AHA Guide® to the Health Care Field

2020 Edition

AHA Guide to the Health Care Field

2020 Edition

AHA Members $299.00
Nonmembers $446.00
AHA Item Number 010020
Telephone ORDERS 1–800–AHA–2626

ISSN 0094–8969
ISBN–13: 978–1–55648–449–0

Contents

Section

v	Acknowledgements and Advisements
vi	Introduction
ix	AHA Offices, Officers, and Historical Data

A — Hospitals Institutional and Associate Members

A1	Contents of Section A
2	AHA Guide Hospital Listing Requirements
3	Explanation of Hospital Listings
5	Annual Survey
13	Hospitals in the United States, by State
714	Hospitals in Areas Associated with the United States, by Area
721	U.S. Government Hospitals Outside the United States, by Area
722	Index of Hospitals
763	Index of Health Care Professionals
1004	AHA Membership Categories
1005	Other Institutional Members
1010	Associate Members

B — Networks, Health Care Systems and Alliances

B1	Contents of Section B
2	Introduction
3	Statistics for Multihospital Health Care Systems and their Hospitals
4	Health Care Systems and their Hospitals
150	Headquarters of Health Care Systems, Geographically
159	Networks and their Hospitals
175	Alliances

C Indexes

C1   Abbreviations Used in the AHA Guide

2   Index

Acknowledgements and Advisements

Acknowledgements

The AHA Guide® to the Health Care Field is published annually by Health Forum LLC, an affiliate of the American Hospital Association. Contributions are made by Information Systems and Technology, Member Relations, Office of the President, Office of the Secretary, Printing Services Group, AHA Resource Center and the following participants:

Jed Cusimano	Kimberly Jackson
Grant Denten	Peter Kralovec
Dianna Doyle	Mary Krzywicki
DeAnn Ellis	Andrea Liebig
Joan Finn	Denise Loggins
Deanna Frazier	Gail Lovinger
Jennifer Gillespie	Bethany Parnell
Tan Harris	Susan Sheffey
Estella Heard	Elaine Singh
Clisby Jackson	Margaret Weglarz
Danny Jackson	

Health Forum LLC acknowledges the cooperation given by many professional groups and government agencies in the health care field, particularly the following: American College of Surgeons; American Medical Association; Council of Teaching Hospitals of the Association of American Medical Colleges; The Joint Commission; DNV Healthcare Inc.; Center for Improvement in Healthcare Quality; Commission on Accreditation of Rehabilitation Facilities; American Osteopathic Association, Centers for Medicare & Medicaid Services; and various offices within the U.S. Department of Health and Human Services.

Advisements

The data published here should be used with the following advisements: The data is based on replies to an annual survey that seeks a variety of information, not all of which is published in this book. The information gathered by the survey includes specific services, but not all of each hospital's services. Therefore, the data does not reflect an exhaustive list of all services offered by all hospitals. For information on the availability of additional data and products, please contact Health Forum LLC at 800/821–2039, or visit our web site.

Health Forum LLC does not assume responsibility for the accuracy of information voluntarily reported by the individual institutions surveyed. **The purpose of this publication is to provide basic data reflecting the delivery of health care in the United States and associated areas, and is not to serve as an official and all inclusive list of services offered by individual hospitals. The information reflected is based on data collected as of September 12, 2019.**

An Introduction to AHA Guide

Welcome, and thank you for purchasing the 2020 edition of *AHA Guide*®. This section is designed to aid you in using the book. While the primary focus of *AHA Guide* is on hospitals, it also contains information on other areas of the health care field, divided across its two major sections:

A. Hospitals

B. Health care systems, networks, and alliances

The information contained within this publication was compiled using AHA membership, and the AHA Annual Survey of Hospitals. *AHA Guide* is the leading hospital directory and represents hospitals with or without AHA membership.

Additional information contained in the front of AHA Guide includes:

- A section by section table of contents
- Recognition of the source of data in the *Acknowledgements and Advisements* section
- Information on AHA's history as well as a listing of our awards in *AHA Offices, Officers, Historical Data, and Awards*

Open the front cover and *AHA Guide* begins with the *2020 AHA Guide Code Chart*. This two page section (front and back) explains how to find and understand the most important elements of each hospital's listing.

The *Code Chart* is a very useful tool to have when reading. It allows new users to become familiar with the data, and it aids returning users in understanding the new design and layout of *AHA Guide*. At the top of the chart, there is a sample listing. If you have used this publication before, you will notice the new columnar listing of all hospital entries by city. The city and county names are highlighted in gray, and all hospitals within the city follow. After the hospital name, you will find the address, telephone number, approval, facility and service codes, and health care systems to which the hospital belongs. Following this are the chief administrators and classifications for the hospital.

Utilization data for the hospital is found in the box at the bottom of each hospital's entry in *AHA Guide*.

The chart further demonstrates how to understand these important elements:

1. **Approval codes** refer to certifications held by a hospital; they represent information supplied by various national approving and reporting bodies. For example, code A–3 indicates accreditation under one of the programs of the Accreditation Council for Graduate Medical Education, evidence that the hospital has been approved for participation in residency training.

2. **Health Care System names** reference specific health care system headquarters to which the hospital belongs. The presence of a system name indicates that the hospital is a member. If no names are listed, the hospital does not belong to a system.

3. **Titles of Chief Administrators** including the Chief Executive Officer and, when available, other C-Suite officers such as the Chief Financial Officer, Chief Information Officer, Chief Medical Officer, Chief Operating Officer, Chief Human Resources Officer, and Chief Nursing Officer.

4. **Classification** refers to two items in *AHA Guide*. **Control** classification indicates the organization that operates the hospital, and **Service** classification refers to the type of service the hospital offers. Previously, this section utilized numerical codes corresponding with a literal value, but the new design of *AHA Guide* bypasses the codes and

---

2020 AHA Guide Code Chart

Sample Hospital Listing:

ANYTOWN, Universal County

■ ★ **ANYTOWN HOSPITAL & CLINICS (777777)**, (Formerly Anytown Area Community Hospital and Clinic), 100 South Main Street, Zip 12345–6789; tel. 123/456–7890 **A9** 10 ①
F10 12 13 23 24 39 30 31 37 39 49 51 55 57 64 65 66 68 70 71 72 77 78 83 87 88 91 96 97 106 107 110 111 113 124 **$** Universal ⑥
County Health System ②
Primary Contact: Ann M. Generic, Chief Executive Officer
COO: Ann M. Generic
CFO: Michael M. Generic ③
CMO: Peter Van Generic, Chief Executive President Medical Staff
CHR: Jerry Generic, Human Resources Director
CNO: Danielle Generic, R.N., Chief Nursing Officer
Web address: www.website.org
Control: Other not-for-profit including NFP Corporation) **Service:** General Medical and Surgical ④

Staffed Beds: 25 **Admissions:** 892 **Census:** 9 **Outpatient Visits:** 44014
Births: 51 **Total Expense ($000):** 19210 **Payroll Expense ($000):** 5864
Personnel: 182 ⑤

① = Approval Codes
② = Health Care System Name
③ = Titles of Chief Administrators
④ = Control and Service Classifications
⑤ = Utilization Data
⑥ = Facility Codes

Hospital, Medicare Provider Number, Address, Telephone, Approval, Facility, and Physician Codes, Health Care System

- ★ American Hospital Association (AHA) membership
- ■ The Joint Commission accreditation
- ◇ Healthcare Facilities Accreditation Program
- ◇ DNV Healthcare Inc. accreditation
- ‡ Center for Improvement in Healthcare Quality Accreditation
- △ Commission on Accreditation of Rehabilitation Facilities (CARF) accreditation

① Approval Codes
Reported by the approving bodies specified, as of the dates noted.

1 Accreditation under the hospital program of The Joint Commission (February 2017).
2 Cancer program approved by American College of Surgeons (January 2017).
3 Participating site recognized for one or more Accreditation Council for Graduate Medical Education accredited programs (April 2017).
5 Medical school affiliation, reported to the American Medical Association (March 2017).
7 Accreditation by Commission on Accreditation of Rehabilitation Facilities (January 2017).

8 Member of Council of Teaching Hospitals of the Association of American Medical Colleges (March 2017).
10 Certified for participation in the Health Insurance for the Aged (Medicare) Program by the Centers for Medicare and Medicaid Services (January 2017).
11 Healthcare Facilities Accreditation Program (April 2017).
12 Internship approved by American Osteopathic Association (March 2016).

13 Residency or fellowship approved by American Osteopathic Association (March 2017).
18 Critical Access Hospitals (March 2017).
19 Rural Referral Center (March 2017).
20 Sole Community Provider (March 2017).
21 Accreditation by DNV Healthcare Inc. (March 2017).
22 Accreditation by Center for Improvement in Healthcare Quality (January 2017).
Nonreporting indicates that the 2016 Annual Survey questionnaire for the hospital was not received prior to publication.

② Healthcare System Name
The inclusion of the letter "S" (1) indicates that the hospital belongs to a health care system and (2) identifies the specific system to which the hospital belongs.

③ Titles of Chief Administrators

④ Control and Service Classification
For a list of control and service classifications, see page A13.
Control–The type of organization that is responsible for establishing policy for overall operation of the hospital.
Service–The type of service the hospital provides to the majority of admissions.

⑤ Utilization Data
Definitions are based on the American Hospital Association's Hospital Administration Terminology. In completing the survey, hospitals were requested to report data for a full year in accord with their fiscal year, ending in 2015.

Beds–Number of beds regularly maintained (set up and staffed for use) for inpatients as of the close of the reporting period. Excludes newborn bassinets.
Admissions–Number of patients accepted for inpatient service during a 12-month period; does not include newborn.
Census–Average number of inpatients receiving care each day during the 12-month reporting period; does not include newborn.

Outpatient Visits–A visit by a patient who is not lodged in the hospital while receiving medical, dental, or other service. Each appearance of an outpatient in each unit constitutes one visit regardless of the number of diagnostic and/or therapeutic treatments that a patient receives.
Births–Number of infants born in the hospital and accepted for service in a newborn infant bassinet during a 12-month period; excludes stillbirths.

Expense: Expense for a 12-month period; both total expense and payroll components are shown. Payroll expenses include all salaries and wages.
Personnel: Represents personnel situations as they existed at the end of the reporting period; includes full-time equivalents of part-time personnel. Full-time equivalents were calculated on the basis that two part-time persons equal one full-time person.

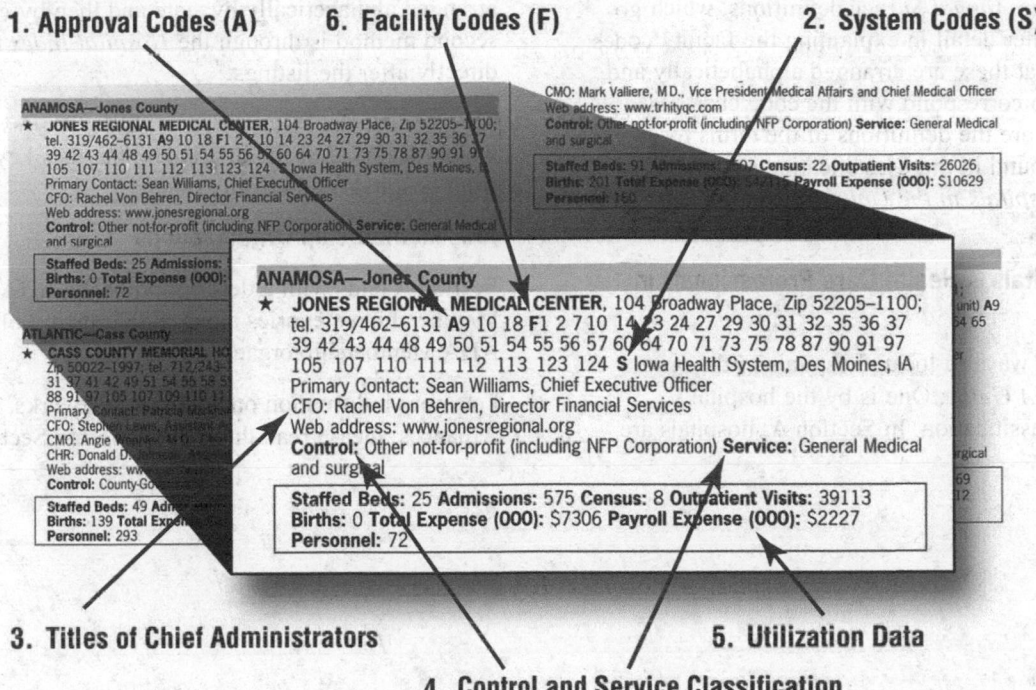

1. Approval Codes (A)   **6. Facility Codes (F)**   **2. System Codes (S)**

3. Titles of Chief Administrators   **5. Utilization Data**

4. Control and Service Classification

instead displays the literal classifications for control and service.

- **Control:** In this section, organizations are divided among nonfederal government hospitals, nongovernment not-for-profit hospitals, investor owned for-profit hospitals, and federal government hospitals.

- **Service:** This section displays the primary type of service that a hospital offers. The most common value is general hospital. Among the other services listed in this section are specialties such as psychiatric hospitals or children's hospitals.

5. **Utilization Data** contains the statistics related to the day-to-day and cumulative operation of the hospital. The information included in this section consists of:

- **Beds:** Number of beds regularly maintained.

- **Admissions:** Amount of patients accepted for inpatient services over a 12-month period.

- **Census:** Average number of patients receiving care each day.

- **Outpatient Visits:** Amount of visits by patients not lodged in the hospital while receiving care.

- **Births:** Number of infants born in the hospital and accepted for service in a newborn infant bassinet.

- **Expense:** Includes all expenses (including payroll) that the hospital had over the 12- month period.

- **Personnel:** Represents personnel situations as they existed at the end of the reporting period. In this area, full time equivalency is calculated on the basis that two part-time persons equal one full-time person.

6. **Facility codes** provide a description of the specific services offered by a hospital. Code F-14, for instance, indicates that the hospital contains a Blood Donor Center.

How To Use This Book

Section A begins with the *AHA Guide Hospital Listing Requirements*. This explains the requisite accreditations or characteristics a hospital must meet to be included in *AHA Guide*.

After this there is *An Explanation of the Hospital Listings*. These two pages review the information included in the Code Chart and are a vital resource in identifying the information, symbols, and codes for each hospital's listing.

Next up are the *Annual Survey* definitions, which go into even greater detail in explaining the facility codes. Please note that these are arranged alphabetically and numerically to correspond with the code chart. Also included here are the definitions of the terms for Control and Service found in the Classification section. The listings of *Hospitals in the United States, by State* follow the definitions.

Finding Hospitals & Health Care Professionals in Section A

There are two ways to locate hospitals in the print version of *AHA Guide*. One is by the hospital's geographic classification. In Section A, hospitals are arranged alphabetically by state and then by city. The second method is through the *Hospital Index* that appears directly after the listings.

There is also an *Index of Health Care Professionals* which begins after the first index that lists key people from hospitals and health systems.

AHA Membership Organizations

Section A ends with a description of the AHA Membership categories along with a listing of various AHA Membership organizations.

For more information on Systems, Networks, and Alliances, please read the introduction to Section B.

AHA Offices, Officers, and Historical Data

Past Presidents/Chairs†

1899	★James S. Knowles	1940 ★Fred G. Carter, M.D.	1981 ★Bernard J. Lachner
1900	★James S. Knowles	1941 ★B. W. Black, M.D.	1982 ★Stanley R. Nelson
1901	★Charles S. Howell	1942 ★Basil C. MacLean, M.D.	1983 ★Elbert E. Gilbertson
1902	★J. T. Duryea	1943 ★James A. Hamilton	1984 Thomas R. Matherlee
1903	★John Fehrenbatch	1944 ★Frank J. Walter	1985 ★Jack A. Skarupa
1904	★Daniel D. Test	1945 ★Donald C. Smelzer, M.D.	1986 Scott S. Parker
1905	★George H. M. Rowe, M.D.	1946 ★Peter D. Ward, M.D.	1987 Donald C. Wegmiller
1906	★George P. Ludlam	1947 ★John H. Hayes	1988 ★Eugene W. Arnett
1907	★Renwick R. Ross, M.D.	1948 ★Graham L. Davis	1989 ★Edward J. Connors
1908	★Sigismund S. Goldwater, M.D.	1949 ★Joseph G. Norby	1990 David A. Reed
1909	★John M. Peters, M.D.	1950 ★John N. Hatfield	1991 C. Thomas Smith
1910	★H. B. Howard, M.D.	1951 ★Charles F. Wilinsky, M.D.	1992 D. Kirk Oglesby, Jr.
1911	★W. L. Babcock, M.D.	1952 ★Anthony J. J. Rourke, M.D.	1993 Larry L. Mathis
1912	★Henry M. Hurd, M.D.	1953 ★Edwin L. Crosby, M.D.	1994 Carolyn C. Roberts
1913	★F. A. Washburn, M.D.	1954 ★Ritz E. Heerman	1995 Gail L. Warden
1914	★Thomas Howell, M.D.	1955 ★Frank R. Bradley	1996 Gordon M. Sprenger
1915	★William O. Mann, M.D.	1956 ★Ray E. Brown	1997 Reginald M. Ballantyne III
1916	★Winford H. Smith, M.D.	1957 ★Albert W. Snoke, M.D.	1998 John G. King
1917	★Robert J. Wilson, M.D.	1958 ★Tol Terrell	1999 Fred L. Brown
1918	★A. B. Ancker, M.D.	1959 ★Ray Amberg	2000 ★Carolyn Boone Lewis
1919	★A. R. Warner, M.D.	1960 ★Russell A. Nelson, M.D.	2001 Gary A. Mecklenburg
1920	★Joseph B. Howland, M.D.	1961 ★Frank S. Groner	2002 Sr. Mary Roch Rocklage, RSM
1921	★Louis B. Baldwin, M.D.	1962 ★Jack Masur, M.D.	2003 Dennis R. Barry
1922	★George O'Hanlon, M.D.	1963 ★T. Stewart Hamilton, M.D.	2004 David L. Bernd
1923	★Asa S. Bacon	1964 ★Stanley A. Ferguson	2005 George F. Lynn
1924	★Malcolm T. MacEachern, M.D.	1965 ★Clarence E. Wonnacott	**January–April 2006** Richard J. Umbdenstock
1925	★E. S. Gilmore	1966 ★Philip D. Bonnet, M.D.	**April–December 2006** George F. Lynn
1926	★Arthur C. Bachmeyer, M.D.	1967 ★George E. Cartmill	2007 Kevin E. Lofton
1927	★R. G. Brodrick, M.D.	1968 ★David B. Wilson, M.D.	2008 William D. Petasnick
1928	★Joseph C. Doane, M.D.	1969 ★George William Graham, M.D.	2009 Thomas M. Priselac
1929	★Louis H. Burlingham, M.D.	1970 ★Mark Berke	2010 Richard P. de Filippi
1930	★Christopher G. Parnall, M.D.	1971 ★Jack A. L. Hahn	2011 John W. Bluford
1931	★Lewis A. Sexton, M.D.	1972 ★Stephen M. Morris	2012 Teri G. Fontenot
1932	★Paul H. Fesler	1973 ★John W. Kauffman	2013 Benjamin K. Chu, MD
1933	★George F. Stephens, M.D.	1974 ★Horace M. Cardwell	2014 James H. Hinton
1934	★Nathaniel W. Faxon, M.D.	1975 Wade Mountz	2015 Jonathan B. Perlin, MD, PhD
1935	★Robert Jolly	1976 ★H. Robert Cathcart	2016 Jim Skogsbergh
1936	★Robin C. Buerki, M.D.	1977 ★John M. Stagl	2017 Eugene A. Woods
1937	★Claude W. Munger, M.D.	1978 ★Samuel J. Tibbitts	2018 Nancy Howell Agee
1938	★Robert E. Neff	1979 W. Daniel Barker	2019 Brian Gragnolati
1939	★G. Harvey Agnew, M.D.	1980 ★Sister Irene Kraus	

Chief Executive Officers

1917–18	★William H. Walsh, M.D.	1954–72	★Edwin L. Crosby, M.D.	1991–2007	★Richard J. Davidson
1919–24	★Andrew Robert Warner, M.D.	1972	★Madison B. Brown, M.D. (acting)	2007–2015	Richard J. Umbdenstock
1925–27	★William H. Walsh, M.D.	1972–86	★J. Alexander McMahon	2015	Richard J. Pollack (current)
1928–42	★Bert W. Caldwell, M.D.	1986–91	Carol M. McCarthy, Ph.D., J.D.		
1943–54	★George Bugbee	1991	★Jack W. Owen (acting)		

★Deceased

Distinguished Service Award

The award recognizes significant lifetime contributions and service to health care institutions and associations.

1934	Matthew O. Foley	1966	Frank S. Groner		Jack W. Owen
1939	Malcolm T. MacEachern, M.D.	1967	Rev. John J. Flanagan, S.J.	1994	George Adams
1940	Sigismund S. Goldwater, M.D.	1968	Stanley W. Martin	1995	Scott S. Parker
1941	Frederic A. Washburn, M.D.	1969	T. Stewart Hamilton, M.D.	1996	John A. Russell
1942	Winford H. Smith, M.D.	1970	Charles Patteson Cardwell, Jr.	1997	D. Kirk Oglesby, Jr.
1943	Arthur C. Bachmeyer, M.D.	1971	Mark Berke	1998	Henry B. Betts, M.D.
1944	Rt. Rev. Msgr. Maurice F. Griffin, LL.D.	1972	Stanley A. Ferguson	1999	Mitchell T. Rabkin, M.D.
1945	Asa S. Bacon	1973	Jack A. L. Hahn	2000	Gail L. Warden
1946	George F. Stephens, M.D.	1974	George William Graham, M.D.	2001	Gordon M. Sprenger
1947	Robin C. Buerki, M.D.	1975	George E. Cartmill	2002	Carolyn Boone Lewis
1948	James A. Hamilton	1976	D. O. McClusky, Jr.	2003	C. Thomas Smith
1949	Claude W. Munger, M.D.	1977	Boone Powell	2004	Michael C. Waters
1950	Nathaniel W. Faxon, M.D.	1978	Richard J. Stull	2005	John G. King
1951	Bert W. Caldwell, M.D.	1979	Horace M. Cardwell	2006	Gary A. Mecklenburg
1952	Fred G. Carter, M.D.	1980	Donald W. Cordes		Sr. Mary Roch Rocklage, RSM
1953	Basil C. MacLean, M.D.	1981	Sister Mary Brigh Cassidy	2007	Richard J. Davidson
1954	George Bugbee	1982	R. Zach Thomas, Jr.	2008	Fred L. Brown
1955	Joseph G. Norby	1983	H. Robert Cathcart	2009	George F. Lynn
1956	Charles F. Wilinsky, M.D.	1984	Matthew F. McNulty, Jr., Sc.D.	2010	James J. Mongan, M.D.
1957	John H. Hayes	1985	J. Alexander McMahon	2011	Thomas C. Royer, M.D.
1958	John N. Hatfield	1986	Sister Irene Kraus	2012	Karen Davis, Ph.D.
1959	Edwin L. Crosby, M.D.	1987	W. Daniel Barker	2013	Thomas C. Dolan, Ph.D., FACHE
1960	Oliver G. Pratt	1988	Elbert E. Gilbertson	2014	Thomas M. Priselac
1961	E. M. Bluestone, M.D.	1989	Donald G. Shropshire	2015	Richard P. de Filippi
1962	Mother Loretto Bernard, S.C., R.N.	1990	John W. Colloton	2016	William Petasnick
1963	Ray E. Brown	1991	Carol M. McCarthy, Ph.D., J.D.	2017	Richard J. Umbdenstock
1964	Russell A. Nelson, M.D.	1992	David H. Hitt	2018	C. Duane Dauner
1965	Albert W. Snoke, M.D.	1993	Edward J. Connors	2019	Ralph W. Muller

†On June 3, 1972, the House of Delegates changed the title of the chief elected officer to chairman of the Board of Trustees, and the title of president was conferred on the chief executive officer of the Association.

Award of Honor

Awarded to individuals, organizations, or groups to recognize an exemplary contribution to the health and well being of the people through leadership on a major health policy or social initiative.

1966	Senator Lister Hill	1998	John E. Curley, Jr.	2010	Jack Bovender
1967	Emory W. Morris, D.D.S.		National Civic League	2011	Cary Medical Center, Caribou, ME
1971	Special Committee on Provision of Health Services (staff also)	1999	Joseph Cardinal Bernardin, Literacy Volunteers of America	2012	Ronald McDonald House Charities
					The Schwartz Center for Compassionate Healthcare
1982	Walter J. McNerney	2000	Institute for Safe Medication Practices	2013	George C. Halvorson
1989	Ruth M. Rothstein	2001	Dennis R. Barry		Reach Out and Read
1990	Joyce C. Clifford, R.N.	2002	Donald M. Berwick, M.D.	2014	Rhonda Anderson, RN
1991	Haynes Rice	2003	Steven A. Schroeder, M.D.		Ohio Hospital Association
1992	Donald W. Dunn		Dan S. Wilford	2015	Spencer C. Johnson
	Ira M. Lane, Jr.	2004	Ron J. Anderson, M.D.		Robert Wood Johnson Foundation
1993	Elliott C. Roberts, Sr.		Johnson & Johnson	2016	Henry J. Kaiser Family Foundation
	William A. Spencer, M.D.	2005	Sr. Mary Jean Ryan	2017	Joel T. Allison
1994	Robert A. Derzon	2006	Jordan J. Cohen, M.D.		Doug Leonard
1995	Russell G. Mawby, Ph.D. John K. Springer		James W. Varnum	2018	Ronald R. Peterson
1996	Stephen J. Hegarty	2007	Edward A. Eckenhoff		Sister Carol Keehan
	Mothers Against Drunk Driving (MADD)		Stanley F. Hupfeld	2019	Darrell G. Kirch, M.D.
1997	Paul B. Batalden, M.D.	2008	Regina M. Benjamin, MD, MBA Alfred G. Stubblefield		John Bluford
	Habitat for Humanity International	2009	The Center to Advance Palliative Care Paul B. Hofmann, Dr.PH		

Justin Ford Kimball Innovators Award

Recognition to individuals or organizations that have made outstanding, innovative contributions to health care financing and/or delivery that improves access or coordination of care.

1958	E. A. van Steenwyk	1975	Earl H. Kammer	1997	Harvey Pettry
1959	George A. Newbury	1976	J. Ed McConnell		D. David Sniff
1960	C. Rufus Rorem, Ph.D.	1978	Edwin R. Werner	1998	Montana Health Research and Education Foundation
1961	James E. Stuart	1979	Robert M. Cunningham, Jr.	1999	Kenneth W. Kizer, M.D.
1962	Frank Van Dyk	1981	Maurice J. Norby	2002	David M. Lawrence, M.D.
1963	William S. McNary	1982	Robert E. Rinehimer	2003	Lowell C. Kruse
1964	Frank S. Groner	1983	John B. Morgan, Jr.	2006	Spencer Foreman, M.D.
1965	J. Douglas Colman	1984	Joseph F. Duplinsky	2009	On Lok
1967	Walter J. McNemey	1985	David W. Stewart	2012	Thomas S. Nesbitt, M.D.
1968	John W. Paynter	1988	Ernest W. Saward, M.D.	2015	Glenn D. Steele, Jr., MD
1970	Edwin L. Crosby, M.D.	1990	James A. Vohs	2016	Dan Wolterman
1971	H. Charles Abbott	1993	John C. Lewin, M.D.	2017	James N. Weinstein, DO
1972	John R. Mannix	1994	Donald A. Brennan	2018	Nicholas Wolter, M.D.
1973	Herman M. Somers	1995	E. George Middleton, Jr.		
1974	William H. Ford, Ph.D.		Glenn R. Mitchell		

Board of Trustees Award

Individuals or groups who have made substantial and noteworthy contributions to the work of the American Hospital Association.

1959	Joseph V. Friel	1982	John Bigelow	2002	Victor L. Campbell
	John H. Hayes		Robert W. O'Leary		Joseph A. Parker
1960	Duncan D. Sutphen, Jr.		Jack W. Owen	2003	J. Richard Gaintner, M.D.
1963	Eleanor C. Lambertsen, R.N., Ed.D.	1984	Howard J. Berman		Donald A. Wilson
1964	John R. Mannix		O. Ray Hurst	2004	Richard L. Clarke
1965	Albert G. Hahn		James R. Neely		Thelma Traut
	Maurice J. Norby	1985	James E. Ferguson	2005	Merrill Gappmayer
1966	Madison B. Brown, M.D.		Cleveland Rodgers		Leo Greenawalt
	Kenneth Williamson	1986	Rex N. Olsen	2006	Robert L. Harman
1967	Alanson W. Wilcox	1987	Michael Lesparre		Kenneth G. Stella
1968	E. Dwight Barnett, M.D.	1988	Barbara A. Donaho, R.N.	2007	Deborah Freund, Ph.D.
1969	Vane M. Hoge, M.D.	1989	Walter H. MacDonald		Michael D. Stephens
	Joseph H. McNinch, M.D.		Donald R. Newkirk	2008	James R. Castle
1972	David F. Drake, Ph.D.	1990	William T. Robinson	2009	Richard M. Knapp, Ph.D.
	Paul W. Earle	1992	Jack C. Bills	2010	Fred Hessler
	Michael Lesparre		Anne Hall Davis		John G. O'Brien
	Andrew Pattullo	1993	Theodore C. Eickhoff, M.D.	2011	Carolyn F. Scanlan
1973	Tilden Cummings		Stephen W. Gamble		Charlotte S. Yeh, MD
	Edmond J. Lanigan		Yoshi Honkawa	2012	Larry S. Gage
1974	James E. Hague	1994	Roger M. Busfield, Jr., Ph.D.		Larry McAndrews
	Sister Marybelle	1995	Stephen E. Dorn	2013	Jeffrey D. Selberg
1975	Helen T. Yast		William L. Yates	2014	Russell D. Harrington, Jr.
1976	Boynton P. Livingston	1996	Leigh E. Morris		Daniel Sisto
	James Ludlam		John Quigley	2015	Todd C. Linden
	Helen McGuire	1998	John D. Leech		R. Timothy Rice
1979	Newton J. Jacobson	1999	Sister Carol Keehan	2016	Sandra Bennett Bruce
	Edward W. Weimer		C. Edward McCauley		Michael G. Rock, M.D.
1980	Robert B. Hunter, M.D.		Stephen Rogness	2017	Kris A. Doody, RN
	Samuel J. Tibbitts	2000	Dennis May		Daniel L. Gross, RN
1981	Vernon A. Knutson	2001	Spencer C. Johnson	2018	Ian Morrison
	John E. Sullivan		Michael M. Mitchel	2019	Jeanette Clough Bruce Bailey

Citation for Meritorious Service

1968	F. R. Knautz		Gordon McLachlan	1983	David M. Kinzer
	Sister Conrad Mary, R.N.	1977	Theodore Cooper, M.D.	1984	Donald L. Custis, M.D.
1971	Hospital Council of Southern California	1979	Norman D. Burkett	1985	John A. D. Cooper, M.D.
1972	College of Misericordia, Dallas, PA		John L. Quigley		Imperial Council of the Ancient Arabic Order of the Nobles of the Mystic Shrine for North America
1973	Madison B. Brown, M.D.		William M. Whelan		
	Samuel J. Tibbitts	1980	Sister Grace Marie Hiltz	1986	Howard F. Cook
1975	Kenneth B. Babcock, M.D.		Leo J. Gehrig, M.D.	1987	David H. Hitt
	Sister Mary Maurita Sengelaube	1981	Richard Davi		Lucile Packard
1976	Chaiker Abbis		Pearl S. Fryar		
	Susan Jenkins	1982	Jorge Brull Nater		

This citation is no longer awarded

Dick Davidson NOVA Award

This award honors effective, collaborative programs focused on improving community health status.

1994
Health Partners of Philadelphi (PA): Albert Einstein Medical Center, Episcopal Hospital, Frankford Hospital, Medical College of Pennsylvania Hospital, St. Christopher's Hospital for Children, Temple University Hospital

Decker Family Development Center: Children's Hospital Medical Center of Akron (OH)
Denver (CO) School–Based Clinics: The Children's Hospital

Basic Health Plan: Dominican Network; Mount Carmel Hospital, Colville, WA; St. Joseph's Hospital, Chewelah, WA; and Holy Family Hospital, Spokane, WA
HealthLink: Lakes Region General Hospital, Laconia, NH

1995
Bladen Community Care Network: Bladen County Hospital, Elizabethtown, NC
Building a Healthier Community: Community– Kimball Health Care System, Toms River, NJ '

Injury Prevention Program: Harlem Hospital Center, New York City, NY
The Community Ministries & Outreach Program: Reaching Out to Our Vickery/Meadow Neighborhood: Presbyterian Healthcare System, Dallas, TX

"CHOICES": Shriners Hospitals for Crippled Children, Tampa, FL

1996
Lincoln and Sunnyslope: John C. Lincoln Hospital and Health Center, Sunnyslope, AZ
Growing into Life Task Force: Aiken (SC) Regional Medical Centers

People Caring for People: Beatrice (NE) Community Hospital and Health Center
Injury Prevention Center of the Greater Dayton (OH) Area: The Children's Medical Center, Good Samaritan Hospital and Health Center, Grandview Hospital, Kettering Memorial

Hospital, Miami Valley Hospital, and St. Elizabeth Medical Center
Family Road: Hutzel Hospital, Detroit, MI

1997
Health Promotion Schools of Excellence Program: Alliant Health System and Kosair Children's Hospital, Louisville, KY
Health, Outreach, Prevention, and Education (HOPE): Health First Holmes Regional Medical Center, Melbourne, FL

Healthy Community Initiative: Roper Care Alliance, Charleston, SC
Obstetrical Care and Prenatal Counseling Program: St. Alexius Medical Center, Bismarck, ND

HIV/AIDS Neighborhood Service Program: Yale–New Haven Hospital, New Haven, CT

1998
Partners for a Healthier Community: Evergreen Community Health Care, Group Health Cooperative of Puget Sound, Overlake Hospital Medical Center, Providence Health System/Medalia HealthCare, Seattle, WA
Glenwood–Lyndale Community Clinic: Hennepin County Medical Center, Minneapolis, MN

Greater Dallas (TX) Injury Prevention Center: Parkland Health & Hospital System, Children's Medical Center of Dallas, Baylor Health Care System, Methodist Hospitals of Dallas, and Presbyterian Healthcare System
Network of Trust: Phoebe Putney Memorial Hospital, Albany, GA

The Lauderdale Court: A Community Partnership:St. Joseph Hospital and Health Centers, Memphis, TN

1999
Making a Case for Community Health: Middletown (OH) Regional Hospital
The Family Resource Center: Mount Carmel Medical Center, Pittsburgh, KO

The Health Neighborhood Project: St. Patrick Hospital, Missoula, MT
Kids for Health: Washington Regional Medical Center, Fayettoville, AR

Children's Village: Yakima Memorial Hospital, Yakima, WA

2000
Community Healthcare Network: Columbus (GA) Regional Healthcare System
Pasadena County Asthma Project: Huntington Memorial Hospital, Pasadena, CA

Ashe County Health Council "Health Carolinias Task Force": Ashe Memorial Hospital, Jefferson, NC
Caritas–Connection Project: St. Mary's Hospital, Passaic, NJ

Correctional Health Care Program: Baystate Health System, Springfield, MA

2001
J.C. Lewis Health Center: Memorial Health and St. Joseph's Candler Health System, Savannah, GA
Project C.A.R.E.: Mercy Medical Center, Canton, OH

TeenHealthFX.com: Atlantic Health System, Florham Park, NJ
Vista ElderCARE: Vista Health, Waukegan, IL

Western Village Enterprise School: INTEGRIS Health, Oklahoma City, OK

2002
Chester Community Connections: Crozer– Keystone Health System, Springfield, PA
The Hope Street Family Center: California Hospital Medical Center, Los Angeles, CA

Mobile Health Outreach Ministry: St. Vincent's Health System, Jacksonville, FL
Operation Access: Kaiser Foundation Hospitals, Oakland; Sutter Health, Sacramento; San Francisco General Hospital,

San Francisco; St. Rose Hospital, Hayward; and Santa Rosa Memorial Hospital, Santa Rosa, CA
Wilmington Health Access for Teens: New Hanover Health Network, Wilmington, NC

2003
C.O.A.C.H. for Kids: Cedars–Sinai Medical Center, Los Angeles, CA
Community Action Network: Trinity Regional Medical Center, Fort Dodge, IA

Hearts N' Health: Glendale Adventist Medical Center, Glendale, CA
Saint Joseph Health Center: Saint Joseph Regional Medical Center, South Bend, IN

St. Mary Medical Center Bensalem Ministries: St. Mary Medical Center, Langhorne, PA

2004
Better Beginnings: Brockton Hospital, Brockton, MA
Buffalo County Community Health Partners: Good Samaritan Health Systems, Kearney, NE

Quad City Health Initiative: Genesis Health System, Davenport, IA and Trinity Regional Health System, Rock Island, IL
Quality of Life in the Truckee Meadows: Washoe Health System, Reno, NV

Solano Coalition for Better Health, Inc.: NorthBay Healthcare Group, Fairfield, CA; Sutter Solano Medical Center, Vallejo, CA; and Kaiser Permanente, Martinez, CA

2005
Children's Health Connection: McKay-Dee Hospital Center, Ogden, UT
Palmetto Health's Vision Health Initiative: Palmetto Health, Columbia, SC

Project Dulce, Whittier Institute for Diabetes: Scripps Health, San Diego, CA
Toledo/Lucas County CareNet: Mercy Health Partners, ProMedica Health System, and Medical University of Ohio, all of Toledo, OH and St. Luke's Hospital, Maumee, O

Volunteer Health Advisor (VHA) Program: Cambridge Health Alliance, Cambridge, MA

2006
Healthy Learners, Columbia, SC: Allendale County Hospital, Fairfax, SC; McLeod Medical Center–Dillon, Dillon, SC; Sisters of Charity Providence Hospitals, Columbia, SC; and Self Regional Healthcare, Greenwood, SC

Primary Care Access Network (PCAN): Health Central, Ocoee, FL; Florida Hospital, Winter Park, FL; and Orlando Regional Healthcare, Orlando, FL **ProHealth Care Community Health Outreach Initiative:** ProHealth Care, Waukesha, WI

St. Joseph Mobile Health Services: Saint Joseph HealthCare Inc., Lexington, KY
Yonkers Childhood Health Initiative: St. John's Riverside, Yonkers, NY

2007
Medical-Legal Partnership for Children: Boston Medical Center, Boston, MA
NOW (Nutritional Options for Wellness) Program: Spectrum Health, Grand Rapids, MI
Richland Care: Palmetto Health, Columbia, SC

Trauma Nurses Talk Tough: Legacy Health System, Portland, OR
UMass Memorial Medical Center Healthy Youth Development Initiative: UMass Memorial Health Care, Worcester, MA

Youth Health Partnership-Patee Market Youth Dental Clinic: Heartland Health, St. Joseph, MO

2008

Partnership for Community Health: California Pacific Medical Center, San Francisco, CA
Every Child Succeeds: Cincinnati Children's Hospital Medical Center, Cincinnati, OH

Memorial Hermann Health Centers for Schools: Memorial Hermann, Houston, TX
Nutrition Center of Maine: Saint Mary's Health System, Lewiston, ME

***ENERGIZE!* Pediatric Diabetes Intervention Program:** WakeMed Health & Hospitals, Raleigh, NC

2009

Lighten Up 4 Life: Mission Health System, Asheville, NC
Project BRIEF: Jacobi Medical Center and North Central Bronx Hospital, Bronx, NY

Really Awesome Health (RAH) and Wholesome Routines: Duke Raleigh Hospital, Raleigh, NC

Student Success Jobs Program: Brigham and Women's Hospital, Boston, MA
Taos First Steps Program: Holy Cross Hospital, Taos, NM

2010

Community-Based Alternatives to the Emergency Room: Lee Memorial Health System, Fort Meyers, FL
Health-e-Access Telemedicine: University of Rochester Medical Center, Rochester, NY

Healthy Futures: Munson Healthcare System, Traverse City, MI
Healthy San Francisco: San Francisco General Hospital, University of California Medical Center, Chinese Hospital, California Pacific Medical Center, Saint Francis Memorial

Hospital, St. Mary's Medical Center, and Kaiser Permanente, San Francisco, CA
Pediatric Asthma Program: Sinai Health System, Chicago, IL

2011

Emergency Department Consistent Care Program: Providence St. Peter Hospital, Olympia, WA
Integrated Community Nursing Program at Parkview Health: Parkview Health, Fort Wayne, IN

Milwaukee Health Care Partnership: Aurora Health Care, Children's Hospital & Health System, Inc., Columbia St. Mary's, and Froedtert Health, all of Milwaukee, WI, and Wheaton Franciscan Healthcare, Glendale, WI

The Diabetes Collaborative: Northwestern Memorial Hospital, Chicago, IL
Rochester Youth Violence Partnership: University of Rochester Medical Center and Rochester General Health System, Rochester, NY

2012

The Beth Embraces Wellness: An Integrated Approach to Prevention in the Community: Newark Beth Israel Medical Center and Children's Hospital of New Jersey, Newark, NJ

CARE Network: St. Joseph Health Queen of the Valley Medical Center, Napa, CA
Fitness in the City: Boston Children's Hospital, Boston, MA
Puff City: Henry Ford Health System, Detroit, MI

Rural Health Initiative: Shawano Medical Center of ThedaCare, Shawano, WI

2013

Bangor Beacon Community: EMHS, Brewer, ME and St. Joseph Healthcare, Bangor, ME
Chippewa Health Improvement Partnership (CHIP): St. Joseph's Hospital, Chippewa Falls, WI

Core Health Program of Healthier Communities: Spectrum Health, Grand Rapids, MI
Free Preventive Screenings Program: Good Samaritan Hospital, Vincennes, IN

Hope Clinic and Pharmacy: Ephraim McDowell Health, Danville, KY

2014

FirstReach: FirstHealth of the Carolinas, Pinehurst, NC
Children's Hospital Center for Pediatric Medicine Asthma Action Team: Greenville Health System, Greenville, SC

Let's Go!: The Barbara Bush Children's Hospital at Maine Medical Center, Portland, ME
Hearts Beat Back: The Heart of New Ulm (HONU) Project: New Ulm Medical Center, part of Allina Health, New Ulm, MN

Finney County Community Health Coalition: St. Catherine Hospital, Garden City, KS

2015

Activate Whittier: PIH Health, Whittier, Calif. And Kaiser Permanente Downey Medical Center, Downey, CA
Bithlo Transformation Effort: Florida Hospital, Orlando, FL

Blood Pressure Advocate Program: University of Rochester Medical Center, Rochester, NY
Community Health: Healthy Eating: Presbyterian Healthcare Services, Albuquerque, NM

Mayor's Healthy City Initiative (Healthy BR): Baton Rouge General Medical Center, Ochsner Medical Center-Baton Rouge, Our Lady of the Lake Regional Medical Center and Woman's Hospital, Baton Rouge, LA

2016

Baylor Scott & White Health's Diabetes Health and Wellness Institute at the Juanita J. Craft Recreation Center: Baylor Scott & White Health, Dallas, TX

Building a Healthy Community Initiative, East Ocean View: Bon Secours Hampton Roads Health System, Norfolk, VA
Memorial Hermann Mobile Dental Program: Memorial Hermann Health System, Houston, TX

Spectrum Health Healthier Communities – Strong Beginnings: Spectrum Health, Grand Rapids, MI
Get Healthy, Live Well: Tanner Health System, Carrollton, GA

2017

Morrison County Community-Based Care Coordination: CHI St. Gabriel's Health, Little Falls, MN
The Health and Wellness Alliance Asthma Collaboration: Children's Health, Dallas, TX

Healthy Youth Transitions: Memorial Healthcare System, Hollywood, FL
Pediatric Care-A-Van: Norwegian American Hospital, Chicago, IL

Palmetto Health Dental Health Initiative: Palmetto Health, Columbia, SC

2018

Unity Center for Behavioral Health: Adventist Health, Kaiser Permanente, Legacy Health, Oregon Health & Science University, Portland, OR
Annapolis Community Health Partnership: Anne Arundel Medical Center, Annapolis, MD

Enos Park Access to Care Collaborative: HSHS St. John's Hospital and Memorial Medical Center, Springfield, IL
Kids Teaching Kids: Medical City Healthcare, Dallas, TX

Healthy Kids Express: St. Louis Children's Hospital, St. Louis, MO

2019

Stark County Toward Health Resiliency for Infant Vitality and Equality (THRIVE): Aultman Hospital and Canton City Public Health, Canton, OH

Project Ujima: Children's Hospital of Wisconsin, Milwaukee, WI
Women-Inspired Neighborhood Network: Henry Ford Health System, Detroit, MI

House of Mercy Homeless Center: Mercyhealth, Janesville, WI
Transforming Communities Initiative: Trinity Health, Livonia, MI

The Carolyn Boone Lewis Living the Vision Award

Organizations and individuals living AHA's vision of a society of healthy communities where all individuals reach their highest potential for health.

1998	Memorial Healthcare System, Hollywood, FL Baptist Health System, Montgomery, AL
1999	Robert A. DeVries, Battle Creek, MI Memorial Health System, South Bend, IN
2000	Rockingham Memorial Hospital, Harrisonburg, VA
2001	Salina Regional Health Center, Salina, KS
2002	Health Improvement Collaborative of Greater Cincinnati, Cincinnati, OH
2003	Franklin Memorial Hospital, Farmington, ME

2004	Jamaica Hospital Medical Center, Jamaica, NY
2005	Fairbanks Memorial Hospital, Fairbanks, AK Boston Medical Center, Boston, MA
2010	Lehigh Valley Health Network, Allentown, PA
2011	Alaska Native Tribal Health Consortium, Anchorage, AK
2013	St. Joseph's Hospital Health Center, Syracuse, NY Cheshire Medical Center/Dartmouth–Hitchcock Keene, Keene, NH

| 2014 | TPR Collaborative, MD |
| 2016 | Saint Elizabeth's Medical Center, Wabasha, MN |

This citation is no longer awarded

Circle of Life Award

This award celebrates innovation in palliative and end-of-life care.

2000

Improving Care through the End of Life, Franciscan Health System, Gig Harbor, WA

The Hospice of The Florida Suncoast, Largo, FL

Louisiana State Penitentiary Hospice Program, Angola, LA

2001

Department of Pain Medicine and Palliative Care, Beth Israel Medical Center, New York, NY

Palliative CareCenter & Hospice of the North Shore, Evanston, IL

St. Joseph's Manor, Trumbull, CT

2002

Children's Program of San Diego Hospice and Children's Hospital and Health Center of San Diego, San Diego, CA
Hospice of the Bluegrass, Lexington, KY

Project Safe Conduct, Hospice of the Western Reserve and Ireland Cancer Center, Cleveland, OH

Special Circle of Life Award Population–based Palliative Care Research Network (PoPCRN), Denver, CO

2003

Hospice & Palliative CareCenter, Winston–Salem, NC

Providence Health System, Portland, OR

University of California Davis Health System, Sacramento, CA

2004

Hope Hospice and Palliative Care, Fort Myers, FL
St. Mary's Healthcare System for Children, Bayside, NY

University of Texas M.D. Anderson Cancer Center Palliative Care, Houston, TX

2005

High Point Regional Health System, High Point, NC

Palliative and End-of-life Care Program, Hoag Memorial Hospital Presbyterian, Newport Beach, CA

Thomas Palliative Care Unit, VCU Massey Cancer Center, Richmond, VA

2006

Continuum Hospice Care, New York, NY

Mercy Supportive Care, St. Joseph Mercy Oakland, Pontiac, MI

Transitions and Life Choices, Fairview Health Services, Minneapolis, MN

2007

UCSF Palliative Care Program, San Francisco, CA
Covenant Hospice, Pensacola, FL

Woodwell: A Program of Presbyterian SeniorCare and Family Hospice and Palliative Care, Oakmont, PA

2008

Children's Hospitals and Clinics of Minnesota, Pain and Palliative Care Program, Minneapolis, MN

Haven Hospice, Gainesville, FL

The Pediatric Advanced Care Team, The Children's Hospital of Philadelphia, Philadelphia, PA

2009

Four Seasons, Flat Rock, NC

Oregon Health and Science University Palliative Medicine & Comfort Care Program, Portland, OR

Wishard Health Services Palliative Care Program, Indianapolis, IN

2010

Department of Veteran Affairs, VA New York/New Jersey Healthcare Network, Brooklyn, NY

Kansas City Hospice & Palliative Care, Kansas City, MO
Snohomish Palliative Partnership, Everett, WA

2011

The Center for Hospice & Palliative Care, Cheektowaga, NY

Gilchrist Hospice Care, Hunt Valley, MD

St. John Providence Health System, Detroit, MI

2012

Haslinger Family Pediatric Palliative Care Center, Akron Children's Hospital, Akron, OH

Calvary Hospital, Bronx, NY
Sharp HealthCare, San Diego, CA

2013

The Denver Hospice and Optio Health Services, Denver, CO

Hertzberg Palliative Care Institute at the Mount Sinai Medical Center, New York, NY

UnityPoint Health, Iowa and Illinois

2014

OACIS/Palliative Medicine, Lehigh Valley Health Network, Allentown, PA

Supportive & Palliative Care, Baylor Health Care System, Dallas, TX

Yakima Valley Memorial Hospital, Yakima, WA

2015

Care Dimensions, Danvers, MA

2016

Bon Secours Palliative Medicine, Richmond, VA

Cambia Palliative Care Center of Excellence at UW Medicine, Seattle, WA

Susquehanna Health Hospice and Palliative Care, Williamsport, PA

2017

Bluegrass Care Navigators, formerly Hospice of the Bluegrass, Lexington, KY

Providence TrinityCare Hospice, Providence Little Company of Mary Medical Center Torrance and Providence Institute for Human Caring, Torrance, CA

2018

Hospice of the Valley, Phoenix, AZ

Western Connecticut Health Network, Danbury, CT

Penn Wissahickon Hospice and Caring Way, Philadelphia, PA

2019

Western Reserve Navigator, Hospice of the Western Reserve, Cleveland, OH

Palliative Care Services, UCHealth University of Colorado Hospital, Aurora, CO

University Health System Palliative Care Team, San Antonio, TX

The American Hospital Association Quest for Quality Prize*

Honoring Leadership and Innovation in Patient Care Quality, Safety, and Commitment

2002
Missouri Baptist Medical Center, St. Louis, MO
Finalist: Fairview Hospital, Greater, Barrington, MA
Finalist: Minnesota Children's Hospital and Clinics, Minneapolis, MN

2003
Abington Memorial Hospital, Abington, PA
Finalist: Beaumont Hospitals, Royal Oak, MI
Finalist: University of Wisconsin Hospital and Clinics, Madison, WI

2004
Sentara Norfolk General Hospital, Norfolk, VA
Finalist: The Johns Hopkins Hospital, Baltimore, MD
Finalist: Mary Lanning Memorial Hospital, Hastings, NE

2005
North Mississippi Medical Center, Tupelo, MS
Finalist: El Camino Hospital, Mountain View, CA
Finalist: NewYork-Presbyterian Hospital, New York, NY

2006
Cincinnati Children's Hospital Medical Center, Cincinnati, OH

2007
Columbus Regional Hospital, Columbus, IN
Finalist: Cedars-Sinai Medical Center, Los Angeles, CA
Finalist: INTEGRIS Baptist Medical Center, Oklahoma City, OK

2008
Munson Medical Center, Traverse City, MI
Finalist: University of Michigan Hospitals & Health Centers, Ann Arbor, MI

2009
Bronson Methodist Hospital, Kalamazoo, MI
Finalist: Beth Israel Deaconess Medical Center, Boston, MA

2010
McLeod Regional Medical Center, Florence, SC
Finalist: Henry Ford Hospital, Detroit, MI

2011
Memorial Regional Hospital, Hollywood, FL
Finalist: AtlantiCare Regional Medical Center, Atlantic City, NJ
Finalist: Northwestern Memorial Hospital, Chicago, IL

2012
University Hospitals Case Medical Center, Cleveland, OH
Finalist: Lincoln Medical and Mental Health Center, Bronx, NY
Finalist: University of North Carolina Hospitals, Chapel Hill, NC and Life Choices, Fairview Health Services, Minneapolis, MN

2013
Beth Israel Deaconess Medical Center, Boston, MA
Finalist: Franklin Woods Community Hospital, Johnson City, TN

2014
VCU Medical Center, Richmond, VA
Finalist: Carolinas Medical Center-Northeast, Concord, NC

2015
Children's Hospital Colorado in Aurora, CO
Finalist: Duke University Hospital, Durham, NC

2016
Memorial Medical Center, Springfield, IL
Finalist: Memorial Hermann Greater Heights, Houston, TX

2018
Northwell Health, New Hyde Park, NY
Finalist: Anne Arundel Medical Center, Annapolis, MD
Finalist: Aurora Health Care, Milwaukee, WI

2019
Carolinas Rehabilitation, Charlotte, NC
Finalist: Finalist: Mission Health, Asheville, NC

(*This award was sponsored from 2001-2016 by McKesson. RLDatix is the current sponsor.)

Foster G. McGaw Prize

Honors health delivery organizations that have demonstrated exceptional commitment to community service.

1986	Lutheran Medical Center, Brooklyn, NY	1997	Bladen County Hospital Rural Health Network, Elizabethtown, NC
1987	Copley Hospital, Morrisville, VT Mount Sinai Hospital, Hartford, CT	1998	Allina Health System, Minneapolis, MN
1988	MetroHealth System, Cleveland, OH	1999	LAC+USC Healthcare Network, Los Angeles, CA
1989	Greater Southeast Healthcare System, Washington, DC	2000	Kaweah Delta Health Care District, Visalia, CA
1990	Mount Zion Medical Center of The University of California-San Francisco, San Francisco, CA	2001	Memorial Hospital of South Bend, South Bend, IN
		2002	John C. Lincoln Health Network, Phoenix, AZ
1991	Franklin Regional Hospital, Franklin, NH	2003	Phoebe Putney Memorial Hospital, Albany, GA
1992	Mount Sinai Hospital Medical Center of Chicago, Chicago, IL	2004	Henry Ford Health System, Detroit, MI
		2005	Venice Family Clinic, Venice, CA
1993	The Cambridge Hospital, Cambridge, MA	2006	Memorial Healthcare System, Hollywood, FL
1994	Parkland Memorial Hospital, Dallas, TX	2007	Harborview Medical Center, Seattle, WA
1995	Our Lady of Lourdes Medical Center, Camden, NJ	2008	St. Mary's Health System, Lewiston, ME
1996	St. Mary's Hospital, Rochester, NY	2009	Heartland Health, St. Joseph, MO
		2010	Allegiance Health, Jackson, MI
		2011	Mt. Ascutney Hospital and Health Center, Windsor, VT
		2012	St. Joseph's/Candler Health System, Savannah, GA
		2013	Crozer–Keystone Health System, Delaware County, PA
		2014	Palmetto Health, Columbia, SC
		2015	Massachusetts General Hospital, Boston
		2016	Spectrum Health, Grand Rapids, MI
		2017	Yale New Haven Hospital, New Haven, CT
		2018	Penn Medicine Lancaster General Health, Lancaster County, PA

Dick Davidson Quality Milestone Award for Allied Association Leadership

The award recognizes state, regional or metropolitan hospital association leadership in improving health care quality.

2011	Michigan Health & Hospital Association	2013	Florida Hospital Association	2015	Minnesota Hospital Association
	South Carolina Hospital Association		Tennessee Hospital Association	2016	Maryland Hospital Association
2012	Iowa Hospital Association	2014	Connecticut Hospital Association	2017	California's Hospital Quality Institute
	Washington State Hospital Association		Wisconsin Hospital Association	2018	Missouri Hospital Association

This citation is no longer awarded

Carolyn Boone Lewis Equity of Care Award

The award is presented to hospitals or care systems that are noteworthy leaders and examples to the field in the area of equitable care.

2014	Massachusetts General Hospital, Boston, MA
2015	Henry Ford Health System, Detroit, MI
	Robert Wood Johnson University Hospital, New Brunswick, NJ
2016	Cleveland Clinic, Cleveland, OH
2017	Kaiser Permanente, Oakland, CA
2018	Navicent Health, Macon, GA
2019	Anne Arundel Medical Center, Annapolis, MD

A

**Hospitals,
Institutional and
Associate Members**

A2   AHA Guide Hospital Listing Requirements

3   Explanation of Hospital Listings

5   Annual Survey

13   Hospitals in the United States, by State

714   Hospitals in Areas Associated with the United States, by Area

721   U.S. Government Hospitals Outside the United States, by Area

722   Index of Hospitals

763   Index of Health Care Professionals

1004   AHA Membership Categories

1005   Other Institutional Members
1005   *Institutional Member Hospitals*
1006   *Associated University Programs in Health Administration*
1007   *Hospital Schools of Nursing*
1008   *Nonhospital Preacute and Postacute Care Facilities*
1009   *Provisional Hospitals*

1010   Associate Members
1010   *Ambulatory Centers and Home Care Agencies*
1010   *Blue Cross Plans*
1011   *Other Associate Members*

An institution is considered a hospital by the American Hospital Association if it is licensed as general or specialty hospital by the appropriate state agency, and accredited as a hospital by one of the following organizations: The Joint Commission; Healthcare Facilities Accreditation Program (HFAP); accreditation by DNV GL Healthcare; Center for Improvement in Healthcare Quality accreditation; or Medicare certified as a provider of acute service under Title 18 of the Social Security Act.

Types of Hospitals

Hospitals are listed as one of four types of hospitals: general, special, rehabilitation and chronic disease, or psychiatric. The following definitions of function by type of hospital and special requirements are:

General

The primary function of the institution is to provide patient services, diagnostic and therapeutic, for a variety of medical conditions. A general hospital also shall provide:

- diagnostic x–ray services with facilities and staff for a variety of procedures
- clinical laboratory service with facilities and staff for a variety of procedures and with anatomical pathology services regularly and conveniently available
- operating room service with facilities and staff.

Special

The primary function of the institution is to provide diagnostic and treatment services for patients who have specified medical conditions, both surgical and nonsurgical. A special hospital also shall provide:

- such diagnostic and treatment services as may be determined by the Executive Committee of the Board of Trustees of the American Hospital Association to be appropriate for the specified medical conditions for which medical services are provided shall be maintained in the institution with suitable facilities and staff. If such conditions do not normally require diagnostic x–ray service, laboratory service, or operating room service, and if any such services are therefore not maintained in the institution, there shall be written arrangements to make them available to patients requiring them.
- clinical laboratory services capable of providing tissue diagnosis when offering pregancy termination services.

Rehabilitation and Chronic Disease

The primary function of the institution is to provide diagnostic and treatment services to handicapped or disabled individuals requiring restorative and adjustive services. A rehabilitation and chronic disease hospital also shall provide:

- arrangements for diagnostic x–ray services, as required, on a regular and conveniently available basis
- arrangements for clinical laboratory service, as required on a regular and conveniently available basis
- arrangements for operating room service, as required, on a regular and conveniently available basis
- a physical therapy service with suitable facilities and staff in the institution

- an occupational therapy service with suitable facilities and staff in the institution
- arrangements for psychological and social work services on a regular and conveniently available basis
- arrangements for educational and vocational services on a regular and conveniently available basis
- written arrangements with a general hospital for the transfer of patients who require medical, obstetrical, or surgical services not available in the institution.

Psychiatric

The primary function of the institution is to provide diagnostic and treatment services for patients who have psychiatric–related illnesses. A psychiatric hospital also shall provide:

- arrangements for clinical laboratory service, as required, on a regular and conveniently available basis
- arrangements for diagnostic x–ray services, as required on a regular and conveniently available basis
- psychiatric, psychological, and social work service with facilities and staff in the institution
- arrangements for electroencephalograph services, as required, on a regular and conveniently available basis
- written arrangements with a general hospital for the transfer of patients who require medical, obstetrical, or surgical services not available in the institution

The American Hospital Association may, at the sole discretion of the Executive Committee of the Board of Trustees, grant, deny, or withdraw the listing of an institution.

---

* Physician–Term used to describe an individual with an M.D. or D.O. degree who is fully licensed to practice medicine in all its phases.

‡ The completed records in general shall contain at least the following: the patient's identifying data and consent forms, medical history, record of physical examination, physicians' progress notes, operative notes, nurses' notes, routine x–ray and laboratory reports, doctors' orders, and final diagnosis.

Explanation of Hospital Listings

Sample Hospital Listing:

Hospital, Medicare Provider Number, Address, Telephone, Approval, Facility, and Health Care System

★ American Hospital Association (AHA) membership
□ The Joint Commission accreditation
○ Healthcare Facilities Accreditation Program
◇ DNV Healthcare Inc. accreditation
⇧ Center for Improvement in Healthcare Quality Accreditation
△ Commission on Accreditation of Rehabilitation Facilities (CARF) accreditation

① Approval Codes

Reported by the approving bodies specified, as of the dates noted.

1 Accreditation under the hospital program of The Joint Commission (February 2019).
2 Cancer program approved by American College of Surgeons (April 2019).
3 Participating site recognized for one or more Accreditation Council for Graduate Medical Education accredited programs (March 2019).
5 Medical school affiliation, reported to the American Medical Association (March 2019).
6 Accreditation by Commission on Accreditation of Rehabilitation Facilities (February 2019).

7 Member of Council of Teaching Hospitals of the Association of American Medical Colleges (January 2019).
10 Certified for participation in the Health Insurance for the Aged (Medicare) Program by the Centers for Medicare and Medicaid Services (January 2019).
11 Healthcare Facilities Accreditation Program (February 2019).
12 Internship approved by American Osteopathic Association (February 2019).

13 Residency or fellowship approved by American Osteopathic Association (February 2019).
18 Critical Access Hospitals (January 2019).
19 Rural Referral Center (January 2019).
20 Sole Community Provider (January 2019).
21 Accreditation by DNV Healthcare Inc. (January 2019).
22 Accreditation by Center for Improvement in Healthcare Quality (January 2019).

Nonreporting indicates that the 2018 Annual Survey questionnaire for the hospital was not received prior to publication.

② Healthcare System Name

The inclusion of the letter "S" (1) indicates that the hospital belongs to a health care system and (2) identifies the specific system to which the hospital belongs.

③ Titles of Chief Administrators

④ Control and Service Classification

For a list of control and service classifications, see page A13.

Control–The type of organization that is responsible for establishing policy for overall operation of the hospital.

Service–The type of service the hospital provides to the majority of admissions.

⑤ Utilization Data

Definitions are based on the American Hospital Association's Hospital Administration Terminology. In completing the survey, hospitals were requested to report data for a full year, in accord with their fiscal year, ending in 2017.

Beds–Number of beds regularly maintained (set up and staffed for use) for inpatients as of the close of the reporting period. Excludes newborn bassinets.

Admissions–Number of patients accepted for inpatient service during a 12–month period; does not include newborn.

Census–Average number of inpatients receiving care each day during the 12–month reporting period; does not include newborn.

Outpatient Visits–A visit by a patient who is not lodged in the hospital while receiving medical, dental, or other services. Each appearance of an outpatient in each unit constitutes one visit regardless of the number of diagnostic and/or therapeutic treatments that a patient receives.

Births–Number of infants born in the hospital and accepted for service in a newborn infant bassinet during a 12–month period; excludes stillbirths.

Expense: Expense for a 12–month period; both total expense and payroll components are shown. Payroll expenses include all salaries and wages.

Personnel: Represents personnel situations as they existed at the end of the reporting period; includes full-time equivalents of part–time personnel. Full–time equivalents were calculated on the basis that two part–time persons equal one full–time person.

Sample Hospital Listing:

ANYTOWN, Universal County

⊠ **ANYTOWN HOSPITAL & CLINICS (777777),** (Formerly Anytown Area Community Hospital and Clinic), 100 South Main Street, Zip 12345–6789; tel. 123/456–7890 **A**9 10] ①
F10 12 23 24 29 30 31 37 39 49 51 55 57 64 65 66 68 70 71 72 77 78 83 87 88 91 96 97 106 107 110 111 113 124 **S** Universal ⎤ ⑥
County Health System ②
Primary Contact: Ann M. Generic, Chief Executive Officer
COO: Ann M. Generic
CFO: Michael M. Generic
CMO: Peterl Van Generic, President Medical Staff ③
CHR: Jerry Generic, Human Resources Director
CNO: Danielle Generic, R.N., Chief Nursing Officer
Web address: www.website.org
Control: Other not–for–profit (including NFP Corporation) **Service:** General ⎤ ④
Medical and Surgical

Staffed Beds: 25 **Admissions:** 892 **Census:** 9 **Outpatient Visits:** 44014
Births: 51 **Total Expense ($000):** 19210 **Payroll Expense ($000):** 5864 ⑤
Personnel: 182

ANYTOWN, Universal County

⊠ **ANYTOWN HOSPITAL & CLINICS (777777),** (Formerly Anytown Area Community Hospital and Clinic), 100 South Main Street, Zip 12345–6789; tel. 123/456–7890 **A**9 10

① = **Approval Codes**
② = **Health Care System Name**
③ = **Titles of Chief Administrators**
④ = **Control and Service Classifications**
⑤ = **Utilization Data**
⑥ = **Facility Codes**

Hospital, Medicare Provider Number, Address, Telephone, Approval, Facility, and Health Care System
★ American Hospital Association (AHA) membership ○ Healthcare Facilities Accreditation Program ⇑ Center for Improvement in Healthcare Quality Accreditation
☐ The Joint Commission accreditation ◇ DNV Healthcare Inc. accreditation △ Commission on Accreditation of Rehabilitation Facilities (CARF) accreditation

⑥ **Facility Codes**

Provided directly by the hospital; for definitions, see page A6.

(Numerical Order)

1 Acute long-term care
2 Adult day care program
3 Airborne infection isolation room
4 Alcoholism-drug abuse or dependency inpatient services
5 Alcoholism-drug abuse or dependency outpatient services
6 Alzheimer center
7 Ambulance services
8 Ambulatory surgery center
9 Arthritis treatment center
10 Assisted living
11 Auxiliary
12 Bariatric/weight control services
13 Birthing room-LDR room-LDRP room
14 Blood donor center
15 Breast cancer screening/mammograms
16 Burn care services
17 Cardiac intensive care
18 Adult cardiology services
19 Pediatric cardiology services
20 Adult diagnostic catheterization
21 Pediatric diagnostic catheterization
22 Adult interventional cardiac catheterization
23 Pediatric interventional cardiac catheterization
24 Adult cardiac surgery
25 Pediatric cardiac surgery
26 Adult cardiac electrophysiology
27 Pediatric cardiac electrophysiology
28 Cardiac rehabilitation
29 Case management
30 Chaplaincy/pastoral care services
31 Chemotherapy
32 Children's wellness program
33 Chiropractic services
34 Community health education
35 Community outreach
36 Complementary and alternative medicine services
37 Computer assisted orthopedic surgery (CAOS)
38 Crisis prevention
39 Dental services
40 On-campus emergency department
41 Pediatric emergency department
42 Off-campus emergency department
43 Trauma center (certified)
44 Enabling services
45 Optical colonoscopy
46 Endoscopic ultrasound
47 Ablation of Barrett's esophagus
48 Esophageal impedance study
49 Endoscopic retrograde cholangiopancreatography (ERCP)
50 Enrollment assistance services
51 Extracorporeal shock wave lithotripter (ESWL)
52 Fertility clinic

53 Fitness center
54 Freestanding outpatient care center
55 Genetic testing/counseling
56 Geriatric services
57 Health fair
58 Health research
59 Health screenings
60 Hemodialysis
61 HIV–AIDS services
62 Home health services
63 Hospice program
64 Hospital–based outpatient care center services
65 Immunization program
66 Indigent care clinic
67 Intermediate nursing care
68 Linguistic/translation services
69 Meal delivery services
70 Medical surgical intensive care services
71 Mobile health services
72 Neonatal intensive care
73 Neonatal intermediate care
74 Neurological services
75 Nutrition programs
76 Obstetrics
77 Occupational health services
78 Oncology services
79 Orthopedic services
80 Other special care
81 Outpatient surgery
82 Pain management program
83 Inpatient palliative care unit
84 Palliative care program
85 Patient controlled analgesia (PCA)
86 Patient education center
87 Patient representative services
88 Pediatric intensive care services
89 Pediatric medical–surgical care
90 Physical rehabilitation inpatient services
91 Assistive technology center
92 Electrodiagnostic services
93 Physical rehabilitation outpatient services
94 Prosthetic and orthotic services
95 Robot-assisted walking therapy
96 Simulated rehabilitation environment
97 Primary care department
98 Psychiatric care
99 Psychiatric pediatric care
100 Psychiatric consultation–liaison services
101 Psychiatric education services
102 Psychiatric emergency services
103 Psychiatric geriatric services
104 Psychiatric outpatient services
105 Psychiatric partial hospitalization services
106 Psychiatric residential treatment
107 CT scanner
108 Diagnostic radioisotope facility

109 Electron beam computed tomography (EBCT)
110 Full–field digital mammography (FFDM)
111 Magnetic resonance imaging (MRI)
112 Intraoperative magnetic resonance imaging
113 Magnetoencephalography (MEG)
114 Multi–slice spiral computed tomography (MSCT) (<64 slice CT)
115 Multi–slice spiral computed tomography (64 + slice CT)
116 Positron emission tomography (PET)
117 Positron emission tomography/CT (PET/CT)
118 Single photon emission computerized tomography (SPECT)
119 Ultrasound
120 Image–guided radiation therapy (IGRT)
121 Intensity–modulated radiation therapy (IMRT)
122 Proton beam therapy
123 Shaped beam radiation therapy
124 Stereotactic radiosurgery
125 Retirement housing
126 Robotic surgery
127 Rural health clinic
128 Skilled nursing care
129 Sleep center
130 Social work services
131 Sports medicine
132 Support groups
133 Swing bed services
134 Teen outreach services
135 Tobacco treatment/cessation program
136 Bone marrow transplant services
137 Heart transplant
138 Kidney transplant
139 Liver transplant
140 Lung transplant
141 Tissue transplant
142 Other transplant
143 Transportation to health services
144 Urgent care center
145 Virtual colonoscopy
146 Volunteer services department
147 Women's health center/services
148 Wound management services
149 Violence prevention programs for the workplace
150 Violence prevention programs for the community
151 Alcoholism-chemical dependency pediatric services
152 Alcoholism-chemical dependency partial hospitalization services
153 Psychiatric intensive outpatient services
154 Telehealth
155 Air ambulance services
156 Diabetes prevention program
157 Employment support services
158 Supportive housing services

Annual Survey

Each year, an annual survey of hospitals is conducted by the American Hospital Association through its Health Forum affiliate.

The facilities and services found below are provided by the hospital. For data products reflecting the services provided by a hospital through its health care system, or network or through a formal arrangement with another provider contact Health Forum at 800/821–2039, or visit www.healthforum.com.

The AHA Guide to the Health Care Field does not include all data collected from the 2018 Annual Survey. Requests for purchasing other Annual Survey data should be directed to Health Forum LLC, an affiliate of the American Hospital Association, 155 N. Wacker Drive, Chicago, IL 60606, 800/821–2039.

Definitions of Facility Codes

1. **Acute long–term care.** Provides specialized acute hospital care to medically complex patients who are critically ill, have multisystem complications and/or failure, and require hospitalization averaging 25 days, in a facility offering specialized treatment programs and therapeutic intervention on a 24–hour/7 day a week basis.

2. **Adult day care program.** Program providing supervision, medical and psychological care, and social activities for older adults who live at home or in another family setting, but cannot be alone or prefer to be with others during the day. May include intake assessment, health monitoring, occupational therapy, personal care, noon meal, and transportation services.

3. **Airborne infection isolation room.** A single–occupancy room for patient care where environmental factors are controlled in an effort to minimize the transmission of those infectious agents, usually spread person to person by droplet nuclei associated with coughing and inhalation. Such rooms typically have specific ventilation requirements for controlled ventilation, air pressure and filtration.

4. **Alcoholism–drug abuse or dependency inpatient unit.** Provides diagnosis and therapeutic services to patients with alcoholism or other drug dependencies. Includes care for inpatient/residential treatment for patients whose course of treatment involves more intensive care than provided in an outpatient setting or where patient requires supervised withdrawal.

5. **Alcoholism–drug abuse or dependency outpatient unit.** Organized hospital services that provide medical care and/or rehabilitative treatment services to outpatients for whom the primary diagnosis is alcoholism or other chemical dependency.

6. **Alzheimer center.** Facility that offers care to persons with Alzheimer's disease and their families through an integrated program of clinical services, research, and education.

7. **Ambulance services.** Provision of ambulance services to the ill and injured who require medical attention on a scheduled or unscheduled basis.

8. **Ambulatory surgery center.** Facility that provides care to patients requiring surgery who are admitted and discharged on the same day. Ambulatory surgery centers are distinct from same day surgical units within the hospital outpatient departments for purposes of Medicare payments.

9. **Arthritis treatment center.** Specifically equipped and staffed center for the diagnosis and treatment of arthritis and other joint disorders.

10. **Assisted living.** A special combination of housing, supportive services, personalized assistance and health care designed to respond to the individual needs of those who need help in activities of daily living and instrumental activities of daily living. Supportive services are available, 24 hours a day, to meet scheduled and unscheduled needs, in a way that promotes maximum independence and dignity for each resident and encourages the involvement of a resident's family, neighbor and friends.

11. **Auxiliary.** A volunteer community organization formed to assist the hospital in carrying out its purpose and to serve as a link between the institution and the community.

12. **Bariatric/weight control services.** Bariatrics is the medical practice of weight reduction.

13. **Birthing room–LDR room–LDRP room.** A single room–type of maternity care with a more homelike setting for families than the traditional three–room unit (labor/delivery/recovery) with a separate postpartum area. A birthing room combines labor and delivery in one room. An LDR room accommodates three stages in the birthing process—labor, delivery, and recovery. An LDRP room accommodates all four stages of the birth process—labor, delivery, recovery and postpartum.

14. **Blood donor center.** A facility that performs, or is responsible for the collection, processing, testing or distribution of blood and components.

15. **Breast cancer screening/ mammograms**. Mammography screening–the use of breast x–ray to detect unsuspected breast cancer in asymptomatic women. Diagnostic mammography–the x–ray imaging of breast tissue in symptomatic women who are considered to have a substantial likelihood of having breast cancer already.

16. **Burn care services**. Provides care to severely burned patients. Severely burned patients are those with any of the following: 1. Second–degree burns of more than 25% total body surface area for adults or 20% total body surface area for children; 2. Third–degree burns of more than 10% total body surface area; 3. Any severe burns of the hands, face, eyes, ears or feet or; 4. All inhalation injuries, electrical burns, complicated burn injuries involving fractures and other major traumas, and all other poor risk factors.

17. **Cardiac intensive care.** Provides patient care of a more specialized nature than the usual medical and surgical care, on the basis of

physicians' orders and approved nursing care plans. The unit is staffed with specially trained nursing personnel and contains monitoring and specialized support or treatment equipment for patients who, because of heart seizure, one-heart surgery, or other life-threatening conditions, require intensified, comprehensive observation and care. May include myocardial infarction, pulmonary care, and heart transplant units.

18. **Adult cardiology services.** An organized clinical service offering diagnostic and interventional procedures to manage the full range of adult heart conditions.

19. **Pediatric cardiology services.**

20. **Adult diagnostic catheterization.** (also called coronary angiography or coronary arteriography) is used to assist in diagnosing complex heart conditions. Cardiac angiography involves the insertion of a tiny catheter up into the artery in the groin then carefully threading the catheter up into the aorta where the coronary arteries originate. Once the catheter is in place, a dye is injected which allows the cardiologist to see the size, shape and distribution of the coronary arteries. These images are used to diagnose heart disease and to determine, among other things, whether or not surgery is indicated.

21. **Pediatric diagnostic catheterization.** (also called coronary angiography or coronary arteriography) is used to assist in diagnosing complex heart conditions. Cardiac angiography involves the insertion of a tiny catheter up into the artery in the groin then carefully threading the catheter up into the aorta where the coronary arteries originate. Once the catheter is in place, a dye is injected which allows the cardiologist to see the size, shape and distribution of the coronary arteries. These images are used to diagnose heart disease and to determine, among other things, whether or not surgery is indicated.

22. **Adult interventional cardiac catheterization.** Nonsurgical procedure that utilizes the same basic principles as diagnostic catheterization and then uses advanced the techniques to improve the heart's function. It can be less invasive alternative to heart surgery.

23. **Pediatric diagnostic catheterization.** Nonsurgical procedure that utilizes the same basic principles as diagnostic catheterization and then uses advanced the techniques to improve the heart's function. It can be less invasive alternative to heart surgery.

24. **Adult cardiac surgery.** Includes minimally invasive procedures that include surgery done with only a small incision or no incision at all, such as through a laparoscope or an endoscope and more invasive major surgical procedures that include open chest and open heart surgery.

25. **Pediatric cardiac surgery.** Includes minimally invasive procedures that include surgery done with only a small incision or no incision at all, such as through a laparoscope or an endoscope and more invasive major surgical procedures that include open chest and open heart surgery defibrillator implantation and follow- up.

26. **Adult cardiac electrophysiology.** Evaluation and management of patients with complex rhythm or conduction abnormalities, including diagnostic testing, treatment of arrhythmias by catheter ablation or drug therapy, and pacemaker/ defibrillator implantation and follow- up.

27. **Pediatric cardiac electrophysiology.**

28. **Cardiac rehabilitation.** A medically supervised program to help heart patients recover quickly and improve their overall physical and mental functioning. The goal is to reduce risk of another cardiac event or to keep an already present heart condition from getting worse. Cardiac rehabilitation programs include: counseling to patients, an exercise program, helping patients modify risk factors such as smoking and high blood pressure, providing vocational guidance to enable the patient to return to work, supplying information on physical limitations and lending emotional support.

29. **Case management.** A system of assessment, treatment planning, referral and follow–up that ensures the provision of comprehensive and continuous services and the coordination of payment and reimbursement for care.

30. **Chaplaincy/pastoral care services.** A service ministering religious activities and providing pastoral counseling to patients, their families, and staff of a health care organization.

31. **Chemotherapy.** An organized program for the treatment of cancer by the use of drugs or chemicals.

32. **Children's wellness program.** A program that encourages improved health status and a healthful lifestyle of children through health education, exercise, nutrition and health promotion.

33. **Chiropractic services.** An organized clinical service including spinal manipulation or adjustment and related diagnostic and therapeutic services.

34. **Community health education.** Education that provides health information to individuals and populations as well as support for personal, family and community health decisions with the objective of improving health status.

35. **Community outreach.** A program that systematically interacts with the community to identify those in need of services, alerting persons and their families to the availability of services, locating needed services, and enabling persons to enter the service delivery system.

36. **Complementary and alternative medicine services.** Organized hospital services or formal arrangements to providers that provide care or treatment not based solely on traditional western allopathic medical teachings as instructed in most U.S. medical schools. Includes any of the following; acupuncture, chiropractic, homeopathy, osteopathy, diet and lifestyle changes, herbal medicine, massage therapy, etc.

37. **Computer assisted orthopedic surgery (CAOS).** Orthopedic surgery using computer technology, enabling three–dimensional graphic models to visualize a patient's anatomy.

38. **Crisis prevention.** Services provided in order to promote physical and mental well being and the early identification of disease and ill health prior to the onset and recognition of symptoms so as to permit early treatment.

39. **Dental services.** An organized dental service, not necessarily involving special facilities, that provides dental or oral services to inpatients or outpatients.

40. **On-campus emergency department.** Hospital facilities for the provision of unscheduled outpatient services to patients whose conditions require immediate care. Must be staffed 24 hours a day.

41. **Pediatric emergency department.** Hospital facilities for the provision of unscheduled outpatient services to patients whose conditions require immediate care.

42. **Off-campus emergency department.** A facility owned and operated by the hospital but physically separate from the hospital for the provision of unscheduled outpatient services to patients whose conditions require immediate care. A freestanding ED is not physically connected to a hospital but has all the necessary emergency staffing and equipment on site.

43. **Trauma center (certified).** A facility certified to provide emergency and specialized intensive care to critically ill and injured patients.

44. **Enabling services.** A program that is designed to help the patient access health care services by offering any of the following linguistic services, transportation services, and/or referrals to local social services agencies.

45. **Optical colonoscopy.** An examination of the interior of the colon using a long, flexible, lighted tube with a small built-in camera.

46. **Endoscopic ultrasound.** Specially designed endoscope that incorporates an ultrasound transducer used to obtain detailed images of organs in the chest and abdomen. The endoscope can be passed through the mouth or the anus. When combined with needle biopsy the procedure can assist in diagnosis and staging of cancer.

47. **Ablation of Barrett's esophagus.** Premalignant condition that can lead to adenocarcinoma of the esophagus. The non surgical ablation of the premalignant tissue in Barrett's esophagus by the application of thermal energy or light through an endoscope passed from the mouth into the esophagus.

48. **Esophageal impedance study.** A test in which a catheter is placed through the nose into the esophagus to measure whether gas or liquids are passing from the stomach into the esophagus and causing symptoms.

49. **Endoscopic retrograde cholangiopancreatography (ERCP).** A procedure in which a catheter is introduced through an endoscope into the bile ducts and pancreatic ducts. Injection of contrast materials permits detailed x-ray of these structures. The procedure is used diagnostically as well as therapeutically to relieve obstruction or remove stones

50. **Enrollment assistance services.** A program that provides enrollment assistance for patients who are potentially eligible for public health insurance programs such as Medicaid, State Children's Health Insurance, or local/state indigent care programs. The specific services offered could include explanation of benefits, assist applicants in completing the application and locating all relevant documents, conduct eligibilty interviews, and/or forward applications and documentation to state/local social service or health agency.

51. **Extracorporeal shock wave lithotripter (ESWL).** A medical device used for treating stones in the kidney or urethra. The device disintegrates kidney stones noninvasively through the transmission of acoustic shock waves directed at the stones.

52. **Fertility clinic.** A specialized program set in an infertility center that provides counseling and education as well as advanced reproductive techniques such as: injectable therapy, reproductive surgeries, treatment for endometriosis, male factor infertility, tubal reversals in vitro fertilization (IVF), donor eggs, and other such services to help patients achieve successful pregnancies.

53. **Fitness center.** Provides exercise, testing, or evaluation programs and fitness activities to the community and hospital employees.

54. **Freestanding outpatient care center.** A facility owned and operated by the hospital, but physically separate from the hospital, that provides various medical treatments on an outpatient basis only. In addition to treating minor illnesses or injuries, the center will stabilize seriously ill or injured patients before transporting them to a hospital. Laboratory and radiology services are usually available.

55. **Genetic testing/counseling.** A service equipped with adequate laboratory facilities and directed by a qualified physician to advise parents and prospective parents on potential problems in cases of genetic defects. A genetic test is the analysis of human DNA, RNA, chromosomes, proteins, and certain metabolites in order to detect heritable disease– related genotypes, mutations, phenotypes, or karyotypes for clinical purposes. Genetic tests can have diverse purposes, including the diagnosis of genetic diseases in newborns, children, and adults; the identification of future health risks; the prediction of drug responses; and the assessment of risks to future children.

56. **Geriatric services.** The branch of medicine dealing with the physiology of aging and the diagnosis and treatment of disease affecting the aged. Services could include: Adult day care program; Alzheimer's diagnostic–assessment services; Comprehensive geriatric assessment; Emergency response system; Geriatric acute care unit; and/or Geriatric clinics.

57. **Health fair.** Community health education events that focus on the prevention of disease and promotion of health through such activities as audiovisual exhibits and free diagnostic services.

58. **Health research.** Organized hospital research program in any of the following areas: basic research, clinical research, community health research, and/or research on innovative health care delivery.

59. **Health screenings.** A preliminary procedure, such as a test or examination to detect the most characteristic sign or signs of a disorder that may require further investigation.

60. **Hemodialysis.** Provision of equipment and personnel for the treatment of renal insufficiency on an inpatient or outpatient basis.

61. **HIV–AIDS services.** Services may include one or more of the following: HIV–AIDS unit (special unit or team designated and equipped specifically for diagnosis, treatment, continuing care planning, and counseling services for HIV–AIDS patients and their families.) General inpatient care for HIV–AIDS (inpatient diagnosis and treatment for human immunodeficiency virus and acquired immunodeficiency syndrome patients, but dedicated unit is not available.) Specialized outpatient program for HIV–AIDS (special outpatient program providing diagnostic, treatment, continuing care planning, and counseling

for HIV–AIDS patients and their families.)

62. **Home health services.** Service providing nursing, therapy, and health–related homemaker or social services in the patient's home.

63. **Hospice program.** A program providing palliative care, chiefly medical relief of pain and supportive services, addressing the emotional, social, financial, and legal needs of terminally ill patients and their families. Care can be provided in a variety of settings, both inpatient and at home.

64. **Hospital–based outpatient care center services.** Organized hospital health care services offered by appointment on an ambulatory basis. Services may include outpatient surgery, examination, diagnosis, and treatment of a variety of medical conditions on a nonemergency basis, and laboratory and other diagnostic testing as ordered by staff or outside physician referral.

65. **Immunization program.** Program that plans, coordinates and conducts immunization services in the community.

66. **Indigent care clinic.** Health care services for uninsured and underinsured persons where care is free of charge or charged on a sliding scale. This would include "free clinics" staffed by volunteer practitioners, but could also be staffed by employees with sponsoring health care organizations subsidizing the cost of service.

67. **Intermediate nursing care.** Provides health–related services (skilled nursing care and social services) to residents with a variety of physical conditions or functional disabilities. These residents do not require the care provided by a hospital or skilled nursing facility, but do need supervision and support services.

68. **Linguistic/translation services.** Services provided by the hospital designed to make health care more accessible to non–English speaking patients and their physicians.

69. **Meal delivery services.** A hospital sponsored program which delivers meals to people, usually the elderly, who are unable to prepare their own meals. Low cost, nutritional meals are delivered to individuals' homes on a regular basis.

70. **Medical surgical intensive care services.** Provides patient care of a more intensive nature than the usual medical and surgical care, on the basis of physicians' orders and approved nursing care plans. These units are staffed with specially trained nursing personnel and contain monitoring and specialized support equipment of patients who, because of shock, trauma, or other life–threatening conditions, require intensified, comprehensive observation and care. Includes mixed intensive care units.

71. **Mobile health services.** Vans and other vehicles used to deliver primary care services.

72. **Neonatal intensive care.** A unit that must be separate from the newborn nursery providing intensive care to all sick infants including those with the very lowest birth weights (less that 1500 grams). NICU has potential for providing mechanical ventilation, neonatal surgery, and special care for the sickest infants born in the hospital or transferred from another institution. A full–time neonatologist serves as director of the NICU.

73. **Neonatal intermediate care.** A unit that must be separate from the normal newborn nursery and that provides intermediate and/or recovery care and some specialized services, including immediate resuscitation, intravenous therapy, and capacity for prolonged oxygen therapy and monitoring.

74. **Neurological services.** Services provided by the hospital dealing with the operative and nonoperative management of disorders of the central, peripheral, and autonomic nervous system.

75. **Nutrition programs.** Those services within a health care facility which are designed to provide inexpensive, nutritionally sound meals to patients.

76. **Obstetrics.** Levels should be designated: (1) unit provides services for uncomplicated maternity and newborn cases; (2) unit provides services for uncomplicated cases, the majority of complicated problems, and special neonatal services; and (3) unit provides services for all serious illnesses and abnormalities and is supervised by a full–time maternal/ fetal specialist.

77. **Occupational health services.** Includes services designed to protect the safety of employees from hazards in the work environment.

78. **Oncology services.** Inpatient and outpatient services for patients with cancer, including comprehensive care, support and guidance in addition to patient education and preventiion, chemotherapy, counseling, and other treatment methods.

79. **Orthopedic services.** Services provided for the prevention or correction of injuries or disorders of the skeletal system and associated muscles, joints, and ligaments.

80. **Other special care.** Provides care to patients requiring care more intensive than that provided in the acute area, yet not sufficiently intensive to require admission to an intensive care unit. Patients admitted to the area are usually transferred here from an intensive care unit once their condition has improved. These units are sometimes referred to as definitive observation, step–down, or progressive care units.

81. **Outpatient surgery.** Scheduled surgical services provided to patients who do not remain in the hospital overnight. The surgery may be performed in operating suites also used for inpatient surgery, specially designated surgical suites for outpatient surgery, or procedure rooms within an outpatient care facility.

82. **Pain management program.** A hospital wide formalized program that includes staff education for the management of chronic and acute pain based on guidelines and protocols like those developed by the agency for Health Care Policy Research, etc.

83. **Inpatient palliative care unit.** An inpatient palliative care ward is a physically discreet, inpatient nursing unit where the focus is palliative care. The patient care focus is on symptom relief for complex patients who may be continuing to undergo primary treatment. Care is delivered by palliative medicine specialists.

84. **Palliative care program.** An organized program providing specialized medical care, drugs or therapies for the management of acute or chronic pain and/or the control of symptoms adminstered by specially trained physicians and

other clinicians; and supportive care services, such as counseling on advanced directives, spiritual care, and social services, to patients with advanced disease and their families.

85. **Patient controlled analgesia (PCA).** Patient Controlled Analgesia (PCA) is intravenously administered pain medicine under the patient's control. The patient has a button on the end of a cord than can be pushed at will, whenever more pain medicine is desired. This button will only deliver more pain medicine at pre-determined intervals, as programmed by the doctor's order.

86. **Patient education center.** Written goals and objectives for the patient and/or family related to therapeutic regimens, medical procedures, and self care.

87. **Patient representative services.** Organized hospital services providing personnel through whom patients and staff can seek solutions to institutional problems affecting the delivery of high-quality care and services.

88. **Pediatric intensive care services.** Provides care to pediatric patients that is of a more intensive nature than that usually provided to pediatric patients. The unit is staffed with specially trained personnel and contains monitoring and specialized support equipment for treatment of patients who, because of shock, trauma, or other life-threatening conditions, require intensified, comprehensive observation and care.

89. **Pediatric medical-surgical care.** Provides acute care to pediatric settings) or in a traditional setting (gymnasium) using motor learning principles.

90. **Physical rehabilitation inpatient services.** Provides care encompassing a comprehensive array of restoration services for the disabled and all support services necessary to help patients attain their maximum functional capacity.

91. **Assistive technology center.** A program providing access to specialized hardware and software with adaptations allowing individuals greater independence with mobility, dexterity, or increased communication options.

92. **Electrodiagnostic services.** Diagnostic testing services for nerve and muscle function including services such as nerve conduction studies and needle electromyography.

93. **Physical rehabilitation outpatient services.** Outpatient program providing medical, health-related, therapy, social, and/or vocational services to help disabled persons attain or retain their maximum functional capacity.

94. **Prosthetic and orthotic services.** Services providing comprehensive prosthetic and orthotic evaluation, fitting, and training.

95. **Robot-assisted walking therapy.** A form of physical therapy that uses a courts, public health nurses, welfare agencies, clergy and so forth. The purpose is to expand the mental health knowledge and competence of personnel not working in the mental health field and to promote good mental health through improved understanding, attitudes, and behavioral patterns.

96. **Simulated rehabilitation environment.** Rehabilitation focused on retraining functional skills in a contextually appropriate environment (simulated home and community settings) or in a traditional setting (gymnasium) using motor learning principles.

97. **Primary care department.** A unit or clinic within the hospital that provides primary care services (e.g. general pediatric care, general internal medicine, family practice and gynecology) through hospital-salaried medical and or nursing staff, focusing on evaluating and diagnosing medical problems and providing medical treatment on an outpatient basis.

98. **Psychiatric care.** Provides acute or long-term care to emotionally disturbed patients, including patients admitted for diagnosis and those admitted for treatment of psychiatric problems, on the basis of physicians' orders and approved nursing care plans. Long-term care may include intervention, and assistance to persons suffering acute emotional or mental distress.

99. **Psychiatric pediatric care.** The branch of medicine focused on the diagnosis, treatment, and prevention of mental, emotional, and behavioral disorders in pediatric patients.

100. **Psychiatric consultation-liaison services.** Provides organized psychiatric consultation/liaison services to nonpsychiatric hospital staff and/or department on psychological aspects of medical care that may be generic or specific to individual patients.

101. **Psychiatric education services.** Provides psychiatric educational services to community agencies and workers such as schools, police, courts, public health nurses, welfare agencies, clergy and so forth. The purpose is to expand the mental health knowledge and competence of personnel not working in the mental health field and to promote good mental health through improved understanding, attitudes, and behavioral patterns.

102. **Psychiatric emergency services.** Services or facilities available on a 24-hour basis to provide immediate unscheduled outpatient care, diagnosis, evaluation, crisis intervention, and assistance to persons suffering acute emotional or mental distress.

103. **Psychiatric geriatric services.** Provides care to emotionally disturbed elderly patients, including those admitted for diagnosis and those admitted for treatment.

104. **Psychiatric outpatient services.** Provides medical care, including diagnosis and treatment of psychiatric outpatients.

105. **Psychiatric partial hospitalization services.** Organized hospital services of intensive day/evening outpatient services of three hours or more duration, distinguished from other outpatient visits of one hour.

106. **Psychiatric residential treatment.**

107. **CT scanner.** Computed tomographic scanner for head and whole body scans.

108. **Diagnostic radioisotope facility.** The use of radioactive isotopes (Radiopharmaceutical) as tracers or indicators to detect an abnormal condition or disease.

109. **Electron beam computed tomography (EBCT).** A high tech computed tomography scan used to detect coronary artery disease by measuring coronary calcifications. This imaging procedure uses electron beams which are magnetically steered to produce a visual of the coronary artery and the images are produced faster than conventional CT scans.

110. **Full–field digital mammography (FFDM).** Combines the x–ray generators and tubes used in analog screen–film mammography (SFM) with a detector plate that converts the x–rays into a digital signal.

111. **Magnetic resonance imaging (MRI).** The use of a uniform magnetic field and radio frequencies to study tissue and structure of the body. This procedure enables the visualization of biochemical activity of the cell in vivo without the use of ionizing radiation, radioisotopic substances, or high–frequency sound.

112. **Intraoperative magnetic resonance imaging.** An integrated surgery system which provides an MRI system in an operating room. The system allows for immediate evaluation of the degree to tumor resection while the patient is undergoing a surgical resection. Intraoperative MRI exists when a MRI (low–field or high–field) is placed in the operating theater and is used during surgical resection without moving the patient from the operating room to the diagnostic imaging suite.

113. **Magnetoencephalography (MEG).** A noninvasive neurophysiological measurement tool used to study magnetic fields generated by neuronal activity of the brain. MEG provides direct information about the dynamics of evoked and spontaneous neural activity and the location of their sources in the brain. The primary uses of MEG include assisting surgeons in localizing the source of epilepsy, sensory mapping and the study of brain function. When it is combined with structural imaging, it is known as magnetic source imaging (MSI).

114. **Multi–slice spiral computed tomography (MSCT) (<64 slice CT).** A specialized computed tomography cycles per second to visualize internal body structures.

115. **Multi–slice spiral computed tomography (64 + slice CT).** Involves the acquisition of volumetric tomographic x–ray absorption data expressed in Hounsfield units using multiple rows of detectors. 64+ systems reconstruct the equivalent of 64 or greater slices to cover the imaged volume.

116. **Positron emission tomography (PET).** A nuclear medicine imaging technology which uses radioactive (positron emitting) isotopes created in a cyclotron or generator and computers to produce composite pictures of the brain and heart at work. PET scanning produces sectional images depicting metabolic activity or blood flow rather than anatomy.

117. **Positron emission tomography/ CT (PET/CT).** Provides metabolic functional information for the monitoring of chemotherapy, radiotherapy and surgical planning.

118. **Single photon emission computerized tomography (SPECT).** A nuclear medicine imaging technology that combines existing technology of gamma camera imaging with computed tomographic imaging technology to provide a more precise and clear image.

119. **Ultrasound.** The use of acoustic waves above the range of 20,000 cycles per second to visualize internal body structures.

120. **Image–guided radiation therapy (IGRT).** Automated system for image– guided radiation therapy that enables clinicians to obtain high–resolution x– ray images to pinpoint tumor sites, adjust patient positioning when necessary, and complete a treatment, all within the standard treatment time slot, allowing for more effective cancer treatments.

121. **Intensity–modulated radiation Therapy (IMRT).** A type of three–dimensional radiation therapy, which improves the targeting of treatment delivery in a way that is likely to decrease damage to normal tissues and allows varying intensities diagnosis of genetic diseases in newborns, children, and adults; the identification of future health risks; arrange for acute and long term care through affiliated institutions.

122. **Proton beam therapy.** A form of radiation therapy which administers proton beams. While producing the same biologic effects as x–ray beams, the energy distribution of protons differs from conventional x–ray beams in that they can be more precisely focused in tissue volumes in a three–dimensional pattern resulting in less surrounding tissue damage than conventional radiation therapy permitting administration of higher doses.

123. **Shaped beam radiation therapy.** A precise, non–invasive treatment that involves targeting beams of radiation that mirror the exact size and shape of a tumor at a specific area of a tumor to shrink or destroy cancerous cells. This procedure delivers a therapeutic dose of radiation that conforms precisely to the shape of the tumor, thus minimizing the risk to nearby tissues.

124. **Stereotactic radiosurgery.** Stereotactic radiosurgery (SRS) is a radiotherapy modality that delivers a high dosage of radiation to a discrete treatment area in as few as one treatment session. Includes gamma knife, cyberknife, etc.

125. **Retirement housing.** A facility which provides social activities to senior citizens, usually retired persons, who do not require health care but some short–term skilled nursing care may be provided. A retirement center may furnish housing and may also have acute hospital and long–term care facilities, or it may arrange for acute and long term care through affiliated institutions.

126. **Robotic surgery.** The use of mechanical guidance devices to remotely manipulate surgical instrumentation.

127. **Rural health clinic.** A clinic located in a rural, medically under-served area in the United States that has a separate reimbursement structure from the standard medical office under the Medicare and Medicaid programs.

128. **Skilled nursing care.** Provides non–acute medical and skilled nursing care services, therapy, and social services under the supervision of a licensed registered nurse on a 24–hour basis.

129. **Sleep center.** Specially equipped and staffed center for the diagnosis and treatment of sleep disorders.

130. **Social work services.** Services may include one or more of the following: Organized social work services (services that are properly directed and sufficiently staffed by qualified individuals who provide assistance and counseling to patients and their families in dealing with social, emotional, and environmental problems associated with illness or disability, often in the context of financial or discharge planning coordination.) Outpatient social work services (social work services provided in ambulatory care areas.) Emergency department social work services (social work services provided to emergency department patients by social workers dedicated to the emergency department or on call.)

131. **Sports medicine.** Provision of diagnostic screening and assessment and clinical and rehabilitation services for the prevention and treatment of sports–related injuries.

132. **Support groups.** A hospital sponsored program which allows a group of individuals with the same or similar problems who meet periodically to share experiences, problems, and solutions, in order to support each other.

133. **Swing bed services.** A hospital bed that can be used to provide either acute or long–term care depending on community or patients needs. To be eligible a hospital must have a Medicare provider agreement in place, have fewer than 100 beds, be located in a rural area, not have a 24 hour nursing service waiver in effect, have not been terminated from the program in the prior two years, and meet various service conditions.

134. **Teen outreach services.** A program focusing on the teenager which encourages an improved health status and a healthful lifestyle including physical, emotional, mental, social, spiritual and economic health through education, exercise, nutrition and health promotion.

135. **Tobacco treatment/cessation program.** Organized hospital services with the purpose of ending tobacco–use habits of patients addicted to tobacco/nicotine.

136.–142. **Transplant services.** The branch of medicine that transfers an organ or tissue from one person to another or from one body part to another to replace a diseased structure or to restore function or to change appearance. Services could include: Bone marrow transplant program (136. Bone marrow); heart (137. Heart transplant), kidney (138. Kidney transplant), liver (139. Liver transplant) lung (140. Lung transplant), tissue (141. Tissue transplant). Please include heart/lung or other multi- transplant surgeries inn other (142. Other Transplant).

143. **Transportation to health services.** A long–term care support service designed to assist the mobility of the elderly. Some programs offer improved financial access by offering reduced rates and barrier–free buses or vans with ramps and lifts to assist the elderly or handicapped; others offer subsidies for public transport systems or operate mini–bus services

144. **Urgent care center.** A facility that provides care and treatment for problems that are not life–threatening but require attention over the short term. These units function like emergency rooms but are separate from hospitals with which they may have backup affiliation arrangements.

145. **Virtual colonoscopy.** Noninvasive screening procedure used to visualize, analyze and detect cancerous or potentially cancerous polyps in the colon.

146. **Volunteer services department.** An organized hospital department responsible for coordinating the services of volunteers working within the institution.

147. **Women's center.** An area set aside for coordinated education and treatment services specifically for and promoted by women as provided by this special unit. Services may or may not include obstetrics but include a range of services other than OB.

148. **Wound management services.** Services for patients with chronic wounds and non–healing wounds often resulting from diabetes, poor circulation, improper seating and immunocompromising conditions. The goals are to progress chronic wounds through stages of healing, reduce and eliminate infections, increase physical function to minimize complications from current wounds and prevent future chronic wounds. Wound management services are provided on an inpatient or outpatient basis, depending on the intensity of service needed.

149. **Violence prevention programs for the workplace.** A violence prevention program with goals and objectives for preventing workplace violence against staff and patients.

150. **Violence prevention programs for the community.** An organized program that attempts to make a positive impact on the type(s) of violence a community is experiencing. For example, it can assist victims of violent crimes, e.g., rape, or incidents, e.g., bullying, to hospital or to community services to prevent further victimization or retaliation. A program that targets the underlying circumstances that contribute to violence such as poor housing, insufficient job training, and/or substance abuse through means such as direct involvement and support, education, mentoring, anger management, crisis intervention and training programs would also qualify.

151. **Alcoholism-chemical dependency pediatric services.** Provides diagnosis and therapeutic services to pediatric patients with alcoholism or other drug dependencies. Includes care for inpatient/residential treatment for patients whose course of treatment involves more intensive care than provided in an outpatient setting or where patient requires supervised withdrawal.

152. **Alcoholism-chemical dependency partial hospitalization services.** Organized hospital services providing intensive day/evening outpatient services of three hour or more duration, distinguished from other outpatient visits of one hour.

153. **Psychiatric intensive outpatient services.** A prescribed course of treatment in which the patient receives outpatient care no less than three times a week (which might include more than one service/day).

154. **Telehealth.** A broad variety of technologies and tactics to deliver virtual medical, public health, health education delivery, and support services using telecommunications technologies. Telehealth is used more commonly as it describes the wide range of diagnosis and management, education, and other related fields of health care. This includes, but are not limited to: dentistry, counseling, physical and occupational therapy, home health, chronic disease monitoring and management, disaster management, and consumer and professional education, and remote patient monitoring.

155. **Air ambulance services.** Aircraft and especially a helicopter equipped for transporting the injured or sick. Most air ambulances carry critically ill or injured patients, whose condition could rapidly change for the worse.

156. **Diabetes prevention program.** Program to prevent or delay the onset of type 2 diabetes by offering evidence-based lifestyle changes based on research studies, which showed modest behavior changes helped individuals with prediabetes reduce their risk of developing type 2 diabetes.

157. **Employment support services.** Services designed to support individuals with significant disabilities to seek and maintain employment.

158. **Supportive housing services.** A hospital program that provides decent, safe, affordable, community-based housing with flexible support services designed to help the individual or family stay housed and live a more productive life in the community.

Control and Service Classifications

Control

Government, nonfederal
State
County
City
City-county
Hospital district or authority

Nongovernment not-for-profit
Church operated
Other

Investor-owned (for-profit)
Individual
Partnership
Corporation

Department of Defense, Government, federal*
Public Health Service other than 47
Veterans Affairs

Osteopathic
Church operated Other not-for-profit
Other
Individual for-profit
Partnership for-profit
Corporation for-profit

Service

General medical and surgical
Hospital unit of an institution (prison hospital, college infirmary, etc.)
Hospital unit within a facility for persons with intellectual disabilities
Surgical
Psychiatric
Tuberculosis and other respiratory diseases
Cancer
Heart
Obstetrics and gynecology

Eye, ear, nose, and throat
Rehabilitation
Orthopedic
Chronic disease
Other specialty
Children's general
Children's hospital unit of an institution
Children's psychiatric
Children's tuberculosis and other respiratory diseases
Children's eye, ear, nose, and throat

Children's rehabilitation
Children's orthopedic
Children's chronic disease
Children's other specialty
Intellectual disabilities
Long-Term Acute Care
Alcoholism and other chemical dependency
Children's Long-Term Acute Care
Children's Cancer
Children's Heart

---

* Starting with the 2018 Annual Survey, Air Force, Army, and Navy are now rolled up into the Department of Defense.

ALABAMA

ALABASTER—Shelby County

☐ **NOLAND HOSPITAL SHELBY (012013)**, 1000 First Street North, 3rd Floor, Zip 35007–8703; tel. 205/620–8641, (Nonreporting) **A**1 10 **S** Noland Health Services, Inc., Birmingham, AL
Primary Contact: Laura S. Wills, Administrator
Web address: www.nolandhospitals.com
Control: Other not–for–profit (including NFP Corporation) **Service:** Acute long–term care hospital

Staffed Beds: 52

☒ **SHELBY BAPTIST MEDICAL CENTER (010016)**, 1000 First Street North, Zip 35007–8703; tel. 205/620–8100, **A**1 10 **F**3 8 11 12 13 15 17 18 20 22 24 26 28 29 30 31 34 35 40 43 45 47 48 49 50 57 59 64 70 72 74 75 76 77 79 81 82 84 85 87 93 98 103 107 108 110 111 114 115 118 119 124 126 127 129 130 131 135 146 147 148 149 156 157 **S** TENET Healthcare Corporation, Dallas, TX
Primary Contact: Daniel Listi, Chief Executive Officer
COO: Megan Drake, Chief Operating Officer
CFO: Jennifer Pittman, Chief Financial Officer
CMO: Jade Brice Roshell, M.D., Chief Medical Officer
CIO: Mike Nighman, Facility Coordinator Information Systems
CHR: Cindy Nicholson, Director Human Resources
CNO: Susan Bria, Chief Nursing Officer
Web address: www.brookwoodbaptisthealth.com
Control: Corporation, Investor–owned (for–profit) **Service:** General medical and surgical

Staffed Beds: 231 Admissions: 11508 Census: 158 Outpatient Visits: 97646 Births: 978

ALEXANDER CITY—Tallapoosa County

☐ **RUSSELL MEDICAL (010065)**, 3316 Highway 280, Zip 35010–3369, Mailing Address: P.O. Box 939, Zip 35011–0939; tel. 256/329–7100, **A**1 3 5 10 19 **F**3 11 13 15 18 20 22 28 29 30 31 34 35 40 43 45 50 51 53 57 59 60 64 67 68 74 75 76 77 78 79 80 81 82 85 89 93 102 107 108 110 111 115 116 119 121 123 126 129 131 132 133 143 144 146 148 149 154
Primary Contact: Lother E. Peace III, President and Chief Executive Officer
CFO: J. Matthew Fisher, Chief Financial Officer
CMO: Michele Goldhagen, M.D., Chief Medical Officer
CIO: Donna Carter, Chief Information Officer and Security Officer
CHR: Mary Shockley, Human Resources Director
Web address: www.russellmedcenter.com
Control: Other not–for–profit (including NFP Corporation) **Service:** General medical and surgical

Staffed Beds: 69 Admissions: 2382 Census: 21 Outpatient Visits: 88335 Births: 330 Total Expense ($000): 74716 Payroll Expense ($000): 24289 Personnel: 515

ANDALUSIA—Covington County

☒ **ANDALUSIA HEALTH (010036)**, 849 South Three Notch Street, Zip 36420–5325, Mailing Address: P.O. Box 760, Zip 36420–1214; tel. 334/222–8466, (Nonreporting) **A**1 10 **S** LifePoint Health, Brentwood, TN
Primary Contact: John C. Yanes, Chief Executive Officer
CFO: Shirley M Smith, Chief Financial Officer
CIO: Matthew Perry, Director Information Systems
CHR: Brian Woods, Human Resources Director
CNO: Pam Aud, Chief Clinical Officer
Web address: www.andalusiahealth.com
Control: Corporation, Investor–owned (for–profit) **Service:** General medical and surgical

Staffed Beds: 88

ANNISTON—Calhoun County

☐ **NOLAND HOSPITAL ANNISTON (012011)**, 400 East 10th Street, 4th Fl, Zip 36207–4716; tel. 256/741–6141, (Nonreporting) **A**1 10 **S** Noland Health Services, Inc., Birmingham, AL
Primary Contact: Trina Woods, Administrator
Web address: www.nolandhealth.com
Control: Other not–for–profit (including NFP Corporation) **Service:** Acute long–term care hospital

Staffed Beds: 38

☒ **RMC ANNISTON (010078)**, 400 East Tenth Street, Zip 36207–4716, Mailing Address: P.O. Box 2208, Zip 36202–2208; tel. 256/235–5121, **A**1 2 10 19 **F**3 11 13 15 17 18 20 22 24 28 29 30 31 34 35 37 40 43 45 46 47 48 49 50 51 53 54 56 57 59 60 61 64 68 70 74 76 77 78 79 81 82 84 85 86 87 89 93 98 100 103 107 108 110 111 114 115 116 117 118 119 120 121 123 124 126 129 130 132 135 146 147 148 149 156 157 **S** Regional Medical Center, Anniston, AL
Primary Contact: Louis A. Bass, Chief Executive Officer
CMO: David Zinn, M.D., Vice President Medical Affairs
CIO: Pete Furlow, Director Information Technology Services
CHR: Doug Scott, Corporate Director Human Resources
CNO: Elaine Davis, Chief Nursing Officer and Vice President Patient Services
Web address: www.rmccares.org
Control: Hospital district or authority, Government, nonfederal **Service:** General medical and surgical

Staffed Beds: 160 Admissions: 12323 Census: 160 Outpatient Visits: 595751 Births: 2044 Total Expense ($000): 158470 Payroll Expense ($000): 70856 Personnel: 1420

☐ **RMC-STRINGFELLOW MEMORIAL HOSPITAL (010038)**, 301 East 18th Street, Zip 36207–3952; tel. 256/235–8900, (Nonreporting) **A**10 **S** Regional Medical Center, Anniston, AL
Primary Contact: Joe Weaver, Chief Executive Officer
CIO: Peggy Henderson, Director Health Information
CHR: Tamatha Johnson, Director Human Resources
Web address: www.stringfellowmemorial.com
Control: Corporation, Investor–owned (for–profit) **Service:** General medical and surgical

Staffed Beds: 88

ASHLAND—Clay County

☐ **CLAY COUNTY HOSPITAL (010073)**, 83825 Highway 9, Zip 36251–7981, Mailing Address: P.O. Box 1270, Zip 36251–1270; tel. 256/354–2131, (Nonreporting) **A**10
Primary Contact: Joel W. Tate, FACHE, Chief Executive Officer
CFO: Kerry W Tomlin, Associate Administrator
CMO: David Hensleigh, Director Medical Staff
CIO: Patrick Smith, Director Information Technology
CHR: Linda T Smith, Director Human Resources
CNO: Charles Griffin, Director of Nursing
Web address: www.claycountyhospital.com
Control: County, Government, nonfederal **Service:** General medical and surgical

Staffed Beds: 129

ATHENS—Limestone County

☐ **ATHENS-LIMESTONE HOSPITAL (010079)**, 700 West Market Street, Zip 35611–2457, Mailing Address: P.O. Box 999, Zip 35612–0999; tel. 256/233–9292, **A**1 5 10 **F**3 7 8 11 13 15 18 28 29 34 35 40 43 46 48 50 51 53 54 56 57 58 59 64 68 70 73 75 76 77 79 81 82 85 86 87 89 93 98 107 108 109 110 111 114 115 118 119 129 130 131 132 143 144 146 147 148 149 **S** Huntsville Hospital Health System, Huntsville, AL
Primary Contact: David Pryor, President
COO: Randy Comer, Chief Operating Officer
CFO: Randy Comer, Chief Financial Officer
CMO: Jon Bignault, M.D., Chief of Staff
CIO: Kim Hoback, Supervisor Information Systems
CHR: Rachel Frey, Director Human Resources
CNO: Jan Lenz, Chief Nursing Officer
Web address: www.athenslimestonehospital.com
Control: Hospital district or authority, Government, nonfederal **Service:** General medical and surgical

Staffed Beds: 71 Admissions: 4014 Census: 41 Outpatient Visits: 127088 Births: 461 Total Expense ($000): 82107 Payroll Expense ($000): 33375 Personnel: 707

Hospital, Medicare Provider Number, Address, Telephone, Approval, Facility, and Physician Codes, Health Care System
★ American Hospital Association (AHA) membership   ○ Healthcare Facilities Accreditation Program   ⇑ Center for Improvement in Healthcare Quality Accreditation ☐ The Joint Commission accreditation   ◇ DNV Healthcare Inc. accreditation   △ Commission on Accreditation of Rehabilitation Facilities (CARF) accreditation

NORTH ALABAMA SPECIALTY HOSPITAL (012014), 700 West Market Street, 2 South, Zip 35611–2457; tel. 256/262–6767, (Nonreporting) **A**10 22
Primary Contact: Gene Smith, Chief Executive Officer
Web address: www.amgnash.com
Control: Corporation, Investor–owned (for–profit) **Service**: Acute long–term care hospital

Staffed Beds: 31

ATMORE—Escambia County

ATMORE COMMUNITY HOSPITAL (010169), 401 Medical Park Drive, Zip 36502–3091; tel. 251/368–2500, (Nonreporting) **A**10 **S** Infirmary Health System, Mobile, AL
Primary Contact: Douglas Tanner, President
CFO: Keith Strickling, Chief Financial Officer
CHR: Linda Lowrey, Human Resources Officer
CNO: Ashley Chunn, Director of Nursing
Web address: www.ebaptisthealthcare.org/AtmoreCommunityHospital/
Control: Other not–for–profit (including NFP Corporation) **Service**: General medical and surgical

Staffed Beds: 33

BAY MINETTE—Baldwin County

NORTH BALDWIN INFIRMARY (010129), 1815 Hand Avenue, Zip 36507–4110, Mailing Address: P.O. Box 1409, Zip 36507–1409; tel. 251/937–5521, (Nonreporting) **A**10 **S** Infirmary Health System, Mobile, AL
Primary Contact: Benjamin K. Hansert, Administrator
CFO: J Patrick Murphy, Chief Financial Officer
Web address: www.mobileinfirmary.org
Control: Other not–for–profit (including NFP Corporation) **Service**: General medical and surgical

Staffed Beds: 50

BESSEMER—Jefferson County

☐ **MEDICAL WEST (010114)**, 995 Ninth Avenue SW, Zip 35022–4527; tel. 205/481–7000, **A**1 3 10 **F**3 11 13 15 18 20 29 30 31 34 40 42 43 45 49 50 53 54 57 59 60 64 68 70 74 75 76 77 78 79 81 82 85 86 90 92 93 94 96 98 100 101 102 103 104 107 108 110 111 114 115 118 119 129 130 132 143 146 147 148 149 154 **S** UAB Health System, Birmingham, AL
Primary Contact: Brian Keith. Pennington, President and Chief Executive Officer
COO: Sean Tinney, FACHE, Chief Operating Officer
CFO: Brandon H Slocum, Senior Vice President and Chief Financial Officer
CMO: Conrad De Los Santos, President Medical Staff
CIO: Bob Duckworth, Director Information Systems
CHR: Gannon Davis, Director Human Resources
CNO: Pamela Spencer Autrey, R.N., Ph.D., MSN, Chief Nursing Officer
Web address: www.medicalwesthospital.org
Control: Hospital district or authority, Government, nonfederal **Service**: General medical and surgical

Staffed Beds: 231 Admissions: 7086 Census: 114 Outpatient Visits: 234273 Births: 316 Total Expense ($000): 125056 Payroll Expense ($000): 50889 Personnel: 1167

BIRMINGHAM—Jefferson County

☒ **BIRMINGHAM VETERANS AFFAIRS MEDICAL CENTER**, 700 South 19th Street, Zip 35233–1927; tel. 205/933–8101, **A**1 2 3 5 8 **F**3 5 8 9 14 15 17 18 20 22 24 26 28 29 30 31 34 35 36 38 39 40 43 45 46 47 48 49 50 51 54 55 56 57 58 59 60 61 62 64 65 68 69 70 71 74 75 77 78 79 81 82 83 84 85 86 87 91 92 93 94 96 97 100 101 102 104 107 108 109 110 111 112 113 114 115 116 117 118 119 126 127 129 130 132 133 135 138 143 146 147 148 149 153 154 156 157 **S** Department of Veterans Affairs, Washington, DC
Primary Contact: Stacy J. Vasquez, Chief Executive Officer
COO: Phyllis J. Smith, Associate Director
CFO: Mary S Mitchell, Chief Resource Management Services
CMO: William F Harper, M.D., Chief of Staff
CIO: Antonia Mohamed, Acting Chief Information Officer
CHR: Jacqueline Caron, Chief Human Resources
CNO: Cynthia Cleveland, Ph.D., R.N., Associate Director for Patient Care Services and Nurse Executive
Web address: www.birmingham.va.gov/
Control: Veterans Affairs, Government, federal **Service**: General medical and surgical

Staffed Beds: 141 Admissions: 7825 Census: 98 Outpatient Visits: 840500 Births: 0 Total Expense ($000): 571309 Payroll Expense ($000): 207107 Personnel: 2668

☒ △ **BROOKWOOD BAPTIST MEDICAL CENTER (010139)**, 2010 Brookwood Medical Center Drive, Zip 35209–6875; tel. 205/877–1000, (Nonreporting) **A**1 2 3 5 7 10 **S** TENET Healthcare Corporation, Dallas, TX
Primary Contact: Timothy Puthoff, Chief Executive Officer
COO: Kathy Healy-Collier, Chief Operating Officer
CFO: Jay M Pennisson, Chief Financial Officer
CMO: Vish Sachdev, M.D., Chief Medical Officer
CIO: Manuel Price, Director Information Systems
CHR: Ronnelle Stewart, Chief Human Resources Officer
CNO: Amy Beard, Chief Nursing Officer
Web address: www.https://www.brookwoodbaptisthealth.com/
Control: Corporation, Investor–owned (for–profit) **Service**: General medical and surgical

Staffed Beds: 607

☒ **CHILDREN'S OF ALABAMA (013300)**, 1600 Seventh Avenue South, Zip 35233–1785; tel. 205/638–9100, **A**1 3 5 10 **F**3 7 8 9 11 12 16 17 19 20 21 22 23 25 27 28 29 30 31 32 34 35 36 37 38 39 40 41 43 44 46 48 50 54 55 57 58 59 60 61 64 65 68 72 74 75 77 78 79 80 81 82 84 85 86 87 88 89 91 92 93 94 95 96 97 98 99 100 101 102 104 107 108 109 111 114 115 116 117 118 119 126 129 130 131 132 134 135 136 137 138 139 142 146 148 149 154 155 156
Primary Contact: Wm. Michael. Warren Jr, President and Chief Executive Officer
COO: Tom Shufflebarger, Chief Operating Officer
CFO: Dawn Walton, Chief Financial Officer
CMO: Crayton A Fargason, M.D., Medical Director
CIO: Robert Sarnecki, Interim Chief Information Officer
CHR: Douglas B Dean, Chief Human Resources Officer
CNO: Deb Wesley, MSN, Chief Nursing Officer
Web address: www.childrensal.org
Control: Other not–for–profit (including NFP Corporation) **Service**: Children's general medical and surgical

Staffed Beds: 341 Admissions: 15630 Census: 259 Outpatient Visits: 677390 Births: 0 Total Expense ($000): 693135 Payroll Expense ($000): 281815 Personnel: 4291

☒ **ENCOMPASS HEALTH LAKESHORE REHABILITATION HOSPITAL (013025)**, 3800 Ridgeway Drive, Zip 35209–5599; tel. 205/868–2000, (Nonreporting) **A**1 10 **S** Encompass Health Corporation, Birmingham, AL
Primary Contact: Michael Bartell, Chief Executive Officer
CFO: Kimberly Thrasher, Controller
CMO: Michael Rosemore, M.D., Medical Director
CHR: Julie Smith, Director Human Resources
CNO: April Cobb, Chief Nursing Officer
Web address: www.encompasshealth.com/lakeshorerehab
Control: Corporation, Investor–owned (for–profit) **Service**: Rehabilitation

Staffed Beds: 100

☒ **GRANDVIEW MEDICAL CENTER (010104)**, 3690 Grandview Parkway, Zip 35243–3326; tel. 205/971–1000, **A**1 2 3 10 **F**1 3 4 11 12 13 15 16 17 18 20 22 24 26 27 28 29 30 34 35 40 43 45 46 47 48 49 50 51 54 57 58 59 64 67 70 72 73 74 75 76 77 78 79 80 81 82 85 87 88 89 90 93 96 98 99 100 102 103 107 108 110 111 115 116 117 118 119 120 121 124 126 128 129 130 131 132 135 146 147 148 149 154 **S** Community Health Systems, Inc., Franklin, TN
Primary Contact: Drew Mason, Chief Executive Officer
COO: Justin O. Bryant, Chief Operating Officer
CFO: Julie Soekoro, Chief Financial Officer
CMO: Rebecca Byrd, President Medical Staff
CIO: Tim Townes, Director Information Systems
CHR: Jeri Wink, Director Human Resources
CNO: James Epperson, Interim Chief Nursing Officer
Web address: www.grandviewhealth.com
Control: Corporation, Investor–owned (for–profit) **Service**: General medical and surgical

Staffed Beds: 414 Admissions: 21431 Census: 289 Outpatient Visits: 307860 Births: 1295 Total Expense ($000): 355004 Payroll Expense ($000): 99050 Personnel: 2118

☐ **HILL CREST BEHAVIORAL HEALTH SERVICES (014000)**, 6869 Fifth Avenue South, Zip 35212–1866; tel. 205/833–9000, (Nonreporting) **A**1 10 **S** Universal Health Services, Inc., King of Prussia, PA
Primary Contact: Steve McCabe, Chief Executive Officer
CFO: Mark Teske, Chief Financial Officer
Web address: www.hillcrestbhs.com
Control: Corporation, Investor–owned (for–profit) **Service**: Psychiatric

Staffed Beds: 80

NOLAND HOSPITAL BIRMINGHAM (012009), 50 Medical Park East Drive, 8th Floor, Zip 35235; tel. 205/808–5100, (Nonreporting) **A**1 10 **S** Noland Health Services, Inc., Birmingham, AL
Primary Contact: Laura S. Wills, Administrator
COO: Sharon Engle, Director Clinical Services
CMO: Mark Middlebrooks, M.D., Medical Director
CHR: Ashley Clark, Coordinator Human Resources
CNO: Rachel Chapman, Nurse Manager
Web address: www.nolandhealth.com
Control: Other not–for–profit (including NFP Corporation) **Service:** Acute long–term care hospital

Staffed Beds: 45

PRINCETON BAPTIST MEDICAL CENTER (010103), 701 Princeton Avenue SW, Zip 35211–1303; tel. 205/783–3000, (Nonreporting) **A**1 2 3 5 10 **S** TENET Healthcare Corporation, Dallas, TX
Primary Contact: Michael Neuendorf, Chief Executive Officer
CFO: Amanda Dyle, Chief Financial Officer
CMO: Alan Craig, M.D., Chief Medical Officer
CHR: Jason Hatter, Chief Human Resource Officer
CNO: Paula Davenport, Chief Nursing Officer
Web address: www.bhsala.com
Control: Church operated, Nongovernment, not–for–profit **Service:** General medical and surgical

Staffed Beds: 311

SELECT SPECIALTY HOSPITAL-BIRMINGHAM (012008), 2010 Brookwood Medical Center Drive, 3rd Floor, Zip 35209–6804; tel. 205/599–4600, (Nonreporting) **A**1 10 **S** Select Medical Corporation, Mechanicsburg, PA
Primary Contact: Clifton Quinn, Chief Executive Officer
CMO: Allan Goldstein, M.D., Medical Director and Chief of Staff
Web address: www.birmingham.selectspecialtyhospitals.com
Control: Corporation, Investor–owned (for–profit) **Service:** Acute long–term care hospital

Staffed Beds: 38

ST. VINCENT'S BIRMINGHAM (010056), 810 St Vincent's Drive, Zip 35205–1695, Mailing Address: P.O. Box 12407, Zip 35202–2407; tel. 205/939–7000, **A**1 2 3 5 10 **F**3 11 13 15 17 18 20 22 24 26 28 29 30 31 34 35 37 40 43 45 53 57 58 59 60 62 68 70 72 74 76 77 79 81 82 84 85 86 87 91 93 94 107 110 111 114 119 120 121 123 124 126 131 132 135 146 147 149 **S** Ascension Healthcare, Saint Louis, MO
Primary Contact: Evan Ray, FACHE, Chief Executive Officer
COO: Andy Davis, Chief Operating Officer
CFO: Wilma Newton, Executive Vice President and Chief Financial Officer
CMO: Gregory L James, D.O., Chief Medical Officer
CIO: Timothy Stetthelmer, Vice President and Chief Information Officer
CHR: Michelle Oulipeau, Director Human Resources
Web address: www.stvhs.com
Control: Other not–for–profit (including NFP Corporation) **Service:** General medical and surgical

Staffed Beds: 409 **Admissions:** 20136 **Census:** 263 **Outpatient Visits:** 165281 **Births:** 3241 **Total Expense ($000):** 441391 **Payroll Expense ($000):** 100792 **Personnel:** 1644

ST. VINCENT'S EAST (010011), 50 Medical Park East Drive, Zip 35235–9987; tel. 205/838–3000, **A**1 2 3 5 10 **F**3 11 12 13 15 17 18 20 22 24 26 28 29 30 31 35 40 43 44 45 46 47 49 50 51 53 57 59 70 72 74 76 77 78 79 81 85 86 87 90 93 98 100 102 103 107 108 111 114 118 119 120 121 123 124 129 130 132 135 146 147 149 **S** Ascension Healthcare, Saint Louis, MO
Primary Contact: Suzannah Campbell, President
COO: Andrew Gnann, Vice President Operations
CFO: Jan DiCesare, Vice President Financial Operations
CMO: Frank Malensek, M.D., Chief Medical Officer
CIO: Beverly Golightly, Director Information Technology
CHR: Carol Maietta, Vice President Human Resources and Chief Learning Officer
CNO: Amy Shelton, Chief Nursing Officer
Web address: www.stvhs.com
Control: Other not–for–profit (including NFP Corporation) **Service:** General medical and surgical

Staffed Beds: 362 **Admissions:** 15708 **Census:** 259 **Outpatient Visits:** 118752 **Births:** 815 **Total Expense ($000):** 228840 **Payroll Expense ($000):** 62442 **Personnel:** 1042

UAB HIGHLANDS See University of Alabama Hospital, Birmingham

UNIVERSITY OF ALABAMA HOSPITAL (010033), 619 19th Street South, Zip 35249–1900; tel. 205/934–4011, (Includes UAB HIGHLANDS, 1201 11th Avenue South, Birmingham, Alabama, Zip 35205–5299; tel. 205/930–7000; Anthony Patterson, FACHE, Chief Operating Officer) **A**1 2 3 5 8 10 **F**1 3 4 5 7 8 9 11 12 13 15 16 17 18 20 22 24 26 27 28 29 30 31 33 34 35 37 38 39 40 43 44 45 46 47 48 49 50 52 53 54 55 56 57 58 59 60 61 62 64 65 66 67 68 70 71 72 73 74 75 76 77 78 79 80 81 82 83 84 85 86 87 88 89 90 91 92 93 94 95 96 97 98 100 101 102 103 104 107 108 110 111 113 114 115 116 117 118 119 120 121 123 124 126 128 129 130 131 132 135 136 137 138 139 140 141 142 143 144 145 146 147 148 149 152 154 155 156 **S** UAB Health System, Birmingham, AL
Primary Contact: Reid F. Jones, Chief Executive Officer
CMO: Loring Rue, M.D., Senior Vice President, Quality Patient Safety and Clinical Effectiveness
CIO: Joan Hicks, Chief Information Officer
CHR: Alesia Jones, Chief Human Resources Officer
CNO: Terri Lyn Poe, Interim Chief Nursing Officer
Web address: www.uabmedicine.org
Control: State, Government, nonfederal **Service:** General medical and surgical

Staffed Beds: 1206 **Admissions:** 48728 **Census:** 986 **Outpatient Visits:** 756423 **Births:** 4344 **Total Expense ($000):** 1699346 **Payroll Expense ($000):** 614549 **Personnel:** 9773

VETERANS AFFAIRS MEDICAL CENTER See Birmingham Veterans Affairs Medical Center

BOAZ—Marshall County

MARSHALL MEDICAL CENTER SOUTH (010005), U S Highway 431 North, Zip 35957–0999, Mailing Address: P.O. Box 758, Zip 35957–0758; tel. 256/593–8310, **A**1 10 19 **F**3 7 8 9 11 12 13 15 18 20 22 26 28 29 31 32 34 35 37 40 43 45 46 50 51 53 54 57 59 64 68 70 74 75 76 77 78 79 81 84 85 86 87 89 92 93 100 107 108 110 111 114 115 117 119 121 123 129 130 131 132 135 141 146 147 148 149 154 **S** Marshall Health System, Guntersville, AL
Primary Contact: John D. Anderson, FACHE, Administrator
CFO: Kathy Nelson, Chief Financial Officer
Web address: www.mmcenters.com//index.php/facilities/marshall_south
Control: Hospital district or authority, Government, nonfederal **Service:** General medical and surgical

Staffed Beds: 114 **Admissions:** 4492 **Census:** 53 **Outpatient Visits:** 330958 **Births:** 688 **Total Expense ($000):** 99045 **Payroll Expense ($000):** 38308 **Personnel:** 696

BREWTON—Escambia County

D. W. MCMILLAN MEMORIAL HOSPITAL (010099), 1301 Belleville Avenue, Zip 36426–1306, Mailing Address: P.O. Box 908, Zip 36427–0908; tel. 251/867–8061, (Nonreporting) **A**1 10
Primary Contact: Rick Owens, Administrator
CIO: Ian Vickery, Director Information Technology
CHR: Autherine Davis, Director Human Resources
CNO: Bob Ellis, Director of Nursing
Web address: www.dwmmh.org
Control: Hospital district or authority, Government, nonfederal **Service:** General medical and surgical

Staffed Beds: 49

BUTLER—Choctaw County

CHOCTAW GENERAL HOSPITAL (011304), 401 Vanity Fair Avenue, Zip 36904–3032; tel. 205/459–9100, (Nonreporting) **A**10 18 **S** Rush Health Systems, Meridian, MS
Primary Contact: J W. Cowan, Administrator
Web address: www.choctawgeneral.com/cgh/
Control: Corporation, Investor–owned (for–profit) **Service:** General medical and surgical

Staffed Beds: 25

Hospital, Medicare Provider Number, Address, Telephone, Approval, Facility, and Physician Codes, Health Care System

★ American Hospital Association (AHA) membership
□ The Joint Commission accreditation
○ Healthcare Facilities Accreditation Program
◇ DNV Healthcare Inc. accreditation
⇑ Center for Improvement in Healthcare Quality Accreditation
△ Commission on Accreditation of Rehabilitation Facilities (CARF) accreditation

CARROLLTON—Pickens County

PICKENS COUNTY MEDICAL CENTER (010109), 241 Robert K Wilson Drive, Zip 35447, Mailing Address: P.O. Box 478, Zip 35447–0478; tel. 205/367–8111, (Nonreporting) **A**10 20
Primary Contact: John O'Neil, Chief Executive Officer
CFO: Janice Winters, Controller
CMO: William R Brooke, M.D., President Medical Staff
CHR: Dottie D Wilson, Director Human Resources
Web address: www.pcmc.care/
Control: County, Government, nonfederal **Service**: General medical and surgical

Staffed Beds: 52

CENTRE—Cherokee County

✠ **FLOYD CHEROKEE MEDICAL CENTER (010022)**, 400 Northwood Drive, Zip 35960–1023; tel. 256/927–5531, (Data for 214 days) **A**1 10 **F**3 11 15 29 30 35 39 40 43 45 48 51 57 77 79 81 85 93 107 108 110 119 130 133 146 152 **S** Floyd Healthcare Management, Rome, GA
Primary Contact: Brandon Reece, Chief Executive Officer
CFO: Zac Allen, CPA, Chief Financial Officer
CHR: Marlene Benefield, Director Human Resources
Web address: www.cherokeemedicalcenter.com
Control: Other not–for–profit (including NFP Corporation) **Service**: General medical and surgical

Staffed Beds: 45 Admissions: 457 Census: 11 Outpatient Visits: 9632
Births: 0 Total Expense ($000): 11428 Payroll Expense ($000): 3337
Personnel: 98

CENTREVILLE—Bibb County

BIBB MEDICAL CENTER (010058), 208 Pierson Avenue, Zip 35042–2918; tel. 205/926–4881, (Total facility includes 131 beds in nursing home-type unit) **A**3 5 10 13 **F**3 11 13 15 29 31 34 35 40 45 50 53 56 57 59 64 66 69 75 76 77 80 81 86 87 93 97 107 114 119 125 127 128 130 133 135 143 144 146 148 149 150 154 158
Primary Contact: Joseph Marchant, Administrator
CFO: Heather Desmond, Chief Financial Officer
CMO: John Meigs, M.D., Jr Chief of Staff
CHR: Karen Daniel, Director Human Resources
Web address: www.bibbmedicalcenter.com
Control: Hospital district or authority, Government, nonfederal **Service**: General medical and surgical

Staffed Beds: 180 Admissions: 762 Census: 123 Outpatient Visits: 48644
Births: 85 Total Expense ($000): 20307 Payroll Expense ($000): 8882
Personnel: 226

CHATOM—Washington County

★ **WASHINGTON COUNTY HOSPITAL (011300)**, 14600 St Stephens Avenue, Zip 36518–9998, Mailing Address: P.O. Box 1299, Zip 36518–1299; tel. 251/847–2223, (Nonreporting) **A**10 18
Primary Contact: Teresa G. Grimes, Chief Executive Officer
CFO: Alyson Overstreet, Chief Financial Officer
CMO: Steve Donald, M.D., Chief of Staff
CIO: Brady Wright, Information Technology Network Administrator
CHR: Linda Randolph, Director Personnel Services
CNO: Michelle Alford, R.N., MSN, Director of Nursing
Web address: www.wchnh.org
Control: County, Government, nonfederal **Service**: General medical and surgical

Staffed Beds: 20

CLANTON—Chilton County

✠ **ST. VINCENT'S CHILTON HOSPITAL (010173)**, 2030 Lay Dam Road, Zip 35045; tel. 205/258–4400, **A**1 10 **F**3 11 15 29 30 35 40 43 45 46 50 59 60 64 68 70 79 81 82 85 87 93 107 108 110 111 119 130 135 146 148 149 **S** Ascension Healthcare, Saint Louis, MO
Primary Contact: John Shanon. Hamilton, Administrator
Web address: www.https://www.stvhs.com/chilton/
Control: Other not–for–profit (including NFP Corporation) **Service**: General medical and surgical

Staffed Beds: 36 Admissions: 785 Census: 7 Outpatient Visits: 29726
Births: 0 Total Expense ($000): 22539 Payroll Expense ($000): 6776
Personnel: 110

CULLMAN—Cullman County

☐ **CULLMAN REGIONAL MEDICAL CENTER (010035)**, 1912 Alabama Highway 157, Zip 35055, Mailing Address: P.O. Box 1108, Zip 35056–1108; tel. 256/737–2000, **A**1 3 10 **F**3 7 12 13 15 18 20 22 26 28 29 30 34 35 37 40 43 45 46 49 50 51 53 54 57 59 62 63 64 68 70 71 74 75 76 79 81 82 84 85 86 87 89 93 97 107 108 110 111 114 115 118 119 120 129 130 131 132 133 134 135 144 146 147 148 149 154 156 157
Primary Contact: James Clements, Chief Executive Officer
COO: Nesha Donaldson, Chief Operating Officer
CMO: William E. Smith, M.D., Chief of Staff
CIO: Nancy Zavatchen, Director Information Technology
CHR: Toni Geddings, Director Human Resources
CNO: Cheryl Bailey, R.N., Chief Nursing Officer Vice President Patient Care Services
Web address: www.crmhospital.com
Control: Other not–for–profit (including NFP Corporation) **Service**: General medical and surgical

Staffed Beds: 145 Admissions: 8069 Census: 85 Outpatient Visits: 95731
Births: 603 Total Expense ($000): 108358 Payroll Expense ($000): 43484
Personnel: 987

DADEVILLE—Tallapoosa County

LAKE MARTIN COMMUNITY HOSPITAL (010052), 201 Mariarden Road, Zip 36853–6251, Mailing Address: P.O. Box 629, Zip 36853–0629; tel. 256/825–7821, (Nonreporting) **A**10
Primary Contact: Michael D. Bruce, Chief Executive Officer
CHR: Karen Treadwell, Director Human Resources
Web address: www.lakemartincommunityhospital.com
Control: Partnership, Investor–owned (for–profit) **Service**: General medical and surgical

Staffed Beds: 25

DAPHNE—Baldwin County

★ **EASTPOINTE HOSPITAL (014017)**, 7400 Roper Lane, Zip 36526–5274; tel. 251/378–6500, **A**10 **F**29 98 106 130 143 **S** AltaPointe Health Systems, Mobile, AL
Primary Contact: Philip L. Cusa, Hospital Director
CFO: Kevin Markham, Chief Financial Officer
CMO: Sandra K Parker, M.D., Chief Medical Officer
CIO: Steve Dolan, Chief Information Officer
CHR: Alicia Donoghue, Director Human Resources
Web address: www.altapointe.org/eastpointe.php
Control: Other not–for–profit (including NFP Corporation) **Service**: Psychiatric

Staffed Beds: 50 Admissions: 1223 Census: 39 Outpatient Visits: 0
Births: 0 Total Expense ($000): 9859 Payroll Expense ($000): 6065
Personnel: 147

DECATUR—Morgan County

☐ **DECATUR MORGAN HOSPITAL (010085)**, 1201 Seventh Street SE, Zip 35601–3303, Mailing Address: P.O. Box 2239, Zip 35609–2239; tel. 256/341–2000, (Includes DECATUR MORGAN HOSPITAL PARKWAY CAMPUS, 1874 Beltline Road SW, Decatur, Alabama, Zip 35601–5509, Mailing Address: P O Box 2239, Zip 35609–2239, tel. 256/350–2211; DECATUR MORGAN HOSPITAL-WEST, 2205 Beltline Road SW, Decatur, Alabama, Zip 35601–3687, Mailing Address: P O Box 2240, Zip 35609–2240, tel. 256/306–4000), (Nonreporting) **A**1 5 10 **S** Huntsville Hospital Health System, Huntsville, AL
Primary Contact: Nathaniel Richardson Jr, President
CFO: Kim Shrewsbury, Vice President and Chief Financial Officer
CMO: Allen J Schmidt, M.D., President, Medical Staff
CIO: Mark Megehee, Vice President and Chief Information Officer
CNO: Anita Walden, Vice President and Chief Nursing Officer
Web address: www.decaturgeneral.org
Control: Hospital district or authority, Government, nonfederal **Service**: General medical and surgical

Staffed Beds: 110

PARKWAY MEDICAL CENTER See Decatur Morgan Hospital Parkway Campus

Many Facility Codes have changed. Please refer to the AHA Guide Code Chart. © 2019 AHA Guide

DEMOPOLIS—Marengo County

BRYAN W. WHITFIELD MEMORIAL HOSPITAL (010112), 105 U S Highway 80 East, Zip 36732–3616, Mailing Address: P.O. Box 890, Zip 36732–0890; tel. 334/289–4000, (Nonreporting) **A**3 10 20 **S** UAB Health System, Birmingham, AL
Primary Contact: Douglas L. Brewer, Chief Executive Officer
COO: Dereck Morrison, Assistant Administrator
CFO: Doug A. Brooker, Chief Financial Officer
CMO: John G. Kahler, M.D., Radiologist
Web address: www.bwwmh.com
Control: Hospital district or authority, Government, nonfederal **Service**: General medical and surgical

Staffed Beds: 47

DOTHAN—Houston County

⊠ **ENCOMPASS HEALTH REHABILITATION HOSPITAL OF DOTHAN (013030)**, 1736 East Main Street, Zip 36301–3040, Mailing Address: P.O. Box 6708, Zip 36302–6708; tel. 334/712–6333, (Nonreporting) **A**1 10 **S** Encompass Health Corporation, Birmingham, AL
Primary Contact: Margaret A. Futch, Chief Executive Officer
CFO: Heath Watson, Controller
CHR: Lydia Christion, Director Human Resources
Web address: www.encompasshealth.com/dothanrehab
Control: Corporation, Investor–owned (for–profit) **Service**: Rehabilitation

Staffed Beds: 51

⊠ **FLOWERS HOSPITAL (010055)**, 4370 West Main Street, Zip 36305–4000, Mailing Address: P.O. Box 6907, Zip 36302–6907; tel. 334/793–5000, **A**1 2 3 10 19 **F**3 4 11 12 13 15 17 18 19 20 22 24 26 28 29 30 31 34 35 37 40 43 46 48 49 50 51 56 57 59 60 61 64 67 68 70 72 74 75 76 77 78 79 81 82 85 86 87 89 90 92 97 98 100 107 108 110 111 114 115 116 117 118 119 126 128 129 130 131 132 134 135 146 147 148 149 154 156 157 **S** Community Health Systems, Inc., Franklin, TN
Primary Contact: Heath Phillips, Chief Executive Officer
COO: Matthew H Blevins, Chief Operating Officer
CFO: Talana Bell, Chief Financial Officer
CIO: Matthew Garrett, Director Information Systems
CHR: Jennifer Odom, Interim Director Human Resources
CNO: Dan L Cumbie, Chief Nursing Officer
Web address: www.flowershospital.com
Control: Corporation, Investor–owned (for–profit) **Service**: General medical and surgical

Staffed Beds: 147 **Admissions**: 12158 **Census**: 145 **Outpatient Visits**: 189566 **Births**: 1362 **Total Expense ($000)**: 181586 **Payroll Expense ($000)**: 55559 **Personnel**: 1271

☐ **LAUREL OAKS BEHAVIORAL HEALTH CENTER (014013)**, 700 East Cottonwood Road, Zip 36301–3644; tel. 334/794–7373, (Nonreporting) **A**1 10 **S** Universal Health Services, Inc., King of Prussia, PA
Primary Contact: Derek Johnson, Chief Executive Officer
CMO: Nelson Handol, M.D., Medical Director
CHR: Lorrie Evans, Director Human Resources
Web address: www.laureloaksbhc.com
Control: Corporation, Investor–owned (for–profit) **Service**: Children's hospital psychiatric

Staffed Beds: 38

☐ **NOLAND HOSPITAL DOTHAN (012010)**, 1108 Ross Clark Circle, 4th Floor, Zip 36301–3022; tel. 334/699–4300, (Nonreporting) **A**1 10 **S** Noland Health Services, Inc., Birmingham, AL
Primary Contact: Kaye Burk, Administrator
Web address: www.nolandhealth.com
Control: Other not–for–profit (including NFP Corporation) **Service**: Acute long–term care hospital

Staffed Beds: 38

⇑ **SOUTHEAST ALABAMA MEDICAL CENTER (010001)**, 1108 Ross Clark Circle, Zip 36301–3024, Mailing Address: P.O. Box 6987, Zip 36302–6987; tel. 334/793–8111, (Nonreporting) **A**2 3 5 10 21
Primary Contact: Richard O. Sutton, FACHE, Chief Executive Officer
COO: Charles C Brannen, Senior Vice President and Chief Operating Officer
CFO: Derek Miller, Senior Vice President and Chief Financial Officer
CMO: Charles Harkness, D.O., Vice President Medical Affairs
CIO: Eric Allen Daffron, Division Director, Information Systems
CHR: Tony Welch, Vice President Human Resources
CNO: Diane Buntyn, MSN, R.N., Vice President Patient Care Services
Web address: www.samc.org
Control: Hospital district or authority, Government, nonfederal **Service**: General medical and surgical

Staffed Beds: 387

ENTERPRISE—Coffee County

⊠ **MEDICAL CENTER ENTERPRISE (010049)**, 400 North Edwards Street, Zip 36330–2510; tel. 334/347–0584, **A**1 10 **F**3 13 15 18 24 28 29 34 40 43 50 57 59 60 65 68 70 76 79 81 82 87 93 107 108 111 115 119 129 130 133 146 147 148 154 **S** Community Health Systems, Inc., Franklin, TN
Primary Contact: Suzanne Woods, Chief Executive Officer
CFO: Greg McGilvray, Chief Financial Officer
CMO: Rick Harrelson, M.D., President Medical Staff
CIO: Stephen Smothers, Director Information Systems
CHR: Toni Kaminski, Director Human Resources
CNO: Bobby Phillips, Chief Nursing Officer
Web address: www.mcehospital.com
Control: Corporation, Investor–owned (for–profit) **Service**: General medical and surgical

Staffed Beds: 99 **Admissions**: 3403 **Census**: 24 **Outpatient Visits**: 68809 **Births**: 791 **Total Expense ($000)**: 48520 **Payroll Expense ($000)**: 19741 **Personnel**: 323

EUFAULA—Barbour County

MEDICAL CENTER BARBOUR (010069), 820 West Washington Street, Zip 36027–1899; tel. 334/688–7000, (Nonreporting) **A**10 20
Primary Contact: Farrell Turner, Chief Executive Officer
CFO: Debbie Norton, Chief Financial Officer
CHR: Cindy Griffin, Director Human Resources
CNO: Christy Moore, Chief Nursing Officer
Web address: www.medctrbarbour.org
Control: Hospital district or authority, Government, nonfederal **Service**: General medical and surgical

Staffed Beds: 47

EUTAW—Greene County

GREENE COUNTY HEALTH SYSTEM (010051), 509 Wilson Avenue, Zip 35462–1099; tel. 205/372–3388, (Nonreporting) **A**10
Primary Contact: Marcia Pugh, Chief Executive Officer
Web address: www.gcheutaw.com
Control: County, Government, nonfederal **Service**: General medical and surgical

Staffed Beds: 92

EVERGREEN—Conecuh County

EVERGREEN MEDICAL CENTER (010148), 101 Crestview Avenue, Zip 36401–3333, Mailing Address: P.O. Box 706, Zip 36401–0706; tel. 251/578–2480, (Nonreporting) **A**10 **S** Gilliard Health Services, Montgomery, AL
Primary Contact: Tom McLendon, Administrator
CFO: Sharon Jones, Chief Financial Officer
CMO: William Farmer, M.D., Chief of Staff
CHR: Tracey Rhodes, Coordinator Human Resources
CNO: Angie Hendrix, Director of Nursing
Web address: www.evergreenmedical.org
Control: Partnership, Investor–owned (for–profit) **Service**: General medical and surgical

Staffed Beds: 39

Hospital, Medicare Provider Number, Address, Telephone, Approval, Facility, and Physician Codes, Health Care System

★ American Hospital Association (AHA) membership
☐ The Joint Commission accreditation
○ Healthcare Facilities Accreditation Program
◇ DNV Healthcare Inc. accreditation
⇑ Center for Improvement in Healthcare Quality Accreditation
△ Commission on Accreditation of Rehabilitation Facilities (CARF) accreditation

FAIRHOPE—Baldwin County

☐ **THOMAS HOSPITAL (010100)**, 750 Morphy Avenue, Zip 36532–1812, Mailing Address: P.O. Box 929, Zip 36533–0929; tel. 251/928–2375, (Nonreporting) **A**1 3 10 19 **S** Infirmary Health System, Mobile, AL
Primary Contact: Ormand P. Thompson, President
COO: Douglas Garner, Vice President
CMO: Michael McBrearty, M.D., Vice President Medical Affairs
CNO: Julie Rowell, R.N., Chief Nursing Officer
Web address: www.thomashospital.com
Control: Other not-for-profit (including NFP Corporation) **Service:** General medical and surgical

Staffed Beds: 136

FAYETTE—Fayette County

☐ **FAYETTE MEDICAL CENTER (010045)**, 1653 Temple Avenue North, Zip 35555–1314, Mailing Address: P O Drawer 710, Zip 35555–0710; tel. 205/932–5966, (Total facility includes 122 beds in nursing home-type unit) **A**1 10 **F**11 15 28 29 30 40 70 81 107 110 111 114 119 127 128 130 133 146 **S** DCH Health System, Tuscaloosa, AL
Primary Contact: Donald J. Jones, FACHE, Administrator
CFO: Jeff Huff, Assistant Administrator Finance
CHR: Felicia Solomon-Owens, Director Human Resources
Web address: www.dchsystem.com
Control: Hospital district or authority, Government, nonfederal **Service:** General medical and surgical

Staffed Beds: 167 **Admissions:** 866 **Census:** 128 **Outpatient Visits:** 50423 **Births:** 0 **Total Expense ($000):** 24805 **Payroll Expense ($000):** 11125 **Personnel:** 196

FLORENCE—Lauderdale County

⊞ **NORTH ALABAMA MEDICAL CENTER (010006)**, 1701 Veterans Drive, Zip 35630–6033; tel. 256/629–1000, **A**1 5 10 19 **F**3 13 15 17 18 20 22 24 26 28 29 34 35 40 43 49 50 54 56 57 60 64 68 70 73 74 75 76 77 79 80 81 83 84 85 86 87 89 90 97 98 102 103 107 108 110 111 115 117 119 126 127 129 130 135 145 146 147 148 156 **S** LifePoint Health, Brentwood, TN
Primary Contact: Russell Pigg, Chief Executive Officer
COO: Mike Howard, Chief Operating Officer
CFO: Steve E. Hobbs, Chief Financial Officer
CMO: Oliver Matthews, M.D., Chief Medical Officer
CIO: Raul Velez, Information Technology Director
CHR: Cheryl Lee, Human Resources Director
Web address: www.https://namccares.com/
Control: Corporation, Investor-owned (for-profit) **Service:** General medical and surgical

Staffed Beds: 321 **Admissions:** 14324 **Census:** 155 **Outpatient Visits:** 100887 **Births:** 1235 **Total Expense ($000):** 141003 **Payroll Expense ($000):** 50306 **Personnel:** 1180

FOLEY—Baldwin County

⊞ **SOUTH BALDWIN REGIONAL MEDICAL CENTER (010083)**, 1613 North McKenzie Street, Zip 36535–2299; tel. 251/949–3400, **A**1 3 5 10 19 **F**3 12 13 15 18 20 28 29 30 31 34 35 37 38 40 43 45 49 50 51 54 57 59 60 62 64 65 66 68 70 74 75 76 77 79 81 82 85 86 87 93 107 108 110 111 115 116 117 118 119 126 129 130 131 132 133 134 135 144 146 147 148 149 154 156 **S** Community Health Systems, Inc., Franklin, TN
Primary Contact: Daniel McKinney, Chief Executive Officer
CFO: Brad Hardcastle, Chief Financial Officer
CMO: Lee Eslava, Chief Medical Officer
CHR: Pamela J Brunson, Director Human Resources
CNO: Margaret Roley, Chief Nursing Officer
Web address: www.southbaldwinrmc.com
Control: Corporation, Investor-owned (for-profit) **Service:** General medical and surgical

Staffed Beds: 112 **Admissions:** 6627 **Census:** 68 **Outpatient Visits:** 112668 **Births:** 616 **Personnel:** 626

FORT PAYNE—Dekalb County

⊞ **DEKALB REGIONAL MEDICAL CENTER (010012)**, 200 Medical Center Drive, Zip 35968–3458, Mailing Address: P.O. Box 680778, Zip 35968–1608; tel. 256/845–3150, (Nonreporting) **A**1 10 20 **S** Quorum Health, Brentwood, TN
Primary Contact: Patrick Trammell, Chief Executive Officer
CFO: Chris Benson, Chief Financial Officer
CMO: Anthony Sims, M.D., Chief of Staff
CIO: Joseph Helms, Director Information Systems
CHR: Diane McMichen, Director Human Resources
CNO: Marquita Bailey, Chief Nursing Officer
Web address: www.dekalbregional.com
Control: Corporation, Investor-owned (for-profit) **Service:** General medical and surgical

Staffed Beds: 115

GADSDEN—Etowah County

⊞ **ENCOMPASS HEALTH REHABILITATION HOSPITAL OF GADSDEN (013032)**, 801 Goodyear Avenue, Zip 35903–1133; tel. 256/439–5000, **A**1 10 **F**28 29 30 90 91 94 95 96 148 **S** Encompass Health Corporation, Birmingham, AL
Primary Contact: Kayla Feazell, Chief Executive Officer
COO: Kayla Feazell, Chief Executive Officer
CFO: Lori Norman, Chief Financial Officer
CMO: Vladimir Slutsker, Medical Director
CIO: Lori Norman, Chief Financial Officer
CHR: Rhonda Young, Human Resource Director
CNO: Barry Eads, Chief Nursing Officer
Web address: www.encompasshealth.com/gadsdenrehab
Control: Corporation, Investor-owned (for-profit) **Service:** Rehabilitation

Staffed Beds: 44 **Admissions:** 1151 **Census:** 38 **Outpatient Visits:** 0 **Births:** 0 **Total Expense ($000):** 15161 **Payroll Expense ($000):** 8423 **Personnel:** 126

⊞ **GADSDEN REGIONAL MEDICAL CENTER (010040)**, 1007 Goodyear Avenue, Zip 35903–1195; tel. 256/494–4000, **A**1 2 10 **F**3 13 15 18 20 22 24 29 30 31 34 35 40 43 45 49 50 56 57 59 64 68 70 74 76 77 78 79 80 81 85 89 93 98 102 103 107 108 110 111 114 115 119 120 121 124 126 129 130 131 146 147 148 149 154 **S** Community Health Systems, Inc., Franklin, TN
Primary Contact: Corey Ewing, Chief Executive Officer
COO: Josh Hester, Chief Operating Officer
CFO: Michael Cotton, Chief Financial Officer
CMO: Arthur Boykin, M.D., Chief of Staff
CIO: Glenn Phillips, Director Information Systems
CHR: Gale H Sanders, Director
CNO: Martha Seahorn, Chief Nursing Officer
Web address: www.gadsdenregional.com
Control: Corporation, Investor-owned (for-profit) **Service:** General medical and surgical

Staffed Beds: 279 **Admissions:** 13238 **Census:** 181 **Outpatient Visits:** 81874 **Births:** 841 **Total Expense ($000):** 175459 **Payroll Expense ($000):** 56066 **Personnel:** 1046

☐ **MOUNTAIN VIEW HOSPITAL (014006)**, 3001 Scenic Highway, Zip 35904–3047, Mailing Address: P.O. Box 8406, Zip 35902–8406; tel. 256/546–9265, (Nonreporting) **A**1 10
Primary Contact: G Michael. Shehi, M.D., Chief Executive Officer
COO: Sara Romano, R.N., Vice President
CFO: Mary Jensen, Controller
CMO: G Michael Shehi, M.D., Medical Director
CHR: Dave Jensen, Director Human Resources, Performance Improvement and Risk Management
Web address: www.mtnviewhospital.com
Control: Corporation, Investor-owned (for-profit) **Service:** Psychiatric

Staffed Beds: 68

⊞ **RIVERVIEW REGIONAL MEDICAL CENTER (010046)**, 600 South Third Street, Zip 35901–5399; tel. 256/543–5200, (Nonreporting) **A**1 10 **S** Prime Healthcare, Ontario, CA
Primary Contact: John Langlois, Chief Executive Officer
CIO: Jay Terrell, Manager Management Information Systems
CHR: Leslie Morton, Manager Human Resources
Web address: www.riverviewregional.com
Control: Corporation, Investor-owned (for-profit) **Service:** General medical and surgical

Staffed Beds: 280

GENEVA—Geneva County

WIREGRASS MEDICAL CENTER (010062), 1200 West Maple Avenue, Zip 36340–1694; tel. 334/684–3655, (Nonreporting) **A**10
Primary Contact: Jeffrey M. Brannon, Chief Executive Officer
CFO: Janet Smith, Chief Financial Officer
CHR: Tim Tidwell, Human Resources Director
CNO: Ashley Tanner, Director of Nursing
Web address: www.wiregrassmedicalcenter.org
Control: Hospital district or authority, Government, nonfederal **Service:** General medical and surgical

Staffed Beds: 165

Many Facility Codes have changed. Please refer to the AHA Guide Code Chart.

© 2019 AHA Guide

GREENSBORO—Hale County

HALE COUNTY HOSPITAL (010095), 508 Green Street, Zip 36744–2316; tel. 334/624–3024, (Nonreporting) **A**10
Primary Contact: Shay Fondren, Administrator
Web address: www.halecountyhospital.com
Control: Hospital district or authority, Government, nonfederal **Service:** General medical and surgical

Staffed Beds: 20

GREENVILLE—Butler County

✠ **REGIONAL MEDICAL CENTER OF CENTRAL ALABAMA (010150)**, 29 L V Stabler Drive, Zip 36037–3800; tel. 334/382–2671, (Nonreporting) **A**1 5 10
Primary Contact: Chad French, Chief Executive Officer
CFO: David Wilcox, Chief Financial Officer
CMO: Norman F McGowin, M.D., III Chief of Staff
CIO: Doug Burkett, Manager Information Technology
CHR: Robert Foster, Director Human Resources
CNO: Kimberli Weaver, Chief Nursing Officer
Web address: www.lvstabler.com
Control: City, Government, nonfederal **Service:** General medical and surgical

Staffed Beds: 61

GROVE HILL—Clarke County

★ **GROVE HILL MEMORIAL HOSPITAL (010091)**, 295 South Jackson Street, Zip 36451–3231, Mailing Address: P.O. Box 935, Zip 36451–0935; tel. 251/275–3191, (Nonreporting) **A**10
Primary Contact: Kenneth Larrimore, Administrator
CFO: Elaine Averett, Chief Financial Officer
CMO: Eniola Fagbongbe, M.D., Chief Medical Staff
CIO: Aaron Harrell, Director
CHR: Aubrey Sheffield, Administrative Assistant Human Resources and Public Relations
CNO: Karen Coleman, Director of Nursing
Web address: www.grovehillmemorial.org
Control: City, Government, nonfederal **Service:** General medical and surgical

Staffed Beds: 34

GUNTERSVILLE—Marshall County

MARSHALL MEDICAL CENTER NORTH (010010), 8000 Alabama Highway 69, Zip 35976; tel. 256/753–8000, **A**5 **F**3 11 12 13 15 26 28 29 32 34 35 37 38 40 43 45 49 50 51 53 54 57 59 64 68 70 74 75 76 77 79 81 82 85 86 87 89 92 93 98 100 102 104 107 108 110 111 114 115 119 130 131 132 135 141 146 147 149 154 **S** Marshall Health System, Guntersville, AL
Primary Contact: Cheryl M. Hays, FACHE, Administrator and Chief Operating Officer
COO: Cheryl M Hays, FACHE, Administrator and Chief Operating Officer
CFO: Kathy Nelson, Chief Financial Officer
CMO: Don Jones, M.D., Chief Medical Officer
CIO: Kim Bunch, Director Information Technology
CHR: Sabrina Weaver, Director of Human Resources
CNO: Kathy Woodruff, R.N., MSN, Chief Nursing Officer
Web address: www.mmcenters.com
Control: Hospital district or authority, Government, nonfederal **Service:** General medical and surgical

Staffed Beds: 90 **Admissions:** 3509 **Census:** 47 **Outpatient Visits:** 112714 **Births:** 462 **Total Expense ($000):** 59153 **Payroll Expense ($000):** 25117 **Personnel:** 347

HALEYVILLE—Winston County

☐ **LAKELAND COMMUNITY HOSPITAL (010125)**, Highway 195 East, Zip 35565–9536, Mailing Address: P.O. Box 780, Zip 35565–0780; tel. 205/486–5213, (Nonreporting) **A**1 10
Primary Contact: Cynthia Nichols, R.N., MSN, Chief Executive Officer
CFO: Penny Westmoreland, Chief Financial Officer
Web address: www.lakelandcommunityhospital.com/
Control: Hospital district or authority, Government, nonfederal **Service:** General medical and surgical

Staffed Beds: 59

HAMILTON—Marion County

✠ **NORTH MISSISSIPPI MEDICAL CENTER-HAMILTON (010044)**, 1256 Military Street South, Zip 35570–5003; tel. 205/921–6200, (Nonreporting) **A**1 10 **S** North Mississippi Health Services, Inc., Tupelo, MS
Primary Contact: Robert Trimm, Administrator
CMO: Jarred Sartain, M.D., President Medical Staff
CHR: Anne Lawler, Director Human Resources
CNO: Jennifer Cagle, Director of Nursing
Web address: www.nmhs.net
Control: Other not–for–profit (including NFP Corporation) **Service:** General medical and surgical

Staffed Beds: 15

HUNTSVILLE—Madison County

✠ **CRESTWOOD MEDICAL CENTER (010131)**, One Hospital Drive, Zip 35801–3403; tel. 256/429–4000, **A**1 5 10 **F**3 11 12 13 15 17 18 20 22 26 28 29 30 31 34 35 40 43 45 47 49 50 51 54 56 57 59 60 64 65 68 70 72 74 75 76 77 78 79 81 85 86 87 89 93 97 107 108 110 111 114 115 119 126 129 130 131 132 136 146 147 148 149 154 156 157 **S** Community Health Systems, Inc., Franklin, TN
Primary Contact: Pamela Hudson, M.D., Chief Executive Officer
COO: Bobby Ginn, Chief Operating Officer
CFO: Sherry J Jones, Chief Financial Officer
CHR: Elyria Sinclair, Director Human Resources
CNO: Martha Delaney Walls, R.N., MSN, Chief Nursing Officer
Web address: www.crestwoodmedcenter.com
Control: Corporation, Investor–owned (for–profit) **Service:** General medical and surgical

Staffed Beds: 180 **Admissions:** 10667 **Census:** 108 **Outpatient Visits:** 109321 **Births:** 1081 **Personnel:** 1112

✠ **ENCOMPASS REHABILITATION HOSPITAL OF NORTH ALABAMA (013029)**, 107 Governors Drive SW, Zip 35801–4326; tel. 256/535–2300, (Nonreporting) **A**1 10 **S** Encompass Health Corporation, Birmingham, AL
Primary Contact: Douglas H. Beverly, Chief Executive Officer
Web address: www.encompasshealth.com/huntsvillerehab
Control: Corporation, Investor–owned (for–profit) **Service:** Rehabilitation

Staffed Beds: 70

☐ **HUNTSVILLE HOSPITAL (010039)**, 101 Sivley Road SW, Zip 35801–4470; tel. 256/265–1000, (Includes HUNTSVILLE HOSPITAL FOR WOMEN AND CHILDREN, 911 Big Cove Road SE, Huntsville, Alabama, Zip 35801–3784; tel. 256/265–1000; MADISON HOSPITAL, 8375 Highway 72 West, Madison, Alabama, Zip 35758–9573; tel. 256/265–2012; Mary Lynne Wright, R.N., President) **A**1 2 3 5 10 **F**5 7 8 12 13 14 15 17 18 19 20 21 22 23 24 25 26 28 29 30 31 35 37 38 40 41 43 46 49 50 51 53 54 56 57 59 60 63 64 68 70 71 72 73 76 78 79 80 81 82 84 85 86 87 88 89 93 98 100 101 102 103 107 108 109 110 111 114 115 116 117 118 119 126 129 130 131 142 145 146 147 148 154 157 **S** Huntsville Hospital Health System, Huntsville, AL
Primary Contact: David S. Spillers, Chief Executive Officer
COO: Jeff Samz, Chief Operating Officer
CFO: Kelli Powers, Chief Financial Officer
CMO: Robert Chappell, M.D., Chief Medical Officer and Chief Quality Officer
CIO: Rick Corn, Chief Information Officer
CHR: Andrea P Rosler, Vice President Human Resources
CNO: Karol Jones, Chief Nursing Officer
Web address: www.huntsvillehospital.org
Control: Hospital district or authority, Government, nonfederal **Service:** General medical and surgical

Staffed Beds: 948 **Admissions:** 48811 **Census:** 674 **Outpatient Visits:** 863560 **Births:** 5416 **Total Expense ($000):** 957723 **Payroll Expense ($000):** 366233 **Personnel:** 7871

UNITY PSYCHIATRIC CARE-HUNTSVILLE (014018), 5315 Millennium Drive NW, Zip 35806–2458; tel. 256/964–6700, **A**10 **F**6 29 34 35 38 56 59 65 75 77 86 87 98 101 103 130 135 148 **S** Tennessee Health Management, Parsons, TN
Primary Contact: Bradley Moss, Administrator
Web address: www.thmgt.com/locations/behavioral-healthcare-center-at-huntsville
Control: Corporation, Investor–owned (for–profit) **Service:** Psychiatric

Staffed Beds: 20 **Admissions:** 196 **Census:** 9 **Outpatient Visits:** 0 **Births:** 0

Hospital, Medicare Provider Number, Address, Telephone, Approval, Facility, and Physician Codes, Health Care System

★ American Hospital Association (AHA) membership
☐ The Joint Commission accreditation
○ Healthcare Facilities Accreditation Program
◇ DNV Healthcare Inc. accreditation
⇑ Center for Improvement in Healthcare Quality Accreditation
△ Commission on Accreditation of Rehabilitation Facilities (CARF) accreditation

© 2019 AHA Guide   *Many Facility Codes have changed. Please refer to the AHA Guide Code Chart.*   Hospitals **A19**

JACKSON—Clarke County

JACKSON MEDICAL CENTER (010128), 220 Hospital Drive, Zip 36545–2459, Mailing Address: P.O. Box 428, Zip 36545–0428; tel. 251/246–9021, (Nonreporting) **A**10 **S** Gilliard Health Services, Montgomery, AL
Primary Contact: Jennifer M. Ryland, R.N., Chief Executive Officer
COO: Jennifer M Ryland, R.N., Chief Administrative Officer
CHR: Kathy Jones, Director Human Resources
Web address: www.jacksonmedicalcenter.org
Control: Partnership, Investor–owned (for–profit) **Service**: General medical and surgical

Staffed Beds: 26

JASPER—Walker County

⊠ **WALKER BAPTIST MEDICAL CENTER (010089)**, 3400 Highway 78 East, Zip 35501–8907, Mailing Address: P.O. Box 3547, Zip 35502–3547; tel. 205/387–4000, **A**1 10 20 **F**3 4 7 8 11 13 15 18 20 26 28 29 30 34 35 39 40 45 46 50 56 57 59 60 65 68 70 74 75 76 77 79 81 82 86 87 91 93 98 100 101 102 103 104 107 110 111 114 115 119 126 130 131 132 146 147 148 153 154 155 156 **S** TENET Healthcare Corporation, Dallas, TX
Primary Contact: Robert A. Phillips, Chief Executive Officer
CFO: Amanda Dyle, Chief Financial Officer
CIO: Kenny Horton, Director Information Systems
CHR: Pat Morrow, Director Human Resources
CNO: Robbie Hindman, Vice President Patient Care Services and Chief Nursing Officer
Web address: www.bhsala.com
Control: Corporation, Investor–owned (for–profit) **Service**: General medical and surgical

Staffed Beds: 178 Admissions: 7614 Census: 98 Outpatient Visits: 73536 Births: 831 Total Expense ($000): 87866 Payroll Expense ($000): 31235 Personnel: 632

LUVERNE—Crenshaw County

☐ **BEACON CHILDREN'S HOSPITAL (014015)**, 150 Hospital Drive, Zip 36049; tel. 334/335–5040, (Nonreporting) **A**1 10
Primary Contact: Bradley Eisemann, Administrator
Web address: www.beaconchildrenshospital.com
Control: Other not–for–profit (including NFP Corporation) **Service**: Children's hospital psychiatric

Staffed Beds: 24

CRENSHAW COMMUNITY HOSPITAL (010008), 101 Hospital Circle, Zip 36049–7344; tel. 334/335–3374, (Nonreporting) **A**10
Primary Contact: David L. Hughes, Administrator
COO: Victoria Lawrenson, Chief Operating Officer
CMO: Charles Tompkins, M.D., Chief of Staff
CHR: Patricia Jarry, Manager Human Resources
Web address: www.crenshawcommunityhospital.com
Control: Corporation, Investor–owned (for–profit) **Service**: General medical and surgical

Staffed Beds: 65

MADISON—Madison County

BRADFORD HEALTH SERVICES AT HUNTSVILLE, 1600 Browns Ferry Road, Zip 35758–9601, Mailing Address: P.O. Box 1488, Zip 35758–0176; tel. 256/461–7272, (Nonreporting) **S** Bradford Health Services, Birmingham, AL
Primary Contact: Bob Hinds, Executive Director
Web address: www.bradfordhealth.com
Control: Corporation, Investor–owned (for–profit) **Service**: Alcoholism and other chemical dependency

Staffed Beds: 84

MOBILE—Mobile County

★ **BAYPOINTE BEHAVIORAL HEALTH (014014)**, 5800 Southland Drive, Zip 36693–3313; tel. 251/661–0153, **A**3 10 **F**38 98 99 100 101 106 130 132 154 **S** AltaPointe Health Systems, Mobile, AL
Primary Contact: Jarett Crum, Hospital Director
Web address: www.altapointe.org
Control: Other not–for–profit (including NFP Corporation) **Service**: Children's hospital psychiatric

Staffed Beds: 60 Admissions: 1418 Census: 46 Outpatient Visits: 0 Births: 0 Total Expense ($000): 9232 Payroll Expense ($000): 6398 Personnel: 205

☐ **INFIRMARY LONG TERM ACUTE CARE HOSPITAL (012006)**, 5 Mobile Infirmary Circle, Zip 36607–3513, Mailing Address: P.O. Box 2226, Zip 36652–2226; tel. 251/660–5239, (Nonreporting) **A**1 10 **S** Infirmary Health System, Mobile, AL
Primary Contact: Susanne Marmande, Administrator
Web address: www.theinfirmary.com/
Control: Other not–for–profit (including NFP Corporation) **Service**: Acute long–term care hospital

Staffed Beds: 38

☐ △ **MOBILE INFIRMARY MEDICAL CENTER (010113)**, 5 Mobile Infirmary Drive North, Zip 36607–3513, Mailing Address: P.O. Box 2144, Zip 36652–2144; tel. 251/435–2400, (Includes ROTARY REHABILITATION HOSPITAL, 5 Mobile Infirmary Circle, Mobile, Alabama, Zip 36607, Mailing Address: P O Box 2144, Zip 36652, tel. 251/435–3400), (Nonreporting) **A**1 2 3 5 7 10 **S** Infirmary Health System, Mobile, AL
Primary Contact: Joe Stough, Interim President
CFO: Joe Denton, Executive Vice President and Chief Financial Officer
CMO: John Dixon, Chief Medical Officer
CIO: Eddy Stephens, Vice President Information Technology
CHR: Sheila Young, Vice President Human Resources
Web address: www.infirmaryhealth.org
Control: Other not–for–profit (including NFP Corporation) **Service**: General medical and surgical

Staffed Beds: 554

⊠ **PROVIDENCE HOSPITAL (010090)**, 6801 Airport Boulevard, Zip 36608–3785, Mailing Address: P.O. Box 850429, Zip 36685–0429; tel. 251/633–1000, **A**1 2 3 5 10 **F**3 11 13 15 17 18 20 22 24 26 28 29 30 31 34 35 40 44 45 49 50 51 53 54 55 57 58 59 60 61 64 65 68 70 73 74 75 76 77 78 79 80 81 82 83 84 85 86 87 89 92 93 96 102 107 108 110 111 114 115 117 119 120 121 124 126 129 130 131 132 135 146 148 149 **S** Ascension Healthcare, Saint Louis, MO
Primary Contact: Todd S. Kennedy, President and Chief Executive Officer
COO: C Susan Cornejo, Chief Operating Officer
CMO: William M Lightfoot, M.D., Vice President Medical Services
CHR: Christopher Cockrell, Executive Director Human Resources
CNO: Peter Lindquist, Vice President and Chief Nursing Officer
Web address: www.providencehospital.org
Control: Church operated, Nongovernment, not–for–profit **Service**: General medical and surgical

Staffed Beds: 305 Admissions: 14147 Census: 187 Outpatient Visits: 309527 Births: 1694 Total Expense ($000): 241975 Payroll Expense ($000): 64699 Personnel: 1446

ROTARY REHABILITATION HOSPITAL See Mobile Infirmary Medical Center, Mobile

☐ **SPRINGHILL MEMORIAL HOSPITAL (010144)**, 3719 Dauphin Street, Zip 36608–1798, Mailing Address: P.O. Box 8246, Zip 36689–0246; tel. 251/344–9630, (Nonreporting) **A**1 10
Primary Contact: Jeffery M. St Clair, President and Chief Executive Officer
COO: Rene Areaux, Vice President and Chief Operating Officer
CFO: Jan Grigsby, Vice President and Chief Financial Officer
CMO: Liston Jones, M.D., Medical Director
CIO: Mark Kilborn, Director Information Systems
CHR: Daniela Batchelor, Director Human Resources
CNO: Paul Read, R.N., MSN, Vice President and Chief Nursing Officer
Web address: www.springhillmedicalcenter.com
Control: Corporation, Investor–owned (for–profit) **Service**: General medical and surgical

Staffed Beds: 207

⊠ **USA CHILDREN'S AND WOMEN'S HOSPITAL (013301)**, 1700 Center Street, Zip 36604–3301; tel. 251/415–1000, (Nonreporting) **A**1 3 5 10 **S** USA Health, Mobile, AL
Primary Contact: Chris Jett, Administrator
CFO: Traci Jones, Chief Financial Officer
CIO: Garry Adkins, Chief Information Officer
CHR: Janice Rehm, Manager Human Resources
CNO: Scotty Roberson, Assistant Administrator and Chief Nursing Officer
Web address: www.usahealthsystem.com/usacwh
Control: State, Government, nonfederal **Service**: Children's general medical and surgical

Staffed Beds: 180

Many Facility Codes have changed. Please refer to the AHA Guide Code Chart.   © 2019 AHA Guide

☒ **USA HEALTH UNIVERSITY HOSPITAL (010087)**, 2451 USA Medical Center Drive, Zip 36617–2293; tel. 251/471–7000, **A**1 2 3 5 8 10 **F**3 7 11 12 16 17 18 20 22 24 26 29 31 34 40 43 45 46 47 48 49 57 58 59 61 64 65 68 70 74 78 79 80 81 85 87 107 108 111 114 115 119 120 121 124 126 130 131 132 145 146 148 149 155 **S** USA Health, Mobile, AL
Primary Contact: Sam Dean, Administrator
CFO: Traci Jones, Chief Financial Officer
CIO: Mark Lauteren, Chief Information Officer
CHR: Anita Shirah, Director Human Resources
CNO: Lisa Mestas, Associate Administrator and System Chief Nursing Officer
Web address: www.usahealthsystem.com/usamc
Control: State, Government, nonfederal **Service:** General medical and surgical

Staffed Beds: 150 **Admissions:** 8920 **Census:** 138 **Outpatient Visits:** 58674 **Births:** 0 **Total Expense ($000):** 214064 **Payroll Expense ($000):** 90414 **Personnel:** 1585

MONROEVILLE—Monroe County

☐ **MONROE COUNTY HOSPITAL (010120)**, 2016 South Alabama Avenue, Zip 36460–3044, Mailing Address: P.O. Box 886, Zip 36461–0886; tel. 251/575–3111, (Nonreporting) **A**1 10 20
Primary Contact: Wes Nall, Interim Chief Executive Officer
CFO: Wes Nall, Chief Financial Officer
CMO: David Stallworth, M.D., Chief of Staff
CIO: Jody Falkenberry, Director Information Systems
CHR: Tara Nowling, Director Human Resources
CNO: Barbara Harned, R.N., MSN, Chief Nursing Officer
Web address: www.mchcare.com
Control: Hospital district or authority, Government, nonfederal **Service:** General medical and surgical

Staffed Beds: 44

MONTGOMERY—Montgomery County

☐ **BAPTIST MEDICAL CENTER EAST (010149)**, 400 Taylor Road, Zip 36117–3512, Mailing Address: P.O. Box 241267, Zip 36124–1267; tel. 334/277–8330, **A**1 3 5 10 **F**3 11 12 13 15 29 30 34 35 40 44 45 47 49 50 56 57 63 64 70 72 73 75 76 77 79 81 82 85 86 89 90 93 94 107 108 111 114 115 119 126 129 130 132 135 146 147 **S** Baptist Health, Montgomery, AL
Primary Contact: Jeff G. Rains, Chief Executive Officer
CFO: Katrina Belt, Chief Financial Officer
CHR: Kay R Bennett, Vice President Human Resources
CNO: Kathy Gaston, Chief Nursing Officer
Web address: www.baptistfirst.org
Control: Hospital district or authority, Government, nonfederal **Service:** General medical and surgical

Staffed Beds: 176 **Admissions:** 10359 **Census:** 128 **Outpatient Visits:** 115513 **Births:** 3479 **Total Expense ($000):** 120788 **Payroll Expense ($000):** 49060 **Personnel:** 903

☐ **BAPTIST MEDICAL CENTER SOUTH (010023)**, 2105 East South Boulevard, Zip 36116–2409, Mailing Address: Box 11010, Zip 36111–0010; tel. 334/288–2100, **A**1 3 5 10 **F**3 5 11 13 15 17 18 20 22 24 26 28 29 30 31 34 35 37 40 43 44 45 46 47 49 50 56 57 58 59 60 63 64 68 70 72 74 75 76 77 78 79 81 82 84 85 86 87 89 94 98 100 101 102 103 104 105 107 108 110 111 114 115 116 117 118 119 126 129 130 131 132 135 146 147 148 **S** Baptist Health, Montgomery, AL
Primary Contact: J Peter. Selman, FACHE, Chief Executive Officer
CFO: Melissa Johnson, Chief Financial Officer
CMO: Donovan Kendrick, M.D., Chief Medical Officer
CIO: Steve Miller, Director Information Systems
CHR: Kay R Bennett, System Director Human Resources
CNO: Karen McCaa, R.N., Vice President Patient Care Services and Chief Nursing Officer
Web address: www.baptistfirst.org
Control: Hospital district or authority, Government, nonfederal **Service:** General medical and surgical

Staffed Beds: 379 **Admissions:** 18095 **Census:** 272 **Outpatient Visits:** 241159 **Births:** 729 **Total Expense ($000):** 442170 **Payroll Expense ($000):** 116836 **Personnel:** 2100

☒ **CENTRAL ALABAMA VETERANS HEALTH CARE SYSTEM**, 215 Perry Hill Road, Zip 36109–3798; tel. 334/272–4670, (Includes MONTGOMERY DIVISION, 215 Perry Hill Road, Montgomery, Alabama, Zip 36109–3798; tel. 334/272–4670; TUSKEGEE DIVISION, 2400 Hospital Road, Tuskegee, Alabama, Zip 36083–5001; tel. 334/727–0550), (Nonreporting) **A**1 3 **S** Department of Veterans Affairs, Washington, DC
Primary Contact: Linda Lake Boyle, R.N., MSN, Director
CFO: Debra Nicholson, Manager Finance
CMO: Cliff Robinson, M.D., Chief of Staff
CIO: Rhoda Tyson, Chief Information Officer
CHR: Janice Hardy, Chief Human Resource Management Service
Web address: www.centralalabama.va.gov/
Control: Veterans Affairs, Government, federal **Service:** General medical and surgical

Staffed Beds: 245

☒ **ENCOMPASS HEALTH REHABILITATION HOSPITAL OF MONTGOMERY (013028)**, 4465 Narrow Lane Road, Zip 36116–2900; tel. 334/284–7700, **A**1 10 **F**3 9 28 29 34 35 56 57 59 64 74 75 77 86 90 93 95 96 97 130 131 132 143 146 148 149 **S** Encompass Health Corporation, Birmingham, AL
Primary Contact: Randy Thompson, Chief Executive Officer
CFO: Heath Watson, Controller
CMO: Jeffrey Eng, M.D., Medical Director
CIO: Anidra Billingslea, Health Insurance Management
CHR: Kim McDaniel, Director Human Resources
CNO: Gretchen Vercher, Chief Nursing Officer
Web address: www.encompasshealth.com/montgomeryrehab
Control: Corporation, Investor–owned (for–profit) **Service:** Rehabilitation

Staffed Beds: 70 **Admissions:** 1945 **Census:** 64 **Outpatient Visits:** 3415 **Births:** 0 **Total Expense ($000):** 26336 **Payroll Expense ($000):** 12863 **Personnel:** 184

☒ **JACKSON HOSPITAL AND CLINIC (010024)**, 1725 Pine Street, Zip 36106–1117; tel. 334/293–8000, **A**1 3 5 10 19 **F**12 13 15 17 18 20 22 24 26 29 30 31 34 35 40 45 46 48 49 54 55 57 59 64 68 70 74 75 76 77 78 79 81 82 83 84 85 86 87 89 97 107 108 110 111 115 116 117 118 119 126 129 130 132 135 144 146 147 148 149 154 156
Primary Contact: Joe B. Riley, FACHE, President and Chief Executive Officer
COO: Michael James, Chief Operations Officer
CFO: Paul Peiffer, Chief Financial Officer and Vice President
CHR: Gilbert Darrington, Director Human Resources
Web address: www.jackson.org
Control: Other not–for–profit (including NFP Corporation) **Service:** General medical and surgical

Staffed Beds: 262 **Admissions:** 14637 **Census:** 195 **Outpatient Visits:** 151331 **Births:** 1185 **Total Expense ($000):** 231489 **Payroll Expense ($000):** 110027 **Personnel:** 1740

LONG TERM CARE HOSPITAL See Noland Hospital Montgomery

MONTGOMERY DIVISION See Central Alabama Veterans Health Care System, Montgomery

☐ **NOLAND HOSPITAL MONTGOMERY (012007)**, 1725 Pine Street, 5 North, Zip 36106–1109; tel. 334/240–0532, (Nonreporting) **A**1 10 **S** Noland Health Services, Inc., Birmingham, AL
Primary Contact: Dale Jones, Administrator
Web address: www.nolandhealth.com
Control: Other not–for–profit (including NFP Corporation) **Service:** Acute long–term care hospital

Staffed Beds: 65

MOULTON—Lawrence County

☐ **LAWRENCE MEDICAL CENTER (010059)**, 202 Hospital Street, Zip 35650–1218, Mailing Address: P.O. Box 39, Zip 35650–0039; tel. 256/974–2200, (Nonreporting) **A**1 10 **S** Huntsville Hospital Health System, Huntsville, AL
Primary Contact: Dean A. Griffin, Chief Executive Officer
CFO: Jim Crawford, Chief Financial Officer
CIO: Jeremy Duncan, Director Information Systems
CHR: Diane K Secor, Director Human Resources
Web address: www.lawrencemedicalcenter.com
Control: County, Government, nonfederal **Service:** General medical and surgical

Staffed Beds: 43

Hospital, Medicare Provider Number, Address, Telephone, Approval, Facility, and Physician Codes, Health Care System

★ American Hospital Association (AHA) membership   ○ Healthcare Facilities Accreditation Program   ⇑ Center for Improvement in Healthcare Quality Accreditation
☐ The Joint Commission accreditation   ◇ DNV Healthcare Inc. accreditation   △ Commission on Accreditation of Rehabilitation Facilities (CARF) accreditation

MUSCLE SHOALS—Colbert County

✠ **SHOALS HOSPITAL (010157)**, 201 Avalon Avenue, Zip 35661–2805, Mailing Address: P.O. Box 3359, Zip 35662–3359; tel. 256/386–1600, (Nonreporting) **A1** 10 **S** LifePoint Health, Brentwood, TN
Primary Contact: Kidada Hawkins, Chief Executive Officer
CFO: Steve E. Hobbs, Chief Financial Officer
CMO: Terry true, M.D., Chief of Staff
CIO: William Johnson, Director Information Systems
CHR: Nancy Bowling, Director Human Resources
Web address: www.shoalshospital.com
Control: Hospital district or authority, Government, nonfederal **Service:** General medical and surgical

Staffed Beds: 137

ONEONTA—Blount County

✠ **ST. VINCENT'S BLOUNT (011305)**, 150 Gilbreath, Zip 35121–2827, Mailing Address: P.O. Box 1000, Zip 35121–0013; tel. 205/274–3000, **A1** 10 18 **F3** 11 15 18 29 30 35 40 45 46 50 57 59 60 64 70 81 85 87 93 97 107 108 110 111 119 127 133 135 146 149 **S** Ascension Healthcare, Saint Louis, MO
Primary Contact: Suzannah Campbell, President
CFO: Jennifer Kingry, Chief Financial Officer
CMO: David R Wilson, M.D., Chief of Staff
CIO: John Laliberte, Chief Information Officer
CHR: Kristin L. Costanzo, Direct-In-Market Lead Human Relations Partner
CNO: Kira Schnittker, Director of Nursing
Web address: www.stvhs.com
Control: Other not–for–profit (including NFP Corporation) **Service:** General medical and surgical

Staffed Beds: 25 **Admissions:** 914 **Census:** 14 **Outpatient Visits:** 37211 **Births:** 0 **Total Expense ($000):** 21846 **Payroll Expense ($000):** 6183 **Personnel:** 104

OPELIKA—Lee County

✠ **EAST ALABAMA MEDICAL CENTER (010029)**, 2000 Pepperell Parkway, Zip 36801–5452; tel. 334/749–3411, (Includes EAST ALABAMA MEDICAL CENTER-LANIER, 4800 48th Street, Valley, Alabama, Zip 36854–3666; tel. 334/756–9180; Greg Nichols, Chief Executive Officer) (Total facility includes 216 beds in nursing home-type unit) **A1** 2 10 19 **F3** 7 11 13 15 17 18 20 22 24 26 28 29 30 31 34 35 40 43 45 47 48 50 53 54 57 59 60 61 64 68 70 75 76 77 78 79 81 82 84 85 86 89 90 93 94 98 99 100 102 107 110 111 114 115 116 117 119 120 121 123 124 125 126 128 129 130 131 132 135 146 148 149 154 156
Primary Contact: Laura D. Grill, R.N., Chief Executive Officer
COO: Sarah Nunnelly, Executive Vice President and Chief Operating Officer
CFO: Sam Price, Executive Vice President Finance/Chief Financial Officer
CMO: William Golden, M.D., Chief Medical Officer
CIO: Sarah Gray, Vice President Information Services
CHR: Susan Johnston, Vice President Human Resources
CNO: Jane Fullum, Vice President Patient Care Services
Web address: www.eamc.org
Control: Hospital district or authority, Government, nonfederal **Service:** General medical and surgical

Staffed Beds: 549 **Admissions:** 16198 **Census:** 435 **Outpatient Visits:** 74905 **Births:** 2061 **Total Expense ($000):** 309917 **Payroll Expense ($000):** 128845 **Personnel:** 3040

OPP—Covington County

MIZELL MEMORIAL HOSPITAL (010007), 702 Main Street, Zip 36467–1626, Mailing Address: P.O. Box 1010, Zip 36467–1010; tel. 334/493–3541, **A10 F8** 11 15 34 40 41 43 44 45 50 51 53 54 56 59 64 70 74 75 77 81 85 87 93 97 98 102 103 107 108 110 111 114 119 129 130 133 135 146 149 154
Primary Contact: Jana Wyatt, Chief Executive Officer
CFO: Amy Bess, Chief Financial Officer
CIO: Elizabeth Cook, Chief Information Officer
CHR: Dianne Morrison, Director Human Resources
CNO: Steven Skeen, R.N., Chief Nursing Officer
Web address: www.mizellmh.com
Control: Other not–for–profit (including NFP Corporation) **Service:** General medical and surgical

Staffed Beds: 59 **Admissions:** 1460 **Census:** 22 **Births:** 0 **Total Expense ($000):** 18414 **Payroll Expense ($000):** 8309 **Personnel:** 204

OZARK—Dale County

DALE MEDICAL CENTER (010021), 126 Hospital Avenue, Zip 36360–2080; tel. 334/774–2601, (Nonreporting) **A10**
Primary Contact: Vernon Johnson, Administrator
CFO: Brad Hull, Chief Financial Officer
CMO: Steve Brandt, M.D., Chief of Staff
CHR: Sheila Dunn, Assistant Administrator Human Resources
Web address: www.dalemedical.org
Control: Corporation, Investor–owned (for–profit) **Service:** General medical and surgical

Staffed Beds: 69

PELHAM—Shelby County

☐ **ENCOMPASS HEALTH REHABILITATION HOSPITAL OF SHELBY COUNTY**, 900 Oak Mountain Commons Lane, Zip 35124; tel. 205/216–7600, (Nonreporting) **A1** 10 **S** Encompass Health Corporation, Birmingham, AL
Primary Contact: Robert Russell, Chief Executive Officer
Web address: www.encompasshealth.com/shelbycountyrehab
Control: Corporation, Investor–owned (for–profit) **Service:** Rehabilitation

Staffed Beds: 35

PELL CITY—St. Clair County

✠ **ST. VINCENT'S ST. CLAIR (010130)**, 7063 Veterans Parkway, Zip 35125–1499; tel. 205/814–2105, **A1** 10 **F3** 11 15 29 30 35 40 43 45 46 50 59 60 64 68 70 79 81 82 85 87 93 107 108 110 111 119 130 135 146 148 149 **S** Ascension Healthcare, Saint Louis, MO
Primary Contact: Suzannah Campbell, President
CFO: Jason Lynn, Director Finance
Web address: www.stvhs.com
Control: Other not–for–profit (including NFP Corporation) **Service:** General medical and surgical

Staffed Beds: 40 **Admissions:** 1815 **Census:** 19 **Outpatient Visits:** 49198 **Births:** 0 **Total Expense ($000):** 29491 **Payroll Expense ($000):** 9312 **Personnel:** 141

PHENIX CITY—Russell County

☐ **JACK HUGHSTON MEMORIAL HOSPITAL (010168)**, 4401 Riverchase Drive, Zip 36867–7483; tel. 334/732–3000, **A1** 3 10 13 **F3** 29 40 45 70 79 81 89 107 111 115 119 130 131
Primary Contact: Mark A. Baker, Chief Executive Officer
COO: Rachel H. Crenshaw, Chief Operating Officer
CFO: Angela Shelton, Chief Financial Officer
CMO: James F. Zumstein, M.D., Chief of Medicine
CHR: Lana Thomas-Folds, System Director Human Resources
CNO: Sylvia Thomas, Chief Nursing Officer
Web address: www.hughston.com
Control: Corporation, Investor–owned (for–profit) **Service:** General medical and surgical

Staffed Beds: 35 **Admissions:** 2941 **Census:** 18 **Outpatient Visits:** 18480 **Births:** 3 **Total Expense ($000):** 53305 **Payroll Expense ($000):** 14954 **Personnel:** 294

✠ **REGIONAL REHABILITATION HOSPITAL (013033)**, 3715 Highway 280/431 North, Zip 36867; tel. 334/732–2200, **A1** 10 **F3** 9 28 29 34 56 57 59 61 64 65 74 75 77 79 86 90 93 95 96 97 130 132 143 148 149 **S** Encompass Health Corporation, Birmingham, AL
Primary Contact: Lora Davis, FACHE, Chief Executive Officer
CFO: Bobby Edmondson, Controller
CMO: Nitin Desei, M.D., Medical Director
CIO: Jacki Cuevas, Director Health Information Services
CHR: Cindy Glynn, Director Human Resources
CNO: Wendy Lee, Chief Nursing Officer
Web address: www.regionalrehabhospital.com
Control: Corporation, Investor–owned (for–profit) **Service:** Rehabilitation

Staffed Beds: 58 **Admissions:** 1560 **Census:** 55 **Outpatient Visits:** 3145 **Births:** 0 **Total Expense ($000):** 18926 **Payroll Expense ($000):** 10515 **Personnel:** 190

Many Facility Codes have changed. Please refer to the AHA Guide Code Chart.   © 2019 AHA Guide

PRATTVILLE—Autauga County

☐ **PRATTVILLE BAPTIST HOSPITAL (010108)**, 124 South Memorial Drive,
Zip 36067–3619, Mailing Address: P.O. Box 681630, Zip 36068–1638;
tel. 334/365–0651, **A**1 10 **F**3 11 12 15 18 29 30 34 35 40 44 45 50 56 57 59
60 63 64 68 70 74 75 77 81 82 84 85 86 87 93 107 111 114 119 129 132
146 154 **S** Baptist Health, Montgomery, AL
Primary Contact: Eric Morgan, Chief Executive Officer
CFO: LaDonna McDaniel, Financial Manager
CIO: B Blaine Brown, Vice President and General Counsel
CHR: Kymberli Skipper, Manager Human Resources
Web address: www.baptistfirst.org/facilities/prattville-baptist-hospital/default.aspx
Control: Hospital district or authority, Government, nonfederal **Service**: General
medical and surgical

Staffed Beds: 50 **Admissions**: 3289 **Census**: 39 **Outpatient Visits**: 79228
Births: 0 **Total Expense ($000)**: 46598 **Payroll Expense ($000)**: 17130
Personnel: 311

RED BAY—Franklin County

★ **RED BAY HOSPITAL (011302)**, 211 Hospital Road, Zip 35582–3858, Mailing
Address: P.O. Box 490, Zip 35582–0490; tel. 256/356–9532, **A**10 18 **F**7 11 15
29 34 35 40 53 57 59 68 77 85 87 93 97 107 110 114 119 127 130 131 133
135 157 **S** Huntsville Hospital Health System, Huntsville, AL
Primary Contact: Sherry Jolley, Director of Operations and Nursing
CFO: Penny Westmoreland, Chief Financial Officer
CMO: Kristy Crandell, M.D., Medical Staff President
CHR: Amy Leigh Bishop, Director Human Resources
CNO: Margaret Thorn, Interim Director of Nursing
Web address: www.redbayhospital.com
Control: Hospital district or authority, Government, nonfederal **Service**: General
medical and surgical

Staffed Beds: 22 **Admissions**: 404 **Census**: 8 **Outpatient Visits**: 10515 **Births**: 0
Total Expense ($000): 10231 **Payroll Expense ($000)**: 4216 **Personnel**: 109

RUSSELLVILLE—Franklin County

☐ **RUSSELLVILLE HOSPITAL (010158)**, 15155 Highway 43, Zip 35653–1975,
Mailing Address: P.O. Box 1089, Zip 35653–1089; tel. 256/332–1611,
(Nonreporting) **A**1 10 **S** Curae Health, Clinton, TN
Primary Contact: Christine R. Stewart, FACHE, Chief Executive Officer
CFO: Penny Westmoreland, Chief Financial Officer
CHR: Stephen Proctor, Director of Human Resources/Risk
CNO: Belinda Johnson, R.N., Chief Nursing Officer/Chief Clinical Officer
Web address: www.russellvillehospital.com
Control: Partnership, Investor–owned (for–profit) **Service**: General medical and surgical

Staffed Beds: 92

SCOTTSBORO—Jackson County

☐ **HIGHLANDS MEDICAL CENTER (010061)**, 380 Woods Cove Road,
Zip 35768–2428, Mailing Address: P.O. Box 1050, Zip 35768–1050;
tel. 256/259–4444, (Nonreporting) **A**1 5 10 20
Primary Contact: Lonnie Albin, M.D., Interim Chief Executive Officer
CFO: Dan Newell, Chief Financial Officer
CIO: Doug Newby, Chief Information Officer
CHR: Susanna S Sivley, Chief Personnel Officer
Web address: www.highlandsmedcenter.com
Control: Hospital district or authority, Government, nonfederal **Service**: General
medical and surgical

Staffed Beds: 92

SELMA—Dallas County

⊞ **VAUGHAN REGIONAL MEDICAL CENTER (010118)**, 1015 Medical Center
Parkway, Zip 36701–6352; tel. 334/418–4100, **A**1 3 5 10 **F**8 11 13 15 17 18
20 22 29 30 34 40 45 50 57 59 60 70 74 76 79 81 85 89 93 107 108 110 111
114 115 118 119 120 127 129 130 131 146 **S** LifePoint Health, Brentwood, TN
Primary Contact: J. David. McCormack, Chief Executive Officer
CFO: Tyler Adkins, Chief Financial Officer
CMO: Walid Freij, M.D., Chief of Staff
CIO: Matthew McHugh, Director Information Services
CHR: Dionne Williams, Director Human Resources
CNO: Patricia Hannon, Chief Nursing Officer
Web address: www.vaughanregional.com
Control: Corporation, Investor–owned (for–profit) **Service**: General medical and
surgical

Staffed Beds: 149 **Admissions**: 5184 **Census**: 46 **Outpatient Visits**: 35183
Births: 448 **Total Expense ($000)**: 50101 **Payroll Expense ($000)**: 20468
Personnel: 433

SHEFFIELD—Colbert County

☐ **HELEN KELLER HOSPITAL (010019)**, 1300 South Montgomery Avenue,
Zip 35660–6334, Mailing Address: P.O. Box 610, Zip 35660–0610; tel. 256/386–
4196, **A**1 10 **F**3 7 8 11 13 15 18 20 21 28 29 30 31 34 35 40 45 47 49 50
51 53 57 59 60 64 65 68 70 74 75 76 77 78 79 80 81 82 83 84 85 86 87
89 91 92 93 94 107 108 110 111 114 115 117 118 119 126 129 130 131
132 135 145 146 147 148 149 154 157 **S** Huntsville Hospital Health System,
Huntsville, AL
Primary Contact: Kyle Buchanan, President
CFO: Morris S Strickland, Chief Financial Officer
CHR: Pam Bryant, Director Human Resources
Web address: www.helenkeller.com
Control: Hospital district or authority, Government, nonfederal **Service**: General
medical and surgical

Staffed Beds: 143 **Admissions**: 7400 **Census**: 77 **Outpatient Visits**: 93069
Births: 791 **Total Expense ($000)**: 105639 **Payroll Expense ($000)**: 39646
Personnel: 816

SYLACAUGA—Talladega County

☐ **COOSA VALLEY MEDICAL CENTER (010164)**, 315 West Hickory Street,
Zip 35150–2996; tel. 256/401–4000, (Nonreporting) **A**1 10
Primary Contact: Glenn C. Sisk, President
CFO: Janice Brown, Chief Financial Officer
CIO: Sandra Murchison, Director Medical Records
CHR: Christy Knowles, Chief Human Resources Officer
Web address: www.cvhealth.net
Control: Other not–for–profit (including NFP Corporation) **Service**: General
medical and surgical

Staffed Beds: 101

TALLADEGA—Talladega County

⊞ **CITIZENS BAPTIST MEDICAL CENTER (010101)**, 604 Stone Avenue,
Zip 35160–2217, Mailing Address: P.O. Box 978, Zip 35161–0978; tel. 256/362–
8111, (Nonreporting) **A**1 10 19 **S** TENET Healthcare Corporation, Dallas, TX
Primary Contact: Frank D. Thomas, Chief Executive Officer
CFO: Zach Abercrombie, Chief Financial Officer
CHR: Sandra Willis, Director of Human Resources
CNO: Ann McEntire, MSN, R.N., Chief Nursing Officer
Web address: www.brookwoodbaptisthealth.org
Control: Church operated, Nongovernment, not–for–profit **Service**: General
medical and surgical

Staffed Beds: 72

TALLASSEE—Elmore County

☐ **COMMUNITY HOSPITAL (010034)**, 805 Friendship Road, Zip 36078–1324;
tel. 334/283–6541, (Nonreporting) **A**10
Primary Contact: Jennie R. Rhinehart, Administrator and Chief Executive Officer
Web address: www.chal.org
Control: Other not–for–profit (including NFP Corporation) **Service**: General
medical and surgical

Staffed Beds: 47

TROY—Pike County

☐ **TROY REGIONAL MEDICAL CENTER (010126)**, 1330 Highway 231 South,
Zip 36081–3058; tel. 334/670–5000, (Nonreporting) **A**1 10
Primary Contact: Ronald Dean, Chief Executive Officer
CFO: Janet Smith, Chief Financial Officer
CMO: Paul Dulaney, M.D., Chief of Staff
CIO: Michael Moore, Director Information Systems
CHR: Beth Nissen, Director Human Resources
CNO: Amy Minor, Chief Nursing Officer
Web address: www.troymedicalcenter.com
Control: Corporation, Investor–owned (for–profit) **Service**: General medical and
surgical

Staffed Beds: 43

Hospital, Medicare Provider Number, Address, Telephone, Approval, Facility, and Physician Codes, Health Care System

★ American Hospital Association (AHA) membership   ○ Healthcare Facilities Accreditation Program   ⇑ Center for Improvement in Healthcare Quality Accreditation
☐ The Joint Commission accreditation   ◇ DNV Healthcare Inc. accreditation   △ Commission on Accreditation of Rehabilitation Facilities (CARF) accreditation

TUSCALOOSA—Tuscaloosa County

☐ **BRYCE HOSPITAL (014007)**, 200 University Boulevard, Zip 35401–1294;
tel. 205/507–8299, (Nonreporting) **A**1 5 10
Primary Contact: Shelia Penn, Facility Director
CFO: Wendell Summerville, Chief Financial Officer
CMO: Cynthia Moore Sledge, M.D., Medical Director
CIO: Ronene Howell, Director Health Information Management
CHR: Jim Elliott, Director Human Resources
Web address: www.mh.alabama.gov/
Control: State, Government, nonfederal **Service**: Psychiatric

Staffed Beds: 820

☐ **DCH REGIONAL MEDICAL CENTER (010092)**, 809 University Boulevard East,
Zip 35401–2029; tel. 205/759–7111, (Includes NORTHPORT MEDICAL CENTER,
2700 Hospital Drive, Northport, Alabama, Zip 35476–3360; tel. 205/333–4500;
Luke Standeffer, Administrator) **A**1 2 3 5 10 20 **F**3 11 12 13 15 18 20 22 24 26
28 29 30 31 34 35 38 40 43 45 46 48 49 50 51 58 59 60 61 62 64 68 70 71
72 74 75 76 77 78 79 81 82 84 86 87 89 90 93 94 98 100 101 102 103 107
108 110 111 114 115 117 118 119 120 121 124 126 129 130 131 132 146
147 148 156 **S** DCH Health System, Tuscaloosa, AL
Primary Contact: Paul Betz, FACHE, Administrator
CFO: Nina Dusang, Vice President Finance and Chief Financial Officer
CMO: Kenneth Aldridge, M.D., Vice President Medical Affairs
CIO: Kim Ligon, Director Information Services
CHR: Peggy Sease, Vice President Human Resources
CNO: Lorraine Yehlen, R.N., Vice President Patient Care Services
Web address: www.dchsystem.com
Control: Hospital district or authority, Government, nonfederal **Service**: General
medical and surgical

Staffed Beds: 607 Admissions: 31829 Census: 458 Outpatient
Visits: 553560 Births: 3321 Total Expense ($000): 485703 Payroll
Expense ($000): 198979 Personnel: 3746

☐ **MARY S HARPER GERIATRIC PSYCHIATRY CENTER (014012)**, 200 University
Boulevard, Zip 35401–1250; tel. 205/759–0900, (Nonreporting) **A**1 10
Primary Contact: Beverly White, MS, Facility Director
CFO: Sarah Mitchell, Director Finance
CMO: Robin Barton Lariscy, M.D., Medical Director
CIO: Sarah Mitchell, Director Finance
CHR: Jim Elliott, Director Human Resources
Web address: www.mh.alabama.gov
Control: Corporation, Investor–owned (for–profit) **Service**: Psychiatric

Staffed Beds: 96

☐ **NOLAND HOSPITAL TUSCALOOSA (012012)**, 809 University Blvd E, 4th Fl,
Zip 35401–2029; tel. 205/759–7241, (Nonreporting) **A**1 10 **S** Noland Health
Services, Inc., Birmingham, AL
Primary Contact: Jack Gibson, Administrator
Web address: www.nolandhealth.com
Control: Other not–for–profit (including NFP Corporation) **Service**: Acute long–
term care hospital

Staffed Beds: 32

☐ **TAYLOR HARDIN SECURE MEDICAL FACILITY (014011)**, 1301 Jack Warner
Parkway, Zip 35404–1060; tel. 205/556–7060, (Nonreporting) **A**1
Primary Contact: Barbara Jackson, Ed.D., Acting Facility Director
Web address: www.mh.alabama.gov/
Control: Corporation, Investor–owned (for–profit) **Service**: Psychiatric

Staffed Beds: 114

✖ **TUSCALOOSA VETERANS AFFAIRS MEDICAL CENTER**, 3701 Loop Road East,
Zip 35404–5015; tel. 205/554–2000, (Total facility includes 134 beds in nursing
home-type unit) **A**1 5 **F**4 5 29 30 34 35 36 38 39 55 56 57 58 59 61 63 65 71
74 75 77 82 83 84 86 87 90 91 94 95 98 100 101 103 104 105 106 107 108
119 127 128 130 132 135 143 146 147 148 149 153 154 156 157 158 **S**
Department of Veterans Affairs, Washington, DC
Primary Contact: John F. Merkle, Medical Center Director
COO: Gary D Trende, FACHE, Associate Director
CFO: Angelia Stevenson, Manager Finance
CMO: Carlos E. Berry, M.D., Acting Chief of Staff
Web address: www.tuscaloosa.va.gov
Control: Veterans Affairs, Government, federal **Service**: Psychiatric

Staffed Beds: 315 Admissions: 1718 Census: 282 Outpatient
Visits: 203835 Births: 0 Total Expense ($000): 160175 Payroll Expense
($000): 97866 Personnel: 1189

TUSKEGEE—Macon County

TUSKEGEE DIVISION See Central Alabama Veterans Health Care System,
Montgomery

UNION SPRINGS—Bullock County

☐ **BULLOCK COUNTY HOSPITAL (010110)**, 102 West Conecuh Avenue,
Zip 36089–1303; tel. 334/738–2140, (Nonreporting) **A**10 20
Primary Contact: Jacques Jarry, Administrator
COO: Victoria Lawrenson, Chief Operating Officer
CMO: Maria Bernardo, M.D., Chief of Staff
Web address: www.unionspringsalabama.com/
Control: Corporation, Investor–owned (for–profit) **Service**: General medical and
surgical

Staffed Beds: 54

WARRIOR—Jefferson County

BRADFORD HEALTH SERVICES AT WARRIOR LODGE, 1189 Allbritt Road,
Zip 35180, Mailing Address: P.O. Box 129, Zip 35180–0129; tel. 205/647–1945,
(Nonreporting) **S** Bradford Health Services, Birmingham, AL
Primary Contact: Roy M. Ramsey, Executive Director
Web address: www.bradfordhealth.com
Control: Corporation, Investor–owned (for–profit) **Service**: Alcoholism and other
chemical dependency

Staffed Beds: 100

WEDOWEE—Randolph County

TANNER MEDICAL CENTER/EAST ALABAMA (010032), 1032 South Main
Street, Zip 36278–7428; tel. 256/357–2111, (Data for 229 days) **A**10 **F**8 11 40
45 50 57 59 68 75 81 87 107 115 119 129 130 133 146 147 154 **S** Tanner
Health System, Carrollton, GA
Primary Contact: Jerry Morris, Administrator
Web address: www.tanner.org/eastalabama
Control: Other not–for–profit (including NFP Corporation) **Service**: General
medical and surgical

Staffed Beds: 15 Admissions: 289 Census: 5 Outpatient Visits: 11913
Births: 0 Total Expense ($000): 6290 Payroll Expense ($000): 2302
Personnel: 88

WETUMPKA—Elmore County

ELMORE COMMUNITY HOSPITAL (010097), 500 Hospital Drive, Zip 36092–
1625, Mailing Address: P.O. Box 130, Zip 36092–0003; tel. 334/567–4311,
(Nonreporting) **A**10
Primary Contact: Michael Ritzus, Chief Executive Officer
CFO: Mike Bruce, Chief Financial Officer
CHR: Cindy Futral, Director Human Resources
Web address: www.elmorehospital.com/
Control: Partnership, Investor–owned (for–profit) **Service**: General medical and
surgical

Staffed Beds: 49

WINFIELD—Marion County

☐ **NORTHWEST MEDICAL CENTER (010086)**, 1530 U S Highway 43, Zip 35594–
5056; tel. 205/487–7000, **A**1 10 **F**3 15 29 30 34 40 41 43 45 50 53 56 57 59
64 68 70 75 77 79 80 81 83 85 87 98 100 102 103 104 107 108 110 111
115 119 127 130 133 135 146 149 154 **S** Curae Health, Clinton, TN
Primary Contact: Michael D. Windham, Chief Executive Officer
CFO: Glenda Reyes, Chief Financial Officer
CMO: David Corbett, M.D., Chief of Staff
Web address: www.northwestmedcenter.com
Control: Hospital district or authority, Government, nonfederal **Service**: General
medical and surgical

Staffed Beds: 56 Admissions: 1125 Census: 16 Outpatient Visits: 44068
Births: 0 Total Expense ($000): 22617 Payroll Expense ($000): 6802
Personnel: 223

YORK—Sumter County

HILL HOSPITAL OF SUMTER COUNTY (010138), 751 Derby Drive, Zip 36925–
2121; tel. 205/392–5263, (Nonreporting) **A**10
Primary Contact: Loretta Wilson, Administrator
CFO: Joyce Wedgeworth, Financial Clerk
CMO: Gary Walton, M.D., Chief Medical Officer
CNO: Cynthia Brown, Director of Nursing
Control: Other not–for–profit (including NFP Corporation) **Service**: General
medical and surgical

Staffed Beds: 33

ALASKA

ANCHORAGE—Anchorage County

⊞ **ALASKA NATIVE MEDICAL CENTER (020026)**, 4315 Diplomacy Drive, Zip 99508–5926; tel. 907/563–2662, **A**1 3 5 10 **F**1 3 8 11 13 15 16 18 20 22 29 30 31 32 34 35 38 39 40 41 43 44 45 47 48 49 50 51 54 55 56 57 58 59 61 63 64 65 66 67 68 70 72 73 74 75 76 77 78 79 80 81 82 84 85 86 87 88 89 92 93 94 107 110 111 114 115 119 127 129 130 135 141 142 143 144 145 146 147 148 149 154 156
Primary Contact: Roald Helgesen, Chief Executive Officer
CMO: Paul Franke, M.D., Chief Medical Officer
CHR: Sonya Conant, Senior Director Human Resources
Web address: www.dhss.alaska.gov/dbh/Pages/api/default.aspx
Control: Other not–for–profit (including NFP Corporation) **Service:** General medical and surgical

Staffed Beds: 173 **Admissions:** 8599 **Census:** 130 **Outpatient Visits:** 447330 **Births:** 1511 **Total Expense ($000):** 481545 **Payroll Expense ($000):** 182104 **Personnel:** 1939

☐ **ALASKA PSYCHIATRIC INSTITUTE (024002)**, 3700 Piper Street, Zip 99508–4677; tel. 907/269–7100, (Nonreporting) **A**1 10
Primary Contact: Gavin H. Carmichael, FACHE, Acting Chief Executive Officer
COO: Gavin H Carmichael, FACHE, Chief Operating Officer
CFO: Gavin H Carmichael, FACHE, Chief Operating Officer
CMO: Claudette A. Zarema, M.D., Medical Officer
CIO: Stephen Schneider, Manager Information Services
CHR: Katie E. Cratrix, Administrative Assistant III
CNO: Sharon Bergstedt, Director of Nursing
Web address: www.hss.state.ak.us/dbh/API/
Control: State, Government, nonfederal **Service:** Psychiatric

Staffed Beds: 80

⊞ **ALASKA REGIONAL HOSPITAL (020017)**, 2801 Debarr Road, Zip 99508–2997; tel. 907/264–1754, (Nonreporting) **A**1 2 5 10 **S** HCA Healthcare, Nashville, TN
Primary Contact: Julie Taylor, FACHE, Chief Executive Officer
COO: Victor Rosenbaum, Chief Operating Officer
CFO: Lynn Kennington, Chief Financial Officer
CMO: David Cadogan, Chief Medical Officer
CIO: Gene Kaplanis, Director Information Technology
CHR: Tammy Kaminski, Director Human Resources
CNO: Linda Doughty, Chief Nursing Officer
Web address: www.alaskaregional.com
Control: Corporation, Investor–owned (for–profit) **Service:** General medical and surgical

Staffed Beds: 132

⊞ **NORTH STAR BEHAVIORAL HEALTH SYSTEM (024001)**, 2530 DeBarr Circle, Zip 99508–2948; tel. 907/258–7575, (Includes NORTH STAR BEHAVIORAL HEALTH, 1650 South Bragaw, Anchorage, Alaska, Zip 99508–3467; tel. 907/258–7575), (Nonreporting) **A**1 5 10 **S** Universal Health Services, Inc., King of Prussia, PA
Primary Contact: Andrew Mayo, Ph.D., Chief Executive Officer and Managing Director
CFO: Alan Barnes, Chief Financial Officer
CMO: Ruth Dukoff, M.D., Medical Director
CIO: Brian O'Connell, Director Information Services
CHR: Sabrina Ben, Director Human Resources
CNO: Brandy Proctor, Director of Nursing
Web address: www.northstarbehavioral.com
Control: Corporation, Investor–owned (for–profit) **Service:** Psychiatric

Staffed Beds: 200

⊞ **PROVIDENCE ALASKA MEDICAL CENTER (020001)**, 3200 Providence Drive, Zip 99508–4615, Mailing Address: P.O. Box 196604, Zip 99519–6604; tel. 907/562–2211, (Includes CHILDREN'S HOSPITAL AT PROVIDENCE, 3200 Providence Drive, Anchorage, Alaska, Zip 99508; tel. 907/212–3130), (Nonreporting) **A**1 2 3 5 10 13 **S** Providence St. Joseph Health, Renton, WA
Primary Contact: Ella M. Goss, MSN, R.N., Chief Executive Officer
CFO: Anthony Dorsch, Chief Financial Officer
CMO: Roy Davis, M.D., Chief Medical Officer
CIO: Stephanie Morton, Chief Information Officer
CHR: Scott Jungwirth, Chief Human Resources Officer
Web address: www.alaska.providence.org/locations/p/pamc
Control: Church operated **Service:** General medical and surgical

Staffed Beds: 401

⊞ **ST. ELIAS SPECIALTY HOSPITAL (022001)**, 4800 Cordova Street, Zip 99503–7218; tel. 907/561–3333, **A**1 10 **F**1 3 18 28 29 30 60 65 68 75 77 86 107 114 119
Primary Contact: Sharon H. Kurz, Ph.D., Chief Executive Officer
CFO: Andrew Fitch, Chief Financial Officer
Web address: www.st-eliashospital.com
Control: Partnership, Investor–owned (for–profit) **Service:** Acute long-term care hospital

Staffed Beds: 59 **Admissions:** 312 **Census:** 36 **Outpatient Visits:** 0 **Births:** 0 **Total Expense ($000):** 35640 **Payroll Expense ($000):** 13800 **Personnel:** 171

BARROW—North Slope County

⊞ **SAMUEL SIMMONDS MEMORIAL HOSPITAL (021312)**, 7000 Uulu Street, Zip 99723, Mailing Address: P.O. Box 29, Zip 99723–0029; tel. 907/852–4611, (Nonreporting) **A**1 10 18
Primary Contact: Richard Hall, Chief Executive Officer
CMO: Devon Allen, M.D., Chief of Medical Staff
Web address: www.arcticslope.org
Control: Other not–for–profit (including NFP Corporation) **Service:** General medical and surgical

Staffed Beds: 14

BETHEL—Bethel County

⊞ **YUKON-KUSKOKWIM DELTA REGIONAL HOSPITAL (020018)**, 700 Chief Eddie Hoffman Highway, Zip 99559–3000, Mailing Address: P.O. Box 528, Zip 99559–0528; tel. 907/543–6300, **A**1 3 5 10 **F**3 5 13 15 29 34 35 38 39 40 45 50 53 54 57 58 59 64 65 66 68 71 75 76 81 82 84 85 87 89 91 93 97 99 100 101 102 103 104 106 107 110 127 130 134 135 144 147 148 151 152 153 154
Primary Contact: Dan Winkelman, President and Chief Executive Officer
CFO: Tommy Tompkins, Vice President, Finance and Chief Financial Officer
CIO: William Pearch, Chief Information Officer
Web address: www.ykhc.org
Control: Other not–for–profit (including NFP Corporation) **Service:** General medical and surgical

Staffed Beds: 37 **Admissions:** 2197 **Census:** 18

CORDOVA—Valdez-Cordova County

★ **CORDOVA COMMUNITY MEDICAL CENTER (021307)**, 602 Chase Avenue, Zip 99574, Mailing Address: P.O. Box 160, Zip 99574–0160; tel. 907/424–8000, (Total facility includes 10 beds in nursing home–type unit) **A**10 18 **F**29 34 35 40 57 59 65 69 75 93 97 100 101 102 104 107 114 119 128 130 133 146 153 154
Primary Contact: Scot Mitchell, FACHE, Chief Executive Officer and Administrator
CFO: Lee W Bennett, Interim Chief Financial Officer
CMO: Sam Blackadar, M.D., Medical Director
CHR: Kim Wilson, Human Resources Coordinator
CNO: Mary Rios, R.N., Interim Director of Nursing
Web address: www.cdvcmc.com
Control: City, Government, nonfederal **Service:** General medical and surgical

Staffed Beds: 23 **Admissions:** 57 **Census:** 13 **Outpatient Visits:** 2233 **Births:** 0 **Total Expense ($000):** 12308 **Payroll Expense ($000):** 3976 **Personnel:** 81

Hospital, Medicare Provider Number, Address, Telephone, Approval, Facility, and Physician Codes, Health Care System

★ American Hospital Association (AHA) membership
☐ The Joint Commission accreditation
○ Healthcare Facilities Accreditation Program
◇ DNV Healthcare Inc. accreditation
⇑ Center for Improvement in Healthcare Quality Accreditation
△ Commission on Accreditation of Rehabilitation Facilities (CARF) accreditation

AK

DILLINGHAM—Dillingham County

✠ **BRISTOL BAY AREA HEALTH CORPORATION (021309)**, 6000 Kanakanak Road, Zip 99576, Mailing Address: P.O. Box 130, Zip 99576–0130; tel. 907/842–5201, (Nonreporting) **A**1 3 10 18
Primary Contact: Robert J. Clark, President and Chief Executive Officer
COO: Lucrecia Scotford, Executive Vice President and Chief Operations Officer
CFO: David Morgan, Vice President and Chief Financial Officer
CMO: Arnold Loera, M.D., Clinical Director
CIO: Bill Wilcox, Chief Information Technology Officer
CHR: John Davis, Chief Human Resources Officer
CNO: Starla Fox, Director of Nursing
Web address: www.bbahc.org
Control: Other not–for–profit (including NFP Corporation) **Service:** General medical and surgical

Staffed Beds: 16

ELMENDORF AFB—Anchorage County

✠ **U. S. AIR FORCE REGIONAL HOSPITAL**, 5955 Zeamer Avenue, Zip 99506–3702; tel. 907/580–3006, (Nonreporting) **A**1 **S** Department of the Air Force, Washington, DC
Primary Contact: Major Mark Lamey, Commander
COO: Colonel Rebecca Seese, Chief Operating Officer
CFO: Major Felicia Burks, Chief Financial Officer
CMO: Colonel Marriner Oldham, M.D., Chief Medical Officer
CIO: Major Phillip Oliphant, Chief Information Officer
CHR: Mark Clark, Human Resources Liaison
Web address: www.elmendorf.af.mil/
Control: Department of Defense, Government, federal **Service:** General medical and surgical

Staffed Beds: 64

FAIRBANKS—Fairbanks North Star County

✠ **FAIRBANKS MEMORIAL HOSPITAL (020012)**, 1650 Cowles Street, Zip 99701–5998; tel. 907/452–8181, (Total facility includes 90 beds in nursing home–type unit) **A**1 2 3 5 10 **F**3 13 15 17 18 20 22 28 29 30 31 35 40 41 43 45 48 50 51 59 60 62 63 64 67 68 70 72 75 76 77 79 81 82 84 85 86 87 89 93 98 102 107 108 110 111 114 115 118 119 120 126 128 129 130 135 144 146 147 148 149
Primary Contact: Jim Lynch, Chief Executive Officer
CFO: Steve Leslie, Chief Financial Officer
CIO: Carl J Kegley, System Director Information Technology
CHR: Nicole Welch, Chief Human Resources Officer
CNO: Karen Justin-Tanner, R.N., Chief Nursing Officer
Web address: www.https://www.foundationhealth.org/fmh
Control: Other not–for–profit (including NFP Corporation) **Service:** General medical and surgical

Staffed Beds: 217 **Admissions:** 4565 **Census:** 127 **Outpatient Visits:** 339043 **Births:** 1069 **Total Expense ($000):** 241332 **Payroll Expense ($000):** 106062 **Personnel:** 1293

FORT WAINWRIGHT—Fairbanks North Star County

✠ **BASSETT ARMY COMMUNITY HOSPITAL**, 1060 Gaffney Road, Box 7400, Zip 99703–5001, Mailing Address: 1060 Gaffney Road, Box 7440, Zip 99703–5001; tel. 907/361–4000, (Nonreporting) **A**1 **S** Department of the Army, Office of the Surgeon General, Falls Church, VA
Primary Contact: Colonel Constance Jenkins, Commander
CMO: Colonel Leo Bennett, M.D., Deputy Commander Clinical Services
CHR: Terri Morefield, Deputy Chief Human Resources Division
Web address: www.alaska.amedd.army.mil
Control: Department of Defense, Government, federal **Service:** General medical and surgical

Staffed Beds: 24

HOMER—Kenai Peninsula County

★ **SOUTH PENINSULA HOSPITAL (021313)**, 4300 Bartlett Street, Zip 99603–7000; tel. 907/235–8101, (Nonreporting) **A**10 18
Primary Contact: Noel Rea, Interim Chief Executive Officer
CMO: Sarah Spencer, M.D., Chief of Staff
CIO: Jim Bartilson, Manager Information Systems
CNO: Von Kilpatrick, Chief Nursing Officer
Web address: www.sphosp.org
Control: Hospital district or authority, Government, nonfederal **Service:** General medical and surgical

Staffed Beds: 50

JUNEAU—Juneau County

✠ **BARTLETT REGIONAL HOSPITAL (020008)**, 3260 Hospital Drive, Zip 99801–7808; tel. 907/796–8900, (Nonreporting) **A**1 5 10 20
Primary Contact: Charles E. Bill, Chief Executive Officer
CFO: Alan Ulrich, Chief Financial Officer
CMO: Sharon Fisher, M.D., Chief of Staff
CIO: Martha Palicka, Director Information Systems
CHR: Dallas Hargrave, Human Resources Director
CNO: William Gardner, Chief Clinical Officer
Web address: www.bartletthospital.org
Control: City, Government, nonfederal **Service:** General medical and surgical

Staffed Beds: 73

KETCHIKAN—Ketchikan Gateway County

★ ⇑ **PEACEHEALTH KETCHIKAN MEDICAL CENTER (021311)**, 3100 Tongass Avenue, Zip 99901–5746; tel. 907/225–5171, (Total facility includes 25 beds in nursing home–type unit) **A**5 10 18 21 **F**70 76 128 **S** PeaceHealth, Vancouver, WA
Primary Contact: Edward E. Freysinger, Chief Administrative Officer
CFO: Ken Tonjes, Chief Financial Officer
CMO: Peter Rice, M.D., Medical Director
CIO: Tim Walker, Manager Information Services
CHR: Lanetta Lundberg, Vice President Culture and People
Web address: www.peacehealth.org
Control: Other not–for–profit (including NFP Corporation) **Service:** General medical and surgical

Staffed Beds: 54 **Admissions:** 1235 **Census:** 35 **Outpatient Visits:** 35075 **Births:** 203 **Total Expense ($000):** 60410 **Payroll Expense ($000):** 27857 **Personnel:** 361

KODIAK—Kodiak Island County

✠ **PROVIDENCE KODIAK ISLAND MEDICAL CENTER (021306)**, 1915 East Rezanof Drive, Zip 99615–6602; tel. 907/486–3281, (Nonreporting) **A**1 10 18 **S** Providence St. Joseph Health, Renton, WA
Primary Contact: Regina L. Bishop, Administrator
COO: Brenda Zawacki, Chief Operating Manager
CFO: Timothy Hocum, Chief Financial Officer
CMO: Steve Smith, M.D., Chief of Staff
CIO: David Johnson, Manager Information Services
CNO: LeeAnn Horn, Chief Nurse Executive
Web address: www.providence.org
Control: Church operated **Service:** General medical and surgical

Staffed Beds: 6

KOTZEBUE—Northwest Arctic County

☐ **MANIILAQ HEALTH CENTER (021310)**, 436 5th Avenue, Zip 99752–0043, Mailing Address: P.O. Box 43, Zip 99752–0043; tel. 907/442–7344, (Nonreporting) **A**1 10 18
Primary Contact: Paul Hansen, Administrator
COO: Timothy Schuerch, President and Chief Executive Officer
CFO: Lucy Nelson, Director Finance, Vice President
CMO: Patricia Clancy, M.D., Director Medical Services
CIO: Eugene Smith, Chief Information Officer
CHR: Gerty Gallahom, Director Human Resources
CNO: Commander Donna K Biagioni, R.N., MSN, Director of Nursing
Web address: www.maniilaq.org
Control: Other not–for–profit (including NFP Corporation) **Service:** General medical and surgical

Staffed Beds: 17

NOME—Nome County

✠ **NORTON SOUND REGIONAL HOSPITAL (021308)**, Bering Straits, Zip 99762, Mailing Address: P.O. Box 966, Zip 99762–0966; tel. 907/443–3311, (Nonreporting) **A**1 10 18
Primary Contact: Angela Gorn, Vice President
COO: Roy Agloinga, Chief Administrative Officer
CMO: David Head, M.D., Chief Medical Staff
CIO: Dan Bailey, Director Information Systems
CHR: Tiffany Martinson, Director Human Resources
Web address: www.nortonsoundhealth.org
Control: Other not–for–profit (including NFP Corporation) **Service:** General medical and surgical

Staffed Beds: 36

Many Facility Codes have changed. Please refer to the AHA Guide Code Chart.
© 2019 AHA Guide

PALMER—Matanuska-Susitna County

✠ **MAT-SU REGIONAL MEDICAL CENTER (020006)**, 2500 South Woodworth Loop, Zip 99645–8984, Mailing Address: P.O. Box 1687, Zip 99645–1687; tel. 907/861–6000, (Nonreporting) **A**1 10 20 **S** Community Health Systems, Inc., Franklin, TN
Primary Contact: David Wallace, Chief Executive Officer
CMO: Christopher Sahlstrom, M.D., Chief of Staff
CIO: Bryan Meurer, Director Information Systems
CHR: Cathy Babuscio, Director Human Resources
CNO: Emily Stevens, Chief Nursing Officer
Web address: www.matsuregional.com
Control: Partnership, Investor–owned (for–profit) **Service**: General medical and surgical

Staffed Beds: 74

PETERSBURG—Petersburg County

★ **PETERSBURG MEDICAL CENTER (021304)**, 103 Fram Street, Zip 99833, Mailing Address: Box 589, Zip 99833–0589; tel. 907/772–4291, (Nonreporting) **A**10 18
Primary Contact: Peter A. Hofstetter, Chief Executive Officer
CFO: Doran Hammett, Chief Financial Officer
CHR: Cynthia Newman, Manager Human Resources
CNO: Jennifer Bryner, Director Nursing
Web address: www.pmcak.org
Control: City, Government, nonfederal **Service**: General medical and surgical

Staffed Beds: 27

SEWARD—Kenai Peninsula County

★ **PROVIDENCE SEWARD MEDICAL CENTER (021302)**, 417 First Avenue, Zip 99664, Mailing Address: P.O. Box 365, Zip 99664–0365; tel. 907/224–5205, (Nonreporting) **A**10 18 **S** Providence St. Joseph Health, Renton, WA
Primary Contact: Don Hanna, Interim Chief Executive Officer
Web address: www.providence.org
Control: Church operated **Service**: General medical and surgical

Staffed Beds: 6

SITKA—Sitka County

✠ **SEARHC MT. EDGECUMBE HOSPITAL (021314)**, 222 Tongass Drive, Zip 99835–9416; tel. 907/966–2411, (Nonreporting) **A**1 5 10 18
Primary Contact: Charles Clement, Chief Executive Officer
COO: Daniel P Neumeister, Senior Vice President and Chief Operating Officer
CFO: Barbara Searls, Chief Financial Officer
CMO: David Vastola, Medical Director
CIO: Bob Cita, Chief Information Officer
CHR: Peggy Bernhardt-Radlec, Chief Human Resources Officer
CNO: Patricia L Giampa, Chief Nursing Officer
Web address: www.searhc.org
Control: Other not–for–profit (including NFP Corporation) **Service**: General medical and surgical

Staffed Beds: 25

★ **SITKA COMMUNITY HOSPITAL (021303)**, 209 Moller Avenue, Zip 99835–7142; tel. 907/747–3241, (Nonreporting) **A**10 18
Primary Contact: Rob Allen, Chief Executive Officer
CFO: Lee W Bennett, Chief Financial Officer
CHR: Shannon Callahan, Director Human Resources
Web address: www.sitkahospital.org
Control: City, Government, nonfederal **Service**: General medical and surgical

Staffed Beds: 27

SOLDOTNA—Kenai Peninsula County

✠ **CENTRAL PENINSULA HOSPITAL (020024)**, 250 Hospital Place, Zip 99669–6999; tel. 907/714–4404, (Total facility Includes 60 beds in nursing home–type unit) **A**1 3 10 20 **F**3 4 5 11 13 15 28 29 30 31 34 35 36 38 40 45 46 47 48 49 51 57 59 65 68 70 74 75 76 77 78 79 81 82 84 85 86 87 93 97 105 106 107 108 110 111 115 119 128 129 130 131 132 133 134 135 145 146 147 148 149 152 153 154 155
Primary Contact: Richard Davis, Chief Executive Officer
COO: Matt Dammeyer, Ph.D., Chief Operating Officer
CMO: Gregg Motonaga, M.D., Chief of Staff
CIO: Bryan Downs, Director Information Systems
CHR: John Dodd, Vice President Human Resources
Web address: www.cpgh.org
Control: Other not–for–profit (including NFP Corporation) **Service**: General medical and surgical

Staffed Beds: 119 Admissions: 2917 Census: 82 Outpatient Visits: 133194 Births: 425 Total Expense ($000): 157218 Payroll Expense ($000): 67407 Personnel: 789

VALDEZ—Valdez-Cordova County

★ **PROVIDENCE VALDEZ MEDICAL CENTER (021301)**, 911 Meals Avenue, Zip 99686–0550, Mailing Address: P.O. Box 550, Zip 99686–0550; tel. 907/835–2249, (Nonreporting) **A**5 10 18 **S** Providence St. Joseph Health, Renton, WA
Primary Contact: Jeremy O'Neil, Administrator
CMO: John Cullen, M.D., Chief of Staff and Medical Director Long Term Care
CHR: Maureen Radotich, Director Human Resources
Web address: www.providence.org/alaska
Control: Church operated **Service**: General medical and surgical

Staffed Beds: 21

WRANGELL—Wrangell County

★ **WRANGELL MEDICAL CENTER (021305)**, First Avenue & Bennett Street, Zip 99929, Mailing Address: P.O. Box 1081, Zip 99929–1081; tel. 907/874–7000, (Nonreporting) **A**10 18
Primary Contact: Leatha N. Merculieff, Hospital Administrator
CIO: Cathy Gross, Director Health Information Management Systems
CNO: Sherri Austin, MSN, R.N., Chief Nursing Officer
Web address: www.wrangellmedicalcenter.org/
Control: City, Government, nonfederal **Service**: General medical and surgical

Staffed Beds: 22

ARIZONA

AZ

APACHE JUNCTION—Pinal County

⊞ **BANNER GOLDFIELD MEDICAL CENTER (030134)**, 2050 West Southern Avenue, Zip 85120–7305; tel. 480/733–3300, **A**1 10 **F**3 29 30 34 35 40 45 49 68 75 81 87 107 115 119 130 135 146 147 148 149 154 156 **S** Banner Health, Phoenix, AZ
Primary Contact: Sharon Lind, MSN, FACHE, Chief Executive Officer
CFO: Tracy French, Chief Financial Officer
CMO: Jason Brown, M.D., Chief Medical Officer
CHR: Rebecca McLaughlin, Chief Human Resource Officer
CNO: Terresa Ann Paulus, Chief Nursing Officer
Web address: www.bannerhealth.com/Locations/Arizona/
Banner+Goldfield+Medical+Center/_Welcome+to+Banner+Goldfield.htm
Control: Other not–for–profit (including NFP Corporation) **Service:** General medical and surgical

Staffed Beds: 20 **Admissions:** 767 **Census:** 6 **Total Expense ($000):** 20103 **Payroll Expense ($000):** 7212 **Personnel:** 78

AVONDALE—Maricopa County

☐ **COPPER SPRINGS HOSPITAL (034032)**, 10550 West Mcdowell Road, Zip 85392–4864; tel. 602/314–7800, (Nonreporting) **A**1
Primary Contact: Jessica Black, Chief Executive Officer
Web address: www.copperspringshealth.com
Control: Corporation, Investor–owned (for–profit) **Service:** Psychiatric

Staffed Beds: 72

BENSON—Cochise County

BENSON HOSPITAL (031301), 450 South Ocotillo Street, Zip 85602–6403, Mailing Address: P.O. Box 2290, Zip 85602–2290; tel. 520/586–2261, **A**10 18 **F**3 11 29 30 34 35 40 43 50 54 57 59 64 75 77 86 87 93 107 111 114 119 132 133 146 148
Primary Contact: Linda Wojtowicz, R.N., MS, Chief Executive Officer
COO: Teresa Vincifora, Chief Operating Officer
CFO: Ken Goranson, Chief Financial Officer
CMO: Barbara Hartley, Chief Medical Officer
CIO: Rob Roberts, Director Information Technology
CHR: Ashley Dickey, Director Human Resources
Web address: www.bensonhospital.org
Control: Other not–for–profit (including NFP Corporation) **Service:** General medical and surgical

Staffed Beds: 22 **Admissions:** 279 **Census:** 4

BISBEE—Cochise County

★ **COPPER QUEEN COMMUNITY HOSPITAL (031312)**, 101 Cole Avenue, Zip 85603–1399; tel. 520/432–5383, **A**10 18 **F**3 7 11 18 29 30 34 40 42 45 46 50 53 57 62 67 77 81 93 97 107 108 110 111 133 147 154 155
Primary Contact: Robert L. Seamon, Chief Executive Officer
COO: Daniel Roe, M.D., Chief Operating Officer
CFO: James Ehasz, Chief Financial Officer
CIO: David Chmura, Chief Information Officer
CHR: Virginia Martinez, Director Human Resources
CNO: Sadie Maestas, Interim Chief Nursing Officer
Web address: www.cqch.org
Control: Other not–for–profit (including NFP Corporation) **Service:** General medical and surgical

Staffed Beds: 14 **Admissions:** 369 **Census:** 4 **Outpatient Visits:** 57617 **Births:** 0 **Total Expense ($000):** 34855 **Payroll Expense ($000):** 16590 **Personnel:** 258

BULLHEAD CITY—Mohave County

⊞ **WESTERN ARIZONA REGIONAL MEDICAL CENTER (030101)**, 2735 Silver Creek Road, Zip 86442–8303; tel. 928/763–2273, **A**1 10 19 **F**3 8 11 13 15 18 20 22 28 29 34 35 40 43 45 50 53 54 56 57 59 64 65 68 69 70 75 76 77 79 80 81 82 85 86 87 93 97 102 107 108 110 111 114 115 118 119 130 131 144 146 147 148 149 156 157 **S** Community Health Systems, Inc., Franklin, TN
Primary Contact: Michael J Stenger, Chief Executive Officer
CFO: Kenneth Pannell, Chief Financial Officer
CNO: Tara Barth, Chief Nursing Officer
Web address: www.warmc.com
Control: Corporation, Investor–owned (for–profit) **Service:** General medical and surgical

Staffed Beds: 106 **Admissions:** 4559 **Census:** 52 **Outpatient Visits:** 68899 **Births:** 260 **Total Expense ($000):** 80710 **Payroll Expense ($000):** 32007 **Personnel:** 543

CASA GRANDE—Pinal County

⊞ **BANNER CASA GRANDE MEDICAL CENTER (030016)**, 1800 East Florence Boulevard, Zip 85122–5399; tel. 520/381–6300, **A**1 10 **F**3 13 15 18 20 22 29 30 34 40 41 43 45 46 47 48 49 57 68 70 73 75 76 77 79 81 85 87 93 107 111 114 115 116 119 126 129 130 131 135 141 146 147 148 149 154 **S** Banner Health, Phoenix, AZ
Primary Contact: Brian Kellar, Chief Executive Officer
CMO: Devin Minior, M.D., Chief Medical Officer
CHR: Carol D'Souza, Chief Human Resources Officer
CNO: Dan Lingle, Chief Nursing Officer
Web address: www.https://www.bannerhealth.com/locations/casa-grande/banner-casa-grande-medical-center
Control: Other not–for–profit (including NFP Corporation) **Service:** General medical and surgical

Staffed Beds: 123 **Admissions:** 5426 **Census:** 60 **Births:** 715 **Total Expense ($000):** 119161 **Payroll Expense ($000):** 42867 **Personnel:** 571

CHANDLER—Maricopa County

☐ **ARIZONA ORTHOPEDIC SURGICAL HOSPITAL (030112)**, 2905 West Warner Road, Suite 1, Zip 85224–1674; tel. 480/603–9000, (Nonreporting) **A**1 10 **S** United Surgical Partners International, Addison, TX
Primary Contact: Patricia K. Alice, Chief Executive Officer
CFO: Shalen Young, Chief Financial Officer
CMO: Randall Hardison, M.D., Chief Medical Officer
CIO: John Langenfeld, Medical Records Coordinator
CNO: Caroline Herpfer, Chief Nursing Officer
Web address: www.azosh.com
Control: Corporation, Investor–owned (for–profit) **Service:** Surgical

Staffed Beds: 24

⊞ **CHANDLER REGIONAL MEDICAL CENTER (030036)**, 1955 West Frye Road, Zip 85224–6282; tel. 480/728–3000, **A**1 3 5 10 19 **F**3 8 11 12 13 15 17 18 20 22 24 26 28 29 30 31 32 34 35 37 40 41 42 43 44 45 46 47 48 49 50 51 54 57 58 59 60 64 65 66 68 70 71 72 73 74 75 76 77 78 79 81 82 83 84 85 86 87 93 96 107 108 110 111 114 115 119 126 130 131 132 135 143 144 146 147 148 156 **S** CommonSpirit Health, Chicago, IL
Primary Contact: Mark F. Slyter, FACHE, President and Chief Operating Officer
COO: Mark F. Slyter, FACHE, President and Chief Operating Officer
CFO: Mark Kem, Vice President Finance and Chief Financial Officer
CMO: Terry J Happel, M.D., Vice President and Chief Medical Officer
CHR: Renea Brunke, Vice President Human Resources
CNO: Peg Smith, Vice President and Chief Nursing Officer
Web address: www.chandlerregional.com
Control: Other not–for–profit (including NFP Corporation) **Service:** General medical and surgical

Staffed Beds: 338 **Admissions:** 26272 **Census:** 285 **Outpatient Visits:** 193644 **Births:** 3810 **Total Expense ($000):** 502363 **Payroll Expense ($000):** 169320 **Personnel:** 2754

☐ **DIGNITY HEALTH EAST VALLEY REHABILITATION HOSPITAL (033040)**, 1515 West Chandler Boulevard, Zip 85224–6141; tel. 602/594–5400, (Nonreporting) **A**1 **S** Kindred Healthcare, Louisville, KY
Primary Contact: Alvin Wendt, Acting Chief Executive Officer
Web address: www.dignityhealthevrehab.com
Control: Partnership, Investor–owned (for–profit) **Service:** Rehabilitation

Staffed Beds: 50

OASIS BEHAVIORAL HEALTH - CHANDLER (034029), 2190 North Grace Boulevard, Zip 85225–3416; tel. 480/917–9301, (Nonreporting) **S** Acadia Healthcare Company, Inc., Franklin, TN
Primary Contact: James Gallagher, Chief Executive Officer
CFO: Dino Quarante, CPA, Chief Financial Officer
CHR: Barbara Mitchell, Director Human Resources
CNO: Charissa Davis, Chief Nursing Officer and Director of Nursing
Web address: www.obhhospital.com/about/location
Control: Corporation, Investor–owned (for–profit) **Service:** Psychiatric

Staffed Beds: 47

Many Facility Codes have changed. Please refer to the AHA Guide Code Chart. © 2019 AHA Guide

CHINLE—Apache County

✠ **CHINLE COMPREHENSIVE HEALTH CARE FACILITY (030084)**, Highway 191, Zip 86503, Mailing Address: Highway 191 Hospital Drive, Zip 86503–8000; tel. 928/674–7001, (Nonreporting) **A**1 10 **S** U. S. Indian Health Service, Rockville, MD
Primary Contact: Darlene Chee, Acting Chief Executive Officer
CFO: Philene Tyler, Chief Finance Officer
CMO: Eric Ritchie, M.D., Clinical Director
CIO: Perry Francis, Supervisory Information Technology Specialist
CHR: Lorraine Begaye, Supervisory Human Resource Specialist
Web address: www.ihs.gov
Control: PHS, Indian Service, Government, federal **Service:** General medical and surgical

Staffed Beds: 60

COTTONWOOD—Yavapai County

★ ⚘ **VERDE VALLEY MEDICAL CENTER (030007)**, 269 South Candy Lane, Zip 86326–4170; tel. 928/639–6000, **A**3 5 10 13 20 21 **F**3 11 13 15 18 20 22 28 29 30 31 32 34 35 40 42 44 45 47 48 49 50 51 53 54 57 58 59 60 61 64 68 70 75 76 77 78 79 81 82 84 85 86 87 91 92 93 94 96 97 98 100 101 102 103 104 107 108 110 111 114 115 118 119 120 121 123 129 130 131 132 135 145 146 147 148 149 154 **S** Northern Arizona Healthcare, Flagstaff, AZ
Primary Contact: Barbara Firminger, Chief Administrative Officer
CFO: Jeffrey Treasure, Chief Financial Officer, Northern Arizona Healthcare
CMO: Amy Gottschalk, M.D., Chief Medical Officer, Verde Valley Medical Center; Vice President Quality, Northern Arizona Healthcare
CIO: Marilynn Black, Chief Information Officer, Northern Arizona Healthcare
CHR: Ronald Haase, Chief Human Resources Officer, Northern Arizona Healthcare
CNO: Lori A Stevens, MSN, R.N., Interim Chief Nursing Officer
Web address: www.https://nahealth.com/
Control: Other not–for–profit (including NFP Corporation) **Service:** General medical and surgical

Staffed Beds: 98 **Admissions:** 4645 **Census:** 54 **Outpatient Visits:** 38889 **Births:** 558 **Total Expense ($000):** 126294 **Payroll Expense ($000):** 50001 **Personnel:** 838

FLAGSTAFF—Coconino County

★ ⚘ **FLAGSTAFF MEDICAL CENTER (030023)**, 1200 North Deaver Street, Zip 86001–3118; tel. 928/779–3366, **A**3 5 10 21 **F**3 5 7 8 11 12 13 15 17 18 19 20 22 28 29 30 31 32 34 35 36 40 43 44 45 46 47 48 49 50 51 53 54 57 58 59 60 61 64 68 70 72 74 75 76 77 78 79 81 82 84 85 86 87 88 89 91 92 93 94 96 97 98 100 101 102 103 104 107 108 110 111 114 115 118 119 120 121 123 124 126 130 131 132 135 146 147 148 149 154 155 **S** Northern Arizona Healthcare, Flagstaff, AZ
Primary Contact: Florence (Flo) Spyrow, Chief Administrative Officer
CFO: Jeffrey Treasure, Chief Financial Officer, Northern Arizona Healthcare
CMO: Richard Neff, M.D., Interim Chief Medical Officer
CIO: Marilynn Black, Chief Information Officer, Northern Arizona Healthcare
CHR: Ronald Haase, Chief Human Resources Officer, Northern Arizona Healthcare
CNO: Katy Wilkens, Chief Nursing Officer and Vice President, Northern Arizona Healthcare
Web address: www.nahealth.com
Control: Other not–for–profit (including NFP Corporation) **Service:** General medical and surgical

Staffed Beds: 264 **Admissions:** 13133 **Census:** 172 **Outpatient Visits:** 62444 **Births:** 1077 **Total Expense ($000):** 394722 **Payroll Expense ($000):** 131686 **Personnel:** 1734

☐ **GUIDANCE CENTER (034023)**, 2187 North Vickey Street, Zip 86004–6121; tel. 928/527–1899, **A**1 10 **F**4 5 29 35 38 44 50 54 68 71 87 98 100 102 103 104 105 106 127 130 132 134 143 152 154 157 158
CFO: Steve Finch, Chief Financial Officer
CMO: Chris Linskey, M.D., Acting Chief Medical Officer
CIO: John Crockett, Chief Information Officer
Web address: www.tgcaz.org
Control: Other not–for–profit (including NFP Corporation) **Service:** Psychiatric

Staffed Beds: 16 **Admissions:** 735 **Census:** 11 **Outpatient Visits:** 0 **Births:** 0 **Total Expense ($000):** 4545 **Payroll Expense ($000):** 2583 **Personnel:** 37

REHABILITATION HOSPITAL OF NORTHERN ARIZONA (033041), 1851 North Gemini Drive, Zip 86001–1607; tel. 928/774–7070, (Nonreporting) **S** Ernest Health, Inc., Albuquerque, NM
Primary Contact: Judy Baum, Chief Executive Officer, Mountain Valley Regional Rehabilitation Hospital
Web address: www.ernesthealth.com/gallery-item/rehabilitation-hospital-of-northern-arizona/
Control: General Investor–owned, for–profit **Service:** Rehabilitation

Staffed Beds: 40

FORT DEFIANCE—Apache County

★ **TSEHOOTSOOI MEDICAL CENTER (030071)**, Highway 12 & Bonito Drive, Zip 86504, Mailing Address: P.O. Box 649, Zip 86504–0649; tel. 928/729–8000, (Nonreporting) **A**3 5 10
Primary Contact: Sandi Aretino, M.D., Chief Executive Officer
COO: Valonia Hardy, Chief Healthy Living Officer
CFO: Rachel Sorrell, Chief Financial Officer
CMO: Michael Tutt, M.D., Chief Medical Officer
CIO: Virgil Chavez, Director Information Technology
CHR: Vivian Santistevan, Chief Human Resources
CNO: Tori Davidson, R.N., Chief Nursing Officer
Web address: www.fdihb.org
Control: Public Health Service other than 47, Government, federal **Service:** General medical and surgical

Staffed Beds: 39

FORT MOHAVE—Mohave County

✠ **VALLEY VIEW MEDICAL CENTER (030117)**, 5330 South Highway 95, Zip 86426–9225; tel. 928/788–2273, **A**1 10 **F**3 8 11 13 15 18 20 22 29 45 50 51 56 59 64 70 76 77 81 85 87 90 93 107 108 111 114 115 116 117 119 135 144 149 154 **S** LifePoint Health, Brentwood, TN
Primary Contact: Feliciano Jiron, Chief Executive Officer
CFO: Emma Canlas, Chief Financial Officer
CIO: Monique Murphy-Mijares, Chief Information Officer
CHR: Bonnie Guerrero, Director Human Resources
CNO: Lesa Lock, Chief Nursing Officer
Web address: www.valleyviewmedicalcenter.net
Control: Corporation, Investor–owned (for–profit) **Service:** General medical and surgical

Staffed Beds: 84 **Admissions:** 2194 **Census:** 23

GANADO—Apache County

✠ **SAGE MEMORIAL HOSPITAL (031309)**, Highway 264, Zip 86505, Mailing Address: P.O. Box 457, Zip 86505–0457; tel. 928/755–4500, (Nonreporting) **A**1 10 18
Primary Contact: Christi J. El-Meligi, Chief Executive Officer
COO: Netrisha Dalgai, Director of Operations
CHR: Gary Pahe, Manager Human Resources
CNO: Ernasha McIntosh, Interim Director of Nursing
Web address: www.sagememorial.com
Control: Other not–for–profit (including NFP Corporation) **Service:** General medical and surgical

Staffed Beds: 25

GILBERT—Maricopa County

✠ **BANNER GATEWAY MEDICAL CENTER (030122)**, 1900 North Higley Road, Zip 85234–1604; tel. 480/543–2000, **A**1 3 10 **F**3 8 11 13 15 18 29 30 31 34 35 36 40 44 45 46 47 49 50 51 55 57 59 60 63 68 70 72 74 75 76 77 78 79 81 84 85 87 93 107 108 110 111 114 116 117 118 119 120 121 124 126 129 132 134 136 141 142 146 147 148 149 154 **S** Banner Health, Phoenix, AZ
Primary Contact: Lamont M. Yoder, R.N., MSN, FACHE, Chief Executive Officer
COO: James R Powell, Associate Administrator
CFO: Thomas M Matenaer, Chief Financial Officer
CMO: Nikunj Doshi, D.O., Chief Medical Officer
CHR: Michele Mustacchia, Chief Human Resources Officer
CNO: Debra Adornetto Garcia, MSN, R.N., Chief Nursing Officer
Web address: www.bannerhealth.com/Locations/Arizona/Banner+Gateway+Medical+Center/
Control: Other not–for–profit (including NFP Corporation) **Service:** General medical and surgical

Staffed Beds: 177 **Admissions:** 13519 **Census:** 146 **Births:** 4456 **Total Expense ($000):** 374255 **Payroll Expense ($000):** 102514 **Personnel:** 1608

✠ **MERCY GILBERT MEDICAL CENTER (030119)**, 3555 South Val Vista Road, Zip 85297–7323; tel. 480/728–8000, **A**1 10 19 **F**3 8 11 13 15 18 20 22 26 28 29 30 31 32 34 35 37 38 40 41 42 44 45 46 47 49 50 51 57 58 59 60 64 65 66 68 70 73 74 75 76 77 78 79 81 82 83 84 85 86 87 96 100 101 102 103 107 108 110 111 114 115 119 126 129 130 131 132 135 144 145 146 147 148 156 **S** CommonSpirit Health, Chicago, IL
Primary Contact: Mark F. Slyter, FACHE, President and Chief Operating Officer
COO: Mark F. Slyter, FACHE, President and Chief Operating Officer
CFO: Chuck Sowers, Vice President Finance and Chief Financial Officer
CMO: Phil Fracica, M.D., Vice President and Chief Medical Officer
CIO: Larissa Spraker, Vice President Business Development and Chief Strategy Officer
CHR: Anita Harger, Director Human Resources
Web address: www.mercygilbert.org
Control: Other not–for–profit (including NFP Corporation) **Service:** General medical and surgical

Staffed Beds: 198 **Admissions:** 15242 **Census:** 151 **Outpatient Visits:** 87094 **Births:** 3450 **Total Expense ($000):** 273532 **Payroll Expense ($000):** 93612 **Personnel:** 1879

Hospital, Medicare Provider Number, Address, Telephone, Approval, Facility, and Physician Codes, Health Care System

★ American Hospital Association (AHA) membership
☐ The Joint Commission accreditation
○ Healthcare Facilities Accreditation Program
◇ DNV Healthcare Inc. accreditation
⚘ Center for Improvement in Healthcare Quality Accreditation
△ Commission on Accreditation of Rehabilitation Facilities (CARF) accreditation

AZ

GLENDALE—Maricopa County

☒ **ABRAZO ARROWHEAD CAMPUS (030094)**, 18701 North 67th Avenue, Zip 85308–7100; tel. 623/561–1000, (Includes ABRAZO ARIZONA HEART HOSPITAL, 1930 East Thomas Road, Phoenix, Arizona, Zip 85016; tel. 602/532–1000; Jeff Patterson, Chief Executive Officer), (Nonreporting) **A**1 3 5 10 **S** TENET Healthcare Corporation, Dallas, TX
Primary Contact: Jeff Patterson, Chief Executive Officer
CMO: Patrick Smith, M.D., Chief Medical Officer
CHR: Sharon M Chadwick, Director Human Resources
Web address: www.arrowheadhospital.com
Control: Corporation, Investor–owned (for–profit) **Service:** General medical and surgical

Staffed Beds: 234

☐ **AURORA BEHAVIORAL HEALTH SYSTEM WEST (034024)**, 6015 West Peoria Avenue, Zip 85302–1213; tel. 623/344–4400, **A**1 **F**5 10 11 29 30 34 35 38 44 50 57 68 75 86 87 98 99 101 102 104 130 132 134 135 146 **S** Signature Healthcare Services, Corona, CA
Primary Contact: Bruce Waldo, Chief Executive Officer
CFO: Rebekah Francis, JD, Chief Financial Officer
CHR: Vicki Thomsen, Director Human Resources
CNO: Lori Milus, R.N., MSN, Director of Nursing
Web address: www.aurorabehavioral.com
Control: Corporation, Investor–owned (for–profit) **Service:** Psychiatric

Staffed Beds: 100 **Admissions:** 4241 **Census:** 84 **Births:** 0

☒ **BANNER THUNDERBIRD MEDICAL CENTER (030089)**, 5555 West Thunderbird Road, Zip 85306–4696; tel. 602/865–5555, (Includes BANNER BEHAVIORAL HEALTH CENTER-THUNDERBIRD CAMPUS, 5555 West Thunderbird Road, Glendale, Arizona, Zip 85306; tel. 602/588–5555) **A**1 3 5 10 **F**3 5 14 17 18 19 20 21 22 23 24 26 27 28 29 30 31 32 34 40 41 43 45 46 49 50 51 59 60 61 64 65 67 68 70 72 74 75 76 77 78 79 81 84 85 87 88 89 92 96 98 100 101 102 104 107 108 109 111 112 114 115 116 117 118 119 120 121 122 123 124 126 129 130 132 135 146 147 148 149 153 154 **S** Banner Health, Phoenix, AZ
Primary Contact: Debra J. Krmpotic, R.N., Chief Executive Officer
CFO: Richard Miller, Administrator Finance
CMO: Kathryn Perkins, M.D., Chief Medical Officer
CHR: Laura Witt, Administrator Human Resources
Web address: www.bannerhealth.com/Locations/Arizona/Banner+Thunderbird+Medical+Center/
Control: Other not–for–profit (including NFP Corporation) **Service:** General medical and surgical

Staffed Beds: 475 **Admissions:** 25535 **Census:** 358 **Births:** 5185
Total Expense ($000): 480336 **Payroll Expense ($000):** 173499
Personnel: 2539

☒ **ENCOMPASS HEALTH VALLEY OF THE SUN REHABILITATION HOSPITAL (033032)**, 13460 North 67th Avenue, Zip 85304–1042; tel. 623/878–8800, **A**1 10 **F**29 62 64 75 90 93 132 **S** Encompass Health Corporation, Birmingham, AL
Primary Contact: Beth Bacher, Chief Executive Officer
CFO: Kathryn Haney, Controller
CMO: Michael Kravetz, M.D., Medical Director
CHR: Danette Garcia, Director Human Resources
CNO: Stephanie Palmer, Chief Nursing Officer
Web address: www.https://www.encompasshealth.com/valleyofthesunrehab
Control: Corporation, Investor–owned (for–profit) **Service:** Rehabilitation

Staffed Beds: 75 **Admissions:** 1130 **Census:** 41 **Births:** 0

GLOBE—Gila County

COBRE VALLEY COMMUNITY HOSPITAL See Cobre Valley Regional Medical Center

★ **COBRE VALLEY REGIONAL MEDICAL CENTER (031314)**, 5880 South Hospital Drive, Zip 85501–9454; tel. 928/425–3261, **A**10 18 **F**3 11 12 13 15 18 20 22 28 29 30 34 35 40 41 43 45 46 49 51 55 57 59 64 70 74 75 76 78 79 81 82 87 92 93 96 97 107 108 110 111 115 117 118 119 127 129 130 133 135 146 147 148 149 154 **S** HealthTech Management Services, Brentwood, TN
Primary Contact: Neal Jensen, Chief Executive Officer
CFO: Frank Napier, Interim Chief Financial Officer
CIO: Sharon Bennett, Manager Information Systems
CHR: Rita Murphy, Director Human Resources
Web address: www.cvrmc.org
Control: Other not–for–profit (including NFP Corporation) **Service:** General medical and surgical

Staffed Beds: 25 **Admissions:** 1639 **Census:** 14 **Births:** 271 **Total Expense ($000):** 52637 **Payroll Expense ($000):** 21377

GOODYEAR—Maricopa County

☒ **ABRAZO WEST CAMPUS (030110)**, 13677 West McDowell Road, Zip 85395–2635; tel. 623/882–1500, **A**1 3 10 **F**3 11 13 18 20 22 24 26 28 29 30 34 35 40 41 42 43 44 45 46 47 49 51 59 64 70 72 74 75 76 78 79 81 85 87 107 108 111 115 119 126 130 132 135 146 148 149 154 **S** TENET Healthcare Corporation, Dallas, TX
Primary Contact: Christina E. Oh, Chief Executive Officer
COO: Jeffrey Dossett, Chief Operating Officer
CFO: Asja DiMuria, Chief Financial Officer
CNO: Scott David Morey, Chief Nursing Officer
Web address: www.abrazohealth.com
Control: Corporation, Investor–owned (for–profit) **Service:** General medical and surgical

Staffed Beds: 188 **Admissions:** 11990 **Census:** 132 **Outpatient Visits:** 85148 **Births:** 1333 **Total Expense ($000):** 172381 **Payroll Expense ($000):** 72938 **Personnel:** 787

☒ **WESTERN REGIONAL MEDICAL CENTER (030138)**, 14200 West Celebrate Life way, Zip 85338–3005; tel. 623/207–3000, **A**1 2 10 **F**18 29 30 31 63 70 75 82 84 100 107 108 110 111 114 115 116 117 118 119 120 121 123 126 130 135 **S** Cancer Treatment Centers of America, Schaumburg, IL
Primary Contact: Robert Gould, President and Chief Executive Officer
Web address: www.cancercenter.com/western-hospital.cfm
Control: Corporation, Investor–owned (for–profit) **Service:** Cancer

Staffed Beds: 12 **Admissions:** 546 **Census:** 6 **Births:** 0

GREEN VALLEY—Cochise County

⇑ **SANTA CRUZ VALLEY REGIONAL HOSPITAL (030137)**, 4455 South I-19 Frontage Road, Zip 85614; tel. 520/393–4700, (Data for 132 days) **A**21 **F**18 20 22 24 29 30 35 40 45 56 60 64 75 79 81 82 93 107 108 111 131 133
Primary Contact: Kelly Adams, Chief Executive Officer
CFO: Sara Ghali, Chief Financial Officer
CNO: Mona R. Smith, Chief Nursing Officer
Web address: www.https://scvrhaz.com/
Control: Corporation, Investor–owned (for–profit) **Service:** General medical and surgical

Staffed Beds: 49 **Admissions:** 640 **Census:** 18

KEAMS CANYON—Navajo County

☒ **HOPI HEALTH CARE CENTER (031305)**, Highway 264 Mile Marker 388, Zip 86042, Mailing Address: P.O. Box 4000, Polacca, Zip 86042–4000; tel. 928/737–6000, (Nonreporting) **A**1 3 5 10 18 **S** U. S. Indian Health Service, Rockville, MD
Primary Contact: Mose Herne, Chief Executive Officer
COO: Leonard H Lopez, Chief Operating Officer
CFO: Dorothy Sulu, Budget Analyst
CMO: Darren Vicenti, M.D., Clinical Director
CHR: Trudy Begay, Human Resources Specialist
Web address: www.ihs.gov/index.asp
Control: PHS, Indian Service, Government, federal **Service:** General medical and surgical

Staffed Beds: 15

KINGMAN—Mohave County

★ ⇑ **KINGMAN REGIONAL MEDICAL CENTER (030055)**, 3269 North Stockton Hill Road, Zip 86409–3691; tel. 928/757–2101, **A**3 5 10 13 21 **F**11 17 20 22 24 28 29 30 31 32 33 34 35 36 40 43 45 46 47 48 53 57 59 60 63 64 65 68 69 70 75 76 77 78 79 81 82 83 84 85 86 87 89 90 92 93 96 97 100 107 108 114 115 117 118 119 121 129 130 131 132 143 144 145 146 147 148
Primary Contact: Brian Turney, Chief Executive Officer
COO: Ryan Kennedy, Chief Operating Officer
CFO: Timothy D Blanchard, Chief Financial Officer
CMO: Thomas Gaughan, M.D., Chief Medical Officer
CIO: Cheryl Martin, Chief Information Officer
CHR: Anita Harger, Chief Human Resource Officer
CNO: Kimberly Miyauchi, R.N., Chief Nursing Officer
Web address: www.azkrmc.com
Control: Hospital district or authority, Government, nonfederal **Service:** General medical and surgical

Staffed Beds: 160 **Admissions:** 8268 **Census:** 106 **Births:** 584

LAKE HAVASU CITY—Mohave County

⊠ **HAVASU REGIONAL MEDICAL CENTER (030069)**, 101 Civic Center Lane, Zip 86403–5683; tel. 928/855–8185, (Nonreporting) **A**1 10 **S** LifePoint Health, Brentwood, TN
Primary Contact: Michael N. Patterson, Chief Executive Officer
COO: Wes Taylor, Chief Operating Officer
CFO: Christina DiMambro, Chief Financial Officer
CMO: Michael Rosen, M.D., Chief Medical Officer
CIO: Linda Toy, Director Information Systems
Web address: www.havasuregional.com
Control: Corporation, Investor–owned (for–profit) **Service:** General medical and surgical

Staffed Beds: 162

LAKESIDE—Navajo County

CCC AT PINEVIEW HOSPITAL (034027), 1920 West Commerce Drive, Zip 85929; tel. 928/368–4110, **A**10 **F**4 98 102 154
Primary Contact: Rosemary Anderson, Administrator
Web address: www.ccc-az.org
Control: Other not–for–profit (including NFP Corporation) **Service:** Psychiatric

Staffed Beds: 16 **Admissions:** 615 **Census:** 10 **Births:** 0

LAVEEN—Maricopa County

☐ **DIGNITY HEALTH ARIZONA GENERAL HOSPITAL (030136)**, 7171 South 51st Avenue, Zip 85339–2923; tel. 623/584–5100, (Nonreporting) **A**1 **S** CommonSpirit Health, Chicago, IL
Primary Contact: Mark F. Slyter, FACHE, President and Chief Executive Officer, East Valley
CFO: Anthony Cirocco, Chief Financial Officer
CMO: Fred Johnson, M.D., Chief Medical Officer
CNO: Victoria Nugent, Chief Nursing Officer
Web address: www.dignityhealth.org/arizonageneral/
Control: Other not–for–profit (including NFP Corporation) **Service:** Acute long–term care hospital

Staffed Beds: 16

MESA—Maricopa County

☐ **ARIZONA SPINE AND JOINT HOSPITAL (030107)**, 4620 East Baseline Road, Zip 85206–4624; tel. 480/832–4770, **A**1 10 **F**29 34 77 79 81 82 85 111 146 **S** National Surgical Healthcare, Chicago, IL
Primary Contact: Todd Greene, Chief Executive Officer
CHR: Diane Hearne, Director Human Resources
CNO: Stacy Hayes, R.N., Chief Nursing Officer
Web address: www.azspineandjoint.com
Control: Corporation, Investor–owned (for–profit) **Service:** Orthopedic

Staffed Beds: 23 **Admissions:** 1432 **Census:** 6 **Births:** 0

⊠ **BANNER BAYWOOD MEDICAL CENTER (030088)**, 6644 East Baywood Avenue, Zip 85206–1797; tel. 480/321–2000, **A**1 10 **F**3 15 18 29 30 31 34 35 36 37 40 41 43 44 45 46 47 49 50 51 56 57 58 59 60 61 63 64 65 68 70 74 75 77 78 79 81 82 84 85 86 87 90 91 92 94 96 100 102 107 108 110 111 115 118 119 126 129 130 135 141 146 147 148 149 154 156 **S** Banner Health, Phoenix, AZ
Primary Contact: Lamont M. Yoder, R.N., MSN, FACHE, Chief Executive Officer
CFO: Derek Lythgoe, Chief Financial Officer
CMO: Michael P O'Connor, M.D., Chief Medical Officer
CIO: Lori Matthews, Vice President Information Technology System
CHR: Tiffany Werner, Senior Human Resource Business Partner
CNO: Kelley Kieffer, Chief Nursing Officer
Web address: www.bannerhealth.com/locations/Arizona/banner+baywood+medical+center
Control: Other not–for–profit (including NFP Corporation) **Service:** General medical and surgical

Staffed Beds: 359 **Admissions:** 15121 **Census:** 206 **Total Expense ($000):** 256917 **Payroll Expense ($000):** 91115 **Personnel:** 1416

BANNER CHILDREN'S HOSPITAL See Cardon Children's Medical Center

⊠ **BANNER DESERT MEDICAL CENTER (030065)**, 1400 South Dobson Road, Zip 85202–4707; tel. 480/412–3000, (Includes CARDON CHILDREN'S MEDICAL CENTER, 1400 South Dobson Road, Mesa, Arizona, Zip 85202–4707; tel. 480/412–3000; Justin Bradshaw, Chief Executive Officer; SAMARITAN BEHAVIORAL HEALTH CENTER-DESERT SAMARITAN MEDICAL CENTER, 2225 West Southern Avenue, Mesa, Arizona, Zip 85202; tel. 602/464–4000) **A**1 3 5 10 **F**3 11 13 17 18 19 20 24 25 26 27 28 29 30 31 32 34 35 36 40 41 43 45 46 47 48 49 50 51 56 58 59 60 61 63 64 68 70 72 74 75 76 77 78 79 81 84 85 86 87 88 89 91 92 96 100 107 108 111 114 115 118 119 120 121 123 124 126 129 130 133 135 146 147 148 149 154 **S** Banner Health, Phoenix, AZ
Primary Contact: Laura Robertson, R.N., Chief Executive Officer
COO: Cristal Mackay, Chief Operating Officer
CFO: Scott Leckey, Chief Financial Officer
CMO: Tanya Kne, M.D., Chief Medical Officer
CIO: Stacey Hinkle, Director Information Technology
CHR: Kevin McVeigh, Chief Human Resources Officer
Web address: www.bannerhealth.com/Locations/Arizona/Banner+Desert+Medical+Center
Control: Other not–for–profit (including NFP Corporation) **Service:** General medical and surgical

Staffed Beds: 595 **Admissions:** 33751 **Census:** 450 **Births:** 3888 **Total Expense ($000):** 610228 **Payroll Expense ($000):** 211517 **Personnel:** 2930

⊠ **BANNER HEART HOSPITAL (030105)**, 6750 East Baywood Avenue, Zip 85206–1749; tel. 480/854–5000, **A**1 3 10 **F**3 8 12 13 15 18 29 30 31 34 35 36 40 44 45 46 47 49 50 51 55 57 59 60 63 68 70 72 74 75 76 77 78 79 81 84 85 87 93 102 107 108 110 111 114 116 117 118 119 120 121 124 126 130 134 136 141 142 146 147 148 149 154 156 **S** Banner Health, Phoenix, AZ
Primary Contact: Lamont M. Yoder, R.N., MSN, FACHE, Chief Executive Officer
CFO: Derek Lythgoe, Chief Financial Officer
CMO: Paul Hurst, M.D., Chief Medical Officer
CIO: Lori Matthews, Vice President, Information Technology System
CHR: Tiffany Werner, Senior Human Resource Business Partner
CNO: Kelley Kieffer, Chief Nursing Officer
Web address: www.bannerhealth.com/Locations/Arizona/Banner+Heart+Hospital/
Control: Other not–for–profit (including NFP Corporation) **Service:** Heart

Staffed Beds: 111 **Admissions:** 4705 **Census:** 55 **Births:** 0 **Total Expense ($000):** 118788 **Payroll Expense ($000):** 29448 **Personnel:** 375

CARDON CHILDREN'S MEDICAL CENTER See Banner Desert Medical Center, Mesa

⊠ **ENCOMPASS HEALTH REHABILITATION HOSPITAL OF EAST VALLEY (033037)**, 5652 East Baseline Road, Zip 85206–4713; tel. 480/567–0350, **A**1 10 **F**28 29 64 74 75 77 79 82 90 91 93 94 95 96 130 132 148 **S** Encompass Health Corporation, Birmingham, AL
Primary Contact: Jeffrey Roberts, Chief Executive Officer
CMO: Martin Yee, M.D., Medical Director
CHR: Nancy Pickler, Director of Human Resources
CNO: Hope Dunn, Chief Nursing Officer
Web address: www.healthsoutheastvalley.com
Control: Corporation, Investor–owned (for–profit) **Service:** Rehabilitation

Staffed Beds: 60 **Admissions:** 1428 **Census:** 52 **Births:** 0

HACIENDA CHILDREN'S HOSPITAL (033303), 610 West Jerome Avenue, Zip 85210; tel. 480/579–2400, (Nonreporting) **A**10 22
Primary Contact: William Timmons, President and Chief Executive Officer
Web address: www.haciendahealthcare.org/careproviders/hacienda-childrens-hospital/
Control: Other not–for–profit (including NFP Corporation) **Service:** Children's general medical and surgical

Staffed Beds: 24

★ ⇑ **MOUNTAIN VISTA MEDICAL CENTER (030121)**, 1301 South Crismon Road, Zip 85209–3767; tel. 480/358–6100, (Nonreporting) **A**3 5 10 13 21 **S** Steward Health Care System, LLC, Dallas, TX
Primary Contact: Jacob Golich, Chief Executive Officer
CFO: Marty Bakos, Chief Financial Officer
CNO: Elizabeth Kearney, R.N., Chief Nursing Officer
Web address: www.mvmedicalcenter.com
Control: Corporation, Investor–owned (for–profit) **Service:** General medical and surgical

Staffed Beds: 172

Hospital, Medicare Provider Number, Address, Telephone, Approval, Facility, and Physician Codes, Health Care System

★ American Hospital Association (AHA) membership
☐ The Joint Commission accreditation
○ Healthcare Facilities Accreditation Program
◇ DNV Healthcare Inc. accreditation
⇑ Center for Improvement in Healthcare Quality Accreditation
△ Commission on Accreditation of Rehabilitation Facilities (CARF) accreditation

PROMISE HOSPITAL OF PHOENIX (032006), 433 East 6th Street, Zip 85203–7104; tel. 480/427–3000, (Nonreporting) **A**10 **S** Promise Healthcare, Boca Raton, FL
Primary Contact: Wayne Kinsey, Chief Executive Officer
COO: Wendy Larson, Chief Clinical Officer
CFO: Theo Clark, Director Financial Services
CMO: Syed Shahryar, M.D., Medical Director
CHR: Christie Brea, Manager Human Resources
Web address: www.promise-phoenix.com
Control: Corporation, Investor–owned (for–profit) **Service:** Acute long–term care hospital

Staffed Beds: 40

SAMARITAN BEHAVIORAL HEALTH CENTER-DESERT SAMARITAN MEDICAL CENTER See Banner Desert Medical Center, Mesa

NOGALES—Santa Cruz County

✠ **CARONDELET HOLY CROSS HOSPITAL (031313)**, 1171 West Target Range Road, Zip 85621–2415; tel. 520/285–3000, **A**1 3 5 10 18 **F**3 13 29 30 31 32 34 35 40 50 51 56 57 59 64 65 68 70 75 76 77 79 81 85 86 87 89 93 107 111 119 130 132 133 134 135 146 149 156 **S** TENET Healthcare Corporation, Dallas, TX
Primary Contact: Debbie Knapheide, MSN, Site Administrator, Chief Nursing Officer and Chief Operating Officer
COO: Debbie Knapheide, MSN, Site Administrator, Chief Nursing Officer and Chief Operating Officer
CFO: Alan Strauss, Chief Financial Officer
CMO: Roy Farrell, M.D., Chief Medical Officer
CNO: Debbie Knapheide, MSN, Site Administrator, Chief Nursing Officer and Chief Operating Officer
Web address: www.carondelet.org
Control: Corporation, Investor–owned (for–profit) **Service:** General medical and surgical

Staffed Beds: 25 Admissions: 1162 Census: 7 Outpatient Visits: 38914 Births: 710 Total Expense ($000): 26732 Payroll Expense ($000): 13512 Personnel: 146

ORO VALLEY—Pima County

✠ **ORO VALLEY HOSPITAL (030114)**, 1551 East Tangerine Road, Zip 85755–6213; tel. 520/901–3500, **A**1 10 **F**3 15 17 20 22 29 30 34 35 37 40 42 45 49 50 54 57 59 60 64 70 74 75 77 79 81 85 86 87 90 93 96 98 100 103 107 108 109 110 111 114 115 118 119 126 129 130 144 146 154 **S** Community Health Systems, Inc., Franklin, TN
Primary Contact: , MSN
CFO: Maurene Polashek, Chief Financial Officer
CNO: Julie Hunt, R.N., MS, Chief Nursing Officer
Web address: www.orovalleyhospital.com
Control: Individual, Investor–owned (for–profit) **Service:** General medical and surgical

Staffed Beds: 146 Admissions: 5493 Census: 59 Outpatient Visits: 66239 Births: 0 Total Expense ($000): 95871 Payroll Expense ($000): 35012 Personnel: 627

PAGE—Coconino County

✠ **PAGE HOSPITAL (031304)**, 501 North Navajo Drive, Zip 86040, Mailing Address: P.O. Box 1447, Zip 86040–1447; tel. 928/645–2424, **A**1 10 18 **F**3 13 15 18 29 34 35 40 43 45 47 49 50 59 68 70 71 75 76 81 82 85 91 93 94 107 110 111 114 119 133 146 148 154 **S** Banner Health, Phoenix, AZ
Primary Contact: Susan Eubanks, Chief Executive Officer
CFO: Darcy Robertson, Chief Financial Officer
CMO: Thomas Wood, M.D., Chief Medical Officer
CIO: Paul Caldwell, Facility Coordinator Information Technology Customer Relations
CHR: Ed Franklin, Chief Human Resources Officer
Web address: www.bannerhealth.com/Locations/Arizona/Page+Hospital
Control: Other not–for–profit (including NFP Corporation) **Service:** General medical and surgical

Staffed Beds: 25 Admissions: 381 Census: 3 Births: 154 Total Expense ($000): 15296 Payroll Expense ($000): 7295 Personnel: 101

PARKER—La Paz County

○ **LA PAZ REGIONAL HOSPITAL (031317)**, 1200 West Mohave Road, Zip 85344–6349; tel. 928/669–9201, (Nonreporting) **A**10 11 18
Primary Contact: Kevin Brown, Chief Executive Officer
CFO: Carl J. Flanagan, Chief Financial Officer
CMO: Jack Dunn, M.D., Chief of Staff
CHR: Regina M Martinez, Director Human Resources
CNO: Maria Martinez, Chief Nursing Officer
Web address: www.lapazhospital.org
Control: Other not–for–profit (including NFP Corporation) **Service:** General medical and surgical

Staffed Beds: 25

✠ **U. S. PUBLIC HEALTH SERVICE INDIAN HOSPITAL (031307)**, 12033 Agency Road, Zip 85344–7718; tel. 928/669–2137, (Nonreporting) **A**1 10 18 **S** U. S. Indian Health Service, Rockville, MD
Primary Contact: Elizabeth Helsel, Chief Executive Officer
CFO: Robin Tahbo, Financial Management Officer
CMO: Laurence Norick, M.D., Clinical Director
CIO: JayLynn Saavedra, Chief Information Officer
Web address: www.ihs.gov
Control: PHS, Indian Service, Government, federal **Service:** General medical and surgical

Staffed Beds: 20

PAYSON—Gila County

✠ **BANNER PAYSON MEDICAL CENTER (031318)**, 807 South Ponderosa Street, Zip 85541–5599; tel. 928/474–3222, **A**1 3 5 10 18 **F**3 11 13 15 18 26 29 30 31 34 35 38 40 44 45 46 50 51 57 59 68 70 75 76 77 79 81 85 87 89 93 100 107 108 110 111 119 127 130 132 135 145 146 147 148 149 154 **S** Banner Health, Phoenix, AZ
Primary Contact: Lance Porter, Chief Executive Officer
CFO: Peter Finelli, Chief Financial Officer
CMO: John Vandruff, M.D., Chief of Staff
CIO: Nick Vandermeer, Director Information Systems
CHR: Shawn M. Thomas, Director Human Resources
CNO: Hartland Hintze, Chief Nursing Officer
Web address: www.paysonhospital.com
Control: Corporation, Investor–owned (for–profit) **Service:** General medical and surgical

Staffed Beds: 25 Admissions: 1408 Census: 10 Births: 167 Total Expense ($000): 40933 Payroll Expense ($000): 13331 Personnel: 208

PEORIA—Maricopa County

CURAHEALTH PHOENIX See Curahealth Phoenix, Phoenix

PERIDOT—Gila County

✠ **SAN CARLOS APACHE HEALTHCARE CORPORATION (030077)**, 103 Medicine Way Road, Zip 85542; tel. 928/475–1400, (Nonreporting) **A**1 10 **S** U. S. Indian Health Service, Rockville, MD
Primary Contact: Victoria D. Began, R.N., MS, President and Chief Executive Officer
CFO: Vivie Hosteenez, Chief Financial Officer
CMO: Douglas Brinkerhoff, M.D., Clinical Director
CIO: Nimmy Mathews, Acting Director Quality Management
CHR: Shirley M Boni, Administrative Officer
Web address: www.ihs.gov
Control: PHS, Indian Service, Government, federal **Service:** General medical and surgical

Staffed Beds: 8

PHOENIX—Maricopa County

★ **ABRAZO CENTRAL CAMPUS (030030)**, 2000 West Bethany Home Road, Zip 85015–2443; tel. 602/249–0212, **A**3 5 10 **F**3 15 18 20 29 30 31 34 35 40 41 44 45 46 48 49 50 51 57 58 59 64 70 74 75 77 78 79 80 81 82 85 87 107 108 110 111 114 119 120 121 124 126 129 130 132 135 146 148 149 154 157 **S** TENET Healthcare Corporation, Dallas, TX
Primary Contact: Frank L. Molinaro, Chief Executive Officer
COO: Jayleen Casano, Ph.D., FACHE, Chief Operations and Nursing Officer
CFO: Paul Hymel, Chief Financial Officer
CHR: Dana George, Chief Human Resources Officer
Web address: www.abrazohealth.com
Control: Corporation, Investor–owned (for–profit) **Service:** General medical and surgical

Staffed Beds: 172 Admissions: 7930 Census: 93 Outpatient Visits: 66107 Births: 887 Total Expense ($000): 127346 Payroll Expense ($000): 53057 Personnel: 684

✠ **ABRAZO SCOTTSDALE CAMPUS (030083)**, 3929 East Bell Road, Zip 85032–2196; tel. 602/923–5000, **A**1 10 **F**3 11 12 20 22 28 29 30 34 35 37 40 41 43 44 45 48 49 50 51 57 59 64 68 69 70 75 77 79 81 82 85 87 93 97 107 108 111 114 119 126 130 131 132 135 146 148 149 154 157 **S** TENET Healthcare Corporation, Dallas, TX
Primary Contact: Frank L. Molinaro, Chief Executive Officer
CFO: Jeffrey Zyla, Chief Financial Officer
CHR: Kendrick Russell, Chief Human Resources Officer
CNO: Vicki Lynn Huber, R.N., MSN, Chief Nursing Officer
Web address: www.abrazoscottsdale.com
Control: Corporation, Investor–owned (for–profit) **Service:** General medical and surgical

Staffed Beds: 116 Admissions: 5516 Census: 55 Outpatient Visits: 44501 Births: 776 Total Expense ($000): 80683 Payroll Expense ($000): 36762 Personnel: 447

ARIZONA STATE HOSPITAL (034021), 2500 East Van Buren Street, Zip 85008–6079; tel. 602/244–1331, **A**1 3 5 10 **F**3 30 39 44 53 58 59 68 75 77 86 87 98 100 101 106 130 132 135 143 147 148 154 156
Primary Contact: Aaron Bowen, Chief Executive Officer
CMO: Steve Dingle, M.D., Chief Medical Officer
CHR: Jeanine Decker, Manager Human Resources
Web address: www.hs.state.az.us
Control: Public Health Service other than 47, Government, federal **Service:** Psychiatric

Staffed Beds: 260 **Admissions:** 62 **Census:** 211 **Outpatient Visits:** 0 **Births:** 0

BANNER - UNIVERSITY MEDICAL CENTER PHOENIX (030002), 1111 East McDowell Road, Zip 85006–2666, Mailing Address: P.O. Box 2989, Zip 85062–2989; tel. 602/239–2000, **A**1 3 5 7 8 10 **F**3 5 6 7 8 9 10 11 12 13 15 17 18 19 20 22 24 26 28 29 30 31 34 35 36 37 38 39 40 43 44 45 46 47 48 49 50 51 53 54 55 56 57 58 59 60 61 64 65 66 68 70 72 74 75 76 77 78 79 81 82 84 85 86 87 90 91 92 93 94 96 97 98 100 101 102 103 104 107 108 110 111 114 115 116 117 118 119 123 124 126 129 130 131 132 135 138 139 141 142 143 145 146 147 148 149 150 156 157 **S** Banner Health, Phoenix, AZ
Primary Contact: Steve Narang, M.D., Chief Executive Officer
CFO: Kathy Kotin, Chief Financial Officer
CMO: Paul Stander, M.D., Chief Medical Officer
CIO: Michael S Warden, Senior Vice President Information Technology
CHR: Michael Fleming, Chief People Officer
Web address: www.bannerhealth.com/Locations/Arizona/Banner+Good+Samaritan+Medical+Center
Control: Other not–for–profit (including NFP Corporation) **Service:** General medical and surgical

Staffed Beds: 727 **Admissions:** 31911 **Census:** 513 **Births:** 5681
Total Expense ($000): 875776 **Payroll Expense ($000):** 261872
Personnel: 3624

BANNER ESTRELLA MEDICAL CENTER (030115), 9201 West Thomas Road, Zip 85037–3332; tel. 623/327–4000, **A**1 3 5 10 **F**3 11 12 13 18 20 22 24 28 29 30 31 34 35 36 37 38 40 41 43 44 45 46 49 50 51 57 58 59 60 61 64 68 70 73 74 75 76 77 78 79 81 82 83 84 85 86 87 96 102 107 108 111 114 115 118 119 126 130 131 132 135 144 145 146 147 148 149 154 157 **S** Banner Health, Phoenix, AZ
Primary Contact: Courtney Ophaug, FACHE, Chief Executive Officer
COO: Gary Foster, R.N., Associate Administrator
CFO: Dean Shepardson, Chief Financial Officer
CHR: Wendy Labadie, Chief Human Resource Officer
CNO: Sheri Dahlstrom, R.N., Chief Nursing Officer
Web address: www.bannerhealth.com/Locations/Arizona/Banner+Estrella+Medical+Center/
Control: Other not–for–profit (including NFP Corporation) **Service:** General medical and surgical

Staffed Beds: 293 **Admissions:** 18076 **Census:** 204 **Births:** 4980
Total Expense ($000): 278762 **Payroll Expense ($000):** 101147
Personnel: 1437

CURAHEALTH PHOENIX (032000), 40 East Indianola Avenue, Zip 85012–2059; tel. 602/280–7000, (Includes CURAHEALTH PHOENIX, 13216 North Plaza Del Rio Boulevard, Peoria, Arizona, Zip 85381–4907; tel. 623/974–5463; Karen Shammas, Chief Executive Officer), (Nonreporting) **A**1 10 **S** Curahealth Hospitals, Garland, TX
Primary Contact: Karen Cawley, Chief Executive Officer
Web address: www.curahealth.com
Control: Corporation, Investor–owned (for–profit) **Service:** Acute long–term care hospital

Staffed Beds: 58

HAVEN SENIOR HORIZONS (034020), 1201 South 7th Avenue, Suite 200, Zip 85007–4076; tel. 623/236–2000, (Nonreporting) **A**10 **S** Haven Behavioral Healthcare, Nashville, TN
Primary Contact: Ashley Ellis, Chief Executive Officer
CHR: Erin McEldowney, Manager Human Resources
CNO: Char Ralstin, Director of Nursing
Web address: www.havenbehavioral.com
Control: Corporation, Investor–owned (for–profit) **Service:** Psychiatric

Staffed Beds: 45

★ ⇑ **HONORHEALTH DEER VALLEY MEDICAL CENTER (030092)**, 19829 North 27th Avenue, Zip 85027–4002; tel. 623/879–6100, **A**3 10 19 21 **F**8 15 17 20 22 24 26 28 29 31 34 35 40 41 45 46 49 54 57 58 59 60 64 65 68 70 74 75 77 78 79 80 81 84 85 89 92 102 107 108 110 111 112 114 115 118 119 126 130 132 133 145 146 148 **S** HonorHealth, Scottsdale, AZ
Primary Contact: David Price, Chief Executive Officer
CMO: Mary Ann Turley, D.O., Medical Director
CHR: Frank L Cummins, Vice President Human Resources
Web address: www.jcl.com
Control: Other not–for–profit (including NFP Corporation) **Service:** General medical and surgical

Staffed Beds: 204 **Admissions:** 13930 **Census:** 146

★ ⇑ **HONORHEALTH JOHN C. LINCOLN MEDICAL CENTER (030014)**, 250 East Dunlap Avenue, Zip 85020–2825; tel. 602/943–2381, **A**3 5 10 19 21 **F**3 11 15 17 18 20 22 24 26 28 29 30 31 34 37 40 43 45 46 47 49 50 53 54 57 58 59 60 64 68 70 74 75 77 78 79 81 85 92 107 108 111 114 115 118 119 126 130 132 135 145 146 147 148 **S** HonorHealth, Scottsdale, AZ
Primary Contact: Margaret Elizabeth. Griffin, Chief Executive Officer
CMO: Christopher Shearer, M.D., Chief Medical Officer
CNO: Jelden Arcilla, R.N., Vice President and Chief Nursing Officer
Web address: www.jcl.com
Control: Other not–for–profit (including NFP Corporation) **Service:** General medical and surgical

Staffed Beds: 262 **Admissions:** 13709 **Census:** 154

LOS NINOS HOSPITAL (033301), 2303 East Thomas Road, Zip 85016–7827; tel. 602/954–7311, (Nonreporting) **A**10
Primary Contact: William Timmons, Chief Executive Officer
Web address: www.losninoshospital.com
Control: Other not–for–profit (including NFP Corporation) **Service:** Children's other specialty

Staffed Beds: 15

★ ⇑ **MARICOPA INTEGRATED HEALTH SYSTEM (030022)**, 2601 East Roosevelt Street, Zip 85008–4956; tel. 602/344–5011, (Includes ARIZONA CHILDREN'S CENTER, 2601 East Roosevelt Street, Phoenix, Arizona, Zip 85008–4973; tel. 602/344–5051) **A**3 5 8 10 21 **F**3 15 16 18 20 22 29 30 31 34 39 40 41 43 45 46 47 48 49 50 51 54 57 58 59 60 61 64 65 68 70 72 74 75 76 77 78 79 81 85 86 87 88 89 93 97 98 100 101 103 104 107 108 110 111 114 115 118 119 126 130 132 135 146 147 148 149 150 153 154
Primary Contact: Stephen A. Purves, FACHE, President and Chief Executive Officer
COO: Kris Gaw, Executive Vice President and Chief Operating Officer
CFO: Kathleen Benaquista, Executive Vice President and Chief Financial Officer
CMO: John Hitt, M.D., Executive Vice President and Chief Medical Officer
CIO: Kelly Summers, Chief Information Officer
CHR: Marshall Jones, Senior Vice President Human Resources
CNO: Sherry Stotler, R.N., MSN, Chief Nursing Officer
Web address: www.mihs.org
Control: Hospital district or authority, Government, nonfederal **Service:** General medical and surgical

Staffed Beds: 544 **Admissions:** 15343 **Census:** 360 **Outpatient Visits:** 385831 **Births:** 2038 **Total Expense ($000):** 534936 **Payroll Expense ($000):** 241467 **Personnel:** 2892

MAYO CLINIC HOSPITAL (030103), 5777 East Mayo Boulevard, Zip 85054–4502; tel. 480/342–2000, **A**1 2 3 5 8 10 19 **F**3 8 9 11 12 14 15 17 18 20 22 24 26 28 29 30 31 34 35 36 37 39 40 44 45 46 47 48 49 50 51 53 54 55 56 57 58 59 60 61 64 65 67 68 70 74 75 77 78 79 80 81 82 83 84 85 86 87 90 92 93 96 97 100 104 107 108 110 111 112 114 115 116 117 118 119 120 121 122 123 124 126 129 130 131 132 135 136 137 138 139 141 142 145 146 147 148 149 154 **S** Mayo Clinic, Rochester, MN
Primary Contact: Lois E. Krahn, M.D., Interim Chief Executive Officer
CFO: Jeffrey R Froisland, Chief Financial Officer
CMO: Alyssa B Chapital, M.D., Medical Director, Mayo Clinic Hospital
CIO: Paul Lenko, Section Head Information Technology
CHR: Nichelle A Baker, Chair Human Resources
CNO: Teresa Connolly, R.N., Chief Nursing Officer
Web address: www.mayoclinic.org/arizona/
Control: Other not–for–profit (including NFP Corporation) **Service:** General medical and surgical

Staffed Beds: 280 **Admissions:** 16486 **Census:** 213 **Outpatient Visits:** 77585 **Births:** 0 **Personnel:** 3702

OASIS HOSPITAL (030131), 750 North 40th Street, Zip 85008–6486; tel. 602/797–7700, (Nonreporting) **A**1 3 5 10
Primary Contact: Tim Bogardus, Chief Executive Officer
Web address: www.oasishospital.com
Control: Partnership, Investor–owned (for–profit) **Service:** Orthopedic

Staffed Beds: 64

Hospital, Medicare Provider Number, Address, Telephone, Approval, Facility, and Physician Codes, Health Care System

★ American Hospital Association (AHA) membership
☐ The Joint Commission accreditation
○ Healthcare Facilities Accreditation Program
◇ DNV Healthcare Inc. accreditation
⇑ Center for Improvement in Healthcare Quality Accreditation
△ Commission on Accreditation of Rehabilitation Facilities (CARF) accreditation

⊞ **PHOENIX CHILDREN'S HOSPITAL (033302)**, 1919 East Thomas Road, Zip 85016–7710; tel. 602/933–1000, **A**1 3 5 10 **F**3 8 11 15 17 19 21 23 25 27 29 30 31 32 34 35 37 38 39 40 41 43 44 46 48 49 50 54 55 57 58 59 60 61 64 65 66 68 71 72 73 74 75 77 78 79 81 82 84 85 86 87 88 89 91 92 93 94 96 97 98 99 100 101 102 104 105 107 108 111 113 114 115 116 117 118 119 129 130 131 132 134 136 137 138 139 144 146 148 153 157
Primary Contact: Robert L. Meyer, President and Chief Executive Officer
COO: Betsy Kuzas, Executive Vice President and Chief Operating Officer
CFO: Douglas Myers, Executive Vice President and Chief Financial Officer
CMO: H. Stacy Nicholson, M.D., M.P.H., Physician in Chief
CIO: David Higginson, Executive Vice President and Chief Administrative Officer
CHR: Lisa Phelps, Senior Vice President, Human Resources
CNO: Julie Bowman, Senior Vice President, Patient Care and Chief Nursing Officer
Web address: www.phoenixchildrens.com
Control: Other not–for–profit (including NFP Corporation) **Service:** Children's general medical and surgical

Staffed Beds: 381 Admissions: 13559 Census: 223 Outpatient Visits: 327521 Births: 0 Total Expense ($000): 857085 Payroll Expense ($000): 395609 Personnel: 4132

⊞ **PHOENIX VETERANS AFFAIRS HEALTH CARE SYSTEM**, 650 East Indian School Road, Zip 85012–1892; tel. 602/277–5551, (Nonreporting) **A**1 3 5 **S** Department of Veterans Affairs, Washington, DC
Primary Contact: RimaAnn O. Nelson, R.N., Director
CFO: Christine Hollingsworth, Chief Financial Officer
CMO: Maureen McCarthy, M.D., Chief of Staff
Web address: www.phoenix.va.gov/
Control: Veterans Affairs, Government, federal **Service:** General medical and surgical

Staffed Beds: 197

QUAIL RUN BEHAVIORAL HEALTH (034031), 2545 West Quail Avenue, Zip 85027–2418; tel. 602/455–5700, (Nonreporting)
Primary Contact: David Carnahan, Chief Executive Officer
Web address: www.quailrunbehavioral.com/
Control: Other not–for–profit (including NFP Corporation) **Service:** Psychiatric

Staffed Beds: 102

⊞ **SELECT SPECIALTY HOSPITAL-PHOENIX (032001)**, 350 West Thomas Road, 3rd Floor Main, Zip 85013–4409; tel. 602/406–6810, **A**1 10 **F**1 29 75 77 87 148 **S** Select Medical Corporation, Mechanicsburg, PA
Primary Contact: Karen Cawley, Chief Executive Officer
Web address: www.https://phoenix.selectspecialtyhospitals.com
Control: Corporation, Investor–owned (for–profit) **Service:** Acute long–term care hospital

Staffed Beds: 48 Admissions: 527 Census: 42 Outpatient Visits: 0 Births: 0 Total Expense ($000): 27449 Payroll Expense ($000): 11301 Personnel: 155

★ **SELECT SPECIALTY HOSPITAL-PHOENIX DOWNTOWN (032005)**, 1012 East Wiletta Street, 4th Floor, Zip 85006; tel. 602/839–6550, **F**1 29 75 77 87 148 **S** Select Medical Corporation, Mechanicsburg, PA
Primary Contact: David Selman, Chief Executive Officer
Web address: www.selectmedicalcorp.com
Control: Corporation, Investor–owned (for–profit) **Service:** Acute long–term care hospital

Staffed Beds: 33 Admissions: 329 Census: 25 Outpatient Visits: 0 Births: 0 Total Expense ($000): 15232 Payroll Expense ($000): 7002 Personnel: 93

⊞ △ **ST. JOSEPH'S HOSPITAL AND MEDICAL CENTER (030024)**, 350 West Thomas Road, Zip 85013–4496, Mailing Address: P.O. Box 2071, Zip 85001–2071; tel. 602/406–3000, (Includes CHILDREN'S HEALTH CENTER, 350 West Thomas Road, Phoenix, Arizona, Zip 85013–4409; tel. 602/344–5051; ST. JOSEPH'S WESTGATE MEDICAL CENTER, 7300 North 99th Avenue, Glendale, Arizona, Zip 85307–3003; tel. 602/406–0000) **A**1 2 3 5 7 10 19 **F**2 3 6 7 10 11 12 13 15 17 18 20 22 24 26 29 30 31 32 34 35 36 37 38 39 40 41 42 43 44 45 46 47 48 49 50 51 53 54 55 56 57 58 59 60 61 62 64 65 66 68 70 71 72 73 74 75 76 77 78 79 80 81 82 84 85 86 87 90 91 92 93 95 96 97 100 101 102 104 107 108 110 111 112 114 115 117 118 119 120 121 123 124 126 127 130 131 132 134 135 138 139 140 141 142 143 144 145 146 147 148 149 150 153 154 156 157 158 **S** CommonSpirit Health, Chicago, IL
Primary Contact: Patty White, R.N., MS, President
CMO: Edward Donahue, M.D., Chief Medical Officer
CHR: Maureen Sterbach, Vice President Human Resources
CNO: Julie Ward, MSN, R.N., Chief Nursing Officer
Web address: www.stjosephs-phx.org
Control: Other not–for–profit (including NFP Corporation) **Service:** General medical and surgical

Staffed Beds: 574 Admissions: 31851 Census: 437 Outpatient Visits: 595191 Births: 4982 Total Expense ($000): 1183251 Payroll Expense ($000): 453240 Personnel: 4989

☐ **ST. LUKE'S BEHAVIORAL HEALTH CENTER (034013)**, 1800 East Van Buren, Zip 85006–3742; tel. 602/251–8546, (Nonreporting) **A**1 10 **S** Steward Health Care System, LLC, Dallas, TX
Primary Contact: Gregory L. Jahn, R.N., Chief Executive Officer
CFO: Ruby Majhail, Chief Financial Officer
CMO: Mario Tafur, M.D., Chief of Staff
CIO: Chris Ulrey, Director Management Information Systems
CHR: Amy M Howell, Director Human Resources
Web address: www.iasishealthcare.com
Control: Corporation, Investor–owned (for–profit) **Service:** Psychiatric

Staffed Beds: 85

★ ⇑ **ST. LUKE'S MEDICAL CENTER (030037)**, 1800 East Van Buren Street, Zip 85006–3742; tel. 602/251–8100, (Includes TEMPE ST. LUKE'S HOSPITAL, 1500 South Mill Avenue, Tempe, Arizona, Zip 85281–6699; tel. 480/784–5510; James Flinn, JD, FACHE, Chief Executive Officer) **A**5 10 21 **F**3 11 12 13 18 20 22 24 26 28 29 30 34 35 37 40 45 46 47 49 50 51 56 57 58 60 61 64 68 70 71 74 75 76 79 81 82 85 87 90 91 92 93 94 98 100 102 103 107 108 111 115 119 126 129 130 131 132 146 147 148 149 **S** Steward Health Care System, LLC, Dallas, TX
Primary Contact: James Flinn, JD, FACHE, Chief Executive Officer
CFO: Ken Walsh, Chief Financial Officer
CHR: Trinise Thompson, Director Human Resources
Web address: www.stlukesmedcenter.com
Control: Corporation, Investor–owned (for–profit) **Service:** General medical and surgical

Staffed Beds: 219 Admissions: 6789 Census: 114

☐ **THE CORE INSTITUTE SPECIALTY HOSPITAL (030108)**, 6501 North 19th Avenue, Zip 85015–1646; tel. 602/795–6020, (Nonreporting) **A**1 10
Primary Contact: Kurt Loveless, Chief Executive Officer
CFO: Barbara Chacon, Chief Financial Officer
CMO: Christopher A. Yeung, M.D., Chief of Staff
CHR: Sherrie A Wagner, Manager Human Resources
CNO: Deborah Roberts, R.N., Chief Nursing Officer
Web address: www.thecoreinstitutehospital.com/
Control: Corporation, Investor–owned (for–profit) **Service:** Surgical

Staffed Beds: 33

⊞ **U. S. PUBLIC HEALTH SERVICE PHOENIX INDIAN MEDICAL CENTER (030078)**, 4212 North 16th Street, Zip 85016–5389; tel. 602/263–1200, (Nonreporting) **A**1 3 5 10 **S** U. S. Indian Health Service, Rockville, MD
Primary Contact: Deanna Dick, Chief Executive Officer
CFO: Geraldine Harney, Chief Financial Officer
CMO: Dave Civic, M.D., Associate Director Clinical Services
CIO: Vina Montour, Director Information Technology
CHR: Betty Weston, Chief Human Resources Officer
Web address: www.ihs.gov
Control: PHS, Indian Service, Government, federal **Service:** General medical and surgical

Staffed Beds: 127

☐ **VALLEY HOSPITAL PHOENIX (034026)**, 3550 East Pinchot Avenue, Zip 85018–7434; tel. 602/957–4000, (Nonreporting) **A**1 10 **S** Universal Health Services, Inc., King of Prussia, PA
Primary Contact: Michelle David, Chief Executive Officer
Web address: www.valleyhospital-phoenix.com
Control: Corporation, Investor–owned (for–profit) **Service:** Psychiatric

Staffed Beds: 122

PRESCOTT—Yavapai County

⊞ **NORTHERN ARIZONA VETERANS AFFAIRS HEALTH CARE SYSTEM**, 500 Highway 89 North, Zip 86313–5000; tel. 928/445–4860, (Nonreporting) **A**1 **S** Department of Veterans Affairs, Washington, DC
Primary Contact: Barbara A. Oemcke, Director
COO: James Belmont, Associate Director
CFO: Ame Callahan, Acting Manager Resource Management Service
CMO: A Panneer Selvam, M.D., Chief of Staff
CIO: Scott McCrimmon, Manager Information Technology
CHR: Jane Lewerke, Manager Human Resources
Web address: www.prescott.va.gov/
Control: Veterans Affairs, Government, federal **Service:** General medical and surgical

Staffed Beds: 147

Many Facility Codes have changed. Please refer to the AHA Guide Code Chart. © 2019 AHA Guide

★ **YAVAPAI REGIONAL MEDICAL CENTER (030012)**, 1003 Willow Creek Road, Zip 86301–1668; tel. 928/445–2700, (Includes YAVAPAI REGIONAL MEDICAL CENTER - EAST, 7700 East Florentine Road, Prescott Valley, Arizona, Zip 86314–2245; tel. 928/445–2700; John R. Amos, Chief Executive Officer **A**5 10 20 **F**3 11 13 15 17 18 20 22 24 26 28 29 30 31 32 34 35 40 45 46 50 53 54 57 59 60 64 68 70 71 72 74 75 76 77 78 79 81 82 84 85 86 87 89 91 93 107 108 111 114 116 117 118 119 130 131 132 135 146 147 148 154 156
Primary Contact: John R. Amos, President and Chief Executive Officer
COO: Larry P Burns Jr Chief Operating Officer
CFO: Lee Livin, Chief Financial Officer
CMO: Anthony Torres, M.D., Chief Medical Officer
CHR: Mark Timm, Executive Director Human Resources
CNO: Diane Drexler, R.N., Chief Nursing Officer
Web address: www.yrmc.org
Control: Other not-for-profit (including NFP Corporation) **Service:** General medical and surgical

Staffed Beds: 206 **Admissions:** 11513 **Census:** 109 **Outpatient Visits:** 145028 **Births:** 960 **Total Expense ($000):** 337625 **Payroll Expense ($000):** 130006 **Personnel:** 1343

PRESCOTT VALLEY—Yavapai County

☐ **MOUNTAIN VALLEY REGIONAL REHABILITATION HOSPITAL (033036)**, 3700 North Windsong Drive, Zip 86314–1253; tel. 928/759–8800, (Nonreporting) **A**1 10 **S** Ernest Health, Inc., Albuquerque, NM
Primary Contact: Judy Baum, Chief Executive Officer
CFO: Mark A. Roth, Chief Financial Officer
CMO: Alan S. Berman, M.D., Medical Director
CHR: Troy Eagar, Director Human Resources
CNO: Leah Walters, R.N., Director of Nursing
Web address: www.mvrrh.ernesthealth.com
Control: Corporation, Investor–owned (for–profit) **Service:** Rehabilitation

Staffed Beds: 16

WINDHAVEN PSYCHIATRIC HOSPITAL (034025), 3347 North Windsong Drive, Zip 86314–2283, Mailing Address: 3343 North Windsong Drive, Zip 86314–1213; tel. 928/445–5211, (Nonreporting) **A**10
Primary Contact: Larry D. Green Jr, Chief Executive Officer
COO: Pamela Pierce, Deputy Chief Executive Officer
CFO: Doug Oliver, Chief Financial Officer
CMO: Shane Russell-Jenkins, M.D., Medical Director
CIO: Laura Norman, Chief Development and Information Officer
CHR: Pamela Pierce, Deputy Chief Executive Officer
CNO: Esther Grear, Director Hospital Social Work and Assistant Hospital Administrator
Web address: www.wygc.org
Control: Other not-for-profit (including NFP Corporation) **Service:** Psychiatric

Staffed Beds: 16

SACATON—Pinal County

☐ **HUHUKAM MEMORIAL HOSPITAL (031308)**, 483 West Seed Farm Road, Zip 85147, Mailing Address: P.O. Box 38, Zip 85147–0001; tel. 602/528–1200, (Nonreporting) **A**1 3 5 10 18
Primary Contact: Lorrie Henderson, Ph.D., Chief Executive Officer
COO: Pamela Thompson, Chief Operations Officer
CMO: Noel Habib, M.D., Chief Medical Officer
CHR: Michael Freeman, Director Human Resources
Web address: www.grhc.org
Control: Other not-for-profit (including NFP Corporation) **Service:** General medical and surgical

Staffed Beds: 15

SAFFORD—Graham County

★ **MT. GRAHAM REGIONAL MEDICAL CENTER (030068)**, 1600 South 20th Avenue, Zip 85546–4097; tel. 928/348–4000, **A**3 5 10 20 **F**3 11 13 15 18 29 30 31 34 35 40 41 43 45 46 47 48 49 50 57 59 64 70 75 77 78 79 81 85 97 107 108 110 111 114 119 127 129 130 132 133 145 146 147 148 154 156
Primary Contact: Mark E. Marchetti, President and Chief Executive Officer
CFO: Keith Bryce, Vice President Finance and Chief Financial Officer
CIO: Anthon Ellsworth, Director Information Technology
CHR: Irvan Wick"" Lewis, Vice President Human Resources
CNO: Lori Burress, Vice President Patient Services and Chief Nursing Officer
Web address: www.mtgraham.org
Control: Hospital district or authority, Government, nonfederal **Service:** General medical and surgical

Staffed Beds: 49 **Admissions:** 1252 **Census:** 13 **Outpatient Visits:** 73715 **Births:** 551 **Total Expense ($000):** 59176 **Payroll Expense ($000):** 25640 **Personnel:** 358

SAN TAN VALLEY—Pinal County

⊞ **BANNER IRONWOOD MEDICAL CENTER (030130)**, 37000 North Gantzel Road, Zip 85140–7303; tel. 480/394–4000, **A**1 10 **F**3 13 30 39 40 41 43 49 64 68 70 75 76 77 79 81 85 87 107 111 115 119 126 130 131 135 146 147 149 154 156 **S** Banner Health, Phoenix, AZ
Primary Contact: Sharon Lind, MSN, FACHE, Chief Executive Officer
CFO: Tracy French, Chief Financial Officer
CMO: Darren West, M.D., Interim Chief Medical Officer
CHR: Janine Polito, Chief Human Resources Officer
CNO: Terresa Ann Paulus, Chief Nursing Officer
Web address: www.bannerhealth.com/Locations/Arizona/Banner+Ironwood/
Control: Other not-for-profit (including NFP Corporation) **Service:** General medical and surgical

Staffed Beds: 53 **Admissions:** 3361 **Census:** 27 **Births:** 1043 **Total Expense ($000):** 70301 **Payroll Expense ($000):** 24415 **Personnel:** 360

SCOTTSDALE—Maricopa County

⊞ **BANNER BEHAVIORAL HEALTH HOSPITAL - SCOTTSDALE (034004)**, 7575 East Earll Drive, Zip 85251–6915; tel. 480/941–7500, **A**1 3 10 **F**4 5 29 30 34 35 38 44 50 57 68 75 86 87 98 99 101 102 104 130 132 134 135 146 149 153 **S** Banner Health, Phoenix, AZ
Primary Contact: William Southwick, MS, R.N., R.N., Chief Executive Officer
CFO: Michael A. Cimino Jr Chief Financial Officer
CMO: Gagandeep Singh, M.D., Chief Medical Officer Behavioral Health
CHR: Zsaber Gere, Chief Human Resource Officer
CNO: Cherri Anderson, Chief Nursing Officer
Web address: www.https://www.bannerhealth.com/locations/scottsdale/banner-behavioral-health-hospital
Control: Other not-for-profit (including NFP Corporation) **Service:** Psychiatric

Staffed Beds: 124 **Admissions:** 6299 **Census:** 106 **Births:** 0 **Total Expense ($000):** 44804 **Payroll Expense ($000):** 20941 **Personnel:** 378

⊞ **ENCOMPASS HEALTH REHABILITATION HOSPITAL OF SCOTTSDALE (033025)**, 9630 East Shea Boulevard, Zip 85260–6267; tel. 480/551–5400, (Nonreporting) **A**1 10 **S** Encompass Health Corporation, Birmingham, AL
Primary Contact: Kenneth Bell, Chief Executive Officer
CFO: Lisa Barrick, Controller
CMO: Keith W Cunningham, M.D., Medical Director
CHR: Mary Beth Giczi, Director Human Resources
CNO: Diane M Caruso, MSN, Chief Nursing Officer
Web address: www.https://www.encompasshealth.com/locations/scottsdalerehab
Control: Corporation, Investor–owned (for–profit) **Service:** Rehabilitation

Staffed Beds: 60

⊞ △ **HONORHEALTH REHABILITATION HOSPITAL (033038)**, 8850 East Pima Center Parkway, Zip 85258–4619; tel. 480/800–3900, **A**1 3 7 10 **F**3 28 29 34 35 38 50 56 57 59 60 68 74 75 79 82 84 86 87 90 91 92 94 96 100 101 119 130 132 143 148 149 156 **S** Select Medical Corporation, Mechanicsburg, PA
Primary Contact: Scott R. Keen, Chief Executive Officer
Web address: www.scottsdale-rehab.com/
Control: Partnership, Investor–owned (for–profit) **Service:** Rehabilitation

Staffed Beds: 50 **Admissions:** 1057 **Census:** 39 **Outpatient Visits:** 0 **Births:** 0

★ ⇑ **HONORHEALTH SCOTTSDALE OSBORN MEDICAL CENTER (030038)**, 7400 East Osborn Road, Zip 85251–6403; tel. 480/882–4000, (Nonreporting) **A**2 3 5 8 10 21 **S** HonorHealth, Scottsdale, AZ
Primary Contact: Kimberly Post, Senior Vice President and Chief Executive Officer
CMO: James Burke, M.D., Senior Vice President and Chief Medical Officer
CIO: James R Cramer, Vice President and Chief Information Officer
Web address: www.shc.org
Control: Other not-for-profit (including NFP Corporation) **Service:** General medical and surgical

Staffed Beds: 347

★ ⇑ **HONORHEALTH SCOTTSDALE SHEA MEDICAL CENTER (030087)**, 9003 East Shea Boulevard, Zip 85260–6771; tel. 480/323–3000, **A**2 3 5 10 19 21 **F**7 8 12 13 15 17 18 20 26 28 29 31 34 35 40 41 45 56 57 58 59 62 64 70 72 73 75 76 78 79 81 82 88 89 91 97 107 111 114 115 119 126 130 131 132 133 135 146 147 148 **S** HonorHealth, Scottsdale, AZ
Primary Contact: Gary E. Baker, Senior Vice President and Chief Executive Officer
CMO: James Burke, M.D., Senior Vice President and Chief Medical Officer
CIO: James R Cramer, Vice President and Chief Information Officer
Web address: www.shc.org
Control: Other not-for-profit (including NFP Corporation) **Service:** General medical and surgical

Staffed Beds: 427 **Admissions:** 21986 **Census:** 272 **Births:** 5023

Hospital, Medicare Provider Number, Address, Telephone, Approval, Facility, and Physician Codes, Health Care System

★ American Hospital Association (AHA) membership ○ Healthcare Facilities Accreditation Program ⇑ Center for Improvement in Healthcare Quality Accreditation
☐ The Joint Commission accreditation ◇ DNV Healthcare Inc. accreditation △ Commission on Accreditation of Rehabilitation Facilities (CARF) accreditation

★ ⇑ **HONORHEALTH SCOTTSDALE THOMPSON PEAK MEDICAL CENTER (030123)**, 7400 East Thompson Peak Parkway, Zip 85255–4109; tel. 480/324–7000, **A**3 5 10 21 **F**3 5 20 22 24 26 29 30 31 34 35 37 40 45 46 49 50 51 57 58 59 70 77 78 79 81 82 107 110 111 112 119 126 130 131 132 133 134 135 143 144 145 146 147 148 149 150 **S** HonorHealth, Scottsdale, AZ
Primary Contact: David Price, Chief Executive Officer
COO: Bruce Pearson, Senior Vice President and Chief Operating Officer
CFO: Alice H Pope, Chief Financial Officer
CMO: Stephanie Jackson, M.D., Vice President and Chief Medical Officer
CIO: Charles Scully, Chief Information Officer
CHR: Wendy Crawford, Chief Human Resource Officer
CNO: Kimberly Post, Senior Vice President and Chief Clinical Officer
Web address: www.shc.org
Control: Other not–for–profit (including NFP Corporation) **Service:** General medical and surgical

Staffed Beds: 92 **Admissions:** 7183 **Census:** 63

⇑ **SCOTTSDALE LIBERTY HOSPITAL**, 17500 North Perimeter Drive, Zip 85255–7808; tel. 480/586–2300, **A**21 **F**29 33 34 36 58 64 80 81 82 85 87 **S** Nobilis Health Corporation, Houston, TX
Primary Contact: Steven M. Siwek, M.D., President and Chief Executive Officer
COO: Michael Adams, Chief Operating Officer
CFO: Douglas B Kell, Chief Financial Officer
CMO: Natalie Shand, M.D., Vice President Integrative Medicine and Chief Medical Officer
CIO: Milad Najjar, Information Technology
CHR: Samantha Mendez, Human Resources
CNO: Jani Manseau, Vice President Operations and Chief Nursing Officer
Web address: www.freedompainhospital.com
Control: Corporation, Investor–owned (for–profit) **Service:** Other specialty treatment

Staffed Beds: 12 **Admissions:** 50 **Census:** 1 **Births:** 0

SELLS—Pima County

⊠ **U. S. PUBLIC HEALTH SERVICE INDIAN HOSPITAL-SELLS (030074)**, Highway 86 & Topawa Road, Zip 85634, Mailing Address: P.O. Box 548, Zip 85634–0548; tel. 520/383–7251, (Nonreporting) **A**1 10 **S** U. S. Indian Health Service, Rockville, MD
Primary Contact: Troy Klarkowski, Administrator and Chief Executive Officer
COO: Diane Shanley, Deputy Service Unit Director
CFO: Vivian Draper, Chief Financial Officer
CNO: Donna Hobbs, Nurse Executive
Web address: www.ihs.gov
Control: PHS, Indian Service, Government, federal **Service:** General medical and surgical

Staffed Beds: 12

SHOW LOW—Navajo County

★ **SUMMIT HEALTHCARE REGIONAL MEDICAL CENTER (030062)**, 2200 East Show Low Lake Road, Zip 85901–7800; tel. 928/537–4375, **A**3 5 10 20 **F**11 13 15 18 20 22 28 29 30 31 32 34 35 36 40 41 43 45 46 47 53 54 55 57 59 62 64 65 68 70 71 73 75 76 77 78 79 81 82 84 91 92 93 97 107 108 110 111 114 115 118 119 121 127 129 130 131 132 133 135 146 147 148 149 154
Primary Contact: Ronald L. McArthur, Chief Executive Officer
COO: Doug Gilchrist, Chief Operating Officer
CFO: David Rothenberger, Chief Financial Officer
CMO: Alan Neil DeWitt, Chief Medical Officer
CIO: Aaron Young, Chief Information Officer
CHR: Connie Kakavas, Chief Human Resources Officer
CNO: Cynthia Ebert-Loomis, R.N., Chief Nursing Officer
Web address: www.summithealthcare.net
Control: Other not–for–profit (including NFP Corporation) **Service:** General medical and surgical

Staffed Beds: 89 **Admissions:** 4598 **Census:** 38 **Births:** 841

SIERRA VISTA—Cochise County

⊠ **CANYON VISTA MEDICAL CENTER (030043)**, 5700 East Highway 90, Zip 85635–9110; tel. 520/263–2000, **A**1 3 5 10 13 20 **F**3 13 15 18 20 22 24 26 28 29 30 31 34 35 40 43 44 45 1 57 59 60 61 63 64 70 72 74 75 76 77 79 80 81 85 93 94 96 98 100 103 107 108 109 111 114 115 118 119 120 122 123 130 131 145 146 147 148 **S** LifePoint Health, Brentwood, TN
Primary Contact: Bob Gomes, FACHE, President and Chief Executive Officer
COO: Ashley L. Johnson, Chief Operations Officer
CIO: Jorge Moreno, Director Information Technology Operations
CHR: Traci Meyer, Director Human Resources
Web address: www.canyonvistamedicalcenter.com/
Control: Corporation, Investor–owned (for–profit) **Service:** General medical and surgical

Staffed Beds: 100 **Admissions:** 5774 **Census:** 49 **Births:** 836

SPRINGERVILLE—Apache County

WHITE MOUNTAIN REGIONAL MEDICAL CENTER (031315), 118 South Mountain Avenue, Zip 85938–5104; tel. 928/333–4368, (Nonreporting) **A**10 18
Primary Contact: Gregory J. Was, CPA, Chief Executive Officer
CFO: James Hamblin, Chief Financial Officer
CMO: Scott Hamblin, M.D., President Medical Staff
Web address: www.wmrmc.com
Control: Other not–for–profit (including NFP Corporation) **Service:** General medical and surgical

Staffed Beds: 20

SUN CITY—Maricopa County

⊠ **BANNER BOSWELL MEDICAL CENTER (030061)**, 10401 West Thunderbird Blvd, Zip 85351–3004, Mailing Address: P.O. Box 1690, Zip 85372–1690; tel. 623/832–4000, (Total facility includes 78 beds in nursing home–type unit) **A**1 2 3 5 10 **F**3 9 11 15 17 18 20 22 24 26 28 29 30 31 34 35 36 37 40 43 44 45 46 47 48 49 50 51 53 56 57 58 59 60 61 63 64 65 69 70 74 75 77 78 79 81 84 85 86 87 90 91 92 93 94 96 107 108 110 111 114 115 117 119 120 121 124 126 128 130 131 132 135 141 145 146 147 148 149 154 157 **S** Banner Health, Phoenix, AZ
Primary Contact: Debbie Flores, Interim Chief Executive Officer
CFO: Jeremy Williams, Chief Financial Officer
CMO: Kathryn Perkins, M.D., Chief Medical Officer
CHR: Brenda Dietrich, Chief Human Resources Officer
Web address: www.bannerhealth.com/locations/sun-city/banner-boswell-medical-center
Control: Other not–for–profit (including NFP Corporation) **Service:** General medical and surgical

Staffed Beds: 436 **Admissions:** 15734 **Census:** 243 **Births:** 0
Total Expense ($000): 324902 **Payroll Expense ($000):** 104488
Personnel: 1608

SUN CITY WEST—Maricopa County

⊠ **BANNER DEL E. WEBB MEDICAL CENTER (030093)**, 14502 West Meeker Boulevard, Zip 85375–5299; tel. 623/524–4000, **A**1 3 5 10 **F**3 4 5 9 11 13 15 18 20 22 28 29 30 31 34 35 36 37 38 40 43 44 45 46 47 49 50 51 53 56 57 58 59 60 61 63 64 65 70 74 75 76 77 78 79 80 81 84 85 86 87 90 91 92 93 94 96 98 100 101 102 103 104 107 108 110 111 114 115 118 119 126 130 131 132 135 141 145 146 147 148 149 153 154 157 **S** Banner Health, Phoenix, AZ
Primary Contact: Debbie Flores, Chief Executive Officer
COO: Nathan Shinagawa, Chief Operating Officer
CFO: Dan Stimpson, Chief Financial Officer
CMO: Scott Anderson, Chief Medical Officer
CHR: Carole Smith, Senior Human Resource Business Partner
CNO: Nancy Adamson, Chief Nursing Officer
Web address: www.bannerhealth.com/Locations/Arizona/Banner+Del+Webb+Medical+Center/
Control: Other not–for–profit (including NFP Corporation) **Service:** General medical and surgical

Staffed Beds: 390 **Admissions:** 17840 **Census:** 235 **Births:** 1886 **Total Expense ($000):** 279960 **Payroll Expense ($000):** 98925 **Personnel:** 1410

SURPRISE—Maricopa County

COBALT REHABILITATION HOSPITAL (033039), 13060 West Bell Road, Zip 85378–1200; tel. 623/499–9100, **A**10 22 **F**28 29 54 65 75 77 90 91 95 96 100 145 154
Primary Contact: Sharon Noe, Chief Executive Officer
Web address: www.colbaltrehab.com
Control: Corporation, Investor–owned (for–profit) **Service:** Rehabilitation

Staffed Beds: 40 **Admissions:** 81 **Census:** 26 **Births:** 0

TEMPE—Maricopa County

☐ **AURORA BEHAVIORAL HEALTH SYSTEM EAST (034028)**, 6350 South Maple Street, Zip 85283–2857; tel. 480/345–5400, (Nonreporting) **A**1 10 **S** Signature Healthcare Services, Corona, CA
Primary Contact: Bruce Waldo, Chief Executive Officer
CFO: Rebekah Francis, JD, Chief Financial Officer
CMO: Jason Friday, M.D., Medical Director
CHR: Vicki Thomsen, Director Human Resources
Web address: www.auroraarizona.com
Control: Partnership, Investor–owned (for–profit) **Service:** Psychiatric

Staffed Beds: 70

TUBA CITY—Coconino County

☒ **TUBA CITY REGIONAL HEALTH CARE CORPORATION (030073)**, 167 Main Street, Zip 86045–0611, Mailing Address: P.O. Box 600, Zip 86045–0600, tel. 928/283–2501, (Nonreporting) **A**1 3 5 10
Primary Contact: Lynette Bonar, FACHE, R.N., Chief Executive Officer
CFO: Christine Keyonnie, CPA, Chief Financial Officer
CMO: Holly Van Dyk, M.D., Interim Chief Medical Officer
CIO: Shawn Davis, Chief Information Officer
CHR: George Hunter, Interim Chief Human Resources Officer
CNO: Alvina Rosales, R.N., Chief Nursing Officer
Web address: www.tchealth.org
Control: Other not-for-profit (including NFP Corporation) **Service**: General medical and surgical

Staffed Beds: 53

TUCSON—Pima County

☒ **BANNER - UNIVERSITY MEDICAL CENTER SOUTH (030111)**, 2800 East Ajo Way, Zip 85713–6289; tel. 520/874–2000, **A**1 3 5 10 **F**3 11 18 20 22 29 30 34 40 41 43 45 47 48 51 54 56 58 59 60 61 64 65 66 67 68 70 71 74 75 77 79 81 82 84 85 86 87 93 97 98 99 100 101 102 103 104 107 108 111 114 115 119 130 131 132 135 146 148 149 154 **S** Banner Health, Phoenix, AZ
Primary Contact: John Scherpf, Chief Executive Officer
CFO: Jeff Buehrle, Chief Financial Officer
CMO: David Sheinbein, Chief Medical Officer
CIO: Ryan K Smith, Senior Vice President Information Technology
CHR: Jennifer L Sherwood, Division, Human Resource Business Partner
CNO: Cathy Townsend, Chief Nursing Officer
Web address: www.bannerhealth.com
Control: Other not-for-profit (including NFP Corporation) **Service**: General medical and surgical

Staffed Beds: 167 **Admissions**: 7742 **Census**: 106 **Births**: 0 **Total Expense ($000)**: 183970 **Payroll Expense ($000)**: 54370 **Personnel**: 692

☒ **BANNER - UNIVERSITY MEDICAL CENTER TUCSON (030064)**, 1501 North Campbell Avenue, Zip 85724–5128; tel. 520/694–0111, (Includes DIAMOND CHILDREN'S HOSPITAL, 1501 North Campbell Avenue, Tucson, Arizona, Zip 85724–0001; tel. 520/694–0111) **A**1 2 3 5 8 10 19 **F**3 11 12 13 15 16 19 20 21 22 23 25 26 27 28 29 30 31 34 35 40 41 43 45 46 47 49 50 51 53 54 55 56 57 58 59 60 61 64 65 67 68 70 71 72 74 75 76 77 78 79 80 81 82 84 85 86 87 88 89 92 93 97 100 104 107 108 110 111 114 115 116 117 118 119 120 121 123 124 126 129 130 131 132 135 136 137 138 139 140 141 142 145 146 147 148 149 154 **S** Banner Health, Phoenix, AZ
Primary Contact: John Scherpf, Chief Executive Officer
CFO: Misty Hansen, Chief Financial Officer
CMO: Andreas Theodorou, Chief Medical Officer
CIO: Dan Critchley, Chief Information Officer
CHR: John Marques, Vice President Human Resources
Web address: www.https://www.bannerhealth.com/locations/tucson/banner-university-medical-center-tucson
Control: Other not-for-profit (including NFP Corporation) **Service**: General medical and surgical

Staffed Beds: 439 **Admissions**: 20990 **Census**: 353 **Births**: 1487 **Total Expense ($000)**: 776284 **Payroll Expense ($000)**: 214212 **Personnel**: 2622

☒ **CARONDELET ST. JOSEPH'S HOSPITAL (030011)**, 350 North Wilmot Road, Zip 85711–2678; tel. 520/873–3000, **A**1 5 10 19 **F**3 5 12 13 18 20 22 24 28 29 30 31 34 35 38 40 44 45 46 47 49 50 57 59 60 64 68 69 70 72 74 75 76 77 78 79 81 82 83 84 85 86 87 90 92 93 98 100 101 102 104 107 108 114 115 118 119 126 129 130 132 135 145 146 147 148 156 **S** TENET Healthcare Corporation, Dallas, TX
Primary Contact: Mark A. Benz, President and Chief Executive Officer
CFO: Alan Strauss, Chief Financial Officer
CMO: Donald Denmark, M.D., Chief Medical Officer
CIO: Sally Zambrello, Chief Information Officer
CHR: Igor Shegolev, Vice President Human Resources
CNO: Robin Conklin, R.N., Chief Nursing Officer
Web address: www.carondelet.org
Control: Corporation, Investor-owned (for-profit) **Service**: General medical and surgical

Staffed Beds: 486 **Admissions**: 15992 **Census**: 183 **Outpatient Visits**: 94519 **Births**: 2385 **Total Expense ($000)**: 236752 **Payroll Expense ($000)**: 102055 **Personnel**: 1189

☒ **CARONDELET ST. MARY'S HOSPITAL (030010)**, 1601 West St Mary's Road, Zip 85745–2682; tel. 520/872–3000, **A**1 5 10 19 **F**3 12 15 17 18 20 22 24 26 28 29 30 31 34 38 40 44 45 46 47 49 50 51 53 56 57 58 59 60 64 68 70 74 77 78 79 81 82 84 85 86 87 90 92 93 96 98 100 101 102 103 107 108 110 111 114 115 118 119 126 129 130 131 132 146 148 149 156 157 **S** TENET Healthcare Corporation, Dallas, TX
Primary Contact: Mark A. Benz, President and Chief Executive Officer
CMO: Donald Denmark, M.D., Chief Medical Officer
Web address: www.carondelet.org
Control: Corporation, Investor-owned (for-profit) **Service**: General medical and surgical

Staffed Beds: 300 **Admissions**: 11677 **Census**: 157 **Outpatient Visits**: 97276 **Births**: 0 **Total Expense ($000)**: 197147 **Payroll Expense ($000)**: 82115 **Personnel**: 963

☐ **CHG HOSPITAL TUCSON, LLC (032004)**, 7220 East Rosewood Drive, Zip 85710–1350; tel. 520/546–4595, **A**1 10 **F**1 3 29 75 148 154 **S** Cornerstone Healthcare Group, Dallas, TX
Primary Contact: Vanessa Acevedo, Interim Chief Executive Officer
CFO: Kurt Schultz, Group Chief Financial Officer
CMO: Haroon Haque, M.D., Medical Director
CIO: Adam Davis, Director Information Technology
CHR: Deborah Darcy, Human Resources
CNO: Jose' Sanchez, Chief Nursing Officer
Web address: www.chghospitals.com
Control: Corporation, Investor-owned (for-profit) **Service**: Acute long-term care hospital

Staffed Beds: 32 **Admissions**: 401 **Census**: 26 **Births**: 0

☐ **CURAHEALTH TUCSON (032002)**, 355 North Wilmot Road, Zip 85711–2601; tel. 520/584–4500, (Nonreporting) **A**1 10 **S** Curahealth Hospitals, Garland, TX
Primary Contact: Camie Overton, Chief Executive Officer
CMO: Sunil Natrajan, M.D., Medical Director
CNO: Globert Empedrad, Chief Clinical Officer
Web address: www.curahealth.com
Control: Corporation, Investor-owned (for-profit) **Service**: Acute long-term care hospital

Staffed Beds: 51

☒ **ENCOMPASS HEALTH REHABILITATION HOSPITAL OF NORTHWEST TUCSON (033029)**, 1921 West Hospital Drive, Zip 85704–7806; tel. 520/742–2800, **A**1 10 **F**3 29 34 59 64 69 90 93 95 96 130 131 132 143 148 **S** Encompass Health Corporation, Birmingham, AL
Primary Contact: Timothy T. Poore, Chief Executive Officer
CFO: Kaleigh Hotchkiss, Controller
CMO: Susan R. Bulen, M.D., Medical Director
CHR: Neil Cullen, Director Human Resources
CNO: Virginia Ragonese-Green, Chief Nursing Officer
Web address: www.https://www.encompasshealth.com/northwesttucsonrehab
Control: Corporation, Investor-owned (for-profit) **Service**: Rehabilitation

Staffed Beds: 60 **Admissions**: 938 **Census**: 32 **Births**: 0

☒ **ENCOMPASS HEALTH REHABILITATION INSTITUTE OF TUCSON (033028)**, 2650 North Wyatt Drive, Zip 85712–6108; tel. 520/325–1300, **A**1 3 5 10 **F**29 34 35 62 90 93 96 130 132 **S** Encompass Health Corporation, Birmingham, AL
Primary Contact: Jeffrey Christensen, Chief Executive Officer
CFO: Mary Donovan, Controller
CMO: Jon Larson, M.D., Medical Director
CHR: Dawn Mosier, Director Human Resources
Web address: www.https://www.encompasshealth.com/rehabinstituteoftucson
Control: Corporation, Investor-owned (for-profit) **Service**: Rehabilitation

Staffed Beds: 80 **Admissions**: 1659 **Census**: 54 **Outpatient Visits**: 0 **Births**: 0

☒ **NORTHWEST MEDICAL CENTER (030085)**, 6200 North La Cholla Boulevard, Zip 85741–3599; tel. 520/742–9000, **A**1 5 10 **F**3 8 12 13 15 17 18 20 22 24 26 28 29 30 31 34 35 40 42 45 46 47 48 49 51 56 57 59 60 67 68 70 72 74 75 76 77 78 79 81 82 85 87 90 93 102 107 108 110 111 114 115 118 119 126 130 131 132 135 144 145 146 147 148 **S** Community Health Systems, Inc., Franklin, TN
Primary Contact: Kevin Stockton, Chief Executive Officer
CFO: Ronald Patrick, Chief Financial Officer
CIO: David Bullock, Director Information Services
CNO: Kay Stubbs, Chief Nursing Officer
Web address: www.northwestmedicalcenter.com
Control: Corporation, Investor-owned (for-profit) **Service**: General medical and surgical

Staffed Beds: 258 **Admissions**: 14364 **Census**: 143 **Outpatient Visits**: 171513 **Births**: 2315 **Total Expense ($000)**: 252951 **Payroll Expense ($000)**: 85650 **Personnel**: 1921

Hospital, Medicare Provider Number, Address, Telephone, Approval, Facility, and Physician Codes, Health Care System

★ American Hospital Association (AHA) membership
☐ The Joint Commission accreditation
○ Healthcare Facilities Accreditation Program
◇ DNV Healthcare Inc. accreditation
⇑ Center for Improvement in Healthcare Quality Accreditation
△ Commission on Accreditation of Rehabilitation Facilities (CARF) accreditation

AZ

☐ **PALO VERDE BEHAVIORAL HEALTH (034030)**, 2695 North Craycroft Road, Zip 85712–2244; tel. 520/322–2888, (Nonreporting) **A**1 3 5 10 **S** Universal Health Services, Inc., King of Prussia, PA
Primary Contact: Melissa Eckstein, Chief Executive Officer
CFO: Richard N England, Chief Financial Officer
CHR: Michelle Carrasco, Director Human Resources
Web address: www.paloverdebh.com/
Control: Other not–for–profit (including NFP Corporation) **Service**: Psychiatric

Staffed Beds: 48

☐ **SONORA BEHAVIORAL HEALTH HOSPITAL (034022)**, 6050 North Corona Road, #3, Zip 85704–1096; tel. 520/469–8700, **A**1 10 **F**5 29 50 98 99 100 102 104 105 153 **S** Acadia Healthcare Company, Inc., Franklin, TN
Primary Contact: Edeli Kinsala, Chief Executive Officer
CMO: Steven Bupp, M.D., Medical Director
CHR: Ciria Soto, Director Human Resources
CNO: Angel Payne, Clinical Director, Director of Nursing
Control: Corporation, Investor–owned (for–profit) **Service**: Psychiatric

Staffed Beds: 106 Admissions: 4227 Census: 88 Births: 0

⊠ △ **SOUTHERN ARIZONA VETERANS AFFAIRS HEALTH CARE SYSTEM**, 3601 Sout 6th Avenue, Zip 85723–0002, Mailing Address: 3601 South 6th Avenue, Zip 85723–0002; tel. 520/792–1450, (Nonreporting) **A**1 3 5 7 **S** Department of Veterans Affairs, Washington, DC
Primary Contact: William J. Caron, Director
CMO: Jayendra H Shah, M.D., Chief Medical Officer
CIO: John Walston, Chief Information Officer
CHR: Patrice Craig, Manager Human Resources
Web address: www.tucson.va.gov
Control: Veterans Affairs, Government, federal **Service**: General medical and surgical

Staffed Beds: 323

TMC FOR CHILDREN See Tmc Healthcare, Tucson

⊠ **TMC HEALTHCARE (030006)**, 5301 East Grant Road, Zip 85712–2874; tel. 520/324–5461, (Includes TMC FOR CHILDREN, 5301 East Grant Road, Tucson, Arizona, Zip 85712–2805; tel. 520/327–5461; Judy F. Rich, MSN, R.N., President and Chief Executive Officer) **A**1 3 5 10 19 **F**3 11 12 13 15 17 18 20 22 24 26 28 29 30 31 32 34 35 37 40 41 45 46 47 48 49 50 53 54 56 57 58 59 63 64 65 66 68 72 74 75 76 77 78 79 81 82 84 85 87 88 89 93 98 102 103 107 108 110 111 114 115 118 119 124 126 127 129 130 132 135 146 147 148 149 154 156 157
Primary Contact: Judy F. Rich, MSN, R.N., President and Chief Executive Officer
COO: Karen Mlawsky, Senior Vice President and Chief Operations Officer
CFO: Stephen Bush, Chief Financial Officer
CMO: Rick Anderson, M.D., Senior Vice President and Chief Medical Officer
CIO: Frank Marini, Senior Vice President and Chief Information Officer
CHR: Alex Horvath, Vice President and Chief Human Resources Officer
CNO: Mimi Coomler, R.N., Vice President and Chief Nursing Officer
Web address: www.tmcaz.com
Control: Other not–for–profit (including NFP Corporation) **Service**: General medical and surgical

Staffed Beds: 586 Admissions: 34512 Census: 403 Outpatient Visits: 172222 Births: 5485 Total Expense ($000): 535369 Payroll Expense ($000): 213413 Personnel: 3747

TUCSON—Pinal County

SIERRA TUCSON, 39580 South Lago Del Oro Parkway, Zip 85739–1091; tel. 520/624–4000, (Nonreporting) **A**3 5 **S** CRC Health Group, Inc., Cupertino, CA
Primary Contact: Stephen P. Fahey, Executive Director
COO: Stephen P Fahey, Executive Director
CFO: Amy Fritton, Controller
CMO: Jerome Lerner, M.D., Medical Director
CHR: Betty Dickens, Director Human Resources
CNO: Sue Menzie, R.N., Director Patient Care
Web address: www.sierratucson.com
Control: Corporation, Investor–owned (for–profit) **Service**: Alcoholism and other chemical dependency

Staffed Beds: 139

WHITERIVER—Navajo County

☐ **U. S. PUBLIC HEALTH SERVICE INDIAN HOSPITAL-WHITERIVER (030113)**, 200 West Hospital Drive, Zip 85941–0860, Mailing Address: State Route 73, Box 860, Zip 85941–0860; tel. 928/338–4911, (Nonreporting) **A**1 3 5 10 **S** U. S. Indian Health Service, Rockville, MD
Primary Contact: Michelle Martinez, Chief Executive Officer
COO: Brian Campbell, Director Professional Services
CFO: Desdemona Leslie, Finance Officer
CMO: John Umhau, M.D., Clinical Director
CIO: Russell Barker, Information Officer
CHR: Lena Fasthorse, Supervisor Human Resource
CNO: Jana Towne, Nurse Executive
Web address: www.ihs.gov
Control: PHS, Indian Service, Government, federal **Service**: General medical and surgical

Staffed Beds: 35

WICKENBURG—Maricopa County

★ **WICKENBURG COMMUNITY HOSPITAL (031300)**, 520 Rose Lane, Zip 85390–1447; tel. 928/684–5421, **A**10 18 **F**3 8 15 18 29 30 34 37 40 43 45 46 47 50 54 57 59 65 68 75 77 79 81 86 87 90 93 97 107 108 110 111 112 119 120 121 122 123 124 127 130 131 133 135 146 148 154 157
Primary Contact: James Tavary, Chief Executive Officer
CFO: Jackie Lundblad, Chief Financial Officer
CMO: Todd Kravetz, Chief of Staff
CIO: Michael McKay, Chief Information Officer
CNO: Linda Brockwell, Director of Nursing, Administrative
Web address: www.wickhosp.com
Control: Other not–for–profit (including NFP Corporation) **Service**: General medical and surgical

Staffed Beds: 19 Admissions: 307 Census: 3

WILLCOX—Cochise County

★ **NORTHERN COCHISE COMMUNITY HOSPITAL (031302)**, 901 West Rex Allen Drive, Zip 85643–1009; tel. 520/384–3541, **A**10 18 **F**11 15 29 34 35 40 41 43 57 59 65 75 77 87 90 93 100 107 110 111 115 119 127 128 133 146 149
Primary Contact: Roland Knox, Chief Executive Officer
CFO: Kim Aguirre, Director Finance
CMO: Hisham Hamam, M.D., Chief of Staff
CIO: Dennis Drury, Director Information Technology
CNO: Pam Noland, Director of Nursing
Web address: www.ncch.com
Control: Hospital district or authority, Government, nonfederal **Service**: General medical and surgical

Staffed Beds: 24 Admissions: 285 Census: 3 Outpatient Visits: 16991 Births: 0 Total Expense ($000): 17217 Payroll Expense ($000): 7150 Personnel: 149

WINSLOW—Navajo County

LITTLE COLORADO MEDICAL CENTER (031311), 1501 Williamson Avenue, Zip 86047–2797; tel. 928/289–4691, **A**3 10 18 **F**29 34 40 50 65 79 81 107 127 130 133
Primary Contact: John J. Dempsey, Chief Executive Officer
CFO: Gina Reffner, Chief Financial Officer
CMO: Perry Mitchell, M.D., Chief of Staff
CIO: Jacob Garcia, Chief Information Officer
CHR: Nina L Ferguson, Director Human Resources
Web address: www.lcmcwmh.com
Control: Other not–for–profit (including NFP Corporation) **Service**: General medical and surgical

Staffed Beds: 25 Admissions: 1114 Census: 10 Births: 174

YUMA—Yuma County

★ ⇑ **YUMA REGIONAL MEDICAL CENTER (030013)**, 2400 South Avenue 'A', Zip 85364–7170; tel. 928/344–2000, **A**3 5 10 21 **F**3 8 12 13 15 18 20 22 24 26 28 29 30 31 32 34 35 40 41 45 46 47 48 49 50 54 57 58 59 64 68 70 72 74 75 76 77 78 79 81 82 83 84 85 86 87 89 97 104 107 108 109 110 111 112 114 115 116 117 118 119 120 121 122 123 124 126 130 132 146 147 148 149 154
Primary Contact: Robert Trenschel, D.O., FACHE, M.P.H., President and Chief Executive Officer
CFO: David Willie, Chief Financial Officer
CMO: Bharat Magu, M.D., Chief Medical Officer
CIO: Fred Peet, Chief Information Officer
CHR: Randal M. Etzler, Chief Human Resources Officer
CNO: Deb Aders, MS, R.N., Vice President Patient Care Services, Chief Nursing Officer
Web address: www.yumaregional.org
Control: Other not–for–profit (including NFP Corporation) **Service**: General medical and surgical

Staffed Beds: 406 Admissions: 17578 Census: 187 Outpatient Visits: 305095 Births: 3340 Total Expense ($000): 450405 Payroll Expense ($000): 172386 Personnel: 2145

⊠ **YUMA REHABILITATION HOSPITAL, A PARTNERSHIP OF ENCOMPASS HEALTH AND YRMC (033034)**, 901 West 24th Street, Zip 85364–6384; tel. 928/726–5000, (Nonreporting) **A**1 10 **S** Encompass Health Corporation, Birmingham, AL
Primary Contact: Ian Hodge, Chief Executive Officer
CMO: Bapu Aluri, M.D., Chief Medical Officer
CHR: Linda Woen, Director Human Resources
CNO: Kristin Parra, Chief Nursing Officer
Web address: www.https://www.encompasshealth.com/yumarehab
Control: Corporation, Investor–owned (for–profit) **Service**: Rehabilitation

Staffed Beds: 41

Many Facility Codes have changed. Please refer to the AHA Guide Code Chart. © 2019 AHA Guide

ARKANSAS

ARKADELPHIA—Clark County

✠ **BAPTIST HEALTH MEDICAL CENTER-ARKADELPHIA (041321)**, 3050 Twin Rivers Drive, Zip 71923–4299; tel. 870/245–2622, **A**1 10 18 **F**3 11 13 15 29 30 34 35 40 41 43 45 46 50 57 59 64 65 68 69 70 75 76 79 81 85 87 93 96 97 102 107 110 111 114 119 127 129 130 131 133 135 146 148 154 156 **S** Baptist Health, Little Rock, AR
Primary Contact: Tony Hardage, PharmD, Assistant Vice President and Administrator
CFO: Robert C Roberts, Vice President and Chief Financial Officer
CMO: Eddie Phillips, M.D., Chief Medical Officer
CIO: David House, Vice President and Chief Information Officer
CHR: Anthony Kendall, Vice President Human Resources
Web address: www.baptist-health.com/locations/accesspoint.aspx?accessPointID=187
Control: Other not–for–profit (including NFP Corporation) **Service:** General medical and surgical

Staffed Beds: 25 **Admissions:** 1145 **Census:** 11 **Outpatient Visits:** 37644 **Births:** 381 **Total Expense ($000):** 25171 **Payroll Expense ($000):** 9788 **Personnel:** 166

ASHDOWN—Little River County

★ **LITTLE RIVER MEMORIAL HOSPITAL (041320)**, 451 West Locke Street, Zip 71822–3325; tel. 870/898–5011, **A**10 18 **F**3 40 56 59 62 65 77 93 97 107 110 115 119 133
Primary Contact: James Dowell, Administrator and Chief Executive Officer
CFO: Jackie Rainey, Chief Financial Officer
CIO: Mitchell Jones, Director Information Technology
CHR: Vicki Keener, Administrative Assistant and Director Human Resources
CNO: Cynthia Metzger, Chief Nursing and Operations Officer
Control: Other not–for–profit (including NFP Corporation) **Service:** General medical and surgical

Staffed Beds: 25 **Admissions:** 120 **Census:** 1 **Outpatient Visits:** 13104 **Births:** 0 **Total Expense ($000):** 9612 **Payroll Expense ($000):** 5436 **Personnel:** 120

BARLING—Sebastian County

☐ **VALLEY BEHAVIORAL HEALTH SYSTEM (044006)**, 10301 Mayo Drive, Zip 72923–1660; tel. 479/494–5700, **A**1 10 **F**29 34 35 75 87 98 99 100 101 102 105 130 135 153 **S** Acadia Healthcare Company, Inc., Franklin, TN
Primary Contact: Andrea Norman, Chief Executive Officer
CFO: Paul D Ervin, Chief Financial Officer
CMO: Richard Livingston, M.D., Medical Director
CHR: Patricia J Moore, Director Human Resource
CNO: Landon Horton, Director of Nursing
Web address: www.valleybehavioral.com
Control: State, Government, nonfederal **Service:** Psychiatric

Staffed Beds: 114 **Admissions:** 2282 **Census:** 75 **Outpatient Visits:** 10749 **Births:** 0 **Total Expense ($000):** 14924 **Payroll Expense ($000):** 7900 **Personnel:** 177

BATESVILLE—Independence County

★ **WHITE RIVER MEDICAL CENTER (040119)**, 1710 Harrison Street, Zip 72501–7303, Mailing Address: P.O. Box 2197, Zip 72503–2197; tel. 870/262–1200, (Total facility includes 11 beds in nursing home–type unit) **A**3 5 10 **F**3 8 11 12 13 15 17 20 22 26 28 29 30 31 34 35 38 40 42 43 44 45 48 50 51 56 57 59 60 64 68 70 74 75 76 77 78 79 81 82 84 85 86 87 90 92 93 98 100 101 102 103 107 108 110 111 114 115 119 121 126 127 128 129 130 131 132 135 144 146 147 148 154 156 **S** White River Health System, Batesville, AR
Primary Contact: Gary Paxson, Administrator
CFO: Phillip Hacker, Chief Financial Officer
CMO: Doug Bernard, M.D., Chief Medical Officer
CHR: Gary McDonald, Chief Facilities and Personnel Officer
CNO: Terri Bunch, MSN, R.N., MSN, Chief Nursing Officer
Web address: www.whiteriverhealthsystem.com
Control: Other not–for–profit (including NFP Corporation) **Service:** General medical and surgical

Staffed Beds: 210 **Admissions:** 8254 **Census:** 101 **Outpatient Visits:** 539928 **Births:** 712 **Total Expense ($000):** 219439 **Payroll Expense ($000):** 91604 **Personnel:** 1657

BENTON—Saline County

☐ **RIVENDELL BEHAVIORAL HEALTH SERVICES OF ARKANSAS (044007)**, 100 Rivendell Drive, Zip 72019–9100; tel. 501/316–1255, **A**1 10 **F**29 38 59 75 98 99 100 101 104 105 130 132 153 **S** Universal Health Services, Inc., King of Prussia, PA
Primary Contact: Ballard Sheppard, Chief Executive Officer
CFO: Mike Rainbolt, Chief Financial Officer
Web address: www.rivendellofarkansas.com
Control: Corporation, Investor–owned (for–profit) **Service:** Psychiatric

Staffed Beds: 80 **Admissions:** 3130 **Census:** 62 **Outpatient Visits:** 3674 **Births:** 0 **Total Expense ($000):** 13567 **Payroll Expense ($000):** 7200 **Personnel:** 132

★ **SALINE MEMORIAL HOSPITAL (040084)**, 1 Medical Park Drive, Zip 72015–3354; tel. 501/776–6000, **A**10 **F**3 7 11 12 13 15 18 20 22 24 26 29 30 34 35 39 40 43 49 50 56 57 59 62 63 68 70 74 75 76 77 79 81 82 83 84 85 87 89 90 98 103 107 108 110 111 114 115 118 119 129 130 132 135 146 147 148 154 **S** LifePoint Health, Brentwood, TN
Primary Contact: Michael K. Stewart, Chief Executive Officer
COO: Carla Robertson, Chief Operating Officer and Chief Financial Officer
CFO: Carla Robertson, Chief Operating Officer and Chief Financial Officer
CIO: Andy Dick, Director Information Services
CHR: Carol Matthews, Director Human Resources
CNO: Katie Lea, Chief Nursing Officer
Web address: www.salinememorial.org
Control: Corporation, Investor–owned (for–profit) **Service:** General medical and surgical

Staffed Beds: 133 **Admissions:** 6137 **Census:** 72 **Outpatient Visits:** 112563 **Births:** 504 **Total Expense ($000):** 103564 **Payroll Expense ($000):** 48120 **Personnel:** 678

BERRYVILLE—Carroll County

✠ **MERCY HOSPITAL BERRYVILLE (041329)**, 214 Carter Street, Zip 72616–4303; tel. 870/423–3355, **A**1 10 18 **F**3 11 15 28 29 30 34 35 40 41 45 46 48 50 57 59 61 64 71 75 81 85 86 87 93 96 107 108 110 111 114 119 129 130 131 132 133 143 144 145 146 148 153 154 156 **S** Mercy, Chesterfield, MO
Primary Contact: VonDa Moore, Administrator
CFO: Sherry Clouse Day, Vice President Finance
CHR: Taya James, Director
CNO: Michele Gann, Vice President Patient Services
Web address: www.https://www.mercy.net/newsroom/mercy-hospital-berryville-quick-facts/
Control: Church operated, Nongovernment, not–for–profit **Service:** General medical and surgical

Staffed Beds: 25 **Admissions:** 372 **Census:** 3 **Outpatient Visits:** 28746 **Births:** 0 **Total Expense ($000):** 16205 **Payroll Expense ($000):** 7961 **Personnel:** 116

BLYTHEVILLE—Mississippi County

✠ **GREAT RIVER MEDICAL CENTER (040069)**, 1520 North Division Street, Zip 72315–1448, Mailing Address: P.O. Box 108, Zip 72316–0108; tel. 870/838–7300, **A**1 10 **F**3 13 15 29 34 43 45 48 53 57 68 70 76 81 89 90 92 93 107 108 110 111 114 119 148 149 154
Primary Contact: Chris Lee. Raymer, MSN, Chief Executive Officer
COO: Paul Pieffer, Chief Operating Officer
CFO: Randy Nichols, Chief Financial Officer
CIO: Tammy Bratcher, Director System Information Technology
CHR: Cheri Blurton, SPHR,SHRM-SCP, Director Human Resources, HIPAA Privacy Officer
CNO: Felicia Pierce, R.N., Chief Nursing Officer
Web address: www.mchsys.org
Control: County, Government, nonfederal **Service:** General medical and surgical

Staffed Beds: 73 **Admissions:** 1422 **Census:** 10 **Outpatient Visits:** 29341 **Births:** 343 **Total Expense ($000):** 22770 **Payroll Expense ($000):** 9668 **Personnel:** 256

Hospital, Medicare Provider Number, Address, Telephone, Approval, Facility, and Physician Codes, Health Care System

★ American Hospital Association (AHA) membership
☐ The Joint Commission accreditation
○ Healthcare Facilities Accreditation Program
◇ DNV Healthcare Inc. accreditation
⇑ Center for Improvement in Healthcare Quality Accreditation
△ Commission on Accreditation of Rehabilitation Facilities (CARF) accreditation

AR

BOONEVILLE—Logan County

★ **MERCY HOSPITAL BOONEVILLE (041318)**, 880 West Main Street, Zip 72927–3443; tel. 479/675–2800, **A**10 18 **F**3 11 15 35 40 43 45 57 59 62 64 65 68 81 85 107 119 127 133 148 149 **S** Mercy, Chesterfield, MO
Primary Contact: Teresa Williams, R.N., Regional Administrator
CMO: Michael Miranda, Chief of Staff
CHR: Doris Whitaker, Vice President and Manager
CNO: Kimberly Russell, Chief Nursing Officer
Web address: www.mercy.net
Control: Church operated, Nongovernment, not–for–profit **Service**: General medical and surgical

Staffed Beds: 25 **Admissions**: 356 **Census**: 4 **Outpatient Visits**: 15411 **Births**: 0 **Total Expense ($000)**: 14556 **Payroll Expense ($000)**: 5209 **Personnel**: 76

CAMDEN—Ouachita County

★ **OUACHITA COUNTY MEDICAL CENTER (040050)**, 638 California Avenue SW, Zip 71701–4699, Mailing Address: P.O. Box 797, Zip 71711–0797; tel. 870/836–1000, **A**10 20 **F**3 4 5 7 11 13 15 18 20 22 26 29 31 34 35 40 41 43 45 50 57 59 62 63 64 69 70 75 79 81 85 87 93 100 102 107 108 110 111 114 115 119 127 129 130 132 133 135 144 146 147 148 149 150 154
Primary Contact: Peggy L. Abbott, President and Chief Executive Officer
CFO: Robert Anders, Chief Financial Officer
CIO: Kenny Frachiseur, Chief Information Officer
CHR: Mary Bridges, Director Human Resources
CNO: Diane Isaacs, Director of Nursing
Web address: www.ouachitamedcenter.com
Control: Other not–for–profit (including NFP Corporation) **Service**: General medical and surgical

Staffed Beds: 67 **Admissions**: 1717 **Census**: 16 **Outpatient Visits**: 48559 **Births**: 245 **Total Expense ($000)**: 47667 **Payroll Expense ($000)**: 13939 **Personnel**: 371

OUACHITA MEDICAL CENTER See Ouachita County Medical Center

CALICO ROCK—Logan County

IZARD COUNTY MEDICAL CENTER (041306), 61 Grasse Street, Zip 72519, Mailing Address: P.O. Box 438, Zip 72519–0438; tel. 870/297–3726, **A**10 18 **F**3 11 29 30 40 43 45 64 81 93 107 119 127 128 130 133 148 154
Primary Contact: Kim Skidmore, Chief Executive Officer
COO: Cathy Franks RN Chief Operating Officer
CMO: Bethany Knight, M.D., Chief of Staff
CIO: Quentin Wildhagen, Systems Administrator
CHR: Crystal R Moody, Director Human Resources
CNO: Dana Hicks, Director of Nursing
Web address: www.cmcofic.org
Control: Corporation, Investor–owned (for–profit) **Service**: General medical and surgical

Staffed Beds: 20 **Admissions**: 359 **Census**: 4 **Outpatient Visits**: 6689 **Births**: 0 **Personnel**: 108

CLARKSVILLE—Johnson County

★ **JOHNSON REGIONAL MEDICAL CENTER (040002)**, 1100 East Poplar Street, Zip 72830–4419, Mailing Address: P.O. Box 738, Zip 72830–0738; tel. 479/754–5454, **A**10 **F**3 7 11 13 15 29 34 35 40 45 50 51 57 62 64 68 70 75 76 77 79 81 85 90 91 93 96 98 103 104 107 108 110 111 115 119 129 130 131 132 147 148 153 154
Primary Contact: Michael A. Dorsey, FACHE, Chief Executive Officer
CFO: Joe Jeans, CPA, Chief Financial Officer
CIO: Scott Cook, Chief Information Officer
CHR: Betty Collier, Human Resources Officer
CNO: Nancy Hill, R.N., Chief Nursing Officer
Web address: www.jrmc.com
Control: Other not–for–profit (including NFP Corporation) **Service**: General medical and surgical

Staffed Beds: 90 **Admissions**: 2037 **Census**: 29 **Outpatient Visits**: 44424 **Births**: 300 **Total Expense ($000)**: 39118 **Payroll Expense ($000)**: 17419 **Personnel**: 331

CLINTON—Van Buren County

OZARK HEALTH MEDICAL CENTER (041313), Highway 65 South, Zip 72031–9045, Mailing Address: P.O. Box 206, Zip 72031–0206; tel. 501/745–7000, (Total facility includes 118 beds in nursing home–type unit) **A**10 18 **F**11 15 28 29 34 35 40 43 45 57 59 62 64 65 75 79 81 93 107 110 111 114 119 128 132 133 146 156
Primary Contact: David Deaton, Chief Executive Officer
CFO: Mike Deaton, Chief Financial Officer
CMO: Steve Schoettle, M.D., Chief Medical Staff
CHR: Sally D Cassell, Manager Human Resources
CNO: Edna Prosser, Chief Nursing Officer
Web address: www.ozarkhealthinc.com
Control: Other not–for–profit (including NFP Corporation) **Service**: General medical and surgical

Staffed Beds: 143 **Admissions**: 834 **Census**: 97 **Outpatient Visits**: 27924 **Births**: 0 **Total Expense ($000)**: 25846 **Payroll Expense ($000)**: 13530 **Personnel**: 274

CONWAY—Faulkner County

★ **BAPTIST HEALTH MEDICAL CENTER - CONWAY (040154)**, 1555 Exchange Avenue, Zip 72032–7824; tel. 501/585–2000, **A**10 **F**3 13 15 18 20 22 28 29 30 35 40 45 46 51 59 60 64 68 70 74 76 79 81 85 87 107 108 110 111 115 118 119 126 130 133 135 141 146 147 148 **S** Baptist Health, Little Rock, AR
Primary Contact: Tim Bowen, Vice President and Administrator
CNO: Stephana Loyd, Vice President, Chief Nursing Officer
Web address: www.baptist-health.com/location/baptist-health-medical-center-conway-conway
Control: Other not–for–profit (including NFP Corporation) **Service**: General medical and surgical

Staffed Beds: 111 **Admissions**: 3133 **Census**: 27 **Outpatient Visits**: 41591 **Births**: 179 **Total Expense ($000)**: 81431 **Payroll Expense ($000)**: 20616 **Personnel**: 235

☐ **CONWAY BEHAVIORAL HEALTH HOSPITAL (044022)**, 2255 Sturgis Road, Zip 72034–8029; tel. 501/858–3048, **A**1 **F**4 29 98 99 100 101 103 104 105 151 153 **S** Acadia Healthcare Company, Inc., Franklin, TN
Primary Contact: Doris Singleton, Chief Executive Officer
CFO: Andrea Lane, Chief Financial Officer
CMO: Thomas Stinnett, M.D., Chief Medical Officer
CHR: Levi J. King, Director Human Resources
CNO: Beth Williams, R.N., Chief Nursing Officer
Web address: www.conwaybh.com
Control: Corporation, Investor–owned (for–profit) **Service**: Psychiatric

Staffed Beds: 60 **Admissions**: 1428 **Census**: 31 **Outpatient Visits**: 137 **Births**: 0 **Total Expense ($000)**: 10509 **Payroll Expense ($000)**: 5783 **Personnel**: 120

⊞ **CONWAY REGIONAL MEDICAL CENTER (040029)**, 2302 College Avenue, Zip 72034–6297; tel. 501/329–3831, **A**1 10 **F**3 8 11 13 15 17 18 20 22 24 26 28 29 30 31 34 35 37 40 43 45 46 49 50 51 53 56 57 59 61 62 64 70 74 75 76 77 78 79 81 82 85 87 89 97 98 104 107 110 111 115 118 119 126 129 130 131 135 144 146 147 148 149 154 156 157
Primary Contact: Matthew Troup, President and Chief Executive Officer
COO: Alan Finley, Chief Operating Officer
CFO: Troy Brooks, Chief Financial Officer
CMO: James France, M.D., Chief of Staff
CHR: Richard Tyler, Corporate Director Human Resources
CNO: Jacquelyn Wilkerson, R.N., Chief Nursing Officer
Web address: www.conwayregional.org
Control: Other not–for–profit (including NFP Corporation) **Service**: General medical and surgical

Staffed Beds: 150 **Admissions**: 7829 **Census**: 87 **Outpatient Visits**: 112654 **Births**: 1700 **Total Expense ($000)**: 170451 **Payroll Expense ($000)**: 64287 **Personnel**: 1147

CONWAY REGIONAL REHABILITATION HOSPITAL (043033), 2210 Robinson Avenue, Zip 72034–4943; tel. 501/932–3500, **A**10 **F**3 29 90 91 96 130 132 143 154
Primary Contact: Alicia Kunert, MS, Executive Director
COO: Christy Scroggin, Chief Operating Officer
CMO: Roy Denton, M.D., Chief Medical Officer
CNO: Darrallyn Webb, R.N., Chief Nursing Officer
Web address: www.conwayregional.org
Control: Partnership, Investor–owned (for–profit) **Service**: Rehabilitation

Staffed Beds: 26 **Admissions**: 415 **Census**: 15 **Outpatient Visits**: 0 **Births**: 0 **Total Expense ($000)**: 5474 **Payroll Expense ($000)**: 1669 **Personnel**: 38

CROSSETT—Ashley County

★ **ASHLEY COUNTY MEDICAL CENTER (041323)**, 1015 Unity Road, Zip 71635–9443, Mailing Address: P.O. Box 400, Zip 71635–0400; tel. 870/364–4111, **A**10 18 **F**3 11 13 15 18 29 31 34 35 40 45 50 53 56 57 59 62 64 68 70 75 76 77 78 79 81 85 93 98 100 103 104 107 108 110 111 115 119 127 129 130 132 133 148 153 154 156
Primary Contact: Phillip K. Gilmore, Ph.D., FACHE, Chief Executive Officer
CFO: Bill Couch, Chief Financial Officer
CMO: Brad Walsh, M.D., Chief of Staff
CIO: Dan Austin, Manager Data Processing
CHR: Shirley White, Director Human Resources
CNO: Emily Bendinelli, Director of Nurses
Web address: www.acmconline.org
Control: Other not–for–profit (including NFP Corporation) **Service**: General medical and surgical

Staffed Beds: 33 **Admissions**: 1000 **Census**: 15 **Outpatient Visits**: 94668 **Births**: 143 **Total Expense ($000)**: 36192 **Payroll Expense ($000)**: 17613 **Personnel**: 311

Many Facility Codes have changed. Please refer to the AHA Guide Code Chart. © 2019 AHA Guide

DANVILLE—Yell County

★ **CHAMBERS MEMORIAL HOSPITAL (040011)**, 719 Detroit Avenue, Zip 72833–9607, Mailing Address: P.O. Box 639, Zip 72833–0639; tel. 479/495–2241, **A**10 20 **F**3 11 15 29 34 35 40 43 45 57 59 62 68 75 77 81 87 93 96 97 98 103 107 110 114 119 128 130 133 154
Primary Contact: Mike McCoy, Chief Executive Officer
CMO: Thomas Tinnesz, M.D., Chief Medical Officer
CIO: Ken Masters, Director Information Technology
CNO: Joeann Bowerman, Director of Nursing
Web address: www.chambershospital.com
Control: Other not–for–profit (including NFP Corporation) **Service:** General medical and surgical

Staffed Beds: 42 **Admissions:** 1590 **Census:** 12 **Outpatient Visits:** 39898 **Births:** 0 **Total Expense ($000):** 19363 **Payroll Expense ($000):** 9466 **Personnel:** 207

DARDANELLE—Yell County

RIVER VALLEY MEDICAL CENTER (041302), 200 North Third Street, Zip 72834–3802, Mailing Address: P.O. Box 578, Zip 72834–0578; tel. 479/229–4677, (Nonreporting) **A**10 18 **S** Allegiance Health Management, Shreveport, LA
Primary Contact: Vicki Andert, R.N., Chief Executive Officer
CMO: William P Scott, M.D., Chief of Staff
CHR: Kathy Hastin, Administrative Assistant Human Resources
Web address: www.rivervalleymedicalcenter.com/
Control: Corporation, Investor–owned (for–profit) **Service:** General medical and surgical

Staffed Beds: 35

DEWITT—Arkansas County

★ **DEWITT HOSPITAL (041314)**, 1641 South Whitehead Drive, Zip 72042–9481, Mailing Address: P.O. Box 32, Zip 72042–0032; tel. 870/946–3571, (Total facility includes 45 beds in nursing home–type unit) **A**10 18 **F**3 7 11 14 15 34 40 43 55 57 59 65 87 90 107 111 119 127 128 129 130 133 145 149
Primary Contact: Brian Miller, Chief Executive Officer
CFO: Brandon Cotten, Chief Financial Officer
CMO: Stan Burleson, M.D., Chief Medical Staff
CIO: Brian Brooks, Information Manager
CHR: Alisa Brown, Administrative Assistant
CNO: Jerrilyn Horton, R.N., Chief Nursing Officer
Web address: www.dhnh.org
Control: Other not–for–profit (including NFP Corporation) **Service:** General medical and surgical

Staffed Beds: 70 **Admissions:** 284 **Census:** 41 **Outpatient Visits:** 12248 **Births:** 0 **Total Expense ($000):** 13413 **Payroll Expense ($000):** 7510 **Personnel:** 137

DUMAS—Desha County

DELTA MEMORIAL HOSPITAL (041326), 811 South Highway 65, Zip 71639–3006, Mailing Address: P.O. Box 887, Zip 71639–0887; tel. 870/382–4303, (Nonreporting) **A**10 18
Primary Contact: Ashley Anthony, R.N., Chief Executive Officer
CMO: Thomas Lewellen, D.O., Chief of Staff
CIO: Chris McTigrit, Manager Information Technology
CHR: Doris Fortenberry, Coordinator Human Resources
CNO: Dana Miles, Chief Nursing Officer and Chief Clinical Officer
Web address: www.deltamem.com
Control: Other not–for–profit (including NFP Corporation) **Service:** General medical and surgical

Staffed Beds: 25

EL DORADO—Union County

⊞ **MEDICAL CENTER OF SOUTH ARKANSAS (040088)**, 700 West Grove Street, Zip 71730–4416; tel. 870/863–2000, **A**1 10 **F**3 11 13 15 17 18 20 22 24 29 31 34 40 41 43 45 46 50 56 57 59 64 65 70 73 76 78 79 80 81 82 85 89 90 93 96 102 107 108 110 111 115 118 119 130 146 147 149 152 **S** Community Health Systems, Inc., Franklin, TN
Primary Contact: Scott Street, Chief Executive Officer
CFO: Dale Maddox, Chief Financial Officer
CMO: Misty Kneeland, Chief Medical Staff
CIO: Rob Robison, Director Information Technology
CHR: LaKeitha Davis, Director Human Resources
CNO: Kathy Degenstein Gartman, Chief Nursing Officer
Web address: www.themedcenter.net
Control: Corporation, Investor–owned (for–profit) **Service:** General medical and surgical

Staffed Beds: 121 **Admissions:** 3420 **Census:** 37 **Outpatient Visits:** 50378 **Births:** 600 **Total Expense ($000):** 56597 **Payroll Expense ($000):** 19754 **Personnel:** 357

EUREKA SPRINGS—Carroll County

EUREKA SPRINGS HOSPITAL (041304), 24 Norris Street, Zip 72632–3541; tel. 479/253 7400, **A**10 18 **F**3 34 40 43 47 57 83 84 91 93 107 111 114 115 119 128 133 148 154 **S** Allegiance Health Management, Shreveport, LA
CFO: Taylor Smith, Chief Financial Officer
CMO: John House, M.D., Chief of Staff
CIO: Drew Wood, Director Information Technology
CHR: Jodi Smith, Administrative Assistant Human Resources
Web address: www.eurekaspringshospital.com
Control: Corporation, Investor–owned (for–profit) **Service:** General medical and surgical

Staffed Beds: 15 **Admissions:** 379 **Census:** 2 **Outpatient Visits:** 2955 **Births:** 0

FAYETTEVILLE—Washington County

⊞ **ENCOMPASS HEALTH REHABILITATION HOSPITAL, A PARTNER OF WASHINGTON REGIONAL (043032)**, 153 East Monte Painter Drive, Zip 72703–4002; tel. 479/444–2200, **A**1 10 **F**3 29 34 57 75 90 91 96 130 132 149 157 **S** Encompass Health Corporation, Birmingham, AL
Primary Contact: Jack C. Mitchell, FACHE, Chief Executive Officer
CMO: Marty Hurlbut, M.D., Medical Director
CHR: Missy Cole, Director Human Resources
CNO: Miriam Irvin, CNO
Web address: www.https://www.encompasshealth.com/fayettevillerehab
Control: Corporation, Investor–owned (for–profit) **Service:** Rehabilitation

Staffed Beds: 80 **Admissions:** 1619 **Census:** 51 **Outpatient Visits:** 0 **Births:** 0 **Total Expense ($000):** 18545 **Payroll Expense ($000):** 9948 **Personnel:** 206

★ **NORTHWEST HEALTH PHYSICIANS' SPECIALTY HOSPITAL (040152)**, 3873 North Parkview Drive, Zip 72703–6286; tel. 479/571–7070, **A**3 10 **F**3 12 29 40 45 79 81 82 85 107 111 114 119 131 **S** Community Health Systems, Inc., Franklin, TN
Primary Contact: Denten Park, Chief Executive Officer
CFO: Joshua Harmond, Assistant Chief Financial Officer
CNO: Tim Kimball, Chief Nursing Officer
Web address: www.pshfay.com
Control: Corporation, Investor–owned (for–profit) **Service:** Surgical

Staffed Beds: 20 **Admissions:** 1330 **Census:** 6 **Outpatient Visits:** 14115 **Births:** 0 **Total Expense ($000):** 34004 **Payroll Expense ($000):** 7265 **Personnel:** 111

⊞ **SPRINGWOODS BEHAVIORAL HEALTH HOSPITAL (044019)**, 1955 West Truckers Drive, Zip 72704–5637; tel. 479/973–6000, **A**1 10 **F**3 29 34 35 38 42 56 57 98 99 100 103 105 130 132 134 135 143 144 147 149 150 152 153 157 **S** Universal Health Services, Inc., King of Prussia, PA
Primary Contact: Jordon Babcock, Chief Executive Officer
Web address: www.springwoodsbehavioral.com
Control: Corporation, Investor–owned (for–profit) **Service:** Psychiatric

Staffed Beds: 80 **Admissions:** 2260 **Census:** 40 **Outpatient Visits:** 2560 **Births:** 0 **Total Expense ($000):** 15771 **Payroll Expense ($000):** 6671 **Personnel:** 188

☐ **VANTAGE POINT OF NORTHWEST ARKANSAS (044004)**, 4253 North Crossover Road, Zip 72703–4596; tel. 479/521–5731, **A**1 10 **F**30 56 87 98 99 100 101 102 103 130 132 153 **S** Acadia Healthcare Company, Inc., Franklin, TN
Primary Contact: Megan Wedgworth, Chief Executive Officer
CFO: Ben Winbery, Chief Financial Officer
CMO: Norman Snyder, M.D., Medical Director
CIO: Margaret Brown, Director Medical Records
CHR: Kathy Vickers, Director Human Resources
CNO: Suzette Branscum, Director of Nursing
Web address: www.vantagepointnwa.com
Control: Corporation, Investor–owned (for–profit) **Service:** Psychiatric

Staffed Beds: 114 **Admissions:** 2673 **Census:** 95 **Outpatient Visits:** 0 **Births:** 0 **Total Expense ($000):** 20486 **Payroll Expense ($000):** 11431 **Personnel:** 204

⊞ **VETERANS HEALTH CARE SYSTEM OF THE OZARKS**, 1100 North College Avenue, Zip 72703–1944; tel. 479/443–4301, (Nonreporting) **A**1 2 3 5 **S** Department of Veterans Affairs, Washington, DC
Primary Contact: Kelvin L. Parks, Interim Director
CMO: Bonnie Baker, M.D., Chief Medical Services
CIO: Michael Gracie, Chief Information Officer
CHR: Kathryn L Barker, Chief Human Resources Management
Web address: www.fayettevillear.va.gov
Control: Veterans Affairs, Government, federal **Service:** General medical and surgical

Staffed Beds: 72

Hospital, Medicare Provider Number, Address, Telephone, Approval, Facility, and Physician Codes, Health Care System

★ American Hospital Association (AHA) membership
☐ The Joint Commission accreditation
○ Healthcare Facilities Accreditation Program
◇ DNV Healthcare Inc. accreditation
⇑ Center for Improvement in Healthcare Quality Accreditation
△ Commission on Accreditation of Rehabilitation Facilities (CARF) accreditation

AR

☒ **WASHINGTON REGIONAL MEDICAL CENTER (040004)**, 3215 North Hills Boulevard, Zip 72703–4424; tel. 479/463–1000, **A**1 3 10 **F**3 11 13 17 18 20 22 24 26 28 29 30 31 34 35 40 41 43 45 48 49 50 56 57 58 59 60 62 63 64 68 70 71 72 74 75 76 77 78 79 80 81 84 85 86 87 92 100 102 107 108 111 115 118 119 126 129 130 132 135 141 146 147 148 149 154 157
Primary Contact: J. Larry. Shackelford, President and Chief Executive Officer
CFO: Dan Eckels, Chief Financial Officer
CMO: David Ratcliff, M.D., Chief Medical Affairs
CIO: Becky Magee, Chief Information Officer
CHR: Laurie Morrow, Executive Director Human Resources
CNO: Meredith Green, Senior Vice President and Chief Nursing Officer
Web address: www.wregional.com
Control: Other not–for–profit (including NFP Corporation) **Service:** General medical and surgical

Staffed Beds: 378 Admissions: 16367 Census: 187 Outpatient Visits: 157304 Births: 2539 Total Expense ($000): 283646 Payroll Expense ($000): 108443 Personnel: 2743

FORDYCE—Dallas County

★ **DALLAS COUNTY MEDICAL CENTER (041317)**, 201 Clifton Street, Zip 71742–3099; tel. 870/352–6300, **A**10 18 **F**3 11 29 30 32 33 34 35 40 41 43 57 59 68 75 77 87 91 93 97 107 119 127 130 133 146 149
Primary Contact: Kenneth Sanders, Administrator and Chief Executive Officer
CFO: Billie Launius, Director Business Finance
CMO: Michael Payne, M.D., Chief of Staff
CHR: Audrey Allen, Coordinator Benefits
CNO: Hollie Raney, Director of Nursing
Web address: www.dallascountymedicalcenter.com
Control: County, Government, nonfederal **Service:** General medical and surgical

Staffed Beds: 25 Admissions: 146 Census: 1 Outpatient Visits: 33403 Births: 0

FORREST CITY—St. Francis County

☒ **FORREST CITY MEDICAL CENTER (040019)**, 1601 Newcastle Road, Zip 72335–2218; tel. 870/261–0000, **A**1 10 20 **F**3 7 13 15 29 30 34 40 43 45 50 56 57 70 76 77 81 85 87 91 92 93 98 100 102 103 107 108 109 110 111 112 114 119 129 130 135 145 146 147 148 154 155 **S** Quorum Health, Brentwood, TN
Primary Contact: Kevin Decker, Chief Executive Officer
CFO: Misty Gates, Chief Financial Officer
CMO: James DeRossitt, M.D., Chief of Staff
CIO: David Shaw, Director Information Technology
CHR: Sherry McLaughlin, Director Human Resources
CNO: Leslie Harris, MSN, R.N., Chief Nursing Officer
Web address: www.forrestcitymedicalcenter.com
Control: Corporation, Investor–owned (for–profit) **Service:** General medical and surgical

Staffed Beds: 55 Admissions: 2238 Census: 19 Outpatient Visits: 37847 Births: 856 Total Expense ($000): 31162 Payroll Expense ($000): 10432 Personnel: 263

FORT SMITH—Sebastian County

☒ **BAPTIST HEALTH - FORT SMITH (040055)**, 1001 Towson Avenue, Zip 72901–4921, Mailing Address: P.O. Box 2406, Zip 72917–7006; tel. 479/441–4000, (Data for 61 days) **A**1 3 5 10 19 **F**3 8 12 13 14 15 17 18 20 21 22 24 26 28 29 30 31 34 35 40 43 45 46 47 48 49 50 51 53 54 56 58 59 60 64 67 70 72 74 75 76 77 78 79 81 82 85 86 87 89 93 97 98 103 107 108 109 110 111 112 113 114 115 116 117 119 120 121 122 124 126 129 130 144 146 147 148 154 156 **S** Baptist Health, Little Rock, AR
Primary Contact: Brandon Bullard, Interim Chief Executive Officer
COO: Aimee Arzoumanian, Chief Operating Officer
CFO: Brandon Bullard, Chief Financial Officer
CMO: Katherine Irish-Clardy, M.D., Chief Medical Officer
CIO: Tom Sallis, Director Information Systems
CHR: Robert Freeman, Director Human Resources
CNO: Stephanie Whitaker, Chief Nursing Officer
Web address: www.https://www.sparkshealth.com/
Control: Other not–for–profit (including NFP Corporation) **Service:** General medical and surgical

Staffed Beds: 272 Admissions: 2305 Census: 169 Outpatient Visits: 30404 Births: 191 Total Expense ($000): 38308 Payroll Expense ($000): 10525 Personnel: 1136

☐ **CHRISTUS DUBUIS HOSPITAL OF FORT SMITH (042008)**, 7301 Rogers Avenue, 4th Floor, Zip 72903–4100; tel. 479/314–4900, **A**1 10 **F**1 3 29 50 62 68 85 157 **S** LHC Group, Lafayette, LA
Primary Contact: Nancy Owens, Administrator
CFO: Paul Veillon, CPA, Chief Financial Officer
Web address: www.christusdubuis.org/fortsmith
Control: Partnership, Investor–owned (for–profit) **Service:** Acute long–term care hospital

Staffed Beds: 25 Admissions: 73 Census: 19 Outpatient Visits: 0 Births: 0 Total Expense ($000): 5936 Payroll Expense ($000): 3335 Personnel: 49

☒ **ENCOMPASS HEALTH REHABILITATION HOSPITAL OF FORT SMITH (043028)**, 1401 South 'J' Street, Zip 72901–5155; tel. 479/785–3300, **A**1 10 **F**29 30 34 77 90 91 94 95 96 130 132 149 157 **S** Encompass Health Corporation, Birmingham, AL
Primary Contact: Dawn Watts, Chief Executive Officer
CFO: Brenda Forbes, Controller
CMO: Cygnet Schroeder, D.O., Medical Director
CHR: S Janette Daniels, Director Human Resources
Web address: www.healthsouthfortsmith.com
Control: Corporation, Investor–owned (for–profit) **Service:** Rehabilitation

Staffed Beds: 60 Admissions: 1489 Census: 47 Outpatient Visits: 0 Births: 0 Total Expense ($000): 16383 Payroll Expense ($000): 9401 Personnel: 167

☒ **MERCY HOSPITAL FORT SMITH (040062)**, 7301 Rogers Avenue, Zip 72903–4189, Mailing Address: P.O. Box 17000, Zip 72917–7000; tel. 479/314–6000, (Includes MERCY ORTHOPEDIC HOSPITAL FORT SMITH, 3601 South 79th Street, Fort Smith, Arkansas, Zip 72903–6255; tel. 479/709–8500; Ryan Gehrig, President) **A**1 2 10 13 19 **F**3 12 13 15 18 20 22 24 26 28 29 30 31 32 34 35 36 38 40 42 43 44 45 48 49 50 53 56 57 58 59 60 61 62 63 64 65 68 70 71 72 74 75 76 77 78 79 81 82 83 84 85 86 87 89 90 91 93 95 96 102 107 108 109 110 111 114 115 116 117 119 120 121 123 124 129 130 134 135 143 146 147 148 149 154 156 157 **S** Mercy, Chesterfield, MO
Primary Contact: Ryan Gehrig, President
COO: Julianne Stec, Chief Operating Officer
CFO: Greta Wilcher, Senior Vice President and Chief Financial Officer
CMO: David Hunton, M.D., Chief Medical Officer
CHR: Bryan Brown, Executive Director
CNO: Marianne Rataj, Chief Nursing Officer
Web address: www.mercy.net/fortsmithar
Control: Church operated, Nongovernment, not–for–profit **Service:** General medical and surgical

Staffed Beds: 352 Admissions: 16554 Census: 202 Outpatient Visits: 269608 Births: 2364 Total Expense ($000): 333669 Payroll Expense ($000): 119642 Personnel: 1736

☒ **SELECT SPECIALTY HOSPITAL-FORT SMITH (042006)**, 1001 Towson Avenue, 6 Central, Zip 72901–4921; tel. 479/441–3960, **A**1 10 **F**1 3 29 34 45 46 57 74 75 78 79 94 148 **S** Select Medical Corporation, Mechanicsburg, PA
Primary Contact: Shannon Grams, Chief Executive Officer
Web address: www.https://fortsmith.selectspecialtyhospitals.com/
Control: Corporation, Investor–owned (for–profit) **Service:** Acute long–term care hospital

Staffed Beds: 34 Admissions: 309 Census: 22 Outpatient Visits: 0 Births: 0 Total Expense ($000): 11077 Payroll Expense ($000): 4879 Personnel: 76

GRAVETTE—Benton County

OZARKS COMMUNITY HOSPITAL (041331), 1101 Jackson Street Sw, Zip 72736–9121; tel. 479/787–5291, **A**10 18 **F**3 29 34 35 40 44 45 50 56 57 59 64 65 74 75 77 79 81 82 85 87 91 93 96 97 100 104 107 111 115 119 127 128 129 130 131 133 143 148 153 154 157
Primary Contact: Paul Taylor, Administrator
Web address: www.ochonline.com/
Control: Corporation, Investor–owned (for–profit) **Service:** General medical and surgical

Staffed Beds: 25 Admissions: 690 Census: 20 Outpatient Visits: 99424 Births: 1 Total Expense ($000): 49272 Payroll Expense ($000): 20928 Personnel: 270

HARRISON—Boone County

★ **NORTH ARKANSAS REGIONAL MEDICAL CENTER (040017)**, 620 North Main Street, Zip 72601–2911; tel. 870/414–4000, **A**10 **F**3 7 11 13 15 17 18 28 29 30 31 32 34 35 39 40 41 43 45 50 53 56 57 59 62 63 64 65 68 70 73 75 76 77 78 79 81 85 86 87 89 93 97 98 102 103 107 108 110 111 114 115 118 119 120 121 123 127 129 130 131 132 135 144 146 147 148 149 154 156 157
Primary Contact: Vincent Leist, President and Chief Executive Officer
CFO: Deana Thomas, Vice President Finance and Chief Financial Officer
CIO: William J Bogle, Director Information Systems
CNO: Sammie Cribbs, Vice President Clinical Services and Chief Nursing Officer
Web address: www.narmc.com
Control: Other not–for–profit (including NFP Corporation) **Service:** General medical and surgical

Staffed Beds: 113 Admissions: 3388 Census: 24 Outpatient Visits: 113672 Births: 653 Total Expense ($000): 95710 Payroll Expense ($000): 40787 Personnel: 803

Many Facility Codes have changed. Please refer to the AHA Guide Code Chart.   © 2019 AHA Guide

AR

HEBER SPRINGS—Cleburne County

✠ **BAPTIST HEALTH MEDICAL CENTER-HEBER SPRINGS (041312)**, 1800 Bypass Road, Zip 72543–9135; tel. 501/887–3000, **A**1 10 18 **F**3 8 11 14 15 18 28 29 30 31 34 35 36 40 43 45 48 50 51 57 59 64 68 75 77 78 79 81 82 85 93 96 102 107 110 111 115 116 117 127 129 131 132 133 143 146 149 154 156 157 **S** Baptist Health, Little Rock, AR
Primary Contact: Kevin L. Storey, Vice President and Administrator
Web address: www.baptist-health.com/maps-directions/bhmc-heber-springs
Control: Other not–for–profit (including NFP Corporation) **Service:** General medical and surgical

Staffed Beds: 25 **Admissions:** 847 **Census:** 9 **Outpatient Visits:** 33067 **Births:** 0 **Total Expense ($000):** 22000 **Payroll Expense ($000):** 7562 **Personnel:** 156	

HELENA—Phillips County

✠ **HELENA REGIONAL MEDICAL CENTER (040085)**, 1801 Martin Luther King Drive, Zip 72342, Mailing Address: P.O. Box 788, Zip 72342–0788; tel. 870/338–5800, **A**1 10 20 **F**3 11 13 15 29 34 40 50 59 62 70 74 76 79 81 82 86 87 89 91 93 97 107 108 111 113 114 119 130 132 133 135 145 146 147 148 **S** Quorum Health, Brentwood, TN
Primary Contact: Amy Rice, Interim Chief Executive Officer
CFO: Amy Rice, Chief Financial Officer
CIO: Christopher Hunt, Director, Information Technologies, FISO
CHR: Juril Fonzie, Director Human Resources
CNO: Judith LeAnn Gerlach, Chief Nursing Officer
Web address: www.helenarmc.com
Control: Corporation, Investor–owned (for–profit) **Service:** General medical and surgical

Staffed Beds: 105 **Admissions:** 1449 **Census:** 11 **Outpatient Visits:** 41299 **Births:** 198 **Total Expense ($000):** 26852 **Payroll Expense ($000):** 9542 **Personnel:** 142	

HOPE—Hempstead County

⇑ **WADLEY REGIONAL MEDICAL CENTER AT HOPE (040153)**, 2001 South Main Street, Zip 71801–8194; tel. 870/722–3800, **A**10 21 **F**3 11 15 18 29 34 35 40 50 56 57 59 64 70 86 93 98 103 107 110 111 114 119 127 130 **S** Steward Health Care System, LLC, Dallas, TX
Primary Contact: Thomas D. Gilbert, FACHE, Chief Executive Officer
CFO: Bonny Sorensen, Chief Financial Officer
CIO: Matt Kesterson, Director Information Services
CHR: Debby Butler, Director Human Resources
CNO: Shelly Strayhorn, R.N., Chief Nursing Officer
Web address: www.wadleyhealthathope.com
Control: Corporation, Investor–owned (for–profit) **Service:** General medical and surgical

Staffed Beds: 79 **Admissions:** 924 **Census:** 13 **Outpatient Visits:** 25815 **Births:** 0 **Total Expense ($000):** 13741 **Payroll Expense ($000):** 6723 **Personnel:** 133	

HOT SPRINGS—Garland County

✠ **CHI ST. VINCENT HOT SPRINGS (040026)**, 300 Werner Street, Zip 71913–6406; tel. 501/622–1000, **A**1 2 10 19 **F**3 11 12 13 15 18 20 22 24 26 28 29 30 31 34 35 38 40 43 47 49 50 51 56 57 59 62 64 65 66 68 69 70 71 74 75 76 77 78 79 81 82 84 85 86 87 89 93 107 108 110 111 112 114 115 116 117 118 119 120 121 123 124 130 132 135 146 147 148 149 150 154 156 157 **S** CommonSpirit Health, Chicago, IL
Primary Contact: Douglas B. Ross, President
CFO: Shawn Barnett, Senior Vice President and Chief Financial Officer
CIO: Tracy Kirby, Assistant Vice President Business Relationship Management
CHR: Aaron Austin, Market Vice President Human Resources
CNO: Bryan Williams, R.N., Vice President Patient Care Services
Web address: www.chistvincent.com/Hospitals/st-vincent-hot-springs
Control: Church operated, Nongovernment, not–for–profit **Service:** General medical and surgical

Staffed Beds: 241 **Admissions:** 11949 **Census:** 140 **Outpatient Visits:** 185136 **Births:** 1032 **Total Expense ($000):** 194663 **Payroll Expense ($000):** 69170 **Personnel:** 991	

☐ **CHI ST. VINCENT HOT SPRINGS REHABILITATION HOSPITAL (043035)**, 1636 Higdon Ferry Road, Zip 71913–6912; tel. 501/651–2000, (Nonreporting) **A**1 **S** Encompass Health Corporation, Birmingham, AL
Primary Contact: Janette Daniels, Chief Executive Officer
Web address: www.https://www.encompasshealth.com
Control: Corporation, Investor–owned (for–profit) **Service:** Rehabilitation

Staffed Beds: 40	

✠ △ **NATIONAL PARK MEDICAL CENTER (040078)**, 1910 Malvern Avenue, Zip 71901–7799; tel. 501/321–1000, **A**1 7 10 19 **F**3 11 12 13 15 17 18 20 22 24 28 29 30 31 34 35 40 45 46 47 48 49 56 57 59 64 70 73 74 75 78 79 81 85 87 90 92 93 98 103 107 110 111 115 119 124 130 131 132 146 148 156 **S** LifePoint Health, Brentwood, TN
Primary Contact: Jerry D. Mabry, FACHE, Chief Executive Officer
COO: Brian Bell, Associate Administrator and Chief Operating Officer
CFO: Robbie Pettey, Chief Financial Officer
CMO: Robert Breving, M.D., Chief of Staff
CIO: Brian Coffman, Director Information System
CHR: Tina Albright, Director Human Resources
CNO: Patsy Sue Crumpton, R.N., Chief Nursing Officer
Web address: www.nationalparkmedical.com
Control: Corporation, Investor–owned (for–profit) **Service:** General medical and surgical

Staffed Beds: 181 **Admissions:** 6631 **Census:** 107 **Outpatient Visits:** 59161 **Births:** 346 **Total Expense ($000):** 89417 **Payroll Expense ($000):** 33315 **Personnel:** 631	

HOT SPRINGS NATIONAL PARK—Garland County

✠ **CHRISTUS DUBUIS HOSPITAL OF HOT SPRINGS (042004)**, 300 Werner Street, 3rd Floor East, Zip 71913–6406; tel. 501/609–4300, **A**1 10 **F**1 3 29 130 135 **S** LHC Group, Lafayette, LA
Primary Contact: Cleta Munholland, Interim Administrator
CFO: Paul Veillon, CPA, Chief Financial Officer
CIO: David Cook, Manager Information Systems
Web address: www.christusdubuis.org/hotsprings
Control: Partnership, Investor–owned (for–profit) **Service:** Acute long–term care hospital

Staffed Beds: 27 **Admissions:** 171 **Census:** 11 **Outpatient Visits:** 0 **Births:** 0 **Total Expense ($000):** 6027 **Payroll Expense ($000):** 2763 **Personnel:** 37	

★ **LEVI HOSPITAL (040132)**, 300 Prospect Avenue, Zip 71901–4097; tel. 501/624–1281, **A**10 **F**3 40 57 59 64 93 98 102 103 104 107 130 131 132 153
Primary Contact: Patrick G. McCabe Jr, FACHE, President and Chief Executive Officer
CFO: Stuart Lisko, Vice President, Chief Financial Officer and Compliance Officer
CMO: P Ross Bandy, M.D., Chief Medical Officer and Chief of Staff
CIO: Stuart Lisko, Vice President, Chief Financial Officer and Compliance Officer
CHR: Susan Kramer, Director of Human Resources
CNO: Steven Boyd, R.N., Nurse Executive
Web address: www.levihospital.com
Control: Other not–for–profit (including NFP Corporation) **Service:** Psychiatric

Staffed Beds: 35 **Admissions:** 1259 **Census:** 14 **Outpatient Visits:** 19520 **Births:** 0 **Total Expense ($000):** 8116 **Payroll Expense ($000):** 4245 **Personnel:** 92	

JACKSONVILLE—Pulaski County

NORTH METRO MEDICAL CENTER (040074), 1400 West Braden Street, Zip 72076–3788; tel. 501/985–7000, **A**10 **F**3 6 9 10 11 12 14 15 29 30 34 35 38 40 41 50 56 57 59 62 64 65 68 70 77 82 83 84 85 86 87 97 98 100 101 102 103 106 107 108 110 115 119 130 146 147 148 149 150 154 156 157 158 **S** Allegiance Health Management, Shreveport, LA
Primary Contact: Dale Anderson, R.N., Chief Executive Officer
CFO: Lynn Muller, Chief Financial Officer
CMO: Ann Layton, M.D., Chief of Staff
CHR: Jane Rockwell, Director Support Services
Web address: www.northmetromed.com
Control: Corporation, Investor–owned (for–profit) **Service:** Psychiatric

Staffed Beds: 113 **Admissions:** 1550 **Census:** 33 **Outpatient Visits:** 24020 **Births:** 0 **Total Expense ($000):** 30198 **Payroll Expense ($000):** 13138 **Personnel:** 207	

JONESBORO—Craighead County

ARKANSAS CONTINUED CARE HOSPITAL (042013), 3024 Red Wolf Boulevard, Zip 72401–7415; tel. 870/819–4040, (Nonreporting) **A**22 **S** Community Hospital Corporation, Plano, TX
Primary Contact: Sally A. Parnell, R.N., Interim Chief Executive Officer
Control: Other not–for–profit (including NFP Corporation) **Service:** Acute long–term care hospital

Staffed Beds: 44	

AR

✠ **ENCOMPASS HEALTH REHABILITATION HOSPITAL OF JONESBORO (043029)**, 1201 Fleming Avenue, Zip 72401–4311, Mailing Address: P.O. Box 1680, Zip 72403–1680; tel. 870/932–0440, (Nonreporting) **A**1 10 **S** Encompass Health Corporation, Birmingham, AL
Primary Contact: Donna Harris, Chief Executive Officer
CFO: Allan Jones, Controller
CMO: Virendar Verma, M.D., Medical Director
CHR: Tammy Barley, Director, Human Resources
CNO: Becky Kimble, R.N., Chief Nursing Officer
Web address: www.healthsouthjonesboro.com
Control: Corporation, Investor–owned (for–profit) **Service**: Rehabilitation

Staffed Beds: 67

✠ **NEA BAPTIST MEMORIAL HOSPITAL (040118)**, 4800 East Johnson Avenue, Zip 72401–8413; tel. 870/936–1000, **A**1 3 5 10 **F**3 11 12 13 15 17 18 20 22 24 26 28 29 30 31 34 39 40 43 45 46 48 49 57 58 59 60 74 75 77 78 79 81 82 84 85 86 87 90 93 96 97 107 108 110 111 115 119 120 121 123 124 126 129 130 135 146 148 **S** Baptist Memorial Health Care Corporation, Memphis, TN
Primary Contact: Brad Parsons, FACHE, Administrator and Chief Executive Officer
CFO: Kyle Sanders, Chief Financial Officer
CMO: Stephen Woodruff, M.D., Chief Medical Officer
CIO: Terry Crider, Information Technology Site Manager
CHR: James Keller, Director Human Resources
CNO: Paula Grimes, R.N., MSN, Chief Nursing Officer
Web address: www.neabaptist.com
Control: Other not–for–profit (including NFP Corporation) **Service**: General medical and surgical

Staffed Beds: 228 **Admissions**: 11183 **Census**: 143 **Outpatient Visits**: 98639 **Births**: 807 **Total Expense ($000)**: 181401 **Payroll Expense ($000)**: 57207 **Personnel**: 986

✠ **ST. BERNARDS MEDICAL CENTER (040020)**, 225 East Jackson Avenue, Zip 72401–3119; tel. 870/207–4100, **A**1 2 3 5 10 13 19 **F**3 5 11 12 13 15 17 18 19 20 22 24 26 27 28 29 30 31 32 34 35 38 39 40 43 44 45 46 48 49 50 51 53 54 55 56 57 58 59 60 62 63 64 66 68 70 71 72 74 75 76 77 78 79 81 82 83 84 85 86 87 89 91 92 93 97 98 100 101 102 103 104 105 107 108 109 110 111 114 115 116 117 118 119 120 121 123 124 126 129 130 131 132 134 135 141 145 146 147 148 149 154 156 157
Primary Contact: Chris B. Barber, FACHE, President and Chief Executive Officer
COO: Michael K Givens, FACHE, Administrator
CFO: Ben Barylske, Chief Financial Officer
CMO: Kasey Holder, M.D., Vice President Medical Affairs
CIO: Josh Melton, Chief Information Officer
CHR: Lori J. Smith, Vice President Human Resources
CNO: Susan Greenwood, R.N., Vice President and Chief Nursing Officer
Web address: www.stbernards.info
Control: Church operated, Nongovernment, not–for–profit **Service**: General medical and surgical

Staffed Beds: 386 **Admissions**: 17877 **Census**: 223 **Outpatient Visits**: 315039 **Births**: 1520 **Total Expense ($000)**: 324743

LAKE VILLAGE—Chicot County

★ **CHICOT MEMORIAL MEDICAL CENTER (041328)**, 2729 Highway 65 and 82 South, Zip 71653; tel. 870/265–5351, **A**10 18 **F**3 7 11 15 16 29 34 35 39 40 43 49 53 57 59 62 64 66 68 75 77 80 81 82 85 86 87 89 93 97 107 110 111 119 127 129 130 132 133 146 147 148 154
Primary Contact: Chris Auerswald, Interim Chief Executive Officer and Chief Financial Officer
CFO: Vicki Allen, Chief Financial Officer
CMO: Michael Bradley Mayfield, M.D., Chief of Staff
CIO: David Andrews, Manager Information Systems
CNO: Eric Selby, R.N., Chief Nursing Officer
Web address: www.chicotmemorial.com
Control: Other not–for–profit (including NFP Corporation) **Service**: General medical and surgical

Staffed Beds: 25 **Admissions**: 681 **Census**: 9 **Outpatient Visits**: 20340 **Births**: 0 **Total Expense ($000)**: 18375 **Payroll Expense ($000)**: 8407 **Personnel**: 162

SOUTHEAST REHABILITATION HOSPITAL (043034), 2729-A Highway 65 and 82 South, Zip 71653; tel. 870/265–4333, **A**10 **F**3 28 29 34 35 90
Primary Contact: Catherine M. Waldrop, Administrator
CNO: Michael Vaughn, Director of Nursing
Web address: www.southeastrehab.com
Control: Partnership, Investor–owned (for–profit) **Service**: Rehabilitation

Staffed Beds: 10 **Admissions**: 222 **Census**: 6 **Outpatient Visits**: 0 **Births**: 0 **Total Expense ($000)**: 963 **Payroll Expense ($000)**: 515 **Personnel**: 57

LITTLE ROCK—Pulaski County

ALLEGIANCE SPECIALTY HOSPITAL OF LITTLE ROCK See Cornerstone Hospital of Little Rock

✠ **ARKANSAS CHILDREN'S HOSPITAL (043300)**, 1 Children's Way, Zip 72202–3500; tel. 501/364–1100, **A**1 3 10 **F**3 7 11 16 17 19 21 23 25 27 28 29 30 31 32 34 35 38 39 40 41 43 45 46 48 50 53 54 55 57 58 59 60 64 68 72 74 75 77 78 79 80 81 82 84 85 86 87 88 89 90 91 92 93 94 96 97 102 107 108 111 115 119 126 129 130 131 132 134 135 136 137 138 146 149 150 154 155 156
Primary Contact: Marcella Doderer, FACHE, President and Chief Executive Officer
COO: Chanda Cashen Chacon, Executive Vice President and Chief Operating Officer
CFO: Gena Wingfield, Senior Vice President and Chief Financial Officer
CMO: Greg Sharp, M.D., Senior Vice President and Chief Medical Officer
CIO: Jonathan Goldberg, Senior Vice President and Chief Information Officer
CHR: Jimmy Duncan, Senior Vice President and Chief People Officer
CNO: Lee Anne Eddy, Senior Vice President and Chief Nursing Officer
Web address: www.archildrens.org
Control: Other not–for–profit (including NFP Corporation) **Service**: Children's general medical and surgical

Staffed Beds: 336 **Admissions**: 15380 **Census**: 230 **Outpatient Visits**: 375132 **Births**: 0 **Total Expense ($000)**: 532414 **Payroll Expense ($000)**: 210872 **Personnel**: 3888

☐ **ARKANSAS HEART HOSPITAL (040134)**, 1701 South Shackleford Road, Zip 72211–4335; tel. 501/219–7000, **A**1 3 5 10 **F**3 11 12 17 18 20 22 24 26 28 29 30 34 35 40 45 46 50 53 54 57 59 64 68 75 81 87 107 108 111 115 119 127 130 135 148 154 156
Primary Contact: Bruce Murphy, M.D., President and Chief Executive Officer
Web address: www.arheart.com
Control: Partnership, Investor–owned (for–profit) **Service**: Heart

Staffed Beds: 110 **Admissions**: 6152 **Census**: 54 **Outpatient Visits**: 213835 **Births**: 0 **Total Expense ($000)**: 192354 **Payroll Expense ($000)**: 54674 **Personnel**: 1100

☐ **ARKANSAS STATE HOSPITAL (044011)**, 305 South Palm Street, Zip 72205–5432; tel. 501/686–9000, **A**1 3 5 10 **F**11 29 30 50 57 59 65 75 86 87 97 98 99 100 101 102 106 130 132 135 143 146 148 154
Primary Contact: James Scoggins, Interim Chief Executive Officer
CFO: Gary W Hollis, Comptroller
CMO: Steven Domon, M.D., Medical Director
CIO: Tina Grissom, Chief Information Technology Officer
CHR: Donna Sadler, Director Human Resources
CNO: James Scoggins, Director of Nursing
Web address: www.https://humanservices.arkansas.gov/about-dhs/dbhs/arkansas-state-hospital
Control: State, Government, nonfederal **Service**: Psychiatric

Staffed Beds: 222 **Admissions**: 504 **Census**: 204 **Outpatient Visits**: 111 **Births**: 0 **Total Expense ($000)**: 49850 **Payroll Expense ($000)**: 25186 **Personnel**: 658

★ **BAPTIST HEALTH EXTENDED CARE HOSPITAL (042012)**, 9601 Baptist Health Drive, Zip 72205–7202; tel. 501/202–1070, **A**10 **F**1 3 29 31 77 87 130 148 158 **S** Baptist Health, Little Rock, AR
Primary Contact: Lee Gentry, FACHE, Vice President and Administrator
CFO: Robert C Roberts, Vice President
CMO: Gail McCracken, M.D., Medical Director
CIO: David House, Vice President
CHR: Anthony Kendall, Vice President Human Resources
CNO: Christopher Cox, Chief Nursing Officer
Web address: www.baptist-health.com/maps-directions/bh_extended_care/default.aspx
Control: Other not–for–profit (including NFP Corporation) **Service**: Acute long–term care hospital

Staffed Beds: 55 **Admissions**: 382 **Census**: 31 **Outpatient Visits**: 0 **Births**: 0 **Total Expense ($000)**: 17983 **Payroll Expense ($000)**: 8317 **Personnel**: 106

✠ **BAPTIST HEALTH MEDICAL CENTER-LITTLE ROCK (040114)**, 9601 Baptist Health Drive, Zip 72205–7299; tel. 501/202–2000, **A**1 3 5 10 **F**3 4 5 7 8 11 12 13 15 17 18 20 22 24 26 28 29 30 31 32 34 35 36 37 38 40 43 44 45 46 47 48 49 50 54 56 57 58 59 60 61 62 64 65 67 68 70 72 73 74 75 76 77 78 79 81 82 84 85 86 87 89 93 98 100 101 102 103 104 107 108 110 111 114 115 119 126 128 129 130 131 132 134 135 137 143 144 146 147 148 154 **S** Baptist Health, Little Rock, AR
Primary Contact: Greg Crain, FACHE, Senior Vice President and Administrator
CFO: Robert C Roberts, Senior Vice President Financial Services
CMO: Anthony Bennett, M.D., Chief Clinical Affairs
CIO: David House, Vice President and Chief Information Officer
CHR: Anthony Kendall, Vice President Human Resources
CNO: Michele Diedrich, R.N., Chief Nursing Officer, Vice President Patient Care
Web address: www.baptist-health.org/maps-directions/bhmc-lr
Control: Other not–for–profit (including NFP Corporation) **Service**: General medical and surgical

Staffed Beds: 682 **Admissions**: 29683 **Census**: 447 **Outpatient Visits**: 142885 **Births**: 2810 **Total Expense ($000)**: 540015 **Payroll Expense ($000)**: 168070 **Personnel**: 2672

Many Facility Codes have changed. Please refer to the AHA Guide Code Chart. © 2019 AHA Guide

⊠ △ **BAPTIST HEALTH REHABILITATION INSTITUTE (043026)**, 9501 Baptist Health Drive, Zip 72205–6225; tel. 501/202–7000, **A**1 3 5 7 10 **F**29 30 34 35 50 53 64 75 86 87 90 91 93 95 96 130 132 143 **S** Baptist Health, Little Rock, AR
Primary Contact: Julie Nix, Vice President and Administrator
CFO: Robert C Roberts, Senior Vice President
CIO: David House, Vice President and Chief Information Officer
CHR: Anthony Kendall, Vice President Human Resources
Web address: www.baptist-health.com/locations/accesspoint. aspx?accessPointID=202
Control: Other not–for–profit (including NFP Corporation) **Service**: Rehabilitation

Staffed Beds: 120 **Admissions**: 1434 **Census**: 51 **Outpatient Visits**: 91270 **Births**: 0 **Total Expense ($000)**: 31803 **Payroll Expense ($000)**: 15286 **Personnel**: 223

⊠ △ **CENTRAL ARKANSAS VETERANS HEALTHCARE SYSTEM**, 4300 West Seventh Street, Zip 72205–5446; tel. 501/257–1000, (Includes NORTH LITTLE ROCK DIVISION, 2200 Fort Roots Drive, North Little Rock, Arkansas, Zip 72114–1706; tel. 501/661–1202) (Total facility includes 152 beds in nursing home–type unit) **A**1 2 3 5 7 8 **F**2 3 5 8 15 17 18 20 22 26 28 29 30 31 33 34 35 36 38 39 40 45 46 49 50 51 54 55 56 57 58 59 60 61 62 63 64 65 66 68 70 71 74 75 77 78 79 81 82 83 84 85 86 87 91 92 93 94 96 97 98 100 101 102 104 105 106 107 108 109 110 111 114 115 119 120 126 127 128 129 130 132 133 135 143 144 146 147 148 149 150 151 152 153 154 157 158 **S** Department of Veterans Affairs, Washington, DC
Primary Contact: Margie A. Scott, M.D., Director
CFO: Colonel Nate Todd, Chief Financial Officer
CIO: Jim Hall, Acting Chief Information Officer
CHR: Richard Nelson, Chief of Human Resources Management Services
Web address: www.littlerock.va.gov/
Control: Veterans Affairs, Government, federal **Service**: General medical and surgical

Staffed Beds: 551 **Admissions**: 12106 **Census**: 344 **Outpatient Visits**: 1359963 **Births**: 0 **Total Expense ($000)**: 662034 **Payroll Expense ($000)**: 263443 **Personnel**: 3242

⊠ **CHI ST. VINCENT INFIRMARY MEDICAL CENTER (040007)**, Two St Vincent Circle, Zip 72205–5499; tel. 501/552–3000, **A**1 3 5 10 **F**3 11 13 15 17 18 20 22 24 26 28 29 30 31 34 35 37 40 43 44 45 46 48 49 50 52 53 54 56 57 59 60 61 62 64 66 67 68 70 72 74 75 76 77 78 79 80 81 82 84 85 86 87 91 93 96 97 98 100 102 104 107 108 111 114 115 116 117 118 119 126 129 130 132 135 143 144 146 147 148 149 157 **S** CommonSpirit Health, Chicago, IL
Primary Contact: Chris Stines, President
CFO: Shawn Barnett, Senior Vice President and Chief Financial Officer
CIO: Tracy Kirby, Assistant Vice President Business Relationship Management
CHR: Aaron Austin, Market Vice President Human Resources
CNO: Kathy E. Neely, R.N., Interim Vice President Patient Care Services
Web address: www.chistvincent.com/
Control: Church operated, Nongovernment, not–for–profit **Service**: General medical and surgical

Staffed Beds: 355 **Admissions**: 19582 **Census**: 294 **Outpatient Visits**: 153817 **Births**: 704 **Total Expense ($000)**: 411538 **Payroll Expense ($000)**: 171258 **Personnel**: 1738

CORNERSTONE HOSPITAL OF LITTLE ROCK (042010), 2 Saint Vincent Circle, 6th Floor, Zip 72205–5423; tel. 501/265–0600, **A**10 22 **F**1 3 29 85 **S** Cornerstone Healthcare Group, Dallas, TX
Primary Contact: James H. Rogers, FACHE, Chief Executive Officer
CNO: Joy Miller, Chief Nursing Officer
Web address: www.chghospitals.com/littlerock/
Control: Corporation, Investor–owned (for–profit) **Service**: Acute long–term care hospital

Staffed Beds: 30 **Admissions**: 373 **Census**: 25 **Outpatient Visits**: 0 **Births**: 0 **Total Expense ($000)**: 10529 **Payroll Expense ($000)**: 5897 **Personnel**: 92

☐ **PINNACLE POINTE HOSPITAL (044013)**, 11501 Financial Center Parkway, Zip 72211–3715; tel. 501/223–3322, **A**1 10 **F**5 29 34 35 38 50 75 87 98 99 101 102 105 130 134 143 **S** Universal Health Services, Inc., King of Prussia, PA
Primary Contact: Shane Frazier, Chief Executive Officer
CFO: Gina Dailey, Chief Financial Officer
CMO: Ben Nimmo, M.D., Medical Director
CIO: James L Howe, Director Human Resources
CHR: James L Howe, Director Human Resources
CNO: Bobby Alexander, R.N., Chief Nursing Officer
Web address: www.pinnaclepointehospital.com
Control: Corporation, Investor–owned (for–profit) **Service**: Children's hospital psychiatric

Staffed Beds: 127 **Admissions**: 3011 **Census**: 112 **Outpatient Visits**: 0 **Births**: 0 **Total Expense ($000)**: 19600 **Payroll Expense ($000)**: 11944 **Personnel**: 238

⊠ **UAMS MEDICAL CENTER (040016)**, 4301 West Markham Street, Zip 72205–7101; tel. 501/686–7000, **A**1 3 5 8 10 **F**3 11 12 13 15 17 18 20 22 24 26 29 30 31 34 40 43 44 45 46 47 48 49 50 52 53 54 55 56 57 58 59 60 61 64 68 70 71 72 73 74 75 76 77 78 79 80 81 82 84 85 86 87 91 92 93 94 96 97 98 99 100 101 102 103 104 105 106 107 108 110 111 114 115 116 117 118 119 120 121 123 124 126 127 128 129 130 131 132 135 136 138 139 141 142 146 147 148 149 153 154 156
Primary Contact: Richard Turnage, M.D., Chief Executive Officer
COO: Timothy Hill, Chief Operating Officer
CFO: William Bowes, Chief Financial Officer
CMO: Nicholas P Lang, M.D., Chief Medical Officer
CHR: Jeff Risinger, Director Human Resources
CNO: Mary Helen Forrest, R.N., Chief Nursing Officer
Web address: www.uams.edu/medcenter
Control: State, Government, nonfederal **Service**: General medical and surgical

Staffed Beds: 508 **Admissions**: 25223 **Census**: 418 **Outpatient Visits**: 562632 **Births**: 3390 **Total Expense ($000)**: 1037197 **Payroll Expense ($000)**: 438076 **Personnel**: 6161

MAGNOLIA—Columbia County

★ **MAGNOLIA REGIONAL MEDICAL CENTER (040067)**, 101 Hospital Drive, Zip 71753–2415, Mailing Address: P.O. Box 629, Zip 71754–0629; tel. 870/235–3000, **A**3 10 20 **F**3 11 13 15 29 31 34 35 40 43 45 50 59 62 64 70 76 81 87 93 107 108 110 111 115 119 129 130 132 133 146 147 148 149
Primary Contact: Rex Jones, Chief Executive Officer
CFO: Roxane Stewart, Chief Financial Officer
CMO: James W Chambliss, Chief of Staff
CHR: Shawnee Cooper, Director Human Resources
CNO: Joycelyn Watkins, R.N., Chief Nursing Officer
Web address: www.magnoliarmc.org
Control: City, Government, nonfederal **Service**: General medical and surgical

Staffed Beds: 36 **Admissions**: 1296 **Census**: 11 **Outpatient Visits**: 26543 **Births**: 195 **Total Expense ($000)**: 23737 **Payroll Expense ($000)**: 11016 **Personnel**: 202

MALVERN—Hot Spring County

★ **BAPTIST HEALTH MEDICAL CENTER-HOT SPRING COUNTY (040076)**, 1001 Schneider Drive, Zip 72104–4811; tel. 501/332–1000, **A**10 **F**3 11 12 15 29 30 34 35 40 43 45 57 59 64 70 75 81 93 98 102 106 107 110 111 115 119 130 132 146 152 154 155 156 **S** Baptist Health, Little Rock, AR
Primary Contact: Sheila Williams, Vice President and Administrator
CMO: Allen Gerber, M.D., Chief of Staff
CHR: Kelli Hopkins, Director Human Resources
CNO: Dee Schall, R.N., Chief Nursing Officer
Web address: www.https://www.baptist-health.com/location/baptist-health-medical-center-hot-spring-county-hot-spring-county
Control: Other not–for–profit (including NFP Corporation) **Service**: General medical and surgical

Staffed Beds: 72 **Admissions**: 2304 **Census**: 26 **Outpatient Visits**: 23243 **Births**: 0 **Total Expense ($000)**: 21969 **Payroll Expense ($000)**: 8886 **Personnel**: 174

MAUMELLE—Pulaski County

☐ **METHODIST BEHAVIORAL HOSPITAL OF ARKANSAS (044017)**, 1601 Murphy Drive, Zip 72113–6187; tel. 501/803–3388, **A**1 10 **F**98 99 104 153 154
Primary Contact: Andy Altom, President and Chief Executive Officer
Web address: www.https://www.methodistfamily.org/
Control: Other not–for–profit (including NFP Corporation) **Service**: Children's hospital psychiatric

Staffed Beds: 60 **Admissions**: 1949 **Census**: 53 **Outpatient Visits**: 88501 **Births**: 0 **Total Expense ($000)**: 21308 **Payroll Expense ($000)**: 8610 **Personnel**: 115

MCGEHEE—Desha County

★ **MCGEHEE HOSPITAL (041308)**, 900 South Third, Zip 71654–2562, Mailing Address: P.O. Box 351, Zip 71654–0351; tel. 870/222–5600, **A**10 18 **F**3 11 29 40 57 59 62 64 68 107 114 119 132 133 135 146 148 154
Primary Contact: John E. Heard, Chief Executive Officer
CFO: Teresa Morgan, Chief Financial Officer
CMO: James Young, M.D., Chief of Staff
CIO: Shaun Perry, Chief Information Officer
CNO: Sarah Calvert, Chief Nursing Officer
Control: Other not–for–profit (including NFP Corporation) **Service**: General medical and surgical

Staffed Beds: 25 **Admissions**: 260 **Census**: 3 **Outpatient Visits**: 24076 **Births**: 0 **Total Expense ($000)**: 13202 **Payroll Expense ($000)**: 6147 **Personnel**: 138

AR

Hospital, Medicare Provider Number, Address, Telephone, Approval, Facility, and Physician Codes, Health Care System

★ American Hospital Association (AHA) membership ○ Healthcare Facilities Accreditation Program ⇑ Center for Improvement in Healthcare Quality Accreditation
☐ The Joint Commission accreditation ◇ DNV Healthcare Inc. accreditation △ Commission on Accreditation of Rehabilitation Facilities (CARF) accreditation

MENA—Polk County

★ **MENA REGIONAL HEALTH SYSTEM (040015)**, 311 North Morrow Street, Zip 71953–2516; tel. 479/394–6100, **A**10 20 **F**3 4 11 13 15 29 30 34 35 40 43 45 56 57 59 64 68 70 75 76 77 79 81 86 87 90 91 93 96 98 100 101 103 104 107 108 110 111 115 119 129 130 131 144 146 147 149
Primary Contact: Jay Quebedeaux, Chief Executive Officer
CFO: Mark Henke, Chief Financial Officer
CMO: Richard Lochala, Chief of Staff
CIO: Nicholas Dunn, Director Information Systems
CHR: Chandler Cox, Director Human Resources
CNO: Teresa Wise, R.N., Chief Nursing Officer
Web address: www.menaregional.com
Control: City, Government, nonfederal **Service**: General medical and surgical

Staffed Beds: 65 **Admissions**: 1525 **Census**: 24 **Outpatient Visits**: 34788 **Births**: 255 **Total Expense ($000)**: 28849 **Payroll Expense ($000)**: 14383 **Personnel**: 293

MONTICELLO—Drew County

★ **DREW MEMORIAL HEALTH SYSTEM (040051)**, 778 Scogin Drive, Zip 71655–5729; tel. 870/367–2411, **A**10 20 **F**11 13 15 18 29 30 31 34 35 39 40 50 57 59 62 68 70 75 76 77 78 79 81 85 86 87 93 94 96 100 102 107 111 115 119 128 129 130 132 133 135 143 147 148 153 154 156
Primary Contact: Scott G. Barrilleaux, FACHE, Chief Executive Officer
COO: Wade Smith, Chief Operating Officer
CFO: Melodie Colwell, Chief Financial Officer
CMO: Julia Nichoson, M.D., Chief Medical Officer
CIO: Rusty Bryant, Director Information Technology
CHR: Seth Givens, Chief Human Resource Officer
CNO: Jonathan Schell, Chief Nursing Officer
Web address: www.drewmemorial.org
Control: Other not–for–profit (including NFP Corporation) **Service**: General medical and surgical

Staffed Beds: 49 **Admissions**: 1937 **Census**: 15 **Outpatient Visits**: 53361 **Births**: 368 **Total Expense ($000)**: 32416 **Payroll Expense ($000)**: 14252 **Personnel**: 332

MORRILTON—Conway County

★ **CHI ST. VINCENT MORRILTON (041324)**, 4 Hospital Drive, Zip 72110–4510; tel. 501/977–2300, **A**10 18 **F**3 11 15 18 28 29 30 34 40 43 44 45 57 59 62 63 64 77 79 80 81 85 87 93 104 107 108 110 111 119 127 129 130 132 133 143 145 146 148 154 **S** CommonSpirit Health, Chicago, IL
Primary Contact: Leslie Arnold, Chief Executive Officer and Administrator
CFO: Shawn Barnett, Senior Vice President and Chief Financial Officer
CIO: Tracy Kirby, Assistant Vice President Business Relationship Management
CHR: Aaron Austin, Market Vice President Human Resources
CNO: Kathy E. Neely, R.N., Interim Vice President Patient Care Services
Web address: www.chistvincent.com/Hospitals/st-vincent-morrilton
Control: Church operated, Nongovernment, not–for–profit **Service**: General medical and surgical

Staffed Beds: 25 **Admissions**: 667 **Census**: 8 **Outpatient Visits**: 31578 **Births**: 0 **Total Expense ($000)**: 21303 **Payroll Expense ($000)**: 9322 **Personnel**: 112

ST. ANTHONY'S MEDICAL CENTER See Chi St. Vincent Morrilton

MOUNTAIN HOME—Baxter County

★ **BAXTER REGIONAL MEDICAL CENTER (040027)**, 624 Hospital Drive, Zip 72653–2955; tel. 870/508–1000, **A**10 **F**7 11 13 15 17 18 20 22 24 28 29 30 31 34 40 43 46 47 49 53 56 57 59 62 63 64 70 74 76 77 78 79 81 82 85 86 87 89 90 93 96 97 98 100 103 107 108 110 111 114 115 116 117 119 124 126 127 129 130 132 135 146 147 148 149 154 156
Primary Contact: Ron Peterson, FACHE, President and Chief Executive Officer
COO: David R. Fox, Vice President and Chief Operating Officer
CFO: Debbie Henry, Vice President and Chief Financial Officer
CHR: Karen Adams, Vice President Human Resources
Web address: www.baxterregional.org
Control: Other not–for–profit (including NFP Corporation) **Service**: General medical and surgical

Staffed Beds: 225 **Admissions**: 9181 **Census**: 86 **Outpatient Visits**: 128669 **Births**: 669 **Total Expense ($000)**: 216515 **Payroll Expense ($000)**: 86960 **Personnel**: 1552

MOUNTAIN VIEW—Stone County

★ **STONE COUNTY MEDICAL CENTER (041310)**, 2106 East Main Street, Zip 72560–6439, Mailing Address: P.O. Box 510, Zip 72560–0510; tel. 870/269–4361, **A**10 18 **F**3 11 15 28 29 34 40 43 45 57 59 64 79 81 85 93 107 110 111 114 119 128 133 135 146 147 148 154 **S** White River Health System, Batesville, AR
Primary Contact: Kevin Spears, Chief Executive Officer
CFO: Phillip Hacker, Chief Financial Officer
CHR: Gary McDonald, Associate Administrator Human Resources
CNO: Diana Shelden, Chief Nursing Officer
Web address: www.whiteriverhealthsystem.com/doctors/facilities/stone-county-medical-center
Control: Other not–for–profit (including NFP Corporation) **Service**: General medical and surgical

Staffed Beds: 25 **Admissions**: 604 **Census**: 5 **Outpatient Visits**: 29119 **Births**: 0 **Total Expense ($000)**: 13785 **Payroll Expense ($000)**: 5866 **Personnel**: 111

NASHVILLE—Howard County

★ **HOWARD MEMORIAL HOSPITAL (041311)**, 130 Medical Circle, Zip 71852–8606; tel. 870/845–4400, **A**10 18 **F**3 11 15 28 29 30 34 35 40 43 45 50 53 57 64 65 70 77 81 85 87 93 107 108 110 115 119 133 146 156
Primary Contact: Debra J. Wright, R.N., Chief Executive Officer
CFO: William J Craig, CPA, Chief Financial Officer
CMO: John Hearnsberger, M.D., Chief of Staff
CHR: Gayla Lacefield, Director Human Resources
CNO: Alesha Danielle Collins, MSN, R.N., Chief Nursing Officer
Web address: www.howardmemorial.com
Control: Other not–for–profit (including NFP Corporation) **Service**: General medical and surgical

Staffed Beds: 20 **Admissions**: 649 **Census**: 7 **Outpatient Visits**: 28064 **Births**: 0 **Total Expense ($000)**: 23575 **Payroll Expense ($000)**: 10953 **Personnel**: 198

NORTH LITTLE ROCK—Pulaski County

○ **ARKANSAS SURGICAL HOSPITAL (040147)**, 5201 North Shore Drive, Zip 72118–5312; tel. 501/748–8000, **A**10 11 **F**3 29 30 35 40 64 74 75 78 79 81 82 85 86 87 107 111 114 119 126 130 131 144 146 148 149
Primary Contact: Carrie Helm, Chief Executive Officer
CFO: Charles Powell, Chief Financial Officer
CMO: Kenneth A Martin, M.D., Chief of Staff
CIO: Scott Davis, Manager Information Technology
CNO: Judy Jones, Chief Clinical Officer
Web address: www.ArkSurgicalHospital.com
Control: Corporation, Investor–owned (for–profit) **Service**: General medical and surgical

Staffed Beds: 49 **Admissions**: 3470 **Census**: 19 **Outpatient Visits**: 16883 **Births**: 0 **Total Expense ($000)**: 53862 **Payroll Expense ($000)**: 13991 **Personnel**: 240

⊞ △ **BAPTIST HEALTH MEDICAL CENTER - NORTH LITTLE ROCK (040036)**, 3333 Springhill Drive, Zip 72117–2922; tel. 501/202–3000, **A**1 3 7 10 **F**3 8 11 13 15 17 18 20 22 24 26 28 29 30 31 38 40 43 45 46 47 48 49 50 53 54 56 59 60 64 65 70 72 74 75 76 77 78 79 81 85 86 87 89 90 93 94 107 108 110 111 114 115 118 119 124 126 128 129 130 135 144 146 147 148 **S** Baptist Health, Little Rock, AR
Primary Contact: Mike Perkins, Vice President and Administrator
COO: Doug Weeks, FACHE, Executive Vice President and Chief Operations Officer
CFO: Robert C Roberts, Senior Vice President Financial Services
CMO: Eddie Phillips, M.D., Chief Medical Affairs
CIO: David House, Vice President and Chief Information Officer
CHR: Cathy C Dickinson, Vice President Human Resources
CNO: Kelley Hamby, Vice President Patient Care
Web address: www.https://www.baptist-health.com/location/baptist-health-medical-center-north-little-rock-north-little-rock
Control: Other not–for–profit (including NFP Corporation) **Service**: General medical and surgical

Staffed Beds: 177 **Admissions**: 11119 **Census**: 135 **Outpatient Visits**: 108408 **Births**: 1276 **Total Expense ($000)**: 184679 **Payroll Expense ($000)**: 60508 **Personnel**: 994

NORTH LITTLE ROCK DIVISION See Central Arkansas Veterans Healthcare System, Little Rock

Many Facility Codes have changed. Please refer to the AHA Guide Code Chart. © 2019 AHA Guide

☐ **THE BRIDGEWAY (044005)**, 21 Bridgeway Road, Zip 72113–9516;
tel. 501/771–1500, **A**1 10 **F**4 5 34 56 98 99 101 102 103 104 105 106 149
151 152 153 154 **S** Universal Health Services, Inc., King of Prussia, PA
Primary Contact: Sherrie James, R.N., Chief Executive Officer
CFO: Fred Woods, Chief Financial Officer
CMO: Philip L Mizell, M.D., Medical Director
CHR: Neely Robison, Director Human Resources
Web address: www.thebridgeway.com
Control: Corporation, Investor–owned (for–profit) **Service:** Psychiatric

Staffed Beds: 124 **Admissions:** 4249 **Census:** 84 **Outpatient Visits:** 7362
Births: 0 **Total Expense ($000):** 25151 **Payroll Expense ($000):** 11027

OSCEOLA—Mississippi County

⊞ **SOUTH MISSISSIPPI COUNTY REGIONAL MEDICAL CENTER (041316)**, 611
West Lee Avenue, Zip 72370–3001, Mailing Address: P.O. Box 108, Blytheville,
Zip 72316–0108; tel. 870/563–7000, **A**1 10 18 **F**3 29 34 40 43 81 90 107 114
133 135 149 154
Primary Contact: Chris Lee. Raymer, MSN, Chief Executive Officer
COO: Paul Pieffer, Chief Operating Officer
CFO: Randy Nichols, Chief Financial Officer
CMO: Pratapji Thakor, M.D., Chief of Staff
CIO: Tammy Bratcher, Director Information Technology
CHR: Cheri Blurton, SPHR, SHRM-SCP, Director Human Resources
CNO: Felicia Pierce, R.N., Chief Nursing Officer
Web address: www.mchsys.org
Control: County, Government, nonfederal **Service:** General medical and surgical

Staffed Beds: 25 **Admissions:** 397 **Census:** 3 **Outpatient Visits:** 14279
Births: 0 **Total Expense ($000):** 10240 **Payroll Expense ($000):** 4005
Personnel: 61

OZARK—Franklin County

★ **MERCY HOSPITAL OZARK (041303)**, 801 West River Street, Zip 72949–3023;
tel. 479/667–4138, **A**10 18 **F**3 15 35 40 43 45 57 59 64 65 68 81 85 107 119
129 133 148 149 **S** Mercy, Chesterfield, MO
Primary Contact: Teresa Williams, R.N., Regional Administrator
COO: Brent Hubbard, FACHE, Chief Operating Officer
CMO: John Lachowsky, M.D., Chief Medical Officer
CIO: Tiana Bolduc, Chief Information Officer
Web address: www.https://www.mercy.net/practice/mercy-hospital-ozark/
Control: Church operated, Nongovernment, not–for–profit **Service:** General
medical and surgical

Staffed Beds: 25 **Admissions:** 316 **Census:** 4 **Outpatient Visits:** 13636
Births: 0 **Total Expense ($000):** 10804 **Payroll Expense ($000):** 4431
Personnel: 56

PARAGOULD—Greene County

⊞ △ **ARKANSAS METHODIST MEDICAL CENTER (040020)**, 900 West
Kingshighway, Zip 72450–5942, Mailing Address: P.O. Box 339, Zip 72451–0339;
tel. 870/239–7000, **A**1 7 10 19 **F**1 3 4 7 10 11 13 15 16 17 18 20 22 28 29
32 34 35 40 43 45 49 50 51 53 54 57 59 62 64 67 68 70 72 73 75 76 79 80
81 85 86 87 88 89 90 93 97 98 107 108 110 111 114 115 119 124 125 128
129 130 131 132 133 135 144 146 147 148 154 156
Primary Contact: Barry L. Davis, FACHE, President and Chief Executive Officer
CFO: Brad Bloemer, Vice President Finance and Chief Financial Officer
CMO: Aaron Thompson, M.D., Chief of Staff
CIO: Dan Austin, Director Information Technology
CHR: Kevin Thielemier, Director Human Resources
CNO: Lana R Williams, Chief Nursing Officer
Web address: www.arkansasmethodist.org
Control: Other not–for–profit (including NFP Corporation) **Service:** General
medical and surgical

Staffed Beds: 125 **Admissions:** 3902 **Census:** 51 **Outpatient
Visits:** 138477 **Births:** 484 **Total Expense ($000):** 69469 **Payroll Expense
($000):** 31443 **Personnel:** 632

PARIS—Logan County

★ **MERCY HOSPITAL PARIS (041300)**, 500 East Academy, Zip 72855–4040;
tel. 479/963–6101, **A**10 18 **F**3 15 35 40 43 45 57 59 64 65 68 81 85 107 119
127 129 133 148 149 **S** Mercy, Chesterfield, MO
Primary Contact: Teresa Williams, R.N., Regional Administrator
COO: Brent Hubbard, FACHE, Chief Operating Officer
Web address: www.https://www.mercy.net/practice/mercy-hospital-paris/
Control: Church operated, Nongovernment, not–for–profit **Service:** General
medical and surgical

Staffed Beds: 16 **Admissions:** 257 **Census:** 3 **Outpatient Visits:** 17087 **Births:** 0
Total Expense ($000): 9551 **Payroll Expense ($000):** 4011 **Personnel:** 62

PIGGOTT—Clay County

★ **PIGGOTT COMMUNITY HOSPITAL (041330)**, 1206 Gordon Duckworth Drive,
Zip 72454–1911; tel. 870/598–3881, **A**10 18 **F**3 7 8 11 29 30 34 35 40 43
45 46 57 59 62 64 65 71 77 81 86 87 93 107 111 114 119 127 129 130 132
133 135 143 146 148 154 156
Primary Contact: James L. Magee, Executive Director
CFO: Linda Ort, Chief Financial Officer
Web address: www.piggottcommunityhospital.com
Control: City, Government, nonfederal **Service:** General medical and surgical

Staffed Beds: 25 **Admissions:** 729 **Census:** 7 **Outpatient Visits:** 15371 **Births:** 0
Total Expense ($000): 18472 **Payroll Expense ($000):** 8766 **Personnel:** 200

PINE BLUFF—Jefferson County

★ △ **JEFFERSON REGIONAL MEDICAL CENTER (040071)**, 1600 West 40th
Avenue, Zip 71603–6301; tel. 870/541–7100, **A**3 5 7 10 20 **F**3 8 11 13 15 17
18 20 22 28 29 30 31 34 35 38 40 43 45 46 48 49 50 51 53 54 56 57 59 60
61 64 65 70 72 73 74 75 76 77 78 79 81 82 85 86 87 89 90 96 97 98 100
101 102 103 105 107 108 110 111 114 115 116 117 118 119 124 130 131
132 135 143 144 145 146 147 148 149 154 156 157
Primary Contact: Brian N. Thomas, President and Chief Executive Officer
CFO: Bryan G Jackson, Vice President and Chief Financial Officer
CMO: Reid Pierce, M.D., Chief Medical Officer
CIO: Patrick Neece, Chief Information Officer
CHR: M Daryl Scott, Assistant Vice President
CNO: Louise Hickman, R.N., Vice President of Patient Care Services
Web address: www.jrmc.org
Control: Other not–for–profit (including NFP Corporation) **Service:** General
medical and surgical

Staffed Beds: 258 **Admissions:** 9996 **Census:** 145 **Outpatient
Visits:** 251266 **Births:** 738 **Total Expense ($000):** 196400 **Payroll Expense
($000):** 81733 **Personnel:** 1359

POCAHONTAS—Randolph County

ST. BERNARDS FIVE RIVERS (040047), 2801 Medical Center Drive,
Zip 72455–9436; tel. 870/892–6000, **A**10 20 **F**3 8 11 29 30 38 40 43 45 50
57 59 62 68 70 77 79 81 85 87 93 97 98 103 107 111 115 119 127 129 130
131 133 146 148 154 157
Primary Contact: Luther J. Lewis, FACHE, Chief Executive Officer
CFO: Joey Radcliff, Chief Financial Officer
CHR: Anita Dickson, Director Human Resources
CNO: Paula Lewis, Interim Chief Nursing Officer
Web address: www.https://www.stbernards.info/news/pocahontas-hospital-now-st-
bernards-five-rivers
Control: Other not–for–profit (including NFP Corporation) **Service:** General
medical and surgical

Staffed Beds: 36 **Admissions:** 814 **Census:** 12 **Outpatient Visits:** 25567
Births: 0 **Personnel:** 180

Hospital, Medicare Provider Number, Address, Telephone, Approval, Facility, and Physician Codes, Health Care System

★ American Hospital Association (AHA) membership ○ Healthcare Facilities Accreditation Program ⇑ Center for Improvement in Healthcare Quality Accreditation
☐ The Joint Commission accreditation ◇ DNV Healthcare Inc. accreditation △ Commission on Accreditation of Rehabilitation Facilities (CARF) accreditation

AR

ROGERS—Benton County

✠ **MERCY HOSPITAL ROGERS (040010)**, 2710 Rife Medical Lane, Zip 72758–1452; tel. 479/338–8000, **A**1 3 5 10 **F**7 8 11 12 13 15 17 18 20 22 24 26 28 29 30 34 35 40 42 43 45 46 48 49 54 57 59 62 64 68 70 71 72 74 75 77 79 81 82 84 85 86 87 89 93 104 107 108 110 111 114 115 118 119 129 130 131 135 146 147 148 153 154 155 156 157 **S** Mercy, Chesterfield, MO
Primary Contact: Eric Pianalto, Chief Executive Officer
COO: Charlotte Rankin, R.N., Chief Operating Officer
CFO: Benny Stover, Vice President Finance
CMO: Chris Johnson, M.D., Chief of Staff
CHR: Rick Barclay, Vice President Support Services
Web address: www.https://www.mercy.net/practice/mercy-hospital-northwest-arkansas/
Control: Church operated, Nongovernment, not–for–profit **Service:** General medical and surgical

Staffed Beds: 194 Admissions: 11186 Census: 115 Outpatient Visits: 241219 Births: 1709 Total Expense ($000): 225482 Payroll Expense ($000): 81097

RUSSELLVILLE—Pope County

✠ **SAINT MARY'S REGIONAL MEDICAL CENTER (040041)**, 1808 West Main Street, Zip 72801–2724; tel. 479/968–2841, (Nonreporting) **A**1 10 19 **S** LifePoint Health, Brentwood, TN
Primary Contact: James Davidson, Chief Executive Officer
COO: Scott Bailey, Chief Operating Officer
CFO: Wendell VanEs, Chief Financial Officer
CMO: Vickie Henderson, M.D., Chief Medical Officer
CHR: Connie Gragg, Director Human Resources
CNO: Carol Gore, MSN, R.N., Chief Nursing Officer
Web address: www.saintmarysregional.com
Control: Corporation, Investor–owned (for–profit) **Service:** General medical and surgical

Staffed Beds: 141

SALEM—Fulton County

FULTON COUNTY HOSPITAL (041322), 679 North Main Street, Zip 72576–9451, Mailing Address: P.O. Box 517, Zip 72576–0517; tel. 870/895–2691, **A**10 18 **F**3 7 11 28 29 30 34 40 43 45 57 59 64 87 107 114 119 133 146 148 154
Primary Contact: Curren Everett, Chief Executive Officer
Web address: www.fultoncountyhospital.org
Control: County, Government, nonfederal **Service:** General medical and surgical

Staffed Beds: 25 Admissions: 762 Census: 6 Outpatient Visits: 8637 Births: 0 Total Expense ($000): 10865 Payroll Expense ($000): 4795 Personnel: 198

SEARCY—White County

ADVANCED CARE HOSPITAL OF WHITE COUNTY (042011), 1200 South Main Street, Zip 72143–7321; tel. 501/278–3155, **A**10 **F**1 3 148
Primary Contact: Terri L. Parsons, Administrator
CMO: Miguel Aguinaga, M.D., FACS, Medical Director
CNO: Mistie Vannatter, Chief Nursing Officer
Web address: www.https://unity-health.org/advanced-care
Control: Other not–for–profit (including NFP Corporation) **Service:** Acute long–term care hospital

Staffed Beds: 27 Admissions: 171 Census: 11 Outpatient Visits: 0 Births: 0 Total Expense ($000): 5809 Payroll Expense ($000): 2815 Personnel: 53

★ **UNITY HEALTH WHITE COUNTY MEDICAL CENTER (040014)**, 3214 East Race Avenue, Zip 72143–4810; tel. 501/268–6121, (Includes UNITY HEALTH HARRIS MEDICAL CENTER, 1205 McLain Street, Newport, Arkansas, Zip 72112–3533; tel. 870/523–8911; Steven B. Webb, FACHE, President and Chief Executive Officer; UNITY HEALTH SPECIALTY CARE, 1200 South Main Street, Searcy, Arkansas, Zip 72143–7397; tel. 501/278–3100; Steven B. Webb, FACHE, President and Chief Executive Officer) **A**3 5 10 **F**1 3 11 13 15 17 18 20 22 28 29 30 31 34 35 38 39 40 43 45 50 51 57 58 59 64 65 68 69 70 74 75 76 77 78 79 81 84 85 86 87 89 90 93 98 100 102 103 104 105 107 108 110 111 114 115 119 126 129 130 132 134 135 144 146 147 148 152 154 157
Primary Contact: Steven B. Webb, FACHE, President and Chief Executive Officer
CFO: Stuart Hill, Vice President and Treasurer
CMO: John Henderson, M.D., Chief Medical Officer
CIO: Phil Miller, Chief Information Officer
CHR: Pamela G Williams, Director Human Resources
CNO: Peggy Turner, Assistant Vice President and Director of Nursing
Web address: www.unity-health.org
Control: Other not–for–profit (including NFP Corporation) **Service:** General medical and surgical

Staffed Beds: 368 Admissions: 12891 Census: 150 Outpatient Visits: 110917 Births: 1398 Total Expense ($000): 248214 Payroll Expense ($000): 120930 Personnel: 1931

SHERWOOD—Pulaski County

★ **CHI ST. VINCENT MEDICAL CENTER-NORTH (040137)**, 2215 Wildwood Avenue, Zip 72120–5089; tel. 501/552–7100, **A**10 **F**3 11 15 18 20 22 26 29 30 35 40 44 45 50 57 58 64 68 70 74 79 81 82 85 87 107 110 111 114 115 118 119 129 130 146 149 150 154 **S** CommonSpirit Health, Chicago, IL
Primary Contact: Chris Stines, President
CFO: Shawn Barnett, Senior Vice President and Chief Financial Officer
Web address: www.stvincenthealth.com
Control: Church operated, Nongovernment, not–for–profit **Service:** General medical and surgical

Staffed Beds: 68 Admissions: 1710 Census: 17 Outpatient Visits: 31585 Births: 0 Total Expense ($000): 31365 Payroll Expense ($000): 12515 Personnel: 271

✠ **CHI ST. VINCENT SHERWOOD REHABILITATION HOSPITAL (043031)**, 2201 Wildwood Avenue, Zip 72120–5074; tel. 501/834–1800, **A**1 10 **F**3 29 50 87 90 91 94 95 96 130 132 135 143 148 149 **S** Encompass Health Corporation, Birmingham, AL
Primary Contact: Lisa Watson, Chief Executive Officer
CFO: Stacy Shilling, Controller
CMO: Kevin J. Collins, M.D., Medical Director
CNO: Carolynn Whitley, Chief Nursing Officer
Web address: www.stvincentrehabhospital.com/
Control: Corporation, Investor–owned (for–profit) **Service:** Rehabilitation

Staffed Beds: 80 Admissions: 1820 Census: 60 Outpatient Visits: 0 Births: 0 Total Expense ($000): 24055 Payroll Expense ($000): 12782 Personnel: 233

SILOAM SPRINGS—Benton County

✠ **SILOAM SPRINGS REGIONAL HOSPITAL (040001)**, 603 North Progress Avenue, Zip 72761–4352; tel. 479/215–3000, **A**1 10 **F**3 11 13 15 28 29 30 34 40 45 50 57 59 64 68 70 75 76 77 79 80 81 85 91 93 107 108 110 111 115 118 119 129 130 144 146 147 154 **S** Community Health Systems, Inc., Franklin, TN
Primary Contact: Adam Bracks, Chief Executive Officer
CFO: Todd Williams, Chief Financial Officer
CMO: Ashish Mathur, M.D., Chief of Staff
CHR: Cindy Ruffing, Director Human Resources
CNO: Maria Wleklinski, Chief Nursing Officer
Web address: www.ssrh.net
Control: Corporation, Investor–owned (for–profit) **Service:** General medical and surgical

Staffed Beds: 44 Admissions: 1711 Census: 11 Outpatient Visits: 56864 Births: 597 Total Expense ($000): 34616 Payroll Expense ($000): 13661 Personnel: 211

SPRINGDALE—Washington County

✠ **ARKANSAS CHILDREN'S NORTHWEST (043301)**, 2601 Gene George Boulevard, Zip 72762; tel. 479/725–6800, (Data for 173 days) **A**1 **F**3 29 30 31 32 34 38 40 41 44 50 55 57 59 64 68 74 75 77 78 79 81 85 86 87 89 93 97 102 107 111 115 119 130 132 146 149 150 154 156
Primary Contact: Marcella Doderer, FACHE, President and Chief Executive Officer
Control: Other not–for–profit (including NFP Corporation) **Service:** General medical and surgical

Staffed Beds: 24 Admissions: 591 Census: 7 Outpatient Visits: 9109 Births: 0 Total Expense ($000): 32531 Payroll Expense ($000): 9736 Personnel: 315

✠ **NORTHWEST MEDICAL CENTER - SPRINGDALE (040022)**, 609 West Maple Avenue, Zip 72764–5394, Mailing Address: P.O. Box 47, Zip 72765–0047; tel. 479/751–5711, (Includes NORTHWEST MEDICAL CENTER - BENTONVILLE, 3000 Medical Center Parkway, Bentonville, Arkansas, Zip 72712; tel. 479/553–1000; Denten Park, Chief Executive Officer; Willow Creek Women's Hospital, 4301 Greathouse Springs Road, Johnson, Arkansas, Zip 72741–0544, Mailing Address: P O Box 544, Zip 72741–0544, tel. 479/684–3000; Denten Park, Chief Executive Officer) **A**1 3 10 **F**3 7 8 11 12 13 15 17 18 20 22 24 26 28 29 30 37 40 43 45 46 47 48 49 50 51 56 60 61 70 72 74 76 77 79 81 82 85 86 87 90 91 92 93 96 98 102 107 108 110 111 114 115 118 119 124 126 129 130 131 135 146 147 148 156 **S** Community Health Systems, Inc., Franklin, TN
Primary Contact: Hans Driessnack, Chief Executive Officer
COO: Tom Sledge, Chief Operating Officer
CMO: James Tanner, M.D., Chief Medical Officer
CIO: Mark Bokon, Chief Information Officer
CNO: Karen Y Labonte, Chief Nursing Officer
Web address: www.northwesthealth.com
Control: Corporation, Investor–owned (for–profit) **Service:** General medical and surgical

Staffed Beds: 345 Admissions: 13552 Census: 162 Outpatient Visits: 141074 Births: 2547 Total Expense ($000): 226534 Payroll Expense ($000): 72975 Personnel: 1120

Many Facility Codes have changed. Please refer to the AHA Guide Code Chart.
© 2019 AHA Guide

⊞ **REGENCY HOSPITAL OF NORTHWEST ARKANSAS - SPRINGDALE (042009)**, 609 West Maple Avenue, 6th Fl, Zip 72764; tel. 479/757–2600, **A**1 10 **F**1 3 29 84 130 148 **S** Select Medical Corporation, Mechanicsburg, PA
Primary Contact: Robert Poole, Chief Executive Officer
COO: Ruth Jones, Chief Clinical Officer
CMO: Gary Templeton, M.D., Medical Director
CHR: Melissa Ross-Cole, Director Human Resources
Web address: www.regencyhospital.com
Control: Corporation, Investor–owned (for–profit) **Service:** Acute long–term care hospital

Staffed Beds: 25 **Admissions:** 263 **Census:** 17 **Outpatient Visits:** 0
Births: 0 **Total Expense ($000):** 9227 **Payroll Expense ($000):** 4297
Personnel: 70

STUTTGART—Arkansas County

★ **BAPTIST HEALTH MEDICAL CENTER-STUTTGART (040072)**, 1703 North Buerkle Road, Zip 72160–1905, Mailing Address: P.O. Box 1905, Zip 72160–1905; tel. 870/673–3511, **A**10 **F**3 11 13 15 18 29 30 34 35 39 40 43 45 53 57 59 64 68 75 76 78 79 81 85 87 97 107 110 111 114 119 127 129 130 132 133 135 146 148 154 156 157 **S** Baptist Health, Little Rock, AR
Primary Contact: Kevin L. Storey, Vice President and Administrator
CMO: Seth M. Kleinbeck, M.D., Chief of Staff
CIO: Warren Horton, Information Technologist
CNO: Susan Williams, R.N., Chief Nursing Officer
Web address: www.https://www.baptist-health.com/location/baptist-health-medical-center-stuttgart-stuttgart
Control: Church operated, Nongovernment, not–for–profit **Service:** General medical and surgical

Staffed Beds: 41 **Admissions:** 1055 **Census:** 10 **Outpatient Visits:** 22875
Births: 192 **Total Expense ($000):** 28245 **Payroll Expense ($000):** 9877
Personnel: 191

TEXARKANA—Miller County

☐ **RIVERVIEW BEHAVIORAL HEALTH (044020)**, 701 Arkansas Boulevard, Zip 71854–2105; tel. 870/772–5028, (Nonreporting) **A**1 10 **S** Acadia Healthcare Company, Inc., Franklin, TN
Primary Contact: Allison De Bruycker, Chief Executive Officer
CFO: Kimberly Hibschman, Chief Financial Officer
CIO: Jim Cruson, Chief Information Officer
CHR: Roberta Bachman, Director Human Resources
CNO: Carrie Gray, Director of Nursing
Web address: www.riverviewbehavioralhealth.com
Control: Corporation, Investor–owned (for–profit) **Service:** Psychiatric

Staffed Beds: 62

VAN BUREN—Crawford County

⊞ **BAPTIST HEALTH - VAN BUREN (040018)**, East Main and South 20th Streets, Zip 72956–5715, Mailing Address: P.O. Box 409, Zip 72957–0409; tel. 479/474–3401, (Data for 61 days) **A**1 10 **F**12 29 40 43 68 70 79 81 107 108 111 116 117 151 152 **S** Baptist Health, Little Rock, AR
Primary Contact: Brandon Bullard, Interim Chief Executive Officer
CHR: James Ford, Director Human Resources
Web address: www.https://www.sparkshealth.com/
Control: Other not–for–profit (including NFP Corporation) **Service:** General medical and surgical

Staffed Beds: 39 **Admissions:** 175 **Census:** 8 **Outpatient Visits:** 7743
Births: 0 **Total Expense ($000):** 2747 **Payroll Expense ($000):** 951
Personnel: 86

WALDRON—Scott County

★ **MERCY HOSPITAL WALDRON (041305)**, 1341 West 6th Street, Zip 72958–7642; tel. 479/637–4135, **A**10 18 **F**3 15 35 40 43 45 57 59 64 65 68 81 85 107 119 127 129 133 148 149 **S** Mercy, Chesterfield, MO
Primary Contact: Teresa Williams, R.N., Regional Administrator
COO: Brent Hubbard, FACHE, Chief Operating Officer
CFO: Greta Wilcher, Senior Vice President and Chief Financial Officer
CNO: Nick Hunt, Interim Director of Nursing
Web address: www.https://www.mercy.net/practice/mercy-hospital-waldron/
Control: Church operated, Nongovernment, not–for–profit **Service:** General medical and surgical

Staffed Beds: 24 **Admissions:** 222 **Census:** 3 **Outpatient Visits:** 16101
Births: 0 **Total Expense ($000):** 10891 **Payroll Expense ($000):** 4922
Personnel: 60

WALNUT RIDGE—Lawrence County

⊞ **LAWRENCE MEMORIAL HOSPITAL (041309)**, 1309 West Main, Zip 72476–1430, Mailing Address: P.O. Box 839, Zip 72476–0839; tel. 870/886–1200, (Total facility includes 150 beds in nursing home–type unit) **A**1 10 18 **F**3 11 15 29 32 34 35 40 45 46 47 57 59 84 85 87 97 107 110 111 114 119 127 128 129 130 133 135 146
Primary Contact: Gary R. Sparks, Interim President
COO: Junior Briner, Chief Operating Officer
CFO: Vanessa Wagner, Chief Financial Officer
CMO: Kevin M. Diamond, M.D., Chief Medical Officer
CIO: Josh Wise, Director Information Technology
CHR: Brigett Montgomery, Director Human Resource
CNO: Rosalind C Casillas, Chief Nursing Officer
Web address: www.lawrencehealth.net
Control: County, Government, nonfederal **Service:** General medical and surgical

Staffed Beds: 175 **Admissions:** 1027 **Census:** 136 **Outpatient Visits:** 34160 **Births:** 0 **Total Expense ($000):** 22700 **Payroll Expense ($000):** 12053 **Personnel:** 271

WARREN—Bradley County

★ **BRADLEY COUNTY MEDICAL CENTER (041327)**, 404 South Bradley Street, Zip 71671–3493; tel. 870/226–3731, **A**10 18 **F**3 11 13 15 29 30 34 35 40 45 49 50 56 57 59 62 76 81 87 98 103 104 107 108 110 111 115 118 119 127 130 132 133 146 147 153 154
Primary Contact: Steve Henson, Chief Executive Officer
CFO: Brandon Gorman, Chief Financial Officer
CMO: Joe H Wharton, M.D., Chief of Staff
CHR: Brooke Hatch, Director Human Resource
CNO: Sarah Tucker, Chief Nursing Officer
Web address: www.bradleycountymedicalcenter.com
Control: Other not–for–profit (including NFP Corporation) **Service:** General medical and surgical

Staffed Beds: 33 **Admissions:** 650 **Census:** 6 **Outpatient Visits:** 60000
Births: 139 **Total Expense ($000):** 21202 **Payroll Expense ($000):** 9467
Personnel: 222

WEST MEMPHIS—Crittenden County

☐ **PERIMETER BEHAVIORAL HOSPITAL OF WEST MEMPHIS (044021)**, 800 North Seventh Street, Zip 72301–3235; tel. 870/394–7100, (Nonreporting) **A**1
Primary Contact: Jennifer Kelly, Chief Executive Officer
Web address: www.https://www.perimeterhealthcare.com
Control: Corporation, Investor–owned (for–profit) **Service:** Psychiatric

Staffed Beds: 24

WYNNE—Cross County

Ⓐ **CROSSRIDGE COMMUNITY HOSPITAL (041307)**, 310 South Falls Boulevard, Zip 72396–3013, Mailing Address: P.O. Box 590, Zip 72396–0590; tel. 870/238–3300, **A**1 10 18 **F**1 3 4 11 15 16 17 28 34 35 40 50 57 59 62 64 67 68 69 70 72 73 80 81 88 89 90 93 98 107 110 111 114 119 128 130 133 146 148
Primary Contact: Gary R. Sparks, Administrator
COO: Bryan Mattes, Associate Administrator
CFO: Janice Morris, Accountant
CIO: Gail Copeland, Director Management Information Systems
CHR: Bertha Ragle, Director Personnel
CNO: Amelia Davis, Director of Nursing
Web address: www.https://www.stbernards.info
Control: Church operated, Nongovernment, not–for–profit **Service:** General medical and surgical

Staffed Beds: 15 **Admissions:** 698 **Census:** 9 **Outpatient Visits:** 20736
Births: 0 **Total Expense ($000):** 15818 **Payroll Expense ($000):** 6430
Personnel: 136

AR

Hospital, Medicare Provider Number, Address, Telephone, Approval, Facility, and Physician Codes, Health Care System

★ American Hospital Association (AHA) membership	○ Healthcare Facilities Accreditation Program	⇑ Center for Improvement in Healthcare Quality Accreditation
☐ The Joint Commission accreditation	◇ DNV Healthcare Inc. accreditation	△ Commission on Accreditation of Rehabilitation Facilities (CARF) accreditation

CALIFORNIA

ALAMEDA—Alameda County

★ **ALAMEDA HOSPITAL (050211)**, 2070 Clinton Avenue, Zip 94501–4397; tel. 510/522–3700, (Total facility includes 181 beds in nursing home–type unit) **A**10 **F**3 11 15 17 18 29 31 34 35 36 39 40 43 46 50 57 58 59 70 77 78 79 81 82 85 93 97 107 108 110 114 118 119 128 130 131 132 146 147 148 **S** Alameda Health System, San Leandro, CA
Primary Contact: Delvecchio Finley, Chief Executive Officer
CFO: Robert C Anderson, Interim Chief Financial Officer
CMO: Aika Sharma, M.D., President Medical Staff
CIO: Robert Lundy-Paine, Director Information Systems
CHR: Phyllis Weiss, Director Human Resources
Web address: www.alamedahealthsystem.org
Control: Hospital district or authority, Government, nonfederal **Service**: General medical and surgical

Staffed Beds: 215 **Admissions**: 2666 **Census**: 206 **Outpatient Visits**: 30814 **Births**: 0 **Total Expense ($000)**: 108260 **Payroll Expense ($000)**: 55322 **Personnel**: 570

ALHAMBRA—Los Angeles County

☐ **ALHAMBRA HOSPITAL MEDICAL CENTER (050281)**, 100 South Raymond Avenue, Zip 91801–3199, Mailing Address: P.O. Box 510, Zip 91802–2510; tel. 626/570–1606, (Nonreporting) **A**1 10 **S** AHMC & Healthcare, Inc., Alhambra, CA
Primary Contact: Iris Lai, Chief Executive Officer
CFO: Linda Marsh, Vice President Financial Services and Chief Financial Officer
CMO: Stephen Chen, M.D., Chief Medicare
CIO: Johnson Legaspi, Director Information Systems
CHR: Elizabeth Sabandit, Director Human Resources
CNO: Eleanor Martinez, Chief Nursing Officer
Web address: www.alhambrahospital.com
Control: Partnership, Investor–owned (for–profit) **Service**: General medical and surgical

Staffed Beds: 144

ALTURAS—Modoc County

MODOC MEDICAL CENTER (051330), 228 West McDowell Avenue, Zip 96101–3934; tel. 530/233–5131, (Nonreporting) **A**10 18
Primary Contact: Kevin Kramer, Chief Executive Officer
CMO: Ed Richert, M.D., Chief of Staff
CHR: Diane Hagelthorn, Human Resources Generalist
Web address: www.modocmedicalcenter.org
Control: County, Government, nonfederal **Service**: General medical and surgical

Staffed Beds: 87

ANAHEIM—Orange County

☐ **AHMC ANAHEIM REGIONAL MEDICAL CENTER (050226)**, 1111 West La Palma Avenue, Zip 92801–2881; tel. 714/774–1450, (Nonreporting) **A**1 10 **S** AHMC & Healthcare, Inc., Alhambra, CA
Primary Contact: Richard Castro, Chief Executive Officer
COO: Mary Anne Monje, Chief Operations Officer
CFO: Mary Anne Monje, Chief Financial Officer
CMO: Amitabh Prakash, M.D., Chief Medical Officer
CIO: Jeff DesRoches, Director Information Systems
CHR: Jason Jaquez, Human Resource Director
CNO: Lisa Hahn, R.N., Chief Nursing Officer
Web address: www.anaheimregionalmc.com
Control: Other not–for–profit (including NFP Corporation) **Service**: General medical and surgical

Staffed Beds: 223

☐ **ANAHEIM GLOBAL MEDICAL CENTER (050744)**, 1025 South Anaheim Boulevard, Zip 92805–5806; tel. 714/533–6220, (Nonreporting) **A**1 10 **S** KPC Healthcare, Inc., Santa Ana, CA
Primary Contact: Scott Rifkin, Chief Executive Officer
CFO: John Collins, Chief Financial Officer
CMO: Beena Shah, M.D., Chief of Staff and Chief Medical Officer
CNO: Bonita Wells Veal, Chief Nursing Officer
Web address: www.anaheim-gmc.com
Control: Corporation, Investor–owned (for–profit) **Service**: General medical and surgical

Staffed Beds: 188

ANAHEIM MEDICAL CENTER See Kaiser Permanente Orange County Anaheim Medical Center

⊞ **KAISER PERMANENTE ORANGE COUNTY ANAHEIM MEDICAL CENTER (050609)**, 3440 East La Palma Avenue, Zip 92806–2020; tel. 714/644–2000, (Includes ORANGE COUNTY IRVINE MEDICAL CENTER, 6640 Alton Parkway, Irvine, California, Zip 92618; tel. 949/932–5000; Mark E Costa, Executive Director) **A**1 3 5 10 **F**3 8 13 15 18 19 20 29 30 31 35 37 40 44 45 46 47 48 49 50 53 55 56 57 59 60 61 62 63 65 66 68 70 72 74 75 76 77 78 79 81 82 84 85 86 87 89 92 93 100 107 108 110 111 114 115 117 119 130 135 143 146 148 149 150 154 155 157 **S** Kaiser Foundation Hospitals, Oakland, CA
Primary Contact: Mark E. Costa, Executive Director
COO: Margie Harrier, MSN, R.N., Medical Center Chief Operations Officer
CFO: Marcus Hoffman, Area Chief Financial Officer
CMO: Nancy Gin, M.D., Area Associate Medical Director
CIO: James Brady, Area Information Officer
CHR: Jocelyn A. Herrera, Director Human Resources
CNO: Martha Dispoto, R.N., I Chief Nurse Executive, Anaheim Medical Center
Web address: www.kp.org
Control: Other not–for–profit (including NFP Corporation) **Service**: General medical and surgical

Staffed Beds: 469 **Admissions**: 25760 **Census**: 275 **Outpatient Visits**: 419051 **Births**: 6584 **Personnel**: 3134

⊞ **WEST ANAHEIM MEDICAL CENTER (050426)**, 3033 West Orange Avenue, Zip 92804–3183; tel. 714/827–3000, (Nonreporting) **A**1 5 10 13 **S** Prime Healthcare, Ontario, CA
Primary Contact: Edward Mirzabegian, Chief Executive Officer
CFO: Kora Guoyavatin, Chief Financial Officer
CMO: Hassan Alkhouli, M.D., Chief Medical Officer
CIO: Vic Mahan, Director Information Technology
CHR: Stephanie Sioson, Director Human Resources
Web address: www.westanaheimmedctr.com
Control: Partnership, Investor–owned (for–profit) **Service**: General medical and surgical

Staffed Beds: 219

ANTIOCH—Contra Costa County

⊞ **KAISER PERMANENTE ANTIOCH MEDICAL CENTER (050760)**, 4501 Sand Creek Road, Zip 94531–8687; tel. 925/813–6500, **A**1 2 5 10 **F**3 8 13 15 18 26 28 29 30 31 34 37 39 40 41 45 49 50 55 56 57 58 59 60 63 64 68 70 73 74 75 76 77 78 79 81 82 84 85 86 102 107 108 110 111 114 115 118 119 126 130 131 134 135 144 146 147 148 149 154 156 157 **S** Kaiser Foundation Hospitals, Oakland, CA
Primary Contact: Colleen McKeown, Senior Vice President and Area Manager
CFO: Kerry Easthope, Area Finance Officer
CMO: Dale Poppert, M.D., Chief of Staff
CIO: Mical Cayton, Area Information Officer
CHR: Davida Lindsay-Bell, Area Human Resources Leader
CNO: Janet Jule, Chief Nurse Executive
Web address: www.https://health.kaiserpermanente.org/wps/portal/facility/100382
Control: Other not–for–profit (including NFP Corporation) **Service**: General medical and surgical

Staffed Beds: 150 **Admissions**: 7347 **Census**: 63 **Outpatient Visits**: 142941 **Births**: 1739 **Personnel**: 814

⊞ **SUTTER DELTA MEDICAL CENTER (050523)**, 3901 Lone Tree Way, Zip 94509–6253; tel. 925/779–7200, (Nonreporting) **A**1 10 **S** Sutter Health, Sacramento, CA
Primary Contact: Sherie C. Hickman, Chief Executive Officer
CFO: Julie Peterson, Chief Financial Officer
CMO: Anupam Mapara, M.D., Chief of Staff
CIO: Kathy Frederickson, Information Systems Site Lead
CHR: Noemi Whitehead, Administrative Director Human Resources
CNO: James Christopher Reedy, Chief Nursing Officer
Web address: www.sutterdelta.org
Control: Other not–for–profit (including NFP Corporation) **Service**: General medical and surgical

Staffed Beds: 132

CA

APPLE VALLEY—San Bernardino County

✠ **ST. MARY MEDICAL CENTER (050300)**, 18300 Highway 18, Zip 92307–2206, Mailing Address: P.O. Box 7025, Zip 92307–0725; tel. 760/242–2311, **A1** 3 5 10 **F**8 11 15 18 20 22 24 26 28 29 30 34 35 40 45 46 50 57 59 60 64 65 68 70 71 72 75 76 77 81 82 83 84 87 89 93 107 108 111 115 119 126 127 130 146 147 148 156 **S** Providence St. Joseph Health, Renton, WA
Primary Contact: Randall Castillo, Chief Executive Officer
CFO: Tracey Fernandez, Chief Financial Officer
CMO: Riad Z. Abdelkarim, M.D., Vice President and Chief Medical Officer
CIO: Doug Kleine, IT Director
CHR: Jean Holtman, Vice President, Human Resources
CNO: Marilyn Drone, R.N., MSN, Vice President, CNO
Web address: www.stmaryapplevalley.com/
Control: Church operated, Nongovernment, not–for–profit **Service:** General medical and surgical

Staffed Beds: 212 **Admissions:** 14051 **Census:** 181 **Outpatient Visits:** 101734 **Births:** 1995 **Total Expense ($000):** 299702 **Payroll Expense ($000):** 127753 **Personnel:** 1542

ARCADIA—Los Angeles County

✠ **METHODIST HOSPITAL OF SOUTHERN CALIFORNIA (050238)**, 300 West Huntington Drive, Zip 91007–3473, Mailing Address: P.O. Box 60016, Zip 91066–6016; tel. 626/898–8000, **A1** 2 3 10 **F**3 12 13 14 15 17 18 20 22 24 26 28 29 30 31 34 35 37 38 40 45 46 48 49 50 51 55 56 57 58 59 60 64 65 68 70 72 74 75 76 77 78 79 81 82 84 85 86 87 90 92 94 96 107 108 110 111 114 115 119 130 132 135 146 147 148 156
Primary Contact: Dan F. Ausman, President and Chief Executive Officer
COO: Steven A. Sisto, Senior Vice President and Chief Operating Officer
CFO: William E. Grigg, Senior Vice President and Chief Financial Officer
CHR: Gwen Chambers, Executive Director Human Resources
CNO: Roberta A McCaffrey, R.N., Vice President and Chief Nursing Officer
Web address: www.methodisthospital.org
Control: Other not–for–profit (including NFP Corporation) **Service:** General medical and surgical

Staffed Beds: 294 **Admissions:** 15391 **Census:** 204 **Outpatient Visits:** 76696 **Births:** 1414 **Total Expense ($000):** 290731 **Payroll Expense ($000):** 131185 **Personnel:** 1424

ARCATA—Humboldt County

◯ **MAD RIVER COMMUNITY HOSPITAL (050028)**, 3800 Janes Road, Zip 95521–4788, Mailing Address: P.O. Box 1115, Zip 95518 1115; tel. 707/822–3621, (Nonreporting) **A10** 11
Primary Contact: Douglas A. Shaw, Chief Executive Officer
CFO: Michael Young, Chief Financial Officer
CMO: Bonnie MacEvoy, Chief of Staff
CIO: Jedd Rudd, Director of Ancillary Services and Safety
CNO: Sara Innanen, Chief Nursing Officer
Web address: www.madriverhospital.com
Control: Corporation, Investor–owned (for–profit) **Service:** General medical and surgical

Staffed Beds: 42

ARROYO GRANDE—San Luis Obispo County

★ **ARROYO GRANDE COMMUNITY HOSPITAL (050016)**, 345 South Halcyon Road, Zip 93420–3896; tel. 805/489–4261, (Nonreporting) **A10**
Primary Contact: Kenneth Dalebout, Site Administrator
CHR: Ami Padilla, Director Human Resources
Web address: www.arroyograndehospital.org
Control: Other not–for–profit (including NFP Corporation) **Service:** General medical and surgical

Staffed Beds: 67

ATASCADERO—San Luis Obispo County

☐ **ATASCADERO STATE HOSPITAL**, 10333 El Camino Real, Zip 93422–5808, Mailing Address: P.O. Box 7001, Zip 93423–7001; tel. 805/468–2000, (Nonreporting) **A1**
Primary Contact: Bob Hushing-Kline, Hospital Administrator
COO: David Landrum, Chief Police Services
CFO: Janie Pagnini, Administrator Accounting
CMO: David Fennell, M.D., Acting Medical Director
CIO: James Grover, Manager Data Processing
CHR: Elizabeth Andres, Director Human Resources
CNO: Liz Souza, Coordinator Nursing Services
Web address: www.dmh.ca.gov/statehospitals/atascadero
Control: State, Government, nonfederal **Service:** Psychiatric

Staffed Beds: 1184

AUBURN—Placer County

✠ **SUTTER AUBURN FAITH HOSPITAL (050498)**, 11815 Education Street, Zip 95602–2410; tel. 530/888–4500, (Nonreporting) **A1** 2 10 **S** Sutter Health, Sacramento, CA
Primary Contact: Mitchell J. Hanna, Chief Executive Officer
CFO: Gary Hubschman, Administrative Director Finance
CMO: John Mesic, M.D., Chief Medical Officer
CIO: Tom Ream, Regional Chief Information Officer
CHR: Yvette Martinez, Director Human Resources
Web address: www.sutterhealth.org
Control: Other not–for–profit (including NFP Corporation) **Service:** General medical and surgical

Staffed Beds: 72

AVALON—Los Angeles County

★ **CATALINA ISLAND MEDICAL CENTER (051307)**, 100 Falls Canyon Road, Zip 90704, Mailing Address: P.O. Box 1563, Zip 90704–1563; tel. 310/510–0700, **A**10 18 **F**3 11 28 34 36 40 50 57 64 65 75 93 96 107 113 119 127 128 130 134 146 154
Primary Contact: Jason Paret, Chief Executive Officer
COO: Stacie Amarantos, Chief Operating Officer
CFO: John Lovrich, Chief Financial Officer
CMO: Laura Ulibarri, M.D., Chief of Staff
CIO: Leah Keeline, Clinical Informatics Specialist
CHR: Lilly Hernandez, Human Resources Director
CNO: Stacie Amarantos, Chief Operating Officer
Web address: www.catalinaislandmedicalcenter.org
Control: Other not–for–profit (including NFP Corporation) **Service:** General medical and surgical

Staffed Beds: 12 **Admissions:** 5 **Census:** 6 **Outpatient Visits:** 24941 **Births:** 0 **Total Expense ($000):** 10804 **Payroll Expense ($000):** 3627 **Personnel:** 90

BALDWIN PARK—Los Angeles County

BALDWIN PARK MEDICAL CENTER See Kaiser Permanente Baldwin Park Medical Center

✠ **KAISER PERMANENTE BALDWIN PARK MEDICAL CENTER (050723)**, 1011 Baldwin Park Boulevard, Zip 91706–5806; tel. 626/851–1011, **A**1 3 10 **F**8 13 15 29 30 31 32 34 35 38 40 41 44 46 50 53 54 56 57 59 60 61 62 63 64 65 66 68 70 72 74 75 76 77 78 79 81 82 83 84 85 86 87 89 92 93 94 97 107 108 110 111 112 114 115 116 117 118 119 130 131 132 135 144 146 147 148 149 154 156 157 **S** Kaiser Foundation Hospitals, Oakland, CA
Primary Contact: Margaret H. Pierce, Executive Director
COO: Payman Roshan, Chief Operating Officer
CFO: Rebecca Wheeler, Director Finance
CMO: John Bigley, M.D., Medical Director
CIO: Linda C Salazar, Information Technology Leader
CNO: Michelle Nowicki, R.N., MSN, Chief Nurse Executive
Web address: www.kp.org
Control: Other not–for–profit (including NFP Corporation) **Service:** General medical and surgical

Staffed Beds: 257 **Admissions:** 12827 **Census:** 106 **Outpatient Visits:** 331544 **Births:** 3135 **Personnel:** 2359

✠ **KINDRED HOSPITAL-BALDWIN PARK (052045)**, 14148 Francisquito Avenue, Zip 91706–6120; tel. 626/388–2700, (Nonreporting) **A1** 10 **S** Kindred Healthcare, Louisville, KY
Primary Contact: Fiona Basa-Reyes, Chief Executive Officer
COO: Dina Garrow, Chief Nursing Officer and Chief Operating Officer
CFO: Christine Saltonstall, Chief Financial Officer
CMO: Anil Gupta, M.D., Chief of Staff
CHR: Antoinette Bibal, Director Human Resources
CNO: Dina Garrow, Chief Nursing Officer and Chief Operating Officer
Web address: www.khbaldwinpark.com
Control: Corporation, Investor–owned (for–profit) **Service:** Acute long–term care hospital

Staffed Beds: 91

VISTA SPECIALTY HOSPITAL OF SAN GABRIEL VALLEY See Kindred Hospital-Baldwin Park

---

Hospital, Medicare Provider Number, Address, Telephone, Approval, Facility, and Physician Codes, Health Care System

★ American Hospital Association (AHA) membership   ◯ Healthcare Facilities Accreditation Program   ⇑ Center for Improvement in Healthcare Quality Accreditation
☐ The Joint Commission accreditation   ◇ DNV Healthcare Inc. accreditation   △ Commission on Accreditation of Rehabilitation Facilities (CARF) accreditation

CA

BAKERSFIELD—Kern County

✠ **ADVENTIST HEALTH BAKERSFIELD (050455)**, 2615 Chester Avenue, Zip 93301–2014, Mailing Address: P.O. Box 2615, Zip 93303–2615; tel. 661/395–3000, **A**1 3 10 **F**3 8 11 12 13 15 18 20 22 24 26 28 29 30 31 34 35 36 40 45 46 47 48 49 50 51 54 55 56 57 59 64 65 70 71 72 74 75 76 77 78 79 81 82 84 85 86 87 89 91 107 108 110 111 114 115 116 117 118 119 120 121 123 124 126 130 132 135 146 147 148 149 154 156 **S** Adventist Health, Roseville, CA
Primary Contact: Sharlet Briggs, Ph.D., Market Chief Executive Officer and President
COO: Sharlet Briggs, Ph.D., Chief Operating Officer
CFO: Brent Soper, Chief Financial Officer
CHR: Marlene Kreidler, Executive Director Human Resources
Web address: www.sanjoaquinhospital.org
Control: Church operated, Nongovernment, not–for–profit **Service:** General medical and surgical

Staffed Beds: 223 **Admissions:** 17163 **Census:** 178 **Outpatient Visits:** 135238 **Births:** 3022 **Total Expense ($000):** 399874 **Payroll Expense ($000):** 110809 **Personnel:** 1739

☐ **BAKERSFIELD HEART HOSPITAL (050724)**, 3001 Sillect Avenue, Zip 93308–6337; tel. 661/316–6000, **A**1 10 **F**3 18 20 22 24 26 28 29 34 45 46 47 50 57 59 68 70 79 81 85 107 111 119 130 141 147 148
Primary Contact: Michelle Oxford, Chief Operating Officer, Acting Chief Executive Officer
COO: Michelle Oxford, Chief Operating Officer, Acting Chief Executive Officer
CFO: Vickie Scharr, Chief Financial Officer
CMO: Brijesh Bhambi, M.D., Chief Medical Officer
CIO: Peter Mayer, Director Information Systems
CHR: Linda Hansen, Director Human Resources
Web address: www.bakersfieldhearthospital.com
Control: Partnership, Investor–owned (for–profit) **Service:** General medical and surgical

Staffed Beds: 47 **Admissions:** 3105 **Census:** 34

✠ **BAKERSFIELD MEMORIAL HOSPITAL (050036)**, 420 34th Street, Zip 93301–2237; tel. 661/327–1792, **A**1 3 5 10 13 **F**3 11 13 15 16 17 18 20 22 24 26 28 29 30 31 37 40 45 50 58 60 68 70 72 74 75 76 77 78 79 81 84 85 86 88 89 93 107 108 109 111 114 115 119 120 124 126 130 146 147 148 149 156 **S** CommonSpirit Health, Chicago, IL
Primary Contact: Ken Keller, President and Chief Executive Officer
COO: Bruce Peters, Vice President and Chief Operating Officer
CFO: Jesica Hanson, Vice President and Chief Financial Officer
CMO: Rodney Mark Root, D.O., Vice President Medical Affairs
CHR: Sheri Comaianni, Vice President Human Resources
Web address: www.bakersfieldmemorial.org
Control: Other not–for–profit (including NFP Corporation) **Service:** General medical and surgical

Staffed Beds: 401 **Admissions:** 15571 **Census:** 170 **Outpatient Visits:** 149549 **Births:** 2947 **Total Expense ($000):** 449352 **Payroll Expense ($000):** 153434 **Personnel:** 1473

✠ **ENCOMPASS HEALTH REHABILITATION HOSPITAL OF BAKERSFIELD (053031)**, 5001 Commerce Drive, Zip 93309–0689; tel. 661/323–5500, **A**1 10 **F**3 29 60 90 91 95 96 119 132 148 156 **S** Encompass Health Corporation, Birmingham, AL
Primary Contact: Martha Samora, R.N., FACHE, Chief Executive Officer
CFO: Robert Mosesian, Controller
CMO: Chris Yoon, M.D., Medical Director
CHR: Lori Brackett, Director Human Resources
CNO: Kathleen Szura, R.N., Chief Nursing Officer
Web address: www.healthsouthbakersfield.com
Control: Corporation, Investor–owned (for–profit) **Service:** Rehabilitation

Staffed Beds: 70 **Admissions:** 1828 **Census:** 60 **Outpatient Visits:** 0 **Births:** 0 **Total Expense ($000):** 28031 **Payroll Expense ($000):** 16874 **Personnel:** 294

☐ **GOOD SAMARITAN HOSPITAL (050257)**, 901 Olive Drive, Zip 93308–4144, Mailing Address: P.O. Box 85002, Zip 93380–5002; tel. 661/215–7500, (Nonreporting) **A**1 10
Primary Contact: Ganesh Acharya, Chief Executive Officer
COO: Anand Manohara, Chief Operating Officer
CFO: Rogelio Monzon, Chief Financial Officer
CMO: Gurmant Singh, Chief of Staff
CHR: Anand Manohara, Chief Operating Officer
CNO: Toby Davis, Chief Nursing Officer
Web address: www.goodsamhospital.com
Control: Partnership, Investor–owned (for–profit) **Service:** General medical and surgical

Staffed Beds: 64

☐ **KERN MEDICAL CENTER (050315)**, 1700 Mount Vernon Avenue, Zip 93306–4018; tel. 661/326–2000, (Nonreporting) **A**1 2 3 5 10
Primary Contact: Russell V. Judd, Chief Executive Officer
COO: Jared Leavitt, Chief Operating Officer
CFO: Andrew Cantu, Chief Financial Officer
CMO: Glenn Goldis, Chief Medical Officer
CHR: Lisa K. Hockersmith, Vice President Human Resources
CNO: Toni Smith, Chief Nursing Officer
Web address: www.kernmedical.com
Control: County, Government, nonfederal **Service:** General medical and surgical

Staffed Beds: 188

✠ **MERCY HOSPITALS OF BAKERSFIELD (050295)**, 2215 Truxtun Avenue, Zip 93301–3698, Mailing Address: P.O. Box 119, Zip 93302–0119; tel. 661/632–5000, (Includes MERCY SOUTHWEST HOSPITAL, 400 Old River Road, Bakersfield, California, Zip 93311; tel. 661/663–6000) **A**1 2 3 10 **F**11 12 13 15 26 29 30 31 34 35 36 40 43 44 45 46 47 48 49 51 54 57 59 62 64 65 68 69 70 71 72 74 75 76 77 78 79 81 84 85 86 87 92 97 100 101 102 107 108 110 111 112 113 114 115 116 117 118 119 120 121 122 124 126 130 131 132 135 146 147 148 149 154 **S** CommonSpirit Health, Chicago, IL
Primary Contact: Bruce Peters, Chief Executive Officer
CFO: Rodney Winegarner, Chief Financial Officer
CIO: Jeff Vague, Regional Manager Information Systems
CHR: Jay King, Vice President Human Resources
Web address: www.mercybakersfield.org
Control: Other not–for–profit (including NFP Corporation) **Service:** General medical and surgical

Staffed Beds: 204 **Admissions:** 11576 **Census:** 111 **Outpatient Visits:** 122131 **Births:** 2685 **Total Expense ($000):** 320145 **Payroll Expense ($000):** 120008 **Personnel:** 1110

BANNING—Riverside County

★ **SAN GORGONIO MEMORIAL HOSPITAL (050054)**, 600 North Highland Springs Avenue, Zip 92220–3046; tel. 951/845–1121, **A**10 22 **F**3 8 11 13 15 18 28 29 30 34 35 40 45 49 50 56 57 68 70 79 81 82 85 87 104 107 108 110 111 115 119 130 146 147 148 149
Primary Contact: Steven R. Barron, Interim Chief Executive Officer
CFO: David Recupero, Chief Financial Officer
CIO: Dan Howard, Director, Information Services
CHR: Annah Karam, Director Human Resources
CNO: Pat Brown, R.N., Chief Nursing Officer
Web address: www.sgmh.org
Control: Hospital district or authority, Government, nonfederal **Service:** General medical and surgical

Staffed Beds: 79 **Admissions:** 3039 **Census:** 31 **Outpatient Visits:** 52714 **Births:** 255 **Total Expense ($000):** 85128 **Payroll Expense ($000):** 36006 **Personnel:** 510

BARSTOW—San Bernardino County

✠ **BARSTOW COMMUNITY HOSPITAL (050298)**, 820 East Mountain View Street, Zip 92311–3004; tel. 760/256–1761, **A**1 10 20 **F**3 11 13 15 18 20 22 24 29 40 45 46 47 48 49 50 64 70 75 76 79 81 86 87 107 111 114 119 **S** Quorum Health, Brentwood, TN
Primary Contact: Matthew H. Blevins, Chief Executive Officer
CFO: Carrie Howell, Chief Financial Officer
CIO: Scott Bullock, Director Information Systems
CNO: Donna M Smith, Chief Nursing Officer
Web address: www.barstowhospital.com
Control: Corporation, Investor–owned (for–profit) **Service:** General medical and surgical

Staffed Beds: 30 **Admissions:** 2160 **Census:** 18 **Outpatient Visits:** 45876 **Births:** 367 **Total Expense ($000):** 44905 **Payroll Expense ($000):** 18778 **Personnel:** 305

BERKELEY—Alameda County

✠ **ALTA BATES SUMMIT MEDICAL CENTER (050305)**, 2450 Ashby Avenue, Zip 94705–2067; tel. 510/204–4444, (Includes ALTA BATES MEDICAL CENTER-HERRICK CAMPUS, 2001 Dwight Way, Berkeley, California, Zip 94704; tel. 510/204–4444), (Nonreporting) **A**1 3 5 10 **S** Sutter Health, Sacramento, CA
Primary Contact: Julie A. Petrini, Chief Executive Officer
CFO: Robert Petrina, Chief Financial Officer
CMO: John Gentile, M.D., Vice President Medical Affairs
Web address: www.altabatessummit.org/
Control: Other not–for–profit (including NFP Corporation) **Service:** General medical and surgical

Staffed Beds: 441

Many Facility Codes have changed. Please refer to the AHA Guide Code Chart. © 2019 AHA Guide

CA

BIG BEAR LAKE—San Bernardino County

★ **BEAR VALLEY COMMUNITY HOSPITAL (051335)**, 41870 Garstin Drive, Zip 92315, Mailing Address: P.O. Box 1649, Zip 92315–1649; tel. 909/866–6501, (Total facility includes 21 beds in nursing home–type unit) **A**10 18 **F**3 15 29 34 35 40 50 57 59 81 93 97 104 107 110 114 119 127 128 133 146 149 150 154 **S** QHR, Brentwood, TN
Primary Contact: John P. Friel, Chief Executive Officer
CFO: Garth Hamblin, Chief Financial Officer
CMO: Steven Knapik, M.D., Chief of Staff
CHR: Erin Wilson, Human Resource Director
CNO: Kerri Jex, R.N., Chief Nursing Officer
Web address: www.bvchd.com
Control: Hospital district or authority, Government, nonfederal **Service**: General medical and surgical

Staffed Beds: 30 Admissions: 143 Census: 20 Outpatient Visits: 42906 Births: 0 Total Expense ($000): 24522 Payroll Expense ($000): 9777 Personnel: 143

BISHOP—Inyo County

⊞ **NORTHERN INYO HOSPITAL (051324)**, 150 Pioneer Lane, Zip 93514–2599; tel. 760/873–5811, (Nonreporting) **A**1 5 10 18
Primary Contact: Kevin Flanigan, M.D., Chief Executive Officer
COO: Kelli Huntsinger, Chief Operating Officer
CMO: Thomas Boo, M.D., Chief of Staff
CIO: Adam Taylor, Manager Information Technology
CHR: Georgan L. Stottlemyre, Chief Human Relations Officer
CNO: Tracy Aspel, Chief Nursing Officer
Web address: www.nih.org
Control: Hospital district or authority, Government, nonfederal **Service**: General medical and surgical

Staffed Beds: 25

BLYTHE—Riverside County

⇑ **PALO VERDE HOSPITAL (050423)**, 250 North First Street, Zip 92225–1702; tel. 760/922–4115, (Nonreporting) **A**10 20 21
Primary Contact: Sandra J. Anaya, R.N., Chief Executive Officer
CFO: Christa Ronde, Assistant Chief Financial Officer
CMO: Hossain Sahlolbei, M.D., Chief of Staff
CIO: Jerome Learson, Manager Information Technology and Chief Security Officer
CHR: Myrna Davis, Manager Human Resources
CNO: Nena Foreman, Chief Nursing Officer
Web address: www.paloverdehospital.org
Control: Hospital district or authority, Government, nonfederal **Service**: General medical and surgical

Staffed Beds: 32

BRAWLEY—Imperial County

★ ⇑ **PIONEERS MEMORIAL HEALTHCARE DISTRICT (050342)**, 207 West Legion Road, Zip 92227–7780; tel. 760/351–3333, **A**3 10 21 **F**13 15 18 29 30 31 34 40 45 46 49 50 51 54 57 60 64 68 70 72 74 76 78 79 80 81 82 85 89 93 107 110 111 115 117 119 127 130 144 146 147 148
Primary Contact: Lawrence E. Lewis, Chief Executive Officer
COO: Stephen J Campbell, Chief Operating Officer
CFO: Roger Armstrong, Interim Chief Financial Officer
CMO: Kestutis V Kuraitis, M.D., Chief of Staff
CIO: Kathleen S. McKernan, Director Information Systems
CHR: Julie Cunningham, Associate Administrator and Chief Human Resources Officer
CNO: Robyn Atadero, R.N., Chief Nursing Officer
Web address: www.pmhd.org
Control: Hospital district or authority, Government, nonfederal **Service**: General medical and surgical

Staffed Beds: 107 Admissions: 5655 Census: 56 Outpatient Visits: 167941 Births: 1699 Total Expense ($000): 125184 Payroll Expense ($000): 50928

BREA—Orange County

⊞ **KINDRED HOSPITAL-BREA (052039)**, 875 North Brea Boulevard, Zip 92821–2699; tel. 714/529–6842, (Nonreporting) **A**1 10 **S** Kindred Healthcare, Louisville, KY
Primary Contact: Rafael Pena, Chief Executive Officer
COO: Denise Jenkins, Chief Clinical Officer
CFO: John Browne, Assistant Administrator Finance
CMO: Jyotika Wali, M.D., Chief of Staff
Web address: www.kindredhospitalbrea.com/
Control: Corporation, Investor–owned (for–profit) **Service**: Acute long–term care hospital

Staffed Beds: 48

BURBANK—Los Angeles County

⊞ △ **PROVIDENCE SAINT JOSEPH MEDICAL CENTER (050235)**, 501 South Buena Vista Street, Zip 91505–4866; tel. 818/843–5111, **A**1 2 3 5 7 10 19 **F**3 9 11 12 13 15 17 18 20 22 24 26 28 29 30 31 34 35 36 39 40 41 44 45 46 47 48 49 50 51 53 54 55 56 57 58 59 62 63 64 65 70 72 74 75 76 77 78 79 81 82 83 84 85 86 87 90 92 93 96 97 100 101 107 108 110 111 114 115 116 117 118 119 120 121 122 123 124 126 130 131 132 143 145 146 147 148 149 154 156 **S** Providence St. Joseph Health, Renton, WA
Primary Contact: Kelly Linden, Chief Executive Officer
CFO: Glenn Bales, Chief Financial Officer
CMO: Nick Testa, M.D., Chief Medical Officer
CIO: Anne Marie Brody, Director Information Systems Customer Service
CHR: LaDonna Najieb, Service Area Director Human Resources
CNO: Elizabeth Hart, R.N., MSN, Chief Nursing Officer
Web address: www.providence.org
Control: Church operated, Nongovernment, not–for–profit **Service**: General medical and surgical

Staffed Beds: 383 Admissions: 16007 Census: 197 Outpatient Visits: 253178 Births: 2202 Total Expense ($000): 335763 Payroll Expense ($000): 156818 Personnel: 1919

BURLINGAME—San Mateo County

⊞ **MILLS-PENINSULA HEALTH SERVICES (050007)**, 1501 Trousdale Drive, Zip 94010–3282; tel. 650/696–5400, (Includes MILLS HEALTH CENTER, 100 South San Mateo Drive, San Mateo, California, Zip 94401; tel. 650/696–4400; Janet Wagner, R.N., Chief Executive Officer; MILLS PENINSULA MEDICAL CENTER, 1501 Trousdale Drive, Burlingame, California, Zip 94010–3205; tel. 650/696–5400; Janet Wagner, R.N., Chief Executive Officer), (Nonreporting) **A**1 10 **S** Sutter Health, Sacramento, CA
Primary Contact: Janet Wagner, R.N., Chief Executive Officer
COO: Dolores S. Gomez, R.N., Chief Operating Officer
CFO: Catherine Messman, Chief Financial Officer
CMO: Ranjit Hundal, M.D., Chief Medical Executive
CIO: Michael Reandeau, Chief Information Officer
CHR: Claudia Christensen, Director, Human Resources
CNO: Vicki White, R.N., MS, Chief Nurse Executive
Web address: www.mills-peninsula.com
Control: Other not–for–profit (including NFP Corporation) **Service**: General medical and surgical

Staffed Beds: 266

CAMARILLO—Ventura County

★ **ST. JOHN'S PLEASANT VALLEY HOSPITAL (050616)**, 2309 Antonio Avenue, Zip 93010–1414; tel. 805/389–5800, (Nonreporting) **A**10 **S** CommonSpirit Health, Chicago, IL
Primary Contact: Darren W. Lee, President and Chief Executive Officer
COO: Richard Montmeny, Vice President Professional Services, On-Site Administrator
CFO: Donald P Bernard, Chief Financial Officer
CMO: Sahin Yanik, M.D., Vice President Medical Associate
CIO: Jeff Perry, Director Information Technology
CHR: Ed Gonzales, Vice President Human Resources
CNO: Dana Littlepage, Interim Chief Nursing Officer
Web address: www.dignityhealth.org/pleasantvalley
Control: Church operated **Service**: General medical and surgical

Staffed Beds: 127

Hospital, Medicare Provider Number, Address, Telephone, Approval, Facility, and Physician Codes, Health Care System

★ American Hospital Association (AHA) membership ○ Healthcare Facilities Accreditation Program ⇑ Center for Improvement in Healthcare Quality Accreditation
☐ The Joint Commission accreditation ◇ DNV Healthcare Inc. accreditation △ Commission on Accreditation of Rehabilitation Facilities (CARF) accreditation

CA

CAMP PENDLETON—San Diego County

⊞ **NAVAL HOSPITAL CAMP PENDLETON**, 200 Mercy Circle, Zip 92055–5191; Mailing Address: P.O. Box 555191, Zip 92055–5191; tel. 760/725–1304, (Nonreporting) **A**1 3 5 **S** Bureau of Medicine and Surgery, Department of the Navy, Falls Church, VA
Primary Contact: Captain Frank P. Pearson, Commanding Officer
CFO: Commander Gordon Blighton, Director Resource Management
CIO: Gabe Vallido, Chief Information Officer
CHR: Lieutenant Jet Ramos, Head Staff Administration
Web address: www.cpen.med.navy.mil/
Control: Department of Defense, Government, federal **Service**: General medical and surgical

Staffed Beds: 72

CARMICHAEL—Sacramento County

⊞ **MERCY SAN JUAN MEDICAL CENTER (050516)**, 6501 Coyle Avenue, Zip 95608–0306; tel. 916/537–5000, (Nonreporting) **A**1 2 3 5 10 **S** CommonSpirit Health, Chicago, IL
Primary Contact: Michael Korpiel, FACHE, Chief Executive Officer
COO: Paul R Luehrs, Chief Operating Officer
CFO: Robert Pascuzzi, Chief Financial Officer
CMO: Mark Owens, M.D., Vice President Medical Affairs
CHR: Donna Utley, Vice President Human Resources
Web address: www.mercysanjuan.org
Control: Church operated **Service**: General medical and surgical

Staffed Beds: 340

CASTRO VALLEY—Alameda County

⊞ **EDEN MEDICAL CENTER (050488)**, 20103 Lake Chabot Road, Zip 94546–5305; tel. 510/537–1234, (Nonreporting) **A**1 2 3 10 **S** Sutter Health, Sacramento, CA
Primary Contact: Stephen Gray, Chief Executive Officer
Web address: www.edenmedcenter.org
Control: Other not–for–profit (including NFP Corporation) **Service**: General medical and surgical

Staffed Beds: 130

CEDARVILLE—Modoc County

SURPRISE VALLEY HEALTH CARE DISTRICT (051308), 741 North Main Street, Zip 96104, Mailing Address: P.O. Box 246, Zip 96104–0246; tel. 530/279–6111, (Total facility includes 22 beds in nursing home–type unit) **A**10 18 **F**3 7 34 35 40 50 54 57 59 65 127 128 133 143 148 154
Primary Contact: Richard Cornwell, Chief Executive Officer
CFO: Renae Sweet, Chief Financial Officer
CMO: Chuck Colas, Medical Director
CHR: William Bostic, Administrative Assistant Human Resources
Web address: www.svhospital.org/
Control: Hospital district or authority, Government, nonfederal **Service**: General medical and surgical

Staffed Beds: 26 Admissions: 25 Census: 19 Outpatient Visits: 45 Births: 0

CERRITOS—Los Angeles County

☐ **COLLEGE HOSPITAL CERRITOS (054055)**, 10802 College Place, Zip 90703–1579; tel. 562/924–9581, (Nonreporting) **A**1 10 **S** College Health Enterprises, Santa Fe Springs, CA
Primary Contact: Stephen Witt, President and Chief Executive Officer
CFO: Roderick Bell, Chief Financial Officer
CHR: Holly Risha, Administrative Director Human Resources
Web address: www.collegehospitals.com
Control: Corporation, Investor–owned (for–profit) **Service**: Psychiatric

Staffed Beds: 187

CHESTER—Plumas County

SENECA HEALTHCARE DISTRICT (051327), 130 Brentwood Drive, Zip 96020–0737, Mailing Address: P.O. Box 737, Zip 96020–0737; tel. 530/258–2151, (Nonreporting) **A**5 10 18
Primary Contact: Linda S. Wagner, R.N., MSN, FACHE, Chief Executive Officer
CFO: Carlene Slusher, Director Finance
CMO: Dana Ware, M.D., Chief of Staff
CIO: Elizabeth Steffen, Director Information Technology
CHR: James Kooyman, Human Resources Manager
CNO: Karen Turner, Chief Nursing Officer
Web address: www.senecahospital.org
Control: Hospital district or authority, Government, nonfederal **Service**: General medical and surgical

Staffed Beds: 26

CHICO—Butte County

⊞ **ENLOE MEDICAL CENTER (050039)**, 1531 Esplanade, Zip 95926–3386; tel. 530/332–7300, (Includes ENLOE MEDICAL CENTER-COHASSET, 560 Cohasset Road, Chico, California, Zip 95926; tel. 530/332–7300) **A**1 10 **F**3 7 8 11 12 13 17 18 19 20 22 24 26 28 29 30 31 34 35 36 38 39 40 43 44 45 46 49 50 51 54 57 59 61 62 63 64 65 68 69 70 73 74 75 77 78 79 81 82 84 85 87 90 91 92 93 94 96 98 100 102 107 108 109 111 114 115 116 117 118 119 120 121 123 124 126 130 131 132 143 144 146 147 148 149 155 157
Primary Contact: Michael C. Wiltermood, President and Chief Executive Officer
CMO: Forrest Olson, M.D., Chief Medical Officer
CHR: Carol Linscheid, Vice President Human Resources
Web address: www.enloe.org
Control: Other not–for–profit (including NFP Corporation) **Service**: General medical and surgical

Staffed Beds: 298 Admissions: 19617 Census: 221 Outpatient Visits: 358693 Births: 1671 Total Expense ($000): 601185 Payroll Expense ($000): 208493 Personnel: 2643

CHINO—San Bernardino County

☐ **CANYON RIDGE HOSPITAL (054111)**, 5353 'G' Street, Zip 91710–5250; tel. 909/590–3700, (Nonreporting) **A**1 3 10 **S** Universal Health Services, Inc., King of Prussia, PA
Primary Contact: Burt Harris, Acting Chief Executive Officer
CFO: Burt Harris, Chief Financial Officer
CMO: Mir Ali-Khan, M.D., Medical Director
CIO: Maria Patterson, Manager Health Information Management
CHR: Ericca Lopez, Director Human Resources
Web address: www.canyonridgehospital.com
Control: Corporation, Investor–owned (for–profit) **Service**: Psychiatric

Staffed Beds: 106

★ ○ **CHINO VALLEY MEDICAL CENTER (050586)**, 5451 Walnut Avenue, Zip 91710–2672; tel. 909/464–8600, **A**5 10 11 12 13 **F**3 15 34 40 61 70 **S** Prime Healthcare, Ontario, CA
Primary Contact: Tim Moran, Chief Executive Officer
CIO: Vic Mahan, Chief Information Officer
Web address: www.cvmc.com
Control: State, Government, nonfederal **Service**: General medical and surgical

Staffed Beds: 112 Admissions: 5213 Census: 41 Outpatient Visits: 47708 Births: 0 Total Expense ($000): 83349 Payroll Expense ($000): 34587 Personnel: 561

CHULA VISTA—San Diego County

SCRIPPS MERCY HOSPITAL CHULA VISTA See Scripps Mercy Hospital, San Diego

⊞ **SHARP CHULA VISTA MEDICAL CENTER (050222)**, 751 Medical Center Court, Zip 91911–6699; tel. 619/502–5800, (Total facility includes 100 beds in nursing home–type unit) **A**1 2 10 **F**8 10 11 12 13 15 17 18 20 22 24 26 28 29 30 31 34 35 40 46 47 49 51 53 54 57 59 60 63 64 65 70 72 75 76 77 78 79 81 82 84 85 86 87 93 107 108 114 115 118 119 120 121 123 124 126 128 130 132 143 146 147 148 156 **S** Sharp HealthCare, San Diego, CA
Primary Contact: Pablo Velez, R.N., Ph.D., Chief Executive Officer
CMO: Lynn Welling, M.D., Chief Medical Officer
CHR: Zoe Gardner, Manager Human Resources
Web address: www.sharp.com
Control: Other not–for–profit (including NFP Corporation) **Service**: General medical and surgical

Staffed Beds: 338 Admissions: 16218 Census: 284 Outpatient Visits: 157856 Births: 2473 Total Expense ($000): 420563 Payroll Expense ($000): 167213 Personnel: 1829

CLEARLAKE—Lake County

⊞ **ADVENTIST HEALTH CLEAR LAKE (051317)**, 15630 18th Avenue, Zip 95422–9336, Mailing Address: P.O. Box 6710, Zip 95422; tel. 707/994–6486, **A**1 10 18 **F**29 30 33 34 35 39 40 45 50 57 64 70 76 77 79 81 82 85 86 87 92 93 96 97 100 107 108 110 111 114 115 119 127 129 130 132 133 146 148 149 154 **S** Adventist Health, Roseville, CA
Primary Contact: David Santos, President and Chief Executive Officer
COO: David Santos, President Chief Executive Officer
CFO: Carlton Jacobson, Vice President of Finance
CMO: Marc Shapiro, M.D., Chief Medical Officer
CIO: Cambria Wheeler, Communications and Marketing
CHR: Audrey Barrall, Director Human Resources
CNO: Colleen Assavapisitkul, R.N., Patient Care Executive
Web address: www.adventisthealth.org
Control: Church operated, Nongovernment, not–for–profit **Service**: General medical and surgical

Staffed Beds: 25 Admissions: 1462 Census: 16 Outpatient Visits: 223502 Births: 159 Total Expense ($000): 84225 Payroll Expense ($000): 29714 Personnel: 527

Many Facility Codes have changed. Please refer to the AHA Guide Code Chart. © 2019 AHA Guide

CLOVIS—Fresno County

CLOVIS COMMUNITY MEDICAL CENTER (050492), 2755 Herndon Avenue, Zip 93611–6801; tel. 559/324–4000, (Nonreporting) **A**10 **S** Community Medical Centers, Fresno, CA
Primary Contact: Craig Castro, Chief Executive Officer
CFO: Tracy Kiritani, Vice President and Chief Financial Officer
CIO: George Vasquez, Chief Technology Officer
CHR: Ginny Burdick, Senior Vice President and Chief Human Resources Officer
Web address: www.communitymedical.org
Control: Other not–for–profit (including NFP Corporation) **Service**: General medical and surgical

Staffed Beds: 109

COLTON—San Bernardino County

⊞ **ARROWHEAD REGIONAL MEDICAL CENTER (050245)**, 400 North Pepper Avenue, Zip 92324–1819; tel. 909/580–1000, **A**1 3 5 10 13 **F**3 8 13 15 16 18 20 22 28 29 30 31 32 34 35 36 39 40 43 45 47 49 50 51 52 54 55 56 57 60 64 66 68 70 71 72 74 75 76 77 78 79 81 82 84 85 86 87 89 91 92 93 97 98 100 101 102 107 108 110 111 114 115 116 118 119 120 121 130 132 135 146 147 148 149 150
Primary Contact: William L. Gilbert, Hospital Director
CFO: Arvind Oswal, Interim Chief Financial Officer
CMO: Varadarajan Subbiah, M.D., Chief Medical Officer
CIO: Felix Ekpo, Manager, Information Systems
CHR: Kevin Saunders, Human Resources Officer III
CNO: Jerome Dayao, Chief Nursing Officer
Web address: www.arrowheadmedcenter.org
Control: County, Government, nonfederal **Service**: General medical and surgical

Staffed Beds: 456 **Admissions:** 21689 **Census:** 306 **Outpatient Visits:** 323886 **Births:** 3205 **Total Expense ($000):** 712266 **Payroll Expense ($000):** 206687 **Personnel:** 3142

CONCORD—Contra Costa County

⊞ **JOHN MUIR BEHAVIORAL HEALTH CENTER (054131)**, 2740 Grant Street, Zip 94520–2265; tel. 925/674–4100, (Nonreporting) **A**1 10 **S** John Muir Health, Walnut Creek, CA
Primary Contact: Cindy Bolter, Chief Nursing and Operations Officer
COO: Arman Danielyan, M.D., Chief of Staff
CFO: Christian Pass, Senior Vice President and Chief Financial Officer
CMO: O B Towery, M.D., Chief of Staff
CIO: Jim Wesley, Senior Vice President and Chief Information Officer
CHR: Lisa Foust, Senior Vice President Human Resources
CNO: Cindy Bolter, Chief Nursing and Operations Officer
Web address: www.johnmuirhealth.com
Control: Other not–for–profit (including NFP Corporation) **Service**: Psychiatric

Staffed Beds: 73

⊞ **JOHN MUIR MEDICAL CENTER, CONCORD (050496)**, 2540 East Street, Zip 94520–1906; tel. 925/682–8200, **A**1 2 3 10 **F**3 12 15 17 18 20 22 24 26 28 29 30 31 34 37 39 40 41 44 45 46 47 48 49 50 55 56 57 58 59 61 64 68 70 74 75 77 78 79 80 81 82 83 84 85 86 87 93 100 102 107 108 110 115 118 119 120 121 123 126 130 132 141 145 146 148 149 156 157 **S** John Muir Health, Walnut Creek, CA
Primary Contact: Michael S. Thomas, President and Chief Administrative Officer
COO: Michael S Thomas, President and Chief Administrative Officer
CFO: Christian Pass, Interim Chief Financial Officer
CMO: John Merson, M.D., Chief of Staff
CIO: Jon Russell, Senior Vice President and Chief Information Officer
CHR: Lisa Foust, Senior Vice President Human Resources
CNO: Donna Brackley, R.N., MSN, Senior Vice President Patient Care Services
Web address: www.johnmuirhealth.com
Control: Other not–for–profit (including NFP Corporation) **Service**: General medical and surgical

Staffed Beds: 207 **Admissions:** 11406 **Census:** 148 **Outpatient Visits:** 158424 **Births:** 0 **Total Expense ($000):** 501292 **Payroll Expense ($000):** 177738 **Personnel:** 1063

CORONA—Riverside County

☐ **CORONA REGIONAL MEDICAL CENTER (050329)**, 800 South Main Street, Zip 92882–3400; tel. 951/737–4343, (Includes CORONA REGIONAL MEDICAL CENTER-REHABILITATION, 730 Magnolia Avenue, Corona, California, Zip 92879; tel. 951/736–7200) **A**1 3 10 **F**3 8 13 15 18 20 22 26 29 30 34 35 40 45 46 47 48 49 50 51 57 59 60 62 63 64 65 67 68 70 75 76 79 81 84 85 87 89 98 100 101 102 104 105 106 107 108 110 111 114 115 119 128 130 143 146 147 148 149 154 **S** Universal Health Services, Inc., King of Prussia, PA
Primary Contact: Mark H. Uffer, Chief Executive Officer
COO: Mitchell Winnik, Chief Operating Officer
CFO: Kanner Tillman, Chief Financial Officer
CMO: Alaa Y Afifi, M.D., Chief of Staff
CIO: De'Niro Pankey, Director Information Systems
CHR: Dale Cole, Director, Human Resources
CNO: Kim Colonnelli, Chief Nursing Officer
Web address: www.coronaregional.com
Control: Individual, Investor–owned (for–profit) **Service**: General medical and surgical

Staffed Beds: 147 **Admissions:** 9323 **Census:** 147 **Outpatient Visits:** 70276 **Births:** 889 **Total Expense ($000):** 152681 **Payroll Expense ($000):** 74246 **Personnel:** 1004

CORONADO—San Diego County

⊞ **SHARP CORONADO HOSPITAL AND HEALTHCARE CENTER (050234)**, 250 Prospect Place, Zip 92118–1999; tel. 619/522–3600, (Total facility includes 108 beds in nursing home–type unit) **A**1 **F**3 8 11 15 29 30 34 35 40 42 44 45 46 47 49 53 57 58 59 60 64 65 68 70 74 75 77 79 81 82 84 85 86 87 91 93 107 111 114 126 128 130 132 135 146 148 149 154 **S** Sharp HealthCare, San Diego, CA
Primary Contact: Susan Stone, R.N., Ph.D., Senior Vice President and Chief Executive Officer
CFO: Victoria Day, Chief Financial Officer and Vice President of Ancillary Services
CHR: Rachel Davis, Director
CNO: Christopher Walker, Chief Nursing Officer and Operating Officer
Web address: www.sharp.com
Control: Other not–for–profit (including NFP Corporation) **Service**: General medical and surgical

Staffed Beds: 181 **Admissions:** 2494 **Census:** 118 **Outpatient Visits:** 77370 **Births:** 0 **Total Expense ($000):** 106109 **Payroll Expense ($000):** 46052 **Personnel:** 465

COSTA MESA—Orange County

☐ **COLLEGE HOSPITAL COSTA MESA (050543)**, 301 Victoria Street, Zip 92627–7131; tel. 949/642–2734, (Nonreporting) **A**1 10 **S** College Health Enterprises, Santa Fe Springs, CA
Primary Contact: Susan L. Taylor, JD, Chief Executive Officer
CFO: Dale Bracy, Chief Financial Officer
CMO: Michael Schwartz, M.D., Chief of Staff
CIO: Eladio Aldana, Manager Information Systems
CHR: Sharon DuBruyne, Director Human Resources
Web address: www.collegehospitals.com/cosHome
Control: Corporation, Investor–owned (for–profit) **Service**: Psychiatric

Staffed Beds: 122

FAIRVIEW DEVELOPMENTAL CENTER (050548), 2501 Harbor Boulevard, Zip 92626; tel. 714/957–5000, (Nonreporting) **A**10
Primary Contact: Cheryl Bright, Executive Director
Web address: www.dds.ca.gov/fairview/index.cfm
Control: State, Government, nonfederal **Service**: Intellectual disabilities

Staffed Beds: 237

COVINA—Los Angeles County

☐ **AURORA CHARTER OAK HOSPITAL (054069)**, 1161 East Covina Boulevard, Zip 91724–1599; tel. 626/966–1632, (Nonreporting) **A**1 10 **S** Signature Healthcare Services, Corona, CA
Primary Contact: Todd A. Smith, Chief Executive Officer
COO: Sheila Cordova, Director Clinical Services and Chief Operating Officer
CMO: Adib Bitar, M.D., Medical Director
CHR: Christine de la Paz, Director Human Resources
CNO: Sheila Cordova, Chief Operating Officer and Chief Nursing Officer
Web address: www.charteroakhospital.com
Control: Corporation, Investor–owned (for–profit) **Service**: Psychiatric

Staffed Beds: 146

CA

Hospital, Medicare Provider Number, Address, Telephone, Approval, Facility, and Physician Codes, Health Care System

★ American Hospital Association (AHA) membership
☐ The Joint Commission accreditation
○ Healthcare Facilities Accreditation Program
◇ DNV Healthcare Inc. accreditation
⇑ Center for Improvement in Healthcare Quality Accreditation
△ Commission on Accreditation of Rehabilitation Facilities (CARF) accreditation

CA

★ **CITRUS VALLEY MEDICAL CENTER-INTER COMMUNITY CAMPUS (050382)**, 210 West San Bernadino Road, Zip 91723–1515, Mailing Address: P.O. Box 6108, Zip 91722–5108; tel. 626/331–7331, (Includes CITRUS VALLEY MEDICAL CENTER-INTER-COMMUNITY CAMPUS, 210 West San Bernadino Road, Covina, California, Zip 91723–1515, Mailing Address: P O Box 6108, Zip 91722–5108, tel. 626/331–7331; Robert H Curry, President and Chief Executive Officer; CITRUS VALLEY MEDICAL CENTER-QUEEN OF THE VALLEY CAMPUS, 1115 South Sunset Avenue, West Covina, California, Zip 91790–3940, Mailing Address: P O Box 1980, Zip 91793–1980, tel. 626/962–4011; Robert H Curry, President and Chief Executive Officer) **A**3 10 **F**3 11 13 15 17 18 20 22 24 26 28 29 30 31 34 35 40 41 45 47 48 49 50 51 53 54 56 57 59 60 64 65 68 69 70 72 74 75 77 78 79 80 81 84 85 86 87 90 93 95 96 98 107 108 110 111 114 115 118 119 121 126 128 130 131 133 146 147 148 149 156 157 **S** Citrus Valley Health Partners, Covina, CA
Primary Contact: Robert H. Curry, President and Chief Executive Officer
CFO: Roger Sharma, Executive Vice President/Chief Financial Officer
CIO: Daniel J Nash, Chief Information Officer
CHR: Ryan Burke Esq Vice President, Human Resources
CNO: Melissa Howard, Chief Nurse Executive, ICH & FPH
Web address: www.cvhp.org
Control: Other not–for–profit (including NFP Corporation) **Service:** General medical and surgical

Staffed Beds: 314 **Admissions:** 23539 **Census:** 291 **Outpatient Visits:** 201496 **Births:** 3758 **Total Expense ($000):** 451892 **Payroll Expense ($000):** 154156 **Personnel:** 1964

CRESCENT CITY—Del Norte County

✠ **SUTTER COAST HOSPITAL (050417)**, 800 East Washington Boulevard, Zip 95531–8359; tel. 707/464–8511, (Nonreporting) **A**1 10 20 **S** Sutter Health, Sacramento, CA
Primary Contact: Mitchell J. Hanna, Chief Executive Officer
CNO: Rose Corcoran, R.N., Chief Nursing Executive
Web address: www.sutterhealth.org
Control: Other not–for–profit (including NFP Corporation) **Service:** General medical and surgical

Staffed Beds: 49

CULVER CITY—Los Angeles County

SOUTHERN CALIFORNIA HOSPITAL AT CULVER CITY (050752), 3828 Delmas Terrace, Zip 90232–6806; tel. 310/836–7000, (Nonreporting) **S** Prospect Medical Holdings, Los Angeles, CA
Primary Contact: Sean Fowler, Chief Executive Officer
CFO: Vincent Rubin, Chief Financial Officer
CMO: Martha Sonnenberg, M.D., Chief of Staff
CIO: Carrie Bonar, Chief Information Officer
CHR: Betty J Harris, Director Human Resources
Web address: www.sch-culvercity.com
Control: Corporation, Investor–owned (for–profit) **Service:** General medical and surgical

Staffed Beds: 239

DALY CITY—San Mateo County

☐ **SETON MEDICAL CENTER (050289)**, 1900 Sullivan Avenue, Zip 94015–2229; tel. 650/992–4000, (Total facility includes 164 beds in nursing home–type unit) **A**1 2 3 10 **F**3 8 15 18 20 22 24 26 29 30 31 34 35 37 39 40 44 45 46 48 49 50 51 56 57 58 59 60 64 66 68 70 74 75 77 78 79 81 82 84 85 87 92 93 96 98 100 102 103 107 108 110 111 114 116 117 118 119 120 121 123 124 126 128 130 132 135 141 143 146 148 149 154 156 **S** Verity Health System, Los Angeles, CA
Primary Contact: Mark Fratzke, R.N., President and Chief Executive Officer
COO: Stephanie Mearns, Vice President Patient Care Services and Chief Nurse Executive
CFO: Richard Wood, Chief Financial Officer
CMO: Timothy Ranney, M.D., Chief Medical Officer
CHR: Patricia White, Vice President Human Resources
CNO: Mark R Brown, Chief Nursing Officer
Web address: www.setonmedicalcenter.org
Control: Other not–for–profit (including NFP Corporation) **Service:** General medical and surgical

Staffed Beds: 397 **Admissions:** 5422 **Census:** 238 **Outpatient Visits:** 27100 **Births:** 0 **Total Expense ($000):** 294119 **Payroll Expense ($000):** 124362 **Personnel:** 869

DAVIS—Yolo County

✠ **SUTTER DAVIS HOSPITAL (050537)**, 2000 Sutter Place, Zip 95616–6201, Mailing Address: P.O. Box 1617, Zip 95617–1617; tel. 530/756–6440, (Nonreporting) **A**1 3 5 10 **S** Sutter Health, Sacramento, CA
Primary Contact: Rachael McKinney, FACHE, Chief Executive Officer
CFO: Patti Pilgrim, Chief Financial Officer
CMO: Deven Merchant, M.D., Chief Medical Executive
CHR: Don Hartman, Director Human Resources
CNO: Tamara Davis, R.N., Chief Nurse Executive Officer
Web address: www.sutterhealth.org
Control: Other not–for–profit (including NFP Corporation) **Service:** General medical and surgical

Staffed Beds: 48

DELANO—Kern County

○ **DELANO REGIONAL MEDICAL CENTER (050608)**, 1401 Garces Highway, Zip 93215–3690, Mailing Address: P.O. Box 460, Zip 93216–0460; tel. 661/725–4800, (Nonreporting) **A**10 11
Primary Contact: Bahram Ghaffari, President
CFO: Bahram Ghaffari, President
CIO: Sandy Bakich, Director Information Management
CHR: Del Garbanzos, Director Human Resources
CNO: Amy Scroggs, Chief Nursing Officer
Web address: www.drmc.com
Control: Other not–for–profit (including NFP Corporation) **Service:** General medical and surgical

Staffed Beds: 100

DOWNEY—Los Angeles County

✠ **KAISER PERMANENTE DOWNEY MEDICAL CENTER (050139)**, 9333 Imperial Highway, Zip 90242–2812; tel. 562/657–9000, **A**1 3 10 **F**2 3 5 11 12 14 15 29 30 31 32 33 34 38 39 40 41 44 45 46 47 48 49 50 51 52 53 54 55 56 57 58 59 60 61 62 63 64 65 66 68 70 71 72 73 74 75 76 77 78 79 81 82 83 84 85 86 87 88 89 93 94 96 97 100 102 104 107 108 110 111 114 115 119 126 129 130 131 132 134 135 141 144 146 147 148 149 150 153 154 156 **S** Kaiser Foundation Hospitals, Oakland, CA
Primary Contact: James Branchick, R.N., MS, Senior Vice President and Area Manager
CNO: Patricia J Clausen, R.N., Chief Nurse Executive
Web address: www.kaiserpermanente.org
Control: Other not–for–profit (including NFP Corporation) **Service:** General medical and surgical

Staffed Beds: 352 **Admissions:** 15830 **Census:** 185 **Outpatient Visits:** 245683 **Births:** 4669 **Personnel:** 3262

★ **PIH HEALTH HOSPITAL - DOWNEY (050393)**, 11500 Brookshire Avenue, Zip 90241–4917; tel. 562/904–5000, **A**3 10 12 13 22 **F**3 11 13 15 18 20 22 24 26 29 30 36 40 41 45 46 48 49 50 51 55 59 60 61 64 68 70 72 74 76 79 81 84 85 87 91 92 93 97 100 107 111 114 115 119 130 146 147 148 149 154 156 **S** PIH Health, Whittier, CA
Primary Contact: James R. West, President and Chief Executive Officer
COO: Ramona Pratt, Chief Operating Officer
CFO: Greg Williams, Chief Financial Officer
CIO: Jason Fischer, Chief Information Officer
CHR: Sherri Hollingsworth, Chief Human Resources Officer
CNO: Judy Pugach, Chief Nursing Officer
Web address: www.PIHHealth.org
Control: Other not–for–profit (including NFP Corporation) **Service:** General medical and surgical

Staffed Beds: 156 **Admissions:** 8125 **Census:** 80 **Outpatient Visits:** 77843 **Births:** 936 **Total Expense ($000):** 165578 **Payroll Expense ($000):** 71482 **Personnel:** 1018

☐ △ **RANCHO LOS AMIGOS NATIONAL REHABILITATION CENTER (050717)**, 7601 East Imperial Highway, Zip 90242–3496; tel. 562/401–7111, (Nonreporting) **A**1 3 5 7 10 **S** Los Angeles County-Department of Health Services, Los Angeles, CA
Primary Contact: Jorge Orozco, Chief Executive Officer
COO: Benjamin Ovando, Chief Operations Officer
CFO: Robin Bayus, Chief Financial Officer
CMO: Mindy Aisen, M.D., Chief Medical Officer
CIO: Francis Tang, Chief Information Officer
CHR: Elizabeth Jacobi, Associate Director Human Resources
CNO: Aries Limbaga, R.N., Chief Nursing Officer
Web address: www.rancho.org
Control: County, Government, nonfederal **Service:** Rehabilitation

Staffed Beds: 207

Many Facility Codes have changed. Please refer to the AHA Guide Code Chart.   © 2019 AHA Guide

CA

DUARTE—Los Angeles County

☒ **CITY OF HOPE'S HELFORD CLINICAL RESEARCH HOSPITAL (050146)**, 1500 East Duarte Road, Zip 91010–3012; tel. 626/256–4673, **A**1 2 3 5 8 10 **F**3 8 11 14 15 18 19 29 30 31 34 35 36 38 44 45 46 47 49 50 55 56 57 58 59 61 64 68 70 74 75 77 78 79 80 81 82 84 85 86 87 88 89 91 92 93 94 96 100 101 104 107 108 110 111 114 115 116 117 118 119 120 121 123 124 126 130 132 135 136 142 144 145 146 147 148 149 154 156
Primary Contact: Robert Stone, President and Chief Executive Officer
COO: Jeff E. Walker, Chief Operating Officer
CFO: Jennifer Parkhurst, Chief Financial Officer
CMO: William D. Boswell, M.D., Jr Chief Medical Officer
CIO: Mark Hulse, MSN, Chief Digital Officer
CHR: Stephanie Neuvirth, Chief Human Resource and Diversity Officer
Web address: www.cityofhope.org
Control: Other not–for–profit (including NFP Corporation) **Service:** Cancer

Staffed Beds: 215 **Admissions:** 6900 **Census:** 200 **Outpatient Visits:** 238400 **Births:** 0 **Total Expense ($000):** 1260403 **Payroll Expense ($000):** 387963 **Personnel:** 4107

EL CENTRO—Imperial County

☒ **EL CENTRO REGIONAL MEDICAL CENTER (050045)**, 1415 Ross Avenue, Zip 92243–4398; tel. 760/339–7100, (Nonreporting) **A**1 3 10
Primary Contact: Adolphe Edward, Chief Executive Officer
COO: Tomas Virgen, R.N., MSN, Chief Operating Officer
CFO: Kathleen Farmer, Assistant Administrator Finance and Chief Financial Officer
CIO: John Gaede, Director Information Systems
CHR: Bill Moore, Chief Human Resources
Web address: www.ecrmc.org
Control: City, Government, nonfederal **Service:** General medical and surgical

Staffed Beds: 161

ELDRIDGE—Sonoma County

SONOMA DEVELOPMENTAL CENTER (050547), 15000 Arnold Drive, Zip 95431–8900, Mailing Address: P.O. Box 1493, Zip 95431–1493; tel. 707/938–6000, (Nonreporting) **A**10
Primary Contact: Aleana Carreon, Executive Director
COO: Karen Clark, Director Administrative Services
CMO: Carol Castillo, Medical Director
CHR: Brenda Dukes, Director Human Resources
Web address: www.dds.ca.gov/sonoma
Control: State, Government, nonfederal **Service:** Intellectual disabilities

Staffed Beds: 546

ENCINITAS—San Diego County

☒ **SCRIPPS MEMORIAL HOSPITAL-ENCINITAS (050503)**, 354 Santa Fe Drive, Zip 92024–5182, Mailing Address: P.O. Box 230817, Zip 92023–0817; tel. 760/633–6501, **A**1 10 **F**3 8 13 14 15 18 20 22 26 29 30 31 34 35 40 44 49 50 54 57 58 59 64 65 68 70 74 75 76 77 78 79 81 82 84 85 86 87 90 91 92 93 94 95 96 107 108 110 111 114 115 118 119 126 130 132 141 146 148 **S** Scripps Health, San Diego, CA
Primary Contact: Carl J. Etter, Chief Executive and Senior Vice President
COO: Jan Zachry, R.N., Vice President Administrator and Chief Operations Executive
CFO: Sharon Creal, Vice President Financial Operations
CHR: Steve Rust, Director, Human Resources
CNO: Jan Zachry, R.N., Vice President Administrator and Chief Operations Executive
Web address: www.scripps.org
Control: Other not–for–profit (including NFP Corporation) **Service:** General medical and surgical

Staffed Beds: 171 **Admissions:** 12480 **Census:** 142 **Outpatient Visits:** 85576 **Births:** 1862 **Total Expense ($000):** 297979 **Payroll Expense ($000):** 111996 **Personnel:** 1334

ENCINO—Los Angeles County; See Los Angeles

ESCONDIDO—San Diego County

☒ △ **PALOMAR MEDICAL CENTER (050115)**, 2185 West Citracado Parkway, Zip 92029–4159; tel. 760/739–3000, **A**1 3 5 7 10 **F**3 12 13 15 17 18 20 22 24 26 28 29 30 31 40 43 45 46 49 50 51 62 64 68 70 74 75 76 77 78 79 81 82 84 85 87 93 96 98 104 107 108 111 112 114 115 119 120 121 123 124 126 129 130 146 147 148 149 153 157 **S** Palomar Health, Escondido, CA
Primary Contact: Mariellena Sudak, R.N., MSN, Vice President and Chief Nursing Officer
CMO: Duane Buringrud, M.D., Chief Medical and Quality Officer
CIO: Prudence August, Chief Information Officer
CHR: Brenda C Turner, Chief Human Resources Officer
CNO: Mariellena Sudak, R.N., MSN, Vice President and Chief Nursing Officer
Web address: www.palomarhealth.org
Control: Hospital district or authority, Government, nonfederal **Service:** General medical and surgical

Staffed Beds: 403 **Admissions:** 22794 **Census:** 254 **Outpatient Visits:** 206399 **Births:** 3165 **Total Expense ($000):** 566424 **Payroll Expense ($000):** 211414 **Personnel:** 1968

EUREKA—Humboldt County

HUMBOLDT COUNTY MENTAL HEALTH (054124), 720 Wood Street, Zip 95501–4413; tel. 707/268–2900, (Nonreporting) **A**10
Primary Contact: Jet L. DeKruse, Administrator
CMO: Harpreet Duggal, M.D., Medical Director, Department of Health and Human Services
CNO: Sherry Gallagher, Director Nursing, Department of Health and Human Services
Web address: www.https://co.humboldt.ca.us/hhs/mhb/
Control: County, Government, nonfederal **Service:** Psychiatric

Staffed Beds: 16

☒ **ST. JOSEPH HOSPITAL (050006)**, 2700 Dolbeer Street, Zip 95501–4799; tel. 707/445–8121, (Includes GENERAL HOSPITAL, 2200 Harrison Avenue, Eureka, California, Zip 95501–3299; tel. 707/445–5111), (Nonreporting) **A**1 2 3 10 19 **S** Providence St. Joseph Health, Renton, WA
Primary Contact: Roberta Luskin-Hawk, M.D., Chief Executive
CFO: Michel Riccioni, Chief Financial Officer
CMO: Mathew Miller, M.D., Vice President and Chief Medical Officer
CIO: Wendy Thorpe, Area Director Information Systems
CHR: Linda Cook, Vice President Human Resources
CNO: Carol Reeder, R.N., Chief Nursing Officer
Web address: www.stjosepheureka.org
Control: Church operated **Service:** General medical and surgical

Staffed Beds: 153

FAIRFIELD—Solano County

☒ **NORTHBAY MEDICAL CENTER (050367)**, 1200 B. Gale Wilson Boulevard, Zip 94533–3587; tel. 707/646–5000, (Includes NORTHBAY VACAVALLEY HOSPITAL, 1000 Nut Tree Road, Vacaville, California, Zip 95687–4100; tel. 707/624–7000; Aimee Brewer, President, NorthBay Healthcare Group) **A**1 2 10 **F**2 3 6 8 11 13 17 18 19 20 22 24 26 28 29 30 31 32 34 35 36 40 41 43 44 45 46 49 50 53 54 55 56 57 59 62 63 64 65 70 72 73 74 75 76 77 78 79 80 81 82 84 85 87 89 92 93 94 95 97 100 105 106 107 114 115 118 119 120 121 124 129 130 131 132 144 146 147 148 149 154 156 157
Primary Contact: Aimee Brewer, President, NorthBay Healthcare Group
CFO: Arthur E DeNio, Vice President and Chief Financial Officer
CMO: Seth Kaufman, M.D., Chief Medical Officer
CIO: Christopher Timbers, Vice President and Chief Information Officer
CNO: Traci A Duncan, Vice President, Chief Nursing Officer
Web address: www.northbay.org
Control: Other not–for–profit (including NFP Corporation) **Service:** General medical and surgical

Staffed Beds: 176 **Admissions:** 6547 **Census:** 121 **Outpatient Visits:** 380824 **Births:** 1157 **Total Expense ($000):** 559295 **Payroll Expense ($000):** 240688 **Personnel:** 1659

Hospital, Medicare Provider Number, Address, Telephone, Approval, Facility, and Physician Codes, Health Care System

★ American Hospital Association (AHA) membership
☐ The Joint Commission accreditation
○ Healthcare Facilities Accreditation Program
◇ DNV Healthcare Inc. accreditation
⇑ Center for Improvement in Healthcare Quality Accreditation
△ Commission on Accreditation of Rehabilitation Facilities (CARF) accreditation

CA

FALL RIVER MILLS—Shasta County

★ **MAYERS MEMORIAL HOSPITAL DISTRICT (051305)**, 43563 Highway 299 East, Zip 96028–0459, Mailing Address: P.O. Box 459, Zip 96028–0459; tel. 530/336–5511, (Nonreporting) **A**10 18
Primary Contact: Louis James. Ward, Interim Chief Executive Officer
COO: Louis James Ward, Chief Operating Officer
CFO: Travis Lakey, Chief Financial Officer
CMO: Thomas Watson, M.D., Chief of Staff
CIO: Chris Broadway, Manager Information Technology
CHR: Julie Thompson, Manager Personnel and Payroll
CNO: Sherry Wilson, R.N., Chief Nursing Officer
Web address: www.mayersmemorial.com
Control: Hospital district or authority, Government, nonfederal **Service**: General medical and surgical

Staffed Beds: 97

FOLSOM—Sacramento County

⊞ **MERCY HOSPITAL OF FOLSOM (050414)**, 1650 Creekside Drive, Zip 95630–3400; tel. 916/983–7400, (Nonreporting) **A**1 5 10 **S** CommonSpirit Health, Chicago, IL
Primary Contact: Randall W. Ross, FACHE, President and Chief Executive Officer
CMO: Robert Allen, M.D., Chief Medical Officer
CHR: Anthony Robinson, Manager, Human Resources
CNO: Josh Freilich, Vice President and Chief Nurse Executive
Web address: www.mercyfolsom.org
Control: Church operated **Service**: General medical and surgical

Staffed Beds: 106

⊞ **VIBRA HOSPITAL OF SACRAMENTO (052033)**, 330 Montrose Drive, Zip 95630–2720; tel. 916/351–9151, **A**1 10 **F**3 29 30 34 46 49 68 70 75 77 84 85 91 119 130 148 149 **S** Vibra Healthcare, Mechanicsburg, PA
Primary Contact: Kimberly C. Long, R.N., MSN, Chief Executive Officer
CFO: Todd Scott, Chief Financial Officer
CMO: S. Kwon Lee, M.D., Chief of Staff
CHR: Glenda Franco, Director, Human Resources
Web address: www.vhsacramento.com
Control: Individual, Investor–owned (for–profit) **Service**: Acute long–term care hospital

Staffed Beds: 58 Admissions: 361 Census: 44 Outpatient Visits: 0 Births: 0 Total Expense ($000): 27760 Payroll Expense ($000): 14372 Personnel: 221

FONTANA—San Bernardino County

⊞ **KAISER PERMANENTE FONTANA MEDICAL CENTER (050140)**, 9961 Sierra Avenue, Zip 92335–6794; tel. 909/427–5000, (Includes KAISER PERMANENTE ONTARIO MEDICAL CENTER, 2295 South Vineyard Avenue, Ontario, California, Zip 91761–7925; tel. 909/724–5000; Greg Christian, Sr Vice President, Area Manager - San Bernardino County Area) **A**1 3 5 10 **F**3 8 11 12 13 15 17 18 20 22 24 26 29 30 31 35 40 41 44 45 46 48 49 50 51 53 57 58 59 60 61 62 63 64 65 68 70 72 73 74 75 76 77 78 79 81 82 84 85 86 87 88 89 100 102 107 108 110 111 114 115 117 118 119 126 130 131 132 135 136 141 143 145 146 148 149 154 **S** Kaiser Foundation Hospitals, Oakland, CA
Primary Contact: Greg Christian, Senior Vice President, Area Manager - San Bernardino County Area
COO: Ken Rivers, Chief Operating Officer, Fontana Medical Center
CFO: Trish Lopez, Area Chief Financial Officer
CMO: Timothy Jenkins, M.D., Area Medical Director and Chief of Staff
CIO: Heather Raymond, Area Public Relations Director
CHR: Irene Ruiz, Area Human Resources Director
CNO: Raye M. Burkhardt, Chief Nurse Executive
Web address: www.kaiserpermanente.org
Control: Other not–for–profit (including NFP Corporation) **Service**: General medical and surgical

Staffed Beds: 490 Admissions: 32057 Census: 374 Outpatient Visits: 185907 Births: 6962 Personnel: 4061

FORT BRAGG—Mendocino County

⊞ **MENDOCINO COAST DISTRICT HOSPITAL (051325)**, 700 River Drive, Zip 95437–5495; tel. 707/961–1234, (Nonreporting) **A**1 10 18
Primary Contact: Wayne Allen, Interim Chief Executive Officer
CFO: Mike Ellis, Chief Financial Officer
CMO: John Kermen, D.O., Chief Medical Staff
CIO: Jeff Edwards, Manager Information Services
CNO: Bonnie Kittner, R.N., Chief Nursing Officer
Web address: www.mcdh.org
Control: Hospital district or authority, Government, nonfederal **Service**: General medical and surgical

Staffed Beds: 25

FORT IRWIN—San Bernardino County

⊞ **WEED ARMY COMMUNITY HOSPITAL**, Inner Loop Road and 4th Street, Building 166, Zip 92310–5065, Mailing Address: P.O. Box 105109, Zip 92310–5109; tel. 760/380–3108, (Nonreporting) **A**1 **S** Department of the Army, Office of the Surgeon General, Falls Church, VA
Primary Contact: Colonel Larry O. France, Commander
CIO: Michael Haenelt, Chief Information Management
Web address: www.https://www.irwin.amedd.army.mil/
Control: Department of Defense, Government, federal **Service**: General medical and surgical

Staffed Beds: 27

FORTUNA—Humboldt County

⊞ **REDWOOD MEMORIAL HOSPITAL (051318)**, 3300 Renner Drive, Zip 95540–3198; tel. 707/725–3361, **A**1 10 18 **F**3 11 13 15 29 30 34 35 39 40 45 50 53 56 57 59 63 64 70 75 77 78 79 81 82 84 85 86 93 107 110 119 127 130 131 132 133 146 **S** Providence St. Joseph Health, Renton, WA
Primary Contact: Roberta Luskin-Hawk, M.D., Chief Executive
COO: Joseph J Rogers, Vice President and Chief Operating Officer
CHR: Bob Sampson, Vice President Human Resources
Web address: www.redwoodmemorial.org/
Control: Church operated, Nongovernment, not–for–profit **Service**: General medical and surgical

Staffed Beds: 25 Admissions: 1380 Census: 15 Outpatient Visits: 46753 Births: 303 Total Expense ($000): 42506 Payroll Expense ($000): 14303 Personnel: 164

FOUNTAIN VALLEY—Orange County

⊞ **FOUNTAIN VALLEY REGIONAL HOSPITAL AND MEDICAL CENTER (050570)**, 17100 Euclid Street, Zip 92708–4043; tel. 714/966–7200, **A**1 2 5 10 **F**3 12 13 17 18 20 22 24 26 29 30 31 34 40 45 49 56 57 60 68 70 72 73 74 75 76 77 78 79 81 82 84 85 87 88 89 100 107 111 114 115 119 126 130 146 148 149 154 156 **S** TENET Healthcare Corporation, Dallas, TX
Primary Contact: Kenneth D. McFarland, Chief Executive Officer
COO: Edward Littlejohn, Chief Operating Officer
CFO: Ken Jordan, Chief Financial Officer
CMO: Daniel Hilton, M.D., Chief of Staff
CIO: Freddie Sanchez, Director Information Systems
CHR: Connie Worden, Chief Human Resources Officer
CNO: Kristin Christophersen, Chief Nursing Officer
Web address: www.fountainvalleyhospital.com
Control: Corporation, Investor–owned (for–profit) **Service**: General medical and surgical

Staffed Beds: 380 Admissions: 19019 Census: 234 Outpatient Visits: 66464 Births: 3076 Total Expense ($000): 330542 Payroll Expense ($000): 148418 Personnel: 1634

⊞ **MEMORIALCARE, ORANGE COAST MEMORIAL MEDICAL CENTER (050678)**, 9920 Talbert Avenue, Zip 92708–5115; tel. 714/378–7000, **A**1 2 10 **F**3 8 11 12 13 15 18 20 22 24 26 28 29 31 34 35 38 40 44 45 46 47 48 49 50 51 53 55 56 57 58 59 64 65 68 70 72 74 75 76 77 78 79 81 82 84 85 86 87 93 107 108 110 111 114 115 116 117 118 119 124 126 130 131 132 135 143 145 146 147 149 154 157 **S** MemorialCare, Fountain Valley, CA
Primary Contact: Marcia Manker, Chief Executive Officer
COO: Emily Randle, Vice President Operations
CFO: Steve McNamara, Chief Financial Officer
CIO: Scott Raymond, Director Information Systems
CHR: Michelle Gutierrez, Executive Director Human Resources
CNO: Dale Vital, Chief Nursing Officer
Web address: www.memorialcare.org
Control: Other not–for–profit (including NFP Corporation) **Service**: General medical and surgical

Staffed Beds: 218 Admissions: 11288 Census: 111 Outpatient Visits: 99000 Births: 1348 Total Expense ($000): 289043 Payroll Expense ($000): 80927 Personnel: 1110

FREMONT—Alameda County

⊞ **FREMONT HOSPITAL (054110)**, 39001 Sundale Drive, Zip 94538–2005; tel. 510/796–1100, **A**1 10 **F**3 5 29 30 38 98 100 101 102 103 104 105 130 132 135 143 **S** Universal Health Services, Inc., King of Prussia, PA
Primary Contact: Tricia Williams, Chief Executive Officer
CMO: Vikas Duvvuri, M.D., Medical Director
CHR: Tom Piz, Director Human Resources
Web address: www.fremonthospital.com
Control: Corporation, Investor–owned (for–profit) **Service**: Psychiatric

Staffed Beds: 148 Admissions: 5517 Census: 102

Many Facility Codes have changed. Please refer to the AHA Guide Code Chart. © 2019 AHA Guide

✠ **KAISER PERMANENTE FREMONT MEDICAL CENTER (050512)**, 39400 Paseo Padre Parkway, Zip 94538–2310; tel. 510/248–3000, **A**1 3 10 **F**3 8 11 12 15 18 20 27 28 29 30 31 34 39 40 41 45 49 50 51 55 56 57 58 59 60 61 63 64 68 70 74 75 77 78 79 81 82 84 85 86 102 107 108 110 111 114 115 118 119 130 131 134 135 144 146 147 148 149 154 156 **S** Kaiser Foundation Hospitals, Oakland, CA
Primary Contact: Victoria O'Gorman, Administrator
Web address: www.kp.org
Control: Other not–for–profit (including NFP Corporation) **Service:** General medical and surgical

Staffed Beds: 76 **Admissions:** 3874 **Census:** 37 **Outpatient Visits:** 249294 **Births:** 8 **Personnel:** 555

✠ **WASHINGTON HOSPITAL HEALTHCARE SYSTEM (050195)**, 2000 Mowry Avenue, Zip 94538–1746; tel. 510/797–1111, (Nonreporting) **A**1 2 10 19
Primary Contact: Nancy D. Farber, Chief Executive Officer
COO: Edward J Fayen, Associate Administrator Operations and Support
CFO: Chris Henry, Associate Administrator and Chief Financial Officer
CMO: Albert Brooks, M.D., Chief Medical Staff Services
CIO: Robert Thorwald, Chief Information Officer
CHR: Bryant Welch, Chief Human Resources
CNO: Stephanie Williams, R.N., Chief Nursing Officer
Web address: www.whhs.com
Control: Hospital district or authority, Government, nonfederal **Service:** General medical and surgical

Staffed Beds: 269

FRENCH CAMP—San Joaquin County

☐ **SAN JOAQUIN GENERAL HOSPITAL (050167)**, 500 West Hospital Road, Zip 95231–9693, Mailing Address: P.O. Box 1020, Stockton, Zip 95201–3120; tel. 209/468–6000, (Nonreporting) **A**1 3 5
Primary Contact: David K. Culberson, Chief Executive Officer
CFO: Ron Kreutner, Chief Financial Officer
CMO: Sheela Kapre, M.D., Chief Medical Officer
CIO: Don Johnston, Chief Information Officer
CHR: Lisa M Lopez, Director Human Resources
CNO: Erlinda Bolor, R.N., Chief Nursing Officer
Web address: www.sjgeneral.org/
Control: County, Government, nonfederal **Service:** General medical and surgical

Staffed Beds: 110

FRESNO—Fresno County

COMMUNITY BEHAVIORAL HEALTH CENTER, 7171 North Cedar Avenue, Zip 93720–3311; tel. 559/449–8000, (Nonreporting) **S** Community Medical Centers, Fresno, CA
Primary Contact: Craig Wagoner, Chief Executive Officer
CFO: Stephen Walter, Senior Vice President and Chief Financial Officer
CMO: Tom Utecht, M.D., Senior Vice President and Chief Quality Officer
CIO: George Vasquez, Vice President Information Services
CHR: Ginny Burdick, Vice President Human Resources
CNO: Karen L Buckley, R.N., Chief Nursing Officer
Web address: www.communitymedical.org
Control: Corporation, Investor–owned (for–profit) **Service:** Psychiatric

Staffed Beds: 61

COMMUNITY REGIONAL MEDICAL CENTER (050060), 2823 Fresno Street, Zip 93721–1324, Mailing Address: P.O. Box 1232, Zip 93715–1232; tel. 559/459–6000, (Nonreporting) **A**2 3 5 8 10 **S** Community Medical Centers, Fresno, CA
Primary Contact: Craig Wagoner, Chief Executive Officer
COO: Patrick W Rafferty, Executive Vice President and Chief Operating Officer
CFO: Stephen Walter, Senior Vice President and Chief Financial Officer
CMO: Tom Utecht, M.D., Chief Medical and Quality Officer
CIO: Craig Castro, Chief Information Officer
CHR: Ginny Burdick, Vice President Human Resources
Web address: www.communitymedical.org
Control: Other not–for–profit (including NFP Corporation) **Service:** General medical and surgical

Staffed Beds: 852

FRESNO HEART AND SURGICAL HOSPITAL (050732), 15 East Audubon Drive, Zip 93720–1542; tel. 559/433–8000, (Nonreporting) **A**3 10 **S** Community Medical Centers, Fresno, CA
Primary Contact: Ben Armfield, Associate Administrator
CFO: Ben Armfield, Chief Financial Officer
CMO: Tom Utecht, M.D., Corporate Chief Quality Officer
CIO: George Vasquez, Corporate Chief Information Officer
CHR: Julie Adair, Interim Corporate Chief Human Resources Officer
CNO: Heather Rodriguez, Chief Nursing Officer
Web address: www.fresnoheartandsurgical.org
Control: Corporation, Investor–owned (for–profit) **Service:** Heart

Staffed Beds: 60

FRESNO MEDICAL CENTER See Kaiser Permanente Fresno Medical Center

☐ **FRESNO SURGICAL HOSPITAL (050708)**, 6125 North Fresno Street, Zip 93710–5207; tel. 559/431–8000, (Nonreporting) **A**1 10
Primary Contact: Kristine Kassahn, Chief Executive Officer
CFO: Bruce Cecil, Chief Financial Officer
CMO: Bruce Witmer, M.D., Medical Director
CHR: Laura Patillo, Manager Human Resources
Web address: www.fresnosurgicalhospital.com
Control: Partnership, Investor–owned (for–profit) **Service:** Surgical

Staffed Beds: 16

✠ **KAISER PERMANENTE FRESNO MEDICAL CENTER (050710)**, 7300 North Fresno Street, Zip 93720–2942; tel. 559/448–4500, **A**1 3 5 10 **F**3 8 11 12 13 15 18 28 29 30 31 34 39 40 41 45 49 50 51 55 56 57 58 59 60 61 63 64 68 70 72 73 74 75 76 77 78 79 81 82 84 85 86 102 107 108 110 111 114 115 118 119 130 131 134 135 144 146 147 148 149 154 156 **S** Kaiser Foundation Hospitals, Oakland, CA
Primary Contact: Debbie Hemker, Senior Vice President and Area Manager
CFO: Paula Armstrong, Chief Financial Officer
CMO: Smita Rouillard, M.D., Physician in Chief
CIO: Patty Thompson, Area Compliance Officer
CHR: Mike Silveira Suffix Human Resources Leader
CNO: Karen S Strauman, R.N., Chief Nurse Executive
Web address: www.kaiserpermanente.org
Control: Other not–for–profit (Including NFP Corporation) **Service:** General medical and surgical

Staffed Beds: 169 **Admissions:** 8263 **Census:** 83 **Outpatient Visits:** 271868 **Births:** 1461 **Personnel:** 717

✠ **SAINT AGNES MEDICAL CENTER (050093)**, 1303 East Herndon Avenue, Zip 93720–3397; tel. 559/450–3000, (Nonreporting) **A**1 2 3 10 **S** Trinity Health, Livonia, MI
Primary Contact: Nancy Hollingsworth, R.N., M3N, President and Chief Executive Officer
COO: Mark T Bateman, Interim Chief Operating Officer
CFO: Phil Robinson, Chief Financial Officer
CMO: Stephen Soldo, M.D., Chief Medical Officer
CIO: Irfan Ali, Director Information Services
CHR: Stacy Vaillancourt, Vice President Marketing, Communications, Advocacy and Human Resources
Web address: www.samc.com
Control: Church operated **Service:** General medical and surgical

Staffed Beds: 436

✠ △ **SAN JOAQUIN VALLEY REHABILITATION HOSPITAL (053032)**, 7173 North Sharon Avenue, Zip 93720–3329; tel. 559/436–3600, (Nonreporting) **A**1 7 10 **S** Vibra Healthcare, Mechanicsburg, PA
Primary Contact: Mary Jo Jacobson, Chief Executive Officer
CFO: Margaret Casarez, Chief Financial Officer
CMO: Michael Azevedo, M.D., Medical Director
CIO: Christi Rolff, Director Business Development
CHR: Jennifer Morrow, Director Human Resources
Web address: www.sanjoaquinrehab.com
Control: Corporation, Investor–owned (for–profit) **Service:** Rehabilitation

Staffed Beds: 62

Hospital, Medicare Provider Number, Address, Telephone, Approval, Facility, and Physician Codes, Health Care System

★ American Hospital Association (AHA) membership
☐ The Joint Commission accreditation
○ Healthcare Facilities Accreditation Program
◇ DNV Healthcare Inc. accreditation
⇑ Center for Improvement in Healthcare Quality Accreditation
△ Commission on Accreditation of Rehabilitation Facilities (CARF) accreditation

CA

✠ **VETERANS AFFAIRS CENTRAL CALIFORNIA HEALTH CARE SYSTEM**, 2615 East Clinton Avenue, Zip 93703–2223; tel. 559/225–6100, (Nonreporting) **A**1 3 5 **S** Department of Veterans Affairs, Washington, DC
Primary Contact: Stephen R. Bauman, Medical Center Director
CMO: Wessel H. Meyer, M.D., Chief of Staff
CHR: Sandra Stein, Chief Human Resources Management
Web address: www.fresno.va.gov/
Control: Veterans Affairs, Government, federal **Service:** General medical and surgical

Staffed Beds: 117

FULLERTON—Orange County

✠ △ **ST. JUDE MEDICAL CENTER (050168)**, 101 East Valencia Mesa Drive, Zip 92835–3875; tel. 714/992–3000, **A**1 2 3 5 7 10 **F**2 3 8 9 11 13 15 18 20 22 24 26 28 29 30 31 34 35 36 38 39 40 44 45 46 47 48 49 50 51 53 54 55 56 57 58 59 60 61 62 63 64 65 66 68 70 71 72 73 74 75 76 77 78 79 81 82 83 84 85 86 87 90 91 92 93 94 95 96 97 100 101 102 107 108 109 110 111 112 114 115 116 117 118 119 120 121 123 124 126 129 130 131 132 134 135 143 145 146 147 148 149 154 156 157 **S** Providence St. Joseph Health, Renton, WA
Primary Contact: Brian Helleland, Chief Executive Officer
CFO: Ed Salvador, Chief Financial Officer
CMO: Eugene P. Kim, M.D., Chief Medical Officer
CHR: Mark Jablonski, Vice President Mission Integration
CNO: Linda Jenkins, R.N., Vice President Patient Care Services
Web address: www.stjudemedicalcenter.org
Control: Church operated, Nongovernment, not-for-profit **Service:** General medical and surgical

Staffed Beds: 320 **Admissions:** 15375 **Census:** 187 **Outpatient Visits:** 513457 **Births:** 2448 **Total Expense ($000):** 524668 **Payroll Expense ($000):** 194070 **Personnel:** 2155

GARBERVILLE—Humboldt County

★ **JEROLD PHELPS COMMUNITY HOSPITAL (051309)**, 733 Cedar Street, Zip 95542–3292; tel. 707/923–3921, (Total facility includes 8 beds in nursing home–type unit) **A**10 18 **F**34 35 40 50 57 59 65 68 97 110 127 128 133 143 149
Primary Contact: Matthew Rees, Administrator
COO: Kent Scown, Director Operations and Information Services
CFO: Harry Jasper, Chief Financial Officer
CMO: Marcin Matuszkiewicz, M.D., Chief of Staff and Medical Director
CIO: Kent Scown, Director Operations and Information Services
CHR: Dee Way, Director Human Resources
CNO: Sarah Beach, Director of Nursing
Web address: www.shchd.org
Control: Hospital district or authority, Government, nonfederal **Service:** General medical and surgical

Staffed Beds: 17 **Admissions:** 66 **Census:** 51 **Outpatient Visits:** 13183 **Births:** 0 **Total Expense ($000):** 11057 **Payroll Expense ($000):** 5007 **Personnel:** 30

GARDEN GROVE—Orange County

✠ **GARDEN GROVE HOSPITAL AND MEDICAL CENTER (050230)**, 12601 Garden Grove Boulevard, Zip 92843–1959; tel. 714/537–5160, (Nonreporting) **A**1 3 10 **S** Prime Healthcare, Ontario, CA
Primary Contact: Richard M. Rowe, PharmD, Chief Executive Officer
CFO: Kora Guoyavatin, Chief Financial Officer
CMO: Hassan Alkhouli, M.D., Chief Medical Officer
CIO: Vic Mahan, Director Information Systems
CHR: Stephanie Sioson, Director Human Resources
CNO: Wanda Ruben, R.N., Chief Nursing Officer
Web address: www.gardengrovehospital.com
Control: Corporation, Investor-owned (for-profit) **Service:** General medical and surgical

Staffed Beds: 167

GARDENA—Los Angeles County

✠ **KINDRED HOSPITAL SOUTH BAY (052050)**, 1246 West 155th Street, Zip 90247–4062; tel. 310/323–5330, (Nonreporting) **A**1 10 **S** Kindred Healthcare, Louisville, KY
Primary Contact: Michael D. Kerr, Chief Executive Officer
CHR: Michelle Parra, Director Human Resources
Web address: www.khsouthbay.com/
Control: Corporation, Investor-owned (for-profit) **Service:** Acute long-term care hospital

Staffed Beds: 84

✠ **MEMORIAL HOSPITAL OF GARDENA (050468)**, 1145 West Redondo Beach Boulevard, Zip 90247–3528; tel. 310/532–4200, (Nonreporting) **A**1 10 **S** Avanti Hospitals, El Segundo, CA
Primary Contact: Kathy Wojno, R.N., MSN, Administrator
CFO: Daniel R Heckathorne, Chief Financial Officer
CMO: Nosratian Farshao, M.D., Chief Medical Staff
CHR: Matthew Kempiak, Director Human Resources and Administrative Services
CNO: Glenda Luce, Chief Nursing Officer
Web address: www.mhglax.com/
Control: Corporation, Investor-owned (for-profit) **Service:** General medical and surgical

Staffed Beds: 172

GILROY—Santa Clara County

☐ **SAINT LOUISE REGIONAL HOSPITAL (050688)**, 9400 No Name Uno, Zip 95020–3528; tel. 408/848–2000, (Nonreporting) **A**1 10
Primary Contact: John Hennelly, Chief Executive Officer
COO: Carol Furgurson, Chief Operating Officer
CFO: Nicole Thomson, Chief Financial Officer
CMO: Arthur Douville, M.D., Chief Medical Officer
CIO: Dick Hutsell, Vice President Information Technology Services
CHR: Lin Velasquez, Vice President Human Resources
CNO: Marilyn Gerrior, R.N., MSN, Chief Nursing Executive
Web address: www.verity.org
Control: County, Government, nonfederal **Service:** General medical and surgical

Staffed Beds: 93

VISTA HOSPITAL OF SOUTH BAY See Kindred Hospital South Bay

GLENDALE—Los Angeles County

✠ **GLENDALE MEMORIAL HOSPITAL AND HEALTH CENTER (050058)**, 1420 South Central Avenue, Zip 91204–2594; tel. 818/502–1900, (Nonreporting) **A**1 10 19 **S** CommonSpirit Health, Chicago, IL
Primary Contact: Jill Welton, President and Chief Executive Officer
COO: Brad Grote, Chief Operating Officer
CFO: Rebecca Cheng, Chief Financial Officer
CIO: Brian Gregor, Manager Information Technology Operations
CHR: Nga Nguyen, Manager Human Resources and Organizational Development
CNO: Jason Black Esq Vice President and Chief Nursing Officer
Web address: www.glendalememorial.com
Control: Other not-for-profit (including NFP Corporation) **Service:** General medical and surgical

Staffed Beds: 334

★ ⇧ **USC VERDUGO HILLS HOSPITAL (050124)**, 1812 Verdugo Boulevard, Zip 91208–1409; tel. 818/790–7100, **A**3 10 21 **F**3 11 12 13 15 17 18 28 29 30 34 35 37 38 40 41 45 46 47 48 49 50 51 53 56 57 59 64 65 68 70 72 74 75 76 77 78 79 81 83 85 87 93 94 96 98 100 101 102 103 104 107 108 110 111 115 119 126 128 130 131 132 135 145 146 147 148 149 153 **S** Keck Medicine of USC, Los Angeles, CA
Primary Contact: Keith Hobbs, Chief Executive Officer
COO: Kenny Pawlek, Chief Operating Officer
CMO: Stephanie Hall, M.D., Chief Medical Officer
CHR: Eva Herberger, Administrator Human Resources
CNO: Theresa Murphy, Chief Nursing Officer
Web address: www.uscvhh.org
Control: Other not-for-profit (including NFP Corporation) **Service:** General medical and surgical

Staffed Beds: 154 **Admissions:** 6891 **Census:** 86 **Outpatient Visits:** 64607 **Births:** 321 **Total Expense ($000):** 129965 **Payroll Expense ($000):** 59162 **Personnel:** 709

GLENDORA—Los Angeles County

✠ **FOOTHILL PRESBYTERIAN HOSPITAL (050597)**, 250 South Grand Avenue, Zip 91741–4218; tel. 626/963–8411, **A**1 3 10 **F**3 7 11 13 15 17 18 29 30 31 34 35 40 41 44 45 49 50 51 60 64 68 70 74 75 76 77 78 79 81 85 86 87 98 107 108 114 119 130 131 143 146 154 **S** Citrus Valley Health Partners, Covina, CA
Primary Contact: Robert H. Curry, President and Chief Executive Officer
COO: Elvia Foulke, Executive Vice President and Chief Operating Officer
CMO: John DiMare, M.D., Medical Director
CIO: David McCobb, Chief Information Officer
Web address: www.cvhp.org/Our_Facilities/Foothill_Presbyterian.aspx
Control: Other not-for-profit (including NFP Corporation) **Service:** General medical and surgical

Staffed Beds: 71 **Admissions:** 5653 **Census:** 63 **Outpatient Visits:** 67490 **Births:** 830 **Total Expense ($000):** 103733 **Payroll Expense ($000):** 39127 **Personnel:** 514

Many Facility Codes have changed. Please refer to the AHA Guide Code Chart.   © 2019 AHA Guide

★ ○ **GLENDORA COMMUNITY HOSPITAL (050205)**, 150 West Route 66, Zip 91740–6207; tel. 626/852–5000, (Nonreporting) **A**10 11 **S** Prime Healthcare, Ontario, CA
Primary Contact: Sofia Abrina, R.N., Chief Executive Officer
CFO: Robert Bonner, Chief Financial Officer
CMO: Oliver Solomon, M.D., Chief Medical Officer
CIO: Jeffrey Cox, Chief Information Officer
CHR: Diana Cancel, Director Human Resources
CNO: Mary Ann Bennett, Chief Nursing Officer
Web address: www.evhmc.com
Control: Other not–for–profit (including NFP Corporation) **Service**: General medical and surgical

Staffed Beds: 128

GRASS VALLEY—Nevada County

⊞ **SIERRA NEVADA MEMORIAL HOSPITAL (050150)**, 155 Glasson Way, Zip 95945–5723, Mailing Address: P.O. Box 1029, Zip 95945–1029; tel. 530/274–6000, (Nonreporting) **A**1 2 10 19 **S** CommonSpirit Health, Chicago, IL
Primary Contact: Brian Evans Esq, M.D., President and Chief Executive Officer
CFO: Carolyn Canady, Chief Financial Officer
CMO: Jeffrey M. Rosenburg, Chief Medical Officer
CIO: Monica Biley, Chief Nursing Officer
CHR: Terri Labriola, Human Resources Officer
CNO: Jill McWilliams, Chief Nursing Officer
Web address: www.snmh.org
Control: Other not–for–profit (including NFP Corporation) **Service**: General medical and surgical

Staffed Beds: 104

GREENBRAE—Marin County

⊞ **MARINHEALTH MEDICAL CENTER (050360)**, 250 Bon Air Road, Zip 94904–1784, Mailing Address: P.O. Box 8010, San Rafael, Zip 94912–8010; tel. 415/925–7000, **A**1 2 **F**3 8 13 15 18 20 22 24 26 29 30 31 34 35 36 37 40 43 45 46 47 48 49 51 57 59 60 63 64 68 70 73 74 75 76 77 78 79 81 84 85 87 89 98 105 107 108 110 112 114 115 118 119 120 121 122 123 124 126 130 132 141 146 148 149 153 154 157
Primary Contact: Lee Domanico, Chief Executive Officer
CFO: David W Cox, Chief Financial Officer
CMO: Joel Sklar, M.D., Chief Medical Officer
CIO: Mark Zielazinski, Chief Information and Technology Integration Officer
CHR: Linda Lang, Chief Human Resources Officer
Web address: www.maringeneral.org
Control: Hospital district or authority, Government, nonfederal **Service**: General medical and surgical

Staffed Beds: 235 **Admissions:** 9181 **Census:** 118 **Outpatient Visits:** 199906 **Births:** 1217 **Total Expense ($000):** 394452 **Payroll Expense ($000):** 178851 **Personnel:** 1434

GRIDLEY—Butte County

★ ⇑ **ORCHARD HOSPITAL (051311)**, 240 Spruce Street, Zip 95948–2216, Mailing Address: P.O. Box 97, Zip 95948–0097; tel. 530/846–5671, (Nonreporting) **A**10 18 21
Primary Contact: Steve Lee. Stark, Chief Executive Officer
COO: Tracy Atkins, Chief Operating and Nursing Officer
CFO: Kristina Sanke, Chief Financial Officer
CMO: Henry Starkes, M.D., Medical Director
CIO: John Helvey, Chief Information Officer
CNO: Tracy Atkins, Chief Operating and Nursing Officer
Web address: www.orchardhospital.com
Control: Other not–for–profit (including NFP Corporation) **Service**: General medical and surgical

Staffed Beds: 45

HANFORD—Kings County

⊞ **ADVENTIST MEDICAL CENTER - HANFORD (050121)**, 115 Mall Drive, Zip 93230–3513; tel. 559/582–9000, (Includes ADVENTIST MEDICAL CENTER-SELMA, 1141 Rose Avenue, Selma, California, Zip 93662–3241; tel. 559/891–1000; Richard L Rawson, President and Chief Executive Officer), (Nonreporting) **A**1 3 5 10 **S** Adventist Health, Roseville, CA
Primary Contact: Wayne Ferch, President and Chief Executive Officer
CIO: Michael Aubry, Director Information Services
Web address: www.adventisthealthcv.com/hospital_newhanfordhospital.aspx
Control: Church operated, Nongovernment, not–for–profit **Service**: General medical and surgical

Staffed Beds: 199

★ **CENTRAL VALLEY GENERAL HOSPITAL (050196)**, 1025 North Douty Street, Zip 93230–3722, Mailing Address: P.O. Box 480, Zip 93232–2113; tel. 559/583–2100, (Nonreporting) **S** Adventist Health, Roseville, CA
Primary Contact: Wayne Ferch, President and Chief Executive Officer
Web address: www.hanfordhealth.com
Control: Corporation, Investor–owned (for–profit) **Service**: General medical and surgical

Staffed Beds: 49

HARBOR CITY—Los Angeles County; See Los Angeles

HAYWARD—Alameda County

☐ **ST. ROSE HOSPITAL (050002)**, 27200 Calaroga Avenue, Zip 94545–4383; tel. 510/264–4000, (Nonreporting) **A**1 10 **S** Alecto Healthcare, Irvine, CA
Primary Contact: Aman Dhuper, President and Chief Executive Officer
CFO: Michael Taylor, Vice President Financial Services and Chief Financial Officer
CMO: Charles S Feldstein, M.D., Vice President Medical Affairs
CHR: John Davini, Vice President
Web address: www.srhca.org
Control: Church operated, Nongovernment, not–for–profit **Service**: General medical and surgical

Staffed Beds: 150

HEALDSBURG—Sonoma County

☐ **HEALDSBURG DISTRICT HOSPITAL (051321)**, 1375 University Avenue, Zip 95448–3382; tel. 707/431–6500, (Nonreporting) **A**1 10 18
Primary Contact: Joseph P. Harrington, Chief Executive Officer
COO: Regina Novello, R.N., Chief Operating Officer
CFO: John S Parigi II Interim Chief Financial Officer
CMO: Judy Widger, M.D., Chief of Staff
CIO: Steven Hansen, Director Information Technology
CHR: Kristina Holloway, Chief Human Resources Officer
CNO: Susan G Spoelma, MSN, R.N., Chief Nursing Officer
Web address: www.nschd.org
Control: Hospital district or authority, Government, nonfederal **Service**: General medical and surgical

Staffed Beds: 38

HEMET—Riverside County

☐ **HEMET VALLEY MEDICAL CENTER (050390)**, 1117 East Devonshire Avenue, Zip 92543–3083; tel. 951/652–2811, (Nonreporting) **A**1 3 5 10 12 13 **S** Physicians for Healthy Hospitals, Hemet, CA
Primary Contact: Dan C. McLaughlin, Chief Hospital Executive Officer
CFO: John R Collins, Chief Financial Officer
CMO: Sumanta Chaudhuri, M.D., Chief Medical Officer
CHR: Michele Bird, Chief Human Resources Officer
CNO: Kathryn McLaughlin, Chief Nursing Officer
Web address: www.physiciansforhealthyhospitals.com
Control: Hospital district or authority, Government, nonfederal **Service**: General medical and surgical

Staffed Beds: 238

HOLLISTER—San Benito County

☐ **HAZEL HAWKINS MEMORIAL HOSPITAL (050296)**, 911 Sunset Drive, Zip 95023–5695; tel. 831/637–5711, (Includes WILLIAM AND INEZ MABIE SKILLED NURSING FACILITY, 911 Sunset Drive, Hollister, California, Zip 95023; tel. 408/637–5711), (Nonreporting) **A**1 10
Primary Contact: Ken Underwood, Chief Executive Officer
CFO: Mark Robinson, Associate Administrator and Chief Financial Officer
CIO: Julio Gil, Manager Information Services
CHR: Ysidro Gallardo, Associate Administrator Human Resources
Web address: www.hazelhawkins.com
Control: Hospital district or authority, Government, nonfederal **Service**: General medical and surgical

Staffed Beds: 181

CA

CA

HUNTINGTON BEACH—Orange County

⊞ **HUNTINGTON BEACH HOSPITAL (050526)**, 17772 Beach Boulevard, Zip 92647–6896; tel. 714/843–5000, (Nonreporting) **A**1 10 **S** Prime Healthcare, Ontario, CA
Primary Contact: Richard M. Rowe, PharmD, Chief Executive Officer
CFO: Alan H Smith, Chief Financial Officer
CMO: Hassan Alkhouli, M.D., Medical Director
CIO: Adam Morquecho, Director Information Technology
CHR: Stephanie Sioson, Director Human Resources
Web address: www.hbhospital.com
Control: Other not–for–profit (including NFP Corporation) **Service:** General medical and surgical

Staffed Beds: 102

HUNTINGTON PARK—Los Angeles County

COMMUNITY AND MISSION HOSPITALS OF HUNTINGTON PARK See Community Hospital of Huntington Park

★ ○ **COMMUNITY HOSPITAL OF HUNTINGTON PARK (050091)**, 2623 East Slauson Avenue, Zip 90255–2926; tel. 323/583–1931, (Nonreporting) **A**10 11 **S** Avanti Hospitals, El Segundo, CA
Primary Contact: Patricia Rives, R.N., MSN, Chief Executive Officer
CFO: Cheryl Tong, Corporate Chief Financial Officer
CMO: Jose Rivas, M.D., Chief of Staff
CIO: Jason Cervantes, Corporate Chief Information Officer
CHR: Paul Celuch, Corporate Human Resources Director
CNO: Lisa Jacobson, Director of Nursing
Web address: www.avantihospitals.com/community-hospital-of-huntington-park
Control: Corporation, Investor–owned (for–profit) **Service:** General medical and surgical

Staffed Beds: 81

INDIO—Riverside County

⊞ **JOHN F. KENNEDY MEMORIAL HOSPITAL (050534)**, 47111 Monroe Street, Zip 92201–6799; tel. 760/347–6191, **A**1 10 **F**3 8 18 20 29 30 34 35 37 40 46 47 48 49 50 54 56 57 59 68 70 74 76 78 79 81 85 87 89 90 97 107 108 111 118 119 126 130 146 148 154 156 **S** TENET Healthcare Corporation, Dallas, TX
Primary Contact: Gary Honts, Chief Executive Officer
COO: Philip Fitzgerald, Chief Operating Officer
CFO: Lorna Curtis, Chief Financial Officer
CHR: Raymond Konieczek, Chief Human Resources Officer
CNO: Heather Adams, Chief Nursing Officer
Web address: www.jfkmemorialhosp.com
Control: Corporation, Investor–owned (for–profit) **Service:** General medical and surgical

Staffed Beds: 145 Admissions: 6246 Census: 47 Outpatient Visits: 56149 Births: 1869 Total Expense ($000): 108562 Payroll Expense ($000): 50255 Personnel: 642

INGLEWOOD—Los Angeles County

⊞ **CENTINELA HOSPITAL MEDICAL CENTER (050739)**, 555 East Hardy Street, Zip 90301–4011, Mailing Address: P.O. Box 720, Zip 90312–6720; tel. 310/673–4660, (Nonreporting) **A**1 10 **S** Prime Healthcare, Ontario, CA
Primary Contact: Linda Bradley, Chief Executive Officer
CFO: Paul Sennett, Chief Financial Officer
CMO: Paryus Patel, M.D., Chief Medical Officer
CIO: Martin Cordova, Director Information Services
CHR: George Akopyan, Director Human Resources
CNO: Mohammad Abdelnaser, Chief Nursing Officer
Web address: www.centinelamed.com
Control: Corporation, Investor–owned (for–profit) **Service:** General medical and surgical

Staffed Beds: 369

IRVINE—Orange County

⇑ **HOAG ORTHOPEDIC INSTITUTE (050769)**, 16250 Sand Canyon Avenue, Zip 92618–3714; tel. 949/517–3149, (Nonreporting) **A**3 10 21
Primary Contact: Carlos Prietto, President and Chief Executive Officer
CMO: Robert Gorab, M.D., Chief Medical Officer
Web address: www.https://www.orthopedichospital.com/
Control: Other not–for–profit (including NFP Corporation) **Service:** Orthopedic

Staffed Beds: 70

ORANGE COUNTY IRVINE MEDICAL CENTER See Kaiser Permanente Orange County Anaheim Medical Center, Anaheim

JACKSON—Amador County

⊞ **SUTTER AMADOR HOSPITAL (050014)**, 200 Mission Boulevard, Zip 95642–2564; tel. 209/223–7500, (Nonreporting) **A**1 5 10 20 **S** Sutter Health, Sacramento, CA
Primary Contact: Thomas C. Dickson, Chief Executive Officer
CFO: Brett Moore, CPA, Assistant Administrator Finance
CMO: Ron Hood, M.D., Chief of Staff
CIO: Joy Bailey, Director Information Technology
CHR: Beverly Revels, Director Human Resources
CNO: Nikki Allen, Patient Care Executive
Web address: www.sutteramador.org
Control: Other not–for–profit (including NFP Corporation) **Service:** General medical and surgical

Staffed Beds: 52

JOSHUA TREE—San Bernardino County

⊞ **HI-DESERT MEDICAL CENTER (050279)**, 6601 White Feather Road, Zip 92284; tel. 760/366–3711, (Total facility includes 120 beds in nursing home-type unit) **A**1 10 20 **F**3 13 15 18 29 30 34 35 40 45 50 54 62 63 64 68 70 75 76 77 79 81 82 85 87 92 93 104 107 108 110 111 115 119 128 130 131 132 146 147 149 154 **S** TENET Healthcare Corporation, Dallas, TX
Primary Contact: Karen Faulis, Chief Executive Officer
COO: David Cooke, R.N., Chief Operating Officer
CMO: Jeffrey Seip, M.D., Chief Medical Staff
CIO: Darrell Goodman, Chief Information Officer
CHR: Nicole Smith, Director Human Resources
CNO: David Cooke, R.N., Chief Operating Officer
Web address: www.hdmc.org
Control: Corporation, Investor–owned (for–profit) **Service:** General medical and surgical

Staffed Beds: 179 Admissions: 2196 Census: 96 Outpatient Visits: 60102 Births: 319 Total Expense ($000): 66547 Payroll Expense ($000): 29284 Personnel: 298

KENTFIELD—Marin County

⊞ **KENTFIELD REHABILITATION AND SPECIALTY HOSPITAL (052043)**, 1125 Sir Francis Drake Boulevard, Zip 94904–1455; tel. 415/456–9680, (Nonreporting) **A**1 10 **S** Vibra Healthcare, Mechanicsburg, PA
Primary Contact: Varun Chauhan, Chief Executive Officer
CFO: Stephanie Lawrence, Chief Financial Officer
CMO: Curtis Roebken, M.D., Chief Medical Staff
CHR: Julene English, Director Human Resources
Web address: www.kentfieldrehab.com
Control: Corporation, Investor–owned (for–profit) **Service:** Acute long–term care hospital

Staffed Beds: 60

KING CITY—Monterey County

☐ **MEE MEMORIAL HOSPITAL (050189)**, 300 Canal Street, Zip 93930–3431; tel. 831/385–6000, (Nonreporting) **A**1 5 10 20
Primary Contact: R. Michael. Hutchinson, Chief Executive Officer
CFO: Gary L Wangsmo, Chief Financial Officer
CMO: Schindelheim Roy, M.D., Chief of Staff
CIO: Mike McNamara, Chief Information Officer
CHR: Karen Wong, Chief Human Resources Officer
Web address: www.meememorial.com
Control: Other not–for–profit (including NFP Corporation) **Service:** General medical and surgical

Staffed Beds: 119

LA JOLLA—San Diego County

⊞ **SCRIPPS GREEN HOSPITAL (050424)**, 10666 North Torrey Pines Road, Zip 92037–1093; tel. 858/455–9100, **A**1 3 5 8 10 **F**3 8 11 12 14 15 17 18 20 22 24 26 29 30 31 34 35 36 37 44 45 46 47 49 50 51 54 57 58 59 61 64 68 70 74 75 77 78 79 80 81 82 84 85 86 87 93 107 108 110 111 115 118 119 120 121 123 124 126 130 131 132 136 138 139 141 142 146 148 156 157 **S** Scripps Health, San Diego, CA
Primary Contact: Carl J. Etter, Chief Executive Officer
CFO: Richard Rothberger, Corporate Executive Vice President and Chief Financial Officer
CMO: James LaBelle, M.D., Chief Medical Officer
CIO: Andy Crowder, Chief Information Officer and Corporate Senior Vice President
CHR: Victor Buzachero, Corporate Senior Vice President for Innovation, Human Resources and Performance Management
Web address: www.scrippshealth.org
Control: Other not–for–profit (including NFP Corporation) **Service:** General medical and surgical

Staffed Beds: 173 Admissions: 8028 Census: 81 Outpatient Visits: 91499 Births: 0 Total Expense ($000): 269464 Payroll Expense ($000): 87607 Personnel: 1077

⊞ **SCRIPPS MEMORIAL HOSPITAL-LA JOLLA (050324)**, 9888 Genesee Avenue, Zip 92037–1200, Mailing Address: P.O. Box 28, Zip 92038–0028; tel. 858/626–4123, **A**1 3 5 10 **F**3 8 11 12 13 14 15 17 18 20 22 24 26 28 29 30 31 34 35 40 43 44 45 46 48 49 50 51 53 54 55 57 58 59 64 65 68 70 74 75 76 77 78 79 81 82 84 85 86 87 91 92 93 94 100 101 102 107 108 110 111 114 115 116 117 118 119 124 126 130 132 141 145 146 147 148 156 157 **S** Scripps Health, San Diego, CA
Primary Contact: Carl J. Etter, Chief Executive Officer
COO: Cindy Steckel, Ph.D., R.N., Vice President Chief Nurse and Operations Executive
CFO: Alan Mandal, Vice President Financial Operations
CMO: James LaBelle, M.D., Chief Medical Officer
CHR: Shelly Blazakis, Director Human Resources Services
CNO: Cindy Steckel, Ph.D., R.N., Vice President Chief Nurse and Operations Executive
Web address: www.scripps.org/locations/hospitals__scripps-memorial-hospital-la-jolla
Control: Other not–for–profit (including NFP Corporation) **Service:** General medical and surgical

Staffed Beds: 365 Admissions: 18731 Census: 231 Outpatient Visits: 96574 Births: 3257 Total Expense ($000): 630980 Payroll Expense ($000): 204325 Personnel: 2476

LA MESA—San Diego County

☐ **ALVARADO PARKWAY INSTITUTE BEHAVIORAL HEALTH SYSTEM (054075)**, 7050 Parkway Drive, Zip 91942–1535; tel. 619/465–4411, (Nonreporting) **A**1 10
Primary Contact: Patrick C. Ziemer, Chief Executive Officer
CFO: Chad Engbrecht, Chief Financial Officer
CMO: R. Bradley Sanders, D.O., Executive Medical Director
CNO: Bonnie Asada, Chief Nursing Officer
Web address: www.apibhs.com
Control: Partnership, Investor–owned (for–profit) **Service:** Psychiatric

Staffed Beds: 66

⊞ △ **SHARP GROSSMONT HOSPITAL (050026)**, 5555 Grossmont Center Drive, Zip 91942–3019, Mailing Address: P.O. Box 158, Zip 91944–0158; tel. 619/740–6000, (Total facility includes 11 beds in nursing home–type unit) **A**1 2 3 7 10 **F**1 3 5 8 11 12 13 15 17 18 20 22 24 26 28 29 30 31 34 35 37 38 40 43 44 45 46 47 48 49 50 51 54 55 57 58 59 60 61 64 65 66 67 68 70 72 73 74 75 76 77 78 79 80 81 82 83 84 85 86 87 90 91 92 93 94 96 97 98 100 101 102 103 104 106 107 108 109 111 114 115 116 117 118 119 120 121 122 123 124 126 128 129 130 132 135 143 146 147 148 149 153 154 156 **S** Sharp HealthCare, San Diego, CA
Primary Contact: Scott Evans, PharmD, FACHE, Senior Vice President and Chief Executive Officer
COO: Maryann Cone, Chief Operating Officer
CFO: Karl Cornicelli, Chief Financial Officer
CMO: Michael Murphy, M.D., JD, Chief Medical Officer
CIO: Kenneth Lawenn, Senior Vice President and Chief Information Officer
CHR: George Holtz, Director Human Resources
Web address: www.sharp.com
Control: Other not–for–profit (including NFP Corporation) **Service:** General medical and surgical

Staffed Beds: 524 Admissions: 28083 Census: 368 Outpatient Visits: 437388 Births: 3241 Total Expense ($000): 740964 Payroll Expense ($000): 304716 Personnel: 3130

LA MIRADA—Los Angeles County

⊞ **KINDRED HOSPITAL-LA MIRADA (052038)**, 14900 East Imperial Highway, Zip 90638–2172; tel. 562/944–1900, (Includes KINDRED HOSPITAL SAN GABRIEL VALLEY, 845 North Lark Ellen Avenue, West Covina, California, Zip 91791–1069; tel. 626/339–5451; Julie Myers, Chief Executive Officer; KINDRED HOSPITAL SANTA ANA, 1901 North College Avenue, Santa Ana, California, Zip 92706–2334; tel. 714/564–7800), (Nonreporting) **A**1 10 **S** Kindred Healthcare, Louisville, KY
Primary Contact: David Kowalski, Chief Executive Officer
CFO: Rishab Punjabi, Chief Financial Officer
CMO: Prakash Chandra Patel, M.D., Chief of Staff
CHR: Susan Bergquist, Human Resources Generalist
CNO: Esperanza Sanchez, Chief Clinical Officer
Web address: www.kindredlamirada.com/
Control: Corporation, Investor–owned (for–profit) **Service:** Acute long–term care hospital

Staffed Beds: 216

LA PALMA—Orange County

⊞ **LA PALMA INTERCOMMUNITY HOSPITAL (050580)**, 7901 Walker Street, Zip 90623 1764; tel. 714/670–7400, (Nonreporting) **A**1 10 **S** Prime Healthcare, Ontario, CA
Primary Contact: Michael Sarian, Interim Chief Executive Officer
CFO: Alan H Smith, Chief Financial Officer
CMO: Sami Shoukair, M.D., Chief Medical Officer
CIO: Vic Mahan, Director Information Technology
CHR: Stephanie Sioson, Director Human Resources
CNO: Hilda Manzo-Luna, Chief Nursing Officer
Web address: www.lapalmaintercommunityhospital.com
Control: Other not–for–profit (including NFP Corporation) **Service:** General medical and surgical

Staffed Beds: 140

LAGUNA HILLS—Orange County

⊞ **MEMORIALCARE, SADDLEBACK MEMORIAL MEDICAL CENTER (050603)**, 24451 Health Center Drive, Zip 92653–3689; tel. 949/837–4500, **A**1 3 10 **F**3 11 13 14 15 18 20 22 24 26 28 29 30 31 34 35 36 38 40 44 45 46 47 48 49 50 51 53 54 55 56 57 58 59 62 63 64 65 68 70 72 74 75 76 77 78 79 81 84 85 86 87 93 94 107 108 110 111 115 116 117 118 119 120 121 123 124 126 130 132 135 141 142 143 145 146 147 148 149 154 157 **S** MemorialCare, Fountain Valley, CA
Primary Contact: Marcia Manker, Chief Executive Officer
COO: Ryan Olsen, Chief Operating Officer
CFO: Aaron Coley, Chief Financial Officer, Orange County
CMO: Kathleen Sullivan, M.D., Chief of Staff
CIO: J Scott Joslyn, Senior Vice President and Chief Information Officer
CHR: Michelle Gutierrez, Executive Director Human Resources, Orange County
CNO: Brandi Cassingham, Chief Nursing Officer
Web address: www.memorialcare.org
Control: Other not–for–profit (including NFP Corporation) **Service:** General medical and surgical

Staffed Beds: 250 Admissions: 12631 Census: 119 Outpatient Visits: 202100 Births: 2392 Total Expense ($000): 308924 Payroll Expense ($000): 92398 Personnel: 1310

LAKE ARROWHEAD—San Bernardino County

⊞ **SAN BERNARDINO MOUNTAINS COMMUNITY HOSPITAL DISTRICT (051312)**, 29101 Hospital Road, Zip 92352–9706, Mailing Address: P.O. Box 70, Zip 92352–0070; tel. 909/336–3651, (Nonreporting) **A**1 10 18
Primary Contact: Charles Harrison, Chief Executive Officer
COO: Terry Pena, Chief Operating Officer and Chief Nursing Officer
CFO: Yvonne Waggener, Chief Financial Officer
CMO: Walter M. Maier, Chief of Staff
CIO: Patrick Miller, Technology Coordinator
CHR: Julie Atwood, Director Human Resources
CNO: Terry Pena, Chief Operating Officer and Chief Nursing Officer
Web address: www.mchcares.com
Control: Hospital district or authority, Government, nonfederal **Service:** General medical and surgical

Staffed Beds: 37

LAKE ISABELLA—Kern County

KERN VALLEY HEALTHCARE DISTRICT (051314), 6412 Laurel Avenue, Zip 93240–9529, Mailing Address: P.O. Box 1628, Zip 93240–1628; tel. 760/379–2681, (Nonreporting) **A**10 18
Primary Contact: Timothy McGlew, Chief Executive Officer
CFO: Chester Beedle, Chief Financial Officer
CMO: Gary A Finstad, M.D., Chief of Staff
CIO: Paul Quinn, Information Systems Manager
CHR: Debra Hoffman, Human Resources Manager
CNO: Mark Gordon, Chief Nursing Officer
Web address: www.kvhd.org
Control: Hospital district or authority, Government, nonfederal **Service:** General medical and surgical

Staffed Beds: 99

CA

LAKEPORT—Lake County

⊞ **SUTTER LAKESIDE HOSPITAL (051329)**, 5176 Hill Road East, Zip 95453–6300; tel. 707/262–5000, (Nonreporting) **A**1 10 18 **S** Sutter Health, Sacramento, CA
Primary Contact: Dan Peterson, Chief Administrative Officer
CFO: Linnea Humble, Director of Finance
CMO: Diane Pege, M.D., Vice President Medical Affairs
CIO: Jack Buell, Director Information Services
CHR: Brenda DeRamus, Manager Human Resources
CNO: Teresa Campbell, R.N., Chief Nursing Executive
Web address: www.sutterlakeside.org
Control: Other not–for–profit (including NFP Corporation) **Service:** General medical and surgical

Staffed Beds: 25

LAKEWOOD—Los Angeles County

⊞ **LAKEWOOD REGIONAL MEDICAL CENTER (050581)**, 3700 East South Street, Zip 90712–1498, Mailing Address: P.O. Box 6070, Zip 90712; tel. 562/531–2550, **A**1 10 **F**3 11 15 17 18 20 22 24 26 29 30 34 35 38 40 45 49 50 51 57 59 64 68 70 74 75 77 79 81 85 87 93 107 108 109 111 115 118 119 120 126 130 132 143 146 148 149 154 **S** TENET Healthcare Corporation, Dallas, TX
Primary Contact: John A. Grah, FACHE, Chief Executive Officer
COO: Robert Shappley, Chief Operating Officer
CFO: Eric Delgado, Chief Financial Officer
CIO: Pat Pierce, Director Information Systems
CHR: Mary Okuhara, Chief Human Resource Officer
CNO: Terri Newton, Chief Nursing Officer
Web address: www.lakewoodregional.com
Control: Corporation, Investor–owned (for–profit) **Service:** General medical and surgical

Staffed Beds: 111 **Admissions:** 8864 **Census:** 111 **Outpatient Visits:** 56304 **Births:** 0 **Total Expense ($000):** 168945 **Payroll Expense ($000):** 77881 **Personnel:** 865

LANCASTER—Los Angeles County

⊞ **ANTELOPE VALLEY HOSPITAL (050056)**, 1600 West Avenue 'J', Zip 93534–2894; tel. 661/949–5000, (Nonreporting) **A**1 2 3 5 10
Primary Contact: Edward Mirzabegian, Chief Executive Officer
COO: Colette Menzel, Ph.D., Chief Operating Officer and Chief Financial Officer
CFO: Colette Menzel, Ph.D., Chief Operating Officer and Chief Financial Officer
CMO: Radha Krishnan, M.D., Chief Medical Officer
CIO: Dale Lepper, Chief Information Officer
CHR: George Leisher Jr Chief Human Resources Officer
CNO: Jack J Burke, MS, R.N., Chief Operating Officer and Chief Nursing Officer
Web address: www.avhospital.org
Control: Hospital district or authority, Government, nonfederal **Service:** General medical and surgical

Staffed Beds: 368

LEMOORE—Kings County

★ **NAVAL HOSPITAL LEMOORE**, 937 Franklin Avenue, Zip 93246–0001; tel. 559/998–4481, (Nonreporting) **S** Bureau of Medicine and Surgery, Department of the Navy, Falls Church, VA
Primary Contact: Captain Kristen Attenbury, Commanding Officer
CFO: Thomas M Brui, Director Resource Management
CMO: Scott Cota, M.D., Director Medical Services
CIO: Victor Dela Torre, Command Legal Officer
CHR: Billy Newman, Department Head
Web address: www.med.navy.mil/sites/nhlem/Pages/index.aspx
Control: Department of Defense, Government, federal **Service:** General medical and surgical

Staffed Beds: 16

LIVERMORE—Alameda County

VALLEY MEMORIAL See Stanford Health Care - Valleycare, Pleasanton

VETERANS AFFAIRS PALO ALTO HEALTH CARE SYSTEM, LIVERMORE DIVISION See Va Palo Alto Health Care System, Palo Alto

LODI—San Joaquin County

⊞ **ADVENTIST HEALTH LODI MEMORIAL (050336)**, 975 South Fairmont Avenue, Zip 95240–5118, Mailing Address: P.O. Box 3004, Zip 95241–1908; tel. 209/334–3411, (Includes LODI MEMORIAL HOSPITAL WEST, 800 South Lower Sacramento Road, Lodi, California, Zip 95242; tel. 209/333–0211), (Nonreporting) **A**1 5 10 **S** Adventist Health, Roseville, CA
Primary Contact: Daniel Wolcott, President and Chief Executive Officer
CFO: Terry Deak, Chief Financial Officer
CHR: Mark T Wallace, Director Human Resources
CNO: Debbie Moreno, R.N., Patient Care Executive
Web address: www.https://www.adventisthealth.org/lodi-memorial/
Control: Other not–for–profit (including NFP Corporation) **Service:** General medical and surgical

Staffed Beds: 190

LOMA LINDA—San Bernardino County

☐ **LOMA LINDA UNIVERSITY CHILDREN'S HOSPITAL (050778)**, 11234 Anderson Street, Zip 92354–2804; tel. 909/558–8000, **A**1 3 5 10 **F**3 11 13 19 21 23 25 27 29 31 34 43 44 45 46 50 54 55 57 58 59 60 61 64 65 68 72 74 75 76 77 78 79 80 81 82 84 85 86 87 88 89 97 119 126 132 134 136 137 138 141 146 147 149 154 156 **S** Loma Linda University Adventist Health Sciences Center, Loma Linda, CA
Primary Contact: Kerry Heinrich, JD, Chief Executive Officer
COO: Trevor Wright, Chief Operating Officer
CFO: Angela Lalas, Senior Vice President, Finance
CMO: Richard Chinnock, Chief Medical Officer, LLUCH
CIO: Mark Zirkelbach, Chief Information Officer
CHR: Lizette O Norton, Vice President, Human Resources
CNO: Helen Staples-Evans, Chief Nursing Officer, LLUCH
Web address: www.llu.edu/lluch
Control: Other not–for–profit (including NFP Corporation) **Service:** Children's general medical and surgical

Staffed Beds: 339 **Admissions:** 13964 **Census:** 229 **Outpatient Visits:** 72912 **Births:** 2952 **Total Expense ($000):** 412854 **Payroll Expense ($000):** 164845 **Personnel:** 1350

LOMA LINDA UNIVERSITY HEART & SURGICAL HOSPITAL See Loma Linda University Medical Center, Loma Linda

⊞ △ **LOMA LINDA UNIVERSITY MEDICAL CENTER (050327)**, 11234 Anderson Street, Zip 92354–2804, Mailing Address: P.O. Box 2000, Zip 92354–0200; tel. 909/558–4000, (Includes LOMA LINDA UNIVERSITY EAST CAMPUS HOSPITAL, 25333 Barton Road, Loma Linda, California, Zip 92354–3053; tel. 909/558–6000; LOMA LINDA UNIVERSITY HEART & SURGICAL HOSPITAL, 26780 Barton Road, Loma Linda, California, Zip 92354; tel. 909/583–2900) **A**1 2 3 5 7 8 10 **F**2 3 8 11 12 15 17 18 20 22 24 26 28 29 30 31 34 35 37 40 41 43 44 45 46 47 48 49 50 54 57 58 59 60 62 64 65 68 70 74 75 77 78 79 81 82 84 85 86 87 90 91 92 93 94 95 96 102 107 108 110 111 114 115 117 118 119 120 121 122 123 124 126 129 130 132 136 137 138 139 141 142 143 144 146 147 148 149 154 156 **S** Loma Linda University Adventist Health Sciences Center, Loma Linda, CA
Primary Contact: Kerry Heinrich, JD, Chief Executive Officer
COO: Trevor Wright, Chief Operating Officer
CMO: H Roger Hadley, M.D., Vice President, Medical Affairs
CIO: Mark Zirkelbach, Chief Information Officer
CNO: Judith Storfjell, Ph.D., R.N., Senior Vice President and Chief Nursing Officer
Web address: www.llumc.edu
Control: Other not–for–profit (including NFP Corporation) **Service:** General medical and surgical

Staffed Beds: 538 **Admissions:** 21896 **Census:** 348 **Outpatient Visits:** 666430 **Births:** 0 **Total Expense ($000):** 1120178 **Payroll Expense ($000):** 328901 **Personnel:** 4653

⊞ △ **VETERANS AFFAIRS LOMA LINDA HEALTHCARE SYSTEM**, 11201 Benton Street, Zip 92357–1000; tel. 909/825–7084, (Nonreporting) **A**1 2 3 5 7 8 **S** Department of Veterans Affairs, Washington, DC
Primary Contact: Andrew Welch, Interim Director
COO: Shane Elliott, Associate Director Administration
CFO: Eric C Sorenson, Chief Financial Officer
CMO: Dwight Evans, M.D., Chief of Staff
CIO: Doug Wirthgen, Facility Chief Information Officer
CHR: Eugene Wylie, Chief Human Resources Officer
CNO: Anne Gillespie, R.N., Associate Director Patient Care and Nursing Services
Web address: www.lomalinda.va.gov
Control: Veterans Affairs, Government, federal **Service:** General medical and surgical

Staffed Beds: 268

LOMPOC—Santa Barbara County

★ **LOMPOC VALLEY MEDICAL CENTER (050110)**, 1515 East Ocean Avenue, Zip 93436–7092, Mailing Address: P.O. Box 1058, Zip 93438–1058; tel. 805/737–3300, (Nonreporting) **A**10 22
Primary Contact: Steven Popkin, Chief Executive Officer
COO: Naishadh Buch, Chief Operating Officer
CFO: Robert M Baden, Chief Financial Officer
CMO: Randall Michel, M.D., Chief of Staff
CIO: Jim White, Chief Information Officer
CHR: Edwin R Braxton, Director Human Resources
CNO: Yvette Renee Cope, Chief Nurse Executive
Web address: www.lompocvmc.com
Control: Hospital district or authority, Government, nonfederal **Service:** General medical and surgical

Staffed Beds: 170

Many Facility Codes have changed. Please refer to the AHA Guide Code Chart.   © 2019 AHA Guide

LONE PINE—Inyo County

SOUTHERN INYO HEALTHCARE DISTRICT (051302), 501 East Locust Street, Zip 93545–1009, Mailing Address: P.O. Box 1009, Zip 93545–1009; tel. 760/876–5501, (Nonreporting) **A**10 18
Primary Contact: Brian Cotter, Chief Operating Officer
CFO: Marise Andrade, Controller
CIO: Phyllis Gregory, Registered Health Information Administrator
CHR: Nancy Erickson, Human Resource Director
CNO: Colleen Wilson, Chief Nursing Officer
Web address: www.sihd.org
Control: Hospital district or authority, Government, nonfederal **Service:** General medical and surgical

Staffed Beds: 4

LONG BEACH—Los Angeles County

⇑ **COLLEGE MEDICAL CENTER (050776)**, 2776 Pacific Avenue, Zip 90806–2613; tel. 562/595–1911, (Nonreporting) **A**3 5 10 12 13 21
Primary Contact: Joseph Avelino, Chief Executive Officer
COO: Jennifer Ensminger, Chief Operating Officer
CFO: Jim Canedo, Chief Financial Officer
CMO: Luke Watson, M.D., Chief of Staff
CIO: Rohan Corea, Director Healthcare Information Technology
CHR: Ann Mattia Schiller, Vice President Human Resources
Web address: www.collegemedicalcenter.com/
Control: Other not–for–profit (including NFP Corporation) **Service:** General medical and surgical

Staffed Beds: 184

⊠ △ **MEMORIALCARE, LONG BEACH MEMORIAL MEDICAL CENTER (050485)**, 2801 Atlantic Avenue, Zip 90806–1701, Mailing Address: P.O. Box 1428, Zip 90801–1428; tel. 562/933–2000, **A**1 2 3 5 7 8 10 **F**3 8 9 11 12 14 15 17 18 20 22 24 26 28 29 30 31 34 35 36 37 38 39 40 43 44 45 47 48 49 50 52 53 55 56 57 58 59 61 63 64 65 68 70 74 75 77 78 79 81 82 84 85 86 87 90 93 96 97 107 108 110 111 114 115 116 117 118 119 120 121 123 124 126 128 129 130 131 132 135 141 142 143 144 146 147 148 149 150 154 156 157 **S** MemorialCare, Fountain Valley, CA
Primary Contact: John Bishop, Chief Executive Officer
COO: Ikenna Mmeje, Chief Operating Officer
CFO: Yair Katz, Chief Financial Officer
CMO: Susan Melvin, D.O., Chief Medical Officer
CIO: Danny Asaoka, Executive Director Information Systems
CHR: Marcie Atchison, Vice President Human Resources
CNO: Antonio M. Garcia, Chief Nursing Officer
Web address: www.memorialcare.org/LongBeach
Control: Other not–for–profit (including NFP Corporation) **Service:** General medical and surgical

Staffed Beds: 458 Admissions: 20815 **Census:** 283 **Outpatient Visits:** 207271 **Births:** 0 **Total Expense ($000):** 822400 **Payroll Expense ($000):** 190010 **Personnel:** 2702

☐ **MEMORIALCARE, MILLER CHILDREN'S & WOMEN'S HOSPITAL LONG BEACH (053309)**, 2801 Atlantic Avenue, Zip 90806–1701; tel. 562/933–5437, **A**1 2 3 5 10 **F**3 11 12 13 14 15 19 21 23 25 27 29 30 31 32 34 35 36 37 38 40 41 43 44 45 47 48 49 50 52 53 54 55 57 58 59 61 64 65 66 68 72 74 75 76 77 78 79 81 82 84 85 86 87 88 89 93 96 97 107 108 111 114 115 116 117 118 119 120 121 123 124 126 130 132 134 135 141 142 143 144 146 147 148 149 154 156 157 **S** MemorialCare, Fountain Valley, CA
Primary Contact: John Bishop, Chief Executive Officer
COO: Tamra Kaplan, PharmD, Chief Operating Officer
CFO: Yair Katz, Chief Financial Officer
CMO: Graham Tse, M.D., Chief Medical Officer
CIO: Danny Asaoka, Executive Director Information Systems
CHR: Marcie Atchison, Vice President Human Resources
CNO: Antonio M. Garcia, Chief Nursing Officer
Web address: www.memorialcare.org
Control: Other not–for–profit (including NFP Corporation) **Service:** Children's general medical and surgical

Staffed Beds: 371 Admissions: 15233 **Census:** 193 **Outpatient Visits:** 99328 **Births:** 3979 **Total Expense ($000):** 429061 **Payroll Expense ($000):** 131843 **Personnel:** 1207

⊠ **ST. MARY MEDICAL CENTER (050191)**, 1050 Linden Avenue, Zip 90813–3321, Mailing Address: P.O. Box 887, Zip 90801–0887; tel. 562/491–9000, **A**1 3 10 **F**3 12 13 15 18 19 20 22 24 25 26 28 34 35 38 39 40 41 43 45 46 47 48 49 50 54 55 56 57 59 61 64 65 66 68 70 71 72 74 75 76 77 78 79 80 81 82 84 85 86 87 89 90 92 96 97 100 104 107 108 110 111 114 115 118 119 120 121 122 123 130 143 145 146 147 148 153 156 **S** CommonSpirit Health, Chicago, IL
Primary Contact: Carolyn P. Caldwell, FACHE, President and Chief Executive Officer
COO: Bonnie Panlasigui, Chief Operating Officer
CFO: Leon Choiniere, Vice President, Chief Financial Officer
CIO: David Ung, Site Director
CHR: Denise Livingston, Director Human Resources
CNO: Nancy Valla, R.N., Chief Nursing Officer
Web address: www.stmarymedicalcenter.org
Control: Other not–for–profit (including NFP Corporation) **Service:** General medical and surgical

Staffed Beds: 302 Admissions: 11132 **Census:** 144 **Outpatient Visits:** 125219 **Births:** 2203 **Total Expense ($000):** 332742 **Payroll Expense ($000):** 122832 **Personnel:** 1111

⊠ △ **VA LONG BEACH HEALTHCARE SYSTEM**, 5901 East 7th Street, Zip 90822–5201; tel. 562/826–8000, (Nonreporting) **A**1 2 3 5 7 8 **S** Department of Veterans Affairs, Washington, DC
Primary Contact: Walt Dannenberg, Director
COO: Anthony DeFrancesco, Associate Director
CFO: Michael J Rupert, Chief Financial Officer
CMO: Sandor Szabo, M.D., Ph.D., M.P.H., Chief of Staff
CIO: Rodney Sagmit, Chief Information Management
CHR: Mary E McCartan, Manager Human Resources
Web address: www.longbeach.va.gov/
Control: Veterans Affairs, Government, federal **Service:** General medical and surgical

Staffed Beds: 356

LOS ALAMITOS—Orange County

⊠ **LOS ALAMITOS MEDICAL CENTER (050551)**, 3751 Katella Avenue, Zip 90720–3164; tel. 562/598–1311, **A**1 10 **F**3 11 15 17 18 20 22 26 28 29 30 31 34 35 37 40 45 49 50 51 54 56 57 58 59 64 65 66 68 70 74 75 77 78 79 81 82 84 85 86 87 92 102 107 108 110 114 115 117 119 120 121 122 123 124 126 146 148 154 156 **S** TFNFT Healthcare Corporation, Dallas, TX
Primary Contact: Kent G. Clayton, Chief Executive Officer
COO: Clay Farell, Chief Operation Officer
CFO: Dave Vickers, Chief Financial Officer
CMO: Nirav Patel, M.D., Chief of Staff
CIO: Sally Andrada, Chief Information Officer
CHR: Mark Fisher, Chief Human Resources Officer
CNO: Judy Chabot, Chief Nursing Officer
Web address: www.losalamitosmedctr.com
Control: Corporation, Investor–owned (for–profit) **Service:** General medical and surgical

Staffed Beds: 120 Admissions: 9235 **Census:** 109 **Outpatient Visits:** 85311 **Births:** 862 **Total Expense ($000):** 190669 **Payroll Expense ($000):** 82662 **Personnel:** 762

LOS ANGELES—Los Angeles County

(Mailing Addresses—Canoga Park, Encino, Granada Hills, Harbor City, Hollywood, Mission Hills, North Hollywood, Northridge, Panorama City, San Pedro, Sepulveda, Sherman Oaks, Sun Valley, Sylmar, Tarzana, Van Nuys, West Hills, West Los Angeles, Woodland Hills)

⊠ ⇑ **ADVENTIST HEALTH GLENDALE (050239)**, 8700 Beverly Blvd, NT-3138, Zip 90048, Mailing Address: 1509 Wilson Terrace, Glendale, Zip 91206–4098; tel. 818/409–8000, **A**1 2 3 5 10 21 **F**3 4 5 8 12 13 15 17 18 20 22 24 26 28 29 30 31 32 34 35 36 37 39 40 44 45 46 47 48 49 50 51 53 54 57 58 59 63 64 65 68 70 71 72 73 74 75 76 77 78 79 81 82 83 84 85 86 87 90 91 92 93 96 98 100 101 102 104 105 107 108 109 110 111 114 115 118 119 120 121 124 126 128 129 130 131 132 135 145 146 147 148 149 152 156 **S** Adventist Health, Roseville, CA
Primary Contact: Alice H. Issai, President
COO: Warren Tetz, Senior Vice President and Chief Operating Officer
CFO: Kelly Turner, Senior Vice President Finance and Chief Financial Officer
CMO: Arby Nahapetian, M.D., Vice President Medical Affairs and Quality
CIO: Sharon Correa, Vice President and Chief Information Officer
CNO: Judy Blair, Senior Vice President Clinical Services and Chief Nursing Officer
Web address: www.glendaleadventist.com
Control: Other not–for–profit (including NFP Corporation) **Service:** General medical and surgical

Staffed Beds: 462 Admissions: 19252 **Census:** 207 **Births:** 1835 **Total Expense ($000):** 476194 **Payroll Expense ($000):** 141774 **Personnel:** 1814

CA

Hospital, Medicare Provider Number, Address, Telephone, Approval, Facility, and Physician Codes, Health Care System

★ American Hospital Association (AHA) membership   ○ Healthcare Facilities Accreditation Program   ⇑ Center for Improvement in Healthcare Quality Accreditation
☐ The Joint Commission accreditation   ◇ DNV Healthcare Inc. accreditation   △ Commission on Accreditation of Rehabilitation Facilities (CARF) accreditation

CA

⊞ **ADVENTIST HEALTH WHITE MEMORIAL (050103)**, 1720 Cesar Chavez Avenue, Zip 90033–2414; tel. 323/268–5000, (Total facility includes 27 beds in nursing home–type unit) **A**1 2 3 5 8 10 **F**3 11 13 15 17 18 19 20 22 24 26 27 28 29 30 31 34 35 40 41 45 46 47 48 49 50 51 53 57 58 59 64 68 70 72 74 75 76 77 78 79 81 82 84 85 86 87 88 89 90 91 92 93 96 97 98 102 103 107 108 109 110 111 114 115 116 117 118 119 120 121 123 126 128 130 131 132 146 147 148 149 154 156 **S** Adventist Health, Roseville, CA
Primary Contact: John Raffoul, Chief Executive Officer
CIO: Ralf Weissenberger, Director Information Systems
CHR: Natasha Milatovich, Association Vice President Human Resources
CNO: Patricia Stone, R.N., MSN, Senior Vice President Operations and Chief Nursing Officer
Web address: www.whitememorial.com
Control: Church operated, Nongovernment, not–for–profit **Service:** General medical and surgical

Staffed Beds: 353 **Admissions:** 19424 **Census:** 241 **Outpatient Visits:** 87614 **Births:** 3492 **Total Expense ($000):** 437028 **Payroll Expense ($000):** 128529 **Personnel:** 1686

⊞ **BARLOW RESPIRATORY HOSPITAL (052031)**, 2000 Stadium Way, Zip 90026–2696; tel. 213/250–4200, **A**1 10 **F**1 3 14 29 30 35 45 46 60 68 84 107 111 119 130 148
Primary Contact: Amit Mohan, President and Chief Executive Officer
CFO: Edward Engesser, Chief Financial Officer and Chief Information Officer
CMO: David Nelson, M.D., Medical Director
CIO: Edward Engesser, Chief Financial Officer and Chief Information Officer
CHR: Rashawn Woods, Vice President Human Resources
CNO: Gladys D'Souza, Chief Nursing Officer
Web address: www.barlow2000.org
Control: Other not–for–profit (including NFP Corporation) **Service:** Acute long–term care hospital

Staffed Beds: 105 **Admissions:** 863 **Census:** 76 **Outpatient Visits:** 0 **Births:** 0

⊞ **CALIFORNIA HOSPITAL MEDICAL CENTER (050149)**, 1401 South Grand Avenue, Zip 90015–3010; tel. 213/748–2411, (Nonreporting) **A**1 3 5 10 **S** CommonSpirit Health, Chicago, IL
Primary Contact: Margaret R. Peterson, Ph.D., R.N., President
CFO: Rebecca Cheng, Chief Financial Officer
CMO: Joseph Nussbaum, M.D., Chief of Staff
CIO: David Ung, Director, Information Technology
CHR: Kristin Anderson, Director, Human Resources
CNO: Valarie McPherson, MSN, Chief Nursing Executive
Web address: www.chmcla.org
Control: Other not–for–profit (including NFP Corporation) **Service:** General medical and surgical

Staffed Beds: 318

⊞ △ **CALIFORNIA REHABILITATION INSTITUTE (053039)**, 2070 Century Park East, Zip 90067–1907; tel. 424/363–1000, **A**1 3 7 10 **F**29 30 34 44 50 68 77 87 90 92 94 96 100 130 132 148 **S** Select Medical Corporation, Mechanicsburg, PA
Primary Contact: Scott T. Rotsted, Chief Executive Officer
Web address: www.californiarehabinstitute.com/
Control: Corporation, Investor–owned (for–profit) **Service:** Rehabilitation

Staffed Beds: 120 **Admissions:** 2744 **Census:** 103 **Outpatient Visits:** 0 **Births:** 0 **Personnel:** 451

⊞ **CEDARS-SINAI MEDICAL CENTER (050625)**, 8700 Beverly Boulevard, Zip 90048–1865; tel. 310/423–5000, **A**1 2 3 5 8 10 19 **F**3 6 8 9 11 12 13 14 15 17 18 19 20 21 22 23 24 25 26 27 28 29 30 31 32 33 34 35 36 37 38 39 40 41 43 44 45 46 47 48 49 50 51 52 54 55 56 57 58 59 60 61 64 65 66 68 69 70 71 72 74 75 76 77 78 79 81 82 83 84 85 86 87 88 89 91 92 93 96 97 100 102 107 108 109 110 111 112 113 114 115 116 117 118 119 120 121 123 124 126 130 131 132 133 134 135 136 137 138 139 140 141 142 144 145 146 147 148 149 150 154 **S** Cedars-Sinai Health System, West Hollywood, CA
Primary Contact: Thomas M. Priselac, President and Chief Executive Officer
COO: Jeffrey A. Smith, M.D., Executive Vice President Hospital Operations and Chief Operating Officer
CFO: Edward M Prunchunas, Executive Vice President and Chief Financial Officer
CMO: Michael L Langberg, M.D., Senior Vice President Medical Affairs and Chief Medical Officer
CIO: Darren Dworkin, Senior Vice President Enterprise Information Systems and Chief Information Officer
CHR: Andrew Ortiz, Senior Vice President, Human Resources and Organization Development
CNO: Linda Burnes Bolton, Dr.PH, R.N., Chief Health Equity Officer
Web address: www.cedars-sinai.edu
Control: Other not–for–profit (including NFP Corporation) **Service:** General medical and surgical

Staffed Beds: 885 **Admissions:** 50300 **Census:** 721 **Outpatient Visits:** 885381 **Births:** 6358 **Total Expense ($000):** 3164509 **Payroll Expense ($000):** 1173698 **Personnel:** 13235

⊞ △ **CHILDREN'S HOSPITAL LOS ANGELES (053302)**, 4650 West Sunset Boulevard, Zip 90027–6062, Mailing Address: 4650 West Sunset Boulevard, MS #1, Zip 90027–6062; tel. 323/660–2450, **A**1 3 5 7 8 10 **F**3 7 8 9 11 14 15 17 19 21 23 25 27 28 29 30 31 33 34 35 36 37 38 39 40 41 43 44 45 46 47 48 49 50 54 55 57 58 59 60 61 64 65 68 70 72 73 74 75 77 78 79 80 81 82 83 84 86 87 88 89 90 91 92 93 94 95 107 111 115 116 117 118 119 120 121 122 124 126 129 130 131 132 134 136 137 138 139 140 141 146 148 149 154 155 156 157
Primary Contact: Paul S. Viviano, President and Chief Executive Officer
CFO: Lannie Tonnu, Senior Vice President and Chief Financial Officer
CMO: Brent Polk, M.D., Chair Department of Pediatrics and Vice President Academic Affairs
CIO: TJ Malseed, Vice President and Chief Information Officer
CHR: Myra Gregorian, Vice President and Chief Human Resources Officer
CNO: Mary Dee Hacker, R.N., Vice President, Patient Care Services and Chief Nursing Officer
Web address: www.chla.org
Control: Other not–for–profit (including NFP Corporation) **Service:** Children's general medical and surgical

Staffed Beds: 361 **Admissions:** 18338 **Census:** 315 **Outpatient Visits:** 382042 **Births:** 0 **Total Expense ($000):** 1187586 **Payroll Expense ($000):** 464468 **Personnel:** 5538

☐ **EAST LOS ANGELES DOCTORS HOSPITAL (050641)**, 4060 Whittier Boulevard, Zip 90023–2526; tel. 323/268–5514, (Nonreporting) **A**1 10 **S** Avanti Hospitals, El Segundo, CA
Primary Contact: Gerald B. Clute, Chief Executive Officer
CFO: Steven Blake, Corporate Chief Financial Officer
CMO: Janine King, M.D., Chief of Staff
CIO: Jason Cervantes, Chief Information Officer
CHR: Paul Celuch, Chief Human Resource Officer
CNO: Kimberly Frazier, R.N., Chief Nursing Officer
Web address: www.avantihospitals.com
Control: Corporation, Investor–owned (for–profit) **Service:** General medical and surgical

Staffed Beds: 127

⊞ **ENCINO HOSPITAL MEDICAL CENTER (050158)**, 16237 Ventura Boulevard, Zip 91436–2272; tel. 818/995–5000, (Nonreporting) **A**1 10 **S** Prime Healthcare, Ontario, CA
Primary Contact: Bockhi Park, Chief Executive Officer
CFO: Kanner Tillman, Chief Financial Officer
CMO: Muhammad Anwar, M.D., Chief Medical Officer
CIO: Edward Barrera, Director Communications
CHR: Barbara Back, Manager Human Resources
CNO: Vilma L Dinham, R.N., Chief Nursing Officer
Web address: www.encinomed.com
Control: Other not–for–profit (including NFP Corporation) **Service:** General medical and surgical

Staffed Beds: 78

○ **GATEWAYS HOSPITAL AND MENTAL HEALTH CENTER (054028)**, 1891 Effie Street, Zip 90026–1793; tel. 323/644–2000, (Nonreporting) **A**10 11
Primary Contact: Philip Wong, PsyD, Chief Executive Officer
COO: Philip Wong, PsyD, Chief Operating Officer
CMO: Imani Walker, M.D., Medical Director
CIO: Rozelle DeVera, Director of Information Systems
CHR: Vahan Demlakian, Director of Human Resources
Web address: www.gatewayshospital.org
Control: Other not–for–profit (including NFP Corporation) **Service:** Psychiatric

Staffed Beds: 55

☐ **GOOD SAMARITAN HOSPITAL (050471)**, 1225 Wilshire Boulevard, Zip 90017–2395; tel. 213/977–2121, **A**1 2 3 5 10 **F**3 7 8 11 13 15 17 18 20 22 24 26 28 29 30 31 34 35 37 40 45 46 47 48 49 51 53 57 58 59 64 65 68 70 72 74 75 76 77 78 79 81 84 85 86 87 93 107 108 110 111 114 115 117 118 119 120 121 123 124 126 129 130 132 134 148 149 156
Primary Contact: Andrew B. Leeka, President and Chief Executive Officer
COO: Phillip Wolfe, Vice President of Professional Operations
CFO: Alan Ino, Chief Financial Officer
CMO: Margaret Bates, Chief of Staff
CIO: Dean Campbell, Vice President Information Services and Chief Information Officer
CHR: Lexie Schuster, Vice President Human Resources
CNO: Margaret Pfeiffer, R.N., MSN, Vice President Patient Care Services
Web address: www.goodsam.org
Control: Other not–for–profit (including NFP Corporation) **Service:** General medical and surgical

Staffed Beds: 374 **Admissions:** 12671 **Census:** 174 **Outpatient Visits:** 74588 **Births:** 2717 **Total Expense ($000):** 350417 **Payroll Expense ($000):** 113000 **Personnel:** 1400

Many Facility Codes have changed. Please refer to the AHA Guide Code Chart. © 2019 AHA Guide

CA

☒ **HOLLYWOOD PRESBYTERIAN MEDICAL CENTER (050063)**, 1300 North Vermont Avenue, Zip 90027–6306; tel. 213/413–3000, **A**1 3 10 **F**3 8 13 15 17 18 20 22 24 26 29 30 31 34 40 41 45 46 49 50 51 56 57 59 60 61 64 68 70 72 74 75 76 77 78 79 80 81 85 87 89 90 92 96 97 107 108 110 111 115 119 126 130 146 147 148 149 154
Primary Contact: Robert Allen, President and Chief Executive Officer
COO: Wontae Cha, Chief Operating Officer
CIO: Steve Giles, Chief Information Officer
CHR: George Leisher Jr Vice President Human Resources
CNO: Farideh Ara, Interim Chief Nursing Officer
Web address: www.hollywoodpresbyterian.com
Control: Partnership, Investor–owned (for–profit) **Service:** General medical and surgical

Staffed Beds: 434 **Admissions:** 12765 **Census:** 222 **Outpatient Visits:** 53163 **Births:** 3422 **Total Expense ($000):** 290315 **Payroll Expense ($000):** 124219 **Personnel:** 1193

KAISER FOUNDATION MENTAL HEALTH CENTER See Kaiser Permanente Los Angeles Medical Center, Los Angeles

☒ **KAISER PERMANENTE LOS ANGELES MEDICAL CENTER (050138)**, 4867 Sunset Boulevard, Zip 90027–5961; tel. 323/783–4011, (Includes KAISER FOUNDATION MENTAL HEALTH CENTER, 765 West College Street, Los Angeles, California, Zip 90012; tel. 213/580–7200) **A**1 3 5 8 10 **F**3 7 8 13 15 17 18 19 20 21 22 23 24 26 29 30 31 34 35 36 38 40 44 45 46 47 49 50 51 52 54 55 56 57 58 59 60 61 62 63 64 65 66 68 70 72 74 75 76 77 78 79 81 82 83 84 85 86 87 88 89 92 93 97 98 99 101 102 103 104 105 107 108 109 110 111 113 114 115 116 117 118 119 120 121 122 123 124 126 129 130 131 132 135 144 146 147 148 149 150 153 154 156 157 **S** Kaiser Foundation Hospitals, Oakland, CA
Primary Contact: William N. Grice, Executive Director
COO: Derek Berz, Chief Operating Officer
CFO: Brad Malsed, Area Chief Financial Officer
CMO: Michael Tome, M.D., Medical Director
CIO: David Strickland, Area Information Officer
CHR: Paul J Martin, Director Human Resources
Web address: www.kaiserpermanente.org
Control: Other not–for–profit (including NFP Corporation) **Service:** General medical and surgical

Staffed Beds: 528 **Admissions:** 30767 **Census:** 391 **Outpatient Visits:** 101046 **Births:** 2873 **Personnel:** 5154

☒ **KAISER PERMANENTE PANORAMA CITY MEDICAL CENTER (050137)**, 13652 Cantara Street, Zip 91402–5497; tel. 818/375–2000, **A**1 3 5 10 **F**3 7 8 11 13 15 18 29 30 31 32 34 35 37 38 40 41 44 45 46 48 49 50 51 54 55 56 57 58 59 60 61 62 63 64 65 66 68 70 74 75 76 77 78 79 81 82 84 85 86 87 89 92 97 101 102 104 107 108 110 111 114 115 116 117 118 119 124 126 129 130 131 132 135 141 143 144 146 147 148 149 154 156 157 **S** Kaiser Foundation Hospitals, Oakland, CA
Primary Contact: Payman Roshan, Senior Vice President and Area Manager
COO: Laura Gallardo, Chief Operating Officer
CFO: Karla Valle, Area Chief Financial Officer
CMO: James Lau, M.D., Area Medical Director
CIO: Earle Johnson, Area Information Officer
CHR: Carole L Erken, Human Resources Leader
CNO: Celeste Farugia, R.N., MSN, Chief Nurse Executive
Web address: www.kaiserpermanente.org
Control: Other not–for–profit (including NFP Corporation) **Service:** General medical and surgical

Staffed Beds: 115 **Admissions:** 8725 **Census:** 87 **Outpatient Visits:** 80851 **Births:** 2607 **Personnel:** 693

☒ **KAISER PERMANENTE SOUTH BAY MEDICAL CENTER (050411)**, 25825 Vermont Avenue, Zip 90710–3599; tel. 310/325–5111, **A**1 3 10 **F**2 3 5 6 9 11 12 13 15 18 29 30 31 32 34 35 36 39 40 44 45 46 47 48 49 50 51 53 54 55 56 57 58 59 60 61 63 64 65 66 68 70 72 74 75 76 77 78 79 81 82 85 86 87 91 92 93 94 96 97 100 107 108 110 111 114 115 116 117 118 119 130 131 132 134 135 144 146 147 148 149 150 154 156 157 **S** Kaiser Foundation Hospitals, Oakland, CA
Primary Contact: Lesley A. Wille, Executive Director
Web address: www.kaiserpermanente.org
Control: Other not–for–profit (including NFP Corporation) **Service:** General medical and surgical

Staffed Beds: 226 **Admissions:** 8000 **Census:** 104 **Outpatient Visits:** 87268 **Births:** 2613 **Personnel:** 2255

☒ **KAISER PERMANENTE WEST LOS ANGELES MEDICAL CENTER (050561)**, 6041 Cadillac Avenue, Zip 90034–1700; tel. 323/857–2201, **A**1 3 5 10 **F**3 6 11 12 13 15 29 30 31 32 34 35 37 40 41 44 45 46 47 48 49 50 55 56 57 58 59 60 61 64 65 68 70 72 73 74 75 76 78 79 80 81 82 85 87 100 101 107 108 110 111 114 115 116 117 119 126 130 132 135 146 148 149 150 154 158 **S** Kaiser Foundation Hospitals, Oakland, CA
Primary Contact: Georgina R. Garcia, R.N., Executive Director
CMO: Fred Alexander, M.D., Medical Director
CIO: Gregory M Sincock, Information Technology Leader
Web address: www.kaiserpermanente.org
Control: Other not–for–profit (including NFP Corporation) **Service:** General medical and surgical

Staffed Beds: 126 **Admissions:** 15965 **Census:** 265 **Outpatient Visits:** 81140 **Births:** 1908 **Personnel:** 1298

☒ **KAISER PERMANENTE WOODLAND HILLS MEDICAL CENTER (050677)**, 5601 DeSoto Avenue, Zip 91367–6798; tel. 818/719–2000, **A**1 3 5 10 **F**3 6 8 9 12 13 15 18 29 30 31 34 35 38 40 41 44 45 46 48 49 50 51 52 53 54 55 56 57 58 59 60 61 63 64 65 66 68 70 73 74 75 76 77 78 79 80 81 82 83 84 85 86 87 92 93 97 100 102 104 107 108 110 111 114 115 117 119 124 129 130 131 132 134 135 141 144 146 147 148 149 150 153 154 156 157 **S** Kaiser Foundation Hospitals, Oakland, CA
Primary Contact: Murtaza Sanwari, Senior Vice President and Area Manager
COO: Richard Trogman, FACHE, Chief Operating Officer
CFO: Marilou Cheung, Assistant Administrator Finance
CMO: Gregory Kelman, M.D., Area Medical Director
CIO: Earle Johnson, Area Information Officer
CHR: Cathy Cousineau, Director Human Resources
CNO: Nancy Tankel, R.N., Chief Nurse Executive
Web address: www.kaiserpermanente.org
Control: Other not–for–profit (including NFP Corporation) **Service:** General medical and surgical

Staffed Beds: 160 **Admissions:** 8557 **Census:** 87 **Outpatient Visits:** 118175 **Births:** 1777 **Personnel:** 1060

☒ **KECK HOSPITAL OF USC (050696)**, 1500 San Pablo Street, Zip 90033–5313; tel. 323/442–8500, **A**1 3 5 8 10 **F**3 6 8 9 11 12 14 15 17 18 22 24 26 29 30 31 34 35 36 37 38 39 43 44 45 46 47 48 49 50 51 52 53 54 55 56 57 58 59 60 61 64 65 68 70 71 74 75 77 78 79 81 82 84 85 86 87 90 91 92 93 94 95 96 97 100 101 104 107 108 109 110 111 112 113 114 115 116 117 118 119 124 126 129 130 131 132 135 137 138 139 140 141 142 144 145 146 147 148 149 150 154 156 157 **S** Keck Medicine of USC, Los Angeles, CA
Primary Contact: Rodney B. Hanners, Chief Executive Officer
CMO: Stephanie Hall, M.D., Chief Medical Officer
CIO: Timothy James Malseed, Chief Information Officer
CHR: Matthew McElrath, Chief Human Resources Officer
CNO: Annette Sy, Chief Nursing Officer
Web address: www.https://www.keckmedicine.org/
Control: Other not–for–profit (including NFP Corporation) **Service:** General medical and surgical

Staffed Beds: 401 **Admissions:** 12309 **Census:** 234 **Outpatient Visits:** 345084 **Births:** 0 **Total Expense ($000):** 1077146 **Payroll Expense ($000):** 369484 **Personnel:** 3820

KEDREN COMMUNITY MENTAL HEALTH CENTER (054083), 4211 South Avalon Boulevard, Zip 90011–5699; tel. 323/233–0425, (Nonreporting) **A**10
Primary Contact: John H. Griffith, Ph.D., President and Chief Executive Officer
COO: Madeline Valencerina, Chief Operating Officer
CFO: Rizwan A. Uraizee, Chief Financial Officer
CMO: Frank L. Williams, Executive Vice President/ Medical Director
CNO: Essie Adams, Director of Nursing
Web address: www.kedrenmentalhealth.com
Control: Other not–for–profit (including NFP Corporation) **Service:** Psychiatric

Staffed Beds: 72

☒ **KINDRED HOSPITAL-LOS ANGELES (052032)**, 5525 West Slauson Avenue, Zip 90056–1067; tel. 310/642–0325, (Nonreporting) **A**1 10 **S** Kindred Healthcare, Louisville, KY
Primary Contact: Phillip R. Wolfe, Chief Executive Officer
CFO: Charles Natcher, Chief Financial Officer
Web address: www.kindredhospitalla.com/
Control: Corporation, Investor–owned (for–profit) **Service:** Acute long–term care hospital

Staffed Beds: 81

Hospital, Medicare Provider Number, Address, Telephone, Approval, Facility, and Physician Codes, Health Care System

★ American Hospital Association (AHA) membership
□ The Joint Commission accreditation
○ Healthcare Facilities Accreditation Program
◇ DNV Healthcare Inc. accreditation
⇑ Center for Improvement in Healthcare Quality Accreditation
△ Commission on Accreditation of Rehabilitation Facilities (CARF) accreditation

CA

□ **LAC-OLIVE VIEW-UCLA MEDICAL CENTER (050040)**, 14445 Olive View Drive, Zip 91342–1438; tel. 818/364–1555, **A**1 3 5 10 **F**3 13 15 18 19 20 22 24 26 29 30 31 34 40 41 44 45 46 48 49 50 51 58 59 60 61 62 63 64 65 66 68 70 72 74 75 76 78 79 80 81 82 84 85 87 89 93 94 97 98 100 102 104 107 108 110 111 114 115 116 117 118 119 129 130 143 144 146 147 148 149 156 **S** Los Angeles County-Department of Health Services, Los Angeles, CA
Primary Contact: Judith Maass, Chief Executive Officer
COO: Niloo Shahi, Chief Operating Officer
CFO: Anthony Gray, Chief Financial Officer
CMO: Shannon Thyne, Chief Medical Officer
CIO: Susan Aintablian, Chief Information Officer
CHR: Thomas Beggane, Manager Human Resources
CNO: Dellone Pascascio, Chief Nursing Officer
Web address: www.dhs.lacounty.gov/wps/portal/dhs/oliveview
Control: County, Government, nonfederal **Service:** General medical and surgical

Staffed Beds: 202 **Admissions:** 11229 **Census:** 181 **Outpatient Visits:** 247092 **Births:** 683 **Total Expense ($000):** 584476 **Payroll Expense ($000):** 233008 **Personnel:** 2553

□ **LAC+USC MEDICAL CENTER (050373)**, 2051 Marengo Street, Zip 90033–1352; tel. 323/409–1000, (Includes GENERAL HOSPITAL, 1200 North State Street, Los Angeles, California, Zip 90033; tel. 909/558–6000; WOMEN'S AND CHILDREN'S HOSPITAL, 1240 North Mission Road, Los Angeles, California, Zip 90033; tel. 909/558–6000), (Nonreporting) **A**2 3 5 10 **S** Los Angeles County-Department of Health Services, Los Angeles, CA
Primary Contact: Dan A. Castillo, FACHE, Chief Executive Officer
COO: Henry Ornelas, Chief Operating Officer
CFO: Mark Corbet, Interim Chief Financial Officer
CMO: Brad Spellberg, M.D., Chief Medical Officer
CIO: Oscar Autelli, Chief Information Officer
CHR: Elizabeth Jacobi, Human Resources Director
CNO: Isabel Milan, R.N., Chief Nursing Officer
Web address: www.lacusc.org
Control: County, Government, nonfederal **Service:** General medical and surgical

Staffed Beds: 664

□ **LOS ANGELES COMMUNITY HOSPITAL AT LOS ANGELES (050663)**, 4081 East Olympic Boulevard, Zip 90023–3330; tel. 323/267–0477, (Includes LOS ANGELES COMMUNITY HOSPITAL OF NORWALK, 13222 Bloomfield Avenue, Norwalk, California, Zip 90650; tel. 562/863–4763), (Nonreporting) **A**1 10 **S** Prospect Medical Holdings, Los Angeles, CA
Primary Contact: Omar Ramirez, Chief Executive Officer
CFO: Johnnette Chong, Chief Financial Officer
Web address: www.altacorp.com/altacorp/our-hospitals/lach-menu.html
Control: Corporation, Investor–owned (for–profit) **Service:** General medical and surgical

Staffed Beds: 180

LOS ANGELES COUNTY CENTRAL JAIL HOSPITAL, 441 Bauchet Street, Zip 90012–2906; tel. 213/473–6100, (Nonreporting)
Primary Contact: Tom Flaherty, Assistant Administrator
Control: County, Government, nonfederal **Service:** Hospital unit of an institution (prison hospital, college infirmary, etc.)

Staffed Beds: 190

LOS ANGELES MEDICAL CENTER See Kaiser Permanente Los Angeles Medical Center

□ **MARTIN LUTHER KING, JR. COMMUNITY HOSPITAL (050779)**, 1680 East 120th Street, Zip 90059–3026; tel. 424/338–8000, (Nonreporting) **A**1 5 10
Primary Contact: Elaine Batchlor, M.D., M.P.H., Chief Executive Officer
COO: Myrna Allen, R.N., MS, Chief Operating and Nursing Officer
CMO: John Fisher, M.D., Chief Medical Officer
CIO: Sajid Ahmed, Chief Information and Innovation Officer
CHR: Susan M Burrows, Vice President Human Resources
CNO: Myrna Allen, R.N., MS, Chief Operating and Nursing Officer
Web address: www.mlkcommunityhospital.org/
Control: Other not–for–profit (including NFP Corporation) **Service:** General medical and surgical

Staffed Beds: 131

□ **MIRACLE MILE MEDICAL CENTER (050751)**, 6000 San Vicente Boulevard, Zip 90036–4404; tel. 323/930–1040, (Nonreporting) **A**1 10
Primary Contact: Gil Tepper, M.D., Chief Executive Officer
COO: Liz Cheever, Administrator
CFO: Bert Roberts, Controller
CMO: Gil Tepper, M.D., Chief of Staff
CIO: Jonathan Lindell, Director Information Technology
CHR: Liz Cheever, Administrator
CNO: Melody Bradley, Chief Nursing Officer
Web address: www.miraclemilemedicalcenter.com
Control: Individual, Investor–owned (for–profit) **Service:** General medical and surgical

Staffed Beds: 17

□ **MISSION COMMUNITY HOSPITAL (050704)**, 14850 Roscoe Boulevard, Zip 91402–4677; tel. 818/787–2222, (Nonreporting) **A**1 10
Primary Contact: James Theiring, Chief Executive Officer
CMO: Glenn Marshak, M.D., Chief of Staff
CIO: Eric Rivers, Chief Information Officer
CHR: Carolyn Fish, Director Human Resources
CNO: Gwendolyn Dianne Wagner, R.N., MSN, Chief Nursing Officer
Web address: www.mchonline.org
Control: Other not–for–profit (including NFP Corporation) **Service:** General medical and surgical

Staffed Beds: 145

□ **MOTION PICTURE AND TELEVISION FUND HOSPITAL AND RESIDENTIAL SERVICES (050552)**, 23388 Mulholland Drive, Zip 91364–2792; tel. 818/876–1888, (Nonreporting) **A**1
Primary Contact: Bob Beitcher, Chief Executive Officer
COO: David Asplund, Chief Operating Officer
CFO: Frank Guarrera, Executive Vice President and Chief Financial Officer
CHR: Nancy Rubin, Vice President Human Resources
Web address: www.mptvfund.org
Control: Other not–for–profit (including NFP Corporation) **Service:** General medical and surgical

Staffed Beds: 20

⊠ △ **NORTHRIDGE HOSPITAL MEDICAL CENTER (050116)**, 18300 Roscoe Boulevard, Zip 91328–4167; tel. 818/885–8500, **A**1 2 3 5 7 10 **F**1 2 3 5 11 13 14 15 17 18 20 22 24 26 28 29 30 31 34 35 38 40 41 43 48 49 56 57 59 60 61 64 68 70 72 73 74 75 76 78 79 81 82 84 85 87 88 89 90 93 97 98 99 100 101 102 103 105 107 108 110 111 115 117 118 119 121 124 126 130 132 146 147 148 152 153 154 **S** CommonSpirit Health, Chicago, IL
Primary Contact: Paul Watkins, JD, President
COO: Betsy Hart, Chief Operating Officer
CFO: Michael Taylor, Vice President Finance
CMO: Mark Dumais, M.D., Chief Medical Officer
CHR: Susan Paulsen, Director Human Resources
CNO: Resha T Holman, Chief Nurse Executive Officer
Web address: www.northridgehospital.org
Control: Other not–for–profit (including NFP Corporation) **Service:** General medical and surgical

Staffed Beds: 394 **Admissions:** 14969 **Census:** 182 **Outpatient Visits:** 109114 **Births:** 751 **Total Expense ($000):** 431716 **Payroll Expense ($000):** 157743 **Personnel:** 1505

⇑ **OLYMPIA MEDICAL CENTER (050742)**, 5900 West Olympic Boulevard, Zip 90036–4671; tel. 310/657–5900, (Nonreporting) **A**10 21 **S** Alecto Healthcare, Irvine, CA
Primary Contact: Matthew Williams, R.N., Chief Executive Officer
CFO: Matthew Williams, R.N., Chief Financial Officer
CMO: Panch Jeyakumar, M.D., Chief of Staff
CIO: Jason Williams, Director Information Systems
CHR: Joseph Ambrosini, Director Human Resources
CNO: Sylvia A Ventura, R.N., MS, Chief Nursing Officer
Web address: www.olympiamc.com
Control: Partnership, Investor–owned (for–profit) **Service:** General medical and surgical

Staffed Beds: 204

□ **PACIFICA HOSPITAL OF THE VALLEY (050378)**, 9449 San Fernando Road, Zip 91352–1489; tel. 818/767–3310, (Nonreporting) **A**1 10 **S** Southwest Healthcare System, Scottsdale, AZ
Primary Contact: Ayman Mousa, R.N., Ph.D., Chief Executive Officer
COO: Daniel Santos, Director Ancillary Services
CFO: Eileen Fisler, Chief Financial Officer
CMO: Joseph Eipe, M.D., Chief Medical Officer
CIO: Mubashir Hashmi, Chief Information Officer
CHR: Patti Alonzo, Manager Human Resources
CNO: Janet B. Latto, Chief Nursing Officer and Disaster Officer
Web address: www.pacificahospital.com
Control: Corporation, Investor–owned (for–profit) **Service:** General medical and surgical

Staffed Beds: 231

PANORAMA CITY MEDICAL CENTER See Kaiser Permanente Panorama City Medical Center

PROMISE HOSPITAL OF EAST LOS ANGELES (052046), 443 South Soto Street, Zip 90033–4398; tel. 323/261–1181, (Includes PROMISE HOSPITAL OF EAST LOS ANGELES, SUBURBAN MEDICAL CENTER CAMPUS, 16453 South Colorado Avenue, Paramount, California, Zip 90723–5011; tel. 562/531–3110; Michael D Kerr, Chief Executive Officer), (Nonreporting) **A**10 **S** Promise Healthcare, Boca Raton, FL
Primary Contact: Michael D. Kerr, Chief Executive Officer
Web address: www.promiseeastla.com
Control: Corporation, Investor–owned (for–profit) **Service:** Acute long–term care hospital

Staffed Beds: 213

Many Facility Codes have changed. Please refer to the AHA Guide Code Chart. © 2019 AHA Guide

✠ △ **PROVIDENCE LITTLE COMPANY OF MARY MEDICAL CENTER SAN PEDRO (050078)**, 1300 West Seventh Street, Zip 90732–3505; tel. 310/832–3311, (Total facility includes 125 beds in nursing home–type unit) **A**1 7 10 **F**2 3 4 5 11 13 14 15 18 29 30 32 34 35 40 41 44 45 49 50 51 56 57 59 60 63 64 65 66 68 70 71 74 75 76 77 78 79 81 82 84 85 86 87 90 92 93 94 95 96 98 100 101 102 103 104 107 108 110 111 114 119 120 123 128 130 131 132 135 145 146 147 149 150 153 154 **S** Providence St. Joseph Health, Renton, WA
Primary Contact: Garry M. Olney, Chief Executive Officer
CFO: Elizabeth Zuanich, Chief Financial Officer
CMO: Richard Glimp, M.D., Chief Medical Officer
CIO: Kim Brant-Lucich, Director, Information Systems
CHR: Melissa Baker, Director, Human Resources
Web address: www.https://california.providence.org/san-pedro
Control: Church operated, Nongovernment, not–for–profit **Service:** General medical and surgical

Staffed Beds: 318 **Admissions:** 6746 **Census:** 207 **Outpatient Visits:** 120814 **Births:** 389 **Total Expense ($000):** 138045 **Payroll Expense ($000):** 78955 **Personnel:** 1122

✠ **PROVIDENCE TARZANA MEDICAL CENTER (050761)**, 18321 Clark Street, Zip 91356–3521; tel. 818/881–0800, **A**1 10 **F**3 7 8 13 15 17 18 19 20 22 24 26 28 29 30 31 34 35 37 40 41 44 45 46 49 50 51 54 56 57 59 63 64 70 72 74 75 76 77 78 79 81 82 83 84 85 86 87 88 89 107 108 110 111 114 115 118 119 126 130 131 132 143 146 147 148 149 154 **S** Providence St. Joseph Health, Renton, WA
Primary Contact: Dale Surowitz, Chief Executive
COO: Phyllis Bushart, R.N., Chief Operating Officer
CMO: Howard Z Davis, M.D., Chief Medical Officer
CIO: Alex Nury, Chief Information Officer
CHR: Beverly Murray, Director of Human Resources
CNO: Deborah Carver, Chief Nursing Officer
Web address: www.providence.org/tarzana.com
Control: Church operated, Nongovernment, not–for–profit **Service:** General medical and surgical

Staffed Beds: 229 **Admissions:** 13041 **Census:** 130 **Outpatient Visits:** 154965 **Births:** 2502 **Total Expense ($000):** 227379 **Payroll Expense ($000):** 109086 **Personnel:** 1242

✠ **RONALD REAGAN UCLA MEDICAL CENTER (050262)**, 757 Westwood Plaza, Zip 90095–8358; tel. 310/825–9111, (Includes MATTEL CHILDREN'S HOSPITAL, 757 Westwood Plaza, Los Angeles, California, Zip 90095; tel. 310/825–9111) **A**1 3 5 8 10 19 **F**3 6 7 8 9 11 12 13 14 15 17 18 19 20 21 22 23 24 25 26 27 28 29 30 31 32 34 35 36 37 39 40 41 43 44 45 46 47 48 49 50 51 52 54 55 56 57 58 59 61 62 64 65 66 68 70 71 72 74 75 76 77 78 79 81 82 84 85 86 87 88 89 92 93 94 96 97 102 107 108 110 111 112 113 114 115 116 117 118 119 120 121 123 124 126 129 130 131 132 135 136 137 138 139 140 141 142 143 145 146 147 148 149 154 156 **S** University of California Systemwide Administration, Oakland, CA
Primary Contact: Johnese Spisso, Chief Executive Officer
COO: J. Shannon O'Kelley, Chief Operating Officer
CFO: Paul Staton, Chief Financial Officer
CMO: Robert Cherry, M.D., Chief Medical and Quality Officer
CIO: Michael Pfeffer, M.D., Chief Information Officer
CHR: Susi Takeuchi, Chief Human Resources and Organization Development Officer
CNO: Karen A Grimley, Chief Nursing Executive
Web address: www.uclahealth.org
Control: State, Government, nonfederal **Service:** General medical and surgical

Staffed Beds: 445 **Admissions:** 23150 **Census:** 454 **Outpatient Visits:** 568608 **Births:** 1836 **Total Expense ($000):** 1882941 **Payroll Expense ($000):** 736234 **Personnel:** 8178

✠ **SHERMAN OAKS HOSPITAL (050755)**, 4929 Van Nuys Boulevard, Zip 91403–1777; tel. 818/981–7111, (Nonreporting) **A**1 5 10 **S** Prime Healthcare, Ontario, CA
Primary Contact: Bockhi Park, Chief Executive Officer
CFO: Daniel Leon, Chief Financial Officer
CMO: Michael Malamed, M.D., Chief of Staff
Web address: www.shermanoakshospital.com
Control: Other not–for–profit (including NFP Corporation) **Service:** General medical and surgical

Staffed Beds: 90

☐ **SILVER LAKE MEDICAL CENTER (050763)**, 1711 West Temple Street, Zip 90026–5421; tel. 213/989–6100, (Includes SILVER LAKE MEDICAL CENTER-INGLESIDE HOSPITAL, 7500 East Hellman Avenue, Rosemead, California, Zip 91770; tel. 626/288–1160), (Nonreporting) **A**1 10 **S** Success Healthcare, Boca Raton, FL
Primary Contact: Brent A. Cope, Chief Executive Officer
CFO: John Cowles, Chief Financial Officer
CMO: Louis Acosta, M.D., Chief of Staff
CIO: Scott Musack, Chief Information Officer
CHR: Sylvia Cloud, Director Human Resources
Web address: www.silverlakemc.com
Control: Corporation, Investor–owned (for–profit) **Service:** General medical and surgical

Staffed Beds: 175

SOUTHERN CALIFORNIA HOSPITAL AT VAN NUYS See Southern California Hospital At Hollywood, Los Angeles

☐ **SOUTHERN CALIFORNIA HOSPITAL AT HOLLYWOOD (050135)**, 6245 De Longpre Avenue, Zip 90028–9001; tel. 323/462–2271, (Includes SOUTHERN CALIFORNIA HOSPITAL AT VAN NUYS, 14433 Emelita Street, Van Nuys, California, Zip 91401; tel. 818/787–1511), (Nonreporting) **A**1 10 **S** Prospect Medical Holdings, Los Angeles, CA
Primary Contact: Bruce P. Grimshaw, FACHE, Chief Executive Officer
Web address: www.hollywoodcommunityhospital.org/
Control: Corporation, Investor–owned (for–profit) **Service:** General medical and surgical

Staffed Beds: 45

☐ **ST. VINCENT MEDICAL CENTER (050502)**, 2131 West Third Street, Zip 90057–1901, Mailing Address: P.O. Box 57992, Zip 90057–0992; tel. 213/484–7111, (Total facility includes 27 beds in nursing home–type unit) **A**1 3 10 **F**3 15 18 20 22 24 26 29 31 34 35 36 40 45 47 49 50 54 57 58 59 60 63 64 65 68 70 71 74 75 77 78 79 81 82 85 87 90 91 96 107 108 110 111 116 118 119 120 121 128 130 136 138 139 142 143 146 148 149 154 **S** Verity Health System, Los Angeles, CA
Primary Contact: Frank J. Cracolici, President and Chief Executive Officer
CFO: Michael Garko, Chief Financial Officer
CMO: Brian Itagaki, M.D., Chief of Staff
CIO: Dan Robbins, Information Technology and Account Executive
CHR: Gail Watts, Director
CNO: Judy McCurdy, R.N., Vice President and Chief Nursing Officer
Web address: www.stvincentmedicalcenter.com
Control: Other not–for–profit (including NFP Corporation) **Service:** General medical and surgical

Staffed Beds: 271 **Admissions:** 11221 **Census:** 179 **Outpatient Visits:** 73548 **Births:** 0 **Total Expense ($000):** 304033 **Payroll Expense ($000):** 93813 **Personnel:** 925

✠ **STEWART & LYNDA RESNICK NEUROPSYCHIATRIC HOSPITAL AT UCLA (054009)**, 150 UCLA Medical Plaza, Zip 90095–8353; tel. 310/825–9989, **A**1 3 5 10 **F**3 5 6 29 30 35 40 43 55 56 64 68 77 86 87 98 99 100 101 102 107 104 105 130 132 134 147 149 153 154 **S** University of California Systemwide Administration, Oakland, CA
Primary Contact: Peter Whybrow, M.D., Chief Executive Officer
COO: Ruth Irwin, Associate Director Clinical Operations
CFO: Ronald Anthony Davis, Chief Financial Officer UCLA Hospital System
CMO: Thomas Strouse, M.D., Medical Director and Professor of Clinical Psych
CIO: Michael Pfeffer, M.D., Chief Medical Informatics Officer, UCLA Health
CHR: Monica Rodriquez, Director of Human Resources
CNO: Patricia Matos, Chief Nursing Officer
Web address: www.semel.ucla.edu/resnick
Control: State, Government, nonfederal **Service:** Psychiatric

Staffed Beds: 74 **Admissions:** 1792 **Census:** 66 **Outpatient Visits:** 19933 **Births:** 0 **Total Expense ($000):** 72025 **Payroll Expense ($000):** 39818 **Personnel:** 390

✠ **USC NORRIS COMPREHENSIVE CANCER CENTER (050660)**, 1441 Eastlake Avenue, Zip 90089–0112; tel. 323/865–3000, **A**1 2 3 5 8 10 **F**3 11 15 18 29 30 31 34 35 36 38 39 44 45 46 47 48 49 50 51 54 55 56 57 58 59 60 61 64 65 68 70 74 75 77 78 79 81 82 84 85 86 87 92 93 94 97 100 101 104 107 108 109 110 111 115 118 119 120 121 123 124 126 132 134 135 136 145 146 147 148 149 150 154 156 157 **S** Keck Medicine of USC, Los Angeles, CA
Primary Contact: Rodney B. Hanners, Chief Executive Officer
COO: Tarek Salaway, R.N., Chief Operating Officer
CMO: Stephanie Hall, M.D., Medical Director
CHR: Matthew McElrath, Chief Human Resources Officer
CNO: Annette Sy, Chief Nursing Officer
Web address: www.uscnorriscancerhospital.org
Control: Other not–for–profit (including NFP Corporation) **Service:** Cancer

Staffed Beds: 60 **Admissions:** 1606 **Census:** 35 **Outpatient Visits:** 118247 **Births:** 0 **Total Expense ($000):** 212939 **Payroll Expense ($000):** 65741 **Personnel:** 501

CA

Hospital, Medicare Provider Number, Address, Telephone, Approval, Facility, and Physician Codes, Health Care System

★ American Hospital Association (AHA) membership
☐ The Joint Commission accreditation
○ Healthcare Facilities Accreditation Program
◇ DNV Healthcare Inc. accreditation
⇑ Center for Improvement in Healthcare Quality Accreditation
△ Commission on Accreditation of Rehabilitation Facilities (CARF) accreditation

USC UNIVERSITY HOSPITAL See Keck Hospital of USC

✠ △ **VA GREATER LOS ANGELES HEALTHCARE SYSTEM**, 11301 Wilshire Boulevard, Zip 90073–1003; tel. 310/478–3711, (Total facility includes 252 beds in nursing home–type unit) **A**1 3 5 7 8 **F**2 3 4 5 9 15 17 18 20 22 24 26 28 29 30 31 33 34 35 36 37 38 39 40 44 45 46 47 48 49 50 51 53 54 55 56 57 58 59 60 61 62 63 64 65 66 68 70 71 74 75 77 78 79 81 82 83 84 85 86 87 90 91 92 93 94 96 97 98 100 101 102 104 105 106 107 108 109 110 111 115 116 117 118 119 120 121 123 124 126 127 128 129 130 131 132 133 135 143 144 146 147 148 149 153 154 156 157 158 **S** Department of Veterans Affairs, Washington, DC

Primary Contact: Ann R. Brown, M.D., Director
COO: Susan Shyshka, Associate Director
CFO: Joseph Schmitt, Chief Financial Officer
CIO: Eugene Archey, Chief Information Technology
CHR: Brenda Cabunoc, Chief Human Resources
Web address: www.losangeles.va.gov/
Control: Veterans Affairs, Government, federal **Service**: General medical and surgical

Staffed Beds: 422 **Admissions**: 4807 **Census**: 304 **Outpatient Visits**: 650775 **Births**: 0 **Personnel**: 4911

★ ⇑ **VALLEY PRESBYTERIAN HOSPITAL (050126)**, 15107 Vanowen Street, Zip 91405–4597; tel. 818/782–6600, **A**1 3 5 7 8 **F**2 3 13 18 20 22 24 28 29 31 34 35 37 40 41 44 45 46 49 50 54 55 57 59 64 65 70 72 75 76 77 78 79 80 81 85 86 87 88 89 90 96 107 108 114 115 118 119 130 146 147 148 149 Primary Contact: Gustavo A. Valdespino, President and Chief Executive Officer
COO: Lori Cardle, Senior Vice President, Chief Operating Officer
CFO: Janice Klostermeier, Senior Vice President and Chief Financial Officer
CMO: Clyde Wesp, M.D., Chief Medical Officer
CIO: Jeff Allport, Vice President, Chief Information Officer
CHR: Deborah Gac, Vice President Human Resources
CNO: Lori Burnell, R.N., Ph.D., Senior Vice President and Chief Nursing Officer
Web address: www.valleypres.org
Control: Other not–for–profit (including NFP Corporation) **Service**: General medical and surgical

Staffed Beds: 325 **Admissions**: 13158 **Census**: 193 **Outpatient Visits**: 110007 **Births**: 2547 **Total Expense ($000)**: 371925 **Payroll Expense ($000)**: 119545 **Personnel**: 1570

✠ **WEST HILLS HOSPITAL AND MEDICAL CENTER (050481)**, 7300 Medical Center Drive, Zip 91307–1900; tel. 818/676–4000, (Nonreporting) **A**1 10 **S** HCA Healthcare, Nashville, TN
Primary Contact: Mark Miller, FACHE, Chief Executive Officer
COO: Isaiah Zirkle, Chief Operating Officer
CFO: David Cantrell, CPA, Vice President and Chief Financial Officer
CMO: Yale D. Podnos, M.D., Chief Medical Officer
CHR: Diana Steel, Vice President Human Resources
CNO: Janeen Gallego, Chief Nursing Officer
Web address: www.westhillshospital.com
Control: Corporation, Investor–owned (for–profit) **Service**: General medical and surgical

Staffed Beds: 225

WEST LOS ANGELES MEDICAL CENTER See Kaiser Permanente West Los Angeles Medical Center

WOODLAND HILLS MEDICAL CENTER See Kaiser Permanente Woodland Hills Medical Center

LOS BANOS—Merced County

✠ **MEMORIAL HOSPITAL LOS BANOS (050528)**, 520 West 'I' Street, Zip 93635–3498; tel. 209/826–0591, **A**1 10 20 **F**2 3 8 11 13 15 18 29 30 34 35 39 40 44 45 46 49 50 54 57 59 60 64 65 68 70 74 75 76 81 82 85 86 87 107 110 111 115 119 127 130 132 135 146 149 154 **S** Sutter Health, Sacramento, CA
Primary Contact: Doug Archer, Administrator
CFO: Timothy J Noakes, Chief Financial Officer
CHR: Shawn Garcia, Manager Human Resources
CNO: Kristie Marion, Chief Nurse Executive
Web address: www.memoriallosbanos.org/
Control: Other not–for–profit (including NFP Corporation) **Service**: General medical and surgical

Staffed Beds: 44 **Admissions**: 1678 **Census**: 12

LYNWOOD—Los Angeles County

☐ **ST. FRANCIS MEDICAL CENTER (050104)**, 3630 East Imperial Highway, Zip 90262–2636; tel. 310/900–8900, (Nonreporting) **A**1 3 10 **S** Verity Health System, Los Angeles, CA
Primary Contact: Gerald T. Kozai, PharmD, President and Chief Executive Officer
CFO: Anil Jain, Chief Financial Officer
CMO: Rahul Dhawan, M.D., Chief Medical Officer
CIO: Judi Binderman, Chief Information Technology Officer and Chief Medical Informatics Officer
CHR: Laura Kato, Vice President Human Resources
CNO: Derek Scott Drake, Chief Nursing Officer
Web address: www.dochs.org
Control: Church operated, Nongovernment, not–for–profit **Service**: General medical and surgical

Staffed Beds: 323

MADERA—Madera County

○ **MADERA COMMUNITY HOSPITAL (050568)**, 1250 East Almond Avenue, Zip 93637–5696, Mailing Address: P.O. Box 1328, Zip 93639–1328; tel. 559/675–5501, **A**10 11 19 **F**3 8 11 15 18 29 30 33 34 35 40 45 50 54 57 59 64 65 68 70 75 76 79 81 89 107 110 111 114 119 127 132 146 149 154 156 157
Primary Contact: Karen Paolinelli, Chief Executive Officer
CFO: Mark Foote, Chief Financial Officer
CIO: Jerry Kovalski, Director Information Systems
CHR: Christine M Watts-Johnson, Assistant Vice President
CNO: Meri Combs, R.N., Vice President and Chief Nursing Officer
Web address: www.maderahospital.org
Control: Other not–for–profit (including NFP Corporation) **Service**: General medical and surgical

Staffed Beds: 106 **Admissions**: 3853 **Census**: 41 **Outpatient Visits**: 153667 **Births**: 908 **Total Expense ($000)**: 90032 **Payroll Expense ($000)**: 33301 **Personnel**: 676

✠ △ **VALLEY CHILDREN'S HEALTHCARE (053300)**, 9300 Valley Children's Place, Zip 93636–8761; tel. 559/353–3000, **A**1 3 5 7 8 10 **F**3 8 9 11 19 21 23 25 27 28 29 30 31 32 34 35 38 40 41 43 44 46 48 49 50 54 55 57 58 59 60 61 62 64 65 68 72 73 74 75 77 78 79 81 82 84 85 86 87 88 89 90 93 94 107 108 111 114 115 119 126 127 129 130 131 132 134 146 147 148 149 Primary Contact: Todd A. Suntrapak, President and Chief Executive Officer
COO: Debra A Flores, R.N., MS, President and Chief Operating Officer
CFO: Michele Waldron, Senior Vice President and Chief Financial Officer
CMO: David Christensen, M.D., Senior Vice President and Chief Medical Officer
CIO: Kevin Shimamoto, Vice President and Chief Informational Officer
CHR: Nat Ponticello, Vice President Human Resources
CNO: Beverly P. Hayden-Pugh, R.N., Senior Vice President and Chief Nursing Officer
Web address: www.valleychildrens.org
Control: Other not–for–profit (including NFP Corporation) **Service**: Children's general medical and surgical

Staffed Beds: 358 **Admissions**: 12010 **Census**: 199 **Outpatient Visits**: 279399 **Births**: 0 **Total Expense ($000)**: 618618 **Payroll Expense ($000)**: 207649 **Personnel**: 2381

MAMMOTH LAKES—Mono County

⇑ **MAMMOTH HOSPITAL (051303)**, 85 Sierra Park Road, Zip 93546–2073, Mailing Address: P.O. Box 660, Zip 93546–0660; tel. 760/934–3311, (Nonreporting) **A**5 10 18 21
Primary Contact: Thomas Parker, Chief Executive Officer
CFO: Melanie Van Winkle, Chief Financial Officer
CMO: Yuri Parisky, M.D., Chief of Staff
CIO: Mark Lind, Chief Information Officer
CHR: Sarah Vigilante, Manager Human Resources
CNO: Kathleen Alo, Chief Nursing Officer
Web address: www.mammothhospital.com
Control: Hospital district or authority, Government, nonfederal **Service**: General medical and surgical

Staffed Beds: 17

MANTECA—San Joaquin County

✠ **DOCTORS HOSPITAL OF MANTECA (050118)**, 1205 East North Street, Zip 95336–4900; tel. 209/823–3111, **A**1 10 **F**3 11 12 13 15 29 31 34 35 40 44 45 49 50 51 64 75 76 78 79 81 85 102 107 108 110 111 115 116 117 118 119 126 130 132 143 146 147 148 149 154 **S** TENET Healthcare Corporation, Dallas, TX
Primary Contact: Brandon May, Chief Executive Officer
COO: Carmen Silva, R.N., Chief Operating Officer
CFO: Ryan Marshall, Chief Financial Officer
CHR: Traci Holzer, Chief Human Resources Officer
CNO: Beverly Fick, Chief Nursing Officer
Web address: www.doctorsmanteca.com
Control: Corporation, Investor–owned (for–profit) **Service**: General medical and surgical

Staffed Beds: 56 **Admissions**: 3827 **Census**: 41 **Outpatient Visits**: 65065 **Births**: 566 **Total Expense ($000)**: 99311 **Payroll Expense ($000)**: 42529 **Personnel**: 440

★ **KAISER PERMANENTE MANTECA MEDICAL CENTER (050748)**, 1777 West Yosemite Avenue, Zip 95337–5187; tel. 209/825–3700, (Includes MODESTO MEDICAL CENTER, 4601 Dale Road, Modesto, California, Zip 95356–9718; tel. 209/735–5000; Corwin N Harper, Administrator) **A**5 10 **F**3 8 11 15 18 20 26 28 29 30 31 34 39 40 41 45 49 50 55 56 57 58 59 60 61 63 64 65 68 70 72 73 74 75 76 77 78 79 81 82 84 85 86 102 107 108 110 111 114 115 118 119 129 130 131 134 135 144 146 147 148 149 154 156 **S** Kaiser Foundation Hospitals, Oakland, CA
Primary Contact: Corwin N. Harper, Senior Vice President and Area Manager
COO: Corwin N Harper, Senior Vice President and Area Manager
CFO: Debra L Brown, Area Financial Officer
CMO: Moses D Elam, M.D., Physician-in-Chief
CIO: Tom J Osteen, Director Area Technology
CHR: Pat McKeldin, Human Resource Business Partner
Web address: www.kaiserpermanente.org
Control: Other not–for–profit (including NFP Corporation) **Service**: General medical and surgical

Staffed Beds: 213 **Admissions:** 11825 **Census:** 112 **Outpatient Visits:** 199560 **Births:** 3299 **Personnel:** 1157

MARINA DEL REY—Los Angeles County

✠ **MARINA DEL REY HOSPITAL (050740)**, 4650 Lincoln Boulevard, Zip 90292–6306; tel. 310/823–8911, (Nonreporting) **A**1 3 10 **S** Cedars-Sinai Health System, West Hollywood, CA
Primary Contact: Paulette Heitmeyer, Administrator and Chief Operating Officer
COO: Phyllis Buchart, Chief Operating Officer
CFO: Stephen A Hargett, Senior Vice President and Chief Financial Officer
CNO: Joanne Laguna, Vice President of Hospital Operations and Chief Nursing Officer
Web address: www.marinahospital.com
Control: Corporation, Investor–owned (for–profit) **Service**: General medical and surgical

Staffed Beds: 145

MARIPOSA—Mariposa County

★ **JOHN C. FREMONT HEALTHCARE DISTRICT (051304)**, 5189 Hospital Road, Zip 95338–9524, Mailing Address: P.O. Box 216, Zip 95338–0216; tel. 209/966–3631, (Nonreporting) **A**10 18
Primary Contact: Matthew Matthiessen, Chief Executive Officer
CFO: Matthew Matthiessen, Chief Financial Officer
CMO: Kenneth P Smith, Chief of Staff
CHR: Martha Robichaux, Chief Human Resources Officer
CNO: Theresa Loya, R.N., Chief Nursing Officer
Web address: www.jcf-hospital.com
Control: Hospital district or authority, Government, nonfederal **Service**: General medical and surgical

Staffed Beds: 33

MARTINEZ—Contra Costa County

✠ **CONTRA COSTA REGIONAL MEDICAL CENTER (050276)**, 2500 Alhambra Avenue, Zip 94553–3156; tel. 925/370–5000, **A**1 2 3 10 **F**3 11 13 15 18 30 31 35 36 39 40 45 49 50 54 56 59 60 61 62 64 65 66 68 70 71 72 73 74 75 76 77 78 79 81 82 84 85 86 87 93 97 98 100 102 104 107 108 111 115 119 130 132 143 146 147 148 149 156
Primary Contact: Anna M. Roth, R.N., MS, M.P.H., Chief Executive Officer
COO: Timothy Thompson-Cook, Chief Operating Officer
CFO: Patrick Godley, Chief Financial Officer
CMO: David Goldstein, M.D., Chief Medical Officer
CNO: Jaspreet Benepal, Chief Nursing Officer
Web address: www.cchealth.org/medical_center/
Control: County, Government, nonfederal **Service**: General medical and surgical

Staffed Beds: 146 **Admissions:** 7318 **Census:** 118 **Outpatient Visits:** 509816 **Births:** 1967 **Total Expense ($000):** 596265 **Payroll Expense ($000):** 213489 **Personnel:** 2718

KAISER FOUNDATION HOSPITAL See Kaiser Permanente Walnut Creek Medical Center, Walnut Creek

MARYSVILLE—Yuba County

★ **ADVENTIST HEALTH AND RIDEOUT (050133)**, 726 Fourth Street, Zip 95901–5600; tel. 530/749–4300, (Includes FREMONT MEDICAL CENTER, 970 Plumas Street, Yuba City, California, Zip 95991–4087; tel. 530/751–4000), (Nonreporting) **A**2 10 20 **S** Adventist Health, Roseville, CA
Primary Contact: Richard Rawson, Chief Executive Officer
COO: Cyndy Gordon, Chief Operating Officer
CFO: Diane Moon, Chief Financial Officer
CMO: Azad Sheikh, Chief Medical Officer
CIO: Daniel Chibaya, Chief Information Officer
CHR: Bart R Minsky, Interim Vice President Human Resources
CNO: Inna Makievsky, Interim Chief Nursing Officer
Web address: www.frhg.org
Control: Other not–for–profit (including NFP Corporation) **Service**: General medical and surgical

Staffed Beds: 219

MENLO PARK—San Mateo County

✠ **MENLO PARK SURGICAL HOSPITAL (050754)**, 570 Willow Road, Zip 94025–2617; tel. 650/324–8500, (Nonreporting) **A**1 10 **S** Sutter Health, Sacramento, CA
Primary Contact: Jeanette Engle-Ramirez, Chief Executive Officer
CMO: Andrew Gutow, M.D., Medical Director
CNO: Marjorie Eckford, Chief Nursing Officer
Web address: www.pamf.org/mpsh
Control: Other not–for–profit (including NFP Corporation) **Service**: General medical and surgical

Staffed Beds: 16

MERCED—Merced County

✠ **MERCY MEDICAL CENTER MERCED (050444)**, 333 Mercy Avenue, Zip 95340–8319; tel. 209/564–5000, (Includes MERCY MEDICAL CENTER MERCED-DOMINICAN CAMPUS, 2740 'M' Street, Merced, California, Zip 95340–2880; tel. 209/384–6444; Charles Kassis, President) **A**1 3 5 10 19 **F**3 8 13 15 18 20 22 28 29 30 32 34 35 37 40 41 45 46 49 50 54 57 59 62 64 65 66 68 69 70 74 75 76 77 79 81 83 84 85 86 87 88 90 92 93 96 97 107 108 110 115 118 119 126 127 130 132 135 146 148 149 154 156 **S** CommonSpirit Health, Chicago, IL
Primary Contact: Charles Kassis, President
CFO: Michael Strasser, Vice President and Chief Financial Officer
CMO: Robert Streeter, M.D., Vice President Medical Affairs
CIO: Daniel Andresen, Chief Information Officer
CHR: Julie Rocha, Vice President Human Resources
CNO: Greg Rouleau, Vice President Nursing
Web address: www.mercymercedcares.org
Control: Other not–for–profit (including NFP Corporation) **Service**: General medical and surgical

Staffed Beds: 186 **Admissions:** 12073 **Census:** 132 **Outpatient Visits:** 179113 **Births:** 2392 **Total Expense ($000):** 310498 **Payroll Expense ($000):** 112023 **Personnel:** 1056

MISSION HILLS—Los Angeles County

✠ △ **PROVIDENCE HOLY CROSS MEDICAL CENTER (050278)**, 15031 Rinaldi Street, Zip 91345–1207; tel. 818/365–8051, (Total facility includes 48 beds in nursing home–type unit) **A**1 2 7 10 19 **F**3 8 11 13 15 17 18 20 22 24 26 28 29 30 31 34 35 36 40 43 44 45 46 49 50 54 55 56 57 58 59 60 61 64 65 68 70 71 72 74 75 77 78 79 81 82 83 84 85 87 90 93 94 97 105 107 108 110 111 114 115 116 117 119 120 121 123 124 126 128 130 131 132 133 143 146 147 148 149 150 153 154 156 157 **S** Providence St. Joseph Health, Renton, WA
Primary Contact: Bernard Klein, M.D., Chief Executive
CMO: Rex Hoffman, M.D., Chief Medical Officer
CHR: Pam Stahl, Regional Chief Human Resources Officer
CNO: Jodi Hein, Chief Nursing Officer
Web address: www.https://california.providence.org/holy-cross/Pages/default.aspx
Control: Church operated, Nongovernment, not–for–profit **Service**: General medical and surgical

Staffed Beds: 377 **Admissions:** 18287 **Census:** 262 **Outpatient Visits:** 323072 **Births:** 3187 **Total Expense ($000):** 337413 **Payroll Expense ($000):** 160730 **Personnel:** 1977

MISSION VIEJO—Orange County

☐ **CHOC CHILDREN'S AT MISSION HOSPITAL (053306)**, 27700 Medical Center Road, Zip 92691–6426; tel. 949/347–8400, **A**1 5 10 **F**3 11 36 71 72 74 79 81 85 88 89 92 129 154
Primary Contact: Kimberly C. Cripe, President and Chief Executive Officer
COO: Matthew S Gerlach, Chief Operating Officer
CFO: Kerri Ruppert Schiller, Senior Vice President and Chief Financial Officer
CMO: Maria Minon, M.D., Vice President Medical Affairs and Chief Medical Officer
CIO: John Henderson, Chief Information Officer
CHR: Thomas Capizzi, Vice President Human Resources
Web address: www.choc.org
Control: Other not–for–profit (including NFP Corporation) **Service:** Children's general medical and surgical

Staffed Beds: 54 **Admissions:** 2032 **Census:** 19 **Outpatient Visits:** 22445 **Births:** 0 **Total Expense ($000):** 55401 **Payroll Expense ($000):** 9847 **Personnel:** 107

✠ △ **MISSION HOSPITAL (050567)**, 27700 Medical Center Road, Zip 92691–6474; tel. 949/364–1400, (Includes MISSION HOSPITAL LAGUNA BEACH, 31872 Coast Highway, Laguna Beach, California, Zip 92651–6775; tel. 949/499–1311; Seth R. Teigen, Chief Executive Officer) **A**1 2 3 7 10 **F**3 4 5 8 11 13 14 15 17 18 20 22 24 26 28 29 30 31 32 34 35 36 37 38 39 40 41 43 44 45 46 48 49 50 51 53 54 55 57 58 59 64 65 68 70 72 74 75 76 77 78 79 80 81 82 84 85 86 87 88 89 90 93 96 98 100 102 104 105 107 108 110 111 114 115 116 117 118 119 120 121 123 126 129 130 131 132 134 135 141 142 144 145 146 147 148 149 150 152 153 154 **S** Providence St. Joseph Health, Renton, WA
Primary Contact: Seth R. Teigen, Chief Executive Officer
COO: Terrence Wooten, Vice President of Operations, Support Services
CFO: Eileen Haubl, Senior Vice President and Chief Financial Officer
CMO: Linda Sieglen, M.D., Chief Medical Officer
CIO: Bill Russell, Senior Chief Information Officer
CHR: Terri Covert, Vice President Human Resources
CNO: Jennifer Cord, R.N., Chief Nursing Officer
Web address: www.mission4health.com
Control: Church operated, Nongovernment, not–for–profit **Service:** General medical and surgical

Staffed Beds: 296 **Admissions:** 19068 **Census:** 219 **Outpatient Visits:** 231762 **Births:** 2316 **Total Expense ($000):** 583746 **Payroll Expense ($000):** 174523 **Personnel:** 2178

MODESTO—Stanislaus County

⇑ **CENTRAL VALLEY SPECIALTY HOSPITAL (052055)**, 730 17th Street, Zip 95354–1209; tel. 209/248–7700, (Nonreporting) **A**10 21
Primary Contact: Gia Smith, Chief Executive Officer
Web address: www.centralvalleyspecialty.org/CVSH/
Control: Partnership, Investor–owned (for–profit) **Service:** Acute long–term care hospital

Staffed Beds: 36

✠ **DOCTORS MEDICAL CENTER OF MODESTO (050464)**, 1441 Florida Avenue, Zip 95350–4418, Mailing Address: P.O. Box 4138, Zip 95352–4138; tel. 209/578–1211, **A**1 2 3 10 **F**3 5 12 13 15 17 18 20 22 24 26 28 29 30 31 34 35 40 43 45 46 47 48 49 50 51 55 56 57 58 59 60 61 63 64 65 70 72 73 74 75 76 77 78 79 80 81 82 84 85 87 89 98 100 101 102 103 104 105 107 108 111 113 114 115 119 126 130 135 146 147 148 149 152 156 157 **S** TENET Healthcare Corporation, Dallas, TX
Primary Contact: Warren J. Kirk, Chief Executive Officer
CFO: Greg Berry, Chief Financial Officer
CMO: Gabrielle Gaspar, M.D., Chief Medical Officer
CIO: Debbie Fuller, Director Health Information Systems and Chief Information Officer
CHR: Michele Bava, Director Human Resources
CNO: Cheryl Harless, Chief Nursing Officer
Web address: www.dmc-modesto.com
Control: Corporation, Investor–owned (for–profit) **Service:** General medical and surgical

Staffed Beds: 461 **Admissions:** 26222 **Census:** 365 **Outpatient Visits:** 156083 **Births:** 3427 **Total Expense ($000):** 538435 **Payroll Expense ($000):** 235558 **Personnel:** 2380

☐ **ENCOMPASS HEALTH REHABILITATION HOSPITAL OF MODESTO (053040)**, 1303 Mable Avenue, Zip 95355; tel. 209/857–3400, (Nonreporting) **A**1 10
Primary Contact: Kay E. Peck, Ph.D., Chief Executive Officer
CFO: Seth Rogers, Controller
CMO: Greg A. Vigna, M.D., Medical Director
CHR: Tina Reed, Director of Human Resources
CNO: Mark Dinardo, Chief Nursing Officer
Web address: www.healthsouthmodesto.com/
Control: Corporation, Investor–owned (for–profit) **Service:** Rehabilitation

Staffed Beds: 50

✠ **MEMORIAL MEDICAL CENTER (050557)**, 1700 Coffee Road, Zip 95355–2869, Mailing Address: P.O. Box 942, Zip 95353–0942; tel. 209/526–4500, (Includes MEMORIAL MEDICAL CENTER, 1700 Coffee Road, Modesto, California, Zip 95355, Mailing Address: Box 942, Zip 95353, tel. 209/526–4500), (Nonreporting) **A**1 2 10 **S** Sutter Health, Sacramento, CA
Primary Contact: Eugene Patrizio, Chief Executive Officer
COO: Steve Mitchell, Chief Operating Officer
CFO: Eric Dalton, Chief Financial Officer
CIO: Patrick Anderson, Chief Information Officer
CHR: Paula Rafala, Director, Human Resources
CNO: Sandra Proctor, R.N., MS, Chief Nurse Executive
Web address: www.memorialmedicalcenter.org
Control: Other not–for–profit (including NFP Corporation) **Service:** General medical and surgical

Staffed Beds: 222

MODESTO MEDICAL CENTER See Kaiser Permanente Manteca Medical Center, Manteca

★ **STANISLAUS SURGICAL HOSPITAL (050726)**, 1421 Oakdale Road, Zip 95355–3356; tel. 209/572–2700, (Nonreporting) **A**10 **S** Sutter Health, Sacramento, CA
Primary Contact: Douglas V. Johnson, Chief Executive Officer
CFO: Richard Hart, Chief Financial Officer
CMO: Wesley Kinzie, M.D., Chief of Staff
CIO: Richard Hart, Chief Financial Officer
CHR: Tyson Hubbard, Director Human Resources
CNO: Susan Gonzalez, Director of Clinical Services
Web address: www.stanislaussurgical.com
Control: Individual, Investor–owned (for–profit) **Service:** General medical and surgical

Staffed Beds: 23

MONROVIA—Los Angeles County

○ **MONROVIA MEMORIAL HOSPITAL (052054)**, 323 South Heliotrope Avenue, Zip 91016–2914; tel. 626/408–9800, (Nonreporting) **A**10 11
Primary Contact: Ron Kupferstein, Chief Executive Officer
Web address: www.monroviamemorial.com
Control: Partnership, Investor–owned (for–profit) **Service:** Acute long–term care hospital

Staffed Beds: 49

MONTCLAIR—San Bernardino County

✠ **MONTCLAIR HOSPITAL MEDICAL CENTER (050758)**, 5000 San Bernardino Street, Zip 91763–2326; tel. 909/625–5411, (Nonreporting) **A**1 3 10 12 13 **S** Prime Healthcare, Ontario, CA
Primary Contact: Sofia Abrina, R.N., Administrator
CFO: Robert Bonner, Chief Financial Officer
CMO: Joseph Hourany, Chief Medical Officer
CNO: Gail Aviado, Chief Nursing Officer
Web address: www.montclair-hospital.com
Control: Other not–for–profit (including NFP Corporation) **Service:** General medical and surgical

Staffed Beds: 102

MONTEBELLO—Los Angeles County

⇑ **BEVERLY HOSPITAL (050350)**, 309 West Beverly Boulevard, Zip 90640–4308; tel. 323/726–1222, **A**10 21 **F**3 13 15 18 20 22 24 29 30 31 34 35 40 41 45 49 50 51 57 59 60 65 68 70 72 74 75 77 78 79 81 86 107 108 110 111 115 118 119 130 132 135 143 145 146 147 148 149 154 156
Primary Contact: Alice Cheng, President and Chief Executive Officer
CFO: Larry Pugh, Vice President and Chief Financial Officer
CIO: Mark Turner, Director Information Systems
CHR: John Barnes, Administrative Director Human Resources
CNO: Kathy Wojno, R.N., MSN, Vice President Nursing Services and Chief Nursing Officer
Web address: www.beverly.org
Control: Other not–for–profit (including NFP Corporation) **Service:** General medical and surgical

Staffed Beds: 202 **Admissions:** 10407 **Census:** 107 **Outpatient Visits:** 58357 **Births:** 658 **Total Expense ($000):** 201225 **Payroll Expense ($000):** 58968 **Personnel:** 761

CA

MONTEREY—Monterey County

⊞ △ **COMMUNITY HOSPITAL OF THE MONTEREY PENINSULA (050145)**, 23625 Holman Highway, Zip 93940–5902, Mailing Address: Box 'HH', Zip 93942–6032; tel. 831/624–5311, (Total facility includes 28 beds in nursing home–type unit) **A**1 2 7 10 **F**3 5 11 12 13 15 17 18 20 22 24 26 28 29 30 31 32 34 35 37 40 44 45 46 47 48 49 50 51 53 54 57 58 59 60 61 62 63 64 66 68 70 71 73 74 75 76 77 78 79 81 82 83 84 85 86 87 89 90 91 92 93 94 96 98 99 100 101 102 103 104 105 107 110 111 114 115 116 117 118 119 120 121 123 124 128 129 130 132 134 135 147 148 149 150 151 153 154 156
Primary Contact: Steven J. Packer, M.D., President and Chief Executive Officer
CFO: Laura Zehm, Vice President and Chief Financial Officer
CMO: Anthony D Chavis, M.D., Vice President Enterprise Medical Officer, Community Hospital Foundation
Web address: www.chomp.org
Control: Other not–for–profit (including NFP Corporation) **Service:** General medical and surgical

Staffed Beds: 248 **Admissions:** 12669 **Census:** 168 **Outpatient Visits:** 348364 **Births:** 1090 **Total Expense ($000):** 536496 **Payroll Expense ($000):** 212950 **Personnel:** 1840

MONTEREY PARK—Los Angeles County

☐ **GARFIELD MEDICAL CENTER (050737)**, 525 North Garfield Avenue, Zip 91754–1205; tel. 626/573–2222, (Nonreporting) **A**1 10 **S** AHMC & Healthcare, Inc., Alhambra, CA
Primary Contact: Patrick A. Petre, Chief Executive Officer
COO: Herbert Villafuerte, Chief Operating Officer/Chief Nursing Officer
CFO: Steve Maekawa, Chief Financial Officer
CMO: Thomas Lam, Chief Medical Officer
CIO: Angelica Ching, Director Information Systems
CHR: Darcy Castro, Director Human Resources
CNO: Herbert Villafuerte, Chief Operating Officer and Chief Nursing Officer
Web address: www.garfieldmedicalcenter.com
Control: Partnership, Investor–owned (for–profit) **Service:** General medical and surgical

Staffed Beds: 195

☐ **MONTEREY PARK HOSPITAL (050736)**, 900 South Atlantic Boulevard, Zip 91754–4780; tel. 626/570–9000, (Nonreporting) **A**1 10 **S** AHMC & Healthcare, Inc., Alhambra, CA
Primary Contact: Philip A. Cohen, Chief Executive Officer
COO: Ericka Smith, Chief Operating Officer
CFO: Daniel Song, Chief Financial Officer
CMO: Ruben Ramirez, M.D., Chief of Staff
CIO: Angelica Ching, Director Information Systems
CHR: Gretchen Lindeman, Director of Human Resources
CNO: Shirley Tang, R.N., Chief Nursing Officer
Web address: www.montereyparkhosp.com
Control: Partnership, Investor–owned (for–profit) **Service:** General medical and surgical

Staffed Beds: 101

MORENO VALLEY—Riverside County

⊞ **KAISER PERMANENTE MORENO VALLEY MEDICAL CENTER (050765)**, 27300 Iris Avenue, Zip 92555–4800; tel. 951/243–0811, **A**1 3 10 **F**3 13 15 17 29 30 35 40 44 45 46 49 50 59 60 64 65 68 70 71 74 75 76 77 78 79 81 82 84 85 87 97 100 101 102 104 107 108 109 110 111 115 117 119 130 135 144 146 148 149 154 156 157 **S** Kaiser Foundation Hospitals, Oakland, CA
Primary Contact: Vita M. Willett, Senior Vice President, Area Manager
COO: Corey A Seale, Chief Operating Officer
CFO: JiJi Abraham, Area Chief Financial Officer
CMO: Frank M. Flowers, M.D., Area Medical Director
CIO: Alfred T Velasquez, Area Information Officer
CHR: Cheryl M Witt, Human Resources Director
CNO: Sonia A. Bravo, Chief Nurse Executive
Control: Other not–for–profit (including NFP Corporation) **Service:** General medical and surgical

Staffed Beds: 94 **Admissions:** 4160 **Census:** 36 **Outpatient Visits:** 54047 **Births:** 1419 **Personnel:** 417

⊞ **RIVERSIDE UNIVERSITY HEALTH SYSTEM-MEDICAL CENTER (050292)**, 26520 Cactus Avenue, Zip 92555–3911; tel. 951/486–4000, **A**1 3 5 10 12 13 **F**3 11 13 15 18 19 26 28 29 30 31 34 35 40 43 45 46 47 49 50 55 57 58 59 64 68 70 72 74 75 76 77 78 79 80 81 84 85 87 88 89 92 93 98 100 102 107 108 110 111 115 119 126 130 132 135 143 146 147 148 149 154
Primary Contact: Jennifer Cruikshank, R.N., Chief Executive Officer
CFO: Christopher Hans, Chief Financial Officer
CMO: Arnold Tabuenca, M.D., Medical Director
CNO: Judi Nightingale, R.N., Dr.PH, Chief Nursing Officer
Web address: www.ruhealth.org/en-us
Control: County, Government, nonfederal **Service:** General medical and surgical

Staffed Beds: 439 **Admissions:** 19160 **Census:** 297 **Outpatient Visits:** 218819 **Births:** 1605 **Total Expense ($000):** 614164 **Payroll Expense ($000):** 243471 **Personnel:** 3136

MOUNT SHASTA—Siskiyou County

⊞ **MERCY MEDICAL CENTER MOUNT SHASTA (051319)**, 914 Pine Street, Zip 96067–2143; tel. 530/926–6111, **A**1 10 18 **F**3 11 13 15 29 30 35 40 43 50 53 56 57 59 62 63 64 68 70 75 76 77 79 81 82 84 93 107 108 110 111 114 118 119 121 127 130 131 132 133 143 146 148 149 154 **S** CommonSpirit Health, Chicago, IL
Primary Contact: Rodger Page, President
CFO: Kimberly Miranda, Chief Financial Officer
CMO: Todd Guthrie, Chief of Staff
CHR: Michelle Michl, Director Human Resources
CNO: Lisa Hubbard, Vice President and Chief Nursing Executive
Web address: www.mercymtshasta.org
Control: Other not–for–profit (including NFP Corporation) **Service:** General medical and surgical

Staffed Beds: 33 **Admissions:** 953 **Census:** 8 **Outpatient Visits:** 61339 **Births:** 125 **Total Expense ($000):** 58640 **Payroll Expense ($000):** 22954 **Personnel:** 243

MOUNTAIN VIEW—Santa Clara County

⊞ **EL CAMINO HOSPITAL (050308)**, 2500 Grant Road, Zip 94040–4302, Mailing Address: P.O. Box 7025, Zip 94039–7025; tel. 650/940–7000, (Includes EL CAMINO HOSPITAL LOS GATOS, 815 Pollard Road, Los Gatos, California, Zip 95032–1438; tel. 408/378–6131), (Nonreporting) **A**1 2 3 10
Primary Contact: Dan Woods, Chief Executive Officer
COO: James D Griffith, Chief Operating Officer
CFO: Iftikhar Hussain, Chief Financial Officer
CMO: Mark C. Adams, M.D., Chief Medical Officer
CIO: Deborah Muro, Chief Information Officer
CHR: Kathryn M Fisk, Chief Human Resources Officer
CNO: Cheryl Reinking, R.N., MS, Chief Nursing Officer
Web address: www.elcaminohospital.org
Control: Hospital district or authority, Government, nonfederal **Service:** General medical and surgical

Staffed Beds: 420

MURRIETA—Riverside County

☐ **LOMA LINDA UNIVERSITY MEDICAL CENTER-MURRIETA (050770)**, 28062 Baxter Road, Zip 92563–1401; tel. 951/290–4000, **A**1 10 **F**3 11 13 15 18 20 22 24 26 28 29 30 31 34 35 40 44 45 46 47 48 49 50 54 57 58 59 60 64 65 70 72 74 75 76 77 78 79 81 82 85 87 91 92 93 96 107 108 110 111 114 115 117 118 119 120 121 123 126 130 132 143 146 147 148 149 154 **S** Loma Linda University Adventist Health Sciences Center, Loma Linda, CA
Primary Contact: Peter Baker, Senior Vice President and Administrator
COO: Richard M Tibbits, Vice President and Chief Operating Officer
CFO: James Uli, Chief Financial Officer
CMO: Jeff Conner, M.D., Chief Medical Staff
Web address: www.llumcmurrieta.org
Control: Other not–for–profit (including NFP Corporation) **Service:** General medical and surgical

Staffed Beds: 111 **Admissions:** 8313 **Census:** 86 **Outpatient Visits:** 62740 **Births:** 1180 **Total Expense ($000):** 196943 **Payroll Expense ($000):** 61403 **Personnel:** 777

CA

Hospital, Medicare Provider Number, Address, Telephone, Approval, Facility, and Physician Codes, Health Care System

★ American Hospital Association (AHA) membership
☐ The Joint Commission accreditation
○ Healthcare Facilities Accreditation Program
◇ DNV Healthcare Inc. accreditation
⇑ Center for Improvement in Healthcare Quality Accreditation
△ Commission on Accreditation of Rehabilitation Facilities (CARF) accreditation

SOUTHWEST HEALTHCARE SYSTEM (050701), 25500 Medical Center Drive, Zip 92562–5965; tel. 951/696–6000, (Includes INLAND VALLEY MEDICAL CENTER, 36485 Inland Valley Drive, Wildomar, California, Zip 92595–9700; tel. 951/677–1111; Bradley D Neet, FACHE, Chief Executive Officer; RANCHO SPRINGS MEDICAL CENTER, 25500 Medical Center Drive, Murrieta, California, Zip 92562–5965; tel. 951/696–6000) **A**1 10 **F**3 8 11 12 13 15 29 30 34 35 37 40 43 45 48 49 50 51 57 59 68 70 72 74 76 77 79 81 84 85 87 93 96 100 102 107 108 110 111 115 119 126 130 132 134 146 147 149 154 155 **S** Universal Health Services, Inc., King of Prussia, PA
Primary Contact: Bradley D. Neet, FACHE, Chief Executive Officer
COO: Jared Giles, Chief Operating Officer
CFO: Jon Zilkow, Chief Financial Officer
CMO: Reza Vaezazizi, M.D., Chief of Staff
CIO: Jeffrey Upcraft, Director Information Services
CHR: Della G Stange, Director Human Resources
CNO: Kristen Johnson, Chief Nursing Officer
Web address: www.swhealthcaresystem.com/
Control: Corporation, Investor–owned (for–profit) **Service**: General medical and surgical

Staffed Beds: 231 Admissions: 15834 Census: 150 Outpatient Visits: 108199 Births: 3084 Total Expense ($000): 238603 Payroll Expense ($000): 102434 Personnel: 1271

NAPA—Napa County

NAPA STATE HOSPITAL (054122), 2100 Napa-Vallejo Highway, Zip 94558–6293; tel. 707/253–5000, **A**1 3 5 10 **F**30 39 53 56 59 61 67 68 77 86 98 128 130 132 135 146 149 154
Primary Contact: Dolly Matteucci, Executive Director
COO: Dolly Matteucci, Executive Director
Web address: www.dmh.ca.gov
Control: State, Government, nonfederal **Service**: Psychiatric

Staffed Beds: 1284 Admissions: 868 Census: 1243 Outpatient Visits: 0 Births: 0 Total Expense ($000): 336736 Payroll Expense ($000): 198091 Personnel: 2348

QUEEN OF THE VALLEY MEDICAL CENTER (050009), 1000 Trancas Street, Zip 94558–2906, Mailing Address: P.O. Box 2340, Zip 94558–0688; tel. 707/252–4411, **A**1 2 10 19 **F**3 11 12 13 15 18 20 22 24 26 29 30 31 34 35 37 39 40 41 43 44 45 46 50 51 53 54 57 59 64 68 70 71 72 74 75 76 77 78 79 81 82 84 85 86 87 90 91 92 93 96 107 108 110 111 115 117 118 119 120 121 123 126 130 132 135 144 146 149 154 156 **S** Providence St. Joseph Health, Renton, WA
Primary Contact: Larry Coomes, Chief Executive Officer
COO: Vincent Morgese, M.D., Executive Vice President, Chief Operating Officer and Chief Medical Officer
CFO: Michel Riccioni, Vice President and Chief Financial Officer, Northern California Region
CMO: Vincent Morgese, M.D., Executive Vice President, Chief Operating Officer and Chief Medical Officer
CHR: Robert A Eisen, Vice President Human Resources, Northern California Region
Web address: www.thequeen.org
Control: Other not–for–profit (including NFP Corporation) **Service**: General medical and surgical

Staffed Beds: 208 Admissions: 6587 Census: 87 Outpatient Visits: 161206 Births: 581 Total Expense ($000): 279944 Payroll Expense ($000): 111252 Personnel: 1136

NATIONAL CITY—San Diego County

△ **PARADISE VALLEY HOSPITAL (050024)**, 2400 East Fourth Street, Zip 91950–2099; tel. 619/470–4321, (Includes BAYVIEW BEHAVIORAL HEALTH CAMPUS, 330 Moss Street, Chula Vista, California, Zip 91911–2005; tel. 619/470–4321; Neerav Jadeja, Administrator), (Nonreporting) **A**1 3 7 10 **S** Prime Healthcare, Ontario, CA
Primary Contact: William J. Comer, Chief Executive Officer
CFO: Becky Levy, Chief Financial Officer
CMO: Rosemarie Lim, M.D., Chief Medical Officer
CIO: Allan Tojino, Director, Information Systems
CHR: Lorraine Villegas, Manager Human Resources
CNO: Gemma Rama-Banaag, R.N., MSN, Chief Nursing Officer
Web address: www.paradisevalleyhospital.org
Control: Corporation, Investor–owned (for–profit) **Service**: General medical and surgical

Staffed Beds: 256

NEEDLES—San Bernardino County

COLORADO RIVER MEDICAL CENTER (051323), 1401 Bailey Avenue, Zip 92363–3198; tel. 760/326–7100, **A**10 18 **F**3 29 30 34 35 40 41 44 45 46 47 48 49 50 53 57 59 64 65 68 79 81 86 87 89 91 92 93 107 111 114 119 130 143 145 146 148 149 154
Primary Contact: Steve Kelley. Lopez, Chief Executive Officer
COO: Knaya Tabora, Chief Operating Officer and Chief Nursing Officer
CFO: Steve Kelley Lopez, Chief Financial Officer
CMO: Robert Strecker, M.D., Chief of Staff
CIO: Ron Chieffo, Chief Information Officer
CHR: Pam Barrett, Human Resources Director
CNO: Knaya Tabora, Chief Operating Officer and Chief Nursing Officer
Web address: www.crmccares.com
Control: Other not–for–profit (including NFP Corporation) **Service**: General medical and surgical

Staffed Beds: 25 Admissions: 508 Census: 4

NEWPORT BEACH—Orange County

★ ⚕ **HOAG MEMORIAL HOSPITAL PRESBYTERIAN (050224)**, One Hoag Drive, Zip 92663–4120, Mailing Address: P.O. Box 6100, Zip 92658–6100; tel. 949/764–4624, (Includes HOAG HOSPITAL IRVINE, 16200 Sand Canyon Avenue, Irvine, California, Zip 92618–3714; tel. 949/764–8240) **A**3 5 10 21 **F**3 4 5 8 11 13 14 15 17 18 20 22 24 26 28 30 31 34 35 36 37 40 44 45 46 47 48 49 50 51 52 53 54 55 57 58 59 64 65 68 70 72 74 75 76 77 78 79 80 81 82 84 85 86 87 90 92 93 94 96 97 100 101 102 104 107 108 109 110 111 113 114 115 116 117 118 119 120 121 123 124 126 129 130 131 132 134 135 141 143 144 145 146 147 148 149 150 152 154 156 **S** Providence St. Joseph Health, Renton, WA
Primary Contact: Robert Braithwaite, President and Chief Executive Officer
COO: Michael Ricks, Chief Operating Officer
CFO: Andrew Guarni, Chief Financial Officer
CIO: Patrick Anderson, Chief Information Officer and Senior Vice President
CHR: Jan L Blue, Vice President Human Resources
CNO: Richard A Martin, MSN, R.N., Senior Vice President and Chief Nursing Officer
Web address: www.hoaghospital.org
Control: Other not–for–profit (including NFP Corporation) **Service**: General medical and surgical

Staffed Beds: 588 Admissions: 34070 Census: 355 Outpatient Visits: 456380 Births: 6830 Total Expense ($000): 1131131 Payroll Expense ($000): 411564 Personnel: 5342

NEWPORT BAY HOSPITAL (054135), 1501 East 16th Street, Zip 92663–5924; tel. 949/650–9750, (Nonreporting) **A**10
Primary Contact: James E. Parkhurst, President and Chief Executive Officer
COO: Garry Hardwick, R.N., Chief Operating Officer
CFO: Rocky Gentner, Chief Financial Officer
CMO: Jason Kellogg, M.D., Chief of Staff
CIO: Nina Swenson, Director Business Services
CHR: Phyllis Parkhurst, Vice President Support Services
CNO: Diana Hakenson, Director of Patient Care Services
Web address: www.newportbayhospital.com
Control: Corporation, Investor–owned (for–profit) **Service**: Psychiatric

Staffed Beds: 34

NORTHRIDGE—Los Angeles County; See Los Angeles

NORWALK—Los Angeles County

COAST PLAZA DOCTORS HOSPITAL See Coast Plaza Hospital

COAST PLAZA HOSPITAL (050771), 13100 Studebaker Road, Zip 90650–2500; tel. 562/868–3751, (Nonreporting) **A**1 10 **S** Avanti Hospitals, El Segundo, CA
Primary Contact: Gregory Padilla, Administrator
CFO: Mihi Lee, Chief Financial Officer
CMO: Galal S Gough, M.D., Chief of Staff
CIO: Linda K Roman, Administrator
Web address: www.avantihospitals.com/coast-plaza-hospital
Control: Corporation, Investor–owned (for–profit) **Service**: General medical and surgical

Staffed Beds: 123

LOS ANGELES COMMUNITY HOSPITAL OF NORWALK See Los Angeles Community Hospital at Los Angeles, Los Angeles

CA

☐ **METROPOLITAN STATE HOSPITAL (054133)**, 11401 Bloomfield Avenue, Zip 90650–2015; tel. 562/863–7011, (Nonreporting) **A**1 10
Primary Contact: Michael Barsom, M.D., Executive Director
CFO: Maybelle Manlagnit, Senior Accounting Officer
CIO: Paul Mello, Manager Data Processing
CHR: Jorge Banuedos, Director Human Resources
Web address: www.dmh.ca.gov
Control: State, Government, nonfederal **Service:** Psychiatric

Staffed Beds: 657

NOVATO—Marin County

☒ **NOVATO COMMUNITY HOSPITAL (050131)**, 180 Rowland Way, Zip 94945–5009, Mailing Address: P.O. Box 1108, Zip 94948–1108; tel. 415/209–1300, (Nonreporting) **A**1 10 **S** Sutter Health, Sacramento, CA
Primary Contact: Michael L. Purvis, Chief Executive Officer
CMO: Barbara Nylund, M.D., Chief of Staff
CIO: Kathryn Graham, Director Communications and Community Relations
CHR: Diana G Johnson, Acting Chief Human Resources Officer
Web address: www.novatocommunity.sutterhealth.org
Control: Other not-for-profit (including NFP Corporation) **Service:** General medical and surgical

Staffed Beds: 40

OAKDALE—Stanislaus County

☒ **OAK VALLEY HOSPITAL DISTRICT (050067)**, 350 South Oak Avenue, Zip 95361–3581; tel. 209/847–3011, (Nonreporting) **A**1 10
Primary Contact: John McCormick, President and Chief Executive Officer
CMO: Chaitanya Mahida, M.D., Chief of Staff
CIO: Sherry Peral, Manager Information Systems
CHR: Brian Beck,PHR,MHROD, Vice President Human Resources
CNO: Joann L. Saporito, R.N., Vice President Nursing Services
Web address: www.oakvalleycares.org
Control: Hospital district or authority, Government, nonfederal **Service:** General medical and surgical

Staffed Beds: 150

OAKLAND—Alameda County

☒ △ **ALTA BATES SUMMIT MEDICAL CENTER - SUMMIT CAMPUS (050043)**, 350 Hawthorne Avenue, Zip 94609–3100; tel. 510/655–4000, (Nonreporting) **A**1 2 7 10 **S** Sutter Health, Sacramento, CA
Primary Contact: Charles Prosper, Chief Executive Officer
CMO: John Gentile, M.D., Vice President Medical Affairs
CHR: Mark Beiting, Vice President Human Resources
Web address: www.altabatessummit.com
Control: Other not-for-profit (including NFP Corporation) **Service:** General medical and surgical

Staffed Beds: 333

☒ **HIGHLAND HOSPITAL (050320)**, 1411 East 31st Street, Zip 94602–1018; tel. 510/437–4800, (Includes FAIRMONT HOSPITAL, 15400 Foothill Boulevard, San Leandro, California, Zip 94578–1009; tel. 510/895–4200; Richard Espinoza, Chief Administrative Officer; JOHN GEORGE PSYCHIATRIC HOSPITAL, 2060 Fairmont Drive, San Leandro, California, Zip 94578–1001; tel. 510/346–1300; Guy C Qvistgaard, Chief Executive Officer) (Total facility includes 109 beds in nursing home–type unit) **A**1 3 5 10 **F**3 5 8 11 13 15 18 20 22 28 29 30 31 32 34 35 36 38 39 40 43 44 45 46 49 50 54 56 57 58 59 60 61 64 65 66 68 70 71 73 74 75 76 77 78 79 81 82 84 85 86 87 90 92 93 94 96 97 98 100 101 102 104 105 107 111 112 114 115 118 130 132 134 135 142 143 144 146 147 148 152 153 154 156 157 **S** Alameda Health System, San Leandro, CA
Primary Contact: Delvecchio Finley, Chief Executive Officer
CFO: Marion Schales, Chief Financial Officer
CMO: Sang-ick Chang, M.D., M.P.H., Chief Medical Officer
CHR: Jeanette L Louden-Corbett, Chief Human Resources Officer
Web address: www.alamedahealthsystem.org
Control: Hospital district or authority, Government, nonfederal **Service:** General medical and surgical

Staffed Beds: 372 **Admissions:** 13507 **Census:** 334 **Outpatient Visits:** 393787 **Births:** 1348 **Total Expense ($000):** 842106 **Payroll Expense ($000):** 383927 **Personnel:** 3032

★ **KAISER PERMANENTE OAKLAND MEDICAL CENTER (050075)**, 3600 Broadway, Zip 94611–5693; tel. 510/752–1000, (Includes KAISER PERMANENTE RICHMOND MEDICAL CENTER, 901 Nevin Avenue, Richmond, California, Zip 94801–2555; tel. 510/307–1500; Jeffrey A Collins, M.D., Chief Executive Officer) **A**2 3 5 8 10 **F**3 8 11 12 15 18 19 20 21 22 23 24 25 26 27 28 29 30 31 34 37 39 40 41 42 45 46 47 48 49 50 51 55 56 57 58 59 60 61 63 64 68 70 72 73 74 75 76 77 78 79 80 81 82 84 85 86 88 89 102 107 108 110 111 112 114 115 117 118 119 120 121 123 124 126 130 131 134 135 144 146 147 148 149 150 154 156 157 **S** Kaiser Foundation Hospitals, Oakland, CA
Primary Contact: Jeffrey A. Collins, M.D., Senior Vice President and Area Manager
CFO: Dennis Morris, Area Finance Officer
CMO: John Loftus, M.D., Chief of Staff
CIO: Johnny Law, Area Information Officer
CHR: Rick Mead, Human Resources Leader
CNO: Charlene Boyer, Chief Nursing Officer
Web address: www.kaiserpermanente.org
Control: Other not-for-profit (including NFP Corporation) **Service:** General medical and surgical

Staffed Beds: 297 **Admissions:** 20682 **Census:** 245 **Outpatient Visits:** 369378 **Births:** 3061 **Personnel:** 2764

OAKLAND MEDICAL CENTER See Kaiser Permanente Oakland Medical Center

☐ **TELECARE HERITAGE PSYCHIATRIC HEALTH CENTER (054146)**, 2633 East 27th Street, Zip 94601–1912; tel. 510/535–5115, (Nonreporting) **A**1 10
Primary Contact: Anne L. Bakar, President and Chief Executive Officer
Web address: www.tbhcare.com/
Control: Partnership, Investor–owned (for–profit) **Service:** Psychiatric

Staffed Beds: 26

☒ **UCSF BENIOFF CHILDREN'S HOSPITAL OAKLAND (053301)**, 747 52nd Street, Zip 94609–1859; tel. 510/428–3000, **A**1 3 5 10 **F**3 7 19 21 23 25 27 29 30 31 32 34 35 40 41 43 50 54 55 57 58 59 61 64 65 68 72 74 75 77 78 79 81 82 83 84 85 86 87 88 89 90 97 99 102 107 108 111 114 118 119 130 131 132 134 136 144 146 148 149 150 155
Primary Contact: Bertram Lubin, M.D., President and Chief Executive Officer
CIO: Don Livsey, Vice President and Chief Information Officer
Web address: www.childrenshospitaloakland.org
Control: Other not-for-profit (including NFP Corporation) **Service:** Children's general medical and surgical

Staffed Beds: 190 **Admissions:** 9185 **Census:** 123 **Outpatient Visits:** 198617 **Births:** 0 **Total Expense ($000):** 552590 **Payroll Expense ($000):** 203729 **Personnel:** 2143

OCEANSIDE—San Diego County

☒ **TRI-CITY MEDICAL CENTER (050128)**, 4002 Vista Way, Zip 92056–4593; tel. 760/724–8411, (Nonreporting) **A**1 2 3 5 10
Primary Contact: Steve Dietlin, Chief Executive Officer
CMO: Scott Worman, Chief of Staff
CIO: Kim Cook, Interim Clinical Applications Services Manager
CHR: Esther Beverly, Vice President Human Resources
CNO: Sharon A Schultz, Chief Nurse Executive and Vice President
Web address: www.tricitymed.org
Control: Hospital district or authority, Government, nonfederal **Service:** General medical and surgical

Staffed Beds: 330

OJAI—Ventura County

⇑ **OJAI VALLEY COMMUNITY HOSPITAL (051334)**, 1306 Maricopa Highway, Zip 93023–3163; tel. 805/646–1401, (Total facility includes 63 beds in nursing home–type unit) **A**10 18 21 **F**8 18 29 30 32 34 35 40 50 54 64 65 66 68 70 75 77 81 82 93 97 104 111 119 127 128 130 133 144 **S** Community Memorial Health System, Ventura, CA
Primary Contact: Haady Lashkari, Chief Administrative Officer
CFO: David Glyer, Vice President Finance
CIO: Mark Turner, Manager Information Technology
CHR: Deborah Gallagher, Manager Human Resources
Web address: www.cmhshealth.org/locations/ojai-valley-community-hospital/
Control: Other not-for-profit (including NFP Corporation) **Service:** General medical and surgical

Staffed Beds: 66 **Admissions:** 546 **Census:** 65 **Outpatient Visits:** 34431 **Births:** 0 **Total Expense ($000):** 32046 **Payroll Expense ($000):** 14027 **Personnel:** 198

CA

ONTARIO—San Bernardino County

✉ **KINDRED HOSPITAL-ONTARIO (052037)**, 550 North Monterey Avenue, Zip 91764–3399; tel. 909/391–0333, (Nonreporting) **A**1 10 **S** Kindred Healthcare, Louisville, KY
Primary Contact: Vincent Trac, Chief Executive Officer
CFO: Omar Oregel, Controller
CMO: Marc Lynch, D.O., Chief of Staff
CHR: Laurel Scharber, Administrative Assistant and Coordinator Human Resources
CNO: Holly Ramos, R.N., Chief Clinical Officer
Web address: www.khontario.com/
Control: Corporation, Investor–owned (for–profit) **Service**: Acute long–term care hospital

Staffed Beds: 81

ORANGE—Orange County

☐ **CHAPMAN GLOBAL MEDICAL CENTER (050745)**, 2601 East Chapman Avenue, Zip 92869–3296; tel. 714/633–0011, (Nonreporting) **A**1 10 **S** KPC Healthcare, Inc., Santa Ana, CA
Primary Contact: Ada Yeh, Chief Executive Officer
CFO: John Collins, Corporate Chief Financial Officer
CMO: Gary Bennett, M.D., Chief of Medical Staff
CHR: JoAnne Suehs, Manager Human Resources
CNO: Ada Yeh, Chief Operating Officer and Chief Nursing Officer
Web address: www.Chapman-GMC.com
Control: Corporation, Investor–owned (for–profit) **Service**: General medical and surgical

Staffed Beds: 100

☐ **CHILDREN'S HOSPITAL OF ORANGE COUNTY (053304)**, 1201 West La Veta Avenue, Zip 92868–4203, Mailing Address: P.O. Box 5700, Zip 92863–5700; tel. 714/997–3000, **A**1 3 5 10 **F**3 14 17 19 21 23 25 27 29 30 31 32 34 35 40 41 43 50 55 57 58 59 60 61 64 65 66 68 71 72 74 75 77 78 79 81 82 84 85 86 87 88 89 91 92 93 97 98 100 101 102 104 105 106 107 111 113 114 115 118 119 121 123 126 129 130 131 132 134 136 144 146 149 153 154
Primary Contact: Kimberly C. Cripe, President and Chief Executive Officer
COO: Matthew S Gerlach, Chief Operating Officer
CFO: Kerri Ruppert Schiller, Senior Vice President and Chief Financial Officer
CMO: Maria Minon, M.D., Vice President Medical Affairs and Chief Medical Officer
CIO: John Henderson, Vice President and Chief Information Officer
CHR: Mamoon Syed, Vice President Human Resources
CNO: Melanie Patterson, R.N., Vice President Patient Care Services and Chief Nursing Officer
Web address: www.choc.org
Control: Other not–for–profit (including NFP Corporation) **Service**: Children's general medical and surgical

Staffed Beds: 334 Admissions: 12337 Census: 180 Outpatient Visits: 617097 Births: 0 Total Expense ($000): 728962 Payroll Expense ($000): 214287 Personnel: 3100

⇑ **HEALTHBRIDGE CHILDREN'S HOSPITAL (053308)**, 393 South Tustin Street, Zip 92866–2501; tel. 714/289–2400, (Nonreporting) **A**10 21 **S** Nexus Health Systems, Houston, TX
Primary Contact: Alex Villarruz, Chief Executive Officer
CIO: Roberta Consolver, Chief Information Officer
Web address: www.HealthBridgeOrange.com
Control: Partnership, Investor–owned (for–profit) **Service**: Rehabilitation

Staffed Beds: 27

✉ **ST. JOSEPH HOSPITAL (050069)**, 1100 West Stewart Drive, Zip 92868–3849, Mailing Address: P.O. Box 5600, Zip 92863–5600; tel. 714/633–9111, **A**1 2 3 5 10 **F**3 5 8 12 13 15 17 18 19 20 22 24 26 28 29 30 31 34 35 37 38 40 41 42 44 45 46 47 48 49 50 51 53 54 55 57 58 59 60 63 64 65 68 69 70 74 75 76 77 78 79 80 81 82 84 85 86 87 91 92 93 98 100 101 102 104 105 107 108 109 110 111 113 114 115 116 117 118 119 120 121 123 124 126 129 130 131 132 135 138 141 146 147 148 149 152 153 154 156 157 **S** Providence St. Joseph Health, Renton, WA
Primary Contact: Jeremy Zoch, Chief Executive
COO: Jeremy Zoch, Executive Vice President and Chief Operating Officer
CFO: Kristi Liberatore, Vice President and Chief Financial Officer
CMO: Scott Rusk, M.D., Chief Medical Officer
CIO: Jeremy Zoch, Executive Vice President and Chief Operating Officer
CHR: Mary P Leahy, Regional Vice President, Chief Human Resources Officer
CNO: Katie Skelton, MSN, R.N., Vice President Nursing and Chief Nursing Officer
Web address: www.sjo.org
Control: Church operated, Nongovernment, not–for–profit **Service**: General medical and surgical

Staffed Beds: 379 Admissions: 20594 Census: 225 Outpatient Visits: 337613 Births: 4878 Total Expense ($000): 634767 Payroll Expense ($000): 213846 Personnel: 2389

✉ **UC IRVINE MEDICAL CENTER (050348)**, 101 The City Drive South, Zip 92868–3298; tel. 714/456–6011, **A**1 2 3 5 8 10 19 **F**3 6 8 9 11 12 13 14 15 16 17 18 19 20 21 22 24 26 27 28 29 30 31 32 34 35 36 37 39 40 41 43 44 45 46 47 48 49 50 51 52 53 54 55 56 57 58 59 60 61 63 64 65 66 68 70 71 72 73 74 75 76 77 78 79 80 81 82 84 85 86 87 88 89 90 91 92 93 96 97 98 99 100 101 102 104 105 107 108 110 111 114 115 116 117 118 119 120 121 123 124 126 130 131 132 134 135 138 141 142 144 145 146 147 148 149 150 153 154 156 **S** University of California Systemwide Administration, Oakland, CA
Primary Contact: Richard Gannotta, Chief Executive Officer
COO: Chad T. Lefteris, Chief Operating Officer
CFO: Ajay Sial, Chief Financial Officer, UC Irvine Health
CMO: William Wilson, M.D., Chief Medical Officer
CIO: Charles H Podesta, Chief Information Officer
CHR: Ramona Agrela, Associate Chancellor & Chief Human Resources Executive
CNO: Sonia Lane, Interim Chief Nursing Officer
Web address: www.ucirvinehealth.org
Control: State, Government, nonfederal **Service**: General medical and surgical

Staffed Beds: 417 Admissions: 22086 Census: 344 Outpatient Visits: 773807 Births: 1693 Total Expense ($000): 1069532 Payroll Expense ($000): 427120 Personnel: 4414

OROVILLE—Butte County

★ **OROVILLE HOSPITAL (050030)**, 2767 Olive Highway, Zip 95966–6118; tel. 530/533–8500, **A**10 **F**3 5 8 11 13 15 18 20 26 27 28 29 30 31 32 33 34 35 36 38 39 40 41 44 45 46 47 48 49 50 51 52 54 56 57 58 59 60 61 62 63 64 65 66 68 70 74 75 76 77 78 79 81 82 83 84 85 86 87 91 93 94 96 97 107 108 110 111 114 115 116 117 118 119 120 121 123 124 126 127 129 130 131 132 134 135 144 145 146 147 148 149 154 156
Primary Contact: Robert J. Wentz, President and Chief Executive Officer
COO: Scott Chapple, Chief Operating Officer
CFO: Ashok Khanchandani, Chief Financial Officer
CMO: Mathew N. Fine, M.D., Chief Medical Officer
CIO: Denise LeFevre, Chief Information Officer
CHR: Scott Chapple, Chief Operating Officer
CNO: Carol Speer-Smith, R.N., Chief Nursing Officer
Web address: www.orovillehospital.com
Control: Other not–for–profit (including NFP Corporation) **Service**: General medical and surgical

Staffed Beds: 133 Admissions: 13390 Census: 124 Outpatient Visits: 505978 Births: 433 Total Expense ($000): 288529 Payroll Expense ($000): 110467 Personnel: 1763

OXNARD—Ventura County

✉ **ST. JOHN'S REGIONAL MEDICAL CENTER (050082)**, 1600 North Rose Avenue, Zip 93030–3723; tel. 805/988–2500, (Nonreporting) **A**1 2 3 5 10 **S** CommonSpirit Health, Chicago, IL
Primary Contact: Darren W. Lee, President and Chief Executive Officer
CFO: Donald P Bernard, Chief Financial Officer
CMO: Sahin Yanik, M.D., Vice President Medical Administration
CIO: Jeff Perry, Director Information Technology
CHR: Ed Gonzales, Vice President Human Resources
Web address: www.stjohnshealth.org
Control: Church operated **Service**: General medical and surgical

Staffed Beds: 139

PALM SPRINGS—Riverside County

✉ **DESERT REGIONAL MEDICAL CENTER (050243)**, 1150 North Indian Canyon Drive, Zip 92262–4872; tel. 760/323–6511, (Total facility includes 30 beds in nursing home–type unit) **A**1 2 3 5 10 13 18 **F**3 12 13 15 17 18 20 22 24 26 28 29 30 31 34 35 40 43 45 46 47 48 49 50 51 52 53 54 55 56 59 60 61 62 64 65 68 70 72 74 75 77 78 79 81 82 85 86 87 89 90 92 93 94 100 102 107 108 109 110 111 114 115 116 117 119 120 124 126 128 130 131 132 144 146 147 148 **S** TENET Healthcare Corporation, Dallas, TX
Primary Contact: Michele Finney, Chief Executive Officer
COO: James Santucci, Chief Operating Officer
CFO: Judi Stimson, Chief Financial Officer
CMO: Charles Anderson, M.D., Chief Medical Officer
CIO: Robert Klingseis, Director Information Systems
CHR: James Kelley, Chief Human Resources Officer
CNO: Beverly Fick, Chief Nursing Officer
Web address: www.desertregional.com
Control: Individual, Investor–owned (for–profit) **Service**: General medical and surgical

Staffed Beds: 385 Admissions: 19832 Census: 259 Outpatient Visits: 163688 Births: 3014 Total Expense ($000): 481055 Payroll Expense ($000): 195482 Personnel: 2059

Many Facility Codes have changed. Please refer to the AHA Guide Code Chart.   © 2019 AHA Guide

PALMDALE—Los Angeles County

☐ **PALMDALE REGIONAL MEDICAL CENTER (050204)**, 38600 Medical Center Drive, Zip 93551–4483; tel. 661/382–5000, **A**1 10 **F**3 11 12 18 20 22 24 26 29 31 34 35 40 41 45 46 47 48 49 50 56 57 60 63 64 68 70 74 78 79 81 85 87 90 93 96 102 107 108 111 114 115 119 126 130 132 135 146 148 149 154 **S** Universal Health Services, Inc., King of Prussia, PA
Primary Contact: Richard Allen, Chief Executive Officer
CFO: Kurt Broten, Chief Financial Officer
CIO: Roy Singleton, Director Computer Information Systems
CHR: Karen Hickling, Director Human Resources
Web address: www.palmdaleregional.com
Control: Corporation, Investor–owned (for–profit) **Service:** General medical and surgical

> **Staffed Beds:** 184 **Admissions:** 8529 **Census:** 104 **Outpatient Visits:** 74552 **Births:** 0 **Total Expense ($000):** 159572 **Payroll Expense ($000):** 63152 **Personnel:** 811

PALO ALTO—Santa Clara County

☒ **LUCILE SALTER PACKARD CHILDREN'S HOSPITAL STANFORD (053305)**, 725 Welch Road, Zip 94304–1614; tel. 650/497–8000, **A**1 3 5 10 **F**3 7 8 11 12 13 17 19 25 27 28 29 30 31 32 34 35 36 38 39 44 45 46 47 48 49 50 52 54 55 57 58 59 60 61 64 65 66 68 71 72 73 74 75 76 77 78 79 81 82 84 85 86 87 88 89 91 92 93 96 97 99 100 101 104 107 108 109 111 112 113 114 115 116 118 119 124 126 129 130 131 132 134 136 137 138 139 140 141 142 144 145 146 148 149 154
Primary Contact: Paul A. King, President and Chief Executive Officer
CMO: Dennis Lund, M.D., Chief Medical Officer
CIO: Kim Roberts, Chief Strategy Officer
CHR: Greg Souza, Vice President Human Resources
CNO: Kelly M Johnson, Chief Nursing Officer
Web address: www.stanfordchildrens.org
Control: Other not–for–profit (including NFP Corporation) **Service:** Children's general medical and surgical

> **Staffed Beds:** 297 **Admissions:** 13163 **Census:** 234 **Outpatient Visits:** 92977 **Births:** 4500 **Total Expense ($000):** 1272821 **Payroll Expense ($000):** 442563 **Personnel:** 4128

★ **STANFORD HEALTH CARE (050441)**, 300 Pasteur Drive, Suite H3200, Zip 94304–2203; tel. 650/723–4000, **A**3 5 8 10 **F**3 5 6 8 9 11 12 14 15 17 18 20 22 24 26 28 29 30 31 33 34 35 36 37 38 40 41 43 45 46 47 48 49 50 54 55 56 57 58 59 60 61 64 65 68 70 74 75 77 78 79 80 81 82 84 85 86 87 92 93 95 96 97 98 100 102 103 104 107 108 110 111 114 115 117 118 119 120 121 123 124 126 129 130 131 132 135 136 137 138 139 140 141 142 145 146 147 148 149 150 154 155 156 **S** Stanford Health Care, Palo Alto, CA
Primary Contact: David Entwistle, President and Chief Executive Officer
COO: Quinn McKenna, Chief Operating Officer
CFO: Daniel Morrisselle, Chief Financial Officer
CMO: Norman Rizk, M.D., Chief Medical Officer
CIO: Pravene Nath, Chief Information Officer
CHR: Kety Duron, Vice President Human Resources
CNO: Nancy Lee, R.N., MSN, Vice President Patient Care Services and Chief Nursing Officer
Web address: www.stanfordhealthcare.org
Control: Other not–for–profit (including NFP Corporation) **Service:** General medical and surgical

> **Staffed Beds:** 477 **Admissions:** 27109 **Census:** 421 **Outpatient Visits:** 1808715 **Births:** 0 **Total Expense ($000):** 3798075 **Payroll Expense ($000):** 1173095 **Personnel:** 11501

☒ △ **VA PALO ALTO HEALTH CARE SYSTEM**, 3801 Miranda Avenue, Zip 94304–1207; tel. 650/493–5000, (Includes PALO ALTO DIVISION, 3801 Miranda Avenue, Palo Alto, California, Zip 94304–1207; tel. 650/493–5000; VETERANS AFFAIRS PALO ALTO HEALTH CARE SYSTEM, LIVERMORE DIVISION, 4951 Arroyo Road, Livermore, California, Zip 94550; tel. 510/447–2560) (Total facility includes 349 beds in nursing home–type unit) **A**1 2 3 5 7 **F**3 4 5 8 9 10 12 15 18 20 22 24 26 28 29 30 31 33 34 35 36 37 38 39 40 44 45 46 47 49 50 51 53 54 56 57 58 59 60 61 62 63 64 65 66 68 70 71 74 75 77 78 79 80 81 82 83 84 85 86 87 90 91 92 93 94 95 96 97 98 100 101 102 103 104 106 107 108 110 111 114 115 116 117 118 119 126 129 130 131 132 135 137 141 146 147 148 149 152 153 154 156 157 158 **S** Department of Veterans Affairs, Washington, DC
Primary Contact: Thomas J. Fitzgerald III, Director
CFO: Mel Niese, Chief Fiscal Service
CMO: Lawrence Leung, M.D., Chief of Staff
CIO: Doug Wirthgen, Chief Information Officer
CHR: Lori Peery, Chief Human Resource Management Services
Web address: www.paloalto.va.gov/
Control: Veterans Affairs, Government, federal **Service:** General medical and surgical

> **Staffed Beds:** 755 **Admissions:** 7198 **Census:** 514 **Outpatient Visits:** 972805 **Births:** 0 **Total Expense ($000):** 1135548 **Payroll Expense ($000):** 428411 **Personnel:** 4226

PANORAMA CITY—Los Angeles County; See Los Angeles

PASADENA—Los Angeles County

☒ **HUNTINGTON MEMORIAL HOSPITAL (050438)**, 100 West California Boulevard, Zip 91105–3097, Mailing Address: P.O. Box 7013, Zip 91109–7013; tel. 626/397–5000, (Nonreporting) **A**1 2 3 5 8 10 19
Primary Contact: Lori J. Morgan, M.D., President and Chief Executive Officer
CFO: Steve Mohr, Senior Vice President and Chief Financial Officer
CMO: Paula Verrette, M.D., Senior Vice President Quality and Physician Services and Chief Medical Officer
CIO: Debbie Tafoya, Vice President and Chief Information Officer
CHR: Debbie Ortega, Chief Human Resource Officer and Vice President Administrative Services
CNO: Gloria Sanchez-Rico, Chief Nursing Officer and Vice President
Web address: www.huntingtonhospital.com
Control: Other not–for–profit (including NFP Corporation) **Service:** General medical and surgical

> **Staffed Beds:** 619

☐ **LAS ENCINAS HOSPITAL (054078)**, 2900 East Del Mar Boulevard, Zip 91107–4399; tel. 626/795–9901, **A**1 10 **F**4 5 29 32 54 98 100 104 105 130 132 152 153 **S** Signature Healthcare Services, Corona, CA
Primary Contact: Thomas J. Mahle, Chief Executive Officer
CMO: Daniel Suzuki, M.D., Medical Director
CIO: Eric Kim, Chief Information Officer
CHR: Veronica Herrera, Director Human Resources
Web address: www.lasencinashospital.com
Control: Individual, Investor–owned (for–profit) **Service:** Psychiatric

> **Staffed Beds:** 118 **Admissions:** 5038 **Census:** 76 **Outpatient Visits:** 11947 **Births:** 0 **Total Expense ($000):** 30482 **Payroll Expense ($000):** 16154 **Personnel:** 285

PATTON—San Bernardino County

☐ **PATTON STATE HOSPITAL**, 3102 East Highland Avenue, Zip 92369–7813; tel. 909/425–7000, (Nonreporting) **A**1 3 5
Primary Contact: Harry Oreol, Acting Chief Executive Officer
CFO: Kathleen Gamble, Fiscal Officer
CMO: George Christison, M.D., Medical Director
CIO: Cindy Barrett, Administrative Assistant
CHR: Nancy Varela, Director Human Resources
Web address: www.dmh.cahwnet.gov/statehospitals/patton
Control: State, Government, nonfederal **Service:** Psychiatric

> **Staffed Beds:** 1527

Hospital, Medicare Provider Number, Address, Telephone, Approval, Facility, and Physician Codes, Health Care System

★ American Hospital Association (AHA) membership
☐ The Joint Commission accreditation
○ Healthcare Facilities Accreditation Program
◇ DNV Healthcare Inc. accreditation
⇧ Center for Improvement in Healthcare Quality Accreditation
△ Commission on Accreditation of Rehabilitation Facilities (CARF) accreditation

CA

CA

PERRIS—Riverside County

★ **KINDRED HOSPITAL RIVERSIDE (052052)**, 2224 Medical Center Drive, Zip 92571–2638; tel. 951/436–3535, (Nonreporting) **A**10 **S** Kindred Healthcare, Louisville, KY
Primary Contact: William Mitchell, Chief Executive Officer and Administrator
COO: Guay Khim Fugate, Chief Operations Officer
CFO: John Browne, Senior Chief Financial Officer
CHR: Tom Wright, Director Human Resources
Web address: www.khriverside.com
Control: Corporation, Investor–owned (for–profit) **Service:** Acute long–term care hospital

Staffed Beds: 40

PETALUMA—Sonoma County

☒ **PETALUMA VALLEY HOSPITAL (050136)**, 400 North McDowell Boulevard, Zip 94954–2366; tel. 707/778–1111, (Nonreporting) **A**1 10
Primary Contact: David Southerland, Vice President of Operations
CFO: Michel Riccioni, Chief Financial Officer
CIO: Patrick Wylie, Director Information Systems
Web address: www.stjosephhealth.org/About-Us/Facilities/Petaluma-Valley-Hospital.aspx
Service: General medical and surgical

Staffed Beds: 51

PLACENTIA—Orange County

☒ **PLACENTIA-LINDA HOSPITAL (050589)**, 1301 North Rose Drive, Zip 92870–3899; tel. 714/993–2000, **A**1 10 **F**3 12 17 18 20 22 29 30 34 35 40 41 45 49 50 51 56 57 59 60 64 65 68 70 74 75 77 79 81 82 84 85 86 87 93 97 107 108 110 111 114 119 126 130 132 135 144 145 146 148 149 154 156 **S** TENET Healthcare Corporation, Dallas, TX
Primary Contact: Kent G. Clayton, Interim Chief Executive Officer
COO: Dwayne Richardson, Chief Operating Officer
CFO: Kelsie Blackwell, Chief Financial Officer
CIO: Eleanor Laneaux, Director Information Systems
CHR: Michelle Miller, Chief Human Resources
CNO: Rhonda Sausedo, Chief Nursing Officer
Web address: www.placentialinda.com
Control: Corporation, Investor–owned (for–profit) **Service:** General medical and surgical

Staffed Beds: 74 Admissions: 2913 Census: 26 Outpatient Visits: 51559 Births: 0 Total Expense ($000): 79812 Payroll Expense ($000): 32644 Personnel: 320

PLACERVILLE—El Dorado County

☒ **MARSHALL MEDICAL CENTER (050254)**, 1100 Marshall Way, Zip 95667–5722; tel. 530/622–1441, (Total facility includes 14 beds in nursing home–type unit) **A**1 2 5 10 **F**3 5 8 11 13 15 18 20 28 29 31 34 35 40 43 46 49 50 51 54 56 57 59 62 64 65 66 70 74 75 76 77 78 79 81 84 85 86 87 93 100 104 107 108 110 111 115 116 117 119 126 127 128 130 131 135 146 147 148 149 156
Primary Contact: James Whipple, Chief Executive Officer
COO: Shannon Truesdell, Chief Operating Officer
CFO: Laurie Eldridge, Chief Financial Officer
CMO: Rajiv Pathak, Chief of Staff
CIO: Mike Jones, Executive Director
CHR: Scott M Comer, Vice President Human Resources
CNO: Kathy Blair Krejci, Chief Nursing Officer
Web address: www.marshallmedical.org
Control: Other not–for–profit (including NFP Corporation) **Service:** General medical and surgical

Staffed Beds: 119 Admissions: 5450 Census: 66 Outpatient Visits: 531079 Births: 517 Total Expense ($000): 265126 Payroll Expense ($000): 95927 Personnel: 1094

PLEASANTON—Alameda County

★ **STANFORD HEALTH CARE - VALLEYCARE (050283)**, 5555 West Las Positas Boulevard, Zip 94588–4000; tel. 925/847–3000, (Includes VALLEY MEMORIAL, 1111 East Stanley Boulevard, Livermore, California, Zip 94550–4115; tel. 925/447–7000) (Total facility includes 22 beds in nursing home–type unit) **A**2 10 **F**3 8 11 12 13 15 17 18 20 22 24 26 28 29 30 31 34 35 39 40 41 45 47 49 50 53 54 57 59 60 64 68 70 72 74 75 76 77 78 79 81 85 89 93 107 110 111 116 119 126 128 130 131 132 144 146 147 155 156 157 **S** Stanford Health Care, Palo Alto, CA
Primary Contact: Tracey Lewis-Taylor, Chief Operating Officer
COO: Tracey Lewis-Taylor, Chief Operating Officer
CMO: David Svec, M.D., Chief Medical Officer
CIO: Bob Woods, Chief Information Officer
CHR: Chris Faber, Human Resources Analyst
Web address: www.valleycare.com
Control: Other not–for–profit (including NFP Corporation) **Service:** General medical and surgical

Staffed Beds: 193 Admissions: 6919 Census: 89 Outpatient Visits: 200090 Births: 1313 Total Expense ($000): 313048 Payroll Expense ($000): 122866 Personnel: 999

POMONA—Los Angeles County

☒ △ **CASA COLINA HOSPITAL AND HEALTH SYSTEMS (053027)**, 255 East Bonita Avenue, Zip 91767–1923, Mailing Address: P.O. Box 6001, Zip 91769–6001; tel. 909/596–7733, **A**1 3 7 10 13 **F**2 3 15 18 26 28 29 30 34 35 37 38 44 45 46 48 49 50 53 54 56 57 58 59 64 65 68 70 74 75 79 81 85 86 87 90 91 92 93 95 96 97 104 107 108 110 111 115 118 119 126 130 131 132 134 145 146 147 148 158
Primary Contact: Felice L. Loverso, Ph.D., President and Chief Executive Officer
CFO: David Morony, Chief Financial Officer
CMO: Christopher Chalian, M.D., Medical Director
CIO: Ross Lesins, Chief Information Officer
CHR: Karen Du Pont, Chief Human Resource Officer
CNO: Kathryn Johnson, Chief Nursing Officer
Web address: www.casacolina.org
Control: Other not–for–profit (including NFP Corporation) **Service:** Rehabilitation

Staffed Beds: 99 Admissions: 2809 Census: 74 Outpatient Visits: 109230 Births: 0 Total Expense ($000): 82964 Payroll Expense ($000): 38474 Personnel: 585

☒ **POMONA VALLEY HOSPITAL MEDICAL CENTER (050231)**, 1798 North Garey Avenue, Zip 91767–2918; tel. 909/865–9500, **A**1 2 3 5 10 **F**3 11 13 15 17 18 20 22 24 26 28 29 30 31 34 35 40 41 43 45 46 47 49 50 51 53 54 55 57 58 59 60 61 63 64 68 69 70 72 74 75 76 77 78 79 81 84 85 87 89 92 93 107 108 110 111 114 115 116 117 118 119 120 121 123 124 126 129 130 131 132 135 144 145 146 147 148 149 154 156
Primary Contact: Richard E. Yochum, FACHE, President and Chief Executive Officer
CFO: Michael Nelson, Executive Vice President and Chief Financial Officer
CMO: Kenneth Nakamoto, M.D., Vice President Medical Affairs
CIO: Kent Hoyos, Chief Information Officer
CHR: Ray Inge, Vice President Human Resources
CNO: Darlene Scafiddi, R.N., MSN, Vice President Nursing and Patient Care Services
Web address: www.pvhmc.org
Control: Other not–for–profit (including NFP Corporation) **Service:** General medical and surgical

Staffed Beds: 412 Admissions: 21392 Census: 243 Outpatient Visits: 589101 Births: 5986 Total Expense ($000): 610785 Payroll Expense ($000): 272526 Personnel: 3028

PORTERVILLE—Tulare County

PORTERVILLE DEVELOPMENTAL CENTER (050546), 26501 Avenue 140, Zip 93257–9109, Mailing Address: P.O. Box 2000, Zip 93258–2000; tel. 559/782–2222, (Nonreporting) **A**10
Primary Contact: Theresa Billeci, Executive Director
COO: Betty Davis, Director Administrative Services
CFO: Karen Warren, Fiscal Officer
CMO: Joseph Mendoza, M.D., Medical Director
CIO: Vincent Chandler, Director Information Services
CHR: Shawna Gregg, Director Human Resources
CNO: Tom Shelton, Coordinator of Nursing Services
Web address: www.pdc.dds.ca.gov
Control: State, Government, nonfederal **Service:** Intellectual disabilities

Staffed Beds: 484

Many Facility Codes have changed. Please refer to the AHA Guide Code Chart. © 2019 AHA Guide

☐ **SIERRA VIEW MEDICAL CENTER (050261)**, 465 West Putnam Avenue, Zip 93257–3320; tel. 559/784–1110, (Total facility includes 35 beds in nursing home–type unit) **A**1 **F**3 8 13 15 20 22 29 30 31 34 35 40 45 49 54 57 59 60 65 68 70 72 75 76 78 79 81 83 84 85 87 89 93 107 108 110 111 114 115 118 119 120 121 123 124 130 132 135 144 146 147 148 149 156
Primary Contact: Donna J. Hefner, R.N., President and Chief Executive Officer
CFO: John Chivers, Senior Vice President Finance
CIO: Traci Follett, Director Clinical Informatics
CHR: Sharon Brown, Vice President Human Resources
Web address: www.sierra-view.com
Control: Hospital district or authority, Government, nonfederal **Service:** General medical and surgical

Staffed Beds: 158 **Admissions:** 5607 **Census:** 93 **Outpatient Visits:** 187146 **Births:** 1377 **Total Expense ($000):** 148520 **Payroll Expense ($000):** 54843 **Personnel:** 860

PORTOLA—Plumas County

EASTERN PLUMAS HEALTH CARE (051300), 500 First Avenue, Zip 96122–9406; tel. 530/832–6500, (Nonreporting) **A**10 18
Primary Contact: Thomas P. Hayes, Chief Executive Officer
CFO: Katherine Pairish, Chief Financial Officer
CMO: Eric Bugna, M.D., Chief of Staff
CHR: Cathy Conant, Chief Human Resources and Personnel
Web address: www.ephc.org
Control: Hospital district or authority, Government, nonfederal **Service:** General medical and surgical

Staffed Beds: 75

POWAY—San Diego County

✠ **PALOMAR MEDICAL CENTER POWAY (050636)**, 15615 Pomerado Road, Zip 92064–2460; tel. 858/613–4000, (Total facility includes 105 beds in nursing home–type unit) **A**1 10 **F**3 11 12 13 15 29 30 34 35 36 38 40 45 46 47 49 50 51 54 55 56 57 58 59 64 65 67 68 70 72 74 75 76 77 79 81 82 84 85 87 91 94 97 98 100 101 102 103 107 108 110 111 119 120 128 130 132 143 144 146 147 148 149 **S** Palomar Health, Escondido, CA
Primary Contact: Cheryl Olson, Vice President
CIO: Steven Tanaka, Chief Information Officer
CHR: Brenda C Turner, Chief Human Resources Officer
Web address: www.pph.org
Control: Hospital district or authority, Government, nonfederal **Service:** General medical and surgical

Staffed Beds: 201 **Admissions:** 6037 **Census:** 150 **Outpatient Visits:** 53904 **Births:** 880 **Total Expense ($000):** 169001 **Payroll Expense ($000):** 66779

QUINCY—Plumas County

☐ **PLUMAS DISTRICT HOSPITAL (051326)**, 1065 Bucks Lake Road, Zip 95971–9599; tel. 530/283–2121, (Nonreporting) **A**1 5 10 18
Primary Contact: JoDee Tittle, Chief Executive Officer
CMO: Vincent Frantz, M.D., Chief of Staff
CIO: Brenda Compton, Manager Information Technology
CHR: Denise Harding, Director Human Resources
Web address: www.pdh.org
Control: Hospital district or authority, Government, nonfederal **Service:** General medical and surgical

Staffed Beds: 25

RANCHO CUCAMONGA—San Bernardino County

✠ **KINDRED HOSPITAL RANCHO (052049)**, 10841 White Oak Avenue, Zip 91730–3811; tel. 909/581–6400, (Nonreporting) **A**1 10 **S** Kindred Healthcare, Louisville, KY
Primary Contact: Victor Carrasco, Chief Executive Officer
COO: Jody Knox, Chief Operating Officer
Web address: www.khrancho.com
Control: Corporation, Investor–owned (for–profit) **Service:** Acute long–term care hospital

Staffed Beds: 55

RANCHO MIRAGE—Riverside County

✠ **EISENHOWER MEDICAL CENTER (050573)**, 39000 Bob Hope Drive, Zip 92270–3221; tel. 760/340–3911, **A**1 2 3 5 8 10 **F**2 3 9 11 12 15 17 18 20 22 24 26 28 29 30 31 34 35 37 40 41 45 47 49 50 53 54 56 57 58 59 60 61 64 65 68 70 74 75 77 78 79 81 82 84 85 86 87 90 93 96 97 100 101 102 104 107 108 109 110 111 112 114 115 118 119 120 121 123 124 126 129 130 131 132 135 143 144 145 146 147 148 149 156
Primary Contact: G Aubrey. Serfling, President and Chief Executive Officer
COO: Martin Massiello, Executive Vice President and Chief Operating Officer
CFO: Ken Wheat, Senior Vice President and Chief Financial Officer
CMO: Alan Williamson, M.D., Chief Medical Officer
CIO: David Perez, Vice President and Chief Information Officer
CHR: Liz Guignier, Vice President Human Resources
CNO: Ann R Mostofi, MSN, R.N., Vice President Patient Care and Chief Nursing Officer
Web address: www.emc.org
Control: Other not–for–profit (including NFP Corporation) **Service:** General medical and surgical

Staffed Beds: 410 **Admissions:** 20582 **Census:** 214 **Outpatient Visits:** 801858 **Births:** 0 **Total Expense ($000):** 802093 **Payroll Expense ($000):** 264526 **Personnel:** 3167

RED BLUFF—Tehama County

✠ **ST. ELIZABETH COMMUNITY HOSPITAL (050042)**, 2550 Sister Mary Columba Drive, Zip 96080–4397; tel. 530/529–8000, (Nonreporting) **A**1 10 20 **S** CommonSpirit Health, Chicago, IL
Primary Contact: Jordan Wright, Chief Executive Officer
CFO: Kim Miranda, Chief Financial Officer
CMO: James DeSoto, M.D., Vice President Medical Affairs
CIO: Henry Niessink, Senior Manager Information Technology Systems
CHR: Denise Little, Director Human Resources
Web address: www.mercy.org
Control: Church operated **Service:** General medical and surgical

Staffed Beds: 65

REDDING—Shasta County

✠ **MERCY MEDICAL CENTER REDDING (050280)**, 2175 Rosaline Avenue, Zip 96001–2549, Mailing Address: P.O. Box 496009, Zip 96049–6009; tel. 530/225–6000, **A**1 2 3 5 10 **F**2 3 7 11 13 15 17 18 20 22 24 28 29 30 31 34 35 37 40 43 45 46 47 48 49 50 54 57 59 61 62 63 64 66 68 70 72 75 76 77 78 79 81 82 84 85 89 91 97 107 108 111 114 115 118 119 126 130 132 135 143 144 145 146 147 148 149 154 **S** CommonSpirit Health, Chicago, IL
Primary Contact: G. Todd. Smith, Chief Executive Officer
COO: Patrick Varga, Chief Operating Officer
CFO: Kimberly Miranda, Regional Vice President Finance and Chief Financial Officer
CMO: James DeSoto, M.D., Vice President Medical Affairs
CIO: Henry Niessink, Regional Director Information Technology Services
CNO: Kimberly Shaw, Vice President Patient Care and Chief Nursing Executive
Web address: www.mercy.org
Control: Church operated, Nongovernment, not–for–profit **Service:** General medical and surgical

Staffed Beds: 267 **Admissions:** 13638 **Census:** 166 **Outpatient Visits:** 160100 **Births:** 2059 **Total Expense ($000):** 465998 **Payroll Expense ($000):** 156884 **Personnel:** 1627

NORTHERN CALIFORNIA REHABILITATION HOSPITAL See Vibra Hospital of Northern California

PATIENTS' HOSPITAL OF REDDING (050697), 2900 Eureka Way, Zip 96001–0220; tel. 530/225–8700, (Nonreporting) **A**10
Primary Contact: Shari Lejsek, Administrator
CFO: Kim Needles, Manager Business Office
CMO: James Tate, M.D., Chief of Staff
CIO: Kim Cameron, Manager Health Information Services
CHR: Brenda Meline, Manager Human Resources
CNO: Diane Rieke, Director Patient Care Services
Web address: www.patientshospital.com
Control: Individual, Investor–owned (for–profit) **Service:** Surgical

Staffed Beds: 10

CA

Hospital, Medicare Provider Number, Address, Telephone, Approval, Facility, and Physician Codes, Health Care System

★ American Hospital Association (AHA) membership   ◯ Healthcare Facilities Accreditation Program   ⇑ Center for Improvement in Healthcare Quality Accreditation
☐ The Joint Commission accreditation   ◇ DNV Healthcare Inc. accreditation   △ Commission on Accreditation of Rehabilitation Facilities (CARF) accreditation

✦ **SHASTA REGIONAL MEDICAL CENTER (050764)**, 1100 Butte Street, Zip 96001–0853, Mailing Address: P.O. Box 496072, Zip 96049–6072; tel. 530/244–5400, (Nonreporting) **A**1 3 5 10 **S** Prime Healthcare, Ontario, CA
Primary Contact: Casey Fatch, Chief Executive Officer
COO: Becky Levy, Chief Operating Officer
CFO: Becky Levy, Chief Financial Officer
CMO: Marcia McCampbell, M.D., Chief Medical Officer
CIO: Tony VanBoekel, Director Information Systems
CHR: Andrew Torge, Director Human Resources
Web address: www.shastaregional.com
Control: Corporation, Investor–owned (for–profit) **Service:** General medical and surgical

Staffed Beds: 100

✦ **VIBRA HOSPITAL OF NORTHERN CALIFORNIA (052047)**, 2801 Eureka Way, Zip 96001–0222; tel. 530/246–9000, (Nonreporting) **A**1 10 **S** Vibra Healthcare, Mechanicsburg, PA
Primary Contact: Chris Jones, Chief Executive Officer
COO: Lisa Stevens, Chief Clinical Officer and Chief Operating Officer
CFO: Rebecca Andrews, Chief Financial Officer
CMO: Nanda Kumar, M.D., Chief of Staff
CIO: Mark Cardenas, Director Plant Operations
CHR: Wendy Tempest, Director Human Resources
Web address: www.norcalrehab.com
Control: Corporation, Investor–owned (for–profit) **Service:** Acute long–term care hospital

Staffed Beds: 88

REDLANDS—San Bernardino County

✦ **LOMA LINDA UNIVERSITY BEHAVIORAL MEDICINE CENTER (054093)**, 1710 Barton Road, Zip 92373–5304; tel. 909/558–9200, **A**1 3 5 10 **F**4 5 29 30 34 44 50 57 87 98 99 100 101 103 104 105 130 132 134 135 152 153 154 **S** Loma Linda University Adventist Health Sciences Center, Loma Linda, CA
Primary Contact: Edward Field, Administrator
COO: Ruthita J Fike, Chief Executive Officer
CMO: William Murdoch, M.D., Medical Director
CIO: Mark Zirkelback, Chief Information Officer
CHR: Mark Hubbard, Vice President Risk Management
CNO: Norie Lee Reyes Bencito Acaac, R.N., MS, Executive Director
Web address: www.llu.edu
Control: Other not–for–profit (including NFP Corporation) **Service:** Psychiatric

Staffed Beds: 89 **Admissions:** 4146 **Census:** 68 **Outpatient Visits:** 46142 **Births:** 0 **Total Expense ($000):** 42836 **Payroll Expense ($000):** 7456 **Personnel:** 324

✦ **REDLANDS COMMUNITY HOSPITAL (050272)**, 350 Terracina Boulevard, Zip 92373–0742, Mailing Address: P.O. Box 3391, Zip 92373–0742; tel. 909/335–5500, (Total facility includes 16 beds in nursing home–type unit) **A**1 10 **F**3 11 13 15 20 28 29 30 31 34 35 40 45 46 47 49 54 57 59 62 63 64 65 66 68 70 72 74 75 76 77 78 79 81 82 84 85 87 93 96 97 98 102 104 105 107 108 110 111 115 117 119 121 126 128 130 132 143 146 147 148 154
Primary Contact: James R. Holmes, President and Chief Executive Officer
CFO: Michelle Mok, Chief Financial Officer
CHR: Lisa Guzman, Human Resource Vice President
CNO: Lauren Spilsbury, R.N., MSN, Vice President for Patient Care Services
Web address: www.redlandshospital.org
Control: Other not–for–profit (including NFP Corporation) **Service:** General medical and surgical

Staffed Beds: 229 **Admissions:** 12101 **Census:** 127 **Outpatient Visits:** 176974 **Births:** 2184 **Total Expense ($000):** 319023 **Payroll Expense ($000):** 110491 **Personnel:** 1509

REDWOOD CITY—San Mateo County

✦ **KAISER PERMANENTE REDWOOD CITY MEDICAL CENTER (050541)**, 1100 Veterans Boulevard, Zip 94063–2087; tel. 650/299–2000, **A**1 3 5 10 **F**3 8 11 13 15 18 20 26 28 29 30 31 34 35 39 40 41 45 49 50 51 55 56 57 58 59 60 61 62 63 64 68 70 72 73 74 75 76 77 78 79 80 81 82 84 85 86 91 102 107 108 110 111 114 115 118 119 130 131 134 135 144 146 147 148 149 154 156 157 **S** Kaiser Foundation Hospitals, Oakland, CA
Primary Contact: Michelle Gaskill-Hames, R.N., Senior Vice President & Area Manager
COO: Sheila Gilson, R.N., Chief Operating Officer
CFO: Doug Reynolds, Area Finance Officer
CMO: William Firtch, M.D., Physician In Chief
CHR: Kimberly A Seitz, Area Human Resources Leader
CNO: Jodi B. Galli, R.N., Chief Nursing Officer
Web address: www.kaiserpermanente.org
Control: Other not–for–profit (including NFP Corporation) **Service:** General medical and surgical

Staffed Beds: 149 **Admissions:** 8273 **Census:** 77 **Outpatient Visits:** 55947 **Births:** 2019 **Personnel:** 841

✦ **SEQUOIA HOSPITAL (050197)**, 170 Alameda De Las Pulgas, Zip 94062–2799; tel. 650/369–5811, **A**1 10 **F**11 12 13 15 18 20 22 24 26 28 29 30 31 32 34 35 37 40 45 46 49 50 53 57 59 60 64 68 70 74 75 76 77 78 79 81 84 86 87 92 93 94 107 108 110 111 115 118 119 120 121 123 124 126 130 132 135 146 147 149 154 156 **S** CommonSpirit Health, Chicago, IL
Primary Contact: Bill Graham, President
CFO: Kim Osborn, Chief Financial Officer
CMO: Anita Chandrasena, M.D., Vice President Medical Affairs
CIO: Ian Vallely, Information Technology Site Leader
CHR: Linde Cheema, Vice President Human Resources
CNO: Sherie Ambrose, Chief Nurse Executive
Web address: www.sequoiahospital.org
Control: Other not–for–profit (including NFP Corporation) **Service:** General medical and surgical

Staffed Beds: 114 **Admissions:** 5405 **Census:** 53 **Outpatient Visits:** 79519 **Births:** 1302 **Total Expense ($000):** 291429 **Payroll Expense ($000):** 89968 **Personnel:** 681

REEDLEY—Fresno County

✦ **ADVENTIST MEDICAL CENTER-REEDLEY (050192)**, 372 West Cypress Avenue, Zip 93654–2199; tel. 559/638–8155, (Nonreporting) **A**1 3 10 **S** Adventist Health, Roseville, CA
Primary Contact: Wayne Ferch, President and Chief Executive Officer
CFO: Teresa Jacques, Interim Chief Financial Officer
CMO: Todd Spencer, M.D., Chief Medical Staff
CIO: Valerie Alvarez, Executive Assistant
CHR: Ramona Alvarado, Interim Manager Human Resources
Web address: www.skdh.org
Control: Hospital district or authority, Government, nonfederal **Service:** General medical and surgical

Staffed Beds: 49

RESEDA—Los Angeles County

☐ **JOYCE EISENBERG-KEEFER MEDICAL CENTER (054147)**, 7150 Tampa Avenue, Zip 91335–3700; tel. 818/774–3000, (Total facility includes 239 beds in nursing home–type unit) **A**1 10 **F**2 29 30 34 35 39 50 53 56 62 63 65 68 74 75 77 82 84 90 98 103 128 130 132 143 146 148 149 154
Primary Contact: Molly Forrest, President and Chief Executive Officer
CNO: Haya Berci, Executive Director of Nursing
Web address: www.jha.org
Control: Other not–for–profit (including NFP Corporation) **Service:** Psychiatric

Staffed Beds: 249 **Admissions:** 495 **Census:** 239 **Outpatient Visits:** 0 **Births:** 0

RICHMOND—Contra Costa County

KAISER PERMANENTE RICHMOND MEDICAL CENTER See Kaiser Permanente Oakland Medical Center, Oakland

RIDGECREST—Kern County

★ ⇑ **RIDGECREST REGIONAL HOSPITAL (051333)**, 1081 North China Lake Boulevard, Zip 93555–3130; tel. 760/446–3551, (Total facility includes 125 beds in nursing home–type unit) **A**10 18 21 **F**8 15 18 28 29 30 31 32 33 34 35 39 40 43 45 46 50 57 59 62 63 64 65 68 69 70 71 75 76 77 78 79 81 84 85 86 87 89 93 94 97 107 108 109 110 111 112 113 114 115 116 117 118 119 127 128 129 130 132 133 135 143 144 146 147 148 149 154
Primary Contact: James A. Suver, FACHE, Chief Executive Officer
CFO: John Chivers, Chief Financial Officer
CHR: Michelle Lemke, Administrator Human Resources and Support Services
Web address: www.rrh.org
Control: Other not–for–profit (including NFP Corporation) **Service:** General medical and surgical

Staffed Beds: 197 **Admissions:** 1794 **Census:** 92 **Outpatient Visits:** 231375 **Births:** 450 **Total Expense ($000):** 116382 **Payroll Expense ($000):** 42504 **Personnel:** 754

Many Facility Codes have changed. Please refer to the AHA Guide Code Chart.

CA

RIVERSIDE—Riverside County

⊠ **KAISER PERMANENTE RIVERSIDE MEDICAL CENTER (050686)**, 10800 Magnolia Avenue, Zip 92505–3000; tel. 951/353–2000, **A**1 3 5 10 **F**3 13 15 17 28 29 30 31 34 35 40 44 45 46 48 49 50 51 53 59 60 62 63 64 65 68 70 71 72 74 75 76 77 78 79 81 82 84 85 86 87 92 93 97 100 102 107 108 109 110 111 114 115 116 117 118 119 130 131 132 135 143 144 146 147 148 149 150 154 156 157 **S** Kaiser Foundation Hospitals, Oakland, CA
Primary Contact: Vita M. Willett, Executive Director
COO: Robin D. Mackenroth, Chief Operating Officer
CFO: JiJi Abraham, Chief Financial Officer
CMO: Frank M. Flowers, M.D., Area Medical Director
CIO: Alfred T Velasquez, Area Information Officer
CHR: Michelle Skipper, Director Human Resources
CNO: Rosemary M Butler, R.N., MSN, Chief Nurse Executive
Web address: www.kaiserpermanente.org
Control: Other not–for–profit (including NFP Corporation) **Service**: General medical and surgical

Staffed Beds: 226 **Admissions**: 9864 **Census**: 114 **Outpatient Visits**: 61636 **Births**: 3166 **Personnel**: 1407

☐ **PACIFIC GROVE HOSPITAL (054130)**, 5900 Brockton Avenue, Zip 92506–1862; tel. 951/275–8400, (Nonreporting) **A**1 5 10 **S** Acadia Healthcare Company, Inc., Franklin, TN
Primary Contact: Nichol Sheffield, Chief Executive Officer
Web address: www.pacificgrovehospital.com
Control: Corporation, Investor–owned (for–profit) **Service**: Psychiatric

Staffed Beds: 68

☐ **PARKVIEW COMMUNITY HOSPITAL MEDICAL CENTER (050102)**, 3865 Jackson Street, Zip 92503–3998; tel. 951/688–2211, **A**1 10 **F**1 3 4 8 11 12 13 15 16 17 18 29 34 35 40 45 46 49 50 51 56 57 59 60 64 65 67 68 70 72 73 74 76 77 79 80 81 84 85 86 87 88 89 90 92 98 100 102 107 110 111 114 115 119 128 130 132 135 145 146 147 148 149 154 156 **S** AHMC & Healthcare, Inc., Alhambra, CA
Primary Contact: Steven Popkin, Chief Executive Officer
COO: Robert Brown, Chief Operating Officer
CFO: Nancy Wilson, Chief Financial Officer
CMO: Serafin Salazar, M.D., Chief of Staff
CIO: John Ciccarelli, Director Information Technology
CHR: Ilyssa DeCasperis, Director of Human Resources
CNO: Karen T. Descent, Chief Nursing Officer
Web address: www.pchmc.org
Control: Other not–for–profit (including NFP Corporation) **Service**: General medical and surgical

Staffed Beds: 193 **Admissions**: 7524 **Census**: 80 **Outpatient Visits**: 63273 **Births**: 1813 **Total Expense ($000)**: 154635 **Payroll Expense ($000)**: 54434 **Personnel**: 1010

RIVERSIDE CENTER FOR BEHAVIORAL MEDICINE See Pacific Grove Hospital

⊠ **RIVERSIDE COMMUNITY HOSPITAL (050022)**, 4445 Magnolia Avenue, Zip 92501–4199; tel. 951/788–3000, (Nonreporting) **A**1 2 3 5 10 **S** HCA Healthcare, Nashville, TN
Primary Contact: Jacqueline DeSouza-Van Blaricum, President and Chief Executive Officer
COO: Daniel Bowers, Chief Operating Officer
CFO: Todd LaCaze, Chief Financial Officer
CMO: David Tito, M.D., President Medical Staff
CIO: Cae Swanger, Chief Information Officer
CHR: Tammy Kaminski, Vice President Human Relations
CNO: Annette June Greenwood, Chief Nursing Officer
Web address: www.riversidecommunityhospital.com
Control: Corporation, Investor–owned (for–profit) **Service**: General medical and surgical

Staffed Beds: 373

RIVERSIDE MEDICAL CENTER See Kaiser Permanente Riverside Medical Center

ROSEMEAD—Los Angeles County

☐ **BHC ALHAMBRA HOSPITAL (054032)**, 4619 North Rosemead Boulevard, Zip 91770–1478, Mailing Address: P.O. Box 369, Zip 91770–0369; tel. 626/286–1191, (Nonreporting) **A**1 3 10 **S** Universal Health Services, Inc., King of Prussia, PA
Primary Contact: Peggy Minnick, R.N., Chief Executive Officer
CFO: Michelle Jackson, Chief Financial Officer
CMO: Wakelin McNeel, M.D., Medical Director
CIO: Debbie Irvin, Director Health Information Management
CHR: Venus Taylor, Director Human Resources
Web address: www.bhcalhambra.com
Control: Corporation, Investor–owned (for–profit) **Service**: Psychiatric

Staffed Beds: 97

ROSEVILLE—Placer County

⊠ **KAISER PERMANENTE ROSEVILLE MEDICAL CENTER (050772)**, 1600 Eureka Road, Zip 95661–3027; tel. 916/784–4000, **A**1 2 5 10 **F**3 8 11 15 18 20 22 26 27 28 29 30 31 34 39 40 41 45 49 50 51 55 56 57 58 59 60 61 63 64 68 70 72 73 74 75 76 77 78 79 81 82 84 85 86 88 89 102 107 108 110 111 114 115 117 118 119 120 121 123 124 129 130 131 134 135 144 146 147 148 149 154 **S** Kaiser Foundation Hospitals, Oakland, CA
Primary Contact: Jordan Herget, Senior Vice President and Manager
Web address: www.kp.org
Control: Other not–for–profit (including NFP Corporation) **Service**: General medical and surgical

Staffed Beds: 340 **Admissions**: 23469 **Census**: 246 **Outpatient Visits**: 194106 **Births**: 6398 **Personnel**: 1836

⊠ △ **SUTTER ROSEVILLE MEDICAL CENTER (050309)**, One Medical Plaza Drive, Zip 95661–3037; tel. 916/781–1000, (Nonreporting) **A**1 2 5 7 10 **S** Sutter Health, Sacramento, CA
Primary Contact: Brian Alexander, Chief Executive Officer
COO: Dionne Miller, Chief Operating Officer
CFO: Gary Hubschman, Administrative Director Finance
CMO: Stuart Bostrom, M.D., Director Medical Affairs
CIO: Nancy Turner, Director Communications
CHR: Lynda Dasaro, Director Human Resources
CNO: Barbara J Nelson, Ph.D., R.N., Chief Nursing Executive
Web address: www.sutterroseville.org
Control: Other not–for–profit (including NFP Corporation) **Service**: General medical and surgical

Staffed Beds: 328

SACRAMENTO—Sacramento County

☐ **HERITAGE OAKS HOSPITAL (054104)**, 4250 Auburn Boulevard, Zip 95841–4164; tel. 916/489–3336, (Nonreporting) **A**1 3 5 10 **S** Universal Health Services, Inc., King of Prussia, PA
Primary Contact: Shawn Silva, Chief Executive Officer
CFO: Art Wong, Chief Financial Officer
CMO: Joseph Sison, M.D., Medical Director
CHR: Lisa Myers, Director Human Resources
Web address: www.heritageoakshospital.com
Control: Corporation, Investor–owned (for–profit) **Service**: Psychiatric

Staffed Beds: 120

⊠ **KAISER PERMANENTE SACRAMENTO MEDICAL CENTER (050425)**, 2025 Morse Avenue, Zip 95825–2100; tel. 916/973–5000, **A**1 2 3 5 10 **F**3 8 11 15 17 18 20 22 26 28 29 30 31 34 39 40 41 45 46 47 49 50 55 56 57 58 59 60 61 63 64 68 70 74 75 77 78 79 81 82 84 85 86 102 107 108 110 111 114 115 118 119 120 121 123 129 130 135 146 148 149 154 **S** Kaiser Foundation Hospitals, Oakland, CA
Primary Contact: Sandy Sharon, Senior Vice President and Area Manager
CFO: Jim Eldridge, Area Financial Officer
CMO: Chris Palkowski, M.D., Physician in Chief
CIO: Philip Fasano, Chief Information Officer
CHR: Gay Westfall, Senior Vice President Human Resources
Web address: www.kp.org
Control: Other not–for–profit (including NFP Corporation) **Service**: General medical and surgical

Staffed Beds: 200 **Admissions**: 12192 **Census**: 138 **Outpatient Visits**: 269238 **Births**: 10 **Personnel**: 1298

Hospital, Medicare Provider Number, Address, Telephone, Approval, Facility, and Physician Codes, Health Care System

★ American Hospital Association (AHA) membership
☐ The Joint Commission accreditation
○ Healthcare Facilities Accreditation Program
◇ DNV Healthcare Inc. accreditation
⇑ Center for Improvement in Healthcare Quality Accreditation
△ Commission on Accreditation of Rehabilitation Facilities (CARF) accreditation

⊠ **KAISER PERMANENTE SOUTH SACRAMENTO MEDICAL CENTER (050674)**, 6600 Bruceville Road, Zip 95823–4691; tel. 916/688–2430, **A**1 3 5 10 **F**3 8 11 12 13 15 18 20 22 26 29 30 31 34 35 37 39 40 41 43 44 45 47 49 50 51 55 56 57 58 59 60 61 62 63 64 65 68 70 73 74 75 76 77 78 79 81 82 84 85 86 87 100 102 107 108 110 111 114 115 118 119 120 126 129 130 131 135 144 146 147 148 149 150 154 156 **S** Kaiser Foundation Hospitals, Oakland, CA
Primary Contact: Patricia M. Rodriguez, Senior Vice President and Area Manager
CFO: Kevin L Smith, Area Finance Officer
CIO: Michelle Odell, Director of Public Affairs
CHR: James Kevin Peterson, Human Resources Leader
CNO: Terri Owensby, R.N., Chief Nursing Executive
Web address: www.kp.org
Control: Other not–for–profit (including NFP Corporation) **Service:** General medical and surgical

Staffed Beds: 217 **Admissions:** 20739 **Census:** 156 **Outpatient Visits:** 218038 **Births:** 2809 **Personnel:** 1249

⊠ △ **MERCY GENERAL HOSPITAL (050017)**, 4001 'J' Street, Zip 95819–3600; tel. 916/453–4545, **A**1 2 3 5 7 10 **F**3 8 11 13 15 17 18 20 22 24 26 28 29 30 31 34 35 36 37 38 39 40 44 45 46 47 48 49 50 51 53 56 57 58 59 62 63 64 66 67 68 70 74 75 76 77 78 79 81 82 84 85 86 87 90 91 92 93 94 96 100 107 108 111 114 115 119 124 126 131 132 135 141 142 143 145 146 149 154 **S** CommonSpirit Health, Chicago, IL
Primary Contact: Edmundo Castaneda, President
COO: Clare Lee, Chief Operating Officer
CFO: Bonnie Jenkins, Chief Financial Officer
CHR: Cyndi Kirch, Vice President Human Resources
CNO: Allison Cotterill, Chief Nursing Officer
Web address: www.mercygeneral.org
Control: Other not–for–profit (including NFP Corporation) **Service:** General medical and surgical

Staffed Beds: 305 **Admissions:** 14400 **Census:** 169 **Outpatient Visits:** 102091 **Births:** 972 **Total Expense ($000):** 593389 **Payroll Expense ($000):** 197280 **Personnel:** 1726

⊠ **METHODIST HOSPITAL OF SACRAMENTO (050590)**, 7500 Hospital Drive, Zip 95823–5477; tel. 916/423–3000, (Total facility includes 171 beds in nursing home–type unit) **A**1 3 5 10 **F**3 8 11 12 13 17 18 29 30 34 35 39 40 45 46 48 49 50 51 56 57 59 60 64 66 68 70 72 74 75 76 79 81 85 87 91 92 93 94 96 107 111 114 115 116 119 128 130 131 132 146 147 149 154 **S** CommonSpirit Health, Chicago, IL
Primary Contact: Phyllis Baltz, Chief Executive Officer
COO: Anita J Kennedy, Vice President Operations
CFO: Bonnie Jenkins, Chief Financial Officer
CMO: Amir Sweha, M.D., Vice President Medical Administration
CHR: Cyndi Kirch, Vice President Human Resources
CNO: Martina Evans-Harrison, R.N., MSN, Chief Nurse Executive
Web address: www.methodistsacramento.org
Control: Other not–for–profit (including NFP Corporation) **Service:** General medical and surgical

Staffed Beds: 329 **Admissions:** 10126 **Census:** 247

☐ **SHRINERS HOSPITALS FOR CHILDREN-NORTHERN CALIFORNIA (053311)**, 2425 Stockton Boulevard, Zip 95817–2215; tel. 916/453–2000, (Nonreporting) **A**1 3 5 10 **S** Shriners Hospitals for Children, Tampa, FL
Primary Contact: Margaret Bryan, Administrator
COO: Margaret Bryan, Administrator
CFO: William Dalby, Director Fiscal Services
CIO: John Bevel, Manager Information Systems
CHR: Deborah Rubens, Director Human Resources
Web address: www.shrinershospitalsforchildren.org/Hospitals/Locations/NorthernCalifornia.aspx
Control: Other not–for–profit (including NFP Corporation) **Service:** Children's general medical and surgical

Staffed Beds: 70

☐ **SIERRA VISTA HOSPITAL (054087)**, 8001 Bruceville Road, Zip 95823–2329; tel. 916/288–0300, (Nonreporting) **A**1 10 **S** Universal Health Services, Inc., King of Prussia, PA
Primary Contact: Mike Zauner, Chief Executive Officer
COO: Ixel Morell, Chief Operating Officer
CFO: Nicole Samuel, Chief Financial Officer
CMO: Alok Banga, M.D., Medical Director
CNO: Gwen Hubbard, Chief Nursing Officer
Web address: www.sierravistahospital.com
Control: Corporation, Investor–owned (for–profit) **Service:** Psychiatric

Staffed Beds: 171

SOUTH SACRAMENTO MEDICAL CENTER See Kaiser Permanente South Sacramento Medical Center

⊠ **SUTTER CENTER FOR PSYCHIATRY (054096)**, 7700 Folsom Boulevard, Zip 95826–2608; tel. 916/386–3000, (Nonreporting) **A**1 3 10 **S** Sutter Health, Sacramento, CA
Primary Contact: John W. Boyd, PsyD, Chief Executive Officer
CFO: Pamela Ansley, Director Finance
CMO: Cindy Thygeson, M.D., Director Medical Affairs
CHR: Kristin Daniels, Manager Human Resources
Web address: www.sutterpsychiatry.org
Control: Other not–for–profit (including NFP Corporation) **Service:** Psychiatric

Staffed Beds: 71

★ **SUTTER MEDICAL CENTER, SACRAMENTO (050108)**, 2801 'L' Street, Zip 95816–5680; tel. 916/454–3333, (Includes SUTTER CHILDREN'S CENTER, 5151 F Street, Sacramento, California, Zip 95819–3223; tel. 800/478–8837; SUTTER GENERAL HOSPITAL, 2801 'L' Street, Sacramento, California, Zip 95816; tel. 916/454–2222), (Nonreporting) **A**2 3 5 10 **S** Sutter Health, Sacramento, CA
Primary Contact: David Cheney, Chief Executive Officer
CFO: Richard SooHoo, Chief Financial Officer
CMO: Muhammed Afzal, M.D., Chief of Staff
CIO: Jim Mills, Regional Director Information Technology
CHR: Colleen Peschel, Director Human Resources
CNO: Marchelle M McGriff, Chief Nursing Executive
Web address: www.sutterhealth.org
Control: Other not–for–profit (including NFP Corporation) **Service:** General medical and surgical

Staffed Beds: 523

⊠ **UNIVERSITY OF CALIFORNIA, DAVIS MEDICAL CENTER (050599)**, 2315 Stockton Boulevard, Zip 95817–2282; tel. 916/734–2011, (Includes UNIVERSITY OF CALIFORNIA DAVIS CHILDREN'S HOSPITAL, 2315 Stockton Boulevard, Sacramento, California, Zip 95817–2201; tel. 800/282–3284) **A**1 2 3 5 8 10 **F**3 5 6 8 9 11 12 13 15 16 17 18 19 20 21 22 23 24 25 26 27 28 29 30 31 32 34 35 36 37 38 39 40 41 43 44 45 46 47 48 49 50 51 53 54 55 56 57 58 59 60 61 62 63 64 65 66 68 70 72 73 74 75 76 77 78 79 81 82 83 84 85 86 87 88 89 90 91 92 93 94 95 96 97 99 100 101 102 103 104 107 108 110 111 114 115 116 117 118 119 120 121 123 124 126 129 130 131 132 134 135 136 138 141 142 145 146 147 148 149 150 153 154 156 157 **S** University of California Systemwide Administration, Oakland, CA
Primary Contact: Brad Simmons, Interim Chief Executive Officer
COO: Brad Simmons, Chief Operating Officer
CFO: Timothy Maurice, Chief Financial Officer
CMO: J. Douglas Kirk, M.D., Chief Medical Officer
CIO: John Cook, Interim Chief Information Officer
CHR: Stephen Chilcott, Associate Director Human Resources
CNO: Toby Marsh, MSN, R.N., Interim Chief Patient Care Services Officer
Web address: www.ucdmc.ucdavis.edu
Control: Other not–for–profit (including NFP Corporation) **Service:** General medical and surgical

Staffed Beds: 611 **Admissions:** 34937 **Census:** 537 **Outpatient Visits:** 1198512 **Births:** 1604 **Total Expense ($000):** 2045569 **Payroll Expense ($000):** 898454 **Personnel:** 8674

SAINT HELENA—Napa County

⊠ **ADVENTIST HEALTH ST. HELENA (050013)**, 10 Woodland Road, Zip 94574–9554; tel. 707/963–3611, **A**1 10 **F**3 8 15 17 18 20 22 24 26 28 29 30 31 34 35 36 37 40 45 47 50 51 53 56 57 58 59 60 62 64 65 70 74 75 76 77 78 79 81 82 84 85 86 87 92 97 98 100 101 102 103 104 105 107 108 110 111 115 117 119 120 121 126 130 131 135 146 147 148 153 154 156 157 **S** Adventist Health, Roseville, CA
Primary Contact: Steven Herber, M.D., FACS, President and Chief Executive Officer
COO: Hal Chilton, Senior Vice President and Chief Operating Officer
CMO: Timothy Lyons, M.D., Chief Medical Officer
CIO: David Noll, Director
CHR: Audrey Barrall, Director Human Resources
CNO: Nia Lendaris, MS, R.N., Regional Vice President Patient Care
Web address: www.sthelenahospital.org
Control: Church operated, Nongovernment, not–for–profit **Service:** General medical and surgical

Staffed Beds: 81 **Admissions:** 4648 **Census:** 70 **Outpatient Visits:** 45550 **Births:** 186

SALINAS—Monterey County

⊠ **NATIVIDAD MEDICAL CENTER (050248)**, 1441 Constitution Boulevard, Zip 93906–3100, Mailing Address: P.O. Box 81611, Zip 93912–1611; tel. 831/647–7611, (Nonreporting) **A**1 3 5 10
Primary Contact: Gary Gray, D.O., Chief Executive Officer
CMO: Craig Walls, M.D., Ph.D., Chief Medical Officer
CIO: Ari Entin, Chief Information Officer
CHR: Lawanda Janine Bouyea, Director Human Resources
Web address: www.natividad.com
Control: County, Government, nonfederal **Service:** General medical and surgical

Staffed Beds: 157

Many Facility Codes have changed. Please refer to the AHA Guide Code Chart. © 2019 AHA Guide

✉ **SALINAS VALLEY MEMORIAL HEALTHCARE SYSTEM (050334)**, 450 East Romie Lane, Zip 93901–4098; tel. 831/757–4333, **A**1 2 10 19 **F**3 13 15 17 18 19 20 22 24 26 28 29 30 31 34 35 37 40 45 46 49 50 54 57 58 59 64 66 68 70 72 74 75 76 77 78 79 81 84 85 87 89 93 97 107 108 110 111 115 117 118 119 127 129 130 131 132 135 144 146 147 148 149 156
Primary Contact: Pete Delgado, President and Chief Executive Officer
COO: Henry Ornelas, Chief Operating Officer
CFO: Augustine Lopez, Chief Financial Officer
CMO: Allen Radner, M.D., Chief Medical Officer
CIO: Audrey Parks, Chief Information Officer
CHR: Michelle Childs, Chief Human Resources Officer
CNO: Christie Gonder, R.N., Chief Nursing Officer
Web address: www.svmh.com
Control: Hospital district or authority, Government, nonfederal **Service**: General medical and surgical

Staffed Beds: 212 **Admissions**: 10872 **Census**: 132 **Outpatient Visits**: 113768 **Births**: 1636 **Total Expense ($000)**: 393251 **Payroll Expense ($000)**: 193125 **Personnel**: 1558

SAN ANDREAS—Calaveras County

✉ **MARK TWAIN MEDICAL CENTER (051332)**, 768 Mountain Ranch Road, Zip 95249–9998; tel. 209/754–3521, (Nonreporting) **A**1 10 18 **S** CommonSpirit Health, Chicago, IL
Primary Contact: Robert Diehl, President
CFO: Jacob Lewis, Chief Financial Officer
CHR: Nancy Vargas, Director Human Resources
Web address: www.marktwainhospital.com
Control: Other not–for–profit (including NFP Corporation) **Service**: General medical and surgical

Staffed Beds: 25

SAN BERNARDINO—San Bernardino County

✉ △ **BALLARD REHABILITATION HOSPITAL (053037)**, 1760 West 16th Street, Zip 92411–1160; tel. 909/473–1200, (Nonreporting) **A**1 7 10 **S** Vibra Healthcare, Mechanicsburg, PA
Primary Contact: Mary Miles Hunt, Chief Executive Officer
CMO: Van Chen, M.D., Medical Director
CNO: Chris Bauman, Director of Nursing
Web address: www.ballardrehab.com
Control: Corporation, Investor–owned (for–profit) **Service**: Rehabilitation

Staffed Beds: 60

✉ **COMMUNITY HOSPITAL OF SAN BERNARDINO (050089)**, 1805 Medical Center Drive, Zip 92411–1214; tel. 909/887–6333, (Nonreporting) **A**1 10 **S** CommonSpirit Health, Chicago, IL
Primary Contact: June Collison, President
COO: Victoria Selby MHA, BSN, Vice President, Ancillary and Support Services
CFO: Dave Evans, Chief Financial Officer
CMO: Andrew Fragen, M.D., Chief Medical Officer
CIO: James Borrenpohl, Market Site Director
CHR: Deena Marano, Human Resources Director
CNO: Roz Nolan, Interim Chief Nursing Officer
Web address: www.dignityhealth.org/san-bernardino
Control: Other not–for–profit (including NFP Corporation) **Service**: General medical and surgical

Staffed Beds: 379

✉ **ST. BERNARDINE MEDICAL CENTER (050129)**, 2101 North Waterman Avenue, Zip 92404–4855; tel. 909/883–8711, (Nonreporting) **A**1 3 10 **S** CommonSpirit Health, Chicago, IL
Primary Contact: Douglas V. Kleam, President
CFO: Paul Steinke, Chief Financial Officer
CMO: Betty Daniels, M.D., Chief of Staff
CIO: James Croker, Director Information Systems
CHR: Dee Webb, Vice President Human Resources
Web address: www.stbernardinemedicalcenter.com
Control: Church operated **Service**: General medical and surgical

Staffed Beds: 342

SAN DIEGO—San Diego County

✉ **ALVARADO HOSPITAL MEDICAL CENTER (050757)**, 6655 Alvarado Road, Zip 92120–5208; tel. 619/287–3270, (Nonreporting) **A**1 3 10 **S** Prime Healthcare, Ontario, CA
Primary Contact: Robin Gomez, R.N., MSN, Administrator
CMO: Larry Emdur, D.O., Chief Medical Officer
CIO: Wayne Bartlett, Director Information Systems
CHR: Sara Turner, Director Human Resources
CNO: Peggy Jezsu, Chief Nursing Officer
Web address: www.alvaradohospital.com
Control: Corporation, Investor–owned (for–profit) **Service**: General medical and surgical

Staffed Beds: 137

□ **AURORA BEHAVIORAL HEALTHCARE SAN DIEGO (054095)**, 11878 Avenue of Industry, Zip 92128–3490; tel. 858/487–3200, (Nonreporting) **A**1 10 **S** Signature Healthcare Services, Corona, CA
Primary Contact: Alain Azcona, Chief Executive Officer
COO: Barbara Kennison, Director Clinical Services
CFO: Gene Fantano, Chief Financial Officer
CMO: Thomas Flanagan, M.D., Medical Director
CIO: Alain Azcona, Director Business Development
CHR: Susan Haas, Director Human Resources
Web address: www.sandiego.aurorabehavioral.com/
Control: Corporation, Investor–owned (for–profit) **Service**: Psychiatric

Staffed Beds: 80

✉ **KAISER PERMANENTE SAN DIEGO MEDICAL CENTER (050515)**, 4647 Zion Avenue, Zip 92120–2507; tel. 619/528–5000, (Includes KAISER PERMANENTE SAN DIEGO MEDICAL CENTER, 9455 Clairemont Mesa Boulevard, San Diego, California, Zip 92123–1297; tel. 510/307–1500; Jane Finley, Senior Vice President and Area Manager) **A**1 3 5 10 **F**3 6 8 9 11 13 15 18 19 26 28 29 30 31 32 34 35 38 40 41 42 45 46 47 48 49 50 51 54 56 57 60 61 64 65 68 70 72 74 75 76 77 78 79 81 82 84 85 86 87 89 94 97 100 102 104 107 108 110 111 114 115 116 117 118 119 120 130 131 143 146 148 149 154 156 157 **S** Kaiser Foundation Hospitals, Oakland, CA
Primary Contact: Jane Finley, Senior Vice President & Area Manager
COO: Sam Totah, Chief Operating Officer
CFO: Lynette Seid, Area Chief Financial Officer
CMO: Paul E Bernstein, M.D., Area Medical Director
CIO: Laura Sullivant, Area Chief Information Officer
CHR: Jocelyn A. Herrera, Human Resources Director
CNO: Anne Marie Watkins, R.N., Chief Nurse Executive
Web address: www.kaiserpermanente.org
Control: Other not–for–profit (including NFP Corporation) **Service**: General medical and surgical

Staffed Beds: 446 **Admissions**: 35961 **Census**: 340 **Outpatient Visits**: 143736 **Births**: 4900 **Personnel**: 3838

✉ **KINDRED HOSPITAL-SAN DIEGO (052036)**, 1940 El Cajon Boulevard, Zip 92104–1096; tel. 619/543–4500, **A**1 10 **F**1 3 29 107 119 130 148 **S** Kindred Healthcare, Louisville, KY
Primary Contact: Kerry Ashment, Chief Executive Officer
CMO: Davies Wong, M.D., Medical Director
CHR: Jody Dewen Moore, District Director Human Resources
CNO: Maureen Bodine, Chief Clinical Officer
Web address: www.kindredsandiego.com
Control: Corporation, Investor–owned (for–profit) **Service**: Acute long–term care hospital

Staffed Beds: 58 **Admissions**: 600 **Census**: 58 **Outpatient Visits**: 0 **Births**: 0 **Total Expense ($000)**: 39300 **Payroll Expense ($000)**: 19601 **Personnel**: 162

✉ **NAVAL MEDICAL CENTER SAN DIEGO**, 34800 Bob Wilson Drive, Zip 92134–5000; tel. 619/532–6400, (Nonreporting) **A**1 2 3 5 **S** Bureau of Medicine and Surgery, Department of the Navy, Falls Church, VA
Primary Contact: Captain Joel A. Roos, Commanding Officer
CFO: Commander Thomas J. Piner, Director for Resources Management
CIO: Lieutenant Commander Ryan Jarmer, Chief Information Officer
Web address: www.med.navy.mil/sites/nmcsd/Pages/default.aspx
Control: Department of Defense, Government, federal **Service**: General medical and surgical

Staffed Beds: 285

Hospital, Medicare Provider Number, Address, Telephone, Approval, Facility, and Physician Codes, Health Care System

★ American Hospital Association (AHA) membership
□ The Joint Commission accreditation
○ Healthcare Facilities Accreditation Program
◇ DNV Healthcare Inc. accreditation
⇑ Center for Improvement in Healthcare Quality Accreditation
△ Commission on Accreditation of Rehabilitation Facilities (CARF) accreditation

☐ **RADY CHILDREN'S HOSPITAL - SAN DIEGO (053303)**, 3020 Childrens Way, Zip 92123–4223; tel. 858/576–1700, (Total facility includes 43 beds in nursing home–type unit) **A**1 3 5 10 **F**1 3 4 7 8 9 10 11 16 17 19 20 21 22 23 24 25 26 27 28 29 30 31 32 34 35 36 38 39 40 41 43 45 46 47 48 50 51 54 55 57 58 59 60 61 62 63 64 65 66 67 68 70 71 72 73 74 75 77 78 79 80 81 82 83 84 85 86 87 88 89 90 91 92 93 94 98 99 100 101 102 104 107 108 111 114 115 118 119 122 124 128 129 131 132 133 134 135 136 137 138 143 144 145 146 148 149 150 153 154 155 156
Primary Contact: Patricio A. Frias, M.D., President and Chief Executive Officer
COO: Meg Norton, Executive Vice President and Chief Administrative Officer
CFO: Roger Roux, Chief Financial Officer
CMO: Irvin A Kaufman, M.D., Chief Medical Officer
CIO: Albert Oriol, Vice President Information Management and Chief Information Officer
CHR: Mamoon Syed, Vice President Human Resources
CNO: Mary Fagan, MSN, R.N., Chief Nursing Officer
Web address: www.rchsd.org
Control: Other not–for–profit (including NFP Corporation) **Service:** Children's general medical and surgical

Staffed Beds: 409 **Admissions:** 20367 **Census:** 317 **Outpatient Visits:** 537490 **Births:** 0 **Total Expense ($000):** 1176415 **Payroll Expense ($000):** 385528 **Personnel:** 4270

RADY CHILDREN'S HOSPITAL AND HEALTH CENTER See Rady Children's Hospital - San Diego

☐ **SAN DIEGO COUNTY PSYCHIATRIC HOSPITAL (054114)**, 3853 Rosecrans Street, Zip 92110–3115, Mailing Address: P.O. Box 85524, Zip 92186–5524; tel. 619/692–8211, (Nonreporting) **A**1 10
Primary Contact: Izabela Karmach, R.N., Administrator
COO: Izabela Karmach, R.N., Administrator
CFO: Raul J Loyo-Rodriguez, Administrative Analyst III
CMO: Michael Krelstein, M.D., Medical Director
CIO: Linda Cannon, Chief Medical Records Services
CHR: Francisco Puentes, Human Resource Officer
Web address: www.sdcounty.ca.gov
Control: County, Government, nonfederal **Service:** Psychiatric

Staffed Beds: 357

SAN DIEGO MEDICAL CENTER See Kaiser Permanente San Diego Medical Center

⊠ **SCRIPPS MERCY HOSPITAL (050077)**, 4077 Fifth Avenue, Zip 92103–2105; tel. 619/294–8111, (Includes SCRIPPS MERCY HOSPITAL CHULA VISTA, 435 'H' Street, Chula Vista, California, Zip 91912–6617, Mailing Address: P O Box 1537, Zip 91910–1537, tel. 619/691–7000; Thomas A Gammiere, Chief Executive Officer) **A**1 2 3 5 10 19 **F**3 8 11 12 13 14 15 17 18 20 22 24 26 28 29 30 31 32 34 35 39 40 43 44 45 46 49 50 51 54 58 59 61 64 65 66 68 70 73 74 75 76 77 78 79 81 82 84 85 86 87 92 93 97 98 100 101 102 103 107 108 110 111 114 115 119 126 130 132 134 135 141 146 147 148 154 156 157 **S** Scripps Health, San Diego, CA
Primary Contact: Thomas A. Gammiere, Chief Executive, Senior Vice President
CFO: Edward Turk, Vice President Finance
CMO: Davis Cracroft, M.D., Senior Director Medical Affairs
CIO: Drexel DeFord, Chief Information Officer
Web address: www.scrippshealth.org
Control: Other not–for–profit (including NFP Corporation) **Service:** General medical and surgical

Staffed Beds: 392 **Admissions:** 30938 **Census:** 386 **Outpatient Visits:** 170615 **Births:** 3774 **Total Expense ($000):** 799157 **Payroll Expense ($000):** 282910 **Personnel:** 3426

⊠ **SELECT SPECIALTY HOSPITAL - SAN DIEGO (052044)**, 555 Washington Street, Zip 92103–2294; tel. 619/260–8300, (Nonreporting) **A**1 10 **S** Select Medical Corporation, Mechanicsburg, PA
Primary Contact: Yameeka Jones, Chief Executive Officer
CFO: Mike Gonzales, Chief Financial Officer
CMO: John Fox, M.D., Medical Director
CHR: Tania Khalique, Director Human Resources
Web address: www.vhsandiego.com/
Control: Corporation, Investor–owned (for–profit) **Service:** Acute long–term care hospital

Staffed Beds: 80

⊠ △ **SHARP MEMORIAL HOSPITAL (050100)**, 7901 Frost Street, Zip 92123–2701; tel. 858/939–3400, **A**1 2 3 7 10 **F**3 11 12 15 17 18 20 22 24 26 28 29 30 31 34 35 36 40 43 44 45 46 49 50 54 55 56 57 58 59 62 64 65 68 70 74 75 77 78 79 80 81 82 84 85 86 87 90 93 94 96 107 108 109 110 114 115 116 117 118 119 120 121 124 126 129 130 131 132 135 137 138 142 143 145 146 148 149 156 **S** Sharp HealthCare, San Diego, CA
Primary Contact: Tim Smith, Senior Vice President and Chief Executive Officer
COO: Janie Kramer, Chief Operating Officer
CFO: Kari Cornicelli, Chief Financial Officer
CMO: Geoffrey Stiles, M.D., Chief Medical Officer
CIO: Kenneth Lawonn, Senior Vice President and Chief Information Officer
CHR: Connie Duquette, Director Human Resources
CNO: Pamela Wells, R.N., MSN, Chief Nursing Officer
Web address: www.sharp.com
Control: Other not–for–profit (including NFP Corporation) **Service:** General medical and surgical

Staffed Beds: 459 **Admissions:** 22444 **Census:** 303 **Outpatient Visits:** 364461 **Births:** 0 **Total Expense ($000):** 817331 **Payroll Expense ($000):** 304175 **Personnel:** 3661

⊠ **SHARP MESA VISTA HOSPITAL (054145)**, 7850 Vista Hill Avenue, Zip 92123–2717; tel. 858/278–4110, (Includes SHARP MCDONALD CENTER, 7989 Linda Vista Road, San Diego, California, Zip 92111–5106; tel. 858/637–6920; Trisha Khaleghi, Chief Executive Officer) **A**1 10 **F**3 4 5 11 29 30 31 34 35 40 44 49 50 56 57 58 59 64 68 87 98 99 100 101 102 103 104 105 130 132 135 143 146 149 150 152 153 **S** Sharp HealthCare, San Diego, CA
Primary Contact: Trisha Khaleghi, Senior Vice President and Chief Executive Officer
CFO: Kari Cornicelli, Chief Financial Officer
CMO: Michael Plopper, M.D., Chief Medical Officer
CIO: Kenneth Lawonn, Senior Vice President Information Systems
CHR: Carlisle Lewis III Senior Vice President Legal and Human Resources
CNO: Cheryl Odell, R.N., Chief Nursing Officer
Web address: www.sharp.com
Control: Other not–for–profit (including NFP Corporation) **Service:** Psychiatric

Staffed Beds: 162 **Admissions:** 5262 **Census:** 137 **Outpatient Visits:** 87336 **Births:** 0 **Total Expense ($000):** 90526 **Payroll Expense ($000):** 49912 **Personnel:** 591

⊠ **UC SAN DIEGO HEALTH (050025)**, 200 West Arbor Drive, Zip 92103–9000; tel. 619/543–6222, (Includes THORNTON HOSPITAL, 9300 Campus Point Drive, La Jolla, California, Zip 92037–1300; tel. 858/657–7000; UC SAN DIEGO SHILEY EYE INSTITUTE, 9415 Campus Point Drive, Room 2411 Dept Of, Department of Ophthalmology, Mail Code 0946, La Jolla, California, Zip 92093–0946, Mailing Address: 9415 Campus Point Drive, Zip 92093–0946, tel. 858/534–6290; Karen Anisko Ryan, Director Business Development and Communications) **A**1 2 3 5 8 10 **F**3 5 6 8 9 11 12 13 15 16 17 18 20 22 24 26 28 29 30 31 34 36 37 40 43 44 45 46 47 48 49 50 51 54 55 56 57 58 59 60 61 63 64 65 66 68 70 72 73 74 75 76 77 78 79 80 81 82 83 84 85 86 87 91 92 93 94 96 97 98 100 101 102 103 104 107 108 109 110 111 112 113 114 115 116 117 118 119 120 121 123 124 126 129 130 131 132 136 137 138 139 140 141 142 144 145 146 147 148 149 153 154 158 **S** University of California Systemwide Administration, Oakland, CA
Primary Contact: Patty Maysent, Chief Executive Officer
COO: Margarita Baggett, MSN, R.N., Interim Chief Operating Officer
CFO: Lori Donaldson, Chief Financial Officer
CMO: Angela Scioscia, M.D., Chief Medical Officer
CIO: Ed Babakanian, Chief Information Officer
CHR: William J Murin, Chief Human Resources Officer
CNO: Margarita Baggett, MSN, R.N., Chief Nursing Officer
Web address: www.health.ucsd.edu
Control: State, Government, nonfederal **Service:** General medical and surgical

Staffed Beds: 701 **Admissions:** 31715 **Census:** 552 **Outpatient Visits:** 943856 **Births:** 3105 **Total Expense ($000):** 1849454 **Payroll Expense ($000):** 627236 **Personnel:** 7300

UNIVERSITY OF CALIFORNIA SAN DIEGO MEDICAL CENTER See UC San Diego Health

⊠ △ **VA SAN DIEGO HEALTHCARE SYSTEM**, 3350 LaJolla Village Drive, Zip 92161–0002; tel. 858/552–8585, (Nonreporting) **A**1 3 5 7 **S** Department of Veterans Affairs, Washington, DC
Primary Contact: Robert M. Smith, M.D., Director
COO: Cynthia Abair, Associate Director
CFO: Ronald Larson, Chief Financial Officer
CIO: Ruey Keller, Acting Chief Information Officer
CHR: Stephanie Wright, Director Human Resources Management
Web address: www.sandiego.va.gov
Control: Veterans Affairs, Government, federal **Service:** General medical and surgical

Staffed Beds: 248

SAN DIMAS—Los Angeles County

☒ **SAN DIMAS COMMUNITY HOSPITAL (050588)**, 1350 West Covina Boulevard, Zip 91773–3219; tel. 909/599–6811, (Nonreporting) **A**1 10 **S** Prime Healthcare, Ontario, CA
Primary Contact: Parrish Scarboro, Chief Executive Officer
CFO: Edward Matthews, Chief Financial Officer
CMO: Rajnish Jandial, M.D., Chief Medical Officer
CIO: Jeffrey Cox, Director Information Technology
CHR: Kristina Mack, Manager, Human Resources
CNO: Holly Nagatoshi, R.N., Chief Nursing Officer
Web address: www.sandimashospital.com/
Control: Corporation, Investor–owned (for–profit) **Service:** General medical and surgical

Staffed Beds: 101

SAN FRANCISCO—San Francisco County

☒ **CALIFORNIA PACIFIC MEDICAL CENTER (050047)**, 2333 Buchanan Street, Zip 94115–1925, Mailing Address: P.O. Box 7999, Zip 94120–7999; tel. 415/600–6000, (Nonreporting) **A**1 2 3 5 8 10 **S** Sutter Health, Sacramento, CA
Primary Contact: Warren S. Browner, M.D., M.P.H., Chief Executive Officer
COO: Hamila Kownacki, Chief Operating Officer
CFO: Henry Yu, Vice President Finance and Chief Financial Officer
CMO: Vernon Giang, M.D., Chief Medical Officer
CIO: Ann Barr, Chief Information Officer - Bay Area
CHR: Edward Battista, Vice President Human Resources
CNO: Diana M. Karner, R.N., MSN, Chief Nursing Officer
Web address: www.cpmc.org
Control: Other not–for–profit (including NFP Corporation) **Service:** General medical and surgical

Staffed Beds: 642

★ △ **CALIFORNIA PACIFIC MEDICAL CENTER-DAVIES CAMPUS (050008)**, Castro and Duboce Streets, Zip 94114; tel. 415/600–6000, (Nonreporting) **A**3 5 7 **S** Sutter Health, Sacramento, CA
Primary Contact: Mary Lanier, Vice President, Post Acute Services and Site Administrator
Web address: www.cpmc.org
Control: Other not–for–profit (including NFP Corporation) **Service:** General medical and surgical

Staffed Beds: 154

☒ **CALIFORNIA PACIFIC MEDICAL CENTER-ST. LUKE'S CAMPUS (050055)**, 3555 Cesar Chavez Street, Zip 94110–4403; tel. 415/600–6000, (Nonreporting) **A**1 3 5 10 **S** Sutter Health, Sacramento, CA
Primary Contact: Warren S. Browner, M.D., M.P.H., Chief Executive Officer
COO: Hamila Kownacki, Chief Operating Officer
CFO: Henry Yu, Vice President Finance and Chief Financial Officer
CMO: Vernon Giang, M.D., Chief Medical Executive
CIO: Ann Barr, Chief Information Officer - Bay Area
CHR: Edward Battista, Vice President Human Resources
CNO: Diana M. Karner, R.N., MSN, Chief Nursing Executive
Web address: www.stlukes-sf.org
Control: Other not–for–profit (including NFP Corporation) **Service:** General medical and surgical

Staffed Beds: 175

☒ **CHINESE HOSPITAL (050407)**, 845 Jackson Street, Zip 94133–4899; tel. 415/982–2400, (Nonreporting) **A**1 10
Primary Contact: Jian Q. Zhang, MSN, Chief Executive Officer
COO: Jian Q Zhang, MSN, Chief Operating Officer
CFO: Scott Goodin, Chief Financial Officer
CMO: William Chung, M.D., Chief of Staff
CIO: Keith Minard, Chief Information Officer
CHR: Lydia Mahr-Chan, Director of Human Resources
CNO: Peggy Cmiel, R.N., Chief Nursing Officer
Web address: www.chinesehospital-sf.org
Control: Other not–for–profit (including NFP Corporation) **Service:** General medical and surgical

Staffed Beds: 28

JEWISH HOME OF SAN FRANCISCO (054089), 302 Silver Avenue, Zip 94112–1510; tel. 415/334–2500, (Nonreporting) **A**3 10
Primary Contact: Daniel R. Ruth, President and Chief Executive Officer
COO: Kevin Ward, Chief Operating Officer
CFO: Victor E Meinke, Chief Financial Officer
CNO: Edwin Cabigao, Chief Nursing Officer
Web address: www.jhsf.org
Control: Other not–for–profit (including NFP Corporation) **Service:** Psychiatric

Staffed Beds: 374

☒ **KAISER PERMANENTE SAN FRANCISCO MEDICAL CENTER (050076)**, 2425 Geary Boulevard, Zip 94115–3358; tel. 415/833–2000, **A**1 2 3 5 10 **F**3 8 11 15 17 18 20 22 24 26 27 28 29 30 31 34 37 39 40 41 45 46 49 50 51 55 56 57 58 59 60 61 62 63 64 68 70 72 73 74 75 76 77 78 79 81 82 84 85 86 89 102 107 108 110 111 114 115 117 118 119 126 130 131 134 135 144 146 147 148 149 154 156 157 **S** Kaiser Foundation Hospitals, Oakland, CA
Primary Contact: Ronald Groepper, Senior Vice President and Area Manager
COO: Helen Archer-Duste, Chief Operating Officer
CFO: Alex Khoo, Interim Area Finance Officer
CMO: Robert Mithun, M.D., Physician in Chief
CIO: Peti Arunamata, Interim Area Director Information Technology
CHR: Diane J Easterwood, Human Resources Business Partner
Web address: www.kaiserpermanente.org
Control: Other not–for–profit (including NFP Corporation) **Service:** General medical and surgical

Staffed Beds: 239 **Admissions:** 11842 **Census:** 152 **Outpatient Visits:** 73689 **Births:** 2975 **Personnel:** 1487

★ **LAGUNA HONDA HOSPITAL AND REHABILITATION CENTER (050668)**, 375 Laguna Honda Boulevard, Zip 94116–1499; tel. 415/759–2300, (Nonreporting) **A**10
Primary Contact: Margaret A. Rykowski, Acting Chief Executive Officer
COO: Michael R Llewellyn, Chief Operating Officer
CFO: Tess Navarro, Chief Financial Officer
CMO: Colleen Riley, M.D., Medical Director
CIO: Pat Skala, Chief Information Officer
CHR: Willie Ramirez, Manager Labor Relations
Web address: www.lagunahonda.org/
Control: City–county, Government, nonfederal **Service:** Rehabilitation

Staffed Beds: 780

SAN FRANCISCO MEDICAL CENTER See Kaiser Permanente San Francisco Medical Center

☒ **SAN FRANCISCO VA MEDICAL CENTER**, 4150 Clement Street, Zip 94121–1545; tel. 415/221–4810, (Nonreporting) **A**1 3 5 **S** Department of Veterans Affairs, Washington, DC
Primary Contact: Bonnie S. Graham, Director
CFO: Brian Kelly, Acting Chief Fiscal Service
CMO: C. Diana Nicoll, M.D., Ph.D., Chief of Staff
CIO: Ryan Chun, Information Resources Management
CHR: Jerry Mills, Chief Human Resources Management Services
CNO: Shirley Pikula, MSN, Associate Director Patient Center Care
Web address: www.sanfrancisco.va.gov/
Control: Veterans Affairs, Government, federal **Service:** General medical and surgical

Staffed Beds: 241

★ △ **SAINT FRANCIS MEMORIAL HOSPITAL (050152)**, 900 Hyde Street, Zip 94109–4899, Mailing Address: P.O. Box 7726, Zip 94120–7726; tel. 415/353–6000, (Nonreporting) **A**2 3 7 10 **S** CommonSpirit Health, Chicago, IL
Primary Contact: David G. Klein, M.D., President
CFO: Alan Fox, Chief Financial Officer
CHR: Richard Mead, Senior Director Human Resources
Web address: www.saintfrancismemorial.org
Control: Other not–for–profit (including NFP Corporation) **Service:** General medical and surgical

Staffed Beds: 239

CA

Hospital, Medicare Provider Number, Address, Telephone, Approval, Facility, and Physician Codes, Health Care System

★ American Hospital Association (AHA) membership
☐ The Joint Commission accreditation
○ Healthcare Facilities Accreditation Program
◇ DNV Healthcare Inc. accreditation
⇑ Center for Improvement in Healthcare Quality Accreditation
△ Commission on Accreditation of Rehabilitation Facilities (CARF) accreditation

✠ △ **ST. MARY'S MEDICAL CENTER (050457)**, 450 Stanyan Street, Zip 94117–1079; tel. 415/668–1000, (Nonreporting) **A**1 2 3 5 7 10 **S** CommonSpirit Health, Chicago, IL
Primary Contact: John P. Allen, President
COO: Deborah Kolhede, Vice President and Chief Operating Officer
CMO: Francis Charlton, M.D., Jr Chief Medical Staff
CHR: Barbara Morrissett, Vice President Human Resources
CNO: Barbara Eusebio, R.N., JD, Vice President, Chief Nurse Executive
Web address: www.stmarysmedicalcenter.com
Control: Church operated **Service:** General medical and surgical

Staffed Beds: 232

✠ **UCSF MEDICAL CENTER (050454)**, 500 Parnassus Avenue, Zip 94143–0296, Mailing Address: 500 Parnassus Avenue, Box 0296, Zip 94143–0296; tel. 415/476–1000, (Includes UCSF BENIOFF CHILDREN'S HOSPITAL, 500 Parnassus Avenue, San Francisco, California, Zip 94143–2203, Mailing Address: 505 Parnassus Avenue, Zip 94143–2203, tel. 888/689–8273; Michael Anderson, M.D., President; UCSF MEDICAL CENTER MISSION BAY, 1975 4th Street, San Francisco, California, Zip 94158–2351; tel. 415/353–3000) **A**1 2 3 5 8 10 **F**3 6 7 8 9 11 12 13 14 15 17 18 19 20 21 22 23 24 25 26 27 29 30 31 32 33 34 35 36 37 38 39 40 41 43 44 45 46 47 48 49 50 51 52 53 54 55 56 57 58 59 60 61 63 64 65 66 68 70 72 74 75 76 77 78 79 81 82 83 84 85 86 87 88 89 90 91 92 93 94 96 97 98 99 100 101 102 103 104 105 107 108 110 111 112 113 114 115 116 117 118 119 120 121 123 124 126 129 130 131 132 134 135 136 137 138 139 140 141 142 143 144 145 146 147 148 149 150 153 154 155 156 **S** University of California Systemwide Administration, Oakland, CA
Primary Contact: Mark R. Laret, Chief Executive Officer
COO: Ken M Jones, Chief Operating Officer
CFO: Raju Iyer, Senior Vice President and Chief Financial Officer
CMO: Josh Adler, M.D., Chief Medical Officer
CIO: Joe Bergfort, Chief Information Officer
CHR: David Odato, Chief Administrative and Chief Human Resources Officer
CNO: Sheila Antrum, R.N., President
Web address: www.ucsfhealth.org
Control: Other not–for–profit (including NFP Corporation) **Service:** General medical and surgical

Staffed Beds: 859 **Admissions:** 36415 **Census:** 626 **Outpatient Visits:** 1385388 **Births:** 3173 **Total Expense ($000):** 3673561 **Payroll Expense ($000):** 1325676 **Personnel:** 14571

VETERANS AFFAIRS MEDICAL CENTER See San Francisco Va Medical Center

✠ **ZUCKERBERG SAN FRANCISCO GENERAL HOSPITAL AND TRAUMA CENTER (050228)**, 1001 Potrero Avenue, Zip 94110–3518; tel. 415/206–8000, (Total facility includes 26 beds in nursing home–type unit) **A**1 2 3 5 8 10 **F**3 13 15 18 20 22 29 30 31 34 35 36 38 39 40 41 43 44 45 46 47 48 49 50 57 58 59 60 61 64 65 68 70 71 72 73 74 75 76 77 78 79 81 82 83 84 85 86 87 89 92 93 94 97 98 100 102 105 107 108 110 111 115 119 128 129 130 131 132 135 144 146 147 148 149 150 154 157
Primary Contact: Susan P. Ehrlich, M.D., Chief Executive Officer
COO: Tosan O. Boyo, Chief Operating Officer
CFO: Valerie Inouye, Chief Financial Officer
CMO: Todd May, M.D., Chief Medical Officer
CIO: Winona Windolovich, Associate Chief Information Officer
CHR: Karen Hill, Departmental Personnel Officer
CNO: Terry Dentoni, Chief Nursing Officer
Web address: www.zuckerbergsanfranciscogeneral.org/
Control: City–county, Government, nonfederal **Service:** General medical and surgical

Staffed Beds: 296 **Admissions:** 17168 **Census:** 303 **Outpatient Visits:** 608699 **Births:** 1157 **Total Expense ($000):** 989750 **Payroll Expense ($000):** 374174 **Personnel:** 2884

☐ **SAN GABRIEL VALLEY MEDICAL CENTER (050132)**, 438 West Las Tunas Drive, Zip 91776–1216, Mailing Address: P.O. Box 1507, Zip 91778–1507; tel. 626/289–5454, (Nonreporting) **A**1 10 **S** AHMC & Healthcare, Inc., Alhambra, CA
Primary Contact: Jonathon F. Aquino, Chief Executive Officer
CFO: Andrew Grim, Chief Financial Officer
CIO: Bernie Sauer, Director Information Technology
CHR: Victor Voisard, Director Human Resources
CNO: Gail Freeman, Chief Nursing Officer
Web address: www.sgvmc.org
Control: Partnership, Investor–owned (for–profit) **Service:** General medical and surgical

Staffed Beds: 273

★ **GOOD SAMARITAN HOSPITAL (050380)**, 2425 Samaritan Drive, Zip 95124–3997, Mailing Address: P.O. Box 240002, Zip 95154–2402; tel. 408/559–2011, (Nonreporting) **A**2 10 **S** HCA Healthcare, Nashville, TN
Primary Contact: Joseph DeSchryver, Chief Executive Officer
COO: Jordan Herget, Chief Operating Officer
CFO: Lana Arad, Chief Financial Officer
CMO: Bruce Wilbur, M.D., Chief Medical Officer
CIO: Darrell O'Dell, Director Information Services
CHR: Edward Battista, Vice President Human Resources
CNO: Darina Kavanagh, R.N., MSN, Chief Nursing Officer
Web address: www.goodsamsanjose.com
Control: Corporation, Investor–owned (for–profit) **Service:** General medical and surgical

Staffed Beds: 349

✠ **KAISER PERMANENTE SAN JOSE MEDICAL CENTER (050604)**, 250 Hospital Parkway, Zip 95119–1199; tel. 408/972–7000, **A**1 2 3 5 10 **F**3 8 11 15 18 20 22 26 28 29 30 31 34 39 40 41 42 45 46 49 50 55 56 57 58 59 60 61 63 64 68 70 71 73 74 75 76 77 78 79 80 81 82 84 85 86 102 107 108 110 111 114 115 118 119 130 131 134 135 144 146 147 148 149 154 156 **S** Kaiser Foundation Hospitals, Oakland, CA
Primary Contact: Irene Chavez, Senior Vice President and Area Manager
COO: Irene Chavez, Senior Vice President and Area Manager
CFO: Stephen L Kalsman, Area Finance Officer
CMO: Raj Bhandari, M.D., Physician-in-Chief
CIO: Greg Tuck, Area Information Officer
CHR: Susan Franzella, Human Resource Business Partner
CNO: Theresa R Nero, R.N., MS, Chief Nursing Officer
Web address: www.kaiserpermanente.org
Control: Other not–for–profit (including NFP Corporation) **Service:** General medical and surgical

Staffed Beds: 247 **Admissions:** 11668 **Census:** 111 **Outpatient Visits:** 153654 **Births:** 2564 **Personnel:** 1175

☐ **O'CONNOR HOSPITAL (050153)**, 2105 Forest Avenue, Zip 95128–1471; tel. 408/947–2500, (Nonreporting) **A**1 2 3 5 10
Primary Contact: Jordan Herget, President and Chief Executive Officer
CMO: Arthur Douville, M.D., Chief Medical Officer
CIO: Richard Hutsell, Vice President and Chief Information Officer, Daughters of Charity Health System
CHR: Julie Hatcher, Vice President Human Resources
CNO: Dawn Marie Goeringer, Chief Clinical Care Officer
Web address: www.oconnorhospital.org
Control: County, Government, nonfederal **Service:** General medical and surgical

Staffed Beds: 202

✠ **REGIONAL MEDICAL CENTER OF SAN JOSE (050125)**, 225 North Jackson Avenue, Zip 95116–1603; tel. 408/259–5000, (Nonreporting) **A**1 2 10 **S** HCA Healthcare, Nashville, TN
Primary Contact: Tomi S. Ryba, President and Chief Executive Officer
COO: Brian J Knecht, Chief Operating Officer
CFO: Fred Ashworth, Chief Financial Officer
CMO: William Scott, M.D., Vice President Medical Affairs
CIO: Shirley Joyal, Director Information Systems
CHR: Nancy Clark, Vice President Human Resources
Web address: www.regionalmedicalsanjose.com
Control: Partnership, Investor–owned (for–profit) **Service:** General medical and surgical

Staffed Beds: 247

☐ **SAN JOSE BEHAVORIAL HEALTH (054154)**, 455 Silicon Valley Boulevard, Zip 95138–1858; tel. 888/210–2484, (Nonreporting) **A**1 10 **S** Acadia Healthcare Company, Inc., Franklin, TN
Primary Contact: Rob Marsh, Chief Executive Officer
Web address: www.sanjosebh.com
Control: Corporation, Investor–owned (for–profit) **Service:** Psychiatric

Staffed Beds: 80

SAN JOSE MEDICAL CENTER See Kaiser Permanente San Jose Medical Center

△ **SANTA CLARA VALLEY MEDICAL CENTER (050038)**, 751 South Bascom Avenue, Zip 95128–2699; tel. 408/885–5000, (Nonreporting) **A**1 3 5 7 10
Primary Contact: Paul E. Lorenz, Chief Executive Officer
COO: Benita McLarin, Chief Operating Officer
CMO: Jeffrey Arnold, M.D., Chief Medical Officer
CIO: Lee Herrmann, Chief Healthcare Technology Officer
CHR: David Manson, Manager Human Resources
CNO: Trudy Johnson, R.N., RN Chief Nursing Officer
Web address: www.scvmed.org
Control: County, Government, nonfederal **Service**: General medical and surgical

Staffed Beds: 481

SAN LEANDRO—Alameda County

FAIRMONT HOSPITAL See Highland Hospital, Oakland

KAISER PERMANENTE SAN LEANDRO MEDICAL CENTER (050777), 2500 Merced Street, Zip 94577–4201; tel. 510/454–1000, **A**1 3 10 **F**3 8 11 13 15 26 28 29 30 31 34 40 41 45 49 50 51 55 56 57 58 59 60 61 63 64 68 70 72 73 74 75 76 77 78 79 81 82 84 85 86 87 102 107 108 110 111 114 115 117 118 119 130 131 134 135 143 144 146 147 148 149 154 156 **S** Kaiser Foundation Hospitals, Oakland, CA
Primary Contact: Thomas S. Hanenburg, Senior Vice President and Area Manager
Web address: www.kaiserpermanente.org
Control: Other not–for–profit (including NFP Corporation) **Service**: General medical and surgical

Staffed Beds: 186 **Admissions:** 11731 **Census:** 114 **Outpatient Visits:** 156138 **Births:** 3815 **Personnel:** 1225

KINDRED HOSPITAL-SAN FRANCISCO BAY AREA (052034), 2800 Benedict Drive, Zip 94577–6840; tel. 510/357–8300, (Nonreporting) **A**1 10 **S** Kindred Healthcare, Louisville, KY
Primary Contact: Jacob M. McCarty, Chief Executive Officer
CFO: Ziba Aflak, Chief Financial Officer
CHR: Erin Greene, Coordinator Human Resources
CNO: Emily Gard, Chief Clinical Officer
Web address: www.kindredhospitalsfba.com
Control: Corporation, Investor–owned (for–profit) **Service**: Acute long–term care hospital

Staffed Beds: 99

SAN LEANDRO HOSPITAL (050773), 13855 East 14th Street, Zip 94578–2600; tel. 510/357–6500, **A**1 10 **F**3 15 18 29 30 31 34 35 40 44 45 50 51 57 59 60 68 70 77 79 81 87 107 108 110 111 114 119 130 146 **S** Alameda Health System, San Leandro, CA
Primary Contact: James E T. Jackson, M.P.H., Chief Administrative Officer
Web address: www.sanleandrohospital.org
Control: Hospital district or authority, Government, nonfederal **Service**: General medical and surgical

Staffed Beds: 48 **Admissions:** 2854 **Census:** 33 **Outpatient Visits:** 34438 **Births:** 0 **Total Expense ($000):** 81069 **Payroll Expense ($000):** 47153 **Personnel:** 365

WILLOW ROCK CENTER (054149), 2050 Fairmont Drive, Zip 94578–1001; tel. 510/895–5502, (Nonreporting) **A**1 10
Primary Contact: Anne L. Bakar, President and Chief Executive Officer
Web address: www.tbhcare.com
Control: County, Government, nonfederal **Service**: Psychiatric

Staffed Beds: 16

SAN LUIS OBISPO—San Luis Obispo County

CALIFORNIA MENS COLONY CORRECTIONAL TREATMENT CENTER, Highway 1, Zip 93409–8101, Mailing Address: P.O. Box 8101, Zip 93403–8101; tel. 805/547–7913, (Nonreporting)
Primary Contact: Martha Wallace, Administrator
CFO: William Cook, Associate Warden Business Service
CIO: Terry Knight, Public Information Officer and Administrative Assistant
Web address: www.yaca.ca.gov/visitors/fac_prison_cmc.html
Control: State, Government, nonfederal **Service**: Hospital unit of an institution (prison hospital, college infirmary, etc.)

Staffed Beds: 39

FRENCH HOSPITAL MEDICAL CENTER (050232), 1911 Johnson Avenue, Zip 93401–4197; tel. 805/543–5353, (Nonreporting) **A**1 2 10 **S** CommonSpirit Health, Chicago, IL
Primary Contact: Alan Iftiniuk, Chief Executive Officer
COO: Julia Fogelson, R.N., Chief Operating Officer and Chief Nursing Executive
CFO: Sue Andersen, Chief Financial Officer
CMO: Chris Voge, Chief of Staff
CIO: Cyndi Lang, Director Information Services
CHR: Barry Nateman, Manager Human Resources
CNO: Julia Fogelson, R.N., Chief Operating Officer and Chief Nursing Executive
Web address: www.frenchmedicalcenter.org
Control: Other not–for–profit (including NFP Corporation) **Service**: General medical and surgical

Staffed Beds: 72

SIERRA VISTA REGIONAL MEDICAL CENTER (050506), 1010 Murray Avenue, Zip 93405–1806, Mailing Address: P.O. Box 1367, Zip 93405; tel. 805/546–7600, (Nonreporting) **A**1 2 10 19 **S** TENET Healthcare Corporation, Dallas, TX
Primary Contact: Mark P. Lisa, FACHE, Chief Executive Officer
COO: Eleze Armstrong, Chief Operating Officer
CFO: Scott Wartelle, Chief Financial Officer
CIO: Robert Leonard, Director Information Services
CHR: Kristin Flynn, Chief Human Resources Officer
CNO: Nicki E Edwards, Ph.D., R.N., Interim Chief Nursing Officer
Web address: www.sierravistaregional.com
Control: Corporation, Investor–owned (for–profit) **Service**: General medical and surgical

Staffed Beds: 164

SAN MATEO—San Mateo County

MILLS HEALTH CENTER See Mills-Peninsula Health Services, Burlingame

SAN MATEO MEDICAL CENTER (050113), 222 West 39th Avenue, Zip 94403–4398; tel. 650/573–2222, (Total facility includes 30 beds in nursing home–type unit) **A**1 3 5 10 **F**3 15 18 19 29 30 31 32 36 39 40 44 45 47 49 51 53 54 55 56 57 58 59 61 64 65 66 68 70 71 74 75 77 78 79 81 82 84 85 87 89 90 92 93 97 98 100 101 102 103 104 105 107 111 115 119 128 130 132 134 144 146 147 148 149 152 154 156
Primary Contact: Chester Kunnappilly, M.D., Interim Chief Executive Officer
COO: John Thomas, Chief Operating Officer
CFO: David S McGrew, Chief Financial Officer
CMO: Susan Fernyak, M.D., Interim Chief Medical Officer & Chief Quality Officer
CIO: Michael Aratow, M.D., Chief Information Officer
CHR: Angela Gonzales, Manager Human Resources
CNO: Joan G Spicer, R.N., Chief Nursing Officer
Web address: www.sanmateomedicalcenter.org
Control: County, Government, nonfederal **Service**: General medical and surgical

Staffed Beds: 97 **Admissions:** 2753 **Census:** 96 **Outpatient Visits:** 502583 **Births:** 0 **Total Expense ($000):** 325170 **Payroll Expense ($000):** 104604 **Personnel:** 1209

SAN PEDRO—Los Angeles County; See Los Angeles

SAN RAFAEL—Marin County

KAISER PERMANENTE SAN RAFAEL MEDICAL CENTER (050510), 99 Montecillo Road, Zip 94903–3397; tel. 415/444–2000, **A**1 5 10 **F**3 11 15 18 20 26 28 29 30 31 34 35 39 40 41 44 45 49 50 51 55 56 57 58 59 60 61 62 63 64 68 70 74 75 77 78 79 81 82 84 85 86 102 107 108 110 111 114 115 118 119 130 131 134 135 142 144 146 147 148 149 154 156 **S** Kaiser Foundation Hospitals, Oakland, CA
Primary Contact: Judy Coffey, R.N., Senior Vice President and Area Manager
CFO: Diane Hernandez, Area Finance Officer
CMO: Gary Mizono, M.D., Physician-in-Chief
CIO: Stanley Dobrawa, Area Information Officer
Web address: www.kaiserpermanente.org
Control: Other not–for–profit (including NFP Corporation) **Service**: General medical and surgical

Staffed Beds: 116 **Admissions:** 4113 **Census:** 41 **Outpatient Visits:** 133277 **Births:** 3 **Personnel:** 615

Hospital, Medicare Provider Number, Address, Telephone, Approval, Facility, and Physician Codes, Health Care System

★ American Hospital Association (AHA) membership
□ The Joint Commission accreditation
○ Healthcare Facilities Accreditation Program
◇ DNV Healthcare Inc. accreditation
⇑ Center for Improvement in Healthcare Quality Accreditation
△ Commission on Accreditation of Rehabilitation Facilities (CARF) accreditation

---

SAN RAMON—Contra Costa County

⊞ **SAN RAMON REGIONAL MEDICAL CENTER (050689)**, 6001 Norris Canyon Road, Zip 94583–5400; tel. 925/275–9200, **A**1 10 **F**3 8 11 13 15 18 20 22 24 26 28 29 30 31 34 35 37 40 45 46 47 48 49 53 57 59 64 70 72 75 76 77 78 79 81 85 86 87 93 107 108 110 118 119 126 130 131 146 147 148 149 **S** TENET Healthcare Corporation, Dallas, TX
Primary Contact: Ann Lucena, Chief Executive Officer
CFO: Beenu Chadha, Chief Financial Officer
CMO: Raymond Cheung, M.D., Chief of Staff
CIO: Anthony Abbate, Director of Information Services
CHR: Dennis Mills, Chief Human Resources Officer
Web address: www.sanramonmedctr.com
Control: Partnership, Investor–owned (for–profit) **Service**: General medical and surgical

> **Staffed Beds**: 123 **Admissions**: 4763 **Census**: 47 **Outpatient Visits**: 65006 **Births**: 577 **Total Expense ($000)**: 148357 **Payroll Expense ($000)**: 70405 **Personnel**: 677

SANTA ANA—Orange County

☐ **ORANGE COUNTY GLOBAL MEDICAL CENTER, INC. (050746)**, 1001 North Tustin Avenue, Zip 92705–3577; tel. 714/953–3500, (Nonreporting) **A**1 3 5 10 **S** KPC Healthcare, Inc., Santa Ana, CA
Primary Contact: Ann Abe, Interim Chief Executive Officer
COO: Ann Abe, Administrator and Chief Operating Officer
CFO: John Collins, Chief Financial Officer
CMO: Steven Bui, M.D., Chief of Staff
CIO: Charles Flack, Interim Chief Information Officer
CHR: Terry Bohn, Director, Human Resources
CNO: Sandra Moreno, Chief Nursing Officer
Web address: www.orangecounty-gmc.com
Control: Corporation, Investor–owned (for–profit) **Service**: General medical and surgical

> **Staffed Beds**: 282

☐ **SOUTH COAST GLOBAL MEDICAL CENTER (050747)**, 2701 South Bristol Street, Zip 92704–6278; tel. 714/754–5454, (Nonreporting) **A**1 10 **S** KPC Healthcare, Inc., Santa Ana, CA
Primary Contact: Ada Yeh, Chief Executive Officer
CFO: John Collins, Chief Financial Officer
CHR: Cynthia Garren-Oster, Human Resource Manager
Web address: www.SouthCoast-GMC.com
Control: Corporation, Investor–owned (for–profit) **Service**: General medical and surgical

> **Staffed Beds**: 178

SANTA BARBARA—Santa Barbara County

COTTAGE REHABILITATION HOSPITAL See Santa Barbara Cottage Hospital, Santa Barbara

⊞ **GOLETA VALLEY COTTAGE HOSPITAL (050357)**, 351 South Patterson Avenue, Zip 93111–2496, Mailing Address: Box 6306, Zip 93160–6306; tel. 805/967–3411, **A**1 10 **F**8 11 12 15 29 40 65 68 70 75 79 81 107 110 114 119 124 130 148 149 **S** Cottage Health, Santa Barbara, CA
Primary Contact: Ronald C. Werft, President and Chief Executive Officer
COO: Steven A Fellows, Executive Vice President and Chief Operating Officer
CFO: Joan Bricher, Senior Vice President Finance and Chief Financial Officer
CMO: Edmund Wroblewski, M.D., Vice President Medical Affairs and Chief Medical Officer
CIO: Alberto Kywi, Chief Information Officer
CHR: Patrice Ryan, Vice President Human Resources
Web address: www.sbch.org
Control: Other not–for–profit (including NFP Corporation) **Service**: General medical and surgical

> **Staffed Beds**: 28 **Admissions**: 1726 **Census**: 10 **Outpatient Visits**: 54697 **Births**: 0 **Total Expense ($000)**: 75056 **Payroll Expense ($000)**: 29694 **Personnel**: 291

⊞ △ **SANTA BARBARA COTTAGE HOSPITAL (050396)**, 400 West Pueblo Street, Zip 93105–4390, Mailing Address: P.O. Box 689, Zip 93102–0689; tel. 805/682–7111, (Includes COTTAGE CHILDREN'S HOSPITAL, 400 West Pueblo Street, Santa Barbara, California, Zip 93105–4353; tel. 805/247–3260; COTTAGE REHABILITATION HOSPITAL, 2415 De la Vina Street, Santa Barbara, California, Zip 93105–3819; tel. 805/687–7444; Melinda Staveley, President and Chief Executive Officer) **A**1 2 3 5 7 10 **F**3 4 5 8 11 12 13 15 17 18 20 22 24 26 28 29 30 31 34 35 40 43 45 46 50 53 54 57 58 59 60 64 65 68 70 72 74 75 76 77 78 79 81 84 86 88 89 90 91 92 93 96 98 100 102 103 104 106 107 110 111 114 115 117 119 126 130 132 135 146 148 149 151 152 153 155 156 **S** Cottage Health, Santa Barbara, CA
Primary Contact: Ronald C. Werft, President and Chief Executive Officer
COO: Steven A Fellows, Executive Vice President and Chief Operating Officer
CFO: Joan Bricher, Senior Vice President Finance and Chief Financial Officer
CMO: Edmund Wroblewski, M.D., Vice President Medical Affairs and Chief Medical Officer
CIO: Alberto Kywi, Chief Information Officer
CHR: Patrice Ryan, Vice President Human Resources
CNO: Herb J Geary, Vice President Patient Care Services and Chief Nursing Officer
Web address: www.cottagehealthsystem.org
Control: Other not–for–profit (including NFP Corporation) **Service**: General medical and surgical

> **Staffed Beds**: 363 **Admissions**: 17898 **Census**: 249 **Outpatient Visits**: 116616 **Births**: 2060 **Total Expense ($000)**: 669435 **Payroll Expense ($000)**: 266396 **Personnel**: 2571

SANTA BARBARA COUNTY PSYCHIATRIC HEALTH FACILITY (054125), 315 Camino Del Remedio, Zip 93110–1332; tel. 805/681–5244, (Nonreporting) **A**10
Primary Contact: Ole Behrendtsen, M.D., Interim Director
CFO: Michael C. Evans, Chief Executive Officer and Deputy Director of Finance and Administration
CMO: Ole Behrendtsen, M.D., Medical Director
CIO: Dana Fahey, Manager Management Information Systems
CHR: Elena Molelus, Manager Human Resources
Web address: www.countyofsb.org
Control: County, Government, nonfederal **Service**: Psychiatric

> **Staffed Beds**: 16

SANTA CLARA—Santa Clara County

⊞ **KAISER PERMANENTE SANTA CLARA MEDICAL CENTER (050071)**, 700 Lawrence Expressway, Zip 95051–5173; tel. 408/851–1000, **A**1 2 3 5 10 **F**3 11 15 16 17 18 20 22 24 26 27 28 29 30 31 34 37 39 40 41 42 45 49 50 55 56 57 58 59 60 61 62 63 64 68 70 72 73 74 75 76 77 78 79 80 81 82 84 85 86 88 89 102 107 108 110 111 114 115 117 118 119 120 121 123 126 130 131 134 135 144 146 147 148 149 154 155 156 **S** Kaiser Foundation Hospitals, Oakland, CA
Primary Contact: Christopher L. Boyd, Senior Vice President and Area Manager
CFO: Tim O'Connor, Area Finance Officer
CMO: Susan Smarr, M.D., Physician-in-Chief
CIO: Scott May, Area Director Technology
CHR: Robert Hyde, Human Resources Business Partner
CNO: Lori Armstrong, R.N., MSN, Chief Nursing Officer
Web address: www.kaiserpermanente.org
Control: Other not–for–profit (including NFP Corporation) **Service**: General medical and surgical

> **Staffed Beds**: 327 **Admissions**: 18663 **Census**: 219 **Outpatient Visits**: 216765 **Births**: 4650 **Personnel**: 2241

SANTA CRUZ—Santa Cruz County

⊞ **DOMINICAN HOSPITAL (050242)**, 1555 Soquel Drive, Zip 95065–1794; tel. 831/462–7700, (Nonreporting) **A**1 2 10 **S** CommonSpirit Health, Chicago, IL
Primary Contact: Nanette Mickiewicz, M.D., President
COO: Chris Wernke, Chief Operating Officer
CFO: Rick Harron, Chief Financial Officer
CMO: Freddie Weinstein, M.D., Chief Medical Officer
CIO: Lee Vanderpool, Vice President
CHR: Vicki Miranda, Vice President Human Resources
Web address: www.dominicanhospital.org
Control: Church operated **Service**: General medical and surgical

> **Staffed Beds**: 223

Many Facility Codes have changed. Please refer to the AHA Guide Code Chart.   © 2019 AHA Guide

CA

⊞ **SUTTER MATERNITY AND SURGERY CENTER OF SANTA CRUZ (050714)**, 2900 Chanticleer Avenue, Zip 95065–1816; tel. 831/477–2200, (Nonreporting) **A**1 10 **S** Sutter Health, Sacramento, CA
Primary Contact: Trina White, President and Chief Executive Officer
CFO: Bonnie Liang, Divisional Finance Officer
CMO: Joseph Fabry, D.O., Chief of Staff
CIO: Ann Barr, Chief Information Officer, Sutter Health Bay Area
CHR: Maynard Jenkins, Regional Vice President Human Resources
CNO: Sherri Stout-Torres, R.N., Chief Nursing Executive
Web address: www.suttersantacruz.org
Control: Other not-for-profit (including NFP Corporation) **Service:** Other specialty treatment

Staffed Beds: 30

SANTA MARIA—Santa Barbara County

⊞ **MARIAN REGIONAL MEDICAL CENTER (050107)**, 1400 East Church Street, Zip 93454–5906; tel. 805/739–3000, (Nonreporting) **A**1 2 3 5 10 **S** CommonSpirit Health, Chicago, IL
Primary Contact: Kerin A. Mase, President and Chief Executive Officer
COO: Mark Allen, Chief Operating Officer
CFO: Sue Andersen, Vice President and Service Area and Chief Financial Officer
CMO: Chuck Merrill, M.D., Vice President Medical Affairs
CIO: Patricia Haase, Director Information Technology and Communications
CHR: Ed Gonzales, Vice President Human Resources
CNO: Candice Monge, R.N., Chief Nurse Executive Officer
Web address: www.marianmedicalcenter.org
Control: Church operated **Service:** General medical and surgical

Staffed Beds: 286

SANTA MONICA—Los Angeles County

⊞ **PROVIDENCE SAINT JOHN'S HEALTH CENTER (050290)**, 2121 Santa Monica Boulevard, Zip 90404–2091; tel. 310/829–5511, (Nonreporting) **A**1 2 10 19 **S** Providence St. Joseph Health, Renton, WA
Primary Contact: Marcel C. Loh, FACHE, Chief Executive Officer
COO: David A Tam, M.D., FACHE, Chief Operating Officer
CFO: James Uli, Chief Financial Officer
CMO: Donald Larsen, M.D., Chief Medical Officer
CIO: Martha Ponce, Director Information Technologies and Telecommunications
CHR: Laura Morton Rowe, Director of Human Resources
CNO: Dawna Hendel, R.N., Chief Nursing Officer and Vice President Patient Care Services
Web address: www.providence.org/saintjohns
Control: Church operated **Service:** General medical and surgical

Staffed Beds: 228

⊞ **UCLA MEDICAL CENTER-SANTA MONICA (050112)**, 1250 16th Street, Zip 90404–1249; tel. 310/319–4000, **A**1 2 6 10 19 **F**2 8 9 11 12 13 15 18 20 22 24 26 29 30 31 34 35 36 37 39 40 41 45 46 47 48 49 50 51 52 54 55 56 57 58 59 62 64 65 68 70 72 74 75 76 78 79 81 82 83 84 85 86 87 89 93 96 97 102 107 108 110 111 114 115 116 117 118 119 130 131 143 145 146 147 149 154 156 **S** University of California Systemwide Administration, Oakland, CA
Primary Contact: Richard Azar, Chief Operating Officer
COO: Robert Azar, Chief Operating Officer
CFO: Paul Staton, Chief Financial Officer
CMO: James Atkinson, M.D., Medical Director
CIO: Virginia McFerran, Chief Information Officer
CHR: Mark Speare, Senior Associate Director Patient Relations and Human Resources
Web address: www.healthcare.ucla.edu
Control: State, Government, nonfederal **Service:** General medical and surgical

Staffed Beds: 265 **Admissions:** 15491 **Census:** 209 **Outpatient Visits:** 187376 **Births:** 1577 **Total Expense ($000):** 557431 **Payroll Expense ($000):** 201101 **Personnel:** 2083

SANTA ROSA—Sonoma County

⊞ **AURORA SANTA ROSA HOSPITAL (054151)**, 1287 Fulton Road, Zip 95401–4923; tel. 707/800–7700, (Nonreporting) **A**10 **S** Signature Healthcare Services, Corona, CA
Primary Contact: Kay E. Seim, Chief Executive Officer
Web address: www.aurorasantarosa.com
Control: Corporation, Investor-owned (for-profit) **Service:** Rehabilitation

Staffed Beds: 95

⊞ **KAISER PERMANENTE SANTA ROSA MEDICAL CENTER (050690)**, 401 Bicentennial Way, Zip 95403–2192; tel. 707/393–4000, **A**1 3 5 10 **F**3 8 11 15 18 26 28 29 30 31 34 35 39 40 41 44 45 49 50 55 56 57 58 59 60 61 63 64 68 70 73 74 75 76 77 78 79 81 82 84 85 86 89 102 107 108 110 111 114 115 118 119 130 131 134 135 142 144 146 147 148 149 154 156 **S** Kaiser Foundation Hospitals, Oakland, CA
Primary Contact: Judy Coffey, R.N., Senior Vice President and Area Manager
COO: Vicky Locey, R.N., MSN, Chief Operating Officer and Chief Nursing Executive
CFO: Diane Hernandez, Area Finance Officer
CMO: Kirk Pappas, M.D., Physician-in-Chief
CIO: Stanley Dobrawa, Area Information Officer
CNO: Vicky Locey, R.N., MSN, Chief Operating Officer and Chief Nursing Executive
Web address: www.kaiserpermanente.org
Control: Other not-for-profit (including NFP Corporation) **Service:** General medical and surgical

Staffed Beds: 173 **Admissions:** 9475 **Census:** 94 **Outpatient Visits:** 134477 **Births:** 1953 **Personnel:** 928

⊞ **SANTA ROSA MEMORIAL HOSPITAL (050174)**, 1165 Montgomery Drive, Zip 95405–4897, Mailing Address: P.O. Box 522, Zip 95402–0522; tel. 707/546–3210, (Nonreporting) **A**1 2 10 19 **S** Providence St. Joseph Health, Renton, WA
Primary Contact: Tyler Hedden, Interim Chief Executive Officer
COO: Tyler Hedden, Chief Operating Officer
CFO: Robert Petrina, Interim Chief Financial Officer
CMO: Chad Krilich, M.D., Chief Medical Officer
CIO: Les Brooks, System Director Information Technology
CHR: John Bibby, Regional Vice President, Human Resources
CNO: Vicki White, Chief Nursing Officer
Web address: www.stjosephhealth.org
Control: Church operated **Service:** General medical and surgical

Staffed Beds: 278

⊞ **SUTTER SANTA ROSA REGIONAL HOSPITAL (050291)**, 30 Mark West Springs Road, Zip 95403; tel. 707/576–4000, (Includes WARRACK CAMPUS, 2449 Summerfield Road, Santa Rosa, California, Zip 95405–7815; tel. 707/576–4200), (Nonreporting) **A**1 3 5 10 **S** Sutter Health, Sacramento, CA
Primary Contact: Mike Purvis, Chief Administrative Officer
CMO: William Carroll, M.D., Chief Medical Executive
Web address: www.sutterhealth.org
Control: Other not-for-profit (including NFP Corporation) **Service:** General medical and surgical

Staffed Beds: 84

SEBASTOPOL—Sonoma County

⇑ **SONOMA WEST MEDICAL CENTER (050781)**, 501 Petaluma Avenue, Zip 95472–4215; (Nonreporting) **A**10 21
Primary Contact: John Peleuses, Interim Chief Executive Officer
CFO: Robert Hehemeier, Interim Chief Financial Officer
Web address: www.sonomawesthealth.org/
Control: Hospital district or authority, Government, nonfederal **Service:** Acute long-term care hospital

Staffed Beds: 25

SHERMAN OAKS—Los Angeles County; See Los Angeles

SIMI VALLEY—Ventura County

⊞ **SIMI VALLEY HOSPITAL (050236)**, 2975 North Sycamore Drive, Zip 93065–1277; tel. 805/955–6000, **A**1 2 10 **F**3 8 11 13 15 18 20 22 24 26 29 30 31 32 34 35 36 40 41 44 45 46 49 50 51 54 56 57 58 59 62 63 64 65 68 70 72 74 75 76 77 78 79 81 82 84 85 86 87 93 96 97 100 101 102 107 108 110 111 114 115 116 117 118 119 120 121 123 130 131 132 134 141 144 146 147 148 149 150 154 **S** Adventist Health, Roseville, CA
Primary Contact: Jennifer Swenson, President and Chief Executive Officer
COO: Caroline Esparza, R.N., Sr. VP, COO & CNO
CFO: Brian Anderson, Chief Financial Officer
CMO: John Dingilian, M.D., Chief Medical Officer
CIO: Bridget Nakamura, Director Information Systems
CHR: Susan Crabtree, Director Human Resources
CNO: Caroline Esparza, R.N., Senior Vice President, Chief Operating Officer and Chief Nurse Officer
Web address: www.simivalleyhospital.com
Control: Other not-for-profit (including NFP Corporation) **Service:** General medical and surgical

Staffed Beds: 144 **Admissions:** 8275 **Census:** 71 **Outpatient Visits:** 68963 **Births:** 526 **Total Expense ($000):** 158576 **Payroll Expense ($000):** 50496 **Personnel:** 676

Hospital, Medicare Provider Number, Address, Telephone, Approval, Facility, and Physician Codes, Health Care System

★ American Hospital Association (AHA) membership ○ Healthcare Facilities Accreditation Program ⇑ Center for Improvement in Healthcare Quality Accreditation
□ The Joint Commission accreditation ◇ DNV Healthcare Inc. accreditation △ Commission on Accreditation of Rehabilitation Facilities (CARF) accreditation

---

CA

SOLVANG—Santa Barbara County

☒ **SANTA YNEZ VALLEY COTTAGE HOSPITAL (051331)**, 2050 Viborg Road, Zip 93463–2295; tel. 805/688–6431, **A**1 10 18 **F**11 15 18 28 40 45 57 68 75 81 85 107 111 114 119 143 146 149 **S** Cottage Health, Santa Barbara, CA
Primary Contact: Ronald C. Werft, President and Chief Executive Officer
COO: Steven A Fellows, Executive Vice President and Chief Operating Officer
CFO: Brett Tande, Chief Financial Officer
CMO: Edmund Wroblewski, M.D., Vice President Medical Affairs and Chief Medical Officer
CHR: Patrice Ryan, Vice President Human Resources
CNO: Herb J Geary, Chief Nursing Officer
Web address: www.cottagehealthsystem.org
Control: Other not–for–profit (including NFP Corporation) **Service**: General medical and surgical

> **Staffed Beds**: 11 **Admissions**: 216 **Census**: 2 **Outpatient Visits**: 20735 **Births**: 0 **Total Expense ($000)**: 17827 **Payroll Expense ($000)**: 8758 **Personnel**: 80

SONOMA—Sonoma County

SONOMA VALLEY HOSPITAL (050090), 347 Andrieux Street, Zip 95476–6811, Mailing Address: P.O. Box 600, Zip 95476–0600; tel. 707/935–5000, (Nonreporting) **A**5 10 22
Primary Contact: Kelly Mather, Chief Executive Officer
CFO: Jeanette Tarver, Director of Finance
CMO: Sabrina Kidd, M.D., Chief Medical Officer
CIO: Fe Sendaydiego, Director Information Systems
CHR: Paula M Davis, Chief Human Resources Officer
CNO: Leslie Lovejoy, R.N., Ph.D., Chief Nursing and Quality Officer
Web address: www.svh.com
Control: Hospital district or authority, Government, nonfederal **Service**: General medical and surgical

> **Staffed Beds**: 65

SONORA—Tuolumne County

☒ **ADVENTIST HEALTH SONORA (050335)**, 1000 Greenley Road, Zip 95370–4819; tel. 209/536–5000, (Total facility includes 68 beds in nursing home–type unit) **A**1 10 **F**3 8 11 13 15 17 18 20 28 29 30 31 34 35 37 39 40 45 49 53 54 56 57 59 62 63 64 66 70 75 76 77 78 79 81 82 84 85 86 87 93 94 96 97 104 107 108 110 111 114 115 117 118 119 120 121 123 126 127 128 129 130 131 132 133 143 144 145 146 148 149 154 156 **S** Adventist Health, Roseville, CA
Primary Contact: Michelle Fuentes, President
CFO: Greg McCulloch, CPA, Vice President of Finance and Chief Financial Officer
CMO: Ed Clinite, D.O., Chief of Staff
CIO: Manty Drews, Chief Information Officer
CNO: Julie Kline, R.N., Senior Vice President Patient Services
Web address: www.sonoramedicalcenter.org/
Control: Church operated, Nongovernment, not–for–profit **Service**: General medical and surgical

> **Staffed Beds**: 152 **Admissions**: 4169 **Census**: 109 **Outpatient Visits**: 342238 **Births**: 551 **Total Expense ($000)**: 247879 **Payroll Expense ($000)**: 73557 **Personnel**: 1052

SOUTH EL MONTE—Los Angeles County

☐ **GREATER EL MONTE COMMUNITY HOSPITAL (050738)**, 1701 Santa Anita Avenue, Zip 91733–3411; tel. 626/579–7777, **A**1 10 **F**3 13 14 17 18 29 34 35 40 41 45 49 50 57 59 64 68 70 75 76 77 78 79 81 82 85 87 89 92 93 107 108 119 128 130 146 **S** AHMC & Healthcare, Inc., Alhambra, CA
Primary Contact: Stanley Toy Jr, M.D., Chief Executive Officer
COO: Jose Ortega, Chief Operating Officer
CFO: Michael Chung, Chief Financial Officer
CMO: Dilip Patel, M.D., Chief of Staff
CIO: Jay Geldhof, Director Information Systems
CHR: Jason Jaquez, Director Human Resources
CNO: Evelyn Calubaquib, Chief Nursing Officer
Web address: www.greaterelmonte.com
Control: Hospital district or authority, Government, nonfederal **Service**: General medical and surgical

> **Staffed Beds**: 117 **Admissions**: 3481 **Census**: 53 **Outpatient Visits**: 23758 **Births**: 131 **Total Expense ($000)**: 67893 **Payroll Expense ($000)**: 24255 **Personnel**: 319

SOUTH LAKE TAHOE—El Dorado County

☒ **BARTON MEMORIAL HOSPITAL (050352)**, 2170 South Avenue, Zip 96150–7026, Mailing Address: P.O. Box 9578, Zip 96158–9578; tel. 530/541–3420, (Total facility includes 48 beds in nursing home–type unit) **A**1 3 5 10 20 **F**3 8 11 13 15 18 29 30 32 34 35 38 40 43 45 46 47 48 49 50 54 57 59 62 63 64 65 66 68 70 75 76 77 79 81 82 83 84 85 86 87 89 90 92 93 94 96 97 100 104 107 109 110 111 112 113 114 115 116 117 118 119 121 122 123 124 126 127 128 129 130 131 132 135 143 144 146 147 148 149
Primary Contact: Clint Purvance, M.D., President and Chief Executive Officer
CFO: Kelly Neiger, Chief Financial Officer
CMO: Matthew Wonnacott, M.D., Chief Medical Officer
CIO: Jason Roberts, Director of Information Services
CNO: Susan Fairley, Chief Nursing Officer
Web address: www.bartonhealth.org
Control: Other not–for–profit (including NFP Corporation) **Service**: General medical and surgical

> **Staffed Beds**: 111 **Admissions**: 2322 **Census**: 62 **Outpatient Visits**: 194399 **Births**: 317 **Total Expense ($000)**: 122713 **Payroll Expense ($000)**: 54076 **Personnel**: 906

SOUTH SAN FRANCISCO—San Mateo County

☒ **KAISER PERMANENTE SOUTH SAN FRANCISCO (050070)**, 1200 El Camino Real, Zip 94080–3208; tel. 650/742–2000, **A**1 3 5 10 **F**3 8 11 12 15 18 26 28 29 30 31 34 39 40 41 45 49 50 51 55 56 57 58 59 60 61 62 63 64 68 70 74 75 77 78 79 81 82 84 85 86 102 107 108 110 111 114 115 118 119 120 121 123 124 129 130 131 134 135 144 146 147 148 149 154 156 157 **S** Kaiser Foundation Hospitals, Oakland, CA
Primary Contact: Ronald Groepper, Senior Vice President and Area Manager
CMO: Michelle Caughey, M.D., Physician In Chief
CIO: Angel Shew, Director Area Technology
CHR: Sharon Barncord, Human Resource Business Partner
Web address: www.kaiserpermanente.org
Control: Other not–for–profit (including NFP Corporation) **Service**: General medical and surgical

> **Staffed Beds**: 120 **Admissions**: 5584 **Census**: 55 **Outpatient Visits**: 93128 **Births**: 0 **Personnel**: 715

STOCKTON—San Joaquin County

☐ **DAMERON HOSPITAL (050122)**, 525 West Acacia Street, Zip 95203–2484; tel. 209/944–5550, (Nonreporting) **A**1 5 10
Primary Contact: Lorraine P. Auerbach, FACHE, President and Chief Executive Officer
COO: Michael Glasberg, Senior Vice President, Chief Operating Officer
CFO: Elizabeth R Propp, Vice President Finance and Chief Financial Officer
CMO: Bradley Reinke, M.D., Vice President Medical Affairs and Chief Medical Officer
CIO: David Kerrins, Vice President Information Services and Chief Information Officer
CHR: Tresha Moreland, MS, Regional Vice President Human Resources
CNO: Denise J. Hair, Vice President of Nursing Services and Chief Nursing Officer
Web address: www.dameronhospital.org
Control: Other not–for–profit (including NFP Corporation) **Service**: General medical and surgical

> **Staffed Beds**: 202

☒ **ST. JOSEPH'S BEHAVIORAL HEALTH CENTER (054123)**, 2510 North California Street, Zip 95204–5568; tel. 209/461–2000, **A**1 10 **F**5 29 38 68 98 100 101 103 104 105 130 132 143 146 153 **S** CommonSpirit Health, Chicago, IL
Primary Contact: Paul Rains, R.N., MSN, President
CFO: Doreen Hartmann, Chief Financial Officer
CMO: David Robinson, D.O., Medical Director
CHR: Nancy Vargas, Chief Human Resources
CNO: Benny Lee Lucas Jr Chief Nursing Executive
Web address: www.stjosephscanhelp.org
Control: Other not–for–profit (including NFP Corporation) **Service**: Psychiatric

> **Staffed Beds**: 35 **Admissions**: 1881 **Census**: 32 **Outpatient Visits**: 9312 **Births**: 0 **Total Expense ($000)**: 17796 **Payroll Expense ($000)**: 9128 **Personnel**: 106

Many Facility Codes have changed. Please refer to the AHA Guide Code Chart. © 2019 AHA Guide

⊠ **ST. JOSEPH'S MEDICAL CENTER (050084)**, 1800 North California Street, Zip 95204–6019, Mailing Address: P.O. Box 213008, Zip 95213–9008; tel. 209/943–2000, (Nonreporting) **A**1 2 3 5 10 19 **S** CommonSpirit Health, Chicago, IL
Primary Contact: Donald J. Wiley, President and Chief Executive Officer
COO: Michaell Rose, Chief Operating Officer
CFO: Nikki Ochoa, Interim Chief Financial Officer
CIO: Randall Gamino, Director Perot Site
CHR: Nancy Vargas, Vice President Human Resources
Web address: www.stjosephsCARES.org
Control: Church operated **Service**: General medical and surgical

Staffed Beds: 273

SUN CITY—Riverside County

☐ **MENIFEE VALLEY MEDICAL CENTER (050684)**, 28400 McCall Boulevard, Zip 92585–9537; tel. 951/679–8888, (Nonreporting) **A**1 3 10 **S** Physicians for Healthy Hospitals, Hemet, CA
Primary Contact: Dan C. McLaughlin, Chief Executive Officer
CMO: Sumanta Chaudhuri, M.D., Chief Medical Officer
CHR: Michele Bird, Chief Human Resources Officer
Web address: www.valleyhealthsystem.com
Control: Hospital district or authority, Government, nonfederal **Service**: General medical and surgical

Staffed Beds: 84

SUN VALLEY—Los Angeles County; See Los Angeles

SUSANVILLE—Lassen County

⊠ **BANNER LASSEN MEDICAL CENTER (051320)**, 1800 Spring Ridge Drive, Zip 96130–6100; tel. 530/252–2000, **A**1 10 18 **F**3 13 15 29 30 31 34 38 39 40 43 45 59 76 79 81 85 87 93 107 110 111 114 119 129 130 146 148 149 **S** Banner Health, Phoenix, AZ
Primary Contact: Catherine S. Harshbarger, R.N., Chief Executive Officer
CFO: Jon R McMillan, Chief Financial Officer
CMO: Hal Meadows, M.D., Chief Medical Officer
CIO: Randy Moore, Chief Information Officer
CHR: Ruth Smith, Division Human Resources Business Partner
CNO: Claudia Helmes, R.N., Chief Nursing Officer
Web address: www.https://www.bannerhealth.com/locations/susanville/banner-lassen-medical-center
Control: Other not–for–profit (including NFP Corporation) **Service**: General medical and surgical

Staffed Beds: 25 **Admissions:** 991 **Census:** 9 **Outpatient Visits:** 50914 **Births:** 230 **Total Expense ($000):** 37423 **Payroll Expense ($000):** 17544 **Personnel:** 160

SYLMAR—Los Angeles County; See Los Angeles

TARZANA—Los Angeles County; See Los Angeles

TEHACHAPI—Kern County

★ ⇧ **ADVENTIST HEALTH MEDICAL CENTER - TEHACHAPI VALLEY (051301)**, 115 West 'E' Street, Zip 93561–1607, Mailing Address: P.O. Box 1900, Zip 93581–1900; tel. 661/823–3000, (Nonreporting) **A**10 18 21 **S** Adventist Health, Roseville, CA
Primary Contact: David Eastman, Interim Chief Executive Officer
CFO: Chester Beedle, Interim Chief Financial Officer
CMO: Susan Cribbs, D.O., Chief of Staff
CIO: Dusty Colvard, Manager Information Technology
CHR: Susan Nelson-Jones, Director Human Resources
CNO: Juliana Kay Kirby, R.N., MSN, Chief Nursing Officer
Web address: www.tvhd.org
Control: Hospital district or authority, Government, nonfederal **Service**: General medical and surgical

Staffed Beds: 24

TEMECULA—Riverside County

⊠ **TEMECULA VALLEY HOSPITAL (050775)**, 31700 Temecula Parkway, Zip 92592–5896; tel. 951/331–2216, (Nonreporting) **A**1 3 10 **S** Universal Health Services, Inc., King of Prussia, PA
Primary Contact: Darlene Wetton, R.N., Chief Executive Officer
Web address: www.temeculavalleyhospital.com
Control: Corporation, Investor–owned (for–profit) **Service**: General medical and surgical

Staffed Beds: 140

TEMPLETON—San Luis Obispo County

⊠ **TWIN CITIES COMMUNITY HOSPITAL (050633)**, 1100 Las Tablas Road, Zip 93465–9796; tel. 805/434–3500, **A**1 10 **F**3 13 29 30 34 40 45 49 50 55 56 57 59 60 64 67 68 70 74 75 76 77 79 81 85 87 91 107 111 114 115 119 130 132 146 148 149 154 **S** TENET Healthcare Corporation, Dallas, TX
Primary Contact: Mark P. Lisa, FACHE, Chief Executive Officer
COO: Mike Lane, Chief Operating Officer
CFO: Lois Johnson, Chief Financial Officer
CHR: Diane M McCluskey, Chief Human Resources Officer
CNO: Robert Cook, Chief Nursing Officer
Web address: www.twincitieshospital.com
Control: Corporation, Investor–owned (for–profit) **Service**: General medical and surgical

Staffed Beds: 89 **Admissions:** 4279 **Census:** 46 **Outpatient Visits:** 44338 **Births:** 554 **Total Expense ($000):** 92249 **Payroll Expense ($000):** 42274 **Personnel:** 427

THOUSAND OAKS—Ventura County

⊠ **LOS ROBLES HOSPITAL AND MEDICAL CENTER (050549)**, 215 West Janss Road, Zip 91360–1899; tel. 805/370–4421, (Includes THOUSAND OAKS SURGICAL HOSPITAL, 401 Rolling Oaks Drive, Thousand Oaks, California, Zip 91361–1050; tel. 805/497–2727; Natalie Mussi, President and Chief Executive Officer), (Nonreporting) **A**1 2 10 **S** HCA Healthcare, Nashville, TN
Primary Contact: Natalie Mussi, President and Chief Executive Officer
COO: Austin Lane Manning, Chief Operating Officer
CMO: Hannah Grossman, M.D., Chief Medical Officer
CIO: Alex Bryer, Director Information Management
CHR: Geoff Washburn, Vice President Human Resources
CNO: Cynthia J Johnson, R.N., Chief Nursing Officer
Web address: www.losrobleshospital.com
Control: Corporation, Investor–owned (for–profit) **Service**: General medical and surgical

Staffed Beds: 325

TORRANCE—Los Angeles County

☐ **DEL AMO HOSPITAL (054053)**, 23700 Camino Del Sol, Zip 90505–5000; tel. 310/530–1151, (Nonreporting) **A**1 10 **S** Universal Health Services, Inc., King of Prussia, PA
Primary Contact: Steven Hytry, PsyD, Chief Executive Officer
CFO: Norma Hudson, Chief Financial Officer
Web address: www.delamohospital.com
Control: Corporation, Investor–owned (for–profit) **Service**: Psychiatric

Staffed Beds: 70

☐ **HARBOR-UCLA MEDICAL CENTER (050376)**, 1000 West Carson Street, Zip 90502–2059; tel. 310/222–2345, (Nonreporting) **A**1 2 3 5 8 10 **S** Los Angeles County-Department of Health Services, Los Angeles, CA
Primary Contact: Kimberly McKenzie, R.N., MSN, Interim Chief Executive Officer
COO: Kimberly McKenzie, R.N., MSN, Chief Nursing Officer and Chief Operations Officer
CFO: Jody Nakasuji, Chief Financial Officer
CMO: Timothy Van Natta, M.D., Chief Medical Officer
CIO: Sandy Mungovan, Chief Information Officer
CHR: Karyl Smith, Director Human Resources
CNO: Kimberly McKenzie, R.N., MSN, Chief Nursing Officer and Chief Operations Officer
Web address: www.harbor-ucla.org
Control: County, Government, nonfederal **Service**: General medical and surgical

Staffed Beds: 373

CA

✠ **PROVIDENCE LITTLE COMPANY OF MARY MEDICAL CENTER - TORRANCE (050353)**, 4101 Torrance Boulevard, Zip 90503–4664; tel. 310/540–7676, (Total facility includes 85 beds in nursing home–type unit) **A1** 2 10 **F**3 7 8 11 12 13 14 15 18 19 20 22 24 26 28 29 30 31 34 35 37 39 40 41 44 45 46 49 50 51 54 55 57 58 59 60 62 63 64 68 70 72 74 75 76 77 78 79 81 82 84 85 86 87 89 91 92 93 94 100 107 108 110 111 114 115 116 117 118 119 120 121 123 126 128 130 131 132 143 145 146 147 148 149 150 154 156 **S** Providence St. Joseph Health, Renton, WA
Primary Contact: Garry M. Olney, Chief Executive Officer
CFO: Elizabeth Zuanich, Chief Financial Officer
CMO: Richard Glimp, M.D., Chief Medical Officer
CIO: Andrea Flores, Director, Information Systems
CHR: Melissa Baker, Director, Human Resources
CNO: Michael Jongsma, R.N., Chief Nursing Officer
Web address: www.providence.org
Control: Church operated, Nongovernment, not–for–profit **Service**: General medical and surgical

Staffed Beds: 386 **Admissions**: 20100 **Census**: 260 **Outpatient Visits**: 284151 **Births**: 2623 **Total Expense ($000)**: 329760 **Payroll Expense ($000)**: 161129 **Personnel**: 2258

✠ **TORRANCE MEMORIAL MEDICAL CENTER (050351)**, 3330 Lomita Boulevard, Zip 90505–5073; tel. 310/325–9110, (Total facility includes 40 beds in nursing home–type unit) **A1** 2 10 **F**3 5 8 9 11 12 13 14 15 16 17 18 19 20 22 24 26 28 29 30 31 32 34 35 36 37 39 40 41 44 45 46 47 48 49 50 51 53 54 55 56 57 58 59 60 61 62 63 64 68 70 72 74 75 76 77 78 79 81 82 83 84 85 86 87 89 91 92 93 96 107 108 109 110 111 114 115 116 117 118 119 120 121 123 124 126 128 129 130 132 134 135 141 143 145 146 147 148 149 154 156 **S** Cedars-Sinai Health System, West Hollywood, CA
Primary Contact: Craig Leach, President and Chief Executive Officer
CFO: Bill Larson, Vice President Finance and Chief Financial Officer
CMO: John McNamara, M.D., Senior Vice President, Chief Medical Officer
CIO: Bernadette Reid, Vice President, Information Technology and Chief Information Officer
CHR: Linda Dobie, R.N., JD, Vice President, Legal Affairs
CNO: Margaret Berwald, R.N., MSN, Senior Vice President Patient Services
Web address: www.torrancememorial.org
Control: Other not–for–profit (including NFP Corporation) **Service**: General medical and surgical

Staffed Beds: 444 **Admissions**: 26693 **Census**: 311 **Outpatient Visits**: 436438 **Births**: 2659 **Total Expense ($000)**: 663647 **Payroll Expense ($000)**: 248010 **Personnel**: 3240

TRACY—San Joaquin County

✠ **SUTTER TRACY COMMUNITY HOSPITAL (050313)**, 1420 North Tracy Boulevard, Zip 95376–3497; tel. 209/835–1500, (Nonreporting) **A1** 10 **S** Sutter Health, Sacramento, CA
Primary Contact: David M. Thompson, Chief Executive Officer
CFO: Eric Dalton, Chief Financial Officer
CIO: Catherine M Larsen, Director Marketing
CHR: Melanie Wallace, Manager Human Resources
Web address: www.suttertracy.org
Control: Other not–for–profit (including NFP Corporation) **Service**: General medical and surgical

Staffed Beds: 77

TRAVIS AFB—Solano County

✠ **DAVID GRANT USAF MEDICAL CENTER**, 101 Bodin Circle, Zip 94535–1809; tel. 707/423–7300, (Nonreporting) **A1** 3 5 **S** Department of the Air Force, Washington, DC
Primary Contact: Lieutenant Michael Higgins, Commander
CFO: Major Jonathan Richards, Chief Financial Officer
CMO: Colonel Chris Scharenbrock, M.D., Chief Medical Staff
Web address: www.travis.af.mil/units/dgmc/index.asp
Control: Department of Defense, Government, federal **Service**: General medical and surgical

Staffed Beds: 116

TRUCKEE—Nevada County

★ ○ **TAHOE FOREST HOSPITAL DISTRICT (051328)**, 10121 Pine Avenue, Zip 96161–4856, Mailing Address: P.O. Box 759, Zip 96160–0759; tel. 530/587–6011, (Nonreporting) **A2** 3 5 10 11 18 **S** Tahoe Forest Health System, Truckee, CA
Primary Contact: Harry Weis, Chief Executive Officer
COO: Judy Newland, R.N., Chief Operating Officer
CFO: Crystal Betts, Chief Financial Officer
CMO: Shawni Coll, D.O., Chief Medical Officer
CIO: Jake Dorst, Chief Information Officer
CHR: Alex MacLennan, Chief Human Resources Officer
CNO: Karen Baffone, R.N., Chief Nursing Officer
Web address: www.tfhd.com
Control: Hospital district or authority, Government, nonfederal **Service**: General medical and surgical

Staffed Beds: 62

TULARE—Tulare County

★ ⇑ **ADVENTIST HEALTH - TULARE (050359)**, 869 North Cherry Street, Zip 93274–2287; tel. 559/688–0821, (Nonreporting) **A21** **S** Adventist Health, Roseville, CA
Primary Contact: Randy Dodd, President
COO: Alan Germany, Chief Operating Officer
CFO: Michael Bernstein, Chief Financial Officer
CMO: Pradeep Kamboj, M.D., Chief Medical Staff
CIO: Jim Peelgren, Chief Information Officer
CHR: John Barbadian, Vice President Human Resources
CNO: Patricia Mathewson, Chief Nursing Officer
Web address: www.tulareregional.org
Control: Hospital district or authority, Government, nonfederal **Service**: General medical and surgical

Staffed Beds: 103

TURLOCK—Stanislaus County

✠ **EMANUEL MEDICAL CENTER (050179)**, 825 Delbon Avenue, Zip 95382–2016, Mailing Address: P.O. Box 819005, Zip 95382; tel. 209/667–4200, **A1** 5 10 **F**3 8 11 15 18 20 22 26 29 30 31 34 35 40 47 48 49 54 59 60 64 68 70 73 75 76 77 78 79 81 89 93 97 107 108 110 111 114 115 117 118 119 120 121 123 126 130 132 146 147 148 149 156 **S** TENET Healthcare Corporation, Dallas, TX
Primary Contact: Lani Dickinson, Chief Executive Officer
CFO: David Neapolitan, Chief Financial Officer
CIO: Beth Walker, Chief Information Officer
CHR: Terry Gray, Vice President Human Resources
CNO: Sharon Perry, Chief Nursing Officer
Web address: www.emanuelmedicalcenter.org
Control: Corporation, Investor–owned (for–profit) **Service**: General medical and surgical

Staffed Beds: 209 **Admissions**: 8941 **Census**: 92 **Outpatient Visits**: 128994 **Births**: 1204 **Total Expense ($000)**: 203897 **Payroll Expense ($000)**: 81134 **Personnel**: 991

TUSTIN—Orange County

✠ **ENCOMPASS HEALTH REHABILITATION HOSPITAL OF TUSTIN (053034)**, 14851 Yorba Street, Zip 92780–2925; tel. 714/832–9200, (Nonreporting) **A1** 10 **S** Encompass Health Corporation, Birmingham, AL
Primary Contact: Diana Hanyak, Chief Executive Officer
CFO: Paula Redmond, Controller
CMO: Ann Vasile, M.D., Medical Director
CHR: JoAnn Roiz, Director Human Resources
CNO: LaDonna Butler Esq Chief Nursing Officer
Web address: www.tustinrehab.com
Control: Corporation, Investor–owned (for–profit) **Service**: Rehabilitation

Staffed Beds: 48

☐ **FOOTHILL REGIONAL MEDICAL CENTER (050780)**, 14662 Newport Avenue, Zip 92780–6064; tel. 714/838–9600, (Nonreporting) **A1** 10 **S** Prospect Medical Holdings, Los Angeles, CA
Primary Contact: Barbara Schneider, R.N., Chief Executive Officer
COO: Kara Bourne, R.N., MSN, Chief Nursing Officer and Chief Operating Officer
CIO: Darla Kennedy, Chief Information Officer
CHR: Aprille Major, Director Human Resources
Web address: www.hfcis.cdph.ca.gov/longtermcare/Facility.aspx?fac=060000013
Control: Corporation, Investor–owned (for–profit) **Service**: Acute long–term care hospital

Staffed Beds: 42

TWENTYNINE PALMS—San Bernardino County

✠ **ROBERT E. BUSH NAVAL HOSPITAL**, 1145 Sturgis Road, Zip 92278, Mailing Address: Box 788250, MCAGCC, Zip 92278–8250; tel. 760/830–2190, (Nonreporting) **A1** 3 **S** Bureau of Medicine and Surgery, Department of the Navy, Falls Church, VA
Primary Contact: Captain Jay C. Sourbeer, Commanding Officer
CHR: Virginia Ward, Human Resources Officer
CNO: Captain Sandra Mason, MSN, R.N., Director Nursing Services and Senior Nurse Executive
Web address: www.med.navy.mil/sites/nhtp/Pages/default.aspx
Control: Department of Defense, Government, federal **Service**: General medical and surgical

Staffed Beds: 29

Many Facility Codes have changed. Please refer to the AHA Guide Code Chart.
© 2019 AHA Guide

UKIAH—Mendocino County

⊞ **UKIAH VALLEY MEDICAL CENTER (050301)**, 275 Hospital Drive, Zip 95482–4531; tel. 707/462–3111, **A**1 3 5 10 **F**8 11 12 13 15 18 29 30 31 32 34 35 36 38 40 44 45 46 48 49 50 51 54 57 59 60 64 65 68 70 72 75 77 78 79 81 82 84 85 86 87 93 94 97 101 111 114 115 116 117 118 119 127 130 131 132 135 144 146 147 148 **S** Adventist Health, Roseville, CA
Primary Contact: Gwen Matthews, R.N., MSN, Chief Executive Officer
CHR: Rebecca Ryan, Interim Director Human Resources and Employee Health
Web address: www.adventisthealth.org
Control: Church operated, Nongovernment, not–for–profit **Service**: General medical and surgical

> **Staffed Beds:** 50 **Admissions:** 4140 **Census:** 33 **Outpatient Visits:** 133420 **Births:** 724 **Total Expense ($000):** 181484 **Payroll Expense ($000):** 45019 **Personnel:** 568

UPLAND—San Bernardino County

⊞ **SAN ANTONIO REGIONAL HOSPITAL (050099)**, 999 San Bernardino Road, Zip 91786–4920, Mailing Address: Box 5001, Zip 91785–5001; tel. 909/985–2811, **A**1 2 3 5 10 **F**3 8 11 13 15 17 18 20 22 24 26 28 29 31 35 38 40 45 46 49 50 54 57 59 60 61 64 65 69 70 72 74 75 76 77 78 79 80 81 82 83 84 85 86 87 89 91 92 93 94 107 108 110 111 114 115 118 119 121 123 124 130 132 146 147 148 157
Primary Contact: Harris F. Koenig, President and Chief Executive Officer
CFO: Wah Chung Hsu, Senior Vice President Finance
CMO: Rohinder Sandhu, M.D., President of the Medical Staff
CIO: Kamel Pandya, Director Information Services
CHR: Laura Kato, Vice President of Human Resources
CNO: Gudrun Moll, R.N., MSN, Chief Nursing Officer
Web address: www.sarh.org
Control: Other not–for–profit (including NFP Corporation) **Service**: General medical and surgical

> **Staffed Beds:** 363 **Admissions:** 17670 **Census:** 185 **Outpatient Visits:** 242953 **Births:** 2231 **Total Expense ($000):** 376271 **Payroll Expense ($000):** 157935 **Personnel:** 1951

VACAVILLE—Solano County

CALIFORNIA MEDICAL FACILITY, 1600 California Drive, Zip 95687; tel. 707/448–6841, (Nonreporting)
Primary Contact: David Horch, Chief Executive
CMO: Raymond Andreasen, M.D., Chief Medical Officer Inpatient
Web address: www.cya.ca.gov/visitors/fac_prison_cmf.html
Control: State, Government, nonfederal **Service**: Hospital unit of an institution (prison hospital, college infirmary, etc.)

> **Staffed Beds:** 215

⊞ **KAISER PERMANENTE VACAVILLE MEDICAL CENTER (050767)**, 1 Quality Drive, Zip 95688–9494; tel. 707/624–4000, **A**1 2 3 10 **F**3 8 11 13 15 18 26 28 29 30 31 34 39 40 41 43 45 49 50 51 55 56 57 58 59 60 61 64 65 68 70 74 75 76 77 78 79 81 82 84 85 86 102 107 108 110 111 114 115 118 119 130 131 134 135 144 146 147 148 149 154 156 **S** Kaiser Foundation Hospitals, Oakland, CA
Primary Contact: Norair Jemjemian, Senior Vice President and Area Manager
Web address: www.kp.org
Control: Other not–for–profit (including NFP Corporation) **Service**: General medical and surgical

> **Staffed Beds:** 140 **Admissions:** 5908 **Census:** 65 **Outpatient Visits:** 139895 **Births:** 1319 **Personnel:** 706

NORTHBAY VACAVALLEY HOSPITAL See Northbay Medical Center, Fairfield

VALENCIA—Los Angeles County

⊞ **HENRY MAYO NEWHALL HOSPITAL (050624)**, 23845 McBean Parkway, Zip 91355–2083; tel. 661/200–2000, (Nonreporting) **A**1 2 10
Primary Contact: Roger E. Seaver, President and Chief Executive Officer
COO: John V Schleif, Senior Vice President and Chief Operating Officer
CFO: Ted Sirotta, Senior Vice President and Chief Financial Officer
CMO: Kingman Ho, M.D., Senior Vice President, Chief Medical and Care Innovation Officer
CIO: Ray Moss, Vice President and Chief Information Officer
CHR: Mark Puleo, Vice President and Chief Human Resources Officer
CNO: Jennifer Castaldo, R.N., Vice President, Patient Care and Chief Nursing Officer
Web address: www.henrymayo.com
Control: Other not–for–profit (including NFP Corporation) **Service**: General medical and surgical

> **Staffed Beds:** 238

VALLEJO—Solano County

⊞ **ADVENTIST HEALTH ST. HELENA (054074)**, 525 Oregon Street, Zip 94590–3201; tel. 707/648–2200, **A**1 10 **F**29 30 50 64 65 68 98 104 105 130 146 153 154 **S** Adventist Health, Roseville, CA
Primary Contact: Steven Herber, M.D., FACS, President and Chief Executive Officer
CFO: Edward A McDonald, Chief Financial Officer
Web address: www.sthelenahospitals.org/location/center-for-behavioral-health
Control: Other not–for–profit (including NFP Corporation) **Service**: Psychiatric

> **Staffed Beds:** 61 **Admissions:** 1974 **Census:** 53 **Births:** 0

⊞ △ **KAISER PERMANENTE VALLEJO MEDICAL CENTER (050073)**, 975 Sereno Drive, Zip 94589–2441; tel. 707/651–1000, **A**1 2 3 5 7 10 **F**3 8 11 15 18 20 22 26 28 29 30 31 34 39 40 41 45 48 49 50 51 55 56 57 58 59 60 61 63 64 68 70 73 74 75 76 77 78 79 81 82 84 85 86 90 102 107 108 110 111 114 115 118 119 130 131 134 135 144 146 147 148 149 154 156 **S** Kaiser Foundation Hospitals, Oakland, CA
Primary Contact: Corwin N. Harper, Senior Vice President and Area Manager
COO: Karen Grisnak, R.N., Chief Operating Officer and Assistant Administrator Quality Services
CFO: Joseph D'Angina, Area Finance Officer
CMO: Steven Stricker, M.D., Physician in Chief
CIO: Gale Austin-Moore, Director Area Technology
CHR: Sherri Stegge, Director Human Resources
Web address: www.kaiserpermanente.org
Control: Other not–for–profit (including NFP Corporation) **Service**: General medical and surgical

> **Staffed Beds:** 248 **Admissions:** 8502 **Census:** 92 **Births:** 1597 **Personnel:** 1074

⊞ **SUTTER SOLANO MEDICAL CENTER (050101)**, 300 Hospital Drive, Zip 94589–2574, Mailing Address: P.O. Box 3189, Zip 94590–0669; tel. 707/554–4444, (Nonreporting) **A**1 2 10 **S** Sutter Health, Sacramento, CA
Primary Contact: Abhishek Dosi, Chief Executive Officer
CHR: Jean Willhite, Director Human Resources
Web address: www.suttersolano.org
Control: Other not–for–profit (including NFP Corporation) **Service**: General medical and surgical

> **Staffed Beds:** 108

VAN NUYS—Los Angeles County; See Los Angeles

VENTURA—Ventura County

★ ⇧ **COMMUNITY MEMORIAL HOSPITAL (050394)**, 147 North Brent Street, Zip 93003–2809; tel. 805/652–5011, (Includes COMMUNITY MEMORIAL HOSPITAL, 147 North Brent Street, Ventura, California, Zip 93003–2854; tel. 805/652–5011) **A**2 3 5 10 13 21 **F**3 8 11 12 13 15 17 18 19 20 22 24 26 28 29 30 31 32 34 35 37 40 45 46 47 48 49 50 53 54 57 59 64 65 66 68 70 71 72 74 75 76 77 78 79 81 82 83 84 85 86 89 91 93 97 104 107 108 110 111 114 115 118 119 126 127 130 131 132 141 142 144 145 146 147 148 154 156 **S** Community Memorial Health System, Ventura, CA
Primary Contact: Gary Wilde, President and Chief Executive Officer
COO: Adam Thunell, Chief Operating Officer and Vice President Operations
CFO: David Glyer, Vice President Finance
CMO: Stanley Frochtzwajg, M.D., Chief Medical Officer
CIO: Ron Sandifer, Chief Information Officer
CHR: Diany Klein, Vice President Human Resources
Web address: www.cmhshealth.org
Control: Other not–for–profit (including NFP Corporation) **Service**: General medical and surgical

> **Staffed Beds:** 126 **Admissions:** 11704 **Census:** 126 **Outpatient Visits:** 453239 **Births:** 2639 **Total Expense ($000):** 372804 **Payroll Expense ($000):** 131883 **Personnel:** 1887

⊞ **VENTURA COUNTY MEDICAL CENTER (050159)**, 3291 Loma Vista Road, Zip 93003–3099; tel. 805/652–6000, (Nonreporting) **A**1 3 5 10
Primary Contact: John Fankhauser, M.D., Chief Executive Officer
CMO: Bryan Wong, M.D., Medical Director
CIO: Terry Theobald, Chief Information Officer
CHR: Tim Rhyne, Personnel Officer
CNO: Susan Scott, Chief Nurse Executive
Web address: www.vchca.org
Control: County, Government, nonfederal **Service**: General medical and surgical

> **Staffed Beds:** 160

CA

Hospital, Medicare Provider Number, Address, Telephone, Approval, Facility, and Physician Codes, Health Care System

★ American Hospital Association (AHA) membership ○ Healthcare Facilities Accreditation Program ⇧ Center for Improvement in Healthcare Quality Accreditation
☐ The Joint Commission accreditation ◇ DNV Healthcare Inc. accreditation △ Commission on Accreditation of Rehabilitation Facilities (CARF) accreditation

☐ **VISTA DEL MAR HOSPITAL (054077)**, 801 Seneca Street, Zip 93001–1411; tel. 805/653–6434, (Nonreporting) **A**1 10 **S** Signature Healthcare Services, Corona, CA
Primary Contact: Mayla Krebsbach, Chief Executive Officer
CFO: Kurt Broten, Chief Financial Officer
CMO: Steve Ruths, M.D., Chief Medical Officer
Web address: www.vistadelmarhospital.com
Control: Corporation, Investor–owned (for–profit) **Service:** Psychiatric

Staffed Beds: 87

VICTORVILLE—San Bernardino County

★ ○ **DESERT VALLEY HOSPITAL (050709)**, 16850 Bear Valley Road, Zip 92395–5795; tel. 760/241–8000, (Nonreporting) **A**10 11 **S** Prime Healthcare, Ontario, CA
Primary Contact: Fred Hunter, R.N., Chief Executive Officer
COO: Luis Leon, Chief Operating Officer
CFO: Martin Mansukhani, Chief Financial Officer
CIO: Sreekant Gotti, Director Information Systems
Web address: www.dvmc.com
Control: Corporation, Investor–owned (for–profit) **Service:** General medical and surgical

Staffed Beds: 110

☐ **VICTOR VALLEY GLOBAL MEDICAL CENTER (050517)**, 15248 Eleventh Street, Zip 92395–3704; tel. 760/245–8691, (Nonreporting) **A**1 10
Primary Contact: Lori Burns, Administrator
COO: Doreen Dann, R.N., Chief Operating Officer
CIO: Joe Archer, Chief Information Officer
CHR: Cesar Lugo, Director Human Resources
Web address: www.vvgmc.com
Control: Other not–for–profit (including NFP Corporation) **Service:** General medical and surgical

Staffed Beds: 101

VISALIA—Tulare County

⊞ △ **KAWEAH DELTA MEDICAL CENTER (050057)**, 400 West Mineral King Boulevard, Zip 93291–6263; tel. 559/624–2000, (Includes SOUTH CAMPUS, 1633 South Court Street, Visalia, California, Zip 93277; tel. 559/624–6090), (Nonreporting) **A**1 3 5 7 10
Primary Contact: Gary Herbst, Chief Executive Officer
COO: Thomas J Rayner, Senior Vice President and Chief Operating Officer
CMO: Edward Hirsch, M.D., Vice President Chief Medical and Quality Officer
CIO: Doug Leeper, Chief Information Officer
CHR: Dianne E Cox, Vice President of Human Resources
CNO: Regina Sawyer, Vice President Chief Nursing Officer
Web address: www.kaweahdelta.org
Control: Hospital district or authority, Government, nonfederal **Service:** General medical and surgical

Staffed Beds: 437

WALNUT CREEK—Contra Costa County

⊞ △ **JOHN MUIR MEDICAL CENTER, WALNUT CREEK (050180)**, 1601 Ygnacio Valley Road, Zip 94598–3194; tel. 925/939–3000, **A**1 2 3 5 7 10 **F**3 11 13 15 17 18 19 20 22 24 26 28 29 30 31 32 34 35 37 39 40 41 43 44 45 46 47 48 49 50 54 55 56 57 58 59 61 62 64 65 68 70 72 74 75 76 77 78 79 80 81 82 83 84 85 86 87 88 89 90 91 93 95 96 100 102 108 110 118 119 120 121 123 124 126 130 131 132 141 145 146 147 148 149 150 154 156 157 **S** John Muir Health, Walnut Creek, CA
Primary Contact: Jane Willemsen, President and Chief Administrative Officer
COO: Raymond Nassief, Senior Vice President, Hospital Operations and Support Services
CFO: Christian Pass, Senior Vice President & Chief Financial Officer
CMO: Irving Pike, M.D., Senior Vice President and Chief Medical Officer
CIO: Jon Russell, Senior Vice President & Chief Information Officer
CHR: Lisa Foust, Senior Vice President, Human Resources
CNO: Michelle Anne Lopes, MSN, R.N., Senior Vice President, Patient Care Services & Chief Nursing Officer
Web address: www.https://www.johnmuirhealth.com/
Control: Other not–for–profit (including NFP Corporation) **Service:** General medical and surgical

Staffed Beds: 420 Admissions: 20253 Census: 282 Outpatient Visits: 311142 Births: 2685 Total Expense ($000): 894392 Payroll Expense ($000): 300265 Personnel: 2006

⊞ **KAISER PERMANENTE WALNUT CREEK MEDICAL CENTER (050072)**, 1425 South Main Street, Zip 94596–5300; tel. 925/295–4000, (Includes KAISER FOUNDATION HOSPITAL, 200 Muir Road, Martinez, California, Zip 94553–4696; tel. 510/372–1000) **A**1 2 3 5 10 **F**3 8 11 15 18 20 22 26 28 29 30 31 34 39 40 41 44 45 49 50 55 56 57 58 59 60 61 63 64 68 70 73 74 75 76 77 78 79 81 82 84 85 86 89 102 107 108 110 111 114 115 117 118 119 126 130 131 134 135 144 146 147 148 149 154 156 157 **S** Kaiser Foundation Hospitals, Oakland, CA
Primary Contact: Colleen McKeown, Senior Vice President and Area Manager
CFO: Yakesun Wing, Business Strategy and Finance Leader
Web address: www.kaiserpermanente.org
Control: Other not–for–profit (including NFP Corporation) **Service:** General medical and surgical

Staffed Beds: 233 Admissions: 11852 Census: 128 Outpatient Visits: 144793 Births: 3211 Personnel: 1210

WATSONVILLE—Santa Cruz County

⊞ **WATSONVILLE COMMUNITY HOSPITAL (050194)**, 75 Nielson Street, Zip 95076–2468; tel. 831/724–4741, **A**1 10 **F**3 13 15 18 29 34 35 40 44 45 49 50 51 57 60 64 68 70 72 74 76 77 79 81 87 89 93 97 107 110 111 114 115 119 126 130 146 148 149 154 **S** Quorum Health, Brentwood, TN
Primary Contact: Audra Earle, FACHE, Chief Executive Officer
CFO: Rachel Jones, Chief Financial Officer
CIO: Sergio Nell, Director Information Systems
CNO: Donna Salvi, Chief Nursing Officer
Web address: www.watsonvillehospital.com
Control: Corporation, Investor–owned (for–profit) **Service:** General medical and surgical

Staffed Beds: 106 Admissions: 3577 Census: 38 Outpatient Visits: 69926 Births: 877 Total Expense ($000): 111655 Payroll Expense ($000): 53397 Personnel: 498

WEAVERVILLE—Trinity County

TRINITY HOSPITAL (051315), 60 Easter Avenue, Zip 96093, Mailing Address: P.O. Box 1229, Zip 96093–1229; tel. 530/623–5541, (Nonreporting) **A**10 18
Primary Contact: Aaron Rogers, Chief Executive Officer
CFO: Kathy Walker, Chief Financial Officer
CMO: Donald Krouse, M.D., Chief of Staff
CIO: Jake Odom, Chief Information Officer
CHR: Heidi Corrigan, Manager Human Resources
CNO: Judy Nordlund, R.N., Chief Nursing Officer
Web address: www.mcmedical.org
Control: Hospital district or authority, Government, nonfederal **Service:** General medical and surgical

Staffed Beds: 47

WEST COVINA—Los Angeles County

☐ **WEST COVINA MEDICAL CENTER (050096)**, 725 South Orange Avenue, Zip 91790–2614; tel. 626/338–8481, (Nonreporting) **A**1 10
Primary Contact: Gerald H. Wallman, Administrator
CFO: Kami Horvat, Chief Financial Officer
CMO: Erich Pollak, M.D., Chief of Staff
CHR: Lourdes Meza, Coordinator Human Resources
CNO: Guadalupe Ojeda, R.N., Chief Nursing Officer
Control: Corporation, Investor–owned (for–profit) **Service:** General medical and surgical

Staffed Beds: 46

WEST HILLS—Los Angeles County; See Los Angeles

WESTMINSTER—Orange County

⊞ **KINDRED HOSPITAL-WESTMINSTER (052035)**, 200 Hospital Circle, Zip 92683–3910; tel. 714/893–4541, (Nonreporting) **A**1 10 **S** Kindred Healthcare, Louisville, KY
Primary Contact: Julie Myers, Chief Executive Officer
CFO: Dale Wagner, Chief Financial Officer
Web address: www.khwestminster.com/
Control: Corporation, Investor–owned (for–profit) **Service:** Acute long–term care hospital

Staffed Beds: 109

CA

WHITTIER—Los Angeles County

⊞ **PIH HEALTH HOSPITAL - WHITTIER (050169)**, 12401 Washington Boulevard, Zip 90602–1099; tel. 562/698–0811, (Total facility includes 19 beds in nursing home–type unit) **A**1 2 3 5 10 22 **F**1 3 8 11 12 13 15 18 20 22 24 26 28 29 30 31 32 34 38 40 45 46 49 50 54 55 56 57 58 59 60 61 62 63 64 65 70 72 74 75 76 77 78 79 81 84 85 86 87 90 93 94 96 97 100 107 108 110 111 114 115 116 117 118 119 120 121 123 128 130 131 132 135 143 145 146 147 148 149 154 156 157 **S** PIH Health, Whittier, CA
Primary Contact: James R. West, President and Chief Executive Officer
COO: Reanna Thompson, R.N., Chief Operating Officer and Chief Nursing Officer
CFO: Greg Williams, Chief Financial Officer
CMO: Rosalio J Lopez, M.D., Senior Vice President and Chief Medical Officer
CIO: Jason Fischer, Chief Information Officer
CNO: Reanna Thompson, R.N., Chief Operating Officer and Chief Nursing Officer
Web address: www.PIHHealth.org
Control: Other not–for–profit (including NFP Corporation) **Service**: General medical and surgical

Staffed Beds: 236 Admissions: 17887 Census: 204 Outpatient Visits: 366284 Births: 1793 Total Expense ($000): 538140 Payroll Expense ($000): 193377 Personnel: 2780

☐ **WHITTIER HOSPITAL MEDICAL CENTER (050735)**, 9080 Colima Road, Zip 90605–1600; tel. 562/945–3561, (Nonreporting) **A**1 10 **S** AHMC & Healthcare, Inc., Alhambra, CA
Primary Contact: Richard Castro, Chief Executive Officer
COO: Mary Anne Monje, Chief Financial Officer and Chief Operating Officer
CFO: Mary Anne Monje, Chief Financial Officer and Chief Operating Officer
CIO: Jay Geldhof, Director Information Systems
CHR: Martha Salcedo, Interim Director Human Resources
CNO: Sarkis Vartanian, Chief Nursing Officer
Web address: www.whittierhospital.com
Control: Corporation, Investor–owned (for–profit) **Service**: General medical and surgical

Staffed Beds: 100

WILLITS—Mendocino County

⊞ **ADVENTIST HEALTH HOWARD MEMORIAL (051310)**, One Marcela Drive, Zip 95490–4298; tel. 707/459–6801, **A**1 3 10 18 **F**11 15 29 30 34 35 40 57 59 69 70 75 79 81 93 97 107 110 111 115 119 127 131 132 133 135 146 147 148 **S** Adventist Health, Roseville, CA
Primary Contact: Jason Wells, President and Chief Executive Officer
CFO: Judson Howe, Chief Financial Officer
CMO: Kimberly Faucher, M.D., Chief Medical Officer
CIO: Cecilia Winiger, Community Outreach and Communication Manager
CHR: Darcy De Leon, Executive Director, Human Resources
CNO: Karen M Scott, Vice President Patient Care
Web address: www.howardhospital.com
Control: Church operated, Nongovernment, not for profit **Service**: General medical and surgical

Staffed Beds: 25 Admissions: 1669 Census: 19 Outpatient Visits: 57111 Births: 0 Total Expense ($000): 65806 Payroll Expense ($000): 20816 Personnel: 236

WILLOWS—Glenn County

GLENN MEDICAL CENTER (051306), 1133 West Sycamore Street, Zip 95988–2745; tel. 530/934–1800, (Nonreporting) **A**10 18
Primary Contact: Timothy M. Moran, Chief Executive Officer
CFO: John Lovrich, Chief Financial Officer
CHR: Deborah McMillan, Director Human Resources
CNO: Timothy Speek I Director of Nursing
Web address: www.glennmed.org
Control: Other not–for–profit (including NFP Corporation) **Service**: General medical and surgical

Staffed Beds: 15

WOODLAND—Yolo County

⊞ **WOODLAND HEALTHCARE (050127)**, 1325 Cottonwood Street, Zip 95695–5199; tel. 530/662–3961, (Nonreporting) **A**1 5 10 **S** CommonSpirit Health, Chicago, IL
Primary Contact: H Kevin. Vaziri, President
CMO: Sarada Mylavarapu, M.D., Chief Medical Officer
Web address: www.woodlandhealthcare.org
Control: Other not–for–profit (including NFP Corporation) **Service**: General medical and surgical

Staffed Beds: 108

WOODLAND HILLS—Los Angeles County; See Los Angeles

YREKA—Siskiyou County

⊞ **FAIRCHILD MEDICAL CENTER (051316)**, 444 Bruce Street, Zip 96097–3450; tel. 530/842–4121, (Nonreporting) **A**1 10 18
Primary Contact: Jonathon Andrus, Chief Executive Officer
CFO: Kelly Martin, Chief Financial Officer
CMO: Moudy Youssef, M.D., Chief Medical Officer
CIO: Randy Ferguson, Information Systems Manager
CHR: Joann Sarmento, Manager Human Resources
CNO: Susan Westphal, Assistant Administrator, Patient Care Services
Web address: www.fairchildmed.org
Control: Other not–for–profit (including NFP Corporation) **Service**: General medical and surgical

Staffed Beds: 25

YUBA CITY—Sutter County

FREMONT MEDICAL CENTER See Adventist Health and Rideout, Marysville

☐ **SUTTER SURGICAL HOSPITAL - NORTH VALLEY (050766)**, 455 Plumas Boulevard, Zip 95991–5074; tel. 530/749–5700, (Nonreporting) **A**1 10 **S** Sutter Health, Sacramento, CA
Primary Contact: Shawndra Simpson, Interim Chief Executive Officer
CHR: Michelle Guina, Manager Human Resources
CNO: David Cooke, R.N., Chief Nursing Officer
Web address: www.sshnv.org
Control: Partnership, Investor–owned (for–profit) **Service**: Surgical

Staffed Beds: 14

Hospital, Medicare Provider Number, Address, Telephone, Approval, Facility, and Physician Codes, Health Care System

★ American Hospital Association (AHA) membership   ○ Healthcare Facilities Accreditation Program   ⇑ Center for Improvement in Healthcare Quality Accreditation
☐ The Joint Commission accreditation   ◇ DNV Healthcare Inc. accreditation   △ Commission on Accreditation of Rehabilitation Facilities (CARF) accreditation

---

COLORADO

ALAMOSA—Alamosa County

★ **SAN LUIS VALLEY HEALTH (060008)**, 106 Blanca Avenue, Zip 81101–2393; tel. 719/589–2511, **A**3 10 20 **F**3 7 11 13 15 18 28 29 30 31 33 34 40 43 45 53 57 59 70 74 75 77 78 79 81 82 85 93 97 107 108 110 111 115 119 129 130 131 146 147 148 154 155 156 **S** San Luis Valley Health, Alamosa, CO
Primary Contact: Konnie Martin, Chief Executive Officer
COO: Patti Thompson, Chief Operating Officer
CFO: Shane Mortensen, Chief Financial Officer
CMO: Gregory McAuliffe, M.D., Chief Medical Officer
CIO: Chuck Laufle, Director of Information Services
CHR: Mandy Lee Crockett, Director Human Resources
Web address: www.sanluisvalleyhealth.org
Control: Other not–for–profit (including NFP Corporation) **Service**: General medical and surgical

Staffed Beds: 44 **Admissions**: 1916 **Census**: 22 **Outpatient Visits**: 143006 **Births**: 440 **Total Expense ($000)**: 91770 **Payroll Expense ($000)**: 42174 **Personnel**: 720

ASPEN—Pitkin County

⊞ **ASPEN VALLEY HOSPITAL (061324)**, 0401 Castle Creek Road, Zip 81611–1159; tel. 970/925–1120, (Nonreporting) **A**1 10 18
Primary Contact: David Ressler, Chief Executive Officer
CFO: Ginette Sebenaler, Associate Chief Financial Officer
CMO: J Christopher Beck, D.O., President Medical Staff
CIO: Ginny Dyche, Director Community Relations
CHR: Alicia Miller, Director Human Resources
CNO: Elaine Gerson, Chief Clinical Officer and General Counsel
Web address: www.avhaspen.org
Control: Hospital district or authority, Government, nonfederal **Service**: General medical and surgical

Staffed Beds: 25

AURORA—Adams County

⊞ **CHILDREN'S HOSPITAL COLORADO (063301)**, 13123 East 16th Avenue, Zip 80045–7106; tel. 720/777–1234, (Includes CHILDREN'S HOSPITAL OF COLORADO AT MEMORIAL, 1400 East Boulder Street, Colorado Springs, Colorado, Zip 80909–5533; tel. 719/365–5000; Greg Raymond, Regional Vice President, Southern Colorado) **A**1 3 5 10 **F**3 11 12 13 14 17 19 21 23 25 27 28 29 30 31 32 34 35 36 38 39 40 41 43 44 45 46 48 49 50 53 54 55 58 59 60 61 64 65 66 68 71 72 74 75 76 77 78 79 80 81 82 84 85 86 87 88 89 91 92 93 95 96 97 98 99 100 101 102 104 107 108 111 114 115 116 117 119 126 129 130 131 132 134 136 137 138 139 141 144 146 147 148
Primary Contact: Jena Hausmann, President and Chief Executive Officer
COO: David Biggerstaff, Chief Operating Officer
CFO: Jeff Harrington, Chief Financial Officer
CMO: Joan Bothner, M.D., Chief Medical Officer
CIO: Dana Moore, Chief Information Officer
CNO: Patricia Givens, R.N., Chief Nursing Officer
Web address: www.thechildrenshospital.org
Control: Other not–for–profit (including NFP Corporation) **Service**: Children's general medical and surgical

Staffed Beds: 486 **Admissions**: 15214 **Census**: 280

AURORA—Arapahoe County

⊞ **KINDRED HOSPITAL-AURORA (062013)**, 700 Potomac Street 2nd Floor, Zip 80011–6844; tel. 720/857–8333, **A**1 10 **F**1 29 30 50 77 83 91 **S** Kindred Healthcare, Louisville, KY
Primary Contact: Jeanette Williams, Chief Executive Officer
CMO: Eric Yaeger, M.D., Chief Medical Officer
CHR: Becky Small, Chief Human Resources Officer
CNO: Paul Green, Chief Clinical Officer
Web address: www.khaurora.com/
Control: Individual, Investor–owned (for–profit) **Service**: Acute long–term care hospital

Staffed Beds: 23 **Admissions**: 184 **Census**: 24 **Outpatient Visits**: 0 **Births**: 0 **Total Expense ($000)**: 16741 **Payroll Expense ($000)**: 7681

⊞ **MEDICAL CENTER OF AURORA (060100)**, 1501 South Potomac Street, Zip 80012–5411; tel. 303/695–2600, (Includes MEDICAL CENTER OF AURORA NORTH, 700 Potomac Street, Aurora, Colorado, Zip 80011–6792; tel. 303/363–7200; MEDICAL CENTER OF AURORA, 700 Potomac Street, Aurora, Colorado, Zip 80011; tel. 303/360–3030; Ryan Simpson, President and Chief Executive Officer; SOUTH CAMPUS, 1501 South Potomac, Aurora, Colorado, Zip 80012; tel. 303/695–2600) **A**1 2 3 10 **F**3 11 15 18 20 22 24 26 28 29 30 31 34 35 38 40 41 42 43 44 45 46 47 48 49 50 54 55 56 59 63 64 68 70 72 74 75 76 77 78 79 80 81 84 87 89 91 97 98 99 100 101 102 103 104 105 107 110 111 114 115 116 117 118 119 126 129 130 131 132 146 147 148 153 154 **S** HCA Healthcare, Nashville, TN
Primary Contact: Ryan Simpson, President and Chief Executive Officer
COO: Mark S Deno, Chief Operating Officer
CFO: Bryce DeHaven, Chief Financial Officer
CMO: Dianne McCallister, M.D., Chief Medical Officer
CNO: Stacy Black, MSN, R.N., Associate Chief Nursing Officer
Web address: www.auroramed.com
Control: Corporation, Investor–owned (for–profit) **Service**: General medical and surgical

Staffed Beds: 261 **Admissions**: 16842 **Census**: 229 **Outpatient Visits**: 149313 **Births**: 1120

AURORA—Adams County

⊞ **SPALDING REHABILITATION HOSPITAL (063027)**, 900 Potomac Steet, Zip 80011–6716; tel. 303/367–1166, (Nonreporting) **A**1 10 **S** HCA Healthcare, Nashville, TN
Primary Contact: Ryan Simpson, President and Chief Executive Officer
COO: Debbie Petersen, R.N., Chief Operating Officer and Chief Nursing Officer
CFO: Joyce Webber, Chief Financial Officer
CHR: Donna Greeley, Director Human Resources
CNO: Stacy Black, MSN, R.N., Chief Nursing Officer
Web address: www.spaldingrehab.com
Control: Partnership, Investor–owned (for–profit) **Service**: Rehabilitation

Staffed Beds: 40

⊞ **UNIVERSITY OF COLORADO HOSPITAL (060024)**, 12401 East 17th Avenue, MS F417, Zip 80045–2545; tel. 720/848–0000, **A**1 2 3 5 8 10 **F**3 4 5 6 8 9 11 12 13 15 16 17 18 20 22 24 26 28 29 30 31 33 34 35 36 37 38 40 42 43 44 45 46 47 48 49 50 53 54 55 56 57 58 59 60 61 63 64 65 68 70 71 72 74 75 76 77 78 79 80 81 82 83 84 85 86 87 90 91 92 93 96 97 98 100 101 102 104 107 108 109 110 111 112 113 114 115 117 118 119 120 121 123 124 126 129 130 131 132 134 135 136 137 138 139 140 141 142 145 146 147 148 149 150 152 154 155 156 157 **S** UCHealth, Fort Collins, CO
Primary Contact: Christopher A. Gessner, President and Chief Executive Officer
COO: Thomas Gronow, Chief Operating Officer
CFO: Barbara Carveth, Chief Financial Officer
CMO: Jean Kutner, M.D., Chief Medical Officer
CIO: Steve Hess, Vice President Information Services and Chief Information Officer
CNO: Carolyn Lucey Sanders, Senior Vice President Patient Services and Chief Nursing Officer
Web address: www.uchealth.org
Control: Hospital district or authority, Government, nonfederal **Service**: General medical and surgical

Staffed Beds: 763 **Admissions**: 32217 **Census**: 567 **Outpatient Visits**: 1352830 **Births**: 3673 **Total Expense ($000)**: 1620534 **Payroll Expense ($000)**: 487665 **Personnel**: 6135

BOULDER—Boulder County

⊞ **BOULDER COMMUNITY HEALTH (060027)**, 4747 Arapahoe Ave, Zip 80303–1133, Mailing Address: P.O. Box 9019, Zip 80301–9019; tel. 303/415–7000, (Includes BOULDER COMMUNITY FOOTHILLS HOSPITAL, 4747 Arapahoe Avenue, Boulder, Colorado, Zip 80303–1133, Mailing Address: P O Box 9047, Zip 80301–9047, tel. 720/854–7000; Robert Vissers, M.D., President and Chief Executive Officer) **A**1 2 3 5 10 **F**3 5 7 8 13 15 18 20 22 24 26 28 29 30 31 34 35 36 37 40 42 43 45 46 49 50 54 56 59 60 61 62 64 65 68 70 72 74 75 76 77 78 79 81 84 85 87 90 93 94 96 97 98 100 101 102 104 107 109 110 111 112 114 115 118 119 126 130 132 144 146 147 148 149 153 155
Primary Contact: Robert Vissers, M.D., President and Chief Executive Officer
CFO: Bill Munson, Vice President and Chief Financial Officer
CNO: Jacqueline M Attlesey-Pries, MS, R.N., Chief Nursing Officer, Vice President
Web address: www.bch.org
Control: Other not–for–profit (including NFP Corporation) **Service**: General medical and surgical

Staffed Beds: 178 **Admissions**: 7792 **Census**: 93 **Outpatient Visits**: 339341 **Births**: 616 **Total Expense ($000)**: 357515 **Payroll Expense ($000)**: 159569 **Personnel**: 2069

CO

BRIGHTON—Adams County

★ **PLATTE VALLEY MEDICAL CENTER (060004)**, 1600 Prairie Center Parkway, Zip 80601–4006; tel. 303/498–1600, **A**5 10 **F**3 7 13 15 18 20 22 26 28 29 30 31 34 35 40 43 45 49 57 65 68 70 72 74 75 76 77 78 79 81 85 87 90 92 93 107 108 110 111 115 119 130 132 135 146 147 148 149 154 **S** SCL Health, Broomfield, CO
Primary Contact: John R. Hicks, President and Chief Executive Officer
COO: Kurt G Gensert, FACHE, R.N., Vice President Operations
CFO: Harold Dupper, Chief Financial Officer
CMO: Kirk Quackenbush, M.D., Chief of Staff
CIO: Timothy Brannigan, Director Information Services
CHR: Jackie J. Dunkin, Director Human Resources
Web address: www.pvmc.org
Control: Other not–for–profit (including NFP Corporation) **Service:** General medical and surgical

Staffed Beds: 70 **Admissions:** 3179 **Census:** 33 **Outpatient Visits:** 87608 **Births:** 655 **Total Expense ($000):** 112502 **Payroll Expense ($000):** 38193 **Personnel:** 518

BROOMFIELD—Denver County

☐ **UCHEALTH BROOMFIELD HOSPITAL (060129)**, 11820 Destination Drive, Zip 80021; tel. 303/460–6000, (Data for 212 days) **A**1 **F**29 30 40 68 75 79 81 85 87 100 107 115 119 130 148 154 **S** UCHealth, Fort Collins, CO
Primary Contact: Lonnie Cramer, President
Web address: www.uchealth.org/pages/OHAM/OrgUnitDetails.aspx?
Control: Hospital district or authority, Government, nonfederal **Service:** General medical and surgical

Staffed Beds: 18 **Admissions:** 85 **Census:** 2 **Outpatient Visits:** 35645 **Births:** 0 **Personnel:** 140

BRUSH—Morgan County

★ **EAST MORGAN COUNTY HOSPITAL (061303)**, 2400 West Edison Street, Zip 80723–1640; tel. 970/842–6200, **A**10 18 **F**3 13 15 28 29 34 35 36 40 43 45 50 53 57 59 61 65 68 75 76 77 79 81 85 86 87 89 93 96 107 108 110 115 119 127 130 131 132 133 135 141 146 147 148 149 154 **S** Banner Health, Phoenix, AZ
Primary Contact: Linda Thorpe, Chief Executive Officer
CFO: Edith Pemberton, Chief Financial Officer
CHR: Cynthia Wentworth, Chief Human Resource Officer
CNO: Linda Lyn Roan, Chief Nursing Officer
Web address: www.emchbrush.com
Control: Other not–for–profit (including NFP Corporation) **Service:** General medical and surgical

Staffed Beds: 19 **Admissions:** 464 **Census:** 4 **Births:** 94 **Total Expense ($000):** 31446 **Payroll Expense ($000):** 14027 **Personnel:** 181

BURLINGTON—Kit Carson County

★ **KIT CARSON COUNTY HEALTH SERVICE DISTRICT (061313)**, 286 16th Street, Zip 80807–1697; tel. 719/346–5311, (Nonreporting) **A**10 18
Primary Contact: Kelly Duke, Chief Operating Officer
CMO: Bong Pham, Chief Medical Officer
CIO: Paul Velasco, IT Manager
CHR: Robin Konecne, Manager Human Resources
CNO: Kandi Kuper, Chief Nursing Officer
Web address: www.kcchsd.org
Control: Hospital district or authority, Government, nonfederal **Service:** General medical and surgical

Staffed Beds: 19

CANON CITY—Fremont County

⊠ **ST. THOMAS MORE HOSPITAL (061344)**, 1338 Phay Avenue, Zip 81212–2302; tel. 719/285–2000, **A**1 10 18 **F**3 8 11 12 13 15 28 29 30 34 35 40 43 51 53 57 59 64 66 69 70 75 76 77 79 81 82 85 86 87 93 97 107 108 110 111 119 127 129 131 132 133 135 146 147 148 154 156 **S** CommonSpirit Health, Chicago, IL
Primary Contact: Kristi Olson, Chief Executive Officer
COO: Dennis Bruens, Vice President Operations
CFO: Gwenyth Howard, Vice President Finance
CMO: Kern Low, M.D., Chief Medical Officer
CIO: Jillian Maes, Director Marketing and Public Relations
CHR: Janet Reedy, Manager Human Resources
CNO: James Woodard, Chief Nursing Officer
Web address: www.stmhospital.org
Control: Church operated, Nongovernment, not–for–profit **Service:** General medical and surgical

Staffed Beds: 25 **Admissions:** 1854 **Census:** 16 **Outpatient Visits:** 45465 **Births:** 228 **Total Expense ($000):** 45855 **Payroll Expense ($000):** 16597

CASTLE ROCK—Douglas County

⊠ **CASTLE ROCK ADVENTIST HOSPITAL (060125)**, 2350 Meadows Boulevard, Zip 80109–8405; tel. 720/455–5000, **A**1 10 **F**3 11 13 15 18 20 22 29 30 32 34 35 37 38 40 41 43 44 45 48 49 50 53 57 59 60 62 64 65 67 68 70 72 74 75 76 77 79 81 85 86 87 89 91 93 101 102 107 108 110 111 114 115 118 119 129 130 131 135 146 147 148 154 156 **S** AdventHealth, Altamonte Springs, FL
Primary Contact: Brandon M. Nudd, Chief Executive Officer
CFO: Jeremy Pittman, Chief Financial Officer
Web address: www.castlerockhospital.org
Control: Church operated, Nongovernment, not–for–profit **Service:** General medical and surgical

Staffed Beds: 53 **Admissions:** 3364 **Census:** 27 **Outpatient Visits:** 40374 **Births:** 790 **Total Expense ($000):** 83940 **Payroll Expense ($000):** 28920 **Personnel:** 550

CHEYENNE WELLS—Cheyenne County

★ **KEEFE MEMORIAL HOSPITAL (061343)**, 602 North 6th Street West, Zip 80810, Mailing Address: P.O. Box 578, Zip 80810–0578; tel. 719/767–5661, (Nonreporting) **A**10 18
Primary Contact: Stella Worley, Interim Chief Executive Officer
CFO: Stella Worley, Director of Finance
CMO: Christine Connolly, M.D., Chief of Staff
CIO: Jeanne Moffat, Manager Information Technology
CHR: Carrie Rico, Chief Human Resource Officer
CNO: Jesse Smith, Director of Nursing
Web address: www.keefememorial.com
Control: County, Government, nonfederal **Service:** General medical and surgical

Staffed Beds: 11

COLORADO SPRINGS—El Paso County

☐ **CEDAR SPRINGS HOSPITAL (064009)**, 2135 Southgate Road, Zip 80906–2693; tel. 719/633–4114, (Nonreporting) **A**1 10 **S** Universal Health Services, Inc., King of Prussia, PA
Primary Contact: Christopher D. Burke, Ph.D., Chief Executive Officer
CFO: Cynthia D Deboer, Chief Financial Officer
CMO: Larry Shores, M.D., Executive Medical Director
CHR: Jessica McCoy, Director Human Resources
CNO: Jodi Mattson, Director of Nursing
Web address: www.cedarspringsbhs.com
Control: Corporation, Investor–owned (for–profit) **Service:** Psychiatric

Staffed Beds: 110

⊠ **HEALTHSOUTH REHABILITATION HOSPITAL OF COLORADO SPRINGS (063030)**, 325 Parkside Drive, Zip 80910–3134; tel. 719/630–8000, (Nonreporting) **A**1 10 **S** Encompass Health Corporation, Birmingham, AL
Primary Contact: Stephen Schaefer, Chief Executive Officer
CFO: Stephanie Davis, Controller
CHR: Diana Crepeau, Director Human Resources
CNO: Cindy Nordell, Chief Nursing Officer
Web address: www.healthsouthcoloradosprings.com
Control: Corporation, Investor–owned (for–profit) **Service:** Rehabilitation

Staffed Beds: 60

☐ **PEAK VIEW BEHAVIORAL HEALTH (064026)**, 7353 Sisters Grove, Zip 80923–2615; tel. 719/444–8484, **A**1 3 10 **F**5 29 35 38 54 56 99 100 101 103 104 105 152 153 **S** Strategic Behavioral Health, LLC, Memphis, TN
Primary Contact: Dan Zarecky, Chief Executive Officer
Web address: www.strategicbh.com/peakview.html
Control: Corporation, Investor–owned (for–profit) **Service:** Psychiatric

Staffed Beds: 112 **Admissions:** 3968 **Census:** 78 **Outpatient Visits:** 1680 **Births:** 0 **Personnel:** 311

CO

CO

⊞ **PENROSE-ST. FRANCIS HEALTH SERVICES (060031)**, 2222 North Nevada Avenue, Zip 80907–6799; tel. 719/776–5000, (Includes PENROSE HOSPITAL, 2222 North Nevada Avenue, Colorado Springs, Colorado, Zip 80907; tel. 719/776–5000; Brian Erling, Interim Chief Executive Officer; ST. FRANCIS MEDICAL CENTER, 6001 East Woodmen Road, Colorado Springs, Colorado, Zip 80923–2601; tel. 719/776–5000; Brian Erling, Interim Chief Executive Officer) **A**1 2 3 5 10 **F**3 5 11 12 13 14 15 17 18 20 22 24 26 28 29 30 31 34 35 36 37 38 39 40 41 43 44 45 46 47 48 49 50 52 53 54 55 56 57 58 59 61 62 64 65 68 70 71 72 74 75 76 77 78 79 81 82 84 85 86 87 89 90 91 92 93 94 96 97 100 101 102 107 108 110 114 115 118 119 120 121 123 124 126 127 129 130 131 132 135 144 146 147 148 149 150 154 **S** CommonSpirit Health, Chicago, IL
Primary Contact: Brian Erling, Interim Chief Executive Officer
COO: Lonnie Cramer, Chief Operating Officer
CFO: Danny Reeves, Chief Financial Officer
CMO: David Dull, M.D., Chief Medical Officer
CHR: James Humphrey, Vice President Talent Resources and Human Resources for South Side Operating Group
CNO: Cynthia Latney, Chief Nursing Officer
Web address: www.penrosestfrancis.org
Control: Church operated, Nongovernment, not–for–profit **Service:** General medical and surgical

Staffed Beds: 444 **Admissions:** 24801 **Census:** 266 **Outpatient Visits:** 201273 **Births:** 3028 **Total Expense ($000):** 520485 **Payroll Expense ($000):** 162268 **Personnel:** 2754

☐ **UCHEALTH GRANDVIEW HOSPITAL (060130)**, 5623 Pulpit Peak View, Zip 80918; tel. 719/272–3600, (Nonreporting) **A**1 **S** UCHealth, Fort Collins, CO
Primary Contact: Derek Rushing, Chief Executive Officer
Web address: www.https://www.uchealth.org/Pages/OHAM/OrgUnitDetails.aspx?OrganizationalUnitId=514
Control: Other not–for–profit (including NFP Corporation) **Service:** General medical and surgical

Staffed Beds: 22

⊞ **UCHEALTH MEMORIAL HOSPITAL (060022)**, 1400 East Boulder Street, Zip 80909–5599; tel. 719/365–5000, (Includes UCHEALTH MEMORIAL HOSPITAL NORTH, 4050 Briargate Parkway, Colorado Springs, Colorado, Zip 80909, Mailing Address: 1400 East Boulder Street, Zip 80909, tel. 719/365–5000; Joel P. Yuhas, FACHE, President and Chief Executive Officer) **A**1 2 3 10 **F**3 8 12 13 15 17 18 19 20 21 22 23 24 26 27 28 29 30 31 34 35 36 37 39 40 41 42 43 44 45 46 47 48 49 54 55 57 58 59 64 68 70 72 74 76 77 78 79 81 82 84 85 86 87 88 89 90 92 93 96 97 107 108 109 110 111 114 115 116 117 118 119 120 121 123 124 126 129 130 131 132 135 141 144 146 148 149 154 156 157 **S** UCHealth, Fort Collins, CO
Primary Contact: Joel P. Yuhas, FACHE, President and Chief Executive Officer
COO: Cherie Gorby, Chief Operations Officer
CFO: Dan Rieber, Chief Financial Officer
CMO: Jose Melendez, M.D., Chief Medical Officer
CHR: Jeffrey Johnson, Vice President
CNO: Kay J Miller, R.N., MSN, Chief Nursing Officer
Web address: www.uchealth.org/southerncolorado
Control: Other not–for–profit (including NFP Corporation) **Service:** General medical and surgical

Staffed Beds: 528 **Admissions:** 28145 **Census:** 335 **Outpatient Visits:** 535846 **Births:** 4579 **Total Expense ($000):** 695244 **Payroll Expense ($000):** 265422 **Personnel:** 2992

CORTEZ—Montezuma County

★ ⇑ **SOUTHWEST HEALTH SYSTEM (061327)**, 1311 North Mildred Road, Zip 81321–2299; tel. 970/565–6666, (Nonreporting) **A**10 18 21
Primary Contact: Anthony G. Sudduth, CPA, Interim Chief Executive Officer
CHR: Travis Parker, Director Human Resources
Web address: www.swhealth.org
Control: Other not–for–profit (including NFP Corporation) **Service:** General medical and surgical

Staffed Beds: 25

CRAIG—Moffat County

★ ⇑ **MEMORIAL REGIONAL HEALTH (061314)**, 750 Hospital Loop, Zip 81625–8750; tel. 970/824–9411, **A**10 18 21 **F**3 7 11 13 15 18 29 31 32 34 35 40 43 45 49 50 51 57 59 68 70 75 76 77 78 79 81 85 86 87 91 93 97 102 107 108 110 111 112 114 119 129 130 131 132 133 135 146 147 148
Primary Contact: Andrew J. Daniels, Chief Executive Officer
COO: Jennifer Riley, Vice President Operations
CFO: Kelsea Henry, Chief Financial Officer
CMO: Scott Ellis, D.O., Chief Medical Officer
CIO: Bryan Curtis, Chief Information Officer
CNO: Amy Peck, R.N., Chief Nursing Officer
Web address: www.thememorialhospital.com
Control: County, Government, nonfederal **Service:** General medical and surgical

Staffed Beds: 25 **Admissions:** 1013 **Census:** 9

DEL NORTE—Rio Grande County

★ **RIO GRANDE HOSPITAL (061301)**, 310 County Road 14, Zip 81132–8719; tel. 719/657–2510, **A**10 18 **F**34 40 43 57 65 81 93 107 111 115 119 127 129 133
Primary Contact: Arlene Harms, Chief Executive Officer
CFO: Greg Porter, Chief Financial Officer
CMO: Heidi E Helgeson, M.D., Chief Medical Officer
CIO: Denise Fietek, Information Technology
CHR: Paula Warner-Pacheco, Chief Human Resources
CNO: Candice Allen, Director of Nursing
Web address: www.rio-grande-hospital.org/
Control: Other not–for–profit (including NFP Corporation) **Service:** General medical and surgical

Staffed Beds: 17 **Admissions:** 590 **Census:** 6 **Outpatient Visits:** 50743

DELTA—Delta County

★ ⇑ **DELTA COUNTY MEMORIAL HOSPITAL (060071)**, 1501 East 3rd Street, Zip 81416–2815, Mailing Address: P.O. Box 10100, Zip 81416–0008; tel. 970/874–7681, **A**10 21 **F**3 8 9 13 15 28 29 30 31 34 40 43 45 50 57 59 62 70 75 76 77 78 79 81 85 87 90 93 107 108 110 111 115 119 129 135 141 144 146 147 148
Primary Contact: Jason Cleckler, Chief Executive Officer
CFO: Bev Carlson, Chief Financial Officer
CMO: John P Knutson, M.D., Chief Medical Staff
CIO: Mitch Van Scoyk, Manager Information Systems
CHR: Larry Vincent, Director Human Resources
Web address: www.deltahospital.org
Control: Hospital district or authority, Government, nonfederal **Service:** General medical and surgical

Staffed Beds: 49 **Admissions:** 1590 **Census:** 14 **Outpatient Visits:** 120097

DENVER—Denver, Adams and Arapaho Coun County

⊞ **COLORADO ACUTE LONG TERM HOSPITAL (062012)**, 1690 North Meade Street, Zip 80204–1552; tel. 303/264–6900, (Nonreporting) **A**1 10 **S** LifeCare Management Services, Plano, TX
Primary Contact: Craig Bailey, MS, Chief Executive Officer and Administrator
Web address: www.lifecare-hospitals.com/hospital/colorado
Control: Corporation, Investor–owned (for–profit) **Service:** Acute long–term care hospital

Staffed Beds: 63

☐ **COLORADO MENTAL HEALTH INSTITUTE AT FORT LOGAN (064003)**, 3520 West Oxford Avenue, Zip 80236–3197; tel. 303/866–7066, (Nonreporting) **A**1 3 5 10
Primary Contact: David M. Polunas, Director
CFO: Sabina Genesio, Finance Officer for Institutes
CMO: Bruce Leonard, M.D., Medical Director and Chief of Psychiatry
CNO: Nancy Kehiayan, Director of Nursing
Web address: www.cdhs.state.co.us/cmhifl
Control: State, Government, nonfederal **Service:** Psychiatric

Staffed Beds: 297

⊞ **DENVER HEALTH (060011)**, 777 Bannock Street, Zip 80204–4507, Mailing Address: 777 Bannock Street, MC0278, Zip 80204–4507; tel. 303/436–6000, **A**1 3 5 8 10 **F**3 5 7 8 11 12 13 15 18 19 20 22 26 28 29 30 31 32 34 35 36 37 38 39 40 41 42 43 44 45 46 49 50 52 53 54 55 56 57 58 59 60 61 64 65 66 68 70 71 72 74 75 76 77 78 79 80 81 82 84 85 86 87 88 89 90 92 93 94 96 97 98 99 100 101 102 103 104 107 108 110 111 114 115 118 119 127 129 130 131 132 134 135 143 144 146 147 148 149 153 154 156
Primary Contact: Robin D. Wittenstein, Ed.D., Chief Executive Officer
COO: Tim Harlin, M.D., Chief Operations Officer
CFO: Peg Burnette, Chief Financial Officer
CMO: Connie Price, M.D., Chief Medical Officer
CIO: Jeff Pelot, Interim Chief Information Officer
CHR: Tim Hansen, Interim Chief Human Resource Officer
CNO: Kathy Boyle, R.N., Ph.D., Chief Nursing Officer
Web address: www.denverhealth.org
Control: Hospital district or authority, Government, nonfederal **Service:** General medical and surgical

Staffed Beds: 431 **Admissions:** 21758 **Census:** 309 **Outpatient Visits:** 908399 **Births:** 3323 **Total Expense ($000):** 1094461 **Payroll Expense ($000):** 513867 **Personnel:** 6862

Many Facility Codes have changed. Please refer to the AHA Guide Code Chart. © 2019 AHA Guide

★ **KINDRED HOSPITAL DENVER SOUTH (062015)**, 2525 South Downing Street, 3 South, Zip 80210–5817; tel. 303/715–7373, (Nonreporting) **S** Kindred Healthcare, Louisville, KY
Primary Contact: Marc Lemon, Chief Executive Officer
Web address: www.kindreddenversouth.com/
Control: Corporation, Investor–owned (for–profit) **Service**: Acute long–term care hospital

Staffed Beds: 28

✠ **KINDRED HOSPITAL-DENVER (062009)**, 1920 High Street, Zip 80218–1213; tel. 303/320–5871, (Nonreporting) **A**1 10 **S** Kindred Healthcare, Louisville, KY
Primary Contact: Janelle Kircher, R.N., MSN, Chief Executive Officer
CFO: Tim Stecker, Chief Financial Officer
CMO: Eric Yaeger, M.D., Medical Director
Web address: www.kh-denver.com
Control: Corporation, Investor–owned (for–profit) **Service**: Acute long–term care hospital

Staffed Beds: 68

✠ **NATIONAL JEWISH HEALTH (060107)**, 1400 Jackson Street, Zip 80206–2762; tel. 303/388–4461, **A**1 3 5 8 10 **A**1 2 3 10 F3 9 11 12 18 20 28 29 30 31 32 34 35 36 44 45 46 48 50 53 54 55 57 58 59 61 62 64 65 66 68 70 74 75 77 78 84 86 87 89 90 93 96 97 98 99 100 101 104 107 108 111 114 115 116 117 118 119 127 129 130 132 134 135 143 145 146 147 149 154 156
Primary Contact: Michael Salem, M.D., President and Chief Executive Officer
COO: Ron Berge, Executive Vice President and Chief Operating Officer
CFO: Christine Forkner, Executive Vice President and Chief Financial Officer
CMO: Gary Cott, M.D., Executive Vice President Medical and Clinical Services
CIO: Lots Pook, Chief Information Officer
CHR: Sarah Taylor, Chief Human Resources
CNO: Jeff Downing, R.N., MS, Chief Nursing Officer
Web address: www.njhealth.org
Control: Other not–for–profit (including NFP Corporation) **Service**: Tuberculosis and other respiratory diseases

Staffed Beds: 76 **Admissions**: 49 **Census**: 1 **Outpatient Visits**: 112341 **Births**: 0 **Total Expense ($000)**: 259222 **Payroll Expense ($000)**: 133203 **Personnel**: 1629

✠ **PORTER ADVENTIST HOSPITAL (060064)**, 2525 South Downing Street, Zip 80210–5876; tel. 303/778–1955, **A**1 2 3 10 F3 4 5 6 0 11 15 17 10 20 22 24 26 28 29 30 31 34 35 36 37 38 39 40 43 44 45 46 47 48 49 50 53 54 55 56 57 58 59 60 63 64 65 68 70 74 75 77 78 79 81 82 83 84 85 86 87 90 91 92 93 94 96 97 98 100 101 102 103 104 105 107 108 109 110 111 112 114 115 116 117 118 119 120 121 122 123 124 125 126 130 131 132 135 138 139 141 143 146 147 148 153 155 156 **S** AdventHealth, Altamonte Springs, FL
Primary Contact: Todd Folkenberg, Chief Executive Officer
COO: David Dookeeram, Chief Operating Officer
CFO: Andrew Gaasch, Chief Financial Officer
CHR: Oz Muller, Director Human Resources
Web address: www.porterhospital.org/poh/home/
Control: Church operated, Nongovernment, not–for–profit **Service**: General medical and surgical

Staffed Beds: 250 **Admissions**: 9924 **Census**: 134 **Outpatient Visits**: 59925 **Births**: 0 **Total Expense ($000)**: 269938 **Payroll Expense ($000)**: 92365 **Personnel**: 1728

✠ **PRESBYTERIAN-ST. LUKE'S MEDICAL CENTER (060014)**, 1719 East 19th Avenue, Zip 80218–1281; tel. 720/754–6000, (Includes ROCKY MOUNTAIN HOSPITAL FOR CHILDREN, 1719 East 19th Avenue, Denver, Colorado, Zip 80218–1235; tel. 720/754–1000; Maureen Tarrant, President and Chief Executive Officer) **A**1 2 3 10 F3 11 12 13 14 18 19 20 21 22 23 24 25 26 27 28 29 30 31 34 35 36 37 40 41 45 46 47 48 49 50 52 53 54 55 56 58 59 60 61 64 65 68 70 72 73 74 75 76 77 78 79 81 82 84 85 86 89 91 92 93 94 95 96 97 102 107 108 111 114 115 116 117 118 119 120 121 123 126 129 130 131 132 135 138 139 146 147 148 156 **S** HCA Healthcare, Nashville, TN
Primary Contact: Maureen Tarrant, President and Chief Executive Officer
CFO: Shari Collier, Chief Financial Officer
CMO: Stephen Cobb, M.D., Chief Medical Officer
CIO: Jason Brakenhoff, Director Information Services
CHR: Keri Moore, Vice President Human Resources and Support Services
CNO: Amanda Veit, R.N., Chief Nursing Officer
Web address: www.pslmc.com
Control: Corporation, Investor–owned (for–profit) **Service**: General medical and surgical

Staffed Beds: 359 **Admissions**: 10989 **Census**: 213 **Outpatient Visits**: 56109

✠ **ROSE MEDICAL CENTER (060032)**, 4567 East Ninth Avenue, Zip 80220–3941; tel. 303/320–2121, **A**1 2 3 5 10 F3 8 11 12 13 15 17 18 20 22 24 26 28 29 30 31 34 35 40 44 45 46 49 50 52 53 54 58 59 60 61 63 64 65 68 70 72 74 75 76 77 78 79 81 82 84 85 86 87 91 92 93 94 96 97 100 101 102 107 108 110 111 112 114 115 116 117 118 119 120 121 122 123 126 129 130 131 132 135 144 146 147 148 149 154 **S** HCA Healthcare, Nashville, TN
Primary Contact: Ryan Tobin, President and Chief Executive Officer
CFO: Jac Connelly, Chief Financial Officer
CMO: Andrew Ziller, M.D., Chief Medical Officer
CIO: Dave Trevathan, Director Information Systems
CHR: Clarence McDavid, Vice President Human Resources
CNO: Lynne Wagner, R.N., Chief Nursing Officer
Web address: www.rosebabies.com
Control: Corporation, Investor–owned (for–profit) **Service**: General medical and surgical

Staffed Beds: 282 **Admissions**: 11462 **Census**: 114 **Outpatient Visits**: 107893

✠ **SAINT JOSEPH HOSPITAL (060028)**, 1375 East 19th Avenue, Zip 80218–1126; tel. 303/837–7111, **A**1 2 3 5 10 F3 8 11 12 13 15 18 20 22 24 26 28 29 30 31 34 35 37 40 42 43 45 46 49 50 55 58 60 63 64 66 68 70 71 72 74 75 76 77 78 79 81 82 84 85 87 93 107 108 110 111 115 116 117 119 120 121 123 124 126 130 145 146 149 154 156 157 **S** SCL Health, Broomfield, CO
Primary Contact: Jameson Smith, President
COO: Barbara A. Jahn, Chief Operating Officer
CFO: Alice W. Rigdon, Vice President Finance
CMO: Shawn Dufford, M.D., Vice President Medical Affairs and Chief Medical Officer
CHR: William R Gould, Vice President Human Resources
CNO: Mary Shepler, R.N., Vice President and Chief Nursing Officer
Web address: www.saintjosephdenver.org/
Control: Other not–for–profit (including NFP Corporation) **Service**: General medical and surgical

Staffed Beds: 379 **Admissions**: 19519 **Census**: 249 **Outpatient Visits**: 131847 **Births**: 4315 **Total Expense ($000)**: 521533 **Payroll Expense ($000)**: 163270 **Personnel**: 2267

★ **VETERANS AFFAIRS EASTERN COLORADO HEALTH CARE SYSTEM**, 1055 Clermont Street, Zip 80220–3877; tel. 303/399–8020, (Nonreporting) **A**5 **S** Department of Veterans Affairs, Washington, DC
Primary Contact: Sallie Houser-Hanfelder, FACHE, Director
CFO: Eliott R Vanderstek, Chief Fiscal Service
CMO: Ellen Manglone, M.D., Chief of Staff
CIO: Don Huckaby, Chief Information Management Service
CHR: Lorene Connel, Chief Human Resources Management Service
Web address: www.denver.va.gov/
Control: Veterans Affairs, Government, federal **Service**: General medical and surgical

Staffed Beds: 271

DURANGO—La Plata County

✠ **ANIMAS SURGICAL HOSPITAL (060117)**, 575 Rivergate Lane, Zip 81301–7487; tel. 970/247–3537, (Nonreporting) **A**10
Primary Contact: Brett Gosney, Chief Executive Officer
Web address: www.animassurgical.com/
Control: Corporation, Investor–owned (for–profit) **Service**: Surgical

Staffed Beds: 12

✠ **MERCY REGIONAL MEDICAL CENTER (060013)**, 1010 Three Springs Boulevard, Zip 81301–8296; tel. 970/247–4311, **A**1 2 10 20 F3 11 13 15 18 20 22 24 26 27 28 29 30 31 35 36 40 43 45 49 50 55 59 60 61 70 74 75 76 78 79 81 83 84 85 87 93 94 96 97 107 108 111 115 119 120 126 127 129 130 131 132 133 135 144 146 147 148 149 150 154 155 156 **S** CommonSpirit Health, Chicago, IL
Primary Contact: William McConnell, Ph.D., President and Chief Executive Officer
CFO: Jane Strobel, Vice President and Chief Financial Officer
CMO: William Plauth, M.D., Vice President Operations and Chief Medical Officer
CIO: Neil Stock, Director Technology and Facilities
CHR: Cathy Roberts, Vice President Mission Integration and Human Resources
CNO: Nancy Gerilyn Hoyt, R.N., Vice President Operations/Clinical and Chief Nursing Officer
Web address: www.mercydurango.org
Control: Church operated, Nongovernment, not–for–profit **Service**: General medical and surgical

Staffed Beds: 82 **Admissions**: 4194 **Census**: 38 **Outpatient Visits**: 135052 **Births**: 801 **Total Expense ($000)**: 149403 **Payroll Expense ($000)**: 47217 **Personnel**: 760

CO

EADS—Kiowa County

★ **WEISBROD MEMORIAL COUNTY HOSPITAL (061300)**, 1208 Luther Street, Zip 81036, Mailing Address: P.O. Box 817, Zip 81036–0817; tel. 719/438–5401, **A**10 18 **F**7 29 30 32 34 40 57 59 64 75 82 84 87 93 96 97 107 119 127 133 135 143 148 156
Primary Contact: Charlene Korrell, Chief Executive Officer
CFO: Shannon Dixon, Manager Business Office
CMO: Jeff Waggoner, M.D., Chief of Staff
CHR: Shannon Dixon, Manager Business Office
CNO: Wendy McDowell, R.N., Director of Nursing
Web address: www.kchd.org
Control: Hospital district or authority, Government, nonfederal **Service**: General medical and surgical

Staffed Beds: 25 **Admissions**: 52 **Census**: 1 **Outpatient Visits**: 3532 **Births**: 0 **Total Expense ($000)**: 7566 **Payroll Expense ($000)**: 3480 **Personnel**: 85

ENGLEWOOD—Arapahoe County

⊠ **CRAIG HOSPITAL (062011)**, 3425 South Clarkson Street, Zip 80113–2899; tel. 303/789–8000, **A**1 3 5 10 **F**29 30 34 35 36 44 50 53 58 64 68 74 75 77 81 86 87 90 91 93 95 96 97 100 104 130 132 146 148 149
Primary Contact: Jandel Allen-Davis, President and Chief Executive Officer
CFO: Daniel Frank, Chief Financial Officer
CMO: Thomas E Balazy, M.D., Medical Director
CHR: Stacy L Abel, Vice President People and Culture
CNO: Diane Reinhard, R.N., Vice President of Patient Care Services
Web address: www.craighospital.org
Control: Other not–for–profit (including NFP Corporation) **Service**: Rehabilitation

Staffed Beds: 93 **Admissions**: 489 **Census**: 79 **Outpatient Visits**: 17375 **Births**: 0 **Total Expense ($000)**: 106289 **Payroll Expense ($000)**: 52052 **Personnel**: 953

DENVER SPRINGS (064028), 8835 American Way, Zip 80112–7056; tel. 720/643–4300, **A**10 **F**4 40 53 64 68 77 87 98 100 101 102 104 105 130 132 133 135 143 153 154 **S** Springstone, Louisville, KY
Primary Contact: Bill Snyder, Chief Executive Officer
Web address: www.denversprings.com/
Control: Corporation, Investor–owned (for–profit) **Service**: Psychiatric

Staffed Beds: 96 **Admissions**: 1200 **Census**: 19 **Births**: 0

⊠ **SWEDISH MEDICAL CENTER (060034)**, 501 East Hampden Avenue, Zip 80113–2702; tel. 303/788–5000, **A**1 2 3 5 10 **F**3 8 11 13 16 18 20 22 24 26 29 30 31 34 35 37 40 42 43 45 46 47 48 49 50 51 53 54 55 56 58 59 60 63 64 65 68 70 72 74 75 76 77 78 79 81 82 85 87 88 89 90 91 92 94 96 97 107 108 109 111 113 114 115 116 117 118 119 121 123 124 126 129 130 132 141 145 146 147 148 149 154 **S** HCA Healthcare, Nashville, TN
Primary Contact: Richard A. Hammett, President and Chief Executive Officer
CFO: Kathy Ashenfelter, Chief Financial Officer
CMO: Monique Butler, Chief Medical Officer
CIO: Jeff Schnoor, Director Information Systems
CHR: Lisa Morris, Vice President Human Resources
CNO: Shari Chavez, Chief Nursing Officer
Web address: www.swedishhospital.com
Control: Corporation, Investor–owned (for–profit) **Service**: General medical and surgical

Staffed Beds: 386 **Admissions**: 20081 **Census**: 270 **Outpatient Visits**: 155068 **Births**: 1728 **Personnel**: 1487

ESTES PARK—Larimer County

⇧ **ESTES PARK MEDICAL CENTER (061312)**, 555 Prospect Avenue, Zip 80517–6312, Mailing Address: P.O. Box 2740, Zip 80517–2740; tel. 970/586–2317, (Nonreporting) **A**10 18 21
Primary Contact: Larry E. Leaming, Ph.D., FACHE, Chief Executive Officer
CFO: Tim Cashman, Chief Financial Officer
CMO: Paul Fonken, M.D., Chief of Staff
CIO: Gary Hall, Vice President of Information Technology
CHR: Randy Brigham, Chief Human Resource Officer
CNO: Cynthia Standlee, R.N., Chief Nursing Officer
Web address: www.epmedcenter.com
Control: Hospital district or authority, Government, nonfederal **Service**: General medical and surgical

Staffed Beds: 79

FORT CARSON—El Paso County

⊠ **EVANS U. S. ARMY COMMUNITY HOSPITAL**, 1650 Cochrane Circle, Building 7500, Zip 80913–4613; tel. 719/526–7200, (Nonreporting) **A**1 3 **S** Department of the Army, Office of the Surgeon General, Falls Church, VA
Primary Contact: Colonel Patrick M. Garman, Commander
COO: Lieutenant Colonel Steven D. Hankins, Chief Operating Officer
CFO: Major Bradley Robinson, Chief Financial Officer
CHR: Lieutenant Colonel Lory Gurr, Chief Human Resources Division
Web address: www.https://evans.amedd.army.mil/
Control: Department of Defense, Government, federal **Service**: General medical and surgical

Staffed Beds: 68

FORT COLLINS—Larimer County

★ **BANNER FORT COLLINS MEDICAL CENTER (060126)**, 4700 Lady Moon Drive, Zip 80528–4426; tel. 970/821–4000, **F**3 13 15 18 29 30 34 35 36 38 40 43 47 57 59 60 68 70 74 76 77 79 81 84 85 86 87 89 107 108 111 114 115 119 130 135 146 149 154 **S** Banner Health, Phoenix, AZ
Primary Contact: Margo Karsten, Ph.D., MSN, Chief Executive Officer
COO: Marilyn Fain, R.N., MSN, Chief Operating Officer
CFO: Lori Sehrt, Associate Chief Financial Officer Northern Colorado
CMO: Bert Honea, M.D., Associate Chief Medical Officer Northern Colorado
CHR: Kelly Hurt, Chief Human Resources Officer Northern Colorado and Western Region
CNO: Roberta Bean, R.N., Associate Chief Nursing Officer
Web address: www.bannerhealth.com/Locations/Colorado/Banner+Fort+Collins+Medical+Center
Control: Other not–for–profit (including NFP Corporation) **Service**: General medical and surgical

Staffed Beds: 23 **Admissions**: 1209 **Census**: 9 **Births**: 420 **Total Expense ($000)**: 43787 **Payroll Expense ($000)**: 12047 **Personnel**: 205

⊠ **UCHEALTH POUDRE VALLEY HOSPITAL (060010)**, 1024 South Lemay Avenue, Zip 80524–3998, Mailing Address: 2315 East Harmony Road, Suite 200, Zip 80528; tel. 970/495–7000, (Includes MOUNTAIN CREST HOSPITAL, 4601 Corbett Drive, Fort Collins, Colorado, Zip 80525; tel. 970/270–4800) **A**1 2 3 5 10 **F**3 5 7 11 12 13 14 15 18 20 22 23 29 30 31 32 33 34 35 38 39 40 42 43 44 45 46 47 48 49 50 53 54 55 57 58 59 60 61 64 65 66 68 69 70 72 73 74 75 76 77 78 79 80 81 82 83 84 85 86 87 89 90 92 93 98 99 100 101 102 103 104 105 106 107 108 110 111 114 115 118 119 120 121 123 124 126 129 130 131 132 134 135 143 146 147 148 149 150 153 154 156 157 **S** UCHealth, Fort Collins, CO
Primary Contact: Kevin L. Unger, Ph.D., FACHE, President and Chief Executive Officer
COO: Ryan Rohman, MSN, R.N., Chief Operating Officer
CFO: Stephanie Doughty, Chief Financial Officer
CIO: Fernando Pedroza, Vice President Information Technology
Web address: www.uchealth.org
Control: Other not–for–profit (including NFP Corporation) **Service**: General medical and surgical

Staffed Beds: 255 **Admissions**: 15669 **Census**: 161 **Outpatient Visits**: 356577 **Births**: 1986 **Total Expense ($000)**: 496976 **Payroll Expense ($000)**: 180990

FORT MORGAN—Morgan County

⊠ **COLORADO PLAINS MEDICAL CENTER (060044)**, 1000 Lincoln Street, Zip 80701–3298; tel. 970/867–3391, **A**1 3 10 20 **F**3 11 13 15 29 31 34 35 40 43 44 45 46 48 50 51 53 56 57 59 64 65 70 75 76 77 79 81 85 86 87 89 93 94 97 98 100 101 103 104 107 108 110 111 115 119 129 130 133 146 147 148 153 154 **S** LifePoint Health, Brentwood, TN
Primary Contact: Kevin Zachary, Chief Executive Officer
CFO: Christina Patton, Chief Financial Officer
CHR: Janet Brinkman, Director Human Resources
CNO: Sonya Bass, MS, Chief Nursing Officer
Web address: www.coloradoplainsmedicalcenter.com
Control: Corporation, Investor–owned (for–profit) **Service**: General medical and surgical

Staffed Beds: 50 **Admissions**: 1106 **Census**: 15

FRISCO—Summit County

⊠ **ST. ANTHONY SUMMIT MEDICAL CENTER (060118)**, 340 Peak One Drive, Zip 80443, Mailing Address: P.O. Box 738, Zip 80443–0738; tel. 970/668–3300, **A**1 10 **F**3 15 29 30 34 35 40 43 45 57 59 66 68 70 75 76 77 79 81 82 84 85 97 107 110 111 119 129 130 132 146 147 **S** CommonSpirit Health, Chicago, IL
Primary Contact: Lee Boyles, Chief Executive Officer
CNO: Trixie VanderSchaaff, Chief Nursing Officer
Web address: www.summitmedicalcenter.org
Control: Church operated, Nongovernment, not–for–profit **Service**: General medical and surgical

Staffed Beds: 34 **Admissions**: 1436 **Census**: 10 **Outpatient Visits**: 25670 **Births**: 409 **Total Expense ($000)**: 54542 **Payroll Expense ($000)**: 18122 **Personnel**: 349

Many Facility Codes have changed. Please refer to the AHA Guide Code Chart. © 2019 AHA Guide

FRUITA—Mesa County

★ **COLORADO CANYONS HOSPITAL AND MEDICAL CENTER (061302)**, 300 West Ottley Avenue, Zip 81521–2118, Mailing Address: P.O. Box 130, Zip 81521–0130; tel. 970/858–9871, **A**10 18 **F**3 9 10 15 29 30 34 35 36 40 41 43 45 50 53 54 56 57 59 64 65 68 74 75 77 79 81 82 85 86 87 90 93 107 110 111 115 119 128 129 130 131 132 133 143 144 146 148 149
Primary Contact: Mark J. Francis, President and Chief Executive Officer
CFO: Mark J Francis, President and Chief Executive Officer
CMO: Christopher Wibblesman, M.D., Chief of Staff
CIO: Derrick Diddle, Chief Information Officer
CHR: Kelly Murphy, Vice President Human Resources
CNO: Lori Henderson, Chief Nursing Officer, Vice President Clinical
Web address: www.fhw.org
Control: Other not–for–profit (including NFP Corporation) **Service:** General medical and surgical

Staffed Beds: 25 Admissions: 463 Census: 14 Outpatient Visits: 84093 Births: 0 Total Expense ($000): 42112 Payroll Expense ($000): 16069 Personnel: 404	

GLENWOOD SPRINGS—Garfield County

✠ **VALLEY VIEW HOSPITAL (060075)**, 1906 Blake Avenue, Zip 81601–4259; tel. 970/945–6535, **A**1 2 10 20 **F**3 4 13 15 18 20 22 24 26 28 29 30 31 32 34 35 36 37 38 40 43 44 45 46 49 50 51 54 57 58 59 64 68 69 70 74 75 76 77 78 79 81 82 84 85 86 87 92 93 94 97 104 107 108 110 111 114 115 116 117 118 119 120 121 123 124 126 129 130 131 132 135 145 146 147 148 151 153 154 156 **S** QHR, Brentwood, TN
Primary Contact: Brian Murphy, M.D., Chief Executive Officer
CFO: Charles Crevling, Chief Financial Officer
CMO: David Brooks, M.D., Chief Medical Officer
CHR: Daniel Biggs, Director Human Resources
CNO: Sandra Hurley, Chief Nursing Officer
Web address: www.vvh.org
Control: Other not–for–profit (including NFP Corporation) **Service:** General medical and surgical

Staffed Beds: 49 Admissions: 2956 Census: 34 Outpatient Visits: 130935 Births: 718 Total Expense ($000): 215314 Payroll Expense ($000): 88421 Personnel: 940	

GRAND JUNCTION—Mesa County

✠ **COMMUNITY HOSPITAL (060054)**, 2351 G Road, Zip 81505; tel. 970/242–0920, (Nonreporting) **A**1 10 **S** QHR, Brentwood, TN
Primary Contact: Chris Thomas, FACHE, President and Chief Executive Officer
CMO: Donald Nicolay, M.D., Chief Medical Officer
CIO: Bart Butzine, Director Information Technology
CNO: Kristin Gundt, Chief Nursing Officer
Web address: www.yourcommunityhospital.com
Control: Other not–for–profit (including NFP Corporation) **Service:** General medical and surgical

Staffed Beds: 78	

✠ **GRAND JUNCTION VETERANS HEALTH CARE SYSTEM**, 2121 North Avenue, Zip 81501–6428; tel. 970/242–0731, (Nonreporting) **A**1 **S** Department of Veterans Affairs, Washington, DC
Primary Contact: Michael T. Kilmer, Director
COO: Patricia A Hitt, Associate Director
CFO: Laquita Gruver, Fiscal Officer
CMO: William R Berryman, M.D., Chief of Staff
CIO: Craig Frerichs, Chief Information Technology Service
CHR: William Chester, Manager Human Resources
Web address: www.grandjunction.va.gov/
Control: Veterans Affairs, Government, federal **Service:** General medical and surgical

Staffed Beds: 23	

✠ **ST. MARY'S HOSPITAL AND MEDICAL CENTER (060023)**, 2635 North 7th Street, Zip 81501–8209, Mailing Address: P.O. Box 1628, Zip 81502–1628; tel. 970/298–2273, **A**1 2 3 10 **F**3 7 11 13 14 15 17 18 19 20 22 24 26 28 29 30 31 34 35 37 40 43 45 46 48 49 50 51 54 55 57 58 59 60 61 64 65 69 70 71 72 74 75 76 77 78 79 81 82 84 85 86 87 89 90 91 92 93 96 97 107 108 109 110 111 113 114 115 116 117 119 120 121 122 123 124 126 129 130 131 132 135 143 145 146 147 148 149 155 156 **S** SCL Health, Broomfield, CO
Primary Contact: Brian Davidson, M.D., President and Chief Medical Officer
COO: Reza Kaleel, Executive Vice President and Chief Operating Officer
CFO: Terri Chinn, Vice President Finance
CIO: John Bullard, Director Information Technology
CHR: Judy White House, Vice President Human Resources
CNO: Shelley Peterson, R.N., Vice President Patient Services and Chief Nursing Officer
Web address: www.stmarygj.com
Control: Other not–for–profit (including NFP Corporation) **Service:** General medical and surgical

Staffed Beds: 309 Admissions: 12842 Census: 183 Outpatient Visits: 189783 Births: 1522 Total Expense ($000): 403908 Payroll Expense ($000): 117729 Personnel: 1818	

VETERANS AFFAIRS MEDICAL CENTER See Grand Junction Veterans Health Care System

WEST SPRINGS HOSPITAL (064023), 515 28 3/4 Road, Zip 81501–5016; tel. 970/263–4918, (Nonreporting) **A**10
Primary Contact: Sharon Raggio, President and Chief Executive Officer
COO: Brandi Kroese, Director Operations
CFO: John Rattle, Chief Financial Officer
CMO: Jules Rosen, M.D., Chief Medical Officer
CIO: Charles Andrews, Director Information Technology
CHR: Karen Birmingham, Director Human Resources
CNO: Deborah Sharpe, R.N., Director of Nursing
Web address: www.WestSpringsHospital.org
Control: Other not–for–profit (including NFP Corporation) **Service:** Psychiatric

Staffed Beds: 32	

GREELEY—Weld County

✠ **NORTH COLORADO MEDICAL CENTER (060001)**, 1801 16th Street, Zip 80631–5154; tel. 970/352–4121, **A**1 2 3 5 10 **F**3 7 8 11 13 15 16 18 20 22 24 26 28 29 30 31 34 35 36 38 40 42 43 44 46 49 50 51 53 54 55 57 58 59 60 61 64 65 68 70 72 73 74 75 76 77 78 79 80 81 82 84 85 86 87 89 93 96 100 102 107 108 110 111 114 115 116 117 118 119 120 121 126 129 130 131 132 135 141 146 148 149 154 155 156 **S** Banner Health, Phoenix, AZ
Primary Contact: Margo Karsten, Ph.D., MSN, Chief Executive Officer
COO: Wendy Sparks, Chief Operating Officer
CFO: Mary McCabe, Chief Financial Officer
CHR: Jeannie Gallagher, Chief Human Resource Officer
CNO: Tiffany Erin Hettinger, Associate Chief Nursing Officer
Web address: www.ncmcgreeley.com
Control: Other not–for–profit (including NFP Corporation) **Service:** General medical and surgical

Staffed Beds: 236 Admissions: 10399 Census: 127 Births: 1542 Total Expense ($000): 336096 Payroll Expense ($000): 101142 Personnel: 1479	

GUNNISON—Gunnison County

✠ **GUNNISON VALLEY HOSPITAL (061320)**, 711 North Taylor Street, Zip 81230–2296; tel. 970/641–1456, **A**1 10 18 **F**3 7 11 13 15 29 30 31 32 34 35 40 43 44 45 56 57 59 64 68 76 77 78 85 87 93 97 107 110 111 114 119 129 132 133 135 146 147 148
Primary Contact: Robert J. Santilli, Chief Executive Officer
CFO: James P Barbuat, Chief Financial Officer
CIO: Trevor Smith, Chief Management Information Services
CHR: Christina Lovelace, Director Human Resources
CNO: Lisa Loughran, Chief Nursing Officer
Web address: www.gvh-colorado.org
Control: County, Government, nonfederal **Service:** General medical and surgical

Staffed Beds: 24 Admissions: 510 Census: 4	

Hospital, Medicare Provider Number, Address, Telephone, Approval, Facility, and Physician Codes, Health Care System

★ American Hospital Association (AHA) membership
□ The Joint Commission accreditation
○ Healthcare Facilities Accreditation Program
◇ DNV Healthcare Inc. accreditation
⇑ Center for Improvement in Healthcare Quality Accreditation
△ Commission on Accreditation of Rehabilitation Facilities (CARF) accreditation

CO

CO

HAXTUN—Phillips County

★ **HAXTUN HOSPITAL DISTRICT (061304)**, 235 West Fletcher Street, Zip 80731–2737; tel. 970/774–6123, **A**10 18 **F**3 7 40 43 54 56 59 64 65 75 77 87 93 97 107 114 119 129 133 146
Primary Contact: Dewane Pace, President and Chief Executive Officer
CFO: Rick Lee Nader, Chief Financial Officer
CMO: Colby Jolley, D.O., Acting Chief of Staff
CIO: Andrea Evers, Director Information Technology
CNO: Gail Phelps, R.N., Chief Nursing Officer
Web address: www.haxtunhealth.org
Control: Hospital district or authority, Government, nonfederal **Service:** General medical and surgical

Staffed Beds: 25 **Admissions:** 102 **Census:** 20 **Births:** 0

HOLYOKE—Phillips County

★ **MELISSA MEMORIAL HOSPITAL (061305)**, 1001 East Johnson Street, Zip 80734–1854; tel. 970/854–2241, **A**10 18 **F**7 8 15 18 28 29 30 34 35 40 41 43 46 47 48 49 50 53 56 57 59 64 65 67 68 71 75 77 79 81 82 85 87 90 91 92 93 97 107 110 111 112 114 119 127 128 129 133 143 146 147 148 149 152 154
Primary Contact: Trampas Hutches, Chief Executive Officer
CFO: Jason McCormick, Interim Chief Financial Officer
CMO: Dennis Jelden, M.D., Chief of Staff
CIO: David Bickford, Chief Information Officer
CHR: Sharon Greenman, Director Human Resources
CNO: Pat Notter, R.N., Chief Nursing Officer and Director Quality
Web address: www.melissamemorial.org
Control: Hospital district or authority, Government, nonfederal **Service:** General medical and surgical

Staffed Beds: 15 **Admissions:** 242 **Census:** 3 **Outpatient Visits:** 11410
Total Expense ($000): 17163 **Payroll Expense ($000):** 6461
Personnel: 102

HUGO—Lincoln County

★ **LINCOLN COMMUNITY HOSPITAL AND NURSING HOME (061306)**, 111 6th Street, Zip 80821–0248, Mailing Address: P.O. Box 248, Zip 80821–0248; tel. 719/743–2421, (Total facility includes 30 beds in nursing home–type unit) **A**10 18 **F**7 15 29 32 34 35 38 43 44 45 50 59 62 63 64 71 77 81 82 84 90 93 97 107 110 111 114 119 128 129 130 133 135 143 146 154 156
Primary Contact: Kevin M. Stansbury, Chief Executive Officer
CMO: Mark Olson, M.D., Chief of Staff
CIO: Michael Gaskins, Director Information Technology
CHR: Susan Petersen, Human Resources
CNO: Dan Walker, Chief Nursing Officer
Web address: www.lincolncommunityhospital.com
Control: County, Government, nonfederal **Service:** General medical and surgical

Staffed Beds: 45 **Admissions:** 233 **Census:** 28 **Births:** 0 **Total Expense ($000):** 18458 **Payroll Expense ($000):** 9756 **Personnel:** 220

JOHNSTOWN—Larimer County

☐ **NORTHERN COLORADO LONG TERM ACUTE HOSPITAL (062017)**, 4401 Union Street, Zip 80534; tel. 970/619–3663, (Nonreporting) **A**1 10 **S** Ernest Health, Inc., Albuquerque, NM
Primary Contact: Blake Sims, Chief Executive Officer
Web address: www.ncltah.ernesthealth.com/
Control: Partnership, Investor–owned (for–profit) **Service:** Acute long–term care hospital

Staffed Beds: 40

☐ **NORTHERN COLORADO REHABILITATION HOSPITAL (063033)**, 4401 Union Street, Zip 80534–2800; tel. 970/619–3400, (Nonreporting) **A**1 10 **S** Ernest Health, Inc., Albuquerque, NM
Primary Contact: Brenda Simon, Chief Executive Officer
CFO: Bonnie Cushman, Chief Financial Officer
CMO: Revelyn Arrogante, M.D., Medical Director
CHR: Amy Lauridsen, Director Human Resources
CNO: Mark Smith, Director Nursing Operations
Web address: www.ncrh.ernesthealth.com
Control: Corporation, Investor–owned (for–profit) **Service:** Rehabilitation

Staffed Beds: 40

JULESBURG—Sedgwick County

SEDGWICK COUNTY HEALTH CENTER (061310), 900 Cedar Street, Zip 80737–1199; tel. 970/474–3323, (Total facility includes 52 beds in nursing home–type unit) **A**10 18 **F**3 10 13 32 40 43 45 53 56 57 59 64 65 66 67 68 76 77 81 89 93 107 111 114 119 127 128 130 133 145 148
Primary Contact: Karla Dunker, Chief Executive Officer
CMO: Donald Regier, M.D., Chief Medical Officer
CHR: Sonja Bell, Coordinator Human Resources
Web address: www.schealth.org/
Control: County, Government, nonfederal **Service:** General medical and surgical

Staffed Beds: 67 **Admissions:** 216 **Census:** 51 **Outpatient Visits:** 14467
Births: 14 **Total Expense ($000):** 10347 **Payroll Expense ($000):** 5241
Personnel: 97

KREMMLING—Grand County

★ **MIDDLE PARK MEDICAL CENTER-KREMMLING (061318)**, 214 South Fourth Street, Zip 80459, Mailing Address: P.O. Box 399, Zip 80459–0399; tel. 970/724–3442, (Includes MIDDLE PARK MEDICAL CENTER - GRANBY, 1000 Granby Park Drive South, Granby, Colorado, Zip 80446, Mailing Address: P.O. Box 399, Kremmling, Zip 80446, tel. 970/887–5800; Robert Flake, Chief Executive Officer), (Nonreporting) **A**10 18
Primary Contact: Robert Flake, Chief Executive Officer
CFO: Robert Flake, Chief Financial Officer
CMO: Thomas C. Coburn, M.D., Chief Medical Officer
CHR: Jason Bryan, Director Human Resources
CNO: Debra Plemmons, Chief Nursing Officer
Web address: www.mpmc.org
Control: Hospital district or authority, Government, nonfederal **Service:** General medical and surgical

Staffed Beds: 10

LA JARA—Conejos County

★ **SAN LUIS VALLEY HEALTH CONEJOS COUNTY HOSPITAL (061308)**, 19021 U S Highway 285, Zip 81140–0639, Mailing Address: P.O. Box 639, Zip 81140–0639; tel. 719/274–5121, **A**10 18 **F**3 29 40 43 54 56 59 64 70 76 87 89 93 97 107 114 119 127 128 133 **S** San Luis Valley Health, Alamosa, CO
Primary Contact: Kelly Gallegos, Administrator
CFO: Shane Mortensen, Chief Financial Officer
CMO: Gregory McAuliffe, M.D., Chief Medical Officer
CIO: Kathy Rogers, Vice President Marketing
CHR: Mandy Lee Crockett, Director Human Resources
CNO: Tandra Dunn, Director of Nursing
Web address: www.sanluisvalleyhealth.org/locations/conejos-county-hospital
Control: Other not–for–profit (including NFP Corporation) **Service:** General medical and surgical

Staffed Beds: 17 **Admissions:** 165 **Census:** 3

LA JUNTA—Otero County

⊞ **ARKANSAS VALLEY REGIONAL MEDICAL CENTER (061336)**, 1100 Carson Avenue, Zip 81050–2799; tel. 719/383–6000, (Nonreporting) **A**1 10 18 **S** QHR, Brentwood, TN
Primary Contact: Lynn Crowell, Chief Executive Officer
CMO: Kent E. Gay, M.D., Chief of Medical Staff
CIO: Heidi Gearhart, Director Information Systems
CHR: Kelsey B. Brundage, Director Human Resources
CNO: Carrie Cutrell, Chief Nursing Officer
Web address: www.avrmc.org
Control: Other not–for–profit (including NFP Corporation) **Service:** General medical and surgical

Staffed Beds: 106

LAFAYETTE—Boulder County

⊞ **GOOD SAMARITAN MEDICAL CENTER (060116)**, 200 Exempla Circle, Zip 80026–3370; tel. 303/689–4000, **A**1 2 10 **F**3 11 12 13 15 18 20 22 26 28 29 30 31 32 34 35 36 40 41 43 45 46 47 49 50 51 60 64 68 70 72 74 75 76 77 78 79 80 81 84 85 86 87 91 92 93 100 102 107 108 110 111 114 115 117 118 119 120 121 123 124 126 130 132 135 143 146 147 148 149 150 154 156 **S** SCL Health, Broomfield, CO
Primary Contact: Jennifer Alderfer, President
COO: Beth Forsyth, Chief Operating Officer
CFO: John Higgins, Vice President and Chief Financial Officer
CMO: Todd Mydler, M.D., Vice President and Chief Medical Officer
CHR: Amy Pacey, Vice President Human Resources
CNO: Susan Kerschen, MS, R.N., Vice President and Chief Nursing Officer
Web address: www.goodsamaritancolorado.org/
Control: Other not–for–profit (including NFP Corporation) **Service:** General medical and surgical

Staffed Beds: 176 **Admissions:** 12500 **Census:** 142 **Outpatient Visits:** 93678 **Births:** 1909 **Total Expense ($000):** 290720 **Payroll Expense ($000):** 92575 **Personnel:** 1237

LAKEWOOD—Jefferson County

⊞ **ORTHOCOLORADO HOSPITAL (060124)**, 11650 West 2nd Place, Zip 80228–1527; tel. 720/321–5000, (Nonreporting) **A**1 10 **S** CommonSpirit Health, Chicago, IL
Primary Contact: Jude Torchia, Chief Executive Officer
Web address: www.orthocolorado.org
Control: Partnership, Investor–owned (for–profit) **Service:** Orthopedic

Staffed Beds: 48

Many Facility Codes have changed. Please refer to the AHA Guide Code Chart. © 2019 AHA Guide

✠ **ST. ANTHONY HOSPITAL (060015)**, 11600 West Second Place, Zip 80228–1527; tel. 720/321–0000, **A**1 2 3 5 10 **F**3 7 8 11 15 17 18 20 22 24 26 28 29 30 31 34 35 36 38 40 42 43 45 46 47 48 49 50 53 56 57 59 64 65 66 68 70 74 75 77 78 79 81 82 84 85 87 90 92 93 96 97 102 107 108 111 114 115 116 117 118 119 120 121 123 124 126 129 130 131 132 133 134 135 144 146 147 148 149 154 155 **S** CommonSpirit Health, Chicago, IL
Primary Contact: Peter Powers, Chief Executive Officer
CMO: Brian Erling, Group Chief Medical Officer
CHR: Michelle Fornier-Johnson, Group Vice President Human Resources
Web address: www.stanthonyhosp.org
Control: Church operated, Nongovernment, not–for–profit **Service:** General medical and surgical

> **Staffed Beds:** 219 **Admissions:** 11875 **Census:** 165 **Outpatient Visits:** 89786 **Births:** 0 **Total Expense ($000):** 331436 **Payroll Expense ($000):** 100479 **Personnel:** 1953

LAMAR—Prowers County

★ ⇑ **PROWERS MEDICAL CENTER (061323)**, 401 Kendall Drive, Zip 81052–3993; tel. 719/336–4343, **A**10 18 21 **F**3 11 13 15 18 20 28 29 31 34 35 40 44 45 50 56 57 59 62 64 65 66 68 76 77 78 81 85 86 93 96 97 107 111 115 119 127 130 131 132 133 135 146 147 148 154 **S** QHR, Brentwood, TN
Primary Contact: Craig Loveless, Chief Executive Officer
COO: Karen Bryant, Chief Support Services Officer
CFO: Audrey Kane, Interim Chief Financial Officer
CMO: Barry Portner, M.D., Chief of Staff
CIO: Jason Spano, Director of Information Technology
CHR: Karen Bryant, Chief Support Services Officer
Web address: www.prowersmedical.com
Control: Hospital district or authority, Government, nonfederal **Service:** General medical and surgical

> **Staffed Beds:** 25 **Admissions:** 1240 **Census:** 12

LEADVILLE—Lake County

⇑ **ST. VINCENT GENERAL HOSPITAL DISTRICT (061319)**, 822 West 4th Street, Zip 80461–3897; tel. 719/486–0230, **A**10 18 21 **F**3 7 29 34 35 40 44 50 57 59 87 93 97 107 119 133 143 157
Primary Contact: Gary Campbell, Chief Executive Officer
CMO: Gary Petry, M.D., Chief of Staff
CHR: Cheryl Snider, Director Human Resources
CNO: Von Kilpatrick, Chief Nursing Officer
Web address: www.svghd.org
Control: Hospital district or authority, Government, nonfederal **Service:** General medical and surgical

> **Staffed Beds:** 8 **Admissions:** 165 **Census:** 1 **Outpatient Visits:** 6190 **Births:** 0 **Total Expense ($000):** 9342 **Payroll Expense ($000):** 5071 **Personnel:** 76

LITTLETON—Jefferson County

FEDERAL CORRECTIONAL INSTITUTE HOSPITAL, 9595 West Quincy Street, Zip 80123–1159; tel. 303/985–1566, (Nonreporting)
Primary Contact: Mike Hudson, Administrator
Control: Department of Justice, Government, federal **Service:** Hospital unit of an institution (prison hospital, college infirmary, etc.)

> **Staffed Beds:** 6

LITTLETON—Arapahoe County

✠ **HEALTHSOUTH REHABILITATION HOSPITAL OF LITTLETON (063034)**, 1001 West Mineral Avenue, Zip 80120–4507; tel. 303/334–1100, (Nonreporting) **A**1 10 **S** Encompass Health Corporation, Birmingham, AL
Primary Contact: David H. Shefte, Chief Executive Officer
CFO: Liz Freudenberg, Chief Financial Officer
CMO: Jill Castro, M.D., Medical Director
CHR: Sarah Thomas, Director of Human Resources
Web address: www.healthsouthdenver.com
Control: Corporation, Investor–owned (for–profit) **Service:** Rehabilitation

> **Staffed Beds:** 28

LITTLETON—Douglas County

☐ **HIGHLANDS BEHAVIORAL HEALTH SYSTEM (064024)**, 8565 South Poplar Way, Zip 80130–3602; tel. 720/348–2800, (Nonreporting) **A**1 10 **S** Universal Health Services, Inc., King of Prussia, PA
Primary Contact: Amy Alexander, Chief Executive Officer
Web address: www.highlandsbhs.com
Control: Corporation, Investor–owned (for–profit) **Service:** Psychiatric

> **Staffed Beds:** 86

LITTLETON—Arapahoe County

✠ **LITTLETON ADVENTIST HOSPITAL (060113)**, 7700 South Broadway Street, Zip 80122–2628; tel. 303/730–8900, **A**1 2 3 5 10 **F**3 11 13 15 17 18 20 22 26 29 30 31 34 35 36 39 40 41 42 43 44 45 46 47 48 49 50 53 54 55 57 58 59 64 68 70 72 74 75 76 77 78 79 81 82 83 84 85 86 87 89 90 91 92 93 97 107 108 110 111 114 115 116 117 118 119 121 126 130 131 132 135 146 147 148 156 **S** AdventHealth, Altamonte Springs, FL
Primary Contact: Geoff Lawton, Interim Chief Executive Officer
COO: Geoff Lawton, Vice President Operations
CFO: Cheryl Curry, Chief Financial Officer
CMO: Lawrence Wood, M.D., Chief Medical Officer
CHR: Rita K Arthur, Director Human Resources
CNO: Rhonda Ward, R.N., MSN, Chief Nursing Officer
Web address: www.centura.org
Control: Church operated, Nongovernment, not–for–profit **Service:** General medical and surgical

> **Staffed Beds:** 176 **Admissions:** 9900 **Census:** 118 **Outpatient Visits:** 56701 **Births:** 1504 **Total Expense ($000):** 208404 **Payroll Expense ($000):** 73638 **Personnel:** 1266

LONE TREE—Douglas County

✠ **SKY RIDGE MEDICAL CENTER (060112)**, 10101 Ridge Gate Parkway, Zip 80124–5522; tel. 720/225–1000, **A**1 2 3 5 10 12 13 **F**3 8 12 15 17 18 20 22 26 28 29 30 31 34 35 36 37 40 41 43 44 45 46 47 48 49 50 54 57 58 59 64 70 72 74 75 76 77 78 79 81 82 84 85 86 87 89 93 107 108 111 114 115 119 120 121 123 126 129 130 131 132 135 146 147 148 149 157 **S** HCA Healthcare, Nashville, TN
Primary Contact: Susan Hicks, Chief Executive Officer
CFO: Craig Sammons, Chief Financial Officer
CMO: David Markenson, M.D., Chief Medical Officer
CIO: Evan Tice, Director Information Technology and Systems
CHR: Jim Ritchey, Director Human Resources
CNO: Marian Savitsky, R.N., Chief Nursing Officer
Web address: www.skyridgemedcenter.com
Control: Corporation, Investor–owned (for–profit) **Service:** General medical and surgical

> **Staffed Beds:** 274 **Admissions:** 16413 **Census:** 149 **Outpatient Visits:** 100201 **Births:** 3324 **Personnel:** 1199

LONGMONT—Boulder County

✠ **LONGMONT UNITED HOSPITAL (060003)**, 1950 West Mountain View Avenue, Zip 80501–3162, Mailing Address: P.O. Box 1659, Zip 80502–1659; tel. 303/651–5111, **A**1 2 10 **F**3 11 13 15 18 20 22 28 29 30 31 34 35 36 37 38 40 43 44 45 47 48 49 50 53 54 56 57 59 61 64 68 70 73 74 75 76 77 78 79 81 82 84 85 86 87 89 92 93 107 108 110 111 114 115 118 119 121 123 126 129 130 131 132 135 146 148 149 150 154 **S** CommonSpirit Health, Chicago, IL
Primary Contact: Christina Johnson, M.D., Chief Executive Officer
CFO: Daniel Frank, Chief Financial Officer
CMO: Wyatt Hall, M.D., Chief Medical Officer
CHR: Warren Laughlin, Vice President Human Resources
CNO: Nancy Driscoll, Chief Nursing Officer
Web address: www.luhcares.org
Control: Other not-for-profit (including NFP Corporation) **Service:** General medical and surgical

> **Staffed Beds:** 131 **Admissions:** 5014 **Census:** 53 **Outpatient Visits:** 74942 **Births:** 605 **Total Expense ($000):** 142672 **Payroll Expense ($000):** 48979 **Personnel:** 599

LONGMONT—Weld County

☐ **UCHEALTH LONGS PEAK HOSPITAL (060128)**, 1750 East Ken Pratt Boulevard, Zip 80504–5311; tel. 970/237–7850, (Data for 303 days) **A**1 **F**3 7 8 11 12 13 15 17 18 20 26 29 30 34 35 37 40 43 45 46 47 48 49 50 56 57 59 64 68 70 73 74 75 76 79 81 82 84 85 87 89 90 93 102 107 108 111 114 115 117 118 119 126 130 131 132 134 146 147 148 149 154 157 **S** UCHealth, Fort Collins, CO
Primary Contact: Lonnie Cramer, President
Web address: www.https://www.uchealth.org/locations/uchealth-longs-peak-hospital/
Control: Other not-for-profit (including NFP Corporation) **Service:** General medical and surgical

> **Staffed Beds:** 47 **Admissions:** 2011 **Census:** 21 **Outpatient Visits:** 14049 **Births:** 563 **Total Expense ($000):** 76051 **Payroll Expense ($000):** 27773 **Personnel:** 233

Hospital, Medicare Provider Number, Address, Telephone, Approval, Facility, and Physician Codes, Health Care System

★ American Hospital Association (AHA) membership
☐ The Joint Commission accreditation
○ Healthcare Facilities Accreditation Program
◇ DNV Healthcare Inc. accreditation
⇑ Center for Improvement in Healthcare Quality Accreditation
△ Commission on Accreditation of Rehabilitation Facilities (CARF) accreditation

CO

LOUISVILLE—Boulder County

✠ **AVISTA ADVENTIST HOSPITAL (060103)**, 100 Health Park Drive, Zip 80027–9583; tel. 303/673–1000, **A**1 3 10 **F**3 8 11 13 15 17 18 20 22 28 29 30 31 34 40 42 43 44 45 47 48 49 50 56 59 60 62 63 64 68 70 72 74 75 76 77 79 81 82 84 85 86 87 90 93 107 108 111 114 115 119 129 130 131 132 135 146 147 157 **S** AdventHealth, Altamonte Springs, FL
Primary Contact: Jillyan McKinney, Chief Executive Officer
CMO: David Ehrenberger, M.D., Chief Medical Officer
CHR: Becky Ortega, Manager Human Resources
CNO: Lavah Boyers Lowe, Chief Nursing Officer
Web address: www.avistahospital.org
Control: Church operated, Nongovernment, not–for–profit **Service**: General medical and surgical

Staffed Beds: 108 **Admissions**: 4616 **Census**: 39 **Outpatient Visits**: 41772 **Births**: 2390 **Total Expense ($000)**: 91107 **Payroll Expense ($000)**: 34216 **Personnel**: 653

☐ **CENTENNIAL PEAKS HOSPITAL (064007)**, 2255 South 88th Street, Zip 80027–9716; tel. 303/673–9990, (Nonreporting) **A**1 10 **S** Universal Health Services, Inc., King of Prussia, PA
Primary Contact: Elicia Bunch, Chief Executive Officer
COO: Lisa Strub, Chief Operating Officer
CFO: Tim Ryan, Chief Financial Officer
CMO: Konoy Mandal, M.D., Medical Director
CHR: Suzanne Martinez, Director Human Resources
CNO: Donia L Andersen, Director of Nursing
Web address: www.centennialpeaks.com
Control: Other not–for–profit (including NFP Corporation) **Service**: Psychiatric

Staffed Beds: 72

LOVELAND—Larimer County

✠ **MCKEE MEDICAL CENTER (060030)**, 2000 Boise Avenue, Zip 80538–4281; tel. 970/669–4640, **A**1 2 10 **F**2 3 8 11 13 14 15 18 20 22 26 28 29 30 31 34 35 36 40 42 43 44 50 54 56 59 60 62 64 65 68 70 74 75 76 77 78 79 81 84 85 87 89 92 93 97 107 108 110 111 114 115 119 120 121 122 123 124 126 129 130 135 144 146 147 148 149 154 **S** Banner Health, Phoenix, AZ
Primary Contact: Margo Karsten, Ph.D., MSN, Chief Executive Officer
COO: Julie Klein, Chief Operating Officer
CFO: Lori Sehrt, Chief Financial Officer
CMO: Bert Honea, M.D., Medical Director
CIO: Steve Rains, Director Information Services
CHR: Jeannie Gallagher, jeanie.gallagher@bannerhealth.com
CNO: Kelly Sturler, Chief Nursing Officer
Web address: www.mckeeloveland.com
Control: Other not–for–profit (including NFP Corporation) **Service**: General medical and surgical

Staffed Beds: 96 **Admissions**: 3067 **Census**: 28 **Births**: 434 **Total Expense ($000)**: 117807 **Payroll Expense ($000)**: 35538 **Personnel**: 497

✠ **UCHEALTH MEDICAL CENTER OF THE ROCKIES (060119)**, 2500 Rocky Mountain Avenue, Zip 80538–9004; tel. 970/624–2500, **A**1 3 5 10 **F**3 11 13 14 15 17 18 20 22 24 26 28 29 30 31 32 34 35 38 39 40 42 43 44 45 47 49 50 54 55 57 58 59 60 61 64 65 68 70 74 75 76 77 78 79 80 81 82 83 84 85 86 87 89 92 93 96 100 102 107 108 110 111 114 115 118 119 126 129 130 131 132 134 135 146 147 148 149 150 154 155 156 157 **S** UCHealth, Fort Collins, CO
Primary Contact: Kevin L. Unger, Ph.D., FACHE, President and Chief Executive Officer
COO: Ryan Rohman, MSN, R.N., Chief Operating Officer
CFO: Stephanie Doughty, Chief Financial Officer
CMO: William Neff, M.D., Chief Medical Officer
CIO: Steve Hess, Vice President & Chief Information Officer
Web address: www.medctrrockies.org
Control: Other not–for–profit (including NFP Corporation) **Service**: General medical and surgical

Staffed Beds: 174 **Admissions**: 11934 **Census**: 134 **Outpatient Visits**: 97224 **Births**: 1485 **Total Expense ($000)**: 417333 **Payroll Expense ($000)**: 121565

MEEKER—Rio Blanco County

★ **PIONEERS MEDICAL CENTER (061325)**, 100 Pioneers Medical Center Drive, Zip 81641–3181; tel. 970/878–5047, (Nonreporting) **A**10 18 **S** QHR, Brentwood, TN
Primary Contact: Kenneth Harman, Chief Executive Officer
COO: Karen Iacuone, Chief Nursing Officer and Chief Operating Officer
CFO: James W Worrell, Chief Financial Officer
CMO: Christopher Williams, M.D., Chief of Staff
CIO: Curtis Cooper, Manager Information Systems
CHR: Twyla Jensen, Director Human Resources
CNO: Karen Iacuone, Chief Nursing Officer
Web address: www.pioneershospital.org
Control: Hospital district or authority, Government, nonfederal **Service**: General medical and surgical

Staffed Beds: 45

MONTROSE—Montrose County

✠ **MONTROSE MEMORIAL HOSPITAL (060006)**, 800 South Third Street, Zip 81401–4212; tel. 970/249–2211, **A**1 10 20 **F**3 13 15 18 20 22 28 29 30 31 34 35 40 43 44 45 46 50 51 57 59 64 68 70 74 75 76 77 78 79 81 82 85 89 90 92 93 96 107 108 110 111 115 118 119 126 129 130 132 135 146 147 148 154 **S** QHR, Brentwood, TN
Primary Contact: James R. Kiser II, Chief Executive Officer
COO: Mary E Snyder, Chief Operations Officer
CFO: Stephan A Wilson, Chief Financial Officer
CMO: Richard Shannon, M.D., Chief of Staff
CIO: Carlos Lovera, Director Information Systems
CHR: Kathy McKie, Director Human Resources
Web address: www.montrosehospital.com
Control: Other not–for–profit (including NFP Corporation) **Service**: General medical and surgical

Staffed Beds: 60 **Admissions**: 2883 **Census**: 25

PAGOSA SPRINGS—Archuleta County

PAGOSA SPRINGS MEDICAL CENTER (061328), 95 South Pagosa Boulevard, Zip 81147–8329; tel. 970/731–3700, **A**10 18 **F**3 7 11 15 18 29 30 31 32 34 35 38 40 43 45 50 54 55 56 57 59 61 64 65 66 68 74 78 79 81 82 84 85 86 87 89 90 93 97 100 102 104 107 110 111 115 119 127 128 130 131 133 135 143 144 145 146 147 148 154 156 157
Primary Contact: Rhonda Webb, M.D., Chief Executive Officer
Web address: www.pagosaspringsmedicalcenter.org/
Control: Hospital district or authority, Government, nonfederal **Service**: General medical and surgical

Staffed Beds: 11 **Admissions**: 453 **Census**: 3 **Outpatient Visits**: 66926 **Births**: 0 **Total Expense ($000)**: 34964 **Payroll Expense ($000)**: 18782 **Personnel**: 232

PARKER—Douglas County

✠ **PARKER ADVENTIST HOSPITAL (060114)**, 9395 Crown Crest Boulevard, Zip 80138–8573; tel. 303/269–4000, **A**1 2 10 **F**3 11 12 13 15 20 22 29 30 31 34 35 36 37 38 40 42 43 45 46 47 48 49 50 54 55 57 59 64 70 72 73 74 75 76 77 78 79 81 82 83 84 85 87 93 96 97 102 107 110 111 114 115 116 117 118 119 120 121 123 126 129 130 131 132 146 147 148 156 **S** AdventHealth, Altamonte Springs, FL
Primary Contact: Michael Goebel, Chief Executive Officer
CFO: Andrew Gaasch, Chief Financial Officer
Web address: www.parkerhospital.org
Control: Church operated, Nongovernment, not–for–profit **Service**: General medical and surgical

Staffed Beds: 167 **Admissions**: 8218 **Census**: 78 **Outpatient Visits**: 77230 **Births**: 1250 **Total Expense ($000)**: 205257 **Payroll Expense ($000)**: 65796 **Personnel**: 1253

PUEBLO—Pueblo County

☐ **COLORADO MENTAL HEALTH INSTITUTE AT PUEBLO (064001)**, 1600 West 24th Street, Zip 81003–1499; tel. 719/546–4000, (Nonreporting) **A**1 3 5 10
Primary Contact: Ron Hale, Superintendent
CFO: Jim Duff, Chief Financial Officer
CMO: Al Singleton, M.D., Chief Psychiatry and Chief Medical Staff
CIO: Eunice Wolther, Public Information Officer
CHR: Mary Young, Director Human Resources
Web address: www.cdhs.state.co.us/cmhip
Control: State, Government, nonfederal **Service**: Psychiatric

Staffed Beds: 514

✠ △ **PARKVIEW MEDICAL CENTER (060020)**, 400 West 16th Street, Zip 81003–2781; tel. 719/584–4000, (Nonreporting) **A**1 3 7 10 13
Primary Contact: Leslie Barnes, Chief Executive Officer
COO: Darrin Smith, Chief Operating Officer
CFO: Leslie Barnes, Chief Financial Officer
CMO: Steve Nafziger, M.D., Vice President Medical Affairs
CIO: Steve Shirley, Chief Information Officer
CNO: Linda Flores, R.N., MSN, Vice President Nursing Services
Web address: www.parkviewmc.org
Control: Other not–for–profit (including NFP Corporation) **Service**: General medical and surgical

Staffed Beds: 370

Many Facility Codes have changed. Please refer to the AHA Guide Code Chart. © 2019 AHA Guide

✠ **ST. MARY-CORWIN MEDICAL CENTER (060012)**, 1008 Minnequa Avenue, Zip 81004–3798; tel. 719/557–4000, **A**1 2 3 5 10 13 **F**3 15 18 29 30 31 34 35 40 43 45 47 48 49 50 53 55 57 59 64 68 70 72 73 76 78 79 81 82 84 85 86 87 89 90 107 108 109 110 111 114 115 117 119 120 121 123 124 126 130 132 135 146 148 149 154 **S** CommonSpirit Health, Chicago, IL
Primary Contact: Michael Cafasso, Chief Executive Officer
COO: Michael Cafasso, Chief Operating Officer
CFO: Janiece McNichols, Chief Financial Officer
CMO: Kern Low, M.D., Chief Medical Officer
CHR: Timea Kennedy, Director Human Resources
CNO: Constance Schmidt, FACHE, R.N., Vice President Patient Care Services and Chief Nursing Officer
Web address: www.stmarycorwin.org
Control: Church operated, Nongovernment, not–for–profit **Service**: General medical and surgical

Staffed Beds: 125 **Admissions**: 5219 **Census**: 62 **Outpatient Visits**: 86991 **Births**: 190 **Total Expense ($000)**: 137397 **Payroll Expense ($000)**: 45875 **Personnel**: 527

RANGELY—Rio Blanco County

★ **RANGELY DISTRICT HOSPITAL (061307)**, 225 Eagle Crest Drive, Zip 81648–2104; tel. 970/675–5011, (Nonreporting) **A**10 18
Primary Contact: Nick Goshe, Chief Executive Officer
COO: Bernard Rice, Chief Compliance Officer
CFO: Jim Dillon, Chief Financial Officer
CMO: Abigail R. Urish, M.D., Chief of Staff
CHR: Cynthia S. Stults, Executive Assistant and Human Resources Director
CNO: Sharma Vaughn Esq Chief Nursing Officer
Web address: www.rangelyhospital.com
Control: Hospital district or authority, Government, nonfederal **Service**: General medical and surgical

Staffed Beds: 25

RIFLE—Garfield County

★ **GRAND RIVER HOSPITAL DISTRICT (061317)**, 501 Airport Road, Zip 81650–8510, Mailing Address: P.O. Box 912, Zip 81650–0912; tel. 970/625–1510, (Total facility includes 50 beds in nursing home–type unit) **A**10 18 **F**3 11 12 15 29 31 32 34 35 36 38 39 40 41 43 45 50 55 57 59 64 68 69 75 77 78 79 81 85 87 93 96 97 107 108 110 111 115 119 127 128 129 130 131 132 133 144 146 147 148 149 156 157
Primary Contact: James Coombs, Chief Executive Officer
COO: Bill Noel, Chief Operating Officer
CFO: Cris Bolin, Chief Financial Officer
CMO: Kevin Coleman, M.D., Chief Medical Officer
CIO: Diana Murray, Director Information Systems
CHR: Dawn Hodges, Director Human Resources
CNO: Stacy Pemberton, Chief Nursing Officer
Web address: www.grhd.org
Control: Hospital district or authority, Government, nonfederal **Service**: General medical and surgical

Staffed Beds: 62 **Admissions**: 652 **Census**: 47 **Outpatient Visits**: 110218 **Births**: 0 **Total Expense ($000)**: 87589 **Payroll Expense ($000)**: 38486 **Personnel**: 485

SALIDA—Chaffee County

★ **HEART OF THE ROCKIES REGIONAL MEDICAL CENTER (061322)**, 1000 Rush Drive, Zip 81201–9627, Mailing Address: P.O. Box 429, Zip 81201–0429; tel. 719/530–2200, **A**10 18 **F**3 5 11 13 15 28 29 31 34 35 40 43 45 50 53 54 57 59 64 68 70 74 75 76 77 78 79 81 82 85 87 91 93 97 102 104 107 110 111 115 119 127 129 130 131 132 133 135 146 147 148 156
Primary Contact: Robert A. Morasko, Chief Executive Officer
CFO: Lesley Fagerberg, Vice President Fiscal Services
CMO: Daniel Wardrop, M.D., Medical Director
CIO: Andy Waldbart, Department Manager
CHR: Barbara Lutz, Vice President Human Resources
CNO: Linda Johnson, R.N., Vice President, Patient Services Risk Management and Chief Nursing Officer
Web address: www.hrrmc.com
Control: Hospital district or authority, Government, nonfederal **Service**: General medical and surgical

Staffed Beds: 25 **Admissions**: 1071 **Census**: 10 **Outpatient Visits**: 98303 **Births**: 92 **Total Expense ($000)**: 67708 **Payroll Expense ($000)**: 30555 **Personnel**: 395

SPRINGFIELD—Baca County

★ **SOUTHEAST COLORADO HOSPITAL DISTRICT (061311)**, 373 East Tenth Avenue, Zip 81073–1699, tel. 719/523–4501, (Total facility includes 56 beds in nursing home–type unit) **A**10 18 **F**3 6 7 11 29 40 50 57 62 63 66 67 68 81 91 97 114 119 127 130 133 135 148 154 **S** QHR, Brentwood, TN
Primary Contact: David Engel, Chief Executive Officer and Administrator
CFO: Dorothy Burke, Chief Financial Officer
CMO: Andrea Wismann, M.D., Chief of Staff
CIO: Chris Westphal, Chief Information Technology Officer
CHR: Sherrilyn Turner, Director Human Resources
CNO: Cecelia Deen Esq Chief Nursing Officer
Web address: www.sechosp.org
Control: Hospital district or authority, Government, nonfederal **Service**: General medical and surgical

Staffed Beds: 79 **Admissions**: 205 **Census**: 48 **Outpatient Visits**: 38484 **Births**: 0 **Total Expense ($000)**: 16441 **Payroll Expense ($000)**: 5672 **Personnel**: 178

STEAMBOAT SPRINGS—Routt County

✠ **UCHEALTH YAMPA VALLEY MEDICAL CENTER (060049)**, 1024 Central Park Drive, Zip 80487–8813; tel. 970/879–1322, (Data for 303 days) **A**1 2 10 20 **F**3 13 15 18 28 29 31 34 35 36 37 40 43 45 46 48 50 51 57 64 68 70 73 75 76 77 78 79 81 82 84 85 86 87 93 97 107 110 111 115 119 126 129 130 131 132 133 135 146 147 148 149 154 156 **S** UCHealth, Fort Collins, CO
Primary Contact: Thomas Downes, M.D., Interim Chief Executive Officer
CMO: Laura Sehnert, Chief Medical Officer
CIO: Mark Clark, Chief Information Officer
CHR: Soniya Fidler, MS, Chief Human Resources and Compliance Officer
CNO: Marie Timlin, R.N., Chief Nursing Officer
Web address: www.https://www.uchealth.org/locations/uchealth-yampa-valley-medical-center/
Control: Other not–for–profit (including NFP Corporation) **Service**: General medical and surgical

Staffed Beds: 39 **Admissions**: 1026 **Census**: 8 **Outpatient Visits**: 52527 **Births**: 198 **Total Expense ($000)**: 79133 **Payroll Expense ($000)**: 27727 **Personnel**: 367

STERLING—Logan County

✠ **STERLING REGIONAL MEDCENTER (060076)**, 615 Fairhurst Street, Zip 80751–4523; tel. 970/522–0122, **A**1 3 10 20 **F**3 13 15 18 28 29 31 34 35 38 40 41 43 57 59 64 70 76 77 78 79 81 85 87 91 93 96 97 107 108 111 115 119 120 121 127 129 130 131 146 147 148 154 **S** Banner Health, Phoenix, AZ
Primary Contact: Wade Tyrell, Chief Executive Officer and Chief Nursing Officer
CFO: Nathan Nichols, Director of Finance
CMO: Jeff Bacon, D.O., Chief Medical Officer
CNO: Wade Alan Tyrrell RN Chief Executive Officer and Chief Nursing Officer
Web address: www.https://www.bannerhealth.com/locations/sterling/sterling-regional-medcenter
Control: Other not–for–profit (including NFP Corporation) **Service**: General medical and surgical

Staffed Beds: 25 **Admissions**: 1106 **Census**: 8 **Births**: 218 **Total Expense ($000)**: 48468 **Payroll Expense ($000)**: 16618 **Personnel**: 225

THORNTON—Adams County

✠ **NORTH SUBURBAN MEDICAL CENTER (060065)**, 9191 Grant Street, Zip 80229–4341; tel. 303/451–7800, **A**1 3 10 **F**3 8 11 12 13 15 20 22 29 30 31 34 35 40 41 43 45 48 50 51 54 59 64 70 72 74 75 76 77 78 79 80 81 82 85 87 89 107 108 110 111 114 115 119 126 130 132 135 146 147 148 149 154 **S** HCA Healthcare, Nashville, TN
Primary Contact: Daphne G. David, President and Chief Executive Officer
CIO: Marty Hoesch, Director Information Systems
CHR: Dena Schmaedecke, Vice President Human Resources
Web address: www.northsuburban.com
Control: Corporation, Investor–owned (for–profit) **Service**: General medical and surgical

Staffed Beds: 139 **Admissions**: 7708 **Census**: 77

CO

⊞ **VIBRA HOSPITAL OF DENVER (062014)**, 8451 Pearl Street, Zip 80229–4804; tel. 303/288–3000, (Nonreporting) **A**1 10 **S** Vibra Healthcare, Mechanicsburg, PA
Primary Contact: Lamar McBride, Chief Executive Officer
CMO: John Buckley, M.D., President Medical Staff
CHR: Lorna Fulton, Director Human Resources
Web address: www.vhdenver.com
Control: Corporation, Investor–owned (for–profit) **Service**: Acute long–term care hospital

Staffed Beds: 71

VIBRA REHABILITATION HOSPITAL OF DENVER (063035), 8451 Pearl Street, Suite 101, Zip 80229–4803; tel. 303/301–8700, (Nonreporting)
Primary Contact: Craig A. Hoover, Chief Executive Officer
Web address: www.https://www.vibrahealthcare.com
Control: Corporation, Investor–owned (for–profit) **Service**: Rehabilitation

Staffed Beds: 31

TRINIDAD—Las Animas County

★ **MT. SAN RAFAEL HOSPITAL (061321)**, 410 Benedicta Avenue, Zip 81082–2093; tel. 719/846–9213, **A**10 18 **F**3 15 28 29 32 34 35 40 43 45 46 47 48 50 59 64 65 66 75 79 81 82 87 90 93 97 107 110 111 115 119 127 129 133 135 146 147 148 149 150 154 156 157
Primary Contact: John Tucker, Chief Executive Officer
CFO: David W Rollins, Chief Financial Officer
CIO: Michael Archuleta, Chief Information Technology Officer
CHR: Tammy Rogers, Director Human Resources
CNO: Mandy Shaiffer, Chief Nursing Officer
Web address: www.msrhc.org
Control: Other not–for–profit (including NFP Corporation) **Service**: General medical and surgical

Staffed Beds: 18 Admissions: 442 Census: 7 Outpatient Visits: 40711
Births: 0 **Total Expense ($000):** 32159 **Payroll Expense ($000):** 15432
Personnel: 210

VAIL—Eagle County

⊞ **VAIL HEALTH (060096)**, 181 West Meadow Drive, Zip 81657–5242, Mailing Address: P.O. Box 40000, Zip 81658–7520; tel. 970/476–2451, **A**1 3 10 20 **F**3 11 13 15 17 18 20 22 24 26 28 29 30 31 34 39 40 42 43 45 46 50 51 54 57 59 64 68 70 72 74 75 76 77 78 79 81 82 85 86 87 89 91 92 93 94 107 108 109 110 111 115 116 117 119 120 121 123 129 130 131 135 141 142 144 145 146 147 148 149 156
Primary Contact: William Cook, President and Chief Executive Officer
CFO: Ted Sirotta, Chief Financial Officer
CMO: Barry Hammaker, M.D., Chief Medical Officer and Chief Clinical Officer
CIO: Brian Foster, Chief Information Officer
CHR: Rick Smith, Senior Vice President Human Resources and Chief Administrative Officer
CNO: Sheila Sherman, Vice President Patient Care Services
Web address: www.vvmc.com
Control: Other not–for–profit (including NFP Corporation) **Service**: General medical and surgical

Staffed Beds: 53 Admissions: 2089 Census: 15 Outpatient Visits: 181136
Births: 405 **Total Expense ($000):** 182109 **Payroll Expense ($000):** 59813
Personnel: 898

WALSENBURG—Huerfano County

★ **SPANISH PEAKS REGIONAL HEALTH CENTER (061316)**, 23500 U S Highway 160, Zip 81089–9524; tel. 719/738–5100, (Nonreporting) **A**10 18 **S** QHR, Brentwood, TN
Primary Contact: Kay L. Whitley, President and Chief Executive Officer
CFO: Lionel J. Montoya, Chief Financial Officer
CMO: Michael A. Moll, M.D., Chief Medical Officer and Chief of Staff
CHR: Tony Marostica, Chief Compliance and Human Resource Officer
CNO: Mary Cope, R.N., Chief Clinical Officer
Web address: www.sprhc.org
Control: Hospital district or authority, Government, nonfederal **Service**: General medical and surgical

Staffed Beds: 140

WESTMINSTER—Adams County

⊞ **ST. ANTHONY NORTH HEALTH CAMPUS (060104)**, 14300 Orchard Parkway, Zip 80023–9206; tel. 720/627–0000, **A**1 2 3 10 **F**3 11 13 15 18 20 22 26 28 29 30 31 34 35 36 40 42 43 45 46 49 54 55 57 59 60 63 64 65 68 70 74 75 76 77 78 79 81 82 84 85 87 91 92 93 97 102 107 108 110 111 114 115 119 130 131 132 135 142 146 147 148 149 150 155 **S** CommonSpirit Health, Chicago, IL
Primary Contact: Kevin Jenkins, President and Chief Executive Officer
CFO: Alison Mizer, Chief Financial Officer
CHR: Robert Archibold, Director, Human Resources
CNO: Carol A Butler, R.N., MSN, VP Patient Care Services & Operations
Web address: www.stanthonynorth.org
Control: Church operated, Nongovernment, not–for–profit **Service**: General medical and surgical

Staffed Beds: 100 Admissions: 5525 Census: 48 Outpatient Visits: 74976
Births: 913 **Total Expense ($000):** 141929 **Payroll Expense ($000):** 45057
Personnel: 527

WHEAT RIDGE—Jefferson County

⊞ **LUTHERAN MEDICAL CENTER (060009)**, 8300 West 38th Avenue, Zip 80033–6005; tel. 303/425–4500, (Includes EXEMPLA WEST PINES, 3400 Lutheran Parkway, Wheat Ridge, Colorado, Zip 80033; tel. 303/467–4000) **A**1 2 3 10 **F**3 4 5 11 12 13 15 18 20 22 24 26 28 29 30 31 33 35 36 40 43 45 47 48 49 50 55 56 58 59 60 61 63 64 68 70 71 72 74 75 76 77 78 79 81 83 84 85 86 87 94 98 100 101 102 103 104 105 106 107 108 110 111 114 115 119 120 121 123 124 126 129 130 132 146 147 148 149 152 153 154 157 **S** SCL Health, Broomfield, CO
Primary Contact: Grant Wicklund, President and Chief Executive Officer
CFO: Karen Scremin, Vice President Finance
CMO: Christina Johnson, M.D., Vice President and Chief Clinical and Quality Officer
CHR: Scott Day, Vice President Human Resources
CNO: Geraldine Towndrow, R.N., Senior Vice President Nursing
Web address: www.https://www.sclhealth.org/locations/lutheran-medical-center/
Control: Other not–for–profit (including NFP Corporation) **Service**: General medical and surgical

Staffed Beds: 368 Admissions: 15179 Census: 193 Outpatient Visits: 181471 **Births:** 2042 **Total Expense ($000):** 363556 **Payroll Expense ($000):** 125186 **Personnel:** 1671

WOODLAND PARK—Teller County

⇧ **PIKES PEAK REGIONAL HOSPITAL (061326)**, 16420 West Highway 24, Zip 80863; tel. 719/687–9999, (Nonreporting) **A**10 18 21 **S** Steward Health Care System, LLC, Dallas, TX
Primary Contact: Kimberly Monjesky, Chief Executive Officer
CFO: Robin Ruff, Chief Financial Officer
CMO: Richard Malyszek, M.D., Chief of Staff
CHR: Arianne Randolph, Director Human Resources
CNO: Marsha Sensat, R.N., Chief Nursing Officer
Web address: www.pprmc.org
Control: Corporation, Investor–owned (for–profit) **Service**: General medical and surgical

Staffed Beds: 15

WRAY—Yuma County

★ **WRAY COMMUNITY DISTRICT HOSPITAL (061309)**, 1017 West 7th Street, Zip 80758–1420; tel. 970/332–4811, **A**3 10 18 **F**3 13 15 28 29 31 34 35 40 43 45 50 57 59 64 65 68 75 81 82 85 87 93 97 107 110 114 119 132 133 135 147 148 149 154 156
Primary Contact: Jennie Sullivan, Chief Executive Officer
CMO: Monte Uyemura, M.D., Chief of Staff
Web address: www.wraycommunitydistricthospital.com/
Control: Hospital district or authority, Government, nonfederal **Service**: General medical and surgical

Staffed Beds: 73 Admissions: 403 Census: 3 Outpatient Visits: 4501
Births: 149 **Total Expense ($000):** 21206 **Payroll Expense ($000):** 6772

YUMA—Yuma County

★ **YUMA DISTRICT HOSPITAL (061315)**, 1000 West 8th Avenue, Zip 80759–2641; tel. 970/848–5405, (Nonreporting) **A**10 18
Primary Contact: Beth Saxton, R.N., Chief Executive Officer
CFO: Rick Korf, Chief Financial Officer
CMO: John Wolz, M.D., Chief Medical Staff
CIO: Jason Hawley, Director of Information Services and Security
CHR: Gini Adams, Director Employee and Public Relations
Web address: www.yumahospital.org
Control: Hospital district or authority, Government, nonfederal **Service**: General medical and surgical

Staffed Beds: 12

CO

Many Facility Codes have changed. Please refer to the AHA Guide Code Chart.
© 2019 AHA Guide

CONNECTICUT

CT

BRANFORD—New Haven County

☐ **THE CONNECTICUT HOSPICE (070038)**, 100 Double Beach Road,
Zip 06405–4909; tel. 203/315–7500, (Nonreporting) **A**1 3 5 10
Primary Contact: Ronny Knight, President and Chief Executive Officer
Web address: www.hospice.com
Control: Other not–for–profit (including NFP Corporation) **Service**: Other specialty
treatment

> **Staffed Beds:** 52

BRIDGEPORT—Fairfield County

⊞ **BRIDGEPORT HOSPITAL (070010)**, 267 Grant Street, Zip 06610–2805, Mailing
Address: P.O. Box 5000, Zip 06610–0120; tel. 203/384–3000, **A**1 2 3 5 8 10
F3 5 6 8 11 12 13 14 15 16 17 18 20 22 24 26 28 29 30 31 32 34 35 36 37
38 39 40 41 43 44 45 46 47 48 49 50 51 52 54 55 56 57 58 59 61 64 65 66
68 70 74 75 76 78 79 80 81 82 84 85 86 87 93 96 97 98 101 102 103 104
107 108 110 111 114 115 116 117 118 119 120 121 123 124 126 129 130
131 132 134 144 145 146 147 148 149 153 154 **S** Yale New Haven Health,
New Haven, CT
Primary Contact: Michael Ivy, M.D., Interim Chief Executive Officer
CFO: Patrick McCabe, Senior Vice President Finance and Chief Financial Officer
CMO: Michael Ivy, M.D., Senior Vice President for Medical Affairs and Chief Medical
Officer
CIO: Daniel Barchi, Senior Vice President, Technical Services and Chief Information
Officer
CHR: Melissa Turner, Senior Vice President Human Resources
CNO: MaryEllen Kosturko, R.N., Senior Vice President Patient Care Operations and
Chief Nursing Officer
Web address: www.bridgeporthospital.org
Control: Other not–for–profit (including NFP Corporation) **Service**: General
medical and surgical

> **Staffed Beds:** 362 **Admissions:** 18995 **Census:** 303 **Outpatient**
> **Visits:** 329925 **Births:** 2450 **Total Expense ($000):** 528591 **Payroll**
> **Expense ($000):** 176245 **Personnel:** 2525

☐ **SOUTHWEST CONNECTICUT MENTAL HEALTH SYSTEM (074012)**, 1635
Central Avenue, Zip 06610–2717; tel. 203/551–7400, (Nonreporting) **A**1 10 **S**
Connecticut Department of Mental Health and Addiction Services, Hartford, CT
Primary Contact: Alicia Feller, Chief Executive Officer
COO: Cindy Perjon, Associate Director
CFO: Linda Woznikaitis, Chief Financial Officer
CMO: Sandra Gomez-Luna, Medical Director
CIO: Bernetta Witcher Boateng, Ph.D., Director Quality Improvement Services and
Compliance
CHR: Nancy Derman, Director Human Resources
Web address: www.ct.gov/dmhas/cwp/view.asp?a=2946&q=378936
Control: State, Government, nonfederal **Service**: Psychiatric

> **Staffed Beds:** 62

⊞ **ST. VINCENT'S MEDICAL CENTER (070028)**, 2800 Main Street,
Zip 06606–4292; tel. 203/576–6000, (Includes ST. VINCENT'S BEHAVIORAL
HEALTH, 47 Long Lots Road, Westport, Connecticut, Zip 06880–3800;
tel. 203/221–8813) **A**1 2 3 5 10 **F**3 5 8 11 12 13 15 18 20 22 24 26 28 29 30
31 34 35 36 38 40 43 44 45 46 47 48 49 54 55 56 57 58 59 61 64 65
70 71 72 74 75 76 77 78 79 80 81 82 84 85 86 87 90 96 97 98 99 100 101
102 104 105 107 108 110 111 114 115 116 117 118 119 120 121 122 123
124 126 130 132 134 135 144 145 146 147 148 149 150 152 153 154
S Ascension Healthcare, Saint Louis, MO
Primary Contact: Dawn Rudolph, President and Chief Executive Officer
CFO: Stephen Franko, Senior Vice President and Chief Financial Officer
CMO: Dan Gottschall, Senior Vice President and Chief Clinical Officer
CNO: Dale G Danowski, R.N., Senior Vice President, Chief Nursing Officer
Web address: www.stvincents.org
Control: Other not–for–profit (including NFP Corporation) **Service**: General
medical and surgical

> **Staffed Beds:** 352 **Admissions:** 13631 **Census:** 223 **Outpatient**
> **Visits:** 224182 **Births:** 788 **Total Expense ($000):** 515854 **Payroll Expense**
> **($000):** 175267 **Personnel:** 1866

BRISTOL—Hartford County

⊞ **BRISTOL HOSPITAL (070029)**, 41 Brewster Road, Zip 06010–5161, Mailing
Address: P.O. Box 977, Zip 06011–0977; tel. 860/585–3000, (Nonreporting) **A**1
2 5 10
Primary Contact: Kurt A. Barwis, FACHE, President and Chief Executive Officer
COO: Marc D Edelman, Vice President Operations
CFO: Peter Freytag, Senior Vice President Finance and Chief Financial Officer
CMO: Leonard Banco, M.D., Senior Vice President and Chief Medical Officer
CIO: David Rackliffe, Assistant Vice President Information Services
CHR: Jeanine Reckdenwald, Vice President Human Resources and Support
Services
Web address: www.bristolhospital.org
Control: Other not–for–profit (including NFP Corporation) **Service**: General
medical and surgical

> **Staffed Beds:** 110

DANBURY—Fairfield County

⊞ **DANBURY HOSPITAL (070033)**, 24 Hospital Avenue, Zip 06810–6099;
tel. 203/739–7000, (Includes NEW MILFORD HOSPITAL, 21 Elm Street, New
Milford, Connecticut, Zip 06776–2993; tel. 860/355–2611; John M Murphy, M.D.,
President and Chief Executive Officer, Western Connecticut Health Network) **A**1
2 3 5 8 10 **F**3 8 9 12 13 14 15 18 20 22 24 26 28 29 30 31 32 34 35 36 37
38 39 40 43 44 45 46 47 49 50 51 54 55 56 57 58 59 61 64 65 66 68 72 74
75 76 77 78 79 81 82 83 84 85 86 87 89 90 93 96 97 98 100 101 102 104
105 107 108 110 111 115 117 119 120 121 123 124 126 129 130 131 132
134 135 144 145 146 147 148 149 153 154 156 **S** Western Connecticut Health
Network, Danbury, CT
Primary Contact: John M. Murphy, M.D., President
COO: Sharon Adams, Chief Operating Officer
CFO: Steven Rosenberg, Chief Financial Officer
CMO: Patricia Tietjen, M.D., Vice President, Medical Affairs
CIO: Kathleen DeMatteo, Chief Information Officer
CHR: Cathy Frierson, Chief Human Resource Officer
CNO: Sharon Adams, Chief Nursing Officer
Web address: www.danburyhospital.org
Control: Other not–for–profit (including NFP Corporation) **Service**: General
medical and surgical

> **Staffed Beds:** 284 **Admissions:** 19111 **Census:** 257 **Outpatient**
> **Visits:** 447570 **Births:** 2007 **Total Expense ($000):** 638619 **Payroll**
> **Expense ($000):** 228580 **Personnel:** 2029

DERBY—New Haven County

⊞ **GRIFFIN HOSPITAL (070031)**, 130 Division Street, Zip 06418–1326;
tel. 203/735–7421, **A**1 2 3 5 10 **F**3 5 12 13 15 18 28 29 30 31 34 35 36 38
40 45 49 50 53 54 56 57 58 59 64 65 66 68 70 71 74 75 76 77 78 79 81 82
84 85 86 87 91 92 93 94 96 97 98 100 101 102 104 107 108 110 111 114
115 118 119 120 121 123 124 126 129 130 131 132 134 135 146 147 148
149 153 154 156
Primary Contact: Patrick Charmel, President and Chief Executive Officer
CMO: Kenneth V Schwartz, M.D., Medical Director
CIO: George Tomas, Director Information Services
CHR: Steve Mordecai, Director Human Resources
CNO: Barbara J Stumpo, R.N., Vice President Patient Care Services
Web address: www.griffinhealth.org
Control: Other not–for–profit (including NFP Corporation) **Service**: General
medical and surgical

> **Staffed Beds:** 111 **Admissions:** 6702 **Census:** 82 **Outpatient**
> **Visits:** 191147 **Births:** 525 **Total Expense ($000):** 180726 **Payroll Expense**
> **($000):** 68657 **Personnel:** 1253

FARMINGTON—Hartford County

☒ **UCONN, JOHN DEMPSEY HOSPITAL (070036)**, 263 Farmington Avenue, Zip 06032–1941; tel. 860/679–2000, **A**1 2 3 5 8 10 12 13 **F**3 7 8 11 13 15 18 20 22 24 26 29 30 31 34 35 36 37 38 39 40 42 45 46 47 48 49 50 51 52 53 54 55 56 57 58 59 60 61 64 65 67 68 70 74 75 76 77 78 79 81 82 83 84 85 86 87 91 92 93 94 97 98 100 101 102 103 104 105 107 108 110 111 114 115 116 117 118 119 120 121 123 124 126 129 130 131 132 135 136 144 145 146 147 148 153 154 157
Primary Contact: Andrew Agwunobi, M.D., Chief Executive Officer
COO: Kevin Larsen, Associate Vice President, Business and Ancillary Services
CFO: Jeffrey Geoghegan, Chief Financial Officer
CMO: Richard Simon, M.D., Chief of Staff
CIO: Jonathan Carroll, Chief Information Officer
CHR: Carolle Andrews, Vice President, Interim Human Resources Officer
CNO: Ann Marie Capo, R.N., Chief Nursing Officer, Vice President, Quality and Patient Services
Web address: www.uchc.edu
Control: State, Government, nonfederal **Service**: General medical and surgical

Staffed Beds: 212 **Admissions**: 9391 **Census**: 112 **Outpatient Visits**: 365936 **Total Expense ($000)**: 467362 **Payroll Expense ($000)**: 138299 **Personnel**: 1265

GREENWICH—Fairfield County

☒ **GREENWICH HOSPITAL (070018)**, 5 Perryridge Road, Zip 06830–4697; tel. 203/863–3000, **A**1 2 3 5 8 10 **F**3 5 11 12 13 14 15 18 20 22 26 28 29 30 31 32 34 35 36 37 38 39 40 41 44 45 46 47 48 49 50 51 52 53 54 55 56 57 58 59 61 63 64 65 66 68 70 72 74 75 76 78 79 80 81 82 84 85 86 87 89 91 93 96 97 100 101 102 107 108 110 111 114 115 116 117 118 119 120 121 123 124 126 129 130 131 132 134 135 146 147 148 149 154 157 **S** Yale New Haven Health, New Haven, CT
Primary Contact: Norman G. Roth, President
COO: Diane Kelly, Chief Operating Officer
CFO: Eugene Colucci, Vice President Finance
CMO: A Michael Marino, M.D., Senior Vice President Medical Administration
Web address: www.greenhosp.org
Control: Other not–for–profit (including NFP Corporation) **Service**: General medical and surgical

Staffed Beds: 184 **Admissions**: 10158 **Census**: 136 **Outpatient Visits**: 276391 **Births**: 2619 **Total Expense ($000)**: 369975 **Payroll Expense ($000)**: 126426 **Personnel**: 1683

HARTFORD—Hartford County

☒ **CONNECTICUT CHILDREN'S MEDICAL CENTER (073300)**, 282 Washington Street, Zip 06106–3322; tel. 860/545–9000, **A**1 3 5 10 **F**3 5 7 11 14 15 18 19 21 23 25 27 29 30 31 32 34 35 36 37 38 39 40 41 43 44 45 48 49 50 51 54 55 57 58 59 60 61 62 63 64 65 68 72 74 75 78 79 81 82 84 85 86 87 88 89 91 92 93 96 97 99 100 101 102 104 107 111 114 115 119 126 129 130 131 132 134 143 146 148 149 150 154 156
Primary Contact: James E. Shmerling, President and Chief Executive Officer
COO: Gil Peri, President and Chief Operating Officer
CFO: Gerald J Boisvert, Vice President and Chief Financial Officer
CMO: Paul Dworkin, M.D., Physician–in–Chief
CIO: Kelly R Styles, Vice President and Chief Information Officer
CHR: Elizabeth Rudden, Vice President Human Resources
Web address: www.connecticutchildrens.org/
Control: Other not–for–profit (including NFP Corporation) **Service**: Children's general medical and surgical

Staffed Beds: 185 **Admissions**: 6181 **Census**: 122 **Outpatient Visits**: 206500 **Births**: 0 **Total Expense ($000)**: 333629 **Payroll Expense ($000)**: 140712 **Personnel**: 2324

☒ **HARTFORD HOSPITAL (070025)**, 80 Seymour Street, Zip 06102–8000, Mailing Address: P.O. Box 5037, Zip 06102–5037; tel. 860/545–5000, (Includes INSTITUTE OF LIVING, 400 Washington Street, Hartford, Connecticut, Zip 06106–3392; tel. 860/545–7000) (Total facility includes 104 beds in nursing home–type unit) **A**1 2 3 5 10 **F**2 3 5 6 7 8 9 10 12 13 15 17 18 20 22 24 26 28 29 30 31 34 35 36 37 38 39 40 43 44 45 46 47 48 49 50 51 52 53 54 55 56 57 58 59 60 61 63 64 65 66 68 70 71 74 75 76 77 78 79 80 81 82 83 84 85 86 87 90 91 92 93 94 95 96 97 98 99 100 101 102 103 104 105 106 107 108 110 111 112 114 115 116 117 118 119 120 121 123 124 125 126 128 129 130 131 132 133 134 135 137 138 139 141 143 145 146 147 148 149 150 151 152 153 154 155 156 157 **S** Hartford HealthCare, Hartford, CT
Primary Contact: Bimal Patel, President
CMO: Stuart Markowitz, M.D., Chief Medical Officer
CIO: Stephan O'Neill, Vice President Information Services
CHR: Richard McAloon, Vice President Human Resources
Web address: www.harthosp.org
Control: Other not–for–profit (including NFP Corporation) **Service**: General medical and surgical

Staffed Beds: 912 **Admissions**: 41294 **Census**: 730 **Outpatient Visits**: 476084 **Births**: 3860 **Total Expense ($000)**: 1352126 **Payroll Expense ($000)**: 474269 **Personnel**: 6129

☒ **MOUNT SINAI REHABILITATION HOSPITAL (073025)**, 490 Blue Hills Avenue, Zip 06112–1513; tel. 860/714–3500, **A**1 10 **F**3 29 30 34 35 54 58 59 64 68 82 90 91 92 93 94 95 96 130 131 132 **S** Trinity Health, Livonia, MI
Primary Contact: Robert J. Krug, M.D., Chief Executive Officer
CFO: David Bittner, Chief Financial Officer
Web address: www.stfranciscare.org
Control: Other not–for–profit (including NFP Corporation) **Service**: Rehabilitation

Staffed Beds: 38 **Admissions**: 917 **Census**: 34 **Outpatient Visits**: 45681 **Births**: 0

☒ **SAINT FRANCIS HOSPITAL AND MEDICAL CENTER (070002)**, 114 Woodland Street, Zip 06105–1208; tel. 860/714–4000, **A**1 2 3 5 8 10 19 **F**3 8 11 12 13 15 17 18 20 22 24 26 28 29 30 31 34 35 36 38 39 40 43 45 46 47 48 49 50 53 54 55 56 57 58 59 61 64 65 66 67 68 70 72 74 75 76 77 78 79 81 82 84 85 86 87 91 92 93 94 95 96 97 98 99 100 101 102 104 107 108 110 111 115 117 118 119 120 121 123 124 126 129 130 131 132 135 146 147 148 150 154 **S** Trinity Health, Livonia, MI
Primary Contact: John F. Rodis, M.D., President
CFO: Jennifer S. Schneider, Vice President of Finance
CMO: Michael Grey, M.D., Interim Chief Medical Officer
CIO: Linda L. Shanley, Vice President, Chief Information Officer
CHR: Dennis W. Sparks, Vice President of Human Resources
Web address: www.saintfranciscare.com
Control: Church operated, Nongovernment, not–for–profit **Service**: General medical and surgical

Staffed Beds: 416 **Admissions**: 29136 **Census**: 384 **Outpatient Visits**: 294744 **Births**: 2503 **Total Expense ($000)**: 859515 **Payroll Expense ($000)**: 249080 **Personnel**: 4613

MANCHESTER—Hartford County

☐ **MANCHESTER MEMORIAL HOSPITAL (070027)**, 71 Haynes Street, Zip 06040–4188; tel. 860/646–1222, (Nonreporting) **A**1 2 3 5 10 12 13 **S** Prospect Medical Holdings, Los Angeles, CA
Primary Contact: Michael F. Collins, Chief Executive Officer
CFO: Michael D. Veillette, Senior Vice President and Chief Financial Officer
CMO: Joel R Reich, M.D., Senior Vice President Medical Affairs
CIO: Richard Daigle, Chief Information Officer
CHR: Natalie Cook, Administrative Director of Human Resources
CNO: Mary Powers, R.N., MSN, Senior Vice President and Chief Nursing Officer
Web address: www.echn.org
Control: Other not–for–profit (including NFP Corporation) **Service**: General medical and surgical

Staffed Beds: 156

MANSFIELD CENTER—Tolland County

☒ **NATCHAUG HOSPITAL (074008)**, 189 Storrs Road, Zip 06250–1683; tel. 860/456–1311, **A**1 10 **F**2 3 4 5 44 50 56 75 77 87 98 99 100 101 104 105 130 132 135 149 151 152 153 **S** Hartford HealthCare, Hartford, CT
Primary Contact: Patricia Rehmer, MSN, FACHE, President
COO: David Klein, Ph.D., Vice President Operations, Behavioral Health Network
CFO: Paul V Maloney, Vice President Finance, Behavioral Health Network
CMO: Deborah Weidner, Medical Director
CIO: Mark Olson, Interim Chief Information Officer, Behavioral Health Network
CHR: Janet Keown, Vice President Human Resources, Behavioral Health Network
CNO: Justin Sleeper, Vice President Clinical Operations, Behavioral Health Network
Web address: www.natchaug.org
Control: Other not–for–profit (including NFP Corporation) **Service**: Psychiatric

Staffed Beds: 57 **Admissions**: 1982 **Census**: 57 **Outpatient Visits**: 0 **Births**: 0 **Personnel**: 439

MERIDEN—New Haven County

☒ **MIDSTATE MEDICAL CENTER (070017)**, 435 Lewis Avenue, Zip 06451–2101; tel. 203/694–8200, **A**1 2 10 **F**3 11 12 13 15 18 26 28 29 30 31 34 35 36 38 39 40 44 45 46 47 48 49 50 51 53 54 56 57 59 61 63 64 68 70 74 75 76 78 79 81 82 84 85 86 87 97 102 107 108 110 111 114 115 117 118 119 120 121 123 124 126 129 130 131 132 144 145 146 147 148 149 154 157 **S** Hartford HealthCare, Hartford, CT
Primary Contact: Gary C. Havican, President
CMO: Kenneth R Kurz, M.D., Chief of Staff
CIO: Jennifer Comerford, Manager Information Services
CHR: Ken Cesca, Vice President Human Resources
Web address: www.midstatemedical.org
Control: Other not–for–profit (including NFP Corporation) **Service**: General medical and surgical

Staffed Beds: 97 **Admissions**: 9419 **Census**: 92 **Outpatient Visits**: 145745 **Births**: 813 **Total Expense ($000)**: 260215 **Payroll Expense ($000)**: 70686 **Personnel**: 931

CT

Many Facility Codes have changed. Please refer to the AHA Guide Code Chart. © 2019 AHA Guide

MIDDLETOWN—Middlesex County

☐ **ALBERT J. SOLNIT PSYCHIATRIC CENTER - SOUTH CAMPUS**, 915 River Road, Zip 06457–3921, Mailing Address: P.O. Box 2792, Zip 06457–9292; tel. 860/704–4000, (Nonreporting) **A**1 3 5 10
Primary Contact: Michelle Sarofin, Superintendent
CFO: Connie Tessarzik, Business Manager
CMO: Lesley Siegel, M.D., Medical Director
CIO: Andrew J A Kass, M.D., Assistant Superintendent
Web address: www.ct.gov/
Control: State, Government, nonfederal **Service**: Children's hospital psychiatric

Staffed Beds: 75

☐ **CONNECTICUT VALLEY HOSPITAL (074003)**, 1000 Silver Street, Zip 06457–3947; tel. 860/262–5000, (Includes WHITING FORENSIC HOSPITAL, 70 O'Brien Drive, Middletown, Connecticut, Zip 6457, Mailing Address: Box 70, Zip 06457–3942, tel. 860/262–5400; Michael A Norko, M.D., Acting Chief Executive Officer) **A**1 3 5 10 **F**4 29 30 34 36 39 50 53 56 57 58 59 60 65 68 74 75 77 82 84 86 87 90 91 96 97 98 100 101 103 106 119 130 132 135 146 148 149 **S** Connecticut Department of Mental Health and Addiction Services, Hartford, CT
Primary Contact: Helene M. Vartelas, MSN, Chief Executive Officer
COO: John D'Eramo, Chief Operating Officer
CFO: Cindy Butterfield, Director, Fiscal and Administrative Services
CMO: Thomas Pisano, M.D., Chief Professional Services
CIO: Kathryn Connelly, Manager Information Technology
CHR: Cheryl Thompson, Facility Director Human Resources
CNO: Jerilynn Lamb-Pagone, Nurse Executive
Web address: www.ct.gov/dmhas/cwp/view.asp?a=3519&q=416778
Control: State, Government, nonfederal **Service**: Psychiatric

Staffed Beds: 361 Admissions: 3349 Census: 529 Outpatient Visits: 0 Births: 0 Personnel: 1060

☒ **MIDDLESEX HOSPITAL (070020)**, 28 Crescent Street, Zip 06457–3650; tel. 860/358–6000, **A**1 2 3 5 10 **F**3 5 7 8 12 13 15 18 20 26 28 29 30 31 32 34 35 36 37 38 40 42 45 46 47 48 49 50 51 54 55 57 58 59 60 61 62 63 64 65 68 70 74 75 76 77 78 79 81 82 83 84 85 86 87 89 92 93 94 97 98 100 101 102 104 105 107 108 110 111 114 115 116 117 118 119 120 121 123 124 126 129 130 131 132 134 135 143 145 146 147 148 149 152 153 154
Primary Contact: Vincent G. Capece Jr, President and Chief Executive Officer
CFO: Susan Martin, Vice President Finance
CMO: Arthur V McDowell, M.D., III Vice President Clinical Affairs
CIO: Evan Jackson, Vice President Information Technology
CHR: Gregory Nokes, Vice President Human Resources
CNO: Jacquelyn Calamari, MSN, MS, Chief Nursing Officer and Vice President, Patient Care Services
Web address: www.middlesexhospital.org
Control: Other not–for–profit (including NFP Corporation) **Service**: General medical and surgical

Staffed Beds: 233 Admissions: 12216 Census: 141 Outpatient Visits: 632889 Births: 1002 Total Expense ($000): 490290 Payroll Expense ($000): 188694 Personnel: 1940

WHITING FORENSIC HOSPITAL See Connecticut Valley Hospital, Middletown

MILFORD—New Haven County

☒ **MILFORD HOSPITAL (070019)**, 300 Seaside Avenue, Zip 06460–4603; tel. 203/876–4000, (Nonreporting) **A**1 10
Primary Contact: Lloyd Friedman, M.D., Interim President and Chief Operating Officer
COO: Lloyd Friedman, M.D., Vice President Medical Affairs and Chief Operating Officer
CFO: Laura Smith, Vice President Finance and Chief Financial Officer
CMO: Lloyd Friedman, M.D., Vice President Medical Affairs and Chief Operating Officer
CIO: Brian Evans, Chief Information Officer
CHR: Jeffrey Komornik, Director Human Resources
CNO: Joan DeMaio, Vice President Nursing
Web address: www.milfordhospital.org
Control: Other not–for–profit (including NFP Corporation) **Service**: General medical and surgical

Staffed Beds: 31

NEW BRITAIN—Hartford County

☒ **HOSPITAL FOR SPECIAL CARE (072004)**, 2150 Corbin Avenue, Zip 06053–2298; tel. 860/223–2761, (Nonreporting) **A**1 3 5 10
Primary Contact: Lynn Ricci, President and Chief Executive Officer
CFO: Laurie A Whelan, Senior Vice President Finance and Chief Financial Officer
CMO: J. Kevin Shushtari, M.D., Chief Medical Officer
CIO: Stan Jankowski, Vice President and Chief Information Officer
CHR: Judi Trczinski, Vice President and Chief Human Resources Officer
Web address: www.hfsc.org
Control: Other not–for–profit (including NFP Corporation) **Service**: Acute long–term care hospital

Staffed Beds: 228

☒ **THE HOSPITAL OF CENTRAL CONNECTICUT (070035)**, 100 Grand Street, Zip 06052–2017, Mailing Address: P.O. Box 100, Zip 06052–2017; tel. 860/224–5011, (Includes BRADLEY MEMORIAL, 81 Meriden Avenue, Southington, Connecticut, Zip 06489–3297; tel. 860/276–5000; NEW BRITAIN GENERAL, 100 Grand Street, New Britain, Connecticut, Zip 06052–2017, Mailing Address: P O Box 100, Zip 06050–0100, tel. 860/224–5011) **A**1 2 3 5 10 **F**3 11 12 13 15 18 20 22 26 28 29 30 31 34 35 38 40 44 45 49 50 51 53 54 57 58 59 60 61 64 65 66 68 70 72 74 75 76 77 78 79 81 84 85 86 87 89 93 97 98 100 101 102 104 107 108 110 111 114 115 117 118 119 120 121 123 124 126 129 130 132 135 144 146 147 148 149 153 154 156 157 **S** Hartford HealthCare, Hartford, CT
Primary Contact: Gary C. Havican, President
CFO: Brian Rogoz, Vice President Finance and Treasurer
CIO: Frank Pinto, Chief Information Officer
CHR: Elizabeth A Lynch, Vice President Human Resources
Web address: www.thocc.org
Control: Other not–for–profit (including NFP Corporation) **Service**: General medical and surgical

Staffed Beds: 179 Admissions: 11834 Census: 172 Outpatient Visits: 406197 Births: 1584 Total Expense ($000): 369054 Payroll Expense ($000): 137856 Personnel: 1685

NEW CANAAN—Fairfield County

☒ **SILVER HILL HOSPITAL (074014)**, 208 Valley Road, Zip 06840–3899; tel. 203/966–3561, (Nonreporting) **A**1 10
Primary Contact: Andrew J. Gerber, M.D., Ph.D., President and Chief Executive Officer
COO: Elizabeth Moore, Chief Operating Officer
CFO: Ruurd Leegstra, Chief Financial Officer
CMO: Andrew J. Gerber, M.D., Ph.D., President and Medical Director
CIO: Maria Klinga, Director Management Information Systems
CHR: Rich Juliana, Director Human Resources
Web address: www.silverhillhospital.org
Control: Other not–for–profit (including NFP Corporation) **Service**: Psychiatric

Staffed Beds: 121

NEW HAVEN—New Haven County

☐ **CONNECTICUT MENTAL HEALTH CENTER (074011)**, 34 Park Street, Zip 06519–1109, Mailing Address: P.O. Box 1842, Zip 06508–1842; tel. 203/974–7144, **A**1 3 5 10 **F**29 30 35 38 51 58 59 98 100 104 106 130 132 157 **S** Connecticut Department of Mental Health and Addiction Services, Hartford, CT
Primary Contact: Michael Sernyak, M.D., Director
COO: Robert Cole, Chief Operating Officer
CFO: Robert Cole, Chief Operating Officer
CMO: Jeanne Steines, D.O., Medical Director
CIO: Paul Moore, Chief Information Officer
CHR: Carolyn Wallace, Director Human Resources
Web address: www.ct.gov/dmhas/cwp/view.asp?a=2906&q=334596
Control: State, Government, nonfederal **Service**: Psychiatric

Staffed Beds: 32 Admissions: 131 Census: 25 Outpatient Visits: 0 Births: 0

HOSPITAL OF SAINT RAPHAEL See Yale-New Haven Hospital-Saint Raphael Campus

CT

Hospital, Medicare Provider Number, Address, Telephone, Approval, Facility, and Physician Codes, Health Care System

★ American Hospital Association (AHA) membership
☐ The Joint Commission accreditation
○ Healthcare Facilities Accreditation Program
◇ DNV Healthcare Inc. accreditation
⇑ Center for Improvement in Healthcare Quality Accreditation
△ Commission on Accreditation of Rehabilitation Facilities (CARF) accreditation

---

☒ **YALE-NEW HAVEN HOSPITAL (070022)**, 20 York Street, Zip 06510–3202; tel. 203/688–4242, (Includes YALE-NEW HAVEN CHILDREN'S HOSPITAL, 1 Park Street, New Haven, Connecticut, Zip 06504–8901; tel. 203/688–4242; Cynthia Sparer, Senior Vice President and Executive Director Women's & Children; YALE-NEW HAVEN HOSPITAL-SAINT RAPHAEL CAMPUS, 1450 Chapel Street, New Haven, Connecticut, Zip 06511–4405; tel. 203/789–3000; Richard D'Aquila, President; YALE-NEW HAVEN PSYCHIATRIC HOSPITAL, 184 Liberty Street, New Haven, Connecticut, Zip 06519–1625; tel. 203/688–9704; Mark Sevilla, Executive Director) **A**1 2 3 5 8 10 19 **F**3 5 6 9 10 11 12 13 14 15 17 18 19 20 21 22 23 24 25 26 27 28 29 30 31 32 34 35 36 37 38 39 40 41 42 43 44 45 46 47 48 49 50 51 52 53 54 55 56 57 58 59 61 64 65 66 68 70 72 73 74 75 76 77 78 79 80 81 82 84 85 86 87 88 89 90 91 92 93 94 96 97 98 99 100 101 102 103 104 105 107 108 109 110 111 112 114 115 116 117 118 119 120 121 123 124 126 129 130 131 132 134 135 136 137 138 139 141 142 143 144 145 146 147 148 149 150 153 154 156 **S** Yale New Haven Health, New Haven, CT
Primary Contact: Marna P. Borgstrom, Chief Executive Officer
CFO: Vincent Tammaro, Chief Financial Officer
CMO: Thomas Balcezak, M.D., Senior Vice President Medical Affairs and Chief Medical Officer
CIO: Lisa Stump, Interim Chief Information Officer
CHR: Kevin A Myatt, Senior Vice President Human Resources
CNO: Patricia Sue Fitzsimons, R.N., Ph.D., Senior Vice President Patient Services
Web address: www.ynhh.org
Control: Other not–for–profit (including NFP Corporation) **Service:** General medical and surgical

Staffed Beds: 1424 **Admissions:** 68404 **Census:** 1172 **Outpatient Visits:** 1429392 **Births:** 5703 **Total Expense ($000):** 2763769 **Payroll Expense ($000):** 900053 **Personnel:** 12597

NEW LONDON—New London County

☒ △ **LAWRENCE + MEMORIAL HOSPITAL (070007)**, 365 Montauk Avenue, Zip 06320–4769; tel. 860/442–0711, **A**1 2 3 5 7 10 19 **F**3 11 13 15 17 18 19 20 22 26 28 29 30 31 34 35 38 39 40 41 42 44 46 49 50 51 54 55 57 59 60 63 64 65 68 70 72 74 75 76 77 78 79 81 82 84 85 86 87 89 90 91 92 93 96 98 100 101 102 104 107 108 110 111 114 115 116 117 118 119 120 121 123 124 126 129 130 131 132 146 147 148 149 153 **S** Yale New Haven Health, New Haven, CT
Primary Contact: Patrick Green, FACHE, President and Chief Executive Officer
CFO: Seth Van Essendelft, Vice President and Chief Financial Officer
CMO: Oliver Mayorga, M.D., Chief Medical Officer
CIO: Kimberly Kalajainen, Vice President Operations and Chief Information Officer
CHR: Donna Epps, Vice President and Chief Human Resources Officer
CNO: Caren Lewis, R.N., Chief Nursing Officer
Web address: www.lmhospital.org
Control: Other not–for–profit (including NFP Corporation) **Service:** General medical and surgical

Staffed Beds: 251 **Admissions:** 11442 **Census:** 172 **Outpatient Visits:** 308613 **Births:** 1997 **Total Expense ($000):** 335705 **Payroll Expense ($000):** 142649 **Personnel:** 999

NORWALK—Fairfield County

☒ **NORWALK HOSPITAL (070034)**, 34 Maple Street, Zip 06850–3894; tel. 203/852–2000, **A**1 2 3 5 8 10 **F**3 7 8 11 12 13 15 17 18 20 22 26 28 29 30 31 34 35 36 39 40 43 44 45 46 47 48 49 50 51 54 55 57 58 59 64 66 68 70 72 74 75 76 77 78 79 80 81 82 84 85 87 89 93 96 97 98 100 101 102 104 105 107 108 110 111 114 115 117 118 119 120 121 123 124 126 129 130 131 132 135 145 146 148 149 153 154 **S** Western Connecticut Health Network, Danbury, CT
Primary Contact: Peter Cordeau, President
CFO: Michael Kruzick, Acting Chief Financial Officer
CMO: Michael Marks, M.D., Chief of Staff
CHR: Anthony Aceto, Vice President Human Resources
Web address: www.norwalkhospital.org
Control: Other not–for–profit (including NFP Corporation) **Service:** General medical and surgical

Staffed Beds: 151 **Admissions:** 11742 **Census:** 138 **Outpatient Visits:** 204532 **Births:** 1146 **Total Expense ($000):** 361307 **Payroll Expense ($000):** 137284 **Personnel:** 1623

NORWICH—New London County

☒ **THE WILLIAM W. BACKUS HOSPITAL (070024)**, 326 Washington Street, Zip 06360–2740; tel. 860/889–8331, **A**1 2 3 5 10 19 **F**3 9 11 12 13 15 18 20 26 28 29 30 31 34 35 36 37 40 43 45 46 49 50 51 54 57 58 59 61 63 64 65 70 71 74 75 76 78 79 81 82 84 85 86 87 89 92 93 97 98 100 101 102 104 105 107 108 110 111 114 115 116 117 118 119 120 121 126 130 132 134 135 144 145 146 147 148 149 153 154 157 **S** Hartford HealthCare, Hartford, CT
Primary Contact: Donna Handley, President
COO: Carolyn Trantalis, R.N., MSN, Regional Vice President, Clinical Services and Operations
CFO: Anthony Mastroianni, Regional Vice President Finance
CMO: Robert Sidman, M.D., Regional Vice President, Medical Affairs
CIO: Angie Mathieu, System Director Information Technology and Regional Chief Information Officer
CHR: Karen James, Regional Director, Human Resources
CNO: Carolyn Trantalis, R.N., MSN, Regional Vice President, Clinical Services and Operations
Web address: www.backushospital.org
Control: Other not–for–profit (including NFP Corporation) **Service:** General medical and surgical

Staffed Beds: 184 **Admissions:** 9453 **Census:** 127 **Births:** 899 **Total Expense ($000):** 308121 **Payroll Expense ($000):** 111080 **Personnel:** 1171

PUTNAM—Windham County

☐ **DAY KIMBALL HOSPITAL (070003)**, 320 Pomfret Street, Zip 06260–1836; tel. 860/928–6541, (Nonreporting) **A**1 2 5 10
Primary Contact: Anne Diamond, President and Chief Executive Officer
CFO: Paul Beaudoin, Chief Financial Officer
CMO: John Graham, M.D., Vice President Medical Affairs
CIO: Odile Romanick, Chief information Officer
CHR: Jeffrey T. Corrigan, Vice President Human Resources
CNO: John O'Keefe, Chief Nursing Officer
Web address: www.daykimball.org
Control: Other not–for–profit (including NFP Corporation) **Service:** General medical and surgical

Staffed Beds: 65

ROCKY HILL—Hartford County

CONNECTICUT VETERANS HOME AND HOSPITAL (072006), 287 West Street, Zip 06067–3501; tel. 860/616–3606, (Nonreporting) **A**10
Primary Contact: Seam Connolly, Commissioner
CFO: Michael Clark, Fiscal Administrative Manager
CMO: Vamseedhar Alla, M.D., Director Medical Staff
CIO: Sheri DeVaux, Information Technology Manager
CHR: Noreen Sinclair, Human Resources Administrator
CNO: Jeff Lord, Director of Nursing
Web address: www.ct.gov/ctva
Control: State, Government, nonfederal **Service:** Acute long–term care hospital

Staffed Beds: 125

SHARON—Litchfield County

☐ **SHARON HOSPITAL (070004)**, 50 Hospital Hill Road, Zip 06069–2096, Mailing Address: P.O. Box 789, Zip 06069–0789; tel. 860/364–4000, (Nonreporting) **A**1 10 20 **S** Health Quest Systems, Inc., LaGrangeville, NY
Primary Contact: Denise George, R.N., Interim Chief Executive Officer
CMO: Michael Parker, M.D., Chief of Staff
CHR: Kathleen Berlinghoff, Director Human Resources
Web address: www.sharonhospital.com
Control: Corporation, Investor–owned (for–profit) **Service:** General medical and surgical

Staffed Beds: 78

SOMERS—Tolland County

CONNECTICUT DEPARTMENT OF CORRECTION'S HOSPITAL, 100 Bilton Road, Zip 06071–1059, Mailing Address: P.O. Box 100, Zip 06071–0100; tel. 860/749–8391, (Nonreporting)
Primary Contact: Edward A. Blanchette, M.D., Director
Control: State, Government, nonfederal **Service:** Hospital unit of an institution (prison hospital, college infirmary, etc.)

Staffed Beds: 29

CT

SOUTHINGTON—Hartford County

BRADLEY MEMORIAL See The Hospital of Central Connecticut, New Britain

STAFFORD SPRINGS—Tolland County

⊞ **JOHNSON MEMORIAL MEDICAL CENTER (070008)**, 201 Chestnut Hill Road, Zip 06076–4005; tel. 860/684–4251, (Nonreporting) **A**1 2 10 **S** Trinity Health, Livonia, MI
Primary Contact: Stuart E. Rosenberg, President
CFO: John Grish, Chief Financial Officer
CMO: Ian Tucker, M.D., Vice President Medical Affairs
CHR: Donna M Megliola, Assistant Vice President
CNO: Patricia Jagoe, Assistant Vice President Patient Care
Web address: www.jmmc.com
Control: Other not–for–profit (including NFP Corporation) **Service**: General medical and surgical

Staffed Beds: 78

STAMFORD—Fairfield County

⊞ **STAMFORD HOSPITAL (070006)**, One Hospital Plaza, Zip 06902, Mailing Address: P.O. Box 9317, Zip 06904–9317; tel. 203/276–1000, **A**1 2 3 5 10 **F**3 8 12 13 15 18 19 20 22 24 26 28 29 30 31 32 34 35 36 37 38 40 41 43 44 45 46 47 48 49 50 52 53 54 55 56 57 58 59 60 61 64 66 68 70 72 74 75 76 77 78 79 81 82 84 85 86 87 89 90 91 92 93 95 96 97 98 100 107 108 110 111 114 115 116 117 118 119 120 121 123 124 126 129 130 131 132 135 144 145 146 147 148 149 150 154 157
Primary Contact: Kathleen A. Silard, R.N., MS, FACHE, President and Chief Executive Officer
COO: Jonathan T Bailey, Chief Operating Officer
CFO: Kevin Gage, Chief Financial Officer
CMO: Sharon Kiely, M.D., Senior Vice President Medical Affairs and Chief Medical Officer
CIO: Steven Sakovits, Vice President Information Systems and Chief Information Officer
CHR: Elaine Guglielmo, Vice President Human Resources and Organizational Development
CNO: Ellen M Komar, R.N., Vice President Patient Care Services and Chief Nursing Officer
Web address: www.stamhealth.org
Control: Other not–for–profit (including NFP Corporation) **Service**: General medical and surgical

Staffed Beds: 305 **Admissions:** 13586 **Census:** 184 **Outpatient Visits:** 488295 **Births:** 2178 **Total Expense ($000):** 548995 **Payroll Expense ($000):** 219955 **Personnel:** 2946

TORRINGTON—Litchfield County

⊞ **CHARLOTTE HUNGERFORD HOSPITAL (070011)**, 540 Litchfield Street, Zip 06790–6679, Mailing Address: P.O. Box 988, Zip 06790–0988; tel. 860/496–6666, **A**1 2 10 **F**3 5 8 11 13 15 18 28 29 30 31 32 34 35 38 40 41 42 44 45 47 48 49 50 51 53 54 57 59 64 68 70 74 75 76 77 78 79 81 82 84 85 86 87 89 93 97 98 100 102 104 105 107 108 110 111 115 117 119 120 121 123 129 130 131 132 144 146 149 152 153 154 **S** Hartford HealthCare, Hartford, CT
Primary Contact: Daniel J. McIntyre, President
CFO: Susan Schapp, Vice President Finance and Treasurer
CMO: Mark Prete, M.D., Vice President Medical Affairs
CHR: R James Elliott, Vice President Human Resources
Web address: www.charlottehungerford.org
Control: Other not–for–profit (including NFP Corporation) **Service**: General medical and surgical

Staffed Beds: 65 **Admissions:** 4987 **Census:** 62 **Outpatient Visits:** 297153 **Births:** 355 **Total Expense ($000):** 128445 **Payroll Expense ($000):** 58737 **Personnel:** 803

VERNON—Tolland County

☐ **ROCKVILLE GENERAL HOSPITAL (070012)**, 31 Union Street, Zip 06066–3160; tel. 860/872–0501, (Nonreporting) **A**1 5 10 **S** Prospect Medical Holdings, Los Angeles, CA
Primary Contact: Michael F. Collins, Chief Executive Officer
CFO: Michael D. Veillette, Senior Vice President and Chief Financial Officer
CMO: Joel R Reich, M.D., Senior Vice President Medical Affairs
CIO: Richard Daigle, Chief Information Officer
CHR: Natalie Cook, Administrative Director, Human Resources
CNO: Mary Powers, R.N., MSN, Senior Vice President and Chief Nursing Officer
Web address: www.echn.com
Control: Other not–for–profit (including NFP Corporation) **Service**: General medical and surgical

Staffed Beds: 47

WALLINGFORD—New Haven County

☐ △ **GAYLORD HOSPITAL (072003)**, 50 Gaylord Farm Road, Zip 06492–7048, Mailing Address: P.O. Box 400, Zip 06492–7048; tel. 203/284–2800, **A**1 3 5 7 10 **F**1 29 30 31 34 35 50 53 54 59 60 64 74 75 82 84 85 86 87 91 93 94 95 96 107 114 119 130 131 132 135 146 148 149
Primary Contact: Sonja LaBarbera, President and Chief Executive Officer
CFO: Art Tedesco, Interim Chief Financial Officer
CMO: Stephen Holland, M.D., Vice President Chief Medical Officer and Medical Director
CIO: Gerry Maroney, Chief Information Officer and Security Officer
CHR: Wally G Harper, Vice President Human Resources
CNO: Lisa Kalafus, MSN, R.N., Chief Nursing Officer
Web address: www.gaylord.org
Control: Other not–for–profit (including NFP Corporation) **Service**: Acute long–term care hospital

Staffed Beds: 122 **Admissions:** 1447 **Census:** 110 **Births:** 0

★ **MASONICARE HEALTH CENTER (070039)**, 22 Masonic Avenue, Zip 06492–3048, Mailing Address: P.O. Box 70, Zip 06492–7001; tel. 203/679–5900, (Nonreporting) **A**3 5 10
Primary Contact: Jon-Paul Venoit, President and Chief Executive Officer
COO: Jon-Paul Venoit, Chief Operating Officer
CFO: Raymond Scott Thelen, Vice President and Chief Financial Officer
CMO: Ronald Schwartz, M.D., Medical Director
CIO: Michael Nichols, Chief Information Officer
CHR: Edward Dooling, Vice President, Human Resources
CNO: Patti Russell, Vice President Nursing
Web address: www.masonicare.org
Control: Other not–for–profit (including NFP Corporation) **Service**: Other specialty treatment

Staffed Beds: 65

WATERBURY—New Haven County

⊞ **SAINT MARY'S HOSPITAL (070016)**, 56 Franklin Street, Zip 06706–1281; tel. 203/709–6000, **A**1 2 3 5 10 **F**3 5 8 11 12 13 14 15 17 18 20 22 24 26 28 29 30 31 34 35 37 38 40 41 42 43 44 45 46 48 49 50 51 54 55 56 57 59 64 65 66 70 72 74 75 76 77 78 79 80 81 82 83 84 85 86 87 91 92 93 97 98 100 101 102 104 105 106 107 108 110 111 115 118 119 120 126 129 130 131 132 135 144 146 147 148 149 152 153 154 157 **S** Trinity Health, Livonia, MI
Primary Contact: Steven E. Schneider, M.D., President
COO: Charles Flinn, Vice President, Chief Operating Officer
CFO: Ralph W Becker, Vice President, Chief Financial Officer
CIO: Michael Novak, Vice President, Operations and Chief Information Officer
CHR: M Clark Kearney, Vice President Human Resources
CNO: Elizabeth Bozzuto, R.N., Chief Nursing Officer and Vice President
Web address: www.stmh.org
Control: Church operated, Nongovernment, not–for–profit **Service**: General medical and surgical

Staffed Beds: 187 **Admissions:** 9937 **Census:** 125 **Outpatient Visits:** 293357 **Births:** 663 **Total Expense ($000):** 292428 **Payroll Expense ($000):** 96701 **Personnel:** 1788

CT

☐ **WATERBURY HOSPITAL (070005)**, 64 Robbins Street, Zip 06708–2600; tel. 203/573–6000, (Nonreporting) **A**1 2 3 5 10 **S** Prospect Medical Holdings, Los Angeles, CA
Primary Contact: Peter J. Adamo, President and Chief Executive Officer
CFO: Colleen M Scott, Vice President Finance
CMO: David Puzzuto, M.D., Vice President Medical Affairs and Chief Medical Officer
CIO: Michael J Cemeno, Chief Information Officer
CHR: Diane Woolley, Vice President Human Resources
CNO: Sandra Ladarola, Chief Nursing Officer
Web address: www.waterburyhospital.org
Control: Other not–for–profit (including NFP Corporation) **Service**: General medical and surgical

Staffed Beds: 183

WEST HARTFORD—Hartford County

HEBREW SENIOR CARE (070040), 1 Abrahms Boulevard, Zip 06117–1525; tel. 860/523–3800, **A**10 **F**2 10 29 56 98 103 130 132 146 149
Primary Contact: Denise Peterson, R.N., FACHE, President and Chief Executive Officer
COO: Marcia H Hickey, Senior Vice President Operations
CFO: David Houle, Executive Vice President and Chief Financial Officer
CMO: Ava Pannullo, M.D., Vice President Medical Services and Physician in Chief
CHR: Sam Vogt, Manager Human Resources
Web address: www.hebrewhealthcare.org
Control: Other not–for–profit (including NFP Corporation) **Service**: Chronic disease

Staffed Beds: 45 **Admissions:** 430 **Census:** 21 **Outpatient Visits:** 0 **Births:** 0 **Personnel:** 61

WEST HAVEN—New Haven County

⊞ **VETERANS AFFAIRS CONNECTICUT HEALTHCARE SYSTEM**, 950 Campbell Avenue, Zip 06516–2770; tel. 203/932–5711, (Includes WEST HAVEN DIVISION, 950 Campbell Avenue, West Haven, Connecticut, Zip 06516–2700; tel. 203/932–5711), (Nonreporting) **A**1 2 3 5 8 **S** Department of Veterans Affairs, Washington, DC
Primary Contact: Gerald F. Culliton, Medical Center Director
CFO: Joseph LaMadeleine, Chief Financial Officer
CMO: Michael Ebert, M.D., Chief of Staff
CIO: Joseph Erdos, M.D., Chief Information Officer
CHR: Mark Bain, Chief Human Resources
Web address: www.connecticut.va.gov
Control: Veterans Affairs, Government, federal **Service**: General medical and surgical

Staffed Beds: 197

WESTPORT—Fairfield County

ST. VINCENT'S BEHAVIORAL HEALTH See St. Vincent's Medical Center, Bridgeport

WILLIMANTIC—Windham County

WINDHAM COMMUNITY MEMORIAL HOSPITAL See Windham Hospital

⊞ **WINDHAM HOSPITAL (070021)**, 112 Mansfield Avenue, Zip 06226–2040; tel. 860/456–9116, **A**1 2 5 10 **F**2 3 6 8 11 13 15 18 28 29 30 31 32 34 35 36 40 43 45 48 50 51 53 54 56 57 59 60 61 64 65 66 68 75 76 77 78 79 81 82 85 86 87 90 93 94 98 99 100 102 107 108 110 111 115 116 117 118 119 126 129 130 131 132 134 135 144 146 147 148 149 151 154 157 **S** Hartford HealthCare, Hartford, CT
Primary Contact: Donna Handley, President
COO: Carolyn Trantalis, R.N., MSN, Chief Operating Officer, East Region
CFO: Daniel E Lohr, Regional Vice President Finance
CMO: Nadia Nashid, M.D., Chief of Staff
CHR: Theresa L Buss, Regional Vice President Human Resources
Web address: www.windhamhospital.org
Control: Other not–for–profit (including NFP Corporation) **Service**: General medical and surgical

Staffed Beds: 99 **Admissions:** 2748 **Census:** 30 **Outpatient Visits:** 78962 **Births:** 110 **Total Expense ($000):** 95677 **Payroll Expense ($000):** 34520 **Personnel:** 394

CT

DELAWARE

DOVER—Kent County

BAYHEALTH MEDICAL CENTER (080004), 640 South State Street, Zip 19901–3530; tel. 302/674–4700, (Includes BAYHEALTH MEDICAL CENTER AT KENT GENERAL, 640 South State Street, Dover, Delaware, Zip 19901–3597; tel. 203/932–5711; BAYHEALTH MEDICAL CENTER, MILFORD MEMORIAL HOSPITAL, 21 West Clarke Avenue, Milford, Delaware, Zip 19963–1840, Mailing Address: P O Box 199, Zip 19963–0199, tel. 302/430–5738; Michael Ashton, Administrator) **A**1 2 3 5 10 **F**3 8 11 12 13 15 17 18 20 22 24 26 28 29 30 31 32 34 35 38 40 41 42 43 44 45 47 48 49 50 51 53 54 55 57 58 59 60 61 64 67 68 70 72 73 74 75 76 77 78 79 81 82 84 85 86 87 88 89 90 93 94 98 99 100 101 102 103 104 107 108 110 111 114 115 117 118 119 120 121 123 124 126 129 130 131 132 134 135 144 146 147 148
Primary Contact: Terry Murphy, President and Chief Executive Officer
COO: Deborah Watson, Senior Vice President and Chief Operating Officer
CFO: Mike Tretina, Senior Vice President and Chief Financial Officer
CMO: Gary M Siegelman, M.D., MSC, Senior Vice President and Chief Medical Officer
CIO: Richard Mohnk, Vice President Corporate Services
CHR: Shana Ross, Vice President Human Resources
CNO: Brenda Blain, MSN, Senior Vice President and Chief Nursing Executive
Web address: www.bayhealth.org
Control: Other not–for–profit (including NFP Corporation) **Service:** General medical and surgical

Staffed Beds: 374 **Admissions:** 19164 **Census:** 276 **Outpatient Visits:** 595196 **Births:** 2303 **Total Expense ($000):** 554780 **Payroll Expense ($000):** 269372 **Personnel:** 2425

DOVER BEHAVIORAL HEALTH SYSTEM (084004), 725 Horsepond Road, Zip 19901–7232; tel. 302/741–0140, (Nonreporting) **A**1 10 **S** Universal Health Services, Inc., King of Prussia, PA
Primary Contact: Jean-Charles Constant, Administrator
Web address: www.doverbehavioral.com
Control: Corporation, Investor–owned (for–profit) **Service:** Psychiatric

Staffed Beds: 80

LEWES—Sussex County

BEEBE HEALTHCARE (080007), 424 Savannah Road, Zip 19958–1462; tel. 302/645–3300, **A**1 2 3 10 19 **F**3 11 12 13 15 17 18 20 22 24 28 29 30 31 32 34 40 41 43 45 46 49 51 54 56 57 59 62 64 67 70 74 75 76 77 78 79 81 82 84 85 87 89 93 96 97 107 108 110 111 114 115 117 118 119 120 121 123 124 130 146 147 148 154 156
Primary Contact: Richard Schaffner, Interim Chief Executive Officer
COO: Richard Schaffner, Executive Vice President and Chief Operating Officer
CFO: Paul Pernice, Vice President Finance
CMO: Jeffrey Hawtof, M.D., Vice President Medical Operations and Informatics
CIO: Michael Maksymow, Vice President Information Systems
CHR: Catherine Halen, Vice President Human Resources
CNO: Steve Rhone, R.N., MS, Vice President Patient Care Services
Web address: www.beebemed.org
Control: Other not–for–profit (including NFP Corporation) **Service:** General medical and surgical

Staffed Beds: 155 **Admissions:** 10534 **Census:** 121 **Outpatient Visits:** 406832 **Births:** 782 **Total Expense ($000):** 349878 **Payroll Expense ($000):** 125240 **Personnel:** 2248

MIDDLETOWN—New Castle County

HEALTHSOUTH REHABILITATION HOSPITAL OF MIDDLETOWN (083026), 250 East Hampden Road, Zip 19709–5303; tel. 302/464–3400, **A**1 10 **F**3 29 90 95 96 146 148 149 **S** Encompass Health Corporation, Birmingham, AL
Primary Contact: Mathew Gooch, Chief Executive Officer
CFO: Lisa Trimble, Controller
CMO: Ashish Khandelwal, M.D., Medical Director
CHR: Anitra Robinson, Human Resources Director
CNO: Rebecca Boney, R.N., Chief Nursing Officer
Web address: www.healthsouthmiddletown.com
Control: Corporation, Investor–owned (for–profit) **Service:** Rehabilitation

Staffed Beds: 37 **Admissions:** 1107 **Census:** 35 **Outpatient Visits:** 0 **Births:** 0 **Total Expense ($000):** 13670 **Payroll Expense ($000):** 7691 **Personnel:** 144

MILFORD—Sussex County

BAYHEALTH MEDICAL CENTER, MILFORD MEMORIAL HOSPITAL See Bayhealth Medical Center, Dover

NEW CASTLE—New Castle County

DELAWARE PSYCHIATRIC CENTER (084001), 1901 North Dupont Highway, Zip 19720–1199; tel. 302/255–2700, **A**1 3 5 10 **F**30 34 39 59 65 68 75 86 87 98 100 101 103 106 130 132 135 143 149
Primary Contact: Norman Vetter, Chief Executive Officer, Division of Substance Abuse and Mental Health
CIO: James Nau, Manager Computer and Applications Support
Web address: www.dhss.delaware.gov
Control: State, Government, nonfederal **Service:** Psychiatric

Staffed Beds: 166 **Admissions:** 236 **Census:** 109 **Outpatient Visits:** 0 **Births:** 0 **Personnel:** 287

MEADOW WOOD BEHAVIORAL HEALTH SYSTEM (084003), 575 South Dupont Highway, Zip 19720–4606; tel. 302/328–3330, (Nonreporting) **A**1 10 **S** Acadia Healthcare Company, Inc., Franklin, TN
Primary Contact: Bill A. Mason, Chief Executive Officer
CFO: Maria Valdenegro, Chief Financial Officer
Web address: www.meadowwoodhospital.com
Control: Corporation, Investor–owned (for–profit) **Service:** Psychiatric

Staffed Beds: 53

NEWARK—New Castle County

CHRISTIANA CARE HEALTH SYSTEM (080001), 4755 Ogletown-Stanton Road, Zip 19718–0002, Mailing Address: P.O. Box 6001, Zip 19718; tel. 302/733–1000, **A**1 2 3 5 8 10 **F**2 3 5 6 7 8 11 12 13 15 17 18 20 22 24 26 28 29 30 31 32 34 35 36 37 38 39 40 41 42 43 44 45 46 47 48 49 50 53 54 55 56 57 58 59 60 61 62 64 65 66 68 70 72 74 75 76 77 78 79 80 81 82 84 85 86 87 89 90 92 93 94 96 97 98 100 101 102 104 107 108 110 111 114 115 117 118 119 120 121 123 124 126 129 130 131 132 134 135 136 138 143 144 145 146 147 148 149 150 154 155 156 **S** Christiana Care Health System, Wilmington, DE
Primary Contact: Janice E. Novin, M.D., M.P.H., Chief Executive Officer
CFO: Rob McMurray, Chief Financial Officer
CMO: Kenneth L Silverstein, M.D., Chief Clinical Officer
CIO: Randall Gaboriault, Chief Information Officer
CHR: Christopher Cowan, Senior Vice President and Chief Human Resources Officer
CNO: Richard Cuming, R.N., MSN, Ed.D., Chief Nurse Executive
Web address: www.christianacare.org
Control: Other not–for–profit (including NFP Corporation) **Service:** General medical and surgical

Staffed Beds: 1082 **Admissions:** 52339 **Census:** 814 **Outpatient Visits:** 603922 **Births:** 6115 **Total Expense ($000):** 1836206 **Payroll Expense ($000):** 879957 **Personnel:** 10491

ROCKFORD CENTER (084002), 100 Rockford Drive, Zip 19713–2121; tel. 302/996–5480, **A**1 3 10 **F**5 98 99 103 105 154 **S** Universal Health Services, Inc., King of Prussia, PA
Primary Contact: John F. McKenna, Chief Executive Officer and Managing Director
CFO: Kumar Purohit, Chief Financial Officer
CMO: Saurabh Gupta, Chief Medical Officer
CHR: Jessi Stewart, Director Human Resources
CNO: Michelle Singletary-Twyman, Chief Nursing Officer
Web address: www.rockfordcenter.com
Control: Corporation, Investor–owned (for–profit) **Service:** Psychiatric

Staffed Beds: 138 **Admissions:** 4896 **Census:** 135 **Outpatient Visits:** 12827 **Births:** 0 **Total Expense ($000):** 28574 **Payroll Expense ($000):** 15141 **Personnel:** 294

DE

Hospital, Medicare Provider Number, Address, Telephone, Approval, Facility, and Physician Codes, Health Care System

★ American Hospital Association (AHA) membership
☐ The Joint Commission accreditation
○ Healthcare Facilities Accreditation Program
◇ DNV Healthcare Inc. accreditation
⇑ Center for Improvement in Healthcare Quality Accreditation
△ Commission on Accreditation of Rehabilitation Facilities (CARF) accreditation

SEAFORD—Sussex County

☒ **NANTICOKE MEMORIAL HOSPITAL (080006)**, 801 Middleford Road,
Zip 19973–3636; tel. 302/629–6611, **A**1 2 10 **F**3 12 13 15 18 20 22 28 29
30 31 32 34 35 37 40 43 45 49 50 54 57 59 64 65 70 74 75 76 77 78 79
81 84 85 86 87 89 93 107 108 111 114 115 119 120 121 123 126 129 130
132 135 144 146 147 148 149 150 154 156 157
Primary Contact: Steven A Rose, R.N., President and Chief Executive Officer
COO: Penny Short, R.N., Chief Operating Officer
CFO: Denise Jester, Chief Financial Officer
CMO: Harry C. Anthony, M.D., Chief Medical Officer
CIO: Charles Palmer, Director Information Technology
CNO: Lori L Lee, Vice President Nursing
Web address: www.nanticoke.org
Control: Other not–for–profit (including NFP Corporation) **Service**: General
medical and surgical

> **Staffed Beds:** 99 **Admissions:** 5676 **Census:** 57 **Outpatient Visits:** 144204
> **Births:** 917 **Total Expense ($000):** 131963 **Payroll Expense ($000):** 45808
> **Personnel:** 1044

WILMINGTON—New Castle County

☒ △ **ALFRED I. DUPONT HOSPITAL FOR CHILDREN (083300)**, 1600
Rockland Road, Zip 19803–3616, Mailing Address: Box 269, Zip 19899–0269;
tel. 302/651–4000, (Nonreporting) **A**1 2 3 5 7 10 **S** Nemours, Jacksonville, FL
Primary Contact: Roy Proujansky, M.D., Chief Executive Officer
CFO: William N Britton, Associate Administrator Finance
CMO: Brent R King, Chief Medical Officer and Chief Physician
Web address: www.nemours.org
Control: Other not–for–profit (including NFP Corporation) **Service**: Children's
general medical and surgical

> **Staffed Beds:** 200

☒ **SELECT SPECIALTY HOSPITAL-WILMINGTON (082000)**, 701 North Clayton
Street, 5th Floor, Zip 19805–3948; tel. 302/421–4545, **A**1 10 **F**1 18 29 74 79
130 148 **S** Select Medical Corporation, Mechanicsburg, PA
Primary Contact: Donna Gares, R.N., FACHE, MSN, Chief Executive Officer
CFO: David Huffman, Vice President and Controller
CMO: Hummayun Ismail, M.D., Medical Director
CHR: Barbara A Foster, Regional Human Resources Director
Web address: www.wilmington.selectspecialtyhospitals.com
Control: Corporation, Investor–owned (for–profit) **Service**: Acute long–term care
hospital

> **Staffed Beds:** 35 **Admissions:** 323 **Census:** 27 **Outpatient Visits:** 0
> **Births:** 0 **Total Expense ($000):** 16996 **Payroll Expense ($000):** 7850
> **Personnel:** 118

☒ **ST. FRANCIS HOSPITAL (080003)**, 701 North Clayton Street, Zip 19805,
Mailing Address: P.O. Box 2500, Zip 19805–0500; tel. 302/421–4100,
(Nonreporting) **A**1 2 3 5 10 **S** Trinity Health, Livonia, MI
Primary Contact: Daniel J. Sinnott, President and Chief Executive Officer
CIO: Paul W Rowe, Director Information Technology
CHR: Charlene J Wilson, Vice President Human Resources
Web address: www.stfrancishealthcare.org
Service: General medical and surgical

> **Staffed Beds:** 154

☒ **WILMINGTON VETERANS AFFAIRS MEDICAL CENTER**, 1601 Kirkwood
Highway, Zip 19805–4989; tel. 302/994–2511, (Nonreporting) **A**1 3 5 **S**
Department of Veterans Affairs, Washington, DC
Primary Contact: Robert W. Callahan Jr, Interim Director
CFO: Mary Ann Kozel, Chief Fiscal
CMO: Enrique Guttin, M.D., FACS, Chief of Staff
CIO: Scott Vlars, Chief Information Technology Services
CHR: Louis McCloskey, Chief Human Resources
Web address: www.va.gov/wilmington
Control: Veterans Affairs, Government, federal **Service**: General medical and
surgical

> **Staffed Beds:** 60

Many Facility Codes have changed. Please refer to the AHA Guide Code Chart. © 2019 AHA Guide

DE

DISTRICT OF COLUMBIA

WASHINGTON—District of Columbia County

☐ **BRIDGEPOINT HOSPITAL CAPITOL HILL (092002)**, 700 Constitution Avenue NE, Zip 20002–6058; tel. 202/546–5700, (Nonreporting) **A**1 10 **S** BridgePoint Healthcare, Portsmouth, NH
Primary Contact: James Linhares, Chief Executive Officer
COO: Delores Clair Oliver, Chief Clinical Officer and Chief Operating Officer
CFO: Michael Grubb, Chief Financial Officer
CMO: Gerald Moawad, Chief Medical Officer
CHR: Karen Brown, Senior Director of Human Resources
CNO: Delores Clair Oliver, Chief Clinical Officer and Chief Operating Officer
Web address: www.bridgepointhealthcare.com/
Control: Corporation, Investor–owned (for–profit) **Service:** Acute long–term care hospital

Staffed Beds: 177

BRIDGEPOINT HOSPITAL NATIONAL HARBOR (092003), 4601 Martin Luther King Jr Avenue, SW, Zip 20032–1131; tel. 202/574–5700, (Nonreporting) **A**10 19 22 **S** BridgePoint Healthcare, Portsmouth, NH
Primary Contact: Swenda Moreh, Interim Chief Executive Officer
COO: Swenda Moreh, Vice President and Chief Operating Officer
CFO: Michael Grubb, Chief Financial Officer
CMO: Khosrow Davachi, Chief Medical Officer
CHR: Antoninette Saldivar, Vice President, Human Resources
CNO: Diane White, Chief Clinical Officer and Chief Nursing Officer
Web address: www.bridgepointhealthcare.com/
Control: Corporation, Investor–owned (for–profit) **Service:** Acute long–term care hospital

Staffed Beds: 82

⊠ **CHILDREN'S NATIONAL HEALTH SYSTEM (093300)**, 111 Michigan Avenue NW, Zip 20010–2916; tel. 202/476–5000; **A**1 3 5 8 10 **F**1 3 4 5 7 8 11 12 14 16 17 18 19 21 23 25 27 29 30 31 32 34 35 36 38 39 40 41 42 43 44 45 46 40 49 50 51 54 55 57 58 59 60 61 64 65 66 67 68 70 71 72 73 74 75 77 78 79 80 81 82 83 84 85 86 87 88 89 90 91 92 93 94 96 97 98 99 100 102 104 105 106 107 111 112 115 116 117 118 119 126 128 129 130 131 132 134 136 137 138 141 142 146 148 155 156 157
Primary Contact: Kurt Newman, M.D., President and Chief Executive Officer
COO: Kathleen Gorman, MSN, R.N., Executive Vice President Patient Care Services and Chief Operating Officer
CMO: Mark L Batshaw, M.D., Physician-in-Chief, Executive Vice President and Chief Academic Officer
CIO: Brian Jacobs, M.D., Vice President Chief Information Officer and Chief Medical Information Officer
CHR: Darryl Varnado, Executive Vice President and Chief People Officer
CNO: Linda Talley, MS, R.N., Vice President and Chief Nursing Officer
Web address: www.childrensnational.org
Control: Other not–for–profit (including NFP Corporation) **Service:** Children's general medical and surgical

Staffed Beds: 313 **Admissions:** 15319 **Census:** 266 **Outpatient Visits:** 553146 **Births:** 0 **Total Expense ($000):** 1060398 **Payroll Expense ($000):** 579789 **Personnel:** 5381

⊠ △ **GEORGE WASHINGTON UNIVERSITY HOSPITAL (090001)**, 900 23rd Street NW, Zip 20037–2342; tel. 202/715–4000, **A**1 2 3 5 7 8 10 **F**3 8 11 12 13 15 17 18 20 22 24 26 29 31 34 35 37 38 39 40 43 44 45 47 48 49 51 53 54 55 56 57 58 59 60 61 63 64 65 68 70 71 72 74 75 76 77 78 79 80 81 82 84 85 86 87 90 91 92 93 94 96 98 102 107 108 110 111 114 115 116 117 118 119 120 121 123 124 126 129 130 131 132 134 135 136 138 141 146 147 148 149 150 156 **S** Universal Health Services, Inc., King of Prussia, PA
Primary Contact: Kimberly Russo, Chief Executive Officer
COO: Kimberly Russo, Chief Operating Officer
CFO: Richard Davis, Chief Financial Officer
CMO: Gary Little, M.D., Medical Director
CIO: Louis Duhe, Senior Director Information Technology
CHR: Erin Fagan, Manager Human Resources
Web address: www.gwhospital.com
Control: Partnership, Investor–owned (for–profit) **Service:** General medical and surgical

Staffed Beds: 385 **Admissions:** 20177 **Census:** 321 **Outpatient Visits:** 190737 **Births:** 3454 **Personnel:** 2776

GEORGETOWN UNIVERSITY HOSPITAL See Medstar Georgetown University Hospital

⊠ **HOWARD UNIVERSITY HOSPITAL (090003)**, 2041 Georgia Avenue NW, Zip 20060–0002; tel. 202/865–6100, **A**1 2 3 5 8 10 **F**8 12 13 15 17 18 24 26 28 29 30 31 32 34 35 36 38 39 40 41 43 44 45 46 50 53 54 55 56 57 58 59 60 61 64 65 66 68 70 71 72 74 75 76 77 78 79 81 82 85 86 87 93 97 98 100 101 102 104 107 108 110 111 114 115 118 119 123 124 129 130 132 146 147 148 156
Primary Contact: John Kerr. Tolmie, Chief Executive Officer
CFO: Ed Gyimah, Chief Financial Officer
CMO: Shelly McDonald-Pinkett, Chief Medical Officer
CIO: Becky Quammen, Chief Information Officer
CHR: Jeronica Goodwin, Senior Director Human Resources
CNO: Shirley Evers-Manly, Chief Nursing Officer
Web address: www.huhealthcare.com
Control: Other not–for–profit (including NFP Corporation) **Service:** General medical and surgical

Staffed Beds: 239 **Admissions:** 8242 **Census:** 95 **Outpatient Visits:** 113787 **Births:** 1138

⊠ **MEDSTAR GEORGETOWN UNIVERSITY HOSPITAL (090004)**, 3800 Reservoir Road NW, Zip 20007–2197; tel. 202/444–2000, **A**1 2 3 5 8 10 **F**3 6 7 9 11 13 15 18 20 26 29 30 31 32 34 35 36 37 38 39 40 41 44 45 46 47 48 49 50 51 53 54 55 56 57 58 59 60 61 63 64 65 66 68 70 71 72 74 75 76 77 78 79 80 81 82 84 85 86 87 88 89 92 93 97 98 100 101 102 104 105 107 108 110 111 114 115 116 117 118 119 120 121 122 123 124 126 129 130 131 132 134 135 136 138 139 141 142 145 146 147 148 149 150 154 156 **S** MedStar Health, Columbia, MD
Primary Contact: Michael Sachtleben, President
CFO: Paul Warda, Chief Financial Officer
CMO: Lisa Boyle, M.D., Vice President Medical Affairs and Medical Director
CIO: John Rasmussen, Vice President for Information Technology
CHR: Mary Jo Schweickhardt, Vice President Human Resources
CNO: Eileen Brennan Ferrell, MS, R.N., Vice President and Chief Nursing Officer
Web address: www.georgetownuniversityhospital.org
Control: Other not–for–profit (including NFP Corporation) **Service:** General medical and surgical

Staffed Beds: 409 **Admissions:** 15640 **Census:** 323 **Outpatient Visits:** 646406 **Births:** 987 **Total Expense ($000):** 1057641 **Payroll Expense ($000):** 492688 **Personnel:** 5476

⊠ △ **MEDSTAR NATIONAL REHABILITATION HOSPITAL (093025)**, 102 Irving Street NW, Zip 20010–2949; tel. 202/877–1000, **A**1 3 5 7 10 **F**9 11 28 29 30 33 34 35 36 44 53 54 56 58 59 60 64 68 74 75 77 78 79 82 86 87 90 91 92 93 94 95 96 119 129 130 131 132 146 148 149 **S** MedStar Health, Columbia, MD
Primary Contact: John D. Rockwood, President
CFO: Michael Boemmel, Vice President and Chief Financial Officer
CMO: Michael R Yocholson, M.D., Vice President and Medical Director
CHR: Pamela Ashby, Vice President Human Resources
CNO: Rosemary C Welch, R.N., Vice President and Chief Nursing Officer
Web address: www.medstarnrh.org
Control: Other not–for–profit (including NFP Corporation) **Service:** Rehabilitation

Staffed Beds: 137 **Admissions:** 2038 **Census:** 93 **Outpatient Visits:** 447660 **Births:** 0 **Total Expense ($000):** 139682 **Payroll Expense ($000):** 79080 **Personnel:** 1320

DC

☒ **MEDSTAR WASHINGTON HOSPITAL CENTER (090011)**, 110 Irving Street NW, Zip 20010–3017; tel. 202/877–7000, **A**1 2 3 5 8 10 F3 5 12 13 15 16 17 18 20 22 24 26 27 28 29 30 31 34 35 37 38 39 40 43 44 45 46 47 48 49 50 51 54 55 56 57 58 59 61 62 64 65 66 68 70 72 73 74 75 76 77 78 79 80 81 82 84 85 86 87 92 97 98 100 101 102 104 107 108 110 111 114 115 116 117 118 119 120 121 123 124 126 130 131 132 134 135 137 146 147 148 149 150 153 154 156 157 **S** MedStar Health, Columbia, MD
Primary Contact: Gregory J. Argyros, M.D., Senior Vice President and President
COO: Robert Ross, Chief Operating Officer
CFO: William Gayne, Chief Financial Officer
CIO: Joe Brothman, Assistant Vice President, Information Systems
CHR: James P Hill, Senior Vice President Administrative Services
CNO: Susan E. Eckert, R.N., MSN, Senior Vice President and Chief Nursing Officer
Web address: www.whcenter.org
Control: Other not–for–profit (including NFP Corporation) **Service**: General medical and surgical

> **Staffed Beds**: 745 **Admissions**: 32558 **Census**: 605 **Outpatient Visits**: 396168 **Births**: 3688 **Total Expense ($000)**: 1286220 **Payroll Expense ($000)**: 576642 **Personnel**: 5225

NATIONAL REHABILITATION HOSPITAL See Medstar National Rehabilitation Hospital

☐ **PSYCHIATRIC INSTITUTE OF WASHINGTON (094004)**, 4228 Wisconsin Avenue NW, Zip 20016–2138; tel. 202/885–5600, (Nonreporting) **A**1 5 10
Primary Contact: Dina Levi, Director, Business Development
COO: Carol Desjeunes, Vice President and Chief Operating Officer
CFO: Aarti Subramanian, Vice President and Chief Financial Officer
CMO: Howard Hoffman, M.D., Medical Director
CIO: Ray Santina, Director Information Systems
CHR: Dawn Hatterer-Hoag, Director Human Resources
Web address: www.psychinstitute.com
Control: Corporation, Investor–owned (for–profit) **Service**: Psychiatric

> **Staffed Beds**: 124

★ **SAINT ELIZABETHS HOSPITAL (094001)**, 1100 Alabama Avenue SE, Zip 20032–4540; tel. 202/299–5000, **A**3 5 10 F29 30 39 56 59 65 74 75 86 91 98 103 130 135 146 148
Primary Contact: Mark J. Chastang, M.P.H., Chief Executive Officer
COO: K. Singh Taneja, Chief Operating Officer
CFO: James V. Jackson, Budget Director
CMO: Hannah Ong, Director, Medical Affairs
CIO: Brady Birdsong, Chief Information Officer
CHR: Frankie Wheeler, Director, Human Resources
CNO: Clotilde Vidoni-Clark, Ph.D., R.N., Chief Nursing Executive
Web address: www.dbh.dc.gov/
Control: State, Government, nonfederal **Service**: Psychiatric

> **Staffed Beds**: 292 **Admissions**: 427 **Census**: 261 **Outpatient Visits**: 0 **Births**: 0 **Personnel**: 757

☒ **SIBLEY MEMORIAL HOSPITAL (090005)**, 5255 Loughboro Road NW, Zip 20016–2633; tel. 202/537–4000, (Total facility includes 45 beds in nursing home–type unit) **A**1 2 3 5 10 F3 6 8 10 12 13 15 20 29 30 31 34 35 36 37 38 44 45 46 47 48 49 50 53 54 55 57 58 59 64 68 70 73 74 75 76 77 78 79 81 82 84 85 86 87 91 92 93 96 97 98 100 101 102 103 104 107 108 109 110 111 113 114 115 116 117 118 119 120 121 123 126 128 130 132 135 146 147 148 154 157 **S** Johns Hopkins Health System, Baltimore, MD
Primary Contact: Richard O. Davis, Ph.D., President
COO: Sanjay K Saha, Chief Operating Officer
CFO: Marty Basso, Chief Financial Officer
CMO: M. Therese McDonnell, M.D., Interim Vice President Patient Safety, Quality and Medical Affairs
CIO: Christopher T Timbers, Chief Information Officer
CHR: Queenie C. Plater, Vice President, Human Resources National Capital Region Johns Hopkins Medicine
CNO: Lynn Meuer, Interim Chief Nursing Officer
Web address: www.sibley.org
Control: Other not–for–profit (including NFP Corporation) **Service**: General medical and surgical

> **Staffed Beds**: 273 **Admissions**: 12122 **Census**: 159 **Outpatient Visits**: 129596 **Births**: 3921 **Total Expense ($000)**: 364904 **Payroll Expense ($000)**: 129724 **Personnel**: 1955

☒ **THE HSC PEDIATRIC CENTER**, 1731 Bunker Hill Road NE, Zip 20017–3096; tel. 202/832–4400, **A**1 3 F12 29 30 31 32 34 35 44 50 54 58 59 64 68 71 75 79 80 83 84 86 90 91 93 94 96 130 132 134 143 146 148 157
Primary Contact: Debbie C. Holson, R.N., MSN, Chief Operating Officer
COO: Debbie C Holson, R.N., MSN, Chief Operating Officer
CFO: Ray Vicks, Senior Vice President, Finance and Chief Financial Officer
CMO: Andrew Metinko, M.D., Chief Medical Officer
CIO: Khalil Bouharoun, Chief Information Officer
CHR: Lynne Hostetter, Vice President Human Resources
Web address: www.hscpediatriccenter.org/
Control: Other not–for–profit (including NFP Corporation) **Service**: Children's chronic disease

> **Staffed Beds**: 118 **Admissions**: 202 **Census**: 23 **Outpatient Visits**: 18070 **Births**: 0 **Total Expense ($000)**: 35818 **Payroll Expense ($000)**: 12495

☒ **UNITED MEDICAL CENTER (090008)**, 1310 Southern Avenue SE, Zip 20032–4623; tel. 202/574–6000, (Nonreporting) **A**1 3 10
Primary Contact: Matthew Hamilton, Chief Executive Officer
CFO: Lilian Chukwuma, Chief Financial Officer
CMO: Eric Li, M.D., Chief Medical Officer
CIO: Alan Johnson, Interim Chief Information Officer
CHR: Eric M. Johnson, Director
Web address: www.united-medicalcenter.com
Control: Other not–for–profit (including NFP Corporation) **Service**: General medical and surgical

> **Staffed Beds**: 354

VETERANS AFFAIRS MEDICAL CENTER See Washington DC Veterans Affairs Medical Center

☒ △ **WASHINGTON DC VETERANS AFFAIRS MEDICAL CENTER**, 50 Irving Street NW, Zip 20422–0002; tel. 202/745–8000, (Nonreporting) **A**1 2 3 5 7 **S** Department of Veterans Affairs, Washington, DC
Primary Contact: Adam M. Robinson, Acting Director
CFO: Frank Filosa, Fiscal Manager
CIO: Amanda Graves, Chief Information Systems
Web address: www.washingtondc.va.gov/
Control: Veterans Affairs, Government, federal **Service**: General medical and surgical

> **Staffed Beds**: 291

WASHINGTON HOSPITAL CENTER See Medstar Washington Hospital Center

DC

FLORIDA

ALTAMONTE SPRINGS—Seminole County

ADVENTHEALTH ALTAMONTE SPRINGS See Adventhealth Orlando, Orlando

⊞ **ENCOMPASS HEALTH REHABILITATION HOSPITAL OF ALTAMONTE SPRINGS (103045)**, 831 South State Road 434, Zip 32714–3502; tel. 407/587–8600, (Nonreporting) **A**1 10 **S** Encompass Health Corporation, Birmingham, AL
Primary Contact: George Welton, Chief Executive Officer
Web address: www.healthsouthaltamontesprings.com
Control: Corporation, Investor–owned (for–profit) **Service:** Rehabilitation

Staffed Beds: 50

APALACHICOLA—Franklin County

GEORGE E. WEEMS MEMORIAL HOSPITAL (101305), 135 Avenue G, Zip 32320–1613, Mailing Address: P.O. Box 580, Zip 32329–0580; tel. 850/653–8853, (Nonreporting) **A**10 18
Primary Contact: David Walker, Interim Chief Executive Officer
CHR: Ginny Griner, Director Human Resources
Web address: www.weemsmemorial.com
Control: Partnership, Investor–owned (for–profit) **Service:** General medical and surgical

Staffed Beds: 15

APOPKA—Orange County

ADVENTHEALTH APOPKA See Adventhealth Orlando, Orlando

ARCADIA—Desoto County

☐ **DESOTO MEMORIAL HOSPITAL (100175)**, 900 North Robert Avenue, Zip 34266–8712, Mailing Address: P.O. Box 2180, Zip 34265–2180; tel. 863/494–3535, **A**1 10 20 **F**5 15 18 28 29 31 34 35 40 45 46 54 55 57 62 64 65 66 70 74 75 77 79 81 82 85 87 93 104 105 107 108 110 111 114 119 120 130 135 146 148 149 154
Primary Contact: Vincent A. Sica, President and Chief Executive Officer
CFO: Dan Hogan, Chief Financial Officer
CMO: Steven Mishkind, M.D., Chief of Staff
CIO: Kristen Opahr, Director of Marketing
CHR: Lois Hilton, Director Human Resources
CNO: Joseph La Cava, Chief Nursing Officer and Director of Anesthesia
Web address: www.dmh.org
Control: Hospital district or authority, Government, nonfederal **Service:** General medical and surgical

Staffed Beds: 45 Admissions: 1177 Census: 9 Outpatient Visits: 74164
Births: 100 Total Expense ($000): 34363 Payroll Expense ($000): 13292
Personnel: 269

ATLANTIS—Palm Beach County

⊞ **JFK MEDICAL CENTER (100080)**, 5301 South Congress Avenue, Zip 33462–1197; tel. 561/965–7300, (Nonreporting) **A**1 2 3 5 10 **S** HCA Healthcare, Nashville, TN
Primary Contact: Gina Melby, Chief Executive Officer
CFO: Jim Leamon, Chief Financial Officer
CIO: Jane Stewart, Director Information Services
CHR: Trudy Bromley, Vice President Human Resources
Web address: www.jfkmc.com
Control: Corporation, Investor–owned (for–profit) **Service:** General medical and surgical

Staffed Beds: 424

AVENTURA—Miami-Dade County

⊞ **AVENTURA HOSPITAL AND MEDICAL CENTER (100131)**, 20900 Biscayne Boulevard, Zip 33180–1407; tel. 305/682–7000, (Nonreporting) **A**1 2 3 5 10 **S** HCA Healthcare, Nashville, TN
Primary Contact: Lee B. Chaykin, Chief Executive Officer
COO: Luanne Ansaldo, Chief Operating Officer
CFO: Alisa Bert, Chief Financial Officer
CMO: Martin Grossman, Chief of Staff
CHR: Rosemarie Amberson, Vice President Human Resources
Web address: www.aventurahospital.com
Control: Corporation, Investor–owned (for–profit) **Service:** General medical and surgical

Staffed Beds: 359

BARTOW—Polk County

⊞ **BARTOW REGIONAL MEDICAL CENTER (100121)**, 2200 Osprey Boulevard, Zip 33830–3308; tel. 863/533–8111, **A**1 10 **F**3 11 12 15 18 20 22 29 30 34 35 40 44 45 46 49 50 51 57 59 60 64 68 70 74 75 77 78 79 81 82 84 85 86 87 93 101 107 108 110 111 114 115 118 119 126 129 130 131 132 135 145 146 147 148 149 154 156 **S** Trinity Health, Livonia, MI
Primary Contact: Karen Kerr, R.N., President
CFO: Michael Boscia, Chief Financial Officer
CMO: Stuart Patterson, M.D., Chief of Staff
CIO: Vilakon Champavannarath, Director Information Systems
CHR: Marie Horton, Director Associate Relations
Web address: www.bartowregional.com
Control: Other not–for–profit (including NFP Corporation) **Service:** General medical and surgical

Staffed Beds: 72 Admissions: 2980 Census: 32 Outpatient Visits: 41412
Births: 0 Total Expense ($000): 59378 Payroll Expense ($000): 21199
Personnel: 346

BAY PINES—Pinellas County

⊞ △ **BAY PINES VETERANS AFFAIRS HEALTHCARE SYSTEM**, 10000 Bay Pines Boulevard, Zip 33744–8200, Mailing Address: P.O. Box 5005, Zip 33744–5005; tel. 727/398–6661, (Nonreporting) **A**1 2 3 5 7 **S** Department of Veterans Affairs, Washington, DC
Primary Contact: Paul M. Russo, FACHE, Director
COO: Kris Brown, Associate Director
CFO: Jeanine Ergle, Chief Financial Officer
CMO: George F Van Buskirk, M.D., Chief of Staff
CIO: John Williams, Chief Information Officer
CHR: Paula Buchele, Chief Human Resources
Web address: www.baypines.va.gov/
Control: Veterans Affairs, Government, federal **Service:** General medical and surgical

Staffed Beds: 396

BELLE GLADE—Palm Beach County

GLADES GENERAL HOSPITAL See Lakeside Medical Center

⊞ **LAKESIDE MEDICAL CENTER (100130)**, 39200 Hooker Highway, Zip 33430–5368; tel. 561/996–6571, (Nonreporting) **A**1 5 10 13
Primary Contact: Janet Moreland, Administrator
COO: Darcy Davis, Chief Financial Officer
CFO: Darcy Davis, Chief Financial Officer
CMO: Ron Wiewora, M.D., Chief Medical Officer
Web address: www.lakesidemedical.org
Control: Hospital district or authority, Government, nonfederal **Service:** General medical and surgical

Staffed Beds: 70

FL

Hospital, Medicare Provider Number, Address, Telephone, Approval, Facility, and Physician Codes, Health Care System

★ American Hospital Association (AHA) membership
☐ The Joint Commission accreditation
○ Healthcare Facilities Accreditation Program
◇ DNV Healthcare Inc. accreditation
⇧ Center for Improvement in Healthcare Quality Accreditation
△ Commission on Accreditation of Rehabilitation Facilities (CARF) accreditation

BLOUNTSTOWN—Calhoun County

CALHOUN-LIBERTY HOSPITAL (101304), 20370 NE Burns Avenue, Zip 32424–1045, Mailing Address: P.O. Box 419, Zip 32424–0419; tel. 850/674–5411, (Nonreporting) **A**10 18 **S** Alliant Management Services, Louisville, KY
Primary Contact: Charles E. Durant Jr, FACHE, Chief Executive Officer
CFO: Nathan Ebersole, Controller
CIO: Michael Flowers, Director Information Management
CHR: Lynn Pitts, Director Human Resources
CNO: Debra Summers, Chief Nursing Officer
Web address: www.calhounlibertyhospital.com
Control: Other not–for–profit (including NFP Corporation) **Service:** General medical and surgical

Staffed Beds: 25

BOCA RATON—Palm Beach County

BOCA RATON COMMUNITY HOSPITAL See Boca Raton Regional Hospital

☐ **BOCA RATON REGIONAL HOSPITAL (100168)**, 800 Meadows Road, Zip 33486–2368; tel. 561/955–7100, **A**1 2 3 5 10 **F**3 6 8 11 12 13 15 17 18 20 22 24 26 28 29 30 31 33 35 36 37 40 44 45 46 47 48 49 50 51 54 55 56 57 58 59 60 61 62 64 68 70 71 73 74 75 76 78 79 81 82 84 85 86 87 92 93 96 97 101 102 107 108 109 110 111 112 114 115 116 117 118 119 120 121 123 124 126 130 131 132 135 144 145 146 147 148 149 154 156
Primary Contact: Lincoln S. Mendez, Chief Executive Officer
COO: Mindy Shikiar, MSN, Chief Operating Officer
CFO: Dawn Jauersack, Vice President and Chief Financial Officer
CMO: Charles Posternack, M.D., Vice President
CIO: Robin Hildwein, Chief Information Officer
CHR: Mindy Raymond, Vice President Human Resources
CNO: Melissa Ann Durbin, R.N., MSN, Chief Nursing Officer
Web address: www.brrh.com
Control: Other not–for–profit (including NFP Corporation) **Service:** General medical and surgical

Staffed Beds: 374 Admissions: 19619 Census: 250 Outpatient Visits: 292035 Births: 2545 Total Expense ($000): 528190 Payroll Expense ($000): 208004 Personnel: 2574

✉ **WEST BOCA MEDICAL CENTER (100268)**, 21644 State Road 7, Zip 33428–1899; tel. 561/488–8000, (Nonreporting) **A**1 3 5 10 **S** TENET Healthcare Corporation, Dallas, TX
Primary Contact: Mitchell S. Feldman, Chief Executive Officer
COO: Ryan Lee, Chief Operating Officer
CFO: Brook Thomas, Chief Financial Officer
CMO: Jack L Harari, M.D., Chief Medical Officer
CIO: Lauren Spagna, Marketing Director
CHR: Stephanie Sherman, Chief Human Resources Officer
CNO: Ruth Schwarzkopf, Chief Nursing Officer
Web address: www.westbocamedctr.com
Control: Corporation, Investor–owned (for–profit) **Service:** General medical and surgical

Staffed Beds: 195

BONIFAY—Holmes County

☐ **DOCTORS MEMORIAL HOSPITAL (101307)**, 2600 Hospital Drive, Zip 32425–4264, Mailing Address: P.O. Box 188, Zip 32425–0188; tel. 850/547–8000, (Nonreporting) **A**1 10 18
Primary Contact: Joann Baker, Administrator
CFO: Celia F Ward, Controller and Chief Financial Officer
CMO: Leisa Bailey, M.D., Chief of Staff
CIO: Rohan Anderson, Chief Information Officer
CHR: Christy Booth, Chief Human Resources Officer
CNO: Karla Rockwell, Director of Nursing
Web address: www.doctorsmemorial.org
Control: Hospital district or authority, Government, nonfederal **Service:** General medical and surgical

Staffed Beds: 20

BOYNTON BEACH—Palm Beach County

✉ **BETHESDA HOSPITAL EAST (100002)**, 2815 South Seacrest Boulevard, Zip 33435–7995; tel. 561/737–7733, (Includes BETHESDA HOSPITAL WEST, 9655 West Boynton Beach Boulevard, Boynton Beach, Florida, Zip 33472–4421; tel. 561/336–7000; Roger L Kirk, President and Chief Executive Officer) **A**1 3 5 10 **F**3 8 11 12 13 17 18 19 20 22 26 28 29 31 40 41 45 46 47 48 49 51 56 68 70 72 74 75 76 77 78 79 81 82 85 87 88 89 90 92 93 96 107 108 109 110 111 114 115 116 117 118 119 120 121 124 126 129 130 131 132 135 146 147 148 **S** Baptist Health South Florida, Coral Gables, FL
Primary Contact: Roger L. Kirk, President and Chief Executive Officer
COO: Ela C Lena, Administrator and Vice President Operations
CFO: Joanne Aquilina, Vice President Finance and Chief Financial Officer
CMO: Albert Biehl, M.D., Vice President Medical Affairs
CIO: Leslie Albright, Vice President Information Systems
CHR: Regina Bellucy, Vice President Human Resources
CNO: Ela C Lena, Interim System Chief Nursing Officer
Web address: www.bethesdaweb.com
Control: Other not–for–profit (including NFP Corporation) **Service:** General medical and surgical

Staffed Beds: 481 Admissions: 21141 Census: 285 Outpatient Visits: 264117 Births: 2548 Total Expense ($000): 331443 Payroll Expense ($000): 117364 Personnel: 2256

BRADENTON—Manatee County

✉ △ **BLAKE MEDICAL CENTER (100213)**, 2020 59th Street West, Zip 34209–4669; tel. 941/792–6611, (Nonreporting) **A**1 2 3 7 10 **S** HCA Healthcare, Nashville, TN
Primary Contact: Randy Currin, Chief Executive Officer
COO: Lisa Nummi, MSN, R.N., Chief Operating Officer
CFO: Andrew Smith, Chief Financial Officer
CMO: Alan Harmatz, M.D., Chief Medical Officer
CIO: Shannon Piatkowski, Director Information Technology
CHR: Veronica Lequeux, Vice President Human Resources
CNO: Kimberly Kay Hatchel, Chief Nursing Officer
Web address: www.blakemedicalcenter.com
Control: Corporation, Investor–owned (for–profit) **Service:** General medical and surgical

Staffed Beds: 383

CENTERSTONE HOSPITAL (104040), 2020 26th Avenue East, Zip 34208–7753, Mailing Address: P.O. Box 9478, Zip 34206–9478; tel. 941/782–4600, (Nonreporting) **A**3 10 13
Primary Contact: Melissa Larkin-Skinner, Chief Executive Officer
CFO: Sean Gingras, CPA, Chief Financial Officer
CMO: Ranjay Halder, M.D., Chief Medical Director
CIO: Heidi L Blair, Vice President Administration
CHR: Colleen O'Connor, Director Human Resources
Web address: www.manateeglens.org
Control: Individual, Investor–owned (for–profit) **Service:** Other specialty treatment

Staffed Beds: 62

☐ **LAKEWOOD RANCH MEDICAL CENTER (100299)**, 8330 Lakewood Ranch Boulevard, Zip 34202–5174; tel. 941/782–2100, (Nonreporting) **A**1 10 **S** Universal Health Services, Inc., King of Prussia, PA
Primary Contact: Andrew Guz, Chief Executive Officer
COO: Linda S Widra, FACHE, Ph.D., R.N., Chief Operating Officer
CFO: Gerald Christine, Chief Financial Officer
CHR: Trish Morales, Director Human Resources
Web address: www.lakewoodranchmedicalcenter.com
Control: Corporation, Investor–owned (for–profit) **Service:** General medical and surgical

Staffed Beds: 120

☐ **MANATEE MEMORIAL HOSPITAL (100035)**, 206 Second Street East, Zip 34208–1000; tel. 941/746–5111, (Nonreporting) **A**1 2 3 5 10 12 13 **S** Universal Health Services, Inc., King of Prussia, PA
Primary Contact: Kevin DiLallo, Chief Executive Officer
COO: Camie Patterson, Chief Operating Officer
CFO: Mark A Tierney, Chief Financial Officer
CMO: Eric Deppert, M.D., Chief Medical Officer
CIO: Troy Beaubien, Director Information Services
CHR: Sheree Threewits, Director Human Resources
CNO: Candace Susan Smith, Chief Nursing Officer
Web address: www.manateememorial.com
Control: Partnership, Investor–owned (for–profit) **Service:** General medical and surgical

Staffed Beds: 319

FL

Many Facility Codes have changed. Please refer to the AHA Guide Code Chart.

☐ **SUNCOAST BEHAVIORAL HEALTH CENTER (104078)**, 4480 51st Street West, Zip 34210–2855; tel. 941/251–5000, (Nonreporting) **A**1 10 **S** Universal Health Services, Inc., King of Prussia, PA
Primary Contact: Brandy Hamilton, Chief Executive Officer
CFO: Linda Weymouth, Chief Financial Officer
CMO: Randolph Hemsath, M.D., Medical Director
CNO: Janey Sweeney, Chief Nursing Officer
Web address: www.suncoastbhc.com
Control: Corporation, Investor–owned (for–profit) **Service**: Children's hospital psychiatric

Staffed Beds: 60

BRANDON—Hillsborough County

☒ **BRANDON REGIONAL HOSPITAL (100243)**, 119 Oakfield Drive, Zip 33511–5779; tel. 813/681–5551, (Nonreporting) **A**1 3 5 10 **S** HCA Healthcare, Nashville, TN
Primary Contact: Bland Eng, Chief Executive Officer
COO: Liz Durrence, Chief Operating Officer
CFO: Gary Searls, Chief Financial Officer
CMO: Joseph C. Corcoran, D.O., Chief Medical Officer
CIO: Aaron Fountain, Chief Information Officer
CHR: Doug Goodman, Vice President Human Resources
CNO: William Kyle Thrift, Chief Nursing Officer
Web address: www.brandonhospital.com
Control: Corporation, Investor–owned (for–profit) **Service**: General medical and surgical

Staffed Beds: 407

BROOKSVILLE—Hernando County

☒ **BAYFRONT HEALTH BROOKSVILLE (100071)**, 17240 Cortez Boulevard, Zip 34601–8921, Mailing Address: P.O. Box 37, Zip 34605–0037; tel. 352/796–5111, (Includes BAYFRONT HEALTH SPRING HILL, 10461 Quality Drive, Spring Hill, Florida, Zip 34609–9634; tel. 352/688–8200; Michael Irvin, Chief Executive Officer), (Nonreporting) **A**1 10 **S** Community Health Systems, Inc., Franklin, TN
Primary Contact: Kenneth R. Wicker, Chief Executive Officer
COO: Scott Hartsell, Chief Operating Officer
CFO: Matthew Seagroves, Chief Financial Officer
CMO: Mohammad A Joud, M.D., Chief of Staff
CIO: Lee Burch, Director Management Information Systems
CHR: Claudia L Jack, Director Associate Relations
Web address: www.brooksvilleregionalhospital.org
Control: Corporation, Investor–owned (for–profit) **Service**: General medical and surgical

Staffed Beds: 120

☒ **ENCOMPASS HEALTH REHABILITATION HOSPITAL OF SPRING HILL (103042)**, 12440 Cortez Boulevard, Zip 34613–2628; tel. 352/592–4250, (Nonreporting) **A**1 10 **S** Encompass Health Corporation, Birmingham, AL
Primary Contact: Jeffrey Alexander, Chief Executive Officer
CFO: Kimberly Lunt, Controller
CMO: Mira Zelin, D.O., Medical Director
CIO: Myra Merillo, Supervisor Health Information Management
CHR: Mary Salamanca, Director Human Resources
Web address: www.healthsouthspringhill.com
Control: Corporation, Investor–owned (for–profit) **Service**: Rehabilitation

Staffed Beds: 80

☒ **OAK HILL HOSPITAL (100264)**, 11375 Cortez Boulevard, Zip 34613–5409; tel. 352/596–6632, (Nonreporting) **A**1 2 3 10 13 **S** HCA Healthcare, Nashville, TN
Primary Contact: Mickey Smith, Chief Executive Officer
COO: Leanne Salazar, Chief Operating Officer
CFO: Matt Romero, Chief Financial Officer
CMO: Ed Nast, M.D., Chief Medical Officer
CHR: Charles Snider, Vice President Human Resources
CNO: Elizabeth Adams, R.N., Chief Nursing Officer
Web address: www.oakhillhospital.com
Control: Corporation, Investor–owned (for–profit) **Service**: General medical and surgical

Staffed Beds: 280

☐ **SPRINGBROOK HOSPITAL (104057)**, 7007 Grove Road, Zip 34609–8610; tel. 352/596–4306, (Nonreporting) **A**1 10
Primary Contact: Timothy Cowart, Administrator
Web address: www.springbrookhospital.org/
Control: Other not–for–profit (including NFP Corporation) **Service**: Psychiatric

Staffed Beds: 66

CAPE CORAL—Lee County

★ ⇑ **CAPE CORAL HOSPITAL (100244)**, 636 Del Prado Boulevard, Zip 33990–2695; tel. 239/424–2000, **A**2 10 21 **F**3 11 13 14 18 20 28 29 30 34 35 40 45 46 48 49 50 51 53 56 57 59 60 66 68 70 74 75 76 77 79 81 82 84 85 86 87 93 94 102 107 108 111 114 119 129 130 132 135 146 147 148 156 **S** Lee Health, Fort Myers, FL
Primary Contact: Lawrence Antonucci, M.D., President and Chief Executive Officer
CFO: Ben Spence, Chief Financial Officer
CMO: Mark Greenberg, M.D., Chief Medical Officer
CIO: Mike Smith, Chief Information Officer
CHR: Jon C Cecil, Chief Human Resource Officer
CNO: Lisa Sgarlata, MSN, Chief Patient Care Officer
Web address: www.leememorial.org
Control: Hospital district or authority, Government, nonfederal **Service**: General medical and surgical

Staffed Beds: 291 **Admissions:** 15732 **Census:** 176 **Outpatient Visits:** 235049 **Births:** 1387 **Total Expense ($000):** 181296 **Payroll Expense ($000):** 79100 **Personnel:** 1315

CELEBRATION—Osceola County

ADVENTHEALTH CELEBRATION See Adventhealth Orlando, Orlando

CHATTAHOOCHEE—Gadsden County

FLORIDA STATE HOSPITAL (104000), U S Highway 90 East, Zip 32324–1000, Mailing Address: P.O. Box 1000, Zip 32324–1000; tel. 850/663–7536, (Nonreporting) **A**10
Primary Contact: Marguerite J. Morgan, Administrator
CFO: Bill Jones, Chief Financial Officer
CMO: Josefina Balulga, M.D., Clinical Director
CIO: Wesley Pelham
CHR: Keri Bassett, Human Resources Business Partner
Web address: www.dcf.state.fl.us/institutions/fsh
Control: State, Government, nonfederal **Service**: Psychiatric

Staffed Beds: 987

CHIPLEY—Washington County

☐ **NORTHWEST FLORIDA COMMUNITY HOSPITAL (101300)**, 1360 Brickyard Road, Zip 32428–6303, Mailing Address: P.O. Box 889, Zip 32428–0889; tel. 850/638–1610, (Total facility includes 34 beds in nursing home–type unit) **A**1 10 18 **F**11 15 28 29 30 34 40 45 56 57 59 65 68 81 82 85 93 97 107 108 110 111 115 119 127 128 130 131 132 133 146 148 153 154 **S** Alliant Management Services, Louisville, KY
Primary Contact: Michael A. Kozar, Chief Executive Officer
COO: Janet Kinney, Chief Operating Officer
CFO: Marcey Black, Chief Financial Officer
CHR: Shelia Schierelbein, Coordinator Human Resources
CNO: Joan Beard, Chief Nursing Officer
Web address: www.nfch.org
Control: Corporation, Investor–owned (for–profit) **Service**: General medical and surgical

Staffed Beds: 59 **Admissions:** 714 **Census:** 40 **Outpatient Visits:** 30680 **Births:** 0

CLEARWATER—Pinellas County

☒ **MORTON PLANT HOSPITAL (100127)**, 300 Pinellas Street, Zip 33756–3804, Mailing Address: P.O. Box 210, Zip 33757–0210; tel. 727/462–7000, (Total facility includes 120 beds in nursing home–type unit) **A**1 2 3 5 10 **F**3 6 11 13 15 17 18 20 22 24 26 28 29 30 31 34 35 36 37 38 40 42 44 45 46 47 48 49 50 51 53 54 55 56 57 58 59 60 61 62 63 64 65 66 68 70 72 74 75 76 77 78 79 80 81 82 84 85 86 87 91 92 93 98 100 101 102 107 108 110 111 112 114 115 118 119 120 121 123 124 126 128 129 130 131 132 135 143 145 146 147 148 149 154 156 **S** Morton Plant Mease Health Care, Clearwater, FL
Primary Contact: Lou Galdieri, R.N., President
CFO: Carl Tremonti, Chief Financial Officer
CMO: Jeff Jensen, D.O., Vice President, Medical Affairs
CIO: Timothy Thompson, Senior Vice President and Chief Information Officer
CHR: Angel Brown, Director Human Resources
CNO: Thomas Doria, Vice President Patient Services - West
Web address: www.mortonplant.com
Control: Other not–for–profit (including NFP Corporation) **Service**: General medical and surgical

Staffed Beds: 710 **Admissions:** 27217 **Census:** 333 **Outpatient Visits:** 397381 **Births:** 2300 **Total Expense ($000):** 571988 **Payroll Expense ($000):** 165547 **Personnel:** 3021

FL

Hospital, Medicare Provider Number, Address, Telephone, Approval, Facility, and Physician Codes, Health Care System

★ American Hospital Association (AHA) membership   ○ Healthcare Facilities Accreditation Program   ⇑ Center for Improvement in Healthcare Quality Accreditation
☐ The Joint Commission accreditation   ◇ DNV Healthcare Inc. accreditation   △ Commission on Accreditation of Rehabilitation Facilities (CARF) accreditation

---

☐ **WINDMOOR HEALTHCARE OF CLEARWATER (104017)**, 11300 U S 19 North, Zip 33764; tel. 727/541–2646, (Nonreporting) **A**1 10 **S** Universal Health Services, Inc., King of Prussia, PA
Primary Contact: Wendy Merson, Chief Executive Officer
Web address: www.windmoor.com
Control: Corporation, Investor–owned (for–profit) **Service**: Psychiatric

Staffed Beds: 100

CLERMONT—Lake County

☐ **SOUTH LAKE HOSPITAL (100051)**, 1900 Don Wickham Drive, Zip 34711–1979; tel. 352/394–4071, (Total facility includes 30 beds in nursing home–type unit) **A**1 3 10 **F**3 8 11 13 15 18 20 22 26 28 29 30 31 32 34 35 40 42 45 46 47 48 49 50 51 53 54 57 59 60 62 64 68 70 74 75 76 77 78 79 81 82 85 86 87 89 92 93 107 108 110 111 114 115 116 117 119 120 121 124 126 128 130 131 132 135 146 147 148 149 154 156 **S** Orlando Health, Orlando, FL
Primary Contact: John Moore, President
COO: Paul Johns, Chief Operating Officer
CFO: Lance Sewell, Chief Financial Officer
CHR: Joy L. Sylvester, Administrator, People Services
CNO: Bonnie Onofre, Chief Nursing Officer
Web address: www.southlakehospital.com
Control: Hospital district or authority, Government, nonfederal **Service**: General medical and surgical

Staffed Beds: 170 Admissions: 11849 Census: 139 Outpatient Visits: 134317 Births: 713 Total Expense ($000): 206942 Payroll Expense ($000): 78238 Personnel: 1374

CLEWISTON—Hendry County

☒ **HENDRY REGIONAL MEDICAL CENTER (101309)**, 524 West Sagamore Avenue, Zip 33440–3514; tel. 863/902–3000, **A**1 10 18 **F**11 15 29 34 35 40 45 50 57 59 64 65 68 75 77 81 82 85 91 93 97 107 110 111 114 119 127 133 135 146 **S** QHR, Brentwood, TN
Primary Contact: R D Williams, Chief Executive Officer
CFO: John Beltz, Chief Financial Officer
CMO: Leonard Carroll, M.D., Chief of Staff
CIO: Harrington Fuller, Information Technology Director
CHR: Lisa Miller, Director Human Resources
CNO: Rebecca Springer, MSN, R.N., Chief Nursing Officer
Web address: www.hendryregional.org
Control: Hospital district or authority, Government, nonfederal **Service**: General medical and surgical

Staffed Beds: 25 Admissions: 442 Census: 3 Outpatient Visits: 36828 Births: 0 Total Expense ($000): 32504 Payroll Expense ($000): 14635

COCOA BEACH—Brevard County

☒ **HEALTH FIRST CAPE CANAVERAL HOSPITAL (100177)**, 701 West Cocoa Beach Causeway, Zip 32931–5595, Mailing Address: P.O. Box 320069, Zip 32932–0069; tel. 321/799–7111, **A**1 10 **F**3 4 11 13 15 18 20 22 26 29 30 31 34 39 40 41 45 46 49 50 54 59 60 62 64 68 70 74 75 76 77 78 79 80 81 85 86 87 92 93 102 107 108 110 111 114 115 118 119 129 130 132 141 146 147 148 149 154 **S** Health First, Inc., Rockledge, FL
Primary Contact: Brett A. Esrock, FACHE, President
COO: Deborah Angerami, Chief Operating Officer, Health First Community Hospitals
CFO: Joseph G Felkner, Senior Vice President Finance and Chief Financial Officer
CMO: Lee Scheinbart, M.D., Vice President Medical Affairs, Health First Community Hospitals
CIO: Alex Popowycz, Senior Vice President and Chief Information Officer
CHR: Paula Just, Chief Human Resources Officer
CNO: Connie Bradley, R.N., MSN, FACHE, Chief Nursing Officer
Web address: www.health-first.org
Control: Other not–for–profit (including NFP Corporation) **Service**: General medical and surgical

Staffed Beds: 144 Admissions: 7672 Census: 83 Outpatient Visits: 116926 Births: 699 Total Expense ($000): 135067 Payroll Expense ($000): 62421 Personnel: 533

CORAL GABLES—Miami-Dade County

☒ **BAPTIST HEALTH SOUTH FLORIDA, DOCTORS HOSPITAL (100296)**, 5000 University Drive, Zip 33146–2094; tel. 786/308–3000, **A**1 3 5 10 **F**3 11 18 29 30 31 34 35 37 40 44 45 47 49 53 57 58 59 60 63 64 68 70 74 75 77 78 79 80 81 82 84 85 86 87 90 93 94 100 102 107 108 111 115 119 124 126 130 131 132 135 141 146 148 149 150 154 **S** Baptist Health South Florida, Coral Gables, FL
Primary Contact: Nelson Lazo, Chief Executive Officer
CFO: Maria J Yanez, Chief Financial Officer
Web address: www.baptisthealth.net
Control: Other not–for–profit (including NFP Corporation) **Service**: General medical and surgical

Staffed Beds: 126 Admissions: 5634 Census: 68 Outpatient Visits: 64197 Births: 0 Total Expense ($000): 172409 Payroll Expense ($000): 58103 Personnel: 802

☒ **CORAL GABLES HOSPITAL (100183)**, 3100 Douglas Road, Zip 33134–6914; tel. 305/445–8461, (Nonreporting) **A**1 10 **S** TENET Healthcare Corporation, Dallas, TX
Primary Contact: Cristina Jimenez, Chief Executive Officer
COO: Madison Workman, Chief Operating Officer
CFO: Henry Capote, Interim Chief Financial Officer
CMO: Pedro Friarte, Director of Physician Services
CIO: Mercy Hermosa, Director of Information System
CHR: Ana Paguaga, Director of Human Resources
Web address: www.coralgableshospital.com
Control: Corporation, Investor–owned (for–profit) **Service**: General medical and surgical

Staffed Beds: 256

CORAL SPRINGS—Broward County

☒ **BROWARD HEALTH CORAL SPRINGS (100276)**, 3000 Coral Hills Drive, Zip 33065–4108; tel. 954/344–3000, **A**1 3 10 **F**3 11 12 13 15 20 29 31 34 35 40 41 48 51 55 57 58 59 61 63 64 66 68 70 72 74 75 77 78 79 80 81 82 84 85 86 87 88 93 107 108 111 114 115 118 119 126 129 130 131 132 143 146 147 148 154 **S** Broward Health, Fort Lauderdale, FL
Primary Contact: Jared M. Smith, Chief Executive Officer
COO: Michael Leopold, Chief Operating Officer
CFO: Onel Rodriguez, Chief Financial Officer
CMO: Kutty Chandran, M.D., Regional Medical Officer
CHR: Janene John, Chief Human Resource Officer
CNO: Carolyn Lizann Carter, Chief Nursing Officer
Web address: www.browardhealth.org
Control: Hospital district or authority, Government, nonfederal **Service**: General medical and surgical

Staffed Beds: 196 Admissions: 11234 Census: 117 Outpatient Visits: 125967 Births: 2165 Total Expense ($000): 146192 Payroll Expense ($000): 63928 Personnel: 969

CRESTVIEW—Okaloosa County

☒ **NORTH OKALOOSA MEDICAL CENTER (100122)**, 151 Redstone Avenue SE, Zip 32539–6026; tel. 850/689–8100, **A**1 10 **F**3 8 11 13 15 18 20 22 28 29 30 34 35 40 45 49 50 51 54 59 60 64 70 75 76 79 81 85 86 87 89 90 107 108 110 111 114 115 116 117 118 119 126 127 129 130 131 132 146 147 148 149 150 154 156 157 **S** Community Health Systems, Inc., Franklin, TN
Primary Contact: Ronnie Daves, Chief Executive Officer
CFO: Jim Andrews, Chief Financial Officer
CMO: Michael Foley, M.D., Chief Medical Officer
CIO: Jenny Zeitler, Network Administrator
CHR: Melody M Miller-Collette, Director Human Resources
CNO: Nina Perez, R.N., MSN, Chief Nursing Officer
Web address: www.northokaloosa.com
Control: Corporation, Investor–owned (for–profit) **Service**: General medical and surgical

Staffed Beds: 110 Admissions: 5162 Census: 57 Outpatient Visits: 82087 Births: 465 Total Expense ($000): 83315 Payroll Expense ($000): 27021 Personnel: 551

CRYSTAL RIVER—Citrus County

☒ **SEVEN RIVERS REGIONAL MEDICAL CENTER (100249)**, 6201 North Suncoast Boulevard, Zip 34428–6712; tel. 352/795–6560, (Nonreporting) **A**1 10 19 **S** Community Health Systems, Inc., Franklin, TN
Primary Contact: Linda Stockton, Interim Chief Executive Officer
CFO: Vickie Magurean, Chief Financial Officer
CHR: Joann Mramor, Director Human Resources
CNO: Cynthia Heitzman, R.N., Chief Nursing Officer
Web address: www.srrmc.com
Control: Corporation, Investor–owned (for–profit) **Service**: General medical and surgical

Staffed Beds: 128

CUTLER BAY—Miami-Dade County

☒ **ENCOMPASS HEALTH REHABILITATION HOSPITAL OF MIAMI (103038)**, 20601 Old Cutler Road, Zip 33189–2400; tel. 305/251–3800, (Nonreporting) **A**1 10 **S** Encompass Health Corporation, Birmingham, AL
Primary Contact: Enrique A. Vicens-Rivera Jr, JD, Chief Executive Officer
CFO: Reyna Hernandez, Chief Financial Officer
CIO: Miguel Cruz, Medical Staff Credentialing Coordinator
CHR: Susan Riley, Director Human Resources
CNO: Ellen Romanowski, Chief Nursing Officer
Web address: www.healthsouthmiami.com
Control: Corporation, Investor–owned (for–profit) **Service**: Rehabilitation

Staffed Beds: 60

HEALTHSOUTH REHABILITATION HOSPITAL See Encompass Health Rehabilitation Hospital of Miami

FL

Many Facility Codes have changed. Please refer to the AHA Guide Code Chart.   © 2019 AHA Guide

DADE CITY—Pasco County

⊞ **ADVENTHEALTH DADE CITY (100211)**, 13100 Fort King Road, Zip 33525–5294; tel. 352/521–1100, (Nonreporting) **A**1 10 **S** AdventHealth, Altamonte Springs, FL
Primary Contact: Amanda Maggard, Chief Executive Officer
CFO: Ann Barr, Interim Chief Financial Officer
CMO: Petros Tsambiras, M.D., Chief of Staff
CIO: Cheryl Kaufman, Director Health Information Management
CHR: Tabatha Wallace, Director Human Resources
Web address: www.floridahospital.com/dade-city
Control: Corporation, Investor–owned (for–profit) **Service:** General medical and surgical

Staffed Beds: 120

DAVENPORT—Polk County

⊞ **ADVENTHEALTH HEART OF FLORIDA (100137)**, 40100 Highway 27, Zip 33837–5906; tel. 863/422–4971, **A**1 10 19 **F**3 12 13 15 17 18 20 22 26 28 29 30 34 35 37 40 42 45 49 50 51 57 59 60 64 68 70 74 75 76 77 79 81 82 85 87 89 92 93 96 100 107 110 111 114 115 116 117 118 119 126 130 132 135 144 146 147 148 149 154 156 **S** AdventHealth, Altamonte Springs, FL
Primary Contact: Brian Adams, Chief Executive Officer
CFO: Tonja Mosley, Chief Financial Officer
CMO: Claudio Manubens, M.D., Chief of Staff
CIO: Louis Jones, Director Management Information Systems
CHR: Joan Allard, Director Human Resources
CNO: Dottie Mileto, Chief Nursing Officer
Web address: www.heartofflorida.com
Control: Corporation, Investor–owned (for–profit) **Service:** General medical and surgical

Staffed Beds: 193 Admissions: 8891 Census: 99 Outpatient Visits: 71984 Births: 809 Total Expense ($000): 144172 Payroll Expense ($000): 56187 Personnel: 674

DAYTONA BEACH—Volusia County

⊞ △ **ADVENTHEALTH DAYTONA BEACH (100068)**, 301 Memorial Medical Parkway, Zip 32117–5167; tel. 386/676–6000, (Includes FLORIDA HOSPITAL-OCEANSIDE, 264 South Atlantic Avenue, Ormond Beach, Florida, Zip 32176–8192; tel. 386/672–4161) **A**1 2 7 10 **F**3 11 12 13 15 17 18 20 22 24 26 28 29 30 31 32 34 35 40 41 45 46 47 49 50 53 54 57 58 60 70 72 74 76 77 78 79 80 81 85 86 87 89 90 91 92 93 96 97 107 108 109 110 111 112 114 115 116 117 119 120 121 123 124 130 131 132 135 146 147 148 149 154 **S** AdventHealth, Altamonte Springs, FL
Primary Contact: Ed Noseworthy, Chief Executive Officer
COO: Darlinda Copeland, Chief Operating Officer
CFO: Debora Thomas, Chief Financial Officer
CMO: Kris David Gray, Chief Medical Officer
CHR: Opal R Howard, Executive Director Human Resources
CNO: Michele Goeb-Burkett, R.N., MSN, Chief Nursing Officer
Web address: www.floridahospitalmemorial.org
Control: Church operated, Nongovernment, not–for–profit **Service:** General medical and surgical

Staffed Beds: 326 Admissions: 17193 Census: 244 Outpatient Visits: 341556 Births: 1620 Total Expense ($000): 359929 Payroll Expense ($000): 142089 Personnel: 2177

☐ **HALIFAX HEALTH MEDICAL CENTER OF DAYTONA BEACH (100017)**, 303 North Clyde Morris Boulevard, Zip 32114–2700; tel. 386/425–4000, (Includes HALIFAX BEHAVIORAL SERVICES, 841 Jimmy Ann Drive, Daytona Beach, Florida, Zip 32117–4599; tel. 386/425–3900; HALIFAX HEALTH MEDICAL CENTER OF PORT ORANGE, 1041 Dunlawton Avenue, Port Orange, Florida, Zip 32127; tel. 386/425–4700; Ann Martorano, Chief Operating Officer) **A**1 2 3 5 10 **F**3 8 12 13 14 17 18 20 22 24 26 28 29 30 31 32 33 34 35 40 41 42 43 45 46 47 49 50 53 55 57 59 60 64 65 66 70 72 74 75 76 77 78 79 81 82 85 86 87 88 89 90 91 93 94 96 97 98 99 100 101 102 103 105 119 120 121 123 124 126 131 132 135 138 145 146 147 148 149 153 156 157
Primary Contact: Jeff Feasel, Chief Executive Officer
COO: Mark Billings, Chief Operating Officer
CFO: Eric Peburn, Chief Financial Officer
CMO: Margaret Crossman, M.D., Chief Medical Officer
CIO: Tom Stafford, Chief Information Officer
CHR: Kimberly Fulcher, Chief Human Resources Officer
CNO: Catherine Luchsinger, MSN, Chief Nursing Officer
Web address: www.halifax.org
Control: Hospital district or authority, Government, nonfederal **Service:** General medical and surgical

Staffed Beds: 678 Admissions: 23361 Census: 357 Outpatient Visits: 264892 Births: 1715 Total Expense ($000): 499866 Payroll Expense ($000): 212827 Personnel: 2965

⊞ **SELECT SPECIALTY HOSPITAL DAYTONA BEACH (102030)**, 301 Memorial Medical Parkway, 11th Floor, Zip 32117–5167; tel. 386/231–3436, (Nonreporting) **A**1 10 **S** Select Medical Corporation, Mechanicsburg, PA
Primary Contact: Adrianne Lutes, Chief Executive Officer
Web address: www.daytonabeach.selectspecialtyhospitals.com
Control: Corporation, Investor–owned (for–profit) **Service:** Acute long–term care hospital

Staffed Beds: 34

DEERFIELD BEACH—Broward County

⊞ △ **BROWARD HEALTH NORTH (100086)**, 201 East Sample Road, Zip 33064–3502; tel. 954/941–8300, **A**1 2 7 10 **F**3 6 11 15 17 18 20 22 29 30 31 34 35 37 40 43 45 46 49 50 51 57 58 59 64 66 68 70 74 75 77 78 79 80 81 85 86 87 90 92 93 94 96 100 107 108 111 114 115 117 118 119 129 130 131 132 143 145 146 148 154 **S** Broward Health, Fort Lauderdale, FL
Primary Contact: Alice Taylor, R.N., MSN, Chief Executive Officer
COO: Susan Newton, Chief Operating Officer
CFO: Kim Braxl-Cole, Chief Financial Officer
CMO: Narendra Maheshwari, M.D., Chief of Staff
CNO: Bettiann S Ruditz, MS, R.N., Chief Nursing Officer
Web address: www.browardhealth.org
Control: Hospital district or authority, Government, nonfederal **Service:** General medical and surgical

Staffed Beds: 331 Admissions: 13577 Census: 208 Outpatient Visits: 96110 Births: 0 Total Expense ($000): 248552 Payroll Expense ($000): 92932 Personnel: 1464

DEFUNIAK SPRINGS—Walton County

HEALTHMARK REGIONAL MEDICAL CENTER (100081), 4413 US Highway 331 South, Zip 32435–6307; tel. 850/951–4500, (Nonreporting) **A**10
Primary Contact: James H. Thompson, Ph.D., FACHE, Owner and Chief Executive Officer
COO: Gerald C Beard, Chief Operating Officer
CFO: Jim Brewer, M.P.H., Chief Financial Officer
CMO: Edward Tenewitz, M.D., Chief of Staff
CIO: Ray Downs, Senior Staff Accountant
CHR: Debra Tiller, Director Personnel and Administrative Secretary
Web address: www.healthmarkregional.com
Control: Corporation, Investor–owned (for–profit) **Service:** General medical and surgical

Staffed Beds: 50

DELAND—Volusia County

⊞ **ADVENTHEALTH DELAND (100045)**, 701 West Plymouth Avenue, Zip 32720–3236; tel. 386/943–4522, (Nonreporting) **A**1 2 10 **S** AdventHealth, Altamonte Springs, FL
Primary Contact: Lorenzo Brown, Chief Executive Officer
COO: Samuel Aguero, Chief Operating Officer
CFO: Kyle Glass, Chief Financial Officer
CMO: Samuel Edwards, M.D., Chief of Staff
CIO: Kevin Piper, Director Information Systems
CNO: Patricia Ann Stark, R.N., CNO
Web address: www.fhdeland.org
Control: Other not–for–profit (including NFP Corporation) **Service:** General medical and surgical

Staffed Beds: 164

DELRAY BEACH—Palm Beach County

⊞ △ **DELRAY MEDICAL CENTER (100258)**, 5352 Linton Boulevard, Zip 33484–6580; tel. 561/498–4440, (Includes FAIR OAKS PAVILION, 5440 Linton Boulevard, Delray Beach, Florida, Zip 33484–6578; tel. 561/495–1000; PINECREST REHABILITATION HOSPITAL, 5360 Linton Boulevard, Delray Beach, Florida, Zip 33484–6538; tel. 561/495–0400) **A**1 3 5 7 10 **F**3 4 11 12 15 17 18 20 22 24 26 28 29 30 31 34 35 37 38 40 42 43 45 46 49 50 51 56 57 58 59 60 64 65 74 75 77 78 79 80 81 82 83 84 85 87 90 91 93 94 96 97 98 100 101 102 103 104 107 108 111 115 118 119 126 129 130 132 135 143 146 147 148 151 154 **S** TENET Healthcare Corporation, Dallas, TX
Primary Contact: Margaret Gill, Chief Executive Officer
COO: Stephen Garner, Chief Operating Officer
CMO: Anthony Dardano, M.D., Chief Medical Officer
CIO: Robens Rosena, Director Information Systems
CHR: Shannon Wills, Director Human Resources
Web address: www.delraymedicalctr.com
Control: Corporation, Investor–owned (for–profit) **Service:** General medical and surgical

Staffed Beds: 536 Admissions: 19454 Census: 294 Outpatient Visits: 91762 Births: 0 Personnel: 1737

FL

Hospital, Medicare Provider Number, Address, Telephone, Approval, Facility, and Physician Codes, Health Care System

★ American Hospital Association (AHA) membership   ○ Healthcare Facilities Accreditation Program   ⇧ Center for Improvement in Healthcare Quality Accreditation
☐ The Joint Commission accreditation   ◇ DNV Healthcare Inc. accreditation   △ Commission on Accreditation of Rehabilitation Facilities (CARF) accreditation

DUNEDIN—Pinellas County

⌑ **BAYCARE ALLIANT HOSPITAL (102021)**, 601 Main Street, Zip 34698–5848; tel. 727/736–9991, **A**1 10 **F**1 3 28 29 34 35 36 57 130 148 154 **S** Trinity Health, Livonia, MI
Primary Contact: Jacqueline Arocho, Administrator
CFO: John Proni, CPA, Manager Finance and Operations
CMO: Leonard Dunn, M.D., Chief Medical Officer
CHR: Darlene Shelton, Coordinator Team Resources
Web address: www.baycare.org
Control: Other not–for–profit (including NFP Corporation) **Service**: Acute long–term care hospital

> **Staffed Beds: 35 Admissions: 358 Census: 28 Outpatient Visits: 0 Births: 0 Total Expense ($000): 19226 Payroll Expense ($000): 7122 Personnel: 117**

⌑ **MEASE DUNEDIN HOSPITAL (100043)**, 601 Main Street, Zip 34698–5891; tel. 727/733–1111, **A**1 10 **F**3 11 12 15 18 26 29 30 31 34 35 37 38 40 44 45 49 50 56 57 59 60 62 63 64 68 70 74 75 78 79 81 84 85 86 87 98 99 100 102 103 107 108 110 111 114 118 119 130 132 135 143 145 146 149 154 156 **S** Trinity Health, Livonia, MI
Primary Contact: Matthew Novak, President
CFO: Carl Tremonti, Chief Financial Officer
CMO: Tony Schuster, M.D., Vice President of Physician Services
CIO: Tim Thompson, Senior Vice President, Information Services and Chief Information Officer
CHR: Kyle J Barr, Senior Vice President, Chief Team Resources Officer
CNO: Thomas Doria, Vice President, Patient Services and Chief Nursing Officer
Web address: www.mpmhealth.com
Control: Other not–for–profit (including NFP Corporation) **Service**: General medical and surgical

> **Staffed Beds: 120 Admissions: 6679 Census: 80 Outpatient Visits: 37164 Births: 0 Total Expense ($000): 96716 Payroll Expense ($000): 37404 Personnel: 576**

EGLIN AFB—Okaloosa County

⌑ **U. S. AIR FORCE REGIONAL HOSPITAL**, 307 Boatner Road, Suite 114, Zip 32542–1282; tel. 850/883–8221, (Nonreporting) **A**1 3 5 **S** Department of the Air Force, Washington, DC
Primary Contact: Colonel Pamela Smith, Commander
Web address: www.eglin.af.mil
Control: Department of Defense, Government, federal **Service**: General medical and surgical

> **Staffed Beds: 57**

ENGLEWOOD—Sarasota County

⌑ **ENGLEWOOD COMMUNITY HOSPITAL (100267)**, 700 Medical Boulevard, Zip 34223–3978; tel. 941/475–6571, (Nonreporting) **A**1 10 **S** HCA Healthcare, Nashville, TN
Primary Contact: Michael Ehrat, Chief Executive Officer
COO: Alex Chang, Chief Operating Officer
CFO: Vickie Magurean, Chief Financial Officer
CMO: L. Craig McAskill, M.D., Chief Medical Officer
CNO: Kathleen Pace, MSN, R.N., Chief Nursing Officer
Web address: www.englewoodcommunityhospital.com
Control: Corporation, Investor–owned (for–profit) **Service**: General medical and surgical

> **Staffed Beds: 100**

FERNANDINA BEACH—Nassau County

⌑ **BAPTIST MEDICAL CENTER NASSAU (100140)**, 1250 South 18th Street, Zip 32034–3098; tel. 904/321–3500, **A**1 10 **F**3 11 13 15 18 26 28 29 30 34 35 40 45 49 64 70 74 76 79 81 82 85 91 92 93 102 107 108 110 111 114 115 119 124 129 132 146 148 149 **S** Baptist Health, Jacksonville, FL
Primary Contact: Edward T. Hubel, FACHE, President
CFO: Patricia K Hausauer, Director Finance
CHR: Erin Jackson, Human Resources Specialist
Web address: www.baptistjax.com/locations/baptist-medical-center-nassau
Control: Other not–for–profit (including NFP Corporation) **Service**: General medical and surgical

> **Staffed Beds: 52 Admissions: 3609 Census: 32 Outpatient Visits: 61387 Births: 519 Total Expense ($000): 63526 Payroll Expense ($000): 19120 Personnel: 326**

FORT LAUDERDALE—Broward County

⌑ **BROWARD HEALTH IMPERIAL POINT (100200)**, 6401 North Federal Highway, Zip 33308–1495; tel. 954/776–8500, **A**1 3 10 **F**3 11 12 15 20 29 34 35 40 45 51 53 57 59 61 64 68 70 74 75 77 78 79 80 81 82 84 85 86 87 93 98 100 102 107 108 110 111 114 115 119 126 130 131 132 143 146 147 148 **S** Broward Health, Fort Lauderdale, FL
Primary Contact: Jonathan Watkins, Chief Executive Officer
COO: Netonua Reyes, MSN, Chief Operating Officer and Chief Nursing Officer
CNO: Netonua Reyes, MSN, Chief Operating Officer and Chief Nursing Officer
Web address: www.browardhealth.org
Control: Hospital district or authority, Government, nonfederal **Service**: General medical and surgical

> **Staffed Beds: 180 Admissions: 8072 Census: 120 Outpatient Visits: 74026 Births: 0 Total Expense ($000): 117557 Payroll Expense ($000): 47048 Personnel: 771**

⌑ **BROWARD HEALTH MEDICAL CENTER (100039)**, 1600 South Andrews Avenue, Zip 33316–2510; tel. 954/355–4400, (Includes CHRIS EVERT CHILDRENS HOSPITAL, 1600 South Andrews Avenue, Fort Lauderdale, Florida, Zip 33316–2510; tel. 954/355–4400; Calvin E Glidewell Jr, Chief Executive Officer) **A**1 2 3 5 10 13 **F**3 11 13 15 17 18 20 22 24 26 28 29 30 31 34 35 40 41 43 45 48 49 50 51 53 57 58 59 60 61 62 63 64 65 66 68 70 71 72 73 74 75 76 77 78 79 80 81 82 83 84 85 87 88 89 91 93 94 98 100 102 105 107 108 110 111 114 115 116 117 119 120 121 126 129 130 139 146 147 149 157 **S** Broward Health, Fort Lauderdale, FL
Primary Contact: Jonathan Turton, FACHE, Chief Executive Officer
COO: Natassia Orr, Chief Operating Officer
CFO: Alexander Fernandez, Chief Financial Officer
CMO: Joshua D. Lenchus, Chief Medical Officer
CHR: Dionne Wong, Vice President and Chief Human Resources Officer
CNO: Robyn Farrington, Chief Nursing Officer
Web address: www.browardhealth.org
Control: Hospital district or authority, Government, nonfederal **Service**: General medical and surgical

> **Staffed Beds: 656 Admissions: 26260 Census: 425 Outpatient Visits: 201362 Births: 3796 Total Expense ($000): 492769 Payroll Expense ($000): 186875 Personnel: 2674**

FLORIDA MEDICAL CENTER See Florida Medical Center - A Campus of North Shore

FORT LAUDERDALE HOSPITAL (104026), 1601 East Las Olas Boulevard, Zip 33301–2393; tel. 954/463–4321, **A**10 **F**6 7 8 9 11 12 13 14 15 34 64 98 99 101 102 104 105 153 155 **S** Universal Health Services, Inc., King of Prussia, PA
Primary Contact: Manuel R. Llano, Chief Executive Officer
CFO: Varonica Oehl, Chief Financial Officer
CMO: Sherrie Bieniek, M.D., Medical Director
CHR: Carlos A Gato, Director of Human Resources
CNO: Maria Spingos, Director of Nursing
Web address: www.fortlauderdalehospital.org
Control: Corporation, Investor–owned (for–profit) **Service**: Psychiatric

> **Staffed Beds: 182 Admissions: 4987 Census: 89 Outpatient Visits: 3064 Births: 0 Total Expense ($000): 19449 Payroll Expense ($000): 10729 Personnel: 338**

⌑ **HOLY CROSS HOSPITAL (100073)**, 4725 North Federal Highway, Zip 33308–4668, Mailing Address: P.O. Box 23460, Zip 33307–3460; tel. 954/771–8000, **A**1 2 3 5 10 **F**3 8 11 12 13 15 17 18 20 22 24 26 28 29 30 31 34 35 36 37 40 44 45 46 47 48 49 50 51 53 54 55 56 57 58 59 61 62 64 65 66 67 70 71 72 74 75 76 77 78 79 81 82 84 85 87 90 91 92 93 96 97 100 107 108 110 111 115 117 118 119 120 121 123 124 126 130 131 132 134 143 144 145 146 147 149 154 156 157 **S** Trinity Health, Livonia, MI
Primary Contact: Patrick Taylor, M.D., President and Chief Executive Officer
COO: Luisa Gutman, Senior Vice President and Chief Operating Officer
CFO: Ronald Brandenburg, Vice President and Chief Financial Officer
CMO: Kenneth Homer, M.D., Chief Medical Officer
CIO: Jeff Smith, Chief Information Officer
CNO: Taren Ruggiero, R.N., MSN, Vice President and Chief Nursing Officer
Web address: www.holy-cross.com
Control: Other not–for–profit (including NFP Corporation) **Service**: General medical and surgical

> **Staffed Beds: 367 Admissions: 15789 Census: 216 Outpatient Visits: 180526 Births: 818 Total Expense ($000): 329702 Payroll Expense ($000): 117490 Personnel: 2626**

IMPERIAL POINT MEDICAL CENTER See Broward Health Imperial Point

Many Facility Codes have changed. Please refer to the AHA Guide Code Chart. © 2019 AHA Guide

FL

⊠ KINDRED HOSPITAL SOUTH FLORIDA-FORT LAUDERDALE (102010), 1516 East Las Olas Boulevard, Zip 33301–2399; tel. 954/764–8900, (Includes KINDRED HOSPITAL SOUTH FLORIDA-CORAL GABLES, 5190 SW Eighth Street, Coral Gables, Florida, Zip 33134–2495; tel. 305/445–1364, Brian Soares, Chief Executive Officer; KINDRED HOSPITAL SOUTH FLORIDA-HOLLYWOOD, 1859 Van Buren Street, Hollywood, Florida, Zip 33020–5127; tel. 954/920–9000; David Wagner, South Florida Market Chief Executive Officer), (Nonreporting) **A**1 10 **S** Kindred Healthcare, Louisville, KY
Primary Contact: Michael S. Roffelsen, Chief Executive Officer
CFO: Dean Card, Chief Financial Officer
Web address: www.khfortlauderdale.com/
Control: Corporation, Investor–owned (for–profit) **Service:** Acute long–term care hospital

Staffed Beds: 123

FORT MYERS—Lee County

GOLISANO CHILDREN'S HOSPITAL OF SOUTHWEST FLORIDA See Lee Memorial Hospital, Fort Myers

★ ⇑ GULF COAST MEDICAL CENTER (100220), 13681 Doctor's Way, Zip 33912–4300; tel. 239/343–1000, **A**10 21 **F**3 11 13 14 20 28 29 40 45 46 49 51 60 70 74 76 77 79 81 85 86 87 93 102 107 108 111 114 115 118 119 130 138 146 154 156 **S** Lee Health, Fort Myers, FL
Primary Contact: Lawrence Antonucci, M.D., President and Chief Executive Officer
CFO: Ben Spence, Chief Financial Officer
CMO: Mark Greenberg, M.D., Medical Director
CIO: Mike Smith, Chief Information Officer
CHR: Jon C Cecil, Chief Human Resource Officer
CNO: Lisa Sgarlata, MSN, Chief Patient Care Officer
Web address: www.leememorial.org
Control: Hospital district or authority, Government, nonfederal **Service:** General medical and surgical

Staffed Beds: 356 Admissions: 22091 Census: 277 Outpatient Visits: 79024 Births: 1335 Total Expense ($000): 295230 Payroll Expense ($000): 114611 Personnel: 1880

★ △ ⇑ LEE MEMORIAL HOSPITAL (100012), 2776 Cleveland Avenue, Zip 33901–5855; Mailing Address: P.O. Box 2218, Zip 33902–2218; tel. 239/343–2000, (Includes GOLISANO CHILDREN'S HOSPITAL OF SOUTHWEST FLORIDA, 9981 South HealthPark Drive, Fort Myers, Florida, Zip 33908; tel. 239/343–5437; HEALTHPARK MEDICAL CENTER, 9981 South HealthPark Drive, Fort Myers, Florida, Zip 33908; tel. 239/433–7799; THE REHABILITATION HOSPITAL, 2776 Cleveland Avenue, Fort Myers, Florida, Zip 33901; tel. 239/343–3900) **A**2 3 5 7 10 21 **F**3 11 12 13 14 15 17 18 19 20 21 22 24 26 28 29 30 31 32 34 40 41 43 45 46 48 49 51 53 54 55 56 57 58 59 60 68 69 70 72 74 75 76 77 78 79 81 82 84 85 86 87 88 89 90 93 94 100 102 104 107 108 110 111 114 115 116 117 119 126 128 129 130 131 132 135 136 146 147 148 156 **S** Lee Health, Fort Myers, FL
Primary Contact: Lawrence Antonucci, M.D., President and Chief Executive Officer
CFO: Ben Spence, Chief Financial Officer
CMO: Alex Daneshmand, D.O., Chief Patient Safety Officer
CIO: Mike Smith, Chief Information Officer
CHR: Jon C Cecil, Chief Human Resource Officer
CNO: Donna Giannuzzi, R.N., Chief Nursing Officer
Web address: www.leememorial.org
Control: Hospital district or authority, Government, nonfederal **Service:** General medical and surgical

Staffed Beds: 803 Admissions: 40924 Census: 654 Outpatient Visits: 184758 Births: 3421

☐ PARK ROYAL HOSPITAL (104074), 9241 Park Royal Drive, Zip 33908–9204; tel. 239/985–2700, **A**1 10 **F**4 5 98 102 103 105 151 152 153 **S** Acadia Healthcare Company, Inc., Franklin, TN
Primary Contact: Michael Ham, Chief Executive Officer
CFO: Amy Ciampa, Chief Financial Officer
CHR: Robert Raynor, Human Resources Director
Web address: www.ParkRoyalHospital.com
Control: Corporation, Investor–owned (for–profit) **Service:** Psychiatric

Staffed Beds: 114 Admissions: 3680 Census: 75 Outpatient Visits: 0 Births: 0 Total Expense ($000): 20814 Payroll Expense ($000): 8747 Personnel: 164

★ PROMISE HOSPITAL OF FORT MYERS (102029), 3050 Champion Ring Road, Zip 33905–5599; tel. 239/313–2900, (Nonreporting) **S** Select Medical Corporation, Mechanicsburg, PA
Primary Contact: Patrick G. Ryan, Chief Executive Officer
Web address: www.promisefortmyers.om
Control: Corporation, Investor–owned (for–profit) **Service:** Acute long–term care hospital

Staffed Beds: 60

FORT PIERCE—St. Lucie County

⊠ △ LAWNWOOD REGIONAL MEDICAL CENTER & HEART INSTITUTE (100246), 1700 South 23rd Street, Zip 34950–4803; tel. 772/461–4000, (Includes LAWNWOOD PAVILION, 1860 North Lawnwood Circle, Fort Pierce, Florida, Zip 34950, Mailing Address: P O Box 1540, Zip 34954–1540, tel. 361/466–1500), (Nonreporting) **A**1 3 7 10 **S** HCA Healthcare, Nashville, TN
Primary Contact: Eric Goldman, Chief Executive Officer
CFO: Robert Dunwoody, Chief Financial Officer
CIO: Eric Castle, Director Information Services
CHR: Pam Burchell, Director Human Resources
Web address: www.lawnwoodmed.com
Control: Corporation, Investor–owned (for–profit) **Service:** General medical and surgical

Staffed Beds: 331

FORT WALTON BEACH—Okaloosa County

⊠ FORT WALTON BEACH MEDICAL CENTER (100223), 1000 Mar–Walt Drive, Zip 32547–6795; tel. 850/862–1111, (Nonreporting) **A**1 2 10 **S** HCA Healthcare, Nashville, TN
Primary Contact: Mitchell P. Mongell, FACHE, Chief Executive Officer
CFO: Jeffrey Steve Moore, Chief Financial Officer
CMO: Colonel Tama Van Decar, M.D., Chief Medical Officer
CIO: Amy Caldeira, Director Information Technology and Systems
CHR: Julia Truman, Vice President Human Resources
CNO: Caroline Stewart, Chief Nursing Officer
Web address: www.fwbmc.com
Control: Corporation, Investor–owned (for–profit) **Service:** General medical and surgical

Staffed Beds: 257

GAINESVILLE—Alachua County

⊠ NORTH FLORIDA REGIONAL MEDICAL CENTER (100204), 6500 Newberry Road, Zip 32605–4392, Mailing Address: P.O. Box 147006, Zip 32614–7006; tel. 352/333–4000, (Nonreporting) **A**1 2 3 5 10 **S** HCA Healthcare, Nashville, TN
Primary Contact: Eric Lawson, Chief Executive Officer
CFO: Jay St Pierre, Chief Financial Officer
CMO: Ann Weber, M.D., Chief Medical Officer
CIO: Eric Strand, Director Information Services
CHR: Jane Fuller, Vice President Human Resources
CNO: Natalie Ransom, Chief Nursing Officer
Web address: www.nfrmc.com
Control: Corporation, Investor–owned (for–profit) **Service:** General medical and surgical

Staffed Beds: 432

⊠ NORTH FLORIDA/SOUTH GEORGIA VETERAN'S HEALTH SYSTEM, 1601 SW Archer Road, Zip 32608–1135; tel. 352/376–1611, (Includes GAINESVILLE VETERANS AFFAIRS MEDICAL CENTER, 1601 SW Archer Road, Gainesville, Florida, Zip 32608–1197, tel. 352/376–1611, LAKE CITY VETERANS AFFAIRS MEDICAL CENTER, 619 South Marion Avenue, Lake City, Florida, Zip 32025–5898; tel. 386/755–3016) (Total facility includes 91 beds in nursing home–type unit) **A**1 3 5 **F**3 4 5 12 17 18 29 30 34 35 36 38 39 40 42 44 45 54 55 56 57 58 59 62 63 64 65 66 67 68 70 75 77 79 81 82 83 84 85 86 87 91 92 93 94 97 100 101 102 103 104 105 106 107 108 111 119 127 128 129 130 132 135 143 144 145 146 147 148 149 152 153 154 156 157 **S** Department of Veterans Affairs, Washington, DC
Primary Contact: Thomas Wisnieski, FACHE, Director
COO: Thomas Sutton, Associate Director
CFO: Jim Taylor, Chief Business Office
CMO: Brad Bender, M.D., Chief of Staff
CIO: Deborah Michel-Ogborn, Chief Information Resource Management
CHR: Michelle Manderino, Chief Human Resources
Web address: www.northflorida.va.gov
Control: Veterans Affairs, Government, federal **Service:** General medical and surgical

Staffed Beds: 255 Admissions: 1724 Census: 95 Outpatient Visits: 205300

⊠ SELECT SPECIALTY HOSPITAL-GAINESVILLE (102022), 1600 SW Archer Road, 5th Floor, Zip 32610; tel. 352/337–3240, (Nonreporting) **A**1 10 **S** Select Medical Corporation, Mechanicsburg, PA
Primary Contact: Ronnie Wagley, Market Chief Executive Officer
Web address: www.gainesville.selectspecialtyhospitals.com/
Control: Corporation, Investor–owned (for–profit) **Service:** Acute long–term care hospital

Staffed Beds: 44

FL

Hospital, Medicare Provider Number, Address, Telephone, Approval, Facility, and Physician Codes, Health Care System		
★ American Hospital Association (AHA) membership	○ Healthcare Facilities Accreditation Program	⇑ Center for Improvement in Healthcare Quality Accreditation
☐ The Joint Commission accreditation	◇ DNV Healthcare Inc. accreditation	△ Commission on Accreditation of Rehabilitation Facilities (CARF) accreditation

★ **UF HEALTH REHAB HOSPITAL (103046)**, 2708 Southwest Archer Road, Zip 32608–1316; tel. 352/265–5499, (Nonreporting) **S** Select Medical Corporation, Mechanicsburg, PA
Primary Contact: Marina T. Cecchini, Administrator
CFO: William J Robinson, Senior Vice President and Chief Financial Officer
Web address: www.https://ufhealth.org/uf-health-shands-rehab-hospital
Control: Other not–for–profit (including NFP Corporation) **Service**: Rehabilitation

Staffed Beds: 121

★ △ **UF HEALTH SHANDS HOSPITAL (100113)**, 1600 SW Archer Road, Zip 32610–3003, Mailing Address: P.O. Box 100326, Zip 32610–0326; tel. 352/265–0111, (Includes UF HEALTH SHANDS CANCER HOSPITAL, 1515 SW Archer Road, Gainesville, Florida, Zip 32608–1134, Mailing Address: P.O. Box 100326, Zip 32610–0326, tel. 352/265–0111; Edward Jimenez, Chief Executive Officer; UF HEALTH SHANDS CHILDREN'S HOSPITAL, 1600 SW Archer Road, Gainesville, Florida, Zip 32610–3003, Mailing Address: P.O. Box 100326, Zip 32610–0326, tel. 352/265–0111; Edward Jimenez, Chief Executive Officer; UF HEALTH SHANDS PSYCHIATRIC HOSPITAL, 4101 NW 89th Boulevard, Gainesville, Florida, Zip 32606; tel. 352/265–5481; Roxane Harcourt, Interim Administrator) **A**2 3 5 7 8 10 **F**2 3 4 5 6 7 9 11 12 13 15 16 17 18 19 20 21 22 23 24 25 26 27 28 29 30 31 32 34 35 36 37 38 39 40 41 42 43 44 45 46 47 48 49 50 51 52 53 54 55 56 57 58 59 60 61 62 63 64 65 66 68 69 70 72 73 74 75 76 77 78 79 80 81 82 83 84 85 86 87 88 89 90 91 92 93 94 96 97 98 99 100 101 102 103 104 105 107 108 109 110 111 112 114 115 116 117 118 119 120 121 123 124 126 129 130 131 132 134 135 136 137 138 139 140 141 142 143 144 145 146 147 148 149 150 152 154 155 156 157 **S** UF Health Shands, Gainesville, FL
Primary Contact: Edward Jimenez, Chief Executive Officer
CFO: James J. Kelly Jr Senior Vice President and Chief Financial Officer
CMO: Parker Gibbs, M.D., Chief Medical Officer
CIO: Kari Cassel, Senior Vice President and Chief Information Officer
CHR: Janet L. Christie, Senior Vice President Human Resources
CNO: Irene Alexaitis, R.N., Vice President of Nursing and Patient Services and Chief Nursing Officer
Web address: www.https://ufhealth.org/
Control: Other not–for–profit (including NFP Corporation) **Service**: General medical and surgical

Staffed Beds: 1052 Admissions: 49339 **Census:** 850 **Outpatient Visits:** 1086650 **Births:** 2754 **Total Expense ($000):** 1409698 **Payroll Expense ($000):** 506674 **Personnel:** 8813

GREEN COVE SPRINGS—Clay County

⊞ **KINDRED HOSPITAL NORTH FLORIDA (102015)**, 801 Oak Street, Zip 32043–4317; tel. 904/284–9230, (Nonreporting) **A**1 10 **S** Kindred Healthcare, Louisville, KY
Primary Contact: Patrick McVey, Chief Executive Officer
CFO: Rickie Simmons, Controller
CMO: Uriel Nazario, M.D., Chief of Medical Staff
CIO: Rick Chapman, Chief Information Officer
CNO: Ashley McRae, Chief Clinical Officer
Web address: www.khnorthflorida.com
Control: Corporation, Investor–owned (for–profit) **Service**: Acute long–term care hospital

Staffed Beds: 80

GULF BREEZE—Santa Rosa County

★ ⇑ **GULF BREEZE HOSPITAL (100266)**, 1110 Gulf Breeze Parkway, Zip 32561–4884; tel. 850/934–2000, **A**3 10 21 **F**3 8 11 15 18 26 29 30 34 35 40 44 45 46 50 54 57 59 64 68 70 74 75 77 78 79 81 82 84 85 86 91 93 100 110 111 114 119 120 121 123 130 131 132 143 146 147 148 **S** Baptist Health Care Corporation, Pensacola, FL
Primary Contact: Scott Raynes, President
CFO: Kerry Vermillion, Senior Vice President Finance and Chief Financial Officer
Web address: www.ebaptisthealthcare.org/GulfBreezeHospital/
Control: Other not–for–profit (including NFP Corporation) **Service**: General medical and surgical

Staffed Beds: 65 Admissions: 3756 **Census:** 37 **Outpatient Visits:** 116561 **Births:** 0 **Total Expense ($000):** 85707 **Payroll Expense ($000):** 26870 **Personnel:** 482

HIALEAH—Miami-Dade County

⊞ **HIALEAH HOSPITAL (100053)**, 651 East 25th Street, Zip 33013–3878; tel. 305/693–6100, (Nonreporting) **A**1 5 10 **S** TENET Healthcare Corporation, Dallas, TX
Primary Contact: Michael J. Bell, Chief Executive Officer
COO: Lourdes Camps, Chief Operating Officer
CFO: Gary Nymoen, Chief Financial Officer
CMO: Orlando Garcia, M.D., Chief Medical Officer
CHR: Yamila Herrera, Director Human Resources
CNO: Maribel Torres, Chief Nursing Officer
Web address: www.hialeahhosp.com
Control: Corporation, Investor–owned (for–profit) **Service**: General medical and surgical

Staffed Beds: 191

□ **LARKIN COMMUNITY HOSPITAL-PALM SPRINGS CAMPUS (100050)**, 1475 West 49th Street, Zip 33012–3275, Mailing Address: P.O. Box 2804, Zip 33012–2804; tel. 305/558–2500, **A**1 5 10 12 13 **F**3 12 18 29 31 34 35 40 45 46 47 49 50 51 53 56 57 60 61 62 64 65 68 70 74 75 77 78 79 81 82 91 92 93 102 103 107 108 109 114 115 117 119 124 130 135 148 149 154
Primary Contact: Nicholas T. Smith, Chief Executive Officer
CFO: Tony Milian, Chief Financial Officer
CHR: Lourdes Anton, Director Human Resources
Web address: www.larkinhospital.com
Control: Individual, Investor–owned (for–profit) **Service**: General medical and surgical

Staffed Beds: 261 Admissions: 8393 **Census:** 64 **Outpatient Visits:** 15777 **Births:** 0 **Total Expense ($000):** 60251 **Payroll Expense ($000):** 29498 **Personnel:** 680

⊞ **PALMETTO GENERAL HOSPITAL (100187)**, 2001 West 68th Street, Zip 33016–1898; tel. 305/823–5000, (Nonreporting) **A**1 3 5 10 13 **S** TENET Healthcare Corporation, Dallas, TX
Primary Contact: Ana J. Mederos, Chief Executive Officer
COO: Georgina Diaz, Chief Operating Officer
CFO: Oscar Vicente, Chief Financial Officer
CMO: Eloy Roman, M.D., Chief of Staff
CHR: Ana Gonzalez-Fajardo, Human Resources Director
CNO: Barbara Vazquez, Chief Nursing Officer
Web address: www.palmettogeneral.com
Control: Corporation, Investor–owned (for–profit) **Service**: General medical and surgical

Staffed Beds: 360

HIALEAH—Dade County

SOUTHERN WINDS HOSPITAL See Westchester General Hospital, Miami

HOLLYWOOD—Broward County

□ **LARKIN COMMUNITY HOSPITAL BEHAVIORAL HEALTH SERVICES (104015)**, 1201 North 37th Avenue, Zip 33021–5498; tel. 954/962–1355, (Nonreporting) **A**1 3 10
Primary Contact: Iris Berges, Chief Executive Officer
COO: Christopher Gabel, Chief Operating Officer
CFO: Rocky Davidson, Chief Financial Officer
CHR: Len Alpert, Director Human Resources
Web address: www.hollywoodpavilion.com
Control: Corporation, Investor–owned (for–profit) **Service**: Psychiatric

Staffed Beds: 50

⊞ **MEMORIAL REGIONAL HOSPITAL (100038)**, 3501 Johnson Street, Zip 33021–5421; tel. 954/987–2000, (Includes JOE DIMAGGIO CHILDREN'S HOSPITAL, 1005 Joe DiMaggio Drive, Hollywood, Florida, Zip 33021–5426; tel. 954/987–2000; Caitlin Beck Stella, Chief Executive Officer; MEMORIAL REGIONAL HOSPITAL SOUTH, 3600 Washington Street, Hollywood, Florida, Zip 33021–8216; tel. 954/966–4500; Douglas Zaren, FACHE, Administrator and CEO) **A**1 2 3 5 8 10 **F**3 5 11 12 13 15 17 19 20 21 22 23 24 25 26 27 28 29 30 31 32 34 37 38 39 40 41 43 44 45 46 47 49 50 51 53 54 55 56 57 58 59 60 61 64 65 66 67 68 70 71 72 73 74 75 76 77 78 79 81 82 84 85 87 88 89 90 93 95 96 97 98 99 100 101 102 103 104 107 108 110 111 114 115 118 119 120 121 123 126 129 130 131 132 134 135 137 138 145 146 147 148 149 150 153 **S** Memorial Healthcare System, Hollywood, FL
Primary Contact: Zeff Ross, FACHE, Executive Vice President and Chief Executive Officer
CFO: Walter Bussell, Chief Financial Officer
CMO: Donald Kim, M.D., Chief Medical Officer
CIO: Forest Blanton, Administrator Process Engineering
CHR: Margie Vargas, Chief Human Resources Officer
Web address: www.mhs.net
Control: Hospital district or authority, Government, nonfederal **Service**: General medical and surgical

Staffed Beds: 1013 Admissions: 36755 **Census:** 646 **Outpatient Visits:** 461203 **Births:** 5314 **Total Expense ($000):** 971528 **Payroll Expense ($000):** 406376 **Personnel:** 5456

SOUTH FLORIDA STATE HOSPITAL (104001), 800 East Cypress Drive, Zip 33025–4543; tel. 954/392–3000, (Nonreporting) **A**10
Primary Contact: Lee Packer, Administrator
Web address: www.geocarellc.com/Locations/SouthFloridaStateHospital
Control: State, Government, nonfederal **Service**: Psychiatric

Staffed Beds: 355

FL

Many Facility Codes have changed. Please refer to the AHA Guide Code Chart. © 2019 AHA Guide

HOMESTEAD—Miami-Dade County

⊞ **BAPTIST HEALTH SOUTH FLORIDA, HOMESTEAD HOSPITAL (100125)**, 975 Baptist Way, Zip 33033-7600; tel. 786/243-8000, **A**1 10 **F**3 11 13 15 18 19 26 29 30 31 34 35 40 41 44 45 49 50 51 53 57 58 59 60 61 63 64 68 70 71 74 75 76 77 78 79 80 81 82 84 85 86 87 89 90 93 100 102 107 108 110 111 115 119 129 130 132 134 135 141 145 146 147 148 149 150 154 156 **S** Baptist Health South Florida, Coral Gables, FL
Primary Contact: Kenneth R. Spell, Chief Executive Officer
CFO: David Abercrombie, Controller
CMO: George R. Tershakovec, M.D., President Medical Staff
CIO: Mimi Taylor, Corporate Vice President Information Technology
CHR: Adriene McCoy, Corporate Vice President
CNO: Nancy Gail Gordon, R.N., MSN, Chief Nursing Officer and Vice President of Nursing
Web address: www.baptisthealth.net
Control: Other not-for-profit (including NFP Corporation) **Service:** General medical and surgical

Staffed Beds: 142 **Admissions:** 9170 **Census:** 88 **Outpatient Visits:** 115290 **Births:** 1330 **Total Expense ($000):** 230924 **Payroll Expense ($000):** 79603 **Personnel:** 1034

HUDSON—Pasco County

⊞ **REGIONAL MEDICAL CENTER BAYONET POINT (100256)**, 14000 Fivay Road, Zip 34667-7199; tel. 727/869-5400, (Nonreporting) **A**1 2 3 10 12 13 **S** HCA Healthcare, Nashville, TN
Primary Contact: Thomas Lawhorne, Interim Chief Executive Officer
COO: Joe Rudisill, Chief Operating Officer
CFO: Thomas Lawhorne, Chief Financial Officer
CMO: Joseph Pino, M.D., Chief Medical Officer
CIO: Mike Wilms, Director Information Systems
CHR: Geoffrey A. Washburn, Vice President
CNO: Melanie Wetmore, MSN, R.N., Chief Nursing Officer
Web address: www.rmchealth.com
Control: Corporation, Investor-owned (for-profit) **Service:** General medical and surgical

Staffed Beds: 290

INVERNESS—Citrus County

⊞ **CITRUS MEMORIAL HEALTH SYSTEM (100023)**, 502 West Highland Boulevard, Zip 34452-4754; tel. 352/726-1551, (Nonreporting) **A**1 3 5 10 19 **S** HCA Healthcare, Nashville, TN
Primary Contact: Ralph A. Aleman, President and Chief Executive Officer
COO: George Mavros, Chief Operating Officer
CMO: Raylene Platel, M.D., Chief Medical Officer
CIO: Nick Brooks, Director of Information Systems
CHR: Lee Glutzback, Director Human Resources
CNO: Caroline Stewart, Chief Nursing Officer
Web address: www.citrusmh.com
Control: Other not-for-profit (including NFP Corporation) **Service:** General medical and surgical

Staffed Beds: 204

JACKSONVILLE—Duval County

⊞ **BAPTIST MEDICAL CENTER JACKSONVILLE (100088)**, 800 Prudential Drive, Zip 32207-8202; tel. 904/202-2000, (Includes BAPTIST MEDICAL CENTER SOUTH, 14550 St Augustine Road, Jacksonville, Florida, Zip 32258-2160; tel. 904/821-6000; Nicole B. Thomas, President; WOLFSON CHILDREN'S HOSPITAL, 800 Prudential Drive, Jacksonville, Florida, Zip 32207; tel. 904/202-8000; Michael D Aubin, President) **A**1 2 3 5 10 **F**3 5 6 8 11 12 13 15 17 18 19 20 21 22 23 24 25 26 27 28 29 30 31 32 34 35 36 37 38 39 40 41 42 45 46 47 48 49 50 51 53 54 55 56 57 58 59 60 61 62 64 68 70 72 73 74 75 76 77 78 79 81 82 83 85 86 87 88 89 92 93 94 98 99 100 101 102 103 104 105 107 108 109 110 111 112 113 114 115 116 117 118 119 120 121 123 124 126 129 130 132 134 135 136 145 146 147 148 149 153 155 156 157 **S** Baptist Health, Jacksonville, FL
Primary Contact: Michael A. Mayo, FACHE, President
COO: John F Wilbanks, FACHE, Chief Operating Officer
CFO: Scott Wooten, Senior Vice President and Chief Financial Officer
CMO: Keith L Stein, M.D., Senior Vice President Medical Affairs and Chief Medical Officer
CIO: Roland Garcia, Senior Vice President and Chief Information Officer
CHR: M. Beth Mehaffey, Senior Vice President Human Resources
Web address: www.e-baptisthealth.com
Control: Other not-for-profit (including NFP Corporation) **Service:** General medical and surgical

Staffed Beds: 955 **Admissions:** 48819 **Census:** 661 **Outpatient Visits:** 600368 **Births:** 4653 **Total Expense ($000):** 1097496 **Payroll Expense ($000):** 304866 **Personnel:** 4348

⊞ △ **BROOKS REHABILITATION HOSPITAL (103039)**, 3599 University Boulevard South, Zip 32216-4252; tel. 904/345-7600, **A**1 3 5 7 10 **F**3 28 29 30 38 44 50 74 75 77 78 79 82 86 90 91 95 96 130 148 149
Primary Contact: Douglas M. Baer, Chief Executive Officer
COO: Michael Spigel, Executive Vice President & Chief Operating Officer
CMO: Trevor Paris, M.D., Medical Director
CIO: Karen Green, Chief Information Officer
CHR: Karen Gallagher, Vice President Human Resources and Learning
CNO: Joanne Hoertz, Vice President of Nursing
Web address: www.brookshealth.org
Control: Other not-for-profit (including NFP Corporation) **Service:** Rehabilitation

Staffed Beds: 146 **Admissions:** 3041 **Census:** 133 **Outpatient Visits:** 0 **Births:** 0 **Total Expense ($000):** 75123 **Payroll Expense ($000):** 28647 **Personnel:** 474

⊞ **MAYO CLINIC HOSPITAL IN FLORIDA (100151)**, 4500 San Pablo Road South, Zip 32224-1865; tel. 904/953-2000, **A**1 2 3 5 8 10 **F**3 6 8 9 11 12 14 15 17 18 20 22 24 26 28 29 30 31 34 35 36 37 40 44 45 46 47 48 49 50 51 54 55 56 57 58 59 60 61 64 65 67 68 70 74 75 77 78 79 80 81 82 84 85 86 87 92 93 96 97 100 104 107 108 109 110 111 112 114 115 116 117 118 119 120 121 123 124 126 129 130 131 132 135 136 137 138 139 140 141 142 145 146 147 148 149 150 154 156 **S** Mayo Clinic, Rochester, MN
Primary Contact: Kent Thielen, M.D., Chief Executive Officer
CFO: Kevin Lockett, Interim Chief Financial Officer
CMO: David Thiel, M.D., Medical Director
CIO: John Crooks, Chair Information Services
CHR: Rosemary McMullan, Chief Human Resources
CNO: Ryannon Frederick, Chief Nursing Officer
Web address: www.mayoclinic.org/jacksonville/
Control: Other not-for-profit (including NFP Corporation) **Service:** General medical and surgical

Staffed Beds: 277 **Admissions:** 14788 **Census:** 200 **Outpatient Visits:** 59638 **Births:** 0 **Personnel:** 3126

⊞ **MEMORIAL HOSPITAL JACKSONVILLE (100179)**, 3625 University Boulevard South, Zip 32216-4207; tel. 904/702-6111, (Nonreporting) **A**1 2 3 10 **S** HCA Healthcare, Nashville, TN
Primary Contact: Bradley S. Talbert, FACHE, President and Chief Executive Officer
COO: Cory Darling, Chief Operating Officer
CFO: Andy Miller, Chief Financial Officer
CMO: John Lazenby, M.D., Chief Medical Officer
CIO: Patrick Adesso, Director Information Technology and Systems
CHR: Stuart Thompson, Vice President Human Resources
CNO: Suzanne Woods, Senior Vice President of Nursing
Web address: www.memorialhospitaljax.com
Control: Corporation, Investor-owned (for-profit) **Service:** General medical and surgical

Staffed Beds: 410

⊞ **NAVAL HOSPITAL JACKSONVILLE**, 2080 Child Street, Zip 32214-5000; tel. 904/542-7300, (Nonreporting) **A**1 3 5 **S** Bureau of Medicine and Surgery, Department of the Navy, Falls Church, VA
Primary Contact: Commander Darryl Green, Director Administration
CFO: Lieutenant Commander Michael Gregonis, Comptroller
CMO: Captain Christopher Quarles, M.D., Director Medical Services
CIO: Mike Haytaian, Head Director Information Resources Management
CHR: Captain Ruby Tennyson, Director Administration
Web address: www.med.navy.mil/SITES/NAVALHOSPITALJAX/Pages/default.aspx
Control: Department of Defense, Government, federal **Service:** General medical and surgical

Staffed Beds: 64

RIVER POINT BEHAVIORAL HEALTH (104016), 6300 Beach Boulevard, Zip 32216-2782; tel. 904/724-9202, (Nonreporting) **A**10 **S** Universal Health Services, Inc., King of Prussia, PA
Primary Contact: Kevin McGee, Chief Executive Officer
CFO: Jenni Stackhouse, Chief Financial Officer
CIO: Bill Willis, Director Information Technology
CHR: Cathy Calhoun, Director Human Resources
Web address: www.riverpointbehavioral.com
Control: Corporation, Investor-owned (for-profit) **Service:** Psychiatric

Staffed Beds: 92

FL

Hospital, Medicare Provider Number, Address, Telephone, Approval, Facility, and Physician Codes, Health Care System

★ American Hospital Association (AHA) membership   ○ Healthcare Facilities Accreditation Program   ⇧ Center for Improvement in Healthcare Quality Accreditation
□ The Joint Commission accreditation   ◇ DNV Healthcare Inc. accreditation   △ Commission on Accreditation of Rehabilitation Facilities (CARF) accreditation

---

⊞ **SPECIALTY HOSPITAL JACKSONVILLE (102012)**, 4901 Richard Street, Zip 32207–7328; tel. 904/737–3120, (Nonreporting) **A**1 10 **S** Curae Health, Clinton, TN
Primary Contact: Barbara McCarthy, Chief Executive Officer
CFO: Joshua Szostek, Chief Financial Officer
CMO: Wendell H Williams, M.D., Jr Medical Director
CIO: Patrick Adesso, Director Information Technology and Systems
CHR: Lisa Ayala, R.N., Director Human Resources
Web address: www.specialtyhospitaljax.com
Control: Corporation, Investor–owned (for–profit) **Service**: Acute long–term care hospital

Staffed Beds: 62

⊞ **ST. VINCENT'S MEDICAL CENTER RIVERSIDE (100040)**, 1 Shircliff Way, Zip 32204–4748, Mailing Address: P.O. Box 2982, Zip 32203–2982; tel. 904/308–7300, **A**1 2 3 10 **F**3 12 13 15 17 18 20 22 24 26 28 29 30 31 34 37 40 44 45 46 47 48 49 53 55 57 58 61 64 65 70 72 74 76 78 79 81 85 86 87 91 93 107 108 110 111 114 115 117 118 119 120 121 123 124 126 130 131 132 146 147 149 154 156 **S** Ascension Healthcare, Saint Louis, MO
Primary Contact: Thomas J. VanOsdol, Chief Executive Officer
CIO: Ann Carey, Vice President and Chief Information Officer
CHR: Michelle Adamolekun, Chief Human Resource Officer
CNO: Lorraine Keith, Chief Nursing Officer
Web address: www.jaxhealth.com
Control: Church operated, Nongovernment, not–for–profit **Service**: General medical and surgical

Staffed Beds: 482 Admissions: 22810 Census: 287 Outpatient Visits: 109698 Births: 1519 Total Expense ($000): 425735 Payroll Expense ($000): 126853 Personnel: 1882

⊞ **ST. VINCENT'S MEDICAL CENTER SOUTHSIDE (100307)**, 4201 Belfort Road, Zip 32216–1431; tel. 904/296–3700, **A**1 3 5 10 **F**3 12 13 15 18 20 22 26 29 30 31 34 40 44 47 49 50 57 60 61 64 65 70 72 74 76 78 79 81 85 86 87 93 96 102 107 108 110 111 114 115 119 126 128 129 130 131 132 146 147 149 154 156 **S** Ascension Healthcare, Saint Louis, MO
Primary Contact: Thomas J. VanOsdol, Chief Executive Officer
CIO: Ann Carey, Chief Information Officer
CHR: Kaye W Lunsford, System Director Human Resources
CNO: Lorraine Keith, Chief Nursing Officer
Web address: www.jaxhealth.com
Control: Church operated, Nongovernment, not–for–profit **Service**: General medical and surgical

Staffed Beds: 289 Admissions: 11957 Census: 133 Outpatient Visits: 45531 Births: 1696 Total Expense ($000): 165344 Payroll Expense ($000): 47824 Personnel: 667

★ **UF HEALTH JACKSONVILLE (100001)**, 655 West Eighth Street, Zip 32209–6595; tel. 904/244–0411, (Total facility includes 56 beds in nursing home–type unit) **A**3 5 8 10 **F**3 5 8 11 12 13 15 17 18 20 22 24 26 28 29 30 31 32 34 35 36 37 38 40 41 43 44 45 46 47 49 50 51 53 54 55 56 57 58 59 60 61 62 63 64 65 66 68 70 71 72 73 74 75 76 77 78 79 80 81 82 84 85 86 87 88 91 92 93 94 96 97 98 100 101 102 103 104 107 108 109 110 111 114 115 116 117 118 119 120 121 123 124 126 128 129 130 131 132 134 135 141 145 146 147 148 149 150 154 156 157 **S** UF Health Shands, Gainesville, FL
Primary Contact: Leon L. Haley Jr, M.D., Chief Executive Officer
COO: Greg Miller, Senior Vice President Operations
CFO: William Ryan, Vice President and Chief Financial Officer
CMO: David Vukich, M.D., Senior Vice President, Chief Medical Officer and Chief Quality Officer
CIO: Kari Cassel, Senior Vice President and Chief Information Officer
CHR: Lesli Ward, Vice President Human Resources
CNO: Patrice I. Jones, R.N., MSN, Vice President and Chief Nursing Officer
Web address: www.ufhealthjax.org/
Control: Other not–for–profit (including NFP Corporation) **Service**: General medical and surgical

Staffed Beds: 644 Admissions: 28107 Census: 464 Outpatient Visits: 587462 Births: 3605 Total Expense ($000): 725466 Payroll Expense ($000): 259410 Personnel: 4384

☐ **WEKIVA SPRINGS (104069)**, 3947 Salisbury Road, Zip 32216–6115; tel. 904/296–3533, (Nonreporting) **A**1 10 **S** Universal Health Services, Inc., King of Prussia, PA
Primary Contact: Sheila Carr, Chief Executive Officer
Web address: www.wekivacenter.com
Control: Other not–for–profit (including NFP Corporation) **Service**: Psychiatric

Staffed Beds: 60

⊞ **BAPTIST MEDICAL CENTER BEACHES (100117)**, 1350 13th Avenue South, Zip 32250–3205; tel. 904/627–2900, **A**1 10 **F**3 8 11 13 15 18 20 28 29 30 34 35 36 40 43 45 49 50 53 54 56 57 59 61 64 74 75 76 77 78 79 80 81 82 85 86 93 107 108 110 111 114 115 118 119 126 129 130 146 147 148 155 156 157 **S** Baptist Health, Jacksonville, FL
Primary Contact: Joseph M. Mitrick, FACHE, President
COO: John F Wilbanks, FACHE, Chief Operating Officer
CFO: Scott Wooten, Senior Vice President and Chief Financial Officer
CMO: Keith L Stein, M.D., Chief Medical Officer
CIO: Roland Garcia, Senior Vice President and Chief Information Officer
CHR: Dana Voiselle, Director Human Resources and Community Relations
Web address: www.community.e-baptisthealth.com/bmc/beaches/index.html
Control: Other not–for–profit (including NFP Corporation) **Service**: General medical and surgical

Staffed Beds: 135 Admissions: 7151 Census: 75 Outpatient Visits: 87413 Births: 875 Total Expense ($000): 111172 Payroll Expense ($000): 34713 Personnel: 577

★ **JAY HOSPITAL (100048)**, 14114 South Alabama Street, Zip 32565–1219; tel. 850/675–8000, **A**10 **F**3 11 15 29 30 34 35 40 45 48 50 57 59 64 75 81 85 93 107 110 114 119 127 130 133 **S** Baptist Health Care Corporation, Pensacola, FL
Primary Contact: Michael T. Hutchins, Administrator
CFO: Keith Strickling, Chief Accountant
CMO: C David Smith, M.D., Chief Medical Officer
CHR: Heather Suggs, Manager Human Resources
CNO: Patsy Jackson, Director of Nursing
Web address: www.bhcpns.org/jayhospital/
Control: Other not–for–profit (including NFP Corporation) **Service**: General medical and surgical

Staffed Beds: 21 Admissions: 560 Census: 8 Outpatient Visits: 17628 Births: 0 Total Expense ($000): 12903 Payroll Expense ($000): 5815 Personnel: 110

⊞ **JUPITER MEDICAL CENTER (100253)**, 1210 South Old Dixie Highway, Zip 33458–7299; tel. 561/263–2234, (Nonreporting) **A**1 2 10
Primary Contact: Donald McKenna, President and Chief Executive Officer
COO: Steven Seeley, Vice President, Chief Operating Officer, Chief Nursing Officer
CFO: Dale E Hocking, Chief Financial Officer
CIO: Thomas Schoenig, Chief Information Officer
CHR: Peter Gloggner, Chief Human Resources Officer
CNO: Steven Seeley, Vice President, Chief Operating Officer, Chief Nursing Officer
Web address: www.jupitermed.com
Control: Other not–for–profit (including NFP Corporation) **Service**: General medical and surgical

Staffed Beds: 207

⊞ **LOWER KEYS MEDICAL CENTER (100150)**, 5900 College Road, Zip 33040–4396, Mailing Address: P.O. Box 9107, Zip 33041–9107; tel. 305/294–5531, (Includes DE POO HOSPITAL, 1200 Kennedy Drive, Key West, Florida, Zip 33041; tel. 305/294–4692), (Nonreporting) **A**1 10 **S** Community Health Systems, Inc., Franklin, TN
Primary Contact: David Clay, Chief Executive Officer
CFO: Henrietta Skeens, Chief Financial Officer
CMO: Jerome Covington, M.D., Chief Medical Officer
Web address: www.lkmc.com
Control: Corporation, Investor–owned (for–profit) **Service**: General medical and surgical

Staffed Beds: 90

ADVENTHEALTH KISSIMMEE See Adventhealth Orlando, Orlando

⊞ **OSCEOLA REGIONAL MEDICAL CENTER (100110)**, 700 West Oak Street, Zip 34741–4996; tel. 407/846–2266, **A**1 2 3 5 8 10 **F**3 8 13 15 17 18 20 22 24 26 28 29 30 34 35 40 41 42 43 45 46 49 50 56 57 64 65 68 70 72 74 75 76 77 78 79 80 81 85 87 88 89 90 92 93 96 97 98 100 101 102 104 105 107 110 111 114 115 116 117 118 119 124 126 130 131 132 135 146 147 148 149 150 153 154 156 157 **S** HCA Healthcare, Nashville, TN
Primary Contact: Davide M. Carbone, FACHE, Chief Executive Officer
COO: Steve Gordon, Chief Operating Officer
CFO: Carrie Biggar, Chief Financial Officer
CMO: Joseph Mazzola, M.D., Chief Medical Officer
CIO: Carrie Biggar, Chief Financial Officer
CHR: Sylvia Lollis, Director Human Resources
CNO: Barbara K Watson, Chief Nursing Officer
Web address: www.osceolaregional.com
Control: Corporation, Investor–owned (for–profit) **Service**: General medical and surgical

Staffed Beds: 404 Admissions: 24866 Census: 323

✠ **POINCIANA MEDICAL CENTER (100320)**, 325 Cypress Parkway, Zip 34758; tel. 407/530–2000, (Nonreporting) **A**1 10 **S** HCA Healthcare, Nashville, TN
Primary Contact: Christopher Cosby, Chief Executive Officer
CFO: Chris Conn, Chief Financial Officer
CNO: Sharon Dillard, Chief Nursing Officer
Web address: www.poincianamedicalcenter.com
Control: Corporation, Investor–owned (for–profit) **Service**: General medical and surgical

Staffed Beds: 24

LAKE BUTLER—Union County

LAKE BUTLER HOSPITAL HAND SURGERY CENTER (101303), 850 East Main Street, Zip 32054–1353, Mailing Address: P.O. Box 748, Zip 32054–0748; tel. 386/496–2323, (Nonreporting) **A**10 18
Primary Contact: Pamela B. Howard, R.N., Chief Executive Officer, Administrator and Risk Manager
COO: Jennifer Thomas, Chief Operating Officer and Director of Public Relations
CFO: Paula Webb, Chief Financial Officer and Compliance Officer
CMO: Cynthia Larimer, M.D., Chief of Staff
CIO: Diane Cason, Chief Information Officer, Controller and Director Human Resources
CNO: Mandy Dicks, Director of Nursing
Web address: www.lakebutlerhospital.com
Control: Corporation, Investor–owned (for–profit) **Service**: General medical and surgical

Staffed Beds: 25

RECEPTION AND MEDICAL CENTER, State Road 231 South, Zip 32054, Mailing Address: P.O. Box 628, Zip 32054–0628; tel. 386/496–6000, (Nonreporting)
Primary Contact: Maxine Streeter, Administrator
Web address: www.dc.state.fl.us
Control: State, Government, nonfederal **Service**: Hospital unit of an institution (prison hospital, college infirmary, etc.)

Staffed Beds: 120

LAKE CITY—Columbia County

▣ **LAKE CITY MEDICAL CENTER (100150)**, 340 NW Commerce Drive, Zip 32055–4709; tel. 386/719–9000, (Nonreporting) **A**1 10 **S** HCA Healthcare, Nashville, TN
Primary Contact: Rick Naegler, Chief Executive Officer
COO: Jennifer B Adams, Chief Operating Officer and Chief Financial Officer
CFO: Jennifer B Adams, Chief Operating Officer and Chief Financial Officer
CMO: Miguel Tepedino, M.D., Chief Medicine
CIO: Taylor Dickerson, Chief Information Officer
CHR: Steve Gordon, Director Human Resources
Web address: www.lakecitymedical.com
Control: Corporation, Investor–owned (for–profit) **Service**: General medical and surgical

Staffed Beds: 67

✠ **SHANDS LAKE SHORE REGIONAL MEDICAL CENTER (100102)**, 368 NE Franklin Street, Zip 32055–3047; tel. 386/292–8000, (Nonreporting) **A**1 3 10 **S** Community Health Systems, Inc., Franklin, TN
Primary Contact: Rhonda Kay. Sherrod, R.N., MSN, Chief Executive Officer
COO: Francis A Pommett Jr Chief Operating Officer
CFO: Steve Davis, Chief Financial Officer
CMO: Mohammad Faisal, President Medical Staff
CHR: Angie Altman, Director Human Resources
CNO: Gary Goelz, R.N., Chief Nursing Officer
Web address: www.shandslakeshore.com
Control: Partnership, Investor–owned (for–profit) **Service**: General medical and surgical

Staffed Beds: 85

VETERANS AFFAIRS MEDICAL CENTER See Lake City Veterans Affairs Medical Center

LAKE WALES—Polk County

✠ **ADVENTHEALTH LAKE WALES (100099)**, 410 South 11th Street, Zip 33853–4256; tel. 863/676–1433, **A**1 10 **F**3 11 15 18 20 29 30 34 35 40 45 46 49 50 56 57 59 64 70 74 75 77 79 81 82 85 86 87 91 92 93 94 96 98 103 107 108 110 111 114 115 119 124 131 132 146 147 148 149 154 156 **S** AdventHealth, Altamonte Springs, FL
Primary Contact: Brian Adams, Chief Executive Officer
COO: Rebecca Brewer, FACHE, Chief Operating Officer
CMO: Sunil Nihalani, M.D., Chief Medical Staff
CIO: Erwin Jaropillo, Director Information Systems
CHR: Renee Latterner, Director Human Resources
CNO: Jennifer Huston, Chief Nursing Officer
Web address: www.lakewalesmedicalcenter.com
Control: Corporation, Investor–owned (for–profit) **Service**: General medical and surgical

Staffed Beds: 150 Admissions: 4054 Census: 54 Outpatient Visits: 46478 Births: 0 Total Expense ($000): 56680 Payroll Expense ($000): 23673 Personnel: 467

LAKE WORTH—Palm Beach County

✠ **SELECT SPECIALTY HOSPITAL-PALM BEACH (102023)**, 3060 Melaleuca Lane, Zip 33461–5174; tel. 561/357–7200, (Nonreporting) **A**1 10 **S** Select Medical Corporation, Mechanicsburg, PA
Primary Contact: Larry Melby, Chief Executive Officer
Web address: www.selectspecialtyhospitals.com/company/locations/palmbeach.aspx
Control: Corporation, Investor–owned (for–profit) **Service**: Acute long–term care hospital

Staffed Beds: 60

LAKELAND—Polk County

✠ **LAKELAND REGIONAL HEALTH MEDICAL CENTER (100157)**, 1324 Lakeland Hills Blvd, Zip 33805–4543, Mailing Address: P.O. Box 95448, Zip 33804–5448; tel. 863/687–1100, **A**1 2 5 10 19 **F**3 4 13 18 20 22 24 26 28 29 30 31 34 37 38 40 41 43 44 45 46 47 49 51 55 56 57 58 59 60 61 64 65 66 70 72 74 75 76 77 78 79 80 81 82 83 84 85 86 87 88 89 93 95 96 98 99 100 101 102 103 107 108 109 110 111 114 115 118 119 120 121 123 124 126 130 131 132 135 143 146 147 148 149 154 156
Primary Contact: Timothy Regan, M.D., President and Chief Medical Officer
COO: Sarah Bhagat, Chief Operating Officer and Vice President of Organizational Effectiveness
CFO: Evan Jones, Executive Vice President and Chief Financial Officer
CMO: Timothy Regan, M.D., President and Chief Medical Officer
CIO: Elizabeth Kerns, Senior Vice President and Chief Information Officer
CHR: Scott Dimmick, Senior Vice President and Chief Human Resources Officer
CNO: Janet Fansler, R.N., Executive Vice President and Chief Nurse Executive
Web address: www.mylrh.org
Control: Other not–for–profit (including NFP Corporation) **Service**: General medical and surgical

Staffed Beds: 841 Admissions: 42447 Census: 560 Outpatient Visits: 288514 Births: 3023 Total Expense ($000): 658345 Payroll Expense ($000): 250233 Personnel: 4358

LAND O'LAKES—Pasco County

✠ **ADVENTHEALTH CONNERTON (102026)**, 9441 Health Center Drive, Zip 34637–5837; tel. 813/903–3701, **A**1 10 **F**1 3 4 16 17 29 30 31 34 67 70 72 73 80 88 89 90 91 98 107 119 128 146 148 **S** AdventHealth, Altamonte Springs, FL
Primary Contact: Brian Adams, President and Chief Executive Officer
COO: Debora Martoccio, R.N., Chief Operating Officer
CMO: Sharad Patel, M.D., Medical Director
Web address: www.elevatinghealthcare.org
Control: Church operated, Nongovernment, not–for–profit **Service**: Acute long–term care hospital

Staffed Beds: 50 Admissions: 693 Census: 49 Outpatient Visits: 0 Births: 0 Total Expense ($000): 26790 Payroll Expense ($000): 12032 Personnel: 224

FL

Hospital, Medicare Provider Number, Address, Telephone, Approval, Facility, and Physician Codes, Health Care System

★ American Hospital Association (AHA) membership
□ The Joint Commission accreditation
○ Healthcare Facilities Accreditation Program
◇ DNV Healthcare Inc. accreditation
⇑ Center for Improvement in Healthcare Quality Accreditation
△ Commission on Accreditation of Rehabilitation Facilities (CARF) accreditation

LARGO—Pinellas County

☒ **ENCOMPASS HEALTH REHABILITATION HOSPITAL OF LARGO (103037)**, 901 North Clearwater-Largo Road, Zip 33770–4126; tel. 727/586–2999, (Nonreporting) **A**1 10 **S** Encompass Health Corporation, Birmingham, AL
Primary Contact: Tripp Smith, Chief Executive Officer
CFO: Judith Johnson, Controller
CMO: Richard A Liles, M.D., Medical Director
CHR: Jackie Chalk, Director Human Resources
CNO: Pattie Brenner, R.N., Chief Nursing Officer
Web address: www.healthsouthlargo.com
Control: Corporation, Investor–owned (for–profit) **Service**: Rehabilitation

Staffed Beds: 70

☒ △ **LARGO MEDICAL CENTER (100248)**, 201 14th Street SW, Zip 33770–3133; tel. 727/588–5200, (Includes LARGO MEDICAL CENTER - INDIAN ROCKS, 2025 Indian Rocks Road, Largo, Florida, Zip 33774–1096, Mailing Address: P O Box 2025, Zip 33779–2025, tel. 727/581–9474), (Nonreporting) **A**1 2 3 5 7 10 12 13 **S** HCA Healthcare, Nashville, TN
Primary Contact: Adam Rudd, Chief Executive Officer
COO: Wyatt Chocklett, Chief Operating Officer
CFO: Glenn Romig, Chief Financial Officer
CMO: David Weiland, M.D., Chief Medical Officer
CIO: David Saly, Director, Information Services
CNO: Brenda Simpson, R.N., Chief Nursing Officer
Web address: www.largomedical.com
Control: Corporation, Investor–owned (for–profit) **Service**: General medical and surgical

Staffed Beds: 243

LAUDERDALE LAKES—Broward County

☐ **ST. ANTHONY'S REHABILITATION HOSPITAL (103027)**, 3485 NW 30th Street, Zip 33311–1890; tel. 954/739–6233, **A**1 10 **F**28 29 30 34 35 60 64 68 74 75 79 86 90 91 93 94 96 130 131 132 148 149 **S** Catholic Health Services, Lauderdale Lakes, FL
Primary Contact: Joseph M. Catania, Chief Executive Officer
COO: James Ball, Chief Operating Officer, Executive
CFO: David D'Amico
CMO: Mark Reiner, Chief Medical Office, Executive
CIO: Dario Achury, Director of Information Management
CHR: Barbara Griffith, Vice President Human Resources
Web address: www.catholichealthservices.org
Control: Church operated, Nongovernment, not–for–profit **Service**: Rehabilitation

Staffed Beds: 26 **Admissions**: 457 **Census**: 17 **Outpatient Visits**: 2415 **Births**: 0 **Total Expense ($000)**: 7552 **Payroll Expense ($000)**: 3517 **Personnel**: 72

LEESBURG—Lake County

☒ **LEESBURG REGIONAL MEDICAL CENTER (100084)**, 600 East Dixie Avenue, Zip 34748–5999; tel. 352/323–5762, **A**1 2 10 **F**3 8 11 13 15 17 18 20 22 24 26 28 29 30 31 34 35 40 45 47 48 49 53 54 57 59 64 68 70 74 75 76 77 78 79 81 82 84 85 87 89 93 96 98 103 107 108 110 111 114 115 119 130 132 135 144 146 147 149 156 **S** Central Florida Health, Leesburg, FL
Primary Contact: Donald G. Henderson, FACHE, President and Chief Executive Officer
COO: Saad Ehtisham, R.N., FACHE, Senior Vice President and Chief Operating Officer
CFO: Diane P Harden, Chief Financial Officer
CIO: David Steele, Vice President Chief Information Officer
CHR: Amie A Richason, Vice President Human Resources
CNO: Joshua Fleming, Vice President Chief Clinical Officer
Web address: www.centralfloridahealth.org
Control: Other not–for–profit (including NFP Corporation) **Service**: General medical and surgical

Staffed Beds: 329 **Admissions**: 13228 **Census**: 181 **Outpatient Visits**: 72267 **Births**: 1231 **Personnel**: 1622

LIFESTREAM BEHAVIORAL CENTER (104018), 2020 Tally Road, Zip 34748–3426, Mailing Address: P.O. Box 491000, Zip 34749–1000; tel. 352/315–7500, (Nonreporting) **A**10
Primary Contact: Jonathan M. Cherry, President and Chief Executive Officer
COO: David Braughton, Chief Operating Officer
CFO: Carol Dozier, Chief Financial Officer
CMO: T. J. Valente, M.D., Medical Director
CIO: Chad Heim, Management Information System Director
CHR: Ben Hargrove, Human Resources Director
Web address: www.lsbc.net
Control: Other not–for–profit (including NFP Corporation) **Service**: Psychiatric

Staffed Beds: 46

LEHIGH ACRES—Lee County

☒ **LEHIGH REGIONAL MEDICAL CENTER (100107)**, 1500 Lee Boulevard, Zip 33936–4835; tel. 239/369–2101, **A**1 10 **F**3 18 29 30 34 40 45 46 49 50 57 63 65 68 70 81 107 111 114 118 119 130 132 135 149 **S** Prime Healthcare, Ontario, CA
Primary Contact: Gary C. Bell, LFACHE, Chief Executive Officer
CFO: Osman Gruhonjic, Chief Financial Officer
CMO: Joe Lemmons, D.O., Chief of Staff
CIO: Jeff Hampton, Director Information Systems
CHR: Mary Gray, Director Human Resources
CNO: Julie G Banker, R.N., MSN, Chief Nursing Officer
Web address: www.lehighregional.com
Control: Corporation, Investor–owned (for–profit) **Service**: General medical and surgical

Staffed Beds: 53 **Admissions**: 2443 **Census**: 26 **Outpatient Visits**: 27908 **Births**: 0 **Total Expense ($000)**: 35711 **Payroll Expense ($000)**: 12494 **Personnel**: 310

LIVE OAK—Suwannee County

☒ **SHANDS LIVE OAK REGIONAL MEDICAL CENTER (101301)**, 1100 SW 11th Street, Zip 32064–3608; tel. 386/362–0800, (Nonreporting) **A**1 10 18 **S** Community Health Systems, Inc., Franklin, TN
Primary Contact: Rhonda Kay. Sherrod, R.N., MSN, Chief Executive Officer
CFO: Jennifer Grafton, Chief Financial Officer
CMO: Andrew C. Bass, M.D., Medical Director
CIO: Justin Marlowe, Information Technology Director
CHR: Dana Abbott, Market Human Resources Director
CNO: Donna Ragan, R.N., Chief Nursing Officer
Web address: www.shandsliveoak.com/
Control: Partnership, Investor–owned (for–profit) **Service**: General medical and surgical

Staffed Beds: 25

LOXAHATCHEE—Palm Beach County

☒ **PALMS WEST HOSPITAL (100269)**, 13001 Southern Boulevard, Zip 33470–9203; tel. 561/798–3300, (Nonreporting) **A**1 3 5 10 **S** HCA Healthcare, Nashville, TN
Primary Contact: Joshua DeTillio, Chief Executive Officer
COO: Lorna Kernivan, Chief Operating Officer
CFO: Steven Burroughs, Chief Financial Officer
CIO: Martha Stinson, Director of Information Technology
CHR: Marcy Mills-Mathews, Director Human Resources
CNO: Silvia Stradi, Chief Nursing Officer
Web address: www.palmswesthospital.com
Control: Corporation, Investor–owned (for–profit) **Service**: General medical and surgical

Staffed Beds: 204

MACCLENNY—Baker County

ED FRASER MEMORIAL HOSPITAL AND BAKER COMMUNITY HEALTH CENTER (100134), 159 North Third Street, Zip 32063–2103, Mailing Address: P.O. Box 484, Zip 32063–0484; tel. 904/259–3151, (Nonreporting) **A**10 20
Primary Contact: Dennis R. Markos, Chief Executive Officer
CFO: W. Steve Dudley, CPA, Chief Financial Officer
CMO: Mark Hardin, M.D., Medical Director
CIO: Ernie Waller, Director Information Technology
CHR: Stacey Conner, Director Personnel
CNO: Valerie Markos, Chief Nursing Officer
Web address: www.bcmedsvcs.com
Control: Other not–for–profit (including NFP Corporation) **Service**: General medical and surgical

Staffed Beds: 68

MADISON—Madison County

MADISON COUNTY MEMORIAL HOSPITAL (101311), 224 NW Crane Avenue, Zip 32340–2561; tel. 850/973–2271, (Nonreporting) **A**10 18
Primary Contact: Tammy Stevens, Chief Executive Officer
CMO: Brett Perkins, M.D., Chief Medical Staff
CIO: Patrick Stiff, Coordinator Information Technology
CHR: Cindi Burnett, Chief Human Resources Officer
Web address: www.mcmh.us/
Control: Other not–for–profit (including NFP Corporation) **Service**: General medical and surgical

Staffed Beds: 25

FL

Many Facility Codes have changed. Please refer to the AHA Guide Code Chart. © 2019 AHA Guide

MARATHON—Monroe County

✠ **FISHERMEN'S HOSPITAL (101312)**, 3301 Overseas Highway, Zip 33050–2329; tel. 305/743–5533, (Nonreporting) **A**1 10 18 **S** Baptist Health South Florida, Coral Gables, FL
Primary Contact: Rick Freeburg, Chief Executive Officer
COO: Lynn Mauck, R.N., Chief Operating Officer and Chief Nursing Officer
CFO: H D Cannington, Interim Chief Financial Officer
CMO: Harlan Pettit, M.D., Chief of Medical Staff
CIO: Patrick Still, Director of Information Systems
CHR: Chris Fletcher, Director of Human Resources
CNO: Lynn Mauck, R.N., Chief Operating Officer and Chief Nursing Officer
Web address: www.fishermenshospital.org
Control: Other not–for–profit (including NFP Corporation) **Service**: General medical and surgical

Staffed Beds: 25

MARGATE—Broward County

✠ **NORTHWEST MEDICAL CENTER (100189)**, 2801 North State Road 7, Zip 33063–5727; tel. 954/974–0400, (Nonreporting) **A**1 10 **S** HCA Healthcare, Nashville, TN
Primary Contact: Erica Gulrich, Chief Executive Officer
CFO: Ananda Rampat, Chief Financial Officer
CMO: Jose Martinez, M.D., Chief Medical Officer
CIO: David Irizarri, Director Information Technology
CHR: Lynda Bryan, Vice President Human Resources
CNO: Sandra Emeott, R.N., Chief Nursing Officer
Web address: www.northwestmed.com
Control: Corporation, Investor–owned (for–profit) **Service**: General medical and surgical

Staffed Beds: 228

MARIANNA—Jackson County

✠ **JACKSON HOSPITAL (100142)**, 4250 Hospital Drive, Zip 32446–1917, Mailing Address: P.O. Box 1608, Zip 32447–5608; tel. 850/526–2200, **A**1 10 20 **F**3 11 13 15 20 28 29 30 31 34 35 40 45 50 53 54 57 59 70 75 76 78 81 85 86 87 97 107 108 110 111 114 118 119 120 127 130 132 133 135 146 147 148 **S** QHR, Brentwood, TN
Primary Contact: James Platt, Chief Executive Officer
CFO: Kevin Rovito, Chief Financial Officer
CMO: Steven Walter Spence, M.D., Chief Medical Officer
CIO: Jamie Hussey, Chief Information Officer
CHR: Brooke G Donaldson, Assistant Administrator Human Resources
CNO: Robbin K Pumphrey, Chief Nursing Officer
Web address: www.jacksonhosp.com
Control: Hospital district or authority, Government, nonfederal **Service**: General medical and surgical

Staffed Beds: 68 **Admissions**: 2748 **Census**: 35 **Outpatient Visits**: 74872 **Births**: 382 **Total Expense ($000)**: 55624 **Payroll Expense ($000)**: 26082 **Personnel**: 511

MELBOURNE—Brevard County

☐ **CIRCLES OF CARE (104024)**, 400 East Sheridan Road, Zip 32901–3184; tel. 321/722–5200, (Nonreporting) **A**1 10
Primary Contact: David L. Feldman, President and Chief Executive Officer
CFO: David L Feldman, Executive Vice President and Treasurer
CMO: Jose Alvarez, M.D., Chief Medical Staff
CHR: Linda Brannon, Vice President Human Resources
Web address: www.circlesofcare.org
Control: Other not–for–profit (including NFP Corporation) **Service**: Psychiatric

Staffed Beds: 134

DEVEREUX HOSPITAL AND CHILDREN'S CENTER OF FLORIDA, 8000 Devereux Drive, Zip 32940–7907; tel. 321/242–9100, (Nonreporting) **S** Devereux, Villanova, PA
Primary Contact: Steven Murphy, Executive Director
COO: Eva Horner, Assistant Executive Director Operations
CFO: Kelly Messer, Director of Finance
CMO: Manal Durgin, Network Medical Director
CIO: Diana Deitrick, Director Information Services
CHR: Tim Dillion, Vice President of Human Resources
Web address: www.devereux.org
Control: Other not–for–profit (including NFP Corporation) **Service**: Children's hospital psychiatric

Staffed Beds: 100

✠ **HEALTH FIRST HOLMES REGIONAL MEDICAL CENTER (100019)**, 1350 South Hickory Street, Zip 32901–3224; tel. 321/434–7000, **A**1 10 **F**3 11 13 17 18 20 22 24 26 29 30 31 34 39 40 41 43 45 46 49 50 54 56 59 60 64 68 70 72 74 75 77 78 79 80 81 82 84 85 86 87 89 92 93 102 107 108 111 114 115 118 119 126 130 132 141 146 148 149 155 **S** Health First, Inc., Rockledge, FL
Primary Contact: Brett A. Esrock, FACHE, Chief Executive Officer
CFO: Joseph G Felkner, Executive Vice President/Chief Financial Officer
CMO: Mark Rosenbloom, M.D., Vice President of Medical Affairs
CIO: Dustin Leek, Vice President of Enterprise Technology Services
CHR: Paula Just, Chief Human Resources Officer
CNO: Barbara Seymour, Vice President of Nursing
Web address: www.health-first.org
Control: Other not–for–profit (including NFP Corporation) **Service**: General medical and surgical

Staffed Beds: 514 **Admissions**: 30075 **Census**: 392 **Outpatient Visits**: 231297 **Births**: 3169 **Total Expense ($000)**: 496464 **Payroll Expense ($000)**: 181158 **Personnel**: 2313

☐ **HEALTH FIRST VIERA HOSPITAL (100315)**, 8745 North Wickham Road, Zip 32940–5997; tel. 321/434–9164, **A**1 5 10 **F**3 12 15 18 20 26 29 30 31 34 39 40 41 45 46 47 48 49 50 54 59 60 64 68 70 74 75 77 78 79 80 81 85 86 87 93 102 107 108 110 111 114 115 117 118 119 126 129 130 132 141 146 148 149 154 **S** Health First, Inc., Rockledge, FL
Primary Contact: Brett A. Esrock, FACHE, President
COO: Deborah Angerami, Chief Operating Officer
CFO: Joseph G Felkner, Chief Financial Officer
CMO: Scott Gettings, M.D., Senior Vice President and Chief Medical Officer
CIO: Alex Popowycz, Chief Information Officer
CHR: Paula Just, Chief Human Resources Officer
CNO: Connie Bradley, R.N., MSN, FACHE, Senior Vice President and Chief Nursing Officer
Web address: www.vierahospital.org
Control: Other not–for–profit (including NFP Corporation) **Service**: General medical and surgical

Staffed Beds: 84 **Admissions**: 5032 **Census**: 49 **Outpatient Visits**: 73907 **Births**: 0 **Total Expense ($000)**: 96564 **Payroll Expense ($000)**: 34387 **Personnel**: 387

✠ **KINDRED HOSPITAL MELBOURNE (102027)**, 765 West Nasa Boulevard, Zip 32901–1815; tel. 321/733–5725, (Nonreporting) **A**1 10 **S** Kindred Healthcare, Louisville, KY
Primary Contact: Pamela R. Reed, Chief Executive Officer
Web address: www.khmelbourne.com
Control: Corporation, Investor–owned (for–profit) **Service**: Acute long–term care hospital

Staffed Beds: 60

☐ **MELBOURNE REGIONAL MEDICAL CENTER (100291)**, 250 North Wickham Road, Zip 32935–8625; tel. 321/752–1200, (Nonreporting) **A**1 10 **S** Steward Health Care System, LLC, Dallas, TX
Primary Contact: Ron Cicca, Chief Executive Officer
CFO: Dale Armour, Chief Financial Officer
Web address: www.wuesthoff.com/locations/wuesthoff-medical-center-melbourne
Control: Corporation, Investor–owned (for–profit) **Service**: General medical and surgical

Staffed Beds: 119

✠ **SEA PINES REHABILITATION HOSPITAL (103034)**, 101 East Florida Avenue, Zip 32901–8301; tel. 321/984–4600, (Nonreporting) **A**1 10 **S** Encompass Health Corporation, Birmingham, AL
Primary Contact: Denise B. McGrath, Chief Executive Officer
CFO: Dana Edwards, Chief Financial Officer
CMO: Juan Lebron, M.D., Medical Director
CHR: James L Henry, Director Human Resources
CNO: Lisa Truman, Chief Nursing Officer
Web address: www.healthsouthseapines.com
Control: Corporation, Investor–owned (for–profit) **Service**: Rehabilitation

Staffed Beds: 90

FL

Hospital, Medicare Provider Number, Address, Telephone, Approval, Facility, and Physician Codes, Health Care System

★ American Hospital Association (AHA) membership   ○ Healthcare Facilities Accreditation Program   ⇑ Center for Improvement in Healthcare Quality Accreditation
☐ The Joint Commission accreditation   ◇ DNV Healthcare Inc. accreditation   △ Commission on Accreditation of Rehabilitation Facilities (CARF) accreditation

MIAMI—Miami-Dade County

✠ △ **BAPTIST HEALTH SOUTH FLORIDA, BAPTIST HOSPITAL OF MIAMI (100008)**, 8900 North Kendall Drive, Zip 33176–2197; tel. 786/596–1960, (Includes BAPTIST CHILDREN'S HOSPITAL, 8900 North Kendall Drive, Miami, Florida, Zip 33176–2118; tel. 786/596–1960; Albert Leon Boulenger, R.N., Chief Executive Officer) **A**1 2 7 10 **F**3 11 13 15 17 18 19 20 22 24 26 28 29 30 31 32 34 35 36 38 39 40 41 44 45 46 47 48 49 50 51 53 54 55 56 57 58 59 60 61 63 64 66 68 70 72 73 74 75 76 77 78 79 80 81 82 84 85 86 87 88 89 90 91 92 93 94 96 100 102 104 107 108 109 110 111 112 115 116 117 118 119 120 121 122 123 124 126 129 130 132 135 136 141 144 145 146 147 148 149 150 154 156 157 **S** Baptist Health South Florida, Coral Gables, FL
Primary Contact: Patricia M. Rosello, Chief Executive Officer
CFO: Ralph E Lawson, Executive Vice President and Chief Financial Officer
CMO: Mark J Hauser, M.D., Chief Medical Officer
CIO: Mimi Taylor, Corporate Vice President Information Technology
CHR: Adriene McCoy, Chief Human Resource Officer
CNO: Becky Montesino-King, MS, R.N., MSN, Vice President and Chief Nursing Officer
Web address: www.baptisthealth.net
Control: Other not–for–profit (including NFP Corporation) **Service:** General medical and surgical

Staffed Beds: 720 **Admissions:** 30533 **Census:** 507 **Outpatient Visits:** 547071 **Births:** 3765 **Total Expense ($000):** 1048953 **Payroll Expense ($000):** 340601 **Personnel:** 5238

✠ **BAPTIST HEALTH SOUTH FLORIDA, SOUTH MIAMI HOSPITAL (100154)**, 6200 SW 73rd Street, Zip 33143–4679; tel. 786/662–4000, **A**1 2 3 10 **F**3 5 11 12 13 15 16 17 18 19 20 22 24 26 28 29 30 31 34 35 36 40 44 45 46 48 49 50 51 52 53 54 57 58 59 60 61 63 64 66 68 70 72 73 74 75 76 77 78 79 80 81 82 84 85 86 87 90 91 93 94 96 100 102 107 108 110 111 115 118 119 126 129 130 132 135 141 144 146 147 148 149 150 154 157 **S** Baptist Health South Florida, Coral Gables, FL
Primary Contact: William M. Duquette, Chief Executive Officer
COO: Jeanette Stone, Vice President Operations
CFO: Erik Long, Controller
CMO: Jeremy Tabak, M.D., President Medical Staff
CIO: Mimi Taylor, Vice President Information Technology
CHR: Diana Montenegro, Director Human Resources
CNO: Kathy Sparger, R.N., MSN, Chief Nursing Officer
Web address: www.baptisthealth.net
Control: Other not–for–profit (including NFP Corporation) **Service:** General medical and surgical

Staffed Beds: 336 **Admissions:** 15526 **Census:** 204 **Outpatient Visits:** 275370 **Births:** 3529 **Total Expense ($000):** 458056 **Payroll Expense ($000):** 156788 **Personnel:** 1886

✠ **BAPTIST HEALTH SOUTH FLORIDA, WEST KENDALL BAPTIST HOSPITAL (100314)**, 9555 SW 162nd Avenue, Zip 33196–6408; tel. 786/467–2000, **A**1 3 5 10 **F**3 11 13 18 19 29 30 31 34 35 40 41 44 45 49 50 51 53 57 58 59 60 63 64 68 70 71 74 75 76 77 78 79 80 81 82 84 85 86 87 90 93 100 102 107 108 109 111 114 115 119 130 131 132 135 145 146 147 148 149 150 154 **S** Baptist Health South Florida, Coral Gables, FL
Primary Contact: Javier Hernandez-Lichtl, Chief Executive Officer
CFO: Odalys Remigio, Assistant Vice President, Finance
CMO: Juan-Carlos Verdeja, M.D., President of Medical Staff
CHR: Hilde Zamora de Aguero, Human Resources Site Director
CNO: Denise H. Harris, R.N., MSN, Chief Nursing Officer
Web address: www.baptisthealth.net/en/facilities/West-Kendall-Baptist-Hospital/Pages/default.aspx
Control: Other not–for–profit (including NFP Corporation) **Service:** General medical and surgical

Staffed Beds: 133 **Admissions:** 8006 **Census:** 86 **Outpatient Visits:** 91836 **Births:** 932 **Total Expense ($000):** 195346 **Payroll Expense ($000):** 71416 **Personnel:** 997

JACKSON BEHAVIORAL HEALTH HOSPITAL See Jackson Health System, Miami

☐ **JACKSON HEALTH SYSTEM (100022)**, 1611 NW 12th Avenue, Zip 33136–1005; tel. 305/585–1111, (Includes HOLTZ CHILDREN'S HOSPITAL, 1611 NW 12th Avenue, Miami, Florida, Zip 33136–1005; tel. 305/585–5437; Don S Steigman, Chief Executive Officer; JACKSON BEHAVIORAL HEALTH HOSPITAL, 1695 NW Ninth Avenue, Miami, Florida, Zip 33136–1409; tel. 305/324–4357; Nicolette B Tessler, Chief Executive Officer of Behavioral Health Hospital; JACKSON MEMORIAL HOSPITAL, 1611 NW 12th Avenue, Miami, Florida, Zip 33136; tel. 305/585–1111; David Zambrana, Ph.D., R.N., Senior Vice President and Chief Executive Officer; JACKSON NORTH MEDICAL CENTER, 160 NW 170th Street, North Miami Beach, Florida, Zip 33169–5576; tel. 305/651–1100; Roy L. Hawkins Jr, Senior Vice President and Chief Executive Officer; JACKSON SOUTH COMMUNITY HOSPITAL, 9333 SW 152nd Street, Miami, Florida, Zip 33157–1780; tel. 305/251–2500; Georgina Diaz, Chief Executive Officer) (Total facility includes 343 beds in nursing home–type unit) **A**1 3 5 8 10 19 **F**1 3 4 5 8 10 11 12 13 15 16 17 18 19 20 21 22 23 24 25 26 27 28 29 30 31 34 35 38 39 40 41 43 44 45 46 49 50 54 55 56 57 58 59 60 61 64 65 66 67 68 70 71 72 73 74 75 76 77 78 79 80 81 82 83 84 85 86 87 88 89 90 93 94 96 97 98 99 100 101 102 103 104 107 108 109 110 111 115 117 118 119 120 121 123 124 126 128 129 130 131 132 135 136 137 138 139 140 141 142 144 146 147 148 149 154 157
Primary Contact: Carlos A. Migoya, President and Chief Executive Officer
COO: Don S Steigman, Chief Operating Officer
CFO: Mark T Knight, Executive Vice President and Chief Financial Officer
CMO: Peter G Paige, Chief Medical Officer
CIO: Michael A Garcia, Vice President and Chief Information Officer
CHR: Julie Staub, Chief Human Resources Officer
Web address: www.jacksonhealth.org
Control: County, Government, nonfederal **Service:** General medical and surgical

Staffed Beds: 2134 **Admissions:** 65477 **Census:** 1851 **Outpatient Visits:** 3141051 **Births:** 6318 **Total Expense ($000):** 1938854 **Payroll Expense ($000):** 923046 **Personnel:** 12105

JACKSON SOUTH COMMUNITY HOSPITAL See Jackson Health System, Miami

✠ **KENDALL REGIONAL MEDICAL CENTER (100209)**, 11750 Bird Road, Zip 33175–3530; tel. 305/223–3000, (Nonreporting) **A**1 3 10 **S** HCA Healthcare, Nashville, TN
Primary Contact: Brandon Haushalter, Chief Executive Officer
COO: Randy Gross, Chief Operating Officer
CFO: Robert Grace, Chief Financial Officer
CIO: Matt Hernandez, Director of Information Technology and System
CHR: Knicole S White, Vice-President, Human Resources
CNO: Maria Villa, Interim Chief Nursing Officer
Web address: www.kendallmed.com
Control: Partnership, Investor–owned (for–profit) **Service:** General medical and surgical

Staffed Beds: 300

☐ **MIAMI JEWISH HOME AND HOSPITAL FOR AGED (100277)**, 5200 NE Second Avenue, Zip 33137–2706; tel. 305/751–8626, (Nonreporting) **A**1 3 5 10
Primary Contact: Jeffrey P. Freimark, Chief Executive Officer
CFO: Lisa Jo Desmarteau, Chief Financial Officer
CMO: Brian Kiedrowski, M.D., Chief Medical Director
CHR: Larry McDonald, Director Human Resources
Web address: www.mjhha.org
Control: Other not–for–profit (including NFP Corporation) **Service:** General medical and surgical

Staffed Beds: 32

✠ △ **MIAMI VETERANS AFFAIRS HEALTHCARE SYSTEM**, 1201 NW 16th Street, Zip 33125–1624; tel. 305/575–7000, (Nonreporting) **A**1 3 5 7 **S** Department of Veterans Affairs, Washington, DC
Primary Contact: David VanMeter, FACHE, Acting Director
COO: Lance Davis, PharmD, Associate Director
CFO: Albert Tucker, Chief Financial Officer
CMO: Vincent DeGennaro, M.D., Chief of Staff
CIO: Anthony Brooks, Chief Information Officer
CHR: Loyman Marin, Chief Human Resources
CNO: Marcia C Lysaght, R.N., MSN, Associate Director Patient Care Services
Web address: www.miami.va.gov/
Control: Veterans Affairs, Government, federal **Service:** General medical and surgical

Staffed Beds: 401

Many Facility Codes have changed. Please refer to the AHA Guide Code Chart.
© 2019 AHA Guide

FL

★ ⇧ **NICKLAUS CHILDREN'S HOSPITAL (103301)**, 3100 SW 62nd Avenue, Zip 33155–3009; tel. 305/666–6511, **A**2 3 5 8 10 21 **F**3 7 17 18 19 20 21 22 23 24 25 26 27 29 30 31 32 34 35 39 40 41 43 44 45 46 47 48 49 50 53 54 55 57 58 59 60 61 64 65 68 71 72 74 75 77 78 79 80 81 82 85 86 87 88 89 93 94 97 98 99 100 101 102 104 105 107 108 109 111 112 115 116 117 118 119 126 129 130 131 132 136 142 143 144 145 146 148 149 153 154 155 156 157 158
Primary Contact: Matthew Love, Interim Chief Executive Officer
COO: Martha McGill, Executive Vice President and Chief Operating Officer
CFO: Matthew Love, Chief Financial Officer
CMO: Deise Granado-Villar, M.D., Chief Medical Officer and Senior Vice President Medical Affairs
CIO: Edward Martinez, Chief Information Officer
CHR: Michael S. Kushner, Senior Vice President and Chief Talent Officer
CNO: Jacqueline Gonzalez, Senior Vice President and Chief Nursing Officer
Web address: www.mch.com
Control: Other not–for–profit (including NFP Corporation) **Service:** Children's general medical and surgical

Staffed Beds: 281 **Admissions:** 19120 **Census:** 180 **Outpatient Visits:** 438543 **Births:** 0 **Total Expense ($000):** 623381 **Payroll Expense ($000):** 219183 **Personnel:** 3747

⊠ **NORTH SHORE MEDICAL CENTER (100029)**, 1100 NW 95th Street, Zip 33150–2098; tel. 305/835–6000, (Includes FLORIDA MEDICAL CENTER - A CAMPUS OF NORTH SHORE, 5000 West Oakland Park Boulevard, Fort Lauderdale, Florida, Zip 33313–1585; tel. 954/735–6000; Trey Abshier, Chief Executive Officer) **A**1 3 10 **F**3 7 13 15 18 20 22 29 30 34 35 40 44 45 49 56 57 59 60 64 68 69 70 72 74 75 76 77 78 79 80 81 82 85 87 93 94 98 102 107 110 111 115 119 126 129 130 146 147 148 149 154 157 **S** TENET Healthcare Corporation, Dallas, TX
Primary Contact: Mark Racicot, Chief Executive Officer
COO: Shana Crittenden, Chief Operating Officer
CFO: Howard Drown, Chief Financial Officer
CMO: Marcia Bierman, M.D., Chief of Staff
CIO: Luis Estrada, Director Multifacility Information Systems
CHR: Carmen Gomez, Director Human Resources
Web address: www.northshoremedical.com
Control: Corporation, Investor–owned (for–profit) **Service:** General medical and surgical

Staffed Beds: 258 **Admissions:** 13221 **Census:** 164 **Outpatient Visits:** 67178 **Births:** 1691 **Total Expense ($000):** 128299 **Payroll Expense ($000):** 74238 **Personnel:** 781

⊠ **SELECT SPECIALTY HOSPITAL-MIAMI (102001)**, 955 NW 3rd Street, Zip 33128–1274; tel. 305/416–5700, (Nonreporting) **A**1 10 **S** Select Medical Corporation, Mechanicsburg, PA
Primary Contact: Loretta Sheffield, Chief Executive Officer
Web address: www.selectspecialtyhospitals.com/company/locations/miami.aspx
Control: Corporation, Investor–owned (for–profit) **Service:** Acute long–term care hospital

Staffed Beds: 47

⊠ **UNIVERSITY OF MIAMI HOSPITAL AND CLINICS (100079)**, 1475 NW 12th Avenue, Zip 33136–1002; tel. 305/689–5511, (Includes BASCOM PALMER EYE INSTITUTE-ANNE BATES LEACH EYE HOSPITAL, 900 NW 17th Street, Miami, Florida, Zip 33136–1199, Mailing Address: Box 016880, Zip 33101–6880; tel. 305/326–6000; Michael B Gittelman, Administrator; UNIVERSITY OF MIAMI HOSPITAL, 1400 NW 12th Avenue, Miami, Florida, Zip 33136–1003; tel. 305/325–5511; Michael B Gittelman, Chief Executive Officer) **A**1 2 3 5 8 10 **F**3 8 11 12 15 17 18 20 22 24 26 28 29 30 31 34 35 36 37 38 39 40 44 45 46 47 48 49 50 51 53 54 55 56 57 58 59 60 61 63 64 66 68 70 71 74 75 77 78 79 80 81 82 83 84 85 86 87 90 92 93 94 96 98 100 102 104 107 108 110 111 114 115 117 118 119 120 121 123 124 126 129 130 131 132 135 136 141 146 147 148 149 156 157
Primary Contact: Stephen Demers, Chief Executive Officer
COO: Stephen Demers, Chief Operating Officer
CFO: Harry Rohrer, Chief Financial Officer
CMO: W Jarrad Goodwin, M.D., Director
Web address: www.uhealthsystem.com
Control: Other not–for–profit (including NFP Corporation) **Service:** Cancer

Staffed Beds: 547 **Admissions:** 20159 **Census:** 309 **Outpatient Visits:** 848982 **Births:** 0 **Total Expense ($000):** 1418169 **Payroll Expense ($000):** 269108 **Personnel:** 3172

VETERANS AFFAIRS MEDICAL CENTER See Miami Veterans Affairs Healthcare System

⊠ △ **WEST GABLES REHABILITATION HOSPITAL (103036)**, 2525 SW 75th Avenue, Zip 33155–2800; tel. 305/262–6800, **A**1 7 10 **F**29 34 74 75 77 82 86 87 90 93 94 95 96 130 131 132 135 148 149 **S** Select Medical Corporation, Mechanicsburg, PA
Primary Contact: Walter Concepcion, Chief Executive Officer
CFO: Sara Reohr, Regional Controller
CMO: Jose L Vargas, M.D., Medical Director
CHR: Barbara Etchason, HR Manager
CNO: Lucia Benjamin, Chief Nursing Officer
Web address: www.westgablesrehabhospital.com/
Control: Corporation, Investor–owned (for–profit) **Service:** Rehabilitation

Staffed Beds: 60 **Admissions:** 1557 **Census:** 58 **Outpatient Visits:** 0 **Births:** 0 **Personnel:** 214

○ **WESTCHESTER GENERAL HOSPITAL (100284)**, 2500 SW 75th Avenue, Zip 33155–2805; tel. 305/264–5252, (Includes SOUTHERN WINDS HOSPITAL, 4225 West 20th Street, Hialeah, Florida, Zip 33012–5835; tel. 305/558–9700) **A**3 10 11 13 **F**3 15 18 29 31 40 45 49 56 65 70 74 75 77 78 79 81 85 87 98 100 102 103 107 108 110 114 115 119 130
Primary Contact: Rudy Garcia, Chief Executive Officer
CFO: Joel Snook, Chief Financial Officer
CMO: Rogelio Zaldivar, M.D., Medical Director
CHR: Jennifer Ricardo, Director of Human Resources
Web address: www.westchestergeneralhospital.com/
Control: Corporation, Investor–owned (for–profit) **Service:** General medical and surgical

Staffed Beds: 125 **Admissions:** 4389 **Census:** 70 **Outpatient Visits:** 24507 **Births:** 0 **Total Expense ($000):** 50540 **Payroll Expense ($000):** 22693 **Personnel:** 481

MIAMI BEACH—Dade County

MIAMI HEART CAMPUS AT MOUNT SINAI MEDICAL CENTER See Mount Sinai Medical Center, Miami Beach

MIAMI BEACH—Miami-Dade County

□ △ **MOUNT SINAI MEDICAL CENTER (100034)**, 4300 Alton Road, Zip 33140–2940; tel. 305/674–2121, (Includes MIAMI HEART CAMPUS AT MOUNT SINAI MEDICAL CENTER, 4701 North Meridian Avenue, Miami Beach, Florida, Zip 33140–2910; tel. 305/672–1111) **A**1 2 3 5 7 8 10 **F**1 2 3 4 6 8 9 12 13 14 15 16 17 18 19 20 22 24 26 28 29 30 31 34 35 36 37 38 39 40 41 42 44 45 46 47 48 49 50 51 53 54 55 56 57 58 59 60 61 62 63 64 65 66 67 68 70 71 72 73 74 75 76 77 78 79 80 81 82 84 85 86 87 88 89 90 91 92 93 96 97 98 100 101 102 103 104 105 107 108 110 111 114 115 118 119 120 121 123 124 126 128 129 130 131 132 135 141 143 145 146 147 148 149 152 154 156 157 158
Primary Contact: Steven D. Sonenreich, President and Chief Executive Officer
COO: Angel Pallin, Senior Vice President of Operations
CFO: Alex A Mendez, Executive Vice President of Operations and Chief Financial Officer
CMO: Robert Goldszer, M.D., Senior Vice President and Chief Medical Officer
CIO: Tom Gillette, Senior Vice President and Chief Information Officer
CHR: Georgia McLean, Director Human Resources
CNO: Karen W Moyer, R.N., Senior Vice President and Chief Nursing Officer
Web address: www.msmc.com
Control: Other not–for–profit (including NFP Corporation) **Service:** General medical and surgical

Staffed Beds: 608 **Admissions:** 23331 **Census:** 338 **Outpatient Visits:** 217700 **Births:** 2813 **Total Expense ($000):** 583866 **Payroll Expense ($000):** 264723 **Personnel:** 4023

MIAMI LAKES—Miami-Dade County

★ **PROMISE HOSPITAL OF MIAMI (100326)**, 14001 NW 82nd Avenue, Zip 33016–1561; tel. 786/609–9200, (Nonreporting) **S** Select Medical Corporation, Mechanicsburg, PA
Primary Contact: Charles Doten, Chief Executive Officer
Web address: www.promise-miami.com
Control: Corporation, Investor–owned (for–profit) **Service:** Acute long–term care hospital

Staffed Beds: 60

Hospital, Medicare Provider Number, Address, Telephone, Approval, Facility, and Physician Codes, Health Care System

★ American Hospital Association (AHA) membership   ○ Healthcare Facilities Accreditation Program   ⇧ Center for Improvement in Healthcare Quality Accreditation
□ The Joint Commission accreditation   ◇ DNV Healthcare Inc. accreditation   △ Commission on Accreditation of Rehabilitation Facilities (CARF) accreditation

FL

MIDDLEBURG—Clay County

☒ **ST. VINCENT'S MEDICAL CENTER CLAY COUNTY (100321)**, 1670 St. Vincent's Way, Zip 32068–8427, Mailing Address: 1670 St. Vincents Way, Zip 32068–8447; tel. 904/602–1000, **A**1 10 **F**3 13 15 18 20 22 29 30 34 37 40 44 49 57 61 64 65 70 74 76 79 81 84 85 86 87 93 107 108 110 111 114 115 118 119 124 130 131 132 146 147 149 156 **S** Ascension Healthcare, Saint Louis, MO
Primary Contact: James Machado, President
Web address: www.jaxhealth.com/
Control: Church operated, Nongovernment, not–for–profit **Service:** General medical and surgical

Staffed Beds: 106 **Admissions:** 7097 **Census:** 67 **Outpatient Visits:** 52043 **Births:** 568 **Total Expense ($000):** 90329 **Payroll Expense ($000):** 28931 **Personnel:** 407

MILTON—Santa Rosa County

☒ **SANTA ROSA MEDICAL CENTER (100124)**, 6002 Berryhill Road, Zip 32570–5062; tel. 850/626–7762, (Nonreporting) **A**1 10 **S** Community Health Systems, Inc., Franklin, TN
Primary Contact: Doug Sills, Chief Executive Officer
CFO: Jared Whipkey, Chief Financial Officer
CIO: Rick Payne, Director Information Systems
CHR: Christopher Foreman, Director Human Resources
CNO: Trish Davis, Chief Nursing Officer
Web address: www.santarosamedicalcenter.org
Control: Corporation, Investor–owned (for–profit) **Service:** General medical and surgical

Staffed Beds: 68

WEST FLORIDA COMMUNITY CARE CENTER (104027), 5500 Stewart Street, Zip 32570–4304; tel. 850/983–5500, (Nonreporting) **A**10
Primary Contact: Joshua Willis, Chief Executive Officer
Web address: www.elakeviewcenter.org/MentalHealth/Adult/Inpatient-WFCCC.aspx
Control: Other not–for–profit (including NFP Corporation) **Service:** Psychiatric

Staffed Beds: 100

MIRAMAR—Broward County

☒ **MEMORIAL HOSPITAL MIRAMAR (100285)**, 1901 SW 172nd Avenue, Zip 33029–5592; tel. 954/538–5000, **A**1 10 **F**3 11 13 15 29 30 32 34 39 40 41 44 45 49 50 55 57 59 64 68 70 72 74 75 76 77 79 81 82 84 85 87 91 93 107 108 110 111 114 115 119 126 130 131 132 145 146 147 **S** Memorial Healthcare System, Hollywood, FL
Primary Contact: Grisel Fernandez-Bravo, R.N., Administrator and Chief Executive Officer
CFO: Judy Sada, Chief Financial Officer
CMO: Stanley Marks, M.D., FACS, Chief Medical Officer
CIO: Forest Blanton, Senior VP and Chief Information Officer
CHR: Ray Kendrick, Chief Human Resources Officer
CNO: Denise Reynolds, Chief Nursing Officer
Web address: www.mhs.net
Control: Hospital district or authority, Government, nonfederal **Service:** General medical and surgical

Staffed Beds: 178 **Admissions:** 10167 **Census:** 100 **Outpatient Visits:** 139910 **Births:** 3854 **Total Expense ($000):** 159098 **Payroll Expense ($000):** 78754 **Personnel:** 835

MIRAMAR BEACH—Walton County

☒ **SACRED HEART HOSPITAL ON THE EMERALD COAST (100292)**, 7800 Highway 98 West, Zip 32550; tel. 850/278–3000, **A**1 10 **F**8 13 15 18 20 22 24 26 28 29 30 31 34 35 40 45 46 49 51 59 60 64 68 70 74 76 77 78 79 80 81 84 85 87 93 107 108 110 111 114 115 116 117 118 119 124 126 130 131 132 146 147 148 154 156 **S** Ascension Healthcare, Saint Louis, MO
Primary Contact: Roger L. Hall, President
CMO: Gary M. Pablo, M.D., Chief Medical Officer
Web address: www.sacredheartemerald.org
Control: Other not–for–profit (including NFP Corporation) **Service:** General medical and surgical

Staffed Beds: 76 **Admissions:** 5490 **Census:** 46 **Outpatient Visits:** 100652 **Births:** 1293 **Total Expense ($000):** 110099 **Payroll Expense ($000):** 30390 **Personnel:** 378

NAPLES—Collier County

LANDMARK HOSPITAL OF SOUTHWEST FLORIDA, 1285 Creekside Boulevard East, Zip 34108; tel. 239/529–1800, (Nonreporting) **A**10 22 **S** Landmark Hospitals, Cape Girardeau, MO
Primary Contact: James Whitacre, Chief Executive Officer
Web address: www.landmarkhospitals.com/our-hospitals/southwest-florida/
Control: Partnership, Investor–owned (for–profit) **Service:** Acute long–term care hospital

Staffed Beds: 50

☒ △ **NCH BAKER HOSPITAL (100018)**, 350 Seventh Street North, Zip 34102–5754, Mailing Address: P.O. Box 413029, Zip 34101–3029; tel. 239/624–4000, (Includes NCH NORTH NAPLES HOSPITAL, 11190 Health Park Blvd, Naples, Florida, Zip 34110–5729, Mailing Address: 11190 Health Park Boulevard, Zip 34110–5729, tel. 239/552–7000) **A**1 2 3 7 10 **F**11 12 13 14 15 17 18 19 20 22 24 26 28 29 30 31 32 34 35 37 40 41 42 44 45 46 47 48 49 50 53 56 57 59 64 68 70 72 74 75 76 77 78 79 81 82 84 85 86 87 88 89 90 91 92 93 95 96 98 100 102 103 107 108 110 111 114 115 116 117 119 126 131 135 145 146 147 148 149 154 156
Primary Contact: Paul C. Hiltz, FACHE, Chief Executive Officer
COO: Phillip C Dutcher, Chief Operating Officer
CFO: Mike Stephens, Chief Financial Officer
CMO: Doug Ardion, M.D., Chief Medical Officer
CHR: John McGirl, Chief Human Resources Officer
CNO: Michele Thoman, R.N., Chief Nursing Officer
Web address: www.nchmd.org
Control: Other not–for–profit (including NFP Corporation) **Service:** General medical and surgical

Staffed Beds: 713 **Admissions:** 29444 **Census:** 401 **Outpatient Visits:** 337566 **Births:** 3437 **Total Expense ($000):** 480498 **Payroll Expense ($000):** 191209 **Personnel:** 3135

☒ **PHYSICIANS REGIONAL - PINE RIDGE (100286)**, 6101 Pine Ridge Road, Zip 34119–3900; tel. 239/348–4000, (Includes PHYSICIANS REGIONAL, 8300 Collier Boulevard, Naples, Florida, Zip 34114; tel. 239/354–6000; C Scott Campbell, Market Chief Executive Officer) **A**1 10 19 **F**3 12 15 18 20 22 24 26 28 29 30 34 35 37 39 40 45 48 49 51 54 56 57 64 68 70 74 75 77 79 80 81 85 87 93 96 107 108 110 111 114 115 118 119 126 129 130 135 141 146 148 149 154 156 **S** Community Health Systems, Inc., Franklin, TN
Primary Contact: Scott Lowe, Market Chief Executive Officer
COO: Susan Takacs, Market Chief Operating Officer
CFO: Ken Warriner, Market Chief Financial Officer
CHR: Jill Gaffoli, Director Human Resources
Web address: www.physiciansregional.com
Control: Corporation, Investor–owned (for–profit) **Service:** General medical and surgical

Staffed Beds: 193 **Admissions:** 10585 **Census:** 117 **Outpatient Visits:** 266155 **Births:** 0 **Total Expense ($000):** 195855 **Payroll Expense ($000):** 66889 **Personnel:** 1273

☐ **THE WILLOUGH AT NAPLES (104063)**, 9001 Tamiami Trail East, Zip 34113–3304; tel. 239/775–4500, (Nonreporting) **A**1 10
Primary Contact: Kathleen Melo, Administrator
CFO: Steve Baldwin, Vice President Finance
Web address: www.thewilloughatnaples.com/
Control: Corporation, Investor–owned (for–profit) **Service:** Psychiatric

Staffed Beds: 80

NEW PORT RICHEY—Pasco County

☒ △ **MORTON PLANT NORTH BAY HOSPITAL (100063)**, 6600 Madison Street, Zip 34652–1900; tel. 727/842–8468, **A**1 7 10 **F**3 11 18 20 22 28 29 30 31 34 35 40 44 49 50 57 58 59 63 64 68 70 74 75 78 79 81 84 85 86 87 90 93 94 96 98 99 100 102 107 108 110 111 114 115 118 119 129 130 131 132 135 143 146 147 149 154 156 **S** Morton Plant Mease Health Care, Clearwater, FL
Primary Contact: Sarah Naumowich, President
CFO: Carl Tremonti, Chief Financial Officer
CMO: Jeff Jensen, D.O., Vice President, Medical Affairs
CIO: Timothy Thompson, Senior Vice President and Chief Information Officer
CHR: Kyle J Barr, Senior Vice President, Chief Team Resources Officer
CNO: Thomas Doria, Vice President and Patient Services - West
Web address: www.mpmhealth.com
Control: Other not–for–profit (including NFP Corporation) **Service:** General medical and surgical

Staffed Beds: 222 **Admissions:** 12924 **Census:** 168 **Outpatient Visits:** 47868 **Births:** 0 **Total Expense ($000):** 148407 **Payroll Expense ($000):** 58628 **Personnel:** 920

Many Facility Codes have changed. Please refer to the AHA Guide Code Chart. © 2019 AHA Guide

FL

NEW SMYRNA BEACH—Volusia County

⊞ **ADVENTHEALTH NEW SMYRNA BEACH (100014)**, 401 Palmetto Street, Zip 32168–7399; tel. 386/424–5000, (Nonreporting) **A**1 10 **S** AdventHealth, Altamonte Springs, FL
Primary Contact: David Ottati, Regional Chief Executive Officer
COO: Steven W Harrell, FACHE, Chief Operating Officer
CFO: Al W Allred, Chief Financial Officer
CMO: Dennis Hernandez, Chief Medical Officer
CIO: Calvin Patrick II Director Information Services
CHR: Nancy K Evolga, Director Human Resources
CNO: Linda G Breum, R.N., MSN, Chief Nursing Officer
Web address: www.https://www.floridahospital.com/new-smyrna
Control: Hospital district or authority, Government, nonfederal **Service:** General medical and surgical

Staffed Beds: 95

NICEVILLE—Okaloosa County

⊞ **TWIN CITIES HOSPITAL (100054)**, 2190 Highway 85 North, Zip 32578–1045; tel. 850/678–4131, (Nonreporting) **A**1 10 **S** HCA Healthcare, Nashville, TN
Primary Contact: David Whalen, Chief Executive Officer
CFO: Mark Day, Chief Financial Officer
CHR: Cyndi Ronca, Director Human Resources
Web address: www.tchealthcare.com
Control: Corporation, Investor–owned (for–profit) **Service:** General medical and surgical

Staffed Beds: 65

NORTH MIAMI—Miami-Dade County

☐ △ **ST. CATHERINE'S REHABILITATION HOSPITAL (103026)**, 1050 NE 125th Street, Zip 33161–5881; tel. 305/357–1735, (Nonreporting) **A**1 7 10 **S** Catholic Health Services, Lauderdale Lakes, FL
Primary Contact: Jaime Gonzalez, Administrator
COO: Jim Ball, Chief Operating Officer
CFO: Mary Jo Frick, Director Finance
CMO: Miriam Feliz, M.D., Medical Director
Web address: www.catholichealthservices.org
Control: Church operated **Service:** Rehabilitation

Staffed Beds: 60

NORTH MIAMI BEACH—Miami-Dade County

JACKSON NORTH MEDICAL CENTER See Jackson Health System, Miami

OCALA—Marion County

⊞ **ADVENTHEALTH OCALA (100062)**, 1500 SW 1st Avenue, Zip 34471–6504, Mailing Address: P.O. Box 6000, Zip 34478–6000; tel. 352/351–7200, (Nonreporting) **A**1 3 5 10 19 **S** AdventHealth, Altamonte Springs, FL
Primary Contact: Joe Johnson, FACHE, Chief Executive Officer
COO: Philoron A. Wright, FACHE, II Chief Operating Officer
CFO: Eric LaChance, Chief Financial Officer
CMO: Lon McPherson, M.D., Senior Vice President Medical Affairs and Chief Quality Officer
CIO: Carl Candullo, Chief Information Officer
CNO: Pamela W Michell, R.N., Vice President, Chief Nursing Officer
Web address: www.munroeregional.com
Control: Church operated, Nongovernment, not–for–profit **Service:** General medical and surgical

Staffed Beds: 300

⊞ **ENCOMPASS HEALTH REHABILITATION HOSPITAL OF OCALA (103043)**, 2275 SW 22nd Lane, Zip 34471–7710; tel. 352/282–4000, (Nonreporting) **A**1 10 **S** Encompass Health Corporation, Birmingham, AL
Primary Contact: Karthik Muthu, Chief Executive Officer
CFO: Sammy King, Controller
CMO: Amy Clunn, M.D., Medical Director
CHR: Tracy Sapp, Director Human Resources
CNO: Wendy Milam, Chief Nursing Officer
Web address: www.healthsouthocala.com
Control: Corporation, Investor–owned (for–profit) **Service:** Rehabilitation

Staffed Beds: 60

⊞ **KINDRED HOSPITAL OCALA (102019)**, 1500 SW 1st Avenue, Zip 34471–6504; tel. 352/369–0513, (Nonreporting) **A**1 10 **S** Kindred Healthcare, Louisville, KY
Primary Contact: Merlene Bhoorasingh, Administrator
CFO: Dean Cocchi, Chief Financial Officer
Web address: www.kindredocala.com/
Control: Corporation, Investor–owned (for–profit) **Service:** Acute long–term care hospital

Staffed Beds: 31

⊞ **OCALA REGIONAL MEDICAL CENTER (100212)**, 1431 SW First Avenue, Zip 34471–6500, Mailing Address: P.O. Box 2200, Zip 34478–2200; tel. 352/401–1000, (Includes WEST MARION COMMUNITY HOSPITAL, 4600 SW 46th Court, Ocala, Florida, Zip 34474; tel. 352/291–3000), (Nonreporting) **A**1 2 3 5 10 13 **S** HCA Healthcare, Nashville, TN
Primary Contact: Chad Christianson, Chief Executive Officer
CMO: Art Osberg, M.D., Chief Medical Officer
CIO: Brandon Holbert, Director, Information Services
CHR: Wayne Nielsen, Director Human Resources
Web address: www.ocalaregional.com
Control: Corporation, Investor–owned (for–profit) **Service:** General medical and surgical

Staffed Beds: 270

THE CENTERS (104068), 5664 SW 60th Avenue, Zip 34474–5677; tel. 352/291–5500, **A**3
Primary Contact: Donald J. Baracskay II, M.D., Chief Executive Officer
Web address: www.thecenters.us
Control: Other not–for–profit (including NFP Corporation) **Service:** Psychiatric

Staffed Beds: 61

THE VINES (104071), 3130 SW 27th Avenue, Zip 34471–4306; tel. 352/671–3130, **A**10 **F**4 5 38 40 98 100 105 132 135 147 151 152 153 154 **S** Universal Health Services, Inc., King of Prussia, PA
Primary Contact: Stephen Quintyne, Chief Executive Officer
Web address: www.thevineshospital.com
Control: Corporation, Investor–owned (for–profit) **Service:** Psychiatric

Staffed Beds: 98 **Admissions:** 3772 **Census:** 58 **Outpatient Visits:** 14368 **Births:** 0 **Total Expense ($000):** 18216 **Payroll Expense ($000):** 7306 **Personnel:** 151

OCOEE—Orange County

⊞ **HEALTH CENTRAL HOSPITAL (100030)**, 10000 West Colonial Drive, Zip 34761–3499; tel. 407/296–1000, (Total facility includes 228 beds in nursing home–type unit) **A**1 3 10 **F**3 6 8 11 12 15 17 18 20 22 26 28 29 30 34 35 37 40 42 45 46 48 49 50 51 57 59 60 61 66 68 74 76 79 80 81 82 85 86 87 93 107 108 110 111 115 118 119 126 128 130 131 132 135 146 147 148 149 150 154 156 157 **S** Orlando Health, Orlando, FL
Primary Contact: Mark A. Marsh, President
COO: Nick Smith, Chief Operating Officer
CFO: Michael E Mueller, Chief Financial Officer
CMO: James Barton Rodier, M.D., Chief Quality Officer
CIO: John T Sills, Chief Information Officer
CHR: Nancy Dinon, Vice President Human Resources
CNO: Christina Marie McGuirk, R.N., Chief Nursing Officer
Web address: www.healthcentral.org
Control: Other not–for–profit (including NFP Corporation) **Service:** General medical and surgical

Staffed Beds: 439 **Admissions:** 12572 **Census:** 355 **Outpatient Visits:** 117431 **Births:** 302 **Total Expense ($000):** 209723 **Payroll Expense ($000):** 89072 **Personnel:** 1442

OKEECHOBEE—Okeechobee County

⊞ **RAULERSON HOSPITAL (100252)**, 1796 Highway 441 North, Zip 34972–1918, Mailing Address: P.O. Box 1307, Zip 34973–1307; tel. 863/763–2151, (Nonreporting) **A**1 10 20 **S** HCA Healthcare, Nashville, TN
Primary Contact: Brian Melear, Chief Executive Officer
CFO: Terry L Brown, Chief Financial Officer
CMO: Arif Shakoor, Chief of Staff
CIO: Tim Hearing, Associate Information Technology Director
CHR: Cynthia Jackson, Vice President Human Resources
CNO: Adam Kless, Chief Nursing Officer
Web address: www.raulersonhospital.com
Control: Corporation, Investor–owned (for–profit) **Service:** General medical and surgical

Staffed Beds: 100

FL

Hospital, Medicare Provider Number, Address, Telephone, Approval, Facility, and Physician Codes, Health Care System

★ American Hospital Association (AHA) membership
☐ The Joint Commission accreditation
○ Healthcare Facilities Accreditation Program
◇ DNV Healthcare Inc. accreditation
⇧ Center for Improvement in Healthcare Quality Accreditation
△ Commission on Accreditation of Rehabilitation Facilities (CARF) accreditation

ORANGE CITY—Volusia County

ADVENTHEALTH FISH MEMORIAL (100072), 1055 Saxon Boulevard, Zip 32763–8468; tel. 386/917–5000, (Nonreporting) **A**1 10 **S** AdventHealth, Altamonte Springs, FL
Primary Contact: Robert Deininger, Chief Executive Officer
COO: Danielle Johnson, Chief Operating Officer
CFO: Eric Osterly, Chief Financial Officer
CMO: Stephen Knych, M.D., Chief Medical Officer
CHR: Jannina Garcia, Director of Human Resources
CNO: Jennifer Shull, R.N., Chief Nursing Officer
Web address: www.fhfishmemorial.org
Control: Church operated, Nongovernment, not–for–profit **Service:** General medical and surgical

Staffed Beds: 175

ORANGE PARK—Clay County

ORANGE PARK MEDICAL CENTER (100226), 2001 Kingsley Avenue, Zip 32073–5156; tel. 904/639–8500, **A**1 2 3 10 **F**3 13 15 17 18 20 22 24 26 29 30 31 32 34 35 37 38 40 41 42 43 45 46 47 48 49 50 56 57 58 60 61 67 68 70 72 73 74 75 76 77 78 79 80 81 82 84 85 88 89 90 93 98 100 102 104 105 107 108 110 111 114 115 119 126 130 132 135 146 147 153 154 **S** HCA Healthcare, Nashville, TN
Primary Contact: Chad Patrick, President and Chief Executive Officer
CFO: Chris Glenn, Chief Financial Officer
CMO: Bradley Shumaker, Chief Medical Officer
CHR: Brad Coburn, Vice President, Human Resources
CNO: Kathy Hester, Chief Nursing Officer
Web address: www.opmedical.com
Control: Corporation, Investor–owned (for–profit) **Service:** General medical and surgical

Staffed Beds: 320 **Admissions:** 18925 **Census:** 250 **Outpatient Visits:** 136930 **Births:** 1902 **Total Expense ($000):** 369341 **Payroll Expense ($000):** 86582 **Personnel:** 1099

ORLANDO—Orange County

ADVENTHEALTH ORLANDO (100007), 601 East Rollins Street, Zip 32803–1248; tel. 407/303–6611, (Includes ADVENTHEALTH ALTAMONTE SPRINGS, 601 East Altamonte Drive, Altamonte Springs, Florida, Zip 32701; tel. 407/830–4321; David Ottati, Regional Chief Executive Officer; ADVENTHEALTH APOPKA, 201 North Park Avenue, Apopka, Florida, Zip 32703; tel. 407/889–1000; Verbelee Neilsen Swanson, Administrator; ADVENTHEALTH CELEBRATION, 400 Celebration Place, Celebration, Florida, Zip 34747; tel. 407/303–4000; Douglas Harcombe, Chief Executive Officer; ADVENTHEALTH EAST ORLANDO, 7727 Lake Underhill Road, Orlando, Florida, Zip 32822; tel. 407/277–8110; ADVENTHEALTH FOR CHILDREN, 601 East Rollins Street, Orlando, Florida, Zip 32803–1248; tel. 407/303–9732; Lars D Houmann, President; ADVENTHEALTH KISSIMMEE, 2269 Santa Lucia St, Kissimmee, Florida, Zip 34743, Mailing Address: 2450 North Orange Blossom Trai, Zip 34741, tel. 407/846–4343; William Haupt, Administrator; ADVENTHEALTH WINTER PARK, 200 North Lakemont Avenue, Winter Park, Florida, Zip 32792–3273; tel. 407/646–7000; Douglas Harcombe, Administrator) **A**2 3 5 7 8 10 21 **F**3 6 7 9 11 12 13 15 17 18 19 20 21 22 23 24 25 26 27 28 29 30 31 32 34 35 36 37 38 39 40 41 42 44 45 46 47 48 49 50 51 53 54 56 57 58 59 60 61 62 64 65 66 68 70 71 72 73 74 75 76 77 78 79 80 81 82 83 84 85 86 87 88 89 90 92 93 94 96 97 98 100 101 102 103 107 108 109 110 111 112 113 114 115 116 117 118 119 120 121 123 124 126 129 130 131 132 134 135 136 137 138 139 140 141 142 145 146 147 148 149 154 155 156 157 **S** AdventHealth, Altamonte Springs, FL
Primary Contact: Daryl Tol, President and Chief Executive Officer
COO: Brian Paradis, Chief Operating Officer
CFO: Eddie Soler, Chief Financial Officer
CMO: David Moorhead, M.D., Chief Medical Officer
CHR: Sheryl Dodds, Chief Clinical Officer
Web address: www.floridahospital.com/orlando
Control: Other not–for–profit (including NFP Corporation) **Service:** General medical and surgical

Staffed Beds: 2875 **Admissions:** 145390 **Census:** 1842 **Outpatient Visits:** 1217572 **Births:** 12792 **Total Expense ($000):** 3316895 **Payroll Expense ($000):** 1131415 **Personnel:** 19265

ARNOLD PALMER HOSPITAL FOR CHILDREN See Orlando Regional Medical Center, Orlando

ASPIRE HEALTH PARTNERS (104067), 1800 Mercy Drive, Zip 32808–5646; tel. 407/875–3700, **A**10 **F**29 35 38 98 100 102 104 130 132 134 153 154
Primary Contact: Jerry Kassab, President and Chief Executive Officer
Web address: www.lakesidecares.org
Control: Other not–for–profit (including NFP Corporation) **Service:** Psychiatric

Staffed Beds: 66 **Admissions:** 2812 **Census:** 54 **Outpatient Visits:** 0 **Births:** 0 **Total Expense ($000):** 6747 **Payroll Expense ($000):** 3468 **Personnel:** 67

CENTRAL FLORIDA BEHAVIORAL HOSPITAL (104072), 6601 Central Florida Parkway, Zip 32821–8064; tel. 407/370–0111, (Nonreporting) **A**1 10 **S** Universal Health Services, Inc., King of Prussia, PA
Primary Contact: Vickie Lewis, Chief Executive Officer
CFO: Marsha Burick, Chief Financial Officer
Web address: www.centralfloridabehavioral.com
Control: Other not–for–profit (including NFP Corporation) **Service:** Psychiatric

Staffed Beds: 126

NEMOURS CHILDREN'S HOSPITAL (103304), 13535 Nemours Parkway, Zip 32827–7402; tel. 407/567–4000, **A**1 3 10 **F**3 17 19 21 23 25 27 29 30 31 32 34 35 40 41 45 46 48 50 53 55 57 58 59 60 64 65 68 72 73 74 75 77 78 79 80 81 82 84 85 86 87 88 90 91 92 93 94 96 97 100 107 108 111 115 119 120 121 130 131 146 149 154 156 **S** Nemours, Jacksonville, FL
Primary Contact: Dana Bledsoe, MS, R.N., President
COO: Randall W Hartley, Chief Operating Officer
CFO: Rodney McKendree, Senior Vice President and Chief Financial Officer
CMO: Andre Hebra, M.D., Chief Medical Officer
CIO: Bernard Rice, Chief Information Officer
CHR: Theresa M Young, Senior Vice President Human Resources
CNO: Helen M Case, Chief Nursing Officer
Web address: www.nemours.org
Control: Other not–for–profit (including NFP Corporation) **Service:** Children's general medical and surgical

Staffed Beds: 92 **Admissions:** 3826 **Census:** 63 **Outpatient Visits:** 86595 **Births:** 0 **Total Expense ($000):** 207226 **Payroll Expense ($000):** 69447 **Personnel:** 920

ORLANDO REGIONAL MEDICAL CENTER (100006), 52 West Underwood Street, Zip 32806; tel. 407/841–5111, (Includes ARNOLD PALMER HOSPITAL FOR CHILDREN, 92 West Miller Street, Orlando, Florida, Zip 32806; tel. 407/649–6960; Cary D'Ortona, President; ORLANDO HEALTH SOUTH SEMINOLE HOSPITAL, 555 West State Road 434, Longwood, Florida, Zip 32750–4999; tel. 407/767–1200; Karen Frenier, President; WINNIE PALMER HOSPITAL FOR WOMEN AND BABIES, 83 West Miller Street, Orlando, Florida, Zip 32806; tel. 321/843–9792; Kelly Nierstedt, President) **A**2 3 5 7 10 **F**3 4 7 8 11 12 13 15 16 17 18 19 20 21 22 23 24 25 26 27 28 29 30 31 34 35 36 37 40 41 42 43 44 45 46 47 48 49 50 51 54 55 57 58 59 60 61 62 64 68 70 71 72 73 74 75 76 77 78 79 80 81 82 84 85 86 87 88 89 90 91 92 93 94 96 97 98 99 100 101 102 104 107 108 110 111 114 115 116 117 118 119 120 121 122 123 124 126 129 130 131 132 134 135 143 146 147 148 149 154 155 156 157 **S** Orlando Health, Orlando, FL
Primary Contact: Mark A. Jones, President
COO: Carlos Carrasco, Chief Operating Officer
CFO: Steve Miglietta, Chief Financial Officer
CMO: Charles Heard, M.D., Chief of Staff
CIO: Rick Schooler, Vice President and Chief Information Officer
CHR: Greg Thompson, Corporate Director, Human Resources
CNO: Jayne Willis, Vice President, System Chief Nurse Executive
Web address: www.orlandohealth.com/facilities/orlando-regional-medical-center
Control: Other not–for–profit (including NFP Corporation) **Service:** General medical and surgical

Staffed Beds: 1331 **Admissions:** 85014 **Census:** 1133 **Outpatient Visits:** 733670 **Births:** 14334 **Total Expense ($000):** 2024960 **Payroll Expense ($000):** 759609 **Personnel:** 11714

ORLANDO VA MEDICAL CENTER, 13800 Veterans Way, Zip 32827–7403; tel. 407/631–1000, (Nonreporting) **A**1 3 5 8 **S** Department of Veterans Affairs, Washington, DC
Primary Contact: Timothy Liezert, Medical Center Director
Web address: www.orlando.va.gov
Control: Veterans Affairs, Government, federal **Service:** General medical and surgical

Staffed Beds: 134

SELECT SPECIALTY HOSPITAL-ORLANDO (102003), 2250 Bedford Road, Zip 32803–1443; tel. 407/303–7869, (Includes SELECT SPECIALTY HOSPITAL-ORLANDO SOUTH, 5579 South Orange Avenue, Orlando, Florida, Zip 32809–3493; tel. 407/241–4800), (Nonreporting) **A**10 **S** Select Medical Corporation, Mechanicsburg, PA
Primary Contact: Theodore Mena, Chief Executive Officer
Web address: www.selectspecialtyhospitals.com/company/locations/orlando.aspx
Control: Corporation, Investor–owned (for–profit) **Service:** Acute long–term care hospital

Staffed Beds: 75

WINNIE PALMER HOSPITAL FOR WOMEN AND BABIES See Orlando Regional Medical Center, Orlando

FL

Many Facility Codes have changed. Please refer to the AHA Guide Code Chart. © 2019 AHA Guide

OVIEDO—Seminole County

OVIEDO MEDICAL CENTER (100329), 8300 Red Bug Lake Road, Zip 32765–6801; tel. 407/890–2273, (Nonreporting) **A**1 10 **S** HCA Healthcare, Nashville, TN
Primary Contact: Kenneth C. Donahey, Chief Executive Officer
Web address: www.oviedomedicalcenter.com
Control: Other not–for–profit (including NFP Corporation) **Service**: General medical and surgical

Staffed Beds: 64

OXFORD—Sumter County

★ **PROMISE HOSPITAL OF FLORIDA AT THE VILLAGES (102028)**, 5050 County Road 472, Zip 34484; tel. 352/689–6400, (Nonreporting) **A**10 **S** Select Medical Corporation, Mechanicsburg, PA
Primary Contact: Hoyt Ross, Chief Executive Officer
CNO: Janice M McCoy, MS, R.N., Chief Clinical Officer
Web address: www.promise-villages.com
Control: Corporation, Investor–owned (for–profit) **Service**: Acute long–term care hospital

Staffed Beds: 40

PALATKA—Putnam County

PUTNAM COMMUNITY MEDICAL CENTER (100232), 611 Zeagler Drive, Zip 32177–3810; tel. 386/328–5711, (Nonreporting) **A**1 10 **S** HCA Healthcare, Nashville, TN
Primary Contact: Mark J. Dooley, Chief Executive Officer
CFO: Stewart Whitmore, Chief Financial Officer
CIO: Yvette A Jones, Health Information Management Director
CHR: John Schneider, Human Resources Director
CNO: Kari Bolin, Chief Nursing Officer
Web address: www.pcmcfl.com
Control: Corporation, Investor–owned (for–profit) **Service**: General medical and surgical

Staffed Beds: 99

PALM BAY—Brevard County

HEALTH FIRST PALM BAY HOSPITAL (100316), 1425 Malabar Road NE, Zip 32907–2506; tel. 321/434–8000, **A**1 10 **F**3 11 12 15 18 20 22 29 30 34 37 39 40 41 45 47 49 50 59 60 64 68 70 74 75 77 79 80 81 85 86 87 93 102 107 108 110 111 114 115 118 119 126 130 132 141 146 148 149 153 154 **S** Health First, Inc., Rockledge, FL
Primary Contact: Brett A. Esrock, FACHE, President
COO: Deborah Angerami, Chief Operating Officer, Health First Community Hospitals
CFO: Joseph G Felkner, Executive Vice President and Chief Financial Officer
CMO: Lee Scheinbart, M.D., Vice President Medical Affairs, Health First Community Hospitals
CIO: Alex Popowycz, Senior Vice President and Chief Information Officer
CHR: Paula Just, Chief Human Resources Officer
CNO: Connie Bradley, R.N., MSN, FACHE, Chief Nursing Officer
Web address: www.health-first.org/hospitals_services/pbch/index.cfm
Control: Other not–for–profit (including NFP Corporation) **Service**: General medical and surgical

Staffed Beds: 120 Admissions: 6962 Census: 82 Outpatient Visits: 89297 Births: 0 Total Expense ($000): 105984 Payroll Expense ($000): 44588 Personnel: 543

PALM BEACH GARDENS—Palm Beach County

PALM BEACH GARDENS MEDICAL CENTER (100176), 3360 Burns Road, Zip 33410–4323; tel. 561/622–1411, **A**1 5 10 **F**3 11 15 17 18 20 22 24 26 28 29 34 35 40 45 49 50 57 58 59 64 67 70 74 77 79 81 85 87 92 93 94 96 107 108 110 111 115 118 119 126 130 131 132 135 146 148 149 **S** TENET Healthcare Corporation, Dallas, TX
Primary Contact: Teresa C. Urquhart, Chief Executive Officer
CFO: Judi Stimson, Chief Financial Officer
CIO: James Vega, Director Information Systems
CHR: Kevin Caracciolo, Chief Human Resources Officer
CNO: Patricia Rosenberg, R.N., MSN, Chief Nursing Officer
Web address: www.pbgmc.com
Control: Corporation, Investor–owned (for–profit) **Service**: General medical and surgical

Staffed Beds: 202 Admissions: 10272 Census: 130 Outpatient Visits: 59064 Births: 0 Total Expense ($000): 191322 Payroll Expense ($000): 55488 Personnel: 636

PALM COAST—Flagler County

ADVENTHEALTH PALM COAST (100118), 60 Memorial Medical Parkway, Zip 32164–5980; tel. 386/586–2000, (Nonreporting) **A**1 2 10 **S** AdventHealth, Altamonte Springs, FL
Primary Contact: Ronald Jimenez, M.D., Chief Executive Officer
COO: JoAnne King, Chief Operating Officer
CFO: Cory Domayer, Chief Financial Officer
CMO: Ron Thomas, M.D., Chief Medical Officer
CHR: Joshua I Champion, Director
CNO: Robert Davis, Chief Nursing Officer
Web address: www.floridahospitalflagler.com/
Control: Church operated, Nongovernment, not–for–profit **Service**: General medical and surgical

Staffed Beds: 99

PANAMA CITY—Bay County

BAY MEDICAL SACRED HEART (100026), 615 North Bonita Avenue, Zip 32401–3600, Mailing Address: P.O. Box 59515, Zip 32412–0515; tel. 850/769–1511, **A**1 2 10 **F**30 35 40 42 43 64 74 77 79 81 93 107 111 115 119 126 **S** Ascension Healthcare, Saint Louis, MO
Primary Contact: Heath Evans, President
CHR: Donna Baird, Vice President Corporate Services
CNO: Jan Thornton, Chief Nursing Officer
Web address: www.baymedical.org
Control: Corporation, Investor–owned (for–profit) **Service**: General medical and surgical

Staffed Beds: 15 Admissions: 11149 Census: 160 Outpatient Visits: 127339 Births: 277 Total Expense ($000): 263518 Payroll Expense ($000): 96578 Personnel: 1207

EMERALD COAST BEHAVIORAL HOSPITAL (104073), 1940 Harrison Avenue, Zip 32405–4542; tel. 850/763–0017, (Nonreporting) **A**1 10 **S** Universal Health Services, Inc., King of Prussia, PA
Primary Contact: Tim Bedford, Chief Executive Officer
CFO: Michael J Zenone, Chief Financial Officer
CMO: Roy Deal, Chief Medical Officer
CNO: Michael B Barbour, Chief Nursing Officer
Web address: www.emeraldcoastbehavioral.com
Control: Corporation, Investor–owned (for–profit) **Service**: Psychiatric

Staffed Beds: 86

ENCOMPASS HEALTH REHABILITATION HOSPITAL OF PANAMA CITY (103040), 1847 Florida Avenue, Zip 32405–4640; tel. 850/914–8600, (Data for 327 days) **A**1 10 **F**3 28 29 34 57 59 68 75 77 85 86 87 90 95 96 130 131 132 148 156 **S** Encompass Health Corporation, Birmingham, AL
Primary Contact: Tony N. Bennett, Chief Executive Officer
CFO: Bradley Tilghman, Controller
CMO: Michael Hennigan, M.D., Medical Director
CHR: Traci Powell, Director Human Resources
CNO: Sharon Hamilton, Chief Nursing Officer
Web address: www.healthsouthpanamacity.com
Control: Corporation, Investor–owned (for–profit) **Service**: Rehabilitation

Staffed Beds: 75 Admissions: 1392 Census: 56 Outpatient Visits: 0 Births: 0 Total Expense ($000): 23278 Payroll Expense ($000): 11806 Personnel: 204

GULF COAST REGIONAL MEDICAL CENTER (100242), 449 West 23rd Street, Zip 32405–4593, Mailing Address: P.O. Box 15309, Zip 32406–5309; tel. 850/769–8341, (Nonreporting) **A**1 2 10 **S** HCA Healthcare, Nashville, TN
Primary Contact: Brad Griffin, Chief Executive Officer
COO: Holly Jackson, Chief Operating Officer
CFO: Laurie Haynes, Chief Financial Officer
CHR: Tracy McGlon, Director Human Resources
CNO: Brian Pinelle, R.N., Chief Nursing Officer
Web address: www.egulfcoastmedical.com
Control: Corporation, Investor–owned (for–profit) **Service**: General medical and surgical

Staffed Beds: 176

FL

Hospital, Medicare Provider Number, Address, Telephone, Approval, Facility, and Physician Codes, Health Care System

★ American Hospital Association (AHA) membership   ○ Healthcare Facilities Accreditation Program   ⇑ Center for Improvement in Healthcare Quality Accreditation
□ The Joint Commission accreditation   ◇ DNV Healthcare Inc. accreditation   △ Commission on Accreditation of Rehabilitation Facilities (CARF) accreditation

✠ **SELECT SPECIALTY HOSPITAL-PANAMA CITY (102017)**, 615 North Bonita Avenue, 3rd Floor, Zip 32401–3623; tel. 850/767–3180, (Nonreporting) **A**1 10 **S** Select Medical Corporation, Mechanicsburg, PA
Primary Contact: Randal S. Hamilton, Chief Executive Officer
CMO: Amir Manzoor, M.D., Medical Director
Web address: www.selectspecialtyhospitals.com/company/locations/panamacity.aspx
Control: Corporation, Investor–owned (for–profit) **Service:** Acute long–term care hospital

Staffed Beds: 30

PEMBROKE PINES—Broward County

✠ **MEMORIAL HOSPITAL PEMBROKE (100230)**, 7800 Sheridan Street, Zip 33024–2536; tel. 954/883–8482, **A**1 5 10 **F**3 12 29 30 34 40 44 45 46 47 48 49 50 51 59 64 65 66 70 74 75 77 79 81 82 84 85 86 87 107 108 111 115 119 126 130 132 141 144 146 148 149 154 **S** Memorial Healthcare System, Hollywood, FL
Primary Contact: Mark Doyle, Administrator and Chief Executive Officer
CFO: Joseph Stuczynski, Assistant Administrator Finance and Support
CMO: Stanley Marks, M.D., FACS, Chief Medical Officer
CIO: Forest Blanton, Chief Information Officer
CNO: Judy Frum, R.N., Chief Nursing Officer
Web address: www.memorialpembroke.com/
Control: Hospital district or authority, Government, nonfederal **Service:** General medical and surgical

Staffed Beds: 186 **Admissions:** 7928 **Census:** 102 **Outpatient Visits:** 101470 **Births:** 0 **Total Expense ($000):** 147653 **Payroll Expense ($000):** 62309

✠ **MEMORIAL HOSPITAL WEST (100281)**, 703 North Flamingo Road, Zip 33028–1014; tel. 954/436–5000, **A**1 2 3 5 10 **F**3 12 13 15 17 18 22 26 28 29 30 31 34 35 36 40 41 45 46 47 49 53 55 56 57 58 60 68 70 72 74 75 76 78 79 81 82 84 85 87 91 93 107 108 110 111 114 115 119 120 121 123 124 126 130 131 132 136 145 146 147 **S** Memorial Healthcare System, Hollywood, FL
Primary Contact: Leah A. Carpenter, Administrator and Chief Executive Officer
CFO: Walter Bussell, Chief Financial Officer
CMO: Eric Freling, M.D., Director Medical Staff Affairs
CIO: Forest Blanton, Chief Information Officer
CHR: Maria Naranjo, Director Human Resources
Web address: www.mhs.net
Control: Hospital district or authority, Government, nonfederal **Service:** General medical and surgical

Staffed Beds: 382 **Admissions:** 21630 **Census:** 299 **Outpatient Visits:** 287538 **Births:** 3735 **Total Expense ($000):** 442013 **Payroll Expense ($000):** 174382 **Personnel:** 2176

PENSACOLA—Escambia County

★ ⇑ **BAPTIST HOSPITAL (100093)**, 1000 West Moreno Street, Zip 32501–2316, Mailing Address: P.O. Box 17500, Zip 32522–7500; tel. 850/434–4011, **A**2 3 10 21 **F**3 8 11 12 13 15 17 18 20 22 24 26 28 29 30 31 34 35 40 43 45 46 47 48 49 50 51 54 55 56 57 58 59 60 61 63 64 70 71 74 75 76 77 78 79 80 81 82 84 85 86 87 91 92 93 97 98 99 100 101 102 103 104 107 108 110 111 114 115 116 117 118 119 120 121 123 126 130 131 132 146 147 148 **S** Baptist Health Care Corporation, Pensacola, FL
Primary Contact: Scott Raynes, President
CFO: Sharon Nobles, Interim Chief Financial Officer
CMO: Mike Oleksyk, M.D., Vice President and Chief Medical Officer
CIO: Steven Sarros, Vice President and Chief Information Officer
CHR: Darlene Stone, Vice President Human Resources
CNO: Cynde Gamache, R.N., Vice President and Chief Nursing Officer
Web address: www.ebaptisthealthcare.org
Control: Other not–for–profit (including NFP Corporation) **Service:** General medical and surgical

Staffed Beds: 340 **Admissions:** 17289 **Census:** 235 **Outpatient Visits:** 279077 **Births:** 868 **Total Expense ($000):** 324913 **Payroll Expense ($000):** 104265 **Personnel:** 1781

✠ **NAVAL HOSPITAL PENSACOLA**, 6000 West Highway 98, Zip 32512–0003; tel. 850/505–6601, (Nonreporting) **A**1 3 5 **S** Bureau of Medicine and Surgery, Department of the Navy, Falls Church, VA
Primary Contact: Commander Devin Morrison, Director Administration
COO: Commander Devin Morrison, Director for Administration
CMO: Commander Carolyn Rice, M.D., Director Medical Services
CIO: Lieutenant Commander William Berg, Chief Information Officer
CHR: Commander Devin Morrison, Director for Administration
CNO: Captain Amy Tarbay, Director Nursing Services
Web address: www.med.navy.mil/sites/pcola/Pages/default.aspx
Control: Department of Defense, Government, federal **Service:** General medical and surgical

Staffed Beds: 28

✠ **SACRED HEART HOSPITAL PENSACOLA (100025)**, 5151 North Ninth Avenue, Zip 32504–8795, Mailing Address: P.O. Box 2700, Zip 32513–2700; tel. 850/416–7000, **A**1 2 3 5 10 **F**3 8 11 12 13 15 17 18 19 20 21 22 24 26 28 29 30 31 34 35 40 41 43 44 45 46 47 48 49 50 54 55 57 58 59 60 61 65 68 70 72 73 74 75 76 77 78 79 81 82 84 85 87 88 89 92 93 96 97 107 108 110 111 112 114 116 117 119 120 124 126 130 131 132 135 138 146 147 148 149 154 156 **S** Ascension Healthcare, Saint Louis, MO
Primary Contact: Henry Stovall, President
COO: Terri Smith, Chief Operating Officer
CFO: C Susan Cornejo, Chief Financial Officer
CMO: Peter Jennings, M.D., Chief Medical Officer
CIO: Donna Roach, Chief Information Officer
CHR: Michelle Adamolekun, Vice President Human Resource Market Lead Florida/Alabama Ministry Market
Web address: www.https://healthcare.ascension.org/Locations/Florida/FLPEN/Pensacola-Sacred-Heart-Hospital-Pensacola
Control: Other not–for–profit (including NFP Corporation) **Service:** General medical and surgical

Staffed Beds: 440 **Admissions:** 25060 **Census:** 337 **Outpatient Visits:** 363573 **Births:** 3902 **Total Expense ($000):** 478346 **Payroll Expense ($000):** 127723 **Personnel:** 1703

✠ **SELECT SPECIALTY HOSPITAL-PENSACOLA (102024)**, 7000 Cobble Creek Drive, Zip 32504–8638; tel. 850/473–4800, (Nonreporting) **A**1 10 **S** Select Medical Corporation, Mechanicsburg, PA
Primary Contact: Adam Principe, Chief Executive Officer
CMO: John Bray, M.D., Medical Director
Web address: www.https://pensacola.selectspecialtyhospitals.com/
Control: Corporation, Investor–owned (for–profit) **Service:** Acute long–term care hospital

Staffed Beds: 75

✠ △ **WEST FLORIDA HOSPITAL (100231)**, 8383 North Davis Highway, Zip 32514–6088; tel. 850/494–4000, (Includes THE PAVILION, 8383 North Davis Highway, Pensacola, Florida, Zip 32523, Mailing Address: P O Box 18900, Zip 32523, tel. 904/494–5000; WEST FLORIDA REHABILITATION INSTITUTE, 8383 North Davis Highway, Pensacola, Florida, Zip 32514, Mailing Address: P O Box 18900, Zip 32523, tel. 850/494–6000), (Nonreporting) **A**1 2 7 10 **S** HCA Healthcare, Nashville, TN
Primary Contact: Gay Nord, Chief Executive Officer
COO: Jessica O'Neal, Chief Operating Officer
CFO: Randy Butler, Chief Financial Officer
CMO: Terry Stallings, M.D., Chief Medical Officer
CIO: Jeff Amerson, Director Information System
CHR: Wanda Salley, Vice President Human Resources
CNO: Karen White-Trevino, Chief Nursing Officer
Web address: www.westfloridahospital.com
Control: Corporation, Investor–owned (for–profit) **Service:** General medical and surgical

Staffed Beds: 339

WEST FLORIDA REHABILITATION INSTITUTE See West Florida Hospital, Pensacola

PERRY—Taylor County

DOCTOR'S MEMORIAL HOSPITAL (100106), 333 North Byron Butler Parkway, Zip 32347–2300; tel. 850/584–0800, **A**10 20 **F**3 7 11 15 17 29 30 34 35 40 45 50 57 59 62 70 76 81 85 89 93 107 110 111 114 119 126 127 129 132 133 146
Primary Contact: Thomas J. Stone, FACHE, Chief Executive Officer
CHR: David Dawkins, Director Human Resources
CNO: Mary Lescher, Chief Clinical Officer
Web address: www.doctorsmemorial.com
Control: Other not–for–profit (including NFP Corporation) **Service:** General medical and surgical

Staffed Beds: 24 **Admissions:** 713 **Census:** 5

PLANT CITY—Hillsborough County

SOUTH FLORIDA BAPTIST HOSPITAL (100132), 301 North Alexander Street,
Zip 33563–4303; tel. 813/757–1200, **A**1 10 **F**3 11 12 13 15 18 20 22 28 29
30 31 34 35 37 40 41 44 45 47 48 49 50 51 57 59 60 64 68 70 71 74 75 76
77 78 79 80 81 85 87 89 93 107 108 110 111 114 115 118 119 124 126 130
131 132 135 145 146 147 148 154 156 **S** Trinity Health, Livonia, MI
Primary Contact: Karen Kerr, R.N., President
COO: Beth Tancredo, Director Operations
CFO: Carl Tremonti, Chief Financial Officer
CMO: Mark Vaaler, M.D., Chief Medical Officer
CIO: Tim Thompson, Senior Vice President, Chief Information Officer
CHR: Pat Lipton, Director Team Resources
CNO: Teresa Colletti, Director Patient Services
Web address: www.https://baycare.org/sfbh
Control: Other not–for–profit (including NFP Corporation) **Service:** General
medical and surgical

**Staffed Beds: 133 Admissions: 7849 Census: 73 Outpatient Visits: 59804
Births: 509 Total Expense ($000): 126426 Payroll Expense ($000): 45089
Personnel: 692**

PLANTATION—Broward County

PLANTATION GENERAL HOSPITAL (100167), 401 NW 42nd Avenue,
Zip 33317–2882; tel. 954/587–5010, (Includes MERCY HOSPITAL - A CAMPUS
OF PLANTATION GENERAL HOSPITAL, 3663 South Miami Avenue, Miami, Florida,
Zip 33133–4237; tel. 305/854–4400; Barbara Simmons, R.N., Chief Executive
Officer), (Nonreporting) **A**1 2 3 5 10 **S** HCA Healthcare, Nashville, TN
Primary Contact: Madeline Nava, Chief Executive Officer
COO: Patrick Rohan, Chief Operating Officer
CFO: Irfan Mirza, Chief Financial Officer
CIO: Mia McGlynn, Director Management Information Systems
CHR: Jennifer Allen, Vice President Human Resources
CNO: Jesse Gabuat, Chief Nursing Officer
Web address: www.plantationgeneral.com/
Control: Church operated **Service:** General medical and surgical

Staffed Beds: 264

WESTSIDE REGIONAL MEDICAL CENTER (100228), 8201 West Broward
Boulevard, Zip 33324–2701; tel. 954/473–6600, (Nonreporting) **A**1 5 10 **S** HCA
Healthcare, Nashville, TN
Primary Contact: Barbara Simmons, R.N., Chief Executive Officer
COO: Shana Sappington-Crittenden, Chief Operating Officer
CFO: Kevin Corcoran, Chief Financial Officer
CMO: Brian Weinstein, M.D., Chief of Staff
CIO: Andres Blanco, Director Management Information Systems
CHR: Maria Rivera, Director Human Resources
Web address: www.westsideregional.com
Control: Corporation, Investor–owned (for–profit) **Service:** General medical and
surgical

Staffed Beds: 224

PORT CHARLOTTE—Charlotte County

BAYFRONT HEALTH PORT CHARLOTTE (100077), 2500 Harbor Boulevard,
Zip 33952–5000; tel. 941/766–4122, **A**1 5 10 **F**12 13 15 17 18 20 22 24 26
29 30 34 40 45 46 48 49 50 54 59 64 70 72 74 75 76 77 79 81 85 89 93
107 110 111 114 115 119 126 131 132 133 146 147 148 154 156 157 **S**
Community Health Systems, Inc., Franklin, TN
Primary Contact: Timothy J. Cerullo, Chief Executive Officer
COO: Brian Cruddas, Chief Operating Officer
CFO: Jeffrey Mullis, Interim Chief Financial Officer
CMO: Thomas Noone, M.D., Chief Medical Officer
CHR: Karen Gardiner, Human Resources Director
CNO: Debra Clark, Chief Nursing Officer
Web address: www.bayfrontcharlotte.com
Control: Corporation, Investor–owned (for–profit) **Service:** General medical and
surgical

**Staffed Beds: 254 Admissions: 10620 Census: 133 Outpatient
Visits: 48886 Births: 1020 Total Expense ($000): 140513 Payroll Expense
($000): 48161 Personnel: 836**

△ **FAWCETT MEMORIAL HOSPITAL (100236)**, 21298 Olean Boulevard,
Zip 33952–6765; tel. 941/629–1181, (Nonreporting) **A**1 2 7 10 **S** HCA
Healthcare, Nashville, TN
Primary Contact: William Hawley, President and Chief Executive Officer
CFO: Vickie Magurean, Chief Financial Officer
CMO: Mark Callman, M.D., Chief Medical Officer
CHR: Linda Bryan, Vice President Human Resources
CNO: Brandy Hershberger, Chief Nursing Officer
Web address: www.fawcetthospital.com
Control: Corporation, Investor–owned (for–profit) **Service:** General medical and
surgical

Staffed Beds: 237

PORT ST JOE—Gulf County

SACRED HEART HOSPITAL ON THE GULF (100313), 3801 East Highway 98,
Zip 32456–5318; tel. 850/229–5600, **A**1 10 **F**29 30 40 68 77 79 81 85 87 93
107 111 114 119 127 130 131 132 133 146 156 **S** Ascension Healthcare,
Saint Louis, MO
Primary Contact: Roger L. Hall, President
CNO: Robin M. Godwin, MSN, Vice President of Nursing
Web address: www.sacred-heart.org/gulf/
Control: Other not–for–profit (including NFP Corporation) **Service:** General
medical and surgical

**Staffed Beds: 12 Admissions: 507 Census: 5 Outpatient Visits: 27655
Births: 0 Total Expense ($000): 19117 Payroll Expense ($000): 6389
Personnel: 56**

PORT ST LUCIE—St. Lucie County

☐ **PORT ST. LUCIE HOSPITAL (104070)**, 2550 SE Walton Road, Zip 34952–7168;
tel. 772/335–0400, (Nonreporting) **A**1 10
Primary Contact: Mercy Estevez, Administrator
Web address: www.portstluciehospitalinc.com
Control: Other not–for–profit (including NFP Corporation) **Service:** Psychiatric

Staffed Beds: 75

ST. LUCIE MEDICAL CENTER (100260), 1800 SE Tiffany Avenue, Zip 34952–
7521; tel. 772/335–4000, (Nonreporting) **A**1 3 5 10 **S** HCA Healthcare,
Nashville, TN
Primary Contact: Jay Finnegan, Chief Executive Officer
COO: Calvin Thomas IV, Chief Operating Officer
CFO: Kevin Keeling, Chief Financial Officer
Web address: www.stluciemed.com
Control: Corporation, Investor owned (for profit) **Service:** General medical and
surgical

Staffed Beds: 194

PUNTA GORDA—Charlotte County

BAYFRONT HEALTH PUNTA GORDA (100047), 809 East Marion Avenue,
Zip 33950–3819, Mailing Address: P.O. Box 51–1328, Zip 33951–1328;
tel. 941/639–3131, (Nonreporting) **A**1 10 **S** Community Health Systems, Inc.,
Franklin, TN
Primary Contact: Andrew Emery, Chief Executive Officer
Web address: www.bayfrontcharlotte.com
Control: Corporation, Investor–owned (for–profit) **Service:** General medical and
surgical

Staffed Beds: 190

RIVIERA BEACH—Palm Beach County

KINDRED HOSPITAL THE PALM BEACHES (102025), 5555 West Blue Heron
Boulevard, Zip 33418–7813; tel. 561/840–0754, (Nonreporting) **A**1 10 **S** Kindred
Healthcare, Louisville, KY
Primary Contact: Elayne Lopreato, Chief Executive Officer
CFO: Dean Card, Chief Financial Officer
CNO: Elayne Lopreato, Chief Clinical Officer
Web address: www.khthepalmbeaches.com/
Control: Corporation, Investor–owned (for–profit) **Service:** Acute long–term care
hospital

Staffed Beds: 70

FL

Hospital, Medicare Provider Number, Address, Telephone, Approval, Facility, and Physician Codes, Health Care System

★ American Hospital Association (AHA) membership   ◯ Healthcare Facilities Accreditation Program   ⇑ Center for Improvement in Healthcare Quality Accreditation
☐ The Joint Commission accreditation   ◇ DNV Healthcare Inc. accreditation   △ Commission on Accreditation of Rehabilitation Facilities (CARF) accreditation

---

ROCKLEDGE—Brevard County

★ **ROCKLEDGE REGIONAL MEDICAL CENTER (100092)**, 110 Longwood Avenue, Zip 32955–2887, Mailing Address: P.O. Box 565002, Mail Stop 1, Zip 32956–5002; tel. 321/636–2211, (Nonreporting) **A**2 10 **S** Steward Health Care System, LLC, Dallas, TX
Primary Contact: Andrew Romine, Chief Executive Officer
CFO: Jonathan R Immordino, Chief Financial Officer
CMO: Vinay Mehindru, M.D., Medical Director
CIO: David Barnhart, Director Information Systems
CHR: Marchita H Marino, Vice President Human Resources
CNO: Mary Sue Zinsmeister, Chief Nursing Officer
Web address: www.wuesthoff.org
Control: Corporation, Investor–owned (for–profit) **Service:** General medical and surgical

Staffed Beds: 298

SAFETY HARBOR—Pinellas County

⊞ **MEASE COUNTRYSIDE HOSPITAL (100265)**, 3231 McMullen Booth Road, Zip 34695–6607; tel. 727/725–6111, **A**1 2 3 10 **F**3 11 13 15 17 18 20 22 26 28 29 30 31 32 34 35 37 38 40 41 44 45 46 49 50 51 55 56 57 59 60 62 63 64 68 70 72 74 75 76 77 78 79 81 84 85 86 87 89 92 93 97 107 108 109 110 111 114 115 116 117 118 119 126 129 130 131 132 135 143 145 146 147 148 149 154 156 **S** Trinity Health, Livonia, MI
Primary Contact: Matthew Novak, President
CFO: Carl Tremonti, Chief Financial Officer
CMO: Tony Schuster, M.D., Vice President of Physician Services
CIO: Tim Thompson, Senior Vice President, Informant Services and Chief Information Officer
CHR: Kyle Barr, Senior Vice President, Chief Team Resources Officer
CNO: Thomas Doria, Vice President, Patient Services and Chief Nursing Officer
Web address: www.mpmhealth.com
Control: Other not–for–profit (including NFP Corporation) **Service:** General medical and surgical

Staffed Beds: 311 Admissions: 17905 Census: 203 Outpatient Visits: 129212 Births: 2223 Total Expense ($000): 301394 Payroll Expense ($000): 103228 Personnel: 1582

SAINT AUGUSTINE—St. Johns County

☐ **FLAGLER HOSPITAL (100090)**, 400 Health Park Boulevard, Zip 32086–5784; tel. 904/819–5155, **A**1 2 10 20 **F**3 5 8 11 12 13 14 15 18 20 22 24 28 29 30 31 34 35 38 40 44 45 49 50 53 56 57 58 59 65 70 72 74 75 76 78 79 81 82 85 86 87 89 98 100 101 102 104 105 107 108 110 111 114 115 117 118 119 120 121 123 124 126 129 130 132 135 144 146 152 153 154
Primary Contact: Jason P. Barrett, Chief Executive Officer
CFO: Lynda I Kirker, Chief Financial Officer
CMO: Douglas Dew, M.D., President Medical Staff
CIO: Bill Rieger, Chief Information Officer
CHR: Jeff Hurley, Vice President Human Resources
Web address: www.flaglerhospital.org
Control: Other not–for–profit (including NFP Corporation) **Service:** General medical and surgical

Staffed Beds: 204 Admissions: 13225 Census: 163 Outpatient Visits: 157606 Births: 1530 Total Expense ($000): 266020 Payroll Expense ($000): 85589 Personnel: 1474

SAINT CLOUD—Osceola County

⊞ **ST. CLOUD REGIONAL MEDICAL CENTER (100302)**, 2906 17th Street, Zip 34769–6099; tel. 407/892–2135, (Nonreporting) **A**1 10 **S** Community Health Systems, Inc., Franklin, TN
Primary Contact: Brent Burish, Chief Executive Officer
COO: Andrea Thomas, Chief Operating Officer
CFO: Carl Caley, Chief Financial Officer
CIO: James Devlin, Director Information Systems
CHR: Jennifer Harmon, Director of Human Resources
CNO: Perry Horne, Chief Nursing Officer
Web address: www.stcloudregional.com
Control: Corporation, Investor–owned (for–profit) **Service:** General medical and surgical

Staffed Beds: 84

SAINT PETERSBURG—Pinellas County

⊞ **BAYFRONT HEALTH ST. PETERSBURG (100032)**, 701 Sixth Street South, Zip 33701–4891; tel. 727/823–1234, (Nonreporting) **A**1 3 5 10 **S** Community Health Systems, Inc., Franklin, TN
Primary Contact: Sharon Hayes, Chief Executive Officer
COO: Austin Brown, Chief Operating Officer
CFO: Eric Smith, Chief Financial Officer
CIO: Kevin Murphy, Director, Information Technology Services
CHR: Jim Reames, Director Human Resources
CNO: Karen Long, R.N., FACHE, Vice President Nursing
Web address: www.bayfrontstpete.com
Control: Corporation, Investor–owned (for–profit) **Service:** General medical and surgical

Staffed Beds: 382

⊞ **JOHNS HOPKINS ALL CHILDREN'S HOSPITAL (103300)**, 501 6th Avenue South, Zip 33701–4634; tel. 727/898–7451, **A**1 3 5 8 10 **F**3 11 12 17 18 19 20 21 22 23 24 25 26 27 29 30 31 32 34 35 36 37 39 40 41 43 44 45 46 47 48 49 50 54 55 57 58 59 60 61 62 64 65 68 72 73 74 75 77 78 79 81 82 84 85 86 87 88 89 90 92 93 96 97 99 100 107 111 114 115 116 118 119 126 129 130 131 132 134 135 137 141 142 143 146 147 148 154 **S** Johns Hopkins Health System, Baltimore, MD
Primary Contact: Thomas D. Kmetz, Interim Chief Executive Officer
CFO: Nancy Templin, Vice President Finance and Chief Financial Officer
CMO: Michael Epstein, M.D., Senior Vice President Medical Affairs
CIO: John McLendon, Vice President and Chief Information Officer
CHR: Jay Kuhns, Vice President Human Resources
CNO: Melissa Macogay, Vice President and Chief Nursing Officer
Web address: www.allkids.org
Control: Other not–for–profit (including NFP Corporation) **Service:** Children's general medical and surgical

Staffed Beds: 259 Admissions: 6613 Census: 153 Outpatient Visits: 351759 Births: 0 Total Expense ($000): 463379 Payroll Expense ($000): 174561 Personnel: 3131

⊞ **NORTHSIDE HOSPITAL (100238)**, 6000 49th Street North, Zip 33709–2145; tel. 727/521–4411, (Nonreporting) **A**1 3 10 13 **S** HCA Healthcare, Nashville, TN
Primary Contact: Valerie L. Powell-Stafford, Chief Executive Officer
COO: Peter Kennedy, Chief Operating Officer
CFO: Peggy Gatliff, Chief Financial Officer
CMO: Ira Siegman, M.D., Chief Medical Officer
CIO: Kirk Hendrick, Director Information Systems
CHR: Maggie Miklos, Director Human Resources
CNO: John Polisknowski, Chief Nursing Officer
Web address: www.northsidehospital.com
Control: Corporation, Investor–owned (for–profit) **Service:** General medical and surgical

Staffed Beds: 217

⊞ **PALMS OF PASADENA HOSPITAL (100126)**, 1501 Pasadena Avenue South, Zip 33707–3798; tel. 727/381–1000, (Nonreporting) **A**1 10 **S** HCA Healthcare, Nashville, TN
Primary Contact: Jacob Fisher, Chief Executive Officer
COO: Glenn J. Saldanha, Chief Operating Officer
CFO: Chase Redden, Chief Financial Officer
CMO: Mitchell Rubinstein, M.D., Chief Medical Officer
CIO: Danny Waters, Director, Information Services
CHR: Karen Casteel, Director Human Resources
CNO: Colleen Thielk, MSN, R.N., Chief Nursing Officer
Web address: www.palmspasadena.com
Control: Corporation, Investor–owned (for–profit) **Service:** General medical and surgical

Staffed Beds: 187

⊞ **ST. ANTHONY'S HOSPITAL (100067)**, 1200 Seventh Avenue North, Zip 33705–1388, Mailing Address: P.O. Box 12588, Zip 33733–2588; tel. 727/825–1100, **A**1 2 5 10 **F**3 11 12 15 17 18 20 22 26 28 29 30 31 34 35 40 44 45 46 49 51 57 59 60 63 64 68 70 74 75 77 78 79 81 84 85 87 93 98 100 102 103 107 108 110 111 114 115 117 118 121 123 124 126 129 130 131 132 135 146 148 149 154 156 **S** Trinity Health, Livonia, MI
Primary Contact: M. Scott Smith, President
CFO: Carl Tremonti, Chief Financial Officer
CMO: James McClintic, M.D., Vice President Medical Affairs
CIO: Tim Thompson, Senior Vice President and Chief Informatics Officer
CHR: Kristen A Betts, Director Team Resources
CNO: Thomas Doria, Vice President and Patient Services West
Web address: www.stanthonys.com/
Control: Other not–for–profit (including NFP Corporation) **Service:** General medical and surgical

Staffed Beds: 358 Admissions: 22890 Census: 284 Outpatient Visits: 113668 Births: 0 Total Expense ($000): 366894 Payroll Expense ($000): 125357 Personnel: 2080

FL

Many Facility Codes have changed. Please refer to the AHA Guide Code Chart.
© 2019 AHA Guide

⊞ **ST. PETERSBURG GENERAL HOSPITAL (100180)**, 6500 38th Avenue North, Zip 33710–1629; tel. 727/384–1414, (Nonreporting) **A**1 2 3 5 10 12 13 **S** HCA Healthcare, Nashville, TN
Primary Contact: Janice Balzano, President and Chief Executive Officer
COO: Stephanie McNulty, Chief Operating Officer
CFO: Shawn Gregory, Chief Financial Officer
CMO: Mitchell Rubinstein, M.D., Chief Medical Officer
CHR: Jennifer B Robinson, Vice President Human Resources
CNO: JoAnne Cattell, Chief Nursing Officer
Web address: www.stpetegeneral.com
Control: Corporation, Investor–owned (for–profit) **Service**: General medical and surgical

> **Staffed Beds:** 219

SANFORD—Seminole County

⊞ △ **CENTRAL FLORIDA REGIONAL HOSPITAL (100161)**, 1401 West Seminole Boulevard, Zip 32771–6764; tel. 407/321–4500, (Nonreporting) **A**1 7 10 **S** HCA Healthcare, Nashville, TN
Primary Contact: Trey Abshier, Chief Executive Officer
COO: Glenn Carney, Chief Operating Officer
CFO: Richard Read, Chief Financial Officer
CIO: Jerry Ballard, Director Information Systems
CHR: Linda V Smith, Vice President Human Resources
CNO: Maria Calloway, R.N., MSN, Chief Nursing Officer
Web address: www.centralfloridaregional.com
Control: Corporation, Investor–owned (for–profit) **Service**: General medical and surgical

> **Staffed Beds:** 226

SARASOTA—Sarasota County

⊞ **COMPLEX CARE HOSPITAL AT RIDGELAKE (102018)**, 6150 Edgelake Drive, Zip 34240–8803; tel. 941/342–3000, (Nonreporting) **A**1 10 **S** LifeCare Management Services, Plano, TX
Primary Contact: Robert E. Mallicoat, Chief Executive Officer
CFO: Leah Drabant, Director of Finance
CMO: Craig Harcup, M.D., Hospital Medical Director
CHR: Jennifer Sparks, Human Resources Generalist
CNO: Timothy Mitchell, R.N., Chief Nursing Officer
Web address: www.lifecarehospitals.com/hospital.php?id=23
Control: Corporation, Investor–owned (for–profit) **Service**: Acute long–term care hospital

> **Staffed Beds:** 40

⊞ **DOCTORS HOSPITAL OF SARASOTA (100166)**, 5731 Bee Ridge Road, Zip 34233–5056; tel. 941/342–1100, (Nonreporting) **A**1 10 **S** HCA Healthcare, Nashville, TN
Primary Contact: Robert C. Meade, Chief Executive Officer
COO: Peter Hemstead, Chief Operating Officer
CFO: Charles Schwaner III Chief Financial Officer
CMO: Thomas Trinchetto, M.D., Chief Medical Officer
CHR: Theresa Levering, Director Human Resources
CNO: Kathy Mitchell, R.N., Chief Nursing Officer
Web address: www.doctorsofsarasota.com
Control: Corporation, Investor–owned (for–profit) **Service**: General medical and surgical

> **Staffed Beds:** 168

⊞ △ **ENCOMPASS HEALTH REHABILITATION HOSPITAL OF SARASOTA (103031)**, 6400 Edgelake Drive, Zip 34240–8813; tel. 941/921–8600, **A**1 7 10 **F**28 29 62 68 75 96 132 143 **S** Encompass Health Corporation, Birmingham, AL
Primary Contact: Marcus Braz, Chief Executive Officer
CFO: Barbara Bierut, Chief Financial Officer
CMO: Alexander De Jesus, M.D., Medical Director
CHR: Brenda Benner, Director Human Resources
Web address: www.healthsouthsarasota.com
Control: Corporation, Investor–owned (for–profit) **Service**: Rehabilitation

> **Staffed Beds:** 96 **Admissions:** 2452 **Census:** 85 **Outpatient Visits:** 0 **Births:** 0 **Total Expense ($000):** 27744 **Payroll Expense ($000):** 16513 **Personnel:** 237

HEALTHSOUTH RIDGELAKE HOSPITAL See Complex Care Hospital at Ridgelake

☐ △ **SARASOTA MEMORIAL HEALTH CARE SYSTEM (100087)**, 1700 South Tamiami Trail, Zip 34239–3555; tel. 941/917–9000, **A**1 2 3 5 7 8 10 **F**3 6 8 11 12 13 15 17 18 19 20 22 24 26 28 29 30 31 32 34 35 36 37 38 39 40 42 43 44 45 46 47 48 49 50 51 53 54 55 56 57 58 59 60 61 64 66 68 70 72 73 74 75 76 77 78 79 80 81 82 84 85 86 87 89 90 91 92 93 95 96 97 98 99 100 101 102 107 108 110 111 114 115 118 119 124 126 129 130 131 132 134 135 143 144 145 146 147 148 149 150 154 156
Primary Contact: David Verinder, President and Chief Executive Officer
COO: David Verinder, President and Chief Executive Officer
CFO: Bill Woeltjen, Chief Financial Officer
CMO: James Fiorica, M.D., Chief Medical Officer
CIO: Denis Baker, Chief Information Officer
CHR: Laurie Bennett, Director Human Resources
CNO: Connie Andersen, R.N., MS, Chief Nursing Officer
Web address: www.smh.com
Control: Hospital district or authority, Government, nonfederal **Service**: General medical and surgical

> **Staffed Beds:** 775 **Admissions:** 36016 **Census:** 473 **Outpatient Visits:** 572657 **Births:** 3626 **Total Expense ($000):** 706024 **Payroll Expense ($000):** 280054 **Personnel:** 5334

SEBASTIAN—Indian River County

☐ **SEBASTIAN RIVER MEDICAL CENTER (100217)**, 13695 North U S Hwy 1, Zip 32958–3230, Mailing Address: Box 780838, Zip 32978–0838; tel. 772/589–3186, (Nonreporting) **A**1 10 **S** Steward Health Care System, LLC, Dallas, TX
Primary Contact: Kyle Sanders, President
CFO: John McEachern, Controller
CMO: Ralph Geiger, M.D., Chief of Staff
CHR: Kam Storey, Director Human Resources
Web address: www.https://www.sebastianrivermedical.org/
Control: Corporation, Investor–owned (for–profit) **Service**: General medical and surgical

> **Staffed Beds:** 154

SEBRING—Highlands County

⊞ **ADVENTHEALTH SEBRING (100109)**, 4200 Sun'n Lake Boulevard, Zip 33872–1986, Mailing Address: P.O. Box 9400, Zip 33871–9400; tel. 863/314–4466, (Includes FLORIDA HOSPITAL LAKE PLACID, 1210 US 27 North, Lake Placid, Florida, Zip 33852–7948, tel. 863/465–3777, Eric Stevens, Chief Executive Officer) **A**1 10 19 **F**11 13 15 18 20 22 24 26 28 29 30 34 35 37 40 45 49 50 53 54 57 59 60 62 64 70 75 76 78 79 81 86 87 89 97 98 100 101 103 104 105 107 108 110 111 114 115 116 117 119 120 121 123 126 127 129 130 132 146 147 148 149 153 154 156 **S** AdventHealth, Altamonte Springs, FL
Primary Contact: Randy Surber, Chief Executive Officer
CFO: Rosalie Oliver, Chief Financial Officer
CMO: Jorge F Gonzalez, M.D., Chief Medical Officer
CHR: Anthony Stahl, Vice President
CNO: Gloria N Santos, R.N., MS, Chief Nursing Officer
Web address: www.floridahospital.com/heartland/our-location
Control: Church operated, Nongovernment, not–for–profit **Service**: General medical and surgical

> **Staffed Beds:** 197 **Admissions:** 10389 **Census:** 124 **Outpatient Visits:** 150567 **Births:** 799 **Total Expense ($000):** 194267 **Payroll Expense ($000):** 84982 **Personnel:** 1334

⊞ **HIGHLANDS REGIONAL MEDICAL CENTER (100049)**, 3600 South Highlands Avenue, Zip 33870–5495, Mailing Address: Drawer 2066, Zip 33871–2066; tel. 863/385–6101, (Nonreporting) **A**1 10 19 **S** HCA Healthcare, Nashville, TN
Primary Contact: Jason Kimbrell, Chief Executive Officer
CFO: Paul Damron, Chief Financial Officer
CIO: Nate Johnson, Chief Information Officer
CHR: Brenda Dane, Director, Human Resources
CNO: Adam Kless, Chief Nursing Officer
Web address: www.highlandsregional.com
Control: Corporation, Investor–owned (for–profit) **Service**: General medical and surgical

> **Staffed Beds:** 80

FL

SOUTH MIAMI—Miami-Dade County

☐ **LARKIN COMMUNITY HOSPITAL-SOUTH MIAMI CAMPUS (100181)**, 7031 SW 62nd Avenue, Zip 33143–4781; tel. 305/284–7500, **A**1 3 5 10 12 13 **F**3 18 26 29 30 31 34 35 40 45 46 47 48 49 50 54 56 57 58 60 62 68 70 74 75 77 78 79 81 82 84 85 87 91 93 98 99 100 101 102 103 104 105 107 111 115 116 117 118 119 124 126 130 135 143 148 149 153 157
Primary Contact: Sandra Sosa-Guerrero, Chief Executive Officer
COO: George J Michel, Chief Operating Officer
CFO: Edgar Castillo, Chief Financial Officer
CMO: Mario Almeida-Suarez, M.D., Chief of Staff
CIO: Orlando Suarez, Director Information Technology
CHR: Carolina Pena, Assistant Director Administrator
CNO: Mercedes Perez, Vice President Nursing
Web address: www.larkinhospital.com
Control: Individual, Investor–owned (for–profit) **Service**: General medical and surgical

| **Staffed Beds**: 146 **Admissions**: 6061 **Census**: 84 **Outpatient Visits**: 9574 **Births**: 0 |

STARKE—Bradford County

SHANDS STARKE See Shands Starke Regional Medical Center

☒ **SHANDS STARKE REGIONAL MEDICAL CENTER (101310)**, 922 East Call Street, Zip 32091–3699; tel. 904/368–2300, (Nonreporting) **A**1 10 18 **S** Community Health Systems, Inc., Franklin, TN
Primary Contact: John Emery, Chief Executive Officer
CFO: Wendy Martin, Chief Financial Officer
Web address: www.shandsstarke.com
Control: Partnership, Investor–owned (for–profit) **Service**: General medical and surgical

| **Staffed Beds**: 49 |

STUART—Martin County

☒ **CLEVELAND CLINIC MARTIN NORTH HOSPITAL (100044)**, 200 SE Hospital Avenue, Zip 34994–2346, Mailing Address: P.O. Box 9010, Zip 34995–9010; tel. 772/287–5200, (Includes CLEVELAND CLINIC MARTIN SOUTH HOSPITAL, 2100 SE Salerno Road, Stuart, Florida, Zip 34997; tel. 772/223–2300; Mark E Robitaille, FACHE, President and Chief Executive Officer; CLEVELAND CLINIC TRADITION HOSPITAL, 10000 SW Innovation Way, Port St Lucie, Florida, Zip 34987–2111; tel. 772/345–8100; Mark E Robitaille, FACHE, President and Chief Executive Officer) **A**1 2 10 **F**3 8 11 12 13 15 17 18 20 22 24 26 28 29 30 31 34 35 36 37 40 42 45 46 47 48 49 50 51 53 55 59 60 64 65 68 70 72 74 75 77 78 79 81 82 85 86 87 91 92 93 94 95 107 108 110 111 112 114 115 118 119 120 121 122 123 124 126 129 130 132 135 143 146 148 149 154 156 **S** Cleveland Clinic Health System, Cleveland, OH
Primary Contact: Robert L. Lord, JD, President and Chief Executive Officer
CFO: Chuck Cleaver, Vice President and Chief Financial Officer
CMO: Fernando Petry, M.D., Vice President and Chief Medical Officer
CIO: Edmund Collins, Chief Information Officer
CHR: Angie L Metcalf, Vice President and Chief Human Resource Officer
CNO: Mary Elizabeth Flippo, R.N., MSN, Vice President and Chief Nursing Officer
Web address: www.martinhealth.org
Control: Other not–for–profit (including NFP Corporation) **Service**: General medical and surgical

| **Staffed Beds**: 509 **Admissions**: 26410 **Census**: 323 **Outpatient Visits**: 152596 **Births**: 2191 **Total Expense ($000)**: 484639 **Payroll Expense ($000)**: 201682 **Personnel**: 4048 |

☒ **HEALTHSOUTH REHABILITATION HOSPITAL AT MARTIN HEALTH (103044)**, 5850 SE Community Drive, Zip 34997–6420; tel. 772/324–3500, (Nonreporting) **A**1 10 **S** Encompass Health Corporation, Birmingham, AL
Primary Contact: Ivette Miranda, Chief Executive Officer
CFO: Dawn Salas, Controller
CMO: Stephen L Chastain, M.D., Chief Medical Officer
CHR: Donna Holder-Hooper, Chief Human Resource Officer
CNO: Charmaine Blanchard, Chief Nursing Officer
Web address: www.healthsouthmartin.com
Control: Corporation, Investor–owned (for–profit) **Service**: Rehabilitation

| **Staffed Beds**: 54 |

SUN CITY CENTER—Hillsborough County

☒ **SOUTH BAY HOSPITAL (100259)**, 4016 Sun City Center Blvd, Zip 33573–5298; tel. 813/634–3301, (Nonreporting) **A**1 10 **S** HCA Healthcare, Nashville, TN
Primary Contact: Daniel Bender, Chief Executive Officer
CFO: Warren Pate, Chief Financial Officer
CMO: Joseph C. Corcoran, D.O., Chief Medical Officer
CIO: Eric Young, Director Information Technology and Systems
CHR: Stacie Novosel, Vice President, Human Resources
CNO: Marcy Frisina, Chief Nursing Officer
Web address: www.southbayhospital.com/
Control: Corporation, Investor–owned (for–profit) **Service**: General medical and surgical

| **Staffed Beds**: 138 |

SUNRISE—Broward County

☒ **ENCOMPASS HEALTH REHABILITATION HOSPITAL OF SUNRISE (103028)**, 4399 North Nob Hill Road, Zip 33351–5899; tel. 954/749–0300, (Nonreporting) **A**1 3 10 **S** Encompass Health Corporation, Birmingham, AL
Primary Contact: Michael S. Roffelsen, Chief Executive Officer
CFO: Ruth Goodstein, Controller
CMO: Scott Tannenbaum, M.D., Medical Director
CIO: Angela Manning, Director Health Information Services
CHR: Barbara Dunkiel, Director Human Resources
CNO: Omaira D. Riano, Chief Nursing Officer
Web address: www.healthsouthsunrise.com
Control: Corporation, Investor–owned (for–profit) **Service**: Rehabilitation

| **Staffed Beds**: 126 |

TALLAHASSEE—Leon County

☒ **CAPITAL REGIONAL MEDICAL CENTER (100254)**, 2626 Capital Medical Boulevard, Zip 32308–4499; tel. 850/325–5000, (Nonreporting) **A**1 2 10 **S** HCA Healthcare, Nashville, TN
Primary Contact: Alan Seesee, Chief Executive Officer
CMO: Steve West, M.D., Chief Medical Officer
CIO: Robert A Steed, Director Information Systems
CHR: Louise Truitt, Vice President Human Resources
Web address: www.capitalregionalmedicalcenter.com
Control: Individual, Investor–owned (for–profit) **Service**: General medical and surgical

| **Staffed Beds**: 198 |

☒ **EASTSIDE PSYCHIATRIC HOSPITAL (104059)**, 2634 Capital Circle NE, Zip 32308–4106; tel. 850/523–3333, (Nonreporting) **A**10
Primary Contact: Jay A. Reeve, Ph.D., President and Chief Executive Officer
COO: Sue Conger, Chief Operating Officer
CFO: Virginia Kelly, Chief Financial Officer
CMO: Ludmila de Faria, M.D., Chief Medical Officer
CIO: Thad Moorer, Chief Information Officer
CHR: Candy Landry, Chief Human Resource Officer
CNO: Judy Goreau, R.N., Director of Nursing
Web address: www.apalacheecenter.org
Control: Other not–for–profit (including NFP Corporation) **Service**: Psychiatric

| **Staffed Beds**: 24 |

☒ **ENCOMPASS HEALTH REHABILITATION HOSPITAL OF TALLAHASSEE (103033)**, 1675 Riggins Road, Zip 32308–5315; tel. 850/656–4800, (Nonreporting) **A**1 10 **S** Encompass Health Corporation, Birmingham, AL
Primary Contact: K. Dale. Neely, FACHE, Chief Executive Officer
CFO: Jennifer Spooner, Controller
CMO: Robert Rowland, M.D., Medical Director
CIO: Michael Spangler, Health Information Management Services Supervisor
CHR: Carol Bugayong, Human Resources Director
CNO: Elizabeth Squires, R.N., Chief Nursing Officer
Web address: www.healthsouthtallahassee.com
Control: Corporation, Investor–owned (for–profit) **Service**: Rehabilitation

| **Staffed Beds**: 76 |

☒ **SELECT SPECIALTY HOSPITAL-TALLAHASSEE (102020)**, 1554 Surgeons Drive, Zip 32308–4631; tel. 850/219–6950, (Nonreporting) **A**1 10 **S** Select Medical Corporation, Mechanicsburg, PA
Primary Contact: Jay Faherty, Chief Executive Officer
Web address: www.tallahassee.selectspecialtyhospitals.com/
Control: Corporation, Investor–owned (for–profit) **Service**: Acute long–term care hospital

| **Staffed Beds**: 29 |

Many Facility Codes have changed. Please refer to the AHA Guide Code Chart. © 2019 AHA Guide

⊞ **TALLAHASSEE MEMORIAL HEALTHCARE (100135)**, 1300 Miccosukee Road, Zip 32308–5054; tel. 850/431–1155, (Total facility includes 42 beds in nursing home–type unit) **A**1 2 3 5 10 **F**2 3 5 8 11 12 15 17 18 19 20 22 24 26 28 29 30 31 34 35 37 40 42 43 44 46 47 48 49 50 51 53 54 55 56 57 58 59 60 61 62 64 65 68 70 72 73 74 75 77 78 79 80 81 82 84 85 86 87 88 91 93 96 97 98 99 100 102 103 104 107 108 110 113 114 115 117 118 119 120 121 123 124 126 127 128 129 130 131 132 133 143 144 146 147 148 149 154 156
Primary Contact: G. Mark. O'Bryant, President and Chief Executive Officer
COO: Jason H Moore, Vice President and Chief Operating Officer
CFO: William A Giudice, Vice President and Chief Financial Officer
CMO: Dean Watson, M.D., Chief Medical Officer
CIO: Don Lindsey, Vice President and Chief Information Officer
CHR: Steven W Adriaanse, Vice President and Chief Human Resources Officer
Web address: www.tmh.org
Control: Other not–for–profit (including NFP Corporation) **Service**: General medical and surgical

> **Staffed Beds:** 495 **Admissions:** 28992 **Census:** 402 **Outpatient Visits:** 841422 **Births:** 3693 **Total Expense ($000):** 704547 **Payroll Expense ($000):** 291661 **Personnel:** 4647

TAMARAC—Broward County

⊞ **UNIVERSITY HOSPITAL AND MEDICAL CENTER (100224)**, 7201 North University Drive, Zip 33321–2996; tel. 954/721–2200, (Includes UNIVERSITY PAVILION, 7425 North University Drive, Tamarac, Florida, Zip 33328; tel. 305/722–9933), (Nonreporting) **A**1 3 5 10 **S** HCA Healthcare, Nashville, TN
Primary Contact: Dana C. Oaks, Chief Executive Officer
CFO: Aurelio Gonzalez, Chief Financial Officer
CMO: Ran Abrahamy, M.D., Chief of Staff
CIO: Tom Scharff, Director Information Services
Web address: www.uhmchealth.com
Control: Corporation, Investor–owned (for–profit) **Service**: General medical and surgical

> **Staffed Beds:** 317

TAMPA—Hillsborough County

⊞ **ADVENTHEALTH CARROLLWOOD (100069)**, 7171 North Dale Mabry Highway, Zip 33614–2665; tel. 813/932–2222, **A**1 3 10 **F**3 12 15 18 20 22 26 29 30 34 35 40 41 44 45 46 47 48 49 50 51 57 58 59 60 65 70 74 75 79 81 82 87 107 108 110 111 115 116 117 118 119 126 130 133 143 146 148 149 157 **S** AdventHealth, Altamonte Springs, FL
Primary Contact: Erika Skula, President and Chief Executive Officer
COO: Mary C Whillock, R.N., MS, Associate Nursing Officer and Chief Operating Officer
CFO: Chris Sauder, Vice President and Chief Financial Officer
CNO: Deborah W Kumar, MSN, Chief Nursing Officer
Web address: www.https://www.floridahospital.com/carrollwood
Control: Church operated, Nongovernment, not–for–profit **Service**: General medical and surgical

> **Staffed Beds:** 96 **Admissions:** 5170 **Census:** 54 **Outpatient Visits:** 50715 **Births:** 0 **Total Expense ($000):** 129500 **Payroll Expense ($000):** 37252 **Personnel:** 416

⊞ △ **ADVENTHEALTH TAMPA (100173)**, 3100 East Fletcher Avenue, Zip 33613–4688; tel. 813/971–6000, **A**1 3 5 7 10 **F**3 11 12 13 15 17 18 19 20 21 22 24 25 26 27 28 29 30 31 34 35 37 40 41 44 45 46 47 48 49 50 54 57 58 59 60 64 65 70 72 74 75 76 77 78 79 80 81 82 84 85 86 87 88 89 90 91 92 93 96 105 107 108 109 110 111 112 114 115 116 117 118 119 120 121 123 124 126 129 130 132 135 143 144 146 147 148 149 152 156 **S** AdventHealth, Altamonte Springs, FL
Primary Contact: Denyse Bales-Chubb, Chief Executive Officer
COO: Dick Tibbits, Vice President and Chief Operating Officer
CFO: Dima Didenko, Chief Financial Officer
CMO: Brad Bjornstad, M.D., Vice President and Chief Medical Officer
CHR: Dick Tibbits, Vice President and Chief Operating Officer
CNO: Theresa Trivette, R.N., Chief Nursing Officer
Web address: www.floridahospital.com/tampa
Control: Other not–for–profit (including NFP Corporation) **Service**: General medical and surgical

> **Staffed Beds:** 536 **Admissions:** 22537 **Census:** 343 **Outpatient Visits:** 136703 **Births:** 1648 **Total Expense ($000):** 501481 **Payroll Expense ($000):** 159517 **Personnel:** 2895

⊞ **H. LEE MOFFITT CANCER CENTER AND RESEARCH INSTITUTE (100271)**, 12902 Magnolia Drive, Zip 33612–9497; tel. 813/745–4673, **A**1 2 3 5 10 **F**3 8 15 26 29 30 31 34 35 36 37 44 45 46 47 49 50 54 55 56 57 58 59 64 68 70 71 74 75 77 78 79 80 81 82 84 85 86 87 91 92 93 96 97 100 101 103 104 107 108 110 111 114 115 117 118 119 120 121 123 124 126 130 132 135 136 144 145 146 147 148 149 154
Primary Contact: Alan F. List, M.D., President and Chief Executive Officer
COO: John A Kolosky, Executive Vice President and Chief Operating Officer
CFO: Yvette Tremonti, Chief Financial Officer
CMO: Bob Keenan, Chief Medical Officer
CIO: Jennifer Greenman, Vice President Chief Information Officer
CHR: Mariana Bugallo-Muros, Vice President Chief Human Resources Officer
CNO: Jane Fusilero, Vice President Chief Nursing Officer
Web address: www.moffitt.org
Control: Other not–for–profit (including NFP Corporation) **Service**: Cancer

> **Staffed Beds:** 206 **Admissions:** 9095 **Census:** 166 **Outpatient Visits:** 406117 **Births:** 0 **Total Expense ($000):** 1236954 **Payroll Expense ($000):** 494123 **Personnel:** 5884

⊞ △ **JAMES A. HALEY VETERANS' HOSPITAL-TAMPA**, 13000 Bruce B Downs Boulevard, Zip 33612–4745; tel. 813/972–2000, (Total facility includes 64 beds in nursing home–type unit) **A**1 3 5 7 8 **F**1 3 4 5 9 12 15 16 17 18 20 22 24 26 28 29 30 31 33 34 35 36 38 39 40 45 46 47 48 49 50 51 53 54 55 56 57 58 59 60 61 62 63 64 65 67 70 71 72 73 74 75 76 77 78 79 80 81 82 83 84 85 86 87 88 89 90 91 92 93 94 95 96 97 98 100 101 102 104 105 107 108 109 110 111 113 114 115 116 117 118 119 120 121 123 126 127 128 129 130 131 132 135 143 144 146 147 148 149 152 153 154 156 157 158 **S** Department of Veterans Affairs, Washington, DC
Primary Contact: Joe Battle, Director
CFO: Robert Konkel, Manager Finance
CMO: Edward Cutolo, M.D., Jr Chief of Staff
CIO: Jose Seymour, Chief Information Resource Management
CHR: Andrew Sutton, Chief, Human Resources Management Service
CNO: Laureen Doloresco, R.N., Associate Director for Patient Care and Nursing Services
Web address: www.tampa.va.gov/
Control: Veterans Affairs, Government, federal **Service**: General medical and surgical

> **Staffed Beds:** 499 **Admissions:** 11720 **Census:** 384 **Outpatient Visits:** 1424039 **Births:** 0

⊞ **KINDRED HOSPITAL BAY AREA-TAMPA (102009)**, 4555 South Manhattan Avenue, Zip 33611–2397; tel. 813/839–6341, (Includes KINDRED HOSPITAL BAY AREA ST. PETERSBURG, 3030 Sixth Street South, Saint Petersburg, Florida, Zip 33705–3720; tel. 727/894–8719; Debra Plummer, Chief Executive Officer), (Nonreporting) **A**1 10 **S** Kindred Healthcare, Louisville, KY
Primary Contact: Suthanthira M. Ratnasamy, R.N., FACHE, Chief Executive Officer
CFO: Frank Billy, Chief Financial Officer
CHR: Deborah Basria, Human Resources Payroll Administrator
Web address: www.khtampa.com/
Control: Corporation, Investor–owned (for–profit) **Service**: Acute long–term care hospital

> **Staffed Beds:** 73

⊞ **KINDRED HOSPITAL CENTRAL TAMPA (102013)**, 4801 North Howard Avenue, Zip 33603–1411; tel. 813/874–7575, (Nonreporting) **A**1 10 **S** Kindred Healthcare, Louisville, KY
Primary Contact: Ralph Selner, Chief Executive Officer
CFO: John Miner, Chief Financial Officer
Web address: www.kindredcentraltampa.com/
Control: Corporation, Investor–owned (for–profit) **Service**: Acute long–term care hospital

> **Staffed Beds:** 109

⊞ **MEMORIAL HOSPITAL OF TAMPA (100206)**, 2901 Swann Avenue, Zip 33609–4057; tel. 813/873–6400, (Includes TAMPA COMMUNITY HOSPITAL, 6001 Webb Road, Tampa, Florida, Zip 33615–3291; tel. 813/888–7060), (Nonreporting) **A**1 5 10 **S** HCA Healthcare, Nashville, TN
Primary Contact: Sonia I. Wellman, Chief Executive Officer
COO: Cathy Edmisten, Chief Operating Officer
CFO: Shelley V Kolseth, Chief Financial Officer
CMO: Christos Politis, M.D., Chief Medical Officer
CIO: John Riton, Director Information Services
Web address: www.memorialhospitaltampa.com
Control: Corporation, Investor–owned (for–profit) **Service**: General medical and surgical

> **Staffed Beds:** 139

FL

☐ **SHRINERS HOSPITALS FOR CHILDREN-TAMPA (103303)**, 12502 USF Pine Drive, Zip 33612–9499; tel. 813/972–2250, **A**1 3 5 10 **F**3 29 34 35 50 57 64 68 74 77 79 81 85 89 91 93 94 95 96 107 119 130 131 146 157 **S** Shriners Hospitals for Children, Tampa, FL
Primary Contact: Fleury Yelvington, Administrator
CFO: Ruth Gregos, Director Finance
CMO: Maureen Maciel, M.D., Chief of Staff
CHR: Amy Schenker, Human Resources Director
Web address: www.shrinershospitalsforchildren.org/Hospitals/Locations/Tampa.aspx
Control: Other not–for–profit (including NFP Corporation) **Service**: Children's orthopedic

Staffed Beds: 60 **Admissions**: 232 **Census**: 1 **Outpatient Visits**: 12593 **Births**: 0 **Total Expense ($000)**: 23821 **Payroll Expense ($000)**: 11800 **Personnel**: 152

⊞ **ST. JOSEPH'S HOSPITAL (100075)**, 3001 West Martin Luther King Jr. Boulevard, Zip 33607–6387, Mailing Address: P.O. Box 4227, Zip 33677–4227; tel. 813/870–4000, (Includes ST. JOSEPH'S CHILDREN'S HOSPITAL, 3001 Dr Martin Luther King Jr Boulevard, Tampa, Florida, Zip 33607; tel. 813/554–8500; Sarah Naumowich, President; ST. JOSEPH'S HOSPITAL - NORTH, 4211 Van Dyke Road, Lutz, Florida, Zip 33558–8005; tel. 813/443–7000; Paula McGinnis, Chief Executive Officer; ST. JOSEPH'S HOSPITAL BEHAVIORAL HEALTH CENTER, 4918 North Habana Avenue, Tampa, Florida, Zip 33614–6815; tel. 813/870–4300; ST. JOSEPH'S HOSPITAL-SOUTH, 6901 Simmons Loop, Riverview, Florida, Zip 33578–9498; tel. 813/302–8000; Philip Minden, President; ST. JOSEPH'S WOMEN'S HOSPITAL, 3030 West Dr Martin L King Boulevard, Tampa, Florida, Zip 33607–6394; tel. 813/872–2950; Sarah Naumowich, President) **A**1 2 3 5 10 **F**3 7 11 12 13 15 17 18 19 20 21 22 23 24 25 26 27 28 29 30 31 32 34 35 36 37 39 40 41 43 44 45 46 48 49 51 55 57 58 59 61 63 64 65 66 68 70 71 72 73 74 75 76 78 79 81 82 84 85 86 87 88 89 92 93 94 98 99 100 101 102 107 108 110 111 112 114 115 116 117 118 119 120 121 123 124 126 127 129 130 131 132 134 135 143 145 146 147 148 149 150 154 156 **S** Trinity Health, Livonia, MI
Primary Contact: Kimberly Guy, President
CFO: Cathy Yoder, Chief Financial Officer
CMO: Peter Charvat, M.D., Chief Medical Officer
CIO: Lindsey Jarrell, Vice President Information Services
CHR: Pat Lipton, Director Team Resources
Web address: www.sjbhealth.org
Control: Other not–for–profit (including NFP Corporation) **Service**: General medical and surgical

Staffed Beds: 1062 **Admissions**: 59931 **Census**: 716 **Outpatient Visits**: 590728 **Births**: 8212 **Total Expense ($000)**: 1100226 **Payroll Expense ($000)**: 373097 **Personnel**: 5962

★ △ **TAMPA GENERAL HOSPITAL (100128)**, 1 Tampa General Circle, Zip 33606–3571, Mailing Address: P.O. Box 1289, Zip 33601–1289; tel. 813/844–7000, (Includes TAMPA GENERAL HOSPITAL CHILDREN'S MEDICAL CENTER, 1 Tampa General Circle, Tampa, Florida, Zip 33606–3571; tel. 813/844–7000) **A**3 5 7 8 10 **F**3 7 8 9 11 12 13 15 16 17 18 19 20 22 24 26 28 29 30 31 32 34 35 36 37 38 39 40 41 42 43 44 45 46 47 48 49 50 52 53 54 55 56 57 58 59 60 61 62 63 64 66 68 70 72 73 74 75 76 77 78 79 81 82 83 84 85 86 87 88 89 90 91 92 93 94 96 97 99 100 101 102 103 107 108 109 110 111 112 114 115 116 117 118 119 120 121 123 124 126 129 130 132 134 135 137 138 139 140 141 142 143 144 145 146 147 148 149 150 154 155 156
Primary Contact: John D. Couris, Chief Executive Officer
COO: Kelly Cullen, R.N., Executive Vice President and Chief Operating Officer
CFO: Judith M. Ploszek, Chief Financial Officer
CMO: Sally Houston, M.D., Executive Vice President and Chief Medical Officer
CIO: Scott Arnold, Senior Vice President Information Systems
CHR: Chris Roederer, Senior Vice President Human Resources
CNO: Janet Davis, R.N., MS, Senior Vice President and Chief Nursing Officer
Web address: www.tgh.org
Control: Other not–for–profit (including NFP Corporation) **Service**: General medical and surgical

Staffed Beds: 1007 **Admissions**: 47630 **Census**: 797 **Outpatient Visits**: 472733 **Births**: 6181 **Total Expense ($000)**: 1311823 **Payroll Expense ($000)**: 483999 **Personnel**: 7098

TARPON SPRINGS—Pinellas County

⊞ **ADVENTHEALTH NORTH PINELLAS (100055)**, 1395 South Pinellas Avenue, Zip 34689–3790; tel. 727/942–5000, **A**1 5 10 **F**3 15 17 18 20 22 26 28 29 30 31 34 35 37 38 40 42 45 46 49 50 51 54 55 56 57 59 64 65 68 70 71 74 75 76 78 79 81 84 85 87 93 94 96 97 107 108 110 111 114 115 117 119 126 128 129 130 131 132 135 146 148 149 154 155 **S** AdventHealth, Altamonte Springs, FL
Primary Contact: Jason Dunkel, President and Chief Executive Officer
CFO: Caleb Heinrich, Chief Financial Officer
CMO: Michael Longley, M.D., Chief Medical Officer
CIO: Brett Peterson, Director of Information Services
CHR: Vernon Elarbee, Director of Human Resources
CNO: Jennifer Segur, Chief Nursing Officer and Chief Clinical Officer
Web address: www.fhnorthpinellas.com/
Control: Church operated, Nongovernment, not–for–profit **Service**: General medical and surgical

Staffed Beds: 187 **Admissions**: 5835 **Census**: 83 **Outpatient Visits**: 48590 **Births**: 74 **Total Expense ($000)**: 115175 **Payroll Expense ($000)**: 39144 **Personnel**: 551

TAVARES—Lake County

⊞ **ADVENTHEALTH WATERMAN (100057)**, 1000 Waterman Way, Zip 32778–5266; tel. 352/253–3333, **A**1 2 10 **F**3 11 13 15 17 18 20 22 24 26 28 29 30 31 32 34 35 36 37 40 45 49 50 53 54 55 56 57 59 62 64 66 70 74 75 76 77 78 79 81 85 86 87 89 91 93 107 108 110 111 114 115 116 117 118 119 120 121 123 124 126 130 132 143 144 146 147 148 149 156 **S** AdventHealth, Altamonte Springs, FL
Primary Contact: Abel Biri, Chief Executive Officer
COO: Anita Young, Chief Operating Officer
CFO: Terri Warren, Chief Financial Officer
CMO: Vinay Mehindru, M.D., Vice President/Chief Medical Officer
CHR: Madge Springer, Director Human Resources
CNO: Michael Stimson, Chief Nursing Officer
Web address: www.fhwat.org
Control: Church operated, Nongovernment, not–for–profit **Service**: General medical and surgical

Staffed Beds: 269 **Admissions**: 15161 **Census**: 179 **Outpatient Visits**: 119030 **Births**: 601 **Total Expense ($000)**: 231983 **Payroll Expense ($000)**: 87932 **Personnel**: 1983

TAVERNIER—Monroe County

⊞ **BAPTIST HEALTH SOUTH FLORIDA, MARINERS HOSPITAL (101313)**, 91500 Overseas Highway, Zip 33070–2547; tel. 305/434–3000, **A**1 10 18 **F**3 11 15 18 28 29 30 31 34 35 44 45 47 50 51 53 57 59 63 64 68 70 74 75 77 78 79 81 82 84 85 87 90 93 97 107 108 110 111 114 115 119 129 130 131 132 133 135 145 146 147 148 149 150 154 **S** Baptist Health South Florida, Coral Gables, FL
Primary Contact: Rick Freeburg, Chief Executive Officer
CFO: David Abercrombie, Controller
CIO: Mimi Taylor, Vice President Information Technology
CHR: John Williamson, Human Resources Site Manager
Web address: www.baptisthealth.net/en/facilities/mariners-hospital/Pages/default.aspx
Control: Other not–for–profit (including NFP Corporation) **Service**: General medical and surgical

Staffed Beds: 25 **Admissions**: 524 **Census**: 5 **Outpatient Visits**: 37450 **Births**: 0 **Total Expense ($000)**: 48379 **Payroll Expense ($000)**: 16543 **Personnel**: 188

THE VILLAGES—Sumter County

THE VILLAGES REGIONAL HOSPITAL See The Villages Regional Hospital

⊞ **THE VILLAGES REGIONAL HOSPITAL (100290)**, 1451 El Camino Real, Zip 32159–0041; tel. 352/751–8000, **A**1 2 10 **F**3 8 11 15 18 20 22 24 26 28 29 30 31 34 35 40 45 49 51 57 59 64 68 70 74 75 77 78 79 81 84 85 87 90 92 93 96 97 107 108 111 114 115 119 126 130 132 135 146 147 149 150 156 **S** Central Florida Health, Leesburg, FL
Primary Contact: Donald G. Henderson, FACHE, President and Chief Executive Officer
CFO: Diane P Harden, Senior Vice President and Chief Financial Officer
CHR: Amie A Richason, Vice President Human Resources
CNO: Mary Jane Curry-Pelyak, R.N., Vice President and Chief Clinical Officer
Web address: www.cfhalliance.org
Control: Other not–for–profit (including NFP Corporation) **Service**: General medical and surgical

Staffed Beds: 297 **Admissions**: 14236 **Census**: 193 **Outpatient Visits**: 50845 **Births**: 0 **Personnel**: 1047

FL

TITUSVILLE—Brevard County

☐ **PARRISH MEDICAL CENTER (100028)**, 951 North Washington Avenue, Zip 32796–2163; tel. 321/268–6111, (Nonreporting) **A**1 2 10
Primary Contact: George Mikitarian Jr, FACHE, President and Chief Executive Officer
CFO: Timothy Skeldon, Senior Vice President and Chief Financial Officer
CMO: Lisa Alexanda, M.D., Vice President Medical Affairs
CIO: William Moore, Chief Information Officer
Web address: www.parrishmed.com
Control: Hospital district or authority, Government, nonfederal **Service:** General medical and surgical

Staffed Beds: 210

TRINITY—Pasco County

COMMUNITY HOSPITAL See Medical Center of Trinity, Trinity

⊞ **MEDICAL CENTER OF TRINITY (100191)**, 9330 State Road 54, Zip 34655–1808; tel. 727/834–4900, (Nonreporting) **A**1 2 3 10 **S** HCA Healthcare, Nashville, TN
Primary Contact: Leigh Massengill, Chief Executive Officer
COO: Sally Seymour, Chief Operating Officer
CFO: Michael Wyers, Chief Financial Officer
CMO: Elbert Barnes, M.D., Chief Medical Officer
CIO: Kurt Hornung, Director
CHR: Christena Miano, Vice President, Human Resources
CNO: Nancy Maysilles, R.N., Chief Nursing Officer
Web address: www.medicalcentertrinity.com
Control: Corporation, Investor–owned (for–profit) **Service:** General medical and surgical

Staffed Beds: 276

VENICE—Sarasota County

⊞ **VENICE REGIONAL BAYFRONT HEALTH (100070)**, 540 The Rialto, Zip 34285–2900; tel. 941/485–7711, **A**1 10 **F**3 8 11 12 15 17 18 20 22 24 26 28 29 34 35 37 40 45 46 47 49 50 51 54 56 57 59 64 70 74 77 79 81 82 85 87 93 96 107 108 110 111 114 115 118 119 126 129 130 146 148 149 154 156 157 **S** Community Health Systems, Inc., Franklin, TN
Primary Contact: Karen Fordham, Chief Executive Officer
COO: Benjamin Brodersen, Chief Operating Officer
CFO: Danny Warren, Chief Financial Officer
CIO: Eloy Rivas, Director of Information Systems
CHR: John Ware, Director of Human Resources
CNO: Dawn Beijin, R.N., Chief Nursing Officer
Web address: www.veniceregional.com
Control: Corporation, Investor–owned (for–profit) **Service:** General medical and surgical

Staffed Beds: 221 **Admissions:** 8326 **Census:** 94 **Outpatient Visits:** 88641
Births: 0 **Total Expense ($000):** 152517 **Payroll Expense ($000):** 52330
Personnel: 1127

VERO BEACH—Indian River County

⊞ **CLEVELAND CLINIC INDIAN RIVER HOSPITAL (100105)**, 1000 36th Street, Zip 32960–6592; tel. 772/567–4311, (Includes BEHAVIORAL HEALTH CENTER, 1190 37th Street, Vero Beach, Florida, Zip 32960–6507; tel. 772/563–4666; Jeffrey L Susi, President and Chief Executive Officer), (Nonreporting) **A**1 2 10 **S** Cleveland Clinic Health System, Cleveland, OH
Primary Contact: Gregory Rosencrance, Chief Executive Officer
COO: Ralph Turner, Chief Operating Officer
CFO: Greg Gardner, Senior Vice President and Chief Financial Officer
CMO: Charles Mackett, M.D., Senior Vice President and Chief Medical Officer
CIO: William Neil, Vice President and Chief Information Officer
CNO: Linda Walton, R.N., MSN, Chief Nursing Officer
Web address: www.https://www.indianrivermedicalcenter.com/
Control: Other not–for–profit (including NFP Corporation) **Service:** General medical and surgical

Staffed Beds: 220

⊞ **ENCOMPASS HEALTH REHABILITATION HOSPITAL OF TREASURE COAST (103032)**, 1600 37th Street, Zip 32960–4863; tel. 772/778–2100, (Nonreporting) **A**1 10 **S** Encompass Health Corporation, Birmingham, AL
Primary Contact: Michael Kissner, Chief Executive Officer
CFO: Kevin Hardy, Chief Financial Officer
CMO: Jimmy Wayne Lockhart, M.D., Medical Director
CHR: Linda Rinehart, Director Human Resources
Web address: www.healthsouthtreasurecoast.com
Control: Corporation, Investor–owned (for–profit) **Service:** Rehabilitation

Staffed Beds: 80

WAUCHULA—Hardee County

★ **ADVENTHEALTH WAUCHULA (101300)**, 533 West Carlton Street, Zip 33873–3407; tel. 863/773–3101, **A**10 18 **F**29 30 34 40 57 59 107 110 111 119 127 130 133 149 156 **S** AdventHealth, Altamonte Springs, FL
Primary Contact: Denise Grimsley, R.N., Vice President and Administrator
CFO: Rosalie Oliver, Senior Vice President and Chief Financial Officer
CMO: Jorge F Gonzalez, M.D., Vice President and Chief Nursing Officer
CIO: Jeff McDonald, Information Technology Manager
CHR: Michelle F. Myers, Director Human Resources
CNO: Gloria N Santos, R.N., MS, Vice President and Chief Nursing Officer
Web address: www.fh.floridahospital.com/heartland/home.aspx
Control: Church operated, Nongovernment, not–for–profit **Service:** General medical and surgical

Staffed Beds: 25 **Admissions:** 841 **Census:** 23 **Outpatient Visits:** 24954
Births: 0 **Total Expense ($000):** 20795 **Payroll Expense ($000):** 9016
Personnel: 130

WELLINGTON—Palm Beach County

☐ **WELLINGTON REGIONAL MEDICAL CENTER (100275)**, 10101 Forest Hill Boulevard, Zip 33414–6199; tel. 561/798–8500, (Nonreporting) **A**1 3 10 13 **S** Universal Health Services, Inc., King of Prussia, PA
Primary Contact: Pamela S. Tahan, Chief Executive Officer
CFO: Tonja Mosley, Chief Financial Officer
CMO: Richard Hays, M.D., Chief Medical Officer
CIO: Pierre Bergeron, Information Services Director
CHR: Mary Jo Caracciolo, Human Resource Director
CNO: Asenath Cassel, Chief Nursing Officer
Web address: www.wellingtonregional.com
Control: Corporation, Investor–owned (for–profit) **Service:** General medical and surgical

Staffed Beds: 233

WESLEY CHAPEL—Pasco County

★ ⇑ **ADVENTHEALTH WESLEY CHAPEL (100319)**, 2600 Bruce B Downs Boulevard, Zip 33544–9207; tel. 813/929–5000, **A**2 5 10 21 **F**3 11 13 15 18 20 22 26 28 29 30 34 35 40 42 45 46 47 49 51 53 57 59 64 70 74 75 77 79 81 85 87 93 107 108 109 110 111 115 117 119 120 126 130 132 145 146 147 148 149 154 **S** AdventHealth, Altamonte Springs, FL
Primary Contact: Erik Wangsness, Chief Executive Officer
Web address: www.https://www.floridahospital.com/wesley-chapel
Control: Other not–for–profit (including NFP Corporation) **Service:** General medical and surgical

Staffed Beds: 145 **Admissions:** 7845 **Census:** 64 **Outpatient Visits:** 72305
Births: 515 **Total Expense ($000):** 177415 **Payroll Expense ($000):** 55921
Personnel: 1004

☐ **NORTH TAMPA BEHAVIORAL HEALTH (104075)**, 29910 State Road 56, Zip 33543–8800; tel. 813/922–3300, (Nonreporting) **A**1 10 **S** Acadia Healthcare Company, Inc., Franklin, TN
Primary Contact: Tracy Rogers, Chief Executive Officer
Web address: www.northtampabehavioralhealth.com
Control: Corporation, Investor–owned (for–profit) **Service:** Psychiatric

Staffed Beds: 78

FL

Hospital, Medicare Provider Number, Address, Telephone, Approval, Facility, and Physician Codes, Health Care System

★ American Hospital Association (AHA) membership   ○ Healthcare Facilities Accreditation Program   ⇑ Center for Improvement in Healthcare Quality Accreditation
☐ The Joint Commission accreditation   ◇ DNV Healthcare Inc. accreditation   △ Commission on Accreditation of Rehabilitation Facilities (CARF) accreditation

© 2019 AHA Guide   *Many Facility Codes have changed. Please refer to the AHA Guide Code Chart.*   Hospitals **A143**

WEST PALM BEACH—Palm Beach County

⊞ **GOOD SAMARITAN MEDICAL CENTER (100287)**, 1309 North Flagler Drive, Zip 33401–3499; tel. 561/655–5511, **A**1 2 5 10 **F**3 11 12 13 15 18 20 22 26 29 30 31 34 35 40 45 46 49 50 51 55 56 57 58 59 60 68 70 72 74 75 76 77 78 79 81 82 84 85 86 87 93 107 108 110 111 114 115 119 126 129 130 131 132 146 147 154 157 **S** TENET Healthcare Corporation, Dallas, TX
Primary Contact: Tara McCoy, Chief Executive Officer
CFO: Cynthia McCauley, Chief Financial Officer
CIO: Candace Helms, Director Information Services
CNO: Joe Lopez-Cepero, Chief Nursing Officer
Web address: www.goodsamaritanmc.com
Control: Corporation, Investor–owned (for–profit) **Service:** General medical and surgical

Staffed Beds: 226 **Admissions:** 9443 **Census:** 122 **Outpatient Visits:** 123553 **Births:** 625 **Total Expense ($000):** 163751 **Payroll Expense ($000):** 75295 **Personnel:** 898

☐ **JEROME GOLDEN CENTER FOR BEHAVIORAL HEALTH, INC. (104008)**, 1041 45th Street, Zip 33407–2494; tel. 561/383–8000, (Nonreporting) **A**1 10
Primary Contact: Linda De Piano, Ph.D., Chief Executive Officer
CFO: America Cordoves, Controller
CMO: Suresh Rajpara, M.D., Chief Medical Officer
CIO: Iris Garcia, Director, Information Services
CHR: Nadine Wilson, Manager, Human Resources
CNO: Holly Horvath, Director of Nursing
Web address: www.goldenctr.org
Control: Other not–for–profit (including NFP Corporation) **Service:** Psychiatric

Staffed Beds: 44

★ **JFK MEDICAL CENTER NORTH CAMPUS (100234)**, 2201 45th Street, Zip 33407–2047; tel. 561/842–6141, (Nonreporting) **A**5 12 13 **S** HCA Healthcare, Nashville, TN
Primary Contact: Patricia Burns, Chief Executive Officer
COO: Patrick Chapman, Assistant Vice President Operations
CMO: Paul Seltzer, M.D., Chief of Staff
CIO: Kenneth Vasquez, Associate Director
CHR: Donna Boyle, Director
CNO: Geraldine DeStefano, R.N., MS, Chief Nursing Officer
Web address: www.westpalmhospital.com
Control: Corporation, Investor–owned (for–profit) **Service:** General medical and surgical

Staffed Beds: 245

⊞ △ **ST. MARY'S MEDICAL CENTER (100288)**, 901 45th Street, Zip 33407–2495; tel. 561/844–6300, (Includes PALM BEACH CHILDREN'S HOSPITAL, 901 45th Street, West Palm Beach, Florida, Zip 33407; tel. 561/844–6300) **A**1 3 7 10 **F**3 8 13 15 17 18 19 20 29 30 31 32 34 35 39 40 41 43 45 46 47 48 49 50 51 56 57 58 59 60 61 64 70 72 73 74 75 76 77 78 79 81 84 85 86 87 88 89 90 91 92 93 94 96 97 98 100 101 102 107 108 110 111 114 115 119 130 131 132 135 146 147 148 149 156 157 **S** TENET Healthcare Corporation, Dallas, TX
Primary Contact: Gabrielle Finley-Hazle, Chief Executive Officer
COO: Joey Bulfin, R.N., Interim Chief Executive Officer
CFO: Michelle Cartwright, Chief Financial Officer
CMO: Jeffrey Davis, D.O., Chief Medical Officer
CIO: Rich Avato, Director
CHR: Thomas J Piszczatoski, Chief Human Resource Officer
CNO: Donna Small, R.N., Chief Nursing Officer
Web address: www.stmarysmc.com
Control: Corporation, Investor–owned (for–profit) **Service:** General medical and surgical

Staffed Beds: 460 **Admissions:** 18633 **Census:** 272 **Outpatient Visits:** 120147 **Births:** 3385 **Total Expense ($000):** 283108 **Payroll Expense ($000):** 111884

VETERANS AFFAIRS MEDICAL CENTER See West Palm Beach Veterans Affairs Medical Center

⊞ **WEST PALM BEACH VETERANS AFFAIRS MEDICAL CENTER**, 7305 North Military Trail, Zip 33410–6400; tel. 561/422–8262, (Nonreporting) **A**1 3 5 **S** Department of Veterans Affairs, Washington, DC
Primary Contact: Donna Katen-Bahensky, Director
CFO: Lori Hancock, Chief Business Officer
CMO: Deepak Mandi, M.D., Chief of Staff
CIO: Karen Gabaldon, Chief Management Information Systems
CHR: David Green, Chief Human Resources
Web address: www.westpalmbeach.va.gov/
Control: Veterans Affairs, Government, federal **Service:** General medical and surgical

Staffed Beds: 300

WESTON—Broward County

⊞ **CLEVELAND CLINIC FLORIDA (100289)**, 2950 Cleveland Clinic Boulevard, Zip 33331–3602; tel. 954/659–5000, **A**1 2 3 5 10 **F**3 7 8 9 11 12 15 17 18 20 22 24 26 28 29 30 31 34 35 36 37 39 40 41 44 45 46 47 48 49 50 51 54 55 56 57 58 59 60 61 63 64 65 68 70 71 74 75 77 78 79 80 81 82 84 85 86 87 91 92 93 96 97 100 107 108 109 110 111 114 115 116 117 119 120 121 123 124 126 129 130 131 132 135 137 138 139 141 145 146 147 148 149 154 155 156 **S** Cleveland Clinic Health System, Cleveland, OH
Primary Contact: Wael Barsoum, M.D., President
CFO: Keith Nilsson, Chief Financial Officer
CMO: Raul Rosenthal, M.D., Interim Chief of Staff
CIO: John Santangelo, Director Information Technology
CHR: Carl McDonald, Senior Director, Human Resources
CNO: Kerry Major, R.N., MSN, Chief Nursing Officer
Web address: www.clevelandclinic.org/florida
Control: Other not–for–profit (including NFP Corporation) **Service:** General medical and surgical

Staffed Beds: 206 **Admissions:** 11573 **Census:** 143 **Outpatient Visits:** 51418 **Births:** 0 **Total Expense ($000):** 297069 **Payroll Expense ($000):** 104467 **Personnel:** 2749

WILLISTON—Levy County

NATURE COAST REGIONAL HOSPITAL See Regional General Hospital

REGIONAL GENERAL HOSPITAL (100322), 125 SW Seventh Street, Zip 32696–2403; tel. 352/528–2801, (Nonreporting) **A**10
Primary Contact: Edith Mears, Chief Executive Officer
CFO: Barbara Miller, Manager Business Office
CMO: Jeremie Young, M.D., Chief of Staff
CHR: Karla Dass, Director Human Resources
Web address: www.regionalgeneral.com/
Control: Partnership, Investor–owned (for–profit) **Service:** General medical and surgical

Staffed Beds: 20

WINTER HAVEN—Polk County

⊞ △ **WINTER HAVEN HOSPITAL (100052)**, 200 Avenue F NE, Zip 33881–4193; tel. 863/293–1121, **A**1 7 10 **F**3 8 11 15 18 19 20 22 24 26 28 29 30 31 34 37 40 45 47 49 57 58 59 60 64 68 70 72 73 74 75 76 77 78 79 81 82 84 85 86 87 89 93 94 98 100 101 102 104 107 108 109 110 111 114 115 118 119 120 121 122 123 126 130 132 135 144 146 147 148 156 **S** Trinity Health, Livonia, MI
Primary Contact: Stephen A. Nierman, President
COO: Jacques Vasconcellos, Director, Operations
CFO: Tina Solomon, Executive Director Finance
CMO: Khurram Kamran, M.D., Vice President, Physician Services
CIO: Cal Cole, Director Information Systems
CHR: Rosemary Myers, Manager, Team Resources
CNO: Carol Koeppel-Olsen, Vice President, Patient Care Services
Web address: www.winterhavenhospital.org
Control: Other not–for–profit (including NFP Corporation) **Service:** General medical and surgical

Staffed Beds: 361 **Admissions:** 20529 **Census:** 233 **Outpatient Visits:** 169107 **Births:** 1727 **Total Expense ($000):** 315238 **Payroll Expense ($000):** 116784 **Personnel:** 1988

WINTER PARK—Orange County

ADVENTHEALTH WINTER PARK See Adventhealth Orlando, Orlando

ZEPHYRHILLS—Pasco County

⊞ **ADVENTHEALTH ZEPHYRHILLS (100046)**, 7050 Gall Boulevard, Zip 33541–1399; tel. 813/788–0411, **A**1 5 10 **F**13 15 18 20 22 26 29 40 45 50 64 69 70 76 79 81 82 89 97 100 107 108 111 112 116 117 119 126 147 148 **S** AdventHealth, Altamonte Springs, FL
Primary Contact: Amanda Maggard, Chief Executive Officer
COO: Donald E Welch, Chief Operating Officer
CFO: Bill Heinrich, Chief Financial Officer
CMO: Hugar McNamee, D.O., Chief Medical Officer
CIO: Kelley Sasser, Director Information Systems
CHR: Laura Asaftei, Administrative Director
CNO: Gwen Alonso, Chief Nursing Officer
Web address: www.fhzeph.org
Control: Church operated, Nongovernment, not–for–profit **Service:** General medical and surgical

Staffed Beds: 149 **Admissions:** 8979 **Census:** 91 **Outpatient Visits:** 96341 **Births:** 573 **Total Expense ($000):** 151934 **Payroll Expense ($000):** 57013 **Personnel:** 797

FL

GEORGIA

ADEL—Cook County

⌖ **COOK MEDICAL CENTER-A CAMPUS OF TIFT REGIONAL MEDICAL CENTER (110101)**, 706 North Parrish Avenue, Zip 31620–1511; tel. 229/896–8000, (Total facility includes 95 beds in nursing home–type unit) **A**1 10 **F**11 15 29 30 34 35 45 56 57 59 63 64 65 68 75 77 81 84 85 86 87 93 97 98 101 103 104 107 108 110 111 114 119 127 129 130 133 135 146 147 148 149 154 156 **S** Tift Regional Health System, Tifton, GA
Primary Contact: Michael L. Purvis, Chief Executive Officer
COO: Kim Wills, Chief Operating Officer
CIO: Barry Medley, Director Information Systems
CHR: Shirley Padgett, Director Human Resources
Web address: www.cookmedicalcenter.com
Control: Hospital district or authority, Government, nonfederal **Service:** General medical and surgical

Staffed Beds: 155 **Admissions:** 596 **Census:** 99 **Outpatient Visits:** 10905 **Births:** 0 **Total Expense ($000):** 17584 **Payroll Expense ($000):** 8667 **Personnel:** 181

ALBANY—Dougherty County

★ ⇑ **PHOEBE PUTNEY MEMORIAL HOSPITAL (110007)**, 417 West Third Avenue, Zip 31701–1943, Mailing Address: P.O. Box 3770, Zip 31706–3770; tel. 229/312–4100, (Includes PHOEBE NORTH, 2000 Palmyra Road, Albany, Georgia, Zip 31701–1528, Mailing Address: P O Box 1908, Zip 31702–1908, tel. 229/434–2000) **A**2 3 5 10 21 **F**3 5 7 11 12 13 15 17 18 20 22 24 26 28 29 30 31 34 35 40 44 45 46 47 48 49 50 53 54 56 57 59 60 61 62 63 64 68 70 72 73 74 75 76 77 78 79 81 82 83 84 85 86 87 89 90 91 92 93 94 96 97 98 100 101 102 103 104 105 107 108 110 111 114 115 116 117 118 119 120 121 123 124 126 127 129 130 131 132 134 135 136 144 145 146 147 148 149 153 154 **S** Phoebe Putney Health System, Albany, GA
Primary Contact: Scott Steiner, FACHE, Chief Executive Officer
COO: Joe Austin, Executive Vice President and Chief Operating Officer
CFO: Brian Church, Senior Vice President and Chief Financial Officer
CMO: Steven Kitchen, M.D., Chief Medical Officer
CIO: Jesse Diaz, Chief Information Officer
CHR: Tony Welch, Senior Vice President and Chief Human Resources Officer
CNO: Laura Shearer, R.N., MSN, Senior Vice President and Chief Nursing Officer
Web address: www.phoebeputney.com
Control: Other not–for–profit (including NFP Corporation) **Service:** General medical and surgical

Staffed Beds: 461 **Admissions:** 18225 **Census:** 277 **Outpatient Visits:** 1532399 **Births:** 2135 **Total Expense ($000):** 528853 **Payroll Expense ($000):** 146517 **Personnel:** 3344

ALMA—Bacon County

⌖ **BACON COUNTY HOSPITAL AND HEALTH SYSTEM (111327)**, 302 South Wayne Street, Zip 31510–2922, Mailing Address: P O Drawer 1987, Zip 31510–0987; tel. 912/632–8961, (Nonreporting) **A**1 10 18
Primary Contact: Cindy R. Turner, Chief Executive Officer
COO: Cindy R Turner, Chief Executive Officer
CFO: Kyle Kimmel, Chief Financial Officer
CMO: Lou Ellen Hutcheson, M.D., Chief of Staff
CIO: Neil O'Steen, Director Information Technology
CHR: Kerry Hancock, Director Human Resources
CNO: Deanna Hoff, R.N., Director of Nursing
Web address: www.baconcountyhospital.com
Control: Other not–for–profit (including NFP Corporation) **Service:** General medical and surgical

Staffed Beds: 113

AMERICUS—Sumter County

★ ⇑ **PHOEBE SUMTER MEDICAL CENTER (110044)**, 126 Highway, 280 West, Zip 31719, Mailing Address: 126 Highway 280 West, Zip 31719; tel. 229/924–6011, (Nonreporting) **A**10 21 **S** Phoebe Putney Health System, Albany, GA
Primary Contact: Brandi Lunneborg, Chief Executive Officer
CHR: Cassandra Haynes Aldridge, Chief Human Resources Officer
CNO: Susan Bruns, Chief Nursing Officer
Web address: www.phoebesumter.org
Control: Other not–for–profit (including NFP Corporation) **Service:** General medical and surgical

Staffed Beds: 44

ATHENS—Clarke County

⌖ **LANDMARK HOSPITAL OF ATHENS (112017)**, 775 Sunset Drive, Zip 30606–2211; tel. 706/425–1500, (Nonreporting) **A**10 22 **S** Landmark Hospitals, Cape Girardeau, MO
Primary Contact: Vivian Goff, R.N., Chief Executive Officer
Web address: www.landmarkhospitals.com
Control: Individual, Investor–owned (for–profit) **Service:** Acute long–term care hospital

Staffed Beds: 42

⌖ **PIEDMONT ATHENS REGIONAL MEDICAL CENTER (110074)**, 1199 Prince Avenue, Zip 30606–2797; tel. 706/475–7000, **A**1 2 3 10 **F**3 8 13 15 17 18 20 22 24 26 28 29 30 31 32 34 35 36 40 43 45 46 47 48 49 50 51 54 55 56 57 58 59 60 61 62 64 66 68 70 71 72 73 74 76 77 78 79 80 81 83 84 85 86 87 89 91 92 93 94 96 100 102 107 108 110 111 114 115 116 117 118 119 120 121 123 124 126 129 130 131 132 135 144 145 146 147 148 156 **S** Piedmont Healthcare, Roswell, GA
Primary Contact: Michael Burnett, Chief Executive Officer
COO: Jason Smith, Chief Operating Officer
CFO: Wendy J. Cook, Chief Financial Officer
CMO: Robert Sinyard, M.D., Chief Medical Officer
CIO: Louis H. Duhe, Executor Director, Information Services
CHR: Robert D. Finch, Director, Human Resources
CNO: Tamara Jackson, Chief Nursing Officer
Web address: www.https://www.piedmont.org/locations/piedmont-athens
Control: Other not–for–profit (including NFP Corporation) **Service:** General medical and surgical

Staffed Beds: 345 **Admissions:** 20494 **Census:** 240 **Outpatient Visits:** 363608 **Births:** 2411 **Total Expense ($000):** 414474 **Payroll Expense ($000):** 164246 **Personnel:** 2994

⌖ △ **ST. MARY'S HEALTH CARE SYSTEM (110006)**, 1230 Baxter Street, Zip 30606–3791; tel. 706/389–3000, **A**1 3 7 10 19 **F**3 11 12 13 15 18 20 22 26 28 29 30 31 34 35 40 41 45 46 47 48 49 50 53 54 57 58 59 61 62 63 64 68 70 73 74 75 76 77 79 80 81 83 84 85 87 89 90 92 93 107 110 111 114 115 118 119 126 129 130 131 132 135 141 145 146 147 148 149 156 **S** Trinity Health, Livonia, MI
Primary Contact: D. Montez Carter, Chief Executive Officer
CFO: Marty Hutson, Chief Financial Officer
CMO: Bruce Middendorf, M.D., Chief Medical Officer
CIO: Kerry Vaughn, Chief Information Officer
CHR: Jeff English, Vice President Human Resources
CNO: Titus E. Gambrell, Vice President and Chief Nursing Officer
Web address: www.stmarysathens.com
Control: Church operated, Nongovernment, not–for–profit **Service:** General medical and surgical

Staffed Beds: 174 **Admissions:** 10149 **Census:** 131 **Outpatient Visits:** 214078 **Births:** 1446 **Total Expense ($000):** 186508 **Payroll Expense ($000):** 70235 **Personnel:** 1215

ATLANTA—Fulton and De Kalb County

☐ **ANCHOR HOSPITAL (114032)**, 5454 Yorktowne Drive, Zip 30349–5317; tel. 770/991–6044, (Nonreporting) **A**1 10 **S** Universal Health Services, Inc., King of Prussia, PA
Primary Contact: Lloyd Noble, Chief Executive Officer
CFO: John Kim, Chief Financial Officer
CMO: Shailesh Patel, M.D., Medical Director
CIO: Chris Hill, Information Technology
CHR: Danna Nordin, Director Human Resources
CNO: Angelica Jackson, Director of Nursing
Web address: www.anchorhospital.com
Control: Corporation, Investor–owned (for–profit) **Service:** Alcoholism and other chemical dependency

Staffed Beds: 122

Hospital, Medicare Provider Number, Address, Telephone, Approval, Facility, and Physician Codes, Health Care System

★ American Hospital Association (AHA) membership ○ Healthcare Facilities Accreditation Program ⇑ Center for Improvement in Healthcare Quality Accreditation
☐ The Joint Commission accreditation ◇ DNV Healthcare Inc. accreditation △ Commission on Accreditation of Rehabilitation Facilities (CARF) accreditation

GA

☐ △ **CHILDREN'S HEALTHCARE OF ATLANTA (113300)**, 1600 Tullie Circle, NE, Zip 30329–2303; tel. 404/785–7000, (Includes CHILDREN'S HEALTHCARE OF ATLANTA at EGLESTON, 1600 Tullie Circle, Atlanta, Georgia, Zip 30329; tel. 404/325–6000; CHILDREN'S HEALTHCARE OF ATLANTA AT HUGHES SPALDING, 35 Jesse Hill Jr Drive, SE, Atlanta, Georgia, Zip 30303–3032; tel. 404/785–9500; CHILDREN'S HEALTHCARE OF ATLANTA AT SCOTTISH RITE, 1001 Johnson Ferry Road NE, Atlanta, Georgia, Zip 30342–1600; tel. 404/256–5252), (Nonreporting) **A**1 3 5 7 8 10
Primary Contact: Donna W. Hyland, President and Chief Executive Officer
COO: Carolyn Kenny, Executive Vice President Clinical Care
CFO: Ruth Fowler, Senior Vice President and Chief Financial Officer
CMO: Daniel Salinas, M.D., Senior Vice President and Chief Medical Officer
CIO: Allana Cummings, Chief Information Officer
CHR: Linda Matzigkeit, Senior Vice President Human Resources
Web address: www.choa.org
Control: Other not–for–profit (including NFP Corporation) **Service**: Children's general medical and surgical

Staffed Beds: 496

☒ △ **EMORY REHABILITATION HOSPITAL (113031)**, 1441 Clifton Road NE, Zip 30322–1004; tel. 404/712–5512, **A**1 7 10 **F**11 29 30 34 35 36 50 56 58 64 68 74 75 77 79 82 85 86 87 90 93 94 95 96 130 131 132 135 146 148 149 **S** Emory Healthcare, Atlanta, GA
Primary Contact: Michael Eric. Garrard, FACHE, Chief Executive Officer
CMO: S. Byron Milton, M.D., Medical Director
CHR: Janine Diaz, Human Resources Manager
CNO: Deborah Almauhy, R.N., Chief Nursing Officer
Web address: www.emoryhealthcare.org/rehabilitation
Control: Partnership, Investor–owned (for–profit) **Service**: Rehabilitation

Staffed Beds: 46 **Admissions:** 1021 **Census:** 40 **Outpatient Visits:** 24954 **Births:** 0 **Total Expense ($000):** 24825 **Payroll Expense ($000):** 13810 **Personnel:** 187

☒ **EMORY SAINT JOSEPH'S HOSPITAL OF ATLANTA (110082)**, 5665 Peachtree Dunwoody Road NE, Zip 30342–1701; tel. 678/843–7001, **A**1 2 3 5 10 **F**3 11 12 15 17 18 20 22 24 26 28 29 30 31 34 35 37 40 44 45 46 47 49 50 51 53 54 55 57 58 59 60 64 68 70 71 74 75 77 78 79 81 82 84 85 86 87 100 102 107 108 110 111 115 117 118 119 120 121 123 124 126 130 132 135 145 146 147 148 149 156 **S** Emory Healthcare, Atlanta, GA
Primary Contact: Heather Dexter, Chief Executive Officer
CFO: Kevin Brenan, Chief Financial Officer
CMO: Thomas P. McGahan, M.D., Chief Medical Officer
CIO: Dedra Cantrell, Chief Information Officer
CHR: Audra Farish, Vice President Human Resources
Web address: www.emoryhealthcare.org/locations/hospitals/emory-saint-josephs-hospital/
Control: Other not–for–profit (including NFP Corporation) **Service**: General medical and surgical

Staffed Beds: 273 **Admissions:** 14657 **Census:** 196 **Outpatient Visits:** 123524 **Births:** 0 **Total Expense ($000):** 360794 **Payroll Expense ($000):** 119631 **Personnel:** 1674

☒ **EMORY UNIVERSITY HOSPITAL (110010)**, 1364 Clifton Road NE, Zip 30322; tel. 404/712–2000, (Includes EMORY UNIVERSITY ORTHOPAEDIC AND SPINE HOSPITAL, 1455 Montreal Road, Tucker, Georgia, Zip 30084; tel. 404/251–3600; June Conner, R.N., Chief Operating Officer; EMORY WESLEY WOODS GERIATRIC HOSPITAL, 1821 Clifton Road NE, Atlanta, Georgia, Zip 30329–4021; tel. 404/728–6200; Jennifer Schuck, Associate Administrator) **A**1 2 3 5 8 10 **F**3 11 12 14 15 17 18 20 22 24 26 29 30 31 34 35 36 38 39 40 44 45 46 47 48 49 50 55 56 57 58 59 60 61 63 64 68 70 74 75 77 78 79 80 81 82 84 85 86 87 90 92 93 98 100 101 102 103 105 107 108 110 111 114 115 116 117 118 119 120 121 123 124 126 129 130 131 132 135 136 137 138 139 140 141 142 145 146 147 148 149 153 154 156 **S** Emory Healthcare, Atlanta, GA
Primary Contact: Bryce D. Gartland, M.D., Chief Executive Officer
CFO: Carla Chandler, Vice President and Chief Financial Officer
CMO: Chad W.M. Ritenour, M.D., Chief Medical Officer
CIO: Sheila M Sanders, Chief Information Officer
CHR: Mary Beth Allen, Vice President Human Resources
CNO: Nancye R. Feistritzer, Chief Nursing Officer
Web address: www.emoryhealthcare.org
Control: Other not–for–profit (including NFP Corporation) **Service**: General medical and surgical

Staffed Beds: 622 **Admissions:** 28172 **Census:** 523 **Outpatient Visits:** 200457 **Births:** 0 **Total Expense ($000):** 922715 **Payroll Expense ($000):** 300477 **Personnel:** 4066

☒ **EMORY UNIVERSITY HOSPITAL MIDTOWN (110078)**, 550 Peachtree Street NE, Zip 30308–2247; tel. 404/686–4411, **A**1 2 3 5 8 10 **F**3 11 12·13 14 15 17 18 20 22 24 26 29 30 31 34 35 36 38 40 44 45 46 47 48 49 50 51 52 55 57 58 59 60 61 63 64 68 70 72 73 74 75 77 78 79 81 82 84 85 86 87 92 93 100 101 102 107 108 110 111 114 115 116 117 118 119 120 121 123 124 126 130 131 132 135 141 146 147 148 149 154 156 157 **S** Emory Healthcare, Atlanta, GA
Primary Contact: Daniel Owens, Chief Executive Officer
CMO: James P Steinberg, M.D., Chief Medical Officer
CIO: Dedra Cantrell, Chief Information Officer
CHR: Dallis Howard-Crow, Chief Human Resources Officer
Web address: www.emoryhealthcare.org
Control: Other not–for–profit (including NFP Corporation) **Service**: General medical and surgical

Staffed Beds: 512 **Admissions:** 25936 **Census:** 358 **Outpatient Visits:** 273790 **Births:** 4623 **Total Expense ($000):** 868701 **Payroll Expense ($000):** 234459 **Personnel:** 3036

☒ **GRADY MEMORIAL HOSPITAL (110079)**, 80 Jesse Hill Jr Drive SE, Zip 30303–3031, Mailing Address: P.O. Box 26189, Zip 31329–0386; tel. 404/616–1000, (Total facility includes 296 beds in nursing home–type unit) **A**1 2 3 5 8 10 **F**2 3 5 7 13 15 16 18 20 22 24 26 29 30 31 34 35 38 39 40 43 45 46 47 49 50 51 52 53 54 55 56 57 58 59 60 61 62 64 65 66 68 70 72 73 74 75 76 77 78 79 81 82 84 85 86 87 93 94 97 98 100 101 102 104 105 107 108 109 110 111 112 113 114 115 116 117 118 119 120 121 126 128 129 130 132 134 135 143 144 146 147 148 153 154 155 156 157
Primary Contact: John M. Haupert, FACHE, President and Chief Executive Officer
COO: Rhonda A Scott, Ph.D., R.N., Chief Operating Officer
CFO: Mark Meyer, Chief Financial Officer
CMO: Robert Jansen, Chief Medical Officer
CIO: Ben McKeeby, Senior Vice President and Chief Information Officer
CHR: Larry A. Callahan, Senior Vice President Human Resources
CNO: Jacqueline Herd, Executive Vice President and Chief Nursing Officer
Web address: www.gradyhealthsystem.org
Control: Other not–for–profit (including NFP Corporation) **Service**: General medical and surgical

Staffed Beds: 1060 **Admissions:** 32900 **Census:** 919 **Outpatient Visits:** 702553 **Births:** 2621 **Total Expense ($000):** 1220320 **Payroll Expense ($000):** 448040 **Personnel:** 6015

☒ **NORTHSIDE HOSPITAL (110161)**, 1000 Johnson Ferry Road NE, Zip 30342–1611; tel. 404/851–8000, **A**1 2 3 10 **F**3 5 8 11 12 13 15 17 18 20 22 26 28 29 30 31 34 35 37 40 44 45 46 47 48 49 50 54 55 57 58 59 60 64 68 70 71 72 73 74 75 76 77 78 79 80 81 82 84 85 86 87 93 100 104 107 108 110 111 114 115 117 118 119 120 121 123 124 126 129 130 131 132 135 136 144 145 146 147 148 156 **S** Northside Healthcare System, Atlanta, GA
Primary Contact: Robert Quattrocchi, President and Chief Executive Officer
CFO: Debbie Mitcham, Chief Financial Officer
CIO: Tina Wakim, Vice President Information
Web address: www.northside.com
Control: Other not–for–profit (including NFP Corporation) **Service**: General medical and surgical

Staffed Beds: 639 **Admissions:** 35153 **Census:** 404 **Outpatient Visits:** 1904490 **Births:** 15667 **Total Expense ($000):** 2097064 **Payroll Expense ($000):** 655684 **Personnel:** 9008

☐ **PEACHFORD BEHAVIORAL HEALTH SYSTEM (114010)**, 2151 Peachford Road, Zip 30338–6599; tel. 770/455–3200, (Nonreporting) **A**1 10 **S** Universal Health Services, Inc., King of Prussia, PA
Primary Contact: Matthew Crouch, Chief Executive Officer and Managing Director
COO: Sharon Stackhouse, Assistant Administrator and Director Risk Management
CFO: April Hughes, Chief Financial Officer
CMO: Asaf Aleem, M.D., Medical Director
CHR: Clay Boyles, Director Human Resources
Web address: www.peachfordhospital.com
Control: Corporation, Investor–owned (for–profit) **Service**: Psychiatric

Staffed Beds: 246

⋔ **PIEDMONT HOSPITAL (110083)**, 1968 Peachtree Road NW, Zip 30309–1281; tel. 404/605–5000, **A**2 3 5 10 21 **F**3 8 11 12 13 15 17 18 20 22 24 26 28 29 30 31 34 35 40 44 45 46 47 48 49 50 51 53 54 55 56 57 58 59 60 61 63 64 65 68 70 72 73 74 75 76 77 78 79 81 82 84 85 86 87 92 93 107 108 110 111 114 115 116 117 118 119 120 121 126 129 130 131 132 135 137 138 139 141 142 145 146 147 148 149 154 156 **S** Piedmont Healthcare, Roswell, GA
Primary Contact: Patrick M. Battey, FACS, M.D., Chief Executive Officer
COO: Ed Lovern, Chief Operating Officer
CFO: Sheryl Klink, Chief Financial Officer
CMO: Mark Cohen, M.D., Chief Medical Officer
CHR: Vicki A Cansler, Chief Human Resource Officer
CNO: Kelly Hulsey, MSN, R.N., Chief Nursing Officer
Web address: www.piedmont.org
Control: Other not–for–profit (including NFP Corporation) **Service**: General medical and surgical

Staffed Beds: 512 **Admissions:** 28270 **Census:** 406 **Outpatient Visits:** 326018 **Births:** 3538 **Personnel:** 2999

SAINT JOSEPH'S HOSPITAL OF ATLANTA See Emory Saint Joseph's Hospital of Atlanta

GA

Many Facility Codes have changed. Please refer to the AHA Guide Code Chart. © 2019 AHA Guide

⊞ **SELECT SPECIALTY HOSPITAL MIDTOWN ATLANTA (112004)**, 705 Juniper Street NE, Zip 30308–1307; tel. 404/873–2871, (Nonreporting) **A**1 10 **S** Select Medical Corporation, Mechanicsburg, PA
Primary Contact: Adriene Kinnaird, Chief Executive Officer
CFO: Michael Nelson, Chief Financial Officer
CMO: David N. DeRuyter, M.D., President Medical Staff
CHR: Armetria Gibson, Human Resources Generalist
CNO: Annette Harrilson, Chief Clinical Officer
Web address: www.selectspecialtyhospitals.com/
Control: Partnership, Investor–owned (for–profit) **Service:** Acute long–term care hospital

Staffed Beds: 72

☐ △ **SHEPHERD CENTER (112003)**, 2020 Peachtree Road NW, Zip 30309–1465; tel. 404/352–2020, **A**1 3 5 7 10 **F**3 10 29 30 34 35 36 50 53 58 59 64 65 70 74 75 77 79 82 86 87 90 91 92 93 94 95 111 119 130 131 132 134 143 146 148 149 157
Primary Contact: Sarah Morrison, President and Chief Executive Officer
CFO: Stephen B Holleman, Chief Financial Officer
CMO: Donald P Leslie, M.D., Medical Director
CIO: Brian Barnette, Chief Information Officer
CHR: Lorie Hutcheson, Vice President of Human Resources
CNO: Tamara King, R.N., MSN, Chief Nurse Executive
Web address: www.https://www.shepherd.org
Control: Other not–for–profit (including NFP Corporation) **Service:** Rehabilitation

Staffed Beds: 132 Admissions: 919 Census: 129 Outpatient Visits: 66412 **Births:** 0 **Total Expense ($000):** 222109 **Payroll Expense ($000):** 101222 **Personnel:** 1288

☐ **VERITAS COLLABORATIVE**, 6600 Peachtree Dunwoody Road, Embassy Row, Building 400, Suite 150, Zip 30328–6773; tel. 770/871–3730, (Nonreporting) **A**1
Primary Contact: Mederic D. McLaughlin, Executive Director
Web address: www.https://veritascollaborative.com
Control: Partnership, Investor–owned (for–profit) **Service:** Psychiatric

Staffed Beds: 50

★ **WELLSTAR ATLANTA MEDICAL CENTER (110115)**, 303 Parkway Drive NE, Zip 30312–1212; tel. 404/265–4000, (Includes WELLSTAR ATLANTA MEDICAL CENTER - SOUTH CAMPUS, 1170 Cleveland Avenue, Atlanta, Georgia, Zip 30344–3665; tel. 404/466–1170; Daniel Jackson, Vice President, Administrator) **A**2 3 5 8 10 **F**3 11 12 13 15 17 18 20 22 24 26 28 29 30 31 34 35 36 37 38 40 43 44 45 46 50 53 54 56 57 59 60 61 64 65 66 68 70 72 73 74 75 76 77 78 79 81 84 85 86 87 90 93 96 97 98 101 102 103 106 107 108 110 111 114 118 119 126 129 130 132 134 144 146 147 148 149 150 154 156 **S** WellStar Health System, Marietta, GA
Primary Contact: Kimberly Ryan, President
CFO: Jason K Limbaugh, Vice President and Chief Financial Officer
CMO: Albert Barrocas, M.D., Chief Medical Officer
CIO: Mike Sharp, Interim Director
CHR: Detra Bickerstaff, Vice President, Human Resources
CNO: Stuart D. Downs, Vice President and Chief Operating Officer
Web address: www.atlantamedcenter.com
Control: Other not–for–profit (including NFP Corporation) **Service:** General medical and surgical

Staffed Beds: 506 Admissions: 17870 **Census:** 306 **Outpatient Visits:** 189460 **Births:** 2494 **Personnel:** 1791

WESLEY WOODS GERIATRIC HOSPITAL OF EMORY UNIVERSITY See Emory Wesley Woods Geriatric Hospital

AUGUSTA—Richmond County

⊞ **AUGUSTA UNIVERSITY MEDICAL CENTER (110034)**, 1120 15th Street, Zip 30912–0004; tel. 706/721–0211, (Includes CHILDREN'S HOSPITAL OF GEORGIA, 1446 Harper Street, Augusta, Georgia, Zip 30912–0012; tel. 706/721–5437; Lee Ann Liska, Chief Executive Officer) **A**1 2 3 5 8 10 **F**3 5 6 9 11 12 13 14 15 17 18 19 20 21 22 23 24 25 26 27 28 29 30 31 32 36 38 40 41 43 45 46 48 49 50 51 54 55 56 58 59 60 61 64 65 66 68 70 72 73 74 75 76 77 78 79 81 82 84 85 86 87 88 89 91 92 93 97 98 99 100 101 102 103 104 107 108 111 113 115 116 117 118 119 120 121 123 124 126 127 129 130 131 132 134 135 136 138 141 142 143 146 147 148 151 154 156
Primary Contact: Katrina Keefer, Chief Executive Officer
COO: Shawn Vincent, Interim Chief Operating Officer
CFO: Greg Damron, Vice President Finance and Chief Financial Officer
CMO: Kevin Dellsperger, M.D., Chief Medical Officer
CIO: Charles Enicks, Chief Information Officer
CHR: Susan Norton, Vice President Human Resources
CNO: Laura E Brower, R.N., MSN, Chief Nursing Officer
Web address: www.grhealth.org
Control: Other not–for–profit (including NFP Corporation) **Service:** General medical and surgical

Staffed Beds: 467 Admissions: 20715 **Census:** 327 **Outpatient Visits:** 437266 **Births:** 1325 **Total Expense ($000):** 687635 **Payroll Expense ($000):** 221240 **Personnel:** 3681

⊞ △ **CHARLIE NORWOOD VETERANS AFFAIRS MEDICAL CENTER**, 1 Freedom Way, Zip 30904–6285; tel. 706/733–0188, (Nonreporting) **A**1 2 3 5 7 8 **S** Department of Veterans Affairs, Washington, DC
Primary Contact: Robin E. Jackson, Ph.D., Interim Acting Director
COO: John D Stenger, Acting Associate Director
CFO: Earline Corder, Chief Fiscal
CIO: Sandy Williford, Chief Health Information Management and Revenue Administration
CHR: Roger W Buterbaugh, Chief Human Resources Officer
Web address: www.augusta.va.gov/
Control: Veterans Affairs, Government, federal **Service:** General medical and surgical

Staffed Beds: 338

⊞ △ **DOCTORS HOSPITAL (110177)**, 3651 Wheeler Road, Zip 30909–6426; tel. 706/651–3232, (Nonreporting) **A**1 2 3 5 7 10 **S** HCA Healthcare, Nashville, TN
Primary Contact: Douglas Welch, Chief Executive Officer
CIO: Dona Hornung, Director Information and Technology Services
Web address: www.doctors-hospital.net
Control: Corporation, Investor–owned (for–profit) **Service:** General medical and surgical

Staffed Beds: 307

EAST CENTRAL REGIONAL HOSPITAL (114029), 3405 Mike Padgett Highway, Zip 30906–3897; tel. 706/790–2011, (Includes EAST CENTRAL REGIONAL HOSPITAL, 100 Myrtle Boulevard, Gracewood, Georgia, Zip 30812–1299; tel. 706/790–2011) **A**3 5 10 **F**29 34 38 39 59 65 67 75 77 98 101 102 128 130 132 135
Primary Contact: Paul Brock, Administrator
CFO: Candace Walker, Chief Financial Officer
Web address: www.dbhdd.ga.gov
Control: State, Government, nonfederal **Service:** Psychiatric

Staffed Beds: 308 Admissions: 644 Census: 299 Outpatient Visits: 0 **Births:** 0 **Total Expense ($000):** 90974 **Payroll Expense ($000):** 37434 **Personnel:** 1035

MEDICAL COLLEGE OF GEORGIA HEALTH See Augusta University Medical Center

⊞ **SELECT SPECIALTY HOSPITAL-AUGUSTA (112013)**, 1537 Walton Way, Zip 30904 3764; tel. 706/731–1200, (Nonreporting) **A**1 10 **S** Select Medical Corporation, Mechanicsburg, PA
Primary Contact: E Rick Lowe, FACHE, Chief Executive Officer
CHR: Terrie Richardson, Coordinator Human Resources
CNO: Kim Pippin, Chief Nursing Officer
Web address: www.augusta.selectspecialtyhospitals.com
Control: Corporation, Investor–owned (for–profit) **Service:** Acute long–term care hospital

Staffed Beds: 80

⊞ **UNIVERSITY HOSPITAL (110028)**, 1350 Walton Way, Zip 30901–2629; tel. 706/722–9011, **A**1 2 3 5 10 **F**3 12 13 15 17 18 20 22 24 26 28 29 30 31 34 35 37 38 40 41 44 48 49 50 54 55 56 57 59 60 62 64 68 70 71 72 73 74 75 76 77 78 79 80 81 82 83 84 85 86 87 89 93 96 100 107 108 110 111 114 115 116 117 118 119 126 129 130 132 133 135 146 147 148 149 150 154 156 **S** University Health Care System, Augusta, GA
Primary Contact: James R. Davis, Chief Executive Officer
CFO: David Belkoski, Senior Vice President and Chief Financial Officer
CMO: William L Farr, M.D., Chief Medical Officer
CIO: Shirley Gabriel, Vice President and Chief Information Officer
CHR: Laurie Ott, Vice President Human Resources and President University Health Care Foundation
Web address: www.universityhealth.org
Control: Other not–for–profit (including NFP Corporation) **Service:** General medical and surgical

Staffed Beds: 566 Admissions: 26315 **Census:** 355 **Outpatient Visits:** 573949 **Births:** 3245 **Total Expense ($000):** 508489 **Payroll Expense ($000):** 175266 **Personnel:** 2629

★ **UNIVERSITY HOSPITAL SUMMERVILLE (110039)**, 2260 Wrightsboro Road, Zip 30904–4726; tel. 706/481–7000, (Nonreporting) **S** University Health Care System, Augusta, GA
Primary Contact: James R. Davis, Chief Executive Officer
CFO: Rodney Sisk, Chief Financial Officer
CMO: C. Judson Pickett, Chief of Staff
CIO: Charlotte Choate, Director Information Systems
CHR: Diana Maxson, Director Human Resources
Web address: www.universityhealth.org/summerville/
Control: Corporation, Investor–owned (for–profit) **Service:** General medical and surgical

Staffed Beds: 105

GA

Hospital, Medicare Provider Number, Address, Telephone, Approval, Facility, and Physician Codes, Health Care System		
★ American Hospital Association (AHA) membership	○ Healthcare Facilities Accreditation Program	⇑ Center for Improvement in Healthcare Quality Accreditation
☐ The Joint Commission accreditation	◇ DNV Healthcare Inc. accreditation	△ Commission on Accreditation of Rehabilitation Facilities (CARF) accreditation

VETERANS AFFAIRS MEDICAL CENTER See Charlie Norwood Veterans Affairs Medical Center

WALTON REHABILITATION HOSPITAL See Walton Rehabilitation Hospital

⊠ **WALTON REHABILITATION HOSPITAL (113030)**, 1355 Independence Drive, Zip 30901–1037; tel. 706/724–7746, (Nonreporting) **A**1 5 10 **S** Encompass Health Corporation, Birmingham, AL
Primary Contact: Eric Crossan, Chief Executive Officer
CMO: Pamela Salazar, M.D., Chief of Staff
CIO: Ann Keller, Supervisor Health Information Management
CHR: Volante Henderson, Director Human Resources
CNO: Lynn Beaulieu, Chief Nursing Officer
Web address: www.healthsouthwalton.com/
Control: Corporation, Investor–owned (for–profit) **Service:** Rehabilitation

Staffed Beds: 50

AUSTELL—Cobb County

⊠ △ **WELLSTAR COBB HOSPITAL (110143)**, 3950 Austell Road, Zip 30106–1121; tel. 470/732–4000, **A**1 2 3 7 10 **F**3 4 5 11 13 15 16 17 18 20 22 26 28 29 30 31 38 40 41 44 45 48 49 50 51 53 54 55 58 59 60 61 64 65 66 68 70 72 73 74 75 76 77 78 79 81 82 84 85 86 87 90 93 94 96 97 98 100 101 102 104 105 106 107 108 110 111 114 115 119 120 121 123 124 126 129 130 131 132 135 141 144 146 147 148 149 153 154 156 **S** WellStar Health System, Marietta, GA
Primary Contact: Callie Andrews, President
CFO: Darold Etheridge, Vice President and Chief Financial Officer
CMO: Thomas McNamara, D.O., Vice President Medical Affairs
CIO: Jonathan B Morris, M.D., Senior Vice President and Chief Information Officer
CHR: Danyale Ziglor, Assistant Vice President Human Resources
CNO: Kay Kennedy, Chief Nurse Executive
Web address: www.wellstar.org
Control: Other not–for–profit (including NFP Corporation) **Service:** General medical and surgical

Staffed Beds: 370 Admissions: 20990 Census: 273 Outpatient Visits: 226495 Births: 3394 Personnel: 2100

BAINBRIDGE—Decatur County

⇑ **MEMORIAL HOSPITAL AND MANOR (110132)**, 1500 East Shotwell Street, Zip 39819–4256; tel. 229/246–3500, (Nonreporting) **A**10 21
Primary Contact: James M. Lambert, FACHE, Chief Executive Officer
COO: Lee Harris, Assistant Administrator Support Services
CFO: Karen Faircloth, Chief Financial Officer
CMO: Shawn Surratt, M.D., Chief of Staff
CIO: Nelda Moore, Director Data Processing
CHR: Angel Sykes, Director Human Resources
CNO: Cynthia Vickers, R.N., Assistant Administrator for Nursing Services
Web address: www.mh-m.org
Control: Hospital district or authority, Government, nonfederal **Service:** General medical and surgical

Staffed Beds: 80

BAXLEY—Appling County

⇑ **APPLING HEALTHCARE SYSTEM (110071)**, 163 East Tollison Street, Zip 31513–0120; tel. 912/367–9841, (Nonreporting) **A**10 20 21
Primary Contact: Randy Crawford, Chief Executive Officer
COO: Judy M Long, R.N., MS, Chief Nursing Officer and Chief Operating Officer
CFO: Raymond J. Leadbetter Jr Revenue Cycle Consultant
CMO: Garland Martin, M.D., Chief of Staff
CIO: Gary Gower, Chief Information Officer
CHR: Carla McLendon, Director Human Resources
CNO: Judy M Long, R.N., MS, Chief Nursing Officer and Chief Operating Officer
Web address: www.appling-hospital.org
Control: County, Government, nonfederal **Service:** General medical and surgical

Staffed Beds: 150

BLAIRSVILLE—Union County

★ ⇑ **UNION GENERAL HOSPITAL (110051)**, 35 Hospital Road, Zip 30512–3139; tel. 706/745–2111, (Total facility includes 150 beds in nursing home–type unit) **A**10 20 21 **F**3 7 11 13 15 28 29 30 34 35 40 45 46 47 48 49 50 53 57 59 64 70 76 77 79 81 82 85 86 87 93 96 107 108 110 111 114 115 119 120 127 131 132 135 143 146 147 148 149 157 **S** Union General Hospital, Inc., Blairsville, GA
Primary Contact: Kevin Bierschenk, Chief Executive Officer
COO: Lewis Kelley, Chief Operating Officer
CFO: Stephanie L Fletcher, CPA, Chief Financial Officer
CMO: Andre Schaeffer, M.D., Chief of Staff
CIO: Mike Johnston, Director Facilities Operations
CHR: Kathy Hood, Administrative Assistant Human Resources
CNO: Julia Barnett, Chief Nursing Officer
Web address: www.uniongeneralhospital.com
Control: Other not–for–profit (including NFP Corporation) **Service:** General medical and surgical

Staffed Beds: 195 Admissions: 2909 Census: 166 Outpatient Visits: 71086 Births: 430 Total Expense ($000): 69551 Payroll Expense ($000): 30936 Personnel: 759

BLAKELY—Early County

★ ⇑ **LIFEBRITE COMMUNITY HOSPITAL OF EARLY (111314)**, 11740 Columbia Street, Zip 39823–2574; tel. 229/723–4241, (Nonreporting) **A**10 18 21 **S** LifeBrite Hospital Group, LLC, Lilburn, GA
Primary Contact: Ginger Cushing, Chief Executive Officer
Web address: www.pchearly.com
Control: Corporation, Investor–owned (for–profit) **Service:** General medical and surgical

Staffed Beds: 152

BLUE RIDGE—Fannin County

⊠ **FANNIN REGIONAL HOSPITAL (110189)**, 2855 Old Highway 5, Zip 30513–6248; tel. 706/632–3711, (Nonreporting) **A**1 10 **S** Quorum Health, Brentwood, TN
Primary Contact: David S. Sanders, Chief Executive Officer
CFO: Phillip Fouts, Chief Financial Officer
CMO: Dillon D Miller, M.D., Chief Medical Officer
CIO: Timothy Snider, Manager Information Systems
CHR: Terrasina Ensley, Director Human Resources
CNO: Jason L. Jones, R.N., Chief Nursing Officer
Web address: www.fanninregionalhospital.com
Control: Corporation, Investor–owned (for–profit) **Service:** General medical and surgical

Staffed Beds: 50

BRASELTON—Hall County

NORTHEAST GEORGIA MEDICAL CENTER BRASELTON, 1400 River Place, Zip 30517–5600; tel. 770/219–9000, (Nonreporting) **A**3 **S** Northeast Georgia Health System, Gainesville, GA
Primary Contact: Carol H. Burrell, Chief Executive Officer
CNO: Cynthia Danner, Chief Nursing Officer
Web address: www.nghs.com/locations/braselton
Control: Other not–for–profit (including NFP Corporation) **Service:** General medical and surgical

Staffed Beds: 100

BREMEN—Haralson County

⊠ **HIGGINS GENERAL HOSPITAL (111320)**, 200 Allen Memorial Drive, Zip 30110–2012; tel. 770/824–2000, **A**1 10 18 **F**3 11 15 29 31 38 40 45 48 50 51 59 60 68 81 97 107 110 114 119 123 124 127 130 133 146 147 154 **S** Tanner Health System, Carrollton, GA
Primary Contact: Jerry Morris, Administrator
CFO: Carol Crews, Chief Financial Officer
CMO: Bill Waters, M.D., Chief Medical Officer
CIO: Terri Lee, Chief Information Officer
CHR: Shari W Gainey, Human Resource Director
CNO: B. J. Brock, Nursing Director
Web address: www.tanner.org/Main/HigginsGeneralHospitalBremen.aspx
Control: Other not–for–profit (including NFP Corporation) **Service:** General medical and surgical

Staffed Beds: 23 Admissions: 728 Census: 15 Outpatient Visits: 79361 Births: 0 Total Expense ($000): 27864 Payroll Expense ($000): 14929 Personnel: 225

BRUNSWICK—Glynn County

⊠ **SOUTHEAST GEORGIA HEALTH SYSTEM BRUNSWICK CAMPUS (110025)**, 2415 Parkwood Drive, Zip 31520–4722, Mailing Address: P.O. Box 1518, Zip 31521–1518; tel. 912/466–7000, (Total facility includes 278 beds in nursing home–type unit) **A**1 2 10 **F**3 6 8 11 12 13 15 17 18 20 22 26 28 29 30 31 34 35 37 40 44 45 46 47 48 49 50 51 54 57 59 64 66 68 70 71 74 75 76 77 78 79 81 84 85 86 87 89 91 93 94 96 100 107 108 110 111 114 115 117 119 120 121 124 126 129 131 132 135 144 146 147 148 149 156 **S** Southeast Georgia Health System, Brunswick, GA
Primary Contact: Michael D. Scherneck, President and Chief Executive Officer
CFO: Janice Dunn, Vice President and Chief Financial Officer
CMO: Robert Bernasek, M.D., Vice President and Chief Medical Officer
CIO: Charles Bumgardner
CNO: Judith Henson, Vice President Patient Care Services
Web address: www.sghs.org
Control: Other not–for–profit (including NFP Corporation) **Service:** General medical and surgical

Staffed Beds: 532 Admissions: 12715 Census: 399 Outpatient Visits: 239183 Births: 1236 Total Expense ($000): 353292 Payroll Expense ($000): 165525 Personnel: 1464

GA

BRYON—Peach County

★ ⇑ **MEDICAL CENTER OF PEACH COUNTY, NAVICENT HEALTH (111310)**, 1960 Highway 247 Connector, Zip 31008; tel. 478/654–2000, (Nonreporting) **A**10 18 21 **S** Navicent Health, Macon, GA
Primary Contact: Laura Gentry, Administrator
CFO: Lisa Urbistondo, Chief Financial Officer
CMO: Crystal Brown, M.D., Medical Director
CNO: Brenda Goodman, Chief Nursing Officer
Web address: www.navicenthealth.org
Control: Hospital district or authority, Government, nonfederal **Service**: General medical and surgical

Staffed Beds: 25

CAIRO—Grady County

⊞ **GRADY GENERAL HOSPITAL (110121)**, 1155 Fifth Street SE, Zip 39828–3142, Mailing Address: P.O. Box 360, Zip 39828–0360; tel. 229/377–1150, (Nonreporting) **A**1 10 **S** Archbold Medical Center, Thomasville, GA
Primary Contact: Crystal Wells, Administrator
COO: Jim Carter, Chief Operating Officer
CFO: Skip Hightower, Chief Financial Officer
CIO: Tracy Gray, Chief Information Officer
CHR: Michelle Pledger, Coordinator Human Resources
Web address: www.archbold.org
Control: Hospital district or authority, Government, nonfederal **Service**: General medical and surgical

Staffed Beds: 48

CALHOUN—Gordon County

⊞ ○ **ADVENTHEALTH GORDON (110023)**, 1035 Red Bud Road, Zip 30701–2082, Mailing Address: P.O. Box 12938, Zip 30703–7013; tel. 706/629–2895, **A**1 2 10 11 19 **F**3 7 11 13 15 18 20 29 30 31 34 35 37 40 46 57 59 62 64 70 75 76 77 78 79 81 82 85 86 87 93 107 108 110 111 115 119 120 121 123 129 130 135 144 146 147 148 154 **S** AdventHealth, Altamonte Springs, FL
Primary Contact: Pete M. Weber, President and Chief Executive Officer
COO: Karen Steely, Chief Operating Officer
CFO: Cory Reeves, Chief Financial Officer
CMO: Will Theus, M.D., Chief of Staff
CHR: Jeni Hasselbrack, Director Human Resources
CNO: Amy Jordan, Chief Nursing Officer/Vice President of Nursing
Web address: www.gordonhospital.com
Control: Church operated, Nongovernment, not-for-profit **Service**: General medical and surgical

Staffed Beds: 83 **Admissions**: 3996 **Census**: 45 **Outpatient Visits**: 290007 **Births**: 548 **Total Expense ($000)**: 151914 **Payroll Expense ($000)**: 65126 **Personnel**: 1195

CAMILLA—Mitchell County

⊞ **MITCHELL COUNTY HOSPITAL (111331)**, 90 East Stephens Street, Zip 31730–1836, Mailing Address: P.O. Box 639, Zip 31730–0639; tel. 229/336–5284, (Total facility includes 156 beds in nursing home–type unit) **A**1 10 18 **F**3 15 29 30 35 40 41 50 54 57 58 59 68 93 100 102 107 110 111 114 119 127 128 133 135 154 **S** Archbold Medical Center, Thomasville, GA
Primary Contact: James Womack, Administrator
CFO: Skip Hightower, Senior Vice President and Chief Financial Officer
CIO: Tracy Gray, Chief Information Officer
CHR: Vickie County-Teemer, Coordinator Human Resources
CNO: Carla Beasley, Director of Nursing
Web address: www.archbold.org
Control: Other not-for-profit (including NFP Corporation) **Service**: General medical and surgical

Staffed Beds: 181 **Admissions**: 508 **Census**: 167 **Outpatient Visits**: 25813 **Births**: 0

CANTON—Cherokee County

⊞ **NORTHSIDE HOSPITAL-CHEROKEE (110008)**, 450 Northside Cherokee Boulevard, Zip 30115–8015, Mailing Address: P.O. Box 906, Zip 30169 0906; tel. 770/720–5100, **A**1 10 **F**3 8 11 12 13 15 18 20 22 26 28 29 30 31 34 35 40 44 45 49 50 54 55 57 59 60 64 68 70 73 74 75 76 77 78 79 81 82 85 86 87 93 107 108 110 111 114 118 119 120 121 123 124 126 129 130 131 132 144 145 146 147 148 156 **S** Northside Healthcare System, Atlanta, GA
Primary Contact: William M. Hayes, Chief Executive Officer
COO: Mike Patterson, Director of Operations
CFO: Brian Jennette, Chief Financial Officer
CMO: Alexander Kessler, M.D., Chief of Staff
CIO: Bill Dunford, Manager
CHR: Roslyn Roberts, Manager
Web address: www.northside.com
Control: Other not-for-profit (including NFP Corporation) **Service**: General medical and surgical

Staffed Beds: 122 **Admissions**: 8940 **Census**: 121 **Outpatient Visits**: 367679 **Births**: 1703 **Total Expense ($000)**: 363971 **Payroll Expense ($000)**: 137130 **Personnel**: 2021

CARROLLTON—Carroll County

⊞ **TANNER MEDICAL CENTER-CARROLLTON (110011)**, 705 Dixie Street, Zip 30117–3818; tel. 770/836–9666, **A**1 2 10 **F**3 11 13 15 18 20 22 26 28 29 30 31 34 35 37 40 45 47 49 56 57 58 59 62 63 64 68 70 71 73 74 75 76 78 79 81 82 84 85 87 89 107 108 109 110 111 115 116 117 118 119 120 121 123 124 126 129 130 132 143 146 147 148 149 154 156 **S** Tanner Health System, Carrollton, GA
Primary Contact: Loy M. Howard, Chief Operating Officer
CFO: Carol Crews, Chief Financial Officer
CMO: William Waters, M.D., IV Chief Medical Officer
CNO: Deborah Matthews, Chief Nursing Officer
Web address: www.tanner.org
Control: Other not-for-profit (including NFP Corporation) **Service**: General medical and surgical

Staffed Beds: 146 **Admissions**: 8668 **Census**: 101 **Outpatient Visits**: 248073 **Births**: 1306 **Total Expense ($000)**: 296758 **Payroll Expense ($000)**: 118495 **Personnel**: 1779

CARTERSVILLE—Bartow County

⊞ **CARTERSVILLE MEDICAL CENTER (110030)**, 960 Joe Frank Harris Parkway, Zip 30120–2129; tel. 770/382–1530, (Nonreporting) **A**1 2 3 10 **S** HCA Healthcare, Nashville, TN
Primary Contact: J. Christopher Mosley, Chief Executive Officer
COO: Lori Rakes, Chief Operating Officer
CNO: Jan Tidwell, Chief Nursing Officer
Web address: www.cartersvillemedical.com
Control: Corporation, Investor owned (for profit) **Service**: General medical and surgical

Staffed Beds: 80

CEDARTOWN—Polk County

⊞ **POLK MEDICAL CENTER (111330)**, 2360 Rockmart Highway, Zip 30125–6029; tel. 770/748–2500, **A**1 10 18 **F**3 15 28 29 30 34 35 40 43 50 56 57 59 64 68 75 77 81 93 103 107 108 110 114 119 130 132 133 135 143 144 146 147 148 149 154 156 **S** Floyd Healthcare Management, Rome, GA
Primary Contact: Tifani Kinard, Administrator and Chief Nursing Officer
CFO: Rick Sheerin, Chief Financial Officer
CHR: Jeanna Smith, Administrative Assistant and Human Resources Officer
CNO: Tifani Kinard, Administrator and Chief Nursing Officer
Web address: www.polkhospital.org
Control: Hospital district or authority, Government, nonfederal **Service**: General medical and surgical

Staffed Beds: 25 **Admissions**: 581 **Census**: 23 **Outpatient Visits**: 38644 **Births**: 0 **Total Expense ($000)**: 25378 **Payroll Expense ($000)**: 10043 **Personnel**: 141

GA

CHATSWORTH—Murray County

⊞ **ADVENTHEALTH MURRAY (110050)**, 707 Old Dalton Ellijay Road, Zip 30705–2060, Mailing Address: P.O. Box 1406, Zip 30705–1406; tel. 706/695–4564, **A**1 10 **F**3 7 15 29 30 34 35 40 57 59 64 79 81 93 107 111 115 119 146 **S** AdventHealth, Altamonte Springs, FL
Primary Contact: Karen Steely, Administrator
COO: Karen Steely, Chief Operating Officer
CMO: Blaine Minor, M.D., Chief of Staff
CIO: Jose C Rios, Director Information Services
CHR: Brandy Rymer, Coordinator Human Resources
CNO: Susan Shook, Interim Chief Executive Officer
Web address: www.murraymedical.org/
Control: Church operated, Nongovernment, not–for–profit **Service:** General medical and surgical

Staffed Beds: 12 **Admissions:** 536 **Census:** 4 **Outpatient Visits:** 71657 **Births:** 0 **Total Expense ($000):** 27361 **Payroll Expense ($000):** 11035 **Personnel:** 229

CLAXTON—Evans County

⇑ **EVANS MEMORIAL HOSPITAL (110142)**, 200 North River Street, Zip 30417–1659, Mailing Address: P.O. Box 518, Zip 30417–0518; tel. 912/739–2611, (Nonreporting) **A**10 21
Primary Contact: Nikki NeSmith, Chief Executive Officer and Chief Nursing Officer
CFO: John Wiggins, Chief Financial Officer
CMO: Kyle Parks, M.D., Chief of Staff
CIO: Steve Schmidt, Director Information Systems
CHR: Gina Waters, Director Human Resources
CNO: Nikki NeSmith, Chief Nursing Officer
Web address: www.evansmemorialhospital.org/
Control: Hospital district or authority, Government, nonfederal **Service:** General medical and surgical

Staffed Beds: 10

CLAYTON—Rabun County

MOUNTAIN LAKES MEDICAL CENTER (111336), 162 Legacy Point, Zip 30525–5354; tel. 706/782–3100, (Nonreporting) **A**10 18
Primary Contact: Tammy L. Coll, Chief Executive Officer
CFO: Jimmy Norman, Chief Financial Officer
CHR: Charles Harbaugh, Director Human Resources
Web address: www.mountainlakesmedicalcenter.com
Control: Hospital district or authority, Government, nonfederal **Service:** General medical and surgical

Staffed Beds: 25

COCHRAN—Bleckley County

⇑ **BLECKLEY MEMORIAL HOSPITAL (111302)**, 145 East Peacock Street, Zip 31014–7846, Mailing Address: P.O. Box 536, Zip 31014–0536; tel. 478/934–6211, (Nonreporting) **A**10 18 21
Primary Contact: Jon Green, R.N., Chief Executive Officer
COO: John Roland, R.N., Chief Operating Officer and Chief Nursing Officer
CFO: Sandra Herndon, CPA, Chief Financial Officer
CIO: Scott Wynne, Chief Information Officer Director
CHR: Jean Allen, Human Resources Director
CNO: John Roland, R.N., Chief Operating Officer and Chief Nursing Officer
Web address: www.bleckleymemorial.com
Control: Hospital district or authority, Government, nonfederal **Service:** General medical and surgical

Staffed Beds: 25

COLQUITT—Miller County

⇑ **MILLER COUNTY HOSPITAL (111305)**, 209 North Cuthbert Street, Zip 39837–3518, Mailing Address: P.O. Box 7, Zip 39837–0007; tel. 229/758–3385, (Nonreporting) **A**10 18 21
Primary Contact: Robin Rau, Chief Executive Officer
CFO: Jill Brown, Chief Financial Officer
CMO: William Swofford, M.D., Chief of Staff
CIO: Keith Lovering, Information Technician
CHR: Karie Spence, Director Human Resources
CNO: Shawn Whittaker, Chief Nursing Officer
Web address: www.millercountyhospital.com
Control: Hospital district or authority, Government, nonfederal **Service:** General medical and surgical

Staffed Beds: 188

COLUMBUS—Muscogee County

BRADLEY CENTER OF ST. FRANCIS See St. Francis Hospital, Columbus

COLUMBUS SPECIALTY HOSPITAL (112012), 616 19th Street, Zip 31901–1528, Mailing Address: P.O. Box 910, Zip 31902–0910; tel. 706/494–4075, (Nonreporting) **A**10
Primary Contact: William Eckstein, Chief Executive Officer and Chief Financial Officer
CFO: William Eckstein, Chief Executive Officer and Chief Financial Officer
CHR: Myra Whitley, Vice President, Human Resources
Web address: www.columbusspecialtyhospital.net
Control: Other not–for–profit (including NFP Corporation) **Service:** Acute long–term care hospital

Staffed Beds: 33

HUGHSTON HOSPITAL See Piedmont Columbus Regional Northside

PIEDMONT COLUMBUS REGIONAL MIDTOWN (110064), 710 Center Street, Zip 31901–1527, Mailing Address: P.O. Box 951, Zip 31902–0951; tel. 706/571–1000, (Includes MIDTOWN MEDICAL CENTER WEST, 616 19th Street, Columbus, Georgia, Zip 31901–1528, Mailing Address: P O Box 2188, Zip 31902–2188, tel. 706/494–4262; Ryan Chandler, Chief Executive Officer) **A**2 3 5 10 13 **F**3 11 12 13 18 20 22 29 30 31 34 35 38 40 41 43 44 45 46 47 48 49 50 51 55 56 57 58 59 60 61 64 65 66 68 70 72 73 74 75 76 77 78 79 81 82 85 86 87 88 89 92 93 94 97 102 107 108 111 114 115 116 117 119 120 121 123 124 126 130 131 132 135 146 147 148 149 156 **S** Piedmont Healthcare, Roswell, GA
Primary Contact: M. Scott. Hill, President and Chief Executive Officer
COO: Bill Tustin, Chief Operating Officer
CMO: Chris Edwards, M.D., Chief Medical Officer
Web address: www.columbusregional.com
Control: Other not–for–profit (including NFP Corporation) **Service:** General medical and surgical

Staffed Beds: 510 **Admissions:** 15526 **Census:** 216 **Outpatient Visits:** 251752 **Births:** 2679 **Total Expense ($000):** 302217 **Payroll Expense ($000):** 104569 **Personnel:** 1659

☐ **PIEDMONT COLUMBUS REGIONAL NORTHSIDE (110200)**, 100 Frist Court, Zip 31909–3578, Mailing Address: P.O. Box 7188, Zip 31908–7188; tel. 706/494–2100, **A**1 3 10 **F**3 11 29 30 32 34 35 38 40 44 45 50 57 59 60 61 64 65 68 70 71 74 75 77 79 81 82 85 86 87 90 92 93 94 96 97 107 108 111 119 129 130 131 135 146 149 156 **S** Piedmont Healthcare, Roswell, GA
Primary Contact: M. Scott. Hill, President and Chief Executive Officer
COO: Laura Drew, Chief Operating Officer
CFO: Roland Thacker, Chief Financial Officer
CMO: Chris Edwards, M.D., Chief Medical Officer
CIO: Douglas Colburn, Chief Information Officer
CHR: Becky Augustyniak, Director Human Resources
Web address: www.columbusregional.com
Control: Other not–for–profit (including NFP Corporation) **Service:** General medical and surgical

Staffed Beds: 100 **Admissions:** 2801 **Census:** 40 **Outpatient Visits:** 19543 **Births:** 0 **Total Expense ($000):** 67000 **Payroll Expense ($000):** 18694 **Personnel:** 327

⊞ **ST. FRANCIS HOSPITAL (110129)**, 2122 Manchester Expressway, Zip 31904–6878, Mailing Address: P.O. Box 7000, Zip 31908–7000; tel. 706/596–4000, (Includes BRADLEY CENTER OF ST. FRANCIS, 2000 16th Avenue, Columbus, Georgia, Zip 31906–0308; tel. 706/320–3700) **A**1 3 10 **F**3 11 13 15 17 18 20 22 24 26 28 29 30 31 34 35 40 45 46 49 50 51 53 54 56 59 60 64 70 74 75 76 77 78 79 81 82 85 86 98 99 100 101 102 103 104 105 106 107 108 110 111 115 119 126 129 130 131 144 145 146 147 148 153 **S** LifePoint Health, Brentwood, TN
Primary Contact: Danny L. Jones Jr, FACHE, Chief Executive Officer
COO: Alan E George, Chief Operating Officer
CFO: Greg Hembree, Senior Vice President and Chief Financial Officer
CMO: Bobbi Farber, M.D., Chief Medical Officer
CIO: Jonathon R Jager, Chief Information Officer
CHR: E Rick Lowe, FACHE, Operations Support Risk Management and Compliance
CNO: Charlene Falgout, Chief Nursing Officer
Web address: www.mystfrancis.com
Control: Corporation, Investor–owned (for–profit) **Service:** General medical and surgical

Staffed Beds: 331 **Admissions:** 13711 **Census:** 182 **Outpatient Visits:** 198632 **Births:** 1311 **Total Expense ($000):** 244612 **Payroll Expense ($000):** 73684 **Personnel:** 1784

Many Facility Codes have changed. Please refer to the AHA Guide Code Chart. © 2019 AHA Guide

☐ **WEST CENTRAL GEORGIA REGIONAL HOSPITAL (114013)**, 3000 Schatulga Road, Zip 31907–3117, Mailing Address: P.O. Box 12435, Zip 31917–2435; tel. 706/568–5000, **A**1 10 **F**39 98 130 135 149
Primary Contact: John L. Robertson, Administrator
COO: Marcia Capshaw, Chief Operating Officer
CFO: John Frederick, Chief Financial Officer
CMO: David Morton, M.D., Clinical Director
CIO: Karen Fisher-Ford, Director of Health Information Management
CHR: Peri Johnson, Human Resources Director
CNO: Nicolise Claassens, Nurse Executive
Web address: www.dbhdd.georgia.gov/west-central-georgia-regional-hospital-columbus
Control: State, Government, nonfederal **Service**: Psychiatric

Staffed Beds: 194 **Admissions**: 249 **Census**: 188 **Outpatient Visits**: 0
Births: 0 **Personnel**: 556

COMMERCE—Jackson County

✠ **NORTHRIDGE MEDICAL CENTER (110040)**, 70 Medical Center Drive, Zip 30529–1078; tel. 706/335–1000, (Nonreporting) **A**1 10
Primary Contact: Judy Warrner, Chief Operating Officer
CMO: Narasimhulu Neelagaru, M.D., Chief of Staff
Web address: www.northridgemc.com
Control: Partnership, Investor–owned (for–profit) **Service**: General medical and surgical

Staffed Beds: 221

CONYERS—Rockdale County

☐ **PIEDMONT ROCKDALE HOSPITAL (110091)**, 1412 Milstead Avenue NE, Zip 30012–3877; tel. 770/918–3000, (Nonreporting) **A**1 5 10 **S** Piedmont Healthcare, Roswell, GA
Primary Contact: Richard Tanzella, Chief Executive Officer
COO: Blake Watts, Chief Operating Officer
CFO: Diane Roth, Chief Financial Officer
CMO: Lisa Gillespie, M.D., Chief Medical Officer
CIO: Gail Waldo, Director Information Technology
CHR: Marianne Freeman, Vice President Human Resources
CNO: Eleanor Post, R.N., Chief Nursing Officer
Web address: www.rockdalemedicalcenter.org
Control: Corporation, Investor–owned (for–profit) **Service**: General medical and surgical

Staffed Beds: 158

CORDELE—Crisp County

✠ **CRISP REGIONAL HOSPITAL (110104)**, 902 North Seventh Street, Zip 31015–3234; tel. 229/276–3100, (Total facility includes 243 beds in nursing home–type unit) **A**1 3 10 20 **F**3 11 13 15 29 30 31 34 35 40 43 44 45 48 49 50 51 54 56 57 58 59 60 61 62 63 64 65 68 70 71 75 76 77 78 79 81 84 85 86 87 89 90 93 96 97 107 108 110 111 114 115 117 118 125 126 127 128 129 130 132 133 135 144 146 147 148 149 154
Primary Contact: Steven Gautney, Chief Executive Officer
COO: Mary Jim Montgomery, R.N., MSN, FACHE, Chief Operating Officer
CFO: Jessica Y Carter, Chief Financial Officer
CMO: David Kavtaradze, M.D., Chief of Staff
CHR: George M Laurin, Interim Director Human Resources
CNO: Marsha L. Mulderig, R.N., MSN, Chief Nursing Officer
Web address: www.crispregional.org
Control: County, Government, nonfederal **Service**: General medical and surgical

Staffed Beds: 316 **Admissions**: 2965 **Census**: 167 **Outpatient Visits**: 99429 **Births**: 265 **Personnel**: 473

COVINGTON—Newton County

⇑ **PIEDMONT NEWTON HOSPITAL (110018)**, 5126 Hospital Drive, Zip 30014–2567; tel. 770/786–7053, **A**10 21 **F**3 7 11 13 15 18 20 28 29 34 35 39 40 45 47 49 50 51 53 54 57 59 60 68 70 73 75 76 79 81 85 93 107 108 110 111 114 115 119 130 131 143 146 147 148 149 154 156 157 **S** Piedmont Healthcare, Roswell, GA
Primary Contact: Eric Bour, M.D., FACS, Chief Executive Officer
CFO: Lauren Matthews, Chief Financial Officer
CMO: B. Carter Rogers, Chief of Staff
CIO: Brad Collier, Director
CHR: Greg H Richardson, Assistant Administrator Human Resources
CNO: Jeremiah Bame, R.N., Chief Nursing Officer
Web address: www.newtonmedical.com
Control: Other not–for–profit (including NFP Corporation) **Service**: General medical and surgical

Staffed Beds: 103 **Admissions**: 5336 **Census**: 46 **Outpatient Visits**: 81485
Births: 710 **Personnel**: 550

CUMMING—Forsyth County

✠ **NORTHSIDE HOSPITAL-FORSYTH (110005)**, 1200 Northside Forsyth Drive, Zip 30041–7659; tel. 770/844–3200, **A**1 10 **F**3 8 11 12 13 15 18 20 22 26 28 29 30 31 34 35 37 40 44 45 48 49 50 54 55 57 59 60 64 68 70 72 73 74 75 76 77 78 79 81 82 85 86 87 93 107 108 110 111 114 115 117 118 119 120 121 123 124 126 129 130 131 132 135 144 145 146 147 148 156 **S** Northside Healthcare System, Atlanta, GA
Primary Contact: Lynn Jackson, Administrator
CFO: Eric Caldwell, Director Finance
Web address: www.northside.com
Control: Other not–for–profit (including NFP Corporation) **Service**: General medical and surgical

Staffed Beds: 325 **Admissions**: 15273 **Census**: 209 **Outpatient Visits**: 411088 **Births**: 3039 **Total Expense ($000)**: 476119 **Payroll Expense ($000)**: 191948 **Personnel**: 2742

CUTHBERT—Randolph County

★ ⇑ **SOUTHWEST GEORGIA REGIONAL MEDICAL CENTER (111300)**, 361 Randolph Street, Zip 39840–6127; tel. 229/732–2181, (Nonreporting) **A**10 18 21 **S** Phoebe Putney Health System, Albany, GA
Primary Contact: Kim Gilman, Chief Executive Officer and Chief Nursing Officer
CFO: Candace Guarnieri, Chief Financial Officer
CNO: Kim Gilman, Chief Executive Officer and Chief Nursing Officer
Web address: www.phoebeputney.com/
Control: Hospital district or authority, Government, nonfederal **Service**: General medical and surgical

Staffed Beds: 25

DALTON—Whitfield County

✠ **HAMILTON MEDICAL CENTER (110001)**, 1200 Memorial Drive, Zip 30720–2529, Mailing Address: P.O. Box 1168, Zip 30722–1168; tel. 706/272–6000, **A**1 2 10 19 **F**3 5 8 12 13 15 18 20 22 26 28 29 30 31 34 35 40 43 44 45 46 47 48 49 50 51 53 54 57 59 60 62 63 64 68 70 72 73 74 75 76 77 78 79 81 82 84 85 86 87 89 93 96 97 98 100 101 102 103 104 105 107 108 110 111 114 115 116 117 118 119 120 121 123 124 126 129 130 131 132 135 144 146 147 148 149
Primary Contact: Jeffrey D. Myers, President and Chief Executive Officer
COO: Sandra D. McKenzie, Executive Vice President and Chief Operating Officer
CFO: Gary L Howard, Senior Vice President and Chief Financial Officer
CMO: Andrew C. Bland, M.D., Vice President and Chief Medical Officer
CIO: John M Forrester, Director Information Services
CHR: Jason Hopkins, Director, Human Resources
CNO: Cathy Ferguson, R.N., MSN, Vice President and Chief Nursing Officer
Web address: www.hamiltonhealth.com
Control: Other not–for–profit (including NFP Corporation) **Service**: General medical and surgical

Staffed Beds: 227 **Admissions**: 9551 **Census**: 111 **Outpatient Visits**: 233322 **Births**: 1707 **Personnel**: 1118

DECATUR—Dekalb County

✠ **ATLANTA VETERANS AFFAIRS MEDICAL CENTER**, 1670 Clairmont Road, Zip 30033–4004; tel. 404/321–6111, (Nonreporting) **A**1 2 3 5 8 **S** Department of Veterans Affairs, Washington, DC
Primary Contact: Ann R. Brown, M.D., Director
CFO: Pamela Watkins, Chief Financial Officer
CMO: David Bower, M.D., Chief of Staff
CIO: William Brock, Chief Information Officer
CHR: Zeta Ferguson, Chief Human Resources
CNO: Sandy Leake, MSN, R.N., Associate Director, Nursing and Patient Care Services
Web address: www.atlanta.va.gov/
Control: Veterans Affairs, Government, federal **Service**: General medical and surgical

Staffed Beds: 239

GA

Hospital, Medicare Provider Number, Address, Telephone, Approval, Facility, and Physician Codes, Health Care System

★ American Hospital Association (AHA) membership   ○ Healthcare Facilities Accreditation Program   ⇑ Center for Improvement in Healthcare Quality Accreditation
☐ The Joint Commission accreditation   ◇ DNV Healthcare Inc. accreditation   △ Commission on Accreditation of Rehabilitation Facilities (CARF) accreditation

⊞ **EMORY DECATUR HOSPITAL (110076)**, 2701 North Decatur Road, Zip 30033–5995; tel. 404/501–1000, **A**1 2 3 10 **F**3 11 12 13 15 18 20 22 24 26 28 29 30 31 34 35 38 40 44 49 50 51 53 55 57 58 59 60 68 70 71 72 73 74 75 76 77 78 79 81 82 84 85 86 87 90 93 96 98 100 102 104 107 108 110 111 114 115 116 117 119 120 121 123 124 126 129 130 131 132 135 146 147 148 156 **S** Emory Healthcare, Atlanta, GA
Primary Contact: Jim Forstner, Chief Executive Officer
CFO: Robin Nichols, Interim Chief Financial Officer
CIO: Beth Patino, Chief Information Officer
CHR: LeRoy Walker, Vice President Human Resources
CNO: Susan Breslin, R.N., MSN, Vice President Patient Care Services and Chief Nursing Officer
Web address: www.dekalbmedical.org
Control: Other not–for–profit (including NFP Corporation) **Service**: General medical and surgical

Staffed Beds: 472 **Admissions**: 18749 **Census**: 281 **Outpatient Visits**: 152296 **Births**: 3763 **Total Expense ($000)**: 349517 **Payroll Expense ($000)**: 134791 **Personnel**: 2491

☐ **EMORY LONG-TERM ACUTE CARE (112006)**, 450 North Candler Street, Zip 30030–2671; tel. 404/501–6700, **A**1 5 10 **F**1 18 45 48 50 78 84 91 135 **S** Emory Healthcare, Atlanta, GA
Primary Contact: Jim Forstner, Chief Executive Officer
CMO: David Snyder, M.D., Chief of Staff
CHR: Tom Crawford, Vice President Human Resources
Web address: www.dekalbmedicalcenter.org
Control: Other not–for–profit (including NFP Corporation) **Service**: Acute long–term care hospital

Staffed Beds: 38 **Admissions**: 307 **Census**: 26 **Outpatient Visits**: 0 **Births**: 0 **Total Expense ($000)**: 18712 **Payroll Expense ($000)**: 9665 **Personnel**: 159

☐ **GEORGIA REGIONAL HOSPITAL AT ATLANTA (114019)**, 3073 Panthersville Road, Zip 30034–3828; tel. 404/243–2100, (Nonreporting) **A**1 3 5 10
Primary Contact: Susan Trueblood, Chief Executive Officer
COO: Sonny Slate, Chief Operating Officer
CFO: Reginald Jones, Business Manager
CMO: Emile Risby, M.D., Clinical Director
CIO: Elfie Early, Manager Data Services
CHR: Lorraine Farr, Manager Human Resources
Web address: www.atlantareg.dhr.state.ga.us
Control: State, Government, nonfederal **Service**: Psychiatric

Staffed Beds: 319

VETERANS AFFAIRS MEDICAL CENTER See Atlanta Veterans Affairs Medical Center

DEMOREST—Habersham County

★ ⋔ **HABERSHAM MEDICAL CENTER (110041)**, 541 Historic Highway 441, Zip 30535–3118, Mailing Address: P.O. Box 37, Zip 30535–0037; tel. 706/754–2161, (Total facility includes 84 beds in nursing home–type unit) **A**10 21 **F**7 8 13 15 28 29 30 34 35 40 45 46 50 53 57 59 64 68 70 75 77 79 81 82 87 91 93 97 102 107 111 114 119 128 129 130 133 143 146 156
Primary Contact: Lynn Ingram. Boggs, Chief Executive Officer
COO: Michael Gay, Chief Operating Officer
CFO: Barbara Duncan, Chief Financial Officer
CMO: Josh Garrett, Chief of Staff
CHR: Ryan Snow, Director Human Resources
Web address: www.habershammedical.com/
Control: Hospital district or authority, Government, nonfederal **Service**: General medical and surgical

Staffed Beds: 137 **Admissions**: 1851 **Census**: 95 **Outpatient Visits**: 72486 **Births**: 400 **Total Expense ($000)**: 40801 **Payroll Expense ($000)**: 17712 **Personnel**: 473

DONALSONVILLE—Seminole County

⋔ **DONALSONVILLE HOSPITAL (110194)**, 102 Hospital Circle, Zip 39845–1199; tel. 229/524–5217, (Nonreporting) **A**10 21
Primary Contact: Charles H. Orrick, Administrator
CFO: James Moody, Chief Financial Officer
CMO: C O Walker, M.D., Chief of Staff
CHR: Jo Adams, Director Human Resources
Control: Other not–for–profit (including NFP Corporation) **Service**: General medical and surgical

Staffed Beds: 140

DOUGLAS—Coffee County

⋔ **COFFEE REGIONAL MEDICAL CENTER (110089)**, 1101 Ocilla Road, Zip 31533–2207, Mailing Address: P.O. Box 1287, Zip 31534–1287; tel. 912/384–1900, **A**10 20 21 **F**3 7 11 13 15 18 20 26 28 29 30 31 34 35 40 41 44 45 47 50 51 53 54 56 57 59 60 61 64 65 68 70 71 74 75 76 77 78 79 81 82 85 86 87 89 92 93 97 107 108 110 111 114 115 119 124 127 130 131 132 133 135 143 146 147 148 149 154
Primary Contact: Vicki Lewis, R.N., MS, FACHE, President and Chief Executive Officer
CFO: Lavonda Cravey, Chief Financial Officer
CHR: Laura Bloom, Director Human Resources
Web address: www.coffeeregional.org
Control: Other not–for–profit (including NFP Corporation) **Service**: General medical and surgical

Staffed Beds: 88 **Admissions**: 4198 **Census**: 45 **Outpatient Visits**: 87701 **Births**: 566 **Total Expense ($000)**: 93091 **Payroll Expense ($000)**: 34160 **Personnel**: 628

DOUGLASVILLE—Douglas County

★ **WELLSTAR DOUGLAS HOSPITAL (110184)**, 8954 Hospital Drive, Zip 30134–2282; tel. 770/949–1500, **A**2 10 **F**3 11 13 15 18 20 22 28 29 30 31 37 38 40 44 45 48 49 50 51 53 54 58 59 60 61 64 68 70 74 75 76 77 78 79 81 82 84 85 86 87 93 94 102 107 108 110 111 114 115 117 118 119 126 129 130 132 135 146 147 148 154 156 **S** WellStar Health System, Marietta, GA
Primary Contact: Craig A. Owens, President
CFO: Bradley Greene, Chief Financial Officer
CMO: Noel Holtz, M.D., Chief Medical Officer
CHR: Danyale Ziglor, Assistant Director Human Resources
Web address: www.wellstar.org
Control: Other not–for–profit (including NFP Corporation) **Service**: General medical and surgical

Staffed Beds: 108 **Admissions**: 6847 **Census**: 76 **Outpatient Visits**: 127166 **Births**: 412 **Personnel**: 786

YOUTH VILLAGES INNER HARBOUR CAMPUS, 4685 Dorsett Shoals Road, Zip 30135–4999; tel. 770/942–2391, (Nonreporting)
Primary Contact: Patrick Lawler, Chief Executive Officer
CFO: J Steve Lewis, Director Finance
CIO: Laura Sellers, Director Information Systems
CHR: Sherry Kollmeyer, Vice President Human Resources
Web address: www.innerharbour.org
Control: Other not–for–profit (including NFP Corporation) **Service**: Children's hospital psychiatric

Staffed Beds: 190

DUBLIN—Laurens County

⊞ **CARL VINSON VETERANS AFFAIRS MEDICAL CENTER**, 1826 Veterans Boulevard, Zip 31021–3620; tel. 478/272–1210, (Nonreporting) **A**1 3 **S** Department of Veterans Affairs, Washington, DC
Primary Contact: David Whitmer, FACHE, Director
COO: Gerald M DeWorth, Associate Director
CFO: Kimberly Johnson-Miller, Chief Financial Officer
CMO: Christopher Blasy, D.O., Chief of Staff
CIO: Mark Cowart, Facility Chief Information Officer
CHR: Kurt Oster, Human Resources Officer
CNO: Connie Hampton, R.N., Associate Director for Patient Care Services
Web address: www.dublin.va.gov/
Control: Veterans Affairs, Government, federal **Service**: General medical and surgical

Staffed Beds: 178

⊞ **FAIRVIEW PARK HOSPITAL (110125)**, 200 Industrial Boulevard, Zip 31021–2997, Mailing Address: P.O. Box 1408, Zip 31040–1408; tel. 478/275–2000, (Nonreporting) **A**1 3 10 19 **S** HCA Healthcare, Nashville, TN
Primary Contact: Donald R. Avery, FACHE, President and Chief Executive Officer
CFO: Ted Short, Chief Financial Officer
CMO: George E. Harrison, M.D., Chief Medical Officer
CIO: Marsha Morris, Manager Information Services
CHR: Jeff Bruton, Director Human Resources
CNO: Donna Trickey, R.N., Chief Nursing Officer
Web address: www.fairviewparkhospital.com
Control: Corporation, Investor–owned (for–profit) **Service**: General medical and surgical

Staffed Beds: 168

DULUTH—De Kalb County

GWINNETT MEDICAL CENTER-DULUTH See Gwinnett Hospital System, Lawrenceville

Many Facility Codes have changed. Please refer to the AHA Guide Code Chart. © 2019 AHA Guide

EAST POINT—Fulton County

★ **REGENCY HOSPITAL OF SOUTH ATLANTA (112014)**, 1170 Cleveland Avenue, 4th Floor, Zip 30344–3615; tel. 404/466–6250, (Nonreporting) **A**3 **S** Select Medical Corporation, Mechanicsburg, PA
Primary Contact: Michelle Tenhengel-deVille, Chief Executive Officer
Web address: www.regencyhospital.com
Control: Corporation, Investor–owned (for–profit) **Service:** Acute long–term care hospital

Staffed Beds: 40

EASTMAN—Dodge County

⇑ **DODGE COUNTY HOSPITAL (110092)**, 901 Griffin Avenue, Zip 31023–6720, Mailing Address: P.O. Box 4309, Zip 31023–4309; tel. 478/374–4000, **A**10 21 **F**3 11 13 15 29 30 31 40 45 57 59 64 69 70 75 76 79 81 85 86 98 103 107 108 110 111 114 119 146 147
Primary Contact: LaDon Toole, Chief Executive Officer
CFO: Jan Hamrick, Chief Financial Officer
CIO: Victor Woodard, Manager Information Technology
CHR: Wendy Selph, Director Human Resources
CNO: Sandra M. Campbell, R.N., Chief Nursing Officer
Web address: www.dodgecountyhospital.com
Control: Hospital district or authority, Government, nonfederal **Service:** General medical and surgical

Staffed Beds: 35 Admissions: 1465 Census: 22 Outpatient Visits: 31185 Births: 117 Total Expense ($000): 19485 Payroll Expense ($000): 9016 Personnel: 237

EATONTON—Putnam County

☐ **PUTNAM GENERAL HOSPITAL (111313)**, 101 Lake Oconee Parkway, Zip 31024–6054; tel. 706/485–2711, **A**1 10 18 **F**3 8 11 15 28 29 40 47 50 51 57 59 63 64 68 75 81 87 107 110 111 114 119 128 129 133 146 154 157
Primary Contact: Alan Horton, Administrator
CFO: Judy Ware, Chief Financial Officer
CMO: Omar Akhras, M.D., Chief of Staff
CIO: Marcel Lundy, Chief Information Officer
CHR: Jeanine Martinez, Director Human Resources
CNO: Pam Douglas, Chief Nursing Officer
Web address: www.putnamgeneral.com
Control: Hospital district or authority, Government, nonfederal **Service:** General medical and surgical

Staffed Beds: 25 Admissions: 551 Census: 10 Outpatient Visits: 18067 Births: 0 Total Expense ($000): 18671 Payroll Expense ($000): 5170 Personnel: 119

ELBERTON—Elbert County

☐ **ELBERT MEMORIAL HOSPITAL (110026)**, 4 Medical Drive, Zip 30635–1897; tel. 706/283–3151, **A**1 10 20 **F**3 11 15 29 40 45 50 53 57 59 70 77 79 81 87 102 107 110 115 119 128 130 133 146 147
Primary Contact: Kerry A. Trapnell, Chief Executive Officer
CIO: Greg Fields, Director Information Technology
CHR: Georgian Walton, Director Human Resources
CNO: Tammy Harlow, Chief Nursing Officer
Web address: www.emhcare.net
Control: Hospital district or authority, Government, nonfederal **Service:** General medical and surgical

Staffed Beds: 35 Admissions: 597 Census: 7 Outpatient Visits: 23342 Births: 0 Total Expense ($000): 12867 Payroll Expense ($000): 5497 Personnel: 166

FAYETTEVILLE—Fayette County

⇑ **PIEDMONT FAYETTE HOSPITAL (110215)**, 1255 Highway 54 West, Zip 30214–4526; tel. 770/719–7000, **A**2 3 10 21 **F**11 13 15 18 20 22 26 28 29 30 31 34 35 36 40 44 45 46 47 48 49 50 51 53 55 57 59 61 63 64 70 72 73 74 75 76 77 78 79 81 83 84 85 86 87 93 94 97 107 108 110 111 114 115 118 119 120 121 123 126 129 130 132 146 147 148 157 **S** Piedmont Healthcare, Roswell, GA
Primary Contact: Stephen D. Porter, Chief Executive Officer
COO: Nathan Nipper, Chief Operating Officer
CFO: Scott A. Wolfe, Chief Financial Officer
CMO: Angela Swayne, M.D., Chief Medical Officer
CIO: Geoffrey Brown, Chief Information Officer
CHR: Holly Sawyer, Director and Human Resources Business Partner
CNO: Merry Heath, Chief Nursing Officer
Web address: www.piedmont.org
Control: Other not–for–profit (including NFP Corporation) **Service:** General medical and surgical

Staffed Beds: 221 Admissions: 16543 Census: 190 Outpatient Visits: 180773 Births: 2569 Personnel: 1737

FITZGERALD—Ben Hill County

⇑ **DORMINY MEDICAL CENTER (110073)**, 200 Perry House Road, Zip 31750–8857, Mailing Address: P.O. Box 1447, Zip 31750–1447; tel. 229/424–7100, (Nonreporting) **A**10 21
Primary Contact: Mel Pyne, Regional Chief Executive Officer
CFO: Paige Wynn, Chief Financial Officer
CMO: Davey Herring, M.D., Chief Medical Officer
CIO: Chris Ward, Director Management Information Systems
CHR: Denise Steverson, Director Human Resources
CNO: Staci Mims, Chief Nursing Officer
Web address: www.dorminymedical.org
Control: Hospital district or authority, Government, nonfederal **Service:** General medical and surgical

Staffed Beds: 58

FORSYTH—Monroe County

⇑ **MONROE COUNTY HOSPITAL (111318)**, 88 Martin Luther King Jr Drive, Zip 31029–1682, Mailing Address: P.O. Box 1068, Zip 31029–1068; tel. 478/994–2521, **A**3 10 18 21 **F**3 11 15 29 35 40 57 59 75 77 81 107 110 114 119 133 149
Primary Contact: Lorraine Smith, Chief Executive Officer
CFO: Judy King Ware, Chief Financial Officer
CMO: Jeremy Goodwin, M.D., President, Medical Staff
CIO: Tiffany Purmont, Supervisor Medical Records
CHR: Deborah Flowers, Director Human Resources
CNO: Casey Fleckenstein, Nurse Manager
Web address: www.monroehospital.org
Control: Hospital district or authority, Government, nonfederal **Service:** General medical and surgical

Staffed Beds: 25 Admissions: 509 Census: 13 Outpatient Visits: 12962 Births: 0 Total Expense ($000): 10788 Payroll Expense ($000): 3002 Personnel: 81

FORT BENNING—Muscogee County

⊞ **MARTIN ARMY COMMUNITY HOSPITAL**, 7950 Martin Loop, Zip 31905–5648, Mailing Address: 7950 Martin Loop, B9200, Room 010, Zip 31905–5648; tel. 706/544–2516, (Nonreporting) **A**1 3 5 **S** Department of the Army, Office of the Surgeon General, Falls Church, VA
Primary Contact: Colonel Marie Dominguez, Commander
CHR: Major Dornita Hightower, Chief Human Resources
Web address: www.martin.amedd.army.mil
Control: Department of Defense, Government, federal **Service:** General medical and surgical

Staffed Beds: 57

FORT GORDON—Richmond County

⊞ **DWIGHT DAVID EISENHOWER ARMY MEDICAL CENTER**, 300 West Hospital Road, Zip 30905–5741; tel. 706/787–5811, (Nonreporting) **A**1 2 3 5 **S** Department of the Army, Office of the Surgeon General, Falls Church, VA
Primary Contact: Colonel John P. Lamoureux, Commander
CMO: Colonel James M Baunchalk, Deputy Chief Clinical Services
CIO: Major Joseph A Ponce, Chief Information Management
CHR: Elizabeth Shelt, Civilian Personnel Officer
Web address: www.ddeamc.amedd.army.mil
Control: Department of Defense, Government, federal **Service:** General medical and surgical

Staffed Beds: 107

FORT OGLETHORPE—Catoosa County

★ ⇑ **CHI MEMORIAL HOSPITAL - GEORGIA (110236)**, 100 Gross Crescent Circle, Zip 30742–3669; tel. 706/858–2000, (Data for 184 days) **A**10 21 **F**7 8 29 30 40 44 46 48 64 68 87 107 114 115 119 130 146 149 **S** CommonSpirit Health, Chicago, IL
Primary Contact: Angie Hullander, Administrator and Special Operations
COO: Kevin Hopkins, Vice President of Operations
CFO: Farrell Hayes, Chief Financial Officer
CMO: John Erdman, M.D., Chief of Staff
CIO: Ruth Wright-Whitaker, Director Information Services
CHR: Cathy Hulsey, Manager of Human Resources
CNO: Sandra Siniard, Vice President of Patient Care Services
Web address: www.memorial.org/chi-memorial-hospital-georgia
Control: Church operated, Nongovernment, not–for–profit **Service:** General medical and surgical

Staffed Beds: 35 Admissions: 297 Census: 4 Outpatient Visits: 13799 Births: 0 Total Expense ($000): 9251 Payroll Expense ($000): 3332 Personnel: 154

GA

Hospital, Medicare Provider Number, Address, Telephone, Approval, Facility, and Physician Codes, Health Care System

★ American Hospital Association (AHA) membership   ○ Healthcare Facilities Accreditation Program   ⇑ Center for Improvement in Healthcare Quality Accreditation
☐ The Joint Commission accreditation   ◇ DNV Healthcare Inc. accreditation   △ Commission on Accreditation of Rehabilitation Facilities (CARF) accreditation

---

GAINESVILLE—Hall County

★ △ ⇑ **NORTHEAST GEORGIA MEDICAL CENTER (110029)**, 743 Spring Street NE, Zip 30501–3899; tel. 770/219–3553, (Total facility includes 252 beds in nursing home–type unit) **A**2 3 7 10 19 21 **F**3 4 7 11 12 13 15 17 18 20 22 24 26 28 29 30 31 34 35 38 40 43 44 45 46 47 48 49 50 51 54 56 57 58 59 60 61 63 64 66 68 70 72 73 74 75 76 77 78 79 81 82 83 84 85 86 87 89 90 93 98 99 100 101 104 105 107 110 111 114 115 116 117 119 120 121 123 124 126 128 129 130 131 132 143 144 146 147 148 149 151 152 153 154 156 **S** Northeast Georgia Health System, Gainesville, GA
Primary Contact: Carol H. Burrell, Chief Executive Officer
CFO: Brian D Steines, Chief Financial Officer
CMO: Sam Johnson, M.D., Chief Medical Officer
CIO: Chris Paravate, Chief Information Officer
CHR: Deborah Weber, Chief Human Resource Officer
CNO: Brenda Simpson, Chief Nursing Officer
Web address: www.nghs.com
Control: Other not–for–profit (including NFP Corporation) **Service**: General medical and surgical

Staffed Beds: 887 Admissions: 39344 Census: 721 Outpatient Visits: 537522 Births: 4370 Personnel: 5147

GRACEWOOD—Richmond County

EAST CENTRAL REGIONAL HOSPITAL See East Central Regional Hospital, Augusta

GREENSBORO—Greene County

⊞ **ST. MARY'S GOOD SAMARITAN HOSPITAL (111329)**, 5401 Lake Oconee Parkway, Zip 30642–4232; tel. 706/453–7331, **A**1 10 18 **F**3 11 15 18 26 29 30 34 35 40 45 50 51 57 64 65 68 74 75 77 79 81 85 87 93 107 108 115 119 130 132 133 146 147 154 156 157 **S** Trinity Health, Livonia, MI
Primary Contact: Tanya M. Adcock, President
CMO: Dave Ringer, M.D., Chief of Staff
CNO: Celia Covington, MSN, R.N., Director of Nursing
Web address: www.stmarysgoodsam.org
Control: Church operated, Nongovernment, not–for–profit **Service**: General medical and surgical

Staffed Beds: 25 Admissions: 978 Census: 12 Outpatient Visits: 42805 Births: 0 Total Expense ($000): 23629 Payroll Expense ($000): 7907 Personnel: 150

GRIFFIN—Spalding County

⊞ **WELLSTAR SPALDING REGIONAL HOSPITAL (110031)**, 601 South Eighth Street, Zip 30224–4294, Mailing Address: P O Drawer 'V', Zip 30224–1168; tel. 770/228–2721, **A**1 2 10 **F**3 7 11 13 15 18 20 22 29 30 31 34 35 40 45 49 50 53 54 57 59 64 70 73 75 76 77 78 79 80 81 85 87 89 93 107 108 110 111 114 115 119 129 130 146 147 148 **S** WellStar Health System, Marietta, GA
Primary Contact: Tamara Ison, Senior Vice President and President
COO: Tamara Ison, Chief Operating Officer
CMO: Philip Osehobo, M.D., Chief Medical Officer
CIO: Steve Brown, Director Information Systems
CHR: Amanda Remington, Director Human Resources
CNO: Wadra McCullough, Chief Nursing Officer
Web address: www.spaldingregional.com
Control: Other not–for–profit (including NFP Corporation) **Service**: General medical and surgical

Staffed Beds: 160 Admissions: 8891 Census: 105 Outpatient Visits: 102123 Births: 1047 Personnel: 712

HAWKINSVILLE—Pulaski County

⇑ **TAYLOR REGIONAL HOSPITAL (110135)**, Macon Highway, Zip 31036, Mailing Address: P.O. Box 1297, Zip 31036–7297; tel. 478/783–0200, (Nonreporting) **A**3 10 21
Primary Contact: E.R. McDannald, Interim Chief Executive Officer
CFO: Lisa Halliday, Director Accounting Services
CMO: Al Baggett, M.D., Interim Chief of Staff
CIO: Dawn Warnock, Director Medical Records
Web address: www.taylorregional.org
Control: Other not–for–profit (including NFP Corporation) **Service**: General medical and surgical

Staffed Beds: 57

HAZLEHURST—Jeff Davis County

⇑ **JEFF DAVIS HOSPITAL (111333)**, 163 South Tallahassee Street, Zip 31539–2921, Mailing Address: P.O. Box 1690, Zip 31539–1690; tel. 912/375–7781, **A**10 18 21 **F**15 29 30 40 45 57 68 70 77 81 85 97 98 103 107 115 119 133 143 149 153 154
Primary Contact: Tammy Mims, Chief Executive Officer
CFO: Cathy Cason, Chief Financial Officer
CIO: Brian Fowler, Information Technology Director
CHR: Brenda McEachin, Human Resources Director
CNO: Allen Crawford, Chief Nursing Officer
Web address: www.jeffdavishospital.org
Control: Hospital district or authority, Government, nonfederal **Service**: General medical and surgical

Staffed Beds: 25 Admissions: 568 Census: 7 Outpatient Visits: 18708 Births: 0 Total Expense ($000): 12053 Payroll Expense ($000): 5198 Personnel: 159

HIAWASSEE—Towns County

CHATUGE REGIONAL HOSPITAL AND NURSING HOME (111324), 110 Main Street, Zip 30546–3408, Mailing Address: P.O. Box 509, Zip 30546–0509; tel. 706/896–2222, (Total facility includes 112 beds in nursing home–type unit) **A**10 18 **F**3 11 15 29 34 35 40 45 56 57 59 64 65 70 75 77 81 82 86 87 92 93 97 98 100 103 104 107 108 110 111 115 119 127 128 130 132 133 135 144 146 148 149 **S** Union General Hospital, Inc., Blairsville, GA
Primary Contact: Ryan Snow, Administrator
CFO: Tim Henry, Accountant
CMO: Robert F Stahlkuppe, M.D., Chief of Staff
CIO: Walt Stafford, Director Information Technology
CHR: Rita Bradshaw, Director Human Resources
Web address: www.chatugeregionalhospital.org
Control: Hospital district or authority, Government, nonfederal **Service**: General medical and surgical

Staffed Beds: 150 Admissions: 978 Census: 121 Outpatient Visits: 22221 Births: 0 Total Expense ($000): 25597 Payroll Expense ($000): 13860 Personnel: 303

HINESVILLE—Liberty County

☐ **LIBERTY REGIONAL MEDICAL CENTER (111335)**, 462 Elma G Miles Parkway, Zip 31313–4000, Mailing Address: P.O. Box 919, Zip 31310–0919; tel. 912/369–9400, (Nonreporting) **A**1 10 18
Primary Contact: Tammy Mims, Interim Chief Executive Officer
CFO: Derek Rozier, Chief Financial Officer
CNO: Donna R. Cochrane, Chief Nursing Officer
Web address: www.libertyregional.org
Control: Hospital district or authority, Government, nonfederal **Service**: General medical and surgical

Staffed Beds: 25

⊞ **WINN ARMY COMMUNITY HOSPITAL**, 1061 Harmon Avenue, Zip 31314–5641, Mailing Address: 1061 Harmon Avenue, Suite 2311B, Zip 31314–5641; tel. 912/435–6965, (Nonreporting) **A**1 5 **S** Department of the Army, Office of the Surgeon General, Falls Church, VA
Primary Contact: Colonel Kirk W. Eggleston, Commanding Officer
CIO: Arthur N Kirshner, Chief Information Management
CHR: Major Yvette McCrea, Chief Human Resources
CNO: Colonel Sharon Brown, Deputy Commander Nursing
Web address: www.winn.amedd.army.mil/
Control: Department of Defense, Government, federal **Service**: General medical and surgical

Staffed Beds: 37

HIRAM—Paulding County

★ **WELLSTAR PAULDING HOSPITAL (110042)**, 2518 Jimmy Lee Smith Parkway, Zip 30141; tel. 470/644–7000, (Total facility includes 182 beds in nursing home–type unit) **A**2 10 **F**3 11 15 18 20 29 30 31 37 38 40 41 44 45 49 50 53 54 55 59 61 64 68 70 75 77 78 79 80 81 82 85 86 87 93 102 107 108 110 111 114 118 119 120 121 123 124 128 129 130 135 146 148 154 156 **S** WellStar Health System, Marietta, GA
Primary Contact: John Kueven, Senior Vice President and President
COO: Lindsay Rehn, Executive Director of Financial Operations
CFO: Lindsay Rehn, Executive Director of Financial Operations
CMO: Guillermo Pierluisi, Vice President of Medical Affairs
CHR: Jessica Bedsole, Director, Human Resources
CNO: Vicky Hogue, R.N., Vice President Patient Services and Chief Nursing Officer
Web address: www.wellstar.org
Control: Other not–for–profit (including NFP Corporation) **Service**: General medical and surgical

Staffed Beds: 294 Admissions: 7570 Census: 233 Outpatient Visits: 134216 Births: 0 Personnel: 890

GA

Many Facility Codes have changed. Please refer to the AHA Guide Code Chart. © 2019 AHA Guide

HOMERVILLE—Clinch County

★ **CLINCH MEMORIAL HOSPITAL (111308)**, 1050 Valdosta Highway, Zip 31634–9701, Mailing Address: P.O. Box 516, Zip 31634–0516; tel. 912/487–5211, **A**10 18 **F**3 7 11 15 29 34 35 40 45 57 59 64 93 107 114 119 129 130 133 146 149
Primary Contact: Angela Ammons, Administrator
COO: Wallace D Mincey, Chief Executive Officer
CFO: Teressia Shook, Chief Financial Officer
CMO: Samuel Cobarrubias, M.D., Chief of Staff
CIO: Shelly Studebaker, Human Resources Assistant
CHR: Shelly Studebaker, Human Resources Assistant
CNO: Kellie Register, Director of Nursing
Web address: www.clinchmemorialhospital.org
Control: County, Government, nonfederal **Service:** General medical and surgical

Staffed Beds: 25 **Admissions:** 229 **Census:** 3 **Outpatient Visits:** 11170 **Births:** 0 **Total Expense ($000):** 10045 **Payroll Expense ($000):** 3870 **Personnel:** 88

JACKSON—Butts County

★ **WELLSTAR SYLVAN GROVE HOSPITAL (111319)**, 1050 McDonough Road, Zip 30233–1599; tel. 770/775–7861, **A**10 18 **F**29 34 35 40 50 57 59 68 77 93 107 119 133 **S** WellStar Health System, Marietta, GA
Primary Contact: Tamara Ison, Senior Vice President and President
CFO: Tamara Ison, Chief Financial Officer
CIO: Steve Brown, Chief Information Officer
CHR: Amanda Remington, Director Human Resources
Web address: www.sylvangrovehospital.com
Control: Other not-for-profit (including NFP Corporation) **Service:** General medical and surgical

Staffed Beds: 24 **Admissions:** 332 **Census:** 11 **Outpatient Visits:** 18773 **Births:** 0 **Personnel:** 76

JASPER—Pickens County

⇑ **PIEDMONT MOUNTAINSIDE HOSPITAL (110225)**, 1266 Highway 515 South, Zip 30143–4872; tel. 706/692–2441, **A**10 21 **F**3 13 15 20 28 29 34 35 40 41 42 45 46 49 53 57 59 64 70 75 76 77 79 81 85 107 108 110 111 114 115 119 124 129 130 132 135 146 148 149 154 **S** Piedmont Healthcare, Roswell, GA
Primary Contact: Denise Ray, Chief Executive Officer
CMO: Moiz Master, M.D., Medical Director of Quality
CIO: Geoffrey Brown, Chief Information Officer
CHR: Frank Leist, Human Resources Manager
CNO: Michelle Breitfelder, Chief Nursing Officer
Web address: www.https://www.piedmont.org
Control: Other not-for-profit (including NFP Corporation) **Service:** General medical and surgical

Staffed Beds: 52 **Admissions:** 3373 **Census:** 33 **Outpatient Visits:** 77411 **Births:** 304 **Total Expense ($000):** 61875 **Payroll Expense ($000):** 27106 **Personnel:** 358

JESUP—Wayne County

☐ **WAYNE MEMORIAL HOSPITAL (110124)**, 865 South First Street, Zip 31545–0210, Mailing Address: P.O. Box 410, Zip 31598–0410; tel. 912/427–6811, (Nonreporting) **A**1 10 20
Primary Contact: Joseph P. Ierardi, Chief Executive Officer
CFO: Greg Jones, Chief Financial Officer
CMO: Dan Collipp, M.D., Chief of Staff
CIO: Deborah Six, Coordinator Data Processing
CHR: John McIwain, Director Human Resources
Web address: www.wmhweb.com
Control: County, Government, nonfederal **Service:** General medical and surgical

Staffed Beds: 84

JOHNS CREEK—Fulton County

⊞ **EMORY JOHNS CREEK HOSPITAL (110230)**, 6325 Hospital Parkway, Zip 30097–5775; tel. 678/474–7000, **A**1 2 3 5 10 **F**3 11 12 13 15 18 20 22 26 29 30 31 34 35 36 40 45 49 50 54 55 57 58 59 60 64 68 70 72 73 74 75 76 77 78 79 81 82 84 85 86 87 93 100 101 102 107 108 110 111 115 116 117 119 126 129 130 131 132 141 146 147 148 149 156 **S** Emory Healthcare, Atlanta, GA
Primary Contact: Marilyn Margolis, MSN, Chief Executive Officer
COO: Laurie Hansen, Vice President of Operations
CFO: JoAnn Manning, Chief Financial Officer
CMO: Adedapo Odetoyinbo, M.D., Chief Medical Office
CHR: Hannah Henry, Interim Vice President of Human Resources
CNO: Heather Redrick, Chief Nursing Officer
Web address: www.emoryjohnscreek.com
Control: Other not-for-profit (including NFP Corporation) **Service:** General medical and surgical

Staffed Beds: 118 **Admissions:** 7945 **Census:** 93 **Outpatient Visits:** 81591 **Births:** 1196 **Total Expense ($000):** 157054 **Payroll Expense ($000):** 56332 **Personnel:** 772

KENNESAW—Cobb County

DEVEREUX ADVANCED BEHAVIORAL HEALTH GEORGIA, 1291 Stanley Road NW, Zip 30152–4359; tel. 770/427–0147, **A**3 **F**98 106 **S** Devereux, Villanova, PA
Primary Contact: Gwendolyn Skinner, Operational Vice President
COO: Mary H Esposito, Assistant Executive Director
CFO: Kathy Goggin, Director of Finance
CMO: Yolanda Graham, M.D., Medical Director
CIO: Sam Maguta, Coordinator Information Systems
CHR: Rudie Delien, Director of Human Resources
CNO: Debra Sharpton, Director of Nursing
Web address: www.devereuxga.org
Control: Other not-for-profit (including NFP Corporation) **Service:** Psychiatric

Staffed Beds: 110 **Admissions:** 169 **Census:** 80 **Outpatient Visits:** 63 **Births:** 0 **Total Expense ($000):** 17388 **Payroll Expense ($000):** 4644 **Personnel:** 354

LAGRANGE—Troup County

Ⓐ **WELLSTAR WEST GEORGIA MEDICAL CENTER (110016)**, 1514 Vernon Road, Zip 30240–4131; tel. 706/882–1411, (Total facility includes 260 beds in nursing home–type unit) **A**1 2 10 19 **F**3 11 12 13 15 18 20 22 26 28 29 30 31 34 35 40 44 47 48 50 51 56 57 58 59 62 63 64 66 68 70 73 74 75 76 77 78 79 80 81 82 84 85 86 87 89 92 93 96 107 108 110 111 114 115 119 120 121 123 124 126 128 129 130 132 135 146 147 148 149 154 **S** WellStar Health System, Marietta, GA
Primary Contact: Coleman Foss, Chief Executive Officer
COO: Charis L Acree, Vice President and Chief Operating Officer
CFO: Paul R Perrotti, CPA, Chief Financial Officer
CIO: Alan Whitehouse, Chief Information Officer
CHR: Tommy Britt, Vice President of Human Resources
CNO: Tracy Gynther, R.N., Vice President and Chief Nursing Officer
Web address: www.wghealth.org/
Control: Other not-for-profit (including NFP Corporation) **Service:** General medical and surgical

Staffed Beds: 390 **Admissions:** 7764 **Census:** 313 **Outpatient Visits:** 127991 **Births:** 977 **Personnel:** 1214

LAKELAND—Lanier County

⊞ **SOUTH GEORGIA MEDICAL CENTER LANIER CAMPUS (111326)**, 116 West Thigpen Avenue, Zip 31635–1011; tel. 229/482–3110, (Total facility includes 62 beds in nursing home–type unit) **A**1 10 18 **F**3 7 15 29 34 35 40 57 59 68 75 77 107 119 128 129 130 133 135 146 148 149 150 **S** South Georgia Medical Center, Valdosta, GA
Primary Contact: Richard Huth, Administrator
CFO: Libby Flemming, Controller and Chief Information Officer
CMO: Bruce Herrington, M.D., Chief Medical Officer
CIO: Libby Flemming, Controller and Chief Information Officer
CHR: Vicki Dinkins, Director Human Resources
Web address: www.sgmc.org
Control: Hospital district or authority, Government, nonfederal **Service:** General medical and surgical

Staffed Beds: 87 **Admissions:** 292 **Census:** 66 **Outpatient Visits:** 12496 **Births:** 0 **Total Expense ($000):** 15150 **Payroll Expense ($000):** 6270 **Personnel:** 166

GA

Hospital, Medicare Provider Number, Address, Telephone, Approval, Facility, and Physician Codes, Health Care System

★ American Hospital Association (AHA) membership
☐ The Joint Commission accreditation
○ Healthcare Facilities Accreditation Program
◇ DNV Healthcare Inc. accreditation
⇑ Center for Improvement in Healthcare Quality Accreditation
△ Commission on Accreditation of Rehabilitation Facilities (CARF) accreditation

LAVONIA—Franklin County

✠ **ST. MARY'S SACRED HEART HOSPITAL (110027)**, 367 Clear Creek Parkway, Zip 30553–4173; tel. 706/356–7800, **A**1 10 **F**3 11 13 15 18 29 30 34 35 40 49 50 53 57 59 70 74 75 76 79 81 85 87 93 107 108 110 111 115 119 129 130 132 149 154 **S** Trinity Health, Livonia, MI
Primary Contact: Jeff English, President
CIO: Tim Vickery, Chief Information Officer
CHR: Lauren Papka, Chief Administrative Officer
CNO: Evelyn Murphy, Chief Nursing Officer
Web address: www.stmaryssacredheart.org/
Control: Church operated, Nongovernment, not–for–profit **Service:** General medical and surgical

Staffed Beds: 41 **Admissions:** 1921 **Census:** 19 **Outpatient Visits:** 49321 **Births:** 314 **Total Expense ($000):** 32459 **Payroll Expense ($000):** 12541 **Personnel:** 212

LAWRENCEVILLE—Gwinnett County

✠ **GWINNETT HOSPITAL SYSTEM (110087)**, 1000 Medical Center Boulevard, Zip 30046–7694, Mailing Address: P.O. Box 348, Zip 30046–0348; tel. 678/312–1000, (Includes GWINNETT MEDICAL CENTER-DULUTH, 3620 Howell Ferry Road, Duluth, Georgia, Zip 30096; tel. 678/312–6800; GWINNETT MEDICAL CENTER, 1000 Medical Center Boulevard, Lawrenceville, Georgia, Zip 30245, Mailing Address: Box 348, Zip 30246, tel. 678/312–1000; Thomas Shepherd, Executive Vice President and Chief Operating Officer) (Total facility includes 89 beds in nursing home–type unit) **A**1 2 3 5 8 10 **F**3 8 11 12 13 15 17 18 20 22 24 26 28 29 30 31 34 35 36 37 38 40 41 43 44 45 46 47 48 49 50 53 54 55 56 58 59 64 67 68 70 71 72 73 74 75 76 77 78 79 81 82 84 85 86 87 90 93 96 97 107 108 110 111 114 115 116 117 118 119 126 128 129 130 131 132 134 135 146 147 148 149 157
Primary Contact: Philip R. Wolfe, President and Chief Executive Officer
COO: Thomas Shepherd, Executive Vice President and Chief Operating Officer
CFO: Thomas Y McBride III Executive Vice President and Chief Financial Officer
CMO: Alan Bier, M.D., Executive Vice President and Chief Medical Officer
CIO: Patricia A Lavely, FACHE, Senior Vice President and Chief Information Officer
CHR: Stephen Nadeau, Senior Vice President Human Resources
CNO: Carol Danielson, R.N., Senior Vice President and Chief Nursing Officer
Web address: www.gwinnettmedicalcenter.org
Control: Other not–for–profit (including NFP Corporation) **Service:** General medical and surgical

Staffed Beds: 569 **Admissions:** 29060 **Census:** 492 **Outpatient Visits:** 390147 **Births:** 4502 **Total Expense ($000):** 721164 **Payroll Expense ($000):** 281696 **Personnel:** 3917

☐ **SUMMITRIDGE HOSPITAL (114004)**, 250 Scenic Highway, Zip 30046–5675; tel. 678/442–5800, **A**1 10 **F**4 5 98 99 102 103 104 105 152 153 154
Primary Contact: Tim E. Merritt, Chief Executive Officer
Web address: www.summitridgehospital.net
Control: Corporation, Investor–owned (for–profit) **Service:** Psychiatric

Staffed Beds: 96 **Admissions:** 3888 **Census:** 87 **Outpatient Visits:** 8406 **Births:** 0 **Total Expense ($000):** 17352 **Payroll Expense ($000):** 10316 **Personnel:** 138

LITHONIA—Dekalb County

☐ **EMORY HILLANDALE HOSPITAL (110226)**, 2801 DeKalb Medical Parkway, Zip 30058–4996; tel. 404/501–8000, **A**1 10 **F**3 15 18 20 22 26 28 29 30 34 35 38 40 44 49 50 51 57 59 60 61 68 70 74 75 77 78 79 81 82 84 85 86 87 93 96 100 107 111 121 129 130 131 132 135 148 149 156 **S** Emory Healthcare, Atlanta, GA
Primary Contact: Jim Forstner, Chief Executive Officer
CMO: Duane Barclay, D.O., Chief Medical Officer
CIO: Mark Trocino, Chief Information Officer
CHR: Tom Crawford, Vice President Human Resources
Web address: www.dekalbmedical.org
Control: Other not–for–profit (including NFP Corporation) **Service:** General medical and surgical

Staffed Beds: 70 **Admissions:** 4114 **Census:** 47 **Outpatient Visits:** 94285 **Births:** 0 **Total Expense ($000):** 80695 **Payroll Expense ($000):** 30881 **Personnel:** 458

LOUISVILLE—Jefferson County

⇑ **JEFFERSON HOSPITAL (110100)**, 1067 Peachtree Street, Zip 30434–1599; tel. 478/625–7000, **A**10 20 21 **F**3 11 15 29 30 34 35 40 43 46 50 57 59 64 65 66 68 75 77 81 86 90 91 93 96 97 102 107 110 115 119 127 129 130 133 146 148 154
Primary Contact: Louis Semrad, Chief Executive Officer
CFO: Lieutenant John Graham, Chief Financial Officer
CMO: James Polhill, M.D., Chief Medical Officer
CHR: Catherine Hall, Manager Human Resources
CNO: Stacey Smith, R.N., Director of Nursing
Web address: www.jeffersonhosp.com
Control: County, Government, nonfederal **Service:** General medical and surgical

Staffed Beds: 37 **Admissions:** 390 **Census:** 4 **Births:** 0

MACON—Bibb County

✠ **COLISEUM MEDICAL CENTERS (110164)**, 350 Hospital Drive, Zip 31217–3871; tel. 478/765–7000, (Includes COLISEUM CENTER FOR BEHAVIORAL HEALTH, 340 Hospital Drive, Macon, Georgia, Zip 31217–3838; tel. 478/741–1355; Stephen J. Daugherty, Interim Chief Executive Officer), (Nonreporting) **A**1 2 3 5 10 **S** HCA Healthcare, Nashville, TN
Primary Contact: Stephen J. Daugherty, Chief Executive Officer
COO: Kelly Lindsay, Chief Operating Officer
CFO: Scott Anderton, Chief Financial Officer
CIO: Joan Morstad, Director Information Systems
CHR: Laura Booras, Vice President Human Resources
Web address: www.coliseumhealthsystem.com
Control: Corporation, Investor–owned (for–profit) **Service:** General medical and surgical

Staffed Beds: 227

✠ **COLISEUM NORTHSIDE HOSPITAL (110201)**, 400 Charter Boulevard, Zip 31210–4853, Mailing Address: P.O. Box 4627, Zip 31208–4627; tel. 478/757–8200, (Nonreporting) **A**1 10 **S** HCA Healthcare, Nashville, TN
Primary Contact: Greg Caples, Chief Executive Officer
CFO: Elmer Polite, Chief Financial Officer
CHR: Louise Truitt, Human Resource Director
CNO: Patricia Derrico, FACHE, R.N., Chief Nursing Officer
Web address: www.coliseumhealthsystem.com
Control: Corporation, Investor–owned (for–profit) **Service:** General medical and surgical

Staffed Beds: 103

★ ⇑ **MEDICAL CENTER, NAVICENT HEALTH (110107)**, 777 Hemlock Street, Zip 31201–2155; tel. 478/633–1000, (Includes CHILDREN'S HOSPITAL, NAVICENT HEALTH, 888 Pine Street, Macon, Georgia, Zip 31201–2155; tel. 478/633–1000) **A**2 3 5 8 10 21 **F**3 7 8 11 12 13 14 15 17 18 20 22 24 26 28 29 30 31 32 34 35 36 39 40 43 44 45 46 47 48 49 50 51 53 54 56 57 58 59 60 61 62 63 64 65 66 68 70 72 73 74 75 76 77 78 79 80 81 82 83 84 85 86 87 88 89 92 93 94 97 98 100 101 102 104 107 108 110 111 114 115 119 126 130 132 135 143 144 145 146 147 148 149 150 154 **S** Navicent Health, Macon, GA
Primary Contact: Ninfa M. Saunders, President and Chief Executive Officer
COO: Susan Harris, R.N., Chief Operating Officer
CFO: Rhonda S. Perry, Chief Financial Officer
CMO: Christopher Hendry, M.D., Chief Medical Officer
CIO: Ed Brown, Chief Information Officer
CHR: Bernard J Price, Chief Human Resources Officer
CNO: Tracey Blalock, MSN, R.N., Chief Nurse Executive
Web address: www.https://www.navicenthealth.org/
Control: Other not–for–profit (including NFP Corporation) **Service:** General medical and surgical

Staffed Beds: 627 **Admissions:** 30198 **Census:** 482

✠ **REGENCY HOSPITAL OF CENTRAL GEORGIA (112016)**, 535 Coliseum Drive, Zip 31217–0104; tel. 478/803–7300, (Nonreporting) **A**1 10 **S** Select Medical Corporation, Mechanicsburg, PA
Primary Contact: Wayne B. Boutwell, Chief Executive Officer
Web address: www.regencyhospital.com
Control: Corporation, Investor–owned (for–profit) **Service:** Acute long–term care hospital

Staffed Beds: 60

GA

Many Facility Codes have changed. Please refer to the AHA Guide Code Chart. © 2019 AHA Guide

★ ⇑ **REHABILITATION HOSPITAL, NAVICENT HEALTH (113029)**, 3351 Northside Drive, Zip 31210–2587; tel. 478/201–6500, (Nonreporting) **A**3 10 21 **S** Navicent Health, Macon, GA
Primary Contact: Regina Tipton, Director of Operations
COO: Darren Pearce, Executive Director
CFO: Beverly Owens, Controller
CMO: Allison Scheetz, M.D., Medical Director
Web address: www.navicenthealth.org/service-center/rehabilitation-hospital-navicent-health
Control: Other not–for–profit (including NFP Corporation) **Service:** Rehabilitation

Staffed Beds: 58

MADISON—Morgan County

☐ **MORGAN MEMORIAL HOSPITAL (111304)**, 1077 South Main Street, Zip 30650–2073, Mailing Address: P.O. Box 860, Zip 30650–0860; tel. 706/342–1667, **A**1 10 18 **F**11 15 29 30 34 35 40 43 49 57 61 64 77 79 81 82 87 89 90 93 94 97 107 110 111 114 119 128 133 146 147 148
Primary Contact: Ralph A. Castillo, CPA, Chief Executive Officer
CFO: Kyle Wilkinson, Chief Financial Officer
CMO: Dan Zant, M.D., Chief of Staff
CIO: Patrick Cook, Vice President Support Services
CHR: Sarah Phillips, Manager Human Resources
CNO: Beth O'Neill, Chief Nursing Officer
Web address: www.mmh.org
Control: Hospital district or authority, Government, nonfederal **Service:** General medical and surgical

Staffed Beds: 25 Admissions: 384 Census: 14 Outpatient Visits: 14216 Births: 0 Total Expense ($000): 15499 Payroll Expense ($000): 6559

MARIETTA—Cobb County

⊞ △ **WELLSTAR KENNESTONE HOSPITAL (110035)**, 677 Church Street, Zip 30060–1148; tel. 770/793–5000, **A**1 2 3 7 10 **F**3 10 11 12 13 15 17 18 20 22 24 26 28 29 30 31 34 36 37 38 40 41 43 44 45 46 47 48 49 50 51 53 54 55 58 59 60 61 64 66 68 70 72 73 74 75 76 77 78 79 80 81 82 84 85 86 87 89 90 93 94 96 97 100 102 107 108 110 111 114 115 116 117 118 119 120 121 123 124 125 126 129 130 132 141 146 147 148 154 156 **S** WellStar Health System, Marietta, GA
Primary Contact: Mary Chatman, Ph.D., Chief Executive Officer
CFO: Douglas Arvin, Vice President Finance and Chief Financial Officer
CMO: Robert Lubitz, M.D., Vice President of Medical Affairs
CIO: Jonathan B Morris, M.D., Senior Vice President and Chief Information Officer
CNO: Lynn Meurer, MSN, R.N., Interim Chief Nursing Officer
Web address: www.wellstar.org
Control: Other not–for–profit (including NFP Corporation) **Service:** General medical and surgical

Staffed Beds: 657 Admissions: 41875 Census: 545 Outpatient Visits: 451255 Births: 5404 Personnel: 4132

⊞ **WELLSTAR WINDY HILL HOSPITAL (112007)**, 2540 Windy Hill Road, Zip 30067–8632; tel. 770/644–1000, **A**1 2 10 **F**1 3 11 15 28 29 30 44 45 50 51 60 61 64 68 75 77 79 81 82 85 86 87 93 100 101 107 108 110 111 114 118 119 129 130 131 135 141 146 147 148 156 **S** WellStar Health System, Marietta, GA
Primary Contact: Mary Chatman, Ph.D., Chief Executive Officer
CFO: Marsha Burke, Senior Vice President and Chief Financial Officer
CMO: Larry Haldeman, M.D., Executive Vice President and Chief Medical Officer
CIO: Leigh Cox, Chief Information Officer
Web address: www.wellstar.org
Control: Other not–for–profit (including NFP Corporation) **Service:** Acute long–term care hospital

Staffed Beds: 55 Admissions: 298 Census: 26 Outpatient Visits: 124817 Births: 0 Personnel: 337

METTER—Candler County

⇑ **CANDLER COUNTY HOSPITAL (111334)**, 400 Cedar Street, Zip 30439–3338, Mailing Address: P.O. Box 597, Zip 30439–0597; tel. 912/685–5741, (Nonreporting) **A**10 18 21
Primary Contact: Karen O'Neal, Chief Executive Officer
COO: David Flanders, Chief Operating Officer
CNO: Christy Blackburn, R.N., Chief Nursing Officer
Web address: www.candlercountyhospital.com
Control: Hospital district or authority, Government, nonfederal **Service:** General medical and surgical

Staffed Beds: 25

MILLEDGEVILLE—Baldwin County

☐ **CENTRAL STATE HOSPITAL**, 2450 Vinson Highway, Zip 31062–0001; tel. 478/445–4128, **A**1 3 **F**30 39 59 75 77 86 87 97 98 100 130 132 149
Primary Contact: Susan Trueblood, Regional Hospital Administrator
COO: Terry McGee, Chief Operations Officer
CMO: Scott VanSant, M.D., Chief Medical Officer
CIO: Betsy Bradley, Coordinator Performance Improvement
CHR: Myra Holloway, Director Human Resources Management
Web address: www.centralstatehospital.org
Control: State, Government, nonfederal **Service:** Psychiatric

Staffed Beds: 182 Admissions: 154 Census: 175 Outpatient Visits: 0 Births: 0 Total Expense ($000): 57903 Payroll Expense ($000): 24734 Personnel: 640

★ ⇑ **NAVICENT HEALTH BALDWIN (110150)**, 821 North Cobb Street, Zip 31061–2351, Mailing Address: P.O. Box 690, Zip 31059–0690; tel. 478/454–3505, (Nonreporting) **A**10 19 21 **S** Navicent Health, Macon, GA
Primary Contact: Todd Dixon, R.N., Chief Executive Officer
CFO: Brenda Qualls, Chief Financial Officer
CNO: Deborah Block, Vice President Nursing and Chief Nursing Officer
Web address: www.navicenthealth.org/nhb/home
Control: Other not–for–profit (including NFP Corporation) **Service:** General medical and surgical

Staffed Beds: 90

MILLEN—Jenkins County

JENKINS COUNTY MEDICAL CENTER (111311), 931 East Winthrope Avenue, Zip 30442–1839; tel. 478/982–4221, (Nonreporting) **A**10 18 **S** National Surgical Healthcare, Chicago, IL
Primary Contact: Earl S. Whiteley, FACHE, Chief Executive Officer
CFO: Cindy Bierschenk, Director of Financial Services
CIO: Christian Rekowski, Information Technology Director
CHR: Natalie Peterson, Director of Human Resources
CNO: Sharon Lagina Evans, R.N., Assistant Chief Nursing Officer
Web address: www.https://jenkinsmedicalcenter.com/
Control: Hospital district or authority, Government, nonfederal **Service:** General medical and surgical

Staffed Beds: 25

MONROE—Walton County

⊞ **PIEDMONT WALTON HOSPITAL (110046)**, 2151 West Spring Street, Zip 30655–3116, Mailing Address: P.O. Box 1346, Zip 30655–1346; tel. 770/267–8461, (Nonreporting) **A**1 10 **S** Piedmont Healthcare, Roswell, GA
Primary Contact: Larry W. Ebert Jr, Chief Executive Officer
CFO: Jeffrey Mullis, Interim Chief Financial Officer
CMO: Robert Shyard, M.D., Chief Medical Officer
CIO: Cory Crayton, Director of Information Systems
CHR: Michele Monsrud, Director Human Resources
CNO: Sharon H Queen, R.N., Chief Nursing Officer
Web address: www.https://www.piedmont.org/locations/piedmont-walton/home
Control: Corporation, Investor–owned (for–profit) **Service:** General medical and surgical

Staffed Beds: 52

MONTEZUMA—Macon County

⇑ **FLINT RIVER COMMUNITY HOSPITAL (110190)**, 509 Sumter Street, Zip 31063–1733, Mailing Address: P.O. Box 770, Zip 31063–2502; tel. 478/472–3100, (Nonreporting) **A**10 21
Primary Contact: Michael C. Patterson, Chief Executive Officer
CMO: Quincy Jordan, M.D., Chief of Staff
CHR: Vicki Stotts, Coordinator Human Resources
CNO: Lee Hughes, R.N., Chief Nursing Officer
Web address: www.flintriverhospital.com/
Control: Corporation, Investor–owned (for–profit) **Service:** General medical and surgical

Staffed Beds: 49

GA

Hospital, Medicare Provider Number, Address, Telephone, Approval, Facility, and Physician Codes, Health Care System

★ American Hospital Association (AHA) membership
☐ The Joint Commission accreditation
○ Healthcare Facilities Accreditation Program
◇ DNV Healthcare Inc. accreditation
⇑ Center for Improvement in Healthcare Quality Accreditation
△ Commission on Accreditation of Rehabilitation Facilities (CARF) accreditation

MONTICELLO—Jasper County

JASPER MEMORIAL HOSPITAL (111303), 898 College Street, Zip 31064–1258; tel. 706/468–6411, (Total facility includes 55 beds in nursing home–type unit) **A**10 18 **F**11 18 29 34 40 57 59 65 77 93 97 107 119 128 133 146 148 149
Primary Contact: Jan Gaston, Administrator
CFO: Stuart Abney, Controller
CHR: Laura E Hudgins, Assistant Administrator
CNO: Robin Carey, Director of Nursing
Web address: www.jaspermemorialhospital.org
Control: Other not–for–profit (including NFP Corporation) **Service:** General medical and surgical

Staffed Beds: 67 **Admissions:** 133 **Census:** 57 **Outpatient Visits:** 8530 **Births:** 0 **Total Expense ($000):** 11398 **Payroll Expense ($000):** 5513 **Personnel:** 139

MOULTRIE—Colquitt County

☒ **COLQUITT REGIONAL MEDICAL CENTER (110105)**, 3131 South Main Street, Zip 31768–6925, Mailing Address: P.O. Box 40, Zip 31776–0040; tel. 229/985–3420, **A**1 3 5 10 13 **F**3 7 11 12 13 15 17 20 29 30 31 32 34 35 40 45 47 48 49 56 57 59 60 61 62 63 65 68 70 74 75 76 77 78 79 81 82 85 86 87 89 91 93 97 107 108 110 111 115 119 126 127 129 130 131 132 133 135 143 146 147 148
Primary Contact: James L. Matney, President and Chief Executive Officer
COO: Greg K Johnson, Chief Operating Officer
CFO: Shamb Purohit, Chief Financial Officer
CMO: Andy Wills, M.D., Medical Director
CIO: Bill Bishop, Chief Information Officer
CHR: Dawn Johns, Director Human Resources
CNO: Dena Zinker, MSN, R.N., Vice President Patient Services
Web address: www.colquittregional.com
Control: Hospital district or authority, Government, nonfederal **Service:** General medical and surgical

Staffed Beds: 99 **Admissions:** 4718 **Census:** 57 **Outpatient Visits:** 151793 **Births:** 562 **Total Expense ($000):** 119013 **Payroll Expense ($000):** 51625 **Personnel:** 920

TURNING POINT HOSPITAL (110209), 3015 Veterans Parkway South, Zip 31788–6705, Mailing Address: P.O. Box 1177, Zip 31776–1177; tel. 229/985–4815, **A**10 **F**4 5 30 75 87 98 130 135 143 152 **S** Universal Health Services, Inc., King of Prussia, PA
Primary Contact: Judy H. Payne, Chief Executive Officer
COO: Mark A Heatley, Associate Administrator
CFO: Edwin Bennett, Controller
CMO: Muhammad M Alam, M.D., Medical Director
CHR: Michelle Hamilton, Human Resource Manager
CNO: Faith Connell, Director of Nursing
Web address: www.turningpointcare.com
Control: Corporation, Investor–owned (for–profit) **Service:** Alcoholism and other chemical dependency

Staffed Beds: 69 **Admissions:** 4066 **Census:** 60 **Outpatient Visits:** 32701 **Births:** 0 **Total Expense ($000):** 26761 **Payroll Expense ($000):** 14674 **Personnel:** 220

NASHVILLE—Berrien County

☒ **SOUTH GEORGIA MEDICAL CENTER BERRIEN CAMPUS (110234)**, 1221 East McPherson Avenue, Zip 31639–2326; tel. 229/433–8600, **A**1 10 **F**15 29 34 35 40 57 59 68 75 77 98 102 103 107 110 119 130 135 149 150 **S** South Georgia Medical Center, Valdosta, GA
Primary Contact: Richard Huth, Administrator
Web address: www.sgmc.org/
Control: Hospital district or authority, Government, nonfederal **Service:** General medical and surgical

Staffed Beds: 39 **Admissions:** 360 **Census:** 8 **Outpatient Visits:** 12345 **Births:** 0 **Total Expense ($000):** 7440 **Payroll Expense ($000):** 3243 **Personnel:** 74

NEWNAN—Coweta County

⇑ **PIEDMONT NEWNAN HOSPITAL (110229)**, 745 Poplar Road, Zip 30265–1618; tel. 770/400–1000, (Nonreporting) **A**2 10 21 **S** Piedmont Healthcare, Roswell, GA
Primary Contact: Michael Robertson, Chief Executive Officer
COO: Nathan Nipper, Vice President and Chief Operating Officer
CFO: John Miles, Chief Financial Officer
CMO: Jeffrey R Folk, M.D., Vice President Medical Affairs and Chief Medical Officer
CIO: Henry Scott, Executive Director, Technical Services
CHR: Clay Boyles, Executive Director, Human Resources
CNO: Jennifer Key, Chief Nursing Officer
Web address: www.piedmont.org/locations/piedmont-newnan/pnh-home
Control: Other not–for–profit (including NFP Corporation) **Service:** General medical and surgical

Staffed Beds: 146

☐ **SOUTHEASTERN REGIONAL MEDICAL CENTER (110233)**, 600 Celebrate Life Parkway, Zip 30265–8000; tel. 770/400–6000, **A**1 2 10 **F**3 8 15 18 29 30 31 33 35 36 45 46 47 49 55 64 67 70 75 77 78 81 82 85 86 87 93 107 108 109 110 111 114 115 116 117 118 119 120 121 123 124 130 132 135 146 148 154 **S** Cancer Treatment Centers of America, Schaumburg, IL
Primary Contact: Anne Meisner, MSN, President and Chief Executive Officer
COO: David Kent, Chief Operating Officer
CFO: Scott Walker, Chief Financial Officer
CNO: Gloria V. Barnes, MSN, Assistant Vice President Patient Care Services
Web address: www.cancercenter.com/southeastern-hospital.cfm
Control: Corporation, Investor–owned (for–profit) **Service:** Cancer

Staffed Beds: 50 **Admissions:** 1810 **Census:** 26 **Births:** 0 **Personnel:** 832

NORCROSS—Gwinnett County

LAKEVIEW BEHAVIORAL HEALTH, 1 Technology Parkway South, Zip 30092–2928; tel. 678/713–2600, (Nonreporting) **A**3 **S** Acadia Healthcare Company, Inc., Franklin, TN
Primary Contact: Bill Anderson, Chief Executive Officer
Web address: www.lakeviewbehavioralhealth.com
Control: Corporation, Investor–owned (for–profit) **Service:** Psychiatric

Staffed Beds: 70

OCILLA—Irwin County

⇑ **IRWIN COUNTY HOSPITAL (110130)**, 710 North Irwin Avenue, Zip 31774–5011; tel. 229/468–3800, (Nonreporting) **A**10 21
Primary Contact: Paige Wynn, Administrator
CFO: Tami Gray, Chief Financial Officer
CMO: Ashfaq Saiyed, M.D., Medical Director
CHR: Becky Edwards, Manager Human Resources
Web address: www.irwincntyhospital.com
Control: County, Government, nonfederal **Service:** General medical and surgical

Staffed Beds: 64

PERRY—Houston County

★ ⇑ **PERRY HOSPITAL (110153)**, 1120 Morningside Drive, Zip 31069–2906; tel. 478/987–3600, **A**10 21 **F**3 11 15 18 29 30 34 35 39 40 45 46 50 57 59 61 64 68 70 75 79 81 82 85 86 87 89 93 100 107 110 111 115 119 129 130 131 132 133 134 135 146 149 **S** Houston Healthcare System, Warner Robins, GA
Primary Contact: David Campbell, Administrator
COO: Charles G Briscoe, FACHE, Chief Operating Officer
CFO: Sean Whilden, Chief Financial Officer
CMO: Larry D. Stewart Jr Chief Medical Officer and Vice President, Medical Affairs
CHR: Michael O'Hara, Senior Executive Director
CNO: Melinda D. Hartley, R.N., Vice President Patient Care Services
Web address: www.hhc.org
Control: Other not–for–profit (including NFP Corporation) **Service:** General medical and surgical

Staffed Beds: 39 **Admissions:** 1442 **Census:** 19 **Outpatient Visits:** 46341 **Births:** 0 **Total Expense ($000):** 26437 **Payroll Expense ($000):** 10555 **Personnel:** 219

QUITMAN—Brooks County

☒ **BROOKS COUNTY HOSPITAL (111332)**, 903 North Court Street, Zip 31643–1315, Mailing Address: P.O. Box 5000, Zip 31643–5000; tel. 229/263–4171, **A**1 10 18 **F**15 29 30 34 40 87 93 107 110 119 133 146 149 154 **S** Archbold Medical Center, Thomasville, GA
Primary Contact: Nancy M. Williams, R.N., Administrator
CFO: Skip Hightower, Chief Financial Officer
CMO: Michael Sopt, M.D., Chief of Staff
CHR: Janet Eldridge, Director Human Resources and Personnel
CNO: June Furney, R.N., Director of Nursing
Web address: www.archbold.org
Control: Other not–for–profit (including NFP Corporation) **Service:** General medical and surgical

Staffed Beds: 25 **Admissions:** 413 **Census:** 15 **Births:** 0

REIDSVILLE—Tattnall County

★ **OPTIM MEDICAL CENTER - TATTNALL (111323)**, 247 South Main Street, Zip 30453–4605; tel. 912/557–1000, (Nonreporting) **A**10 18 **S** National Surgical Healthcare, Chicago, IL
Primary Contact: Rob Snipes, Administrator
Web address: www.optimmedicalcenter.com
Control: Corporation, Investor–owned (for–profit) **Service:** Orthopedic

Staffed Beds: 25

GA

Many Facility Codes have changed. Please refer to the AHA Guide Code Chart. © 2019 AHA Guide

RIVERDALE—Clayton County

☐ **RIVERWOODS BEHAVIORAL HEALTH SYSTEM (114035)**, 233 Medical Center Drive, Zip 30274–2640; tel. 770/991–8500, (Nonreporting) **A**1 5 10 **S** Acadia Healthcare Company, Inc., Franklin, TN
Primary Contact: John B. Warburton, Chief Executive Officer
COO: Jenifer Harcourt, Chief Operating Officer
CFO: Tricia Nelson, Chief Financial Officer
CIO: Hema Patel, Director Medical Records
CHR: Tareka Beasley, Director Human Resources
Web address: www.riverwoodsbehavioral.com
Control: Corporation, Investor–owned (for–profit) **Service:** Psychiatric

Staffed Beds: 75

⊞ **SOUTHERN REGIONAL MEDICAL CENTER (110165)**, 11 Upper Riverdale Road SW, Zip 30274–2615; tel. 770/991–8000, (Nonreporting) **A**1 2 10 **S** Prime Healthcare, Ontario, CA
Primary Contact: Charlotte W. Dupre, Chief Executive Officer
COO: Therese O Sucher, Senior Vice President Operations
CFO: Richard G Stovall, Senior Vice President Fiscal Services and Chief Financial Officer
CMO: Willie Cochran, M.D., Jr Chief of Staff
CIO: Karen Moore, Vice President Information Technology and Chief Information Officer
CHR: Norma Adams, Director Human Resources
Web address: www.southernregional.org
Control: Other not–for–profit (including NFP Corporation) **Service:** General medical and surgical

Staffed Beds: 331

ROME—Floyd County

⊞ **FLOYD MEDICAL CENTER (110054)**, 304 Turner McCall Boulevard, Zip 30165–5621, Mailing Address: P.O. Box 233, Zip 30162–0233; tel. 706/509–5000, **A**1 2 3 5 10 19 **F**3 4 5 6 7 8 9 10 11 12 13 15 17 18 20 22 26 28 29 30 31 32 34 35 36 37 38 39 40 43 44 45 46 48 49 50 51 53 54 56 57 58 59 61 63 64 65 66 68 70 71 72 73 74 75 76 77 78 79 81 82 84 85 86 87 89 90 93 96 97 98 100 101 102 103 104 105 107 108 110 111 114 115 118 119 129 130 131 132 134 135 143 144 146 147 148 149 151 152 154 156 **S** Floyd Healthcare Management, Rome, GA
Primary Contact: Kurt Stuenkel, FACHE, President and Chief Executive Officer
COO: Warren Alston Rigas, Executive Vice President and Chief Operating Officer
CFO: Rick Sheerin, Vice President Fiscal Services
CMO: Joseph Biuso, M.D., Vice President and Chief of Medical Affairs
CIO: Jeff Duda, Chief Information Officer
CHR: Beth Bradford, Director Human Resources
CNO: Sheila Bennett, R.N., Vice President & Chief Nursing Officer
Web address: www.floyd.org
Control: Other not–for–profit (including NFP Corporation) **Service:** General medical and surgical

Staffed Beds: 327 **Admissions:** 16061 **Census:** 248 **Outpatient Visits:** 277693 **Births:** 2213 **Total Expense ($000):** 430168 **Payroll Expense ($000):** 192003 **Personnel:** 2687

⊞ **KINDRED HOSPITAL ROME (112010)**, 304 Turner McCall Boulevard, Zip 30165–5621; tel. 706/378–6800, (Nonreporting) **A**1 10 **S** Kindred Healthcare, Louisville, KY
Primary Contact: Al Diaz, M.D., Chief Executive Officer
CFO: Julia Smith, Chief Financial Officer
CMO: Brij Singh, Medical Staff Director
CHR: Holly Murdock, Human Resources Coordinator
CNO: Jennifer Johnstone, Chief Clinical Officer
Web address: www.kindredrome.com
Control: Corporation, Investor–owned (for–profit) **Service:** Acute long–term care hospital

Staffed Beds: 45

⊞ **REDMOND REGIONAL MEDICAL CENTER (110168)**, 501 Redmond Road, Zip 30165–1415, Mailing Address: P.O. Box 107001, Zip 30164–7001; tel. 706/291–0291, (Nonreporting) **A**1 2 3 5 10 13 19 **S** HCA Healthcare, Nashville, TN
Primary Contact: John Quinlivan, Chief Executive Officer
COO: David Bradley Stockton, Chief Operating Officer
CFO: Kenneth Metteauer, Chief Financial Officer
CMO: Julie Coffman Barnes, M.D., Chief Medical Officer
CIO: Brad Treglown, Director Information Systems
CHR: Patsy Adams, Vice President Human Resources
CNO: Stephanie Jones, R.N., Chief Nursing Officer
Web address: www.redmondregional.com
Control: Corporation, Investor–owned (for–profit) **Service:** General medical and surgical

Staffed Beds: 230

SPECIALTY HOSPITAL See Kindred Hospital Rome

ROSWELL—Fulton County

⊞ **WELLSTAR NORTH FULTON HOSPITAL (110198)**, 3000 Hospital Boulevard, Zip 30076–3899; tel. 770/751–2500, **A**1 2 3 10 13 **F**3 13 15 18 20 22 26 28 29 30 31 34 35 37 40 43 45 48 49 55 57 59 63 67 68 70 73 74 75 76 77 78 79 81 82 85 86 87 90 91 92 93 107 108 110 111 114 115 118 119 126 130 132 141 146 147 148 152 **S** WellStar Health System, Marietta, GA
Primary Contact: Jon-Paul Croom, President
COO: Lindsey Petrini, Chief Operating Officer
CFO: Felix Sotoizaguirre, Chief Financial Officer
CMO: Karim Godamunne, M.D., Chief Medical Officer
CHR: Susan Brown, Chief Human Resources Officer
CNO: Nancy Melcher, Chief Nursing Officer
Web address: www.nfultonhospital.com
Control: Other not–for–profit (including NFP Corporation) **Service:** General medical and surgical

Staffed Beds: 173 **Admissions:** 7053 **Census:** 102 **Outpatient Visits:** 83753 **Births:** 924 **Personnel:** 748

SAINT MARYS—Camden County

⊞ **SOUTHEAST GEORGIA HEALTH SYSTEM CAMDEN CAMPUS (110146)**, 2000 Dan Proctor Drive, Zip 31558–3810; tel. 912/576–6200, **A**1 10 20 **F**3 11 13 15 18 29 30 31 34 35 40 45 46 47 48 49 50 57 59 64 68 70 71 75 76 77 78 79 81 85 86 87 93 94 107 108 110 111 114 116 117 119 120 129 130 131 132 146 149 **S** Southeast Georgia Health System, Brunswick, GA
Primary Contact: Howard W. Sepp Jr, Vice-President and Administrator
CFO: Janice Dunn, Chief Financial Officer
CMO: Robert Bernasek, M.D., Chief Medical Officer
CIO: Charles Bumgardner, Director
CNO: Judith Henson, Vice President, Patient Care Services
Web address: www.sghs.org
Control: Other not–for–profit (including NFP Corporation) **Service:** General medical and surgical

Staffed Beds: 40 **Admissions:** 1969 **Census:** 18 **Outpatient Visits:** 86285 **Births:** 696 **Total Expense ($000):** 44974 **Payroll Expense ($000):** 16552 **Personnel:** 292

SAINT SIMONS ISLAND—Glynn County

☐ **SAINT SIMONS BY THE SEA HOSPITAL (114016)**, 2927 Demere Road, Zip 31522–1620; tel. 912/638–1999, (Nonreporting) **A**1 10 **S** Universal Health Services, Inc., King of Prussia, PA
Primary Contact: Chuck Flavio, Chief Executive Officer
CMO: Kim Masters, M.D., Medical Director
CIO: Chisty Mccoly, Director Information Management
Web address: www.ssbythesea.com
Control: Corporation, Investor–owned (for–profit) **Service:** Psychiatric

Staffed Beds: 101

SANDERSVILLE—Washington County

☐ **WASHINGTON COUNTY REGIONAL MEDICAL CENTER (110086)**, 610 Sparta Road, Zip 31082–1860, Mailing Address: P.O. Box 636, Zip 31082–0636; tel. 478/240–2000, (Nonreporting) **A**1 10 20
Primary Contact: Antoine Poythress, Interim Chief Executive Officer
CFO: Antoine Poythress, Chief Financial Officer
CMO: Rob Gatliff, Chief of Medical Staff
CHR: Misty Ivey, Human Resources Manager
CNO: Pamela Stewart, Director of Nursing
Web address: www.wcrmc.com
Control: Hospital district or authority, Government, nonfederal **Service:** General medical and surgical

Staffed Beds: 116

GA

Hospital, Medicare Provider Number, Address, Telephone, Approval, Facility, and Physician Codes, Health Care System
★ American Hospital Association (AHA) membership   ○ Healthcare Facilities Accreditation Program   ⇑ Center for Improvement in Healthcare Quality Accreditation
☐ The Joint Commission accreditation   ◇ DNV Healthcare Inc. accreditation   △ Commission on Accreditation of Rehabilitation Facilities (CARF) accreditation

SAVANNAH—Chatham County

☒ △ **CANDLER HOSPITAL (110024)**, 5353 Reynolds Street, Zip 31405–6015; tel. 912/819–6000, (Total facility includes 11 beds in nursing home–type unit) **A**1 7 10 **F**2 3 11 13 15 18 20 29 30 31 32 34 35 36 38 39 40 44 45 46 47 48 49 50 53 54 57 58 59 60 61 64 65 68 70 71 73 74 75 76 77 78 80 81 82 84 85 86 87 89 90 93 94 96 107 108 110 111 114 117 119 120 121 123 124 126 128 129 130 131 132 135 146 147 148 149 156
Primary Contact: Paul P. Hinchey, President and Chief Executive Officer
CFO: Gregory J Schaack, CPA, Vice President and Chief Financial Officer
CMO: James Scott, M.D., Vice President Medical Affairs
CIO: George Evans, Vice President and Chief Information Officer
CHR: Don Stubbs, Vice President Human Resources
CNO: Sherry Danello, MSN, R.N., Vice President and Chief Nursing Officer
Web address: www.sjchs.org
Control: Church operated, Nongovernment, not–for–profit **Service:** General medical and surgical

> **Staffed Beds: 264 Admissions: 11423 Census: 160 Outpatient Visits: 272940 Births: 2729 Total Expense ($000): 290403 Payroll Expense ($000): 100830 Personnel: 1486**

☐ **COASTAL HARBOR TREATMENT CENTER (114008)**, 1150 Cornell Avenue, Zip 31406–2702; tel. 912/354–3911, **A**1 10 **F**5 98 99 100 103 104 105 106 153 **S** Universal Health Services, Inc., King of Prussia, PA
Primary Contact: Sally Perry, Chief Executive Officer
COO: Ray Heckerman, Chief Executive Officer and Managing Director
CFO: Brad Lavoie, Chief Financial Officer
CMO: Reemon Bishara, M.D., Medical Director
CHR: Kellie Carlson, Director Human Resources
CNO: Jillisa Thornton, Director of Nursing
Web address: www.coastalharbor.com
Control: Corporation, Investor–owned (for–profit) **Service:** Psychiatric

> **Staffed Beds: 191 Admissions: 3760 Census: 146 Outpatient Visits: 21383 Births: 0 Total Expense ($000): 27744 Payroll Expense ($000): 14433 Personnel: 274**

GEORGE AND MARIE BACKUS CHILDREN'S HOSPITAL See Memorial Children's Hospital

☐ **GEORGIA REGIONAL HOSPITAL AT SAVANNAH (114028)**, 1915 Eisenhower Drive, Zip 31406–5098; tel. 912/356–2011, (Nonreporting) **A**1 3 10
Primary Contact: Andy Mannich, Regional Administrator
COO: Thomas F Kurtz Jr Chief Operating Officer
CFO: Janet Edenfield, Director Financial Services
CMO: Donald Manning, M.D., Clinical Director
CHR: Jamekia Powers, Assistant Director Human Resources
Web address: www.dbhdd.georgia.gov/georgia-regional-hospital-savannah
Control: State, Government, nonfederal **Service:** Psychiatric

> **Staffed Beds: 105**

LANDMARK HOSPITAL OF SAVANNAH (112018), 800 East 68th Street, Zip 31405–4710; tel. 912/298–1000, (Nonreporting) **A**22 **S** Landmark Hospitals, Cape Girardeau, MO
Primary Contact: John Salandi, Chief Executive Officer
Web address: www.landmarkhospitals.com/savannah
Control: Partnership, Investor–owned (for–profit) **Service:** Acute long–term care hospital

> **Staffed Beds: 50**

☒ **MEMORIAL HEALTH (110036)**, 4700 Waters Avenue, Zip 31404–6283, Mailing Address: P.O. Box 23089, Zip 31403–3089; tel. 912/350–8000, (Includes MEMORIAL CHILDREN'S HOSPITAL, 4700 Waters Avenue, Savannah, Georgia, Zip 31404–6220, Mailing Address: P.O. Box 23089, Zip 31403–3089, tel. 912/350–7337), (Nonreporting) **A**1 2 3 5 8 10 **S** HCA Healthcare, Nashville, TN
Primary Contact: Shayne George, Chief Executive Officer
COO: Matthew Steven Hasbrouck, Chief Operating Officer
CFO: Laura Dow, Chief Financial Officer
CMO: Ramon V Meguiar, M.D., Chief Medical Officer
CIO: Kathryn McClellan, Chief Information Officer
CHR: Alisa R Griner, Director, Human Resources
CNO: Todd Isbell, R.N., MSN, Chief Nursing Officer
Web address: www.memorialhealth.com
Control: Other not–for–profit (including NFP Corporation) **Service:** General medical and surgical

> **Staffed Beds: 508**

☒ **REHABILITATION HOSPITAL OF SAVANNAH (113033)**, 6510 Seawright DR, Zip 31406–2752; tel. 800/622–7269, (Nonreporting) **A**1 10 **S** Encompass Health Corporation, Birmingham, AL
Primary Contact: Kathy Kleinsteuber, Chief Executive Officer
Web address: www.rehabilitationhospitalsavannah.com
Control: Corporation, Investor–owned (for–profit) **Service:** Rehabilitation

> **Staffed Beds: 50**

☒ **SELECT SPECIALTY HOSPITAL-SAVANNAH (112011)**, 5353 Reynolds Street, 4 South, Zip 31405–6015; tel. 912/819–7982, (Nonreporting) **A**1 10 **S** Select Medical Corporation, Mechanicsburg, PA
Primary Contact: Greg Wuchter, R.N., MSN, Chief Executive Officer
Web address: www.savannah.selectspecialtyhospitals.com
Control: Corporation, Investor–owned (for–profit) **Service:** Acute long–term care hospital

> **Staffed Beds: 40**

SAVANNAH—Chatham County

ST. JOSEPH'S CANDLER HOSPITAL See Candler Hospital

☐ △ **ST. JOSEPH'S HOSPITAL (110043)**, 11705 Mercy Boulevard, Zip 31419–1791; tel. 912/819–4100, (Total facility includes 11 beds in nursing home–type unit) **A**1 2 7 10 **F**2 3 11 15 17 18 20 22 24 26 28 29 30 34 35 36 37 38 39 40 41 44 45 49 50 56 57 58 59 60 65 70 74 75 77 79 80 81 82 84 85 86 90 94 96 107 108 110 111 114 115 119 126 128 130 131 132 135 146 148 149 150
Primary Contact: Paul P. Hinchey, President and Chief Executive Officer
COO: Kyle McCann, Chief Operating Officer
CFO: Gregory J Schaack, CPA, Vice President and Chief Financial Officer
CMO: James Scott, M.D., Vice President Medical Affairs
CIO: Nolan Henessee, Vice President and Chief Information Officer
CHR: Steve Pound, Vice President Human Resources
CNO: Sherry Danello, MSN, R.N., Vice President and Chief Nursing Officer
Web address: www.sjchs.org
Control: Church operated, Nongovernment, not–for–profit **Service:** General medical and surgical

> **Staffed Beds: 227 Admissions: 12056 Census: 171 Outpatient Visits: 86759 Births: 0 Total Expense ($000): 226336 Payroll Expense ($000): 78435 Personnel: 1195**

SMYRNA—Cobb County

☒ **RIDGEVIEW INSTITUTE (114012)**, 3995 South Cobb Drive SE, Zip 30080–6397; tel. 770/434–4567, (Nonreporting) **A**1 3 10
Primary Contact: Margaret P. Collier, Chief Executive Officer
CFO: Ruth Jenkins, Chief Financial Officer
CMO: Thomas Bradford Johns, M.D., Medical Director
CIO: Lynn Leger, Director Information Systems
CHR: Betty Sonderman, Manager Human Resources
Web address: www.ridgeviewinstitute.com
Control: Other not–for–profit (including NFP Corporation) **Service:** Psychiatric

> **Staffed Beds: 110**

SNELLVILLE—Gwinnett County

☒ **EASTSIDE MEDICAL CENTER (110192)**, 1700 Medical Way, Zip 30078–2195; tel. 770/979–0200, (Nonreporting) **A**1 2 10 **S** HCA Healthcare, Nashville, TN
Primary Contact: Trent Lind, Chief Executive Officer
COO: John Hoover, Chief Operating Officer
CMO: Michael O'Neill, M.D., Chief Medical Officer
CIO: Pattie Page, Director Marketing and Public Relations
CNO: Tracey Smithson, MSN, R.N., Chief Nursing Officer
Web address: www.eastsidemedical.com
Control: Corporation, Investor–owned (for–profit) **Service:** General medical and surgical

> **Staffed Beds: 294**

SPRINGFIELD—Effingham County

☒ **EFFINGHAM HOSPITAL (111306)**, 459 Highway 119 South, Zip 31329–3021, Mailing Address: P.O. Box 386, Zip 31329–0386; tel. 912/754–6451, (Total facility includes 105 beds in nursing home–type unit) **A**1 10 18 **F**3 6 11 15 29 34 35 40 43 45 50 57 59 74 77 81 85 97 107 110 111 114 119 127 128 130 133 135 146 147 154
Primary Contact: Francine Baker-Witt, R.N., Chief Executive Officer
CFO: Matthew Moore, Director of Financial Reporting
CMO: Claude Sanks, Chief Medical Staff
CIO: Mary Pizzino, Chief Information Officer
CHR: Marie Murphy, Director Human Resources
CNO: Betsy Smith, Chief Nursing Officer
Web address: www.effinghamhospital.org
Control: Hospital district or authority, Government, nonfederal **Service:** General medical and surgical

> **Staffed Beds: 130 Admissions: 1110 Census: 106 Outpatient Visits: 42866 Births: 0 Total Expense ($000): 54067 Payroll Expense ($000): 20065 Personnel: 364**

GA

STATESBORO—Bulloch County

☒ **EAST GEORGIA REGIONAL MEDICAL CENTER (110075)**, 1499 Fair Road, Zip 30458–1683, Mailing Address: P.O. Box 1048, Zip 30459–1048; tel. 912/486–1000, (Nonreporting) **A**1 10 **S** Community Health Systems, Inc., Franklin, TN
Primary Contact: Stephen G. Pennington, Chief Executive Officer
COO: Erin Smith, Chief Operating Officer
CFO: Christine Markowitz, Chief Financial Officer
CMO: Mark McCracken, M.D., Chief of Staff
CIO: Brian Girardeau, Director Information System
CHR: Michael Black, Director Human Resources
CNO: Marie Burdette, Chief Nursing Officer
Web address: www.eastgeorgiaregional.com
Control: Corporation, Investor–owned (for–profit) **Service**: General medical and surgical

Staffed Beds: 149

WILLINGWAY HOSPITAL, 311 Jones Mill Road, Zip 30458–4765; tel. 912/764–6236, (Nonreporting) **A**3
Primary Contact: Cherie Tolley, Chief Executive Officer
CMO: Robert W Mooney, M.D., Medical Director
Web address: www.willingway.com
Control: Corporation, Investor–owned (for–profit) **Service**: Alcoholism and other chemical dependency

Staffed Beds: 40

STOCKBRIDGE—Henry County

⇑ **PIEDMONT HENRY HOSPITAL (110191)**, 1133 Eagle's Landing Parkway, Zip 30281–5099; tel. 678/604–1000, **A**2 10 21 **F**3 8 11 13 15 18 20 22 26 28 29 30 31 34 35 37 40 45 49 54 57 59 61 64 70 72 73 74 75 76 77 78 79 81 82 84 85 86 87 93 94 100 107 108 110 111 114 115 118 119 120 121 123 130 132 135 146 147 148 154 156 **S** Piedmont Healthcare, Roswell, GA
Primary Contact: Deborah Armstrong, Chief Executive Officer
COO: James Atkins, PharmD, Chief Operating Officer
CFO: Wesley James, Chief Financial Officer
CMO: Lily Henson, M.D., Chief Medical Officer
CHR: Jana Warren, Human Resources Business Partner
CNO: Paula Yvonne Butts, Chief Nursing Officer
Web address: www.piedmont.org
Control: Other not–for–profit (including NFP Corporation) **Service**: General medical and surgical

Staffed Beds: 236 **Admissions**: 15198 **Census**: 192 **Outpatient Visits**: 156085 **Births**: 2324 **Total Expense ($000)**: 217163 **Payroll Expense ($000)**: 90976 **Personnel**: 1460

SWAINSBORO—Emanuel County

⇑ **EMANUEL MEDICAL CENTER (110109)**, 117 Kite Road, Zip 30401–3231, Mailing Address: P.O. Box 879, Zip 30401–0879; tel. 478/289–1100, (Nonreporting) **A**10 20 21
Primary Contact: Mel Pyne, Chief Executive Officer
CFO: Rhonda Durden, Chief Financial Officer
CMO: Cedric Porter, M.D., President Medical Staff
CIO: Damien Scott, Chief Information Officer
CHR: Ellen Boyd, Director Human Resources
Web address: www.emanuelmedical.org
Control: Hospital district or authority, Government, nonfederal **Service**: General medical and surgical

Staffed Beds: 91

SYLVANIA—Screven County

OPTIM MEDICAL CENTER - SCREVEN (111312), 215 Mims Road, Zip 30467–2097; tel. 912/564–7426, (Nonreporting) **A**10 18 **S** National Surgical Healthcare, Chicago, IL
Primary Contact: Michael G. Layfield, Interim Chief Executive Officer
CFO: Cindy Bierschenk, Finance Director
CMO: Sherma Peter, M.D., Chief of Staff
CIO: Christian Rekowski, Information Technology Manager
CHR: Natalie Peterson, Director of Human Resources
CNO: Sharon Lagina Evans, R.N., Assistant Chief Nursing Officer
Web address: www.optimhealth.com
Control: County, Government, nonfederal **Service**: General medical and surgical

Staffed Beds: 25

SYLVESTER—Worth County

★ ⇑ **PHOEBE WORTH MEDICAL CENTER (111328)**, 807 South Isabella Street, Zip 31791–7554, Mailing Address: P.O. Box 545, Zip 31791–0545; tel. 229/776–6961, (Nonreporting) **A**10 18 21 **S** Phoebe Putney Health System, Albany, GA
Primary Contact: Kim Gilman, Chief Executive Officer
CFO: Candace Guarnieri, Chief Financial Officer
CMO: Natu M Patel, M.D., Chief of Staff
CHR: Mandy Gordon, Human Resource Coordinator
CNO: Kim Gilman, Chief Nursing Officer
Web address: www.phoebeputney.com
Control: Other not–for–profit (including NFP Corporation) **Service**: General medical and surgical

Staffed Beds: 18

THOMASTON—Upson County

★ ⇑ **UPSON REGIONAL MEDICAL CENTER (110002)**, 801 West Gordon Street, Zip 30286–3426, Mailing Address: P.O. Box 1059, Zip 30286–0027; tel. 706/647–8111, **A**10 21 **F**11 13 15 20 21 22 23 28 29 30 31 34 35 36 40 45 46 49 50 57 59 61 64 68 70 76 78 79 80 81 82 85 86 87 89 98 103 107 108 109 111 114 115 118 119 124 130 131 132 135 148 154 156 **S** HealthTech Management Services, Brentwood, TN
Primary Contact: Jeffrey S. Tarrant, FACHE, Chief Executive Officer
CFO: John Williams, Chief Financial Officer
CIO: Douglas Thompson, Chief Information Officer
CHR: Rich Williams, Director Human Resources
CNO: Marilyn Ray, MSN, Chief Nursing Officer
Web address: www.urmc.org
Control: Other not–for–profit (including NFP Corporation) **Service**: General medical and surgical

Staffed Beds: 83 **Admissions**: 3440 **Census**: 39 **Outpatient Visits**: 77489 **Births**: 350 **Total Expense ($000)**: 75186 **Payroll Expense ($000)**: 27702 **Personnel**: 621

THOMASVILLE—Thomas County

☒ **JOHN D. ARCHBOLD MEMORIAL HOSPITAL (110038)**, 915 Gordon Avenue, Zip 31792–6614, Mailing Address: P.O. Box 1018, Zip 31799–1018; tel. 229/228–2000, (Nonreporting) **A**1 2 10 19 **S** Archbold Medical Center, Thomasville, GA
Primary Contact: J. Perry Mustian, President and Chief Executive Officer
CFO: Skip Hightower, Senior Vice President and Chief Financial Officer
CIO: Tracy Gray, Senior Vice President Information Services
CHR: Zachariah P Wheeler, Senior Vice President Human Resources
CNO: Amy Griffin, Vice President Patient Care Services
Web address: www.archbold.org
Control: Other not–for–profit (including NFP Corporation) **Service**: General medical and surgical

Staffed Beds: 328

THOMSON—McDuffie County

☒ **UNIVERSITY HOSPITAL MCDUFFIE (110111)**, 2460 Washington Road, NE, Zip 30824; tel. 706/595–1411, **A**1 10 **F**3 11 15 29 30 40 45 50 59 64 68 79 81 85 87 107 110 114 119 130 132 133 146 148 149 **S** University Health Care System, Augusta, GA
Primary Contact: Bob Kepshire, R.N., MS, Administrator and Chief Nursing Officer
CFO: Dave Belkoski, Chief Financial Officer
CNO: Bob Kepshire, R.N., MS, Administrator and Chief Nursing Officer
Web address: www.universityhealth.org/mcduffie
Control: Other not–for–profit (including NFP Corporation) **Service**: General medical and surgical

Staffed Beds: 22 **Admissions**: 695 **Census**: 15 **Outpatient Visits**: 35668 **Births**: 1 **Total Expense ($000)**: 19360 **Payroll Expense ($000)**: 5587 **Personnel**: 95

GA

TIFTON—Tift County

☒ **TIFT REGIONAL MEDICAL CENTER (110095)**, 901 East 18th Street, Zip 31794–3648, Mailing Address: Drawer 747, Zip 31793–0747; tel. 229/382–7120, **A**1 2 5 10 19 **F**3 8 9 11 12 13 15 18 20 22 26 28 29 30 31 33 34 35 40 45 47 49 50 51 54 57 59 60 63 64 68 70 74 75 76 77 78 79 81 82 84 85 86 87 89 92 93 97 100 104 107 108 110 111 114 115 118 119 120 121 123 126 129 130 131 132 135 143 144 146 147 148 149 154 156 **S** Tift Regional Health System, Tifton, GA
Primary Contact: Christopher Dorman, President and Chief Executive Officer
CFO: Dennis L Crum, Senior Vice President and Chief Financial Officer
CMO: William Guest, M.D., Senior Vice President and Chief Medical Officer
CIO: Guy McAllister, Vice President and Chief Information Officer
CHR: Lori S Folsom, Assistant Vice President Human Resources
CNO: Carol Smith, Vice President Patient Care and Chief Nursing Officer
Web address: www.tiftregional.com
Control: Hospital district or authority, Government, nonfederal **Service**: General medical and surgical

> **Staffed Beds**: 181 **Admissions**: 9873 **Census**: 117 **Outpatient Visits**: 195025 **Births**: 1411 **Total Expense ($000)**: 364901 **Payroll Expense ($000)**: 155680 **Personnel**: 2073

TOCCOA—Stephens County

☐ **STEPHENS COUNTY HOSPITAL (110032)**, 163 Hospital Drive, Zip 30577–6820; tel. 706/282–4200, (Nonreporting) **A**1 10
Primary Contact: Michael Hester, Chief Executive Officer
CFO: Jeff Laird, Controller
CHR: Diane Hardeman, Director Personnel
CNO: Faye M Taylor, R.N., Director of Nursing
Web address: www.stephenscountyhospital.com
Control: Hospital district or authority, Government, nonfederal **Service**: General medical and surgical

> **Staffed Beds**: 188

VALDOSTA—Lowndes County

☐ **GREENLEAF BEHAVIORAL HEALTH HOSPITAL (114036)**, 2209 Pineview Drive, Zip 31602–7316; tel. 229/247–4357, (Nonreporting) **A**1 10 **S** Acadia Healthcare Company, Inc., Franklin, TN
Primary Contact: Bryan D. Adams, Chief Executive Officer
Web address: www.greenleafcounseling.net
Control: Corporation, Investor–owned (for–profit) **Service**: Psychiatric

> **Staffed Beds**: 73

☒ **SOUTH GEORGIA MEDICAL CENTER (110122)**, 2501 North Patterson Street, Zip 31602–1735, Mailing Address: P.O. Box 1727, Zip 31603–1727; tel. 229/333–1000, (Includes SMITH NORTHVIEW HOSPITAL, 4280 North Valdosta Road, Valdosta, Georgia, Zip 31602, Mailing Address: P O Box 10010, Zip 31604, tel. 229/671–2000; Leonard Carter, Campus Administrator) **A**1 2 10 19 **F**3 7 8 11 13 15 18 20 21 22 23 24 25 26 27 28 29 30 31 32 34 35 38 40 44 45 46 48 49 50 51 54 56 57 58 59 60 64 68 70 71 72 73 74 75 76 77 78 79 81 82 84 85 86 87 89 90 91 92 96 97 107 108 111 114 115 116 117 119 120 121 124 126 129 130 132 135 143 144 146 147 148 149 150 154 156 **S** South Georgia Medical Center, Valdosta, GA
Primary Contact: Bill Forbes, Chief Executive Officer
COO: Andrew Flemer, Chief Operating Officer
CMO: Kimberly Megow, M.D., Chief Medical Officer
CIO: Bob Foster, Chief Information Officer
CHR: Johnny Percy Ball III Assistant Administrator Human Resources
CNO: Denida A. Cox, Chief Nursing Officer
Web address: www.sgmc.org
Control: Hospital district or authority, Government, nonfederal **Service**: General medical and surgical

> **Staffed Beds**: 203 **Admissions**: 13426 **Census**: 188 **Outpatient Visits**: 184756 **Births**: 1987 **Total Expense ($000)**: 377235 **Payroll Expense ($000)**: 133339 **Personnel**: 2525

VIDALIA—Toombs County

★ ⇑ **MEADOWS REGIONAL MEDICAL CENTER (110128)**, One Meadows Parkway, Zip 30474–8759, Mailing Address: P.O. Box 1048, Zip 30475–1048; tel. 912/535–5555, (Nonreporting) **A**10 20 21
Primary Contact: Alan Kent, Chief Executive Officer
COO: James Nixon, Chief Operating Officer
CFO: Tony O'Steen, Chief Financial Officer
CMO: Karen McColl, M.D., Chief Medical Officer
CIO: Charles Bondurant, Chief Information Officer
CNO: Jeffrey M Harden, Chief Nursing Officer
Web address: www.meadowsregional.org
Control: Other not–for–profit (including NFP Corporation) **Service**: General medical and surgical

> **Staffed Beds**: 57

VILLA RICA—Carroll County

☒ **TANNER MEDICAL CENTER–VILLA RICA (110015)**, 601 Dallas Highway, Zip 30180–1202; tel. 770/456–3000, (Includes WILLOWBROOKE AT TANNER, 20 Herrell Road, Villa Rica, Georgia, Zip 30180–5527; tel. 770/812–3266; Paula Gresham, Vice President, Hospital Administrator) **A**1 10 **F**3 5 11 13 15 18 20 22 29 30 31 34 38 40 49 50 59 60 64 68 70 74 76 78 79 81 87 98 100 101 102 103 104 105 107 108 110 111 115 118 119 129 130 146 147 149 152 153 154 156 **S** Tanner Health System, Carrollton, GA
Primary Contact: Eric Dalton, Administrator
CFO: Carol Crews, Senior Vice President and Chief Financial Officer
CMO: William Waters, M.D., IV Executive Vice President
CIO: Terri Lee, Chief Information Officer
CHR: Shari W Gainey, Chief Human Resource Officer
CNO: Deborah Matthews, Senior Vice President
Web address: www.tanner.org
Control: Other not–for–profit (including NFP Corporation) **Service**: General medical and surgical

> **Staffed Beds**: 132 **Admissions**: 7006 **Census**: 101 **Outpatient Visits**: 140015 **Births**: 499 **Total Expense ($000)**: 102673 **Payroll Expense ($000)**: 40227 **Personnel**: 645

WARM SPRINGS—Meriwether County

☐ **ROOSEVELT WARM SPRINGS REHABILITATION AND SPECIALTY HOSPITALS - LTAC (112000)**, 6135 Roosevelt Highway, Zip 31830–2757, Mailing Address: P.O. Box 280, Zip 31830–2757; tel. 706/655–5291, **A**1 10 **F**1 29 30 34 35 57 60 74 75 77 84 86 87 91 100 146 148
Primary Contact: David L. Mork Jr, Chief Executive Officer
CFO: Susan Wilder, Director Financial Services
CMO: Carlos Parrado, M.D., Sr Chief Medical Officer
CHR: Laura Stokes, Director Human Resources
CNO: Cathy Harbin, Chief Nursing Officer
Web address: www.augustahealth.org/roosevelt-warm-springs/rwsh
Control: Other not–for–profit (including NFP Corporation) **Service**: Acute long–term care hospital

> **Staffed Beds**: 32 **Admissions**: 162 **Census**: 12 **Outpatient Visits**: 0 **Births**: 0

☒ **ROOSEVELT WARM SPRINGS REHABILITATION HOSPITAL - REHAB (113028)**, 6135 Roosevelt Highway, Zip 31830–2757, Mailing Address: P.O. Box 280, Zip 31830–0280; tel. 706/655–5515, **A**1 10 **F**29 30 60 74 77 82 85 87 90 119 146 148
Primary Contact: David L. Mork Jr, Chief Executive Officer
CFO: Susan Wilder, Director Financial Services
CMO: Ara Chitchyan, M.D., Medical Director
CIO: Christen Carter, Director Public Relations
CHR: Laura Stokes, Director Human Resources
CNO: Cathy Harbin, Chief Nursing Officer
Web address: www.augustahealth.org/roosevelt-warm-springs/rwsh
Control: Other not–for–profit (including NFP Corporation) **Service**: Rehabilitation

> **Staffed Beds**: 52 **Admissions**: 396 **Census**: 17 **Outpatient Visits**: 0 **Births**: 0

☒ **WARM SPRINGS MEDICAL CENTER (111316)**, 5995 Spring Street, Zip 31830–2149, Mailing Address: P.O. Box 8, Zip 31830–0008; tel. 706/655–3331, (Total facility includes 79 beds in nursing home–type unit) **A**1 10 18 **F**3 15 29 30 34 35 40 41 45 46 47 48 57 59 60 64 65 68 75 81 107 110 114 119 128 130 133 135 143 146 148 149 156
Primary Contact: Karen Daniel, Chief Executive Officer
CFO: Patrick Flynn, Chief Financial Officer
CMO: Alan Thompson, M.D., President Medical Staff
CIO: Milo Varnadoe, Director Information Systems
CHR: Theresa Passarelli, Human Resources Generalist
CNO: Lynda Ligon, Chief Nursing Officer
Web address: www.warmspringsmc.org
Control: Partnership, Investor–owned (for–profit) **Service**: General medical and surgical

> **Staffed Beds**: 104 **Admissions**: 406 **Census**: 82 **Outpatient Visits**: 8252 **Births**: 0

GA

Many Facility Codes have changed. Please refer to the AHA Guide Code Chart. © 2019 AHA Guide

WARNER ROBINS—Houston County

★ ⇑ **HOUSTON MEDICAL CENTER (110069)**, 1601 Watson Boulevard, Zip 31093–3431, Mailing Address: P.O. Box 2886, Zip 31099–2886; tel. 478/922–4281, **A**3 5 10 13 21 **F**3 8 11 13 15 18 20 22 26 28 29 30 31 34 35 38 39 40 44 45 46 49 50 51 57 59 60 61 64 68 70 73 74 75 76 78 79 81 82 85 86 87 89 93 98 100 102 103 107 108 110 111 115 118 119 129 130 131 132 134 135 144 146 147 148 149 150 **S** Houston Healthcare System, Warner Robins, GA
Primary Contact: Cary Martin, Chief Executive Officer
COO: Charles G Briscoe, FACHE, Chief Operating Officer
CFO: Sean Whilden, Chief Financial Officer
CIO: George Curtis, Chief Information Officer
CHR: Michael O'Hara, Senior Executive Director Human Resources
Web address: www.hhc.org
Control: Other not–for–profit (including NFP Corporation) **Service:** General medical and surgical

Staffed Beds: 237 **Admissions:** 13183 **Census:** 171 **Outpatient Visits:** 237055 **Births:** 1887 **Total Expense ($000):** 219726 **Payroll Expense ($000):** 89472 **Personnel:** 1866

WASHINGTON—Wilkes County

☐ **WILLS MEMORIAL HOSPITAL (111325)**, 120 Gordon Street, Zip 30673–1602, Mailing Address: P.O. Box 370, Zip 30673–0370; tel. 706/678–2151, (Nonreporting) **A**1 10 18
Primary Contact: Tracie Haughey, Chief Executive Officer and Chief Financial Officer
CFO: Tracie Haughey, Chief Executive Officer and Chief Financial Officer
CMO: Robert J. Williams, M.D., Chief Medical Staff
CIO: David Harper, Chief Information Officer
CHR: Susan Pope, Director Human Resources
CNO: Angie Radford, R.N., Director of Nursing
Web address: www.willsmemorialhospital.com
Control: Hospital district or authority, Government, nonfederal **Service:** General medical and surgical

Staffed Beds: 25

WAYCROSS—Ware County

⊠ **MEMORIAL SATILLA HEALTH (110003)**, 1900 Tebeau Street, Zip 31501–6357, Mailing Address: P.O. Box 139, Zip 31502–0139; tel. 912/283–3030, (Nonreporting) **A**1 2 3 5 10 **S** HCA Healthcare, Nashville, TN
Primary Contact: Bobby McCullough, Chief Executive Officer
COO: Mark Roberts, Chief Operating Officer
CFO: Patrick Sloan, Chief Financial Officer
CIO: Barry Rudd, Chief Information Officer
CHR: Brigitte Churchill, Director of Human Resources
CNO: Holli Sweat, Associate Administrator and Chief Nursing Officer
Web address: www.memorialsatillahealth.com/
Control: Other not–for–profit (including NFP Corporation) **Service:** General medical and surgical

Staffed Beds: 199

WAYNESBORO—Burke County

☐ **BURKE MEDICAL CENTER (110113)**, 351 Liberty Street, Zip 30830–9686; tel. 706/554–4435, (Nonreporting) **A**1 10
Primary Contact: Thomas K. Steiner, Interim Chief Executive Officer
CFO: Karen ONeal, Chief Financial Officer
CHR: Kim Anthony, Director Human Resources
CNO: Debra Burch, Chief Nursing Officer
Web address: www.burkemedical.net
Control: Hospital district or authority, Government, nonfederal **Service:** General medical and surgical

Staffed Beds: 40

WINDER—Barrow County

★ ⇑ **NORTHEAST GEORGIA MEDICAL CENTER BARROW (110045)**, 316 North Broad Street, Zip 30680–2150, Mailing Address: P.O. Box 688, Zip 30680–0688; tel. 770/867–3400, **A**10 21 **F**3 11 15 29 30 34 35 38 40 44 45 50 57 59 60 68 70 74 75 77 79 81 82 85 107 108 110 111 114 115 118 119 124 130 131 132 135 143 146 147 148 149 154 156 **S** Northeast Georgia Health System, Gainesville, GA
Primary Contact: Chad Hatfield, Chief Executive Officer
CMO: Jon Horn, M.D., Chief of Staff
CIO: Cory Crayton, Director Information Systems
CHR: Carlotta Hannah Newman, Human Resources Manager
CNO: Heather Standard, Chief Nursing Officer
Web address: www.barrowregional.com
Control: Other not–for–profit (including NFP Corporation) **Service:** General medical and surgical

Staffed Beds: 30 **Admissions:** 1242 **Census:** 11 **Outpatient Visits:** 33668 **Births:** 0 **Personnel:** 194

Hospital, Medicare Provider Number, Address, Telephone, Approval, Facility, and Physician Codes, Health Care System

★ American Hospital Association (AHA) membership
☐ The Joint Commission accreditation
○ Healthcare Facilities Accreditation Program
◇ DNV Healthcare Inc. accreditation
⇑ Center for Improvement in Healthcare Quality Accreditation
△ Commission on Accreditation of Rehabilitation Facilities (CARF) accreditation

GA

HAWAII

AIEA—Honolulu County

⊞ **PALI MOMI MEDICAL CENTER (120026)**, 98–1079 Moanalua Road,
Zip 96701–4713; tel. 808/486–6000, **A**1 2 3 5 10 **F**3 12 15 18 20 22 26 29 31
34 35 36 40 43 44 45 46 49 50 54 58 59 63 64 65 68 70 74 75 77 78 79 80
81 84 85 86 87 92 107 108 110 111 115 118 119 126 130 132 135 146 147
148 149 154 156 **S** Hawaii Pacific Health, Honolulu, HI
Primary Contact: Art Gladstone, R.N., Chief Executive Officer
CFO: David Okabe, Executive Vice President, Chief Financial Officer and Treasurer
CMO: James Kakuda, M.D., Chief of Staff
CIO: Steve Robertson, Senior Vice President
CHR: Gail Lerch, R.N., Vice President Human Resources
CNO: Brigitte McKale, MSN, FACHE, Vice President and Chief Nurse Executive
Web address: www.palimomi.org
Control: Other not–for–profit (including NFP Corporation) **Service**: General
medical and surgical

Staffed Beds: 118 **Admissions**: 5699 **Census**: 81 **Outpatient**
Visits: 232393 **Births**: 0 **Total Expense ($000)**: 227289 **Payroll Expense**
($000): 81986 **Personnel**: 939

EWA BEACH—Honolulu County

⊞ **SUTTER HEALTH KAHI MOHALA (124001)**, 91–2301 Old Fort Weaver Road,
Zip 96706–3602; tel. 808/671–8511, (Nonreporting) **A**1 3 10 **S** Sutter Health,
Sacramento, CA
Primary Contact: Leonard Licina, Chief Executive Officer
CFO: Quin Ogawa, Chief Financial Officer
CMO: Steven Chaplin, M.D., Medical Director
CHR: Christina Enoka, Director Human Resources and Risk Management
CNO: Charles St. Louis, Director of Patient Care Services
Web address: www.kahimohala.org
Control: Other not–for–profit (including NFP Corporation) **Service**: Psychiatric

Staffed Beds: 76

HILO—Hawaii County

⊞ **HILO MEDICAL CENTER (120005)**, 1190 Waianuenue Avenue, Zip 96720–
2089; tel. 808/932–3000, (Nonreporting) **A**1 3 5 10 20 **S** Hawaii Health Systems
Corporation, Honolulu, HI
Primary Contact: Dan Brinkman, R.N., Chief Executive Officer
COO: Dan Brinkman, R.N., Chief Operating Officer
CMO: Ted Peskin, M.D., Acute Care Medical Director
CIO: Money Atwal, Chief Information Officer
CHR: Holly Ka'akimaka, Director Human Resources
CNO: Arthur Sampaga, Assistant Director Nursing
Web address: www.https://www.hilomedicalcenter.org/
Control: State, Government, nonfederal **Service**: General medical and surgical

Staffed Beds: 199

HONOKAA—Hawaii County

★ **HALE HO'OLA HAMAKUA (121307)**, 45–547 Plumeria Street, Zip 96727–6902;
tel. 808/932–4100, (Nonreporting) **A**10 18 **S** Hawaii Health Systems Corporation,
Honolulu, HI
Primary Contact: Denise Mackey, Administrator
CMO: Bruce Graves, M.D., Chief of Staff
CNO: Gayle Green, Director of Nursing
Web address: www.halehoolahamakua.org
Control: State, Government, nonfederal **Service**: General medical and surgical

Staffed Beds: 77

HONOLULU—Honolulu County

⊞ **KAISER PERMANENTE MEDICAL CENTER (120011)**, 3288 Moanalua Road,
Zip 96819–1469; tel. 808/432–0000, **A**1 2 3 5 10 **F**3 12 13 15 17 18 19 20 21
22 24 26 29 30 31 32 34 35 36 38 40 41 45 46 47 48 49 50 51 54 55 56 57
58 59 60 61 62 64 65 68 70 72 74 75 76 77 78 79 80 81 82 83 84 85 86 87
88 89 92 93 94 97 100 101 104 107 108 110 111 115 119 126 129 130 131
134 135 146 148 149 154 **S** Kaiser Foundation Hospitals, Oakland, CA
Primary Contact: James Y. Lee, Hospital Administrator
CFO: Thomas Risse, Chief Financial Officer and Vice President Business Services
CMO: Keith Ogasawara, M.D., Associate Medical Director and Professional Chief
of Staff
CIO: Donna Scannell, Vice President Information Technology
CHR: Jean Melnikoff, Vice President Human Resources
CNO: Kecia Kelly, R.N., Chief Nurse Executive
Web address: www.kaiserpermanente.org
Control: Other not–for–profit (including NFP Corporation) **Service**: General
medical and surgical

Staffed Beds: 295 **Admissions**: 11663 **Census**: 181 **Outpatient**
Visits: 61400 **Births**: 1403 **Total Expense ($000)**: 376255 **Payroll Expense**
($000): 143882 **Personnel**: 1401

☐ **KAPIOLANI MEDICAL CENTER FOR WOMEN & CHILDREN (123300)**, 1319
Punahou Street, Zip 96826–1001; tel. 808/983–6000, (Nonreporting) **A**1 2 3 5
10 **S** Hawaii Pacific Health, Honolulu, HI
Primary Contact: Martha Smith, Chief Executive Officer
CFO: David Okabe, Senior Vice President, Chief Financial Officer and Treasurer
CIO: Steve Robertson, Vice President
CHR: Gail Lerch, R.N., Vice President
Web address: www.kapiolani.org
Control: Other not–for–profit (including NFP Corporation) **Service**: Children's
general medical and surgical

Staffed Beds: 180

⊞ **KUAKINI MEDICAL CENTER (120007)**, 347 North Kuakini Street, Zip 96817–
2381; tel. 808/536–2236, **A**1 2 3 5 10 **F**3 15 17 18 20 22 24 26 28 29 31 34
35 40 45 46 49 57 58 59 60 64 68 70 74 75 77 78 79 80 81 82 84 85 86 87
107 108 110 111 115 117 118 119 120 121 129 130 131 132 135 145 146
147 148 149
Primary Contact: Gary K. Kajiwara, President and Chief Executive Officer
CFO: Quin Ogawa, Vice President Finance and Chief Financial Officer
CMO: Nobuyuki Miki, M.D., Vice President Medical Services and Chief Medical
Officer
CIO: Gary K Kajiwara, President and Chief Executive Officer
CHR: Ann N. Choy, Manager Human Resources and Payroll
CNO: Virginia Walker, Vice President Nursing Services and Chief Nursing Officer
Web address: www.kuakini.org
Control: Other not–for–profit (including NFP Corporation) **Service**: General
medical and surgical

Staffed Beds: 100 **Admissions**: 3648 **Census**: 64 **Outpatient Visits**: 52462
Births: 0 **Total Expense ($000)**: 144283 **Payroll Expense ($000)**: 56087
Personnel: 844

★ **LEAHI HOSPITAL (122001)**, 3675 Kilauea Avenue, Zip 96816–2398;
tel. 808/733–8000, (Total facility includes 117 beds in nursing home–type
unit) **A**10 **F**3 77 128 130 146 148 149 **S** Hawaii Health Systems Corporation,
Honolulu, HI
Primary Contact: Derek Akiyoshi, Chief Executive Officer
CFO: Edward Chu, Chief Financial Officer
CMO: Albert Yazawa, M.D., Regional Medical Director
CHR: Russel Higa, JD, Regional Director Human Resources
CNO: Amy Vasunaga, Chief Nurse Executive
Web address: www.hhsc.org
Control: State, Government, nonfederal **Service**: Acute long–term care hospital

Staffed Beds: 126 **Admissions**: 130 **Census**: 108

HI

Many Facility Codes have changed. Please refer to the AHA Guide Code Chart. © 2019 AHA Guide

⊠ **REHABILITATION HOSPITAL OF THE PACIFIC (123025)**, 226 North Kuakini Street, Zip 96817–2488; tel. 808/531–3511, (Nonreporting) **A**1 10
Primary Contact: Timothy J. Roe, M.D., President and Chief Executive Officer
CFO: Wendy Manuel, Vice President and Chief Financial Officer
CMO: Jason Chang, Chief Medical Officer and Vice President of Medical Affairs
CIO: Colbert Seto, Chief Information Officer
CHR: Faye Miyamoto, Assistant Vice President Human Resources
CNO: Brenda Hiromoto, Director of Nursing
Web address: www.rehabhospital.org
Control: Other not–for–profit (including NFP Corporation) **Service**: Rehabilitation

Staffed Beds: 68

☐ **SHRINERS HOSPITALS FOR CHILDREN-HONOLULU (123301)**, 1310 Punahou Street, Zip 96826–1099; tel. 808/941–4466, (Nonreporting) **A**1 3 5 10 **S** Shriners Hospitals for Children, Tampa, FL
Primary Contact: Anton C. Smith, Administrator
CFO: Patricia Miyasawa, CPA, Director Fiscal Service
CMO: Craig Ono, M.D., Chief of Staff
CIO: Gregory A Wolf, Director Information Systems
CHR: Derek Ito, Director Human Resources
CNO: Andrea Kubota, R.N., MSN, Director Patient Care Services and Nurse Executive
Web address: www.shrinershospitalsforchildren.org/honolulu
Control: Other not–for–profit (including NFP Corporation) **Service**: Children's orthopedic

Staffed Beds: 16

☐ **STRAUB MEDICAL CENTER (120022)**, 888 South King Street, Zip 96813–3097; tel. 808/522–4000, **A**1 2 3 5 10 **F**3 9 15 16 18 20 21 22 23 24 26 27 28 29 31 34 35 40 44 45 46 47 48 49 50 54 56 57 58 59 63 64 65 68 70 74 75 77 78 79 80 81 84 85 86 87 92 93 97 100 104 107 108 110 111 115 119 129 130 131 132 135 144 145 146 147 148 149 154 156 **S** Hawaii Pacific Health, Honolulu, HI
Primary Contact: Art Gladstone, R.N., Chief Executive Officer
COO: Maureen Flannery, Vice President Clinic Operations
CFO: David Okabe, Executive Vice President, Chief Financial Officer and Treasurer
CMO: Randy Yates, M.D., Chief Medical Officer
CIO: Steve Robertson, Executive Vice President and Chief Information Officer
CHR: Gail Lerch, R.N., Executive Vice President Human Resources
CNO: Patricia Boeckmann, R.N., Chief Operating Officer and Chief Nursing Officer
Web address: www.straubhealth.org
Control: Other not–for–profit (including NFP Corporation) **Service**: General medical and surgical

Staffed Beds: 121 **Admissions**: 6759 **Census**: 112 **Outpatient Visits**: 861920 **Births**: 0 **Total Expense ($000)**: 467506 **Payroll Expense ($000)**: 205876 **Personnel**: 1849

⊠ **THE QUEEN'S MEDICAL CENTER (120001)**, 1301 Punchbowl Street, Zip 96813–2499; tel. 808/691–5100, (Includes QUEEN'S MEDICAL CENTER - WEST OAHU, 91–2141 Fort Weaver Road, Ewa Beach, Hawaii, Zip 96706–1993; tel. 808/691–3000; Susan Murray, FACHE, Chief Operating Officer) **A**1 2 3 5 10 **F**3 4 5 11 12 13 15 17 18 20 22 24 26 28 29 30 31 34 35 37 38 40 43 44 45 46 47 48 49 51 54 55 56 57 58 59 60 61 62 63 64 66 68 70 73 74 75 76 77 78 79 81 82 84 85 86 87 89 93 96 97 98 99 100 101 102 104 105 107 108 110 111 115 117 118 119 120 121 124 126 129 130 131 132 134 135 138 139 142 143 144 147 148 149 150 151 152 153 154 156 **S** Queen's Health Systems, Honolulu, HI
Primary Contact: Jill Hoggard Green, Ph.D., R.N., Chief Executive Officer
COO: Jason Chang, Executive Vice President and Chief Operating Officer
CFO: Michel Riccioni, Chief Financial Officer
CMO: Whitney Limm, M.D., Executive Vice President and Chief Physician Executive
CIO: Brian Yoshii, Vice President Information Technology and Chief Information Officer
CHR: Nona Tamanaha, Vice President Human Resources
CNO: Madeline Harris, R.N., Vice President and Chief Nursing Officer
Web address: www.queensmedicalcenter.org
Control: Other not–for–profit (including NFP Corporation) **Service**: General medical and surgical

Staffed Beds: 637 **Admissions**: 28048 **Census**: 488 **Outpatient Visits**: 150305 **Births**: 1590 **Total Expense ($000)**: 1102063 **Payroll Expense ($000)**: 416618 **Personnel**: 4638

⊠ **TRIPLER ARMY MEDICAL CENTER**, 1 Jarret White Road, Zip 96859–5001; tel. 808/433–6661, **A**1 2 3 5 **F**1 3 4 5 7 8 11 12 13 14 15 17 18 19 20 22 24 26 27 28 29 30 31 32 33 34 35 36 38 39 40 41 43 45 46 47 48 49 50 52 53 54 55 56 57 58 59 60 61 64 65 67 68 69 70 72 74 75 76 77 78 79 80 81 82 84 85 86 87 88 89 92 93 94 97 98 100 101 102 104 105 106 107 108 110 111 114 115 116 117 118 119 120 121 123 124 126 127 128 129 130 131 132 133 134 135 141 143 144 145 146 147 148 149 153 154 155 156 157 **S** Department of the Army, Office of the Surgeon General, Falls Church, VA
Primary Contact: Colonel Mary Krueger, Commanding Officer
COO: Major Elias B. Lozano, Executive Officer
CFO: Lieutenant Colonel Christopher A. Wodarz, Chief, Resource Management Division
CMO: Captain Andrew L. Findlay, Deputy Commander Clinical Services
CIO: Lieutenant Colonel Donna E Beed, Chief Information Management Division
CHR: Colonel James N. Davidson, Troop Commander
CNO: Colonel Jennifer L. Bedick, Deputy Commander Nursing
Web address: www.tamc.amedd.army.mil
Control: Department of Defense, Government, federal **Service**: General medical and surgical

Staffed Beds: 181 **Admissions**: 9736 **Census**: 119 **Outpatient Visits**: 973129 **Births**: 2555 **Personnel**: 4161

★ **VETERANS AFFAIRS PACIFIC ISLANDS HEALTH CARE SYSTEM**, 459 Patterson Road, Zip 96819–1522; tel. 808/433–0600, (Nonreporting) **A**3 5 **S** Department of Veterans Affairs, Washington, DC
Primary Contact: Jennifer S. Gutowski, FACHE, Director
Web address: www.hawaii.va.gov/
Control: Veterans Affairs, Government, federal **Service**: General medical and surgical

Staffed Beds: 80

KAHUKU—Honolulu County

⊠ **KAHUKU MEDICAL CENTER (121304)**, 56–117 Pualalea Street, Zip 96731–2052; tel. 808/293–9221, (Nonreporting) **A**1 10 18
Primary Contact: Alan MacPhee, Chief Executive Officer
COO: Jerome Flores, Chief Financial Officer and Chief Operating Officer
CFO: Jerome Flores, Chief Financial Officer and Chief Operating Officer
CMO: P Douglas Nielson, M.D., Chief of Staff
Web address: www.kahuku.hhsc.org/
Control: Other not–for–profit (including NFP Corporation) **Service**: General medical and surgical

Staffed Beds: 21

KAILUA—Honolulu County

⊞ **ADVENTIST HEALTH CASTLE (120006)**, 640 Ulukahiki Street, Zip 96734–4454; tel. 808/263–5500, **A**1 3 10 **F**3 8 12 13 15 18 20 22 24 26 29 30 31 32 34 36 37 40 45 46 49 50 51 54 56 57 59 64 68 69 70 74 75 76 78 79 81 84 85 86 91 92 93 97 98 102 105 107 108 110 111 114 119 120 126 127 130 135 146 147 149 152 156 **S** Adventist Health, Roseville, CA
Primary Contact: Kathryn A. Raethel, R.N., M.P.H., President and Chief Executive Officer
COO: Travis Clegg, Vice President, Operations
CFO: Heidar Thordarson, Chief Financial Officer
CMO: Alan Cheung, M.D., Vice President Medical Affairs
CHR: Todd Reese, Director Human Performance
CNO: Laura R. Westphal, R.N., Vice President Patient Care Services
Web address: www.castlemed.org
Control: Church operated, Nongovernment, not–for–profit **Service**: General medical and surgical

Staffed Beds: 160 **Admissions**: 7674 **Census**: 85 **Outpatient Visits**: 104008 **Births**: 1069 **Total Expense ($000)**: 171625 **Payroll Expense ($000)**: 55898 **Personnel**: 891

KAMUELA—Hawaii County

⊠ **NORTH HAWAII COMMUNITY HOSPITAL (120028)**, 67–1125 Mamalahoa Highway, Zip 96743–8496; tel. 808/885–4444, **A**1 3 10 20 **F**3 8 13 15 18 26 29 30 31 34 35 36 40 41 43 44 49 50 53 54 57 59 62 64 68 70 75 76 77 78 79 81 85 86 87 93 97 102 107 108 110 111 115 119 130 131 132 146 147 148 154 156 157 **S** Queen's Health Systems, Honolulu, HI
Primary Contact: Cynthia Kamikawa, R.N., MSN, President
CFO: Michel Riccioni, Chief Financial Officer
CMO: Gary Goldberg, M.D., Chief Medical Officer
CNO: Miquel Noelani Simms, R.N., Chief Nursing Officer
Web address: www.nhch.com
Control: Other not–for–profit (including NFP Corporation) **Service**: General medical and surgical

Staffed Beds: 35 **Admissions**: 1787 **Census**: 15 **Outpatient Visits**: 83985 **Births**: 479 **Total Expense ($000)**: 71823 **Payroll Expense ($000)**: 26715 **Personnel**: 297

HI

KANEOHE—Honolulu County

☐ **HAWAII STATE HOSPITAL**, 45–710 Keaahala Road, Zip 96744–3597;
tel. 808/247–2191, (Nonreporting) **A**1 3 5
Primary Contact: William J. May, Administrator
COO: Anthony Fraiola, Associate Administrator Administrative and Support Services
CFO: Stephen Teeter, Business Manager
CMO: James Westphal, M.D., AMHD Medical Director
CIO: John Jansen, Management Information Specialist
CHR: Karen Hara, Personnel Management Specialist
CNO: Lani Tsuneishi, Nursing Services Manager
Web address: www.hawaii.gov/health/
Control: State, Government, nonfederal **Service**: Psychiatric

Staffed Beds: 178

KAPAA—Kauai County

★ **SAMUEL MAHELONA MEMORIAL HOSPITAL (121306)**, 4800 Kawaihau Road,
Zip 96746–1971; tel. 808/822–4961, (Nonreporting) **A**10 18 **S** Hawaii Health
Systems Corporation, Honolulu, HI
Primary Contact: Lance Segawa, Chief Executive Officer
CFO: Michael Perel, Regional Chief Financial Officer
CMO: Gerald Tomory, M.D., Regional Medical Director
CIO: Sandra McMaster, Regional Chief Information Officer
CHR: Lani Aranio, Regional Director Human Resources
Web address: www.smmh.hhsc.org
Control: State, Government, nonfederal **Service**: General medical and surgical

Staffed Beds: 80

KAUNAKAKAI—Maui County

✉ **MOLOKAI GENERAL HOSPITAL (121303)**, 280 Home Olu Place, Zip 96748–
0408, Mailing Address: P.O. Box 408, Zip 96748–0408; tel. 808/553–5331,
(Nonreporting) **A**1 10 18 **S** Queen's Health Systems, Honolulu, HI
Primary Contact: Janice Kalanihuia, President
CFO: Zessica L Apiki, Accountant
CMO: William Thomas, M.D., Jr Medical Director Clinical and Internal Affairs
CIO: Sampson Wescoatt, Manager Information Technology
CHR: Alicia Teves, Coordinator Human Resources
Web address: www.queens.org
Control: Other not–for–profit (including NFP Corporation) **Service**: General
medical and surgical

Staffed Beds: 15

KEALAKEKUA—Hawaii County

✉ **KONA COMMUNITY HOSPITAL (120019)**, 79–1019 Haukapila Street,
Zip 96750–7920; tel. 808/322–9311, **A**1 10 20 **F**3 8 11 12 13 29 30 31 34
35 40 43 44 47 50 68 70 76 77 78 79 81 84 98 106 107 108 109 111 115
119 120 121 123 130 132 146 149 **S** Hawaii Health Systems Corporation,
Honolulu, HI
Primary Contact: Jay E. Kreuzer, FACHE, Chief Executive Officer
CFO: Dean Herzog, Chief Financial Officer
CMO: Richard McDowell, M.D., Medical Director
CHR: Kathryn Salomon, Director Human Resources
CNO: Patricia Kalua, Chief Nurse Executive
Web address: www.kch.hhsc.org
Control: State, Government, nonfederal **Service**: General medical and surgical

Staffed Beds: 94 **Admissions**: 3756 **Census**: 52 **Outpatient Visits**: 57983
Births: 498 **Personnel**: 425

KOHALA—Hawaii County

★ **KOHALA HOSPITAL (121302)**, 54–383 Hospital Road, Zip 96755, Mailing
Address: P.O. Box 10, Kapaau, Zip 96755–0010; tel. 808/889–6211,
(Nonreporting) **A**10 18 **S** Hawaii Health Systems Corporation, Honolulu, HI
Primary Contact: Eugene Amar Jr, Administrator
CMO: Silvia Sonnenschein, M.D., Chief of Staff
Web address: www.koh.hhsc.org
Control: State, Government, nonfederal **Service**: General medical and surgical

Staffed Beds: 28

KULA—Maui County

★ **KULA HOSPITAL (121308)**, 100 Keokea Place, Zip 96790–7450; tel. 808/878–
1221, (Total facility includes 105 beds in nursing home–type unit) **A**10 18 **F**11 40
50 67 68 97 128 130 133 143 148 **S** Kaiser Foundation Hospitals, Oakland, CA
Primary Contact: Kerry Pitcher, Chief Executive Officer
CFO: Nerissa Garrity, Chief Financial Officer
CMO: Nicole Apoliona, M.D., Medical Director
Web address: www.https://www.mauihealthsystem.org/kula-hospital/
Control: Other not–for–profit (including NFP Corporation) **Service**: General
medical and surgical

Staffed Beds: 114 **Admissions**: 84 **Census**: 87 **Outpatient Visits**: 3384
Births: 0 **Total Expense ($000)**: 21569 **Payroll Expense ($000)**: 10877
Personnel: 126

LANAI CITY—Maui County

★ **LANAI COMMUNITY HOSPITAL (121305)**, 628 Seventh Street, Zip 96763–0650,
Mailing Address: P.O. Box 630650, Zip 96763–0650; tel. 808/565–8450, (Total
facility includes 10 beds in nursing home–type unit) **A**10 18 **F**11 34 40 50 59 68
128 **S** Kaiser Foundation Hospitals, Oakland, CA
Primary Contact: Kerry Pitcher, Administrator
Web address: www.https://www.mauihealthsystem.org/lanai-hospital/
Control: Other not–for–profit (including NFP Corporation) **Service**: General
medical and surgical

Staffed Beds: 14 **Admissions**: 15 **Census**: 9 **Outpatient Visits**: 3499
Births: 0 **Total Expense ($000)**: 5296 **Payroll Expense ($000)**: 2152
Personnel: 29

LIHUE—Kauai County

☐ **WILCOX MEDICAL CENTER (120014)**, 3–3420 Kuhio Highway,
Zip 96766–1099; tel. 808/245–1100, **A**1 2 10 20 **F**3 9 13 15 28 29 31 32 34 35
37 40 41 43 44 45 49 50 53 56 57 58 59 61 63 64 65 70 74 75 76 77 78 79
81 82 84 85 86 87 93 107 108 110 111 114 115 119 126 130 131 132 133
135 145 146 147 148 149 154 156 **S** Hawaii Pacific Health, Honolulu, HI
Primary Contact: Jen Chahanovich, President and Chief Executive Officer
CFO: David Okabe, Executive Vice President, Chief Financial Officer and Treasurer
CMO: Craig Netzer, M.D., President Medical Staff
CIO: Steve Robertson, Executive Vice President Revenue Cycle Management and
Chief Information Officer
CNO: Mary Ann England, Chief Nurse Executive
Web address: www.wilcoxhealth.org
Control: Other not–for–profit (including NFP Corporation) **Service**: General medical
and surgical

Staffed Beds: 65 **Admissions**: 3412 **Census**: 45 **Outpatient Visits**: 97823
Births: 501 **Total Expense ($000)**: 120164 **Payroll Expense ($000)**: 39112
Personnel: 478

PAHALA—Hawaii County

★ **KA'U HOSPITAL (121301)**, 1 Kamani Street, Zip 96777, Mailing Address: P.O.
Box 40, Zip 96777–0040; tel. 808/932–4200, (Nonreporting) **A**10 18 **S** Hawaii
Health Systems Corporation, Honolulu, HI
Primary Contact: Merilyn Harris, Administrator
CMO: Clifford Field, M.D., Medical Director
Web address: www.hhsc.org
Control: State, Government, nonfederal **Service**: General medical and surgical

Staffed Beds: 21

WAHIAWA—Honolulu County

✉ **WAHIAWA GENERAL HOSPITAL (120004)**, 128 Lehua Street, Zip 96786–2036;
tel. 808/621–8411, (Nonreporting) **A**1 3 5 10
Primary Contact: Brian Cunningham, Chief Executive Officer
CMO: Manuel Abundo, M.D., Chief of Staff
CIO: Jason Fujinaka, Manager Information System
CHR: Liflor Barrera, Manager Human Resources
CNO: Tammy Kohrer, Director of Nursing-Acute
Web address: www.wahiawageneral.org
Control: Other not–for–profit (including NFP Corporation) **Service**: General
medical and surgical

Staffed Beds: 160

WAILUKU—Maui County

✉ **MAUI MEMORIAL MEDICAL CENTER (120002)**, 221 Mahalani Street, Zip 96793–
2581; tel. 808/244–9056, **A**1 10 20 **F**3 8 11 12 15 18 20 22 24 26 28 29 30 31
34 35 36 39 40 43 46 47 48 49 50 51 53 57 59 60 64 68 70 75 76 77 78 79 81
84 85 87 89 93 98 102 104 105 107 108 110 111 114 115 119 124 130 132
135 141 142 146 148 149 **S** Kaiser Foundation Hospitals, Oakland, CA
Primary Contact: Michael A. Rembis, FACHE, Chief Executive Officer
COO: Debbie Walsh, MSN, Chief Operating Officer
CIO: Dana Mendoza, Chief Information Officer
Web address: www.https://www.mauihealthsystem.org/maui-memorial/
Control: Other not–for–profit (including NFP Corporation) **Service**: General
medical and surgical

Staffed Beds: 214 **Admissions**: 8821 **Census**: 164 **Outpatient
Visits**: 95657 **Births**: 1570 **Total Expense ($000)**: 281070 **Payroll Expense
($000)**: 105598 **Personnel**: 1000

WAIMEA—Kauai County

✉ **KAUAI VETERANS MEMORIAL HOSPITAL (121300)**, 4643 Waimea Canyon Road,
Zip 96796, Mailing Address: P.O. Box 337, Zip 96796–0337; tel. 808/338–9431,
(Nonreporting) **A**1 10 18 **S** Hawaii Health Systems Corporation, Honolulu, HI
Primary Contact: Lance Segawa, Chief Executive Officer
CFO: Michael Perel, Regional Chief Financial Officer
CMO: Gerald Tomory, M.D., Regional Medical Director
CIO: Sandra McMaster, Regional Chief Information Officer
CHR: Solette Perry, Regional Director Human Resources
Web address: www.kvmh.hhsc.org
Control: State, Government, nonfederal **Service**: General medical and surgical

Staffed Beds: 45

HI

IDAHO

AMERICAN FALLS—Power County

★ ⇧ **POWER COUNTY HOSPITAL DISTRICT (131304)**, 510 Roosevelt Street,
Zip 83211–1362, Mailing Address: P.O. Box 420, Zip 83211–0420; tel. 208/226–
3200, (Nonreporting) **A**10 18 21
Primary Contact: Dallas Clinger, Administrator
COO: Rock Roy, Professional Services Director
CFO: Jeremy Claunch, Chief Financial Officer
CMO: Spencer Garrett Seibold, M.D., Chief of Medical Staff
CIO: Mindy Earl, Health Information Manager
CHR: Kendra Sweat, Director Human Resources
CNO: June Mortenson, R.N., Director of Nursing
Web address: www.pchd.net
Control: Hospital district or authority, Government, nonfederal **Service:** General
medical and surgical

Staffed Beds: 10

ARCO—Butte County

⇧ **LOST RIVERS MEDICAL CENTER (131324)**, 551 Highland Drive,
Zip 83213–9771, Mailing Address: P.O. Box 145, Zip 83213–0145;
tel. 208/527–8206, (Nonreporting) **A**5 10 18 21
Primary Contact: Brad Huerta, Chief Executive Officer and Administrator
CFO: Jon Smith, Chief Financial Officer
CMO: Jeffrey Haskell, M.D., Chief Medical Staff
CHR: Tina Akins, Director Human Resources
CNO: Geri Cammack, R.N., Director of Nursing
Web address: www.lostriversmedical.com
Control: Hospital district or authority, Government, nonfederal **Service:** General
medical and surgical

Staffed Beds: 43

BLACKFOOT—Bingham County

⊠ **BINGHAM MEMORIAL HOSPITAL (131325)**, 98 Poplar Street,
Zip 83221–1799; tel. 208/785–4100, (Nonreporting) **A**1 3 5 10 18
Primary Contact: Jake Erickson, Chief Executive Officer
CFO: John Fullmer, Chief Financial Officer
CIO: Robert Weis, Director Information Systems
CHR: Tara Preston, Director Human Resources
CNO: Carolyn Hansen, Chief Nursing Officer
Web address: www.binghammemorial.org
Control: Other not-for-profit (including NFP Corporation) **Service:** General
medical and surgical

Staffed Beds: 85

MOUNTAIN RIVER BIRTHING AND SURGERY CENTER (130067), 350 North
Meridian Street, Zip 83221–1625; tel. 208/782–0300, (Data for 240 days) **A**10
F3 13 29 35 68 73 76 79 81 85 119 130
Primary Contact: D. Jeffery. Daniels, Chief Executive Officer
COO: Dan Cochran, Chief Operating Officer
CIO: Robert Weis, Director Information Technology
CHR: Tara Preston, Director Human Resources
CNO: Nathan Buck, R.N., Nursing Manager
Web address: www.binghammemorial.org
Control: Other not-for-profit (including NFP Corporation) **Service:** General
medical and surgical

Staffed Beds: 8 **Admissions:** 53 **Census:** 1 **Outpatient Visits:** 2931
Births: 16 **Total Expense ($000):** 3189 **Payroll Expense ($000):** 649
Personnel: 26

□ **STATE HOSPITAL SOUTH (134010)**, 700 East Alice Street, Zip 83221–4925,
Mailing Address: P.O. Box 400, Zip 83221–0400; tel. 208/785–1200,
(Nonreporting) **A**1 5 10
Primary Contact: James Price, Hospital Administrator
COO: Greg Horton, Director Support Services
CFO: Angela Loosli, Assistant Administrator, Operations
CMO: Kelly Palmer, D.O., Medical Director
CIO: Julie Sutton, Director Performance Improvement
CHR: Sheryl Donnelly, Human Resources Specialist
CNO: Randy Walker, Director Nursing Services
Web address: www.healthandwelfare.idaho.gov
Control: State, Government, nonfederal **Service:** Psychiatric

Staffed Beds: 135

BOISE—Ada County

BOISE BEHAVIORAL HEALTH HOSPITAL See Safe Haven Hospital of Treasure Valley

⊠ **BOISE VETERANS AFFAIRS MEDICAL CENTER**, 500 West Fort Street,
Zip 83702–4598; tel. 208/422–1000, (Total facility includes 32 beds in nursing
home–type unit) **A**1 3 5 **F**1 2 3 4 5 8 9 10 12 29 30 31 34 35 38 39 40 43 45
46 47 50 53 54 56 57 58 59 60 61 62 63 64 65 66 67 68 70 71 74 75 77
78 79 81 82 83 84 85 86 87 90 91 92 93 94 96 97 98 100 101 102 104 107
108 111 112 119 120 121 122 123 124 127 128 129 130 132 133 135 143
144 145 146 147 148 149 150 152 154 156 **S** Department of Veterans Affairs,
Washington, DC
Primary Contact: David P. Wood, FACHE, Director
CFO: Ron Blanton, Chief Fiscal Services
CMO: Paul Lambert, M.D., Chief of Staff
CHR: Randy Turner, Chief Human Resource Management Services
Web address: www.boise.va.gov/
Control: Veterans Affairs, Government, federal **Service:** General medical and
surgical

Staffed Beds: 87 **Admissions:** 3320 **Census:** 71 **Outpatient Visits:** 394051
Births: 0 **Total Expense ($000):** 275000 **Payroll Expense ($000):** 170000
Personnel: 1449

IDAHO ELKS REHABILITATION HOSPITAL See St. Luke's Rehabilitation Hospital

□ **INTERMOUNTAIN HOSPITAL (134002)**, 303 North Allumbaugh Street,
Zip 83704–9208; tel. 208/377–8400, **A**1 10 **F**4 98 99 103 105 130 151 152
153 **S** Universal Health Services, Inc., King of Prussia, PA
Primary Contact: Jeffrey F. Morrell, Chief Executive Officer
CFO: JeDonne Hines, Chief Financial Officer
CMO: Charles Novak, M.D., Chief Medical Officer
CHR: Nancy Nelson, Director Human Resources
CNO: Jennifer Beaulieu, Director of Nursing
Web address: www.intermountainhospital.com
Control: Corporation, Investor–owned (for–profit) **Service:** Psychiatric

Staffed Beds: 135 **Admissions:** 3562 **Census:** 89 **Births:** 0

SAFE HAVEN HOSPITAL OF TREASURE VALLEY (134009), 8050 Northview
Street, Zip 83704–7126; tel. 208/327–0504, (Nonreporting) **A**10 **S** Safe Haven
Health Care, Pocatello, ID
Primary Contact: Scott Proctor, Chief Executive Officer
CMO: David Kent, M.D., Chief Medical Officer
CIO: Debra Alexander, Chief Information Officer
CHR: Kathy Cady, Coordinator Human Resources, Accounts Payable and Payroll
Web address: www.boisepsychhospital.com
Control: Corporation, Investor–owned (for–profit) **Service:** Psychiatric

Staffed Beds: 22

ID

⊠ △ **SAINT ALPHONSUS REGIONAL MEDICAL CENTER (130007)**, 1055 N Curtis Rd, Zip 83706–1309, Mailing Address: 1055 North Curtis Road, Zip 83706–1309; tel. 208/367–2121, **A**1 2 3 5 7 10 **F**3 11 12 13 15 17 18 20 22 24 26 28 29 30 31 32 33 34 35 36 37 38 39 40 42 43 44 45 49 50 54 55 56 57 58 59 64 65 66 68 70 71 72 74 75 76 77 78 79 81 82 84 85 86 87 89 90 91 93 94 96 97 98 99 100 102 103 104 107 108 110 111 114 115 118 119 121 124 126 131 132 134 135 144 146 147 148 149 150 154 156 **S** Trinity Health, Livonia, MI
Primary Contact: Andrew B. Cosentino, President
CFO: Kenneth Fry, Chief Financial Officer
CMO: Steve Brown, M.D., Chief Quality Officer
CIO: Dwight Pond, TIS Boise
CHR: Teresa Sargent, Vice President Human Resources
CNO: Sherry Parks, R.N., MS, Chief Nursing Officer
Web address: www.saintalphonsus.org
Control: Other not–for–profit (including NFP Corporation) **Service**: General medical and surgical

> **Staffed Beds: 392 Admissions: 18213 Census: 243 Outpatient Visits: 1212580 Births: 1408 Total Expense ($000): 634780 Payroll Expense ($000): 264363 Personnel: 3451**

★ **ST. LUKE'S REGIONAL MEDICAL CENTER (130006)**, 190 East Bannock Street, Zip 83712–6241; tel. 208/381–2222, (Includes ST. LUKE'S CHILDREN'S HOSPITAL, 190 East Bannock Street, Boise, Idaho, Zip 83712–6241; tel. 208/381–2222; ST. LUKE'S MERIDIAN MEDICAL CENTER, 520 South Eagle Road, Meridian, Idaho, Zip 83642, Mailing Address: 520 S Eagle RD, Zip 83642–6351, tel. 208/706–5000; Dennis Mesaros, Administrator) **A**2 3 5 10 **F**7 8 11 12 13 15 17 18 19 20 21 22 23 24 25 26 27 28 29 30 31 32 34 35 36 37 40 41 46 47 48 49 53 54 55 56 57 59 62 63 64 68 69 70 71 72 74 75 76 77 78 79 81 82 84 86 87 88 89 90 93 107 108 110 111 114 115 116 117 118 119 120 121 124 126 127 128 129 130 131 132 134 135 136 144 146 147 155 156 **S** St. Luke's Health System, Boise, ID
Primary Contact: David M. McFadyen, Administrator
CFO: Jeff Taylor, Vice President Finance
CMO: Jim Souza, Chief Medical Officer
CIO: Marc Chasin, M.D., Chief Information Officer
CHR: Phillip Johnson, Vice President, Chief Human Resources Officer
CNO: Barbara Hocking, Chief Nursing Officer
Web address: www.stlukesonline.org/boise
Control: Other not–for–profit (including NFP Corporation) **Service**: General medical and surgical

> **Staffed Beds: 604 Admissions: 31628 Census: 361 Outpatient Visits: 1637205 Births: 4913 Total Expense ($000): 1555383 Payroll Expense ($000): 757416 Personnel: 9656**

★ △ **ST. LUKE'S REHABILITATION HOSPITAL (133025)**, 600 North Robbins Road, Zip 83702–4565, Mailing Address: P.O. Box 1100, Zip 83701–1100; tel. 208/489–4444, (Nonreporting) **A**5 7 10 **S** St. Luke's Health System, Boise, ID
Primary Contact: Nolan Hoffer, Senior Director
COO: Melissa Honsinger, Chief Operating Officer
CFO: Doug Lewis, Chief Financial Officer
CMO: Lee Kornfield, M.D., Medical Director
CIO: Scott Pyrah, Director Information Systems
CHR: Jim Atkins, Director Employee Services
Web address: www.idahoelksrehab.org
Control: Other not–for–profit (including NFP Corporation) **Service**: Rehabilitation

> **Staffed Beds: 30**

☐ **TREASURE VALLEY HOSPITAL (130063)**, 8800 West Emerald Street, Zip 83704–8205; tel. 208/373–5000, (Nonreporting) **A**1 3 10
Primary Contact: Nick Genna, Administrator
CMO: Jeffrey Hessing, M.D., Medical Director
CHR: Kathleen Phelps, Director Human Resources
Web address: www.treasurevalleyhospital.com
Control: Corporation, Investor–owned (for–profit) **Service**: General medical and surgical

> **Staffed Beds: 9**

VETERANS AFFAIRS MEDICAL CENTER See Boise Veterans Affairs Medical Center

⊠ **VIBRA HOSPITAL OF BOISE (132002)**, 6651 West Franklin Road, Zip 83709–0914; tel. 877/801–2244, (Nonreporting) **A**1 3 10 **S** Vibra Healthcare, Mechanicsburg, PA
Primary Contact: Cynthia Newsom, Chief Executive Officer
Web address: www.vhboise.com
Control: Corporation, Investor–owned (for–profit) **Service**: Acute long–term care hospital

> **Staffed Beds: 60**

BONNERS FERRY—Boundary County

★ ⇧ **BOUNDARY COMMUNITY HOSPITAL (131301)**, 6640 Kaniksu Street, Zip 83805–7532; tel. 208/267–3141, (Total facility includes 28 beds in nursing home–type unit) **A**10 18 21 **F**3 11 15 28 29 34 35 40 41 50 57 59 64 75 77 79 81 85 93 97 107 110 111 115 119 127 128 130 132 133 143 149
Primary Contact: Craig A. Johnson, Chief Executive Officer
CFO: Holly McDonald, Controller
CMO: Chuck Newhouse, M.D., Chief of Staff
CHR: Ann Coughlin, Director Human Resources
CNO: Tari Yourzek, Chief Nursing Officer
Web address: www.boundarycommunityhospital.org
Control: County, Government, nonfederal **Service**: General medical and surgical

> **Staffed Beds: 48 Admissions: 149 Census: 28**

BURLEY—Cassia County

⊠ **CASSIA REGIONAL HOSPITAL (131326)**, 1501 Hiland Avenue, Zip 83318–2688; tel. 208/678–4444, **A**1 10 18 **F**3 7 13 15 18 29 31 34 35 38 39 40 44 45 46 47 48 49 50 57 64 68 70 75 76 77 79 81 85 86 87 89 92 93 97 100 102 107 108 110 111 114 119 129 130 132 154 157 **S** Intermountain Healthcare, Inc., Salt Lake City, UT
Primary Contact: Ben Smalley, Administrator
CFO: Mark Christensen, Director, Finance
CMO: Bernard Boehmer, M.D., Medical Director
CIO: Carie Call, Computer Support
CHR: Keri Perrigot, Manager Human Resources
CNO: Michele Pond-Bell, R.N., Nurse Administrator
Web address: www.cassiaregional.org
Control: Other not–for–profit (including NFP Corporation) **Service**: General medical and surgical

> **Staffed Beds: 25 Admissions: 1987 Census: 12 Outpatient Visits: 59777 Births: 541 Total Expense ($000): 50773 Payroll Expense ($000): 20289 Personnel: 277**

CALDWELL—Canyon County

⊠ **WEST VALLEY MEDICAL CENTER (130014)**, 1717 Arlington, Zip 83605–4802; tel. 208/459–4641, **A**1 3 5 10 **F**3 8 11 13 15 18 20 22 26 28 29 30 34 35 40 41 45 50 51 54 57 59 60 64 68 70 72 74 75 76 77 79 81 82 84 85 86 87 89 91 92 93 98 100 101 102 104 105 107 108 110 111 114 115 119 126 130 131 135 146 147 148 149 154 **S** HCA Healthcare, Nashville, TN
Primary Contact: Elizabeth Hunsicker, Chief Executive Officer
COO: Jennifer Opsut, Interim Chief Operating Officer
CFO: Kate Fowler, Chief Financial Officer
CMO: Richard Augustus, M.D., Chief Medical Officer
CIO: Jason Martinez, Director Information Technology
CHR: Senta Cornelius, Director Human Resources
CNO: Edith E Irving, R.N., MS, FACHE, Chief Nursing Officer
Web address: www.westvalleymedctr.com
Control: Corporation, Investor–owned (for–profit) **Service**: General medical and surgical

> **Staffed Beds: 105 Admissions: 4113 Census: 45**

CASCADE—Valley County

CASCADE MEDICAL CENTER (131308), 402 Lake Cascade Pkwy, Zip 83611–7702, Mailing Address: P.O. Box 1330, Zip 83611–1330; tel. 208/382–4242, **A**5 10 18 **F**11 28 29 32 34 35 40 41 53 57 59 64 65 66 87 89 93 94 97 102 107 127 133 154
Primary Contact: Tom Reinhardt, Chief Executive Officer
CFO: Penny Lancaster, Controller
CMO: Mikael Bedell, M.D., Medical Director
CNO: Teri Coombs, R.N., Director Nursing Services
Web address: www.cascademedicalcenter.net
Control: Hospital district or authority, Government, nonfederal **Service**: General medical and surgical

> **Staffed Beds: 8 Admissions: 56 Census: 1 Outpatient Visits: 9946 Births: 0 Total Expense ($000): 4367 Payroll Expense ($000): 2262 Personnel: 42**

ID

Many Facility Codes have changed. Please refer to the AHA Guide Code Chart. © 2019 AHA Guide

COEUR D'ALENE—Kootenai County

★ ⥣ **KOOTENAI HEALTH (130049)**, 2003 Kootenai Health Way, Zip 83814–2677; tel. 208/625–4000, (Includes KOOTENAI BEHAVIORAL HEALTH, 2301 North Ironwood Place, Coeur D'Alene, Idaho, Zip 83814–2650; tel. 208/625–4800) **A**2 3 5 10 19 21 **F**3 4 5 9 11 13 14 15 17 18 20 22 24 26 28 29 30 31 32 34 35 37 40 41 43 44 45 46 47 48 49 50 51 53 54 56 57 58 59 60 63 64 65 68 70 71 72 74 75 76 78 79 81 82 83 84 85 86 87 89 91 93 95 96 97 98 99 100 101 102 104 107 108 110 111 114 115 116 117 119 121 124 126 127 129 130 131 132 135 143 145 146 148 149 154 156
Primary Contact: Jon Ness, Chief Executive Officer
COO: Jeremy Evans, Vice President Operations
CFO: Kimberly Webb, Chief Financial Officer
CMO: Walter Fairfax, M.D., Chief Medical Officer
CHR: Daniel Klocko, Vice President Human Resources
CNO: Joan M. Simon, R.N., FACHE, Chief Nursing Officer
Web address: www.kh.org
Control: Hospital district or authority, Government, nonfederal **Service**: General medical and surgical

Staffed Beds: 297 **Admissions:** 16491 **Census:** 189 **Outpatient Visits:** 546815 **Births:** 1815 **Total Expense ($000):** 531756 **Payroll Expense ($000):** 234226 **Personnel:** 3208

COTTONWOOD—Idaho County

★ **ST. MARY'S HOSPITAL (131321)**, 701 Lewiston Street, Zip 83522–9750, Mailing Address: P.O. Box 137, Zip 83522–0137; tel. 208/962–3251, **A**5 10 18 **F**7 8 13 28 29 30 34 35 40 43 45 59 64 65 75 76 81 82 91 93 97 104 107 114 119 128 130 133 154 156 **S** Essentia Health, Duluth, MN
Primary Contact: Lenne Bonner, President
CFO: Jyl Ruland, Chief Financial Officer
CHR: Debbie Schumacher, Chief Human Resource Officer
Web address: www.smh-cvhc.org/getpage.php?name=index
Control: Other not–for–profit (including NFP Corporation) **Service**: General medical and surgical

Staffed Beds: 25 **Admissions:** 562 **Census:** 7 **Outpatient Visits:** 25131 **Births:** 41

DRIGGS—Teton County

★ **TETON VALLEY HEALTH CARE (131313)**, 120 East Howard Street, Zip 83422–5112; tel. 208/354–2383, **A**10 18 **F**3 15 18 29 30 31 34 35 38 39 40 41 43 45 50 55 56 57 59 64 65 68 74 75 77 78 79 81 82 84 85 87 93 97 100 102 104 107 110 111 114 119 127 131 133 135 146 147 148 154
Primary Contact: Keith Gnagey, Chief Executive Officer
CFO: Wesley D White, Chief Financial Officer
CMO: Nathan Levanger, M.D., Chief of Staff
CHR: Dory Harris, Director Human Resource
CNO: Angela Booker, Director of Nursing Services
Web address: www.tvhcare.org
Control: Other not–for–profit (including NFP Corporation) **Service**: General medical and surgical

Staffed Beds: 13 **Admissions:** 182 **Census:** 2

EMMETT—Gem County

⥣ **VALOR HEALTH (131318)**, 1202 East Locust Street, Zip 83617–2715; tel. 208/365–3561, **A**10 18 21 **F**11 13 29 34 35 40 45 48 50 57 59 65 68 75 79 81 83 85 97 107 111 115 119 127 128 129 130 131 133 135 144 148 149
Primary Contact: Brad Turpen, FACHE, Interim Chief Executive Officer
CHR: Susan Vahlberg, Director Employee and Community Relations
Web address: www.wkmh.org
Control: County, Government, nonfederal **Service**: General medical and surgical

Staffed Beds: 12 **Admissions:** 216 **Census:** 2 **Outpatient Visits:** 64440 **Births:** 53

GOODING—Gooding County

★ ⥣ **NORTH CANYON MEDICAL CENTER (131302)**, 267 North Canyon Drive, Zip 83330–5500; tel. 208/934–4433, **A**5 10 18 21 **F**3 5 11 12 15 29 32 33 34 35 36 37 40 41 44 45 50 54 56 57 59 63 64 65 68 75 77 79 81 84 85 87 90 93 97 107 110 111 114 119 126 127 129 130 131 133 135 143 144 148 154 156
Primary Contact: Tim Powers, Chief Executive Officer
COO: J'Dee Adams, Chief Operating Officer
CFO: Sara DeMoe, Chief Financial Officer
CMO: Jennifer Olsen, M.D., Chief of Staff
CIO: Margie McLeod, Director Information Technology
CHR: Sara Otto, Chief Compliance Officer
CNO: Lisa Mangum, Chief Nursing Officer
Web address: www.ncm-c.org
Control: Other not–for–profit (including NFP Corporation) **Service**: General medical and surgical

Staffed Beds: 18 **Admissions:** 589 **Census:** 6 **Outpatient Visits:** 25003 **Births:** 0 **Total Expense ($000):** 29146 **Payroll Expense ($000):** 11160 **Personnel:** 206

GRANGEVILLE—Idaho County

★ **SYRINGA HOSPITAL AND CLINICS (131315)**, 607 West Main Street, Zip 83530–1396; tel. 208/983–1700, **A**5 10 18 **F**3 7 13 29 34 35 40 45 50 57 58 63 64 76 81 85 87 93 97 102 107 115 119 127 130 133 146 148 156
Primary Contact: Abner King, Chief Executive Officer
CFO: Betty A Watson, Chief Financial Officer
CMO: Daniel Griffis, M.D., Chief Medical Officer
CIO: Darla Whitley, Manager Health Information Technology
CHR: Katy Eimers, Human Resources Officer
CNO: Cindy Daly, R.N., Director of Nursing
Web address: www.syringahospital.org
Control: Hospital district or authority, Government, nonfederal **Service**: General medical and surgical

Staffed Beds: 14 **Admissions:** 365 **Census:** 3 **Births:** 32 **Total Expense ($000):** 15585 **Payroll Expense ($000):** 8377 **Personnel:** 154

IDAHO FALLS—Bonneville County

☒ **EASTERN IDAHO REGIONAL MEDICAL CENTER (130018)**, 3100 Channing Way, Zip 83404–7533, Mailing Address: P.O. Box 2077, Zip 83403–2077; tel. 208/529–6111, **A**1 3 5 10 19 **F**3 7 11 12 13 15 18 20 21 22 23 24 28 29 30 31 34 35 36 39 40 43 44 46 49 50 53 57 59 62 65 68 70 74 75 76 77 78 79 81 82 85 86 87 89 90 91 92 93 98 102 106 107 108 111 114 115 118 119 120 121 123 130 131 132 135 146 147 148 157 **S** HCA Healthcare, Nashville, TN
Primary Contact: Jeff Sollis, Chief Executive Officer
COO: Sandee Moore, Chief Operating Officer
CFO: Judd Taylor, Chief Financial Officer
CMO: R. Lee Biggs, M.D., Chief Medical Officer
CHR: Wendy Andersen, Director Human Resources
CNO: Ann Marie Kjosa, R.N., MSN, Chief Nursing Officer
Web address: www.eirmc.com
Control: Corporation, Investor–owned (for–profit) **Service**: General medical and surgical

Staffed Beds: 280 **Admissions:** 10333 **Census:** 125 **Outpatient Visits:** 176459 **Births:** 1204

MOUNTAIN VIEW HOSPITAL (130065), 2325 Coronado Street, Zip 83404–7407; tel. 208/557–2700, (Nonreporting) **A**3 5 10
Primary Contact: James Adamson, Chief Executive Officer
COO: Peter Fabrick, Vice President Clinical Operations
CHR: Eilene Horne, Manager Human Resources
Web address: www.mountainviewhospital.org
Control: Corporation, Investor–owned (for–profit) **Service**: General medical and surgical

Staffed Beds: 22

JEROME—Jerome County

★ **ST. LUKE'S JEROME (131310)**, 709 North Lincoln Street, Zip 83338–1851, Mailing Address: 709 North Lincoln Avenue, Zip 83338–1851; tel. 208/814–9500, **A**3 10 18 **F**7 13 15 29 30 32 34 39 40 56 57 59 64 65 68 76 77 81 87 97 107 111 119 127 130 133 146 147 148 152 154 **S** St. Luke's Health System, Boise, ID
Primary Contact: Curtis Maier, Administrator
CMO: Elizabeth Sugden, M.D., Chief Medical Officer
CHR: Mark Stevens, Director Human Resources
CNO: Jill Howell, Chief Nursing Officer
Web address: www.stlukesonline.org/jerome/
Control: Other not–for–profit (including NFP Corporation) **Service**: General medical and surgical

Staffed Beds: 25 **Admissions:** 485 **Census:** 6 **Outpatient Visits:** 40292 **Births:** 139 **Total Expense ($000):** 19824 **Payroll Expense ($000):** 10468 **Personnel:** 147

KELLOGG—Shoshone County

⥣ **SHOSHONE MEDICAL CENTER (131314)**, 25 Jacobs Gulch, Zip 83837–2023; tel. 208/784–1221, (Nonreporting) **A**10 18 21
Primary Contact: Jerry Brantz, Chief Executive Officer and Chief Financial Officer
CMO: David Lawhorn, M.D., Chief Medical Officer
CIO: John Wohlman, Manager Information Systems
CHR: Dana Hemphill, Manager Human Resources
CNO: Karen Mann, R.N., Chief Nursing Officer
Web address: www.shoshonehealth.com
Control: Hospital district or authority, Government, nonfederal **Service**: General medical and surgical

Staffed Beds: 25

ID

Hospital, Medicare Provider Number, Address, Telephone, Approval, Facility, and Physician Codes, Health Care System

★ American Hospital Association (AHA) membership
□ The Joint Commission accreditation
○ Healthcare Facilities Accreditation Program
◇ DNV Healthcare Inc. accreditation
⥣ Center for Improvement in Healthcare Quality Accreditation
△ Commission on Accreditation of Rehabilitation Facilities (CARF) accreditation

KETCHUM—Blaine County

✠ **ST. LUKE'S WOOD RIVER MEDICAL CENTER (131323)**, 100 Hospital Drive, Zip 83340, Mailing Address: P.O. Box 100, Zip 83340–0100; tel. 208/727–8800, **A**1 5 10 18 **F**3 7 11 13 15 29 30 31 32 34 35 36 37 40 43 45 50 54 56 57 59 62 64 65 68 74 75 76 77 79 81 82 85 86 87 91 93 97 99 101 103 104 107 108 110 111 114 115 119 126 130 131 132 133 134 135 143 146 147 148 154 **S** St. Luke's Health System, Boise, ID
Primary Contact: Cody Langbehn, Administrator
CNO: Suzanne Miller, R.N., MSN, Senior Director Patient Care Services and Nursing
Web address: www.slrmc.org
Control: Other not–for–profit (including NFP Corporation) **Service**: General medical and surgical

Staffed Beds: 25 **Admissions**: 1100 **Census**: 8 **Outpatient Visits**: 104958 **Births**: 189 **Total Expense ($000)**: 69821 **Payroll Expense ($000)**: 32767 **Personnel**: 354

LEWISTON—Nez Perce County

✠ **ST. JOSEPH REGIONAL MEDICAL CENTER (130003)**, 415 Sixth Street, Zip 83501–2431; tel. 208/743–2511, **A**1 2 10 **F**8 11 15 18 20 22 26 29 30 31 34 35 40 41 43 44 45 46 47 48 49 50 54 57 59 60 63 64 68 69 70 71 74 75 76 77 78 79 80 81 83 84 86 87 89 91 93 97 98 101 102 104 107 108 109 110 111 114 115 116 117 118 119 120 121 122 123 124 129 130 132 135 146 148 **S** LifePoint Health, Brentwood, TN
Primary Contact: Blain Claypool, Chief Executive Officer
CFO: Thomas Safley, Chief Financial Officer
CHR: Susan Dokken, Chief Human Resources
CNO: Joan Agee, Vice President Patient Care Services
Web address: www.sjrmc.org
Control: Church operated, Nongovernment, not–for–profit **Service**: General medical and surgical

Staffed Beds: 123 **Admissions**: 5881 **Census**: 44 **Births**: 770 **Total Expense ($000)**: 157821

MALAD CITY—Oneida County

NELL J. REDFIELD MEMORIAL HOSPITAL (131303), 150 North 200 West, Zip 83252–1239, Mailing Address: Box 126, Zip 83252–0126; tel. 208/766–2231, (Nonreporting) **A**10 18
Primary Contact: John Williams, Administrator and Chief Executive Officer
CFO: Cindy Howard, Director Financial Services
CHR: Kathy Hubbard, Manager Human Resources
Web address: www.oneidahospital.com
Control: County, Government, nonfederal **Service**: General medical and surgical

Staffed Beds: 11

MCCALL—Valley County

★ **ST. LUKE'S MCCALL (131312)**, 1000 State Street, Zip 83638–3704; tel. 208/634–2221, **A**5 10 18 **F**3 8 9 11 13 15 30 32 34 35 36 38 40 45 46 50 57 59 64 66 68 79 81 85 86 87 93 97 107 111 115 119 130 132 133 134 135 146 148 149 154 156 **S** St. Luke's Health System, Boise, ID
Primary Contact: Amber Green, R.N., Chief Operating Officer and Chief Nursing Officer
COO: Amber Green, R.N., Chief Operating Officer and Chief Nursing Officer
CFO: Matt Groenig, Vice President Finance
CNO: Amber Green, R.N., Chief Operating Officer and Chief Nursing Officer
Web address: www.https://www.stlukesonline.org/communities-and-locations/facilities/hospitals-and-medical-centers/st-lukes-mccall-medical-center
Control: Other not–for–profit (including NFP Corporation) **Service**: General medical and surgical

Staffed Beds: 15 **Admissions**: 594 **Census**: 4 **Outpatient Visits**: 56476 **Births**: 103 **Total Expense ($000)**: 38004 **Payroll Expense ($000)**: 16764 **Personnel**: 211

MERIDIAN—Ada County

ST. LUKE'S MERIDIAN MEDICAL CENTER See St. Luke's Regional Medical Center, Boise

MONTPELIER—Bear Lake County

★ ⇑ **BEAR LAKE MEMORIAL HOSPITAL (131316)**, 164 South Fifth Street, Zip 83254–1597; tel. 208/847–1630, (Nonreporting) **A**10 18 21
Primary Contact: Leslie Crane, Interim Chief Executive Officer
Web address: www.blmhospital.com
Control: County, Government, nonfederal **Service**: General medical and surgical

Staffed Beds: 57

MOSCOW—Latah County

✠ **GRITMAN MEDICAL CENTER (131327)**, 700 South Main Street, Zip 83843–3056; tel. 208/882–4511, **A**1 10 18 **F**3 8 11 13 15 19 28 29 34 35 36 37 40 45 46 49 51 53 54 56 57 59 64 65 70 75 76 77 79 81 82 85 86 87 89 91 93 96 97 107 108 110 111 115 119 124 127 129 130 131 132 133 135 143 146 147 148 149 **S** QHR, Brentwood, TN
Primary Contact: Kara Besst, President and Chief Executive Officer
CMO: Michael Patmas, M.D., Chief Medical Officer
CIO: Kane Francetich, Chief Information Officer
CHR: Dennis Cockrell, Director Human Resources
Web address: www.gritman.org
Control: Other not–for–profit (including NFP Corporation) **Service**: General medical and surgical

Staffed Beds: 25 **Admissions**: 1368 **Census**: 14

MOUNTAIN HOME—Elmore County

✠ **ST. LUKE'S ELMORE (131311)**, 895 North Sixth East Street, Zip 83647–2207, Mailing Address: P.O. Box 1270, Zip 83647–1270; tel. 208/587–8401, (Total facility includes 34 beds in nursing home–type unit) **A**1 10 18 **F**3 7 11 13 15 29 30 34 35 40 50 57 59 64 68 75 77 81 85 107 111 114 119 127 128 129 130 133 146 149 154 **S** St. Luke's Health System, Boise, ID
Primary Contact: Lisa Melchiorre, R.N., MS, Chief Operating Officer and Chief Nursing Officer
COO: Lisa Melchiorre, R.N., MS, Chief Operating Officer and Chief Nursing Officer
CFO: Tricia Senger, Chief Financial Officer
CNO: Lisa Melchiorre, R.N., MS, Chief Operating Officer and Chief Nursing Officer
Web address: www.stlukesonline.org/elmore/
Control: Other not–for–profit (including NFP Corporation) **Service**: General medical and surgical

Staffed Beds: 63 **Admissions**: 926 **Census**: 26 **Outpatient Visits**: 60423 **Births**: 181 **Total Expense ($000)**: 38994 **Payroll Expense ($000)**: 16344 **Personnel**: 236

NAMPA—Canyon County

⇑ **MERCY MEDICAL CENTER** See Saint Alphonsus Medical Center - NAMPA

✠ ⇑ **SAINT ALPHONSUS MEDICAL CENTER - NAMPA (130013)**, 4300 East Flamingo Avenue, Zip 83686–6008; tel. 208/205–1000, **A**1 3 5 10 19 21 **F**3 8 11 12 13 14 15 18 20 22 28 29 30 31 32 34 35 37 39 40 41 42 44 45 50 51 57 59 64 65 66 68 69 70 71 72 75 76 77 78 79 81 82 85 86 87 92 107 108 110 111 115 118 119 120 121 123 126 129 130 132 133 134 135 141 143 145 146 147 148 149 154 **S** Trinity Health, Livonia, MI
Primary Contact: Travis Leach, President
CFO: Lannie Checketts, Chief Financial Officer
CMO: Dustan Hughes, M.D., Vice President Medical Affairs
CIO: Daniel Wright, Director Information Technology
CHR: Stefanie Thiel, Senior Human Resources Business Partner
CNO: Clint L Child, R.N., Chief Nursing Officer
Web address: www.https://www.saintalphonsus.org/nampa
Control: Church operated, Nongovernment, not–for–profit **Service**: General medical and surgical

Staffed Beds: 106 **Admissions**: 5903 **Census**: 55 **Outpatient Visits**: 111230 **Births**: 994 **Total Expense ($000)**: 136318 **Payroll Expense ($000)**: 44144 **Personnel**: 700

NAMPA—Elmore County

ST. LUKE'S NAMPA (130071), 9850 West St.Luke's Drive, Zip 83687; tel. 208/505–2000, **A**3 5 10 **F**3 7 11 13 15 18 20 22 29 30 40 41 50 53 63 68 70 72 75 76 77 81 85 87 92 93 107 108 109 110 111 114 115 118 119 120 130 134 135 146 154 157 **S** St. Luke's Health System, Boise, ID
Primary Contact: Ed Castledine, Chief Executive Officer
Control: Other not–for–profit (including NFP Corporation) **Service**: General medical and surgical

Staffed Beds: 87 **Admissions**: 2506 **Census**: 23 **Outpatient Visits**: 90914 **Births**: 677 **Total Expense ($000)**: 96660 **Payroll Expense ($000)**: 34612 **Personnel**: 514

OROFINO—Clearwater County

★ **CLEARWATER VALLEY HOSPITAL AND CLINICS (131320)**, 301 Cedar, Zip 83544–9029; tel. 208/476–4555, (Nonreporting) **A**10 18 **S** Essentia Health, Duluth, MN
Primary Contact: Lenne Bonner, President
CFO: Jyl Ruland, Chief Financial Officer
CMO: Kelly McGrath, Chief Medical Officer
CHR: Debbie Schumacher, Chief Human Resource Officer
Web address: www.smh-cvhc.org
Control: Other not–for–profit (including NFP Corporation) **Service**: General medical and surgical

Staffed Beds: 23

ID

Many Facility Codes have changed. Please refer to the AHA Guide Code Chart. © 2019 AHA Guide

STATE HOSPITAL NORTH, 300 Hospital Drive, Zip 83544–9034; tel. 208/476–4511, **A**5 **F**98 106 154
Primary Contact: Todd Hurt, Administrator
CMO: Karla Eisele, M.D., Clinical Director
CIO: James Sarbacher, Chief Information Officer
CHR: Heather Vandenbark, Human Resources Specialist
Web address: www.healthandwelfare.idaho.gov
Control: State, Government, nonfederal **Service:** Psychiatric

Staffed Beds: 55 **Admissions:** 277 **Census:** 44 **Outpatient Visits:** 0 **Births:** 0 **Total Expense ($000):** 9454 **Payroll Expense ($000):** 4879 **Personnel:** 100

POCATELLO—Bannock County

✉ **PORTNEUF MEDICAL CENTER (130028)**, 777 Hospital Way, Zip 83201–5175; tel. 208/239–1000, **A**1 3 5 10 20 **F**3 8 11 12 13 15 17 18 19 20 22 24 26 28 29 31 34 35 37 39 40 43 44 45 46 47 48 49 50 56 57 58 59 61 64 65 68 70 71 72 74 75 76 77 78 79 80 81 82 85 86 87 88 89 90 93 96 97 98 100 101 102 104 107 108 109 110 111 114 115 118 119 120 121 123 124 126 127 129 130 132 143 146 149 154 156 **S** Ardent Health Services, Nashville, TN
Primary Contact: Daniel Ordyna, Chief Executive Officer
COO: Don Wadle, Vice President Clinical and Support Services
CFO: John Abreu, Vice President and Chief Financial Officer
CMO: Dan Snell, Chief Medical Officer
CHR: Don Wadle, Interim Director Human Resources
CNO: Angela Treasure, Chief Nursing Officer
Web address: www.portmed.org
Control: Corporation, Investor–owned (for–profit) **Service:** General medical and surgical

Staffed Beds: 175 **Admissions:** 8342 **Census:** 97 **Outpatient Visits:** 284198 **Births:** 1251 **Total Expense ($000):** 239940 **Payroll Expense ($000):** 83603 **Personnel:** 1136

SAFE HAVEN HOSPITAL OF POCATELLO (134011), 1200 Hospital Way, Zip 83201–2708; tel. 208/232–2570, (Nonreporting) **A**10 **S** Safe Haven Health Care, Pocatello, ID
Primary Contact: Karen Neilson, Administrator
Web address: www.safehavenhealthcare.org/safehaven_hospital/index.html
Control: Individual, Investor–owned (for–profit) **Service:** Rehabilitation

Staffed Beds: 87

POST FALLS—Kootenai County

☐ **NORTHERN IDAHO ADVANCED CARE HOSPITAL (132001)**, 600 North Cecil Road, Zip 83854–6200; tel. 208/262–2800, (Nonreporting) **A**1 10 **S** Ernest Health, Inc., Albuquerque, NM
Primary Contact: Una Alderman, Chief Executive Officer
Web address: www.niach.ernesthealth.com
Control: Corporation, Investor–owned (for–profit) **Service:** Acute long–term care hospital

Staffed Beds: 40

☐ **NORTHWEST SPECIALTY HOSPITAL (130066)**, 1593 East Polston Avenue, Zip 83854–5326; tel. 208/262–2300, (Nonreporting) **A**1 10 **S** National Surgical Healthcare, Chicago, IL
Primary Contact: Rick Rasmussen, Chief Executive Officer
CIO: Craig McIntosh, Chief Information Officer
CHR: Gina Schneider, Director Human Resources
CNO: Christi Nance, R.N., MSN, Chief Nursing Officer
Web address: www.northwestspecialtyhospital.com
Control: Corporation, Investor–owned (for–profit) **Service:** Surgical

Staffed Beds: 34

△ **REHABILITATION HOSPITAL OF THE NORTHWEST (133027)**, 3372 East Jenalan Avenue, Zip 83854–7787; tel. 208/262–8700, (Nonreporting) **A**7 **S** Ernest Health, Inc., Albuquerque, NM
Primary Contact: Darby Brockette, Chief Executive Officer
Web address: www.ernesthealth.com
Control: Corporation, Investor–owned (for–profit) **Service:** Rehabilitation

Staffed Beds: 25

PRESTON—Franklin County

★ **FRANKLIN COUNTY MEDICAL CENTER (131322)**, 44 North First East Street, Zip 83263–1399; tel. 208/852–0137, **A**5 10 18 **F**3 8 13 15 29 34 35 39 40 41 45 46 49 50 56 57 59 62 63 64 65 68 76 77 79 81 83 84 85 87 91 92 93 96 100 105 107 110 127 129 130 131 132 133 135 143 144 146 147 148 149 154
Primary Contact: Darin Dransfield, Chief Executive Officer
CFO: Paul Smart, CPA, Chief Financial Officer
CHR: Courtney Dursteler, Chief Human Resources Officer
CNO: Patrica Bowles, R.N., Chief Nursing Officer
Web address: www.fcmc.org
Control: County, Government, nonfederal **Service:** General medical and surgical

Staffed Beds: 20 **Admissions:** 539 **Census:** 8 **Births:** 57

REXBURG—Madison County

★ ⇑ **MADISON MEMORIAL HOSPITAL (130025)**, 450 East Main Street, Zip 83440–2048, Mailing Address: P.O. Box 310, Zip 83440–0310; tel. 208/359–6900, **A**3 5 10 21 **F**3 11 13 28 29 31 34 35 39 40 41 43 45 54 57 59 60 65 68 70 72 75 76 77 78 79 81 82 85 86 87 89 91 93 107 108 111 115 118 119 126 129 130 131 146 147 148 149 157
Primary Contact: Rachel Ann. Gonzales, Chief Executive Officer
COO: Audrey Fletcher, Chief Operating Officer
CFO: Troy Christensen, Chief Financial Officer
CMO: Clay Prince, M.D., Chief Medical Officer
Web address: www.https://madisonmemorial.org/
Control: County, Government, nonfederal **Service:** General medical and surgical

Staffed Beds: 49 **Admissions:** 2599 **Census:** 19 **Outpatient Visits:** 44859 **Births:** 1367 **Total Expense ($000):** 68827 **Payroll Expense ($000):** 24080 **Personnel:** 432

RUPERT—Minidoka County

★ ⇑ **MINIDOKA MEMORIAL HOSPITAL (131319)**, 1224 Eighth Street, Zip 83350–1599; tel. 208/436–0481, (Total facility includes 43 beds in nursing home–type unit) **A**5 10 18 21 **F**3 7 8 11 15 29 30 34 35 37 40 45 50 56 57 59 62 63 64 65 68 70 75 77 79 81 83 84 85 86 87 97 107 108 111 114 119 127 128 130 131 132 133 134 143 146 147 148 149 154 156 157
Primary Contact: Tom Murphy, Chief Executive Officer
CFO: Jason Gibbons, Chief Financial Officer
CMO: Brian Muir, Chief of Staff
CIO: Nick Martin, Chief Information Officer
CHR: Eric Gochnour, SPHR, SHRM-SCP, Manager Human Resources
CNO: Erinn Neilson, Chief Nursing Officer
Web address: www.minidokamemorial.com
Control: County, Government, nonfederal **Service:** General medical and surgical

Staffed Beds: 72 **Admissions:** 580 **Census:** 45 **Outpatient Visits:** 20181 **Births:** 0 **Total Expense ($000):** 25246 **Payroll Expense ($000):** 15043 **Personnel:** 216

⇑ **MINIDOKA MEMORIAL HOSPITAL AND EXTENDED CARE FACILITY** See Minidoka Memorial Hospital

SAINT MARIES—Benewah County

⇑ **BENEWAH COMMUNITY HOSPITAL (131317)**, 229 South Seventh Street, Zip 83861–1803; tel. 208/245–5551, **A**5 10 18 21 **F**13 15 29 31 34 35 40 56 57 59 64 76 79 81 89 90 93 96 97 107 110 111 114 119 127 129 130 131 133 135 146 147 **S** QHR, Brentwood, TN
Primary Contact: Liz Sellers, R.N., MSN, Chief Executive Officer
CFO: Lori Minier, Chief Financial Officer
CMO: William Wheeler, M.D., Chief of Staff
CIO: Joseph Getchius, Director Information Technology
CHR: Marlana Martin, Director Human Resources
CNO: Rhonda Smith, Chief Nursing Officer
Web address: www.bchmed.org
Control: County, Government, nonfederal **Service:** General medical and surgical

Staffed Beds: 19 **Admissions:** 315 **Census:** 5 **Total Expense ($000):** 19194

ID

Hospital, Medicare Provider Number, Address, Telephone, Approval, Facility, and Physician Codes, Health Care System

★ American Hospital Association (AHA) membership   ○ Healthcare Facilities Accreditation Program   ⇑ Center for Improvement in Healthcare Quality Accreditation
☐ The Joint Commission accreditation   ◇ DNV Healthcare Inc. accreditation   △ Commission on Accreditation of Rehabilitation Facilities (CARF) accreditation

SALMON—Lemhi County

★ **STEELE MEMORIAL MEDICAL CENTER (131305)**, 203 South Daisy Street, Zip 83467–4709; tel. 208/756–5600, **A**10 18 **F**3 11 13 15 18 28 29 31 34 35 40 45 55 57 59 64 65 66 68 75 76 77 78 79 81 82 85 86 87 90 93 97 104 107 110 111 115 119 127 131 132 133 135 146 148 **S** QHR, Brentwood, TN
Primary Contact: Jeanine Gentry, Chief Executive Officer
COO: Abner King, Chief Operating Officer
CFO: Jim Peterson, Chief Financial Officer
CMO: Richard Natelson, M.D., Chief of Staff
CHR: Libby Brittain, Director Human Resources
CNO: Stephanie Orr, Chief Nursing Officer
Web address: www.steelemh.org
Control: County, Government, nonfederal **Service**: General medical and surgical

Staffed Beds: 18 **Admissions**: 384 **Census**: 3 **Births**: 43 **Total Expense ($000)**: 26348

SANDPOINT—Bonner County

★ ⇑ **BONNER GENERAL HOSPITAL (131328)**, 520 North Third Avenue, Zip 83864–1507; tel. 208/263–1441, **A**10 18 21 **F**3 11 13 15 17 22 26 28 29 30 34 35 40 43 45 46 47 48 54 57 59 62 63 64 68 75 76 77 79 81 85 86 87 93 102 104 107 108 110 111 114 118 119 127 130 131 132 144 146 148 156
Primary Contact: Sheryl Rickard, Chief Executive Officer
CFO: John Hennessy, Chief Financial Officer
CIO: Jeremy Welser, Director Information Systems
CHR: Brad Waterbury, Director Human Resources
CNO: Misty Robertson, R.N., Chief Nursing Officer
Web address: www.bonnergeneral.org
Control: Other not–for–profit (including NFP Corporation) **Service**: General medical and surgical

Staffed Beds: 25 **Admissions**: 1749 **Census**: 12 **Outpatient Visits**: 69297 **Births**: 283 **Total Expense ($000)**: 56798 **Payroll Expense ($000)**: 24587 **Personnel**: 363

SODA SPRINGS—Caribou County

★ ⇑ **CARIBOU MEMORIAL HOSPITAL AND LIVING CENTER (131309)**, 300 South Third West, Zip 83276–1598; tel. 208/547–3341, **A**5 10 18 21 **F**70 81
Primary Contact: Christina Thomas, R.N., FACHE, Chief Executive Officer
CMO: John K Franson, M.D., Chief Medical Staff
CIO: Johnathan Inskeep, Chief Information Officer
CHR: Michael D Peck, Assistant Administrator
CNO: Brenda Bergholm, MSN, R.N., Chief Nursing Officer
Web address: www.cmhlc.org/
Control: County, Government, nonfederal **Service**: General medical and surgical

Staffed Beds: 18 **Admissions**: 265 **Census**: 3 **Outpatient Visits**: 18054

TWIN FALLS—Twin Falls County

⊠ △ **ST. LUKE'S MAGIC VALLEY MEDICAL CENTER (130002)**, 801 Pole Line Road West, Zip 83301–5810, Mailing Address: P.O. Box 409, Zip 83303–0409; tel. 208/814–1000, **A**1 2 3 5 7 10 **F**3 5 7 8 11 13 15 18 20 22 29 30 31 35 40 51 57 62 63 68 70 72 76 77 78 79 81 85 87 89 90 93 96 98 104 107 110 111 114 119 130 143 146 154 155 **S** St. Luke's Health System, Boise, ID
Primary Contact: Michael A. Fenello, Administrator and West Region Chief Executive Officer
CFO: Joshua Custer, Director Finance
CIO: Melissa Capps, Site Leader Information Technology
CHR: Mark Stevens, Senior Director Human Resources
CNO: Amy Bearden, R.N., MSN, Vice President Patient Care Services and Chief Nursing Officer
Web address: www.stlukesonline.org
Control: Other not–for–profit (including NFP Corporation) **Service**: General medical and surgical

Staffed Beds: 224 **Admissions**: 11985 **Census**: 119 **Outpatient Visits**: 596736 **Births**: 1721 **Total Expense ($000)**: 391024 **Payroll Expense ($000)**: 117324 **Personnel**: 1898

WEISER—Washington County

★ ⇑ **WEISER MEMORIAL HOSPITAL (131307)**, 645 East Fifth Street, Zip 83672–2202; tel. 208/549–0370, **A**5 10 18 21 **F**3 11 13 29 34 35 40 43 45 46 56 57 59 65 68 75 76 79 81 82 85 89 91 97 107 115 119 127 129 130 131 133 135 144 146 147 148 149 154 **S** St. Luke's Health System, Boise, ID
Primary Contact: Steven D. Hale, FACHE, Chief Executive Officer
CFO: Mark Christensen, Chief Financial Officer
CMO: Lore Wooton, M.D., Chief of Medical Staff
CHR: Terri Kautz, Manager Human Resources
Web address: www.weisermemorialhospital.org
Control: Hospital district or authority, Government, nonfederal **Service**: General medical and surgical

Staffed Beds: 18 **Admissions**: 349 **Census**: 3 **Outpatient Visits**: 18926 **Births**: 52 **Total Expense ($000)**: 17873 **Payroll Expense ($000)**: 6384 **Personnel**: 138

ID

ILLINOIS

ALEDO—Mercer County

☒ **GENESIS MEDICAL CENTER-ALEDO (141304)**, 409 NW Ninth Avenue,
Zip 61231–1296; tel. 309/582–9100, **A**1 10 18 **F**3 11 15 28 29 34 40 45 56
57 59 64 75 81 82 87 89 93 94 97 104 107 108 110 115 119 127 128 130
131 133 144 146 149 154 **S** Genesis Health System, Davenport, IA
Primary Contact: Ted Rogalski, Administrator
CFO: Mark G Rogers, Vice President, Finance and Chief Financial Officer
CMO: Julio Santiago, M.D., Chief of Staff
CIO: Robert Frieden, Vice President, Information Services and Chief Information
Officer
CHR: Tammy Hagedorn, Chief Human Resource Officer
CNO: Heidi Hess, Chief Nursing Officer
Web address: www.genesishealth.com
Control: Other not–for–profit (including NFP Corporation) **Service**: General
medical and surgical

Staffed Beds: 22 **Admissions**: 201 **Census**: 3 **Outpatient Visits**: 14440
Births: 0 **Total Expense ($000)**: 16600 **Payroll Expense ($000)**: 6625
Personnel: 48

ALTON—Madison County

☒ **ALTON MEMORIAL HOSPITAL (140002)**, One Memorial Drive, Zip 62002–6722;
tel. 618/463–7311, (Total facility includes 64 beds in nursing home–type unit) **A**1
10 **F**3 6 7 11 13 15 18 20 22 29 30 31 34 35 36 38 39 40 45 46 49 50 51 56
57 59 64 70 74 75 76 77 78 79 81 82 85 86 87 89 92 93 96 98 103 104 107
108 110 111 114 115 116 117 118 119 120 121 123 129 130 131 132 135
146 148 149 154 **S** BJC HealthCare, Saint Louis, MO
Primary Contact: David A. Braasch, President
COO: Brad Goacher, Vice President Administration
CFO: Susan Koesterer, Vice President, Finance
CMO: Sebastian Rueckert, M.D., Vice President and Chief Medical Officer
CIO: Jerry Fox Jr Chief Information Officer
CHR: Bryan Hartwick, Vice President Human Resources
CNO: Debra Turpin, R.N., MSN, Vice President Patient Care Services and Chief
Nursing Officer
Web address: www.altonmemorialhospital.org
Control: Other not–for–profit (including NFP Corporation) **Service**: General
medical and surgical

Staffed Beds: 200 **Admissions**: 7431 **Census**: 120 **Outpatient
Visits**: 157005 **Births**: 769 **Total Expense ($000)**: 144274 **Payroll Expense
($000)**: 52999 **Personnel**: 830

☐ **ALTON MENTAL HEALTH CENTER (144016)**, 4500 College Avenue,
Zip 62002–5099; tel. 618/474–3800, **A**1 10 **F**39 68 75 98 130 143 149 154 **S**
Division of Mental Health, Department of Human Services, Springfield, IL
Primary Contact: Brian E. Thomas, Administrator
CFO: Susan Shobe, Director Administration and Support Services
CMO: Claudia Kachigion, M.D., Medical Director
Control: State, Government, nonfederal **Service**: Psychiatric

Staffed Beds: 115 **Admissions**: 111 **Census**: 103 **Outpatient Visits**: 0
Births: 0 **Total Expense ($000)**: 31870 **Payroll Expense ($000)**: 17064
Personnel: 259

☒ **OSF HEALTHCARE SAINT ANTHONY'S HEALTH CENTER (140052)**, 1 Saint
Anthony's Way, Zip 62002–4579, Mailing Address: P.O. Box 340, Zip 62002–
0340; tel. 618/465–2571, (Includes OSF HEALTHCARE SAINT CLARE'S HOSPITAL,
915 East Fifth Street, Alton, Illinois, Zip 62002–6434; tel. 618/463–5151) **A**1 2
10 **F**3 5 10 11 13 15 18 20 22 29 30 31 34 35 37 38 39 40 41 44 45 47 48
49 50 51 56 57 58 59 60 64 65 68 69 70 74 75 76 77 78 79 81 82 84 85 86
87 91 92 93 95 96 100 101 102 104 107 108 110 111 114 115 116 117 118
119 120 121 123 125 129 130 131 132 134 135 146 147 148 149 154 156
158 **S** OSF Healthcare, Peoria, IL
Primary Contact: Ajay Pathak, President
COO: Sister M. Anselma Belongea, Chief Operating Officer
CFO: Mathew Hanley, Chief Financial Officer
CMO: Dennis Sands, Chief Medical Officer
CIO: Georgia Henke, Operational Account Manager
CHR: Robyn Grissom, Director of Human Resources
CNO: Colleen Becker, Chief Nursing Officer
Web address: www.osfsaintanthonys.org
Control: Church operated, Nongovernment, not–for–profit **Service**: General
medical and surgical

Staffed Beds: 140 **Admissions**: 2926 **Census**: 30 **Outpatient Visits**: 89047
Births: 177 **Total Expense ($000)**: 84682 **Payroll Expense ($000)**: 26845
Personnel: 414

ANNA—Union County

☐ **CHOATE MENTAL HEALTH CENTER (144038)**, 1000 North Main Street,
Zip 62906–1699; tel. 618/833–5161, **A**1 10 **F**34 39 59 65 75 86 98 101
102 103 130 143 149 154 **S** Division of Mental Health, Department of Human
Services, Springfield, IL
Primary Contact: Elaine Ray, Administrator
COO: Elaine Ray, Administrator
CMO: John Larcas, M.D., Acting Medical Director
CIO: Cindy Flamm, Manager Quality
CHR: Tammy Tellor, Acting Director Human Resources
Control: State, Government, nonfederal **Service**: Psychiatric

Staffed Beds: 79 **Admissions**: 65 **Census**: 41 **Outpatient Visits**: 134
Births: 0 **Total Expense ($000)**: 40592 **Payroll Expense ($000)**: 32768

☒ **UNION COUNTY HOSPITAL (141342)**, 517 North Main Street, Zip 62906–1696;
tel. 618/833–4511, (Total facility includes 22 beds in nursing home–type unit)
A1 10 18 **F**3 4 11 15 28 29 34 35 40 45 49 50 57 59 64 68 75 77 81 85 87
93 97 107 110 111 114 119 127 129 130 133 146 148 **S** Quorum Health,
Brentwood, TN
Primary Contact: James R. Farris, FACHE, Chief Executive Officer
CFO: Terry Paligo, Chief Financial Officer
CMO: Christine Lucas, Chief of Staff
CIO: John Hegger, Director Information Systems
CHR: Tammy Davis, Director Human Resources
CNO: Tammy H. Wheaton, Interim Chief Nursing Officer
Web address: www.unioncountyhospital.com
Control: Corporation, Investor–owned (for–profit) **Service**: General medical and
surgical

Staffed Beds: 47 **Admissions**: 584 **Census**: 20 **Outpatient Visits**: 33775
Births: 0 **Total Expense ($000)**: 21257 **Payroll Expense ($000)**: 8899
Personnel: 149

ARLINGTON HEIGHTS—Cook County

☒ **NORTHWEST COMMUNITY HOSPITAL (140252)**, 800 West Central Road,
Zip 60005–2392; tel. 847/618–1000, **A**1 2 10 **F**3 5 8 12 13 15 18 20 22 24 26
28 29 30 31 32 33 34 35 37 38 39 40 41 43 44 45 46 47 48 49 50 53 54 55
56 57 59 61 62 63 64 65 68 70 71 72 73 74 75 76 77 78 79 81 82 85 86 87
89 90 91 92 93 94 96 98 99 100 102 103 104 107 108 110 111 114 115 116
117 118 119 120 121 123 124 126 129 130 131 132 135 144 145 146 147
148 149 152 154 156 157
Primary Contact: Stephen Scogna, President and Chief Executive Officer
COO: Michael Hartke, Executive Vice President, Chief Operating Officer
CFO: Marsha Liu, Executive Vice President and Chief Financial Officer
CIO: Glen Malan, Vice President Information Technology and Chief Information
Officer
CHR: Ann M Patrick, Vice President Human Resources
Web address: www.nch.org
Control: Other not–for–profit (including NFP Corporation) **Service**: General
medical and surgical

Staffed Beds: 395 **Admissions**: 21726 **Census**: 274 **Outpatient
Visits**: 498275 **Births**: 2483 **Total Expense ($000)**: 467701 **Payroll
Expense ($000)**: 196626 **Personnel**: 3392

AURORA—Du Page and Kane Counties County

☒ **AMITA HEALTH MERCY MEDICAL CENTER (140174)**, 1325 North Highland
Avenue, Zip 60506–1449; tel. 630/859–2222, **A**1 2 10 **F**3 5 12 13 15 18 20 22
24 26 28 29 30 31 34 35 36 38 40 43 45 46 49 56 57 59 61 65 68 70 75 76
77 78 79 81 82 85 86 87 89 93 97 98 99 100 101 102 103 104 105 107 111
114 115 119 125 126 130 132 135 144 146 147 153 **S** Ascension Healthcare,
Saint Louis, MO
Primary Contact: Michael L. Brown, Regional President and Chief Executive Officer
COO: Roxann E Barber, Regional Ambulatory Care and Ancillary Services Officer
CFO: Kevin Larkin, Regional Chief Financial Officer
CMO: Anil Gopinath, FACHE, M.D., Regional Chief Medical Officer
CHR: Michael O'Rourke, Regional Human Resource Officer
CNO: Grace McBride, Regional Chief Nursing Officer
Web address: www.presencehealth.org/mercy/
Control: Church operated, Nongovernment, not–for–profit **Service**: General
medical and surgical

Staffed Beds: 292 **Admissions**: 8040 **Census**: 102 **Births**: 195 **Total
Expense ($000)**: 187496 **Payroll Expense ($000)**: 47785 **Personnel**: 750

Hospital, Medicare Provider Number, Address, Telephone, Approval, Facility, and Physician Codes, Health Care System

★ American Hospital Association (AHA) membership ○ Healthcare Facilities Accreditation Program ⇑ Center for Improvement in Healthcare Quality Accreditation
☐ The Joint Commission accreditation ◇ DNV Healthcare Inc. accreditation △ Commission on Accreditation of Rehabilitation Facilities (CARF) accreditation

IL

PROVENA MERCY MEDICAL CENTER See Amita Health Mercy Medical Center

✠ △ **RUSH-COPLEY MEDICAL CENTER (140029)**, 2000 Ogden Avenue, Zip 60504–7222; tel. 630/978–6200, **A**1 2 3 5 7 10 **F**3 7 8 13 15 17 18 19 20 22 24 26 28 29 30 31 32 34 35 36 38 39 40 42 43 44 45 46 47 48 49 50 51 52 53 54 55 57 58 59 60 61 64 65 66 68 70 72 73 74 75 76 78 79 81 82 84 85 86 87 89 90 92 93 94 96 97 107 108 110 111 114 115 117 118 119 120 121 123 124 126 130 131 132 134 135 143 144 145 146 147 148 149 154 **S** Rush University Medical Center, Chicago, IL
Primary Contact: Barry C. Finn, President and Chief Executive Officer
COO: John A Diederich, Senior Vice President Operations and Chief Operating Officer
CFO: Brenda VanWyhe, Senior Vice President Finance and Chief Financial Officer
CMO: Steve B Lowenthal, M.D., M.P.H., FACS, Senior Vice President Medical Affairs and Chief Medical Officer
CIO: Dennis DeMasie, Vice President Information Systems and Chief Information Officer
CNO: Mary Shilkaitis, Vice President Patient Care and Chief Nursing Officer
Web address: www.rushcopley.com
Control: Other not–for–profit (including NFP Corporation) **Service**: General medical and surgical

Staffed Beds: 210 **Admissions**: 11526 **Census**: 134 **Outpatient Visits**: 216853 **Births**: 3110 **Total Expense ($000)**: 294542 **Payroll Expense ($000)**: 122334 **Personnel**: 1721

BARRINGTON—Lake County

★ ⇑ **ADVOCATE GOOD SHEPHERD HOSPITAL (140291)**, 450 West Highway 22, Zip 60010–1919; tel. 847/381–0123, **A**2 10 21 **F**3 11 12 13 15 17 18 20 22 24 26 28 29 30 31 34 35 36 37 40 43 45 46 47 48 49 54 57 59 63 64 65 68 70 74 75 76 77 78 79 81 82 84 87 89 91 92 93 94 97 100 107 108 110 111 114 115 116 117 118 119 120 121 123 124 126 129 130 131 132 135 144 146 154 156 **S** Advocate Aurora Health, Downers Grove, IL
Primary Contact: Karen A. Lambert, President
CFO: George Teufel, Vice President Finance
CMO: Barry Rosen, M.D., Vice President Medical Management
CIO: Chuck Malik, Director Information Systems
CHR: Jason Spigner, Vice President Human Resources
CNO: Marianne D Araujo, R.N., Ph.D., FACHE, Vice President Nursing and Chief Nurse Executive
Web address: www.advocatehealth.com/gshp/
Control: Church operated, Nongovernment, not–for–profit **Service**: General medical and surgical

Staffed Beds: 176 **Admissions**: 9712 **Census**: 104 **Outpatient Visits**: 253961 **Births**: 1150 **Total Expense ($000)**: 255350 **Payroll Expense ($000)**: 77739 **Personnel**: 958

BELLEVILLE—St. Clair County

★ ○ **MEMORIAL HOSPITAL (140185)**, 4500 Memorial Drive, Zip 62226–5399; tel. 618/233–7750, (Total facility includes 76 beds in nursing home–type unit) **A**3 10 11 **F**3 11 13 15 18 20 22 24 26 28 29 30 31 34 40 45 46 47 48 49 51 53 54 57 59 62 64 67 70 74 76 77 79 81 82 84 85 87 91 92 93 94 107 108 110 111 114 115 118 119 126 128 129 130 131 132 145 146 147 148 149 156 **S** BJC HealthCare, Saint Louis, MO
Primary Contact: Mark J. Turner, FACHE, President
COO: Michael T McManus, Chief Operating Officer
CFO: Jane Gusmano, Interim Vice President Finance
CMO: William Casperson, M.D., Vice President Medical Affairs
CIO: Jennifer Meinkoth, Executive Director, IS
CHR: John C Ziegler, FACHE, Vice President Human Resources
CNO: Teresa Halloran, Ph.D., R.N., Vice President Nursing Services
Web address: www.memhosp.com
Control: Other not–for–profit (including NFP Corporation) **Service**: General medical and surgical

Staffed Beds: 304 **Admissions**: 11202 **Census**: 202 **Outpatient Visits**: 183887 **Births**: 549 **Total Expense ($000)**: 240190 **Payroll Expense ($000)**: 106860 **Personnel**: 1915

BENTON—Franklin County

FRANKLIN HOSPITAL DISTRICT (141321), 201 Bailey Lane, Zip 62812–1969; tel. 618/439–3161, **A**10 18 **F**11 15 29 30 34 35 40 45 56 57 59 63 66 68 75 77 81 97 107 115 119 127 130 133
Primary Contact: James Johnson, Chief Executive Officer
COO: Derek Johnson Sr Chief Operating Officer
CFO: Rikki S Bonthron, Chief Financial Officer
CMO: Richard Rethorst, Chief of Medical Staff
CIO: David Williams, Director Information Technology
CNO: Terri Hermann, R.N., Chief Nursing Officer
Web address: www.franklinhospital.net
Control: Hospital district or authority, Government, nonfederal **Service**: General medical and surgical

Staffed Beds: 16 **Admissions**: 402 **Census**: 3 **Outpatient Visits**: 44095 **Births**: 0 **Total Expense ($000)**: 25126 **Payroll Expense ($000)**: 8536 **Personnel**: 172

BERWYN—Cook County

⊞ **MACNEAL HOSPITAL (140054)**, 3249 South Oak Park Avenue, Zip 60402–0715; tel. 708/783–9100, **A**1 2 3 5 8 10 19 **F**3 5 12 13 15 18 19 20 22 24 26 28 29 30 31 34 35 37 38 40 41 43 44 45 46 47 48 49 50 54 56 57 58 59 64 65 68 70 74 75 76 77 78 79 81 82 85 86 87 89 90 91 93 96 97 98 100 101 102 103 104 105 107 108 110 111 114 115 118 119 126 128 130 131 132 144 146 147 148 149 150 152 153 **S** Trinity Health, Livonia, MI
Primary Contact: Mary Elizabeth. Cleary, President
CMO: Charles Bareis, M.D., Medical Director
CIO: Tom Haslett, Interim Chief Information Officer
Web address: www.macneal.com
Control: Other not–for–profit (including NFP Corporation) **Service**: General medical and surgical

Staffed Beds: 358 **Admissions**: 13997 **Census**: 179 **Outpatient Visits**: 220893 **Births**: 1407 **Personnel**: 1514

BLOOMINGTON—Mclean County

⊞ **OSF ST. JOSEPH MEDICAL CENTER (140162)**, 2200 East Washington Street, Zip 61701–4323; tel. 309/662–3311, (Total facility includes 12 beds in nursing home–type unit) **A**1 2 10 **F**3 11 12 13 15 18 20 22 24 26 28 30 31 34 35 37 40 43 45 49 50 51 53 54 57 59 60 61 64 65 68 70 74 75 76 77 78 79 81 82 84 85 86 87 89 92 93 96 97 107 108 110 111 114 115 118 119 126 127 128 129 131 132 135 144 146 147 148 149 150 154 156 157 **S** OSF Healthcare, Peoria, IL
Primary Contact: Lynn Fulton, President
CFO: John R Zell, Chief Financial Officer
CMO: Paul E Pedersen, M.D., Vice President and Chief Medical Officer
CHR: Misti Tompkins, Employee Relations Director
Web address: www.osfstjoseph.org
Control: Church operated, Nongovernment, not–for–profit **Service**: General medical and surgical

Staffed Beds: 149 **Admissions**: 7362 **Census**: 80 **Outpatient Visits**: 165205 **Births**: 722 **Total Expense ($000)**: 152796 **Payroll Expense ($000)**: 47500 **Personnel**: 673

BLUE ISLAND—Cook County

⊞ **METROSOUTH MEDICAL CENTER (140118)**, 12935 South Gregory Street, Zip 60406–2470; tel. 708/597–2000, (Nonreporting) **A**1 10 **S** Quorum Health, Brentwood, TN
Primary Contact: John D. Baird, Chief Executive Officer
CHR: Alanna Barker, Director Human Resources
CNO: Kathleen Hartman, Chief Nursing Officer
Web address: www.metrosouthmedicalcenter.com
Control: Corporation, Investor–owned (for–profit) **Service**: General medical and surgical

Staffed Beds: 285

BOLINGBROOK—Will County

⊞ **ADVENTIST MEDICAL CENTER BOLINGBROOK (140304)**, 500 Remington Boulevard, Zip 60440–4906; tel. 630/312–5000, **A**1 10 **F**3 12 13 15 18 20 22 28 29 30 31 34 35 37 40 41 43 44 45 46 49 50 54 56 57 59 61 64 70 73 74 76 78 79 81 82 85 86 87 98 100 101 102 103 107 108 110 111 114 115 119 130 132 146 147 149 154 **S** AdventHealth, Altamonte Springs, FL
Primary Contact: Bruce C. Christian, Chief Executive Officer
COO: Richard Roehr, Chief Operating Officer
CFO: Rebecca Mathis, Chief Financial Officer
CMO: Richard Carroll, M.D., Chief Medical officer
CIO: John McLendon, Senior Vice President and Chief Information Officer
CHR: Katie Baio, Human Resource Director
CNO: Obed Cruz, Vice President and Chief Nursing Officer
Web address: www.keepingyouwell.com/abh/
Control: Church operated, Nongovernment, not–for–profit **Service**: General medical and surgical

Staffed Beds: 134 **Admissions**: 6247 **Census**: 72 **Outpatient Visits**: 103014 **Births**: 871 **Total Expense ($000)**: 130911 **Payroll Expense ($000)**: 39534 **Personnel**: 556

BREESE—Clinton County

⊞ **HSHS ST. JOSEPH'S HOSPITAL (140145)**, 9515 Holy Cross Lane, Zip 62230–3618, Mailing Address: P.O. Box 99, Zip 62230–0099; tel. 618/526–4511, (Nonreporting) **A**1 10 **S** HSHS Hospital Sisters Health System, Springfield, IL
Primary Contact: Chris Klay, President and Chief Executive Officer
CFO: John Jeffries, Director Finance
CHR: Jason T Snow, Director Human Resources
Web address: www.stjoebreese.com
Control: Church operated **Service**: General medical and surgical

Staffed Beds: 65

Many Facility Codes have changed. Please refer to the AHA Guide Code Chart. © 2019 AHA Guide

IL

CANTON—Fulton County

☒ **GRAHAM HOSPITAL ASSOCIATION (140001)**, 210 West Walnut Street, Zip 61520–2497; tel. 309/647–5240, (Total facility includes 38 beds in nursing home–type unit) **A**1 3 10 20 **F**3 11 13 15 26 28 29 30 33 40 45 50 53 54 57 59 64 65 67 70 75 76 79 81 82 85 87 89 91 97 107 108 110 111 115 119 124 127 128 129 130 131 132 135 143 144 145 146
Primary Contact: Robert G. Senneff, FACHE, President and Chief Executive Officer
CFO: Eric Franz, Vice President, Finance and Chief Financial Officer
CIO: Jim Schreiner, Chief Information Officer
CHR: Canise A McComb, Director Human Resources
CNO: Teresa L McConkey, MSN, R.N., Vice President of Nursing and Chief Nursing Officer
Web address: www.grahamhealthsystem.org
Control: Other not–for–profit (including NFP Corporation) **Service**: General medical and surgical

> **Staffed Beds**: 87 **Admissions**: 2371 **Census**: 46 **Outpatient Visits**: 249717 **Births**: 246 **Total Expense ($000)**: 85264 **Payroll Expense ($000)**: 31185 **Personnel**: 625

CARBONDALE—Jackson County

☒ **MEMORIAL HOSPITAL OF CARBONDALE (140164)**, 405 West Jackson Street, Zip 62901–1467, Mailing Address: P.O. Box 10000, Zip 62902–9000; tel. 618/549–0721, **A**1 2 3 5 10 13 19 **F**3 11 13 17 18 20 22 24 26 28 29 30 31 34 35 40 45 46 47 48 49 54 56 57 59 64 68 70 72 74 75 76 77 78 79 81 82 83 84 85 86 87 89 100 101 102 104 107 108 111 112 114 115 116 117 118 119 120 121 124 126 130 131 132 135 145 146 147 148 149 154 156 **S** Southern Illinois Healthcare, Carbondale, IL
Primary Contact: Al Taylor, Vice President and Administrator
CFO: Michael Kasser, Vice President Chief Financial Officer and Treasurer
CMO: Marci Moore-Connelly, M.D., Vice President Chief Medical Officer
CIO: David Holland, Vice President Chief Innovation Officer
CHR: Pamela S Henderson, Vice President Human Resources
Web address: www.sih.net
Control: Other not–for–profit (including NFP Corporation) **Service**: General medical and surgical

> **Staffed Beds**: 167 **Admissions**: 11049 **Census**: 102 **Outpatient Visits**: 125220 **Births**: 1845 **Total Expense ($000)**: 288512 **Payroll Expense ($000)**: 67610 **Personnel**: 1133

CARLINVILLE—Macoupin County

★ ○ **CARLINVILLE AREA HOSPITAL (141347)**, 20733 North Broad Street, Zip 62626–1499, tel. 217/854–3141, **A**3 10 11 18 **F**11 15 28 29 34 35 40 45 64 77 79 81 91 93 107 110 115 127 129 133 148 149 150 154 **S** HealthTech Management Services, Brentwood, TN
Primary Contact: Kenneth G. Reid, President and Chief Executive Officer
CFO: Mike Brown, Chief Financial Officer
CMO: Therese Polo, Medical Staff President
CIO: Jerod Cottingham, Director Information Systems
CHR: Tracy Koster, Director Human Resources
CNO: Sara McPeak, Chief Nursing Officer
Web address: www.cahcare.com
Control: Other not–for–profit (including NFP Corporation) **Service**: General medical and surgical

> **Staffed Beds**: 25 **Admissions**: 579 **Census**: 7 **Outpatient Visits**: 25498 **Births**: 0 **Total Expense ($000)**: 25175 **Payroll Expense ($000)**: 10001 **Personnel**: 196

CARROLLTON—Greene County

THOMAS H. BOYD MEMORIAL HOSPITAL (141300), 800 School Street, Zip 62016–1498; tel. 217/942–6946, (Nonreporting) **A**10 18
Primary Contact: Deborah Campbell, Administrator
CHR: Lisa Eldridge, Human Resources Officer
Control: Other not–for–profit (including NFP Corporation) **Service**: General medical and surgical

> **Staffed Beds**: 65

CARTHAGE—Hancock County

☐ **MEMORIAL HOSPITAL (141305)**, 1454 North County Road 2050, Zip 62321–3551, Mailing Address: P.O. Box 160, Zip 62321–0160; tel. 217/357–8500, **A**1 10 18 **F**3 13 15 28 29 30 31 34 35 40 45 57 59 68 76 80 81 82 85 87 107 108 110 115 119 127 129 130 132 133 146 147 156 **S** QHR, Brentwood, TN
Primary Contact: Ada Bair, Chief Executive Officer
COO: Florine Dixon, Chief Operating Officer
CFO: Teresa Smith, Chief Financial Officer
CIO: Syndi Horn, Director Information Systems
CHR: Dan Smith, Director Human Resources
Web address: www.mhtlc.org
Control: Other not–for–profit (including NFP Corporation) **Service**: General medical and surgical

> **Staffed Beds**: 18 **Admissions**: 603 **Census**: 6 **Outpatient Visits**: 5176 **Births**: 107 **Total Expense ($000)**: 28928 **Payroll Expense ($000)**: 12027 **Personnel**: 205

CENTRALIA—Marion County

☒ **SSM HEALTH ST. MARY'S HOSPITAL CENTRALIA (140034)**, 400 North Pleasant Avenue, Zip 62801–3056; tel. 618/436–8000, **A**1 2 10 **F**3 5 11 12 13 15 18 20 26 28 29 30 31 32 34 35 37 38 40 44 45 46 50 51 54 56 57 59 60 61 64 68 70 73 74 75 76 77 78 79 80 81 82 84 85 86 87 89 90 91 92 93 94 98 99 100 101 102 103 104 105 107 108 110 111 114 118 119 120 121 123 127 129 130 131 132 135 144 146 147 148 149 152 153 156 157 **S** SSM Health, Saint Louis, MO
Primary Contact: Damon R. Harbison, President
COO: Mark A Clark, Vice President Operations
CFO: Deland Evischi, Chief Financial Officer
CMO: Rajendra Shroff, M.D., Administrative Medical Director
CIO: Steve Murphy, Director Information Systems
CHR: Brenda Alexander, System Vice President, Human Resources
CNO: Sherry Dunlay, R.N., MSN, Vice President Patient Care Services and Chief Nursing Officer
Web address: www.https://www.ssmhealth.com/locations/st-marys-hospital-centralia
Control: Church operated, Nongovernment, not–for–profit **Service**: General medical and surgical

> **Staffed Beds**: 124 **Admissions**: 5137 **Census**: 57 **Outpatient Visits**: 200797 **Births**: 295 **Total Expense ($000)**: 95668 **Payroll Expense ($000)**: 33609 **Personnel**: 653

CENTREVILLE—St. Clair County

☐ **TOUCHETTE REGIONAL HOSPITAL (140077)**, 5900 Bond Avenue, Zip 62207–2326; tel. 618/332–3060, **A**1 5 10 **F**3 11 13 15 18 29 30 39 40 45 47 50 54 55 62 64 68 70 75 76 79 81 85 87 92 98 101 102 104 105 107 108 110 114 119 129 130 135 143 146 148 149 150 153 156
Primary Contact: Larry W. McCulley, President and Chief Executive Officer
COO: Tom Mikkelson, M.D., Interim Chief Operating Officer
CFO: John Majchrzak, Chief Financial Officer
CMO: Tom Mikkelson, M.D., Vice President Medical Affairs
Web address: www.touchette.org
Control: Other not–for–profit (including NFP Corporation) **Service**: General medical and surgical

> **Staffed Beds**: 119 **Admissions**: 2534 **Census**: 27 **Outpatient Visits**: 52510 **Births**: 34 **Total Expense ($000)**: 58648 **Payroll Expense ($000)**: 25160 **Personnel**: 442

CHAMPAIGN—Champaign County

☐ **THE PAVILION (144029)**, 809 West Church Street, Zip 61820–3399; tel. 217/373–1700, **A**1 10 **F**98 99 101 102 105 106 152 **S** Universal Health Services, Inc., King of Prussia, PA
Primary Contact: Mark Littrell, Group Director
CFO: Edith Frasca, Controller and Chief Financial Officer
Web address: www.pavilionhospital.com
Control: Corporation, Investor–owned (for–profit) **Service**: Psychiatric

> **Staffed Beds**: 106 **Admissions**: 2766 **Census**: 97 **Outpatient Visits**: 8436 **Births**: 0 **Total Expense ($000)**: 19137 **Payroll Expense ($000)**: 9678 **Personnel**: 132

IL

CHESTER—Randolph County

☐ **CHESTER MENTAL HEALTH CENTER**, Chester Road, Zip 62233–0031, Mailing Address: Box 31, Zip 62233–0031; tel. 618/826–4571, **A**1 **F**39 65 75 97 98 100 101 102 130 132 135 143 149 154 156 **S** Division of Mental Health, Department of Human Services, Springfield, IL
Primary Contact: Leah Hammel, Acting Administrator
CFO: Sarah Imhoff, Business Administrator
CMO: Maitra Rupa, M.D., Acting Medical Director
CIO: Anthony Young, Information Services Specialist
CHR: Kim Holsapple, Human Resource Specialist
CNO: Jennifer Klingeman, Director of Nursing
Control: State, Government, nonfederal **Service**: Psychiatric

Staffed Beds: 271 Admissions: 180 Census: 5 Outpatient Visits: 0 Births: 0

☐ **MEMORIAL HOSPITAL (141338)**, 1900 State Street, Zip 62233–1116, Mailing Address: P.O. Box 609, Zip 62233–0609; tel. 618/826–4581, (Nonreporting) **A**1 10 18
Primary Contact: Brett Bollmann, Administrator
CFO: Gail Miesner, Chief Financial Officer
CMO: Alan Liefer, M.D., President Medical Staff
CIO: Becky Bunselmeyer, Director Information Services
CHR: May Rose, Director Human Resources
Web address: www.mhchester.com
Control: Hospital district or authority, Government, nonfederal **Service**: General medical and surgical

Staffed Beds: 25

CHICAGO—Cook County

ADVOCATE BETHANY HOSPITAL See Rml Specialty Hospital

★ ⇧ **ADVOCATE ILLINOIS MASONIC MEDICAL CENTER (140182)**, 836 West Wellington Avenue, Zip 60657–5147; tel. 773/975–1600, **A**2 3 5 8 10 21 **F**3 5 12 13 15 17 18 19 20 22 24 26 28 29 30 31 34 35 37 38 40 43 44 45 46 47 48 49 50 53 54 55 56 57 58 59 60 61 64 66 68 70 71 72 73 74 75 76 77 78 79 81 82 84 85 86 87 89 90 92 93 96 97 98 100 101 102 104 107 110 111 115 117 118 119 120 121 123 124 126 129 130 131 132 134 135 141 143 146 147 148 149 153 154 **S** Advocate Aurora Health, Downers Grove, IL
Primary Contact: Susan Nordstrom. Lopez, President
CFO: Jack Gilbert, Vice President Finance and Facilities
CMO: Clifton Clarke, Vice President Medical Management
CIO: Chuck Malik, Director Information Systems
CHR: Katie Bata, Vice President Human Resources
CNO: Donna King, R.N., FACHE, Vice President Clinical Operations and Chief Nursing Executive
Web address: www.advocatehealth.com/masonic
Control: Other not–for–profit (including NFP Corporation) **Service**: General medical and surgical

Staffed Beds: 335 Admissions: 13256 Census: 170 Outpatient Visits: 215463 Births: 1909 Total Expense ($000): 382058 Payroll Expense ($000): 142751 Personnel: 2079

★ ⇧ **ADVOCATE TRINITY HOSPITAL (140048)**, 2320 East 93rd Street, Zip 60617–3909; tel. 773/967–2000, **A**10 21 **F**3 13 15 18 20 22 24 26 28 29 30 31 34 35 40 45 49 50 55 56 57 58 59 60 61 64 65 68 70 74 75 76 77 78 79 81 82 87 89 92 93 107 110 111 114 115 119 126 130 132 135 146 148 154 **S** Advocate Aurora Health, Downers Grove, IL
Primary Contact: Rashard Johnson, President
COO: Dan Doherty, Vice President, Operations
CFO: Maureen Morrison, Vice President, Finance
CMO: James Keller, M.D., Vice President, Medical Management
CIO: Bonita Brown-Roberts, Director Information Systems
CHR: Kristin Landini, Vice President, Human Resources
CNO: Jacquelyn Whitten, MSN, R.N., Chief Nursing Executive, Vice President of Nursing
Web address: www.https://www.advocatehealth.com/trin/
Control: Church operated, Nongovernment, not–for–profit **Service**: General medical and surgical

Staffed Beds: 174 Admissions: 7347 Census: 79 Outpatient Visits: 72827 Births: 684 Total Expense ($000): 153411 Payroll Expense ($000): 53075 Personnel: 780

⊠ △ **AMITA HEALTH RESURRECTION MEDICAL CENTER (140117)**, 7435 West Talcott Avenue, Zip 60631–3746; tel. 773/774–8000, **A**1 2 3 5 7 10 13 **F**3 11 13 15 17 18 19 20 22 24 26 28 29 30 31 34 35 37 38 39 40 41 45 46 47 49 50 53 57 58 59 60 62 64 66 68 70 73 74 75 76 78 79 81 82 83 84 85 86 87 89 90 93 96 97 100 107 108 110 111 113 114 115 117 118 119 120 121 123 124 126 130 131 132 133 135 146 147 148 154 **S** Ascension Healthcare, Saint Louis, MO
Primary Contact: Robert Dahl, President and Chief Executive Officer
CFO: Colleen Koppenhaver, Interim Chief Financial Officer
CMO: David Bordo, M.D., Chief Medical Officer
CHR: Ivy McKinley, Regional Lead Human Resources
CNO: Pam Bell, Vice President Patient Care Services and Chief Nursing Officer
Web address: www.presencehealth.org
Control: Church operated, Nongovernment, not–for–profit **Service**: General medical and surgical

Staffed Beds: 337 Admissions: 12432 Census: 173 Outpatient Visits: 129460 Births: 963 Total Expense ($000): 262813 Payroll Expense ($000): 86953 Personnel: 1362

⊠ **AMITA HEALTH SAINT JOSEPH HOSPITAL (140224)**, 2900 North Lake Shore Drive, Zip 60657–6274; tel. 773/665–3000, **A**1 2 3 5 10 **F**3 5 7 11 12 13 15 18 19 20 22 24 25 26 28 29 30 31 32 33 34 35 36 38 39 40 41 45 46 47 48 49 50 53 54 55 56 57 58 59 60 61 63 64 65 66 68 70 72 74 75 76 77 78 79 81 82 84 85 86 87 89 90 92 93 96 97 98 101 102 103 104 107 108 110 111 114 115 117 118 119 120 121 122 123 124 126 128 129 130 131 132 135 143 145 146 147 148 151 152 154 156 **S** Ascension Healthcare, Saint Louis, MO
Primary Contact: James L. Robinson III, President
CFO: Stanley Kazmierczak, Controller
CMO: M Todd Grendon, M.D., President Medical Staff
CIO: George Chessum, Senior Vice President Information Systems and Chief Information Officer
CHR: Denise Brown, Vice President Human Resources
Web address: www.reshealth.org
Control: Church operated, Nongovernment, not–for–profit **Service**: General medical and surgical

Staffed Beds: 361 Admissions: 10891 Census: 153 Outpatient Visits: 77196 Births: 1039 Total Expense ($000): 225806 Payroll Expense ($000): 73163 Personnel: 1152

⊠ **AMITA HEALTH SAINTS MARY & ELIZABETH MEDICAL CENTER (140180)**, 2233 West Division Street, Zip 60622–3086; tel. 312/770–2000, (Includes PRESENCE SAINTS MARY & ELIZABETH MEDICAL CENTER, CLAREMONT AVENUE, 1431 North Claremont Avenue, Chicago, Illinois, Zip 60622–1791; tel. 773/278–2000; Martin H. Judd, Regional President and Chief Executive Officer) **A**1 2 3 5 10 **F**2 3 4 13 15 18 19 20 22 24 26 28 29 30 31 32 34 35 36 38 40 45 46 47 49 50 52 57 58 59 60 61 63 64 66 68 70 74 75 76 77 78 79 81 82 84 85 86 87 89 90 91 92 93 94 96 98 99 100 101 102 103 107 108 110 111 114 115 116 117 119 120 121 123 126 128 129 130 132 135 143 146 147 148 149 151 154 **S** Ascension Healthcare, Saint Louis, MO
Primary Contact: Martin H. Judd, Regional President and Chief Executive Officer
CFO: Bob Cech, Regional Finance Officer
CMO: Laura Concannon, M.D., Regional Chief Medical Officer
CIO: Cheryl Rodenfels, System Vice President, IT Operations
CHR: Melanie Saenz, Regional Human Resources Officer
CNO: Suzanne Lambert, R.N., Regional Chief Nursing Officer and Support Services
Web address: www.presencehealth.org/presence-saints-mary-and-elizabeth-medical-center-chicago
Control: Church operated, Nongovernment, not–for–profit **Service**: General medical and surgical

Staffed Beds: 495 Admissions: 18433 Census: 280 Outpatient Visits: 166929 Births: 1109 Total Expense ($000): 321122 Payroll Expense ($000): 99141 Personnel: 1515

⊠ **ANN & ROBERT H. LURIE CHILDREN'S HOSPITAL OF CHICAGO (143300)**, 225 East Chicago Avenue, Zip 60611–2991; tel. 312/227–4000, **A**1 3 5 8 10 **F**3 8 9 11 12 17 18 19 20 21 22 23 24 25 26 27 28 29 30 31 32 34 35 36 37 38 39 40 41 43 44 45 46 48 49 50 51 52 54 55 57 58 59 60 61 63 64 65 68 72 74 75 78 79 81 82 84 85 86 87 88 89 91 92 93 94 96 97 98 99 100 101 102 104 105 107 108 111 115 116 117 119 124 126 129 130 131 132 134 136 137 138 139 141 142 144 146 148 149 150 154
Primary Contact: Patrick M. Magoon, President and Chief Executive Officer
COO: Michelle Stephenson, R.N., Executive Vice President & Chief Operations Officer
CFO: Ron Blaustein, Chief Financial Officer
CMO: Michael Kelleher, Chief Medical Officer
CIO: Lisa Dykstra, Senior Vice President and Chief Information Officer
CHR: Joani Duncan, Chief Human Resource Officer
CNO: Brian M Stahulak, R.N., Chief Nursing Officer
Web address: www.luriechildrens.org
Control: Other not–for–profit (including NFP Corporation) **Service**: Children's general medical and surgical

Staffed Beds: 312 Admissions: 10423 Census: 229 Outpatient Visits: 655368 Births: 0 Total Expense ($000): 825580 Payroll Expense ($000): 355045 Personnel: 6006

IL

Many Facility Codes have changed. Please refer to the AHA Guide Code Chart. © 2019 AHA Guide

BERNARD MITCHELL HOSPITAL See University of Chicago Medical Center, Chicago

☐ **CHICAGO LAKESHORE HOSPITAL (144005)**, 4840 North Marine Drive, Zip 60640–4296; tel. 773/878–9700, **A**1 3 5 10 **F**4 98 99 100 101 102 103 104 105 143 153 154 **S** Signature Healthcare Services, Corona, CA
Primary Contact: David Fletcher–Janzen, Chief Executive Officer
CFO: Carol Peart, Chief Financial Officer
CMO: Peter Nierman, M.D., Chief Medical Officer
CHR: Michelle Culpepper, Director Human Resources
Web address: www.chicagolakeshorehospital.com
Control: Corporation, Investor–owned (for–profit) **Service:** Psychiatric

Staffed Beds: 161 **Admissions:** 4427 **Census:** 100 **Outpatient Visits:** 6844
Births: 0 **Total Expense ($000):** 37901 **Payroll Expense ($000):** 16552
Personnel: 251

CHICAGO LYING-IN (CLI) See University of Chicago Medical Center, Chicago

☐ **CHICAGO-READ MENTAL HEALTH CENTER (144010)**, 4200 North Oak Park Avenue, Zip 60634–1457; tel. 773/794–4000, (Nonreporting) **A**1 10 **S** Division of Mental Health, Department of Human Services, Springfield, IL
Primary Contact: Ellen Otomo, Interim Hospital Administrator
Control: State, Government, nonfederal **Service:** Psychiatric

Staffed Beds: 200

CHILDREN'S MEMORIAL HOSPITAL See Ann & Robert H. Lurie Children's Hospital of Chicago

COMER CHILDREN'S HOSPITAL See University of Chicago Medical Center, Chicago

☐ **COMMUNITY FIRST MEDICAL CENTER (140251)**, 5645 West Addison Street, Zip 60634–4403; tel. 773/282–7000, (Nonreporting) **A**1 3 10
Primary Contact: Sheila Senn, PsyD, Chief Clinical and Administrative Officer
COO: Dennis FitzMaurice, Vice President, Professional Services
CFO: Richard Franco, Chief Financial Officer
CMO: David Bordo, M.D., Vice President and Chief Medical Officer
CIO: George Chessum, Senior Vice President and Chief Information Officer
CHR: Ivy McKinley, Regional Human Resources Officer
Web address: www.cfmedicalcenter.com
Control: Church operated, Nongovernment, not–for–profit **Service:** General medical and surgical

Staffed Beds: 279

☐ **GARFIELD PARK HOSPITAL (144039)**, 520 North Ridgeway Avenue, Zip 60624–1232; tel. 773/265–3700, **A**1 10 **F**98 99 101 102 104 105 130 132 135 153 154 **S** Universal Health Services, Inc., King of Prussia, PA
Primary Contact: Steven Airhart, Chief Executive Officer
CMO: Tina Mohera, M.D., Chief Medical Officer
CHR: Janice Clark, Manager Human Resources
Web address: www.garfieldparkhospital.com
Control: Corporation, Investor–owned (for–profit) **Service:** Children's hospital psychiatric

Staffed Beds: 88 **Admissions:** 1125 **Census:** 40 **Outpatient Visits:** 0
Births: 0 **Total Expense ($000):** 12220 **Payroll Expense ($000):** 6668

☐ **HARTGROVE HOSPITAL (144026)**, 5730 West Roosevelt Road, Zip 60644–1580; tel. 773/413–1700, (Nonreporting) **A**1 3 10 **S** Universal Health Services, Inc., King of Prussia, PA
Primary Contact: Steven Airhart, Chief Executive Officer
CFO: Srbo Nikolic, Chief Financial Officer
CMO: Johnny Williamson, M.D., Chief Medical Officer
CHR: Anthony Rivera, Director Human Resources
CNO: Jody Bhambra, Chief Nursing Officer
Web address: www.hartgrovehospital.com
Control: Corporation, Investor–owned (for–profit) **Service:** Psychiatric

Staffed Beds: 128

★ ○ **HOLY CROSS HOSPITAL (140133)**, 2701 West 68th Street, Zip 60629–1882; tel. 773/884–9000, **A**3 10 11 **F**3 9 11 13 15 17 18 20 22 24 26 29 30 34 35 38 40 44 45 46 49 50 56 57 59 64 66 68 70 74 75 76 78 79 81 85 86 87 93 97 98 100 101 102 104 107 108 110 111 114 115 118 119 121 123 130 132 134 148 153 154 **S** Sinai Health System, Chicago, IL
Primary Contact: Lori Pacura, MSN, R.N., President
COO: Donnica Austin, Vice President, Operations
CFO: Charles Weis, Executive Vice President and Chief Financial Officer
CMO: James Richardson, Chief Medical Officer
CHR: Ann Hatches, Director, Human Resources
CNO: Deborah Davisson, MSN, Chief Nursing Officer and Vice President, Patient Care Services
Web address: www.holycrosshospital.org
Control: Other not–for–profit (including NFP Corporation) **Service:** General medical and surgical

Staffed Beds: 209 **Admissions:** 8843 **Census:** 112 **Outpatient Visits:** 72863 **Births:** 248 **Total Expense ($000):** 127203 **Payroll Expense ($000):** 58804 **Personnel:** 747

☐ **JACKSON PARK HOSPITAL AND MEDICAL CENTER (140177)**, 7531 Stony Island Avenue, Zip 60649–3993; tel. 773/947–7500, (Nonreporting) **A**1 3 10
Primary Contact: William Dorsey, M.D., Board Chairman and Chief Executive Officer
COO: Randall Smith, Executive Vice President
CFO: Nelson Vasquez, Vice President Finance
CMO: Bangalore Murthy, M.D., Director Medical Staff
CIO: Thomas Pankow, Chief Information Officer
CHR: Tracey Jones, Director Human Resources
Web address: www.jacksonparkhospital.org
Control: Other not–for–profit (including NFP Corporation) **Service:** General medical and surgical

Staffed Beds: 118

⊞ △ **JESSE BROWN VETERANS AFFAIRS MEDICAL CENTER**, 820 South Damen, Zip 60612–3776; tel. 312/569–8387, (Nonreporting) **A**1 3 5 7 8 **S** Department of Veterans Affairs, Washington, DC
Primary Contact: Marc Magill, MS, Medical Center Director
COO: Michelle Blakely, FACHE, Ph.D., Associate Director
CFO: Kalpana Mehta, Chief Fiscal Services
CMO: Wendy W Brown, M.D., M.P.H., Chief of Staff
CIO: Howard Loewenstein, Chief Information Resource Management Services
CHR: Wayne Davis, Manager Human Resources
Web address: www.chicago.va.gov/
Control: Veterans Affairs, Government, federal **Service:** General medical and surgical

Staffed Beds: 207

⊞ **JOHN H. STROGER JR. HOSPITAL OF COOK COUNTY (140124)**, 1969 West Ogden Avenue, Zip 60612–3714; tel. 312/864–6000, **A**1 2 3 5 8 10 13 **F**3 5 11 13 15 16 17 18 19 20 22 24 29 30 31 34 35 36 38 39 40 41 43 44 45 46 47 48 49 50 51 52 54 55 56 57 58 59 60 61 64 65 68 70 72 74 75 76 77 78 79 81 82 84 85 86 87 88 89 91 92 93 94 97 99 100 101 102 103 104 107 108 110 111 114 115 118 119 120 121 122 123 129 130 132 134 135 143 146 147 148 149 154 156 **S** Cook County Health and Hospitals System, Chicago, IL
Primary Contact: John Jay. Shannon, M.D., Chief Executive Officer
CFO: John R Morales, Chief Financial Officer
CMO: Claudia Fegan, M.D., Chief Medical Officer
CIO: Bala Hota, Interim Chief Information Officer
CHR: Paris I Partee, Associate Administrator and Director Human Resources
CNO: Antoinette Williams, Chief Nursing Officer
Web address: www.cookcountyhealth.net
Control: County, Government, nonfederal **Service:** General medical and surgical

Staffed Beds: 450 **Admissions:** 16876 **Census:** 235 **Outpatient Visits:** 893283 **Births:** 952 **Total Expense ($000):** 858859 **Payroll Expense ($000):** 457037 **Personnel:** 6108

IL

JOHNSTON R. BOWMAN HEALTH CENTER See Rush University Medical Center, Chicago

KINDRED CHICAGO LAKESHORE See Kindred Chicago-Central Hospital, Chicago

⊞ **KINDRED CHICAGO-CENTRAL HOSPITAL (142009)**, 4058 West Melrose Street, Zip 60641–4797; tel. 773/736–7000, (Includes KINDRED CHICAGO LAKESHORE, 6130 North Sheridan Road, Chicago, Illinois, Zip 60660; tel. 773/381–1222; Diane Otteman, Chief Executive Officer; KINDRED HOSPITAL CHICAGO NORTH, 2544 West Montrose Avenue, Chicago, Illinois, Zip 60618–1589; tel. 773/267–2622; Larry Foster, R.N., MSN, Chief Executive Officer), (Non-reporting) **A**1 10 **S** Kindred Healthcare, Louisville, KY
Primary Contact: , R.N., MSN
COO: Joanne Garcia, Chief Operating Officer
CFO: Mary Treacy Shiff, Chief Financial Officer
Web address: www.khchicagocentral.com
Control: Corporation, Investor–owned (for–profit) **Service**: Acute long–term care hospital

Staffed Beds: 187

KINDRED HOSPITAL CHICAGO NORTH See Kindred Chicago-Central Hospital, Chicago

⊞ **LA RABIDA CHILDREN'S HOSPITAL (143301)**, 6501 South Promontory Drive, Zip 60649–1003; tel. 773/363–6700, **A**1 3 5 10 **F**3 29 32 34 35 38 41 50 57 59 64 65 74 75 79 82 84 85 86 87 89 91 93 94 96 97 99 100 101 104 119 130 132 134 143 144 146 148 149 156
Primary Contact: Brenda J. Wolf, President and Chief Executive Officer
CFO: Mark Renfree, Chief Financial Officer
CMO: David Soglin, Chief Medical Officer
CIO: Sheelah Cabrera, Chief Information Officer
CHR: Frances Lefkow, Director Human Resources
CNO: Aden Henry, R.N., Vice President, Patient Care
Web address: www.larabida.org
Control: Other not–for–profit (including NFP Corporation) **Service**: Children's chronic disease

Staffed Beds: 30 **Admissions:** 356 **Census:** 26 **Outpatient Visits:** 33387 **Births:** 0 **Total Expense ($000):** 61958 **Payroll Expense ($000):** 30066 **Personnel:** 448

LORETTO HOSPITAL (140083), 645 South Central Avenue, Zip 60644–5059; tel. 773/626–4300, **A**10 **F**3 4 5 15 18 20 29 30 31 34 35 39 40 41 43 45 46 50 57 58 59 60 61 64 68 70 74 75 78 79 81 82 85 86 87 91 92 93 97 98 102 103 104 107 108 110 111 115 119 130 132 135 143 144 145 146 147 148 149 153 154 156 157
Primary Contact: George Miller, President and Chief Executive Officer
CFO: Kenneth Mcghee, Vice President and Chief Financial Officer
CMO: Sonia Mehta, M.D., Chief Medical Officer
CIO: Syed Haque, Vice President and Chief Information Officer
CHR: Tania A White, Director Human Resources
Web address: www.lorettohospital.org
Control: Other not–for–profit (including NFP Corporation) **Service**: General medical and surgical

Staffed Beds: 177 **Admissions:** 3809 **Census:** 58 **Outpatient Visits:** 21467 **Births:** 0 **Total Expense ($000):** 68896 **Payroll Expense ($000):** 30643 **Personnel:** 525

⊞ **LOUIS A. WEISS MEMORIAL HOSPITAL (140082)**, 4646 North Marine Drive, Zip 60640–5759; tel. 773/878–8700, **A**1 2 3 5 10 **F**1 3 4 8 15 16 17 18 20 28 29 30 31 34 35 36 37 40 44 45 49 56 57 58 59 61 64 65 66 67 68 70 72 73 74 75 76 77 78 79 80 81 82 85 86 87 88 89 90 91 92 93 96 97 98 100 101 102 103 107 108 109 110 111 114 115 119 121 128 129 130 131 132 135 141 143 146 147 148 149 154 157
Primary Contact: Mary Shehan, R.N., MSN, Chief Executive Officer
CFO: Jeffrey L Meigs, Chief Financial Officer
CIO: Thomas Crawford, Chicago Market Chief Information Officer
CHR: Keoni Nader, Director Human Resources
Web address: www.weisshospital.com
Control: Corporation, Investor–owned (for–profit) **Service**: General medical and surgical

Staffed Beds: 152 **Admissions:** 5202 **Census:** 80 **Outpatient Visits:** 62713 **Births:** 0 **Total Expense ($000):** 111511 **Payroll Expense ($000):** 46451 **Personnel:** 719

★ ○ **MERCY HOSPITAL AND MEDICAL CENTER (140158)**, 2525 South Michigan Avenue, Zip 60616–2333; tel. 312/567–2000, **A**2 3 5 10 11 **F**3 5 12 13 15 17 18 20 22 24 26 28 29 30 31 34 35 40 44 45 46 49 50 54 55 56 57 58 59 61 64 65 66 68 70 74 75 76 77 78 79 81 82 84 85 86 87 90 91 92 93 96 97 98 99 100 101 102 103 104 107 108 110 111 114 115 117 118 119 120 121 123 124 126 129 130 131 132 134 135 143 144 145 146 147 148 149 150 153 154 156 **S** Trinity Health, Livonia, MI
Primary Contact: Carol L. Schneider, President and Chief Executive Officer
COO: Richard Cerceo, Executive Vice President and Chief Operating Officer
CFO: Eric Krueger, Chief Financial Officer
CMO: Michael McDonnell, M.D., Chief Medical Officer
CIO: John Romeo, Chief Information Officer
CHR: Nancy L Hill-Davis, Vice President Human Resources
Web address: www.mercy-chicago.org
Control: Other not–for–profit (including NFP Corporation) **Service**: General medical and surgical

Staffed Beds: 402 **Admissions:** 12971 **Census:** 160 **Outpatient Visits:** 352689 **Births:** 1778 **Personnel:** 1766

○ **METHODIST HOSPITAL OF CHICAGO (140197)**, 5025 North Paulina Street, Zip 60640–2772; tel. 773/271–9040, (Nonreporting) **A**10 11
Primary Contact: Joseph Chandy, Administrator
CFO: Jim Gregory, Controller
Web address: www.bethanymethodist.org
Control: Other not–for–profit (including NFP Corporation) **Service**: General medical and surgical

Staffed Beds: 189

⊞ **MOUNT SINAI HOSPITAL (140018)**, 1500 South Fairfield Avenue, Zip 60608–1729; tel. 773/542–2000, (Includes SINAI CHILDREN'S HOSPITAL, California Avenue at 15th Street, Chicago, Illinois, Zip 60608; tel. 773/542–2000; Karen Teitelbaum, President and Chief Executive Officer) **A**1 2 3 5 10 **F**3 9 11 12 13 15 17 18 19 20 22 24 26 29 30 31 34 35 38 40 43 44 45 46 50 56 57 59 60 61 64 66 68 70 72 74 75 76 78 79 81 85 86 87 97 98 100 101 102 104 107 108 110 111 114 115 118 119 121 123 130 132 134 135 143 147 154 **S** Sinai Health System, Chicago, IL
Primary Contact: Loren Chandler, President
CFO: Charles Weis, Chief Financial Officer
CMO: Mark Multach, M.D., Chief Medical Officer
CHR: Ann Hatches, Interim Director Human Resources
CNO: Michele A Mazurek, Interim Vice President Patient Care Services and Chief Nursing Officer
Web address: www.sinai.org
Control: Other not–for–profit (including NFP Corporation) **Service**: General medical and surgical

Staffed Beds: 276 **Admissions:** 10725 **Census:** 138 **Outpatient Visits:** 240640 **Births:** 1749 **Total Expense ($000):** 291116 **Payroll Expense ($000):** 108632

⊞ **NORTHWESTERN MEMORIAL HOSPITAL (140281)**, 251 East Huron Street, Zip 60611–2908; tel. 312/926–2000, (Includes PRENTICE WOMEN'S HOSPITAL, 250 East Superior Street, Chicago, Illinois, Zip 60611; tel. 312/926–2000; STONE INSTITUTE OF PSYCHIATRY, 251 East Huron Street, Chicago, Illinois, Zip 60611; tel. 312/926–2000) **A**1 2 3 5 8 10 19 **F**3 4 5 6 9 11 12 13 14 15 17 18 20 22 24 26 28 29 30 31 33 34 35 36 38 39 40 43 44 45 46 47 48 49 50 51 52 54 55 56 57 58 59 61 63 64 65 66 68 70 72 73 74 75 76 77 78 79 80 81 82 84 85 86 87 92 93 94 96 97 98 100 101 102 103 104 107 108 110 111 112 114 115 116 117 118 119 120 121 123 124 126 129 130 131 132 134 135 136 137 138 139 140 141 142 144 145 146 147 148 149 150 152 153 154 156 157 **S** Northwestern Memorial HealthCare, Chicago, IL
Primary Contact: Julie L. Creamer, President, Northwestern Memorial Hospital and Senior Vice President Northwestern Memorial HealthCare
CFO: Francis D Fraher, Vice President, Finance, Northwestern Memorial Hospital
CMO: Gary Noskin, Senior Vice President and Chief Medical Officer, Northwestern Memorial Hospital
CIO: Carl Christensen, Senior Vice President and Chief Information Officer, Northwestern Memorial HealthCare
CHR: Michael Vivoda, Senior Vice President, Administration
CNO: Kristin Ramsey, R.N., Senior Vice President and Chief Nursing Executive, Northwestern Memorial Hospital
Web address: www.nm.org
Control: Other not–for–profit (including NFP Corporation) **Service**: General medical and surgical

Staffed Beds: 894 **Admissions:** 46320 **Census:** 694 **Outpatient Visits:** 1952760 **Births:** 11960 **Total Expense ($000):** 2753649 **Payroll Expense ($000):** 887366 **Personnel:** 11708

Many Facility Codes have changed. Please refer to the AHA Guide Code Chart.   © 2019 AHA Guide

✠ **NORWEGIAN AMERICAN HOSPITAL (140206)**, 1044 North Francisco Avenue, Zip 60622–2743; tcl. 773/292–8200, (Nonreporting) **A**1 3 10
Primary Contact: Jose R. Sanchez, President and Chief Executive Officer
COO: Michelle Blakely, FACHE, Ph.D., Chief Operating Officer
CFO: Gary M Krugel, Chief Financial Officer
CIO: Stephen DePooter, Chief Information Officer
CHR: Neil Teatsorth, Vice President Human Resources
CNO: William Duffy, Interim Chief Nursing Officer
Web address: www.nahospital.org
Control: Other not–for–profit (including NFP Corporation) **Service:** General medical and surgical

Staffed Beds: 195

OUR LADY OF THE RESURRECTION MEDICAL CENTER See Community First Medical Center

PRENTICE WOMEN'S HOSPITAL See Northwestern Memorial Hospital, Chicago

✠ **PROVIDENT HOSPITAL OF COOK COUNTY (140300)**, 500 East 51st Street, Zip 60615–2494; tel. 312/572–2000, **A**1 3 5 10 **F**3 8 15 18 29 30 34 35 40 45 50 53 57 59 61 64 66 68 78 81 87 92 94 104 107 119 130 132 135 143 146 147 149 154 156 **S** Cook County Health and Hospitals System, Chicago, IL
Primary Contact: John Jay. Shannon, M.D., Chief Executive Officer
CFO: Barbara Patterson, Chief Financial Officer
CMO: Aaron Hamb, M.D., Chief Medical Officer
CIO: Donna Hart, Chief Information Officer
Web address: www.ccbhs.org/pages/ProvidentHospitalofCookCounty.htm
Control: County, Government, nonfederal **Service:** General medical and surgical

Staffed Beds: 25 **Admissions:** 569 **Census:** 8 **Outpatient Visits:** 127403
Births: 0 **Personnel:** 345

RESURRECTION MEDICAL CENTER See Amita Health Resurrection Medical Center

◯ **ROSELAND COMMUNITY HOSPITAL (140068)**, 45 West 111th Street, Zip 60628–4294; tel. 773/995–3000, (Nonreporting) **A**10 11
Primary Contact: Timothy Egan, President and Chief Executive Officer
CFO: Marlo Kemp, Vice President and Chief Financial Officer
CMO: Alan Jackson, M.D., Medical Director
CIO: Mariusz Mazek, Vice President Information Technology and Chief Information Officer
CHR: Paulette Clark, Chief Human Resource Officer
CNO: Jeraldene Shaffer, MSN, Chief Nursing Officer
Web address: www.roselandhospital.org
Control: Other not–for–profit (including NFP Corporation) **Service:** General medical and surgical

Staffed Beds: 134

✠ △ **RUSH UNIVERSITY MEDICAL CENTER (140119)**, 1653 West Congress Parkway, Zip 60612–3833; tel. 312/942–5000, (Includes JOHNSTON R. BOWMAN HEALTH CENTER, 700 South Paulina, Chicago, Illinois, Zip 60612; tel. 312/942–7000; RUSH CHILDREN'S HOSPITAL, 1653 Wes Congress Parkway, Chicago, Illinois, Zip 60612–3833; tel. 888/352–7874) **A**1 2 3 5 7 8 10 **F**2 3 6 8 9 11 12 13 14 15 17 18 19 20 21 22 23 24 25 26 27 28 29 30 31 32 34 35 36 37 38 40 41 43 44 45 46 47 48 49 50 51 52 53 54 55 56 57 58 59 60 61 62 63 64 65 66 68 70 72 74 75 76 77 78 79 81 82 83 84 85 86 87 88 89 90 91 92 93 94 95 96 97 98 99 100 101 102 104 105 106 107 108 110 111 114 115 117 118 119 120 121 123 124 125 126 129 130 131 132 134 135 136 137 138 139 141 142 144 145 146 147 148 149 153 154 156 157 **S** Rush University Medical Center, Chicago, IL
Primary Contact: Omar Lateef, D.O., Chief Executive Officer
COO: Michael J Dandorph, President and Chief Operating Officer
CFO: John P Mordach, Senior Vice President and Chief Financial Officer
CIO: Lac Tran, Senior Vice President Information Services
CHR: Mary Ellen Schopp, Senior Vice President Human Resources
CNO: Angelique Richard, R.N., Ph.D., Vice President Clinical Nursing, Chief Nursing Officer and Associate Dean for Practice, College of Nursing
Web address: www.rush.edu
Control: Other not–for–profit (including NFP Corporation) **Service:** General medical and surgical

Staffed Beds: 701 **Admissions:** 33784 **Census:** 494 **Outpatient Visits:** 660931 **Births:** 2260 **Total Expense ($000):** 1256099 **Payroll Expense ($000):** 467538 **Personnel:** 9556

✠ **SAINT ANTHONY HOSPITAL (140095)**, 2875 West 19th Street, Zip 60623–3596; tel. 773/484–1000, **A**1 3 10 **F**3 13 15 18 19 29 30 31 32 34 35 40 41 44 48 49 50 51 54 56 57 59 60 64 65 68 70 74 75 76 77 78 79 81 82 85 86 87 89 93 96 97 98 100 101 102 107 108 110 111 114 115 118 119 130 131 132 143 144 146 147 148 149 150 156 157
Primary Contact: Guy A. Medaglia, President and Chief Executive Officer
CFO: Justin Bynum, Chief Financial Officer
CIO: Mark Jennings, Chief Information Officer
CHR: Malinda Yvonne Carter, Vice President Human Resources
Web address: www.sahchicago.org
Control: Church operated, Nongovernment, not–for–profit **Service:** General medical and surgical

Staffed Beds: 151 **Admissions:** 5795 **Census:** 69 **Outpatient Visits:** 137506 **Births:** 1358 **Total Expense ($000):** 111054 **Payroll Expense ($000):** 53296 **Personnel:** 820

SAINT JOSEPH HOSPITAL See Amita Health Saint Joseph Hospital

SAINTS MARY & ELIZABETH MEDICAL CENTER See Amita Health Saints Mary & Elizabeth Medical Center

✠ **SCHWAB REHABILITATION HOSPITAL (143025)**, 1401 South California Avenue, Zip 60608–1858; tel. 773/522–2010, **A**1 3 5 10 **F**11 29 30 34 35 44 50 57 59 60 64 66 68 74 86 87 90 91 92 93 94 96 97 100 119 128 131 132 143 150 **S** Sinai Health System, Chicago, IL
Primary Contact: Karen Teitelbaum, Chief Executive Officer
CFO: Charles Weis, Chief Financial Officer
CMO: Michelle Gittler, M.D., Medical Director
CNO: Mary A Gollinger, MS, R.N., Director of Nursing
Web address: www.schwabrehab.org
Control: Other not–for–profit (including NFP Corporation) **Service:** Rehabilitation

Staffed Beds: 73 **Admissions:** 1210 **Census:** 50 **Outpatient Visits:** 9255
Births: 0 **Personnel:** 266

✠ **SHIRLEY RYAN ABILITYLAB (143026)**, 345 East Erie Street, Zip 60611–2654, Mailing Address: 355 East Erie Street, Zip 60611–2654; tel. 312/238–1000, **A**1 3 5 10 **F**3 9 29 30 34 35 36 53 54 58 64 68 75 79 82 86 90 91 92 93 94 95 96 107 111 119 131 132 148 157
Primary Contact: Joanne C. Smith, M.D., President and Chief Executive Officer
COO: Peggy Kirk, Senior Vice President Clinical Operations
CFO: Ed Case, Executive Vice President and Chief Financial Officer
CMO: James Sliwa, M.D., Chief Medical Officer
CIO: Tim McKula, Vice President Information Systems and Chief Information Officer
CHR: Lois Huggins, Chief Human Resources Officer and Senior Vice President Human Resources
CNO: Karen M Colby, MS, Chief Nursing Officer
Web address: www.ric.org
Control: Other not–for–profit (including NFP Corporation) **Service:** Rehabilitation

Staffed Beds: 242 **Admissions:** 3172 **Census:** 107 **Outpatient Visits:** 225486 **Births:** 0 **Total Expense ($000):** 312131 **Payroll Expense ($000):** 151232 **Personnel:** 1917

☐ **SHRINERS HOSPITALS FOR CHILDREN-CHICAGO (143302)**, 2211 North Oak Park Avenue, Zip 60707–3392; tel. 773/622–5400, (Nonreporting) **A**1 3 5 10 **S** Shriners Hospitals for Children, Tampa, FL
Primary Contact: Mark L. Niederpruem, FACHE, Administrator
CFO: Philip Magid, Director Fiscal Services
CMO: Jeffrey D. Ackman, M.D., Chief of Staff
CHR: James E Pawlowicz, Director Human Resources
CNO: Terry Wheat, R.N., M.P.H., Director of Patient Care Services
Web address: www.shrinershospitalsforchildren.org/Hospitals/Locations/Chicago.aspx
Control: Other not–for–profit (including NFP Corporation) **Service:** Children's orthopedic

Staffed Beds: 36

◯ **SOUTH SHORE HOSPITAL (140181)**, 8012 South Crandon Avenue, Zip 60617–1124; tel. 773/768–0810, (Nonreporting) **A**10 11
Primary Contact: Timothy Caveney, President
CFO: Scott Spencer, Chief Financial Officer
CMO: James Bob Achebe, M.D., President Medical Staff
CIO: Jim Ritchie, Director Management Information Systems
CHR: Roger Rak, Director Human Resources
CNO: Laura Gonzalez, Interim Chief Nurse Executive
Web address: www.southshorehospital.com
Control: Other not–for–profit (including NFP Corporation) **Service:** General medical and surgical

Staffed Beds: 136

Hospital, Medicare Provider Number, Address, Telephone, Approval, Facility, and Physician Codes, Health Care System

★ American Hospital Association (AHA) membership   ◯ Healthcare Facilities Accreditation Program   ⇑ Center for Improvement in Healthcare Quality Accreditation
☐ The Joint Commission accreditation   ◇ DNV Healthcare Inc. accreditation   △ Commission on Accreditation of Rehabilitation Facilities (CARF) accreditation

IL

☐ **ST. BERNARD HOSPITAL AND HEALTH CARE CENTER (140103)**, 326 West 64th Street, Zip 60621–3146; tel. 773/962–3900, (Nonreporting) **A**1 10
Primary Contact: Charles Holland, President and Chief Executive Officer
COO: Roland Abellera, Vice President and Chief Operating Officer
CFO: James P Porter, Chief Financial Officer
CNO: Evelyn Jones, R.N., Vice President Nursing Services
Web address: www.stbernardhospital.com
Control: Church operated **Service:** General medical and surgical

Staffed Beds: 100

★ ○ **SWEDISH COVENANT HOSPITAL (140114)**, 5145 North California Avenue, Zip 60625–3661; tel. 773/878–8200, **A**2 3 5 10 11 13 15 18 19 20 22 24 26 28 29 30 31 32 33 34 35 36 38 39 40 45 46 47 49 50 53 56 57 58 59 60 64 68 70 74 75 76 78 79 81 82 84 85 86 87 89 90 92 93 95 96 97 98 100 101 102 107 110 111 114 115 116 117 118 119 120 121 123 124 126 128 129 130 131 132 134 135 143 144 146 147 148 149 154 158
Primary Contact: Anthony Guaccio, President and Chief Executive Officer
COO: Jonathan Lind, Chief Operating Officer
CFO: Thomas J Garvey, Senior Vice President Operations and Chief Financial Officer
CMO: Bruce McNulty, Chief Medical Officer
CIO: Karen Sheehan, Vice President and Chief Information Officer
CNO: Kathryn Donofrio, Chief Nursing Officer
Web address: www.schosp.org
Control: Church operated, Nongovernment, not-for-profit **Service:** General medical and surgical

Staffed Beds: 267 **Admissions:** 12613 **Census:** 170 **Outpatient Visits:** 300470 **Births:** 2112 **Total Expense ($000):** 265464 **Payroll Expense ($000):** 108036

○ **THOREK MEMORIAL HOSPITAL (140115)**, 850 West Irving Park Road, Zip 60613–3077; tel. 773/525–6780, (Nonreporting) **A**3 10 11
Primary Contact: Edward Budd, President and Chief Executive Officer
COO: Peter N Kamberos, Chief Operating Officer
CMO: Ilona Carlos, M.D., President Medical Staff
CIO: Tony Vavarutsos, Director Information Systems
CHR: Brett Wakefield, Director Human Resources
CNO: Mary McCahill, Chief Nursing Officer
Web address: www.thorek.org
Control: Other not-for-profit (including NFP Corporation) **Service:** General medical and surgical

Staffed Beds: 134

⊞ **UNIVERSITY OF CHICAGO MEDICAL CENTER (140088)**, 5841 South Maryland Avenue, Zip 60637–1443; tel. 773/702–1000, (Includes BERNARD MITCHELL HOSPITAL, 5815 South Maryland Avenue, Chicago, Illinois, Zip 60637, Mailing Address: 5841 S. Maryland Ave., Zip 60637, tel. 773/702–1000; Sharon L O'Keefe, President, University of Chicago Medical Center; CHICAGO LYING-IN (CLI), 5815 South Maryland Avenue, Chicago, Illinois, Zip 60637, Mailing Address: 5841 South Maryland Avenue, Zip 60637, tel. 773/702–1000; Sharon L O'Keefe, President, University of Chicago Medical Center; COMER CHILDREN'S HOSPITAL, 5721 South Maryland Avenue, Chicago, Illinois, Zip 60637, Mailing Address: 5841 South Maryland Avenue, Zip 60637, tel. 773/702–1000; Sharon L O'Keefe, President, University of Chicago Medical Center) **A**1 2 3 5 8 10 19 **F**3 5 6 9 11 12 13 14 15 16 17 18 19 20 21 22 23 24 25 26 27 28 29 30 31 32 34 35 36 37 38 40 41 43 44 45 46 47 48 49 50 51 52 54 55 56 57 58 59 64 65 66 67 68 70 71 72 73 74 75 76 77 78 79 81 82 83 84 85 86 87 88 89 92 93 97 100 101 102 104 107 108 109 110 111 112 114 115 116 117 118 119 120 121 123 124 126 129 130 131 132 134 135 136 137 138 139 140 141 142 143 145 146 147 148 149 150 156 **S** University of Chicago Medicine, Chicago, IL
Primary Contact: Sharon L. O'Keefe, President
COO: Jason Keeler, Executive Vice President and Chief Operating Officer
CFO: Rich Silveria, Executive Vice President and Chief Financial Officer
CMO: Stephen Weber, M.D., Chief Medical Officer
CHR: Bob Hanley, Chief Human Resources Officer
CNO: Debra Albert, MSN, R.N., Senior Vice President Patient Care and Chief Nursing Officer
Web address: www.uchospitals.edu
Control: Other not-for-profit (including NFP Corporation) **Service:** General medical and surgical

Staffed Beds: 668 **Admissions:** 31577 **Census:** 545 **Outpatient Visits:** 709774 **Births:** 2774 **Total Expense ($000):** 1784575 **Payroll Expense ($000):** 628730 **Personnel:** 9222

⊞ **UNIVERSITY OF ILLINOIS HOSPITAL & HEALTH SCIENCES SYSTEM (140150)**, 1740 West Taylor Street, Zip 60612–7232; tel. 312/996–7000, **A**1 2 3 5 8 10 **F**3 9 12 13 15 17 18 19 20 21 22 23 24 25 26 28 29 30 31 32 34 35 37 38 39 40 41 45 46 47 48 49 50 52 54 55 56 57 58 59 60 61 64 65 66 68 70 72 74 75 76 77 78 79 81 82 84 85 86 87 88 89 91 92 93 96 97 98 99 100 101 102 103 104 107 108 110 111 114 115 116 117 118 119 120 121 123 124 126 129 130 131 132 134 135 136 138 139 141 142 144 145 146 147 148 149 150 154 156 157
Primary Contact: Michael B. Zenn, Chief Executive Officer
COO: David Loffing, Chief Operating Officer
CMO: Bernard Pygon, M.D., Chief Medical Officer
CIO: Audrius Polikaitis, Chief Information Officer
Web address: www.hospital.uillinois.edu/
Control: State, Government, nonfederal **Service:** General medical and surgical

Staffed Beds: 405 **Admissions:** 18880 **Census:** 296 **Outpatient Visits:** 650654 **Births:** 2182 **Total Expense ($000):** 1087738 **Payroll Expense ($000):** 332524 **Personnel:** 3929

CLINTON—De Witt County

WARNER HOSPITAL AND HEALTH SERVICES (141303), 422 West White Street, Zip 61727–2272; tel. 217/935–9571, (Nonreporting) **A**10 18
Primary Contact: Paul Skowron, Chief Executive Officer
CFO: Donna Wisner, Chief Financial Officer
CMO: Brit Williams, M.D., President Medical Staff
CIO: Larry Schleicher, Manager Information Services
CHR: Sarah Gerke, Manager Human Resources
CNO: Heidi Cook, Chief Nursing Officer
Web address: www.djwhospital.org
Control: City, Government, nonfederal **Service:** General medical and surgical

Staffed Beds: 25

DANVILLE—Vermilion County

⊞ **OSF SACRED HEART MEDICAL CENTER (140093)**, 812 North Logan, Zip 61832–3788; tel. 217/443–5000, (Data for 242 days) **A**1 2 5 10 19 **F**3 8 12 13 15 18 20 24 26 28 29 30 31 35 40 45 46 47 48 49 59 60 64 68 70 74 75 76 78 79 81 82 87 89 92 93 94 96 97 102 107 108 110 111 114 115 118 119 120 121 122 123 129 130 132 146 147 148 154 **S** OSF Healthcare, Peoria, IL
Primary Contact: Jared Rogers, M.D., President and Chief Executive Officer
CFO: Lucas Morton, Regional Chief Financial Officer
CMO: Vincent Kucich, FACHE, FACS, M.D., Chief Medical Officer
CIO: Paula Keele, Manager Information Systems
CHR: Michael Zimmerman, Human Resource Officer
CNO: Molly Nicholson, MS, R.N., Vice President of Patient Care/Chief Nurse Executive
Web address: www.presencehealth.org/usmc
Control: Church operated, Nongovernment, not-for-profit **Service:** General medical and surgical

Staffed Beds: 117 **Admissions:** 3200 **Census:** 42 **Outpatient Visits:** 40068 **Births:** 340 **Total Expense ($000):** 59432 **Payroll Expense ($000):** 18498 **Personnel:** 428

⊞ **VETERANS AFFAIRS ILLIANA HEALTH CARE SYSTEM**, 1900 East Main Street, Zip 61832–5198; tel. 217/554–3000, (Nonreporting) **A**1 3 5 **S** Department of Veterans Affairs, Washington, DC
Primary Contact: Diana Carranza, Interim Director
COO: Diana Carranza, Associate Director
CFO: Becky Tissier, Chief Fiscal Service
CMO: Khiem Tran, M.D., Acting Chief of Staff
CIO: Frank D. Jackson III Facility Chief Information Officer
CHR: Connie Ohl, Acting Chief Human Resources
Web address: www.danville.va.gov/
Control: Veterans Affairs, Government, federal **Service:** General medical and surgical

Staffed Beds: 221

DECATUR—Macon County

⊞ △ **DECATUR MEMORIAL HOSPITAL (140135)**, 2300 North Edward Street, Zip 62526–4192; tel. 217/876–8121, **A**1 2 3 5 7 10 19 **F**3 8 11 12 13 15 18 19 20 22 24 26 28 29 30 31 34 35 37 40 43 45 46 47 48 49 51 53 54 56 57 58 59 60 61 62 63 64 65 69 70 71 73 74 75 76 77 78 79 81 82 84 85 86 87 89 91 92 93 94 96 97 98 100 102 103 104 107 108 110 111 112 114 115 116 117 118 119 120 121 123 124 126 129 130 131 132 135 141 143 144 145 146 147 148 149 153 154 156
Primary Contact: Timothy D. Stone Jr, President and Chief Executive Officer
COO: John Ridley, Executive Vice President & Chief Operating Officer
CFO: Deborah L Bragg, Senior Vice President, Finance
CMO: Larry T Hegland, M.D., Chief Medical Officer
CIO: Linda L Fahey, R.N., Chief Information Officer and Senior Vice President Quality Systems
CHR: Kevin Horath, Vice President Human Resources
CNO: Robyn Reising, R.N., Chief Nursing Officer
Web address: www.dmhcares.com
Control: Other not-for-profit (including NFP Corporation) **Service:** General medical and surgical

Staffed Beds: 304 **Admissions:** 9213 **Census:** 113 **Outpatient Visits:** 251528 **Births:** 726 **Total Expense ($000):** 334114 **Payroll Expense ($000):** 131702 **Personnel:** 2013

IL

⊠ △ **HSHS ST. MARY'S HOSPITAL (140166)**, 1800 East Lake Shore Drive, Zip 62521–3883; tel. 217/464–2966, **A**1 3 7 10 **F**2 3 5 7 11 13 15 18 20 22 28 29 30 31 34 35 40 44 45 50 54 56 57 59 64 66 70 74 75 76 77 78 79 81 82 85 86 87 89 90 91 92 93 96 98 99 100 101 102 103 104 107 108 110 111 114 115 117 119 120 121 123 124 126 129 130 131 132 141 142 146 148 149 150 **S** HSHS Hospital Sisters Health System, Springfield, IL
Primary Contact: Michael Hicks, President and Chief Executive Officer
CMO: Phil Barnell, Chief Medical Officer
CHR: Denise Smith, Director People Services
CNO: Michelle Oliver, Chief Nursing Officer
Web address: www.stmarysdecatur.com
Control: Church operated, Nongovernment, not–for–profit **Service:** General medical and surgical

Staffed Beds: 230 **Admissions:** 6604 **Census:** 85 **Outpatient Visits:** 150765 **Births:** 693 **Total Expense ($000):** 142683 **Payroll Expense ($000):** 43188

DEKALB—DeKalb County

⊠ **NORTHWESTERN MEDICINE KISHWAUKEE HOSPITAL (140286)**, 1 Kish Hospital Drive, Zip 60115–9602, Mailing Address: P.O. Box 707, Zip 60115–0707; tel. 815/756–1521, **A**1 2 10 **F**3 5 8 11 13 15 18 20 22 26 28 29 30 31 32 34 35 36 38 40 41 43 44 45 46 48 49 50 51 54 57 58 59 60 64 65 66 68 70 71 73 74 75 76 77 78 79 80 81 82 84 85 86 87 89 93 94 96 97 98 100 101 102 104 107 108 110 111 114 115 117 118 119 127 129 130 131 132 135 144 145 146 147 148 149 150 152 154 157 158 **S** Northwestern Memorial HealthCare, Chicago, IL
Primary Contact: Jay Anderson, President
COO: Brad Copple, Vice President, Operations
CFO: John Orsini, Senior Vice President, Chief Financial Officer
CMO: Michael Kulisz, D.O., Chief Medical Officer
CIO: Carl Christensen, Senior Vice President, Chief Information Officer
CHR: Michael Vivoda, Senior Vice President, Human Resources
CNO: Pamela Duffy, MSN, R.N., Vice President Operations and Chief Nursing Officer
Web address: www.nm.org
Control: Other not–for–profit (including NFP Corporation) **Service:** General medical and surgical

Staffed Beds: 98 **Admissions:** 5115 **Census:** 56 **Outpatient Visits:** 328293 **Births:** 795 **Total Expense ($000):** 234708 **Payroll Expense ($000):** 82722 **Personnel:** 1354

DES PLAINES—Cook County

⊠ **AMITA HEALTH HOLY FAMILY MEDICAL CENTER (142011)**, 100 North River Road, Zip 60016–1255; tel. 847/297–1800, **A**1 10 **F**1 3 5 15 18 29 30 34 35 45 46 50 53 57 59 60 63 64 65 66 81 82 84 85 87 92 93 107 110 111 118 119 124 129 130 132 135 141 143 146 147 148 149 150 154 **S** Ascension Healthcare, Saint Louis, MO
Primary Contact: Yolande Wilson-Stubbs, President
CFO: Gene Yakovenko, Director of Finance
CMO: David Bordo, M.D., Chief Medical Officer
CIO: David Lundal, Senior Vice President Information Systems and Chief Information Officer
CHR: Ivy McKinley, Director Human Resources
Web address: www.presencehealth.org
Control: Church operated, Nongovernment, not–for–profit **Service:** Acute long–term care hospital

Staffed Beds: 178 **Admissions:** 1465 **Census:** 84 **Outpatient Visits:** 18425 **Births:** 0 **Total Expense ($000):** 71008 **Payroll Expense ($000):** 28415 **Personnel:** 516

HOLY FAMILY MEDICAL CENTER See Amita Health Holy Family Medical Center

DIXON—Lee County

★ **KATHERINE SHAW BETHEA HOSPITAL (140012)**, 403 East First Street, Zip 61021–3187; tel. 815/288–5531, **A**3 5 10 **F**3 11 13 15 18 20 22 28 29 30 34 35 38 39 40 44 45 46 47 50 54 56 57 59 61 62 64 69 70 74 75 76 79 81 82 85 86 87 89 91 92 93 94 96 97 98 101 102 104 107 108 110 111 112 115 119 127 129 130 131 132 135 145 146 147 148 149 150 154 156 157
Primary Contact: David L. Schreiner, FACHE, President and Chief Executive Officer
COO: Julie D Mann, Vice President and Chief Administrative Officer
CFO: Anthony Evers, Chief Financial Officer
CMO: Pratip Nag, Vice President, Chief Medical Officer
CHR: Christy Pierce, Director of Human Resources
CNO: Linda Clemen, Vice President and Chief Nursing Officer
Web address: www.ksbhospital.com
Control: Other not–for–profit (including NFP Corporation) **Service:** General medical and surgical

Staffed Beds: 80 **Admissions:** 3190 **Census:** 27 **Outpatient Visits:** 271948 **Births:** 322 **Total Expense ($000):** 129861 **Payroll Expense ($000):** 61988 **Personnel:** 783

DOWNERS GROVE—Dupage County

★ ⇑ **ADVOCATE GOOD SAMARITAN HOSPITAL (140288)**, 3815 Highland Avenue, Zip 60515–1590; tel. 630/275–5900, **A**2 5 10 21 **F**3 5 11 12 13 15 17 18 20 22 24 26 28 29 30 31 32 34 35 36 37 38 40 41 43 44 45 46 47 49 50 53 54 55 56 57 59 60 63 64 68 70 72 74 75 76 77 78 79 81 82 84 85 86 87 89 93 97 98 100 101 102 104 105 107 108 109 110 111 114 115 118 119 120 121 123 124 126 129 130 131 132 135 144 145 146 147 148 149 152 153 154 156 157 **S** Advocate Aurora Health, Downers Grove, IL
Primary Contact: Nancy M. Tinsley, R.N., FACHE, President
COO: Sandi Churchill, Vice President Business Development and Operations, Professional Services
CFO: Mary Treacy-Shiff, Vice President Finance
CMO: Charles Derus, M.D., Vice President Medical Management
CHR: Elizabeth Calby, Vice President Human Resources
CNO: Susan K Okuno-Jones, Vice President Patient Care Services and Chief Nursing Executive
Web address: www.advocatehealth.com/gsam
Control: Church operated, Nongovernment, not–for–profit **Service:** General medical and surgical

Staffed Beds: 288 **Admissions:** 15832 **Census:** 185 **Outpatient Visits:** 127413 **Births:** 1772 **Total Expense ($000):** 350383 **Payroll Expense ($000):** 120259 **Personnel:** 1521

DU QUOIN—Perry County

⊠ **MARSHALL BROWNING HOSPITAL (141331)**, 900 North Washington Street, Zip 62832–1233, Mailing Address: P.O. Box 192, Zip 62832–0192; tel. 618/542–2146, **A**1 10 18 **F**3 11 15 28 29 34 35 40 57 59 81 93 97 104 107 114 119 125 127 129 133 144 148 154 156
Primary Contact: Dan Eaves, Chief Executive Officer
CFO: Brice Harsy, Chief Financial Officer
CIO: Brian Schandl, Chief Information Officer
CHR: Sarah J. Dickey, Human Resource Director
CNO: Laurie Kellerman, MSN, Chief Clinical Officer
Web address: www.marshallbrowninghospital.com
Control: Other not–for–profit (including NFP Corporation) **Service:** General medical and surgical

Staffed Beds: 25 **Admissions:** 506 **Census:** 7 **Outpatient Visits:** 41434 **Births:** 0 **Total Expense ($000):** 23642 **Payroll Expense ($000):** 9367 **Personnel:** 190

EFFINGHAM—Effingham County

⊠ **HSHS ST. ANTHONY'S MEMORIAL HOSPITAL (140032)**, 503 North Maple Street, Zip 62401–2099; tel. 217/342–2121, **A**1 2 3 5 10 19 **F**3 11 13 15 18 20 28 29 30 31 32 34 35 37 40 45 50 57 59 62 63 64 68 70 75 76 79 81 82 84 85 87 89 93 107 108 110 111 114 115 117 118 119 126 129 130 131 132 144 146 147 154 **S** HSHS Hospital Sisters Health System, Springfield, IL
Primary Contact: Theresa Rutherford, R.N., MS, FACHE, President and Chief Executive Officer
CFO: Dave Storm, Director Business Support
CNO: Kelly Sage, Chief Nursing Officer
Web address: www.stanthonyshospital.org
Control: Church operated, Nongovernment, not–for–profit **Service:** General medical and surgical

Staffed Beds: 123 **Admissions:** 4769 **Census:** 42 **Outpatient Visits:** 159871 **Births:** 767 **Total Expense ($000):** 128681 **Payroll Expense ($000):** 43893 **Personnel:** 674

ELDORADO—Saline County

★ **FERRELL HOSPITAL (141324)**, 1201 Pine Street, Zip 62930–1634; tel. 618/273–3361, (Nonreporting) **A**10 18
Primary Contact: Alisa Coleman, Chief Executive Officer
CFO: Joseph Hohenberger, Chief Financial Officer
CIO: Brent Volkert, Director Information Technology
CHR: Caleigh Bruce, Vice President Human Resources
CNO: Rachael Prather, Chief Nursing Officer
Web address: www.ferrellhosp.org
Control: Other not–for–profit (including NFP Corporation) **Service:** General medical and surgical

Staffed Beds: 25

IL

ELGIN—Kane County

★ ⇑ **ADVOCATE SHERMAN HOSPITAL (140030)**, 1425 North Randall Road, Zip 60123–2300; tel. 847/742–9800, **A**2 10 21 **F**3 11 13 15 18 20 22 24 26 28 29 30 31 34 35 38 40 41 43 45 46 47 48 49 50 54 57 59 64 65 68 70 71 73 74 75 76 77 78 79 81 82 85 87 89 92 93 100 102 107 108 110 111 114 115 116 117 118 119 120 121 123 126 129 130 132 135 144 146 147 148 149 154 **S** Advocate Aurora Health, Downers Grove, IL
Primary Contact: Linda Deering, MSN, R.N., President
CMO: Bruce Hyman, M.D., Vice President Clinical Performance
CHR: Melissa O'Neill, Vice President Human Resources
CNO: Cheri Goll, MSN, R.N., Chief Nursing Executive
Web address: www.advocatehealth.com/sherman
Control: Other not–for–profit (including NFP Corporation) **Service**: General medical and surgical

Staffed Beds: 255 **Admissions:** 14400 **Census:** 150 **Outpatient Visits:** 310145 **Births:** 2435 **Total Expense ($000):** 307792 **Payroll Expense ($000):** 102003 **Personnel:** 1442

☒ △ **AMITA HEALTH SAINT JOSEPH HOSPITAL (140217)**, 77 North Airlite Street, Zip 60123–4912; tel. 847/695–3200, **A**1 2 7 10 **F**5 11 12 17 18 20 22 24 26 28 29 30 31 34 35 36 37 38 40 43 44 49 50 53 54 56 57 58 59 60 61 62 63 64 65 68 69 70 74 75 77 78 79 81 82 84 85 86 87 90 93 94 96 97 98 99 100 101 102 103 104 105 107 108 111 114 115 117 119 120 121 123 124 130 132 134 135 143 146 147 148 153 **S** Ascension Healthcare, Saint Louis, MO
Primary Contact: Michael L. Brown, Regional President and Chief Executive Officer
CFO: Kevin Larkin, Regional Chief Financial Officer
CIO: Trevor O'Malley, Site Manager
CHR: Michael O'Rourke, Regional Human Resources Lead
Web address: www.provena.org
Control: Church operated, Nongovernment, not–for–profit **Service**: General medical and surgical

Staffed Beds: 184 **Admissions:** 6841 **Census:** 103 **Births:** 0 **Total Expense ($000):** 141663 **Payroll Expense ($000):** 40401 **Personnel:** 620

☐ **ELGIN MENTAL HEALTH CENTER (144037)**, 750 South State Street, Zip 60123–7692; tel. 847/742–1040, **A**1 3 5 10 **F**29 30 38 39 50 59 65 68 87 98 101 130 132 143 **S** Division of Mental Health, Department of Human Services, Springfield, IL
Primary Contact: Meredith Kiss, Administrator
CFO: Tajudeen Ibrahim, Interim Business Administrator
CMO: Malini Patel, M.D., Medical Director
CIO: Kelly Callahan, Public Information Officer
CHR: Darek Williams, Director Human Resources
Web address: www.dhs.state.il.us
Control: State, Government, nonfederal **Service**: Psychiatric

Staffed Beds: 383 **Admissions:** 790 **Census:** 353 **Outpatient Visits:** 0 **Births:** 0 **Total Expense ($000):** 51246 **Personnel:** 566

PROVENA SAINT JOSEPH HOSPITAL See Amita Health Saint Joseph Hospital

⇑ **SHERMAN HOSPITAL** See Advocate Sherman Hospital

ELK GROVE VILLAGE—Cook County

☒ **AMITA HEALTH ELK GROVE VILLAGE (140258)**, 800 Biesterfield Road, Zip 60007–3397; tel. 847/437–5500, (Includes AMITA HEALTH REHABILITATION HOSPITAL, 935 Beisner Road, Elk Grove Village, Illinois, Zip 60007; tel. 847/640–5600; John Dunkin, Executive Director) **A**1 2 3 5 10 **F**3 10 11 12 13 15 17 18 19 20 22 23 24 26 27 28 29 30 31 34 35 37 38 39 40 41 42 43 44 45 46 47 48 49 50 54 55 57 59 63 64 70 73 74 76 78 79 81 82 84 85 86 87 89 90 91 92 93 95 96 97 98 103 107 108 110 111 114 115 116 117 118 119 120 121 124 126 129 130 132 135 143 145 146 147 148 149 154 156 157 **S** Ascension Healthcare, Saint Louis, MO
Primary Contact: John P. Werrbach, President and Chief Executive Officer
COO: Laurence Dry, Chief Operating Officer, Acute Care Hospitals Northern Region
CFO: Henry Zeisel, Chief Financial Officer, Northern Region
CIO: Sherrie Russell, Senior Vice President & Chief Information Officer
CHR: Donald Russell, Senior Vice President and Chief Human Resources Officer
CNO: Chris Budzinsky, Vice President, Nursing and Chief Nursing Officer
Web address: www.AMITAHealth.org
Control: Church operated, Nongovernment, not–for–profit **Service**: General medical and surgical

Staffed Beds: 401 **Admissions:** 17808 **Census:** 267 **Outpatient Visits:** 346079 **Births:** 1778 **Total Expense ($000):** 458428 **Payroll Expense ($000):** 142169 **Personnel:** 2031

ELMHURST—Dupage County

☒ **ELMHURST HOSPITAL (140200)**, 155 East Brush Hill Road, Zip 60126–5658; tel. 331/221–1000, **A**1 2 5 10 **F**3 12 13 15 18 19 20 22 24 26 28 29 30 31 34 35 36 37 38 39 40 41 43 44 45 46 47 48 49 50 54 55 57 58 59 61 63 64 65 70 73 74 75 76 77 78 79 81 82 84 85 86 87 89 91 92 93 96 97 99 100 101 102 103 107 108 110 111 115 117 119 120 121 126 129 130 131 132 135 144 146 147 148 149 154 156 **S** Edward-Elmhurst Healthcare, Naperville, IL
Primary Contact: Pamela L. Dunley, MS, R.N., Chief Executive Officer
CMO: Daniel Sullivan, D.O., Chief Medical Officer, Vice President Medical Administration
CHR: Robert Blazek, System Director, Human Resources Business Partners
CNO: Jean Lydon, MS, R.N., System Vice President Operations, Chief Nursing Officer
Web address: www.eehealth.org
Control: Other not–for–profit (including NFP Corporation) **Service**: General medical and surgical

Staffed Beds: 269 **Admissions:** 17581 **Census:** 187 **Outpatient Visits:** 725128 **Births:** 2329 **Total Expense ($000):** 461522 **Payroll Expense ($000):** 131775 **Personnel:** 2206

EUREKA—Woodford County

★ ⇑ **ADVOCATE EUREKA HOSPITAL (141309)**, 101 South Major Street, Zip 61530–1246; tel. 309/467–2371, **A**10 18 21 **F**3 4 11 15 17 18 28 29 30 34 35 39 40 44 45 50 56 57 59 64 65 67 68 70 73 74 75 76 77 78 79 81 82 85 86 87 89 90 93 97 98 107 108 110 111 114 119 127 128 129 130 132 133 144 146 149 154 156 157 **S** Advocate Aurora Health, Downers Grove, IL
Primary Contact: Colleen Kannaday, FACHE, President
CFO: Aron Klein, Vice President of Finance
CMO: Steven K Jones, M.D., Medical Director
CIO: David Harper, Director, Site Information Systems
CHR: Antonio Coletta, Vice President Human Resources
CNO: Nancy Allen, R.N., MS, Director, Patient Services and Chief Nursing Executive
Web address: www.advocatehealth.com/eureka/
Control: Church operated, Nongovernment, not–for–profit **Service**: General medical and surgical

Staffed Beds: 11 **Admissions:** 172 **Census:** 3 **Outpatient Visits:** 49220 **Births:** 0 **Total Expense ($000):** 20693 **Payroll Expense ($000):** 8950 **Personnel:** 112

⇑ **EUREKA COMMUNITY HOSPITAL** See Advocate Eureka Hospital

EVANSTON—Cook County

☒ **AMITA HEALTH SAINT FRANCIS HOSPITAL EVANSTON (140080)**, 355 Ridge Avenue, Zip 60202–3399; tel. 847/316–4000, **A**1 2 3 5 10 **F**3 11 12 13 15 18 20 22 24 26 28 29 30 31 34 35 38 40 41 42 43 44 45 47 48 49 56 57 58 59 60 61 64 68 70 74 75 76 77 78 79 81 82 84 85 86 87 91 92 93 97 100 107 108 111 114 115 117 118 119 121 123 125 126 129 130 131 132 146 147 148 154 156 **S** Ascension Healthcare, Saint Louis, MO
Primary Contact: Kenneth Jones, President
CMO: David DiLoreto, Executive Vice President and Chief Medical Officer
CIO: George Chessum, Vice President Information Systems
CHR: Paul Skiem, Senior Vice President Human Resources
CNO: Trisha E. Musich, R.N., Chief Nursing Officer
Web address: www.reshealth.org
Control: Church operated, Nongovernment, not–for–profit **Service**: General medical and surgical

Staffed Beds: 215 **Admissions:** 7591 **Census:** 82 **Outpatient Visits:** 86911 **Births:** 502 **Total Expense ($000):** 154966 **Payroll Expense ($000):** 54415 **Personnel:** 826

☒ **NORTHSHORE UNIVERSITY HEALTH SYSTEM (140010)**, 2650 Ridge Avenue, Zip 60201–1613; tel. 847/570–2000, (Includes NORTHSHORE EVANSTON HOSPITAL, 2650 Ridge Avenue, Evanston, Illinois, Zip 60201–1797; tel. 847/570–2000; Douglas M Silverstein, President; NORTHSHORE GLENBROOK HOSPITAL, 2100 Pfingsten Road, Glenview, Illinois, Zip 60025; tel. 847/657–5800; Jesse Peterson Hall, President; NORTHSHORE HIGHLAND PARK HOSPITAL, 718 Glenview Avenue, Highland Park, Illinois, Zip 60035–2497; tel. 847/432–8000; Gabrielle Cummings, President; NORTHSHORE SKOKIE HOSPITAL, 9600 Gross Point Road, Skokie, Illinois, Zip 60076–1257; tel. 847/677–9600; David Rahija, FACHE, President) **A**1 2 3 5 8 10 **F**3 5 8 9 11 12 13 14 15 17 18 19 20 22 24 26 28 29 30 31 32 34 35 36 37 38 39 40 43 44 45 46 47 48 49 50 54 55 56 57 58 59 60 61 62 63 64 66 68 70 72 74 75 76 77 78 79 81 82 84 85 86 87 88 89 90 92 93 96 97 98 99 100 101 102 103 104 105 107 108 110 111 114 115 116 117 118 119 120 121 123 124 126 129 130 131 132 134 135 136 144 145 146 147 148 149 153 154 156
Primary Contact: J. P. Gallagher, President and Chief Executive Officer
CFO: Gary Weiss, Chief Financial Officer
CIO: Steven Smith, Chief Information Officer
CHR: Bill Luehrs, Chief Human Resources Officer
CNO: Nancy Semerdjian, R.N., Chief Nursing Officer
Web address: www.northshore.org
Control: Other not–for–profit (including NFP Corporation) **Service**: General medical and surgical

Staffed Beds: 673 **Admissions:** 40850 **Census:** 486 **Outpatient Visits:** 2189093 **Births:** 4802 **Total Expense ($000):** 1424541 **Payroll Expense ($000):** 537374 **Personnel:** 6304

Many Facility Codes have changed. Please refer to the AHA Guide Code Chart.

© 2019 AHA Guide

SAINT FRANCIS HOSPITAL See Amita Health Saint Francis Hospital Evanston

EVERGREEN PARK—Cook County

☐ **LITTLE COMPANY OF MARY HOSPITAL AND HEALTH CARE CENTERS (140179)**, 2800 West 95th Street, Zip 60805–2795; tel. 708/422–6200, **A**1 2 3 5 10 **F**3 4 5 11 12 13 15 18 20 22 26 29 30 31 34 35 36 38 40 41 45 46 47 49 50 54 56 57 59 60 62 63 64 65 70 71 72 74 75 76 77 78 79 81 82 83 84 85 86 87 89 92 93 94 98 100 101 102 104 105 107 108 110 111 114 115 119 120 121 124 126 129 130 131 132 133 135 144 146 147 148 149 150 152 153 154 156 157 **S** American Province of Little Company of Mary Sisters, Evergreen Park, IL
Primary Contact: John Hanlon, M.D., President and Chief Executive Officer
COO: Mary Freyer, Chief Operating Officer
CFO: Robert Tarola, Chief Financial Officer
CMO: Kent A W Armbruster, M.D., Vice President Medical Affairs
CIO: Darryl Mazzuca, Director Management Information Systems
CHR: Colleen Rohan, Director Human Resources
CNO: Lisa DiMarco, R.N., FACHE, Vice President Patient Care Service and Chief Nursing Officer
Web address: www.lcmh.org
Control: Other not–for–profit (including NFP Corporation) **Service:** General medical and surgical

Staffed Beds: 231 **Admissions:** 11357 **Census:** 141 **Outpatient Visits:** 191386 **Births:** 1005 **Total Expense ($000):** 216104 **Payroll Expense ($000):** 89539 **Personnel:** 1715

FAIRFIELD—Wayne County

✉ **FAIRFIELD MEMORIAL HOSPITAL (141311)**, 303 NW 11th Street, Zip 62837–1203; tel. 618/842–2611, (Total facility includes 30 beds in nursing home–type unit) **A**1 10 18 **F**3 11 15 18 28 31 34 35 38 40 41 45 46 50 56 57 59 62 64 65 69 70 71 75 77 81 85 86 87 93 97 102 104 107 108 110 111 115 119 124 127 128 129 130 132 135 144 146 149 153 154 156
Primary Contact: Katherine Bunting Esq, Chief Executive Officer
COO: Dana Shantel Taylor, Director Organizational Development
CFO: Amy Marsh, Chief Financial Officer
CMO: Wesley Thompson, M.D., President Medical Staff
CIO: Brad August, Director Information Systems
CHR: Robert Musoiu, Director Human Resources
CNO: Tracy Taylor, Chief Nurse Executive
Web address: www.fairfieldmemorial.org
Control: Other not–for–profit (including NFP Corporation) **Service:** General medical and surgical

Staffed Beds: 55 **Admissions:** 747 **Census:** 27 **Outpatient Visits:** 42158 **Births:** 0 **Total Expense ($000):** 30708 **Payroll Expense ($000):** 13077 **Personnel:** 308

FLORA—Clay County

✉ **CLAY COUNTY HOSPITAL (141351)**, 911 Stacy Burk Drive, Zip 62839–3241, Mailing Address: P.O. Box 280, Zip 62839–0280; tel. 618/662–2131, **A**1 10 18 **F**3 7 11 15 28 29 45 48 57 77 81 92 93 97 100 104 107 110 111 114 115 116 117 119 127 129 133 156 **S** SSM Health, Saint Louis, MO
Primary Contact: Chris Hunt, President
COO: Jamie Veach, Chief Operating Officer
CFO: Mike Hobbs, Chief Financial Officer
CMO: Colleen Murphy, M.D., Chief of Staff
CIO: Phil Bute, Manager Information Technology
CHR: Chelsea Musgrave, Director of Human Resources
Web address: www.claycountyhospital.org
Control: County, Government, nonfederal **Service:** General medical and surgical

Staffed Beds: 10 **Admissions:** 642 **Census:** 8 **Outpatient Visits:** 44070 **Total Expense ($000):** 31680 **Payroll Expense ($000):** 13630 **Personnel:** 236

FOREST PARK—Cook County

☐ **RIVEREDGE HOSPITAL (144009)**, 8311 West Roosevelt Road, Zip 60130–2500; tel. 708/771–7000, (Nonreporting) **A**1 10 **S** Universal Health Services, Inc., King of Prussia, PA
Primary Contact: Carey Carlock, Chief Executive Officer
COO: Joseph Baw, Chief Operating Officer
CFO: Mark Hennessy, Chief Financial Officer
CMO: Lucyna M. Puszkarska, M.D., Medical Director
CIO: Kyle Heinze, Coordinator Information Technology
CHR: Joseph Rinke, Director of Human Resources
Web address: www.riveredgehospital.com
Control: Corporation, Investor–owned (for–profit) **Service:** Psychiatric

Staffed Beds: 224

FREEPORT—Stephenson County

★ **FHN MEMORIAL HOSPITAL (140160)**, 1045 West Stephenson Street, Zip 61032–4899; tel. 815/599–6000, **A**10 **F**3 13 14 15 18 20 22 28 29 30 31 34 38 40 45 46 47 48 49 50 51 53 55 57 58 59 61 63 64 65 68 69 74 75 76 77 78 79 81 82 84 85 86 87 93 97 100 101 102 104 107 108 109 110 111 114 119 129 130 131 132 135 145 146 149 153 154 156
Primary Contact: Mark Gridley, FACHE, President and Chief Executive Officer
CFO: Michael Clark, Executive Vice President and Chief Financial Officer
CMO: Keith Martin, M.D., Chief Medical Officer
CIO: Mike Willams, Chief Information Officer
CHR: Leonard M Carter, Chief Human Resources Officer
CNO: Kathryn J Martinez, Chief Nursing Officer
Web address: www.fhn.org
Control: Other not–for–profit (including NFP Corporation) **Service:** General medical and surgical

Staffed Beds: 100 **Admissions:** 3835 **Census:** 38 **Outpatient Visits:** 102718 **Births:** 285 **Total Expense ($000):** 113469 **Payroll Expense ($000):** 33861 **Personnel:** 461

GALENA—Jo Daviess County

★ **MIDWEST MEDICAL CENTER (141302)**, One Medical Center Drive, Zip 61036–1697; tel. 815/777–1340, (Nonreporting) **A**10 18
Primary Contact: Tracy Bauer, Chief Executive Officer
COO: Steve Busch, Chief Operating Officer
CMO: Grant Westenfelder, M.D., Chief Medical Officer
CHR: Melissa Conley, Director Human Resources
Web address: www.midwestmedicalcenter.org
Control: Corporation, Investor–owned (for–profit) **Service:** General medical and surgical

Staffed Beds: 25

GALESBURG—Knox County

✉ **GALESBURG COTTAGE HOSPITAL (140040)**, 695 North Kellogg Street, Zip 61401–2885; tel. 309/343–8131, (Nonreporting) **A**1 10 **S** Quorum Health, Brentwood, TN
Primary Contact: James Flynn, Chief Executive Officer
COO: James Stanley, Interim Chief Operating Officer
CFO: Patricia Ellison, Chief Financial Officer
CMO: Parthasarathy Srinivasan, M.D., President Medical Staff
CIO: Richard Tran, Director Information Technology
CHR: Barbara Hendricks, Interim Human Resources Director
CNO: Pam Davis, Chief Nursing Officer
Web address: www.cottagehospital.com
Control: Other not–for–profit (including NFP Corporation) **Service:** General medical and surgical

Staffed Beds: 119

✉ **OSF ST. MARY MEDICAL CENTER (140064)**, 3333 North Seminary Street, Zip 61401–1299; tel. 309/344–3161, **A**1 10 **F**3 11 13 15 18 26 28 29 30 31 32 34 35 40 45 46 49 50 51 53 56 57 59 64 70 75 78 79 81 82 84 85 87 93 96 102 107 108 110 111 115 118 119 129 130 131 132 146 147 148 149 154 **S** OSF Healthcare, Peoria, IL
Primary Contact: Jennifer Junis, MSN, R.N., President
COO: Don Shadensack, Vice President Clinical Services
CFO: Curt Lipe, Vice President, Chief Financial Officer
CMO: Clifford G Martin, M.D., Regional Vice President and Chief Medical Officer
CIO: Becky Lynch, Manager Business Entity Management and Information Systems
CHR: Jenny Jacobs, Director Human Resources
CNO: Alice Snyder, Vice President, Chief Nursing Officer
Web address: www.osfstmary.org
Control: Church operated, Nongovernment, not–for–profit **Service:** General medical and surgical

Staffed Beds: 71 **Admissions:** 3215 **Census:** 34 **Outpatient Visits:** 104721 **Births:** 407 **Total Expense ($000):** 75713 **Payroll Expense ($000):** 26720 **Personnel:** 374

IL

GENESEO—Henry County

★ ⇑ **HAMMOND-HENRY HOSPITAL (141319)**, 600 North College Avenue, Zip 61254–1099; tel. 309/944–6431, (Total facility includes 38 beds in nursing home–type unit) **A**10 18 21 **F**3 11 15 28 29 34 35 40 45 49 50 57 59 62 70 75 81 87 93 97 107 111 114 119 128 129 130 131 132 133 144 146 154 **S** HealthTech Management Services, Brentwood, TN
Primary Contact: Mark Kuhn, Chief Executive Officer
CFO: Jodie Criswell, Vice President of Fiscal Services
CIO: Heather Henry, Information Technology Manager
CHR: Hazel Butter, Manager Human Resources
Web address: www.hammondhenry.com
Control: Hospital district or authority, Government, nonfederal **Service:** General medical and surgical

Staffed Beds: 61 **Admissions:** 935 **Census:** 43 **Outpatient Visits:** 118389 **Births:** 0 **Total Expense ($000):** 40161 **Payroll Expense ($000):** 17449 **Personnel:** 310	

GENEVA—Kane County

⊠ **NORTHWESTERN MEDICINE DELNOR HOSPITAL (140211)**, 300 Randall Road, Zip 60134–4200; tel. 630/208–3000, **A**1 2 3 10 **F**3 12 13 15 18 20 22 26 28 29 30 31 33 34 35 36 37 39 40 41 43 44 45 46 47 48 49 50 51 53 55 57 59 64 65 68 70 73 74 75 76 77 78 79 81 82 84 85 86 87 89 92 93 94 96 97 100 101 102 104 105 107 108 110 111 114 115 116 117 119 120 121 123 126 129 130 131 132 135 146 147 148 149 153 154 156 157 **S** Northwestern Memorial HealthCare, Chicago, IL
Primary Contact: Maureen A. Bryant, FACHE, President
CFO: John Orsini, Executive Vice President and Chief Financial Officer
CMO: Mark Daniels, M.D., Vice President Physician Enterprise
CIO: Daniel F Kinsella, Executive Vice President Information Technology
Web address: www.nm.org
Control: Other not–for–profit (including NFP Corporation) **Service:** General medical and surgical

Staffed Beds: 142 **Admissions:** 7948 **Census:** 79 **Outpatient Visits:** 462696 **Births:** 1329 **Total Expense ($000):** 389336 **Payroll Expense ($000):** 126607 **Personnel:** 1771	

GIBSON CITY—Ford County

★ **GIBSON AREA HOSPITAL AND HEALTH SERVICES (141317)**, 1120 North Melvin Street, Zip 60936–1477, Mailing Address: P.O. Box 429, Zip 60936–0429; tel. 217/784–4251, (Total facility includes 42 beds in nursing home–type unit) **A**10 18 **F**3 7 8 11 13 15 18 20 26 28 29 31 34 35 39 40 44 45 46 50 51 53 56 57 59 64 67 68 69 70 75 76 77 78 79 81 82 85 86 87 89 90 93 97 98 100 102 104 107 110 111 115 118 119 127 128 129 130 131 132 133 135 141 143 144 146 148 149 154 **S** Alliant Management Services, Louisville, KY
Primary Contact: Robert C. Schmitt II, CPA, FACHE, Chief Executive Officer
COO: Robin Rose, R.N., Chief Operating and Clinical Officer
CFO: Matthew Ertel, Chief Financial Officer
CMO: Mark Spangler, M.D., Chief Medical Officer
CHR: Ty Royal, Executive Director of Human Resources and Support Services
CNO: Barb Meyer, Executive Director of Nursing
Web address: www.gibsonhospital.org
Control: Other not–for–profit (including NFP Corporation) **Service:** General medical and surgical

Staffed Beds: 67 **Admissions:** 1100 **Census:** 46 **Outpatient Visits:** 135260 **Births:** 223 **Total Expense ($000):** 98963 **Payroll Expense ($000):** 47777 **Personnel:** 722	

GLENDALE HEIGHTS—DuPage County

⊠ **ADVENTIST MEDICAL CENTER GLENOAKS (140292)**, 701 Winthrop Avenue, Zip 60139–1403; tel. 630/545–8000, **A**1 10 **F**3 11 13 15 18 20 22 26 29 30 31 34 35 38 40 41 43 44 45 49 50 56 57 59 61 64 70 73 74 76 78 79 81 82 85 86 87 89 98 100 101 103 107 108 110 119 128 129 130 131 132 146 147 148 149 154 157 **S** AdventHealth, Altamonte Springs, FL
Primary Contact: Bruce C. Christian, President and Chief Executive Officer
COO: Richard Roehr, Vice President and Chief Operating Officer
CFO: Chase Aalborg, Vice President and Chief Financial Officer
CMO: Richard Carroll, M.D., Vice President and Chief Medical Officer
CIO: Sherrie Russell, AMITA Health Senior Vice President and Chief Information Officer
CHR: Donald Russell, AMITA Health Senior Vice President and Chief Human Resources Officer
CNO: Suzette Mahneke, Associate Vice President of Nursing
Web address: www.AMITAHealth.org
Control: Church operated, Nongovernment, not–for–profit **Service:** General medical and surgical

Staffed Beds: 138 **Admissions:** 5532 **Census:** 75 **Outpatient Visits:** 36309 **Births:** 296 **Total Expense ($000):** 89836 **Payroll Expense ($000):** 35123 **Personnel:** 481	

GLENVIEW—Cook County

NORTHSHORE GLENBROOK HOSPITAL See Northshore University Health System, Evanston

GRANITE CITY—Madison County

⊠ **GATEWAY REGIONAL MEDICAL CENTER (140125)**, 2100 Madison Avenue, Zip 62040–4799; tel. 618/798–3000, **A**1 10 **F**3 8 11 13 15 17 18 20 22 24 26 28 29 31 34 35 40 45 49 50 51 54 59 64 70 75 76 77 78 79 80 81 82 85 87 91 92 93 94 97 98 99 100 101 102 103 104 107 108 110 111 114 115 119 126 129 130 132 135 144 146 147 148 149 157 **S** Quorum Health, Brentwood, TN
Primary Contact: M Edward. Cunningham, Chief Executive Officer
CMO: Mike Adams, M.D., Chief Medical Officer
CIO: Dennis Kampwerth, Director Management Information Systems
CHR: Reva S Weems, Director Human Resources
CNO: Sam R White, Chief Nursing Officer
Web address: www.gatewayregional.net
Control: Corporation, Investor–owned (for–profit) **Service:** General medical and surgical

Staffed Beds: 127 **Admissions:** 7030 **Census:** 91 **Births:** 251	

GREENVILLE—Bond County

★ ○ **HSHS HOLY FAMILY HOSPITAL IN GREENVILLE (140137)**, 200 Healthcare Drive, Zip 62246–1154; tel. 618/664–1230, **A**10 11 **F**3 11 13 15 18 30 31 34 40 41 45 49 50 56 57 59 76 78 79 81 85 89 93 94 97 98 103 104 107 110 111 115 119 125 127 129 130 132 133 135 154 **S** HSHS Hospital Sisters Health System, Springfield, IL
Primary Contact: Kelly Sager, R.N., President and Chief Executive Officer
CFO: Mark S Ennen, Director of Finance
CHR: Vicki Kloeckner, Director Human Resources
CNO: Lorna Keaster, Interim Chief Nursing Officer
Web address: www.greenvilleregionalhospital.com
Control: Other not–for–profit (including NFP Corporation) **Service:** General medical and surgical

Staffed Beds: 42 **Admissions:** 1098 **Census:** 13 **Outpatient Visits:** 30055 **Births:** 184 **Total Expense ($000):** 31456 **Payroll Expense ($000):** 10476 **Personnel:** 187	

HARRISBURG—Saline County

⊠ **HARRISBURG MEDICAL CENTER (140210)**, 100 Dr Warren Tuttle Drive, Zip 62946–2718, Mailing Address: P.O. Box 428, Zip 62946–0428; tel. 618/253–7671, **A**1 10 20 **F**3 8 11 15 28 29 30 31 34 40 45 50 56 57 59 61 62 64 75 77 78 79 81 85 87 91 93 94 97 98 100 101 102 103 104 107 108 110 114 118 119 127 129 130 131 133 146 154
Primary Contact: Donald Hutson, President and Chief Executive Officer
COO: Danny Lampley, Chief Operating Officer
CFO: June Hayes, Chief Financial Officer
CIO: Rick Pyle, Director Information Systems
CHR: Dorene L Ewell, Director Human Resources and Education
CNO: Leslie Ferrell, Chief Nursing Officer
Web address: www.harrisburgmc.com
Control: Other not–for–profit (including NFP Corporation) **Service:** General medical and surgical

Staffed Beds: 69 **Admissions:** 2926 **Census:** 40 **Outpatient Visits:** 105254 **Births:** 0 **Total Expense ($000):** 69553 **Payroll Expense ($000):** 29029 **Personnel:** 551	

HARVARD—Mchenry County

⊠ **MERCYHEALTH HOSPITAL AND MEDICAL CENTER - HARVARD (141335)**, 901 Grant Street, Zip 60033–1898, Mailing Address: P.O. Box 850, Zip 60033–0850; tel. 815/943–5431, (Total facility includes 45 beds in nursing home–type unit) **A**1 10 18 **F**3 11 15 28 29 30 35 40 45 46 57 59 64 69 70 75 77 79 81 82 85 87 93 96 107 108 110 119 128 129 130 131 132 143 146 149 **S** Mercy Health System, Janesville, WI
Primary Contact: Javon R. Bea, Chief Executive Officer
COO: Jennifer Hallatt, Chief Operating Officer
CFO: Shannon Dunphy-Alexander, Director
CMO: Douglas Bryan, President, Medical Staff
CHR: Heather Niles, Director Human Resources Operations
CNO: Caryn Lynn Oleston, FACHE, MSN, R.N., Chief Nursing Officer
Web address: www.mercyhealthsystem.org
Control: Other not–for–profit (including NFP Corporation) **Service:** General medical and surgical

Staffed Beds: 50 **Admissions:** 651 **Census:** 46 **Outpatient Visits:** 59459 **Births:** 0 **Total Expense ($000):** 23624 **Payroll Expense ($000):** 9058 **Personnel:** 137	

HARVEY—Cook County

★ △ ⇑ **INGALLS MEMORIAL HOSPITAL (140191)**, One Ingalls Drive, Zip 60426–3591; tel. 708/333–2300, **A**2 3 5 7 10 21 **F**3 4 5 7 8 11 12 13 15 18 20 22 24 26 28 29 30 31 34 35 36 37 40 42 45 46 47 49 50 51 54 56 57 58 59 60 62 63 64 68 70 74 75 76 77 78 79 81 82 84 85 86 87 89 90 92 93 96 97 98 99 100 101 102 103 104 105 107 108 110 111 113 114 115 116 117 118 119 120 121 123 124 126 129 130 131 132 135 143 144 146 147 148 152 153 156 **S** University of Chicago Medicine, Chicago, IL
Primary Contact: Jonathan R. Goble, FACHE, Interim President
COO: Michael L Hicks, Senior Vice President and Chief Operating Officer
CFO: Michael Lawrence, Chief Financial Officer
CNO: Kathleen A Mikos, Vice President and Chief Nursing Officer
Web address: www.ingallshealthsystem.org
Control: Other not–for–profit (including NFP Corporation) **Service**: General medical and surgical

Staffed Beds: 270 **Admissions**: 13541 **Census**: 194 **Outpatient Visits**: 358417 **Births**: 942 **Total Expense ($000)**: 325589 **Payroll Expense ($000)**: 100693 **Personnel**: 1442

HAVANA—Mason County

⊞ **MASON DISTRICT HOSPITAL (141313)**, 615 North Promenade Street, Zip 62644–1243, Mailing Address: P.O. Box 530, Zip 62644–0530; tel. 309/543–4431, (Nonreporting) **A**1 10 18
Primary Contact: Douglas D. Kosier, Chief Executive Officer
CMO: Tad A. Yetter, M.D., President Medical Staff
CIO: Aaron Coots, Information Technology Director
CHR: Anne Davis, Director Human Resources
CNO: Rhonda Hine, R.N., Interim Chief Nursing Executive
Web address: www.masondistricthospital.org
Control: Hospital district or authority, Government, nonfederal **Service**: General medical and surgical

Staffed Beds: 20

HAZEL CREST—Cook County

★ ⇑ **ADVOCATE SOUTH SUBURBAN HOSPITAL (140250)**, 17800 South Kedzie Avenue, Zip 60429–0989; tel. 708/799–8000, **A**2 10 21 **F**3 11 13 15 18 20 22 24 26 28 29 30 31 34 35 36 40 46 47 49 50 51 53 55 57 59 60 63 64 68 70 75 76 78 79 81 82 85 87 89 92 93 100 107 108 110 111 114 115 118 119 126 130 132 145 146 147 148 149 154 156 **S** Advocate Aurora Health, Downers Grove, IL
Primary Contact: Rashard Johnson, President
COO: Karen Clark, MS, R.N., Vice President Operations
CFO: Brian Kelly, Vice President Finance
CMO: Richard Multack, D.O., Vice President Medical Management
CIO: Beth Turek, Site Manager Information Systems
CHR: Kristin Landini, Vice President Human Resources
CNO: Sharon A. Otten, Vice President Nursing
Web address: www.advocatehealth.com/ssub/
Control: Church operated, Nongovernment, not–for–profit **Service**: General medical and surgical

Staffed Beds: 217 **Admissions**: 9821 **Census**: 105 **Outpatient Visits**: 144889 **Births**: 60 **Total Expense ($000)**: 218900 **Payroll Expense ($000)**: 72169 **Personnel**: 1024

HERRIN—Williamson County

☐ **HERRIN HOSPITAL (140011)**, 201 South 14th Street, Zip 62948–3631; tel. 618/942–2171, **A**1 5 10 **F**3 11 12 18 28 29 30 34 35 40 45 47 49 50 51 54 56 57 59 60 61 64 68 70 74 75 78 79 81 82 84 85 86 87 90 92 93 100 107 108 111 114 115 119 130 131 132 135 143 146 148 149 154 156 **S** Southern Illinois Healthcare, Carbondale, IL
Primary Contact: Rodney Smith, Vice President and Administrator
CFO: Michael Kasser, Chief Financial Officer
CMO: Michelle Jenkins, M.D., President Medical Staff
CIO: David Holland, Chief Information Officer
CHR: Teresa A Lovellette, Manager Human Resources
Web address: www.sih.net
Control: Other not–for–profit (including NFP Corporation) **Service**: General medical and surgical

Staffed Beds: 114 **Admissions**: 6770 **Census**: 80 **Outpatient Visits**: 170201 **Births**: 0 **Total Expense ($000)**: 157726 **Payroll Expense ($000)**: 45808 **Personnel**: 925

HIGHLAND—Madison County

⊞ **HSHS ST. JOSEPH'S HOSPITAL (141336)**, 12866 Troxler Avenue, Zip 62249–1698; tel. 618/651–2600, **A**1 10 18 **F**3 8 11 15 26 27 28 29 30 34 35 37 40 41 44 45 47 49 51 53 57 59 64 70 75 79 81 84 86 87 93 97 107 108 110 111 114 119 124 126 129 130 131 132 133 135 143 146 147 154 157 **S** HSHS Hospital Sisters Health System, Springfield, IL
Primary Contact: John A. Ludwig, President and Chief Operating Officer
COO: Chris Govero, Director of Operations
CFO: David Nosacka, Southern Illinois Division Chief Financial Officer
CHR: Christie Silvey, Director People Services
CNO: Teresa Cornelius, R.N., Interim Chief Nursing Officer
Web address: www.stjosephshighland.com
Control: Church operated, Nongovernment, not–for–profit **Service**: General medical and surgical

Staffed Beds: 25 **Admissions**: 1258 **Census**: 18 **Outpatient Visits**: 58918 **Births**: 0 **Total Expense ($000)**: 39454 **Payroll Expense ($000)**: 11696 **Personnel**: 218

HIGHLAND PARK—Lake County

NORTHSHORE HIGHLAND PARK HOSPITAL See Northshore University Health System, Evanston

HILLSBORO—Montgomery County

⊞ **HILLSBORO AREA HOSPITAL (141332)**, 1200 East Tremont Street, Zip 62049–1900; tel. 217/532–6111, **A**1 10 18 **F**2 3 10 15 28 29 30 34 35 40 56 57 59 64 65 75 77 79 81 85 86 87 89 92 93 94 97 107 110 111 115 125 129 130 131 133 135 146 148 **S** HealthTech Management Services, Brentwood, TN
Primary Contact: Rex H. Brown, President and Chief Executive Officer
CFO: Terri L Carroll, Vice President Financial Services
CHR: Sharon Clark, Director Human Resources
Web address: www.hillsborohealth.org
Control: Other not–for–profit (including NFP Corporation) **Service**: General medical and surgical

Staffed Beds: 25 **Admissions**: 353 **Census**: 7 **Outpatient Visits**: 15088 **Births**: 0 **Total Expense ($000)**: 21060 **Payroll Expense ($000)**: 8004 **Personnel**: 179

HINES—Cook County

⊞ △ **EDWARD HINES, JR. VETERANS AFFAIRS HOSPITAL**, 5000 South Fifth Avenue, Zip 60141–3030, Mailing Address: P.O. Box 5000, Zip 60141–5000; tel. 708/202–8387, (Nonreporting) **A**1 2 3 5 7 **S** Department of Veterans Affairs, Washington, DC
Primary Contact: Steven E. Braverman, M.D., Director
CFO: Yolanda Martinez, Chief Fiscal Services
CMO: Jack Bulmash, M.D., Chief of Staff
CIO: Robert Tanjuakio, Chief Information Resources Management
CNO: Marianne Locke, R.N., MSN, Associate Director Patient Care Services
Web address: www.hines.va.gov/
Control: Veterans Affairs, Government, federal **Service**: General medical and surgical

Staffed Beds: 485

☐ **JOHN J. MADDEN MENTAL HEALTH CENTER (144028)**, 1200 South First Avenue, Zip 60141–0800; tel. 708/338–7202, (Nonreporting) **A**1 3 5 10 **S** Division of Mental Health, Department of Human Services, Springfield, IL
Primary Contact: Edith Newman, Interim Administrator
CFO: Janice Evans, Chief Financial Officer
Control: State, Government, nonfederal **Service**: Psychiatric

Staffed Beds: 125

VETERANS AFFAIRS EDWARD HINES, JR. HOSPITAL See Edward Hines, Jr. Veterans Affairs Hospital

IL

HINSDALE—DuPage County

☒ **ADVENTIST MEDICAL CENTER - HINSDALE (140122)**, 120 North Oak Street, Zip 60521–3890; tel. 630/856–6001, **A**1 2 3 5 10 13 **F**3 4 13 15 18 20 22 24 26 28 29 30 31 34 37 38 39 40 41 43 44 45 47 49 54 55 57 58 59 61 64 70 72 76 78 79 81 82 84 85 86 87 89 92 93 97 98 99 100 107 108 114 115 126 129 130 131 132 135 143 146 147 149 151 154 156 **S** AdventHealth, Altamonte Springs, FL
Primary Contact: Steven Province, President and Chief Executive Officer
CFO: Rebecca Mathis, Vice President and Chief Financial Officer
CMO: Bonny Chen, M.D., Vice President and Chief Medical Officer
CHR: Mary P Leurck, Human Resources Director
CNO: Mary S Murphy, MSN, Vice President and Chief Nursing Officer
Web address: www.AMITAhealth.org
Control: Church operated, Nongovernment, not–for–profit **Service:** General medical and surgical

> **Staffed Beds:** 261 **Admissions:** 11744 **Census:** 139 **Outpatient Visits:** 251486 **Births:** 2641 **Total Expense ($000):** 280567 **Payroll Expense ($000):** 92595 **Personnel:** 1415

☒ **RML SPECIALTY HOSPITAL (142010)**, 5601 South County Line Road, Zip 60521–4875; tel. 630/286–4000, (Includes RML SPECIALTY HOSPITAL, 3435 West Van Buren Street, Chicago, Illinois, Zip 60624–3312; tel. 773/826–6300; James R Prister, President and Chief Executive Officer) **A**1 3 5 10 **F**1 3 18 29 30 31 45 53 58 74 85 87 107 114 115 119 130 148 149
Primary Contact: James R. Prister, President and Chief Executive Officer
COO: Ken Pawola, Chief Operating Officer
CFO: Tom Pater, Chief Financial Officer
CMO: Patrick Fahey, M.D., Chief Medical Officer
CIO: Vincent S Vitali, Chief Information Officer
CHR: John Landstrom, Director Human Resources
CNO: Marti Edwards, MSN, R.N., Chief Nursing Officer
Web address: www.rmlspecialtyhospital.org
Control: Other not–for–profit (including NFP Corporation) **Service:** Acute long–term care hospital

> **Staffed Beds:** 165 **Admissions:** 1350 **Census:** 135 **Outpatient Visits:** 0 **Births:** 0 **Total Expense ($000):** 93141 **Payroll Expense ($000):** 46402 **Personnel:** 702

HOFFMAN ESTATES—Cook County

☒ **ALEXIAN BROTHERS BEHAVIORAL HEALTH HOSPITAL (144031)**, 1650 Moon Lake Boulevard, Zip 60169–1010; tel. 847/882–1600, (Nonreporting) **A**1 10 **S** Ascension Healthcare, Saint Louis, MO
Primary Contact: Clayton Ciha, President and Chief Executive Officer
COO: Christopher Novak, Chief Operating Officer
CFO: David Jones, Chief Financial Officer
CMO: Gregory Teas, M.D., Chief Medical Officer
CIO: Sherrie Russell, Vice President and Chief Information Officer
CNO: Christine Quinlan, MS, R.N., Chief Nursing Officer
Web address: www.abbhh.org
Control: Church operated **Service:** Psychiatric

> **Staffed Beds:** 141

☒ **AMITA HEALTH HOFFMAN ESTATES (140290)**, 1555 Barrington Road, Zip 60169–1019; tel. 847/843–2000, (Includes AMITA HEALTH WOMEN & CHILDREN'S HOSPITAL, 1555 Barrington Road, Hoffman Estates, Illinois, Zip 60169–1019; tel. 847/843–2000; Kevin Rath, Vice President and Executive Director) **A**1 2 3 5 10 **F**3 8 11 12 13 15 18 19 20 22 26 29 30 31 32 34 35 37 39 40 41 42 43 44 45 46 47 48 49 50 51 54 55 57 59 63 64 70 72 73 74 76 77 78 79 81 82 84 85 86 87 88 89 93 107 108 110 111 114 115 118 119 120 121 124 126 130 132 145 146 147 148 149 154 156 157 **S** Ascension Healthcare, Saint Louis, MO
Primary Contact: Leonard Wilk, President and Chief Executive Officer
COO: Laurence Dry, Chief Operating Officer, Acute Care Hospitals Northern Region
CFO: Henry Zeisel, Chief Financial Officer, Northern Region
CIO: Sherrie Russell, Senior Vice President and Chief Information Officer
CHR: Donald Russell, Senior Vice President and Chief Human Resources Officer
CNO: Chris Budzinsky, Vice President Nursing and Chief Nursing Officer Alexian Brothers Acute Care Ministries
Web address: www.AMITAHealth.org
Control: Church operated, Nongovernment, not–for–profit **Service:** General medical and surgical

> **Staffed Beds:** 298 **Admissions:** 16814 **Census:** 199 **Outpatient Visits:** 191493 **Births:** 3371 **Total Expense ($000):** 458428 **Payroll Expense ($000):** 143842 **Personnel:** 1424

HOOPESTON—Vermilion County

★ ⇑ **CARLE HOOPESTON REGIONAL HEALTH CENTER (141316)**, 701 East Orange Street, Zip 60942–1801; tel. 217/283–5531, **A**3 10 18 21 **F**3 15 29 35 40 45 57 59 65 79 81 85 89 90 93 107 108 110 111 115 119 128 133 **S** Carle Foundation, Urbana, IL
Primary Contact: Harry Brockus, Chief Executive Officer
CHR: Melodee Bowers, Director Human Resources
Web address: www.carle.org
Control: Other not–for–profit (including NFP Corporation) **Service:** General medical and surgical

> **Staffed Beds:** 13 **Admissions:** 362 **Census:** 3 **Outpatient Visits:** 11375 **Births:** 0 **Total Expense ($000):** 30685 **Payroll Expense ($000):** 6177 **Personnel:** 99

HOPEDALE—Tazewell County

HOPEDALE MEDICAL COMPLEX (141330), 107 Tremont Street, Zip 61747–7525, Mailing Address: P.O. Box 267, Zip 61747–7525; tel. 309/449–3321, (Total facility includes 52 beds in nursing home–type unit) **A**10 18 28 29 30 32 34 35 40 45 49 53 56 57 59 64 65 67 70 78 79 81 97 107 110 111 115 119 129 130 131 133 145 146 147 149 157 158
Primary Contact: Alfred N. Rossi, M.D., Chief Executive Officer
COO: Mark F Rossi, Chief Operating Officer and General Counsel
CFO: Nicholas A. Penn, Chief Financial Officer
CHR: Andrea Halley, Vice President of Non-Clinical Operations/Director Human Resources
CNO: Timothy Sondag, Senior Nursing Officer
Web address: www.hopedalemc.com
Control: Other not–for–profit (including NFP Corporation) **Service:** General medical and surgical

> **Staffed Beds:** 82 **Admissions:** 522 **Census:** 52 **Outpatient Visits:** 61744 **Births:** 0 **Total Expense ($000):** 26376 **Payroll Expense ($000):** 10644 **Personnel:** 173

JACKSONVILLE—Morgan County

☒ **PASSAVANT AREA HOSPITAL (140058)**, 1600 West Walnut Street, Zip 62650–1136; tel. 217/245–9541, (Total facility includes 15 beds in nursing home–type unit) **A**1 10 **F**3 13 14 15 28 29 30 31 34 35 40 41 45 50 51 57 58 59 64 68 69 70 75 76 78 79 81 82 85 86 87 89 93 97 98 104 107 108 110 111 115 118 119 121 124 127 128 129 130 131 141 146 147 148 **S** Memorial Health System, Springfield, IL
Primary Contact: Harry M. Schmidt, President and Chief Executive Officer
CFO: David Bolen, Vice President and Chief Financial Officer
CMO: Scott Boston, M.D., Chief Medical Officer
CIO: Janie Cook, Director Information Systems
CHR: Jim Bormann, Director Human Resources
CNO: Karen Daum, R.N., MS, Vice President and Chief Nursing Officer
Web address: www.passavanthospital.com
Control: Church operated, Nongovernment, not–for–profit **Service:** General medical and surgical

> **Staffed Beds:** 118 **Admissions:** 3885 **Census:** 49 **Outpatient Visits:** 89708 **Births:** 374

JERSEYVILLE—Jersey County

☒ **JERSEY COMMUNITY HOSPITAL (140059)**, 400 Maple Summit Road, Zip 62052–2028, Mailing Address: P.O. Box 426, Zip 62052–0426; tel. 618/498–6402, (Nonreporting) **A**1 10
Primary Contact: Jonathan O. Wade, Chief Executive Officer
CFO: Beth King, Chief Financial Officer
CMO: Michael McNear, M.D., Chief Medical Officer
CIO: Shane Winters, Chief Information Officer
CHR: Sharon K Sanford, Director Human Resources
CNO: Julie Smith, R.N., MSN, Director of Nursing
Web address: www.jch.org
Control: Hospital district or authority, Government, nonfederal **Service:** General medical and surgical

> **Staffed Beds:** 46

Many Facility Codes have changed. Please refer to the AHA Guide Code Chart. © 2019 AHA Guide

JOLIET—Will County

⊞ △ **AMITA HEALTH SAINT JOSEPH MEDICAL CENTER (140007)**, 333 North Madison Street, Zip 60435–8200; tel. 815/725–7133, **A**1 2 3 7 10 **F**3 11 12 13 15 17 18 20 22 24 26 28 29 30 31 32 34 35 36 38 39 40 41 43 44 45 46 47 49 50 53 54 56 57 58 59 60 61 64 65 68 70 72 74 75 76 77 78 79 80 81 82 84 85 86 87 89 90 92 93 96 97 98 99 100 101 102 103 105 107 108 110 111 114 115 118 119 120 121 123 124 126 129 130 131 132 134 135 143 145 146 147 149 154 **S** Ascension Healthcare, Saint Louis, MO
Primary Contact: Robert J. Erickson, President
CFO: Deb Schimerowski, Regional Finance Officer
CMO: Gary Lipinski, M.D., Chief Medical Officer
CHR: Monica Simzyk, Regional Human Resource Officer
CNO: Lynn Watson, Interim Chief Nursing Officer
Web address: www.presencehealth.org/stjoes
Control: Church operated, Nongovernment, not–for–profit **Service**: General medical and surgical

Staffed Beds: 485 **Admissions**: 18871 **Census**: 235 **Outpatient Visits**: 173144 **Births**: 1062 **Total Expense ($000)**: 393195 **Payroll Expense ($000)**: 114336 **Personnel**: 1736

PROVENA SAINT JOSEPH MEDICAL CENTER See Amita Health Saint Joseph Medical Center

KANKAKEE—Kankakee County

⊞ **AMITA HEALTH ST. MARY'S HOSPITAL (140155)**, 500 West Court Street, Zip 60901–3661; tel. 815/937–2400, **A**1 2 3 10 **F**3 5 11 12 13 15 18 20 22 26 28 29 30 31 32 34 35 36 38 39 40 43 44 45 46 47 48 49 50 54 56 57 58 59 60 61 64 65 68 70 74 75 76 77 78 79 81 82 84 85 86 87 89 92 93 97 98 100 101 102 103 104 105 107 108 110 111 114 115 119 120 121 123 129 130 131 132 135 143 146 147 149 152 153 154 **S** Ascension Healthcare, Saint Louis, MO
Primary Contact: Chris Shride, President
CFO: Deb Schimerowski, Regional Chief Financial Officer
CMO: Kalisha Hill, M.D., Chief Medical Officer
CIO: Russell Soliman, Director Information Services
CHR: Monica Simzyk, Regional Chief Human Resources Officer
CNO: Karen M Gallagher, MSN, Chief Nursing Office, Vice President Operations
Web address: www.presencehealth.org/presence-st-marys-hospital-kankakee
Control: Church operated, Nongovernment, not–for–profit **Service**: General medical and surgical

Staffed Beds: 182 **Admissions**: 5562 **Census**: 59 **Outpatient Visits**: 80363 **Births**: 373 **Total Expense ($000)**: 122932 **Payroll Expense ($000)**: 34652 **Personnel**: 631

PROVENA ST. MARY'S HOSPITAL See Amita Health St. Mary's Hospital

★ △ ⇧ **RIVERSIDE MEDICAL CENTER (140186)**, 350 North Wall Street, Zip 60901–2901; tel. 815/933–1671, **A**2 3 5 7 10 21 **F**3 4 5 6 7 8 9 12 13 15 17 18 20 22 24 26 28 29 30 31 32 34 35 36 38 39 40 41 43 44 45 46 47 49 50 51 54 55 56 57 58 59 61 62 64 65 66 68 70 71 74 75 76 77 78 79 81 82 84 85 86 87 89 90 92 93 96 97 98 99 100 101 102 103 104 105 107 108 110 111 114 115 118 119 120 121 123 124 126 127 129 130 131 132 134 135 141 143 144 145 146 147 148 149 150 151 152 153 154 156 157
Primary Contact: Phillip M. Kambic, President and Chief Executive Officer
CFO: John Seal, Interim Chief Financial Officer Director Human Resources
CMO: Keith A Moss, Vice President & Chief Medical Informatics Officers
CIO: Kyle Hansen, Corporate Director Information Systems
CHR: Becky Kay Hinrichs, Vice President Human Resources
CNO: Michael Mutterer, Senior Vice President and Chief Nursing Officer
Web address: www.riversidehealthcare.org
Control: Other not–for–profit (including NFP Corporation) **Service**: General medical and surgical

Staffed Beds: 318 **Admissions**: 12030 **Census**: 165 **Outpatient Visits**: 567233 **Births**: 1033 **Total Expense ($000)**: 343333 **Payroll Expense ($000)**: 156264 **Personnel**: 2218

KEWANEE—Henry County

★ **OSF SAINT LUKE MEDICAL CENTER (141325)**, 1051 West South Street, Zip 61443–8354, Mailing Address: P.O. Box 747, Zip 61443–0747; tel. 309/852–7500, **A**10 18 **F**3 11 15 29 30 32 34 35 36 38 40 45 50 57 59 64 65 66 70 75 77 78 79 81 82 85 86 87 92 93 96 97 108 110 111 115 119 127 129 130 131 132 133 135 146 147 148 149 154 156 **S** OSF Healthcare, Peoria, IL
Primary Contact: Jacqueline D. Kernan, President
CFO: John Bowser, Vice President, Chief Financial Officer
CMO: Clifford G Martin, M.D., Regional Vice President and Chief Medical Officer
CHR: Renee A Salisbury, Director Human Resources
CNO: Shelley Wiborg, MS, R.N., Chief Nursing Officer
Web address: www.osfsaintluke.org
Control: Other not–for–profit (including NFP Corporation) **Service**: General medical and surgical

Staffed Beds: 25 **Admissions**: 601 **Census**: 5 **Outpatient Visits**: 41454 **Births**: 0 **Total Expense ($000)**: 30587 **Payroll Expense ($000)**: 11198 **Personnel**: 125

LA GRANGE—Cook County

⊞ **ADVENTIST MEDICAL CENTER LAGRANGE (140065)**, 5101 South Willow Spring Road, Zip 60525–2600; tel. 708/245–9000, **A**1 2 3 5 10 **F**3 4 13 15 18 20 22 24 29 30 31 34 37 40 41 43 44 45 49 51 54 57 58 59 61 62 64 68 70 73 76 77 78 79 81 82 84 85 86 87 90 91 93 96 97 100 101 107 108 110 111 114 115 119 126 130 131 143 146 147 148 154 **S** AdventHealth, Altamonte Springs, FL
Primary Contact: Michael Murrill, President and Chief Executive Officer
CFO: Rebecca Mathis, Chief Financial Officer
CIO: Thomas Schoenig, Chief Information Officer
CHR: Garry Giertuga, Site Manager Human Resources
CNO: Mary S Murphy, MSN, Regional Chief Nursing Officer
Web address: www.keepingyouwell.com
Control: Church operated, Nongovernment, not–for–profit **Service**: General medical and surgical

Staffed Beds: 200 **Admissions**: 7843 **Census**: 103 **Outpatient Visits**: 82999 **Births**: 133 **Total Expense ($000)**: 112661 **Payroll Expense ($000)**: 54356 **Personnel**: 750

LAKE FOREST—Lake County

LAKE FOREST HOSPITAL See Northwestern Medicine Lake Forest Hospital

⊞ **NORTHWESTERN MEDICINE LAKE FOREST HOSPITAL (140130)**, 1000 North Westmoreland Road, Zip 60045–1696, Mailing Address: 1000 N Westmoreland Road, Zip 60045–1658; tel. 847/234–5600, **A**1 2 3 5 10 **F**3 8 9 11 13 15 18 20 22 26 28 29 30 31 32 34 35 36 38 40 41 42 43 44 45 46 48 49 50 51 52 53 54 55 56 57 58 59 60 62 64 65 66 68 70 73 74 75 76 77 78 79 81 82 84 85 86 87 92 93 96 97 100 102 104 107 108 110 111 114 115 116 117 119 120 121 123 126 129 130 131 132 135 144 146 147 148 149 150 154 156 **S** Northwestern Memorial HealthCare, Chicago, IL
Primary Contact: Thomas J. McAfee, President, North Region
CFO: Richard A. Franco, Vice President and Chief Financial Officer
CMO: Jeffrey D. Kopin, Senior Vice President and Chief Medical Officer
CNO: Denise Majeski, MSN, R.N., Vice President Operations and Chief Nurse Executive
Web address: www.nm.org
Control: Other not–for–profit (including NFP Corporation) **Service**: General medical and surgical

Staffed Beds: 120 **Admissions**: 8368 **Census**: 76 **Outpatient Visits**: 539528 **Births**: 1709 **Total Expense ($000)**: 446012 **Payroll Expense ($000)**: 176715 **Personnel**: 2243

LAWRENCEVILLE—Lawrence County

LAWRENCE COUNTY MEMORIAL HOSPITAL (141344), 2200 West State Street, Zip 62439–1852; tel. 618/943–1000, **A**10 18 **F**3 11 15 28 29 30 35 40 75 77 81 93 107 110 114 127 130 133 149 **S** QHR, Brentwood, TN
Primary Contact: Donald Robbins, Chief Executive Officer
CFO: Larry Spore, Chief Financial Officer
CIO: Gary Theriac, Director Information Technology
CHR: Kim Alldredge, Director Human Resources
CNO: Rita Garvey, Chief Nursing Officer
Web address: www.lcmhosp.org
Control: Other not–for–profit (including NFP Corporation) **Service**: General medical and surgical

Staffed Beds: 25 **Admissions**: 479 **Census**: 6 **Outpatient Visits**: 47078 **Births**: 0 **Total Expense ($000)**: 16317 **Payroll Expense ($000)**: 7009 **Personnel**: 148

IL

Hospital, Medicare Provider Number, Address, Telephone, Approval, Facility, and Physician Codes, Health Care System

★ American Hospital Association (AHA) membership
☐ The Joint Commission accreditation
○ Healthcare Facilities Accreditation Program
◇ DNV Healthcare Inc. accreditation
⇧ Center for Improvement in Healthcare Quality Accreditation
△ Commission on Accreditation of Rehabilitation Facilities (CARF) accreditation

LIBERTYVILLE—Lake County

★ ⬆ **ADVOCATE CONDELL MEDICAL CENTER (140202)**, 801 South Milwaukee Avenue, Zip 60048–3199; tel. 847/362–2900, **A**2 10 21 **F**1 3 4 11 12 13 15 16 17 18 19 20 22 24 26 28 29 30 31 32 34 35 36 37 39 40 41 43 44 45 46 47 48 49 50 51 53 54 55 56 57 59 60 64 65 67 68 70 72 73 74 75 76 77 78 79 80 81 82 85 86 87 88 89 90 92 93 94 96 98 107 108 110 111 114 115 117 118 119 120 121 123 124 126 128 130 132 135 144 145 146 147 148 154 **S** Advocate Aurora Health, Downers Grove, IL
Primary Contact: Michael A. Ploszek, President
CFO: David A Cartwright, Vice President Finance and Support Services
CMO: Debra Susie-Lattner, M.D., Vice President Medical Management
CIO: Harold Kromer, Director Site Information Systems
CHR: Amy Antani Logue, Ph.D., Vice President Human Resources
Web address: www.advocatehealth.com/condell/
Control: Other not–for–profit (including NFP Corporation) **Service**: General medical and surgical

Staffed Beds: 286 **Admissions**: 15638 **Census**: 189 **Outpatient Visits**: 236215 **Births**: 1129 **Total Expense ($000)**: 309603 **Payroll Expense ($000)**: 105567

LINCOLN—Logan County

⊠ **ABRAHAM LINCOLN MEMORIAL HOSPITAL (141322)**, 200 Stahlhut Drive, Zip 62656–5066; tel. 217/732–2161, **A**1 10 18 **F**13 15 28 29 30 34 35 40 57 59 64 75 76 77 78 79 81 82 87 93 107 108 110 111 119 129 130 131 132 133 144 146 149 156 **S** Memorial Health System, Springfield, IL
Primary Contact: Dolan Dalpoas, President and Chief Executive Officer
CFO: Andrew Costic, Regional Chief Financial Officer
CMO: Amir J. Wahab, M.D., Medical Staff President
CIO: Keenan Leesman, Director Information Systems
CHR: Michelle Long, Regional Human Resource Manager
CNO: Roxanne Harling, Chief Nursing Officer
Web address: www.almh.org
Control: Other not–for–profit (including NFP Corporation) **Service**: General medical and surgical

Staffed Beds: 25 **Admissions**: 890 **Census**: 11 **Outpatient Visits**: 46299 **Births**: 195 **Total Expense ($000)**: 44289 **Payroll Expense ($000)**: 16955 **Personnel**: 301

LITCHFIELD—Montgomery County

⊠ **HSHS ST. FRANCIS HOSPITAL (141350)**, 1215 Franciscan Drive, Zip 62056–1799, Mailing Address: P.O. Box 1215, Zip 62056–0999; tel. 217/324–2191, **A**1 10 18 **F**3 8 11 13 15 18 28 29 30 31 34 35 40 44 45 46 50 56 57 59 64 68 70 74 75 76 77 78 79 81 82 85 86 87 92 93 107 111 114 117 118 119 129 131 132 133 134 135 146 147 149 154 **S** HSHS Hospital Sisters Health System, Springfield, IL
Primary Contact: John Peipert, R.N., Interim President and Chief Executive Officer
CFO: Marisa Murray, CPA, Director Finance
CNO: John Peipert, R.N., Chief Nursing Officer
Web address: www.stfrancis-litchfield.org
Control: Church operated, Nongovernment, not–for–profit **Service**: General medical and surgical

Staffed Beds: 25 **Admissions**: 1320 **Census**: 12 **Outpatient Visits**: 65866 **Births**: 235 **Total Expense ($000)**: 35614 **Payroll Expense ($000)**: 11612 **Personnel**: 223

MACOMB—Mcdonough County

⊠ **MCDONOUGH DISTRICT HOSPITAL (140089)**, 525 East Grant Street, Zip 61455–3318; tel. 309/833–4101, **A**1 10 20 **F**3 5 11 13 15 28 29 31 34 35 38 40 45 47 48 50 51 54 56 57 59 62 63 64 68 70 76 77 78 79 81 84 85 86 91 93 94 96 97 98 100 101 102 103 104 107 108 110 115 119 124 127 129 130 131 132 133 135 146 147 148
Primary Contact: Brian Dietz, Interim Chief Executive Officer
CFO: Linda Dace, Vice President Finance
CMO: Edwin Card, President Medical Staff
CIO: Harlan T Baker, Department Leader Information Systems
CHR: Sue Dexter, Administrative Department Leader Human Resources
CNO: Wanda Foster, R.N., MS, FACHE, MSN, Vice President Nursing
Web address: www.mdh.org
Control: Hospital district or authority, Government, nonfederal **Service**: General medical and surgical

Staffed Beds: 60 **Admissions**: 1642 **Census**: 20 **Outpatient Visits**: 213762 **Births**: 249 **Total Expense ($000)**: 84192 **Payroll Expense ($000)**: 38176 **Personnel**: 496

MARION—Williamson County

⊠ **HEARTLAND REGIONAL MEDICAL CENTER (140184)**, 3333 West DeYoung, Zip 62959–5884; tel. 618/998–7000, (Nonreporting) **A**1 10 **S** Quorum Health, Brentwood, TN
Primary Contact: Melisa Adkins, Chief Executive Officer
COO: Kolbe Sheridan, Chief Operating Officer
CFO: Jeff Thomas, Chief Financial Officer
CHR: Sam Hood, Director Human Resources
Web address: www.heartlandregional.com
Control: Corporation, Investor–owned (for–profit) **Service**: General medical and surgical

Staffed Beds: 92

⊠ **MARION VETERANS AFFAIRS MEDICAL CENTER**, 2401 West Main Street, Zip 62959–1188; tel. 618/997–5311, (Nonreporting) **A**1 **S** Department of Veterans Affairs, Washington, DC
Primary Contact: Jo-Ann M. Ginsberg, R.N., MSN, Director
COO: Frank Kehus, Associate Director for Operations
CFO: Connie McDonald, Chief Financial Officer
CMO: Michael Ladwig, M.D., Chief of Staff
CIO: Adam Powell, Program Manager
CHR: Tim Hartwell, Chief Human Resources
CNO: Rose Burke, Associate Director Patient Care Services
Web address: www.marion.va.gov
Control: Veterans Affairs, Government, federal **Service**: General medical and surgical

Staffed Beds: 54

MARYVILLE—Madison County

⊠ △ **ANDERSON HOSPITAL (140289)**, 6800 State Route 162, Zip 62062–8500; tel. 618/288–5711, **A**1 7 10 **F**3 11 13 15 18 20 22 28 29 30 31 34 35 40 49 57 59 62 64 70 74 75 76 78 79 81 85 90 93 107 110 111 115 117 118 119 120 121 123 126 129 130 132 144 146 147 148 149 154 156
Primary Contact: Keith Allen. Page, President and Chief Executive Officer
CFO: Michael Marshall, Vice President Finance and Chief Financial Officer
CMO: Charles A. Lane, Chief Medical Officer
CIO: Michael Ward, Director Information Services
CHR: Robin Steinmann, Administrative Director Human Resources
CNO: Lisa Klaustermeier, R.N., MSN, Chief Nursing Officer
Web address: www.andersonhospital.org
Control: Other not–for–profit (including NFP Corporation) **Service**: General medical and surgical

Staffed Beds: 154 **Admissions**: 7301 **Census**: 79 **Outpatient Visits**: 169934 **Births**: 1473 **Total Expense ($000)**: 140210 **Payroll Expense ($000)**: 54068 **Personnel**: 1220

MATTOON—Coles County

⊠ **SARAH BUSH LINCOLN HEALTH CENTER (140189)**, 1000 Health Center Drive, Zip 61938–9253; tel. 217/258–2525, **A**1 10 20 **F**3 11 12 13 15 28 29 30 31 32 34 35 36 38 39 40 44 45 49 50 53 54 56 57 59 61 62 63 64 65 66 68 69 70 71 74 75 76 77 78 79 81 82 84 85 86 87 89 93 97 98 100 101 102 104 105 107 110 111 115 117 119 120 121 123 127 129 130 131 132 134 135 144 145 146 147 148 154 156
Primary Contact: Jerry Esker, President and Chief Executive Officer
COO: Dennis Pluard, Vice President Finance and Operations
CFO: Dennis Pluard, Vice President Finance and Operations
CMO: James Hildebrandt, D.O., Vice President Medical Affairs
CIO: Maggie Ratliff, Vice President Information Systems
CHR: Eric Benson, Vice President Human Resources & Wellness
CNO: Lisa J. Hernandez, R.N., Vice President, Patient Care Continuum and Chief Nursing Officer
Web address: www.sarahbush.org
Control: Other not–for–profit (including NFP Corporation) **Service**: General medical and surgical

Staffed Beds: 132 **Admissions**: 7291 **Census**: 65 **Outpatient Visits**: 470856 **Births**: 751 **Total Expense ($000)**: 305972 **Payroll Expense ($000)**: 147096 **Personnel**: 2178

IL

Many Facility Codes have changed. Please refer to the AHA Guide Code Chart. © 2019 AHA Guide

MAYWOOD—Cook County

LOYOLA UNIVERSITY MEDICAL CENTER (140276), 2160 South First Avenue, Zip 60153–3328; tel. 708/216–9000, (Includes RONALD MCDONALD CHILDREN'S HOSPITAL, 2160 South 1St Avenue, Maywood, Illinois, Zip 60153–3328; tel. 888/584–7888) **A**1 2 3 5 8 10 19 **F**3 6 7 8 9 11 12 13 14 15 16 17 18 19 20 21 22 23 24 25 26 27 28 29 30 31 32 33 34 35 36 37 38 39 40 41 43 44 45 46 47 48 49 50 51 54 55 56 57 58 59 60 61 64 65 66 68 70 71 72 73 74 75 76 77 78 79 80 81 82 84 85 86 87 88 89 91 92 93 94 96 97 100 101 102 104 107 108 110 111 114 115 116 117 118 119 120 121 123 124 126 129 130 131 132 134 135 136 137 138 139 140 141 142 143 144 145 146 147 148 149 150 154 155 **S** Trinity Health, Livonia, MI
Primary Contact: Daniel J. Post, Interim President
CFO: Jay Sial, Chief Financial Officer
CMO: Joshua Lee, M.D., Chief Medical Officer
CIO: Arthur J Krumrey, Chief Information Officer
CHR: Vicky Piper, Vice President Human Resources
Web address: www.loyolamedicine.org/Medical_Services/index.cfm
Control: Other not–for–profit (including NFP Corporation) **Service:** General medical and surgical

Staffed Beds: 524 **Admissions:** 22054 **Census:** 358 **Outpatient Visits:** 1344744 **Births:** 1379 **Personnel:** 6708

MCHENRY—Mchenry County

NORTHWESTERN MEDICINE MCHENRY (140116), 4201 Medical Center Drive, Zip 60050–8409; tel. 815/344–5000, (Includes NORTHWESTERN MEDICINE HUNTLEY, 10400 Haligus Road, Huntley, Illinois, Zip 60142; tel. 224/654–0000; Michael S Eesley, Chief Executive Officer; NORTHWESTERN MEDICINE WOODSTOCK, 3701 Doty Road, Woodstock, Illinois, Zip 60098–7509, Mailing Address: P O Box 1990, Zip 60098–1990, tel. 815/338–2500; Michael S Eesley, Chief Executive Officer) **A**1 2 3 5 10 **F**3 11 12 13 15 17 18 19 20 22 24 26 28 29 30 31 34 35 37 38 39 40 41 43 44 45 47 49 50 51 54 55 58 59 64 65 68 69 70 71 74 75 76 78 79 81 82 85 86 87 89 90 92 93 96 97 98 100 101 102 103 104 105 107 108 110 111 114 115 117 118 119 120 121 123 124 126 130 131 132 135 143 144 146 147 148 153 154 156 157 **S** Northwestern Memorial HealthCare, Chicago, IL
Primary Contact: Michael S. Eesley, Chief Executive Officer
COO: Jason Sciarro, President and Chief Operating Officer
CFO: David Tomlinson, Executive Vice President Chief Financial Officer and Chief Information Officer
CMO: Irfan Hafiz, Vice President Medical Affairs
CIO: David Tomlinson, Executive Vice President Chief Financial Officer and Chief Information Officer
CHR: Bernadette S Szczepanski, Senior Vice President, Human Resources
Web address: www.centegra.org
Control: Other not–for–profit (including NFP Corporation) **Service:** General medical and surgical

Staffed Beds: 326 **Admissions:** 18020 **Census:** 208 **Outpatient Visits:** 368855 **Births:** 1853 **Total Expense ($000):** 404084 **Payroll Expense ($000):** 145082 **Personnel:** 2830

MCLEANSBORO—Hamilton County

HAMILTON MEMORIAL HOSPITAL DISTRICT (141326), 611 South Marshall Avenue, Zip 62859–1213, Mailing Address: P.O. Box 429, Mc Leansboro, Zip 62859–0429; tel. 618/643–2361, (Nonreporting) **A**10 18
Primary Contact: Victoria Woodrow, Chief Executive Officer
CFO: Kent Mitchell, Chief Financial Officer
CIO: Mark Todd, Senior Systems Administrator
CHR: Sheila Thompson, Director Human Resources
CNO: Patty Blazier, Chief Nursing Officer
Web address: www.hmhospital.org
Control: Hospital district or authority, Government, nonfederal **Service:** General medical and surgical

Staffed Beds: 25

MELROSE PARK—Cook County

△ **GOTTLIEB MEMORIAL HOSPITAL (140008)**, 701 West North Avenue, Zip 60160–1612; tel. 708/681–3200, **A**1 3 5 7 10 19 **F**2 3 11 12 15 18 20 22 24 26 28 29 30 31 34 35 36 39 40 43 44 45 47 49 50 51 54 56 57 59 60 64 65 68 70 74 75 77 78 79 81 85 86 87 89 90 92 93 96 97 98 103 107 108 110 111 114 116 117 118 119 126 128 129 130 131 132 143 144 145 146 147 148 149 150 **S** Trinity Health, Livonia, MI
Primary Contact: Lori Price, President
CFO: Ellyn Chin, Vice President Finance
CMO: Gerald Luger, M.D., President Medical Staff
CIO: Maurita Adler, Director Information Services
CHR: Brett Wakefield, Vice President Human Resources
Web address: www.gottliebhospital.org
Control: Other not–for–profit (including NFP Corporation) **Service:** General medical and surgical

Staffed Beds: 171 **Admissions:** 6556 **Census:** 113 **Outpatient Visits:** 101748 **Births:** 0 **Personnel:** 825

WESTLAKE HOSPITAL (140240), 1225 Lake Street, Zip 60160–4000; tel. 708/681–3000, (Nonreporting) **A**1 10
Primary Contact: Joseph Ottolino, Chief Executive Officer
COO: Michael Ditoro, Chief Operating Officer
CFO: Jennifer Lamont, Chief Financial Officer
CMO: Robert Chase, M.D., Chief Medical Officer
CHR: Nancy Gunnell, Chief Human Resource Officer
CNO: Ruth Matthei, R.N., MS, Chief Nursing Officer
Web address: www.westlakehosp.com
Control: Corporation, Investor–owned (for–profit) **Service:** General medical and surgical

Staffed Beds: 181

MENDOTA—Lasalle County

★ **OSF SAINT PAUL MEDICAL CENTER (141310)**, 1401 East 12th Street, Zip 61342–9216; tel. 815/539–7461, **A**10 18 **F**3 11 15 28 29 30 31 34 40 49 57 59 64 69 70 77 78 79 81 82 85 93 107 110 111 115 127 129 130 133 146 154 **S** OSF Healthcare, Peoria, IL
Primary Contact: Dawn Trompeter, President
CMO: Leonardo Lopez, President Medical Staff
CHR: Kimberly Kennedy, Manager Human Resources
CNO: Heather Bomstad, MSN, R.N., Vice President Patient Care Services and Chief Nursing Officer
Web address: www.https://www.osfhealthcare.org/saint-paul
Control: Other not–for–profit (including NFP Corporation) **Service:** General medical and surgical

Staffed Beds: 25 **Admissions:** 529 **Census:** 7 **Outpatient Visits:** 33597 **Births:** 0 **Total Expense ($000):** 33234 **Payroll Expense ($000):** 12000 **Personnel:** 121

METROPOLIS—Massac County

★ **MASSAC MEMORIAL HOSPITAL (141323)**, 28 Chick Street, Zip 62960–2467, Mailing Address: P.O. Box 850, Zip 62960–0850; tel. 618/524–2176, (Nonreporting) **A**10 18
Primary Contact: Rick Goins, Chief Executive Officer
CFO: Randy Rushing, Chief Financial Officer
CHR: Johnna Douglas, Human Resources Manager
Web address: www.massachealth.org
Control: Hospital district or authority, Government, nonfederal **Service:** General medical and surgical

Staffed Beds: 25

MOLINE—Rock Island County

UNITYPOINT HEALTH - TRINITY MOLINE See Unitypoint Health - Trinity Rock Island, Rock Island

MONMOUTH—Warren County

★ **OSF HOLY FAMILY MEDICAL CENTER (141318)**, 1000 West Harlem Avenue, Zip 61462–1007; tel. 309/734–3141, **A**10 18 **F**11 15 28 29 30 34 40 45 46 57 59 64 65 68 75 81 85 87 93 97 107 110 115 118 119 127 129 130 132 133 145 146 154 156 **S** OSF Healthcare, Peoria, IL
Primary Contact: Patricia A. Luker, President
CFO: Theresa Springer, Chief Financial Officer
CMO: Clifford G Martin, M.D., Regional Vice President and Chief Medical Officer
CIO: Lew McCann, Director Management Information Systems
CHR: Jenny Jacobs, Director Human Resources
CNO: Shelley Wiborg, MS, R.N., Director of Nursing
Web address: www.osfholyfamily.org
Control: Church operated, Nongovernment, not–for–profit **Service:** General medical and surgical

Staffed Beds: 23 **Admissions:** 315 **Census:** 4 **Outpatient Visits:** 64249 **Births:** 0 **Total Expense ($000):** 28670 **Payroll Expense ($000):** 10688 **Personnel:** 91

IL

Hospital, Medicare Provider Number, Address, Telephone, Approval, Facility, and Physician Codes, Health Care System

★ American Hospital Association (AHA) membership
□ The Joint Commission accreditation
○ Healthcare Facilities Accreditation Program
◇ DNV Healthcare Inc. accreditation
⇑ Center for Improvement in Healthcare Quality Accreditation
△ Commission on Accreditation of Rehabilitation Facilities (CARF) accreditation

MONTICELLO—Piatt County

KIRBY MEDICAL CENTER (141301), 1000 Medical Center Drive, Zip 61856–2116; tel. 217/762–2115, (Nonreporting) **A**1 10 18
Primary Contact: Steven D. Tenhouse, FACHE, Chief Executive Officer
COO: Mark Fred, R.N., Chief Operating Officer
CFO: Alexander Nazarian, CPA, Chief Financial Officer
CMO: Narain Mandhan, M.D., Chief Medical Officer
CIO: Alexander Nazarian, CPA, Director Information Technology
CHR: Andrew Buffenbarger, Chief Compliance Officer
CNO: Jennifer Moss, MS, R.N., Chief Clinical Officer
Web address: www.kirbyhealth.org
Control: Other not–for–profit (including NFP Corporation) **Service:** General medical and surgical

Staffed Beds: 16

MORRIS—Grundy County

★ ○ **MORRIS HOSPITAL & HEALTHCARE CENTERS (140101)**, 150 West High Street, Zip 60450–1497; tel. 815/942–2932, **A**2 10 11 **F**3 11 13 15 18 20 22 26 28 29 34 35 40 43 45 47 49 50 54 57 59 64 65 66 69 70 75 76 77 78 79 81 82 85 86 87 89 93 97 102 107 108 110 111 114 115 118 119 120 121 123 129 130 132 135 143 144 146 149 154 156
Primary Contact: Mark B. Steadham, President and Chief Executive Officer
CFO: Mary Lou Tate, Chief Financial Officer
CHR: Erin Murphy-Frobish, Vice President Human Resources
CNO: Kimberly A. Landers, MS, R.N., Vice President Patient Care Services
Web address: www.morrishospital.org
Control: Other not–for–profit (including NFP Corporation) **Service:** General medical and surgical

Staffed Beds: 89 **Admissions:** 4070 **Census:** 38 **Outpatient Visits:** 367482 **Births:** 553 **Total Expense ($000):** 174080 **Payroll Expense ($000):** 77960 **Personnel:** 933

MORRISON—Whiteside County

MORRISON COMMUNITY HOSPITAL (141329), 303 North Jackson Street, Zip 61270–3042; tel. 815/772–4003, **A**10 18 **F**3 7 11 29 34 35 38 40 45 51 59 64 65 66 74 81 90 93 94 97 104 107 114 119 127 128 130 133 135 143 146 148 154
Primary Contact: Pam Pfister, Chief Executive Officer
COO: Pam Pfister, Chief Executive Officer
CFO: Cami Megli, Controller
CMO: Duncan Dinkha, M.D., Chief of Staff
CIO: Pam Pfister, Chief Executive Officer
CHR: Amber L Temple, Director Human Resources
Web address: www.morrisonhospital.com
Control: Hospital district or authority, Government, nonfederal **Service:** General medical and surgical

Staffed Beds: 23 **Admissions:** 288 **Census:** 8 **Outpatient Visits:** 24206 **Births:** 0 **Total Expense ($000):** 15386 **Payroll Expense ($000):** 8140 **Personnel:** 154

MOUNT CARMEL—Wabash County

WABASH GENERAL HOSPITAL (141327), 1418 College Drive, Zip 62863–2638; tel. 618/262–8621, (Nonreporting) **A**1 10 18 **S** Alliant Management Services, Louisville, KY
Primary Contact: Jay Purvis, President and Chief Executive Officer
COO: Karissa Turner, Vice President Operations
CFO: Steve McGill, Vice President Finance and Chief Financial Officer
CMO: Lawrence Jennings, Chief of Staff
CIO: Bobby Gage, Director Information Technology
CHR: Bridget Shepard, Vice President Human Resources
CNO: Tamara Gould, R.N., Vice President Clinical Services and Chief Nursing Officer
Web address: www.wabashgeneral.com
Control: County, Government, nonfederal **Service:** General medical and surgical

Staffed Beds: 25

MOUNT VERNON—Jefferson County

CROSSROADS COMMUNITY HOSPITAL (140294), 8 Doctors Park Road, Zip 62864–6224; tel. 618/244–5500, (Nonreporting) **A**1 10 **S** Quorum Health, Brentwood, TN
Primary Contact: Amanda J. Basso, Chief Executive Officer
CIO: Bryan Delaney, Director Information Technology
CHR: Jessica Connaway, Director Human Resources
CNO: Stephanie Maines, Chief Nursing Officer
Web address: www.crossroadshospital.com
Control: Corporation, Investor–owned (for–profit) **Service:** General medical and surgical

Staffed Beds: 31

GOOD SAMARITAN REGIONAL HEALTH CENTER (140046), 1 Good Samaritan Way, Zip 62864–2402; tel. 618/242–4600, **A**1 2 10 19 **F**3 4 8 11 12 13 15 18 20 22 24 26 28 29 30 31 34 35 38 40 44 45 46 50 51 54 56 57 59 60 61 64 68 70 73 74 75 76 77 78 79 80 81 82 84 85 86 87 89 90 92 93 94 96 102 104 107 108 110 111 114 115 119 123 124 126 130 131 132 135 144 146 147 148 149 154 156 157 **S** SSM Health, Saint Louis, MO
Primary Contact: Kerry Swanson, Regional President, President Good Samaritan
COO: Mark A Clark, Vice President Operations
CFO: Deland Evischi, Regional Chief Financial Officer, Southern Illinois
CMO: Daniel Hoffman, M.D., Administrative Medical Director
CIO: Steve Murphy, FM-East Region IS
CHR: Thomas W Blythe, System Vice President Human Resources
CNO: Chris Adams, Vice President Patient Care Services
Web address: www.smgsi.com
Control: Church operated, Nongovernment, not–for–profit **Service:** General medical and surgical

Staffed Beds: 134 **Admissions:** 7406 **Census:** 83 **Outpatient Visits:** 264358 **Births:** 1151 **Total Expense ($000):** 183399 **Payroll Expense ($000):** 53841 **Personnel:** 982

MURPHYSBORO—Jackson County

★ **ST. JOSEPH MEMORIAL HOSPITAL (141334)**, 2 South Hospital Drive, Zip 62966–3333; tel. 618/684–3156, **A**10 18 **F**3 11 18 28 29 30 31 34 35 40 45 49 50 56 57 59 64 74 75 77 78 79 81 82 84 85 86 87 93 104 107 111 114 119 129 130 132 133 135 146 148 154 156 **S** Southern Illinois Healthcare, Carbondale, IL
Primary Contact: Susan Odle, Administrator
CMO: Emily Hanson, M.D., President, Medical Staff
CIO: David Holland, Vice President Information Services
CHR: Kelly Stevens, Manager Human Resources
Web address: www.sih.net
Control: Other not–for–profit (including NFP Corporation) **Service:** General medical and surgical

Staffed Beds: 25 **Admissions:** 660 **Census:** 13 **Outpatient Visits:** 72561 **Births:** 0 **Total Expense ($000):** 55498 **Payroll Expense ($000):** 13777 **Personnel:** 270

NAPERVILLE—Dupage County

EDWARD HOSPITAL (140231), 801 South Washington Street, Zip 60540–7499; tel. 630/527–3000, **A**1 2 10 **F**3 7 12 13 15 17 18 19 20 22 24 26 28 29 30 31 34 35 36 37 38 39 40 41 42 43 44 45 46 47 48 49 50 53 54 55 57 58 59 61 63 64 65 70 72 74 75 76 77 78 79 81 82 84 85 86 87 88 89 91 92 93 96 97 99 100 101 102 103 107 108 110 111 114 115 117 118 119 120 121 123 124 126 129 130 131 132 135 144 146 147 148 149 154 156 **S** Edward-Elmhurst Healthcare, Naperville, IL
Primary Contact: Bill Kottmann, President and Chief Executive Officer
CMO: Sanjeeb Khatua, M.D., Chief Medical Officer and Vice President
CHR: Chris Devereux, Human Resources Director, Business Partner
CNO: Lynn Cochran, R.N., System Vice President Operations, Chief Nursing Officer
Web address: www.eehealth.org
Control: Other not–for–profit (including NFP Corporation) **Service:** General medical and surgical

Staffed Beds: 358 **Admissions:** 22738 **Census:** 242 **Outpatient Visits:** 1052213 **Births:** 3252 **Total Expense ($000):** 645345 **Payroll Expense ($000):** 186036 **Personnel:** 2396

LINDEN OAKS HOSPITAL (144035), 852 South West Street, Zip 60540–6400; tel. 630/305–5500, **A**1 3 10 **F**4 5 29 34 35 38 44 56 57 59 64 75 86 87 98 99 100 101 103 104 105 130 132 134 149 150 151 152 153 **S** Edward-Elmhurst Healthcare, Naperville, IL
Primary Contact: Gina Sharp, FACHE, President and Chief Executive Officer
CFO: Kristen Refness, Director, Financial Operations
CMO: Barry Rabin, M.D., Regional Medical Director
CIO: David Pickering, System Director, Applications
CHR: Lisa Dixon, Business Partner and Human Resource Director
CNO: Trish Fairbanks, R.N., Associate Vice President and Chief Nursing Officer
Web address: www.https://www.eehealth.org/services/behavioral-health
Control: Other not–for–profit (including NFP Corporation) **Service:** Psychiatric

Staffed Beds: 108 **Admissions:** 4188 **Census:** 83 **Outpatient Visits:** 66431 **Births:** 0 **Total Expense ($000):** 48958 **Payroll Expense ($000):** 28397 **Personnel:** 443

Many Facility Codes have changed. Please refer to the AHA Guide Code Chart. © 2019 AHA Guide

NASHVILLE—Washington County

☐ **WASHINGTON COUNTY HOSPITAL (141308)**, 705 South Grand Avenue, Zip 62263–1534; tel. 618/327–8236, (Total facility includes 28 beds in nursing home–type unit) **A**1 10 18 **F**8 11 15 28 29 31 34 40 49 57 59 64 65 75 78 81 85 93 97 107 115 119 127 132 133 145 146 148 154 156
Primary Contact: Nancy M. Newby, FACHE, Ph.D., R.N., President and Chief Executive Officer
CFO: Elaine Matzenbacher, Chief Financial Officer
CMO: Alfonso Urdaneta, M.D., President Medical Staff
CIO: Kim Larkin, Chief Information Officer
CHR: David Davenport, Director Human Resources
CNO: Lisa Little, Chief Nursing Officer
Web address: www.washingtoncountyhospital.org
Control: Hospital district or authority, Government, nonfederal **Service:** General medical and surgical

Staffed Beds: 42 **Admissions:** 222 **Census:** 26 **Outpatient Visits:** 29720 **Births:** 0 **Total Expense ($000):** 13855 **Payroll Expense ($000):** 6030 **Personnel:** 128

NEW LENOX—Will County

☒ △ **SILVER CROSS HOSPITAL (140213)**, 1900 Silver Cross Boulevard, Zip 60451–9509; tel. 815/300–1100, **A**1 2 3 7 10 **F**3 13 15 18 20 22 26 28 29 30 34 35 37 40 42 43 44 45 46 47 48 49 50 53 54 56 57 58 59 60 62 64 65 68 70 71 73 74 75 76 78 79 81 82 83 84 85 86 87 89 90 97 98 100 101 102 103 107 108 109 110 111 112 113 114 115 116 117 119 120 121 122 123 124 126 129 130 131 132 144 145 146 147 148 149 150 154 156 157
Primary Contact: Ruth A. Colby, President and Chief Executive Officer
COO: Mary Bakken, Executive Vice President and Chief Operating Officer
CFO: Vincent Pryor, Senior Vice President and Chief Financial Officer
CMO: Christopher Udovich, M.D., Chief of Staff
CIO: Kevin Lane, Vice President Information Systems
CHR: Mark Jepson, Vice President
CNO: Peggy Gricus, R.N., Vice President, Patient Care Services and Chief Nursing Officer
Web address: www.silvercross.org
Control: Other not–for–profit (including NFP Corporation) **Service:** General medical and surgical

Staffed Beds: 302 **Admissions:** 20470 **Census:** 217 **Outpatient Visits:** 273511 **Births:** 2731 **Total Expense ($000):** 367790 **Payroll Expense ($000):** 127586 **Personnel:** 1854

SILVER OAKS BEHAVIORAL HOSPITAL (144041), 1004 Pawlak Parkway, Zip 60451–9401; tel. 844/580–5000, (Nonreporting)
Primary Contact: Scott Hullinger, Chief Executive Officer
Web address: www.https://silveroaksbehavioralhospital.com
Control: Other not–for–profit (including NFP Corporation) **Service:** Psychiatric

Staffed Beds: 100

NORMAL—Mclean County

★ ⇑ **ADVOCATE BROMENN MEDICAL CENTER (140127)**, 1304 Franklin Avenue, Zip 61761–3558, Mailing Address: P.O. Box 2850, Bloomington, Zip 61702–2850; tel. 309/454–1400, (Includes ADVOCATE BROMENN REGIONAL MEDICAL CENTER, 1304 Franklin Avenue, Normal, Illinois, Zip 61761–3558, Mailing Address: P.O. Box 2850, Bloomington, Zip 61702–2850, tel. 309/454–1400; Colleen Kannaday, FACHE, President) **A**2 5 10 13 21 **F**2 3 4 5 11 12 13 15 18 20 22 24 26 28 29 30 31 32 34 35 37 38 39 40 43 44 45 48 49 50 51 54 55 57 59 64 65 66 68 70 73 74 75 76 77 78 79 81 82 84 85 86 87 89 90 93 96 97 98 100 101 102 103 107 108 110 111 114 115 118 119 126 129 130 131 132 135 141 146 147 148 149 152 154 156 157 **S** Advocate Aurora Health, Downers Grove, IL
Primary Contact: Colleen Kannaday, FACHE, President
CFO: Aron Klein, Vice President Finance
CMO: James Nevin, M.D., Vice President Medical Management
CHR: Antonio Coletta, Vice President Human Resources
CNO: Laurie Round, MS, R.N., Chief Nurse Executive
Web address: www.advocatehealth.com
Control: Church operated, Nongovernment, not–for–profit **Service:** General medical and surgical

Staffed Beds: 203 **Admissions:** 9027 **Census:** 96 **Outpatient Visits:** 117551 **Births:** 1461 **Total Expense ($000):** 170403 **Payroll Expense ($000):** 60788 **Personnel:** 1089

⇑ **ADVOCATE BROMENN REGIONAL MEDICAL CENTER** See Advocate Bromenn Medical Center

NORTH CHICAGO—Lake County

☒ **CAPTAIN JAMES A. LOVELL FEDERAL HEALTH CARE CENTER**, 3001 Green Bay Road, Zip 60064–3049; tel. 847/688–1900, (Total facility includes 104 beds in nursing home–type unit) **A**1 3 5 8 **F**3 4 8 11 14 15 18 29 30 31 32 34 35 36 38 39 40 44 45 46 48 49 54 56 58 59 61 62 63 64 65 68 70 71 74 75 77 78 79 81 83 84 86 87 90 91 92 96 97 98 100 101 102 103 104 107 108 110 111 115 118 119 128 129 130 131 132 133 135 143 146 147 148 149 154 156 **S** Department of Veterans Affairs, Washington, DC
Primary Contact: Daniel Zomcheck, Interim Director
CFO: Barbara Meadows, Chief Financial Manager
CMO: Tariq Hassan, M.D., Associate Director of Patient Care
CIO: Jonathan Friedman, Public Affairs Officer
CHR: Amy Sanders, Chief Human Resources
CNO: Sarah Fouse, Associate Director of Patient Services
Web address: www.lovell.fhcc.va.gov
Control: Veterans Affairs, Government, federal **Service:** General medical and surgical

Staffed Beds: 297 **Admissions:** 5051 **Census:** 190 **Outpatient Visits:** 1095193 **Births:** 0 **Personnel:** 1824

NORTHLAKE—Cook County

☒ **KINDRED HOSPITAL CHICAGO–NORTHLAKE (142008)**, 365 East North Avenue, Zip 60164–2628; tel. 708/345–8100, (Nonreporting) **A**1 10 **S** Kindred Healthcare, Louisville, KY
Primary Contact: Brinsley Lewis, FACHE, Chief Executive Officer
COO: Sandra Buckhoy, Chief Clinical Officer
CFO: Jay Schweikart, Chief Financial Officer
CMO: Maher Najjar, M.D., Medical Director
Web address: www.kindrednorthlake.com/
Control: Corporation, Investor–owned (for–profit) **Service:** Acute long–term care hospital

Staffed Beds: 94

OAK LAWN—Cook County

★ ⇑ **ADVOCATE CHRIST MEDICAL CENTER (140208)**, 4440 West 95th Street, Zip 60453–2699; tel. 708/684–8000, (Includes ADVOCATE HOPE CHILDREN'S HOSPITAL, 4440 West 95th Street, Oak Lawn, Illinois, Zip 60453–2600; tel. 708/684–8000) **A**2 3 5 8 10 21 **F**3 4 5 9 11 13 15 17 18 19 20 21 22 23 24 25 26 27 28 29 30 31 32 34 35 37 38 39 40 41 43 44 45 46 47 48 49 50 52 54 55 56 57 58 59 60 61 62 63 64 65 66 68 70 71 72 74 75 76 77 78 79 81 82 84 85 86 87 88 89 90 92 93 96 97 98 100 101 102 103 104 105 107 108 109 110 111 114 115 116 117 118 119 120 121 123 124 126 130 131 132 134 135 137 138 140 141 143 145 146 147 148 149 152 154 156 **S** Advocate Aurora Health, Downers Grove, IL
Primary Contact: Matthew Lee. Primack, President
CFO: Robert Pekofske, Vice President Finance
CMO: Robert Stein, M.D., Vice President Medical Management
CIO: Brian Banbury, Director Site Information Systems
Web address: www.advocatehealth.com/christ
Control: Other not–for–profit (including NFP Corporation) **Service:** General medical and surgical

Staffed Beds: 767 **Admissions:** 44705 **Census:** 666 **Outpatient Visits:** 362448 **Births:** 4367 **Total Expense ($000):** 1141857 **Payroll Expense ($000):** 368920 **Personnel:** 4687

OAK PARK—Cook County

☒ **RUSH OAK PARK HOSPITAL (140063)**, 520 South Maple Avenue, Zip 60304–1097; tel. 708/383–9300, (Total facility includes 21 beds in nursing home–type unit) **A**1 3 5 10 **F**3 11 15 18 20 22 29 30 34 35 40 45 47 49 50 56 57 58 59 64 70 74 75 77 79 81 82 85 87 91 92 93 94 96 107 108 110 111 114 115 119 128 130 141 145 146 148 149 154 **S** Rush University Medical Center, Chicago, IL
Primary Contact: Bruce M. Elegant, FACHE, President and Chief Executive Officer
COO: Robert S Spadoni, Vice President of Hospital Operations
CFO: Elvy Yap, Director of Finance
CMO: Michael R. Silver, M.D., Vice President Medical Affairs
CIO: Michael R. Silver, M.D., Chief Information Officer
CHR: Arlene Cruz, Director
CNO: Karen M Mayer, Ph.D., R.N., FACHE, Senior Vice President Patient Care Services
Web address: www.roph.org
Control: Other not–for–profit (including NFP Corporation) **Service:** General medical and surgical

Staffed Beds: 108 **Admissions:** 4093 **Census:** 56 **Outpatient Visits:** 144105 **Births:** 0 **Total Expense ($000):** 128083 **Payroll Expense ($000):** 60455 **Personnel:** 904

IL

⊞ **WEST SUBURBAN MEDICAL CENTER (140049)**, 3 Erie Court, Zip 60302–2599; tel. 708/383–6200, (Nonreporting) **A**1 2 3 5 10 13
Primary Contact: Joseph Ottolino, Chief Executive Officer
CFO: Jennifer Lamont, Chief Financial Officer
CMO: Robert Chase, M.D., Physician Advisor
CHR: Nancy Gunnell, Chief Human Resource Officer
CNO: Roslyn J Lennon, R.N., MS, Chief Nursing Officer
Web address: www.westsuburbanmc.com/Home.aspx
Control: Corporation, Investor–owned (for–profit) **Service**: General medical and surgical

Staffed Beds: 172

O'FALLON—St. Clair County

⊞ △ **HSHS ST. ELIZABETH'S HOSPITAL (140187)**, One St. Elizabeth's Boulevard, Zip 62269; tel. 618/234–2120, (Nonreporting) **A**1 3 5 7 10 **S** HSHS Hospital Sisters Health System, Springfield, IL
Primary Contact: Patricia Fischer, FACHE, R.N., President and Chief Executive Officer
CFO: David Nosacka, Chief Financial Officer
CMO: Shelly Harkins, M.D., Chief Medical Officer
CIO: Leslee Martin, Manager Information Technology
CHR: Jason T Snow, Director People Services
Web address: www.steliz.org
Control: Church operated **Service**: General medical and surgical

Staffed Beds: 224

OLNEY—Richland County

★ ○ **CARLE RICHLAND MEMORIAL HOSPITAL (140147)**, 800 East Locust Street, Zip 62450–2553; tel. 618/395–2131, (Total facility includes 34 beds in nursing home–type unit) **A**10 11 20 **F**3 7 11 13 15 18 28 29 31 34 35 40 45 57 59 62 63 64 68 69 70 75 76 78 79 81 85 87 89 93 97 104 107 108 110 111 115 119 127 128 130 131 132 133 135 143 146 147 148 **S** Carle Foundation, Urbana, IL
Primary Contact: Harry Brockus, Chief Executive Officer
COO: Jennifer Emmons, Chief Operating Officer & Director of Physician Services
CFO: Christina Bare, Director of Business Operations
CMO: Robert Nash, M.D., Chief of Staff
CIO: Tim Gillespie, Manager Information Systems
CHR: Jill Van Hyning, Director Human Resources
CNO: Gina Thomas, Chief Nursing Officer & Director of Patient Care Services
Web address: www.richlandmemorial.com
Control: Other not–for–profit (including NFP Corporation) **Service**: General medical and surgical

Staffed Beds: 86 Admissions: 1443 Census: 38 Outpatient Visits: 108795 Births: 236 Total Expense ($000): 59553 Payroll Expense ($000): 25903 Personnel: 472

OLYMPIA FIELDS—Cook County

★ ○ △ **FRANCISCAN HEALTH OLYMPIA FIELDS (140172)**, 20201 South Crawford Avenue, Zip 60461–1010; tel. 708/747–4000, (Includes FRANCISCAN HEALTH OLYMPIA FIELDS, 20201 Crawford Avenue, Olympia Fields, Illinois, Zip 60461–1010; tel. 708/747–4000) **A**3 7 10 11 12 13 **F**12 13 15 18 20 22 24 26 28 29 30 31 35 40 45 46 49 50 53 60 62 64 66 68 70 75 76 77 78 81 82 84 90 91 93 97 107 111 114 115 116 117 119 120 121 124 126 129 130 132 133 135 143 144 146 148 **S** Franciscan Health, Mishawaka, IN
Primary Contact: Allan M. Spooner, President and Chief Executive Officer
CIO: Stephen Maes, Director Information Systems
Web address: www.franciscanalliance.org/hospitals/olympiafields/pages/default.aspx
Control: Church operated, Nongovernment, not–for–profit **Service**: General medical and surgical

Staffed Beds: 206 Admissions: 11649 Census: 132 Outpatient Visits: 152804 Births: 845 Total Expense ($000): 323742 Payroll Expense ($000): 116737

ST. JAMES HOSPITAL AND HEALTH CENTERS See Franciscan Health Olympia Fields

OTTAWA—Lasalle County

⊞ **OSF SAINT ELIZABETH MEDICAL CENTER (140110)**, 1100 East Norris Drive, Zip 61350–1687; tel. 815/433–3100, **A**1 10 19 **F**3 11 13 15 18 28 29 30 34 35 40 42 45 48 49 53 56 57 59 68 70 75 76 77 79 81 82 84 85 86 87 93 94 98 99 100 101 102 103 104 105 107 108 110 111 115 116 117 118 119 120 121 129 130 131 132 135 143 144 146 148 149 153 154 155 156 157 **S** OSF Healthcare, Peoria, IL
Primary Contact: Kenneth Beutke, President
CMO: Brian S Rosborough, M.D., Chief Medical Officer
CHR: Karen M Russell, Director of Employee Relations
CNO: Pat Torrico, Chief Nursing Officer
Web address: www.osfsaintelizabeth.org
Control: Church operated, Nongovernment, not–for–profit **Service**: General medical and surgical

Staffed Beds: 87 Admissions: 4463 Census: 43 Outpatient Visits: 154683 Births: 393 Total Expense ($000): 104747 Payroll Expense ($000): 41117 Personnel: 541

PALOS HEIGHTS—Cook County

☐ **PALOS HEALTH (140062)**, 12251 South 80th Avenue, Zip 60463–0930; tel. 708/923–4000, (Nonreporting) **A**1 2 10
Primary Contact: Terrence Moisan, M.D., Chief Executive Officer
CFO: Hugh Rose, Vice President Fiscal Management
CIO: Peggy Carroll, Chief Information Officer
CHR: Mary Denisienko, Vice President Human Resources
Web address: www.https://www.paloshealth.com/
Control: Other not–for–profit (including NFP Corporation) **Service**: General medical and surgical

Staffed Beds: 362

PANA—Christian County

★ ○ **PANA COMMUNITY HOSPITAL (141341)**, 101 East Ninth Street, Zip 62557–1785; tel. 217/562–2131, **A**10 11 18 **F**3 11 15 28 29 30 31 34 35 40 45 46 49 50 53 55 57 61 62 63 69 75 77 78 79 81 87 91 93 107 115 124 127 130 131 132 133 143 146 148 149 156
Primary Contact: Trina Casner, President and Chief Executive Officer
CFO: James Moon, Chief Financial Officer
CMO: Alan Frigy, M.D., President Medical Staff
CIO: Dianne Bailey, Chief Information Officer
CHR: Luann A Funk, Administrative Assistant and Manager Human Resources
CNO: Vickie Coen, Chief Clinical Officer and Nurse Executive
Web address: www.panahospital.com
Control: Other not–for–profit (including NFP Corporation) **Service**: General medical and surgical

Staffed Beds: 22 Admissions: 458 Census: 5 Outpatient Visits: 49613 Births: 0 Total Expense ($000): 24569 Payroll Expense ($000): 11614 Personnel: 247

PARIS—Edgar County

⊞ **PARIS COMMUNITY HOSPITAL (141320)**, 721 East Court Street, Zip 61944–2460; tel. 217/465–4141, **A**1 10 18 **F**3 7 12 15 18 28 29 30 31 34 35 40 45 47 50 57 59 64 65 69 74 75 77 78 79 81 82 85 86 87 93 107 108 110 111 115 119 127 129 130 131 132 133 135 144 146 148 149 154 156 157 **S** Alliant Management Services, Louisville, KY
Primary Contact: Oliver Smith, President and Chief Executive Officer
CFO: Martin D. Adams, CPA, Vice President Finance and Chief Financial Officer
CIO: Ed Weeks, Manager Information Services
CHR: Cathy Thompson, Manager Human Resources
CNO: Tiffany Turner, MSN, R.N., Vice President of Nursing and Chief Nursing Officer
Web address: www.pariscommunityhospital.com
Control: Other not–for–profit (including NFP Corporation) **Service**: General medical and surgical

Staffed Beds: 25 Admissions: 717 Census: 6 Outpatient Visits: 144152 Births: 0 Total Expense ($000): 52798 Payroll Expense ($000): 27777 Personnel: 366

PARK RIDGE—Cook County

★ △ ⋔ **ADVOCATE LUTHERAN GENERAL HOSPITAL (140223)**, 1775 Dempster Street, Zip 60068–1174; tel. 847/723–2210, **A**2 3 5 7 8 10 13 21 **F**2 3 5 6 8 9 11 13 15 17 18 19 20 22 24 25 26 27 28 29 30 31 32 34 35 37 38 39 40 41 43 44 45 48 49 50 53 55 56 57 58 59 60 61 63 64 65 66 68 69 70 72 74 75 76 78 79 80 81 82 84 85 86 87 88 89 90 92 93 94 96 97 98 99 100 101 102 103 104 105 106 107 108 110 111 114 115 116 117 118 119 120 121 124 126 129 130 131 132 134 135 136 143 146 147 148 149 150 152 153 154 156 157 **S** Advocate Aurora Health, Downers Grove, IL
Primary Contact: Terika Richardson, M.P.H., President
COO: Allyson Wyler, Vice President, Operations
CFO: Beth Hickey, Vice President, Finance
CMO: Leo Kelly, Vice President Medical Management
CIO: Mark Beitzel, Director Information Systems
CHR: Katie Bata, Vice President Human Resources
CNO: Jane Denten, MSN, R.N., Chief Nurse Executive
Web address: www.advocatehealth.com/luth/
Control: Other not–for–profit (including NFP Corporation) **Service**: General medical and surgical

Staffed Beds: 629 Admissions: 29491 Census: 449 Outpatient Visits: 353054 Births: 3904 Total Expense ($000): 755328 Payroll Expense ($000): 255758 Personnel: 3541

IL

Many Facility Codes have changed. Please refer to the AHA Guide Code Chart. © 2019 AHA Guide

PEKIN—Tazewell County

⊞ **UNITYPOINT HEALTH-PEKIN HOSPITAL (140120)**, 600 South 13th Street, Zip 61554–4936; tel. 309/347–1151, **A**1 10 **F**8 11 13 15 18 20 22 28 29 30 31 34 35 40 45 46 47 48 49 50 57 59 60 62 64 68 69 74 75 78 79 81 82 85 86 87 93 97 107 108 110 111 115 119 129 130 132 135 144 145 146 147 148 **S** UnityPoint Health, West Des Moines, IA
Primary Contact: Keith Knepp, M.D., President and Chief Executive Officer
COO: Jeanine R. Spain, R.N., MS, Vice President, Chief Operating Officer and Chief Nursing Officer
CFO: Steve Hall, Chief Financial Officer
CMO: Kathryn Kramer, M.D., President Medical Staff
CHR: Anne Dierker, Vice President Hospital Services
CNO: Jeanine R. Spain, R.N., MS, Vice President, Chief Operating Officer and Chief Nursing Officer
Web address: www.pekinhospital.org
Control: Other not-for-profit (including NFP Corporation) **Service:** General medical and surgical

Staffed Beds: 98 **Admissions:** 2498 **Census:** 25 **Outpatient Visits:** 80300 **Births:** 321 **Total Expense ($000):** 57379 **Payroll Expense ($000):** 21380 **Personnel:** 346

PEORIA—Peoria County

GREATER PEORIA SPECIALTY HOSPITAL See Kindred Hospital Peoria

⊞ **KINDRED HOSPITAL PEORIA (142013)**, 500 West Romeo B Garrett Avenue, Zip 61605–2301; tel. 309/680–1500, (Nonreporting) **A**1 10 **S** Kindred Healthcare, Louisville, KY
Primary Contact: Christopher Curry, Chief Executive Officer
CMO: Michael Peil, M.D., Chief Medical Director
Web address: www.khpeoria.com/
Control: Corporation, Investor-owned (for-profit) **Service:** Acute long-term care hospital

Staffed Beds: 50

METHODIST MEDICAL CENTER OF ILLINOIS See Unitypoint Health - Peoria

⊞ **OSF SAINT FRANCIS MEDICAL CENTER (140067)**, 530 NE Glen Oak Avenue, Zip 61637–0001; tel. 309/655–2000, (Includes CHILDREN'S HOSPITAL OF ILLINOIS, 530 NE Glen Oak Avenue, Peoria, Illinois, Zip 61637–0001; tel. 309/655–7171; Kelly Nierstedt, President) **A**1 2 3 5 8 10 **F**3 9 11 12 13 15 17 18 19 20 21 22 23 24 25 26 27 28 29 30 31 32 34 35 37 38 39 40 41 43 44 45 46 47 48 49 50 51 52 54 56 57 58 59 60 64 65 66 70 71 72 73 74 75 76 77 78 79 80 81 82 83 84 85 86 87 88 89 90 92 93 95 96 100 102 104 105 107 108 109 110 111 112 114 115 117 118 119 121 125 126 129 130 138 142 145 146 147 148 149 153 154 **S** OSF Healthcare, Peoria, IL
Primary Contact: Robert G. Anderson Jr, President
CFO: Ken Harbaugh, Vice President and Chief Financial Officer
CMO: Robert T. Sparrow, M.D., Vice President, Chief Medical Officer
CHR: Jacki L. Fugitt, Director Employee Relations
CNO: Jennifer Hopwood, Chief Nursing Officer, Vice President Patient Care
Web address: www.osfsaintfrancis.org
Control: Church operated, Nongovernment, not-for-profit **Service:** General medical and surgical

Staffed Beds: 629 **Admissions:** 35607 **Census:** 521 **Outpatient Visits:** 607171 **Births:** 2933 **Total Expense ($000):** 883691 **Payroll Expense ($000):** 335334 **Personnel:** 5187

⊞ **UNITYPOINT HEALTH - PEORIA (140209)**, 221 NE Glen Oak Avenue, Zip 61636–4310; tel. 309/672–5522, **A**1 2 5 10 **F**3 9 11 12 13 15 17 18 20 22 24 26 29 30 31 32 34 35 36 38 40 43 44 45 46 47 48 49 50 53 54 56 57 58 59 60 62 63 64 68 70 74 75 76 77 78 79 81 82 84 85 86 87 89 90 92 93 96 98 99 100 101 102 104 105 107 108 110 111 114 115 116 117 118 119 120 121 126 127 129 130 131 132 134 135 136 143 144 145 146 147 148 149 150 154 156 **S** UnityPoint Health, West Des Moines, IA
Primary Contact: Keith Knepp, M.D., President and Chief Executive Officer
COO: Jeanine R. Spain, R.N., MS, Vice President, Chief Operating Officer and Chief Nursing Officer
CFO: Robert Quin, Regional Vice President Finance, and Chief Financial Officer
CMO: Gary Knepp, D.O., Regional Chief Medical Officer and Chief Quality Officer
CHR: Joy Ledbetter, Regional Chief Human Resources Officer
CNO: Jeanine R. Spain, R.N., MS, Vice President, Chief Operating Officer and Chief Nursing Officer
Web address: www.unitypoint.org/peoria
Control: Other not-for-profit (including NFP Corporation) **Service:** General medical and surgical

Staffed Beds: 269 **Admissions:** 13526 **Census:** 180 **Outpatient Visits:** 578775 **Births:** 1568 **Total Expense ($000):** 428831 **Payroll Expense ($000):** 196185 **Personnel:** 2390

☐ **UNITYPOINT HEALTH - PROCTOR (140013)**, 5409 North Knoxville Avenue, Zip 61614–5069; tel. 309/691–1000, (Total facility includes 30 beds in nursing home–type unit) **A**1 3 5 10 **F**3 4 5 11 15 18 20 22 24 28 29 30 34 40 45 51 53 57 59 60 64 70 74 75 79 81 98 99 103 104 107 108 110 111 114 115 118 119 128 130 132 135 143 145 146 148 149 150 151 152 154 **S** UnityPoint Health, West Des Moines, IA
Primary Contact: Keith Knepp, M.D., President and Chief Executive Officer
COO: Jeanine R. Spain, R.N., MS, Vice President, Chief Operating Officer and Chief Nursing Officer
CFO: Roger Armstrong, Vice President Finance and Chief Financial Officer
CHR: Linda K Buck, Vice President Human Resources
CNO: Jeanine R. Spain, R.N., MS, Vice President, Chief Operating Officer and Chief Nursing Officer
Web address: www.proctor.org
Control: Other not-for-profit (including NFP Corporation) **Service:** General medical and surgical

Staffed Beds: 131 **Admissions:** 4535 **Census:** 74 **Outpatient Visits:** 64236 **Births:** 0 **Total Expense ($000):** 101918 **Payroll Expense ($000):** 31982 **Personnel:** 573

PERU—Lasalle County

★ **ILLINOIS VALLEY COMMUNITY HOSPITAL (140234)**, 925 West Street, Zip 61354–2757; tel. 815/223–3300, **A**10 **F**2 3 11 13 15 18 28 29 30 31 34 35 38 40 45 46 47 48 49 50 51 54 57 59 63 64 65 66 68 69 70 74 75 76 77 79 81 82 85 87 93 96 97 104 107 110 111 114 115 118 119 127 129 130 131 132 133 135 143 144 146 147 148 149 154 156 157
Primary Contact: Tommy Hobbs, Chief Executive Officer
COO: Bobby Smith, Vice President Physician Services and Quality
CFO: Lisa Lynch, Chief Financial Officer
CMO: Mark Fernandez, M.D., Chief of Staff and President Medical Staff
CIO: Nancy McDonnell, Manager Information Systems
CHR: Mary Beth Herron, Director of Human Resources
CNO: Robert Fortney, MS, R.N., Chief Nursing Officer and Vice President of Patient Care
Web address: www.ivch.org
Control: Other not-for-profit (including NFP Corporation) **Service:** General medical and surgical

Staffed Beds: 49 **Admissions:** 2322 **Census:** 18 **Outpatient Visits:** 202364 **Births:** 404 **Total Expense ($000):** 86123 **Payroll Expense ($000):** 35984 **Personnel:** 539

PINCKNEYVILLE—Perry County

★ **PINCKNEYVILLE COMMUNITY HOSPITAL (141307)**, 5383 State Route 154, Zip 62274–1099, Mailing Address: P.O. Box 437, Zip 62274–1099; tel. 618/357–2187, **A**10 18 **F**3 11 15 28 29 31 34 40 43 45 50 53 56 57 65 78 81 85 93 107 108 110 119 127 130 132 133 146 149
Primary Contact: Randall W. Dauby, CPA, Chief Executive Officer
CFO: Kara Jo Carson, Chief Financial Officer
CIO: Jeff Roberts, Director Information Technology
CHR: Christie Gajewski, Director Human Resources
CNO: Eva Hopp, Chief Nurse Executive
Web address: www.pvillehosp.org/
Control: Hospital district or authority, Government, nonfederal **Service:** General medical and surgical

Staffed Beds: 17 **Admissions:** 488 **Census:** 8 **Outpatient Visits:** 44904 **Births:** 0 **Total Expense ($000):** 25693 **Payroll Expense ($000):** 10057 **Personnel:** 189

PITTSFIELD—Pike County

★ ⇑ **ILLINI COMMUNITY HOSPITAL (141315)**, 640 West Washington Street, Zip 62363–1350; tel. 217/285–2113, **A**10 18 21 **F**15 18 19 28 29 30 31 34 40 46 50 53 59 64 65 68 70 75 77 78 81 85 87 97 98 100 101 103 104 107 110 115 119 127 129 130 131 132 133 144 146 149 154 156
Primary Contact: Kathy Hull, President and Chief Executive Officer
CFO: Tim Moore, Vice President Finance
CMO: Bashar Alzein, M.D., President Medical Staff
CHR: Becky Myers, Human Resources Specialist
CNO: Holly A Jones, Administrative Director Nursing Services
Web address: www.illinihospital.org
Control: Other not-for-profit (including NFP Corporation) **Service:** General medical and surgical

Staffed Beds: 25 **Admissions:** 520 **Census:** 7 **Outpatient Visits:** 9172 **Births:** 0 **Total Expense ($000):** 26276 **Payroll Expense ($000):** 9389 **Personnel:** 195

IL

Hospital, Medicare Provider Number, Address, Telephone, Approval, Facility, and Physician Codes, Health Care System

★ American Hospital Association (AHA) membership
☐ The Joint Commission accreditation
○ Healthcare Facilities Accreditation Program
◇ DNV Healthcare Inc. accreditation
⇑ Center for Improvement in Healthcare Quality Accreditation
△ Commission on Accreditation of Rehabilitation Facilities (CARF) accreditation

PONTIAC—Livingston County

⊞ **OSF SAINT JAMES - JOHN W. ALBRECHT MEDICAL CENTER (140161)**, 2500 West Reynolds, Zip 61764–9774; tel. 815/842–2828, **A**1 10 20 **F**3 8 11 13 15 18 28 29 30 32 34 35 40 45 50 51 56 57 59 64 68 70 75 76 81 82 84 85 86 87 89 90 91 93 107 110 111 115 117 118 119 128 129 130 131 132 133 135 146 147 149 156 **S** OSF Healthcare, Peoria, IL
Primary Contact: Bradley V. Solberg, FACHE, President
CFO: Paula Corrigan, Vice President and Chief Financial Officer
CMO: John M. Rinker, Chief Medical Officer
CNO: Elizabeth Davidson, R.N., MSN, Vice President, Patient Care Services
Web address: www.osfsaintjames.org
Control: Church operated, Nongovernment, not–for–profit **Service**: General medical and surgical

Staffed Beds: 42 **Admissions**: 1846 **Census**: 17 **Outpatient Visits**: 72657 **Births**: 216 **Total Expense ($000)**: 51726 **Payroll Expense ($000)**: 19030 **Personnel**: 246

PRINCETON—Bureau County

PERRY MEMORIAL HOSPITAL (141337), 530 Park Avenue East, Zip 61356–2598; tel. 815/875–2811, **A**10 18 **F**3 11 15 18 28 29 30 31 32 34 35 40 41 45 48 49 51 56 57 59 64 65 70 75 77 78 79 81 82 83 85 86 87 93 97 100 104 105 107 108 110 111 115 116 118 119 127 129 130 131 132 133 144 145 146 148 149 153 154 156
Primary Contact: Annette Schnabel, FACHE, President and Chief Executive Officer
COO: Chris J. Williams, FACHE, Vice President Operations
CFO: Mike DeFoe, Chief Financial Officer
CMO: T Doran, M.D., Chief of Staff
CIO: Karen Behrens, Director Technology Services
CHR: James Lewandowski, Vice President Human Resources
Web address: www.perry-memorial.org
Control: City, Government, nonfederal **Service**: General medical and surgical

Staffed Beds: 25 **Admissions**: 857 **Census**: 6 **Outpatient Visits**: 87316 **Births**: 1 **Total Expense ($000)**: 44742 **Payroll Expense ($000)**: 19115 **Personnel**: 281

QUINCY—Adams County

★ △ ⇑ **BLESSING HOSPITAL (140015)**, Broadway at 11th Street, Zip 62305–7005, Mailing Address: P.O. Box 7005, Zip 62305–7005; tel. 217/223–1200, (Includes BLESSING HOSPITAL, Broadway & 14th Street, Quincy, Illinois, Zip 62301, Mailing Address: P O Box 7005, Zip 62305–7005, tel. 217/223–1200) (Total facility includes 20 beds in nursing home–type unit) **A**2 3 5 7 10 13 21 **F**3 5 8 11 12 13 15 17 18 20 22 24 26 28 29 30 31 32 33 34 35 40 42 43 44 48 49 50 53 56 57 58 59 60 61 62 63 64 66 68 70 73 74 75 76 77 78 79 81 82 84 85 86 87 89 90 94 96 98 99 100 101 102 104 105 107 108 110 111 114 115 118 119 120 121 123 124 126 127 128 129 130 131 132 135 144 146 147 148 149 152 153 154 156
Primary Contact: Maureen A. Kahn, R.N., President and Chief Executive Officer
COO: Tim Moore, Chief Accounting Officer and Vice President Ancillary Services and Finance
CFO: Patrick M Gerveler, Vice President Finance and Chief Financial Officer
CMO: George Liesmann, M.D., Chief Medical Officer
CNO: Jill K Mason, MS, R.N., Chief Nursing Officer
Web address: www.blessinghospital.org
Control: Other not–for–profit (including NFP Corporation) **Service**: General medical and surgical

Staffed Beds: 314 **Admissions**: 15558 **Census**: 200 **Outpatient Visits**: 291589 **Births**: 1103 **Total Expense ($000)**: 390359 **Payroll Expense ($000)**: 136259 **Personnel**: 2463

RED BUD—Randolph County

⊞ **RED BUD REGIONAL HOSPITAL (141348)**, 325 Spring Street, Zip 62278–1105; tel. 618/282–3831, (Nonreporting) **A**1 10 18 **S** Quorum Health, Brentwood, TN
Primary Contact: Shane Watson, Chief Executive Officer
CFO: Zach Schmitt, Chief Financial Officer
CMO: Julie Kelley, M.D., Chief of Staff
CIO: Nick Behnken, IT Director
CHR: Lori Brooks, Director Human Resources
Web address: www.redbudregional.com
Control: Corporation, Investor–owned (for–profit) **Service**: General medical and surgical

Staffed Beds: 140

ROBINSON—Crawford County

★ ○ **CRAWFORD MEMORIAL HOSPITAL (141343)**, 1000 North Allen Street, Zip 62454–1167; tel. 618/544–3131, (Total facility includes 38 beds in nursing home–type unit) **A**10 11 18 **F**3 11 12 13 15 28 30 31 40 46 53 59 62 64 76 78 79 80 81 82 85 93 107 108 111 119 127 128 129 130 132 133 146 147 **S** QHR, Brentwood, TN
Primary Contact: Douglas Florkowski, Chief Executive Officer
CFO: Richard Carlson, Chief Financial Officer
CMO: Gary Tennison, M.D., Chief of Staff
CIO: Tim Richard, IT Coordinator
CHR: Kristi Zane, Chief Human Resources Officer
CNO: Tammy Fralicker, MS, R.N., Chief Nursing Officer
Web address: www.crawfordmh.net
Control: Hospital district or authority, Government, nonfederal **Service**: General medical and surgical

Staffed Beds: 63 **Admissions**: 778 **Census**: 24 **Outpatient Visits**: 48790 **Births**: 207 **Total Expense ($000)**: 43409 **Payroll Expense ($000)**: 21872 **Personnel**: 381

ROCHELLE—Ogle County

⊞ **ROCHELLE COMMUNITY HOSPITAL (141312)**, 900 North Second Street, Zip 61068–1764; tel. 815/562–2181, **A**1 10 18 **F**3 15 29 30 31 34 35 40 41 45 50 53 57 59 64 68 70 74 75 77 78 81 82 85 86 87 97 107 110 111 115 130 132 133 135 144 146 149 156 157
Primary Contact: Mark Batty, Chief Executive Officer
CFO: Lori Gutierrez, Chief Financial Officer
CMO: Jason Popp, Chief of Medical Staff
CIO: Scott Stewart, Manager Information Services
CHR: Laura Cirone, Manager Human Resources
CNO: Julie Norem, MSN, Chief Nursing Officer
Web address: www.rcha.net
Control: Other not–for–profit (including NFP Corporation) **Service**: General medical and surgical

Staffed Beds: 17 **Admissions**: 428 **Census**: 3 **Outpatient Visits**: 43453 **Births**: 0 **Total Expense ($000)**: 31668 **Payroll Expense ($000)**: 12127 **Personnel**: 210

ROCK ISLAND—Rock Island County

⊞ △ **UNITYPOINT HEALTH - TRINITY ROCK ISLAND (140280)**, 2701 17th Street, Zip 61201–5393; tel. 309/779–5000, (Includes UNITYPOINT HEALTH - TRINITY MOLINE, 500 John Deere Road, Moline, Illinois, Zip 61265; tel. 309/779–5000) (Total facility includes 29 beds in nursing home–type unit) **A**1 3 7 10 **F**3 5 11 12 13 15 18 20 22 24 26 28 29 30 31 34 35 37 38 40 43 44 45 46 47 48 49 50 57 58 59 64 68 70 74 76 78 79 81 82 85 86 87 90 93 96 97 98 102 104 105 107 108 110 114 115 118 119 120 121 123 126 128 129 130 132 146 147 148 149 150 152 153 154 **S** UnityPoint Health, West Des Moines, IA
Primary Contact: John C. Sheehan, FACHE, Interim President and Chief Executive Officer
CFO: Katie A Marchik, Chief Financial Officer
CMO: Paul McLoone, M.D., Chief Medical Officer
CHR: Cara Fuller, Vice President Human Resources
CNO: Ginger L Renkiewicz, Chief Clinical Officer, Chief Nursing Executive, and Chief Quality Officer
Web address: www.trinityqc.com
Control: Other not–for–profit (including NFP Corporation) **Service**: General medical and surgical

Staffed Beds: 343 **Admissions**: 13236 **Census**: 155 **Outpatient Visits**: 365446 **Births**: 1273 **Total Expense ($000)**: 328937 **Payroll Expense ($000)**: 113084 **Personnel**: 1958

ROCKFORD—Winnebago County

⊞ **JAVON BEA HOSPITAL-ROCKTON (140239)**, 2400 North Rockton Avenue, Zip 61103–3655; tel. 815/971–5000, (Includes MERCYHEALTH JAVON BEA HOSPITAL - RIVERSIDE CAMPUS, 8201 East Riverside Boulevard, Rockford, Illinois, Zip 61114–2300; tel. 815/971–7000; Javon R. Bea, President and Chief Executive Officer) **A**1 2 3 5 10 **F**3 11 12 13 18 19 20 22 24 26 27 28 29 30 31 32 34 35 39 40 41 43 44 45 46 47 48 49 50 51 54 55 56 57 59 64 65 68 70 71 72 74 75 76 77 78 79 81 82 83 84 85 86 87 88 89 91 93 97 98 100 101 102 103 107 108 111 114 115 118 119 120 121 123 126 129 130 131 132 135 145 146 147 148 149 154 156 157 **S** Mercy Health System, Janesville, WI
Primary Contact: Javon R. Bea, President and Chief Executive Officer
COO: Sue Ripsch, Senior Vice President & Chief Operating Officer
CFO: John Cook, Senior Vice President & Chief Financial Officer
CMO: John T Dorsey, M.D., Vice President Physician Services and Chief Medical Officer
CIO: Ruth Yarbrough, Vice President
CHR: Heidi Elsbree, Vice President People and Culture
CNO: Doreen Timm, MSN, Senior Director and Chief Nursing Officer
Web address: www.rhsnet.org
Control: Other not–for–profit (including NFP Corporation) **Service**: General medical and surgical

Staffed Beds: 288 **Admissions**: 12702 **Census**: 180 **Outpatient Visits**: 315970 **Births**: 2257 **Total Expense ($000)**: 319836 **Payroll Expense ($000)**: 118278 **Personnel**: 2239

IL

Many Facility Codes have changed. Please refer to the AHA Guide Code Chart. © 2019 AHA Guide

⊞ **OSF SAINT ANTHONY MEDICAL CENTER (140233)**, 5666 East State Street, Zip 61108–2425; tel. 815/226–2000, **A**1 2 3 5 10 **F**3 11 12 13 15 16 17 18 19 20 22 24 26 28 29 30 31 32 34 35 36 37 38 40 41 43 44 45 46 49 50 51 53 55 56 57 58 59 63 64 66 70 73 74 75 76 77 78 79 81 82 84 85 86 87 89 92 93 107 108 110 111 114 115 116 117 118 119 120 121 123 124 126 129 130 131 132 135 145 146 147 148 149 150 154 **S** OSF Healthcare, Peoria, IL
Primary Contact: Paula A. Carynski, MS, R.N., President
COO: James Girardy, M.D., Vice President, Chief Surgical Officer
CFO: David Stenerson, Vice President and Chief Financial Officer
CMO: Harneet Bath, M.D., Vice President, Chief Medicine Officer
CIO: Kathy Peterson, Director Information Services
CHR: Karen C Brown, Vice President Chief Operating Officer
Web address: www.osfhealth.com
Control: Church operated, Nongovernment, not–for–profit **Service**: General medical and surgical

Staffed Beds: 235 **Admissions**: 12287 **Census**: 142 **Outpatient Visits**: 222601 **Births**: 477 **Total Expense ($000)**: 355510 **Payroll Expense ($000)**: 109146 **Personnel**: 1382

⊞ **SWEDISHAMERICAN - A DIVISION OF UW HEALTH (140228)**, 1401 East State Street, Zip 61104–2315; tel. 815/968–4400, **A**1 2 3 5 10 **F**3 13 15 17 18 20 22 24 26 28 29 30 31 34 35 36 38 39 40 43 44 45 46 48 49 50 51 56 57 58 59 60 61 63 64 65 68 70 71 73 74 76 77 78 79 81 84 85 86 87 89 92 93 98 99 100 102 105 107 108 110 111 115 118 119 126 129 130 132 135 146 147 148 149 154 156
Primary Contact: Michael J. Born, M.D., President and Chief Executive Officer
COO: Don Daniels, Executive Vice President and Chief Operating Officer
CFO: Patti DeWane, Vice President Finance and Treasurer
CMO: Mike Polizzotto, Chief Medical Officer
CIO: Sheryl Johnson, Chief Information Officer
CHR: Gerard Guinane, Vice President Human Resources
CNO: Ann M Gantzer, Ph.D., R.N., Vice President Patient Services and Chief Nursing Officer
Web address: www.swedishamerican.org
Control: Other not–for–profit (including NFP Corporation) **Service**: General medical and surgical

Staffed Beds: 280 **Admissions**: 14195 **Census**: 160 **Outpatient Visits**: 272860 **Births**: 1661 **Total Expense ($000)**: 338207 **Payroll Expense ($000)**: 126132 **Personnel**: 2087

⊞ **VAN MATRE ENCOMPASS HEALTH (143028)**, 950 South Mulford Road, Zip 61108–4274; tel. 815/381–8500, (Nonreporting) **A**1 10 **S** Encompass Health Corporation, Birmingham, AL
Primary Contact: Jeffrey Reese, Chief Executive Officer
CFO: Tim Anderson, Controller
CMO: Ricardo Knight, Interim Medical Director
CIO: Angela Bergman, Director of Quality, Risk and Health Information Management
CHR: Dorothy Richardson, Director Human Resources
CNO: Chrisi Karcz, Chief Nursing Officer
Web address: www.healthsouth.com
Control: Corporation, Investor–owned (for–profit) **Service**: Rehabilitation

Staffed Beds: 61

ROSICLARE—Hardin County

★ **HARDIN COUNTY GENERAL HOSPITAL (141328)**, 6 Ferrell Road, Zip 62982, Mailing Address: P.O. Box 2467, Zip 62982–2467; tel. 618/285–6634, **A**10 18 **F**34 40 44 45 46 50 57 59 65 68 93 97 107 119 127 129 130 133
Primary Contact: Roby D. Williams, Administrator
CFO: Janie Parker, Chief Financial Officer
CMO: Marcos N Sunga, M.D., Chief of Staff
CIO: Brian Casteel, Information Technology Technician
CHR: Joyce Shelby, Manager Human Resources
CNO: Courtney Spivey, Chief Nursing Officer
Web address: www.ilhcgh.org
Control: Other not–for–profit (including NFP Corporation) **Service**: General medical and surgical

Staffed Beds: 25 **Admissions**: 623 **Census**: 10 **Outpatient Visits**: 16294 **Births**: 0 **Total Expense ($000)**: 11562 **Payroll Expense ($000)**: 6078 **Personnel**: 128

RUSHVILLE—Schuyler County

★ **SARAH D. CULBERTSON MEMORIAL HOSPITAL (141333)**, 238 South Congress Street, Zip 62681–1472; tel. 217/322–4321, **A**10 18 **F**11 15 28 29 30 31 34 40 56 59 65 68 69 75 77 81 85 93 96 97 104 107 110 114 119 125 127 129 130 132 133 146 148 149
Primary Contact: John E. Kessler, Chief Executive Officer
CFO: Alan Palo, Chief Financial Officer
CMO: Marguerite Taillefer, M.D., Acting President Medical Staff
CIO: Dan Wise, Manager Information Technology
CNO: Lisa M Downs, R.N., Chief Nursing Officer
Web address: www.cmhospital.com
Control: Hospital district or authority, Government, nonfederal **Service**: General medical and surgical

Staffed Beds: 22 **Admissions**: 274 **Census**: 4 **Outpatient Visits**: 36621 **Births**: 0 **Total Expense ($000)**: 23370 **Payroll Expense ($000)**: 8853 **Personnel**: 177

SALEM—Marion County

★ ○ **SALEM TOWNSHIP HOSPITAL (141345)**, 1201 Ricker Drive, Zip 62881–4263; tel. 618/548–3194, (Nonreporting) **A**10 11 18
Primary Contact: Kendra Taylor, MSN, R.N., President and Chief Executive Officer
CFO: Teresa Stroud, Chief Financial Officer
CMO: Seth Hahs, Chief of Staff
CIO: Steve Turner, Director Information Technology
CHR: Diane Boswell, Director Human Resources and Marketing
Web address: www.sthcares.org
Control: City–county, Government, nonfederal **Service**: General medical and surgical

Staffed Beds: 22

SANDWICH—Dekalb County

⊞ **NORTHWESTERN MEDICINE VALLEY WEST HOSPITAL (141340)**, 1302 North Main Street, Zip 60548–2587; tel. 815/786–8484, **A**1 10 18 **F**3 11 13 15 18 28 29 30 31 32 34 35 36 38 40 41 44 45 46 49 50 51 57 58 59 60 64 68 70 71 73 75 76 77 78 79 81 82 84 85 87 89 93 102 104 107 108 110 111 115 119 129 130 131 132 135 146 147 149 150 153 154 **S** Northwestern Memorial HealthCare, Chicago, IL
Primary Contact: Jay Anderson, President
COO: Brad Copple, Vice President Operations
CFO: Matthew J Flynn, Chief Financial Officer West Region
CMO: Michael Kulisz, D.O., Vice President, Chief Medical Officer
CIO: Heath Bell, Vice President, Information Services
CHR: Michael Vivoda, Senior Vice President Human Resources
CNO: Pamela Duffy, MSN, R.N., Vice President Operations and Chief Nursing Executive
Web address: www.nm.org
Control: Other not–for–profit (including NFP Corporation) **Service**: General medical and surgical

Staffed Beds: 25 **Admissions**: 760 **Census**: 5 **Outpatient Visits**: 30614 **Births**: 182 **Total Expense ($000)**: 43635 **Payroll Expense ($000)**: 12666 **Personnel**: 266

SHELBYVILLE—Shelby County

★ ⇑ **HSHS GOOD SHEPHERD HOSPITAL (140019)**, 200 South Cedar Street, Zip 62565–1838; tel. 217/774–3961, **A**10 20 21 **F**3 15 28 29 30 34 35 40 45 50 57 59 62 64 77 79 81 97 107 108 110 115 118 119 127 129 131 132 133 146 154 **S** HSHS Hospital Sisters Health System, Springfield, IL
Primary Contact: Aaron Puchbauer, President
CFO: Marilyn Sears, Chief Financial Officer
CMO: David Oligschlaeger, Medical Staff President
CIO: Ian Kuhlman, Manager Information Technology
CHR: Amy Koehler, Director Human Resources
CNO: Michelle Oliver, Chief Nursing Executive
Web address: www.mysmh.org
Control: Church operated, Nongovernment, not–for–profit **Service**: General medical and surgical

Staffed Beds: 30 **Admissions**: 610 **Census**: 5 **Outpatient Visits**: 21887 **Births**: 0 **Total Expense ($000)**: 16064 **Payroll Expense ($000)**: 5404 **Personnel**: 127

IL

SHILOH—St. Clair County

★ ○ **MEMORIAL HOSPITAL EAST (140307)**, 1404 Cross Street, Zip 62269–2988; tel. 618/607–1000, **A**10 11 **F**3 11 13 15 18 20 22 26 29 30 40 41 45 49 57 64 70 73 74 76 78 79 81 85 87 91 92 93 94 107 110 111 115 118 119 130 131 132 146 148 149 154 **S** BJC HealthCare, Saint Louis, MO
Primary Contact: Mark J. Turner, FACHE, President
COO: Michael T McManus, Chief Operating Officer
CFO: Jane Gusmano, Interim Vice President Finance
CMO: William Casperson, Vice President Medical Affairs
CIO: Jennifer Meinkoth, Executive Director I.S.
CHR: John Ç Ziegler, FACHE, Vice President Human Resources
CNO: Teresa Halloran, Ph.D., R.N., Vice President Nursing Services
Web address: www.memhospeast.com
Control: Other not–for–profit (including NFP Corporation) **Service**: General medical and surgical

Staffed Beds: 94 **Admissions:** 4311 **Census:** 42 **Outpatient Visits:** 76232 **Births:** 1038 **Total Expense ($000):** 86785 **Payroll Expense ($000):** 31479 **Personnel:** 517

SILVIS—Rock Island County

☒ **GENESIS MEDICAL CENTER, SILVIS (140275)**, 801 Illini Drive, Zip 61282–1893; tel. 309/281–4000, **A**1 10 **F**3 7 13 15 18 20 22 26 28 29 30 31 34 35 40 43 45 46 47 50 51 53 59 60 62 64 65 68 70 75 76 77 79 81 84 85 87 107 108 110 111 114 119 129 130 132 135 146 147 149 157 **S** Genesis Health System, Davenport, IA
Primary Contact: Theresa Summers-Main, R.N., President
CFO: Mark G Rogers, Interim Vice President Finance and Chief Financial Officer
CMO: Peter Metcalf, M.D., President Medical Staff
CIO: Robert Frieden, Vice President Information Systems
CHR: Heidi Kahly-McMahon, Vice President Human Resources
Web address: www.genesishealth.com
Control: Other not–for–profit (including NFP Corporation) **Service**: General medical and surgical

Staffed Beds: 127 **Admissions:** 3979 **Census:** 30 **Outpatient Visits:** 125550 **Births:** 365 **Total Expense ($000):** 81114 **Payroll Expense ($000):** 24170 **Personnel:** 295

SPARTA—Randolph County

○ **SPARTA COMMUNITY HOSPITAL (141349)**, 818 East Broadway Street, Zip 62286–1820, Mailing Address: P.O. Box 297, Zip 62286–0297; tel. 618/443–2177, **A**10 11 18 **F**3 11 15 28 30 34 35 40 41 44 45 53 57 59 62 64 75 77 81 85 93 97 107 110 111 115 119 127 130 132 133 135 143 146 149 156
Primary Contact: Joann Emge, Chief Executive Officer
CFO: Paul Mueller, Chief Financial Officer
CMO: Mark Pruess, M.D., Chief Medical Staff
CIO: Susan Gutjahr, Reimbursement Specialist
CHR: Darla Shawgo, Director Human Resources
CNO: Lori Clinton, Chief Nursing Officer
Web address: www.spartahospital.com
Control: Hospital district or authority, Government, nonfederal **Service**: General medical and surgical

Staffed Beds: 25 **Admissions:** 455 **Census:** 5 **Outpatient Visits:** 42484 **Births:** 0 **Total Expense ($000):** 36579 **Payroll Expense ($000):** 14473 **Personnel:** 249

SPRING VALLEY—Bureau County

ST. MARGARET'S HOSPITAL (140143), 600 East First Street, Zip 61362–1512; tel. 815/664–5311, **A**10 **F**3 11 13 15 28 29 30 31 32 34 35 37 38 40 44 45 46 47 49 53 57 58 59 63 70 74 75 76 77 79 81 82 84 85 87 93 96 107 108 110 111 115 118 119 125 129 130 131 132 133 135 143 144 146 147 148 149 154 156 157 **S** Sisters of Mary of the Presentation Health System, Fargo, ND
Primary Contact: Tim Muntz, President and Chief Executive Officer
CFO: Kim D Santman, Vice President Finance
CIO: John Sabotta, Director Information Systems
CHR: Lisa R Blackburn, Director Human Resources
CNO: Mary Vega, R.N., MSN, Vice President Nursing
Web address: www.aboutsmh.org
Control: Church operated, Nongovernment, not–for–profit **Service**: General medical and surgical

Staffed Beds: 44 **Admissions:** 1942 **Census:** 18 **Outpatient Visits:** 299796 **Births:** 326 **Total Expense ($000):** 89511 **Payroll Expense ($000):** 37527 **Personnel:** 569

SPRINGFIELD—Sangamon County

☐ **ANDREW MCFARLAND MENTAL HEALTH CENTER (144021)**, 901 East Southwind Road, Zip 62703–5125; tel. 217/786–6994, **A**1 10 **F**29 30 38 87 98 100 101 130 146 149 154 157 **S** Division of Mental Health, Department of Human Services, Springfield, IL
Primary Contact: Karen Schweighart, R.N., MS, Administrator
CFO: Jeff Frey, Business Administrator
CMO: Kasturi Kripakaran, M.D., Medical Director
CIO: Josh Kates, Information Technology Analyst
CNO: Frances Collins, Director of Nursing
Control: State, Government, nonfederal **Service**: Psychiatric

Staffed Beds: 142 **Admissions:** 252 **Census:** 139 **Outpatient Visits:** 0 **Births:** 0 **Personnel:** 225

☒ **HSHS ST. JOHN'S HOSPITAL (140053)**, 800 East Carpenter Street, Zip 62769–0002; tel. 217/544–6464, (Includes ST. JOHN'S CHILDREN'S HOSPITAL, 800 East Carpenter Street, Springfield, Illinois, Zip 62769; tel. 217/544–6464) **A**1 2 3 5 10 **F**3 11 13 15 17 18 20 22 24 26 28 29 30 31 34 35 36 37 39 40 41 43 44 45 46 47 48 49 50 51 53 54 56 57 58 59 60 61 62 63 64 68 70 72 74 75 76 77 78 79 81 82 83 84 85 86 87 88 89 92 93 94 96 98 103 104 107 110 111 114 115 117 118 119 120 121 122 123 124 126 129 130 131 132 135 146 147 148 149 150 154 157 **S** HSHS Hospital Sisters Health System, Springfield, IL
Primary Contact: Evert J. Kuiper, President and Chief Executive Officer
COO: David R Olejniczak, Chief Operating Officer
CFO: Patty Allen, St. John's Vice President Finance
CIO: Ryan Leach, Chief Information Officer
CHR: Becky Puclik, Division Chief People Officer
CNO: Allison Kay Paul, R.N., Chief Nursing Officer
Web address: www.st-johns.org
Control: Other not–for–profit (including NFP Corporation) **Service**: General medical and surgical

Staffed Beds: 404 **Admissions:** 19429 **Census:** 277 **Outpatient Visits:** 227866 **Births:** 2015 **Total Expense ($000):** 515861 **Payroll Expense ($000):** 146816 **Personnel:** 2737

☐ **LINCOLN PRAIRIE BEHAVIORAL HEALTH CENTER**, 5230 South Sixth Street, Zip 62703–5128; tel. 217/585–1180, **A**1 3 5 **F**29 35 98 99 101 102 104 105 153 **S** Universal Health Services, Inc., King of Prussia, PA
Primary Contact: Mark Littrell, Chief Executive Officer
CFO: Chris Statz, Chief Financial Officer
CMO: Pamela Campbell, M.D., Medical Director
CNO: Renae Hale, Chief Nursing Officer
Web address: www.lincolnprairiebhc.com/
Control: Corporation, Investor–owned (for–profit) **Service**: Children's hospital psychiatric

Staffed Beds: 97 **Admissions:** 2208 **Census:** 73 **Births:** 0 **Total Expense ($000):** 20142 **Payroll Expense ($000):** 8330

☒ △ **MEMORIAL MEDICAL CENTER (140148)**, 701 North First Street, Zip 62781–0001; tel. 217/788–3000, **A**1 2 3 5 7 8 10 **F**3 8 11 12 13 14 15 16 17 18 20 22 24 26 28 29 30 31 32 34 35 36 37 40 43 44 45 46 47 48 49 50 51 54 57 58 59 60 61 63 64 68 69 70 74 75 76 77 78 79 81 82 84 85 86 87 89 90 92 93 96 97 98 102 105 107 110 111 114 115 116 117 118 119 120 121 123 124 126 129 130 131 132 134 135 138 141 145 146 147 148 149 154 156 **S** Memorial Health System, Springfield, IL
Primary Contact: Edgar J. Curtis, FACHE, President and Chief Executive Officer
COO: Charles D Callahan, Ph.D., Executive Vice President and Chief Operating Officer
CFO: Robert W Kay, Senior Vice President and Chief Financial Officer
CMO: Rajesh G. Govindaiah, M.D., Chief Medical Officer
CIO: David B Graham, M.D., Senior Vice President and Chief Information Officer
CHR: Robert F Scott, Vice President and Chief Human Resources Officer
CNO: Marsha A Prater, Ph.D., R.N., Senior Vice President and Chief Nursing Officer
Web address: www.memorialmedical.com
Control: Other not–for–profit (including NFP Corporation) **Service**: General medical and surgical

Staffed Beds: 451 **Admissions:** 24287 **Census:** 334 **Outpatient Visits:** 471709 **Births:** 1507 **Total Expense ($000):** 666273 **Payroll Expense ($000):** 214982 **Personnel:** 3771

IL

Many Facility Codes have changed. Please refer to the AHA Guide Code Chart. © 2019 AHA Guide

STAUNTON—Macoupin County

COMMUNITY HOSPITAL OF STAUNTON (141306), 400 Caldwell Street,
Zip 62088–1499; tel. 618/635–2200, (Nonreporting) **A**10 18
Primary Contact: Susie Campbell, Chief Executive Officer
CFO: Brian Engelke, Chief Financial Officer
CMO: Joshua Poos, M.D., President Medical Staff
CIO: Cheryl Horner, Supervisor Data Processing
CHR: Marilyn Herbeck, Coordinator Human Resources
CNO: Roberta Brown, Chief Nursing Officer
Web address: www.stauntonhospital.org
Control: Other not–for–profit (including NFP Corporation) **Service**: General
medical and surgical

Staffed Beds: 25

STERLING—Whiteside County

CGH MEDICAL CENTER (140043), 100 East LeFevre Road, Zip 61081–1279;
tel. 815/625–0400, **A**1 10 **F**3 7 8 11 13 15 18 20 22 28 29 30 31 34 35 40 45
47 49 50 51 57 59 62 64 68 70 74 76 78 79 81 82 85 86 87 89 92 93 97 107
108 110 111 112 115 116 117 118 119 124 129 130 132 135 144 145 146
147 148 149 156
Primary Contact: Paul Steinke, D.O., President and Chief Executive Officer
CFO: Ben Schaab, Vice President, Chief Financial Officer
CIO: Randy Davis, Vice President and Chief Information Officer
CHR: Paul Steinke, D.O., President and Chief Executive Officer
CNO: Kristie A Geil, Vice President, Chief Nursing Officer
Web address: www.cghmc.com
Control: City, Government, nonfederal **Service**: General medical and surgical

Staffed Beds: 99 **Admissions**: 4079 **Census**: 36 **Outpatient Visits**: 373101
Births: 575 **Total Expense ($000)**: 218189 **Payroll Expense ($000)**: 97388
Personnel: 1004

STREAMWOOD—Cook County

STREAMWOOD BEHAVIORAL HEALTH CENTER (144034), 1400 East Irving
Park Road, Zip 60107–3203; tel. 630/837–9000, **A**1 10 **F**50 98 99 100 101
104 105 130 153 **S** Universal Health Services, Inc., King of Prussia, PA
Primary Contact: Ron Weglarz, Chief Executive Officer and Managing Director
CMO: Joseph McNally, M.D., Medical Director
CHR: Joseph Rinke, Director Human Resources
CNO: Olieth Lightbourne, Chief Nursing Officer
Web address: www.streamwoodhospital.com
Control: Corporation, Investor–owned (for–profit) **Service**: Psychiatric

Staffed Beds: 178 **Admissions**: 2974 **Census**: 111 **Outpatient
Visits**: 28198 **Births**: 0 **Total Expense ($000)**: 32550 **Payroll Expense
($000)**: 20722 **Personnel**: 303

SYCAMORE—Dekalb County

KINDRED HOSPITAL-SYCAMORE (142006), 225 Edward Street,
Zip 60178–2137; tel. 815/895–2144, (Nonreporting) **A**1 10 **S** Kindred
Healthcare, Louisville, KY
Primary Contact: Jim Cohick, Chief Executive Officer
CFO: Jay Schweikart, Chief Financial Officer
CMO: Manav Salwan, Medical Director
CNO: Beth Ann Navarro, Chief Clinical Officer
Web address: www.kindredhospitalsyc.com/
Control: Corporation, Investor–owned (for–profit) **Service**: Acute long–term care
hospital

Staffed Beds: 69

TAYLORVILLE—Christian County

TAYLORVILLE MEMORIAL HOSPITAL (141339), 201 East Pleasant Street,
Zip 62568–1597; tel. 217/824–3331, **A**1 3 5 10 18 **F**8 15 28 29 30 34 35 40
45 46 50 57 59 64 75 77 79 81 87 89 93 103 107 108 110 111 115 119 129
130 131 132 133 144 146 149 **S** Memorial Health System, Springfield, IL
Primary Contact: Kimberly L. Bourne, Chief Executive Officer
CFO: Andrew Costic, Regional Chief Financial Officer
CHR: Michelle Long, Regional Human Resource Manager
CNO: Tracy Seaton, Director of Nursing
Web address: www.taylorvillememorial.org
Control: Other not–for–profit (including NFP Corporation) **Service**: General
medical and surgical

Staffed Beds: 25 **Admissions**: 641 **Census**: 6 **Outpatient Visits**: 34511
Births: 0 **Total Expense ($000)**: 38986 **Payroll Expense ($000)**: 15612
Personnel: 257

URBANA—Champaign County

★ △ ⇑ **CARLE FOUNDATION HOSPITAL (140091)**, 611 West Park Street,
Zip 61801–2529; tel. 217/383–3311, **A**2 3 5 7 10 13 21 **F**3 8 12 13 15 17 18
20 22 24 26 28 29 30 31 34 35 40 43 44 45 46 47 48 49 50 51 53 56 57 58
59 60 61 62 63 64 68 70 72 73 74 75 76 77 78 79 80 81 82 84 85 86 87 89
90 91 92 93 96 97 104 107 108 110 111 114 115 117 118 119 120 121 123
124 126 129 130 131 132 146 148 149 154 **S** Carle Foundation, Urbana, IL
Primary Contact: James C. Leonard, M.D., President and Chief Executive Officer
COO: John Snyder, Executive Vice President and System Chief Operating Officer
CFO: Dennis Hesch, Executive Vice President Finance, System Chief Financial
Officer
CMO: Matthew Gibb, M.D., Executive Vice President and System Chief Medical
Officer
CIO: Rick Rinehart, Vice President, Chief Information Officer
CHR: L J Fallon, JD, Executive Vice President, Chief Legal and Human Resources
Officer
CNO: Pamela Bigler, R.N., Senior Vice President, Chief Nursing Officer
Web address: www.carle.org
Control: Other not–for–profit (including NFP Corporation) **Service**: General
medical and surgical

Staffed Beds: 436 **Admissions**: 25433 **Census**: 338 **Outpatient
Visits**: 1467485 **Births**: 2823 **Total Expense ($000)**: 797262 **Payroll
Expense ($000)**: 204927 **Personnel**: 3450

OSF HEART OF MARY MEDICAL CENTER (140113), 1400 West Park
Street, Zip 61801–2396, Mailing Address: P.O. Box 6259, Peoria, Zip 61601;
tel. 217/337–2000, (Data for 334 days) **A**1 3 10 **F**3 8 12 13 15 18 20 22 24 26
28 29 30 35 40 45 46 47 48 49 57 59 60 64 68 70 73 74 75 76 79 81 82 84
87 89 90 92 94 96 97 98 100 102 107 108 110 111 112 113 114 115 119
126 130 132 146 147 148 154 **S** OSF Healthcare, Peoria, IL
Primary Contact: Jared Rogers, M.D., President and Chief Executive Officer
CFO: Lucas Morton, Regional Chief Financial Officer
CMO: Vincent Kucich, FACHE, FACS, M.D., Chief Medical Officer
CIO: Paula Keele, Manager Information Systems
CHR: Michael Zimmerman, Human Resource Officer
CNO: Molly Nicholson, MS, R.N., Chief Nurse Executive
Web address: www.presencehealth.org/covenant
Control: Church operated, Nongovernment, not–for–profit **Service**: General
medical and surgical

Staffed Beds: 101 **Admissions**: 4200 **Census**: 60 **Outpatient Visits**: 27475
Births: 381 **Total Expense ($000)**: 84950 **Payroll Expense ($000)**: 24701
Personnel: 581

VANDALIA—Fayette County

FAYETTE COUNTY HOSPITAL (141346), 650 West Taylor Street,
Zip 62471–1296; tel. 618/283–1231, (Nonreporting) **A**1 10 18 **S** Alliant
Management Services, Louisville, KY
Primary Contact: Gregory D. Starnes, Chief Executive Officer
CFO: David H Wiesman, Interim Chief Financial Officer
CMO: Joseph Blaser, Chief Medical Officer
CIO: Gary Hood, Chief Information Officer
CHR: Susan Crawford, Manager Human Resources
CNO: Marci Barth, Chief Nursing Officer
Web address: www.fayettecountyhospital.org
Control: Corporation, Investor–owned (for–profit) **Service**: General medical and
surgical

Staffed Beds: 110

WATSEKA—Iroquois County

IROQUOIS MEMORIAL HOSPITAL AND RESIDENT HOME (140167), 200
Fairman Avenue, Zip 60970–1644; tel. 815/432–5841, (Total facility includes 35
beds in nursing home–type unit) **A**1 3 10 20 **F**3 7 11 14 15 18 20 28 29 30 31
34 35 38 40 43 45 46 49 56 57 59 62 63 65 69 70 75 77 81 82 85 86 87 92
93 97 107 108 110 115 119 127 128 130 132 133 135 145 146 147 154
Primary Contact: Tim Smith, Chief Executive Officer
CFO: Lori Yelenick, Chief Financial Officer
CMO: Aravind Reddy, M.D., Chief of Staff
CHR: Jamie Neumann, Director Human Resources
CNO: Mary Cahoe, Chief Nursing Officer
Web address: www.imhrh.org
Control: Other not–for–profit (including NFP Corporation) **Service**: General
medical and surgical

Staffed Beds: 60 **Admissions**: 704 **Census**: 32 **Outpatient Visits**: 40199
Births: 2 **Total Expense ($000)**: 34539 **Payroll Expense ($000)**: 16801
Personnel: 303

IL

Hospital, Medicare Provider Number, Address, Telephone, Approval, Facility, and Physician Codes, Health Care System

★ American Hospital Association (AHA) membership   ○ Healthcare Facilities Accreditation Program   ⇑ Center for Improvement in Healthcare Quality Accreditation
□ The Joint Commission accreditation   ◇ DNV Healthcare Inc. accreditation   △ Commission on Accreditation of Rehabilitation Facilities (CARF) accreditation

WAUKEGAN—Lake County

☒ **VISTA HEALTH (140033)**, 2615 Washington Street, Zip 60085–4988; tel. 847/249–3900, (Nonreporting) **A**1 10
Primary Contact: Norman F. Stephens, Interim Chief Executive Officer
COO: Kim Needham, Assistant Chief Executive Officer
CFO: Kerry Hill, Chief Financial Officer
CMO: Daniel Liesen, M.D., Chief Medical Officer
CHR: Michael R Isaacs, Vice President Human Resources
Web address: www.vistahealth.com
Control: Corporation, Investor–owned (for–profit) **Service**: General medical and surgical

Staffed Beds: 67

☒ **VISTA HEALTH (140084)**, 1324 North Sheridan Road, Zip 60085–2161; tel. 847/360–3000, (Nonreporting) **A**1 2 3 5 10 **S** Quorum Health, Brentwood, TN
Primary Contact: Norman F. Stephens, Interim Chief Executive Officer
COO: Kim Needham, Assistant Chief Executive Officer
CFO: Kerry Hill, Chief Financial Officer
CMO: Daniel Liesen, M.D., Chief Medical Officer
CHR: Michael R Isaacs, Vice President Human Resources
Web address: www.vistahealth.com
Control: Corporation, Investor–owned (for–profit) **Service**: General medical and surgical

Staffed Beds: 190

WHEATON—Du Page County

☒ △ **NORTHWESTERN MEDICINE MARIANJOY REHABILITATION HOSPITAL (143027)**, 26 West 171 Roosevelt Road, Zip 60187–0795, Mailing Address: P.O. Box 795, Zip 60187–0795; tel. 630/909–8000, (Total facility includes 27 beds in nursing home–type unit) **A**1 3 7 10 **F**3 11 29 30 34 35 36 44 50 53 54 57 58 64 68 74 75 77 79 82 86 87 90 91 92 93 95 96 119 128 130 131 132 143 146 148 149 154 **S** Northwestern Memorial HealthCare, Chicago, IL
Primary Contact: Brian J. Lemon, President
COO: John Brady, Vice President Physician Services and Organizational Planning
CFO: Michael Hedderman, Senior Vice President Finance and Chief Financial Officer
CMO: Jeffrey Oken, Vice President of Medical Affairs
CIO: Robert Sinickas, Director Information Services
CHR: Teresa Chapman, Vice President Human Resources
Web address: www.marianjoy.org
Control: Other not–for–profit (including NFP Corporation) **Service**: Rehabilitation

Staffed Beds: 127 **Admissions:** 3019 **Census:** 118 **Outpatient Visits:** 59680 **Births:** 0 **Total Expense ($000):** 103775 **Payroll Expense ($000):** 55401 **Personnel:** 721

WINFIELD—DuPage County

☒ **NORTHWESTERN MEDICINE CENTRAL DUPAGE HOSPITAL (140242)**, 25 North Winfield Road, Zip 60190; tel. 630/933–1600, (Includes BEHAVIORAL HEALTH CENTER, 27 West 350 High Lake Road, Winfield, Illinois, Zip 60190; tel. 630/653–4000) **A**1 2 3 5 10 **F**3 4 5 6 8 9 11 12 13 15 17 18 19 20 22 24 26 28 29 30 31 32 34 35 36 37 38 39 40 41 43 44 45 46 47 48 49 50 54 55 57 58 59 60 64 65 68 70 71 72 73 74 75 76 77 78 79 81 82 84 85 86 87 88 89 91 92 93 94 96 97 98 99 100 101 102 103 104 105 107 108 110 111 112 114 115 116 117 118 119 120 121 122 123 124 126 129 130 131 132 135 144 145 146 147 148 149 152 153 154 156 157 **S** Northwestern Memorial HealthCare, Chicago, IL
Primary Contact: Brian J. Lemon, President
CFO: John Orsini, Executive Vice President and Chief Financial Officer
CMO: Kevin Most, D.O., Vice President Medical Affairs
CIO: Daniel F Kinsella, Vice President and Chief Information Officer
Web address: www.nm.org
Control: Other not–for–profit (including NFP Corporation) **Service**: General medical and surgical

Staffed Beds: 419 **Admissions:** 21158 **Census:** 262 **Outpatient Visits:** 1060823 **Births:** 2785 **Total Expense ($000):** 1086063 **Payroll Expense ($000):** 367581 **Personnel:** 5439

ZION—Lake County

☒ **MIDWESTERN REGIONAL MEDICAL CENTER (140100)**, 2520 Elisha Avenue, Zip 60099–2587; tel. 847/872–4561, **A**1 2 3 10 **F**3 8 15 29 30 31 33 34 36 37 38 40 44 45 46 47 48 49 50 55 57 58 59 64 68 70 74 75 77 78 79 81 82 85 86 87 92 93 94 95 107 108 110 111 115 116 117 118 119 120 121 123 124 126 129 130 132 133 136 143 144 146 147 148 154 **S** Cancer Treatment Centers of America, Schaumburg, IL
Primary Contact: Scott Jones, President and Chief Executive Officer
COO: Pete Govorchin, Senior Vice President Operations
CFO: Cecilia Taylor, Chief Financial Officer
CMO: Bradford Tan, M.D., Chief Medical Officer
CHR: Amy VanStrien, Director Talent Operations
CNO: Jacklynn Lesniak, R.N., MS, Vice President Patient Care Services and Chief Nursing Officer
Web address: www.cancercenter.com
Control: Corporation, Investor–owned (for–profit) **Service**: Cancer

Staffed Beds: 72 **Admissions:** 1554 **Census:** 23 **Outpatient Visits:** 32724 **Births:** 0 **Personnel:** 760

IL

Many Facility Codes have changed. Please refer to the AHA Guide Code Chart. © 2019 AHA Guide

INDIANA

ANDERSON—Madison County

⊞ **COMMUNITY HOSPITAL OF ANDERSON & MADISON COUNTY (150113)**, 1515 North Madison Avenue, Zip 46011–3453; tel. 765/298–4242, **A**1 2 10 **F**3 10 11 13 15 18 20 22 28 29 30 31 32 34 35 40 43 44 46 49 50 51 54 55 56 57 58 59 60 61 64 68 70 74 75 76 77 78 79 81 82 85 86 87 89 93 107 108 109 110 111 114 115 119 120 121 122 123 126 129 130 132 135 143 144 146 147 148 149 156 157 **S** Community Health Network, Indianapolis, IN
Primary Contact: Beth S. Tharp, R.N., President and Chief Executive Officer
CFO: John B. Harris, Vice President Finance and Chief Financial Officer
CHR: Michael Harpe, Vice President Human Resources
CNO: Carol Whitesel, MSN, R.N., Vice President Patient Care Services and Chief Nursing Officer
Web address: www.communityanderson.com
Control: Other not–for–profit (including NFP Corporation) **Service:** General medical and surgical

Staffed Beds: 140 **Admissions:** 6200 **Census:** 72 **Outpatient Visits:** 226538 **Births:** 862 **Total Expense ($000):** 173780 **Payroll Expense ($000):** 70917 **Personnel:** 1132

⊞ **ST. VINCENT ANDERSON (150088)**, 2015 Jackson Street, Zip 46016–4339; tel. 765/649–2511, **A**1 2 10 **F**3 4 5 8 11 13 14 15 18 20 22 30 31 32 34 35 36 38 39 40 43 44 45 46 49 50 51 54 55 56 57 58 59 60 61 64 65 66 68 70 74 75 76 77 78 79 81 82 84 85 86 87 89 90 92 93 94 96 98 99 100 101 102 103 104 105 106 107 108 110 111 114 115 116 117 118 119 120 121 123 124 126 129 130 132 134 135 145 146 147 148 149 151 153 154 156 **S** Ascension Healthcare, Saint Louis, MO
Primary Contact: Mike K. Schroyer, FACHE, MSN, R.N., President
COO: Nick Theohares, Executive Director, Operations
CFO: Laura L Rose, Chief Financial Officer
CIO: Robert A. Pope, Director I
CHR: Ross Brodhead, Senior Director, Human Resource
Web address: www.stvincent.org/anderson
Control: Church operated, Nongovernment, not–for–profit **Service:** General medical and surgical

Staffed Beds: 154 **Admissions:** 5944 **Census:** 86 **Outpatient Visits:** 248282 **Births:** 402 **Total Expense ($000):** 189628 **Payroll Expense ($000):** 51030

ANGOLA—Steuben County

★ **CAMERON MEMORIAL COMMUNITY HOSPITAL (151315)**, 416 East Maumee Street, Zip 46703–2015, tel. 260/665–2141, **A**10 **F**3 11 13 15 18 20 29 30 34 35 40 44 45 50 53 57 59 62 63 65 68 75 76 77 79 81 85 86 87 90 93 97 103 104 107 108 110 111 114 115 117 119 125 127 129 130 131 132 133 144 146 147 149 156
Primary Contact: Connie McCahill, R.N., President and Chief Executive Officer
CFO: Douglas Bomba, Chief Financial Officer
CMO: Jon Alley, D.O., President Medical Staff
CIO: Kris Keen, Chief Information Officer
CHR: Nancy Covell, Director Human Resources
Web address: www.cameronmch.com
Control: Other not–for–profit (including NFP Corporation) **Service:** General medical and surgical

Staffed Beds: 25 **Admissions:** 1388 **Census:** 10 **Outpatient Visits:** 135127 **Births:** 236 **Total Expense ($000):** 68204 **Payroll Expense ($000):** 24214

AUBURN—Dekalb County

DEKALB HEALTH (150045), 1316 East Seventh Street, Zip 46706–2515, Mailing Address: P.O. Box 542, Zip 46706–0542; tel. 260/925–4600, **A**10 **F**3 7 11 13 15 28 29 32 34 35 36 40 45 53 56 57 59 62 63 64 70 73 75 76 77 79 81 82 84 85 86 87 89 93 97 107 108 110 111 114 115 119 129 130 132 135 144 146 147 148 149
Primary Contact: Natasha Eicher, President and Chief Executive Officer
CMO: Emilio Vazquez, M.D., Chief Medical Officer
CIO: Ed Hobbs, Director Information Services
CNO: Donna S Wisemore, R.N., Vice President and Chief Nursing Officer
Web address: www.dekalbhealth.com
Control: Other not–for–profit (including NFP Corporation) **Service:** General medical and surgical

Staffed Beds: 56 **Admissions:** 2289 **Census:** 15

NORTHEASTERN CENTER (154050), 1850 Wesley Road, Zip 46706–3653; tel. 260/927–0726, (Nonreporting) **A**10
Primary Contact: Jerry Hollister, Chief Executive Officer
Web address: www.necmh.org
Control: Other not–for–profit (including NFP Corporation) **Service:** Psychiatric

Staffed Beds: 16

AVON—Hendricks County

CLARIAN WEST MEDICAL CENTER See Indiana University Health West Hospital

⊞ **INDIANA UNIVERSITY HEALTH WEST HOSPITAL (150158)**, 1111 North Ronald Reagan Parkway, Zip 46123–7085; tel. 317/217–3000, **A**1 2 3 5 10 **F**3 13 15 18 20 22 26 28 29 30 34 35 40 41 46 47 48 49 50 51 57 59 64 68 70 74 75 76 77 78 79 81 82 85 86 87 89 93 100 107 110 111 113 114 117 119 120 121 129 130 132 135 146 147 148 156 157 **S** Indiana University Health, Indianapolis, IN
Primary Contact: Arthur Vasquez, President
CMO: Andrew Nigh, M.D., Chief of Staff
CHR: Tamarah Brownlee, Vice President, Human Resources
CNO: Lisa Sparks, R.N., Chief Nursing Officer and Vice President Patient Care Services
Web address: www.iuhealth.org
Control: Other not–for–profit (including NFP Corporation) **Service:** General medical and surgical

Staffed Beds: 127 **Admissions:** 7151 **Census:** 84 **Outpatient Visits:** 242414 **Births:** 865 **Total Expense ($000):** 170445 **Payroll Expense ($000):** 49995 **Personnel:** 768

BATESVILLE—Ripley County

⊞ **MARGARET MARY HEALTH (151329)**, 321 Mitchell Avenue, Zip 47006–8909, Mailing Address: P.O. Box 226, Zip 47006–0226; tel. 812/934–6624, (Nonreporting) **A**1 2 10 18
Primary Contact: Timothy L. Putnam, FACHE, President and Chief Executive Officer
CFO: Brian Daeger, Chief Financial Officer and Vice President Financial Services
CMO: Charles McGovern, Chief of Staff
CIO: Trisha Prickel, Information Systems Director
CHR: Kimberly Inscho, Vice President Human Resources and Marketing
CNO: Elizabeth Leising, Chief Nursing Officer and Vice President Patient Services
Web address: www.mmhealth.org
Control: Other not–for–profit (including NFP Corporation) **Service:** General medical and surgical

Staffed Beds: 25

BEDFORD—Lawrence County

BEDFORD REGIONAL MEDICAL CENTER See Indiana University Health Bedford Hospital

DUNN MEMORIAL HOSPITAL See St. Vincent Dunn Hospital

⊞ **INDIANA UNIVERSITY HEALTH BEDFORD HOSPITAL (151328)**, 2900 West 16th Street, Zip 47421–3583; tel. 812/275–1200, **A**1 2 10 18 **F**3 7 11 15 18 28 29 30 31 34 35 38 40 41 45 46 49 50 57 64 68 70 74 75 77 78 79 81 85 86 87 93 102 107 108 110 111 115 118 119 129 130 132 133 135 146 149 154 156 **S** Indiana University Health, Indianapolis, IN
Primary Contact: Bradford W. Dykes, President and Chief Executive Officer
CFO: Mike Craig, Vice President, Chief Financial Officer
CMO: Joanne F Smart, M.D., Director Medical Affairs
CHR: Bruce Wade, Vice President Human Resources
CNO: Brenda Davis, Vice President Patient Services
Web address: www.iuhealth.org
Control: Other not–for–profit (including NFP Corporation) **Service:** General medical and surgical

Staffed Beds: 25 **Admissions:** 1109 **Census:** 11 **Outpatient Visits:** 80742 **Births:** 0 **Total Expense ($000):** 55473 **Payroll Expense ($000):** 15326 **Personnel:** 215

✠ **ST. VINCENT DUNN HOSPITAL (151335)**, 1600 23rd Street, Zip 47421–4704; tel. 812/275–3331, **A**1 10 18 **F**2 3 12 13 15 18 28 29 30 34 35 40 45 50 53 59 64 65 66 68 75 76 77 79 81 82 85 86 87 107 108 109 111 115 119 130 133 135 146 148 149 **S** Ascension Healthcare, Saint Louis, MO
Primary Contact: Jerry Laue, Administrator
CFO: Crystal Plano, Controller
CMO: Deborah W Craton, M.D., Chief Medical Officer
CIO: Chad Damon, Contractor
CHR: Darci Medlock, Manager Human Resources
CNO: Michelle Dotts-McCool, Chief Nursing Officer
Web address: www.stvincent.org/St-Vincent-Dunn/Default.aspx
Control: Other not–for–profit (including NFP Corporation) **Service**: General medical and surgical

> **Staffed Beds**: 35 **Admissions**: 686 **Census**: 6 **Outpatient Visits**: 32831 **Births**: 287 **Total Expense ($000)**: 20046 **Payroll Expense ($000)**: 5744 **Personnel**: 400

BLOOMINGTON—Monroe County

BLOOMINGTON HOSPITAL See Indiana University Health Bloomington Hospital

✠ **BLOOMINGTON MEADOWS HOSPITAL (154041)**, 3600 North Prow Road, Zip 47404–1616; tel. 812/331–8000, (Nonreporting) **A**1 10 **S** Universal Health Services, Inc., King of Prussia, PA
Primary Contact: Christopher Dowers, Chief Executive Officer
CFO: Becky T Nyberg, Chief Financial Officer
CMO: David Gilliam, M.D., Medical Director
CHR: Amanda Shettlesworth, Director Human Resources
CNO: Penny Caswell, Director of Nursing
Web address: www.bloomingtonmeadows.com
Control: Corporation, Investor–owned (for–profit) **Service**: Psychiatric

> **Staffed Beds**: 67

✠ **INDIANA UNIVERSITY HEALTH BLOOMINGTON HOSPITAL (150051)**, 601 West Second Street, Zip 47403–2317, Mailing Address: P.O. Box 1149, Zip 47402–1149; tel. 812/336–6821, **A**1 2 10 19 **F**3 7 8 11 12 17 18 19 20 22 24 26 28 29 30 31 32 34 35 38 40 43 45 46 47 48 49 50 53 54 55 57 59 61 62 63 64 65 69 70 72 75 76 77 78 79 81 82 84 85 86 87 89 90 92 93 94 97 98 100 101 102 104 107 108 111 114 115 119 120 121 124 126 129 130 131 132 135 143 144 146 147 148 149 153 154 156 158 **S** Indiana University Health, Indianapolis, IN
Primary Contact: Brian T. Shockney, FACHE, President
CFO: Mike Craig, Chief Financial Officer
CMO: Daniel Handel, M.D., Vice President, Chief Medical Officer
CIO: Mark W McMath, Chief Information Officer
CHR: Steven D Deckard, Vice President Human Resources
Web address: www.iuhealth.org
Control: Other not–for–profit (including NFP Corporation) **Service**: General medical and surgical

> **Staffed Beds**: 282 **Admissions**: 12552 **Census**: 167 **Outpatient Visits**: 225092 **Births**: 1968 **Total Expense ($000)**: 337105 **Payroll Expense ($000)**: 109978 **Personnel**: 1713

✠ **MONROE HOSPITAL (150183)**, 4011 South Monroe Medical Park Boulevard, Zip 47424; tel. 812/825–1111, **A**1 10 **F**3 15 18 29 34 35 40 41 44 45 46 47 48 50 56 57 59 64 65 68 70 75 78 79 80 81 85 86 87 91 97 107 108 109 110 111 114 115 119 135 148 149 154 156 **S** Prime Healthcare, Ontario, CA
Primary Contact: Nancy Bakewell, Administrator
CFO: Hilary Dolbee, Chief Financial Officer
CMO: Amandeep Singh, Chief Medical Officer
CIO: LaDonna Cagle, HIM Appeals Coordinator III
CHR: Karyn Batdorf, Director of Human Resources
CNO: Nancy Bakewell, Chief Nursing Officer
Web address: www.monroehospital.com
Control: Corporation, Investor–owned (for–profit) **Service**: General medical and surgical

> **Staffed Beds**: 32 **Admissions**: 1163 **Census**: 12 **Outpatient Visits**: 27518 **Births**: 0 **Total Expense ($000)**: 28644 **Payroll Expense ($000)**: 12327 **Personnel**: 263

BLUFFTON—Wells County

✠ **BLUFFTON REGIONAL MEDICAL CENTER (150075)**, 303 South Main Street, Zip 46714–2503; tel. 260/824–3210, (Total facility includes 13 beds in nursing home–type unit) **A**1 10 19 **F**3 13 15 18 28 29 30 34 35 40 41 45 49 50 57 59 64 70 74 75 76 79 81 85 86 87 89 91 93 94 96 97 107 108 110 111 114 119 128 129 130 132 135 146 147 148 149 150 154 **S** Community Health Systems, Inc., Franklin, TN
Primary Contact: Brent Parsons, Chief Executive Officer
COO: Julie Thompson, Chief Operating Officer and Chief Nursing Officer
CFO: Larry W DeBolt, Chief Financial Officer
CMO: Harish Ardeshna, Pulmonologist & Chief Medical Officer
CHR: Patricia Sprinkle, Vice President, Human Resources
CNO: Julie Thompson, Chief Operating Officer and Chief Nursing Officer
Web address: www.blufftonregional.com
Control: Corporation, Investor–owned (for–profit) **Service**: General medical and surgical

> **Staffed Beds**: 54 **Admissions**: 1355 **Census**: 20 **Outpatient Visits**: 60847 **Births**: 208 **Total Expense ($000)**: 36859 **Payroll Expense ($000)**: 13238 **Personnel**: 212

BOONVILLE—Warrick County

✠ **ST. VINCENT WARRICK (151325)**, 1116 Millis Avenue, Zip 47601–2204; tel. 812/897–4800, **A**1 10 18 **F**7 8 11 15 29 30 38 40 56 59 68 77 79 81 93 97 100 104 106 107 111 114 115 116 117 119 126 148 155 **S** Ascension Healthcare, Saint Louis, MO
Primary Contact: Kathy J. Hall, Administrator
CFO: Crystal Heaton, Director of Finance
CNO: Karen Waters, Chief Nursing Officer
Web address: www.stmarys.org/warrick
Control: Other not–for–profit (including NFP Corporation) **Service**: General medical and surgical

> **Staffed Beds**: 35 **Admissions**: 565 **Census**: 18 **Outpatient Visits**: 22228 **Births**: 0 **Total Expense ($000)**: 17868 **Payroll Expense ($000)**: 5523 **Personnel**: 106

BRAZIL—Clay County

✠ **ST. VINCENT CLAY HOSPITAL (151309)**, 1206 East National Avenue, Zip 47834–2797, Mailing Address: 1206 East National Ave, Zip 47834–0489; tel. 812/442–2500, **A**1 10 18 **F**3 12 15 18 29 30 34 35 40 45 50 57 59 65 68 75 77 79 81 82 85 86 87 107 108 110 111 115 119 128 130 132 133 135 146 148 154 **S** Ascension Healthcare, Saint Louis, MO
Primary Contact: Jerry Laue, Administrator
CFO: Wayne Knight, Director Finance
CMO: Stephen Tharp, Regional Chief Medical Officer
CHR: Lainie Collins, Human Resources Partner
CNO: Paulette Sue Gaskill, Executive Director of Nursing
Web address: www.stvincent.org
Control: Church operated, Nongovernment, not–for–profit **Service**: General medical and surgical

> **Staffed Beds**: 25 **Admissions**: 269 **Census**: 3 **Outpatient Visits**: 35747 **Total Expense ($000)**: 17869 **Payroll Expense ($000)**: 4362 **Personnel**: 61

BREMEN—Marshall County

★ **COMMUNITY HOSPITAL OF BREMEN (151300)**, 1020 High Road, Zip 46506–1093, Mailing Address: P.O. Box 8, Zip 46506–0008; tel. 574/546–2211, **A**10 18 **F**3 11 13 15 29 34 35 40 45 50 57 59 64 69 75 76 77 79 81 82 85 93 107 110 111 115 119 129 130 132 133 135 146 149
Primary Contact: David Bailey, FACHE, Chief Executive Officer
CFO: Amy Lashbrook, Chief Financial Officer
CMO: Lindy Sergeant, Medical Staff President
CHR: Patricia Board, Vice President Human Resources
CNO: Sue Bettcher, R.N., Vice President of Nursing Services
Web address: www.bremenhospital.com
Control: Other not–for–profit (including NFP Corporation) **Service**: General medical and surgical

> **Staffed Beds**: 24 **Admissions**: 253 **Census**: 2 **Outpatient Visits**: 46692 **Births**: 108 **Total Expense ($000)**: 19172 **Payroll Expense ($000)**: 8060 **Personnel**: 133

□ **DOCTORS NEUROPSYCHIATRIC HOSPITAL AND RESEARCH INSTITUTE (154058)**, 417 South Whitlock Street, Zip 46506–1626; tel. 574/546–0330, **A**1 10 **F**29 98 **S** NeuroPsychiatric Hospitals, Mishawaka, IN
Primary Contact: Christy Gilbert, Interim Chief Executive Officer
Control: Individual, Investor–owned (for–profit) **Service**: Psychiatric

> **Staffed Beds**: 37 **Admissions**: 808 **Census**: 35 **Outpatient Visits**: 0 **Births**: 0 **Total Expense ($000)**: 8177 **Personnel**: 81

IN

Many Facility Codes have changed. Please refer to the AHA Guide Code Chart. © 2019 AHA Guide

CARMEL—Hamilton County

CLARIAN NORTH MEDICAL CENTER See Indiana University Health North Hospital

○ **FRANCISCAN HEALTH CARMEL (150182)**, 12188B North Meridian Street, Zip 46032–4840; tel. 317/705–4500, (Nonreporting) **A**10 11 **S** Franciscan Health, Mishawaka, IN
Primary Contact: Stephen J. Wheatley, Director of Operations
CFO: Keith A. Lauter, Chief Financial Officer
CMO: Christopher Doehring, M.D., Vice President of Medical Affairs
CIO: Rebecca Merkel, Privacy Officer
CHR: Corey Baute, Vice President of Human Resource
CNO: Agnes Therady, MSN, FACHE, Vice President and Chief Nursing Officer
Web address: www.franciscanalliance.org/hospitals/carmel/Pages/default.aspx
Control: Church operated **Service:** General medical and surgical

Staffed Beds: 6

✠ **INDIANA UNIVERSITY HEALTH NORTH HOSPITAL (150161)**, 11700 North Meridian Avenue, Zip 46032–4656; tel. 317/688–2000, **A**1 3 5 10 **F**3 13 15 18 19 20 22 26 29 30 31 34 35 36 37 40 45 47 48 49 50 55 57 59 60 64 68 70 72 74 75 76 77 78 79 81 85 86 87 88 89 91 92 93 107 108 110 111 115 119 124 126 129 130 132 135 146 147 148 154 155 156 157 **S** Indiana University Health, Indianapolis, IN
Primary Contact: Alicia Schulhof, President and Chief Executive Officer
COO: Randall C. Yust, Chief Operating Officer and Chief Financial Officer
CFO: Randall C. Yust, Chief Operating Officer and Chief Financial Officer
CMO: Paul Calkins, M.D., Chief Medical Officer
CIO: Steve Bodenham, Senior Manager Clinical Engineering
CHR: Steven E Kile, Vice President Human Resources
Web address: www.iuhealth.org/north
Control: Other not–for–profit (including NFP Corporation) **Service:** General medical and surgical

Staffed Beds: 161 **Admissions:** 7443 **Census:** 82 **Outpatient Visits:** 206313 **Births:** 2308 **Total Expense ($000):** 202030 **Payroll Expense ($000):** 59337 **Personnel:** 892

✠ **ST. VINCENT CARMEL HOSPITAL (150157)**, 13500 North Meridian Street, Zip 46032–1456; tel. 317/582–7000, **A**1 5 10 **F**3 12 13 15 34 35 36 37 40 44 45 49 50 54 57 58 59 61 64 65 69 70 72 75 76 78 79 80 81 85 87 92 96 107 108 110 111 114 115 119 126 130 132 135 146 147 148 149 154 157 **S** Ascension Healthcare, Saint Louis, MO
Primary Contact: Julie Manas, Regional President
COO: Daniel LaReau, Executive Director, Operations and Information
CFO: Robert A Dates, Chief Financial Officer
CMO: Steven Priddy, M.D., VP of Physician Affairs/Chief Medical Officer
CIO: Daniel LaReau, Executive Director, Operations and Information
CHR: Ross Brodhead, Senior Director, Human Resources
CNO: Ted Eads, Interim Chief Nursing Officer
Web address: www.https://www.stvincent.org
Control: Church operated, Nongovernment, not–for–profit **Service:** General medical and surgical

Staffed Beds: 111 **Admissions:** 5273 **Census:** 48 **Outpatient Visits:** 91946 **Births:** 1622 **Total Expense ($000):** 137157 **Payroll Expense ($000):** 36883

CLINTON—Vermillion County

○ **UNION HOSPITAL CLINTON (151326)**, 801 South Main Street, Zip 47842–2261; tel. 765/832–1234, **A**10 11 18 **F**3 11 15 18 29 30 34 35 40 45 50 57 59 64 65 68 70 75 81 85 86 87 91 93 97 107 108 110 115 119 130 132 133 146 156 157
Primary Contact: Stephanie Laws, Vice President, Administrator
CFO: Wayne Hutson, Chief Financial Officer
CMO: John Albrecht, Chief of Staff
CIO: Jack Hill, Vice President and Chief Operating Officer
Web address: www.myunionhospital.org/unionhospital/union-hospital-clinton
Control: Other not–for–profit (including NFP Corporation) **Service:** General medical and surgical

Staffed Beds: 21 **Admissions:** 627 **Census:** 5 **Outpatient Visits:** 43534 **Births:** 0 **Total Expense ($000):** 21463 **Payroll Expense ($000):** 7114 **Personnel:** 111

COLUMBIA CITY—Whitley County

✠ **PARKVIEW WHITLEY HOSPITAL (150101)**, 1260 East State Road 205, Zip 46725–9492; tel. 260/248–9000, **A**1 10 **F**3 7 13 15 28 29 30 34 35 38 40 42 45 50 54 59 64 70 75 76 79 81 82 85 87 89 91 93 96 102 107 108 110 111 115 119 129 132 135 143 146 148 154 156 **S** Parkview Health, Fort Wayne, IN
Primary Contact: Scott F. Gabriel, President
COO: Scott F Gabriel, President
CFO: Lisa Peppler, Financial Manager
CMO: Jeffrey Brookes, M.D., Medical Director
Web address: www.parkview.com
Control: Other not–for–profit (including NFP Corporation) **Service:** General medical and surgical

Staffed Beds: 30 **Admissions:** 1690 **Census:** 12 **Outpatient Visits:** 69044 **Births:** 399 **Total Expense ($000):** 68161 **Payroll Expense ($000):** 18212 **Personnel:** 282

COLUMBUS—Bartholomew County

★ ○ **COLUMBUS REGIONAL HOSPITAL (150112)**, 2400 East 17th Street, Zip 47201–5360; tel. 812/379–4441, **A**2 10 11 19 **F**3 7 11 12 13 15 18 20 22 24 26 28 29 30 31 34 35 38 39 40 45 46 47 49 50 51 53 58 59 70 73 74 75 76 77 78 79 81 85 86 87 89 90 93 97 98 100 101 102 103 107 108 110 111 114 115 117 118 119 120 121 123 124 126 129 130 131 132 135 146 147 148 149 156
Primary Contact: Jim Bickel, President and Chief Executive Officer
CFO: Marlene Weatherwax, Vice President and Chief Financial Officer
CMO: Thomas Sonderman, M.D., Vice President and Chief Medical Officer
CIO: Steve Baker, Vice President and Chief Technology and Information Officer
CHR: John R Loya, Vice President Human Resources and Organizational Development
CNO: Holly Cheek, Vice President and Chief Nursing Officer
Web address: www.crh.org
Control: County, Government, nonfederal **Service:** General medical and surgical

Staffed Beds: 229 **Admissions:** 9473 **Census:** 97 **Outpatient Visits:** 252735 **Births:** 1240 **Total Expense ($000):** 273766 **Payroll Expense ($000):** 83949 **Personnel:** 1590

CONNERSVILLE—Fayette County

○ **FAYETTE REGIONAL HEALTH SYSTEM (150064)**, 1941 Virginia Avenue, Zip 47331–2833; tel. 765/825–5131, (Nonreporting) **A**10 11
Primary Contact: Randall White, President and Chief Executive Officer
CFO: Debra Michalek, Chief Financial Officer
CMO: Mike Rowe, M.D., Chief of Staff
CIO: Andy Merida, Director Management Information Systems
CHR: Rhonda McPherson, Vice President Human Resources
CNO: Beth A Wampler, R.N., Chief Nursing Officer
Web address: www.fayetteregional.org
Control: Other not–for–profit (including NFP Corporation) **Service:** General medical and surgical

Staffed Beds: 75

CORYDON—Harrison County

★ ○ **HARRISON COUNTY HOSPITAL (151331)**, 1141 Hospital Drive N W, Zip 47112–1774; tel. 812/738–4251, (Nonreporting) **A**10 11 18
Primary Contact: Steven L. Taylor, Chief Executive Officer
CFO: Jeff Davis, Chief Financial Officer
CIO: Chuck Wiley, Manager Information Systems
CHR: Loren Haverstock, Manager Human Resources
CNO: Ruth Donahue, R.N., Chief Nursing Officer
Web address: www.hchin.org
Control: County, Government, nonfederal **Service:** General medical and surgical

Staffed Beds: 25

IN

CRAWFORDSVILLE—Montgomery County

○ **FRANCISCAN HEALTH CRAWFORDSVILLE (150022)**, 1710 Lafayette Road, Zip 47933–1099; tel. 765/362–2800, **A**10 11 **F**3 11 15 18 19 28 29 30 31 34 35 40 45 50 54 56 57 64 69 70 74 75 77 78 79 81 82 85 87 93 98 103 107 108 110 111 114 115 118 119 120 121 126 129 130 131 132 135 145 146 148 154 **S** Franciscan Health, Mishawaka, IN
Primary Contact: Terrence Klein, Ph.D., Vice President and Chief Operating Officer
COO: Terrence Klein, Ph.D., Vice President and Chief Operating Officer
CFO: Keith A. Lauter, Vice President Finance
Web address: www.stclaremedical.org
Control: Church operated, Nongovernment, not–for–profit **Service**: General medical and surgical

> **Staffed Beds**: 40 **Admissions**: 1127 **Census**: 15 **Outpatient Visits**: 64495 **Births**: 0 **Total Expense ($000)**: 52896 **Payroll Expense ($000)**: 15054 **Personnel**: 185

ST. CLARE MEDICAL CENTER See Franciscan Health Crawfordsville

CROWN POINT—Lake County

○ **FRANCISCAN HEALTH CROWN POINT (150126)**, 1201 South Main Street, Zip 46307–8483; tel. 219/738–2100, (Nonreporting) **A**2 10 11 **S** Franciscan Health, Mishawaka, IN
Primary Contact: Daniel McCormick, M.D., President and Chief Executive Officer
CFO: Marc Golan, Chief Financial Officer
CIO: Tim Loosemore, Director
CNO: Carol E Schuster, R.N., Chief Nursing Officer and Vice President Patient Care Services
Web address: www.franciscanalliance.org
Control: Church operated **Service**: General medical and surgical

> **Staffed Beds**: 254

○ **PINNACLE HOSPITAL (150166)**, 9301 Connecticut Drive, Zip 46307–7486; tel. 219/756–2100, (Nonreporting) **A**10 11
Primary Contact: Haroon Naz, Chief Executive Officer
Web address: www.pinnaclehealthcare.net
Control: Partnership, Investor–owned (for–profit) **Service**: General medical and surgical

> **Staffed Beds**: 18

ST. ANTHONY MEDICAL CENTER See Franciscan Health Crown Point

⊞ **VIBRA HOSPITAL OF NORTHWESTERN INDIANA (152028)**, 9509 Georgia Street, Zip 46307–6518; tel. 219/472–2200, (Nonreporting) **A**1 10 **S** Vibra Healthcare, Mechanicsburg, PA
Primary Contact: Craig L. Johnson, FACHE, Chief Executive Officer
CFO: Douglas Morris, Chief Financial Officer
CMO: Raja Devanathan, M.D., Chief Medical Officer
CNO: Robert Beard, Chief Clinical Officer
Web address: www.vhnwindiana.com/
Control: Corporation, Investor–owned (for–profit) **Service**: Acute long–term care hospital

> **Staffed Beds**: 40

DANVILLE—Hendricks County

★ ○ **HENDRICKS REGIONAL HEALTH (150005)**, 1000 East Main Street, Zip 46122–1948, Mailing Address: P.O. Box 409, Zip 46122–0409; tel. 317/745–4451, **A**2 5 10 11 **F**3 8 9 11 13 15 17 18 20 22 28 29 30 31 32 34 35 38 40 41 42 43 44 45 47 48 50 53 54 55 56 57 58 59 60 61 64 65 70 73 74 75 76 77 78 79 81 82 83 84 85 86 87 89 90 92 93 94 95 96 97 107 108 110 111 115 116 117 119 120 121 123 127 128 129 130 131 132 133 135 143 144 146 147 148 149 150 154 156
Primary Contact: Kevin Speer, President and Chief Executive Officer
CFO: Dennis Ressler, Vice President, Finance and Chief Financial Officer
CMO: Michelle Fenoughty, M.D., Chief Medical Officer, Vice President of Medical Affairs
CIO: Todd Davis, Executive Director of Information Systems
CHR: Nancy Foster, Vice President, Human Resources
Web address: www.https://www.hendricks.org
Control: County, Government, nonfederal **Service**: General medical and surgical

> **Staffed Beds**: 133 **Admissions**: 5794 **Census**: 53 **Outpatient Visits**: 316975 **Births**: 1340 **Total Expense ($000)**: 338351 **Payroll Expense ($000)**: 140290 **Personnel**: 1780

DECATUR—Adams County

★ ○ **ADAMS MEMORIAL HOSPITAL (151330)**, 1100 Mercer Avenue, Zip 46733–2303, Mailing Address: P.O. Box 151, Zip 46733–0151; tel. 260/724–2145, (Total facility includes 195 beds in nursing home–type unit) **A**10 11 18 **F**3 5 7 10 13 15 28 29 30 34 35 38 40 47 50 53 56 57 59 64 65 66 67 70 74 75 76 77 79 81 82 85 86 87 93 97 101 102 104 105 107 108 110 111 115 119 125 127 128 129 130 131 132 133 135 143 144 146 147 148 149 152 153 156
Primary Contact: JoEllen Eidam, FACHE, Chief Executive Officer
CFO: Dane Wheeler, Chief Financial Officer
CMO: Scott Smith, M.D., Chief Medical Officer
CIO: Nick Nelson, Director Support Services
CHR: Alison Kukelhan, Manager Human Resources
CNO: Theresa Bradtmiller DNP, RN, MSN, R.N., Chief Nursing Officer
Web address: www.adamshospital.com
Control: County, Government, nonfederal **Service**: General medical and surgical

> **Staffed Beds**: 224 **Admissions**: 2588 **Census**: 170 **Outpatient Visits**: 146166 **Births**: 225 **Total Expense ($000)**: 83024 **Payroll Expense ($000)**: 37675 **Personnel**: 687

DYER—Lake County

○ △ **FRANCISCAN HEALTH DYER (150090)**, 24 Joliet Street, Zip 46311–1799; tel. 219/865–2141, (Nonreporting) **A**3 7 10 11 **S** Franciscan Health, Mishawaka, IN
Primary Contact: Patrick J. Maloney, Chief Executive Officer
Control: Church operated **Service**: General medical and surgical

> **Staffed Beds**: 341

SAINT MARGARET MERCY HEALTHCARE CENTERS-SOUTH CAMPUS See Franciscan Health Dyer

EAST CHICAGO—Lake County

⊞ **REGENCY HOSPITAL OF NORTHWEST INDIANA (152024)**, 4321 Fir Street, 4th Floor, Zip 46312–3049; tel. 219/392–7799, (Includes REGENCY HOSPITAL OF PORTER COUNTY, 3630 Willow Creek Road, Portage, Indiana, Zip 46368; tel. 219/364–3800), (Non-reporting) **A**1 10 **S** Select Medical Corporation, Mechanicsburg, PA
Primary Contact: Eleyce Winn, Chief Executive Officer
Web address: www.regencyhospital.com/company/locations/indiana-northwest-indiana.aspx
Control: Corporation, Investor–owned (for–profit) **Service**: Acute long–term care hospital

> **Staffed Beds**: 61

□ △ **ST. CATHERINE HOSPITAL (150008)**, 4321 Fir Street, Zip 46312–3097; tel. 219/392–1700, **A**1 7 10 **F**3 11 13 15 17 18 20 22 24 26 28 29 30 31 34 35 40 46 49 50 51 57 59 61 64 66 68 74 75 76 78 79 80 81 82 85 86 87 89 90 92 93 96 98 100 101 102 103 104 107 108 110 111 112 115 119 124 126 129 130 131 132 135 146 148 149 153 154 156 **S** Community Healthcare System, Hammond, IN
Primary Contact: Leo Correa, Chief Executive Officer and Administrator
COO: Craig Bolda, Chief Operating Officer
CMO: John Griep, M.D., Chief Medical Director
CIO: Gary Weiner, Chief Information Officer
CNO: Paula C Swenson, R.N., Vice President and Chief Nursing Officer
Web address: www.stcatherinehospital.org
Control: Other not–for–profit (including NFP Corporation) **Service**: General medical and surgical

> **Staffed Beds**: 211 **Admissions**: 6998 **Census**: 106 **Outpatient Visits**: 121251 **Births**: 595 **Total Expense ($000)**: 219739 **Payroll Expense ($000)**: 57985 **Personnel**: 801

ELKHART—Elkhart County

⊞ △ **ELKHART GENERAL HOSPITAL (150018)**, 600 East Boulevard, Zip 46514–2499, Mailing Address: P.O. Box 1329, Zip 46515–1329; tel. 574/294–2621, **A**1 2 7 10 **F**3 12 13 15 17 18 20 22 24 26 28 29 30 31 34 35 40 45 46 48 49 50 57 59 64 65 68 70 72 74 75 76 77 78 79 81 82 84 85 86 87 89 90 91 92 93 98 100 102 104 107 108 110 111 114 115 118 119 120 121 123 126 129 130 131 132 134 135 145 146 147 148 155 156 **S** Beacon Health System, South Bend, IN
Primary Contact: Carl W. Risk II, President
CFO: Jeff Costello, Chief Financial Officer
CMO: Gene Grove, M.D., Chief of Staff
CIO: Mark Warlick, Chief Information Officer
CHR: Steven M Eller, Vice President Human Resources
Web address: www.egh.org
Control: Other not–for–profit (including NFP Corporation) **Service**: General medical and surgical

> **Staffed Beds**: 230 **Admissions**: 10558 **Census**: 120 **Outpatient Visits**: 160318 **Births**: 1304 **Total Expense ($000)**: 323318 **Payroll Expense ($000)**: 82149 **Personnel**: 1483

IN

Many Facility Codes have changed. Please refer to the AHA Guide Code Chart. © 2019 AHA Guide

ELWOOD—Madison County

✠ **ST. VINCENT MERCY HOSPITAL (151308)**, 1331 South 'A' Street, Zip 46036–1942; tel. 765/552–4600, **A**1 2 10 18 **F**3 8 15 28 29 30 31 34 35 40 44 45 50 51 57 59 64 68 74 75 77 78 79 81 85 89 93 107 108 110 111 115 119 128 129 130 132 133 135 146 148 149 150 154 **S** Ascension Healthcare, Saint Louis, MO
Primary Contact: Ann C. Yates, R.N., MSN, Administrator and Chief Nursing Officer
CFO: John Arthur, Chief Financial Officer
CMO: Gary Brazel, M.D., Chief Medical Officer
CHR: Ross Brodhead, Manager Human Resources
CNO: Ann C Yates, R.N., MSN, Chief Nursing Officer
Web address: www.stvincent.org
Control: Church operated, Nongovernment, not–for–profit **Service:** General medical and surgical

Staffed Beds: 12 **Admissions:** 357 **Census:** 4 **Outpatient Visits:** 34618 **Births:** 0 **Total Expense ($000):** 22800 **Payroll Expense ($000):** 6082 **Personnel:** 73

EVANSVILLE—Vanderburgh County

★ ○ **DEACONESS MIDTOWN HOSPITAL (150082)**, 600 Mary Street, Zip 47710–1658; tel. 812/450–5000, (Includes DEACONESS CROSS POINTE CENTER, 7200 East Indiana Street, Evansville, Indiana, Zip 47715; tel. 812/476–7200; Cheryl Rietman, Chief Administrative Officer) **A**2 3 10 11 **F**3 4 5 9 11 12 15 17 18 19 20 22 24 26 29 30 31 32 36 38 39 40 43 44 45 46 47 48 49 50 51 53 54 56 57 58 59 60 61 62 63 64 65 66 68 70 71 74 75 77 78 79 81 82 85 86 87 88 89 92 93 94 96 97 98 99 100 101 102 104 105 107 108 110 111 114 115 116 117 118 119 120 121 123 124 126 129 130 132 134 135 143 145 146 148 149 150 153 154 156 **S** Deaconess Health System, Evansville, IN
Primary Contact: Shawn W. McCoy, Chief Executive Officer
CFO: Cheryl A Wathen, Interim Chief Financial Officer
CHR: Larry Pile, Director Human Resources
Web address: www.deaconess.com
Control: Other not–for–profit (including NFP Corporation) **Service:** General medical and surgical

Staffed Beds: 547 **Admissions:** 30411 **Census:** 365 **Outpatient Visits:** 642574 **Births:** 0 **Total Expense ($000):** 769322 **Payroll Expense ($000):** 269951 **Personnel:** 4034

EVANSVILLE PSYCHIATRIC CHILDREN CENTER (15J200), 3300 East Morgan Avenue, Zip 47715–2232; tel. 812/477–6436, (Nonreporting) **A**10
Primary Contact: Lottie Cook, Superintendent
COO: Melinda Kendle, Manager Business Office
CMO: Shannon Jones, M.D., Medical Director and Attending Psychiatrist
CIO: David Wirtz, Supervisor Information Technology
CHR: Jennifer Sontz, Director Human Resources
CNO: Elizabeth Angermeier, Director of Nursing
Web address: www.ih.gov
Control: State, Government, nonfederal **Service:** Children's hospital psychiatric

Staffed Beds: 24

☐ **EVANSVILLE STATE HOSPITAL (154056)**, 3400 Lincoln Avenue, Zip 47714–0146; tel. 812/469–6800, **A**1 5 10 **F**30 98 130 132 135 146
Primary Contact: Cathe Fulcher, Superintendent
CFO: Melinda Kendle, Director Fiscal Management
CMO: Melba Briones, M.D., Medical Director
CIO: David Wirtz, Senior LAN Administrator
CHR: Jennifer Sontz, Director Human Resources
Control: State, Government, nonfederal **Service:** Psychiatric

Staffed Beds: 168 **Admissions:** 105 **Census:** 149 **Outpatient Visits:** 0 **Births:** 0

✠ **HEALTHSOUTH DEACONESS REHABILITATION HOSPITAL (153025)**, 4100 Covert Avenue, Zip 47714–5567, Mailing Address: P.O. Box 5349, Zip 47716–5349; tel. 812/476–9983, **A**1 10 **F**28 29 57 68 75 87 90 91 94 95 96 130 132 143 148 149 **S** Encompass Health Corporation, Birmingham, AL
Primary Contact: Blake Bunner, Chief Executive Officer
CFO: Rhonda Ramsey, Controller
CMO: Mohammed Adeel, Medical Director
CHR: Wendy Gumbel, Director of Human Resources
CNO: Trish Draeger, Chief Nursing Officer
Web address: www.healthsouthdeaconess.com
Control: Corporation, Investor–owned (for–profit) **Service:** Rehabilitation

Staffed Beds: 103 **Admissions:** 2190 **Census:** 81 **Outpatient Visits:** 4598 **Births:** 0 **Total Expense ($000):** 28283 **Payroll Expense ($000):** 13916 **Personnel:** 272

✠ **SELECT SPECIALTY HOSPITAL-EVANSVILLE (152014)**, 400 SE 4th Street, Zip 47713–1206; tel. 812/421–2500, **A**1 10 **F**1 3 29 45 46 48 60 63 75 77 96 107 108 114 119 **S** Select Medical Corporation, Mechanicsburg, PA
Primary Contact: Scott A. Butler, Chief Executive Officer
Web address: www.selectspecialtyhospitals.com/company/locations/evansville.aspx
Control: Corporation, Investor–owned (for–profit) **Service:** Acute long–term care hospital

Staffed Beds: 51 **Admissions:** 600 **Census:** 43 **Outpatient Visits:** 0 **Births:** 0

✠ △ **ST. VINCENT EVANSVILLE (150100)**, 3700 Washington Avenue, Zip 47714–0541; tel. 812/485–4000, **A**1 2 7 10 **F**3 7 8 11 12 13 15 17 18 19 20 22 24 26 28 29 30 31 32 34 35 36 37 39 40 43 45 46 47 48 49 50 51 53 54 55 56 57 58 59 60 61 64 65 68 70 71 72 73 74 75 76 77 78 79 81 82 83 84 85 86 87 88 89 90 91 92 93 96 98 100 101 102 107 108 110 111 114 115 116 117 118 119 126 129 130 131 132 133 134 135 138 143 144 146 147 148 149 150 154 156 157 **S** Ascension Healthcare, Saint Louis, MO
Primary Contact: Daniel A. Parod, President
COO: Gwynn Perlich, Chief Operating Officer
CFO: Craig Polkow, Vice President, Finance
CMO: Vernon Maas, M.D., Vice President, Medical Affairs
CIO: Jose Diaz, Director Information Systems
CHR: Marty Mattingly, Chief Human Resources Officer
CNO: Darcy Ellison, R.N., MSN, Senior Vice President, Chief Nursing Officer and Inpatient Flow
Web address: www.stmarys.org
Control: Church operated, Nongovernment, not–for–profit **Service:** General medical and surgical

Staffed Beds: 468 **Admissions:** 15793 **Census:** 200 **Outpatient Visits:** 399529 **Births:** 1463 **Total Expense ($000):** 468707 **Payroll Expense ($000):** 125216 **Personnel:** 2431

FISHERS—Hamilton County

✠ **ST. VINCENT FISHERS HOSPITAL (150181)**, 13861 Olio Road, Zip 46037–3487; tel. 317/415–9000, **A**1 10 **F**3 8 13 15 29 30 31 34 35 39 40 45 46 49 50 53 57 59 60 64 75 77 78 79 81 82 87 91 93 97 107 110 111 119 129 130 131 132 146 148 149 **S** Ascension Healthcare, Saint Louis, MO
Primary Contact: Julie Manas, Regional President
CMO: Craig Wilson, Chief Medical Officer
Web address: www.stvincent.org
Control: Church operated, Nongovernment, not–for–profit **Service:** General medical and surgical

Staffed Beds: 48 **Admissions:** 1393 **Census:** 9 **Outpatient Visits:** 56984 **Births:** 647 **Total Expense ($000):** 51019 **Payroll Expense ($000):** 13491 **Personnel:** 150

FORT WAYNE—Allen County

✠ **DUPONT HOSPITAL (150150)**, 2520 East Dupont Road, Zip 46825–1675; tel. 260/416–3000, **A**1 10 **F**3 8 13 15 18 29 30 34 35 39 40 45 50 56 57 58 59 60 64 65 68 70 72 74 75 77 78 79 81 82 83 84 85 86 87 88 107 110 111 114 115 118 119 126 129 130 131 132 135 141 146 147 148 154 157 **S** Community Health Systems, Inc., Franklin, TN
Primary Contact: Lorenzo Suter, Chief Executive Officer
COO: Darrick Hoopingarner, Chief Operating Officer
CFO: Brian Schneider, Chief Financial Officer
CIO: Janis Gray, Chief Information Officer
CNO: Kimberly Fulkerson, Chief Nursing Officer
Web address: www.thedupontdifference.com
Control: Partnership, Investor–owned (for–profit) **Service:** General medical and surgical

Staffed Beds: 131 **Admissions:** 4511 **Census:** 48 **Outpatient Visits:** 88409 **Births:** 2288 **Total Expense ($000):** 108102 **Payroll Expense ($000):** 36222 **Personnel:** 562

Hospital, Medicare Provider Number, Address, Telephone, Approval, Facility, and Physician Codes, Health Care System

★ American Hospital Association (AHA) membership
☐ The Joint Commission accreditation
○ Healthcare Facilities Accreditation Program
◇ DNV Healthcare Inc. accreditation
⇑ Center for Improvement in Healthcare Quality Accreditation
△ Commission on Accreditation of Rehabilitation Facilities (CARF) accreditation

---

IN

LUTHERAN HOSPITAL OF INDIANA (150017), 7950 West Jefferson Boulevard, Zip 46804–4140; tel. 260/435–7001, **A**1 2 3 5 10 **F**3 7 11 12 13 15 17 18 20 23 24 26 28 29 30 31 32 34 35 40 41 43 44 45 46 47 48 49 50 51 54 57 58 59 60 64 65 68 70 72 74 75 76 77 78 79 80 81 84 85 86 87 88 89 91 92 93 94 96 107 108 109 110 111 112 113 114 115 116 117 118 119 120 121 122 123 124 126 129 130 132 137 138 141 144 145 146 147 149 154 **S** Community Health Systems, Inc., Franklin, TN
CFO: Cully Chapman, Chief Financial Officer
CIO: Keith A. Neuman, Chief Information Officer
CHR: Maria Kurtz, Director Human Resources
CNO: Angela Logan, Chief Nursing Officer
Web address: www.lutheranhospital.com
Control: Corporation, Investor–owned (for–profit) **Service:** General medical and surgical

Staffed Beds: 407 **Admissions:** 20520 **Census:** 275

ORTHOPAEDIC HOSPITAL OF LUTHERAN HEALTH NETWORK (150168), 7952 West Jefferson Boulevard, Zip 46804–4140; tel. 260/435–2999, **A**1 10 **F**3 8 29 30 34 35 37 64 77 79 80 81 82 90 93 94 96 111 131 **S** Community Health Systems, Inc., Franklin, TN
Primary Contact: Lorie Ailor, Chief Executive Officer
CFO: Amy Hochstetler, Chief Financial Officer
CMO: Kevin Rahn, President Medical Staff
CIO: Keith A. Neuman, Chief Information Officer
CHR: Maria Kurtz, Director Human Resources
CNO: Marci Hamilton, Chief Nursing Officer
Web address: www.theorthohospital.com
Control: Corporation, Investor–owned (for–profit) **Service:** Orthopedic

Staffed Beds: 43 **Admissions:** 2392 **Census:** 15 **Outpatient Visits:** 52693
Births: 0

PARKVIEW ORTHO HOSPITAL (150167), 11130 Parkview Circle Drive, Zip 46845–1735; tel. 260/672–5000, **A**1 10 **F**3 8 29 30 34 45 50 58 65 68 79 81 82 84 85 86 87 90 91 93 94 96 107 111 119 131 135 141 149 **S** Parkview Health, Fort Wayne, IN
Primary Contact: Julie Fleck, Chief Operating Officer
Web address: www.parkview.com
Control: Corporation, Investor–owned (for–profit) **Service:** Orthopedic

Staffed Beds: 37 **Admissions:** 2984 **Census:** 15 **Outpatient Visits:** 8438
Births: 0 **Total Expense ($000):** 70151 **Payroll Expense ($000):** 12924
Personnel: 175

PARKVIEW REGIONAL MEDICAL CENTER (150021), 11109 Parkview Plaza Drive, Zip 46845–1701; tel. 260/266–1000, (Includes PARKVIEW HOSPITAL RANDALLIA, 2200 Randallia Drive, Fort Wayne, Indiana, Zip 46805–4699; tel. 260/373–4000; Marlon Wardlow, Chief Operating Officer; PARKVIEW NORTH HOSPITAL, 11115 Parkview Plaza Drive, Fort Wayne, Indiana, Zip 46845; tel. 260/672–4000) (Total facility includes 31 beds in nursing home–type unit) **A**1 2 10 **F**3 5 7 11 12 13 14 15 17 18 19 20 22 24 26 28 29 30 31 32 34 35 39 40 41 43 44 45 46 47 48 49 50 51 53 54 55 56 57 58 59 60 61 62 63 64 65 67 68 70 72 74 75 76 78 79 80 81 82 83 84 85 86 87 88 89 90 91 92 93 95 96 98 99 100 101 102 103 104 105 107 108 109 111 114 115 118 119 120 121 123 124 126 128 129 130 131 132 135 141 146 147 148 149 152 153 154 155 156 **S** Parkview Health, Fort Wayne, IN
Primary Contact: Ben Miles, President
CNO: Judy Boerger, MSN, Chief Nursing Executive
Web address: www.parkview.com
Control: Other not–for–profit (including NFP Corporation) **Service:** General medical and surgical

Staffed Beds: 753 **Admissions:** 39651 **Census:** 550 **Outpatient Visits:** 601386 **Births:** 3639 **Total Expense ($000):** 1046517 **Payroll Expense ($000):** 274683 **Personnel:** 4116

△ **REHABILITATION HOSPITAL OF FORT WAYNE (153030)**, 7970 West Jefferson Boulevard, Zip 46804–4140; tel. 260/435–6100, **A**1 7 10 **F**29 30 60 68 69 90 94 96 130 132 146 148 **S** Community Health Systems, Inc., Franklin, TN
Primary Contact: Ryan Cassedy, Chief Administrative Officer
COO: Shelley Boxell, R.N., Interim Chief Operating Officer
CFO: Edward Romero, Chief Financial Officer
CMO: Preeti Dembla, Chief Medical Officer and Medical Director
CIO: Janis Gray, Chief Information Officer
CHR: Deborah Giardina, Director Human Resources and Medical Staff Services
CNO: Shelley Boxell, R.N., Chief Nursing Officer
Web address: www.rehabhospital.com
Control: Corporation, Investor–owned (for–profit) **Service:** Rehabilitation

Staffed Beds: 36 **Admissions:** 662 **Census:** 24 **Births:** 0

ST. JOSEPH HOSPITAL (150047), 700 Broadway, Zip 46802–1493; tel. 260/425–3000, (Nonreporting) **A**1 3 10 **S** Community Health Systems, Inc., Franklin, TN
Primary Contact: Lisa Dolan, Interim Chief Executive Officer
COO: Vince Green, Chief Operating Officer
CHR: Steve Heggen, Administrative Director Human Resources
Web address: www.stjoehospital.com
Control: Corporation, Investor–owned (for–profit) **Service:** General medical and surgical

Staffed Beds: 182

VETERANS AFFAIRS NORTHERN INDIANA HEALTH CARE SYSTEM, 2121 Lake Avenue, Zip 46805–5100; tel. 260/426–5431, (Includes VETERANS AFFAIRS NORTHERN INDIANA HEALTH CARE SYSTEM-MARION CAMPUS, 1700 East 38th Street, Marion, Indiana, Zip 46953–4589; tel. 765/674–3321), (Non-reporting) **A**1 **S** Department of Veterans Affairs, Washington, DC
Primary Contact: Michael Hershmann, Medical Center Director
COO: Helen Rhodes, R.N., Associate Director Operations
CFO: Jay H Vandermark, Chief Financial Officer
CMO: Ajay Dhawan, M.D., Chief of Staff
CIO: David Troyer, Chief Information Officer
CHR: Brian Flynn, Chief Human Resources Officer
Web address: www.northernindiana.va.gov/
Control: Veterans Affairs, Government, federal **Service:** General medical and surgical

Staffed Beds: 217

FRANKFORT—Clinton County

INDIANA UNIVERSITY HEALTH FRANKFORT (151316), 1300 South Jackson Street, Zip 46041–3313; tel. 765/656–3000, **A**1 10 18 **F**3 11 15 18 28 29 30 34 35 40 45 50 57 59 61 64 68 75 79 81 85 86 90 93 107 110 111 114 119 133 146 148 154 **S** Indiana University Health, Indianapolis, IN
Primary Contact: Kelly Braverman, President
CFO: Wayne Knight, Chief Financial Officer
CMO: Stephen Tharp, Medical Director
CHR: Krista Wright, Director Human Resources
Web address: www.stvincent.org
Control: Other not–for–profit (including NFP Corporation) **Service:** General medical and surgical

Staffed Beds: 25 **Admissions:** 418 **Census:** 4 **Outpatient Visits:** 22962
Births: 0 **Total Expense ($000):** 21741 **Payroll Expense ($000):** 6725
Personnel: 98

FRANKFORT—Marion County

INDIANA UNIVERSITY HEALTH METHODIST HOSPITAL See Indiana University Health University Hospital, Indianapolis

METHODIST HOSPITAL See Indiana University Health Methodist Hospital

FRANKLIN—Johnson County

★ ○ **JOHNSON MEMORIAL HOSPITAL (150001)**, 1125 West Jefferson Street, Zip 46131–2140, Mailing Address: P.O. Box 549, Zip 46131–0549; tel. 317/736–3300, **A**5 10 11 **F**12 13 15 18 20 22 28 29 30 31 34 35 36 40 44 45 49 50 54 57 59 62 64 68 70 74 75 76 77 78 79 81 82 85 87 90 93 97 107 108 110 111 113 114 118 119 129 130 131 132 134 135 144 146 147 148 154 156
Primary Contact: Larry Heydon, President and Chief Executive Officer
COO: Steve Wohlford, Chief Operating Officer
CFO: Tim Balasia, Chief Financial Officer
CMO: David Dunkle, Vice President Medical Affairs
CIO: Scott Krodel, Vice President Information Systems
CHR: Judy Ware, Director Human Resources
CNO: Anita M. Keller, R.N., MSN, Chief Nursing Officer
Web address: www.johnsonmemorial.org
Control: County, Government, nonfederal **Service:** General medical and surgical

Staffed Beds: 87 **Admissions:** 1936 **Census:** 18 **Outpatient Visits:** 149224
Births: 405 **Total Expense ($000):** 86020 **Payroll Expense ($000):** 39964
Personnel: 640

IN

Many Facility Codes have changed. Please refer to the AHA Guide Code Chart. © 2019 AHA Guide

GARY—Lake County

✉ △ **METHODIST HOSPITALS (150002)**, 600 Grant Street, Zip 46402–6099; tel. 219/886–4000, (Includes SOUTHLAKE CAMPUS, 8701 Broadway, Merrillville, Indiana, Zip 46410; tel. 219/738–5500) **A**1 2 3 5 7 10 **F**3 8 11 12 13 15 18 20 22 24 26 28 29 30 31 34 35 37 40 43 45 46 47 48 49 50 51 54 55 57 58 59 61 62 64 67 70 72 73 74 75 76 77 78 79 81 82 85 86 87 89 90 91 93 96 98 100 101 102 103 107 108 110 111 114 115 118 119 120 121 123 124 126 130 132 133 134 135 146 147 148 150 154 156
Primary Contact: Raymond Grady, FACHE, President and Chief Executive Officer
CFO: Matthew Doyle, Chief Financial Officer
CIO: Timothy Diamond, Chief Information Officer
CHR: Alex Horvath, Vice President Human Resources
CNO: James M Renneker, FACHE, MSN, R.N., Vice President and Chief Nursing Officer
Web address: www.methodisthospitals.org
Control: Other not–for–profit (including NFP Corporation) **Service**: General medical and surgical

Staffed Beds: 500 Admissions: 14993 Census: 258 Outpatient Visits: 328089 Births: 1246 Total Expense ($000): 351453 Payroll Expense ($000): 150821 Personnel: 2042

GOSHEN—Elkhart County

GOSHEN GENERAL HOSPITAL See Goshen Health

✉ **GOSHEN HEALTH (150026)**, 200 High Park Avenue, Zip 46526–4899, Mailing Address: P.O. Box 139, Zip 46527–0139; tel. 574/533–2141, **A**1 2 10 **F**3 8 11 12 13 15 17 18 20 22 24 26 28 29 30 31 34 35 36 40 45 46 47 49 50 54 57 58 59 62 63 64 68 70 71 74 75 76 77 78 79 80 81 82 83 84 85 86 87 91 92 93 97 107 109 110 111 112 114 115 116 117 118 119 120 121 122 123 124 126 130 131 132 135 141 142 144 146 147 154
Primary Contact: Randal Christophel, President and Chief Executive Officer
COO: Robert T Myers, Chief Operating Officer
CMO: Randall Cammenga, M.D., Vice President Medical Affairs
CHR: Alan Weldy, Vice President Human Resources, Compliance and Legal Services
Web address: www.https://goshenhealth.com/Home
Control: Other not–for–profit (including NFP Corporation) **Service**: General medical and surgical

Staffed Beds: 122 Admissions: 5652 Census: 59

OAKLAWN PSYCHIATRIC CENTER (154031), 330 Lakeview Drive, Zip 46528–9365, Mailing Address: P.O. Box 809, Zip 46527–0809; tel. 574/533–1234, (Nonreporting) **A**10
Primary Contact: Laurie N. Nafziger, President and Chief Executive Officer
CFO: Joseph Barkman, Vice President Financial Services
CMO: Daniel Kinsey, M.D., Medical Director
CIO: Jennifer Glick, Manager Clinical Informatics
CHR: Jill Seifer, Vice President Human Resources
CNO: Elaine G Miller, Director of Nursing
Web address: www.oaklawn.org
Control: Other not–for–profit (including NFP Corporation) **Service**: Psychiatric

Staffed Beds: 16

GREENCASTLE—Putnam County

○ **PUTNAM COUNTY HOSPITAL (151333)**, 1542 South Bloomington Street, Zip 46135–2297; tel. 765/653–5121, (Nonreporting) **A**2 10 11 18
Primary Contact: Dennis Weatherford, Chief Executive Officer
CFO: Kevin Fowler, Director Finance
Web address: www.pchosp.org/
Control: County, Government, nonfederal **Service**: General medical and surgical

Staffed Beds: 25

GREENFIELD—Hancock County

★ ○ **HANCOCK REGIONAL HOSPITAL (150037)**, 801 North State Street, Zip 46140–1270, Mailing Address: P.O. Box 827, Zip 46140–0827; tel. 317/462–5544, **A**10 11 **F**3 13 15 17 18 20 22 28 29 30 31 32 34 35 36 37 38 40 41 44 45 46 47 48 49 51 53 54 55 56 57 58 59 63 64 65 70 74 75 76 78 79 81 82 83 84 85 86 87 89 92 93 98 100 101 102 103 104 107 108 110 111 114 115 119 120 121 123 124 127 129 130 132 134 135 144 145 146 147 149 156
Primary Contact: Steven V. Long, FACHE, President and Chief Executive Officer
COO: Robert Lawrence Matt, Vice President and Chief Operating Officer
CFO: Rick Edwards, Vice President and Chief Financial Officer
CMO: Michael Fletcher, M.D., Vice President and Chief Medical Officer
CIO: Jon Miller, Director Accounting and Information Services
CHR: Laura L Nichols, Director Human Resources
Web address: www.hancockregional.org
Control: County, Government, nonfederal **Service**: General medical and surgical

Staffed Beds: 68 Admissions: 2945 Census: 31 Outpatient Visits: 141632 Births: 356 Total Expense ($000): 131036 Payroll Expense ($000): 47561 Personnel: 773

GREENSBURG—Decatur County

★ ⇑ **DECATUR COUNTY MEMORIAL HOSPITAL (151332)**, 720 North Lincoln Street, Zip 47240–1398; tel. 812/663–1171, (Total facility includes 370 beds in nursing home–type unit) **A**2 10 18 21 **F**3 7 11 13 15 18 28 29 30 31 32 34 35 36 40 44 45 50 51 53 54 57 59 64 65 68 74 75 76 77 78 79 80 81 85 87 89 92 93 96 97 104 107 108 110 111 115 118 119 127 128 129 130 131 132 133 135 143 144 146 147 156 157
Primary Contact: Rex McKinney, President and Chief Executive Officer
COO: Eric Stokes, Vice President of Operations
CFO: Jerry Marks, Vice President Finance
CMO: Jennifer Fletcher, Chief of Staff
CHR: Amy Lynn Wickens, Executive Director Human Resources
CNO: Kathy Stephens, Vice President of Patient Care
Web address: www.dcmh.net
Control: County, Government, nonfederal **Service**: General medical and surgical

Staffed Beds: 395 Admissions: 1623 Census: 241 Outpatient Visits: 88695 Births: 237 Total Expense ($000): 76354 Payroll Expense ($000): 40207 Personnel: 825

GREENWOOD—Johnson County

☐ **VALLE VISTA HEALTH SYSTEM (154024)**, 898 East Main Street, Zip 46143–1400; tel. 317/887–1348, (Nonreporting) **A**1 10 **S** Universal Health Services, Inc., King of Prussia, PA
Primary Contact: Sherri R. Jewell, Chief Executive Officer
CFO: Tim Sides, Chief Financial Officer
CMO: Jennifer Comer, M.D., Medical Director
CIO: Karen Hayden, Director Health Information Services, Performance Improvement and Risk Management
CHR: Ismael Santos, Director Human Resources
Web address: www.vallevistahospital.com
Control: Corporation, Investor–owned (for–profit) **Service**: Psychiatric

Staffed Beds: 102

HAMMOND—Lake County

○ △ **FRANCISCAN HEALTH HAMMOND (150004)**, 5454 Hohman Avenue, Zip 46320–1999; tel. 219/932–2300, (Includes SAINT MARGARET MERCY HEALTHCARE CENTERS–NORTH CAMPUS, 5454 Hohman Avenue, Hammond, Indiana, Zip 46320; tel. 219/932–2300), (Nonreporting) **A**2 3 7 10 11 **S** Franciscan Health, Mishawaka, IN
Primary Contact: Patrick J. Maloney, Chief Executive Officer
CFO: Marc Golan, Chief Financial Officer
Web address: www.https://www.franciscanhealth.org/healthcare-facilities/franciscan-health-hammond-18
Control: Church operated **Service**: General medical and surgical

Staffed Beds: 406

✉ **KINDRED HOSPITAL NORTHWEST INDIANA (152012)**, 5454 Hohman Avenue, 5th Floor, Zip 46320–1931; tel. 219/937–9900, (Nonreporting) **A**1 10 **S** Kindred Healthcare, Louisville, KY
Primary Contact: Frank A. Solare, Chief Executive Officer
Web address: www.khnwindiana.com
Control: Corporation, Investor–owned (for–profit) **Service**: Acute long–term care hospital

Staffed Beds: 70

IN

SAINT MARGARET MERCY HEALTHCARE CENTERS See Franciscan Health Hammond

TRIUMPH HOSPITAL NORTHWEST INDIANA See Kindred Hospital Northwest Indiana

HARTFORD CITY—Blackford County

BLACKFORD COMMUNITY HOSPITAL See Indiana University Health Blackford Hospital

☒ **INDIANA UNIVERSITY HEALTH BLACKFORD HOSPITAL (151302)**, 410 Pilgrim Boulevard, Zip 47348–1897; tel. 765/348–0300, **A**1 10 18 **F**3 11 15 28 29 34 35 40 44 45 50 57 59 64 75 81 85 87 93 107 110 115 119 130 132 133 157 **S** Indiana University Health, Indianapolis, IN
Primary Contact: David W. Hyatt, President
CFO: John Vanator, CPA, Chief Financial Officer
CNO: Rodney Stevens, East Central Region Director of Nursing Practice
Web address: www.iuhealth.org/blackford
Control: Other not–for–profit (including NFP Corporation) **Service**: General medical and surgical

> **Staffed Beds:** 15 **Admissions:** 431 **Census:** 6 **Outpatient Visits:** 38121
> **Births:** 0 **Total Expense ($000):** 18293 **Payroll Expense ($000):** 6559
> **Personnel:** 82

HOBART—Lake County

☐ △ **ST. MARY MEDICAL CENTER (150034)**, 1500 South Lake Park Avenue, Zip 46342–6699; tel. 219/942–0551, **A**1 2 7 10 **F**3 8 11 12 13 15 18 20 22 24 26 28 29 30 31 34 35 36 37 38 39 40 44 45 47 49 50 51 54 55 57 58 59 62 64 65 67 70 74 75 76 77 78 79 81 82 84 85 86 87 89 90 91 92 93 96 107 108 110 111 114 115 116 117 118 119 120 121 123 126 129 130 131 132 135 146 147 148 149 156 157 **S** Community Healthcare System, Hammond, IN
Primary Contact: Janice L. Ryba, JD, Chief Executive Officer
CFO: Mary Sudicky, Chief Financial Officer
CIO: Gary Weiner, Vice President Information Technology and Chief Information Officer
CHR: Tony Ferracane, Vice President Human Resources
Web address: www.comhs.org
Control: Other not–for–profit (including NFP Corporation) **Service**: General medical and surgical

> **Staffed Beds:** 200 **Admissions:** 10104 **Census:** 140 **Outpatient Visits:** 254743 **Births:** 678 **Total Expense ($000):** 228661 **Payroll Expense ($000):** 69457 **Personnel:** 1078

HUNTINGTON—Huntington County

☒ **PARKVIEW HUNTINGTON HOSPITAL (150091)**, 2001 Stults Road, Zip 46750–1291; tel. 260/355–3000, **A**1 10 **F**3 7 8 13 15 28 29 30 31 32 34 35 36 38 39 40 44 45 46 50 53 56 57 59 64 68 69 70 75 76 77 78 79 81 85 86 87 93 96 97 107 108 111 119 129 130 131 132 134 135 146 148 154 156 **S** Parkview Health, Fort Wayne, IN
Primary Contact: Juli Johnson, MSN, R.N., President
CMO: Jeffrey Brooks, M.D., Chief Medical Officer
CIO: Ron Double, Chief Information Officer
CHR: Dena M Jacquay, Chief Human Resource Officer
CNO: Doug R Selig, MSN, R.N., Vice President of Patient Services
Web address: www.parkview.com
Control: Other not–for–profit (including NFP Corporation) **Service**: General medical and surgical

> **Staffed Beds:** 36 **Admissions:** 1894 **Census:** 13 **Outpatient Visits:** 47761
> **Births:** 385 **Total Expense ($000):** 52862 **Payroll Expense ($000):** 15475
> **Personnel:** 239

INDIANAPOLIS—Hamilton County

☒ **ST. VINCENT HEART CENTER (150153)**, 10580 North Meridian Street, Zip 46290–1028; tel. 317/583–5000, **A**1 10 **F**3 18 20 22 24 26 28 29 30 34 35 40 43 45 46 58 59 75 81 85 86 87 107 111 115 119 129 130 135 149 154 **S** Ascension Healthcare, Saint Louis, MO
Primary Contact: Lori Shannon, President
CFO: Becky Jacobson, Vice President Finance
CMO: Don Stogsdill, Chief Medical Officer
CIO: Jeremy Long, Chief Information Officer
Web address: www.bestheartcare.com/
Control: Partnership, Investor–owned (for–profit) **Service**: Heart

> **Staffed Beds:** 80 **Admissions:** 4360 **Census:** 53 **Outpatient Visits:** 12893
> **Births:** 0 **Total Expense ($000):** 108177 **Payroll Expense ($000):** 27655
> **Personnel:** 347

INDIANAPOLIS—Marion County

CLARIAN HEALTH PARTNERS See Indiana University Health University Hospital

☒ **COMMUNITY HOSPITAL EAST (150074)**, 1500 North Ritter Avenue, Zip 46219–3095; tel. 317/355–1411, (Includes COMMUNITY HEART AND VASCULAR HOSPITAL, 8075 North Shadeland Avenue, Indianapolis, Indiana, Zip 46250–2693; tel. 317/621–8000; Kathleen R Krusie, FACHE, President), (Non-reporting) **A**1 2 3 10 13 **S** Community Health Network, Indianapolis, IN
Primary Contact: Scott L. Teffeteller, Senior Vice President and President of East Region
Web address: www.ecommunity.com/east/
Control: Other not–for–profit (including NFP Corporation) **Service**: General medical and surgical

> **Staffed Beds:** 335

☒ △ **COMMUNITY HOSPITAL NORTH (150169)**, 7150 Clearvista Drive, Zip 46256–1695, Mailing Address: 7250 Clearvista Drive, Suite 200, Zip 46256–1695; tel. 317/355–2469, **A**1 3 7 10 **F**3 11 13 29 30 31 34 35 40 41 43 45 46 47 48 49 50 52 56 57 59 65 70 72 74 75 76 77 78 79 80 81 85 87 88 89 96 107 111 114 119 126 129 130 132 145 146 147 148 **S** Community Health Network, Indianapolis, IN
Primary Contact: Kathleen R. Krusie, FACHE, President
CFO: Amy Campbell, Chief Financial Officer
CMO: Wesley Wong, M.D., Acting Vice President Medical and Academic Affairs
CIO: Ron Thieme, Ph.D., Chief Knowledge and Information Officer
CHR: Steve Pearcy, Director Human Resources
Web address: www.ecommunity.com/north
Control: Other not–for–profit (including NFP Corporation) **Service**: General medical and surgical

> **Staffed Beds:** 343 **Admissions:** 17784 **Census:** 227 **Outpatient Visits:** 243556 **Births:** 3787 **Total Expense ($000):** 405926 **Payroll Expense ($000):** 253685

☒ **COMMUNITY HOSPITAL SOUTH (150128)**, 1402 East County Line Road South, Zip 46227–0963; tel. 317/887–7000, **A**1 3 10 **F**3 11 12 13 15 18 20 22 28 29 30 31 35 37 40 45 46 47 48 49 54 60 64 69 73 74 75 76 77 78 79 81 82 84 85 86 89 107 108 110 111 114 115 119 126 129 130 131 135 145 146 147 148 **S** Community Health Network, Indianapolis, IN
Primary Contact: David Kiley, M.D., Vice President
COO: Nichole Goddard, Chief Operating Officer, South Region
CFO: Leslie Yoder, Executive Director, Finance
CMO: Randy Lee, M.D., Senior Vice President Medical Affairs
CHR: Edie Garriott, Director Human Resources
CNO: Anita Capps, R.N., Chief Nursing Executive
Web address: www.ecommunity.com
Control: Other not–for–profit (including NFP Corporation) **Service**: General medical and surgical

> **Staffed Beds:** 158 **Admissions:** 9954 **Census:** 100 **Outpatient Visits:** 138689 **Births:** 1679 **Total Expense ($000):** 203834 **Payroll Expense ($000):** 62147

☐ **ESKENAZI HEALTH (150024)**, 720 Eskenazi Avenue, Zip 46202–5166; tel. 317/880–0000, **A**1 3 5 8 10 **F**3 5 7 10 13 14 15 16 18 20 22 28 29 30 31 32 34 35 36 38 39 40 43 44 47 48 49 50 53 54 55 56 57 59 61 62 64 65 66 68 70 71 72 74 75 76 77 78 79 81 82 83 84 85 86 87 93 97 98 100 101 102 103 104 105 106 107 110 111 115 119 130 132 134 135 143 144 145 146 147 148 150 153 156
Primary Contact: Lisa E. Harris, M.D., Chief Executive Officer
COO: Neil Johnson, Chief Operating Officer
CFO: Kathi Johnson, Chief Financial Officer
CMO: David W Crabb, M.D., Chief Medical Officer
CIO: Scott Morris, Vice President Information Systems
CHR: Christia Hicks, Vice President Human Resources
CNO: Lee Ann Blue, MSN, R.N., Chief Nursing Officer and Executive Vice President Patient Care Services
Web address: www.eskenazihealth.edu
Control: County, Government, nonfederal **Service**: General medical and surgical

> **Staffed Beds:** 343 **Admissions:** 17056 **Census:** 223 **Outpatient Visits:** 859145 **Births:** 2677 **Personnel:** 4057

☐ **FAIRBANKS (150179)**, 8102 Clearvista Parkway, Zip 46256–4698; tel. 317/849–8222, **A**1 3 10 **F**4 5 30 75 87 100 135 151 152 158
Primary Contact: Barb Elliott, Interim President and Chief Executive Officer
CFO: Barb Elliott, Chief Financial Officer
CMO: Dennis Rhyne, M.D., Acting Medical Director
CIO: Randy Walls, Manager Information Services
CHR: Sharon Baker, Director Support Services
CNO: Jennifer M Horstman, R.N., Chief Nursing Officer and Chief Information Officer
Web address: www.fairbankscd.org
Control: Other not–for–profit (including NFP Corporation) **Service**: Alcoholism and other chemical dependency

> **Staffed Beds:** 86 **Admissions:** 3230 **Census:** 44 **Outpatient Visits:** 23097
> **Births:** 0 **Total Expense ($000):** 26500 **Payroll Expense ($000):** 12215

IN

Many Facility Codes have changed. Please refer to the AHA Guide Code Chart. © 2019 AHA Guide

○ △ **FRANCISCAN HEALTH INDIANAPOLIS (150162)**, 8111 South Emerson Avenue, Zip 46237–8601; tel. 317/528–5000, (Nonreporting) **A**2 3 5 7 10 11 **S** Franciscan Health, Mishawaka, IN
Primary Contact: James Callaghan III, M.D., President and Chief Executive Officer
CFO: Keith A. Lauter, Regional Chief Financial Officer
CMO: Christopher Doehring, M.D., Vice President Medical Affairs
CIO: Barbara Coulter, Director Information Systems
CHR: Corey Baute, Vice President Human Resources
CNO: Agnes Therady, MSN, FACHE, Vice President and Chief Nursing Officer
Web address: www.stfrancishospitals.org
Control: Church operated **Service:** General medical and surgical

Staffed Beds: 485

⊞ **INDIANA UNIVERSITY HEALTH UNIVERSITY HOSPITAL (150056)**, 550 University Boulevard, Zip 46202–5149, Mailing Address: P.O. Box 1367, Zip 46206–1367; tel. 317/944–5000, (Includes INDIANA UNIVERSITY HEALTH METHODIST HOSPITAL, 1300 South jackson St, Frankfort, Indiana, Zip 46041, Mailing Address: 1701 North Senate Boulevard, Indianapolis, Zip 46202, tel. 317/962–2000; Ryan Nagy, M.D., President and Chief Medical Officer; INDIANA UNIVERSITY HEALTH SAXONY HOSPITAL, 13000 East 136th Street, Fishers, Indiana, Zip 46037–9478; tel. 317/678–2000; Alicia Schulhof, President and Chief Executive Officer; INDIANA UNIVERSITY HOSPITAL, 550 North University Boulevard, Indianapolis, Indiana, Zip 46202–5262; tel. 317/274–5000; RILEY HOSPITAL FOR CHILDREN AT INDIANA UNIVERSITY HEALTH, 702 Barnhill Drive, Indianapolis, Indiana, Zip 46202–5225, Mailing Address: 705 Riley Hospital Dr, Zip 46202, tel. 317/274–5000) **A**1 2 3 5 8 10 **F**3 5 6 7 8 9 11 12 13 15 16 17 18 19 20 21 22 23 24 25 26 27 28 29 30 31 32 33 34 35 36 37 38 39 40 41 43 44 45 46 47 48 49 50 51 52 53 54 55 56 57 58 59 60 61 62 63 64 65 68 69 70 71 72 73 74 75 76 77 78 79 80 81 82 83 84 85 86 87 88 89 90 91 92 93 94 95 96 97 98 99 100 101 102 103 104 105 106 107 108 109 110 111 112 113 114 115 116 117 118 119 120 121 122 123 124 126 129 130 131 132 134 135 136 137 138 139 140 141 142 144 145 146 147 148 149 150 151 152 153 154 155 157 **S** Indiana University Health, Indianapolis, IN
Primary Contact: Ryan Nagy, M.D., President and Chief Medical Officer
Web address: www.iuhealth.org
Control: Other not–for–profit (including NFP Corporation) **Service:** General medical and surgical

Staffed Beds: 1288 **Admissions:** 48166 **Census:** 931 **Outpatient Visits:** 1518637 **Births:** 2988 **Total Expense ($000):** 3068555 **Payroll Expense ($000):** 1042141 **Personnel:** 14211

INDIANA UNIVERSITY HOSPITAL See Indiana University Health University Hospital, Indianapolis

⊞ **KINDRED HOSPITAL INDIANAPOLIS NORTH (152013)**, 8060 Knue Road, Zip 46250–1976; tel. 317/813–8900, (Nonreporting) **A**1 10 **S** Kindred Healthcare, Louisville, KY
Primary Contact: Nakia Tremble, Chief Executive Officer
CHR: Kelly Becker, Administrative Coordinator Human Resources
Web address: www.kindredindynorth.com/
Control: Corporation, Investor–owned (for–profit) **Service:** Acute long–term care hospital

Staffed Beds: 45

⊞ **KINDRED HOSPITAL–INDIANAPOLIS (152007)**, 1700 West 10th Street, Zip 46222–3802; tel. 317/636–4400, (Nonreporting) **A**1 10 **S** Kindred Healthcare, Louisville, KY
Primary Contact: Bryan Chatterton, Chief Executive Officer
COO: Angela Lynne Rotert, Chief Clinical Officer
CFO: William Brenner, Chief Financial Officer
CHR: Joe Housh, District Director Human Resources
Web address: www.kindredhospitalindy.com/
Control: Corporation, Investor–owned (for–profit) **Service:** Acute long–term care hospital

Staffed Beds: 59

□ **LARUE D. CARTER MEMORIAL HOSPITAL (154008)**, 2601 Cold Spring Road, Zip 46222–2273; tel. 317/941–4000, (Nonreporting) **A**1 5 10
Primary Contact: Robert Clover, Interim Superintendent
CFO: Michael Logar, Assistant Superintendent
CMO: Beth Pfau, M.D., Chief Medical Officer
CIO: Denton Gross, Director Information Services
CHR: Rebecca Dutton, Director Human Resources
CNO: Todd Rittman, Director of Nursing
Control: State, Government, nonfederal **Service:** Psychiatric

Staffed Beds: 148

NEURODIAGNOSTIC INSTITUTE AND ADVANCED TREATMENT CENTER, 5435 East 16th Street, Zip 46218; tel. 317/941–4000, (Nonreporting)
Primary Contact: Robert Clover, Superintendent
CNO: Cynthia Wilson, Director, NDI Advanced Treatment Center, Nursing and BHRA Unit Services
Web address: www.https://www.in.gov/fssa/dmha/index.htm
Control: State, Government, nonfederal **Service:** Psychiatric

Staffed Beds: 318

□ **NEUROPSYCHIATRIC HOSPITAL OF INDIANAPOLIS (154063)**, 6720 Parkdale Place, Zip 46254–4668; tel. 317/744–9200, (Nonreporting) **A**1 10 **S** NeuroPsychiatric Hospitals, Mishawaka, IN
Primary Contact: Tracy Davis, Chief Executive Officer
Web address: www.https://www.neuropsychiatrichospitals.net
Control: Corporation, Investor–owned (for–profit) **Service:** Psychiatric

Staffed Beds: 50

□ **OPTIONS BEHAVIORAL HEALTH SYSTEM (154057)**, 5602 Caito Drive, Zip 46226–1346; tel. 317/544–4340, (Nonreporting) **A**1 10 **S** Acadia Healthcare Company, Inc., Franklin, TN
Primary Contact: Chris Rupert, Chief Executive Officer
Web address: www.optionsbehavioralhealthsystem.com/
Control: Corporation, Investor–owned (for–profit) **Service:** Psychiatric

Staffed Beds: 84

○ **ORTHOINDY HOSPITAL (150160)**, 8400 Northwest Boulevard, Zip 46278–1381; tel. 317/956–1000, **A**3 10 11 **F**3 29 30 34 35 37 57 64 68 69 71 79 81 82 83 84 86 87 92 93 107 111 114 115 119 131 135
Primary Contact: Timothy Dicke, M.D., Chief Executive Officer
COO: Stacie Vance, Chief Nursing Officer and
CFO: Anthony Gioia, Chief Financial Officer
CMO: Joseph Randolph, M.D., Chairman Medical Executive Committee
CIO: Paul Frey, Director Information Technology Applications
CHR: Kristy Hensley, Director Human Resources
CNO: Stacie Vance, Chief Nursing Officer and Vice President Operations
Web address: www.orthoindy.com
Control: Partnership, Investor–owned (for–profit) **Service:** Orthopedic

Staffed Beds: 38 **Admissions:** 3186 **Census:** 14 **Births:** 0

□ △ **REHABILITATION HOSPITAL OF INDIANA (153028)**, 4141 Shore Drive, Zip 46254–2607; tel. 317/329–2000, **A**1 3 5 7 10 **F**28 29 30 33 35 54 57 58 64 75 79 86 87 90 91 92 93 96 130 131 132 146 148 **S** Indiana University Health, Indianapolis, IN
Primary Contact: Daniel D. Woloszyn, Chief Executive Officer
COO: Monte Spence, Chief Operating Officer
CFO: Marjorie Basey, Chief Financial Officer
CMO: Flora Hammond, M.D., Chief Medical Affairs
CIO: Gary Skinner, Director Information Technology
CHR: Joni Brown, Director Human Resources
CNO: Debra Cordes, Chief Nursing Officer
Web address: www.rhin.com
Control: Other not–for–profit (including NFP Corporation) **Service:** Rehabilitation

Staffed Beds: 83 **Admissions:** 1302 **Census:** 54 **Outpatient Visits:** 22616 **Births:** 0 **Total Expense ($000):** 42312 **Payroll Expense ($000):** 21385 **Personnel:** 313

⊞ △ **RICHARD L. ROUDEBUSH VETERANS AFFAIRS MEDICAL CENTER**, 1481 West Tenth Street, Zip 46202–2884; tel. 317/554–0000, **A**1 2 3 5 7 8 **F**3 5 18 20 22 24 26 28 29 30 31 33 34 35 36 38 39 40 42 44 45 46 47 49 50 53 54 56 57 58 59 60 61 62 63 64 65 66 67 70 71 74 75 77 78 79 80 81 82 83 84 85 86 87 90 91 92 93 94 96 97 98 100 101 102 103 104 105 106 107 108 111 115 117 118 119 120 121 123 124 126 127 130 132 135 143 144 146 147 148 149 152 153 154 155 156 157 158 **S** Department of Veterans Affairs, Washington, DC
Primary Contact: Brian Hancock, M.D., Director
COO: Ginny L Creasman, Associate Director
CFO: Colin Lennon, Chief Financial Officer
CMO: Imtiaz A Munshi, M.D., Chief of Staff
CIO: Steve Stoner, Chief Information Officer
CHR: Chari Weddle, Chief Human Resource Management Service
CNO: Patricia Mathis, Associate Director Patient Care Service
Web address: www.indianapolis.va.gov
Control: Veterans Affairs, Government, federal **Service:** General medical and surgical

Staffed Beds: 209 **Admissions:** 9234 **Census:** 152 **Outpatient Visits:** 736282 **Births:** 0 **Total Expense ($000):** 591140 **Payroll Expense ($000):** 243823 **Personnel:** 2852

IN

Hospital, Medicare Provider Number, Address, Telephone, Approval, Facility, and Physician Codes, Health Care System

★ American Hospital Association (AHA) membership   ○ Healthcare Facilities Accreditation Program   ⇈ Center for Improvement in Healthcare Quality Accreditation
□ The Joint Commission accreditation   ◇ DNV Healthcare Inc. accreditation   △ Commission on Accreditation of Rehabilitation Facilities (CARF) accreditation

RILEY HOSPITAL FOR CHILDREN See Riley Hospital for Children at Indiana University Health

RILEY HOSPITAL FOR CHILDREN AT INDIANA UNIVERSITY HEALTH See Indiana University Health University Hospital, Indianapolis

ST. FRANCIS HOSPITAL AND HEALTH CENTERS - SOUTH CAMPUS See Franciscan Health Indianapolis

☒ **ST. VINCENT INDIANAPOLIS HOSPITAL (150084)**, 2001 West 86th Street, Zip 46260–1991, Mailing Address: P.O. Box 40970, Zip 46240–0970; tel. 317/338–2345, (Includes PEYTON MANNING CHILDREN'S HOSPITAL AT ST. VINCENT, 2001 West 86th Street, Indianapolis, Indiana, Zip 46260, Mailing Address: P O Box 40970, Zip 46240–0970, tel. 317/415–8111; Hossain Marandi, M.D., FACHE, President and Chief Executive Officer; PEYTON MANNING CHILDREN'S HOSPITAL, 1707 West 86th Street, Indianapolis, Indiana, Zip 46240, Mailing Address: P O Box 40407, Zip 46240, tel. 317/415–5500; Hossain Marandi, M.D., FACHE, President and Chief Executive Officer; ST. VINCENT STRESS CENTER, 8401 Harcourt Road, Indianapolis, Indiana, Zip 46260, Mailing Address: P O Box 80160, Zip 46280, tel. 317/338–4600; Sheila Mishler, Chief Executive Officer; ST. VINCENT WOMEN'S HOSPITAL, 8111 Township Line Road, Indianapolis, Indiana, Zip 46260–8043; tel. 317/415–8111; Anne Coleman, Administrator) **A**1 2 3 5 8 10 **F**3 4 5 7 8 9 11 13 15 17 18 19 20 21 22 23 24 25 26 27 28 29 30 31 32 34 35 36 37 38 39 40 41 43 44 45 46 47 48 49 50 51 53 54 55 56 57 58 59 61 62 63 64 65 66 68 70 71 72 73 74 75 76 77 78 79 81 82 83 84 85 86 87 88 89 90 91 92 93 94 95 96 97 98 99 100 101 102 103 104 105 107 108 109 110 111 114 115 117 118 119 120 121 124 126 129 130 131 132 134 135 137 138 141 142 143 146 147 148 149 151 152 153 154 **S** Ascension Healthcare, Saint Louis, MO
Primary Contact: Joel Feldman, Regional President
COO: Erica Wehrmeister, Chief Operating Officer
CFO: Terry Metzger, Vice President, Finance
CMO: Richard Freeman, Chief Medical Officer
CIO: Randy Cox, Chief Information Officer
CHR: Audra Pratt, Chief Human Resource Officer
CNO: Mary Myers, R.N., MSN, Chief Nursing Officer
Web address: www.stvincent.org
Control: Church operated, Nongovernment, not–for–profit **Service:** General medical and surgical

Staffed Beds: 840 **Admissions:** 30904 **Census:** 520 **Outpatient Visits:** 699888 **Births:** 2996 **Total Expense ($000):** 1095892 **Payroll Expense ($000):** 343536 **Personnel:** 3844

☒ **ST. VINCENT SETON SPECIALTY HOSPITAL (152020)**, 8050 Township Line Road, Zip 46260–2478; tel. 317/415–8500, **A**1 10 **F**1 3 29 30 31 35 44 68 75 85 107 114 119 130 132 148 154 **S** Ascension Healthcare, Saint Louis, MO
Primary Contact: Joel Feldman, Regional President
CFO: Terry Metzger, Chief Financial Officer
CMO: Alain Broccard, M.D., Chief Medical Officer
Web address: www.stvincent.org/
Control: Church operated, Nongovernment, not–for–profit **Service:** Acute long–term care hospital

Staffed Beds: 74 **Admissions:** 425 **Census:** 41 **Outpatient Visits:** 0 **Births:** 0 **Total Expense ($000):** 34591 **Payroll Expense ($000):** 14057 **Personnel:** 169

JASPER—Dubois County

☒ **MEMORIAL HOSPITAL AND HEALTH CARE CENTER (150115)**, 800 West Ninth Street, Zip 47546–2516; tel. 812/996–2345, (Total facility includes 14 beds in nursing home–type unit) **A**1 2 10 19 **F**3 5 7 8 11 12 13 15 18 20 22 24 26 28 29 30 31 34 35 36 40 41 43 45 46 47 48 49 50 51 53 54 56 57 59 62 64 66 68 70 74 75 76 77 78 79 81 82 84 85 86 87 89 90 93 97 98 100 101 102 103 104 107 108 110 111 112 113 114 115 116 117 118 119 120 121 126 127 128 129 130 131 132 135 144 146 147 148 149 154 156 **S** American Province of Little Company of Mary Sisters, Evergreen Park, IL
Primary Contact: E Kyle Bennett, President and Chief Executive Officer
CFO: Ted Miller, Vice President and Chief Financial Officer
CMO: Stan Tretter, M.D., Chief Medical Officer
CIO: Gary Light, Vice President and Chief Information Officer
CHR: Richard Pea, Director Human Resources
CNO: Tonya Heim, R.N., MSN, Vice President Patient Services and Chief Nursing Officer
Web address: www.mhhcc.org
Control: Church operated, Nongovernment, not–for–profit **Service:** General medical and surgical

Staffed Beds: 137 **Admissions:** 5445 **Census:** 61 **Outpatient Visits:** 249455 **Births:** 902 **Total Expense ($000):** 212976 **Payroll Expense ($000):** 98125 **Personnel:** 1302

JEFFERSONVILLE—Clark County

☒ **CLARK MEMORIAL HEALTH (150009)**, 1220 Missouri Avenue, Zip 47130–3743, Mailing Address: P.O. Box 69, Zip 47131–0600; tel. 812/282–6631, **A**1 3 5 10 **F**3 5 8 11 15 17 18 20 22 26 28 29 30 31 34 35 38 40 45 46 49 50 51 54 56 57 59 64 65 70 73 74 75 76 77 78 79 81 82 85 86 87 92 98 101 102 103 104 105 107 108 110 111 114 115 119 124 129 130 131 132 135 144 145 146 147 148 149 153 156 **S** LifePoint Health, Brentwood, TN
Primary Contact: Martin Padgett, President and Chief Executive Officer
CFO: Kirk Strack, Vice President and Chief Financial Officer
CMO: William Templeton, M.D., III Medical Director
CIO: Larry Reverman, Director Information Systems
CHR: Scott Hicks, Vice President
CNO: Kathy Neuner, R.N., Chief Nursing Officer
Web address: www.clarkmemorial.org
Control: Corporation, Investor–owned (for–profit) **Service:** General medical and surgical

Staffed Beds: 185 **Admissions:** 9836 **Census:** 102 **Outpatient Visits:** 108499 **Births:** 1452 **Total Expense ($000):** 152605 **Payroll Expense ($000):** 50888 **Personnel:** 1188

☐ **WELLSTONE REGIONAL HOSPITAL (154051)**, 2700 Vissing Park Road, Zip 47130–5989; tel. 812/284–8000, **A**1 10 **F**4 5 29 35 38 40 56 65 87 98 99 100 101 102 103 104 105 130 149 152 153 154 **S** Universal Health Services, Inc., King of Prussia, PA
Primary Contact: Greg Stewart, Chief Executive Officer
CFO: Gracia Winsett, Chief Financial Officer
CMO: Asad Ismail, M.D., Medical Director
CIO: Billy Leftwitch, Director, Information Technology
CHR: Tiffany Pierce, Director Human Resources
CNO: Anthony Aemmer, Director of Nursing
Web address: www.wellstonehospital.com
Control: Corporation, Investor–owned (for–profit) **Service:** Psychiatric

Staffed Beds: 100 **Admissions:** 3460 **Census:** 69 **Outpatient Visits:** 8257 **Births:** 0 **Total Expense ($000):** 15978 **Payroll Expense ($000):** 9809 **Personnel:** 231

KENDALLVILLE—Noble County

☒ **PARKVIEW NOBLE HOSPITAL (150146)**, 401 Sawyer Road, Zip 46755–2568; tel. 260/347–8700, **A**1 10 **F**3 7 13 15 28 29 34 35 40 45 46 47 50 54 57 59 64 70 74 75 76 79 81 82 85 87 93 94 97 107 108 110 111 114 118 119 129 130 132 135 143 145 146 154 156 **S** Parkview Health, Fort Wayne, IN
Primary Contact: Gary W. Adkins, President
COO: Gary W Adkins, Chief Executive Officer
CFO: Kem Prince, Manager of Finance
CMO: Gerald Warrener, M.D., Chief Medical Officer
CIO: Ron Double, Chief Information Officer
CHR: Bruce Buttermore, Manager Human Resources
CNO: Catherine Byrd, Vice President Patient Services
Web address: www.parkview.com
Control: Other not–for–profit (including NFP Corporation) **Service:** General medical and surgical

Staffed Beds: 31 **Admissions:** 1870 **Census:** 14 **Outpatient Visits:** 60284 **Births:** 228 **Total Expense ($000):** 55852 **Payroll Expense ($000):** 15622 **Personnel:** 226

KNOX—Starke County

☒ **STARKE HOSPITAL (150102)**, 102 East Culver Road, Zip 46534–2216, Mailing Address: P.O. Box 339, Zip 46534–0339; tel. 574/772–6231, **A**1 10 **F**3 15 18 29 30 32 34 35 38 40 45 46 49 50 53 57 59 65 68 74 75 77 79 81 85 87 93 94 107 108 110 111 114 115 116 117 119 130 146 149 **S** Community Health Systems, Inc., Franklin, TN
Primary Contact: Jeff Vice, Chief Operating Officer and Interim Chief Executive Officer
COO: Jeff Vice, Chief Operating Officer
CFO: Drew Keesbury, Chief Financial Officer
CMO: A N Damodaran, M.D., President Medical Staff
CIO: Ashley Norem, Chief Information Systems
CHR: Doug Jesch, Director Human Resources
CNO: Anetra Jones, R.N., M.P.H., Chief Nursing Officer
Web address: www.iuhealth.org/starke/
Control: Corporation, Investor–owned (for–profit) **Service:** General medical and surgical

Staffed Beds: 15 **Admissions:** 486 **Census:** 4 **Outpatient Visits:** 28969 **Births:** 0 **Total Expense ($000):** 15245 **Payroll Expense ($000):** 6464 **Personnel:** 105

IN

STARKE MEMORIAL HOSPITAL See Starke Hospital

KNOX—St. Joseph County

☐ **MEDICAL BEHAVIORAL HOSPITAL OF MISHAWAKA (154061)**, 5985 E 200 S, Zip 46534, Mailing Address: 1625 East Jefferson Boulevard, Mishawaka, Zip 46545–7103; tel. 574/255–1400, (Nonreporting) **A**1 10 **S** NeuroPsychiatric Hospitals, Mishawaka, IN
Primary Contact: Emily Ryan, Chief Executive Officer
COO: Christy Gilbert, President and Chief Operating Officer
Web address: www.physicianshospitalsystem.net/
Control: Partnership, Investor–owned (for–profit) **Service**: Acute long–term care hospital

Staffed Beds: 30

KOKOMO—Howard County

✠ **COMMUNITY HOWARD REGIONAL HEALTH (150007)**, 3500 South Lafountain Street, Zip 46902–3803, Mailing Address: P.O. Box 9011, Zip 46904–9011; tel. 765/453–0702, (Nonreporting) **A**1 2 10 **S** Community Health Network, Indianapolis, IN
Primary Contact: Joseph Hooper, President and Chief Executive Officer
COO: Theodore Brown, Chief Operating Officer
CFO: Theodore Brown, Vice President Financial Services
CIO: Kevin Purvis, Chief Information Officer
CHR: Michael L Williams, FACHE, Vice President Human Resources
CNO: Melodi Greene, R.N., MS, Chief Nursing Officer
Web address: www.howardregional.org
Control: Other not–for–profit (including NFP Corporation) **Service**: General medical and surgical

Staffed Beds: 159

✠ **COMMUNITY HOWARD SPECIALTY HOSPITAL (153039)**, 829 North Dixon Road, Zip 46901–7709; tel. 765/452–6700, **A**1 10 **F**28 29 30 34 57 77 90 93 129 131 132 154 **S** Community Health Network, Indianapolis, IN
Primary Contact: Michelle L. Russell, Administrator
CFO: Julie Pena, Director Finance
CMO: Brad Vossberg, M.D., Chief Rehabilitation
CNO: Claudia Jean Lowry, R.N., Director of Nursing
Web address: www.ecommunity.com
Control: Partnership, Investor–owned (for–profit) **Service**: Rehabilitation

Staffed Beds: 30 **Admissions**: 398 **Census**: 13 **Births**: 0

HOWARD REGIONAL HEALTH SYSTEM See Community Howard Regional Health

HOWARD REGIONAL HEALTH SYSTEM WEST CAMPUS SPECIALTY HOSPITAL See Community Howard Specialty Hospital

✠ **ST. VINCENT KOKOMO (150010)**, 1907 West Sycamore Street, Zip 46901–4197; tel. 765/452–5611, **A**1 10 **F**3 4 5 7 8 13 15 18 20 28 29 30 31 34 35 36 40 44 45 49 50 51 53 55 57 59 64 66 68 69 70 73 74 75 76 77 78 79 81 82 85 86 87 89 90 93 96 98 100 101 102 104 105 107 108 110 111 115 118 119 120 121 123 126 129 130 131 132 135 143 145 146 147 148 149 151 155 156 **S** Ascension Healthcare, Saint Louis, MO
Primary Contact: Margaret M. Johnson, President, St. Vincent Northwest Region
CMO: David L Williams, M.D., Chief Medical Officer
CIO: Jeffrey Scott, Chief Information Officer
CHR: Cindy Babb, Executive Director Human Resources and Organizational Effectiveness
CNO: Kathleen K Peoples, R.N., MS, Vice President of Nursing
Web address: www.stvincent.org/stjoseph
Control: Church operated, Nongovernment, not–for–profit **Service**: General medical and surgical

Staffed Beds: 129 **Admissions**: 5103 **Census**: 57 **Outpatient Visits**: 183575 **Births**: 834 **Total Expense ($000)**: 133539 **Payroll Expense ($000)**: 35934

LA PORTE—Laporte County

✠ **LA PORTE HOSPITAL (150006)**, 1007 Lincolnway, Zip 46350–3201, Mailing Address: P.O. Box 250, Zip 46352–0250; tel. 219/326–1234, **A**1 2 10 19 **F**3 11 13 15 17 18 20 22 24 26 28 29 30 31 32 34 35 36 39 40 44 45 46 47 48 49 50 51 53 54 56 57 59 60 64 65 66 68 70 71 74 75 77 78 79 81 85 86 87 91 92 93 96 97 107 108 110 111 114 115 118 119 126 129 130 131 132 135 144 145 146 147 148 149 154 156 **S** Community Health Systems, Inc., Franklin, TN
Primary Contact: Ashley Dickinson, Chief Executive Officer
CFO: Drew Keesbury, Chief Financial Officer
CNO: Anetra Jones, R.N., M.P.H., Chief Nursing Officer
Web address: www.iuhealth.org
Control: Corporation, Investor–owned (for–profit) **Service**: General medical and surgical

Staffed Beds: 91 **Admissions**: 4517 **Census**: 49 **Outpatient Visits**: 107589 **Births**: 668 **Total Expense ($000)**: 145159 **Payroll Expense ($000)**: 39992 **Personnel**: 862

LA PORTE REGIONAL HEALTH SYSTEM See La Porte Hospital

LAFAYETTE—Tippecanoe County

CLARIAN ARNETT HOSPITAL See Indiana University Health Arnett Hospital

○ **FRANCISCAN HEALTH LAFAYETTE EAST (150109)**, 1701 South Creasy Lane, Zip 47905–4972; tel. 765/502–4000, (Includes FRANCISCAN HEALTH LAFAYETTE CENTRAL, 1501 Hartford Street, Lafayette, Indiana, Zip 47904–2134; tel. 765/423–6011; Terrance E. Wilson, President and Chief Executive Officer) **A**2 5 10 11 **F**3 11 13 15 17 18 19 20 22 24 26 28 29 30 31 34 35 37 40 43 45 49 50 51 54 55 57 60 62 63 64 68 69 70 72 75 76 77 78 79 81 82 84 85 87 89 90 93 94 96 97 107 110 111 114 115 118 119 120 121 126 129 130 131 132 135 145 146 147 148 154 156 **S** Franciscan Health, Mishawaka, IN
Primary Contact: Terrance E. Wilson, President and Chief Executive Officer
Web address: www.ste.org
Control: Church operated, Nongovernment, not–for–profit **Service**: General medical and surgical

Staffed Beds: 203 **Admissions**: 10409 **Census**: 126 **Outpatient Visits**: 389262 **Total Expense ($000)**: 309610 **Payroll Expense ($000)**: 114230 **Personnel**: 1648

★ ○ **INDIANA UNIVERSITY HEALTH ARNETT HOSPITAL (150173)**, 5165 McCarty Lane, Zip 47905–8764, Mailing Address: P.O. Box 5545, Zip 47903–5545; tel. 765/448–8000, **A**2 3 5 10 11 **F**3 8 11 12 13 15 17 18 20 22 24 26 28 29 30 31 34 35 40 43 45 46 49 50 51 54 55 57 59 61 64 65 68 69 70 72 74 75 76 77 78 79 81 82 84 85 87 89 92 93 97 100 104 107 108 110 111 114 115 116 117 118 119 120 121 126 129 130 131 132 135 144 145 146 147 148 154 156 **S** Indiana University Health, Indianapolis, IN
Primary Contact: Daniel Neufelder, President
CFO: Cara Breidster, Chief Financial Officer
CMO: Jeffrey P Brown, M.D., Chief Medical Officer
CIO: Rusty McGill, System Director Information Technology
CHR: Koreen H Kyhnell, Vice President Human Resources
Web address: www.iuhealth.org
Control: Other not–for–profit (including NFP Corporation) **Service**: General medical and surgical

Staffed Beds: 192 **Admissions**: 9828 **Census**: 119 **Outpatient Visits**: 101170 **Births**: 1567 **Total Expense ($000)**: 432831 **Payroll Expense ($000)**: 180266 **Personnel**: 1873

✠ **LAFAYETTE REGIONAL REHABILITATION HOSPITAL (153042)**, 950 Park East Boulevard, Zip 47905–0792; tel. 765/447–4040, (Nonreporting) **A**1 10 **S** Ernest Health, Inc., Albuquerque, NM
Primary Contact: Greg Floyd, Chief Executive Officer
Web address: www.lrrh.ernesthealth.com
Control: Corporation, Investor–owned (for–profit) **Service**: Rehabilitation

Staffed Beds: 40

ST. ELIZABETH CENTRAL See Franciscan Health Lafayette Central

---

IN

☐ **SYCAMORE SPRINGS HOSPITAL (154059)**, 833 Park East Boulevard, Zip 47905–0785; tel. 765/743–4400, (Nonreporting) **A**1 10 **S** Springstone, Louisville, KY
Primary Contact: Shelley Zimmerman, Chief Executive Officer
CFO: Michael Huth, Chief Financial Officer
CMO: Nizar El Khalili, M.D., Medical Director
CHR: Pam Sichts, Director Human Resources
CNO: Brooke Lavignette, Director of Nursing
Web address: www.sycamorespringshealth.com
Control: Corporation, Investor–owned (for–profit) **Service:** Psychiatric

Staffed Beds: 48

LAGRANGE—Lagrange County

☒ **PARKVIEW LAGRANGE HOSPITAL (151323)**, 207 North Townline Road, Zip 46761–1325; tel. 260/463–9000, **A**1 10 18 **F**3 7 13 15 17 26 29 30 34 35 40 45 50 51 57 59 63 64 70 75 76 79 81 82 83 84 85 86 87 89 90 93 96 107 108 109 110 111 114 118 119 128 130 132 133 143 146 148 154 156 **S** Parkview Health, Fort Wayne, IN
Primary Contact: Jordi K. Disler, President
CFO: Vickie Stanski, Financial Manager
CMO: Jeffrey Brookes, M.D., Chief Medical Officer
CIO: Ron Double, Chief Information Technology Officer
CHR: Bruce Buttermore, Director Human Resources
CNO: Jared Beasley, R.N., Vice President Patient Care
Web address: www.parkview.com
Control: Other not–for–profit (including NFP Corporation) **Service:** General medical and surgical

Staffed Beds: 25 **Admissions:** 1118 **Census:** 9 **Outpatient Visits:** 27134
Births: 222 **Total Expense ($000):** 37600 **Payroll Expense ($000):** 10477
Personnel: 156

LAWRENCEBURG—Dearborn County

COMMUNITY MENTAL HEALTH CENTER (154011), 285 Bielby Road, Zip 47025–1055; tel. 812/537–1302, (Nonreporting) **A**10
Primary Contact: Tom Talbot, Chief Executive Officer
CFO: Georgii Zhirkin, Chief Financial Officer
CMO: Hasan Bakhtier, M.D., Medical Director
CIO: John McKinley, Director, Information Technology
CHR: Kelly Stewart, Director of Human Resources
Web address: www.cmhcinc.org
Control: Other not–for–profit (including NFP Corporation) **Service:** Psychiatric

Staffed Beds: 16

★ ○ **HIGHPOINT HEALTH (150086)**, 600 Wilson Creek Road, Zip 47025–2751; tel. 812/537–1010, **A**10 11 **F**3 11 13 15 18 20 26 28 29 30 34 35 37 40 43 44 45 46 47 49 50 57 59 62 63 64 70 75 76 77 79 81 84 85 86 87 92 93 107 108 110 111 115 116 117 118 119 129 130 131 132 146 148 157
Primary Contact: Michael W. Schwebler, President and Chief Executive Officer
CMO: Nancy A. Kennedy, M.D., Chief Medical Officer
CIO: Kathy Dickman, Director of Information Systems
CNO: Angela K. Scudder, MSN, R.N., Vice President Patient Care Services
Web address: www.dch.org
Control: County, Government, nonfederal **Service:** General medical and surgical

Staffed Beds: 64 **Admissions:** 3093 **Census:** 29 **Outpatient Visits:** 139659
Births: 384 **Total Expense ($000):** 74834 **Payroll Expense ($000):** 32430
Personnel: 598

LEBANON—Boone County

☒ **WITHAM HEALTH SERVICES (150104)**, 2605 North Lebanon Street, Zip 46052–1476, Mailing Address: P.O. Box 1200, Zip 46052–3005; tel. 765/485–8000, **A**1 10 **F**3 7 8 13 15 18 20 22 24 28 29 30 34 40 42 44 45 53 54 56 57 59 64 65 67 69 70 75 76 77 79 81 82 83 85 86 87 93 94 97 98 107 111 116 121 128 129 130 132 135 143 144 146 147 148 156
Primary Contact: Raymond V. Ingham, Ph.D., President and Chief Executive Officer
COO: Diane Feder, R.N., FACHE, Senior Vice President and Chief Operating Officer
CFO: George Pogas, CPA, Senior Vice President and Chief Financial Officer
CMO: Anthony Steele, M.D., Chief Medical Officer
CIO: George Pogas, CPA, Senior Vice President and Chief Financial Officer
CHR: Gary A Deater, Vice President Administration, Human Resources and Risk Management
CNO: Diane Feder, R.N., FACHE, Senior Vice President and Chief Operating Officer
Web address: www.witham.org
Control: County, Government, nonfederal **Service:** General medical and surgical

Staffed Beds: 70 **Admissions:** 2824 **Census:** 43 **Outpatient Visits:** 146090
Births: 471 **Total Expense ($000):** 142967 **Payroll Expense ($000):** 60233
Personnel: 824

LINTON—Greene County

☒ **GREENE COUNTY GENERAL HOSPITAL (151317)**, 1185 North 1000 West, Zip 47441–5282; tel. 812/847–2281, **A**1 10 18 **F**1 3 6 11 13 15 26 27 28 29 31 34 35 39 40 41 44 45 55 56 57 58 59 62 64 65 66 67 68 70 75 76 77 78 79 81 85 86 87 89 90 91 93 96 97 107 108 110 111 114 119 127 128 130 133 135 146 147 148 149 154 156
Primary Contact: Brenda Reetz, FACHE, Chief Executive Officer
CFO: April Settles, Chief Financial Officer
CMO: Frederick R. Ridge, M.D., Chief of Staff
CIO: Steve Phillips, Information Officer
CHR: Jean Prather, Director of Human Resources
CNO: Kristin Crynes, Executive Director of Nursing
Web address: www.greenecountyhospital.com
Control: County, Government, nonfederal **Service:** General medical and surgical

Staffed Beds: 25 **Admissions:** 722 **Census:** 6 **Outpatient Visits:** 833597
Births: 93 **Total Expense ($000):** 34355 **Payroll Expense ($000):** 16666
Personnel: 291

LOGANSPORT—Cass County

FOUR COUNTY COUNSELING CENTER (154035), 1015 Michigan Avenue, Zip 46947–1526; tel. 574/722–5151, (Nonreporting) **A**10
Primary Contact: Carrie Cadwell, PsyD, Chief Executive Officer
CFO: Jason Cadwell, Chief Financial Officer
CMO: John Yarling, M.D., Medical Director
CIO: Becky Mulis, Director of Health Information Management Systems
CHR: Steve Curry, Regional Director Human Resources
CNO: Donna Henry, Vice President of Nursing Services
Web address: www.fourcounty.org
Control: Other not–for–profit (including NFP Corporation) **Service:** Psychiatric

Staffed Beds: 15

★ ○ **LOGANSPORT MEMORIAL HOSPITAL (150072)**, 1101 Michigan Avenue, Zip 46947–1528, Mailing Address: P.O. Box 7013, Zip 46947–7013; tel. 574/753–7541, **A**10 11 20 **F**3 11 13 15 28 29 32 34 35 36 40 44 45 48 49 50 51 57 59 64 65 68 69 70 75 76 77 78 79 81 85 86 87 93 97 107 108 110 111 114 119 120 121 129 130 131 132 135 146 147 149 156
Primary Contact: Perry Gay, President and Chief Executive Officer
CFO: Sherri Gehlhausen, Assistant Chief Financial Officer
CMO: Todd S Weinstein, M.D., Chief of Staff
CIO: Beth Jump, Chief Information Officer
CHR: Lynda J Shrock, Vice President Human Resources
CNO: Tara McVay, Chief Nursing Officer
Web address: www.logansportmemorial.org
Control: County, Government, nonfederal **Service:** General medical and surgical

Staffed Beds: 83 **Admissions:** 1661 **Census:** 12 **Outpatient Visits:** 117399
Births: 486 **Total Expense ($000):** 82720 **Payroll Expense ($000):** 32615
Personnel: 518

☐ **LOGANSPORT STATE HOSPITAL**, 1098 South State Road 25, Zip 46947–6723; tel. 574/737–3633, (Nonreporting) **A**1
Primary Contact: Robert Clover, Superintendent and Chief Executive Officer
CFO: Misty Moss, Director Business Administration
CMO: Danny Meadows, M.D., Medical Director
CIO: Joe McIntosh, Director Management Information Systems
CHR: Dianne Renner, Director Human Resources
Web address: www.lshonline.org
Control: State, Government, nonfederal **Service:** Psychiatric

Staffed Beds: 170

MADISON—Jefferson County

★ ○ **KING'S DAUGHTERS' HEALTH (150069)**, 1373 East State Road 62, Zip 47250–3357, Mailing Address: P.O. Box 447, Zip 47250–0447; tel. 812/801–0800, **A**2 10 11 **F**3 7 8 12 13 15 18 28 29 30 31 32 34 35 40 45 48 50 55 56 57 59 62 63 64 65 68 70 74 75 76 77 78 79 81 82 84 85 86 87 89 91 93 94 97 107 108 110 111 115 119 120 121 123 129 130 131 132 134 135 144 145 146 147 148 149 150 156
Primary Contact: Carol Dozier, President and Chief Executive Officer
CFO: John Price, Chief Financial Officer
CIO: Linda Darnell, Director Management Information Systems
CHR: Susan Poling, Director Human Resources
CNO: Jennifer Lynn Liter, Vice President of Inpatient Services
Web address: www.kdhhs.org
Control: Other not–for–profit (including NFP Corporation) **Service:** General medical and surgical

Staffed Beds: 77 **Admissions:** 3089 **Census:** 30 **Outpatient Visits:** 200367
Births: 466 **Total Expense ($000):** 125761 **Payroll Expense ($000):** 52041
Personnel: 790

IN

Many Facility Codes have changed. Please refer to the AHA Guide Code Chart. © 2019 AHA Guide

☐ **MADISON STATE HOSPITAL (154019)**, 711 Green Road, Zip 47250–2199; tel. 812/265–2611, (Nonreporting) **A**1 10
Primary Contact: Peggy Stephens, M.D., Superintendent and Medical Director
COO: Peggy Stephens, M.D., Superintendent and Medical Director
CFO: Carolyn Copeland, Business Administrator
CMO: Peggy Stephens, M.D., Superintendent and Medical Director
CIO: Ric Martin, Information Specialist
Web address: www.in.gov/fssa/msh
Control: State, Government, nonfederal **Service**: Psychiatric

Staffed Beds: 150

MARION—Grant County

☐ **GRANT-BLACKFORD MENTAL HEALTH CENTER (154021)**, 505 North Wabash Avenue, Zip 46952–2608; tel. 765/662–3971, (Nonreporting) **A**1 10
Primary Contact: Paul Kuczora, Chief Executive Officer
Web address: www.cornerstone.org/
Control: Other not-for-profit (including NFP Corporation) **Service**: Psychiatric

Staffed Beds: 16

★ ○ **MARION GENERAL HOSPITAL (150011)**, 441 North Wabash Avenue, Zip 46952–2690; tel. 765/660–6000, **A**2 10 11 **F**3 7 8 11 13 15 18 20 22 26 28 29 30 31 34 35 40 41 44 45 47 50 54 57 58 59 64 68 70 76 77 78 79 81 82 85 86 87 89 90 91 92 93 96 97 107 108 110 111 114 115 117 118 119 129 130 132 135 146 147 148 149 154 156
Primary Contact: Stephanie Hilton-Siebert, MSN, President and Chief Executive Officer
CFO: Jeff Wakefield, CPA, Chief Financial Officer
CMO: Edward L. Keppler, M.D., Chief Medical Officer
CIO: Emmanuel Ndow, Chief Information Officer
CHR: Karen Jones, Administrative Director Human Resources
CNO: Cynthia Futrell, MSN, R.N., Chief Nursing Officer
Web address: www.mgh.net
Control: Other not-for-profit (including NFP Corporation) **Service**: General medical and surgical

Staffed Beds: 117 **Admissions:** 5200 **Census:** 56 **Outpatient Visits:** 249449 **Births:** 620 **Total Expense ($000):** 171180 **Payroll Expense ($000):** 64150 **Personnel:** 1021

VETERANS AFFAIRS NORTHERN INDIANA HEALTH CARE SYSTEM-MARION CAMPUS See Veterans Affairs Northern Indiana Health Care System, Fort Wayne

MERRILLVILLE—Lake County

REGIONAL MENTAL HEALTH CENTER (154020), 8555 Taft Street, Zip 46410–6123; tel. 219/769–4005, (Nonreporting) **A**10
Primary Contact: Robert D. Krumwied, President and Chief Executive Officer
Web address: www.regionalmentalhealth.org/
Control: Corporation, Investor-owned (for-profit) **Service**: Psychiatric

Staffed Beds: 16

SOUTHLAKE CAMPUS See Methodist Hospitals, Gary

MICHIGAN CITY—Laporte County

○ **FRANCISCAN HEALTH MICHIGAN CITY (150015)**, 301 West Homer Street, Zip 46360–4358; tel. 219/879–8511, (Nonreporting) **A**2 10 11 19 **S** Franciscan Health, Mishawaka, IN
Primary Contact: Dean Mazzoni, President and Chief Executive Officer
CFO: Marc Golan, Regional Chief Financial Officer
CIO: Tim Loosemore, Regional Director Information Systems
CHR: John Barrett, Regional Director Human Resources
CNO: Trish Weber, R.N., FACHE, Vice President Operations and Chief Nursing Officer
Web address: www.franciscanalliance.org
Control: Church operated **Service**: General medical and surgical

Staffed Beds: 171

SAINT ANTHONY MEMORIAL See Franciscan Health Michigan City

MISHAWAKA—St. Joseph County

⊞ **SAINT JOSEPH HEALTH SYSTEM (150012)**, 5215 Holy Cross Parkway, Zip 46545–1469; tel. 574/335–5000, **A**1 2 3 5 10 **F**3 11 13 15 17 18 19 20 21 22 23 24 26 28 29 30 31 34 35 36 37 39 40 41 44 45 46 47 48 49 50 51 52 54 55 57 58 59 60 61 63 64 65 66 70 71 72 73 74 75 76 77 78 79 80 81 82 83 84 85 86 87 89 90 91 92 93 96 97 100 107 108 110 114 115 117 118 119 120 121 124 126 129 130 131 132 135 144 146 147 148 149 154 156 **S** Trinity Health, Livonia, MI
Primary Contact: Chad Towner, Chief Executive Officer
COO: Christopher J Karam, Chief Operating Officer
CFO: Kevin J Higdon, Chief Financial Officer
CMO: Genevieve Lankowicz, M.D., Chief Medical Officer
CIO: Gary L Miller, Senior Director Information Systems
CHR: Kurt A Meyer, Chief Human Resource Officer
CNO: Kenneth C Hall, R.N., Chief Nursing Officer
Web address: www.sjmed.com
Control: Other not-for-profit (including NFP Corporation) **Service**: General medical and surgical

Staffed Beds: 300 **Admissions:** 15014 **Census:** 188 **Outpatient Visits:** 177608 **Births:** 1905 **Total Expense ($000):** 418866 **Payroll Expense ($000):** 93538 **Personnel:** 1646

○ **UNITY MEDICAL & SURGICAL HOSPITAL (150177)**, 4455 Edison Lakes Parkway, Zip 46545–1442; tel. 574/968–0867, (Nonreporting) **A**10 11
Primary Contact: John M. Day, Chief Executive Officer
COO: Donald Allen, Chief Operating Officer
CFO: Matthew M Sherwood, Chief Financial Officer
CMO: Viraj Patel, M.D., Chief Medical Officer
CIO: Richard Leighton, Financial Application Analyst
CHR: Emyle Kruyer-Collins, Chief Human Resources Officer
CNO: Sylvia K Coffing, R.N., MSN, Chief Nursing and Compliance Officer
Web address: www.umsh.net
Control: Partnership, Investor-owned (for-profit) **Service**: Surgical

Staffed Beds: 15

MONTICELLO—White County

⊞ ○ **INDIANA UNIVERSITY HEALTH WHITE MEMORIAL HOSPITAL (151312)**, 720 South Sixth Street, Zip 47960–8182; tel. 574/583–7111, **A**1 10 11 18 **F**3 11 15 29 30 31 34 35 40 45 50 57 59 64 75 77 78 79 81 93 03 107 108 110 111 114 119 129 133 135 146 147 148 149 150 **S** Indiana University Health, Indianapolis, IN
Primary Contact: Mary Minier, President
CMO: Adel Khdour, M.D., Chief Medical Officer
CIO: Michelle Baker, Director Information Systems
CHR: JoEllyn Brockmeyer, Director Human Resources
CNO: Robin C Smith, Chief Nursing Officer
Web address: www.iuhealth.org/white-memorial
Control: Other not-for-profit (including NFP Corporation) **Service**: General medical and surgical

Staffed Beds: 25 **Admissions:** 609 **Census:** 6 **Outpatient Visits:** 40219 **Births:** 0 **Total Expense ($000):** 28115 **Payroll Expense ($000):** 7764 **Personnel:** 134

MOORESVILLE—Morgan County

○ **FRANCISCAN HEALTH MOORESVILLE (150057)**, 1201 Hadley Road, Zip 46158–1789; tel. 317/831–1160, (Nonreporting) **A**3 5 10 11 **S** Franciscan Health, Mishawaka, IN
Primary Contact: Peter J. Murphy, Senior Vice President and Chief Operating Officer
CIO: Barbara Coulter, Director Information Systems
CHR: John Ross, Vice President
CNO: Agnes Therady, MSN, FACHE, Vice President and Chief Nursing Officer
Web address: www.franciscanalliance.org/hospitals/mooresville/Pages/default.aspx
Control: Church operated **Service**: General medical and surgical

Staffed Beds: 115

ST. FRANCIS HOSPITAL-MOORESVILLE See Franciscan Health Mooresville

MUNCIE—Delaware County

BALL MEMORIAL HOSPITAL See Indiana University Health Ball Memorial Hospital

IN

Hospital, Medicare Provider Number, Address, Telephone, Approval, Facility, and Physician Codes, Health Care System

★ American Hospital Association (AHA) membership
☐ The Joint Commission accreditation
○ Healthcare Facilities Accreditation Program
◇ DNV Healthcare Inc. accreditation
⇑ Center for Improvement in Healthcare Quality Accreditation
△ Commission on Accreditation of Rehabilitation Facilities (CARF) accreditation

○ **CENTRAL INDIANA AMG SPECIALTY HOSPITAL (152025)**, 2401 West University Avenue, 8th Floor, Zip 47303–3428; tel. 765/751–5253, (Nonreporting) **A**10 11
Primary Contact: Victor J. Galfano, FACHE, Chief Executive Officer
CNO: Lisa G. Hayes, Chief Clinical Officer
Web address: www.amgmuncie.com/
Control: Corporation, Investor–owned (for–profit) **Service**: Acute long–term care hospital

Staffed Beds: 32

✠ **INDIANA UNIVERSITY HEALTH BALL MEMORIAL HOSPITAL (150089)**, 2401 West University Avenue, Zip 47303–3499; tel. 765/747–3111, **A**1 2 3 5 10 19 **F**3 11 12 13 15 17 18 20 22 24 26 28 29 30 31 32 34 35 37 39 40 43 45 46 49 50 51 53 54 56 57 58 59 60 64 65 66 70 72 73 74 75 76 77 78 79 80 81 82 84 85 86 87 89 90 92 93 94 96 97 98 100 101 102 105 107 108 110 111 114 115 116 117 118 119 120 121 123 124 126 129 130 132 141 142 146 147 148 149 154 156 157 **S** Indiana University Health, Indianapolis, IN
Primary Contact: Jeffrey C. Bird, M.D., President
COO: Lori Luther, CPA, Chief Operating Officer
CFO: John Vanator, CPA, Chief Financial Officer
CMO: Peter Voss, M.D., Chief Medical Officer
CHR: Ann M. McGuire, Regional Vice President Human Resources
CNO: Carla C. Cox, Chief Nursing Officer
Web address: www.iuhealth.org
Control: Other not–for–profit (including NFP Corporation) **Service**: General medical and surgical

Staffed Beds: 344 **Admissions**: 16029 **Census**: 238 **Outpatient Visits**: 260036 **Births**: 1253 **Total Expense ($000)**: 385434 **Payroll Expense ($000)**: 111845 **Personnel**: 1850

MERIDIAN HEALTH SERVICES (154053), 240 North Tillotson Avenue, Zip 47304; tel. 765/747–3281, (Nonreporting) **A**10
Primary Contact: Hank A. Milius, Chief Executive Officer
CMO: Sarfraz Khan, Medical Director
Web address: www.meridianhs.org
Control: Other not–for–profit (including NFP Corporation) **Service**: Psychiatric

Staffed Beds: 20

RENAISSANCE SPECIALTY HOSPITAL OF CENTRAL INDIANA See Central Indiana Amg Specialty Hospital

MUNSTER—Lake County

☐ △ **COMMUNITY HOSPITAL (150125)**, 901 Macarthur Boulevard, Zip 46321–2959; tel. 219/836–1600, **A**1 2 7 10 **F**8 11 12 13 15 17 18 20 22 24 26 28 29 30 31 34 35 36 38 39 40 45 46 47 49 50 53 54 55 57 58 59 62 64 67 70 72 73 74 75 77 78 79 80 81 82 85 86 87 90 92 93 96 107 108 110 111 114 115 116 119 120 121 123 124 126 129 130 131 132 135 144 146 147 148 149 156 **S** Community Healthcare System, Hammond, IN
Primary Contact: Luis F. Molina, Chief Executive Officer and Administrator
CFO: Daniel R. O'Brien, Vice President and Chief Financial Officer
CMO: David Robinson, President Medical and Dental Staff
CIO: Gary Weiner, Vice President Information Technology, Chief Information Officer
CHR: Debbie Brandt, Director Human Resources
CNO: Ronda McKay, R.N., Vice President Patient Care Services, Chief Nursing Officer
Web address: www.comhs.org
Control: Other not–for–profit (including NFP Corporation) **Service**: General medical and surgical

Staffed Beds: 510 **Admissions**: 19093 **Census**: 297 **Outpatient Visits**: 334363 **Births**: 1950 **Total Expense ($000)**: 482271 **Payroll Expense ($000)**: 169815 **Personnel**: 2528

○ **FRANCISCAN HEALTHCARE MUNSTER (150165)**, 701 Superior Avenue, Zip 46321–4037; tel. 219/924–1300, (Nonreporting) **A**3 10 11 **S** Franciscan Health, Mishawaka, IN
Primary Contact: Patrick J. Maloney, Chief Executive Officer
CFO: Harold E Collins, JD, Chief Financial Officer
CMO: Vijay D Gupta, M.D., President and Chief Executive Officer
CIO: Steven Krause, Manager Information Technology
Web address: www.franciscanphysicianshospital.org
Control: Church operated **Service**: General medical and surgical

Staffed Beds: 32

NEW ALBANY—Floyd County

★ ○ **BAPTIST HEALTH FLOYD (150044)**, 1850 State Street, Zip 47150–4997; tel. 812/949–5500, **A**2 3 5 10 11 **F**3 8 11 12 13 15 17 18 20 22 24 26 28 29 30 31 32 34 35 36 40 43 44 45 46 47 49 50 53 54 55 57 58 59 62 64 70 74 75 76 77 78 79 80 81 82 84 85 86 87 89 92 93 100 107 108 109 110 111 114 115 116 117 118 119 120 121 123 124 129 130 131 132 135 144 145 146 147 148 149 154 156 **S** Baptist Health, Louisville, KY
Primary Contact: Daniel J. Eichenberger, M.D., President and Chief Executive Officer
COO: Mark Truman, Vice President of Operations
CIO: Brian Cox, Director Information Systems
CHR: Sue Christopher, Vice President, Human Resources
CNO: Kelly McMinoway, R.N., Vice President, Nursing
Web address: www.floydmemorial.com
Control: Other not–for–profit (including NFP Corporation) **Service**: General medical and surgical

Staffed Beds: 244 **Admissions**: 12361 **Census**: 126 **Outpatient Visits**: 270739 **Births**: 1020 **Total Expense ($000)**: 266314 **Payroll Expense ($000)**: 88154 **Personnel**: 2266

☐ **PHYSICIANS' MEDICAL CENTER (150172)**, 4023 Reas Lane, Zip 47150–2228; tel. 812/206–7660, **A**1 10 **F**3 12 29 45 51 77 79 81 82 85 89 94 107 111 144
Primary Contact: Dennis Medley, Chief Executive Officer and Administrator
COO: Rob Jones, Director of Nursing and Operations
CFO: Dennis Medley, Chief Executive Officer
CMO: Perry Cassady, M.D., Medical Director
CIO: Rob Jones, Director of Nursing and Operations
CHR: Mary Arntz, Manager Business Office and Executive Assistant
CNO: Rob Jones, Director of Nursing and Operations
Web address: www.pmcindiana.com
Control: Partnership, Investor–owned (for–profit) **Service**: General medical and surgical

Staffed Beds: 19 **Admissions**: 1353 **Census**: 8 **Outpatient Visits**: 24482 **Births**: 0 **Total Expense ($000)**: 50813 **Payroll Expense ($000)**: 12872 **Personnel**: 268

✠ △ **SOUTHERN INDIANA REHABILITATION HOSPITAL (153037)**, 3104 Blackiston Boulevard, Zip 47150–9579; tel. 812/941–8300, (Nonreporting) **A**1 7 10 **S** Vibra Healthcare, Mechanicsburg, PA
Primary Contact: William Boso, Executive Director, Administrator
CFO: Robert Steltenpohl, Vice President
CMO: John C Shaw, M.D., Medical Director
CHR: Lisa Burris, Director Human Resources
CNO: Suzann Byers, Director of Nursing
Web address: www.sirh.org
Control: Other not–for–profit (including NFP Corporation) **Service**: Rehabilitation

Staffed Beds: 60

NEW CASTLE—Henry County

★ ○ **HENRY COMMUNITY HEALTH (150030)**, 1000 North 16th Street, Zip 47362–4319, Mailing Address: P.O. Box 490, Zip 47362–0490; tel. 765/521–0890, (Nonreporting) **A**10 11
Primary Contact: Paul Janssen, President and Chief Executive Officer
COO: Brian K Ring, Chief Operating Officer
CFO: Darin Brown, Vice President Finance
CMO: Arun Tewari, M.D., Chief Medical Officer
CIO: Mike Spencer, Chief Information Officer
CHR: Deanna Malott, Director Human Resources
CNO: Leslie Cowan, R.N., Chief Nursing Officer
Web address: www.hcmhcares.org
Control: County, Government, nonfederal **Service**: General medical and surgical

Staffed Beds: 90

NEWBURGH—Warrick County

☐ **BRENTWOOD SPRINGS (154055)**, 4488 Roslin Road, Zip 47630; tel. 812/858–7200, (Nonreporting) **A**1 10 **S** Springstone, Louisville, KY
Primary Contact: Mark Puckett, Chief Executive Officer
Web address: www.brentwoodmeadows.com
Control: Partnership, Investor–owned (for–profit) **Service**: Psychiatric

Staffed Beds: 48

Many Facility Codes have changed. Please refer to the AHA Guide Code Chart. © 2019 AHA Guide

★ **DEACONESS GATEWAY HOSPITAL (150175)**, 4007 Gateway Boulevard, Zip 47630–8947; tel. 812/842–4784, (Nonreporting) **A**10 **S** Deaconess Health System, Evansville, IN
Primary Contact: Rebecca Malotte, Executive Director and Chief Nursing Officer
COO: Rebecca Malotte, Executive Director and Chief Nursing Officer
CFO: Tracy Hoefling, Chief Financial Officer
CMO: Lee Wagmeister, M.D., President Medical Staff
CIO: Lisa Hobgood, Chief Information Officer
CHR: Sarah Bryan, Manager Human Resources
CNO: Rebecca Malotte, Executive Director and Chief Nursing Officer
Web address: www.deaconess.com/
Control: Partnership, Investor–owned (for–profit) **Service**: Heart

Staffed Beds: 24

★ ○ **THE WOMEN'S HOSPITAL (150149)**, 4199 Gateway Boulevard, Zip 47630–8940; tel. 812/842–4200, **A**3 10 11 **F**3 13 15 29 30 34 35 36 40 50 53 55 57 59 63 64 65 72 75 76 77 81 84 85 86 87 93 110 119 126 130 132 134 135 147 154 **S** Deaconess Health System, Evansville, IN
Primary Contact: Christina M. Ryan, R.N., Chief Executive Officer
CFO: Tina Cady, Controller
CIO: Jenny Skelton, System Integration Manager
CHR: Jerri Sue Traylor, Director Human Resources
CNO: Christina M Ryan, R.N., Chief Executive Officer and Chief Nursing Officer
Web address: www.deaconess.com
Control: Partnership, Investor–owned (for–profit) **Service**: Obstetrics and gynecology

Staffed Beds: 74 **Admissions**: 3653 **Census**: 46 **Outpatient Visits**: 42720
Births: 3052 **Total Expense ($000)**: 88277 **Payroll Expense ($000)**: 38630
Personnel: 579

NOBLESVILLE—Hamilton County

○ △ **RIVERVIEW HEALTH (150059)**, 395 Westfield Road, Zip 46060–1425, Mailing Address: P.O. Box 220, Zip 46061–0220; tel. 317/773–0760, **A**2 7 10 11 **F**3 11 13 15 17 18 20 22 24 26 28 29 30 31 34 35 37 40 45 46 49 50 53 54 56 57 59 60 64 65 70 73 74 75 76 77 78 79 81 82 85 86 87 89 90 93 94 97 107 108 110 111 114 115 116 118 119 120 121 123 128 129 130 131 132 144 146 147 148 149
Primary Contact: Seth Warren, President and Chief Executive Officer
COO: Lawrence Christman, Chief Financial Officer and Chief Operating Officer
CFO: Brenda Baker, Chief Financial Officer
CMO: Eric Marcotte, M.D., Chief Medical Officer
CIO: Brant Bucciarelli, Chief Information Officer
CHR: Ann Kuzee, Executive Director Human Resources
CNO: Joyce Wood, Vice President Organizational Improvement and Chief Nursing Officer
Web address: www.riverview.org
Control: County, Government, nonfederal **Service**: General medical and surgical

Staffed Beds: 176 **Admissions**: 4898 **Census**: 69 **Outpatient Visits**: 469620 **Births**: 566 **Total Expense ($000)**: 210020 **Payroll Expense ($000)**: 78327 **Personnel**: 1007

NORTH VERNON—Jennings County

✠ **ST. VINCENT JENNINGS HOSPITAL (151303)**, 301 Henry Street, Zip 47265–1097; tel. 812/352–4200, **A**1 10 18 **F**3 11 29 30 34 35 40 44 45 50 56 57 59 64 65 66 77 81 85 107 111 115 119 128 133 135 144 146 148 **S** Ascension Healthcare, Saint Louis, MO
Primary Contact: Dana M. Muntz, Chief Executive Officer
CFO: Joseph Kubala, Chief Financial Officer
CMO: Jennifer Stanley, M.D., Chief Medical Officer
CHR: Kathryn Johnson, Manager Human Resources, Marketing and Public Relations
Web address: www.stvincent.org
Control: Other not–for–profit (including NFP Corporation) **Service**: General medical and surgical

Staffed Beds: 17 **Admissions**: 449 **Census**: 2 **Outpatient Visits**: 33475 **Births**: 0 **Total Expense ($000)**: 14443 **Payroll Expense ($000)**: 3473 **Personnel**: 57

PAOLI—Orange County

BLOOMINGTON HOSPITAL OF ORANGE COUNTY See Indiana University Health Paoli Hospital

✠ **INDIANA UNIVERSITY HEALTH PAOLI HOSPITAL (151306)**, 642 West Hospital Road, Zip 47454–9672, Mailing Address: P.O. Box 499, Zip 47454–0499; tel. 812/723–2811, **A**1 10 18 **F**3 13 15 29 30 35 40 45 50 53 57 59 64 76 77 81 84 85 89 93 107 110 111 114 119 129 132 133 135 146 148 149 150 154 **S** Indiana University Health, Indianapolis, IN
Primary Contact: Larry Bailey, President
COO: Sonya M. Zeller, R.N., Vice President, Chief Operating Officer and Chief Nursing Officer
CMO: Jose Lopez, M.D., Medical Staff President
CNO: Sonya M. Zeller, R.N., Vice President, Chief Operating Officer and Chief Nursing Officer
Web address: www.iuhealth.org/paoli
Control: Other not–for–profit (including NFP Corporation) **Service**: General medical and surgical

Staffed Beds: 25 **Admissions**: 260 **Census**: 2 **Outpatient Visits**: 28143 **Births**: 118 **Total Expense ($000)**: 24095 **Payroll Expense ($000)**: 7527 **Personnel**: 115

PERU—Miami County

✠ **DUKES MEMORIAL HOSPITAL (151318)**, 275 West 12th Street, Zip 46970–1638; tel. 765/472–8000, **A**1 10 18 **F**7 8 15 18 28 29 34 35 40 50 56 57 59 64 68 69 70 75 77 81 93 97 107 108 109 110 111 115 119 129 130 133 144 146 147 149 154 **S** Community Health Systems, Inc., Franklin, TN
Primary Contact: Debra Close, Chief Executive Officer
CFO: Adam Cumbo, Chief Financial Officer
CMO: Neil Stalker, M.D., Chief of Staff
Web address: www.dukesmemorialhosp.com
Control: Corporation, Investor–owned (for–profit) **Service**: General medical and surgical

Staffed Beds: 25 **Admissions**: 1047 **Census**: 9 **Outpatient Visits**: 41273 **Births**: 129

PLYMOUTH—Marshall County

□ **MICHIANA BEHAVIORAL HEALTH CENTER (154047)**, 1800 North Oak Drive, Zip 46563–3492; tel. 574/936–3784, (Nonreporting) **A**1 10 **S** Universal Health Services, Inc., King of Prussia, PA
Primary Contact: Michael Perry, Chief Executive Officer
CFO: Jeff Calvin, Chief Financial Officer
CMO: Robert Raster, M.D., Medical Director
CIO: Leslie McLaughlin, Director of Business Development
CHR: Becky Nowicki, Director Human Resources
CNO: Brandi Richard, Chief Nursing Officer
Web address: www.michianabhc.com
Control: Corporation, Investor–owned (for–profit) **Service**: Psychiatric

Staffed Beds: 75

✠ **PLYMOUTH MEDICAL CENTER (150076)**, 1915 Lake Avenue, Zip 46563–9366, Mailing Address: P.O. Box 670, Zip 46563–0670; tel. 574/948–4000, **A**1 10 **F**3 8 13 15 18 20 29 30 34 35 40 45 46 50 51 54 57 59 64 65 66 68 70 74 75 76 78 79 81 84 85 86 87 89 91 92 93 97 107 108 110 114 115 118 119 120 121 123 124 129 131 132 135 146 149 154 156 **S** Trinity Health, Livonia, MI
Primary Contact: Christopher J. Karam, President
COO: Tamara Awald, Chief Nursing Officer and Chief Operating Officer
CFO: Janice Dunn, Chief Financial Officer
CMO: Stephen Anderson, M.D., Chief Medical Officer
CIO: Gary L Miller, Regional Director Information Systems
CHR: Kurt A Meyer, Chief Human Resources Officer
Web address: www.sjmed.com
Control: Other not–for–profit (including NFP Corporation) **Service**: General medical and surgical

Staffed Beds: 48 **Admissions**: 2156 **Census**: 17 **Outpatient Visits**: 82769 **Births**: 284 **Total Expense ($000)**: 60258 **Payroll Expense ($000)**: 17693 **Personnel**: 308

PORTLAND—Jay County

✠ **INDIANA UNIVERSITY HEALTH JAY HOSPITAL (151320)**, 500 West Votaw Street, Zip 47371–1322; tel. 260/726–7131, (Data for 306 days) **A**1 10 18 **F**3 8 11 13 15 28 29 30 32 34 35 40 45 50 57 59 68 75 76 77 81 85 86 87 98 104 107 108 110 111 114 115 119 129 130 132 133 135 146 148 157 **S** Indiana University Health, Indianapolis, IN
Primary Contact: David W. Hyatt, President
CIO: Jeff Horn, Director of Support Services
CHR: Linda Guise, Senior Human Resource Consultant
CNO: Lisa Craiger, Chief Nursing Officer
Web address: www.jaycountyhospital.com
Control: Other not–for–profit (including NFP Corporation) **Service**: General medical and surgical

Staffed Beds: 35 **Admissions**: 798 **Census**: 10 **Outpatient Visits**: 70998 **Births**: 72 **Total Expense ($000)**: 31629 **Payroll Expense ($000)**: 11619 **Personnel**: 225

IN

Hospital, Medicare Provider Number, Address, Telephone, Approval, Facility, and Physician Codes, Health Care System

★ American Hospital Association (AHA) membership
□ The Joint Commission accreditation
○ Healthcare Facilities Accreditation Program
◇ DNV Healthcare Inc. accreditation
⇑ Center for Improvement in Healthcare Quality Accreditation
△ Commission on Accreditation of Rehabilitation Facilities (CARF) accreditation

PRINCETON—Gibson County

☒ **GIBSON GENERAL HOSPITAL (151319)**, 1808 Sherman Drive, Zip 47670–1043; tel. 812/385–3401, (Total facility includes 45 beds in nursing home–type unit) **A**1 10 18 **F**3 11 15 28 29 31 34 35 38 40 44 45 49 50 57 58 59 62 64 68 70 75 77 81 82 89 93 97 102 107 110 115 119 127 128 129 130 132 133 148 **S** Deaconess Health System, Evansville, IN
Primary Contact: Claudia Eisenmann, Chief Executive Officer
CFO: James R Childers, Vice President & Chief Financial Officer
CMO: Krishna Murthy, M.D., Chief of Medical Staff
CIO: Steve Paddock, Director of Information Services
CHR: D Deann Hunt, Director of Human Resources
CNO: Lois Morgan, R.N., MSN, Vice President and Chief Nursing Officer
Web address: www.gibsongeneral.com
Control: Other not–for–profit (including NFP Corporation) **Service**: General medical and surgical

Staffed Beds: 70 **Admissions**: 415 **Census**: 40 **Outpatient Visits**: 26833 **Births**: 0 **Total Expense ($000)**: 26752 **Payroll Expense ($000)**: 10498 **Personnel**: 278

RENSSELAER—Jasper County

FRANCISCAN HEALTH RENSSELAER (151324), 1104 East Grace Street, Zip 47978–3296; tel. 219/866–5141, (Total facility includes 21 beds in nursing home–type unit) **A**10 18 **F**1 3 10 15 29 31 34 35 40 49 50 51 54 57 62 63 64 69 70 75 77 78 79 81 85 91 93 94 107 108 110 111 115 118 119 127 129 130 132 133 135 145 148 154 156 **S** Franciscan Health, Mishawaka, IN
Primary Contact: Carlos Vasquez, Vice President and Chief Operating Officer
CFO: Jeffrey D Webb, CPA, Chief Financial Officer
CIO: Kirby Reed, Director Information Systems
CHR: Deana Brown, Director Administrative Services
CNO: Stacie Klingler, R.N., Vice President of Patient Services
Web address: www.franciscanhealth.org
Control: Church operated, Nongovernment, not–for–profit **Service**: General medical and surgical

Staffed Beds: 46 **Admissions**: 430 **Census**: 13 **Outpatient Visits**: 56737 **Births**: 0 **Total Expense ($000)**: 35948 **Payroll Expense ($000)**: 13411 **Personnel**: 166

RICHMOND—Wayne County

★ ○ **REID HEALTH (150048)**, 1100 Reid Parkway, Zip 47374–1157; tel. 765/983–3000, **A**2 3 10 11 **F**3 8 11 13 15 18 20 22 24 26 28 29 30 31 34 35 37 38 40 43 44 45 47 49 50 51 54 55 56 57 58 59 61 63 64 68 69 70 74 75 76 77 78 79 81 82 84 85 86 87 89 90 91 92 93 95 96 97 98 100 101 102 103 104 107 108 110 111 114 115 116 117 118 119 120 121 123 124 126 127 129 130 131 132 135 144 146 147 148 149 154 156
Primary Contact: Craig C. Kinyon, President and Chief Executive Officer
CFO: Christopher D. Knight, Vice President Finance and Chief Financial Officer
CMO: Thomas Huth, M.D., Vice President Medical Affairs
CIO: Tim Love, Director Information Services
CHR: Scott C Rauch, Vice President Human Resources
CNO: Misti Foust-Cofield, R.N., Vice President and Chief Nursing Officer
Web address: www.reidhealth.org
Control: Other not–for–profit (including NFP Corporation) **Service**: General medical and surgical

Staffed Beds: 221 **Admissions**: 12551 **Census**: 145 **Outpatient Visits**: 328898 **Births**: 772 **Total Expense ($000)**: 475817 **Payroll Expense ($000)**: 203566 **Personnel**: 2650

☐ **RICHMOND STATE HOSPITAL (154018)**, 498 NW 18th Street, Zip 47374–2851; tel. 765/966–0511, **A**1 10 **F**56 98 103 106 130 135 146
Primary Contact: Warren Fournier, Chief Executive Officer and Medical Director
CFO: Dave Shelford, Assistant Superintendent
CMO: Donald Graber, M.D., Medical Director
CIO: Robert Boatman, Director Information Technology
CHR: Sarah Witt, Director Human Resources
Web address: www.richmondstatehospital.org
Control: State, Government, nonfederal **Service**: Psychiatric

Staffed Beds: 180 **Admissions**: 123 **Census**: 169 **Outpatient Visits**: 0 **Births**: 0

ROCHESTER—Fulton County

★ ○ **WOODLAWN HOSPITAL (151313)**, 1400 East Ninth Street, Zip 46975–8937; tel. 574/223–3141, **A**10 11 18 **F**3 11 13 15 28 29 30 31 34 40 46 56 57 59 65 68 69 70 75 76 77 78 79 81 82 93 94 97 107 108 111 115 119 129 130 132 133 135 146 147 148 149
Primary Contact: John L. Alley, Chief Executive Officer
CFO: Dave Cholger, Chief Financial Officer
CHR: Debra J Lemasters, Director Human Resources
Web address: www.woodlawnhospital.com
Control: County, Government, nonfederal **Service**: General medical and surgical

Staffed Beds: 25 **Admissions**: 1033 **Census**: 10 **Outpatient Visits**: 50034 **Births**: 162 **Total Expense ($000)**: 58448 **Payroll Expense ($000)**: 25957 **Personnel**: 348

RUSHVILLE—Rush County

★ **RUSH MEMORIAL HOSPITAL (151304)**, 1300 North Main Street, Zip 46173–1198; tel. 765/932–4111, **A**10 18 **F**3 7 11 15 18 24 28 29 31 35 36 40 46 50 51 57 59 63 64 65 74 75 77 78 79 81 82 85 93 97 107 111 114 117 120 121 122 130 131 132 133 135 144 146 147 148 156
Primary Contact: Bradley Smith, President and Chief Executive Officer
COO: Gretchen Smith, Vice President of Operations, Risk and Compliance, and Chief Operating Officer
CFO: Karen Meyer, Vice President Finance and Chief Financial Officer
CMO: Daniel Stahl, D.O., Chief Medical Officer
CIO: Jim Boyer, Vice President Information Technology and Chief Information Officer
CHR: Brian R Bane, Vice President Human Resources
CNO: Carrie Tressler, Vice President of Nursing and Chief Nursing Officer
Web address: www.rushmemorial.com
Control: County, Government, nonfederal **Service**: General medical and surgical

Staffed Beds: 25 **Admissions**: 487 **Census**: 4 **Outpatient Visits**: 32808 **Births**: 0 **Total Expense ($000)**: 35441 **Payroll Expense ($000)**: 15636 **Personnel**: 289

SALEM—Washington County

☒ **ST. VINCENT SALEM HOSPITAL (151314)**, 911 North Shelby Street, Zip 47167–1694; tel. 812/883–5881, **A**1 10 18 **F**3 11 15 28 29 30 32 34 40 45 47 49 57 59 75 77 79 81 82 85 93 107 111 114 119 124 129 130 131 132 133 144 148 154 **S** Ascension Healthcare, Saint Louis, MO
Primary Contact: Dana M. Muntz, Chief Executive Officer
CFO: Joseph Kubala, Director Financial and Support Services
CMO: S E Kemker, M.D., President Medical Staff
CIO: Jeremy Long, Manager Information Systems
CHR: Val Potter, Director Human Resources
Web address: www.stvincent.org/St-Vincent-Salem/Default.aspx
Control: Other not–for–profit (including NFP Corporation) **Service**: General medical and surgical

Staffed Beds: 25 **Admissions**: 97 **Census**: 1 **Outpatient Visits**: 33655 **Births**: 0 **Total Expense ($000)**: 16150 **Payroll Expense ($000)**: 4935 **Personnel**: 71

SCOTTSBURG—Scott County

☒ **SCOTT MEMORIAL HEALTH (151334)**, 1415 North Gardner Street, Zip 47170, Mailing Address: Box 430, Zip 47170–0430; tel. 812/752–3456, (Nonreporting) **A**1 10 18 **S** LifePoint Health, Brentwood, TN
Primary Contact: Martin Padgett, Acting Chief Executive Officer
CFO: Angela Doan, Chief Financial Officer
CNO: Dawn Mays, Chief Nursing Officer
Web address: www.scottmemorial.com
Control: County, Government, nonfederal **Service**: General medical and surgical

Staffed Beds: 25

SEYMOUR—Jackson County

☒ **SCHNECK MEDICAL CENTER (150065)**, 411 West Tipton Street, Zip 47274–2363, Mailing Address: P.O. Box 2349, Zip 47274–5000; tel. 812/522–2349, **A**1 2 10 **F**3 5 12 13 15 18 28 29 30 31 34 35 36 40 45 48 53 56 57 59 62 63 64 65 68 69 70 74 75 76 77 78 79 81 82 84 85 87 89 93 97 100 101 104 107 108 110 111 114 115 119 120 121 123 124 126 129 130 131 132 133 135 144 146 147 148
Primary Contact: Warren Forgey, CPA, FACHE, President and Chief Executive Officer
CFO: Deborah Ridlen, CPA, Vice President Finance and Chief Financial Officer
CMO: Eric Fish, M.D., Vice President of Medical Affairs and Chief Medical Officers
CIO: Craig Rice, Director Information Technology
CHR: Kathy Covert, MSN, Vice President Workforce Development and Organizational Development
CNO: Amy Pettit, R.N., Vice President Nursing Services and Chief Nursing Officer
Web address: www.schneckmed.org
Control: County, Government, nonfederal **Service**: General medical and surgical

Staffed Beds: 93 **Admissions**: 2613 **Census**: 25 **Outpatient Visits**: 288286 **Births**: 684 **Total Expense ($000)**: 143513 **Payroll Expense ($000)**: 64880 **Personnel**: 917

SHELBYVILLE—Shelby County

★ ○ **MAJOR HOSPITAL (150097)**, 150 West Washington Street, Zip 46176–1236, Mailing Address: 2451 Intelliplex Drive, Zip 46176; tel. 317/392–3211, **A**2 10 11 **F**3 13 15 28 29 30 31 34 35 36 38 40 45 47 50 56 57 59 62 64 68 69 70 73 74 75 76 77 78 79 81 82 84 85 87 92 93 94 97 104 107 108 109 110 111 114 115 118 119 120 121 123 124 127 129 130 131 132 135 144 146 147 148 154 156
Primary Contact: John M. Horner, President and Chief Executive Officer
CFO: Ralph Mercuri, Vice President and Chief Financial Officer
CMO: Douglas S Carter, M.D., Vice President and Chief Medical Officer
CIO: Carol Huesman, Chief Information Officer
CHR: Nicki Sparling, Manager Human Resources
CNO: Valerie L Miller, MSN, R.N., Director of Nursing
Web address: www.majorhospital.org
Control: City–county, Government, nonfederal **Service**: General medical and surgical

Staffed Beds: 46 **Admissions**: 2787 **Census**: 25 **Outpatient Visits**: 172374 **Births**: 343 **Total Expense ($000)**: 136258 **Payroll Expense ($000)**: 52097 **Personnel**: 1016

IN

Many Facility Codes have changed. Please refer to the AHA Guide Code Chart. © 2019 AHA Guide

SOUTH BEND—St. Joseph County

☒ △ **MEMORIAL HOSPITAL OF SOUTH BEND (150058)**, 615 North Michigan Street, Zip 46601–1033; tel. 574/647–1000, (Includes BEACON CHILDREN'S HOSPITAL, 615 North Michigan Street, South Bend, Indiana, Zip 46601; tel. 574/647–1000) **A**1 2 3 7 10 **F**3 7 8 11 12 13 15 17 18 19 20 22 24 26 28 29 30 31 34 35 36 38 40 43 45 46 47 49 50 53 55 56 58 59 60 61 64 65 67 68 70 72 73 74 75 76 77 78 79 81 82 84 85 86 87 88 89 90 91 92 93 96 98 99 100 102 103 107 108 110 114 115 116 117 118 119 120 121 123 124 126 129 130 131 132 135 145 146 147 148 150 154 155 156 **S** Beacon Health System, South Bend, IN
Primary Contact: Larry A. Tracy Jr, FACHE, President
CFO: Jeff Costello, Chief Financial Officer, Beacon Health System
CMO: Cheryl Wibbens, M.D., Vice President Medical Staff Affairs
CIO: Mark Warlick, Chief Information Officer
CHR: Steven M Eller, Chief Human Resources Officer
Web address: www.beaconhealthsystem.org
Control: Other not–for–profit (including NFP Corporation) **Service:** General medical and surgical

Staffed Beds: 418 **Admissions:** 19099 **Census:** 273 **Outpatient Visits:** 203873 **Births:** 2419 **Total Expense ($000):** 447627 **Payroll Expense ($000):** 151191 **Personnel:** 2619

SULLIVAN—Sullivan County

★ ○ **SULLIVAN COUNTY COMMUNITY HOSPITAL (151327)**, 2200 North Section Street, Zip 47882–7523, Mailing Address: P.O. Box 10, Zip 47882–0010; tel. 812/268–4311, **A**10 11 18 **F**3 8 11 13 15 28 29 32 34 35 40 44 45 47 48 50 53 56 57 59 61 62 65 69 70 75 76 77 78 79 81 86 87 93 97 107 110 111 114 116 117 118 119 127 129 130 131 133 146 147 148 154 156 **S** QHR, Brentwood, TN
Primary Contact: Michelle Franklin, Chief Executive Officer
CFO: Jim Bishop, Chief Financial Officer
CMO: Divyesh Purohit, M.D., Chief of Staff
CIO: Hap Beckes, Director Information Systems
CHR: Denise Hart, Director Human Resources
CNO: Lori Resler, R.N., Chief Nurse
Web address: www.schosp.com
Control: County, Government, nonfederal **Service:** General medical and surgical

Staffed Beds: 25 **Admissions:** 629 **Census:** 5 **Outpatient Visits:** 58469 **Births:** 120 **Total Expense ($000):** 33924 **Payroll Expense ($000):** 16248 **Personnel:** 198

TELL CITY—Perry County

★ **PERRY COUNTY MEMORIAL HOSPITAL (151322)**, 8885 State Road 237, Zip 47586–2750; tel. 812/547–7011, **A**10 18 **F**3 7 11 13 15 17 18 28 29 30 31 34 35 40 41 45 50 53 56 57 59 62 64 65 68 70 76 77 78 79 81 82 85 87 89 107 110 111 115 119 124 127 128 129 130 133 135 144 146 148 154 **S** Alliant Management Services, Louisville, KY
Primary Contact: Brian J. Herwig, President and Chief Executive Officer
CMO: Juan Cornejo, M.D., Chief of Staff
CIO: Mark Miller, Director Information Systems
CHR: Sheila Gaynor, Director Human Resources
CNO: Michele Howard, Vice President Nursing Services
Web address: www.pchospital.org
Control: County, Government, nonfederal **Service:** General medical and surgical

Staffed Beds: 25 **Admissions:** 1450 **Census:** 13 **Outpatient Visits:** 60837 **Births:** 84 **Total Expense ($000):** 53598 **Payroll Expense ($000):** 13727 **Personnel:** 269

TERRE HAUTE—Vigo County

HAMILTON CENTER (154009), 620 Eighth Avenue, Zip 47804–2744; tel. 812/231–8323, **A**10 **F**35 38 98 102 106 130
Primary Contact: Melvin Burks, Chief Executive Officer
COO: Robb Johnson, Director Operations
CFO: Renee Utley, Chief Financial Officer
CMO: Ahsan Mahmood, M.D., Chief Medical Officer
CIO: Hans Eilbracht, Chief Information Officer
CHR: Margie Anshutz, Chief Development Officer
CNO: Rose Christy, Executive Director of Medical Services
Web address: www.hamiltoncenter.org
Control: State, Government, nonfederal **Service:** Psychiatric

Staffed Beds: 16 **Admissions:** 785 **Census:** 15 **Births:** 0 **Personnel:** 37

☐ **HARSHA BEHAVIORAL CENTER (154054)**, 1980 East Woodsmall Drive, Zip 47802–4937; tel. 866/644–8880, (Nonreporting) **A**1 10
Primary Contact: Roopam Harshawat, President and Chief Executive Officer
COO: Holly Near, Chief Administrative Officer
CFO: Holly Near, Chief Administrative Officer
CMO: Paras Harshawat, M.D., Medical Director
CHR: Karen Hunt, Executive Director
CNO: Cindy Dowers, Chief Nursing Officer
Web address: www.harshacenter.com
Control: Corporation, Investor–owned (for–profit) **Service:** Psychiatric

Staffed Beds: 44

☒ **TERRE HAUTE REGIONAL HOSPITAL (150046)**, 3901 South Seventh Street, Zip 47802–5709; tel. 812/232–0021, (Nonreporting) **A**1 2 10 **S** HCA Healthcare, Nashville, TN
Primary Contact: Nathan Vooys, Chief Executive Officer
COO: Andrea Gwyn, Chief Operating Officer
CIO: Mike Kuckewich, Director Information Systems
CNO: Angela Ellis, R.N., Chief Nursing Officer
Web address: www.regionalhospital.com
Control: Corporation, Investor–owned (for–profit) **Service:** General medical and surgical

Staffed Beds: 208

★ ○ **UNION HOSPITAL (150023)**, 1606 North Seventh Street, Zip 47804–2780; tel. 812/238–7000, **A**2 3 10 11 19 **F**3 8 13 15 18 20 22 24 26 28 29 30 31 34 35 36 40 43 45 46 47 48 49 50 51 53 54 57 59 64 68 70 72 73 74 75 76 77 78 79 81 83 85 86 87 89 90 91 92 93 94 95 96 97 107 108 110 111 112 114 115 116 117 118 119 120 121 123 124 126 127 130 131 132 135 144 146 147 149 157
Primary Contact: Steve M. Holman, Chief Executive Officer
CFO: Wayne Hutson, Executive Vice President and Chief Financial Officer
CMO: John Bolinger, M.D., Vice President Medical Affairs
CIO: Kym Pfrank, Senior Vice President and Chief Operating Officer
CHR: Sally Zuel, Vice President Human Resources
Web address: www.uhhg.org
Control: Other not–for–profit (including NFP Corporation) **Service:** General medical and surgical

Staffed Beds: 214 **Admissions:** 15634 **Census:** 167 **Outpatient Visits:** 426864 **Births:** 1752 **Total Expense ($000):** 404401 **Payroll Expense ($000):** 108352 **Personnel:** 1720

TIPTON—Tipton County

☒ **INDIANA UNIVERSITY HEALTH TIPTON HOSPITAL (151311)**, 1000 South Main Street, Zip 46072–9799; tel. 765/675–8500, **A**1 10 18 **F**3 11 15 18 28 29 30 31 34 35 39 40 45 46 47 48 57 59 70 74 75 77 78 79 81 82 85 86 87 93 107 108 110 111 115 119 129 130 131 132 133 135 146 147 148 156 **S** Indiana University Health, Indianapolis, IN
Primary Contact: Michael Harlowe, President and Chief Executive Officer
CFO: Randall C. Yust, Chief Financial Officer NCR
CMO: Larry Hopkins, Chief Medical Officer
CHR: Shelly E Huff, Manager Human Resources
CNO: Jo Ellen Scott, R.N., MS, Senior Vice President of Patient Care Services and Chief Nursing Officer
Web address: www.iuhealth.org
Control: Other not–for–profit (including NFP Corporation) **Service:** General medical and surgical

Staffed Beds: 25 **Admissions:** 783 **Census:** 8 **Outpatient Visits:** 39486 **Births:** 0 **Total Expense ($000):** 36109 **Payroll Expense ($000):** 11256 **Personnel:** 177

TIPTON HOSPITAL See Indiana University Health Tipton Hospital

VALPARAISO—Porter County

☒ **PORTER REGIONAL HOSPITAL (150035)**, 85 East U. S. Highway 6, Zip 46383–8947; tel. 219/983–8300, (Nonreporting) **A**1 10 **S** Community Health Systems, Inc., Franklin, TN
Primary Contact: Sean T. Dardeau, FACHE, Chief Executive Officer
COO: Lauren Hull, Chief Operating Officer
CFO: Jeffrey Daneff, Chief Financial Officer
CMO: Ramireddy K Tummuru, M.D., Chief Medical Officer
CIO: Robert Richardson, Information Technology Administrator
CHR: Angie Hampton, Director Human Resources
CNO: Judy Davidson, R.N., I Chief Nursing Officer
Web address: www.porterhealth.com
Control: Corporation, Investor–owned (for–profit) **Service:** General medical and surgical

Staffed Beds: 276

IN

Hospital, Medicare Provider Number, Address, Telephone, Approval, Facility, and Physician Codes, Health Care System

★ American Hospital Association (AHA) membership
☐ The Joint Commission accreditation
○ Healthcare Facilities Accreditation Program
◇ DNV Healthcare Inc. accreditation
⇑ Center for Improvement in Healthcare Quality Accreditation
△ Commission on Accreditation of Rehabilitation Facilities (CARF) accreditation

PORTER-STARKE SERVICES (154052), 601 Wall Street, Zip 46383–2512; tel. 219/531–3500, (Nonreporting) **A**10
Primary Contact: Matthew J. Burden, President and Chief Executive Officer
CFO: Mary Idstein, Chief Financial Officer
CMO: Anand Popli, Medical Director
Web address: www.porterstarke.org
Control: Other not–for–profit (including NFP Corporation) **Service**: Psychiatric

Staffed Beds: 16

VINCENNES—Knox County

⊞ △ **GOOD SAMARITAN HOSPITAL (150042)**, 520 South Seventh Street, Zip 47591–1038; tel. 812/882–5220, **A**1 2 7 10 19 **F**3 4 5 8 11 13 15 18 20 22 28 29 30 31 34 35 37 38 40 41 43 44 45 46 47 48 49 53 54 56 57 59 63 64 65 67 70 74 75 76 77 78 79 80 81 84 85 87 89 90 93 96 98 102 104 106 107 108 110 111 115 118 119 120 121 123 127 129 130 131 132 134 135 144 146 147 149 150 154 156 157
Primary Contact: Robert D. McLin, President and Chief Executive Officer
COO: Adam Thacker, Chief Operating Officer
CFO: Thomas M Cook, Chief Financial Officer
CMO: Charles C Hedde, M.D., Chief Medical Officer
CIO: Daniel Scott, Director of Information Systems
CHR: Dean Wagoner, Director Human Resources
CNO: Karen S. Haak, R.N., MSN, Chief Nursing Officer
Web address: www.gshvin.org/goodsamaritan
Control: County, Government, nonfederal **Service**: General medical and surgical

Staffed Beds: 158 **Admissions**: 6975 **Census**: 90 **Outpatient Visits**: 538938 **Births**: 412 **Total Expense ($000)**: 246352 **Payroll Expense ($000)**: 104551 **Personnel**: 1742

WABASH—Wabash County

⊞ **PARKVIEW WABASH HOSPITAL (151310)**, 10 John Kissinger Drive, Zip 46992–1648; tel. 260/563–3131, **A**1 10 18 **F**3 13 15 28 29 30 31 34 35 40 44 45 46 47 50 56 57 59 62 63 68 69 70 75 76 77 78 79 81 85 93 107 108 110 111 119 129 130 131 132 133 135 146 148 154 156 **S** Parkview Health, Fort Wayne, IN
Primary Contact: Marilyn J. Custer-Mitchell, President
CMO: Jeff Miller, M.D., Chief of Staff
CIO: David Brinson, Director Information Technology
CHR: Kimberly R Shininger, Manger, Human Resources
CNO: Cathy Allyson Wolfe, Chief Nursing Officer
Web address: www.wchospital.com
Control: Other not–for–profit (including NFP Corporation) **Service**: General medical and surgical

Staffed Beds: 18 **Admissions**: 1036 **Census**: 8 **Outpatient Visits**: 33470 **Births**: 21 **Total Expense ($000)**: 51244 **Payroll Expense ($000)**: 11464 **Personnel**: 160

WARSAW—Kosciusko County

⊞ **KOSCIUSKO COMMUNITY HOSPITAL (150133)**, 2101 East Dubois Drive, Zip 46580–3288; tel. 574/267–3200, **A**1 10 19 **F**3 7 8 13 15 18 28 29 30 31 32 35 40 49 50 51 54 55 57 58 59 64 65 68 69 74 75 76 77 78 79 81 85 86 89 90 93 107 108 110 111 114 115 116 117 118 119 120 121 129 130 131 132 144 146 147 148 154 **S** Community Health Systems, Inc., Franklin, TN
Primary Contact: Jae Dale, Chief Executive Officer
CFO: Douglas J BeMent, Chief Financial Officer
CMO: Patrick Silveus, M.D., Medical Director
CIO: Tammy Lukens, Director Information
CHR: Joe Jarboe, Director Human Resources
CNO: Kim Finch, Chief Nursing Officer
Web address: www.kch.com
Control: Corporation, Investor–owned (for–profit) **Service**: General medical and surgical

Staffed Beds: 72 **Admissions**: 2739 **Census**: 24

★ **OTIS R. BOWEN CENTER FOR HUMAN SERVICES (154014)**, 2621 East Jefferson Street, Zip 46580–3880; tel. 574/267–7169, (Nonreporting) **A**10
Primary Contact: Kurt Carlson, Chief Executive Officer
Web address: www.bowencenter.org
Control: Other not–for–profit (including NFP Corporation) **Service**: Psychiatric

Staffed Beds: 16

WASHINGTON—Daviess County

⊞ △ **DAVIESS COMMUNITY HOSPITAL (150061)**, 1314 East Walnut Street, Zip 47501–2860, Mailing Address: P.O. Box 760, Zip 47501–0760; tel. 812/254–2760, **A**1 7 10 **F**3 11 13 15 18 28 29 30 31 34 35 36 40 41 45 51 54 56 57 59 61 63 64 65 66 68 70 71 74 75 76 77 78 79 81 85 86 87 89 90 92 93 94 96 97 98 100 101 102 103 104 107 108 110 111 115 118 119 127 129 130 131 132 135 146 147 148 149 153 154 **S** Ascension Healthcare, Saint Louis, MO
Primary Contact: Tracy Conroy, Chief Executive Officer
COO: Keith Miller, Chief Operating Officer
CFO: Amanda Rodewald, Interim Chief Financial Officer
CNO: Nancy Case, Chief Nursing Officer
Web address: www.dchosp.org
Control: County, Government, nonfederal **Service**: General medical and surgical

Staffed Beds: 72 **Admissions**: 2115 **Census**: 33 **Outpatient Visits**: 301669 **Births**: 478 **Total Expense ($000)**: 67157 **Payroll Expense ($000)**: 26207

WEST LAFAYETTE—Tippecanoe County

⊞ **RIVER BEND HOSPITAL (154005)**, 2900 North River Road, Zip 47906–3744; tel. 765/464–0400, (Nonreporting) **A**1 10
Primary Contact: Stephanie Long, President and Chief Executive Officer
COO: Tom Gillian, Chief Operating Officer
CFO: Jeff Nagy, Chief Financial Officer
CMO: Richard Rahdert, M.D., Medical Director
CIO: Craig Anderson, Director Management Information Systems
CHR: Jan Shaw, Director Personnel
CNO: Megan Gibson, Nurse Manager
Web address: www.nchsi.com/riverbendhospital.cfm
Control: Other not–for–profit (including NFP Corporation) **Service**: Psychiatric

Staffed Beds: 16

WABASH VALLEY HOSPITAL See River Bend Hospital

WILLIAMSPORT—Warren County

⊞ **ST. VINCENT WILLIAMSPORT HOSPITAL (151307)**, 412 North Monroe Street, Zip 47993–1049; tel. 765/762–4000, **A**1 10 18 **F**3 7 15 29 34 35 40 45 50 57 59 64 75 77 79 81 85 86 87 93 97 107 110 111 114 119 127 131 132 133 135 143 149 156 **S** Ascension Healthcare, Saint Louis, MO
Primary Contact: Jane Craigin, Chief Executive Officer
CFO: Janet Merritt, Chief Financial Officer
Web address: www.stvincent.org
Control: Other not–for–profit (including NFP Corporation) **Service**: General medical and surgical

Staffed Beds: 16 **Admissions**: 575 **Census**: 6 **Outpatient Visits**: 66312 **Births**: 0 **Total Expense ($000)**: 20630 **Payroll Expense ($000)**: 7884 **Personnel**: 123

WINAMAC—Pulaski County

★ ○ **PULASKI MEMORIAL HOSPITAL (151305)**, 616 East 13th Street, Zip 46996–1117, Mailing Address: P.O. Box 279, Zip 46996–0279; tel. 574/946–2100, **A**10 11 18 **F**3 11 12 13 15 28 29 30 31 34 40 43 45 50 56 57 59 62 64 65 73 74 75 76 77 78 79 81 82 86 87 90 93 96 97 100 103 107 110 111 118 119 127 128 130 131 132 133 135 146 147 148 149 153 154
Primary Contact: Thomas Barry, Chief Executive Officer
CFO: Gregg Malott, Chief Financial Officer
CMO: Rex Allman, M.D., President Medical Staff
CIO: Jeff Boer, Director Information Technology
CHR: Mark Fenn, Director Human Resources
CNO: Linda Webb, R.N., Chief Nursing Executive
Web address: www.pmhnet.com
Control: County, Government, nonfederal **Service**: General medical and surgical

Staffed Beds: 25 **Admissions**: 629 **Census**: 9 **Outpatient Visits**: 27887 **Births**: 82 **Total Expense ($000)**: 34428 **Payroll Expense ($000)**: 16326 **Personnel**: 237

WINCHESTER—Randolph County

⊞ **ST. VINCENT RANDOLPH HOSPITAL (151301)**, 473 Greenville Avenue, Zip 47394–9436; tel. 765/584–0004, **A**1 10 18 **F**3 13 15 18 28 29 30 31 34 35 40 44 45 50 57 59 64 65 68 75 77 79 81 85 86 87 93 107 110 111 115 119 129 130 131 132 133 135 146 147 148 149 150 154 **S** Ascension Healthcare, Saint Louis, MO
Primary Contact: Carla Fouse, Administrator and Chief Nursing Officer
CFO: John Arthur, Chief Financial Officer
CNO: Carla Fouse, Chief Nursing Officer
Web address: www.stvincent.org
Control: Other not–for–profit (including NFP Corporation) **Service**: General medical and surgical

Staffed Beds: 18 **Admissions**: 532 **Census**: 5 **Outpatient Visits**: 46434 **Births**: 216 **Total Expense ($000)**: 22365 **Payroll Expense ($000)**: 6109 **Personnel**: 93

IN

Many Facility Codes have changed. Please refer to the AHA Guide Code Chart. © 2019 AHA Guide

IOWA

ALBIA—Monroe County

★ **MONROE COUNTY HOSPITAL AND CLINICS (161342)**, 6580 165th Street, Zip 52531–8793; tel. 641/932–2134, **A**10 18 **F**7 11 15 28 29 31 34 40 43 47 50 57 59 77 81 89 93 107 110 114 119 127 128 130 132 133 **S** MercyOne, Clive, IA
Primary Contact: Veronica Fuhs, Chief Executive Officer
Web address: www.mchalbia.com
Control: County, Government, nonfederal **Service**: General medical and surgical

> **Staffed Beds**: 25 **Admissions**: 280 **Census**: 4 **Outpatient Visits**: 47629
> **Births**: 0 **Total Expense ($000)**: 21102 **Payroll Expense ($000)**: 9181
> **Personnel**: 130

ALGONA—Kossuth County

★ **KOSSUTH REGIONAL HEALTH CENTER (161353)**, 1515 South Phillips Street, Zip 50511–3649; tel. 515/295–2451, **A**10 18 **F**11 13 15 17 28 29 30 31 32 34 35 36 40 41 43 50 56 57 59 62 63 64 65 67 68 70 75 76 77 78 81 82 84 86 87 89 92 93 97 107 114 119 127 128 130 131 132 133 146 147 148 149 154 156 **S** Trinity Health, Livonia, MI
Primary Contact: Darlene M. Elbert, R.N., MS, Chief Executive Officer and Chief Nursing Officer
CFO: Jason Feucht, Chief Financial Officer
CMO: Michael Lampe, M.D., Chief of Staff
CIO: Nancy Erickson, Administrator Information Systems
CHR: Paula Seely, Manager Human Resources
CNO: Darlene M Elbert, R.N., MS, Assistant Administrator and Chief Nursing Officer
Web address: www.krhc.com
Control: County, Government, nonfederal **Service**: General medical and surgical

> **Staffed Beds**: 23 **Admissions**: 828 **Census**: 10 **Outpatient Visits**: 30812
> **Births**: 125 **Total Expense ($000)**: 35466 **Payroll Expense ($000)**: 12050
> **Personnel**: 195

AMES—Story County

⊞ △ **MARY GREELEY MEDICAL CENTER (160030)**, 1111 Duff Avenue, Zip 50010–5745; tel. 515/239–2011, **A**1 2 7 10 19 **F**3 7 11 12 13 15 17 18 20 22 26 28 29 30 31 34 35 36 37 38 40 43 45 46 47 48 49 50 53 55 57 58 59 61 62 63 64 65 69 70 72 74 75 76 77 78 79 81 82 84 85 86 87 89 90 92 93 96 98 100 101 102 104 107 108 110 111 114 115 118 119 120 121 123 124 126 129 130 131 132 135 146 147 148 149 156
Primary Contact: Brian Dieter, President and Chief Executive Officer
CFO: Gary Botine, Vice President, Chief Financial Officer
CIO: Scott Carlson, Director
CHR: Betsy V Schoeller, Director Human Resources and Education
Web address: www.mgmc.org
Control: City, Government, nonfederal **Service**: General medical and surgical

> **Staffed Beds**: 190 **Admissions**: 8510 **Census**: 100 **Outpatient Visits**: 153228 **Births**: 1119 **Total Expense ($000)**: 185167 **Payroll Expense ($000)**: 66004 **Personnel**: 1084

ANAMOSA—Jones County

★ **UNITYPOINT HEALTH - JONES REGIONAL MEDICAL CENTER (161306)**, 1795 Highway 64 East, Zip 52205–2112; tel. 319/462–6131, **A**10 18 **F**3 7 8 11 15 28 29 30 31 34 35 40 43 45 50 56 57 59 65 68 71 75 77 78 79 81 82 84 87 90 91 93 96 97 102 104 107 110 111 114 118 119 127 128 129 130 131 132 133 135 144 146 147 148 149 154 156 **S** UnityPoint Health, West Des Moines, IA
Primary Contact: Eric Briesemeister, Chief Executive Officer
CFO: Rachel Von Behren, Director Financial Services
CMO: Victor Salas, M.D., President Medical Staff
CHR: Donna Condry, Director Human Resources
Web address: www.jonesregional.org
Control: Other not–for–profit (including NFP Corporation) **Service**: General medical and surgical

> **Staffed Beds**: 22 **Admissions**: 369 **Census**: 5 **Outpatient Visits**: 87607
> **Births**: 0 **Total Expense ($000)**: 32407 **Payroll Expense ($000)**: 9866
> **Personnel**: 164

ATLANTIC—Cass County

★ **CASS COUNTY MEMORIAL HOSPITAL (161376)**, 1501 East Tenth Street, Zip 50022–1997; tel. 712/243–3250, **A**10 18 **F**3 13 15 28 29 31 34 35 40 45 50 57 59 64 65 70 75 76 77 78 79 81 82 85 93 97 98 101 102 107 108 110 111 115 119 124 127 129 130 131 132 133 135 146 147 148 154 156
Primary Contact: Brett Altman, Chief Executive Officer
COO: Alison Bruckner, Chief Operating Officer
CFO: Abbey Stangl, Chief Financial Officer
CMO: Todd Bean, Chief Medical Officer
CIO: Jeff Osegard, Chief Information Officer
CHR: Denise Coder, Chief Human Resource Officer
Web address: www.casshealth.org
Control: County, Government, nonfederal **Service**: General medical and surgical

> **Staffed Beds**: 29 **Admissions**: 1050 **Census**: 12 **Outpatient Visits**: 96873
> **Births**: 120 **Total Expense ($000)**: 50884 **Payroll Expense ($000)**: 21287
> **Personnel**: 327

AUDUBON—Audubon County

AUDUBON COUNTY MEMORIAL HOSPITAL AND CLINICS (161330), 515 Pacific Street, Zip 50025–1056; tel. 712/563–2611, **A**10 18 **F**3 15 28 31 34 40 43 45 53 57 59 64 67 78 79 81 82 85 93 110 119 127 128 133 135
Primary Contact: Suzanne Cooner, R.N., MSN, Chief Executive Officer
CFO: Melinda Alt, Chief Financial Officer
CMO: James Cunnigham, D.O., Chief of Staff
CIO: Mike Card, Chief Information Officer
CNO: Holly Kjergaard, Chief Nursing Officer
Web address: www.acmhhosp.org
Control: County, Government, nonfederal **Service**: General medical and surgical

> **Staffed Beds**: 25 **Admissions**: 165 **Census**: 2 **Outpatient Visits**: 14840
> **Births**: 0 **Total Expense ($000)**: 13448 **Payroll Expense ($000)**: 6007
> **Personnel**: 96

BELMOND—Wright County

★ ⇑ **IOWA SPECIALTY HOSPITAL-BELMOND (161301)**, 403 1st Street SE, Zip 50421–1201; tel. 641/444–3223, **A**10 18 21 **F**7 11 12 15 28 29 32 34 35 40 43 45 46 50 56 57 59 62 63 64 65 67 68 70 75 77 79 81 82 85 87 89 92 93 96 97 100 101 102 104 107 110 119 127 128 129 130 131 132 133 135 146 148 149 150 154 **S** Iowa Specialty Hospitals, Clarion, IA
Primary Contact: Amy McDaniel, Chief Executive Officer
CFO: Greg Polzin, Chief Financial Officer
CMO: Charles B Brindle, M.D., Chief Medical Staff
CHR: Holly Martin, Director Human Resource
CNO: Lisa Weatherwax, R.N., Chief Nursing Officer
Web address: www.iowaspecialtyhospital.com
Control: City, Government, nonfederal **Service**: General medical and surgical

> **Staffed Beds**: 22 **Admissions**: 474 **Census**: 3 **Outpatient Visits**: 43598
> **Births**: 0 **Total Expense ($000)**: 27267 **Payroll Expense ($000)**: 7565
> **Personnel**: 152

BETTENDORF—Scott County

⊞ **UNITYPOINT HEALTH - TRINITY BETTENDORF (160104)**, 4500 Utica Ridge Road, Zip 52722–1626; tel. 563/742–5000, **A**1 10 **F**3 11 13 15 18 20 22 24 26 29 30 34 35 37 40 44 45 46 48 50 57 59 64 68 70 73 74 75 76 79 81 82 85 86 87 89 93 96 97 102 104 107 108 110 114 119 130 132 135 146 147 148 149 150 154 157 **S** UnityPoint Health, West Des Moines, IA
Primary Contact: John C. Sheehan, FACHE, Interim President and Chief Executive Officer
COO: Jay Willsher, Chief Operating Officer
CFO: Greg Pagliuzza, Chief Financial Officer
CMO: Paul McLoone, M.D., Chief Medical Officer
CHR: Cara Fuller, Vice President Human Resources
CNO: Jean B Doerge, MS, R.N., Chief Nursing Executive
Web address: www.trinityqc.com
Control: Other not–for–profit (including NFP Corporation) **Service**: General medical and surgical

> **Staffed Beds**: 86 **Admissions**: 4702 **Census**: 37 **Outpatient Visits**: 81826
> **Births**: 972 **Total Expense ($000)**: 82488 **Payroll Expense ($000)**: 23621
> **Personnel**: 462

IA

BLOOMFIELD—Davis County

★ **DAVIS COUNTY HOSPITAL (161327)**, 509 North Madison Street, Zip 52537–1271; tel. 641/664–2145, **A**10 18 **F**3 7 11 15 28 29 34 35 40 44 45 50 57 59 63 64 65 69 75 79 81 84 85 86 87 97 107 110 111 115 119 127 132 133 135 146 **S** MercyOne, Clive, IA
Primary Contact: Veronica Fuhs, Chief Executive Officer
CFO: Kendra Warning, Chief Financial Officer
CMO: Robert Floyd, D.O., Chief Medical Staff
CIO: Kendra Warning, Chief Financial Officer
CHR: Pam Young, Director Human Resources
CNO: Susan Kay Pankey, Chief Nursing Officer
Web address: www.daviscountyhospital.org
Control: County, Government, nonfederal **Service:** General medical and surgical

Staffed Beds: 13 **Admissions:** 235 **Census:** 2 **Outpatient Visits:** 41632 **Births:** 0 **Total Expense ($000):** 24567 **Payroll Expense ($000):** 9473 **Personnel:** 163

BOONE—Boone County

★ **BOONE COUNTY HOSPITAL (161372)**, 1015 Union Street, Zip 50036–4821; tel. 515/432–3140, **A**10 18 **F**2 3 7 11 13 15 28 29 30 31 34 35 40 43 45 50 56 57 59 62 64 65 69 70 75 76 77 78 79 81 82 85 86 87 89 91 93 97 107 110 111 114 119 131 132 133 134 145 146 147 148 156 **S** QHR, Brentwood, TN
Primary Contact: Joseph S. Smith, Chief Executive Officer
CFO: Joseph Devin, Chief Financial Officer
CMO: Brian Mehlhaus, M.D., Chief of Staff
CIO: Paul Sliva, Chief Information Officer
CHR: Kim Schwartz, Assistant Administrator Human Resources and Operations
Web address: www.boonehospital.com
Control: County, Government, nonfederal **Service:** General medical and surgical

Staffed Beds: 25 **Admissions:** 1030 **Census:** 11 **Outpatient Visits:** 79255 **Births:** 125 **Total Expense ($000):** 46448 **Payroll Expense ($000):** 19897 **Personnel:** 361

BRITT—Hancock County

★ **HANCOCK COUNTY HEALTH SYSTEM (161307)**, 532 First Street NW, Zip 50423–1227; tel. 641/843–5000, **A**10 18 **F**3 15 29 34 35 36 40 43 45 46 50 53 56 57 59 62 64 65 75 77 81 82 85 93 97 100 104 107 110 114 119 129 130 131 132 133 135 146 148 154 156 **S** Trinity Health, Livonia, MI
Primary Contact: Laura Zwiefel, Chief Executive Officer
CFO: Julie Damm, Chief Financial Officer
CMO: Catherine Butler, M.D., Chief Medical Staff
CIO: Julie Damm, Chief Financial Officer
CHR: Denise Jakoubeck, Director Human Resources
Web address: www.trusthchs.com/hancock-county-health-system
Control: County, Government, nonfederal **Service:** General medical and surgical

Staffed Beds: 25 **Admissions:** 446 **Census:** 9 **Outpatient Visits:** 20961 **Births:** 0 **Total Expense ($000):** 24902 **Payroll Expense ($000):** 8224 **Personnel:** 173

CARROLL—Carroll County

★ **ST. ANTHONY REGIONAL HOSPITAL (160005)**, 311 South Clark Street, Zip 51401–3038, Mailing Address: P.O. Box 628, Zip 51401–0628; tel. 712/792–3581, (Total facility includes 79 beds in nursing home–type unit) **A**10 20 **F**6 11 13 15 28 29 30 31 34 35 37 38 39 40 43 44 45 46 57 59 60 61 62 63 64 65 67 68 69 70 74 75 76 77 78 79 81 82 84 85 86 87 89 93 97 98 100 101 102 103 104 107 108 110 111 115 118 119 120 121 122 123 125 126 127 129 130 131 132 133 134 135 145 146 147 148 156
Primary Contact: Edward H. Smith, President and Chief Executive Officer
CFO: John Munson, Vice President and Chief Financial Officer
CMO: Kyle Ulveling, M.D., Chief of Staff
CIO: Chad Lawson, Chief Information Officer
CHR: Anna Fitzpatrick, Director Human Resources
CNO: Karen Timm, R.N., MSN, Vice President Patient Services
Web address: www.stanthonyhospital.org
Control: Church operated, Nongovernment, not–for–profit **Service:** General medical and surgical

Staffed Beds: 155 **Admissions:** 2139 **Census:** 106 **Outpatient Visits:** 121078 **Births:** 358 **Total Expense ($000):** 78563 **Payroll Expense ($000):** 34226 **Personnel:** 597

CEDAR FALLS—Black Hawk County

⊞ **MERCYONE CEDAR FALLS MEDICAL CENTER (160040)**, 515 College Street, Zip 50613–2500; tel. 319/268–3000, **A**1 10 **F**3 7 8 11 12 15 29 30 35 40 43 44 46 53 57 59 64 68 70 75 77 79 81 91 93 97 98 103 107 110 111 119 130 131 132 146 **S** Trinity Health, Livonia, MI
Primary Contact: MaryJo Kavalier, Administrator
CFO: Timothy Huber, Vice President and Chief Financial Officer
CMO: James Lehman, M.D., Vice President Medical Affairs
CNO: Kelly Richards, MSN, Senior Vice President and Chief Nursing Officer
Web address: www.wheatoniowa.org
Control: Church operated, Nongovernment, not–for–profit **Service:** General medical and surgical

Staffed Beds: 50 **Admissions:** 1294 **Census:** 17 **Outpatient Visits:** 40383 **Births:** 0 **Total Expense ($000):** 36257 **Payroll Expense ($000):** 11464 **Personnel:** 175

CEDAR RAPIDS—Linn County

⊞ **MERCY MEDICAL CENTER - CEDAR RAPIDS (160079)**, 701 Tenth Street SE, Zip 52403–1292; tel. 319/398–6011, (Total facility includes 76 beds in nursing home–type unit) **A**1 2 3 10 **F**3 5 11 12 13 15 18 19 20 22 24 26 28 29 30 31 32 34 35 37 38 40 43 44 45 46 48 49 50 51 54 55 56 57 58 59 60 61 62 63 64 65 67 68 70 72 74 75 76 77 78 79 81 82 84 85 86 87 88 89 90 91 92 93 96 98 99 100 101 102 103 104 107 108 109 110 114 115 116 117 118 119 120 121 123 124 126 128 130 131 132 134 135 145 146 147 148 149 150 153 154
Primary Contact: Timothy L. Charles, President and Chief Executive Officer
CFO: Nathan Van Genderen, Executive Vice President and Chief Financial Officer
CMO: Tim Quinn, M.D., Executive Vice President and Chief of Clinical Operations and President Mercy Care Management
CIO: Jeff Cash, Senior Vice President and Chief Information Officer
CHR: Doug Jontz, Senior Vice President Human Resources
CNO: Mary Brobst, R.N., MSN, Senior Vice President Patient Care Services and Chief Nursing Officer
Web address: www.mercycare.org
Control: Church operated, Nongovernment, not–for–profit **Service:** General medical and surgical

Staffed Beds: 302 **Admissions:** 11012 **Census:** 168 **Outpatient Visits:** 357146 **Births:** 830 **Total Expense ($000):** 321957 **Payroll Expense ($000):** 126353 **Personnel:** 1872

ST. LUKE'S HOSPITAL See Unitypoint Health - St. Luke's Hospital

⊞ △ **UNITYPOINT HEALTH - ST. LUKE'S HOSPITAL (160045)**, 1026 'A' Avenue NE, Zip 52402–3026, Mailing Address: P.O. Box 3026, Zip 52406–3026; tel. 319/369–7211, **A**1 2 3 5 7 10 **F**3 5 11 12 13 15 17 18 19 20 22 24 26 28 29 30 31 32 34 35 36 37 39 40 43 45 46 49 50 54 55 56 57 59 60 61 62 63 64 65 66 68 70 72 74 75 76 77 78 79 81 82 84 85 86 87 89 90 91 92 93 95 96 98 99 100 101 103 104 105 107 108 110 115 117 118 119 120 121 123 124 126 130 131 132 134 135 145 146 147 148 149 152 153 154 155 157 **S** UnityPoint Health, West Des Moines, IA
Primary Contact: Michelle Niermann, President and Chief Executive Officer
COO: Casey Greene, Vice President and Chief Operating Officer
CFO: Michael G. Heinrich, Senior Vice President and Chief Financial Officer
CMO: Dustin Arnold, D.O., Chief Medical Officer
CHR: Susan L Slattery, Director Human Resources
CNO: Carmen Kleinsmith, MSN, R.N., Vice President, Chief Nurse Executive
Web address: www.unitypoint.org
Control: Other not–for–profit (including NFP Corporation) **Service:** General medical and surgical

Staffed Beds: 345 **Admissions:** 16357 **Census:** 204 **Outpatient Visits:** 517936 **Births:** 2400 **Total Expense ($000):** 360665 **Payroll Expense ($000):** 123196 **Personnel:** 2396

CENTERVILLE—Appanoose County

★ **MERCYONE CENTERVILLE MEDICAL CENTER (161377)**, 1 St Joseph's Drive, Zip 52544–8055; tel. 641/437–4111, (Total facility includes 19 beds in nursing home–type unit) **A**10 18 **F**1 3 4 8 11 15 16 17 28 29 30 31 34 40 45 46 50 54 57 59 64 67 70 72 73 75 77 78 80 81 85 86 87 88 89 90 93 97 98 107 110 111 113 115 117 119 127 128 129 130 132 133 135 156 157 **S** CommonSpirit Health, Chicago, IL
Primary Contact: Matthew Johnson, President
CHR: Tonya Clawson, Manager Human Resources
CNO: Sherri L Doggett, Vice President Patient Services
Web address: www.mercycenterville.org
Control: Church operated, Nongovernment, not–for–profit **Service:** General medical and surgical

Staffed Beds: 44 **Admissions:** 370 **Census:** 22 **Outpatient Visits:** 92866 **Births:** 0 **Total Expense ($000):** 27666 **Payroll Expense ($000):** 11727 **Personnel:** 197

CHARITON—Lucas County

★ **LUCAS COUNTY HEALTH CENTER (161341)**, 1200 North Seventh Street, Zip 50049–1258; tel. 641/774–3000, **A**10 18 **F**3 11 15 28 29 30 31 34 40 43 44 45 46 47 50 55 64 66 70 75 81 85 87 93 97 107 110 115 119 127 130 131 132 133 143 145 146 148 156 **S** UnityPoint Health, West Des Moines, IA
Primary Contact: Brian Sims, Chief Executive Officer
CMO: David Marcowitz, M.D., Chief of Staff
CIO: Terri Black, Network Manager
CHR: Lana Kuball, Director Administrative Services
CNO: JoBeth Lawless, Chief Nursing Officer, Nursing Services and Director Emergency Management Services
Web address: www.lchcia.com
Control: County, Government, nonfederal **Service**: General medical and surgical

Staffed Beds: 25 **Admissions**: 337 **Census**: 4 **Outpatient Visits**: 19258 **Births**: 74 **Total Expense ($000)**: 20374 **Payroll Expense ($000)**: 9349 **Personnel**: 182

CHARLES CITY—Floyd County

FLOYD COUNTY MEDICAL CENTER (161347), 800 Eleventh Street, Zip 50616–3499; tel. 641/228–6830, **A**10 18 **F**11 13 15 28 29 34 35 40 45 57 59 64 75 79 81 86 91 93 107 115 119 127 130 132 146 148 149 154 156 **S** Mayo Clinic, Rochester, MN
Primary Contact: Rod Nordeng, Administrator
CFO: Ron Timpe, Chief Financial Officer
CHR: Don Nosbisch, Director Human Resources
CNO: Viva Boerschel, Director of Nursing
Web address: www.fcmc.us.com/
Control: County, Government, nonfederal **Service**: General medical and surgical

Staffed Beds: 25 **Admissions**: 611 **Census**: 9 **Outpatient Visits**: 57732 **Births**: 76 **Total Expense ($000)**: 27889 **Payroll Expense ($000)**: 11306 **Personnel**: 179

CHEROKEE—Cherokee County

★ **CHEROKEE REGIONAL MEDICAL CENTER (161362)**, 300 Sioux Valley Drive, Zip 51012–1205; tel. 712/225–5101, **A**10 18 **F**7 11 13 15 17 28 29 34 35 40 43 45 53 56 57 59 62 63 64 65 67 68 69 75 76 77 78 81 84 86 87 89 93 96 97 107 111 114 119 125 129 130 131 132 133 135 146 147 148 154 156 **S** UnityPoint Health, West Des Moines, IA
Primary Contact: Gary W. Jordan, FACHE, Chief Executive Officer
CFO: Joan Bierman, Vice President Finance
CIO: Kevin Naslund, Manager Information Technology
CHR: Theresa Conley, Manager Human Resources
CNO: Christy Syndergaard, Vice President Nursing
Web address: www.cherokeermc.org
Control: Other not–for–profit (including NFP Corporation) **Service**: General medical and surgical

Staffed Beds: 25 **Admissions**: 914 **Census**: 9 **Outpatient Visits**: 52163 **Births**: 126 **Total Expense ($000)**: 24664 **Payroll Expense ($000)**: 10742 **Personnel**: 176

☐ **MENTAL HEALTH INSTITUTE (164002)**, 1251 West Cedar Loop, Zip 51012–1599; tel. 712/225–2594, **A**1 10 **F**29 30 68 75 98 99 100 101 130 135 149
Primary Contact: Chris Tosteberg, Superintendent
CFO: Tony Morris, Business Manager
CHR: Mary Ann Hanson, Director Personnel
Web address: www.dhs.state.ia.us
Control: State, Government, nonfederal **Service**: Psychiatric

Staffed Beds: 36 **Admissions**: 358 **Census**: 31 **Outpatient Visits**: 62 **Births**: 0 **Total Expense ($000)**: 15611 **Payroll Expense ($000)**: 8686 **Personnel**: 140

CLARINDA—Page County

★ **CLARINDA REGIONAL HEALTH CENTER (161352)**, 220 Essie Davison Drive, Zip 51632–2915, Mailing Address: P.O. Box 217, Zip 51632–0217; tel. 712/542–2176, **A**10 18 **F**3 7 11 15 28 29 31 34 36 40 43 50 57 59 64 65 69 75 79 81 85 86 87 93 97 107 110 111 114 118 119 127 128 129 130 133 135 143 146 148 150 152 154 155 156 **S** Bryan Health, Lincoln, NE
Primary Contact: Charles Nordyke, Chief Executive Officer
COO: Elaine Otte, Chief Operating Officer
CFO: Milton Trabal, Chief Financial Officer
CMO: Autumn Morales, Chief Medical Staff Officer
CIO: Richard Morgan-Fine, IT Director
CHR: Melissa Walter, Director Human Resources
CNO: Sherrie L Laubenthal, R.N., Chief Nursing Officer
Web address: www.clarindahealth.com
Control: City, Government, nonfederal **Service**: General medical and surgical

Staffed Beds: 25 **Admissions**: 435 **Census**: 4 **Outpatient Visits**: 66813 **Births**: 0 **Total Expense ($000)**: 32579 **Payroll Expense ($000)**: 12080 **Personnel**: 204

CLARION—Wright County

★ ⇑ **IOWA SPECIALTY HOSPITAL-CLARION (161302)**, 1316 South Main Street, Zip 50525–2019; tel. 515/532–2811, **A**10 18 21 **F**11 13 15 28 29 31 32 34 35 40 43 45 46 50 56 57 59 63 64 65 68 69 71 75 76 77 79 81 82 85 86 87 92 93 96 97 102 110 111 116 119 125 127 130 131 132 133 134 135 146 147 148 149 154 156 **S** Iowa Specialty Hospitals, Clarion, IA
Primary Contact: Steven J. Simonin, President and Chief Executive Officer
COO: Kirk Rier, Chief Operating Officer
CFO: Greg Polzin, Chief Financial Officer
CMO: Dennis Colby, M.D., Chief of Staff
CHR: Holly Martin, Human Resources Leader
CNO: Abby Young, Chief Nursing Officer
Web address: www.iowaspecialtyhospital.com
Control: City, Government, nonfederal **Service**: General medical and surgical

Staffed Beds: 25 **Admissions**: 1177 **Census**: 9 **Outpatient Visits**: 57123 **Births**: 364 **Total Expense ($000)**: 54378 **Payroll Expense ($000)**: 19751 **Personnel**: 327

CLINTON—Clinton County

⊞ **MERCYONE CLINTON MEDICAL CENTER (160080)**, 1410 North Fourth Street, Zip 52732–2940; tel. 563/244–5555, (Includes MERCY SERVICES FOR AGING, 600 14th Avenue North, Clinton, Iowa, Zip 52732; tel. 563/244–3888) (Total facility includes 86 beds in nursing home–type unit) **A**1 10 **F**3 11 13 15 18 20 22 28 29 30 31 34 35 36 38 40 44 45 47 49 50 53 56 57 59 60 61 62 63 64 68 70 74 75 76 77 78 79 80 81 82 84 85 87 89 93 98 100 101 102 107 108 110 111 115 118 119 121 123 128 129 130 132 146 148 **S** Trinity Health, Livonia, MI
Primary Contact: Amy Berentes, R.N., MSN, Executive Vice President and Chief Operating Officer
CFO: Paul Mangin, Vice President Finance
CHR: Shane Buer, Vice President, Human Resources
CNO: Amy Berentes, R.N., MSN, Vice President Patient Care Services
Web address: www.mercyclinton.com
Control: Church operated, Nongovernment, not–for–profit **Service**: General medical and surgical

Staffed Beds: 193 **Admissions**: 4064 **Census**: 148 **Outpatient Visits**: 70408 **Births**: 377 **Total Expense ($000)**: 102326 **Payroll Expense ($000)**: 41862 **Personnel**: 730

CLIVE—Polk County

☐ **MERCYONE CLIVE REHABILITATION HOSPITAL (163025)**, 1401 Campus Drive, Zip 50325–6500; tel. 515/381–6519. (Data for 203 days) **A**1 10 **F**3 29 30 56 90 94 95 96 132 143 148
Primary Contact: Nicole Nigg, Chief Executive Officer
Web address: www.mercydesmoines.org
Control: Partnership, Investor–owned (for–profit) **Service**: Rehabilitation

Staffed Beds: 50 **Admissions**: 282 **Census**: 15 **Outpatient Visits**: 0 **Births**: 0 **Total Expense ($000)**: 5849 **Payroll Expense ($000)**: 3146 **Personnel**: 102

CORALVILLE—Johnson County

IOWA MEDICAL AND CLASSIFICATION CENTER, 2700 Coral Ridge Avenue, Zip 52241–4708, Mailing Address: 2700 Coral Rigde Avenue, Zip 52241; tel. 319/626–2391, **F**29 30 38 39 59 75 98 101 102 103 130 132 143 154
Primary Contact: James McKinney, Warden
Web address: www.oakdaleprison.com/
Control: State, Government, nonfederal **Service**: Psychiatric

Staffed Beds: 20 **Admissions**: 92 **Census**: 12 **Outpatient Visits**: 0 **Births**: 0 **Personnel**: 26

CORNING—Adams County

★ **CHI HEALTH MERCY CORNING (161304)**, 603 Rosary Drive, Zip 50841–1683; tel. 641/322–3121, **A**10 18 **F**3 11 15 28 30 31 34 40 43 46 50 53 56 57 59 64 67 69 74 75 77 78 79 81 85 89 90 97 107 110 115 119 127 128 129 130 132 133 135 146 147 148 149 154 156 157 **S** CommonSpirit Health, Chicago, IL
Primary Contact: Lisa Wolfe, President
CMO: Maen Haddadin, M.D., President Medical Staff
CIO: Kenneth Lawonn, Senior Vice President and Chief Information Officer
CHR: Sandra Lammers, Coordinator Human Resources and Finance
Web address: www.alegent.com
Control: Church operated, Nongovernment, not–for–profit **Service**: General medical and surgical

Staffed Beds: 22 **Admissions**: 161 **Census**: 2 **Outpatient Visits**: 20341 **Births**: 0 **Total Expense ($000)**: 14588 **Payroll Expense ($000)**: 4437 **Personnel**: 78

IA

Hospital, Medicare Provider Number, Address, Telephone, Approval, Facility, and Physician Codes, Health Care System

★ American Hospital Association (AHA) membership
☐ The Joint Commission accreditation
○ Healthcare Facilities Accreditation Program
◇ DNV Healthcare Inc. accreditation
⇑ Center for Improvement in Healthcare Quality Accreditation
△ Commission on Accreditation of Rehabilitation Facilities (CARF) accreditation

CORYDON—Wayne County

★ ○ **WAYNE COUNTY HOSPITAL (161358)**, 417 South East Street, Zip 50060–1860, Mailing Address: P.O. Box 305, Zip 50060–0305; tel. 641/872–2260, **A**10 11 18 **F**7 13 15 28 29 31 34 35 40 43 51 56 57 59 60 64 69 70 75 76 77 78 79 81 85 87 89 91 92 93 97 107 110 115 119 126 127 130 131 133 148 149 154 **S** MercyOne, Clive, IA
Primary Contact: Daren Relph, Chief Executive Officer
COO: Michael Thomas, Associate Administrator
CFO: Diane Hook, Chief Financial Officer
CMO: Joel Baker, D.O., Chief Medical Officer
CIO: Laurie Ehrich, Chief Communications Officer
CHR: Dave Carlyle, Director Human Resources
CNO: Sheila Mattly, Chief Nursing Officer
Web address: www.waynecountyhospital.org
Control: County, Government, nonfederal **Service:** General medical and surgical

> **Staffed Beds:** 25 **Admissions:** 631 **Census:** 6 **Outpatient Visits:** 29029
> **Births:** 158 **Total Expense ($000):** 31224 **Payroll Expense ($000):** 12707
> **Personnel:** 202

COUNCIL BLUFFS—Pottawattamie County

⊠ **CHI HEALTH MERCY COUNCIL BLUFFS (160028)**, 800 Mercy Drive, Zip 51503–3128; tel. 712/328–5000, **A**1 2 10 **F**3 11 13 15 18 20 22 26 28 29 30 31 34 35 37 40 41 43 45 47 48 49 50 57 59 68 70 72 74 76 77 78 79 81 82 84 85 87 89 91 93 98 99 100 101 102 104 105 107 108 110 111 114 115 119 126 129 130 132 146 147 154 **S** CommonSpirit Health, Chicago, IL
Primary Contact: Ann Schumacher, R.N., MSN, FACHE, President
CFO: Jeanette Wojtalewicz, Chief Financial Officer
CMO: Joseph Hoagbin, M.D., Chief Quality Officer
CIO: Thomas Haley, Information Technology Services Site Director
CHR: Nancy Wallace, Senior Vice President Human Resources
Web address: www.chihealth.com/chi-health-mercy-council-bluffs
Control: Church operated, Nongovernment, not–for–profit **Service:** General medical and surgical

> **Staffed Beds:** 148 **Admissions:** 6943 **Census:** 70 **Outpatient Visits:** 80522
> **Births:** 310 **Total Expense ($000):** 93352 **Payroll Expense ($000):** 29967
> **Personnel:** 433

JENNIE EDMUNDSON HOSPITAL See Methodist Jennie Edmundson Hospital

⊠ **METHODIST JENNIE EDMUNDSON HOSPITAL (160047)**, 933 East Pierce Street, Zip 51503–4652, Mailing Address: P.O. Box 2C, Zip 51502–3002; tel. 712/396–6000, **A**1 2 3 5 10 **F**3 11 13 15 18 20 22 26 28 29 30 31 34 35 39 40 43 44 45 47 49 50 57 58 59 61 64 68 70 74 75 76 78 79 81 82 85 86 87 89 92 93 98 100 101 102 107 108 110 111 115 118 119 120 121 123 124 126 129 130 131 132 135 143 145 146 147 148 149 **S** Nebraska Methodist Health System, Inc., Omaha, NE
Primary Contact: Steven P. Baumert, President and Chief Executive Officer
CFO: Jeffrey Francis, Vice President Finance and Chief Financial Officer
CMO: Scott Bomgaars, M.D., Vice President Medical Affairs
CIO: Steven Zuber, Vice President
CHR: Holly Huerter, Vice President Human Resources
CNO: Peggy Helget, R.N., MSN, Vice President Patient Services and Chief Nursing Officer
Web address: www.bestcare.org
Control: Other not–for–profit (including NFP Corporation) **Service:** General medical and surgical

> **Staffed Beds:** 114 **Admissions:** 5777 **Census:** 63 **Outpatient Visits:** 62364
> **Births:** 593 **Total Expense ($000):** 105112 **Payroll Expense ($000):** 41638
> **Personnel:** 599

CRESCO—Howard County

★ **REGIONAL HEALTH SERVICES OF HOWARD COUNTY (161328)**, 235 Eighth Avenue West, Zip 52136–1098; tel. 563/547–2101, **A**10 18 **F**3 7 11 13 15 28 29 34 35 36 38 40 41 43 44 45 50 53 56 57 59 62 63 64 65 76 81 82 85 87 89 96 104 107 110 115 119 127 128 130 132 133 146 147 148 149 150 154 156 **S** Trinity Health, Livonia, MI
Primary Contact: Robin M. Schluter, Chief Executive Officer
CFO: Greg Burkel, Chief Financial Officer
CMO: Paul Jensen, M.D., Chief of Staff
CIO: Greg Burkel, Chief Financial Officer
CHR: Jennalee Pedretti, Vice President Operations
CNO: Carol Kerian-Masters, RN, Chief Nursing Officer
Web address: www.rhshc.com
Control: County, Government, nonfederal **Service:** General medical and surgical

> **Staffed Beds:** 19 **Admissions:** 253 **Census:** 3 **Outpatient Visits:** 23530
> **Births:** 57 **Total Expense ($000):** 21510 **Payroll Expense ($000):** 8088
> **Personnel:** 160

CRESTON—Union County

★ ⇑ **GREATER REGIONAL MEDICAL CENTER (161365)**, 1700 West Townline Street Suite 3, Zip 50801–1099; tel. 641/782–7091, **A**10 18 21 **F**3 7 8 11 13 15 28 29 31 34 35 40 43 44 45 47 48 50 51 56 57 59 64 65 66 70 75 76 77 78 79 81 82 85 86 93 96 97 102 104 107 108 110 111 115 119 120 121 122 123 124 125 127 128 129 131 132 133 146 147 148 149 156 **S** UnityPoint Health, West Des Moines, IA
Primary Contact: Monte Neitzel, Chief Executive Officer
CFO: Matt McCutchan, Chief Financial Officer
CMO: Steve Reeves, M.D., Chief Medical Staff
CIO: Karla Alford, Chief Information Officer
CHR: Amy Rieck, Human Resources Officer
CNO: Amanda Mohr, Chief Nursing Officer
Web address: www.greaterregional.org
Control: County, Government, nonfederal **Service:** General medical and surgical

> **Staffed Beds:** 25 **Admissions:** 842 **Census:** 7 **Outpatient Visits:** 120658
> **Births:** 167 **Total Expense ($000):** 57437 **Payroll Expense ($000):** 24908
> **Personnel:** 382

DAVENPORT—Scott County

⊠ △ **GENESIS MEDICAL CENTER, DAVENPORT (160033)**, 1227 East Rusholme Street, Zip 52803–2498; tel. 563/421–1000, (Includes GENESIS MEDICAL CENTER-EAST CAMPUS, 1227 East Rusholme Street, Davenport, Iowa, Zip 52803; tel. 563/421–1000; GENESIS MEDICAL CENTER-WEST CAMPUS, 1401 West Central Park, Davenport, Iowa, Zip 52804–1769; tel. 563/421–1000) **A**1 2 3 5 7 10 **F**3 7 11 12 13 15 17 18 20 22 24 26 28 29 30 31 34 35 37 38 40 43 44 46 49 50 53 54 57 58 59 63 64 68 70 72 74 75 76 77 78 79 81 82 84 85 86 87 89 90 91 92 93 94 96 97 98 100 102 107 111 114 115 118 119 120 121 123 124 126 129 130 131 132 135 146 147 148 153 154 156 157 **S** Genesis Health System, Davenport, IA
Primary Contact: Jordan Voigt, Administrator
CFO: Mark G Rogers, Interim Vice President Finance and Chief Financial Officer
CMO: Frank Claudy, M.D., Vice President Medical Staff Affairs
CIO: Robert Frieden, Vice President Information Systems
CHR: Heidi Kahly-McMahon, Interim Vice President Human Resources
Web address: www.genesishealth.com
Control: Other not–for–profit (including NFP Corporation) **Service:** General medical and surgical

> **Staffed Beds:** 368 **Admissions:** 19705 **Census:** 198 **Outpatient Visits:** 212291 **Births:** 1884 **Total Expense ($000):** 343901 **Payroll Expense ($000):** 92598 **Personnel:** 1256

⊠ **SELECT SPECIALTY HOSPITAL-QUAD CITIES (162001)**, 1111 West Kimberly Road, Zip 52806–5711; tel. 563/468–2000, **A**1 10 **F**1 3 29 45 75 85 119 130 148 **S** Select Medical Corporation, Mechanicsburg, PA
Primary Contact: Codie Dillie, Chief Executive Officer
Web address: www.selectmedicalcorp.com
Control: Corporation, Investor–owned (for–profit) **Service:** Acute long–term care hospital

> **Staffed Beds:** 50 **Admissions:** 313 **Census:** 22 **Outpatient Visits:** 0
> **Births:** 0 **Total Expense ($000):** 15236 **Payroll Expense ($000):** 6199
> **Personnel:** 110

DE WITT—Clinton County

⊠ **GENESIS MEDICAL CENTER, DEWITT (161313)**, 1118 11th Street, Zip 52742–1296; tel. 563/659–4200, (Total facility includes 75 beds in nursing home–type unit) **A**1 10 18 **F**3 7 8 11 15 28 29 30 34 35 38 40 41 43 44 45 49 50 53 57 59 64 68 69 77 79 81 82 85 86 87 93 96 102 107 110 115 119 129 130 131 132 133 146 148 149 154 **S** Genesis Health System, Davenport, IA
Primary Contact: Curt Coleman, FACHE, Chief Executive Officer
CMO: Steven Fowler, M.D., President Medical Staff
CHR: Kristin Nicholson, Coordinator Human Resources
CNO: Wanda Haack, MSN, R.N., Chief Nursing Officer
Web address: www.genesishealth.com
Control: Other not–for–profit (including NFP Corporation) **Service:** General medical and surgical

> **Staffed Beds:** 88 **Admissions:** 345 **Census:** 69 **Outpatient Visits:** 21287
> **Births:** 0 **Total Expense ($000):** 20652 **Payroll Expense ($000):** 7954
> **Personnel:** 78

IA

DECORAH—Winneshiek County

⊞ **WINNESHIEK MEDICAL CENTER (161371)**, 901 Montgomery Street, Zip 52101–2325; tel. 563/382–2911, **A**1 10 18 **F**3 7 8 11 13 15 28 29 31 34 35 36 38 40 43 44 45 50 56 57 59 61 62 63 64 65 68 69 75 76 77 78 79 81 82 86 87 93 94 97 101 102 104 106 107 111 115 119 128 129 130 131 132 133 135 144 146 147 148 149 153 156 **S** Mayo Clinic, Rochester, MN
Primary Contact: Lisa Radtke, Chief Administrative Officer
COO: David Rooney, Administrator Operations
CFO: Lynn Luloff, Chief Financial Officer
CMO: Robert Flinchbaugh, D.O., Chief Medical Officer
CHR: Laurie Bulman, Director Human Resources
Web address: www.winmedical.org
Control: County, Government, nonfederal **Service**: General medical and surgical

Staffed Beds: 25 **Admissions**: 983 **Census**: 11 **Outpatient Visits**: 111887
Births: 243 **Total Expense ($000)**: 63142 **Payroll Expense ($000)**: 21552
Personnel: 387

DENISON—Crawford County

★ **CRAWFORD COUNTY MEMORIAL HOSPITAL (161369)**, 100 Medical Parkway, Zip 51442–2299; tel. 712/265–2500, **A**10 18 **F**3 7 8 11 13 15 17 28 29 31 34 35 40 45 50 54 56 57 59 64 65 67 68 70 75 76 77 78 79 81 82 85 87 89 93 97 101 104 107 110 111 115 119 127 128 133 135 143 148 156
Primary Contact: Bill Bruce, FACHE, Chief Executive Officer
CFO: Rachel Melby, Vice President, Chief Financial Officer
CIO: Angie Anderson, Director Information Technology
CHR: Brad L. Bonner, Executive Director, Human Resources and General Counsel
CNO: Erin Muck, Vice President, Clinical Nursing
Web address: www.ccmhia.com
Control: County, Government, nonfederal **Service**: General medical and surgical

Staffed Beds: 25 **Admissions**: 619 **Census**: 5 **Outpatient Visits**: 49347
Births: 120 **Total Expense ($000)**: 37496 **Payroll Expense ($000)**: 17003
Personnel: 251

DES MOINES—Polk County

⊞ **BROADLAWNS MEDICAL CENTER (160101)**, 1801 Hickman Road, Zip 50314–1597; tel. 515/282–2200, **A**1 3 5 10 **F**3 5 11 13 15 18 29 30 31 32 34 35 38 39 40 43 44 45 48 50 52 53 56 57 58 59 64 65 66 68 70 74 75 76 77 78 79 81 82 85 86 87 92 93 94 97 98 99 100 101 102 103 104 105 106 107 111 114 119 127 129 130 131 132 135 144 146 147 148 153 154 156
Primary Contact: Jody J. Jenner, President and Chief Executive Officer
CFO: Karlis Viluma, Chief Financial Officer
CMO: Vincent Mandracchia, DPM, Chief Medical Officer
CHR: Julie Kilgore, Vice President, Human Resources
CNO: Susan N. Kirstein, R.N., MSN, Chief Nursing Officer
Web address: www.broadlawns.org
Control: County, Government, nonfederal **Service**: General medical and surgical

Staffed Beds: 135 **Admissions**: 2881 **Census**: 59 **Outpatient Visits**: 263562 **Births**: 408 **Total Expense ($000)**: 175364 **Payroll Expense ($000)**: 83120 **Personnel**: 1055

DES MOINES DIVISION See Veterans Affairs Central Iowa Health Care System, Des Moines

⇑ **IOWA LUTHERAN HOSPITAL** See Unitypoint Health-Iowa Lutheran Hospital

⊞ **MERCYONE DES MOINES MEDICAL CENTER (160083)**, 1111 6th Avenue, Zip 50314–2611; tel. 515/247–3121, (Includes MERCYONE WEST DES MOINES MEDICAL CENTER, 1755 59th Place, West Des Moines, Iowa, Zip 50266–7737; tel. 515/358–8000; Karl Keeler, President) **A**1 2 3 5 10 13 **F**3 5 6 7 8 9 11 12 13 15 17 18 19 20 21 22 23 24 25 26 27 28 29 30 31 32 34 35 36 38 39 40 41 43 44 46 48 49 50 53 54 55 56 57 58 59 60 61 62 63 64 65 66 68 70 71 72 73 74 75 76 77 78 79 81 82 84 85 86 87 88 89 91 92 93 94 96 97 98 99 100 101 102 103 104 105 107 108 109 110 111 114 115 116 117 118 119 120 121 123 124 126 129 130 131 132 134 135 138 141 142 143 144 145 146 147 148 149 150 152 153 154 156 157 158 **S** CommonSpirit Health, Chicago, IL
Primary Contact: Karl Keeler, President
COO: Linda Goodwin, Chief Operating Officer and Chief Nursing Executive
CFO: Randy Rubin, Senior Vice President and Chief Financial Officer
CIO: James Strother, Site Director Information Technology Systems
CHR: Kevin Elsberry, Senior Vice President Human Resources
CNO: Linda Goodwin, Chief Operating Officer and Chief Nursing Executive
Web address: www.mercydesmoines.org
Control: Church operated, Nongovernment, not–for–profit **Service**: General medical and surgical

Staffed Beds: 606 **Admissions**: 32121 **Census**: 445 **Outpatient Visits**: 254769 **Births**: 4230 **Total Expense ($000)**: 726080 **Payroll Expense ($000)**: 267703 **Personnel**: 5896

⊞ **SELECT SPECIALTY HOSPITAL-DES MOINES (162003)**, 1111 6th Avenue, 4th Floor Main, Zip 50314–2610; tel. 515/247–4400, **A**1 10 **F**1 29 75 148 **S** Select Medical Corporation, Mechanicsburg, PA
Primary Contact: Brent Hanson, Chief Executive Officer
Web address: www.selectspecialtyhospitals.com
Control: Corporation, Investor–owned (for–profit) **Service**: Acute long–term care hospital

Staffed Beds: 30 **Admissions**: 307 **Census**: 24 **Outpatient Visits**: 0
Births: 0 **Total Expense ($000)**: 13707 **Payroll Expense ($000)**: 5980
Personnel: 88

★ ⇑ **UNITYPOINT HEALTH-IOWA LUTHERAN HOSPITAL (160024)**, 700 East University Avenue, Zip 50316–2392; tel. 515/263–5612, (Total facility includes 16 beds in nursing home–type unit) **A**5 10 21 **F**3 4 5 8 11 13 15 17 18 20 22 26 28 29 30 34 35 37 38 39 40 43 44 45 49 50 51 53 56 57 58 59 60 61 64 65 68 70 74 75 76 79 81 82 84 85 86 87 91 92 93 95 96 97 98 99 100 101 102 103 104 105 107 108 110 111 114 115 118 119 126 128 130 132 134 135 146 147 148 149 152 153 154 **S** UnityPoint Health, West Des Moines, IA
Primary Contact: David A. Stark, FACHE, President and Chief Executive Officer
COO: Eric L Lothe, FACHE, Senior Vice President and Chief Operating Officer
CMO: Mark Purtle, M.D., Vice President Medical Affairs
CHR: Joyce McDanel, Vice President Human Resources and Education
CNO: Debra Moyer, R.N., Chief Nurse Executive
Web address: www.unitypoint.org
Control: Other not–for–profit (including NFP Corporation) **Service**: General medical and surgical

Staffed Beds: 207 **Admissions**: 8145 **Census**: 119 **Outpatient Visits**: 60456 **Births**: 283 **Total Expense ($000)**: 143826 **Payroll Expense ($000)**: 58621 **Personnel**: 838

★ △ ⇑ **UNITYPOINT HEALTH - IOWA METHODIST MEDICAL CENTER (160082)**, 1200 Pleasant Street, Zip 50309–1406; tel. 515/241–6212, (Includes POWELL CONVALESCENT CENTER, 1200 Pleasant, Des Moines, Iowa, Zip 50309; tel. 515/241–6212; UNITY POINT HEALTH - JOHN STODDARD CANCER CENTER, 1221 Pleasant Street, Des Moines, Iowa, Zip 50309-1423; tel. 515/241–6212; UNITYPOINT HEALTH - BLANK CHILDREN'S HOSPITAL, 1200 Pleasant Street, Des Moines, Iowa, Zip 50309–1406; tel. 515/241–5437; Steve R. Stephenson, M.D., President and Chief Operating Officer; UNITYPOINT HEALTH - METHODIST WEST HOSPITAL, 1660 60th Street, West Des Moines, Iowa, Zip 50266–7700; tel. 515/343–1000; David A. Stark, FACHE, President and Chief Executive Officer; YOUNKER MEMORIAL REHABILITATION CENTER, 1200 Pleasant Road, Des Moines, Iowa, Zip 50308; tel. 515/241–6212) **A**2 3 5 7 10 21 **F**3 7 8 11 12 13 17 18 20 22 24 26 28 29 30 31 32 34 35 39 40 41 43 44 46 47 48 49 50 53 54 55 56 57 58 59 60 61 64 65 68 70 71 72 74 75 76 77 78 79 81 82 84 85 86 87 88 89 90 91 92 93 95 96 97 100 107 108 111 114 115 116 117 118 119 120 121 123 124 126 129 130 131 132 134 135 138 146 147 148 149 154 156 157 **S** UnityPoint Health, West Des Moines, IA
Primary Contact: David A. Stark, FACHE, President and Chief Executive Officer
COO: Eric L Lothe, FACHE, Executive Vice President and Chief Operating Officer
CFO: Michael Dewerff, Chief Financial Officer
CMO: Mark Purtle, M.D., Vice President Medical Affairs
CHR: Joyce McDanel, Vice President Human Resources and Education
CNO: Debra Moyer, R.N., Chief Nursing Executive and Vice President Nursing Services
Web address: www.unitypoint.org
Control: Other not–for–profit (including NFP Corporation) **Service**: General medical and surgical

Staffed Beds: 544 **Admissions**: 27066 **Census**: 378 **Outpatient Visits**: 316625 **Births**: 4903 **Total Expense ($000)**: 631677 **Payroll Expense ($000)**: 266818 **Personnel**: 4262

⊞ △ **VETERANS AFFAIRS CENTRAL IOWA HEALTH CARE SYSTEM**, 3600 30th Street, Zip 50310 5753; tel. 515/699–5999, (Includes DES MOINES DIVISION, 3600 30th Street, Des Moines, Iowa, Zip 50310–5774; tel. 515/699–5999; KNOXVILLE DIVISION, 1515 West Pleasant, Knoxville, Iowa, Zip 50138–3399; tel. 515/842–3101) (Total facility includes 108 beds in nursing home–type unit) **A**1 3 5 7 **F**1 3 4 5 6 8 11 12 15 18 20 22 24 28 29 30 31 33 34 35 36 37 38 39 40 44 45 46 50 53 54 55 56 57 59 61 62 63 64 65 66 70 71 74 75 77 78 79 81 82 83 84 85 86 87 93 94 96 97 98 100 101 102 103 104 106 107 108 110 111 114 115 117 118 119 127 129 130 132 135 137 138 139 140 141 142 143 144 145 147 148 149 153 154 156 157 **S** Department of Veterans Affairs, Washington, DC
Primary Contact: Gail L. Graham, Director
CMO: Fredrick Bahls, M.D., Chief of Staff
CIO: James Danuser, Chief Information Officer
CHR: Sabrina Owen, Human Resources Officer
Web address: www.centraliowa.va.gov/
Control: Veterans Affairs, Government, federal **Service**: General medical and surgical

Staffed Beds: 223 **Admissions**: 3884 **Census**: 152 **Outpatient Visits**: 364662 **Births**: 0 **Total Expense ($000)**: 266036 **Payroll Expense ($000)**: 112297 **Personnel**: 1642

IA

Hospital, Medicare Provider Number, Address, Telephone, Approval, Facility, and Physician Codes, Health Care System

★ American Hospital Association (AHA) membership ○ Healthcare Facilities Accreditation Program ⇑ Center for Improvement in Healthcare Quality Accreditation
☐ The Joint Commission accreditation ◇ DNV Healthcare Inc. accreditation △ Commission on Accreditation of Rehabilitation Facilities (CARF) accreditation

---

DUBUQUE—Dubuque County

FINLEY HOSPITAL See Unitypoint Health - Finley Hospital

✠ △ **MERCY MEDICAL CENTER-DUBUQUE (160069)**, 250 Mercy Drive, Zip 52001–7360; tel. 563/589–8000, (Total facility includes 40 beds in nursing home–type unit) **A**1 7 10 **F**3 4 5 8 11 13 15 18 20 22 24 26 28 29 30 31 32 34 35 36 38 39 40 43 44 49 50 51 53 56 57 58 59 61 62 64 65 67 70 72 74 75 76 77 78 79 80 81 84 85 86 87 89 90 91 93 97 98 99 100 101 102 103 104 107 108 110 111 114 115 117 118 119 126 128 129 130 131 132 134 135 144 146 147 148 149 150 156 **S** Trinity Health, Livonia, MI
Primary Contact: Kay Takes, R.N., President
CFO: Robert Shafer, Vice President Finance
CIO: Joe Billmeyer, Director, Information Services
CHR: Kathryn Roberts, Director Human Resources
CNO: Robert Wethal, R.N., Vice President and Chief Nursing Officer
Web address: www.mercydubuque.com
Control: Church operated, Nongovernment, not–for–profit **Service**: General medical and surgical

> **Staffed Beds:** 231 **Admissions:** 8632 **Census:** 135 **Outpatient Visits:** 44711 **Births:** 755 **Total Expense ($000):** 162473 **Payroll Expense ($000):** 57083 **Personnel:** 1071

✠ △ **UNITYPOINT HEALTH - FINLEY HOSPITAL (160117)**, 350 North Grandview Avenue, Zip 52001–6393; tel. 563/582–1881, **A**1 7 10 **F**3 13 15 18 20 22 28 29 30 31 34 35 39 40 43 44 45 46 47 48 49 50 56 57 59 60 61 62 64 65 70 72 74 75 76 77 78 79 81 82 84 85 86 87 90 91 92 93 96 97 98 103 107 108 110 111 114 115 118 119 120 121 123 124 126 130 131 132 135 144 146 147 148 149 153 154 156 **S** UnityPoint Health, West Des Moines, IA
Primary Contact: Chad Wolbers, President and Chief Executive Officer
CMO: Bryan Pechous, M.D., Vice President Medical Affairs
CIO: Tim Loeffelholz, Account Executive Information Technology
CHR: Karla Waldbillig, Director Human Resources
CNO: Mary Peters, Chief Nursing Officer
Web address: www.unitypoint.org
Control: Other not–for–profit (including NFP Corporation) **Service**: General medical and surgical

> **Staffed Beds:** 109 **Admissions:** 4587 **Census:** 53 **Outpatient Visits:** 163018 **Births:** 700 **Total Expense ($000):** 124273 **Payroll Expense ($000):** 53884 **Personnel:** 807

DYERSVILLE—Dubuque County

★ **MERCY MEDICAL CENTER-DYERSVILLE (161378)**, 1111 Third Street SW, Zip 52040–1725; tel. 563/875–7101, **A**10 18 **F**11 15 34 35 36 39 40 44 50 56 57 59 64 65 75 79 81 85 86 93 119 130 131 132 133 134 135 146 147 149 156 **S** Trinity Health, Livonia, MI
Primary Contact: Kay Takes, R.N., President
CFO: Robert Shafer, Vice President Finance
Web address: www.mercydubuque.com/mercy-dyersville
Control: Church operated, Nongovernment, not–for–profit **Service**: General medical and surgical

> **Staffed Beds:** 20 **Admissions:** 71 **Census:** 2 **Outpatient Visits:** 3589 **Births:** 0 **Total Expense ($000):** 5953 **Payroll Expense ($000):** 2645 **Personnel:** 52

ELKADER—Clayton County

★ **MERCYONE ELKADER MEDICAL CENTER (161319)**, 901 Davidson Street NW, Zip 52043–9015; tel. 563/245–7000, **A**10 18 **F**7 11 15 28 34 35 40 43 45 50 57 59 64 67 68 75 81 85 87 91 93 102 107 110 114 128 133 146 **S** Trinity Health, Livonia, MI
Primary Contact: Brooke Kensinger, Chief Executive Officer
CFO: Patricia Borel, Chief Financial Officer
CIO: Jonathan Holliday, Manager Information Technology
CHR: Angie Gerndt, Human Resources Manager
CNO: Natalie Shea, Chief Nursing Officer
Web address: www.centralcommunityhospital.com
Control: Other not–for–profit (including NFP Corporation) **Service**: General medical and surgical

> **Staffed Beds:** 15 **Admissions:** 139 **Census:** 2 **Outpatient Visits:** 14758 **Births:** 0 **Total Expense ($000):** 7860 **Payroll Expense ($000):** 2913 **Personnel:** 63

EMMETSBURG—Palo Alto County

★ **PALO ALTO COUNTY HEALTH SYSTEM (161357)**, 3201 First Street, Zip 50536–2516; tel. 712/852–5500, (Total facility includes 22 beds in nursing home–type unit) **A**10 18 **F**3 7 11 13 15 28 29 34 35 37 40 43 45 46 50 57 59 62 63 64 65 67 69 71 75 77 81 82 85 87 93 97 107 110 114 119 127 130 132 133 143 146 154 158 **S** Trinity Health, Livonia, MI
Primary Contact: Brett Antczak, Chief Executive Officer
CFO: Collette Johnson, Chief Financial Officer
CMO: Madhan Prabhakaran, M.D., Chief Medical Officer
CHR: Tara Helle, Human Resources Lead
CNO: Sara Travis, Chief Nursing Officer and Assistant Administrator
Web address: www.pachs.com
Control: County, Government, nonfederal **Service**: General medical and surgical

> **Staffed Beds:** 47 **Admissions:** 387 **Census:** 26 **Outpatient Visits:** 23652 **Births:** 80 **Total Expense ($000):** 25951 **Payroll Expense ($000):** 9059 **Personnel:** 176

ESTHERVILLE—Emmet County

★ **AVERA HOLY FAMILY HOSPITAL (161351)**, 826 North Eighth Street, Zip 51334–1598; tel. 712/362–2631, **A**10 18 **F**3 11 13 15 28 29 30 31 34 35 37 40 45 57 59 64 68 69 70 75 76 77 78 79 81 85 87 93 97 107 110 111 114 119 130 131 132 133 146 154 156 **S** Avera Health, Sioux Falls, SD
Primary Contact: Deborah L. Herzberg, R.N., MS, FACHE, Administrator
CFO: Shannon Adams, Chief Financial Officer
CMO: Anthony Cook, M.D., Chief of Staff
CHR: Janette Jensen, Manager Human Resources
CNO: Cathi Rae Scharnberg, R.N., M.P.H., Vice President Patient Services
Web address: www.avera-holyfamily.org
Control: Church operated, Nongovernment, not–for–profit **Service**: General medical and surgical

> **Staffed Beds:** 25 **Admissions:** 550 **Census:** 5 **Outpatient Visits:** 36006 **Births:** 0 **Total Expense ($000):** 26593 **Payroll Expense ($000):** 10799 **Personnel:** 177

FAIRFIELD—Jefferson County

★ **JEFFERSON COUNTY HEALTH CENTER (161364)**, 2000 S Main, Zip 52556–9572, Mailing Address: P.O. Box 588, Zip 52556–0010; tel. 641/472–4111, **A**10 18 **F**11 15 28 30 31 34 35 36 40 43 45 50 57 59 67 68 70 75 77 78 79 81 85 89 93 96 102 107 110 111 112 114 115 119 127 128 129 132 133 135 143 144 146 148 156
Primary Contact: Bryan Hunger, Chief Executive Officer
CFO: Larry Peach, Chief Financial Officer
CHR: Nanette Everly, Manager Human Resources and Administrative Assistant
Web address: www.jeffersoncountyhealthcenter.org
Control: County, Government, nonfederal **Service**: General medical and surgical

> **Staffed Beds:** 25 **Admissions:** 607 **Census:** 9 **Outpatient Visits:** 134667 **Births:** 0 **Total Expense ($000):** 47568 **Payroll Expense ($000):** 17432 **Personnel:** 333

FORT DODGE—Webster County

★ ⇑ **UNITYPOINT HEALTH - TRINITY REGIONAL MEDICAL CENTER (160016)**, 802 Kenyon Road, Zip 50501–5795; tel. 515/573–3101, **A**2 10 21 **F**3 11 13 15 18 20 22 26 28 29 30 31 32 34 35 38 40 43 44 45 47 49 50 53 57 59 64 68 70 75 76 77 81 82 84 85 86 87 89 93 96 101 102 104 107 108 110 111 115 118 119 120 121 123 127 129 130 135 146 147 149 150 153 156 **S** UnityPoint Health, West Des Moines, IA
Primary Contact: Leah Glasgo, Chief Executive Officer
COO: Troy Martens, Chief Operating Officer
CFO: Brent Feickert, Chief Financial Officer
CHR: Ted W Vaughn, Director Human Resources
CNO: Debra Shriver, R.N., MSN, Chief Nurse Executive
Web address: www.trmc.org
Control: Other not–for–profit (including NFP Corporation) **Service**: General medical and surgical

> **Staffed Beds:** 49 **Admissions:** 3291 **Census:** 32 **Outpatient Visits:** 67586 **Births:** 480 **Total Expense ($000):** 125285 **Payroll Expense ($000):** 60171 **Personnel:** 275

Many Facility Codes have changed. Please refer to the AHA Guide Code Chart. © 2019 AHA Guide

FORT MADISON—Lee County

⊞ **FORT MADISON COMMUNITY HOSPITAL (160122)**, 5445 Avenue 'O', Zip 52627–9611, Mailing Address: P.O. Box 174, Zip 52627–0174; tel. 319/372–6530, **A**1 10 **F**3 11 13 15 28 29 31 34 40 43 45 50 51 53 57 59 62 64 67 68 70 74 75 76 77 78 79 81 85 86 87 90 91 93 94 96 97 99 100 101 102 103 104 107 108 110 111 115 117 118 119 128 129 130 131 132 133 143 144 146 147 148 149
Primary Contact: Jeremy Alexander, Chief Executive Officer
CFO: Bradley J Kokjohn, Chief Financial Officer
CMO: David Wenger-Keller, M.D., Chief of Staff
CIO: Shane Tapper, Director Management Information Systems
CHR: Vicki Kokjohn, Director Employee Relations
CNO: Shelby Dickens, Director, Patient Care Services
Web address: www.fmchosp.com
Control: Other not–for–profit (including NFP Corporation) **Service:** General medical and surgical

Staffed Beds: 50 **Admissions:** 1037 **Census:** 8 **Outpatient Visits:** 96148 **Births:** 241 **Total Expense ($000):** 61425 **Payroll Expense ($000):** 28961 **Personnel:** 534

GREENFIELD—Adair County

★ **ADAIR COUNTY HEALTH SYSTEM (161310)**, 609 SE Kent Street, Zip 50849–9454; tel. 641/743–2123, **A**10 18 **F**3 7 8 11 15 18 28 34 35 40 43 45 50 57 59 64 65 69 75 81 97 107 108 110 115 119 127 128 133 144 149 154 **S** MercyOne, Clive, IA
Primary Contact: Marcia Hendricks, FACHE, R.N., Chief Executive Officer
CFO: Heather Shaull, Chief Financial Officer
CMO: Jessica Kennedy, D.O., Chief Medical Officer
CIO: Gary Bateman, Chief Information Technology
CHR: Angie Frankl, Director Human Resources
CNO: Cindy K Peeler, R.N., Chief Nursing Officer
Web address: www.adaircountyhealthsystem.org
Control: County, Government, nonfederal **Service:** General medical and surgical

Staffed Beds: 17 **Admissions:** 65 **Census:** 1 **Outpatient Visits:** 8284 **Births:** 0 **Total Expense ($000):** 13817 **Payroll Expense ($000):** 5739 **Personnel:** 78

GRINNELL—Poweshiek County

★ ○ **UNITYPOINT HEALTH - GRINNELL REGIONAL MEDICAL CENTER (160147)**, 210 Fourth Avenue, Zip 50112–1898; tel. 641/236–7511, **A**10 11 **F**3 11 12 13 15 28 29 30 31 32 34 35 36 38 40 43 44 45 46 47 50 53 54 56 57 59 61 62 63 64 65 66 70 75 77 78 04 05 06 87 93 97 107 110 111 115 118 119 126 127 130 131 132 133 134 135 144 146 147 148 149 150 154 156 **S** UnityPoint Health, West Des Moines, IA
Primary Contact: Jennifer Havens, Chief Executive Officer
CFO: Kyle M Wilcox, Vice President Finance
CIO: David L Ness, Vice President Operations
CHR: Debra S. Nowachek, Director Human Resources
CNO: Doris Rindels, Vice President Operations
Web address: www.grmc.us
Control: Other not–for–profit (including NFP Corporation) **Service:** General medical and surgical

Staffed Beds: 49 **Admissions:** 1231 **Census:** 11 **Outpatient Visits:** 46855 **Births:** 153 **Total Expense ($000):** 51161 **Payroll Expense ($000):** 21191 **Personnel:** 341

GRUNDY CENTER—Grundy County

★ **GRUNDY COUNTY MEMORIAL HOSPITAL (161303)**, 201 East 'J' Avenue, Zip 50638–2096; tel. 319/824–5421, **A**10 18 **F**15 28 29 34 35 40 43 50 57 59 63 64 68 75 78 79 81 82 86 87 93 107 110 111 114 119 128 129 130 131 132 133 135 146 148 154 156 **S** UnityPoint Health, West Des Moines, IA
Primary Contact: Adam Scherling, President
COO: Ryan Bingman, Director Operations
CFO: Lisa Zinkula, Chief Financial Officer
CMO: Douglas Cooper, M.D., Chief Medical Officer
CIO: Steve Bantz, Manager Information Technology
CHR: Keagan Brunscheon, Manager, Human Resources
CNO: Jody Schipper, Director of Nursing
Web address: www.https://www.unitypoint.org
Control: County, Government, nonfederal **Service:** General medical and surgical

Staffed Beds: 25 **Admissions:** 266 **Census:** 25 **Outpatient Visits:** 45886 **Births:** 0 **Total Expense ($000):** 20075 **Payroll Expense ($000):** 8811 **Personnel:** 108

GUTHRIE CENTER—Guthrie County

★ **GUTHRIE COUNTY HOSPITAL (161314)**, 710 North 12th Street, Zip 50115–1544; tel. 641/332–2201, **A**10 18 **F**11 15 18 28 29 34 35 40 43 45 53 56 57 59 64 69 75 79 81 85 93 107 110 114 119 128 130 132 133 143 148 154 156 **S** UnityPoint Health, West Des Moines, IA
Primary Contact: Patrick Peters, Chief Executive Officer
CFO: Troy Eller, Chief Financial Officer
CMO: Donald Fillman, M.D., Chief Medical Officer
CIO: Jeff Cobb, Information Technologist
CHR: Kimberly Myers, Director Human Resources
CNO: Gregory Opseth, Chief Nursing Officer
Web address: www.guthriecountyhospital.org
Control: County, Government, nonfederal **Service:** General medical and surgical

Staffed Beds: 17 **Admissions:** 309 **Census:** 3 **Outpatient Visits:** 30208 **Births:** 0 **Total Expense ($000):** 16972 **Payroll Expense ($000):** 7640 **Personnel:** 103

GUTTENBERG—Clayton County

⊞ **GUTTENBERG MUNICIPAL HOSPITAL (161312)**, 200 Main Street, Zip 52052–9108, Mailing Address: P.O. Box 550, Zip 52052–0550; tel. 563/252–1121, **A**1 10 18 **F**3 7 11 15 28 34 35 40 43 45 50 57 59 64 68 81 85 89 93 97 102 107 110 111 115 119 126 127 128 130 132 133 **S** MercyOne, Clive, IA
Primary Contact: Tim Ahlers, Chief Executive Officer
COO: Lisa Manson, Director Ambulatory Services
CFO: Jill DeMoss, Finance Manager
CMO: Chris Hugo, M.D., Chief of Staff
CIO: Scott R Pauls, Director Information Technology- HealthNet Connect
CHR: Chelsea Greene, Manager Human Resources
Web address: www.guttenberghospital.org
Control: City, Government, nonfederal **Service:** General medical and surgical

Staffed Beds: 20 **Admissions:** 288 **Census:** 4 **Outpatient Visits:** 26461 **Births:** 9 **Total Expense ($000):** 17313 **Payroll Expense ($000):** 7316 **Personnel:** 137

HAMBURG—Fremont County

GEORGE C GRAPE COMMUNITY HOSPITAL (161324), 2959 US Highway 275, Zip 51640–5067; tel. 712/382–1515, (Total facility includes 6 beds in nursing home–type unit) **A**10 18 **F**11 15 18 28 31 34 35 40 43 46 50 53 59 62 64 65 68 75 77 78 79 81 82 85 91 93 107 115 119 128 129 130 133 135 148
Primary Contact: Michael O'Neal, Chief Executive Officer
CFO: Hilary Christiansen, Chief Financial Officer
CMO: Kelli Woltemath, D.O., Chief Medical Staff
CIO: Craig Wells, Chief Information Officer
CHR: Jackie Wertz, Director Human Resources
CNO: Gloria Mattice, R.N., Director Patient Care
Web address: www.grapehospital.com
Control: Other not–for–profit (including NFP Corporation) **Service:** General medical and surgical

Staffed Beds: 25 **Admissions:** 159 **Census:** 3 **Outpatient Visits:** 17233 **Births:** 0 **Total Expense ($000):** 10895 **Payroll Expense ($000):** 4405 **Personnel:** 97

HAMPTON—Franklin County

★ **FRANKLIN GENERAL HOSPITAL (161308)**, 1720 Central Avenue East, Suite A, Zip 50441–1867; tel. 641/456–5000, (Total facility includes 52 beds in nursing home–type unit) **A**10 18 **F**7 10 11 15 28 30 34 40 43 57 59 63 64 65 67 68 75 77 79 81 82 85 86 89 90 93 103 107 111 115 119 127 128 129 130 131 132 133 135 146 147 148 154 **S** Trinity Health, Livonia, MI
Primary Contact: Kim Price, Chief Executive Officer
CFO: Deb Rosburg, Chief Financial Officer
CHR: Victoria Kruse, Manager Human Resources
CNO: Ronda Reimer, R.N., Chief Nursing Officer and Assistant Administrator
Web address: www.franklingeneral.com
Control: County, Government, nonfederal **Service:** General medical and surgical

Staffed Beds: 77 **Admissions:** 281 **Census:** 54 **Outpatient Visits:** 24575 **Births:** 0 **Total Expense ($000):** 20716 **Payroll Expense ($000):** 6025 **Personnel:** 133

IA

HARLAN—Shelby County

★ **MYRTUE MEDICAL CENTER (161374)**, 1213 Garfield Avenue, Zip 51537–2057; tel. 712/755–5161, **A**10 18 **F**3 5 11 13 15 28 29 31 32 34 35 38 40 43 45 46 50 53 56 57 59 62 63 64 65 68 75 77 78 81 85 87 92 93 97 99 101 102 103 104 107 110 114 119 127 128 129 130 131 132 133 135 146 148 154 156 157
Primary Contact: Barry Jacobsen, CPA, Chief Executive Officer
CFO: Kristy Hansen, CPA, Chief Financial Officer
CMO: Brian A. Anderson, D.O., Chief of Staff
CIO: David Sirek, Chief Information Officer
CHR: Donna Christensen-Mores, JD, Director Human Resources
CNO: Karen Buman, MSN, Chief Nursing Executive
Web address: www.myrtuemedical.org
Control: County, Government, nonfederal **Service:** General medical and surgical

Staffed Beds: 25 **Admissions:** 874 **Census:** 10 **Outpatient Visits:** 109217 **Births:** 65 **Total Expense ($000):** 41464 **Payroll Expense ($000):** 16054 **Personnel:** 352

HAWARDEN—Sioux County

★ **HAWARDEN REGIONAL HEALTHCARE (161311)**, 1111 11th Street, Zip 51023–1999; tel. 712/551–3100, **A**10 18 **F**11 15 28 29 31 34 35 40 43 53 56 59 64 68 75 77 81 82 92 93 104 107 108 110 114 119 127 128 129 131 132 133 135 144 148 156 **S** Trinity Health, Livonia, MI
Primary Contact: Jayson Pullman, Chief Executive Officer
CFO: Jessica Hughes, Director Finance
CMO: Dale Nystrom, M.D., Chief Medical Officer, Physician
CHR: Maggie Hofer, Human Resources Representative
Web address: www.hawardenregionalhealthcare.com/
Control: City, Government, nonfederal **Service:** General medical and surgical

Staffed Beds: 18 **Admissions:** 186 **Census:** 3 **Outpatient Visits:** 19129 **Births:** 0 **Total Expense ($000):** 11111 **Payroll Expense ($000):** 3544 **Personnel:** 67

HUMBOLDT—Humboldt County

★ **HUMBOLDT COUNTY MEMORIAL HOSPITAL (161334)**, 1000 North 15th Street, Zip 50548–1008; tel. 515/332–4200, (Total facility includes 28 beds in nursing home–type unit) **A**10 18 **F**7 8 10 11 12 14 15 28 29 31 34 35 40 41 43 45 47 50 51 59 62 63 65 68 75 77 78 79 81 82 84 85 87 93 102 104 107 110 111 114 119 125 127 128 129 130 133 135 156 **S** UnityPoint Health, West Des Moines, IA
Primary Contact: Michelle Sleiter, Chief Executive Officer
CFO: Betty Etherington, Chief Financial Officer
CHR: Mary Moritz, Administrator Human Resources
Web address: www.humboldthospital.org
Control: County, Government, nonfederal **Service:** General medical and surgical

Staffed Beds: 49 **Admissions:** 492 **Census:** 32 **Outpatient Visits:** 86916 **Births:** 0 **Total Expense ($000):** 18931 **Payroll Expense ($000):** 8641 **Personnel:** 188

IDA GROVE—Ida County

★ **HORN MEMORIAL HOSPITAL (161354)**, 701 East Second Street, Zip 51445–1699; tel. 712/364–3311, **A**10 18 **F**11 15 28 29 34 40 45 50 57 59 62 63 64 65 66 68 75 77 79 81 82 85 89 93 97 100 107 108 110 111 115 117 119 127 128 129 130 131 132 133 135 146 147 148 154 156
Primary Contact: Glen Winekauf, Chief Executive Officer
CFO: Marcia Fehring, Chief Financial Officer
CIO: Robbie Todd, Director Information Technology
CHR: Lorraine Davis, Vice President Human Resources
CNO: Jo Hayes, Chief Nursing Officer
Web address: www.hornmemorialhospital.org
Control: Other not–for–profit (including NFP Corporation) **Service:** General medical and surgical

Staffed Beds: 20 **Admissions:** 385 **Census:** 6 **Outpatient Visits:** 48174 **Births:** 0 **Total Expense ($000):** 20406 **Payroll Expense ($000):** 9132 **Personnel:** 159

INDEPENDENCE—Buchanan County

★ **BUCHANAN COUNTY HEALTH CENTER (161335)**, 1600 First Street East, Zip 50644–3155; tel. 319/332–0999, (Total facility includes 39 beds in nursing home–type unit) **A**10 18 **F**3 11 15 28 29 32 34 35 40 43 45 50 53 56 57 59 64 65 67 75 77 79 81 82 84 85 86 87 91 93 97 107 110 111 114 119 125 127 128 129 130 131 132 133 135 144 146 148 156 **S** UnityPoint Health, West Des Moines, IA
Primary Contact: Steve Robert. Slessor, Chief Executive Officer
CFO: Ben Stevens, Chief Financial Officer
CNO: Rachel Goldenstein, R.N., Chief Nursing Officer
Web address: www.bchealth.info
Control: County, Government, nonfederal **Service:** General medical and surgical

Staffed Beds: 58 **Admissions:** 295 **Census:** 42 **Outpatient Visits:** 58065 **Births:** 0 **Total Expense ($000):** 29513 **Payroll Expense ($000):** 12486 **Personnel:** 203

☐ **MENTAL HEALTH INSTITUTE (164003)**, 2277 Iowa Avenue, Zip 50644–9106; tel. 319/334–2583, **A**1 10 **F**59 65 75 98 99 101 102 130 135 143 146 149
Primary Contact: Bhasker J. Dave, M.D., Superintendent
CFO: Kevin Jimmerson, Business Manager
CMO: Bhasker J Dave, M.D., Superintendent
Web address: www.dhs.state.ia.us
Control: State, Government, nonfederal **Service:** Psychiatric

Staffed Beds: 56 **Admissions:** 160 **Census:** 55 **Outpatient Visits:** 36 **Births:** 0 **Total Expense ($000):** 19930 **Payroll Expense ($000):** 11528 **Personnel:** 185

IOWA CITY—Johnson County

⊞ **IOWA CITY VETERANS AFFAIRS HEALTH CARE SYSTEM**, 601 Highway 6 West, Zip 52246–2208; tel. 319/338–0581, **A**1 3 5 **F**3 5 8 11 12 17 18 20 22 24 29 30 31 33 34 35 36 38 39 40 43 44 45 46 47 50 51 53 54 57 58 59 60 61 62 64 65 70 71 74 75 78 79 81 82 83 84 85 86 87 91 92 93 94 97 98 100 101 102 103 104 105 107 108 110 111 114 115 116 117 118 119 129 130 135 138 142 143 146 147 148 149 152 153 154 156 157 158 **S** Department of Veterans Affairs, Washington, DC
Primary Contact: Judith Johnson-Mekota, Director
COO: Kevin Kosek, Associate Director Operations
CFO: Jennifer Ruppert, Chief Financial Officer
CMO: Richard A Charlat, Chief of Staff
CIO: Dwight Schuessler, Chief Information Officer
CHR: Dan Helle, Human Resources Officer
CNO: Dawn Oxley, R.N., Associate Director Patient Care Services and Nurse Executive
Web address: www.iowacity.va.gov/
Control: Veterans Affairs, Government, federal **Service:** General medical and surgical

Staffed Beds: 78 **Admissions:** 3573 **Census:** 54 **Outpatient Visits:** 603693 **Births:** 0 **Total Expense ($000):** 318548 **Payroll Expense ($000):** 152963 **Personnel:** 2254

⊞ **MERCYONE IOWA CITY MEDICAL CENTER (160029)**, 500 East Market Street, Zip 52245–2689; tel. 319/339–0300, **A**1 2 10 **F**3 5 8 12 13 15 18 20 22 24 26 28 29 30 31 34 35 38 40 43 44 45 47 48 50 51 54 57 59 62 63 64 65 70 72 73 74 75 76 77 78 79 81 85 86 87 89 97 98 100 101 102 104 105 107 108 110 111 114 115 116 117 119 126 127 129 130 132 135 144 145 146 148 152 156 157 **S** MercyOne, Clive, IA
Primary Contact: Sean J. Williams, President and Chief Executive Officer
CFO: Douglas Davenport, Interim Chief Financial Officer
CMO: Martin Izakovic, M.D., Vice President Medical Staff Affairs and Chief Medical Officer
CIO: David Fishbaugher, Chief Medical Information
CHR: Dena M Brockhouse, Director Human Resources
CNO: Cindy L Penney, R.N., Vice President Nursing
Web address: www.mercyiowacity.org
Control: Church operated, Nongovernment, not–for–profit **Service:** General medical and surgical

Staffed Beds: 223 **Admissions:** 6879 **Census:** 66 **Outpatient Visits:** 113902 **Births:** 1129 **Total Expense ($000):** 148474 **Payroll Expense ($000):** 56325 **Personnel:** 842

UNIVERSITY HOSPITAL SCHOOL See Center for Disabilities and Development

⊞ **UNIVERSITY OF IOWA HOSPITALS AND CLINICS (160058)**, 200 Hawkins Drive, Zip 52242–1009; tel. 319/356–1616, (Includes CENTER FOR DISABILITIES AND DEVELOPMENT, 200 Hawkins Drive, Iowa City, Iowa, Zip 52242; tel. 319/356–1347; CHEMICAL DEPENDENCY CENTER, 200 Hawkins Drive, Iowa City, Iowa, Zip 52242–1007; tel. 319/384–8765; STATE PSYCHIATRIC HOSPITAL, 200 Hawkins Drive, Iowa City, Iowa, Zip 52242; tel. 319/356–4658; UNIVERSITY OF IOWA STEAD FAMILY CHILDREN'S HOSPITAL, 200 Hawkins Drive, Iowa City, Iowa, Zip 52242–1009; tel. 888/573–5437) **A**1 2 3 5 8 10 **F**3 5 6 7 8 9 11 12 13 14 15 16 17 18 19 20 21 22 23 24 25 26 27 28 29 30 31 32 33 34 35 36 37 38 39 40 41 43 44 45 46 47 48 49 50 51 52 53 54 55 56 57 58 59 60 61 62 63 64 65 66 68 70 72 73 74 75 76 77 78 79 80 81 82 83 84 85 86 87 88 89 90 91 92 93 94 96 97 98 99 100 101 102 103 104 105 107 108 109 110 111 114 115 116 117 118 119 120 121 123 124 126 127 129 130 131 132 135 136 137 138 139 140 141 142 143 145 146 147 148 152 153 154 155 156
Primary Contact: Suresh Gunasekaran, Chief Executive Officer
COO: Scott Turner, Chief Operating Officer
CFO: Bradley Haws, Chief Financial Officer
CMO: Theresa Brennan, M.D., Chief Medical Officer
CIO: Lee Carmen, Associate Vice President Health Care Information Systems
CHR: Jana Wessels, Associate Vice President Human Resources
CNO: Cindy Dawson, MSN, R.N., Chief Nursing Executive
Web address: www.uihealthcare.org
Control: State, Government, nonfederal **Service:** General medical and surgical

Staffed Beds: 747 **Admissions:** 35074 **Census:** 639 **Outpatient Visits:** 1502523 **Births:** 2371 **Total Expense ($000):** 1616346 **Payroll Expense ($000):** 533741 **Personnel:** 8873

IA

Many Facility Codes have changed. Please refer to the AHA Guide Code Chart. © 2019 AHA Guide

IOWA FALLS—Hardin County

★ **HANSEN FAMILY HOSPITAL (161380)**, 920 South Oak, Zip 50126–9506;
tel. 641/648–4631, **A**10 18 **F**3 11 13 15 28 29 30 34 40 41 43 45 50 53 57
59 64 65 75 76 77 81 82 85 86 87 89 93 97 100 102 104 107 110 115 119
128 133 135 146 147 149 156 **S** Trinity Health, Livonia, MI
Primary Contact: Douglas E. Morse, Chief Executive Officer and Administrator
CFO: Mike White, Chief Financial Officer
CMO: George Pfaltzgraff, Chief Medical Officer
CHR: Cheri Geitz, Director Human Resources
CNO: Katie Rieks, Chief Nursing Officer
Web address: www.hansenfamilyhospital.com
Control: City, Government, nonfederal **Service**: General medical and surgical

Staffed Beds: 21 **Admissions**: 500 **Census**: 7 **Outpatient Visits**: 25956
Births: 105 **Total Expense ($000)**: 24787 **Payroll Expense ($000)**: 9771
Personnel: 193

JEFFERSON—Greene County

★ **GREENE COUNTY MEDICAL CENTER (161325)**, 1000 West Lincolnway,
Zip 50129–1645; tel. 515/386–2114, (Total facility includes 60 beds in nursing
home–type unit) **A**10 18 **F**3 11 15 28 29 31 34 35 36 40 46 55 56 57 59 63 64
65 67 68 75 77 79 81 82 85 93 107 110 114 119 125 128 130 131 132 133
147 149 150 156 **S** UnityPoint Health, West Des Moines, IA
Primary Contact: Carl P. Behne, Chief Executive Officer
CFO: Mark A VanderLinden, Chief Financial Officer
CMO: Jon Van Der Veer, D.O., Vice President Medical Affairs
CIO: Roger Overby, Executive Director Information Systems
CHR: Cathy Krieger, Human Resources Director
CNO: Katie Heldt, Chief Nursing Officer
Web address: www.gcmchealth.com
Control: County, Government, nonfederal **Service**: General medical and surgical

Staffed Beds: 85 **Admissions**: 319 **Census**: 41 **Outpatient Visits**: 18242
Births: 0 **Total Expense ($000)**: 26170 **Payroll Expense ($000)**: 9233
Personnel: 215

KEOKUK—Lee County

⊠ **UNITYPOINT HEALTH-KEOKUK (160008)**, 1600 Morgan Street, Zip 52632–
3456; tel. 319/524–7150, **A**1 10 **F**3 11 15 28 29 34 35 40 43 45 46 57 59 62
64 68 70 81 85 86 87 93 96 107 108 111 115 118 119 129 132 133 140 140
149 156 **S** UnityPoint Health, West Des Moines, IA
Primary Contact: John Winenger, FACHE, Interim Chief Executive Officer
CFO: Kris Karre, Director Finance and Accounting
CMO: Neville Crenshaw, D.O., Chief of Staff
CIO: Linda Atterberg, Chief Information Officer
CHR: Lora Taylor, Director Human Resources and Compliance Officer
CNO: Vickie White, Director of Nursing
Web address: www.keokukhealthsystems.org
Control: Other not–for–profit (including NFP Corporation) **Service**: General
medical and surgical

Staffed Beds: 42 **Admissions**: 523 **Census**: 4 **Outpatient Visits**: 27995
Births: 0 **Total Expense ($000)**: 21651 **Payroll Expense ($000)**: 8457
Personnel: 188

KEOSAUQUA—Van Buren County

★ **VAN BUREN COUNTY HOSPITAL (161337)**, 304 Franklin Street, Zip 52565–
1164; tel. 319/293–3171, **A**10 18 **F**3 7 10 11 13 15 28 29 32 34 35 40 43 45
46 50 56 57 59 64 65 70 75 81 82 85 89 93 97 102 107 110 115 119 125
127 128 130 132 133 135 146 147 154 156 157
Primary Contact: Ray Brownsworth, Chief Executive Officer
CFO: Kara McEntee, Chief Financial Officer
CIO: Chris McEntee, Network Specialist
CNO: Rhonda Fellows, R.N., Chief Nursing Officer
Web address: www.vbch.org
Control: County, Government, nonfederal **Service**: General medical and surgical

Staffed Beds: 25 **Admissions**: 262 **Census**: 3 **Outpatient Visits**: 16212
Births: 59 **Total Expense ($000)**: 16797 **Payroll Expense ($000)**: 8226
Personnel: 156

KNOXVILLE—Marion County

KNOXVILLE DIVISION See Veterans Affairs Central Iowa Health Care System, Des
Moines

★ **KNOXVILLE HOSPITAL & CLINICS (161355)**, 1002 South Lincoln Street,
Zip 50138–3155; tel. 641/842–2151, **A**10 18 **F**3 8 11 15 28 29 31 34 35
37 40 43 45 47 48 49 50 54 57 59 64 65 75 77 81 85 86 93 97 107 108
110 111 114 118 119 126 129 130 131 133 135 146 148 154 156 **S**
CommonSpirit Health, Chicago, IL
Primary Contact: Kevin Kincaid, Chief Executive Officer
CFO: Maggie Hamilton-Beyer, Chief Financial Officer
CMO: Brent Hoehns, M.D., Chief of Medical Staff
CIO: Thom Richards, Director Information Technology
CNO: MaryJane Hunt, Chief Clinical Officer
Web address: www.knoxvillehospital.org
Control: Other not–for–profit (including NFP Corporation) **Service**: General
medical and surgical

Staffed Beds: 25 **Admissions**: 1074 **Census**: 8 **Outpatient Visits**: 63125
Births: 0 **Total Expense ($000)**: 32259 **Payroll Expense ($000)**: 13119
Personnel: 246

LAKE CITY—Calhoun County

★ **STEWART MEMORIAL COMMUNITY HOSPITAL (161350)**, 1301 West Main,
Zip 51449–1585; tel. 712/464–3171, **A**10 18 **F**11 12 13 15 28 29 30 31 34 40
43 45 50 59 64 65 69 75 76 77 80 81 82 86 93 94 107 110 114 119 127 130
133 135 147 154 156 **S** UnityPoint Health, West Des Moines, IA
Primary Contact: Cynthia L. Carstens, R.N., Chief Executive Officer
CFO: Jim Henkenius, Chief Financial Officer
CHR: Bill Albright, Director Human Resources
Web address: www.stewartmemorial.org
Control: Other not–for–profit (including NFP Corporation) **Service**: General
medical and surgical

Staffed Beds: 25 **Admissions**: 377 **Census**: 3 **Outpatient Visits**: 46241
Births: 92 **Total Expense ($000)**: 31539 **Payroll Expense ($000)**: 14472
Personnel: 223

LE MARS—Plymouth County

★ **FLOYD VALLEY HEALTHCARE (161368)**, 714 Lincoln Street NE, Zip 51031–
3314; tel. 712/546–7871, **A**10 18 **F**3 10 11 13 28 29 31 32 34 35 40 43 45
50 53 57 59 62 64 65 67 68 76 78 79 80 81 85 86 87 107 110 111 114 119
128 130 132 133 135 146 148 154 156 157 **S** Avera Health, Sioux Falls, SD
Primary Contact: Dustin Wright, Chief Executive Officer
CFO: Daryl Friedenbach, Director Fiscal Services
CMO: Andrew Geha, D.O., President Medical Staff
CIO: Jacob Jorgensen, Chief Information Officer
CHR: Mary Helen Gibson, Director Human Resources
CNO: Lorrie Mortensen, MSN, R.N., Director, Patient Care
Web address: www.floydvalley.org
Control: City, Government, nonfederal **Service**: General medical and surgical

Staffed Beds: 25 **Admissions**: 605 **Census**: 6 **Outpatient Visits**: 50133
Births: 99 **Total Expense ($000)**: 39608 **Payroll Expense ($000)**: 14050
Personnel: 290

LEON—Decatur County

★ ○ **DECATUR COUNTY HOSPITAL (161340)**, 1405 NW Church Street,
Zip 50144–1299; tel. 641/446–4871, **A**10 11 18 **F**3 7 11 28 29 31 34 40 41
45 50 57 59 64 68 69 71 75 78 79 81 82 85 93 104 107 111 114 117 119
130 133 146 148 149 157 **S** MercyOne, Clive, IA
Primary Contact: Mike Johnston, Chief Executive Officer
CFO: Tara Spidle, Chief Financial Officer
CMO: Ed Wehling, Chief Medical Staff
CHR: Jo Beth Smith, Vice President Human Resources
Web address: www.decaturcountyhospital.org
Control: County, Government, nonfederal **Service**: General medical and surgical

Staffed Beds: 11 **Admissions**: 179 **Census**: 2 **Outpatient Visits**: 9013
Births: 0 **Total Expense ($000)**: 13831 **Payroll Expense ($000)**: 4479
Personnel: 92

IA

MANCHESTER—Delaware County

★ **REGIONAL MEDICAL CENTER (161343)**, 709 West Main Street, Zip 52057–1526, Mailing Address: P.O. Box 359, Zip 52057–0359; tel. 563/927–3232, **A**10 18 **F**3 7 11 13 15 17 28 29 34 35 36 40 43 44 50 53 57 59 61 62 63 64 65 66 68 70 75 76 77 79 81 82 85 86 89 93 94 97 100 104 107 110 111 114 119 126 127 128 129 130 131 132 133 144 146 148
Primary Contact: Charlie A. Button, Chief Executive Officer
CFO: Danette Kramer, Chief Financial Officer
CIO: Amy Mensen, Chief Administrative Officer
CHR: Amy Mensen, Chief Administrative Officer
CNO: Heather Ries, MSN, R.N., Chief Nursing Officer
Web address: www.regmedctr.org
Control: County, Government, nonfederal **Service:** General medical and surgical

Staffed Beds: 25 **Admissions:** 785 **Census:** 7 **Outpatient Visits:** 185812 **Births:** 196 **Total Expense ($000):** 54338 **Payroll Expense ($000):** 25579 **Personnel:** 371

MANNING—Carroll County

★ **MANNING REGIONAL HEALTHCARE CENTER (161332)**, 1550 6th Street, Zip 51455–1093; tel. 712/655–2072, (Total facility includes 46 beds in nursing home–type unit) **A**10 18 **F**3 4 5 8 11 15 18 29 31 32 34 35 36 40 45 50 51 56 57 59 64 68 75 78 79 81 82 83 85 97 107 114 119 128 130 131 132 133 152 154 157 **S** MercyOne, Clive, IA
Primary Contact: John O'Brien, Chief Executive Officer
CFO: Amy McLaughlin, CPA, Chief Financial Officer
CMO: Douglas McLaws, D.O., Chief Medical Officer
CIO: Kim C Jahn, Chief Plant Operations and Chief Information Officer
CHR: Shelli Lorenzen, Chief Human Resources Officer
CNO: Linn Block, R.N., Chief Nursing Officer
Web address: www.mrhcia.com
Control: Other not–for–profit (including NFP Corporation) **Service:** General medical and surgical

Staffed Beds: 79 **Admissions:** 181 **Census:** 35 **Outpatient Visits:** 8253 **Births:** 0 **Total Expense ($000):** 18267 **Payroll Expense ($000):** 7384 **Personnel:** 166

MAQUOKETA—Jackson County

✇ **JACKSON COUNTY REGIONAL HEALTH CENTER (161329)**, 700 West Grove Street, Zip 52060–2163; tel. 563/652–2474, **A**1 10 18 **F**3 7 11 15 28 34 40 43 45 50 53 64 75 81 82 85 87 93 107 110 114 119 128 129 133 146 148 156 **S** Genesis Health System, Davenport, IA
Primary Contact: Curt Coleman, FACHE, Administrator
CFO: Donna Roeder, Chief Financial Officer
CHR: Shannon Langenberg, Director Human Resources
Web address: www.jcrhc.org
Control: County, Government, nonfederal **Service:** General medical and surgical

Staffed Beds: 12 **Admissions:** 244 **Census:** 4 **Outpatient Visits:** 18034 **Births:** 0 **Total Expense ($000):** 15852 **Payroll Expense ($000):** 5612 **Personnel:** 119

MARENGO—Iowa County

★ **COMPASS MEMORIAL HEALTHCARE (161317)**, 300 West May Street, Zip 52301–1261; tel. 319/642–5543, **A**10 18 **F**3 15 28 29 31 34 35 38 40 43 45 50 59 64 65 69 75 77 78 79 81 85 87 93 96 97 107 110 111 115 119 127 129 130 131 132 133 135 145 146 149 **S** UnityPoint Health, West Des Moines, IA
Primary Contact: Barry Goettsch, FACHE, Chief Executive Officer
COO: Mikaela Gehring, Chief Operating Officer
CFO: Matthew Murphy, Chief Financial Officer
CHR: Lesa Waddell, Director Human Resources
CNO: Teresa Sauerbrei, Chief Nursing Officer
Web address: www.compassmemorial.org
Control: City, Government, nonfederal **Service:** General medical and surgical

Staffed Beds: 25 **Admissions:** 326 **Census:** 6 **Outpatient Visits:** 18162 **Births:** 0 **Total Expense ($000):** 24033 **Payroll Expense ($000):** 10046 **Personnel:** 157

MARSHALLTOWN—Marshall County

★ **UNITYPOINT HEALTH - MARSHALLTOWN (160001)**, 3 South Fourth Avenue, Zip 50158–2998; tel. 641/754–5151, **A**10 **F**3 7 11 12 13 15 28 29 30 40 41 43 50 54 56 62 64 68 69 75 76 77 79 81 83 85 87 89 102 107 108 110 111 114 115 119 127 129 130 132 135 144 146 147 148 149 **S** UnityPoint Health, West Des Moines, IA
Primary Contact: Jennifer Friedly, President
COO: Shari King, Interim Vice President of Operations
CMO: Russell Adams, M.D., Chief Medical Officer
CHR: Jill Petermeier, Senior Executive Human Resources
Web address: www.https://marshalltown.unitypoint.org
Control: Other not–for–profit (including NFP Corporation) **Service:** General medical and surgical

Staffed Beds: 37 **Admissions:** 1858 **Census:** 16 **Outpatient Visits:** 128656 **Births:** 427 **Total Expense ($000):** 75839 **Payroll Expense ($000):** 39451 **Personnel:** 435

MASON CITY—Cerro Gordo County

✉ **MERCYONE NORTH IOWA MEDICAL CENTER (160064)**, 1000 Fourth Street SW, Zip 50401–2800; tel. 641/428–7000, **A**1 2 3 5 10 13 **F**3 11 12 13 15 18 20 22 24 26 28 29 30 31 34 35 37 40 43 45 48 50 55 56 57 58 59 61 62 63 64 65 68 69 70 71 72 74 75 76 77 78 79 81 82 84 85 87 89 90 91 92 93 96 97 98 100 102 104 105 107 108 109 110 111 112 114 115 116 117 118 119 120 121 122 123 125 126 127 128 129 130 131 132 135 144 146 147 148 149 153 154 **S** Trinity Health, Livonia, MI
Primary Contact: Rod G. Schlader, President and Chief Executive Officer
COO: Diane Fischels, Senior Vice President and Chief Operating Officer
CFO: Danette Zook, Chief Financial Officer
CMO: Paul Manternach, M.D., Senior Vice President Physician Integration
CIO: Terry Chartier, Director, Information Systems
CHR: Jackie Luecht, Chief Human Resources Officer
CNO: Kim Chamberlin, Vice President Patient Services and Chief Nursing Officer
Web address: www.mercynorthiowa.com
Control: Church operated, Nongovernment, not–for–profit **Service:** General medical and surgical

Staffed Beds: 222 **Admissions:** 9945 **Census:** 116 **Outpatient Visits:** 415442 **Births:** 897 **Total Expense ($000):** 367056 **Payroll Expense ($000):** 147645 **Personnel:** 2048

MISSOURI VALLEY—Harrison County

★ **CHI HEALTH MISSOURI VALLEY (161309)**, 631 North Eighth Street, Zip 51555–1102; tel. 712/642–2784, **A**10 18 **F**3 15 18 28 29 30 31 34 35 40 43 44 45 46 47 50 54 57 58 59 60 61 64 71 75 81 82 83 85 86 87 93 94 97 99 100 101 107 110 119 127 129 133 135 144 146 148 154 156 157 **S** CommonSpirit Health, Chicago, IL
Primary Contact: Jonathan Moe, President
CMO: Daniel Richter, M.D., Chief of Staff
CIO: Ravae Smallwood, IS Coordinator
CHR: Heidi Winters, Business Partner Human Resources
CNO: Darcy Behrendt, R.N., Vice President, Patient Care Services
Web address: www.chihealth.com/chi-health-missouri-valley
Control: Other not–for–profit (including NFP Corporation) **Service:** General medical and surgical

Staffed Beds: 16 **Admissions:** 366 **Census:** 4 **Outpatient Visits:** 27221 **Births:** 0 **Total Expense ($000):** 17653 **Payroll Expense ($000):** 6462 **Personnel:** 77

MOUNT AYR—Ringgold County

RINGGOLD COUNTY HOSPITAL (161373), 504 North Cleveland Street, Zip 50854–2201; tel. 641/464–3226, **A**10 18 **F**3 7 15 28 29 31 34 35 36 38 40 43 56 57 59 64 65 81 93 97 119 127 133 148 **S** MercyOne, Clive, IA
Primary Contact: Gordon W. Winkler, Administrator and Chief Executive Officer
CFO: Teresa Roberts, Chief Financial Officer
CIO: Beth Kosman, Director Health Information Management
CHR: Mitzi Hymbaugh, Chief Personnel
Web address: www.rchmtayr.org
Control: Hospital district or authority, Government, nonfederal **Service:** General medical and surgical

Staffed Beds: 16 **Admissions:** 255 **Census:** 3 **Outpatient Visits:** 35448 **Births:** 0 **Total Expense ($000):** 20197 **Payroll Expense ($000):** 7251 **Personnel:** 133

IA

Many Facility Codes have changed. Please refer to the AHA Guide Code Chart. © 2019 AHA Guide

MOUNT PLEASANT—Henry County

★ **HENRY COUNTY HEALTH CENTER (161356)**, 407 South White Street, Zip 52641–2263; tel. 319/385–3141, (Total facility includes 49 beds in nursing home–type unit) **A**10 18 **F**3 7 11 13 15 28 29 31 34 35 40 41 43 45 50 53 54 59 64 68 70 75 76 78 79 81 82 85 86 87 89 93 97 107 108 110 115 118 119 128 129 130 131 132 133 146 147 156
Primary Contact: Robb Gardner, Chief Executive Officer
CFO: David Muhs, Chief Financial Officer
CMO: Joel Ryon, M.D., Chief of Staff
CHR: Lynn Humphreys, Director Human Resources
CNO: Jodi Geerts, Chief Nursing Officer
Web address: www.hchc.org
Control: County, Government, nonfederal **Service**: General medical and surgical

Staffed Beds: 74 **Admissions**: 586 **Census**: 47 **Outpatient Visits**: 48851 **Births**: 120 **Total Expense ($000)**: 37907 **Payroll Expense ($000)**: 14324 **Personnel**: 218

MUSCATINE—Muscatine County

✉ **UNITYPOINT HEALTH - TRINITY MUSCATINE (160013)**, 1518 Mulberry Avenue, Zip 52761–3499; tel. 563/264–9100, **A**1 10 20 **F**3 5 11 13 15 18 28 29 34 38 40 43 45 50 55 56 57 59 61 64 65 66 68 69 70 75 76 77 81 85 87 97 102 107 108 110 111 114 119 129 130 131 132 134 135 147 148 149 156 **S** UnityPoint Health, West Des Moines, IA
Primary Contact: Angela Johnson, Executive Director
CFO: Katie A Marchik, Vice President, Consolidated Services, UnityPoint Health and Chief Financial Officer, Trinity Regional Health System
CMO: Manasi Nadkarni, M.D., Vice President Medical Affairs
CIO: Sean Liddell, Manager Regional Service Information Technology
CHR: Karla Blaser, Director Human Resources
CNO: Pam Askew, R.N., Vice President Patient Care Services
Web address: www.unitypoint.org/quadcities/trinity-muscatine.aspx
Control: Other not–for–profit (including NFP Corporation) **Service**: General medical and surgical

Staffed Beds: 45 **Admissions**: 1363 **Census**: 10 **Outpatient Visits**: 89319 **Births**: 261 **Total Expense ($000)**: 45574 **Payroll Expense ($000)**: 15565 **Personnel**: 285

NEVADA—Story County

★ **STORY COUNTY MEDICAL CENTER (161333)**, 640 South 19th Street, Zip 50201–2902; tel. 515/382–2111, (Total facility includes 65 beds in nursing home–type unit) **A**10 18 **F**3 7 11 28 29 32 34 35 36 40 43 50 53 57 59 64 65 75 81 85 87 97 107 114 116 119 127 130 133 146 147 **S** UnityPoint Health, West Des Moines, IA
Primary Contact: Nate Thompson, Chief Executive Officer
CFO: Jane Ramthun, Chief Financial Officer
CMO: Arthur Check, M.D., Chief Medical Officer
CHR: Jessica Lingo, Human Resource Generalist
CNO: Beth Rehbein, Chief Nursing and Quality Officer
Web address: www.storymedical.org
Control: County, Government, nonfederal **Service**: General medical and surgical

Staffed Beds: 82 **Admissions**: 298 **Census**: 66 **Outpatient Visits**: 52204 **Births**: 0 **Total Expense ($000)**: 27065 **Payroll Expense ($000)**: 10852 **Personnel**: 261

NEW HAMPTON—Chickasaw County

★ **MERCYONE NEW HAMPTON MEDICAL CENTER (161331)**, 308 North Maple Avenue, Zip 50659–1142; tel. 641/394–4121, **A**10 18 **F**3 11 13 15 28 29 34 35 40 43 48 56 57 59 64 65 68 74 76 77 79 81 85 93 97 107 110 119 131 133 146 149 **S** Trinity Health, Livonia, MI
Primary Contact: Aaron Flugum, Chief Executive Officer
CFO: Jennifer Rapenske, Manager Financial Services
CMO: Jack Kline, M.D., Chief of Staff
CIO: Terry Chartier, Director, Information Systems
CHR: Jackie Luecht, Director, Human Resources
CNO: Cheryl Kay Haggerty, Chief Nursing Officer, Assistant Chief Executive Officer
Web address: www.mercynewhampton.com
Control: Church operated, Nongovernment, not–for–profit **Service**: General medical and surgical

Staffed Beds: 18 **Admissions**: 292 **Census**: 3 **Outpatient Visits**: 21962 **Births**: 65 **Total Expense ($000)**: 17929 **Payroll Expense ($000)**: 6756 **Personnel**: 117

NEWTON—Jasper County

★ **MERCYONE NEWTON MEDICAL CENTER (160032)**, 204 North Fourth Avenue East, Zip 50208–3100; tel. 641/792–1273, **A**10 **F**3 11 13 15 17 28 29 30 31 34 35 40 43 44 45 50 57 59 63 64 70 75 76 77 78 79 81 82 85 89 90 93 96 102 107 108 110 111 115 119 128 129 130 131 132 133 135 145 146 148 149 156 **S** CommonSpirit Health, Chicago, IL
Primary Contact: Laurie A. Conner, FACHE, President
COO: Sonja Ranck, MSN, R.N., Chief Operating Officer and Chief Nursing Officer
CIO: Amber Wentz, Director of Clinical Information Systems & Clinical Informatics
CHR: Heather Wolf, Human Resources Business Partner
CNO: Sonja Ranck, MSN, R.N., Chief Operating Officer and Chief Nursing Officer
Web address: www.skiffmed.com
Control: Other not–for–profit (including NFP Corporation) **Service**: General medical and surgical

Staffed Beds: 26 **Admissions**: 915 **Census**: 9 **Outpatient Visits**: 78078 **Births**: 154 **Total Expense ($000)**: 34409 **Payroll Expense ($000)**: 11442 **Personnel**: 185

OELWEIN—Fayette County

★ **MERCYONE OELWEIN MEDICAL CENTER (161338)**, 201 Eighth Avenue SE, Zip 50662–2447; tel. 319/283–6000, (Total facility includes 39 beds in nursing home–type unit) **A**10 18 **F**7 11 15 29 30 34 35 40 57 59 69 75 79 93 97 107 110 111 119 127 128 130 132 133 146 147 **S** Trinity Health, Livonia, MI
Primary Contact: Terri Derflinger, Site Administrator
CFO: Timothy Huber, Vice President and Chief Financial Officer
CMO: James Lehman, M.D., Vice President Medical Affairs
CNO: Kelly Richards, MSN, Senior Vice President and Chief Nursing Officer
Web address: www.wheatoniowa.org
Control: Church operated, Nongovernment, not–for–profit **Service**: General medical and surgical

Staffed Beds: 64 **Admissions**: 250 **Census**: 37 **Outpatient Visits**: 23655 **Births**: 0 **Total Expense ($000)**: 14221 **Payroll Expense ($000)**: 5632 **Personnel**: 110

ONAWA—Monona County

★ **BURGESS HEALTH CENTER (161359)**, 1600 Diamond Street, Zip 51040–1548; tel. 712/423–2311, **A**10 18 **F**3 7 11 13 15 28 29 31 32 34 35 40 45 50 53 56 57 60 62 63 64 65 67 68 70 75 76 77 78 79 81 82 85 93 97 100 101 104 107 110 111 115 119 127 128 130 132 133 135 146 147 148 149 154 156
Primary Contact: Francis G. Tramp, President
CFO: Shawn Gosch, Chief Financial Officer
CMO: John Garred, M.D., Sr Chief Medical Officer
CIO: Grady Warner, Director of Information Technology
CHR: Erin Brekke, Director Human Resources
CNO: Patty Sandmann, Senior Director of Nursing
Web address: www.burgesshc.org
Control: Other not–for–profit (including NFP Corporation) **Service**: General medical and surgical

Staffed Beds: 25 **Admissions**: 618 **Census**: 7 **Outpatient Visits**: 63788 **Births**: 49 **Total Expense ($000)**: 28928 **Payroll Expense ($000)**: 12605 **Personnel**: 243

ORANGE CITY—Sioux County

★ **ORANGE CITY AREA HEALTH SYSTEM (161360)**, 1000 Lincoln Circle SE, Zip 51041–1862; tel. 712/737–4984, (Total facility includes 89 beds in nursing home–type unit) **A**10 18 **F**7 10 11 13 15 18 28 29 31 34 35 40 45 50 53 56 57 59 62 64 67 68 70 75 76 77 78 79 81 82 85 86 87 89 93 97 99 100 101 102 103 104 107 110 111 114 117 119 120 125 127 130 131 132 133 146 147 148 154 156 **S** Sanford Health, Sioux Falls, SD
Primary Contact: Martin W. Guthmiller, Chief Executive Officer
COO: Daniel P McCarty, Chief Operating Officer
CFO: Dina Baas, Director Financial Services
CMO: Alan Laird, M.D., Chief Medical Officer
CHR: Jason Jauron, Director Human Resources
CNO: Laurie Gebauer, Director Patient Care
Web address: www.ochealthsystem.org
Control: City, Government, nonfederal **Service**: General medical and surgical

Staffed Beds: 114 **Admissions**: 989 **Census**: 94 **Outpatient Visits**: 75353 **Births**: 216 **Total Expense ($000)**: 48591 **Payroll Expense ($000)**: 20191 **Personnel**: 425

IA

OSAGE—Mitchell County

★ **MITCHELL COUNTY REGIONAL HEALTH CENTER (161323)**, 616 North Eighth Street, Zip 50461–1498; tel. 641/732–6000, **A**10 18 **F**7 8 11 15 18 28 29 34 35 40 45 50 56 57 59 63 64 65 68 75 81 85 87 93 107 110 114 119 127 129 130 132 133 144 146 156 **S** Trinity Health, Livonia, MI
Primary Contact: Shelly Russell, Chief Executive Officer
CFO: Gregory Burkel, Chief Financial Officer
CMO: Jeff Nasstrom, D.O., Chief of Staff
CHR: Jodie Anderson, Director Human Resources
CNO: Shelly Russell, Chief Nursing Officer
Web address: www.mitchellcohospital-clinics.com
Control: County, Government, nonfederal **Service:** General medical and surgical

> **Staffed Beds:** 25 **Admissions:** 327 **Census:** 4 **Outpatient Visits:** 63065
> **Total Expense ($000):** 25101 **Payroll Expense ($000):** 8590
> **Personnel:** 186

OSCEOLA—Clarke County

★ **CLARKE COUNTY HOSPITAL (161348)**, 800 South Fillmore Street, Zip 50213–1619; tel. 641/342–2184, **A**10 18 **F**7 11 15 18 28 29 31 34 35 40 42 44 45 51 57 59 64 67 68 75 77 78 79 81 82 89 90 93 94 96 97 107 110 111 115 116 117 118 119 128 129 130 131 132 133 135 148 154 156 **S** UnityPoint Health, West Des Moines, IA
Primary Contact: Brian G. Evans, FACHE, Chief Executive Officer
CFO: Michael Thilges, Chief Financial Officer
CMO: George Fotiadis, M.D., Chief of Staff
CIO: Dennis Blazek, Chief Information Officer
CHR: Kate Emanuel, Director Human Resources
Web address: www.clarkehosp.org
Control: County, Government, nonfederal **Service:** General medical and surgical

> **Staffed Beds:** 25 **Admissions:** 288 **Census:** 10 **Outpatient Visits:** 27392
> **Births:** 0 **Total Expense ($000):** 22307 **Payroll Expense ($000):** 7237
> **Personnel:** 145

OSKALOOSA—Mahaska County

⊞ **MAHASKA HEALTH PARTNERSHIP (161379)**, 1229 'C' Avenue East, Zip 52577–4298; tel. 641/672–3100, **A**1 10 18 **F**3 5 7 11 13 15 28 29 34 35 40 43 50 54 57 59 62 63 64 65 68 70 75 77 79 81 84 85 87 93 97 100 101 102 104 107 110 111 115 119 126 129 130 132 133 146 148 149 150 156
Primary Contact: Kevin DeRonde, Chief Executive Officer
COO: Erin Baldwin, M.P.H., Chief Operating Officer
CMO: Matt Whitis, Chief Medical Officer
CHR: Sarah S. Dickey, Executive Director, Human Resource People and Culture
Web address: www.mahaskahealth.com
Control: County, Government, nonfederal **Service:** General medical and surgical

> **Staffed Beds:** 25 **Admissions:** 1117 **Census:** 13 **Outpatient Visits:** 154515
> **Births:** 182 **Total Expense ($000):** 58862 **Payroll Expense ($000):** 28569
> **Personnel:** 346

OTTUMWA—Wapello County

⊞ △ **OTTUMWA REGIONAL HEALTH CENTER (160089)**, 1001 Pennsylvania Avenue, Zip 52501–2186; tel. 641/684–2300, **A**1 7 10 **F**3 7 11 13 15 18 20 22 26 28 29 30 34 35 40 41 43 45 46 47 48 50 51 53 54 56 57 59 60 62 64 73 75 76 77 79 81 82 85 87 89 90 93 96 98 102 103 107 108 110 111 114 115 116 117 118 119 120 121 123 126 129 130 131 132 135 146 147 148 154 **S** LifePoint Health, Brentwood, TN
Primary Contact: Philip J. Noel III, Chief Executive Officer
COO: Dennis Hunger, Chief Operating Officer
CFO: Jason Hotchkiss, CPA, Chief Financial Officer
CMO: Sandro Younadam, M.D., Chief Medical Officer
CIO: Scott Garrett, Director of IS
CHR: Lidia Bryant, Director Human Resources
CNO: Lori Bailey, R.N., Vice President and Chief Nursing Officer
Web address: www.ottumwaregionalhealth.com
Control: Corporation, Investor–owned (for–profit) **Service:** General medical and surgical

> **Staffed Beds:** 101 **Admissions:** 3098 **Census:** 42 **Outpatient Visits:** 134655 **Births:** 418 **Total Expense ($000):** 74216 **Payroll Expense ($000):** 22597 **Personnel:** 533

PELLA—Marion County

⊞ **PELLA REGIONAL HEALTH CENTER (161367)**, 404 Jefferson Street, Zip 50219–1257; tel. 641/628–3150, **A**1 10 18 **F**3 11 13 15 18 28 29 30 31 32 34 35 40 43 45 50 51 53 57 59 62 63 64 65 66 70 74 75 76 77 78 79 81 82 84 85 86 87 93 94 97 102 107 108 110 111 115 119 126 127 129 130 131 132 133 146 147 148 149 154 156 157
Primary Contact: Robert D. Kroese, FACHE, Chief Executive Officer
COO: Robert D Kroese, FACHE, Chief Executive Officer
CFO: Bruce Heifner, Chief Financial Officer
CIO: Tait Smock, Manager Information Systems
CHR: Ashley Arkema, Director of Human Resources
CNO: Deborah Willyard, R.N., MSN, Chief Nursing Officer
Web address: www.pellahealth.org
Control: Other not–for–profit (including NFP Corporation) **Service:** General medical and surgical

> **Staffed Beds:** 25 **Admissions:** 1349 **Census:** 12 **Outpatient Visits:** 150306
> **Births:** 531 **Total Expense ($000):** 57575 **Payroll Expense ($000):** 20427
> **Personnel:** 608

PERRY—Dallas County

★ **DALLAS COUNTY HOSPITAL (161322)**, 610 10th Street, Zip 50220–2221; tel. 515/465–3547, **A**10 18 **F**15 18 28 29 30 31 34 35 39 40 41 43 45 47 50 56 57 59 68 75 77 78 79 81 82 89 93 107 110 114 119 128 130 132 133 135 146 148 156 **S** MercyOne, Clive, IA
Primary Contact: Angela Mortoza, Chief Executive Officer
CFO: Randy Loomis, Chief Financial Officer
CMO: Steven Sohn, M.D., President Medical Staff
CHR: Sherry Smith, Manager Human Resources
CNO: Tonya Summerson, Chief Clinical Officer
Web address: www.dallascohospital.org
Control: County, Government, nonfederal **Service:** General medical and surgical

> **Staffed Beds:** 15 **Admissions:** 153 **Census:** 2 **Outpatient Visits:** 22048
> **Births:** 1 **Total Expense ($000):** 15169 **Payroll Expense ($000):** 4619
> **Personnel:** 86

POCAHONTAS—Pocahontas County

★ **POCAHONTAS COMMUNITY HOSPITAL (161305)**, 606 NW Seventh Street, Zip 50574–1099; tel. 712/335–3501, **A**10 18 **F**7 11 15 28 29 34 35 40 43 45 50 59 64 67 75 77 78 79 81 82 85 90 93 107 110 115 119 128 129 130 132 133 135 146 148 **S** UnityPoint Health, West Des Moines, IA
Primary Contact: James D. Roetman, President and Chief Executive Officer
CFO: Lynn Raveling, Chief Financial Officer
CNO: Susie Aden, Director of IP Services
Web address: www.pocahontashospital.org
Control: City, Government, nonfederal **Service:** General medical and surgical

> **Staffed Beds:** 20 **Admissions:** 221 **Census:** 3 **Outpatient Visits:** 19811
> **Births:** 0 **Total Expense ($000):** 10715 **Payroll Expense ($000):** 3801
> **Personnel:** 84

PRIMGHAR—O'brien County

★ **MERCYONE PRIMGHAR MEDICAL CENTER (161300)**, 255 North Welch Avenue, Zip 51245–7765, Mailing Address: P.O. Box 528, Zip 51245–0528; tel. 712/957–2300, **A**10 18 **F**11 15 28 29 34 35 40 45 53 57 59 64 67 75 77 81 89 107 110 119 127 128 132 133 156 **S** Trinity Health, Livonia, MI
Primary Contact: Misty Dulin, CAH, Director
CFO: Sue E McCauley, Director Finance
CMO: Shailesh Desai, M.D., Chief of Staff
Web address: www.baumharmon.org
Control: Hospital district or authority, Government, nonfederal **Service:** General medical and surgical

> **Staffed Beds:** 11 **Admissions:** 75 **Census:** 1 **Outpatient Visits:** 20148
> **Births:** 0 **Total Expense ($000):** 8789 **Payroll Expense ($000):** 4093
> **Personnel:** 52

RED OAK—Montgomery County

★ **MONTGOMERY COUNTY MEMORIAL HOSPITAL (161363)**, 2301 Eastern Avenue, Zip 51566–1300, Mailing Address: P.O. Box 498, Zip 51566–0498; tel. 712/623–7000, **A**10 18 **F**3 11 12 13 15 28 29 31 34 35 40 44 45 50 53 55 57 59 64 65 68 69 70 71 75 76 77 78 79 81 82 85 86 87 93 107 110 111 114 115 118 119 129 130 132 133 135 146 147 148 154 156
Primary Contact: David E. Abercrombie, Chief Executive Officer
CFO: Rick J Leinen, Chief Financial Officer
CMO: Warren Hayes, Chief of Staff
CIO: Ron Kloewer, Chief Information Officer
CHR: Shayla Jennings, Human Resources Director
CNO: Diane McGrew, Chief Nurse Executive
Web address: www.mcmh.org
Control: County, Government, nonfederal **Service:** General medical and surgical

> **Staffed Beds:** 25 **Admissions:** 1016 **Census:** 13 **Outpatient Visits:** 47203
> **Births:** 59 **Total Expense ($000):** 44391 **Payroll Expense ($000):** 18546
> **Personnel:** 307

IA

Many Facility Codes have changed. Please refer to the AHA Guide Code Chart. © 2019 AHA Guide

ROCK RAPIDS—Lyon County

★ **AVERA MERRILL PIONEER HOSPITAL (161321)**, 1100 South 10th Avenue, Zip 51246–2020; tel. 712/472–5400, (Nonreporting) **S** Avera Health, Sioux Falls, SD
Primary Contact: Craig Hohn, Chief Executive Officer
Web address: www.https://www.avera.org
Control: Church operated, Nongovernment, not–for–profit **Service**: General medical and surgical

Staffed Beds: 11

ROCK VALLEY—Sioux County

★ **HEGG HEALTH CENTER AVERA (161336)**, 1202 21st Avenue, Zip 51247–1497; tel. 712/476–8000, (Total facility includes 60 beds in nursing home–type unit) **A**10 18 **F**3 11 13 15 28 29 31 34 35 36 40 41 43 44 45 50 53 57 59 62 64 65 67 68 75 76 77 78 79 81 82 85 89 91 93 96 97 107 110 115 119 128 130 131 132 133 135 144 146 147 148 154 156 **S** Avera Health, Sioux Falls, SD
Primary Contact: Glenn Zevenbergen, Chief Executive Officer
CFO: Kari Timmer, Chief Financial Officer
CMO: Jon Engbers, M.D., President
CHR: Tammy Faber, Director Human Resources
Web address: www.hegghc.org
Control: Other not–for–profit (including NFP Corporation) **Service**: General medical and surgical

Staffed Beds: 85 Admissions: 336 Census: 63 Outpatient Visits: 35145 Births: 67 Total Expense ($000): 20219 Payroll Expense ($000): 10449 Personnel: 188

SAC CITY—Sac County

★ **LORING HOSPITAL (161370)**, 211 Highland Avenue, Zip 50583–2424; tel. 712/662–7105, **A**10 18 **F**3 11 15 28 29 30 31 34 35 40 43 45 50 57 59 64 68 75 77 79 81 83 85 86 87 93 102 107 110 115 125 130 133 146 148 149 156 157 **S** UnityPoint Health, West Des Moines, IA
Primary Contact: Stacy Johnson, Chief Executive Officer
CMO: Les Marczewski, M.D., Chief Medical Officer
CIO: Leah Snyder, Director Health Information Services
CHR: Becky Pontious, Human Resources/Accounting
Web address: www.loringhospital.org
Control: Other not–for–profit (including NFP Corporation) **Service**: General medical and surgical

Staffed Beds: 25 Admissions: 257 Census: 3 Outpatient Visits: 24708 Births: 0 Total Expense ($000): 12454 Payroll Expense ($000): 4319 Personnel: 104

SHELDON—O'brien County

★ **SANFORD SHELDON MEDICAL CENTER (161381)**, 118 North Seventh Avenue, Zip 51201–1235, Mailing Address: P.O. Box 250, Zip 51201–0250; tel. 712/324–5041, (Total facility includes 70 beds in nursing home–type unit) **A**10 18 **F**3 15 28 29 31 32 34 35 38 40 43 45 50 53 57 59 62 63 64 65 66 67 68 74 75 76 77 78 79 81 82 84 86 87 91 93 96 97 99 100 101 102 103 104 107 108 110 111 114 119 127 130 131 132 133 135 146 148 149 150 154 156 **S** Sanford Health, Sioux Falls, SD
Primary Contact: Richard E. Nordahl, Senior Director
CFO: Richard E. Nordahl, Senior Director
CMO: Scott Lichty, M.D., Physician
CIO: Jason Brown, Director Information Systems
CHR: Dianne Wolthuizen, Director Human Resources
CNO: Joni DeKok, Chief Nursing Officer
Web address: www.sanfordsheldon.org
Control: Other not–for–profit (including NFP Corporation) **Service**: General medical and surgical

Staffed Beds: 95 Admissions: 712 Census: 67 Outpatient Visits: 43829 Births: 83 Total Expense ($000): 30366 Payroll Expense ($000): 14667 Personnel: 241

SHENANDOAH—Page County

★ **SHENANDOAH MEDICAL CENTER (161366)**, 300 Pershing Avenue, Zip 51601–2355; tel. 712/246–1230, (Total facility includes 50 beds in nursing home–type unit) **A**10 18 **F**1 3 4 13 15 16 17 18 28 29 31 34 36 38 40 41 43 45 50 53 56 57 59 62 63 64 65 67 68 69 70 72 73 74 75 76 77 78 79 80 81 83 84 85 87 88 89 90 91 93 98 104 107 108 110 111 115 117 118 119 127 128 129 130 131 132 133 135 144 146 147 148 149 154
Primary Contact: Matt Sells, Chief Executive Officer
COO: Jonathan Moe, Chief Operating Officer
CFO: Kaley Neal, Chief Financial Officer
CMO: Heather Babe, M.D., Chief of Staff
CIO: Chuck Dougherty, Chief Information Officer
CHR: Keli Royal, Chief Human Resources Officer
CNO: Laura Stofferson, Chief Nursing Officer
Web address: www.smchospital.com/
Control: Other not–for–profit (including NFP Corporation) **Service**: General medical and surgical

Staffed Beds: 75 Admissions: 583 Census: 45 Outpatient Visits: 208419 Births: 94 Total Expense ($000): 44166 Payroll Expense ($000): 21426 Personnel: 277

SIBLEY—Page County

★ **OSCEOLA COMMUNITY HOSPITAL (161345)**, 600 Ninth Avenue North, Zip 51249–1012, Mailing Address: P.O. Box 258, Zip 51249–0258; tel. 712/754–2574, **A**10 18 **F**3 8 9 10 11 12 15 17 18 26 28 29 31 32 34 35 36 40 43 45 46 50 53 56 57 59 61 62 64 65 67 68 70 75 77 78 79 81 82 84 85 86 87 89 107 108 110 114 119 125 128 129 130 131 132 133 135 143 144 145 146 147 148 149 154 156 **S** Avera Health, Sioux Falls, SD
Primary Contact: Ben Davis, Chief Executive Officer
CFO: Lorrie Reed, Chief Financial Officer
CMO: Gregory J Kosters, D.O., Chief Medical Officer
Web address: www.osceolacommunityhospital.org
Control: Other not–for–profit (including NFP Corporation) **Service**: General medical and surgical

Staffed Beds: 25 Admissions: 211 Census: 2 Outpatient Visits: 14547 Births: 8 Total Expense ($000): 12253 Payroll Expense ($000): 4141 Personnel: 87

SIGOURNEY—Keokuk County

KEOKUK COUNTY HEALTH CENTER (161315), 23019 Highway 149, Zip 52591–8341; tel. 641/622–2720, **A**10 18 **F**1 2 3 7 11 12 15 28 29 30 34 35 38 40 43 44 45 46 50 56 57 59 64 65 66 67 75 77 82 84 86 87 90 91 93 97 107 110 114 117 127 128 129 130 131 132 133 135 146 147 148 156
Primary Contact: Matthew Ives, Chief Executive Officer and Chief Financial Officer
CFO: Matthew Ives, Interim Chief Executive Officer and Chief Financial Officer
Web address: www.kchc.net
Control: County, Government, nonfederal **Service**: General medical and surgical

Staffed Beds: 14 Admissions: 136 Census: 4 Outpatient Visits: 23517 Births: 0 Total Expense ($000): 11904 Payroll Expense ($000): 6140 Personnel: 106

SIOUX CENTER—Sioux County

★ **SIOUX CENTER HEALTH (161346)**, 1101 9th Street SE, Zip 51250; tel. 712/722–8107, (Total facility includes 69 beds in nursing home–type unit) **A**10 18 **F**3 8 10 12 13 15 18 26 28 29 30 31 34 35 40 41 43 45 50 56 57 59 62 63 64 65 67 68 74 75 76 77 78 79 80 81 82 84 85 86 87 89 93 96 97 100 101 104 107 108 110 111 114 119 125 128 130 131 132 133 144 146 147 148 149 154 156 157 **S** Avera Health, Sioux Falls, SD
Primary Contact: Cory D. Nelson, Administrator
CFO: Jackson Schuiteman, Chief Financial Officer
CHR: Theresa Tucker, Human Resources Officer
Web address: www.siouxcenterhealth.org
Control: Other not–for–profit (including NFP Corporation) **Service**: General medical and surgical

Staffed Beds: 88 Admissions: 549 Census: 73 Outpatient Visits: 52374 Births: 174 Total Expense ($000): 41546 Payroll Expense ($000): 17414 Personnel: 353

IA

SIOUX CITY—Woodbury County

☒ **MERCYONE SIOUXLAND MEDICAL CENTER (160153)**, 801 Fifth Street, Zip 51101–1326, Mailing Address: P.O. Box 3168, Zip 51102–3168; tel. 712/279–2010, **A**1 2 3 5 10 19 **F**3 5 8 11 12 13 15 17 18 20 22 24 26 28 29 30 31 32 34 35 37 40 43 44 45 49 50 56 57 59 64 65 68 70 71 74 75 76 77 78 79 81 82 84 85 87 89 90 91 92 93 96 97 98 100 102 107 108 110 111 114 115 118 119 124 126 127 128 129 130 144 145 146 148 149 150 154 156 157 **S** Trinity Health, Livonia, MI
Primary Contact: Beth Hughes, President
CFO: Hugh DePaulis, Interim Vice President and Chief Financial Officer
CMO: Jerome Pierson, Chief Medical Officer
CIO: Steve Larson, M.D., Director Information Systems
CHR: Julie Anfinson, Director Human Resources
CNO: Tracy Larson, MS, Vice President Patient Care Services and Chief Nursing Officer
Web address: www.mercysiouxcity.com
Control: Church operated, Nongovernment, not–for–profit **Service**: General medical and surgical

Staffed Beds: 197 **Admissions**: 9187 **Census**: 120 **Outpatient Visits**: 205685 **Births**: 268 **Total Expense ($000)**: 208630 **Payroll Expense ($000)**: 77788 **Personnel**: 1312

★ ⇑ **UNITYPOINT HEALTH - ST. LUKES'S SIOUX CITY (160146)**, 2720 Stone Park Boulevard, Zip 51104–3734; tel. 712/279–3500, **A**3 5 10 21 **F**3 11 13 15 17 18 20 22 26 28 29 30 31 34 35 39 40 43 45 49 50 51 54 56 57 58 59 60 64 68 70 72 73 74 75 76 77 78 79 81 82 84 85 86 88 89 90 91 92 93 96 97 98 102 104 107 108 111 114 115 118 119 126 129 130 131 132 135 142 143 144 145 146 147 149 154 156 157 **S** UnityPoint Health, West Des Moines, IA
Primary Contact: Lynn Wold, President and Chief Executive Officer
COO: Chad Markham, Chief Operating Officer
CFO: James Gobell, Chief Financial Officer
CIO: James Gobell, Chief Financial Officer
CHR: Tammy Hartnett, Employee Relations Manager
CNO: Priscilla Stokes, MS, R.N., Vice President Patient Care and Hospital Operations
Web address: www.stlukes.org
Control: Other not–for–profit (including NFP Corporation) **Service**: General medical and surgical

Staffed Beds: 152 **Admissions**: 9000 **Census**: 101 **Outpatient Visits**: 87029 **Births**: 1947 **Total Expense ($000)**: 164823 **Payroll Expense ($000)**: 69879 **Personnel**: 1252

SPENCER—Clay County

★ **SPENCER HOSPITAL (160112)**, 1200 First Avenue East, Suite 1, Zip 51301–4342; tel. 712/264–6111, **A**10 **F**3 7 8 11 13 15 28 29 30 31 34 35 37 39 40 43 45 50 53 57 59 60 62 63 64 65 70 75 76 77 78 79 81 82 85 86 87 93 96 98 107 108 109 110 111 115 118 119 120 121 123 126 127 129 130 131 132 133 135 144 146 147 148 149
Primary Contact: William J. Bumgarner, President
CFO: Stacy E Mol, CPA, Director Finance
CMO: Sonia Sather, M.D., President Medical Staff
CIO: Brenda Marie Tiefenthaler, R.N., MSN, Vice President Patient Care and Informatics
CHR: Stephen Deutsch, Vice President Operations and Support
CNO: Brenda Marie Tiefenthaler, R.N., MSN, Vice President Patient Care and Informatics
Web address: www.spencerhospital.org
Control: City, Government, nonfederal **Service**: General medical and surgical

Staffed Beds: 64 **Admissions**: 2400 **Census**: 25 **Outpatient Visits**: 125619 **Births**: 289 **Total Expense ($000)**: 88721 **Payroll Expense ($000)**: 23875 **Personnel**: 425

SPIRIT LAKE—Dickinson County

★ **LAKES REGIONAL HEALTHCARE (160124)**, 2301 Highway 71 South, Zip 51360–0159; tel. 712/336–1230, **A**10 **F**3 7 11 13 15 28 29 30 31 34 35 37 40 41 43 45 50 57 59 62 63 64 65 70 75 76 77 78 79 81 85 89 91 93 97 107 111 115 119 126 128 129 130 132 133 143 146 148 149 154 156 **S** Avera Health, Sioux Falls, SD
Primary Contact: Jason Harrington, FACHE, President and Chief Executive Officer
CFO: Steve Alger, Senior Vice President and Chief Financial Officer
CMO: Zachary A. Borus, M.D., Medical Chief of Staff
CIO: Derek Larson, Information Technology Network
CHR: Sonja Hamm, Vice President Human and Foundation Resources
CNO: Connie Lange, R.N., Vice President Quality, Inpatient and Community Services
Web address: www.lakeshealth.org
Control: County, Government, nonfederal **Service**: General medical and surgical

Staffed Beds: 30 **Admissions**: 921 **Census**: 8 **Outpatient Visits**: 103730 **Births**: 157 **Total Expense ($000)**: 40212 **Payroll Expense ($000)**: 12343 **Personnel**: 218

STORM LAKE—Buena Vista County

☒ **BUENA VISTA REGIONAL MEDICAL CENTER (161375)**, 1525 West Fifth Street, Zip 50588–3027, Mailing Address: P.O. Box 309, Zip 50588–0309; tel. 712/732–4030, **A**1 10 18 **F**3 7 8 11 13 15 18 28 29 30 31 34 40 43 45 53 55 56 57 59 63 64 68 70 74 75 76 77 78 79 81 82 84 85 86 87 93 96 98 103 107 108 110 111 115 117 118 119 128 129 130 131 132 133 135 146 147 148 **S** UnityPoint Health, West Des Moines, IA
Primary Contact: Steven Colerick, Chief Executive Officer
CFO: Krista Ketcham, Chief Financial Officer
CMO: Lisa Shepherd, M.D., Chief of Staff
CIO: Steve Spurlock, Director Information Systems
CHR: Carrie Turnquist, Director Human Resources
CNO: Dawn M Bach, MS, Chief Clinical Officer
Web address: www.bvrmc.org
Control: County, Government, nonfederal **Service**: General medical and surgical

Staffed Beds: 35 **Admissions**: 1261 **Census**: 15 **Outpatient Visits**: 65833 **Births**: 321 **Total Expense ($000)**: 51654 **Payroll Expense ($000)**: 20098 **Personnel**: 334

SUMNER—Bremer County

★ **COMMUNITY MEMORIAL HOSPITAL (161320)**, 909 West First Street, Zip 50674–1203, Mailing Address: P.O. Box 148, Zip 50674–0148; tel. 563/578–3275, **A**10 18 **F**3 11 15 28 29 34 40 45 57 59 64 77 81 82 85 86 97 107 110 114 119 128 129 131 133 135 148 149 156 **S** UnityPoint Health, West Des Moines, IA
Primary Contact: Dawn Everding, President and Chief Financial Officer
CFO: Dawn Everding, President and Chief Financial Officer
CMO: Jeff Roske, D.O., Chief Medical Staff
CHR: Robin Elliott, Personnel Officer
CNO: Lynne Niemann, Director Nurses and Patient Care
Web address: www.cmhsumner.org
Control: Other not–for–profit (including NFP Corporation) **Service**: General medical and surgical

Staffed Beds: 16 **Admissions**: 175 **Census**: 2 **Outpatient Visits**: 34713 **Births**: 0 **Total Expense ($000)**: 13968 **Payroll Expense ($000)**: 5107 **Personnel**: 83

VINTON—Benton County

★ **VIRGINIA GAY HOSPITAL (161349)**, 502 North 9th Avenue, Zip 52349–2299; tel. 319/472–6200, (Total facility includes 40 beds in nursing home–type unit) **A**10 18 **F**3 15 28 29 34 40 43 45 53 57 59 62 63 64 65 75 77 81 85 86 87 91 93 96 97 100 107 110 111 114 119 125 127 129 130 131 132 133 143 146 148 149 154 156
Primary Contact: Michele Schoonover, Chief Executive Officer
CFO: Barry Dietsch, Chief Financial Officer
CMO: Brian Meeker, D.O., President Medical Staff
CIO: Sherri Isbell, Chief Information Officer
CHR: Kim Frank, Chief Human Resources Officer
CNO: Tina M Eden, Director of Nursing
Web address: www.myvgh.org
Control: Other not–for–profit (including NFP Corporation) **Service**: General medical and surgical

Staffed Beds: 65 **Admissions**: 375 **Census**: 42 **Outpatient Visits**: 82220 **Births**: 0 **Total Expense ($000)**: 27868 **Payroll Expense ($000)**: 12898 **Personnel**: 238

WASHINGTON—Washington County

★ **WASHINGTON COUNTY HOSPITAL AND CLINICS (161344)**, 400 East Polk Street, Zip 52353–1237, Mailing Address: P.O. Box 909, Zip 52353–0909; tel. 319/653–5481, (Total facility includes 43 beds in nursing home–type unit) **A**10 18 **F**3 13 15 18 28 29 34 40 43 45 50 57 59 64 67 68 74 75 76 81 85 86 93 96 97 107 110 111 115 119 127 130 132 133 146 147 148 **S** QHR, Brentwood, TN
Primary Contact: Todd Patterson, Chief Executive Officer
CFO: Steve Sanders, Chief Financial Officer
CMO: Matt Prihoda, M.D., Chief of Staff
CIO: Makyla Maize, Director Information Services
CHR: Tracy Ousey, Director Human Resources
CNO: Andrea Leyden RN Chief Nursing Officer
Web address: www.wchc.org
Control: County, Government, nonfederal **Service**: General medical and surgical

Staffed Beds: 68 **Admissions**: 1231 **Census**: 42 **Outpatient Visits**: 55022 **Births**: 118 **Total Expense ($000)**: 44563 **Payroll Expense ($000)**: 18706 **Personnel**: 302

IA

Many Facility Codes have changed. Please refer to the AHA Guide Code Chart. © 2019 AHA Guide

WATERLOO—Black Hawk County

ALLEN MEMORIAL HOSPITAL See Unitypoint Health - Allen Hospital

☒ △ **MERCYONE WATERLOO MEDICAL CENTER (160067)**, 3421 West Ninth Street, Zip 50702–5401; tel. 319/272–8000, (Includes KIMBALL-RIDGE CENTER, 2101 Kimball Avenue, Waterloo, Iowa, Zip 50702; tel. 319/272–8000; Jack Dusenbery, President and Chief Executive Officer) **A**1 2 3 5 7 10 **F**3 4 5 7 11 13 15 18 19 20 22 26 28 29 30 31 33 34 35 40 43 44 46 49 50 51 53 56 57 58 59 60 61 62 64 68 70 71 72 74 75 76 77 78 79 81 82 86 87 89 90 93 97 98 99 100 101 102 104 107 108 110 111 114 115 116 118 119 120 126 127 129 130 131 132 135 143 144 146 147 148 152 154 155 **S** Trinity Health, Livonia, MI
Primary Contact: Jack Dusenbery, President and Chief Executive Officer
CFO: Timothy Huber, Vice President and Chief Financial Officer
CMO: James Lehman, M.D., Vice President Medical Affairs
CIO: Marge Ray, Director Information Systems
CHR: Suzanne M. Burt, Director Human Resources
CNO: Kelly Richards, MSN, Senior Vice President and Chief Nursing Officer
Web address: www.wheatoniowa.org
Control: Church operated, Nongovernment, not–for–profit **Service**: General medical and surgical

Staffed Beds: 229 **Admissions**: 7709 **Census**: 89 **Outpatient Visits**: 655034 **Births**: 1344 **Total Expense ($000)**: 308476 **Payroll Expense ($000)**: 136590 **Personnel**: 1805

☒ △ **UNITYPOINT HEALTH - ALLEN HOSPITAL (160110)**, 1825 Logan Avenue, Zip 50703–1916; tel. 319/235–3941, **A**1 3 5 7 10 **F**3 8 11 13 15 18 20 22 24 26 28 29 30 31 34 35 37 40 43 45 46 48 49 50 51 54 56 57 59 63 64 66 68 70 72 74 75 76 77 78 79 81 82 84 85 86 87 88 90 91 92 93 96 97 98 99 100 101 102 103 104 107 108 110 111 114 115 118 119 126 127 129 130 132 135 146 147 148 149 153 **S** UnityPoint Health, West Des Moines, IA
Primary Contact: Pamela K. Delagardelle, President and Chief Executive Officer
COO: Jennifer Friedly, Chief Operating Officer and Vice President
CFO: Craig Flanagan, Chief Financial Officer
CMO: Timothy Horrigan, M.D., Chief Quality Officer
CIO: Daniel Norman, Regional Service Manager
CHR: Steven Sesterhenn, Vice President
CNO: Mary Hagen, R.N., MSN, VP and Chief Nursing Officer
Web address: www.unitypoint.org/waterloo
Control: Other not–for–profit (including NFP Corporation) **Service**: General medical and surgical

Staffed Beds: 201 **Admissions**: 9394 **Census**: 94 **Outpatient Visits**: 304225 **Births**: 1102 **Total Expense ($000)**: 274805 **Payroll Expense ($000)**: 102373 **Personnel**: 1331

WAUKON—Allamakee County

★ **VETERANS MEMORIAL HOSPITAL (101010)**, 40 First Street SE, Zip 52172–2099; tel. 563/568–3411, **A**10 18 **F**7 11 13 15 28 34 35 40 45 46 57 59 62 64 65 75 76 77 79 81 93 107 110 111 119 131 132 133 134 144 146 156
Primary Contact: Michael D. Myers, R.N., Chief Executive Officer
CFO: Scott Knode, Chief Financial Officer
CHR: Erin Berns, Director Human Resources
Web address: www.vmhospital.com
Control: City, Government, nonfederal **Service**: General medical and surgical

Staffed Beds: 25 **Admissions**: 516 **Census**: 7 **Outpatient Visits**: 42246 **Births**: 128 **Total Expense ($000)**: 19344 **Payroll Expense ($000)**: 9276 **Personnel**: 159

WAVERLY—Bremer County

☒ **WAVERLY HEALTH CENTER (161339)**, 312 Ninth Street SW, Zip 50677–2999; tel. 319/352–4120, **A**1 10 18 **F**3 7 8 11 12 13 15 26 28 29 34 35 36 40 43 45 50 57 59 63 64 75 76 77 81 85 86 97 104 107 110 111 114 119 127 130 132 133 135 144 146 147 156
Primary Contact: James Atty, Chief Executive Officer
CFO: Lisa Bennett, Chief Financial Officer
CMO: Clay Dahlquist, M.D., Chief Medical Officer
CIO: Jerry Tiedt, Director Information Systems
CHR: Angie Tye, Director Human Resources
CNO: Joanne Nathem, MSN, R.N., Chief Clinical and Nursing Officer
Web address: www.waverlyhealthcenter.org
Control: City, Government, nonfederal **Service**: General medical and surgical

Staffed Beds: 25 **Admissions**: 822 **Census**: 6 **Outpatient Visits**: 118433 **Births**: 258 **Total Expense ($000)**: 56369 **Payroll Expense ($000)**: 26555 **Personnel**: 336

WEBSTER CITY—Hamilton County

HAMILTON HOSPITAL See Van Diest Medical Center

★ **VAN DIEST MEDICAL CENTER (161361)**, 2350 Hospital Drive, Zip 50595–6600, Mailing Address: P.O. Box 430, Zip 50595–0430; tel. 515/832–9400, **A**10 18 **F**3 7 8 11 15 28 29 31 36 40 43 45 50 75 77 79 81 82 85 93 96 97 107 110 111 115 119 127 130 133 157 **S** MercyOne, Clive, IA
Primary Contact: Lisa Ridge, Chief Executive Officer
CFO: Alice Heinrichs, CPA, Chief Financial Officer
CMO: Nicole Ehn, M.D., Chief of Staff
CIO: Erick Schrier, Supervisor Information Technology
CHR: Jodie Harker, Director Human Resources
CNO: Janet Naset-Payne, MS, R.N., Chief Nursing Officer
Web address: www.vandiestmc.org
Control: County, Government, nonfederal **Service**: General medical and surgical

Staffed Beds: 25 **Admissions**: 870 **Census**: 9 **Outpatient Visits**: 54952 **Births**: 74 **Total Expense ($000)**: 33877 **Payroll Expense ($000)**: 14719 **Personnel**: 223

WEST BURLINGTON—Des Moines County

★ △ **GREAT RIVER HEALTH SYSTEM (160057)**, 1221 South Gear Avenue, Zip 52655–1681; tel. 319/768–1000, (Total facility includes 160 beds in nursing home–type unit) **A**7 10 19 **F**3 5 7 11 13 15 18 20 22 28 29 30 31 32 34 35 36 38 40 43 45 48 50 53 57 59 60 62 63 64 68 69 70 73 75 77 78 79 81 82 84 85 86 87 90 91 92 93 96 98 99 100 101 102 103 104 107 108 110 111 114 115 116 117 118 119 120 121 123 128 129 130 131 132 143 146 147 148 154 156 157
Primary Contact: Matthew Wenzel, President and Chief Executive Officer
CFO: Todd J. Sladky, Chief Financial Officer and Vice President Finance
CMO: Michael Jerry McCoy, M.D., Chief Medical Officer
CIO: Levi Nathan Gause, M.D., Chief Information Officer and Vice President Health System Informatics
CHR: James M. Kammerer, Vice President Support Services
CNO: Teresa Colgan, Vice President Nursing
Web address: www.greatrivermedical.org
Control: Other not–for–profit (including NFP Corporation) **Service**: General medical and surgical

Staffed Beds: 314 **Admissions**: 6795 **Census**: 226 **Outpatient Visits**: 299440 **Births**: 585 **Total Expense ($000)**: 177177 **Payroll Expense ($000)**: 69908 **Personnel**: 1288

WEST UNION—Fayette County

★ **GUNDERSEN PALMER LUTHERAN HOSPITAL AND CLINICS (161316)**, 112 Jefferson Street, Zip 52175–1022; tel. 563/422–3811, **A**10 18 **F**3 11 13 15 28 29 30 31 32 34 35 36 38 40 43 44 45 50 53 56 57 59 62 63 64 65 68 75 76 77 78 79 81 82 85 86 87 89 91 93 96 100 101 107 110 111 115 119 127 128 129 130 131 132 133 135 146 148 154 156
Primary Contact: Patrice Kuennen, Chief Executive Officer
CFO: Joni Gisleson, Director Finance
CMO: Chaudri Rasool, D.O., Chief of Staff
CIO: Kurt Chicken, Director Support Services
CHR: Cheryl Meyer, Director Human Resources
CNO: Kathy Begalske, Chief Nursing Officer
Web address: www.palmerlutheran.org
Control: Other not–for–profit (including NFP Corporation) **Service**: General medical and surgical

Staffed Beds: 25 **Admissions**: 256 **Census**: 3 **Outpatient Visits**: 89712 **Births**: 89 **Total Expense ($000)**: 29722 **Payroll Expense ($000)**: 9846 **Personnel**: 195

WINTERSET—Madison County

★ **MADISON COUNTY HEALTH CARE SYSTEM (161326)**, 300 West Hutchings Street, Zip 50273–2109; tel. 515/462–2373, **A**10 18 **F**3 15 18 28 31 35 37 40 43 45 57 64 78 79 81 89 93 97 107 110 114 119 127 128 130 131 133 135 144 146 149 156 **S** CommonSpirit Health, Chicago, IL
Primary Contact: Marcia Hendricks, FACHE, R.N., Chief Executive Officer
CFO: Rebekah Mitchell, Chief Financial Officer
CMO: David Smith, D.O., Chief of Staff
CIO: Dan VandenBosch, Chief Information Officer
CHR: Jennifer Jackson, Director Human Resources
CNO: Kim Hulbert, R.N., Chief Clinical and Nursing Officer
Web address: www.madisonhealth.com
Control: County, Government, nonfederal **Service**: General medical and surgical

Staffed Beds: 25 **Admissions**: 395 **Census**: 5 **Outpatient Visits**: 63594 **Births**: 0 **Total Expense ($000)**: 22553 **Payroll Expense ($000)**: 8855 **Personnel**: 152

IA

KANSAS

ABILENE—Dickinson County

★ **MEMORIAL HEALTH SYSTEM (171381)**, 511 NE Tenth Street, Zip 67410–2153; tel. 785/263–2100, (Total facility includes 74 beds in nursing home–type unit) **A**10 18 **F**2 3 11 13 15 18 28 29 34 40 45 53 57 59 62 63 64 68 69 75 76 77 78 79 81 82 85 87 89 93 97 98 103 104 107 108 110 111 115 119 127 128 129 130 131 132 133 143 145 146 148 149 154 158
Primary Contact: Harold Courtois, Chief Executive Officer
CFO: Elgin Glanzer, Chief Financial Officer
CMO: W L Short, M.D., Chief Medical Officer
CIO: Blaine Cappel, Director Information Systems
CNO: Brenda L. Moffitt, Chief Nursing Officer
Web address: www.mhsks.org
Control: Hospital district or authority, Government, nonfederal **Service:** General medical and surgical

Staffed Beds: 109 **Admissions:** 834 **Census:** 86 **Outpatient Visits:** 25161
Births: 28 **Total Expense ($000):** 34380 **Payroll Expense ($000):** 14878
Personnel: 310

ANDOVER—Butler County

KANSAS MEDICAL CENTER (170197), 1124 West 21st Street, Zip 67002–5500; tel. 316/300–4000, **A**10 **F**3 18 20 22 24 28 29 30 40 42 49 60 64 68 70 75 77 79 81 85 87 93 102 107 108 111 115 117 119 126 130 131 146 148 157
Primary Contact: Badr Idbeis, M.D., Chief Executive Officer
COO: Daryl W Thornton, Chief Operating Officer
CFO: Steven N Hadley, Chief Financial Officer
CMO: G. Whitney Reader, M.D., Chief Medical Officer
CIO: Mike Buffington, Manager Information Technology
CHR: Norm Nevins, Manager Human Resources
CNO: Janet Kaiser, R.N., Chief Nursing Officer
Web address: www.ksmedcenter.com/
Control: Corporation, Investor–owned (for–profit) **Service:** General medical and surgical

Staffed Beds: 58 **Admissions:** 2650 **Census:** 27 **Outpatient Visits:** 14233
Births: 0 **Personnel:** 266

ARKANSAS CITY—Cowley County

★ **SOUTH CENTRAL KANSAS MEDICAL CENTER (170150)**, 6401 Patterson Parkway, Zip 67005–5701, Mailing Address: P.O. Box 1107, Zip 67005–1107; tel. 620/442–2500, **A**10 20 **F**3 8 11 12 13 15 19 29 30 34 35 39 40 41 45 47 48 50 54 56 57 59 64 68 70 75 76 79 81 82 85 87 93 97 98 100 103 107 108 110 111 115 119 127 130 132 133 135 146 147 148 149 154 156 157
Primary Contact: Jeff Bowman, Interim Chief Executive Officer
CFO: Holly Beaty, Chief Financial Officer
CMO: Kamran Shahzada, M.D., Chief Medical Staff
CHR: Clayton Pappan, Director Human Resources and Marketing
CNO: Patricia Davis, Chief Nursing Officer
Web address: www.sckrmc.org
Control: City, Government, nonfederal **Service:** General medical and surgical

Staffed Beds: 44 **Admissions:** 974 **Census:** 17 **Outpatient Visits:** 18282
Births: 84

ASHLAND—Clark County

★ **ASHLAND HEALTH CENTER (171304)**, 709 Oak Street, Zip 67831–0188, Mailing Address: P.O. Box 188, Zip 67831–0188; tel. 620/635–2241, **A**10 18 **F**2 30 34 40 53 59 62 64 68 85 87 93 107 127 128 133 143 154 156 **S** Great Plains Health Alliance, Inc., Wichita, KS
Primary Contact: Michael Mages, Chief Executive Officer
CFO: Debbie Filson, Chief Financial Officer
CMO: Daniel Shuman, D.O., Chief Medical Officer
CIO: Alan Romans, Director Information Technology
CHR: Debbie Filson, Chief Financial Officer
CNO: Patty Young, R.N., Chief Nursing Officer
Web address: www.ashlandhc.org
Control: Hospital district or authority, Government, nonfederal **Service:** General medical and surgical

Staffed Beds: 25 **Admissions:** 128 **Census:** 19 **Outpatient Visits:** 6415
Births: 0 **Total Expense ($000):** 7983 **Payroll Expense ($000):** 3201
Personnel: 77

ATCHISON—Atchison County

★ ○ **ATCHISON HOSPITAL (171382)**, 800 Raven Hill Drive, Zip 66002–9204; tel. 913/367–2131, **A**10 11 18 **F**3 11 13 15 28 29 30 31 34 35 39 40 45 49 50 57 59 62 63 64 65 68 70 75 76 77 79 81 82 85 87 89 92 93 96 97 107 108 110 111 114 118 119 127 129 130 131 132 133 135 144 146 147 148 149
Primary Contact: Jeffery Perry, President and Chief Executive Officer
COO: Sandra Leggett, Chief Operating Officer
CFO: Gary R Foll, Chief Financial Officer
CMO: McGarrett Groth, Chief of Staff
CIO: Terry Davis, Manager Information Systems
CHR: Jill Wenger, Chief Human Resources Officer
Web address: www.atchisonhospital.org
Control: Other not–for–profit (including NFP Corporation) **Service:** General medical and surgical

Staffed Beds: 25 **Admissions:** 964 **Census:** 10 **Outpatient Visits:** 85379
Births: 143 **Total Expense ($000):** 40507 **Payroll Expense ($000):** 19324
Personnel: 296

ATWOOD—Rawlins County

★ **RAWLINS COUNTY HEALTH CENTER (171307)**, 707 Grant Street, Zip 67730–1526, Mailing Address: P.O. Box 47, Zip 67730–0047; tel. 785/626–3211, **A**10 18 **F**3 28 29 34 35 40 41 43 45 50 53 59 64 65 66 67 75 81 83 85 87 93 97 107 115 125 127 128 130 131 132 133 135 147 148 149 154 156
Primary Contact: Ronald R. Robinson, M.D., M.P.H., FACHE, Chief Executive Officer and Chief Medical Officer
COO: Ryan Marvin, Support Services Director
CFO: Heather Prideaux, Chief Financial Officer
CMO: Ronald R. Robinson, M.D., M.P.H., FACHE, Chief Executive Officer and Chief Medical Officer
CIO: Destiny Schroeder, Information Systems Director
CHR: Tara Bowles, Employee Relations Director
CNO: Amber Withington, R.N., Chief Clinical Officer
Web address: www.rchc.us
Control: County, Government, nonfederal **Service:** General medical and surgical

Staffed Beds: 15 **Admissions:** 175 **Census:** 2 **Outpatient Visits:** 6338
Births: 0 **Total Expense ($000):** 8200 **Payroll Expense ($000):** 3185
Personnel: 67

BELLEVILLE—Republic County

★ **REPUBLIC COUNTY HOSPITAL (171361)**, 2420 'G' Street, Zip 66935–2400; tel. 785/527–2254, **A**10 18 **F**3 13 15 28 29 30 31 34 35 40 43 45 56 57 59 64 68 75 76 77 78 79 81 82 85 86 87 89 91 93 94 104 107 108 110 114 119 128 129 130 131 133 153 156 **S** Great Plains Alliance, Inc., Wichita, KS
Primary Contact: David-Paul Cavazos, Chief Executive Officer
CFO: Barry Bottger, Chief Financial Officer
Web address: www.rphospital.org
Control: Other not–for–profit (including NFP Corporation) **Service:** General medical and surgical

Staffed Beds: 25 **Admissions:** 707 **Census:** 16 **Outpatient Visits:** 15976
Births: 52 **Total Expense ($000):** 13477 **Payroll Expense ($000):** 5969
Personnel: 117

BELOIT—Mitchell County

★ **MITCHELL COUNTY HOSPITAL HEALTH SYSTEMS (171375)**, 400 West Eighth, Zip 67420–1605, Mailing Address: P.O. Box 399, Zip 67420–0399; tel. 785/738–2266, (Total facility includes 40 beds in nursing home–type unit) **A**10 18 **F**2 3 11 13 15 28 29 31 34 40 43 45 48 50 56 59 63 64 68 69 74 76 77 81 82 84 86 87 93 98 103 107 111 114 119 128 129 130 132 133 148 149
Primary Contact: Jeremy Armstrong, FACHE, Chief Executive Officer
CFO: Eldon Koepke, Chief Financial Officer
CIO: Nate Richards, Director Information Technology
CHR: Phyllis Oetting, Director Human Resources
CNO: Jan Kemmerer, Director of Nursing
Web address: www.mchks.com
Control: County, Government, nonfederal **Service:** General medical and surgical

Staffed Beds: 75 **Admissions:** 1293 **Census:** 56 **Outpatient Visits:** 17111
Births: 97 **Total Expense ($000):** 26131 **Payroll Expense ($000):** 11763
Personnel: 252

Many Facility Codes have changed. Please refer to the AHA Guide Code Chart.

BURLINGTON—Coffey County

★ ⇑ **COFFEY COUNTY HOSPITAL (170094)**, 801 North 4th Street, Zip 66839–2602; tel. 620/364–2121, (Total facility includes 30 beds in nursing home–type unit) **A**10 18 21 **F**3 7 10 11 13 15 17 29 30 31 34 40 45 57 59 62 64 65 67 68 70 75 76 77 78 79 81 82 85 87 93 107 110 111 114 119 125 127 128 130 133 146 149
Primary Contact: Leonard Hernandez, Chief Executive Officer
CFO: Jim Van Hoet, Chief Financial Officer
CMO: John Shell, M.D., Chief Medical Officer
CIO: Adam Haag, Manager Information Technology
CHR: Theresa Thoele, Director Human Resources
CNO: Melissa Hall, Chief Nursing Officer
Web address: www.coffeyhealth.org
Control: County, Government, nonfederal **Service:** General medical and surgical

Staffed Beds: 55 **Admissions:** 514 **Census:** 28 **Outpatient Visits:** 25869
Births: 77 **Total Expense ($000):** 25443 **Payroll Expense ($000):** 14056
Personnel: 165

CALDWELL—Sumner County

★ **SUMNER COUNTY HOSPITAL DISTRICT 1 (171329)**, 601 South Osage Street, Zip 67022–1654; tel. 620/845–6492, **A**10 18 **F**7 11 40 45 46 50 64 67 75 81 82 85 89 90 93 107 114 119 128 133 146 148
Primary Contact: Teresa Tomlin, R.N., Administrator
CFO: Jennifer Marcrum, Chief Financial Officer
CMO: Jim Blunk, D.O., Chief Medical Officer
CIO: Trey Watson, Network Administrator
Web address: www.sumnercountyhospital.org
Control: Hospital district or authority, Government, nonfederal **Service:** General medical and surgical

Staffed Beds: 25 **Admissions:** 52 **Census:** 2 **Outpatient Visits:** 1204
Births: 0 **Total Expense ($000):** 4745 **Payroll Expense ($000):** 1976
Personnel: 42

CHANUTE—Neosho County

★ ⇑ **NEOSHO MEMORIAL REGIONAL MEDICAL CENTER (171380)**, 629 South Plummer, Zip 66720–1928, Mailing Address: P.O. Box 426, Zip 66720–0426; tel. 620/431–4000, **A**10 18 21 **F**3 7 13 15 28 29 30 40 43 47 48 50 62 63 64 76 79 81 85 107 108 110 111 114 119 126 127 129 130 133 143 146 147 149 154 **S** QHR, Brentwood, TN
Primary Contact: Dennis Franks, FACHE, Chief Executive Officer
COO: Wendy Brazil, Chief Operating Officer
CFO: Nancy Woodyard, Chief Financial Officer
CMO: Charles Van Houden, M.D., Chief Medical Officer
CIO: Gretchen Keller, Director Health Information
CHR: R C Rowan, Director Human Resources
CNO: Jennifer Newton, R.N., Chief Nursing Officer
Web address: www.nmrmc.com
Control: County, Government, nonfederal **Service:** General medical and surgical

Staffed Beds: 25 **Admissions:** 1388 **Census:** 6 **Outpatient Visits:** 56082
Births: 362 **Total Expense ($000):** 53164 **Payroll Expense ($000):** 22093
Personnel: 333

CLAY CENTER—Clay County

★ **CLAY COUNTY MEDICAL CENTER (171371)**, 617 Liberty Street, Zip 67432–1564, Mailing Address: P.O. Box 512, Zip 67432–0512; tel. 785/632–2144, **A**10 18 **F**13 15 18 19 28 29 30 31 40 45 50 53 55 57 59 63 64 68 70 74 75 76 77 78 79 81 82 84 85 86 87 93 96 97 107 108 111 114 119 127 130 132 133 135 146 148 149
Primary Contact: Austin M. Gillard, Chief Executive Officer
CFO: James Garbarino, Chief Financial Officer
CIO: Chris Wolf, Director Information Technology
CHR: Cindy Rush, Director Human Resources
CNO: Sara Beikman, Director of Nursing
Web address: www.ccmcks.org
Control: County, Government, nonfederal **Service:** General medical and surgical

Staffed Beds: 25 **Admissions:** 815 **Census:** 11 **Outpatient Visits:** 85612
Births: 45 **Total Expense ($000):** 26991 **Payroll Expense ($000):** 11615
Personnel: 215

COFFEYVILLE—Montgomery County

⊠ **COFFEYVILLE REGIONAL MEDICAL CENTER (170145)**, 1400 West Fourth, Zip 67337–3306; tel. 620/251–1200, (Total facility includes 20 beds in nursing home–type unit) **A**1 10 20 **F**3 7 11 13 15 28 29 30 31 34 40 45 50 51 57 59 62 64 65 66 70 74 76 77 78 79 81 82 85 86 87 93 97 107 108 109 110 111 113 117 119 120 121 123 127 128 130 131 132 135 146 147 148 154 156 **S** QHR, Brentwood, TN
Primary Contact: Lori Rexwinkle, Chief Executive Officer
CIO: Kris Penco, Director Information Systems
CHR: Becky McCune, Director Human Resources, Community Relations and Education
Web address: www.https://www.crmcinc.org
Control: Other not–for–profit (including NFP Corporation) **Service:** General medical and surgical

Staffed Beds: 87 **Admissions:** 1564 **Census:** 15 **Outpatient Visits:** 49408
Births: 263 **Total Expense ($000):** 44124 **Payroll Expense ($000):** 20289
Personnel: 326

COLBY—Thomas County

★ **CITIZENS MEDICAL CENTER (171362)**, 100 East College Drive, Zip 67701–3799; tel. 785/462–7511, (Total facility includes 60 beds in nursing home–type unit) **A**10 18 **F**3 11 13 15 28 29 30 31 34 35 40 43 50 57 64 67 68 75 76 77 78 81 82 85 86 87 93 97 107 108 110 111 114 119 127 130 133 146 148 156
Primary Contact: Greg Unruh, Chief Executive Officer
CFO: Darcy Howard, Chief Financial Officer
CMO: Kelly Gabel, Chief of Staff
CIO: Jacee Dobbs, Chief Information Officer
CHR: Margaret Kummer, Chief Human Resource Officer
CNO: Jenny Niblock, Chief Clinical Officer
Web address: www.cmciks.com
Control: Other not–for–profit (including NFP Corporation) **Service:** General medical and surgical

Staffed Beds: 85 **Admissions:** 842 **Census:** 64 **Outpatient Visits:** 161590
Births: 166 **Total Expense ($000):** 3903549 **Payroll Expense ($000):** 19448 **Personnel:** 335

COLDWATER—Comanche County

★ **COMANCHE COUNTY HOSPITAL (171312)**, 202 South Frisco Street, Zip 67029–9101, Mailing Address: HC 65, Box 8A, Zip 67029–9500; tel. 620/582–2144, **A**10 18 **F**3 11 30 31 40 43 53 59 61 68 75 78 93 102 107 128 133 156 **S** Great Plains Health Alliance, Inc., Wichita, KS
Primary Contact: Nancy Zimmerman, R.N., Administrator
CFO: Lisa Brooks, Chief Financial Officer
CMO: Daniel Schowengerdt, M.D., Chief of Staff
CIO: LaNell Wagnon, Director Medical Records
CHR: Lisa Brooks, Chief Financial Officer
CNO: Sandra Dobrinski, Director of Nursing
Web address: www.gpha.com
Control: County, Government, nonfederal **Service:** General medical and surgical

Staffed Beds: 12 **Admissions:** 101 **Census:** 3 **Outpatient Visits:** 10416
Births: 0 **Total Expense ($000):** 5461 **Payroll Expense ($000):** 2580
Personnel: 55

COLUMBUS—Cherokee County

★ **MERCY HOSPITAL COLUMBUS (171308)**, 220 North Pennsylvania Avenue, Zip 66725–1110; tel. 620/429–2545, **A**10 18 **F**11 15 40 45 59 77 93 119 133 **S** Mercy, Chesterfield, MO
Primary Contact: Angie Saporito, Administrator
Web address: www.mercy.net/newsroom-mercy-maude-norton-hospital-quick-facts
Control: Church operated, Nongovernment, not–for–profit **Service:** General medical and surgical

Staffed Beds: 18 **Admissions:** 66 **Census:** 1 **Births:** 0

CONCORDIA—Cloud County

★ **CLOUD COUNTY HEALTH CENTER (171349)**, 1100 Highland Drive, Zip 66901–3923; tel. 785/243–1234, **A**10 18 **F**3 11 15 28 31 34 35 40 41 45 56 57 59 64 65 70 74 75 77 79 81 82 85 86 87 89 93 96 97 102 107 108 114 118 119 127 130 133 135 146 148 154 **S** Salina Regional Health Center, Salina, KS
Primary Contact: David Garnas, Administrator
CFO: Pamela Blochlinger, Acting Vice President Finance
CMO: Justin Poore, D.O., Chief Medical Staff
CIO: Jenny Bergstrom, Project Manager Information Technology
CHR: Dawn Thoman, Vice President Human Resources
CNO: Michelle Metro, Vice President Nursing
Web address: www.cchc.com
Control: Other not–for–profit (including NFP Corporation) **Service**: General medical and surgical

Staffed Beds: 25 **Admissions:** 333 **Census:** 5 **Outpatient Visits:** 37046 **Births:** 0 **Total Expense ($000):** 14325 **Payroll Expense ($000):** 7405 **Personnel:** 134

COUNCIL GROVE—Morris County

★ **MORRIS COUNTY HOSPITAL (171379)**, 600 North Washington Street, Zip 66846–1422; tel. 620/767–6811, **A**10 18 **F**7 11 13 15 18 28 35 40 45 59 64 65 70 77 81 87 93 94 96 107 110 111 130 132 133 146 148 149 156
Primary Contact: Kevin Leeper, Chief Executive Officer
CFO: Ron Christenson, Chief Financial Officer
CMO: Lora Siegle, M.D., Chief Medical Officer
CIO: Bill Lauer, Chief Information Officer
CHR: Don Zimmerman, Director Human Resources
CNO: Stephanne Wolf, Chief Nursing Officer
Web address: www.mrcohosp.com
Control: County, Government, nonfederal **Service**: General medical and surgical

Staffed Beds: 25 **Admissions:** 339 **Census:** 4 **Outpatient Visits:** 14394 **Births:** 33 **Total Expense ($000):** 10835 **Payroll Expense ($000):** 4110 **Personnel:** 103

DERBY—Sedgwick County

ROCK REGIONAL HOSPITAL, 3251 North Rock Road, Zip 67037–3850; tel. 316/425–2400, (Nonreporting)
Primary Contact: Jason Eitutus, Chief Executive Officer
Web address: www.https://rockregionalhospitalderby.com
Control: Corporation, Investor–owned (for–profit) **Service**: General medical and surgical

Staffed Beds: 31

DIGHTON—Lane County

★ **LANE COUNTY HOSPITAL (171303)**, 235 West Vine, Zip 67839–0969, Mailing Address: P.O. Box 969, Zip 67839–0969; tel. 620/397–5321, **A**10 18 **F**40 59 77 93 97 127 128 133 156 **S** Great Plains Health Alliance, Inc., Wichita, KS
Primary Contact: Mike Ruggiero, Interim Chief Executive Officer
CFO: Marcia Gabel, Chief Financial Officer
CMO: Paul Chinburg, M.D., Medical Director
CHR: Dina Casey, Human Resources Officer
CNO: Jennifer Whipple, Director Nursing
Web address: www.lanecountyhospital.com/
Control: County, Government, nonfederal **Service**: General medical and surgical

Staffed Beds: 25 **Admissions:** 71 **Census:** 16 **Outpatient Visits:** 9233 **Births:** 0 **Total Expense ($000):** 5705 **Payroll Expense ($000):** 2589 **Personnel:** 48

DODGE CITY—Ford County

⊞ **WESTERN PLAINS MEDICAL COMPLEX (170175)**, 3001 Avenue 'A', Zip 67801–6508, Mailing Address: P.O. Box 1478, Zip 67801–1478; tel. 620/225–8400, **A**1 3 5 10 20 **F**3 8 11 13 15 18 20 22 28 29 30 34 35 40 50 57 60 64 68 70 74 75 76 77 79 81 82 85 88 89 93 107 108 110 111 115 119 130 131 132 133 144 146 149 150 154 **S** LifePoint Health, Brentwood, TN
Primary Contact: Scott M. Smith, Chief Executive Officer
CFO: Ryan Pugh, Chief Financial Officer
CMO: Merrill Conant, M.D., Chief of Staff
CIO: Shawna Culver, Director Information Systems
CHR: Corry Israel, Director Human Resources
CNO: Jay Trevor Fogg, Chief Nursing Officer
Web address: www.westernplainsmc.com
Control: Corporation, Investor–owned (for–profit) **Service**: General medical and surgical

Staffed Beds: 45 **Admissions:** 1756 **Census:** 12 **Outpatient Visits:** 31458 **Births:** 650 **Total Expense ($000):** 36378 **Payroll Expense ($000):** 12671

EL DORADO—Butler County

⊞ **SUSAN B. ALLEN MEMORIAL HOSPITAL (170017)**, 720 West Central Avenue, Zip 67042–2112; tel. 316/321–3300, **A**1 10 **F**3 11 13 15 28 34 35 40 45 55 57 59 60 62 64 68 69 70 75 76 79 81 85 92 93 96 97 107 108 110 111 115 119 120 121 123 130 133 144 146 148 149 154 155
Primary Contact: James B. Kirkbride, President and Chief Executive Officer
COO: Mark Rooker, Chief Operations and Information Officer
CFO: Gene Kaberline, Chief Financial Officer
CMO: Paige Dodson, M.D., M.P.H., Chief Medical Officer
CIO: Mark Rooker, Chief Operations and Information Officer
CHR: D. Gay Kimble, Chief Human Resource Officer
CNO: Cecilia B Goebel, R.N., Chief Nursing Officer
Web address: www.sbamh.com
Control: Other not–for–profit (including NFP Corporation) **Service**: General medical and surgical

Staffed Beds: 38 **Admissions:** 1605 **Census:** 18 **Outpatient Visits:** 87423 **Births:** 148 **Total Expense ($000):** 52165 **Payroll Expense ($000):** 21421 **Personnel:** 350

ELKHART—Morton County

MORTON COUNTY HEALTH SYSTEM (170166), 445 Hilltop Street, Zip 67950–0937, Mailing Address: P.O. Box 937, Zip 67950–0937; tel. 620/697–2141, **A**10 20 **F**3 28 29 34 40 54 56 57 59 64 70 83 86 87 93 94 96 97 104 107 114 119 127 130 131 132 133 154
Primary Contact: Chad Thompson, Chief Executive Officer
CHR: Sonja May, Director Human Resources
Web address: www.mchswecare.com
Control: County, Government, nonfederal **Service**: General medical and surgical

Staffed Beds: 28 **Admissions:** 209 **Census:** 2 **Outpatient Visits:** 8695 **Births:** 0 **Total Expense ($000):** 8140 **Payroll Expense ($000):** 3913 **Personnel:** 55

ELLINWOOD—Barton County

★ **ELLINWOOD DISTRICT HOSPITAL (171301)**, 605 North Main Street, Zip 67526–1440; tel. 620/564–2548, **A**10 18 **F**11 40 64 65 93 107 127 128 133 154 156 **S** Great Plains Health Alliance, Inc., Wichita, KS
Primary Contact: Kile Magner, Administrator
CFO: Summer Zink, Chief Financial Officer
CMO: Charlie Joslin, M.D., Chief of Staff
CIO: Becky L Burns, Manager Health Information Management
CHR: Chris Robl, Human Resources
CNO: Jill Ritchie, Director of Nursing
Web address: www.ellinwooddistricthospital.org
Control: Other not–for–profit (including NFP Corporation) **Service**: General medical and surgical

Staffed Beds: 25 **Admissions:** 209 **Census:** 4 **Outpatient Visits:** 13415 **Births:** 0 **Total Expense ($000):** 6805 **Payroll Expense ($000):** 3273 **Personnel:** 73

ELLSWORTH—Ellsworth County

★ **ELLSWORTH COUNTY MEDICAL CENTER (171327)**, 1604 Aylward Street, Zip 67439–0087, Mailing Address: P.O. Box 87, Zip 67439–0087; tel. 785/472–3111, **A**10 18 **F**3 11 28 29 34 35 40 45 47 53 57 59 64 75 77 85 86 87 93 97 107 115 119 127 130 133 146 156
Primary Contact: Andrew P. Bair, Chief Executive Officer
CFO: Preston Sauers, Chief Financial Officer
CIO: Lynette Dick, Director of Support Services
CHR: Christa N Bohnen, Director Human Resources
CNO: Amanda Thrasher, Director Nursing
Web address: www.ewmed.com
Control: County, Government, nonfederal **Service**: General medical and surgical

Staffed Beds: 19 **Admissions:** 526 **Census:** 6 **Outpatient Visits:** 17312 **Births:** 0 **Total Expense ($000):** 17121 **Payroll Expense ($000):** 8612 **Personnel:** 160

EMPORIA—Lyon County

○ **NEWMAN REGIONAL HEALTH (171384)**, 1201 West 12th Avenue, Zip 66801–2597; tel. 620/343–6800, (Nonreporting) **A**10 11 18
Primary Contact: Robert N. Wright, Chief Executive Officer
CFO: Holly French, Chief Financial Officer
CMO: James Geitz, M.D., Chief of Staff
CHR: Kathy Orear, Director Human Resources
CNO: Julia Pyle, R.N., Chief Nursing Officer
Web address: www.newmanrh.org
Control: County, Government, nonfederal **Service**: General medical and surgical

Staffed Beds: 32

Many Facility Codes have changed. Please refer to the AHA Guide Code Chart. © 2019 AHA Guide

EUREKA—Greenwood County

GREENWOOD COUNTY HOSPITAL (171339), 100 West 16th Street, Zip 67045–1064; tel. 620/583–7451, **A**10 18 **F**3 40 43 53 57 62 81 93 96 107 119 127 128 133 135 146
Primary Contact: Sandra Dickerson, Chief Executive Officer
CFO: Marian Drake, Chief Financial Officer
CIO: Jason Clark, Director Quality Improvement, Risk Management and Information System
CHR: Janel M Palmer, Director Human Resources
CNO: Tracy Harrod, Director of Nursing
Web address: www.gwch.org
Control: County, Government, nonfederal **Service:** General medical and surgical

Staffed Beds: 25 **Admissions:** 422 **Census:** 7 **Outpatient Visits:** 11926 **Births:** 0 **Total Expense ($000):** 12089 **Payroll Expense ($000):** 6441 **Personnel:** 119

FREDONIA—Wilson County

★ **FREDONIA REGIONAL HOSPITAL (171374)**, 1527 Madison Street, Zip 66736–1751, Mailing Address: P.O. Box 579, Zip 66736–0579; tel. 620/378–2121, **A**10 18 **F**3 7 11 15 30 40 57 59 81 82 85 91 93 103 107 110 111 115 119 128 133 154 156 **S** Great Plains Health Alliance, Inc., Wichita, KS
Primary Contact: Johnathan Durrett, Chief Executive Officer
CFO: Tracy Row, Manager Business Office
CMO: Jennifer McKenney, M.D., Chief Medical Officer
CIO: Tyler Row, Director Information Technology
CHR: Debbie Marr, Administrative Assistant and Director Human Resources
CNO: Ryan Duft, R.N., Chief Nursing Officer
Web address: www.fredoniaregionalhospital.org
Control: City, Government, nonfederal **Service:** General medical and surgical

Staffed Beds: 25 **Admissions:** 504 **Census:** 9 **Outpatient Visits:** 29384 **Births:** 0 **Total Expense ($000):** 14623 **Payroll Expense ($000):** 5441 **Personnel:** 111

GALENA—Cherokee County

⇈ **PREMIER SURGICAL INSTITUTE (170203)**, 1619 West 7th Street, Zip 66739; tel. 620/783–1732, (Nonreporting) **A**10 21
Primary Contact: Travis W. Roderick, Chief Executive Officer
Web address: www.premiersurgicalinstitute.com/
Control: City, Government, nonfederal **Service:** General medical and surgical

Staffed Beds: 25

GARDEN CITY—Finney County

⊠ **ST. CATHERINE HOSPITAL (170023)**, 401 East Spruce Street, Zip 67846–5679; tel. 620/272–2561, **A**1 10 20 **F**3 8 13 15 18 20 22 29 30 31 34 35 40 45 49 51 57 59 60 63 64 65 68 69 70 73 74 75 76 77 78 79 81 82 83 84 85 86 87 89 90 91 92 93 94 96 97 98 100 102 107 108 109 110 111 112 113 114 115 116 117 118 119 120 121 122 123 124 127 130 131 132 135 144 146 147 148 154 156 **S** CommonSpirit Health, Chicago, IL
Primary Contact: Scott J. Taylor, President and Chief Executive Officer
CFO: Amanda Vaughan, Chief Financial Officer
CMO: Matthew C Byrnes, M.D., Chief Medical Officer
CIO: Lance Kellenbarger, Site Director Information Systems
CHR: Kathy E Morrison, Executive Director Human Resources
CNO: Margaret Elizabeth Prewitt, Vice President Patient Services and Chief Nursing Officer
Web address: www.StCatherineHosp.org
Control: Church operated, Nongovernment, not–for–profit **Service:** General medical and surgical

Staffed Beds: 100 **Admissions:** 3926 **Census:** 42 **Outpatient Visits:** 249430 **Births:** 634 **Total Expense ($000):** 113707 **Payroll Expense ($000):** 42105 **Personnel:** 568

GARDNER—Johnson County

★ △ **MEADOWBROOK REHABILITATION HOSPITAL (173033)**, 427 West Main Street, Zip 66030–1183; tel. 913/856–8747, (Nonreporting) **A**7 10
Primary Contact: Peter Kautz, Chief Executive Officer
CFO: Kelly Taul, Business Manager
CMO: David Edalati, M.D., Medical Director
CHR: Carrie Moore, Director Human Resources
CNO: Lisa Perez, R.N., Director Nursing
Web address: www.meadowbrookrehab.com
Control: Partnership, Investor–owned (for–profit) **Service:** Rehabilitation

Staffed Beds: 96

GARNETT—Anderson County

★ **ANDERSON COUNTY HOSPITAL (171316)**, 421 South Maple, Zip 66032–1334, Mailing Address: P.O. Box 309, Zip 66032–0309; tel. 785/448–3131, (Total facility includes 36 beds in nursing home–type unit) **A**10 18 **F**3 7 11 15 18 29 30 34 35 40 43 44 45 50 56 57 59 64 65 67 75 77 79 81 85 86 87 93 96 97 102 107 108 110 115 118 119 127 130 131 133 135 141 146 148 149 154 **S** Saint Luke's Health System, Kansas City, MO
Primary Contact: Rick McKain, Chief Executive Officer
CFO: Vicki L Mills, Chief Financial Officer
CMO: Mackenzie Peterson, M.D., Chief of Staff
CHR: Karen Gillespie, Director Human Resources
CNO: Margo L Williams, R.N., Chief Nursing Officer
Web address: www.saint-lukes.org
Control: Other not–for–profit (including NFP Corporation) **Service:** General medical and surgical

Staffed Beds: 48 **Admissions:** 224 **Census:** 34 **Outpatient Visits:** 47405 **Births:** 0 **Total Expense ($000):** 27145 **Payroll Expense ($000):** 11078 **Personnel:** 216

GIRARD—Crawford County

★ **GIRARD MEDICAL CENTER (171376)**, 302 North Hospital Drive, Zip 66743–2000; tel. 620/724–8291, **A**10 18 **F**3 6 8 11 12 15 28 29 34 35 40 43 44 45 47 50 51 53 56 57 59 62 63 64 65 68 70 75 77 79 81 86 87 93 97 98 100 101 103 104 107 114 119 127 128 130 131 132 133 144 146 148 149 154
Primary Contact: Ruth Duling, Chief Executive Officer
CFO: Holly Koch, Chief Financial Officer
CIO: Jeff Barnes, Director Information Technology
CHR: Gregory Sullivan, Manager Human Resources
CNO: Joyce Geier, Director Nursing
Web address: www.girardmedicalcenter.com
Control: Hospital district or authority, Government, nonfederal **Service:** General medical and surgical

Staffed Beds: 35 **Admissions:** 566 **Census:** 11 **Outpatient Visits:** 21878 **Births:** 0 **Total Expense ($000):** 18488 **Payroll Expense ($000):** 9271 **Personnel:** 196

GOODLAND—Sherman County

★ **GOODLAND REGIONAL MEDICAL CENTER (171370)**, 220 West Second Street, Zip 67735–1602; tel. 785/890–3625, (Nonreporting) **A**10 18
Primary Contact: Ronald R. Robinson, M.D., M.P.H., FACHE, Chief Executive Officer and Chief Medical Officer
CFO: Derick Lorentz, Chief Financial Officer
CMO: Ronald R. Robinson, M.D., M.P.H., FACHE, Chief Executive Officer and Chief Medical Officer
CIO: Christopher Biel, Chief Information Officer
CHR: Kim Horineck, Chief Human Resource Officer
Web address: www.goodlandregional.com
Control: County, Government, nonfederal **Service:** General medical and surgical

Staffed Beds: 25

GREAT BEND—Barton County

★ **UNIVERSITY OF KANSAS HEALTH SYSTEM GREAT BEND CAMPUS (170191)**, 514 Cleveland Street, Zip 67530–3562; tel. 620/792–8833, (Nonreporting) **A**10 20 22 **S** The University of Kansas Health System, Kansas City, KS
Primary Contact: Jesse Mock, Chief Executive Officer
COO: Adina Gregory, Chief Operating Officer
CFO: Timothy Latimer, Chief Financial Officer
CMO: Randall Hildebrand, M.D., Chief Medical Officer
CHR: Brenda Kaiser, Director Human Resources
CNO: Adina Gregory, Chief Nursing Officer
Web address: www.gbregional.com
Control: Hospital district or authority, Government, nonfederal **Service:** Surgical

Staffed Beds: 33

Hospital, Medicare Provider Number, Address, Telephone, Approval, Facility, and Physician Codes, Health Care System

★ American Hospital Association (AHA) membership
□ The Joint Commission accreditation
○ Healthcare Facilities Accreditation Program
◇ DNV Healthcare Inc. accreditation
⇈ Center for Improvement in Healthcare Quality Accreditation
△ Commission on Accreditation of Rehabilitation Facilities (CARF) accreditation

KS

GREENSBURG—Kiowa County

★ ⋔ **KIOWA COUNTY MEMORIAL HOSPITAL (171332)**, 721 West Kansas Avenue, Zip 67054–1633; tel. 620/723–3341, **A**10 18 21 **F**3 7 34 40 50 53 59 64 68 107 114 127 128 133 149 156 **S** Great Plains Health Alliance, Inc., Wichita, KS
Primary Contact: Mary Sweet, Administrator
CFO: Ron Tucker, Business Office Manager
CMO: Nizar Kibar, M.D., Chief Medical Staff
CIO: Jeremy Steven Hoover, Chief Information Officer
CHR: Cathy McFall, Human Resources Manager
CNO: Vanessa Kirk, Director of Nursing
Web address: www.kcmh.net
Control: Other not–for–profit (including NFP Corporation) **Service**: General medical and surgical

Staffed Beds: 15 **Admissions**: 103 **Census**: 6 **Outpatient Visits**: 11153 **Births**: 0 **Total Expense ($000)**: 9114 **Payroll Expense ($000)**: 3494 **Personnel**: 74

HANOVER—Washington County

★ **HANOVER HOSPITAL (171365)**, 205 South Hanover, Zip 66945–8924, Mailing Address: P.O. Box 38, Zip 66945–0038; tel. 785/337–2214, **A**10 18 **F**2 7 28 40 53 69 81 127 133
Primary Contact: Brittni Oehmke, Administrator
CFO: Sheryl Adam, Chief Financial Officer
Control: Hospital district or authority, Government, nonfederal **Service**: General medical and surgical

Staffed Beds: 25 **Admissions**: 108 **Census**: 4 **Outpatient Visits**: 3463 **Births**: 1 **Total Expense ($000)**: 5168 **Payroll Expense ($000)**: 2525 **Personnel**: 49

HARPER—Harper County

★ **HOSPITAL DISTRICT 6 - HARPER CAMPUS (171366)**, 700 West 13th Street, Zip 67058–1401; tel. 620/896–7324, (Includes HOSPITAL DISTRICT 6 - ANTHONY CAMPUS, 1101 East Spring Street, Anthony, Kansas, Zip 67003–2122; tel. 620/842–5111; Pat Patton, Chief Executive Officer) **A**10 18 **F**10 15 28 29 34 35 40 43 45 50 53 57 64 67 69 81 93 97 100 107 114 119 127 128 130 133 148
Primary Contact: Pat Patton, Chief Executive Officer
CFO: Sandra Owen, Director Fiscal and Accounting
CMO: Ralph Imlay, M.D., Chief of Staff
CIO: Cindi Beadman, Director Medical Records
CHR: Troy Hickman, Director Human Resources
CNO: Teresa Tomlin, R.N., Chief Nursing Officer
Web address: www.hhd5.com
Control: Hospital district or authority, Government, nonfederal **Service**: General medical and surgical

Staffed Beds: 25 **Admissions**: 372 **Census**: 5 **Outpatient Visits**: 41786 **Births**: 0 **Total Expense ($000)**: 18356 **Payroll Expense ($000)**: 8501 **Personnel**: 176

HAYS—Ellis County

★ ⋔ **HAYS MEDICAL CENTER (170013)**, 2220 Canterbury Drive, Zip 67601–2370, Mailing Address: P.O. Box 8100, Zip 67601–8100; tel. 785/623–5000, **A**5 10 21 **F**3 11 12 13 15 18 20 22 24 26 28 29 30 31 32 34 35 36 37 38 40 41 43 45 51 53 55 56 57 59 60 63 64 65 66 68 69 70 71 72 73 75 76 77 78 79 80 81 82 84 85 86 87 89 92 93 96 97 107 108 110 111 115 118 119 120 121 123 124 126 127 129 130 131 132 135 144 146 147 148 149 154 156 **S** The University of Kansas Health System, Kansas City, KS
Primary Contact: Edward Herrman, R.N., FACHE, President and Chief Executive Officer
COO: Bryce A Young, Chief Operating Officer
CFO: George Harms, Chief Financial Officer
CIO: Scott Rohleder, Chief Information Officer
CHR: Bryce A Young, Chief Operating Officer
CNO: Terry Siek, MSN, R.N., Chief Nursing Officer
Web address: www.haysmed.com
Control: Other not–for–profit (including NFP Corporation) **Service**: General medical and surgical

Staffed Beds: 127 **Admissions**: 4537 **Census**: 50 **Outpatient Visits**: 168809 **Births**: 581 **Total Expense ($000)**: 177589 **Payroll Expense ($000)**: 75296 **Personnel**: 1221

HERINGTON—Dickinson County

HERINGTON MUNICIPAL HOSPITAL (171340), 100 East Helen Street, Zip 67449–1606; tel. 785/258–2207, (Nonreporting) **A**10 18
Primary Contact: Isabel Schmedemann, Chief Executive Officer and Administrator
CFO: Alan Meisinger, Chief Financial Officer
CMO: John Mosier, D.O., Chief of Staff
CHR: Nicole Will, Human Resources Officer
CNO: Roni Baker, Director of Nursing
Web address: www.heringtonhospital.org
Control: City, Government, nonfederal **Service**: General medical and surgical

Staffed Beds: 25

HIAWATHA—Brown County

★ **HIAWATHA COMMUNITY HOSPITAL (171341)**, 300 Utah Street, Zip 66434–2314; tel. 785/742–2131, **A**10 18 **F**8 11 13 15 28 29 40 43 45 67 69 70 76 81 85 107 111 114 119 127 128 130 133 143 146 149 155 156
Primary Contact: John Broberg, Chief Executive Officer
CFO: Jenny Knudson, Controller
CMO: Steffen Shamburg, M.D., Chief of Staff
CIO: Cheryl Wenger, Manager Health Information and Quality Assurance
CHR: Alison Keri, Director Human Resources
CNO: Lisa Thompson, MSN, R.N., Director of Nursing
Web address: www.hch-ks.org
Control: Other not–for–profit (including NFP Corporation) **Service**: General medical and surgical

Staffed Beds: 25 **Admissions**: 836 **Census**: 9 **Outpatient Visits**: 32473 **Births**: 94 **Total Expense ($000)**: 25813 **Payroll Expense ($000)**: 12905 **Personnel**: 266

HILL CITY—Graham County

★ **GRAHAM COUNTY HOSPITAL (171325)**, 304 West Prout Street, Zip 67642–1435; tel. 785/421–2121, **A**10 18 **F**3 11 34 40 50 53 59 64 67 68 81 82 84 93 107 114 127 128 133 148 149
Primary Contact: Melissa Atkins, CPA, Chief Executive Officer
CHR: Donella Belleau, Director Human Resources
Web address: www.grahamcountyhospital.org
Control: County, Government, nonfederal **Service**: General medical and surgical

Staffed Beds: 20 **Admissions**: 296 **Census**: 4 **Outpatient Visits**: 6874 **Births**: 0 **Total Expense ($000)**: 7271 **Payroll Expense ($000)**: 3457 **Personnel**: 68

HILLSBORO—Marion County

HILLSBORO COMMUNITY HOSPITAL (171357), 701 South Main Street, Zip 67063–1553; tel. 620/947–3114, **A**10 18 **F**3 29 40 57 59 64 81 82 104 107 115 117 119 148 149 154 **S** Rural Community Hospitals of America, Kansas City, MO
Primary Contact: Marion Regier, Chief Executive Officer
COO: Johna Magnuson, Director Nursing
CIO: Marsha Setzkorn-Meyer, Director Public Relations and Marketing
CHR: Wendy McCarty, Director Human Resources
Web address: www.hchks.com
Control: Other not–for–profit (including NFP Corporation) **Service**: General medical and surgical

Staffed Beds: 15 **Admissions**: 405 **Census**: 1 **Outpatient Visits**: 16663 **Births**: 0 **Total Expense ($000)**: 9425 **Payroll Expense ($000)**: 3836 **Personnel**: 50

HOISINGTON—Barton County

★ **CLARA BARTON HOSPITAL (171333)**, 250 West Ninth Street, Zip 67544–1706; tel. 620/653–2114, **A**10 18 **F**11 15 28 40 56 57 59 64 77 81 85 92 93 97 107 114 127 128 133 148
Primary Contact: James Blackwell, President and Chief Executive Officer
CMO: Nathan Knackstedt, D.O., Chief of Staff
CHR: John Moshier, Director Human Resources
CNO: Jane Schepmann, Vice President and Chief Nursing Officer
Web address: www.clarabartonhospital.org
Control: Other not–for–profit (including NFP Corporation) **Service**: General medical and surgical

Staffed Beds: 23 **Admissions**: 547 **Census**: 8 **Outpatient Visits**: 70977 **Births**: 0 **Total Expense ($000)**: 24240 **Payroll Expense ($000)**: 11228 **Personnel**: 203

Many Facility Codes have changed. Please refer to the AHA Guide Code Chart.

HOLTON—Jackson County

★ **HOLTON COMMUNITY HOSPITAL (171319)**, 1110 Columbine Drive,
Zip 66436–8824; tel. 785/364–2116, **A**10 18 **F**3 11 15 18 28 29 34 40 43 45
50 57 59 62 63 64 65 75 77 79 81 82 87 90 93 97 107 114 119 127 128 130
131 132 133 135 146 147 148 156 157
Primary Contact: Carrie L. Saia, Chief Executive Officer
CFO: Bart Kenton, Chief Financial Officer
CMO: Joel Hutchsin, M.D., Chief Medical Staff
CIO: Holll Peters, Director Health Information Management
CHR: Gretchen Snavely, Director Human Resources
CNO: Mandy Bontrager, Director Nursing
Web address: www.holtonhospital.com
Control: Other not–for–profit (including NFP Corporation) **Service:** General
medical and surgical

Staffed Beds: 12 **Admissions:** 189 **Census:** 2 **Outpatient Visits:** 49419
Births: 28 **Total Expense ($000):** 16299 **Payroll Expense ($000):** 7955
Personnel: 155

HOXIE—Sheridan County

SHERIDAN COUNTY HEALTH COMPLEX (171347), 826 18th Street,
Zip 67740–0167, Mailing Address: P.O. Box 167, Zip 67740–0167; tel. 785/675–
3281, (Total facility includes 32 beds in nursing home–type unit) **A**10 18 **F**7 10 11
29 34 35 40 45 50 53 56 57 59 64 66 67 68 69 75 81 85 87 93 107 115 119
130 133
Primary Contact: Niceta Farber, Chief Executive Officer
CFO: Michael O'Dell, Chief Financial Officer
CMO: Victor Nemechek, M.D., Chief of Staff and Chief Medical Officer
CHR: Shelby Moss, Human Resource Officer
CNO: Hannah Schoendaler, Chief Nursing Officer
Web address: www.sheridancountyhospital.com
Control: County, Government, nonfederal **Service:** General medical and surgical

Staffed Beds: 50 **Admissions:** 292 **Census:** 32 **Outpatient Visits:** 7338
Births: 0 **Total Expense ($000):** 12274 **Payroll Expense ($000):** 6360
Personnel: 143

HUGOTON—Stevens County

STEVENS COUNTY HOSPITAL (171335), 1006 South Jackson Street,
Zip 67951–2858, Mailing Address: P.O. Box 10, Zip 67951–0010; tel. 620/544–
8511, (Nonreporting) **A**10 18
Primary Contact: Linda Stalcup, Chief Executive Officer
CMO: Samer Al-hashmi, M.D., Chief Medical Staff
Web address: www.stevenscountyhospital.com/
Control: County, Government, nonfederal **Service:** General medical and surgical

Staffed Beds: 100

HUTCHINSON—Reno County

✉ △ **HUTCHINSON REGIONAL MEDICAL CENTER (170020)**, 1701 East 23rd
Avenue, Zip 67502–1191; tel. 620/665–2000, **A**1 7 10 **F**3 7 11 13 18 20 22 24
26 28 29 30 31 34 35 40 43 45 47 48 49 50 51 53 57 60 64 68 70 74 76 77
78 79 81 82 83 85 87 89 90 93 98 102 106 107 108 111 114 115 119 120
121 123 126 128 129 130 143 146 148 154 156
Primary Contact: Ken Johnson, President and Chief Executive Officer
CFO: Cassie Dolen, Vice President Finance and Chief Financial Officer
CMO: Thomas Smith, M.D., Vice President Medical Affairs
CIO: Calvin Wright, Chief Information Officer
CHR: Kevin Chiles, Vice President Human Resources
CNO: Julie R. Ward, MSN, R.N., Vice President Patient Care Services
Web address: www.hutchregional.com
Control: Other not–for–profit (including NFP Corporation) **Service:** General
medical and surgical

Staffed Beds: 146 **Admissions:** 5832 **Census:** 68 **Outpatient**
Visits: 115836 **Births:** 571 **Total Expense ($000):** 127223 **Payroll Expense**
($000): 45188 **Personnel:** 886

SUMMIT SURGICAL (170198), 1818 East 23rd Avenue, Zip 67502–1106;
tel. 620/663–4800, **A**10 **F**29 45 53 64 77 79 81 82 85 86 87 93 94
Primary Contact: Ann Hentzen Page, M.D., Chief Executive Officer
COO: Nancy Corwin, Chief Operating Officer
CMO: Ann Hentzen Page, M.D., Medical Director
CNO: Nancy Corwin, Chief Nursing Officer
Web address: www.summitks.com/index_surgical.htm
Control: Corporation, Investor–owned (for–profit) **Service:** Surgical

Staffed Beds: 10 **Admissions:** 282 **Census:** 1 **Births:** 0

IOLA—Allen County

✉ **ALLEN COUNTY REGIONAL HOSPITAL (171373)**, 3066 N. Kentucky St,
Zip 66749, Mailing Address: P.O. Box 540, Zip 66749–0540; tel. 620/365–1000, **A**1
10 18 **F**3 11 13 29 30 31 34 35 40 43 45 57 59 62 63 64 65 75 76 77 78 79 81
82 84 85 86 89 92 103 104 107 115 119 127 129 130 133 146 148 149
Primary Contact: Marion A. Thompson, FACHE, Chief Executive Officer
CFO: Larry Peterson, Chief Financial Officer
CMO: Brian Wolfe, Chief of Staff
CHR: Paula Sell, Director Human Resources
CNO: Patty McGuffin, Chief Nursing Officer
Web address: www.allencountyhospital.com
Control: County, Government, nonfederal **Service:** General medical and surgical

Staffed Beds: 25 **Admissions:** 693 **Census:** 9 **Outpatient Visits:** 19500
Births: 49 **Total Expense ($000):** 23864 **Payroll Expense ($000):** 7186
Personnel: 154

JETMORE—Hodgeman County

★ **HODGEMAN COUNTY HEALTH CENTER (171369)**, 809 Bramley Street,
Zip 67854–9320, Mailing Address: P.O. Box 310, Zip 67854–0310; tel. 620/357–
8361, (Total facility includes 17 beds in nursing home–type unit) **A**10 18 **F**3 29 32
33 40 53 59 64 67 81 93 97 107 114 125 127 130 133 143 148
Primary Contact: Phil Ginder, Chief Executive Officer
Web address: www.hchconline.org
Control: County, Government, nonfederal **Service:** General medical and surgical

Staffed Beds: 25 **Admissions:** 221 **Census:** 24 **Outpatient Visits:** 4278
Births: 0 **Total Expense ($000):** 7590 **Payroll Expense ($000):** 3546
Personnel: 76

JOHNSON—Stanton County

STANTON COUNTY HOSPITAL (171343), 404 North Chestnut Street,
Zip 67855–5001, Mailing Address: P.O. Box 779, Zip 67855–0779; tel. 620/492–
6250, (Total facility includes 25 beds in nursing home–type unit) **A**10 18 **F**3 11
13 34 35 40 41 45 50 54 56 57 59 64 68 75 81 82 86 87 93 97 107 114 127
130 131 133 143 154
Primary Contact: Jay Tusten, Chief Executive Officer
CMO: Bill Troup, M.D., Chief of Staff
CIO: Marco Medina, Chief Information Officer
CHR: Camille Davidson, Director Human Resources
CNO: Marianne Mills, R.N., Chairperson
Web address: www.stantoncountyhospital.com
Control: County, Government, nonfederal **Service:** General medical and surgical

Staffed Beds: 40 **Admissions:** 132 **Census:** 24 **Outpatient Visits:** 12279
Total Expense ($000): 8519 **Payroll Expense ($000):** 4865 **Personnel:** 80

JUNCTION CITY—Geary County

✉ **GEARY COMMUNITY HOSPITAL (170074)**, 1102 St Mary's Road, Zip 66441–
4196, Mailing Address: P.O. Box 490, Zip 66441–0490; tel. 785/238–4131, **A**1
10 **F**3 8 11 12 13 15 29 30 32 34 35 40 45 50 57 59 64 65 70 75 76 77 79
81 85 86 87 97 107 108 109 110 111 113 115 117 118 119 127 129 130
131 132 133 144 146 148 154 156
Primary Contact: Joseph Stratton, FACHE, Chief Executive Officer
CFO: William Kloppe, Chief Financial Officer
CMO: Jimmy Jenkins, M.D., Chief Medical Officer
CIO: Kyle Ibarra, Director Information Systems
CHR: Loren Streit, Director Human Resources
CNO: Dawn M Engel, Chief Nursing Officer
Web address: www.gchks.org
Control: County, Government, nonfederal **Service:** General medical and surgical

Staffed Beds: 49 **Admissions:** 962 **Census:** 9 **Outpatient Visits:** 97836
Births: 272 **Total Expense ($000):** 40977 **Payroll Expense ($000):** 18390
Personnel: 294

✉ **IRWIN ARMY COMMUNITY HOSPITAL**, 600 Caisson Hill Road, Zip 66442–
7037; tel. 785/239–7000, (Nonreporting) **A**1 3 5 **S** Department of the Army,
Office of the Surgeon General, Falls Church, VA
Primary Contact: Colonel Risa Ware, Commander
CMO: Lieutenant Colonel Mark S Ochoa, M.D., Deputy Commander, Clinical
Services
CIO: David Dougherty, Chief Information Management Officer
CHR: Hope Brunton, Chief Manpower Branch
Web address: www.iach.amedd.army.mil
Control: Department of Defense, Government, federal **Service:** General medical
and surgical

Staffed Beds: 44

KANSAS CITY—Wyandotte County

☐ **KVC PRAIRIE RIDGE PSYCHIATRIC HOSPITAL**, 4300 Brenner Drive, Zip 66104–1163; tel. 913/334–0294, **A**1 5 **F**32 38 50 98 99 100 106 154
Primary Contact: Jason R. Hooper, President and Chief Executive Officer
COO: Ryan Speier, Vice President Administration
CMO: Vishal Adma, M.D., Medical Director
Web address: www.kvc.org
Control: Other not–for–profit (including NFP Corporation) **Service:** Children's hospital psychiatric

Staffed Beds: 122 **Admissions:** 2659 **Census:** 122 **Outpatient Visits:** 0 **Births:** 0 **Total Expense ($000):** 24324 **Payroll Expense ($000):** 12102 **Personnel:** 287

✉ **PROVIDENCE MEDICAL CENTER (170146)**, 8929 Parallel Parkway, Zip 66112–1689; tel. 913/596–4000, (Total facility includes 45 beds in nursing home–type unit) **A**1 10 **F**3 13 15 17 18 20 22 24 28 29 30 31 34 35 40 41 44 45 49 50 53 56 57 59 64 70 74 75 76 77 78 79 81 82 84 85 87 93 97 102 107 108 110 111 114 119 120 121 123 124 126 128 129 130 131 132 135 143 146 147 148 149 156 **S** Prime Healthcare, Ontario, CA
Primary Contact: Karen Orr, Administrator and Chief Nursing Officer
CFO: David Dulny, Chief Financial Officer
CMO: Sabato Sisillo, M.D., Chief Medical Officer
CIO: Charles Soeken, Director Information Technology
CHR: Brenda Farwell, Director Human Resources
CNO: Karen Orr, Chief Nursing Officer
Web address: www.providencekc.com
Control: Individual, Investor–owned (for–profit) **Service:** General medical and surgical

Staffed Beds: 215 **Admissions:** 9161 **Census:** 127 **Outpatient Visits:** 217557 **Births:** 396 **Total Expense ($000):** 150256 **Payroll Expense ($000):** 60427 **Personnel:** 868

✉ **SELECT SPECIALTY HOSPITAL-KANSAS CITY (172005)**, 1731 North 90th Street, Zip 66112–1515; tel. 913/732–5900, (Nonreporting) **A**1 10 **S** Select Medical Corporation, Mechanicsburg, PA
Primary Contact: Bridgette Hunter, Chief Executive Officer
Web address: www.selectspecialtyhospitals.com
Control: Corporation, Investor–owned (for–profit) **Service:** Acute long–term care hospital

Staffed Beds: 40

✉ **THE UNIVERSITY OF KANSAS HOSPITAL (170040)**, 4000 Cambridge Street, MS 3011, Zip 66160; tel. 913/588–5000, (Includes THE UNIVERSITY OF KANSAS HOSPITAL - INDIAN CREEK CAMPUS, 10720 Nall Avenue, Overland Park, Kansas, Zip 66211–1206; tel. 913/754–5000) **A**1 2 3 5 8 10 **F**3 5 8 9 11 12 13 15 16 17 18 19 20 22 24 26 28 29 30 31 32 34 35 36 37 38 39 40 41 43 44 45 46 47 48 49 50 51 52 54 55 56 57 58 59 60 61 63 64 65 68 70 71 72 74 75 76 77 78 79 80 81 82 83 84 85 86 87 88 89 90 92 93 96 97 98 99 100 101 102 103 104 105 107 108 110 111 112 114 115 116 117 118 119 120 121 123 124 126 129 130 131 132 135 136 137 138 139 141 142 144 145 146 147 148 149 154 156 157 **S** The University of Kansas Health System, Kansas City, KS
Primary Contact: Bob Page, Chief Executive Officer
COO: Tammy Peterman, R.N., MS, Executive Vice President, Chief Operating Officer and Chief Nursing Officer
CFO: Bill Marting, Senior Vice President and Chief Financial Officer
CMO: Lou Wetzel, M.D., Chief of Staff
CIO: Chris Hansen, Senior Vice President and Chief Information Officer
CHR: Alisa Ford, Vice President Human Resources
CNO: Tammy Peterman, R.N., MS, Executive Vice President, Chief Operating Officer and Chief Nursing Officer
Web address: www.kumed.com
Control: Hospital district or authority, Government, nonfederal **Service:** General medical and surgical

Staffed Beds: 897 **Admissions:** 40828 **Census:** 609 **Outpatient Visits:** 1482964 **Births:** 2253 **Total Expense ($000):** 2145395 **Payroll Expense ($000):** 972487 **Personnel:** 10981

KINGMAN—Kingman County

★ **KINGMAN COMMUNITY HOSPITAL (171378)**, 750 Avenue D West, Zip 67068–0376; tel. 620/532–3147, **A**10 18 **F**3 11 15 17 18 28 29 31 34 35 40 45 50 54 56 57 59 64 70 75 77 78 81 86 87 89 90 93 97 107 114 119 127 128 129 130 132 133 145 146 148 154 156
Primary Contact: Shannan Flach, Chief Executive Officer
CFO: Kent Hudson, Chief Financial Officer
CIO: Jay Gehring, Director Information Systems
CHR: Nancy Stucky, Director Human Resources and Public Relations
CNO: Nita McFarland, Director of Nursing
Web address: www.kchks.com
Control: Other not–for–profit (including NFP Corporation) **Service:** General medical and surgical

Staffed Beds: 25 **Admissions:** 407 **Census:** 5 **Outpatient Visits:** 20943 **Births:** 0 **Total Expense ($000):** 10617 **Payroll Expense ($000):** 5258 **Personnel:** 94

KINSLEY—Edwards County

EDWARDS COUNTY MEDICAL CENTER (171317), 620 West Eighth Street, Zip 67547–2329, Mailing Address: P.O. Box 99, Zip 67547–0099; tel. 620/659–3621, (Nonreporting) **A**10 18
Primary Contact: Jimmie W. Hansel, Ph.D., Chief Executive Officer
CHR: Tammy K Lampe, Director Human Resources
Web address: www.edwardscohospital.com
Control: County, Government, nonfederal **Service:** General medical and surgical

Staffed Beds: 22

KIOWA—Barber County

★ **KIOWA DISTRICT HEALTHCARE (171331)**, 1002 South Fourth Street, Zip 67070–1825, Mailing Address: P.O. Box 184, Zip 67070–0184; tel. 620/825–4131, (Total facility includes 29 beds in nursing home–type unit) **A**10 18 **F**1 2 3 4 12 16 17 34 40 41 45 55 56 57 59 64 65 67 69 70 72 73 76 80 81 84 85 87 88 89 90 91 92 93 97 98 107 114 119 127 128 133 148 150 154
Primary Contact: Robert Whitaker, Chief Executive Officer
CFO: Robin Lewis, Chief Financial Officer
CMO: Paul Wilhelm, M.D., Chief of Staff
CHR: Tara Girty, Director Human Resources
Web address: www.k-d-h.com
Control: Hospital district or authority, Government, nonfederal **Service:** General medical and surgical

Staffed Beds: 39 **Admissions:** 352 **Census:** 24 **Outpatient Visits:** 6587 **Births:** 0 **Total Expense ($000):** 7098 **Payroll Expense ($000):** 3532 **Personnel:** 70

LA CROSSE—Rush County

★ **RUSH COUNTY MEMORIAL HOSPITAL (171342)**, 801 Locust Street, Zip 67548–9673, Mailing Address: P.O. Box 520, Zip 67548–0520; tel. 785/222–2545, **A**10 18 **F**3 34 40 45 53 59 64 67 77 82 93 97 107 114 119 127 128 133 148
Primary Contact: Brenda Legleiter, R.N., Chief Executive Officer
CFO: Jane Oborny, Chief Financial Officer
CMO: Harley Calvin, D.O., Chief Medical Officer
CHR: Charlene Goodman, Director Human Resources
Web address: www.rushcountymemorialhospital.com
Control: County, Government, nonfederal **Service:** General medical and surgical

Staffed Beds: 25 **Admissions:** 175 **Census:** 24 **Outpatient Visits:** 17207 **Births:** 0 **Total Expense ($000):** 5811 **Payroll Expense ($000):** 2617 **Personnel:** 70

LAKIN—Kearny County

★ **KEARNY COUNTY HOSPITAL (171313)**, 500 Thorpe Street, Zip 67860–9625; tel. 620/355–7111, (Total facility includes 75 beds in nursing home–type unit) **A**10 18 **F**2 3 6 10 13 28 29 34 35 40 45 50 56 57 58 59 64 67 68 69 75 76 79 81 82 85 86 87 89 93 97 107 111 114 119 125 127 128 130 131 132 133 143 149 156
Primary Contact: Benjamin Anderson, Chief Executive Officer and Administrator
COO: Shari Campbell, Chief Operating Officer
CFO: Kelly Ann Speckman, Chief Financial Officer
CMO: Arlo Reimer, M.D., Chief of Staff
CIO: Lisa Kay-Garcia, Chief Information Officer
CHR: Laci Williams, Director Human Resources
CNO: Susan D Stingley, Chief Nursing Officer
Web address: www.kearnycountyhospital.com
Control: County, Government, nonfederal **Service:** General medical and surgical

Staffed Beds: 100 **Admissions:** 582 **Census:** 69 **Outpatient Visits:** 50422 **Births:** 337 **Total Expense ($000):** 26333 **Payroll Expense ($000):** 13456 **Personnel:** 257

LARNED—Pawnee County

☐ **LARNED STATE HOSPITAL (174006)**, 1301 Kansas Highway 264, Zip 67550; tel. 620/285–2131, **A**1 10 **F**3 29 30 38 50 53 57 68 75 77 86 87 97 98 100 101 102 103 130 132 135 143 146 149 154 156
Primary Contact: Thomas Kinlen, Superintendent
COO: Steve Spain, Chief Operating Officer
CMO: Sayed Jehan, M.D., Interim Medical Director
CIO: Sid Smith, Director Information Resources
CHR: Kerri Barnard, Director Human Resources
CNO: Holly Hertel, Director Nursing
Web address: www.larnedstatehospital.org
Control: State, Government, nonfederal **Service:** Psychiatric

Staffed Beds: 517 **Admissions:** 1489 **Census:** 480 **Outpatient Visits:** 0 **Births:** 0 **Total Expense ($000):** 65279 **Payroll Expense ($000):** 33086 **Personnel:** 647

Many Facility Codes have changed. Please refer to the AHA Guide Code Chart.

★ **UNIVERSITY OF KANSAS HEALTH SYSTEM PAWNEE VALLEY CAMPUS (171345)**, 923 Carroll Avenue, Zip 67550–2429; tel. 620/285–3161, **A**10 18 **F**3 11 28 29 30 34 40 43 45 46 57 68 77 81 82 84 85 86 87 91 93 94 102 107 111 115 127 129 130 131 132 133 135 147 148 149 156 **S** The University of Kansas Health System, Kansas City, KS
Primary Contact: Kendra Barker, Administrator
COO: Bryce A Young, Chief Operating Officer
CFO: George Harms, Chief Financial Officer
CMO: David Sanger, M.D., Chief Medical Officer
CHR: Bruce Whittington, Vice President Human Resources
Web address: www.pawneevalleyhospital.com
Control: County, Government, nonfederal **Service:** General medical and surgical

Staffed Beds: 22 **Admissions:** 199 **Census:** 4 **Outpatient Visits:** 50989 **Births:** 0 **Total Expense ($000):** 15586 **Payroll Expense ($000):** 6875 **Personnel:** 109

LAWRENCE—Douglas County

✣ **LMH HEALTH (170137)**, 325 Maine Street, Zip 66044–1360; tel. 785/505–5000, (Total facility includes 17 beds in nursing home–type unit) **A**1 3 5 10 20 **F**3 11 13 15 18 19 20 22 26 28 29 30 31 34 35 38 39 40 43 44 45 49 50 51 54 55 56 57 59 61 64 65 67 69 70 73 74 75 76 77 78 79 81 82 84 85 86 87 89 90 93 94 96 97 100 102 107 110 111 114 115 118 119 120 124 126 128 130 131 132 135 145 146 147 148 154 156
Primary Contact: Russell W. Johnson, President and Chief Executive Officer
COO: Karen J Shumate, R.N., Chief Operating Officer
CFO: Joe Pedley, CPA, Vice President and Chief Financial Officer
CIO: Michael Williams, Chief Information Officer
CHR: Carolyn Bowmer
CNO: Traci Hoopingarner, R.N., Chief Nursing Officer
Web address: www.lmh.org
Control: Other not–for–profit (including NFP Corporation) **Service:** General medical and surgical

Staffed Beds: 142 **Admissions:** 7042 **Census:** 71 **Outpatient Visits:** 237889 **Births:** 1017 **Total Expense ($000):** 272612 **Payroll Expense ($000):** 114307 **Personnel:** 1565

LEAVENWORTH—Leavenworth County

✣ **SAINT JOHN HOSPITAL (170009)**, 3500 South Fourth Street, Zip 66048–5043; tel. 913/680 6000, **A**1 10 **F**2 15 18 20 29 30 34 40 44 45 46 50 54 56 57 59 64 68 70 74 75 77 84 85 87 93 98 100 103 107 114 119 130 133 146 148 149 154 **S** Prime Healthcare, Ontario, CA
Primary Contact: Paula Ellis, Administrator
CFO: David Dulny, Chief Financial Officer
CMO: Sabato Sisillo, M.D., Chief Medical Officer
CIO: Charles Soeken, Director Information Technology
CHR: Brenda Farwell, Director Human Resources
CNO: Jodi Fincher, R.N., Vice President Patient Care Services
Web address: www.providence.health.org/sjh
Control: Individual, Investor–owned (for–profit) **Service:** General medical and surgical

Staffed Beds: 58 **Admissions:** 1845 **Census:** 31 **Outpatient Visits:** 25475 **Births:** 0 **Total Expense ($000):** 26552 **Payroll Expense ($000):** 11691 **Personnel:** 147

✣ **SAINT LUKE'S CUSHING HOSPITAL (170133)**, 711 Marshall Street, Zip 66048–3235; tel. 913/684–1100, (Nonreporting) **A**1 10 **S** Saint Luke's Health System, Kansas City, MO
Primary Contact: Bobby Olm-Shipman, President and Chief Executive Officer
CFO: Jackie Martin, Chief Financial Officer
CMO: Nicholas Brockert, President
CHR: Donna Kunz, System Director Human Resources
CNO: Karin Sundblom, MSN, R.N., Chief Nursing Officer
Web address: www.saintlukeshealthsystem.org/locations/saint-lukes-cushing-hospital
Control: Other not–for–profit (including NFP Corporation) **Service:** General medical and surgical

Staffed Beds: 25

VETERANS AFFAIRS EASTERN KANSAS HEALTH CARE SYSTEM-DWIGHT D. EISENHOWER VETERANS AFFAIRS MEDICAL CENTER See Veterans Affairs Eastern Kansas Health Care System, Topeka

---

LEAWOOD—Johnson County

☐ **DOCTOR'S HOSPITAL (170194)**, 4901 College Boulevard, Zip 66211–1602; tel. 913/529–1801, (Nonreporting) **A**1 10
Primary Contact: Phil Harness, Chief Executive Officer
Web address: www.dshospital.net
Control: Partnership, Investor–owned (for–profit) **Service:** General medical and surgical

Staffed Beds: 9

○ **KANSAS CITY ORTHOPAEDIC INSTITUTE (170188)**, 3651 College Boulevard, Zip 66211–1910; tel. 913/338–4100, **A**3 5 10 11 **F**29 77 79 81 82 93 111
Primary Contact: Charles E. Rhoades, M.D., Chief Executive Officer
CIO: Jim Leveling, Director Information Technology
CHR: Laura Sinclair, Director Human Resources
Web address: www.kcoi.com
Control: Partnership, Investor–owned (for–profit) **Service:** Orthopedic

Staffed Beds: 17 **Admissions:** 945 **Census:** 5 **Outpatient Visits:** 34901 **Births:** 0 **Personnel:** 141

⇑ **SAINT LUKE'S COMMUNITY HOSPITAL AT LEAWOOD**, 13200 State Line Road, Zip 66209; tel. 913/222–8380, (Nonreporting) **A**21 **S** Saint Luke's Health System, Kansas City, MO
Primary Contact: Teresa Collins, R.N., Chief Executive Officer and Chief Nursing Officer
Web address: www.saintlukescommunityhospital.org
Control: Church operated, Nongovernment, not–for–profit **Service:** General medical and surgical

Staffed Beds: 8

LENEXA—Johnson County

☐ **MINIMALLY INVASIVE SURGERY HOSPITAL (170199)**, 11217 Lakeview Avenue, Zip 66219–1399; tel. 913/322–7401, **A**1 10 **F**3 18 26 31 45 64 68 70 78 79 81 82 85 86 107 111 115 119 129
Primary Contact: Parajeet Sabharrwal, Chief Executive Officer
Web address: www.mishhospital.com
Control: Corporation, Investor–owned (for–profit) **Service:** Surgical

Staffed Beds: 9 **Admissions:** 283 **Census:** 1 **Outpatient Visits:** 4946 **Births:** 0 **Total Expense ($000):** 5316 **Payroll Expense ($000):** 121 **Personnel:** 30

LEOTI—Wichita County

★ **WICHITA COUNTY HEALTH CENTER (171306)**, 211 East Earl Street, Zip 67861–9620; tel. 620/375–2233, (Total facility includes 17 beds in nursing home–type unit) **A**10 18 **F**2 3 11 29 34 35 40 41 45 50 56 57 59 64 69 75 77 86 87 93 97 102 107 119 127 130 133 135 146 148 156 **S** Great Plains Health Alliance, Inc., Wichita, KS
Primary Contact: Teresa Clark, Chief Executive Officer and Administrator
CFO: Janice Campas, Chief Financial Officer
CMO: Jeffrey Alpert, M.D., Medical Director
CHR: Patti Whalen, Manager Human Resources
Web address: www.wichitacountyhealthcenter.com
Control: County, Government, nonfederal **Service:** General medical and surgical

Staffed Beds: 42 **Admissions:** 129 **Census:** 28 **Outpatient Visits:** 5744 **Births:** 0 **Total Expense ($000):** 8901 **Payroll Expense ($000):** 3725 **Personnel:** 73

LIBERAL—Seward County

☐ **SOUTHWEST MEDICAL CENTER (170068)**, 315 West 15th Street, Zip 67901–2455, Mailing Address: Box 1340, Zip 67905–1340; tel. 620/624–1651, (Total facility includes 18 beds in nursing home–type unit) **A**1 10 **F**3 11 13 15 28 29 31 34 40 45 48 49 57 59 68 70 73 75 76 77 79 81 85 87 89 93 96 98 103 107 108 110 111 114 118 119 128 129 130 131 145 146 147 148 149 154 157
Primary Contact: William Ermann, President and Chief Executive Officer
CFO: Amber Williams, Vice President and Chief Financial Officer
CHR: Lisa L Mathes, Human Resources Director
CNO: Jo L Harrison, Vice President of Patient Care Services
Web address: www.swmedcenter.com
Control: County, Government, nonfederal **Service:** General medical and surgical

Staffed Beds: 101 **Admissions:** 2360 **Census:** 21 **Outpatient Visits:** 55374 **Births:** 740 **Total Expense ($000):** 58214 **Payroll Expense ($000):** 25827 **Personnel:** 434

Hospital, Medicare Provider Number, Address, Telephone, Approval, Facility, and Physician Codes, Health Care System

★ American Hospital Association (AHA) membership
☐ The Joint Commission accreditation
○ Healthcare Facilities Accreditation Program
◇ DNV Healthcare Inc. accreditation
⇑ Center for Improvement in Healthcare Quality Accreditation
△ Commission on Accreditation of Rehabilitation Facilities (CARF) accreditation

KS

LINCOLN—Lincoln County

LINCOLN COUNTY HOSPITAL (171360), 624 North Second Street, Zip 67455–1738, Mailing Address: P.O. Box 406, Zip 67455–0406; tel. 785/524–4403, **A**10 18 **F**3 11 15 40 68 69 77 93 107 110 111 115 119 127 129 133 154
Primary Contact: Steven L. Granzow, Chief Executive Officer
CFO: Tawnya Seitz, Chief Financial Officer
CNO: Christa Haesemeyer, Chief Nursing Officer
Web address: www.lincolncountyhospital.net
Control: County, Government, nonfederal **Service:** General medical and surgical

Staffed Beds: 14 Admissions: 101 Census: 1 Outpatient Visits: 4994
Births: 0 Total Expense ($000): 8440 **Payroll Expense ($000):** 3394
Personnel: 71

LINDSBORG—Mcpherson County

★ **LINDSBORG COMMUNITY HOSPITAL (171358)**, 605 West Lincoln Street, Zip 67456–2328; tel. 785/227–3308, **A**10 18 **F**3 11 28 29 36 40 45 46 53 57 59 62 64 65 67 81 87 93 97 107 115 119 128 130 133 144 **S** Salina Regional Health Center, Salina, KS
Primary Contact: Larry VanDerWege, Administrator
CFO: Laraine Gengler, Chief Financial Officer
CIO: Jeremy Snapp, Director Information Systems
CHR: Brad Malm, Director Human Resources and Education
CNO: Beth Hedberg, R.N., Director Nursing
Web address: www.lindsborghospital.org
Control: Other not–for–profit (including NFP Corporation) **Service:** General medical and surgical

Staffed Beds: 21 Admissions: 216 Census: 4 Outpatient Visits: 23321
Births: 0 Total Expense ($000): 11446 **Payroll Expense ($000):** 5293
Personnel: 103

LYONS—Rice County

★ **HOSPITAL DISTRICT NO 1 OF RICE COUNTY (171330)**, 619 South Clark Street, Zip 67554–3003, Mailing Address: P.O. Box 828, Zip 67554–0828; tel. 620/257–5173, **A**10 18 **F**3 13 28 29 30 34 35 40 43 45 65 75 77 81 93 107 125 127 130 132 133 143
Primary Contact: George M. Stover, Chief Executive Officer
CFO: Terry Pound, Chief Financial Officer
CMO: Kristina Darnauer, M.D., Chief of Staff
CNO: Judy Hogdson, R.N., Chief Nursing Officer
Web address: www.ricecountyhospital.com
Control: Hospital district or authority, Government, nonfederal **Service:** General medical and surgical

Staffed Beds: 25 Admissions: 372 Census: 13 Outpatient Visits: 30690
Births: 88 Total Expense ($000): 14553 **Payroll Expense ($000):** 6933
Personnel: 125

MANHATTAN—Riley County

★ ○ **ASCENSION VIA CHRISTI HOSPITAL, MANHATTAN (170142)**, 1823 College Avenue, Zip 66502–3346; tel. 785/776–3322, **A**10 11 19 **F**3 11 12 13 15 18 22 28 29 30 31 34 35 37 40 41 44 45 49 50 51 60 67 70 76 77 79 81 82 83 84 85 86 87 89 90 92 94 95 96 102 104 107 108 109 110 111 115 119 126 129 130 132 133 145 146 147 148 149 154 **S** Ascension Healthcare, Saint Louis, MO
Primary Contact: Robert C. Copple, FACHE, Senior Administrator
CFO: James Fraser, Administrator Finance
CIO: Andy Gagnon, Manager Information Technology
CHR: Renee Reed, Director Human Resources
CNO: Jennifer Goehring, R.N., Assistant Chief Nursing Officer
Web address: www.https://www.viachristi.org/manhattan
Control: Other not–for–profit (including NFP Corporation) **Service:** General medical and surgical

Staffed Beds: 96 Admissions: 4441 Census: 44 Outpatient Visits: 102941
Births: 1103 Total Expense ($000): 85920 **Payroll Expense ($000):** 27810
Personnel: 340

MANHATTAN SURGICAL (170190), 1829 College Avenue, Zip 66502–3381; tel. 785/776–5100, **A**10 **F**78 79 81 82 85 97 107 115 120 121 122 123 124
Primary Contact: Christopher R. Stipe, FACHE, Chief Executive Officer
Web address: www.manhattansurgical.com
Control: Corporation, Investor–owned (for–profit) **Service:** Surgical

Staffed Beds: 13 Admissions: 11145 Census: 2 Outpatient Visits: 5176
Births: 0

MANKATO—Jewell County

JEWELL COUNTY HOSPITAL (171309), 100 Crestvue Avenue, Zip 66956–2407, Mailing Address: P.O. Box 327, Zip 66956–0327; tel. 785/378–3137, **A**10 18 **F**2 3 29 40 50 64 75 77 87 93 107 127 128 130 133 148 156
Primary Contact: Doyle L. McKimmy, FACHE, Chief Executive Officer
COO: Eric Borden, Chief Operating Officer and Chief Financial Officer
CFO: Eric Borden, Chief Operating Officer and Chief Financial Officer
Web address: www.jewellcountyhospital.com
Control: County, Government, nonfederal **Service:** General medical and surgical

Staffed Beds: 25 Admissions: 92 Census: 18 Outpatient Visits: 16215
Births: 0 Total Expense ($000): 5636 **Payroll Expense ($000):** 2798
Personnel: 61

MARION—Marion County

ST. LUKE HOSPITAL AND LIVING CENTER (171356), 535 South Freeborn, Zip 66861–1256; tel. 620/382–2177, (Nonreporting) **A**10 18
Primary Contact: Jeremy Ensey, Chief Executive Officer
CFO: Bev Reid, Chief Financial Officer
CMO: Don Hodson, M.D., Chief Medical Officer
CIO: Jeff Methvin, Manager Information Technology
CHR: Sharon Zogelman, Director Human Resources
Web address: www.slhmarion.org
Control: Hospital district or authority, Government, nonfederal **Service:** General medical and surgical

Staffed Beds: 39

MARYSVILLE—Marshall County

★ **COMMUNITY MEMORIAL HEALTHCARE (171363)**, 708 North 18th Street, Zip 66508–1338; tel. 785/562–2311, **A**10 18 **F**3 13 15 28 29 34 35 40 45 47 50 57 59 62 64 69 75 76 81 87 97 107 108 114 119 127 128 129 130 131 132 133 135 146
Primary Contact: Curtis R. Hawkinson, Chief Executive Officer
CFO: Therese Landoll, Interim Chief Financial Officer
CMO: John Haefele, M.D., Chief Medical Officer
CIO: Colleen Behrens, Director Information Technology
CHR: Jessie Schneider, Director Human Resources
CNO: Diane Luebcke, R.N., Director Nursing
Web address: www.cmhcare.org
Control: Other not–for–profit (including NFP Corporation) **Service:** General medical and surgical

Staffed Beds: 25 Admissions: 683 Census: 10 Outpatient Visits: 27362
Births: 44 Total Expense ($000): 22216 **Payroll Expense ($000):** 9916
Personnel: 185

MCPHERSON—McPherson County

★ **MCPHERSON HOSPITAL (170105)**, 1000 Hospital Drive, Zip 67460–2326; tel. 620/241–2250, **A**10 **F**3 7 11 13 15 28 29 34 35 40 45 50 53 54 59 64 65 70 75 76 77 81 82 85 86 87 97 107 110 111 114 119 130 133 144 146 147 148 154
Primary Contact: Terri Gehring, President and Chief Executive Officer
COO: Terri Gehring, Vice President Operations
CFO: George Halama, Vice President Finance
CHR: Cathy Dunham, Vice President Human Resources
CNO: Beth Worden, Director Nursing Services
Web address: www.mcphersonhospital.org
Control: Other not–for–profit (including NFP Corporation) **Service:** General medical and surgical

Staffed Beds: 33 Admissions: 722 Census: 7 Outpatient Visits: 69154
Births: 94 Total Expense ($000): 30622 **Payroll Expense ($000):** 15291
Personnel: 269

MEMORIAL HOSPITAL See Mcpherson Hospital

MEADE—Meade County

★ **MEADE DISTRICT HOSPITAL (171321)**, 510 East Carthage Street, Zip 67864–6401, Mailing Address: P.O. Box 820, Zip 67864–0820; tel. 620/873–2141, (Total facility includes 45 beds in nursing home–type unit) **A**10 18 **F**3 34 40 45 50 53 56 57 59 62 64 67 79 81 82 85 87 92 93 94 107 108 114 119 127 128 129 130 131 133 148 156
Primary Contact: Tara Ramlochan, Chief Executive Officer
CIO: Matt Bobo, Chief Information Officer
Web address: www.meadehospital.com
Control: Hospital district or authority, Government, nonfederal **Service:** General medical and surgical

Staffed Beds: 65 Admissions: 218 Census: 34 Outpatient Visits: 12175
Births: 0 Total Expense ($000): 16513 **Payroll Expense ($000):** 8766
Personnel: 161

MEDICINE LODGE—Barber County

MEDICINE LODGE MEMORIAL HOSPITAL (171334), 710 North Walnut Street, Zip 67104–1019; tel. 620/886–3771, **A**10 18 **F**3 7 11 40 44 45 56 64 81 93 107 119 127 128 133 148 154 156 **S** Great Plains Health Alliance, Inc., Wichita, KS
Primary Contact: Kevin A. White, Administrator
CFO: Thomas G Lee, Chief Financial Officer
CHR: Johnnie Davis, Director Human Resources
CNO: Kathryn I. Burns, R.N., Director of Nursing
Web address: www.mlmh.net/
Control: Hospital district or authority, Government, nonfederal **Service**: General medical and surgical

Staffed Beds: 25 **Admissions**: 187 **Census**: 17 **Outpatient Visits**: 16294
Births: 0 **Total Expense ($000)**: 10117 **Payroll Expense ($000)**: 4724
Personnel: 87

MINNEAPOLIS—Ottawa County

★ **OTTAWA COUNTY HEALTH CENTER (171328)**, 215 East Eighth, Zip 67467–1902, Mailing Address: P.O. Box 290, Zip 67467–0290; tel. 785/392–2122, (Total facility includes 10 beds in nursing home–type unit) **A**10 18 **F**28 29 34 35 40 53 56 64 67 85 86 93 107 114 128 130 133 143 154 156 **S** Great Plains Health Alliance, Inc., Wichita, KS
Primary Contact: Jody Parks, Administrator
CFO: Cheryl Lanoue, Chief Financial Officer
CIO: Linda Wright, Director Information
CNO: Marlene Gawith, Director of Nursing
Web address: www.ottawacountyhealthcenter.com
Control: Other not–for–profit (including NFP Corporation) **Service**: General medical and surgical

Staffed Beds: 35 **Admissions**: 241 **Census**: 20 **Outpatient Visits**: 6550
Births: 0 **Total Expense ($000)**: 6609 **Payroll Expense ($000)**: 2859
Personnel: 74

MINNEOLA—Ford County

★ **MINNEOLA DISTRICT HOSPITAL (171368)**, 212 Main Street, Zip 67865–8511, Mailing Address: P.O. Box 127, Zip 67865–0127; tel. 620/885–4264, (Total facility includes 36 beds in nursing home–type unit) **A**10 18 **F**29 40 45 46 56 57 64 65 67 81 83 93 102 107 127 128 130 133 148 156 **S** Great Plains Health Alliance, Inc., Wichita, KS
Primary Contact: Deborah Bruner, Chief Executive Officer and Administrator
CFO: Marion Zirger, Chief Financial Officer
CMO: Tony Luna, M.D., Chief of Staff
CHR: Vena Harris, Director Human Resources
CNO: Amanda Stout, Chief Nursing Officer
Web address: www.minneolahealthcare.com
Control: Hospital district or authority, Government, nonfederal **Service**: General medical and surgical

Staffed Beds: 54 **Admissions**: 332 **Census**: 34 **Outpatient Visits**: 22909
Births: 0 **Total Expense ($000)**: 13552 **Payroll Expense ($000)**: 6063
Personnel: 103

MOUNDRIDGE—Mcpherson County

★ **MERCY HOSPITAL (170075)**, 218 East Pack Street, Zip 67107–8815, Mailing Address: P.O. Box 180, Zip 67107–0180; tel. 620/345–6391, **A**10 **F**29 30 40 45 59 67 77 81 86 87 89 92 93 128 130 133 146 149 154
Primary Contact: Aaron Herbel, Administrator
CFO: Royce Holdeman, Chief Financial Officer
Web address: www.mercyh.org/
Control: Church operated, Nongovernment, not–for–profit **Service**: General medical and surgical

Staffed Beds: 16 **Admissions**: 315 **Census**: 4 **Outpatient Visits**: 7851
Births: 0 **Total Expense ($000)**: 3412 **Payroll Expense ($000)**: 1657
Personnel: 39

MULVANE—Sedgwick County

✠ **ASCENSION VIA CHRISTI ST. FRANCIS (170122)**, 211 N College Ave, Zip 67110, Mailing Address: 929 North St Francis Street, Wichita, Zip 67214–3882; tel. 316/268–5000, (Includes GOOD SHEPHERD CAMPUS, 8901 East Orme, Wichita, Kansas, Zip 67207; tel. 316/858–0333; Kevin Strecker, President; ST. FRANCIS CAMPUS, 929 North St Francis Street, Wichita, Kansas, Zip 67214–3882; tel. 316/268–5000; Kevin Strecker, President; ST. JOSEPH CAMPUS, 3600 East Harry Street, Wichita, Kansas, Zip 67218–3713; tel. 316/685–1111; Kevin Strecker, President) **A**1 2 3 5 10 13 **F**3 7 11 12 13 15 16 17 18 19 20 21 22 23 24 26 27 28 29 30 31 32 34 35 38 40 43 44 45 46 48 49 50 51 54 56 57 58 59 60 61 62 64 68 70 72 74 75 76 77 78 79 80 81 82 84 85 86 87 88 89 92 93 97 98 99 100 102 103 104 105 107 108 110 111 114 115 117 118 119 120 121 123 124 126 130 131 132 135 136 141 142 143 146 147 148 153 154 **S** Ascension Healthcare, Saint Louis, MO
Primary Contact: Kevin Strecker, President
CFO: Jeff Seirer, Interim Chief Financial Officer
CMO: Darrell Youngman, D.O., Chief Medical Officer
CIO: Donna Roach, Chief Information Officer
CHR: Judy Espinoza, Chief Human Resources Officer
Web address: www.via-christi.org
Control: Church operated, Nongovernment, not–for–profit **Service**: General medical and surgical

Staffed Beds: 647 **Admissions**: 30404 **Census**: 420 **Outpatient Visits**: 283331 **Births**: 2482 **Total Expense ($000)**: 496235 **Payroll Expense ($000)**: 157804 **Personnel**: 2591

VIA CHRISTI REGIONAL MEDICAL CENTER See Ascension Via Christi St. Francis

NEODESHA—Wilson County

★ **WILSON MEDICAL CENTER (171344)**, 2600 Ottawa Road, Zip 66757–1897, Mailing Address: P.O. Box 360, Zip 66757–0360; tel. 620/325–2611, **A**10 18 **F**3 11 15 29 32 34 35 40 42 44 45 53 57 59 64 75 77 81 82 85 86 89 90 93 107 110 114 119 127 128 130 133 146 148 149 154 **S** QHR, Brentwood, TN
Primary Contact: Dennis R. Shelby, Chief Executive Officer
CFO: John Gutschenritter, Chief Financial Officer
CIO: Kevin Myers, Director Information Technology
CHR: Laura L Dean, Director Human Resources
CNO: Temple Monroe, Director Nursing Operations
Web address: www.wilsonmedical.org
Control: County, Government, nonfederal **Service**: General medical and surgical

Staffed Beds: 15 **Admissions**: 313 **Census**: 7 **Outpatient Visits**: 19126
Births: 0 **Total Expense ($000)**: 19289 **Payroll Expense ($000)**: 6043
Personnel: 158

NESS CITY—Ness County

★ **NESS COUNTY HOSPITAL DISTRICT NO 2 (171336)**, 312 Custer Street, Zip 67560–1654; tel. 785/798–2291, (Total facility includes 30 beds in nursing home–type unit) **A**10 18 **F**7 15 40 45 59 62 67 93 114 125 127 133 154
Primary Contact: Curt Thomas, Administrator
CFO: Debra Frank, Chief Financial Officer
CMO: Mikhail Imseis, M.D., Chief of Staff
CIO: Vicki Howe, Health Information Management
CHR: Shelly McDonald, Chief Human Resources Officer
CNO: Cindy Maier, R.N., Director of Nursing
Web address: www.nchospital.org
Control: Hospital district or authority, Government, nonfederal **Service**: General medical and surgical

Staffed Beds: 55 **Admissions**: 193 **Census**: 34 **Outpatient Visits**: 8814
Births: 0 **Total Expense ($000)**: 10421 **Payroll Expense ($000)**: 4637
Personnel: 103

NEWTON—Harvey County

★ ○ **NEWTON MEDICAL CENTER (170103)**, 600 Medical Center Drive, Zip 67114–8780, Mailing Address: P.O. Box 308, Zip 67114–0308; tel. 316/283–2700, **A**3 10 11 **F**3 11 13 15 20 22 28 29 30 31 34 35 37 40 45 51 59 62 64 68 70 73 74 75 76 77 79 81 84 85 86 90 93 98 102 103 107 108 110 111 115 118 119 126 130 131 132 133 145 146 147 148 149 154 156 157
Primary Contact: Vallerie L. Gleason, President and Chief Executive Officer
COO: Todd Tangeman, Chief Operating Officer
CFO: Todd Kasitz, Vice President Finance
CIO: Mike Cottle, Chief Information Officer
CHR: Todd Tangeman, Chief Operating Officer and Chief Human Resource Officer
CNO: Heather Renee Porter, Chief Clinical Officer
Web address: www.newtonmedicalcenter.com
Control: Other not–for–profit (including NFP Corporation) **Service**: General medical and surgical

Staffed Beds: 103 **Admissions**: 2799 **Census**: 35 **Outpatient Visits**: 62163
Births: 463 **Total Expense ($000)**: 79263 **Payroll Expense ($000)**: 38604
Personnel: 692

Hospital, Medicare Provider Number, Address, Telephone, Approval, Facility, and Physician Codes, Health Care System

★ American Hospital Association (AHA) membership ○ Healthcare Facilities Accreditation Program ⇑ Center for Improvement in Healthcare Quality Accreditation
□ The Joint Commission accreditation ◇ DNV Healthcare Inc. accreditation △ Commission on Accreditation of Rehabilitation Facilities (CARF) accreditation

KS

☐ **PRAIRIE VIEW (174016)**, 1901 East First Street, Zip 67114–5010, Mailing Address: P.O. Box 467, Zip 67114–0467; tel. 316/284–6400, (Nonreporting) **A**1 10
Primary Contact: Jessie Kaye, Chief Executive Officer
CFO: Lisa Ramsey, Chief Financial Officer
CMO: Gary Fast, M.D., Medical Director
CIO: Chad Roth, Director Information Services
CHR: Joy Robb, Vice President Human Resources
CNO: Patrick Flaming, R.N., Director Inpatient Operations
Web address: www.prairieview.org
Control: Other not–for–profit (including NFP Corporation) **Service:** Psychiatric

Staffed Beds: 38

NORTON—Norton County

★ **NORTON COUNTY HOSPITAL (171348)**, 102 East Holme, Zip 67654–1406, Mailing Address: P.O. Box 250, Zip 67654–0250; tel. 785/877–3351, **A**10 18 **F**3 13 15 18 28 29 30 31 34 35 40 45 50 59 64 65 67 76 77 78 79 81 85 86 87 93 97 107 110 112 119 127 128 129 130 131 133 154
Primary Contact: Gina Frack, Chief Executive Officer
CHR: Shannan Hempler, Director Human Resources
Web address: www.ntcohosp.com
Control: County, Government, nonfederal **Service:** General medical and surgical

Staffed Beds: 25 **Admissions:** 447 **Census:** 8 **Outpatient Visits:** 37613 **Births:** 45 **Total Expense ($000):** 15320 **Payroll Expense ($000):** 7085 **Personnel:** 128

OAKLEY—Logan County

LOGAN COUNTY HOSPITAL (171326), 211 Cherry Street, Zip 67748–1201; tel. 785/672–3211, **A**10 18 **F**28 29 32 34 40 45 53 54 56 57 59 69 71 77 81 91 93 107 111 115 127 128 130 133 148 154
Primary Contact: Meldon L. Snow, Chief Executive Officer
COO: Aimee Zimmerman, R.N., Chief Operations Officer
CFO: Bonnie Hagel, Chief Financial Officer
CMO: Celeste Rains, D.O., Chief of Staff
CIO: Russ Kahle, Chief Information Officer
CHR: Steve Allison, Director Human Resources
CNO: Marcia Kruse, R.N., Director Nursing
Web address: www.logancountyhospital.org
Control: County, Government, nonfederal **Service:** General medical and surgical

Staffed Beds: 25 **Admissions:** 98 **Census:** 1 **Outpatient Visits:** 6950 **Births:** 0 **Total Expense ($000):** 11169 **Payroll Expense ($000):** 4430

OBERLIN—Decatur County

DECATUR HEALTH SYSTEMS (171352), 810 West Columbia Street, Zip 67749–2450, Mailing Address: P.O. Box 268, Zip 67749–0268; tel. 785/475–2208, **A**10 18 **F**3 15 34 40 41 45 50 53 56 59 64 69 77 82 83 84 85 93 97 107 110 114 125 127 130 131 133 135 148 149 154 158
Primary Contact: Kristopher Matthews, Chief Operating Officer
CFO: Amanda Fortin, Manager Finance
CMO: Elizabeth Sliter, M.D., Chairman Medical Staff
CIO: Natasha Weishapl, Manager Business Office and Human Resources
CHR: Natasha Weishapl, Manager Business Office and Human Resources
Web address: www.decaturhealthsystems.org
Control: Other not–for–profit (including NFP Corporation) **Service:** General medical and surgical

Staffed Beds: 12 **Admissions:** 126 **Census:** 1 **Outpatient Visits:** 11859 **Births:** 0 **Total Expense ($000):** 8265 **Payroll Expense ($000):** 3721 **Personnel:** 83

OLATHE—Johnson County

☐ **COTTONWOOD SPRINGS HOSPITAL (174020)**, 13351 South Arapaho Drive, Zip 66062–1520; tel. 913/353–3000, (Nonreporting) **A**1 10 **S** Springstone, Louisville, KY
Primary Contact: Jason Toalson, Chief Executive Officer
Web address: www.cottonwoodsprings.com
Control: Corporation, Investor–owned (for–profit) **Service:** Psychiatric

Staffed Beds: 72

☐ **OLATHE MEDICAL CENTER (170049)**, 20333 West 151st Street, Zip 66061–5350; tel. 913/791–4200, **A**1 2 10 **F**3 11 12 13 15 18 20 22 24 26 28 29 30 31 34 35 39 40 45 46 47 48 49 56 57 58 59 61 62 63 64 65 68 70 73 74 75 76 77 78 79 80 81 82 84 85 86 87 89 92 93 107 108 110 111 115 116 117 118 119 120 121 123 124 126 129 130 131 132 135 145 146 147 148 149 156
Primary Contact: Stan Holm, President and Chief Executive Officer
COO: John Staton, Senior Vice President Operations
CFO: Tierney Lynn Grasser, Senior Vice President and Chief Financial Officer
CMO: James L Wetzel, M.D., Senior Vice President, Chief Medical Officer
CIO: Randy Rahman, Vice President and Chief Information Officer
CHR: David Klimek, Vice President Human Resources
CNO: Amy J Meglemre, R.N., MSN, Senior Vice President and Chief Nursing Officer
Web address: www.olathehealth.org
Control: Other not–for–profit (including NFP Corporation) **Service:** General medical and surgical

Staffed Beds: 254 **Admissions:** 10474 **Census:** 109 **Outpatient Visits:** 349350 **Births:** 1283 **Personnel:** 1300

ONAGA—Pottawatomie County

★ **COMMUNITY HEALTHCARE SYSTEM (171354)**, 120 West Eighth Street, Zip 66521–9574; tel. 785/889–4272, (Total facility includes 78 beds in nursing home–type unit) **A**10 18 **F**2 3 5 6 10 11 12 13 15 29 31 32 34 35 36 40 43 45 50 53 56 57 59 62 64 65 67 74 75 77 78 81 82 84 85 86 87 93 97 99 100 101 102 103 104 105 106 107 110 111 114 119 125 127 128 130 131 132 133 134 135 143 144 145 146 147 148 151 152 153 154 156
Primary Contact: Todd Willert, Chief Executive Officer
COO: Marcia S Walsh, M.P.H., Chief Operating Officer
CFO: Monica Holthaus, Chief Financial Officer
CMO: Marcus Weiser, D.O., Chief of Staff
CIO: Rod Evans, Chief Information Officer
CHR: Terry D. Bernatis, Director Human Resources
CNO: Rosalind Lewis, R.N., MSN, Director of Ancillary Services
Web address: www.chcsks.org
Control: Other not–for–profit (including NFP Corporation) **Service:** General medical and surgical

Staffed Beds: 150 **Admissions:** 1136 **Census:** 77 **Outpatient Visits:** 103449 **Births:** 77 **Total Expense ($000):** 36675 **Payroll Expense ($000):** 19859 **Personnel:** 265

OSAWATOMIE—Miami County

OSAWATOMIE STATE HOSPITAL AT ADAIR ACUTE CARE (174022), 500 State Hospital Drive, Zip 66064–1813, Mailing Address: P.O. Box 500, Zip 66064–0500; tel. 913/755–7000, **A**10 **F**30 50 86 87 98 100 101 130 135 146 156
Primary Contact: Sherman W. Cole, Interim Chief Executive Officer
CMO: Maria Gustilo, M.D., Medical Director
CHR: Dezerae Curran, Director Human Resources
Web address: www.srskansas.org/osh/osh-rmhf_info.html
Control: State, Government, nonfederal **Service:** Psychiatric

Staffed Beds: 166 **Admissions:** 1250 **Census:** 138 **Outpatient Visits:** 0 **Births:** 0 **Total Expense ($000):** 41775 **Payroll Expense ($000):** 23978 **Personnel:** 432

OSBORNE—Osborne County

OSBORNE COUNTY MEMORIAL HOSPITAL (171364), 424 West New Hampshire Street, Zip 67473–2314, Mailing Address: P.O. Box 70, Zip 67473–0070; tel. 785/346–2121, **A**10 18 **F**11 13 40 45 64 69 81 82 91 93 107 119 127 133 154 **S** Great Plains Health Alliance, Inc., Wichita, KS
Primary Contact: Marianna Harris, Administrator
CFO: Linda Murphy, Chief Financial Officer
CMO: Erin Baxa, M.D., Chief Medical Officer
CNO: Monica Mullender, Director of Nursing
Web address: www.ocmh.org
Control: County, Government, nonfederal **Service:** General medical and surgical

Staffed Beds: 25 **Admissions:** 157 **Census:** 1 **Outpatient Visits:** 7206 **Births:** 7 **Total Expense ($000):** 6226 **Payroll Expense ($000):** 2723

OTTAWA—Franklin County

⊞ **RANSOM MEMORIAL HOSPITAL (170014)**, 1301 South Main Street, Zip 66067–3598; tel. 785/229–8200, **A**1 10 20 **F**3 11 13 15 28 29 30 32 34 35 40 41 43 44 45 50 53 56 57 59 64 68 70 75 76 77 78 79 81 82 85 86 87 89 92 93 94 96 97 107 108 110 111 114 115 118 119 127 129 130 131 132 134 135 144 146 147 148 149 154 156
Primary Contact: Matthew M. Heyn, Chief Executive Officer
Web address: www.ransom.org
Control: County, Government, nonfederal **Service:** General medical and surgical

Staffed Beds: 44 **Admissions:** 1296 **Census:** 10 **Outpatient Visits:** 135424 **Births:** 182 **Total Expense ($000):** 45650 **Payroll Expense ($000):** 21267 **Personnel:** 304

Many Facility Codes have changed. Please refer to the AHA Guide Code Chart.

OVERLAND PARK—Johnson County

☐ **CHILDREN'S MERCY HOSPITAL KANSAS (173300)**, 5808 West 110th Street, Zip 66211–2504; tel. 913/696–8000, **A**1 10 **F**7 9 12 29 30 32 35 36 38 40 41 44 48 50 55 58 59 62 64 65 68 75 77 79 81 82 85 87 89 93 100 104 107 111 115 119 129 130 131 132 134 144 146 148 149 150 154 157
Primary Contact: Paul D. Kempinski, Chief Executive Officer
CFO: Sandra A J Lawrence, Executive Vice President and Chief Financial Officer
CMO: Charles Roberts, M.D., Medical Director
CIO: Jean Ann Breedlove, Chief Information Officer
CHR: Dan Wright, Vice President Human Resources
Web address: www.childrens-mercy.org
Control: Other not–for–profit (including NFP Corporation) **Service:** Children's general medical and surgical

Staffed Beds: 50 **Admissions:** 2532 **Census:** 16 **Outpatient Visits:** 153978 **Births:** 0 **Total Expense ($000):** 103630 **Payroll Expense ($000):** 68329 **Personnel:** 797

HEARTLAND SPINE & SPECIALTY HOSPITAL See The University of Kansas Hospital - Indian Creek Campus

☒ **MENORAH MEDICAL CENTER (170182)**, 5721 West 119th Street, Zip 66209–3722; tel. 913/498–6000, **A**1 2 3 10 **F**3 12 13 15 18 20 22 24 26 28 29 30 31 34 35 38 40 45 46 47 49 55 57 58 59 60 64 65 68 70 72 74 75 76 77 78 79 81 82 84 85 86 87 90 93 100 102 107 108 110 111 114 115 116 117 119 120 121 126 129 130 131 132 135 145 146 148 149 154 **S** HCA Healthcare, Nashville, TN
Primary Contact: Phil Buttell, Chief Executive Officer
CFO: Deborah Gafford, Chief Financial Officer
CMO: James Cheray, M.D., Chief Medical Officer
CIO: Christina McGinnis, Director Information Technology
CHR: Amy Hunt, Director Human Resources
CNO: Kelly Reno, R.N., Chief Nursing Officer
Web address: www.menorahmedicalcenter.com
Control: Corporation, Investor–owned (for–profit) **Service:** General medical and surgical

Staffed Beds: 158 **Admissions:** 8858 **Census:** 95 **Outpatient Visits:** 71992 **Births:** 604 **Total Expense ($000):** 216795 **Payroll Expense ($000):** 58078 **Personnel:** 792

☒ **OVERLAND PARK REGIONAL MEDICAL CENTER (170176)**, 10500 Quivira Road, Zip 66215–2306, Mailing Address: P.O. Box 15959, Zip 66215–5959; tel. 913/541–5000, **A**1 2 3 5 10 **F**3 8 13 15 18 19 20 22 24 26 28 29 30 31 34 35 37 40 41 42 43 45 49 50 52 55 56 57 59 60 61 64 65 67 70 72 73 74 75 76 77 78 79 81 82 83 84 85 86 87 88 91 92 93 107 108 110 111 114 115 119 126 129 130 131 135 144 145 146 147 149 156 **S** HCA Healthcare, Nashville, TN
Primary Contact: Matt Sogard, Chief Executive Officer
COO: Jim Beatty, Chief Operating Officer
CFO: Steven R Cleary, Chief Financial Officer
CMO: George D. Stamos, M.D., Chief Medical Officer
CHR: Connie Miller, Vice President Human Resources
Web address: www.oprmc.com
Control: Corporation, Investor–owned (for–profit) **Service:** General medical and surgical

Staffed Beds: 283 **Admissions:** 12012 **Census:** 151 **Outpatient Visits:** 98272 **Births:** 2847 **Total Expense ($000):** 205340 **Payroll Expense ($000):** 72598 **Personnel:** 829

☐ **PROMISE HOSPITAL OF OVERLAND PARK (172004)**, 6509 West 103rd Street, Zip 66212–1728; tel. 913/649–3701, (Nonreporting) **A**1 10 **S** Promise Healthcare, Boca Raton, FL
Primary Contact: Kristen Barrett, Chief Executive Officer
CFO: William Scott, Chief Financial Officer
CHR: Darren Enochs, Director Human Resources
Web address: www.promise-overlandpark.com
Control: Corporation, Investor–owned (for–profit) **Service:** Acute long–term care hospital

Staffed Beds: 104

☐ **REHABILITATION HOSPITAL OF OVERLAND PARK (173032)**, 5100 Indian Creek Parkway, Zip 66207–4115; tel. 913/544–1957, **A**1 10 **F**3 34 35 56 64 74 75 79 86 87 90 91 93 96 100 131 148 154 **S** Post Acute Medical, LLC, Enola, PA
Primary Contact: Portlyn Brogger, Divisional President
Web address: www.warmsprings.org
Control: Partnership, Investor–owned (for–profit) **Service:** Rehabilitation

Staffed Beds: 45 **Admissions:** 1118 **Census:** 37 **Outpatient Visits:** 2400 **Births:** 0 **Personnel:** 159

☒ **SAINT LUKE'S SOUTH HOSPITAL (170185)**, 12300 Metcalf Avenue, Zip 66213–1324; tel. 913/317–7000, **A**1 10 **F**3 12 13 15 18 20 22 26 28 29 30 31 34 35 38 39 40 44 45 47 48 49 50 54 56 58 59 60 64 65 68 70 73 74 75 76 77 78 79 80 81 82 84 85 86 87 89 90 93 94 95 96 100 102 107 108 110 111 114 115 117 118 119 120 121 123 126 129 130 131 132 135 141 146 147 148 149 154 **S** Saint Luke's Health System, Kansas City, MO
Primary Contact: Bobby Olm-Shipman, Chief Executive Officer
CFO: Shelby Frigon, Chief Financial Officer
CMO: Lisa Heath, M.D., President Medical Staff
CIO: Deborah Gash, Chief Information Officer
CHR: Donna Kunz, System Director Human Resources
CNO: Julia Woods, R.N., MSN, Vice President and Chief Nursing Officer
Web address: www.saintlukeshealthsystem.org/south
Control: Church operated, Nongovernment, not–for–profit **Service:** General medical and surgical

Staffed Beds: 104 **Admissions:** 5984 **Census:** 61 **Outpatient Visits:** 99569 **Births:** 504 **Total Expense ($000):** 138268 **Payroll Expense ($000):** 39061 **Personnel:** 551

PAOLA—Miami County

☐ **MIAMI COUNTY MEDICAL CENTER (170109)**, 2100 Baptiste Drive, Zip 66071–1314, Mailing Address: P.O. Box 365, Zip 66071–0365; tel. 913/294–2327, **A**1 5 10 **F**3 11 15 18 28 34 40 43 57 59 64 68 75 77 78 79 81 82 85 87 93 107 108 110 111 115 119 127 130 131 135 145 146 148 156
Primary Contact: Paul W. Luce, R.N., MSN, Vice President Operations
CFO: Cheryl Sharp, Chief Financial Office
CMO: Christopher Eckland, M.D., Chief Medical Officer
CIO: Randy Rahman, Chief Information Officer
CHR: David Klimek, Chief Human Resources Officer
CNO: Aubree Slayman, Director Patient Services
Web address: www.olathehealth.org
Control: Other not–for–profit (including NFP Corporation) **Service:** General medical and surgical

Staffed Beds: 18 **Admissions:** 488 **Census:** 3 **Outpatient Visits:** 55995 **Births:** 0 **Personnel:** 124

PARSONS—Labette County

★ ○ **LABETTE HEALTH (170120)**, 1902 South U S Highway 59, Zip 67357–7404; tel. 620/421–4880, **A**10 11 **F**3 11 13 15 29 30 34 40 42 43 50 53 59 62 70 74 75 76 77 79 81 86 90 93 97 107 108 110 111 114 119 126 127 129 130 143 144 146 147 148 149 154 156
Primary Contact: Brian A. Williams, Chief Executive Officer
CFO: Thomas Macaronas, Chief Financial Officer
CHR: Christina Sykes, Director Human Resources
Web address: www.labettehealth.com
Control: County, Government, nonfederal **Service:** General medical and surgical

Staffed Beds: 56 **Admissions:** 1955 **Census:** 18 **Outpatient Visits:** 91887 **Births:** 200 **Total Expense ($000):** 73382 **Payroll Expense ($000):** 32344 **Personnel:** 580

PARSONS STATE HOSPITAL AND TRAINING CENTER, 2601 Gabriel Avenue, Zip 67357–2341, Mailing Address: P.O. Box 738, Zip 67357–0738; tel. 620/421–6550, (Nonreporting)
Primary Contact: Jerry A. Rea, Ph.D., Superintendent
CFO: John Spare, Accountant
CMO: Rema Menon, M.D., Clinical Director
CIO: Ron Malmstrom, Information Research Specialist
CHR: Tim B Posch, Business Manager and Director Personnel
Web address: www.pshtc.org
Control: State, Government, nonfederal **Service:** Intellectual disabilities

Staffed Beds: 188

PHILLIPSBURG—Phillips County

★ **PHILLIPS COUNTY HEALTH SYSTEMS (171353)**, 1150 State Street, Zip 67661–1743, Mailing Address: P.O. Box 607, Zip 67661–0607; tel. 785/543–5226, **A**10 18 **F**3 11 15 28 30 40 45 50 59 64 68 75 77 81 86 87 91 107 110 114 127 130 132 133 145 146 148 154
Primary Contact: Rex D. Walk, Chief Executive Officer
CFO: Christi Driggs, Chief Financial Officer
CMO: Ben Stephenson, M.D., Chief of Staff
CIO: Steven Seems, Director of Information Technology
CHR: Peggy Fabin, Director Human Resources
CNO: Vickie Gibbs, Director Nursing
Web address: www.phillipshospital.org
Control: Other not–for–profit (including NFP Corporation) **Service:** General medical and surgical

Staffed Beds: 25 **Admissions:** 199 **Census:** 7 **Outpatient Visits:** 24000 **Births:** 0 **Total Expense ($000):** 12340 **Payroll Expense ($000):** 5399 **Personnel:** 104

Hospital, Medicare Provider Number, Address, Telephone, Approval, Facility, and Physician Codes, Health Care System

★ American Hospital Association (AHA) membership
☐ The Joint Commission accreditation
○ Healthcare Facilities Accreditation Program
◇ DNV Healthcare Inc. accreditation
⇑ Center for Improvement in Healthcare Quality Accreditation
△ Commission on Accreditation of Rehabilitation Facilities (CARF) accreditation

KS

© 2019 AHA Guide   *Many Facility Codes have changed. Please refer to the AHA Guide Code Chart.*   Hospitals **A243**

PITTSBURG—Crawford County

⊠ **ASCENSION VIA CHRISTI HOSPITAL (170006)**, 1 Mt. Carmel Way, Zip 66762–7587; tel. 620/231–6100, **A**1 2 10 **F**3 5 11 12 13 15 18 20 22 26 28 29 30 31 34 35 40 42 43 45 46 47 48 50 51 53 54 56 57 58 59 62 64 68 69 70 74 75 76 77 78 79 81 82 84 85 86 89 90 93 104 107 108 109 110 111 112 114 115 116 117 118 119 120 121 122 123 126 129 130 131 132 133 135 143 145 146 147 148 154 156 157 **S** Ascension Healthcare, Saint Louis, MO
Primary Contact: Randall R. Cason, FACHE, Senior Administrator
CFO: Mike Joy, Administrator, Finance
CIO: Missy McDown, Director Information Systems
CHR: Laurie Johnson, Director - Human Resources
CNO: Amy Katherine Renn, Interim Administrator, Patient Care and Nursing
Web address: www.viachristi.org/pittsburg
Control: Church operated, Nongovernment, not–for–profit **Service**: General medical and surgical

> **Staffed Beds: 89 Admissions: 2965 Census: 32 Outpatient Visits: 82432**
> **Births: 535 Total Expense ($000): 80507 Payroll Expense ($000): 29610**
> **Personnel: 376**

PLAINVILLE—Rooks County

★ **ROOKS COUNTY HEALTH CENTER (171311)**, 1210 North Washington Street, Zip 67663–1632, Mailing Address: P.O. Box 389, Zip 67663–0389; tel. 785/434–4553, **A**10 18 **F**3 13 15 28 29 31 34 35 40 43 45 47 50 57 59 64 67 76 77 79 81 85 86 87 93 96 107 108 110 111 114 119 125 128 130 131 133 135 143 144 146 148 149
Primary Contact: Anthony Thomas, Chief Executive Officer
COO: William D Stahl, Chief Operating Officer
CFO: Frank A Rajewski, Chief Financial Officer
CMO: Lynn Fisher, M.D., Chief of Staff
CHR: Cindi Knipp, Director Human Resources
Web address: www.rookscountyhealthcenter.com
Control: Hospital district or authority, Government, nonfederal **Service**: General medical and surgical

> **Staffed Beds: 20 Admissions: 406 Census: 5 Outpatient Visits: 25158**
> **Births: 52 Total Expense ($000): 17380 Payroll Expense ($000): 6467**
> **Personnel: 135**

PRATT—Pratt County

★ **PRATT REGIONAL MEDICAL CENTER (170027)**, 200 Commodore Street, Zip 67124–2903; tel. 620/672–7451, (Total facility includes 45 beds in nursing home–type unit) **A**10 20 **F**3 7 11 13 15 30 31 34 40 45 49 50 56 57 59 61 62 64 68 70 75 76 77 79 81 82 85 86 87 93 107 108 114 118 119 124 127 130 131 133 145 146 147 148 155 156
Primary Contact: Susan M. Page, President and Chief Executive Officer
CFO: Vincent Scot Wilczek, Controller
CIO: Vikki Mader, Director Health Information Services
CHR: Kenneth A Brown, Vice President and Chief Human Resource Officer
CNO: Jack L Kennedy, R.N., MS, Vice President and Chief Nursing Officer
Web address: www.prmc.org
Control: Other not–for–profit (including NFP Corporation) **Service**: General medical and surgical

> **Staffed Beds: 80 Admissions: 1419 Census: 50 Outpatient Visits: 103920**
> **Births: 221 Total Expense ($000): 54404 Payroll Expense ($000): 23918**
> **Personnel: 484**

QUINTER—Gove County

GOVE COUNTY MEDICAL CENTER (171367), 520 West Fifth Street, Zip 67752–0129, Mailing Address: P.O. Box 129, Zip 67752–0129; tel. 785/754–3341, (Total facility includes 42 beds in nursing home–type unit) **A**10 18 **F**3 11 13 28 29 34 40 45 57 67 75 81 82 86 93 107 115 119 125 129 133 135 143 148 156
Primary Contact: Coleen Tummons, Chief Executive Officer
CFO: Alan Waites, Chief Financial Officer
CIO: Brad Mullins, Director Information Technology
CHR: Valerie Schneider, Director Human Resources
CNO: Renee Wagoner, R.N., Director of Nursing
Web address: www.govecountymedicalcenter.org
Control: County, Government, nonfederal **Service**: General medical and surgical

> **Staffed Beds: 63 Admissions: 427 Census: 41 Outpatient Visits: 10530**
> **Births: 44 Total Expense ($000): 14124 Payroll Expense ($000): 6317**
> **Personnel: 156**

RANSOM—Ness County

★ **GRISELL MEMORIAL HOSPITAL DISTRICT ONE (171300)**, 210 South Vermont Avenue, Zip 67572–9525; tel. 785/731–2231, (Total facility includes 30 beds in nursing home–type unit) **A**10 18 **F**3 40 67 69 85 93 97 127 128 133 156 **S** Great Plains Health Alliance, Inc., Wichita, KS
Primary Contact: David Caudill, Administrator
CFO: Jolene Schuster, Chief Financial Officer
CMO: Allen McLain, M.D., Chief of Staff
CNO: Joni Pfaff, Chief Nursing Officer
Web address: www.grisellmemorialhospital.org
Control: Hospital district or authority, Government, nonfederal **Service**: General medical and surgical

> **Staffed Beds: 42 Admissions: 67 Census: 26 Outpatient Visits: 4179**
> **Births: 0 Total Expense ($000): 6563 Payroll Expense ($000): 2855**
> **Personnel: 92**

RUSSELL—Russell County

★ **RUSSELL REGIONAL HOSPITAL (171350)**, 200 South Main Street, Zip 67665–2920; tel. 785/483–3131, (Total facility includes 22 beds in nursing home–type unit) **A**10 18 **F**9 11 15 29 34 40 45 46 50 53 57 59 64 65 66 67 69 75 81 85 87 93 97 107 108 109 110 115 119 127 129 130 131 133 135 145 146 147 148 154
Primary Contact: Sharon Collins, Chief Executive Officer
CFO: Kevin Kreutzer, Chief Financial Officer
CMO: Tyrel Somers, M.D., Chief Medical Officer
CIO: David Schraeder, Director Information Systems
CNO: Deb Strobel, R.N., Chief Nursing Officer
Web address: www.russellhospital.org
Control: Other not–for–profit (including NFP Corporation) **Service**: General medical and surgical

> **Staffed Beds: 47 Admissions: 407 Census: 27 Outpatient Visits: 36083**
> **Births: 0 Total Expense ($000): 13818 Payroll Expense ($000): 9191**
> **Personnel: 183**

SABETHA—Nemaha County

★ **SABETHA COMMUNITY HOSPITAL (171338)**, 14th and Oregon Streets, Zip 66534–0229, Mailing Address: P.O. Box 229, Zip 66534–0229; tel. 785/284–2121, **A**10 18 **F**3 11 13 15 28 34 35 40 43 45 50 56 57 59 62 63 64 68 75 76 77 78 79 81 82 84 85 86 93 107 110 114 119 128 130 132 133 146 148 156 **S** Great Plains Health Alliance, Inc., Wichita, KS
Primary Contact: Lora Key, Chief Executive Officer
CFO: Lori Lackey, Chief Financial Officer
CMO: James Longabaugh, M.D., Chief Medical Staff
CIO: Garrett Colglazier, Director Health Information Management
CHR: Julie K Holthaus, Director Human Resources
CNO: Rhonda Spellmeier, R.N., Director of Nursing
Web address: www.sabethahospital.com
Control: Other not–for–profit (including NFP Corporation) **Service**: General medical and surgical

> **Staffed Beds: 25 Admissions: 339 Census: 5 Outpatient Visits: 39420**
> **Births: 44 Total Expense ($000): 12859 Payroll Expense ($000): 5933**
> **Personnel: 106**

SAINT FRANCIS—Cheyenne County

★ **CHEYENNE COUNTY HOSPITAL (171310)**, 210 West First Street, Zip 67756–3540, Mailing Address: P.O. Box 547, Zip 67756–0547; tel. 785/332–2104, **A**10 18 **F**3 8 11 13 28 29 34 40 57 59 64 65 66 68 76 77 81 89 97 107 119 127 128 133 148 156 **S** Great Plains Health Alliance, Inc., Wichita, KS
Primary Contact: Kelly Pottorff, Chief Executive Officer
CFO: Heidi Tice, Chief Financial Officer
CMO: Mary Beth Miller, M.D., Chief of Staff
CIO: Carol Sloper, Manager Information Technology
CHR: Sara Wilson, Director Human Resources
CNO: Judith Ann Hodgson, Chief Nursing Officer
Web address: www.cheyennecountyhospital.com
Control: Other not–for–profit (including NFP Corporation) **Service**: General medical and surgical

> **Staffed Beds: 16 Admissions: 203 Census: 3 Outpatient Visits: 21054**
> **Births: 0 Total Expense ($000): 11615 Payroll Expense ($000): 4640**
> **Personnel: 79**

KS

Many Facility Codes have changed. Please refer to the AHA Guide Code Chart.
© 2019 AHA Guide

SALINA—Saline County

★ ○ **SALINA REGIONAL HEALTH CENTER (170012)**, 400 South Santa Fe Avenue, Zip 67401–4198, Mailing Address: P.O. Box 5080, Zip 67402–5080; tel. 785/452–7000, (Includes SALINA REGIONAL HEALTH CENTER- PENN CAMPUS, 139 North Penn Street, Salina, Kansas, Zip 67401, Mailing Address: P O Box 5080, Zip 67402–5080, tel. 913/452–7000; SALINA REGIONAL HEALTH CENTER-SANTA FE CAMPUS, 400 South Santa Fe Avenue, Salina, Kansas, Zip 67401, Mailing Address: Box 5080, Zip 67402–5080, tel. 913/452–7000) **A**3 5 10 11 20 **F**3 13 15 18 19 20 22 24 28 29 30 31 40 43 45 46 47 48 49 51 53 54 55 57 59 63 64 65 68 70 71 72 73 74 76 77 78 79 81 85 86 87 89 90 98 100 101 102 104 105 107 108 110 111 114 115 116 117 118 119 120 121 122 123 124 126 129 130 143 144 145 146 147 148 149 153 154 **S** Salina Regional Health Center, Salina, KS
Primary Contact: Micheal Terry, President and Chief Executive Officer
COO: Joel Phelps, President and Chief Operating Officer
CFO: Joe Tallon, Vice President Finance
CIO: Larry Barnes, Vice President Information Technology
CHR: David Moody, Vice President Human Resources
Web address: www.srhc.com
Control: Other not–for–profit (including NFP Corporation) **Service**: General medical and surgical

Staffed Beds: 205 **Admissions:** 8718 **Census:** 112 **Outpatient Visits:** 292894 **Births:** 1082 **Total Expense ($000):** 248400 **Payroll Expense ($000):** 107002 **Personnel:** 1519

SALINA SURGICAL HOSPITAL (170187), 401 South Santa Fe Avenue, Zip 67401–4143, Mailing Address: 401 South Sante Fe Avenue, Zip 67401–4143; tel. 785/827–0610, **A**5 10 **F**29 45 48 49 51 59 74 79 81 85 89 131
Primary Contact: LuAnn Puvogel, R.N., Chief Executive Officer
CFO: Elizabeth Bishop, Business Office Manager
CMO: Michael Johnson, M.D., Medical Director
CIO: Earl Akers, Supervisor Information Technology
CHR: Elizabeth Bishop, Business Office Manager
CNO: Jolene Glavin, R.N., MSN, Director Nursing
Web address: www.salinasurgical.com/
Control: Partnership, Investor–owned (for–profit) **Service**: Surgical

Staffed Beds: 16 **Admissions:** 876 **Census:** 6 **Outpatient Visits:** 8175 **Births:** 0 **Total Expense ($000):** 19200 **Payroll Expense ($000):** 6358 **Personnel:** 98

SATANTA—Haskell County

★ **SATANTA DISTRICT HOSPITAL AND LONG TERM CARE (171324)**, 401 South Cheyenne Street, Zip 67870–0159, Mailing Address: P.O. Box 159, Zip 67870–0159; tel. 620/649–2761, (Total facility includes 44 beds in nursing home–type unit) **A**10 18 **F**3 11 40 43 45 57 64 67 68 75 81 87 93 104 107 119 127 128 130 133 156 **S** Great Plains Health Alliance, Inc., Wichita, KS
Primary Contact: Jeremy Clingenpeel, Administrator
CFO: Libby Anderson, Chief Financial Officer
CMO: Virgilio Taduran, M.D., Chief Medical Officer
CIO: Ben Leppke, Chief Information Officer
CHR: Samantha Hett, Manager Human Resources
CNO: Tina Pendergraft, Chief Nursing Officer
Web address: www.satantahospital.org
Control: Hospital district or authority, Government, nonfederal **Service**: General medical and surgical

Staffed Beds: 57 **Admissions:** 152 **Census:** 41 **Outpatient Visits:** 20378 **Births:** 0 **Total Expense ($000):** 12720 **Payroll Expense ($000):** 6338 **Personnel:** 128

SCOTT CITY—Scott County

★ **SCOTT COUNTY HOSPITAL (171372)**, 201 East Albert Avenue, Zip 67871–1203; tel. 620/872–5811, **A**10 18 **F**3 7 11 13 15 28 29 30 31 32 34 40 41 45 46 56 57 59 64 65 68 69 74 75 76 77 81 82 85 87 93 97 107 108 110 111 114 119 127 128 129 130 131 132 133 135 146 147 148 149 152 154 156 157
Primary Contact: Mark Burnett, President and Chief Executive Officer
COO: Karma Huck, Chief Operating Officer
CFO: Joe S Meyer, Chief Financial Officer
CMO: Elizabeth Hineman, M.D., Chief Medical Staff
CHR: Pamela R Wheeler, Director Human Resources
Web address: www.scotthospital.net
Control: County, Government, nonfederal **Service**: General medical and surgical

Staffed Beds: 22 **Admissions:** 500 **Census:** 8 **Outpatient Visits:** 34239 **Births:** 57 **Total Expense ($000):** 21361 **Payroll Expense ($000):** 11354 **Personnel:** 215

SEDAN—Chautauqua County

SEDAN CITY HOSPITAL (171318), 300 North Street, Zip 67361–1051, Mailing Address: P.O. Box 'C', Zip 67361–0427; tel. 620/725–3115, **A**10 18 **F**29 34 40 57 64 93 107 119 128 130 133 148
Primary Contact: Michelle Williams, Administrator
CFO: Jennifer Seever, Regional Chief Financial Officer
CMO: James McDermott, M.D., Chief of Staff
Control: City, Government, nonfederal **Service**: General medical and surgical

Staffed Beds: 20 **Admissions:** 157 **Census:** 2 **Outpatient Visits:** 10414 **Births:** 0 **Total Expense ($000):** 4509 **Payroll Expense ($000):** 2080 **Personnel:** 39

SENECA—Nemaha County

★ **NEMAHA VALLEY COMMUNITY HOSPITAL (171315)**, 1600 Community Drive, Zip 66538–9739; tel. 785/336–6181, **A**10 18 **F**11 12 13 15 28 31 40 56 57 59 64 65 75 76 77 78 79 81 84 85 89 93 107 114 119 127 129 130 131 132 133
Primary Contact: Kiley Floyd, Chief Executive Officer
CFO: Connie Ingwerson, Chief Financial Officer
CMO: Angela Stueve, M.D., Chief Medical Officer
CHR: Lynn E Hartter Jr Director Human Resources
CNO: Lynda Cross, R.N., Director of Nurses
Web address: www.nemvch.org
Control: Other not–for–profit (including NFP Corporation) **Service**: General medical and surgical

Staffed Beds: 24 **Admissions:** 355 **Census:** 5 **Outpatient Visits:** 21741 **Births:** 67 **Total Expense ($000):** 16550 **Payroll Expense ($000):** 8076 **Personnel:** 156

SHAWNEE MISSION—Johnson County

✉ **ADVENTHEALTH SHAWNEE MISSION (170104)**, 9100 West 74th Street, Zip 66204–4004, Mailing Address: Box 2923, Zip 66201–1323; tel. 913/676–2000, **A**1 2 3 5 10 **F**3 4 5 8 11 12 13 15 17 18 20 22 24 26 28 29 30 31 32 34 35 36 40 42 45 46 47 48 49 52 53 54 55 56 57 58 59 60 61 62 64 65 70 72 74 75 76 77 78 79 80 81 82 83 84 85 86 87 89 93 96 97 98 100 101 102 103 104 105 106 107 108 110 111 114 115 117 118 119 120 121 123 124 126 129 130 131 132 135 144 145 146 147 148 149 153 154 156 157 **S** AdventHealth, Altamonte Springs, FL
Primary Contact: Sam D. Huenergardt, Chief Executive Officer
CFO: Karsten Randolph, Executive Vice President and Chief Financial Officer
CMO: Sherri Martin, M.D., President Medical Staff
CIO: Mike Allen, Director Information Services
CHR: Brad Hoffman, Administrative Director Human Resources
CNO: Sheri Hawkins, Chief Nursing Officer
Web address: www.shawneemission.org
Control: Church operated, Nongovernment, not–for–profit **Service**: General medical and surgical

Staffed Beds: 397 **Admissions:** 21695 **Census:** 245 **Outpatient Visits:** 625763 **Births:** 5024 **Total Expense ($000):** 467038 **Payroll Expense ($000):** 186373 **Personnel:** 2822

✉ **MID-AMERICA REHABILITATION HOSPITAL (173026)**, 5701 West 110th Street, Zip 66211–2503, Mailing Address: Overland Park, tel. 913/491–2400, **A**1 10 **F**29 34 36 56 62 68 82 87 90 93 94 95 96 100 130 132 135 148 **S** Encompass Health Corporation, Birmingham, AL
Primary Contact: Tiffany Kiehl, Chief Executive Officer
CFO: Richard Lane, Chief Financial Officer
CMO: Cielo Dehning, M.D., Medical Director
CHR: Elizabeth Gibson, Director Human Resources
CNO: Amy McKay, Chief Nursing Officer
Web address: www.midamericarehabhospital.com
Control: Corporation, Investor–owned (for–profit) **Service**: Rehabilitation

Staffed Beds: 98 **Admissions:** 1774 **Census:** 59 **Outpatient Visits:** 8694 **Births:** 0 **Total Expense ($000):** 26531 **Payroll Expense ($000):** 13650 **Personnel:** 160

Hospital, Medicare Provider Number, Address, Telephone, Approval, Facility, and Physician Codes, Health Care System

★ American Hospital Association (AHA) membership
□ The Joint Commission accreditation
○ Healthcare Facilities Accreditation Program
◇ DNV Healthcare Inc. accreditation
⇈ Center for Improvement in Healthcare Quality Accreditation
△ Commission on Accreditation of Rehabilitation Facilities (CARF) accreditation

KS

SMITH CENTER—Smith County

★ **SMITH COUNTY MEMORIAL HOSPITAL (171377)**, 921 East Highway 36, Zip 66967; tel. 785/282–6845, **A**10 18 **F**3 13 15 28 29 30 31 34 40 43 45 53 64 65 68 69 75 76 81 85 89 91 93 107 110 114 119 127 128 130 133 135 154 156 **S** Great Plains Health Alliance, Inc., Wichita, KS
Primary Contact: Allen Van Driel, FACHE, Administrator
CFO: Julie Williams, Chief Financial Officer
CIO: Tammy Gaston, Chief Information Officer
CHR: Jody Maxwell, Manager Business Office
CNO: Sarah Ragsdale, R.N., Chief Nursing Officer
Web address: www.gpha.com
Control: Other not–for–profit (including NFP Corporation) **Service**: General medical and surgical

Staffed Beds: 25 Admissions: 527 Census: 14 Outpatient Visits: 26837 Births: 41 Total Expense ($000): 15069 Payroll Expense ($000): 6302 Personnel: 122

STAFFORD—Stafford County

★ **STAFFORD COUNTY HOSPITAL (171323)**, 502 South Buckeye Street, Zip 67578–2035, Mailing Address: P.O. Box 190, Zip 67578–0190; tel. 620/234–5221, (Total facility includes 10 beds in nursing home–type unit) **A**10 18 **F**3 15 29 35 40 57 59 62 64 67 77 93 107 128 130 133
Primary Contact: Todd Taylor, Chief Executive Officer
Web address: www.staffordcounty.org
Control: Hospital district or authority, Government, nonfederal **Service**: General medical and surgical

Staffed Beds: 25 Admissions: 84 Census: 5 Outpatient Visits: 44493 Births: 0

SYRACUSE—Hamilton County

★ **HAMILTON COUNTY HOSPITAL (171322)**, 700 North Huser Street, Zip 67878–0948, Mailing Address: P.O. Box 948, Zip 67878–0948; tel. 620/384–7461, (Nonreporting) **A**10 18
Primary Contact: Malachi Lones, Interim Administrator
CMO: Richard Carter, M.D., Chief Medical Director
CIO: Merlin Kuder, Chief Information Officer
CHR: Angela Talbot, Manager Human Resources
CNO: Stacey Perry, Director, Nursing
Web address: www.myhch.org
Control: County, Government, nonfederal **Service**: General medical and surgical

Staffed Beds: 25

TOPEKA—Shawnee County

KANSAS NEUROLOGICAL INSTITUTE, 3107 West 21st Street, Zip 66604–3298; tel. 785/296–5301, (Nonreporting)
Primary Contact: Brent Widick, Superintendent
CFO: Sara Hoyer, Director Administrative Services
CMO: Mary Gingrich, Director Health Care Services
CIO: Cheryl Fuller, Director Information Resources
CHR: Shawna Mercer, Director Human Resources
Web address: www.kdads.ks.gov/state-hospitals-and-institutions/kansas-neurological-institute
Control: State, Government, nonfederal **Service**: Intellectual disabilities

Staffed Beds: 142

⊠ **KANSAS REHABILITATION HOSPITAL (173025)**, 1504 SW Eighth Avenue, Zip 66606–1632; tel. 785/235–6600, **A**1 10 **F**29 75 86 90 91 95 96 130 132 148 149 **S** Encompass Health Corporation, Birmingham, AL
Primary Contact: William J. Overbey, Chief Executive Officer
CMO: Joseph Sankoorikal, M.D., Chief Medical Staff
CHR: Dina Cox, Director Human Resources
CNO: Carol Swanger, Chief Nursing Officer
Web address: www.kansasrehabhospital.com
Control: Corporation, Investor–owned (for–profit) **Service**: Rehabilitation

Staffed Beds: 57 Admissions: 1150 Census: 36 Outpatient Visits: 0 Births: 0 Total Expense ($000): 16426 Payroll Expense ($000): 7832 Personnel: 133

⊠ **STORMONT VAIL HEALTH (170086)**, 1500 SW Tenth Avenue, Zip 66604–1353; tel. 785/354–6000, **A**1 2 10 **F**3 8 11 12 13 15 17 18 19 20 22 24 26 28 29 30 31 34 35 37 40 43 44 45 46 47 49 50 51 54 55 56 57 58 59 60 61 64 65 68 70 71 72 74 75 76 77 78 79 81 82 84 85 86 87 88 89 91 92 93 97 98 99 100 101 102 103 104 105 107 108 110 111 112 114 115 116 117 118 119 120 121 123 126 129 130 131 132 135 143 144 145 146 147 148 149 150 153 154 156
Primary Contact: Rob Kenagy, M.D., President and Chief Executive Officer
COO: Janet Stanek, Senior Vice President and Chief Operating Officer
CFO: Robert Langland, Senior Vice President and Chief Financial Officer
CMO: Rob Kenagy, M.D., Senior Vice President and Chief Medical Officer
CIO: Judy Corzine, Administrative Director and Chief Information Officer
CNO: Carol Perry, R.N., Vice President and Chief Nursing Officer
Web address: www.stormontvail.org
Control: Other not–for–profit (including NFP Corporation) **Service**: General medical and surgical

Staffed Beds: 390 Admissions: 25310 Census: 286 Outpatient Visits: 145097 Births: 1752 Total Expense ($000): 680948 Payroll Expense ($000): 360637 Personnel: 4119

⊠ **UNIVERSITY OF KANSAS HEALTH SYSTEM ST. FRANCIS CAMPUS (170016)**, 1700 SW 7th Street, Zip 66606–1690; tel. 785/295–8000, **A**1 2 10 **F**3 12 13 15 18 20 22 24 26 28 29 30 31 34 35 36 37 38 40 45 47 48 49 50 51 53 54 56 57 58 59 60 61 62 64 65 66 70 71 73 74 75 76 77 78 79 80 81 82 85 86 87 89 90 92 93 95 96 107 108 110 111 114 115 116 117 118 119 120 121 123 130 131 132 135 144 146 147 148 149 **S** Ardent Health Services, Nashville, TN
Primary Contact: Steven Anderson, Chief Executive Officer
CFO: Samuel Moore, Chief Financial Officer
CMO: Jaquelyn Hyland, M.D., Chief Medical Officer
CIO: Jamie Hilliard, Director of Information Technology
CHR: Steve Saffa, Director Human Resources
CNO: Lisa Alexander, Vice President Patient Services and Chief Nursing Officer
Web address: www.stfrancistopeka.org
Control: Partnership, Investor–owned (for–profit) **Service**: General medical and surgical

Staffed Beds: 242 Admissions: 7457 Census: 84 Outpatient Visits: 191148 Births: 959 Total Expense ($000): 225769 Payroll Expense ($000): 89733 Personnel: 1246

⊠ **VETERANS AFFAIRS EASTERN KANSAS HEALTH CARE SYSTEM**, 2200 South West Gage Boulevard, Zip 66622–0002; tel. 785/350–3111, (Includes VETERANS AFFAIRS EASTERN KANSAS HEALTH CARE SYSTEM-COLMERY-O'NEIL VETERANS AFFAIRS MEDICAL CENTER, 2200 South West Gage Boulevard, Topeka, Kansas, Zip 66622–0002; tel. 785/350–3111; VETERANS AFFAIRS EASTERN KANSAS HEALTH CARE SYSTEM-DWIGHT D. EISENHOWER VETERANS AFFAIRS MEDICAL CENTER, 4101 South 4th Street Trafficway, Leavenworth, Kansas, Zip 66048–5055; tel. 913/682–2000), (Non-reporting) **A**1 3 5 **S** Department of Veterans Affairs, Washington, DC
Primary Contact: Anthony Rudy. Klopfer, FACHE, Director
COO: John Moon, Associate Director
CMO: Rajeev Trehan, M.D., M.P.H., Chief of Staff
CIO: Joni Davin, Director Information and Business Management Service Line
Web address: www.topeka.va.gov/
Control: Veterans Affairs, Government, federal **Service**: General medical and surgical

Staffed Beds: 213

VETERANS AFFAIRS EASTERN KANSAS HEALTH CARE SYSTEM-COLMERY-O'NEIL VETERANS AFFAIRS MEDICAL CENTER See Veterans Affairs Eastern Kansas Health Care System, Topeka

TRIBUNE—Greeley County

★ **GREELEY COUNTY HEALTH SERVICES (171359)**, 506 Third Street, Zip 67879–9684, Mailing Address: P.O. Box 338, Zip 67879–0338; tel. 620/376–4221, (Total facility includes 32 beds in nursing home–type unit) **A**10 18 **F**3 28 29 32 34 40 45 50 57 59 64 65 66 69 81 93 97 107 127 133 147 **S** QHR, Brentwood, TN
Primary Contact: Burke Kline, Chief Executive Officer
CMO: Wendel Ellis, D.O., Chief Medical Staff
CIO: Shanon Schneider, Chief Information Officer
CHR: Katelyn Reynolds, Manager Human Resources
CNO: Janie Schmidt, Director of Nursing
Web address: www.mygchs.com
Control: Other not–for–profit (including NFP Corporation) **Service**: General medical and surgical

Staffed Beds: 50 Admissions: 257 Census: 35 Outpatient Visits: 12098 Births: 0 Total Expense ($000): 11415 Payroll Expense ($000): 6007 Personnel: 117

Many Facility Codes have changed. Please refer to the AHA Guide Code Chart. © 2019 AHA Guide

ULYSSES—Grant County

★ **BOB WILSON MEMORIAL GRANT COUNTY HOSPITAL (170110)**, 415 North Main Street, Zip 67880–2133; tel. 620/356–1266, **A**10 20 **F**3 11 13 15 29 30 34 35 40 45 50 57 59 64 68 75 76 79 81 82 85 86 87 91 93 96 97 107 119 127 130 133 146 148 154 157 **S** CommonSpirit Health, Chicago, IL
Primary Contact: Amanda Vaughan, Interim Administrator
CFO: Amanda Vaughan, Chief Financial Officer
CIO: Chris Moffet, Director Information Services
CHR: Tammy Oxford, Director Human Resources
Web address: www.bwmgch.com
Control: Corporation, Investor–owned (for–profit) **Service**: General medical and surgical

Staffed Beds: 26 Admissions: 191 Census: 2 Outpatient Visits: 7486 **Births:** 11 **Total Expense ($000):** 14879 **Payroll Expense ($000):** 5126 **Personnel:** 72

WAKEENEY—Trego County

★ **TREGO COUNTY-LEMKE MEMORIAL HOSPITAL (171355)**, 320 North 13th Street, Zip 67672–2099; tel. 785/743–2182, (Total facility includes 37 beds in nursing home–type unit) **A**10 18 **F**3 8 10 11 15 28 29 34 40 45 53 57 59 62 64 67 69 71 81 86 89 93 107 110 114 127 128 130 133 143 146 148 154 156 **S** Great Plains Health Alliance, Inc., Wichita, KS
Primary Contact: David Augustine, Chief Executive Officer
CFO: ReChelle Horinek, Chief Financial Officer
CMO: Gordon Lang, M.D., Chief of Staff
CHR: Jeff Bieker, Director Human Resource
CNO: Sandy Purinton, Chief Nursing Officer
Web address: www.tclmh.org
Control: County, Government, nonfederal **Service**: General medical and surgical

Staffed Beds: 62 Admissions: 599 Census: 45 Outpatient Visits: 30113 **Births:** 0 **Total Expense ($000):** 16793 **Payroll Expense ($000):** 7966 **Personnel:** 177

WAMEGO—Pottawatomie County

★ **WAMEGO HEALTH CENTER (171337)**, 711 Genn Drive, Zip 66547–1179, tel. 785/456–2295, **A**10 18 **F**3 11 15 28 29 34 40 45 56 59 64 65 75 77 81 93 97 107 114 119 127 130 131 132 133 143 146 147 148 149
Primary Contact: Steve Land, Senior Administrator
COO: Brian Smith, Director of Operations
CFO: Keith Zachariasen, Chief Financial Officer
CMO: Roland Darey, M.D., Medical Director
CIO: Wes Janzen, Chief Information Officer
CHR: Renee Reed, Director Human Resources
CNO: Tresha Flanary, R.N., Chief Clinical Services Officer
Web address: www.https://www.wamegohealthcenter.com
Control: Other not–for–profit (including NFP Corporation) **Service**: General medical and surgical

Staffed Beds: 18 Admissions: 195 Census: 5 Outpatient Visits: 40738 **Births:** 0 **Total Expense ($000):** 11658 **Payroll Expense ($000):** 5788 **Personnel:** 86

WASHINGTON—Washington County

WASHINGTON COUNTY HOSPITAL (171351), 304 East Third Street, Zip 66968–2033; tel. 785/325–2211, (Nonreporting) **A**10 18
Primary Contact: Roxanne Schottel, Chief Executive Officer
CFO: Linda Rettig, Director Financial Services
CNO: Kelly Otott, R.N., Chief Nursing Officer
Web address: www.washingtoncountyhospital.net
Control: County, Government, nonfederal **Service**: General medical and surgical

Staffed Beds: 18

WELLINGTON—Sumner County

SUMNER REGIONAL MEDICAL CENTER (170039), 1323 North 'A' Street, Zip 67152–4350; tel. 620/326–7451, (Nonreporting) **A**10
Primary Contact: Les Dean, President and Chief Executive Officer
CFO: Barry Harding, Interim Chief Executive Officer and Chief Financial Officer
CHR: Allen Keller, Director Human Resources
CNO: Darlene Cooney, Director Nursing
Web address: www.srmcks.org
Control: City, Government, nonfederal **Service**: General medical and surgical

Staffed Beds: 61

WINCHESTER—Jefferson County

★ **F. W. HUSTON MEDICAL CENTER (171314)**, 408 Delaware Street, Zip 66097–4003; tel. 913/774–4340, (Total facility includes 38 beds in nursing home–type unit) **A**10 18 **F**3 10 40 56 57 64 67 69 75 77 93 97 103 104 107 111 125 128 130 133 143 144
Primary Contact: LaMont Cook, Administrator
CFO: Jason Johnson, Controller
CMO: William Greiner, M.D., Chief of Staff
CIO: Jason Johnson, Controller
CHR: Melody Keirns, Manager Human Resources
CNO: Heather R Aranda, R.N., MSN, Chief Nursing Officer
Web address: www.jcmhospital.org
Control: Other not–for–profit (including NFP Corporation) **Service**: General medical and surgical

Staffed Beds: 69 Admissions: 69 Census: 36 Outpatient Visits: 14418 **Births:** 0 **Total Expense ($000):** 6113 **Payroll Expense ($000):** 3956 **Personnel:** 71

JEFFERSON COUNTY MEMORIAL HOSPITAL See F. W. Huston Medical Center

WICHITA—Sedgwick County

AMG SPECIALTY HOSPITAL-WICHITA (172003), 8080 East Pawnee Street, Zip 67207–5475; tel. 316/682–0004, (Nonreporting) **A**10 **S** AMG Integrated Healthcare Management, Lafayette, LA
Primary Contact: Robert A. Loepp Jr, FACHE, Chief Executive Officer
CFO: Myra Dick, Manager Business Office
CIO: Michelle Bradley, Director Health Information Management
CHR: Adrienne Burkholder, Director Human Resources
Web address: www.amgwichita.com/
Control: Corporation, Investor–owned (for–profit) **Service**: Acute long–term care hospital

Staffed Beds: 26

⊞ **ASCENSION VIA CHRISTI HOSPITAL ON ST. TERESA (170200)**, 14800 West St. Teresa, Zip 67235–9602; tel. 316/796–7000, **A**1 10 **F**3 8 18 20 22 29 30 34 35 40 45 50 64 68 70 75 78 79 81 85 87 90 92 93 96 107 108 111 114 118 119 130 146 147 148 154 **S** Ascension Healthcare, Saint Louis, MO
Primary Contact: Robyn Chadwick, President
Web address: www.via-christi.org/st-teresa
Control: Church operated, Nongovernment, not–for–profit **Service**: General medical and surgical

Staffed Beds: 49 Admissions: 1547 Census: 21 Outpatient Visits: 27185 **Births:** 0 **Total Expense ($000):** 30477 **Payroll Expense ($000):** 9200 **Personnel:** 125

⊞ **ASCENSION VIA CHRISTI REHABILITATION HOSPITAL (173028)**, 1151 North Rock Road, Zip 67206–1262; tel. 316/634–3400, **A**1 10 **F**11 29 30 34 35 44 50 54 57 59 64 77 86 87 90 92 93 95 96 119 129 130 131 132 143 146 148 **S** Ascension Healthcare, Saint Louis, MO
Primary Contact: Kevin Strecker, President
CMO: Kevin Rieg, M.D., President Medical Staff
CNO: Cindy Hagerty, Assistant Chief Nurse Officer and Administrator of Operations
Web address: www.via-christi.org
Control: Church operated, Nongovernment, not–for–profit **Service**: Rehabilitation

Staffed Beds: 58 Admissions: 679 Census: 21 Outpatient Visits: 101335 **Births:** 0 **Total Expense ($000):** 19961 **Payroll Expense ($000):** 9047 **Personnel:** 162

KANSAS HEART HOSPITAL (170186), 3601 North Webb Road, Zip 67226–8129; tel. 316/630–5000, (Nonreporting) **A**10
Primary Contact: Thomas L. Ashcom, M.D., Ph.D., Chief Executive Officer
COO: Joyce Heismeyer, Chief Operating Officer
CFO: Steve Smith, Chief Financial Officer
CHR: Teresa E Wolfe, Manager Human Resources
CNO: Susan Bradford, Director Nursing
Web address: www.kansasheart.com
Control: Corporation, Investor–owned (for–profit) **Service**: Heart

Staffed Beds: 54

Hospital, Medicare Provider Number, Address, Telephone, Approval, Facility, and Physician Codes, Health Care System

★ American Hospital Association (AHA) membership ○ Healthcare Facilities Accreditation Program ⇑ Center for Improvement in Healthcare Quality Accreditation
□ The Joint Commission accreditation ◇ DNV Healthcare Inc. accreditation △ Commission on Accreditation of Rehabilitation Facilities (CARF) accreditation

KS

KANSAS SPINE AND SPECIALTY HOSPITAL (170196), 3333 North Webb Road, Zip 67226–8123; tel. 316/462–5000, **A**10 **F**3 29 79 81 82 85 87 107 111 114 126 149
Primary Contact: Thomas M. Schmitt, Chief Executive Officer
CFO: Kevin P Vaughn, Chief Financial Officer
CIO: Michael Knocke, Chief Information Officer
CHR: Jean-Marie Jimeson, Manager Human Resources
CNO: John Coslett, R.N., Chief Nursing Officer
Web address: www.ksspine.com
Control: Corporation, Investor–owned (for–profit) **Service**: General medical and surgical

Staffed Beds: 36 **Admissions**: 2198 **Census**: 13 **Outpatient Visits**: 9134 **Births**: 0 **Personnel**: 200

○ **KANSAS SURGERY AND RECOVERY CENTER (170183)**, 2770 North Webb Road, Zip 67226–8112; tel. 316/634–0090, **A**10 11 **F**45 51 64 68 79 81 85 87 93 107 111 114 119 126
Primary Contact: Ely Bartal, M.D., Chief Executive Officer
CFO: Ashley Simon, Chief Financial Officer
CMO: Ely Bartal, M.D., Chief Executive Officer and Medical Director
CIO: Jonathan Wells, Supervisor Information Technology
CNO: Becky Bailey, R.N., Director Nursing
Web address: www.ksrc.org
Control: Partnership, Investor–owned (for–profit) **Service**: Surgical

Staffed Beds: 32 **Admissions**: 2013 **Census**: 12 **Outpatient Visits**: 10456 **Births**: 0 **Total Expense ($000)**: 30189 **Payroll Expense ($000)**: 8024 **Personnel**: 144

✉ **ROBERT J. DOLE VETERANS AFFAIRS MEDICAL CENTER**, 5500 East Kellogg, Zip 67218–1607; tel. 316/685–2221, (Nonreporting) **A**1 3 5 **S** Department of Veterans Affairs, Washington, DC
Primary Contact: Rick Ament, Chief Executive Officer
CFO: Ronald Dreher, Finance Officer
CMO: Kent Murray, M.D., Chief of Staff
CIO: Sharon Williamson, Chief Information Technology
CHR: Nancy Gerstner, Manager Human Resources
Web address: www.wichita.va.gov
Control: Veterans Affairs, Government, federal **Service**: General medical and surgical

Staffed Beds: 41

✉ **SELECT SPECIALTY HOSPITAL-WICHITA (172007)**, 929 North St Francis Street, Zip 67214–3821; tel. 316/261–8303, (Nonreporting) **A**1 10 **S** Select Medical Corporation, Mechanicsburg, PA
Primary Contact: Christopher Keith, Chief Executive Officer
CHR: Renee Schaffer, Coordinator Human Resources
CNO: Lindsey Cahoj, Chief Nursing Officer
Web address: www.selectspecialtyhospitals.com/company/locations/wichita.aspx
Control: Corporation, Investor–owned (for–profit) **Service**: Acute long–term care hospital

Staffed Beds: 48

✉ **WESLEY HEALTHCARE CENTER (170123)**, 550 North Hillside, Zip 67214–4976; tel. 316/962–2000, (Includes WESLEY CHILDREN'S HOSPITAL, 550 North Hillside Street, Wichita, Kansas, Zip 67214–4910; tel. 316/962–2000; WESLEY WOODLAWN HOSPITAL & ER, 2610 North Woodlawn, Wichita, Kansas, Zip 67220; tel. 316/858–2610; Thomas Owings, Chief Executive Officer) **A**1 2 3 5 10 **F**3 7 11 12 13 15 17 18 19 20 22 24 26 28 29 30 31 32 34 35 37 38 39 40 41 42 43 44 45 46 47 48 49 50 51 54 55 56 57 58 59 60 64 65 68 70 72 73 74 76 78 79 81 82 85 86 87 88 89 92 93 94 97 100 102 107 108 110 111 114 115 119 120 121 123 124 126 129 130 131 132 134 135 146 147 148 149 **S** HCA Healthcare, Nashville, TN
Primary Contact: Bill Voloch, President and Chief Executive Officer
CFO: Bradley Schultz, Chief Financial Officer
CMO: Francie H Ekengren, M.D., Chief Medical Officer
CIO: Jeffrey Schauf, Director Information Systems
CHR: Jennifer Krier, Vice President Human Resources
Web address: www.wesleymc.com
Control: Corporation, Investor–owned (for–profit) **Service**: General medical and surgical

Staffed Beds: 573 **Admissions**: 29224 **Census**: 376

✉ **WESLEY REHABILITATION HOSPITAL (173027)**, 8338 West 13th Street North, Zip 67212–2984; tel. 316/729–9999, **A**1 10 **F**29 34 35 62 63 64 68 90 91 93 95 96 132 148 **S** Encompass Health Corporation, Birmingham, AL
Primary Contact: James F. Grocholski, FACHE, Chief Executive Officer
CFO: Bob Peck, Chief Financial Officer
CIO: Debbie Patterson, Director Health Information Management
CHR: Betty Shuman, Director Human Resources
CNO: Jessika M Workman, Chief Nursing Officer
Web address: www.wesleyrehabhospital.com
Control: Corporation, Investor–owned (for–profit) **Service**: Rehabilitation

Staffed Beds: 65 **Admissions**: 1078 **Census**: 37 **Outpatient Visits**: 8381 **Births**: 0 **Total Expense ($000)**: 18318 **Payroll Expense ($000)**: 8576 **Personnel**: 148

WICHITA SPECIALTY HOSPITAL See Amg Specialty Hospital-Wichita

WINFIELD—Cowley County

★ **WILLIAM NEWTON HOSPITAL (171383)**, 1300 East Fifth Street, Zip 67156–2407; tel. 620/221–2300, **A**3 5 10 18 **F**3 8 11 13 15 17 28 29 34 35 40 45 50 56 57 59 62 64 65 69 70 75 76 77 79 81 85 89 91 93 94 107 108 110 111 114 119 127 130 133 146 148 149 150 156
Primary Contact: J. Ben. Quinton, Administrator
COO: Shona Salzman, Chief Operating Officer
CFO: Brian Barta, Assistant Administrator and Chief Financial Officer
CMO: Bryan Dennett, M.D., Chief of Staff
CIO: Randy Mayo, Director Information Technology
CHR: Cathy McClurg, Director Human Resources
Web address: www.wnmh.org
Control: Other not–for–profit (including NFP Corporation) **Service**: General medical and surgical

Staffed Beds: 25 **Admissions**: 1167 **Census**: 12 **Outpatient Visits**: 77993 **Births**: 260 **Total Expense ($000)**: 38164 **Payroll Expense ($000)**: 15964 **Personnel**: 290

KS

Many Facility Codes have changed. Please refer to the AHA Guide Code Chart. © 2019 AHA Guide

KENTUCKY

ALBANY—Clinton County

THE MEDICAL CENTER ALBANY (180106), 723 Burkesville Road, Zip 42602–1654; tel. 606/387–8000, (Nonreporting) **A**10 **S** Med Center Health, Bowling Green, KY
Primary Contact: Laura Belcher, Administrator
CFO: Ronald G. Sowell, FACHE, Executive Vice President, Chief Financial Officer
CIO: Mark Brookman, Chief Information Officer
CHR: Lynn Williams, Vice President, Human Resources
Web address: www.chc.net/services/hospitals/the_medical_center_at_albany.aspx
Control: Other not–for–profit (including NFP Corporation) **Service**: General medical and surgical

Staffed Beds: 42

ASHLAND—Boyd County

☐ **KING'S DAUGHTERS MEDICAL CENTER (180009)**, 2201 Lexington Avenue, Zip 41101–2874, Mailing Address: P.O. Box 151, Zip 41105–0151; tel. 606/408–4000, (Nonreporting) **A**1 2 3 10
Primary Contact: Kristie Whitlatch, President
COO: Bob Lucas, Vice President Operations
CFO: Paul L McDowell, Vice President Finance and Chief Financial Officer
CMO: Phil Fioret, M.D., Vice President Medical Affairs
CIO: David Oliver, Director Information Systems
CHR: Larry Higgins, Vice President Human Resources
Web address: www.kdmc.com
Control: Other not–for–profit (including NFP Corporation) **Service**: General medical and surgical

Staffed Beds: 448

☐ **OUR LADY OF BELLEFONTE HOSPITAL (180036)**, St Christopher Drive, Zip 41101, Mailing Address: P.O. Box 789, Zip 41105–0789; tel. 606/833–3333, **A**1 2 10 **F**3 4 8 11 15 18 20 22 28 29 30 31 34 35 37 39 40 44 48 49 50 53 54 55 56 57 58 59 62 64 65 66 69 70 74 75 77 78 79 81 82 84 85 86 87 89 93 96 97 98 100 101 102 103 104 105 106 107 108 110 111 114 115 118 119 129 130 131 132 135 143 144 145 146 147 148 154 **S** Bon Secours Mercy Health, Marriottsville, MD
Primary Contact: Kevin Halter, Chief Executive Officer
CFO: Joe Buchheit, Chief Financial Officer
CMO: Dan Goulson, M.D., Chief Medical Officer
CIO: Mike Gomez, Site Manager Medical Information Systems
CHR: Judy Daniels, Vice President Human Resources
Web address: www.olbh.com
Control: Church operated, Nongovernment, not–for–profit **Service**: General medical and surgical

Staffed Beds: 151 **Admissions:** 7169 **Census:** 82 **Outpatient Visits:** 273289 **Births:** 0 **Total Expense ($000):** 160870 **Payroll Expense ($000):** 52694 **Personnel:** 804

BARBOURVILLE—Knox County

⇑ **BARBOURVILLE ARH HOSPITAL (181328)**, 80 Hospital Drive, Zip 40906–7363, Mailing Address: P.O. Box 10, Zip 40906–0010; tel. 606/546–4175, **A**10 18 21 **F**3 11 15 28 29 30 34 35 39 40 50 57 59 64 70 81 85 87 107 108 110 114 119 127 130 133 146 154 **S** Pacer Health Corporation, Miami Lakes, FL
Primary Contact: Charles D. Lovell Jr, FACHE, Chief Executive Officer
CFO: Amanda Ellis, Chief Financial Officer
CMO: Kamran Hasni, M.D., Chief of Medical Staff
CIO: Evan Davis, Director Technology and Environmental Services
CHR: Janet Wilder, Director Human Resources
CNO: Brenda Graham, Chief Nursing Officer
Web address: www.knoxcohospital.com
Control: Other not–for–profit (including NFP Corporation) **Service**: General medical and surgical

Staffed Beds: 25 **Admissions:** 1018 **Census:** 10 **Outpatient Visits:** 28639 **Births:** 0 **Total Expense ($000):** 19777 **Payroll Expense ($000):** 7142 **Personnel:** 135

BARDSTOWN—Nelson County

⊞ **CHI FLAGET MEMORIAL HOSPITAL (180025)**, 4305 New Shepherdsville Road, Zip 40004–9019; tel. 502/350–5000, **A**1 2 3 10 **F**3 11 12 13 15 18 29 30 31 34 35 37 40 45 49 55 59 60 62 63 64 70 76 78 79 81 82 84 85 87 91 93 96 107 111 116 117 119 120 128 129 130 132 144 146 147 148 **S** CommonSpirit Health, Chicago, IL
Primary Contact: Jennifer Nolan, President and Chief Executive Officer
CFO: Jim Wentz, Chief Financial Officer
CMO: Mickey Anderson, M.D., Vice President Medical Affairs
CHR: Tanja Oquendo, Chief Human Resources Officer
CNO: Norma Goss, R.N., Chief Nursing Officer
Web address: www.kentuckyonehealth.org/flaget
Control: Other not–for–profit (including NFP Corporation) **Service**: General medical and surgical

Staffed Beds: 42 **Admissions:** 2202 **Census:** 27 **Outpatient Visits:** 70622 **Births:** 285 **Total Expense ($000):** 60622 **Payroll Expense ($000):** 17140 **Personnel:** 285

BENTON—Marshall County

⊞ **MARSHALL COUNTY HOSPITAL (181327)**, 615 Old Symsonia Road, Zip 42025–5042; tel. 270/527–4800, **A**1 10 18 **F**3 11 15 18 19 28 29 30 34 35 40 57 59 62 77 79 81 85 90 93 107 108 119 127 130 132 133 135 148 149
Primary Contact: David G. Fuqua, Chief Executive Officer
CFO: Janice Kelley, Chief Financial Officer
CMO: Edwin Perez, M.D., Chief of Medical Staff
CIO: Dave Cope, Director Information Systems
CHR: Janice Bone, Human Resources
Web address: www.marshallcountyhospital.org
Control: Hospital district or authority, Government, nonfederal **Service**: General medical and surgical

Staffed Beds: 25 **Admissions:** 755 **Census:** 7 **Outpatient Visits:** 16818 **Births:** 0 **Total Expense ($000):** 22026 **Payroll Expense ($000):** 9155 **Personnel:** 261

BEREA—Madison County

△ **CHI SAINT JOSEPH BEREA (181329)**, 305 Estill Street, Zip 40403–1909; tel. 859/986–3151, **A**1 10 18 **F**3 29 40 45 70 77 79 81 82 91 97 107 111 114 119 133 156 **S** CommonSpirit Health, Chicago, IL
Primary Contact: Terrence G. Deis, CPA, FACHE, President
CFO: Christy Spitser, Vice President Finance
CMO: Joshua Huffman, M.D., Chief Medical Staff
CHR: Sandra Turqueza, Human Resources Business Partner
CNO: Leslie Adams, Chief Nursing Executive
Web address: www.kentuckyonehealth.org/berea
Control: Other not–for–profit (including NFP Corporation) **Service**: General medical and surgical

Staffed Beds: 25 **Admissions:** 885 **Census:** 11 **Outpatient Visits:** 53672 **Births:** 0 **Total Expense ($000):** 29481 **Payroll Expense ($000):** 10108 **Personnel:** 175

BOWLING GREEN—Warren County

☐ **COMMONWEALTH REGIONAL SPECIALTY HOSPITAL (182005)**, 250 Park Drive, 6th Floor, Zip 42101–1760, Mailing Address: P.O. Box 90010, Zip 42102–9010; tel. 270/796–6200, **A**1 10 **F**1 3 29 30 34 35 50 57 68 85 87 130 135 143 146 148 149 **S** Med Center Health, Bowling Green, KY
Primary Contact: Christa Atkins, Administrator
CFO: Ronald G. Sowell, FACHE, Executive Vice President
CMO: Doug Thomson, M.D., Chief Medical Officer
CIO: Jean Cherry, Executive Vice President
CHR: Lynn Williams, Vice President Human Resources
Web address: www.commonwealthregionalspecialtyhospital.org
Control: Other not–for–profit (including NFP Corporation) **Service**: Acute long–term care hospital

Staffed Beds: 28 **Admissions:** 233 **Census:** 15 **Outpatient Visits:** 0 **Births:** 0 **Personnel:** 48

☐ **MEDICAL CENTER AT BOWLING GREEN (180013)**, 250 Park Street, Zip 42101–1795, Mailing Address: P.O. Box 90010, Zip 42102–9010; tel. 270/745–1000, **A**1 2 3 10 19 **F**1 3 7 12 13 15 17 18 20 22 24 26 28 29 30 31 34 37 39 40 45 46 48 49 50 51 56 57 58 59 60 62 64 69 70 73 74 75 76 78 79 81 82 84 85 86 87 91 92 93 98 100 102 103 104 107 108 110 111 114 115 116 117 118 119 120 121 122 123 124 126 129 130 132 135 145 146 147 148 149 154 **S** Med Center Health, Bowling Green, KY
Primary Contact: Connie Smith, FACHE, MSN, R.N., Chief Executive Officer
CFO: Ronald G. Sowell, FACHE, Executive Vice President
CIO: Mark Brookman, Chief Information Officer
CHR: Lynn Williams, Vice President Human Resources
CNO: Betsy Kullman, R.N., MSN, Executive Vice President and Chief Nursing Officer
Web address: www.themedicalcenter.org
Control: Other not–for–profit (including NFP Corporation) **Service:** General medical and surgical

Staffed Beds: 337 **Admissions:** 16105 **Census:** 235 **Outpatient Visits:** 141500 **Births:** 2557 **Personnel:** 1766

☐ **RIVENDELL BEHAVIORAL HEALTH (184017)**, 1035 Porter Pike, Zip 42103–9581; tel. 270/843–1199, (Nonreporting) **A**1 10 **S** Universal Health Services, Inc., King of Prussia, PA
Primary Contact: Matt Ours, Chief Executive Officer and Managing Director
CFO: Tim Gore, Chief Financial Officer
Web address: www.rivendellbehavioral.com
Control: Corporation, Investor–owned (for–profit) **Service:** Psychiatric

Staffed Beds: 125

⊠ △ **SOUTHERN KENTUCKY REHABILITATION HOSPITAL (183029)**, 1300 Campbell Lane, Zip 42104–4162; tel. 270/782–6900, (Nonreporting) **A**1 7 10 **S** Vibra Healthcare, Mechanicsburg, PA
Primary Contact: Stuart Locke, Chief Executive Officer
COO: Dana Lewis, Director Clinical Services
CMO: Jim Farrage, M.D., Medical Director
CHR: Suzanne Cornett, Director Human Resources
Web address: www.skyrehab.com
Control: Corporation, Investor–owned (for–profit) **Service:** Rehabilitation

Staffed Beds: 60

⊠ **TRISTAR GREENVIEW REGIONAL HOSPITAL (180124)**, 1801 Ashley Circle, Zip 42104–3362; tel. 270/793–1000, (Nonreporting) **A**1 10 19 **S** HCA Healthcare, Nashville, TN
Primary Contact: Michael Sherrod, Chief Executive Officer
COO: Andrew Bedi, Chief Operating Officer
CMO: Wayne Bush, M.D., Chief of Staff
CIO: Cyndi Talley, Director Information Systems
CHR: Judy Fulkerson, Director Human Resources
CNO: Anne Leonard, R.N., Chief Nursing Officer
Web address: www.greenviewhospital.com
Control: Corporation, Investor–owned (for–profit) **Service:** General medical and surgical

Staffed Beds: 148

BURKESVILLE—Cumberland County

CUMBERLAND COUNTY HOSPITAL (181317), 299 Glasgow Road, Zip 42717–9696, Mailing Address: P.O. Box 280, Zip 42717–0280; tel. 270/864–2511, (Nonreporting) **A**10 18
Primary Contact: Richard Neikirk, Chief Executive Officer
COO: Steve Burns, Chief Operating Officer
CFO: Rick Capps, Chief Financial Officer
CMO: Christian Konsavage, M.D., Chief of Staff
CHR: Martha Young, Director Human Resources
CNO: Susan S Flowers, MSN, R.N., Chief Nursing Officer
Web address: www.cchospital.org
Control: Other not–for–profit (including NFP Corporation) **Service:** General medical and surgical

Staffed Beds: 25

CADIZ—Trigg County

TRIGG COUNTY HOSPITAL (181304), 254 Main Street, Zip 42211–9153, Mailing Address: P.O. Box 312, Zip 42211–0312; tel. 270/522–3215, (Nonreporting) **A**10 18
Primary Contact: John Sumner, Chief Executive Officer
CFO: Liz Snodgrass, Chief Financial Officer
CMO: Stuart Harris, M.D., Chief of Staff
CHR: Janet James, Director Human Resources
Web address: www.trigghospital.org
Control: County, Government, nonfederal **Service:** General medical and surgical

Staffed Beds: 19

CAMPBELLSVILLE—Taylor County

⊠ **TAYLOR REGIONAL HOSPITAL (180087)**, 1700 Old Lebanon Road, Zip 42718–9600; tel. 270/465–3561, **A**1 2 10 **F**3 8 11 13 15 18 20 28 29 30 31 32 34 35 39 40 41 43 45 46 48 49 50 51 54 56 57 59 64 65 68 70 74 75 76 77 78 79 81 85 86 87 93 97 107 108 111 115 118 119 127 129 130 131 132 134 135 141 143 146 147 148 149 150 **S** CommonSpirit Health, Chicago, IL
Primary Contact: Jane Wheatley, Chief Executive Officer
CFO: Paul Phillips, Chief Financial Officer
CIO: Christopher Michael Gibbs, Director Information Management Systems
CHR: Andrea Settle, Director Human Resources
CNO: Dana M. Garrett, R.N., Nursing Services Administrator
Web address: www.trhosp.org
Control: Hospital district or authority, Government, nonfederal **Service:** General medical and surgical

Staffed Beds: 90 **Admissions:** 2542 **Census:** 28 **Outpatient Visits:** 94476 **Births:** 307 **Total Expense ($000):** 82215 **Payroll Expense ($000):** 36895 **Personnel:** 633

CARROLLTON—Carroll County

CARROLL COUNTY MEMORIAL HOSPITAL (181310), 309 11th Street, Zip 41008–1400; tel. 502/732–4321, (Nonreporting) **A**10 18 **S** Alliant Management Services, Louisville, KY
Primary Contact: Harry Hays, Chief Executive Officer
CMO: Winston Yap, M.D., Chief Medical Officer
CHR: Kimberly Adams, Manager Human Resources
CNO: Lisa Penick, R.N., Chief Nursing Officer
Web address: www.ccmhosp.com
Control: County, Government, nonfederal **Service:** General medical and surgical

Staffed Beds: 25

COLUMBIA—Adair County

☐ **T.J. HEALTH COLUMBIA (180149)**, 901 Westlake Drive, Zip 42728–1123, Mailing Address: P.O. Box 1269, Zip 42728–6269; tel. 270/384–4753, (Nonreporting) **A**1 10
Primary Contact: Neil Thornbury, Chief Executive Officer
CFO: David R Hayes, Chief Financial Officer
CMO: Charles Giles, M.D., President Medical Staff
CHR: Tonya Grant, Director Human Resources
CNO: Gidgett Warren, Director of Nursing
Web address: www.healthiercolumbia.org/
Control: Hospital district or authority, Government, nonfederal **Service:** General medical and surgical

Staffed Beds: 32

CORBIN—Whitley County

★ ⇑ **BAPTIST HEALTH CORBIN (180080)**, 1 Trillium Way, Zip 40701–8420; tel. 606/528–1212, **A**10 19 21 **F**1 3 4 5 13 15 18 20 22 26 28 29 30 31 32 34 35 36 38 40 45 47 48 49 51 54 57 59 64 67 68 70 72 73 76 78 79 80 81 84 85 86 87 89 90 93 96 98 100 101 102 104 105 106 107 108 110 111 114 115 118 119 126 130 132 133 135 145 146 147 148 152 153 154 156 **S** Baptist Health, Louisville, KY
Primary Contact: Anthony Powers, Interim President and Vice President of Patient Services
CFO: Pamela K. Jones, Executive Director of Finance
CMO: David Worthy, M.D., Vice President and Chief Medical Officer
CIO: Rodney Richardson, Director of Information Technology
CHR: Tim Perry, Executive Director of Human Resources
CNO: Sherrie Mays, MSN, R.N., Vice President and Chief Nursing Officer
Web address: www.baptisthealth.com/corbin
Control: Other not–for–profit (including NFP Corporation) **Service:** General medical and surgical

Staffed Beds: 273 **Admissions:** 8625 **Census:** 115 **Outpatient Visits:** 154230 **Births:** 959 **Total Expense ($000):** 169135 **Payroll Expense ($000):** 59482 **Personnel:** 1106

★ **CONTINUECARE HOSPITAL AT BAPTIST HEALTH CORBIN (182006)**, 1 Trillium Way, Lower Level, Zip 40701–8727; tel. 606/523–5150, **A**10 22 **F**1 3 29 30 34 57 59 85 148 **S** Community Hospital Corporation, Plano, TX
Primary Contact: Tuan Le, Chief Executive Officer
COO: Wilson Weber, Chief Operating Officer
CFO: Lisa Young, CPA, Chief Financial Officer
CMO: Steve Morton, M.D., Chief Medical Officer
CIO: Brian Doerr, Chief Information Officer
CHR: Amie Marcum, Human Resources Coordinator
CNO: Della Rains, Chief Nursing Officer
Web address: www.continuecare.org
Control: Other not–for–profit (including NFP Corporation) **Service:** Acute long–term care hospital

Staffed Beds: 32 **Admissions:** 298 **Census:** 24 **Outpatient Visits:** 0 **Births:** 0 **Total Expense ($000):** 10793 **Payroll Expense ($000):** 4250 **Personnel:** 75

COVINGTON—Kenton County

ST. ELIZABETH MEDICAL CENTER-NORTH See St. Elizabeth Covington

CYNTHIANA—Harrison County

☒ **HARRISON MEMORIAL HOSPITAL (180079)**, 1210 KY Highway 36E, Zip 41031–7498; tel. 859/234–2300, **A**1 10 **F**3 8 11 13 15 18 20 22 26 28 29 30 31 34 35 36 39 40 43 44 45 47 49 50 53 57 59 61 64 68 69 70 74 75 76 77 78 79 81 82 85 86 87 89 93 97 107 108 111 115 118 119 129 130 131 132 133 135 144 146 147 148
Primary Contact: Sheila Currans, Chief Executive Officer
CFO: David Mellett, Chief Financial Officer
CIO: Martha Sullivan, Chief Information Officer
CHR: Rebecca Jenkins, Director Human Resources Management
CNO: Wendy Reeder, R.N., Chief Nursing Officer
Web address: www.harrisonmemhosp.com
Control: Other not–for–profit (including NFP Corporation) **Service**: General medical and surgical

Staffed Beds: 34 Admissions: 1282 Census: 11 Outpatient Visits: 77202 Births: 214 Total Expense ($000): 59050 Payroll Expense ($000): 25388 Personnel: 408

DANVILLE—Boyle County

☐ **EPHRAIM MCDOWELL REGIONAL MEDICAL CENTER (180048)**, 217 South Third Street, Zip 40422–1823; tel. 859/239–1000, (Nonreporting) **A**1 3 5 10 19 **S** Ephraim McDowell Health, Danville, KY
Primary Contact: Daniel E. McKay, Chief Executive Officer
COO: Burt Piper, Chief Operating Officer
CFO: William R Snapp III Executive Vice President Finance and Chief Financial Officer
CMO: Kryder Van Buskirk III Medical Staff President at EMRMC
CIO: Gary Neat, Chief Information Officer
CHR: Libby Mayes, Human Resource Director
CNO: Mark W Milner, Chief Nursing Officer
Web address: www.emrmc.org
Control: Other not–for–profit (including NFP Corporation) **Service**: General medical and surgical

Staffed Beds: 159

EDGEWOOD—Kenton County

☒ **HEALTHSOUTH NORTHERN KENTUCKY REHABILITATION HOSPITAL (183027)**, 201 Medical Village Drive, Zip 41017–3407; tel. 859/341–2044, (Nonreporting) **A**1 10 **S** Encompass Health Corporation, Birmingham, AL
Primary Contact: Jeremy Yates, Chief Executive Officer
CFO: Lisa McGue, Controller
CMO: Neal Moser, M.D., Medical Director
CHR: Bridgette Keith, Director Human Resources
CNO: Terri Ballard, Chief Nursing Officer
Web address: www.healthsouthkentucky.com
Control: Partnership, Investor–owned (for–profit) **Service**: Rehabilitation

Staffed Beds: 40

☐ **ST. ELIZABETH EDGEWOOD (180035)**, 1 Medical Village Drive, Zip 41017–3403; tel. 859/301–2000, (Includes ST. ELIZABETH COVINGTON, 1500 James Simpson Jr. Way, Covington, Kentucky, Zip 41014–1585; tel. 859/655–8800) **A**1 2 3 5 10 **F**3 5 8 9 11 13 14 15 17 18 20 22 24 26 28 29 30 31 34 35 36 37 38 39 40 44 45 46 47 48 49 50 53 55 57 58 59 60 61 63 64 65 70 71 72 73 74 75 76 77 78 79 80 81 82 83 84 85 86 87 92 93 97 98 100 101 102 103 104 105 107 108 109 110 111 114 115 117 118 119 120 121 123 124 126 129 130 131 132 135 141 145 146 147 148 149 150 152 153 154 **S** St. Elizabeth Healthcare, Edgewood, KY
Primary Contact: Garren Colvin, Chief Executive Officer
CMO: Karl Schmitt, M.D., Chief of Staff
CIO: Alex Rodriguez, Vice President and Chief Information Officer
CHR: Martin Oscadal, Vice President Human Resources
Web address: www.stelizabeth.com
Control: Church operated, Nongovernment, not–for–profit **Service**: General medical and surgical

Staffed Beds: 510 Admissions: 27276 Census: 334 Outpatient Visits: 1314848 Births: 4376 Total Expense ($000): 778674 Payroll Expense ($000): 292900 Personnel: 3149

ST. ELIZABETH HEALTHCARE-EDGEWOOD See St. Elizabeth Edgewood

ELIZABETHTOWN—Hardin County

☒ **ENCOMPASS REHABILITATION HOSPITAL OF LAKEVIEW (183028)**, 134 Heartland Drive, Zip 42701–2778; tel. 270/769–3100, (Nonreporting) **A**1 10 **S** Encompass Health Corporation, Birmingham, AL
Primary Contact: Lori Jarboe, Chief Executive Officer
CFO: Scott Hart, Controller
CMO: Toni Abang, M.D., Medical Director
CHR: Janet Morris, Director Human Resources
Web address: www.healthsouthlakeview.com
Control: Corporation, Investor–owned (for–profit) **Service**: Rehabilitation

Staffed Beds: 40

☒ **HARDIN MEMORIAL HEALTH (180012)**, 913 North Dixie Avenue, Zip 42701–2503; tel. 270/737–1212, (Total facility includes 15 beds in nursing home–type unit) **A**1 2 5 10 19 **F**3 8 11 12 13 15 17 18 20 22 24 28 29 30 31 32 34 35 37 39 40 44 45 48 49 50 51 52 54 57 58 59 64 68 70 71 72 74 75 76 77 78 79 80 81 82 84 85 86 87 89 93 94 96 98 102 107 108 110 111 114 115 117 118 119 120 121 124 126 127 128 129 130 131 132 134 135 144 146 147 148 149 154 **S** Baptist Health, Louisville, KY
Primary Contact: Dennis B. Johnson, President and Chief Executive Officer
COO: Tom Carrico, Vice President of Operations
CFO: Lennis Thompson II Vice President and Chief Financial Officer
CMO: John Godfrey, M.D., Vice President and Chief Executive Officer
CIO: Trey Hyberger, Director Information Technology
CHR: Myra Covault, Associate Vice President of Human Resources
CNO: Sharon Wright, R.N., Vice President and Chief Nursing Officer
Web address: www.hmh.net
Control: County, Government, nonfederal **Service**: General medical and surgical

Staffed Beds: 268 Admissions: 13450 Census: 160

ERLANGER—Kenton County

☒ **SUN BEHAVIORAL KENTUCKY (184006)**, 820 Dolwick Drive, Zip 41018, Mailing Address: 3900 Olympic Blvd., Ste 400, Zip 41018; tel. 859/429–5188, (Nonreporting) **A**1 10
Primary Contact: Chris Lockey, Chief Executive Officer
COO: Carol Parke, Chief Operating Officer, SUN Kentucky
Web address: www https://www.sunkentucky.com/
Control: Corporation, Investor–owned (for–profit) **Service**: Psychiatric

Staffed Beds: 197

FLEMINGSBURG—Fleming County

☒ **FLEMING COUNTY HOSPITAL (180053)**, 55 Foundation Drive, Zip 41041–9815, Mailing Address: P.O. Box 388, Zip 41041–0388; tel. 606/849–5000, (Nonreporting) **A**1 10 **S** LifePoint Health, Brentwood, TN
Primary Contact: Brian Springate, Chief Executive Officer
CFO: Theresa Fite, R.N., Chief Financial Officer
CMO: Samuel Gehring, M.D., Chief of Staff
CIO: Don Daugherty, Director Information Systems
CHR: Marsha Mitchell, Director Human Resources
CNO: Lynda Skaggs, Chief Nursing Officer
Web address: www.flemingcountyhospital.org
Control: Other not–for–profit (including NFP Corporation) **Service**: General medical and surgical

Staffed Beds: 52

FLORENCE—Boone County

☐ △ **GATEWAY REHABILITATION HOSPITAL (183030)**, 5940 Merchant Street, Zip 41042–1158; tel. 859/426–2400, (Nonreporting) **A**1 7 10 **S** Vibra Healthcare, Mechanicsburg, PA
Primary Contact: Frank Schneider, FACHE, Chief Executive Officer
CFO: Margaret Cesarez, Chief Financial Officer
CNO: Jenna Wellbrock, Chief Nursing Officer
Web address: www.gatewayflorence.com/
Control: Corporation, Investor–owned (for–profit) **Service**: Rehabilitation

Staffed Beds: 40

Hospital, Medicare Provider Number, Address, Telephone, Approval, Facility, and Physician Codes, Health Care System

★ American Hospital Association (AHA) membership
☐ The Joint Commission accreditation
○ Healthcare Facilities Accreditation Program
◇ DNV Healthcare Inc. accreditation
⇑ Center for Improvement in Healthcare Quality Accreditation
△ Commission on Accreditation of Rehabilitation Facilities (CARF) accreditation

☐ **ST. ELIZABETH FLORENCE (180045)**, 4900 Houston Road, Zip 41042–4824; tel. 859/212–5200, (Total facility includes 16 beds in nursing home–type unit) **A**1 10 **F**3 9 11 12 15 20 28 29 30 34 35 39 40 44 45 46 47 48 49 50 53 55 56 57 59 60 61 64 65 70 74 75 77 78 79 80 81 82 84 85 86 87 92 93 97 98 100 101 102 107 108 110 111 115 118 119 126 128 129 130 132 135 141 145 146 147 148 149 150 152 154 **S** St. Elizabeth Healthcare, Edgewood, KY
Primary Contact: Garren Colvin, Chief Executive Officer
COO: Chris Carle, Senior Vice President and Chief Operating Officer
CMO: George Hall, M.D., Vice President Medical Affairs
CIO: Alex Rodriguez, Vice President and Chief Information Officer
CHR: Martin Oscadal, Senior Vice President Human Resources
Web address: www.stelizabeth.com
Control: Church operated, Nongovernment, not–for–profit **Service**: General medical and surgical

Staffed Beds: 147 **Admissions:** 10038 **Census:** 113 **Outpatient Visits:** 184546 **Births:** 0 **Total Expense ($000):** 151126 **Payroll Expense ($000):** 62568 **Personnel:** 857

ST. ELIZABETH HEALTHCARE FLORENCE See St. Elizabeth Florence

FORT CAMPBELL—Christian County

✉ **COLONEL FLORENCE A. BLANCHFIELD ARMY COMMUNITY HOSPITAL**, 650 Joel Drive, Zip 42223–5318; tel. 270/798–8040, (Nonreporting) **A**1 3 5 **S** Department of the Army, Office of the Surgeon General, Falls Church, VA
Primary Contact: Colonel Telita Crosland, Commander
CHR: Major Travis Burchett, Troop Commander Human Resources
Web address: www.campbell.amedd.army.mil/
Control: Department of Defense, Government, federal **Service**: General medical and surgical

Staffed Beds: 66

FORT THOMAS—Campbell County

CARDINAL HILL SPECIALTY HOSPITAL See Select Specialty Hospital-Northern Kentucky

✉ **SELECT SPECIALTY HOSPITAL-NORTHERN KENTUCKY (182004)**, 85 North Grand Avenue, Zip 41075–1793; tel. 859/572–3880, (Nonreporting) **A**1 10 **S** Select Medical Corporation, Mechanicsburg, PA
Primary Contact: Mavis Bechtle, MSN, R.N., FACHE, Chief Executive Officer
Web address: www.selectspecialtyhospitals.com
Control: Corporation, Investor–owned (for–profit) **Service**: Acute long–term care hospital

Staffed Beds: 33

☐ **ST. ELIZABETH FORT THOMAS (180001)**, 85 North Grand Avenue, Zip 41075–1796; tel. 859/572–3100, (Includes ST. ELIZABETH FALMOUTH, 512 South Maple Avenue, Falmouth, Kentucky, Zip 41040–1422; tel. 859/572–3500; Garren Colvin, Chief Executive Officer) (Total facility includes 26 beds in nursing home–type unit) **A**1 2 10 **F**3 4 5 9 11 15 18 20 28 29 30 31 34 35 39 40 44 45 47 48 49 50 51 53 55 56 57 58 59 60 61 63 64 65 70 71 74 75 77 78 79 80 81 82 85 86 87 91 92 93 94 97 100 102 107 108 110 111 115 118 119 120 121 123 126 128 129 130 135 141 146 147 149 150 152 153 154 **S** St. Elizabeth Healthcare, Edgewood, KY
Primary Contact: Garren Colvin, Chief Executive Officer
COO: Thomas Saalfeld, Senior Vice President and Chief Operating Officer
CMO: George Hall, M.D., Vice President Medical Affairs
CIO: Alex Rodriguez, Vice President and Chief Information Officer
CHR: Martin Oscadal, Senior Vice President Human Resources
Web address: www.stelizabeth.com
Control: Church operated, Nongovernment, not–for–profit **Service**: General medical and surgical

Staffed Beds: 147 **Admissions:** 7346 **Census:** 100 **Outpatient Visits:** 143484 **Births:** 0 **Total Expense ($000):** 137669 **Payroll Expense ($000):** 56374 **Personnel:** 683

ST. ELIZABETH HEALTHCARE FORT THOMAS See St. Elizabeth Fort Thomas

FRANKFORT—Franklin County

✉ **FRANKFORT REGIONAL MEDICAL CENTER (180127)**, 299 King's Daughters Drive, Zip 40601–4186; tel. 502/875–5240, (Nonreporting) **A**1 2 10 19 **S** HCA Healthcare, Nashville, TN
Primary Contact: Chip Peal, Chief Executive Officer
CMO: Willis P McKee, M.D., Jr Chief Medical Officer
CIO: Craig Willard, Director Information Technology and Systems
CHR: Bev Young, Director Human Resources
Web address: www.frankfortregional.com
Control: Corporation, Investor–owned (for–profit) **Service**: General medical and surgical

Staffed Beds: 115

FRANKLIN—Simpson County

☐ **MEDICAL CENTER AT FRANKLIN (181318)**, 1100 Brookhaven Road, Zip 42134–2746; tel. 270/598–4800, **A**1 10 18 **F**3 15 28 29 30 34 35 40 46 50 57 59 64 68 75 77 81 82 86 87 93 107 108 110 111 114 119 127 130 133 135 146 148 149 **S** Med Center Health, Bowling Green, KY
Primary Contact: Annette Runyon, Vice President and Administrator
CFO: Ronald G. Sowell, FACHE, Executive Vice President
CIO: Mark Brookman, Vice President and Chief Information Officer
Web address: www.themedicalcenterfranklin.org
Control: Other not–for–profit (including NFP Corporation) **Service**: General medical and surgical

Staffed Beds: 25 **Admissions:** 890 **Census:** 21 **Outpatient Visits:** 21641 **Births:** 0 **Personnel:** 120

GEORGETOWN—Scott County

✉ **GEORGETOWN COMMUNITY HOSPITAL (180101)**, 1140 Lexington Road, Zip 40324–9362; tel. 502/868–1100, **A**1 10 **F**3 11 12 13 15 18 28 29 30 31 34 35 40 45 46 47 48 49 50 51 57 59 60 64 65 66 70 74 75 76 77 78 79 81 82 85 87 92 93 100 107 108 109 110 111 114 115 116 119 124 126 129 130 131 132 133 135 144 146 147 148 149 154 156 **S** LifePoint Health, Brentwood, TN
Primary Contact: William Haugh, Administrator
CFO: Patrick C Bolander, Chief Financial Officer
CMO: Brian Allen, M.D., President Medical Staff
CHR: Marrianne Slonina, Director Human Resources
Web address: www.georgetowncommunityhospital.com
Control: Corporation, Investor–owned (for–profit) **Service**: General medical and surgical

Staffed Beds: 58 **Admissions:** 1943 **Census:** 16 **Outpatient Visits:** 77694 **Births:** 355 **Total Expense ($000):** 56014 **Payroll Expense ($000):** 17716 **Personnel:** 410

GLASGOW—Barren County

☐ **T. J. SAMSON COMMUNITY HOSPITAL (180017)**, 1301 North Race Street, Zip 42141–3483; tel. 270/651–4444, (Nonreporting) **A**1 3 5 10 19
Primary Contact: Neil Thornbury, Chief Executive Officer
COO: Margie Gentry, Controller
CFO: Mei Deng, Chief Financial Officer
CIO: Chad Friend, Director
CHR: LaDonna Rogers, Executive Vice President Human Resources
CNO: Shea Wilson, Chief Nursing Officer
Web address: www.tjsamson.org
Control: Other not–for–profit (including NFP Corporation) **Service**: General medical and surgical

Staffed Beds: 114

GREENSBURG—Green County

JANE TODD CRAWFORD HOSPITAL (181325), 202–206 Milby Street, Zip 42743–1100, Mailing Address: P.O. Box 220, Zip 42743–0220; tel. 270/932–4211, (Nonreporting) **A**10 18
Primary Contact: Rex A. Tungate, Chief Executive Officer
CFO: Richard Hendershot, Chief Financial Officer
CMO: Shane DeSimone, M.D., Chief of Staff
CHR: Mary Ann Quinn, Administrative Assistant
CNO: Roxie Montgomery, Director of Nursing
Web address: www.janetoddhospital.com
Control: County, Government, nonfederal **Service**: General medical and surgical

Staffed Beds: 45

GREENVILLE—Muhlenberg County

☐ **OWENSBORO HEALTH MUHLENBERG COMMUNITY HOSPITAL (180004)**, 440 Hopkinsville Street, Zip 42345–1172, Mailing Address: P.O. Box 387, Zip 42345–0378; tel. 270/338–8000, (Nonreporting) **A**1 10 **S** Owensboro Health, Owensboro, KY
Primary Contact: Ed Heath, FACHE, Chief Executive Officer
CMO: Vincent P Genovese, M.D., President Medical Staff
CIO: Alan Trail, Director Information Systems
CHR: Lisa R Hope, Director Human Resources
CNO: Kathy Mitchell, Chief Nursing Officer
Web address: www.mchky.org
Control: Other not–for–profit (including NFP Corporation) **Service**: General medical and surgical

Staffed Beds: 105

HARDINSBURG—Breckinridge County

☒ **BRECKINRIDGE MEMORIAL HOSPITAL (181319)**, 1011 Old Highway 60, Zip 40143–2597; tel. 270/756–7000, (Nonreporting) **A**1 10 18 **S** Alliant Management Services, Louisville, KY
Primary Contact: Angela Portman, Chief Executive Officer
CFO: Timothy D Crockett, Chief Financial Officer
CMO: Brian O'Donoghue, M.D., Chief Medical Officer
CHR: James Turpin, Human Resources
CNO: Tiffany Kennedy, Chief Nursing Officer
Web address: www.breckinridgehealth.org/
Control: Other not–for–profit (including NFP Corporation) **Service:** General medical and surgical

Staffed Beds: 43

HARLAN—Harlan County

⇑ **HARLAN ARH HOSPITAL (180050)**, 81 Ball Park Road, Zip 40831–1792; tel. 606/573–8100, **A**5 10 21 **F**3 11 13 15 18 20 28 29 30 32 34 35 40 43 50 54 57 59 62 64 70 75 76 77 78 79 81 82 85 86 87 89 93 97 98 99 102 103 107 108 111 115 118 119 127 129 130 132 146 147 148 154 **S** Appalachian Regional Healthcare, Inc., Lexington, KY
Primary Contact: Donald R. Fields, Community Chief Executive Officer
CFO: Brad Burkhart, Assistant Administrator
CHR: Sabra Howard, Manager Human Resources
Web address: www.arh.org
Control: Other not–for–profit (including NFP Corporation) **Service:** General medical and surgical

Staffed Beds: 103 **Admissions:** 4410 **Census:** 51 **Outpatient Visits:** 69929 **Births:** 188 **Total Expense ($000):** 61447 **Payroll Expense ($000):** 17480 **Personnel:** 455

HARRODSBURG—Mercer County

☒ **EPHRAIM MCDOWELL JAMES B. HAGGIN MEMORIAL HOSPITAL (181302)**, 464 Linden Avenue, Zip 40330–1862; tel. 859/734–5441, (Nonreporting) **A**1 10 18 **S** Ephraim McDowell Health, Danville, KY
Primary Contact: Lynne Warner Lynn, R.N., Administrator
CFO: Tony Patterson, Chief Financial Officer
Web address: www.hagginhosp.org
Control: Other not–for–profit (including NFP Corporation) **Service:** General medical and surgical

Staffed Beds: 25

HARTFORD—Ohio County

☒ **OHIO COUNTY HOSPITAL (181323)**, 1211 Main Street, Zip 42347–1619; tel. 270/298–7411, **A**1 10 18 **F**3 15 18 26 28 29 30 35 36 40 48 49 50 59 63 64 65 74 75 77 79 81 82 84 85 87 92 93 97 100 107 110 111 115 119 127 120 130 132 133 135 146 147 148 149 154 156 157 **S** QHR, Brentwood, TN
Primary Contact: Blaine Pieper, Chief Executive Officer
CFO: John Tichenor, Chief Financial Officer
CMO: Joshua Skibba, Chief Medical Officer
CHR: Sue Wydick, Director Human Resources
CNO: Athena Minor, Chief Nursing Officer
Web address: www.ohiocountyhospital.com
Control: Other not–for–profit (including NFP Corporation) **Service:** General medical and surgical

Staffed Beds: 30 **Admissions:** 900 **Census:** 9 **Outpatient Visits:** 53874 **Births:** 0 **Total Expense ($000):** 36402 **Payroll Expense ($000):** 19631 **Personnel:** 498

HAZARD—Perry County

☐ ⇑ **HAZARD ARH REGIONAL MEDICAL CENTER (180029)**, 100 Medical Center Drive, Zip 41701–9421; tel. 606/439–6600, **A**1 2 3 5 10 19 21 **F**3 11 12 13 14 15 17 18 20 22 24 26 28 29 30 31 32 34 35 40 43 46 47 48 49 50 54 55 57 59 61 62 64 70 71 73 74 75 76 77 78 79 81 82 85 86 87 89 90 93 97 98 101 102 103 107 108 110 111 115 118 119 120 121 124 127 129 130 132 146 147 148 154 **S** Appalachian Regional Healthcare, Inc., Lexington, KY
Primary Contact: Dan Stone, Senior Community Chief Executive Officer
CMO: J D Miller, M.D., Chief Medical Officer
CIO: Jeff Brady, Director Information Systems
CHR: Sheila Cornett, Manager Human Resources
Web address: www.arh.org
Control: Other not–for–profit (including NFP Corporation) **Service:** General medical and surgical

Staffed Beds: 358 **Admissions:** 11988 **Census:** 195 **Outpatient Visits:** 153041 **Births:** 314 **Total Expense ($000):** 189515 **Payroll Expense ($000):** 38033 **Personnel:** 1114

HENDERSON—Henderson County

☐ **METHODIST HOSPITAL (180056)**, 1305 North Elm Street, Zip 42420–2775, Mailing Address: P.O. Box 48, Zip 42419–0048; tel. 270/827–7700, **A**1 2 10 13 **F**3 11 13 15 18 29 30 31 34 35 36 40 45 46 47 49 50 51 53 54 57 58 59 64 66 68 70 72 74 75 76 77 78 79 81 82 85 86 87 92 93 107 108 110 111 114 115 118 119 127 129 130 131 132 135 146 147 148 149 156
Primary Contact: Benny Nolen, President and Chief Executive Officer
CFO: David Massengale, Vice President and Chief Financial Officer
CMO: John Logan, M.D., Chief Medical Officer
CIO: Randy McCleese, Chief Information Officer
CHR: Ty Kahle, Vice President Human Resources
Web address: www.methodisthospital.net
Control: Church operated, Nongovernment, not–for–profit **Service:** General medical and surgical

Staffed Beds: 121 **Admissions:** 3589 **Census:** 43 **Outpatient Visits:** 270915 **Births:** 642 **Total Expense ($000):** 96815 **Payroll Expense ($000):** 33401 **Personnel:** 887

HOPKINSVILLE—Christian County

☐ **CUMBERLAND HALL HOSPITAL (184014)**, 270 Walton Way, Zip 42240–6808; tel. 270/886–1919, **A**1 10 **F**98 100 101 102 105 130 132 133 143 152 154 **S** Universal Health Services, Inc., King of Prussia, PA
Primary Contact: Jason Staats, Chief Executive Officer
CFO: Mark Wallace, Chief Financial Officer
CMO: Deepak Patel, M.D., Medical Director
CIO: Patricia Gray, Director Health Information Management
CHR: Kelly Hagy, Director Human Resources
CNO: Denise Lyons, Chief Nursing Officer
Web address: www.cumberlandhallhospital.com
Control: Corporation, Investor–owned (for–profit) **Service:** Psychiatric

Staffed Beds: 97 **Admissions:** 1715 **Census:** 64 **Outpatient Visits:** 0 **Births:** 0 **Total Expense ($000):** 11843 **Payroll Expense ($000):** 6587 **Personnel:** 144

☐ **JENNIE STUART MEDICAL CENTER (180051)**, 320 West 18th Street, Zip 42240–1965, Mailing Address: P.O. Box 2400, Zip 42241–2400; tel. 270/887–0100, (Nonreporting) **A**1 10 20 **S** QHR, Brentwood, TN
Primary Contact: Eric A. Lee, President and Chief Executive Officer
CMO: Casey Covington, M.D., President Elect, Medical Staff
CIO: Jerry Houston, Director Information Systems
CHR: Austin Moss, Vice President Human Resources
Web address: www.jsmc.org
Control: Other not–for–profit (including NFP Corporation) **Service:** General medical and surgical

Staffed Beds: 139

☐ **WESTERN STATE HOSPITAL (181002)**, Russellville Road, Zip 42240–3017, Mailing Address: P.O. Box 2200, Zip 42241–2200; tel. 270/889–6025, **A**1 10 **F**98 100 101 102 103 130 149
Primary Contact: Roger Westfall, Director
CFO: Jessica Cates, Fiscal Manager
CMO: Nayyar Iqbal, M.D., Director Medical Staff
CIO: Valerie Majors, Director Information Services
CHR: James L Hayes, Director Human Resources
CNO: Jill Thomas, Director of Nursing
Web address: www.westernstatehospital.ky.gov
Control: State, Government, nonfederal **Service:** Psychiatric

Staffed Beds: 205 **Admissions:** 2262 **Census:** 115 **Outpatient Visits:** 0 **Births:** 0

HORSE CAVE—Hart County

THE MEDICAL CENTER AT CAVERNA (181314), 1501 South Dixie Street, Zip 42749–1477; tel. 270/786–2191, (Nonreporting) **A**10 18 **S** Med Center Health, Bowling Green, KY
Primary Contact: Alan B. Alexander, FACHE, Vice President and Administrator
CFO: Ronald G. Sowell, FACHE, Executive Vice President and Chief Financial Officer
CIO: Mark Brookman, Vice President, Chief Information Officer
CHR: Lynn Williams, Vice President, Human Resources
Web address: www.TheMedicalCenterCaverna.org
Control: Corporation, Investor–owned (for–profit) **Service:** General medical and surgical

Staffed Beds: 25

Hospital, Medicare Provider Number, Address, Telephone, Approval, Facility, and Physician Codes, Health Care System

★ American Hospital Association (AHA) membership
☐ The Joint Commission accreditation
○ Healthcare Facilities Accreditation Program
◇ DNV Healthcare Inc. accreditation
⇑ Center for Improvement in Healthcare Quality Accreditation
△ Commission on Accreditation of Rehabilitation Facilities (CARF) accreditation

---

Many Facility Codes have changed. Please refer to the AHA Guide Code Chart.

HYDEN—Leslie County

⇑ **MARY BRECKINRIDGE ARH HOSPITAL (181316)**, 130 Kate Ireland Drive, Zip 41749–9071, Mailing Address: P.O. Box 447-A, Zip 41749–0717; tel. 606/672–2901, **A**10 18 21 **F**2 3 11 15 29 30 32 34 35 40 50 57 59 62 65 68 75 77 81 86 87 93 107 110 115 119 130 132 133 135 146 154 **S** Appalachian Regional Healthcare, Inc., Lexington, KY
Primary Contact: Mallie S. Noble, Administrator
COO: Nathan W Lee, Chief Executive Officer
CFO: Robert Besten, Chief Financial Officer
CMO: Roy Varghese, M.D., Chief of Staff
CIO: Frank Baker, Chief Information Officer
CHR: Beulah Couch, Director Human Resources
Web address: www.frontiernursing.org
Control: Other not–for–profit (including NFP Corporation) **Service**: General medical and surgical

Staffed Beds: 25 **Admissions:** 352 **Census:** 10 **Outpatient Visits:** 20686 **Births:** 0 **Total Expense ($000):** 12216 **Payroll Expense ($000):** 4438 **Personnel:** 133

IRVINE—Estill County

MERCY HEALTH - MARCUM AND WALLACE (181301), 60 Mercy Court, Zip 40336–1331; tel. 606/723–2115, **A**10 18 **F**3 15 29 30 34 35 40 43 45 50 56 57 59 64 75 77 81 83 93 107 115 119 127 129 130 131 133 146 147 148 156 **S** Mercy Health, Cincinnati, OH
Primary Contact: Susan Starling, President and Chief Executive Officer
CFO: Lori Witt, Site Finance Director
CMO: Maher Kassis, M.D., Chief Medical Staff
CHR: Dana Stepp, Human Resources Officer
CNO: Trena Stocker, Chief Nursing Executive
Web address: www.marcumandwallace.org
Control: Church operated, Nongovernment, not–for–profit **Service**: General medical and surgical

Staffed Beds: 25 **Admissions:** 1024 **Census:** 13 **Outpatient Visits:** 72129 **Births:** 0 **Total Expense ($000):** 22915 **Payroll Expense ($000):** 9310 **Personnel:** 149

JACKSON—Breathitt County

⊞ **KENTUCKY RIVER MEDICAL CENTER (180139)**, 540 Jett Drive, Zip 41339–9622; tel. 606/666–6000, (Nonreporting) **A**1 10 20 **S** Quorum Health, Brentwood, TN
Primary Contact: John Ballard, Ph.D., Chief Executive Officer
CFO: Michael Ackley, Chief Financial Officer
CMO: Eunice Johnson, M.D., Chief Medical Staff
CIO: Diana Tyra, Director Health Information
CHR: Naomi Mitchell, Director Human Resources
Web address: www.kentuckyrivermc.com
Control: Corporation, Investor–owned (for–profit) **Service**: General medical and surgical

Staffed Beds: 54

LA GRANGE—Oldham County

⊞ **BAPTIST HEALTH LA GRANGE (180138)**, 1025 New Moody Lane, Zip 40031–9154; tel. 502/222–5388, (Total facility includes 24 beds in nursing home–type unit) **A**1 5 10 **F**3 7 11 13 15 18 28 29 30 31 34 35 40 45 46 49 50 54 56 57 59 64 70 74 75 76 78 79 81 82 85 86 87 93 97 107 108 110 111 114 119 128 129 130 131 132 135 146 147 148 149 156 **S** Baptist Health, Louisville, KY
Primary Contact: Clint Kaho, President
CFO: Jim Morris, Vice President Finance
CMO: Matt McDanald, M.D., Chief Medical Officer
CIO: David Bensema, Chief Information Officer
CHR: Kayla Batts, Manager Human Resources
CNO: Nathan Wilson, R.N., Vice President and Chief Nursing Officer
Web address: www.baptisthealthlagrange.com
Control: Other not–for–profit (including NFP Corporation) **Service**: General medical and surgical

Staffed Beds: 65 **Admissions:** 2095 **Census:** 33 **Outpatient Visits:** 183494 **Births:** 506 **Total Expense ($000):** 123038 **Payroll Expense ($000):** 28414 **Personnel:** 455

LEBANON—Marion County

⊞ **SPRING VIEW HOSPITAL (180024)**, 320 Loretto Road, Zip 40033–1300; tel. 270/692–3161, (Nonreporting) **A**1 10 **S** LifePoint Health, Brentwood, TN
Primary Contact: Timothy R. Trottier, Chief Executive Officer
CFO: Denise Thomas, Chief Financial Officer
CIO: Douglas Bland, Manager Information Services
CHR: Ann Dabney, Manager Human Resources
CNO: Linda Hunter, Chief Nursing Officer
Web address: www.springviewhospital.com
Control: Corporation, Investor–owned (for–profit) **Service**: General medical and surgical

Staffed Beds: 60

LEITCHFIELD—Grayson County

☐ **TWIN LAKES REGIONAL MEDICAL CENTER (180070)**, 910 Wallace Avenue, Zip 42754–2414; tel. 270/259–9400, (Nonreporting) **A**1 10 **S** Alliant Management Services, Louisville, KY
Primary Contact: Wayne Meriwether, Chief Executive Officer
COO: Deneace Clemons, Chief Operating Officer
CFO: Scott Arndell, Chief Financial Officer
CIO: Robbie Lindsey, Chief Information Officer
CHR: Kim Rayls, Director Human Resources
CNO: David Logdson, Chief Nursing Officer
Web address: www.tlrmc.com
Control: Other not–for–profit (including NFP Corporation) **Service**: General medical and surgical

Staffed Beds: 75

LEXINGTON—Fayette County

⊞ **BAPTIST HEALTH LEXINGTON (180103)**, 1740 Nicholasville Road, Zip 40503–1499; tel. 859/260–6100, **A**1 2 3 10 **F**3 11 12 13 15 17 18 20 22 24 26 28 29 30 31 34 35 36 39 40 44 45 46 47 48 49 54 55 56 57 58 59 60 64 65 68 70 72 74 75 76 77 78 79 81 82 85 86 87 92 93 97 107 108 110 111 114 115 117 118 119 120 121 124 126 129 130 131 132 135 144 146 147 148 154 156 157 **S** Baptist Health, Louisville, KY
Primary Contact: William G. Sisson, FACHE, President
COO: Karen S Hill, R.N., FACHE, Chief Operating Officer and Chief Nursing Officer
CFO: John Franke, Chief Financial Officer
CMO: James Borders, M.D., Chief Medical Officer
CIO: Lisa Fluty, Director Information Services
CHR: Lynette Walker, R.N., Ph.D., Vice President Human Resources
CNO: Karen S Hill, R.N., FACHE, Chief Operating Officer and Chief Nursing Officer
Web address: www.baptisthealthlexington.com
Control: Other not–for–profit (including NFP Corporation) **Service**: General medical and surgical

Staffed Beds: 391 **Admissions:** 19352 **Census:** 266 **Outpatient Visits:** 312366 **Births:** 3752 **Total Expense ($000):** 482259 **Payroll Expense ($000):** 142374 **Personnel:** 2259

⊞ **CARDINAL HILL REHABILITATION HOSPITAL (183026)**, 2050 Versailles Road, Zip 40504–1405; tel. 859/254–5701, (Total facility includes 74 beds in nursing home–type unit) **A**1 3 5 10 **F**3 28 29 56 58 60 64 75 87 90 91 93 95 96 128 130 132 146 148 149 **S** Encompass Health Corporation, Birmingham, AL
Primary Contact: Tara Diebling, Chief Executive Officer
CFO: Marty Lautner, Vice President Finance and Chief Financial Officer
CMO: William Lester, M.D., Vice President Medical Affairs
CIO: LouAnn Hyder, Director Information Integrity Management
CHR: Barry K Lindeman, Director Human Resources
CNO: Maureen Couture, Chief Nursing Officer and Vice President Nursing
Web address: www.cardinalhillhealthsouth.com
Control: Corporation, Investor–owned (for–profit) **Service**: Rehabilitation

Staffed Beds: 232 **Admissions:** 4199 **Census:** 163 **Outpatient Visits:** 40063 **Births:** 0 **Total Expense ($000):** 71776 **Payroll Expense ($000):** 37149 **Personnel:** 570

⊞ **CHI SAINT JOSEPH EAST (180143)**, 150 North Eagle Creek Drive, Zip 40509–1805; tel. 859/967–5000, (Includes WOMEN'S HOSPITAL SAINT JOSEPH EAST, 170 North Eagle Creek Drive, Lexington, Kentucky, Zip 40509–9087; tel. 316/962–2000) **A**1 2 5 10 **F**3 11 12 13 15 18 29 30 31 35 37 40 47 49 50 60 68 70 72 74 75 76 77 78 79 81 82 85 86 93 107 108 111 114 118 119 120 121 122 123 126 129 142 146 147 148 **S** CommonSpirit Health, Chicago, IL
Primary Contact: Eric Gilliam, President
COO: Christine Mays, Chief Operating Officer and Chief Nurse Executive
CFO: Melinda S Evans, Vice President Finance
CIO: Janie Fergus, Director and Chief Information Officer
Web address: www.sjhlex.org
Control: Church operated, Nongovernment, not–for–profit **Service**: General medical and surgical

Staffed Beds: 150 **Admissions:** 8085 **Census:** 80 **Outpatient Visits:** 117857 **Births:** 2433 **Total Expense ($000):** 181956 **Payroll Expense ($000):** 49854 **Personnel:** 787

Many Facility Codes have changed. Please refer to the AHA Guide Code Chart. © 2019 AHA Guide

✠ **CHI SAINT JOSEPH HEALTH (180010)**, One St Joseph Drive, Zip 40504–3754; tel. 859/278–3436, **A**1 2 3 10 **F**3 8 11 12 15 17 18 19 20 22 24 25 26 27 28 29 30 31 34 35 37 40 41 45 47 49 50 51 54 55 56 57 58 59 64 65 66 68 70 74 77 78 79 81 82 83 84 85 86 87 91 92 93 94 97 107 110 111 114 115 116 117 118 119 120 121 123 126 127 129 130 132 135 144 146 147 148 156 **S** CommonSpirit Health, Chicago, IL
Primary Contact: Bruce J. Tassin, President
COO: Christine Mays, Chief Operating Officer and Chief Nurse Executive
CFO: Melinda S Evans, Vice President Finance
CIO: Janie Fergus, Director and Chief Information Officer
Web address: www.sjhlex.org
Control: Church operated, Nongovernment, not–for–profit **Service:** General medical and surgical

Staffed Beds: 307 Admissions: 12052 Census: 168 Outpatient Visits: 101130 Births: 0 Total Expense ($000): 267545 Payroll Expense ($000): 77471 Personnel: 1208

★ **CONTINUING CARE HOSPITAL (182002)**, 1 Saint Joseph Drive, Zip 40504–3742; tel. 859/967–5744, (Nonreporting) **A**10 **S** CommonSpirit Health, Chicago, IL
Primary Contact: Robert C. Desotelle, President and Chief Executive Officer
CMO: Michael Miedler, M.D., Chief Medical Officer
CNO: Regina Masters, R.N., MSN, Director of Nursing
Web address: www.kentuckyonehealth.org
Control: Church operated **Service:** Acute long–term care hospital

Staffed Beds: 43

☐ **EASTERN STATE HOSPITAL (184004)**, 1350 Bull Lea Road, Zip 40511; tel. 859/246–8000, **A**1 3 5 10 **F**30 35 98 101 103 130 132 135 143 146 149 150
Primary Contact: Carrie Rudzik, Chief Administrative Officer
CFO: Brett Russell, Finance Business Partner Specialist
CMO: Andrew Cooley, M.D., Chief Medical Officer
CIO: Steve Kincaid, Information Technology Manager
CHR: Daniel Hacker, Human Resource Business Partner
CNO: Marc Anthony Woods, Assistant Chief Nurse Executive
Web address: www.ukhealthcare.uky.edu/ESH/
Control: State, Government, nonfederal **Service:** Psychiatric

Staffed Beds: 140 Admissions: 2637 Census: 126 Outpatient Visits: 0 Births: 0 Personnel: 413

FEDERAL MEDICAL CENTER, 3301 Leestown Road, Zip 40511–8799, tel. 859/255–6812, (Nonreporting)
Primary Contact: Francisco Quintana, Warden
CFO: Mike Kinsel, Controller
CMO: Michael Growse, M.D., Clinical Director
Control: Department of Justice, Government, federal **Service:** Hospital unit of an institution (prison hospital, college infirmary, etc.)

Staffed Beds: 22

✠ △ **LEXINGTON VETERANS AFFAIRS MEDICAL CENTER**, 1101 Veterans Drive, Zip 40502–2235; tel. 859/281–4901, (Nonreporting) **A**1 3 5 7 **S** Department of Veterans Affairs, Washington, DC
Primary Contact: James Belmont, Interim Director
CFO: Patricia Swisshelm, Acting Chief Fiscal Service
CMO: Patricia Breeden, M.D., Chief of Staff
CIO: Jeffrey Sutton, Chief Information Officer
CHR: Laura Faulkner, Chief Human Resource Management Service
CNO: Mary Kelly McCullough, Associate Director Patient Care Services
Web address: www.lexington.va.gov/
Control: Veterans Affairs, Government, federal **Service:** General medical and surgical

Staffed Beds: 45

☐ **RIDGE BEHAVIORAL HEALTH SYSTEM (184009)**, 3050 Rio Dosa Drive, Zip 40509–1540; tel. 859/269–2325, (Nonreporting) **A**1 5 10 **S** Universal Health Services, Inc., King of Prussia, PA
Primary Contact: Nina W. Eisner, Chief Executive Officer and Managing Director
CFO: Richard McDowell, Chief Financial Officer
CMO: Michael Rieser, M.D., Medical Director
CNO: Georgia Swank, Chief Nursing Officer
Web address: www.ridgebhs.com
Control: Corporation, Investor–owned (for–profit) **Service:** Psychiatric

Staffed Beds: 110

✠ **SELECT SPECIALTY HOSPITAL-LEXINGTON (182003)**, 310 South Limestone Street, 3rd Floor, Zip 40508–3008; tel. 859/226–7096, (Nonreporting) **A**1 10 **S** Select Medical Corporation, Mechanicsburg, PA
Primary Contact: Kim Pennington, Chief Executive Officer
CMO: Fadi Bacha, M.D., Chief Medical Officer
CHR: Tina Kirkland-Rose, Coordinator Human Resources
CNO: Katie Meredith, Chief Nursing Officer
Web address: www.lexington.selectspecialtyhospitals.com/
Control: Corporation, Investor–owned (for–profit) **Service:** Acute long–term care hospital

Staffed Beds: 41

✠ **UNIVERSITY OF KENTUCKY ALBERT B. CHANDLER HOSPITAL (180067)**, 800 Rose Street, Zip 40536–0293; tel. 859/323–5000, (Includes KENTUCKY CHILDREN'S HOSPITAL, N-100 - 800 Rose Street, Lexington, Kentucky, Zip 40536–0293; tel. 859/257–1000; UK HEALTHCARE GOOD SAMARITAN HOSPITAL, 310 South Limestone Street, Lexington, Kentucky, Zip 40508–3008; tel. 859/226–7000) **A**1 2 3 5 8 10 **F**3 5 6 7 9 11 12 13 15 16 17 18 19 20 21 22 23 24 25 26 27 28 29 30 31 32 34 35 36 37 38 39 40 41 43 44 45 46 47 48 49 50 52 54 55 56 57 58 59 60 61 64 65 66 68 70 72 73 74 75 76 77 78 79 81 82 84 85 86 87 88 89 91 92 93 94 95 96 97 98 99 100 101 102 103 104 107 110 111 114 115 116 118 119 120 121 123 124 126 127 129 130 131 132 133 135 136 137 138 139 140 141 142 143 145 146 147 148 149 150 154 155 156 157
Primary Contact: Mark Newman, M.D., Executive Vice President of Health Affairs
CHR: Kimberly P Wilson, Director Human Resources
Web address: www.ukhealthcare.uky.edu
Control: State, Government, nonfederal **Service:** General medical and surgical

Staffed Beds: 913 Admissions: 41044 Census: 755 Outpatient Visits: 1689362 Births: 2053 Total Expense ($000): 1396178 Payroll Expense ($000): 505027 Personnel: 8630

UNIVERSITY OF KENTUCKY HOSPITAL See University of Kentucky Albert B. Chandler Hospital

LIBERTY—Casey County

☐ **CASEY COUNTY HOSPITAL (181309)**, 187 Wolford Avenue, Zip 42539–3278; tel. 606/787–6275, (Nonreporting) **A**1 10 18
Primary Contact: Rex A. Tungate, Chief Executive Officer
CFO: Richard Hendershot, Chief Financial Officer
CMO: Housam Haddad, M.D., Chief of Staff
CHR: Mary Ann Quinn, Administrative Assistant
CNO: Sue Antle, Director of Nursing
Web address: www.caseycountyhospital.com
Control: County, Government, nonfederal **Service:** General medical and surgical

Staffed Beds: 24

LONDON—Laurel County

✠ **CHI SAINT JOSEPH LONDON (180011)**, 1001 Saint Joseph Lane, Zip 40741–8345; tel. 606/330–6000, (Nonreporting) **A**1 10 19 **S** CommonSpirit Health, Chicago, IL
Primary Contact: Terrence G. Deis, CPA, FACHE, President
CFO: Christy Spitser, Vice President Finance and Business Development
CMO: Shelley Stanko, M.D., Chief Medical Officer
CHR: Sandra Turqueza, Senior Human Resources Business Partner
CNO: Lewis Stephen O'Neal, R.N., MSN, Chief Nursing Officer
Web address: www.saintjosephhealthsystem.org
Control: Church operated **Service:** General medical and surgical

Staffed Beds: 116

LOUISA—Lawrence County

✠ **THREE RIVERS MEDICAL CENTER (180128)**, 2485 Highway 644, Zip 41230–9242, Mailing Address: P.O. Box 769, Zip 41230–0769; tel. 606/638–9451, **A**1 10 20 **F**3 11 12 15 18 29 35 38 40 45 49 50 51 68 70 75 79 81 84 85 87 93 98 100 104 107 108 111 115 119 129 130 133 146 147 149 150 154 157 **S** Quorum Health, Brentwood, TN
Primary Contact: Greg Kiser, Chief Executive Officer
CFO: Michael Ackley, Chief Financial Officer
CHR: Pat Hart, Director Human Resources
CNO: Cathy Heston, Chief Nursing Officer
Web address: www.threeriversmedicalcenter.com
Control: Corporation, Investor–owned (for–profit) **Service:** General medical and surgical

Staffed Beds: 90 Admissions: 2448 Census: 26 Outpatient Visits: 51446 Births: 0 Personnel: 321

Hospital, Medicare Provider Number, Address, Telephone, Approval, Facility, and Physician Codes, Health Care System

★ American Hospital Association (AHA) membership
☐ The Joint Commission accreditation
○ Healthcare Facilities Accreditation Program
◇ DNV Healthcare Inc. accreditation
⇑ Center for Improvement in Healthcare Quality Accreditation
△ Commission on Accreditation of Rehabilitation Facilities (CARF) accreditation

LOUISVILLE—Jefferson County

☒ △ **BAPTIST HEALTH LOUISVILLE (180130)**, 4000 Kresge Way, Zip 40207–4676; tel. 502/897–8100, **A**1 2 3 5 7 10 **F**3 5 6 8 11 12 13 15 17 18 20 22 24 26 28 29 30 31 34 35 36 37 38 40 44 45 46 47 48 49 50 51 54 56 57 58 59 61 64 70 72 74 75 76 78 79 81 82 83 84 85 86 87 90 91 92 93 98 100 101 102 103 104 105 107 108 110 111 114 115 116 117 118 119 120 121 123 124 126 129 130 132 135 141 146 147 148 149 153 154 156 **S** Baptist Health, Louisville, KY
Primary Contact: Larry W. Gray, President
COO: Clint Kaho, Vice President
CFO: Jim Morris, Vice President Finance
CMO: Kenneth Anderson, M.D., Vice President and Chief Medical Officer
CIO: Shari Price, Director Information Services
CHR: Kim Scaglione, Vice President Human Resources
CNO: Karen Newman, Ed.D., MSN, R.N., Vice President and Chief Nursing Officer
Web address: www.baptisthealthlouisville.com
Control: Other not–for–profit (including NFP Corporation) **Service**: General medical and surgical

Staffed Beds: 500 **Admissions**: 26182 **Census**: 343 **Outpatient Visits**: 428156 **Births**: 3170 **Total Expense ($000)**: 482600 **Payroll Expense ($000)**: 164262 **Personnel**: 2694

☐ **CENTRAL STATE HOSPITAL (184015)**, 10510 LaGrange Road, Zip 40223–1228; tel. 502/253–7060, (Nonreporting) **A**1 3 5 10
Primary Contact: Josie Goodman, Hospital Director
CFO: Robert Underhill, Director of Business Services
CMO: Vital Shah, M.D., Associate Director and Chief Medical Officer
CIO: Randy Spicer, Information Technology Supervisor
CHR: Sonya Wheatley, Human Resources Manager
CNO: Jennifer Fowler
Control: State, Government, nonfederal **Service**: Psychiatric

Staffed Beds: 112

★ **CHI OUR LADY OF PEACE**, 2020 Newburg Road, Zip 40205–1879; tel. 502/479–4500, **A**5 **F**5 29 30 35 98 99 100 101 104 105 130 132 143 152 153 154 **S** CommonSpirit Health, Chicago, IL
Primary Contact: Jennifer Nolan, President and Chief Executive Officer
COO: Martha S Mather, Chief Operating Officer and Vice President
CFO: Beckie Kistler, Director of Finance
CHR: Jan Ostbloom, Human Resources Consultant
CNO: Brad Lincks, R.N., Chief Nursing Officer and Vice President
Web address: www.kentuckyonehealth.org/our-lady-of-peace
Control: Other not–for–profit (including NFP Corporation) **Service**: Psychiatric

Staffed Beds: 220 **Admissions**: 8533 **Census**: 178 **Outpatient Visits**: 32701 **Births**: 0 **Total Expense ($000)**: 55464 **Payroll Expense ($000)**: 30221 **Personnel**: 469

☒ **JEWISH HOSPITAL (180040)**, 200 Abraham Flexner Way, Zip 40202–1886; tel. 502/587–4011, (Includes FRAZIER REHAB INSTITUTE, 220 Abraham Flexner Way, Louisville, Kentucky, Zip 40202–1887; tel. 502/582–7400; Cathy Spalding, Vice President of Operations) **A**1 2 3 5 10 **F**3 8 12 15 17 18 20 22 24 26 28 29 30 34 39 40 42 45 46 47 48 49 50 53 54 59 60 64 65 67 68 70 74 75 77 79 81 83 85 87 90 91 92 93 94 95 96 107 108 109 110 111 112 114 115 118 119 126 130 131 137 138 139 140 141 142 146 148 149 154 156 157 **S** CommonSpirit Health, Chicago, IL
Primary Contact: Deborah M. Lee-Eddie, Interim President and Chief Executive Officer
CFO: Ronald Farr, Chief Financial Officer
CMO: James P Ketterhagen, M.D., Senior Vice President and Chief Medical Officer
CIO: Thomas Wittman, Chief Information Officer
CHR: Julie McGregor, Vice President and Chief People Officer
CNO: Cheryl Fugatte, MSN, Vice President and Chief Nursing Officer
Web address: www.kentuckyonehealth.org/jewish-hospital
Control: Other not–for–profit (including NFP Corporation) **Service**: General medical and surgical

Staffed Beds: 421 **Admissions**: 16614 **Census**: 290 **Outpatient Visits**: 180236 **Births**: 0 **Total Expense ($000)**: 442056 **Payroll Expense ($000)**: 131340 **Personnel**: 2109

KINDRED HOSPITAL LOUISVILLE AT JEWISH HOSPITAL See Kindred Hospital-Louisville, Louisville

☒ **KINDRED HOSPITAL-LOUISVILLE (182001)**, 1313 Saint Anthony Place, Zip 40204–1740; tel. 502/587–7001, (Includes KINDRED HOSPITAL LOUISVILLE AT JEWISH HOSPITAL, 200 Abraham Flexner Way, 2nd Floor, Louisville, Kentucky, Zip 40202; tel. 502/587–3999; David Johnson, Chief Executive Officer), (Nonreporting) **A**1 3 5 10 **S** Kindred Healthcare, Louisville, KY
Primary Contact: Jack Nicholson, Chief Executive Officer
Web address: www.kindredlouisville.com
Control: Corporation, Investor–owned (for–profit) **Service**: Acute long–term care hospital

Staffed Beds: 117

★ **NORTON CHILDREN'S HOSPITAL (189801)**, 231 East Chestnut Street, Zip 40202–1821; tel. 502/629–6000, **A**2 3 5 8 **F**3 8 11 16 19 21 23 24 25 27 29 30 31 32 34 35 36 38 39 40 41 42 43 44 45 47 48 49 50 51 54 57 58 59 60 61 64 65 67 68 72 73 74 75 78 79 81 82 84 85 86 87 88 89 91 92 93 96 98 99 101 102 107 108 111 114 115 116 117 119 126 130 131 132 134 136 137 138 145 146 148 149 150 154 155 156 **S** Norton Healthcare, Louisville, KY
Primary Contact: Emmett Ramser, Chief Administrative Officer
Web address: www.kosairchildrens.com/
Control: Other not–for–profit (including NFP Corporation) **Service**: Children's general medical and surgical

Staffed Beds: 279 **Admissions**: 9694 **Census**: 200 **Outpatient Visits**: 129953 **Births**: 0 **Total Expense ($000)**: 332532 **Payroll Expense ($000)**: 102767 **Personnel**: 1578

NORTON HEALTHCARE PAVILION See Norton Hospital, Louisville

☒ **NORTON HOSPITAL (180088)**, 200 East Chestnut Street, Zip 40202–1800, Mailing Address: P.O. Box 35070, Zip 40232–5070; tel. 502/629–8000, (Includes NORTON AUDUBON HOSPITAL, One Audubon Plaza Drive, Louisville, Kentucky, Zip 40217–1300, Mailing Address: P O Box 17550, Zip 40217–0550, tel. 502/636–7111; Jon Cooper, Chief Administrative Officer; NORTON BROWNSBORO HOSPITAL, 4960 Norton Healthcare Boulevard, Louisville, Kentucky, Zip 40241–2831; tel. 502/446–8000; Andrew Strausbaugh, Chief Administrative Officer; NORTON HEALTHCARE PAVILION, 315 East Broadway, Louisville, Kentucky, Zip 40202–1703; tel. 502/629–2000; NORTON WOMEN'S AND CHILDREN'S HOSPITAL, 4001 Dutchmans Lane, Louisville, Kentucky, Zip 40207–4799; tel. 502/893–1000; Charlotte Ipsan, Chief Administrative Officer) **A**1 2 3 5 8 10 **F**3 11 12 13 15 17 18 20 22 24 26 28 29 30 31 34 35 36 38 40 44 45 46 47 48 49 50 51 53 55 56 57 59 64 68 70 72 73 74 75 76 78 79 81 82 84 85 86 87 89 91 92 93 95 96 98 100 101 102 107 108 110 111 114 115 116 117 118 119 120 121 123 124 126 129 130 131 132 133 134 135 146 147 148 149 150 154 156 157 **S** Norton Healthcare, Louisville, KY
Primary Contact: Matthew Ayers, Chief Administrative Officer
CFO: Carl Amorose, Vice President Finance
Web address: www.nortonhealthcare.com/nortonhospital
Control: Other not–for–profit (including NFP Corporation) **Service**: General medical and surgical

Staffed Beds: 1232 **Admissions**: 62661 **Census**: 797 **Outpatient Visits**: 543126 **Births**: 7704 **Total Expense ($000)**: 1093246 **Payroll Expense ($000)**: 343577 **Personnel**: 5535

☒ **ROBLEY REX VETERANS AFFAIRS MEDICAL CENTER**, 800 Zorn Avenue, Zip 40206–1499; tel. 502/287–4000, (Nonreporting) **A**1 3 5 **S** Department of Veterans Affairs, Washington, DC
Primary Contact: Marylee Rothschild, M.D., Chief of Staff
CFO: Barbara Roberts, Chief Financial Officer
CMO: Marylee Rothschild, M.D., Chief of Staff
CIO: Augustine Bittner, Chief Information Officer
CHR: Angela Dutton, Chief Human Resources Management Service
Web address: www.louisville.va.gov
Control: Veterans Affairs, Government, federal **Service**: General medical and surgical

Staffed Beds: 116

★ **STS. MARY & ELIZABETH HOSPITAL**, 1850 Bluegrass Avenue, Zip 40215–1199; tel. 502/361–6000, **A**3 5 **F**3 11 12 15 18 20 22 29 30 31 34 35 40 44 45 47 49 50 53 56 59 60 63 64 68 69 70 74 75 78 79 81 82 84 85 86 87 107 108 110 111 114 115 118 119 130 132 135 154 **S** CommonSpirit Health, Chicago, IL
Primary Contact: Charles Powell, President
COO: Kenneth Johnson, Vice President
CFO: Elaine Hayes, Controller
CMO: Val Slayton, M.D., Vice President Medical Affairs
CHR: Julie McGregor, Director Human Resources
Web address: www.jhsmh.org
Control: Other not–for–profit (including NFP Corporation) **Service**: General medical and surgical

Staffed Beds: 170 **Admissions**: 7762 **Census**: 89 **Outpatient Visits**: 86688 **Births**: 0 **Total Expense ($000)**: 122088 **Payroll Expense ($000)**: 45423 **Personnel**: 564

TEN BROECK DUPONT See The Brook at Dupont

☐ **THE BROOK AT DUPONT (184007)**, 1405 Browns Lane, Zip 40207–4608; tel. 502/896–0495, (Nonreporting) **A**1 10 **S** Universal Health Services, Inc., King of Prussia, PA
Primary Contact: Paul Andrews, Chief Executive Officer
Web address: www.thebrookhospitals.com/
Control: Corporation, Investor–owned (for–profit) **Service**: Psychiatric

Staffed Beds: 88

Many Facility Codes have changed. Please refer to the AHA Guide Code Chart. © 2019 AHA Guide

☐ **THE BROOK HOSPITAL - KMI (184008)**, 8521 Old LaGrange Road, Zip 40242–3800; tel. 502/426–6380, (Nonreporting) **A**1 3 5 10 **S** Universal Health Services, Inc., King of Prussia, PA
Primary Contact: Paul Andrews, Chief Executive Officer
COO: Kim Peabody, Chief Operating Officer
CFO: Dennis Collins, Chief Financial Officer
CMO: Timothy Burke, M.D., Medical Director
CIO: Joel Roy, Manager Information Systems
CHR: Christina Taylor, Director Human Resources
Web address: www.thebrookhospitals.com
Control: Corporation, Investor–owned (for–profit) **Service**: Psychiatric

Staffed Beds: 98

☒ **UNIVERSITY OF LOUISVILLE HOSPITAL (180141)**, 530 South Jackson Street, Zip 40202–3611; tel. 502/562–3000, **A**1 2 3 5 8 10 **F**3 8 12 13 15 16 17 18 20 22 24 26 28 29 30 31 34 35 36 37 38 40 43 45 46 47 48 49 50 51 54 56 57 58 59 60 64 66 68 70 71 72 73 74 75 76 77 78 79 80 81 82 84 85 86 87 91 92 93 96 98 100 101 102 103 107 108 109 110 111 112 114 115 116 117 118 119 120 121 123 124 126 130 132 135 136 144 145 146 147 148 149 150 154
Primary Contact: Thomas Miller, Chief Executive Officer
COO: Kenneth P. Marshall, Chief Operating Officer
CMO: Mark P Pfeifer, M.D., Senior Vice President and Chief Medical Officer
CIO: Troy May, Chief Information Officer
CNO: Mary Jane Adams, R.N., MSN, Senior Vice President and Chief Nursing Officer
Web address: www.ulh.org
Control: Other not–for–profit (including NFP Corporation) **Service**: General medical and surgical

Staffed Beds: 329 **Admissions**: 15645 **Census**: 263 **Outpatient Visits**: 188785 **Births**: 1872 **Total Expense ($000)**: 555212 **Payroll Expense ($000)**: 153469 **Personnel**: 2831

VETERANS AFFAIRS MEDICAL CENTER-LOUISVILLE See Robley Rex Veterans Affairs Medical Center

MADISONVILLE—Hopkins County

☒ **BAPTIST HEALTH MADISONVILLE (180093)**, 900 Hospital Drive, Zip 42431–1694, tel. 270/825–5100, **A**1 2 3 6 10 22 **F**2 8 11 13 14 18 20 22 24 26 28 29 30 31 34 35 40 44 45 49 51 53 57 58 59 70 73 75 76 78 79 81 85 87 89 90 93 94 96 98 100 102 103 107 108 111 114 115 117 118 119 120 121 123 129 130 131 132 146 148 149 **S** Baptist Health, Louisville, KY
Primary Contact: Robert L. Ramey, President
COO: Kevin Moser, Vice President of Operations
CFO: Kim Ashby, Vice President of Finance
CMO: Wayne Lipson, M.D., Chief Physician Executive
CIO: Karla Durham, Director of Information Systems
CHR: Lorie A. Oglesby, Director of Human Resources
CNO: Denise Dunn, R.N., Chief Nursing Officer
Web address: www.baptisthealthmadisonville.com
Control: Other not–for–profit (including NFP Corporation) **Service**: General medical and surgical

Staffed Beds: 172 **Admissions**: 6550 **Census**: 92 **Outpatient Visits**: 140630 **Births**: 794 **Total Expense ($000)**: 170744 **Payroll Expense ($000)**: 59955 **Personnel**: 1152

★ **CONTINUECARE HOSPITAL AT MADISONVILLE (182009)**, 900 Hospital Drive, 4th Floor, Zip 42431–1644; tel. 270/825–5450, **A**10 **F**1 3 28 29 34 50 57 85 87 91 **S** Community Hospital Corporation, Plano, TX
Primary Contact: Melissa Nagle, Chief Executive Officer
CNO: Melissa Nagle, Chief Nursing Officer
Web address: www.continuecare.org/madisonville/
Control: Other not–for–profit (including NFP Corporation) **Service**: Acute long–term care hospital

Staffed Beds: 35 **Admissions**: 198 **Census**: 14 **Outpatient Visits**: 0 **Births**: 0 **Total Expense ($000)**: 7128 **Payroll Expense ($000)**: 2584 **Personnel**: 67

MANCHESTER—Clay County

☒ ○ **ADVENTHEALTH MANCHESTER (180043)**, 210 Marie Langdon Drive, Zip 40962–6388; tel. 606/598–5104, (Nonreporting) **A**1 10 11 **S** AdventHealth, Altamonte Springs, FL
Primary Contact: Chris Self, Chief Executive Officer
CFO: Paul Merklin, Vice President Finance and Chief Financial Officer
CMO: Jeff Newswanger, M.D., Chief Medical Officer
CHR: Joe Skula, Director Human Resources
Web address: www.manchestermemorial.org
Control: Church operated, Nongovernment, not–for–profit **Service**: General medical and surgical

Staffed Beds: 63

MARION—Crittenden County

CRITTENDEN COUNTY HOSPITAL (180095), 520 West Gum Street, Zip 42064–1516, Mailing Address: P.O. Box 386, Zip 42064–0386; tel. 270/965–5281, (Nonreporting) **A**10 20
Primary Contact: Daniel Hiben, Chief Executive Officer
COO: Robin Curnel, MSN, Chief Operating Officer and Chief Nursing Officer
CFO: Karen Paris, Controller
CMO: Steven Burkhart, M.D., Chief Medical Officer
CIO: Reese Baker, Director Information Systems
CHR: Jan Gregory, Chief of Human Resources
CNO: Robin Curnel, MSN, Chief Operating Officer and Chief Nursing Officer
Web address: www.crittenden-health.org
Control: Other not–for–profit (including NFP Corporation) **Service**: General medical and surgical

Staffed Beds: 48

MARTIN—Floyd County

★ ⇑ **ARH OUR LADY OF THE WAY (181305)**, 11203 Main Street, Zip 41649; tel. 606/285–6400, (Nonreporting) **A**10 18 21 **S** Appalachian Regional Healthcare, Inc., Lexington, KY
Primary Contact: Kathy Stumbo, President
CFO: Robert Brock, Vice President Finance
CMO: John Triplett, D.O., President Medical Staff
CIO: Chris Dye, Director Information Systems
Web address: www.saintjosephmartin.org
Control: Church operated **Service**: General medical and surgical

Staffed Beds: 25

MAYFIELD—Graves County

☒ **JACKSON PURCHASE MEDICAL CENTER (180116)**, 1099 Medical Center Circle, Zip 42066–1159; tel. 270/251–4100, (Nonreporting) **A**1 10 19 **S** LifePoint Health, Brentwood, TN
Primary Contact: David Anderson, Chief Executive Officer
CFO: Vicki Parks, Chief Financial Officer
CMO: Rudy Triana, M.D., Chief of Staff
CIO: Randy McDaniel, Information Systems Director
CHR: Tressa B Hargrove, Director Human Resources
CNO: Julia Grove, Chief Nursing Officer
Web address: www.jacksonpurchase.com
Control: Corporation, Investor–owned (for–profit) **Service**: General medical and surgical

Staffed Beds: 227

MAYSVILLE—Mason County

☒ **MEADOWVIEW REGIONAL MEDICAL CENTER (180019)**, 989 Medical Park Drive, Zip 41056–8750; tel. 606/759–5311, **A**1 10 **F**3 13 15 18 20 22 26 28 29 30 31 34 35 40 45 50 51 57 59 60 70 75 76 77 78 79 81 85 87 92 93 107 108 110 111 114 115 118 119 129 130 131 133 144 145 154 **S** LifePoint Health, Brentwood, TN
Primary Contact: Joseph G. Koch, Chief Executive Officer
CFO: Clayton Kolodziejczyk, Chief Financial Officer
CMO: Eric Lohman, M.D., Chief of Staff
CHR: Diana Kennedy, Director Human Resources
Web address: www.meadowviewregional.com
Control: Corporation, Investor–owned (for–profit) **Service**: General medical and surgical

Staffed Beds: 100 **Admissions**: 2332 **Census**: 18 **Outpatient Visits**: 68470

Hospital, Medicare Provider Number, Address, Telephone, Approval, Facility, and Physician Codes, Health Care System

★ American Hospital Association (AHA) membership
☐ The Joint Commission accreditation
○ Healthcare Facilities Accreditation Program
◇ DNV Healthcare Inc. accreditation
⇑ Center for Improvement in Healthcare Quality Accreditation
△ Commission on Accreditation of Rehabilitation Facilities (CARF) accreditation

MCDOWELL—Floyd County

⇑ **MCDOWELL ARH HOSPITAL (181331)**, Route 122, Zip 41647, Mailing Address: P.O. Box 247, Zip 41647–0247; tel. 606/377–3400, **A**10 18 21 **F**3 11 15 29 30 34 35 40 50 57 59 62 64 65 75 77 81 82 86 87 89 93 97 107 111 115 119 127 130 131 133 146 154 **S** Appalachian Regional Healthcare, Inc., Lexington, KY
Primary Contact: Russell Barker, Community Chief Executive Officer
COO: Russell Barker, Community Chief Executive Officer
CMO: Mary A Hall, Chief Medical Staff
CIO: Jeff Brady, Director Information Systems
CHR: Stephanie Owens, Manager Human Resources
Web address: www.arh.org
Control: Other not–for–profit (including NFP Corporation) **Service**: General medical and surgical

Staffed Beds: 25 **Admissions:** 372 **Census:** 5 **Outpatient Visits:** 29475 **Births:** 0 **Total Expense ($000):** 15146 **Payroll Expense ($000):** 5419 **Personnel:** 135

MIDDLESBORO—Bell County

⇑ **MIDDLESBORO ARH HOSPITAL (180020)**, 3600 West Cumberland Avenue, Zip 40965–2614, Mailing Address: P.O. Box 340, Zip 40965–0340; tel. 606/242–1100, **A**10 21 **F**3 11 13 15 17 18 20 28 29 30 31 34 35 39 40 45 46 49 50 57 59 62 64 65 70 75 76 77 78 79 81 85 86 87 89 90 93 97 107 108 110 111 115 118 119 127 129 132 133 146 147 148 154 **S** Appalachian Regional Healthcare, Inc., Lexington, KY
Primary Contact: Michael Slusher, Community Chief Executive Officer
CFO: Jeremy Hall, Assistant Administrator and Chief Financial Officer
CMO: Maria Hortillosa, M.D., Chief of Staff
CIO: Lisa Dooley, Health Information Officer
CHR: Marina Cawood, Administrative Assistant
CNO: Stacy England, Community Chief Nursing Officer
Web address: www.arh.org/middlesboro
Control: Other not–for–profit (including NFP Corporation) **Service**: General medical and surgical

Staffed Beds: 73 **Admissions:** 1527 **Census:** 23 **Outpatient Visits:** 70659 **Births:** 232 **Total Expense ($000):** 39726 **Payroll Expense ($000):** 13166 **Personnel:** 274

MONTICELLO—Wayne County

WAYNE COUNTY HOSPITAL (181321), 166 Hospital Street, Zip 42633–2416; tel. 606/348–9343, **A**10 18 **F**3 15 29 30 40 47 75 81 107 108 114 119 127 133 135 146
Primary Contact: Joseph Murrell, Chief Executive Officer
CFO: Anne Sawyer, Chief Financial Officer
CMO: David Mayer, Chief of Staff
CIO: Angela Burton, Privacy Officer
CHR: Mollie Dick, Coordinator Human Resources
CNO: Lora Elam, R.N., Chief Nursing Officer
Web address: www.waynehospital.org
Control: Other not–for–profit (including NFP Corporation) **Service**: General medical and surgical

Staffed Beds: 25 **Admissions:** 371 **Census:** 4 **Outpatient Visits:** 14679 **Births:** 0 **Total Expense ($000):** 14328 **Payroll Expense ($000):** 6042 **Personnel:** 161

MOREHEAD—Rowan County

⊞ **ST. CLAIRE HEALTHCARE (180018)**, 222 Medical Circle, Zip 40351–1179; tel. 606/783–6500, (Nonreporting) **A**1 2 3 5 10 13
Primary Contact: Mark J. Neff, FACHE, President and Chief Executive Officer
CFO: Chris McClurg, Vice President Finance and Chief Financial Officer
CMO: William L Melahn, M.D., Vice President Medical Affairs and Chief Medical Officer
CIO: Randy McCleese, Vice President Information Services and Chief Information Officer
CHR: Travis A Bailey, Vice President Administration
CNO: Lerae Wilson, Vice President Patient Services and Chief Nursing Officer
Web address: www.st-claire.org
Control: Church operated **Service**: General medical and surgical

Staffed Beds: 133

MORGANFIELD—Union County

⊞ **METHODIST HOSPITAL UNION COUNTY (181306)**, 4604 Highway 60 West, Zip 42437–9570; tel. 270/389–5000, **A**1 10 18 **F**3 11 15 29 30 34 40 43 45 57 68 75 77 81 85 87 93 107 114 119 130 133 135 146 149
Primary Contact: Lynn R. Steinwachs, Vice President and Administrator
CFO: David Massengale, Chief Financial Officer
CMO: William Clapp, M.D., Chief of Medical Staff
CIO: Randy McCleese, Chief Information Officer
CHR: Ty Kahle, Assistant Vice President Human Resources
CNO: Peggy F Creighton, R.N., Director of Nursing
Web address: www.methodisthospital.net
Control: Church operated, Nongovernment, not–for–profit **Service**: General medical and surgical

Staffed Beds: 25 **Admissions:** 594 **Census:** 13 **Outpatient Visits:** 24223 **Births:** 0 **Total Expense ($000):** 15991 **Payroll Expense ($000):** 5945 **Personnel:** 127

MOUNT STERLING—Montgomery County

⊞ **SAINT JOSEPH MOUNT STERLING (180064)**, 225 Falcon Drive, Zip 40353–1158, Mailing Address: P.O. Box 7, Zip 40353–0007; tel. 859/497–5000, **A**1 10 **F**3 13 15 17 28 29 34 35 40 45 46 57 59 64 68 70 74 75 76 77 78 79 81 86 87 93 97 107 114 119 129 130 132 133 135 146 147 148 156 **S** CommonSpirit Health, Chicago, IL
Primary Contact: Terrence G. Deis, CPA, FACHE, President
CFO: Amanda Kinman, Director of Finance
CMO: Jeff McGinnis, M.D., President Medical Staff
CIO: Jeff Ryder, Director Information Systems
CHR: Annette Saadat, Human Resources Business Partner
CNO: Cinda Fluke, R.N., Chief Nursing Officer
Web address: www.sjhlex.org
Control: Other not–for–profit (including NFP Corporation) **Service**: General medical and surgical

Staffed Beds: 42 **Admissions:** 1632 **Census:** 18 **Outpatient Visits:** 75038 **Births:** 235 **Total Expense ($000):** 46914 **Payroll Expense ($000):** 11853 **Personnel:** 235

MOUNT VERNON—Rockcastle County

⊞ **ROCKCASTLE REGIONAL HOSPITAL AND RESPIRATORY CARE CENTER (180115)**, 145 Newcomb Avenue, Zip 40456–2728, Mailing Address: P.O. Box 1310, Zip 40456–1310; tel. 606/256–2195, (Nonreporting) **A**1 10
Primary Contact: Stephen A. Estes, Chief Executive Officer
CFO: Charles Black Jr Chief Financial Officer
CMO: Jon A Arvin, M.D., Chief Medical Officer
CIO: Maleigha Amyx, Chief Information Officer
CHR: Carmen Poynter, Director Human Resources
CNO: Tammy Brock, MSN, R.N., Chief Nursing Officer
Web address: www.rockcastleregional.org
Control: Other not–for–profit (including NFP Corporation) **Service**: General medical and surgical

Staffed Beds: 105

MURRAY—Calloway County

⊞ **MURRAY-CALLOWAY COUNTY HOSPITAL (180027)**, 803 Poplar Street, Zip 42071–2432; tel. 270/762–1100, (Total facility includes 150 beds in nursing home–type unit) **A**1 2 10 19 **F**3 7 11 12 13 14 15 18 20 28 29 30 31 34 35 40 45 47 49 50 51 53 57 59 62 63 66 68 70 74 75 76 77 78 79 81 82 84 85 87 90 92 93 94 98 103 104 107 108 111 114 115 119 121 127 128 129 130 131 132 135 141 146 147 148
Primary Contact: Colonel Jerome Penner, Chief Executive Officer
COO: John R Wilson, Chief Operating Officer
CFO: John Bradford, Chief Financial Officer
CIO: Brian Benedict, Director of Information Technology
CHR: John R Wilson, Vice President, Human Resources
CNO: Jeffrey L Eye, R.N., Vice President Patient Care Services
Web address: www.murrayhospital.org
Control: City–county, Government, nonfederal **Service**: General medical and surgical

Staffed Beds: 259 **Admissions:** 4880 **Census:** 193

OWENSBORO—Daviess County

⊞ △ **OWENSBORO HEALTH REGIONAL HOSPITAL (180038)**, 1201 Pleasant Valley Road, Zip 42303; tel. 270/417–2000, (Includes HEALTHPARK, 1006 Ford Avenue, Owensboro, Kentucky, Zip 42301, Mailing Address: P O Box 2839, Zip 42302, tel. 270/688–5433) (Total facility includes 30 beds in nursing home–type unit) **A**1 2 3 5 7 10 **F**3 5 11 13 15 17 18 20 22 24 26 28 29 30 31 32 34 35 40 43 44 45 46 49 53 54 56 57 58 59 61 62 64 65 66 70 72 74 75 76 77 78 79 81 82 83 84 85 86 87 89 90 91 92 93 97 98 100 101 102 103 104 105 107 108 110 111 114 115 116 117 118 119 120 121 123 124 126 127 128 129 130 131 132 135 144 145 146 147 148 149 153 156 **S** Owensboro Health, Owensboro, KY
Primary Contact: Greg Strahan, Interim Chief Executive Officer
COO: Greg Strahan, Chief Operating Officer
CFO: John Hackbarth, CPA, Senior Vice President Finance and Chief Financial Officer
CMO: Wathen Medley, M.D., Chief Medical Officer
CIO: Michael Elley, Chief Information Officer
CHR: Mia Suter, Chief Administration Officer
CNO: Vicki Stogsdill, R.N., MSN, Chief Nursing Officer
Web address: www.owensborohealth.org
Control: Other not–for–profit (including NFP Corporation) **Service**: General medical and surgical

Staffed Beds: 360 **Admissions:** 15899 **Census:** 206 **Outpatient Visits:** 1048408 **Births:** 2060 **Total Expense ($000):** 451198 **Payroll Expense ($000):** 154519 **Personnel:** 2265

RIVERVALLEY BEHAVIORAL HEALTH HOSPITAL (184013), 1000 Industrial Drive, Zip 42301–8715; tel. 270/689–6500, **A**10 **F**29 34 35 38 40 41 50 58 59 64 68 86 98 99 100 101 102 104 130 132
Primary Contact: Wanda Figuerora Peralta, President and Chief Executive Officer
COO: Michelle Parks, Administrator
CFO: J Michael Mountain, Chief Financial Officer
CMO: David Harmon, D.O., Vice President Medical Services
CIO: Travis Taggart, Director Information Technology
CHR: Cathryn H Gaddis, Director Human Resources
Web address: www.rvbh.com
Control: Other not–for–profit (including NFP Corporation) **Service**: Children's hospital psychiatric

Staffed Beds: 80 Admissions: 896 Census: 31 Outpatient Visits: 1439
Births: 0 Total Expense ($000): 7356 Payroll Expense ($000): 3259
Personnel: 83

PADUCAH—Mccracken County

⊞ **BAPTIST HEALTH PADUCAH (180104)**, 2501 Kentucky Avenue, Zip 42003–3200; tel. 270/575–2100, **A**1 2 10 19 **F**3 11 12 13 15 17 18 20 22 24 26 28 29 30 31 32 34 35 40 45 46 48 50 51 57 58 59 64 68 70 72 73 74 75 76 77 78 79 81 82 84 85 86 87 89 91 92 93 96 107 108 109 110 111 112 113 114 115 116 117 118 119 120 121 124 126 129 130 131 132 134 135 145 146 147 148 149 154 156 157 **S** Baptist Health, Louisville, KY
Primary Contact: Christopher Roty, President
COO: Bonnie W Schrock, FACHE, Chief Operating Officer
CMO: Bradley W. Housman, M.D., Chief Medical Officer
CIO: Jay Orazine, Director Information Services
CNO: Sharon Freyer, R.N., Chief Nursing Officer
Web address: www.baptisthealthpaducah.com
Control: Other not–for–profit (including NFP Corporation) **Service**: General medical and surgical

Staffed Beds: 292 Admissions: 9837 Census: 116 Outpatient
Visits: 167827 Births: 1181 Total Expense ($000): 244223 Payroll
Expense ($000): 73707 Personnel: 1316

★ **CONTINUECARE HOSPITAL AT BAPTIST HEALTH PADUCAH (180153)**, 2501 Kentucky Avenue, 5th Floor, Zip 42003–3813; tel. 270/575–2598, **A**10 22 **F**1 3 29 34 35 148 154 **S** Community Hospital Corporation, Plano, TX
Primary Contact: Mary Lou Young, Acting Administrator
CNO: Mary Lou Young, Chief Nursing Officer
Web address: www.continuecare.org/paducah//
Control: Other not–for–profit (including NFP Corporation) **Service**: Acute long–term care hospital

Staffed Beds: 37 Admissions: 232 Census: 16 Outpatient Visits: 0
Births: 0 Total Expense ($000): 8240 Payroll Expense ($000): 3680
Personnel: 47

☐ △ **LOURDES HOSPITAL (180102)**, 1530 Lone Oak Road, Zip 42003–7900, Mailing Address: P.O. Box 7100, Zip 42002–7100; tel. 270/444–2444, (Nonreporting) **A**1 7 10 19 **S** Mercy Health, Cincinnati, OH
Primary Contact: Michael Yungmann, President and Chief Executive Officer
CHR: Kim Lindsey, Chief Human Resources Officer
Web address: www.lourdes-pad.org
Control: Church operated **Service**: General medical and surgical

Staffed Beds: 281

PAINTSVILLE—Johnson County

⊞ **PAUL B. HALL REGIONAL MEDICAL CENTER (180078)**, 625 James S. Trimble Boulevard, Zip 41240–0000; tel. 606/789–3511, (Nonreporting) **A**1 10 **S** Quorum Health, Brentwood, TN
Primary Contact: Deborah Trimble, R.N., Chief Executive Officer
CFO: Pattie Major, Chief Financial Officer
CMO: F K Belhasen, M.D., Medical Director
CHR: Carla J. Stapleton, Director Human Resources
Web address: www.pbhrmc.com
Control: Corporation, Investor–owned (for–profit) **Service**: General medical and surgical

Staffed Beds: 72

PARIS—Bourbon County

⊞ **BOURBON COMMUNITY HOSPITAL (180046)**, 9 Linville Drive, Zip 40361–2196; tel. 859/987–3600, **A**1 10 **F**3 4 15 28 29 30 34 35 38 39 40 45 49 50 56 57 59 61 63 64 65 68 70 71 75 77 79 81 82 85 87 93 94 97 98 99 100 101 102 103 104 105 107 108 110 111 114 117 119 120 127 129 130 131 132 133 135 146 149 150 151 152 154 156 157 **S** LifePoint Health, Brentwood, TN
Primary Contact: Matt Smith, Interim Chief Executive Officer
CFO: Michael Snedegar, Chief Financial Officer
CMO: C. Ray Young, M.D., Chief Medical Officer
CIO: Phil Osborne, Director Information Technology
CHR: Roger K Davis, Director Human Resources
Web address: www.bourbonhospital.com
Control: Corporation, Investor–owned (for–profit) **Service**: General medical and surgical

Staffed Beds: 58 Admissions: 2000 Census: 66 Outpatient Visits: 15000
Births: 0

PIKEVILLE—Pike County

☐ **PIKEVILLE MEDICAL CENTER (180044)**, 911 Bypass Road, Zip 41501–1689; tel. 606/218–3500, **A**1 2 3 10 **F**3 11 12 13 15 18 20 22 24 26 28 29 30 31 32 34 35 39 40 43 45 49 50 51 55 57 59 60 61 62 64 65 66 68 69 70 72 74 75 76 77 78 79 81 82 84 85 86 87 89 90 93 95 96 97 107 108 110 111 115 116 117 118 119 121 123 124 126 127 129 130 131 132 135 146 147 148 154 156
Primary Contact: Donovan Blackburn, Chief Executive Officer
COO: Kansas Justice, Senior Vice President and Chief Operating Officer
CFO: Michelle Hagy, Senior Vice President and Chief Financial Officer
CMO: Aaron Crum, M.D., Senior Vice President, Assistant Chief Executive Officer and Chief Medical Officer
CIO: Tony Damron, Senior Vice President and Chief Information Officer
CNO: Michelle L. Rainey, Senior Vice President and Chief Nursing Officer
Web address: www.pikevillehospital.org
Control: Other not–for–profit (including NFP Corporation) **Service**: General medical and surgical

Staffed Beds: 328 Admissions: 14944 Census: 250 Outpatient
Visits: 478817 Births: 1054 Total Expense ($000): 537909 Payroll
Expense ($000): 223606 Personnel: 2769

PINEVILLE—Bell County

SOUTHEASTERN KENTUCKY MEDICAL CENTER (180021), 850 Riverview Avenue, Zip 40977–1452; tel. 606/337–3051, (Nonreporting) **A**10
Primary Contact: Grant White, Chief Executive Officer
CFO: Colan Kelly, Chief Financial Officer
CMO: Michael Peterson, M.D., Chief of Staff
CIO: David Hall, Chief Information Officer
CHR: Josh Collett, Director Human Resources
CNO: Dinah Jarvis, Director of Nursing
Web address: www.southeasternkyhealth.com
Control: Other not–for–profit (including NFP Corporation) **Service**: General medical and surgical

Staffed Beds: 150

PRESTONSBURG—Floyd County

★ ⇑ **HIGHLANDS ARH REGIONAL MEDICAL CENTER (180005)**, 5000 Kentucky Route 321, Zip 41653–1273, Mailing Address: P.O. Box 668, Zip 41653–0668; tel. 606/886–8511, (Nonreporting) **A**2 10 19 21 **S** Appalachian Regional Healthcare, Inc., Lexington, KY
Primary Contact: Trena F. Hall, Interim Chief Executive Officer
COO: Chris Hoffman, Chief Operating Officer
CFO: Jack Blackwell, Chief Financial Officer
CIO: Michael Roberts, Chief Information Officer
CHR: Susan Renee' Ellis, R.N., MSN, Vice President of Patient Care Service
CNO: Terresa O. Booher, Vice President of Patient Care Services
Web address: www.hrmc.org
Control: Other not–for–profit (including NFP Corporation) **Service**: General medical and surgical

Staffed Beds: 139

Hospital, Medicare Provider Number, Address, Telephone, Approval, Facility, and Physician Codes, Health Care System

★ American Hospital Association (AHA) membership
☐ The Joint Commission accreditation
○ Healthcare Facilities Accreditation Program
◇ DNV Healthcare Inc. accreditation
⇑ Center for Improvement in Healthcare Quality Accreditation
△ Commission on Accreditation of Rehabilitation Facilities (CARF) accreditation

PRINCETON—Caldwell County

☒ **CALDWELL MEDICAL CENTER (181322)**, 100 Medical Center Drive, Zip 42445–2430, Mailing Address: P.O. Box 410, Zip 42445–0410; tel. 270/365–0300, (Nonreporting) **A**1 10 18 **S** QHR, Brentwood, TN
Primary Contact: Daniel Odegaard, FACHE, Chief Executive Officer
CFO: Shane Whittington, Chief Financial Officer
CHR: Rhonda Burns, Director Human Resources
CNO: Douglas James, Chief Nursing Officer
Web address: www.caldwellhosp.org
Control: Other not–for–profit (including NFP Corporation) **Service:** General medical and surgical

Staffed Beds: 25

RADCLIFF—Hardin County

☐ **LINCOLN TRAIL BEHAVIORAL HEALTH SYSTEM (184012)**, 3909 South Wilson Road, Zip 40160–8944, Mailing Address: P.O. Box 369, Zip 40159–0369; tel. 270/351–9444, (Nonreporting) **A**1 10 **S** Universal Health Services, Inc., King of Prussia, PA
Primary Contact: Charles L. Webb Jr, Chief Executive Officer
CFO: Debbie Ditto, CPA, Controller
CMO: Muhammad W. Sajid, M.D., Medical Director
CHR: Charlotte C Davis, Director Human Resources
Web address: www.lincolnbehavioral.com
Control: Corporation, Investor–owned (for–profit) **Service:** Psychiatric

Staffed Beds: 140

RICHMOND—Madison County

★ ○ **BAPTIST HEALTH RICHMOND (180049)**, 801 Eastern Bypass, Zip 40475–2405, Mailing Address: P.O. Box 1600, Zip 40476–2603; tel. 859/623–3131, **A**10 11 19 **F**3 11 12 15 18 20 22 28 29 30 31 34 35 40 45 49 50 51 54 59 68 70 74 75 77 78 79 81 85 87 92 107 108 110 111 114 115 118 119 129 130 132 135 146 147 148 156 **S** Baptist Health, Louisville, KY
Primary Contact: Greg Donavan. Gerard, President
CMO: Richard Shelton, M.D., Chief Medical Officer
CIO: Kelly Bonzo, Director
CHR: Joy M Benedict, Director Human Resources
CNO: Melinda Lee Blair, Vice President and Chief Nursing Officer
Web address: www.baptisthealthrichmond.com
Control: Other not–for–profit (including NFP Corporation) **Service:** General medical and surgical

Staffed Beds: 58 Admissions: 2976 Census: 31 Outpatient Visits: 80655 Births: 518 Total Expense ($000): 93881 Payroll Expense ($000): 27665 Personnel: 480

RUSSELL SPRINGS—Russell County

★ **RUSSELL COUNTY HOSPITAL (181330)**, 153 Dowell Road, Zip 42642–4579, Mailing Address: P.O. Box 1610, Zip 42642–1610; tel. 270/866–4141, **A**10 18 **F**3 15 28 29 30 34 40 45 57 59 64 70 81 85 91 93 107 111 118 119 127 129 130 133 135 146 147 148
Primary Contact: Scott Thompson, Chief Executive Officer
CFO: Janie Landis, Chief Financial Officer
CMO: Jerry D. Westerfield, M.D., Chief of Medical Staff
CIO: Monte Monsanto, Chief Information Officer
CHR: Jennifer Goode, Director Human Resources
CNO: Judy Chenoweth, Chief Nursing Officer
Web address: www.russellcohospital.org
Control: Hospital district or authority, Government, nonfederal **Service:** General medical and surgical

Staffed Beds: 25 Admissions: 519 Census: 9 Outpatient Visits: 22677 Births: 0 Total Expense ($000): 23602 Payroll Expense ($000): 11580 Personnel: 208

RUSSELLVILLE—Logan County

☒ **LOGAN MEMORIAL HOSPITAL (180066)**, 1625 South Nashville Road, Zip 42276–8834, Mailing Address: P.O. Box 10, Zip 42276–0010; tel. 270/726–4011, **A**1 10 **F**3 15 28 29 30 34 40 45 50 51 64 70 75 79 81 87 93 107 108 110 111 114 119 127 129 130 133 146 **S** LifePoint Health, Brentwood, TN
Primary Contact: James Bills, Chief Executive Officer
CFO: Tim Prestridge, Interim Chief Financial Officer
CIO: Randy Compton, Information Technology and System Director
CHR: Susan Renodin Deaton, Human Resources Director
CNO: Deborah Brown, Chief Nursing Officer
Web address: www.loganmemorial.com
Control: Corporation, Investor–owned (for–profit) **Service:** General medical and surgical

Staffed Beds: 30 Admissions: 706 Census: 8 Outpatient Visits: 27522 Births: 0 Total Expense ($000): 20332 Payroll Expense ($000): 7177 Personnel: 191

SALEM—Livingston County

LIVINGSTON HOSPITAL AND HEALTHCARE SERVICES (181320), 131 Hospital Drive, Zip 42078–8043; tel. 270/988–2299, (Nonreporting) **A**10 18
Primary Contact: Elizabeth Snodgrass, Chief Executive Officer
CMO: William Guyette, M.D., President Medical Staff
CIO: Shannan Landreth, Information Systems
CHR: Carla Wiggins, Director Human Resources
CNO: Joanna Stone, Chief Nursing Officer
Web address: www.lhhs.org
Control: Other not–for–profit (including NFP Corporation) **Service:** General medical and surgical

Staffed Beds: 25

SCOTTSVILLE—Allen County

MEDICAL CENTER AT SCOTTSVILLE (181324), 456 Burnley Road, Zip 42164–6355; tel. 270/622–2800, (Total facility includes 110 beds in nursing home–type unit) **A**10 18 **F**3 15 28 29 30 34 35 40 45 50 56 57 59 64 68 75 81 82 85 86 87 93 97 103 104 107 110 111 114 119 127 128 130 132 133 135 143 146 148 149 154 **S** Med Center Health, Bowling Green, KY
Primary Contact: Eric Hagan, R.N., Executive Vice President and Administrator
CFO: Ronald G. Sowell, FACHE, Chief Financial Officer
CIO: Mark Brookman, Chief Information Officer
CHR: Lynn Williams, Vice President Human Resources
Web address: www.themedicalcenterscottsville.org/
Control: Other not–for–profit (including NFP Corporation) **Service:** General medical and surgical

Staffed Beds: 135 Admissions: 711 Census: 127 Outpatient Visits: 23885 Births: 0 Personnel: 205

SHELBYVILLE—Shelby County

☒ **JEWISH HOSPITAL-SHELBYVILLE (180016)**, 727 Hospital Drive, Zip 40065–1699; tel. 502/647–4000, **A**1 10 **F**3 11 15 18 28 29 34 35 40 41 44 45 46 50 57 59 63 64 68 71 75 77 79 80 81 82 85 87 93 94 96 107 108 110 111 115 119 129 132 135 146 149 154 156 **S** CommonSpirit Health, Chicago, IL
Primary Contact: Annessa Baker, Site Executive and Chief Nursing Officer
CFO: Erika McGimsey, Controller
CMO: Tony Perez, M.D., President Medical Staff
CHR: Cindy Stewart Rattray, Director Human Resources
Web address: www.kentuckyonehealth.org/jewish-hospital-shelbyville
Control: Other not–for–profit (including NFP Corporation) **Service:** General medical and surgical

Staffed Beds: 30 Admissions: 641 Census: 5 Outpatient Visits: 35530 Births: 0 Total Expense ($000): 26528 Payroll Expense ($000): 8515 Personnel: 139

SOMERSET—Pulaski County

☒ **LAKE CUMBERLAND REGIONAL HOSPITAL (180132)**, 305 Langdon Street, Zip 42503–2750, Mailing Address: P.O. Box 620, Zip 42502–0620; tel. 606/679–7441, (Nonreporting) **A**1 2 3 10 13 **S** LifePoint Health, Brentwood, TN
Primary Contact: Robert Parker, Chief Executive Officer
COO: Elizabeth Jones, Chief Operating Officer
CFO: Steve Sloan, Chief Financial Officer
CMO: Michael Citak, M.D., Chief Medical Officer
CIO: Thomas Gilbert, Director Information Technology Services
CHR: James Hughes, Director Human Resources
CNO: Sheryl Glasscock, Chief Nursing Officer
Web address: www.lakecumberlandhospital.com
Control: Corporation, Investor–owned (for–profit) **Service:** General medical and surgical

Staffed Beds: 295

SOUTH WILLIAMSON—Pike County

☐ ⇑ **TUG VALLEY ARH REGIONAL MEDICAL CENTER (180069)**, 260 Hospital Drive, Zip 41503–4072; tel. 606/237–1710, (Total facility includes 35 beds in nursing home–type unit) **A**1 10 19 21 **F**3 11 13 15 29 30 34 35 40 43 50 54 57 59 60 62 64 67 70 74 75 76 77 79 81 82 85 86 87 89 93 97 107 108 110 111 115 118 119 127 128 129 130 132 146 147 154 **S** Appalachian Regional Healthcare, Inc., Lexington, KY
Primary Contact: Timothy A. Hatfield, Community Chief Executive Officer
CMO: J D Miller, M.D., Vice President Medical Affairs
CIO: Jeff Brady, Chief Information Officer
Web address: www.arh.org/locations/tug_valley/about_us.aspx
Control: Other not–for–profit (including NFP Corporation) **Service:** General medical and surgical

Staffed Beds: 123 Admissions: 2447 Census: 65 Outpatient Visits: 58714 Births: 132 Total Expense ($000): 44398 Payroll Expense ($000): 13796 Personnel: 332

Many Facility Codes have changed. Please refer to the AHA Guide Code Chart. © 2019 AHA Guide

STANFORD—Lincoln County

☐ **EPHRAIM MCDOWELL FORT LOGAN HOSPITAL (181315)**, 110 Metker Trail, Zip 40484–1020; tel. 606/365–4600, (Nonreporting) **A**1 10 18 **S** Ephraim McDowell Health, Danville, KY
Primary Contact: Ina Louise Glass, Administrator
CFO: William R Snapp III Vice President and Chief Financial Officer
CMO: James Turpin, Chief of Staff
CIO: Gary Neat, Director Information Systems
CHR: Carl Metz, Vice President
CNO: Ina Louise Glass, Administrator
Web address: www.fortloganhospital.org
Control: Other not–for–profit (including NFP Corporation) **Service:** General medical and surgical

Staffed Beds: 25

TOMPKINSVILLE—Monroe County

✠ **MONROE COUNTY MEDICAL CENTER (180105)**, 529 Capp Harlan Road, Zip 42167–1840; tel. 270/487–9231, (Nonreporting) **A**1 10 20
Primary Contact: Vicky McFall, Chief Executive Officer
CFO: Rickie F Brown, Chief Financial Officer
CIO: Paul McKiddy, Director Information Technology
CHR: Sue Page, Director Human Resources
Web address: www.mcmccares.com
Control: Other not–for–profit (including NFP Corporation) **Service:** General medical and surgical

Staffed Beds: 49

VERSAILLES—Woodford County

★ **BLUEGRASS COMMUNITY HOSPITAL (181308)**, 360 Amsden Avenue, Zip 40383–1286; tel. 859/873–3111, (Nonreporting) **A**10 18 **S** LifePoint Health, Brentwood, TN
Primary Contact: Tommy Haggard, Chief Executive Officer
CFO: Shellie Shouse, Chief Financial Officer
CMO: Michele Welling, M.D., Chief of Staff
CHR: Marcia Carter, Director Human Resources
CNO: Kathy Russell, R.N., Chief Nursing Officer
Web address: www.bluegrasscommunityhospital.com
Control: Other not–for–profit (including NFP Corporation) **Service:** General medical and surgical

Staffed Beds: 17

WEST LIBERTY—Morgan County

⇑ **MORGAN COUNTY ARH HOSPITAL (181307)**, 476 Liberty Road, Zip 41472–2049, Mailing Address: P O Box 579, Zip 41472–0579; tel. 606/743–3186, **A**10 18 21 **F**11 15 28 29 30 34 35 40 43 50 56 57 59 62 64 75 82 85 86 87 93 107 110 115 119 129 130 132 133 146 148 154 **S** Appalachian Regional Healthcare, Inc., Lexington, KY
Primary Contact: Stephen M. Gavalchik, FACHE, Community Chief Executive Officer
COO: Paul V Miles, Chief Operating Officer
CMO: J D Miller, M.D., Vice President Medical Affairs
CIO: Jeff Brady, Director Information Systems
CHR: Lisa Redding, Manager Human Resources
Web address: www.arh.org
Control: Other not–for–profit (including NFP Corporation) **Service:** General medical and surgical

Staffed Beds: 25 **Admissions:** 130 **Census:** 2 **Outpatient Visits:** 27460 **Births:** 0 **Total Expense ($000):** 14129 **Payroll Expense ($000):** 4237 **Personnel:** 114

WHITESBURG—Letcher County

⇑ **WHITESBURG ARH HOSPITAL (180002)**, 240 Hospital Road, Zip 41858–7627; tel. 606/633–3500, **A**10 20 21 **F**3 11 13 15 18 20 28 29 30 31 32 34 35 40 43 50 54 57 59 62 64 70 75 76 77 81 82 85 86 87 89 93 97 107 108 110 111 115 118 119 127 129 130 133 146 147 154 **S** Appalachian Regional Healthcare, Inc., Lexington, KY
Primary Contact: Dena C. Sparkman, Community Chief Executive Officer
COO: Paul V Miles, Vice President Administration
CMO: Ricky M Collins, M.D., Chief of Staff
CIO: Brent Styer, Director Information Technology
CHR: Daniel Fitzpatrick, Director Human Resources
Web address: www.arh.org/whitesburg
Control: Other not–for–profit (including NFP Corporation) **Service:** General medical and surgical

Staffed Beds: 89 **Admissions:** 3442 **Census:** 43 **Outpatient Visits:** 58499 **Births:** 473 **Total Expense ($000):** 44252 **Payroll Expense ($000):** 13851 **Personnel:** 314

WILLIAMSTOWN—Grant County

ST. ELIZABETH GRANT (181311), 238 Barnes Road, Zip 41097–9482; tel. 859/824–8240, **A**10 18 **F**3 11 15 18 26 28 29 30 31 34 35 38 40 44 45 50 53 57 59 63 64 65 74 75 78 79 84 93 97 107 108 110 111 115 119 128 129 130 131 132 133 135 141 146 148 149 152 153 154 **S** St. Elizabeth Healthcare, Edgewood, KY
Primary Contact: Garren Colvin, Chief Executive Officer
Web address: www.stelizabeth.com
Control: Church operated, Nongovernment, not–for–profit **Service:** General medical and surgical

Staffed Beds: 24 **Admissions:** 205 **Census:** 2 **Outpatient Visits:** 56114 **Births:** 0 **Total Expense ($000):** 25599 **Payroll Expense ($000):** 8783 **Personnel:** 98

ST. ELIZABETH MEDICAL CENTER-GRANT COUNTY See St. Elizabeth Grant

WINCHESTER—Clark County

✠ **CLARK REGIONAL MEDICAL CENTER (180092)**, 175 Hospital Drive, Zip 40391–9591; tel. 859/745–3500, (Nonreporting) **A**1 10 **S** LifePoint Health, Brentwood, TN
Primary Contact: Aphreikah DuHaney-West, Chief Executive Officer
CFO: Amber Goodpaster, Chief Financial Officer
CMO: Ben McQuaide, M.D., Chief of Staff
CHR: Deidre Bradley, Vice President Human Resources
CNO: Barbara Kinder, R.N., Chief Clinical Officer
Web address: www.clarkregional.org
Control: Corporation, Investor–owned (for–profit) **Service:** General medical and surgical

Staffed Beds: 79

Hospital, Medicare Provider Number, Address, Telephone, Approval, Facility, and Physician Codes, Health Care System

★ American Hospital Association (AHA) membership ○ Healthcare Facilities Accreditation Program ⇑ Center for Improvement in Healthcare Quality Accreditation
☐ The Joint Commission accreditation ◇ DNV Healthcare Inc. accreditation △ Commission on Accreditation of Rehabilitation Facilities (CARF) accreditation

LA

LOUISIANA

ABBEVILLE—Vermilion Parish

⊞ **ABBEVILLE GENERAL HOSPITAL (190034)**, 118 North Hospital Drive, Zip 70510–4077, Mailing Address: P.O. Box 580, Zip 70511–0580; tel. 337/893–5466, **A**1 10 **F**3 11 13 15 29 30 31 34 40 45 50 54 59 60 64 66 68 70 75 76 79 81 82 85 86 87 89 97 98 103 105 107 108 114 119 127 128 130 133 144 146 149 153 156
Primary Contact: Ray A. Landry, FACHE, Chief Executive Officer
COO: Charles W Guidry, Chief Operating Officer
CFO: Troy Hair, Chief Financial Officer
CMO: Weston Miller, M.D., Chief Medical Officer
CIO: Kelly Hair, Director Information Systems and Data Analytics
CNO: Heidi Broussard, Chief Nursing Officer
Web address: www.abbgen.net
Control: Hospital district or authority, Government, nonfederal **Service**: General medical and surgical

Staffed Beds: 60 **Admissions**: 1753 **Census**: 28 **Outpatient Visits**: 103462 **Births**: 224 **Total Expense ($000)**: 51853 **Payroll Expense ($000)**: 24630 **Personnel**: 416

ALEXANDRIA—Rapides Parish

⇑ **CENTRAL LOUISIANA SURGICAL HOSPITAL (190298)**, 651 North Bolton Avenue, Zip 71301–7449, Mailing Address: P.O. Box 8646, Zip 71306–1646; tel. 318/443–3511, (Nonreporting) **A**10 21
Primary Contact: Louise Barker, R.N., Chief Executive Officer
CFO: Michael Fuselier, FACHE, CPA, R.N., Chief Financial Officer
CMO: Renick Webb, M.D., Chief Medical Director
CHR: Debbie Norman, Director Human Resources
CNO: Carol Wells, R.N., MSN, Chief Nursing Officer
Web address: www.clshospital.com
Control: Corporation, Investor–owned (for–profit) **Service**: Surgical

Staffed Beds: 24

☐ **CHRISTUS DUBUIS HOSPITAL OF ALEXANDRIA (192012)**, 3330 Masonic Drive, 4th Floor, Zip 71301–3841; tel. 318/448–4938, (Nonreporting) **A**1 10 **S** LHC Group, Lafayette, LA
Primary Contact: Beth Parsons, R.N., Administrator
CNO: Kimberly Bennett, R.N., Director of Nursing
Web address: www.christusdubuis.org/CHRISTUSDubuisHospitalofAlexandriaLA
Service: Acute long–term care hospital

Staffed Beds: 25

⊞ **CHRISTUS ST. FRANCES CABRINI HOSPITAL (190019)**, 3330 Masonic Drive, Zip 71301–3899; tel. 318/487–1122, **A**1 2 10 **F**3 11 12 13 15 18 20 22 24 26 28 29 30 31 34 35 40 45 46 49 57 58 59 64 66 70 72 74 75 76 78 79 81 82 84 85 86 87 89 90 91 93 98 102 104 105 107 108 111 114 115 116 117 118 119 120 121 124 126 129 130 131 132 135 144 146 147 148 149 156 **S** CHRISTUS Health, Irving, TX
Primary Contact: Chris Karam, FACHE, President and Chief Executive Officer, Senior Vice President Group Operations
COO: Lisa R. Lauve, R.N., Regional Chief Nursing Executive and Chief Operating Officer
CFO: Gary Karg, Interim Vice President Finance
CHR: Wendy Chandler, Regional Vice President Human Resources
Web address: www.cabrini.org/
Control: Church operated, Nongovernment, not–for–profit **Service**: General medical and surgical

Staffed Beds: 293 **Admissions**: 12203 **Census**: 183 **Outpatient Visits**: 235420 **Births**: 1195 **Total Expense ($000)**: 241772 **Payroll Expense ($000)**: 77362 **Personnel**: 1243

☐ **COMPASS BEHAVIORAL CENTER OF ALEXANDRIA (194106)**, 6410 Masonic Drve, Zip 71301–2319; tel. 318/442–3163, (Nonreporting) **A**1 10 **S** Compass Health, Crowley, LA
Primary Contact: William Lancaster, Administrator
CNO: Cheryl Lachney, Director of Nursing
Web address: www.https://www.compasshealthcare.com
Control: Other not–for–profit (including NFP Corporation) **Service**: Psychiatric

Staffed Beds: 16

★ **ENCOMPASS HEALTH REHABILITATION HOSPITAL OF ALEXANDRIA (193031)**, 104 North Third Street, Zip 71301–8581; tel. 318/449–1370, (Nonreporting) **A**10 **S** Encompass Health Corporation, Birmingham, AL
Primary Contact: David Goodson, Chief Executive Officer
CFO: Linda Wright, Chief Financial Officer
CMO: Vasudeva Dhulipala, M.D., Medical Director
CHR: Suzie Wagner, Director Human Resources
Web address: www.healthsouthalexandria.com
Control: Partnership, Investor–owned (for–profit) **Service**: Rehabilitation

Staffed Beds: 47

☐ **LONGLEAF HOSPITAL (194022)**, 44 Versailles Boulevard, Zip 71303–3960; tel. 318/445–5111, **A**1 10 **F**4 5 29 34 35 38 68 98 100 101 102 103 104 105 130 132 151 152 153 **S** Acadia Healthcare Company, Inc., Franklin, TN
Primary Contact: Claire Hick, Chief Executive Officer
CFO: John Montanio, Chief Financial Officer
Web address: www.longleafhospital.com/
Control: Corporation, Investor–owned (for–profit) **Service**: Psychiatric

Staffed Beds: 92 **Admissions**: 3419 **Census**: 84 **Births**: 0

☐ **OCEANS BEHAVIORAL HOSPITAL OF ALEXANDRIA (194096)**, 2621 North Bolton Avenue, Zip 71303–4506; tel. 318/448–8473, (Nonreporting) **A**1 10 **S** Oceans Healthcare, Lake Charles, LA
Primary Contact: Ben Cooper, Administrator
Web address: www.obha.info/
Control: Corporation, Investor–owned (for–profit) **Service**: Psychiatric

Staffed Beds: 24

⊞ **RAPIDES REGIONAL MEDICAL CENTER (190026)**, 211 4th ST, Zip 71301–8421, Mailing Address: 211 Fourth Street, Zip 71301–8421; tel. 318/769–3000, **A**1 2 3 5 10 **F**3 11 13 15 17 18 19 20 22 24 26 28 29 30 31 32 34 35 36 38 40 41 43 44 45 46 47 48 49 50 51 52 54 55 57 59 60 61 64 65 66 68 70 72 74 75 76 77 78 79 81 82 84 85 86 87 88 89 97 107 108 110 111 114 115 118 119 120 121 123 124 126 129 130 131 132 135 144 146 147 148 149 154 156 157 **S** HCA Healthcare, Nashville, TN
Primary Contact: Jason E. Cobb, FACHE, Chief Executive Officer
COO: Cindy Bergmeier, Chief Operating Officer
CFO: Nathan Crabdree, Chief Financial Officer
CMO: David Rhodes, M.D., Senior Vice President Medical Affairs and Chief Medical Officer
CHR: Stephen W Scull, Vice President Ethics and Compliance officer
CNO: Barbara J Griffin, MSN, R.N., Chief Nursing Officer
Web address: www.rapidesregional.com
Control: Partnership, Investor–owned (for–profit) **Service**: General medical and surgical

Staffed Beds: 357 **Admissions**: 15109 **Census**: 228 **Outpatient Visits**: 217748 **Births**: 1759 **Total Expense ($000)**: 238688 **Payroll Expense ($000)**: 84239 **Personnel**: 1422

☐ **RIVERSIDE HOSPITAL OF LOUISIANA (192043)**, 13 Heyman Lane, Zip 71303–3574; tel. 318/767–2900, (Nonreporting) **A**1 10
Primary Contact: Wade K. Lester, Chief Executive Officer
Web address: www.riversidehospital.net
Control: Corporation, Investor–owned (for–profit) **Service**: Acute long–term care hospital

Staffed Beds: 27

AMITE—Tangipahoa Parish

★ **HOOD MEMORIAL HOSPITAL (191309)**, 301 Walnut Street, Zip 70422–2098; tel. 985/748–9485, (Nonreporting) **A**10 18
Primary Contact: Michael Whittington, R.N., Chief Executive Officer and Administrator
CFO: Mike Estay, Chief Financial Officer
CMO: Richard Bridges, M.D., Chief of Staff
CIO: Schley Harvin, Information Technology Technician
CHR: Alicia Chatelain, Director Human Resource
CNO: Todd Acosta, R.N., Chief Nursing Officer
Web address: www.hoodmemorial.com
Control: Hospital district or authority, Government, nonfederal **Service**: General medical and surgical

Staffed Beds: 25

Many Facility Codes have changed. Please refer to the AHA Guide Code Chart. © 2019 AHA Guide

ARCADIA—Bienville Parish

BIENVILLE MEDICAL CENTER (191320), 1175 Pine Street, Suite 200, Zip 71001-3122; tel. 318/263-4700, (Nonreporting) **A**10 18 **S** Allegiance Health Management, Shreveport, LA
Primary Contact: Kirk Lemoine, Chief Executive Officer
Web address: www.bienvillemedicalcenter.net/
Control: Other not-for-profit (including NFP Corporation) **Service:** General medical and surgical

Staffed Beds: 21

BASTROP—Morehouse Parish

☐ **CYPRESS GROVE BEHAVIORAL HEALTH (194083)**, 4673 Eugene Ware Boulevard, Zip 71220-1425; tel. 318/281-2448, (Nonreporting) **A**1 10
Primary Contact: Venicea Austin. Preston, Administrator
COO: Christine Murphy, MS, Chief Operating Officer
CFO: Paul Coburn, Chief Financial Officer
CMO: Tommy Dansby, Chief Medical Officer
CHR: Lindsay Cobb, Director Human Resources
CNO: Carla Sams, R.N., Director of Nursing
Web address: www.libertybh.com/
Control: Corporation, Investor-owned (for-profit) **Service:** Psychiatric

Staffed Beds: 60

★ **MOREHOUSE GENERAL HOSPITAL (190116)**, 323 West Walnut Avenue, Zip 71220-4521, Mailing Address: P.O. Box 1060, Zip 71221-1060; tel. 318/283-3600, (Nonreporting) **A**3 10 **S** Community Hospital Corporation, Plano, TX
Primary Contact: Derrick A. Frazier, FACHE, Chief Executive Officer
CFO: Tom Ramsey, Chief Financial Officer
CMO: John Coats, M.D., Chief Medical Staff
CIO: B J Vail, Director Information Systems
CHR: Debbie Spann, Director Human Resources
CNO: Melinda Jones, R.N., Chief Nursing Officer
Web address: www.mghospital.com
Control: Hospital district or authority, Government, nonfederal **Service:** General medical and surgical

Staffed Beds: 49

STERLINGTON REHABILITATION HOSPITAL (193069), 370 W Hickory Ave, Zip 71220-4442, Mailing Address: P.O. Box 627, Sterlington, Zip 71280-0627; tel. 318/665-9950, **A**10 **F**28 34 35 56 59 64 65 66 75 86 90 91 93 96 97 104 127 130 143 147 148 153 154
Primary Contact: Catherine M, Waldrop, Administrator
Web address: www.https://sterlingtonrehab.com/
Control: Corporation, Investor-owned (for-profit) **Service:** Rehabilitation

Staffed Beds: 10 **Admissions:** 272 **Census:** 10 **Outpatient Visits:** 1375 **Births:** 0 **Total Expense ($000):** 15088 **Payroll Expense ($000):** 5390 **Personnel:** 50

BATON ROUGE—East Baton Rouge Parish

☐ **APOLLO BEHAVIORAL HEALTH HOSPITAL (194105)**, 9938 Airline Highway, Zip 70816-8193; tel. 225/663-2881, (Nonreporting) **A**1
Primary Contact: Gopinath Gopalam, Chief Executive Officer
Web address: www.apollo-bhh.com/about-us/
Control: Other not-for-profit (including NFP Corporation) **Service:** Psychiatric

Staffed Beds: 25

☐ **BATON ROUGE BEHAVIORAL HOSPITAL (194107)**, 4040 North Boulevard, Zip 70806-3829; tel. 225/300-8470, (Nonreporting) **A**1 10
Primary Contact: Michael Gomila, Administrator
COO: James O'Shea, Chief Operating Officer
CFO: Warren Knight, Chief Financial Officer
CMO: Richard Capiola, M.D., Chief Medical Officer
CNO: Francine Mineau, Chief Nursing Officer
Web address: www.batonrougebehavioral.com
Control: Corporation, Investor-owned (for-profit) **Service:** Psychiatric

Staffed Beds: 15

☐ **BATON ROUGE REHABILITATION HOSPITAL (193028)**, 8595 United Plaza Boulevard, Zip 70809-2251; tel. 225/927-0567, (Nonreporting) **A**1 10
Primary Contact: Trisha Guidry, Administrator
CFO: Nicholas Hluchy, Business Analyst, Support Services Manager
CMO: Sundararama R Vatsavai, M.D., Medical Director
CIO: John Derrick Landreneau, Director of Nursing and Marketing Manager
CHR: Michelle Smith, Coordinator Human Resources
CNO: John Derrick Landreneau, Director of Nursing
Web address: www.brrehab.com
Control: Corporation, Investor-owned (for-profit) **Service:** Rehabilitation

Staffed Beds: 80

⊞ **BATON ROUGE GENERAL MEDICAL CENTER (190065)**, 8585 Picardy Avenue, Zip 70809-3679; tel. 225/763-4000, (Includes BATON ROUGE GENERAL MEDICAL CENTER-BLUEBONNET, 8585 Picardy Avenue, Baton Rouge, Louisiana, Zip 70809-3679, Mailing Address: P O Box 84330, Zip 70884-4330, tel. 225/763-4000; Edgardo J Tenreiro, FACHE, Chief Executive Officer and Chief Operating Officer) **A**1 2 3 5 10 19 **F**3 8 11 12 13 15 16 18 20 22 24 28 29 30 31 34 35 38 40 44 45 46 50 53 54 56 57 58 59 60 61 64 65 68 70 72 74 75 76 77 78 79 81 82 84 86 87 89 90 91 93 96 97 98 99 100 101 102 103 104 107 108 110 111 114 115 117 118 119 120 121 123 124 126 128 129 130 131 132 135 143 144 146 147 148 153 154 155 157
Primary Contact: Edgardo J. Tenreiro, FACHE, Chief Executive Officer and Chief Operating Officer
COO: Stephen Mumford, Chief Operating Officer
CFO: Kendall Johnson, Chief Financial Officer
CIO: Bennett Cheramie, Vice President Information Technology
CHR: Paul Douglas, Vice President Human Resources
CNO: Monica Nijoka, Chief Nursing Officer
Web address: www.brgeneral.org
Control: Other not-for-profit (including NFP Corporation) **Service:** General medical and surgical

Staffed Beds: 357 **Admissions:** 16616 **Census:** 229 **Outpatient Visits:** 360851 **Births:** 986 **Total Expense ($000):** 415413 **Payroll Expense ($000):** 118566 **Personnel:** 2674

BETHESDA REHABILITATION HOSPITAL (193092), 8225 Summa Avenue, Suite B, Zip 70809-3422; tel. 225/767-2034, (Nonreporting) **A**10
Primary Contact: Lionel Murphy, Chief Executive Officer and Administrator
Web address: www.bethesdarh.com/
Control: Corporation, Investor-owned (for-profit) **Service:** Rehabilitation

Staffed Beds: 18

HEALTHSOUTH REHABILITATION HOSPITAL OF BATON ROUGE See Baton Rouge Rehabilitation Hospital

OCEANS BEHAVIORAL HOSPITAL OF BATON ROUGE (194086), 11135 Florida Boulevard, Zip 70815-2013; tel. 225/356-7030, (Nonreporting) **A**10 **S** Oceans Healthcare, Lake Charles, LA
Primary Contact: Valerie Dalton, R.N., Administrator
Web address: www.obhbr.info/
Control: Corporation, Investor-owned (for-profit) **Service:** Psychiatric

Staffed Beds: 20

⊞ **OCHSNER MEDICAL CENTER - BATON ROUGE (190202)**, 17000 Medical Center Drive, Zip 70816-3224; tel. 225/752-2470, **A**1 3 10 **F**3 11 12 13 15 18 20 22 24 26 28 29 30 31 34 35 36 40 41 42 44 45 46 47 48 49 54 57 58 59 60 64 68 70 72 74 75 76 77 78 79 81 82 85 86 87 93 97 102 104 107 108 110 111 114 116 117 119 126 129 130 131 132 135 144 146 147 148 154 **S** Ochsner Health System, New Orleans, LA
Primary Contact: Eric McMillen, FACHE, Chief Executive Officer
CFO: Stephanie Bushart, Chief Financial Officer
CMO: F Ralph Dauterive, M.D., Vice President Medical Affairs
CHR: Jan Rivers, Director Human Resources
Web address: www.ochsner.org/page.cfm?id=103
Control: Other not-for-profit (including NFP Corporation) **Service:** General medical and surgical

Staffed Beds: 152 **Admissions:** 7013 **Census:** 71 **Outpatient Visits:** 106531 **Births:** 1457 **Total Expense ($000):** 208016 **Payroll Expense ($000):** 72735 **Personnel:** 997

Hospital, Medicare Provider Number, Address, Telephone, Approval, Facility, and Physician Codes, Health Care System

★ American Hospital Association (AHA) membership
☐ The Joint Commission accreditation
○ Healthcare Facilities Accreditation Program
◇ DNV Healthcare Inc. accreditation
⇧ Center for Improvement in Healthcare Quality Accreditation
△ Commission on Accreditation of Rehabilitation Facilities (CARF) accreditation

LA

✠ **OUR LADY OF THE LAKE REGIONAL MEDICAL CENTER (190064)**, 5000 Hennessy Boulevard, Zip 70808–4375; tel. 225/765–6565, (Includes OUR LADY OF THE LAKE ASCENSION, 1125 West Highway 30, Gonzales, Louisiana, Zip 70737–5004; tel. 225/647–5000; Scott Wester, President and Chief Executive Officer; OUR LADY OF THE LAKE CHILDREN'S HOSPITAL, 5000 Hennessy Boulevard, Baton Rouge, Louisiana, Zip 70808–4375; tel. 225/765–8886; Trey Dunbar, M.D., President) (Total facility includes 390 beds in nursing home–type unit) **A**1 2 3 5 8 10 **F**3 8 9 11 12 14 15 17 18 19 20 21 22 24 26 28 29 30 31 32 34 35 37 38 39 40 41 42 43 44 45 46 47 48 49 50 51 53 54 55 56 57 58 59 60 61 64 66 68 70 71 74 75 77 78 79 81 82 83 84 85 86 87 88 89 90 91 92 93 94 95 96 97 98 99 100 101 102 103 104 105 107 108 110 111 114 115 116 117 118 119 124 125 126 127 129 130 131 132 135 141 142 143 144 145 146 147 148 149 153 154 **S** Franciscan Missionaries of Our Lady Health System, Inc., Baton Rouge, LA
Primary Contact: K Scott. Wester, FACHE, President and Chief Executive Officer
COO: Stephanie Manson, Chief Operating Officer
CFO: Jeff Limbocker, Chief Financial Officer
CMO: Richard Vath, M.D., Vice President Medical Affairs
CIO: Vindell Washington, M.D., Vice President Performance Excellence and Technology
CHR: Cora Ford, Vice President Human Resources
CNO: Nicole Telhiard, MSN, Chief Nursing Officer
Web address: www.ololrmc.com
Control: Church operated, Nongovernment, not–for–profit **Service**: General medical and surgical

Staffed Beds: 1189 **Admissions**: 38673 **Census**: 786 **Outpatient Visits**: 1810454 **Births**: 0 **Total Expense ($000)**: 1343768 **Payroll Expense ($000)**: 483140 **Personnel**: 7182

☐ **PROMISE HOSPITAL BATON ROUGE - MAIN CAMPUS (192004)**, 5130 Mancuso Lane, Zip 70809–3583; tel. 225/490–9600, **A**1 **F**1 3 29 38 56 60 65 68 75 77 82 91 94 119 143 148 149 **S** Promise Healthcare, Boca Raton, FL
Primary Contact: Kiley P. Cedotal, FACHE, Chief Executive Officer
COO: Michael R Sanders, MS, Chief Operating Officer
CFO: Trina Arceneaux, Assistant Chief Financial Officer
CMO: Subhaker Gummadi, M.D., Chief Medical Staff
CIO: Charmaine T Mosby, Area Director Health Information Management
CHR: Marilyn Hamilton, Director Human Resources
CNO: Larrie Arceneaux, Chief Clinical Officer
Web address: www.promise-batonrouge.com
Control: Corporation, Investor–owned (for–profit) **Service**: Acute long–term care hospital

Staffed Beds: 39 **Admissions**: 50 **Census**: 3 **Outpatient Visits**: 0 **Births**: 0

SAGE REHABILITATION HOSPITAL (193078), 8000 Summa Avenue, Zip 70809–3423, Mailing Address: P.O. Box 82681, Zip 70884–2681; tel. 225/819–0703, (Total facility includes 24 beds in nursing home–type unit) **A**10 **F**29 75 77 87 90 93 128 130 148 **S** The Carpenter Health Network, Baton Rouge, LA
Primary Contact: Scott McClelland, Administrator
CMO: Christopher Belleau, M.D., Medical Director
CHR: Kathy Ringe, Director Human Resources
CNO: Beth Sibley, Director of Nursing
Web address: www.sage-rehab.org
Control: Individual, Investor–owned (for–profit) **Service**: Rehabilitation

Staffed Beds: 42 **Admissions**: 694 **Census**: 30 **Outpatient Visits**: 0 **Births**: 0 **Total Expense ($000)**: 10718 **Payroll Expense ($000)**: 5386 **Personnel**: 98

☐ **SEASIDE HEALTH SYSTEM (194103)**, 4363 Convention Street, Zip 70806–3906, Mailing Address: 4363 Convention Stret, Zip 70806–3906; tel. 225/238–3043, (Nonreporting) **A**1 10
Primary Contact: Eric M. Gintoli, Administrator
Web address: www.seasidehc.com/seaside-health-system-locations/
Control: Partnership, Investor–owned (for–profit) **Service**: Psychiatric

Staffed Beds: 24

SPINE HOSPITAL OF LOUISIANA (FORMALLY THE NEUROMEDICAL CENTER SURGICAL HOSPITAL) (190266), 10105 Park Rowe Circle, Suite 250, Zip 70810–1684; tel. 225/763–9900, (Nonreporting) **A**10
Primary Contact: Robert D. Blair, Chief Executive Officer
CFO: Allison Doherty, Chief Financial Officer
CMO: Greg Fautheree, M.D., Medical Director
CIO: Jeremy Deprato, Director Information Technology
CHR: Kimberly Jones, Director Human Resources
CNO: Kim Pettijohn, R.N., MSN, Chief Nursing Officer
Web address: www.theneuromedicalcenter.com
Control: Corporation, Investor–owned (for–profit) **Service**: Surgical

Staffed Beds: 23

☐ **SURGICAL SPECIALTY CENTER OF BATON ROUGE (190251)**, 8080 Bluebonnet Boulevard, Zip 70810–7827; tel. 225/408–8080, (Nonreporting) **A**1 10
Primary Contact: Ann Heine, Chief Executive Officer
CNO: Kelli Firmin, Interim Chief Nursing Officer, Pre-Op and PACU Manager
Web address: www.sscbr.com
Control: Corporation, Investor–owned (for–profit) **Service**: Surgical

Staffed Beds: 14

THE NEUROMEDICAL CENTER REHABILITATION HOSPITAL (193090), 10101 Park Rowe Avenue, Suite 500, Zip 70810–1685; tel. 225/906–2999, (Nonreporting) **A**10 **S** AMG Integrated Healthcare Management, Lafayette, LA
Primary Contact: Sherry Mix, Chief Executive Officer and Administrator
Web address: www.theneuromedicalcenter.com
Control: Corporation, Investor–owned (for–profit) **Service**: Rehabilitation

Staffed Beds: 23

✠ **WOMAN'S HOSPITAL (190128)**, 100 Woman's Way, Zip 70817–5100, Mailing Address: P.O. Box 95009, Zip 70895–9009; tel. 225/927–1300, **A**1 2 3 5 10 **F**3 11 12 13 15 29 31 32 34 35 36 38 40 45 50 53 54 55 57 58 59 61 64 65 66 68 70 71 72 75 76 77 78 79 81 83 84 85 86 87 93 102 107 108 110 111 115 116 117 119 120 121 123 126 129 130 131 132 134 135 146 147 148 149 154 156
Primary Contact: Stephanie Anderson, Interim Chief Executive Officer
COO: Stephanie Anderson, Executive Vice President and Chief Operating Officer
CFO: Gina Dugas, Chief Financial Officer
CMO: Dore Binder, M.D., Chief Medical Officer
CIO: Paul Kirk, Vice President
CHR: Donna L Bodin, Vice President
CNO: Patricia Johnson, R.N., Senior Vice President
Web address: www.womans.org
Control: Other not–for–profit (including NFP Corporation) **Service**: Obstetrics and gynecology

Staffed Beds: 228 **Admissions**: 10963 **Census**: 138 **Outpatient Visits**: 148551 **Births**: 8097 **Total Expense ($000)**: 270615 **Payroll Expense ($000)**: 133967 **Personnel**: 1820

BERNICE—Union Parish

REEVES MEMORIAL MEDICAL CENTER (191326), 409 First Street, Zip 71222–4001, Mailing Address: P.O. Box 697, Zip 71222–0697; tel. 318/285–9066, (Nonreporting) **A**10 18
Primary Contact: Kerry D. Goff, Chief Executive Officer
COO: Beth Jones, Chief Operating Officer
CFO: Charolette Thompson, Chief Financial Officer
CMO: R Brian Harris, M.D., Chief of Staff
CIO: Scott Dickson, Director Information Technology
CHR: Robin Adams, Director Human Resources
CNO: Beth Jones, Director of Nursing
Web address: www.reevesmemorial.com/
Control: Hospital district or authority, Government, nonfederal **Service**: General medical and surgical

Staffed Beds: 11

TRI-WARD GENERAL HOSPITAL See Reeves Memorial Medical Center

BOGALUSA—Washington Parish

✠ **OUR LADY OF THE ANGELS HOSPITAL (190312)**, 433 Plaza Street, Zip 70427–3793; tel. 985/730–6700, (Includes BOGALUSA COMMUNITY MEDICAL CENTER, 433 Plaza Street, Bogalusa, Louisiana, Zip 70427–3793; tel. 985/730–6700), (Non-reporting) **A**1 3 5 10 **S** Franciscan Missionaries of Our Lady Health System, Inc., Baton Rouge, LA
Primary Contact: Rene J. Ragas, Chief Operating Officer
COO: Rene J. Ragas, Chief Operating Officer
CFO: Brooke Cummings, Chief Financial Officer
CMO: Hamid Hussain, M.D., Medical Director
CIO: Mike Gilly, Chief Information Officer
CHR: Christi Brown, Director Human Resources
CNO: Mark Kellar, R.N., Interim Chief Nursing Officer
Web address: www.oloah.org
Service: General medical and surgical

Staffed Beds: 57

Many Facility Codes have changed. Please refer to the AHA Guide Code Chart. © 2019 AHA Guide

BOSSIER CITY—Bossier Parish

☐ **CORNERSTONE HOSPITAL OF BOSSIER CITY (192006)**, 4900 Medical Drive, Zip 71112–4521; tel. 318/747–9500, (Nonreporting) **A**1 10 **S** Cornerstone Healthcare Group, Dallas, TX
Primary Contact: Sheri Burnette, R.N., Chief Executive Officer and Administrator
CMO: James Jackson, M.D., Chief of Staff
CNO: Tamara Grimm, R.N., Chief Clinical Officer and Chief Nursing Officer
Web address: www.chghospitals.com/
Control: Corporation, Investor–owned (for–profit) **Service:** Acute long–term care hospital

Staffed Beds: 54

⇑ **PATHWAY REHABILITATION HOSPITAL (193094)**, 4900 Medical Drive, Zip 71112–4521; tel. 318/841–5555, (Nonreporting) **A**10 21
Primary Contact: James Manning, Administrator
Web address: www.pathrehab.com
Control: Corporation, Investor–owned (for–profit) **Service:** Rehabilitation

Staffed Beds: 24

RED RIVER BEHAVIORAL CENTER (194079), 2800 Melrose Avenue, Zip 71111–5870; tel. 318/549–2033, **A**10 **F**29 38 56 98 100 101 103 130 135 143 154
Primary Contact: Susan Kottenbrook, Chief Executive Officer
Web address: www.redriverbc.com
Control: Partnership, Investor–owned (for–profit) **Service:** Psychiatric

Staffed Beds: 20 **Admissions:** 314 **Census:** 15 **Outpatient Visits:** 0 **Births:** 0 **Total Expense ($000):** 3570 **Payroll Expense ($000):** 1526

WILLIS-KNIGHTON BOSSIER HEALTH CENTER See Wk Bossier Health Center

BREAUX BRIDGE—St. Martin Parish

GENESIS BEHAVIORAL HOSPITAL (194089), 606 Latiolais Drive, Zip 70517–4231, Mailing Address: P.O. Box 159, Zip 70517–0159; tel. 337/442–6084, (Nonreporting) **A**10
Primary Contact: William Arledge, Administrator and Chief Financial Officer
COO: Gretchen Kaltenbach, R.N., Chief Operating Officer
CFO: William Arledge, Administrator and Chief Financial Officer
Web address: www.genesisbh.com/
Control: Corporation, Investor–owned (for–profit) **Service:** Psychiatric

Staffed Beds: 18

★ **ST. MARTIN HOSPITAL (191302)**, 210 Champagne Boulevard, Zip 70517–3700, Mailing Address: P.O. Box 357, Zip 70517–0357; tel. 337/332–2178, **A**10 18 **F**3 15 18 28 29 30 34 35 40 54 57 59 64 68 75 77 87 91 93 107 110 111 114 119 130 133 146 148 149 154 **S** Lafayette General Health, Lafayette, LA
Primary Contact: Karen O. Wyble, R.N., Chief Executive Officer
CFO: Shadelle Huval, Director Finance
CHR: Rena B Mouisset, Director Human Resources and Contract Compliance
Web address: www.stmartinhospital.org
Control: Other not–for–profit (including NFP Corporation) **Service:** General medical and surgical

Staffed Beds: 25 **Admissions:** 434 **Census:** 14 **Outpatient Visits:** 172405 **Births:** 0 **Total Expense ($000):** 19615 **Payroll Expense ($000):** 7384 **Personnel:** 132

BROUSSARD—Lafayette Parish

☐ **OCEANS BEHAVIORAL HOSPITAL OF BROUSSARD (194073)**, 418 Albertson Parkway, Zip 70518–4971; tel. 337/237–6444, (Nonreporting) **A**1 10 **S** Oceans Healthcare, Lake Charles, LA
Primary Contact: Amy Dysart-Credeur, Administrator
Web address: www.obhb.info/
Control: Corporation, Investor–owned (for–profit) **Service:** Psychiatric

Staffed Beds: 38

BUNKIE—Avoyelles Parish

BEACON BEHAVIORAL HOSPITAL (194112), 323 Evergreen Street, Zip 71322–1307; tel. 318/346–3143, (Nonreporting) **S** Beacon Health System, South Bend, IN
Primary Contact: Randall Johnson, Administrator
Web address: www.beaconbh.com
Control: Other not–for–profit (including NFP Corporation) **Service:** Psychiatric

Staffed Beds: 17

BUNKIE GENERAL HOSPITAL (191311), 427 Evergreen Highway, Zip 71322, Mailing Address: P.O. Box 380, Zip 71322–0380; tel. 318/346–6681, (Nonreporting) **A**10 18
Primary Contact: Linda F. Deville, Chief Executive Officer
CFO: Layla Chase, Interim Chief Financial Officer
CMO: Mohit Srivastava, M.D., Chief of Staff
CIO: Kiland Jackson, Chief Information Officer
CHR: Tina Louise Juneau, Director Human Resources
CNO: Corey Jeansonne, Chief Nursing Officer
Web address: www.bunkiegeneral.com
Control: Hospital district or authority, Government, nonfederal **Service:** General medical and surgical

Staffed Beds: 18

CAMERON—Cameron Parish

SOUTH CAMERON MEMORIAL HOSPITAL (190307), 5360 West Creole Highway, Zip 70631–5127; tel. 337/542–4111, (Includes CALCASIEU OAKS GERIATRIC PSYCHIATRIC HOSPITAL, 2837 Ernest Street, Lake Charles, Louisiana, Zip 70601–8785; tel. 337/439–8111; Erica Williams, Assistant Chief Executive Officer), (Non-reporting) **A**10
Primary Contact: Leslie T. Trahan, Chief Executive Officer
Control: Hospital district or authority, Government, nonfederal **Service:** General medical and surgical

Staffed Beds: 30

CHALMETTE—Saint Bernard Parish

⊠ **ST. BERNARD PARISH HOSPITAL (190308)**, 8000 West Judge Perez Drive, Zip 70043–1668; tel. 504/826–9500, **A**1 3 10 **F**3 15 18 20 22 26 29 34 35 40 44 45 50 53 57 59 64 65 70 77 79 81 82 85 86 87 93 107 108 110 111 115 119 130 135 146 148 154 156 **S** Ochsner Health System, New Orleans, LA
Primary Contact: Kimberly Keene, R.N., Chief Executive Officer
CFO: Anthony Bonnecarrere, Controller
CMO: Paul Verrette, M.D., Chief Medical Officer
CIO: Zane Looney, Chief Information Officer
CHR: Melody M O'Connell, Director Human Resources
CNO: Janice Kishner, R.N., FACHE, Chief Clinical Officer
Web address: www.sbph.net
Control: Hospital district or authority, Government, nonfederal **Service:** General medical and surgical

Staffed Beds: 40 **Admissions:** 1336 **Census:** 16 **Outpatient Visits:** 33648 **Births:** 0 **Total Expense ($000):** 41791 **Payroll Expense ($000):** 6702 **Personnel:** 269

CHURCH POINT—Acadia Parish

ACADIA-ST. LANDRY HOSPITAL (191319), 810 South Broadway Street, Zip 70525–4497; tel. 337/684–5435, (Nonreporting) **A**10 18
Primary Contact: Cindy Walters, Chief Executive Officer
CFO: Lucille LeJeune, Assistant Administrator and Chief Financial Officer
CMO: Ty Hargroder, M.D., Chief of Staff
Web address: www.aslh.org
Control: Other not–for–profit (including NFP Corporation) **Service:** General medical and surgical

Staffed Beds: 25

COLUMBIA—Caldwell Parish

CALDWELL MEMORIAL HOSPITAL (190190), 411 Main Street, Zip 71418–6704, Mailing Address: P.O. Box 899, Zip 71418–0899; tel. 318/649–6111, **A**10 **F**34 50 59 90 107 119 127 149
Primary Contact: Danielle Williams, Assistant Administrator
COO: Lisa Patrick, Chief Operating Officer
CFO: William H Clark, Chief Financial Officer
Web address: www.https://www.mycaldwellmemorial.com/
Control: Other not–for–profit (including NFP Corporation) **Service:** General medical and surgical

Staffed Beds: 47 **Admissions:** 744 **Census:** 11 **Outpatient Visits:** 0 **Births:** 0

Hospital, Medicare Provider Number, Address, Telephone, Approval, Facility, and Physician Codes, Health Care System

★ American Hospital Association (AHA) membership
☐ The Joint Commission accreditation
○ Healthcare Facilities Accreditation Program
◇ DNV Healthcare Inc. accreditation
⇑ Center for Improvement in Healthcare Quality Accreditation
△ Commission on Accreditation of Rehabilitation Facilities (CARF) accreditation

LA

CITIZENS MEDICAL CENTER (190184), 7939 U S Highway 165, Zip 71418–1079, Mailing Address: P.O. Box 1079, Zip 71418–1079; tel. 318/649–6106, (Nonreporting) **A**10
Primary Contact: Steve Barbo, R.N., Chief Executive Officer
Web address: www.citizensmedcenter.com/
Control: Hospital district or authority, Government, nonfederal **Service:** General medical and surgical

Staffed Beds: 40

COUSHATTA—Red River Parish

CHRISTUS COUSHATTA HEALTH CARE CENTER (191312), 1635 Marvel Street, Zip 71019–9022, Mailing Address: P.O. Box 589, Zip 71019–0589; tel. 318/932–2000, (Nonreporting) **A**1 10 18 **S** CHRISTUS Health, Irving, TX
Primary Contact: Brandon Hillman, R.N., Interim Administrator, Director of Hospital Services
CFO: Scott Merryman, Chief Financial Officer
CMO: Jonathan Weisul, M.D., Vice President Medical Affairs and Chief Medical Officer
CIO: Bruce Honea, Director Information Services
CHR: Donnette Craig, Director Human Resources
Web address: www.christuscoushatta.org
Service: General medical and surgical

Staffed Beds: 25

SPECIALTY REHABILITATION HOSPITAL OF COUSHATTA (193080), 1110 Ringgold Avenue Suite B, Zip 71019–9073; tel. 318/932–1770, (Nonreporting) **A**10
Primary Contact: Craig Ball, Chief Executive Officer
COO: Charlie Ball, Chief Operating Officer
CFO: Connie Ball, Chief Financial Officer
CMO: Jalal Joudeh, M.D., Chief Medical Officer
CHR: Denise Logan, Director Human Resources
Web address: www.specialtyhealthcare.com
Control: Individual, Investor–owned (for–profit) **Service:** Rehabilitation

Staffed Beds: 12

COVINGTON—St. Tammany Parish

AMG PHYSICAL REHABILITATION HOSPITAL (193097), 5025 Keystone Boulevard, Suite 200, Zip 70433; tel. 985/888–0301, (Nonreporting) **A**1 10 **S** AMG Integrated Healthcare Management, Lafayette, LA
Primary Contact: Natalie Stols, Interim Chief Executive Officer
Web address: www.amgcovingtonprh.com/
Control: Partnership, Investor–owned (for–profit) **Service:** Rehabilitation

Staffed Beds: 24

AVALA (190267), 67252 Industry Lane, Zip 70433–8704; tel. 985/809–9888, (Nonreporting) **A**10 21
Primary Contact: Scott Boudreaux, Chief Executive Officer
CFO: Denise Businelle, Chief Financial Officer
CMO: William Preau, M.D., Medical Director
CIO: Skip Federico, Director Information Systems
CHR: Pam Collins, Director Human Resources
Web address: www.fairwaymedical.com
Control: Corporation, Investor–owned (for–profit) **Service:** General medical and surgical

Staffed Beds: 21

COVINGTON BEHAVIORIAL HEALTH (194069), 201 Greenbrier Boulevard, Zip 70433–7236; tel. 985/893–2970, (Nonreporting) **A**1 10 **S** Acadia Healthcare Company, Inc., Franklin, TN
Primary Contact: Tanmay Mathur, Chief Executive Officer
CFO: Terri Logsdon, Chief Financial Officer
CMO: Jason Coe, M.D., Medical Director
Web address: www.greenbrierhospital.com/
Control: Corporation, Investor–owned (for–profit) **Service:** Psychiatric

Staffed Beds: 60

NORTHSHORE SPECIALTY HOSPITAL See Pam Specialty Hospital of Covington

PAM SPECIALTY HOSPITAL OF COVINGTON (192048), 20050 Crestwood Boulevard, Zip 70433–5207; tel. 985/875–7525, (Nonreporting) **A**1 10 **S** Post Acute Medical, LLC, Enola, PA
Primary Contact: J Cullen. Meyers, Chief Executive Officer
COO: John Bauer, Chief Operating Officer
CFO: Karick Stober, Chief Financial Officer
CMO: Adam Burick, M.D., Chief Medical Officer
CIO: Bryan Munchel, Senior Vice President and Chief Information Officer
CHR: Waynea Finley, Senior Vice President Human Resources
CNO: Marsha Medlin, Senior Vice President of Clinical and Operations
Web address: www.postacutemedical.com
Control: Corporation, Investor–owned (for–profit) **Service:** Acute long–term care hospital

Staffed Beds: 58

ST. TAMMANY PARISH HOSPITAL (190045), 1202 South Tyler Street, Zip 70433–2330; tel. 985/898–4000, **A**1 2 10 **F**3 8 11 12 13 15 17 18 20 22 24 26 28 29 30 31 34 35 37 40 41 42 44 45 46 48 49 50 54 57 59 62 63 64 65 69 70 72 74 75 76 77 78 79 81 82 84 85 86 87 89 90 92 93 96 97 107 108 109 110 111 114 115 119 124 126 129 130 132 135 146 147 148 149 154 156
Primary Contact: Joan Coffman, FACHE, President and Chief Executive Officer
COO: Sharon A Toups, Senior Vice President and Chief Operating Officer
CFO: Sandra P Dipietro, Chief Financial Officer
CMO: Robert Capitelli, M.D., Senior Vice President and Chief Medical Officer
CIO: Craig Doyle, Director and Chief Information Officer
CHR: Carolyn Adema, Vice President, Human Resources
CNO: Kerry K. Milton, R.N., Chief Nursing Officer
Web address: www.stph.org
Control: Hospital district or authority, Government, nonfederal **Service:** General medical and surgical

Staffed Beds: 218 Admissions: 12075 Census: 147 Outpatient Visits: 410048 Births: 2008 Total Expense ($000): 306557 Payroll Expense ($000): 130796 Personnel: 2014

CROWLEY—Acadia Parish

★ **ACADIA GENERAL HOSPITAL (190044)**, 1305 Crowley Rayne Highway, Zip 70526–8202; tel. 337/783–3222, (Nonreporting) **A**10 **S** Lafayette General Health, Lafayette, LA
Primary Contact: Joe J. Mitchell, FACHE, Chief Executive Officer
CNO: Caroline Marceaux, MSN, R.N., Chief Nursing Officer
Web address: www.acadiageneral.com
Control: Other not–for–profit (including NFP Corporation) **Service:** General medical and surgical

Staffed Beds: 140

CUT OFF—Lafourche Parish

★ **LADY OF THE SEA GENERAL HOSPITAL (191325)**, 200 West 134th Place, Zip 70345–4143; tel. 985/632–6401, **A**10 18 21 **F**3 15 29 34 35 40 45 50 57 59 60 62 70 81 85 87 107 108 110 111 114 119 127 130 132 133 146 148 149 156
Primary Contact: Karen S. Collins, R.N., Chief Executive Officer
COO: Lloyd Guidry, Chief Operating Officer
CFO: Jacquelyn Richoux, Chief Financial Officer
CMO: William Crenshaw, M.D., Chief of Staff
CIO: Bennie Smith, Chief Information Officer
CHR: Bennie Smith, Director Human Resources and Risk Management
CNO: Holly Griffin, R.N., Chief Nursing Officer
Web address: www.losgh.org
Control: Hospital district or authority, Government, nonfederal **Service:** General medical and surgical

Staffed Beds: 25 Admissions: 598 Census: 7 Outpatient Visits: 86707 Births: 0 Total Expense ($000): 33949 Payroll Expense ($000): 13937 Personnel: 314

DE RIDDER—Beauregard Parish

BEAUREGARD HEALTH SYSTEM (190050), 600 South Pine Street, Zip 70634–4942, Mailing Address: P.O. Box 730, Zip 70634–0730; tel. 337/462–7100, **A**1 10 **F**3 11 13 15 18 20 26 28 29 30 31 34 35 39 40 45 46 50 53 57 64 70 75 76 78 79 81 85 89 91 93 96 107 108 110 111 114 119 127 129 130 131 133 144 148 154 156
Primary Contact: William F. Barrow II, Chief Executive Officer
CFO: Darrell L Kingham, CPA, Vice President Finance
CMO: David Jones, M.D., Chief Medical Officer
CIO: Meg Jackson, Director Information Technology
CHR: Kelli C Broocks, Director Human Resources, Public Relations and Physician Recruitment
CNO: Anita Thibodeaux, Chief Nursing Officer
Web address: www.beauregard.org
Control: Hospital district or authority, Government, nonfederal **Service:** General medical and surgical

Staffed Beds: 49 Admissions: 2163 Census: 22 Outpatient Visits: 78830 Births: 348 Total Expense ($000): 42182 Payroll Expense ($000): 20307 Personnel: 381

DELHI—Richland Parish

RICHLAND PARISH HOSPITAL (191323), 407 Cincinnati Street, Zip 71232–3007, tel. 318/878–5171, (Nonreporting) **A**10 18
Primary Contact: Michael W. Carroll, Administrator
CIO: Barbra Hutchison, Director Medical Records
CHR: Patsy Stout, Director Personnel
Web address: www.delhihospital.com
Control: Hospital district or authority, Government, nonfederal **Service:** General medical and surgical

Staffed Beds: 25

DENHAM SPRINGS—Livingston Parish

SAGE SPECIALTY HOSPITAL (LTAC) (192008), 8375 Florida Boulevard, Zip 70726–7806; tel. 225/665–2664, **A**10 **F**1 29 98 100 130 154 **S** The Carpenter Health Network, Baton Rouge, LA
Primary Contact: Sharon Faulkner, Administrator
CFO: Jessica McGee, Chief Financial Officer
CMO: Durwin Walker, M.D., Chief Medical Officer
CHR: Kim Hernandez, Chief Human Resources Officer
CNO: Sharon Faulkner, Chief Nursing Officer
Web address: www.amgdenham.com/
Control: Corporation, Investor–owned (for–profit) **Service:** Acute long–term care hospital

Staffed Beds: 59 Admissions: 57 Census: 25 Outpatient Visits: 0 Births: 0

DEQUINCY—Calcasieu Parish

DEQUINCY MEMORIAL HOSPITAL (191307), 110 West Fourth Street, Zip 70633–3508, Mailing Address: P.O. Box 1166, Zip 70633–1166; tel. 337/786–1200, (Nonreporting) **A**10 18
Primary Contact: Heath Hairgrove, Chief Executive Officer
CFO: Vicky Kelley, Chief Financial Officer
CMO: Jalal Joudeh, M.D., Chief of Staff
CNO: Darrell Ross, Chief Nursing Officer
Web address: www.dequincymemorial.com/
Control: City, Government, nonfederal **Service:** General medical and surgical

Staffed Beds: 19

DERIDDER—Beauregard Parish

☐ **OCEANS BEHAVIORAL HOSPITAL OF DE RIDDER (194081)**, 1420 Blankenship Drive, Zip 70634–4604; tel. 337/460–9472, (Nonreporting) **A**1 10 **S** Oceans Healthcare, Lake Charles, LA
Primary Contact: Stuart Archer, Chief Executive Officer, Oceans Healthcare
Web address: www.obhd.info/
Control: Corporation, Investor–owned (for–profit) **Service:** Psychiatric

Staffed Beds: 20

DONALDSONVILLE—Ascension Parish

✠ **PREVOST MEMORIAL HOSPITAL (191308)**, 301 Memorial Drive, Zip 70346–4376; tel. 225/473–7931, (Nonreporting) **A**1 10 18
Primary Contact: Vincent A. Cataldo, Administrator
CFO: Nobie Landry, Chief Financial Officer
CMO: Glenn Sche	xnayder, M.D., Chief of Staff
CHR: Linda Cataldo, Human Resources Secretary
Web address: www.prevosthospital.net
Control: Hospital district or authority, Government, nonfederal **Service:** General medical and surgical

Staffed Beds: 25

FARMERVILLE—Union Parish

UNION GENERAL HOSPITAL (191301), 901 James Avenue, Zip 71241–2234, Mailing Address: P.O. Box 398, Zip 71241–0398; tel. 318/368–9751, **A**10 18 **F**15 29 32 34 35 40 45 50 56 81 93 104 107 110 114 119 127 128 133 134 143 149 153
Primary Contact: Evalyn Ormond, Chief Executive Officer
COO: Dianne Davidson, Chief Operating Officer
CFO: William Adcock, Chief Financial Officer
CHR: Sheri Taylor, Director Human Resources
CNO: Darra Jung, Director of Nursing
Web address: www.uniongen.com
Control: Other not–for–profit (including NFP Corporation) **Service:** General medical and surgical

Staffed Beds: 15 Admissions: 249 Census: 2 Outpatient Visits: 33924 Births: 0 Total Expense ($000): 13684 Payroll Expense ($000): 5437 Personnel: 108

FERRIDAY—Concordia Parish

RIVERLAND MEDICAL CENTER (191318), 1700 EE Wallace Boulevard North, Zip 71334–2239, Mailing Address: P.O. Box 111, Zip 71334–0111; tel. 318/757–6551, **A**10 18 **F**3 15 29 34 35 40 45 57 59 68 70 75 77 81 85 86 87 93 107 110 114 119 127 133 153 154
Primary Contact: Sam Ellard, Chief Executive Officer
COO: Nekisha Smith, Chief Operating Officer
CFO: Spencer Holder, Chief Financial Officer
CMO: Carrie Bonomo, M.D., Chief of Staff
CHR: Debra Stephens, Director Personnel
CNO: Shelia James, Director of Nursing
Web address: www.riverlandmedical.com/
Control: Hospital district or authority, Government, nonfederal **Service:** General medical and surgical

Staffed Beds: 25 Admissions: 860 Census: 11 Outpatient Visits: 105169 Births: 0 Total Expense ($000): 18419 Payroll Expense ($000): 7469 Personnel: 174

FORT POLK—Vernon Parish

✠ **BAYNE-JONES ARMY COMMUNITY HOSPITAL**, 1585 3rd Street, Building 283, Zip 71459–5102; tel. 337/531–3928, (Nonreporting) **A**1 **S** Department of the Army, Office of the Surgeon General, Falls Church, VA
Primary Contact: Colonel Marla J. Ferguson, Commanding Officer
COO: Larry R. Patterson, Deputy Commander Administration
CFO: Captain Dustin Mullins, Chief Resource Management
CIO: Major William Callahan, Chief Information Management Division
CHR: Captain Dustin Mullins, Chief Human Resources
Web address: www.polk.amedd.army.mil
Control: Department of Defense, Government, federal **Service:** General medical and surgical

Staffed Beds: 13

FRANKLIN—St. Mary Parish

✠ **FRANKLIN FOUNDATION HOSPITAL (191310)**, 1097 Northwest Boulevard, Zip 70538–3407, Mailing Address: P.O. Box 577, Zip 70538–0577; tel. 337/828–0760, **A**1 10 18 **F**3 11 13 15 18 26 29 34 35 40 45 50 57 58 59 68 70 75 76 77 79 81 85 93 107 110 111 119 130 132 133 135 145 147 148 149 154 **S** QHR, Brentwood, TN
Primary Contact: Stephanie A. Guidry, Chief Executive Officer
CFO: Ron Bailey, Chief Financial Officer
CMO: Jesus Chua, M.D., Chief of Staff
CIO: John Spradlin, Information Systems Director
CHR: Elmo Viñas, Director Human Resources
CNO: Michelle Skillings, Chief Nursing Officer
Web address: www.franklinfoundation.org
Control: Hospital district or authority, Government, nonfederal **Service:** General medical and surgical

Staffed Beds: 22 Admissions: 627 Census: 9 Outpatient Visits: 29257 Births: 59 Total Expense ($000): 25238 Payroll Expense ($000): 11708 Personnel: 187

FRANKLINTON—Washington Parish

☐ **RIVERSIDE MEDICAL CENTER (191313)**, 1900 Main Street, Zip 70438–3688; tel. 985/839–4431, (Nonreporting) **A**1 10 18
Primary Contact: Peter Sullivan, Chief Executive Officer
CFO: Brandon Anzaldua, Chief Financial Officer
CMO: Chris Foret, M.D., Chief of Staff
CHR: John Seal, Director Human Resources
Web address: www.rmchospital.com
Control: Hospital district or authority, Government, nonfederal **Service:** General medical and surgical

Staffed Beds: 25

GONZALES—Ascension Parish

SOUTH BATON ROUGE REHABILITATION HOSPITAL See United Medical Rehabilitation Hospital - Gonzales

☐ **ST. JAMES BEHAVIORAL HEALTH HOSPITAL (194088)**, 3136 South Saint Landry Avenue, Zip 70737–5801; tel. 225/647–7524, (Nonreporting) **A**1 10
Primary Contact: Andrew Hines, Administrator
COO: Wendell Smith, Chief Operating Officer
CFO: Rama Kongara, Chief Financial Officer
CMO: Lance Bullock, M.D., Medical Director
CHR: Dessa Frederick, Manager Human Resources
Web address: www.sjbhh.net
Control: Corporation, Investor–owned (for–profit) **Service:** Psychiatric

Staffed Beds: 10

LA

GREENSBURG—St. Helena Parish

ST. HELENA PARISH HOSPITAL (191300), 16874 Highway 43, Zip 70441–4834; tel. 225/222–6111, (Nonreporting) **A**10 18
Primary Contact: Naveed Awan, FACHE, Chief Executive Officer
CFO: Theresa Brinkhaus, Chief Financial Officer
CMO: Anjanette Varnado, M.D., Chief Medical Officer
CHR: Lorraine L Ballard, Director Human Resources
CNO: Julie Morgan, Director of Nursing
Web address: www.sthelenaparishhospital.com
Control: Other not–for–profit (including NFP Corporation) **Service**: General medical and surgical

Staffed Beds: 75

GRETNA—Jefferson Parish

UNITED MEDICAL REHABILITATION HOSPITAL (193074), 3201 Wall Boulevard, Suite B, Zip 70056–7755; tel. 504/433–5551, **A**10 **F**28 77 82 90 94 96 119 130 154 **S** United Medical Rehabilitation Hospitals, Gretna, LA
Primary Contact: Elisha Johnson, Interim Administrator
Web address: www.umrhospital.com/
Control: Corporation, Investor–owned (for–profit) **Service**: Rehabilitation

Staffed Beds: 26 **Admissions**: 299 **Census**: 14 **Outpatient Visits**: 0
Births: 0

HAMMOND—Tangipahoa Parish

⇧ **CYPRESS POINTE SURGICAL HOSPITAL (190303)**, 42570 South Airport Road, Zip 70403–0946; tel. 985/510–6200, (Nonreporting) **A**10 21
Primary Contact: Glenda Dobson, Chief Executive Officer
COO: Scot Treitler, Chief Operating Officer
CFO: Donna Varnado, Vice President Finance
CNO: Denise Fortenberry, Chief Nursing Officer and Chief Compliance Officer
Web address: www.cpsh.org
Control: Corporation, Investor–owned (for–profit) **Service**: Surgical

Staffed Beds: 24

⊠ **NORTH OAKS MEDICAL CENTER (190015)**, 15790 Paul Vega, MD, Drive, Zip 70403–1436, Mailing Address: P.O. Box 2668, Zip 70404–2668; tel. 985/345–2700, **A**1 3 10 19 **F**3 12 13 15 18 20 22 24 26 28 29 30 31 32 34 40 43 45 49 50 54 56 57 58 59 63 64 68 70 72 73 74 75 77 78 79 81 82 84 85 86 87 93 94 96 102 107 108 110 111 114 115 118 119 126 129 130 131 132 135 143 144 146 147 148 149 154 156 **S** North Oaks Health System, Hammond, LA
Primary Contact: Michele Kidd. Sutton, FACHE, President and Chief Executive Officer
COO: Michael Watkins, Chief Operating Officer
CFO: Mark Anderson, Chief Financial Officer
CMO: Robert Peltier, M.D., Chief Medical Officer
CIO: Doug Bankston, Director Technical Services
CHR: Jeff Jarreau, Chief Human Resources Officer
Web address: www.northoaks.org
Control: Hospital district or authority, Government, nonfederal **Service**: General medical and surgical

Staffed Beds: 231 **Admissions**: 11362 **Census**: 148 **Outpatient Visits**: 489141 **Births**: 1235 **Total Expense ($000)**: 301777 **Payroll Expense ($000)**: 165748 **Personnel**: 1715

☐ **NORTH OAKS REHABILITATION HOSPITAL (193044)**, 1900 South Morrison Boulevard, Zip 70403–5742; tel. 985/542–7777, **A**1 10 **F**29 56 75 86 87 90 130 132 143 154 **S** North Oaks Health System, Hammond, LA
Primary Contact: Sybil K. Paulson, R.N., MSN, Administrator
CFO: Mark Anderson, Chief Financial Officer
CMO: Robert Peltier, M.D., Senior Vice President, Chief Medical Officer, North Oaks Health System
CIO: Herbert Robinson, M.D., Vice President, Chief Medical Information Officer, North Oaks Health System
CHR: Jeff Jarreau, Senior Vice President, Human Resources, North Oaks Health System
Web address: www.northoaks.org
Control: Hospital district or authority, Government, nonfederal **Service**: Rehabilitation

Staffed Beds: 27 **Admissions**: 529 **Census**: 17 **Outpatient Visits**: 0
Births: 0 **Total Expense ($000)**: 11267 **Payroll Expense ($000)**: 2453
Personnel: 44

⊠ **PAM SPECIALTY HOSPITAL OF HAMMOND (192036)**, 42074 Veterans Avenue, Zip 70403–1408; tel. 985/902–8148, **A**1 10 **F**1 29 75 77 148 149 **S** Post Acute Medical, LLC, Enola, PA
Primary Contact: Nicholas Paul. Mendez, Chief Executive Officer
Web address: www.postacutemedical.com
Control: Partnership, Investor–owned (for–profit) **Service**: Acute long–term care hospital

Staffed Beds: 40 **Admissions**: 547 **Census**: 28 **Outpatient Visits**: 0
Births: 0 **Total Expense ($000)**: 13958 **Payroll Expense ($000)**: 5509
Personnel: 104

UNITED MEDICAL REHABILITATION HOSPITAL (193079), 15717 Belle Drive, Zip 70403–1439; tel. 985/340–5998, (Includes UNITED MEDICAL REHABILITATION HOSPITAL - GONZALES, 333 East Worthy Road, Gonzales, Louisiana, Zip 70737–4234; tel. 225/450–2231; Laura Begnaud, Administrator), (Non-reporting) **A**10 **S** United Medical Rehabilitation Hospitals, Gretna, LA
Primary Contact: Jonathan Landreth, Administrator
CFO: Warren Swenson, Chief Financial Officer
CMO: Luis Franco, M.D., Medical Director
CHR: Mark Gros, Director Human Resources
Web address: www.umrhospital.com
Control: Corporation, Investor–owned (for–profit) **Service**: Rehabilitation

Staffed Beds: 20

HOMER—Claiborne Parish

⇧ **CLAIBORNE MEMORIAL MEDICAL CENTER (190114)**, 620 East College Street, Zip 71040–3202; tel. 318/927–2024, (Nonreporting) **A**10 21
Primary Contact: Tina Haynes, Interim Chief Executive Officer
CFO: Michelle Stillwell, Chief Financial Officer
CMO: Mark Haynes, M.D., Chief of Staff
CIO: Angie Costakis, Chief Information Officer
CHR: William Colvin, Human Resources Officer
CNO: Kristie M. Copeland, Interim Chief Nursing Officer
Web address: www.clairbornemedical.com/
Control: City, Government, nonfederal **Service**: General medical and surgical

Staffed Beds: 57

HOUMA—Terrebonne Parish

AMG SPECIALTY HOSPITAL-HOUMA (192037), 629 Dunn Street, Zip 70360–4707; tel. 985/274–0001, (Nonreporting) **A**10 22 **S** AMG Integrated Healthcare Management, Lafayette, LA
Primary Contact: Jody Robichaux, R.N., Chief Executive Officer
Web address: www.amghouma.com/
Control: Corporation, Investor–owned (for–profit) **Service**: Acute long–term care hospital

Staffed Beds: 40

☐ **COMPASS BEHAVIORAL CENTER OF HOUMA (194109)**, 4701 West Park Avenue, Zip 70364–4426; tel. 985/876–1715, (Nonreporting) **A**1 10 **S** Compass Health, Crowley, LA
Primary Contact: Cleveland Obey, Administrator
Web address: www.compasshealthcare.com/site83.php
Control: Corporation, Investor–owned (for–profit) **Service**: Psychiatric

Staffed Beds: 20

⊠ **LEONARD J. CHABERT MEDICAL CENTER (190183)**, 1978 Industrial Boulevard, Zip 70363–7094; tel. 985/873–2200, **A**1 3 5 10 **F**3 4 15 18 20 22 24 26 29 31 34 35 38 40 44 45 46 48 49 50 51 56 57 58 59 61 64 66 68 70 74 77 78 79 81 82 84 85 86 87 89 93 97 98 102 107 108 110 111 115 119 130 146 147 148 149 154 156 **S** Ochsner Health System, New Orleans, LA
Primary Contact: Timothy J. Allen, FACHE, Chief Executive Officer
COO: Kendrick Duet, Chief Operating Officer
CNO: Jana Semere, Chief Nursing Officer
Web address: www.ochsner.org/locations/leonard_j_chabert_medical_center/
Control: State, Government, nonfederal **Service**: General medical and surgical

Staffed Beds: 78 **Admissions**: 3213 **Census**: 44 **Outpatient Visits**: 176842
Births: 0 **Total Expense ($000)**: 108148 **Payroll Expense ($000)**: 31781
Personnel: 852

PHYSICIANS ALLIANCE HOSPITAL OF HOUMA See Amg Specialty Hospital-Houma

☐ **PHYSICIANS MEDICAL CENTER (190241)**, 218 Corporate Drive, Zip 70360–2768; tel. 985/853–1390, **A**1 10 **F**12 15 29 45 51 65 75 79 81 82 85 87 107 110 115 119 120 124 132
Primary Contact: Carter Ilgenfritz, Chief Executive Officer
Web address: www.physicianshouma.com/
Control: Corporation, Investor–owned (for–profit) **Service**: Surgical

Staffed Beds: 15 **Admissions**: 342 **Census**: 2 **Outpatient Visits**: 9770
Births: 0 **Total Expense ($000)**: 18519 **Payroll Expense ($000)**: 5771
Personnel: 114

Many Facility Codes have changed. Please refer to the AHA Guide Code Chart. © 2019 AHA Guide

⊞ △ **TERREBONNE GENERAL MEDICAL CENTER (190008)**, 8166 Main Street, Zip 70360–3498; tel. 985/873–4141, (Total facility includes 8 beds in nursing home–type unit) **A**1 2 5 7 10 19 **F**8 11 13 14 15 17 18 20 22 24 26 29 30 31 34 35 40 44 49 50 53 55 57 58 59 64 65 68 70 72 74 75 76 77 78 79 81 84 85 86 87 89 90 91 92 93 96 102 107 108 109 110 111 112 115 116 117 118 119 121 123 124 128 130 131 132 134 135 143 146 147 148 149 157
Primary Contact: Phyllis L. Peoples, President and Chief Executive Officer
COO: Diane Yeates, Chief Operating Officer
CFO: Dean Verret, Vice President Financial Services
CMO: Robert Gamble, M.D., Chief of Staff
CIO: Jeff Sardella, Director Information Technology
CHR: Mickie Rousseau, Director Human Resources
CNO: Teresita McNabb, R.N., FACHE, Vice President Nursing Services
Web address: www.tgmc.com
Control: Hospital district or authority, Government, nonfederal **Service:** General medical and surgical

Staffed Beds: 230 **Admissions:** 8062 **Census:** 118 **Outpatient Visits:** 120015 **Births:** 1700 **Total Expense ($000):** 191886 **Payroll Expense ($000):** 72492 **Personnel:** 1339

INDEPENDENCE—Tangipahoa Parish

☐ **LALLIE KEMP MEDICAL CENTER (191321)**, 52579 Highway 51 South, Zip 70443–2231; tel. 985/878–9421, (Nonreporting) **A**1 3 5 10 18
Primary Contact: Rhonda G. Green, R.N., Administrator
COO: Lisa G Bruhl, Chief Operating Officer
CFO: Chad Thompson, Chief Financial Officer
CMO: Kathy Willis, M.D., Medical Director
CIO: Charles Tate, Director Information Technology
CHR: Diane Farnham, Acting Director Human Resources
Web address: www.lsuhospitals.org/Hospitals/LK/LK.aspx
Control: State, Government, nonfederal **Service:** General medical and surgical

Staffed Beds: 24

JACKSON—East Feliciana Parish

☐ **EASTERN LOUISIANA MENTAL HEALTH SYSTEM (194008)**, 4502 Highway 10, Zip 70748, Mailing Address: P.O. Box 498, Zip 70748–0498; tel. 225/634–0100, (Nonreporting) **A**1 3 10 **S** Louisiana State Hospitals, Baton Rouge, LA
Primary Contact: Hampton P S. Lea, Acting Chief Executive Officer
CFO: Laura Lott, Administrative Director
CMO: John W Thompson, M.D., Chief of Staff
CIO: Deborah Brandon, Director Total Quality Management
CHR: Vikki Riggle, Director Human Resources
CNO: Mary Fontenelle, Executive Nurse Director
Web address: www.new.dhh.louisiana.gov/index.cfm/directory/detail/219
Control: State, Government, nonfederal **Service:** Psychiatric

Staffed Beds: 473

VILLA FELICIANA MEDICAL COMPLEX (190199), 5002 Highway 10, Zip 70748–3627, Mailing Address: P.O. Box 438, Zip 70748–0438; tel. 225/634–4017, (Nonreporting) **A**10
Primary Contact: Mark Anders, Administrator
CFO: Kim Jelks, Fiscal Officer
CMO: John F Piker, M.D., Medical Director
CIO: Michael James, Information Technology Technical Support Specialist 1
CHR: Sandra Delatte, Director Human Resources
CNO: Linda Williams, Director of Nursing
Web address: www.dhh.state.la.us/
Control: State, Government, nonfederal **Service:** Other specialty treatment

Staffed Beds: 299

JEFFERSON—Jefferson Parish

⊞ **OCHSNER REHABILITATON HOSPITAL WEST CAMPUS (193099)**, 2614 Jefferson Highway, Zip 70121–3828; tel. 504/291–5100, (Data for 245 days) **A**1 **F**3 29 34 44 60 68 75 90 96 119 130 132 148 **S** Select Medical Corporation, Mechanicsburg, PA
Primary Contact: Sara Wriborg, Chief Executive Officer
Web address: www.https://www.ochsner.org/services/rehabilitation
Control: Corporation, Investor–owned (for–profit) **Service:** Rehabilitation

Staffed Beds: 42 **Admissions:** 478 **Census:** 29 **Outpatient Visits:** 0 **Births:** 0 **Personnel:** 132

JENA—La Salle Parish

★ **LASALLE GENERAL HOSPITAL (190145)**, 187 Ninth Street, Zip 71342–3901, Mailing Address: P.O. Box 2780, Zip 71342–2780; tel. 318/992–9200, **A**3 10 **F**7 11 15 18 29 33 34 35 40 53 57 59 62 64 81 93 97 98 103 107 108 110 111 115 119 127 130 133 149
Primary Contact: Lana B. Francis, Chief Executive Officer
CHR: Allyson Fannin, Human Resources Officer
CNO: Carolyn Francis, R.N., MSN, Director of Nursing
Web address: www.lasallegeneralhospital.com
Control: Hospital district or authority, Government, nonfederal **Service:** General medical and surgical

Staffed Beds: 46 **Admissions:** 971 **Census:** 17 **Outpatient Visits:** 53439 **Births:** 0 **Total Expense ($000):** 20866 **Payroll Expense ($000):** 8457 **Personnel:** 210

JENNINGS—Jefferson Davis Parish

☐ **JENNINGS AMERICAN LEGION HOSPITAL (190053)**, 1634 Elton Road, Zip 70546–3614; tel. 337/616–7000, **A**1 10 **F**3 15 18 20 22 28 29 40 45 64 70 76 79 81 89 107 108 111 115 119 127 133 146 147 149
Primary Contact: Dana D. Williams, Chief Executive Officer
COO: Keith J Simpson, Chief Operating Officer
CIO: Gary Courrege, Chief Information Officer
CHR: Ruth Carnes, Manager Human Resources
CNO: Theresa L Woods, MSN, R.N., FACHE, Chief Nursing Officer
Web address: www.jalh.com
Control: Other not–for–profit (including NFP Corporation) **Service:** General medical and surgical

Staffed Beds: 49 **Admissions:** 2387 **Census:** 25 **Outpatient Visits:** 39412 **Births:** 437 **Total Expense ($000):** 44666 **Payroll Expense ($000):** 20203 **Personnel:** 398

JENNINGS SENIOR CARE HOSPITAL (194082), 1 Hospital Drive, Suite 201, Zip 70546–3641; tel. 337/824–1558, **A**10 **F**98 100 101 104 105 153
Primary Contact: Andre' Robichaux, Administrator
Web address: www.compasshealthcare.com/site74.php
Control: Corporation, Investor–owned (for–profit) **Service:** Psychiatric

Staffed Beds: 16 **Admissions:** 305 **Census:** 13 **Births:** 0 **Total Expense ($000):** 5537 **Payroll Expense ($000):** 2655 **Personnel:** 36

REHABILITATION HOSPITAL OF JENNINGS (193067), 1 Hospital Drive, Suite 101, Zip 70546–3641; tel. 337/821–5353, (Nonreporting) **A**10
Primary Contact: Michael Holland, M.D., Chief Executive Officer
Web address: www.jenningsrehab.com
Control: Partnership, Investor–owned (for–profit) **Service:** Rehabilitation

Staffed Beds: 16

JONESBORO—Jackson Parish

★ **JACKSON PARISH HOSPITAL (191317)**, 165 Beech Springs Road, Zip 71251–2059; tel. 318/259–4435, **A**10 18 **F**8 29 34 35 44 45 50 57 59 64 65 66 68 77 78 81 87 93 107 110 111 115 119 127 128 130 132 133 134 135 146 148 154 157
Primary Contact: John Morgan, R.N., Chief Executive Officer
CFO: Bill Stansbury, Chief Financial Officer
CMO: W. James (Jamie) Slusher, M.D., Chief of Staff
CIO: Monie Phillips III Director Clinical Informatics
CHR: Phillip Thomas Jr Director Human Resources
CNO: Christy Wyatt, R.N., Interim Chief Nursing Officer
Web address: www.jacksonparishhospital.com
Control: Hospital district or authority, Government, nonfederal **Service:** General medical and surgical

Staffed Beds: 25 **Admissions:** 1163 **Census:** 6 **Outpatient Visits:** 24183 **Births:** 0 **Total Expense ($000):** 18819 **Payroll Expense ($000):** 8876

LA

KAPLAN—Vermilion Parish

ABROM KAPLAN MEMORIAL HOSPITAL (191322), 1310 West Seventh Street, Zip 70548–2910; tel. 337/643–8300, (Nonreporting) **A**10 18 **S** Lafayette General Health, Lafayette, LA
Primary Contact: Bryce Quebodeaux, Chief Executive Officer
CFO: Michael G. Johnson, CPA, Chief Financial Officer
CMO: Scott Bergeaux, M.D., Chief Medical Staff
CIO: Michael Cardiff, Systems Supervisor
CHR: Linda Guidry, Human Resources Generalist
CNO: Sally Roberts, R.N., Director of Nursing
Web address: www.lafayettegeneral.com
Control: Hospital district or authority, Government, nonfederal **Service:** General medical and surgical

Staffed Beds: 35

KENNER—Jefferson Parish

☐ **LAKE PINES HOSPITAL (194113)**, 3639 Loyola Drive, Zip 70065; tel. 504/305–2700, (Nonreporting) **A**1
Primary Contact: Debbie Tullier, Chief Executive Officer
Web address: www.https://www.lakepineshospital.com/
Control: Individual, Investor–owned (for–profit) **Service:** Psychiatric

Staffed Beds: 36

☐ **OCEANS BEHAVIORAL HOSPITAL OF GREATER NEW ORLEANS (194098)**, 716 Village Road, Zip 70065–2751; tel. 504/464–8895, (Includes OCEANS BEHAVIORAL HOSPITAL GREATER NEW ORLEANS - MARRERO, 4500 Wichers Drive, Marrero, Louisiana, Zip 70072–3184; tel. 504/349–1661; Deborah Spier, Administrator), (Non-reporting) **A**1 10 **S** Oceans Healthcare, Lake Charles, LA
Primary Contact: Deborah Spier, Administrator
Web address: www.obhgno.info/
Control: Corporation, Investor–owned (for–profit) **Service:** Psychiatric

Staffed Beds: 30

⊞ **OCHSNER MEDICAL CENTER - KENNER (190274)**, 180 West Esplanade Avenue, Zip 70065–6001; tel. 504/468–8600, **A**1 3 5 10 **F**3 13 15 18 20 22 29 30 31 34 35 37 38 40 41 42 44 45 46 49 50 51 53 54 56 57 58 59 60 61 64 65 66 68 70 72 74 75 76 77 78 79 81 82 83 84 85 86 87 93 97 102 107 110 114 116 117 120 129 130 131 132 135 146 147 148 154 157 **S** Ochsner Health System, New Orleans, LA
Primary Contact: Stephen Robinson Jr, FACHE, Chief Executive Officer
COO: Eddy Ramirez, Assistant Vice President Business Development
CFO: Mark Eckert, Vice President Finance
CMO: James Tebbe, M.D., Vice President Medical Affairs
CIO: Dere Krummel, Director Information Systems
Web address: www.https://www.ochsner.org/locations/ochsner-medical-center-kenner/
Control: Other not–for–profit (including NFP Corporation) **Service:** General medical and surgical

Staffed Beds: 110 **Admissions:** 6584 **Census:** 70 **Outpatient Visits:** 171075 **Births:** 1102 **Total Expense ($000):** 145715 **Payroll Expense ($000):** 52274 **Personnel:** 966

ST. THERESA SPECIALTY HOSPITAL (192030), 3601 Loyola Drive, Zip 70065–1797; tel. 504/904–7600, (Nonreporting) **A**10
Primary Contact: Sam Liljebert, Chief Executive Officer
CMO: Ricardo Febry, M.D., Medical Director
CHR: Nicole Wilson, Manager Human Resources
CNO: Collette Jackson, R.N., Director of Clinical Services
Web address: www.stmck.com
Control: Corporation, Investor–owned (for–profit) **Service:** Acute long–term care hospital

Staffed Beds: 73

KENTWOOD—Tangipahoa Parish

OCEANS BEHAVIORAL HOSPITAL OF KENTWOOD (194091), 921 Avenue G, Zip 70444–2636; tel. 985/229–0717, (Nonreporting) **A**10 **S** Oceans Healthcare, Lake Charles, LA
Primary Contact: Marty Dean, Administrator
Web address: www.https://oceanshealthcare.com/kentwood
Control: Corporation, Investor–owned (for–profit) **Service:** Psychiatric

Staffed Beds: 16

SOUTHEAST REGIONAL MEDICAL CENTER (192040), 719 Avenue G, Zip 70444–2601; tel. 985/229–9193, (Nonreporting) **A**10
Primary Contact: Lionel Murphy, Chief Executive Officer
Control: Corporation, Investor–owned (for–profit) **Service:** Acute long–term care hospital

Staffed Beds: 14

KINDER—Allen Parish

ALLEN PARISH COMMUNITY HEALTHCARE (190133), 108 Sixth Avenue, Zip 70648–3187, Mailing Address: P.O. Box 1670, Zip 70648–1670; tel. 337/738–2527, (Nonreporting) **A**10
Primary Contact: Jackie Reviel, R.N., Chief Executive Officer
COO: Terry Willet, Chief Financial Officer
CFO: Stephen Thames, Chief Financial Officer
CMO: Ejiro Ughouwa, M.D., Chief of Staff
CIO: Bill Marcantel, Chief Information Systems
CHR: Amand Lambert, Director Human Resources
Web address: www.allenparishhospital.com
Control: Hospital district or authority, Government, nonfederal **Service:** General medical and surgical

Staffed Beds: 49

LA PLACE—St. John The Baptist Parish

☐ **RIVER PLACE BEHAVIORAL HEALTH (194114)**, 500 Rue De Sante, Zip 70068–5418; tel. 985/303–2327, (Nonreporting) **A**1 **S** Acadia Healthcare Company, Inc., Franklin, TN
Primary Contact: Jeremy Pitzer, Chief Executive Officer
Web address: www.riverplacebh.com
Control: Corporation, Investor–owned (for–profit) **Service:** Psychiatric

Staffed Beds: 82

LACOMBE—St. Tammany Parish

BEACON BEHAVIORAL HOSPITAL NORTHSHORE (194080), 64026 Highway 434, Suite 300, Zip 70445–5417; tel. 985/882–0226, (Nonreporting) **A**10
Primary Contact: Jessika Scallion, Administrator
Web address: www.magnoliabh.com/
Control: Corporation, Investor–owned (for–profit) **Service:** Psychiatric

Staffed Beds: 22

LAFAYETTE—Lafayette Parish

AMG SPECIALTY HOSPITAL-LAFAYETTE (192029), 310 Youngsville Highway, Zip 70508–4524; tel. 337/839–9880, **A**10 **F**1 29 **S** AMG Integrated Healthcare Management, Lafayette, LA
Primary Contact: Rachel Mayeaux, Chief Executive Officer
CFO: Jessica McGee, Chief Financial Officer
CMO: Maximo LaMarche, M.D., Chief Medical Officer
CHR: Heather Lamarche, Manager Human Resources
CNO: Mary Bollich, Director of Nurses
Web address: www.amglafayette.com
Control: Corporation, Investor–owned (for–profit) **Service:** Acute long–term care hospital

Staffed Beds: 18 **Admissions:** 230 **Census:** 15 **Outpatient Visits:** 0 **Births:** 0

★ **COMPASS BEHAVIORAL CENTER OF LAFAYETTE (194085)**, 312 Youngsville Highway, Zip 70508; tel. 337/534–4655, **F**98 100 101 104 105 153 **S** Compass Health, Crowley, LA
Primary Contact: Aimee Monaghan, Chief Executive Officer
Web address: www.compasshealthcare.com/site184.php
Control: Corporation, Investor–owned (for–profit) **Service:** Psychiatric

Staffed Beds: 16 **Admissions:** 266 **Census:** 11 **Outpatient Visits:** 17469 **Births:** 0 **Total Expense ($000):** 5616 **Payroll Expense ($000):** 2846 **Personnel:** 36

⊞ **HEART HOSPITAL OF LAFAYETTE (190263)**, 1105 Kaliste Saloom Road, Zip 70508–5705; tel. 337/521–1000, **A**1 10 **F**3 17 18 20 22 24 26 28 29 30 34 35 40 46 50 57 59 64 68 74 75 81 85 87 107 108 115 135
Primary Contact: Michelle B. Crain, R.N., MSN, Administrator and Chief Operating Officer
CFO: Rachel Hebert, Chief Financial Officer
CHR: Thomas Duhon, Director Human Resources
Web address: www.hearthospitaloflafayette.com
Control: Partnership, Investor–owned (for–profit) **Service:** Heart

Staffed Beds: 32 **Admissions:** 1714 **Census:** 17 **Outpatient Visits:** 17862 **Births:** 0 **Total Expense ($000):** 40206 **Payroll Expense ($000):** 12828 **Personnel:** 228

Many Facility Codes have changed. Please refer to the AHA Guide Code Chart. © 2019 AHA Guide

LAFAYETTE GENERAL MEDICAL CENTER (190002), 1214 Coolidge Boulevard, Zip 70503–2696, Mailing Address: P.O. Box 52009 OCS, Zip 70505–2009; tel. 337/289–7991, (Includes LAFAYETTE BEHAVIORAL HEALTH, 302 Dulles Drive, Lafayette, Louisiana, Zip 70506–3008; tel. 337/289–8595; Sandra Armand, Director; LAFAYETTE GENERAL ORTHOPEDIC HOSPITAL, 2810 Ambassador Caffery Parkway, Lafayette, Louisiana, Zip 70506–5906; tel. 337/981–2949; Jude Fontenot, Administrator) **A**1 2 3 5 10 **F**3 8 11 12 13 15 18 20 22 24 26 28 29 30 31 34 35 37 40 41 43 45 46 47 48 49 50 53 54 55 56 57 58 59 64 65 70 72 74 75 76 77 78 79 81 82 85 87 89 90 92 93 96 98 107 108 110 111 115 117 118 119 120 121 123 124 126 129 130 132 135 146 147 148 149 **S** Lafayette General Health, Lafayette, LA
Primary Contact: Patrick W. Gandy Jr, CPA, Executive Vice President and Chief Executive Officer
COO: Al Patin, R.N., Senior Vice President and Chief Operating Officer
CFO: Lana Adams, Chief Financial Officer
CMO: Stephen G. Rees, M.D., Vice President Medical Affairs
CIO: Michael Dozier, Vice President, Chief Information Officer
CHR: Sheena Bouquet, Vice President
CNO: Rebecca Benoit, R.N., Chief Nursing Officer
Web address: www.lafayettegeneral.com
Control: Other not–for–profit (including NFP Corporation) **Service:** General medical and surgical

Staffed Beds: 420 Admissions: 24558 Census: 310

LAFAYETTE GENERAL SURGICAL HOSPITAL (190268), 1000 West Pinhook Road, Suite 100, Zip 70503–2460; tel. 337/289–8088, (Nonreporting) **A**10 **S** Lafayette General Health, Lafayette, LA
Primary Contact: Kimberly H. Dooley, R.N., Administrator
CFO: Sandi Hernandez, Controller
CHR: Sheena Bouquet, Vice President
CNO: Veronica Els, Chief Nursing Officer
Web address: www.lafayettegeneral.com/our_facilities/main_facilities/lafayette_general_surgical_hospital.aspx
Control: Partnership, Investor–owned (for–profit) **Service:** General medical and surgical

Staffed Beds: 10

LAFAYETTE PHYSICAL REHABILITATION HOSPITAL (193093), 307 Polly Lane, Zip 70508–4960; tel. 337/314–1111, (Nonreporting) **A**10 22 **S** AMG Integrated Healthcare Management, Lafayette, LA
Primary Contact: Bruce J. Bartels, Interim Chief Executive Officer
Web address: www.lafayettephysicalrehab.com/
Control: Corporation, Investor–owned (for–profit) **Service:** Rehabilitation

Staffed Beds: 32

LAFAYETTE SURGICAL SPECIALTY HOSPITAL (190259), 1101 Kaliste Saloom Road, Zip 70508 5705; tel. 337/769–4100, (Nonreporting) **A**1 10 **S** National Surgical Healthcare, Chicago, Il
Primary Contact: Buffy Domingue, Chief Executive Officer
CFO: Chris Kohlenberg, Chief Financial Officer
CNO: Ruth Guidry, Chief Nursing Officer
Web address: www.lafayettesurgical.com
Control: Corporation, Investor–owned (for–profit) **Service:** Surgical

Staffed Beds: 20

LONG TERM ACUTE CARE OF ACADIANA See Amg Specialty Hospital-Lafayette

LOUISIANA EXTENDED CARE HOSPITAL OF LAFAYETTE (192032), 2810 Ambassador Caffery Parkway, 6th Floor, Zip 70506–5906; tel. 337/289–8180, (Includes EUNICE EXTENDED CARE HOSPITAL, 3879 Highway 190, Eunice, Louisiana, Zip 70535; tel. 337/546–0024; Kermit C. Simmons, Chief Executive Officer; IBERIA EXTENDED CARE HOSPITAL, 2315 East Main Street, 3rd Floor, New Iberia, Louisiana, Zip 70560–4031; tel. 337/369–1100; Kermit C. Simmons, Chief Executive Officer), (Non-reporting) **A**10 **S** LHC Group, Lafayette, LA
Primary Contact: Kermit C. Simmons, Chief Executive Officer
CMO: David Ashton Reed, M.D., Chief Medical Officer
CNO: Monica Lake, Chief Nursing Officer
Web address: www.lhcgroup.com
Control: Other not–for–profit (including NFP Corporation) **Service:** Acute long–term care hospital

Staffed Beds: 42

OPTIMA SPECIALTY HOSPITAL See Vermilion Behavioral Health Systems - South Campus

OUR LADY OF LOURDES REGIONAL MEDICAL CENTER (190102), 4801 Ambassador Caffery Parkway, Zip 70508–6917; tel. 337/470–2000, (Includes OUR LADY OF LOURDES WOMEN'S AND CHILDREN'S HOSPITAL, 4600 Ambassador Caffery Parkway, Lafayette, Louisiana, Zip 70508–6923, Mailing Address: P O Box 88030, Zip 70598–8030, tel. 337/521–9100; W. Bryan Lee, Chief Executive Officer) **A**1 2 10 **F**3 9 11 12 15 16 18 20 22 24 26 28 29 30 31 32 34 35 38 39 40 42 43 46 48 49 50 51 53 54 56 57 58 59 60 61 64 65 66 68 70 74 75 77 78 79 81 82 84 85 86 87 90 93 94 96 107 108 110 111 114 115 117 118 119 126 127 129 130 132 134 135 143 144 146 147 148 149 150 154 **S** Franciscan Missionaries of Our Lady Health System, Inc., Baton Rouge, LA
Primary Contact: W. Bryan. Lee, Chief Executive Officer
COO: Donna F. Landry, Chief Operating Officer
CMO: Anthony P. Blalock, M.D., Chief Medical Officer
CIO: Ryan J Latiolais, Director Information Systems
CHR: Jennifer Lynch Trahan, Assistant Vice President Human Resources
CNO: Gilbert Glenn Humbert, R.N., Jr Chief Nursing Officer
Web address: www.lourdesrmc.com
Control: Church operated, Nongovernment, not–for–profit **Service:** General medical and surgical

Staffed Beds: 186 Admissions: 9996 Census: 142 Outpatient Visits: 102048 Births: 0 Total Expense ($000): 238069 Payroll Expense ($000): 60653 Personnel: 1260

PARK PLACE SURGICAL HOSPITAL (190255), 4811 Ambassador Caffery Parkway, Zip 70508–6917; tel. 337/237–8119, (Nonreporting) **A**10 21
Primary Contact: Brandon Moore, FACHE, Administrator and Chief Executive Officer
Web address: www.parkplacesurgery.com/
Control: Partnership, Investor–owned (for–profit) **Service:** Surgical

Staffed Beds: 10

UNIVERSITY HOSPITAL AND CLINICS (190006), 2390 West Congress Street, Zip 70506–4298; tel. 337/261–6000, (Nonreporting) **A**1 2 3 5 10 **S** Lafayette General Health, Lafayette, LA
Primary Contact: Katherine D. Hebert, MS, Chief Executive Officer
CMO: James B Falterman, M.D., Jr Medical Director
CNO: Laurence Marie Vincent, Chief Nursing Officer
Web address: www.lafayettegeneral.com
Control: Other not–for–profit (including NFP Corporation) **Service:** General medical and surgical

Staffed Beds: 52

VERMILION BEHAVIORAL HEALTH SYSTEMS - NORTH CAMPUS (194044), 2520 North University Avenue, Zip 70507–5306; tel. 337/234–5614, (Includes VERMILION BEHAVIORAL HEALTH SYSTEMS - SOUTH CAMPUS, 1131 Rue De Belier, Lafayette, Louisiana, Zip 70506–6532; tel. 337/991–0571; Stephanie Hrdlicka, Chief Executive Officer), (Non-reporting) **A**10 **S** Acadia Healthcare Company, Inc., Franklin, TN
Primary Contact: Stephanie Hrdlicka, Chief Executive Officer
CFO: Margot Mokdessi, Interim Chief Financial Officer
CMO: Bob Winston, M.D., Medical Director
CHR: Claire Rowland, Director Human Resources
CNO: Amy Lallood, R.N., Director of Nursing
Web address: www.acadiavermilion.com
Control: Corporation, Investor–owned (for–profit) **Service:** Psychiatric

Staffed Beds: 78

LAKE CHARLES—Calcasieu Parish

AVAIL HEALTH LAKE CHARLES HOSPITAL, 3730 Nelson Road, Zip 70605; tel. 337/656–7700, (Nonreporting) **A**1
Primary Contact: Lance Armentor, Chief Executive Officer
Control: Other not–for–profit (including NFP Corporation) **Service:** General medical and surgical

Staffed Beds: 10

Hospital, Medicare Provider Number, Address, Telephone, Approval, Facility, and Physician Codes, Health Care System

★ American Hospital Association (AHA) membership ○ Healthcare Facilities Accreditation Program ⇧ Center for Improvement in Healthcare Quality Accreditation
□ The Joint Commission accreditation ◇ DNV Healthcare Inc. accreditation △ Commission on Accreditation of Rehabilitation Facilities (CARF) accreditation

☒ **CHRISTUS OCHSNER LAKE AREA HOSPITAL (190201)**, 4200 Nelson Road, Zip 70605–4118; tel. 337/474–6370, **A**1 10 **F**8 11 12 13 15 29 30 31 32 34 35 40 41 50 55 56 57 58 59 60 61 64 65 68 70 72 73 76 78 79 81 86 87 89 93 97 107 108 110 111 114 115 118 119 126 132 135 146 147 157 **S** CHRISTUS Health, Irving, TX
Primary Contact: Kevin Holland, Chief Executive Officer, CHRISTUS Southwestern Louisiana
CFO: Dawn Johnson-Hatcher, Chief Financial Officer
CIO: Aaron Cook, Director Information Services
CHR: Lisa Friday, Director Human Resources
CNO: Robbin Odom, R.N., MSN, Chief Nursing Officer
Web address: www.Lakeareamc.com
Control: Church operated, Nongovernment, not–for–profit **Service**: Obstetrics and gynecology

Staffed Beds: 88 **Admissions**: 3112 **Census**: 29 **Outpatient Visits**: 38888 **Births**: 1295 **Total Expense ($000)**: 54576 **Payroll Expense ($000)**: 21016 **Personnel**: 286

☒ △ **CHRISTUS OCHSNER ST. PATRICK HOSPITAL SOUTHWEST LOUISIANA (190027)**, 524 Dr Michael Debakey Drive, Zip 70601–5799, Mailing Address: P.O. Box 3401, Zip 70602–3401; tel. 337/436–2511, **A**1 2 7 10 **F**3 11 15 17 18 20 22 24 26 28 29 30 31 32 34 35 37 38 40 44 45 46 47 48 49 50 56 57 59 61 64 65 70 74 75 78 79 81 84 85 86 87 89 90 93 96 97 98 100 101 102 103 104 105 107 108 110 115 118 119 120 121 122 123 124 126 130 131 132 134 135 146 147 148 153 154 **S** CHRISTUS Health, Irving, TX
Primary Contact: Kevin Holland, Chief Executive Officer, CHRISTUS Southwestern Louisiana
CFO: Scott Merryman, Chief Financial Officer
CMO: Timothy Haman, M.D., Vice President Medical Affairs
CHR: Wendy Chandler, Assistant Administrator Human Resources
Web address: www.stpatrickhospital.org
Control: Church operated, Nongovernment, not–for–profit **Service**: General medical and surgical

Staffed Beds: 160 **Admissions**: 8131 **Census**: 105 **Outpatient Visits**: 103474 **Births**: 0 **Total Expense ($000)**: 149531 **Payroll Expense ($000)**: 42582 **Personnel**: 644

☐ **CORNERSTONE HOSPITAL OF SOUTHWEST LOUISIANA (192013)**, 524 Doctor Michael Debakey Drive, Zip 70601–5725; tel. 337/310–6000, (Nonreporting) **A**1 10 **S** Cornerstone Healthcare Group, Dallas, TX
Primary Contact: Austin B. Cleveland, Chief Executive Officer
CFO: Amy Bryant, Chief Financial Officer
CNO: Jeffrey Clark, Chief Nursing Officer
Web address: www.chghospitals.com/sulphur/
Control: Partnership, Investor–owned (for–profit) **Service**: Acute long–term care hospital

Staffed Beds: 30

☒ **LAKE CHARLES MEMORIAL HOSPITAL (190060)**, 1701 Oak Park Boulevard, Zip 70601–8911; tel. 337/494–3000, (Includes LAKE CHARLES MEMORIAL HOSPITAL FOR WOMEN, 1900 West Gauthier Road, Lake Charles, Louisiana, Zip 70605–7170; tel. 337/480–7000; Nancy Coffey, Interim Administrator and Director Emergency Department) **A**1 2 3 5 10 19 **F**3 8 11 13 15 17 18 20 22 24 26 28 29 30 31 34 37 40 45 49 50 53 54 56 57 58 60 62 64 66 70 72 73 74 75 76 77 78 79 81 82 84 85 86 87 88 89 90 93 98 99 102 103 107 108 110 111 114 115 119 120 121 123 124 126 127 129 130 131 132 144 146 147 148 149 153 156 157
Primary Contact: Larry M. Graham, FACHE, President and Chief Executive Officer
COO: Anna Leah Cazes, Interim Chief Nursing Officer, Senior Vice President, Chief Operating Officer
CFO: Charles P Whitson, CPA, Senior Vice President Finance
CMO: Manley Jordan, M.D., Chief Medical Officer
CIO: Belinda Sommers, Chief Information Officer
CHR: Ginger Consigney, Vice President Human Resources
CNO: Anna Leah Cazes, Interim Chief Nursing Officer, Senior Vice President and Chief Operating Officer
Web address: www.lcmh.com
Control: Other not–for–profit (including NFP Corporation) **Service**: General medical and surgical

Staffed Beds: 356 **Admissions**: 13448 **Census**: 185 **Outpatient Visits**: 313053 **Births**: 2119 **Total Expense ($000)**: 297454 **Payroll Expense ($000)**: 97964 **Personnel**: 2491

MEMORIAL SPECIALTY HOSPITAL (192019), 524 Doctor Michael Debakey Drive, 3rd Floor, Zip 70601–5725; tel. 337/480–8990, (Nonreporting) **A**10 **S** Cornerstone Healthcare Group, Dallas, TX
Primary Contact: Jeffrey Clark, Administrator
CNO: Julie LeBlanc, Director of Nursing
Web address: www.lcmh.com/
Control: Other not–for–profit (including NFP Corporation) **Service**: Acute long–term care hospital

Staffed Beds: 29

OCEANS BEHAVIORAL HOSPITAL OF LAKE CHARLES (194090), 4250 5th Avenue, Zip 70607–3900; tel. 337/474–7581, (Nonreporting) **A**10 **S** Oceans Healthcare, Lake Charles, LA
Primary Contact: Nicholas D. Guillory, MSN, Administrator
Web address: www.obhlc.info/
Control: Corporation, Investor–owned (for–profit) **Service**: Psychiatric

Staffed Beds: 40

LAKE PROVIDENCE—East Carroll Parish

EAST CARROLL PARISH HOSPITAL (190208), 336 North Hood Street, Zip 71254–2140; tel. 318/559–4023, (Nonreporting) **A**10
Primary Contact: LaDonna Englerth, Administrator
Control: Hospital district or authority, Government, nonfederal **Service**: General medical and surgical

Staffed Beds: 11

LEESVILLE—Vernon Parish

☒ **BYRD REGIONAL HOSPITAL (190164)**, 1020 West Fertitta Boulevard, Zip 71446–4645; tel. 337/239–9041, (Nonreporting) **A**1 10 **S** Allegiance Health Management, Shreveport, LA
Primary Contact: F. Peter. Savoy III, Chief Executive Officer
CFO: Jared Graves, Chief Financial Officer
CMO: Charles Caldwell, M.D., Chief of Staff
CHR: Karolyne Christian, Director Human Resources
CNO: Beth Westerchil, Chief Nursing Officer
Web address: www.byrdregional.com
Control: Corporation, Investor–owned (for–profit) **Service**: General medical and surgical

Staffed Beds: 60

☐ **LEESVILLE REHABILITATION HOSPITAL (193086)**, 900 South 6th Street, Zip 71446–4723; tel. 337/392–8118, (Nonreporting) **A**1 10
Primary Contact: Jack M. Causey, Chief Executive Officer
CMO: Gregory D Lord, M.D., Chief Medical Officer
CHR: Jackie Rubar, Administrative Assistant and Director Human Resources
Web address: www.leesvillerehab.com
Control: Corporation, Investor–owned (for–profit) **Service**: Rehabilitation

Staffed Beds: 16

☐ **TRI PARISH REHABILITATION HOSPITAL (193050)**, 8088 Hawks Road, Zip 71446–6649; tel. 337/462–8880, (Nonreporting) **A**1 10
Primary Contact: Elizabeth Bennett, Interim Chief Executive Officer
Web address: www.triparishrehab.com
Control: Corporation, Investor–owned (for–profit) **Service**: Rehabilitation

Staffed Beds: 20

LULING—St. Charles Parish

☒ **ST. CHARLES PARISH HOSPITAL (190079)**, 1057 Paul Maillard Road, Zip 70070–4349, Mailing Address: P.O. Box 87, Zip 70070–0087; tel. 985/785–6242, **A**1 10 **F**3 7 11 15 20 22 28 29 30 34 40 45 50 51 60 64 68 70 75 79 81 82 85 86 87 93 96 97 98 100 102 107 108 110 111 115 119 130 131 135 146 148 154 157 **S** Ochsner Health System, New Orleans, LA
Primary Contact: Austin Reeder, M.P.H., Chief Executive Officer
COO: Terrell Neal, R.N., Chief Operating Officer and Chief Nursing Officer
CFO: Peter Torsch, Chief Financial Officer
CMO: Vadakkipalayam N. Devarajan, Chief Medical Staff
CIO: Angela Boudreaux, Director Information Technology
CHR: Karen Ann Judlin, Director Human Resources
CNO: Terrell Neal, R.N., Chief Operating Officer and Chief Nursing Officer
Web address: www.https://www.ochsner.org/locations/st-charles-parish-hospital/
Control: Hospital district or authority, Government, nonfederal **Service**: General medical and surgical

Staffed Beds: 59 **Admissions**: 1445 **Census**: 22 **Outpatient Visits**: 32753 **Births**: 0 **Total Expense ($000)**: 42294 **Payroll Expense ($000)**: 7959 **Personnel**: 86

LUTCHER—St. James Parish

BEACON BEHAVIORAL HOSPITAL (194102), 2471 Louisiana Avenue, Zip 70071–5413; tel. 225/258–6103, (Nonreporting)
Primary Contact: Denise White, Administrator
Web address: www.beaconbh.com
Control: Other not–for–profit (including NFP Corporation) **Service**: Psychiatric

Staffed Beds: 19

Many Facility Codes have changed. Please refer to the AHA Guide Code Chart. © 2019 AHA Guide

⊞ **ST. JAMES PARISH HOSPITAL (191305)**, 1645 Lutcher Avenue, Zip 70071–5150; tel. 225/869–5512, **A**1 10 18 **F**3 15 29 34 35 40 45 46 50 51 57 59 64 75 77 80 81 85 93 107 108 110 111 114 119 128 129 130 132 133 144 149 154
Primary Contact: MaryEllen Pratt, FACHE, Chief Executive Officer
CFO: Tracy L George, Chief Financial Officer
CIO: Jeremy Martin, Chief Support Services Officer
CHR: Lisa Faucheux, Director Human Resources
CNO: Rhonda Zeringue, R.N., Chief Nursing Officer
Web address: www.sjph.org
Control: Hospital district or authority, Government, nonfederal **Service**: General medical and surgical

Staffed Beds: 25 **Admissions**: 518 **Census**: 8 **Outpatient Visits**: 32392 **Births**: 1 **Total Expense ($000)**: 27056 **Payroll Expense ($000)**: 11251 **Personnel**: 215

MAMOU—Evangeline Parish

⊞ **SAVOY MEDICAL CENTER (190025)**, 801 Poinciana Avenue, Zip 70554–2298; tel. 337/468–5261, (Nonreporting) **A**1 10 **S** CHRISTUS Health, Irving, TX
Primary Contact: Eugene H. Burge Jr, Chief Executive Officer
COO: Gerald Fuselier, Chief Operating Officer
CMO: Greg Savoy, M.D., Chief Medical Officer
CIO: Daniel Lahaye, Manager
CHR: Annette Thibodeaux, Director Human Resources
Web address: www.savoymedical.com/
Control: City, Government, nonfederal **Service**: General medical and surgical

Staffed Beds: 180

MANDEVILLE—St. Tammany Parish

☐ **NORTHLAKE BEHAVIORAL HEALTH SYSTEM (194007)**, 23515 Highway 190, Zip 70448–7334; tel. 985/626–6300, (Nonreporting) **A**1 3 5 10
Primary Contact: Billie Whittington, Interim Chief Executive Officer and Director Risk Management and Quality Assurance
CFO: Melissa S. Clayton, CPA, Chief Financial Officer
CMO: Hyon Su Kim, M.D., Medical Director
CIO: Archie Carriere, Information Technology Technician
CHR: Nicole Messa-Gill, Manager Human Resources
CNO: Jo Nell King, Director of Nursing
Web address: www.northlakebehavioralhealth.com
Control: State, Government, nonfederal **Service**: Psychiatric

Staffed Beds: 153

MANSFIELD—De Soto Parish

DE SOTO REGIONAL HEALTH SYSTEM (190118), 207 Jefferson Street, Zip 71052–2603, Mailing Address: P.O. Box 1636, Zip 71052–1636; tel. 318/872–4610, (Nonreporting) **A**10 20 **S** Willis Knighton Health System, Shreveport, LA
Primary Contact: Todd Eppler, FACHE, Chief Executive Officer
CFO: Eric Cripps, Chief Financial Officer
CMO: Denis Kamberov, M.D., Chief of Staff
CNO: Shane Goodman, Chief Nursing Officer
Web address: www.desotoregional.com
Control: Other not-for-profit (including NFP Corporation) **Service**: General medical and surgical

Staffed Beds: 10

MANY—Sabine Parish

SABINE MEDICAL CENTER (190218), 240 Highland Drive, Zip 71449–3718; tel. 318/256–5691, (Nonreporting) **A**10 20 **S** Allegiance Health Management, Shreveport, LA
Primary Contact: Chris Beddoe, Chief Executive Officer
COO: Doug Plummer, Chief Operating Officer
CFO: Frances F Hopkins, Chief Financial Officer
CNO: Karen Ford, Chief Nursing Officer
Web address: www.sabinemedicalcenter.net
Control: Individual, Investor-owned (for-profit) **Service**: General medical and surgical

Staffed Beds: 24

MARKSVILLE—Avoyelles Parish

AVOYELLES HOSPITAL (190099), 4231 Highway 1192, Zip 71351–4711, Mailing Address: P.O. Box 249, Zip 71351–0249; tel. 318/253–8611, **A**10 **F**3 15 29 30 34 40 43 45 54 56 57 64 65 70 81 82 85 86 107 110 114 119 127 133 146 149 154
Primary Contact: Timothey Curry, Chief Executive Officer
CFO: Christina Faust, Chief Financial Officer
CMO: Donna Breen, M.D., Chief of Staff
CIO: Johnny Bergeron, Manager Information Technology
CHR: Allison Ferguson, Director Human Resources
CNO: Cindy K Juneau, Chief Nursing Officer, Manger Quality and Risk
Web address: www.avoyelleshospital.com
Control: Corporation, Investor-owned (for-profit) **Service**: General medical and surgical

Staffed Beds: 32 **Admissions**: 1645 **Census**: 9 **Outpatient Visits**: 37446 **Births**: 0 **Total Expense ($000)**: 16896 **Payroll Expense ($000)**: 7794 **Personnel**: 184

MARRERO—Jefferson Parish

BRIDGEPOINT CONTINUING CARE HOSPITAL (192007), 1101 Medical Center Boulevard, 7th Floor, Zip 70072–3147; tel. 504/349–2581, (Nonreporting) **A**10
Primary Contact: John Rivoire, R.N., MSN, Administrator
Web address: www.https://www.bridgepointhealthcare.com/
Control: Corporation, Investor-owned (for-profit) **Service**: Acute long-term care hospital

Staffed Beds: 56

⊞ △ **WEST JEFFERSON MEDICAL CENTER (190039)**, 1101 Medical Center Boulevard, Zip 70072–3191; tel. 504/347–5511, **A**1 2 3 5 7 10 **F**3 7 8 11 12 13 15 17 18 20 22 24 26 28 29 30 31 34 35 37 38 39 40 41 43 45 46 47 48 49 50 51 53 56 57 59 61 64 65 68 70 72 74 75 76 78 79 81 82 84 85 86 87 90 91 93 96 97 98 100 101 102 104 105 107 108 109 110 111 112 114 115 117 118 119 120 121 124 126 127 129 130 132 135 146 147 148 149 154 157 **S** LCMC Health, New Orleans, LA
Primary Contact: Dodie McElmurray, Interim Chief Executive Officer and Chief Operating Officer
CFO: Daniel Riley
CMO: Robert Chugden, M.D., Chief Medical Officer
CHR: Floyd Riedlinger, Director Human Resources
CNO: Monica Bologna, R.N., Chief Nursing Officer
Web address: www.wjmc.org
Control: Other not-for-profit (including NFP Corporation) **Service**: General medical and surgical

Staffed Beds: 229 **Admissions**: 9787 **Census**: 159 **Outpatient Visits**: 345689 **Births**: 1026 **Total Expense ($000)**: 290057 **Payroll Expense ($000)**: 95177 **Personnel**: 1363

METAIRIE—Jefferson Parish

☐ △ **EAST JEFFERSON GENERAL HOSPITAL (190146)**, 4200 Houma Boulevard, Zip 70006–2996; tel. 504/503–4000, (Includes DOCTORS HOSPITAL OF JEFFERSON, 4320 Houma Boulevard, Metairie, Louisiana, Zip 70006–2973; tel. 504/849–4000) **A**1 2 3 5 7 10 **F**3 7 8 11 13 14 15 17 18 20 22 24 26 28 29 30 31 34 35 36 37 40 44 45 46 47 48 49 50 51 53 54 55 56 57 58 59 64 65 70 72 73 74 75 76 77 78 79 81 82 84 85 86 87 90 91 92 93 96 97 98 102 103 107 108 110 111 114 115 117 118 119 120 121 123 124 126 128 129 130 131 132 135 141 142 145 146 147 148 149 156
Primary Contact: Gerald L. Parton, FACHE, Chief Executive Officer
COO: Paolo Zambito, R.N., Chief Operating Officer
CFO: Robert Riley, Interim Chief Financial Officer
CMO: Raymond P DeCorte, M.D., Chief Medical Officer
CHR: Frank Martinez, Senior Vice President Human Resources
CNO: Ruby Brewer RN Senior Vice President, Chief Nursing and Quality Officer
Web address: www.ejgh.org
Control: Hospital district or authority, Government, nonfederal **Service**: General medical and surgical

Staffed Beds: 412 **Admissions**: 13783 **Census**: 191 **Outpatient Visits**: 215513 **Births**: 952 **Total Expense ($000)**: 353897 **Payroll Expense ($000)**: 102216 **Personnel**: 1927

⇑ **OMEGA HOSPITAL (190302)**, 2525 Severn Avenue, Zip 70002–5932; tel. 504/832–4200, (Nonreporting) **A**10 21
Primary Contact: Karen Rousselle, Administrator
Web address: www.omegahospital.com
Control: Individual, Investor-owned (for-profit) **Service**: Surgical

Staffed Beds: 10

Hospital, Medicare Provider Number, Address, Telephone, Approval, Facility, and Physician Codes, Health Care System

★ American Hospital Association (AHA) membership
☐ The Joint Commission accreditation
○ Healthcare Facilities Accreditation Program
◇ DNV Healthcare Inc. accreditation
⇑ Center for Improvement in Healthcare Quality Accreditation
△ Commission on Accreditation of Rehabilitation Facilities (CARF) accreditation

LA

MINDEN—Webster Parish

✉ **MINDEN MEDICAL CENTER (190144)**, 1 Medical Plaza Place, Zip 71055–3330, Mailing Address: P.O. Box 5003, Zip 71058–5003; tel. 318/377–2321, (Nonreporting) **A**1 10 19 **S** Allegiance Health Management, Shreveport, LA
Primary Contact: Gregory Pearson, Chief Executive Officer
CFO: James R. Williams, Chief Financial Officer
CMO: G Max Stell, M.D., Medical Director
CIO: Mace Morgan, Director Information Systems
CHR: Mary Winget, Director Human Resources
CNO: Donna Carter, MSN, R.N., Chief Nursing Officer
Web address: www.mindenmedicalcenter.com
Control: Corporation, Investor–owned (for–profit) **Service**: General medical and surgical

Staffed Beds: 161

MONROE—Ouachita Parish

BASTROP REHABILITATION HOSPITAL (193058), 4310 South Grand Street, Zip 71202–6322; tel. 318/654–8300, (Nonreporting) **A**10
Primary Contact: Patrick King, Administrator
CMO: Jeffery Combetta, M.D., Medical Director
CHR: Rhonda Church, Director Human Resources
Web address: www.ldh.la.gov/index.cfm/directory/detail/1772/catid/169
Control: Corporation, Investor–owned (for–profit) **Service**: Rehabilitation

Staffed Beds: 12

E. A. CONWAY MEDICAL CENTER See Ochsner Lsu Health Shreveport - Monroe Medical Center

⇑ **MONROE SURGICAL HOSPITAL (190245)**, 2408 Broadmoor Boulevard, Zip 71201–2963; tel. 318/410–0002, (Nonreporting) **A**10 21
Primary Contact: Robyn Hemphill, Chief Executive Officer and Chief Nursing Officer
Web address: www.monroesurgical.com
Control: Corporation, Investor–owned (for–profit) **Service**: Surgical

Staffed Beds: 10

☐ **OCHSNER LSU HEALTH SHREVEPORT - MONROE MEDICAL CENTER (190011)**, 4864 Jackson Street, Zip 71202–6497, Mailing Address: P.O. Box 1881, Zip 71210–8005; tel. 318/330–7000, (Nonreporting) **A**1 3 5 10 **S** University Health System, Shreveport, LA
Primary Contact: Jonathan Phillips, Interim Administrator
CFO: Dorothy Whittington, Chief Financial Officer
CMO: Richard Cavell, M.D., Medical Director
CIO: Todd Walters, Director of UHC Information Technology Services
CHR: Rob Hartmann, Assistant Director Human Resources Management
CNO: Traci S. Jordan, MS, R.N., Chief Nursing Officer
Web address: www.uhsystem.com
Control: State, Government, nonfederal **Service**: General medical and surgical

Staffed Beds: 108

SPECIALTY HOSPITAL (192016), 309 Jackson Street, 7th Floor, Zip 71201–7407, Mailing Address: P.O. Box 1532, Zip 71210–1532; tel. 318/966–7045, (Nonreporting) **A**10 **S** LHC Group, Lafayette, LA
Primary Contact: Cleta Munholland, Administrator
COO: Pamela Chappell, R.N., Assistant Administrator
CNO: Jerry Rogers, R.N., Director Nurses and Infection Control
Web address: www.lhcgroup.com
Control: Church operated, Nongovernment, not–for–profit **Service**: Acute long–term care hospital

Staffed Beds: 32

✉ **ST. FRANCIS MEDICAL CENTER (190125)**, 309 Jackson Street, Zip 71201–7407, Mailing Address: P.O. Box 1901, Zip 71210–1901; tel. 318/966–4000, **A**1 3 10 **F**3 12 13 15 17 18 19 20 21 22 23 24 25 26 27 28 29 30 31 32 34 35 37 39 40 44 45 46 49 50 54 55 56 57 59 64 65 68 69 70 71 72 74 75 76 77 78 79 81 84 85 87 88 89 90 92 93 96 97 107 108 110 111 114 115 118 119 124 126 128 129 130 131 132 135 146 147 148 156 157 **S** Franciscan Missionaries of Our Lady Health System, Inc., Baton Rouge, LA
Primary Contact: Kristin Wolkart, R.N., President and Chief Executive Officer
CFO: Jeremy Rogers, Chief Financial Officer
CNO: Kayla Johnson, R.N., Vice President Patient Care Services and Chief Nursing Officer
Web address: www.stfran.com
Control: Church operated, Nongovernment, not–for–profit **Service**: General medical and surgical

Staffed Beds: 365 Admissions: 15033 Census: 196 Outpatient Visits: 221504 Births: 1702 Total Expense ($000): 254715 Payroll Expense ($000): 87356

ST. FRANCIS SPECIALTY HOSPITAL See Specialty Hospital

MORGAN CITY—St. Mary Parish

✉ **TECHE REGIONAL MEDICAL CENTER (190014)**, 1125 Marguerite Street, Zip 70380–1855, Mailing Address: P.O. Box 2308, Zip 70381–2308; tel. 985/384–2200, (Nonreporting) **A**1 10 20 **S** LifePoint Health, Brentwood, TN
Primary Contact: Anthony Young, Chief Executive Officer
COO: Don Knight, Assistant Administrator and Risk Manager
CFO: Leonard Binkley Jr Interim Chief Financial Officer
CMO: Eric Melancon, Chief of Staff
CIO: Rene Bilello, Manager Information System
CHR: Timothy Hebert, Director Human Resources
Web address: www.techeregional.com
Control: Corporation, Investor–owned (for–profit) **Service**: General medical and surgical

Staffed Beds: 164

NAPOLEONVILLE—Assumption Parish

★ **ASSUMPTION COMMUNITY HOSPITAL (191303)**, 135 Highway 402, Zip 70390–2217; tel. 985/369–3600, (Nonreporting) **A**10 18 **S** Franciscan Missionaries of Our Lady Health System, Inc., Baton Rouge, LA
Primary Contact: Christina P. Hockaday, FACHE, Chief Executive Officer
CHR: Letonia Pierre, Coordinator Human Resources
CNO: Donna Mullings, Director of Nursing
Web address: www.https://ololrmc.com
Service: General medical and surgical

Staffed Beds: 6

NATCHITOCHES—Natchitoches Parish

LOUISIANA EXTENDED CARE HOSPITAL OF NATCHITOCHES (192035), 501 Keyser Avenue, Zip 71457–6018; tel. 318/354–2044, **A**10 **F**1 3 4 16 17 28 29 30 34 50 57 59 67 68 70 72 73 74 75 76 80 85 86 87 88 89 90 91 97 98 128 130 148 **S** LHC Group, Lafayette, LA
Primary Contact: John Rivoire, R.N., MSN, Administrator
Web address: www.lhcgroup.com
Control: Partnership, Investor–owned (for–profit) **Service**: Acute long–term care hospital

Staffed Beds: 21 Admissions: 248 Census: 15 Outpatient Visits: 0 Births: 0

✉ **NATCHITOCHES REGIONAL MEDICAL CENTER (190007)**, 501 Keyser Avenue, Zip 71457–6036, Mailing Address: P.O. Box 2009, Zip 71457–2009; tel. 318/214–4200, (Nonreporting) **A**1 10 20 **S** CHRISTUS Health, Irving, TX
Primary Contact: D. Kirk. Soileau, FACHE, Chief Executive Officer
CFO: Brad McCormick, Chief Financial Officer
CMO: Phyllis Mason, M.D., Chief Medical Officer
CHR: Ernie Scott, Director Human Resources
CNO: Dawna DeBlieux, Vice President Patient Care Services and Chief Nurse Executive
Web address: www.nrmchospital.org
Control: Hospital district or authority, Government, nonfederal **Service**: General medical and surgical

Staffed Beds: 91

NEW IBERIA—Iberia Parish

☐ **IBERIA MEDICAL CENTER (190054)**, 2315 East Main Street, Zip 70560–4031, Mailing Address: P.O. Box 13338, Zip 70562–3338; tel. 337/364–0441, **A**1 10 **F**3 4 11 13 15 16 17 18 20 22 28 29 30 31 34 39 40 45 46 47 48 49 50 53 57 64 67 70 72 73 74 75 76 78 79 80 81 85 88 89 90 93 97 98 103 107 108 110 111 115 119 127 128 130 135 146 149 **S** HealthTech Management Services, Brentwood, TN
Primary Contact: Parker A. Templeton, FACHE, Chief Executive Officer
COO: Shane P Myers, Chief Operating Officer
CFO: Dionne Viator, CPA, FACHE, Chief Financial Officer
CMO: Shawn Baquet, Chief of Staff
CIO: Vance Robinson, Chief Information Officer
CHR: Lori Spann, Director Human Resources
CNO: Sandy Morein, Chief Nursing Officer
Web address: www.iberiamedicalcenter.com
Control: Hospital district or authority, Government, nonfederal **Service**: General medical and surgical

Staffed Beds: 123 Admissions: 4853 Census: 54 Outpatient Visits: 124839 Births: 285 Total Expense ($000): 94319 Payroll Expense ($000): 35379 Personnel: 682

Many Facility Codes have changed. Please refer to the AHA Guide Code Chart.

© 2019 AHA Guide

☐ **IBERIA REHABILITATION HOSPITAL (193096)**, 532 Jefferson Terrace, Zip 70560–4948; tel. 337/364–6923, (Nonreporting) **A**1 10
Primary Contact: Athan J. Olivier III, R.N., MSN, FACHE, Administrator and Chief Executive Officer
Web address: www.iberiarehab.net/
Control: Partnership, Investor–owned (for–profit) **Service**: Rehabilitation

Staffed Beds: 24

NEW ORLEANS—Orleans Parish

☐ **BEACON BEHAVIORAL HOSPITAL - NEW ORLEANS (194084)**, 14500 Hayne Boulevard, Suite 200, Zip 70128–1751; tel. 504/210–0460, (Nonreporting) **A**1 10
Primary Contact: Sean Wendell, CPA, Chief Executive Officer
Control: Corporation, Investor–owned (for–profit) **Service**: Psychiatric

Staffed Beds: 24

☐ △ **CHILDREN'S HOSPITAL (193300)**, 200 Henry Clay Avenue, Zip 70118–5720; tel. 504/899–9511, (Nonreporting) **A**1 2 3 5 7 10 **S** LCMC Health, New Orleans, LA
Primary Contact: John R. Nickens IV, President and Chief Executive Officer
COO: Matthew Schaefer, Chief Operating Officer
CFO: Courtney Garrett, CPA, Senior Vice President, Chief Financial Officer
CMO: George Bisset, M.D., III Chief Medical Officer
CIO: Tanya Townsend, Senior Vice President, Chief Information Officer (part of LCMC)
CHR: Wendy L Willis, Vice President Human Resources
CNO: Diane Michel, Senior Vice President, Chief Nursing Officer
Web address: www.chnola.org
Control: Other not–for–profit (including NFP Corporation) **Service**: Children's general medical and surgical

Staffed Beds: 210

COBALT REHABILITATION HOSPITAL OF NEW ORLEANS (193098), 3801 Bienville Street, Zip 70119; tel. 504/930–3500, (Nonreporting) **A**10 22
Primary Contact: Scott Tranchina, R.N., MSN, Administrator
Control: Partnership, Investor–owned (for–profit) **Service**: Rehabilitation

Staffed Beds: 60

☐ **COMMUNITY CARE HOSPITAL (194056)**, 1421 General Taylor Street, Zip 70115–3717; tel. 504/899–2500, (Nonreporting) **A**1 10
Primary Contact: Paul B. Kavanaugh, President and Chief Executive Officer
Web address: www.communitycarehospital.com
Control: State, Government, nonfederal **Service**: Psychiatric

Staffed Beds: 36

☐ **CURAHEALTH NEW ORLEANS (192009)**, 3601 Coliseum Street, Zip 70115–3606; tel. 504/899–1555, (Nonreporting) **A**1 10 **S** Curahealth Hospitals, Garland, TX
Primary Contact: Kristy Caleyo, Chief Executive Officer
CFO: Laurie Champagne, Controller
Web address: www.curahealth.com
Control: Corporation, Investor–owned (for–profit) **Service**: Acute long–term care hospital

Staffed Beds: 80

MEDICAL CENTER OF LOUISIANA AT NEW ORLEANS See University Medical Center

☐ **NEW ORLEANS EAST HOSPITAL (190313)**, 5620 Read Boulevard, Zip 70127–3106, Mailing Address: 5620 Read Blvd, Zip 70127–3106; tel. 504/592–6600, **A**1 **F**3 11 15 18 20 26 29 30 34 35 38 40 44 45 50 57 58 59 63 64 65 68 70 74 75 77 79 81 82 85 86 87 91 93 97 107 108 110 111 115 118 119 129 130 131 132 133 134 146 147 148 149 156 157 **S** LCMC Health, New Orleans, LA
Primary Contact: Takeisha C. Davis, M.D., M.P.H., President and Chief Executive Officer
COO: Dante Green, Assistant Vice President Operations
CFO: Danielle S. Willis, CPA, Interim Chief Financial Officer, Manager Finance
CHR: Brion Stanford, Director Human Resources
CNO: Martha Smith, R.N., Chief Nursing Officer
Web address: www.noehospital.org
Control: Hospital district or authority, Government, nonfederal **Service**: General medical and surgical

Staffed Beds: 34 Admissions: 1339 Census: 12 Outpatient Visits: 83600 Births: 0 Total Expense ($000): 58354 Payroll Expense ($000): 23296

PSYCHIATRIC PAVILION NEW ORLEANS See Beacon Behavioral Hospital - New Orleans

☐ **UNIVERSITY MEDICAL CENTER (190005)**, 2000 Canal Street, Zip 70112–3018; tel. 504/702–3000, **A**1 2 3 5 8 10 **F**3 11 12 15 16 18 20 22 24 26 29 30 31 34 35 39 40 43 45 46 47 49 50 51 55 57 58 59 61 63 64 65 66 70 74 75 77 78 79 80 81 83 84 85 86 87 92 93 94 97 98 100 102 107 108 110 111 112 114 115 116 117 118 119 123 126 129 130 135 141 142 145 146 147 148 149 150 156 **S** LCMC Health, New Orleans, LA
Primary Contact: Danny Hardman, FACHE, R.N., Chief Executive Officer
COO: Lisa Miranda, Vice President Operations
CFO: Christine Williams, Chief Financial Officer
CNO: Denise Danna Esq Chief Nursing Officer
Web address: www.umcno.org
Control: Other not–for–profit (including NFP Corporation) **Service**: General medical and surgical

Staffed Beds: 324 Admissions: 14158 Census: 263 Outpatient Visits: 393071 Births: 0 Total Expense ($000): 675913 Payroll Expense ($000): 153495 Personnel: 2671

NEW ORLEANS—Jefferson Parish

EXTENDED CARE HOSPITAL (192015), 2614 Jefferson Highway, 2nd Floor, Zip 70121–3828; tel. 504/314–4242, (Nonreporting) **A**10 **S** LHC Group, Lafayette, LA
Primary Contact: Len McDade, Chief Executive Officer
Web address: www.lhcgroup.com/
Control: Corporation, Investor–owned (for–profit) **Service**: Acute long–term care hospital

Staffed Beds: 32

LOUISIANA EXTENDED CARE HOSPITAL OF KENNER See Extended Care Hospital

⊞ **OCHSNER MEDICAL CENTER (190036)**, 1514 Jefferson Highway, Zip 70121–2429; tel. 504/842–3000, (Includes OCHSNER BAPTIST MEDICAL CENTER, 2700 Napoleon Avenue, New Orleans, Louisiana, Zip 70115–6914; tel. 504/899–9311; Beth Walker, Chief Executive Officer; OCHSNER MEDICAL CENTER - WEST BANK, 2500 Belle Chasse Highway, Gretna, Louisiana, Zip 70056–7127; tel. 504/392–3131; Mary Deynoodt, Interim Chief Executive Officer and Chief Operating Officer; OCHSNER MEDICAL CENTER FOR CHILDREN, 1514 Jefferson Highway, New Orleans, Louisiana, Zip 70121–2429; tel. 504/842–3000) (Total facility includes 32 beds in nursing home–type unit) **A**1 2 5 8 10 **F**3 4 5 6 7 8 9 11 12 13 14 15 17 18 19 20 21 22 23 24 25 26 27 28 29 30 31 32 34 35 36 37 38 40 41 42 43 44 45 46 47 48 49 50 53 54 55 56 57 58 59 60 61 63 64 65 68 70 71 72 73 74 75 76 77 78 79 80 81 82 84 85 86 87 88 89 90 91 92 93 94 96 97 98 99 100 101 102 103 104 105 107 108 110 111 114 115 116 117 118 119 120 121 123 124 126 128 129 130 131 132 134 135 136 137 138 139 140 141 142 145 146 147 148 151 152 153 154 156 **S** Ochsner Health System, New Orleans, LA
Primary Contact: Robert K. Wolterman, Chief Executive Officer
CFO: Scott J Posecai, Executive Vice President and Chief Financial Officer
CMO: Patrick J Quinlan, M.D., Chief Executive Officer, Ochsner Clinic Foundation & International Services, Exec. Director Ochsner Center for Community
CIO: Lynn Witherspoon, Vice President and Chief Information Officer
CHR: Joan Mollohan, Vice President Human Resources
Web address: www.ochsner.org
Control: Other not–for–profit (including NFP Corporation) **Service**: General medical and surgical

Staffed Beds: 934 Admissions: 42453 Census: 677 Outpatient Visits: 322869 Births: 4552 Total Expense ($000): 1499376 Payroll Expense ($000): 508729 Personnel: 7789

☐ **RIVER OAKS HOSPITAL (194031)**, 1525 River Oaks Road West, Zip 70123–2162; tel. 504/734–1740, (Includes RIVER OAKS CHILD AND ADOLESCENT HOSPITAL, 1525 River Oaks Road West, New Orleans, Louisiana, Zip 70123–2162; tel. 504/734–1740), (Non-reporting) **A**1 3 10 **S** Universal Health Services, Inc., King of Prussia, PA
Primary Contact: Deagan Watson, Chief Executive Officer
CFO: Brandon Frazier, Chief Financial Officer
CMO: Lincoln Paine, M.D., Medical Director
CIO: Vincent Chatelain, Director Business Development
CHR: Wanda Hoffmann, Director Human Resources
CNO: Jason Krause, R.N., Director of Nursing
Web address: www.riveroakshospital.com
Control: Corporation, Investor–owned (for–profit) **Service**: Psychiatric

Staffed Beds: 126

Hospital, Medicare Provider Number, Address, Telephone, Approval, Facility, and Physician Codes, Health Care System
★ American Hospital Association (AHA) membership	○ Healthcare Facilities Accreditation Program	⇑ Center for Improvement in Healthcare Quality Accreditation
☐ The Joint Commission accreditation	◇ DNV Healthcare Inc. accreditation	△ Commission on Accreditation of Rehabilitation Facilities (CARF) accreditation

LA

NEW ORLEANS—Orleans Parish

SEASIDE BEHAVIORAL CENTER (194100), 4201 Woodland Drive, Zip 70131–7339; tel. 504/393–4223, **A**3 10 **F**35 98 100 101 102 103 105 130 143 153
Primary Contact: Mary L. Matamoros, R.N., Chief Executive Officer
CHR: Sherry May Campbell, Director of Human Resources, Medical Records
CNO: Justin Bernier, R.N., Director of Nursing
Web address: www.seasidehc.com
Control: Corporation, Investor–owned (for–profit) **Service**: Psychiatric

Staffed Beds: 47 **Admissions:** 1745 **Census:** 41 **Outpatient Visits:** 0 **Births:** 0

☐ **ST. CATHERINE MEMORIAL HOSPITAL (192023)**, 14500 Hayne Boulevard, Zip 70128–1751; tel. 504/210–3000, (Nonreporting) **A**1 10
Primary Contact: Lexis Landry Nunez, Chief Executive Officer
Web address: www.stcatherine-hospital.com
Control: Corporation, Investor–owned (for–profit) **Service**: Acute long–term care hospital

Staffed Beds: 21

ST. CHARLES SURGICAL HOSPITAL (190300), 1717 Saint Charles Avenue, Zip 70130–5223; tel. 504/529–6600, (Nonreporting) **A**10 22
Primary Contact: Cheri Saltaformaggio, Chief Executive Officer
Web address: www.scsh.com
Control: Corporation, Investor–owned (for–profit) **Service**: Surgical

Staffed Beds: 39

⊞ △ **TOURO INFIRMARY (190046)**, 1401 Foucher Street, Zip 70115–3593; tel. 504/897–7011, (Includes TOURO REHABILITATION CENTER, 1401 Foucher Street, New Orleans, Louisiana, Zip 70115–3515; tel. 504/897–8560; Susan E. Andrews, Chief Executive Officer) **A**1 2 3 5 7 10 **F**3 8 10 11 13 15 18 20 22 24 26 28 29 30 31 34 35 37 39 40 44 45 46 50 53 54 55 57 58 59 60 61 62 64 68 70 72 74 75 76 77 78 79 81 83 84 85 86 87 90 92 93 96 107 108 109 110 111 114 115 116 117 118 119 120 121 123 124 125 126 130 131 132 135 143 144 146 147 148 149 154 **S** LCMC Health, New Orleans, LA
Primary Contact: Manuel Linares, President and Chief Executive Officer
COO: Stephen Baldwin, Chief Operating Officer
CFO: Bradley Sinclair, Chief Financial Officer
CMO: Jeffrey Coco, M.D., Chief Medical Officer
CIO: Leann Hughes-Mickel, Chief Information Officer
CHR: Cindy Mousa, Director Human Resources
CNO: Danita S Sullivan, R.N., Chief Nursing Officer
Web address: www.touro.com
Control: Other not–for–profit (including NFP Corporation) **Service**: General medical and surgical

Staffed Beds: 280 **Admissions:** 10845 **Census:** 186 **Births:** 3204

⊞ **TULANE HEALTH SYSTEM (190176)**, 1415 Tulane Avenue, Zip 70112–2600; tel. 504/988–5263, (Includes LAKEVIEW REGIONAL MEDICAL CENTER, 95 Judge Tanner Boulevard, Covington, Louisiana, Zip 70433–7507; tel. 985/867–3800; Hiral Patel, M.D., Chief Executive Officer; TULANE-LAKESIDE HOSPITAL, 4700 South I 10 Service Road West, Metairie, Louisiana, Zip 70001–1269; tel. 504/780–4200), (Non-reporting) **A**1 2 3 5 8 10 **S** HCA Healthcare, Nashville, TN
Primary Contact: William Lunn, M.D., President and Chief Executive Officer
COO: Thomas Patrias, FACHE, Chief Operating Officer
CFO: Regina Ramazani, Chief Financial Officer
CMO: John Pigott, M.D., Chief Medical Officer
CIO: Sue Rachuig, Director Information Services
CHR: Leah Grau, Director Human Resources
CNO: Jana S Stonestreet, R.N., Ph.D., Chief Nursing Officer
Web address: www.tuhc.com
Control: Corporation, Investor–owned (for–profit) **Service**: General medical and surgical

Staffed Beds: 294

NEW ROADS—Pointe Coupee Parish

⊞ **POINTE COUPEE GENERAL HOSPITAL (191316)**, 2202 False River Drive, Zip 70760–2614; tel. 225/638–6331, **A**1 10 18 **F**3 29 34 40 75 77 81 107 110 111 119 130 133 146 148 154
Primary Contact: Chad E. Olinde, CPA, Administrator and Chief Executive Officer
CFO: John Cazayoux, Chief Financial Officer
CMO: Paul Rachal, M.D., Chief Medical Officer
CIO: Anthony Sauro, Chief Information Officer
CHR: Lisa Patterson, Director Human Resources
CNO: Valerie Sparks Jarreau, R.N., Chief Nursing Officer
Web address: www.pcgh.org
Control: Hospital district or authority, Government, nonfederal **Service**: General medical and surgical

Staffed Beds: 25 **Admissions:** 277 **Census:** 4 **Outpatient Visits:** 49886 **Births:** 0 **Total Expense ($000):** 17106 **Payroll Expense ($000):** 7789 **Personnel:** 162

OAK GROVE—West Carroll Parish

WEST CARROLL MEMORIAL HOSPITAL (190081), 706 Ross Street, Zip 71263–9798; tel. 318/428–3237, (Nonreporting) **A**10
Primary Contact: R Randall. Morris, Administrator
Control: Other not–for–profit (including NFP Corporation) **Service**: General medical and surgical

Staffed Beds: 21

OAKDALE—Allen Parish

OAKDALE COMMUNITY HOSPITAL (190106), 130 North Hospital Drive, Zip 71463–3035, Mailing Address: P.O. Box 629, Zip 71463–0629; tel. 318/335–3700, (Nonreporting) **A**10
Primary Contact: George Patrick. Derouen, Chief Executive Officer
CFO: Suzette Fatula, Chief Financial Officer
CMO: Tommy Davis, M.D., Chief of Staff
CIO: Sheri Dugas, Director Health Information Management
CHR: Becky Johnson, Director Human Resources
CNO: Kari Broussard, Chief Nursing Officer
Web address: www.oakdalecommunityhospital.com/
Control: Partnership, Investor–owned (for–profit) **Service**: General medical and surgical

Staffed Beds: 27

OLLA—Caldwell Parish

HARDTNER MEDICAL CENTER (191315), 1102 North Pine Road, Zip 71465–4804; tel. 318/495–3131, (Nonreporting) **A**10 18
Primary Contact: Paul G. Mathews, CPA, Administrator
CIO: Sarah Thompson, Director Health Information Management
CNO: Cherry B Salter, Director of Nursing
Web address: www.hardtnermedical.com
Control: Hospital district or authority, Government, nonfederal **Service**: General medical and surgical

Staffed Beds: 35

OPELOUSAS—St. Landry Parish

☐ **OCEANS BEHAVIORAL HOSPITAL OF OPELOUSAS (194095)**, 1310 Heather Drive, Zip 70570–7714; tel. 337/948–8820, (Nonreporting) **A**1 10 **S** Oceans Healthcare, Lake Charles, LA
Primary Contact: Katherine Simoneaux, Administrator
Web address: www.obho.info/
Control: Corporation, Investor–owned (for–profit) **Service**: Psychiatric

Staffed Beds: 20

⊞ **OPELOUSAS GENERAL HEALTH SYSTEM (190017)**, 539 East Prudhomme Street, Zip 70570–6499, Mailing Address: P.O. Box 1389, Zip 70571–1389; tel. 337/948–3011, (Includes OPELOUSAS GENERAL HEALTH SYSTEM-SOUTH CAMPUS, 3983 I-49 South Service Road, Opelousas, Louisiana, Zip 70570–8975; tel. 337/948–2100; Kenneth Cochran, R.N., FACHE, President and Chief Executive Officer) **A**1 2 10 19 **F**3 13 15 28 29 31 34 37 40 44 45 48 49 50 57 60 64 68 70 76 77 78 79 80 81 85 87 90 91 93 96 97 98 102 103 104 105 107 108 110 111 112 114 115 116 117 119 121 126 129 130 131 132 146 147 148 149 153
Primary Contact: Kenneth Cochran, R.N., FACHE, President and Chief Executive Officer
COO: Bob Hardy, Chief Operating Officer
CFO: James B Juneau, Chief Financial Officer
CMO: Hunt Deblanc, M.D., Chief of Staff
CIO: Jared Lormand, Vice President Information Technology
CHR: Suzanne F Kidder, Human Resources Officer
CNO: Kimberly Probus, Chief Nursing Officer
Web address: www.opelousasgeneral.com
Control: Other not–for–profit (including NFP Corporation) **Service**: General medical and surgical

Staffed Beds: 187 **Admissions:** 7160 **Census:** 89 **Outpatient Visits:** 142465 **Births:** 984 **Total Expense ($000):** 137755 **Payroll Expense ($000):** 48715 **Personnel:** 939

ST. LANDRY EXTENDED CARE HOSPITAL (192034), 539 East Prudhomme Street, 6th Floor, Zip 70570–6499; tel. 337/948–2251, (Nonreporting) **A**10 **S** LHC Group, Lafayette, LA
Primary Contact: Biff David, R.N., Administrator
CNO: Shelia B. Johnson, Director of Nursing
Web address: www.lhcgroup.com
Control: Corporation, Investor–owned (for–profit) **Service**: Acute long–term care hospital

Staffed Beds: 41

Many Facility Codes have changed. Please refer to the AHA Guide Code Chart.   © 2019 AHA Guide

PINEVILLE—Rapides Parish

✠ **ALEXANDRIA VETERANS AFFAIRS HEALTH CARE SYSTEM**, 2495 Shreveport Highway, 71 N, Zip 71360–4044, Mailing Address: P.O. Box 69004, Alexandria, Zip 71306–9004; tel. 318/473–0010, (Nonreporting) **A**1 5 **S** Department of Veterans Affairs, Washington, DC
Primary Contact: Peter C. Dancy Jr, FACHE, Director
CFO: Bianca A. Obey, Chief Financial Officer
CMO: Robert Bernard, M.D., Chief of Staff
CIO: Robin McBryde, Chief Information Officer
CHR: Alex Love, Acting Manager Human Resources
CNO: Amy Lesniewski, Associate Director Patient Care Services
Web address: www.alexandria.va.gov/
Control: Veterans Affairs, Government, federal **Service:** General medical and surgical

Staffed Beds: 143

☐ **CENTRAL LOUISIANA STATE HOSPITAL (194025)**, 242 West Shamrock Avenue, Zip 71360–6439, Mailing Address: P.O. Box 5031, Zip 71361–5031; tel. 318/484–6200, **A**1 10 **F**98 100 102 **S** Louisiana State Hospitals, Baton Rouge, LA
Primary Contact: Sandra Duck, Administrator
COO: Paul Benoit, Associate Administrator
CFO: Tina Darbonne, Chief Financial Officer
CMO: L Lee Tynes, M.D., Ph.D., Jr Medical Director
CIO: William Haynes, Director Information Technology
CHR: Tom Crout, MS, Director Human Resources
Web address: www.dhh.louisiana.gov/index.cfm/directory/detail/217
Control: State, Government, nonfederal **Service:** Psychiatric

Staffed Beds: 120 **Admissions:** 31 **Census:** 118 **Outpatient Visits:** 0 **Births:** 0

VETERANS AFFAIRS MEDICAL CENTER - ALEXANDRIA See Alexandria Veterans Affairs Health Care System

PLAQUEMINE—Iberville Parish

ACCORD REHABILIATION HOSPITAL (193070), 59213 Riverwest Drive, Zip 70764–6552; tel. 225/687–8100, (Nonreporting) **A**10
Primary Contact: Julene Mcalister, Administrator
Web address: www.mmoinc.com
Control: Other not–for–profit (including NFP Corporation) **Service:** Rehabilitation

Staffed Beds: 8

RACELAND—Lafourche Parish

✠ **OCHSNER ST. ANNE GENERAL HOSPITAL (191324)**, 4608 Highway 1, Zip 70294–2623; tel. 985/537–6841 **A**1 10 18 **F**3 4 13 15 17 18 29 30 34 35 38 40 44 45 50 51 56 57 59 64 65 68 70 74 75 76 77 81 82 85 86 87 89 90 97 98 102 104 107 110 111 114 119 128 130 133 135 146 147 149 154 156 **S** Ochsner Health System, New Orleans, LA
Primary Contact: Timothy J. Allen, FACHE, Chief Executive Officer
COO: Fernis LeBlanc, Chief Operating Officer
CNO: Jana Semere, Chief Nursing Officer
Web address: www.ochsner.org/locations/ochsner-st-anne
Control: Other not–for–profit (including NFP Corporation) **Service:** General medical and surgical

Staffed Beds: 35 **Admissions:** 2031 **Census:** 18 **Outpatient Visits:** 82217 **Births:** 380 **Total Expense ($000):** 52292 **Payroll Expense ($000):** 17569 **Personnel:** 427

RAYNE—Acadia Parish

OCEANS BEHAVIORAL HOSPITAL OF CROWLEY (194097), 2021 Crowley Rayne Highway, Zip 70578–4027; tel. 337/788–0091, (Nonreporting) **A**10
Primary Contact: Katherine Simoneaux, Administrator
Control: Corporation, Investor–owned (for–profit) **Service:** Psychiatric

Staffed Beds: 16

RAYVILLE—Richland Parish

RICHARDSON MEDICAL CENTER (190151), 254 Highway 3048, Zip 71269–0388, Mailing Address: P.O. Box 388, Zip 71269–0388; tel. 318/728–4181, (Nonreporting) **A**10
Primary Contact: James W. Barrett Jr, Chief Executive Officer
CFO: Mallory Gulley Wells, CPA, Chief Financial Officer
CMO: David Thompson, M.D., Chief of Staff
CHR: Rita Brown, Director Human Resources
CNO: Earlene Chriceol, Chief Nursing Officer
Web address: www.richardsonmed.org
Control: Hospital district or authority, Government, nonfederal **Service:** General medical and surgical

Staffed Beds: 37

RUSTON—Lincoln Parish

LIBERTY HEALTHCARE SYSTEMS See Serenity Springs Specialty Hospital

✠ **NORTHERN LOUISIANA MEDICAL CENTER (190086)**, 401 East Vaughn Avenue, Zip 71270–5950; tel. 318/254–2100, (Includes GREEN CLINIC SURGICAL HOSPITAL, 1118 Farmerville Street, Ruston, Louisiana, Zip 71270–5914; tel. 318/232–7700; Chad Conner, Administrator), (Non-reporting) **A**1 10 19 **S** Community Health Systems, Inc., Franklin, TN
Primary Contact: Keith Newton, Chief Executive Officer
CFO: Michael Lockridge, Chief Financial Officer
CMO: Derek McClusky, M.D., Chief of Staff
CIO: Heather Nolan, Director Information Services
CHR: Tonya Duggan, Director Human Resources
CNO: Hartland Hintze, Chief Nursing Officer
Web address: www.northernlouisianamedicalcenter.com
Control: Other not–for–profit (including NFP Corporation) **Service:** General medical and surgical

Staffed Beds: 104

☐ **RUSTON REGIONAL SPECIALTY HOSPITAL (192022)**, 1401 Ezell Street, Zip 71270–7218; tel. 318/251–3126, (Nonreporting) **A**1 10
Primary Contact: Mark J. Rice, Administrator
Web address: www.rustonregional.com/
Control: Corporation, Investor–owned (for–profit) **Service:** Acute long–term care hospital

Staffed Beds: 55

SERENITY SPRINGS SPECIALTY HOSPITAL (194074), 1495 Frazier Road, Zip 71270–1632, tel. 318/202–3000, (Nonreporting) **A**10
Primary Contact: Adrian Williams, Chief Executive Officer
Web address: www.serenityhospital.com
Control: Corporation, Investor–owned (for–profit) **Service:** Psychiatric

Staffed Beds: 18

SAINT FRANCISVILLE—West Feliciana Parish

✠ **WEST FELICIANA PARISH HOSPITAL (191306)**, 5266 Commerce Street, Zip 70775, Mailing Address: P.O. Box 368, Zip 70775–0368; tel. 225/635–3811, (Nonreporting) **A**1 10 18
Primary Contact: Lee Chastant, Chief Executive Officer
CFO: Linda Harvey, Chief Financial Officer
CHR: Neta F Leake, Administrative Assistant Human Resources
CNO: Angela Noble, Director of Nursing
Web address: www.wfph.org
Control: Hospital district or authority, Government, nonfederal **Service:** General medical and surgical

Staffed Beds: 22

Hospital, Medicare Provider Number, Address, Telephone, Approval, Facility, and Physician Codes, Health Care System

★ American Hospital Association (AHA) membership   ○ Healthcare Facilities Accreditation Program   ⇑ Center for Improvement in Healthcare Quality Accreditation
☐ The Joint Commission accreditation   ◇ DNV Healthcare Inc. accreditation   △ Commission on Accreditation of Rehabilitation Facilities (CARF) accreditation

LA

SHREVEPORT—Caddo Parish

☐ **BRENTWOOD HOSPITAL (194020)**, 1006 Highland Avenue, Zip 71101–4103; tel. 318/678–7500, **A**1 3 10 **F**4 5 29 35 38 87 98 99 100 101 102 103 104 105 135 151 152 153 154 **S** Universal Health Services, Inc., King of Prussia, PA
Primary Contact: William Weaver, Chief Executive Officer
CFO: Kae Bell, Chief Financial Officer
CMO: Colonel Daniel Feeney, M.D., Medical Director
CHR: Talicia Johnson, Director Human Resources
CNO: Ravon Dominique, Chief Nursing Officer
Web address: www.brentwoodbehavioral.com
Control: State, Government, nonfederal **Service:** Psychiatric

> **Staffed Beds:** 176 **Admissions:** 6280 **Census:** 158 **Outpatient Visits:** 14203 **Births:** 0 **Total Expense ($000):** 30055 **Payroll Expense ($000):** 15328 **Personnel:** 320

⊞ **CHRISTUS HEALTH SHREVEPORT-BOSSIER (190041)**, 1453 East Bert Kouns Industrial Loop, Zip 71105–6800; tel. 318/681–5000, (Includes CHRISTUS BOSSIER EMERGENCY HOSPITAL, 2531 Viking Drive, Bossier City, Louisiana, Zip 71111; tel. 318/681–7000; Jennifer Varnadore, Administrator; CHRISTUS HIGHLAND MEDICAL CENTER, 1453 East Bert Kouns Industrial Loop, Shreveport, Louisiana, Zip 71105–6050; tel. 318/681–5000; Thomas S. Trawick, M.D., Chief Executive Officer) **A**1 2 10 **F**3 11 12 13 15 17 18 20 22 24 26 28 29 30 31 32 34 35 40 42 45 46 47 48 49 50 53 54 55 56 57 58 59 61 64 70 72 73 74 75 76 77 78 79 80 81 82 84 85 86 87 90 93 96 97 102 107 108 110 111 114 115 119 120 121 123 124 126 130 131 132 134 135 146 147 148 149 156 **S** CHRISTUS Health, Irving, TX
Primary Contact: Thomas S. Trawick, M.D., Chief Executive Officer
COO: Joshua Lamb, Vice President Operations
CFO: Scott Merryman, Chief Financial Officer
CMO: Marisa Johnson, M.D., Vice President Medical Affairs
CIO: Mary Merryman, Regional Director Information Management
CHR: Wendy Chandler, Vice President Human Resources
CNO: Ginger Disante, Chief Nursing Executive
Web address: www.christushealthsb.org
Control: Church operated, Nongovernment, not–for–profit **Service:** General medical and surgical

> **Staffed Beds:** 200 **Admissions:** 8353 **Census:** 110 **Outpatient Visits:** 190528 **Births:** 973 **Total Expense ($000):** 208843 **Payroll Expense ($000):** 55194 **Personnel:** 889

⊞ **LIFECARE HOSPITALS OF SHREVEPORT-WILLIS KNIGHTON (192011)**, 8001 Youree Drive, Zip 71115–2302; tel. 318/212–2200, (Includes LIFECARE HOSPITALS OF SOUTH SHREVEPORT-WILLIS KNIGHTON NORTH, 2550 Kings Highway, Shreveport, Louisiana, Zip 71103–3922; tel. 318/681–7000; Keith Cox, Chief Executive Officer and Administrator), (Non-reporting) **A**1 **S** LifeCare Management Services, Plano, TX
Primary Contact: Brent Martin, Administrator
Web address: www.https://www.lifecarehealthpartners.com/region/shreveport
Control: Corporation, Investor–owned (for–profit) **Service:** Acute long–term care hospital

> **Staffed Beds:** 54

OCHSNER LSU HEALTH SHREVPORT - ACADEMIC MEDICAL CENTER (190098), 1501 Kings Highway, Zip 71103–4228, Mailing Address: P.O. Box 33932, Zip 71130–3932; tel. 318/675–5000, (Includes CHILDREN'S HOSPITAL OF SHREVEPORT, 1501 Kings Highway, Shreveport, Louisiana, Zip 71103–4228, Mailing Address: P.O. Box 33932, Zip 71130–3932, tel. 318/675–5000), (Non-reporting) **A**2 3 5 10 **S** University Health System, Shreveport, LA
Primary Contact: Mark Randolph, President
COO: Betty Johnson, Associate Administrator
CFO: Harold White, Vice Chancellor
CMO: Kevin Sittig, M.D., Senior Associate Dean and Chief Medical Officer
CIO: Marcus Hobgood, Director Information Services
CHR: David Fuqua, Director Human Resources Management
Web address: www.lsuhscshreveport.edu
Control: State, Government, nonfederal **Service:** General medical and surgical

> **Staffed Beds:** 395

⊞ **OVERTON BROOKS VETERANS AFFAIRS MEDICAL CENTER**, 510 East Stoner Avenue, Zip 71101–4295; tel. 318/221–8411, (Nonreporting) **A**1 2 3 5 **S** Department of Veterans Affairs, Washington, DC
Primary Contact: Richard Crockett, Director
CFO: Kim Lane, Chief Fiscal Service
CIO: Janey Taylor, Chief Information and Technology
CHR: Michael L Palmier, Chief Human Resources Management
Web address: www.shreveport.va.gov/
Control: Veterans Affairs, Government, federal **Service:** General medical and surgical

> **Staffed Beds:** 100

PHYSICIANS BEHAVIORAL HOSPITAL (194094), 2025 Desoto Street, Zip 71103–4717; tel. 318/550–0520, (Nonreporting) **A**10
Primary Contact: Allison Cooper, Administrator
Control: Corporation, Investor–owned (for–profit) **Service:** Psychiatric

> **Staffed Beds:** 24

☐ **PROMISE HOSPITAL OF LOUISIANA - SHREVEPORT CAMPUS (192010)**, 1800 Irving Place, Zip 71101–4608; tel. 318/425–4096, (Includes PROMISE HOSPITAL OF LOUISIANA - BOSSIER CITY CAMPUS, 2525 Viking Drive, Bossier City, Louisiana, Zip 71111–2103; tel. 318/841–2525), (Nonreporting) **A**1 3 10 **S** Promise Healthcare, Boca Raton, FL
Primary Contact: Rick Stockton, Chief Executive Officer
Web address: www.promise-shreveport.com
Control: Corporation, Investor–owned (for–profit) **Service:** Acute long–term care hospital

> **Staffed Beds:** 146

PROMISE SPECIALTY HOSPITAL OF SHREVEPORT See Promise Hospital of Louisiana - Shreveport Campus

☐ **SHRINERS HOSPITALS FOR CHILDREN-SHREVEPORT (193301)**, 3100 Samford Avenue, Zip 71103–4289; tel. 318/222–5704, **A**1 3 5 10 **F**34 50 55 59 64 68 77 79 81 85 89 93 119 130 131 146 154 **S** Shriners Hospitals for Children, Tampa, FL
Primary Contact: Garry Kim. Green, FACHE, Administrator
CFO: Clarissa Brown-Smith, Director Fiscal Services
CMO: John A. Fox, M.D., Chief of Staff
CIO: Michael Lyons, Regional Information Systems Director
CHR: Rena Arbuthnot, Director Human Resources
CNO: Kathleen A. Redler, Director Patient Care Services
Web address: www.shrinershospitalsforchildren.org/Hospitals/Locations/Shreveport.aspx
Control: Other not–for–profit (including NFP Corporation) **Service:** Children's orthopedic

> **Staffed Beds:** 45 **Admissions:** 277 **Census:** 2 **Outpatient Visits:** 18330 **Births:** 0 **Personnel:** 181

SPECIALISTS HOSPITAL - SHREVEPORT (190278), 1500 Line Avenue, Zip 71101–4639; tel. 318/213–3800, (Nonreporting) **A**10
Primary Contact: Kandi Moore, R.N., Administrator
CFO: Daniel Montgomery, Chief Financial Officer
CNO: Mary Virginia Loftus, Chief Nursing Officer
Web address: www.specialistshospitalshreveport.com/
Control: Corporation, Investor–owned (for–profit) **Service:** Orthopedic

> **Staffed Beds:** 15

⊞ **WILLIS-KNIGHTON MEDICAL CENTER (190111)**, 2600 Greenwood Road, Zip 71103–3908, Mailing Address: P.O. Box 32600, Zip 71130–2600; tel. 318/212–4600, (Includes WILLIS-KNIGHTON PIERREMONT HEALTH CENTER, 8001 Youree Drive, Shreveport, Louisiana, Zip 71115; tel. 318/212–3000; WILLIS-KNIGHTON SOUTH - THE CENTER FOR WOMEN'S HEALTH, 2510 Bert Kouns Industrial Loop, Shreveport, Louisiana, Zip 71118; tel. 318/212–5000; Keri Elrod, Administrator; WK BOSSIER HEALTH CENTER, 2400 Hospital Drive, Bossier City, Louisiana, Zip 71111–2385; tel. 318/212–7000; Todd Blanchard, Administrator) (Total facility includes 155 beds in nursing home–type unit) **A**1 2 3 5 10 **F**3 4 5 7 8 12 13 15 18 20 22 24 26 28 29 30 31 32 34 35 39 40 44 45 46 47 48 49 50 51 52 53 54 55 56 57 58 59 60 62 63 64 65 66 68 70 72 74 75 76 77 78 79 81 82 84 85 86 87 88 89 90 91 92 93 94 96 97 98 100 101 102 104 105 107 108 109 110 111 112 114 115 116 117 118 119 120 121 122 123 124 125 126 127 128 129 130 131 132 134 135 138 139 142 143 144 145 147 148 149 152 153 156 **S** Willis-Knighton Health System, Shreveport, LA
Primary Contact: James K. Elrod, LFACHE, Chief Executive Officer
CMO: Dan Moller, M.D., Chief Medical Officer
CHR: Mike Chandler, Administrator
CNO: Debbie D Olds, R.N., MSN, Director of Nursing
Web address: www.wkhs.com
Control: Other not–for–profit (including NFP Corporation) **Service:** General medical and surgical

> **Staffed Beds:** 758 **Admissions:** 34738 **Census:** 539 **Outpatient Visits:** 507569 **Births:** 3078 **Personnel:** 6759

SLIDELL—St. Tammany Parish

NORTHSHORE REGIONAL MEDICAL CENTER See Ochsner Medical Center - North Shore

Many Facility Codes have changed. Please refer to the AHA Guide Code Chart.

© 2019 AHA Guide

⊞ **OCHSNER MEDICAL CENTER - NORTH SHORE (190204)**, 100 Medical Center Drive, Zip 70461–5520; tel. 985/649–7070, **A1** 10 **F3** 12 15 18 24 29 30 31 32 34 35 38 40 41 44 45 46 49 50 51 57 59 60 61 64 68 70 74 75 77 78 79 81 84 85 86 87 90 91 93 95 96 97 102 107 110 111 114 118 119 126 130 132 135 146 147 148 154 **S** Ochsner Health System, New Orleans, LA
Primary Contact: John J. Herman, FACHE, Chief Executive Officer
CFO: Forrest Whichard, Chief Financial Officer
CMO: James Newcomb, M.D., Vice President Medical
CHR: Terri Joseph-Taylor, Chief Human Resource Manager
CNO: Cheryl Woods, Chief Nursing Officer
Web address: www.https://www.ochsner.org/locations/ochsner-medical-center-north-shore/
Control: Other not–for–profit (including NFP Corporation) **Service:** General medical and surgical

> **Staffed Beds:** 163 **Admissions:** 4774 **Census:** 57 **Outpatient Visits:** 88684 **Births:** 0 **Total Expense ($000):** 88860 **Payroll Expense ($000):** 35904 **Personnel:** 531

⊞ **SLIDELL MEMORIAL HOSPITAL (190040)**, 1001 Gause Boulevard, Zip 70458–2987; tel. 985/280–2200, **A1** 2 3 5 10 **F3** 11 13 15 17 18 20 22 24 26 28 29 30 31 32 34 35 40 45 47 49 54 56 57 59 62 64 65 70 72 75 76 77 78 79 81 82 85 86 87 91 93 96 97 102 107 108 110 111 114 115 116 117 118 119 120 121 124 129 130 132 135 154 **S** Ochsner Health System, New Orleans, LA
Primary Contact: Kerry Tirman, JD, FACHE, Chief Executive Officer
COO: Bruce Clement, Chief Operating Officer
CFO: Sandy Badinger, Chief Financial Officer
CMO: James Newcomb, M.D., Vice President Medical Affairs
CNO: Lynn Strain, R.N., MSN, Chief Nursing Officer
Web address: www.slidellmemorial.org
Control: Hospital district or authority, Government, nonfederal **Service:** General medical and surgical

> **Staffed Beds:** 175 **Admissions:** 8524 **Census:** 96 **Outpatient Visits:** 148403 **Births:** 1203 **Total Expense ($000):** 195547 **Payroll Expense ($000):** 80725 **Personnel:** 1090

☐ **SOUTHERN SURGICAL HOSPITAL (190270)**, 1700 Lindberg Drive, Zip 70458–8062; tel. 985/641–0600, **A1** 10 **F8** 12 18 26 29 34 35 37 45 47 51 57 59 60 64 66 68 74 75 79 81 82 85 86 87 107 111 112 114 119 126 130 131 132 135 143
Primary Contact: Michael J. Pisciotta, Chief Executive Officer
CFO: Michael J Maurin, Chief Financial Officer
CMO: J Gooey, M.D., Medical Director
CIO: Buddy Graves, Chief Information Officer
CHR: Lorrie Alfred. Director Human Resources
Web address: www.sshla.com/
Control: Corporation, Investor–owned (for–profit) **Service:** General medical and surgical

> **Staffed Beds:** 37 **Admissions:** 1404 **Census:** 12 **Outpatient Visits:** 5900 **Births:** 0 **Total Expense ($000):** 26677 **Payroll Expense ($000):** 8770

STERLING SURGICAL HOSPITAL (190256), 989 Robert Boulevard, Zip 70458–2009; tel. 985/690–8200, (Nonreporting) **A**10
Primary Contact: Christopher W. Daniel, Administrator
Web address: www.sterlingsurgical.net/
Control: Corporation, Investor–owned (for–profit) **Service:** Surgical

> **Staffed Beds:** 10

SPRINGHILL—Webster Parish

☐ **SPRINGHILL MEDICAL CENTER (190088)**, 2001 Doctors Drive, Zip 71075–4526, Mailing Address: P.O. Box 920, Zip 71075–0920; tel. 318/539–1000, (Nonreporting) **A**1 10 20 **S** Willis-Knighton Health System, Shreveport, LA
Primary Contact: Michael Patronis, Chief Executive Officer
COO: Dana R. Jones, R.N., MSN, Chief Nursing Officer and Chief Operating Officer
CFO: David Sanders, Chief Financial Officer
CMO: Jerry W. Sessions, M.D., Chief Medical Staff
CIO: Brian Griffin, Director Information Services
CHR: Ashley Ortego, Director Human Resources and Marketing
CNO: Dana R. Jones, R.N., MSN, Chief Nursing Officer and Chief Operating Officer
Web address: www.smccare.com
Control: Other not–for–profit (including NFP Corporation) **Service:** General medical and surgical

> **Staffed Beds:** 58

SULPHUR—Calcasieu Parish

☐ **WEST CALCASIEU CAMERON HOSPITAL (190013)**, 701 Cypress Street, Zip 70663–5000, Mailing Address: P.O. Box 2509, Zip 70664–2509; tel. 337/527–7034, **A1** 10 **F3** 7 8 11 13 15 18 20 22 26 28 29 30 31 34 35 37 38 39 40 44 45 46 50 51 53 54 57 59 62 65 68 70 75 76 77 78 79 81 85 86 87 89 91 93 94 96 97 107 108 110 111 114 115 118 119 127 129 130 132 134 135 141 145 146 147 148 149 154 156
Primary Contact: Janie Fruge, FACHE, Chief Executive Officer
CFO: Jobie James, Chief Financial Officer
CIO: Trey Rion, Chief Information Officer
CHR: Christi Kingsley, Vice President Human Resources
CNO: Brenda Quesnel, R.N., Vice President of Patient Care and Chief Nursing Officer
Web address: www.wcch.com
Control: Hospital district or authority, Government, nonfederal **Service:** General medical and surgical

> **Staffed Beds:** 79 **Admissions:** 2359 **Census:** 24 **Outpatient Visits:** 93995 **Births:** 317 **Total Expense ($000):** 73226 **Payroll Expense ($000):** 31826 **Personnel:** 610

TALLULAH—Madison Parish

MADISON PARISH HOSPITAL (191314), 900 Johnson Street, Zip 71282–4537; tel. 318/574–2374, (Nonreporting) **A**10 18
Primary Contact: Ted Topolewski, Chief Executive Officer
CFO: W Robert Laurents, CPA, Chief Financial Officer
CIO: Charles Whitaker, Director Information Technology
CHR: Chasity Whitaker, Administrative Assistant
Web address: www.madisonparishhospital.com
Control: Other not–for–profit (including NFP Corporation) **Service:** General medical and surgical

> **Staffed Beds:** 25

THIBODAUX—Lafourche Parish

⊞ △ **THIBODAUX REGIONAL MEDICAL CENTER (190004)**, 602 North Acadia Road, Zip 70301–4847, Mailing Address: P.O. Box 1118, Zip 70302–1118; tel. 985/447–5500, **A1** 2 7 10 **F3** 8 11 12 13 15 18 19 20 22 24 28 29 30 31 32 34 39 40 46 49 50 53 57 59 62 64 70 73 74 75 76 78 79 81 82 85 86 87 89 90 92 93 96 97 98 103 104 107 108 110 111 115 116 117 119 120 121 123 124 126 127 129 130 131 132 134 135 146 147 148 149 153 156 **S** QHR, Brentwood, TN
Primary Contact: Greg K. Stock, FACHE, Chief Executive Officer
COO: Scott Flowers, Vice President Professional Services
CFO: Steve C Gaubert, Chief Financial Officer
CMO: Allen Vander, M.D., Chief Medical Staff
CIO: Bernie Clement, Chief Information Officer
CHR: Eric Degravelle, Director Human Resources
Web address: www.thibodaux.com
Control: Hospital district or authority, Government, nonfederal **Service:** General medical and surgical

> **Staffed Beds:** 154 **Admissions:** 6483 **Census:** 78 **Outpatient Visits:** 292066 **Births:** 1050 **Total Expense ($000):** 178577 **Payroll Expense ($000):** 69630 **Personnel:** 1094

VIDALIA—Concordia Parish

☐ **PROMISE HOSPITAL OF MISS LOU (192028)**, 209 Front Street, Zip 71373–2837; tel. 318/336–6500, **A1** 10 **F1** 29 60 64 85 93 130 143 148 **S** Promise Healthcare, Boca Raton, FL
Primary Contact: Michael Harrell, R.N., Chief Executive Officer
COO: Howard B Koslow, President and Chief Executive Officer
CFO: James Hopwood, Chief Financial Officer
CMO: Randy Tillman, M.D., Chief Medical Staff
CIO: Robert Greene, Director Information Technology
CHR: Roxan Houghton, Director Human Resources
CNO: Regetta Woods, Chief Nursing Officer and Chief Clinical Officer
Web address: www.promise-misslou.com
Control: Corporation, Investor–owned (for–profit) **Service:** Acute long–term care hospital

> **Staffed Beds:** 40 **Admissions:** 488 **Census:** 28 **Outpatient Visits:** 0 **Births:** 0

Hospital, Medicare Provider Number, Address, Telephone, Approval, Facility, and Physician Codes, Health Care System

★ American Hospital Association (AHA) membership
☐ The Joint Commission accreditation
○ Healthcare Facilities Accreditation Program
◇ DNV Healthcare Inc. accreditation
⇑ Center for Improvement in Healthcare Quality Accreditation
△ Commission on Accreditation of Rehabilitation Facilities (CARF) accreditation

© 2019 AHA Guide   *Many Facility Codes have changed. Please refer to the AHA Guide Code Chart.*   Hospitals **A279**

LA

VILLE PLATTE—Evangeline Parish

★ **MERCY REGIONAL MEDICAL CENTER (190167)**, 800 East Main Street, Zip 70586–4618; tel. 337/363–5684, (Includes ACADIAN MEDICAL CENTER, 3501 Highway 190, Eunice, Louisiana, Zip 70535–5129; tel. 337/580–7500; Kevin Frank, Chief Executive Officer), (Non-reporting) **A**10 **S** Allegiance Health Management, Shreveport, LA
Primary Contact: Calvin Green, Chief Executive Officer
CFO: Janice G Jones, Interim Chief Financial Officer, Controller and Compliance Officer
CMO: Zebediah Stearns, M.D., Chief of Staff
CIO: Courtney Bieber, Director Information Systems
CHR: Cody Ardoin, Director Human Resources
Web address: www.mercyregionalmedicalcenter.com
Control: Corporation, Investor–owned (for–profit) **Service:** General medical and surgical

Staffed Beds: 109

VIVIAN—Caddo Parish

NORTH CADDO MEDICAL CENTER (191304), 815 South Pine Street, Zip 71082–3353, Mailing Address: P.O. Box 792, Zip 71082–0792; tel. 318/375–3235, (Nonreporting) **A**3 5 10 18
Primary Contact: David C. Jones, Administrator
CFO: Dakota Robinson, Interim Chief Financial Officer and Controller
CMO: John H Haynes, M.D., Jr Chief of Medical Staff
Web address: www.ncmcla.com/
Control: Hospital district or authority, Government, nonfederal **Service:** General medical and surgical

Staffed Beds: 27

WEST MONROE—Ouachita Parish

ALLEGIANCE BEHAVIORAL HEALTH CENTERS OF MONROE (194087), 222 Bell Lane, Suite 3, Zip 71291–6302; tel. 318/329–2174, (Includes ALLEGIANCE HEALTH CENTER OF RUSTON, 1401 Ezell Street, Ruston, Louisiana, Zip 71270–7218; tel. 318/255–8085; Chris Young, Chief Executive Officer), (Non-reporting)
Primary Contact: Chris Young, Chief Executive Officer
Web address: www.ahmgt.com
Control: Corporation, Investor–owned (for–profit) **Service:** Psychiatric

Staffed Beds: 38

CORNERSTONE HOSPITAL-WEST MONROE (192031), 6198 Cypress Street, Zip 71291–9010; tel. 318/396–5600, (Nonreporting) **A**10 22 **S** Cornerstone Healthcare Group, Dallas, TX
Primary Contact: Chris Simpson, Chief Executive Officer
CFO: Kurt Schultz, Chief Financial Officer
CMO: Khaled Shafici, M.D., President Medical Staff
CIO: Adam Davis, Chief Information Officer
CHR: Dan Perkins, Corporate Director Human Resources
Web address: www.chghospitals.com/chwm.html
Control: Corporation, Investor–owned (for–profit) **Service:** Acute long–term care hospital

Staffed Beds: 40

⇑ **GLENWOOD REGIONAL MEDICAL CENTER (190160)**, 503 McMillan Road, Zip 71291–5327; tel. 318/329–4200, (Includes GLENWOOD SURGERY CENTER, 1275 Glenwood Drive, West Monroe, Louisiana, Zip 71291–5539, Mailing Address: 503 McMillan Road, Zip 71291–5327, tel. 318/322–1339; Jeremy M. Tinnerello, MSN, R.N., President) **A**10 21 **F**3 8 12 13 15 17 18 20 22 24 26 28 29 30 31 34 35 37 38 40 41 45 46 47 48 49 50 51 54 55 56 57 58 59 60 61 62 63 64 68 70 71 72 74 75 76 78 79 81 82 83 84 85 86 87 89 90 91 92 93 94 96 97 98 100 101 102 103 104 107 108 110 111 113 114 115 116 117 119 120 121 126 128 129 130 131 132 134 146 147 148 149 153 154 **S** Steward Health Care System, LLC, Dallas, TX
Primary Contact: Jeremy M. Tinnerello, MSN, R.N., President
COO: Jeremy M. Tinnerello, MSN, R.N., President
CFO: Lisa Bradley, CPA, Chief Financial Officer
CMO: Steve McMahan, M.D., Chief Medical Officer
CIO: Ronnie Maxwell, Director Information Systems
CHR: Jan Walker, Director Human Resources
CNO: Lori Mathieu, MSN, Chief Nursing Officer
Web address: www.grmc.com
Control: Corporation, Investor–owned (for–profit) **Service:** General medical and surgical

Staffed Beds: 278 **Admissions:** 11897 **Census:** 171 **Births:** 750

LOUISIANA EXTENDED CARE HOSPITAL WEST MONROE (192055), 503

McMillan Road, 3rd Floor, Zip 71291–5327; tel. 318/329–4378, (Nonreporting) **A**10 **S** LHC Group, Lafayette, LA
Primary Contact: Cleta Munholland, Administrator
COO: Pamela Chappell, R.N., Assistant Administrator
CNO: Shelly Nugent, R.N., Director Nurses and Infection Control
Control: Corporation, Investor–owned (for–profit) **Service:** Acute long–term care hospital

Staffed Beds: 18

WINNFIELD—Winn Parish

WINN PARISH MEDICAL CENTER (190090), 301 West Boundary Avenue, Zip 71483–3427, Mailing Address: P.O. Box 152, Zip 71483–0152; tel. 318/648–3000, (Nonreporting) **A**10
Primary Contact: Bryan Bogle, Chief Executive Officer
CFO: Suzette Fatula, Chief Financial Officer
CMO: Mark Shelton, Chief of Staff
CHR: Ashley S Files, Director Human Resources and Public Relations and Marketing
CNO: Toby Wise, Chief Nursing Officer
Web address: www.winnparishmedical.com
Control: Partnership, Investor–owned (for–profit) **Service:** General medical and surgical

Staffed Beds: 60

WINNSBORO—Franklin Parish

FRANKLIN MEDICAL CENTER (190140), 2106 Loop Road, Zip 71295–3344, Mailing Address: P.O. Box 1300, Zip 71295–1300; tel. 318/435–9411, (Nonreporting) **A**3 5 10
Primary Contact: Blake Kramer, Chief Executive Officer
CFO: William E Page, CPA, Chief Financial Officer
CMO: Jay Busby, M.D., President Medical Staff
CIO: Judy Ogden, Director Information Technology
Web address: www.fmc-cares.com
Control: Hospital district or authority, Government, nonfederal **Service:** General medical and surgical

Staffed Beds: 43

ZACHARY—East Baton Rouge Parish

AMG SPECIALTY HOSPITAL-ZACHARY (192041), 4601 McHugh Road, Building B, Zip 70791–5348; tel. 225/683–1600, (Nonreporting) **A**10 **S** AMG Integrated Healthcare Management, Lafayette, LA
Primary Contact: April Ebeling, Chief Executive Officer
Web address: www.amgzachary.com/
Control: Corporation, Investor–owned (for–profit) **Service:** Acute long–term care hospital

Staffed Beds: 16

⊞ **LANE REGIONAL MEDICAL CENTER (190020)**, 6300 Main Street, Zip 70791–4037; tel. 225/658–4000, (Total facility includes 39 beds in nursing home–type unit) **A**1 10 **F**3 8 11 13 15 20 22 26 29 34 35 36 39 40 45 46 50 54 57 59 62 64 67 70 73 75 76 77 78 79 80 81 85 86 87 90 107 108 110 111 114 115 119 130 132 144 146 148 154 157 **S** QHR, Brentwood, TN
Primary Contact: Larry R. Meese Jr, FACHE, Chief Executive Officer
COO: David Beck, Chief Operating Officer
CFO: Phil Hacker, Chief Financial Officer
CMO: Thomas Trahan, M.D., Chief of Medical Staff
CIO: Paul Murphy, Chief Information Officer
CNO: Staci Sullivan, R.N., Chief Nursing Officer
Web address: www.lanermc.org
Control: Hospital district or authority, Government, nonfederal **Service:** General medical and surgical

Staffed Beds: 179 **Admissions:** 4273 **Census:** 85 **Outpatient Visits:** 73722 **Births:** 379 **Total Expense ($000):** 88744 **Payroll Expense ($000):** 33735 **Personnel:** 572

Many Facility Codes have changed. Please refer to the AHA Guide Code Chart. © 2019 AHA Guide

MAINE

AUGUSTA—Kennebec County

MAINEGENERAL MEDICAL CENTER (200039), 35 Medical Center Parkway, Zip 04330; tel. 207/626–1000, (Includes MAINEGENERAL MEDICAL CENTER-AUGUSTA CAMPUS, 35 Medical Center Parkway, Augusta, Maine, Zip 04330–9988; tel. 207/626–1000; Chuck Hays, President and Chief Executive Officer) **A**1 2 3 10 19 **F**3 4 5 8 11 12 13 15 17 18 20 26 28 29 30 31 34 35 36 40 42 44 45 46 47 48 49 50 51 54 55 56 57 58 59 61 64 65 70 73 74 75 76 77 78 79 81 82 84 85 86 87 89 90 92 93 96 97 98 99 100 101 102 104 107 108 110 115 116 117 118 119 120 121 123 124 126 129 130 131 132 134 135 144 145 146 147 148 149 153 154 156
Primary Contact: Chuck Hays, President and Chief Executive Officer
COO: Paul Stein, Chief Operating Officer
CFO: Terry Brann, Chief Financial Officer
CMO: Steve Diaz, M.D., Chief Medical Officer
CIO: Daniel Burgess, Chief Information Officer
CHR: Rebecca Lamey, Vice President Human Resources
CNO: Jennifer Riggs, R.N., Chief Nurse Officer
Web address: www.mainegeneral.org
Control: Other not–for–profit (including NFP Corporation) **Service:** General medical and surgical

Staffed Beds: 197 **Admissions:** 11458 **Census:** 160 **Outpatient Visits:** 821429 **Births:** 1048 **Total Expense ($000):** 474649 **Payroll Expense ($000):** 203463 **Personnel:** 3697

MAINE VETERANS AFFAIRS MEDICAL CENTER, 1 VA Center, Zip 04330–6719; tel. 207/623–8411, (Total facility includes 65 beds in nursing home–type unit) **A**1 3 5 **F**3 5 10 18 20 28 29 30 31 33 34 35 36 38 39 40 44 45 53 54 56 57 58 59 60 61 62 63 64 65 66 68 70 71 74 75 77 78 79 81 82 83 84 85 87 93 94 97 98 100 102 104 105 107 108 111 114 115 118 119 127 129 130 132 135 143 146 147 148 149 153 154 156 157 158 **S** Department of Veterans Affairs, Washington, DC
Primary Contact: Ryan S. Lilly, Director
CFO: Daniel Howard, Chief Financial Officer
CMO: Timothy J Richardson, M.D., Chief of Staff
CIO: Richard McNaughton, Chief Information Management Service
CHR: Christine Miller, Chief Human Resources Management Services
Web address: www.maine.va.gov/
Control: Veterans Affairs, Government, federal **Service:** General medical and surgical

Staffed Beds: 109 **Admissions:** 2581 **Census:** 92 **Outpatient Visits:** 462859 **Births:** 0 **Total Expense ($000):** 301112 **Payroll Expense ($000):** 112302 **Personnel:** 1449

MAINEGENERAL MEDICAL CENTER-AUGUSTA CAMPUS See Mainegeneral Medical Center, Augusta

RIVERVIEW PSYCHIATRIC CENTER (204007), 250 Arsenal Street, Zip 04330–5742; tel. 207/624–3900, (Nonreporting) **A**1
Primary Contact: Rodney Bouffard, Superintendent
COO: David Lovejoy, Chief Operations Officer
CFO: Samantha Kavanaugh, Chief Financial Officer
CMO: Brendan Kirby, M.D., Medical Director
CHR: Aimee Rice, Human Resources Manager
CNO: Roland Pushard, Director of Nursing
Web address: www.state.me.us/dhhs/riverview
Control: State, Government, nonfederal **Service:** Psychiatric

Staffed Beds: 92

VETERANS AFFAIRS MEDICAL CENTER See Maine Veterans Affairs Medical Center

BANGOR—Penobscot County

DOROTHEA DIX PSYCHIATRIC CENTER (204004), 656 State Street, Zip 04401–5609, Mailing Address: P.O. Box 926, Zip 04402–0926; tel. 207/941–4000, (Nonreporting) **A**1 10
Primary Contact: Carolyn Dimek, Acting Superintendent
CMO: Michelle Gardner, M.D., Clinical Director
CHR: Tamra Hanson, Human Resource Manager
CNO: Christine Bellatty, Acting Director of Nursing
Web address: www.maine.gov/dhhs/ddpc/index.shtml
Control: State, Government, nonfederal **Service:** Psychiatric

Staffed Beds: 51

NORTHERN LIGHT EASTERN MAINE MEDICAL CENTER (200033), 489 State Street, Zip 04401–6674, Mailing Address: P.O. Box 404, Zip 04402–0404; tel. 207/973–7000, **A**1 2 3 5 10 13 **F**3 11 12 13 15 17 18 19 20 22 24 26 27 28 29 30 31 32 34 36 37 39 40 43 44 45 46 47 48 49 50 51 53 54 55 56 57 58 59 61 64 70 72 74 75 76 77 78 79 81 82 84 85 86 87 88 89 90 92 93 94 96 97 107 108 110 111 114 115 117 118 119 120 121 123 124 126 129 130 131 132 144 145 146 147 148 149 154 156 **S** Northern Light Health, Brewer, ME
Primary Contact: Timothy Dentry, Interim President
CMO: James Raczek, M.D., Sr. Vice President of Operations and Chief Medical Officer
CIO: Catherine Bruno, FACHE, Chief Information Officer
CHR: Greg Howat, Vice President Human Resources
Web address: www.https://northernlighthealth.org/Eastern-Maine-Medical-Center
Control: Other not–for–profit (including NFP Corporation) **Service:** General medical and surgical

Staffed Beds: 385 **Admissions:** 20062 **Census:** 299 **Outpatient Visits:** 599694 **Births:** 1735 **Total Expense ($000):** 870395 **Payroll Expense ($000):** 345805 **Personnel:** 3875

★ **ST. JOSEPH HOSPITAL (200001)**, 360 Broadway, Zip 04401–3979, Mailing Address: P.O. Box 403, Zip 04402–0403; tel. 207/262–1000, **A**10 **F**3 8 15 18 29 30 31 34 45 46 48 49 51 55 56 57 62 64 70 75 77 81 82 84 85 86 87 97 107 108 110 111 114 118 119 129 130 132 135 145 146 147 148 149 154 **S** Covenant Health, Tewksbury, MA
Primary Contact: Mary Prybylo, President and Chief Executive Officer
CFO: Michael A. Hendrix Jr Chief Financial Officer
CMO: William Wood, M.D., Vice President Medical Affairs
CHR: Paige A Hagerstrom, System Director of Talent Management
CNO: Dianne Swandal, R.N., MSN, Vice President Patient Care
Web address: www.sjhhealth.com
Control: Church operated, Nongovernment, not–for–profit **Service:** General medical and surgical

Staffed Beds: 84 **Admissions:** 3936 **Census:** 51

THE ACADIA HOSPITAL (204006), 268 Stillwater Avenue, Zip 04401–3945, Mailing Address: P.O. Box 422, Zip 04402–0422; tel. 207/973–6100, **A**1 5 10 **F**5 29 30 50 56 57 66 68 75 77 87 98 99 100 101 103 104 105 130 132 152 153 154 **S** Northern Light Health, Brewer, ME
Primary Contact: Scott Oxley, President
CFO: Marie Suitter, Chief Financial Officer
CMO: Anthony Ng, M.D., Vice President and Chief Medical Officer
CIO: Jeanne Paradis, Director Information Services
CHR: Paul Bolin, Vice President and Chief Human Resources Officer
CNO: Wayne Steller, Vice President Chief Nursing Officer
Web address: www.acadiahospital.org
Control: Other not–for–profit (including NFP Corporation) **Service:** Psychiatric

Staffed Beds: 68 **Admissions:** 1466 **Census:** 61 **Outpatient Visits:** 122130 **Births:** 0 **Total Expense ($000):** 54291 **Payroll Expense ($000):** 30581 **Personnel:** 558

BAR HARBOR—Hancock County

★ **MOUNT DESERT ISLAND HOSPITAL (201304)**, 10 Wayman Lane, Zip 04609–1625, Mailing Address: P.O. Box 8, Zip 04609–0008; tel. 207/288–5081, **A**10 18 **F**3 5 6 10 11 13 15 28 29 31 34 35 36 39 40 50 54 56 57 59 64 65 70 74 75 76 77 78 79 81 82 84 85 87 91 92 93 97 100 104 107 110 111 115 118 119 125 127 130 131 132 133 135 145 146 147 154
Primary Contact: Arthur J. Blank, President and Chief Executive Officer
COO: Christina Maguire, Senior Vice President and Chief Operating Officer
CFO: Christina Harding, Vice President Finance
CMO: Stuart Davidson, President Medical Staff
CIO: Bruce Donlin, Director Information Services
CHR: Joanne Harris, Director Human Resources
CNO: Karen Mueller, R.N., Chief Nursing Officer
Web address: www.mdihospital.org
Control: Other not–for–profit (including NFP Corporation) **Service:** General medical and surgical

Staffed Beds: 25 **Admissions:** 787 **Census:** 8 **Outpatient Visits:** 186553 **Births:** 48 **Total Expense ($000):** 56195 **Payroll Expense ($000):** 25734 **Personnel:** 367

Hospital, Medicare Provider Number, Address, Telephone, Approval, Facility, and Physician Codes, Health Care System

★ American Hospital Association (AHA) membership ○ Healthcare Facilities Accreditation Program ⇑ Center for Improvement in Healthcare Quality Accreditation
☐ The Joint Commission accreditation ◇ DNV Healthcare Inc. accreditation △ Commission on Accreditation of Rehabilitation Facilities (CARF) accreditation

ME

BELFAST—Waldo County

WALDO COUNTY GENERAL HOSPITAL MAINE HEALTH (201312), 118 Northport Avenue, Zip 04915–6072, Mailing Address: P.O. Box 287, Zip 04915–0287; tel. 207/338–2500, **A**5 10 18 **F**3 11 13 15 18 27 29 30 31 34 35 39 40 45 46 55 57 59 62 63 64 70 74 75 76 77 78 79 81 82 83 84 85 87 93 97 102 107 110 111 115 117 119 125 129 130 131 132 133 145 146 147 148 154 156 **S** MaineHealth, Portland, ME
Primary Contact: Mark Fourre, Chief Executive Officer
CFO: Linda Drinkwater, Chief Financial Officer
CMO: Kent Clark, M.D., Chief Medical Affairs and Quality
CIO: David Felton, Manager Information Systems
CHR: Karen Littlefield, Director Human Resources
CNO: Paula Delahanty, Regional Chief Nursing Officer
Web address: www.wcgh.org
Control: Other not–for–profit (including NFP Corporation) **Service**: General medical and surgical

Staffed Beds: 25 **Admissions:** 1327 **Census:** 16 **Outpatient Visits:** 16249
Births: 134 **Total Expense ($000):** 100318 **Payroll Expense ($000):** 43876
Personnel: 652

BIDDEFORD—York County

SOUTHERN MAINE HEALTH CARE - BIDDEFORD MEDICAL CENTER (200019), One Medical Center Drive, Zip 04005–9496, Mailing Address: P.O. Box 626, Zip 04005–0626; tel. 207/283–7000, (Includes SOUTHERN MAINE HEALTH CARE - BIDDEFORD MEDICAL CENTER, One Medical Center Drive, Biddeford, Maine, Zip 04005–9496, Mailing Address: P.O. Box 626, Zip 04005–0626, tel. 207/283–7000; Edward J McGeachey, President and Chief Executive Officer) (Total facility includes 112 beds in nursing home–type unit) **A**1 2 3 10 **F**8 10 11 12 13 15 18 20 22 26 28 29 30 31 32 33 34 35 40 42 44 45 46 49 50 54 56 57 59 61 64 65 68 70 74 75 76 77 78 79 81 82 84 86 87 89 93 97 98 100 102 104 105 107 108 110 111 115 117 119 128 129 130 131 132 135 144 146 147 148 149 154 156
Primary Contact: Nathan Howell, Chief Executive Officer
COO: Patricia Aprile, Chief Operating Officer
CFO: Norman Belair, Senior Vice President and Chief Financial Officer
CMO: Michael Albaum, M.D., Senior Vice President and Chief Medical Officer
CIO: Ralph Johnson, Chief Information Officer
CHR: Yvonne McAllister, Senior Director Human Resources
CNO: Joanna Salamone, Senior Vice President Clinical Services and Chief Nursing Officer
Web address: www.smhc.org
Control: Other not–for–profit (including NFP Corporation) **Service**: General medical and surgical

Staffed Beds: 196 **Admissions:** 7039 **Census:** 150 **Outpatient Visits:** 497397 **Births:** 513 **Total Expense ($000):** 296411 **Payroll Expense ($000):** 138694 **Personnel:** 1660

BLUE HILL—Hancock County

★ **NORTHERN LIGHT BLUE HILL HOSPITAL (201300)**, 57 Water Street, Zip 04614–5231, Mailing Address: P.O. Box 1029, Zip 04614–1029; tel. 207/374–3400, (Nonreporting) **A**10 18 **S** Northern Light Health, Brewer, ME
Primary Contact: John Ronan, President
CFO: Wendy Jones, Interim Chief Financial Officer
CHR: David Wheaton, Director Human Resources
CNO: Kathy Lirakis, R.N., Chief Nursing Officer
Web address: www.bhmh.org
Control: Other not–for–profit (including NFP Corporation) **Service**: General medical and surgical

Staffed Beds: 23

BRIDGTON—Cumberland County

★ **BRIDGTON HOSPITAL (201310)**, 10 Hospital Drive, Zip 04009–1148; tel. 207/647–6000, **A**10 18 **F**3 7 8 11 13 15 18 29 30 31 34 35 40 43 44 45 50 57 59 64 65 67 68 75 76 77 78 79 80 81 85 87 90 91 93 94 96 97 107 108 110 114 119 128 130 131 132 133 135 143 144 146 148 **S** Central Maine Healthcare, Lewiston, ME
Primary Contact: Peter J. Wright, FACHE, President
COO: Robert Slattery, Vice President of Operations
CMO: Alan Verrill, M.D., President Medical Staff
CHR: Kirk Miklavic, Director Human Resources
Web address: www.bridgtonhospital.org
Control: Other not–for–profit (including NFP Corporation) **Service**: General medical and surgical

Staffed Beds: 22 **Admissions:** 951 **Census:** 11 **Outpatient Visits:** 142373
Births: 89 **Total Expense ($000):** 46478 **Payroll Expense ($000):** 17497
Personnel: 229

BRUNSWICK—Cumberland County

✉ **MID COAST HOSPITAL (200021)**, 123 Medical Center Drive, Zip 04011–2652; tel. 207/373–6000, **A**1 2 10 **F**3 5 11 12 13 15 18 20 28 29 30 31 32 34 35 36 40 41 44 45 46 47 48 49 51 53 54 56 57 58 59 61 64 65 66 68 70 74 75 76 77 78 79 81 82 84 85 86 87 89 92 93 97 98 101 102 103 105 107 108 110 111 115 119 129 130 131 132 134 135 144 146 147 148 149 150 152 153 154 156
Primary Contact: Lois N. Skillings, R.N., MSN, FACHE, President and Chief Executive Officer
COO: Philip A Ortolani, Vice President Operations
CFO: Robert N McCue, Vice President Finance
CMO: Scott Mills, M.D., Vice President Medical Staff Administration and Chief Medical Officer
CIO: Gale Stoy, Manager Information Systems
CHR: Coleen M Farrell, Vice President Human Resources
CNO: Deborah MacLeod, MS, R.N., Vice President Nursing and Patient Care Services
Web address: www.midcoasthealth.com
Control: Other not–for–profit (including NFP Corporation) **Service**: General medical and surgical

Staffed Beds: 93 **Admissions:** 4884 **Census:** 63 **Outpatient Visits:** 239638
Births: 570 **Total Expense ($000):** 189722 **Payroll Expense ($000):** 88358
Personnel: 1148

CALAIS—Washington County

★ **CALAIS REGIONAL HOSPITAL (201305)**, 24 Hospital Lane, Zip 04619–1398; tel. 207/454–7521, **A**10 18 **F**3 8 11 15 28 29 32 34 35 36 40 41 45 46 50 54 55 57 59 62 64 65 68 75 76 77 79 81 82 83 84 85 87 93 97 107 110 114 119 127 129 130 132 133 146 148 149 154 156 157
Primary Contact: Rodney Boula, Chief Executive Officer
CFO: Nancy Glidden, Chief Financial Officer
CMO: Francis Lee, M.D., Chief Medical Officer
CIO: Dee Dee Travis, Vice President Community Relations
CHR: Kristi K Saunders, Director and Compliance Officer
CNO: Erika Marshall, Interim Chief Nursing Officer
Web address: www.calaishospital.com
Control: Other not–for–profit (including NFP Corporation) **Service**: General medical and surgical

Staffed Beds: 25 **Admissions:** 701 **Census:** 9 **Outpatient Visits:** 35694
Births: 0 **Total Expense ($000):** 30170 **Payroll Expense ($000):** 17105
Personnel: 218

CARIBOU—Aroostook County

✉ **CARY MEDICAL CENTER (200031)**, 163 Van Buren Road, Suite 1, Zip 04736–3567; tel. 207/498–3111, (Total facility includes 9 beds in nursing home–type unit) **A**1 10 **F**3 8 11 13 15 28 29 31 32 34 35 36 38 40 43 44 51 53 54 56 57 59 61 64 67 68 70 75 76 77 78 79 81 82 84 85 86 87 89 90 93 97 107 108 111 115 118 119 121 130 131 132 135 144 146 147 148 156 **S** QHR, Brentwood, TN
Primary Contact: Kris A. Doody, R.N., Chief Executive Officer
COO: Shawn Anderson, Chief Operating Officer
CFO: Chelsea Lee Desrosiers, Chief Financial Officer
CMO: Regen Gallagher, D.O., Chief Medical Officer
CIO: Dave Silsbee, Chief Information Officer
CHR: Paula A. Parent, Chief Nursing Officer and Director of Human Resources
CNO: Paula A. Parent, Chief Nursing Officer
Web address: www.carymedicalcenter.org
Control: City, Government, nonfederal **Service**: General medical and surgical

Staffed Beds: 49 **Admissions:** 1696 **Census:** 29 **Outpatient Visits:** 70338
Births: 201 **Total Expense ($000):** 55944 **Payroll Expense ($000):** 21799
Personnel: 400

DAMARISCOTTA—Lincoln County

★ **LINCOLNHEALTH (201302)**, 35 Miles Street, Zip 04543–4047; tel. 207/563–1234, (Includes LINCOLNHEALTH MILES CAMPUS, 35 Miles Street, Damariscotta, Maine, Zip 04543–4047; tel. 207/563–1234; James W Donovan, President and Chief Executive Officer; LINCOLNHEALTH ST. ANDREWS CAMPUS, 6 St Andrews Lane, Boothbay Harbor, Maine, Zip 04538–1732, Mailing Address: P O Box 417, Zip 04538–0417, tel. 207/633–2121) (Total facility includes 66 beds in nursing home–type unit) **A**10 18 **F**3 10 11 13 15 29 30 32 34 35 40 44 45 50 57 59 64 65 67 70 75 76 79 81 84 85 86 87 93 96 97 107 108 110 111 114 115 119 125 127 128 130 132 133 135 144 146 147 148 149 156 **S** MaineHealth, Portland, ME
Primary Contact: James W. Donovan, President and Chief Executive Officer
COO: Cynthia Wade, R.N., RN, BSN, Executive Vice President and Chief Operating Officer
CFO: Wayne Printy, Chief Financial Officer and Senior Vice President Finance
CIO: David Felton, Regional Chief Information Officer
CHR: Thomas R Girard, Vice President Human Resources
CNO: Christine Anderson, Chief Nursing Officer and Vice President of Patient Care Services
Web address: www.lchcare.org
Control: Other not–for–profit (including NFP Corporation) **Service**: General medical and surgical

Staffed Beds: 91 **Admissions:** 1899 **Census:** 72 **Outpatient Visits:** 114966
Births: 107 **Total Expense ($000):** 84573 **Payroll Expense ($000):** 24740
Personnel: 508

Many Facility Codes have changed. Please refer to the AHA Guide Code Chart. © 2019 AHA Guide

DOVER—FOXCROFT-Piscataquis County

★ **MAYO REGIONAL HOSPITAL (201309)**, 897 West Main Street, Zip 04426–1099; tel. 207/564–8401, **A**10 18 **F**3 5 7 8 11 13 15 28 29 30 31 34 35 38 40 45 50 57 65 71 75 76 77 78 79 80 81 82 85 86 87 93 96 97 104 107 110 111 114 119 127 129 130 132 133 134 135 146 147 148 149 153 156
Primary Contact: Marie E. Vienneau, FACHE, President and Chief Executive Officer
CFO: Nancy Glidden, Chief Financial Officer and Vice President Finance
CMO: Challa Reddy, M.D., President Medical Staff
CHR: James R Godley, Vice President of Human Resources
CNO: Denise Scuderi, Vice President Patient Care Services
Web address: www.mayohospital.com
Control: Hospital district or authority, Government, nonfederal **Service:** General medical and surgical

Staffed Beds: 25 Admissions: 1223 Census: 12 Outpatient Visits: 132087 Births: 121 Total Expense ($000): 52378 Payroll Expense ($000): 26282 Personnel: 423

ELLSWORTH—Hancock County

⊞ **NORTHERN LIGHT MAINE COAST HOSPITAL (200050)**, 50 Union Street, Zip 04605–1599; tel. 207/664–5311, (Nonreporting) **A**1 10 **S** Northern Light Health, Brewer, ME
Primary Contact: John Ronan, President
CFO: Chris Frauenhofer, Chief Financial Officer
CMO: Sheena Whittaker, M.D., Chief Medical Officer
CIO: Scott Burtchell, Director Information Systems
CHR: Noah Lundy, Director of Human Resources
CNO: Kristin Cyr, R.N., MSN, Senior Nursing Executive and Vice President of Patient Care Services
Web address: www.mainehospital.org
Control: Other not–for–profit (including NFP Corporation) **Service:** General medical and surgical

Staffed Beds: 52

FARMINGTON—Franklin County

⊞ **FRANKLIN MEMORIAL HOSPITAL (200037)**, 111 Franklin Health Commons, Zip 04938–6144; tel. 207/778–6031, **A**1 5 10 20 **F**3 5 7 8 11 13 15 28 29 30 31 32 34 40 45 46 50 54 55 67 70 75 76 77 78 79 81 83 85 86 87 93 94 97 101 102 107 108 110 111 115 118 119 129 130 131 135 143 146 147 149
Primary Contact: Timothy A. Churchill, Interim Chief Executive Officer
CFO: Wayne Bennett, Chief Financial Officer
CMO: Michael Rowland, M.D., Vice President Medical Affairs
CIO: Ralph Johnson, Chief Information Officer
CHR: Joline Hart, Vice President Human Resources
Web address: www.fchn.org
Control: Other not–for–profit (including NFP Corporation) **Service:** General medical and surgical

Staffed Beds: 48 Admissions: 1781 Census: 19 Births: 219 Total Expense ($000): 88741 Payroll Expense ($000): 37558 Personnel: 825

FORT FAIRFIELD—Aroostook County

COMMUNITY GENERAL HEALTH CENTER See The Aroostook Medical Center, Presque Isle

FORT KENT—Aroostook County

⊞ **NORTHERN MAINE MEDICAL CENTER (200052)**, 194 East Main Street, Zip 04743–1497; tel. 207/834–3155, (Total facility includes 45 beds in nursing home–type unit) **A**1 10 20 **F**3 13 15 29 31 34 40 45 50 54 57 59 62 64 67 68 70 75 76 77 78 79 81 82 86 87 89 98 99 100 101 102 103 104 107 108 110 111 115 119 127 128 130 131 132 133 135 146 147 148 156
Primary Contact: Peter Sirois, Chief Executive Officer
CFO: Cindy Daigle, Chief Financial Officer
CMO: Michael Sullivan, M.D., Chief Medical Officer
CIO: Adam Landry, Director of Information Systems
CHR: Robin Damboise, Director Human Resources
CNO: Alain Bois, R.N., Director of Nursing
Web address: www.nmmc.org
Control: Other not–for–profit (including NFP Corporation) **Service:** General medical and surgical

Staffed Beds: 81 Admissions: 1433 Census: 67 Outpatient Visits: 52052 Births: 41 Total Expense ($000): 54675 Payroll Expense ($000): 28828 Personnel: 444

GREENVILLE—Piscataquis County

★ **NORTHERN LIGHT CA DEAN HOSPITAL (201301)**, 364 Pritham Avenue, Zip 04441–1395, Mailing Address: P.O. Box 1129, Zip 04441–1129; tel. 207/695–5200, **A**10 18 **F**7 11 28 29 30 34 35 40 53 54 56 59 64 77 85 93 97 102 104 107 119 127 128 130 133 143 148 154 **S** Northern Light Health, Brewer, ME
Primary Contact: Terri Vieira, President
CFO: Edward Olivier, Chief Financial Officer
CMO: Darin Peck, M.D., Chief of Staff
Web address: www.cadean.org
Control: Other not–for–profit (including NFP Corporation) **Service:** General medical and surgical

Staffed Beds: 50 Admissions: 169 Census: 17 Outpatient Visits: 21045 Births: 0 Total Expense ($000): 17162 Payroll Expense ($000): 8617 Personnel: 142

HOULTON—Aroostook County

★ **HOULTON REGIONAL HOSPITAL (201308)**, 20 Hartford Street, Zip 04730–1891; tel. 207/532–9471, **A**10 18 **F**1 3 4 11 13 15 16 17 28 29 30 34 40 43 45 46 50 59 65 67 70 72 73 75 76 77 79 80 81 83 84 85 86 87 88 89 90 93 97 98 107 108 110 111 114 119 127 128 129 130 132 133 146 148 149 156
Primary Contact: Thomas J. Moakler, Chief Executive Officer
CHR: Vicky Moody, Director Human Resources
Web address: www.houlton.net/hrh
Control: Other not–for–profit (including NFP Corporation) **Service:** General medical and surgical

Staffed Beds: 25 Admissions: 1209 Census: 14 Outpatient Visits: 96063 Births: 135 Total Expense ($000): 47840 Payroll Expense ($000): 21258 Personnel: 336

LEWISTON—Androscoggin County

⊞ △ **CENTRAL MAINE MEDICAL CENTER (200024)**, 300 Main Street, Zip 04240–7027; tel. 207/795–0111, **A**1 2 3 5 7 10 13 19 **F**3 11 12 13 15 18 19 20 22 24 26 28 29 30 31 32 34 35 36 40 41 43 44 45 46 47 48 49 50 51 52 54 55 56 57 58 59 61 64 65 66 67 68 70 71 73 74 75 76 77 78 79 81 82 84 85 86 87 89 90 91 92 93 97 101 104 107 108 110 114 115 118 119 120 121 123 124 127 130 131 132 135 143 146 147 148 149 150 **S** Central Maine Healthcare, Lewiston, ME
Primary Contact: David Tupponce, M.D., President
CFO: David Thompson, Chief Financial Officer
CMO: David Lauver, M.D., Chief Division Hospital Based Care
CIO: Denis Tanguay, Chief Information Officer
CHR: Kirk Miklavic, Director, Human Resources
Web address: www.cmmc.org
Control: Other not–for–profit (including NFP Corporation) **Service:** General medical and surgical

Staffed Beds: 190 Admissions: 10405 Census: 127 Outpatient Visits: 708196 Births: 650 Total Expense ($000): 386838 Payroll Expense ($000): 148853 Personnel: 1565

★ ⇑ **ST. MARY'S REGIONAL MEDICAL CENTER (200034)**, 93 Campus Avenue, Zip 04240–6030, Mailing Address: P.O. Box 291, Zip 04243–0291; tel. 207/777–8100, (Nonreporting) **A**2 3 5 10 21 **S** Covenant Health, Tewksbury, MA
Primary Contact: Steven C. Jorgensen, Chief Executive Officer
CFO: Michael Hendrix, Chief Financial Officer
CMO: Christopher Bowe, M.D., Chief Medical Officer, Medical Affairs
CIO: Karen Bowling, Chief Information Officer
CHR: Nicole Morin-Scribner, Director Human Resources
CNO: Karen Clark, Vice President Patient Care Services
Web address: www.stmarysmaine.com
Control: Church operated **Service:** General medical and surgical

Staffed Beds: 353

LINCOLN—Penobscot County

★ **PENOBSCOT VALLEY HOSPITAL (201303)**, 7 Transalpine Road, Zip 04457–4222, Mailing Address: P.O. Box 368, Zip 04457–0368; tel. 207/794–3321, (Nonreporting) **A**10 18
Primary Contact: Crystal Landry, R.N., Chief Executive Officer
CFO: Ann Marie Rush, Chief Financial Officer
CHR: Sarah Loman, Director Human Resources
Web address: www.pvhme.org
Control: Other not–for–profit (including NFP Corporation) **Service:** General medical and surgical

Staffed Beds: 25

Hospital, Medicare Provider Number, Address, Telephone, Approval, Facility, and Physician Codes, Health Care System

★ American Hospital Association (AHA) membership ○ Healthcare Facilities Accreditation Program ⇑ Center for Improvement in Healthcare Quality Accreditation
□ The Joint Commission accreditation ◇ DNV Healthcare Inc. accreditation △ Commission on Accreditation of Rehabilitation Facilities (CARF) accreditation

ME

MACHIAS—Washington County

★ **DOWN EAST COMMUNITY HOSPITAL (201311)**, 11 Hospital Drive, Zip 04654–3325; tel. 207/255–3356, **A**10 18 **F**3 13 15 28 29 34 35 40 45 57 64 65 75 77 79 81 82 83 84 85 93 97 107 108 110 111 114 119 127 130 133 146 147
Primary Contact: Steve Lail, Chief Executive Officer
CFO: Lynnette Parr, Chief Financial Officer
CMO: Aziz Massaad, M.D., Medical Staff President
CHR: Ernestine O Reisman, Vice President Human Resources
CNO: Kevin K McEwan, MSN, R.N., Chief Nursing Officer
Web address: www.dech.org
Control: Other not–for–profit (including NFP Corporation) **Service**: General medical and surgical

> **Staffed Beds:** 25 **Admissions:** 915 **Census:** 20 **Outpatient Visits:** 43426 **Births:** 187 **Total Expense ($000):** 46971 **Payroll Expense ($000):** 19983 **Personnel:** 260

MARS HILL—Aroostook County

AROOSTOOK HEALTH CENTER See The Aroostook Medical Center, Presque Isle

MILLINOCKET—Penobscot County

★ **MILLINOCKET REGIONAL HOSPITAL (201307)**, 200 Somerset Street, Zip 04462–1298; tel. 207/723–5161, **A**10 18 **F**3 8 11 15 29 31 34 35 40 41 45 50 53 54 56 57 59 64 65 68 75 77 78 79 80 81 82 85 87 93 96 97 107 108 110 111 114 118 119 127 128 130 131 132 133 135 144 145 148 154 156
Primary Contact: Robert Peterson I, Chief Executive Officer
CFO: Catherine LeMay, Vice President Finance
CMO: Daniel Herbert, M.D., Medical Administrative Officer
CHR: Lisa Arsenault, Vice President Human Resources and Compliance
CNO: Mary Tatro Esq Chief Nursing Officer
Web address: www.mrhme.org
Control: Other not–for–profit (including NFP Corporation) **Service**: General medical and surgical

> **Staffed Beds:** 25 **Admissions:** 572 **Census:** 7 **Outpatient Visits:** 26916 **Births:** 1 **Total Expense ($000):** 33682 **Payroll Expense ($000):** 16281 **Personnel:** 202

NORWAY—Oxford County

★ **STEPHENS MEMORIAL HOSPITAL (201315)**, 181 Main Street, Zip 04268–5664; tel. 207/743–5933, **A**3 10 18 **F**3 7 13 15 28 29 30 31 34 35 40 43 45 57 59 61 64 65 68 75 76 78 79 80 81 85 87 89 93 96 97 102 107 108 110 111 115 119 127 130 132 146 148 149 154 156 **S** MaineHealth, Portland, ME
Primary Contact: Timothy A. Churchill, President
CMO: James Eshleman, D.O., President Medical Staff
CHR: Roberta Metivier, Vice President Human Resources and Administrator, Western Main Nursing Home
Web address: www.https://mainehealth.org
Control: Other not–for–profit (including NFP Corporation) **Service**: General medical and surgical

> **Staffed Beds:** 25 **Admissions:** 1356 **Census:** 11 **Outpatient Visits:** 94830 **Births:** 162 **Total Expense ($000):** 70832 **Payroll Expense ($000):** 30278 **Personnel:** 453

PITTSFIELD—Somerset County

✠ **NORTHLIGHT SEBASTICOOK VALLEY HOSPITAL (201313)**, 447 North Main Street, Zip 04967–3707; tel. 207/487–4000, **A**1 10 18 **F**3 7 11 15 18 28 29 30 32 34 35 40 45 46 50 51 57 59 64 65 70 75 77 78 79 81 87 93 96 97 104 107 108 111 119 127 129 130 132 133 135 143 146 147 148 156 **S** Northern Light Health, Brewer, ME
Primary Contact: Terri Vieira, President
COO: Michael Peterson, FACHE, Chief Operating Officer
CFO: Randal Clark, Vice President Finance
CMO: Robert Schlager, M.D., Chief Medical Officer
CIO: Michael Peterson, FACHE, Chief Operating Officer
CHR: Tammy Hatch, Manager
Web address: www.sebasticookvalleyhealth.org
Control: Other not–for–profit (including NFP Corporation) **Service**: General medical and surgical

> **Staffed Beds:** 25 **Admissions:** 821 **Census:** 12 **Outpatient Visits:** 84893 **Births:** 0 **Total Expense ($000):** 39373 **Payroll Expense ($000):** 17522 **Personnel:** 304

PORTLAND—Cumberland County

✠ **MAINE MEDICAL CENTER (200009)**, 22 Bramhall Street, Zip 04102–3175; tel. 207/662–0111, (Includes BARBARA BUSH CHILDREN'S HOSPITAL, 22 Bramhall Street, Portland, Maine, Zip 04102–3134; tel. 207/662–0111; Richard W Petersen, President and Chief Executive Officer; MAINE MEDICAL CENTER, BRIGHTON CAMPUS, 335 Brighton Avenue, Portland, Maine, Zip 04102–9735, Mailing Address: P O Box 9735, Zip 04102–9735, tel. 207/879–8000; Richard W Petersen, President and Chief Executive Officer) (Total facility includes 121 beds in nursing home–type unit) **A**1 2 3 5 8 10 **F**1 3 5 6 11 12 13 15 17 18 19 20 21 22 23 24 25 26 27 28 29 30 31 32 34 35 36 38 40 41 43 44 45 46 47 48 49 51 54 55 56 57 58 59 60 61 64 65 66 68 70 71 72 73 74 75 76 78 79 80 81 82 84 85 86 87 88 89 91 92 93 94 97 98 99 100 101 102 103 104 105 107 108 110 111 115 116 117 118 119 120 121 123 124 126 128 129 130 131 132 134 135 138 141 144 146 147 148 149 151 153 154 **S** MaineHealth, Portland, ME
Primary Contact: Richard W. Petersen, President and Chief Executive Officer
COO: Jeff Sanders, Senior Vice President, Chief Operating Officer
CFO: Lou Inzana, Senior Vice President and Chief Financial Officer
CMO: Joel Botler, M.D., Chief Medical Officer
CHR: Judith M West, Senior Vice President Human Resources and Chief Human Resources Officer
CNO: Marjorie Wiggins, Senior Vice President, Chief Nursing Officer
Web address: www.mmc.org
Control: Other not–for–profit (including NFP Corporation) **Service**: General medical and surgical

> **Staffed Beds:** 637 **Admissions:** 29664 **Census:** 538 **Outpatient Visits:** 1015977 **Births:** 2895 **Total Expense ($000):** 1492417 **Payroll Expense ($000):** 694201 **Personnel:** 8471

✠ **NEW ENGLAND REHABILITATION HOSPITAL OF PORTLAND (203025)**, 335 Brighton Avenue, Zip 04102–2363; tel. 207/775–4000, **A**1 3 10 **F**29 34 35 90 93 95 96 132 135 146 148 **S** Encompass Health Corporation, Birmingham, AL
Primary Contact: Jeanine Chesley, Chief Executive Officer
CFO: James Paladino, Controller
CMO: Thomas Morrione, Medical Director
CHR: Mary Cote, Director Human Resources
CNO: Sharon Kuhrt, Chief Nursing Officer
Web address: www.nerhp.org
Control: Partnership, Investor–owned (for–profit) **Service**: Rehabilitation

> **Staffed Beds:** 90 **Admissions:** 1795 **Census:** 62 **Outpatient Visits:** 9760 **Births:** 0 **Total Expense ($000):** 27088 **Payroll Expense ($000):** 14514 **Personnel:** 227

✠ **NORTHERN LIGHT MERCY HOSPITAL (200008)**, 144 State Street, Zip 04101–3795; tel. 207/879–3000, **A**1 2 10 **F**3 11 13 15 18 20 29 30 31 34 35 36 40 44 45 48 49 50 51 54 55 56 57 58 59 61 64 68 70 73 74 75 76 78 79 81 82 84 86 87 93 96 97 100 102 104 107 108 110 111 114 115 119 130 132 135 143 144 146 147 148 149 154 156 **S** Northern Light Health, Brewer, ME
Primary Contact: Charles D. Therrien, President
CFO: Michael Hachey, Senior Vice President and Chief Financial Officer
CIO: Craig Dreher, Chief Information Officer
CHR: Elizabeth B Christensen, Director Human Resources
CNO: Bette Neville, R.N., MSN, Vice President and Chief Nursing Officer
Web address: www.https://northernlighthealth.org/Mercy-Hospital
Control: Other not–for–profit (including NFP Corporation) **Service**: General medical and surgical

> **Staffed Beds:** 104 **Admissions:** 4578 **Census:** 43 **Outpatient Visits:** 355225 **Births:** 693 **Total Expense ($000):** 221590 **Payroll Expense ($000):** 88954 **Personnel:** 1026

PRESQUE ISLE—Aroostook County

✠ **THE AROOSTOOK MEDICAL CENTER (200018)**, 140 Academy Street, Zip 04769–3171, Mailing Address: P.O. Box 151, Zip 04769–0151; tel. 207/768–4000, (Includes AROOSTOOK HEALTH CENTER, 15 Highland Avenue, Mars Hill, Maine, Zip 4758; tel. 207/768–4900; ARTHUR R. GOULD MEMORIAL HOSPITAL, 140 Academy Street, Presque Isle, Maine, Zip 4769, Mailing Address: P O Box 151, Zip 4769, tel. 207/768–4000; COMMUNITY GENERAL HEALTH CENTER, 3 Green Street, Fort Fairfield, Maine, Zip 4742; tel. 207/768–4700) (Total facility includes 64 beds in nursing home–type unit) **A**1 10 **F**3 7 8 12 13 15 18 20 28 29 30 31 32 34 35 36 38 40 43 45 51 52 53 54 55 57 59 60 61 64 65 67 70 74 75 76 78 79 81 82 84 85 86 87 89 90 91 93 96 97 104 107 108 110 114 115 116 117 118 119 120 121 123 128 129 130 131 132 133 134 135 143 144 146 147 148 149 150 154 156 **S** Northern Light Health, Brewer, ME
Primary Contact: Gregory LaFrancois, President
COO: Jay Reynolds, M.D., Chief Medical Officer and Chief Clinical Officer
CFO: C Bruce Sandstrom, Vice President and Chief Financial Officer
CMO: Jay Reynolds, M.D., Chief Medical Officer and Chief Clinical Officer
CIO: Kyle Johnson, Chief Information Officer
CHR: Joseph Siddiqui, Vice President Human Resources
Web address: www.tamc.org
Control: Other not–for–profit (including NFP Corporation) **Service**: General medical and surgical

> **Staffed Beds:** 120 **Admissions:** 2569 **Census:** 83 **Outpatient Visits:** 219904 **Births:** 197 **Total Expense ($000):** 137155 **Payroll Expense ($000):** 66166 **Personnel:** 863

Many Facility Codes have changed. Please refer to the AHA Guide Code Chart.   © 2019 AHA Guide

ROCKPORT—Knox County

☐ **PEN BAY MEDICAL CENTER (200063)**, 6 Glen Cove Drive, Zip 04856–4240; tel. 207/921–8000, (Total facility includes 70 beds in nursing home–type unit) **A**1 2 10 20 **F**3 5 13 15 28 30 31 32 35 36 38 40 43 44 45 46 47 48 49 50 56 58 59 70 74 75 76 77 78 79 81 82 83 84 85 86 87 89 91 93 94 96 98 100 104 107 108 110 111 115 117 118 119 130 131 132 135 146 147 148 154 156 157 **S** MaineHealth, Portland, ME
Primary Contact: Mark Fourre, President and Chief Executive Officer
COO: Eric Waters, Vice President Operations
CFO: Maura Kelly, Vice President Fiscal Services
CMO: Dana L Goldsmith, M.D., Vice President Medical Affairs
CIO: Brooks Betts, Director Information Systems and Chief Information Officer
CHR: Thomas R Girard, Vice President Human Resources
CNO: Paula Delahanty, Regional Chief Nursing Officer
Web address: www.penbayhealthcare.org
Control: Other not–for–profit (including NFP Corporation) **Service:** General medical and surgical

Staffed Beds: 151 **Admissions:** 3597 **Census:** 115 **Outpatient Visits:** 181157 **Births:** 283 **Total Expense ($000):** 139622 **Payroll Expense ($000):** 63834 **Personnel:** 824	

PENOBSCOT BAY MEDICAL CENTER See Pen Bay Medical Center

RUMFORD—Oxford County

★ **RUMFORD HOSPITAL (201306)**, 420 Franklin Street, Zip 04276–2145; tel. 207/369–1000, **A**3 10 18 **F**3 8 11 13 15 18 28 29 30 31 34 35 40 43 44 45 50 53 57 59 64 65 67 68 75 76 77 78 79 80 81 85 87 89 90 91 93 94 96 97 107 110 114 119 127 128 130 132 133 135 143 144 146 148 **S** Central Maine Healthcare, Lewiston, ME
Primary Contact: Peter J. Wright, FACHE, President
CNO: Becky Hall, R.N., Director Nursing
Web address: www.rumfordhospital.org
Control: Other not–for–profit (including NFP Corporation) **Service:** General medical and surgical

Staffed Beds: 25 **Admissions:** 936 **Census:** 10 **Outpatient Visits:** 72271 **Births:** 100 **Total Expense ($000):** 40604 **Payroll Expense ($000):** 15915 **Personnel:** 212	

SKOWHEGAN—Somerset County

⅄ **REDINGTON FAIRVIEW GENERAL HOSPITAL (201314)**, 46 Fairview Avenue, Zip 04976, Mailing Address: P.O. Box 468, Zip 04976–0468; tel. 207/474–5121, **A**10 18 **F**3 7 11 13 15 18 28 29 31 34 35 40 45 47 50 53 56 57 59 65 68 70 74 75 76 77 79 81 82 84 85 91 92 93 97 107 108 110 114 115 118 119 130 131 132 133 134 135 146 147 148 149 155 156
Primary Contact: Richard Willett, Chief Executive Officer
CFO: Elmer H Doucette, Chief Financial Officer
CMO: Gust Stringos, M.D., Medical Staff Director
CHR: Lisa G. Landry, Human Resources Director
CNO: Sherry L Rogers, MS, R.N., Chief Nursing Officer
Web address: www.rfgh.net
Control: Other not–for–profit (including NFP Corporation) **Service:** General medical and surgical

Staffed Beds: 25 **Admissions:** 1430 **Census:** 13 **Outpatient Visits:** 26372 **Births:** 139 **Total Expense ($000):** 92466 **Payroll Expense ($000):** 45597 **Personnel:** 595	

WATERVILLE—Kennebec County

★ ○ **NORTHERN LIGHT INLAND HOSPITAL (200041)**, 200 Kennedy Memorial Drive, Zip 04901–4595; tel. 207/861–3000, **A**10 11 **F**3 13 15 18 28 29 30 34 35 40 44 45 46 50 51 56 57 59 64 68 70 74 75 76 77 79 81 82 85 92 93 97 107 108 109 110 111 115 119 127 129 130 132 146 147 148 149 151 154 **S** Northern Light Health, Brewer, ME
Primary Contact: John Dalton, President
COO: Daniel Booth, Vice President Operations and Chief Human Resources Officer
CFO: Dean Bither, Chief Financial Officer
CMO: Michael Palumbo, D.O., Vice President Medical Affairs and Chief Education
CIO: Kevin Dieterich, Director Information Services
CHR: Daniel Booth, Vice President Operations
Web address: www.inlandhospital.org
Control: Other not–for–profit (including NFP Corporation) **Service:** General medical and surgical

Staffed Beds: 29 **Admissions:** 1308 **Census:** 12 **Outpatient Visits:** 14911 **Births:** 332 **Total Expense ($000):** 78301 **Payroll Expense ($000):** 29068 **Personnel:** 486	

WESTBROOK—Cumberland County

⊠ **SPRING HARBOR HOSPITAL (204005)**, 123 Andover Road, Zip 04092–3850; tel. 207/761–2200, **A**1 3 10 **F**50 59 68 75 80 87 98 99 100 103 104 130 132 157 **S** MaineHealth, Portland, ME
Primary Contact: Mary Jane Krebs, FACHE, President
CFO: Michael Abbatiello, Chief Financial Officer
CMO: Girard Robinson, M.D., Senior Vice President Medical and Clinical Affairs
CIO: Susan Moulton, Director Health Information Management
CHR: Timothy McNulty, Director Human Resources
Web address: www.springharbor.org
Control: Other not–for–profit (including NFP Corporation) **Service:** Psychiatric

Staffed Beds: 100 **Admissions:** 2212 **Census:** 84 **Outpatient Visits:** 1722 **Births:** 0 **Total Expense ($000):** 39174 **Payroll Expense ($000):** 19966 **Personnel:** 301	

YORK—York County

★ **YORK HOSPITAL (200020)**, 15 Hospital Drive, Zip 03909–1099; tel. 207/363–4321, (Nonreporting) **A**10
Primary Contact: Jud Knox, Chief Executive Officer
CFO: Robin LaBonte, Leader Financial Care
CMO: Lawrence Petrovich, M.D., Chief Medical Officer
CIO: Robin LaBonte, Leader Financial Care
CHR: Olivia Chayer, Director, Human Resources
Web address: www.yorkhospital.com
Control: Other not–for–profit (including NFP Corporation) **Service:** General medical and surgical

Staffed Beds: 58	

Hospital, Medicare Provider Number, Address, Telephone, Approval, Facility, and Physician Codes, Health Care System

★ American Hospital Association (AHA) membership
☐ The Joint Commission accreditation
○ Healthcare Facilities Accreditation Program
◇ DNV Healthcare Inc. accreditation
⇧ Center for Improvement in Healthcare Quality Accreditation
△ Commission on Accreditation of Rehabilitation Facilities (CARF) accreditation

MARYLAND

MD

ANNAPOLIS—Anne Arundel County

⊞ **ANNE ARUNDEL MEDICAL CENTER (210023)**, 2001 Medical Parkway, Zip 21401–3019; tel. 443/481–1000, (Total facility includes 40 beds in nursing home–type unit) **A**1 2 3 5 10 **F**3 4 5 9 11 12 13 14 15 18 20 22 26 28 29 30 31 32 34 35 37 38 39 40 41 44 45 46 47 49 50 53 54 55 56 57 58 59 60 61 63 64 65 66 68 70 72 74 75 76 77 78 79 81 82 83 84 85 87 89 91 92 93 94 96 97 100 101 102 107 108 110 111 114 115 116 117 118 119 120 121 123 124 126 130 131 132 134 135 146 147 148 149 150 152 153 154 156 157
Primary Contact: Victoria Bayless, President and Chief Executive Officer
COO: Maulik Joshi, Executive Vice President, Integrated Care Delivery and Chief Operating Officer
CFO: Robert Reilly, Vice President and Chief Financial Officer
CMO: Mitchell B Schwartz, M.D., Chief Medical Officer
CIO: Barbara Baldwin, Chief Information Officer
CHR: Julie McGovern, Vice President Human Resources
CNO: Barbara S Jacobs, MSN, Vice President, Nursing and Chief Nursing Officer
Web address: www.aahs.org
Control: Other not–for–profit (including NFP Corporation) **Service**: General medical and surgical

Staffed Beds: 407 **Admissions:** 25791 **Census:** 279 **Outpatient Visits:** 495310 **Births:** 5402 **Total Expense ($000):** 558534 **Payroll Expense ($000):** 213523 **Personnel:** 3882

BALTIMORE—Baltimore City County

☐ **BON SECOURS BALTIMORE HEALTH SYSTEM (210013)**, 2000 West Baltimore Street, Zip 21223–1558; tel. 410/362–3000, **A**1 10 **F**3 15 18 20 26 29 30 40 44 49 58 59 60 64 66 70 77 78 79 81 84 85 87 97 98 99 100 101 102 103 104 105 107 108 110 111 115 119 130 143 146 148 153 154 156 158 **S** Bon Secours Mercy Health, Marriottsville, MD
Primary Contact: Samuel Lee. Ross, M.D., MS, Chief Executive Officer
CFO: Laura Ellison, Chief Financial Officer
CMO: Arsalan Sheikh, Chief of Medicine
CIO: Sanjay Purushotham, Executive Director Information Systems
CHR: Danielle Jorden-Ellis, Director
CNO: Shelly Buck, Chief Nursing Executive and Chief Operating Officer
Web address: www.bonsecoursbaltimore.com
Control: Church operated, Nongovernment, not–for–profit **Service**: General medical and surgical

Staffed Beds: 69 **Admissions:** 3292 **Census:** 49 **Outpatient Visits:** 337097 **Births:** 0 **Total Expense ($000):** 113802 **Payroll Expense ($000):** 42504 **Personnel:** 699

GOOD SAMARITAN HOSPITAL OF MARYLAND See Medstar Good Samaritan Hospital

HARBOR HOSPITAL See Medstar Harbor Hospital

⊞ △ **JOHNS HOPKINS BAYVIEW MEDICAL CENTER (210029)**, 4940 Eastern Avenue, Zip 21224–2780; tel. 410/550–0100, **A**1 3 5 7 8 10 **F**1 2 3 4 5 6 8 9 11 12 13 15 16 17 18 20 22 26 28 29 30 31 32 34 35 36 38 40 41 43 44 45 46 47 48 49 50 51 54 55 56 57 58 59 60 61 64 65 66 68 70 71 72 74 75 76 77 78 79 80 81 82 84 85 86 87 89 90 92 93 96 97 98 99 100 101 102 103 104 107 108 110 111 115 116 117 118 119 120 121 123 126 130 131 132 134 135 141 143 146 147 148 149 153 154 157 **S** Johns Hopkins Health System, Baltimore, MD
Primary Contact: Richard G. Bennett, M.D., President
COO: Charles B. Reuland, Sc.D., Executive Vice President and Chief Operating Officer
CFO: Carl H Francioli, Vice President Finance
CIO: Sandy Reckert, Director Communications and Public Affairs
CHR: Craig R Brodian, Vice President Human Resources
Web address: www.hopkinsbayview.org
Control: Other not–for–profit (including NFP Corporation) **Service**: General medical and surgical

Staffed Beds: 414 **Admissions:** 19651 **Census:** 308 **Outpatient Visits:** 423851 **Births:** 1253 **Total Expense ($000):** 566558 **Payroll Expense ($000):** 193050 **Personnel:** 3252

⊞ △ **JOHNS HOPKINS HOSPITAL (210009)**, 600 North Wolfe Street, Admin 104, Zip 21287–1629; tel. 410/955–5000, (Includes JOHNS HOPKINS CHILDREN'S CENTER, 1800 Orleans Street, Baltimore, Maryland, Zip 21287–0010; tel. 410/955–5000) **A**1 2 3 5 7 8 10 **F**3 4 5 6 7 8 9 11 13 14 15 16 17 18 19 20 21 22 23 24 25 26 27 28 29 30 31 32 34 35 36 38 39 40 41 43 44 45 46 47 48 49 50 51 52 54 55 56 57 58 59 60 61 63 64 65 66 68 70 72 74 75 76 77 78 79 80 81 82 83 84 85 86 87 88 89 90 91 92 93 94 95 96 97 98 99 100 101 102 103 104 105 106 107 108 109 110 111 112 113 114 115 116 117 118 119 120 121 123 124 126 129 130 131 132 134 135 136 137 138 139 140 141 142 143 145 146 147 148 149 150 152 153 154 155 156 157 **S** Johns Hopkins Health System, Baltimore, MD
Primary Contact: Redonda G. Miller, M.D., President
COO: Charles B. Reuland, Sc.D., Executive Vice President and Chief Operations Officer
CFO: Ronald J Werthman, Senior Vice President Finance, Chief Financial Officer and Treasurer
CIO: Stephanie L Reel, Senior Vice President Information Services
CHR: Bonnie Windsor, Senior Vice President Human Resources
CNO: Deborah Baker, Vice President, Nursing
Web address: www.hopkinsmedicine.org
Control: Other not–for–profit (including NFP Corporation) **Service**: General medical and surgical

Staffed Beds: 988 **Admissions:** 44049 **Census:** 866 **Outpatient Visits:** 653244 **Births:** 2481 **Total Expense ($000):** 2354591 **Payroll Expense ($000):** 633393 **Personnel:** 10059

☐ △ **KENNEDY KRIEGER INSTITUTE (213301)**, 707 North Broadway, Zip 21205–1890; tel. 443/923–9200, (Nonreporting) **A**1 3 5 7 10
Primary Contact: Bradley Schlagger, M.D., President and Chief Executive Officer
COO: James M Anders Jr Administrator and Chief Operating Officer
CFO: Michael J Neuman, Vice President Finance
CMO: Michael V Johnston, M.D., Chief Medical Officer and Senior Vice President Medical Programs
CIO: Kenneth Davis, Assistant Vice President Information Systems
CHR: Michael Loughran, Vice President Human Resources
Web address: www.kennedykrieger.org
Control: Other not–for–profit (including NFP Corporation) **Service**: Children's other specialty

Staffed Beds: 70

☐ △ **LEVINDALE HEBREW HOSPITAL AND NURSING (210064)**, 2434 West Belvedere Avenue, Zip 21215–5267; tel. 410/601–2400, (Nonreporting) **A**1 7 10 **S** LifeBridge Health, Baltimore, MD
Primary Contact: Deborah Graves, R.N., President and Chief Operating Officer
CMO: Susan M Levy, M.D., Vice President Medical Affairs
CIO: Tressa Springmann, Vice President and Chief Information Officer
CHR: Cheryl T. Boyer, Vice President Human Resources
CNO: Candy Hamner, Vice President and Chief Nursing Officer
Web address: www.sinai-balt.com
Control: Other not–for–profit (including NFP Corporation) **Service**: Acute long–term care hospital

Staffed Beds: 490

⊞ △ **MEDSTAR GOOD SAMARITAN HOSPITAL (210056)**, 5601 Loch Raven Boulevard, Zip 21239–2995; tel. 443/444–8000, **A**1 2 3 5 7 10 **F**3 6 9 11 15 17 18 20 26 28 29 30 31 34 35 36 37 38 40 44 45 49 50 51 53 55 56 57 58 59 60 61 63 64 65 66 68 70 74 75 77 78 79 80 81 82 84 85 86 87 90 91 92 93 96 97 100 101 104 107 108 110 111 114 115 116 117 118 119 120 121 123 129 130 131 132 135 143 146 148 149 156 **S** MedStar Health, Columbia, MD
Primary Contact: Bradley Chambers, President and Senior Vice President, MedStar Health
CFO: Deana Stout, Vice President Financial Services
Web address: www.goodsam-md.org
Control: Other not–for–profit (including NFP Corporation) **Service**: General medical and surgical

Staffed Beds: 227 **Admissions:** 8530 **Census:** 125 **Outpatient Visits:** 279309 **Births:** 0 **Total Expense ($000):** 262106 **Payroll Expense ($000):** 114537 **Personnel:** 1422

Many Facility Codes have changed. Please refer to the AHA Guide Code Chart. © 2019 AHA Guide

☒ **MEDSTAR HARBOR HOSPITAL (210034)**, 3001 South Hanover Street, Zip 21225–1290; tel. 410/350–3200, **A**1 2 3 5 10 **F**3 9 11 13 15 18 20 26 29 30 34 35 36 40 43 44 45 46 48 49 50 51 53 54 55 56 57 58 59 60 61 63 64 65 66 68 70 72 74 75 76 77 78 79 81 82 84 85 86 87 89 92 93 94 97 98 100 102 103 104 105 107 108 110 111 114 115 118 119 129 130 131 132 135 146 147 149 153 **S** MedStar Health, Columbia, MD
Primary Contact: Stuart M. Levine, M.D., President and Chief Medical Officer
COO: Jill Donaldson, Vice President Operations
CFO: David R Pitman, Vice President Finance
CMO: Allan Birenberg, Vice President Medical Affairs
CIO: Cynthia Tanebaum, Director Information Services
CHR: Karen Evelius, Director Human Resources
CNO: Lenora Addison, Vice President Patient Care and Nursing
Web address: www.harborhospital.org
Control: Other not–for–profit (including NFP Corporation) **Service**: General medical and surgical

Staffed Beds: 127 **Admissions**: 7538 **Census**: 96 **Outpatient Visits**: 148120 **Births**: 1307 **Total Expense ($000)**: 189034 **Payroll Expense ($000)**: 83803 **Personnel**: 916

☒ **MEDSTAR UNION MEMORIAL HOSPITAL (210024)**, 201 East University Parkway, Zip 21218–2895; tel. 410/554–2000, **A**1 2 3 5 10 **F**3 9 11 15 17 18 20 22 24 26 28 29 30 31 34 35 37 38 39 40 43 44 45 46 47 48 49 50 51 53 54 55 56 57 58 59 60 61 63 64 65 66 68 70 74 75 77 78 79 80 81 82 84 85 86 87 91 92 93 94 96 97 100 101 102 104 105 107 108 110 111 114 115 118 119 121 123 130 131 132 135 141 145 146 149 153 **S** MedStar Health, Columbia, MD
Primary Contact: Bradley Chambers, President
COO: Neil MacDonald, Vice President, Operations
CFO: Deana Stout, Vice President, Finance
CMO: Stuart Bell, M.D., Vice President, Medical Affairs
CIO: Janet Decker, Assistant Vice President, Information Systems
CHR: Ashley Handwerk, Director, Human Resources
CNO: Karen Owings, MSN, Vice President, Patient Care Services
Web address: www.medstarunionmemorial.org
Control: Other not–for–profit (including NFP Corporation) **Service**: General medical and surgical

Staffed Beds: 215 **Admissions**: 10905 **Census**: 133 **Outpatient Visits**: 316308 **Births**: 0 **Total Expense ($000)**: 449852 **Payroll Expense ($000)**: 195718 **Personnel**: 1801

☒ △ **MT. WASHINGTON PEDIATRIC HOSPITAL (213300)**, 1708 West Rogers Avenue, Zip 21209–4545; tel. 410/578–8600, (Nonreporting) **A**1 3 5 7 10 **S** University of Maryland Medical System, Baltimore, MD
Primary Contact: Sheldon J. Stein, President and Chief Executive Officer
CFO: Mary Miller, Vice President Finance and Business Development
CMO: Richard Katz, M.D., Vice President Medical Affairs
CIO: Tim Brady, Director Information Systems
CHR: Thomas J Ellis, Vice President Human Resources
Web address: www.mwph.org
Control: Other not–for–profit (including NFP Corporation) **Service**: Children's other specialty

Staffed Beds: 61

☒ **SAINT AGNES HEALTHCARE (210011)**, 900 Caton Avenue, Zip 21229–5201; tel. 667/234–6000, **A**1 2 3 5 10 **F**3 8 11 12 13 14 15 17 18 20 22 26 28 29 30 31 32 34 35 40 41 44 46 49 50 53 54 55 56 57 58 59 60 61 64 65 68 70 72 74 75 76 77 78 79 81 82 84 85 86 87 88 89 92 93 96 97 100 107 108 110 111 114 115 117 118 119 120 121 123 124 126 129 130 131 132 134 135 144 146 147 148 149 150 154 156 157 **S** Ascension Healthcare, Saint Louis, MO
Primary Contact: Keith Vander Kolk, President and Chief Executive Officer
CFO: Scott Furniss, Vice President and Chief Financial Officer
CMO: Nancy Hammond, M.D., Vice President, Chief Medical Officer
CHR: James Bobbitt, Vice President Human Resources, Group Ministry Market
CNO: Yolanda Copeland, R.N., Senior Vice President Patient Care Services and Chief Nursing Officer
Web address: www.stagnes.org
Control: Church operated, Nongovernment, not–for–profit **Service**: General medical and surgical

Staffed Beds: 367 **Admissions**: 15101 **Census**: 186 **Outpatient Visits**: 477957 **Births**: 2126 **Total Expense ($000)**: 410214 **Payroll Expense ($000)**: 216742 **Personnel**: 2472

☒ △ **SINAI HOSPITAL OF BALTIMORE (210012)**, 2401 West Belvedere Avenue, Zip 21215–5271; tel. 410/601–9000, **A**1 2 3 5 7 10 **F**3 5 6 8 9 12 13 15 17 18 19 20 22 24 26 29 30 31 32 34 35 36 38 39 40 41 43 44 46 47 49 50 51 54 55 56 57 58 59 60 61 63 64 65 66 68 70 72 73 74 75 76 77 78 79 80 81 82 83 84 85 86 87 88 89 90 91 92 93 94 95 96 97 98 100 101 102 104 107 108 110 111 114 115 116 117 118 119 120 121 123 124 126 129 130 131 132 134 135 143 146 147 148 149 150 153 154 156 157 **S** LifeBridge Health, Baltimore, MD
Primary Contact: Jonathan Ringo, M.D., President and Chief Operating Officer
CFO: David Krajewski, Senior Vice President and Chief Financial Officer
CMO: Daniel C Silverman, M.D., Vice President and Chief Medical Officer
CIO: Karen Barker, Vice President and Chief Information Officer
CHR: Cheryl T. Boyer, Vice President Human Resources
CNO: Linda Kosnik, R.N., MSN, Chief Nursing Officer and Vice President, Patient Care Services
Web address: www.lifebridgehealth.org
Control: Other not–for–profit (including NFP Corporation) **Service**: General medical and surgical

Staffed Beds: 404 **Admissions**: 17262 **Census**: 290 **Outpatient Visits**: 176450 **Births**: 1794 **Total Expense ($000)**: 764960 **Payroll Expense ($000)**: 324721 **Personnel**: 3397

UNION MEMORIAL HOSPITAL See Medstar Union Memorial Hospital

☒ **UNIVERSITY OF MARYLAND MEDICAL CENTER (210002)**, 22 South Greene Street, Zip 21201–1595; tel. 410/328–9199, (Includes UNIVERSITY OF MARYLAND HOSPITAL FOR CHILDREN, 22 South Greene Street, Baltimore, Maryland, Zip 21201–1544; tel. 800/492–5538) **A**1 2 3 8 10 **F**3 5 6 7 8 9 11 12 13 14 15 17 18 19 20 21 22 23 24 25 26 27 28 29 30 31 32 34 35 36 37 38 39 40 41 43 44 45 46 47 48 49 50 51 52 54 55 56 57 58 59 60 61 64 65 66 68 70 71 72 74 75 76 77 78 79 81 82 85 86 87 88 89 92 93 94 97 98 99 100 101 102 103 104 105 106 107 108 109 110 111 114 115 116 117 118 119 120 121 122 123 124 126 129 130 131 132 134 135 136 137 138 139 140 141 142 143 144 145 146 147 148 149 150 153 154 155 157 **S** University of Maryland Medical System, Baltimore, MD
Primary Contact: Mohan Suntha, M.D., President and Chief Executive Officer
CFO: Joseph E Hoffman III Senior Vice President and Chief Financial Officer
CMO: Jonathan Gottlieb, M.D., Senior Vice President and Chief Medical Officer
CIO: Jon P Burns, Chief Information Officer
CHR: R Keith Allen, Senior Vice President Human Resources
CNO: Lisa Rowen, R.N., Senior Vice President and Chief Nursing Officer
Web address: www.umm.edu
Control: Other not–for–profit (including NFP Corporation) **Service**: General medical and surgical

Staffed Beds: 693 **Admissions**: 28011 **Census**: 615 **Outpatient Visits**: 319529 **Births**: 1836 **Total Expense ($000)**: 1522227 **Payroll Expense ($000)**: 498883 **Personnel**: 8495

☒ **UNIVERSITY OF MARYLAND MEDICAL CENTER MIDTOWN CAMPUS (210038)**, 827 Linden Avenue, Zip 21201–4606; tel. 410/225–8000, **A**1 3 5 10 **F**1 5 11 15 18 20 29 30 31 34 35 40 44 49 56 57 59 60 61 63 64 65 66 68 70 74 75 77 78 79 81 82 84 87 91 93 94 96 97 98 100 101 102 104 106 107 108 111 114 115 118 119 129 130 143 146 148 149 153 154 156 **S** University of Maryland Medical System, Baltimore, MD
Primary Contact: Mohan Suntha, M.D., President and Chief Executive Officer
COO: Donald Ray, Vice President Operations
CFO: Craig Fleischmann, Vice President Finance
CMO: W Eugene Egerton, M.D., Chief Medical Officer
CIO: Jon P Burns, Senior Vice President and Chief Information Officer
CHR: Paula Henderson, Vice President Human Resources
CNO: Lisa Rowen, R.N., Chief Nursing Officer
Web address: www.ummidtown.org/
Control: Other not–for–profit (including NFP Corporation) **Service**: General medical and surgical

Staffed Beds: 170 **Admissions**: 4640 **Census**: 88 **Outpatient Visits**: 101398 **Births**: 0 **Total Expense ($000)**: 223093 **Payroll Expense ($000)**: 78626 **Personnel**: 1206

Hospital, Medicare Provider Number, Address, Telephone, Approval, Facility, and Physician Codes, Health Care System

★ American Hospital Association (AHA) membership
□ The Joint Commission accreditation
○ Healthcare Facilities Accreditation Program
◇ DNV Healthcare Inc. accreditation
îi Center for Improvement in Healthcare Quality Accreditation
△ Commission on Accreditation of Rehabilitation Facilities (CARF) accreditation

MD

☒ △ **UNIVERSITY OF MARYLAND REHABILITATION & ORTHOPAEDIC INSTITUTE (210058)**, 2200 Kernan Drive, Zip 21207–6697; tel. 410/448–2500, **A**1 3 5 7 10 **F**1 29 30 34 35 38 39 50 57 64 68 74 75 77 79 81 82 85 86 87 90 91 93 94 95 96 100 107 115 119 128 130 131 146 148 149 154 157 **S** University of Maryland Medical System, Baltimore, MD
Primary Contact: Cynthia Kelleher, M.P.H., President and Chief Executive Officer
CFO: W Walter Augustin, CPA, III Vice President Financial Services and Chief Financial Officer
CMO: John P. Straumanis, M.D., Vice President Medical Affairs and Chief Medical Officer
CIO: Linda Hines, Vice President Information Technology and Information Systems
CHR: Paula Henderson, Vice President Human Resources
CNO: Cheryl D Lee, R.N., MSN, Vice President of Patient Care Services and Chief Nursing Officer
Web address: www.umrehabortho.org
Control: Other not–for–profit (including NFP Corporation) **Service**: Rehabilitation

Staffed Beds: 117 Admissions: 2478 Census: 98 Outpatient Visits: 55199 Births: 0 Total Expense ($000): 109216 Payroll Expense ($000): 43193 Personnel: 550

☒ **VETERANS AFFAIRS MARYLAND HEALTH CARE SYSTEM-BALTIMORE DIVISION**, 10 North Greene Street, Zip 21201–1524; tel. 410/605–7001, (Includes VETERANS AFFAIRS MARYLAND HEALTH CARE SYSTEM-PERRY POINT DIVISION, Circle Drive, Perry Point, Maryland, Zip 21902; tel. 410/642–2411; Adam M. Robinson, Director), (Non-reporting) **A**1 2 3 5 **S** Department of Veterans Affairs, Washington, DC
Primary Contact: Adam M. Robinson, Director
CFO: Major Tom Scheffler, Chief Fiscal Officer
CMO: Dorothy Snow, M.D., Chief of Staff
CIO: Sharon Zielinski, Chief Information Resource Officer
CHR: Jeff Craig, Chief Human Resource Management
Web address: www.maryland.va.gov/
Control: Veterans Affairs, Government, federal **Service**: General medical and surgical

Staffed Beds: 727

BALTIMORE—Baltimore County

FRANKLIN SQUARE HOSPITAL CENTER See Medstar Franklin Square Medical Center

☒ **GREATER BALTIMORE MEDICAL CENTER (210044)**, 6701 North Charles Street, Zip 21204–6892; tel. 443/849–2000, (Total facility includes 27 beds in nursing home–type unit) **A**1 2 3 5 10 **F**8 11 12 13 18 20 22 26 29 30 31 34 35 38 40 41 44 45 46 47 48 49 50 51 53 55 56 57 58 59 60 61 62 63 64 68 70 72 73 74 75 76 77 78 79 80 81 82 83 84 85 86 87 89 92 93 96 97 102 107 108 114 115 119 120 121 123 124 126 128 129 130 132 135 136 142 145 146 147 148 154 156 157
Primary Contact: John B. Chessare, M.D., M.P.H., FACHE, President and Chief Executive Officer
COO: Keith R Poisson, Executive Vice President and Chief Operating Officer
CFO: Eric L Melchior, Executive Vice President and Chief Financial Officer
CMO: John R Saunders, M.D., Senior Vice President Medical Affairs and Chief Medical Officer
CHR: Deloris Simpson-Tuggle, Vice President Human Resources and Organizational Development and Chief Human Resources Officer
CNO: Jody Porter, R.N., Senior Vice President Patient Care Services and Chief Nursing Officer
Web address: www.gbmc.org
Control: Other not–for–profit (including NFP Corporation) **Service**: General medical and surgical

Staffed Beds: 402 Admissions: 17313 Census: 173 Outpatient Visits: 501880 Births: 3959 Total Expense ($000): 504348 Payroll Expense ($000): 264554 Personnel: 3194

☒ **MEDSTAR FRANKLIN SQUARE MEDICAL CENTER (210015)**, 9000 Franklin Square Drive, Zip 21237–3901; tel. 443/777–7000, **A**1 2 3 5 8 10 **F**3 5 9 11 12 13 15 18 20 22 26 28 29 30 31 32 34 35 36 37 38 39 40 41 44 45 46 47 48 49 50 51 55 56 57 58 59 60 61 63 64 65 66 68 70 71 72 74 75 76 77 78 79 81 82 84 85 86 87 89 92 93 94 97 98 99 100 101 102 104 107 108 110 111 114 115 118 119 120 121 123 124 126 129 130 131 132 134 135 145 146 147 148 149 154 **S** MedStar Health, Columbia, MD
Primary Contact: Samuel E. Moskowitz, President
CFO: Robert P Lally Jr Vice President Finance
CMO: Tony Sclama, M.D., Vice President Medical Affairs
CIO: Stephen Mannion, Assistant Vice President Information Systems Customer Service
CNO: Lawrence F Strassner III, Ph.D., FACHE, R.N., MS, Senior Vice President Operations and Chief Nursing Officer
Web address: www.medstarfranklin.org
Control: Other not–for–profit (including NFP Corporation) **Service**: General medical and surgical

Staffed Beds: 369 Admissions: 21544 Census: 245 Outpatient Visits: 422598 Births: 2574 Total Expense ($000): 518897 Payroll Expense ($000): 231994 Personnel: 2575

☒ **SHEPPARD PRATT HEALTH SYSTEM (214000)**, 6501 North Charles Street, Zip 21204–6819, Mailing Address: P.O. Box 6815, Zip 21285–6815; tel. 410/938–3000, **A**1 3 5 10 **F**4 10 29 30 34 35 36 38 50 56 57 58 64 68 75 77 87 98 99 100 101 103 104 105 106 130 132 135 143 144 146 149 150 152 153 154 157 158
Primary Contact: Harsh Trivedi, M.D., President and Chief Executive Officer
COO: Armando Colombo, Chief Operating Officer
CFO: Ray R Dziesinski, Vice President and Chief Financial Officer
CMO: Robert Roca, M.D., Vice President Medical Affairs
CIO: Matthew Knudsen, Director, Information Systems
CHR: Cathy Doughty, Vice President Human Resources
CNO: Ernestine Y. Cosby, Vice President Clinical Services and Chief Nursing Officer
Web address: www.sheppardpratt.org
Control: Other not–for–profit (including NFP Corporation) **Service**: Psychiatric

Staffed Beds: 338 Admissions: 8345 Census: 296 Outpatient Visits: 86905 Births: 0 Total Expense ($000): 229288 Payroll Expense ($000): 119859 Personnel: 2422

☐ **SPRING GROVE HOSPITAL CENTER (214018)**, 55 Wade Avenue, Zip 21228–4663; tel. 410/402–6000, (Nonreporting) **A**1 3 5 10
Primary Contact: David S. Helsel, M.D., Chief Executive Officer
CFO: Edward Swartz, Chief Financial Officer
CMO: Kelly Phillips, M.D., M.P.H., Clinical Director and Chief Staff
Web address: www.springgrove.com
Control: State, Government, nonfederal **Service**: Psychiatric

Staffed Beds: 425

BALTIMORE—Baltimore (City) County

☒ **MERCY MEDICAL CENTER (210008)**, 301 St Paul Place, Zip 21202–2165; tel. 410/332–9000, **A**1 2 3 10 **F**3 4 11 13 14 15 18 20 29 30 31 34 35 36 37 39 40 41 44 45 46 47 48 49 50 51 55 57 58 59 64 65 66 68 70 72 74 75 76 77 78 79 81 82 84 85 86 87 89 92 93 94 100 102 107 108 110 111 114 115 116 117 118 119 120 121 123 124 126 128 129 130 131 132 135 141 142 143 144 145 146 147 148 149 150 154 156 157 158
Primary Contact: Thomas R. Mullen, President and Chief Executive Officer
COO: Susan D Finlayson, MSN, R.N., Senior Vice President of MMC Operations
CFO: Justin Deibel, Senior Vice President and Chief Financial Officer
CMO: Wilma Rowe, M.D., Senior Vice President Medical Affairs
CIO: Kathleen Perry, Senior Vice President and Chief Information Officer
CHR: Tammy Janus, Senior Vice President Human Resources
CNO: Kim Bushnell, MSN, R.N., Vice President, Patient Care Services
Web address: www.mdmercy.com
Control: Church operated, Nongovernment, not–for–profit **Service**: General medical and surgical

Staffed Beds: 233 Admissions: 14084 Census: 168 Outpatient Visits: 276570 Births: 2622 Total Expense ($000): 488281 Payroll Expense ($000): 177871 Personnel: 3628

BEL AIR—Harford County

☒ **UNIVERSITY OF MARYLAND UPPER CHESAPEAKE MEDICAL CENTER (210049)**, 500 Upper Chesapeake Drive, Zip 21014–4324; tel. 443/643–1000, (Nonreporting) **A**1 2 3 10 **S** University of Maryland Medical System, Baltimore, MD
Primary Contact: Lyle Ernest. Sheldon, FACHE, President and Chief Executive Officer
CMO: Peggy Vaughan, M.D., Senior Vice President Medical Affairs
CIO: Rick Casteel, Vice President Management Information Systems and Chief Information Officer
CHR: Toni M Shivery, Vice President Human Resources
Web address: www.uchs.org
Control: Other not–for–profit (including NFP Corporation) **Service**: General medical and surgical

Staffed Beds: 162

BERLIN—Worcester County

☒ **ATLANTIC GENERAL HOSPITAL (210061)**, 9733 Healthway Drive, Zip 21811–1155; tel. 410/641–1100, (Nonreporting) **A**1 10
Primary Contact: Michael A. Franklin, FACHE, President and Chief Executive Officer
COO: Kim Justice, Vice President Planning and Operations
CFO: Cheryl Nottingham, Chief Financial Officer
CMO: Stephen F Waters, M.D., Medical Director
CIO: Andrew Fowler, Vice President Information Services
CHR: Jim Brannon, Vice President Human Resources
CNO: Colleen Wareing, Vice President Patient Care Services
Web address: www.atlanticgeneral.org
Control: Other not–for–profit (including NFP Corporation) **Service**: General medical and surgical

Staffed Beds: 45

Many Facility Codes have changed. Please refer to the AHA Guide Code Chart. © 2019 AHA Guide

BETHESDA—Montgomery County

✠ **NATIONAL INSTITUTES OF HEALTH CLINICAL CENTER**, 9000 Rockville Pike, Building 10, Room 6–2551, Zip 20892–1504; tel. 301/496–4000, (Includes CHILDREN'S INN AT NIH, 7 West Drive, Bethesda, Maryland, Zip 20814–1509; tel. 301/496–5672) **A**1 3 5 8 **F**3 4 5 14 20 22 26 30 31 36 39 45 53 55 58 59 60 61 63 64 65 67 68 70 74 75 77 78 79 80 81 82 83 84 85 86 87 89 91 92 93 94 95 96 98 99 100 101 104 107 108 111 112 114 115 116 117 118 119 120 121 124 126 129 130 132 135 136 141 145 146 148 149 152 156 **S** U. S. Indian Health Service, Rockville, MD
Primary Contact: James K. Gilman, M.D., Chief Executive Officer
COO: Captain Pius Aiyelawo, Chief Operating Officer
CFO: Maria Joyce, Chief Financial Officer
CMO: David K Henderson, M.D., Deputy Director Clinical Care
CIO: Jon W McKeeby, Chief Information Officer
CHR: Bonnie Tuma, Human Resources Team Lead
CNO: Clare Hastings, R.N., Ph.D., Chief Nurse Officer
Web address: www.clinicalcenter.nih.gov
Control: Public Health Service other than 47, Government, federal **Service:** Other specialty treatment

Staffed Beds: 121 **Admissions:** 4531 **Census:** 114 **Outpatient Visits:** 95220 **Total Expense ($000):** 494343 **Payroll Expense ($000):** 180990 **Personnel:** 1793

NATIONAL NAVAL MEDICAL CENTER See Walter Reed National Military Medical Center

✠ **SUBURBAN HOSPITAL (210022)**, 8600 Old Georgetown Road, Zip 20814–1497; tel. 301/896–3100, **A**1 2 3 5 10 **F**3 5 8 11 15 17 18 20 22 24 26 28 29 30 31 34 35 36 37 38 39 40 41 43 44 45 46 49 50 51 53 56 57 58 59 60 64 70 71 74 75 77 78 79 81 82 84 85 87 89 92 93 98 100 101 102 104 105 106 107 108 110 111 114 115 118 119 120 121 123 126 130 132 135 146 148 149 150 152 153 156 157 **S** Johns Hopkins Health System, Baltimore, MD
Primary Contact: Jacky Schultz, MSN, R.N., President
COO: Joseph Linstrom, Vice President Operations
CFO: Marty Basso, Senior Vice President Finance
CMO: Eric D Dobkin, M.D., Vice President Medical Affairs
CIO: Jason Cole, Senior Director, Management Information Systems
CHR: Queenie C. Plater, Vice President, Human Resources National Capital Region Johns Hopkins Medicine
CNO: LeighAnn Sidone, MSN, R.N., Chief Nursing Officer
Web address: www.suburbanhospital.org
Control: Other not–for–profit (including NFP Corporation) **Service:** General medical and surgical

Staffed Beds: 208 **Admissions:** 14156 **Census:** 167 **Outpatient Visits:** 59832 **Births:** 0 **Total Expense ($000):** 295192 **Payroll Expense ($000):** 107635 **Personnel:** 1525

✠ **WALTER REED NATIONAL MILITARY MEDICAL CENTER**, 8901 Wisconsin Avenue, Zip 20889–5600; tel. 301/295–4611, **A**1 2 3 5 **F**3 5 8 9 12 13 14 15 18 19 20 21 22 23 24 26 27 28 29 30 31 32 33 34 35 36 37 38 39 40 43 44 45 46 47 48 49 50 51 52 53 54 55 56 57 58 59 60 61 64 65 70 72 74 75 76 77 78 79 80 81 82 83 84 85 86 87 88 89 91 92 93 94 96 97 98 100 101 102 104 107 108 109 110 111 112 113 114 115 116 117 118 119 120 121 122 123 124 125 129 130 131 132 134 135 138 141 143 144 145 146 147 148 149 153 154 156 157 158 **S** Bureau of Medicine and Surgery, Department of the Navy, Falls Church, VA
Primary Contact: Captain Mark A. Kobelja, MC, USN, Director
CFO: Commander Joseph Pickel, Director Resource Management
CIO: Commander Cayetano Thornton, Chief Information Officer
CHR: Captain Jaime Carroll, Department Head
Web address: www.wrnmmc.capmed.mil/SitePages/home.aspx
Control: Department of Defense, Government, federal **Service:** General medical and surgical

Staffed Beds: 257 **Admissions:** 12325 **Census:** 141 **Outpatient Visits:** 1173671 **Births:** 1240 **Total Expense ($000):** 927524 **Payroll Expense ($000):** 377341 **Personnel:** 6895

CAMBRIDGE—Dorchester County

☐ **EASTERN SHORE HOSPITAL CENTER (214002)**, 5262 Woods Road, Zip 21613–3796, Mailing Address: P.O. Box 800, Zip 21613–0800; tel. 410/221–2300, (Nonreporting) **A**1 10
Primary Contact: Randy L. Bradford, Chief Executive Officer
COO: William Webb, Assistant Superintendent
CFO: William Webb, Assistant Superintendent
CMO: Evangeline Garcia, M.D., Clinical Director
CHR: Cassandra Stanley, Director Personnel
CNO: Lisa Hines, Director Nursing
Web address: www.dhmh.state.md.us/eshc
Control: State, Government, nonfederal **Service:** Psychiatric

Staffed Beds: 80

✠ **UNIVERSITY OF MARYLAND SHORE MEDICAL CENTER AT DORCHESTER**, 300 Byrn Street, Zip 21613–1908; tel. 410/228–5511, (Nonreporting) **A**1 **S** University of Maryland Medical System, Baltimore, MD
Primary Contact: Kenneth D. Kozel, FACHE, President and Chief Executive Officer
COO: Robert A Frank, Senior Vice President Operations
CFO: Joanne A Hahey, Senior Vice President and Chief Financial Officer
CMO: William Huffner, M.D., Vice President Medical Affairs
CIO: Elizabeth Fish, Chief Information Officer
CHR: Susan Coe, Regional Vice President Human Resources
Web address: www.shorehealth.org
Control: Other not–for–profit (including NFP Corporation) **Service:** General medical and surgical

Staffed Beds: 47

CHESTERTOWN—Kent County

CHESTER RIVER HOSPITAL CENTER See University of Maryland Shore Medical Center at Chestertown

✠ **UNIVERSITY OF MARYLAND SHORE MEDICAL CENTER AT CHESTERTOWN (210030)**, 100 Brown Street, Zip 21620–1499; tel. 410/778–3300, (Nonreporting) **A**1 10 **S** University of Maryland Medical System, Baltimore, MD
Primary Contact: Kenneth D. Kozel, FACHE, President and Chief Executive Officer
COO: Robert A Frank, Senior Vice President of Operations
CFO: Joanne A Hahey, Vice President Finance and Chief Financial Officer
CMO: William Huffner, M.D., Chief Medical Officer
CIO: Elizabeth Fish, Senior Director Site Executive and Information Technology
CHR: Susan Coe, Vice President Human Resources
CNO: Ruth Ann Jones, Ed.D., MSN, R.N., Senior Vice President, Chief Nursing Officer
Web address: www.umms.org/hospitals/shore-health-system.htm
Control: Other not–for–profit (including NFP Corporation) **Service:** General medical and surgical

Staffed Beds: 124

CHEVERLY—Prince George's County

☐ △ **UNIVERSITY OF MARYLAND CAPITAL REGION HEALTH PRINCE GEORGE'S HOSPITAL CENTER (210003)**, 3001 Hospital Drive, Zip 20785–1189; tel. 301/618–2000, (Includes GLADYS SPELLMAN SPECIALTY HOSPITAL AND NURSING CENTER, 3001 Hospital Drive, Sixth Floor, Cheverly, Maryland, Zip 20785–1189; tel. 301/618–6666; Trudy Hall, M.D., Vice President, Medical Affairs; UNIVERSITY OF MARYLAND CAPITAL REGION HEALTH AT LAUREL MEDICAL CENTER, 7300 Van Dusen Road, Laurel, Maryland, Zip 20707–9463; tel. 301/725–4300; Trudy Hall, M.D., Vice President Medical Affairs and Interim Chief Executive Officer), (Non-reporting) **A**1 3 5 7 10 **S** University of Maryland Medical System, Baltimore, MD
Primary Contact: Sherry B. Perkins, Ph.D., R.N., President and Chief Executive Officer
CFO: William Drosius, Chief Financial Officer
CIO: Henry Archibong, Vice President, Information Services and Technology
CHR: Veronica Ford, Vice President Human Resources
CNO: Katie Boston-Leary, Vice President and Chief Nursing Officer, UMPGHC
Web address: www.princegeorgeshospital.org
Control: Other not–for–profit (including NFP Corporation) **Service:** General medical and surgical

Staffed Beds: 177

CLINTON—Prince George's County

✠ **MEDSTAR SOUTHERN MARYLAND HOSPITAL CENTER (210062)**, 7503 Surratts Road, Zip 20735–3358; tel. 301/868–8000, **A**1 2 5 10 **F**3 13 15 17 18 20 22 26 28 29 30 31 34 35 37 38 39 40 44 45 46 47 48 49 50 51 57 58 59 60 61 64 65 66 68 70 74 75 76 77 78 79 80 81 82 83 84 85 86 87 89 93 98 100 101 102 104 105 107 114 115 119 126 129 130 132 135 141 143 146 147 148 149 154 156 **S** MedStar Health, Columbia, MD
Primary Contact: Christine R. Wray, President
CFO: Daniel Feeley, Interim Chief Financial Officer
CMO: Yvette Johnson-Threat, Vice President Medical Affairs
CIO: Lou Mavromatis, Vice President Information Technology
CHR: Paul Zeller, Vice President Human Resources
CNO: Patricia A Scalfari, Vice President Nursing
Web address: www.medstarsouthernmaryland.org
Control: Other not–for–profit (including NFP Corporation) **Service:** General medical and surgical

Staffed Beds: 206 **Admissions:** 9891 **Census:** 127 **Outpatient Visits:** 121140 **Births:** 1239 **Total Expense ($000):** 230059 **Payroll Expense ($000):** 93162 **Personnel:** 1066

Hospital, Medicare Provider Number, Address, Telephone, Approval, Facility, and Physician Codes, Health Care System

★ American Hospital Association (AHA) membership
☐ The Joint Commission accreditation
○ Healthcare Facilities Accreditation Program
◇ DNV Healthcare Inc. accreditation
⇑ Center for Improvement in Healthcare Quality Accreditation
△ Commission on Accreditation of Rehabilitation Facilities (CARF) accreditation

MD

SOUTHERN MARYLAND HOSPITAL CENTER See Medstar Southern Maryland Hospital Center

COLUMBIA—Howard County

⊞ **HOWARD COUNTY GENERAL HOSPITAL (210048)**, 5755 Cedar Lane, Zip 21044–2999; tel. 410/740–7890, **A**1 2 3 5 10 **F**3 8 11 13 15 18 20 22 26 28 29 30 31 32 34 35 36 39 40 41 44 45 46 47 49 50 51 55 56 57 58 59 60 61 64 65 68 70 72 74 75 76 77 78 79 81 82 84 85 86 87 89 91 92 93 96 98 99 100 101 102 103 107 108 110 111 115 118 119 130 131 132 134 135 146 147 148 149 154 156 **S** Johns Hopkins Health System, Baltimore, MD
Primary Contact: Steven C. Snelgrove, President
CFO: Claro M Pio Roda, Dr.PH, Vice President, Finance and Chief Financial Officer
CMO: Mohammed Shafeeq Ahmed, M.D., Vice President of Medical Affairs and Chief Medical Officer
CHR: Jon Oravec, Vice President, Human Resources
CNO: Karen Davis, Chief Nursing Officer and Vice President, Nursing
Web address: www.hcgh.org
Control: Other not–for–profit (including NFP Corporation) **Service**: General medical and surgical

Staffed Beds: 259 **Admissions**: 15454 **Census**: 171 **Outpatient Visits**: 137954 **Births**: 3369 **Total Expense ($000)**: 263388 **Payroll Expense ($000)**: 102375 **Personnel**: 1486

CRISFIELD—Somerset County

☐ **MCCREADY HEALTH (210045)**, 201 Hall Highway, Zip 21817–1299; tel. 410/968–1200, (Nonreporting) **A**1 10
Primary Contact: Kathleen Harrison, Chief Executive Officer
CFO: Gary W Broadwater, Chief Financial Officer
Web address: www.https://www.mccreadyhealth.org
Control: Other not–for–profit (including NFP Corporation) **Service**: General medical and surgical

Staffed Beds: 89

CUMBERLAND—Allegany County

☐ **THOMAS B. FINAN CENTER (214012)**, 10102 Country Club Road SE, Zip 21502–8339, Mailing Address: P.O. Box 1722, Zip 21501–1722; tel. 301/777–2405, **A**1 10 **F**30 86 98 130 132 149
Primary Contact: John Cullen, Chief Executive Officer
COO: Craig Alexander, Chief Operating Officer
CFO: Gina Spears, Chief Financial Officer
CMO: David Millis, M.D., Clinical Director
CHR: Chris Loney, Director Personnel
CNO: Gayle Walter, Director of Nursing
Web address: www.dhmh.state.md.us
Control: State, Government, nonfederal **Service**: Psychiatric

Staffed Beds: 88 **Admissions**: 85 **Census**: 83 **Outpatient Visits**: 0 **Births**: 0 **Total Expense ($000)**: 19828 **Payroll Expense ($000)**: 8400 **Personnel**: 191

⊞ △ **WESTERN MARYLAND REGIONAL MEDICAL CENTER (210027)**, 12500 Willowbrook Road SE, Zip 21502–6393, Mailing Address: P.O. Box 539, Zip 21501–0539; tel. 240/964–7000, (Total facility includes 88 beds in nursing home–type unit) **A**1 2 3 7 10 **F**3 5 11 13 14 15 17 18 20 22 24 26 28 29 30 31 32 34 35 43 44 45 49 50 53 54 56 57 58 59 60 62 63 64 66 68 70 73 74 75 76 77 78 79 80 81 82 84 85 86 87 89 90 93 94 96 97 98 100 101 102 104 107 108 110 111 114 115 116 117 119 120 121 124 126 128 129 130 132 134 135 144 145 146 148 150 153 154 156
Primary Contact: Barry P. Ronan, President and Chief Executive Officer
COO: Nancy D. Adams, R.N., Senior Vice President and Chief Operating Officer
CFO: Kimberly S Repac, Senior Vice President and Chief Financial Officer
CMO: Gerald Goldstein, M.D., Senior Vice President and Chief Medical Officer
CIO: William J. Byers, Chief Information Officer
CHR: Christopher Bumbaugh, Executive Director Human Resource and Organizational Development
CNO: James M. Karstetter, R.N., II Vice President & Chief Nursing Officer
Web address: www.wmhs.com
Control: Other not–for–profit (including NFP Corporation) **Service**: General medical and surgical

Staffed Beds: 321 **Admissions**: 11280 **Census**: 228 **Outpatient Visits**: 543972 **Births**: 948 **Total Expense ($000)**: 323338 **Payroll Expense ($000)**: 116518 **Personnel**: 1685

EASTON—Talbot County

⊞ △ **UNIVERSITY OF MARYLAND SHORE MEDICAL CENTER AT EASTON (210037)**, 219 South Washington Street, Zip 21601–2996; tel. 410/822–1000, (Nonreporting) **A**1 2 7 10 **S** University of Maryland Medical System, Baltimore, MD
Primary Contact: Kenneth D. Kozel, FACHE, President and Chief Executive Officer
COO: Robert A Frank, Senior Vice President of Operations
CFO: Joanne A Hahey, Senior Vice President and Chief Financial Officer
CMO: William Huffner, M.D., Chief Medical Officer
CIO: Elizabeth Fish, Chief Information Officer
CHR: Susan Coe, Regional Vice President Human Resources
CNO: Ruth Ann Jones, Ed.D., MSN, R.N., Senior Vice President, Chief Nursing Officer
Web address: www.shorehealth.org
Control: Other not–for–profit (including NFP Corporation) **Service**: General medical and surgical

Staffed Beds: 132

ELKTON—Cecil County

⊞ **UNION HOSPITAL (210032)**, 106 Bow Street, Zip 21921–5596; tel. 410/398–4000, **A**1 2 10 **F**2 3 11 12 13 15 18 26 29 30 31 34 35 38 40 44 45 46 49 50 51 53 54 57 59 61 64 69 70 74 75 76 77 78 79 81 82 84 85 86 87 89 92 93 97 98 100 102 104 107 108 110 111 114 118 119 129 130 131 132 135 146 147 148 149 154 156
Primary Contact: Richard C. Szumel, M.D., Chief Executive Officer
CFO: Laurie Beyer, Senior Vice President and Chief Financial Officer
CMO: Cydney Teal, M.D., Vice President Medical Affairs
CIO: Anne Lara, Chief Information Officer
CHR: Terrence Lovell, Vice President Human Resources
Web address: www.uhcc.com
Control: Other not–for–profit (including NFP Corporation) **Service**: General medical and surgical

Staffed Beds: 109 **Admissions**: 5140 **Census**: 51 **Outpatient Visits**: 138028 **Births**: 623 **Total Expense ($000)**: 164054 **Payroll Expense ($000)**: 71630 **Personnel**: 994

FREDERICK—Frederick County

⊞ **FREDERICK REGIONAL HEALTH SYSTEM (210005)**, 400 West Seventh Street, Zip 21701–4593; tel. 240/566–3300, **A**1 2 10 **F**3 11 12 13 15 18 20 22 26 28 29 30 31 34 35 38 40 41 44 45 46 48 49 50 53 54 57 58 59 60 61 62 63 64 66 68 70 72 74 75 76 77 78 79 81 82 84 85 86 87 89 93 98 100 102 105 107 108 110 111 114 115 117 118 119 120 121 123 124 126 129 130 131 132 135 146 147 148 149 153 154 157
Primary Contact: Thomas A. Kleinhanzl, President and Chief Executive Officer
COO: John R Verbus, Senior Vice President and Chief Operating Officer
CFO: Michelle K Mahan, Senior Vice President and Chief Financial Officer
CMO: Manuel Casiano, M.D., Senior Vice President Medical Affairs
CIO: David Quirke, Vice President Information Services
CNO: Cheryl Cioffi, R.N., Senior Vice President Patient Care Services and Chief Nursing Officer
Web address: www.fmh.org
Control: Other not–for–profit (including NFP Corporation) **Service**: General medical and surgical

Staffed Beds: 281 **Admissions**: 16523 **Census**: 205 **Outpatient Visits**: 577645 **Births**: 2113 **Total Expense ($000)**: 340036 **Payroll Expense ($000)**: 124657 **Personnel**: 1825

GERMANTOWN—Montgomery County

★ **HOLY CROSS GERMANTOWN HOSPITAL (210065)**, 19801 Observation Drive, Zip 20876–4070; tel. 301/754–7000, **A**3 10 **F**3 11 12 13 18 23 26 29 30 31 35 39 40 45 46 49 50 56 58 59 64 66 68 70 73 74 75 76 77 78 79 81 84 85 86 87 93 97 98 100 102 107 108 111 115 118 119 126 132 146 147 148 149 **S** Trinity Health, Livonia, MI
Primary Contact: Doug Ryder, President
Web address: www.holycrosshealth.org/germantown
Control: Church operated, Nongovernment, not–for–profit **Service**: General medical and surgical

Staffed Beds: 72 **Admissions**: 5166 **Census**: 51 **Outpatient Visits**: 31766 **Births**: 924 **Total Expense ($000)**: 100707 **Payroll Expense ($000)**: 35242 **Personnel**: 533

Many Facility Codes have changed. Please refer to the AHA Guide Code Chart. © 2019 AHA Guide

GLEN BURNIE—Anne Arundel County

☒ **UNIVERSITY OF MARYLAND BALTIMORE WASHINGTON MEDICAL CENTER (210043)**, 301 Hospital Drive, Zip 21061–5899; tel. 410/787-4000, **A**1 2 3 5 10 **F**3 11 13 15 18 20 22 26 28 29 30 31 34 35 37 40 41 44 45 46 48 49 50 51 54 55 56 57 58 59 60 61 63 64 65 68 70 74 75 76 77 78 79 81 82 83 84 85 86 87 89 93 98 100 101 102 104 105 107 108 111 114 115 118 119 120 121 123 124 126 130 132 135 146 147 148 149 150 156 **S** University of Maryland Medical System, Baltimore, MD
Primary Contact: Karen E. Olscamp, President and Chief Executive Officer
COO: Kathleen McCollum, Senior Vice President, Clinical Integration and Chief Operating Officer
CFO: Al Pietsch, CPA, Senior Vice President and Chief Financial Officer
CMO: Neel Vibhakar, M.D., Senior Vice President and Chief Medical Officer
CIO: Jon P Burns, Senior Vice President and Chief Information Officer
CHR: Kathy Poehler, Vice President, Human Resources
CNO: Catherine Whitaker, MSN, R.N., Vice President and Chief Nursing Officer
Web address: www.mybwmc.org
Control: Other not–for–profit (including NFP Corporation) **Service:** General medical and surgical

Staffed Beds: 272 Admissions: 15742 Census: 194 Outpatient Visits: 125165 Births: 962 Total Expense ($000): 344997 Payroll Expense ($000): 138354 Personnel: 2278

HAGERSTOWN—Washington County

☐ **BROOK LANE HEALTH SERVICES (214003)**, 13121 Brook Lane, Zip 21742–1435, Mailing Address: P.O. Box 1945, Zip 21742–1945; tel. 301/733–0330, (Nonreporting) **A**1 10
Primary Contact: R Lynn. Rushing, Chief Executive Officer
COO: Jason Allen, Chief Operating Officer
CFO: David Schey, Chief Financial Officer
CMO: David Gonzalez, M.D., Medical Director
CIO: Robert Fritz, Chief Information Officer
CHR: Nicole Twigg, Director Human Resources
CNO: Jason Allen, Director Patient Care Services
Web address: www.brooklane.org
Control: Other not–for–profit (including NFP Corporation) **Service:** Psychiatric

Staffed Beds: 57

☒ △ **MERITUS MEDICAL CENTER (210001)**, 11116 Medical Campus Road, Zip 21742–6710; tel. 301/790–8000, **A**1 2 7 10 13 **F**3 5 11 12 13 15 17 18 20 22 26 28 29 30 31 34 35 38 40 43 44 49 51 52 54 55 56 57 58 59 60 61 62 64 65 70 74 75 76 77 78 79 81 82 83 84 85 86 87 89 90 93 94 96 97 98 99 100 101 102 103 104 107 108 110 111 114 115 118 119 120 121 123 130 131 132 135 143 144 145 146 147 148 153 154 155 157
Primary Contact: Carolyn Simonsen, President and Interim Chief Executive Officer
CFO: Thomas T. Chan, Chief Financial Officer
CMO: Heather Lorenzo, M.D., Vice President and Chief Medical Officer
CHR: Laura Minteer, Chief Human Resource Officer
CNO: Melanie M Heuston, Chief Nursing Office
Web address: www.meritushealth.com
Control: Other not–for–profit (including NFP Corporation) **Service:** General medical and surgical

Staffed Beds: 278 Admissions: 15315 Census: 178 Outpatient Visits: 190708 Births: 1820 Total Expense ($000): 314735 Payroll Expense ($000): 110454 Personnel: 1828

WASHINGTON COUNTY HEALTH SYSTEM See Meritus Medical Center

☐ △ **WESTERN MARYLAND HOSPITAL CENTER (212002)**, 1500 Pennsylvania Avenue, Zip 21742–3194; tel. 301/745–4200, (Total facility includes 36 beds in nursing home–type unit) **A**1 7 10 **F**1 11 29 30 39 53 75 77 96 128 130 143 146 148
Primary Contact: Michael Reyka, Ph.D., Chief Executive Officer
COO: David Davis, Chief Operating Officer
CFO: Kelly Edmonds, Chief Financial Officer
CMO: Monica Stallworth, M.D., Chief of Staff
CIO: Ron Keplinger, Chief Information Officer
CHR: David Davis, Chief Operating Officer
Web address: www.wmhc.us
Control: State, Government, nonfederal **Service:** Chronic disease

Staffed Beds: 91 Admissions: 83 Census: 51 Outpatient Visits: 0 Births: 0

HAVRE DE GRACE—Harford County

☒ **UNIVERSITY OF MARYLAND HARFORD MEMORIAL HOSPITAL (210006)**, 501 South Union Avenue, Zip 21078–3493; tel. 443/843–5000, **A**1 10 **F**11 12 15 29 30 31 34 35 36 38 40 46 49 50 51 57 59 60 64 65 66 68 70 71 74 75 77 78 79 81 82 84 85 86 87 92 93 96 98 102 103 104 107 108 110 111 114 115 118 119 130 131 132 135 146 148 **S** University of Maryland Medical System, Baltimore, MD
Primary Contact: Lyle Ernest. Sheldon, FACHE, President and Chief Executive Officer
CMO: Peggy Vaughan, M.D., Senior Vice President Medical Affairs
CIO: Rick Casteel, Vice President Management Information Systems and Chief Information Officer
CHR: Toni M Shivery, Vice President Human Resources
Web address: www.uchs.org
Control: Other not–for–profit (including NFP Corporation) **Service:** General medical and surgical

Staffed Beds: 85 Admissions: 4399 Census: 59 Births: 0

JESSUP—Howard County

☐ **CLIFTON T. PERKINS HOSPITAL CENTER**, 8450 Dorsey Run Road, Zip 20794–9486; tel. 410/724–3000, (Nonreporting) **A**1 3 5
Primary Contact: John Robison, Chief Executive Officer
COO: Thomas D Lewis, Chief Operating Officer
CFO: George Parnel, Chief Financial Officer
CMO: Muhammed Ajanah, M.D., Clinical Director
CIO: Chanda Hamilton, Chief Information Officer
CHR: Beverly Stacie, Director Human Resources
Web address: www.dhmh.state.md.us/perkins/
Control: State, Government, nonfederal **Service:** Psychiatric

Staffed Beds: 250

LA PLATA—Charles County

☒ **UNIVERSITY OF MARYLAND CHARLES REGIONAL MEDICAL CENTER (210035)**, 5 Garrett Avenue, Zip 20646–5960, Mailing Address: P.O. Box 1070, Zip 20646–1070; tel. 301/609–4000, **A**1 2 10 **F**11 13 28 29 30 31 34 35 38 40 44 45 50 51 56 57 59 61 64 70 74 76 77 78 79 81 82 84 85 86 87 89 91 92 93 107 108 111 115 118 119 130 132 135 144 145 146 148 149 156 **S** University of Maryland Medical System, Baltimore, MD
Primary Contact: Noel A. Cervino, President and Chief Executive Officer
CFO: Erik Boas, Chief Financial Officer
CMO: Joseph Moser, M.D., Chief Medical Officer
CIO: John Czahor, IT Site Executive
CHR: Stacey M Cook, MS, Vice President, Human Resources
CNO: Dana Levy, Chief Nursing Officer
Web address: www.charlesregional.org
Control: Other not–for–profit (including NFP Corporation) **Service:** General medical and surgical

Staffed Beds: 109 Admissions: 6541 Census: 71 Outpatient Visits: 76782 Births: 893 Total Expense ($000): 120994 Payroll Expense ($000): 46291 Personnel: 702

LANHAM—Prince George's County

☒ **DOCTORS COMMUNITY HOSPITAL (210051)**, 8118 Good Luck Road, Zip 20706–3574; tel. 301/552–8118, **A**1 10 **F**3 8 12 15 18 20 26 27 28 29 30 31 34 35 40 44 45 46 47 49 50 51 53 54 57 59 64 70 71 75 77 78 79 81 82 84 85 93 107 108 111 114 115 118 119 123 126 129 130 131 132 135 146 149 154 156
Primary Contact: Philip B. Down, Chief Executive Officer
COO: Paul Grenaldo, Executive Vice President and Chief Operating Officer
CFO: Camille Bash, Chief Financial Officer
CMO: Sunil Madan, M.D., Chief Medical Officer and Chief Population Health Officer
CIO: Joyce Hanscome, Chief Information Officer
CHR: Paul Hagens, Vice President Human Resources
Web address: www.dchweb.org
Control: Other not–for–profit (including NFP Corporation) **Service:** General medical and surgical

Staffed Beds: 210 Admissions: 9420 Census: 132 Outpatient Visits: 67684 Births: 0 Total Expense ($000): 195812 Payroll Expense ($000): 87832 Personnel: 1376

MD

LEONARDTOWN—St. Mary's County

✠ **MEDSTAR ST. MARY'S HOSPITAL (210028)**, 25500 Point Lookout Road, Zip 20650–2015, Mailing Address: P.O. Box 527, Zip 20650–0527; tel. 301/475–6001, **A**1 2 10 **F**3 11 13 15 18 28 29 30 31 32 34 35 36 39 40 44 45 48 50 51 53 54 57 59 63 64 65 66 68 70 71 74 75 76 77 78 79 81 82 84 85 86 87 89 93 97 98 100 101 102 103 104 105 107 108 110 111 114 115 116 117 118 119 129 130 132 134 135 143 146 147 148 149 150 154 156 **S** MedStar Health, Columbia, MD
Primary Contact: Christine R. Wray, President
COO: Stephen T. Michaels, M.D., Chief Operating Officer and Chief Medical Officer
CIO: Donald Sirk, Director Information Systems
Web address: www.medstarstmarys.org
Control: Other not–for–profit (including NFP Corporation) **Service**: General medical and surgical

Staffed Beds: 109 Admissions: 6777 Census: 68 Outpatient Visits: 167315 Births: 1136 Total Expense ($000): 162146 Payroll Expense ($000): 64881 Personnel: 977

OAKLAND—Garrett County

✠ **GARRETT REGIONAL MEDICAL CENTER (210017)**, 251 North Fourth Street, Zip 21550–1375; tel. 301/533–4000, (Total facility includes 10 beds in nursing home–type unit) **A**1 10 **F**3 11 13 28 29 30 31 32 34 35 38 40 45 50 53 56 57 59 64 65 68 70 75 77 78 79 81 83 84 85 87 102 107 108 114 119 128 130 132 135 141 143 144 146 147 148 149 154 156
Primary Contact: Mark G. Boucot, FACHE, President and Chief Executive Officer
CFO: Tracy Lipscomb, CPA, Vice President Financial Services and Chief Financial Officer
CMO: Marjorie Fridkin, M.D., Chief Medical Officer
CIO: Steven Peterson, Chief Information Officer, Vice President of Operations
CHR: Laura M Waters, Vice President Human Resources
CNO: Kendra Thayer, MSN, R.N., Chief Nursing Officer, Vice President Clinical Services
Web address: www.https://www.gcmh.com
Control: Other not–for–profit (including NFP Corporation) **Service**: General medical and surgical

Staffed Beds: 59 Admissions: 2097 Census: 20 Outpatient Visits: 77392 Births: 283 Total Expense ($000): 58036 Payroll Expense ($000): 22210 Personnel: 416

OLNEY—Montgomery County

✠ **MEDSTAR MONTGOMERY MEDICAL CENTER (210018)**, 18101 Prince Philip Drive, Zip 20832–1512; tel. 301/774–8882, **A**1 2 3 5 10 **F**3 4 5 11 12 13 15 18 19 20 26 28 29 30 31 34 35 36 37 38 39 40 41 44 45 46 48 50 53 55 56 57 58 59 61 64 65 68 70 74 75 76 77 78 79 80 81 82 84 85 86 87 89 92 93 97 98 99 100 101 102 103 104 105 107 108 110 111 114 115 118 119 120 121 123 124 126 129 130 131 132 134 135 146 147 148 149 153 154 156 **S** MedStar Health, Columbia, MD
Primary Contact: Thomas J. Senker, FACHE, President
CFO: David A Havrilla, Chief Financial Officer
CMO: Frederick Finelli, M.D., Vice President Medical Affairs
CIO: Chistiane Brown, Assistant Vice President
CHR: Kevin Mell, Vice President Operations
CNO: Connie Stone, R.N., Chief Nursing Officer
Web address: www.medstarmontgomery.org
Control: Other not–for–profit (including NFP Corporation) **Service**: General medical and surgical

Staffed Beds: 147 Admissions: 6997 Census: 80 Outpatient Visits: 78923 Births: 558 Total Expense ($000): 165432 Payroll Expense ($000): 66698 Personnel: 833

OXEN HILL—Prince George's County

✠ **FORT WASHINGTON MEDICAL CENTER (210060)**, 174 Waterfront Street, Suite 225, Zip 20744; tel. 301/292–7000, (Nonreporting) **A**1 10
Primary Contact: Joseph B. Tucker, Interim President and Chief Executive Officer
COO: Al Campbell, Senior Vice President and Chief Operating Officer
CFO: Joseph B Tucker, Senior Vice President and Chief Financial Officer
CMO: Elias Debbas, M.D., President Medical Staff
CIO: Fred Ashby, Director Information Technology
CHR: Alexander Morris, Corporate Director Human Resources
CNO: Marjorie Quint-Bouzid, Chief Nursing Officer and Vice President Patient Care Services
Web address: www.fortwashingtonmc.org
Control: Other not–for–profit (including NFP Corporation) **Service**: General medical and surgical

Staffed Beds: 37

PERRY POINT—Cecil County

VETERANS AFFAIRS MARYLAND HEALTH CARE SYSTEM-PERRY POINT DIVISION See Veterans Affairs Maryland Health Care System-Baltimore Division, Baltimore

PRINCE FREDERICK—Calvert County

✠ **CALVERTHEALTH MEDICAL CENTER (210039)**, 100 Hospital Road, Zip 20678–4017; tel. 410/535–4000, (Total facility includes 18 beds in nursing home–type unit) **A**1 10 **F**3 8 11 13 18 20 26 28 29 30 31 32 34 35 36 38 39 40 41 43 45 46 47 48 49 50 51 54 56 57 59 61 64 65 66 68 70 71 74 75 76 77 78 79 81 82 85 86 87 89 93 98 99 100 101 102 104 105 107 108 111 112 114 115 119 124 127 129 130 132 134 135 144 146 147 148 149 150 156 157
Primary Contact: Dean Teague, FACHE, Chief Executive Officer
CFO: Carolyn Heithaus, Chief Financial Officer
CMO: J Michael Brooks, M.D., Chief Medical Officer
CIO: Philip Campbell, Vice President Information Services
CHR: Anthony M. Bladen, Vice President Human Resources
CNO: Diane Couchman, Vice President Patient Care Services and Chief Nursing Executive
Web address: www.calverthospital.com
Control: Other not–for–profit (including NFP Corporation) **Service**: General medical and surgical

Staffed Beds: 92 Admissions: 5565 Census: 56 Outpatient Visits: 154533 Births: 647 Total Expense ($000): 131907 Payroll Expense ($000): 57457 Personnel: 999

RANDALLSTOWN—Baltimore County

☐ **NORTHWEST HOSPITAL (210040)**, 5401 Old Court Road, Zip 21133–5185; tel. 410/521–2200, **A**1 2 3 5 10 **F**1 3 4 8 9 11 12 15 18 28 29 30 31 34 35 38 39 40 44 49 51 54 55 56 58 60 61 63 64 68 69 70 75 77 78 79 81 82 85 86 87 93 94 96 97 98 100 101 102 107 108 110 111 114 115 118 119 126 129 130 131 134 143 146 147 148 149 154 157 **S** LifeBridge Health, Baltimore, MD
Primary Contact: Faraaz Yousuf, President and Chief Operating Officer
COO: Kelly Corbi, Chief Operating Officer
CFO: Nancy Kane, Assistant Vice President Finance LifeBridge Health
CMO: Ronald L Ginsberg, M.D., Vice President Medical Affairs
CIO: Tressa Springmann, Vice President and Chief Information Officer
CHR: Valerie Brandenburg, Director Human Resources
CNO: Susan L Jalbert, R.N., MS, Vice President Patient Care Services and Chief Nursing Officer
Web address: www.lifebridgehealth.org
Control: Other not–for–profit (including NFP Corporation) **Service**: General medical and surgical

Staffed Beds: 171 Admissions: 11027 Census: 172 Outpatient Visits: 71894 Total Expense ($000): 244797 Payroll Expense ($000): 92753 Personnel: 1412

ROCKVILLE—Montgomery County

☐ △ **ADVENTIST HEALTHCARE PHYSICAL HEALTH AND REHABILITATION (213029)**, 9909 Medical Center Drive, Zip 20850–6361; tel. 240/864–6000, (Nonreporting) **A**1 7 10 **S** Adventist HealthCare, Gaithersburg, MD
Primary Contact: Brent Reitz, President
COO: Jason Makaroff, Chief Operating Officer and Associate Vice President
CMO: Terrence P Sheehan, M.D., Medical Director
CHR: Carrie Hibbard, Human Resource Business Partner
CNO: Valerie Summerlin, R.N., MS, Chief Nursing Officer
Web address: www.adventistrehab.com
Control: Other not–for–profit (including NFP Corporation) **Service**: Rehabilitation

Staffed Beds: 77

☐ **ADVENTIST HEALTHCARE SHADY GROVE MEDICAL CENTER (210057)**, 9901 Medical Center Drive, Zip 20850–3395; tel. 240/826–6000, (Includes ADVENTIST BEHAVIORAL HEALTH AND WELLNESS SERVICES, 14901 Broschart Road, Rockville, Maryland, Zip 20850–3318; tel. 301/251–4500; John Sackett, President SGMC and Executive Vice President and Chief Operating Officer) **A**1 2 3 5 10 **F**3 12 13 15 18 20 22 26 28 29 30 31 36 39 40 41 45 46 47 48 50 51 53 55 57 60 61 64 66 68 70 72 74 75 76 77 78 79 81 82 83 84 85 87 89 98 99 100 102 103 104 105 106 107 108 110 111 114 115 116 117 119 120 121 126 129 130 135 146 148 149 153 155 **S** Adventist HealthCare, Gaithersburg, MD
Primary Contact: John Sackett, President SGMC and Executive Vice President and Chief Operating Officer
COO: Eunmee Shim, R.N., MSN, Vice President Operations
CFO: Daniel Cochran, Vice President and Chief Financial Officer
CMO: Kevin Smothers, M.D., Vice President Chief Medical Officer
CIO: christopher Ghion, Vice President and Chief Information Officer
CNO: Joan M Vincent, MSN, MS, R.N., Vice President Patient Care Services and Chief Nurse Executive
Web address: www.adventisthealthcare.com
Control: Church operated, Nongovernment, not–for–profit **Service**: General medical and surgical

Staffed Beds: 523 Admissions: 19701 Census: 266 Outpatient Visits: 105823 Births: 4491 Total Expense ($000): 411857 Payroll Expense ($000): 153864 Personnel: 2100

Many Facility Codes have changed. Please refer to the AHA Guide Code Chart.   © 2019 AHA Guide

POTOMAC RIDGE BEHAVIORAL HEALTH See Adventist Behavioral Health and Wellness Services

SALISBURY—Wicomico County

☒ **DEER'S HEAD HOSPITAL CENTER (212003)**, 351 Deer's Head Hospital Road, Zip 21801–3201, Mailing Address: P.O. Box 2018, Zip 21802–2018; tel. 410/543–4000, (Total facility includes 61 beds in nursing home–type unit) **A**1 10 **F**1 3 11 28 29 30 44 50 56 57 59 60 61 65 68 75 77 82 84 85 86 87 90 91 93 94 96 128 130 132 135 146 148 149 156
Primary Contact: Mary Beth Waide, JD, MS, R.N., Chief Executive Officer
CFO: Kenneth Waller, Fiscal Administrator
CMO: Michael P. Buchness, M.D., Director Medical
CIO: Mac Beattie, Computer Network Specialist
CHR: Luanne G Dashield, Personnel Administrator
CNO: Cheri Porcelli, MSN, R.N., Chief Nursing Officer
Web address: www.deershead.org
Control: State, Government, nonfederal **Service**: Chronic disease

Staffed Beds: 73 Admissions: 94 Census: 43 Outpatient Visits: 8225 **Births:** 0 **Total Expense ($000):** 24144 **Payroll Expense ($000):** 9703 **Personnel:** 229

☒ △ **HEALTHSOUTH CHESAPEAKE REHABILITATION HOSPITAL (213028)**, 220 Tilghman Road, Zip 21804–1921; tel. 410/546–4600, (Nonreporting) **A**1 7 10 **S** Encompass Health Corporation, Birmingham, AL
Primary Contact: Steven Walas, Chief Executive Officer
CFO: Karen Rounsley, Controller
CHR: Belinda Thompson, Coordinator Human Resources
CNO: Belle Goslee, Chief Nursing Officer
Web address: www.healthsouthchesapeake.com
Control: Corporation, Investor–owned (for–profit) **Service**: Rehabilitation

Staffed Beds: 54

☒ **PENINSULA REGIONAL MEDICAL CENTER (210019)**, 100 East Carroll Street, Zip 21801–5422; tel. 410/546–6400, **A**1 2 3 10 **F**3 11 12 13 15 17 18 20 22 24 26 28 29 30 31 32 34 35 37 40 43 44 45 46 47 48 49 50 51 53 54 57 58 59 60 61 64 68 70 71 73 74 75 76 77 78 79 81 82 84 85 86 87 89 92 97 98 100 102 104 105 107 108 110 111 114 115 118 119 120 121 123 124 126 130 132 134 135 143 144 145 146 147 148 149 153 154 156
Primary Contact: Steven E. Leonard, President and Chief Executive Officer
COO: Cindy Lunsford, Executive Vice President and Chief Operating Officer
CFO: Bruce Ritchie, Vice President of Finance and Chief Financial Officer
CMO: Charles B Silvia, M.D., Chief Medical Officer and Vice President Medical Affairs
CIO: Raymond Adkins, Chief Information Officer
CHR: Scott Peterson, Vice President of People and Organizational Development
CNO: Karen C Poisker, MSN, Vice President Patient Care Services and Chief Nursing Officer
Web address: www.peninsula.org
Control: Other not–for–profit (including NFP Corporation) **Service**: General medical and surgical

Staffed Beds: 299 Admissions: 17223 Census: 205 Outpatient Visits: 564532 **Births:** 1873 **Total Expense ($000):** 435951 **Payroll Expense ($000):** 179887 **Personnel:** 2740

SILVER SPRING—Montgomery County

☒ **HOLY CROSS HOSPITAL (210004)**, 1500 Forest Glen Road, Zip 20910–1487; tel. 301/754–7000, **A**1 2 3 10 **F**3 7 11 12 13 15 18 20 29 30 31 40 41 45 46 49 50 56 58 60 64 66 67 68 69 70 72 74 75 76 77 78 79 81 82 84 85 86 87 89 93 97 100 102 107 108 110 111 115 118 119 120 121 123 124 126 129 130 132 141 146 147 148 149 154 **S** Trinity Health, Livonia, MI
Primary Contact: Louis Damiano, M.D., President
CFO: Anne Gillis, Chief Financial Officer
CMO: Blair Eig, M.D., Senior Vice President Medical Affairs
CIO: Matthew Trimmer, Director Information Services
CHR: J Manuel Ocasio, Vice President Human Resources
CNO: Celia Guarino, R.N., MSN, Vice President and Chief Nursing Officer
Web address: www.holycrosshealth.org
Control: Church operated, Nongovernment, not–for–profit **Service**: General medical and surgical

Staffed Beds: 367 Admissions: 30973 Census: 354 Outpatient Visits: 159466 **Births:** 9597 **Total Expense ($000):** 431926 **Payroll Expense ($000):** 201132 **Personnel:** 2908

SILVER SPRING—Prince George's County

SAINT LUKE INSTITUTE, 8901 New Hampshire Avenue, Zip 20903–3611; tel. 301/445–7970, (Nonreporting)
Primary Contact: David Songy, President and Chief Executive Officer
COO: Sister Danile Lynch, Chief Operating Officer
Web address: www.sli.org
Control: Other not–for–profit (including NFP Corporation) **Service**: Psychiatric

Staffed Beds: 24

SYKESVILLE—Carroll County

☐ **SPRINGFIELD HOSPITAL CENTER (214004)**, 6655 Sykesville Road, Zip 21784–7966; tel. 410/970–7000, **A**1 3 10 **F**11 30 35 39 44 50 53 56 57 68 75 77 86 87 98 101 103 130 132 135 146 149
Primary Contact: Paula A. Langmead, Chief Executive Officer
COO: Daniel Triplett, Acting Chief Operating Officer
CFO: Keith Hardesty, Chief Financial Officer
CMO: Kim Bright, M.D., Clinical Director
CIO: Denise Maskell, Chief Information Officer
CNO: Gloria Merek, Director of Nursing
Web address: www.dhmh.state.md.us/springfield
Control: State, Government, nonfederal **Service**: Psychiatric

Staffed Beds: 220 Admissions: 278 Census: 218 Outpatient Visits: 0 **Births:** 0

TAKOMA PARK—Montgomery County

☐ △ **ADVENTIST HEALTHCARE WASHINGTON ADVENTIST HOSPITAL (210016)**, 7600 Carroll Avenue, Zip 20912–6392; tel. 301/891–7600, (Nonreporting) **A**1 2 3 5 7 10 **S** Adventist HealthCare, Gaithersburg, MD
Primary Contact: Erik Wangsness, President
Web address: www.adventisthealthcare.com
Control: Other not–for–profit (including NFP Corporation) **Service**: General medical and surgical

Staffed Beds: 230

TOWSON—Baltimore County

☒ **UNIVERSITY OF MARYLAND ST. JOSEPH MEDICAL CENTER (210063)**, 7601 Osler Drive, Zip 21204–7582; tel. 410/337–1000, **A**1 2 3 10 **F**3 11 13 15 17 18 20 22 24 26 28 29 30 31 34 35 36 37 40 41 44 45 46 47 48 49 50 54 55 56 57 58 59 60 61 64 65 66 68 70 71 72 74 75 76 77 78 79 81 82 84 85 86 87 89 91 92 93 97 98 100 101 102 103 104 107 108 114 115 118 119 120 121 122 123 124 126 130 131 132 134 135 144 146 147 148 149 153 156 157 **S** University of Maryland Medical System, Baltimore, MD
Primary Contact: Thomas Smyth, President and Chief Executive Officer
COO: Craig Carmichael, Vice President, Operations
CMO: Gail Cunningham, Interim Chief Medical Officer
CIO: Thomas Gronert, Chief Information Officer
CNO: Pamela Jamieson, Vice President Patient Care Services and Chief Nursing Officer
Web address: www.stjosephtowson.com/home.aspx
Control: Other not–for–profit (including NFP Corporation) **Service**: General medical and surgical

Staffed Beds: 287 Admissions: 15011 Census: 164 Outpatient Visits: 110628 **Births:** 2166 **Total Expense ($000):** 337973 **Payroll Expense ($000):** 111709 **Personnel:** 1796

WESTMINSTER—Carroll County

☒ **CARROLL HOSPITAL CENTER (210033)**, 200 Memorial Avenue, Zip 21157–5799; tel. 410/848–3000, **A**1 2 3 10 **F**3 7 11 13 15 18 19 20 22 26 28 29 30 31 32 34 35 36 38 39 40 44 45 46 49 50 51 54 55 56 57 58 59 61 62 63 64 68 70 74 75 76 77 78 79 81 82 83 84 85 86 87 89 94 96 97 98 99 100 101 102 103 105 107 108 109 110 111 114 115 116 117 119 126 127 129 130 131 132 134 135 143 146 147 148 149 153 154 155 156 157 **S** LifeBridge Health, Baltimore, MD
Primary Contact: Leslie Simmons, FACHE, R.N., President
CFO: Kevin Kelbly, Senior Vice President Finance and Corporate Fiscal Affairs
CMO: Mark Olszyk, M.D., Vice President Medical Affairs and Chief Medical Officer
CHR: Holly Phipps Adams, Vice President of Human Resources
CNO: Stephanie Reid, R.N., Vice President of Patient Care Services and Chief Nursing Officer
Web address: www.carrollhospitalcenter.org
Control: Other not–for–profit (including NFP Corporation) **Service**: General medical and surgical

Staffed Beds: 146 Admissions: 10106 Census: 112 Outpatient Visits: 137385 **Births:** 1024 **Total Expense ($000):** 221936 **Payroll Expense ($000):** 89870 **Personnel:** 1625

MD

Hospital, Medicare Provider Number, Address, Telephone, Approval, Facility, and Physician Codes, Health Care System

★ American Hospital Association (AHA) membership
☐ The Joint Commission accreditation
○ Healthcare Facilities Accreditation Program
◇ DNV Healthcare Inc. accreditation
⇧ Center for Improvement in Healthcare Quality Accreditation
△ Commission on Accreditation of Rehabilitation Facilities (CARF) accreditation

MASSACHUSETTS

ATHOL—Worcester County

☐ **ATHOL HOSPITAL (221303)**, 2033 Main Street, Zip 01331–3598; tel. 978/249–3511, (Nonreporting) **A**1 10 18 **S** Heywood Healthcare, Gardner, MA
Primary Contact: Winfield S. Brown, FACHE, President and Chief Executive Officer
COO: Michael Grimmer, Chief Operating Officer
CFO: Robert Crosby, Chief Financial Officer
CMO: Mohsen Noreldin, M.D., President Medical Staff
CIO: Carol Roosa, Vice President Information Services and Chief Information Officer
CNO: Lucille Songer, Chief Nursing Officer
Web address: www.atholhospital.org
Control: Other not–for–profit (including NFP Corporation) **Service:** General medical and surgical

Staffed Beds: 25

ATTLEBORO—Bristol County

ARBOUR-FULLER HOSPITAL (224021), 200 May Street, Zip 02703–5520; tel. 508/761–8500, (Nonreporting) **A**10 **S** Universal Health Services, Inc., King of Prussia, PA
Primary Contact: Rachel Legend, Chief Executive Officer
CFO: James Rollins, Chief Financial Officer
CMO: Aminadav Zakai, M.D., Medical Director
CHR: Brian Jenkins, Director Human Resources
Web address: www.arbourhealth.com
Control: Corporation, Investor–owned (for–profit) **Service:** Psychiatric

Staffed Beds: 46

★ ⇑ **STURDY MEMORIAL HOSPITAL (220008)**, 211 Park Street, Zip 02703–3137, Mailing Address: P.O. Box 2963, Zip 02703–0963; tel. 508/222–5200, **A**2 10 21 **F**3 8 13 15 18 20 28 29 30 31 32 34 35 36 40 44 45 46 49 50 53 54 57 58 59 64 70 74 75 76 77 78 79 81 82 85 86 87 89 93 97 100 107 108 109 110 111 115 118 119 129 130 131 132 134 144 146 147 148
Primary Contact: Joseph Casey, Interim President and Chief Executive Officer
CFO: Amy Pfeffer, Chief Financial Officer
CMO: Brian Kelly, M.D., Vice President Medical Affairs and Medical Director
CHR: Cheryl Barrows, Vice President Human Resources
CNO: David Spoor, R.N., Vice President, Patient Care Services and Chief Nursing Officer
Web address: www.sturdymemorial.org
Control: Other not–for–profit (including NFP Corporation) **Service:** General medical and surgical

Staffed Beds: 132 Admissions: 7191 Census: 86 Outpatient Visits: 207287 Births: 641 Total Expense ($000): 179076 Payroll Expense ($000): 92401 Personnel: 1140

AYER—Middlesex County

☐ **NASHOBA VALLEY MEDICAL CENTER (220098)**, 200 Groton Road, Zip 01432–3300; tel. 978/784–9000, (Nonreporting) **A**1 10 **S** Steward Health Care System, LLC, Dallas, TX
Primary Contact: Korry Dow, President
CFO: Ben Moll, Assistant Chief Financial Officer
CMO: Michael Older, M.D., President Medical Staff
CNO: Cheryl L Bonasoro, MSN, R.N., Vice President of Nursing and Chief Operating Officer
Web address: www.https://www.nashobamed.org
Control: Corporation, Investor–owned (for–profit) **Service:** General medical and surgical

Staffed Beds: 48

BEDFORD—Middlesex County

✚ **BEDFORD VETERANS AFFAIRS MEDICAL CENTER, EDITH NOURSE ROGERS MEMORIAL VETERANS HOSPITAL**, 200 Springs Road, Zip 01730–1198; tel. 781/687–2000, **A**1 3 5 **F**4 34 39 54 56 57 58 59 61 62 63 64 65 66 68 69 74 75 77 82 83 84 87 90 91 92 93 94 97 98 100 101 103 104 105 106 119 128 130 132 133 135 143 144 146 147 148 149 153 154 156 157 158 **S** Department of Veterans Affairs, Washington, DC
Primary Contact: Joan Clifford, R.N., FACHE, Medical Center Director and Chief Executive Officer
COO: Mark Fontaine-Westhart, Associate Director
CFO: Edward Koetting, Chief Financial Officer
CMO: Dan Berlowitz, M.D., M.P.H., Acting Chief of Staff
CHR: Robert Colpitts, Chief Human Resource Service
CNO: Mary Ann Petrillo, R.N., MSN, Acting Associate Director Nursing and Patient Clinical Services
Web address: www.bedford.va.gov
Control: Veterans Affairs, Government, federal **Service:** Children's acute long–term Care

Staffed Beds: 324 Admissions: 1950 Census: 342 Births: 0

BELMONT—Middlesex County

✚ **MCLEAN HOSPITAL (224007)**, 115 Mill Street, Zip 02478–1064; tel. 617/855–2000, **A**1 3 5 10 **F**4 5 29 50 53 56 58 68 77 86 98 101 103 104 105 106 111 119 130 132 134 146 152 153 157 **S** Partners HealthCare System, Inc., Boston, MA
Primary Contact: Scott L. Rauch, M.D., President and Psychiatrist in Chief
COO: Michele L Gougeon, Executive Vice President and Chief Operating Officer
CFO: David A Lagasse, Senior Vice President Fiscal Affairs
CMO: Joseph Gold, M.D., Chief Medical Officer
CHR: Lisa D. Pratt, Vice President, Human Resources
CNO: Linda Flaherty, R.N., Senior Vice President, Patient Care Services
Web address: www.mcleanhospital.org
Control: Other not–for–profit (including NFP Corporation) **Service:** Psychiatric

Staffed Beds: 217 Admissions: 6166 Census: 195 Outpatient Visits: 43907 Births: 0 Total Expense ($000): 234809 Payroll Expense ($000): 97248 Personnel: 1782

BEVERLY—Essex County

✚ **BEVERLY HOSPITAL (220033)**, 85 Herrick Street, Zip 01915–1777; tel. 978/922–3000, (Includes ADDISON GILBERT HOSPITAL, 298 Washington Street, Gloucester, Massachusetts, Zip 01930–4887; tel. 978/283–4000), (Nonreporting) **A**1 2 3 5 10 **S** Beth Israel Lahey Health, Boston, MA
Primary Contact: Philip M. Cormier, Chief Executive Officer
COO: Pauline Pike, Chief Operating Officer
CFO: Gary P Marlow, Chief Financial Officer
CMO: Peter H Short, M.D., Senior Vice President Medical Affairs
CIO: Robert Laramie, Chief Information Officer
CHR: Althea C Lyons, Vice President Human Resources and Development
Web address: www.beverlyhospital.org
Control: Other not–for–profit (including NFP Corporation) **Service:** General medical and surgical

Staffed Beds: 320

BOSTON—Suffolk County

☐ **ARBOUR HOSPITAL (224013)**, 49 Robinwood Avenue, Zip 02130–2156; tel. 617/522–4400, (Nonreporting) **A**1 10 **S** Universal Health Services, Inc., King of Prussia, PA
Primary Contact: Eric Kennedy, Chief Executive Officer
Web address: www.arbourhealth.com
Control: Other not–for–profit (including NFP Corporation) **Service:** Psychiatric

Staffed Beds: 118

✚ **BETH ISRAEL DEACONESS MEDICAL CENTER (220086)**, 330 Brookline Avenue, Zip 02215–5491; tel. 617/667–7000, **A**1 2 3 5 8 10 **F**3 5 6 9 11 12 13 14 15 17 18 20 22 24 26 28 29 30 31 34 35 36 37 38 40 43 44 45 46 47 48 49 50 51 52 53 54 55 56 57 58 59 60 61 63 64 65 66 68 70 71 72 73 74 75 76 77 78 79 81 82 84 85 86 87 92 93 97 98 100 101 102 103 104 107 108 109 110 111 112 113 114 115 116 117 118 119 120 121 123 124 126 129 130 131 132 135 136 138 139 141 142 143 144 145 146 147 148 149 150 154 156 157 **S** Beth Israel Lahey Health, Boston, MA
Primary Contact: Kevin Tabb, M.D., Chief Executive Officer
CFO: Steven P Fischer, Chief Financial Officer
CMO: Anthony Weiss, M.D., Chief Medical Officer
CIO: John Halamka, M.D., Chief Information Officer
CHR: Judi Bieber, Senior Vice President Human Resources
CNO: Marsha L. Maurer, R.N., MS, Chief Nursing Officer Patient Care Services
Web address: www.bidmc.harvard.edu
Control: Other not–for–profit (including NFP Corporation) **Service:** General medical and surgical

Staffed Beds: 719 Admissions: 35499 Census: 572 Outpatient Visits: 1046333 Births: 5206 Total Expense ($000): 1767222 Payroll Expense ($000): 693527 Personnel: 8363

BOSTON CHILDREN'S HOSPITAL (223302), 300 Longwood Avenue, Zip 02115–5737; tel. 617/355–6000, **A**1 3 5 8 10 **F**3 5 8 11 12 14 18 19 20 21 22 23 24 25 26 27 28 29 30 31 32 34 35 36 37 38 39 40 41 42 43 44 45 46 48 49 50 51 54 55 57 58 59 60 61 62 63 64 65 67 68 72 74 75 77 78 79 80 81 82 83 84 85 86 87 88 89 92 93 94 97 98 99 100 101 102 104 105 106 107 108 109 111 112 113 114 115 116 117 118 119 120 121 123 124 126 129 130 131 132 134 135 136 137 138 139 140 141 142 143 144 146 147 148 149 150 153 154 156 157
Primary Contact: Sandra L. Fenwick, M.P.H., Chief Executive Officer
COO: Kevin B Churchwell, M.D., President and Chief Operating Officer
CFO: Douglas M Vanderslice, Senior Vice President and Chief Financial Officer
CIO: Daniel Nigrin, M.D., Vice President Information Services and Chief Information Officer
Web address: www.childrenshospital.org/
Control: Other not–for–profit (including NFP Corporation) **Service**: Children's general medical and surgical

Staffed Beds: 415 Admissions: 15196 Census: 330 Outpatient Visits: 720968 Births: 0 Total Expense ($000): 1712419 Payroll Expense ($000): 595024 Personnel: 10386

BOSTON MEDICAL CENTER (220031), 1 Boston Medical Center Place, Zip 02118–2908; tel. 617/638–8000, **A**1 2 3 5 8 10 **F**3 5 8 9 12 13 15 17 18 20 22 24 26 28 29 30 31 32 34 35 36 38 40 41 43 44 45 46 47 48 49 50 54 55 56 57 58 59 60 61 64 65 66 68 70 72 73 74 75 76 77 78 79 81 82 84 85 86 87 88 89 93 97 99 100 101 102 103 104 107 108 110 111 114 116 117 118 119 120 121 123 124 126 129 130 131 132 134 135 136 138 142 143 144 145 146 147 148 149 150
Primary Contact: Kate Walsh, M.P.H., President and Chief Executive Officer
CFO: Ronald E Bartlett, Chief Financial Officer
CMO: Ravin Davidoff, M.D., Chief Medical Officer
CHR: Stephanie Lovell, Vice President and General Counsel
Web address: www.bmc.org
Control: Other not–for–profit (including NFP Corporation) **Service**: General medical and surgical

Staffed Beds: 459 Admissions: 26078 Census: 364 Outpatient Visits: 1356814 Births: 2891 Total Expense ($000): 1425236 Payroll Expense ($000): 496244 Personnel: 6986

BRIGHAM AND WOMEN'S FAULKNER HOSPITAL (220119), 1153 Centre Street, Zip 02130–3446; tel. 617/983–7000, (Nonreporting) **A**1 3 5 10 **S** Partners HealthCare System, Inc., Boston, MA
Primary Contact: David O. McCready, President
CFO: Gerard Hadley, Vice President Finance for Brigham & Women's Faulkner Hospital and Vice President Finance and Controller
CMO: Margaret M. Duggan, M.D., Chief Medical Officer
CIO: Catherine Schroeder, Deputy Chief Information Officer
CHR: Laura Barnett, Executive Director, Human Resources
CNO: Cori Loescher, R.N., Chief Nursing Officer and Vice President of Patient Care Services
Web address: www.brighamandwomensfaulkner.org/index.asp
Control: Other not–for–profit (including NFP Corporation) **Service**: General medical and surgical

Staffed Beds: 125

BRIGHAM AND WOMEN'S HOSPITAL (220110), 75 Francis Street, Zip 02115–6110; tel. 617/732–5500, **A**1 2 3 5 8 10 **F**3 5 6 8 9 11 12 13 14 15 16 17 18 20 22 24 26 28 29 30 31 32 33 34 35 36 37 38 39 40 43 44 45 46 47 48 49 50 51 52 54 55 56 57 58 59 60 61 64 65 66 68 70 71 72 73 74 75 76 77 78 79 81 82 83 84 85 86 87 92 93 97 100 101 102 104 105 107 108 110 111 112 114 115 116 117 118 119 120 121 123 124 126 129 130 131 132 133 134 135 136 137 138 140 141 142 143 144 145 146 147 148 149 150 151 152 153 154 157 **S** Partners HealthCare System, Inc., Boston, MA
Primary Contact: Elizabeth Nabel, M.D., President
COO: Ron Walls, M.D., Executive Vice President and Chief Operating Officer
CFO: Christopher Dunleavy, Senior Vice President Finance and Chief Financial Officer
CMO: Stanley Ashley, M.D., Senior Vice President Medical Affairs and Chief Medical Officer
CIO: Adam Landman, M.D., Chief Information Officer
CHR: Sabrina Williams, Interim Vice President Human Resources
CNO: Madelyn Pearson, R.N., Senior Vice President Patient Care Services and Chief Nursing Officer
Web address: www.brighamandwomens.org
Control: Other not–for–profit (including NFP Corporation) **Service**: General medical and surgical

Staffed Beds: 781 Admissions: 41113 Census: 707 Outpatient Visits: 1125659 Births: 6310 Total Expense ($000): 3085395 Payroll Expense ($000): 815833 Personnel: 13893

CARNEY HOSPITAL (220017), 2100 Dorchester Avenue, Zip 02124–5615; tel. 617/296–4000, (Nonreporting) **A**1 3 5 10 **S** Steward Health Care System, LLC, Dallas, TX
Primary Contact: Tom Sands, Interim Chief Executive Officer
COO: Christian Stroucken, Chief Operating Officer
CFO: David McGrail, Vice President Finance
CMO: Alexander White, Vice President Medical Affairs
CHR: Mary Orlandi, Manager Human Resources
Web address: www.carneyhospital.org
Control: Church operated **Service**: General medical and surgical

Staffed Beds: 81

DANA-FARBER CANCER INSTITUTE (220162), 450 Brookline Avenue, Zip 02215–5418; tel. 617/632–3000, **A**1 2 3 5 8 10 **F**3 11 15 29 30 31 32 34 35 36 44 50 54 55 56 57 58 59 64 65 66 68 71 75 77 78 82 83 84 85 86 87 99 100 101 104 107 108 110 111 114 115 117 118 119 120 121 123 124 130 132 134 135 136 144 146 147 148 149 150 154
Primary Contact: Laurie H. Glimcher, M.D., President and Chief Executive Officer
COO: James G Terwilliger, Executive Vice President and Chief Operating Officer
CIO: Jeffrey R Kessler, Vice President Information Services
CHR: Emily Barclay, Vice President Human Resources
Web address: www.dana-farber.org
Control: Other not–for–profit (including NFP Corporation) **Service**: Cancer

Staffed Beds: 30 Admissions: 1307 Census: 29 Outpatient Visits: 465569 Births: 0 Total Expense ($000): 1662558 Payroll Expense ($000): 441837 Personnel: 5199

DR. SOLOMON CARTER FULLER MENTAL HEALTH CENTER (224040), 85 East Newton Street, Zip 02118–2340; tel. 617/626–8700, (Nonreporting) **A**3 5 10
Primary Contact: Mary-Louise White, M.D., Chief Operating Officer
Web address: www.https://www.mass.gov/service-details/metro-boston-area
Control: State, Government, nonfederal **Service**: Psychiatric

Staffed Beds: 32

MASSACHUSETTS EYE AND EAR (220075), 243 Charles Street, Zip 02114–3002; tel. 617/523–7900, **A**1 3 5 10 **F**3 7 8 11 29 30 31 32 34 41 44 50 54 55 56 57 58 59 64 65 66 68 74 75 77 78 81 82 85 86 87 89 107 111 114 119 126 129 130 132 141 146 **S** Partners HealthCare System, Inc., Boston, MA
Primary Contact: John R. Fernandez, President and Chief Executive Officer
CFO: CarolAnn Williams, Chief Financial Officer
CIO: Leo Hill, Chief Information Officer
CHR: Martha Pyle Farrell, Vice President Human Resources and General Counsel
Web address: www.masseyeandear.org
Control: Other not–for–profit (including NFP Corporation) **Service**: Eye, ear, nose and throat

Staffed Beds: 41 Admissions: 1187 Census: 13 Outpatient Visits: 467249 Births: 0 Total Expense ($000): 286269 Payroll Expense ($000): 76608 Personnel: 1863

MASSACHUSETTS GENERAL HOSPITAL (220071), 55 Fruit Street, Zip 02114–2696; tel. 617/726–2000, (Includes MASSGENERAL HOSPITAL FOR CHILDREN, 55 Fruit Street, Boston, Massachusetts, Zip 02114–2621; tel. 888/644–3248) **A**1 3 5 8 10 **F**3 5 6 8 9 11 12 13 14 15 16 17 18 19 20 21 22 23 24 25 26 27 28 29 30 31 32 33 34 35 36 37 38 39 40 41 43 44 45 46 47 48 49 50 51 52 53 54 55 56 57 58 59 60 61 62 63 64 65 66 68 70 71 72 73 74 75 76 77 78 79 80 81 82 84 85 86 87 88 89 91 92 93 94 96 97 98 99 100 101 102 103 104 105 107 108 110 111 112 113 114 115 116 117 118 119 120 121 122 123 124 126 129 130 131 132 134 135 136 137 138 139 140 141 142 143 144 145 146 147 148 149 150 152 153 154 156 157 **S** Partners HealthCare System, Inc., Boston, MA
Primary Contact: Peter L. Slavin, M.D., President
CFO: Sally Mason Boemer, Senior Vice President Finance
CMO: Britain Nicholson, M.D., Chief Medical Officer
CIO: Keith Jennings, Chief Information Officer
CHR: Jovita Thomas-Williams, Senior Vice President of Human Resources
CNO: Jeanette R Ives Erickson, MS, R.N., Senior Vice President Patient Care and Chief Nurse
Web address: www.massgeneral.org
Control: Other not–for–profit (including NFP Corporation) **Service**: General medical and surgical

Staffed Beds: 1032 Admissions: 50338 Census: 856 Outpatient Visits: 856482 Births: 3896 Total Expense ($000): 3820595 Payroll Expense ($000): 1106478 Personnel: 17292

MA

Hospital, Medicare Provider Number, Address, Telephone, Approval, Facility, and Physician Codes, Health Care System

★ American Hospital Association (AHA) membership   ○ Healthcare Facilities Accreditation Program   ⇑ Center for Improvement in Healthcare Quality Accreditation
□ The Joint Commission accreditation   ◇ DNV Healthcare Inc. accreditation   △ Commission on Accreditation of Rehabilitation Facilities (CARF) accreditation

MA

⊞ **NEW ENGLAND BAPTIST HOSPITAL (220088)**, 125 Parker Hill Avenue, Zip 02120–2847; tel. 617/754–5800, **A**1 3 5 10 **F**3 8 9 14 18 29 30 34 35 37 44 45 50 53 54 57 58 59 64 65 66 70 74 75 77 79 81 82 85 86 87 92 93 97 107 108 111 115 119 130 131 141 146 148 157 **S** Beth Israel Lahey Health, Boston, MA
Primary Contact: David Passafaro, Chief Executive Officer
CFO: Thomas Gheringhelli, Senior Vice President, Chief Financial Officer
CHR: Linda Thompson, Senior Vice President, Human Resources and Service Excellence
CNO: Mary Sullivan Smith, R.N., MS, Senior Vice President, Chief Operating Officer and Chief Nursing Officer
Web address: www.nebh.org
Control: Other not–for–profit (including NFP Corporation) **Service:** Orthopedic

> **Staffed Beds:** 113 **Admissions:** 8562 **Census:** 57 **Outpatient Visits:** 123821 **Births:** 0 **Total Expense ($000):** 237209 **Payroll Expense ($000):** 85716 **Personnel:** 904

☐ **SHRINERS HOSPITALS FOR CHILDREN-BOSTON (223304)**, 51 Blossom Street, Zip 02114–2601; tel. 617/722–3000, **A**1 3 5 10 **F**3 16 29 30 32 34 35 36 39 57 58 59 64 68 69 75 79 81 82 85 87 88 89 93 94 100 119 130 132 134 143 146 148 154 158 **S** Shriners Hospitals for Children, Tampa, FL
Primary Contact: Eileen F. Skinner, FACHE, Administrator
CFO: Maria Chung, CPA, Director Fiscal Services
CMO: Matthias B Donelan, M.D., Chief of Staff
CIO: Mary Dolan, Regional Director Information Services and HIPAA Security Official
CHR: John Donlin, Regional Director Human Resources - Boston, Erie, and Springfield
Web address: www.shrinershospitalsforchildren.org/Hospitals/Locations/Boston
Control: Other not–for–profit (including NFP Corporation) **Service:** Children's other specialty

> **Staffed Beds:** 12 **Admissions:** 164 **Census:** 5 **Outpatient Visits:** 6916 **Births:** 0 **Total Expense ($000):** 39651 **Payroll Expense ($000):** 14521 **Personnel:** 180

⊞ **TUFTS MEDICAL CENTER (220116)**, 800 Washington Street, Zip 02111–1552; tel. 617/636–5000, **A**1 2 3 5 8 10 **F**3 4 5 12 13 14 15 17 18 19 20 21 22 23 24 25 26 27 28 29 30 31 32 34 35 37 39 40 41 42 43 44 45 46 47 49 50 51 52 55 56 57 58 59 61 64 65 68 70 71 72 74 75 76 77 78 79 81 82 84 85 86 87 88 89 93 97 98 100 102 104 107 108 110 111 114 115 116 117 118 119 120 121 123 124 126 129 130 131 132 134 135 136 137 138 141 143 146 147 148 149 154 156 157
Primary Contact: Michael Apkon, M.D., Ph.D., Chief Executive Officer
CFO: Kristine Hanscom, Chief Financial Officer
CMO: David Fairchild, M.D., Chief Medical Officer
CIO: William Shickolovich, Chief Information Officer
CNO: Therese M. Hudson-Jinks, R.N., MSN, Chief Nursing Officer
Web address: www.tuftsmedicalcenter.org
Control: Other not–for–profit (including NFP Corporation) **Service:** General medical and surgical

> **Staffed Beds:** 287 **Admissions:** 16363 **Census:** 263 **Outpatient Visits:** 446145 **Births:** 1336 **Total Expense ($000):** 823872 **Payroll Expense ($000):** 322225 **Personnel:** 4910

BRADFORD—Essex County

⊞ **WHITTIER REHABILITATION HOSPITAL (222047)**, 145 Ward Hill Avenue, Zip 01835–6928; tel. 978/372–8000, **A**1 10 **F**1 29 56 60 62 64 74 75 79 92 93 94 95 96 119 130 131 148 154 **S** Whittier Health Network, Haverhill, MA
Primary Contact: Alfred J. Arcidi, M.D., Senior Vice President
Web address: www.whittierhealth.com
Control: Individual, Investor–owned (for–profit) **Service:** Children's acute long-term Care

> **Staffed Beds:** 60 **Admissions:** 750 **Census:** 47 **Outpatient Visits:** 21000 **Births:** 0 **Personnel:** 299

BRAINTREE—Norfolk County

⊞ **ENCOMPASS HEALTH REHABILITATION HOSPITAL OF BRAINTREE (223027)**, 250 Pond Street, Zip 02184–5351; tel. 781/348–2500, **A**1 5 10 **F**29 34 35 57 59 64 74 75 77 78 79 86 87 90 91 92 93 108 119 130 131 132 146 148 149 150 157 **S** Encompass Health Corporation, Birmingham, AL
Primary Contact: Randy Doherty, CPA, Chief Executive Officer
CFO: Barry Leonard I Vice President of Finance
CMO: Arthur Williams, M.D., Medical Director
CHR: Cathryn Wigman, Director Human Resources
CNO: Jinia Drinkwater, R.N., Director Patient Care Services
Web address: www.braintreerehabhospital.com
Control: Individual, Investor–owned (for–profit) **Service:** Rehabilitation

> **Staffed Beds:** 187 **Admissions:** 2640 **Census:** 96 **Outpatient Visits:** 41418 **Births:** 0 **Total Expense ($000):** 36739 **Payroll Expense ($000):** 23796 **Personnel:** 364

BRIDGEWATER—Plymouth County

BRIDGEWATER STATE HOSPITAL, 20 Administration Road, Zip 02324–3201; tel. 508/279–4521, (Nonreporting) **A**3 5
Primary Contact: Daniel Calais Jr, Superintendent
CFO: Diane Wholley, Director Fiscal Services
Control: State, Government, nonfederal **Service:** Psychiatric

> **Staffed Beds:** 350

BRIGHTON—Suffolk County

CARITAS ST. ELIZABETH'S MEDICAL CENTER See St. Elizabeth's Medical Center

⊞ **FRANCISCAN CHILDREN'S (223300)**, 30 Warren Street, Zip 02135–3680; tel. 617/254–3800, **A**1 5 10 **F**1 29 30 34 35 38 39 50 58 59 64 65 68 77 81 86 87 90 91 93 94 97 98 99 100 101 104 105 106 130 132 146
Primary Contact: John D. Nash, FACHE, President and Chief Executive Officer
COO: Donna Polselli, Chief Operating Officer
CFO: Alex Denucci, Chief Financial Officer
CMO: Jane E O'Brien, M.D., Medical Director
CIO: Sean McKeon, Director, Information Technology
CHR: Nancy Murphy, Vice President, Human Resources
CNO: Mary Lou Kelleher, R.N., MSN, Vice President, Nursing
Web address: www.franciscanhospital.org
Control: Other not–for–profit (including NFP Corporation) **Service:** Children's rehabilitation

> **Staffed Beds:** 74 **Admissions:** 781 **Census:** 65 **Outpatient Visits:** 34820 **Births:** 0 **Total Expense ($000):** 62533 **Payroll Expense ($000):** 36083 **Personnel:** 641

BROCKTON—Plymouth County

CARITAS GOOD SAMARITAN MEDICAL CENTER See Good Samaritan Medical Center

☐ **GOOD SAMARITAN MEDICAL CENTER (220111)**, 235 North Pearl Street, Zip 02301–1794; tel. 508/427–3000, (Includes GOOD SAMARITAN MEDICAL CENTER - CUSHING CAMPUS, 235 North Pearl Street, Brockton, Massachusetts, Zip 02401–1794; tel. 508/427–3000), (Nonreporting) **A**1 2 3 5 10 **S** Steward Health Care System, LLC, Dallas, TX
Primary Contact: Harrison Bane, President
COO: Donna Rubinate, R.N., Chief Operating Officer
CFO: Thomas Whalen, Vice President Finance
CMO: Scott Stewart, M.D., Vice President Medical Management
CIO: Lori Caswell, Director Information Technology
CHR: David J Cronin, Regional Vice President Human Resources
Web address: www.goodsamaritanmedical.org
Control: Church operated **Service:** General medical and surgical

> **Staffed Beds:** 190

⊞ **SIGNATURE HEALTHCARE BROCKTON HOSPITAL (220052)**, 680 Centre Street, Zip 02302–3395; tel. 508/941–7000, **A**1 2 3 10 **F**3 12 13 15 17 18 20 22 28 29 30 31 34 35 38 40 44 45 46 47 48 49 50 51 52 54 57 59 61 64 65 68 70 73 74 75 76 77 78 79 81 82 85 86 87 89 93 97 98 100 102 104 107 108 110 111 114 115 116 117 118 119 120 121 123 124 130 131 132 135 144 146 147 148 149
Primary Contact: Kim Norton. Hollon, FACHE, President and Chief Executive Officer
CFO: James Papadakos, Chief Financial Officer
CIO: Gerald Greeley, Chief Information Officer
CHR: David Fisher, Vice President Human Resources
CNO: Kim Walsh, Chief Nursing Officer
Web address: www.signature-healthcare.org
Control: Other not–for–profit (including NFP Corporation) **Service:** General medical and surgical

> **Staffed Beds:** 216 **Admissions:** 10189 **Census:** 121 **Outpatient Visits:** 371044 **Births:** 937 **Total Expense ($000):** 274086 **Payroll Expense ($000):** 119504 **Personnel:** 1431

☐ **ST. ELIZABETH'S MEDICAL CENTER (220036)**, 736 Cambridge Street, Zip 02135–2997; tel. 617/789–3000, (Nonreporting) **A**1 2 3 5 10 **S** Steward Health Care System, LLC, Dallas, TX
Primary Contact: Craig T. Williams, President
CMO: Dicken S.C. Ko, M.D., Vice President of Medical Affairs and Chief Medical Officer
CIO: Joseph Schmitt, Chief Information Officer
CHR: Claudia Henderson, Chief Human Resources
Web address: www.semc.org/
Control: Church operated **Service:** General medical and surgical

> **Staffed Beds:** 338

Many Facility Codes have changed. Please refer to the AHA Guide Code Chart. © 2019 AHA Guide

★ **VETERANS AFFAIRS BOSTON HEALTHCARE SYSTEM BROCKTON DIVISION**, 940 Belmont Street, Zip 02301–5596; tel. 508/583–4500, (Includes VETERANS AFFAIRS MEDICAL CENTER WEST ROXBURY DIVISION, 1400 VFW Parkway, West Roxbury, Massachusetts, Zip 2132, Mailing Address: 1400 VVF Parkway, West Roxbury, Boston, Zip 2132, tel. 617/323–7700; William H Kelleher, Director), (Non-reporting) **A**3 5 8 **S** Department of Veterans Affairs, Washington, DC
Primary Contact: Vincent Ng, Director
CFO: Joe Costa, Acting Chief Fiscal Officer
Web address: www.boston.va.gov/
Control: Veterans Affairs, Government, federal **Service**: General medical and surgical

Staffed Beds: 375

BROOKLINE—Norfolk County

☐ **ARBOUR H. R. I. HOSPITAL (224018)**, 227 Babcock Street, Zip 02446–6799; tel. 617/731–3200, **A**1 10 **F**4 5 29 30 34 35 36 38 57 59 61 68 75 77 82 86 87 98 100 101 102 105 119 130 132 135 143 147 149 150 152 153 154 **S** Universal Health Services, Inc., King of Prussia, PA
Primary Contact: Jameson Pinette, Chief Executive Officer
CFO: James Rollins, Chief Financial Officer
CMO: Anthony Raynes, M.D., Psychiatrist in Chief
CHR: Kris Munson, Director Human Resources
Web address: www.arbourhealth.com
Control: Corporation, Investor–owned (for–profit) **Service**: Psychiatric

Staffed Beds: 76 **Admissions**: 2207 **Census**: 60 **Outpatient Visits**: 18241 **Births**: 0 **Total Expense ($000)**: 19433 **Payroll Expense ($000)**: 10214 **Personnel**: 152

BOURNEWOOD HEALTH SYSTEMS (224022), 300 South Street, Zip 02467–3658; tel. 617/469–0300, (Nonreporting) **A**3 5 10
Primary Contact: Marcia Fowler, Chief Executive Officer
CFO: Michael Gale, Chief Financial Officer
CMO: Carmel Heinsohn, M.D., Medical Director
CHR: Paula Berardi, Manager Human Resources
Web address: www.bournewood.com
Control: Corporation, Investor–owned (for–profit) **Service**: Psychiatric

Staffed Beds: 90

BURLINGTON—Middlesex County

⊞ **LAHEY HOSPITAL & MEDICAL CENTER, BURLINGTON (220171)**, 41 Mall Road, Zip 01805–0001, Mailing Address: 31 Mall Road, Zip 01805–0001; tel. 781/744–5100, (Includes LAHEY MEDICAL CENTER, PEABODY, 1 Essex Center Drive, Peabody, Massachusetts, Zip 01960–2901; tel. 978/538–4000) **A**1 2 3 5 8 10 19 **F**3 6 8 9 11 12 15 17 18 20 22 24 26 28 29 30 31 34 35 36 37 38 40 43 44 45 46 47 48 49 50 51 52 54 55 56 57 58 59 60 61 63 64 65 68 70 74 75 77 78 79 81 82 84 85 86 87 91 92 93 96 97 100 101 102 104 107 108 110 111 114 115 116 117 118 119 120 121 123 124 126 129 130 131 132 135 136 138 139 141 142 144 145 146 147 148 149 150 153 154 157 **S** Beth Israel Lahey Health, Boston, MA
Primary Contact: David L. Longworth, M.D., Chief Executive Officer
COO: Richard R Bias, Chief Operating Officer
CFO: Timothy P. O'Connor, Executive Vice President and Chief Financial Officer
CMO: Timothy Liesching, M.D., Chief Medical Officer
CIO: Bruce Metz, Ph.D., Senior Vice President and Chief Information Officer
CHR: Elizabeth P. Conrad, Senior Vice President and Chief Human Resource Officer
Web address: www.lahey.org
Control: Other not–for–profit (including NFP Corporation) **Service**: General medical and surgical

Staffed Beds: 345 **Admissions**: 23997 **Census**: 311 **Outpatient Visits**: 811164 **Births**: 0 **Total Expense ($000)**: 945382 **Payroll Expense ($000)**: 289957 **Personnel**: 3895

CAMBRIDGE—Middlesex County

⊞ **CAMBRIDGE HEALTH ALLIANCE (220011)**, 1493 Cambridge Street, Zip 02139–1099; tel. 617/665–1000, (Includes CAMBRIDGE HOSPITAL, 1493 Cambridge Street, Cambridge, Massachusetts, Zip 02139–1099; tel. 617/498–1000; SOMERVILLE HOSPITAL, 230 Highland Avenue, Somerville, Massachusetts, Zip 2143; tel. 617/666–4400; WHIDDEN MEMORIAL HOSPITAL, 103 Garland Street, Everett, Massachusetts, Zip 02149–5095; tel. 617/389–6270) **A**1 2 3 5 8 10 **F**2 5 8 11 12 13 15 29 30 31 32 34 35 36 38 39 40 44 45 46 47 48 49 50 56 57 58 59 61 64 65 66 68 70 75 76 77 78 79 80 81 82 86 87 89 93 97 98 99 100 101 102 103 104 107 108 110 111 114 115 119 129 130 131 132 134 135 141 143 145 146 147 148 149 150 152 153 156
Primary Contact: Assaad Sayah, M.D., Interim Chief Executive Officer
CFO: Jill I Batty, Chief Financial Officer
CMO: Assaad Sayah, M.D., Chief Medical Officer
CIO: Brian Herrick, M.D., Chief Information Officer
CHR: Joy U Curtis, Senior Vice President Human Resources
CNO: Elizabeth Cadigan, R.N., MSN, Senior Vice President Patient Care Services and Chief Nursing Officer
Web address: www.challiance.org
Control: City, Government, nonfederal **Service**: General medical and surgical

Staffed Beds: 256 **Admissions**: 10683 **Census**: 154 **Outpatient Visits**: 658611 **Births**: 1174 **Total Expense ($000)**: 653024 **Payroll Expense ($000)**: 343107 **Personnel**: 3606

⊞ **MOUNT AUBURN HOSPITAL (220002)**, 330 Mount Auburn Street, Zip 02138–5597; tel. 617/492–3500, **A**1 2 3 5 8 10 **F**3 5 11 12 13 14 15 17 18 20 22 24 26 28 29 30 31 34 35 36 37 40 45 49 50 51 52 55 56 57 58 59 60 61 62 63 64 65 68 70 73 74 75 76 77 78 79 81 82 86 87 93 97 98 100 101 102 103 104 107 108 110 111 114 115 117 118 119 120 121 123 124 125 129 130 131 132 135 144 145 146 147 154 **S** Beth Israel Lahey Health, Boston, MA
Primary Contact: Jeanette G. Clough, President and Chief Executive Officer
COO: Nicholas T Dileso, R.N., Chief Operating Officer
CFO: William Sullivan
CIO: Kendall White, Chief Information Officer
CHR: Tom Fabiano, Director Human Resources
CNO: Deborah Baker, Vice President, Patient Care Services
Web address: www.mountauburnhospital.org
Control: Other not–for–profit (including NFP Corporation) **Service**: General medical and surgical

Staffed Beds: 205 **Admissions**: 12040 **Census**: 142 **Outpatient Visits**: 205714 **Births**: 2699 **Total Expense ($000)**: 326477 **Payroll Expense ($000)**: 139141 **Personnel**: 2500

SPAULDING HOSPITAL CAMBRIDGE See Spaulding Hospital for Continuing Medical Care Cambridge

⊞ **SPAULDING HOSPITAL FOR CONTINUING MEDICAL CARE CAMBRIDGE (222000)**, 1575 Cambridge Street, Zip 02138–4308; tel. 617/876–4344, **A**1 10 **F**1 3 7 30 31 34 35 36 50 54 57 58 60 64 68 71 74 75 77 78 85 86 87 91 92 93 94 95 96 100 119 130 131 132 146 148 149 154 157 **S** Partners HealthCare System, Inc., Boston, MA
Primary Contact: Maureen Banks, FACHE, MS, R.N., President
CFO: Mary Shaughnessy, Vice President Finance
CMO: Jonathon Schwartz, M.D., Chief Medical Officer
CIO: John Campbell, Chief Information Officer
CHR: Jack Carroll, Director Human Resources
CNO: Adrienne Sarnecki, R.N., Chief Nurse Executive
Web address: www.spauldingnetwork.org
Control: Other not–for–profit (including NFP Corporation) **Service**: Acute long–term care hospital

Staffed Beds: 118 **Admissions**: 1190 **Census**: 117 **Outpatient Visits**: 0 **Births**: 0 **Total Expense ($000)**: 79437 **Payroll Expense ($000)**: 35500 **Personnel**: 480

CANTON—Norfolk County

☐ **PAPPAS REHABILITATION HOSPITAL FOR CHILDREN (222025)**, 3 Randolph Street, Zip 02021–2351; tel. 781/828–2440, (Nonreporting) **A**1 10 **S** Massachusetts Department of Public Health, Boston, MA
Primary Contact: Brian V. Devin, Chief Executive Officer
CFO: Sharon Porter, Chief Financial Officer
CMO: Aruna Sachdev, M.D., Medical Director
CIO: Robert Lima, Director Information Systems
CHR: Trish Scully, Manager Employment Services
Web address: www.mhsf.us/
Control: State, Government, nonfederal **Service**: Children's acute long–term Care

Staffed Beds: 80

MA

Hospital, Medicare Provider Number, Address, Telephone, Approval, Facility, and Physician Codes, Health Care System

★ American Hospital Association (AHA) membership ○ Healthcare Facilities Accreditation Program ⇑ Center for Improvement in Healthcare Quality Accreditation
☐ The Joint Commission accreditation ◇ DNV Healthcare Inc. accreditation △ Commission on Accreditation of Rehabilitation Facilities (CARF) accreditation

CHARLESTOWN—Suffolk County

☒ △ **SPAULDING REHABILITATION HOSPITAL (223034)**, 300 First Avenue, Zip 02129–3109; tel. 617/952–5000, **A**1 3 5 7 10 **F**3 7 28 29 30 34 35 36 50 54 57 58 60 64 68 71 74 75 77 82 86 87 90 91 92 93 94 95 96 100 119 130 131 132 146 148 149 154 157 **S** Partners HealthCare System, Inc., Boston, MA
Primary Contact: David E. Storto, President
COO: Maureen Banks, FACHE, MS, R.N., Chief Operating Officer
CFO: Mary Shaughnessy, Vice President Finance
CMO: Ross Zafonte, D.O., Chief, Physical Medicine and Rehabilitation and Vice President Medical Affairs, Research and Education
CIO: John Campbell, Chief Information Officer
CHR: Russell Averna, Vice President Human Resources
Web address: www.spauldingrehab.org
Control: Other not–for–profit (including NFP Corporation) **Service**: Rehabilitation

Staffed Beds: 132 **Admissions:** 2164 **Census:** 123 **Outpatient Visits:** 349260 **Births:** 0 **Total Expense ($000):** 166201 **Payroll Expense ($000):** 72353 **Personnel:** 1130

CONCORD—Middlesex County

☒ **EMERSON HOSPITAL (220084)**, 133 Old Road to Nine Acre Corner, Zip 01742–9120; tel. 978/369–1400, **A**1 5 10 **F**3 5 7 8 11 12 13 14 15 17 18 28 29 30 31 32 34 35 36 37 38 40 45 48 49 50 51 54 57 59 60 62 64 65 68 70 73 74 75 76 77 78 79 81 82 85 86 87 89 93 98 100 101 102 103 104 105 107 110 111 114 115 119 128 129 130 131 132 135 144 145 146 148 152 153 156 157
Primary Contact: Christine C. Schuster, R.N., President and Chief Executive Officer
CFO: Michael Hachey, Senior Vice President and Chief Financial Officer
CMO: Barrett Kitch, M.D., Senior Vice President, Clinical Affairs and Chief Medical Officer
CIO: Renee Fosberg, Chief Information Officer
CNO: Joyce Welsh, R.N., MS, Vice President of Clinical Services and Chief Nursing Officer
Web address: www.emersonhospital.org
Control: Other not–for–profit (including NFP Corporation) **Service**: General medical and surgical

Staffed Beds: 175 **Admissions:** 7297 **Census:** 96 **Outpatient Visits:** 290000 **Births:** 1226 **Total Expense ($000):** 244836 **Payroll Expense ($000):** 111941 **Personnel:** 1343

DARTMOUTH—Bristol County

☐ **SOUTHCOAST BEHAVIORAL HEALTH (224041)**, 581 Faunce Corner Road, Zip 02747–1242; tel. 888/210–2475, **A**1 10 **F**29 56 98 101 102 103 130 **S** Acadia Healthcare Company, Inc., Franklin, TN
Primary Contact: Richard Remley, Chief Executive Officer
Web address: www.southcoastbehavioral.com
Control: Partnership, Investor–owned (for–profit) **Service**: Psychiatric

Staffed Beds: 120 **Admissions:** 4379 **Census:** 110 **Outpatient Visits:** 0 **Births:** 0 **Total Expense ($000):** 28152 **Payroll Expense ($000):** 18512 **Personnel:** 12

EAST SANDWICH—Barnstable County

☒ △ **SPAULDING REHABILITATION HOSPITAL CAPE COD (223032)**, 311 Service Road, Zip 02537–1370; tel. 508/833–4000, **A**1 7 10 **F**3 29 30 32 34 35 36 50 60 64 74 75 77 79 82 90 91 92 93 96 130 131 132 135 146 147 148 **S** Partners HealthCare System, Inc., Boston, MA
Primary Contact: Maureen Banks, FACHE, MS, R.N., President
COO: Stephanie Nadolny, Vice President of Hospital Operations
CFO: Mary Shaughnessy, Vice President Finance
CMO: David Lowell, M.D., Chief Medical Officer
CIO: John Campbell, Chief Information Officer
CHR: Russell Averna, Vice President of Human Resources
CNO: Adrienne Sarnecki, R.N., Chief Nursing Officer
Web address: www.spauldingrehab.org
Control: Other not–for–profit (including NFP Corporation) **Service**: Rehabilitation

Staffed Beds: 60 **Admissions:** 1053 **Census:** 40 **Outpatient Visits:** 118760 **Births:** 0 **Total Expense ($000):** 44855 **Payroll Expense ($000):** 22682 **Personnel:** 430

EVERETT—Middlesex County

WHIDDEN MEMORIAL HOSPITAL See Cambridge Health Alliance, Cambridge

FALL RIVER—Bristol County

CHARLTON MEMORIAL HOSPITAL See Southcoast Hospitals Group, Fall River

☐ **DR. J. CORRIGAN MENTAL HEALTH CENTER (224028)**, 49 Hillside Street, Zip 02720–5266; tel. 508/235–7200, (Nonreporting) **A**1 3 10 **S** Massachusetts Department of Mental Health, Boston, MA
Primary Contact: Frank O'Reilly, Director
Control: State, Government, nonfederal **Service**: Psychiatric

Staffed Beds: 16

☐ **SAINT ANNE'S HOSPITAL (220020)**, 795 Middle Street, Zip 02721–1798; tel. 508/674–5741, (Nonreporting) **A**1 2 3 10 **S** Steward Health Care System, LLC, Dallas, TX
Primary Contact: Michael Bushell, President
CMO: John Conlon, M.D., Chief Medical Officer
CIO: Julie Berry, Chief Information Officer
CHR: Sandra Dellicker, Director of Human Resources
CNO: Carole Billington, R.N., MSN, Vice President Operations, Chief Nursing Officer
Web address: www.saintanneshospital.org
Control: Church operated **Service**: General medical and surgical

Staffed Beds: 160

☒ **SOUTHCOAST HOSPITALS GROUP (220074)**, 363 Highland Avenue, Zip 02720–3703; tel. 508/679–3131, (Includes CHARLTON MEMORIAL HOSPITAL, 363 Highland Avenue, Fall River, Massachusetts, Zip 02720–3703; tel. 508/679–3131; Keith A Hovan, R.N., President and Chief Executive Officer; ST. LUKE'S HOSPITAL, 101 Page Street, New Bedford, Massachusetts, Zip 2740; tel. 508/997–1515; Keith A Hovan, R.N., President and Chief Executive Officer; TOBEY HOSPITAL, 43 High Street, Wareham, Massachusetts, Zip 2571; tel. 508/295–0880; Keith A Hovan, R.N., President and Chief Executive Officer) **A**1 2 10 **F**3 8 11 12 13 15 17 18 20 22 24 26 28 29 30 31 34 35 37 40 41 44 45 46 47 48 49 50 51 54 56 57 58 59 60 61 64 65 68 70 71 73 74 75 76 77 78 79 81 82 84 85 86 87 89 90 91 92 93 96 100 102 107 108 110 111 114 115 116 117 118 119 120 121 123 124 126 130 131 132 134 135 146 147 148 149 157
Primary Contact: Keith A. Hovan, R.N., President and Chief Executive Officer
COO: Renee Clark, Senior Vice President and Chief Operating Officer
CFO: Wade Broughman, Chief Financial Officer
CMO: Robert Caldas, D.O., Chief Medical Officer
CIO: Jim Feen, Senior Vice President and Chief Information Officer
CHR: David DeJesus, Senior Vice President Human Resources
CNO: Timothy D. Eixenberger, Chief Nursing Officer
Web address: www.southcoast.org
Control: Other not–for–profit (including NFP Corporation) **Service**: General medical and surgical

Staffed Beds: 497 **Admissions:** 33054 **Census:** 405 **Outpatient Visits:** 905964 **Births:** 3293 **Total Expense ($000):** 777437 **Payroll Expense ($000):** 333897 **Personnel:** 4070

FALMOUTH—Barnstable County

☒ **FALMOUTH HOSPITAL (220135)**, 100 Ter Heun Drive, Zip 02540–2599; tel. 508/548–5300, **A**1 2 10 **F**3 8 11 13 15 18 28 29 30 34 35 36 38 40 45 50 53 54 58 59 61 64 65 68 70 74 75 76 77 79 81 82 85 86 87 89 93 96 100 101 102 104 107 108 110 111 115 119 120 121 123 124 129 130 131 132 143 144 146 147 148 149 **S** Cape Cod Healthcare, Inc., Hyannis, MA
Primary Contact: Lori Jewett, R.N., Chief Executive Officer
CFO: Michael Connors, Senior Vice President and Chief Financial Officer
CMO: Alex Heard, M.D., Chief Medical Officer
CIO: Jeanne M. Fallon, Chief Information Officer
CHR: Emily Schorer, Vice President, Human Resources
CNO: Mary Johnson, Chief Nursing Officer
Web address: www.capecodhealth.org
Control: Other not–for–profit (including NFP Corporation) **Service**: General medical and surgical

Staffed Beds: 95 **Admissions:** 5909 **Census:** 63 **Outpatient Visits:** 157189 **Births:** 323 **Total Expense ($000):** 155726 **Payroll Expense ($000):** 71415 **Personnel:** 682

FRAMINGHAM—Middlesex County

☒ **METROWEST MEDICAL CENTER (220175)**, 115 Lincoln Street, Zip 01702–6342; tel. 508/383–1000, (Includes FRAMINGHAM UNION HOSPITAL, 115 Lincoln Street, Framingham, Massachusetts, Zip 1702; tel. 508/383–1000; LEONARD MORSE HOSPITAL, 67 Union Street, Natick, Massachusetts, Zip 1760; tel. 508/650–7000) **A**1 2 3 5 10 **F**3 4 5 11 12 13 14 15 18 20 22 26 28 29 30 31 32 34 35 36 40 41 44 45 46 49 50 54 56 57 59 61 64 65 68 70 73 74 75 76 77 78 79 81 84 85 87 89 93 97 98 99 100 102 103 104 105 107 108 110 114 115 117 118 119 120 121 126 129 130 131 132 134 135 143 146 147 148 149 152 156 157 **S** TENET Healthcare Corporation, Dallas, TX
Primary Contact: Andrew D. Harding, R.N., Chief Executive Officer
CHR: Rebecca Heffernan, Director Human Resources
CNO: Susan A Mangini, MSN, R.N., Chief Nursing Officer
Web address: www.mwmc.com
Control: Corporation, Investor–owned (for–profit) **Service**: General medical and surgical

Staffed Beds: 160 **Admissions:** 9261 **Census:** 148 **Outpatient Visits:** 326395 **Births:** 1076 **Total Expense ($000):** 234736 **Payroll Expense ($000):** 111425 **Personnel:** 1813

MA

GARDNER—Worcester County

☐ **HEYWOOD HOSPITAL (220095)**, 242 Green Street, Zip 01440–1373; tel. 978/632–3420, (Nonreporting) **A**1 3 5 10 **S** Heywood Healthcare, Gardner, MA
Primary Contact: Winfield S. Brown, FACHE, President and Chief Executive Officer
CFO: Robert Crosby, Senior Vice President and Chief Financial Officer
CHR: Thomas Cady, Vice President Human Resources
Web address: www.heywood.org
Control: Other not–for–profit (including NFP Corporation) **Service**: General medical and surgical

Staffed Beds: 93

GEORGETOWN—Essex County

BALDPATE HOSPITAL (224033), 83 Baldpate Road, Zip 01833–2303; tel. 978/352–2131, (Nonreporting)
Primary Contact: Lucille M. Batal, Administrator
Web address: www.detoxma.com/
Control: Corporation, Investor–owned (for–profit) **Service**: Psychiatric

Staffed Beds: 59

GLOUCESTER—Essex County

ADDISON GILBERT HOSPITAL See Beverly Hospital, Beverly

GREAT BARRINGTON—Berkshire County

☒ **FAIRVIEW HOSPITAL (221302)**, 29 Lewis Avenue, Zip 01230–1713; tel. 413/528–0790, **A**1 5 10 18 **F**3 11 13 15 18 28 29 32 34 35 36 40 50 54 56 57 59 64 65 68 70 75 76 77 79 81 85 86 87 89 92 93 94 107 108 110 115 119 130 131 132 133 134 135 145 146 147 148 149 150 154 156 157 **S** Berkshire Health Systems, Inc., Pittsfield, MA
Primary Contact: Eugene A. Dellea, President
COO: Doreen M Sylvia-Hutchinson, Vice President Operations and Chief Nurse Executive
CFO: Anthony Rinaldi, Executive Vice President
CMO: Brian Burke, M.D., President Medical Staff
CHR: Laura Farkas, Director Human Resources
Web address: www.bhs1.org/body_fh.cfm?id=39
Control: Other not–for–profit (including NFP Corporation) **Service**: General medical and surgical

Staffed Beds: 25 Admissions: 902 Census: 9 Outpatient Visits: 50518 Births: 126 Total Expense ($000): 52605 Payroll Expense ($000): 25529 Personnel: 279

GREENFIELD—Franklin County

☒ **BAYSTATE FRANKLIN MEDICAL CENTER (220010)**, 164 High Street, Zip 01301–2613; tel. 413/773–0211, **A**1 3 5 10 **F**3 11 12 13 14 15 18 26 28 29 30 31 34 35 36 40 45 46 47 48 49 50 51 55 57 59 64 68 70 74 75 77 78 79 81 82 85 86 87 93 98 100 101 105 107 108 110 111 115 118 119 129 130 131 132 146 147 148 154 157 **S** Baystate Health, Inc., Springfield, MA
Primary Contact: Ronald Bryant, President
CFO: Andrea Nathanson, Director Finance
CMO: Thomas Higgins, M.D., Chief Medical Officer
CHR: Kerry Damon, Director Human Resources
CNO: Deborah A Provost, Chief Nursing Officer
Web address: www.baystatehealth.org
Control: Other not–for–profit (including NFP Corporation) **Service**: General medical and surgical

Staffed Beds: 89 Admissions: 4532 Census: 51 Outpatient Visits: 112621 Births: 410 Total Expense ($000): 101009 Payroll Expense ($000): 36674 Personnel: 717

HAVERHILL—Essex County

WHITTIER PAVILION (224039), 76 Summer Street, Zip 01830–5814; tel. 978/373–8222, (Nonreporting) **A**1 **S** Whittier Health Network, Haverhill, MA
Primary Contact: Alfred L. Arcidi, M.D., Chief Executive Officer
Web address: www.whittierhealth.com
Control: Partnership, Investor–owned (for–profit) **Service**: Psychiatric

Staffed Beds: 65

HOLYOKE—Hampden County

⇑ **HOLYOKE MEDICAL CENTER (220024)**, 575 Beech Street, Zip 01040–2223; tel. 413/534–2500, **A**2 5 10 21 **F**3 12 13 14 15 18 26 28 29 30 31 34 35 38 40 46 48 49 50 51 54 55 57 58 59 60 64 65 67 68 70 74 75 76 77 78 79 81 82 85 87 89 93 96 98 101 102 104 105 107 108 110 111 114 115 118 119 129 130 132 135 143 145 146 147 148 149 157
Primary Contact: Spiros Hatiras, FACHE, President and Chief Executive Officer
CFO: Michael J Koziol, Chief Financial Officer
CMO: Karen Ferroni, M.D., Medical Director
CIO: Carl Cameron, Director Information Systems
CHR: Mary Kelleher, Vice President Human Resources
CNO: Colleen Desai, Chief Nursing Officer
Web address: www.holyokehealth.com
Control: Other not–for–profit (including NFP Corporation) **Service**: General medical and surgical

Staffed Beds: 196 Admissions: 6543 Census: 76 Outpatient Visits: 321297 Births: 454 Total Expense ($000): 160624 Payroll Expense ($000): 81533 Personnel: 1212

HYANNIS—Barnstable County

☒ **CAPE COD HOSPITAL (220012)**, 27 Park Street, Zip 02601–5230; tel. 508/771–1800, **A**1 2 3 5 10 20 **F**3 11 13 14 15 17 18 20 22 24 26 28 29 30 31 34 35 37 38 40 45 46 50 51 54 57 58 61 64 65 68 70 74 75 76 77 78 79 81 82 85 86 87 89 93 97 98 99 100 101 102 103 104 105 107 108 110 111 114 115 119 120 121 123 124 126 130 131 132 143 144 146 147 148 149 153 **S** Cape Cod Healthcare, Inc., Hyannis, MA
Primary Contact: Michael K. Lauf, President and Chief Executive Officer
CFO: Michael Connors, Senior Vice President and Chief Financial Officer
CMO: Donald Guadagnoli, M.D., Chief Medical Officer
CIO: Jeanne M. Fallon, Senior Vice President and Chief Information Officer
CHR: Emily Schorer, Senior Vice President Human Resources
CNO: Judith Quinn, Vice President Patient Care Services
Web address: www.capecodhealth.org
Control: Other not–for–profit (including NFP Corporation) **Service**: General medical and surgical

Staffed Beds: 259 Admissions: 16180 Census: 196 Outpatient Visits: 539267 Births: 807 Total Expense ($000): 730256 Payroll Expense ($000): 205902 Personnel: 1965

JAMAICA PLAIN—Suffolk County

☐ **LEMUEL SHATTUCK HOSPITAL (222006)**, 170 Morton Street, Zip 02130–3735; tel. 617/522–8110, (Nonreporting) **A**1 3 5 10 **S** Massachusetts Department of Public Health, Boston, MA
Primary Contact: Rosette Martinez, Acting Chief Executive Officer
CFO: Mike Donovan, Chief Financial Officer
CMO: Kenneth Freedman, M.D., Chief Medical Officer
CIO: Kathryn Noonan, Director Information Management
CHR: Jill Sampson, Director Human Resources
Web address: www.mass.gov/shattuckhospital
Control: State, Government, nonfederal **Service**: Acute long–term care hospital

Staffed Beds: 260

LAWRENCE—Essex County

☒ **LAWRENCE GENERAL HOSPITAL (220010)**, 1 General Street, Zip 01841–2961, Mailing Address: P.O. Box 189, Zip 01842–0389; tel. 978/683–4000, **A**1 2 3 5 10 **F**3 7 11 12 13 15 18 20 22 28 29 30 32 34 35 40 41 43 45 46 47 49 50 54 57 59 64 65 68 70 73 74 75 76 77 78 79 81 84 85 87 89 100 107 108 110 115 118 119 129 130 132 135 146 147 148 149 150 157
Primary Contact: Dianne J. Anderson, MS, R.N., President and Chief Executive Officer
CFO: Felix V. Mercado, Chief Financial Officer
CMO: Pracha Eamranond, M.D., Senior Vice President Population Health and Medical Affairs
CHR: Cynthia Phelan, Vice President Human Resources
CNO: Karen O. Moore, FACHE, Senior Vice President Operations and Chief Nursing Officer
Web address: www.lawrencegeneral.org
Control: Other not–for–profit (including NFP Corporation) **Service**: General medical and surgical

Staffed Beds: 196 Admissions: 10959 Census: 118 Outpatient Visits: 179850 Births: 1505 Total Expense ($000): 252533 Payroll Expense ($000): 117544 Personnel: 1126

Hospital, Medicare Provider Number, Address, Telephone, Approval, Facility, and Physician Codes, Health Care System

★ American Hospital Association (AHA) membership
☐ The Joint Commission accreditation
○ Healthcare Facilities Accreditation Program
◇ DNV Healthcare Inc. accreditation
⇑ Center for Improvement in Healthcare Quality Accreditation
△ Commission on Accreditation of Rehabilitation Facilities (CARF) accreditation

MA

LEEDS—Hampshire County

☒ **VETERANS AFFAIRS CENTRAL WESTERN MASSACHUSETTS HEALTHCARE SYSTEM**, 421 North Main Street, Zip 01053–9764; tel. 413/582–3000, (Nonreporting) **A**1 3 5 **S** Department of Veterans Affairs, Washington, DC
Primary Contact: John P. Collins, FACHE, Medical Center Director
COO: Joyce Fredrick, Associate Director
CFO: Andrew McMahon, Chief Fiscal Officer
CMO: Neil Nusbaum, M.D., Chief of Staff
CIO: Michael Marley, Chief Information Officer
CHR: Pablo Feliciano, Manager Human Resources
Web address: www.centralwesternmass.va.gov/
Control: Veterans Affairs, Government, federal **Service**: Psychiatric

Staffed Beds: 117

LEOMINSTER—Worcester County

☒ **UMASS MEMORIAL HEALTHALLIANCE-CLINTON HOSPITAL (220001)**, 60 Hospital Road, Zip 01453–2205; tel. 978/466–2000, (Includes UMASS MEMORIAL HEALTHALLIANCE-CLINTON HOSPITAL, 201 Highland Street, Clinton, Massachusetts, Zip 01510–1096; tel. 978/368–3000; Steven P Roach, FACHE, Interim President) **A**1 2 3 5 10 **F**3 5 11 13 15 18 28 29 30 31 34 35 36 40 42 45 47 49 50 51 54 56 57 58 59 60 61 62 63 64 65 66 68 70 74 75 76 77 78 79 80 81 84 85 87 89 93 98 103 104 107 108 110 114 115 118 119 130 131 132 135 146 147 149 154 156 **S** UMass Memorial Health Care, Inc., Worcester, MA
Primary Contact: Steven P. Roach, FACHE, Interim Chief Executive Officer
COO: Paul MacKinnon, R.N., Chief Operating Officer
CFO: John Bronhard, CPA, II Corporate Vice President, Chief Financial Officer and Treasurer
CMO: Daniel H O'Leary, M.D., Chief Medical Officer
CHR: Julie DeBono, Director, Human Resources
CNO: Judith Thorpe, R.N., MSN, Vice President and Chief Nursing Officer
Web address: www.healthalliance.com
Control: Other not-for-profit (including NFP Corporation) **Service**: General medical and surgical

Staffed Beds: 163 Admissions: 7323 Census: 95 Outpatient Visits: 261592 Births: 659 Total Expense ($000): 213784 Payroll Expense ($000): 78758 Personnel: 954

LOWELL—Middlesex County

☒ **LOWELL GENERAL HOSPITAL (220063)**, 295 Varnum Avenue, Zip 01854–2134; tel. 978/937–6000, (Includes LOWELL GENERAL HOSPITAL, SAINTS CAMPUS, 1 Hospital Drive, Lowell, Massachusetts, Zip 01852–1311, Mailing Address: 295 Varnum Ave, Zip 01854–2134, tel. 978/458–1411; Normand E. Deschene, FACHE, Chief Executive Officer) **A**1 2 3 5 10 **F**3 11 12 13 15 18 20 22 26 28 29 30 31 32 34 35 36 40 41 43 44 45 46 47 48 49 50 51 54 56 57 58 59 60 61 62 63 64 65 68 70 73 74 75 76 78 79 81 82 83 84 85 86 87 89 93 97 100 107 108 110 114 115 118 119 120 121 123 124 126 129 130 131 132 133 134 143 146 147 149 150 156 157
Primary Contact: Joseph White, FACHE, President and Chief Executive Officer
COO: Amy J Hoey, R.N., MS, Executive Vice President and Chief Operating Officer
CFO: Susan Green, Senior Vice President Finance, Chief Financial Officer
CMO: Arthur Lauretano, M.D., Chief Medical Officer
CIO: Brian Sandager, Chief Information Officer
CHR: Sabrina M Granville, Senior Vice President and Chief Human Resources Officer
CNO: Cecelia Lynch, R.N., MS, Vice President Patient Care Services and Chief Nursing Officer
Web address: www.lowellgeneral.org
Control: Other not-for-profit (including NFP Corporation) **Service**: General medical and surgical

Staffed Beds: 327 Admissions: 19366 Census: 226 Outpatient Visits: 525625 Births: 2230 Total Expense ($000): 457141 Payroll Expense ($000): 188200 Personnel: 2734

SAINTS MEDICAL CENTER See Lowell General Hospital, Saints Campus

LUDLOW—Hampden County

☒ **ENCOMPASS HEALTH REHABILITATION HOSPITAL OF WESTERN MASSACHUSETTS (223030)**, 222 State Street, Zip 01056–3437; tel. 413/308–3300, (Nonreporting) **A**1 10 **S** Encompass Health Corporation, Birmingham, AL
Primary Contact: John R. Hunt, Chief Executive Officer
CFO: John Flaherty, Chief Financial Officer
CMO: Adnan Dahdul, M.D., Medical Director
CHR: Mary Mazza, Director Human Resources
CNO: Deborah Santos, R.N., Chief Nursing Officer
Web address: www.healthsouthrehab.org
Control: Corporation, Investor–owned (for–profit) **Service**: Rehabilitation

Staffed Beds: 53

LYNN—Essex County

UNION CAMPUS See North Shore Medical Center, Salem

UNION HOSPITAL See Union Campus

MARLBOROUGH—Middlesex County

☒ **UMASS MEMORIAL-MARLBOROUGH HOSPITAL (220049)**, 157 Union ST, Zip 01752–1297; tel. 508/481–5000, **A**1 3 10 **F**3 11 15 18 24 28 29 30 34 35 40 49 50 51 53 57 63 68 70 77 79 81 82 85 93 98 100 101 105 107 108 115 119 132 146 147 149 154 157 **S** UMass Memorial Health Care, Inc., Worcester, MA
Primary Contact: Steven P. Roach, FACHE, President and Chief Executive Officer
COO: John Kelly, R.N., Chief Nursing Officer and Chief Operating Officer
CFO: Steven McCue, Chief Financial Officer
CMO: Habib Sioufi, M.D., Chief Medical Officer
CHR: Francis Meringolo, Vice President Human Resources
CNO: John Kelly, R.N., Chief Nursing Officer and Chief Operating Officer
Web address: www.marlboroughhospital.org
Control: Other not-for-profit (including NFP Corporation) **Service**: General medical and surgical

Staffed Beds: 67 Admissions: 4260 Census: 48 Outpatient Visits: 28881 Births: 0 Total Expense ($000): 82864 Payroll Expense ($000): 30558 Personnel: 421

MEDFORD—Middlesex County

LAWRENCE MEMORIAL HOSPITAL OF MEDFORD See Melrosewakefield Healthcare, Melrose

MELROSE—Middlesex County

☒ **MELROSEWAKEFIELD HEALTHCARE (220070)**, 585 Lebanon Street, Zip 02176–3225; tel. 781/979–3000, (Includes LAWRENCE MEMORIAL HOSPITAL OF MEDFORD, 170 Governors Avenue, Medford, Massachusetts, Zip 02155–1643; tel. 781/306–6000; MELROSE-WAKEFIELD HOSPITAL, 585 Lebanon Street, Melrose, Massachusetts, Zip 2176; tel. 781/979–3000; Michael V Sack, FACHE, Chief Executive Officer) **A**1 2 3 10 **F**2 3 11 12 13 15 18 20 22 26 28 29 30 31 34 35 36 38 40 41 45 46 47 49 50 51 54 55 56 57 58 59 60 61 62 63 64 65 68 70 72 74 75 76 77 78 79 81 82 84 85 86 87 93 97 98 100 101 102 103 104 105 107 108 110 111 114 115 116 117 118 119 120 121 123 124 129 130 131 132 135 144 146 147 148 149 154 157
Primary Contact: Susan Sandberg, R.N., Chief Executive Officer
CFO: Michael P. Connelly, CPA, FACHE, Executive Vice President and Chief Financial Officer
CMO: Steven P. Sbardella, M.D., FABC, President Clinical Operations and Chief Medical Officer
CHR: David P. Ryan, Vice President Human Resources
CNO: Deborah L Cronin-Waelde, MSN, R.N., Senior Vice President Clinical Operations and Chief Nursing Officer
Web address: www.melrosewakefield.org
Control: Other not-for-profit (including NFP Corporation) **Service**: General medical and surgical

Staffed Beds: 216 Admissions: 8994 Census: 138 Outpatient Visits: 450465 Births: 777 Total Expense ($000): 233538 Payroll Expense ($000): 115838 Personnel: 1039

METHUEN—Essex County

☐ **HOLY FAMILY HOSPITAL (220080)**, 70 East Street, Zip 01844–4597; tel. 978/687–0151, (Includes HOLY FAMILY HOSPITAL AT MERRIMACK VALLEY, 140 Lincoln Avenue, Haverhill, Massachusetts, Zip 01830–6798; tel. 978/374–2000; Craig A Jesiolowski, FACHE, President), (Non-reporting) **A**1 2 3 10 **S** Steward Health Care System, LLC, Dallas, TX
Primary Contact: Craig A. Jesiolowski, FACHE, President
COO: Martha M McDrury, R.N., Chief Operating Officer and Chief Nursing Officer
CFO: Jeffrey P. Dion, Vice President and Chief Financial Officer
CHR: Patricia Gauron, Director Human Resources
CNO: Martha M McDrury, R.N., Chief Operating Officer and Chief Nursing Officer
Web address: www.stewardhealth.org/Holy-Family-Hospital
Control: Church operated **Service**: General medical and surgical

Staffed Beds: 329

Many Facility Codes have changed. Please refer to the AHA Guide Code Chart. © 2019 AHA Guide

MA

MILFORD—Worcester County

MILFORD REGIONAL MEDICAL CENTER (220090), 14 Prospect Street, Zip 01757–3003; tel. 508/473–1190, (Includes WHITINSVILLE MEDICAL CENTER, 18 Granite Street, Whitinsville, Massachusetts, Zip 1588; tel. 508/234–6311) **A**1 2 3 5 10 **F**3 11 12 13 15 18 20 26 28 29 30 31 32 34 35 40 41 45 46 47 48 49 50 51 52 57 59 64 65 68 70 74 75 76 77 79 80 81 84 85 86 87 89 93 96 107 108 110 115 118 119 126 130 131 132 134 135 145 146 147 148 149 154 156
Primary Contact: Edward Kelly, Chief Executive Officer and President
COO: Peggy Novick, Vice President, Clinical Support and Outpatient Services
CFO: Jeanne Lynskey, Vice President and Chief Financial Officer
CMO: Mary Czymbor, Chief Medical Officer
CIO: Nicole Heim, Chief Information Officer
CHR: Linda Greason, Vice President Human Resources
CNO: Nancy Tomaso, Vice President, Patient Care Services
Web address: www.milfordregional.org
Control: Other not-for-profit (including NFP Corporation) **Service:** General medical and surgical

Staffed Beds: 145 **Admissions:** 8763 **Census:** 85 **Outpatient Visits:** 425726 **Births:** 900 **Total Expense ($000):** 212847 **Payroll Expense ($000):** 97715 **Personnel:** 1718

MILTON—Norfolk County

BETH ISRAEL DEACONESS HOSPITAL-MILTON (220108), 199 Reedsdale Road, Zip 02186–3926; tel. 617/696–4600, (Nonreporting) **A**1 3 10 **S** Beth Israel Lahey Health, Boston, MA
Primary Contact: Richard W. Fernandez, President and Chief Executive Officer
CIO: Jean Fernandez, Chief Information Officer
CHR: Kathleen Harrington, Vice President Human Resources
Web address: www.miltonhospital.org
Control: Other not-for-profit (including NFP Corporation) **Service:** General medical and surgical

Staffed Beds: 100

NANTUCKET—Nantucket County

NANTUCKET COTTAGE HOSPITAL (220177), 57 Prospect Street, Zip 02554–2799; tel. 508/825–8100, **A**1 10 **F**13 15 29 31 35 40 45 50 57 59 60 64 68 70 75 76 77 78 79 81 82 84 85 86 87 89 93 97 100 102 107 110 111 115 119 130 132 133 147 148 154 **S** Partners HealthCare System, Inc., Boston, MA
Primary Contact: Jeannette Ives Erickson, Interim President and Chief Executive Officer
COO: Jim Kelly, Chief Operating Officer
CFO: David J Burke, Director Finance and Chief Financial Officer
CMO: Jock Lawrason, M.D., Chief Medical Officer
CIO: Terry Hughes, Director Information Systems
CHR: Susan Partridge, Director Human Resources
CNO: Ronnie J Kector, R.N., MSN, Vice President Patient Care Services and Chief Nursing Officer
Web address: www.nantuckethospital.org
Control: Other not-for-profit (including NFP Corporation) **Service:** General medical and surgical

Staffed Beds: 19 **Admissions:** 579 **Census:** 6 **Outpatient Visits:** 87299 **Births:** 143 **Total Expense ($000):** 62296 **Payroll Expense ($000):** 25738 **Personnel:** 237

NATICK—Middlesex County

LEONARD MORSE HOSPITAL See Metrowest Medical Center, Framingham

NEEDHAM—Norfolk County

BETH ISRAEL DEACONESS HOSPITAL-NEEDHAM CAMPUS (220083), 148 Chestnut Street, Zip 02492; tel. 781/453–3000, **A**1 2 3 10 **F**3 15 18 29 30 34 35 40 45 50 51 54 59 60 64 65 68 69 70 74 75 77 79 81 82 84 85 87 92 93 100 102 107 108 110 111 114 115 118 119 129 130 131 144 145 146 148 149 154 **S** Beth Israel Lahey Health, Boston, MA
Primary Contact: John M. Fogarty, President and Chief Executive Officer
CFO: Brian Smith, Chief Financial Officer
CMO: Peter Ostrow, M.D., President Medical Staff
Web address: www.bidneedham.org/
Control: Other not-for-profit (including NFP Corporation) **Service:** General medical and surgical

Staffed Beds: 46 **Admissions:** 2832 **Census:** 34 **Outpatient Visits:** 188035 **Births:** 0 **Total Expense ($000):** 91887 **Payroll Expense ($000):** 37708 **Personnel:** 505

NEW BEDFORD—Bristol County

ST. LUKE'S HOSPITAL See Southcoast Hospitals Group, Fall River

VIBRA HOSPITAL OF SOUTHEASTERN MASSACHUSETTS (222043), 4499 Acushnet Avenue, Zip 02745–4707; tel. 508/995–6900, (Nonreporting) **A**1 10 **S** Vibra Healthcare, Mechanicsburg, PA
Primary Contact: Edward B. Leary, Chief Executive Officer
CFO: Cheryl Perry, Chief Financial Officer
CMO: Albert Loerinc, M.D., Medical Director
CHR: Ilene Mirabella, Director Human Resources
CNO: Emmanuel Berthil, Chief Clinical Officer
Web address: www.newbedfordrehab.com
Control: Corporation, Investor–owned (for–profit) **Service:** Acute long–term care hospital

Staffed Beds: 90

NEWBURYPORT—Essex County

ANNA JAQUES HOSPITAL (220029), 25 Highland Avenue, Zip 01950–3894; tel. 978/463–1000, **A**1 10 **F**3 8 13 14 15 18 20 26 28 29 31 34 37 40 43 45 46 50 59 65 70 75 77 78 79 80 81 82 85 92 93 98 99 102 105 107 108 110 114 115 118 119 129 130 135 146 148 149 **S** Beth Israel Lahey Health, Boston, MA
Primary Contact: Mark L. Goldstein, President and Chief Executive Officer
CMO: Gail Fayre, M.D., Medical Director
CIO: Robert Buchanan, Chief Information Officer
CHR: Stephen Salvo, Vice President Human Resources
CNO: Richard Maki, R.N., Vice President Nursing and Chief Nursing Officer
Web address: www.ajh.org
Control: Other not-for-profit (including NFP Corporation) **Service:** General medical and surgical

Staffed Beds: 123 **Admissions:** 6691 **Census:** 79 **Outpatient Visits:** 257257 **Births:** 731 **Total Expense ($000):** 130604 **Payroll Expense ($000):** 56950 **Personnel:** 698

NEWTON LOWER FALLS—Middlesex County

NEWTON-WELLESLEY HOSPITAL (220101), 2014 Washington Street, Zip 02462–1699; tel. 617/243–6000, (Includes MASSGENERAL FOR CHILDREN AT NEWTON WELLESLEY HOSPITAL, 2000 Washington Street, Newton, Massachusetts, Zip 02462–1650; tel. 617/243–6585) **A**1 2 3 5 10 19 **F**3 8 12 13 15 17 18 19 26 20 29 30 31 34 35 36 40 41 45 46 47 49 50 51 52 53 54 55 56 57 58 59 60 64 65 66 68 70 73 74 75 76 77 78 79 81 82 84 85 86 87 89 92 93 97 98 100 101 102 104 107 108 110 111 114 115 117 118 119 126 129 130 131 132 134 135 144 145 146 147 148 149 150 154 156 157 **S** Partners HealthCare System, Inc., Boston, MA
Primary Contact: Michael R. Jaff, D.O., President
CMO: Timothy Foster, Acting Chief Medical Officer
CIO: Beth Downie, Chief Information Officer
CHR: Beth Taylor, Vice President, Human Resources
Web address: www.nwh.org
Control: Other not-for-profit (including NFP Corporation) **Service:** General medical and surgical

Staffed Beds: 220 **Admissions:** 15800 **Census:** 169 **Outpatient Visits:** 555406 **Births:** 3819 **Total Expense ($000):** 517968 **Payroll Expense ($000):** 201486 **Personnel:** 2559

NORTHAMPTON—Hampshire County

COOLEY DICKINSON HOSPITAL (220015), 30 Locust Street, Zip 01060–2093, Mailing Address: P.O. Box 5001, Zip 01061–5001; tel. 413/582–2000, **A**1 2 10 19 **F**3 11 13 15 18 20 22 26 28 29 30 31 34 35 36 38 40 49 50 51 54 55 57 59 60 61 64 68 70 74 75 76 77 78 79 81 84 85 86 87 89 93 96 98 100 107 108 110 111 115 119 120 121 123 130 131 132 146 147 148 149 154 157 **S** Partners HealthCare System, Inc., Boston, MA
Primary Contact: Joanne Marqusee, President and Chief Executive Officer
CFO: Laurie Lamoureux, Director of Finance
CMO: Estevan Garcia, M.D., Chief Medical Officer
CIO: Lee Martinez, Chief Information Officer
CHR: Lori A Kerwood, Director Human Resources
Web address: www.cooleydickinson.org
Control: Other not-for-profit (including NFP Corporation) **Service:** General medical and surgical

Staffed Beds: 56 **Admissions:** 6512 **Census:** 82 **Outpatient Visits:** 214672 **Births:** 543 **Total Expense ($000):** 187073 **Payroll Expense ($000):** 78163 **Personnel:** 1052

MA

NORWOOD—Norfolk County

☐ **NORWOOD HOSPITAL (220126)**, 800 Washington Street, Zip 02062–3487; tel. 781/769–4000, (Nonreporting) **A**1 2 5 10 **S** Steward Health Care System, LLC, Dallas, TX
Primary Contact: Salvatore Perla, President
COO: William P Fleming, Chief Operating Officer
CFO: Mark Johnson, Chief Financial Officer
CHR: Kimberly Brosnan, Director Human Resources
CNO: Mary Kinneman, R.N., MSN, Chief Nursing Officer, Vice President Patient Care Services
Web address: www.norwood-hospital.org
Control: Church operated **Service:** General medical and surgical

Staffed Beds: 188

OAK BLUFFS—Dukes County

☒ **MARTHA'S VINEYARD HOSPITAL (221300)**, One Hospital Road, Zip 02557, Mailing Address: P.O. Box 1477, Zip 02557–1477; tel. 508/693–0410, (Total facility includes 61 beds in nursing home–type unit) **A**1 10 18 **F**3 13 15 28 29 30 31 37 39 40 44 45 50 57 59 60 64 68 69 70 75 76 78 79 81 82 85 86 87 89 93 97 107 110 111 113 115 119 128 130 133 135 146 147 154 **S** Partners HealthCare System, Inc., Boston, MA
Primary Contact: Denise Schepici, M.P.H., Chief Executive Officer and President
CFO: Edward Olivier, Chief Financial Officer
CMO: Pieter Pil, M.D., Chief Medical Staff
CHR: Christine Gould, Director Human Resources
CNO: Carol A Bardwell, R.N., MSN, Chief Nurse Executive
Web address: www.mvhospital.com/
Control: Other not–for–profit (including NFP Corporation) **Service:** General medical and surgical

Staffed Beds: 86 Admissions: 1177 Census: 72 Outpatient Visits: 335414 Births: 125 Total Expense ($000): 95595 Payroll Expense ($000): 54358 Personnel: 367

PALMER—Hampden County

☒ **BAYSTATE WING HOSPITAL (220030)**, 40 Wright Street, Zip 01069–1138; tel. 413/283–7651, **A**1 5 10 **F**3 5 11 15 18 29 33 34 35 36 38 40 42 45 46 49 50 54 56 57 59 61 64 65 68 70 74 75 77 79 81 82 85 86 87 93 97 98 100 101 103 104 107 108 110 115 119 129 130 132 135 146 147 149 150 154 **S** Baystate Health, Inc., Springfield, MA
Primary Contact: Michael Francis. Moran, President and Chief Administrative Officer
CFO: Keary T Allicon, Vice President Finance and Chief Financial Officer
CMO: David L Maguire, M.D., Vice President Medical Affairs
CIO: Kenneth Riley, Director Information Systems
CHR: Thomas Guilfoil, Director Human Resources
Web address: www.baystatewinghospital.org/
Control: Other not–for–profit (including NFP Corporation) **Service:** General medical and surgical

Staffed Beds: 74 Admissions: 3270 Census: 49 Outpatient Visits: 155125 Births: 0 Total Expense ($000): 85186 Payroll Expense ($000): 36201 Personnel: 727

PEMBROKE—Plymouth County

☐ **PEMBROKE HOSPITAL**, 199 Oak Street, Zip 02359–1953; tel. 781/829–7000, (Nonreporting) **A**1 **S** Universal Health Services, Inc., King of Prussia, PA
Primary Contact: Raymond Robinson, Chief Executive Officer
CFO: Diane Airosus, Chief Financial Officer
CMO: Gary Jacobson, M.D., Chief Medical Officer
Web address: www.arbourhealth.com/organizations/pembroke-hospital/
Control: Partnership, Investor–owned (for–profit) **Service:** Psychiatric

Staffed Beds: 115

PITTSFIELD—Berkshire County

☒ **BERKSHIRE MEDICAL CENTER (220046)**, 725 North ST, Zip 01201–4124, Mailing Address: 725 North Street, Zip 01201–4124; tel. 413/447–2000, (Includes HILLCREST HOSPITAL, 165 Tor Court, Pittsfield, Massachusetts, Zip 01201–3099, Mailing Address: Box 1155, Zip 01202–1155, tel. 413/443–4761) **A**1 2 3 5 10 12 13 **F**3 4 8 12 13 14 15 17 18 20 26 28 29 30 31 32 34 35 37 38 40 42 43 44 45 46 48 49 50 51 53 54 55 56 57 58 59 60 61 62 63 64 65 68 70 71 74 75 76 77 78 79 81 82 83 85 86 87 89 90 92 93 95 98 100 101 102 103 104 105 107 108 110 111 112 114 115 116 117 118 119 120 121 122 123 124 126 129 130 131 132 134 135 144 145 146 147 148 149 150 156 157 **S** Berkshire Health Systems, Inc., Pittsfield, MA
Primary Contact: David E. Phelps, President and Chief Executive Officer
CFO: Darlene Rodowicz, Chief Financial Officer
CIO: William Young, Chief Information Officer
CHR: Arthur D Milano, Vice President Human Resources
CNO: Brenda E Cadorette, Chief Nursing Officer
Web address: www.berkshirehealthsystems.org
Control: Other not–for–profit (including NFP Corporation) **Service:** General medical and surgical

Staffed Beds: 275 Admissions: 14559 Census: 190 Outpatient Visits: 303495 Births: 753 Total Expense ($000): 478564 Payroll Expense ($000): 210158 Personnel: 2707

PLYMOUTH—Plymouth County

☒ **BETH ISRAEL DEACONESS HOSPITAL PLYMOUTH (220060)**, 275 Sandwich Street, Zip 02360–2196; tel. 508/746–2000, (Nonreporting) **A**1 2 5 10 **S** Beth Israel Lahey Health, Boston, MA
Primary Contact: Kevin B. Coughlin, President and Chief Executive Officer
CFO: Jason Radzevich, Vice President Finance
CIO: Ronald Rutherford, Chief Information Officer
CHR: Lisa Berry-Barbosa, Vice President Human Resources
CNO: Donna Doherty, R.N., Vice President of Nursing and Chief Nursing Officer
Web address: www.bidplymouth.org
Control: Other not–for–profit (including NFP Corporation) **Service:** General medical and surgical

Staffed Beds: 170

POCASSET—Barnstable County

☐ **POCASSET MENTAL HEALTH CENTER (224031)**, 830 County Road, Zip 02559–2110; tel. 508/564–9600, (Nonreporting) **A**1 10
Primary Contact: Steven Jochim, Administrator
Control: State, Government, nonfederal **Service:** Psychiatric

Staffed Beds: 24

ROCHDALE—Worcester County

VIBRA HOSPITAL OF WESTERN MASSACHUSETTS-CENTRAL CAMPUS See Vibra Hospital of Western Massachusetts, Springfield

ROSLINDALE—Suffolk County

★ △ **HEBREW REHABILITATION CENTER (222007)**, 1200 Centre Street, Zip 02131–1097; tel. 617/363–8000, (Total facility includes 675 beds in nursing home–type unit) **A**7 10 **F**1 2 6 10 29 30 35 39 50 58 59 60 64 65 68 69 75 77 82 83 84 93 97 100 104 119 125 128 130 132 143 146 148 149 158
Primary Contact: Mary K. Moscato, FACHE, President
COO: Brian Murphy, Senior Director Admissions and Referral Services
CFO: Lise Paul, Vice President Reimbursement and Network Planning
CMO: Helen Chen, M.D., Chief Medical Officer
CIO: Eric Rogers, Chief Information Officer
CHR: Deborah Lemmerman, Chief People Officer
CNO: Tammy B. Retalic, R.N., MS, Chief Nursing Officer
Web address: www.hebrewseniorlife.org
Control: Other not–for–profit (including NFP Corporation) **Service:** Acute long–term care hospital

Staffed Beds: 725 Admissions: 1260 Census: 642 Outpatient Visits: 55902 Births: 0 Total Expense ($000): 127014 Payroll Expense ($000): 76253 Personnel: 1215

MA

SALEM—Essex County

NORTH SHORE CHILDREN'S HOSPITAL See Massgeneral for Children at North Shore Medical Center

☒ **NORTH SHORE MEDICAL CENTER (220035)**, 81 Highland Avenue, Zip 01970–2714; tel. 978/741–1200, (Includes MASSGENERAL FOR CHILDREN AT NORTH SHORE MEDICAL CENTER, 57 Highland Avenue, Salem, Massachusetts, Zip 01970–6508; tel. 978/745–2100; SALEM CAMPUS, 81 Highland Avenue, Salem, Massachusetts, Zip 1970; tel. 978/741–1200; Robert G Norton, President; UNION CAMPUS, 500 Lynnfield Street, Lynn, Massachusetts, Zip 01904–1487; tel. 781/581–9200; Robert G Norton, President) **A**1 3 5 10 **F**5 12 13 15 18 20 22 26 28 29 30 32 34 35 36 38 40 41 43 44 45 46 47 48 49 50 51 55 56 57 59 60 63 64 68 70 73 74 75 76 77 79 81 82 84 85 86 87 92 98 99 100 101 102 103 104 105 107 108 110 111 114 115 119 129 130 132 135 143 145 146 147 148 149 150 152 153 154 156 157 **S** Partners HealthCare System, Inc., Boston, MA
Primary Contact: David J. Roberts, M.D., President
CFO: Sally Mason Boemer, Chief Financial Officer
CMO: Mitchell S Rein, M.D., Chief Medical Officer
CIO: Fran X. Hinckley, Chief Information Officer
CHR: Arthur Bowes, Senior Vice President Human Resources
CNO: Cheryl Bhima Merrill, MSN, R.N., Senior Vice President Patient Care Services and Chief Nursing Officer
Web address: www.nsmc.partners.org/
Control: Other not-for-profit (including NFP Corporation) **Service:** General medical and surgical

Staffed Beds: 362 **Admissions:** 18304 **Census:** 247 **Outpatient Visits:** 589309 **Births:** 1197 **Total Expense ($000):** 455291 **Payroll Expense ($000):** 188177 **Personnel:** 2282

SALEM HOSPITAL See Salem Campus

SOMERVILLE—Middlesex County

SOMERVILLE HOSPITAL See Cambridge Health Alliance, Cambridge

SOUTH WEYMOUTH—Norfolk County

☒ **SOUTH SHORE HOSPITAL (220100)**, 55 Fogg Road, Zip 02190–2432; tel. 781/624–8000, **A**1 2 3 5 10 **F**3 7 11 12 13 15 17 18 20 22 24 26 28 29 30 31 32 34 35 36 37 40 41 43 44 45 46 49 50 51 53 54 55 57 58 59 60 62 63 64 65 68 70 72 73 74 75 76 78 79 81 82 84 85 86 87 89 91 92 93 96 107 108 110 111 114 115 118 119 124 126 129 130 132 134 135 143 146 147 148 149 150 156
Primary Contact: Gene E. Green, M.D., President and Chief Executive Officer
COO: Joseph Cahill, Executive Vice President and Chief Operating Officer
CFO: Michael Cullen, Senior Vice President and Chief Financial Officer
CMO: John Stevenson, M.D., Senior Vice President and Chief Medical Officer
CIO: Del Dixon, Chief Information Officer
CHR: Robert Wheeler, Vice President Human Resources
Web address: www.southshorehospital.org
Control: Other not-for-profit (including NFP Corporation) **Service:** General medical and surgical

Staffed Beds: 411 **Admissions:** 26604 **Census:** 312 **Outpatient Visits:** 538020 **Births:** 3203 **Total Expense ($000):** 606109 **Payroll Expense ($000):** 340569 **Personnel:** 3773

SOUTHBRIDGE—Worcester County

☒ **HARRINGTON HOSPITAL (220019)**, 100 South Street, Zip 01550–4051; tel. 508/765–9771, **A**1 2 5 10 **F**3 5 11 15 17 18 19 28 29 30 31 32 34 35 38 39 40 45 48 49 50 51 54 57 59 61 64 65 68 70 71 74 75 77 78 79 81 82 85 86 87 89 92 93 94 96 98 99 100 101 102 103 104 105 107 108 110 111 114 115 117 118 119 129 130 131 132 134 135 145 146 147 148 149 150 152 153 156
Primary Contact: Edward H. Moore, President and Chief Executive Officer
COO: Kristin Morales, Chief Operating Officer
CFO: Thomas Sullivan, Vice President Fiscal Services
CMO: Arthur Russo, M.D., Director Medical Affairs
CIO: Harry Lemieux, Chief Information Officer
CHR: Christopher Canniff, Executive Director, Human Resources
CNO: Thomas W. Hijeck, R.N., MS, Vice President Nursing Services and Chief Nursing Officer
Web address: www.harringtonhospital.org
Control: Other not-for-profit (including NFP Corporation) **Service:** General medical and surgical

Staffed Beds: 119 **Admissions:** 4112 **Census:** 55 **Outpatient Visits:** 378876 **Births:** 0 **Total Expense ($000):** 129705 **Payroll Expense ($000):** 62826 **Personnel:** 827

SPRINGFIELD—Hampden County

☒ **BAYSTATE MEDICAL CENTER (220077)**, 759 Chestnut Street, Zip 01199–0001; tel. 413/794–0000, (Includes BAYSTATE CHILDREN'S HOSPITAL, 759 Chestnut Street, Springfield, Massachusetts, Zip 01199–1001; tel. 413/794–0000; Mark A. Keroack, M.D., M.P.H., President and Chief Executive Officer, Baystate Health) **A**1 3 5 8 10 19 **F**3 8 12 13 14 15 17 18 19 20 22 24 26 28 29 30 31 32 34 35 37 38 40 41 43 44 45 46 47 48 49 50 51 52 54 55 56 57 58 59 60 61 64 65 66 68 70 72 73 74 75 76 77 78 79 81 82 83 84 85 86 87 88 89 93 96 97 98 100 101 102 103 104 105 107 108 110 111 114 115 118 119 120 121 123 124 126 129 130 131 132 135 138 141 143 145 146 147 148 149 154 156 157 **S** Baystate Health, Inc., Springfield, MA
Primary Contact: Nancy Shendell-Falik, R.N., President
COO: Tejas Gandhi, Ph.D., Chief Operating Officer
CFO: Dennis Chalke, Senior Vice President, Chief Financial Officer and Treasurer
CMO: Andrew Artenstein, M.D., Chief Physician Executive, Chief Academic Officer and President, Baystate Medical Practices
CIO: Joel L. Vengco, MS, Vice President, Chief Information Officer
CHR: Paula C Squires, Senior Vice President, Chief Human Resources Officer and Chief Human Resources Officer
CNO: Nancy Shendell-Falik, R.N., Senior Vice President, Chief Operating Officer and Chief Nursing Officer
Web address: www.baystatehealth.org/bmc
Control: Other not-for-profit (including NFP Corporation) **Service:** General medical and surgical

Staffed Beds: 734 **Admissions:** 38602 **Census:** 555 **Outpatient Visits:** 883265 **Births:** 3988 **Total Expense ($000):** 1199956 **Payroll Expense ($000):** 436106 **Personnel:** 7463

KINDRED HOSPITAL PARK VIEW See Vibra Hospital of Western Massachusetts

☒ △ **MERCY MEDICAL CENTER (220066)**, 271 Carew Street, Zip 01104–2398, Mailing Address: P.O. Box 9012, Zip 01102–9012; tel. 413/748–9000, **A**1 2 7 10 **F**3 4 5 8 11 13 15 18 20 26 29 30 31 34 40 43 44 45 46 47 48 49 50 55 56 57 58 59 64 66 67 68 70 71 74 75 76 77 78 79 81 82 85 86 87 90 93 96 97 98 99 100 101 103 104 107 108 110 115 118 119 120 121 123 124 126 129 130 132 135 143 146 147 148 154 **S** Trinity Health, Livonia, MI
Primary Contact: Mark M. Fulco, President
CFO: Thomas W. Robert, Senior Vice President of Finance and Chief Financial Officer
CMO: Robert Roose, M.D., Chief Medical Officer
CIO: Joan Methe, Chief Information Officer
CHR: Leonard F Pansa, Senior Vice President Human Resources and Administrative Services
CNO: Frances Marthone, Chief Nursing Officer
Web address: www.mercycares.com
Control: Other not-for-profit (including NFP Corporation) **Service:** General medical and surgical

Staffed Beds: 317 **Admissions:** 16238 **Census:** 223 **Outpatient Visits:** 648689 **Births:** 1292 **Total Expense ($000):** 313745 **Payroll Expense ($000):** 115722 **Personnel:** 2520

☐ **SHRINERS HOSPITALS FOR CHILDREN-SPRINGFIELD (223303)**, 516 Carew Street, Zip 01104 2396; tel. 413/787 2000, **A**1 3 5 10 **F**29 32 34 35 37 39 44 55 57 58 59 64 66 68 75 77 79 81 82 85 86 87 89 90 91 92 93 94 95 96 119 130 131 132 134 143 146 148 154 **S** Shriners Hospitals for Children, Tampa, FL
Primary Contact: H Lee. Kirk Jr, FACHE, Administrator
CFO: Richard Fulkerson, Director Fiscal Services
CMO: David M Drvaric, M.D., Chief of Staff
CIO: Eric Kamens, Regional Director Information Systems
CHR: John Donlin, Director Human Resources
CNO: Diane Brunelle, MSN, R.N., Director Patient Care Services and Chief Nursing Officer
Web address: www.shrinershospitalsforchildren.org/Hospitals/Locations/Springfield.aspx
Control: Other not-for-profit (including NFP Corporation) **Service:** Children's orthopedic

Staffed Beds: 20 **Admissions:** 142 **Census:** 2 **Outpatient Visits:** 16323 **Births:** 0 **Total Expense ($000):** 23866 **Payroll Expense ($000):** 12775 **Personnel:** 183

Hospital, Medicare Provider Number, Address, Telephone, Approval, Facility, and Physician Codes, Health Care System

★ American Hospital Association (AHA) membership
☐ The Joint Commission accreditation
○ Healthcare Facilities Accreditation Program
◇ DNV Healthcare Inc. accreditation
⇑ Center for Improvement in Healthcare Quality Accreditation
△ Commission on Accreditation of Rehabilitation Facilities (CARF) accreditation

MA

☒ **VIBRA HOSPITAL OF WESTERN MASSACHUSETTS (222046)**, 1400 State Street, Zip 01109–2550; tel. 413/726–6700, (Includes VIBRA HOSPITAL OF WESTERN MASSACHUSETTS-CENTRAL CAMPUS, 111 Huntoon Memorial Highway, Rochdale, Massachusetts, Zip 1542; tel. 508/892–6000; Scott MacLean, Administrator), (Nonreporting) **A**1 10 **S** Vibra Healthcare, Mechanicsburg, PA
Primary Contact: Edward B. Leary, Interim Chief Executive Officer
CFO: Anna Dyrkacz, Chief Financial Officer
CHR: Donna Ciarefella, Director Human Resources
Web address: www.vhwmass.com
Control: Corporation, Investor–owned (for–profit) **Service**: Acute long–term care hospital

Staffed Beds: 174

STOCKBRIDGE—Berkshire County

☒ **AUSTEN RIGGS CENTER**, 25 Main Street, Zip 01262, Mailing Address: P.O. Box 962, Zip 01262–0962; tel. 413/298–5511, **A**1 3 **F**98 104 106 130
Primary Contact: Eric M. Plakun, M.D., Medical Center Director and Chief Executive Officer
COO: Chauncey Collins, Chief Operating Officer and Chief Financial Officer
CFO: Chauncey Collins, Chief Operating Officer and Chief Financial Officer
CIO: Ave Schwartz, Chief Information Officer
CHR: Bertha Mary Connelley, Director Human Resources
CNO: Barbara Turner, Director of Nursing
Web address: www.austenriggs.org
Control: Other not–for–profit (including NFP Corporation) **Service**: Psychiatric

Staffed Beds: 69 Admissions: 65 Census: 50 Outpatient Visits: 3297
Births: 0 Total Expense ($000): 20660 Payroll Expense ($000): 11945
Personnel: 136

STOUGHTON—Norfolk County

☐ **CURAHEALTH HOSPITAL STOUGHTON (222002)**, 909 Sumner Street, 1st Floor, Zip 02072–3396; tel. 781/297–8200, (Nonreporting) **A**1 10 **S** Curahealth Hospitals, Garland, TX
Primary Contact: MacGregor Morgan, R.N., Chief Executive Officer
Web address: www.curahealth.com
Control: Corporation, Investor–owned (for–profit) **Service**: Acute long–term care hospital

Staffed Beds: 111

☐ **NEW ENGLAND SINAI HOSPITAL AND REHABILITATION CENTER (222027)**, 150 York Street, Zip 02072–1881; tel. 781/344–0600, (Nonreporting) **A**1 3 5 10 **S** Steward Health Care System, LLC, Dallas, TX
Primary Contact: Mary Beth. Urquhart, Interim President, Vice President Patient Care Services and Chief Nursing Officer
CFO: Victoria Lobban, Vice President Finance
CMO: Lawrence S Hotes, M.D., Chief Medical Officer
CIO: Michael West, Manager Systems Account
CHR: Julie Burke, Director Human Resources
CNO: Mary Beth Urquhart, Vice President Patient Care Services and Director of Quality
Web address: www.newenglandsinai.org
Control: Other not–for–profit (including NFP Corporation) **Service**: Acute long–term care hospital

Staffed Beds: 212

TAUNTON—Bristol County

☐ **MORTON HOSPITAL AND MEDICAL CENTER (220073)**, 88 Washington Street, Zip 02780–2465; tel. 508/828–7000, (Nonreporting) **A**1 2 10 **S** Steward Health Care System, LLC, Dallas, TX
Primary Contact: Heidi Taylor, President
COO: Donna Maher, R.N., Chief Operating Officer
CMO: Charles Thayer, M.D., Chief Medical Officer
CNO: Lisa Coggins, Chief Nursing Officer
Web address: www.mortonhospital.org
Control: Other not–for–profit (including NFP Corporation) **Service**: General medical and surgical

Staffed Beds: 153

☐ **TAUNTON STATE HOSPITAL (224001)**, 60 Hodges Avenue Extension, Zip 02780–3034, Mailing Address: P.O. Box 4007, Zip 02780–0997; tel. 508/977–3000, (Nonreporting) **A**1 10 **S** Massachusetts Department of Mental Health, Boston, MA
Primary Contact: Joyce O Connor, Chief Operating Officer
CHR: Trish Scully, Director Human Resources
Control: State, Government, nonfederal **Service**: Psychiatric

Staffed Beds: 45

TEWKSBURY—Middlesex County

☐ **TEWKSBURY HOSPITAL (222003)**, 365 East Street, Zip 01876–1998; tel. 978/851–7321, (Nonreporting) **A**1 3 10 **S** Massachusetts Department of Public Health, Boston, MA
Primary Contact: Debra Tosti, Chief Executive Officer
COO: Betsy L Schwechheimer, Chief Operating Officer
CFO: Maureen DiPalma, Chief Financial Officer
CMO: James DeVita, M.D., Chief Medical Officer
CNO: Janice E Bishop, R.N., Chief Nursing Officer
Web address: www.mass.gov
Control: State, Government, nonfederal **Service**: Acute long–term care hospital

Staffed Beds: 381

WALTHAM—Middlesex County

☐ **WALDEN BEHAVIORAL CARE (224038)**, 9 Hope Avenue, Zip 02453–2741; tel. 781/647–6700, **A**1 10 **F**98 100 101 104 105 106 153 154
Primary Contact: Stuart Koman, Ph.D., President and Chief Executive Officer
COO: Paula Vass, Vice President Clinical Operations
CFO: Lawrence Behan, Vice President Administration and Finance, Chief Financial Officer
CMO: James Greenblatt, M.D., Chief Medical Officer, Vice President Medical Clinical Services
CIO: Lawrence Behan, Vice President Administration and Finance, Chief Financial Officer
CHR: Carol Pender, Assistant Vice President Human Resources
Web address: www.waldenbehavioralcare.com/
Control: Corporation, Investor–owned (for–profit) **Service**: Psychiatric

Staffed Beds: 69 Admissions: 1622 Census: 45 Outpatient Visits: 21981

WAREHAM—Plymouth County

TOBEY HOSPITAL See Southcoast Hospitals Group, Fall River

WEST ROXBURY—Suffolk County

☒ △ **VETERANS AFFAIRS BOSTON HEALTHCARE SYSTEM**, 1400 VFW Parkway, Zip 02132–4927; tel. 617/323–7700, (Nonreporting) **A**1 3 5 7 8 **S** Department of Veterans Affairs, Washington, DC
Primary Contact: Vincent Ng, Director
CFO: Joe Costa, Chief Financial Officer
CMO: Brian Hoffman, M.D., Chief Medical Services
CIO: David M Goodman, Ph.D., Chief Information Officer
CHR: William Warfield, Chief Human Resources Management
Web address: www.boston.va.gov/
Control: Veterans Affairs, Government, federal **Service**: General medical and surgical

Staffed Beds: 361

VETERANS AFFAIRS MEDICAL CENTER WEST ROXBURY DIVISION See Veterans Affairs Boston Healthcare System Brockton Division, Brockton

WESTBOROUGH—Worcester County

☐ **WHITTIER REHABILITATION HOSPITAL (222048)**, 150 Flanders Road, Zip 01581–1017; tel. 508/871–2000, (Nonreporting) **A**1 10 **S** Whittier Health Network, Haverhill, MA
Primary Contact: Alfred J. Arcidi, M.D., Senior Vice President
Web address: www.whittierhealth.com
Control: Partnership, Investor–owned (for–profit) **Service**: Acute long–term care hospital

Staffed Beds: 60

WESTFIELD—Hampden County

☒ **BAYSTATE NOBLE HOSPITAL (220065)**, 115 West Silver Street, Zip 01085–3628; tel. 413/568–2811, **A**1 2 5 10 **F**8 14 15 18 28 29 31 34 38 40 57 59 68 70 75 77 79 80 81 86 89 90 93 98 100 101 102 104 105 107 108 110 111 115 119 130 132 144 145 146 147 148 149 154 **S** Baystate Health, Inc., Springfield, MA
Primary Contact: Ronald Bryant, President
CFO: John Shaver, Chief Financial Officer
CMO: Stanley Strzempko, M.D., Vice President Medical Affairs and Chief Medical Officer
CIO: Steven Cummings, Chief Operating Officer and Chief Information Officer
CHR: Joanne Ollson, Vice President Human Resources
Web address: www.baystatehealth.org/locations/noble-hospital
Control: Other not–for–profit (including NFP Corporation) **Service**: General medical and surgical

Staffed Beds: 97 Admissions: 2959 Census: 43 Outpatient Visits: 58522
Births: 0 Total Expense ($000): 56938 Payroll Expense ($000): 27606
Personnel: 393

Many Facility Codes have changed. Please refer to the AHA Guide Code Chart. © 2019 AHA Guide

☐ **WESTERN MASSACHUSETTS HOSPITAL (222023)**, 91 East Mountain Road, Zip 01085–1801; tel. 413/562–4131, (Nonreporting) **A**1 10 **S** Massachusetts Department of Public Health, Boston, MA
Primary Contact: Valenda M. Liptak, Chief Executive Officer
CMO: Chabilal Neergheen, M.D., Medical Director
CHR: James E Duggan, Director Human Resources
Web address: www.mass.gov/eohhs/gov/departments/dph/programs/western-massachusetts-hospital.html
Control: State, Government, nonfederal **Service**: Acute long–term care hospital

Staffed Beds: 80

WHITINSVILLE—Worcester County

WHITINSVILLE MEDICAL CENTER See Milford Regional Medical Center, Milford

WINCHESTER—Middlesex County

⊞ **WINCHESTER HOSPITAL (220105)**, 41 Highland Avenue, Zip 01890–1496; tel. 781/729–9000, **A**1 2 3 5 10 **F**3 8 12 13 15 18 26 28 29 30 31 32 34 35 36 38 40 41 44 45 46 49 50 51 54 55 56 57 59 64 70 73 74 75 77 78 79 81 82 85 86 87 89 91 92 93 107 108 110 114 115 118 119 120 121 126 129 130 131 132 135 144 145 146 147 148 149 156 **S** Beth Israel Lahey Health, Boston, MA
Primary Contact: Richard I. Weiner, M.D., Chief Executive Officer and Chief Medical Officer
COO: Kathy Schuler, R.N., MS, Chief Operating Officer and Chief Nursing Officer
CFO: Matthew Woods, Vice President Finance
CMO: Richard I. Weiner, M.D., Chief Executive Officer and Chief Medical Officer
CHR: Stephanie M Bettinelli, Vice President of Human Resources
CNO: Kathy Schuler, R.N., MS, Chief Operating Officer and Chief Nursing Officer
Web address: www.winchesterhospital.org
Control: Other not–for–profit (including NFP Corporation) **Service**: General medical and surgical

Staffed Beds: 197 Admissions: 10924 Census: 115 Outpatient Visits: 459915 Births: 2320 Total Expense ($000): 276740 Payroll Expense ($000): 107933 Personnel: 1492

WOBURN—Middlesex County

⊞ **ENCOMPASS HEALTH REHABILITATION HOSPITAL OF NEW ENGLAND (223026)**, Two Rehabilitation Way, Zip 01801–6098; tel. 781/935–5050, **A**1 3 10 **F**28 29 30 34 58 59 64 75 77 82 86 90 91 94 96 100 101 103 104 132 146 140 **S** Encompass Health Corporation, Birmingham, AL
Primary Contact: David Coggins, MS, Chief Executive Officer
CFO: Lester Felege, Controller
CHR: Annamarie Cronin, Director Human Resources
Web address: www.newenglandrehab.com
Control: Corporation, Investor–owned (for–profit) **Service**: Rehabilitation

Staffed Beds: 210 Admissions: 2399 Census: 107 Births: 0 Total Expense ($000): 51916 Payroll Expense ($000): 26814 Personnel: 270

WORCESTER—Worcester County

ADCARE HOSPITAL OF WORCESTER (220062), 107 Lincoln Street, Zip 01605–2499; tel. 508/799–9000, (Nonreporting) **A**3 5 10
Primary Contact: David W. Hillis, Chairman and Chief Executive Officer
COO: Jeffrey W Hillis, Chief Operating Officer
CFO: Christine Judycki-Crepeault, Chief Financial Officer
CMO: Ronald F Pike, M.D., Medical Director
CHR: Joan L. Bertrand, Vice President Human Resources
CNO: Judith Richards, Director of Nursing
Web address: www.adcare.com
Control: Other not–for–profit (including NFP Corporation) **Service**: Alcoholism and other chemical dependency

Staffed Beds: 114

⊞ **FAIRLAWN REHABILITATION HOSPITAL (223029)**, 189 May Street, Zip 01602–4339; tel. 508/791–6351, **A**1 3 5 10 **F**28 29 34 35 57 60 64 74 75 77 79 82 90 91 93 94 95 96 130 131 132 148 154 **S** Encompass Health Corporation, Birmingham, AL
Primary Contact: Anne Roper, Interim Chief Executive Officer
CFO: John Flaherty, Controller
CMO: Debra Twehous, Medical Director
CHR: Rosalie Lawless, Director Human Resources
CNO: Sonja Cooley-Johnson, Chief Nursing Officer
Web address: www.fairlawnrehab.com
Control: Corporation, Investor–owned (for–profit) **Service**: Rehabilitation

Staffed Beds: 110 Admissions: 2355 Census: 77 Outpatient Visits: 8292 Births: 0

⊞ **SAINT VINCENT HOSPITAL (220176)**, 123 Summer Street, Zip 01608–1216; tel. 508/363–5000, **A**1 2 3 5 10 **F**3 12 13 15 17 18 20 22 24 26 28 29 30 31 34 35 38 40 45 46 48 49 50 54 55 56 57 59 60 64 68 70 74 75 76 77 78 79 81 82 84 85 86 87 89 92 93 98 100 101 102 105 107 108 110 111 114 115 116 117 119 120 121 123 124 126 129 130 131 132 135 144 146 147 **S** TENET Healthcare Corporation, Dallas, TX
Primary Contact: Carolyn Jackson, Chief Executive Officer
COO: Ava Jo Collins, FACHE, Chief Operating Officer
CFO: Peter D'Elia, Chief Financial Officer
CMO: Douglas Waite, M.D., Chief Medical Officer
CHR: Jan Peters, Vice President Human Resources
CNO: JoAnn Piedrafite, R.N., Chief Nursing Officer
Web address: www.stvincenthospital.com
Control: Corporation, Investor–owned (for–profit) **Service**: General medical and surgical

Staffed Beds: 283 Admissions: 17324 Census: 185 Outpatient Visits: 257399 Births: 1843 Total Expense ($000): 413320 Payroll Expense ($000): 154790 Personnel: 1961

⊞ **UMASS MEMORIAL MEDICAL CENTER (220163)**, 119 Belmont Street, Zip 01605–2982; tel. 508/334–1000, (Includes HAHNEMANN CAMPUS, 281 Lincoln Street, Worcester, Massachusetts, Zip 1605; tel. 508/334–1000; MEMORIAL CAMPUS, 119 Belmont Street, Worcester, Massachusetts, Zip 1605; tel. 508/334–1000; UMASS MEMORIAL CHILDREN'S MEDICAL CENTER, 55 Lake Avenue North, Worcester, Massachusetts, Zip 01655–0002; tel. 508/334–1000; UNIVERSITY CAMPUS, 55 Lake Avenue North, Worcester, Massachusetts, Zip 01655–0002; tel. 508/334–1000) **A**1 2 3 5 8 10 19 **F**3 6 7 8 9 12 13 14 15 16 17 18 19 20 22 24 26 29 30 31 32 38 40 41 43 45 46 47 48 49 50 51 52 55 56 59 60 61 64 65 68 70 71 72 73 74 75 76 77 78 79 81 82 84 85 86 87 88 89 92 97 98 100 101 102 103 104 107 108 110 114 115 118 119 120 121 123 124 126 127 131 132 135 136 138 139 141 145 146 147 148 149 150 154 156 **S** UMass Memorial Health Care, Inc., Worcester, MA
Primary Contact: Michael Gustafson, M.D., President
COO: Andrew Sussman, M.D., Chief Operating Officer
CFO: Therese Day, Chief Financial Officer
CMO: Charles E Cavagnaro, M.D., III Interim Chief Medical officer
CIO: George Brenkle, Chief Information Officer
CNO: Justin Precourt, Chief Nursing Officer
Web address: www.umassmemorial.org
Control: Other not–for–profit (including NFP Corporation) **Service**: General medical and surgical

Staffed Beds: 661 Admissions: 37668 Census: 560 Outpatient Visits: 962800 Births: 4232 Total Expense ($000): 1710073 Payroll Expense ($000): 515771 Personnel: 7404

☐ **WORCESTER RECOVERY CENTER AND HOSPITAL (224032)**, 309 Belmont Street, Zip 01604–1695; tel. 508/368–3300, (Nonreporting) **A**1 3 5 10 **S** Massachusetts Department of Mental Health, Boston, MA
Primary Contact: Anthony Riccitelli, Chief Operating Officer
COO: Anthony Riccitelli, Chief Operating Officer
CIO: Ron Medciros, Director Applied Information Technology
Control: State, Government, nonfederal **Service**: Psychiatric

Staffed Beds: 126

MA

MICHIGAN

MI

ADRIAN—Lenawee County

★ ○ **PROMEDICA BIXBY HOSPITAL (230005)**, 818 Riverside Avenue, Zip 49221–1446; tel. 517/265–0900, **A**2 10 11 **F**3 8 11 15 18 19 26 28 29 30 31 34 35 38 39 40 45 48 53 57 59 62 63 64 65 68 70 74 76 77 78 79 81 82 85 87 92 93 97 100 101 102 104 107 108 109 111 114 115 119 121 126 127 130 132 135 146 148 149 154 157 **S** ProMedica Health System, Toledo, OH
Primary Contact: Julie Yaroch, D.O., President
CFO: Bernie Nawrocki, Administrative Director Finance
CIO: Stephanie Sonnenberg, Director Information Technology
CHR: Kim Langley, Business Partner
CNO: Kathryn M Greenlee, R.N., Vice President, Clinical Services/CNO
Web address: www.promedica.org
Control: Other not–for–profit (including NFP Corporation) **Service:** General medical and surgical

Staffed Beds: 66 **Admissions:** 3293 **Census:** 28 **Outpatient Visits:** 108232 **Births:** 564 **Total Expense ($000):** 75266 **Payroll Expense ($000):** 25056 **Personnel:** 420

ALLEGAN—Allegan County

★ **ALLEGAN GENERAL HOSPITAL (231328)**, 555 Linn Street, Zip 49010–1524; tel. 269/673–8424, **A**10 18 **F**3 12 15 28 29 31 34 35 40 43 45 47 48 50 59 75 77 78 79 81 82 85 86 87 96 97 99 100 101 104 107 108 110 115 118 119 127 129 130 131 132 135 144 146 149 153 154 156 **S** QHR, Brentwood, TN
Primary Contact: Gerald J. Barbini, President and Chief Executive Officer
CFO: Woody White, Interim Chief Financial Officer
CMO: Nabil Nouna, M.D., Chief of Staff
CIO: David Federinko, Chief Information Officer
CHR: Denise A Eberth, Chief Human Resources Officer
CNO: Kathy Chapman, R.N., Chief Clinical Officer and Vice President of Patient Services
Web address: www.aghosp.org
Control: Other not–for–profit (including NFP Corporation) **Service:** General medical and surgical

Staffed Beds: 25 **Admissions:** 688 **Census:** 6 **Outpatient Visits:** 66532 **Births:** 0 **Total Expense ($000):** 46580 **Payroll Expense ($000):** 15930 **Personnel:** 254

ALMA—Gratiot County

GRATIOT MEDICAL CENTER See Midmichigan Medical Center-Gratiot

⊞ △ **MIDMICHIGAN MEDICAL CENTER-GRATIOT (230030)**, 300 East Warwick Drive, Zip 48801–1014; tel. 989/463–1101, **A**1 3 5 7 10 **F**3 12 13 15 18 20 28 29 31 34 35 38 40 42 43 45 50 51 54 56 57 59 61 64 65 68 70 74 75 76 77 78 79 81 82 85 86 87 89 90 92 93 96 98 100 101 103 104 105 107 108 110 111 115 117 118 119 127 129 130 132 135 144 145 146 148 149 154 156 **S** MidMichigan Health, Midland, MI
Primary Contact: Marita Hattem-Schiffman, President
CFO: Jeff Provenzano, Vice President and Chief Financial Officer
CNO: Robin Whitmore, Chief Nursing Officer
Web address: www.midmichigan.org/gratiot
Control: Other not–for–profit (including NFP Corporation) **Service:** General medical and surgical

Staffed Beds: 96 **Admissions:** 4532 **Census:** 65 **Outpatient Visits:** 144044 **Births:** 513 **Total Expense ($000):** 123755 **Payroll Expense ($000):** 36326 **Personnel:** 555

ALPENA—Alpena County

⊞ **MIDMICHIGAN MEDICAL CENTER - ALPENA (230036)**, 1501 West Chisholm Street, Zip 49707–1401; tel. 989/356–7000, **A**1 2 10 **F**3 11 13 15 20 26 28 29 31 34 35 40 44 45 46 47 48 49 50 59 60 62 64 65 70 71 73 74 75 76 77 78 79 81 82 85 86 87 90 92 93 96 97 98 100 101 102 103 104 107 108 110 111 114 115 118 119 129 130 131 132 135 146 147 148 149 154 **S** MidMichigan Health, Midland, MI
Primary Contact: Charles H. Sherwin, President
CFO: George J Smart, Vice President Finance and Information Technology
CMO: Richard Bates, Vice President of Medical Affairs
CHR: Diane Shields, Chief Human Resources Officer
Web address: www.alpenaregionalmedicalcenter.org
Control: Other not–for–profit (including NFP Corporation) **Service:** General medical and surgical

Staffed Beds: 125 **Admissions:** 4585 **Census:** 49 **Outpatient Visits:** 130454 **Births:** 408 **Total Expense ($000):** 136641 **Payroll Expense ($000):** 50190 **Personnel:** 735

ANN ARBOR—Washtenaw County

⊞ **MICHIGAN MEDICINE (230046)**, 1500 East Medical Center Drive, Zip 48109; tel. 734/936–4000, (Includes C. S. MOTT CHILDREN'S HOSPITAL, 1540 East Hospital Drive, Ann Arbor, Michigan, Zip 48109–5475; tel. 734/936–4000; Paul A King, Executive Director) **A**1 2 3 5 8 10 **F**3 5 6 8 9 11 12 13 15 16 17 18 19 20 21 22 23 24 25 26 27 28 29 30 31 32 34 35 36 37 38 39 40 41 43 44 45 46 47 48 49 50 51 52 53 54 55 56 57 58 59 60 61 62 64 65 66 68 69 70 72 74 75 76 77 78 79 80 81 82 83 84 85 86 87 88 89 90 91 92 93 94 95 96 97 98 99 100 101 102 103 104 107 108 110 111 112 114 115 116 117 118 119 120 121 123 124 126 127 129 130 131 132 134 135 136 137 138 139 140 141 142 145 146 147 148 149 150 151 153 154 156
Primary Contact: David Spahlinger, M.D., President
COO: Tony Denton, JD, Senior Vice President and Chief Operating Officer, University of Michigan Health System
CFO: Paul Castillo, Chief Financial Officer
CMO: Jeffrey Desmond, M.D., Chief Medical Officer
CIO: Andrew Rosenberg, M.D., Chief Information Officer
CHR: Deloris Hunt, Chief Human Resources Officer
CNO: Marge Calarco, Chief Nursing Executive
Web address: www.med.umich.edu
Control: Other not–for–profit (including NFP Corporation) **Service:** General medical and surgical

Staffed Beds: 1002 **Admissions:** 50407 **Census:** 857 **Outpatient Visits:** 3311516 **Births:** 4738 **Total Expense ($000):** 3326102 **Payroll Expense ($000):** 1188662 **Personnel:** 17016

⊞ **VETERANS AFFAIRS ANN ARBOR HEALTHCARE SYSTEM**, 2215 Fuller Road, Zip 48105–2399; tel. 734/769–7100, **A**1 2 3 5 8 **F**3 5 12 18 20 22 24 26 28 29 30 31 34 35 36 38 39 40 45 46 48 49 50 54 56 57 58 59 60 61 62 63 64 65 68 70 71 74 75 77 78 79 81 82 83 84 85 86 87 91 92 93 94 96 97 98 100 101 102 103 104 107 108 111 114 115 116 117 118 119 120 121 123 126 128 129 130 132 135 143 144 146 147 148 149 153 154 156 157 **S** Department of Veterans Affairs, Washington, DC
Primary Contact: Andrew Pacyna, Acting Director
COO: Himanshu Singh, M.D., Associate Director
CFO: Joel Wallinga, Chief Financial Officer
CMO: Eric Young, M.D., Chief of Staff
CIO: Rob Whitehurst, Chief, Office of Information and Technology
CHR: Stephanie Hunter, Chief Human Resources Officer
CNO: Stacey Breedveld, R.N., MSN, Associate Director for Patient Care
Web address: www.annarbor.va.gov
Control: Veterans Affairs, Government, federal **Service:** General medical and surgical

Staffed Beds: 109 **Admissions:** 5322 **Census:** 84 **Outpatient Visits:** 596185 **Births:** 0 **Total Expense ($000):** 528170 **Payroll Expense ($000):** 213857 **Personnel:** 3134

AUBURN HILLS—Oakland County

☐ **HAVENWYCK HOSPITAL (234023)**, 1525 University Drive, Zip 48326–2673; tel. 248/373–9200, **A**1 10 **F**98 99 103 105 106 130 154 **S** Universal Health Services, Inc., King of Prussia, PA
Primary Contact: Julie Szyska, Chief Executive Officer and Managing Director
CFO: Steve Sacharski, Chief Financial Officer
CMO: Hani Mekhael, M.D., Chief Staff
CHR: Amy Giannosa, Director Human Resources
CNO: Mitzi Sawicki, Director of Nursing
Web address: www.havenwyckhospital.com
Control: Corporation, Investor–owned (for–profit) **Service:** Psychiatric

Staffed Beds: 243 **Admissions:** 6903 **Census:** 204 **Outpatient Visits:** 5306 **Births:** 0 **Total Expense ($000):** 50069 **Payroll Expense ($000):** 20210 **Personnel:** 429

Many Facility Codes have changed. Please refer to the AHA Guide Code Chart. © 2019 AHA Guide

BAD AXE—Huron County

MCLAREN THUMB REGION (230118), 1100 South Van Dyke Road, Zip 48413–9615; tel. 989/269–9521, **A**10 20 **F**3 11 13 14 15 18 20 28 29 31 32 34 35 40 45 53 56 57 59 64 70 74 75 76 77 78 79 81 82 85 93 97 107 108 114 119 127 130 132 134 135 144 146 148 149 154 156 **S** McLaren Health Care Corporation, Grand Blanc, MI
Primary Contact: Michael Eric. Johnston, President and Chief Executive Officer
CFO: Kevin J Cawley, Interim Chief Financial Officer
CMO: Craig McManaman, M.D., Chief of Staff
CHR: Nancy Bouck, Senior Director of Human Resources
CNO: Jane Christner, Chief Nursing Officer
Web address: www.huronmedicalcenter.org
Control: Other not–for–profit (including NFP Corporation) **Service:** General medical and surgical

Staffed Beds: 49 **Admissions:** 1329 **Census:** 10 **Outpatient Visits:** 47435 **Births:** 372 **Total Expense ($000):** 47704 **Payroll Expense ($000):** 17223 **Personnel:** 317

BATTLE CREEK—Calhoun County

BATTLE CREEK VETERANS AFFAIRS MEDICAL CENTER, 5500 Armstrong Road, Zip 49037–7314; tel. 269/966–5600, (Total facility includes 75 beds in nursing home–type unit) **A**1 3 5 **F**3 4 5 7 12 18 29 30 33 34 35 36 38 39 50 53 54 56 57 58 59 61 62 63 64 65 68 74 75 77 82 83 84 86 87 93 94 96 97 98 100 101 102 103 104 106 107 108 111 114 115 119 127 128 130 132 135 143 144 146 147 148 149 153 154 156 157 **S** Department of Veterans Affairs, Washington, DC
Primary Contact: James Doelling, Executive Director
COO: Edward G. Dornoff, Associate Director
CFO: James M. Rupert, Chief Fiscal Services
CMO: Wilfredo Rodriguez, M.D., Chief of Staff
CIO: Scott Hershberger, Acting Chief Information Management Services
CHR: Palma Simkins, Chief Human Resources Management Services
CNO: Kay Bower, Associate Director for Patient Care Services
Web address: www.battlecreek.va.gov/
Control: Veterans Affairs, Government, federal **Service:** Psychiatric

Staffed Beds: 242 **Admissions:** 1618 **Census:** 182 **Outpatient Visits:** 525882 **Births:** 0 **Personnel:** 1666

BRONSON BATTLE CREEK HOSPITAL (230075), 300 North Avenue, Zip 49017–3307; tel. 269/245–8000, (Includes FIELDSTONE CENTER, 165 North Washington Avenue, Battle Creek, Michigan, Zip 49037; tel. 269/245–8570; MAIN CAMPUS, 300 North Avenue, Battle Creek, Michigan, Zip 49017; tel. 616/966–8000) **A**1 2 5 10 19 **F**3 4 6 9 11 15 18 28 29 30 31 34 35 36 38 40 43 44 45 46 49 50 51 54 55 56 57 58 59 60 61 63 64 65 66 68 70 71 74 75 76 77 78 79 81 82 84 85 86 87 89 97 98 100 101 102 103 104 107 110 111 114 115 117 118 119 120 121 123 126 129 130 131 132 134 135 143 144 146 147 148 149 154 156 **S** Bronson Healthcare Group, Kalamazoo, MI
Primary Contact: Frank J. Sardone, President and Chief Executive Officer
COO: James E. Mckernan, Chief Operating Officer
CMO: Daniel Stewart, M.D., Vice President Medical Affairs
CHR: John Hayden, Senior Vice President and Human Resources Officer
CNO: Susan Watson, MSN, R.N., Vice President
Web address: www.bronsonhealth.com
Control: Other not–for–profit (including NFP Corporation) **Service:** General medical and surgical

Staffed Beds: 198 **Admissions:** 7954 **Census:** 103 **Outpatient Visits:** 493051 **Births:** 814 **Total Expense ($000):** 268939 **Payroll Expense ($000):** 148091 **Personnel:** 1479

SELECT SPECIALTY HOSPITAL-BATTLE CREEK (232035), 300 North Avenue, Zip 49017–3307; tel. 269/245–4675, (Nonreporting) **A**1 10 **S** Select Medical Corporation, Mechanicsburg, PA
Primary Contact: Robert Mach, Chief Executive Officer
Web address: www.battlecreek.selectspecialtyhospitals.com/
Control: Corporation, Investor–owned (for–profit) **Service:** Acute long–term care hospital

Staffed Beds: 25

VETERANS AFFAIRS MEDICAL CENTER See Battle Creek Veterans Affairs Medical Center

BAY CITY—Bay County

☐ △ **MCLAREN BAY REGION (230041)**, 1900 Columbus Avenue, Zip 48708–6831; tel. 989/894–3000, (Includes MCLAREN BAY REGION-WEST CAMPUS, 3250 East Midland Road, Bay City, Michigan, Zip 48706; tel. 989/667–6750; Monica Baranski, MS, R.N., President) **A**1 2 3 7 10 13 **F**3 7 11 13 15 17 18 20 22 24 26 28 29 30 31 32 34 35 36 38 40 44 45 46 47 48 49 50 54 57 58 59 64 65 68 70 73 74 75 76 78 79 81 82 85 86 87 89 90 92 93 96 97 98 100 102 103 107 108 110 111 114 115 119 120 121 123 124 129 130 131 132 135 141 143 144 146 147 148 149 157 **S** McLaren Health Care Corporation, Grand Blanc, MI
Primary Contact: Clarence Sevillian, President and Chief Executive Officer
COO: Mitch Southwick, Chief Operating Officer
CFO: Damon Sorensen, Chief Financial Officer
CMO: Jason White, M.D., Chief Medical Officer
CIO: Ronald Strachan, Chief Information Officer
CHR: Carolyn Potter, Chief Human Resources Officer
CNO: Ellen E Talbott, MSN, R.N., Vice President Patient Care Services
Web address: www.mclaren.org/bayregion
Control: Other not–for–profit (including NFP Corporation) **Service:** General medical and surgical

Staffed Beds: 338 **Admissions:** 15686 **Census:** 207 **Outpatient Visits:** 349521 **Births:** 743 **Total Expense ($000):** 281795 **Payroll Expense ($000):** 110176 **Personnel:** 2106

☐ **MCLAREN BAY SPECIAL CARE (232020)**, 3250 East Midland Road, Suite 1, Zip 48706–2835; tel. 989/667–6851, (Nonreporting) **A**1 10 **S** McLaren Health Care Corporation, Grand Blanc, MI
Primary Contact: Monica Baranski, MS, R.N., President
CMO: Janet Sutton, D.O., Medical Director
CIO: Greg Jacobs, Manager
CHR: Carolyn Potter, Vice President Human Resources
Web address: www.mclaren/bayspecialcare
Control: Other not–for–profit (including NFP Corporation) **Service:** Acute long–term care hospital

Staffed Beds: 21

BIG RAPIDS—Mecosta County

SPECTRUM HEALTH BIG RAPIDS HOSPITAL (230093), 605 Oak Street, Zip 49307–2099; tel. 231/796–8691, **A**1 10 20 **F**3 13 15 28 29 34 35 40 43 45 50 57 64 65 68 69 70 71 74 75 76 77 79 81 82 85 87 93 97 107 108 110 111 115 118 119 126 127 129 130 131 132 135 146 147 149 154 155 156 **S** Spectrum Health, Grand Rapids, MI
Primary Contact: Andrea M. Leslie, MSN, R.N., President
CFO: Thomas Khoerl, Vice President Finance
CMO: Christopher Skinner, Chief of Staff
CIO: Patrick Whiteside, Manager Information Services
CHR: Melonie Jackson, Human Resource Business Partner
CNO: Caroline A Ring, Chief Nursing Officer
Web address: www.spectrumhealth.org
Control: Other not–for–profit (including NFP Corporation) **Service:** General medical and surgical

Staffed Beds: 48 **Admissions:** 2071 **Census:** 15 **Outpatient Visits:** 458097 **Births:** 561 **Total Expense ($000):** 67710 **Payroll Expense ($000):** 24067 **Personnel:** 457

BRIGHTON—Livingston County

★ **ASCENSION BRIGHTON CENTER FOR RECOVERY (230279)**, 12851 Grand River Road, Zip 48116–8506; tel. 810/227–1211, **A**10 **F**4 5 30 34 35 36 38 44 57 68 75 82 86 100 101 104 130 132 135 146 149 150 152 153 157 **S** Ascension Healthcare, Saint Louis, MO
Primary Contact: Raymond A. Waller, Director and Administrator
COO: Raymond A. Waller, Director and Administrator
CFO: Marie Allard, Finance Manager
CMO: Ismael David Yanga, M.D., Chief Medical Officer
CIO: Frank Sanzone, Manager Information Technology
CHR: Marney Daugherty, Worklife Services Consultant
CNO: Barbara Shoup, R.N., Chief Nursing Officer
Web address: www.brightonrecovery.org
Control: Church operated, Nongovernment, not–for–profit **Service:** Alcoholism and other chemical dependency

Staffed Beds: 99 **Admissions:** 3649 **Census:** 77 **Outpatient Visits:** 18113 **Births:** 0 **Total Expense ($000):** 16304 **Payroll Expense ($000):** 7825 **Personnel:** 109

MI

Hospital, Medicare Provider Number, Address, Telephone, Approval, Facility, and Physician Codes, Health Care System

★ American Hospital Association (AHA) membership
☐ The Joint Commission accreditation
○ Healthcare Facilities Accreditation Program
◇ DNV Healthcare Inc. accreditation
⇑ Center for Improvement in Healthcare Quality Accreditation
△ Commission on Accreditation of Rehabilitation Facilities (CARF) accreditation

MI

CADILLAC—Wexford County

⊞ **MUNSON HEALTHCARE CADILLAC HOSPITAL (230081)**, 400 Hobart Street, Zip 49601–2389; tel. 231/876–7200, **A**1 10 20 **F**3 11 13 15 18 28 29 30 31 34 35 40 44 45 50 51 59 64 68 70 76 77 78 79 81 85 87 93 97 107 111 114 115 116 119 127 129 130 132 146 154 156 157 **S** Munson Healthcare, Traverse City, MI
Primary Contact: Tonya Smith, President
COO: Michael Zdrodowski, Vice President of Operations and Ambulatory Services
CFO: Kristin Ellis, Controller
CMO: Joe Santangelo, M.D., Vice President of Medical Affairs
CIO: Randi Terry, Site Director Management Information Systems
CHR: Kelley Whittington-Geppert, Director Human Resources
CNO: Kathryn Bandfield-Keough, Vice President Patient Care Services
Web address: www.mercyhealthcadillac.com/welcome-cadillac
Control: Other not–for–profit (including NFP Corporation) **Service**: General medical and surgical

Staffed Beds: 49 **Admissions**: 3151 **Census**: 26 **Outpatient Visits**: 158745
Births: 352 **Total Expense ($000)**: 95690 **Payroll Expense ($000)**: 37141
Personnel: 600

CARO—Tuscola County

☐ **CARO CENTER (234025)**, 2000 Chambers Road, Zip 48723–9296; tel. 989/673–3191, (Nonreporting) **A**1 10
Primary Contact: Rose Laskowski, R.N., Director
COO: Rose Laskowski, R.N., Director
CFO: Mary Jo Drzewiecki-Burger, Administrative Manager
CMO: William Clark, M.D., Chief Clinical Affairs
CIO: Michele Wills, Registered Health Information Administrator
CHR: Barbara Frank, Human Resource Specialist
Control: State, Government, nonfederal **Service**: Psychiatric

Staffed Beds: 193

★ **MCLAREN CARO REGION (231329)**, 401 North Hooper Street, Zip 48723–1476, Mailing Address: P.O. Box 435, Zip 48723–0435; tel. 989/673–3141, (Data for 273 days) **A**10 18 **F**3 11 15 29 34 35 40 45 50 54 57 59 65 75 77 81 84 85 87 89 92 93 97 107 108 110 115 119 130 135 144 149 154 156 **S** McLaren Health Care Corporation, Grand Blanc, MI
Primary Contact: Marc Augsburger, R.N., President and Chief Executive Officer
CFO: Ron Srebinski, Chief Financial Officer
CMO: T Gard Adams, M.D., Chief of Staff
CHR: Allyson Joyce, Vice President Human Resources
CNO: Kelly Whittaker, Vice President Nursing
Web address: www.cch-mi.org
Control: Other not–for–profit (including NFP Corporation) **Service**: General medical and surgical

Staffed Beds: 25 **Admissions**: 72 **Census**: 1 **Outpatient Visits**: 17530
Births: 0 **Total Expense ($000)**: 11704 **Payroll Expense ($000)**: 4742
Personnel: 109

CARSON CITY—Montcalm County

★ ○ **SPARROW CARSON HOSPITAL (230208)**, 406 East Elm Street, Zip 48811–9693, Mailing Address: P.O. Box 879, Zip 48811–0879; tel. 989/584–3131, **A**3 10 11 19 **F**3 11 13 15 18 20 30 31 34 35 40 45 46 50 53 57 59 64 65 70 75 76 78 79 81 82 85 86 87 93 97 107 108 110 111 115 118 119 126 127 129 130 132 146 147 148 156 **S** Sparrow Health System, Lansing, MI
Primary Contact: William Roeser, Interim President and Chief Executive Officer
CFO: Richard Reid, Vice President Chief Finance Officer
CMO: Robert Seals, D.O., Medical Director
CIO: Richard Terry, Vice President & Chief Information Officer
CHR: Georgette Russell, Vice President of Talent & Organizational Effectiveness
Web address: www.carsoncityhospital.com
Control: Other not–for–profit (including NFP Corporation) **Service**: General medical and surgical

Staffed Beds: 48 **Admissions**: 726 **Census**: 6 **Outpatient Visits**: 71484
Births: 80 **Total Expense ($000)**: 53909 **Payroll Expense ($000)**: 23747
Personnel: 404

CASS CITY—Tuscola County

★ ○ **HILLS & DALES GENERAL HOSPITAL (231316)**, 4675 Hill Street, Zip 48726–1099; tel. 989/872–2121, **A**10 11 18 **F**3 11 15 29 30 31 32 34 35 40 45 46 53 56 57 59 61 64 68 74 75 77 79 81 86 87 93 97 107 108 109 110 115 118 119 127 129 130 131 132 133 135 144 146 147 148 149 156
Primary Contact: Jean Anthony, R.N., President and Chief Executive Officer
CFO: Kenneth Baranski, Chief Financial Officer
CMO: Donald Robbins, M.D., Jr Chief Staff
CNO: Jennifer TerBush, Vice President, Patient Services
Web address: www.hdghmi.org
Control: Other not–for–profit (including NFP Corporation) **Service**: General medical and surgical

Staffed Beds: 25 **Admissions**: 453 **Census**: 5 **Outpatient Visits**: 106527
Births: 0 **Total Expense ($000)**: 33410 **Payroll Expense ($000)**: 16205
Personnel: 394

CHARLEVOIX—Charlevoix County

⊞ **MUNSON HEALTHCARE CHARLEVOIX HOSPITAL (231322)**, 14700 Lake Shore Drive, Zip 49720–1999; tel. 231/547–4024, **A**1 10 18 **F**3 11 13 14 15 26 28 29 30 31 34 35 40 50 55 56 59 64 65 75 76 77 78 79 81 85 87 93 97 100 104 107 114 115 116 117 119 127 129 130 131 132 133 135 144 146 147 149 156 **S** Munson Healthcare, Traverse City, MI
Primary Contact: Joanne Schroeder, President
COO: John Singer IV Chief Operating Officer
CFO: Robert Wilcox, Chief Financial Officer
CMO: James Jeakle, Chief Medical Officer
CIO: David Priest, Director Information Systems
CHR: Patty Fitzgerald, Staff Services
CNO: Bernadette Green Cole, R.N., Chief Nursing Officer
Web address: www.cah.org
Control: Other not–for–profit (including NFP Corporation) **Service**: General medical and surgical

Staffed Beds: 25 **Admissions**: 1143 **Census**: 7 **Outpatient Visits**: 96385
Births: 233 **Total Expense ($000)**: 52740 **Payroll Expense ($000)**: 24145
Personnel: 350

CHARLOTTE—Eaton County

⊞ **HAYES GREEN BEACH MEMORIAL HOSPITAL (231327)**, 321 East Harris Street, Zip 48813–1629; tel. 517/543–1050, **A**1 3 10 18 **F**3 7 11 15 18 26 28 29 34 35 36 40 45 46 50 53 59 64 65 68 69 75 77 79 81 82 85 87 89 92 93 97 107 108 110 111 114 118 119 129 130 131 132 135 143 144 146 147 148 149 154
Primary Contact: Matthew Rush, FACHE, President and Chief Executive Officer
CFO: Kim Capps, Chief Financial Officer
CMO: Hugh Lindsey, M.D., Chief Medical Officer
CIO: Kevin Neugent, Chief Information Officer
CHR: Mandy Rood, Vice President Human Resources
CNO: Maureen Hillary, Chief Nursing Officer
Web address: www.hgbhealth.com
Control: Other not–for–profit (including NFP Corporation) **Service**: General medical and surgical

Staffed Beds: 25 **Admissions**: 738 **Census**: 5 **Outpatient Visits**: 174807
Births: 0 **Total Expense ($000)**: 55838 **Payroll Expense ($000)**: 22865
Personnel: 385

CHELSEA—Washtenaw County

⊞ **ST. JOSEPH MERCY CHELSEA (230259)**, 775 South Main Street, Zip 48118–1383; tel. 734/593–6000, **A**1 3 5 10 **F**3 5 8 11 15 18 28 29 30 31 34 35 40 45 50 51 56 57 59 64 65 70 74 75 77 78 79 81 82 84 85 86 87 90 91 92 93 97 98 100 101 102 103 104 107 110 111 114 115 119 120 121 129 130 131 132 134 135 146 147 149 154 156 **S** Trinity Health, Livonia, MI
Primary Contact: Nancy Kay. Graebner, President and Chief Executive Officer
CFO: Barb Fielder, Vice President Finance
CMO: Randall T Forsch, M.D., M.P.H., Chief Medical Officer
CHR: Jeremy Stephens, Vice President and Chief Human Resources Officer
CNO: Kathy M. Brubaker, R.N., MSN, Vice President and Chief Nursing Officer
Web address: www.cch.org
Control: Church operated, Nongovernment, not–for–profit **Service**: General medical and surgical

Staffed Beds: 96 **Admissions**: 4442 **Census**: 48 **Outpatient Visits**: 321520
Births: 0 **Total Expense ($000)**: 158789 **Payroll Expense ($000)**: 64426
Personnel: 911

Many Facility Codes have changed. Please refer to the AHA Guide Code Chart.   © 2019 AHA Guide

CLARE—Clare County

☒ **MIDMICHIGAN MEDICAL CENTER-CLARE (230180)**, 703 North McEwan Street, Zip 48617–1440, tel. 989/802–5000, **A1** 10 **F3** 11 15 18 20 28 29 30 34 35 40 43 45 50 53 57 58 59 61 64 75 77 79 80 81 85 86 87 93 97 107 108 110 111 115 118 119 127 129 130 135 144 146 148 154 156 157 **S** MidMichigan Health, Midland, MI
Primary Contact: Raymond Stover, President and Chief Executive Officer
CFO: Jeff Provenzano, Vice President and Chief Financial Officer
CMO: David Bremer, D.O., Chief of Staff
CIO: Michael Larson, Vice President Chief Information Officer
CNO: Glenn King, R.N., MSN, Vice President, Chief Nursing Officer
Web address: www.midmichigan.org
Control: Other not-for-profit (including NFP Corporation) **Service:** General medical and surgical

Staffed Beds: 49 **Admissions:** 984 **Census:** 7 **Outpatient Visits:** 94803 **Births:** 0 **Total Expense ($000):** 50757 **Payroll Expense ($000):** 14991 **Personnel:** 241

CLINTON TOWNSHIP—Macomb County

☒ **HENRY FORD MACOMB HOSPITALS (230047)**, 15855 19 Mile Road, Zip 48038–6324; tel. 586/263–2300, (Includes HENRY FORD MACOMB HOSPITAL - MOUNT CLEMENS CAMPUS, 215 North Avenue, Mount Clemens, Michigan, Zip 48043; tel. 586/466–9300; ST. JOSEPH'S MERCY HOSPITAL-WEST, 15855 19 Mile Road, Clinton Township, Michigan, Zip 48038; tel. 586/263–2707; ST. JOSEPH'S MERCY-NORTH, 80650 North Van Dyke, Romeo, Michigan, Zip 48065; tel. 810/798–3551) **A1** 2 3 10 13 **F3** 4 7 8 11 12 13 15 18 20 22 24 26 28 29 30 31 32 34 35 36 38 40 41 42 43 44 45 46 47 49 50 51 54 56 57 58 59 60 61 62 63 64 65 66 68 69 70 73 74 75 76 77 78 79 81 82 83 84 85 86 87 89 90 92 93 94 95 96 97 98 100 101 102 103 107 108 110 111 112 114 115 116 117 118 119 120 121 123 124 126 129 130 131 132 134 135 146 147 148 149 150 154 156 157 **S** Henry Ford Health System, Detroit, MI
Primary Contact: Barbara W. Rossmann, R.N., President and Chief Executive Officer
COO: Gary Beaulac, Chief Operating Officer
CFO: Terry Goodbalian, Vice President Finance and Chief Financial Officer
CMO: Charles Kelly, D.O., Vice President Medical Affairs and Chief Medical Officer
CHR: Joel Gibson, Vice President Human Resources
Web address: www.henryfordmacomb.com
Control: Other not-for-profit (including NFP Corporation) **Service:** General medical and surgical

Staffed Beds: 415 **Admissions:** 20303 **Census:** 270 **Outpatient Visits:** 678287 **Births:** 1667 **Total Expense ($000):** 490834 **Payroll Expense ($000):** 182452 **Personnel:** 2804

COLDWATER—Branch County

★ **PROMEDICA COLDWATER REGIONAL HOSPITAL (230022)**, 274 East Chicago Street, Zip 49036–2041; tel. 517/279–5400, **A6** 10 13 19 **F3** 8 11 13 15 18 28 29 30 31 32 34 40 45 50 57 59 62 63 64 70 74 75 76 77 78 79 81 85 87 91 92 93 96 97 98 100 101 102 108 110 111 115 119 127 129 130 132 146 154 **S** ProMedica Health System, Toledo, OH
Primary Contact: Randy DeGroot, President and Chief Executive Officer
COO: Mary R Rose, R.N., Chief Clinical Officer
CFO: Amy Crouch, Chief Financial Officer
CMO: Joudat Daoud, M.D., Chief of Staff
CIO: Joel Lederman, Director Information Systems
CHR: Amy Jensen, Director Human Resources
Web address: www.chcbc.com
Control: Other not-for-profit (including NFP Corporation) **Service:** General medical and surgical

Staffed Beds: 62 **Admissions:** 2955 **Census:** 32 **Outpatient Visits:** 123734 **Births:** 214 **Total Expense ($000):** 67377 **Payroll Expense ($000):** 29409 **Personnel:** 435

COMMERCE TOWNSHIP—Oakland County

☒ **DMC HURON VALLEY-SINAI HOSPITAL (230277)**, 1 William Carls Drive, Zip 48382–2201; tel. 248/937–3300, **A1** 3 5 10 **F3** 11 12 13 15 18 20 22 26 28 29 30 31 34 35 37 39 40 44 45 46 47 49 50 51 53 55 57 58 59 61 64 65 70 73 74 75 76 77 78 79 81 82 85 86 87 89 91 96 107 108 110 111 114 115 116 117 118 119 121 123 124 126 129 130 131 132 141 145 146 147 148 149 150 154 156 **S** TENET Healthcare Corporation, Dallas, TX
Primary Contact: Karima Bentounsi, Chief Executive Officer
COO: Samuel Pieh, Chief Operating Officer
CFO: William Lantzy, Chief Financial Officer
CHR: Nicole Williams, Director of Human Resources Operations
CNO: Lori Stallings-Sicard, R.N., Chief Nursing Officer
Web address: www.hvsh.org
Control: Corporation, Investor-owned (for-profit) **Service:** General medical and surgical

Staffed Beds: 156 **Admissions:** 7570 **Census:** 75 **Outpatient Visits:** 96206 **Births:** 998 **Total Expense ($000):** 159411 **Payroll Expense ($000):** 55397 **Personnel:** 892

DEARBORN—Wayne County

☒ **BEAUMONT HOSPITAL - DEARBORN (230020)**, 18101 Oakwood Boulevard, Zip 48124–4089, Mailing Address: P.O. Box 2500, Zip 48123–2500; tel. 313/593–7000, **A1** 2 3 5 10 19 **F3** 11 12 13 15 17 18 19 20 22 24 26 28 29 30 31 32 34 35 37 38 39 40 41 43 44 45 46 47 49 50 52 54 55 56 57 58 59 60 61 64 65 68 70 72 74 75 76 77 78 79 81 82 84 85 86 87 89 92 93 96 97 100 102 107 108 110 111 114 115 117 118 119 120 121 123 124 126 129 130 131 132 135 146 147 149 154 **S** Beaumont Health, Southfield, MI
Primary Contact: David Claeys, FACHE, Chief Executive Officer
COO: Carolyn Wilson, Chief Operating Officer
CFO: Timothy Jodway, Chief Financial Administrator
CMO: Paolo G Marciano, M.D., Chief Medical Officer
CIO: Subra Sripada, Executive Vice President, Chief Transformation Officer and Chief Information Officer
CHR: Sherry Huffman, Administrator Human Resources
CNO: Mary Ellen Kochis, MSN, R.N., Administrator Nursing Operations
Web address: www.beaumont.org
Control: Other not-for-profit (including NFP Corporation) **Service:** General medical and surgical

Staffed Beds: 571 **Admissions:** 30982 **Census:** 444 **Outpatient Visits:** 424675 **Births:** 4252 **Total Expense ($000):** 602243 **Payroll Expense ($000):** 240932 **Personnel:** 3596

DECKERVILLE—Sanilac County

DECKERVILLE COMMUNITY HOSPITAL (231311), 3559 Pine Street, Zip 48427–7703, Mailing Address: P.O. Box 126, Zip 48427–0126; tel. 810/376–2835, **A10** 18 **F3** 15 34 35 40 41 43 44 50 56 57 59 64 65 66 68 81 86 87 89 93 97 107 110 115 119 127 133 135 154 156
Primary Contact: Angela McConnachie, Chief Executive Officer and Chief Nursing Officer
CFO: Kim Gentner, Chief Financial Officer
CMO: Josh White, Chief Medical Officer
Web address: www.deckervillehosp.org
Control: Other not-for-profit (including NFP Corporation) **Service:** General medical and surgical

Staffed Beds: 15 **Admissions:** 54 **Census:** 1 **Outpatient Visits:** 6108 **Births:** 0 **Total Expense ($000):** 8760 **Payroll Expense ($000):** 3183 **Personnel:** 92

DETROIT—Wayne County

▣ **ASCENSION ST. JOHN HOSPITAL (230165)**, 22101 Moross Road, Zip 48236–2148; tel. 313/343–4000, **A1** 2 3 5 8 10 19 **F3** 8 9 11 13 15 17 18 20 22 24 26 28 29 30 31 32 34 35 36 37 38 39 40 41 42 43 44 45 46 47 48 49 50 54 55 56 57 58 59 60 61 63 64 65 66 68 70 72 74 75 76 77 78 79 80 81 82 84 85 86 87 88 89 90 91 92 93 95 96 97 98 100 101 102 107 108 110 111 114 115 118 119 120 121 123 124 126 130 131 132 135 138 141 143 144 146 147 148 149 150 155 156 157 **S** Ascension Healthcare, Saint Louis, MO
Primary Contact: Robert E. Hoban, President
COO: Brant Russell, R.N., Chief Operating Officer
CMO: Kevin Grady, M.D., Chief Medical Officer
CIO: Ralph Tenney, Chief Information Officer
CHR: Joanne E Tuscany, Director Human Resources
Web address: www.stjohnprovidence.org/stjohnhospital/
Control: Church operated, Nongovernment, not-for-profit **Service:** General medical and surgical

Staffed Beds: 592 **Admissions:** 28265 **Census:** 383 **Outpatient Visits:** 853084 **Births:** 2999 **Total Expense ($000):** 820688 **Payroll Expense ($000):** 264916 **Personnel:** 2974

BCA STONECREST HOSPITAL See Stonecrest Center

☒ △ **DMC - CHILDREN'S HOSPITAL OF MICHIGAN (233300)**, 3901 Beaubien Street, Zip 48201–2119; tel. 313/745–5852, **A1** 3 5 7 10 **F3** 7 8 11 16 17 18 19 20 21 22 23 24 25 26 27 29 30 31 32 34 35 37 38 39 40 41 42 43 44 45 48 49 50 51 54 55 57 58 59 60 61 64 65 66 68 72 74 75 77 78 79 80 81 82 84 85 86 87 88 89 90 91 92 93 95 96 97 100 107 108 111 114 115 116 117 119 120 121 123 124 129 132 136 137 138 139 141 146 148 149 150 154 156 **S** TENET Healthcare Corporation, Dallas, TX
Primary Contact: Luanne T. Ewald, Chief Executive Officer
CFO: Lisa Hutchings, Chief Financial Officer
CMO: Rudolph Valentini, M.D., Chief Medical Officer
CHR: Jonita Edwards, Director Human Resources
CNO: Brenda VanWallaghen, Interim Chief Nursing Officer
Web address: www.chmkids.org
Control: Corporation, Investor-owned (for-profit) **Service:** Children's general medical and surgical

Staffed Beds: 227 **Admissions:** 10390 **Census:** 146 **Outpatient Visits:** 300248 **Births:** 0 **Total Expense ($000):** 365665 **Payroll Expense ($000):** 133986 **Personnel:** 2177

Hospital, Medicare Provider Number, Address, Telephone, Approval, Facility, and Physician Codes, Health Care System

★ American Hospital Association (AHA) membership
☐ The Joint Commission accreditation
○ Healthcare Facilities Accreditation Program
◇ DNV Healthcare Inc. accreditation
⇧ Center for Improvement in Healthcare Quality Accreditation
△ Commission on Accreditation of Rehabilitation Facilities (CARF) accreditation

☒ **DMC - DETROIT RECEIVING HOSPITAL (230273)**, 4201 Saint Antoine Street, Zip 48201–2153; tel. 313/745–3000, **A**1 3 5 10 **F**3 16 17 18 29 30 34 35 38 39 40 41 43 44 49 50 56 57 58 59 60 61 64 65 66 67 70 74 75 77 79 81 82 84 85 86 87 93 97 98 100 102 103 104 107 114 115 119 129 130 131 132 135 141 144 145 146 148 149 150 **S** TENET Healthcare Corporation, Dallas, TX
Primary Contact: Scott Steiner, FACHE, Chief Executive Officer
COO: Tina Wood, Chief Operations Officer
CFO: Bridgett Feagin, Chief Financial Officer
CMO: Patricia Wilkerson-Uddyback, M.D., Chief Medical Officer
CIO: Michael LeRoy, Senior Vice President and Chief Information Officer
Web address: www.dmc.org
Control: Corporation, Investor–owned (for–profit) **Service**: General medical and surgical

Staffed Beds: 187 **Admissions:** 11417 **Census:** 183 **Outpatient Visits:** 129524 **Births:** 0 **Total Expense ($000):** 251319 **Payroll Expense ($000):** 87623 **Personnel:** 1483

☒ **DMC HARPER UNIVERSITY HOSPITAL (230104)**, 3990 John 'R' Street, Zip 48201–2018; tel. 313/745–8040, (Includes DMC HUTZEL WOMEN'S HOSPITAL, 3980 John R Street, Detroit, Michigan, Zip 48201; tel. 313/745–7555; Scott Steiner, FACHE, Chief Executive Officer) **A**1 3 5 10 19 **F**3 8 9 11 12 13 15 17 18 20 22 24 26 28 29 30 31 34 35 37 40 44 45 46 47 48 49 50 51 52 54 55 57 58 59 60 61 64 65 66 70 74 75 77 78 79 81 82 84 85 86 87 92 93 97 100 107 108 111 115 118 119 126 130 131 132 134 135 138 141 145 146 147 148 149 150 **S** TENET Healthcare Corporation, Dallas, TX
Primary Contact: Scott Steiner, FACHE, Chief Executive Officer
COO: Tina Wood, Chief Operating Officer
CFO: Bridgett Feagin, Chief Financial Officer
CMO: Patricia Wilkerson-Uddyback, M.D., Chief Medical Officer
CIO: Michael LeRoy, Senior Vice President and Chief Information Officer
CNO: Christine Bowen, R.N., Chief Nursing Officer
Web address: www.harperhospital.org
Control: Corporation, Investor–owned (for–profit) **Service**: General medical and surgical

Staffed Beds: 348 **Admissions:** 19885 **Census:** 247 **Outpatient Visits:** 193339 **Births:** 4103 **Total Expense ($000):** 457617 **Payroll Expense ($000):** 145621 **Personnel:** 2047

☒ △ **DMC - REHABILITATION INSTITUTE OF MICHIGAN (233027)**, 261 Mack Avenue, Zip 48201–2495; tel. 313/745–1203, **A**1 3 5 7 10 **F**11 28 29 30 34 35 44 50 53 54 58 59 64 65 75 82 86 87 90 91 92 93 95 96 130 131 132 134 146 149 154 **S** TENET Healthcare Corporation, Dallas, TX
Primary Contact: William Restum, Chief Executive Officer
COO: Patty Jobbitt, Chief Operating Officer
CFO: Dan Babb, Chief Financial Officer
CMO: Ali Bitar, M.D., Vice President Medical Affairs
CHR: Paul Sturgis, Director Human Resources
CNO: Julia Libcke, R.N., MSN, VP Patient Care Services
Web address: www.rimrehab.org
Control: Corporation, Investor–owned (for–profit) **Service**: Rehabilitation

Staffed Beds: 69 **Admissions:** 1239 **Census:** 54 **Outpatient Visits:** 238233 **Births:** 0 **Total Expense ($000):** 69590 **Payroll Expense ($000):** 37332 **Personnel:** 571

☒ △ **DMC - SINAI-GRACE HOSPITAL (230024)**, 6071 West Outer Drive, Zip 48235–2679; tel. 313/966–3300, **A**1 3 5 7 10 12 13 19 **F**3 8 11 13 15 18 20 22 24 26 28 29 30 31 32 34 35 37 38 39 40 43 44 45 49 50 51 53 54 55 57 58 59 60 61 64 65 66 70 72 74 75 77 78 79 80 81 82 84 85 86 87 90 93 96 97 98 100 102 104 107 108 110 111 114 115 117 118 119 120 121 123 126 129 130 131 132 134 135 141 146 147 148 149 150 154 **S** TENET Healthcare Corporation, Dallas, TX
Primary Contact: Conrad L. Mallett Jr, Chief Executive Officer
COO: London Quicci, Chief Operating Officer
CFO: Michael Prusatis, Vice President Finance
CHR: Paulette Griffin, Director Human Resources
Web address: www.sinaigrace.org
Control: Corporation, Investor–owned (for–profit) **Service**: General medical and surgical

Staffed Beds: 285 **Admissions:** 19226 **Census:** 252 **Outpatient Visits:** 196650 **Births:** 1268 **Total Expense ($000):** 328049 **Payroll Expense ($000):** 126370 **Personnel:** 1926

HARPER UNIVERSITY HOSPITAL See Dmc Harper University Hospital

☒ **HENRY FORD HOSPITAL (230053)**, 2799 West Grand Boulevard, Zip 48202–2608; tel. 313/916–2600, **A**1 2 3 5 8 10 19 **F**3 6 8 9 11 12 13 15 17 18 19 20 22 24 26 28 29 30 31 32 33 34 35 36 38 39 40 41 42 43 44 45 46 47 48 49 50 51 52 53 54 55 56 57 58 59 60 61 62 63 64 65 66 67 68 69 70 71 72 73 74 75 76 77 78 79 80 81 82 83 84 85 86 87 91 92 93 96 97 99 100 101 102 103 104 107 108 110 111 112 113 114 115 116 117 118 119 120 121 123 124 126 129 130 131 132 134 135 136 137 138 139 140 141 142 143 144 145 146 147 148 149 150 154 156 **S** Henry Ford Health System, Detroit, MI
Primary Contact: Veronica Hall, R.N., Interim President and Chief Executive Officer
CFO: Joseph Schmitt III Senior Vice President Finance and Chief Financial Officer
CIO: Mary Alice Annecharico, System Vice President and Chief Information Officer
CHR: Antonina Ramsey, Senior Vice President and Chief Human Resource Officer
CNO: Gwen Gnam, R.N., MSN, Chief Nursing Officer
Web address: www.henryfordhealth.org
Control: Other not–for–profit (including NFP Corporation) **Service**: General medical and surgical

Staffed Beds: 773 **Admissions:** 38217 **Census:** 572 **Outpatient Visits:** 3175192 **Births:** 2717 **Total Expense ($000):** 2147925 **Payroll Expense ($000):** 1054217 **Personnel:** 11871

☒ △ **JOHN D. DINGELL VETERANS AFFAIRS MEDICAL CENTER**, 4646 John 'R' Street, Zip 48201–1932; tel. 313/576–1000, (Total facility includes 40 beds in nursing home–type unit) **A**1 2 3 5 7 **F**3 4 5 8 9 11 12 18 20 28 29 30 31 33 34 35 36 37 38 39 40 44 45 46 49 50 53 54 56 57 58 59 60 61 62 63 64 65 66 67 70 74 75 77 78 79 81 82 84 85 86 87 90 91 92 93 94 97 98 100 101 102 103 104 105 107 108 111 114 115 118 119 120 121 126 127 128 129 130 132 133 135 143 144 145 146 147 148 149 152 153 154 156 157 158 **S** Department of Veterans Affairs, Washington, DC
Primary Contact: Pamela J. Reeves, M.D., Director
COO: Annette Walker, Associate Director
CFO: Sherry Riedel, Chief Financial Management Service
CMO: Scott Gruber, M.D., Chief of Staff
CIO: Jonathan Small, Chief Operations Information and Technology
CHR: Kathleen Osinski, Chief Human Resources Service
CNO: Belina Brown-Tezera, MSN, Associate Director Patient Care Services
Web address: www.detroit.va.gov/
Control: Veterans Affairs, Government, federal **Service**: General medical and surgical

Staffed Beds: 209 **Admissions:** 5331 **Census:** 135 **Outpatient Visits:** 513130 **Births:** 0 **Total Expense ($000):** 412641 **Payroll Expense ($000):** 155304 **Personnel:** 1926

☐ **KARMANOS CANCER CENTER (230297)**, 4100 John 'R' Street, Zip 48201–2013; tel. 313/576–8670, **A**1 2 3 5 10 **F**3 8 14 15 29 30 31 34 35 36 39 44 45 46 47 48 49 50 54 55 57 58 59 60 63 64 68 70 74 75 77 78 79 81 82 83 84 85 86 87 100 107 108 110 111 112 113 114 115 116 117 118 119 120 121 123 124 126 130 132 135 136 146 147 148 149 154 157 Primary Contact: Gerold Bepler, M.D., Ph.D., President and Chief Executive Officer
CFO: Brian Gamble, Chief Financial Officer
CMO: George Yoo, M.D., Chief Medical Officer
CIO: Scott McCarter, Chief Information Officer
CHR: David Jansen, Vice President Human Resources
Web address: www.karmanos.org
Control: Other not–for–profit (including NFP Corporation) **Service**: Cancer

Staffed Beds: 84 **Admissions:** 3155 **Census:** 67 **Outpatient Visits:** 130864 **Births:** 0 **Total Expense ($000):** 263767 **Payroll Expense ($000):** 53081 **Personnel:** 982

☐ **STONECREST CENTER (234038)**, 15000 Gratiot Avenue, Zip 48205–1973; tel. 313/245–0600, **A**1 10 **F**98 99 100 101 103 130 149 **S** Acadia Healthcare Company, Inc., Franklin, TN
Primary Contact: Steve Savage, Chief Executive Officer
Web address: www.stonecrestcenter.com
Control: Corporation, Investor–owned (for–profit) **Service**: Psychiatric

Staffed Beds: 162 **Admissions:** 4334 **Census:** 133 **Outpatient Visits:** 0 **Births:** 0 **Total Expense ($000):** 28132 **Payroll Expense ($000):** 12903 **Personnel:** 236

DOWAGIAC—Cass County

☒ **ASCENSION BORGESS-LEE HOSPITAL (231315)**, 420 West High Street, Zip 49047–1943; tel. 269/782–8681, **A**1 10 18 **F**3 11 15 18 28 29 30 31 34 35 40 41 50 54 57 59 64 65 68 70 75 77 78 79 81 85 86 87 93 97 100 104 107 108 110 114 119 127 128 130 132 133 135 146 148 149 **S** Ascension Healthcare, Saint Louis, MO
Primary Contact: Natalie Ryder, Chief Administrative Officer
CMO: Robert Hill, M.D., Chief Medical Officer
CIO: James Keller, Chief Information Officer
Web address: www.borgess.com
Control: Church operated, Nongovernment, not–for–profit **Service**: General medical and surgical

Staffed Beds: 25 **Admissions:** 255 **Census:** 2 **Outpatient Visits:** 125431 **Births:** 0 **Total Expense ($000):** 24406 **Payroll Expense ($000):** 10337 **Personnel:** 147

MI

Many Facility Codes have changed. Please refer to the AHA Guide Code Chart. © 2019 AHA Guide

EAST CHINA—St. Clair County

ASCENSION RIVER DISTRICT HOSPITAL (230241), 4100 River Road, Zip 48054–2909; tel. 810/329–7111, **A**1 3 10 **F**3 7 11 13 15 18 29 30 34 35 36 40 44 45 49 50 57 59 60 64 65 68 75 76 77 79 81 82 84 85 86 87 92 93 97 107 108 110 111 115 119 129 130 132 141 144 146 147 149 157 **S** Ascension Healthcare, Saint Louis, MO
Primary Contact: Robert E. Hoban, President
CMO: H Lee Bacheldor, D.O., Chief Medical Officer
CHR: Dawn Beindit, Labor Relations Partner
CNO: Kim Ronnisch, R.N., Vice President Nursing and Operations
Web address: www.stjohnprovidence.org/RiverDistrict/
Control: Church operated, Nongovernment, not–for–profit **Service**: General medical and surgical

Staffed Beds: 18 **Admissions**: 1548 **Census**: 11 **Outpatient Visits**: 73049 **Births**: 339 **Total Expense ($000)**: 41440 **Payroll Expense ($000)**: 16795 **Personnel**: 156

EATON RAPIDS—Eaton County

★ ⇑ **EATON RAPIDS MEDICAL CENTER (231324)**, 1500 South Main Street, Zip 48827–1952, Mailing Address: P.O. Box 130, Zip 48827–0130; tel. 517/663–2671, **A**10 18 21 **F**3 11 14 15 18 28 29 34 35 36 40 41 45 50 53 57 59 64 65 66 68 75 77 81 86 87 91 93 94 96 97 107 110 115 119 127 129 130 131 132 133 144 146 148 149
Primary Contact: Timothy Johnson, President and Chief Executive Officer
CFO: Shari Glynn, Vice President Finance and Chief Financial Officer
CMO: Ashok K Gupta, M.D., Chief of Staff
CIO: Mark Rodge, Director Information Systems
CHR: Laurie Field, Director Human Resources
Web address: www.eatonrapidsmedicalcenter.org
Control: Other not–for–profit (including NFP Corporation) **Service**: General medical and surgical

Staffed Beds: 20 **Admissions**: 512 **Census**: 5 **Outpatient Visits**: 63285 **Births**: 0 **Total Expense ($000)**: 28872 **Payroll Expense ($000)**: 11864 **Personnel**: 231

ESCANABA—Delta County

OSF ST. FRANCIS HOSPITAL AND MEDICAL GROUP (231337), 3401 Ludington Street, Zip 49829–1377; tel. 906/786–3311, **A**1 10 18 **F**3 11 13 15 18 28 29 30 31 34 35 40 44 45 53 56 57 59 62 63 64 65 66 68 70 75 76 77 78 79 81 82 83 84 85 86 92 93 96 97 107 108 110 111 115 119 127 129 130 131 132 133 144 146 147 148 149 154 **S** OSF Healthcare, Peoria, IL
Primary Contact: David Lord, President
COO: Kelly Jefferson, Vice President, Operations
CFO: Fred Wagner, Chief Financial Officer
CMO: Mark Povich, D.O., Medical Director
CIO: Mark Irving, Manager Management Information Systems
CHR: Elizabeth Zorza, Assistant Administrator
CNO: Joy Hopkins, Vice President Patient Care Services
Web address: www.osfstfrancis.org
Control: Church operated, Nongovernment, not–for–profit **Service**: General medical and surgical

Staffed Beds: 25 **Admissions**: 1588 **Census**: 11 **Outpatient Visits**: 109119 **Births**: 285 **Total Expense ($000)**: 88639 **Payroll Expense ($000)**: 33702 **Personnel**: 369

FARMINGTON HILLS—Oakland County

BEAUMONT HOSPITAL - FARMINGTON HILLS (230151), 28050 Grand River Avenue, Zip 48336–5933; tel. 248/471–8000, **A**1 2 3 5 10 12 13 19 **F**3 9 11 13 15 18 20 22 28 29 30 31 32 34 35 36 38 39 40 41 43 44 45 46 47 48 49 50 51 54 56 57 58 59 60 61 64 65 68 70 74 75 76 77 78 79 81 82 84 85 87 89 90 92 93 96 97 98 100 101 102 103 107 110 111 114 115 118 119 120 121 123 124 126 130 131 132 134 135 145 146 147 148 149 156 **S** Beaumont Health, Southfield, MI
Primary Contact: Constance O'Malley, President
COO: Carolyn Wilson, R.N., Chief Operating Officer
CFO: Barbara Hrit, Controller
CMO: Michael Rebock, Chief Medical Officer
CIO: Subra Sripada, Executive Vice President, Chief Transportation Officer and Chief Information Officer
CHR: Dalph Watson, Director of Human Resources
CNO: Kim Guesman, R.N., Chief Nursing Officer
Web address: www.beaumont.org
Control: Other not–for–profit (including NFP Corporation) **Service**: General medical and surgical

Staffed Beds: 288 **Admissions**: 13358 **Census**: 192 **Outpatient Visits**: 144554 **Births**: 771 **Total Expense ($000)**: 334887 **Payroll Expense ($000)**: 122976 **Personnel**: 1917

FERNDALE—Oakland County

HENRY FORD KINGSWOOD HOSPITAL (234011), 10300 West Eight Mile Road, Zip 48220–2100; tel. 248/398–3200, **A**1 10 **F**29 34 35 44 50 57 58 59 68 75 86 87 98 99 101 103 130 134 135 149 154 **S** Henry Ford Health System, Detroit, MI
Primary Contact: Cathrine Frank, M.D., Chairperson
CMO: Robert Lagrou, D.O., Medical Director
CNO: Cheryl Taylor, R.N., Director of Nursing
Web address: www.henryford.com
Control: Other not–for–profit (including NFP Corporation) **Service**: Psychiatric

Staffed Beds: 94 **Admissions**: 3589 **Census**: 63 **Outpatient Visits**: 0 **Births**: 0 **Total Expense ($000)**: 23598 **Payroll Expense ($000)**: 15231 **Personnel**: 216

FLINT—Genesee County

HURLEY MEDICAL CENTER (230132), One Hurley Plaza, Zip 48503–5993; tel. 810/262–9000, (Includes HURLEY CHILDREN'S HOSPITAL, 1 Hurley Plaza, Flint, Michigan, Zip 48503–5902; tel. 586/263–2707) **A**1 2 3 5 8 10 **F**3 5 11 12 13 15 16 17 18 19 20 22 26 28 29 30 31 32 35 39 40 41 43 45 46 49 50 52 54 55 56 57 58 59 61 64 66 70 72 74 75 76 77 78 79 80 81 82 84 85 86 87 88 89 90 93 96 97 98 100 101 102 103 104 107 108 110 111 114 115 118 119 120 121 123 124 126 129 130 131 132 135 141 143 144 146 147 148 154 156
Primary Contact: Melany Gavulic, President & Chief Executive Officer
COO: Melany Gavulic, Senior Vice President Operations & COO
CFO: Cass Wisniewski, Interim Chief Financial Officer
CMO: Michael Jaggi, D.O., Vice President and Chief Medical Officer
CIO: Gary Townsend, Chief Information Officer
CHR: Beth Brophy, Interim VP for Human Resources
CNO: Teresa Bourque, Sr. Administrator for Nursing/Chief Nurse
Web address: www.hurleymc.com
Control: City, Government, nonfederal **Service**: General medical and surgical

Staffed Beds: 418 **Admissions**: 18409 **Census**: 277 **Outpatient Visits**: 479805 **Births**: 2653 **Total Expense ($000)**: 423266 **Payroll Expense ($000)**: 171032 **Personnel**: 2544

MCLAREN FLINT (230141), 401 South Ballenger Highway, Zip 48532–3685; tel. 810/342–2000, **A**1 2 3 5 8 10 **F**3 8 11 12 13 15 17 18 20 22 24 26 28 29 30 31 34 35 36 37 38 39 40 43 44 45 47 48 49 50 53 54 55 56 57 58 59 60 61 64 66 68 70 74 75 76 77 78 79 81 82 85 86 87 90 91 93 95 96 97 98 100 101 102 104 105 107 108 110 111 114 115 118 119 120 121 123 124 126 129 130 131 132 135 141 144 145 146 147 148 149 154 **S** McLaren Health Care Corporation, Grand Blanc, MI
Primary Contact: Chad M. Grant, President and Chief Executive Officer
COO: Brent Wheeler, Vice President of Operations
CFO: Fred Korte, Chief Financial Officer
CMO: Binesh Patel, M.D., Chief Medical Officer
CIO: Ronald Strachan, Chief Information Officer
CHR: Rachelle Hulett, Vice President Human Resources
CNO: James Williams, Vice President and Chief Nursing Officer
Web address: www.mclaren.org/flint
Control: Other not–for–profit (including NFP Corporation) **Service**: General medical and surgical

Staffed Beds: 371 **Admissions**: 19689 **Census**: 279 **Outpatient Visits**: 323085 **Births**: 615 **Total Expense ($000)**: 417433 **Payroll Expense ($000)**: 183216 **Personnel**: 2223

SELECT SPECIALTY HOSPITAL-FLINT (232012), 401 South Ballenger Highway, 5th Floor Central, Zip 48532–3638; tel. 810/342–4545, (Nonreporting) **A**1 10 **S** Select Medical Corporation, Mechanicsburg, PA
Primary Contact: Christina DeBlouw, Chief Executive Officer
CMO: Jitendra P. Katneni, M.D., Medical Director
CHR: Gayle Barthel, Coordinator Human Resources
CNO: Kathleen Gallardo, Chief Nursing Officer
Web address: www.selectspecialtyhospitals.com/company/locations/flint.aspx
Control: Corporation, Investor–owned (for–profit) **Service**: Acute long–term care hospital

Staffed Beds: 26

Hospital, Medicare Provider Number, Address, Telephone, Approval, Facility, and Physician Codes, Health Care System

★ American Hospital Association (AHA) membership ○ Healthcare Facilities Accreditation Program ⇑ Center for Improvement in Healthcare Quality Accreditation
□ The Joint Commission accreditation ◇ DNV Healthcare Inc. accreditation △ Commission on Accreditation of Rehabilitation Facilities (CARF) accreditation

FRANKFORT—Benzie County

★ **PAUL OLIVER MEMORIAL HOSPITAL (231300)**, 224 Park Avenue, Zip 49635–9658; tel. 231/352–2200, (Total facility includes 39 beds in nursing home–type unit) **A**10 18 **F**11 15 28 30 34 35 40 45 50 53 57 59 60 64 75 77 81 86 87 93 107 110 111 115 119 129 130 132 133 143 146 148 154 156 157 **S** Munson Healthcare, Traverse City, MI
Primary Contact: Peter Marinoff, President
CMO: George Ryckman, D.O., Chief of Staff
CHR: Julie Banktson, Manager Human Resources
Web address: www.munsonhealthcare.org
Control: Other not–for–profit (including NFP Corporation) **Service**: General medical and surgical

Staffed Beds: 47 **Admissions:** 119 **Census:** 26 **Outpatient Visits:** 55807 **Births:** 0 **Total Expense ($000):** 18558 **Payroll Expense ($000):** 7465 **Personnel:** 126

FREMONT—Newaygo County

⊠ **SPECTRUM HEALTH GERBER MEMORIAL (231338)**, 212 South Sullivan Avenue, Zip 49412–1548; tel. 231/924–3300, **A**1 5 10 18 **F**3 11 13 15 28 29 30 31 32 34 35 36 40 43 45 50 53 59 64 68 70 75 76 77 78 79 81 86 87 89 93 96 107 108 110 111 115 118 119 127 129 130 131 132 135 146 147 156 **S** Spectrum Health, Grand Rapids, MI
Primary Contact: Randall Kelley, FACHE, President
COO: Shelly Johnson, Chief Operating Officer
CMO: P. Kevin Gerth, Chief of Staff
CIO: Dave Mitchell, Manager Information Services
CHR: Christine Schurkamp, Senior Human Resources Business Partner
CNO: Meleah Mariani, Chief Nursing Officer
Web address: www.spectrumhealth.org
Control: Other not–for–profit (including NFP Corporation) **Service**: General medical and surgical

Staffed Beds: 25 **Admissions:** 1859 **Census:** 12 **Outpatient Visits:** 114523 **Births:** 485 **Total Expense ($000):** 97393 **Payroll Expense ($000):** 31487 **Personnel:** 602

GARDEN CITY—Wayne County

★ ○ **GARDEN CITY HOSPITAL (230244)**, 6245 Inkster Road, Zip 48135–4001; tel. 734/421–3300, **A**3 5 10 11 12 13 **F**3 11 13 15 17 18 20 22 26 28 29 31 34 35 36 40 43 44 45 46 47 49 50 59 62 64 65 68 70 74 75 76 77 78 79 80 81 85 87 89 90 91 92 93 96 107 109 110 111 112 114 115 119 121 129 130 131 132 135 143 146 147 148 149 154 156 157 **S** Prime Healthcare, Ontario, CA
Primary Contact: Saju George, Chief Executive Officer
CFO: Gina Butcher, Chief Financial Officer
CMO: H. Rex Reuttinger, D.O., Chief Medical Officer, Administration
CIO: Randall Sanborn, Director Information Systems
CHR: Josie Ciccone, Director, Human Resources
Web address: www.gch.org
Control: Corporation, Investor–owned (for–profit) **Service**: General medical and surgical

Staffed Beds: 152 **Admissions:** 8345 **Census:** 93 **Outpatient Visits:** 105090 **Births:** 512 **Total Expense ($000):** 122953 **Payroll Expense ($000):** 50754 **Personnel:** 871

GAYLORD—Otsego County

⊠ **MUNSON HEALTHCARE OTSEGO MEMORIAL HOSPITAL (230133)**, 825 North Center Avenue, Zip 49735–1592; tel. 989/731–2100, (Total facility includes 34 beds in nursing home–type unit) **A**1 10 20 **F**3 13 15 28 29 31 32 34 35 36 40 43 44 45 46 49 50 51 54 56 57 59 64 65 70 75 76 77 78 79 81 82 85 86 87 93 96 97 107 108 110 111 115 118 119 124 126 127 128 130 131 132 134 135 144 146 147 148 149 156 **S** Munson Healthcare, Traverse City, MI
Primary Contact: Thomas R. Lemon, Chief Executive Officer
COO: James Flickema, Vice President Market Development
CFO: Robert Courtois, Vice President Finance
CMO: Kevin Smith, D.O., Chief of Staff
CIO: Timothy Hella, Chief Information Officer
CHR: Terra Deming, Director Human Resources
CNO: Diane Fisher, R.N., VP, Patient Care Services
Web address: www.myomh.org
Control: Other not–for–profit (including NFP Corporation) **Service**: General medical and surgical

Staffed Beds: 80 **Admissions:** 2263 **Census:** 46 **Outpatient Visits:** 340960 **Births:** 402 **Total Expense ($000):** 102606 **Payroll Expense ($000):** 52185 **Personnel:** 727

GLADWIN—Gladwin County

⊠ **MIDMICHIGAN MEDICAL CENTER-GLADWIN (231325)**, 515 Quarter Street, Zip 48624–1959; tel. 989/426–9286, **A**1 10 18 **F**3 11 15 18 28 29 30 31 34 35 40 45 53 57 59 64 75 77 81 85 86 87 93 97 107 108 110 111 114 119 127 129 130 132 135 144 146 154 156 157 **S** MidMichigan Health, Midland, MI
Primary Contact: Raymond Stover, President and Chief Executive Officer
CFO: Jeff Provenzano, Vice President and Chief Financial Officer
CMO: Cheryl Loubert, M.D., Chief Medical Staff
CIO: Dan Waltz, Vice President and Chief Information Officer
CNO: Glenn King, R.N., MSN, Vice President and Chief Nursing Officer
Web address: www.midmichigan.org
Control: Other not–for–profit (including NFP Corporation) **Service**: General medical and surgical

Staffed Beds: 25 **Admissions:** 547 **Census:** 4 **Outpatient Visits:** 54611 **Births:** 0 **Total Expense ($000):** 28961 **Payroll Expense ($000):** 8517 **Personnel:** 130

GRAND BLANC—Genesee County

⊠ **ASCENSION GENESYS HOSPITAL (230197)**, One Genesys Parkway, Zip 48439–8066; tel. 810/606–5000, (Total facility includes 12 beds in nursing home–type unit) **A**1 3 5 10 12 13 **F**3 11 12 13 18 20 22 24 26 28 29 30 31 34 35 40 43 44 45 46 47 48 49 50 51 57 58 59 60 61 63 64 68 70 73 74 75 76 77 78 79 81 82 84 85 86 87 89 90 91 92 96 97 102 107 108 111 114 115 117 118 119 126 128 129 130 132 135 145 146 147 148 149 154 **S** Ascension Healthcare, Saint Louis, MO
Primary Contact: Chris Palazzolo, President and Chief Executive Officer
COO: Joy Finkenbiner, Vice President, Operations
CFO: Nancy Haywood, Chief Financial Officer
CMO: Charles Husson, Regional Chief Medical Officer
CIO: Daniel Stross, Chief Information Officer
CNO: Julie A Gorczyca, R.N., Chief Nursing Officer
Web address: www.genesys.org
Control: Church operated, Nongovernment, not–for–profit **Service**: General medical and surgical

Staffed Beds: 427 **Admissions:** 20064 **Census:** 273 **Outpatient Visits:** 501771 **Births:** 1564 **Total Expense ($000):** 419046 **Payroll Expense ($000):** 171569 **Personnel:** 2518

GRAND HAVEN—Ottawa County

★ ⋔ **NORTH OTTAWA COMMUNITY HOSPITAL (230174)**, 1309 Sheldon Road, Zip 49417–2488; tel. 616/842–3600, **A**10 21 **F**3 7 11 12 13 15 29 30 34 35 37 40 45 46 47 50 51 57 59 63 64 65 68 70 74 75 77 79 81 83 84 85 86 87 92 107 108 110 115 119 124 126 129 130 131 132 135 143 144 145 146 147 148 149 155 157
Primary Contact: Shelleye Yaklin, President and Chief Executive Officer
CFO: Mark Gross, Vice President Finance and Chief Financial Officer
CMO: Haney Assaad, Vice President Medical Affairs
CHR: Tim F Gengle, Director Human Resources
CNO: Cindy Van Kampen, Chief Nursing Officer
Web address: www.noch.org
Control: Other not–for–profit (including NFP Corporation) **Service**: General medical and surgical

Staffed Beds: 81 **Admissions:** 1457 **Census:** 11 **Outpatient Visits:** 102143 **Births:** 284 **Total Expense ($000):** 67369 **Payroll Expense ($000):** 26006 **Personnel:** 427

GRAND RAPIDS—Kent County

☐ **FOREST VIEW PSYCHIATRIC HOSPITAL (234030)**, 1055 Medical Park Drive SE, Zip 49546–3607; tel. 616/942–9610, **A**1 10 **F**87 98 99 100 101 102 103 104 105 130 132 154 **S** Universal Health Services, Inc., King of Prussia, PA
Primary Contact: Andrew Hotaling, Chief Executive Officer
CFO: Andre Pierre, Chief Financial Officer
CMO: James VanHaren, M.D., Medical Director
CHR: Mike Henderson, Human Resources Director
CNO: Jo ell Harris, R.N., Chief Nursing Officer
Web address: www.forestviewhospital.com
Control: Corporation, Investor–owned (for–profit) **Service**: Psychiatric

Staffed Beds: 108 **Admissions:** 3474 **Census:** 91 **Outpatient Visits:** 15888 **Births:** 0 **Personnel:** 178

⊠ △ **MARY FREE BED REHABILITATION HOSPITAL (233026)**, 235 Wealthy Street SE, Zip 49503–5247; tel. 616/840–8000, **A**1 3 5 7 10 **F**12 28 29 30 34 53 54 57 58 62 64 66 68 75 77 78 79 82 86 87 90 91 92 93 94 95 96 100 119 130 131 132 143 146 149 154
Primary Contact: Kent Riddle, Chief Executive Officer
CFO: Randall DeNeff, Vice President Finance
CMO: Michael Jakubowski, M.D., Chief Medical Officer
CIO: Jeff Burns, Manager of Information Technology
CHR: Karen S. Powell, Vice President, Human Resources
CNO: Ingrid Cheslek, R.N., Chief Nursing Officer
Web address: www.maryfreebed.com
Control: Other not–for–profit (including NFP Corporation) **Service**: Rehabilitation

Staffed Beds: 119 **Admissions:** 1922 **Census:** 101 **Outpatient Visits:** 103286 **Births:** 0 **Total Expense ($000):** 103045 **Payroll Expense ($000):** 60256 **Personnel:** 940

Many Facility Codes have changed. Please refer to the AHA Guide Code Chart. © 2019 AHA Guide

MI

⊞ **MERCY HEALTH SAINT MARY'S (230059)**, 200 Jefferson Avenue Southeast, Zip 49503–4598, Mailing Address: 200 Jefferson Avenue SE, Zip 49503–4598; tel. 616/685–5000, (Includes MERCY HEALTH ROCKFORD, 6050 Northland Drive NE, Rockford, Michigan, Zip 49341–9244; tel. 616/685–7950) **A**1 2 3 5 10 **F**3 6 12 13 15 18 20 22 26 28 29 30 34 35 36 37 38 39 40 42 43 44 45 46 47 48 49 50 54 55 56 57 58 59 61 64 66 70 72 74 75 76 77 78 79 80 81 84 85 86 87 97 98 100 101 107 108 110 111 114 115 116 117 118 119 120 121 123 124 126 129 130 132 135 138 144 146 147 148 149 154 156 **S** Trinity Health, Livonia, MI
Primary Contact: David Baumgartner, M.D., Interim President
COO: Randall J Wagner, Chief Operating Officer
CFO: Steve Eavenson, Vice President Finance
CMO: Rolland Mambourg, M.D., Vice President Medical Affairs
CIO: Jim Keller, Site Director Information Services
CHR: Thomas L Karel, Vice President Organization and Talent Effectiveness
CNO: Elizabeth A Murphy, R.N., FACHE, Vice President for Patient Care Services
Web address: www.mercyhealthsaintmarys.org
Control: Church operated, Nongovernment, not–for–profit **Service**: General medical and surgical

Staffed Beds: 283 **Admissions**: 19770 **Census**: 240 **Outpatient Visits**: 1208505 **Births**: 2122 **Total Expense ($000)**: 572576 **Payroll Expense ($000)**: 191314 **Personnel**: 3748

☐ **PINE REST CHRISTIAN MENTAL HEALTH SERVICES (234006)**, 300 68th Street SE, Zip 49548–6927, Mailing Address: P.O. Box 165, Zip 49501–0165; tel. 616/455–5000, **A**1 3 5 10 **F**4 5 6 29 30 32 34 35 38 56 58 59 66 68 75 77 82 86 87 98 99 100 101 102 103 104 105 106 130 132 134 135 146 147 149 150 154 158
Primary Contact: Mark C. Eastburg, Ph.D., President and Chief Executive Officer
COO: Robert Nykamp, Vice President and Chief Operating Officer
CFO: Paul H Karsten, Vice President Finance and Chief Financial Officer
CMO: Alan Armstrong, M.D., Chief Medical Officer
Web address: www.pinerest.org
Control: Other not–for–profit (including NFP Corporation) **Service**: Psychiatric

Staffed Beds: 431 **Admissions**: 9146 **Census**: 173 **Outpatient Visits**: 309973 **Births**: 0 **Total Expense ($000)**: 156450 **Payroll Expense ($000)**: 88710 **Personnel**: 1444

⊞ △ **SELECT SPECIALTY HOSPITAL - SPECTRUM HEALTH (232029)**, 1840 Wealthy Street, Southeast, Zip 49506–2921; tel. 616/774–3800, (Nonreporting) **A**1 7 10 **S** Select Medical Corporation, Mechanicsburg, PA
Primary Contact: Jim Aldrich, Chief Executive Officer
Web address: www.https://grandrapids.selectspecialtyhospitals.com
Control: Corporation, Investor–owned (for–profit) **Service**: Acute long–term care hospital

Staffed Beds: 30

⊞ **SPECTRUM HEALTH - BUTTERWORTH HOSPITAL (230038)**, 100 Michigan Street NE, Zip 49503–2560; tel. 616/391–1774, (Includes HELEN DEVOS CHILDREN'S HOSPITAL, 100 Michigan Street NE, Grand Rapids, Michigan, Zip 49503–2560; tel. 616/391–9000; Robert Connors, M.D., President, Helen DeVos Children's Hospital; SPECTRUM HEALTH - BLODGETT CAMPUS, 1840 Wealthy Street SE, Grand Rapids, Michigan, Zip 49506–2921; tel. 616/774–7444; Julie Wolowitz, Vice President, Imaging, Lab; SPECTRUM HEALTH, 100 Michigan Street NE, Grand Rapids, Michigan, Zip 49503–2551; tel. 616/391–1774; Christina Freese Decker, FACHE, President and Chief Executive Officer) **A**1 2 3 5 8 10 19 **F**1 3 5 8 9 11 12 13 15 16 17 18 19 20 21 22 23 24 25 26 27 28 29 30 31 32 34 35 36 37 38 40 41 43 44 45 46 47 48 49 50 51 52 54 55 56 57 58 59 60 61 64 65 66 68 70 71 72 73 74 75 76 77 78 79 80 81 82 84 85 86 87 88 89 90 93 96 100 101 104 107 108 110 111 112 114 115 116 117 118 119 120 121 123 124 126 128 130 131 132 134 135 136 137 138 140 145 146 147 148 149 156 157 **S** Spectrum Health, Grand Rapids, MI
Primary Contact: Gwen Sandefur, President, Spectrum Health Hospital Group
CFO: Doug Welday, Senior Vice President Finance
CMO: David Krhovsky, M.D., Vice President, Medical Affairs
CIO: Jason Joseph, Vice President, Information Services
CHR: Ovell Barbee, Senior Vice President, Human Resources
CNO: Shawn Ulreich, MSN, R.N., Vice President Clinical Operations and Chief Nursing Executive
Web address: www.spectrumhealth.org
Control: Other not–for–profit (including NFP Corporation) **Service**: General medical and surgical

Staffed Beds: 1412 **Admissions**: 62636 **Census**: 842 **Outpatient Visits**: 1636899 **Births**: 7714 **Total Expense ($000)**: 1962843 **Payroll Expense ($000)**: 537049 **Personnel**: 9073

GRAYLING—Crawford County

⊞ **MUNSON HEALTHCARE GRAYLING HOSPITAL (230058)**, 1100 East Michigan Avenue, Zip 49738–1312; tel. 989/348–5461, (Total facility includes 39 beds in nursing home–type unit) **A**1 5 10 20 **F**3 11 15 28 29 30 32 34 35 36 38 40 44 45 50 51 53 54 56 57 58 59 60 64 65 66 70 75 76 77 78 79 81 85 86 87 93 97 107 108 111 115 119 127 129 130 131 135 146 147 148 154 156 157 **S** Munson Healthcare, Traverse City, MI
Primary Contact: Kirsten Korth-White, President
CFO: Lori Shively, Vice President of Finance
CMO: Vince Schultz, Chief Medical Officer
CNO: Carla Gardner, Director of Nursing
Web address: www.https://www.munsonhealthcare.org
Control: Other not–for–profit (including NFP Corporation) **Service**: General medical and surgical

Staffed Beds: 110 **Admissions**: 3025 **Census**: 55 **Outpatient Visits**: 144831 **Births**: 328 **Total Expense ($000)**: 88765 **Payroll Expense ($000)**: 36955 **Personnel**: 526

GREENVILLE—Montcalm County

⊞ **SPECTRUM HEALTH UNITED HOSPITAL (230035)**, 615 South Bower Street, Zip 48838–2614; tel. 616/754–4691, (Includes SPECTRUM HEALTH KELSEY HOSPITAL, 418 Washington Avenue, Lakeview, Michigan, Zip 48850; tel. 989/352–7211; Andrea M. Leslie, MSN, R.N., President) (Total facility includes 70 beds in nursing home–type unit) **A**1 3 10 **F**3 8 13 15 18 28 29 30 31 34 35 40 41 43 45 46 47 50 54 57 59 64 65 66 68 70 71 75 76 77 78 79 81 85 87 93 96 97 107 108 110 111 115 119 124 126 127 128 129 130 131 132 133 134 135 146 147 148 154 156 157 **S** Spectrum Health, Grand Rapids, MI
Primary Contact: Andrea M. Leslie, MSN, R.N., President
COO: Priscilla Mahar, Chief Operating Officer
CFO: Ryan K Johnson, Controller
CMO: Kevin O'Connor, D.O., President, Medical Staff
CIO: David Dutmers, Manager, Information Services
CHR: Jennifer Nelson, Senior Human Resource Business Partner
CNO: Linda Schaltz, MSN, R.N., Chief Nursing Officer
Web address: www.spectrumhealth.org
Control: Other not–for–profit (including NFP Corporation) **Service**: General medical and surgical

Staffed Beds: 116 **Admissions**: 3036 **Census**: 90 **Outpatient Visits**: 205199 **Births**: 511 **Total Expense ($000)**: 106720 **Payroll Expense ($000)**: 38514 **Personnel**: 720

GROSSE POINTE—Wayne County

⊞ **BEAUMONT HOSPITAL - GROSSE POINTE (230089)**, 468 Cadieux Road, Zip 48230–1507; tel. 313/473–1000, **A**1 2 3 5 10 **F**3 11 12 13 15 18 20 22 26 28 29 30 31 32 34 35 36 39 40 43 45 46 47 48 49 50 51 53 54 55 56 57 58 59 60 61 64 65 68 69 70 71 74 75 76 77 78 79 80 81 82 84 85 86 87 91 92 93 96 100 107 108 110 111 114 115 117 118 119 126 129 130 131 132 134 135 145 146 147 148 149 150 154 156 **S** Beaumont Health, Southfield, MI
Primary Contact: James Lynch, M.D., Interim Chief Executive Officer
COO: Carolyn Wilson, R.N., Chief Operating Officer
CFO: Maria Miller, Controller
CMO: Donna Hoban, M.D., Senior Vice President and Chief Medical Officer
CIO: Subra Sripada, Executive Vice President, Chief Transportation Officer and Chief Information Officer
CHR: Pandora Walker, Director, Human Resources
CNO: Anne Stewart, Vice President and Chief Nursing Officer
Web address: www.beaumont.org
Control: Other not–for–profit (including NFP Corporation) **Service**: General medical and surgical

Staffed Beds: 280 **Admissions**: 12836 **Census**: 132 **Outpatient Visits**: 329227 **Births**: 703 **Total Expense ($000)**: 228236 **Payroll Expense ($000)**: 84443 **Personnel**: 1414

⊞ **SELECT SPECIALTY HOSPITAL-GROSSE POINTE (232038)**, 468 Cadieux Road, 3 North East, Zip 48230–1507, Mailing Address: 22101 Moross Road, 6th Floor, Detroit, Zip 48236; tel. 313/473–6131, (Nonreporting) **A**1 10 **S** Select Medical Corporation, Mechanicsburg, PA
Primary Contact: Zaahra Butt, Chief Executive Officer
Web address: www.grossepointe.selectspecialtyhospitals.com/
Control: Corporation, Investor–owned (for–profit) **Service**: Acute long–term care hospital

Staffed Beds: 30

HANCOCK—Houghton County

✉ **UP HEALTH SYSTEM-PORTAGE (230108)**, 500 Campus Drive, Zip 49930–1569; tel. 906/483–1000, (Total facility includes 60 beds in nursing home–type unit) **A**1 10 20 **F**3 8 13 15 28 29 30 31 34 35 40 43 50 53 56 57 59 60 64 65 67 68 70 75 77 78 79 81 85 86 87 93 94 97 100 102 107 108 110 111 115 119 129 130 131 132 133 144 145 146 148 154 156 157 **S** LifePoint Health, Brentwood, TN
Primary Contact: Randy Neiswonger, Chief Executive Officer
CFO: Steve Bishop, Chief Financial Officer
CMO: Mary Beth Hines, D.O., Chief Medical Officer
CHR: Robbyn Lucier, Director Human Resources
CNO: Debra Young, R.N., MSN, Vice President, Patient Services and Chief Nursing Officer
Web address: www.portagehealth.org
Control: Corporation, Investor–owned (for–profit) **Service:** General medical and surgical

Staffed Beds: 96 **Admissions:** 1148 **Census:** 69 **Outpatient Visits:** 81462 **Births:** 192 **Total Expense ($000):** 67624 **Payroll Expense ($000):** 30787 **Personnel:** 456

HARBOR BEACH—Huron County

HARBOR BEACH COMMUNITY HOSPITAL (231313), 210 South First Street, Zip 48441–1236; tel. 989/479–3201, (Nonreporting) **A**10 18
Primary Contact: Paul Clabuesch, President and Chief Executive Officer
CFO: Jill Wehner, Vice President Financial Services
CMO: Richard Lloyd, D.O., Chief of Staff
CIO: Tami Nickrand, Director Information Technology
CHR: Tina Osantoski, Director Human Resources
CNO: Deb Geiger, Executive Director of Acute Care
Web address: www.hbch.org
Control: Other not–for–profit (including NFP Corporation) **Service:** General medical and surgical

Staffed Beds: 54

HASTINGS—Barry County

✉ **SPECTRUM HEALTH PENNOCK (230040)**, 1009 West Green Street, Zip 49058–1710; tel. 269/945–3451, **A**1 10 **F**3 11 13 15 29 30 31 32 34 35 36 39 40 44 45 50 53 54 56 57 59 62 63 64 65 68 70 74 75 76 77 79 81 82 84 85 86 87 89 91 92 93 96 97 107 108 110 111 115 119 125 126 127 130 131 132 135 144 146 147 148 149 **S** Spectrum Health, Grand Rapids, MI
Primary Contact: Angela Ditmar, R.N., President
COO: Carla Wilson-Neil, FACHE, Chief Operating Officer
CFO: Micheal King, Controller
CMO: Douglas Smendik, M.D., Hospital Medical Director
CIO: Teri VanTongeren, Director Information Services
CHR: Sherri Thrasher, Executive Human Resources Partner
CNO: Steve Marzolf, R.N., Chief Nursing Officer
Web address: www.spectrumhealth.org
Control: Other not–for–profit (including NFP Corporation) **Service:** General medical and surgical

Staffed Beds: 39 **Admissions:** 2178 **Census:** 18 **Outpatient Visits:** 426811 **Births:** 304 **Total Expense ($000):** 76360 **Payroll Expense ($000):** 26796 **Personnel:** 532

HILLSDALE—Hillsdale County

★ ○ **HILLSDALE HOSPITAL (230037)**, 168 South Howell Street, Zip 49242–2081; tel. 517/437–4451, (Total facility includes 39 beds in nursing home–type unit) **A**5 10 11 19 **F**3 11 12 13 15 28 29 31 34 35 38 40 45 46 48 49 50 57 59 62 70 74 75 76 78 79 81 82 87 93 97 98 102 105 106 107 110 111 115 119 127 128 130 131 132 135 146 147 148 154 156
Primary Contact: Duke Anderson, President and Chief Executive Officer
COO: Terri Draper, Director of Operations
CFO: Leya VanDeusen, Interim Chief Financial Officer
CMO: Nichole Ellis, Chief Medical Officer
CIO: Sheila Puffenberger, Manager Information Technology
CHR: Stacy Feltz, Manager Human Resource
CNO: Julie Walters, Chief Nursing Officer
Web address: www.hillsdalehospital.com
Control: Other not–for–profit (including NFP Corporation) **Service:** General medical and surgical

Staffed Beds: 93 **Admissions:** 2559 **Census:** 51 **Outpatient Visits:** 98409 **Births:** 309 **Total Expense ($000):** 60336 **Payroll Expense ($000):** 22920 **Personnel:** 418

HOLLAND—Ottawa County

★ ⚕ **HOLLAND HOSPITAL (230072)**, 602 Michigan Avenue, Zip 49423–4999; tel. 616/392–5141, (Nonreporting) **A**10 21
Primary Contact: Dale Sowders, President and Chief Executive Officer
CFO: Terry L Steele, Vice President Finance and Chief Financial Officer
CMO: William Vandervliet, M.D., Vice President Medical Affairs
CIO: Randy J Paruch, Director, Information Systems
CHR: Michael Matthews, Vice President Human Resources
CNO: Patti J VanDort, MSN, R.N., Vice President Nursing/Chief Nursing Officer
Web address: www.hollandhospital.org
Control: Other not–for–profit (including NFP Corporation) **Service:** General medical and surgical

Staffed Beds: 130

HOWELL—Livingston County

✉ **ST. JOSEPH MERCY LIVINGSTON HOSPITAL (230069)**, 620 Byron Road, Zip 48843–1093; tel. 517/545–6000, **A**1 3 5 10 **F**3 8 11 12 15 18 28 29 30 34 35 40 41 45 50 51 54 56 57 59 61 62 63 64 65 66 68 70 74 75 77 78 79 81 82 84 85 86 87 93 97 100 107 108 110 111 115 117 118 119 120 121 123 126 129 130 131 132 134 135 141 145 146 147 148 149 154 156 157 **S** Trinity Health, Livonia, MI
Primary Contact: John F. O'Malley, FACHE, President
COO: Robin Damschroder, Chief Operating Officer
CFO: Kathy O'Connor, Vice President Finance and Controller
CMO: Rosalie Tocco-Bradley, Ph.D., M.D., Chief Medical Officer
CIO: Frank Rademacher, Director, Information Systems
CHR: Tonia Schemer, Interim Chief Human Resources
CNO: Joyce Young, Ph.D., R.N., Vice President, Patient Services and Chief Nursing Officer
Web address: www.stjoeslivingston.org/livingston
Control: Church operated, Nongovernment, not–for–profit **Service:** General medical and surgical

Staffed Beds: 38 **Admissions:** 2762 **Census:** 24 **Outpatient Visits:** 272302 **Births:** 0 **Total Expense ($000):** 130117 **Payroll Expense ($000):** 43776 **Personnel:** 530

IONIA—Ionia County

✉ **SPARROW IONIA HOSPITAL (231331)**, 3565 South State Road, Zip 48846–1870; tel. 616/523–1400, **A**1 10 18 **F**3 12 15 18 29 31 34 35 40 45 50 54 57 59 64 65 68 70 75 77 78 79 81 85 93 97 107 108 110 111 115 119 127 129 130 131 146 148 149 156 **S** Sparrow Health System, Lansing, MI
Primary Contact: William Roeser, President and Chief Executive Officer
COO: Kevin A Price, Vice President and Chief Operating Officer
CFO: Mark Brisboe, VP and Chief Financial Officer
CMO: Amy Jentz, M.D., Chief of Staff
CIO: Bob Neal, Information Technology
CHR: Debbie Olsen, Human Resource Partner
Web address: www.sparrow.org/sparrowionia
Control: Other not–for–profit (including NFP Corporation) **Service:** General medical and surgical

Staffed Beds: 22 **Admissions:** 789 **Census:** 6 **Outpatient Visits:** 142992 **Births:** 1 **Total Expense ($000):** 49872 **Payroll Expense ($000):** 20698 **Personnel:** 284

IRON MOUNTAIN—Dickinson County

✉ **DICKINSON COUNTY HEALTHCARE SYSTEM (230055)**, 1721 South Stephenson Avenue, Zip 49801–3637; tel. 906/774–1313, **A**1 10 20 **F**3 11 13 15 28 29 30 31 32 34 35 40 45 46 50 53 59 62 64 65 67 70 75 76 77 78 79 80 81 85 87 89 91 92 93 96 107 108 110 111 114 115 119 120 121 127 129 130 131 132 133 144 145 146 147 148 149 156 157
Primary Contact: Jeanne Goche, Interim Chief Executive Officer
COO: Peggy Freeman, Chief Physicians Services Officer
CFO: Debbie Hanson, Interim Chief Financial Officer
CMO: Don Kube, M.D., Chief Medical Officer
CIO: Dean Decremer, Information Systems Manager
CHR: Paula Swartout, Human Resources Manager
CNO: Susan Hadley, MS, Chief Nursing Officer
Web address: www.dchs.org
Control: County, Government, nonfederal **Service:** General medical and surgical

Staffed Beds: 49 **Admissions:** 2295 **Census:** 21 **Outpatient Visits:** 280718 **Births:** 402 **Total Expense ($000):** 108109 **Payroll Expense ($000):** 44541 **Personnel:** 535

Many Facility Codes have changed. Please refer to the AHA Guide Code Chart. © 2019 AHA Guide

MI

OSCAR G. JOHNSON VETERANS AFFAIRS MEDICAL CENTER, 325 East 'H' Street, Zip 49801–4792; tel. 906/774–3300, (Nonreporting) **A**1 **S** Department of Veterans Affairs, Washington, DC
Primary Contact: James W. Rice, Director
Web address: www.ironmountain.va.gov/
Control: Veterans Affairs, Government, federal **Service**: General medical and surgical

> **Staffed Beds**: 17

VETERANS AFFAIRS MEDICAL CENTER See Oscar G. Johnson Veterans Affairs Medical Center

IRON RIVER—Iron County

ASPIRUS IRON RIVER HOSPITALS & CLINICS, INC. (231318), 1400 West Ice Lake Road, Zip 49935–9526; tel. 906/265–6121, **A**1 10 18 **F**11 15 28 29 31 32 34 35 40 43 50 54 56 57 59 60 63 64 70 75 77 78 79 81 86 87 89 93 97 107 111 115 119 128 130 131 132 133 135 144 145 146 147 148 156 **S** Aspirus, Inc., Wausau, WI
Primary Contact: Connie L. Koutouzos, R.N., MSN, Chief Executive Officer
CFO: Glenn E Dobson, Vice President, Finance and Chief Financial Officer
CMO: Nasseem Rizkalla, M.D., Chief Medical Officer
CHR: Carol Bastianello, Director Human Resources
CNO: Nancy Lynn Ponozzo, MSN, R.N., Chief Nursing Officer
Web address: www.aspirus.org
Control: Other not–for–profit (including NFP Corporation) **Service**: General medical and surgical

> **Staffed Beds**: 12 **Admissions**: 721 **Census**: 7 **Outpatient Visits**: 64973 **Births**: 0 **Total Expense ($000)**: 44748 **Payroll Expense ($000)**: 15864 **Personnel**: 285

IRONWOOD—Gogebic County

ASPIRUS IRONWOOD HOSPITALS & CLINICS, INC. (231333), N10561 Grand View Lane, Zip 49938–9622; tel. 906/932–2525, **A**1 10 18 **F**3 11 13 15 28 29 31 34 35 40 46 50 57 59 64 65 70 75 76 78 79 81 85 87 89 93 104 107 110 114 115 119 127 130 132 133 135 146 147 148 149 **S** Aspirus, Inc., Wausau, WI
Primary Contact: Paula L. Chermside, Chief Executive Officer
COO: Paula L. Chermside, Chief Executive Officer
CFO: Mick Hagwell, Chief Financial Officer
CMO: Chris Pogliano, M.D., Chief Medical Staff
CHR: Keri Van Epern, Manager Human Resources
CNO: Grace Tousignant, R.N., MSN, Chief Nursing Officer
Web address: www.aspirus.org
Control: Other not–for–profit (including NFP Corporation) **Service**: General medical and surgical

> **Staffed Beds**: 25 **Admissions**: 1101 **Census**: 10 **Outpatient Visits**: 65823 **Births**: 129 **Total Expense ($000)**: 62281 **Payroll Expense ($000)**: 23715 **Personnel**: 70

ISHPEMING—Marquette County

UP HEALTH SYSTEM-BELL (231321), 901 Lakeshore Drive, Zip 49849–1367; tel. 906/486–4431, **A**1 10 18 **F**3 11 13 15 29 30 34 40 50 53 57 59 64 65 68 70 75 76 77 79 81 82 85 87 90 93 96 97 107 108 110 114 119 129 133 135 144 145 146 147 156 **S** LifePoint Health, Brentwood, TN
Primary Contact: Mitchell D. Leckelt, Chief Executive Officer
CFO: Teresa J Perry, Chief Financial Officer
CMO: Douglas LaBelle, M.D., Chief Medical Officer
CIO: Mike Brady, Director Information Technology
CHR: Tami Ketchem, Human Resource Director
CNO: Sandra McGovern, Chief Nursing Officer
Web address: www.bellhospital.org
Control: Corporation, Investor–owned (for–profit) **Service**: General medical and surgical

> **Staffed Beds**: 25 **Admissions**: 930 **Census**: 7 **Outpatient Visits**: 52955 **Births**: 297 **Total Expense ($000)**: 38151 **Payroll Expense ($000)**: 13788 **Personnel**: 268

JACKSON—Jackson County

DUANE L. WATERS HOSPITAL, 3857 Cooper Street, Zip 49201–7521; tel. 517/780–5600, (Nonreporting)
Primary Contact: Carol Griffes, Administrator
Control: State, Government, nonfederal **Service**: Hospital unit of an institution (prison hospital, college infirmary, etc.)

> **Staffed Beds**: 150

HENRY FORD ALLEGIANCE HEALTH (230092), 205 North East Avenue, Zip 49201–1753; tel. 517/205–4800, **A**1 2 3 5 10 12 13 **F**3 4 5 7 8 9 11 13 15 17 18 20 22 24 26 28 29 30 31 34 35 38 40 43 44 45 46 47 48 49 50 51 53 56 57 58 59 61 62 63 64 65 68 70 71 73 74 75 76 77 78 79 80 81 82 84 85 87 89 91 92 93 96 97 98 100 101 102 103 104 105 107 108 110 111 115 118 119 120 121 123 126 128 129 130 131 132 135 143 146 147 148 149 152 153 154 **S** Henry Ford Health System, Detroit, MI
Primary Contact: Paula R. Autry, FACHE, President and Chief Executive Officer
COO: Ondrea Bates, Senior Vice President, Operations and Continuum of Care
CFO: Kevin Leonard, Vice President, Finance
CMO: Ray King, M.D., Senior Vice President, Medical Affairs and Chief Medical Officer
CIO: Aaron Wootton, Vice President, Health Information Systems and Chief Information Officer
CHR: Patricia Seagram, Vice President Human Resources
CNO: Wendy Boersma, Vice President, Nursing and Chief Nursing Officer
Web address: www.allegiancehealth.org
Control: Other not–for–profit (including NFP Corporation) **Service**: General medical and surgical

> **Staffed Beds**: 404 **Admissions**: 18983 **Census**: 232 **Outpatient Visits**: 534511 **Births**: 1580 **Total Expense ($000)**: 585008 **Payroll Expense ($000)**: 265634 **Personnel**: 3640

HENRY FORD ALLEGIANCE SPECIALTY HOSPITAL (232036), 110 North Elm Avenue, Zip 49202–3595; tel. 517/205–4463, **A**1 10 **F**1 3 29 30 68 77 87 148 **S** Henry Ford Health System, Detroit, MI
Primary Contact: J Mark. Fall, Chief Executive Officer
COO: Charlotte Hyatt, MSN, R.N., Chief Operating Officer and Chief Nursing Officer
CFO: Dale L Friesen, Chief Financial Officer
CMO: Robert Albertson, M.D., Chief Medical Officer
CNO: Charlotte Hyatt, MSN, R.N., Chief Operating Officer and Chief Nursing Officer
Web address: www.carelinkofjackson.org
Control: Other not–for–profit (including NFP Corporation) **Service**: Acute long–term care hospital

> **Staffed Beds**: 44 **Admissions**: 297 **Census**: 23 **Outpatient Visits**: 0 **Births**: 0 **Total Expense ($000)**: 14801 **Payroll Expense ($000)**: 5492 **Personnel**: 92

KALAMAZOO—Kalamazoo County

ASCENSION BORGESS HOSPITAL (230117), 1521 Gull Road, Zip 49048–1640; tel. 269/226–7000, (Includes BORGESS-PIPP HOSPITAL, 411 Naomi Street, Plainwell, Michigan, Zip 49080–1222; tel. 269/685–6811; Donna Cassidy, Administrator) **A**1 3 5 10 **F**3 7 8 9 11 12 13 15 17 10 20 22 24 26 28 29 30 31 32 33 34 35 36 37 38 39 40 43 44 45 46 47 49 50 53 54 56 57 58 59 60 61 64 68 70 74 75 76 77 78 79 81 82 83 84 85 86 87 90 91 92 93 94 96 97 98 99 100 101 102 103 105 107 108 110 114 118 119 126 127 129 130 131 132 135 144 146 147 148 149 154 156 157 **S** Ascension Healthcare, Saint Louis, MO
Primary Contact: Tim Stover, M.D., Interim Chief Executive Officer
COO: Mark Anthony, Executive Vice President and Chief Operating Officer
CMO: Robert Hill, M.D., Vice President Medical Staff Affairs
CHR: Laura Lentenbrink, Vice President, Human Resources
Web address: www.borgess.com
Control: Church operated, Nongovernment, not–for–profit **Service**: General medical and surgical

> **Staffed Beds**: 422 **Admissions**: 17930 **Census**: 239 **Outpatient Visits**: 421001 **Births**: 998 **Total Expense ($000)**: 448197 **Payroll Expense ($000)**: 140710

BRONSON METHODIST HOSPITAL (230017), 601 John Street, Zip 49007–5346; tel. 269/341–6000, (Includes BRONSON VICKSBURG HOSPITAL, 13326 North Boulevard, Vicksburg, Michigan, Zip 49097–1099; tel. 269/649–2321; Frank J Sardone, President and Chief Executive Officer; CHILDREN'S HOSPITAL AT BRONSON, 601 John Street, Kalamazoo, Michigan, Zip 49007–5341; tel. 269/341–7654) **A**1 3 5 10 **F**3 8 9 11 12 15 16 17 18 19 20 22 24 26 28 29 30 31 32 34 35 36 37 39 40 41 43 44 45 46 47 48 49 50 51 54 55 56 57 58 59 60 61 63 64 65 66 68 70 71 72 74 75 76 77 78 79 80 81 82 84 85 86 87 88 89 92 93 97 101 102 107 110 111 114 115 117 118 119 126 129 130 131 132 134 135 141 143 146 147 148 149 154 155 156 157 158 **S** Bronson Healthcare Group, Kalamazoo, MI
Primary Contact: Frank J. Sardone, President and Chief Executive Officer
COO: Kenneth L Taft, Executive Vice President and Chief Operating Officer
CMO: Scott Larson, M.D., Vice President Medical Affairs and Chief Medical Officer
CHR: John Hayden, Vice President and Chief Human Resources Officer
CNO: Denise Neely, Vice President and Chief Nursing Officer
Web address: www.bronsonhealth.com
Control: Other not–for–profit (including NFP Corporation) **Service**: General medical and surgical

> **Staffed Beds**: 415 **Admissions**: 23217 **Census**: 281 **Outpatient Visits**: 1068261 **Births**: 3865 **Total Expense ($000)**: 820995 **Payroll Expense ($000)**: 405341 **Personnel**: 5162

MI

MI

☐ **KALAMAZOO PSYCHIATRIC HOSPITAL (234026)**, 1312 Oakland Drive, Zip 49008–1205; tel. 269/337–3000, (Nonreporting) **A**1 10
Primary Contact: Jill A. Krause, Director
CMO: V.R. Kanaparti, M.D., Director Medical Services
CIO: Brian Bayer, Information Technology Site Leader
CHR: Holly Hiday, Director Human Resources
CNO: Kathleen Millard, Acting Director Nursing
Control: State, Government, nonfederal **Service**: Psychiatric

| Staffed Beds: 203 |

KALKASKA—Kalkaska County

★ **KALKASKA MEMORIAL HEALTH CENTER (231301)**, 419 South Coral Street, Zip 49646–2503; tel. 231/258–7500, (Total facility includes 104 beds in nursing home–type unit) **A**10 18 **F**2 10 15 28 35 40 44 45 50 64 65 66 79 81 84 87 93 97 107 110 111 115 119 125 127 128 129 130 132 134 143 144 146 147 148 154 156 157 **S** Munson Healthcare, Traverse City, MI
Primary Contact: Kevin L. Rogols, FACHE, Administrator
CHR: Kimberly Babcock, Administrative Director of Operations
CNO: Christine Bissonette, R.N., Service Line Director for Acute Services
Web address: www.munsonhealthcare.org
Control: Hospital district or authority, Government, nonfederal **Service**: General medical and surgical

| Staffed Beds: 112 Admissions: 263 Census: 98 Outpatient Visits: 75243 Births: 0 Total Expense ($000): 43418 Payroll Expense ($000): 21179 Personnel: 343 |

LAKEVIEW—Montcalm County

SPECTRUM HEALTH KELSEY HOSPITAL See Spectrum Health United Hospital, Greenville

L'ANSE—L'Anse County

☐ **BARAGA COUNTY MEMORIAL HOSPITAL (231307)**, 18341 U.S. Highway 41, Zip 49946–8024; tel. 906/524–3300, **A**1 10 18 **F**3 11 15 28 31 34 35 40 45 50 53 57 59 62 63 64 75 77 78 79 81 82 84 85 89 93 107 108 110 114 118 119 127 130 132 133 146 154 156
Primary Contact: Margie Hale, R.N., MSN, Chief Executive Officer
CFO: Gail Jestila-Peltola, Chief Financial Officer
CMO: Sharon Gilliland, Chief of Staff
CIO: Taylor Makela, Director Information Technology
CHR: Janelle E Beeler, Human Resource Manager
CNO: Bonny Cotter, Chief Nursing Officer
Web address: www.bcmh.org
Control: County, Government, nonfederal **Service**: General medical and surgical

| Staffed Beds: 15 Admissions: 442 Census: 6 Outpatient Visits: 23203 Births: 0 Total Expense ($000): 22275 Payroll Expense ($000): 8566 Personnel: 124 |

LANSING—Ingham County

☐ **MCLAREN GREATER LANSING (230167)**, 401 West Greenlawn Avenue, Zip 48910–2819; tel. 517/975–6000, (Includes MCLAREN GREATER LANSING, 401 West Greenlawn Avenue, Lansing, Michigan, Zip 48910–2819; tel. 517/795–6000; MCLAREN ORTHOPEDIC HOSPITAL, 2727 South Pennsylvania Avenue, Lansing, Michigan, Zip 48910–3490; tel. 517/975–6000; Casey Kandow, Interim President and Chief Executive Officer), (Non-reporting) **A**1 2 3 5 10 13 **S** McLaren Health Care Corporation, Grand Blanc, MI
Primary Contact: Kirk M. Ray, President and Chief Executive Officer
COO: Casey Kandow, Chief Operating Officer
CFO: Dale Thompson, Chief Financial Officer
CMO: Linda Peterson, M.D., Vice President Medical Affairs
CHR: Amy Dorr, Vice President Human Resources
Web address: www.mclaren.org
Control: Other not–for–profit (including NFP Corporation) **Service**: General medical and surgical

| Staffed Beds: 321 |

☒ △ **SPARROW HOSPITAL (230230)**, 1215 East Michigan Avenue, Zip 48912–1811; tel. 517/364–1000, (Includes SPARROW CHILDREN'S CENTER, 1215 East Michigan Avenue, Lansing, Michigan, Zip 48912–1811; tel. 517/364–1000) **A**1 2 3 5 7 10 12 13 **F**2 5 11 12 13 15 17 18 20 22 24 26 28 29 30 31 34 35 38 40 41 43 44 45 46 49 50 51 54 56 57 58 59 60 63 64 65 67 70 72 74 75 76 77 78 79 81 82 84 85 86 87 88 89 90 91 92 93 94 96 97 98 99 100 101 102 103 104 105 107 108 109 110 111 114 115 116 117 118 119 120 121 123 124 126 129 130 131 132 135 144 146 147 148 149 156 **S** Sparrow Health System, Lansing, MI
Primary Contact: Mark Brett, Chief Executive Officer
COO: Joseph Ruth, Executive Vice President and Chief Operating Officer
CFO: Paula Reichle, Senior Vice President and Chief Operating Officer
CMO: Brian D. Schroeder, M.D., Senior Vice President and Chief Medical Officer
CIO: Thomas Bres, Senior Vice President and Chief Administrative Officer
CHR: Paul Sturgis, Vice President and Chief Human Resources Officer
CNO: Mary Lou Wesley, R.N., Senior Vice President and Chief Nursing Officer
Web address: www.sparrow.org
Control: Other not–for–profit (including NFP Corporation) **Service**: General medical and surgical

| Staffed Beds: 632 Admissions: 32766 Census: 457 Outpatient Visits: 859907 Births: 4151 Total Expense ($000): 926342 Payroll Expense ($000): 430747 Personnel: 4858 |

★ ○ **SPARROW SPECIALTY HOSPITAL (232037)**, 8 West Sparrow Hospital Tower, Zip 48912; tel. 517/364–4840, **A**10 11 **F**1 3 29 30 60 68 85 100 101 119 130 148 **S** Sparrow Health System, Lansing, MI
Primary Contact: Lou Little, President and Chief Executive Officer
CFO: David Przybylski, Controller
CMO: Paul Entler, D.O., Medical Director
CHR: Paul Sturgis, Chief Human Resource Officer
CNO: Tina Gross, MSN, R.N., Chief Nursing Officer
Web address: www.sparrowspecialty.org
Control: Other not–for–profit (including NFP Corporation) **Service**: Acute long–term care hospital

| Staffed Beds: 30 Admissions: 323 Census: 23 Outpatient Visits: 0 Births: 0 Total Expense ($000): 12605 Payroll Expense ($000): 5931 Personnel: 93 |

LAPEER—Lapeer County

☐ **MCLAREN LAPEER REGION (230193)**, 1375 North Main Street, Zip 48446–1350; tel. 810/667–5500, (Total facility includes 19 beds in nursing home–type unit) **A**1 2 10 **F**3 13 15 18 20 26 28 29 30 31 34 35 40 43 44 45 49 54 56 57 59 61 64 68 70 74 76 77 79 81 82 84 85 86 87 92 93 94 97 98 100 101 102 107 108 110 111 114 115 119 126 128 129 130 131 135 143 144 146 148 149 154 157 **S** McLaren Health Care Corporation, Grand Blanc, MI
Primary Contact: Chris Candela, President and Chief Executive Officer
CFO: Mary Beth Callahan, Chief Financial Officer
CMO: Gary Salem, M.D., Vice President Medical Affairs
CIO: Gayle Consiglio, Chief Information Officer
CHR: Amy Dorr, Vice President Human Resources
Web address: www.lapeerregional.org
Control: Other not–for–profit (including NFP Corporation) **Service**: General medical and surgical

| Staffed Beds: 159 Admissions: 6759 Census: 89 Outpatient Visits: 151142 Births: 262 Total Expense ($000): 113578 Payroll Expense ($000): 51891 Personnel: 644 |

LAURIUM—Houghton County

☒ **ASPIRUS KEWEENAW HOSPITAL, INC. (231319)**, 205 Osceola Street, Zip 49913–2134; tel. 906/337–6500, **A**1 10 18 **F**3 11 13 15 18 28 29 30 31 34 35 36 40 43 45 52 53 56 57 61 64 65 66 68 70 75 77 78 79 81 85 87 89 93 97 107 108 110 114 118 119 127 130 131 132 133 135 146 147 148 154 156 **S** Aspirus, Inc., Wausau, WI
Primary Contact: Rick L. Nevers, Interim President
CFO: Glenn E Dobson, Regional Chief Financial Officer
CMO: Michael Luoma, M.D., Chief of Staff
CHR: Chad Rowe, Human Resource Director
CNO: Grace Tousignant, R.N., MSN, Chief Nursing Officer
Web address: www.aspirus.org
Control: Other not–for–profit (including NFP Corporation) **Service**: General medical and surgical

| Staffed Beds: 25 Admissions: 1175 Census: 9 Outpatient Visits: 50159 Births: 169 Total Expense ($000): 54279 Payroll Expense ($000): 20291 Personnel: 287 |

LINCOLN PARK—Wayne County

✠ **VIBRA HOSPITAL OF SOUTHEASTERN MICHIGAN, LLC (232019)**, 26400 West Outer Drive, Zip 48146–2088; tel. 313/386–2000, (Nonreporting) **A**1 10 **S** Vibra Healthcare, Mechanicsburg, PA
Primary Contact: Reginald Lee, Chief Executive Officer
COO: Cindy Brassinger, Chief Operating Officer
CFO: Douglas Morris, Chief Financial Officer
CHR: Karen D Gray, Director Human Resources
Web address: www.vhsemichigan.com/
Control: Corporation, Investor–owned (for–profit) **Service**: Acute long–term care hospital

Staffed Beds: 220

LIVONIA—Wayne County

✠ **ST. MARY MERCY HOSPITAL (230002)**, 36475 Five Mile Road, Zip 48154–1988; tel. 734/655–4800, **A**1 2 3 5 10 **F**3 4 5 8 12 13 15 18 20 22 26 28 29 30 31 34 35 38 40 43 44 45 46 47 49 50 51 53 54 55 56 57 58 59 63 64 68 70 74 75 76 77 78 79 81 84 85 87 90 93 97 98 100 101 102 107 108 110 111 114 115 116 117 118 119 120 121 126 129 130 131 132 135 143 144 145 146 147 148 149 153 154 **S** Trinity Health, Livonia, MI
Primary Contact: David A. Spivey, President and Chief Executive Officer
CFO: Mike Samyn, Vice President, Finance and Chief Financial Officer
CMO: Matthew Griffin, M.D., Chief Medical Officer
CIO: Janet Yim, Director Information Services
CHR: Kenneth Antczak, Vice President Human Resources
Web address: www.stmarymercy.org
Control: Church operated, Nongovernment, not–for–profit **Service**: General medical and surgical

Staffed Beds: 304 **Admissions:** 18111 **Census:** 214 **Outpatient Visits:** 284960 **Births:** 788 **Total Expense ($000):** 321382 **Payroll Expense ($000):** 143506 **Personnel:** 1906

LUDINGTON—Mason County

★ ⇑ **SPECTRUM HEALTH LUDINGTON HOSPITAL (230110)**, One Atkinson Drive, Zip 49431–1906, Mailing Address: P.O. Box 2408, Grand Rapids, Zip 49501–2408; tel. 231/843–2591, **A**10 20 21 **F**3 8 11 13 15 28 31 32 34 35 38 40 41 43 44 45 49 50 51 53 54 57 59 64 65 68 70 75 76 77 78 79 81 82 85 86 87 92 93 96 100 102 107 108 110 111 114 115 118 119 127 129 130 131 132 135 146 147 148 149 154 156 **S** Spectrum Health, Grand Rapids, MI
Primary Contact: Randall Kelley, FACHE, President
CFO: Kerri Nelson, Chief Financial Officer
CMO: Steve Strbich, D.O., Chief of Staff
CIO: Jeremy Vronko, Manager, Information Services
CHR: Jill Vasquez, Manager Human Resources
CNO: Helen Johnson, R.N., MSN, Vice President Patient Services
Web address: www.mmcwm.com
Control: Other not–for–profit (including NFP Corporation) **Service**: General medical and surgical

Staffed Beds: 30 **Admissions:** 2101 **Census:** 22 **Outpatient Visits:** 122886 **Births:** 276 **Total Expense ($000):** 83212 **Payroll Expense ($000):** 26151 **Personnel:** 549

MANISTEE—Manistee County

✠ **MUNSON HEALTHCARE MANISTEE HOSPITAL (230303)**, 1465 East Parkdale Avenue, Zip 49660–9709; tel. 231/398–1000, **A**1 10 20 **F**3 7 11 13 15 28 29 31 34 35 39 40 45 48 50 53 54 57 59 64 74 76 77 78 79 80 81 85 92 93 96 97 107 108 110 111 115 118 119 127 129 131 135 146 147 148 149 **S** Munson Healthcare, Traverse City, MI
Primary Contact: James Barker, Chief Executive Officer
COO: Donn J Lemmer, Chief Financial Officer and Chief Operating Officer
CFO: Donn J Lemmer, Chief Financial Officer and Chief Operating Officer
CMO: Marion Fuller, Chief of Staff
CHR: Kim Weckesser, Director Human Resources
CNO: Thomas Kane, R.N., Vice President Patient Services and Chief Nursing Officer
Web address: www.westshoremedcenter.org
Control: Other not–for–profit (including NFP Corporation) **Service**: General medical and surgical

Staffed Beds: 45 **Admissions:** 1307 **Census:** 11 **Outpatient Visits:** 95844 **Births:** 196 **Total Expense ($000):** 72043 **Payroll Expense ($000):** 28518 **Personnel:** 333

MANISTIQUE—Schoolcraft County

★ **SCHOOLCRAFT MEMORIAL HOSPITAL (231303)**, 7870W US Highway 2, Zip 49854–8992; tel. 906/341–3200, **A**10 18 **F**3 11 15 18 19 28 29 30 31 32 34 35 40 41 45 50 53 56 57 59 62 63 64 65 68 70 75 77 78 79 81 82 85 90 93 97 100 107 108 110 114 115 118 119 127 129 130 132 133 144 146 147 148 154 156
Primary Contact: Robert Crumb, MS, Chief Executive Officer
CMO: John P Galey, M.D., Chief Medical Officer
CIO: Kent La Croix, Chief Information Officer
CHR: Fawn Freeborn, Human Resources Generalist
CNO: Cindy Olli, R.N., Chief Nursing Officer
Web address: www.scmh.org
Control: County, Government, nonfederal **Service**: General medical and surgical

Staffed Beds: 12 **Admissions:** 387 **Census:** 5 **Outpatient Visits:** 49433 **Births:** 0 **Total Expense ($000):** 37491 **Payroll Expense ($000):** 18131 **Personnel:** 261

MARLETTE—Sanilac County

○ **MARLETTE REGIONAL HOSPITAL (231330)**, 2770 Main Street, Zip 48453–1141, Mailing Address: P.O. Box 307, Zip 48453–0307; tel. 989/635–4000, (Nonreporting) **A**10 11 18
Primary Contact: Daniel Babcock, Chief Executive Officer
CFO: James L Singles, Chief Financial Officer
CMO: Daniel Kulick, M.D., Chief of Staff
CIO: Paul Gugel, Manager Information Technology
CHR: Connie Kennedy, Director Human Resources
CNO: Hilda Hebberd, R.N., MSN, Senior Director Clinical Services
Web address: www.marletteregionalhospital.org
Control: Other not–for–profit (including NFP Corporation) **Service**: General medical and surgical

Staffed Beds: 74

MARQUETTE—Marquette County

✠ **UP HEALTH SYSTEM-MARQUETTE (230054)**, 580 West College Avenue, Zip 49855–2736; tel. 906/228–9440, **A**1 2 3 5 10 **F**3 4 5 7 8 11 12 13 14 15 17 18 19 20 22 24 26 28 29 30 31 32 34 35 37 38 40 43 45 46 49 50 51 53 55 56 57 58 59 60 64 65 68 70 72 74 75 76 77 78 79 81 82 84 85 86 87 89 90 93 94 98 100 101 104 107 108 110 111 114 115 116 118 119 120 121 123 124 127 129 130 131 132 135 145 147 148 149 155 156 157 **O** Duke LifePoint Healthcare, Brentwood, TN
Primary Contact: Brian Sinotte, Chief Executive Officer
COO: Steven Salyer, Chief Operating Officer
CFO: Steve Embree, Chief Financial Officer
CMO: Tom Noren, M.D., Chief Medical Officer
CIO: Doug Stacy, Director Information Technology
CHR: Ruth Solinski, Senior Director Human Resources
Web address: www.mgh.org
Control: Corporation, Investor–owned (for–profit) **Service**: General medical and surgical

Staffed Beds: 260 **Admissions:** 9852 **Census:** 132 **Outpatient Visits:** 261112 **Births:** 541 **Total Expense ($000):** 318083 **Payroll Expense ($000):** 111397 **Personnel:** 1591

MARSHALL—Calhoun County

★ ⇑ **OAKLAWN HOSPITAL (230217)**, 200 North Madison Street, Zip 49068–1199; tel. 269/781–4271, (Nonreporting) **A**10 21
Primary Contact: Gregg M. Beeg, FACHE, Interim President and Chief Executive Officer
COO: Sharon Thomas-Boyd, Chief Operating Officer
CFO: Andrew J. Poole III Interim Chief Financial Officer
CNO: Theresa Dawson, MSN, R.N., Chief Nursing Officer
Web address: www.oaklawnhospital.org
Control: Other not–for–profit (including NFP Corporation) **Service**: General medical and surgical

Staffed Beds: 78

MI

Hospital, Medicare Provider Number, Address, Telephone, Approval, Facility, and Physician Codes, Health Care System

★ American Hospital Association (AHA) membership
□ The Joint Commission accreditation
○ Healthcare Facilities Accreditation Program
◇ DNV Healthcare Inc. accreditation
⇑ Center for Improvement in Healthcare Quality Accreditation
△ Commission on Accreditation of Rehabilitation Facilities (CARF) accreditation

MI

MIDLAND—Midland County

☒ **MIDMICHIGAN MEDICAL CENTER-MIDLAND (230222)**, 4000 Wellness Drive, Zip 48670–2000; tel. 989/839–3000, **A**1 2 3 5 10 **F**3 7 8 11 12 13 15 17 18 20 22 24 26 28 29 31 32 34 35 36 37 38 40 43 45 46 47 48 49 50 51 53 54 56 57 58 59 60 61 62 63 64 65 68 70 71 74 75 77 78 79 80 81 82 84 85 86 87 91 92 93 94 97 98 100 101 102 104 107 108 109 110 111 114 115 116 117 118 119 120 121 122 123 124 126 127 129 130 131 132 135 143 144 146 147 148 149 154 156 157 **S** MidMichigan Health, Midland, MI
Primary Contact: Gregory H. Rogers, President
CFO: Scott D Currie, Vice President and Chief Financial Officer
CMO: Margueritte Kuhn, M.D., Vice President Medical Affairs
CIO: C Harlan Goodrich, Vice President and Chief Information Officer
CNO: Jan Penney, R.N., Vice President and Chief Nursing Officer
Web address: www.midmichigan.org
Control: Other not–for–profit (including NFP Corporation) **Service**: General medical and surgical

Staffed Beds: 270 **Admissions:** 14037 **Census:** 151 **Outpatient Visits:** 273321 **Births:** 1296 **Total Expense ($000):** 392345 **Payroll Expense ($000):** 117366 **Personnel:** 1840

MONROE—Monroe County

☒ **PROMEDICA MONROE REGIONAL HOSPITAL (230099)**, 718 North Macomb Street, Zip 48162–7815; tel. 734/240–8400, **A**1 2 3 5 10 12 13 **F**3 5 11 13 15 18 20 21 28 29 30 31 34 35 36 38 40 41 43 44 45 46 49 50 51 53 54 56 57 59 65 66 69 70 71 74 75 76 77 78 79 81 82 85 86 87 92 93 97 98 100 101 102 104 107 108 109 110 111 113 114 115 116 117 118 119 124 126 129 130 132 135 145 146 147 148 149 150 154 156 **S** ProMedica Health System, Toledo, OH
Primary Contact: Daniel Schwanke, President
CMO: Gary L. Moorman, D.O., Chief Medical Officer and Senior Vice President Medical Affairs
CNO: Pamela A Urbanski, R.N., MSN, Chief Nursing Officer, Senior Vice President, Patient Care Services
Web address: www.promedica.org
Control: Other not–for–profit (including NFP Corporation) **Service**: General medical and surgical

Staffed Beds: 100 **Admissions:** 5972 **Census:** 67 **Outpatient Visits:** 158562 **Births:** 634 **Total Expense ($000):** 142424 **Payroll Expense ($000):** 50754 **Personnel:** 848

MOUNT CLEMENS—Macomb County

☐ **MCLAREN MACOMB (230227)**, 1000 Harrington Boulevard, Zip 48043–2992; tel. 586/493–8000, **A**1 2 3 5 10 12 13 **F**3 8 11 12 13 14 15 18 19 20 22 24 26 28 29 30 31 34 35 36 37 40 41 43 45 46 47 48 49 50 51 54 55 56 59 62 63 64 65 66 68 70 71 74 75 76 77 78 79 81 82 84 85 87 89 92 93 94 96 100 102 107 110 111 114 115 118 119 120 121 123 124 126 129 130 131 132 135 145 146 147 148 149 154 156 **S** McLaren Health Care Corporation, Grand Blanc, MI
Primary Contact: Thomas M. Brisse, President and Chief Executive Officer
COO: Sue Durst, R.N., MS, Vice President Plant Operations
CFO: Brian Baluntanski, Chief Financial Officer
CMO: Dennis J. Cunningham, M.D., Chief Medical Officer
CNO: Julia Libcke, R.N., MSN, Chief Nursing Officer
Web address: www.mclaren.org/macomb/macomb.aspx
Control: Other not–for–profit (including NFP Corporation) **Service**: General medical and surgical

Staffed Beds: 288 **Admissions:** 14621 **Census:** 165 **Outpatient Visits:** 165936 **Births:** 1132 **Total Expense ($000):** 323850 **Payroll Expense ($000):** 129365 **Personnel:** 1614

☒ **SELECT SPECIALTY HOSPITAL-MACOMB COUNTY (232023)**, 215 North Avenue, Zip 48043–1700; tel. 586/307–9000, (Nonreporting) **A**1 10 **S** Select Medical Corporation, Mechanicsburg, PA
Primary Contact: Jon P. O'Malley, Chief Executive Officer
CFO: Sharon Ryan, Regional Controller
CMO: Arsenio V Deleon, M.D., Chief Medical Officer
CHR: Katelyn Andre, Human Resource Coordinator
CNO: Lydia Alaszewski, Chief Nursing Officer
Web address: www.macomb.selectspecialtyhospitals.com/
Control: Corporation, Investor–owned (for–profit) **Service**: Acute long–term care hospital

Staffed Beds: 36

MOUNT PLEASANT—Isabella County

☐ **MCLAREN CENTRAL MICHIGAN (230080)**, 1221 South Drive, Zip 48858–3257; tel. 989/772–6700, **A**1 2 10 19 **F**3 11 12 13 15 18 20 22 26 28 29 30 31 34 35 40 44 45 48 49 50 51 54 57 59 62 64 65 68 70 74 75 76 77 78 79 81 82 85 86 87 89 96 97 107 108 110 111 114 117 118 119 120 121 123 124 129 130 131 132 144 145 146 147 148 156 **S** McLaren Health Care Corporation, Grand Blanc, MI
Primary Contact: Martin Tursky, President and Chief Executive Officer
CMO: Ashok Vashishta, M.D., Vice President Medical Affairs
CIO: Nicolette Zalud, Customer Site Manager
CHR: Carolyn Potter, Vice President Human Resources
CNO: Sheri Myers, Vice President Patient Care Services
Web address: www.cmch.org
Control: Other not–for–profit (including NFP Corporation) **Service**: General medical and surgical

Staffed Beds: 78 **Admissions:** 2762 **Census:** 23 **Outpatient Visits:** 109006 **Births:** 469 **Total Expense ($000):** 85544 **Payroll Expense ($000):** 37451 **Personnel:** 429

MUNISING—Alger County

MUNISING MEMORIAL HOSPITAL (231308), 1500 Sand Point Road, Zip 49862–1406; tel. 906/387–4110, (Nonreporting) **A**10 18
Primary Contact: Melissa Hall, Chief Executive Officer
CFO: Wendy Rautio, Chief Financial Officer
CMO: Christine Krueger, M.D., Chief of Staff
CNO: Andrea Wills, R.N., Chief Nursing Executive
Web address: www.munisingmemorial.org
Control: Other not–for–profit (including NFP Corporation) **Service**: General medical and surgical

Staffed Beds: 25

MUSKEGON—Muskegon County

☒ **MERCY HEALTH HACKLEY CAMPUS (230066)**, 1700 Clinton Street, Zip 49442–5502, Mailing Address: P.O. Box 3302, Zip 49443–3302; tel. 231/726–3511, (Includes MERCY HEALTH, GENERAL CAMPUS, 1700 Oak Avenue, Muskegon, Michigan, Zip 49442; tel. 231/672–3311; Greg Loomis, Interim President and Chief Operating Officer; MERCY HEALTH, MERCY CAMPUS, 1500 East Sherman Boulevard, Muskegon, Michigan, Zip 49444–1849; tel. 231/672–2000; Gary Allore, President) **A**1 2 3 10 **F**3 7 11 12 13 15 18 20 22 24 26 28 29 30 34 35 36 38 40 43 44 45 46 47 48 49 50 51 54 56 57 59 61 64 67 68 70 76 77 79 81 82 84 85 86 87 89 90 92 93 96 97 98 104 107 110 111 114 115 118 119 120 121 123 124 126 127 129 130 131 132 144 146 147 148 149 153 154 156 **S** Trinity Health, Livonia, MI
Primary Contact: Gary Allore, President
CMO: F. Remington Sprague, M.D., Chief Medical Officer
CIO: William Stefl, Director Information Systems
CNO: Kimberly Maguire, Chief Nursing Officer
Web address: www.mercyhealthmuskegon.com
Control: Other not–for–profit (including NFP Corporation) **Service**: General medical and surgical

Staffed Beds: 366 **Admissions:** 18868 **Census:** 214 **Outpatient Visits:** 1052862 **Births:** 1981 **Total Expense ($000):** 568942 **Payroll Expense ($000):** 250052 **Personnel:** 3644

☒ **SELECT SPECIALTY HOSPITAL-MUSKEGON (232021)**, 1700 Clinton Street, 3 South, Zip 49442–5502; tel. 231/728–5811, (Nonreporting) **A**1 10 **S** Select Medical Corporation, Mechanicsburg, PA
Primary Contact: Kerry McLane, Chief Executive Officer
Web address: www.greatlakesspecialtyhospital.com
Control: Corporation, Investor–owned (for–profit) **Service**: Acute long–term care hospital

Staffed Beds: 31

SELECT SPECIALTY HOSPITAL-WESTERN MICHIGAN See Select Specialty Hospital-Muskegon

NEW BALTIMORE—Macomb County

HARBOR OAKS HOSPITAL (234021), 35031 23 Mile Road, Zip 48047–3649; tel. 586/725–5777, **A**10 **F**4 98 99 103 105 **S** Acadia Healthcare Company, Inc., Franklin, TN
Primary Contact: Briana Jacob, Chief Executive Officer
CFO: Michael Ferguson, Chief Financial Officer
CMO: James D. Adamo, M.D., Medical Director
CHR: Zena Ridley, Director Human Resources
CNO: Leeann Duncan, Director Patient Care Services
Web address: www.harboroaks.com
Control: Corporation, Investor–owned (for–profit) **Service**: Psychiatric

Staffed Beds: 99 **Admissions:** 3046 **Census:** 92 **Outpatient Visits:** 1772 **Total Expense ($000):** 19436 **Payroll Expense ($000):** 10244 **Personnel:** 200

Many Facility Codes have changed. Please refer to the AHA Guide Code Chart. © 2019 AHA Guide

NEWBERRY—Luce County

★ ⇑ **HELEN NEWBERRY JOY HOSPITAL (231304)**, 502 West Harrie Street, Zip 49868–1209; tel. 906/293–9200, (Total facility includes 39 beds in nursing home-type unit) **A**10 18 21 **F**3 15 28 29 31 34 35 40 43 45 53 57 59 64 65 75 78 79 81 87 93 97 107 108 115 118 119 127 128 129 130 131 132 133 143 144 154
Primary Contact: Scott Pillion, Chief Executive Officer
CFO: Hunter Nostrant, Chef Financial Officer
CMO: Michael Gregory Beaulieu, M.D., Chief Medical Officer
CIO: Howard Bliss, Director of Information Systems
CNO: Deborah Baker, Chief Nursing Officer
Web address: www.hnjh.org
Control: County, Government, nonfederal **Service**: General medical and surgical

Staffed Beds: 64 **Admissions**: 398 **Census**: 39 **Outpatient Visits**: 32815 **Births**: 0 **Total Expense ($000)**: 31942 **Payroll Expense ($000)**: 13897 **Personnel**: 262

NORTHVILLE—Wayne County

☐ **HAWTHORN CENTER**, 18471 Haggerty Road, Zip 48168–9575; tel. 248/735–6771, (Nonreporting) **A**1 3
Primary Contact: George Mellows, Facility Director
CIO: Robert W Bailey, Chief Information Officer
Web address: www.https://www.michigan.gov
Control: State, Government, nonfederal **Service**: Children's hospital psychiatric

Staffed Beds: 69

NOVI—Oakland County

PROVIDENCE - PROVIDENCE PARK HOSPITAL, NOVI CAMPUS See Ascension of Providence Hospital, Southfield Campus, Southfield

ONTONAGON—Ontonagon County

⊠ **ASPIRUS ONTONAGON HOSPITAL, INC. (231309)**, 601 South Seventh Street, Zip 49953–1459; tel. 906/884–8000, (Total facility includes 46 beds in nursing home-type unit) **A**1 10 18 **F**3 15 28 29 31 34 35 40 41 43 45 53 56 59 64 65 68 75 77 78 79 81 85 87 93 94 97 107 110 114 119 127 128 131 132 133 147 149 154 156 **S** Aspirus, Inc., Wausau, WI
Primary Contact: Dylan Taylor, Chief Administrative Officer
CMO: Richard Chaltry, M.D., Director Medical Staff
CHR: Gina Kasten, Manager Human Resources
Web address: www.aspirus.org
Control: Other not–for–profit (including NFP Corporation) **Service**: General medical and surgical

Staffed Beds: 56 **Admissions**: 226 **Census**: 39 **Outpatient Visits**: 13680 **Births**: 0 **Total Expense ($000)**: 15566 **Payroll Expense ($000)**: 5923 **Personnel**: 109

OWOSSO—Shiawassee County

⊠ **MEMORIAL HEALTHCARE (230121)**, 826 West King Street, Zip 48867–2120; tel. 989/723–5211, (Total facility includes 32 beds in nursing home–type unit) **A**1 2 10 **F**3 11 13 15 28 29 30 31 32 34 35 36 38 40 45 50 51 56 57 58 59 62 63 64 65 69 70 74 75 76 77 78 79 81 82 85 87 89 93 97 98 100 101 102 107 108 110 111 115 119 127 128 129 130 131 132 143 144 146 147 148 154 156
Primary Contact: Brian Long, FACHE, President and Chief Executive Officer
COO: Tim Susterich, Chief Financial Officer and Chief Operating Officer
CFO: Tim Susterich, Chief Financial Officer and Chief Operating Officer
CMO: Wael Salman, M.D., Vice President Medical Affairs
CIO: Tom Kurtz, Vice President Information Services and Chief Information Officer
CNO: Jim Nemeth, Senior Vice President of Patient Care Services and Chief Nursing Officer
Web address: www.memorialhealthcare.org
Control: Other not–for–profit (including NFP Corporation) **Service**: General medical and surgical

Staffed Beds: 150 **Admissions**: 4042 **Census**: 76 **Outpatient Visits**: 433051 **Births**: 466 **Total Expense ($000)**: 168594 **Payroll Expense ($000)**: 70601 **Personnel**: 1330

PAW PAW—Van Buren County

⊠ **BRONSON LAKEVIEW HOSPITAL (231332)**, 408 Hazen Street, Zip 49079–1019, Mailing Address: P.O. Box 209, Zip 49079–0209; tel. 269/657–3141, **A**1 10 18 **F**3 6 9 11 15 18 29 30 34 35 36 40 44 55 56 57 58 59 63 64 65 66 68 71 74 75 77 79 81 82 84 85 86 87 93 97 98 100 101 102 103 107 110 111 115 118 119 127 129 130 132 135 143 146 147 148 149 154 156 **S** Bronson Healthcare Group, Kalamazoo, MI
Primary Contact: Kirk Richardson, R.N., Vice President, Chief Operating Officer, and Chief Nursing Officer
COO: Kirk Richardson, R.N., Vice President, Chief Operating Officer, and Chief Nursing Officer
CFO: Becky East, CPA, Senior Vice President, Chief Financial Officer
CMO: Matthew Dommer, M.D., Chief Medical Officer
CIO: Ash Goel, Senior Vice President Information Technology & Chief Information Officer
CHR: John Hayden, Senior Vice President and Chief Human Resources Officer
CNO: Kirk Richardson, R.N., Vice President, Chief Operating Officer, and Chief Nursing Officer
Web address: www.bronsonhealth.com/lakeview
Control: Other not–for–profit (including NFP Corporation) **Service**: General medical and surgical

Staffed Beds: 35 **Admissions**: 711 **Census**: 11 **Outpatient Visits**: 115110 **Births**: 0 **Total Expense ($000)**: 47959 **Payroll Expense ($000)**: 26139 **Personnel**: 291

PETOSKEY—Emmet County

☐ **MCLAREN NORTHERN MICHIGAN (230105)**, 416 Connable Avenue, Zip 49770–2297; tel. 231/487–4000, **A**1 2 10 **F**3 13 15 17 18 20 22 24 26 28 29 30 31 32 34 35 36 38 40 42 44 45 49 50 51 53 57 58 59 60 64 68 70 74 75 76 77 78 79 81 82 85 86 87 89 90 91 93 94 96 107 108 110 111 114 115 119 120 121 123 124 129 130 132 135 146 148 149 154 157 **S** McLaren Health Care Corporation, Grand Blanc, MI
Primary Contact: David M. Zechman, FACHE, President and Chief Executive Officer
CFO: David Bellamy, Chief Financial Officer
CMO: Kirk Lufkin, M.D., VPMA
CIO: David Bellamy, Chief Financial Officer
CHR: Gene Kaminski, Vice President Human Resources and Hospitality Services
CNO: Jennifer Woods, R.N., MSN, Chief Nursing Officer
Web address: www.northernhealth.org
Control: Other not–for–profit (including NFP Corporation) **Service**: General medical and surgical

Staffed Beds: 188 **Admissions**: 9773 **Census**: 105 **Outpatient Visits**: 192599 **Births**: 534 **Total Expense ($000)**: 252863 **Payroll Expense ($000)**: 85558 **Personnel**: 1306

PIGEON—Huron County

⊠ **SCHEURER HOSPITAL (231310)**, 170 North Caseville Road, Zip 48755–9781; tel. 989/453–3223, (Total facility includes 19 beds in nursing home–type unit) **A**1 10 18 **F**3 7 8 10 11 15 28 29 30 31 32 34 35 40 44 45 50 53 54 56 57 59 64 65 68 69 75 77 78 79 81 85 86 87 91 93 97 107 108 110 115 118 119 125 127 130 131 132 133 134 144 146 149 156
Primary Contact: Terrance Lerash, President and Chief Executive Officer
CFO: Terry Lutz, Chief Financial Officer
CMO: Ross Ramsey, M.D., Chief of Staff
CIO: Carleen Giddings, Information Technology System Leader
CHR: Gregory S. Foy, Human Resources System Leader
CNO: Kendra Kretzschmer, Patient Care System Leader
Web address: www.scheurer.org
Control: Other not–for–profit (Including NFP Corporation) **Service**: General medical and surgical

Staffed Beds: 44 **Admissions**: 404 **Census**: 26 **Outpatient Visits**: 44537 **Births**: 0 **Total Expense ($000)**: 40750 **Payroll Expense ($000)**: 19878 **Personnel**: 347

MI

Hospital, Medicare Provider Number, Address, Telephone, Approval, Facility, and Physician Codes, Health Care System

★ American Hospital Association (AHA) membership
☐ The Joint Commission accreditation
○ Healthcare Facilities Accreditation Program
◇ DNV Healthcare Inc. accreditation
⇑ Center for Improvement in Healthcare Quality Accreditation
△ Commission on Accreditation of Rehabilitation Facilities (CARF) accreditation

PONTIAC—Oakland County

☐ **MCLAREN OAKLAND (230207)**, 50 North Perry Street, Zip 48342–2253; tel. 248/338–5000, (Total facility includes 120 beds in nursing home–type unit) **A**1 2 3 5 10 12 **F**3 4 7 8 11 12 14 15 18 20 24 26 28 29 30 31 32 33 34 35 36 40 42 43 44 45 50 53 54 57 59 62 63 64 65 66 68 70 74 75 77 78 79 81 82 85 90 92 93 94 98 103 107 108 111 114 118 119 124 126 128 129 130 131 132 135 136 137 138 139 140 141 142 143 144 146 148 149 **S** McLaren Health Care Corporation, Grand Blanc, MI
Primary Contact: Margaret Dimond, Ph.D., President and Chief Executive Officer
COO: Nicholle Mehr, Vice President Operations
CFO: Lynn Marcotte, Chief Financial Officer
CMO: Steven Calkin, D.O., Vice President Medical Affairs
CIO: Kelly Finley, Customer Site Executive
CHR: Dwan Cosby, Manager Human Resources
CNO: Calandra Anderson, Vice President Patient Care and Chief Nursing Officer
Web address: www.mclaren.org/oakland
Control: Other not–for–profit (including NFP Corporation) **Service**: General medical and surgical

Staffed Beds: 253 **Admissions**: 5257 **Census**: 191 **Outpatient Visits**: 169062 **Births**: 0 **Total Expense ($000)**: 192337 **Payroll Expense ($000)**: 75412 **Personnel**: 1225

☐ **PIONEER SPECIALTY HOSPITAL (230304)**, 50 North Perry Street, 6th Floor, Zip 48342–2217; tel. 248/338–5430, (Nonreporting) **A**1
Primary Contact: Denise Wayne, Chief Executive Officer
Web address: www.pioneerspecialtyhospital.com
Control: Individual, Investor–owned (for–profit) **Service**: Acute long–term care hospital

Staffed Beds: 30

PONTIAC GENERAL HOSPITAL (230013), 461 West Huron Street, Zip 48341–1601; tel. 248/857–7200, (Nonreporting) **A**10
Primary Contact: Robert Barrow, Chief Executive Officer
COO: Dennis Franks, Vice President Operations
CFO: Dennis Franks, Interim Chief Financial Officer
CMO: Ray Breitenbach, M.D., Chief of Staff
CIO: Albert Sinisi, Director Information Systems
Web address: www.pontiacgeneral.com
Control: Other not–for–profit (including NFP Corporation) **Service**: General medical and surgical

Staffed Beds: 106

★ **SELECT SPECIALTY HOSPITAL-PONTIAC (232030)**, 44405 Woodward Avenue, 8th Floor, Zip 48341–5023; tel. 248/452–5252, (Nonreporting) **S** Select Medical Corporation, Mechanicsburg, PA
Primary Contact: Peggy Kingston, Chief Executive Officer
CMO: Fadi Salloum, M.D., Medical Director
CNO: Cathy Boyd, Chief Nursing Officer
Web address: www.selectspecialtyhospitals.com/company/locations/pontiac.aspx
Control: Corporation, Investor–owned (for–profit) **Service**: Acute long–term care hospital

Staffed Beds: 30

⊞ **ST. JOSEPH MERCY OAKLAND (230029)**, 44405 Woodward Avenue, Zip 48341–5023; tel. 248/858–3000, **A**1 2 3 5 10 **F**3 8 11 12 13 15 17 18 20 22 24 26 28 29 30 31 34 35 36 39 40 41 43 44 45 46 48 49 50 53 54 55 56 57 58 59 61 64 65 66 68 70 72 74 75 76 77 78 79 81 82 84 85 86 87 89 90 93 94 96 97 98 100 102 105 107 108 110 111 114 115 118 119 126 129 130 131 132 135 144 146 147 148 149 150 154 **S** Trinity Health, Livonia, MI
Primary Contact: Shannon Striebich, Chief Executive Officer
CFO: Michael Gusho, Chief Financial Officer
CMO: Fabian Fregoli, M.D., Chief Medical Officer
CIO: Robert Jones, Director Management Information Systems
CHR: Ane McNeil, Vice President Human Resources
CNO: Douglas R Dascenzo, MSN, R.N., Chief Nursing Officer
Web address: www.stjoesoakland.com
Control: Church operated, Nongovernment, not–for–profit **Service**: General medical and surgical

Staffed Beds: 396 **Admissions**: 20445 **Census**: 270 **Outpatient Visits**: 360832 **Births**: 1764 **Total Expense ($000)**: 444187 **Payroll Expense ($000)**: 179538 **Personnel**: 2705

PORT HURON—St. Clair County

⊞ **LAKE HURON MEDICAL CENTER (230031)**, 2601 Electric Avenue, Zip 48060–6518; tel. 810/985–1500, **A**1 2 10 **F**3 12 15 18 20 28 29 30 31 34 35 40 45 46 47 49 50 54 56 57 58 59 64 66 70 74 75 77 78 79 81 82 85 86 87 90 91 93 96 97 107 108 110 114 115 118 119 120 121 123 126 130 131 132 146 147 148 149 154 156 **S** Prime Healthcare, Ontario, CA
Primary Contact: Jay De los Reyes, Chief Executive Officer
COO: Ken Sanger, R.N., Chief Nursing Officer and Chief Operations Officer
CFO: Chris Fulks, Vice President Finance
CMO: Sridhar Reddy, M.D., Chief Medical Officer
CIO: Jefferey Wagner, Director, Information Technology
CHR: Debra A Seifert, Director Human Resources
CNO: Ken Sanger, R.N., Chief Nursing Officer and Chief Operations Officer
Web address: www.mymercy.us
Control: Corporation, Investor–owned (for–profit) **Service**: General medical and surgical

Staffed Beds: 119 **Admissions**: 4081 **Census**: 41 **Outpatient Visits**: 114792 **Births**: 0 **Total Expense ($000)**: 67677 **Payroll Expense ($000)**: 26211 **Personnel**: 481

⊞ **MCLAREN PORT HURON (230216)**, 1221 Pine Grove Avenue, Zip 48060–3511; tel. 810/987–5000, **A**1 2 10 **F**1 3 4 5 11 12 13 15 16 17 18 20 22 24 26 28 29 30 31 32 34 35 36 39 40 43 44 45 46 48 49 50 51 54 56 57 58 59 61 64 65 66 67 68 70 72 73 74 75 76 77 78 79 80 81 82 84 85 86 87 88 89 90 92 93 94 96 97 98 99 100 101 102 103 104 107 108 110 111 114 115 116 117 118 119 120 121 126 128 129 130 131 132 134 135 144 145 146 147 148 149 153 154 156 157 **S** McLaren Health Care Corporation, Grand Blanc, MI
Primary Contact: Jennifer Montgomery, FACHE, R.N., President and Chief Executive Officer
COO: John Liston, Chief Operating Officer
CFO: Bridget Sholtis, Chief Financial Officer
CMO: Michael W Tawney, D.O., Vice President Medical Affairs
CIO: John McGrath, Chief Information Officer
CHR: Doris A Seidl, Vice President Human Resources
CNO: Christine R Sansom, Chief Nursing Officer
Web address: www.porthuronhospital.org
Control: Other not–for–profit (including NFP Corporation) **Service**: General medical and surgical

Staffed Beds: 186 **Admissions**: 12170 **Census**: 125 **Outpatient Visits**: 232425 **Births**: 926 **Total Expense ($000)**: 192204 **Payroll Expense ($000)**: 74359 **Personnel**: 1240

REED CITY—Osceola County

⊞ **SPECTRUM HEALTH REED CITY HOSPITAL (231323)**, 300 North Patterson Road, Zip 49677–8041, Mailing Address: P.O. Box 75, Zip 49677–0075; tel. 231/832–3271, (Total facility includes 50 beds in nursing home–type unit) **A**1 10 18 **F**3 15 29 31 34 35 36 40 45 47 50 59 64 65 68 69 71 74 75 78 79 81 82 86 87 93 97 100 107 110 115 119 120 121 122 127 128 129 130 132 133 135 146 147 149 154 155 156 157 **S** Spectrum Health, Grand Rapids, MI
Primary Contact: Andrea M. Leslie, MSN, R.N., President
COO: Cathy Rybicki, Chief Operating Officer
CFO: Thomas Knoerl, Vice President Finance
CMO: Thomas Campana, M.D., Chief of Staff
CIO: Brandi Johnson, Site Manager Technology Information Systems
CHR: Kris Miller, Senior Human Resources Business Partner
Web address: www.spectrumhealth.org/reedcity
Control: Other not–for–profit (including NFP Corporation) **Service**: General medical and surgical

Staffed Beds: 75 **Admissions**: 601 **Census**: 51 **Outpatient Visits**: 312641 **Births**: 0 **Total Expense ($000)**: 54385 **Payroll Expense ($000)**: 17461 **Personnel**: 345

ROCHESTER—Oakland County

⊞ △ **ASCENSION CRITTENTON HOSPITAL MEDICAL CENTER (230254)**, 1101 West University Drive, Zip 48307–1831; tel. 248/652–5000, **A**1 3 5 7 10 **F**3 8 13 15 17 18 20 22 24 26 28 29 30 34 35 36 38 40 43 44 46 48 49 50 51 53 54 56 57 58 59 64 65 66 68 70 73 74 75 76 77 79 81 85 86 87 90 93 97 98 100 107 108 110 111 114 115 119 126 129 130 131 132 134 135 143 146 147 148 149 154 156 **S** Ascension Healthcare, Saint Louis, MO
Primary Contact: Chris Palazzolo, President and Chief Executive Officer
COO: Tomasine Marx, Chief Financial Officer and Chief Operating Officer
CFO: Tomasine Marx, Chief Financial Officer and Chief Operating Officer
CMO: Sheryl Wissman, M.D., Chief Medical Officer
CIO: Ralph Tenney, Chief Information Officer
CHR: Ann Vano, Vice President, Human Resources
Web address: www.crittenton.com
Control: Other not–for–profit (including NFP Corporation) **Service**: General medical and surgical

Staffed Beds: 226 **Admissions**: 9809 **Census**: 122 **Outpatient Visits**: 146153 **Births**: 569 **Total Expense ($000)**: 220322 **Payroll Expense ($000)**: 74249 **Personnel**: 1062

Many Facility Codes have changed. Please refer to the AHA Guide Code Chart.   © 2019 AHA Guide

ROMEO—Macomb County

ST. JOSEPH'S MERCY-NORTH See Henry Ford Macomb Hospitals, Clinton Township

ROYAL OAK—Oakland County

✠ **BEAUMONT HOSPITAL - ROYAL OAK (230130)**, 3601 West Thirteen Mile Road, Zip 48073–6712; tel. 248/898–5000, (Includes BEAUMONT CHILDREN'S HOSPITAL, 3601 West 13 Mile Road, Royal Oak, Michigan, Zip 48073–6712; tel. 248/898–5000) **A**1 2 3 5 8 10 19 **F**3 6 8 11 12 13 15 17 18 19 20 22 24 26 28 29 30 31 32 34 35 36 37 38 39 40 41 43 44 45 46 47 48 49 50 51 54 55 56 57 58 59 60 61 64 65 66 68 70 71 72 74 75 76 77 78 79 80 81 82 83 84 85 86 87 88 89 90 91 92 93 95 96 97 98 100 101 102 104 105 107 108 109 110 111 114 115 117 118 119 120 121 122 123 124 126 129 130 131 132 134 135 138 139 141 142 143 144 145 146 147 148 149 150 154 156 157 **S** Beaumont Health, Southfield, MI
Primary Contact: Nancy Susick, MSN, President
COO: Carolyn Wilson, R.N., Chief Operating Officer
CFO: John Kerndl, Executive Vice President and Chief Financial Officer
CMO: Leslie Rocher, Senior Vice President and Chief Medical Officer
CIO: Subra Sripada, Executive Vice President, Chief Transportation Officer and Chief Information Officer
CHR: Michael L Dixon, Vice President, Human Resources
CNO: Maureen Bowman, Vice President and Chief Nursing Officer
Web address: www.beaumont.org
Control: Other not-for-profit (including NFP Corporation) **Service:** General medical and surgical

Staffed Beds: 1100 **Admissions:** 58510 **Census:** 820 **Outpatient Visits:** 1630039 **Births:** 6788 **Total Expense ($000):** 1353400 **Payroll Expense ($000):** 494985 **Personnel:** 7527

SAGINAW—Saginaw County

✠ △ **ALEDA E. LUTZ VETERANS AFFAIRS MEDICAL CENTER**, 1500 Weiss Street, Zip 48602–5298; tel. 989/497–2500, (Total facility includes 81 beds in nursing home–type unit) **A**1 3 7 **F**3 5 8 11 12 15 18 29 30 31 34 35 36 38 39 44 45 50 53 54 56 57 58 59 61 63 64 68 74 75 77 78 81 82 83 84 85 86 87 93 94 97 100 101 102 104 107 108 119 127 128 130 131 132 133 135 136 137 138 139 140 141 142 143 144 146 147 148 149 154 156 157 **S** Department of Veterans Affairs, Washington, DC
Primary Contact: Karandeep Oraon, Interim Director
COO: Stephanie Young, Associate Director
CFO: Jeff Drew, Fiscal Officer
CMO: Gregory Movsesian, M.D., Acting Chief of Staff
CIO: Angie Schmus, Chief Information Technology
CHR: Thomas Strodnoy, Chief Human Resources Management Service
CNO: Penny Holland, Associate Director for Patient Care Services
Web address: www.saginaw.va.gov/
Control: Veterans Affairs, Government, federal **Service:** General medical and surgical

Staffed Beds: 89 **Admissions:** 895 **Census:** 32 **Outpatient Visits:** 414518 **Births:** 0 **Total Expense ($000):** 267771 **Payroll Expense ($000):** 93724 **Personnel:** 1204

✠ **ASCENSION ST. MARY'S OF MICHIGAN (230077)**, 800 South Washington Avenue, Zip 48601–2594; tel. 989/907–8000, (Total facility includes 29 beds in nursing home–type unit) **A**1 2 3 5 10 19 **F**2 3 11 12 15 17 18 20 22 24 26 28 29 30 31 34 35 40 42 43 44 45 49 50 54 57 58 59 64 66 68 70 74 77 78 79 80 81 82 84 85 86 87 92 93 96 97 100 102 107 108 110 111 114 115 118 119 120 121 123 124 126 128 130 131 132 133 135 146 149 154 **S** Ascension Healthcare, Saint Louis, MO
Primary Contact: Chris Palazzolo, Health System President and Chief Executive Officer Mid-Michigan
CFO: Nancy Haywood, Chief Financial Officer
CMO: Raghu Sarvepalli, M.D., Vice President of Medical Affairs
CIO: Daniel Stross, Chief Information Officer
CHR: Paula Coffee, Director Human Resources
CNO: Bernie Jore, Chief Nursing Officer
Web address: www.stmarysofmichigan.org
Control: Church operated, Nongovernment, not-for-profit **Service:** General medical and surgical

Staffed Beds: 279 **Admissions:** 10382 **Census:** 157 **Outpatient Visits:** 230765 **Births:** 0 **Total Expense ($000):** 297863 **Payroll Expense ($000):** 104986 **Personnel:** 1469

★ ○ **COVENANT HEALTHCARE (230070)**, 1447 North Harrison Street, Zip 48602–4727; tel. 989/583–0000, (Includes COVENANT MEDICAL CENTER-COOPER, 700 Cooper Avenue, Saginaw, Michigan, Zip 48602–5399; tel. 989/583–0000; Edward Bruff, President and Chief Executive Officer; COVENANT MEDICAL CENTER-HARRISON, 1447 North Harrison Street, Saginaw, Michigan, Zip 48602–4785; tel. 989/583–0000; Edward Bruff, President and Chief Executive Officer) (Total facility includes 20 beds in nursing home–type unit) **A**2 3 5 10 11 12 13 15 17 18 19 20 22 24 25 26 27 28 29 30 31 35 36 40 41 42 43 45 46 47 48 49 50 54 57 58 59 60 61 62 63 64 65 70 72 74 75 76 77 78 79 81 82 83 84 86 87 88 89 90 91 92 93 94 97 107 108 110 111 113 114 115 118 119 120 121 123 124 126 128 129 130 131 132 135 143 144 146 147 148 154
Primary Contact: Edward Bruff, President and Chief Executive Officer
COO: Daniel M George, Executive Vice President, Operations
CFO: Kevin Albosta, Vice President, Chief Financial Officer
CMO: John Kosanovich, M.D., Executive Vice President Physician Enterprise and Chief Executive Officer, Covenant Medical Group
CHR: Kevin Birchmeier, Director Human Resources
CNO: Beth Charlton, Vice President Patient Services and Chief Nursing Officer
Web address: www.covenanthealthcare.com
Control: Other not-for-profit (including NFP Corporation) **Service:** General medical and surgical

Staffed Beds: 542 **Admissions:** 28202 **Census:** 420 **Outpatient Visits:** 458986 **Births:** 3050 **Total Expense ($000):** 628908 **Payroll Expense ($000):** 290462 **Personnel:** 4304

□ **HEALTHSOURCE SAGINAW, INC. (230275)**, 3340 Hospital Road, Zip 48603–9622; tel. 989/790–7700, (Total facility includes 213 beds in nursing home–type unit) **A**1 3 5 10 **F**4 5 64 90 91 93 96 98 99 100 101 104 128 130 143 146
Primary Contact: Lisa Lapham, President and Chief Executive Officer
CFO: Glen Chipman, Chief Financial Officer
CMO: Daniel Duffy, D.O., Chief Medical Director
CIO: Greg Sieg, Director Information Technology
CHR: Krystal Hadaway, Director Human Resources
CNO: Susan Graham, R.N., Nurse Executive
Web address: www.healthsourcesaginaw.org
Control: Other not-for-profit (including NFP Corporation) **Service:** Psychiatric

Staffed Beds: 343 **Admissions:** 4273 **Census:** 274 **Outpatient Visits:** 11249 **Births:** 0 **Total Expense ($000):** 51871 **Payroll Expense ($000):** 24448 **Personnel:** 512

✠ **SELECT SPECIALTY HOSPITAL-SAGINAW (232033)**, 1447 North Harrison Street, 8th Floor, Zip 48602–4785; tel. 989/583–4235, (Nonreporting) **A**1 10 **S** Select Medical Corporation, Mechanicsburg, PA
Primary Contact: Matthew J. Campbell Esq, Chief Executive Officer
CNO: Shannon Sequin, MSN, Chief Nursing Officer
Web address: www.selectspecialtyhospitals.com/company/locations/saginaw.aspx
Control: Corporation, Investor–owned (for–profit) **Service:** Acute long–term care hospital

Staffed Beds: 32

SAINT IGNACE—Mackinac County

★ ⇑ **MACKINAC STRAITS HEALTH SYSTEM, INC. (231306)**, 1140 North State Street, Zip 49781–1048; tel. 906/643–8585, (Total facility includes 48 beds in nursing home type unit) **A**10 18 21 **F**3 8 15 28 29 31 40 42 45 51 54 56 59 64 65 74 75 77 78 79 81 91 93 97 107 110 111 115 119 127 128 130 133 135 146 147 148 154 156
Primary Contact: Karen Cheeseman, Chief Executive Officer
CFO: Jason Anderson, Chief Financial Officer
CMO: Edward Smith, Chief of Staff
CHR: Kevin McElroy, Chief Human Resources Officer
CNO: Mary Kaye Ruegg, Chief Nursing Officer
Web address: www.mackinacstraitshealth.org
Control: Other not-for-profit (including NFP Corporation) **Service:** General medical and surgical

Staffed Beds: 63 **Admissions:** 422 **Census:** 54 **Outpatient Visits:** 37871 **Births:** 0 **Total Expense ($000):** 43706 **Payroll Expense ($000):** 15109 **Personnel:** 186

MI

Hospital, Medicare Provider Number, Address, Telephone, Approval, Facility, and Physician Codes, Health Care System

★ American Hospital Association (AHA) membership ○ Healthcare Facilities Accreditation Program ⇑ Center for Improvement in Healthcare Quality Accreditation
□ The Joint Commission accreditation ◇ DNV Healthcare Inc. accreditation △ Commission on Accreditation of Rehabilitation Facilities (CARF) accreditation

SAINT JOHNS—Clinton County

✠ **SPARROW CLINTON HOSPITAL (231326)**, 805 South Oakland Street,
Zip 48879–2253; tel. 989/227–3400, **A**1 10 18 **F**3 11 15 18 31 32 34 35 40
43 45 50 53 57 59 64 68 70 75 77 78 79 81 85 93 97 107 108 110 111 115
119 129 130 131 133 146 148 149 156 **S** Sparrow Health System, Lansing, MI
Primary Contact: Edward Bruun, President and Chief Executive Officer
COO: Kevin A Price, Vice President and Chief Operating Officer
CFO: Mark Brisboe, VP and Chief Financial Officer
CMO: Christopher Beal, M.D., Chief of Staff
CNO: Beth Ann Daugherty, R.N., M.P.H., Vice President Care Services and Chief
Nursing Executive
Web address: www.sparrowclinton.org
Control: Other not–for–profit (including NFP Corporation) **Service**: General
medical and surgical

Staffed Beds: 25 **Admissions:** 796 **Census:** 7 **Outpatient Visits:** 94240
Births: 0 **Total Expense ($000):** 43583 **Payroll Expense ($000):** 17279
Personnel: 220

SAINT JOSEPH—Berrien County

✠ **SPECTRUM HEALTH LAKELAND (230021)**, 1234 Napier Avenue, Zip 49085–
2158; tel. 269/983–8300, (Includes LAKELAND HOSPITAL, NILES, 31 North Saint
Joseph Avenue, Niles, Michigan, Zip 49120; tel. 269/683–5510; Debra Johnson,
R.N., Chief Administrator), (Non–reporting) **A**1 2 3 5 8 10 13 **S** Spectrum Health,
Grand Rapids, MI
Primary Contact: Loren Hamel, M.D., President and Chief Executive Officer
CFO: Timothy Calhoun, Vice President Finance and Chief Financial Officer
CMO: Stephen Hempel, M.D., President Medical Staff
CIO: Emily Gallay, Vice President and Chief Information Officer
Web address: www.lakelandhealth.org
Control: Other not–for–profit (including NFP Corporation) **Service**: General
medical and surgical

Staffed Beds: 303

SALINE—Washtenaw County

☐ **CENTER FOR FORENSIC PSYCHIATRY (234041)**, 8303 Platt Rd,
Zip 48176–9773, Mailing Address: P.O. Box 2060, Ann Arbor, Zip 48106–2060;
tel. 734/429–2531, (Nonreporting) **A**1 3 10
Primary Contact: Diane Heisel, Acting Director
Web address: www.michigan.gov
Control: County, Government, nonfederal **Service**: Psychiatric

Staffed Beds: 210

SANDUSKY—Sanilac County

MCKENZIE HEALTH SYSTEM (231314), 120 North Delaware Street,
Zip 48471–1087; tel. 810/648–3770, (Nonreporting) **A**10 18
Primary Contact: Steve Barnett, President and Chief Executive Officer
COO: Billi Jo Hennika, Vice President Operations
CFO: Amy Ruedisueli, Vice President of Finance
CMO: James C. Sams, Chief of Staff
CHR: Carrie Krampits, Director Human Resources
CNO: Patricia Schafsnitz, Director of Nursing Services
Web address: www.mckenziehealth.org
Control: Other not–for–profit (including NFP Corporation) **Service**: General
medical and surgical

Staffed Beds: 25

SAULT SAINTE MARIE—Chippewa County

★ ⇑ **WAR MEMORIAL HOSPITAL (230239)**, 500 Osborn Boulevard, Zip 49783–
1884; tel. 906/635–4460, (Total facility includes 51 beds in nursing home–type
unit) **A**10 20 21 **F**3 11 12 13 15 18 28 29 30 31 34 35 36 38 40 43 44 50 51
53 54 56 57 59 60 61 64 65 66 68 70 75 76 77 78 79 81 82 85 87 92 93 96
97 98 100 101 103 104 106 107 108 110 111 115 119 126 127 128 129 130
131 132 133 135 143 144 146 147 148 154 156
Primary Contact: David B. Jahn, President and Chief Executive Officer
COO: Marla Bunker, Vice President Nursing and Chief Operating Officer
CFO: Kevin Kalchik, Chief Financial Officer
CMO: Paula Rechner, M.D., Chief Medical Officer
CIO: Sandy DePlonty, Senior Director Clinical Services
CHR: Susan Sliger, Director Human Resources
CNO: Marla Bunker, Vice President Nursing and Chief Operating Officer
Web address: www.warmemorialhospital.org
Control: Other not–for–profit (including NFP Corporation) **Service**: General
medical and surgical

Staffed Beds: 120 **Admissions:** 3151 **Census:** 87 **Outpatient
Visits:** 214636 **Births:** 351 **Total Expense ($000):** 109804 **Payroll Expense
($000):** 47819 **Personnel:** 787

SHELBY—Oceana County

✠ **MERCY HEALTH, LAKESHORE CAMPUS (231320)**, 72 South State Street,
Zip 49455–1299; tel. 231/861–2156, **A**1 10 18 **F**3 11 15 29 30 34 35 40 43
45 47 50 57 59 68 81 83 84 85 87 89 97 107 110 111 114 119 127 129 131
132 146 **S** Trinity Health, Livonia, MI
Primary Contact: John T. Foss, Vice President, Operations
CFO: Mark Gross, Senior Business Director Finance
Web address: www.mercyhealthmuskegon.com
Control: Other not–for–profit (including NFP Corporation) **Service**: General
medical and surgical

Staffed Beds: 24 **Admissions:** 269 **Census:** 2 **Outpatient Visits:** 89604
Births: 0 **Total Expense ($000):** 30520 **Payroll Expense ($000):** 14079
Personnel: 197

SHERIDAN—Montcalm County

○ **SHERIDAN COMMUNITY HOSPITAL (231312)**, 301 North Main Street,
Zip 48884–9235, Mailing Address: P.O. Box 279, Zip 48884–0279; tel. 989/291–
3261, (Nonreporting) **A**10 11 18
Primary Contact: Randolph K. Flechsig, Administrator
COO: Steve Scott, Chief Operating Officer
CFO: Randolph K. Flechsig, Administrator
CMO: Maria Charlotte Alvarez, M.D., Chief of Staff
CIO: David Bussler, Chief Information Officer
CHR: Sharon Bowers, R.N., Manager of Community, Public and Employee Relations
CNO: Kim Christensen, Interim Chief Nursing Executive
Web address: www.sheridanhospital.com
Control: Other not–for–profit (including NFP Corporation) **Service**: General
medical and surgical

Staffed Beds: 22

SOUTH HAVEN—Van Buren County

✠ **BRONSON SOUTH HAVEN HOSPITAL (230085)**, 955 South Bailey Avenue,
Zip 49090–6743; tel. 269/637–5271, **A**1 10 **F**3 11 15 18 28 29 30 31 34 35
36 39 40 45 50 53 54 57 59 62 65 68 70 75 77 78 79 81 82 84 85 86 87 93
97 107 110 111 114 115 117 118 119 127 129 130 131 132 135 144 146
147 148 149 154 156 **S** Bronson Healthcare Group, Kalamazoo, MI
Primary Contact: Kirk Richardson, R.N., Vice President, Chief Operating Officer and
Chief Nursing Officer
CFO: Mark Gross, Executive Vice President and Chief Financial Officer
CMO: Allan Caudill, M.D., Chief of Staff
CIO: Dennis Sorenson, Supervisor Information Technology
CHR: Kim Wise, Director Human Resources
CNO: Donna Cassidy, Chief Nursing Executive
Web address: www.sh-hs.org
Control: Other not–for–profit (including NFP Corporation) **Service**: General
medical and surgical

Staffed Beds: 49 **Admissions:** 535 **Census:** 3 **Outpatient Visits:** 98256
Births: 0 **Total Expense ($000):** 41823 **Payroll Expense ($000):** 21600
Personnel: 238

SOUTH HAVEN COMMUNITY HOSPITAL See Bronson South Haven Hospital

SOUTHFIELD—Oakland County

✠ **ASCENSION OF PROVIDENCE HOSPITAL, SOUTHFIELD CAMPUS (230019)**,
16001 West Nine Mile Road, Zip 48075; tel. 248/849–3400, (Includes
PROVIDENCE - PROVIDENCE PARK HOSPITAL, NOVI CAMPUS, 47601 Grand River
Avebue, Novi, Michigan, Zip 48374–1233; tel. 248/465–4100; Joseph R. Hurshe,
President) **A**1 2 3 5 10 19 **F**3 9 11 12 13 15 17 18 20 22 24 26 28 29 30 31
34 35 36 37 38 39 40 43 44 45 46 47 48 49 50 51 54 55 56 57 58 59 60 61
63 64 65 66 68 70 72 74 75 76 77 78 79 80 81 82 84 85 86 87 90 91 92
93 96 97 98 100 101 102 107 108 110 111 114 115 118 119 120 121 123
124 126 129 130 131 132 135 141 146 147 148 149 150 154 156 157 **S**
Ascension Healthcare, Saint Louis, MO
Primary Contact: Joseph R. Hurshe, President
CFO: Douglas Winner, Chief Financial Officer, Acute Care Operations
CHR: Ann Vano, Vice President Human Resources
Web address: www.https://ascension.org/michigan
Control: Church operated, Nongovernment, not–for–profit **Service**: General
medical and surgical

Staffed Beds: 628 **Admissions:** 33230 **Census:** 401 **Outpatient
Visits:** 326010 **Births:** 3440 **Total Expense ($000):** 728796 **Payroll
Expense ($000):** 239975 **Personnel:** 2715

Many Facility Codes have changed. Please refer to the AHA Guide Code Chart. © 2019 AHA Guide

MI

☒ **STRAITH HOSPITAL FOR SPECIAL SURGERY (230071)**, 23901 Lahser Road, Zip 48033–6035; tel. 248/357–3360, (Nonreporting) **A**1 10
Primary Contact: Jan Rys, R.N., Chief Executive Officer
CFO: Bradley Bescoe, Chief Financial Officer
CNO: Michelle Holder, Nurse Executive
Web address: www.straith.org/
Control: Other not–for–profit (including NFP Corporation) **Service:** Surgical

Staffed Beds: 24

○ **SURGEONS CHOICE MEDICAL CENTER (230301)**, 22401 Foster Winter Drive, Zip 48075–3724; tel. 248/423–5100, (Nonreporting) **A**10 11
Primary Contact: Steven Craig, Ph.D., Chief Operating Officer and Acting Chief Executive Officer
COO: Steven Craig, Ph.D., Chief Operating Officer and Acting Chief Executive Officer
CMO: John Jack Ryan, M.D., Chief Medical Officer
CIO: William Moncrief, ORH IT Client Executive
CHR: Gordon Meyer, Director Human Resources
CNO: Lola Evans, Director of Nursing
Web address: www.oaklandregionalhospital.com
Control: Corporation, Investor–owned (for–profit) **Service:** Surgical

Staffed Beds: 71

STANDISH—Arenac County

☒ **ASCENSION STANDISH HOSPITAL (231305)**, 805 West Cedar Street, Zip 48658–9526; tel. 989/846–4521, (Nonreporting) **A**1 10 18 **S** Ascension Healthcare, Saint Louis, MO
Primary Contact: Chris Palazzolo, President and Chief Executive Officer
CFO: Tony Doud, Controller
CMO: Jaya Sankaran, M.D., Chief of Staff
CIO: Tammy Copes, Director Information Systems
CHR: Renee Reetz, Director Human Resources
Web address: www.stmarysofmichigan.org/standish
Control: Church operated **Service:** General medical and surgical

Staffed Beds: 64

STURGIS—St. Joseph County

★ ⇑ **STURGIS HOSPITAL (230006)**, 916 Myrtle Street, Zip 49091–2326; tel. 269/651–7824, **A**10 21 **F**3 11 13 15 28 29 30 31 34 35 40 45 49 50 57 59 62 63 64 65 68 70 75 76 77 79 81 82 85 87 89 93 97 102 107 108 110 115 118 119 127 129 130 132 144 145 146 147 148 149 154 156
Primary Contact: Robert J. LaBarge, President and Chief Executive Officer
CFO: Robert J. Morin, Vice President Finance and Chief Financial Officer
CMO: James Grannell, Chief Medical Officer
CIO: Rita Denison, Director of Information Systems
CHR: Mary Kay Schultz, Director Human Resources
CNO: Charlotte J Paullants, R.N., Vice President of Clinical Services and Chief Nursing Officer
Web address: www.sturgishospital.com
Control: Other not–for–profit (including NFP Corporation) **Service:** General medical and surgical

Staffed Beds: 49 **Admissions:** 1341 **Census:** 10 **Outpatient Visits:** 147381 **Births:** 306 **Total Expense ($000):** 46455 **Payroll Expense ($000):** 21053 **Personnel:** 304

TAWAS CITY—Iosco County

☒ **ASCENSION ST. JOSEPH HOSPITAL (230100)**, 200 Hemlock Street, Zip 48763–9237, Mailing Address: P.O. Box 659, Zip 48764–0659; tel. 989/362–3411, (Nonreporting) **A**1 10 20 **S** Ascension Healthcare, Saint Louis, MO
Primary Contact: Jan Jacob, R.N., Interim Administrator
CFO: Tony Doud, Controller
CIO: Daniel Stross, Chief Information Officer
CHR: Nancy Bodenner, Director Human Resources
Web address: www.sjhsys.org
Control: Church operated **Service:** General medical and surgical

Staffed Beds: 20

TAYLOR—Wayne County

☒ **BEAUMONT HOSPITAL - TAYLOR (230270)**, 10000 Telegraph Road, Zip 48180–3330; tel. 313/295–5000, **A**1 3 5 10 **F**3 11 15 29 30 34 35 37 38 39 40 44 46 49 50 56 57 59 61 64 65 68 70 74 75 79 81 82 85 86 87 90 92 93 96 98 100 101 102 104 105 107 108 111 114 117 118 119 126 130 131 132 135 146 148 149 **S** Beaumont Health, Southfield, MI
Primary Contact: Lee Ann Odom, Division President
COO: Carolyn Wilson, R.N., Chief Operating Officer
CFO: Mark Deming, Administrator, Finance and Support
CMO: Kassem Charara, Chief Medical Officer
CIO: Subra Sripada, Exec. Vice President, Chief Transformation Officer and Chief Information Officer
CHR: Karen Krolicki, Director, Human Resources
CNO: Kristine Marie Donahue, Administrator, Clinical Operations
Web address: www.beaumont.org
Control: Other not–for–profit (including NFP Corporation) **Service:** General medical and surgical

Staffed Beds: 189 **Admissions:** 8088 **Census:** 129 **Outpatient Visits:** 81756 **Births:** 0 **Total Expense ($000):** 147229 **Payroll Expense ($000):** 65198 **Personnel:** 1052

TECUMSEH—Lenawee County

★ ○ **PROMEDICA HERRICK HOSPITAL (231334)**, 500 East Pottawatamie Street, Zip 49286–2018; tel. 517/424–3000, **A**10 11 18 **F**8 11 15 18 26 29 34 35 36 39 40 53 57 59 65 68 74 75 77 81 82 87 90 92 93 96 97 104 107 108 110 114 119 129 130 132 135 146 147 148 149 150 154 156 157 **S** ProMedica Health System, Toledo, OH
Primary Contact: Julie Yaroch, D.O., President
CFO: Bernie Nawrocki, Administrative Director Finance
CIO: Stephanie Sonnenberg, Director Information Technology
CHR: Kim Langley, Business Partner
CNO: Kathryn M Greenlee, R.N., Vice President, Clinical Services/CNO
Web address: www.promedica.org
Control: Other not–for–profit (including NFP Corporation) **Service:** General medical and surgical

Staffed Beds: 25 **Admissions:** 87 **Census:** 1 **Outpatient Visits:** 38724 **Births:** 0 **Total Expense ($000):** 24049 **Payroll Expense ($000):** 6448 **Personnel:** 80

THREE RIVERS—St. Joseph County

★ ○ **THREE RIVERS HEALTH (230015)**, 701 South Health Parkway, Zip 49093–8352; tel. 269/278–1145, **A**10 11 **F**3 13 15 50 62 63 65 70 71 75 76 77 81 90 107 111 119 129 130 131 133 147 148 154 156 **S** QHR, Brentwood, TN
Primary Contact: David A. Shannon, Interim Chief Executive Officer
COO: Laurie Herbert, Vice President Operations
CFO: Steve Andrews, Chief Financial Officer
CIO: Dave Parks, Chief Information Officer
Web address: www.threerivershealth.org
Control: Other not–for–profit (including NFP Corporation) **Service:** General medical and surgical

Staffed Beds: 60 **Admissions:** 1107 **Census:** 11 **Outpatient Visits:** 221756 **Births:** 217 **Total Expense ($000):** 60139 **Payroll Expense ($000):** 21657 **Personnel:** 435

TRAVERSE CITY—Grand Traverse County

☒ **MUNSON MEDICAL CENTER (230097)**, 1105 Sixth Street, Zip 49684–2386; tel. 231/935–5000, **A**1 2 3 5 10 13 **F**2 4 10 15 17 28 34 35 39 40 43 44 45 47 48 49 50 53 54 55 56 57 58 59 60 61 62 63 65 68 70 71 72 74 75 76 77 78 79 81 82 84 85 86 87 89 90 92 93 94 96 97 98 100 101 102 103 104 105 107 108 110 111 115 116 117 118 119 120 121 123 124 126 129 130 131 132 134 135 141 142 143 144 145 146 147 148 149 154 156 157 **S** Munson Healthcare, Traverse City, MI
Primary Contact: Derk F. Pronger, Interim President and Chief Executive Officer
COO: Derk F. Pronger, Chief Operating Officer
CFO: Mark A Helper, Corporate Vice President and Chief Financial Officer
CMO: Christine Nefcy, Chief Medical Officer, Munson Healthcare
CIO: Christopher J Podges, Vice President Outpatient Services and Chief Information Officer
CHR: Suzanne K Peters, Vice President Human Resources
CNO: Loraine Frank-Lightfoot, Vice President, Patient Care Services and Chief Nursing Officer
Web address: www.munsonhealthcare.org
Control: Other not–for–profit (including NFP Corporation) **Service:** General medical and surgical

Staffed Beds: 442 **Admissions:** 21792 **Census:** 272 **Outpatient Visits:** 557693 **Births:** 1844 **Total Expense ($000):** 598747 **Payroll Expense ($000):** 221187 **Personnel:** 3203

Hospital, Medicare Provider Number, Address, Telephone, Approval, Facility, and Physician Codes, Health Care System

★ American Hospital Association (AHA) membership   ○ Healthcare Facilities Accreditation Program   ⇑ Center for Improvement in Healthcare Quality Accreditation
☐ The Joint Commission accreditation   ◇ DNV Healthcare Inc. accreditation   △ Commission on Accreditation of Rehabilitation Facilities (CARF) accreditation

TRENTON—Wayne County

BEAUMONT HOSPITAL - TRENTON (230176), 5450 Fort Street, Zip 48183–4625; tel. 734/671–3800, **A**1 3 5 10 12 13 **F**3 8 11 12 13 15 18 20 22 26 28 29 30 34 35 38 39 40 43 44 45 46 47 49 50 51 56 57 59 60 61 62 63 64 65 68 70 74 75 76 78 79 80 81 82 84 85 87 91 92 93 100 102 107 108 110 111 114 115 117 118 119 126 130 131 132 135 146 147 148 149 150 154 157 **S** Beaumont Health, Southfield, MI
Primary Contact: Christine Stesney-Ridenour, FACHE, President
COO: Carolyn Wilson, R.N., Chief Operating Officer
CFO: Paul Lauzau, Controller
CMO: Jonathan Kaper, Chief Medical Officer
CIO: Subra Sripada, Executive Vice President, Chief Transformation Officer and Chief Information Officer
CHR: Michelle Cora, Director Human Resources
CNO: Susan G Schulz, Director Patient Care Services
Web address: www.beaumont.org
Control: Other not–for–profit (including NFP Corporation) **Service**: General medical and surgical

Staffed Beds: 193 **Admissions**: 10155 **Census**: 110 **Outpatient Visits**: 102732 **Births**: 653 **Total Expense ($000)**: 173658 **Payroll Expense ($000)**: 71599 **Personnel**: 923

TROY—Oakland County

BEAUMONT HOSPITAL - TROY (230269), 44201 Dequindre Road, Zip 48085–1117; tel. 248/964–5000, **A**1 2 3 5 10 13 19 **F**3 8 11 12 13 15 17 18 19 20 22 24 26 28 29 30 31 32 34 35 36 37 38 39 40 41 43 44 45 46 47 48 49 50 53 54 55 57 58 59 60 61 64 65 66 68 70 71 72 74 75 76 77 78 79 80 81 82 84 85 86 87 89 90 91 92 93 96 97 100 102 107 108 109 110 111 114 115 117 118 119 120 121 123 124 126 129 130 131 132 135 141 142 143 145 146 147 148 149 150 157 **S** Beaumont Health, Southfield, MI
Primary Contact: James Lynch, M.D., Interim President
COO: Carolyn Wilson, R.N., Chief Operating Officer
CFO: Mark Leonard, Vice President Finance
CMO: James Lynch, M.D., Senior Vice President and Chief Medical Officer
CIO: Subra Sripada, Executive Vice President, Chief Transportation Officer and Chief Information Officer
CHR: Lisa Ouelette, Director Human Resources
CNO: Debra Guido-Allen, Vice President and Chief Nursing Officer
Web address: www.beaumont.org
Control: Other not–for–profit (including NFP Corporation) **Service**: General medical and surgical

Staffed Beds: 520 **Admissions**: 36933 **Census**: 417 **Outpatient Visits**: 919424 **Births**: 3543 **Total Expense ($000)**: 641296 **Payroll Expense ($000)**: 250845 **Personnel**: 4165

VICKSBURG—Kalamazoo County

BRONSON VICKSBURG HOSPITAL See Bronson Methodist Hospital, Kalamazoo

WARREN—Macomb County

ASCENSION MACOMB-OAKLAND HOSPITAL (230195), 11800 East 12 Mile Road, Zip 48093–3472; tel. 586/573–5000, (Includes ST. JOHN MACOMB-OAKLAND HOSPITAL, MADISON HEIGHTS CAMPUS, 27351 Dequindre, Madison Heights, Michigan, Zip 48071–3487; tel. 248/967–7000; Terry Hamilton, President; ST. JOHN MACOMB-OAKLAND HOSPITAL, WARREN CAMPUS, 11800 East Twelve Mile Road, Warren, Michigan, Zip 48093–3472; tel. 586/573–5000; Terry Hamilton, President) **A**1 2 3 5 10 12 **F**3 11 12 13 15 17 18 20 22 24 26 28 29 30 31 34 35 36 38 39 40 43 44 45 46 47 48 49 50 51 54 56 57 58 59 60 61 63 64 65 68 70 74 75 76 77 78 79 80 81 82 84 85 86 87 90 92 93 96 97 98 100 101 102 105 107 108 110 111 115 118 119 121 123 126 129 130 131 132 135 141 146 147 148 149 150 156 157 **S** Ascension Healthcare, Saint Louis, MO
Primary Contact: Terry Hamilton, President
COO: William Mott, Chief Operating Officer
CFO: Patrick McGuire, Chief Financial Officer, Michigan Market
CMO: Gary L Berg, D.O., Chief Medical Officer
CIO: Ralph Tenney, Chief Information Officer
CHR: Joanne E Tuscany, Senior Director Human Resources
Web address: www.stjohnprovidence.org/macomb-oakland/
Control: Church operated, Nongovernment, not–for–profit **Service**: General medical and surgical

Staffed Beds: 535 **Admissions**: 24718 **Census**: 339 **Outpatient Visits**: 407731 **Births**: 732 **Total Expense ($000)**: 401919 **Payroll Expense ($000)**: 157620 **Personnel**: 2040

BEHAVIORAL CENTER OF MICHIGAN (234042), 4050 East 12 Mile Road, Zip 48092–2534; tel. 586/261–2266, (Nonreporting) **A**1 10
Primary Contact: Ryan Gunabalan, Chief Executive Officer
COO: Efren Lusterio, Director of Nursing
CFO: Mark Corey, Chief Financial Officer
CMO: Eleanor Medina, M.D., Chief Medical Officer
CIO: Kashmira Khade, Coordinator Non-Clinical Services
CHR: Erin R Youngblood, Chief Human Resources Officer
Web address: www.behavioralcenter.com
Control: Corporation, Investor–owned (for–profit) **Service**: Psychiatric

Staffed Beds: 42

SOUTHEAST MICHIGAN SURGICAL HOSPITAL (230264), 21230 Dequindre, Zip 48091–2287; tel. 586/427–1000, (Nonreporting) **A**1 10 **S** National Surgical Healthcare, Chicago, IL
Primary Contact: Barry Cullen, Chief Executive Officer
CMO: Benjamin Paolucci, D.O., Chief of Staff
CHR: Dawn Meiers, Coordinator Medical Staff and Personnel Services
Web address: www.nshinc.com
Control: Corporation, Investor–owned (for–profit) **Service**: Surgical

Staffed Beds: 13

WATERVLIET—Berrien County

COMMUNITY HOSPITAL See Lakeland Hospital, Watervliet

△ **LAKELAND HOSPITAL, WATERVLIET (230078)**, 400 Medical Park Drive, Zip 49098–9225; tel. 269/463–3111, **A**1 7 10 **F**3 11 15 29 30 34 35 38 40 45 50 54 57 59 64 68 75 77 81 86 87 90 93 94 96 97 107 119 127 130 131 132 135 144 146 148 149 154 **S** Spectrum Health, Grand Rapids, MI
Primary Contact: Ray Cruse, Chief Executive Officer
CFO: Timothy Calhoun, Vice President Finance, Chief Financial Officer
CIO: Norma Tirado, Vice President, Human Resources and Health Information Technology
CHR: Norma Tirado, Vice President, Human Resources and Health Information Technology
CNO: Connie Harmon, Director of Nursing
Control: Other not–for–profit (including NFP Corporation) **Service**: General medical and surgical

Staffed Beds: 44 **Admissions**: 524 **Census**: 14 **Outpatient Visits**: 152820 **Births**: 0 **Total Expense ($000)**: 40331 **Payroll Expense ($000)**: 18866 **Personnel**: 255

WAYNE—Wayne County

BEAUMONT HOSPITAL, WAYNE (230142), 33155 Annapolis Street, Zip 48184–2405; tel. 734/467–4000, **A**1 3 5 10 **F**3 11 12 13 15 18 20 22 26 28 29 30 31 34 35 38 40 42 43 44 45 46 47 49 50 57 59 60 61 64 65 68 70 74 75 76 77 78 79 81 82 84 85 86 87 91 92 93 96 100 102 107 108 110 111 115 117 118 119 126 130 131 132 134 135 143 146 147 148 149 154 **S** Beaumont Health, Southfield, MI
Primary Contact: Eric W. Widner, FACHE, Division President
COO: Carolyn Wilson, R.N., Chief Operating Officer
CFO: Jacqueline Nash, Controller
CMO: Ashok Jain, M.D., Senior Vice President and Chief Medical Officer
CIO: Subra Sripada, Executive Vice President, Chief Transformation Officer and Chief Information Officer
CHR: Robert L James, Director Human Resources
CNO: Diane L Hartley, Director of Patient Care Services
Web address: www.beaumont.org
Control: Other not–for–profit (including NFP Corporation) **Service**: General medical and surgical

Staffed Beds: 185 **Admissions**: 7852 **Census**: 84 **Outpatient Visits**: 50687 **Births**: 986 **Total Expense ($000)**: 155746 **Payroll Expense ($000)**: 65701 **Personnel**: 993

WEST BLOOMFIELD—Oakland County

HENRY FORD WEST BLOOMFIELD HOSPITAL (230302), 6777 West Maple Road, Zip 48322–3013; tel. 248/661–4100, **A**1 2 3 10 **F**3 6 11 12 13 15 18 20 22 26 28 29 30 31 32 33 34 35 36 37 38 40 41 43 44 45 46 47 49 50 51 53 54 55 56 57 58 59 60 61 62 63 64 65 66 70 73 74 75 76 77 78 79 80 81 82 84 85 86 87 89 92 93 96 97 100 101 102 107 108 109 110 111 114 115 117 118 119 120 121 123 124 126 130 131 132 134 135 141 143 146 147 148 149 150 153 154 156 **S** Henry Ford Health System, Detroit, MI
Primary Contact: Lynn M. Torossian, President and Chief Executive Officer
COO: Karen Harris, R.N., Chief Nursing and Operations Officer
CFO: Terry Goodbalian, Regional Chief Financial Officer
CMO: Betty Chu, M.D., Chief Medical Officer and Vice President of Medical Affairs
CIO: Mary Alice Annecharico, System Vice President and Chief Information Officer
CNO: Karen Harris, R.N., Chief Nursing and Operations Officer
Web address: www.henryford.com
Control: Other not–for–profit (including NFP Corporation) **Service**: General medical and surgical

Staffed Beds: 212 **Admissions**: 12664 **Census**: 130 **Outpatient Visits**: 230599 **Births**: 2100 **Total Expense ($000)**: 289283 **Payroll Expense ($000)**: 111480 **Personnel**: 1975

Many Facility Codes have changed. Please refer to the AHA Guide Code Chart. © 2019 AHA Guide

MI

WEST BRANCH—Ogemaw County

★ ○ **MIDMICHIGAN MEDICAL CENTER - WEST BRANCH (230095)**, 2463 South M-30, Zip 48661-1199; tel. 989/345-3660, **A**10 11 20 **F**3 11 15 17 20 28 29 30 34 35 40 50 59 63 64 75 77 79 81 93 97 107 111 115 117 119 130 135 146 148 156 **S** MidMichigan Health, Midland, MI
Primary Contact: Robert McGrail, Chief Executive Officer
CFO: Kathy Kohr, Chief Financial Officer
CMO: Mark Weber, M.D., President Medical Staff
CHR: Kent Allen, Director Human Resources
CNO: Nicole Gillette, R.N., Chief Nursing Officer
Web address: www.wbrmc.com
Control: Other not-for-profit (including NFP Corporation) **Service:** General medical and surgical

Staffed Beds: 88 **Admissions:** 2136 **Census:** 20 **Outpatient Visits:** 63409 **Births:** 0 **Total Expense ($000):** 45203 **Payroll Expense ($000):** 14624 **Personnel:** 319

WESTLAND—Wayne County

☐ **WALTER P. REUTHER PSYCHIATRIC HOSPITAL (234035)**, 30901 Palmer Road, Zip 48186-5389; tel. 734/367-8400, (Nonreporting) **A**1 10
Primary Contact: Richard T. Young, FACHE, Director
CMO: H. Bandla, M.D., Chief Clinical Affairs
CHR: Deborah Moore, Director Human Resources
Web address: www.mhweb.org/wayne/reuther.htm
Control: State, Government, nonfederal **Service:** Psychiatric

Staffed Beds: 239

WYANDOTTE—Wayne County

⊞ △ **HENRY FORD WYANDOTTE HOSPITAL (230146)**, 2333 Biddle Avenue, Zip 48192-4668; tel. 734/246-6000, **A**1 3 5 7 10 **F**3 8 11 12 13 15 18 19 20 22 26 28 29 30 31 32 34 35 36 38 40 41 42 43 44 45 46 47 49 50 51 54 56 57 58 59 60 61 62 63 64 65 66 68 70 73 74 75 76 77 78 79 80 81 82 84 85 86 87 90 92 93 96 97 98 100 101 102 103 107 108 110 111 114 115 116 117 118 119 126 129 130 131 132 135 144 146 147 148 149 150 154 **S** Henry Ford Health System, Detroit, MI
Primary Contact: Peter Karadjoff, Interim President
CFO: Terry Goodbalian, Vice President, Finance and Chief Financial Officer
CMO: Dennis R Lemanski, D.O., Senior Vice President Medical Affairs and Medical Education/CMO
CIO: Mary Alice Annecharico, System Vice President and Chief Information Officer
CNO: Josephine Sclafani Wahl, R.N., MS, FACHE, VP, Patient Care Services & CNO
Web address: www.henryfordhealth.org
Control: Other not-for-profit (including NFP Corporation) **Service:** General medical and surgical

Staffed Beds: 334 **Admissions:** 15656 **Census:** 200 **Outpatient Visits:** 401200 **Births:** 1520 **Total Expense ($000):** 310857 **Payroll Expense ($000):** 129249 **Personnel:** 2023

⊞ **SELECT SPECIALTY HOSPITAL-DOWNRIVER (232031)**, 2333 Biddle Avenue, 8th Floor, Zip 48192-4668; tel. 734/246-5500, (Includes SELECT SPECIALTY HOSPITAL-NORTHWEST DETROIT, 6071 West Outer Drive, Detroit, Michigan, Zip 48235-2624; tel. 313/966-4747; Marilouise Riska, Chief Executive Officer), (Non-reporting) **A**1 10 **S** Select Medical Corporation, Mechanicsburg, PA
Primary Contact: John Ponczocha, Chief Executive Officer
CMO: Roderick Boyer, M.D., Medical Director
CHR: Barb Wierzbicki, Manager Human Resources
CNO: Angela Kudla, MSN, R.N., Chief Nursing Officer
Web address: www.downriver.selectspecialtyhospitals.com/
Control: Corporation, Investor-owned (for-profit) **Service:** Acute long-term care hospital

Staffed Beds: 71

WYOMING—Kent County

★ ○ **METRO HEALTH - UNIVERSITY OF MICHIGAN HEALTH (230236)**, 5900 Byron Center Avenue SW, Zip 49519-9606, Mailing Address: P.O. Box 916, Zip 49509-0916; tel. 616/252-7200, **A**3 5 10 11 13 **F**3 12 13 15 18 19 20 22 26 28 29 30 31 34 35 40 43 44 45 48 49 50 54 57 58 59 64 65 66 70 74 75 76 77 78 79 80 81 85 86 87 92 97 107 108 110 111 115 119 126 129 130 131 132 135 144 146 147 148 149 150 154 156
Primary Contact: Peter Hahn, M.D., President and Chief Executive Officer
COO: David R Olejniczak, Chief Operating Officer
CFO: Kris Kurtz, Chief Financial Officer
CIO: Joshua Wilda, Chief Information Officer
CNO: Steve Polega, Chief Nursing Officer
Web address: www.metrohealth.net
Control: Other not-for-profit (including NFP Corporation) **Service:** General medical and surgical

Staffed Beds: 208 **Admissions:** 10123 **Census:** 107 **Outpatient Visits:** 610669 **Births:** 1634 **Total Expense ($000):** 456394 **Payroll Expense ($000):** 178666 **Personnel:** 2520

YPSILANTI—Washtenaw County

☐ **FOREST HEALTH MEDICAL CENTER (230144)**, 135 South Prospect Street, Zip 48198-7914; tel. 734/547-4700, **A**1 10 **F**12 30 64 74 75 79 81 82 85 111 119 130 132 149
Primary Contact: Trevor J. Dyksterhouse, President
COO: Andrea Walrath, Chief Operating Officer
CFO: David Althoen, Director Financial Planning and Analysis
CMO: Jason Adams, M.D., Medical Staff President
CIO: Andrea Walrath, Chief Operating Officer
CHR: Amy Mohr, Coordinator Human Resources
Web address: www.fhmc-mi.com
Control: Corporation, Investor-owned (for-profit) **Service:** General medical and surgical

Staffed Beds: 24 **Admissions:** 1229 **Census:** 5 **Outpatient Visits:** 17119 **Births:** 0 **Personnel:** 50

⊞ **SELECT SPECIALTY HOSPITAL-ANN ARBOR (232024)**, 5301 East Huron River Drive, 7th Floor, Zip 48197-1051; tel. 734/712-6751, (Nonreporting) **A**1 10 **S** Select Medical Corporation, Mechanicsburg, PA
Primary Contact: Bryan Cutliff, Chief Executive Officer
CMO: Hamid Halimi, M.D., Medical Director
CHR: Cindy Hardick, Human Resources Coordinator
CNO: Tim Varney, R.N., Chief Nursing Officer
Web address: www.annarbor.selectspecialtyhospitals.com/
Control: Corporation, Investor-owned (for-profit) **Service:** Acute long-term care hospital

Staffed Beds: 36

★ **ST. JOSEPH MERCY ANN ARBOR (230156)**, 5301 Mcauley Drive, Zip 48197-1051, Mailing Address: P.O. Box 995, Ann Arbor, Zip 48106-0995; tel. 734/712-3456, **A**2 5 10 **F**3 4 5 8 11 12 13 15 17 18 20 22 24 26 28 29 30 31 32 34 35 36 37 38 40 41 43 44 45 46 47 48 49 50 51 53 54 55 56 57 58 59 61 64 65 66 68 70 71 72 73 74 75 76 77 78 79 80 81 82 83 84 85 86 87 89 90 91 92 93 94 95 96 97 98 100 101 102 103 104 105 107 108 109 110 111 114 115 118 119 120 121 123 124 126 129 130 131 132 134 135 141 143 144 146 147 148 149 153 154 156 157 **S** Trinity Health, Livonia, MI
Primary Contact: Bill Manns, President
CFO: Kathy O'Connor, Vice President Finance
CMO: Rosalie Tocco-Bradley, Ph.D., M.D., Chief Medical Officer
CIO: Frank Rademacher, Senior Director Information Systems
CNO: Joyce Young, Ph.D., R.N., Vice President, Patient Services and Chief Nursing Officer
Web address: www.sjmercyhealth.org
Control: Church operated, Nongovernment, not-for-profit **Service:** General medical and surgical

Staffed Beds: 483 **Admissions:** 31215 **Census:** 377 **Outpatient Visits:** 1096359 **Births:** 3936 **Total Expense ($000):** 775070 **Payroll Expense ($000):** 282281 **Personnel:** 4844

✠ **SPECTRUM HEALTH ZEELAND COMMUNITY HOSPITAL (230003)**, 8333 Felch Street, Zip 49464–2608; tel. 616/772–4644, **A**1 10 **F**3 12 13 15 18 29 32 34 35 38 39 40 43 44 45 46 47 50 57 59 64 65 68 70 74 75 76 78 79 81 85 86 87 89 91 92 93 107 108 110 111 115 118 119 126 129 130 132 134 135 144 146 147 148 154 **S** Spectrum Health, Grand Rapids, MI
Primary Contact: Ron Lewis, President
CFO: Ryan J. Powers, Vice President Finance
CMO: Ruel R. Lirio, M.D., Clinical Physician Advisor
CIO: Imran Syed, Manager Technology Information Services
CHR: Jennifer F Becksvoort, Senior Human Resource Business Partner
CNO: Jane Czerew, Vice President Clinical Services and Quality
Web address: www.spectrumhealth.org/zeeland
Control: Other not–for–profit (including NFP Corporation) **Service**: General medical and surgical

Staffed Beds: 50 **Admissions:** 2576 **Census:** 20 **Outpatient Visits:** 101650 **Births:** 512 **Total Expense ($000):** 57649 **Payroll Expense ($000):** 20132 **Personnel:** 361

ZEELAND COMMUNITY HOSPITAL See Spectrum Health Zeeland Community Hospital

MI

Many Facility Codes have changed. Please refer to the AHA Guide Code Chart.   © 2019 AHA Guide

MINNESOTA

ADA—Norman County

BRIDGES MEDICAL CENTER See Essentia Health Ada

★ **ESSENTIA HEALTH ADA (241313)**, 201 9th Street West, Zip 56510–1279; tel. 218/784–5000, (Nonreporting) **A**10 18 **S** Essentia Health, Duluth, MN
Primary Contact: Erin Stoltman, Administrator
CMO: Jeff Peterson, M.D., Chief of Staff
CHR: Shayla Hennenberg, Director Human Resources
Web address: www.essentiahealth.org
Control: Other not–for–profit (including NFP Corporation) **Service**: General medical and surgical

Staffed Beds: 14

AITKIN—Aitkin County

✉ **RIVERWOOD HEALTHCARE CENTER (241305)**, 200 Bunker Hill Drive, Zip 56431–1865; tel. 218/927–2121, (Nonreporting) **A**1 2 10 18
Primary Contact: Todd Sandberg, Chief Executive Officer
COO: Cindi Baker, Chief Operating Officer
CFO: Casey R Johnson, Chief Financial Officer
CMO: Mark Heggem, M.D., Chief Medical Officer
CIO: Daryl Kallevig, Chief Information Officer
CHR: Cindi Hills, Director Human Resources
CNO: Kristine Layne, R.N., Chief Nursing Officer
Web address: www.riverwoodhealthcare.org
Control: Other not–for–profit (including NFP Corporation) **Service**: General medical and surgical

Staffed Beds: 25

ALBERT LEA—Freeborn County

☐ **MAYO CLINIC HEALTH SYSTEM - ALBERT LEA AND AUSTIN (240043)**, 404 West Fountain Street, Zip 56007–2473; tel. 507/373–2384, (Includes MAYO CLINIC HEALTH SYSTEM - ALBERT LEA AND AUSTIN, 1000 First Drive NW, Austin, Minnesota, Zip 55912–2904; tel. 507/433 7351; Mark Ciota, M.D., Chief Executive Officer) **A**1 3 5 10 20 **F**3 5 13 15 18 28 29 30 31 32 34 35 40 43 45 46 57 59 63 64 65 70 74 75 76 77 78 79 81 82 85 86 87 92 93 97 98 104 106 107 110 111 115 119 129 130 131 132 135 146 147 148 149 154 **S** Mayo Clinic, Rochester, MN
Primary Contact: Mark Ciota, M.D., Chief Executive Officer
CMO: John Grzybowski, M.D., Medical Director
CHR: Monica Fleegel, Director Human Resources
CNO: Lori Routh, R.N., Nurse Administrator
Web address: www.almedcenter.org
Control: Other not–for–profit (including NFP Corporation) **Service**: General medical and surgical

Staffed Beds: 85 Admissions: 4225 Census: 41 Outpatient Visits: 298251 Births: 671 Personnel: 1111

ALEXANDRIA—Douglas County

★ ○ **ALOMERE HEALTH (240030)**, 111 17th Avenue East, Zip 56308–3798; tel. 320/762–1511, **A**2 10 11 **F**3 8 11 13 15 28 29 30 31 32 34 35 36 40 43 50 57 61 64 65 68 70 76 77 78 79 81 82 85 86 87 89 91 93 97 107 108 111 115 117 118 119 126 129 130 131 132 135 144 146 149 154 157
Primary Contact: Carl P. Vaagenes, Chief Executive Officer
CFO: Nate Meyer, Director Finance
CMO: Deborah S. Dittberner, M.D., Chief Medical Officer
CHR: Shelly Gompf, Director Human Resources
Web address: www.dchospital.com
Control: County, Government, nonfederal **Service**: General medical and surgical

Staffed Beds: 99 Admissions: 3529 Census: 30 Outpatient Visits: 71330 Births: 606 Total Expense ($000): 157216 Payroll Expense ($000): 46818 Personnel: 746

ALEXANDRIA—Sherburne County

☐ **COMMUNITY BEHAVIORAL HEALTH HOSPITAL - ALEXANDRIA (244012)**, 1610 8th Avenue East, Zip 56308–2472; tel. 320/335–6201, (Nonreporting) **A**1 10 **S** Minnesota Department of Human Services, Saint Paul, MN
Primary Contact: Jennifer Westrum, Administrator
CFO: Shirley Jacobson, Chief Financial Officer
Web address: www.health.state.mn.us
Control: State, Government, nonfederal **Service**: Psychiatric

Staffed Beds: 16

ANNANDALE—Wright County

☐ **COMMUNITY BEHAVIORAL HEALTH HOSPITAL - ANNANDALE (244011)**, 400 Annandale Boulevard, Zip 55302–3141; tel. 651/259–3850, (Nonreporting) **A**1 10 **S** Minnesota Department of Human Services, Saint Paul, MN
Primary Contact: James P. Kelly, FACHE, Administrator
CMO: Shabeer A Ahmed, M.D., Clinical Director
CNO: Lennetta M Reynolds, Administrative Supervisor
Web address: www.health.state.mn.us
Control: State, Government, nonfederal **Service**: Psychiatric

Staffed Beds: 16

ANOKA—Anoka County

ANOKA-METROPOLITAN REGIONAL TREATMENT CENTER (244002), 3301 Seventh Avenue, Zip 55303–4516, Mailing Address: 3301 Seventh Avenue North, Zip 55303–4516; tel. 651/431–5000, (Nonreporting) **A**10 **S** Minnesota Department of Human Services, Saint Paul, MN
Primary Contact: Wade Brost, Executive Director
Web address: www.health.state.mn.us
Control: State, Government, nonfederal **Service**: Psychiatric

Staffed Beds: 200

APPLETON—Swift County

APPLETON AREA HEALTH SERVICES (241341), 30 South Behl Street, Zip 56208–1699; tel. 320/289–2422, (Nonreporting) **A**10 18
Primary Contact: Lori Andreas, Chief Executive Officer and Administrator
CFO: Anne Kells, Interim Chief Financial Officer
Web address: www.appletonareahealth.com
Control: City, Government, nonfederal **Service**: General medical and surgical

Staffed Beds: 15

ARLINGTON—Sibley County

★ ⇑ **RIDGEVIEW SIBLEY MEDICAL CENTER (241311)**, 601 West Chandler Street, Zip 55307–2127; tel. 507/964–2271, **A**10 18 21 **F**3 15 28 29 31 34 35 40 43 45 46 57 59 64 65 66 77 78 81 86 87 93 96 97 107 110 115 119 127 128 130 133 135 144 154 **S** Ridgeview Medical Center, Waconia, MN
Primary Contact: Michael Phelps, President and Chief Executive Officer
CFO: Darla Anderson, Chief Financial Officer
CMO: Ehtaisham Mohammed, M.D., Chief Medical Officer
CIO: Chris Bulau, Manager Information Technology
CHR: Sara Christiansen, Interim Director Human Resources
CNO: Sandy Domeier, Director Patient Care Services
Web address: www.sibleymedical.org
Control: Other not–for–profit (including NFP Corporation) **Service**: General medical and surgical

Staffed Beds: 6 Admissions: 194 Census: 2 Outpatient Visits: 34229 Births: 0 Total Expense ($000): 14573 Payroll Expense ($000): 6773 Personnel: 124

Hospital, Medicare Provider Number, Address, Telephone, Approval, Facility, and Physician Codes, Health Care System

★ American Hospital Association (AHA) membership
☐ The Joint Commission accreditation
○ Healthcare Facilities Accreditation Program
◇ DNV Healthcare Inc. accreditation
⇑ Center for Improvement in Healthcare Quality Accreditation
△ Commission on Accreditation of Rehabilitation Facilities (CARF) accreditation

AURORA—St. Louis County

★ **ESSENTIA HEALTH NORTHERN PINES MEDICAL CENTER (241340)**, 5211 Highway 110, Zip 55705–1599; tel. 218/229–2211, (Total facility includes 50 beds in nursing home–type unit) **A**10 18 **F**3 28 29 34 40 43 50 56 57 59 64 65 75 81 82 85 87 93 96 97 100 102 107 127 128 130 133 135 148 149 154 157 **S** Essentia Health, Duluth, MN
Primary Contact: Laura Ackman, Chief Operating Officer and Administrator
CFO: Kevin Boren, Chief Financial Officer
CMO: Michelle Oman, D.O., Chief Medical Officer
CHR: Kim Carlson, Director Human Resources
CNO: Cindy Loe, R.N., Director of Nursing
Web address: www.essentiahealth.org/NorthernPines/FindaClinic/Essentia-HealthNorthern-Pines-36.aspx
Control: Other not–for–profit (including NFP Corporation) **Service**: General medical and surgical

Staffed Beds: 58 **Admissions**: 192 **Census**: 31 **Outpatient Visits**: 28145 **Births**: 0 **Total Expense ($000)**: 15939 **Payroll Expense ($000)**: 7675 **Personnel**: 86

WHITE COMMUNITY HOSPITAL See Essentia Health Northern Pines Medical Center

BAGLEY—Clearwater County

★ **SANFORD BAGLEY MEDICAL CENTER (241328)**, 203 Fourth Street NW, Zip 56621–8307; tel. 218/694–6501, **A**10 18 **F**7 8 29 33 34 35 40 50 53 54 57 59 65 68 75 77 81 86 93 96 97 107 115 127 132 133 134 135 146 147 149 157 **S** Sanford Health, Sioux Falls, SD
Primary Contact: Robert Belanger, Administrator Director
CMO: Andre Spence, Chief Medical Staff
CNO: Stephanie McKnight, Hospital Nursing Manager
Web address: www.sanfordhealth.org
Control: Other not–for–profit (including NFP Corporation) **Service**: General medical and surgical

Staffed Beds: 8 **Admissions**: 116 **Census**: 2 **Outpatient Visits**: 6938 **Births**: 0 **Total Expense ($000)**: 11620 **Payroll Expense ($000)**: 5080 **Personnel**: 85

BAUDETTE—Lake of The Woods County

★ **CHI LAKEWOOD HEALTH (241301)**, 600 Main Avenue South, Zip 56623–2855; tel. 218/634–2120, (Nonreporting) **A**10 18 **S** CommonSpirit Health, Chicago, IL
Primary Contact: Benjamin Koppelman, Interim President
CFO: Jay Ross, Vice President of Finance
CMO: Justin Quo, Chief of Staff
CIO: Dan Leadbetter, Information Technology Systems Site Lead
CNO: Danielle Abel, Vice President of Patient Care Services
Web address: www.lakewoodhealthcenter.org
Control: Church operated **Service**: General medical and surgical

Staffed Beds: 55

BAXTER—Crow Wing County

☐ **COMMUNITY BEHAVIORAL HEALTH HOSPITAL - BAXTER (244015)**, 14241 Grand Oaks Drive, Zip 56425–8749; tel. 218/316–3101, (Nonreporting) **A**1 10 **S** Minnesota Department of Human Services, Saint Paul, MN
Primary Contact: James Coughenour, Administrator
Web address: www.business.explorebrainerdlakes.com/list/member/community-behavioral-health-hospital-baxter-8647
Control: State, Government, nonfederal **Service**: Psychiatric

Staffed Beds: 16

BEMIDJI—Beltrami County

☐ **COMMUNITY BEHAVIORAL HEALTH HOSPITAL - BEMIDJI (244014)**, 800 Bemidji Avenue North, Zip 56601–3054; tel. 218/308–2400, (Nonreporting) **A**1 10 **S** Minnesota Department of Human Services, Saint Paul, MN
Primary Contact: Larry A. Laudon, Administrator
Control: State, Government, nonfederal **Service**: Psychiatric

Staffed Beds: 16

NORTH COUNTRY REGIONAL HOSPITAL See Sanford Bemidji Medical Center

⊞ **SANFORD BEMIDJI MEDICAL CENTER (240100)**, 1300 Anne Street NW, Zip 56601–5103; tel. 218/751–5430, (Total facility includes 78 beds in nursing home–type unit) **A**1 2 10 **F**3 8 11 13 15 17 18 20 22 28 29 30 31 32 33 34 35 38 40 41 45 49 50 51 53 54 56 57 58 59 60 61 62 63 64 65 68 70 73 74 75 76 77 78 79 81 82 83 84 85 86 87 88 89 90 91 93 94 96 97 101 102 104 107 108 110 111 114 115 118 119 120 121 123 124 126 127 128 129 130 131 132 134 135 144 146 147 148 149 153 154 155 156 157 **S** Sanford Health, Sioux Falls, SD
Primary Contact: Bryan Nermoe, Executive Vice President
CFO: Craig Boyer, Vice President Finance
CMO: Daniel DeKrey, M.D., Chief of Staff
CIO: Dan Moffatt, Chief Information Officer
Web address: www.sanfordhealth.org/bemidji
Control: Other not–for–profit (including NFP Corporation) **Service**: General medical and surgical

Staffed Beds: 196 **Admissions**: 6828 **Census**: 138 **Outpatient Visits**: 273710 **Births**: 867 **Total Expense ($000)**: 281868 **Payroll Expense ($000)**: 126812 **Personnel**: 1423

BENSON—Swift County

SWIFT COUNTY - BENSON HEALTH SERVICES (241365), 1815 Wisconsin Avenue, Zip 56215–1653; tel. 320/843–1311, **A**10 18 **F**7 8 10 11 15 17 28 29 31 34 40 45 56 57 59 64 65 68 69 70 77 78 79 81 82 85 89 93 110 119 125 127 128 130 132 133 143 144 148 149 154 156
Primary Contact: Mary Ellen Wells, FACHE, Interim Chief Executive Officer
CFO: Jayne Thielke, Chief Financial Officer
CMO: Richard Horecka, Chief Medical Officer
CIO: Jayne Thielke, Chief Financial Officer
Web address: www.scbh.org
Control: Hospital district or authority, Government, nonfederal **Service**: General medical and surgical

Staffed Beds: 10 **Admissions**: 204 **Census**: 1 **Outpatient Visits**: 2156 **Births**: 0 **Total Expense ($000)**: 16387 **Payroll Expense ($000)**: 5688

BIGFORK—Itasca County

★ **BIGFORK VALLEY HOSPITAL (241316)**, 258 Pine Tree Drive, Zip 56628, Mailing Address: P.O. Box 258, Zip 56628–0258; tel. 218/743–3177, (Total facility includes 47 beds in nursing home–type unit) **A**10 18 **F**2 10 28 33 34 40 45 46 53 54 57 62 64 79 81 93 107 110 117 118 119 125 128 129 130 133
Primary Contact: Aaron Saude, Chief Executive Officer
CFO: Christine Lokken, Chief Financial Officer
CMO: Edwin Anderson, M.D., Chief of Staff and Chief Medical Officer
CIO: Amanda Niemala, Director of Information Services
CHR: Angela Kleffman, Director of Ancillary Services
CNO: Nancy Probst, R.N., Chief Nursing Officer
Web address: www.bigforkvalley.org
Control: Hospital district or authority, Government, nonfederal **Service**: General medical and surgical

Staffed Beds: 67 **Admissions**: 291 **Census**: 45 **Outpatient Visits**: 17297 **Births**: 0 **Total Expense ($000)**: 24233 **Payroll Expense ($000)**: 8717

BLUE EARTH—Faribault County

⊞ **UNITED HOSPITAL DISTRICT (241369)**, 515 South Moore Street, Zip 56013–2158, Mailing Address: P.O. Box 160, Zip 56013–0160; tel. 507/526–3273, **A**1 10 18 **F**3 5 7 8 11 13 15 28 29 30 34 35 40 43 45 47 48 50 56 57 59 62 63 64 65 68 69 70 75 77 79 81 82 85 86 91 93 96 97 104 107 110 111 114 115 119 129 130 131 132 133 135 144 146 148 149 154 155 156
Primary Contact: Richard M. Ash, Chief Executive Officer
CFO: Patrick Justin, Chief Financial Officer
CMO: Bob Karp, M.D., Chief Medical Officer
CIO: Mary Hynes, Manager Information Services
CHR: Shanna Gudahl, Manager Human Resources
CNO: Candace Arends, R.N., Chief Nursing Officer
Web address: www.uhd.org
Control: Other not–for–profit (including NFP Corporation) **Service**: General medical and surgical

Staffed Beds: 25 **Admissions**: 731 **Census**: 9 **Outpatient Visits**: 62260 **Births**: 78 **Total Expense ($000)**: 34088 **Payroll Expense ($000)**: 14416 **Personnel**: 189

Many Facility Codes have changed. Please refer to the AHA Guide Code Chart. © 2019 AHA Guide

MN

BRAINERD—Crow Wing County

✠ **ESSENTIA HEALTH ST. JOSEPH'S MEDICAL CENTER (240075)**, 523 North Third Street, Zip 56401–3098; tel. 218/829–2861, **A**1 2 10 **F**3 4 5 11 13 15 18 20 22 26 28 29 30 31 32 34 35 40 43 45 49 50 51 54 57 59 64 65 70 74 75 76 77 78 81 82 86 87 89 91 93 96 97 98 100 102 105 107 111 118 119 126 130 131 132 135 144 145 146 148 152 154 **S** Essentia Health, Duluth, MN
Primary Contact: Adam Rees, President
COO: Mike Larson, Chief Operating Officer
CFO: Dave Pilot, Chief Financial Officer
CMO: Peter Henry, M.D., Chief Medical Officer
CIO: Pam Marlatt, Business Systems Director
CHR: Sarah Carlson, Director Human Resources
CNO: Patricia DeLong, Chief Nursing Officer
Web address: www.essentiahealth.org
Control: Church operated, Nongovernment, not–for–profit **Service**: General medical and surgical

Staffed Beds: 122 Admissions: 4867 Census: 51 Outpatient Visits: 96254 Births: 448 Total Expense ($000): 191587 Payroll Expense ($000): 89359 Personnel: 846

ST. JOSEPH'S MEDICAL CENTER See Essentia Health St. Joseph's Medical Center

BRECKENRIDGE—Wilkin County

✠ **CHI ST. FRANCIS HEALTH (241377)**, 2400 St Francis Drive, Zip 56520–1025; tel. 218/643–3000, (Total facility includes 80 beds in nursing home–type unit) **A**1 10 18 **F**3 13 15 17 28 29 30 34 35 38 40 43 45 50 56 57 59 64 65 70 75 76 79 81 87 89 93 96 97 99 100 101 103 104 107 110 111 115 119 125 127 128 129 130 131 132 133 146 154 **S** CommonSpirit Health, Chicago, IL
Primary Contact: David A. Nelson, President and Chief Executive Officer
CFO: Joshua Senger, Chief Financial Officer
CHR: Gail Grant, Director Human Resources
CNO: Alice Pesonen–Johnson, Chief Nursing Officer
Web address: www.sfcare.org
Control: Church operated, Nongovernment, not–for–profit **Service**: General medical and surgical

Staffed Beds: 105 Admissions: 633 Census: 80 Outpatient Visits: 20324 Births: 72 Total Expense ($000): 29136 Payroll Expense ($000): 10999 Personnel: 149

BROOKLYN PARK—Hennepin County

☐ **PRAIRIECARE - BROOKLYN PARK (244016)**, 9400 Zane Avenue North, Zip 55443, Mailing Address: 12915 63rd Avenue North, Maple Grove, Zip 55369–6001; tel. 763/383–5800, (Nonreporting) **A**1
Primary Contact: Joel V. Oberstar, M.D., Chief Executive Officer and Chief Medical Officer
Web address: www.prairie-care.com
Control: General investor–owned, for–profit **Service**: Psychiatric

Staffed Beds: 50

BUFFALO—Wright County

✠ **BUFFALO HOSPITAL (240076)**, 303 Catlin Street, Zip 55313–1947; tel. 763/682–1212, **A**1 10 **F**3 13 15 18 28 29 30 31 32 34 35 36 40 43 44 45 50 53 57 59 64 75 76 77 78 79 80 81 85 86 87 93 107 110 111 114 115 119 129 130 131 132 135 146 148 149 150 154 **S** Allina Health, Minneapolis, MN
Primary Contact: Heather Johnson, Interim President
COO: Heather Johnson, Director of Finance, Operations and Business Development
CFO: Heather Johnson, Director of Finance, Operations and Business Development
CMO: Corey Martin, M.D., Director Medical Affairs
CIO: Jonathan Cloutier, Manager, Information Services
CHR: Leah Schmoyer, Human Resources Director
CNO: Gretchen A Frederick, R.N., Director Patient Care Services
Web address: www.buffalohospital.org
Control: Other not–for–profit (including NFP Corporation) **Service**: General medical and surgical

Staffed Beds: 44 Admissions: 2185 Census: 16 Outpatient Visits: 77562 Births: 606 Total Expense ($000): 63211 Payroll Expense ($000): 29274 Personnel: 328

BURNSVILLE—Dakota County

✠ **FAIRVIEW RIDGES HOSPITAL (240207)**, 201 East Nicollet Boulevard, Zip 55337–5799; tel. 952/892–2000, **A**1 2 3 5 10 **F**3 13 15 18 20 22 28 29 30 31 34 35 40 41 43 44 45 46 49 50 53 55 57 59 64 65 68 70 72 74 75 76 77 78 79 81 82 84 85 86 87 89 93 96 107 108 110 111 114 115 116 117 118 119 126 130 132 146 148 149 154 **S** Fairview Health Services, Minneapolis, MN
Primary Contact: Jeoff Will, Chief Operating Officer, Acute Care Services
COO: Brian A Knapp, Vice President Operations
CFO: Alan Lem, Vice President Finance
CMO: Paul Kettler, M.D., Vice President Medical Affairs
CHR: Michelle LeDell, Director Human Resource
CNO: Julie Sethney, R.N., Vice President Patient Care
Web address: www.fairview.org
Control: Other not–for–profit (including NFP Corporation) **Service**: General medical and surgical

Staffed Beds: 162 Admissions: 11601 Census: 119 Outpatient Visits: 126587 Births: 2258 Total Expense ($000): 237414 Payroll Expense ($000): 104373 Personnel: 1018

CAMBRIDGE—Isanti County

✠ **CAMBRIDGE MEDICAL CENTER (240020)**, 701 South Dellwood Street, Zip 55008–1920; tel. 763/689–7700, **A**1 2 10 **F**4 5 11 13 14 15 18 28 29 30 31 32 34 35 38 40 43 45 50 55 56 57 59 61 64 65 69 70 74 75 76 77 78 79 81 82 85 86 87 89 93 97 98 100 101 102 104 107 108 111 114 115 119 125 129 130 131 132 134 135 144 145 146 147 148 149 154 156 **S** Allina Health, Minneapolis, MN
Primary Contact: Kelly Spratt, President
CFO: Nancy Treacy, Director Finance
CHR: Diane Rasmussen, Director Human Resources
CNO: Sherri Abrahamson–Baty, Director Patient Care Services
Web address: www.allina.com/ahs/cambridge.nsf
Control: Other not–for–profit (including NFP Corporation) **Service**: General medical and surgical

Staffed Beds: 58 Admissions: 2873 Census: 27 Outpatient Visits: 82805 Births: 300 Total Expense ($000): 79032 Payroll Expense ($000): 34420 Personnel: 612

CANBY—Yellow Medicine County

★ **SANFORD CANBY MEDICAL CENTER (241347)**, 112 St Olaf Avenue South, Zip 56220–1433; tel. 507/223–7277, (Total facility includes 53 beds in nursing home type unit) **A**10 18 **F**3 7 9 10 11 13 15 28 29 31 34 35 39 40 46 46 63 56 59 60 62 64 65 70 71 75 79 81 85 89 92 93 107 110 119 127 128 130 132 133 135 144 149 156 158 **S** Sanford Health, Sioux Falls, SD
Primary Contact: Lori Sisk, R.N., Chief Executive Officer
CFO: Allison Nelson, Chief Financial Officer
CMO: Maritza Lopez, M.D., Chief of Staff
CIO: Cheryl L Ferguson, Associate Administrator
Web address: www.sanfordcanby.org
Control: Other not–for–profit (including NFP Corporation) **Service**: General medical and surgical

Staffed Beds: 78 Admissions: 269 Census: 46 Outpatient Visits: 26726 Births: 0 Total Expense ($000): 21502 Payroll Expense ($000): 10319 Personnel: 180

CANNON FALLS—Goodhue County

☐ **MAYO CLINIC HEALTH SYSTEM IN CANNON FALLS (241346)**, 32021 County Road 24 Boulevard, Zip 55009–1898; tel. 507/263–4221, **A**1 10 18 **F**3 11 15 18 28 29 34 35 40 45 53 57 59 64 65 67 74 75 77 79 81 87 93 97 104 107 111 115 119 130 133 149 154 **S** Mayo Clinic, Rochester, MN
Primary Contact: Brian Whited, M.D., Vice Chair Mayo Clinic Health System
COO: Glenn Christian, Administrator
CFO: Edward A Tusa, Chief Financial Officer
CMO: Tarlochan Turna, M.D., Medical Director
CHR: Mary Garlets, Director Human Resources
Web address: www.mayoclinichealthsystem.org/locations/cannon-falls
Control: Other not–for–profit (including NFP Corporation) **Service**: General medical and surgical

Staffed Beds: 15 Admissions: 361 Census: 9 Outpatient Visits: 24301 Births: 0 Personnel: 104

MN

Hospital, Medicare Provider Number, Address, Telephone, Approval, Facility, and Physician Codes, Health Care System

★ American Hospital Association (AHA) membership
☐ The Joint Commission accreditation
○ Healthcare Facilities Accreditation Program
◇ DNV Healthcare Inc. accreditation
⇧ Center for Improvement in Healthcare Quality Accreditation
△ Commission on Accreditation of Rehabilitation Facilities (CARF) accreditation

MN

CASS LAKE—Cass County

★ **U. S. PUBLIC HEALTH SERVICE INDIAN HOSPITAL (241358)**, 425 7th Street North West, Zip 56633; tel. 218/335–3200, (Nonreporting) **A**10 18 **S** U. S. Indian Health Service, Rockville, MD
Primary Contact: Louis P. Erdrich, Acting Chief Executive Officer
CMO: Antonio Guimaraes, M.D., Clinical Director
CHR: Terrance Lascano, Administrative Officer
CNO: Roberta A Williams, Director of Nursing
Web address: www.ihs.gov
Control: PHS, Indian Service, Government, federal **Service**: General medical and surgical

Staffed Beds: 9

CLOQUET—Carlton County

★ **COMMUNITY MEMORIAL HOSPITAL (241364)**, 512 Skyline Boulevard, Zip 55720–1199; tel. 218/879–4641, (Total facility includes 44 beds in nursing home–type unit) **A**10 18 **F**13 15 28 29 30 31 34 35 40 43 45 46 47 48 49 50 64 70 75 76 77 79 81 82 85 93 107 108 110 111 115 118 124 128 129 130 131 132 147 148
Primary Contact: Rick Breuer, Chief Executive Officer and Administrator
CFO: Brad Anderson, Chief Financial Officer
CIO: Sam Jacobson, Director Management Information Systems
Web address: www.cloquethospital.com
Control: Other not–for–profit (including NFP Corporation) **Service**: General medical and surgical

Staffed Beds: 69 Admissions: 1006 Census: 51

COOK—St. Louis County

★ **COOK HOSPITAL & CARE CENTER (241312)**, 10 Fifth Street SE, Zip 55723–9745; tel. 218/666–5945, (Nonreporting) **A**10 18
Primary Contact: Teresa Debevec, Chief Executive Officer and Administrator
CFO: Kaylee S. Hoard, Chief Financial Officer
Web address: www.cookhospital.org
Control: Hospital district or authority, Government, nonfederal **Service**: General medical and surgical

Staffed Beds: 42

COON RAPIDS—Anoka County

⊞ **MERCY HOSPITAL (240115)**, 4050 Coon Rapids Boulevard, Zip 55433–2586; tel. 763/236–6000, (Includes UNITY HOSPITAL, 550 Osborne Road NE, Fridley, Minnesota, Zip 55432–2799; tel. 763/236–5000; Sara J. Criger, President) **A**1 2 3 5 10 **F**3 4 5 8 11 13 17 18 20 22 24 26 28 29 30 31 34 35 36 37 38 40 43 45 46 49 50 53 55 56 57 59 64 65 68 69 70 74 75 76 77 78 79 81 82 85 86 87 93 96 97 98 100 101 102 103 104 105 107 108 111 114 115 119 126 130 131 132 135 145 146 152 153 154 **S** Allina Health, Minneapolis, MN
Primary Contact: Sara J. Criger, President
CFO: Gerald Pietz, Vice President Finance
CMO: Ryan Else, M.D., Vice President Medical Affairs
CIO: Susan Heichert, Chief Information Officer
CHR: Nancy Watson, Director Human Resources
CNO: MariBeth Olson, R.N., Vice President Patient Care Services
Web address: www.allinamercy.org
Control: Other not–for–profit (including NFP Corporation) **Service**: General medical and surgical

Staffed Beds: 471 Admissions: 31725 Census: 348 Outpatient Visits: 232701 Births: 3171 Total Expense ($000): 675593 Payroll Expense ($000): 250813 Personnel: 2258

CROOKSTON—Polk County

⊞ **RIVERVIEW HEALTH (241320)**, 323 South Minnesota Street, Zip 56716–1601; tel. 218/281–9200, (Nonreporting) **A**1 10 18 **S** QHR, Brentwood, TN
Primary Contact: Carrie Michalski, President and Chief Executive Officer
COO: Chris Bruggeman, Chief Operating Officer
CFO: Betty Arvidson, Chief Financial Officer
CMO: Colin Fennell, M.D., Chief Medical Officer
CIO: Nichole Beauchane, Director Information Technology
CHR: Jean Tate, Vice President Human Resources
CNO: April Grunhovd, Vice President of Patient Care Services and Chief Nursing Officer
Web address: www.riverviewhealth.org
Control: Other not–for–profit (including NFP Corporation) **Service**: General medical and surgical

Staffed Beds: 49

CROSBY—Crow Wing County

★ **CUYUNA REGIONAL MEDICAL CENTER (241353)**, 320 East Main Street, Zip 56441–1690; tel. 218/546–7000, (Total facility includes 113 beds in nursing home–type unit) **A**2 3 5 10 18 **F**3 7 12 13 15 18 28 29 31 34 35 40 45 46 47 48 49 50 51 56 57 59 62 63 64 65 68 70 75 76 77 78 79 81 82 84 85 86 87 91 92 93 94 97 99 100 101 103 104 107 110 111 115 116 117 118 119 124 127 128 130 131 132 133 143 144 146 147 148 149 150 154 156
Primary Contact: Kyle Bauer, Chief Executive Officer
COO: Amy Hart, Chief Operating Officer
CFO: Katie Berg, Chief Financial Officer
CMO: Robert Westin, M.D., Chief Medical Officer
CHR: Caity Eggen, Chief Human Resource Officer
CNO: Renee Steffin, Chief Nursing Officer
Web address: www.cuyunamed.org
Control: Other not–for–profit (including NFP Corporation) **Service**: General medical and surgical

Staffed Beds: 142 Admissions: 2058 Census: 97 Outpatient Visits: 184230 Births: 182

DAWSON—Lac Qui Parle County

JOHNSON MEMORIAL HEALTH SERVICES (241314), 1282 Walnut Street, Zip 56232–2333; tel. 320/769–4323, (Total facility includes 56 beds in nursing home–type unit) **A**10 18 **F**3 7 8 10 11 12 15 28 31 32 34 40 41 43 45 50 56 57 59 62 64 65 66 69 71 75 77 81 82 93 97 107 110 111 115 119 127 128 129 130 133 135 145 147 148 154
Primary Contact: Stacey Lee, CPA, JD, Chief Executive Officer
CFO: Crystal Bothun, Chief Financial Officer
CMO: Ayaz Virji, M.D., Chief of Staff
CIO: Derrick Ochsendorf, Manager Information Technology and Systems
CHR: Megan Lynch, Manager Human Resources
Web address: www.jmhsmn.org
Control: Hospital district or authority, Government, nonfederal **Service**: General medical and surgical

Staffed Beds: 76 Admissions: 312 Census: 64 Outpatient Visits: 13314 Births: 0 Total Expense ($000): 17095 Payroll Expense ($000): 8857 Personnel: 151

DEER RIVER—Itasca County

★ **ESSENTIA HEALTH-DEER RIVER (241360)**, 115 10th Avenue NE, Zip 56636–8795; tel. 218/246–2900, (Total facility includes 32 beds in nursing home–type unit) **A**10 18 **F**3 7 8 10 11 12 13 15 28 29 31 34 35 40 45 46 50 56 57 59 62 64 65 70 71 74 75 76 77 79 81 82 85 91 92 93 96 97 107 108 110 115 118 119 125 127 128 130 131 133 135 143 146 147 148 149 154 156 **S** Essentia Health, Duluth, MN
Primary Contact: Marsha Green, Administrator and Chief Operating Officer
COO: Marsha Green, Administrator and Chief Operating Officer
CMO: David Goodall, M.D., Chief Medical Staff
CHR: Brittany Mohler, Director Human Resources
Web address: www.essentiahealth.org
Control: Other not–for–profit (including NFP Corporation) **Service**: General medical and surgical

Staffed Beds: 52 Admissions: 431 Census: 25 Outpatient Visits: 49192 Births: 78 Total Expense ($000): 33285 Payroll Expense ($000): 14823 Personnel: 176

DETROIT LAKES—Becker County

⊞ **ESSENTIA HEALTH ST. MARY'S - DETROIT LAKES (240101)**, 1027 Washington Avenue, Zip 56501–3409; tel. 218/847–5611, (Total facility includes 96 beds in nursing home–type unit) **A**1 10 20 **F**10 11 13 15 18 28 29 30 31 34 35 40 41 43 45 56 57 59 62 64 65 70 75 76 77 78 79 81 82 85 87 89 91 93 97 104 107 110 111 114 115 119 125 127 128 130 131 132 135 144 146 147 148 149 154 156 **S** Essentia Health, Duluth, MN
Primary Contact: Ryan Hill, Interim Administrator
CFO: Ryan Hill, Senior Financial Advisor
CMO: Rich Vetter, M.D., Associate Chief
CIO: Ken Gilles, Associate Chief Information Officer
CHR: Diane Sundrud, Human Resource Service Partner
CNO: Kay Larson, R.N., Chief Nursing Officer
Web address: www.essentiahealth.org
Control: Other not–for–profit (including NFP Corporation) **Service**: General medical and surgical

Staffed Beds: 132 Admissions: 2456 Census: 99 Outpatient Visits: 274861 Births: 475 Total Expense ($000): 121384 Payroll Expense ($000): 58054 Personnel: 633

ST. MARY'S INNOVIS HEALTH See Essentia Health St. Mary's - Detroit Lakes

Many Facility Codes have changed. Please refer to the AHA Guide Code Chart.
© 2019 AHA Guide

DULUTH—St. Louis County

⊠ △ **ESSENTIA HEALTH DULUTH (240019)**, 502 East Second Street, Zip 55805–1982; tel. 218/727–8762, **A**1 3 7 10 **F**3 5 11 12 15 16 29 30 31 32 34 35 49 50 51 52 54 55 56 57 59 61 64 65 70 74 75 77 78 79 81 82 84 85 86 87 90 91 92 93 94 96 97 98 99 100 101 103 104 105 107 108 110 111 114 115 116 117 118 119 120 121 123 124 130 131 132 134 135 141 144 146 147 148 149 151 153 154 157 **S** Essentia Health, Duluth, MN
Primary Contact: James Garvey, Hospital Operations
CFO: Kevin Boren, Chief Financial Officer
CMO: Hugh Renier, M.D., Vice President Medical Affairs
CIO: Dennis Dassenko, Chief Information Officer
CHR: Diane Davidson, Senior Vice President Human Resources
CNO: Sandee Carlson, Director of Nursing
Web address: www.smdcmedicalcenter.org
Control: Other not–for–profit (including NFP Corporation) **Service**: General medical and surgical

Staffed Beds: 154 **Admissions:** 2866 **Census:** 75 **Outpatient Visits:** 553606 **Births:** 0 **Total Expense ($000):** 423440 **Payroll Expense ($000):** 229595 **Personnel:** 1563

⊠ **ESSENTIA HEALTH ST. MARY'S MEDICAL CENTER (240002)**, 407 East Third Street, Zip 55805–1984; tel. 218/786–4000, (Includes ST. MARY'S CHILDREN'S HOSPITAL, 407 East Third Street, Duluth, Minnesota, Zip 55805–1950; tel. 218/786–5437) **A**1 2 3 5 10 **F**3 11 12 13 17 18 20 22 24 26 28 29 30 34 35 37 38 40 41 43 45 46 47 48 49 50 57 59 63 65 67 70 72 74 76 78 79 81 83 84 85 86 87 88 89 91 102 107 108 111 115 119 126 129 130 132 135 141 146 149 154 157 **S** Essentia Health, Duluth, MN
Primary Contact: James Garvey, Senior Vice President Hospital Practice, Essentia Health East
CMO: Hugh Renier, M.D., Vice President Medical Affairs
CIO: Tess Jettergren, Director Clinical Informatics
CHR: Glen Porter, Vice President Human Resources
Web address: www.essentiahealth.org/StMarysMedicalCenter/FindaClinic/Essentia-HealthSt-Marys-Medical-Center-46.aspx
Control: Other not–for–profit (including NFP Corporation) **Service**: General medical and surgical

Staffed Beds: 310 **Admissions:** 18560 **Census:** 226 **Outpatient Visits:** 131458 **Births:** 1300 **Total Expense ($000):** 408804 **Payroll Expense ($000):** 162349 **Personnel:** 1757

SMDC MEDICAL CENTER See Essentia Health Duluth

★ △ ⇑ **ST. LUKE'S HOSPITAL (240047)**, 915 East First Street, Zip 55805–2193; tel. 218/249–5555, **A**2 3 7 10 19 21 **F**3 8 9 11 12 13 15 18 20 22 24 26 28 29 30 31 34 35 39 40 43 45 46 47 48 49 51 53 54 57 58 59 60 61 62 63 64 65 70 74 75 76 77 78 79 81 82 83 84 85 86 87 89 90 91 92 93 97 98 100 102 104 107 108 110 114 115 117 118 119 120 121 123 124 126 129 130 131 132 144 145 146 147 148 149 154 155 156
Primary Contact: Kevin J. Nokels, FACHE, President and Chief Executive Officer
CFO: Eric Lohn, Vice President and Chief Financial Officer
CMO: Gary Peterson, M.D., Vice President Medical Affairs and Chief Medical Officer
CIO: Clark Averill, Director Information Technology
CHR: Marla Halvorson, Director Human Resources
CNO: Susan Hamel, Chief Nursing Officer
Web address: www.slhduluth.com
Control: Other not–for–profit (including NFP Corporation) **Service**: General medical and surgical

Staffed Beds: 267 **Admissions:** 12152 **Census:** 170 **Outpatient Visits:** 556076 **Births:** 865 **Total Expense ($000):** 482505 **Payroll Expense ($000):** 232437 **Personnel:** 2298

ST. MARY'S MEDICAL CENTER See Essentia Health St. Mary's Medical Center

EDINA—Hennepin County

⊠ **FAIRVIEW SOUTHDALE HOSPITAL (240078)**, 6401 France Avenue South, Zip 55435–2199; tel. 952/924–5000, **A**1 2 3 5 10 **F**3 13 15 17 18 20 22 24 26 28 29 30 31 35 40 43 44 45 46 49 50 51 59 64 65 68 70 71 74 75 76 77 78 79 81 84 85 87 92 93 98 100 101 107 108 110 111 114 115 116 117 119 121 126 130 132 146 148 149 154 **S** Fairview Health Services, Minneapolis, MN
Primary Contact: Jeoff Will, Chief Operating Officer, Acute Care Services
COO: Jeoff Will, Chief Operating Officer, Acute Care Services
CFO: Alan Lem, Vice President Finance
CHR: Michelle LeDell, Director Human Resources
Web address: www.fairview.org
Control: Other not–for–profit (including NFP Corporation) **Service**: General medical and surgical

Staffed Beds: 316 **Admissions:** 18761 **Census:** 210 **Outpatient Visits:** 135144 **Births:** 3094 **Total Expense ($000):** 437415 **Payroll Expense ($000):** 177647 **Personnel:** 1746

ELBOW LAKE—Grant County

ELEAH MEDICAL CENTER See Prairie Ridge Hospital and Health Services

★ **PRAIRIE RIDGE HOSPITAL AND HEALTH SERVICES (241379)**, 1411 Highway 79 East, Zip 56531–4645; tel. 218/685–7300, **A**10 18 **F**3 7 8 15 18 24 26 28 34 40 43 45 48 53 54 59 64 68 77 79 81 91 93 94 96 97 104 107 108 110 111 114 119 127 132 133 135 148 149 154 156
Primary Contact: Danielle Lesmeister, Chief Executive Officer
CFO: Brett Longtin, Chief Financial Officer
CMO: Phillip Walter Holmes, M.D., Chief of Staff
CHR: Kim Blank, Director Human Resources
CNO: Alycia Athey, Director of Nursing
Web address: www.prairiehealth.org
Control: Other not–for–profit (including NFP Corporation) **Service**: General medical and surgical

Staffed Beds: 9 **Admissions:** 144 **Census:** 2 **Outpatient Visits:** 28828 **Births:** 0 **Total Expense ($000):** 18176 **Payroll Expense ($000):** 4939 **Personnel:** 114

ELY—St. Louis County

★ **ELY-BLOOMENSON COMMUNITY HOSPITAL (241318)**, 328 West Conan Street, Zip 55731–1198; tel. 218/365–3271, **A**10 18 **F**3 15 28 31 40 45 53 62 64 81 107 110 119 130 133 148 149 154
Primary Contact: Michael F. Coyle, Chief Executive Officer
CFO: Scott Kellerman, Chief Financial Officer
CHR: Rochelle Sjoberg, Director Human Resources
CNO: Becky Gaulke, Chief Nursing Officer
Web address: www.ebch.org
Control: Other not–for–profit (including NFP Corporation) **Service**: General medical and surgical

Staffed Beds: 21 **Admissions:** 275 **Census:** 2 **Outpatient Visits:** 6087 **Births:** 0 **Total Expense ($000):** 18443 **Payroll Expense ($000):** 6152 **Personnel:** 91

FAIRMONT—Martin County

☐ **MAYO CLINIC HEALTH SYSTEM IN FAIRMONT (240166)**, 800 Medical Center Drive, Zip 56031–4575; tel. 507/238–8100, **A**1 10 20 **F**3 11 12 13 15 18 28 29 30 31 34 35 36 40 43 45 57 59 64 65 68 74 75 76 77 78 79 80 81 85 86 87 92 93 97 100 101 104 107 108 110 111 115 118 119 128 129 130 132 133 144 146 148 149 **S** Mayo Clinic, Rochester, MN
Primary Contact: Amy Long, Administrator
COO: Gayle B Hansen, R.N., Chief Operating Officer
CFO: Brian Suter, Chief Financial Officer
CMO: Rufus Rodriguez, M.D., Medical Director
Web address: www.fairmontmedicalcenter.org
Control: Other not–for–profit (including NFP Corporation) **Service**: General medical and surgical

Staffed Beds: 23 **Admissions:** 1269 **Census:** 12 **Outpatient Visits:** 80796 **Births:** 250 **Personnel:** 284

MN

Hospital, Medicare Provider Number, Address, Telephone, Approval, Facility, and Physician Codes, Health Care System

★ American Hospital Association (AHA) membership
☐ The Joint Commission accreditation
○ Healthcare Facilities Accreditation Program
◇ DNV Healthcare Inc. accreditation
⇑ Center for Improvement in Healthcare Quality Accreditation
△ Commission on Accreditation of Rehabilitation Facilities (CARF) accreditation

FARIBAULT—Rice County

✠ **DISTRICT ONE HOSPITAL (240071)**, 200 State Avenue, Zip 55021–6345;
tel. 507/334–6451, (Nonreporting) **A**1 2 10 **S** Allina Health, Minneapolis, MN
Primary Contact: David L. Albrecht, President
COO: Rick Miller, Director, Operations and Finance
CFO: Rick Miller, Chief Financial Officer
CMO: Amy Elliott, M.D., Director Medical Affairs
Web address: www.allinahealth.org/District-One-Hospital/
Control: Hospital district or authority, Government, nonfederal **Service:** General
medical and surgical

Staffed Beds: 42

FERGUS FALLS—Otter Tail County

☐ **COMMUNITY BEHAVIORAL HEALTH HOSPITAL - FERGUS FALLS (244013)**,
1801 West Alcott Avenue, Zip 56537–2661, Mailing Address: P.O. Box 478,
Zip 56538–0478; tel. 218/332–5001, (Nonreporting) **A**1 10 **S** Minnesota
Department of Human Services, Saint Paul, MN
Primary Contact: Brenda Schleske, Administrator
Control: State, Government, nonfederal **Service:** Psychiatric

Staffed Beds: 16

✠ **LAKE REGION HEALTHCARE (240052)**, 712 South Cascade Street, Zip 56537–
2900, Mailing Address: P.O. Box 728, Zip 56538–0728; tel. 218/736–8000,
(Nonreporting) **A**1 10 20
Primary Contact: Kyle Richards, Chief Executive Officer
CFO: Brett Longtin, Chief Financial Officer
CMO: Greg Smith, Chief Medical Officer
CIO: Wade A Jyrkas, Director Computer Information Systems
CHR: Kim Blank, Director Human Resources
CNO: Lucia E Anderson, Senior Vice President Operations and Chief Nurse
Executive
Web address: www.lrhc.org
Control: Other not–for–profit (including NFP Corporation) **Service:** General
medical and surgical

Staffed Beds: 108

FOSSTON—Polk County

★ **ESSENTIA HEALTH FOSSTON (241357)**, 900 Hilligoss Boulevard SE,
Zip 56542–1599; tel. 218/435–1133, (Total facility includes 50 beds in nursing
home–type unit) **A**10 18 **F**3 7 10 11 13 15 28 29 31 34 40 43 44 50 56
57 59 62 63 65 68 70 75 76 77 78 79 80 81 82 84 85 87 93 97 104 107 110
114 127 128 129 130 131 132 133 135 146 148 149 154 157 **S** Essentia
Health, Duluth, MN
Primary Contact: Kevin Gish, Administrator and Vice President
CFO: Kim Bodensteiner, Chief Financial Officer
CHR: Diane Sundrud, Director Human Resources
Web address: www.essentiahealth.org
Control: Other not–for–profit (including NFP Corporation) **Service:** General
medical and surgical

Staffed Beds: 74 Admissions: 651 Census: 47 Outpatient Visits: 60239
Births: 91 Total Expense ($000): 27779 Payroll Expense ($000): 13184
Personnel: 213

FIRST CARE MEDICAL SERVICES See Essentia Health Fosston

GLENCOE—Mcleod County

★ **GLENCOE REGIONAL HEALTH (241355)**, 1805 Hennepin Avenue North,
Zip 55336–1416; tel. 320/864–3121, (Total facility includes 110 beds in nursing
home–type unit) **A**10 18 **F**3 11 13 15 28 29 31 34 40 43 45 48 50 56 64 68 75
76 77 78 79 81 85 86 87 89 93 97 107 110 111 115 118 119 125 128 130
132 133 135 144 146 148 149 **S** HealthPartners, Bloomington, MN
Primary Contact: Jeffrey Mason, President and Chief Executive Officer
CFO: John C Doidge, Vice President Finance
CMO: Kristine Knudten, M.D., Vice President Medical Affairs
CIO: Ryan Lake, Director Information Technology
CHR: Jill Hatlestad, Vice President Human Resources and Marketing
CNO: Patricia Henderson, R.N., Vice President Nursing and Clinical Services
Web address: www.grhsonline.org
Control: Other not–for–profit (including NFP Corporation) **Service:** General
medical and surgical

Staffed Beds: 135 Admissions: 811 Census: 97

GLENWOOD—Pope County

★ **GLACIAL RIDGE HEALTH SYSTEM (241376)**, 10 Fourth Avenue SE,
Zip 56334–1898; tel. 320/634–4521, **A**10 18 **F**11 12 13 15 17 28 31 34 35 40
41 43 45 53 59 62 63 64 75 77 79 81 93 107 110 111 115 119 127 130 133
146 148 149 154 155
Primary Contact: Kirk A. Stensrud, Chief Executive Officer
CFO: Kyle Chase, Chief Financial Officer
CMO: Gustave Mellgren, M.D., Chief of Staff
CIO: Jeff Ofstedal, Manager Information Technology
CHR: Gordon Paulson, Manager Human Resources
CNO: Lynn Flesner, Director of Nursing
Web address: www.glacialridge.org
Control: Hospital district or authority, Government, nonfederal **Service:** General
medical and surgical

Staffed Beds: 22 Admissions: 758 Census: 9 Outpatient Visits: 18800
Births: 104 Total Expense ($000): 40394 Payroll Expense ($000): 18933
Personnel: 309

GOLDEN VALLEY—Hennepin County

✠ **REGENCY HOSPITAL OF MINNEAPOLIS (242005)**, 1300 Hidden Lakes
Parkway, Zip 55422–4286; tel. 763/588–2750, (Nonreporting) **A**1 10 **S** Select
Medical Corporation, Mechanicsburg, PA
Primary Contact: Sean Stricker, Chief Executive Officer
CMO: Alaka Nagaraj, M.D., Medical Director
CNO: Caren Gaytko, Chief Nursing Officer
Web address: www.regencyhospital.com
Control: Corporation, Investor–owned (for–profit) **Service:** Acute long–term care
hospital

Staffed Beds: 92

GRACEVILLE—Big Stone County

★ **ESSENTIA HEALTH-GRACEVILLE (241321)**, 115 West Second Street,
Zip 56240–4845, Mailing Address: P.O. Box 157, Zip 56240–0157; tel. 320/748–
7223, (Total facility includes 40 beds in nursing home–type unit) **A**10 18 **F**3 15 28
30 33 34 40 41 43 56 57 59 62 64 65 68 75 77 81 82 85 87 93 97 107 110
115 127 128 133 135 146 147 148 149 154 156 **S** Essentia Health, Duluth, MN
Primary Contact: Julie Rosenberg, Administrator
CMO: Arthur Van Vranken, M.D., Chief Medical Officer
CIO: Brad Tostenson, Chief Information Officer
CHR: Jenny Lee, Human Resources Generalist
CNO: Jill Johnsrud, Director of Nursing
Web address: www.essentiahealth.org/HolyTrinityHospital/FindaClinic/Essentia-
HealthHoly-Trinity-Hospital-96.aspx
Control: Other not–for–profit (including NFP Corporation) **Service:** General
medical and surgical

Staffed Beds: 55 Admissions: 89 Census: 38 Outpatient Visits: 7185
Births: 0 Total Expense ($000): 10225 Payroll Expense ($000): 4670
Personnel: 101

GRACEVILLE HEALTH CENTER See Essentia Health-Graceville

GRAND MARAIS—Cook County

★ **NORTH SHORE HEALTH (241317)**, 515 5th Avenue West, Zip 55604–3017;
tel. 218/387–3040, (Total facility includes 37 beds in nursing home–type unit) **A**10
18 **F**3 7 15 28 40 45 50 56 59 62 64 75 84 85 89 93 107 110 111 115 119
128 130 133 148 149
Primary Contact: Kimber L. Wraalstad, FACHE, Administrator
CFO: Vera Schumann, Director of Finance and Controller
CMO: Milan Schmidt, Medical Director
CIO: Greg Johnson, IT Coordinator
CHR: Robert Willis, Director Human Resources
CNO: Amy Lacina, R.N., Director of Nursing
Web address: www.nshorehospitalhealthgm.com
Control: Hospital district or authority, Government, nonfederal **Service:** General
medical and surgical

Staffed Beds: 53 Admissions: 165 Census: 39 Births: 0

Many Facility Codes have changed. Please refer to the AHA Guide Code Chart. © 2019 AHA Guide

MN

GRAND RAPIDS—Itasca County

☒ **GRAND ITASCA CLINIC AND HOSPITAL (240064)**, 1601 Golf Course Road, Zip 55744–8648; tel. 218/326–5000, **A**1 10 20 **F**13 15 18 26 28 29 31 32 33 34 35 40 43 44 45 50 53 57 59 62 65 68 69 70 75 76 77 78 79 81 82 92 93 97 107 111 115 117 119 130 131 132 135 144 146 148 156 **S** Fairview Health Services, Minneapolis, MN
Primary Contact: Jean MacDonell, Interim Chief Executive Officer
CFO: Todd Christensen, Vice President, Finance
CMO: Dan Soular, M.D., Vice President, Medical Affairs
CHR: Katherine Burns-Chistenson, Human Resource Director
CNO: Sandy Lenarz, Chief Nursing Officer
Web address: www.granditasca.org
Control: Other not–for–profit (including NFP Corporation) **Service**: General medical and surgical

Staffed Beds: 49 Admissions: 1785 Census: 14 Outpatient Visits: 106346 **Births:** 318 **Total Expense ($000):** 90941 **Payroll Expense ($000):** 48225 **Personnel:** 581

GRANITE FALLS—Yellow Medicine County

★ **GRANITE FALLS HEALTH (241343)**, 345 Tenth Avenue, Zip 56241–1499; tel. 320/564–3111, (Nonreporting) **A**10 18
Primary Contact: Thomas Kooiman, Chief Executive Officer
CFO: Val Hoffman, Chief Financial Officer
CIO: Kris Wilke, Manager Health Information
CHR: Sue Tollefson, Coordinator Payroll Personnel
CNO: Patty Massman, Director of Nursing
Web address: www.granitefallshealthcare.com
Control: City, Government, nonfederal **Service**: General medical and surgical

Staffed Beds: 82

HALLOCK—Kittson County

★ **KITTSON MEMORIAL HEALTHCARE CENTER (241336)**, 1010 South Birch Street, Zip 56728–4215, Mailing Address: P.O. Box 700, Zip 56728–0700; tel. 218/843–3612, (Nonreporting) **A**10 18
Primary Contact: Ashley Rivera, Chief Financial Officer and Chief Executive Officer
CMO: Thomas Lohstreter, M.D., Chief of Staff
CIO: Holly Knutson, Manager Information Technology
CHR: Carlene Cole, Manager Human Resources
CNO: Tawnya Sorenson, Director of Nursing
Web address: www.kmhc.net
Control: Other not–for–profit (including NFP Corporation) **Service**: General medical and surgical

Staffed Beds: 75

HASTINGS—Dakota County

☒ **REGINA HOSPITAL (240059)**, 1175 Nininger Road, Zip 55033–1098; tel. 651/480–4100, **A**1 10 **F**3 8 11 13 15 28 29 31 34 35 40 43 45 46 50 59 75 76 77 78 79 80 81 82 87 93 98 103 107 110 111 114 119 129 130 132 145 146 148 149 154 157 **S** Allina Health, Minneapolis, MN
Primary Contact: Helen J. Strike, R.N., President
CFO: Andy Rolling, Director of Finance
CMO: James Noreen, M.D., Chief Medical Officer
Web address: www.reginamedical.org
Control: Other not–for–profit (including NFP Corporation) **Service**: General medical and surgical

Staffed Beds: 43 Admissions: 1589 Census: 20 Outpatient Visits: 54638 **Births:** 211 **Total Expense ($000):** 57220 **Payroll Expense ($000):** 20335 **Personnel:** 260

HENDRICKS—Lincoln County

★ **HENDRICKS COMMUNITY HOSPITAL ASSOCIATION (241339)**, 503 East Lincoln Street, Zip 56136–9598, Mailing Address: P.O. Box 106, Zip 56136–0106; tel. 507/275–3134, (Total facility includes 50 beds in nursing home–type unit) **A**10 18 **F**2 3 7 11 15 17 28 29 31 34 40 50 59 62 63 70 81 89 93 107 125 127 128 130 132 133 146 148 156 158
Primary Contact: Jeffrey Gollaher, Chief Executive Officer
CMO: Tabb McCluskey, M.D., Chief Medical Officer
CHR: Lynn R Olson, Director Human Resources
Web address: www.hendrickshosp.org
Control: Other not–for–profit (including NFP Corporation) **Service**: General medical and surgical

Staffed Beds: 61 Admissions: 160 Census: 53 Outpatient Visits: 10659 **Births:** 0 **Total Expense ($000):** 14278 **Payroll Expense ($000):** 7381 **Personnel:** 128

HIBBING—St. Louis County

☒ **RANGE REGIONAL HEALTH SERVICES (240040)**, 750 East 34th Street, Zip 55746–4600; tel. 218/262–4881, **A**1 2 10 **F**3 6 11 13 15 18 28 29 30 31 32 33 34 35 36 40 43 45 50 54 56 57 58 59 62 63 64 65 68 70 75 76 77 78 79 81 82 83 84 85 87 89 93 97 98 100 102 104 105 107 108 110 111 115 118 119 120 121 123 129 130 131 132 135 143 144 145 146 147 148 149 150 154 **S** Fairview Health Services, Minneapolis, MN
Primary Contact: Patrick Sharp, Chief Executive Officer
CFO: Tom Fink, Vice President Regional Finance Officer
CMO: Susan Rudberg, M.D., Chief Medical Officer
CIO: Jessica Valento, Director Information Systems
CHR: Mitchell S Vincent, Vice President Organizational Support
CNO: Connie Harle, Chief Nursing Officer
Web address: www.range.fairview.org
Control: Other not–for–profit (including NFP Corporation) **Service**: General medical and surgical

Staffed Beds: 72 Admissions: 2683 Census: 38 Outpatient Visits: 51336 **Births:** 300 **Total Expense ($000):** 119175 **Payroll Expense ($000):** 63130 **Personnel:** 990

HUTCHINSON—Mcleod County

☐ **HUTCHINSON HEALTH (240187)**, 1095 Highway 15 South, Zip 55350–3182; tel. 320/234–5000, (Nonreporting) **A**1 10 20 **S** HealthPartners, Bloomington, MN
Primary Contact: Jim Lyons, President
COO: Glen Kegley, Chief Operating Officer
CFO: Pamela Larson, Division Director Financial Services
CMO: Brian Pollman, Chief Medical Officer
CIO: Jim Lyons, Chief Clinic Officer
CHR: Rebecca Streich, Manager Human Resources and Education Manager
CNO: Terry J. Graner, R.N., Chief Nursing Officer
Web address: www.hutchhealth.com
Control: Other not–for–profit (including NFP Corporation) **Service**: General medical and surgical

Staffed Beds: 49

INTERNATIONAL FALLS—Koochiching County

RAINY LAKE MEDICAL CENTER (241322), 1400 Highway 71, Zip 56649–2189; tel. 218/283–4481, (Nonreporting) **A**10 18 **S** QHR, Brentwood, TN
Primary Contact: Robert Pastor II, R.N., Chief Executive Officer
CFO: Melissa Marcotte, Chief Financial Officer
CIO: Michael Blesi, Director Information Technology
CNO: Donita Ettestad, R.N., MS, Chief Nursing Officer
Web address: www.rainylakemedical.com
Control: Other not–for–profit (including NFP Corporation) **Service**: General medical and surgical

Staffed Beds: 25

JACKSON—Jackson County

★ **SANFORD JACKSON MEDICAL CENTER (241315)**, 1430 North Highway, Zip 56143–1093; tel. 507/847–2420, **A**10 18 **F**3 28 29 31 32 34 35 40 41 43 44 49 50 56 57 59 62 64 65 68 77 81 85 86 87 89 91 93 97 101 102 104 107 108 114 125 127 130 131 132 133 135 143 149 154 156 **S** Sanford Health, Sioux Falls, SD
Primary Contact: Dawn Schnell, Chief Nursing Officer and Interim Senior Director
CFO: Gail Eike, Chief Financial Officer
CMO: Sister Marie Paul Lockerd, M.D., Chief Medical Officer
CNO: Dawn Schnell, Chief Nursing Officer
Web address: www.sanfordjackson.org
Control: Other not–for–profit (including NFP Corporation) **Service**: General medical and surgical

Staffed Beds: 16 Admissions: 195 Census: 3 Outpatient Visits: 27169 **Births:** 0 **Total Expense ($000):** 10423 **Payroll Expense ($000):** 4632 **Personnel:** 62

MN

LAKE CITY—Goodhue County

□ **MAYO CLINIC HEALTH SYSTEM IN LAKE CITY (241338)**, 500 West Grant Street, Zip 55041–1143; tel. 651/345–3321, (Total facility includes 90 beds in nursing home–type unit) **A**1 10 18 **F**15 18 28 29 30 34 35 40 45 57 59 64 67 69 75 79 81 87 92 93 97 107 110 111 114 119 128 130 132 133 146 148 149 154 **S** Mayo Clinic, Rochester, MN
Primary Contact: Brian Whited, M.D., President and Chief Executive Officer
CFO: David Biren, Chief Financial Officer
CMO: Dennis Spano, M.D., Medical Director
CHR: Jacqueline Ryan, Director Human Resources
Web address: www.lakecitymedicalcenter.org
Control: Other not–for–profit (including NFP Corporation) **Service**: General medical and surgical

Staffed Beds: 98 **Admissions**: 412 **Census**: 86 **Outpatient Visits**: 25072
Births: 0 **Personnel**: 100

LE SUEUR—Le Sueur County

★ **RIDGEVIEW LE SUEUR MEDICAL CENTER (241375)**, 621 South Fourth Street, Zip 56058–2298; tel. 507/665–3375, (Total facility includes 40 beds in nursing home–type unit) **A**10 18 **F**2 3 7 15 40 43 45 69 81 87 97 107 114 128 130 133 144 154 **S** Ridgeview Medical Center, Waconia, MN
Primary Contact: Pamela Williams, Vice President
CFO: Patricia Schlegel, Executive Director Finance
CMO: Carolyn Stelter, M.D., Chief of Staff
CHR: Bonnie Barnhardt, Executive Director Human Resources
CNO: Kim Putz, R.N., Director, Nursing Hospital
Web address: www.mvhc.org
Control: Other not–for–profit (including NFP Corporation) **Service**: General medical and surgical

Staffed Beds: 49 **Admissions**: 143 **Census**: 33 **Outpatient Visits**: 12160
Births: 0 **Total Expense ($000)**: 8781 **Payroll Expense ($000)**: 2644
Personnel: 101

LITCHFIELD—Meeker County

★ **MEEKER MEMORIAL HOSPITAL (241366)**, 612 South Sibley Avenue, Zip 55355–3398; tel. 320/693–4500, (Nonreporting) **A**10 18
Primary Contact: Kurt Waldbillig, Chief Executive Officer
CFO: Stephen Plaisance, Chief Financial Officer
CMO: Tim Peterson, M.D., Chief of Staff
CIO: Troy Bruning, Director Information Technology
CHR: Cindi Twardy, Manager Human Resources
CNO: Joan Bitz, Chief Nursing Officer
Web address: www.meekermemorial.org
Control: County, Government, nonfederal **Service**: General medical and surgical

Staffed Beds: 38

LITTLE FALLS—Morrison County

⊞ **CHI ST. GABRIEL'S HEALTH (241370)**, 815 Second Street SE, Zip 56345–3596; tel. 320/632–5441, (Nonreporting) **A**1 10 18 **S** CommonSpirit Health, Chicago, IL
Primary Contact: Lee Boyles, President
CFO: Steve Smith, Assistant Vice President Finance
CMO: Susan Okoniewski, M.D., Chief of Staff
Web address: www.stgabriels.com
Control: Church operated **Service**: General medical and surgical

Staffed Beds: 25

LONG PRAIRIE—Todd County

★ **CENTRACARE HEALTH-LONG PRAIRIE (241326)**, 20 Ninth Street SE, Zip 56347–1404; tel. 320/732–2141, (Nonreporting) **A**5 10 18 **S** CentraCare Health, Saint Cloud, MN
Primary Contact: Daniel J. Swenson, FACHE, Administrator
CFO: Larry Knutson, Director Finance
CMO: Rene Eldidy, M.D., Chief of Staff
Web address: www.centracare.com
Control: Other not–for–profit (including NFP Corporation) **Service**: General medical and surgical

Staffed Beds: 20

LONG PRAIRIE MEMORIAL HOSPITAL AND HOME See Centracare Health-Long Prairie

LUVERNE—Rock County

★ **SANFORD LUVERNE MEDICAL CENTER (241371)**, 1600 North Kniss Avenue, Zip 56156–1067; tel. 507/283–2321, **A**10 18 **F**3 4 5 7 8 11 13 15 18 19 28 29 31 32 34 35 40 43 45 56 57 59 63 64 65 67 68 74 75 76 77 78 79 81 82 83 84 85 86 87 90 93 96 97 107 111 114 118 119 128 129 131 132 133 135 146 147 148 149 152 154 156 157 **S** Sanford Health, Sioux Falls, SD
Primary Contact: Tammy Loosbrock, Senior Director
COO: Nancy E Drenth, R.N., Director Ancillary Services
CFO: Stanley Knobloch, Director Fiscal Services
CMO: Judy S Chesley, M.D., Chief of Staff
CNO: Nyla H Sandbulte, R.N., Director of Nursing
Web address: www.sanfordluverne.org
Control: Other not–for–profit (including NFP Corporation) **Service**: General medical and surgical

Staffed Beds: 25 **Admissions**: 532 **Census**: 6 **Outpatient Visits**: 41557
Births: 58 **Total Expense ($000)**: 24166 **Payroll Expense ($000)**: 10994
Personnel: 158

MADELIA—Watonwan County

⊞ **MADELIA COMMUNITY HOSPITAL (241323)**, 121 Drew Avenue SE, Zip 56062–1899; tel. 507/642–3255, **A**1 5 10 18 **F**3 11 13 15 34 35 40 57 59 62 64 68 69 75 76 77 81 82 84 85 86 93 102 104 107 110 114 128 130 132 133 144 145 148 149 154
Primary Contact: Jeff Mengenhausen, Chief Executive Officer
CFO: Donna M Klinkner, Chief Financial Officer
CMO: Todd Gavin, Chief Medical Officer
CIO: Valerie Juhl, Director of Health
CHR: Donna M Klinkner, Chief Financial Officer
CNO: Deidre Hruby, Director of Patient Care
Web address: www.mchospital.org
Control: Other not–for–profit (including NFP Corporation) **Service**: General medical and surgical

Staffed Beds: 21 **Admissions**: 160 **Census**: 2 **Outpatient Visits**: 9705
Births: 0 **Total Expense ($000)**: 11456 **Payroll Expense ($000)**: 4375
Personnel: 92

MADISON—Lac Qui Parle County

MADISON HEALTHCARE SERVICES (241372), 900 Second Avenue, Zip 56256–1006; tel. 320/598–7556, (Nonreporting) **A**10 18
Primary Contact: Erik Bjerke, Chief Executive Officer
CFO: Carol Borgerson, Chief Financial Officer
CIO: Jerry Harberts, Information Technologist
CHR: Kelly Johnson, Director Human Resources
Web address: www.mlhmn.org/
Control: Other not–for–profit (including NFP Corporation) **Service**: General medical and surgical

Staffed Beds: 12

MAHNOMEN—Mahnomen County

MAHNOMEN HEALTH CENTER (241300), 414 West Jefferson Avenue, Zip 56557–4912, Mailing Address: P.O. Box 396, Zip 56557–0396; tel. 218/935–2511, (Nonreporting) **A**10 18 **S** Sanford Health, Sioux Falls, SD
Primary Contact: Dale K. Kruger, Chief Executive Officer
CFO: Mary Pazdernik, Chief Financial Officer
CMO: Anju Gurung, M.D., Chief Medical Officer
CHR: Kristi Stall, Chief Human Resources Officer
Web address: www.mahnomenhealthcenter.com
Control: City–county, Government, nonfederal **Service**: General medical and surgical

Staffed Beds: 50

MANKATO—Blue Earth County

⊞ **MAYO CLINIC HEALTH SYSTEM IN MANKATO (240093)**, 1025 Marsh Street, Zip 56001–4752; tel. 507/625–4031, **A**1 3 5 10 **F**3 12 13 15 18 19 20 22 26 28 29 30 31 32 33 34 35 36 37 38 40 41 43 45 49 53 54 56 57 58 59 60 61 63 64 65 68 70 73 74 75 76 77 78 79 81 82 83 84 85 87 89 91 92 93 97 98 100 102 104 107 108 110 111 114 115 118 119 120 121 126 129 130 131 132 135 144 146 147 148 149 154 155 156 **S** Mayo Clinic, Rochester, MN
Primary Contact: James Hebl, M.D., Regional Vice President
CMO: Susan Pearson, M.D., Chief Medical Officer
CIO: Sarah Daniels, Vice President, Information Technology
CHR: Beth Dittbenner, Regional Director, Human Resources
CNO: Laura Evenson, Chief Nursing Officer
Web address: www.mayoclinichealthsystem.org
Control: Other not–for–profit (including NFP Corporation) **Service**: General medical and surgical

Staffed Beds: 172 **Admissions**: 10182 **Census**: 106 **Outpatient Visits**: 266576 **Births**: 1392 **Personnel**: 1586

Many Facility Codes have changed. Please refer to the AHA Guide Code Chart. © 2019 AHA Guide

MN

MAPLE GROVE—Hennepin County

⬆ **MAPLE GROVE HOSPITAL (240214)**, 9875 Hospital Drive, Zip 55369–4648; tel. 763/581–1000, **A**3 10 21 **F**3 13 15 18 29 30 40 43 45 47 53 60 68 70 72 76 77 79 81 84 85 89 100 102 107 108 111 115 118 119 126 130 146 148 149 **S** North Memorial Health Care, Robbinsdale, MN
Primary Contact: Andrew S. Cochrane, Chief Executive Officer
CFO: Aaron Bloomquist, Chief Financial Officer
CMO: Pamela Doorenbos, M.D., Vice President, Medical Affairs
CHR: Rebecca A. Rauen, Director Human Resources
CNO: Wendy Ulferts, Vice President and Chief Nursing Officer
Web address: www.maplegrovehospital.org
Control: Other not–for–profit (including NFP Corporation) **Service:** General medical and surgical

Staffed Beds: 108 **Admissions:** 9562 **Census:** 81 **Outpatient Visits:** 228644 **Births:** 4852 **Total Expense ($000):** 166636 **Payroll Expense ($000):** 59764 **Personnel:** 1098

MAPLEWOOD—Ramsey County

⊠ **ST. JOHN'S HOSPITAL (240210)**, 1575 Beam Avenue, Zip 55109–1126; tel. 651/232–7000, **A**1 3 5 10 **F**3 5 13 15 18 28 29 30 31 34 35 36 37 38 40 44 45 46 49 50 53 54 55 61 63 64 68 70 72 74 75 76 77 78 79 81 82 85 86 87 93 97 100 102 104 107 108 110 111 114 115 116 117 119 120 121 123 126 129 130 131 132 135 146 147 148 149 **S** Fairview Health Services, Minneapolis, MN
Primary Contact: Lia Christiansen, Chief Operating Officer, Acute Care Hospitals
COO: M. Osman Akhtar, Chief Operating Officer
CFO: Daniel Fromm, Chief Financial Officer
CMO: Mark Welton, M.D., Chief Medical Officer
CIO: Alistar Jacques, Chief Information Officer
CHR: Carolyn Jacobson, Chief Human Resources Officer
CNO: Laura Reed, R.N., Chief Nursing Executive
Web address: www.stjohnshospital-mn.org
Control: Other not–for–profit (including NFP Corporation) **Service:** General medical and surgical

Staffed Beds: 192 **Admissions:** 12098 **Census:** 110 **Outpatient Visits:** 115860 **Births:** 2673 **Total Expense ($000):** 250517 **Payroll Expense ($000):** 105770 **Personnel:** 1048

MARSHALL—Lyon County

★ ○ **AVERA MARSHALL REGIONAL MEDICAL CENTER (241359)**, 300 South Bruce Street, Zip 56258–3900; tel. 507/532–9661, (Total facility includes 76 beds in nursing home–type unit) **A**10 11 18 **F**2 3 11 12 13 15 17 18 28 29 30 31 33 34 35 40 41 43 45 50 56 57 59 60 62 63 64 65 70 75 76 78 79 81 82 84 85 87 89 97 98 101 102 104 107 110 111 115 119 120 121 123 128 129 130 131 132 133 144 146 148 149 156 157 **S** Avera Health, Sioux Falls, SD
Primary Contact: Mary B. Maertens, FACHE, President and Chief Executive Officer
CFO: Sharon Williams, Vice President Finance and Information Technology
CMO: Edward Woiske, M.D., Chief Medical Officer
CIO: Sharon Williams, Vice President Finance and Information Technology
CHR: Sonya J Kayser, Human Resources Officer
CNO: Dodie Derynck, Chief Nursing Officer
Web address: www.avera.org
Control: Church operated, Nongovernment, not–for–profit **Service:** General medical and surgical

Staffed Beds: 111 **Admissions:** 2154 **Census:** 92 **Outpatient Visits:** 58372 **Births:** 538 **Total Expense ($000):** 60505 **Payroll Expense ($000):** 23411 **Personnel:** 394

MELROSE—Stearns County

★ **CENTRACARE HEALTH-MELROSE (241330)**, 525 Main Street West, Zip 56352–1043; tel. 320/256–4231, (Total facility includes 75 beds in nursing home–type unit) **A**10 18 **F**3 6 7 10 13 15 28 30 34 35 40 43 56 57 64 65 76 77 78 79 81 82 85 89 91 92 93 96 107 110 111 115 119 121 125 127 128 129 130 132 133 135 146 148 154 **S** CentraCare Health, Saint Cloud, MN
Primary Contact: Gerry Gilbertson, FACHE, Administrator
COO: Gerry Gilbertson, FACHE, Administrator
CFO: Adam Paulson, Director Finance
CMO: Dante Beretta, M.D., Chief of Staff
CIO: Janet Kruzel, Business Office Manager
CHR: Joyce Chan, Chief Human Resources Officer
CNO: Keri Wimmer, R.N., Patient Care Director
Web address: www.centracare.com
Control: Other not–for–profit (including NFP Corporation) **Service:** General medical and surgical

Staffed Beds: 89 **Admissions:** 623 **Census:** 81 **Total Expense ($000):** 36702 **Payroll Expense ($000):** 16669 **Personnel:** 278

MINNEAPOLIS—Hennepin County

⊠ △ **ABBOTT NORTHWESTERN HOSPITAL (240057)**, 800 East 28th Street, Zip 55407–3799; tel. 612/863–4000, (Includes SISTER KENNY REHABILITATION INSTITUTE, 810 East 27th Street, Minneapolis, Minnesota, Zip 55407; tel. 612/874–4000) (Total facility includes 48 beds in nursing home–type unit) **A**1 2 3 5 7 10 **F**3 8 9 11 12 13 15 17 18 19 20 22 24 26 28 29 30 31 34 35 36 38 39 40 42 43 44 45 46 47 48 49 50 51 52 53 54 55 56 57 58 59 60 61 63 64 65 66 68 70 71 74 75 76 77 78 79 81 82 83 84 85 86 87 90 91 92 93 95 96 97 98 99 100 101 102 104 105 107 108 109 110 111 112 113 114 115 116 117 118 119 120 121 123 124 126 128 129 130 131 132 135 137 138 141 143 144 145 146 147 148 149 153 154 157 **S** Allina Health, Minneapolis, MN
Primary Contact: Ann Madden Rice, President
CFO: Brian Weinreis, Vice President Operations and Finance
CMO: Penny Ann Wheeler, M.D., President and Chief Medical Officer
CIO: Susan Heichert, Senior Vice President and Chief Information Officer
CHR: Margaret Butler, Vice President Human Resources
CNO: Mandy Richards, R.N., MSN, System Chief Nursing Officer, Allina Health Vice President of Care
Web address: www.abbottnorthwestern.com
Control: Other not–for–profit (including NFP Corporation) **Service:** General medical and surgical

Staffed Beds: 685 **Admissions:** 36026 **Census:** 506 **Outpatient Visits:** 524189 **Births:** 4907 **Total Expense ($000):** 1206650 **Payroll Expense ($000):** 514015 **Personnel:** 4583

⊠ **CHILDREN'S HOSPITALS AND CLINICS OF MINNESOTA (243302)**, 2525 Chicago Avenue South, Zip 55404–4518; tel. 612/813–6100, (Includes CHILDREN'S HOSPITALS AND CLINICS OF MINNESOTA, 345 North Smith Avenue, Saint Paul, Minnesota, Zip 55102–2346; tel. 651/220–6000; Robert Bonar Jr, Chief Executive Officer) **A**1 3 5 10 **F**3 8 9 17 18 19 20 21 22 23 24 25 26 27 28 29 30 31 32 34 35 36 38 39 40 43 45 50 51 54 55 57 58 59 61 62 63 64 65 68 71 72 73 74 75 77 78 79 80 81 82 84 85 86 87 88 89 92 93 97 100 101 102 104 107 108 111 112 114 115 119 129 130 131 132 134 135 136 143 145 146 148 154 156
Primary Contact: Marc Gorelick, M.D., President and Chief Executive Officer
COO: Trevor Sawallish, Senior Vice President Clinical Operations and Chief Operating Officer
CFO: Rebecca Woitalewicz, Chief Financial Officer
CMO: Emily Chapman, Chief Medical Officer
CIO: Jeffrey D Young, Chief Information Officer
CHR: Samantha Hanson, Chief Human Resources Officer
CNO: Roxanne Fernandes, R.N., Chief Nursing Officer
Web address: www.childrensmn.org
Control: Other not–for–profit (including NFP Corporation) **Service:** Children's general medical and surgical

Staffed Beds: 430 **Admissions:** 15748 **Census:** 207 **Outpatient Visits:** 487115 **Births:** 0 **Total Expense ($000):** 898299 **Payroll Expense ($000):** 417363 **Personnel:** 4039

FAIRVIEW RIVERSIDE HOSPITAL See University of Minnesota Medical Center, Fairview, Minneapolis

☐ △ **HENNEPIN HEALTHCARE (240004)**, 701 Park Avenue South, Zip 55415–1829; tel. 612/873–3000, (Includes HCMC DEPARTMENT OF PEDIATRICS, 701 Park Avenue, Minneapolis, Minnesota, Zip 55415–1623; tel. 612/873–2064) **A**1 2 3 5 7 8 10 **F**3 5 7 8 12 13 15 16 18 20 22 24 26 28 29 30 31 32 33 34 35 36 38 39 40 41 43 44 45 46 47 48 49 50 51 53 54 55 56 57 58 59 60 61 62 63 64 65 66 68 70 72 74 75 76 77 78 79 81 82 84 85 86 87 88 89 90 92 93 94 96 97 98 99 100 101 102 103 104 105 106 107 108 110 111 112 114 115 117 118 119 120 121 126 129 130 131 132 134 135 136 138 139 140 141 144 145 146 147 148 149 150 153 154 156 157
Primary Contact: John Cumming, M.D., Interim Chief Executive Officer
COO: Emily Blomberg, Chief Operating Officer
CFO: Derrick O. Hollings, Chief Financial Officer
CMO: William Heegaard, M.D., Chief Medical Officer
CIO: Nancy Garrett, Chief Analytics and Information Technology Officer
CHR: Walter Chesley, Senior Vice President Human Resources
CNO: Lori J. Brown, R.N., FACHE, Chief Nursing Officer
Web address: www.hcmc.org
Control: County, Government, nonfederal **Service:** General medical and surgical

Staffed Beds: 439 **Admissions:** 22287 **Census:** 332 **Outpatient Visits:** 726572 **Births:** 1913 **Total Expense ($000):** 1001959 **Payroll Expense ($000):** 545825 **Personnel:** 5789

MN

Hospital, Medicare Provider Number, Address, Telephone, Approval, Facility, and Physician Codes, Health Care System

★ American Hospital Association (AHA) membership
☐ The Joint Commission accreditation
○ Healthcare Facilities Accreditation Program
◇ DNV Healthcare Inc. accreditation
⬆ Center for Improvement in Healthcare Quality Accreditation
△ Commission on Accreditation of Rehabilitation Facilities (CARF) accreditation

✉ △ **MINNEAPOLIS VETERANS AFFAIRS HEALTH CARE SYSTEM**, One Veterans Drive, Zip 55417–2399; tel. 612/725–2000, (Nonreporting) **A**1 2 3 5 7 8 **S** Department of Veterans Affairs, Washington, DC
Primary Contact: Patrick J. Kelly, FACHE, Director
COO: Kurt Thielen, Associate Director
CFO: LeAnn Stomberg, Chief Financial Officer
CMO: Kent Crossley, M.D., Chief of Staff
CIO: Brian Bornick, Chief Information Officer
CHR: Tom Johnson, Chief Human Resource Officer
CNO: Helen Pearlman, Nurse Executive
Web address: www.minneapolis.va.gov
Control: Veterans Affairs, Government, federal **Service**: General medical and surgical

Staffed Beds: 309

✉ **PHILLIPS EYE INSTITUTE (240196)**, 2215 Park Avenue, Zip 55404–3756; tel. 612/775–8800, (Nonreporting) **A**1 10 **S** Allina Health, Minneapolis, MN
Primary Contact: Daniel S. Conrad, M.D., President
CFO: Chris Verdon, Director Finance
CMO: Emmett Carpel, M.D., Medical Director and Chief of Staff
CNO: Margaret Watry, Director of Patient Care Services and Nurse Executive
Web address: www.allinahealth.org/ahs/pei.nsf/
Control: Other not–for–profit (including NFP Corporation) **Service**: Eye, ear, nose and throat

Staffed Beds: 8

SISTER KENNY REHABILITATION INSTITUTE See Abbott Northwestern Hospital, Minneapolis

ST. MARY'S HOSPITAL AND REHABILITATION CENTER See University of Minnesota Medical Center, Fairview, Minneapolis

UNIVERSITY OF MINNESOTA HOSPITAL AND CLINIC See University of Minnesota Medical Center, Fairview, Minneapolis

✉ △ **UNIVERSITY OF MINNESOTA MEDICAL CENTER, FAIRVIEW (240080)**, 2450 Riverside Avenue, Zip 55454–1400; tel. 612/672–6000, (Includes FAIRVIEW RIVERSIDE HOSPITAL, 2312 South Sixth Street, Minneapolis, Minnesota, Zip 55454; tel. 612/371–6300; ST. MARY'S HOSPITAL AND REHABILITATION CENTER, 2414 South Seventh Street, Minneapolis, Minnesota, Zip 55454; tel. 612/338–2229; UNIVERSITY OF MINNESOTA HOSPITAL AND CLINIC, 420 SE Delaware Street, Minneapolis, Minnesota, Zip 55455–0392; tel. 612/626–3000; UNIVERSITY OF MINNESOTA MASONIC CHILDREN'S HOSPITAL, 420 Delaware Street, SE, Minneapolis, Minnesota, Zip 55455–0341; tel. 888/543–7866) (Total facility includes 20 beds in nursing home–type unit) **A**1 3 5 7 8 10 **F**3 4 5 11 12 13 15 17 18 19 20 21 22 23 24 25 26 27 28 29 30 31 32 33 34 35 36 37 38 39 40 41 43 44 45 46 47 48 49 50 51 55 56 57 58 59 60 61 64 65 68 70 72 74 75 76 77 78 79 80 81 82 84 85 86 87 88 89 90 91 92 93 96 97 98 99 100 101 102 103 104 105 106 107 108 109 110 111 112 113 114 115 116 117 118 119 120 121 123 124 126 128 130 132 134 135 136 137 138 139 140 141 142 145 146 147 148 149 151 153 154 156 **S** Fairview Health Services, Minneapolis, MN
Primary Contact: John Doherty, Co-President, M Health
CFO: John Doherty, Vice President Finance
CMO: Barbara Gold, M.D., Chief Medical Officer
CHR: Don Moschkau, Senior Director Human Resources
Web address: www.fairview.org
Control: Other not–for–profit (including NFP Corporation) **Service**: General medical and surgical

Staffed Beds: 861 **Admissions**: 33566 **Census**: 637 **Outpatient Visits**: 565553 **Births**: 2368 **Total Expense ($000)**: 1642843 **Payroll Expense ($000)**: 584555 **Personnel**: 5018

VETERANS AFFAIRS MEDICAL CENTER See Minneapolis Veterans Affairs Health Care System

★ **CCM HEALTH (241325)**, 824 North 11th Street, Zip 56265–1683; tel. 320/269–8877, (Nonreporting) **A**10 18
Primary Contact: Brian A. Lovdahl, Chief Executive Officer
CFO: Darlene Boike, Chief Financial Officer
CIO: Jeff Plemel, Director Health Information
CHR: Vonnie Erickson, Human Resource Manager
CNO: Terry Anderson, R.N., Director of Nursing Services
Web address: www.montevideomedical.com
Control: City–county, Government, nonfederal **Service**: General medical and surgical

Staffed Beds: 25

★ ⇑ **CENTRACARE HEALTH-MONTICELLO (241362)**, 1013 Hart Boulevard, Zip 55362–8230; tel. 763/295–2945, (Nonreporting) **A**5 10 18 21 **S** CentraCare Health, Saint Cloud, MN
Primary Contact: Mary Ellen Wells, FACHE, Administrator
CFO: Kristine Hammer, Director of Finance
CMO: John Hering, M.D., Chief Medical Officer
CNO: Lynn Christian, R.N., MSN, Division Director, Acute Care Nursing
Web address: www.centracare.com
Control: Hospital district or authority, Government, nonfederal **Service**: General medical and surgical

Staffed Beds: 126

★ **MERCY HOSPITAL (241350)**, 4572 County Road 61, Zip 55767–9405; tel. 218/485–4481, **A**10 18 **F**3 7 11 13 15 28 29 31 34 35 40 43 45 51 53 57 59 62 64 68 70 75 76 77 78 79 81 82 85 86 87 93 107 110 111 114 119 124 129 130 131 132 133 135 144 146 148 149 156
Primary Contact: Michael Youso, Chief Executive Officer
CHR: Sonya Towle, Director Human Resources
CNO: Donita Korpela, R.N., Director of Patient Care Services
Web address: www.mercymooselake.org
Control: Hospital district or authority, Government, nonfederal **Service**: General medical and surgical

Staffed Beds: 25 **Admissions**: 613 **Census**: 7 **Outpatient Visits**: 33367 **Births**: 97 **Total Expense ($000)**: 36992 **Payroll Expense ($000)**: 14342 **Personnel**: 210

✉ **FIRSTLIGHT HEALTH SYSTEM (241367)**, 301 South Highway 65 South, Zip 55051–1899; tel. 320/679–1212, **A**1 10 18 **F**3 7 11 13 15 28 31 34 35 40 43 51 53 68 70 75 76 77 78 79 81 84 85 87 93 94 97 107 108 110 111 115 119 127 130 131 132 133 135 146 147 148 149 154
Primary Contact: Randy Ulseth, Chief Executive Officer
COO: Sandy Zutz-Wiczek, Chief Operating Officer
CFO: Gordy Forbort, Chief Financial Officer
CIO: Becky Gallik, Information Systems Manager
CNO: Diane Bankers, Chief Nursing Officer
Web address: www.firstlighthealthsystem.org
Control: County, Government, nonfederal **Service**: General medical and surgical

Staffed Beds: 25 **Admissions**: 1288 **Census**: 9 **Outpatient Visits**: 171353 **Births**: 209 **Total Expense ($000)**: 82737 **Payroll Expense ($000)**: 26815 **Personnel**: 330

★ **STEVENS COMMUNITY MEDICAL CENTER (241363)**, 400 East First Street, Zip 56267–1408; tel. 320/589–1313, **A**10 18 **F**3 11 13 15 28 29 31 34 35 40 43 44 45 50 54 57 59 64 70 75 76 77 79 81 85 86 87 89 97 107 110 111 115 119 127 128 130 131 132 135 144 146 148 149
Primary Contact: John Rau, President and Chief Executive Officer
CFO: Kerrie Erickson, Vice President Finance
CIO: Kerrie Erickson, Vice President Finance
CHR: Karla Larson, Director Human Resources
Web address: www.scmcinc.org
Control: Other not–for–profit (including NFP Corporation) **Service**: General medical and surgical

Staffed Beds: 25 **Admissions**: 842 **Census**: 7 **Outpatient Visits**: 71226 **Births**: 97 **Total Expense ($000)**: 39301 **Payroll Expense ($000)**: 17971 **Personnel**: 237

☐ **MAYO CLINIC HEALTH SYSTEM IN NEW PRAGUE (241361)**, 301 Second Street NE, Zip 56071–1799; tel. 952/758–4431, **A**1 3 10 18 **F**11 13 15 18 28 29 30 31 34 35 40 43 45 46 53 57 59 64 65 68 74 75 76 77 78 79 81 82 85 86 87 92 93 97 107 108 110 111 114 116 117 119 125 128 129 130 131 132 133 146 147 149 154 156 **S** Mayo Clinic, Rochester, MN
Primary Contact: Mary J. Klimp, FACHE, Interim Administrator
Web address: www.mayoclinichealthsystem.org/locations/new-prague
Control: Other not–for–profit (including NFP Corporation) **Service**: General medical and surgical

Staffed Beds: 19 **Admissions**: 701 **Census**: 11 **Outpatient Visits**: 45982 **Births**: 156 **Personnel**: 164

Many Facility Codes have changed. Please refer to the AHA Guide Code Chart.   © 2019 AHA Guide

NEW ULM—Brown County

⊞ **NEW ULM MEDICAL CENTER (241378)**, 1324 Fifth Street North, Zip 56073–1553; tel. 507/217–5000, **A**1 3 5 10 18 **F**3 4 5 8 13 15 28 29 31 32 34 35 36 40 42 43 46 50 55 56 57 59 64 65 68 70 75 76 77 78 79 81 82 84 85 87 93 94 97 98 100 101 102 104 107 108 111 115 119 129 130 131 132 135 144 146 148 149 154 156 **S** Allina Health, Minneapolis, MN
Primary Contact: Toby Freier, President
CFO: Steve Schneider, Manager Behavioral Services and Director Operations
CMO: Daniel Holmberg, M.D., Director of Medical Affairs
CHR: Anne Makepeace, Director Human Resources
CNO: Jennifer Brehmer, Director of Patient Care
Web address: www.newulmmedicalcenter.com
Control: Other not–for–profit (including NFP Corporation) **Service:** General medical and surgical

Staffed Beds: 44 **Admissions:** 2078 **Census:** 19 **Personnel:** 418

NORTHFIELD—Dakota County

★ **NORTHFIELD HOSPITAL AND CLINICS (240014)**, 2000 North Avenue, Zip 55057–1498; tel. 507/646–1000, (Total facility includes 40 beds in nursing home–type unit) **A**10 **F**3 7 11 13 15 30 31 40 43 47 48 62 63 64 68 69 70 75 76 77 78 79 81 85 87 89 93 107 110 111 115 119 128 129 130 131 132 133 144 146 149 154
Primary Contact: Steve Underdahl, President and Chief Executive Officer
COO: Jerry Ehn, Chief Operating Officer
CFO: Scott D Edin, Vice President, Finance and Chief Financial Officer
CMO: Jeff Meland, M.D., Vice President, Chief Medical Officer
CHR: Vicki Stevens, Human Resources Executive
CNO: Tammy A. Hayes, R.N., MS, Chief Nurse Executive and Long Term Care Administrator
Web address: www.northfieldhospital.org
Control: City, Government, nonfederal **Service:** General medical and surgical

Staffed Beds: 77 **Admissions:** 2071 **Census:** 50 **Outpatient Visits:** 143986
Births: 550 **Total Expense ($000):** 107320 **Payroll Expense ($000):** 48631
Personnel: 562

OLIVIA—Renville County

★ **RC HOSPITAL AND CLINICS (241306)**, 100 Healthy Way, Zip 56277–1117; tel. 320/523–1261, **A**10 18 **F**3 8 15 17 28 29 34 35 40 41 43 45 46 57 59 63 64 65 68 70 75 76 77 79 81 82 85 86 89 93 94 96 97 107 111 114 119 126 127 129 130 131 132 133 146 148 149 156
Primary Contact: Nathan Blad, Chief Executive Officer
CFO: Nathan Blad, Chief Financial Officer
CIO: Cherry Weigel, Director Health Information Management
Web address: www.rchospital.com
Control: County, Government, nonfederal **Service:** General medical and surgical

Staffed Beds: 16 **Admissions:** 397 **Census:** 3 **Outpatient Visits:** 75896
Births: 49 **Total Expense ($000):** 28636 **Payroll Expense ($000):** 11510
Personnel: 164

ONAMIA—Mille Lacs County

★ **MILLE LACS HEALTH SYSTEM (241356)**, 200 North Elm Street, Zip 56359–7901; tel. 320/532–3154, (Total facility includes 57 beds in nursing home–type unit) **A**10 18 **F**7 11 15 28 29 31 33 34 40 43 45 50 59 62 64 75 77 81 85 93 97 98 103 107 114 115 127 129 130 132 133 135 144 149 156 157
Primary Contact: Bill Nelson, Chief Executive Officer
COO: Kim Kucera, Chief Operating Officer
CFO: John Unzen, Chief Financial Officer
CMO: Thomas H Bracken, M.D., Vice President Medical Affairs
Web address: www.mlhealth.org
Control: Other not–for–profit (including NFP Corporation) **Service:** General medical and surgical

Staffed Beds: 85 **Admissions:** 998 **Census:** 66 **Outpatient Visits:** 24534
Births: 4 **Total Expense ($000):** 40971 **Payroll Expense ($000):** 21060
Personnel: 432

ORTONVILLE—Big Stone County

★ **ORTONVILLE AREA HEALTH SERVICES (241342)**, 450 Eastvold Avenue, Zip 56278–1133; tel. 320/839–2502, (Nonreporting) **A**10 18 **S** Sanford Health, Sioux Falls, SD
Primary Contact: David Rogers, Chief Executive Officer
CFO: Kevin Benson, Chief Financial Officer
CMO: Stacy Longnecker, Chief of Staff
CIO: Barbara Voecks, Chief Information Officer
CHR: Kim McCrea, Chief Human Resources Officer
CNO: Jennifer Wiik, Chief Nursing Officer
Web address: www.oahs.us
Control: City, Government, nonfederal **Service:** General medical and surgical

Staffed Beds: 102

OWATONNA—Steele County

⊞ **OWATONNA HOSPITAL (240069)**, 2250 NW 26th Street, Zip 55060–5503; tel. 507/451–3850, **A**1 10 **F**11 13 28 29 34 35 40 57 77 79 80 81 93 98 100 101 102 107 108 119 129 130 131 145 149 154 **S** Allina Health, Minneapolis, MN
Primary Contact: David L. Albrecht, President
COO: Mark T Gillen, Director of Operations
CFO: Mark T Gillen, Director Finance and Operations
CHR: Sarah Stumme, Director Human Resources
CNO: Anne Draeger, Chief Nursing Officer
Web address: www.owatonnahospital.com
Control: Other not–for–profit (including NFP Corporation) **Service:** General medical and surgical

Staffed Beds: 42 **Admissions:** 2423 **Census:** 24 **Outpatient Visits:** 40304
Total Expense ($000): 54596 **Payroll Expense ($000):** 20209
Personnel: 233

PARK RAPIDS—Hubbard County

⊞ **CHI ST. JOSEPH'S HEALTH (241380)**, 600 Pleasant Avenue, Zip 56470–1431; tel. 218/732–3311, **A**1 10 18 **F**3 11 12 13 15 28 29 30 32 34 35 39 40 43 45 47 50 57 59 63 64 65 70 75 76 77 79 81 82 84 85 93 107 108 110 115 118 129 130 131 132 133 134 146 149 150 154 **S** CommonSpirit Health, Chicago, IL
Primary Contact: Benjamin Koppelman, President
CFO: Jay Ross, Chief Financial Officer
CMO: Kia Parsi, M.D., Chief Medical Officer
CHR: John Tormanen, Director Mission and Human Resources
CNO: Deb Haagenson, R.N., Vice President of Patient Care
Web address: www.sjahs.org
Control: Church operated, Nongovernment, not–for–profit **Service:** General medical and surgical

Staffed Beds: 25 **Admissions:** 1188 **Census:** 11

PAYNESVILLE—Stearns County

★ **CENTRACARE HEALTH-PAYNESVILLE (241349)**, 200 West 1st Street, Zip 56362–1496; tel. 320/243–3767, (Total facility includes 51 beds in nursing home–type unit) **A**5 10 18 **F**2 7 10 11 13 15 28 31 34 40 43 45 50 56 57 64 65 71 76 81 82 85 89 93 107 110 111 115 119 125 128 130 133 135 145 146 148 149 150 **S** CentraCare Health, Saint Cloud, MN
Primary Contact: Brandon E. Pietsch, Administrator
CFO: Jennifer Holtz, Director Finance
CMO: Timothy Malling, M.D., Chief of Staff
CHR: Paulette Hagen, Human Resources and Administrative Services Director
CNO: Rachel A Walz, Director Patient Care
Web address: www.centracare.com
Control: Other not–for–profit (including NFP Corporation) **Service:** General medical and surgical

Staffed Beds: 66 **Admissions:** 493 **Census:** 53 **Outpatient Visits:** 4458
Births: 78 **Total Expense ($000):** 39662 **Payroll Expense ($000):** 19749
Personnel: 86

PERHAM—Otter Tail County

⊞ **PERHAM HEALTH (241373)**, 1000 Coney Street West, Zip 56573–1108; tel. 218/347–4500, (Total facility includes 96 beds in nursing home–type unit) **A**1 10 18 **F**2 3 10 13 15 28 29 30 32 33 34 35 36 40 43 45 50 56 57 59 62 64 65 66 69 75 76 77 81 85 86 89 91 93 97 107 110 111 119 125 128 130 131 132 133 135 144 146 147 148 149 154 156 **S** Sanford Health, Sioux Falls, SD
Primary Contact: Chuck Hofius, Chief Executive Officer
CFO: Brad D Wurgler, Chief Financial Officer
CMO: Tim Studer, President Medical Staff
CIO: Jim Rieber, Director Information Systems
CNO: Bonnie Johnson, R.N., Vice President of Patient Services
Web address: www.perhamhealth.org
Control: Hospital district or authority, Government, nonfederal **Service:** General medical and surgical

Staffed Beds: 121 **Admissions:** 807 **Census:** 95 **Outpatient Visits:** 367429
Births: 138 **Total Expense ($000):** 53903 **Payroll Expense ($000):** 24752
Personnel: 252

MN

Hospital, Medicare Provider Number, Address, Telephone, Approval, Facility, and Physician Codes, Health Care System

★ American Hospital Association (AHA) membership
☐ The Joint Commission accreditation
○ Healthcare Facilities Accreditation Program
◇ DNV Healthcare Inc. accreditation
⇧ Center for Improvement in Healthcare Quality Accreditation
△ Commission on Accreditation of Rehabilitation Facilities (CARF) accreditation

PIPESTONE—Pipestone County

★ **PIPESTONE COUNTY MEDICAL CENTER AVERA (241374)**, 916 4th Avenue SW, Zip 56164–1890; tel. 507/825–5811, **A**10 18 **F**3 8 13 15 28 29 30 31 34 35 40 45 46 47 48 50 53 56 57 59 62 63 64 65 68 75 76 77 79 81 82 85 93 96 97 107 110 111 115 119 130 131 132 133 135 146 148 149 156 **S** Avera Health, Sioux Falls, SD
Primary Contact: Bradley D. Burris, Chief Executive Officer
CFO: Dave Keeler, Chief Financial Officer
CHR: Judy Raschke, Director Human Resources
CNO: Jessica Smidt, R.N., Director of Nursing
Web address: www.pcmchealth.org
Control: County, Government, nonfederal **Service**: General medical and surgical

Staffed Beds: 18 Admissions: 336 Census: 3 Outpatient Visits: 35942 **Births:** 79 **Total Expense ($000):** 30825 **Payroll Expense ($000):** 12889 **Personnel:** 166

PRINCETON—Sherburne County

✉ **FAIRVIEW NORTHLAND MEDICAL CENTER (240141)**, 911 Northland Drive, Zip 55371–2173; tel. 763/389–1313, **A**1 5 10 **F**3 11 13 15 18 34 35 40 41 43 47 48 50 51 57 59 64 69 70 75 76 77 78 79 81 85 86 87 89 93 94 101 107 110 111 115 119 130 131 132 146 148 149 154 **S** Fairview Health Services, Minneapolis, MN
Primary Contact: Lia Christiansen, Chief Operating Officer, Acute Care Hospitals
CFO: Kim Ericson, Vice President Finance
CMO: Greg Schoen, M.D., Regional Medical Director
CHR: Erich Spencer, Chief Human Resource Officer
CNO: Karen Whiley, Vice President Patient Care Services
Web address: www.northland.fairview.org
Control: Other not–for–profit (including NFP Corporation) **Service**: General medical and surgical

Staffed Beds: 23 Admissions: 1622 Census: 13 Outpatient Visits: 53722 **Births:** 394 **Total Expense ($000):** 60554 **Payroll Expense ($000):** 27443 **Personnel:** 224

RED LAKE—Beltrami County

☐ **RED LAKE INDIAN HEALTH SERVICE HOSPITAL (240206)**, 24760 Hospital Drive, Zip 56671, Mailing Address: P.O. Box 497, Zip 56671–0497; tel. 218/679–3912, (Nonreporting) **A**1 10 **S** U. S. Indian Health Service, Rockville, MD
Primary Contact: Norine Smith, Chief Executive Officer
CMO: Paul Ditmanson, M.D., Clinical Director
CNO: Mary Ann Cook, R.N., Director of Nursing
Web address: www.rlnnredlakehospital.com/
Control: PHS, Indian Service, Government, federal **Service**: General medical and surgical

Staffed Beds: 19

RED WING—Goodhue County

☐ **MAYO CLINIC HEALTH SYSTEM IN RED WING (240018)**, 701 Hewitt Boulevard, Zip 55066–2848, Mailing Address: P.O. Box 95, Zip 55066–0095; tel. 651/267–5000, **A**1 3 5 10 **F**3 11 13 15 18 28 29 30 31 34 35 36 40 43 45 57 59 64 65 70 74 75 76 77 78 79 81 82 86 87 93 94 97 100 104 107 111 115 119 129 130 131 132 146 147 149 154 **S** Mayo Clinic, Rochester, MN
Primary Contact: Brian Whited, M.D., President and Chief Executive Officer
CMO: Jack Alexander, M.D., Chief Medical Officer
CHR: Kim Trittin, Manager Human Resources
Web address: www.mayoclinichealthsystem.org/locations/red-wing
Control: Other not–for–profit (including NFP Corporation) **Service**: General medical and surgical

Staffed Beds: 30 Admissions: 1929 Census: 13 Outpatient Visits: 138962 **Births:** 303 **Personnel:** 458

REDWOOD FALLS—Redwood County

★ **CARRIS HEALTH - REDWOOD (241351)**, 100 Fallwood Road, Zip 56283–1828; tel. 507/637–4500, **A**10 18 **F**2 3 11 13 15 29 31 34 35 40 45 46 57 59 62 63 75 77 79 81 82 84 93 107 111 115 119 129 130 131 133 146 148 149 154
Primary Contact: Bryan Lydick, Chief Executive Officer
CFO: Thomas Richard, Director Budget and Revenue Cycle
CIO: Tom Balko, Manager Information Systems
CHR: Jody Rindfleisch, Manager Human Resources
CNO: Dawn Allen, R.N., Chief Clinical Officer
Web address: www.redwoodareahospital.org
Control: City, Government, nonfederal **Service**: General medical and surgical

Staffed Beds: 25 Admissions: 589 Census: 5 Outpatient Visits: 23615 **Births:** 99 **Total Expense ($000):** 19454 **Payroll Expense ($000):** 9864 **Personnel:** 147

ROBBINSDALE—Hennepin County

△ ⇑ **NORTH MEMORIAL HEALTH HOSPITAL (240001)**, 3300 Oakdale Avenue North, Zip 55422–2926; tel. 763/520–5200, **A**2 3 5 7 10 21 **F**3 7 11 12 13 15 17 18 20 22 24 26 28 29 30 31 34 35 38 40 43 44 45 46 49 50 53 54 55 56 57 58 59 60 61 63 64 68 70 72 73 74 75 76 77 78 79 80 81 82 84 85 86 87 88 89 90 91 92 93 96 97 98 100 102 103 104 105 107 108 110 111 114 115 117 118 119 124 126 127 129 130 132 135 144 146 147 148 149 150 153 154 155 156 157 158 **S** North Memorial Health Care, Robbinsdale, MN
Primary Contact: Jeff Wicklander, President
COO: Steve Horstmann, Vice President Operations
CFO: Aaron Bloomquist, Chief Financial Officer
CMO: Andrew Houlton, M.D., Chief Medical Officer
CIO: Patrick Taffe, Vice President Information Services
CHR: Melissa Smith, Interim Vice President Human Resources
CNO: Kelly Lynn White, Vice President of Patient Care and Chief Nursing Officer
Web address: www.northmemorial.com
Control: Other not–for–profit (including NFP Corporation) **Service**: General medical and surgical

Staffed Beds: 358 Admissions: 19345 Census: 251 Outpatient Visits: 170083 **Births:** 909 **Total Expense ($000):** 423050 **Payroll Expense ($000):** 191852 **Personnel:** 3188

ROCHESTER—Olmsted County

☐ **COMMUNITY BEHAVIORAL HEALTH HOSPITAL - ROCHESTER (244017)**, 251 Wood Lake Drive SE, Zip 55904–5530; tel. 507/206–2561, (Nonreporting) **A**1 10 **S** Minnesota Department of Human Services, Saint Paul, MN
Primary Contact: James Pierce, Administrator
CFO: Shirley Jacobson, Chief Financial Officer
CMO: Peter S Millen, Chief Medical Officer MHSATS
CIO: Thomas Baden Jr Chief Information Officer
CHR: Connie Jones, Director Human Resources
CNO: Pamela R Bajari, R.N., Nurse Executive MHSATS
Web address: www.health.state.mn.us
Control: State, Government, nonfederal **Service**: Psychiatric

Staffed Beds: 8

✉ △ **MAYO CLINIC HOSPITAL - ROCHESTER (240010)**, 1216 Second Street SW, Zip 55902–1906; tel. 507/255–5123, (Includes MAYO CLINIC HOSPITAL - METHODIST CAMPUS, 201 West Center Street, Rochester, Minnesota, Zip 55902–3084; tel. 507/266–7890; MAYO CLINIC HOSPITAL - SAINT MARYS CAMPUS, 1216 Second Street SW, Rochester, Minnesota, Zip 55902–1970; tel. 507/255–5123; Kenneth F. Ackerman, FACHE, Chair, Hospital Operation; MAYO EUGENIO LITTA CHILDREN'S HOSPITAL, 200 First Street, SW, Rochester, Minnesota, Zip 55905–0001; tel. 507/255–5123) **A**1 2 3 5 7 8 10 20 **F**3 6 7 8 9 11 12 13 14 15 17 18 19 20 21 22 23 24 25 26 27 28 29 30 31 34 35 36 37 38 39 40 41 43 44 45 46 47 48 49 50 51 52 53 54 55 56 57 58 59 60 61 63 64 65 68 70 71 72 73 74 75 76 77 78 79 80 81 82 84 85 86 87 88 89 90 91 92 93 94 95 96 97 98 99 100 101 102 103 104 105 106 107 108 110 111 112 114 115 116 117 118 119 120 121 122 123 124 126 130 132 134 135 136 137 138 139 140 141 142 143 145 146 147 148 149 150 153 154 155 157 **S** Mayo Clinic, Rochester, MN
Primary Contact: Kenneth F. Ackerman, FACHE, Hospital Administrator
COO: Jeffrey W. Bolton, Chief Administrative Officer
CFO: Kedrick D. Adkins, Chief Financial Officer
CMO: Robert R. Cima, M.D., Medical Director, Hospital Operations
CIO: Christopher J. Ross, Chief Information Technology Officer
CHR: Cathryn H. Fraser, Chief Human Resources Officer
CNO: Pamela O. Johnson, MS, R.N., Chief Nursing Officer
Web address: www.mayoclinic.org
Control: Other not–for–profit (including NFP Corporation) **Service**: General medical and surgical

Staffed Beds: 1283 Admissions: 59667 Census: 904 Outpatient Visits: 415385 **Births:** 2271 **Personnel:** 32751

★ ⇑ **OLMSTED MEDICAL CENTER (240006)**, 1650 Fourth Street SE, Zip 55904–4717, Mailing Address: 210 Ninth Street SE, Zip 55904–6756; tel. 507/288–3443, **A**10 21 **F**3 11 12 13 15 18 26 28 29 30 34 35 40 44 45 46 50 53 54 56 57 58 59 64 65 68 74 75 76 77 79 80 81 82 84 85 86 87 92 93 97 99 100 102 104 107 108 110 111 115 119 129 130 131 132 135 146 147 148 149 154 156
Primary Contact: Tim W. Weir, FACHE, Chief Executive Officer
CFO: Kevin A Higgins, Chief Financial Officer
CIO: Michelle Majerus, Chief Information Officer
CHR: Tom Hunsberger, Director Human Resources
CNO: Susan Klenner, Chief Nursing Officer and Vice President of Hospital Operations
Web address: www.olmmed.org
Control: Other not–for–profit (including NFP Corporation) **Service**: General medical and surgical

Staffed Beds: 42 Admissions: 2011 Census: 12 Outpatient Visits: 325311 **Births:** 982 **Total Expense ($000):** 197745 **Payroll Expense ($000):** 100725 **Personnel:** 907

Many Facility Codes have changed. Please refer to the AHA Guide Code Chart. © 2019 AHA Guide

MN

ROSEAU—Roseau County

☒ **LIFECARE MEDICAL CENTER (241344)**, 715 Delmore Drive, Zip 56751–1599; tel. 218/463–2500, (Total facility includes 90 beds in nursing–type unit) **A1** 10 18 **F3** 7 10 11 13 15 28 29 30 31 32 34 35 36 40 43 45 53 56 57 59 62 63 64 65 68 75 76 77 81 82 84 85 86 93 104 107 110 111 115 118 119 128 129 130 132 133 135 144 146 147 148 149 156
Primary Contact: Keith Okeson, President and Chief Executive Officer
COO: Susan C Lisell, Vice President of Clinical Services
CFO: Cathy Huss, Chief Financial Officer
CIO: Kevin Schumacher, Director of Information Systems
CHR: Lois Slick, Director Human Resources
CNO: Roxanne Fabian, Director of Nursing-Acute Care
Web address: www.lifecaremedicalcenter.org
Control: Other not–for–profit (including NFP Corporation) **Service:** General medical and surgical

Staffed Beds: 115 **Admissions:** 763 **Census:** 97 **Outpatient Visits:** 44084 **Births:** 151 **Total Expense ($000):** 44365 **Payroll Expense ($000):** 20413 **Personnel:** 323

SAINT CLOUD—Stearns County

☒ △ **ST. CLOUD HOSPITAL (240036)**, 1406 Sixth Avenue North, Zip 56303–1901; tel. 320/251–2700, **A1** 2 3 5 7 10 20 **F3** 5 11 12 13 14 15 17 18 19 20 22 24 26 28 29 30 31 32 34 35 36 37 38 39 40 43 44 45 46 47 48 49 50 51 54 56 57 58 59 60 61 62 63 64 66 68 69 70 72 74 75 76 77 78 79 80 81 82 84 85 86 87 88 89 90 92 93 96 97 98 99 100 101 102 103 104 105 106 107 108 110 111 115 117 118 119 120 121 123 124 126 129 130 131 132 134 135 141 144 145 146 147 148 149 150 151 152 153 156 157 **S** CentraCare Health, Saint Cloud, MN
Primary Contact: Craig J. Broman, FACHE, President
COO: Joy Plamann, R.N., Chief Nursing and Operating Officer
CFO: Greg Klugherz, Vice President Corporate Services and Chief Financial Officer
CMO: Mark Matthias, M.D., Vice President of Medical Affairs
CIO: Amy Porwoll, Vice President of Information Systems
CHR: Duane Rasmusson, Vice President Human Resources
CNO: Joy Plamann, R.N., Chief Nursing and Operating Officer
Web address: www.centracare.com
Control: Other not–for–profit (including NFP Corporation) **Service:** General medical and surgical

Staffed Beds: 471 **Admissions:** 28548 **Census:** 343 **Outpatient Visits:** 524649 **Births:** 2660 **Total Expense ($000):** 790230 **Payroll Expense ($000):** 341549 **Personnel:** 4584

☒ **ST. CLOUD VETERANS AFFAIRS HEALTH CARE SYSTEM**, 4801 Veterans Drive, Zip 56303–2099; tel. 320/252–1670, (Total facility includes 225 beds in nursing home–type unit) **A1** 3 **F2** 3 4 5 6 8 9 11 12 18 29 30 31 33 34 35 36 38 39 44 45 47 50 53 54 56 57 58 59 63 64 65 68 74 75 77 78 79 81 82 83 84 85 86 87 91 92 93 94 97 98 100 101 102 103 104 105 106 107 108 111 115 119 128 130 132 135 143 144 146 147 148 149 152 153 154 156 157 **S** Department of Veterans Affairs, Washington, DC
Primary Contact: Stephen Black, MS, Health Care System Director
COO: Barry I Bahl, Director
CFO: Joseph Schmitz, Chief Financial Officer
CMO: Susan Markstrom, M.D., Chief of Staff
CIO: Denise Hanson, Information Technology Specialist
CHR: Lisa Rosendahl, Director Human Resources
CNO: Meri Hauge, R.N., MSN, Associate Director of Patient Care Services and Nurse Executive
Web address: www.stcloud.va.gov
Control: Veterans Affairs, Government, federal **Service:** General medical and surgical

Staffed Beds: 388 **Admissions:** 2672 **Census:** 361 **Outpatient Visits:** 377439 **Births:** 0 **Total Expense ($000):** 340593 **Payroll Expense ($000):** 131583 **Personnel:** 1783

VETERANS AFFAIRS MEDICAL CENTER See St. Cloud Veterans Affairs Health Care System

SAINT JAMES—Watonwan County

☐ **MAYO CLINIC HEALTH SYSTEM IN SAINT JAMES (241333)**, 1101 Moulton and Parsons Drive, Zip 56081–5550; tel. 507/375–3261, **A1** 10 18 **F3** 15 28 30 34 35 40 59 64 75 81 97 107 110 115 128 130 133 135 144 146 149 **S** Mayo Clinic, Rochester, MN
Primary Contact: Scott D. Thoreson, FACHE, Administrator
COO: Richard Grace, Chief Administrative Officer
CFO: James Tarasovich, Chief Financial Officer
CMO: Jennifer Langbehn, Medical Director
CHR: Gayle B Hansen, R.N., Chief Integration Officer
Web address: www.mayoclinichealthsystem.org/locations/st-james
Control: Other not–for–profit (including NFP Corporation) **Service:** General medical and surgical

Staffed Beds: 8 **Admissions:** 228 **Census:** 6 **Outpatient Visits:** 21965 **Births:** 0 **Personnel:** 62

SAINT LOUIS PARK—Hennepin County

☐ **PARK NICOLLET METHODIST HOSPITAL (240053)**, 6500 Excelsior Boulevard, Zip 55426–4702; tel. 952/993–5000, **A1** 2 3 5 10 **F3** 8 11 12 13 15 17 18 20 22 24 26 28 29 30 31 34 38 40 42 43 44 45 46 47 49 50 55 54 55 56 57 58 59 62 63 64 68 70 71 73 74 75 76 77 78 79 81 82 83 84 85 86 87 89 93 94 97 100 102 107 108 111 114 115 117 119 120 121 123 124 126 129 130 132 144 145 146 147 148 149 154 156 **S** HealthPartners, Bloomington, MN
Primary Contact: Jennifer Myster, President
COO: Michael Kaupa, Executive Vice President and Chief Operating Officer
CFO: Sheila McMillan, Chief Financial Officer
CMO: Steven Connelly, M.D., President and Chief Medical Officer
CIO: Julie Flaschenriem, Chief Information Officer
CHR: Paul Dominski, Vice President Human Resources
Web address: www.parknicollet.com
Control: Other not–for–profit (including NFP Corporation) **Service:** General medical and surgical

Staffed Beds: 365 **Admissions:** 23098 **Census:** 235 **Outpatient Visits:** 64415 **Births:** 2998 **Total Expense ($000):** 563338 **Payroll Expense ($000):** 241808

SAINT PAUL—Ramsey County

☒ **BETHESDA HOSPITAL (242004)**, 559 Capitol Boulevard, Zip 55103–2101; tel. 651/232–2000, **A1** 5 10 **F1** 3 6 11 29 30 38 44 50 53 56 64 68 74 75 77 82 84 85 86 87 91 93 96 100 104 107 119 130 132 148 156 **S** Fairview Health Services, Minneapolis, MN
Primary Contact: Jeoff Will, Chief Operating Office, Acute Care Services
COO: Jeoff Will, Chief Operating Officer, Acute Care Services
CFO: Daniel Fromm, Chief Financial Officer
CMO: Mark Welton, M.D., Chief Medical Officer
CIO: Alistar Jacques, Chief Information Officer
CHR: Carolyn Jacobson, Chief Human Resources Officer
CNO: Laura Reed, R.N., Chief Nursing Executive
Web address: www.healtheast.org
Control: Other not–for–profit (including NFP Corporation) **Service:** Acute long–term care hospital

Staffed Beds: 114 **Admissions:** 1064 **Census:** 85 **Outpatient Visits:** 6250 **Births:** 0 **Total Expense ($000):** 84441 **Payroll Expense ($000):** 43789 **Personnel:** 416

☒ △ **GILLETTE CHILDREN'S SPECIALTY HEALTHCARE (243300)**, 200 University Avenue East, Zip 55101–2507; tel. 651/291–2848, **A1** 3 5 7 10 **F3** 29 32 34 35 36 37 39 43 44 50 54 58 59 64 68 74 75 79 81 82 83 84 85 86 87 88 89 90 91 92 93 94 95 96 107 111 114 115 119 127 129 130 144 146 148 149 154
Primary Contact: Barbara Walczyk-Joers, President and Chief Executive Officer
CFO: Patrick Nolan, Vice President Finance and Chief Financial Officer
CMO: Steven Koop, M.D., Chief Medical Officer, Medical Director
CIO: Timothy Getsay, Chief Information Officer, Vice President of Performance & Information Mgmt
CHR: Kit Brady, Vice President Human Resources, Education and Guest Experience
CNO: Karen Brill, R.N., Chief Nursing Officer, Vice President Care
Web address: www.gillettechildrens.org
Control: Other not–for–profit (including NFP Corporation) **Service:** Children's general medical and surgical

Staffed Beds: 60 **Admissions:** 2393 **Census:** 32 **Outpatient Visits:** 138397 **Births:** 0 **Total Expense ($000):** 240720 **Payroll Expense ($000):** 126426 **Personnel:** 1095

MN

Hospital, Medicare Provider Number, Address, Telephone, Approval, Facility, and Physician Codes, Health Care System

★ American Hospital Association (AHA) membership   ○ Healthcare Facilities Accreditation Program   ⇑ Center for Improvement in Healthcare Quality Accreditation
☐ The Joint Commission accreditation   ◇ DNV Healthcare Inc. accreditation   △ Commission on Accreditation of Rehabilitation Facilities (CARF) accreditation

MN

☐ △ **REGIONS HOSPITAL (240106)**, 640 Jackson Street, Zip 55101–2595; tel. 651/254–3456, **A**1 2 3 5 7 8 10 **F**3 4 5 7 8 13 15 16 17 18 20 22 24 26 28 29 30 31 34 35 36 38 40 43 45 46 47 48 49 50 51 53 54 55 56 57 58 59 60 64 65 68 70 71 72 74 75 76 77 78 79 81 82 84 85 86 87 88 90 91 93 95 96 98 100 101 102 103 104 105 106 107 108 110 111 114 115 116 117 118 119 120 121 124 126 129 130 131 132 135 143 146 147 148 149 152 153 154 155 **S** HealthPartners, Bloomington, MN
Primary Contact: Megan Remark, President and Chief Executive Officer
CFO: Heidi Conrad, Vice President and Chief Financial Officer
CMO: Charles Fazio, Chief Health Officer and Medical Director Health Plan
CIO: Kim LaReau, Vice President and Chief Information Officer
CHR: Kim Egan, Executive Director Human Resources
CNO: Chris Boese, Vice President and Chief Nursing Officer
Web address: www.regionshospital.com
Control: Other not–for–profit (including NFP Corporation) **Service:** General medical and surgical

Staffed Beds: 457 **Admissions:** 27551 **Census:** 378 **Outpatient Visits:** 151838 **Births:** 2346 **Total Expense ($000):** 778838 **Payroll Expense ($000):** 374933 **Personnel:** 4012

⊞ **ST. JOSEPH'S HOSPITAL (240063)**, 45 West 10th Street, Zip 55102–1053; tel. 651/232–3000, **A**1 2 3 5 10 **F**1 3 4 5 12 15 17 18 20 22 24 26 28 29 30 35 36 37 38 40 44 45 49 50 53 58 61 63 64 67 68 70 72 73 74 75 76 77 79 80 81 84 85 86 87 88 89 90 92 93 96 97 98 100 101 102 103 104 107 108 110 111 114 115 118 119 120 121 124 128 130 132 146 148 149 152 **S** Fairview Health Services, Minneapolis, MN
Primary Contact: Lia Christiansen, Chief Operating Officer, Acute Care Hospitals
COO: Lia Christiansen, Chief Operating Officer, Acute Care Hospitals
CFO: Daniel Fromm, Chief Financial Officer
CMO: Kevin C. Garrett, M.D., Medical Executive East Region
CIO: Joanne Sunquist, Chief Information Officer East Region
CHR: Carolyn Jacobson, Chief Human Resource Officer
CNO: Debra J. Hurd, MS, R.N., Vice President and Chief Nursing Officer
Web address: www.healtheast.org
Control: Other not–for–profit (including NFP Corporation) **Service:** General medical and surgical

Staffed Beds: 239 **Admissions:** 11704 **Census:** 89 **Outpatient Visits:** 47976 **Total Expense ($000):** 328563 **Payroll Expense ($000):** 157351 **Personnel:** 1344

⊞ △ **UNITED HOSPITAL (240038)**, 333 North Smith Avenue, Zip 55102–2389; tel. 651/241–8000, **A**1 2 3 5 7 10 **F**3 8 12 13 15 17 18 20 22 24 26 28 29 30 31 34 35 36 37 40 43 44 45 46 47 48 49 50 51 53 54 56 58 59 60 61 64 65 68 70 74 75 76 77 78 79 80 81 82 83 84 85 86 87 90 91 92 93 95 96 97 98 99 100 102 103 104 105 107 108 110 111 112 113 114 115 118 119 120 121 123 124 126 129 130 132 134 135 146 148 149 153 154 156 157 **S** Allina Health, Minneapolis, MN
Primary Contact: Thomas O'Connor, President
CFO: John Bien, Vice President Finance
CMO: Alison Peterson, Vice President Medical Affairs
CIO: Susan Heichert, Senior Vice President
CHR: James McGlade, Director Human Resources
CNO: Janet K. Pestle, R.N., MSN, Chief Nursing Officer
Web address: www.allina.com
Control: Other not–for–profit (including NFP Corporation) **Service:** General medical and surgical

Staffed Beds: 379 **Admissions:** 24579 **Census:** 282 **Outpatient Visits:** 187100 **Total Expense ($000):** 592210 **Payroll Expense ($000):** 229284 **Personnel:** 2405

SAINT PETER—Nicollet County

★ ⋔ **RIVER'S EDGE HOSPITAL AND CLINIC (241334)**, 1900 North Sunrise Drive, Zip 56082–5376; tel. 507/931–2200, **A**10 18 21 **F**3 15 28 29 34 40 43 45 46 53 75 81 87 90 93 107 110 119 130 132 133 144 156 **S** QHR, Brentwood, TN
Primary Contact: George A. Rohrich, FACHE, Chief Executive Officer
CFO: Lori Zook, Chief Financial Officer
CIO: Kevin Schaefer, Manager Information Services
CHR: Jackie Kimmet, Chief Human Resource Officer
CNO: Paula Meskan, R.N., Chief Nursing Officer
Web address: www.rehc.org
Control: City, Government, nonfederal **Service:** General medical and surgical

Staffed Beds: 17 **Admissions:** 1043 **Census:** 8 **Outpatient Visits:** 21534 **Births:** 0 **Total Expense ($000):** 35872 **Payroll Expense ($000):** 9456 **Personnel:** 143

SANDSTONE—Pine County

★ **ESSENTIA HEALTH SANDSTONE (241309)**, 705 Lundorff Drive, Zip 55072–5009; tel. 320/245–2212, **A**10 18 **F**3 7 11 12 15 28 29 30 34 35 40 43 45 59 64 65 75 77 80 81 82 85 87 91 92 93 107 110 115 119 129 130 132 133 135 143 144 148 149 154 156 **S** Essentia Health, Duluth, MN
Primary Contact: Michael D. Hedrix, Administrator and President
CMO: Sarah Aldredge, M.D., Chief Medical Officer
Web address: www.pinemedicalcenter.org
Control: Hospital district or authority, Government, nonfederal **Service:** General medical and surgical

Staffed Beds: 9 **Admissions:** 255 **Census:** 3 **Outpatient Visits:** 14375 **Births:** 0 **Total Expense ($000):** 19239 **Payroll Expense ($000):** 7176 **Personnel:** 89

SAUK CENTRE—Stearns County

★ **CENTRACARE HEALTH-SAUK CENTRE (241368)**, 425 North Elm Street, Zip 56378–1010; tel. 320/352–2221, (Nonreporting) **A**5 10 18 **S** CentraCare Health, Saint Cloud, MN
Primary Contact: Delano Christianson, Administrator
CFO: Delano Christianson, Administrator
Web address: www.centracare.com/hospitals/sauk_centre/index.html
Control: City, Government, nonfederal **Service:** General medical and surgical

Staffed Beds: 85

SHAKOPEE—Scott County

⊞ **ST. FRANCIS REGIONAL MEDICAL CENTER (240104)**, 1455 St Francis Avenue, Zip 55379–3380; tel. 952/428–3000, **A**1 2 5 10 **F**3 12 13 15 28 29 30 31 34 35 36 38 40 41 43 45 46 50 57 58 59 64 68 75 76 77 78 79 80 81 82 84 86 87 89 93 107 108 110 111 114 117 118 119 124 129 130 131 132 144 146 147 148 154 **S** Allina Health, Minneapolis, MN
Primary Contact: Amy L. Jerdee, R.N., President
CFO: Cynthia Vincent, Vice President Finance and Operations
CMO: Monte Johnson, Vice President, Medical Affairs
CIO: Joe Delveaux, Manager Information Services
CHR: Sally Haack, Vice President and Director of Human Resources
CNO: Debora Ryan, R.N., Vice President Patient Care
Web address: www.stfrancis-shakopee.com
Control: Other not–for–profit (including NFP Corporation) **Service:** General medical and surgical

Staffed Beds: 89 **Admissions:** 6250 **Census:** 46 **Outpatient Visits:** 132344 **Births:** 1133 **Total Expense ($000):** 153900 **Payroll Expense ($000):** 60376 **Personnel:** 603

SLAYTON—Murray County

★ **MURRAY COUNTY MEDICAL CENTER (241319)**, 2042 Juniper Avenue, Zip 56172–1017; tel. 507/836–6111, **A**10 18 **F**3 7 8 28 29 31 35 40 41 43 45 50 53 56 59 64 65 70 79 81 82 85 86 87 89 97 102 107 110 111 115 119 127 130 131 133 146 154 156 **S** Sanford Health, Sioux Falls, SD
Primary Contact: Michael Ladevich, FACHE, Interim Chief Executive Officer
CFO: Renee Logan, Chief Financial Officer
CMO: Joyce Tarbet, M.D., Chief Medical Officer
CIO: Justin Keller, Chief Information Officer
CHR: Nancy Andert, Director Human Resources
Web address: www.murraycountymed.org
Control: County, Government, nonfederal **Service:** General medical and surgical

Staffed Beds: 20 **Admissions:** 276 **Census:** 3 **Outpatient Visits:** 1682 **Births:** 0 **Total Expense ($000):** 14999 **Payroll Expense ($000):** 6255 **Personnel:** 87

SLEEPY EYE—Brown County

SLEEPY EYE MEDICAL CENTER (241327), 400 Fourth Avenue NW, Zip 56085–1109, Mailing Address: P.O. Box 323, Zip 56085–0323; tel. 507/794–3571, (Nonreporting) **A**10 18
Primary Contact: Kevin Sellheim, Administrator
CHR: Connie Dahlberg, Director Business and Employee
CNO: Karee Schmiesing, Director of Nursing
Web address: www.semedicalcenter.org
Control: City, Government, nonfederal **Service:** General medical and surgical

Staffed Beds: 16

SPRINGFIELD—Brown County

☐ **MAYO CLINIC HEALTH SYSTEM IN SPRINGFIELD (241352)**, 625 North Jackson Avenue, Zip 56087–1714, Mailing Address: P.O. Box 146, Zip 56087–0146; tel. 507/723–6201, **A**1 10 18 **F**3 15 34 35 40 57 59 64 65 75 81 93 97 107 110 114 128 133 135 146 148 149 156 **S** Mayo Clinic, Rochester, MN
Primary Contact: Scott D. Thoreson, FACHE, Administrator
CFO: James Tarasovich, Chief Financial Officer
CMO: Jennifer White, Chief of Staff
Web address: www.mayoclinichealthsystem.org
Control: Other not–for–profit (including NFP Corporation) **Service**: General medical and surgical

Staffed Beds: 10 **Admissions**: 159 **Census**: 3 **Outpatient Visits**: 13349
Births: 0 **Personnel**: 42

STAPLES—Todd County

LAKEWOOD HEALTH SYSTEM (241329), 49725 County 83, Zip 56479–5280; tel. 218/894–1515, (Total facility includes 100 beds in nursing home–type unit) **A**10 18 **F**3 6 7 8 10 11 12 13 15 28 29 30 31 34 35 36 39 40 43 45 50 52 56 57 59 62 63 64 65 68 70 75 76 77 78 79 81 82 84 85 86 87 93 97 98 100 101 102 103 104 107 110 114 115 119 125 127 128 129 130 131 132 133 135 143 146 147 148 149 153 156
Primary Contact: Tim Rice, President and Chief Executive Officer
CMO: John Halfen, M.D., Medical Officer
CHR: Janet Jacobson, Director Human Resources
CNO: Teresa Fisher, Chief Nursing Officer
Web address: www.lakewoodhealthsystem.com
Control: Other not–for–profit (including NFP Corporation) **Service**: General medical and surgical

Staffed Beds: 135 **Admissions**: 1506 **Census**: 111 **Outpatient Visits**: 139033 **Births**: 439 **Total Expense ($000)**: 99998 **Payroll Expense ($000)**: 41796 **Personnel**: 708

STILLWATER—Washington County

☐ **LAKEVIEW HOSPITAL (240066)**, 927 Churchill Street West, Zip 55082–6605; tel. 651/439–5330, **A**1 3 5 10 **F**3 7 13 15 18 26 28 29 30 31 34 35 36 40 41 43 45 50 51 57 62 63 64 70 73 75 76 78 79 81 84 85 87 89 107 108 110 111 115 117 118 119 129 130 132 135 146 147 149 154 156 **S** HealthPartners, Bloomington, MN
Primary Contact: Theodore Wegleitner, Chief Executive Officer and President
CFO: Douglas E Johnson, Chief Financial Officer
CMO: Thomas Anderson, Vice President Medical Affairs
CIO: Emad Awwad, Director Care Delivery Sites Information Systems and Technology
CHR: Angy Duchesneau, Senior Director Human Resources
CNO: Robbi Hagelberg, Vice President Nursing Services and Chief Nursing Officer
Web address: www.lakeview.org
Control: Other not–for–profit (including NFP Corporation) **Service**: General medical and surgical

Staffed Beds: 67 **Admissions**: 4011 **Census**: 30 **Outpatient Visits**: 61502 **Births**: 579 **Total Expense ($000)**: 114046 **Payroll Expense ($000)**: 49972 **Personnel**: 600

THIEF RIVER FALLS—Pennington County

MERITCARE THIEF RIVER FALLS NORTHWEST MEDICAL CENTER See Sanford Medical Center Thief River Falls

★ **SANFORD MEDICAL CENTER THIEF RIVER FALLS (241381)**, 3001 Sanford Parkway, Zip 56701–2700; tel. 218/681–4747, **A**10 18 **F**3 8 11 13 15 28 29 31 32 33 34 35 39 40 45 53 57 64 65 68 76 78 79 81 82 85 86 87 97 107 110 111 115 119 129 130 131 132 133 135 144 146 147 148 156 **S** Sanford Health, Sioux Falls, SD
Primary Contact: Brian J. Carlson, FACHE, Executive Director
COO: Rob Lovejoy, Director, Operations
CMO: Brook Redd, M.D., Chief of Staff
CNO: Janell Hudson, Director, Nursing and Clinical Services
Web address: www.sanfordhealth.org
Control: Other not–for–profit (including NFP Corporation) **Service**: General medical and surgical

Staffed Beds: 25 **Admissions**: 1196 **Census**: 10 **Outpatient Visits**: 95911 **Births**: 108 **Total Expense ($000)**: 64845 **Payroll Expense ($000)**: 26150 **Personnel**: 315

SANFORD THIEF RIVER FALLS BEHAVIORAL HEALTH CENTER (244018), 120 LaBree Avenue South, Zip 56701–2819, Mailing Address: 3001 Sanford Parkway, Zip 56701–2819; tel. 218/683–4349, **A**10 **F**38 64 98 100 101 102 104 154 **S** Sanford Health, Sioux Falls, SD
Primary Contact: Brian J. Carlson, FACHE, Chief Executive Officer
COO: Rob Lovejoy, Chief Operating Officer
Web address: www.sanfordhealth.org/Locations/1766896362
Control: Other not–for–profit (including NFP Corporation) **Service**: Psychiatric

Staffed Beds: 16 **Admissions**: 557 **Census**: 13 **Outpatient Visits**: 9
Births: 0 **Total Expense ($000)**: 12594 **Payroll Expense ($000)**: 7030
Personnel: 91

TRACY—Lyon County

★ **SANFORD TRACY MEDICAL CENTER (241303)**, 251 Fifth Street East, Zip 56175–1536; tel. 507/629–8400, **A**10 18 **F**3 28 29 31 32 34 35 40 41 43 44 49 50 56 57 59 62 64 65 68 77 81 85 86 87 89 91 93 97 102 104 107 108 114 125 127 130 131 132 133 135 143 149 154 156 **S** Sanford Health, Sioux Falls, SD
Primary Contact: Stacy Barstad, Chief Executive Officer
CMO: Muhammad Ali, M.D., Chief Medical Officer
CIO: Janet Theisen, Chief Information Officer
CHR: Becky Foster, Employee Relations Specialist
CNO: Jeri Schons, R.N., Chief Nursing Officer
Web address: www.sanfordtracy.org
Control: Other not–for–profit (including NFP Corporation) **Service**: General medical and surgical

Staffed Beds: 25 **Admissions**: 161 **Census**: 2 **Outpatient Visits**: 16530
Births: 0 **Total Expense ($000)**: 9529 **Payroll Expense ($000)**: 3802
Personnel: 67

TWO HARBORS—Lake County

LAKE VIEW HOSPITAL (241308), 325 11th Avenue, Zip 55616–1360; tel. 218/834–7300, (Nonreporting) **A**10 18
Primary Contact: Greg Ruberg, President and Chief Executive Officer
CFO: Eric Lohn, Chief Financial Officer
Web address: www.lvmhospital.com
Control: Other not–for–profit (including NFP Corporation) **Service**: General medical and surgical

Staffed Beds: 16

TYLER—Lincoln County

AVERA TYLER HOSPITAL (241348), 240 Willow Street, Zip 56178–1166; tel. 507/247–5521, (Total facility includes 30 beds in nursing home type unit) **A**10 18 **F**7 34 35 40 53 57 59 64 65 81 97 107 108 119 127 128 133 **S** Avera Health, Sioux Falls, SD
Primary Contact: Allen Anderson, Administrator
CNO: Kris Vollmer, Director Patient Care Services
Web address: www.avera.org
Control: Church operated, Nongovernment, not–for–profit **Service**: General medical and surgical

Staffed Beds: 39 **Admissions**: 158 **Census**: 29 **Outpatient Visits**: 12619
Births: 0 **Total Expense ($000)**: 8452 **Payroll Expense ($000)**: 3816
Personnel: 53

VIRGINIA—St. Louis County

⊠ △ **ESSENTIA HEALTH-VIRGINIA (240084)**, 901 Ninth Street North, Zip 55792–2398; tel. 218/741–3340, (Total facility includes 90 beds in nursing home–type unit) **A**1 7 10 **F**3 11 13 15 18 28 29 30 31 34 35 40 41 43 45 47 48 56 59 63 64 65 70 75 76 77 81 84 85 87 89 90 93 96 97 104 107 108 110 111 115 119 128 129 130 132 135 144 146 147 148 149 154 157 **S** Essentia Health, Duluth, MN
Primary Contact: Sam Stone, Operations Administrator
CFO: Steven Feltman, CPA, Chief Financial Officer
CMO: Michelle Oman, D.O., Chief Medical Officer
Web address: www.essentiahealth.org
Control: Other not–for–profit (including NFP Corporation) **Service**: General medical and surgical

Staffed Beds: 144 **Admissions**: 1683 **Census**: 72 **Outpatient Visits**: 136720 **Births**: 232 **Total Expense ($000)**: 100417 **Payroll Expense ($000)**: 44834 **Personnel**: 467

MN

Hospital, Medicare Provider Number, Address, Telephone, Approval, Facility, and Physician Codes, Health Care System

★ American Hospital Association (AHA) membership
☐ The Joint Commission accreditation
○ Healthcare Facilities Accreditation Program
◇ DNV Healthcare Inc. accreditation
⇑ Center for Improvement in Healthcare Quality Accreditation
△ Commission on Accreditation of Rehabilitation Facilities (CARF) accreditation

WABASHA—Wabasha County

★ **SAINT ELIZABETH'S MEDICAL CENTER (241335)**, 1200 Grant Boulevard West, Zip 55981–1042; tel. 651/565–4531, (Total facility includes 143 beds in nursing home–type unit) **A**10 18 **F**2 3 6 10 11 12 15 28 29 30 34 35 36 40 43 45 46 49 50 53 56 59 62 64 65 75 77 79 81 82 84 85 86 93 94 97 107 114 119 125 127 128 130 133 135 143 145 146 147 148 149 154 156 **S** Ascension Healthcare, Saint Louis, MO
Primary Contact: Thomas Crowley, President and Chief Executive Officer
CFO: John Wolfe, Chief Financial Officer
CMO: Brian E. Kelly, M.D., President Medical Staff
CHR: Jim Root, Vice President Human Resources
CNO: Kathy Lueders, R.N., Director of Nursing-Acute Care
Web address: www.stelizabethswabasha.org
Control: Church operated, Nongovernment, not–for–profit **Service:** General medical and surgical

Staffed Beds: 153 **Admissions:** 435 **Census:** 134 **Outpatient Visits:** 25382
Births: 0 **Total Expense ($000):** 40627 **Payroll Expense ($000):** 16639
Personnel: 280

WACONIA—Carver County

★ ⇧ **RIDGEVIEW MEDICAL CENTER (240056)**, 500 South Maple Street, Zip 55387–1791; tel. 952/442–2191, **A**2 10 21 **F**3 7 12 13 15 18 20 22 28 29 30 31 32 34 35 36 38 40 41 42 43 45 46 48 49 54 57 58 59 62 63 64 65 70 73 74 75 76 77 78 79 81 82 84 85 86 87 89 93 96 98 103 107 108 110 111 114 115 118 119 126 127 129 130 131 132 135 144 146 147 148 149 156 **S** Ridgeview Medical Center, Waconia, MN
Primary Contact: Michael Phelps, President and Chief Executive Officer
CFO: Gordon Gablenz, Vice President Finance
CMO: Alvaro Sanchez, M.D., Chief Medical Officer
CIO: Tamara Korbel, Director Management Information Systems
CHR: Sarah M Hastings, Executive Director
Web address: www.ridgeviewmedical.org
Control: Other not–for–profit (including NFP Corporation) **Service:** General medical and surgical

Staffed Beds: 108 **Admissions:** 6662 **Census:** 66 **Outpatient Visits:** 330943 **Births:** 1172 **Total Expense ($000):** 268924 **Payroll Expense ($000):** 133040 **Personnel:** 901

WADENA—Wadena County

⊞ **TRI-COUNTY HOSPITAL (241354)**, 415 Jefferson Street North, Zip 56482–1297; tel. 218/631–3510, **A**1 10 18 **F**3 7 11 13 15 17 28 29 31 34 35 40 43 45 48 50 54 57 59 64 65 68 70 75 76 77 79 81 85 86 87 89 93 104 107 108 110 111 114 115 118 119 127 129 130 131 132 133 135 146 147 148 149 154 156
Primary Contact: Joel Beiswenger, Chief Executive Officer
CFO: Kim Aagard, Chief Financial Officer
CMO: John Pate, M.D., Chief Medical Officer
CIO: Bill Blaha, Manager Information Technology
CHR: Bryan Pederson, Human Resources Manager
CNO: Kathy Kleen, Chief Nursing Officer
Web address: www.tchc.org
Control: Other not–for–profit (including NFP Corporation) **Service:** General medical and surgical

Staffed Beds: 25 **Admissions:** 774 **Census:** 6 **Outpatient Visits:** 131963
Births: 131 **Total Expense ($000):** 63823 **Payroll Expense ($000):** 26129
Personnel: 483

WARREN—Marshall County

★ **NORTH VALLEY HEALTH CENTER (241337)**, 300 West Good Samaritan Drive, Zip 56762; tel. 218/745–4211, (Nonreporting) **A**10 18
Primary Contact: Jon E. Linnell, Chief Executive Officer
CFO: Mitchell Kotrba, Chief Financial Officer
CNO: Sara Marie Kazmierczak, R.N., Director of Nursing
Web address: www.northvalleyhealth.org
Control: Other not–for–profit (including NFP Corporation) **Service:** General medical and surgical

Staffed Beds: 20

WASECA—Waseca County

☐ **MAYO CLINIC HEALTH SYSTEM IN WASECA (241345)**, 501 North State Street, Zip 56093–2811; tel. 507/835–1210, **A**1 5 10 18 **F**3 11 15 18 28 29 30 34 35 40 43 45 53 57 59 64 65 68 74 75 77 79 81 82 85 86 87 93 97 107 110 115 119 128 130 132 133 144 146 148 149 154 156 **S** Mayo Clinic, Rochester, MN
Primary Contact: April Lanz, Interim Administrator
CMO: Christopher Schimming, M.D., Medical Director
Web address: www.mayoclinichealthsystem.org
Control: Other not–for–profit (including NFP Corporation) **Service:** General medical and surgical

Staffed Beds: 12 **Admissions:** 233 **Census:** 7 **Outpatient Visits:** 28708
Births: 0 **Personnel:** 82

WESTBROOK—Cottonwood County

★ **SANFORD WESTBROOK MEDICAL CENTER (241302)**, 920 Bell Avenue, Zip 56183–9669, Mailing Address: P.O. Box 188, Zip 56183–0188; tel. 507/274–6121, **A**10 18 **F**3 29 31 32 34 35 40 41 43 44 45 50 56 57 59 62 64 65 68 75 77 81 85 86 87 89 91 93 97 101 102 104 107 108 114 125 127 130 131 132 133 135 143 149 154 **S** Sanford Health, Sioux Falls, SD
Primary Contact: Stacy Barstad, Chief Executive Officer
COO: Gordon Kopperud, Director Operations
CIO: Janet Theisen, Chief Information Officer
CHR: Becky Foster, Employee Relations Specialist
Web address: www.sanfordwestbrook.org
Control: Other not–for–profit (including NFP Corporation) **Service:** General medical and surgical

Staffed Beds: 8 **Admissions:** 90 **Census:** 1 **Outpatient Visits:** 10467
Births: 0 **Total Expense ($000):** 7465 **Payroll Expense ($000):** 2827
Personnel: 36

WHEATON—Traverse County

★ **SANFORD WHEATON MEDICAL CENTER (241304)**, 401 12th Street North, Zip 56296–1099; tel. 320/563–8226, **A**10 18 **F**3 7 11 15 18 28 29 30 34 40 43 45 57 59 64 65 81 86 97 107 111 114 119 127 128 132 133 154 **S** Sanford Health, Sioux Falls, SD
Primary Contact: JoAnn M. Foltz, R.N., Chief Executive Officer
CFO: Shane Ayres, Chief Financial Officer
CHR: Brenda Petersen, Human Resources
CNO: Chelsie Falk, Chief Nursing Officer
Web address: www.sanfordhealth.org
Control: Other not–for–profit (including NFP Corporation) **Service:** General medical and surgical

Staffed Beds: 15 **Admissions:** 94 **Census:** 1 **Outpatient Visits:** 13321
Births: 0 **Total Expense ($000):** 7623 **Payroll Expense ($000):** 3246
Personnel: 47

WILLMAR—Kandiyohi County

☐ **CHILD AND ADOLESCENT BEHAVIORAL HEALTH SERVICES (244005)**, 1701 Technology Drive Northeast, Zip 56201–2275; tel. 320/231–5421, (Nonreporting) **A**1 10
Primary Contact: Jacquelyn Sammons, R.N., Supervisor
Web address: www.dhs.state.mn.us
Control: County, Government, nonfederal **Service:** Psychiatric

Staffed Beds: 16

⊞ **RICE MEMORIAL HOSPITAL (240088)**, 301 Becker Avenue SW, Zip 56201–3395; tel. 320/235–4543, (Total facility includes 78 beds in nursing home–type unit) (Data for 181 days) **A**1 2 10 **F**3 7 8 11 12 13 28 29 30 34 35 39 40 43 45 47 48 49 50 57 59 60 63 64 65 68 70 73 75 76 78 79 81 82 85 86 87 89 90 93 98 100 101 102 103 104 105 107 108 111 115 116 117 118 119 121 126 128 130 132 143 146 148 149 150 153 154 **S** CentraCare Health, Saint Cloud, MN
Primary Contact: Michael Schramm, Chief Executive Officer
CFO: Bill Fenske, Chief Financial Officer
CMO: Kenneth Flowe, M.D., Chief Medical Officer
CIO: Teri Beyer, Chief Information Officer, Quality
Web address: www.ricehospital.com
Control: Other not–for–profit (including NFP Corporation) **Service:** General medical and surgical

Staffed Beds: 164 **Admissions:** 2153 **Census:** 104 **Outpatient Visits:** 41149 **Births:** 344 **Total Expense ($000):** 61066 **Payroll Expense ($000):** 25501 **Personnel:** 640

Many Facility Codes have changed. Please refer to the AHA Guide Code Chart. © 2019 AHA Guide

MN

WINDOM—Cottonwood County

★ **WINDOM AREA HOSPITAL (241332)**, 2150 Hospital Drive, Zip 56101–0339, Mailing Address: P.O. Box 339, Zip 56101–0339; tel. 507/831–2400, **A**10 18 **F**11 13 15 28 31 34 35 40 45 53 57 64 76 77 81 93 107 114 119 130 133 148 149 **S** Sanford Health, Sioux Falls, SD
Primary Contact: Shelby Medina, Chief Executive Officer
CFO: Kim Armstrong, Chief Financial Officer
CIO: Lori Ling, Information Technician
CHR: Emily Masters, Chief Human Relations Officer
CNO: Kari Witte, Director Patient Care
Web address: www.windomareahospital.com
Control: City, Government, nonfederal **Service:** General medical and surgical

Staffed Beds: 18 **Admissions:** 393 **Census:** 3

WINONA—Winona County

★ **WINONA HEALTH (240044)**, 855 Mankato Avenue, Zip 55987–4868, Mailing Address: P.O. Box 5600, Zip 55987–0600; tel. 507/454–3650, **A**2 10 20 **F**6 10 11 13 15 28 29 30 31 32 34 35 36 38 40 43 45 50 53 56 57 58 59 60 61 62 63 64 65 70 75 76 77 78 79 81 82 83 84 85 86 87 89 93 96 97 98 100 101 102 104 107 108 110 111 115 116 118 119 127 129 130 131 132 133 135 144 146 147 148 153 154 156
Primary Contact: Rachelle H. Schultz, Ed.D., President and Chief Executive Officer
CFO: Jan Brosnahan, Chief Financial Officer
CMO: Brett Whyte, M.D., Chief of Medical Staff
CIO: Luke Keninger, Information Technology Client Leader
CHR: Kathy Wade, Chief Human Resource Officer
Web address: www.winonahealth.org
Control: Other not–for–profit (including NFP Corporation) **Service:** General medical and surgical

Staffed Beds: 46 **Admissions:** 2050 **Census:** 20 **Outpatient Visits:** 251980
Births: 240 **Total Expense ($000):** 112620 **Payroll Expense ($000):** 53965
Personnel: 791

WOODBURY—Washington County

✛ **WOODWINDS HEALTH CAMPUS (240213)**, 1925 Woodwinds Drive, Zip 55125–4445; tel. 651/232–0228, **A**1 3 10 **F**3 13 15 28 29 30 31 35 36 37 38 40 43 49 50 59 64 68 70 74 75 76 77 78 79 81 85 86 87 93 94 96 97 100 102 107 108 110 111 115 118 119 120 121 124 130 132 146 149 **S** Fairview Health Services, Minneapolis, MN
Primary Contact: Lia Christiansen, Chief Operating Officer, Acute Care Hospitals
COO: Lia Christiansen, Chief Operating Officer, Acute Care Hospitals
CFO: Daniel Fromm, Chief Financial Officer
CMO: Kevin C. Garrett, M.D., Medical Executive, East Region
CIO: Joanne Sunquist, Chief Information Officer
CHR: Carolyn Jacobson, Chief Human Resource Officer
CNO: Debra J. Hurd, MS, R.N., Vice President and Chief Nursing Officer
Web address: www.woodwinds.org
Control: Other not–for–profit (including NFP Corporation) **Service:** General medical and surgical

Staffed Beds: 86 **Admissions:** 8017 **Census:** 59 **Outpatient Visits:** 61546
Births: 2157 **Total Expense ($000):** 147912 **Payroll Expense ($000):** 54612 **Personnel:** 565

WORTHINGTON—Nobles County

SANFORD REGIONAL HOSPITAL WORTHINGTON See Sanford Worthington Medical Center

★ **SANFORD WORTHINGTON MEDICAL CENTER (240022)**, 1018 Sixth Avenue, Zip 56187–2202, Mailing Address: P.O. Box 997, Zip 56187–0997; tel. 507/372–2941, **A**10 20 **F**3 7 11 13 15 26 27 28 31 34 35 40 43 45 50 57 59 60 62 64 68 69 70 75 76 78 79 81 85 86 93 97 107 110 111 114 116 119 120 121 129 130 131 132 135 144 146 147 148 149 154 **S** Sanford Health, Sioux Falls, SD
Primary Contact: Jennifer Weg, MS, R.N., Executive Director
CFO: Linda Wagner, Chief Financial Officer
CMO: Charles Dike, M.D., Chief of Staff
CIO: Brad Klassen, Information Technology Coordinator
CNO: Gwen Post, R.N., Chief Nursing Officer
Web address: www.sanfordhealth.org
Control: Other not–for–profit (including NFP Corporation) **Service:** General medical and surgical

Staffed Beds: 48 **Admissions:** 1224 **Census:** 8 **Outpatient Visits:** 68404
Births: 276 **Total Expense ($000):** 45971 **Payroll Expense ($000):** 20625
Personnel: 249

WYOMING—Chisago County

✛ **FAIRVIEW LAKES HEALTH SERVICES (240050)**, 5200 Fairview Boulevard, Zip 55092–8013; tel. 651/982–7000, **A**1 10 **F**3 11 13 15 18 28 29 30 34 35 40 41 43 45 50 51 57 59 64 65 68 70 75 76 81 84 85 86 87 89 93 96 101 107 110 111 115 119 130 131 132 134 144 146 148 149 154 **S** Fairview Health Services, Minneapolis, MN
Primary Contact: Lia Christiansen, Chief Operating Officer, Acute Care Hospitals
CFO: Kim Ericson, Vice President Finance
CMO: David Milbrandt, M.D., Vice President Medical Affairs
CNO: Karen Whiley, Vice President Patient Care Services
Web address: www.fairview.org/
Control: Other not–for–profit (including NFP Corporation) **Service:** General medical and surgical

Staffed Beds: 37 **Admissions:** 3169 **Census:** 25 **Outpatient Visits:** 86475
Births: 619 **Total Expense ($000):** 80921 **Payroll Expense ($000):** 42672
Personnel: 416

MN

Hospital, Medicare Provider Number, Address, Telephone, Approval, Facility, and Physician Codes, Health Care System

★ American Hospital Association (AHA) membership ○ Healthcare Facilities Accreditation Program ⇧ Center for Improvement in Healthcare Quality Accreditation
□ The Joint Commission accreditation ◇ DNV Healthcare Inc. accreditation △ Commission on Accreditation of Rehabilitation Facilities (CARF) accreditation

MISSISSIPPI

ABERDEEN—Monroe County

★ ⇑ **MONROE REGIONAL HOSPITAL (251302)**, 400 South Chestnut Street,
Zip 39730–3335, Mailing Address: P.O. Box 548, Zip 39730–0548; tel. 662/369–
2455, **A**10 18 21 **F**3 8 10 11 29 35 39 40 45 56 77 81 82 85 86 87 93 96 97
98 100 101 103 104 105 107 112 115 127 130 133 135 143 146
Primary Contact: Christopher Chandler, Chief Executive Officer
CFO: Julie Gieger, Chief Financial Officer
CMO: Kevin Hayes, M.D., Chief of Staff
CHR: Lee Rob, Director Human Resources
Control: Corporation, Investor–owned (for–profit) **Service:** General medical and
surgical

> **Staffed Beds:** 35 **Admissions:** 477 **Census:** 9 **Outpatient Visits:** 13502
> **Births:** 0 **Total Expense ($000):** 20222 **Payroll Expense ($000):** 9758
> **Personnel:** 225

ACKERMAN—Choctaw County

⇑ **CHOCTAW REGIONAL MEDICAL CENTER (251334)**, 8613 Highway 12,
Zip 39735–8708; tel. 662/285–6235, (Total facility includes 73 beds in nursing
home–type unit) **A**10 18 21 **F**3 29 34 40 43 50 57 58 65 77 87 89 93 104 107
114 119 127 128 130 133
Primary Contact: Jamie Rodgers, Chief Executive Officer
Web address: www.choctawregional.com
Control: County, Government, nonfederal **Service:** General medical and surgical

> **Staffed Beds:** 88 **Admissions:** 338 **Census:** 63 **Outpatient Visits:** 44132
> **Births:** 0 **Total Expense ($000):** 19549 **Payroll Expense ($000):** 10419
> **Personnel:** 289

AMORY—Monroe County

⊞ **NORTH MISSISSIPPI MEDICAL CENTER GILMORE-AMORY (250025)**,
1105 Earl Frye Boulevard, Zip 38821–5500, Mailing Address: P.O. Box 459,
Zip 38821–0459; tel. 662/256–7111, **A**1 10 **F**3 13 15 17 18 29 32 34 35 40
41 43 45 49 50 53 55 57 59 64 65 68 70 72 73 75 76 77 81 85 86 87 88 89
90 107 108 110 111 114 115 119 126 130 135 146 147 **S** North Mississippi
Health Services, Inc., Tupelo, MS
Primary Contact: J Allen. Tyra, Chief Executive
CFO: Bert Pickard, Chief Financial Officer
CMO: William Rogers, Chief Medical Officer
CIO: Jeff Wideman, Director Information Systems
CHR: Angie L Weaver, Director Human Resources
Web address: www.gilmorehealth.com
Control: Other not–for–profit (including NFP Corporation) **Service:** General
medical and surgical

> **Staffed Beds:** 95 **Admissions:** 2380 **Census:** 25 **Outpatient Visits:** 57898
> **Births:** 592 **Total Expense ($000):** 41149 **Payroll Expense ($000):** 13259
> **Personnel:** 314

BATESVILLE—Panola County

PANOLA MEDICAL CENTER (250128), 303 Medical Center Drive, Zip 38606–
8608; tel. 662/563–5611, **A**10 **F**3 4 5 11 12 13 15 18 19 28 29 30 32 34 35
38 40 43 45 48 50 56 57 59 64 65 68 70 76 77 81 85 87 89 97 98 100 101
102 103 107 108 114 119 127 129 130 132 146 147
Primary Contact: Wayne D. Thompson, Interim Chief Executive Officer
CMO: Michael R. Hovens, M.D., Chief Medical Officer
CIO: Will Morris, Director Information Technology
CHR: Arthur A Wasek, Director Human Resources
Web address: www.panolamedicalcenter.org/
Control: Other not–for–profit (including NFP Corporation) **Service:** General
medical and surgical

> **Staffed Beds:** 112 **Admissions:** 1532 **Census:** 17 **Births:** 184 **Total
> Expense ($000):** 38092 **Payroll Expense ($000):** 16697 **Personnel:** 309

BAY SAINT LOUIS—Hancock County

⊞ **HANCOCK MEDICAL CENTER (250162)**, 149 Drinkwater Boulevard,
Zip 39520–1658, Mailing Address: Bay St Louis, tel. 228/467–8600, **A**1 10 **F**3
11 12 13 15 17 18 19 28 29 34 35 39 40 43 45 46 54 57 59 64 65 68 70 74
75 76 77 79 81 85 86 87 89 90 93 94 97 107 108 110 111 115 118 119 124
127 130 131 146 147 148 **S** Ochsner Health System, New Orleans, LA
Primary Contact: Alan Hodges, Chief Executive Officer
CFO: Thomas Ramsey, Chief Financial Officer
CIO: Craig Hodges, Director Information Services
CHR: Cathy Benvenutti, Human Resource Director
CNO: Virginia Kenny, Chief Nursing Officer
Web address: www.ochsner.org/locations/hancock-medical-center
Control: Other not–for–profit (including NFP Corporation) **Service:** General
medical and surgical

> **Staffed Beds:** 102 **Admissions:** 1014 **Census:** 11 **Outpatient Visits:** 46057
> **Births:** 160 **Total Expense ($000):** 37478 **Payroll Expense ($000):** 18073
> **Personnel:** 209

BAY SPRINGS—Jasper County

★ **JASPER GENERAL HOSPITAL (250018)**, 15 'A' South Sixth Street, Zip 39422–
9738, Mailing Address: P.O. Box 527, Zip 39422–0527; tel. 601/764–2101,
(Total facility includes 110 beds in nursing home–type unit) **A**10 **F**10 55 59 62 64
108 119 128 130 133
Primary Contact: Eric Jordan, Chief Executive Officer
CFO: Steve Green, Comptroller
CMO: A K Lay, M.D., Jr Chief Medical Officer
CHR: Beth Gable, Administrative Assistant
CNO: Becky Ulmer, R.N., Director of Nursing
Web address: www.jaspergeneralhospital.com
Control: County, Government, nonfederal **Service:** General medical and surgical

> **Staffed Beds:** 126 **Admissions:** 171 **Census:** 114 **Outpatient Visits:** 0
> **Births:** 0 **Total Expense ($000):** 9989 **Payroll Expense ($000):** 6862
> **Personnel:** 181

BILOXI—Harrison County

⊞ **MERIT HEALTH BILOXI (250007)**, 150 Reynoir Street, Zip 39530–4199, Mailing
Address: P.O. Box 128, Zip 39533–0128; tel. 228/432–1571, **A**1 10 **F**13 15 29
35 40 43 61 70 75 76 77 81 82 86 87 89 90 93 97 98 99 100 102 103 104
107 108 111 116 118 119 130 143 146 147 **S** Community Health Systems,
Inc., Franklin, TN
Primary Contact: Robert Calhoun, Chief Executive Officer
COO: Tonda V. Haigler, Chief Operating Officer
CFO: Charles Brinkley III Chief Financial Officer
CMO: George Loukatos, M.D., President Medical Staff Affairs
CIO: George Bickel, Director, Information Systems
CNO: James Wells, Chief Nursing Officer
Web address: www.merithealthbiloxi.com
Control: Corporation, Investor–owned (for–profit) **Service:** General medical and
surgical

> **Staffed Beds:** 198 **Admissions:** 6902 **Census:** 80 **Outpatient Visits:** 89664
> **Births:** 907 **Total Expense ($000):** 117131 **Payroll Expense ($000):** 43251
> **Personnel:** 503

⊞ **VETERANS AFFAIRS GULF COAST VETERANS HEALTH CARE SYSTEM**, 400
Veterans Avenue, Zip 39531–2410; tel. 228/523–5000, (Nonreporting) **A**1 3 5 **S**
Department of Veterans Affairs, Washington, DC
Primary Contact: Bryan C. Matthews, Medical Center Director
COO: Alexander Murray, Interim Associate Director
CFO: John D Williams Jr Chief Financial Officer
CMO: Kenneth B Simon, M.D., Chief of Staff
CIO: David D Wagner, Chief Information Management Service
CHR: Andrew Roberts, Interim Chief Human Resources Officer
CNO: Deatosha D. Haynes, Interim Associates Director for Patient
Web address: www.biloxi.va.gov/
Control: Veterans Affairs, Government, federal **Service:** General medical and
surgical

> **Staffed Beds:** 392

Many Facility Codes have changed. Please refer to the AHA Guide Code Chart.
© 2019 AHA Guide

BOONEVILLE—Prentiss County

☒ **BAPTIST MEMORIAL HOSPITAL-BOONEVILLE (250044)**, 100 Hospital Street, Zip 38829–3359; tel. 662/720–5000, **A**1 10 **F**3 15 17 28 29 30 34 35 40 43 56 57 59 63 68 70 74 75 77 81 85 86 87 89 90 93 98 103 107 108 111 115 118 119 130 132 133 145 146 148 154 **S** Baptist Memorial Health Care Corporation, Memphis, TN
Primary Contact: James Grantham, Administrator and Chief Executive Officer
CFO: Donavan Leonard, Chief Financial Officer
CMO: Nathan Baldwin, M.D., President Medical Staff
CIO: Linda Chaffin, Director Medical Review
CHR: Shannon Bolen, Director Human Resources
Web address: www.bmhcc.org/booneville
Control: Other not–for–profit (including NFP Corporation) **Service:** General medical and surgical

Staffed Beds: 66 **Admissions:** 904 **Census:** 1/ **Outpatient Visits:** 22445 **Births:** 1 **Total Expense ($000):** 19262 **Payroll Expense ($000):** 8199 **Personnel:** 150

BRANDON—Rankin County

☒ **MERIT HEALTH RANKIN (250096)**, 350 Crossgates Boulevard, Zip 39042–2698; tel. 601/825–2811, **A**1 5 10 **F**3 15 17 29 30 34 35 39 40 43 50 57 59 64 65 70 74 79 81 82 85 87 90 93 97 98 103 107 108 110 111 114 119 129 130 146 153 **S** Community Health Systems, Inc., Franklin, TN
Primary Contact: Heather Sistrunk, R.N., Chief Executive Officer
CFO: Christy Wilson, Chief Financial Officer
CMO: Edward Rigdon, M.D., Chief Medical Officer
CIO: Heather Holmes, Director Health Information Systems
CHR: Joy M Hutson, Director Human Resources
CNO: Cynthia Ellis, Chief Nursing Officer
Web address: www.merithealthrankin.com/
Control: Corporation, Investor–owned (for–profit) **Service:** General medical and surgical

Staffed Beds: 134 **Admissions:** 2292 **Census:** 43 **Outpatient Visits:** 45053 **Births:** 0 **Personnel:** 209

BROOKHAVEN—Lincoln County

★ ⇑ **KING'S DAUGHTERS MEDICAL CENTER (250057)**, 427 Highway 51 North, Zip 39601–2350, Mailing Address: P.O. Box 948, Zip 39602–0948; tel. 601/833–6011, **A**10 20 21 **F**3 7 11 15 17 29 30 34 35 40 41 45 53 54 57 59 64 65 68 70 73 74 75 76 77 79 80 81 82 86 89 93 96 97 107 108 110 111 114 115 119 126 129 130 131 132 135 143 145 146 147 149 156 **S** QHR, Brentwood, TN
Primary Contact: Alvin Hoover, FACHE, Chief Executive Officer
COO: Thomas Hood, Chief Operating Officer
CFO: Randy B Pirtle, Chief Financial Officer
CMO: Jeffrey Ross, M.D., Chief of Staff
CIO: Carl Smith, Director Information Systems
CHR: Celine H Craig, Director Human Resources
CNO: Cheri Walker, R.N., Chief Nursing Officer
Web address: www.kdmc.org
Control: Other not–for–profit (including NFP Corporation) **Service:** General medical and surgical

Staffed Beds: 79 **Admissions:** 4037 **Census:** 29 **Outpatient Visits:** 157828 **Births:** 718 **Total Expense ($000):** 85769 **Payroll Expense ($000):** 35702 **Personnel:** 588

CALHOUN CITY—Calhoun County

★ **BAPTIST MEMORIAL HOSPITAL - CALHOUN (251331)**, 140 Burke-Calhoun City Road, Zip 38916–9690; tel. 662/628–6611, (Total facility includes 120 beds in nursing home–type unit) **A**10 18 **F**3 30 40 43 59 64 68 89 107 114 119 127 128 130 133 154 **S** Baptist Memorial Health Care Corporation, Memphis, TN
Primary Contact: Collin Cheek, Administrator
CFO: Kenneth Conley, Chief Financial Officer
CMO: Bruce Longest, M.D., President Medical Staff
Web address: www.baptistonline.org/calhoun/
Control: Other not–for–profit (including NFP Corporation) **Service:** General medical and surgical

Staffed Beds: 145 **Admissions:** 455 **Census:** 104 **Outpatient Visits:** 11503 **Births:** 0 **Total Expense ($000):** 11567 **Payroll Expense ($000):** 4405 **Personnel:** 196

CANTON—Madison County

☒ **MERIT HEALTH MADISON (250038)**, 161 River Oaks Drive, Zip 39046–5375, Mailing Address: P.O. Box 1607, Zip 39046–5375; tel. 601/855–4000, **A**1 5 10 **F**3 13 15 18 29 34 35 40 43 50 59 64 68 70 73 76 79 81 82 85 87 89 96 108 110 112 114 119 126 129 130 135 146 148 149 154 156 **S** Community Health Systems, Inc., Franklin, TN
Primary Contact: Britton Phelps, Chief Executive Officer
CFO: Shea Sutherland, Chief Financial Officer
CMO: Vibha Vig, Chief of Staff
CIO: Rick Hartzog, Chief Information Officer
CHR: Jackie Williams, Director Human Resources
CNO: Tim Lolley, MSN, Chief Nursing Officer
Web address: www.merithealthmadison.com
Control: Corporation, Investor–owned (for–profit) **Service:** General medical and surgical

Staffed Beds: 43 **Admissions:** 1588 **Census:** 15

CARTHAGE—Leake County

★ **BAPTIST MEDICAL CENTER LEAKE (251315)**, 1100 Highway 16 E, Zip 39051–3809, Mailing Address: P.O. Box 909, Zip 39051–0909; tel. 601/267–1100, **A**10 18 **F**15 29 35 40 43 45 56 59 81 87 107 109 111 114 115 119 127 130 133 146 148 154 **S** Baptist Memorial Health Care Corporation, Memphis, TN
Primary Contact: Daryl W. Weaver, Chief Executive Officer
COO: C Gerald Cotton, Interim Chief Operating Officer
CFO: David Jackson, Chief Financial Officer
CMO: Doug Perry, M.D., Chief of Staff
Web address: www.mbhs.com/locations/baptist-medical-center-leake/
Control: Other not–for–profit (including NFP Corporation) **Service:** General medical and surgical

Staffed Beds: 25 **Admissions:** 704 **Census:** 16 **Outpatient Visits:** 22747 **Births:** 1 **Total Expense ($000):** 21882 **Payroll Expense ($000):** 7619 **Personnel:** 144

CENTREVILLE—Wilkinson County

☒ **FIELD MEMORIAL COMMUNITY HOSPITAL (251309)**, 178 Highway 24, Zip 39631–4171; tel. 601/645–5221, **A**1 10 18 **F**15 18 29 34 39 40 43 45 57 59 64 75 77 79 81 89 90 93 107 108 110 118 119 130 133 148
Primary Contact: Chad Netterville, Administrator and Chief Executive Officer
CFO: Bryan N Stevens, Chief Financial Officer
CIO: Locke Wheeles, Information Technology Manager
CHR: Dana McNabb, Human Resources Manager
CNO: Robin Walker, Chief Nursing Officer
Web address: www.fmch.org
Control: County, Government, nonfederal **Service:** General medical and surgical

Staffed Beds: 16 **Admissions:** 443 **Census:** 9 **Outpatient Visits:** 12078 **Births:** 0 **Total Expense ($000):** 18272 **Payroll Expense ($000):** 8796 **Personnel:** 164

CHARLESTON—Tallahatchie County

⇑ **TALLAHATCHIE GENERAL HOSPITAL (251304)**, 201 South Market, Zip 38921–2236, Mailing Address: P.O. Box 230, Zip 38921–0240; tel. 662/647–5535, (Total facility includes 98 beds in nursing home–type unit) **A**10 18 21 **F**29 34 40 43 53 57 64 86 87 93 107 114 127 130 133 143
Primary Contact: Jim Blackwood, Chief Executive Officer
CFO: Sammie Bell Jr, Chief Financial Officer
Control: County, Government, nonfederal **Service:** General medical and surgical

Staffed Beds: 116 **Admissions:** 623 **Census:** 107 **Births:** 0 **Total Expense ($000):** 32851 **Payroll Expense ($000):** 15885 **Personnel:** 215

CLARKSDALE—Coahoma County

☐ **NORTHWEST MISSISSIPPI MEDICAL CENTER (250042)**, 1970 Hospital Drive, Zip 38614–7202, Mailing Address: P.O. Box 1218, Zip 38614–1218; tel. 662/627–3211, (Data for 334 days) **A**1 10 19 **F**3 13 15 17 18 20 22 28 29 30 31 34 35 40 43 53 57 59 64 70 73 74 76 79 80 81 85 89 93 107 108 110 111 114 115 118 119 126 130 131 132 **S** Curae Health, Clinton, TN
Primary Contact: Joel Southern, R.N., MSN, Chief Executive Officer
CFO: Charles H. Hester, CPA, Jr Chief Financial Officer
CMO: Richard Brownstein, M.D., Chief of Staff
CIO: Adrienne Taylor, Director of Health Information Management
CHR: Devasha Patterson, Director of Human Resources
CNO: Steven W Brackeen, R.N., Chief Nursing Officer
Web address: www.merithealthnorthwestms.com
Control: Other not–for–profit (including NFP Corporation) **Service:** General medical and surgical

Staffed Beds: 181 **Admissions:** 2311 **Census:** 29 **Outpatient Visits:** 51423 **Births:** 585 **Personnel:** 397

MS

Hospital, Medicare Provider Number, Address, Telephone, Approval, Facility, and Physician Codes, Health Care System

★ American Hospital Association (AHA) membership
☐ The Joint Commission accreditation
○ Healthcare Facilities Accreditation Program
◇ DNV Healthcare Inc. accreditation
⇑ Center for Improvement in Healthcare Quality Accreditation
△ Commission on Accreditation of Rehabilitation Facilities (CARF) accreditation

CLEVELAND—Bolivar County

☒ **BOLIVAR MEDICAL CENTER (250093)**, 901 East Sunflower Road, Zip 38732–2833, Mailing Address: P.O. Box 1380, Zip 38732–1380; tel. 662/846–0061, (Total facility includes 35 beds in nursing home–type unit) **A**1 10 20 **F**13 15 29 30 35 39 40 43 56 60 70 73 76 81 82 87 88 89 93 98 103 107 108 111 116 118 119 128 130 132 133 146 148 **S** LifePoint Health, Brentwood, TN
Primary Contact: Robert L. Marshall Jr, FACHE, Chief Executive Officer
CMO: Mark Blackwood, M.D., Chief of Staff
CIO: Cagri Sapmaz, Information Technology Director
CHR: Ben Bufkin, Human Resource Director
CNO: Joann McCollum, Chief Nursing Officer
Web address: www.bolivarmedical.com
Control: Corporation, Investor–owned (for–profit) **Service**: General medical and surgical

Staffed Beds: 129 **Admissions**: 3143 **Census**: 69 **Births**: 379 **Total Expense ($000)**: 52450 **Payroll Expense ($000)**: 18989 **Personnel**: 367

COLLINS—Covington County

★ ⇑ **COVINGTON COUNTY HOSPITAL (251325)**, 701 South Holly Avenue, Zip 39428–3894, Mailing Address: P.O. Box 1149, Zip 39428–1149; tel. 601/765–6711, (Total facility includes 60 beds in nursing home–type unit) **A**10 18 21 **F**2 3 7 29 34 35 39 40 43 45 50 54 57 59 60 64 65 66 68 81 89 93 94 98 103 104 107 114 119 127 128 130 133 143 144 146 147
Primary Contact: Gregg Gibbes, Chief Executive Officer
CFO: Delilah Hudson, Controller
CMO: Word Johnston, Medical Director
CHR: Beverly K Ponder, Executive Assistant and Human Resources Coordinator
CNO: Martha Lynn Scott, Chief Patient Care Officer
Web address: www.covingtoncountyhospital.com
Control: County, Government, nonfederal **Service**: General medical and surgical

Staffed Beds: 95 **Admissions**: 550 **Census**: 70 **Outpatient Visits**: 23422 **Births**: 0 **Total Expense ($000)**: 30847 **Payroll Expense ($000)**: 11551 **Personnel**: 264

COLUMBIA—Marion County

MARION GENERAL HOSPITAL (250085), 1560 Sumrall Road, Zip 39429–2654, Mailing Address: P.O. Box 630, Zip 39429–0630; tel. 601/736–6303, **A**10 **F**3 11 29 34 35 39 40 43 57 59 64 65 66 68 70 81 85 87 92 97 107 114 119 127 130 133 146 148 149 154
Primary Contact: Alaina Cedillo, Interim Administrator
CMO: Mark Stevens, M.D., Chief Medical Staff
CIO: Donny Bracey, Director Information Services
CNO: Patricia Reid, Director of Nursing
Web address: www.mgh.net/
Control: County, Government, nonfederal **Service**: General medical and surgical

Staffed Beds: 49 **Admissions**: 613 **Census**: 9 **Outpatient Visits**: 27910 **Births**: 0 **Total Expense ($000)**: 12656 **Payroll Expense ($000)**: 5869 **Personnel**: 114

COLUMBUS—Lowndes County

☒ **BAPTIST MEMORIAL HOSPITAL-GOLDEN TRIANGLE (250100)**, 2520 Fifth Street North, Zip 39705–2095, Mailing Address: P.O. Box 1307, Zip 39703–1307; tel. 662/244–1000, **A**1 3 10 19 **F**3 4 5 11 13 15 17 18 20 22 24 26 28 29 30 31 34 38 39 40 43 45 49 51 57 59 61 64 70 73 75 76 77 79 80 81 84 85 87 88 89 91 93 94 96 98 102 104 106 107 108 109 110 111 114 115 116 117 118 119 120 121 123 124 126 128 129 130 132 134 146 147 148 149 153 154 156 157 **S** Baptist Memorial Health Care Corporation, Memphis, TN
Primary Contact: Paul Cade, Administrator and Chief Executive Officer
CFO: David Webb, Chief Financial Officer
CMO: John E Reed, M.D., Medical Director
CIO: Sheila Bardwell, Director Information Systems
CHR: Bob McCallister, Director Human Resources
CNO: Mary Ellen Sumrall, Chief Nursing Officer
Web address: www.baptistonline.org/golden-triangle/
Control: Other not–for–profit (including NFP Corporation) **Service**: General medical and surgical

Staffed Beds: 236 **Admissions**: 9017 **Census**: 115 **Outpatient Visits**: 114734 **Births**: 820 **Total Expense ($000)**: 157799 **Payroll Expense ($000)**: 46869 **Personnel**: 966

CORINTH—Alcorn County

☒ **MAGNOLIA REGIONAL HEALTH CENTER (250009)**, 611 Alcorn Drive, Zip 38834–9321; tel. 662/293–1000, **A**1 3 5 10 19 **F**13 15 17 22 24 29 30 35 39 40 43 51 53 60 62 63 70 75 76 77 81 82 86 87 89 93 98 100 101 102 103 107 108 111 116 118 119 127 129 130 131 132 143 146 147 148 **S** QHR, Brentwood, TN
Primary Contact: Ronny Humes, Chief Executive Officer
CMO: Felton Combest, M.D., Vice President Medical Affairs
CIO: David Parker, VP Information Technology
CHR: Regenia Brown, Vice President Human Resources
CNO: Pam B Wallis, MSN, Vice President Nursing Services
Web address: www.mrhc.org
Control: City–county, Government, nonfederal **Service**: General medical and surgical

Staffed Beds: 200 **Admissions**: 8929 **Census**: 102 **Outpatient Visits**: 233896 **Births**: 604 **Total Expense ($000)**: 167420 **Payroll Expense ($000)**: 82419 **Personnel**: 1291

DE KALB—Kemper County

JOHN C. STENNIS MEMORIAL HOSPITAL (251335), 14365 Highway 16 West, Zip 39328–7974; tel. 769/486–1000, **A**10 18 **F**29 40 43 75 81 107 119 127 128 133 **S** Rush Health Systems, Meridian, MS
Primary Contact: Justin Palmer, Administrator
Web address: www.johncstennismemorialhospital.com/jcsmh/
Control: Other not–for–profit (including NFP Corporation) **Service**: General medical and surgical

Staffed Beds: 25 **Admissions**: 469 **Census**: 9 **Outpatient Visits**: 6729 **Births**: 0 **Total Expense ($000)**: 8548 **Payroll Expense ($000)**: 2886 **Personnel**: 163

EUPORA—Webster County

☒ **NORTH MISSISSIPPI MEDICAL CENTER-EUPORA (250020)**, 70 Medical Plaza, Zip 39744–4018; tel. 662/258–6221, (Total facility includes 35 beds in nursing home–type unit) **A**1 10 20 **F**3 11 15 28 29 30 32 34 35 38 40 43 50 53 57 59 64 65 68 71 74 87 89 90 107 114 119 127 129 130 132 133 135 146 148 149 150 154 156 **S** North Mississippi Health Services, Inc., Tupelo, MS
Primary Contact: Robin Mixon, Administrator
CFO: Adonna Mitchell, Director Fiscal Services
CMO: Christy Vowell, D.O., Chief of Staff
CIO: Helen Reed, Director Health Information
CHR: Dorothy Castle, Director Human Resources
Web address: www.nmhs.net/eupora
Control: Other not–for–profit (including NFP Corporation) **Service**: General medical and surgical

Staffed Beds: 73 **Admissions**: 1396 **Census**: 55 **Outpatient Visits**: 50963 **Births**: 0 **Total Expense ($000)**: 25726 **Payroll Expense ($000)**: 12328 **Personnel**: 170

FAYETTE—Jefferson County

JEFFERSON COUNTY HOSPITAL (250060), 870 South Main Street, Zip 39069–5695, Mailing Address: P.O. Box 577, Zip 39069–0577; tel. 601/786–3401, **A**10 **F**3 40 107 130
Primary Contact: Ada Wilson, R.N., Chief Executive Officer
CMO: Khar Omolara, M.D., Chief Medical Staff
CHR: Patricia Selmon, Director Public Relations and Chief Human Resources
Control: County, Government, nonfederal **Service**: General medical and surgical

Staffed Beds: 30 **Admissions**: 264 **Census**: 6 **Outpatient Visits**: 20822 **Births**: 0 **Total Expense ($000)**: 8112 **Payroll Expense ($000)**: 3348 **Personnel**: 99

FLOWOOD—Rankin County

☒ **MERIT HEALTH RIVER OAKS (250138)**, 1030 River Oaks Drive, Zip 39232–9553, Mailing Address: P.O. Box 5100, Jackson, Zip 39296–5100; tel. 601/932–1030, **A**1 3 10 **F**3 11 12 13 18 20 22 29 30 31 34 35 37 39 40 43 45 49 51 57 59 64 65 70 72 73 74 76 79 81 82 85 87 89 93 107 108 111 115 119 126 130 144 146 147 148 149 **S** Community Health Systems, Inc., Franklin, TN
Primary Contact: L Dwayne. Blaylock, Chief Executive Officer
CIO: Pat Jones, Director Information Systems
CHR: Warren Weed, Director Human Resources
CNO: Sherry P Cook, R.N., MSN, Chief Nursing Executive
Web address: www.https://www.merithealthriveroaks.com/
Control: Corporation, Investor–owned (for–profit) **Service**: General medical and surgical

Staffed Beds: 158 **Admissions**: 4528 **Census**: 53 **Births**: 1493 **Total Expense ($000)**: 103518 **Payroll Expense ($000)**: 30078 **Personnel**: 547

MS

☒ **MERIT HEALTH WOMAN'S HOSPITAL (250136)**, 1026 North Flowood Drive, Zip 39232–9532, Mailing Address: 1026 North Flowood Drive, Zip 39232; tel. 601/932–1000, **A**1 3 5 10 **F**13 15 35 39 50 64 65 72 73 76 81 85 108 110 119 126 130 147 **S** Community Health Systems, Inc., Franklin, TN
Primary Contact: Sherry J. Pitts, Chief Executive Officer
CFO: Nick Renda, Chief Financial Officer
CMO: Ed Barham, M.D., Chief of Staff
CHR: Warren Weed, Director Associate Relations
CNO: Linda Atwood, Chief Nursing Officer
Web address: www.merithealthwomanshospital.com
Control: Corporation, Investor–owned (for–profit) **Service**: Obstetrics and gynecology

> **Staffed Beds**: 60 **Admissions**: 1260 **Census**: 15

FOREST—Scott County

★ ⇑ **LACKEY MEMORIAL HOSPITAL (251300)**, 330 Broad Street, Zip 39074–3508, Mailing Address: P.O. Box 428, Zip 39074–0428; tel. 601/469–4151, (Total facility includes 20 beds in nursing home–type unit) **A**10 18 21 **F**3 8 11 15 18 29 34 35 38 39 40 41 45 50 54 55 56 57 59 60 64 65 66 68 81 86 87 89 92 97 98 103 104 107 108 110 111 119 127 128 130 133
Primary Contact: Sydney Sawyer, R.N., Chief Executive Officer
CFO: Julie Gieger, Chief Financial Officer
CMO: John Paul Lee, M.D., Chief of Staff
CIO: Eddie Pope, Chief Information Officer
CHR: Donn Paul, Chief Human Resources
Web address: www.lackeymemorialhospital.com
Control: Other not–for–profit (including NFP Corporation) **Service**: General medical and surgical

> **Staffed Beds**: 55 **Admissions**: 1075 **Census**: 38 **Births**: 0 **Total Expense ($000)**: 23294 **Payroll Expense ($000)**: 11146 **Personnel**: 233

GREENVILLE—Washington County

★ ⇑ **ALLEGIANCE SPECIALTY HOSPITAL OF GREENVILLE (252013)**, 300 South Washington Avenue, 3rd Floor, Zip 38701–4719; tel. 662/332–7344, **A**10 21 **F**1 3 29 34 57 68 85 130 148 149 153 **S** Allegiance Health Management, Shreveport, LA
Primary Contact: Vearnail Herzog, Chief Executive Officer
CMO: Parvez Karim, M.D., Chief Medical Officer
CIO: Sharon Scott, Health Information Director
CHR: Sharon Taylor, Human Resources Director
CNO: John Read, Chief Nursing Officer
Web address: www.ahmgt.com
Control: Corporation, Investor–owned (for–profit) **Service**: Acute long–term care hospital

> **Staffed Beds**: 39 **Admissions**: 364 **Census**: 23 **Outpatient Visits**: 0 **Births**: 0 **Total Expense ($000)**: 11517 **Payroll Expense ($000)**: 4423 **Personnel**: 90

★ **DELTA REGIONAL MEDICAL CENTER (250082)**, 1400 East Union Street, Zip 38704–5247; tel. 662/378–3783, (Includes THE KING'S DAUGHTERS HOSPITAL, 300 Washington Avenue, Greenville, Mississippi, Zip 38701–3614, Mailing Address: P O Box 1857, Zip 38702–1857, tel. 662/378–2020, Scott Christensen, FACHE, Chief Executive Officer) **A**10 19 **F**3 4 8 11 13 15 18 20 22 28 29 30 31 34 35 39 40 43 45 47 50 55 56 57 59 60 62 63 64 65 68 70 72 73 75 76 78 79 81 85 87 89 90 92 93 96 97 98 100 102 103 104 105 107 108 110 111 115 116 118 119 124 127 129 130 131 132 135 144 145 146 147 148 149 153 157
Primary Contact: Scott Christensen, FACHE, Chief Executive Officer
CFO: C Thomas Moore, FACHE, Chief Financial Officer
CHR: Chrissy Nicholson, Vice President of Human Resources
CNO: Amy Walker, MSN, Chief Nursing Officer
Web address: www.deltaregional.com
Control: County, Government, nonfederal **Service**: General medical and surgical

> **Staffed Beds**: 171 **Admissions**: 6138 **Census**: 91 **Outpatient Visits**: 88170 **Births**: 669 **Personnel**: 800

GREENWOOD—Leflore County

☐ △ **GREENWOOD LEFLORE HOSPITAL (250099)**, 1401 River Road, Zip 38930–4030, Mailing Address: Drawer 1410, Zip 38935–1410; tel. 662/459–7000, **A**1 7 10 19 **F**3 13 15 17 18 20 26 28 29 32 34 35 39 40 41 43 45 46 47 48 50 53 56 57 59 64 65 68 70 74 75 76 79 81 82 85 86 87 89 90 93 96 98 103 107 108 109 110 111 114 118 119 120 121 127 129 130 132 135 146 147 148 149 156
Primary Contact: Dawne Holmes, Interim Chief Executive Officer
CFO: Dawne Holmes, Chief Financial Officer
CMO: Abhash Thakur, M.D., Chief of Staff
CHR: Key Britt, Associate Director
Web address: www.glh.org
Control: City–county, Government, nonfederal **Service**: General medical and surgical

> **Staffed Beds**: 208 **Admissions**: 4622 **Census**: 54

GRENADA—Grenada County

★ ⇑ **UNIVERSITY OF MISSISSIPPI MEDICAL CENTER GRENADA (250168)**, 960 Avent Drive, Zip 38901–5230; tel. 662/227–7000, **A**10 21 **F**3 11 13 15 17 29 30 32 34 35 39 40 43 44 45 46 50 54 57 59 60 62 64 65 66 70 73 76 77 79 80 81 82 84 85 87 89 90 93 97 107 108 110 111 115 116 118 119 124 127 130 139 143 146 147 148 149 154 156 **S** University Hospitals and Health System, Jackson, MS
Primary Contact: Wes Sigler, Chief Executive Officer
COO: Molly B. Brown, Chief Operating Officer
CFO: Scott Whittemore, Chief Financial Officer
CIO: John Farrish, Health Information Director
CHR: Claudette Hathcock, Administrative Director Human Resources
Web address: www.glmc.net/
Control: State, Government, nonfederal **Service**: General medical and surgical

> **Staffed Beds**: 58 **Admissions**: 2178 **Census**: 24 **Outpatient Visits**: 58865 **Births**: 351 **Total Expense ($000)**: 52067 **Payroll Expense ($000)**: 24487 **Personnel**: 313

GULFPORT—Harrison County

☐ △ **ENCOMPASS HEALTH REHABILITATION HOSPITAL OF GULFPORT (253027)**, 4500 13th Street, Suite 900, Zip 39501–2515; tel. 228/822–6965, **A**1 7 10 **F**29 90 **S** Encompass Health Corporation, Birmingham, AL
Primary Contact: Amber Hester, Chief Executive Officer
Web address: www.healthsouthgulfport.com
Control: Corporation, Investor–owned (for–profit) **Service**: Rehabilitation

> **Staffed Beds**: 33 **Admissions**: 807 **Census**: 28 **Outpatient Visits**: 0 **Births**: 0 **Total Expense ($000)**: 12548 **Payroll Expense ($000)**: 6326 **Personnel**: 86

☒ **GARDEN PARK MEDICAL CENTER (250123)**, 15200 Community Road, Zip 39503–3085, Mailing Address: P.O. Box 1240, Zip 39502–1240; tel. 228/575–7000, **A**1 10 **F**3 12 13 15 18 29 30 34 35 37 40 43 45 46 47 48 50 57 58 59 64 65 68 70 74 76 79 81 83 84 85 86 89 90 98 103 106 107 108 110 111 114 115 126 135 147 148 149 150 154 **S** HCA Healthcare, Nashville, TN
Primary Contact: Randy Rogers, FACHE, Chief Executive Officer
COO: Regina Ramazani, Chief Operating Officer
CFO: Regina Ramazani, Chief Financial Officer
CMO: T. Paul Mace, Chief Medical Officer
CIO: Chris Oubre, Information Technology Director
CHR: Michael Pocchiari, Director Human Resources
CNO: Cheryl Thompson, Chief Nursing Officer
Web address: www.gpmedical.com
Control: Corporation, Investor–owned (for–profit) **Service**: General medical and surgical

> **Staffed Beds**: 130 **Admissions**: 3854 **Census**: 53 **Outpatient Visits**: 59969 **Births**: 547 **Total Expense ($000)**: 73146 **Payroll Expense ($000)**: 24154 **Personnel**: 337

☐ **GULFPORT BEHAVIORAL HEALTH SYSTEM (254011)**, 11150 Highway 49 North, Zip 39503–4110; tel. 228/831–1700, (Data for 273 days) **A**1 **F**4 98 99 100 104 **S** Universal Health Services, Inc., King of Prussia, PA
Primary Contact: Michael A. Zieman, FACHE, Administrator
Web address: www.gulfportmemorial.com
Control: Corporation, Investor–owned (for–profit) **Service**: Psychiatric

> **Staffed Beds**: 48 **Admissions**: 796 **Census**: 20 **Births**: 0 **Total Expense ($000)**: 11745 **Payroll Expense ($000)**: 5268 **Personnel**: 133

☒ **MEMORIAL HOSPITAL AT GULFPORT (250019)**, 4500 13th Street, Zip 39501–2569, Mailing Address: P.O. Box 1810, Zip 39502–1810; tel. 228/867–4000, **A**1 2 3 10 **F**2 3 11 12 13 15 17 18 20 22 24 28 29 30 31 34 35 40 43 44 45 46 47 48 49 50 53 54 57 59 64 65 68 70 71 72 73 74 76 77 78 79 80 81 82 84 85 87 89 107 108 110 111 114 115 116 117 118 119 120 121 123 124 126 130 132 145 146 148 149
Primary Contact: Kent Nicaud, President and Chief Executive Officer
CFO: Mark Wack, Chief Financial Officer
CMO: Larry Couvillon, M.D., Chief Medical Officer
CIO: Gene Thomas, Vice President, Information Systems, Chief Information Officer
CHR: Cathy Wood, Vice President, Human Resources
CNO: Jennifer Dumal, R.N., Chief Operating Officer of Clinical and Chief Nursing Officer
Web address: www.gulfportmemorial.com
Control: City–county, Government, nonfederal **Service**: General medical and surgical

> **Staffed Beds**: 281 **Admissions**: 14840 **Census**: 190 **Outpatient Visits**: 746271 **Births**: 1276 **Total Expense ($000)**: 527638 **Payroll Expense ($000)**: 226865 **Personnel**: 3070

Hospital, Medicare Provider Number, Address, Telephone, Approval, Facility, and Physician Codes, Health Care System

★ American Hospital Association (AHA) membership
☐ The Joint Commission accreditation
○ Healthcare Facilities Accreditation Program
◇ DNV Healthcare Inc. accreditation
⇑ Center for Improvement in Healthcare Quality Accreditation
△ Commission on Accreditation of Rehabilitation Facilities (CARF) accreditation

MS

⊠ **SELECT SPECIALTY HOSPITAL-GULFPORT (252005)**, 1520 Broad Avenue, Suite 300, Zip 39501–3601; tel. 228/575–7500, **A**1 10 **F**1 29 75 82 87 90 **S** Select Medical Corporation, Mechanicsburg, PA
Primary Contact: John O'Keefe, Chief Executive Officer
Web address: www.selectspecialtyhospitals.com/company/locations/gulfcoast.aspx
Control: Corporation, Investor–owned (for–profit) **Service**: Acute long–term care hospital

Staffed Beds: 61 **Admissions**: 361 **Census**: 28 **Outpatient Visits**: 0
Births: 0 **Total Expense ($000)**: 17004 **Payroll Expense ($000)**: 6978
Personnel: 128

HATTIESBURG—Forrest County

★ △ ⇑ **FORREST GENERAL HOSPITAL (250078)**, 6051 U S Highway 49, Zip 39401–7200, Mailing Address: P.O. Box 16389, Zip 39404–6389; tel. 601/288–7000, (Includes PINE GROVE BEHAVIORAL HEALTH AND ADDICTION SERVICES, 2255 Broadway Drive, Hattiesburg, Mississippi, Zip 39402–3254; tel. 888/574–4673; Debbie F Sanford, R.N., MS, Administrator) **A**2 3 5 7 10 19 21 **F**3 4 5 8 12 13 15 17 18 20 22 24 26 28 29 30 31 34 35 37 39 40 43 45 46 47 48 49 53 55 57 58 59 62 63 64 68 70 72 73 75 76 77 79 81 84 85 86 87 89 90 93 96 97 98 99 100 101 102 103 104 105 106 107 108 111 114 115 118 119 120 121 123 124 126 128 130 132 146 147 149 151 152 154
Primary Contact: Andy Woodard, President and Chief Executive Officer
COO: Douglas A Jones, Chief Operating Officer
CMO: Steven E Farrell, M.D., Chief Medical Officer
CHR: Troy P Daniels, Chief Human Resources Officer
CNO: Micah Rehm, Chief Nursing Officer
Web address: www.forrestgeneral.com
Control: County, Government, nonfederal **Service**: General medical and surgical

Staffed Beds: 545 **Admissions**: 29302 **Census**: 370 **Outpatient Visits**: 155992 **Births**: 2466 **Total Expense ($000)**: 456111 **Payroll Expense ($000)**: 174040 **Personnel**: 3314

HATTIESBURG—Lamar County

⊠ **MERIT HEALTH WESLEY (250094)**, 5001 Hardy Street, Zip 39402–1308, Mailing Address: P.O. Box 16509, Zip 39404–6509; tel. 601/268–8000, **A**1 3 10 12 13 19 **F**3 8 11 12 13 15 17 18 20 22 24 26 28 29 30 32 34 35 37 39 40 41 43 45 46 49 53 54 57 58 59 60 61 64 65 70 71 72 73 74 75 76 77 78 79 81 82 85 87 89 90 91 93 96 97 98 103 107 108 110 111 114 115 117 118 119 126 128 129 130 132 135 146 148 **S** Community Health Systems, Inc., Franklin, TN
Primary Contact: Carol Upton, Interim Chief Executive Officer
CFO: Randy Humphrey, Chief Financial Officer
CMO: William Reno, M.D., III President Medical Staff
CIO: Jesse Folds, Director of Information Technologies
CHR: Terry Trigg, Director Human Resources
Web address: www.wesley.com
Control: Corporation, Investor–owned (for–profit) **Service**: General medical and surgical

Staffed Beds: 211 **Admissions**: 6608 **Census**: 92 **Outpatient Visits**: 75731
Births: 111 **Personnel**: 783

HAZLEHURST—Copiah County

★ **COPIAH COUNTY MEDICAL CENTER (251327)**, 27190 Highway 28, Zip 39083–2228, Mailing Address: P.O. Box 889, Zip 39083–0889; tel. 601/574–7000, **A**10 18 **F**3 15 29 30 34 35 39 40 50 51 57 59 64 77 81 93 104 107 110 111 115 119 133 148 149 153 154 156
Primary Contact: Benjamin Lott, Chief Executive Officer
CFO: Bryan N Stevens, Interim Chief Financial Officer
CNO: Alison Mathis, Chief Nursing Officer
Web address: www.myccmc.org/
Control: County, Government, nonfederal **Service**: General medical and surgical

Staffed Beds: 25 **Admissions**: 746 **Census**: 16 **Births**: 0 **Total Expense ($000)**: 14913 **Payroll Expense ($000)**: 5876 **Personnel**: 153

HOLLY SPRINGS—Marshall County

ALLIANCE HEALTHCARE SYSTEM (250012), 1430 Highway 4 East, Zip 38635–2140, Mailing Address: P.O. Box 6000, Zip 38634–6000; tel. 662/252–1212, **A**10 20 **F**15 29 35 40 43 57 63 75 87 89 98 103 107 114 119 130 132 133
Primary Contact: Perry E. Williams Sr, Administrator and Chief Executive Officer
COO: Cecelia Bost, Chief Operating Officer
CFO: William F Magee, Chief Financial Officer
CMO: Subbu Rayudu, M.D., Chief of Staff
CIO: Saul Mbenga, Manager Information Technology
CHR: Judy Eggers, Manager Human Resources
Web address: www.alliancehealth.us
Control: Corporation, Investor–owned (for–profit) **Service**: General medical and surgical

Staffed Beds: 40 **Admissions**: 448 **Census**: 10 **Births**: 0 **Personnel**: 101

HOUSTON—Chickasaw County

TRACE REGIONAL HOSPITAL (250017), Highway 8 East, Zip 38851–9396, Mailing Address: P.O. Box 626, Zip 38851–0626; tel. 662/456–3700, **A**10 **F**3 11 15 30 34 35 45 57 59 61 64 66 75 82 90 91 93 98 103 107 111 119 127 130 133 135 146 148
Primary Contact: Gary L. Staten, Chief Executive Officer
CFO: Pamela W Cook, Chief Financial Officer
CMO: Bill Brohawn, Chief of Staff
CHR: Sherry Craig, Director Human Resources
CNO: Marianne Johnson, Chief Nursing Officer
Web address: www.traceregional.com
Control: Corporation, Investor–owned (for–profit) **Service**: General medical and surgical

Staffed Beds: 84 **Admissions**: 461 **Census**: 14 **Outpatient Visits**: 8084
Births: 0 **Total Expense ($000)**: 10884 **Payroll Expense ($000)**: 6220
Personnel: 207

INDIANOLA—Sunflower County

★ **SOUTH SUNFLOWER COUNTY HOSPITAL (250095)**, 121 East Baker Street, Zip 38751–2498; tel. 662/635–7201, **A**10 20 **F**3 8 13 34 40 43 50 61 64 65 76 81 85 89 107 119 127 133
Primary Contact: Courtney Phillips, Chief Executive Officer
COO: Holly H. Sparks, Chief Clinical Officer
CFO: Katie Yates, Chief Financial Officer
CMO: Eric Lessmann, Chief of Staff
CIO: Benjamin Rosenthal, Information Systems Director
CHR: Meredith Taylor, Controller
Web address: www.southsunflower.com
Control: County, Government, nonfederal **Service**: General medical and surgical

Staffed Beds: 48 **Admissions**: 1040 **Census**: 14 **Births**: 83 **Total Expense ($000)**: 16619 **Payroll Expense ($000)**: 6093 **Personnel**: 138

IUKA—Tishomingo County

⊠ **NORTH MISSISSIPPI MEDICAL CENTER-IUKA (250002)**, 1777 Curtis Drive, Zip 38852–1001, Mailing Address: P.O. Box 860, Zip 38852–0860; tel. 662/423–6051, **A**1 10 **F**3 15 29 35 40 53 80 82 86 87 89 90 93 107 108 111 114 119 127 129 130 132 133 134 146 **S** North Mississippi Health Services, Inc., Tupelo, MS
Primary Contact: Fred A. Truesdale Jr, Administrator
CFO: Betty Moore, Business Manager
CMO: Margaret Glynn, M.D., Chief Medical Officer
CIO: Fred A Truesdale Jr Administrator
CHR: Jane Chamblee, Manager Human Resources
Web address: www.nmhs.net
Control: Other not–for–profit (including NFP Corporation) **Service**: General medical and surgical

Staffed Beds: 48 **Admissions**: 716 **Census**: 6 **Outpatient Visits**: 20432
Births: 0 **Personnel**: 130

JACKSON—Hinds County

☐ **BRENTWOOD BEHAVIORAL HEALTHCARE OF MISSISSIPPI (254007)**, 3531 East Lakeland Drive, Zip 39232–8839; tel. 601/936–2024, **A**1 10 **F**35 98 99 101 102 104 105 130 132 134 153 **S** Universal Health Services, Inc., King of Prussia, PA
Primary Contact: Michael J. Carney, Chief Executive Officer
Web address: www.brentwoodjackson.com
Control: Corporation, Investor–owned (for–profit) **Service**: Psychiatric

Staffed Beds: 105 **Admissions**: 2474 **Census**: 63 **Outpatient Visits**: 3556
Births: 0 **Personnel**: 250

⊠ **G.V. (SONNY) MONTGOMERY VETERANS AFFAIRS MEDICAL CENTER**, 1500 East Woodrow Wilson Drive, Zip 39216–5199; tel. 601/362–4471, (Nonreporting) **A**1 3 5 **S** Department of Veterans Affairs, Washington, DC
Primary Contact: David M. Walker, M.D., Medical Center Director
COO: Jed Fillingim, Acting Chief Operating Officer and Associate Director
CFO: Joy Willis, Acting Chief Fiscal Service
CMO: Kent Kirchner, M.D., Chief of Staff
CIO: Robert Wolak, Chief Information Resource Management Service
CHR: Sam Evans, Chief Human Resources Management
Web address: www.jackson.va.gov/
Control: Veterans Affairs, Government, federal **Service**: General medical and surgical

Staffed Beds: 323

MS

Many Facility Codes have changed. Please refer to the AHA Guide Code Chart. © 2019 AHA Guide

⊞ **MERIT HEALTH CENTRAL (250072)**, 1850 Chadwick Drive, Zip 39204–3479, Mailing Address: P.O. Box 59001, Zip 39284–9001; tel. 601/376–1000, **A**1 3 10 **F**3 13 15 16 17 18 20 22 24 26 29 30 31 34 35 37 38 40 43 45 46 47 49 50 57 59 64 65 70 72 74 75 76 77 78 79 81 85 87 90 91 92 94 98 100 102 107 108 109 110 111 112 113 114 115 116 117 118 119 121 123 124 126 129 130 132 135 141 146 148 149 154 157 **S** Community Health Systems, Inc., Franklin, TN
Primary Contact: Barry Moss, Chief Executive Officer
COO: Tom Wills, R.N., Chief Operating Officer
CFO: Justin Stroud, Chief Financial Officer
CMO: Greg Oden, Chief Medical Officer
CIO: Tracy Holifield, Director Information Systems
CHR: Sean Jones, Director Human Resources
CNO: Laura Knight, Chief Nursing Officer
Web address: www.merithealthcentral.com/
Control: Corporation, Investor–owned (for–profit) **Service:** General medical and surgical

Staffed Beds: 254 Admissions: 8205 Census: 110 Outpatient Visits: 175533 Births: 634 Total Expense ($000): 149101 Payroll Expense ($000): 46486 Personnel: 785

⊞ △ **METHODIST REHABILITATION CENTER (250152)**, 1350 Woodrow Wilson Drive, Zip 39216–5198; tel. 601/981–2611, (Total facility includes 60 beds in nursing home–type unit) **A**1 5 7 10 **F**30 34 35 50 57 58 59 64 68 74 81 82 86 87 90 91 92 93 94 95 96 119 130 131 132 135 146
Primary Contact: Mark A. Adams, President and Chief Executive Officer
COO: Joseph M Morette, Executive Vice President
CFO: Gary Armstrong, Executive Vice President
CIO: Gary Armstrong, Executive Vice President
CHR: Steve Hope, Vice President Corporate Services
Web address: www.methodistrehab.org
Control: Other not–for–profit (including NFP Corporation) **Service:** Rehabilitation

Staffed Beds: 184 Admissions: 1333 Census: 117 Outpatient Visits: 54355 Births: 0 Total Expense ($000): 47973 Payroll Expense ($000): 26545 Personnel: 572

⊞ **MISSISSIPPI BAPTIST MEDICAL CENTER (250102)**, 1225 North State Street, Zip 39202–2064; tel. 601/968–1000, **A**1 2 3 5 10 **F**3 12 13 15 17 18 20 22 24 26 28 29 30 31 34 35 37 40 46 47 49 50 53 57 58 59 60 64 65 68 70 72 74 75 76 79 80 81 84 85 87 89 92 93 98 103 107 108 110 111 114 115 116 117 118 119 120 121 122 123 124 126 129 130 132 141 146 147 149 3 Baptist Memorial Health Care Corporation, Memphis, TN
Primary Contact: Bobbie K. Ware, R.N., FACHE, Chief Executive Officer
COO: Bobbie K. Ware, R.N., FACHE, Vice President Patient Care and Chief Nursing Officer
CFO: William Thompson, Chief Financial Officer
CMO: Michael Maples, M.D., Vice President and Chief Medical Officer
CIO: Steve M Stanic, Vice President and Chief Information Officer
CHR: Lee Ann Foreman, Vice President Human Resources
CNO: Bobbie K. Ware, R.N., FACHE, Vice President Patient Care and Chief Nursing Officer
Web address: www.mbhs.org
Control: Other not–for–profit (including NFP Corporation) **Service:** General medical and surgical

Staffed Beds: 423 Admissions: 20317 Census: 275 Outpatient Visits: 253975 Births: 1716 Total Expense ($000): 444099 Payroll Expense ($000): 132217 Personnel: 2683

★ **SELECT SPECIALTY HOSPITAL - BELHAVEN (252003)**, 1225 North State Street, Zip 39202–2097, Mailing Address: P.O. Box 23695, Zip 39225–3695; tel. 601/968–1000, **A**10 **F**1 3 29 56 61 82 130 **S** Select Medical Corporation, Mechanicsburg, PA
Primary Contact: Robert Shannon. Canard, Chief Executive Officer
CFO: Russell W York, Vice President and Chief Financial Officer
CMO: Holland M Addison, M.D., Medical Director
CIO: Steve M Stanic, Vice President and Chief Information Officer
CHR: Lee Ann Foreman, Vice President Human Resources
Web address: www.https://belhaven.selectspecialtyhospitals.com/
Control: Corporation, Investor–owned (for–profit) **Service:** Acute long–term care hospital

Staffed Beds: 25 Admissions: 272 Census: 20 Outpatient Visits: 0 Births: 0 Total Expense ($000): 13706 Payroll Expense ($000): 6427 Personnel: 118

⊞ **SELECT SPECIALTY HOSPITAL-JACKSON (252007)**, 5903 Ridgewood Road, Suite 100, Zip 39211–3700; tel. 601/899–3800, **A**1 10 **F**1 107 119 **S** Select Medical Corporation, Mechanicsburg, PA
Primary Contact: Chandler Ewing, Chief Executive Officer
CFO: Melissa Smith, Controller
CIO: Jacqueline Barnes, Manager Health Information
CHR: Vicki Watson, Manager Human Resources
Web address: www.selectspecialtyhospitals.com/company/locations/jackson.aspx
Control: Corporation, Investor–owned (for–profit) **Service:** Acute long–term care hospital

Staffed Beds: 53 Admissions: 647 Census: 45 Outpatient Visits: 0 Births: 0 Total Expense ($000): 23944 Payroll Expense ($000): 10615 Personnel: 217

⊞ **ST. DOMINIC-JACKSON MEMORIAL HOSPITAL (250048)**, 969 Lakeland Drive, Zip 39216–4606; tel. 601/200–2000, **A**1 2 3 5 10 **F**3 4 11 12 13 15 17 18 20 22 24 26 28 29 30 31 34 36 37 38 39 40 43 46 47 49 50 51 53 58 60 61 64 65 68 70 72 73 74 75 76 77 79 80 81 82 84 85 86 87 89 90 92 93 96 97 98 100 101 102 103 107 108 109 110 111 114 115 116 117 118 119 120 121 123 124 126 130 131 146 147 148 154
Primary Contact: Lester K. Diamond, President
CFO: Sam Scott, Vice President Financial Services
CMO: Eric A McVey, M.D., Executive Vice President Medical Affairs and Quality
CIO: Keith Van Camp, Vice President Information Services
CHR: Frank Lenior, Vice President Human Resources
Web address: www.stdom.com
Control: Church operated, Nongovernment, not–for–profit **Service:** General medical and surgical

Staffed Beds: 502 Admissions: 33743 Census: 422 Outpatient Visits: 217125 Births: 1487 Total Expense ($000): 487557 Payroll Expense ($000): 201250 Personnel: 2932

⊞ **UNIVERSITY OF MISSISSIPPI MEDICAL CENTER (250001)**, 2500 North State Street, Zip 39216–4505; tel. 601/984–1000, (Includes BLAIR E. BATSON HOSPITAL FOR CHILDREN, 2500 North State State Room W019, Jackson, Mississippi, Zip 39216–4500; tel. 601/984–1000; CHILDREN'S HEALTHCARE OF MISSISSIPPI, 2500 North State Street, Jackson, Mississippi, Zip 39216–4500; tel. 601/984–1000) **A**1 2 3 5 8 10 13 **F**3 6 7 8 11 12 13 15 17 18 19 20 21 22 23 24 25 26 27 28 29 30 31 32 34 35 38 39 40 43 45 46 47 48 49 50 52 53 54 55 56 57 58 59 60 61 64 65 66 68 70 71 72 73 74 75 76 77 79 80 81 82 84 85 86 87 88 89 90 92 93 94 96 97 98 99 100 101 102 103 104 107 108 110 111 112 114 115 116 117 118 119 120 121 123 124 126 129 130 131 132 134 135 136 137 138 139 141 142 143 144 146 147 148 149 152 154 155 156 **S** University Hospitals and Health System, Jackson, MS
Primary Contact: Kevin S. Cook, Chief Executive Officer
CFO: Dan Janicak, Chief Financial Officer
CMO: William H Cleland, M.D., Chief Medical Officer
CHR: Paula Henderson, Chief Human Resources Officer
Web address: www.umc.edu
Control: State, Government, nonfederal **Service:** General medical and surgical

Staffed Beds: 680 Admissions: 29367 Census: 540 Outpatient Visits: 581753 Births: 2179 Total Expense ($000): 820412 Payroll Expense ($000): 327072 Personnel: 5045

KEESLER AFB—Harrison County

⊞ **U. S. AIR FORCE MEDICAL CENTER KEESLER**, 301 Fisher Street, Room 1A132, Zip 39534–2519; tel. 228/376–2550, (Nonreporting) **A**1 2 3 5 **S** Department of the Air Force, Washington, DC
Primary Contact: Colonel Thomas Harrell, M.D., Commander
COO: Brigadier General James Dougherty, Commander
CFO: Major Brenda Yi, Director Medical Resource Management and Chief Financial Officer
CMO: Colonel James Gasque, M.D., Chief Hospital Services
CIO: Major Samuel Silverthorne, Chief Information Officer
CHR: Major Brenda Yi, Director Medical Resource Management and Chief Financial Officer
Web address: www.keesler.af.mil
Control: Department of Defense, Government, federal **Service:** General medical and surgical

Staffed Beds: 56

Hospital, Medicare Provider Number, Address, Telephone, Approval, Facility, and Physician Codes, Health Care System

★ American Hospital Association (AHA) membership ☐ The Joint Commission accreditation ○ Healthcare Facilities Accreditation Program ◇ DNV Healthcare Inc. accreditation ⇑ Center for Improvement in Healthcare Quality Accreditation △ Commission on Accreditation of Rehabilitation Facilities (CARF) accreditation

KOSCIUSKO—Attala County

★ ⇑ **BAPTIST MEDICAL CENTER ATTALA (251336)**, 220 Highway 12 West, Zip 39090–3208, Mailing Address: P.O. Box 887, Zip 39090–0887; tel. 662/289–4311, **A**10 18 21 **F**2 3 8 15 30 40 45 64 65 81 90 107 108 110 115 118 119 127 133 148 153 **S** Baptist Memorial Health Care Corporation, Memphis, TN
Primary Contact: Robert Coleman, Chief Executive Officer
CHR: Stephanie Washington, Human Resources Director
CNO: Allison Schuler, R.N., Chief Nursing Officer
Web address: www.mbhs.org/locations/baptist-medical-center-attala/
Control: Other not–for–profit (including NFP Corporation) **Service**: General medical and surgical

Staffed Beds: 25 **Admissions**: 483 **Census**: 8 **Outpatient Visits**: 19291 **Births**: 0 **Personnel**: 123

LAUREL—Jones County

★ ⇑ **SOUTH CENTRAL REGIONAL MEDICAL CENTER (250058)**, 1220 Jefferson Street, Zip 39440–4374, Mailing Address: P.O. Box 607, Zip 39441–0607; tel. 601/426–4000, (Total facility includes 248 beds in nursing home–type unit) **A**10 21 **F**3 4 7 12 13 15 17 18 20 26 28 29 30 31 32 34 35 39 40 43 44 45 48 49 50 51 52 53 57 59 62 63 64 65 68 70 73 74 75 76 77 79 81 82 85 86 87 89 90 91 92 93 100 102 104 105 107 108 110 111 115 118 119 126 128 130 131 132 134 135 143 144 146 147 148 152 154 157
Primary Contact: G Douglas Higginbotham, President and Chief Executive Officer
CFO: Tom Canizaro, Vice President and Chief Financial Officer
CIO: Dell Blakeney, Vice President and Chief Information Officer
CHR: Janet Staples, Vice President Human Resources
CNO: Beth W Endom, R.N., MSN, Vice President and Chief Nursing Officer
Web address: www.scrmc.com
Control: County, Government, nonfederal **Service**: General medical and surgical

Staffed Beds: 424 **Admissions**: 7896 **Census**: 343 **Outpatient Visits**: 201566 **Births**: 863 **Total Expense ($000)**: 182292 **Payroll Expense ($000)**: 92399 **Personnel**: 1802

LEAKESVILLE—Greene County

GREENE COUNTY HOSPITAL (251329), 1017 Jackson Avenue, Zip 39451–9105; tel. 601/394–4139, **A**10 18 **F**40 43 107 133
Primary Contact: Deborah Berry, Director of Operations
CFO: Debbie Brannan, Chief Financial Officer
CMO: Larry Henderson, M.D., Medical Director
CHR: Carla Shows, Payroll Clerk
Web address: www.georgeregional.com
Control: County, Government, nonfederal **Service**: General medical and surgical

Staffed Beds: 7 **Admissions**: 121 **Census**: 4 **Births**: 0 **Total Expense ($000)**: 4866 **Payroll Expense ($000)**: 2110 **Personnel**: 45

LEXINGTON—Holmes County

✉ **UNIVERSITY OF MISSISSIPPI MEDICAL CENTER HOLMES COUNTY (251319)**, 239 Bowling Green Road, Zip 39095–5167; tel. 601/496–5200, **A**1 10 18 **F**3 15 29 34 40 43 50 56 57 59 64 86 87 89 93 104 107 114 119 127 130 133 146 148 149 153 **S** University Hospitals and Health System, Jackson, MS
Primary Contact: Wes Sigler, Chief Executive Officer
COO: Paige Lawrence, Assistant Administrator
CFO: Scott Whittemore, Chief Financial Officer
CMO: Mark Smothers, M.D., Chief Medical Officer
CIO: Sammuel Townsend, LAN Administrator
CHR: Claudette Hathcock, Human Resources Director
Web address: www.ummchealth.com/holmes/
Control: State, Government, nonfederal **Service**: General medical and surgical

Staffed Beds: 25 **Admissions**: 326 **Census**: 7 **Outpatient Visits**: 16677 **Births**: 0 **Total Expense ($000)**: 13257 **Payroll Expense ($000)**: 6838 **Personnel**: 109

LOUISVILLE—Winston County

WINSTON MEDICAL CENTER (250027), 562 East Main Street, Zip 39339–2742, Mailing Address: P.O. Box 967, Zip 39339–0967; tel. 662/773–6211, (Total facility includes 120 beds in nursing home–type unit) **A**10 20 **F**15 29 34 35 40 43 57 59 65 89 93 98 103 107 110 114 119 127 128 130 133 146
Primary Contact: Paul S. Black, Chief Executive Officer
Web address: www.winstonmedical.org
Control: Other not–for–profit (including NFP Corporation) **Service**: General medical and surgical

Staffed Beds: 144 **Admissions**: 1277 **Census**: 121 **Outpatient Visits**: 28943 **Births**: 0 **Total Expense ($000)**: 27801 **Payroll Expense ($000)**: 11820 **Personnel**: 303

LUCEDALE—George County

GEORGE REGIONAL HOSPITAL (250036), 859 Winter Street, Zip 39452–6603, Mailing Address: P.O. Box 607, Zip 39452–0607; tel. 601/947–3161, **A**10 20 **F**3 11 13 15 18 29 30 34 35 40 43 45 47 48 49 53 54 57 59 65 68 70 76 77 81 82 86 87 93 97 107 108 111 119 127 129 130 133 135 146 148
Primary Contact: Greg Havard, Chief Executive Officer
CFO: Debbie Brannan, Chief Financial Officer
CMO: Jay Pinkerton, Chief Medical Officer
CIO: Anthoney Fryfogle, Chief Information Officer
CHR: Carla Shows, Human Resource and Payroll Clerk
CNO: Tabatha Pinter, Director of Nursing
Web address: www.georgeregional.com
Control: County, Government, nonfederal **Service**: General medical and surgical

Staffed Beds: 48 **Admissions**: 996 **Census**: 9 **Outpatient Visits**: 45017 **Births**: 276 **Total Expense ($000)**: 22906 **Payroll Expense ($000)**: 12546 **Personnel**: 252

MACON—Noxubee County

NOXUBEE GENERAL HOSPITAL (251307), 606 North Jefferson Street, Zip 39341–2242, Mailing Address: P.O. Box 480, Zip 39341–0480; tel. 662/726–4231, (Total facility includes 60 beds in nursing home–type unit) **A**10 18 **F**40 89 107 111 127 128 130 133
Primary Contact: Danny H. McKay, Administrator
Web address: www.noxubeecountyms.com/quality-of-life-noxubee-mississipp/health-care-noxubee-mississippi/
Control: County, Government, nonfederal **Service**: General medical and surgical

Staffed Beds: 85 **Admissions**: 547 **Census**: 64 **Outpatient Visits**: 32147 **Births**: 0 **Total Expense ($000)**: 14964 **Payroll Expense ($000)**: 7775 **Personnel**: 198

MAGEE—Simpson County

MAGEE GENERAL HOSPITAL (250124), 300 Third Avenue SE, Zip 39111–3698; tel. 601/849–5070, **A**10 **F**15 29 35 40 43 81 89 107 108 111 119 129 130 133 146 148
Primary Contact: Gregg Gibbes, Chief Executive Officer
CMO: Kelli Smith, M.D., Chief of Staff
CIO: Kirby Craft, Chief Information Officer
CHR: Steve Beckham, Director Human Resources
CNO: Cindy McIntyre, R.N., Administrative Director Clinical Services
Web address: www.mghosp.org
Control: Other not–for–profit (including NFP Corporation) **Service**: General medical and surgical

Staffed Beds: 44 **Admissions**: 699 **Census**: 13 **Births**: 0 **Total Expense ($000)**: 17301 **Payroll Expense ($000)**: 5835 **Personnel**: 3

MAGNOLIA—Pike County

BEACHAM MEMORIAL HOSPITAL (250049), 205 North Cherry Street, Zip 39652–2819, Mailing Address: P.O. Box 351, Zip 39652–0351; tel. 601/783–2351, **A**10 **F**3 34 35 36 57 59 65 68 98 100 101 103 107 114 127 130 133 146 148
Primary Contact: Jason Reed, Chief Executive Officer
CMO: Lucius Lampton, M.D., Medical Director
CHR: Jackie McKenzie, Director Administrative Services
Web address: www.beachammemorial.org
Control: Corporation, Investor–owned (for–profit) **Service**: General medical and surgical

Staffed Beds: 31 **Admissions**: 1271 **Census**: 27 **Outpatient Visits**: 0 **Births**: 0 **Total Expense ($000)**: 5194 **Payroll Expense ($000)**: 2253 **Personnel**: 67

MCCOMB—Pike County

★ ⇑ **SOUTHWEST MISSISSIPPI REGIONAL MEDICAL CENTER (250097)**, 215 Marion Avenue, Zip 39648–2705, Mailing Address: P.O. Box 1307, Zip 39649–1307; tel. 601/249–5500, **A**10 19 21 **F**3 8 9 11 13 15 17 18 20 22 24 28 29 30 31 34 35 37 39 40 41 43 44 45 46 47 48 49 50 53 55 57 59 64 65 70 72 73 74 75 76 77 79 81 84 85 86 87 93 94 96 107 108 110 111 115 118 119 120 121 127 129 130 131 132 135 145 146 148 149 **S** Southwest Health Systems, Mccomb, MS
Primary Contact: Norman M. Price, FACHE, Chief Executive Officer
COO: Richard Williams, Chief Operating Officer
CFO: Charla Rowley, Chief Financial Officer
CMO: Kevin Richardson, M.D., Chief of Staff
CIO: David Hamilton, Chief Information Officer
CHR: Don Haskins, Administrative Director Human Resources
CNO: Michelle Gough MSN, RN-B Chief Nursing Officer
Web address: www.smrmc.com
Control: Hospital district or authority, Government, nonfederal **Service**: General medical and surgical

Staffed Beds: 143 **Admissions**: 4727 **Census**: 44 **Outpatient Visits**: 83723 **Births**: 575 **Personnel**: 810

Many Facility Codes have changed. Please refer to the AHA Guide Code Chart.   © 2019 AHA Guide

MS

MEADVILLE—Franklin County

FRANKLIN COUNTY MEMORIAL HOSPITAL (251330), 40 Union Church Road, Zip 39653–8336, Mailing Address: P.O. Box 636, Zip 39653–0636; tel. 601/384–5801, **A**10 18 **F**29 35 39 40 43 56 86 93 104 107 119 127 130 133 143 148
Primary Contact: Mike Boleware, Administrator
Web address: www.fcmh.net
Control: County, Government, nonfederal **Service**: General medical and surgical

Staffed Beds: 25 **Admissions**: 238 **Census**: 18 **Births**: 0

MENDENHALL—Simpson County

SIMPSON GENERAL HOSPITAL (251317), 1842 Simpson Highway 149, Zip 39114–3438; tel. 601/847–2221, **A**10 18 **F**3 11 29 30 34 35 40 43 44 54 56 57 59 61 64 65 66 68 81 85 86 87 93 98 100 101 102 103 104 105 107 114 119 127 130 132 133 134 143 146
Primary Contact: David Welch, Chief Executive Officer
COO: Al Gary, COO
CFO: Al Gary, COO
CMO: Chip Holbrook, M.D., Chief of Staff
CIO: David Welch, Director Information Technology
CHR: Randall Neely, CEO
CNO: Sharon Burnham, Director of Nursing
Web address: www.simpsongeneralhospital.com
Control: Other not–for–profit (including NFP Corporation) **Service**: General medical and surgical

Staffed Beds: 35 **Admissions**: 638 **Census**: 16 **Outpatient Visits**: 11375 **Births**: 0 **Total Expense ($000)**: 28700 **Payroll Expense ($000)**: 8430 **Personnel**: 169

MERIDIAN—Lauderdale County

ALLIANCE HEALTH CENTER (250151), 5000 Highway 39 North, Zip 39301–1021; tel. 601/483–6211, **A**1 10 **F**4 6 35 38 64 86 87 98 99 101 102 103 105 106 135 152 153 154 **S** Universal Health Services, Inc., King of Prussia, PA
Primary Contact: Jay Shehi, Chief Executive Officer
CFO: Robert Jackson, Chief Financial Officer
CMO: Terry Jordan, M.D., Chief of Staff
CIO: Brenda Smith, Director Financial Services
CHR: Shrea Johnson, Director Human Resources
Web address: www.alliancehealthcenter.com
Control: Corporation, Investor–owned (for–profit) **Service**: Psychiatric

Staffed Beds: 154 **Admissions**: 3770 **Census**: 135 **Outpatient Visits**: 0 **Births**: 0 **Total Expense ($000)**: 39447 **Payroll Expense ($000)**: 11657 **Personnel**: 223

ANDERSON REGIONAL HEALTH SYSTEM (250104), 2124 14th Street, Zip 39301–4040; tel. 601/553–6000, **A**1 2 3 10 19 **F**3 7 11 12 13 15 17 18 20 22 24 26 28 29 30 31 34 36 38 40 41 43 44 45 47 48 49 50 53 54 57 58 59 64 65 68 70 72 73 75 76 77 79 80 81 85 86 87 88 89 90 91 92 93 96 107 110 111 115 116 119 120 121 123 124 126 127 129 130 131 132 135 146 148 149
Primary Contact: John G. Anderson, FACHE, President and Chief Executive Officer
CFO: Steven Brown, Vice President Finance
CMO: Scot Bell, Chief Medical Officer
CHR: Joel Windham, Vice President Human Resources
CNO: Matt Edwards, Vice President Nursing Services and Chief Nursing Officer
Web address: www.andersonregional.org
Control: Other not–for–profit (including NFP Corporation) **Service**: General medical and surgical

Staffed Beds: 260 **Admissions**: 11823 **Census**: 142 **Outpatient Visits**: 142546 **Births**: 1202 **Total Expense ($000)**: 172135 **Payroll Expense ($000)**: 55501 **Personnel**: 1241

△ **ANDERSON REGIONAL HEALTH SYSTEM SOUTH (250081)**, 1102 Constitution Avenue, Zip 39301–4001; tel. 601/553–6000, **A**1 7 10 **F**3 13 29 32 34 35 54 60 64 65 68 81 82 86 87 90 91 92 96 97 98 103 105 119 127 130 132 133 135 146 148 149
Primary Contact: John G. Anderson, FACHE, President and Chief Executive Officer
CFO: Steven Brown, Vice President Finance
CIO: Steve Taylor, Chief Information Officer
CHR: Joel Windham, Vice President Human Resources
CNO: Betty Cryer, R.N., Administrator/Chief Nursing Officer
Web address: www.andersonregional.org
Control: Other not–for–profit (including NFP Corporation) **Service**: General medical and surgical

Staffed Beds: 69 **Admissions**: 1381 **Census**: 47 **Outpatient Visits**: 26026 **Births**: 0 **Total Expense ($000)**: 19749 **Payroll Expense ($000)**: 6101 **Personnel**: 163

EAST MISSISSIPPI STATE HOSPITAL, 1818 College Drive, Zip 39307, Mailing Address: Box 4128, West Station, Zip 39304–4128; tel. 601/482–6186, (Total facility includes 158 beds in nursing home–type unit) **A**1 **F**29 30 39 65 82 86 87 98 103 128 130 135 143 146 148 **S** Mississippi State Department of Mental Health, Jackson, MS
Primary Contact: Charles Carlisle, Director
CFO: Geri Doggett, Director Business
CMO: Gloria Gomez, M.D., Medical Director
CIO: Scotty Taylor, Information Technology Director
CHR: Shearmaine Calaway, Director Human Resources
CNO: Diane Nobles, Nurse Executive
Web address: www.emsh.state.ms.us
Control: State, Government, nonfederal **Service**: Psychiatric

Staffed Beds: 266 **Admissions**: 548 **Census**: 279 **Outpatient Visits**: 0 **Births**: 0 **Total Expense ($000)**: 49190 **Payroll Expense ($000)**: 23705 **Personnel**: 750

REGENCY HOSPITAL OF MERIDIAN (252006), 1102 Constitution Avenue, 2nd Floor, Zip 39301–4001; tel. 601/484–7900, **A**1 10 **F**1 **S** Select Medical Corporation, Mechanicsburg, PA
Primary Contact: William Heath, Chief Executive Officer
Web address: www.regencyhospital.com
Control: Corporation, Investor–owned (for–profit) **Service**: Acute long–term care hospital

Staffed Beds: 40 **Admissions**: 264 **Census**: 19 **Outpatient Visits**: 0 **Births**: 0 **Total Expense ($000)**: 10029 **Payroll Expense ($000)**: 4800 **Personnel**: 93

RILEY HOSPITAL See Anderson Regional Health System South

★ ⇧ **RUSH FOUNDATION HOSPITAL (250069)**, 1314 19th Avenue, Zip 39301–4195; tel. 601/483–0011, **A**3 10 19 21 **F**13 15 29 35 39 40 43 70 72 73 76 77 81 82 86 89 90 93 107 108 118 119 130 131 146 147 148 **S** Rush Health Systems, Meridian, MS
Primary Contact: Larkin Kennedy, Chief Executive Officer
COO: Jason Payne, Executive Vice President and Chief Operating Officer
CMO: W Scot Bell, M.D., Chief Medical Officer
CIO: Angela Sherrill, Corporate Director Information System
CHR: Donnie Smith, Director Human Resources
CNO: Casey Bland, Director of Nursing
Web address: www.rushhealthsystems.org/rfh/
Control: Other not–for–profit (including NFP Corporation) **Service**: General medical and surgical

Staffed Beds: 182 **Admissions**: 5390 **Census**: 56 **Outpatient Visits**: 177773 **Births**: 1016 **Total Expense ($000)**: 133255 **Payroll Expense ($000)**: 34061 **Personnel**: 698

SPECIALTY HOSPITAL OF MERIDIAN (252004), 1314 19th Avenue, Zip 39301–4116; tel. 601/703–4211, **A**10 **F**1 3 18 20 34 50 57 59 68 74 79 85 87 94 96 112 133 144 145 149 **S** Rush Health Systems, Meridian, MS
Primary Contact: Elizabeth C. Mitchell, Chief Executive Officer and Chief Operating Officer
COO: Elizabeth C Mitchell, Chief Operating Officer
CFO: Christopher Rush, Chief Financial Officer
CMO: John Johnston, Chief Medical Officer
CIO: Angela Sherrill, Corporate Director Information System
CHR: Donnie Smith, Director of Human Resources
CNO: Kawanda Johnson, Director of Nursing
Web address: www.specialtyhospitalofmeridian.com/shm/
Control: Other not–for–profit (including NFP Corporation) **Service**: Acute long–term care hospital

Staffed Beds: 49 **Admissions**: 618 **Census**: 42 **Outpatient Visits**: 0 **Births**: 0 **Personnel**: 124

MONTICELLO—Lawrence County

LAWRENCE COUNTY HOSPITAL (251305), Highway 84 East, Zip 39654–0788, Mailing Address: P.O. Box 788, Zip 39654–0788; tel. 601/587–4051, **A**10 18 **F**3 18 34 40 43 50 57 59 64 87 107 115 119 127 133 149 153 **S** Southwest Health Systems, Mccomb, MS
Primary Contact: Phillip W. Langston, Administrator
CFO: Jennifer Moak, Business Office Manager
Web address: www.smrmc.com
Control: County, Government, nonfederal **Service**: General medical and surgical

Staffed Beds: 25 **Admissions**: 377 **Census**: 6 **Outpatient Visits**: 8566 **Births**: 0 **Total Expense ($000)**: 10342 **Payroll Expense ($000)**: 5762 **Personnel**: 106

Hospital, Medicare Provider Number, Address, Telephone, Approval, Facility, and Physician Codes, Health Care System

★ American Hospital Association (AHA) membership
☐ The Joint Commission accreditation
○ Healthcare Facilities Accreditation Program
◇ DNV Healthcare Inc. accreditation
⇧ Center for Improvement in Healthcare Quality Accreditation
△ Commission on Accreditation of Rehabilitation Facilities (CARF) accreditation

---

MORTON—Scott County

SCOTT REGIONAL HOSPITAL (251323), 317 Highway 13 South, Zip 39117–3353, Mailing Address: P.O. Box 259, Zip 39117–0259; tel. 601/732–6301, **A**10 18 **F**3 30 35 40 43 55 57 77 81 89 93 107 111 112 114 119 127 130 133 **S** Rush Health Systems, Meridian, MS
Primary Contact: Heather Davis, Administrator
CFO: Paul S Black, Chief Financial Officer
CHR: Amy Sugg, Director Human Resources
Web address: www.scottregional.org/srh/
Control: Other not–for–profit (including NFP Corporation) **Service**: General medical and surgical

Staffed Beds: 25 **Admissions:** 370 **Census:** 10 **Outpatient Visits:** 9129
Births: 0 **Total Expense ($000):** 8895 **Payroll Expense ($000):** 3670
Personnel: 125

NATCHEZ—Adams County

★ △ **MERIT HEALTH NATCHEZ (250084)**, 54 Seargent 'S' Prentiss Drive, Zip 39120–4726; tel. 601/443–2100, **A**7 10 20 **F**3 13 15 17 18 26 28 29 35 40 43 45 46 47 60 70 73 74 75 76 77 79 81 82 85 86 87 88 89 90 92 93 94 98 103 106 107 108 109 110 111 112 114 115 116 118 119 126 129 130 131 132 134 146 147 156 **S** Community Health Systems, Inc., Franklin, TN
Primary Contact: Lance Boyd, Chief Executive Officer
CFO: Charles Mack, Vice President Finance and Chief Financial Officer
CMO: Leslie England, Chief of Staff
CIO: Leslie Makoro, Director Information management Systems
CHR: Jean E Juchnowicz, Director Human Resources
CNO: Lee Hinson, Chief Nursing Officer
Web address: www.natchezregional.com
Control: Corporation, Investor–owned (for–profit) **Service**: General medical and surgical

Staffed Beds: 136 **Admissions:** 4410 **Census:** 62 **Outpatient Visits:** 53041
Births: 789 **Total Expense ($000):** 93167 **Payroll Expense ($000):** 25903
Personnel: 435

NEW ALBANY—Union County

⊞ **BAPTIST MEMORIAL HOSPITAL-UNION COUNTY (250006)**, 200 Highway 30 West, Zip 38652–3112; tel. 662/538–7631, **A**1 10 **F**3 11 13 15 17 29 30 31 34 35 40 45 51 57 59 64 68 70 75 76 77 79 81 84 85 86 87 89 90 91 93 96 107 108 110 111 114 115 118 119 124 130 132 133 135 146 147 148 149 154 156 **S** Baptist Memorial Health Care Corporation, Memphis, TN
Primary Contact: Walter Grace, Chief Executive Officer and Administrator
CFO: Kim High, Chief Financial Officer
CMO: H F Mason, M.D., Chief Medical Officer
CIO: Missy Coltharp, Director
CHR: Lori Goode, Director Human Resources
CNO: Randy White, Chief Nursing Officer
Web address: www.baptistonline.org/union-county/
Control: Other not–for–profit (including NFP Corporation) **Service**: General medical and surgical

Staffed Beds: 153 **Admissions:** 2949 **Census:** 26 **Outpatient Visits:** 61462
Births: 946 **Total Expense ($000):** 54681 **Payroll Expense ($000):** 19172
Personnel: 284

OCEAN SPRINGS—Jackson County

OCEAN SPRINGS HOSPITAL See Singing River Health System, Pascagoula

OLIVE BRANCH—Desoto County

★ ⇑ **METHODIST HEALTHCARE OLIVE BRANCH HOSPITAL (250167)**, 4250 Bethel Road, Zip 38654–8737; tel. 662/932–9000, **A**10 21 **F**3 11 13 15 18 20 22 29 34 35 40 43 44 45 46 47 49 50 57 59 64 68 70 71 74 76 79 80 81 84 85 86 87 88 90 91 92 93 96 107 108 109 110 111 112 114 115 119 130 132 135 145 146 147 149 150 156 157 **S** Methodist Le Bonheur Healthcare, Memphis, TN
Primary Contact: David G. Baytos, President
CFO: Kris Sanders, Chief Financial Officer
CHR: Robin Mathis, Director Human Resources
CNO: Annelise Jensen, Vice President and Chief Nursing Officer
Web address: www.methodisthealth.org/olivebranch
Control: Other not–for–profit (including NFP Corporation) **Service**: General medical and surgical

Staffed Beds: 53 **Admissions:** 3301 **Census:** 29 **Births:** 627 **Total Expense ($000):** 58477 **Payroll Expense ($000):** 21897 **Personnel:** 368

PARKWOOD BEHAVIORAL HEALTH SYSTEM (254005)

☐ **PARKWOOD BEHAVIORAL HEALTH SYSTEM (254005)**, 8135 Goodman Road, Zip 38654–2103; tel. 662/895–4900, (Total facility includes 40 beds in nursing home–type unit) **A**1 10 **F**4 5 29 34 35 54 57 64 71 75 82 86 87 98 99 100 101 102 103 104 105 128 130 135 151 153 **S** Universal Health Services, Inc., King of Prussia, PA
Primary Contact: Vince Brummett, Chief Executive Officer
CFO: David Denegri, Chief Financial Officer
CMO: Paul King, M.D., Medical Director
CHR: Julie Dorman, Human Resources Director
CNO: Alicia Plunkett, Chief Nurse Executive
Web address: www.parkwoodbhs.com
Control: Corporation, Investor–owned (for–profit) **Service**: Psychiatric

Staffed Beds: 148 **Admissions:** 2917 **Census:** 103 **Outpatient Visits:** 3648
Births: 0 **Personnel:** 168

OXFORD—Lafayette County

⊞ △ **BAPTIST MEMORIAL HOSPITAL-NORTH MISSISSIPPI (250034)**, 2301 South Lamar Boulevard, Zip 38655–5373, Mailing Address: P.O. Box 946, Zip 38655–6002; tel. 662/232–8100, **A**1 2 3 7 10 19 **F**3 8 9 11 12 13 15 17 18 20 22 24 26 28 29 30 31 34 35 40 43 45 46 47 48 49 54 57 58 59 64 65 70 73 74 76 79 81 83 84 85 86 87 89 90 91 93 96 107 108 110 111 115 116 117 118 119 120 121 123 124 126 129 130 132 146 148 154 **S** Baptist Memorial Health Care Corporation, Memphis, TN
Primary Contact: William C. Henning, Administrator and Chief Executive Officer
CFO: Dana Williams, Chief Financial Officer
CMO: Dennis P Morgan, Chief of Staff
CIO: Linda Britt, Director Information Systems
CHR: Josh Lowery, Director of Human Resources
CNO: Mark Ottens, Chief Nursing Officer
Web address: www.baptistonline.org/north-mississippi/
Control: Other not–for–profit (including NFP Corporation) **Service**: General medical and surgical

Staffed Beds: 172 **Admissions:** 8718 **Census:** 101 **Outpatient Visits:** 98577 **Births:** 877 **Personnel:** 748

PASCAGOULA—Jackson County

△ ⇑ **SINGING RIVER HEALTH SYSTEM (250040)**, 2809 Denny Avenue, Zip 39581–5301; tel. 228/809–5000, (Includes OCEAN SPRINGS HOSPITAL, 3109 Bienville Boulevard, Ocean Springs, Mississippi, Zip 39564–4361; tel. 228/818–1111; Heath Thompson, R.N., Administrator; SINGING RIVER HOSPITAL, 2809 Denny Avenue, Pascagoula, Mississippi, Zip 39581–5301; tel. 228/809–5000; Laurin St. Pe', Administrator - Singing River Hospital) **A**2 7 10 21 **F**3 7 8 9 11 12 13 15 17 18 20 22 24 26 28 29 30 31 32 34 38 39 40 41 43 44 45 46 47 48 49 50 53 54 55 56 57 58 59 61 64 65 66 68 70 71 73 74 76 78 79 80 81 82 83 84 85 86 87 88 89 90 91 92 94 95 96 98 99 100 101 102 104 105 106 107 108 110 111 114 115 118 119 120 121 123 124 126 127 129 130 135 144 145 146 148 152 153 154
Primary Contact: Lee Bond, Chief Executive Officer
CFO: Sandra Albrecht, Interim Chief Financial Officer
CMO: Randy Roth, Chief Medical Officer
CHR: Craig Summerlin, Chief Human Resources Officer
CNO: Susan Russell, Chief Nursing Officer
Web address: www.singingriverhealthsystem.com
Control: County, Government, nonfederal **Service**: General medical and surgical

Staffed Beds: 361 **Admissions:** 17303 **Census:** 189 **Personnel:** 2275

PHILADELPHIA—Neshoba County

⇑ **CHOCTAW HEALTH CENTER (250127)**, 210 Hospital Circle, Zip 39350–6781; tel. 601/656–2211, (Nonreporting) **A**10 21
Primary Contact: Tina Scott, Acting Health Director
CFO: Myrna Hancock, Director Financial Services
CMO: Juantina Johnson, Chief of Staff
CIO: Raymond Willis, IT Manager
CHR: Anna Denson, Human Resources Specialist
CNO: Regina Isaac, Director of Nursing
Web address: www.choctaw.org
Control: Public Health Service other than 47, Government, federal **Service**: General medical and surgical

Staffed Beds: 26

Many Facility Codes have changed. Please refer to the AHA Guide Code Chart. © 2019 AHA Guide

⇑ **NESHOBA COUNTY GENERAL HOSPITAL (250043)**, 1001 Holland Avenue, Zip 39350–2161, Mailing Address: P.O. Box 648, Zip 39350–0648; tel. 601/663–1200, (Total facility includes 160 beds in nursing home–type unit) **A**10 20 21 **F**3 6 7 11 15 29 31 32 34 38 40 43 57 59 64 65 81 82 89 90 92 93 96 98 103 104 106 107 108 110 111 115 118 119 127 128 129 130 132 133 143 144 146 148 149 153
Primary Contact: Lee McCall, Chief Executive Officer
CFO: Scott McNair, Chief Financial Officer
CMO: Heather Cannon, M.D., Medical Director
CHR: Hedda Stewart, Director Human Resources
CNO: Scott Breazeale, Chief Nursing Officer
Web address: www.neshobageneral.com
Control: County, Government, nonfederal **Service**: General medical and surgical

Staffed Beds: 208 **Admissions**: 1745 **Census**: 171 **Outpatient Visits**: 71570 **Births**: 0 **Total Expense ($000)**: 40129 **Payroll Expense ($000)**: 19505 **Personnel**: 524

PICAYUNE—Pearl River County

HIGHLAND COMMUNITY HOSPITAL (250117), 130 Highland Parkway, Zip 39466–5574, Mailing Address: P.O. Box 909, Zip 39466–0909; tel. 601/358–9400, **A**10 **F**3 11 13 15 18 29 34 40 41 43 44 45 46 50 56 57 59 64 65 70 75 76 81 85 86 87 89 93 96 98 103 107 108 110 111 114 118 119 127 131 133 135 146 147 148 156
Primary Contact: Bryan K. Maxie, Administrator
CMO: Robert Lopez, Chief Medical Officer
CHR: Cynthia Render-Leach, Director Human Resources
CNO: Kim Varnado, R.N., Chief Nursing Officer
Web address: www.highlandch.com
Control: County, Government, nonfederal **Service**: General medical and surgical

Staffed Beds: 49 **Admissions**: 1785 **Census**: 21 **Outpatient Visits**: 87683 **Births**: 271 **Total Expense ($000)**: 36141 **Payroll Expense ($000)**: 13786 **Personnel**: 289

PONTOTOC—Pontotoc County

⊠ **NORTH MISSISSIPPI MEDICAL CENTER-PONTOTOC (251308)**, 176 South Main Street, Zip 38863–3311, Mailing Address: P.O. Box 790, Zip 38863–0790; tel. 662/488–7640, (Total facility includes 44 beds in nursing home–type unit) **A**1 10 18 **F**3 11 15 34 35 40 43 57 65 68 82 83 84 86 87 93 104 107 114 119 128 130 133 146 **S** North Mississippi Health Services, Inc., Tupelo, MS
Primary Contact: Leslia Carter, Administrator
CFO: M Denise Heard, Director Business Services
CHR: P. Marie Barnes, Director, Human Resources
CNO: Cathy Waldrop, Director, Hospital Nursing Services
Web address: www.nmhs.net
Control: Other not–for–profit (including NFP Corporation) **Service**: General medical and surgical

Staffed Beds: 69 **Admissions**: 468 **Census**: 59 **Outpatient Visits**: 38484 **Births**: 0 **Total Expense ($000)**: 22359 **Payroll Expense ($000)**: 12372 **Personnel**: 241

POPLARVILLE—Pearl River County

★ **PEARL RIVER COUNTY HOSPITAL (251333)**, 305 West Moody Street, Zip 39470–7338, Mailing Address: P.O. Box 392, Zip 39470–0392; tel. 601/795–4543, **A**10 18 **F**3 35 40 43 64 65 90 93 107 119 127 128 130 133 143 146
Primary Contact: James Williams, Chief Executive Officer
CNO: Lisa Brown, Director of Nursing
Web address: www.prc-med.com/
Control: County, Government, nonfederal **Service**: General medical and surgical

Staffed Beds: 18 **Admissions**: 298 **Census**: 10 **Births**: 0 **Total Expense ($000)**: 18690 **Payroll Expense ($000)**: 10258 **Personnel**: 197

PORT GIBSON—Claiborne County

CLAIBORNE COUNTY MEDICAL CENTER (251320), 123 McComb Avenue, Zip 39150–2915, Mailing Address: P.O. Box 1004, Zip 39150–1004; tel. 601/437–5141, **A**10 18 **F**40 43 86 89 98 100 101 103 104 106 107 119 130 133 146
Primary Contact: Ada Ratliff, Chief Executive Officer
CFO: Linda Caho-Mooney, Chief Financial Officer
CIO: Ada Ratliff, Chief Information Officer
Control: County, Government, nonfederal **Service**: General medical and surgical

Staffed Beds: 22 **Admissions**: 940 **Census**: 11 **Births**: 0 **Total Expense ($000)**: 12586 **Payroll Expense ($000)**: 4917 **Personnel**: 130

PRENTISS—Jefferson Davis County

JEFFERSON DAVIS COMMUNITY HOSPITAL (251326), 1102 Rose Street, Zip 39474–5200, Mailing Address: P.O. Box 1288, Zip 39474–1288; tel. 601/792–4276, (Total facility includes 60 beds in nursing home–type unit) **A**10 18 **F**3 29 35 39 40 43 53 57 59 64 65 66 68 87 89 92 97 104 107 115 119 127 128 130 133 148 149 154
Primary Contact: Jimmy Graves, Interim Chief Executive Officer
CHR: Diane Daughdrill, Director Human Resources
Web address: www.jdchospital.com
Control: County, Government, nonfederal **Service**: General medical and surgical

Staffed Beds: 95 **Admissions**: 317 **Census**: 48 **Outpatient Visits**: 12299 **Births**: 0 **Total Expense ($000)**: 11396 **Payroll Expense ($000)**: 4606 **Personnel**: 117

PURVIS—Lamar County

☐ **SOUTH MISSISSIPPI STATE HOSPITAL (254008)**, 823 Highway 589, Zip 39475–4194; tel. 601/794–0100, **A**1 10 **F**3 50 98 105 130 146 149 **S** Mississippi State Department of Mental Health, Jackson, MS
Primary Contact: Sabrina Young, Director
CFO: Andy Tucker, Chief Financial Officer
CMO: Allen Harris, M.D., Clinical Director
CIO: Sabrina Young, Administrative Support Director
CHR: Kelly Reid, Human Resources Director
CNO: Pam Brinson, Nurse Executive
Web address: www.smsh.ms.gov/
Control: State, Government, nonfederal **Service**: Psychiatric

Staffed Beds: 50 **Admissions**: 522 **Census**: 45 **Outpatient Visits**: 0 **Births**: 0 **Total Expense ($000)**: 7384 **Payroll Expense ($000)**: 3863 **Personnel**: 91

QUITMAN—Clarke County

H. C. WATKINS MEMORIAL HOSPITAL (251316), 605 South Archusa Avenue, Zip 39355–2331; tel. 601/776–6925, **A**10 18 **F**29 34 40 43 57 59 68 89 104 107 114 119 127 129 130 133 153 154 **S** Rush Health Systems, Meridian, MS
Primary Contact: Michael Nester, Administrator
CFO: Paul S Black, Controller
CMO: O Wayne Byrd, M.D., Chief of Staff
CIO: Melinda Smith, Chief Information Systems
CHR: Leigh Moore, Administrative Assistant Human Resources
Web address: www.watkinsmemorialhospital.com/hcwmh/
Control: Other not–for–profit (including NFP Corporation) **Service**: General medical and surgical

Staffed Beds: 25 **Admissions**: 418 **Census**: 12 **Outpatient Visits**: 27267 **Births**: 0 **Personnel**: 165

RALEIGH—Smith County

PATIENTS CHOICE MEDICAL CENTER OF SMITH COUNTY (250163), 347 Magnolia Drive, Zip 39153–6011; tel. 601/782–9997, **A**10 **F**98 101 103 104 130
Primary Contact: Tim Cockrell, Chief Executive Officer
Control: Corporation, Investor–owned (for–profit) **Service**: General medical and surgical

Staffed Beds: 10 **Admissions**: 173 **Census**: 6 **Births**: 0 **Personnel**: 36

RICHTON—Perry County

PERRY COUNTY GENERAL HOSPITAL (251306), 206 Bay Avenue, Zip 39476–2941; tel. 601/788–6316, **A**10 18 **F**3 34 40 57 59 64 65 107 119 127 130 133 146
Primary Contact: David Paris, Chief Executive Officer
Web address: www.pcghospital.com/
Control: Partnership, Investor–owned (for–profit) **Service**: General medical and surgical

Staffed Beds: 22 **Admissions**: 144 **Census**: 4 **Outpatient Visits**: 11119 **Births**: 0 **Total Expense ($000)**: 3049 **Payroll Expense ($000)**: 2497 **Personnel**: 52

MS

RIPLEY—Tippah County

★ **TIPPAH COUNTY HOSPITAL (251337)**, 1005 City Avenue North, Zip 38663–1414, Mailing Address: P.O. Box 499, Zip 38663–0499; tel. 662/837–9221, (Total facility includes 40 beds in nursing home–type unit) **A**10 18 **F**29 40 43 53 81 90 93 97 107 119 128 130 131 133
Primary Contact: Patrick Chapman, Ed.D., Chief Executive Officer
CFO: Stephanie McAlister, Controller
CMO: Troy Cappleman, M.D., Chief of Staff
CHR: Heather Taylor, Human Resources Manager
CNO: Carol Anne Hurt, Chief Nursing Officer
Web address: www.tippahcountyhospital.com/
Control: County, Government, nonfederal **Service**: General medical and surgical

Staffed Beds: 65 **Admissions**: 605 **Census**: 50 **Outpatient Visits**: 14231
Births: 0 **Total Expense ($000)**: 13218 **Payroll Expense ($000)**: 5276
Personnel: 191

ROLLING FORK—Sharkey County

SHARKEY-ISSAQUENA COMMUNITY HOSPITAL (250079), 108 South Fourth Street, Zip 39159–5146, Mailing Address: P.O. Box 339, Zip 39159–0339; tel. 662/873–4395, **A**10 **F**40 53 98 103 104 105 107 133
Primary Contact: Jerry Keever, Administrator
Control: County, Government, nonfederal **Service**: General medical and surgical

Staffed Beds: 29 **Admissions**: 375 **Census**: 7 **Births**: 0 **Total Expense ($000)**: 9425 **Payroll Expense ($000)**: 4956 **Personnel**: 75

RULEVILLE—Sunflower County

★ **NORTH SUNFLOWER MEDICAL CENTER (251318)**, 840 North Oak Avenue, Zip 38771–3227, Mailing Address: P.O. Box 369, Zip 38771–0369; tel. 662/756–2711, (Total facility includes 60 beds in nursing home–type unit) **A**10 18 **F**15 28 29 30 34 35 40 43 44 45 47 53 54 56 57 59 63 64 74 75 77 81 82 84 85 87 90 92 93 96 97 98 103 104 107 110 115 119 127 128 129 130 133 143 147 149 153 154
Primary Contact: Sam Miller, Chief Executive Officer
COO: Rodney Clark, Chief Operating Officer
CFO: Drew Weissinger, Chief Financial Officer
CMO: Michael W Montesi, M.D., Chief of Staff
CIO: Roger Goss, Chief Information Officer
CHR: Robbie Taylor, Director Human Resources
CNO: Hannah Barrett, Director of Nursing
Web address: www.northsunflower.com
Control: County, Government, nonfederal **Service**: General medical and surgical

Staffed Beds: 95 **Admissions**: 1126 **Census**: 83 **Outpatient Visits**: 58696
Births: 0 **Total Expense ($000)**: 58461 **Payroll Expense ($000)**: 26779
Personnel: 566

SENATOBIA—Tate County

NORTH OAK REGIONAL MEDICAL CENTER (250126), 401 Getwell Drive, Zip 38668–2213, Mailing Address: P.O. Box 648, Zip 38668–0648; tel. 662/562–3100, (Nonreporting) **A**10
Primary Contact: Philip S. Hanna, Chief Executive Officer
CHR: Olga Burris, Human Resource/Executive Assistant
CNO: Pam Ayers, Chief Nursing Officer
Web address: www.northoakregional.com/
Control: Corporation, Investor–owned (for–profit) **Service**: General medical and surgical

Staffed Beds: 41

SOUTHAVEN—Desoto County

⊠ △ **BAPTIST MEMORIAL HOSPITAL-DESOTO (250141)**, 7601 Southcrest Parkway, Zip 38671–4742; tel. 662/772–4000, **A**1 3 7 10 **F**3 8 11 13 15 17 18 20 22 24 26 28 29 30 31 35 39 40 43 44 45 46 47 48 49 50 57 59 60 68 70 73 74 75 76 77 79 80 81 82 84 85 86 87 90 93 96 107 108 109 110 111 114 115 116 117 118 119 120 121 123 124 126 129 130 131 132 135 143 144 146 147 148 154 156 **S** Baptist Memorial Health Care Corporation, Memphis, TN
Primary Contact: James Huffman, Chief Executive Officer and Administrator
CFO: Joe McWherter, Chief Financial Officer
CMO: Joann Wood, M.D., Chief Medical Officer
CHR: Walter Banks, Director Human Resources
Web address: www.baptistonline.org/desoto/
Control: Other not–for–profit (including NFP Corporation) **Service**: General medical and surgical

Staffed Beds: 339 **Admissions**: 17518 **Census**: 226 **Outpatient Visits**: 127122 **Births**: 1355 **Total Expense ($000)**: 240162 **Payroll Expense ($000)**: 90692

STARKVILLE—Oktibbeha County

★ ⇑ **OCH REGIONAL MEDICAL CENTER (250050)**, 400 Hospital Road, Zip 39759–2163, Mailing Address: P.O. Box 1506, Zip 39760–1506; tel. 662/323–4320, **A**10 21 **F**3 7 11 13 15 17 28 29 32 34 35 40 41 43 45 47 48 51 53 57 59 61 64 65 70 73 74 75 76 77 79 81 82 87 88 89 90 93 94 97 98 107 108 110 111 114 115 118 119 126 129 130 131 132 133 135 146 147 149 156
Primary Contact: James H. Jackson Jr, Chief Executive Officer
COO: Mike Andrews, Associate Administrator and Chief Operating Officer
CFO: Susan Russell, Chief Financial Officer
CIO: Chamath Wijewardane, Chief Information Technology Officer
CHR: Mike Andrews, Associate Administrator and Chief Operating Officer
CNO: Martha Fulcher, Chief Nursing Officer
Web address: www.och.org
Control: County, Government, nonfederal **Service**: General medical and surgical

Staffed Beds: 96 **Admissions**: 2242 **Census**: 22 **Outpatient Visits**: 233876
Births: 932 **Total Expense ($000)**: 73193 **Payroll Expense ($000)**: 36618
Personnel: 606

TUPELO—Lee County

⊠ △ **NORTH MISSISSIPPI MEDICAL CENTER - TUPELO (250004)**, 830 South Gloster Street, Zip 38801–4934; tel. 662/377–3000, (Total facility includes 107 beds in nursing home–type unit) **A**1 2 3 5 7 10 **F**3 4 5 6 7 8 9 11 12 13 15 17 18 20 22 24 26 28 29 30 31 32 34 35 40 43 44 45 46 47 48 49 50 51 53 54 55 56 57 58 59 61 62 63 64 65 66 68 70 71 72 73 74 75 76 77 78 79 81 83 84 85 86 87 88 89 90 91 92 93 94 95 96 97 98 100 101 103 104 107 108 109 110 111 112 113 114 115 116 117 118 119 120 121 122 123 124 126 128 129 130 131 132 133 134 135 146 147 148 152 154 **S** North Mississippi Health Services, Inc., Tupelo, MS
Primary Contact: David C. Wilson, President
CFO: Sharon Nobles, Chief Financial Officer
CMO: C K White, M.D., Esq Chief Medical Officer
CIO: James Weldon, Chief Information Officer
Web address: www.nmhs.net
Control: Other not–for–profit (including NFP Corporation) **Service**: General medical and surgical

Staffed Beds: 747 **Admissions**: 26580 **Census**: 460 **Outpatient Visits**: 652630 **Births**: 2325 **Personnel**: 4185

☐ **NORTH MISSISSIPPI STATE HOSPITAL (254009)**, 1937 Briar Ridge Road, Zip 38804–5963; tel. 662/690–4200, **A**1 10 **F**3 29 30 34 87 98 101 130 143 146 **S** Mississippi State Department of Mental Health, Jackson, MS
Primary Contact: Paul A. Callens, Ph.D., Director
CFO: Joe Rials, Director Fiscal Services
CMO: Ken Lippincott, M.D., Chief of Staff
CIO: James Wilhite, Director Systems Information
Web address: www.nmsh.state.ms.us
Control: State, Government, nonfederal **Service**: Psychiatric

Staffed Beds: 50 **Admissions**: 494 **Census**: 46 **Outpatient Visits**: 0
Births: 0 **Total Expense ($000)**: 7289 **Payroll Expense ($000)**: 3764
Personnel: 91

TYLERTOWN—Walthall County

★ **WALTHALL COUNTY GENERAL HOSPITAL (251324)**, 100 Hospital Drive, Zip 39667–2099; tel. 601/876–2122, **A**10 18 **F**3 34 40 43 45 57 59 64 65 66 68 81 85 89 92 93 107 111 115 119 127 133 146 148 149 154
Primary Contact: TaDren Kennedy, Administrator
Web address: www.co.walthall.ms.us/walthall-general-hospital.html
Control: County, Government, nonfederal **Service**: General medical and surgical

Staffed Beds: 25 **Admissions**: 254 **Census**: 5 **Outpatient Visits**: 16055
Births: 0 **Total Expense ($000)**: 8050 **Payroll Expense ($000)**: 4260
Personnel: 85

UNION—Newton County

LAIRD HOSPITAL (251322), 25117 Highway 15, Zip 39365–9099; tel. 601/774–8214, **A**5 10 18 **F**15 29 35 40 43 81 87 89 93 104 107 119 130 132 133 146 **S** Rush Health Systems, Meridian, MS
Primary Contact: Thomas G. Bartlett III, Administrator
COO: Morris A Reece, EVP/COO
CFO: Jennifer Flint, Chief Financial Officer
CMO: John Mutziger, M.D., Chief Medical Officer
CIO: Angela Sherrill, Chief Information Officer
CHR: Donnie Smith, Chief Human Resources Officer
CNO: Pam Rigdon, Director Nursing
Web address: www.lairdhospital.com/lh/
Control: Other not–for–profit (including NFP Corporation) **Service**: General medical and surgical

Staffed Beds: 25 **Admissions**: 506 **Census**: 15 **Outpatient Visits**: 15042
Births: 0 **Total Expense ($000)**: 13631 **Payroll Expense ($000)**: 5398
Personnel: 253

MS

Many Facility Codes have changed. Please refer to the AHA Guide Code Chart. © 2019 AHA Guide

VICKSBURG—Warren County

⊞ **MERIT HEALTH RIVER REGION (250031)**, 2100 Highway 61 North, Zip 39183–8211, Mailing Address: P.O. Box 590, Zip 39181–0590; tel. 601/883–5000, (Includes RIVER REGION WEST CAMPUS, 1111 North Frontage Road, Vicksburg, Mississippi, Zip 39180–5102; tel. 601/883–5000) **A**1 10 **F**3 4 11 13 15 17 18 19 20 22 24 28 29 34 35 38 39 40 43 49 50 51 56 59 60 64 68 70 73 75 76 77 81 82 87 89 90 93 97 98 103 107 108 110 111 115 118 119 126 130 131 132 146 147 149 151 **S** Community Health Systems, Inc., Franklin, TN
Primary Contact: Benjamin Richaud, Interim Chief Executive Officer
CFO: John Milazzo, Chief Financial Officer
CMO: W Briggs Hopson, M.D., Clinical Medical Director
CIO: J B White, Director Information Systems
CHR: Hal Harrington, Vice President Human Resources
Web address: www.riverregion.com
Control: Corporation, Investor–owned (for–profit) **Service**: General medical and surgical

Staffed Beds: 361 **Admissions**: 7281 **Census**: 106 **Outpatient Visits**: 173564 **Births**: 404 **Total Expense ($000)**: 143162 **Payroll Expense ($000)**: 32964 **Personnel**: 656

PROMISE HOSPITAL OF VICKSBURG (252008), 1111 North Frontage Road, 2nd Floor, Zip 39180–5102; tel. 601/619–3526, **A**10 **F**1 3 11 148 **S** Promise Healthcare, Boca Raton, FL
Primary Contact: Michael Harrell, R.N., Chief Executive Officer
COO: Dawn Posey, Chief Operating Officer
CFO: Christopher A Stegall, Regional Chief Financial Officer and Chief Operating Officer
CMO: Daniel Edney, M.D., Chief of Staff
CIO: Barbara Whiting, Director Health Information Management
CHR: Debbie Carson, Director Human Resources
Web address: www.promise-vicksburg.com
Control: Corporation, Investor–owned (for–profit) **Service**: Acute long–term care hospital

Staffed Beds: 33 **Admissions**: 349 **Census**: 24 **Outpatient Visits**: 0 **Births**: 0 **Personnel**: 67

WATER VALLEY—Yalobusha County

YALOBUSHA GENERAL HOSPITAL (250061), 630 South Main, Zip 38965–3468, Mailing Address: P.O. Box 728, Zip 38965–0728; tel. 662/473–1411, (Total facility includes 122 beds in nursing home–type unit) **A**10 **F**3 7 15 29 33 34 50 57 59 65 84 107 109 110 114 119 127 128 129 130 133 143 146 148 153 154 157
Primary Contact: Terry Varner, Administrator
COO: Ashlee Langdon, Controller
CHR: Katie Rotenberry-Baggett, Administrative Assistant and Human Resources
Web address: www.yalobushageneral.com/
Control: County, Government, nonfederal **Service**: General medical and surgical

Staffed Beds: 148 **Admissions**: 745 **Census**: 123 **Births**: 0 **Total Expense ($000)**: 25150 **Payroll Expense ($000)**: 15526 **Personnel**: 207

WAYNESBORO—Wayne County

⇑ **WAYNE GENERAL HOSPITAL (250077)**, 950 Matthew Drive, Zip 39367–2590, Mailing Address: P.O. Box 1249, Zip 39367–1249; tel. 601/735–5151, **A**3 10 20 21 **F**3 7 11 13 15 29 34 40 43 53 59 62 63 64 70 76 81 85 89 93 107 108 115 119 127 130 133 146 148 154
Primary Contact: Kathy Waddell, Administrator
Web address: www.waynegeneralhospital.org
Control: County, Government, nonfederal **Service**: General medical and surgical

Staffed Beds: 80 **Admissions**: 1738 **Census**: 26 **Outpatient Visits**: 29307 **Births**: 182 **Personnel**: 357

WEST POINT—Clay County

⊞ **NORTH MISSISSIPPI MEDICAL CENTER-WEST POINT (250067)**, 835 Medical Center Drive, Zip 39773–9320; tel. 662/495–2300, **A**1 10 **F**3 11 13 15 17 28 29 30 31 32 34 35 40 43 45 48 53 57 59 64 65 70 73 75 76 79 80 81 85 86 87 89 97 107 108 109 110 114 119 120 127 129 130 132 133 135 145 146 147 148 **S** North Mississippi Health Services, Inc., Tupelo, MS
Primary Contact: Barry L. Keel, Administrator
CFO: Kay Lawler, Business Office Manager
CMO: B Keith Watson, M.D., Chief Medical Staff
CIO: Stacie Griggs, MIS Analyst
CHR: Brenda Johnson, Director Human Resources
CNO: Pam White, Chief Nursing Officer
Web address: www.nmhs.net/westpoint
Control: Other not–for–profit (including NFP Corporation) **Service**: General medical and surgical

Staffed Beds: 49 **Admissions**: 1677 **Census**: 18 **Outpatient Visits**: 69001 **Births**: 478 **Total Expense ($000)**: 42373 **Payroll Expense ($000)**: 14451 **Personnel**: 239

WHITFIELD—Rankin County

⊞ **MISSISSIPPI STATE HOSPITAL (254010)**, 3550 Highway 468 West, Zip 39193–5529, Mailing Address: P.O. Box 157-A, Zip 39193–0157; tel. 601/351–8000, (Includes WHITFIELD MEDICAL SURGICAL HOSPITAL, 3550 Highway 468 West, Building 60, Whitfield, Mississippi, Zip 39193–5529, Mailing Address: P O Box 157-A, Zip 39193–0157, tel. 601/351–8023) **A**1 3 5 10 **F**3 4 29 32 39 50 55 56 59 65 68 74 75 86 87 98 99 100 101 103 104 107 115 119 128 130 143 146 149 151 **S** Mississippi State Department of Mental Health, Jackson, MS
Primary Contact: James G. Chastain, FACHE, Director
COO: Kelly R Breland, CPA, Director Support Services
CFO: Alicia Harris, Director Fiscal Services
CMO: Duncan Stone, D.D.S., Chief Medical Staff
CIO: Bart Uharriet, Director Information Services
CHR: Katie Storr, Director of Human Resources
CNO: Jackie Yates, R.N., Nurse Executive
Web address: www.msh.state.ms.us
Control: State, Government, nonfederal **Service**: Psychiatric

Staffed Beds: 316 **Admissions**: 1496 **Census**: 290 **Outpatient Visits**: 1236 **Births**: 0 **Total Expense ($000)**: 119880 **Payroll Expense ($000)**: 50367 **Personnel**: 934

WIGGINS—Stone County

STONE COUNTY HOSPITAL (251303), 1434 East Central Avenue, Zip 39577–9602; tel. 601/928–6600, **A**10 18 **F**3 5 7 29 34 35 40 43 46 57 59 64 81 82 89 97 100 101 103 112 114 115 119 130 133 143 146
Primary Contact: Lynn Truelove, Chief Executive Officer
Web address: www.schospital.net/
Control: Corporation, Investor–owned (for–profit) **Service**: General medical and surgical

Staffed Beds: 25 **Admissions**: 512 **Census**: 14 **Outpatient Visits**: 15681 **Births**: 0 **Total Expense ($000)**: 24956 **Payroll Expense ($000)**: 7806 **Personnel**: 152

WINONA—Montgomery County

TYLER HOLMES MEMORIAL HOSPITAL (251312), 409 Tyler Holmes Drive, Zip 38967–1599; tel. 662/283–4114, **A**10 18 **F**3 11 15 29 34 35 40 43 50 57 59 64 68 87 104 107 110 111 115 119 130 133 149 153
Primary Contact: Sean Johnson, Chief Executive Officer
CFO: Cori Bailey, Accountant
CMO: Eddie Rutherford, Director of Pharmacy
CHR: Becky Corley, Director Human Resources
Web address: www.thmh.org/
Control: County, Government, nonfederal **Service**: General medical and surgical

Staffed Beds: 25 **Admissions**: 421 **Census**: 11 **Outpatient Visits**: 12357 **Births**: 0 **Total Expense ($000)**: 13024 **Payroll Expense ($000)**: 6701 **Personnel**: 142

YAZOO CITY—Yazoo County

★ **BAPTIST MEDICAL CENTER YAZOO (251313)**, 823 Grand Avenue, Zip 39194–3233; tel. 662/746–2261, **A**10 18 **F**8 11 15 18 29 30 40 41 45 46 54 56 64 68 71 81 97 107 108 110 111 112 115 119 127 133 145 148 149 153 154 **S** Baptist Memorial Health Care Corporation, Memphis, TN
Primary Contact: Robert Coleman, Chief Executive Officer
COO: Marsha Jones, R.N., Director Nursing
CFO: James L Miller, Chief Financial Officer
CMO: Marion Sigrest, M.D., Chief of Staff
CIO: Benton D Estes, Materials Management
CHR: Stephanie Washington, Director Community Relations and Human Resources
CNO: Marsha Jones, R.N., Director of Nursing
Web address: www.mbhs.org/locations/baptist-medical-center-yazoo/
Control: Other not–for–profit (including NFP Corporation) **Service**: General medical and surgical

Staffed Beds: 25 **Admissions**: 616 **Census**: 11 **Outpatient Visits**: 23934 **Births**: 8 **Total Expense ($000)**: 14167 **Payroll Expense ($000)**: 8028 **Personnel**: 119

MS

Hospital, Medicare Provider Number, Address, Telephone, Approval, Facility, and Physician Codes, Health Care System

★ American Hospital Association (AHA) membership
□ The Joint Commission accreditation
○ Healthcare Facilities Accreditation Program
◇ DNV Healthcare Inc. accreditation
⇑ Center for Improvement in Healthcare Quality Accreditation
△ Commission on Accreditation of Rehabilitation Facilities (CARF) accreditation

MISSOURI

ALBANY—Gentry County

★ **MOSAIC MEDICAL CENTER - ALBANY (261328)**, 705 North College Street, Zip 64402–1433; tel. 660/726–3941, **A**10 18 **F**3 11 15 18 28 29 32 34 35 39 40 41 44 45 47 50 53 56 57 59 62 64 65 68 74 75 77 79 81 84 85 86 87 89 90 93 97 99 103 104 107 108 110 111 114 118 119 127 128 130 131 133 135 143 148 149 154 156 **S** Mosaic Life Care, Saint Joseph, MO
Primary Contact: Jon D. Doolittle, Regional President
CMO: Angelia Martin, M.D., Chief of Staff
CIO: James Crouch, Vice President Technical Services
CHR: Vickie Cline, Director Human Resources
CNO: Miranda Floyd, R.N., Chief Nursing Officer
Web address: www.northwestmedicalcenter.org
Control: Other not–for–profit (including NFP Corporation) **Service**: General medical and surgical

Staffed Beds: 25 **Admissions**: 441 **Census**: 6 **Outpatient Visits**: 34472
Births: 0 **Total Expense ($000)**: 19924 **Payroll Expense ($000)**: 8907
Personnel: 147

APPLETON CITY—St. Clair County

★ **ELLETT MEMORIAL HOSPITAL (261301)**, 610 North Ohio Avenue, Zip 64724–1609, Mailing Address: P.O. Box 6, Zip 64724–0006; tel. 660/476–2111, **A**10 18 **F**3 7 11 26 34 40 45 50 57 59 64 77 79 90 93 97 107 111 114 119 127 128 129 130 133 143 146 147 154
Primary Contact: Julie Tootle, Chief Executive Officer
CMO: Richard R Dailey, D.O., President Medical Staff
CIO: Gina Raybourn, Director Health Information
CHR: Cathy Grishow, Director Human Resources
CNO: Laura Smith, Chief Nursing Officer and Director of Infection Control
Web address: www.ellettmemorial.com
Control: Hospital district or authority, Government, nonfederal **Service**: General medical and surgical

Staffed Beds: 12 **Admissions**: 136 **Census**: 2 **Outpatient Visits**: 6896
Births: 0 **Total Expense ($000)**: 8887 **Payroll Expense ($000)**: 3077
Personnel: 94

AURORA—Lawrence County

⊞ **MERCY HOSPITAL AURORA (261316)**, 500 Porter Street, Zip 65605–2365; tel. 417/678–2122, **A**1 10 18 **F**3 11 13 15 28 29 30 34 35 40 41 45 50 57 59 64 65 75 76 77 81 85 86 87 89 93 94 96 107 108 110 111 114 119 129 132 133 135 148 149 154 **S** Mercy, Chesterfield, MO
Primary Contact: Nicki Gamet, R.N., Administrator
CFO: Sherry Clouse Day, CPA, Vice President Finance and Regional Chief Financial Officer
CMO: Christie Hurt, M.D., Chief of Staff and Medical Director
CHR: George Roden, Vice President Human Resources
Web address: www.stjohns.com/aboutus/aurora.aspx
Control: Church operated, Nongovernment, not–for–profit **Service**: General medical and surgical

Staffed Beds: 25 **Admissions**: 654 **Census**: 6 **Outpatient Visits**: 31728
Births: 254 **Total Expense ($000)**: 18747 **Payroll Expense ($000)**: 9017
Personnel: 153

BELTON—Cass County

⊞ **BELTON REGIONAL MEDICAL CENTER (260214)**, 17065 South 71 Highway, Zip 64012–4631; tel. 816/348–1200, **A**1 2 10 **F**3 15 18 20 29 30 31 34 35 37 40 43 45 57 59 65 68 70 74 75 77 78 79 81 82 85 87 90 93 107 108 110 111 114 115 118 119 129 130 131 132 146 **S** HCA Healthcare, Nashville, TN
Primary Contact: Todd Krass, Chief Executive Officer
COO: Patrick Avila, Chief Operating Officer
CFO: Ronnie Thompson, Chief Financial Officer
CMO: Douglas Bradley, M.D., Chief Medical Officer
CIO: Sarah Richardson, Director Information Systems
CHR: Jessica Sulzen, Director Human Resources
CNO: Karen Lee, MSN, R.N., Chief Nursing Officer
Web address: www.beltonregionalmedicalcenter.com
Control: Corporation, Investor–owned (for–profit) **Service**: General medical and surgical

Staffed Beds: 48 **Admissions**: 3568 **Census**: 29 **Outpatient Visits**: 98112
Births: 0 **Total Expense ($000)**: 60125 **Payroll Expense ($000)**: 19833
Personnel: 260

RESEARCH BELTON HOSPITAL See Belton Regional Medical Center

BETHANY—Harrison County

★ **HARRISON COUNTY COMMUNITY HOSPITAL (261312)**, 2600 Miller Street, Zip 64424–2701; tel. 660/425–2211, **A**10 18 **F**3 11 15 28 29 34 35 40 41 44 45 50 53 54 57 59 62 64 67 75 77 81 82 87 89 90 92 93 94 96 97 98 104 107 108 110 111 115 119 127 128 129 130 131 133 135 143 147 148 149
Primary Contact: Christina L. Gillespie, Chief Executive Officer
CFO: Lee Ann Miles, Chief Financial Officer
CMO: Terry E. Hall, Chief of Staff
CIO: Will Holt, Director Information Technology
CHR: Cathie Chalfant, Director Human Resources
CNO: Crystal Hicks, R.N., Chief Nursing Officer
Web address: www.hcchospital.org
Control: Hospital district or authority, Government, nonfederal **Service**: General medical and surgical

Staffed Beds: 19 **Admissions**: 358 **Census**: 6 **Outpatient Visits**: 63680
Births: 0 **Total Expense ($000)**: 23898 **Payroll Expense ($000)**: 10525
Personnel: 262

BLUE SPRINGS—Jackson County

⊞ **ST. MARY'S MEDICAL CENTER (260193)**, 201 Northwest R D Mize Road, Zip 64014–2518; tel. 816/228–5900, **A**1 3 10 **F**3 8 15 18 20 22 28 29 30 34 35 40 49 50 53 56 57 59 60 62 63 64 68 70 74 77 78 79 80 81 82 83 84 85 87 90 93 96 107 108 110 111 113 114 115 119 129 130 131 135 143 145 146 148 154 **S** Prime Healthcare, Ontario, CA
Primary Contact: Drew Grossman, Chief Executive Officer
Web address: www.stmaryskc.com/
Control: Corporation, Investor–owned (for–profit) **Service**: General medical and surgical

Staffed Beds: 83 **Admissions**: 4886 **Census**: 55 **Outpatient Visits**: 59888
Births: 0 **Total Expense ($000)**: 78479 **Payroll Expense ($000)**: 28894
Personnel: 482

BOLIVAR—Polk County

⊞ **CITIZENS MEMORIAL HOSPITAL (260195)**, 1500 North Oakland Avenue, Zip 65613–3011; tel. 417/326–6000, **A**1 10 20 **F**3 7 11 13 15 18 20 22 26 28 29 31 34 36 40 43 44 50 51 54 56 57 59 64 66 70 74 75 76 77 78 79 80 81 82 85 86 87 89 90 93 94 96 97 98 100 102 103 104 107 108 110 111 115 117 119 126 127 128 129 130 131 132 133 135 146 147 148 149 154 155 156
Primary Contact: Donald J. Babb, Chief Executive Officer
COO: Jeff Miller, Chief Operating Officer
CFO: Gary D. Fullbright, Comptroller
CMO: Ronald A. Evans, M.D., Chief Medical Officer
CIO: Denni McColm, Chief Information Officer
CHR: Jeremy MacLaughlin, Director Human Resources
CNO: Lesa Stock, R.N., Chief Clinical Officer
Web address: www.citizensmemorial.com
Control: Hospital district or authority, Government, nonfederal **Service**: General medical and surgical

Staffed Beds: 72 **Admissions**: 3387 **Census**: 34 **Outpatient Visits**: 392784
Births: 496 **Total Expense ($000)**: 159349 **Payroll Expense ($000)**: 71601
Personnel: 1215

BONNE TERRE—St. Francois County

★ **PARKLAND HEALTH CENTER-BONNE TERRE (261315)**, 7245 Raider Road, Zip 63628; tel. 573/358–1400, **A**10 18 **F**3 11 29 30 31 34 35 40 50 53 57 59 64 65 68 75 77 78 86 90 102 107 119 129 130 143 146 149 154 157 **S** BJC HealthCare, Saint Louis, MO
Primary Contact: Laura Lynn Rasnick, R.N., Administrator
CFO: Cheri L. Goldsmith, Director Financial Services
Web address: www.parklandhealthcenter.org
Control: Other not–for–profit (including NFP Corporation) **Service**: General medical and surgical

Staffed Beds: 3 **Admissions**: 13 **Census**: 1 **Outpatient Visits**: 23296
Births: 0 **Personnel**: 46

Many Facility Codes have changed. Please refer to the AHA Guide Code Chart. © 2019 AHA Guide

BOONVILLE—Cooper County

○ **PINNACLE REGIONAL HOSPITAL (260004)**, 17651 'B' Highway, Zip 65233–2839, Mailing Address: P.O. Box 88, Zip 65233–0088; tel. 660/882–7461, (Nonreporting) **A**10 11 20
Primary Contact: Randy Simmons, Chief Executive Officer
CFO: Patricia Nowlin, Director Accounting
CMO: Mona Brownfield, M.D., Chief Medical Staff
CIO: Bill Fletcher, Director Information Technology
CHR: Patricia Nowlin, Director Human Resources
CNO: Nancy Fredrich, R.N., Chief Clinical Officer
Web address: www.coopercmh.com
Control: County, Government, nonfederal **Service:** General medical and surgical

Staffed Beds: 32

BRANSON—Taney County

★ △ ⇑ **COX MEDICAL CENTER BRANSON (260094)**, 525 Branson Landing Boulevard, Zip 65616–2052, Mailing Address: P.O. Box 650, Zip 65615–0650; tel. 417/335–7000, **A**7 10 21 **F**3 11 13 15 17 18 20 22 26 28 29 30 31 32 34 35 40 41 45 48 50 53 56 57 59 60 62 64 65 66 68 70 74 75 76 77 78 79 80 81 85 86 87 89 90 98 107 108 110 111 114 117 119 120 121 129 130 131 132 135 144 146 147 148 149 150 154 156 **S** CoxHealth, Springfield, MO
Primary Contact: William K. Mahoney, FACHE, President and Senior Vice President, Community Hospital Group
CFO: David Strong, Chief Financial Officer/Vice President Finance
CMO: James Duff, M.D., Chief Medical Officer
CHR: Carol Murrow, Vice President Business Development
Web address: www.coxhealth.com
Control: Other not–for–profit (including NFP Corporation) **Service:** General medical and surgical

Staffed Beds: 120 **Admissions:** 6473 **Census:** 83 **Outpatient Visits:** 186784 **Births:** 555 **Total Expense ($000):** 182174 **Payroll Expense ($000):** 66081 **Personnel:** 1146

BRIDGETON—St. Louis County

⌧ △ **SSM HEALTH DEPAUL HOSPITAL - ST. LOUIS (260104)**, 12303 De Paul Drive, Zip 63044–2512; tel. 314/344–6000, (Total facility includes 52 beds in nursing home–type unit) **A**1 2 3 5 7 10 **F**3 4 5 11 12 13 15 17 18 20 22 24 26 28 29 30 31 34 35 36 38 40 43 44 45 49 50 51 53 54 55 56 57 58 59 60 61 64 68 70 73 74 75 76 78 79 81 82 84 85 86 87 89 98 99 100 101 102 104 105 107 108 110 111 114 115 117 118 119 120 121 126 128 129 130 132 135 144 146 147 148 153 154 156 **S** SSM Health, Saint Louis, MO
Primary Contact: Ellis Hawkins, President
CFO: Hal Holder, Director Finance
CMO: John Moore, M.D., Vice President Medical Affairs
CIO: Scott Feldmann, Director Information Technology
CHR: Gloria Reed, Leader Human Resources
CNO: Shelly L. Cordum, R.N., MSN, Vice President Nursing and Chief Nursing Officer
Web address: www.ssmdepaul.com
Control: Church operated, Nongovernment, not–for–profit **Service:** General medical and surgical

Staffed Beds: 529 **Admissions:** 24552 **Census:** 352 **Outpatient Visits:** 250984 **Births:** 1070 **Total Expense ($000):** 412346 **Payroll Expense ($000):** 126208 **Personnel:** 1944

BROOKFIELD—Linn County

PERSHING MEMORIAL HOSPITAL (261307), 130 East Lockling Avenue, Zip 64628–2337, Mailing Address: P.O. Box 408, Zip 64628–0408; tel. 660/258–2222, **A**10 18 **F**11 15 28 29 34 40 57 59 64 75 77 81 85 89 93 97 107 111 114 119 127 129 130 133 146 149
Primary Contact: Phil Hamilton, R.N., Chief Executive Officer
CFO: Gary R Tandy, Chief Financial Officer
CMO: B K Knowles, D.O., Chief of Staff
CIO: Elaine Sutton, Chief Information Officer
CHR: Amy Sayre, Director Human Resources
Web address: www.phsmo.org
Control: Other not–for–profit (including NFP Corporation) **Service:** General medical and surgical

Staffed Beds: 25 **Admissions:** 209 **Census:** 4 **Outpatient Visits:** 39104 **Births:** 0 **Total Expense ($000):** 16618 **Payroll Expense ($000):** 6846 **Personnel:** 139

BUTLER—Bates County

★ **BATES COUNTY MEMORIAL HOSPITAL (260034)**, 615 West Nursery Street, Zip 64730–1840, Mailing Address: P.O. Box 370, Zip 64730–0370; tel. 660/200–7000, **A**10 20 **F**3 7 11 15 28 29 30 31 34 40 45 50 59 64 68 70 77 78 79 81 87 90 93 107 108 109 110 111 115 118 119 127 129 130 132 133 154
Primary Contact: John P. Bustle, M.D., Chief Executive Officer
CFO: Terri Floyd, Chief Financial Officer
CMO: William F. Joyce, D.O., Chief of Staff
CIO: Marcia Cook, Director Information Technology
CHR: Melinda R Jackson, Director Human Resources
CNO: Rebecca Tarver, Chief Nursing Officer
Web address: www.bcmhospital.com
Control: County, Government, nonfederal **Service:** General medical and surgical

Staffed Beds: 49 **Admissions:** 851 **Census:** 12 **Outpatient Visits:** 74896 **Births:** 0 **Total Expense ($000):** 39506 **Payroll Expense ($000):** 15146 **Personnel:** 267

CAMERON—Clinton County

CAMERON REGIONAL MEDICAL CENTER (260057), 1600 East Evergreen, Zip 64429–2400, Mailing Address: P.O. Box 557, Zip 64429–0557; tel. 816/632–2101, **A**3 5 10 **F**3 11 12 13 15 28 29 30 31 34 35 39 46 47 49 56 57 59 61 62 63 64 70 74 75 76 77 78 79 81 82 84 85 86 87 89 90 98 100 103 104 107 110 111 115 119 129 130 131 133 143 146 147 148
Primary Contact: Joseph F. Abrutz Jr, Administrator
CFO: Rosa Patti, Chief Financial Officer
CIO: Bill Walser, Coordinator Technology
CHR: Pat Bestgen, Manager Human Resources
Web address: www.cameronregional.org
Control: Other not–for–profit (including NFP Corporation) **Service:** General medical and surgical

Staffed Beds: 58 **Admissions:** 2210 **Census:** 29 **Outpatient Visits:** 310912 **Births:** 153 **Total Expense ($000):** 59894 **Payroll Expense ($000):** 26282 **Personnel:** 387

CAPE GIRARDEAU—Cape Girardeau County

LANDMARK HOSPITAL OF CAPE GIRARDEAU (262015), 3255 Independence Street, Zip 63701–4914; tel. 573/335–1091, **A**10 22 **F**1 3 29 60 74 75 77 79 94 100 107 111 119 130 154 **S** Landmark Hospitals, Cape Girardeau, MO
Primary Contact: Deborah Sabella, R.N., Chief Executive Officer
COO: Michael L Norman, Executive Vice President and Chief Operating Officer
CFO: Richard H Hogan, CPA, Chief Financial Officer
CMO: William Fritsch, M.D., Medical Director
CIO: Renee Hesselrode, Director Health Information Management
CHR: Angela Kisler, Director Human Resources and Coordinator Medical Staff
Web address: www.landmarkhospitals.com
Control: Corporation, Investor–owned (for–profit) **Service:** Acute long–term care hospital

Staffed Beds: 30 **Admissions:** 246 **Census:** 18 **Outpatient Visits:** 0 **Births:** 0 **Total Expense ($000):** 10798 **Payroll Expense ($000):** 4100 **Personnel:** 7

⌧ **SAINT FRANCIS MEDICAL CENTER (260183)**, 211 St Francis Drive, Zip 63703–5049; tel. 573/331–3000, **A**1 2 10 19 **F**3 9 11 12 13 15 17 18 20 22 24 26 28 29 30 31 34 35 40 43 44 45 46 47 48 49 50 51 53 54 55 56 57 58 59 60 61 62 63 64 65 68 70 72 73 74 75 76 77 78 79 80 81 82 83 84 85 86 87 89 90 91 92 93 96 97 107 108 110 111 115 117 118 119 120 121 123 124 126 127 129 130 131 132 135 141 142 144 145 146 147 148 149
Primary Contact: Maryann Reese, R.N., FACHE, President and Chief Executive Officer
CFO: Tony Balsano, Vice President Finance
CMO: James Schell, M.D., Vice President Medical Affairs
CIO: Edward E Duryee, Director Information Systems
CHR: Teri Kreitzer, Director Human Resources
CNO: Jeannie Fadler, R.N., Vice President Patient Care Services
Web address: www.sfmc.net
Control: Church operated, Nongovernment, not–for–profit **Service:** General medical and surgical

Staffed Beds: 308 **Admissions:** 11391 **Census:** 147 **Outpatient Visits:** 745248 **Births:** 1077 **Total Expense ($000):** 478715 **Payroll Expense ($000):** 189807 **Personnel:** 2410

MO

Hospital, Medicare Provider Number, Address, Telephone, Approval, Facility, and Physician Codes, Health Care System

★ American Hospital Association (AHA) membership
☐ The Joint Commission accreditation
○ Healthcare Facilities Accreditation Program
◇ DNV Healthcare Inc. accreditation
⇑ Center for Improvement in Healthcare Quality Accreditation
△ Commission on Accreditation of Rehabilitation Facilities (CARF) accreditation

☒ **SOUTHEAST HOSPITAL (260110)**, 1701 Lacey Street, Zip 63701–5230; tel. 573/334–4822, **A**1 10 19 **F**3 13 15 17 18 20 22 24 26 28 29 30 31 32 34 35 40 44 47 48 49 50 51 53 54 57 58 59 60 61 62 63 64 65 70 72 73 74 75 76 77 78 79 80 81 82 84 85 86 87 88 89 90 92 93 96 97 102 104 107 108 110 111 114 117 118 119 120 121 123 124 126 127 129 130 131 132 135 146 147 148 149 154 156 **S** SoutheastHEALTH, Cape Girardeau, MO
Primary Contact: Kenneth Bateman, CPA, President and Chief Executive Officer
COO: Sylvia Moore, Vice President and Chief Operating Officer
CFO: Bruce Fairbanks, Vice President and Chief Financial Officer
CMO: Matt Shoemaker, D.O., Vice President and Chief Medical Officer
CIO: Mike Dozier, Chief Information Officer
CHR: Lincoln Scott, Vice President Human Resources
CNO: Judy Aslin, MSN, R.N., Vice President and Chief Nursing Officer
Web address: www.sehealth.org/
Control: Other not–for–profit (including NFP Corporation) **Service**: General medical and surgical

Staffed Beds: 146 Admissions: 8792 Census: 116 Outpatient Visits: 435256 Births: 936 Total Expense ($000): 323009 Payroll Expense ($000): 125408 Personnel: 1919

CARROLLTON—Carroll County

★ **CARROLL COUNTY MEMORIAL HOSPITAL (261332)**, 1502 North Jefferson Street, Zip 64633–1948; tel. 660/542–1695, **A**10 18 **F**3 11 15 28 29 30 31 34 35 38 40 45 50 53 56 57 59 62 64 65 68 69 74 75 77 78 79 81 82 85 86 87 90 91 92 93 96 97 103 104 107 108 110 111 115 119 125 127 128 129 130 131 132 133 135 143 146 148 149 153 154
Primary Contact: Jeff A. Tindle, Chief Executive Officer
COO: Tim Braun, Chief Operation Officer
CFO: Amy Ireland, Chief Financial Officer
CMO: Richard Smith, Chief of Staff
CIO: Bill Bollinger, Chief Information Officer
CHR: Michael Schubach, Chief People Officer
CNO: Jeanne Rector, Chief Nursing Officer
Web address: www.carrollcountyhospital.org
Control: Other not–for–profit (including NFP Corporation) **Service**: General medical and surgical

Staffed Beds: 25 Admissions: 223 Census: 5 Outpatient Visits: 59560 Births: 0 Total Expense ($000): 31229 Payroll Expense ($000): 10251 Personnel: 231

CARTHAGE—Jasper County

★ **MERCY HOSPITAL CARTHAGE (261338)**, 3125 Dr Russell Smith Way, Zip 64836–7402; tel. 417/358–8121, **A**10 18 **F**3 7 11 15 28 29 30 31 34 35 40 45 50 53 57 59 62 64 67 68 69 75 79 81 89 98 104 107 108 110 111 115 119 126 127 129 130 131 132 133 135 146 147 154 156 **S** Mercy, Chesterfield, MO
Primary Contact: Scott Watson, Administrator
CFO: Douglas Culver, Chief Financial Officer
CIO: Cheryl Lease-Homeyer, Lead Information Technology Business Partner
CHR: Colette St. Peter, Senior Manager Human Resources
Web address: www.mercy.net
Control: Church operated, Nongovernment, not–for–profit **Service**: General medical and surgical

Staffed Beds: 25 Admissions: 675 Census: 11 Outpatient Visits: 110672 Births: 0 Total Expense ($000): 41476 Payroll Expense ($000): 16704 Personnel: 240

CASSVILLE—Barry County

☒ **MERCY HOSPITAL CASSVILLE (261317)**, 94 Main Street, Zip 65625–1610; tel. 417/847–6000, **A**1 10 18 **F**3 11 15 28 29 30 34 35 40 41 45 50 53 57 59 64 65 68 75 77 81 85 86 87 89 93 94 96 103 107 108 110 111 114 119 132 133 135 148 149 153 154 **S** Mercy, Chesterfield, MO
Primary Contact: Nicki Gamet, R.N., Administrator
CFO: Sherry Clouse Day, CPA, Chief Financial Officer
CMO: Jamie Zengotita, M.D., Chief Medical Staff
CHR: George Roden, Vice President Human Resources
Web address: www.mercy.net/northwestarar/practice/mercy-hospital-cassville
Control: Church operated, Nongovernment, not–for–profit **Service**: General medical and surgical

Staffed Beds: 18 Admissions: 306 Census: 3 Outpatient Visits: 35248 Births: 0 Total Expense ($000): 15858 Payroll Expense ($000): 7351 Personnel: 107

CHESTERFIELD—St. Louis County

☐ △ **MERCY REHABILITATION HOSPITAL ST. LOUIS (263029)**, 14561 North Outer Forty Road, Zip 63017; tel. 314/881–4000, **A**1 7 10 **F**16 29 30 90 130 132 148 **S** Kindred Healthcare, Louisville, KY
Primary Contact: Jerald W. Rumph, Chief Executive Officer
CMO: Siresha Samudrala, M.D., Medical Director
Web address: www.https://www.mercy.net/practice/mercy-rehabilitation-hospital-st-louis/
Control: Partnership, Investor–owned (for–profit) **Service**: Rehabilitation

Staffed Beds: 90 Admissions: 1845 Census: 71 Outpatient Visits: 0 Births: 0 Total Expense ($000): 29492 Payroll Expense ($000): 12875 Personnel: 233

☒ **ST. LUKE'S HOSPITAL (260179)**, 232 South Woods Mill Road, Zip 63017–3417; tel. 314/434–1500, (Total facility includes 140 beds in nursing home–type unit) **A**1 2 3 10 **F**3 10 11 13 15 17 18 20 22 24 26 28 29 30 31 32 34 35 38 39 40 41 44 45 46 49 50 52 53 54 55 56 57 58 59 60 61 62 63 64 65 66 68 69 70 71 73 74 75 76 77 78 79 81 82 83 84 85 86 87 89 90 93 97 107 110 111 114 115 117 118 119 120 121 123 124 126 128 129 130 131 132 135 144 145 146 147 148 149 156
Primary Contact: Christine M. Candio, R.N., FACHE, President and Chief Executive Officer
COO: Diane Ray, R.N., FACHE, Senior Vice President and Chief Operating Officer; Network Chief Nursing Officer
CFO: Scott H. Johnson, Vice President Finance and Chief Financial Officer
CIO: William Meyers, Chief Information Officer
CHR: Janette Taaffe, Vice President, Human Resource
CNO: Diane Ray, R.N., FACHE, Senior Vice President and Chief Operating Officer; Network Chief Nursing Officer
Web address: www.stlukes-stl.com
Control: Church operated, Nongovernment, not–for–profit **Service**: General medical and surgical

Staffed Beds: 548 Admissions: 15342 Census: 270 Outpatient Visits: 1108688 Births: 1739 Total Expense ($000): 533010 Payroll Expense ($000): 239503 Personnel: 2120

☐ △ **ST. LUKE'S REHABILITATION HOSPITAL (263030)**, 14709 Olive Boulevard, Zip 63017–2221; tel. 314/317–5700, **A**1 7 10 **F**3 12 18 28 29 34 75 79 90 96 100 130 132 148 156
Primary Contact: Don Foster, Chief Executive Officer
Web address: www.khrehabstluke.com
Control: Partnership, Investor–owned (for–profit) **Service**: Rehabilitation

Staffed Beds: 35 Admissions: 686 Census: 23 Outpatient Visits: 0 Births: 0 Total Expense ($000): 8917 Payroll Expense ($000): 5241 Personnel: 64

CHILLICOTHE—Livingston County

☒ **HEDRICK MEDICAL CENTER (261321)**, 2799 North Washington Street, Zip 64601–2902; tel. 660/646–1480, **A**1 10 18 **F**3 11 13 15 17 18 28 29 30 31 34 35 39 40 43 44 45 50 59 64 68 69 70 74 75 76 77 78 79 81 82 85 86 87 89 90 92 93 96 97 100 102 104 107 108 110 111 115 118 119 127 130 131 133 141 146 147 148 154 **S** Saint Luke's Health System, Kansas City, MO
Primary Contact: Steven M. Schieber, FACHE, Chief Executive Officer
CHR: Lisa Hecker, Director Human Resources
CNO: Catherine Hamilton, Chief Nursing Officer
Web address: www.saintlukeskc.org
Control: Church operated, Nongovernment, not–for–profit **Service**: General medical and surgical

Staffed Beds: 25 Admissions: 1364 Census: 15 Outpatient Visits: 112360 Births: 303 Total Expense ($000): 51240 Payroll Expense ($000): 19834 Personnel: 309

CLINTON—Henry County

☒ **GOLDEN VALLEY MEMORIAL HEALTHCARE (260175)**, 1600 North Second Street, Zip 64735–1192; tel. 660/885–5511, **A**1 10 **F**3 7 11 13 15 17 18 28 29 30 31 34 35 40 45 47 48 49 53 57 59 61 62 63 64 68 70 74 75 76 77 78 79 81 85 86 87 89 90 93 96 107 108 111 115 118 127 128 129 130 131 132 133 143 146 147 148 149 155 156
Primary Contact: Craig Thompson, Chief Executive Officer
CFO: Tammy R Nadler, Chief Financial Officer
CIO: Mike Gaul, Director Information Technology
CHR: Greg Shannon, Chief Human Resources Officer
CNO: Lynnette Hayes, Chief Nursing Officer
Web address: www.gvmh.org
Control: Hospital district or authority, Government, nonfederal **Service**: General medical and surgical

Staffed Beds: 53 Admissions: 2108 Census: 18 Outpatient Visits: 315992 Births: 0 Total Expense ($000): 99743 Payroll Expense ($000): 43002 Personnel: 819

MO

Many Facility Codes have changed. Please refer to the AHA Guide Code Chart. © 2019 AHA Guide

COLUMBIA—Boone County

⊠ **BOONE HOSPITAL CENTER (260068)**, 1600 East Broadway, Zip 65201–5844; tel. 573/815–8000, **A**1 2 3 5 10 **F**3 7 11 12 13 15 17 18 20 22 24 26 28 29 31 34 35 36 40 45 46 47 48 49 50 51 53 54 56 57 58 59 60 61 64 65 68 70 71 72 73 74 75 76 77 78 79 80 81 82 84 85 86 87 90 93 96 107 110 111 114 115 117 118 119 126 129 130 131 132 133 135 143 144 145 146 147 148 149 156 **S** BJC HealthCare, Saint Louis, MO
Primary Contact: James J. Sinek, FACHE, President
CFO: Randy Morrow, Vice President and Chief Operating Officer
CMO: Jerry Kennett, M.D., Chief Medical Officer
CHR: Michelle Zvanut, Vice President Human Resources
Web address: www.boone.org
Control: Other not–for–profit (including NFP Corporation) **Service:** General medical and surgical

Staffed Beds: 311 **Admissions:** 13093 **Census:** 156 **Outpatient Visits:** 179584 **Births:** 1640 **Total Expense ($000):** 324807 **Payroll Expense ($000):** 87103 **Personnel:** 1355

☐ **CENTERPOINTE HOSPITAL OF COLUMBIA (264032)**, 1201 International Drive, Zip 65202; tel. 573/615–2001, (Nonreporting) **A**1
Primary Contact: Phil Sheridan, Chief Executive Officer
Web address: www.centerpointehospitalcolumbia.com
Control: Corporation, Investor–owned (for–profit) **Service:** Psychiatric

Staffed Beds: 72

ELLIS FISCHEL CANCER CENTER See University of Missouri Health Care, Columbia

⊠ **HARRY S. TRUMAN MEMORIAL VETERANS HOSPITAL**, 800 Hospital Drive, Zip 65201–5275; tel. 573/814–6000, (Total facility includes 35 beds in nursing home–type unit) **A**1 3 5 **F**3 4 5 17 18 20 22 24 26 29 30 31 34 35 36 38 39 40 45 46 49 56 57 58 59 60 61 62 63 64 65 70 74 75 78 79 81 82 84 85 86 87 90 92 93 97 98 100 102 104 105 106 107 111 115 116 117 118 119 128 130 132 135 146 147 149 153 154 156 158 **S** Department of Veterans Affairs, Washington, DC
Primary Contact: David Isaacks, Director
COO: Robert G Ritter, FACHE, Associate Director
CFO: Deborah Henderson, Acting Chief Financial Officer
CMO: Lana Zerrer, M.D., Chief of Staff
CIO: Donna Krause, Chief Information Officer
CHR: Jimmy Powell, Manager Human Resources
Web address: www.columbiamo.va.gov
Control: Veterans Affairs, Government, federal **Service:** General medical and surgical

Staffed Beds: 126 **Admissions:** 4424 **Census:** 101 **Outpatient Visits:** 702120 **Births:** 0 **Total Expense ($000):** 377812 **Payroll Expense ($000):** 134586 **Personnel:** 1677

LANDMARK HOSPITAL OF COLUMBIA (262020), 604 Old 63 North, Zip 65201–6308; tel. 573/499–6600, **A**3 5 10 22 **F**1 3 29 30 70 77 82 84 85 90 130 148 154 **S** Landmark Hospitals, Cape Girardeau, MO
Primary Contact: Glenn Piche, Chief Executive Officer
Web address: www.landmarkhospitals.com
Control: Corporation, Investor–owned (for–profit) **Service:** Acute long–term care hospital

Staffed Beds: 23 **Admissions:** 267 **Census:** 18 **Outpatient Visits:** 0 **Births:** 0 **Total Expense ($000):** 14509 **Payroll Expense ($000):** 5783 **Personnel:** 59

⊠ **RUSK REHABILITATION HOSPITAL (263027)**, 315 Business Loop 70 West, Zip 65203–3248; tel. 573/817–2703, **A**1 3 5 10 **F**29 30 90 143 148 **S** Encompass Health Corporation, Birmingham, AL
Primary Contact: John M. Dawes, FACHE, Chief Executive Officer
CFO: Jeff Reese, Chief Financial Officer
CMO: Gregory Worsowicz, M.D., Medical Director
CHR: Robin Prater, Director Human Resources
CNO: Lori Mann, R.N., MSN, Chief Nursing Officer
Web address: www.ruskrehab.com
Control: Partnership, Investor–owned (for–profit) **Service:** Rehabilitation

Staffed Beds: 60 **Admissions:** 1074 **Census:** 40 **Outpatient Visits:** 0 **Births:** 0 **Total Expense ($000):** 19718 **Payroll Expense ($000):** 9220 **Personnel:** 129

★ ⇑ **UNIVERSITY OF MISSOURI HEALTH CARE (260141)**, One Hospital Drive, Zip 65212–0001; tel. 573/882–4141, (Includes ELLIS FISCHEL CANCER CENTER, 115 Business Loop 70 West, Columbia, Missouri, Zip 65203; tel. 573/882–5460; WOMEN'S AND CHILDREN'S HOSPITAL, 404 Keene Street, Columbia, Missouri, Zip 65201–6626; tel. 573/875–9000; Keri Simon, Executive Director) **A**2 3 5 8 10 21 **F**3 4 7 9 11 12 13 15 16 17 18 19 20 22 24 26 28 29 30 31 32 33 34 35 36 37 38 39 40 41 42 43 44 45 46 47 48 49 50 51 52 53 54 55 56 57 58 59 60 61 64 65 66 68 70 71 72 73 74 75 76 77 78 79 81 82 83 84 85 86 87 88 89 91 92 93 97 98 99 100 101 102 103 104 107 108 110 111 114 115 116 117 118 119 120 121 123 124 126 127 129 130 131 132 134 135 138 141 142 143 144 146 147 148 154 157 **S** University of Missouri Health Care, Columbia, MO
Primary Contact: Jonathan W. Curtright, Chief Executive Officer
CFO: Kevin Necas, Chief Financial Officer
CMO: Stevan Whitt, M.D., Chief Medical Officer
CHR: Sue Kopfle, Chief Human Resources Officer
Web address: www.muhealth.org
Control: State, Government, nonfederal **Service:** General medical and surgical

Staffed Beds: 602 **Admissions:** 26752 **Census:** 404 **Outpatient Visits:** 1025840 **Births:** 2417 **Total Expense ($000):** 952719 **Payroll Expense ($000):** 296142 **Personnel:** 5567

DEXTER—Stoddard County

SOUTHEAST HEALTH CENTER OF STODDARD COUNTY (260160), 1200 North One Mile Road, Zip 63841–1000; tel. 573/624–5566, **A**10 **F**11 15 28 29 31 34 39 40 59 62 65 70 75 77 78 81 85 89 90 93 97 98 107 110 111 115 118 119 127 129 130 133 135 146 154 **S** SoutheastHEALTH, Cape Girardeau, MO
Primary Contact: Sue Ann Williams, Chief Executive Officer
Web address: www.sehealth.org
Control: Other not–for–profit (including NFP Corporation) **Service:** General medical and surgical

Staffed Beds: 31 **Admissions:** 1550 **Census:** 14 **Outpatient Visits:** 98144 **Births:** 0 **Total Expense ($000):** 31494 **Payroll Expense ($000):** 11755 **Personnel:** 242

EL DORADO SPRINGS—Cedar County

CEDAR COUNTY MEMORIAL HOSPITAL (261323), 1401 South Park Street, Zip 64744–2037; tel. 417/876–2511, **A**10 18 **F**11 15 18 28 30 34 35 40 45 53 56 57 59 62 64 65 68 74 77 81 85 87 89 90 102 110 111 114 119 124 127 129 133 143 147 148 149
Primary Contact: Jana Witt, Chief Executive Officer
CFO: Carla Gilbert, Director Finance
CMO: R. John Torontow, M.D., Chief Medical Staff
CIO: Lois Willmore, Supervisor Health Information Management
CHR: Diana Pyle, Director Human Resources and Executive Assistant to Chief Executive Officer
CNO: Drew Alexander, Chief Nursing Officer
Web address: www.cedarcountyhospital.org
Control: County, Government, nonfederal **Service:** General medical and surgical

Staffed Beds: 25 **Admissions:** 334 **Census:** 6 **Outpatient Visits:** 19368 **Births:** 0 **Total Expense ($000):** 13230 **Payroll Expense ($000):** 4274 **Personnel:** 109

EXCELSIOR SPRINGS—Clay County

★ **EXCELSIOR SPRINGS HOSPITAL (261322)**, 1700 Rainbow Boulevard, Zip 64024–1190; tel. 816/630–6081, (Total facility includes 80 beds in nursing home–type unit) **A**10 18 **F**3 10 11 15 18 19 20 29 31 32 34 35 39 40 45 56 57 59 62 63 64 67 68 70 75 77 78 79 81 82 84 85 86 87 89 90 93 102 103 107 108 110 111 115 116 117 118 119 125 128 130 133 143 146 154
Primary Contact: Kristen DeHart, Chief Executive Officer
CFO: Cameron Meyer, CPA, Chief Financial Officer
CMO: H. Andrew Pickett, M.D., Medical Staff President
CHR: Joni Schwan, Director Human Resources
CNO: Nanette Houck, R.N., Chief Nursing Executive
Web address: www.ESHospital.org
Control: City, Government, nonfederal **Service:** General medical and surgical

Staffed Beds: 105 **Admissions:** 420 **Census:** 65 **Outpatient Visits:** 41096 **Births:** 0 **Total Expense ($000):** 33314 **Payroll Expense ($000):** 12018 **Personnel:** 240

MO

Hospital, Medicare Provider Number, Address, Telephone, Approval, Facility, and Physician Codes, Health Care System

★ American Hospital Association (AHA) membership
☐ The Joint Commission accreditation
○ Healthcare Facilities Accreditation Program
◇ DNV Healthcare Inc. accreditation
⇑ Center for Improvement in Healthcare Quality Accreditation
△ Commission on Accreditation of Rehabilitation Facilities (CARF) accreditation

FAIRFAX—Atchison County

⇧ **COMMUNITY HOSPITAL ASSOCIATION** See Community Hospital-Fairfax

★ ⇧ **COMMUNITY HOSPITAL-FAIRFAX (261303)**, 26136 US Highway 59, Zip 64446–9105, Mailing Address: P.O. Box 107, Zip 64446–0107; tel. 660/686–2211, **A**10 18 21 **F**3 11 13 15 18 28 29 30 34 40 45 50 57 59 62 64 75 76 79 81 85 87 89 90 93 96 97 101 103 104 107 110 114 119 127 130 131 132 133 148 149
Primary Contact: Julie L. Jones, Chief Executive Officer
COO: Ann Schlueter, Chief Operating Officer
CFO: Jon Davis, Chief Financial Officer
CMO: Richard Aron Burke, M.D., Chief Medical Officer
CIO: Chris Hedlund, Director Information Systems
Web address: www.fairfaxmed.com
Control: Other not–for–profit (including NFP Corporation) **Service**: General medical and surgical

Staffed Beds: 18 **Admissions**: 529 **Census**: 6 **Outpatient Visits**: 41064 **Births**: 47 **Total Expense ($000)**: 19385 **Payroll Expense ($000)**: 7792 **Personnel**: 77

FARMINGTON—St. Francois County

⊞ **PARKLAND HEALTH CENTER - FARMINGTON COMMUNITY (260163)**, 1101 West Liberty Street, Zip 63640–1921; tel. 573/756–6451, **A**1 10 20 **F**3 11 13 15 18 28 29 30 34 35 40 45 46 49 50 53 57 59 65 68 69 70 75 76 77 79 81 85 86 87 93 98 102 103 107 108 115 118 119 130 143 146 147 148 149 154 157 **S** BJC HealthCare, Saint Louis, MO
Primary Contact: Thomas P. Karl, President
COO: Steven R Marler, Assistant Administrator
CFO: Cheri L. Goldsmith, Director Financial Services
CMO: Scott Kirkley, M.D., BJC Chief Medical Officer Group Liaison
Web address: www.parklandhealthcenter.org
Control: Other not–for–profit (including NFP Corporation) **Service**: General medical and surgical

Staffed Beds: 103 **Admissions**: 3614 **Census**: 33 **Outpatient Visits**: 97248 **Births**: 614 **Total Expense ($000)**: 105084 **Payroll Expense ($000)**: 40476 **Personnel**: 569

☐ **SOUTHEAST MISSOURI MENTAL HEALTH CENTER (264005)**, 1010 West Columbia Street, Zip 63640–2997; tel. 573/218–6792, **A**1 10 **F**4 11 30 39 53 65 75 86 87 98 101 103 106 130 132 135 143 146 157
Primary Contact: Julie Inman, Regional Executive Officer
CMO: Jay Englehart, M.D., Medical Director
CHR: Mark Remspecher, Director Human Resources
Web address: www.dmh.missouri.gov/southeast/
Control: State, Government, nonfederal **Service**: Psychiatric

Staffed Beds: 348 **Admissions**: 33 **Census**: 316 **Outpatient Visits**: 0 **Births**: 0 **Total Expense ($000)**: 71227 **Payroll Expense ($000)**: 36941 **Personnel**: 1004

FENTON—St. Louis County

⊞ **SSM HEALTH ST. CLARE HOSPITAL - FENTON (260081)**, 1015 Bowles Avenue, Zip 63026–2394; tel. 636/496–2000, **A**1 3 10 **F**3 11 13 15 17 18 20 22 24 28 29 30 31 34 35 40 41 44 45 49 50 51 53 54 56 57 58 59 61 64 70 73 74 75 76 78 79 81 82 84 85 86 87 89 100 102 103 105 107 108 110 111 115 117 119 120 121 129 130 132 135 143 144 146 147 148 154 **S** SSM Health, Saint Louis, MO
Primary Contact: Tina Garrison, President
COO: Lee Bernstein, Regional Executive Vice President and Chief Operating Officer
CFO: Hal Holder, Regional Chief Financial Officer-Hospital Operations
CMO: Timothy J Pratt, M.D., Vice President Medical Affairs and Chief Medical Officer
CIO: Michael Paasch, Vice President, Regional Chief Information Officer
CHR: Renee Roach, System Vice President, Human Resources
CNO: Wayne Laramie, Vice President Nursing
Web address: www.ssmstclare.com
Control: Church operated, Nongovernment, not–for–profit **Service**: General medical and surgical

Staffed Beds: 184 **Admissions**: 10521 **Census**: 117 **Outpatient Visits**: 134888 **Births**: 1194 **Total Expense ($000)**: 195629 **Payroll Expense ($000)**: 62281 **Personnel**: 836

FESTUS—Jefferson County

⊞ △ **MERCY HOSPITAL JEFFERSON (260023)**, 1400 US Highway 61 South, Zip 63028–4100, Mailing Address: P.O. Box 350, Crystal City, Zip 63019–0350; tel. 636/933–1000, **A**1 7 10 **F**3 8 11 12 13 15 18 20 22 24 26 28 29 30 31 34 35 40 44 45 46 49 50 51 53 54 57 59 60 62 63 64 68 70 74 75 76 77 78 79 81 82 84 85 86 87 89 90 93 96 97 98 100 103 104 107 108 110 111 114 115 117 118 119 129 130 131 132 135 143 144 146 147 148 149 153 154 156 157 **S** Mercy, Chesterfield, MO
Primary Contact: Eric Ammons, President
COO: Michele C. Meyer, R.N., Vice President of Operations
CMO: Mark Briete, M.D., Vice President Medical Affairs
CIO: Jan Poneta, Director Information Services
CHR: Saundra G Turner, Director Human Resources
Web address: www.mercy.net/crystalcitymo
Control: Other not–for–profit (including NFP Corporation) **Service**: General medical and surgical

Staffed Beds: 204 **Admissions**: 9959 **Census**: 125 **Outpatient Visits**: 216112 **Births**: 463 **Total Expense ($000)**: 172890 **Payroll Expense ($000)**: 68159 **Personnel**: 1195

FORT LEONARD WOOD—Pulaski County

⊞ **GENERAL LEONARD WOOD ARMY COMMUNITY HOSPITAL**, 4430 Missouri Avenue, Zip 65473–8952, Mailing Address: P.O. Box 4430, Zip 65473–8952; tel. 573/596–0414, (Nonreporting) **A**1 **S** Department of the Army, Office of the Surgeon General, Falls Church, VA
Primary Contact: Colonel Kimberlie Biever, Hospital Commander
CFO: Major Michael Hogan, Chief Resource Management
CMO: Lieutenant Colonel John Lowery, M.D., Deputy Commander Clinical Services
CHR: Major Sandra Roper, Chief Human Resources
Web address: www.glwach.amedd.army.mil/
Control: Department of Defense, Government, federal **Service**: General medical and surgical

Staffed Beds: 42

FREDERICKTOWN—Madison County

MADISON MEDICAL CENTER (261302), 611 West Main Street, Zip 63645–1111; tel. 573/783–3341, (Total facility includes 80 beds in nursing home–type unit) **A**10 18 **F**6 11 15 18 28 35 45 59 62 64 67 70 77 78 79 81 85 87 92 93 97 103 107 111 119 127 128 130 133 144 146
Primary Contact: Lisa Twidwell, Administrator
CMO: P A George, M.D., Chief of Staff
CHR: Jennifer Penuel, Director Human Resources
Web address: www.madisonmedicalcenter.net
Control: County, Government, nonfederal **Service**: General medical and surgical

Staffed Beds: 97 **Admissions**: 423 **Census**: 72 **Outpatient Visits**: 56272 **Births**: 0 **Total Expense ($000)**: 19464 **Payroll Expense ($000)**: 9677 **Personnel**: 244

FULTON—Callaway County

FULTON MEDICAL CENTER (260209), 10 South Hospital Drive, Zip 65251–2510; tel. 573/642–3376, **A**5 10 **F**3 4 11 18 29 30 34 40 50 57 59 64 65 68 75 77 90 93 97 98 102 103 107 112 115 119 127 129 130 149
Primary Contact: Mike Reece, Chief Executive Officer
Web address: www.fultonmed.com
Control: Corporation, Investor–owned (for–profit) **Service**: General medical and surgical

Staffed Beds: 37 **Admissions**: 371 **Census**: 13 **Outpatient Visits**: 24512 **Births**: 0 **Total Expense ($000)**: 20462 **Payroll Expense ($000)**: 4906 **Personnel**: 158

☐ **FULTON STATE HOSPITAL (264004)**, 600 East Fifth Street, Zip 65251–1753; tel. 573/592–4100, **A**1 3 5 10 **F**3 4 11 29 30 39 44 50 53 56 57 58 59 65 75 77 82 86 87 98 100 101 102 103 130 132 135 143 146 149
Primary Contact: Robert Reitz, Ph.D., Chief Executive Officer
COO: Andrew Atkinson, Chief Operating Officer
CFO: Susie Kemp, Chief Financial Officer
CMO: Sanjiv Sethi, M.D., Medical Director
CIO: Keith Jones, Chief Information Officer
CHR: Lori French, Manager Human Resources
CNO: Susan Knoepflein, Chief Nurse Executive
Web address: www.dmh.missouri.gov/fulton
Control: State, Government, nonfederal **Service**: Psychiatric

Staffed Beds: 411 **Admissions**: 123 **Census**: 411 **Outpatient Visits**: 0 **Births**: 0 **Total Expense ($000)**: 101424 **Payroll Expense ($000)**: 49922 **Personnel**: 1262

MO

HANNIBAL—Marion County

✠ **HANNIBAL REGIONAL HOSPITAL (260025)**, 6000 Hospital Drive, Zip 63401-6887, Mailing Address: P.O. Box 551, Zip 63401-0551; tel. 573/248-1300, **A**1 2 10 **F**3 13 15 20 22 26 28 29 31 34 35 40 45 47 49 51 57 59 62 64 68 70 74 75 76 78 79 81 85 86 87 89 90 92 107 108 110 111 115 117 118 119 120 121 123 124 129 130 132 135 148
Primary Contact: C Todd. Ahrens, President and Chief Executive Officer
CFO: Roger J Dix, Vice President Finance
CMO: Bryson McHardy, M.D., President Medical Staff
CIO: Jeff W. Evans, Vice President Information and Technology
CHR: Susan R Wathen, Vice President Human Resources
Web address: www.hannibalhealth.org
Control: Other not-for-profit (including NFP Corporation) **Service**: General medical and surgical

Staffed Beds: 99 **Admissions**: 4377 **Census**: 49 **Outpatient Visits**: 193536
Births: 605 **Total Expense ($000)**: 163473 **Payroll Expense ($000)**: 73882
Personnel: 860

HARRISONVILLE—Cass County

✠ **CASS REGIONAL MEDICAL CENTER (261324)**, 2800 East Rock Haven Road, Zip 64701-4411; tel. 816/380-3474, **A**1 10 18 **F**3 11 12 15 17 18 28 29 30 31 32 34 35 40 44 45 46 48 50 54 56 57 59 64 65 66 70 74 75 77 78 79 80 81 82 84 85 86 87 93 97 98 102 103 107 110 111 114 115 119 127 129 130 131 132 133 135 146 149 156
Primary Contact: John Christopher. Lang, FACHE, Chief Executive Officer
CFO: Brent Probasco, Chief Financial Officer
CIO: Lester Vohs, Manager Information Systems
CHR: Carla Wallen, Manager Human Resources
CNO: Twila Buckner, R.N., Chief Nursing Officer
Web address: www.cassregional.org
Control: County, Government, nonfederal **Service**: General medical and surgical

Staffed Beds: 35 **Admissions**: 1114 **Census**: 15 **Outpatient Visits**: 114288
Births: 0 **Total Expense ($000)**: 66422 **Payroll Expense ($000)**: 25729
Personnel: 49

HAYTI—Pemiscot County

PEMISCOT MEMORIAL HEALTH SYSTEM (260070), 946 East Reed Street, Zip 63851-1245, Mailing Address: P.O. Box 489, Zip 63851-0489; tel. 573/359-1372, (Total facility includes 66 beds in nursing home-type unit) **A**10 **F**3 28 29 30 34 39 40 50 57 59 64 67 68 70 75 79 81 82 85 87 90 93 97 98 99 103 104 107 119 127 128 130 133 143 144 149 156
Primary Contact: Jonna Green, Interim Administrator
CHR: Jackie Powell, Director Human Resources
Web address: www.pemiscot.org/
Control: County, Government, nonfederal **Service**: General medical and surgical

Staffed Beds: 167 **Admissions**: 1447 **Census**: 81 **Outpatient Visits**: 27912
Births: 0 **Total Expense ($000)**: 33628 **Payroll Expense ($000)**: 14333
Personnel: 369

HERMANN—Gasconade County

HERMANN AREA DISTRICT HOSPITAL (261314), 509 West 18th Street, Zip 65041-1547, Mailing Address: P.O. Box 470, Zip 65041-0470; tel. 573/486-2191, **A**10 18 **F**3 11 12 15 18 28 29 34 35 40 41 44 45 56 57 59 62 64 67 69 71 75 77 78 81 85 86 87 89 90 93 96 97 104 107 110 111 114 119 127 128 129 130 133 143 146
Primary Contact: Dan McKinney, Administrator
COO: Matt Siebert, Assistant Administrator Ancillary Services
CFO: Christine Lewis, Assistant Administrator, Finance
CMO: Michael Rothermich, M.D., Chief of Staff
CIO: Jeffrey Wehmeyer, Director Information Technology
CHR: Brandon Hughes, Director Human Resources
CNO: Sue Daller, R.N., Assistant Administrator Nursing
Web address: www.hadh.org
Control: Hospital district or authority, Government, nonfederal **Service**: General medical and surgical

Staffed Beds: 24 **Admissions**: 402 **Census**: 10 **Outpatient Visits**: 53328
Births: 0 **Total Expense ($000)**: 17926 **Payroll Expense ($000)**: 9325
Personnel: 157

HOUSTON—Texas County

TEXAS COUNTY MEMORIAL HOSPITAL (260024), 1333 South Sam Houston Boulevard, Zip 65483-2046; tel. 417/967-3311, **A**10 20 **F**3 7 28 29 34 45 57 59 62 63 64 70 76 81 85 86 89 93 97 107 110 111 115 119 127 129 130 133 143 148 149
Primary Contact: Wesley E. Murray, Chief Executive Officer
CFO: Linda Pamperien, Chief Financial Officer
CMO: Charles Mueller, M.D., Chief of Staff
CHR: Anita Kuhn, Controller
Web address: www.tcmh.org
Control: County, Government, nonfederal **Service**: General medical and surgical

Staffed Beds: 47 **Admissions**: 1324 **Census**: 13 **Outpatient Visits**: 103104
Births: 170 **Total Expense ($000)**: 33735 **Payroll Expense ($000)**: 16949
Personnel: 339

INDEPENDENCE—Jackson County

✠ **CENTERPOINT MEDICAL CENTER (260095)**, 19600 East 39th Street, Zip 64057-2301; tel. 816/698-7000, **A**1 2 10 **F**3 8 12 13 15 18 20 22 24 26 28 29 30 31 34 35 38 40 43 46 47 48 49 50 52 54 55 56 57 59 60 64 68 70 72 74 75 76 77 78 79 80 81 82 85 86 87 90 92 93 107 108 110 111 114 115 116 117 118 119 120 121 123 126 129 130 131 132 144 145 146 147 148 149 154 **S** HCA Healthcare, Nashville, TN
Primary Contact: Bret Kolman, CPA, FACHE, Chief Executive Officer
CFO: James H Brown, Chief Financial Officer
CMO: Christopher Sullivan, M.D., Chief Medical Officer
CIO: Carl Sifers, Director Information Technology and System Services
CHR: Kyla Stoltz, Vice President Human Resources
CNO: Lynn Barrett, Chief Nursing Officer
Web address: www.centerpointmedical.com
Control: Corporation, Investor-owned (for-profit) **Service**: General medical and surgical

Staffed Beds: 285 **Admissions**: 15538 **Census**: 178 **Outpatient Visits**: 161104 **Births**: 1431 **Total Expense ($000)**: 285232 **Payroll Expense ($000)**: 82537 **Personnel**: 1222

JEFFERSON CITY—Cole County

✠ **CAPITAL REGION MEDICAL CENTER (260047)**, 1125 Madison Street, Zip 65101-5200, Mailing Address: P.O. Box 1128, Zip 65102-1128; tel. 573/632-5000, **A**1 3 5 10 12 13 **F**11 13 15 17 18 20 22 24 26 28 29 30 31 34 35 36 38 40 45 46 47 48 50 51 53 57 58 59 60 61 62 64 65 68 70 73 74 75 76 77 78 79 80 81 82 85 87 89 90 92 93 96 97 100 107 108 110 111 115 117 118 119 120 121 123 126 129 130 131 132 135 144 146 147 148 149 150 154 **S** University of Missouri Health Care, Columbia, MO
Primary Contact: Gaspare Calvaruso, President
COO: Janet Weckenborg, Vice President Operations
CFO: Tom Luebbering, Vice President Finance
CMO: Mitchell Godbee, Chief of Staff
CIO: Jason Cecil, Vice President, Information
CHR: Sarah Morrow, Vice President Human Resources
Web address: www.crmc.org
Control: Other not-for-profit (including NFP Corporation) **Service**: General medical and surgical

Staffed Beds: 114 **Admissions**: 5513 **Census**: 56 **Outpatient Visits**: 464088 **Births**: 584 **Total Expense ($000)**: 201147 **Payroll Expense ($000)**: 84845 **Personnel**: 1192

✠ **SSM HEALTH ST. MARY'S HOSPITAL - JEFFERSON CITY (260011)**, 2505 Mission Drive, Zip 65109; tel. 573/681-3000, **A**1 10 19 **F**3 5 11 13 15 17 18 20 22 24 28 29 30 31 34 40 45 46 47 48 49 50 51 53 54 57 59 60 62 64 68 70 73 74 75 76 77 78 79 81 82 83 84 85 86 87 89 90 93 96 98 100 101 102 104 107 108 110 111 115 118 119 120 121 122 123 127 129 130 131 132 135 144 146 147 148 149 153 154 157 **S** SSM Health, Saint Louis, MO
Primary Contact: Michael A. Baumgartner, President
CFO: James Stratton, Vice President Finance
CMO: Stephen Stewart, M.D., Vice President Medical Affairs
CHR: Susan Mankoski, Vice President Human Resources
CNO: Alice M Chatley, R.N., MSN, Vice President Acute Care Services
Web address: www.lethealingbegin.com
Control: Church operated, Nongovernment, not-for-profit **Service**: General medical and surgical

Staffed Beds: 92 **Admissions**: 6863 **Census**: 69 **Outpatient Visits**: 219688
Births: 867 **Total Expense ($000)**: 281734 **Payroll Expense ($000)**: 53422
Personnel: 867

MO

Hospital, Medicare Provider Number, Address, Telephone, Approval, Facility, and Physician Codes, Health Care System

★ American Hospital Association (AHA) membership   ○ Healthcare Facilities Accreditation Program   ⇑ Center for Improvement in Healthcare Quality Accreditation
□ The Joint Commission accreditation   ◇ DNV Healthcare Inc. accreditation   △ Commission on Accreditation of Rehabilitation Facilities (CARF) accreditation

© 2019 AHA Guide   *Many Facility Codes have changed. Please refer to the AHA Guide Code Chart.*   Hospitals   **A361**

JOPLIN—Newton County

★ ○ **FREEMAN HEALTH SYSTEM (260137)**, 1102 West 32nd Street, Zip 64804–3503; tel. 417/347–1111, (Includes FREEMAN HOSPITAL EAST, 932 East 34th Street, Joplin, Missouri, Zip 64804–3999, Mailing Address: 1102 West 32nd Street, Zip 64804–3999, tel. 417/347–1111; Paula F Baker, President and Chief Executive Officer) **A**3 10 11 13 19 **F**3 7 8 11 12 13 15 17 18 20 22 24 26 28 30 31 34 35 40 43 44 45 46 47 48 49 50 54 56 57 59 60 61 62 64 65 68 70 72 73 74 75 76 77 78 79 81 82 83 84 85 86 87 89 90 93 96 97 98 100 102 103 107 108 110 111 115 117 119 120 121 124 129 130 131 132 144 145 146 147 148 156 **S** Freeman Health System, Joplin, MO
Primary Contact: Paula F. Baker, President and Chief Executive Officer
CFO: Steve W Graddy, Chief Financial Officer
CMO: Saba Habis, M.D., Chief Medical Officer
CIO: Skip Rollins, Chief Information Officer
CHR: Mary Frerer, Chief Human Resources Officer
CNO: Jeffrey Carrier, R.N., Chief Clinical Officer
Web address: www.freemanhealth.com
Control: Other not–for–profit (including NFP Corporation) **Service**: General medical and surgical

Staffed Beds: 381 **Admissions:** 17608 **Census:** 245 **Outpatient Visits:** 639600 **Births:** 1923 **Total Expense ($000):** 489066 **Payroll Expense ($000):** 226218 **Personnel:** 3224		

LANDMARK HOSPITAL OF JOPLIN (262016), 2040 West 32nd Street, Zip 64804–3512; tel. 417/627–1300, **A**10 22 **F**1 3 29 60 65 75 77 84 90 119 130 143 148 **S** Landmark Hospitals, Cape Girardeau, MO
Primary Contact: Lee A. Simpson, Chief Executive Officer
CMO: Jack Rhoads, M.D., Medical Director
CHR: Janice Nordstrom, Director Human Resources
CNO: Stephanie Slater-Nesuold, Director of Nursing
Web address: www.landmarkhospitals.com
Control: Corporation, Investor–owned (for–profit) **Service**: Acute long–term care hospital

Staffed Beds: 30 **Admissions:** 228 **Census:** 16 **Outpatient Visits:** 0 **Births:** 0 **Total Expense ($000):** 11977 **Payroll Expense ($000):** 4919 **Personnel:** 90		

⊞ **MERCY HOSPITAL JOPLIN (260001)**, 100 Mercy Way, Zip 64804–1626; tel. 417/781–2727, (Includes ST. JOHN'S REHABILITATION CENTER, 2727 McClelland Boulevard, Joplin, Missouri, Zip 64804; tel. 417/659–6716) **A**1 2 10 19 **F**3 5 7 11 12 13 14 15 17 18 19 20 22 24 26 28 29 30 31 34 35 38 39 40 43 44 45 46 47 48 49 51 54 57 58 59 60 61 62 63 64 65 66 68 70 72 73 74 75 76 77 78 79 81 82 84 85 86 87 89 93 94 97 98 99 100 101 102 104 107 108 110 111 114 115 118 119 120 121 123 124 126 127 129 130 131 132 135 144 146 147 148 154 156 **S** Mercy, Chesterfield, MO
Primary Contact: Jeremy Drinkwitz, President and Chief Executive Officer
CFO: Thomas Mathews, Vice President, Finance
CHR: Timothy Murphy, Vice President Human Resources
CNO: Kelli Bigando, Chief Nursing Officer
Web address: www.mercy.net/joplinmo
Control: Church operated, Nongovernment, not–for–profit **Service**: General medical and surgical

Staffed Beds: 236 **Admissions:** 11852 **Census:** 150 **Outpatient Visits:** 275520 **Births:** 1180 **Total Expense ($000):** 239068 **Payroll Expense ($000):** 94878 **Personnel:** 1503		

KANSAS CITY—Jackson County

☐ **CENTER FOR BEHAVIORAL MEDICINE (264008)**, 1000 East 24th Street, Zip 64108–2776; tel. 816/512–7000, (Total facility includes 36 beds in nursing home–type unit) **A**1 3 5 10 **F**4 53 86 87 98 106 128
Primary Contact: Denise Norbury, MS, R.N., Regional Chief Executive Officer
COO: Jeanette Simmons, Chief Operating Officer
CFO: Randy Riley, Chief Financial Officer
CMO: Nashaat Boutros, M.D., Clinical Director
CIO: Robert Curren, Director Information Technology
CHR: Silva Ward, Director Human Resources
CNO: John Tucker, Chief Nursing Executive
Web address: www.dmhonline.dmh.state.mo.us
Control: State, Government, nonfederal **Service**: Psychiatric

Staffed Beds: 101 **Admissions:** 49 **Census:** 96 **Outpatient Visits:** 0 **Births:** 0 **Total Expense ($000):** 24527 **Payroll Expense ($000):** 13734 **Personnel:** 232		

⊞ **CHILDREN'S MERCY HOSPITAL KANSAS CITY (263302)**, 2401 Gilham Road, Zip 64108–4619; tel. 816/234–3000, **A**1 2 3 5 8 10 **F**3 7 8 9 11 12 16 19 20 21 22 23 24 25 26 27 29 30 31 32 34 35 36 38 39 40 41 43 44 48 50 54 55 57 58 59 60 61 62 64 65 68 72 73 74 75 77 78 79 81 82 84 85 86 87 88 89 90 91 92 93 94 96 97 100 101 104 107 108 111 115 117 118 119 130 131 132 134 136 137 138 139 141 142 144 146 148 149 150 154 155 156 157
Primary Contact: Paul D. Kempinski, Chief Executive Officer
COO: Jo W. Stueve, Executive Vice President and Co-Chief Operating Officer
CFO: David Cauble, Executive Vice President and Chief Financial Officer
CMO: Charles Roberts, M.D., Executive Vice President and Executive Medical Director
CIO: David Chou, Vice President, Chief Information and Digital Officer
CNO: Cheri Hunt, R.N., Vice President Patient Care Services and Chief Nursing Officer
Web address: www.childrensmercy.org
Control: Other not–for–profit (including NFP Corporation) **Service**: Children's general medical and surgical

Staffed Beds: 314 **Admissions:** 12666 **Census:** 230 **Outpatient Visits:** 469304 **Births:** 172 **Total Expense ($000):** 1227015 **Payroll Expense ($000):** 570805 **Personnel:** 6264		

⊞ **KANSAS CITY VETERANS AFFAIRS MEDICAL CENTER**, 4801 East Linwood Boulevard, Zip 64128–2226; tel. 816/861–4700, (Nonreporting) **A**1 2 3 5 **S** Department of Veterans Affairs, Washington, DC
Primary Contact: Kathleen R. Fogarty, MS, Director
CFO: Bryan Bieri, Manager Finance
CMO: Ahmad Batrash, Chief of Staff
CIO: Eddie Johnson, Chief Information Technology Officer
CHR: Kathi Nippert, Acting Chief Human Resources Officer
Web address: www.kansascity.va.gov/
Control: Veterans Affairs, Government, federal **Service**: General medical and surgical

Staffed Beds: 157		

⊞ **KINDRED HOSPITAL NORTHLAND (262018)**, 500 Northwest 68th Street, Zip 64118–2455; tel. 816/420–6300, **A**1 10 **F**1 3 29 80 85 130 148 149 **S** Kindred Healthcare, Louisville, KY
Primary Contact: Laura Inge, MSN, R.N., Chief Executive Officer
CFO: Brett Stevenson, Controller
CMO: Sean R Muldoon, M.D., Senior Vice President and Chief Medical Officer-Kindred Healthcare, Hospital Division
Web address: www.khnorthland.com
Control: Corporation, Investor–owned (for–profit) **Service**: Acute long–term care hospital

Staffed Beds: 35 **Admissions:** 371 **Census:** 31 **Outpatient Visits:** 0 **Births:** 0 **Total Expense ($000):** 19125 **Payroll Expense ($000):** 7864 **Personnel:** 98		

NORTHLAND LTAC HOSPITAL See Kindred Hospital Northland

⊞ **RESEARCH MEDICAL CENTER (260027)**, 2316 East Meyer Boulevard, Zip 64132–1136; tel. 816/276–4000, (Includes RESEARCH PSYCHIATRIC CENTER, 2323 East 63rd Street, Kansas City, Missouri, Zip 64130–3462; tel. 816/444–8161; Shannon Griggs, Interim Chief Executive Officer) **A**1 2 3 5 10 **F**3 8 11 13 15 16 17 18 20 22 24 26 28 29 30 31 34 35 36 37 38 39 40 41 42 43 45 46 47 49 50 52 53 54 55 56 57 58 59 60 61 63 64 65 68 70 72 73 74 75 76 77 78 79 80 81 82 83 84 85 86 87 90 91 92 93 94 96 97 98 99 100 101 102 103 104 105 107 108 109 110 111 112 114 115 116 117 118 119 120 121 123 124 126 129 130 131 132 134 135 138 142 143 146 147 148 149 153 154 156 157 **S** HCA Healthcare, Nashville, TN
Primary Contact: Ashley McClellan, FACHE, Chief Executive Officer
COO: Eric Becker, Chief Operating Officer
CFO: Susan Shreeve, Chief Financial Officer
CMO: James Bower, M.D., Chief Medical Officer
CIO: Shawn Kegley, Director Information Services
CHR: Charlotte O'Neal, Vice President Human Resources
Web address: www.researchmedicalcenter.com
Control: Corporation, Investor–owned (for–profit) **Service**: General medical and surgical

Staffed Beds: 472 **Admissions:** 20148 **Census:** 323 **Outpatient Visits:** 165896 **Births:** 1165 **Total Expense ($000):** 508748 **Payroll Expense ($000):** 142132 **Personnel:** 2094		

MO

Many Facility Codes have changed. Please refer to the AHA Guide Code Chart. © 2019 AHA Guide

▣ **SAINT LUKE'S HOSPITAL OF KANSAS CITY (260138)**, 4401 Wornall Road, Zip 64111–3220; tel. 816/932–3800, (Includes SAINT LUKE'S HOSPITAL OF KANSAS CITY CRITTENTON CHILDREN'S CENTER, 10918 Elm Avenue, Kansas City, Missouri, Zip 64134–4108; tel. 816/765–6600; Jerrie Jacobs-Kenner, President) **A**1 2 3 5 8 10 **F**3 6 8 9 11 12 13 15 17 18 20 22 24 26 28 29 30 31 32 34 35 36 37 38 39 40 43 44 45 46 47 49 50 55 56 57 58 59 60 61 64 65 66 68 70 72 73 74 75 76 77 78 79 80 81 82 84 85 86 87 89 90 91 92 93 94 95 96 97 98 99 100 101 102 103 104 106 107 108 110 111 114 115 116 117 118 119 120 121 123 124 126 129 130 131 132 134 135 137 138 139 141 145 146 147 148 149 150 151 153 155 158 **S** Saint Luke's Health System, Kansas City, MO
Primary Contact: Jani L. Johnson, R.N., MSN, Chief Executive Officer
COO: Brad Simmons, Chief Operating Officer
CFO: Amy Nachtigal, Chief Financial Officer
CMO: Peter Holt, M.D., Director Medical Affairs
CIO: Deborah Gash, Chief Information Officer
CHR: Doris Rogers, Vice President Human Resources
CNO: Debra Wilson, Vice President and Chief Nursing Officer
Web address: www.saint-lukes.org
Control: Church operated, Nongovernment, not–for–profit **Service:** General medical and surgical

Staffed Beds: 485 **Admissions:** 22271 **Census:** 360 **Outpatient Visits:** 312832 **Births:** 2296 **Total Expense ($000):** 828525 **Payroll Expense ($000):** 209578 **Personnel:** 3382

▣ **ST. JOSEPH MEDICAL CENTER (260085)**, 1000 Carondelet Drive, Zip 64114–4673; tel. 816/942–4400, **A**1 2 10 **F**3 11 12 15 17 18 20 22 24 26 28 29 30 31 34 35 40 45 48 49 50 51 56 57 59 60 62 64 68 70 74 75 77 78 79 80 81 82 84 85 86 90 93 98 102 103 107 108 110 111 114 115 119 129 130 135 145 146 148 149 154 156 **S** Prime Healthcare, Ontario, CA
Primary Contact: Jodi Fincher, R.N., Administrator
CFO: Debra Cartwright, Chief Financial Officer
CMO: Tommy Ko, M.D., Chief Medical Officer
CIO: Cheryl Johnson, Regional Chief Information Officer
CHR: Donna Sumner, Director, Human Resources and Organizational Development
CNO: Greg Simpson, Chief Nursing Officer
Web address: www.stjosephkc.com/
Control: Individual, Investor–owned (for–profit) **Service:** General medical and surgical

Staffed Beds: 171 **Admissions:** 6622 **Census:** 80 **Outpatient Visits:** 84624 **Births:** 0 **Total Expense ($000):** 140529 **Payroll Expense ($000):** 43945 **Personnel:** 1040

▣ **TRUMAN MEDICAL CENTER-HOSPITAL HILL (260040)**, 2301 Holmes Street, Zip 64108–2640; tel. 816/404–1000, **A**1 2 3 5 8 10 **F**3 4 5 8 11 12 13 14 15 17 18 20 22 26 28 29 30 31 34 35 36 38 39 40 41 43 44 45 46 48 49 50 52 53 55 57 58 59 61 64 65 66 68 70 71 72 73 74 75 76 77 78 79 81 82 84 85 86 87 90 93 94 97 98 99 100 101 102 103 104 107 108 110 111 114 115 119 129 130 131 132 134 135 142 143 146 147 148 154 157 158 **S** Truman Medical Centers, Kansas City, MO
Primary Contact: Charlie Shields, President and Chief Executive Officer
CFO: Allen Johnson, Chief Financial Officer
CMO: Mark Steele, M.D., Chief Medical Officer
CIO: Mitzi Cardenas, Chief Administrative Officer
CHR: Ruth Pullins, Chief Human Resources Officer
CNO: Amy Peters, R.N., Chief Nursing Officer
Web address: www.trumed.org
Control: Other not–for–profit (including NFP Corporation) **Service:** General medical and surgical

Staffed Beds: 249 **Admissions:** 16817 **Census:** 201 **Outpatient Visits:** 499864 **Births:** 1825 **Total Expense ($000):** 386032 **Payroll Expense ($000):** 143675 **Personnel:** 2536

▣ **TRUMAN MEDICAL CENTER-LAKEWOOD (260102)**, 7900 Lee's Summit Road, Zip 64139–1236; tel. 816/404–7000, (Total facility includes 188 beds in nursing home–type unit) **A**1 3 5 10 **F**3 4 6 11 13 15 29 30 32 34 35 36 38 39 40 44 45 50 53 56 57 58 59 64 65 66 67 68 70 71 72 74 75 76 77 78 79 81 84 85 86 87 89 90 92 93 94 97 98 99 100 101 102 103 104 107 112 115 119 126 128 129 130 131 132 134 135 143 146 147 154 156 157 **S** Truman Medical Centers, Kansas City, MO
Primary Contact: Charlie Shields, Chief Executive Officer
COO: Lynette Wheeler, MSN, Chief Operating Officer
CFO: Allen Johnson, Chief Financial Officer
CMO: Mark Steele, M.D., Chief Medical Officer
CIO: Mitzi Cardenas, Chief Administrative Officer
CHR: Ruth Pullins, Chief Human Resources Officer
CNO: Amy Peters, R.N., Chief Nursing Officer
Web address: www.trumed.org
Control: Other not–for–profit (including NFP Corporation) **Service:** General medical and surgical

Staffed Beds: 298 **Admissions:** 5785 **Census:** 223 **Outpatient Visits:** 400568 **Births:** 1588 **Total Expense ($000):** 151857 **Payroll Expense ($000):** 61733 **Personnel:** 863

▢ **TWO RIVERS BEHAVIORAL HEALTH SYSTEM (264017)**, 5121 Raytown Road, Zip 64133–2141; tel. 816/382–6300, (Nonreporting) **A**1 10 **S** Universal Health Services, Inc., King of Prussia, PA
Primary Contact: Greg Shannon, Chief Executive Officer
CMO: Shahbaz Khan, M.D., Medical Director
CNO: Cindy Bearden, Chief Nursing Officer
Web address: www.tworivershospital.com
Control: Corporation, Investor–owned (for–profit) **Service:** Psychiatric

Staffed Beds: 105

VETERANS AFFAIRS MEDICAL CENTER See Kansas City Veterans Affairs Medical Center

KANSAS CITY—Platte County

▣ **SAINT LUKE'S NORTH HOSPITAL - BARRY ROAD (260062)**, 5830 NW Barry Road, Zip 64154–2778; tel. 816/891–6000, (Includes SAINT LUKE'S NORTH HOSPITAL-SMITHVILLE CAMPUS, 601 South 169 Highway, Smithville, Missouri, Zip 64089–9317; tel. 816/532–3700; Adele Ducharme, MSN, R.N., Chief Executive Officer) **A**1 2 10 **F**3 11 12 13 15 18 20 22 26 28 29 30 31 34 35 38 40 44 45 46 49 50 53 56 57 58 59 60 61 64 68 69 70 73 74 75 76 77 78 79 80 81 82 84 85 86 87 89 90 91 92 93 96 98 100 101 102 107 108 110 111 114 115 116 117 118 129 130 131 132 135 141 143 146 147 148 149 154 **S** Saint Luke's Health System, Kansas City, MO
Primary Contact: Adele Ducharme, MSN, R.N., Chief Executive Officer
CFO: Julie Murphy, Chief Financial Officer
CMO: Leonardo J Lozada, M.D., Chief Physician Executive
CIO: LaDonna Seger, Director Information Services
CHR: Donna Kunz, System Director Human Resources
CNO: Amy Brummer, R.N., MSN, Chief Nursing Officer
Web address: www.saint-lukes.org
Control: Church operated, Nongovernment, not–for–profit **Service:** General medical and surgical

Staffed Beds: 139 **Admissions:** 7696 **Census:** 86 **Outpatient Visits:** 94488 **Births:** 726 **Total Expense ($000):** 135921 **Payroll Expense ($000):** 46767 **Personnel:** 676

KANSAS CITY—Clay County

▢ **SIGNATURE PSYCHIATRIC HOSPITAL (264030)**, 2900 Clay Edwards Drive, Zip 64116–0235; tel. 816/691–5101, **A**1 **F**2 24 59 98 101 102 103 104 105 130 132 153
Primary Contact: Lisa St. Aubyn, Chief Executive Officer
CFO: Robert Jackson, Chief Financial Officer
CMO: Azfar Malik, M.D., Chief Medical Officer
CIO: Tariq Nazir, Interim Director Information Technology
CHR: Maria Griffith, Director Human Resources
Web address: www.sphkc.net
Control: Corporation, Investor–owned (for–profit) **Service:** Psychiatric

Staffed Beds: 72 **Admissions:** 1892 **Census:** 44 **Outpatient Visits:** 11096 **Births:** 0 **Total Expense ($000):** 15557 **Payroll Expense ($000):** 8434

KIRKSVILLE—Adair County

★ ○ **NORTHEAST REGIONAL MEDICAL CENTER (260022)**, 315 South Osteopathy Street, Zip 63501–6401, Mailing Address: P.O. Box C8502, Zip 63501–8599; tel. 660/785–1000, **A**3 5 10 11 12 13 **F**3 13 15 17 18 20 22 24 28 29 34 39 40 43 45 48 49 50 57 59 60 64 68 70 73 74 75 76 77 79 81 82 84 85 86 87 89 90 107 108 110 111 115 119 127 128 129 131 133 135 146 147 148 154 156 **S** Community Health Systems, Inc., Franklin, TN
Primary Contact: Ranee C. Brayton, FACHE, MSN, R.N., Chief Executive Officer
CFO: Carol Cross, CPA, Chief Financial Officer
CMO: Benjamin Schrant, M.D., Chief of Staff
CIO: Chad Tatro, Supervisor Information Systems
CHR: Jim Bergman, Director Human Resources
CNO: Peggy Parks, R.N., Chief Nursing Officer
Web address: www.nermc.com
Control: Corporation, Investor–owned (for–profit) **Service:** General medical and surgical

Staffed Beds: 50 **Admissions:** 2458 **Census:** 27 **Outpatient Visits:** 58504 **Births:** 550 **Total Expense ($000):** 47230 **Payroll Expense ($000):** 18276 **Personnel:** 366

MO

Hospital, Medicare Provider Number, Address, Telephone, Approval, Facility, and Physician Codes, Health Care System

★ American Hospital Association (AHA) membership ○ Healthcare Facilities Accreditation Program ⇑ Center for Improvement in Healthcare Quality Accreditation
▢ The Joint Commission accreditation ◇ DNV Healthcare Inc. accreditation △ Commission on Accreditation of Rehabilitation Facilities (CARF) accreditation

LAKE SAINT LOUIS—St. Charles County

⊞ **SSM HEALTH ST. JOSEPH HOSPITAL - LAKE SAINT LOUIS (260200)**, 100 Medical Plaza, Zip 63367–1366; tel. 636/625–5200, **A**1 2 10 **F**3 11 13 15 17 18 20 22 28 29 30 31 34 35 36 38 40 41 43 44 46 49 50 51 53 54 55 56 57 59 60 61 64 68 70 73 74 75 76 78 79 81 82 84 85 86 87 89 102 107 108 110 111 117 119 129 130 132 135 145 146 147 148 149 156 157 **S** SSM Health, Saint Louis, MO
Primary Contact: Lisle Wescott, President
COO: Lee Bernstein, Regional Executive Vice President of Hospital and Chief Operating Officer
CFO: Hal Holder, Regional Chief Financial Officer
CMO: Michael Handler, M.D., Vice President Medical Affairs and Chief Medical Officer
CIO: Sharon Gardner, Manager Information Systems
CHR: Renee Roach, System Vice President
Web address: www.ssmstjoseph.com
Control: Church operated, Nongovernment, not–for–profit **Service**: General medical and surgical

Staffed Beds: 215 **Admissions**: 9608 **Census**: 99 **Outpatient Visits**: 176200 **Births**: 939 **Total Expense ($000)**: 167279 **Payroll Expense ($000)**: 60548 **Personnel**: 818

LAMAR—Barton County

COX BARTON COUNTY MEMORIAL HOSPITAL (261325), 29 NW First Lane, Zip 64759–8105; tel. 417/681–5100, (Data for 273 days) **A**10 18 **F**3 11 15 18 28 30 34 35 40 44 45 50 57 59 64 68 74 75 77 79 81 84 85 86 87 89 90 92 93 97 107 108 110 111 114 119 127 128 129 130 132 133 135 146 148 149 156 **S** CoxHealth, Springfield, MO
Primary Contact: Christopher B. Wyatt, President
CIO: Brad Butler, Network Administrator
CNO: Marlys Buckner, Chief Nursing Officer
Web address: www.bcmh.net
Control: Other not–for–profit (including NFP Corporation) **Service**: General medical and surgical

Staffed Beds: 25 **Admissions**: 353 **Census**: 6 **Outpatient Visits**: 26760 **Births**: 0 **Total Expense ($000)**: 16753 **Payroll Expense ($000)**: 7602 **Personnel**: 169

LEBANON—Laclede County

⊞ **MERCY HOSPITAL LEBANON (260059)**, 100 Hospital Drive, Zip 65536–9210; tel. 417/533–6100, **A**1 10 20 **F**3 11 13 15 28 29 30 31 35 36 40 45 47 50 51 57 59 64 65 68 70 71 74 75 76 77 78 79 81 82 83 85 86 87 89 90 93 94 102 107 108 110 111 114 119 129 130 131 132 135 146 147 148 149 156 **S** Mercy, Chesterfield, MO
Primary Contact: Scott W. Childers, FACHE, Administrator
CFO: Douglas M Hoban, Vice President and Chief Financial Officer
CNO: Judy O'Connor-Snyder, Chief Nursing Officer
Web address: www.mercy.net/practice/mercy-hospital-lebanon
Control: Church operated, Nongovernment, not–for–profit **Service**: General medical and surgical

Staffed Beds: 58 **Admissions**: 2301 **Census**: 17 **Outpatient Visits**: 131848 **Births**: 334 **Total Expense ($000)**: 70787 **Payroll Expense ($000)**: 28641 **Personnel**: 451

LEE'S SUMMIT—Jackson County

⊞ **LEE'S SUMMIT MEDICAL CENTER (260190)**, 2100 SE Blue Parkway, Zip 64063–1007; tel. 816/282–5000, **A**1 3 10 **F**3 12 15 18 20 22 28 29 30 31 34 40 48 49 57 59 60 64 65 68 70 74 75 77 78 79 80 81 82 84 87 93 107 110 111 114 115 119 126 129 130 131 145 146 148 149 154 **S** HCA Healthcare, Nashville, TN
Primary Contact: John McDonald, Chief Executive Officer
COO: Patrick Kueny, Chief Operating Officer
CFO: John Heurtin, Chief Financial Officer
CIO: Andrew Beechy, Manager Information Technology Systems
CHR: Linda Duncan, Director Human Resources
CNO: Paige Baker, MSN, R.N., Chief Nursing Officer
Web address: www.leessummitmedicalcenter.com
Control: Corporation, Investor–owned (for–profit) **Service**: General medical and surgical

Staffed Beds: 80 **Admissions**: 4303 **Census**: 41 **Outpatient Visits**: 107952 **Births**: 0 **Total Expense ($000)**: 78754 **Payroll Expense ($000)**: 28484 **Personnel**: 319

⊞ **SAINT LUKE'S EAST HOSPITAL (260216)**, 100 NE Saint Luke's Boulevard, Zip 64086–6000; tel. 816/347–5000, **A**1 10 **F**3 12 13 15 18 20 22 26 28 29 30 31 34 35 38 40 44 45 46 47 49 50 51 56 57 58 59 60 61 64 65 70 72 73 74 75 76 77 78 79 80 81 82 84 85 86 87 89 90 91 92 93 94 96 100 102 103 107 108 110 111 114 115 117 118 119 120 121 123 126 129 130 131 132 135 141 145 146 147 148 149 154 **S** Saint Luke's Health System, Kansas City, MO
Primary Contact: Ron Baker, FACHE, Chief Executive Officer
CFO: Joseph P Stasi, Chief Financial Officer
CHR: John Clabaugh, Director Human Resources
CNO: Gloria Solis, R.N., MSN, Chief Nursing Officer
Web address: www.saintlukeskc.org
Control: Church operated, Nongovernment, not–for–profit **Service**: General medical and surgical

Staffed Beds: 203 **Admissions**: 14031 **Census**: 148 **Outpatient Visits**: 157680 **Births**: 1820 **Total Expense ($000)**: 247151 **Payroll Expense ($000)**: 73062 **Personnel**: 1037

LEXINGTON—Lafayette County

⊞ **LAFAYETTE REGIONAL HEALTH CENTER (261320)**, 1500 State Street, Zip 64067–1107; tel. 660/259–2203, **A**1 10 18 **F**11 15 29 31 40 68 70 75 78 79 81 85 93 107 110 111 114 116 119 127 129 130 133 147 149 156 **S** HCA Healthcare, Nashville, TN
Primary Contact: Darrel Box, Chief Executive Officer
COO: Daniel Astleford, Vice President Operations
CFO: Teri James, Chief Financial Officer
CIO: Keith Richcreek, Manager Technical Services
CHR: Stephen Davidson, Director Human Resources
CNO: Kim Leakey, R.N., Chief Nursing Officer
Web address: www.lafayetteregionalhealthcenter.com
Control: Corporation, Investor–owned (for–profit) **Service**: General medical and surgical

Staffed Beds: 25 **Admissions**: 811 **Census**: 7 **Outpatient Visits**: 66568 **Births**: 0 **Total Expense ($000)**: 29478 **Payroll Expense ($000)**: 9621 **Personnel**: 174

LIBERTY—Clay County

⊞ **LIBERTY HOSPITAL (260177)**, 2525 Glenn Hendren Dive, Zip 64068–9600, Mailing Address: P.O. Box 1002, Zip 64069–1002; tel. 816/781–7200, **A**1 2 10 **F**3 8 11 13 15 17 18 20 22 24 26 28 29 30 31 34 35 37 40 43 45 46 47 48 49 59 61 62 63 64 69 70 73 74 75 76 77 78 79 80 81 82 83 84 85 86 87 90 92 93 96 97 107 108 110 111 114 115 117 118 119 126 129 130 131 132 144 146 147 148 149 154 156
Primary Contact: David Feess, CPA, President and Chief Executive Officer
CFO: Dan Williams, Vice President Finance and Support
CMO: Robert Haas, M.D., Chief Medical Officer
CIO: Paul Klehn, Chief Information Technology Officer
CHR: Nancy E Cattell, Vice President Human Resources
CNO: Shirley Heintz, R.N., MS, Vice President Patient Care
Web address: www.Libertyhospital.org
Control: Hospital district or authority, Government, nonfederal **Service**: General medical and surgical

Staffed Beds: 179 **Admissions**: 7585 **Census**: 85 **Outpatient Visits**: 297704 **Births**: 1150 **Total Expense ($000)**: 213593 **Payroll Expense ($000)**: 99099 **Personnel**: 1392

LOUISIANA—Pike County

⊞ **PIKE COUNTY MEMORIAL HOSPITAL (261333)**, 2305 Georgia Street, Zip 63353–2559; tel. 573/754–5531, **A**1 10 18 **F**3 7 11 15 18 28 29 30 34 35 40 45 50 53 54 56 57 59 64 65 68 74 75 77 79 81 85 86 87 89 90 93 97 100 107 110 115 127 130 131 132 133 147 148 149 156
Primary Contact: Tylie Mills, R.N., Chief Executive Officer
CFO: Ann Tran, Chief Financial Officer
CIO: Jeremy Gruen, Director Information Systems
CHR: Connie Bair, Human Resources Assistant
CNO: Judith Prater, Director of Nursing
Web address: www.pcmh-mo.org
Control: County, Government, nonfederal **Service**: General medical and surgical

Staffed Beds: 25 **Admissions**: 346 **Census**: 4 **Outpatient Visits**: 44512 **Births**: 0 **Total Expense ($000)**: 19272 **Payroll Expense ($000)**: 8894 **Personnel**: 155

MO

Many Facility Codes have changed. Please refer to the AHA Guide Code Chart. © 2019 AHA Guide

MACON—Macon County

SAMARITAN HOSPITAL (261313), 1205 North Missouri Street, Zip 63552–2095; tel. 660/385–8700, **A**10 18 **F**3 7 8 9 11 29 34 35 40 45 46 53 56 57 59 63 64 65 68 74 75 79 81 82 84 85 86 87 89 90 93 94 107 111 115 119 127 128 129 130 133 146 148 157
Primary Contact: Bernard A. Orman Jr, FACHE, Chief Executive Officer
CFO: Susan Spencer, Chief Financial Officer
CHR: Suzanne Britt, Director Human Resources
Web address: www.samaritanhospital.net
Control: County, Government, nonfederal **Service**: General medical and surgical

Staffed Beds: 25 **Admissions**: 732 **Census**: 11 **Outpatient Visits**: 59488
Births: 4 **Total Expense ($000)**: 25535 **Payroll Expense ($000)**: 9363
Personnel: 190

MARSHALL—Saline County

★ **FITZGIBBON HOSPITAL (260142)**, 2305 South 65 Highway, Zip 65340–0250, Mailing Address: P.O. Box 250, Zip 65340–0250; tel. 660/886–7431, **A**10 20 **F**3 11 13 15 30 31 33 34 35 40 45 56 57 59 62 63 64 65 68 70 74 75 76 77 78 79 81 85 87 89 90 93 98 103 104 107 108 110 111 115 118 120 121 127 128 129 130 131 132 133 146 147 148
Primary Contact: Darin L. Haug, D.O., President and Chief Executive Officer
COO: Angela P. Littrell, CPA, Chief Financial Officer and Chief Operating Officer
CFO: Angela P. Littrell, CPA, Chief Financial Officer and Chief Operating Officer
CMO: Darin L. Haug, D.O., President & Chief Executive Officer
CIO: Tom Jones, Chief Information Officer
CHR: Jessica Henderson, Manager Human Resources
CNO: Angela Igo, MSN, R.N., Chief Nursing Officer
Web address: www.fitzgibbon.org
Control: Other not–for–profit (including NFP Corporation) **Service**: General medical and surgical

Staffed Beds: 52 **Admissions**: 2009 **Census**: 17 **Outpatient Visits**: 103208
Births: 223 **Total Expense ($000)**: 53771 **Payroll Expense ($000)**: 23968
Personnel: 478

MARYLAND HEIGHTS—St. Louis County

★ **RANKEN JORDAN PEDIATRIC BRIDGE HOSPITAL (263303)**, 11365 Dorsett Road, Zip 63043–3411; tel. 314/872–6400, **A**3 5 10 **F**1 3 12 29 30 32 34 35 44 50 53 80 86 87 89 90 91 92 93 94 96 99 130 132 146 148 149
Primary Contact: Brett Moorehouse, FACHE, Chief Executive Officer
CFO: Kenneth Marx, Chief Financial Officer
CMO: Nicholas Holekamp, M.D., Chief Medical Officer
CHR: Erin Bachelier, Human Resource Administrator
Web address: www.rankenjordan.org
Control: Other not–for–profit (including NFP Corporation) **Service**: Children's rehabilitation

Staffed Beds: 60 **Admissions**: 278 **Census**: 31 **Outpatient Visits**: 6112
Births: 0 **Total Expense ($000)**: 32394 **Payroll Expense ($000)**: 17070
Personnel: 340

MARYVILLE—Nodaway County

⊞ **MOSAIC MEDICAL CENTER - MARYVILLE (260050)**, 2016 South Main Street, Zip 64468–2655; tel. 660/562–2600, **A**1 10 20 **F**3 11 13 15 18 28 29 30 31 34 35 38 40 45 57 59 64 65 68 70 75 76 77 78 79 81 82 84 85 86 89 90 93 96 97 98 99 102 103 104 107 110 111 115 116 117 118 119 127 128 130 131 132 133 135 146 149 154 **S** Mosaic Life Care, Saint Joseph, MO
Primary Contact: Nate Blackford, President
COO: Frank Grispino, Vice President Operations
CFO: Jocelyn Skidmore, Director Finance
CMO: Shirley Harris, M.D., President Medical Staff
CIO: Dave Lewis, Director Information Services
CHR: Krista Barcus, Human Resources Leader
CNO: Debbie Hoffman, Vice President Patient Services
Web address: www.mymosaiclifecare.org
Control: Church operated, Nongovernment, not–for–profit **Service**: General medical and surgical

Staffed Beds: 50 **Admissions**: 1604 **Census**: 18 **Outpatient Visits**: 129024
Births: 256 **Total Expense ($000)**: 65580 **Payroll Expense ($000)**: 27318
Personnel: 367

MEMPHIS—Scotland County

★ **SCOTLAND COUNTY HOSPITAL (261310)**, 450 Sigler Avenue, Zip 63555–1726, Mailing Address: 450 E Sigler Avenue, Zip 63555–1726; tel. 660/465–8511, (Nonreporting) **A**10 18
Primary Contact: Randy Tobler, M.D., Chief Executive Officer
CFO: Sheryl Templeton, Chief Financial Officer
CMO: Randy Tobler, M.D., Chief Medical Officer
CIO: Ken McMinn, Director Information Technology
CHR: Missy Smith, Coordinator Human Resources
CNO: Carla Cook, Director of Nursing
Web address: www.scotlandcountyhospital.com
Control: Hospital district or authority, Government, nonfederal **Service**: General medical and surgical

Staffed Beds: 25

SCOTLAND COUNTY MEMORIAL HOSPITAL See Scotland County Hospital

MEXICO—Audrain County

⊞ **SSM HEALTH ST. MARY'S HOSPITAL - AUDRAIN (260064)**, 620 East Monroe Street, Zip 65265–2919; tel. 573/582–5000, **A**1 2 10 **F**3 11 13 15 18 20 22 26 28 29 30 31 34 40 45 54 57 59 64 65 70 73 75 76 77 78 79 81 82 85 86 87 89 90 93 98 103 107 108 110 111 115 118 119 121 123 127 129 130 131 132 144 146 147 149 **S** SSM Health, Saint Louis, MO
Primary Contact: Donna K. Jacobs, FACHE, President
CFO: James Stratton, Regional Vice President Finance
CMO: Diane Jacobi, Chief of Staff
CIO: Dawn Evans, Manager Information Technology
CHR: Christy Smiley, Leader Human Resources
CNO: Kari Wilson, R.N., Chief Nursing Officer
Web address: www.ssmhealthmidmo.com
Control: Church operated, Nongovernment, not–for–profit **Service**: General medical and surgical

Staffed Beds: 60 **Admissions**: 1781 **Census**: 24 **Outpatient Visits**: 137336
Births: 183 **Total Expense ($000)**: 63564 **Payroll Expense ($000)**: 22241
Personnel: 332

MILAN—Sullivan County

★ **SULLIVAN COUNTY MEMORIAL HOSPITAL (261306)**, 630 West Third Street, Zip 63556–1076; tel. 660/265–4212, **A**10 18 **F**28 29 32 33 34 40 57 59 65 67 68 77 81 93 97 107 111 114 119 127 128 130 133 147 148 149 154
Primary Contact: Jerry Dover, Chief Executive Officer
COO: Amy J Michael, Chief Operating Officer
CMO: Dale Essmyer, M.D., Chief of Staff
CIO: Vern Johnson, Director Information Technology
CHR: Rae A. Ashby, Director Human Resources
CNO: Tina Sears, Director Patient Care Services
Web address: www.scmhospital.org
Control: County, Government, nonfederal **Service**: General medical and surgical

Staffed Beds: 25 **Admissions**: 208 **Census**: 9 **Outpatient Visits**: 25176
Births: 0 **Total Expense ($000)**: 9182 **Payroll Expense ($000)**: 3899
Personnel: 79

MOBERLY—Randolph County

⊞ **MOBERLY REGIONAL MEDICAL CENTER (260074)**, 1515 Union Avenue, Zip 65270–9449; tel. 660/263–8400, **A**1 10 20 **F**3 4 18 20 22 26 28 29 30 34 35 38 40 44 45 50 53 56 57 59 64 70 74 75 77 79 81 85 86 87 89 90 93 97 98 100 101 103 107 111 115 118 119 126 127 128 130 131 133 135 141 146 148 149 154 **S** Community Health Systems, Inc., Franklin, TN
Primary Contact: Ranee C. Brayton, FACHE, MSN, R.N., Chief Executive Officer
COO: Tracey Matheis, Chief Operating Officer
CFO: Tracey Matheis, Chief Financial Officer
CMO: Heather Gessling, M.D., Chief Medical Officer
CHR: Michael Turner, Director Human Resources
CNO: Patsy Lewellen, Interim Chief Nursing Officer
Web address: www.moberlyhospital.com
Control: Corporation, Investor–owned (for–profit) **Service**: General medical and surgical

Staffed Beds: 99 **Admissions**: 1194 **Census**: 17 **Outpatient Visits**: 50072
Births: 0 **Total Expense ($000)**: 44026 **Payroll Expense ($000)**: 12886
Personnel: 276

MO

MONETT—Barry County

⋔ **COX MONETT HOSPITAL (261329)**, 801 North Lincoln Avenue, Zip 65708–1641; tel. 417/235–3144, **A**10 18 21 **F**3 11 13 15 18 28 29 30 32 34 35 40 45 50 56 57 59 64 76 77 81 85 89 90 93 107 111 114 119 127 128 129 130 131 133 135 144 146 147 154 **S** CoxHealth, Springfield, MO
Primary Contact: Darren Bass, President
CFO: Josh Powell, Facility Controller
CMO: Frank Romero, M.D., Vice President Medical Affairs and Chief Medical Officer
CHR: Debra Isenmann, Human Resources Generalist
CNO: Bev Eli, Chief Nursing Officer
Web address: www.coxhealth.com
Control: Other not–for–profit (including NFP Corporation) **Service**: General medical and surgical

Staffed Beds: 25 **Admissions**: 901 **Census**: 7 **Outpatient Visits**: 104368 **Births**: 292 **Total Expense ($000)**: 40821 **Payroll Expense ($000)**: 19765 **Personnel**: 314

MOUNTAIN VIEW—Howell County

⊠ **MERCY ST. FRANCIS HOSPITAL (261335)**, 100 West Highway 60, Zip 65548–7125; tel. 417/934–7000, **A**1 10 18 **F**3 11 15 28 29 30 34 45 50 57 59 64 65 75 77 81 85 89 93 107 110 111 114 119 129 131 132 133 148 154 **S** Mercy, Chesterfield, MO
Primary Contact: Cynthia Weatherford, R.N., Administrator and Director of Nursing
CFO: Sherry Clouse Day, CPA, Chief Financial Officer
CMO: Barry Spoon, M.D., Chief of Staff
CHR: Tracy Smith, Director Human Resources
Web address: www.stjohns.com/aboutus/stfrancis.aspx
Control: Church operated, Nongovernment, not–for–profit **Service**: General medical and surgical

Staffed Beds: 20 **Admissions**: 190 **Census**: 2 **Outpatient Visits**: 24040 **Births**: 0 **Total Expense ($000)**: 12737 **Payroll Expense ($000)**: 6544 **Personnel**: 89

NEOSHO—Newton County

★ **FREEMAN NEOSHO HOSPITAL (261331)**, 113 West Hickory Street, Zip 64850–1705; tel. 417/455–4352, **A**10 18 **F**3 11 15 28 30 34 35 40 44 45 47 50 56 57 59 64 68 70 75 77 79 81 84 85 86 87 90 93 97 107 110 111 114 119 127 130 131 132 133 146 147 148 **S** Freeman Health System, Joplin, MO
Primary Contact: Renee Denton, Chief Operating Officer
CFO: Steve W Graddy, Chief Financial Officer
CMO: Rodney McFarland, M.D., Medical Director
CIO: Sue Annesser, Director Information Systems
CHR: Mary Frerer, Chief Human Resources Officer
Web address: www.freemanhealth.com
Control: Other not–for–profit (including NFP Corporation) **Service**: General medical and surgical

Staffed Beds: 25 **Admissions**: 862 **Census**: 9 **Outpatient Visits**: 74096 **Births**: 1 **Total Expense ($000)**: 25791 **Payroll Expense ($000)**: 11766 **Personnel**: 187

NEVADA—Vernon County

☐ **HEARTLAND BEHAVIORAL HEALTH SERVICES**, 1500 West Ashland Street, Zip 64772–1710; tel. 417/667–2666, **A**1 3 **F**98 99 101 **S** Universal Health Services, Inc., King of Prussia, PA
Primary Contact: Alyson Wysong-Harder, Chief Executive Officer
CFO: Bryan Bishop, Chief Financial Officer
CMO: Ahmad Tarar, M.D., Medical Director
CHR: Carri Compton, Administrative Officer
CNO: Nathan Taylor, Director of Nursing
Web address: www.heartlandbehavioral.com
Control: Corporation, Investor–owned (for–profit) **Service**: Children's hospital psychiatric

Staffed Beds: 69 **Admissions**: 2486 **Census**: 47 **Outpatient Visits**: 0 **Births**: 0 **Total Expense ($000)**: 15751 **Payroll Expense ($000)**: 8739 **Personnel**: 175

★ **NEVADA REGIONAL MEDICAL CENTER (260061)**, 800 South Ash Street, Zip 64772–3223; tel. 417/667–3355, **A**10 22 **F**3 11 13 14 15 18 26 27 28 29 30 31 32 34 35 39 40 45 50 54 57 59 64 65 66 70 74 75 76 77 78 79 81 82 84 85 86 87 89 90 91 93 94 96 98 101 102 103 104 107 111 115 119 127 129 130 131 132 133 135 143 144 146 147 148 **S** Freeman Health System, Joplin, MO
Primary Contact: Steve Branstetter, Chief Executive Officer
CMO: Warren Lovinger, M.D., Chief Medical Officer
CIO: Marci Hardin, Manager Information Technology
CHR: Heather Brockmeyer, Human Resource Administrative Officer
CNO: Cory Vokoun, Chief Nursing Officer
Web address: www.nrmchealth.com
Control: City, Government, nonfederal **Service**: General medical and surgical

Staffed Beds: 71 **Admissions**: 2397 **Census**: 28 **Outpatient Visits**: 60416 **Total Expense ($000)**: 41422 **Payroll Expense ($000)**: 16015 **Personnel**: 268

NORTH KANSAS CITY—Clay County

⊠ **NORTH KANSAS CITY HOSPITAL (260096)**, 2800 Clay Edwards Drive, Zip 64116–3220; tel. 816/691–2000, **A**1 2 3 5 10 **F**3 11 12 13 15 17 18 20 22 24 26 28 29 30 31 34 35 37 43 44 45 46 47 48 49 50 51 53 54 57 58 59 60 62 64 70 72 74 75 76 77 78 79 80 81 82 83 84 85 86 87 89 90 93 96 100 107 108 110 111 114 115 116 117 118 119 120 121 123 124 126 129 130 132 135 146 147 148 149
Primary Contact: Peggy Schmitt, President and Chief Executive Officer
COO: Jody Abbott, Senior Vice President and Chief Operating Officer
CFO: Jim McNey, Senior Vice President Finance and Chief Financial Officer
CMO: Gary L Carter, M.D., Vice President and Chief Medical Officer
CIO: Doug Abel, Chief Information Officer
CHR: Dawn Bryant, Vice President Human Resources
CNO: Sarah G Oakley, Vice President Nursing
Web address: www.nkch.org
Control: City, Government, nonfederal **Service**: General medical and surgical

Staffed Beds: 411 **Admissions**: 21475 **Census**: 277 **Outpatient Visits**: 305304 **Births**: 1902 **Total Expense ($000)**: 504196 **Payroll Expense ($000)**: 183244 **Personnel**: 2779

O'FALLON—St. Charles County

⊠ **PROGRESS WEST HOSPITAL (260219)**, Two Progress Point Parkway, Zip 63368–2208; tel. 636/344–1000, **A**1 5 10 **F**3 13 15 18 20 22 26 29 30 34 35 40 41 45 49 51 57 59 60 70 76 77 79 81 85 86 87 89 90 107 108 110 111 115 118 119 130 135 146 148 149 154 **S** BJC HealthCare, Saint Louis, MO
Primary Contact: Chris Watts, President
CFO: Glen Schwaegel, Chief Financial Officer
CMO: Dane Glueck, M.D., Chief of Staff
CHR: Michael J Miller, Director Human Resources
Web address: www.progresswest.org
Control: Other not–for–profit (including NFP Corporation) **Service**: General medical and surgical

Staffed Beds: 74 **Admissions**: 3318 **Census**: 30 **Outpatient Visits**: 61352 **Births**: 815 **Total Expense ($000)**: 80226 **Payroll Expense ($000)**: 29077 **Personnel**: 348

OSAGE BEACH—Camden County

⊠ **LAKE REGIONAL HEALTH SYSTEM (260186)**, 54 Hospital Drive, Zip 65065–3050; tel. 573/348–8000, (Total facility includes 16 beds in nursing home–type unit) **A**1 2 10 **F**3 11 12 13 15 17 18 20 22 24 28 29 30 34 39 40 43 44 45 46 48 49 50 51 53 57 59 60 62 63 64 65 68 70 73 74 75 76 77 78 79 81 82 84 85 86 87 89 93 96 107 108 111 114 115 118 119 120 121 122 123 124 126 127 128 129 130 131 132 135 144 145 146 148 149 150
Primary Contact: Dane W. Henry, Chief Executive Officer
COO: Kevin G McRoberts, FACHE, Senior Vice President of Operations
CFO: David Halsell, Senior Vice President and Chief Financial Officer
CMO: Patrick O'Neil, Senior Vice President Medical Affairs
CIO: Scott Poest, Chief Information Officer
CHR: Tom Williams, Vice President Employee and Community Development
CNO: Melissa Hunter, Chief Nursing Officer
Web address: www.lakeregional.com
Control: Other not–for–profit (including NFP Corporation) **Service**: General medical and surgical

Staffed Beds: 116 **Admissions**: 5353 **Census**: 54 **Outpatient Visits**: 573704 **Births**: 624 **Total Expense ($000)**: 189768 **Payroll Expense ($000)**: 78146 **Personnel**: 1249

☐ **OSAGE BEACH CENTER FOR COGNITIVE DISORDERS (264031)**, 840 Passover Road, Zip 65065; tel. 573/302–0319, **A**1 10 **F**50 56 68 74 75 86 87 98 101 103 130 132 135 149 154
Primary Contact: Tom Flanagan, Chief Executive Officer
CNO: Lorri Steffen, Director of Nursing
Web address: www.osagebeachccd.com
Control: Partnership, Investor–owned (for–profit) **Service**: Psychiatric

Staffed Beds: 14 **Admissions**: 637 **Census**: 10 **Outpatient Visits**: 0 **Births**: 0 **Total Expense ($000)**: 4483 **Payroll Expense ($000)**: 2264 **Personnel**: 30

MO

Many Facility Codes have changed. Please refer to the AHA Guide Code Chart. © 2019 AHA Guide

PERRYVILLE—Perry County

⊞ ○ **PERRY COUNTY MEMORIAL HOSPITAL (261311)**, 434 North West Street, Zip 63775–1398; tel. 573/547–2536, **A**1 10 11 18 **F**3 7 8 11 13 15 28 29 30 31 34 35 40 44 45 49 53 54 56 57 59 62 64 66 68 75 76 77 78 79 81 85 87 89 90 92 93 97 100 101 102 103 104 107 111 115 117 119 129 130 131 132 133 135 143 144 145 146 147 148 154 156
Primary Contact: Patrick E. Carron, FACHE, President and Chief Executive Officer
CFO: Randall Wolf, Vice President Finance
CMO: Michael Steele, M.D., Chief of Staff
CIO: Ron Heuring, Director Information Systems
CHR: Christopher Wibbenmeyer, Director Human Resources
Web address: www.pchmo.org
Control: Other not–for–profit (including NFP Corporation) **Service:** General medical and surgical

Staffed Beds: 25 **Admissions:** 1612 **Census:** 17 **Outpatient Visits:** 53256 **Births:** 122 **Total Expense ($000):** 45730 **Payroll Expense ($000):** 18025 **Personnel:** 358

PILOT KNOB—Iron County

IRON COUNTY MEDICAL CENTER (261336), 301 North Highway 21, Zip 63663–0548, Mailing Address: P.O. Box 548, Zip 63663–0548; tel. 573/546–1260, **A**10 18 **F**3 11 15 18 29 34 35 38 40 41 44 45 50 57 59 64 66 79 81 82 89 90 93 96 97 102 107 111 114 119 127 128 130 133 135 147 154
Primary Contact: Joshua Gilmore, Chief Executive Officer
CNO: Cindy Sadler, Chief Nursing Officer
Web address: www.icmedcenter.org/
Control: Hospital district or authority, Government, nonfederal **Service:** General medical and surgical

Staffed Beds: 15 **Admissions:** 321 **Census:** 4 **Outpatient Visits:** 19696 **Births:** 0 **Personnel:** 129

POPLAR BLUFF—Butler County

⊞ **JOHN J. PERSHING VETERANS AFFAIRS MEDICAL CENTER**, 1500 North Westwood Boulevard, Zip 63901–3318; tel. 573/686–4151, (Nonreporting) **A**1 **S** Department of Veterans Affairs, Washington, DC
Primary Contact: Patricia Hall, MSN, Ph.D., R.N., Director
COO: Seth Barlage, Associate Medical Center Director
CFO: Kristy Williams, Manager Finance
CMO: Vijayachandran Nair, M.D., Chief of Staff
CIO: Michael Gustin, Information Technology
CHR: Genise Denton, Manager Human Resources
CNO: Chandra Miller, Director of Nursing
Web address: www.poplarbluff.va.gov
Control: Veterans Affairs, Government, federal **Service:** General medical and surgical

Staffed Beds: 69

⊞ **POPLAR BLUFF REGIONAL MEDICAL CENTER (260119)**, 3100 Oak Grove Road, Zip 63901, Mailing Address: P.O. Box 88, Zip 63902–0088; tel. 573/776–2000, (Includes POPLAR BLUFF REGIONAL MEDICAL CENTER-SOUTH CAMPUS, 621 Pine Boulevard, Poplar Bluff, Missouri, Zip 63901; tel. 573/785–7721) **A**1 2 10 **F**3 11 13 15 17 18 20 22 24 29 30 31 34 35 45 46 49 50 51 53 54 56 57 59 60 64 65 68 70 74 75 76 77 78 79 80 81 85 87 89 90 98 102 107 108 111 114 117 118 119 120 121 126 127 129 130 131 132 146 148 154 **S** Community Health Systems, Inc., Franklin, TN
Primary Contact: Bryan Bateman, Chief Executive Officer
COO: Christian Jones, Chief Operating Officer
CFO: Steve Dorris, Chief Financial Officer
CMO: Steve Pu, D.O., Chief Medical Officer
CIO: Gary Dollins, Director Management Information Systems
CHR: Denise Rushin, Director Human Resources
Web address: www.poplarbluffregional.com
Control: Individual, Investor–owned (for–profit) **Service:** General medical and surgical

Staffed Beds: 255 **Admissions:** 11157 **Census:** 134 **Outpatient Visits:** 81168 **Births:** 1450 **Total Expense ($000):** 168320 **Payroll Expense ($000):** 44100 **Personnel:** 992

POTOSI—Washington County

WASHINGTON COUNTY MEMORIAL HOSPITAL (261308), 300 Health Way, Zip 63664–1420; tel. 573/438–5451, **A**10 18 **F**3 15 28 29 30 33 34 35 40 45 47 51 57 59 64 65 68 81 82 85 87 90 93 97 98 104 107 108 110 111 115 119 127 129 130 133 135 143 144 145 146 154
Primary Contact: Michele C. Meyer, R.N., Chief Executive Officer
CFO: Yvonne Fourez, Chief Financial Officer
CMO: Jonathan Borchers, M.D., Chief Medical Officer
CIO: Jim Smith, Director Information Systems
CHR: Christy Aubuchon, Director Personnel
CNO: Beverly Williams, R.N., Chief Nursing Officer
Web address: www.wcmhosp.org
Control: County, Government, nonfederal **Service:** General medical and surgical

Staffed Beds: 25 **Admissions:** 616 **Census:** 9 **Outpatient Visits:** 61592 **Births:** 0 **Total Expense ($000):** 23012 **Payroll Expense ($000):** 9826 **Personnel:** 189

RICHMOND—Ray County

★ **RAY COUNTY MEMORIAL HOSPITAL (261327)**, 904 Wollard Boulevard, Zip 64085–2229; tel. 816/470–5432, **A**10 18 **F**3 11 15 28 29 30 31 45 56 57 62 64 75 78 79 81 82 85 87 93 103 107 108 110 111 115 119 130 133 146 Primary Contact: Earl Nielsen. Sheehy, FACHE, Chief Executive Officer
CFO: Donald Harr, Controller
CHR: Donna Strain, Director Human Resources
Web address: www.raycountyhospital.com
Control: County, Government, nonfederal **Service:** General medical and surgical

Staffed Beds: 25 **Admissions:** 609 **Census:** 8 **Outpatient Visits:** 15136 **Births:** 0 **Total Expense ($000):** 26176 **Payroll Expense ($000):** 11154 **Personnel:** 214

RICHMOND HEIGHTS—St. Louis County

⊞ △ **SSM SELECT REHABILITATION HOSPITAL (263031)**, 1027 Bellevue Avenue, 3rd Floor, Zip 63117–1851, Mailing Address: 1027 Bellevue Avenue, Zip 63117–1851; tel. 314/768–5300, (Includes SSM HEALTH REHABILITATION HOSPITAL - LAKE SAINT LOUIS, 100 Medical Plaza, Fifth Floor, Lake Saint Louis, Missouri, Zip 63367–1366; tel. 636/755–6500; John Grubbs, Chief Operating Officer; SSM SELECT REHABILITATION HOSPITAL, 12380 De Paul Drive, Bridgeton, Missouri, Zip 63044–2511; tel. 314/447–9700; Robert Pritts, Chief Executive Officer) **A**1 7 10 **F**3 29 44 64 74 75 77 78 79 85 86 87 90 91 93 96 130 131 132 143 148 149 156 **S** Select Medical Corporation, Mechanicsburg, PA
Primary Contact: Patti Finnegan, Chief Operating Officer
COO: Patti Finnegan, Chief Operating Officer
Web address: www.ssm-select.com
Control: Partnership, Investor–owned (for–profit) **Service:** Rehabilitation

Staffed Beds: 125 **Admissions:** 2559 **Census:** 95 **Outpatient Visits:** 490679 **Births:** 0 **Personnel:** 867

⊞ △ **SSM SELECT REHABILITATION HOSPITAL (263031)**, 1027 Bellevue Avenue, 3rd Floor, Zip 63117–1851, Mailing Address: 1027 Bellevue Avenue, Zip 63117–1851; tel. 314/768–5300, (Includes SSM HEALTH REHABILITATION HOSPITAL - LAKE SAINT LOUIS, 100 Medical Plaza, Fifth Floor, Lake Saint Louis, Missouri, Zip 63367–1366; tel. 636/755–6500; John Grubbs, Chief Operating Officer; SSM SELECT REHABILITATION HOSPITAL, 12380 De Paul Drive, Bridgeton, Missouri, Zip 63044–2511; tel. 314/447–9700; Robert Pritts, Chief Executive Officer) **A**1 7 10 **F**3 29 44 64 74 75 77 78 79 85 86 87 90 91 93 96 130 131 132 143 148 149 156 **S** Select Medical Corporation, Mechanicsburg, PA
Primary Contact: Patti Finnegan, Chief Operating Officer
COO: Patti Finnegan, Chief Operating Officer
Web address: www.ssm-select.com
Control: Partnership, Investor–owned (for–profit) **Service:** Rehabilitation

Staffed Beds: 125 **Admissions:** 2556 **Census:** 95 **Outpatient Visits:** 504152 **Births:** 0 **Total Expense ($000):** 115355 **Payroll Expense ($000):** 64480 **Personnel:** 998

Hospital, Medicare Provider Number, Address, Telephone, Approval, Facility, and Physician Codes, Health Care System

★ American Hospital Association (AHA) membership ○ Healthcare Facilities Accreditation Program ⇑ Center for Improvement in Healthcare Quality Accreditation
□ The Joint Commission accreditation ◇ DNV Healthcare Inc. accreditation △ Commission on Accreditation of Rehabilitation Facilities (CARF) accreditation

ROLLA—Phelps County

⊠ △ **PHELPS HEALTH (260017)**, 1000 West Tenth Street, Zip 65401–2905; tel. 573/458–8899, (Total facility includes 18 beds in nursing home–type unit) **A**1 2 7 10 **F**3 7 8 11 13 15 18 20 22 26 28 29 30 31 34 35 39 40 45 47 49 50 51 54 56 57 59 60 62 63 64 68 70 73 74 75 76 77 78 79 81 82 84 85 86 87 89 90 93 94 96 98 100 102 107 108 110 111 114 115 117 118 119 120 121 123 126 127 128 129 130 132 135 143 146 147 148 149 155
Primary Contact: Edward Clayton, Chief Executive Officer
COO: Jason Shenefield, Senior Vice President and Chief Operating Officer
CFO: Jana Cook, Vice President and Chief Financial Officer
CMO: Donald James, D.O., Senior Vice President and Chief Medical Officer
CIO: Jeff McKune, Chief Health Informatics Officer
CHR: Frank A. Lazzaro III Chief Human Resources Officer
CNO: Keri S. Brookshire-Heavin, Senior Vice President and Chief Nursing Officer
Web address: www.pcrmc.com
Control: County, Government, nonfederal **Service**: General medical and surgical

Staffed Beds: 176 **Admissions**: 6502 **Census**: 87 **Outpatient Visits**: 542952 **Births**: 803 **Total Expense ($000)**: 254346 **Payroll Expense ($000)**: 111239 **Personnel**: 1362

SAINT CHARLES—St. Charles County

⊠ **CENTERPOINTE HOSPITAL (264012)**, 4801 Weldon Spring Parkway, Zip 63304–9101; tel. 636/441–7300, **A**1 10 **F**4 5 34 35 38 40 44 54 80 87 98 99 100 101 102 103 104 105 106 143 152 153
Primary Contact: Scott Williams, Chief Executive Officer
CFO: Tom Croffut, Chief Financial Officer
CMO: Azfar Malik, M.D., Chief Medical Officer
CIO: Jennifer Bourn, Director, Health Information Services and Medical Staff Services
CHR: Kelli White, Director, Human Resources
Web address: www.centerpointehospital.com
Control: Corporation, Investor–owned (for–profit) **Service**: Psychiatric

Staffed Beds: 150 **Admissions**: 4572 **Census**: 110 **Outpatient Visits**: 0 **Births**: 0 **Total Expense ($000)**: 38361 **Payroll Expense ($000)**: 20334 **Personnel**: 328

SAINT CHARLES—Saint Charles County

⊠ **SELECT SPECIALTY HOSPITAL-ST. LOUIS (262013)**, 300 First Capitol Drive, Unit 1, Zip 63301–2844; tel. 636/947–5010, (Includes SELECT SPECIALTY HOSPITAL - TOWN AND COUNTRY, 3015 North Ballas Road, Fifth Floor, St. Louis, Missouri, Zip 63131–2329; tel. 314/996–6500; Marie T Droege, Chief Executive Officer) **A**1 10 **F**1 29 74 75 148 **S** Select Medical Corporation, Mechanicsburg, PA
Primary Contact: Phillip Readinger, Chief Executive Officer
Web address: www.selectspecialtyhospitals.com/company/locations/stlouis.aspx
Control: Corporation, Investor–owned (for–profit) **Service**: Acute long–term care hospital

Staffed Beds: 33 **Admissions**: 294 **Census**: 24 **Outpatient Visits**: 0 **Births**: 0 **Total Expense ($000)**: 15168 **Payroll Expense ($000)**: 6967 **Personnel**: 83

SAINT CHARLES—St. Charles County

⊠ **SSM HEALTH ST. JOSEPH - ST. CHARLES (260005)**, 300 First Capitol Drive, Zip 63301–2844; tel. 636/947–5000, (Includes SSM HEALTH ST. JOSEPH - WENTZVILLE, 500 Medical Drive, Wentzville, Missouri, Zip 63385–3421; tel. 636/327–1000; Lisle Wescott, President) **A**1 2 3 10 **F**3 4 5 11 13 15 17 18 20 22 24 26 28 29 30 31 34 35 38 40 41 42 43 44 45 46 49 50 53 54 55 56 57 58 59 60 64 67 68 70 73 74 75 76 78 79 81 82 84 85 86 87 90 96 97 98 99 100 101 102 103 104 105 107 108 109 110 111 114 118 119 120 121 129 130 132 135 144 146 147 148 152 153 154 **S** SSM Health, Saint Louis, MO
Primary Contact: Lisle Wescott, President
COO: Lee Bernstein, Regional Executive Vice President and Chief Operating Officer
CFO: Karen Rewerts, System Vice President Finance
CMO: Douglas Barton, M.D., Chief Medical Officer
CIO: Margaret Feilner, Director Information Services
CHR: Debbie G Walkenhorst, System Vice President Talent Management
Web address: www.ssmstjoseph.com
Control: Church operated, Nongovernment, not–for–profit **Service**: General medical and surgical

Staffed Beds: 341 **Admissions**: 13791 **Census**: 184 **Outpatient Visits**: 197256 **Births**: 548 **Total Expense ($000)**: 250930 **Payroll Expense ($000)**: 86167 **Personnel**: 1204

SAINT JOSEPH—Buchanan County

★ **LONG-TERM ACUTE CARE HOSPITAL, MOSAIC LIFE CARE AT ST. JOSEPH (262019)**, 5325 Faraon Street, Zip 64506–3488; tel. 816/271–6000, **A**10 **F**1 29 85 130 148 149 150 **S** Mosaic Life Care, Saint Joseph, MO
Primary Contact: Dana Anderson, R.N., Administrator
CNO: Douglas Schmitz, Director of Nursing
Web address: www.https://www.mymosaiclifecare.org/General/Long-Term-Acute-Care-Hospital/
Control: Other not–for–profit (including NFP Corporation) **Service**: Acute long–term care hospital

Staffed Beds: 41 **Admissions**: 216 **Census**: 19 **Outpatient Visits**: 0 **Births**: 0 **Total Expense ($000)**: 10722 **Payroll Expense ($000)**: 3305 **Personnel**: 54

⊠ **MOSAIC LIFE CARE AT ST. JOSEPH - MEDICAL CENTER (260006)**, 5325 Faraon Street, Zip 64506–3488; tel. 816/271–6000, **A**1 2 10 20 **F**3 9 11 12 13 15 17 18 20 22 24 26 28 29 30 31 32 33 34 35 36 39 40 43 45 46 47 48 49 50 51 53 54 56 57 58 59 61 62 63 64 65 70 73 74 75 76 78 79 80 81 82 84 85 86 87 89 90 92 93 94 96 97 98 100 101 102 103 104 107 108 110 111 114 115 118 119 120 121 123 124 129 130 131 132 134 135 143 144 145 146 147 148 149 150 154 **S** Mosaic Life Care, Saint Joseph, MO
Primary Contact: Samuel Mark. Laney, M.D., Chief Executive Officer
COO: Curt Kretzinger, Chief Operating Officer
CFO: Dwain Stilson, Chief Financial Officer
CIO: Brennan Lehman, Chief Information Officer
CHR: Michael Pulido, Chief Administrative Officer
Web address: www.https://www.mymosaiclifecare.org/Main/Location/st-joseph-mo/mosaic-life-care-at-st.joseph/
Control: Other not–for–profit (including NFP Corporation) **Service**: General medical and surgical

Staffed Beds: 352 **Admissions**: 17027 **Census**: 197 **Outpatient Visits**: 1118000 **Births**: 1498 **Total Expense ($000)**: 648061 **Payroll Expense ($000)**: 284064 **Personnel**: 3582

☐ **NORTHWEST MISSOURI PSYCHIATRIC REHABILITATION CENTER (264007)**, 3505 Frederick Avenue, Zip 64506–2914; tel. 816/387–2300, **A**1 3 10 **F**4 29 30 65 68 75 77 86 87 97 98 101 102 103 130 132 135 143
Primary Contact: Denise Norbury, MS, R.N., Regional Executive Officer
COO: Mary Attebury, Chief Operating Officer
CFO: Randy Riley, Fiscal and Administrative Manager
CMO: James B Reynolds, M.D., Medical Director
CIO: Robert Curren, Western Region Chief Information Technology Officer
CHR: Mary Blakey Gorman, Director Human Resources
CNO: Pam Nold, Chief Nurse Executive
Web address: www.https://dmh.mo.gov
Control: State, Government, nonfederal **Service**: Psychiatric

Staffed Beds: 108 **Admissions**: 52 **Census**: 107 **Outpatient Visits**: 0 **Births**: 0 **Total Expense ($000)**: 23186 **Payroll Expense ($000)**: 11736 **Personnel**: 306

SAINT LOUIS—St. Louis County

⊠ **MERCY HOSPITAL ST. LOUIS (260020)**, 615 South New Ballas Road, Zip 63141–8277; tel. 314/251–6000, (Includes MERCY CHILDREN'S HOSPITAL ST. LOUIS, 615 South New Ballas Road, Saint Louis, Missouri, Zip 63141–8221; tel. 314/251–6000) **A**1 2 3 5 8 10 **F**3 4 5 8 11 12 13 14 15 16 17 18 19 20 22 24 25 26 27 28 29 30 31 32 33 34 35 36 38 39 40 41 43 45 46 47 48 49 50 51 52 53 54 55 56 57 58 59 60 61 64 66 68 69 70 71 72 73 74 75 76 77 78 79 80 81 82 84 85 86 87 88 89 90 92 93 94 96 98 99 100 101 102 103 104 105 106 107 108 110 111 114 115 116 117 118 119 120 121 123 124 126 129 130 131 132 134 135 143 144 146 147 148 149 153 154 156 157 **S** Mercy, Chesterfield, MO
Primary Contact: Stephen Mackin, President
CFO: Cheryl Matejka, Chief Financial Officer
CMO: Paul Hintze, M.D., Vice President Medical Affairs
CIO: Eugene Roth, Vice President Information Services
CHR: Rocky Ruello, Vice President Human Resources
Web address: www.mercy.net/stlouismo
Control: Other not–for–profit (including NFP Corporation) **Service**: General medical and surgical

Staffed Beds: 859 **Admissions**: 39590 **Census**: 565 **Outpatient Visits**: 1218328 **Births**: 8653 **Total Expense ($000)**: 923099 **Payroll Expense ($000)**: 336662 **Personnel**: 5251

ST. JOHN'S MERCY MEDICAL CENTER See Mercy Hospital St. Louis

MO

Many Facility Codes have changed. Please refer to the AHA Guide Code Chart. © 2019 AHA Guide

SAINT LOUIS—St. Louis City County

⊞ BARNES-JEWISH HOSPITAL (260032), 1 Barnes-Jewish Hospital Plaza, Zip 63110–1003; tel. 314/747–3000, (Includes BARNES-JEWISH HOSPITAL PSYCHIATRIC SUPPORT CENTER, 5355 Delmar Boulevard, Saint Louis, Missouri, Zip 63112–3146; tel. 314/286–1700; John M Eiler, Ph.D., Administrative Director) (Total facility includes 120 beds in nursing home–type unit) **A**1 2 3 5 8 10 **F**3 4 5 6 8 9 11 12 13 15 16 17 18 20 22 24 26 28 29 30 31 34 35 36 37 38 39 40 43 44 45 46 47 48 49 50 51 52 53 54 55 56 57 58 59 60 61 63 64 65 66 68 70 71 73 74 75 76 77 78 79 80 81 82 84 85 86 87 89 90 91 92 93 94 95 96 97 98 100 101 102 103 104 107 108 109 110 111 112 114 115 116 117 118 119 120 121 122 123 124 125 126 128 129 130 131 132 134 135 136 137 138 139 140 141 142 143 145 146 147 148 149 150 154 156 157 158 **S** BJC HealthCare, Saint Louis, MO
Primary Contact: Robert W. Cannon, President
CFO: Mark Krieger, Vice President and Chief Financial Officer
CMO: John Lynch, M.D., Vice President and Chief Medical Officer
CIO: Jerry Vuchak, Vice President Healthcare Delivery
CHR: Betsy Rodriguez, Vice President Human Resources
CNO: Coreen Vlodarchyk, R.N., Vice President, Patient Care Services and Chief Nursing Officer
Web address: www.barnesjewish.org
Control: Other not–for–profit (including NFP Corporation) **Service:** General medical and surgical

Staffed Beds: 1413 **Admissions:** 54608 **Census:** 957 **Outpatient Visits:** 658280 **Births:** 3551 **Total Expense ($000):** 2160088 **Payroll Expense ($000):** 666476 **Personnel:** 11853

SAINT LOUIS—St. Louis County

⊞ BARNES-JEWISH WEST COUNTY HOSPITAL (260162), 12634 Olive Boulevard, Zip 63141–6337; tel. 314/996–8000, **A**1 3 5 10 **F**3 12 15 18 29 34 35 40 45 46 47 49 50 51 57 59 60 64 65 70 74 75 77 78 79 81 82 85 90 93 107 110 111 114 115 119 120 121 123 126 129 130 131 142 145 146 148 149 154 **S** BJC HealthCare, Saint Louis, MO
Primary Contact: Trisha Lollo, President
CFO: Diane M Glen, Assistant Administrator
CMO: Sam B Bhayani, M.D., Chief Medical Officer
CIO: Jerry Vuchak, Vice President Information Systems
CNO: Yoany Finelli, R.N., Vice President Patient Care Services Chief Nurse Officer
Web address: www.barnesjewishwestcounty.org
Control: Other not–for–profit (including NFP Corporation) **Service:** General medical and surgical

Staffed Beds: 77 **Admissions:** 2862 **Census:** 17 **Outpatient Visits:** 177296 **Births:** 0 **Total Expense ($000):** 128961 **Payroll Expense ($000):** 37120 **Personnel:** 446

⊞ CHRISTIAN HOSPITAL (260180), 11133 Dunn Road, Zip 63136–6119; tel. 314/653–5000, **A**1 2 3 10 **F**3 4 5 7 11 15 17 18 20 22 24 26 28 29 30 34 35 36 38 40 42 44 45 46 47 49 50 51 53 56 57 58 59 60 63 64 65 68 69 70 71 74 75 77 78 79 80 81 82 83 84 85 86 87 90 92 93 94 96 102 104 107 108 109 110 111 112 113 114 115 116 117 118 119 120 121 123 126 129 130 132 135 146 147 148 149 153 **S** BJC HealthCare, Saint Louis, MO
Primary Contact: Rick Stevens, President
COO: Douglas Black, Vice President of Operations
CMO: Sebastian Rueckert, M.D., Chief Medical Officer
CIO: Michael Kelly, Vice President
CHR: Bryan Hartwick, Vice President Human Resources
CNO: Jennifer Cordia, Vice President and Chief Nursing Executive
Web address: www.christianhospital.org
Control: Other not–for–profit (including NFP Corporation) **Service:** General medical and surgical

Staffed Beds: 220 **Admissions:** 13005 **Census:** 179 **Outpatient Visits:** 284528 **Births:** 0 **Total Expense ($000):** 320979 **Payroll Expense ($000):** 122418 **Personnel:** 1783

☐ HAWTHORN CHILDREN PSYCHIATRIC HOSPITAL (264028), 1901 Pennsylvania, Mailing Address: 1901 Pennsylvania Avenue, Zip 63133–1325; tel. 314/512–7800, **A**1 3 5 10 **F**98 99 106
Primary Contact: Laurent D. Javois, Regional Executive Officer
COO: Marcia F Ford, Chief Operating Officer
CFO: James D Martin, Chief Financial Officer
CMO: Joshua Calhoun, M.D., Medical Director
CHR: Michael McFarlane, Director Human Resource
CNO: Melody Chilese, Chief Nurse Executive
Web address: www.dmh.missouri.gov/hcph
Control: State, Government, nonfederal **Service:** Children's hospital psychiatric

Staffed Beds: 52 **Admissions:** 111 **Census:** 36 **Outpatient Visits:** 0 **Births:** 0 **Total Expense ($000):** 14646 **Payroll Expense ($000):** 8622 **Personnel:** 226

SAINT LOUIS—St. Louis City County

⊞ KINDRED HOSPITAL-ST. LOUIS (262010), 4930 Lindell Boulevard, Zip 63108–1510; tel. 314/361–8700, (Includes KINDRED HOSPITAL ST. LOUIS-ST. ANTHONY'S, 10018 Kennerly Road, 3rd Floor, Saint Louis, Missouri, Zip 63128; tel. 314/525–8100; Angela Green, Chief Executive Officer) **A**1 10 **F**1 29 107 111 148 **S** Kindred Healthcare, Louisville, KY
Primary Contact: Kevin L. Shrake, Chief Executive Officer
COO: Dakota Redd, R.N., Chief Clinical Officer
CFO: Maureen Roach, Senior Chief Financial Officer
CMO: Michael Holtzman, M.D., Medical Director
CIO: Thomas C Christman, Director Plant Operations
CHR: Cindy Sander, Coordinator Human Resources
Web address: www.kindredstlouis.com/
Control: Corporation, Investor–owned (for–profit) **Service:** Acute long–term care hospital

Staffed Beds: 98 **Admissions:** 595 **Census:** 47 **Outpatient Visits:** 0 **Births:** 0 **Total Expense ($000):** 31462 **Payroll Expense ($000):** 13608 **Personnel:** 178

SAINT LOUIS—St. Louis County

⊞ △ MERCY HOSPITAL SOUTH (260077), 10010 Kennerly Road, Zip 63128–2106; tel. 314/525–1000, **A**1 2 3 5 7 10 **F**3 4 5 11 12 13 15 17 18 20 22 24 26 28 29 30 31 34 35 36 38 40 41 43 47 48 49 50 53 54 56 57 58 59 60 61 62 63 64 65 68 69 70 73 74 75 76 77 78 79 80 81 82 84 85 86 87 90 91 92 93 96 97 98 99 100 101 102 103 104 107 108 109 110 111 114 115 116 117 118 119 120 121 123 124 126 129 130 132 135 143 144 146 147 148 149 153 **S** Mercy, Chesterfield, MO
Primary Contact: Sean Hogan, FACHE, President
COO: Bill Hoefer, Chief Operating Officer
Web address: www.stanthonysmedcenter.com
Control: Other not–for–profit (including NFP Corporation) **Service:** General medical and surgical

Staffed Beds: 523 **Admissions:** 26474 **Census:** 342 **Outpatient Visits:** 676256 **Births:** 899 **Total Expense ($000):** 490103 **Payroll Expense ($000):** 208111 **Personnel:** 3258

SAINT LOUIS—St. Louis City County

☐ METROPOLITAN ST. LOUIS PSYCHIATRIC CENTER (264025), 5351 Delmar, Zip 63112–3198; tel. 314/877–0501, (Nonreporting) **A**1 3 10
Primary Contact: Laurent D. Javois, Regional Executive Officer
COO: Michael Bruce Anderson, Ph.D., Chief Operating Officer
CFO: James D Martin, Chief Financial Officer
CMO: Davinder Hayreh, M.D., Medical Director
CHR: Michael McFarlane, Director Human Resources
CNO: Sarah Jones, Chief Nurse Executive
Web address: www.dmh.missouri.gov/mpc
Control: State, Government, nonfederal **Service:** Psychiatric

Staffed Beds: 50

SAINT LOUIS—St. Louis County

⊞ MISSOURI BAPTIST MEDICAL CENTER (260108), 3015 North Ballas Road, Zip 63131–2329; tel. 314/996–5000, **A**1 2 3 5 10 **F**3 11 13 14 15 17 18 19 20 22 24 26 28 29 30 31 34 35 36 40 41 45 46 48 49 50 51 52 54 55 56 57 58 59 60 63 64 65 68 70 71 72 73 74 75 76 77 78 79 81 82 83 84 85 87 89 90 92 93 94 96 97 100 102 107 108 110 111 114 115 116 117 118 119 120 121 123 124 126 130 132 135 145 146 147 148 149 154 155 157 **S** BJC HealthCare, Saint Louis, MO
Primary Contact: John Antes, President
COO: Michael Kelly, Vice President Operations
CFO: Amy Desart, Vice President, Chief Financial Officer
CMO: Mitchell Botney, M.D., Vice President Medical Affairs and Chief Medical Officer
CIO: Tracie Jones, Director Information Services
CHR: Cyndy Donato, Vice President, Human Resources
Web address: www.missouribaptist.org
Control: Other not–for–profit (including NFP Corporation) **Service:** General medical and surgical

Staffed Beds: 449 **Admissions:** 21250 **Census:** 259 **Outpatient Visits:** 353512 **Births:** 4016 **Total Expense ($000):** 593607 **Payroll Expense ($000):** 191079 **Personnel:** 2444

MO

Hospital, Medicare Provider Number, Address, Telephone, Approval, Facility, and Physician Codes, Health Care System

★ American Hospital Association (AHA) membership
☐ The Joint Commission accreditation
○ Healthcare Facilities Accreditation Program
◇ DNV Healthcare Inc. accreditation
⇑ Center for Improvement in Healthcare Quality Accreditation
△ Commission on Accreditation of Rehabilitation Facilities (CARF) accreditation

☐ **SHRINERS HOSPITALS FOR CHILDREN-ST. LOUIS (263304)**, 4400 Clayton Avenue, Zip 63110–1624; tel. 314/432–3600, **A**1 3 5 10 **F**3 29 58 64 74 75 79 81 85 86 87 89 93 94 130 131 143 146 154 **S** Shriners Hospitals for Children, Tampa, FL
Primary Contact: Phillip L. Grady, FACHE, Administrator
CFO: Sandra K. Lawson, Interim Director Fiscal Services
CMO: Perry L Schoenecker, M.D., Chief of Staff
CIO: Jeanne Hall, Director Information Systems
CHR: Mark Venable, Interim Director Human Resources
Web address: www.https://www.shrinershospitalsforchildren.org
Control: Other not–for–profit (including NFP Corporation) **Service:** Children's orthopedic

Staffed Beds: 12 **Admissions:** 304 **Census:** 3 **Outpatient Visits:** 9320
Births: 0 **Total Expense ($000):** 26550 **Payroll Expense ($000):** 8034
Personnel: 143

SAINT LOUIS—St. Louis City County

★ **SSM CARDINAL GLENNON CHILDREN'S HOSPITAL (269807)**, 1465 South Grand Boulevard, Zip 63104–1095; tel. 314/577–5600, **A**3 5 10 **F**3 11 12 19 21 23 25 27 29 30 31 32 34 35 38 39 40 41 43 44 45 46 47 48 49 50 51 54 55 57 59 60 61 64 66 68 72 73 74 75 77 78 79 80 81 82 84 85 86 87 88 89 90 93 94 97 99 100 101 102 104 107 108 111 115 118 119 124 127 129 130 131 132 134 136 137 138 139 141 142 146 148 154 156 **S** SSM Health, Saint Louis, MO
Primary Contact: Steven Burghart, President
CFO: Karen Rewerts, System Vice President of Finance
CMO: John Peter, M.D., Vice President Medical Affairs
CIO: Michael Paasch, Regional Vice President and Chief Information Officer
CHR: Debbie G Walkenhorst, Network Vice President
Web address: www.cardinalglennon.com
Control: Church operated, Nongovernment, not–for–profit **Service:** Children's general medical and surgical

Staffed Beds: 176 **Admissions:** 7221 **Census:** 133 **Outpatient Visits:** 247344 **Births:** 0 **Total Expense ($000):** 340420 **Payroll Expense ($000):** 104257 **Personnel:** 1493

SAINT LOUIS—St. Louis (City) County

☒ **SSM HEALTH SAINT LOUIS UNIVERSITY HOSPITAL (260105)**, 3635 Vista at Grand Boulevard, Zip 63110–0250, Mailing Address: P.O. Box 15250, Zip 63110–0250; tel. 314/577–8000, (Includes SSM HEALTH SAINT LOUIS UNIVERSITY HOSPITAL-SOUTH, 1755 South Grand Boulevard, Saint Louis, Missouri, Zip 63104–1540; tel. 314/577–6027; Raymond Alvey, Chief Financial Officer) **A**1 2 3 5 8 10 **F**3 4 6 7 8 9 11 14 15 17 18 20 22 24 26 28 29 30 31 34 35 38 39 40 43 44 45 46 47 48 49 50 51 55 56 57 58 59 60 61 63 64 65 68 70 74 75 77 78 79 81 82 84 85 86 87 90 91 92 93 94 96 97 98 100 101 102 104 107 108 110 111 112 113 114 115 116 117 118 119 121 123 124 126 129 130 131 132 135 136 138 139 141 142 146 147 148 149 150 156 157 **S** SSM Health, Saint Louis, MO
Primary Contact: Steven M. Scott, President
COO: Gretchen Leiterman, Chief Operating Officer
CFO: Raymond Alvey, Chief Financial Officer
CMO: Nirav Patel, M.D., Interim Chief Medical Officer
CIO: Patrick Brennan, Director Information System Technology
CNO: Patti Kelley, MSN, R.N., Vice President, Nursing and Chief Nursing Officer
Web address: www.sluhospital.com
Control: Church operated, Nongovernment, not–for–profit **Service:** General medical and surgical

Staffed Beds: 356 **Admissions:** 15772 **Census:** 272 **Outpatient Visits:** 187536 **Births:** 0 **Total Expense ($000):** 575183 **Payroll Expense ($000):** 143839 **Personnel:** 1525

SAINT LOUIS—St. Louis County

☒ **SSM HEALTH ST. MARY'S HOSPITAL - ST. LOUIS (260091)**, 6420 Clayton Road, Zip 63117–1811; tel. 314/768–8000, **A**1 2 3 5 **F**3 4 5 13 15 17 18 20 22 26 28 29 30 31 34 35 37 38 40 44 45 46 48 49 50 51 52 55 56 57 58 59 60 61 64 66 70 72 73 74 75 76 78 79 81 82 84 85 86 87 97 98 100 101 102 103 104 107 108 110 111 115 119 120 121 126 129 130 132 135 143 144 146 147 148 149 153 154 156 **S** SSM Health, Saint Louis, MO
Primary Contact: Travis Capers, FACHE, President
CFO: Karen Rewerts, System Vice President of Finance
CMO: Stephen Kelly, M.D., Chief Medical Officer
CIO: Michael Paasch, Regional Chief Information Officer
Web address: www.stmarys-stlouis.com
Control: Church operated, Nongovernment, not–for–profit **Service:** General medical and surgical

Staffed Beds: 394 **Admissions:** 17372 **Census:** 252 **Outpatient Visits:** 238664 **Births:** 3353 **Total Expense ($000):** 382180 **Payroll Expense ($000):** 116344 **Personnel:** 1692

☐ **ST. ALEXIUS HOSPITAL - BROADWAY CAMPUS (260210)**, 3933 South Broadway, Zip 63118–4601; tel. 314/865–7000, (Includes SOUTHPOINTE HOSPITAL, 2639 Miami Street, Saint Louis, Missouri, Zip 63118–3929; tel. 314/772–1456; ST. ALEXIUS HOSPITAL - FOREST PARK CAMPUS, 6150 Oakland Avenue, Saint Louis, Missouri, Zip 63139–3215; tel. 314/768–3000; Michael J. Motte, Chief Executive Officer) **A**1 3 5 10 **F**3 11 12 20 29 34 35 38 39 40 43 45 50 51 56 57 59 60 64 65 68 70 74 77 79 81 85 86 87 98 101 102 103 104 107 108 111 118 119 130 135 143 146 148 149 **S** Success Healthcare, Boca Raton, FL
Primary Contact: Russell Kraeger, M.D., Interim Chief Executive Officer
CFO: Matthew Brandt, Chief Financial Officer
Web address: www.stalexiushospital.com
Control: Corporation, Investor–owned (for–profit) **Service:** General medical and surgical

Staffed Beds: 190 **Admissions:** 2986 **Census:** 70 **Outpatient Visits:** 24936
Births: 0 **Total Expense ($000):** 54493 **Payroll Expense ($000):** 31115
Personnel: 495

ST. JOHN'S MERCY CHILDREN'S HOSPITAL See Mercy Children's Hospital St. Louis

☒ △ **ST. LOUIS CHILDREN'S HOSPITAL (263301)**, One Children's Place, Zip 63110–1002; tel. 314/454–6000, **A**1 3 5 7 8 10 **F**7 8 11 16 17 19 20 21 22 23 24 25 26 27 29 30 31 32 34 35 38 39 40 41 43 44 45 46 47 48 49 50 51 54 57 58 59 60 61 62 63 64 65 68 71 72 73 74 75 77 78 79 81 82 83 84 85 86 87 88 89 90 91 92 93 95 96 99 100 101 102 104 107 108 109 111 114 115 118 119 126 129 130 131 132 134 136 137 138 139 140 141 142 143 145 146 148 149 150 154 155 156 **S** BJC HealthCare, Saint Louis, MO
Primary Contact: Peggy Gordin, Acting President
CFO: Michele McKee, Vice President and Chief Financial Officer
CMO: F Sessions Cole, M.D., Chief Medical Officer
CNO: Peggy Gordin, Vice President, Patient Care Services and Chief Nursing Officer
Web address: www.stlouischildrens.org
Control: Other not–for–profit (including NFP Corporation) **Service:** Children's general medical and surgical

Staffed Beds: 390 **Admissions:** 11319 **Census:** 248 **Outpatient Visits:** 362720 **Births:** 0 **Total Expense ($000):** 670316 **Payroll Expense ($000):** 236018 **Personnel:** 2827

☐ **ST. LOUIS PSYCHIATRIC REHABILITATION CENTER (264010)**, 5300 Arsenal Street, Zip 63139–1463; tel. 314/877–6501, **A**1 10 **F**11 30 39 65 68 75 86 87 98 100 101 106 130 143 146 157
Primary Contact: Laurent D. Javois, Chief Executive Officer
COO: Felix T Vincenz, Chief Operating Officer
CFO: James D Martin, Chief Financial Officer
CMO: Roy Wilson, M.D., Medical Director
CHR: Michael McFarlane, Chief Human Resource Officer
CNO: Deborah Mokry, Chief Nurse Executive
Web address: www.dmh.missouri.gov
Control: State, Government, nonfederal **Service:** Psychiatric

Staffed Beds: 180 **Admissions:** 44 **Census:** 175 **Outpatient Visits:** 0
Births: 0 **Total Expense ($000):** 36883 **Payroll Expense ($000):** 19037
Personnel: 530

☒ **ST. LUKE'S DES PERES HOSPITAL (260176)**, 2345 Dougherty Ferry Road, Zip 63122–3313; tel. 314/966–9100, (Data for 61 days) **A**1 3 5 10 12 13 **F**3 12 15 18 20 22 24 26 29 30 34 35 36 40 44 48 49 50 58 59 60 64 68 69 70 75 77 79 81 85 86 87 93 107 108 110 111 115 119 126 130 132 146 149
Primary Contact: David E. Loving, FACHE, Chief Executive Officer
CFO: Steven Downs, Chief Financial Officer
CIO: Mary Estes, Director Information Systems
CHR: Kathaleen Clutts, Chief Human Resources Officer
CNO: Mary Ann Hampton, MSN, R.N., Chief Nursing Officer
Web address: www.despereshospital.com
Control: Church operated, Nongovernment, not–for–profit **Service:** General medical and surgical

Staffed Beds: 88 **Admissions:** 620 **Census:** 29 **Outpatient Visits:** 3208
Births: 0 **Total Expense ($000):** 14746 **Payroll Expense ($000):** 5146
Personnel: 449

SAINT LOUIS—St. Louis City County

⊠ △ **THE REHABILITATION INSTITUTE OF ST. LOUIS (263028)**, 4455 Duncan Avenue, Zip 63110–1111; tel. 314/658–3800, **A**1 3 5 7 10 **F**29 34 40 44 56 58 60 64 68 74 75 79 87 90 91 93 94 100 130 132 143 148 149 150 **S** Encompass Health Corporation, Birmingham, AL
Primary Contact: Mark Dwyer, FACHE, Chief Executive Officer
CMO: David Carr, M.D., Physician Medical Director
CHR: Heather Savage, Director Human Resources
CNO: Angelina Sherman, R.N., MSN, Chief Nursing Officer
Web address: www.rehabinstitutestl.com
Control: Partnership, Investor–owned (for–profit) **Service:** Rehabilitation

Staffed Beds: 131 **Admissions:** 2481 **Census:** 96 **Outpatient Visits:** 23296 **Births:** 0 **Total Expense ($000):** 47353 **Payroll Expense ($000):** 23233 **Personnel:** 303

⊠ △ **VETERANS AFFAIRS ST. LOUIS HEALTH CARE SYSTEM**, 915 North Grand Boulevard, Zip 63106–1621; tel. 314/652–4100, (Nonreporting) **A**1 3 5 7 **S** Department of Veterans Affairs, Washington, DC
Primary Contact: Keith D. Repko, Director
CFO: Karen Westerheide, Chief Financial Officer
CIO: Steve Warmbold, Director Information Management Service Line
CHR: Marie Lewis, Human Resources Liaison
CNO: Richard Holt, R.N., Associate Director Patient Care Services
Web address: www.stlouis.va.gov/
Control: Veterans Affairs, Government, federal **Service:** General medical and surgical

Staffed Beds: 356

SAINT PETERS—St. Charles County

⊠ **BARNES-JEWISH ST. PETERS HOSPITAL (260191)**, 10 Hospital Drive, Zip 63376–1659; tel. 636/916–9000, **A**1 3 5 10 **F**3 7 8 11 12 15 17 18 20 22 26 28 29 30 31 34 35 40 45 46 49 51 57 59 60 64 70 75 77 78 79 81 85 86 90 93 107 108 110 111 115 117 118 119 120 121 123 129 130 132 135 146 147 148 149 154 156 **S** BJC HealthCare, Saint Louis, MO
Primary Contact: Chris Watts, President
CFO: Glen Schwaegel, Vice President and Chief Financial Officer
CMO: Feliipe Orellana, Chief Medical Officer
CIO: Cindy Gross, Director of Finance
CHR: Michael J Miller, Director Human Resources
CNO: Lauren Beckmann, Vice President Patient Services and Chief Nursing Officer
Web address: www.bjsph.org/
Control: Other not–for–profit (including NFP Corporation) **Service:** General medical and surgical

Staffed Beds: 101 **Admissions:** 5375 **Census:** 57 **Outpatient Visits:** 120568 **Births:** 0 **Total Expense ($000):** 126725 **Payroll Expense ($000):** 42069 **Personnel:** 538

SALEM—Dent County

★ **SALEM MEMORIAL DISTRICT HOSPITAL (261318)**, 35629 Highway 72, Zip 65560–7217, Mailing Address: P.O. Box 774, Zip 65560–0774; tel. 573/729–6626, (Nonreporting) **A**10 18
Primary Contact: Kasey Lucas, Chief Executive Officer, Hospital Administrator
CFO: Becky Cunningham, Controller
CMO: John Demorlis, M.D., Chief Medical Staff
CHR: Jodie Gorman, Director Human Resources
Web address: www.smdh.net
Control: Hospital district or authority, Government, nonfederal **Service:** General medical and surgical

Staffed Beds: 43

SEDALIA—Pettis County

⊠ **BOTHWELL REGIONAL HEALTH CENTER (260009)**, 601 East 14th Street, Zip 65301–5972, Mailing Address: P.O. Box 1706, Zip 65302–1706; tel. 660/826–8833, (Total facility includes 10 beds in nursing home–type unit) **A**1 10 **F**3 9 11 14 15 18 20 22 28 29 30 31 34 35 39 51 54 57 59 60 64 65 68 70 73 74 75 76 77 78 79 80 81 82 84 85 86 87 89 92 93 107 108 110 111 114 115 116 117 118 119 120 121 123 124 127 128 129 130 131 132 135 146 147 148
Primary Contact: Lori Wightman, R.N., MSN, FACHE, Chief Executive Officer
COO: Thomas Bailey, Chief Operating Officer
CIO: Tom Fairfax, Director Information Systems
CHR: Deb Clemmer, Vice President Human Resources
CNO: Regina W Crow, Chief Nursing Officer
Web address: www.brhc.org
Control: City, Government, nonfederal **Service:** General medical and surgical

Staffed Beds: 137 **Admissions:** 4276 **Census:** 58 **Outpatient Visits:** 160648 **Births:** 474 **Total Expense ($000):** 111848 **Payroll Expense ($000):** 43221 **Personnel:** 825

SIKESTON—Scott County

☐ **MISSOURI DELTA MEDICAL CENTER (260113)**, 1008 North Main Street, Zip 63801–5044; tel. 573/471–1600, **A**1 10 **F**3 11 13 15 18 28 29 30 31 34 35 37 40 45 50 51 53 54 56 57 59 60 62 63 64 68 70 74 75 76 77 78 79 81 82 84 85 86 87 89 90 93 97 98 103 104 107 108 109 110 111 115 116 117 118 119 126 127 129 130 131 132 146 147 148 149
Primary Contact: Jason Schrumpf, President
CFO: Greg Carda, Vice President Finance
Web address: www.missouridelta.com
Control: Other not–for–profit (including NFP Corporation) **Service:** General medical and surgical

Staffed Beds: 110 **Admissions:** 3884 **Census:** 52 **Outpatient Visits:** 238704 **Births:** 393 **Total Expense ($000):** 103348 **Payroll Expense ($000):** 43852 **Personnel:** 770

SPRINGFIELD—Greene County

★ ⇧ **COX MEDICAL CENTERS (260040)**, 1423 North Jefferson Street, Zip 65802–1988; tel. 417/269–3000, (Includes COX MEDICAL CENTER NORTH, 1423 North Jefferson Avenue, Springfield, Missouri, Zip 65802; tel. 417/269–3000; COX MEDICAL CENTER SOUTH, 3801 South National Avenue, Springfield, Missouri, Zip 65807; tel. 417/269–6000) **A**3 5 10 21 **F**3 4 5 7 11 12 13 15 17 18 19 20 22 24 26 28 29 30 31 32 34 35 38 39 40 41 42 43 44 45 46 47 49 50 51 52 53 54 55 56 57 58 59 60 61 62 64 65 68 69 70 71 72 74 75 76 77 78 79 80 81 82 84 85 86 87 88 89 90 92 93 94 96 97 98 99 100 101 102 103 104 107 108 110 111 114 115 116 117 118 119 120 121 124 126 128 129 130 131 132 134 135 143 144 146 147 148 149 150 152 154 155 156 **S** CoxHealth, Springfield, MO
Primary Contact: Steven D. Edwards, President and Chief Executive Officer
CFO: Jacob McWay, Senior Vice President and Chief Financial Officer
CMO: Frank Romero, M.D., Chief Medical Officer
CIO: Bruce Robison, Vice President and Chief Information Officer
CHR: John Hursh, Vice President Human Resources
CNO: Karen Kramer, R.N., Vice President and System Chief Nursing Officer
Web address: www.coxhealth.com
Control: Other not–for–profit (including NFP Corporation) **Service:** General medical and surgical

Staffed Beds: 665 **Admissions:** 33606 **Census:** 479 **Outpatient Visits:** 1867592 **Births:** 3409 **Total Expense ($000):** 1097942 **Payroll Expense ($000):** 352355 **Personnel:** 8084

☐ **LAKELAND BEHAVIORAL HEALTH SYSTEM (264024)**, 440 South Market Street, Zip 65806–2026; tel. 417/865–5581, **A**1 10 **F**98 99 103 106 130 **S** Acadia Healthcare Company, Inc., Franklin, TN
Primary Contact: Nathan Duncan, Chief Executive Officer
COO: Randy Fox, Director Performance Improvement and Risk Management
CFO: Rick Crump, Chief Financial Officer
CMO: Richard Alken, M.D., Medical Director
CIO: Brad Strothkamp, Chief Information Systems
CHR: Dave England, Director Human Resources
Web address: www.lakeland-hospital.com
Control: Corporation, Investor–owned (for–profit) **Service:** Psychiatric

Staffed Beds: 206 **Admissions:** 2846 **Census:** 161 **Outpatient Visits:** 0 **Births:** 0 **Total Expense ($000):** 24049 **Payroll Expense ($000):** 14187 **Personnel:** 314

⊠ **MERCY HOSPITAL SPRINGFIELD (260065)**, 1235 East Cherokee Street, Zip 65804–2263; tel. 417/820–2000, (Includes MERCY CHILDREN'S HOSPITAL SPRINGFIELD, 1235 East Cherokee Street, Springfield, Missouri, Zip 65804–2203; tel. 417/820–2000; MERCY ORTHOPEDIC HOSPITAL SPRINGFIELD, 3050 East Riverbluff Boulevard, Ozark, Missouri, Zip 65721; tel. 417/820–5611; Robert Steele, M.D., President) **A**1 3 5 10 **F**3 4 5 7 9 11 12 13 15 16 17 18 19 20 22 24 26 28 29 30 31 32 34 35 37 38 39 40 41 43 44 45 46 49 50 51 54 55 56 57 58 59 60 61 62 63 64 65 66 67 68 70 71 72 73 74 75 76 77 78 79 81 82 84 85 86 87 88 89 90 91 92 93 94 96 97 98 102 103 104 107 108 110 111 114 115 117 118 119 120 121 123 124 126 129 130 131 132 135 143 146 147 148 149 154 155 157 **S** Mercy, Chesterfield, MO
Primary Contact: Brent Hubbard, FACHE, President and Chief Operating Officer
COO: Brent Hubbard, FACHE, Chief Operating Officer
CFO: Scott Reynolds, Vice President Finance
CMO: Allan Allphin, M.D., Chief of Staff
CIO: Lori Sturgill, Vice President Business Partnership
CHR: Tanya Maricn, Interim Vice President Human Resources
Web address: www.mercy.net/springfieldmo
Control: Church operated, Nongovernment, not–for–profit **Service:** General medical and surgical

Staffed Beds: 660 **Admissions:** 34723 **Census:** 469 **Outpatient Visits:** 557880 **Births:** 2917 **Total Expense ($000):** 943665 **Payroll Expense ($000):** 369374 **Personnel:** 8020

MO

Hospital, Medicare Provider Number, Address, Telephone, Approval, Facility, and Physician Codes, Health Care System

★ American Hospital Association (AHA) membership
☐ The Joint Commission accreditation
◯ Healthcare Facilities Accreditation Program
◇ DNV Healthcare Inc. accreditation
⇧ Center for Improvement in Healthcare Quality Accreditation
△ Commission on Accreditation of Rehabilitation Facilities (CARF) accreditation

☐ △ **MERCY REHABILITATION HOSPITAL SPRINGFIELD (263032)**, 5904 South Southwood Road, Zip 65804–5234; tel. 417/227–9000, **A**1 7 10 **F**3 29 30 90 95 96 130 132 148
Primary Contact: Jay Guffey, Chief Executive Officer
CFO: Melissa Campbell, Chief Financial Officer and Controller
CMO: Hollis Bell, M.D., Esq Medical Director
CHR: Melissa Mooney, Director Human Resources
CNO: Paul Moore, R.N., Chief Clinical Officer
Web address: www.mercy.net
Control: Partnership, Investor–owned (for–profit) **Service**: Rehabilitation

Staffed Beds: 60 Admissions: 1399 Census: 43 Outpatient Visits: 0
Births: 0 Total Expense ($000): 16967 Payroll Expense ($000): 7944
Personnel: 172

PERIMETER BEHAVIORAL HOSPITAL OF SPRINGFIELD (264033), 2828 North National Avenue, Zip 65803–4306; tel. 417/799–7474, (Nonreporting)
Primary Contact: Rick Harding, Chief Executive Officer
Web address: www.perimeterhealthcare.com
Control: Corporation, Investor–owned (for–profit) **Service**: Psychiatric

Staffed Beds: 32

⊞ **SELECT SPECIALTY HOSPITAL-SPRINGFIELD (262017)**, 1630 East Primrose Street, Zip 65804–7929; tel. 417/885–4700, **A**1 10 **F**1 3 29 45 85 107 114 148 **S** Select Medical Corporation, Mechanicsburg, PA
Primary Contact: Steve Patterson, Chief Executive Officer
CHR: Tonya Eddington, Coordinator Human Resources
Web address: www.selectspecialtyhospitals.com/company/locations/springfield.aspx
Control: Corporation, Investor–owned (for–profit) **Service**: Acute long–term care hospital

Staffed Beds: 44 Admissions: 427 Census: 29 Outpatient Visits: 0
Births: 0 Total Expense ($000): 19063 Payroll Expense ($000): 8619
Personnel: 113

★ **STE. GENEVIEVE COUNTY MEMORIAL HOSPITAL (261330)**, 800 Ste Genevieve Drive, Zip 63670–1434; tel. 573/883–2751, **A**10 18 **F**2 3 11 13 14 15 18 28 29 31 34 35 40 50 53 56 57 59 62 64 65 66 68 75 76 77 78 79 81 82 85 86 87 89 92 93 107 110 111 115 119 124 127 129 130 131 132 133 135 145 146 147 148 154 156
Primary Contact: Thomas Keim, Chief Executive Officer
CFO: Susan Eckenfels, Chief Financial Officer
CMO: Joseph Sharlow, M.D., Chief of Staff
CHR: Sarah Jo Kelley, Executive Director of Human Resources and Support Services
CNO: Rita Brumfield, R.N., MSN, Chief Nursing Officer
Web address: www.stegenevievehospital.org
Control: County, Government, nonfederal **Service**: General medical and surgical

Staffed Beds: 25 Admissions: 1037 Census: 12 Outpatient Visits: 117488
Births: 160 Total Expense ($000): 47450 Payroll Expense ($000): 20239
Personnel: 364

★ **MISSOURI BAPTIST SULLIVAN HOSPITAL (261337)**, 751 Sappington Bridge Road, Zip 63080–2354; tel. 573/468–4186, **A**10 18 **F**3 4 7 11 12 13 15 28 29 30 31 34 35 40 50 53 56 57 59 63 64 65 70 75 76 77 78 79 81 82 83 84 85 86 87 89 90 93 97 98 102 103 104 107 111 115 119 127 129 130 131 132 133 146 148 152 154 **S** BJC HealthCare, Saint Louis, MO
Primary Contact: Tony Schwarm, FACHE, President
CFO: Angela Wilks, Finance Director
CMO: Alison Baker, M.D., Chief of Staff
CHR: Kathleen Reed, Manager Human Resources
CNO: Carmen J. Bartolotta, R.N., Vice President, Patient Care Services and Chief Nursing Officer
Web address: www.missouribaptistsullivan.org
Control: Other not–for–profit (including NFP Corporation) **Service**: General medical and surgical

Staffed Beds: 35 Admissions: 2000 Census: 21 Outpatient Visits: 104984
Births: 255 Total Expense ($000): 54659 Payroll Expense ($000): 21653
Personnel: 371

★ **WRIGHT MEMORIAL HOSPITAL (261309)**, 191 Iowa Boulevard, Zip 64683–8343; tel. 660/358–5700, **A**10 18 **F**3 11 15 18 28 29 30 31 34 35 40 44 45 50 59 64 68 74 75 77 78 79 81 82 85 87 89 90 93 97 102 104 107 108 110 111 115 119 127 129 130 133 141 146 148 154 156 **S** Saint Luke's Health System, Kansas City, MO
Primary Contact: Steven M. Schieber, FACHE, Interim Chief Executive Officer
CFO: Leslie Reed, Chief Financial Officer
CMO: Gerald C Zabielski, M.D., Chief Medical Staff
CHR: Jenny Donovan, Director Human Resources
Web address: www.saintlukeshealthsystem.org
Control: Church operated, Nongovernment, not–for–profit **Service**: General medical and surgical

Staffed Beds: 15 Admissions: 451 Census: 8 Outpatient Visits: 65264
Births: 0 Total Expense ($000): 31291 Payroll Expense ($000): 11069
Personnel: 146

⊞ **MERCY HOSPITAL LINCOLN (261319)**, 1000 East Cherry Street, Zip 63379–1513; tel. 636/528–8551, **A**1 10 18 **F**3 11 15 18 28 29 30 34 35 40 44 45 50 51 57 59 63 64 65 68 70 75 77 79 81 85 86 87 90 93 104 107 110 111 113 114 119 127 129 130 131 132 133 135 144 146 149 154 156 157 **S** Mercy, Chesterfield, MO
Primary Contact: Anthony Rothermich, Administrator
CFO: Mark Thorn, FACHE, Executive Director, Finance
CIO: Travis Boyd, Manager, Information Technology
CHR: Mary Kay Kunza, Manager Human Resources
Web address: www.mercy.net
Control: Other not–for–profit (including NFP Corporation) **Service**: General medical and surgical

Staffed Beds: 25 Admissions: 721 Census: 9 Outpatient Visits: 114080
Births: 0 Total Expense ($000): 34575 Payroll Expense ($000): 17136
Personnel: 250

PUTNAM COUNTY MEMORIAL HOSPITAL (261305), 1926 Oak Street, Zip 63565–1180, Mailing Address: P.O. Box 389, Zip 63565–0389; tel. 660/947–2411, **A**10 18 **F**3 4 5 15 29 32 34 35 39 50 57 59 75 77 81 82 85 90 93 97 102 107 110 111 115 119 127 128 130 133 135 147 148 149 156
Primary Contact: Gayle Pickens, Chief Executive Officer
COO: Jerry Cummings, Chief Operating Officer
CMO: Dawn Ann Fairley, M.D., Chief of Staff
CHR: Debbie Douglas, Director Human Resources
CNO: Nathan Baughman, Chief Nursing Officer
Web address: www.pcmhosp.com
Control: County, Government, nonfederal **Service**: General medical and surgical

Staffed Beds: 15 Admissions: 192 Census: 5 Outpatient Visits: 10344
Births: 0 Total Expense ($000): 39492 Payroll Expense ($000): 4369
Personnel: 81

☐ **WESTERN MISSOURI MEDICAL CENTER (260097)**, 403 Burkarth Road, Zip 64093–3101; tel. 660/747–2500, **A**1 10 20 **F**3 8 11 12 13 15 17 18 28 29 30 31 32 34 35 40 43 45 47 56 57 59 60 61 64 65 68 70 74 75 76 77 78 79 81 82 85 89 90 93 98 102 103 107 108 110 111 115 117 118 119 127 129 130 131 132 133 135 144 146 147 148 154 156
Primary Contact: Darinda Reberry, MSN, R.N., President and Chief Executive Officer
CFO: Dean Ohmart, Vice President Financial Services and Chief Financial Officer
CIO: Bill Ladd, Director Information Services
CHR: Dennis Long, Director Human Resources
CNO: Jennifer Koepke, R.N., Vice President of Patient Care Services and Chief Nursing Officer
Web address: www.wmmc.com
Control: County, Government, nonfederal **Service**: General medical and surgical

Staffed Beds: 57 Admissions: 2675 Census: 27 Outpatient Visits: 149784
Births: 657 Total Expense ($000): 95308 Payroll Expense ($000): 38213
Personnel: 559

MO

WASHINGTON—Franklin County

☒ **MERCY HOSPITAL WASHINGTON (260052)**, 901 East Fifth Street, Zip 63090–3127; tel. 636/239–8000, **A**1 10 **F**3 5 8 11 12 13 14 15 17 18 20 22 26 28 29 30 31 32 34 35 39 40 43 44 46 48 49 50 51 52 53 54 56 57 58 59 61 64 66 68 69 70 73 74 75 76 77 78 79 80 81 82 84 85 86 87 89 90 92 93 94 96 97 98 99 100 101 104 107 108 110 111 114 116 117 118 119 120 121 123 127 129 130 131 132 134 135 143 144 146 147 148 149 154 156 157 **S** Mercy, Chesterfield, MO
Primary Contact: Eric J. Eoloff, President
COO: Joan Frost, R.N., Chief Operating Officer
CFO: Cheryl Matejka, Chief Financial Officer
CMO: Thomas Riechers, M.D., Chief Medical Staff
CIO: Michael McCreary, Chief of Services
CHR: Barbara Grayson, Vice President Human Resources
CNO: Anna Landon, Chief Nursing Officer
Web address: www.mercy.net
Control: Other not–for–profit (including NFP Corporation) **Service**: General medical and surgical

Staffed Beds: 148 **Admissions**: 5891 **Census**: 48 **Outpatient Visits**: 353888 **Births**: 837 **Total Expense ($000)**: 167058 **Payroll Expense ($000)**: 62822 **Personnel**: 858

WENTZVILLE—St. Charles County

SSM HEALTH ST. JOSEPH - WENTZVILLE See Ssm Health St. Joseph - St. Charles, Saint Charles

WEST PLAINS—Howell County

☒ **OZARKS MEDICAL CENTER (260078)**, 1100 Kentucky Avenue, Zip 65775–2029, Mailing Address: P.O. Box 1100, Zip 65775–1100; tel. 417/256–9111, **A**1 10 **F**2 3 5 11 12 13 15 17 18 20 22 24 28 29 30 31 34 38 40 44 45 49 50 57 59 61 62 63 64 68 70 74 75 76 77 78 79 81 82 83 84 85 86 87 89 90 91 93 94 98 99 100 101 102 103 104 107 108 110 111 115 118 119 120 121 127 129 130 131 132 135 144 145 146 147 148 154
Primary Contact: Thomas W. Keller, President and Chief Executive Officer
COO: Pamela R. Lee, Chief Operating Officer
CFO: Kim Thompson, Vice President and Chief Financial Officer
CMO: Walter R Holloway, Chief Medical Officer
CIO: John Wilcox, Chief Information Officer
CHR: Connie Schott, Vice President, Human Resources
CNO: Kurt Abbey, Chief Nursing Officer
Web address: www.ozarksmedicalcenter.com
Control: Other not–for–profit (including NFP Corporation) **Service**: General medical and surgical

Staffed Beds: 103 **Admissions**: 5792 **Census**: 52 **Outpatient Visits**: 552648 **Births**: 650 **Total Expense ($000)**: 167017 **Payroll Expense ($000)**: 72657 **Personnel**: 1486

WINDSOR—Henry County

☐ **ROYAL OAKS HOSPITAL (264020)**, 307 North Main, Zip 65360–1449; tel. 660/647–2182, (Nonreporting) **A**1 3 5 10
Primary Contact: Alan W. Greiman, Chief Executive Officer and President
CFO: Jake Matthew Krafve, Chief Financial Officer
CMO: Syed Arshad Husain, M.D., Executive Vice President and Chief Medical Officer
CIO: Richard Colvert, Chief Information Officer
CHR: Diane Coletta, Vice President Human Resources
CNO: Saundra Overton, R.N., Chief Nursing Officer
Web address: www.compasshealthnetwork.org
Control: Other not–for–profit (including NFP Corporation) **Service**: Psychiatric

Staffed Beds: 41

MO

Hospital, Medicare Provider Number, Address, Telephone, Approval, Facility, and Physician Codes, Health Care System

★ American Hospital Association (AHA) membership   ○ Healthcare Facilities Accreditation Program   ⇧ Center for Improvement in Healthcare Quality Accreditation
☐ The Joint Commission accreditation   ◇ DNV Healthcare Inc. accreditation   △ Commission on Accreditation of Rehabilitation Facilities (CARF) accreditation

© 2019 AHA Guide   *Many Facility Codes have changed. Please refer to the AHA Guide Code Chart.*   Hospitals **A373**

MONTANA

ANACONDA—Deer Lodge County

★ **COMMUNITY HOSPITAL OF ANACONDA (271335)**, 401 West Pennsylvania
Street, Zip 59711; tel. 406/563–8500, (Total facility includes 32 beds in nursing
home–type unit) **A**5 10 18 **F**3 8 11 13 15 29 30 31 34 35 40 43 45 50 54 57
59 62 63 64 70 74 75 76 77 78 79 81 82 87 89 93 97 99 104 107 111 114
116 119 128 132 133 135 143 144 146 148 156
Primary Contact: Jo Ellen Villa, R.N., Chief Executive Officer
CFO: Meg Hickey-Boynton, Chief Financial Officer
CMO: Freddy Bartoletti, M.D., Chief of Staff
CHR: Meg Hickey-Boynton, Director Human Resources and Marketing
CNO: Jamie Johnson, R.N., Vice President Nursing
Web address: www.communityhospitalofanaconda.org
Control: Other not–for–profit (including NFP Corporation) **Service:** General
medical and surgical

Staffed Beds: 57	**Admissions:** 1343	**Census:** 42	**Outpatient Visits:** 72095
Births: 214	**Total Expense ($000):** 63592	**Payroll Expense ($000):** 31580	
Personnel: 381			

BAKER—Fallon County

FALLON MEDICAL COMPLEX (271301), 202 South 4th Street West,
Zip 59313–9156, Mailing Address: P.O. Box 820, Zip 59313–0820;
tel. 406/778–3331, **A**10 18 **F**11 15 32 34 40 56 57 59 62 64 65 66 68 69 75
93 97 107 110 114 119 127 130 133 146 148 149
Primary Contact: David Espeland, Chief Executive Officer
CFO: Selena Nelson, Chief Financial Officer
CMO: Darryl Espeland, D.O., Chief Medical Staff
CIO: Susan Stevens, Information Technology Specialist
CHR: Theresa Myers, Personnel Director
CNO: Susan Lunde, R.N., Director of Nursing
Web address: www.fallonmedical.org
Control: Other not–for–profit (including NFP Corporation) **Service:** General
medical and surgical

Staffed Beds: 25	**Admissions:** 169	**Census:** 17	**Outpatient Visits:** 17717
Births: 0	**Total Expense ($000):** 10347	**Payroll Expense ($000):** 3899	
Personnel: 79			

BIG SANDY—Chouteau County

★ **BIG SANDY MEDICAL CENTER (271311)**, 166 Montana Avenue East,
Zip 59520–8474, Mailing Address: P.O. Box 530, Zip 59520–0530;
tel. 406/378–2188, (Total facility includes 22 beds in nursing home–type unit)
A10 18 **F**40 64 93 127 128 133 154
Primary Contact: Leah Griffith, Chief Executive Officer
CFO: Nora Grubb, Chief Financial Officer
Web address: www.bsmc.org
Control: Other not–for–profit (including NFP Corporation) **Service:** General
medical and surgical

Staffed Beds: 30	**Admissions:** 53	**Census:** 15	**Outpatient Visits:** 2574
Births: 0	**Total Expense ($000):** 3579	**Payroll Expense ($000):** 1370	
Personnel: 41			

BIG SKY—Gallatin County

BIG SKY MEDICAL CENTER (270089), 334 Town Center Avenue, Zip 59716,
Mailing Address: P.O. Box 161529, Zip 59716–1529; tel. 406/995–6995, **A**10
F3 34 35 40 45 57 59 65 87 97 107 111 114
Primary Contact: Chris Darnell, Administrator
Web address: www.https://www.bigskymedicalcenter.org/
Control: Other not–for–profit (including NFP Corporation) **Service:** General
medical and surgical

Staffed Beds: 4	**Admissions:** 33	**Census:** 1	**Outpatient Visits:** 17178
Births: 0	**Personnel:** 47		

BIG TIMBER—Sweet Grass County

★ **PIONEER MEDICAL CENTER (271313)**, 301 West Seventh Avenue,
Zip 59011–7893, Mailing Address: P.O. Box 1228, Zip 59011–1228;
tel. 406/932–4603, **A**10 18 **F**2 3 7 10 11 12 28 29 30 34 35 40 41 45 56 57
59 63 64 65 66 67 68 75 77 82 87 93 97 100 101 102 104 107 114 119 127
128 130 131 132 133 134 143 146 148 149 154 156
Primary Contact: Bradley C. Howell, Chief Executive Officer
CFO: Kyle Gee, Chief Financial Officer
CMO: Benjamin P Bullington, M.D., Chief of Staff
CHR: Miki Gregorich, Director Human Resources
CNO: Randi Pike, Director of Nursing
Web address: www.pmcmt.org/
Control: Other not–for–profit (including NFP Corporation) **Service:** General
medical and surgical

Staffed Beds: 25	**Admissions:** 78	**Census:** 1	**Outpatient Visits:** 15897
Births: 0	**Total Expense ($000):** 8692	**Payroll Expense ($000):** 3126	
Personnel: 105			

BILLINGS—Yellowstone County

☐ **ADVANCED CARE HOSPITAL OF MONTANA (272001)**, 3528 Gabel Road,
Zip 59102–7307; tel. 406/373–8000, (Nonreporting) **A**1 10 **S** Ernest Health, Inc.,
Albuquerque, NM
Primary Contact: Judi Powers, Chief Executive Officer
Web address: www.achm.ernesthealth.com
Control: Corporation, Investor–owned (for–profit) **Service:** Acute long–term care
hospital

Staffed Beds: 40

✠ **BILLINGS CLINIC (270004)**, 2800 10th Avenue North, Zip 59101–0703, Mailing
Address: P.O. Box 37000, Zip 59107–7000; tel. 406/657–4000, **A**1 2 3 5 8 10
19 **F**3 8 9 11 12 13 15 17 18 19 20 22 24 26 27 28 29 30 34 35 36 38
40 41 43 44 45 46 47 48 49 50 51 52 54 55 56 57 58 59 60 61 62 64 65 66
68 70 72 74 75 76 77 78 79 80 81 82 84 85 86 87 89 91 92 93 97 98 99 100
101 102 103 104 105 107 108 110 111 114 115 116 117 118 119 120 121
124 126 129 130 131 132 134 135 136 146 147 148 154 155 156
Primary Contact: Randall K. Gibb, M.D., Chief Executive Officer
CFO: Connie F Prewitt, Chief Financial Officer
CMO: Randall K. Gibb, M.D., Chief Executive Officer
CIO: Chris E Stevens, Chief Information Officer
CHR: Karla Stauffer, Executive Director People Resources
CNO: Lu Byrd, R.N., MSN, Vice President Hospital Operations and Chief Nursing
Officer
Web address: www.billingsclinic.com
Control: Other not–for–profit (including NFP Corporation) **Service:** General
medical and surgical

Staffed Beds: 291	**Admissions:** 15863	**Census:** 204	**Outpatient**
Visits: 871956	**Births:** 1130	**Total Expense ($000):** 682673	**Payroll**
Expense ($000): 334373	**Personnel:** 3604		

✠ △ **ST. VINCENT HEALTHCARE (270049)**, 1233 North 30th Street,
Zip 59101–0165, Mailing Address: P.O. Box 35200, Zip 59107–5200;
tel. 406/237–7000, **A**1 2 3 5 7 10 **F**3 7 9 11 12 13 15 18 19 20 22 24 26 28
29 30 31 32 34 35 36 37 38 40 41 43 44 46 47 49 50 51 56 57 58 59 60 61
64 68 70 71 72 74 75 76 77 78 79 81 82 84 85 86 87 88 89 90 92 93 97 100
101 107 108 110 111 114 115 116 117 118 119 120 121 123 124 126 129
130 131 132 134 135 143 144 145 146 147 148 149 154 155 156 **S**
SCL Health, Broomfield, CO
Primary Contact: Steve Loveless, President and Chief Executive Officer
CMO: Michael Schweitzer, M.D., Chief Medical Officer
CIO: Al Rooney, Director Information Systems
Web address: www.svh-mt.org
Control: Other not–for–profit (including NFP Corporation) **Service:** General
medical and surgical

Staffed Beds: 225	**Admissions:** 12093	**Census:** 152	**Outpatient**
Visits: 137430	**Births:** 1429	**Total Expense ($000):** 382743	**Payroll**
Expense ($000): 113885	**Personnel:** 1404		

MT

Many Facility Codes have changed. Please refer to the AHA Guide Code Chart.   © 2019 AHA Guide

BOZEMAN—Gallatin County

★ ⇑ **BOZEMAN HEALTH (270057)**, 915 Highland Boulevard, Zip 59715–6902; tel. 406/585–5000, **A**2 10 20 21 **F**3 8 10 13 18 20 22 28 29 30 31 32 34 35 36 37 40 43 45 49 50 51 54 55 56 57 58 59 61 64 65 70 71 74 75 76 77 78 79 81 82 83 84 85 86 87 92 93 96 97 100 107 108 111 115 119 120 121 123 125 126 129 130 131 132 135 146 147 148 149 154 156 157
Primary Contact: John Hill, President and Chief Executive Officer
CIO: Brad Ludford, Chief Financial Officer
Web address: www.bozemandeaconess.org
Control: Other not–for–profit (including NFP Corporation) **Service:** General medical and surgical

Staffed Beds: 83 **Admissions:** 5618 **Census:** 53 **Outpatient Visits:** 486488 **Births:** 1185 **Personnel:** 1413

BUTTE—Silver Bow County

⊠ **ST. JAMES HEALTHCARE (270017)**, 400 South Clark Street, Zip 59701–2328; tel. 406/723–2500, **A**1 5 10 **F**3 11 13 15 18 20 22 28 29 30 31 34 35 40 43 45 47 48 50 51 53 56 57 59 64 65 68 70 71 72 75 76 77 78 79 81 82 85 86 87 89 93 97 107 108 110 111 114 115 117 118 119 120 121 123 124 126 127 130 131 132 135 146 147 148 149 156 157 **S** SCL Health, Broomfield, CO
Primary Contact: Jay Doyle, President and Chief Executive Officer
CFO: David Brain, Interim Vice President Finance
CMO: Dennis Salisbury, M.D., Vice President for Medical Affairs
CHR: Trisha Palmer, Director
CNO: Mary Winters, Interim Chief Nursing Officer
Web address: www.stjameshealthcare.org
Control: Other not–for–profit (including NFP Corporation) **Service:** General medical and surgical

Staffed Beds: 73 **Admissions:** 3558 **Census:** 40 **Outpatient Visits:** 55583 **Births:** 255 **Total Expense ($000):** 107405 **Payroll Expense ($000):** 37037 **Personnel:** 458

CHESTER—Liberty County

LIBERTY MEDICAL CENTER (271334), 315 West Madison Avenue, Zip 59522, Mailing Address: P.O. Box 705, Zip 59522–0705; tel. 406/759–5181, **A**10 18 **F**2 3 10 11 34 35 40 43 45 56 59 64 67 81 86 87 93 97 107 114 119 127 128 130 133 154
Primary Contact: Matthew Waller, Chief Executive Officer
CMO: Gladys Young, M.D., Chief of Staff
CHR: Bev Halter, Director Human Resources and Payroll
CNO: Shirley Morkrid, Chief Nursing Officer
Web address: www.lchnh.org
Control: Other not–for–profit (including NFP Corporation) **Service:** General medical and surgical

Staffed Beds: 25 **Admissions:** 60 **Census:** 1 **Outpatient Visits:** 8775 **Births:** 0 **Total Expense ($000):** 7502 **Payroll Expense ($000):** 3489 **Personnel:** 84

CHOTEAU—Teton County

BENEFIS TETON MEDICAL CENTER (271307), 915 4th Street North West, Zip 59422–9123; tel. 406/466–5763, **A**10 18 **F**2 34 35 40 41 43 53 56 57 59 63 64 68 93 102 104 107 127 133 154 **S** Benefis Health System, Great Falls, MT
Primary Contact: Louie King, Chief Executive Officer
Web address: www.tetonmedicalcenter.net
Control: Other not–for–profit (including NFP Corporation) **Service:** General medical and surgical

Staffed Beds: 25 **Admissions:** 83 **Census:** 23 **Outpatient Visits:** 5564 **Births:** 0 **Total Expense ($000):** 6887 **Payroll Expense ($000):** 3204 **Personnel:** 69

CIRCLE—McCone County

★ **MCCONE COUNTY HEALTH CENTER (271305)**, 605 Sullivan Avenue, Zip 59215, Mailing Address: P.O. Box 48, Zip 59215–0048; tel. 406/485–3381, **A**10 18 **F**2 3 11 34 40 41 57 58 59 65 69 86 87 93 133 135 143 146 149 154
Primary Contact: Nancy Rosaaen, Chief Executive Officer
CFO: Nancy Rosaaen, Chief Executive Officer
CHR: Jacque Gardner, Administrative Assistant, Clinic Manager, Co-Chief Financial Officer and Chief Human Resources
Web address: www.mcconehealth.org/
Control: County, Government, nonfederal **Service:** General medical and surgical

Staffed Beds: 30 **Admissions:** 39 **Census:** 17 **Outpatient Visits:** 652 **Total Expense ($000):** 3686 **Payroll Expense ($000):** 1482 **Personnel:** 37

COLUMBUS—Stillwater County

★ **STILLWATER BILLINGS CLINIC (271330)**, 44 West Fourth Avenue North, Zip 59019–0959, Mailing Address: P.O. Box 959, Zip 59019–0959; tel. 406/322–5316, **A**10 18 **F**3 15 28 32 34 35 40 43 45 59 62 64 65 68 77 93 107 110 115 127 133 144 148 154 156
Primary Contact: David Ryerse, Chief Executive Officer
Web address: www.billingsclinic.com
Control: Other not–for–profit (including NFP Corporation) **Service:** General medical and surgical

Staffed Beds: 10 **Admissions:** 166 **Census:** 3 **Outpatient Visits:** 15343 **Births:** 0 **Total Expense ($000):** 11339 **Payroll Expense ($000):** 5194 **Personnel:** 93

CONRAD—Pondera County

PONDERA MEDICAL CENTER (271324), 805 Sunset Boulevard, Zip 59425–1717, Mailing Address: P.O. Box 668, Zip 59425–0668; tel. 406/271–3211, (Nonreporting) **A**10 18 **S** QHR, Brentwood, TN
Primary Contact: Bill O'Leary, Chief Executive Officer
CFO: Brigid Burke, Chief Financial Officer
CMO: Jay Taylor, M.D., Chief of Medical Staff
CIO: Sean Kavanagh, Director Information Technology
CHR: Patrick Johnson, Director Human Resources
CNO: Laura Erickson, R.N., Chief Nursing Officer
Web address: www.ponderamedical.org
Control: Other not–for–profit (including NFP Corporation) **Service:** General medical and surgical

Staffed Beds: 79

CROW AGENCY—Big Horn County

CROW/NORTHERN CHEYENNE HOSPITAL (271339), 10110 South 7650 East, Zip 59022–0009, Mailing Address: P.O. Box 9, Zip 59022–0009; tel. 406/638–2626, (Nonreporting) **A**10 18 **S** U. S. Indian Health Service, Rockville, MD
Primary Contact: Darren Crowe, Chief Executive Officer
CMO: Jim Upchurch, M.D., Chief Medical Officer
CIO: Melanie Falls Down, Site Manager
Web address: www.https://www.ihs.gov/billings/healthcarefacilities/crow/
Control: PHS, Indian Service, Government, federal **Service:** General medical and surgical

Staffed Beds: 24

CULBERTSON—Roosevelt County

★ **ROOSEVELT MEDICAL CENTER (271308)**, 818 Second Avenue East, Zip 59218, Mailing Address: P.O. Box 419, Zip 59218–0419; tel. 406/787–6401, (Total facility includes 27 beds in nursing home–type unit) **A**10 18 **F**2 7 15 34 35 40 43 56 57 59 65 69 77 93 97 127 128 133 140 143 146 147 154 156
Primary Contact: Audrey Stromberg, Administrator
CFO: Jennifer Kessner, Financial Director
CMO: Don Helland, M.D., Chief Medical Officer
CIO: Brian Fordyce, Director Information Technology
CHR: Elizabeth Raaum, Manger Business Office
CNO: Jessica Schmitz, Director of Nursing
Web address: www.roosmem.org
Control: Other not–for–profit (including NFP Corporation) **Service:** General medical and surgical

Staffed Beds: 33 **Admissions:** 60 **Census:** 20 **Outpatient Visits:** 8338 **Births:** 1 **Total Expense ($000):** 5582 **Payroll Expense ($000):** 3109 **Personnel:** 53

CUT BANK—Glacier County

★ **NORTHERN ROCKIES MEDICAL CENTER (271337)**, 802 Second Street SE, Zip 59427–3329; tel. 406/873–2251, **A**10 18 **F**13 34 40 43 57 59 64 65 76 77 81 82 83 84 93 97 107 119 127 128 133 149 154 156 **S** QHR, Brentwood, TN
Primary Contact: Cherie Taylor, Chief Executive Officer
CFO: Treasure Berkram, Chief Financial Officer
CMO: Adron Medley, M.D., Chief Medical Staff
CHR: Kandie Lemieux, Administrative Assistant and Director Human Resources
Web address: www.nrmcinc.org
Control: Other not–for–profit (including NFP Corporation) **Service:** General medical and surgical

Staffed Beds: 29 **Admissions:** 137 **Census:** 1 **Outpatient Visits:** 10734 **Births:** 32 **Total Expense ($000):** 9469 **Payroll Expense ($000):** 4847 **Personnel:** 72

MT

DEER LODGE—Powell County

DEER LODGE MEDICAL CENTER (271314), 1100 Hollenbeck Lane, Zip 59722–2317; tel. 406/846–2212, **A**10 18 **F**8 11 15 18 28 32 33 34 35 40 43 45 50 55 56 57 59 64 65 79 81 82 84 85 86 87 90 91 93 97 107 108 110 119 127 133 147 148 154 156
Primary Contact: Tony Pfaff, Chief Executive Officer
CFO: Jaena Richards, Chief Financial Officer
CMO: Michelle Corbin, M.D., Chief of Staff
CIO: Chris Foster, Director Health Information Management
Web address: www.dlmed.org/
Control: Corporation, Investor–owned (for–profit) **Service**: General medical and surgical

Staffed Beds: 16 **Admissions**: 231 **Census**: 4 **Outpatient Visits**: 9788 **Births**: 0 **Total Expense ($000)**: 13649 **Payroll Expense ($000)**: 5676 **Personnel**: 108

DILLON—Beaverhead County

★ **BARRETT HOSPITAL & HEALTHCARE (271318)**, 600 Mt Highway 91 South, Zip 59725–7379; tel. 406/683–3000, **A**5 10 18 **F**3 13 15 28 29 31 34 40 45 50 52 55 57 59 62 63 64 65 69 75 76 77 79 80 81 83 84 85 87 89 93 96 97 107 110 111 115 119 129 130 131 132 133 135 146 148 154 156 **S** HealthTech Management Services, Brentwood, TN
Primary Contact: Ken Westman, Chief Executive Officer
CFO: Dick Achter, Chief Financial Officer
CMO: Carol Kennedy, Chief Clinical Officer
CIO: Dick Achter, Chief Financial Officer
CHR: Geoff Roach, Director Human Resources
Web address: www.barretthospital.org
Control: Other not–for–profit (including NFP Corporation) **Service**: General medical and surgical

Staffed Beds: 18 **Admissions**: 523 **Census**: 5 **Outpatient Visits**: 29763 **Births**: 90 **Total Expense ($000)**: 33346 **Payroll Expense ($000)**: 15066 **Personnel**: 204

EKALAKA—Carter County

DAHL MEMORIAL HEALTHCARE ASSOCIATION (271302), 215 Sandy Street, Zip 59324, Mailing Address: P.O. Box 46, Zip 59324–0046; tel. 406/775–8730, (Nonreporting) **A**10 18
Primary Contact: Ryan Tooke, Chief Executive Officer
CFO: Nadine Elmore, Chief Executive Officer
CMO: Darryl Espeland, D.O., Medical Director
CIO: Davie Ann Barrere, Coordinator Information Technology
CHR: Melissa Matthews, Director Human Resources
CNO: Patricia Rogers, Director of Nursing
Web address: www.dahlmemorial.com
Control: Other not–for–profit (including NFP Corporation) **Service**: General medical and surgical

Staffed Beds: 25

ENNIS—Madison County

MADISON VALLEY MEDICAL CENTER (271329), 305 North Main Street, Zip 59729–8001; tel. 406/682–4222, **A**10 18 **F**11 18 28 29 32 34 35 38 40 45 46 50 53 55 56 57 59 64 65 68 69 71 75 77 78 79 82 84 87 92 93 94 97 100 102 107 114 119 127 130 131 132 133 135 144 148 154 156
Primary Contact: Allen Rohrback, Chief Executive Officer
CMO: Cindy Sharp, M.D., Chief Medical Officer
CIO: Bo Nix, Chief Information Officer
Web address: www.mvmedcenter.org
Control: Other not–for–profit (including NFP Corporation) **Service**: General medical and surgical

Staffed Beds: 10 **Admissions**: 193 **Census**: 3 **Outpatient Visits**: 6070 **Births**: 0

FORSYTH—Rosebud County

★ **ROSEBUD HEALTH CARE CENTER (271327)**, 383 North 17th Avenue, Zip 59327–0268, Mailing Address: P.O. Box 268, Zip 59327–0268; tel. 406/346–2161, (Nonreporting) **A**10 18
Primary Contact: Mindy Price, R.N., Chief Executive Officer
CMO: William Anderson, Medical Director
CHR: Karla Allies, Director Human Resources
Web address: www.rosebudhealthcare.com/
Control: Other not–for–profit (including NFP Corporation) **Service**: General medical and surgical

Staffed Beds: 55

FORT BENTON—Chouteau County

MISSOURI RIVER MEDICAL CENTER (271304), 1501 St Charles Street, Zip 59442–0249, Mailing Address: P.O. Box 249, Zip 59442–0249; tel. 406/622–3331, **A**10 18 **F**2 40 41 50 59 65 67 84 107 127 128 130 133 135 143 148 154 **S** Benefis Health System, Great Falls, MT
Primary Contact: Louie King, President, Harry Bold Nursing Home Administrator
CMO: Jace Bird, M.D., Chief Medical Officer
CIO: Bryan Cartwright, Chief Information Technology Officer
CHR: Carolyn Johnsrud, Manager Human Resources
CNO: Janice Woodhouse, Director of Nursing
Web address: www.mrmcfb.org
Control: Hospital district or authority, Government, nonfederal **Service**: Acute long–term care hospital

Staffed Beds: 25 **Admissions**: 22 **Census**: 1 **Outpatient Visits**: 10746 **Births**: 0 **Total Expense ($000)**: 5265 **Payroll Expense ($000)**: 2800 **Personnel**: 67

FORT HARRISON—Lewis and Clark County

⊞ **VETERANS AFFAIRS MONTANA HEALTH CARE SYSTEM**, 3687 Veterans Drive, Zip 59636–9703, Mailing Address: P.O. Box 1500, Zip 59636–1500; tel. 406/442–6410, (Nonreporting) **A**1 **S** Department of Veterans Affairs, Washington, DC
Primary Contact: Paul Gregory, Acting Director
CFO: Brian Gustafson, Chief Financial Officer
CMO: Kurt Werner, M.D., Chief of Staff
CIO: Paul Gauthier, Chief Information Resources Management
CHR: Aggie Hamilton, Chief Human Resources
Web address: www.montana.va.gov/
Control: Veterans Affairs, Government, federal **Service**: General medical and surgical

Staffed Beds: 94

GLASGOW—Valley County

⊞ **FRANCES MAHON DEACONESS HOSPITAL (271316)**, 621 Third Street South, Zip 59230–2699; tel. 406/228–3500, **A**1 10 18 **F**3 7 11 13 15 28 29 31 34 35 40 43 53 56 57 59 61 64 70 75 76 78 79 81 82 86 87 89 93 100 102 107 108 110 111 115 118 119 127 128 130 131 133 145 146 149
Primary Contact: Randall G. Holom, Chief Executive Officer
COO: Ellen Guttenberg, Chief Operating Officer
CFO: Cami Kalinski, Director Financial Services
CMO: Gordon Bell, M.D., Chief of Staff
CIO: David L Nixdorf, Director Support Services
CHR: Charam Orth, Director Human Resources
CNO: Brenda Koessl, R.N., Director of Nursing Services
Web address: www.fmdh.org
Control: Other not–for–profit (including NFP Corporation) **Service**: General medical and surgical

Staffed Beds: 25 **Admissions**: 497 **Census**: 4 **Outpatient Visits**: 36786 **Births**: 128 **Total Expense ($000)**: 27780 **Payroll Expense ($000)**: 12230 **Personnel**: 167

GLENDIVE—Dawson County

★ **GLENDIVE MEDICAL CENTER (271332)**, 202 Prospect Drive, Zip 59330–1999; tel. 406/345–3306, (Total facility includes 56 beds in nursing home–type unit) **A**5 10 18 **F**1 8 10 11 13 15 28 29 30 31 34 40 41 45 51 56 57 59 62 63 64 65 67 70 75 76 77 79 81 85 89 90 93 97 100 102 104 107 110 111 115 119 125 127 128 130 132 133 146 147 148 154 156
Primary Contact: Parker Powell, Chief Executive Officer
CFO: Barbara Markham, Chief Financial Officer
CMO: Joseph M Leal, M.D., Jr Chief of Staff
CIO: Barbara Markham, Chief Financial Officer
CHR: Joetta J Pearcy, Director, Human Resources
Web address: www.gmc.org
Control: Other not–for–profit (including NFP Corporation) **Service**: General medical and surgical

Staffed Beds: 88 **Admissions**: 479 **Census**: 43 **Outpatient Visits**: 22028 **Births**: 58 **Total Expense ($000)**: 48867 **Payroll Expense ($000)**: 21412 **Personnel**: 388

MT

GREAT FALLS—Cascade County

△ **BENEFIS HEALTH SYSTEM (270012)**, 1101 26th Street South, Zip 59405–5104; tel. 406/455–5000, (Includes BENEFIS HEALTH CARE-EAST CAMPUS, 1101 26th Street, Great Falls, Montana, Zip 59405; tel. 406/455–5000; BENEFIS HEALTH CARE-WEST CAMPUS, 500 15th Avenue South, Great Falls, Montana, Zip 59405; tel. 406/455–5000) (Total facility includes 217 beds in nursing home–type unit) **A**2 5 7 10 20 **F**3 4 5 6 8 9 10 11 12 13 15 18 20 22 24 26 28 29 30 31 34 35 36 37 38 40 43 45 46 47 48 49 50 52 53 54 55 56 57 58 59 61 62 63 64 65 70 71 72 73 74 75 76 77 78 79 81 82 83 84 85 86 87 88 89 90 91 92 93 96 97 98 100 101 102 104 105 107 108 110 111 114 115 117 119 120 121 123 124 126 127 128 130 131 132 133 135 143 144 146 147 148 149 152 154 155 158 **S** Benefis Health System, Great Falls, MT
Primary Contact: John H. Goodnow, Chief Executive Officer
CFO: Forrest Ehlinger, System Chief Financial Officer
CMO: Gregory Tierney, M.D., President, BMG and BHS Chief Medical Officer
CIO: Mark Simon, System Chief Information Officer
CNO: Rayn Ginnaty, Vice President Nursing
Web address: www.benefis.org
Control: Other not–for–profit (including NFP Corporation) **Service**: General medical and surgical

Staffed Beds: 502 Admissions: 10926 Census: 365 Outpatient Visits: 502488 Births: 1409 Total Expense ($000): 427566 Payroll Expense ($000): 202150 Personnel: 2630

GREAT FALLS CLINIC HOSPITAL (270086), 3010 15th Avenue South, Zip 59405–5240, Mailing Address: 3010 15th Street South, Zip 59405–5240; tel. 406/216–8000, **A**10 **F**3 15 18 24 26 27 29 30 31 34 35 38 40 41 44 45 46 47 51 58 59 64 65 68 74 75 77 78 79 81 82 85 86 87 91 92 93 94 107 108 110 111 114 115 119 120 121 123 124 126 130 135 144 146 148 149 156
Primary Contact: Vicki Newmiller, Chief Executive Officer
CFO: Cheryl Cornwell, Chief Financial Officer
CMO: Nicholas Bonfilio, M.D., Chief of Staff
Web address: www.gfclinic.com/location/great-falls-clinic-hospital/
Control: Partnership, Investor–owned (for–profit) **Service**: General medical and surgical

Staffed Beds: 20 Admissions: 1274 Census: 10 Outpatient Visits: 90628 Births: 0 Total Expense ($000): 61573 Payroll Expense ($000): 17275 Personnel: 272

HAMILTON—Ravalli County

★ **MARCUS DALY MEMORIAL HOSPITAL (271340)**, 1200 Westwood Drive, Zip 59840–2345; tel. 406/363–2211, **A**10 18 **F**3 7 8 11 13 15 17 18 28 29 30 34 35 40 45 50 57 59 62 63 64 65 70 74 75 76 77 79 81 83 84 89 93 97 102 107 110 111 115 119 127 129 130 131 132 133 144 145 146 148 154
Primary Contact: John Bishop, Chief Executive Officer
CFO: Donja Erdman, Chief Financial Officer
CMO: John Moreland, M.D., Chief Medical Officer
CIO: Brad Kowalski, Director Information Technology
CHR: Debbie M Morris, Director Human Resources
CNO: Kathy Padilla, Director of Nursing
Web address: www.mdmh.org
Control: Other not–for–profit (including NFP Corporation) **Service**: General medical and surgical

Staffed Beds: 25 Admissions: 1621 Census: 15 Outpatient Visits: 48903 Births: 123 Total Expense ($000): 63592 Payroll Expense ($000): 34936 Personnel: 494

HARDIN—Big Horn County

★ **BIG HORN COUNTY MEMORIAL HOSPITAL (271338)**, 17 North Miles Avenue, Zip 59034–2323; (Total facility includes 36 beds in nursing home–type unit) **A**10 18 **F**10 15 29 34 40 41 43 45 59 64 67 81 89 90 93 107 110 111 114 119 125 128 130 133 143 146 149 154 158
Primary Contact: Kristi Gatrell, Chief Executive Officer
CFO: Roxie Cain, Chief Financial Officer
CNO: Kirsten Willoughby, Director of Nursing
Control: Other not–for–profit (including NFP Corporation) **Service**: General medical and surgical

Staffed Beds: 61 Admissions: 360 Census: 41 Outpatient Visits: 8688 Births: 5 Total Expense ($000): 15739 Payroll Expense ($000): 7429 Personnel: 166

HARLEM—Blaine County

FORT BELKNAP SERVICE UNIT (271315), 669 Agency Main Street, Zip 59526–9455; tel. 406/353–3100, (Nonreporting) **A**10 18 **S** U. S. Indian Health Service, Rockville, MD
Primary Contact: Gregory Smith, M.D., Chief Executive Officer
CMO: Ethel L Moore, M.D., Director of Medical Affairs
CIO: Mikki Grant, Chief Information Officer
CHR: Charlotte Lamebull, Administrative Officer
CNO: Diana Hunter, Director of Nursing
Web address: www.ihs.gov
Control: PHS, Indian Service, Government, federal **Service**: General medical and surgical

Staffed Beds: 6

HARLOWTON—Wheatland County

★ **WHEATLAND MEMORIAL HEALTHCARE (271321)**, 530 Third Street North West, Zip 59036, Mailing Address: P.O. Box 287, Zip 59036–0287; tel. 406/632–4351, (Nonreporting) **A**10 18
Primary Contact: Rick Poss, Interim Chief Executive Officer
CFO: Doug Lewis, Chief Financial Officer
CMO: Kathy Jutila, M.D., Chief of Staff
CIO: Ray Hetherington, Network Administrator
CHR: Peggy Hiner, Director Human Resources
CNO: Lauri Ann Cooney, Director Nursing
Web address: www.wheatlandmemorial.org
Control: Other not–for–profit (including NFP Corporation) **Service**: General medical and surgical

Staffed Beds: 25

HAVRE—Hill County

★ **NORTHERN MONTANA HEALTH CARE (270032)**, 30 13th Street, Zip 59501–5222, Mailing Address: P.O. Box 1231, Zip 59501–1231; tel. 406/265–2211, (Total facility includes 115 beds in nursing home–type unit) **A**10 20 **F**2 5 10 11 13 15 28 29 34 35 36 38 40 43 45 53 56 57 59 60 63 64 68 70 75 76 77 78 79 81 82 84 85 89 93 97 99 101 102 103 104 107 108 110 111 115 118 119 127 128 129 130 132 133 135 146 148 153 154 156
Primary Contact: David Henry, President and Chief Executive Officer
CFO: Kim Lucke, Vice President Finance
CNO: Eric Koch, Chief Nursing Officer
Web address: www.nmhcare.org
Control: Other not–for–profit (including NFP Corporation) **Service**: General medical and surgical

Staffed Beds: 142 Admissions: 1260 Census: 92 Outpatient Visits: 92311 Births: 349 Total Expense ($000): 61792 Payroll Expense ($000): 31944 Personnel: 520

HELENA—Lewis and Clark County

⊞ **SHODAIR CHILDREN'S HOSPITAL (274004)**, 2755 Colonial Drive, Zip 59601–4926, Mailing Address: P.O. Box 5539, Zip 59604–5539; tel. 406/444–7500, **A**1 10 **F**55 98 99 101 104 106 130 149 154
Primary Contact: Craig E. Aasved, Chief Executive Officer
CFO: Ron Wiens, Chief Financial Officer
CMO: Heather Zaluski, M.D., President Medical Staff
CIO: Judy Jackson, Director Health Information Management and Privacy Officer
CNO: Christine Bates, Chief Nursing Officer
Web address: www.shodair.org
Control: Other not–for–profit (including NFP Corporation) **Service**: Children's hospital psychiatric

Staffed Beds: 74 Admissions: 1111 Census: 60 Outpatient Visits: 2013 Births: 0 Total Expense ($000): 24502 Payroll Expense ($000): 14132 Personnel: 282

★ ⇑ **ST. PETER'S HOSPITAL (270003)**, 2475 Broadway, Zip 59601–4928; tel. 406/442–2480, **A**2 10 20 21 **F**3 7 11 13 15 18 22 26 28 29 30 31 34 35 40 43 44 45 46 49 50 51 54 56 57 59 60 62 63 64 68 70 76 77 78 79 81 82 84 87 89 93 97 98 100 103 104 107 108 110 111 114 115 116 117 118 119 120 121 122 123 124 129 130 135 144 146 148 153 154 156
Primary Contact: Wade C. Johnson, MS, FACHE, Chief Executive Officer
CFO: John Green, Vice President Finance
CMO: Shelly Harkins, M.D., Chief Medical Officer
CHR: Karla Smith, Director Human Resources
CNO: Cheryl Hunt Esq Chief Nursing Officer
Web address: www.stpetes.org
Control: Other not–for–profit (including NFP Corporation) **Service**: General medical and surgical

Staffed Beds: 123 Admissions: 5209 Census: 67 Outpatient Visits: 402065 Births: 751 Total Expense ($000): 214979 Payroll Expense ($000): 89560 Personnel: 1243

MT

Hospital, Medicare Provider Number, Address, Telephone, Approval, Facility, and Physician Codes, Health Care System

★ American Hospital Association (AHA) membership ○ Healthcare Facilities Accreditation Program ⇑ Center for Improvement in Healthcare Quality Accreditation
☐ The Joint Commission accreditation ◇ DNV Healthcare Inc. accreditation △ Commission on Accreditation of Rehabilitation Facilities (CARF) accreditation

JORDAN—Garfield County

GARFIELD COUNTY HEALTH CENTER (271310), 332 Leavitt Avenue,
Zip 59337, Mailing Address: P.O. Box 389, Zip 59337-0389; tel. 406/557-2500,
(Nonreporting) **A**10 18
Primary Contact: Landon Dybdal, Chief Executive Officer
CFO: Charlotte Herbold, Manager Business Officer
CMO: David M. Kidder, D.O., Chief Medical Officer
CIO: Charlotte Herbold, Manager Business Officer
CNO: Sarah Nordlund, Director of Nursing
Web address: www.garfieldco.us/garfield-county-health-center.html
Control: County, Government, nonfederal **Service**: General medical and surgical

Staffed Beds: 28

KALISPELL—Flathead County

HEALTHCENTER NORTHWEST See The Healthcenter

★ **KALISPELL REGIONAL HEALTHCARE (270051)**, 310 Sunnyview Lane,
Zip 59901-3129; tel. 406/752-5111, (Includes PATHWAYS TREATMENT CENTER,
200 Heritage Way, Kalispell, Montana, Zip 59901; tel. 406/756-3950) **A**2 3 5 10
F3 4 5 7 8 13 15 18 19 20 22 24 26 28 29 30 31 34 35 36 40 43 45 46 49 50
56 57 58 59 62 63 64 70 71 72 74 75 77 78 79 81 83 84 85 86 87 88 89 93
97 98 99 100 101 102 103 104 105 107 114 115 118 119 120 121 123 126
129 130 131 132 143 144 145 146 147 148 149 151 152 153 154 155 156
157 **S** QHR, Brentwood, TN
Primary Contact: Craig Lambrecht, M.D., President and Chief Executive Officer
COO: Ted W Hirsch, Senior Executive Director
CFO: Tracey Talley, Chief Financial and Information Officer
CHR: Deb Wilson, Director Human Resources
Web address: www.krmc.org
Control: Other not-for-profit (including NFP Corporation) **Service**: General
medical and surgical

Staffed Beds: 178 **Admissions**: 8594 **Census**: 105 **Outpatient
Visits**: 219593 **Births**: 650 **Total Expense ($000)**: 434992 **Payroll Expense
($000)**: 193339 **Personnel**: 2652

★ **THE HEALTHCENTER (270087)**, 320 Sunnyview Lane, Zip 59901-3129;
tel. 406/751-7550, **A**10 **F**3 15 33 36 39 45 59 64 71 81 82 85 90 91 95 96
107 110 111 112 114 115 117 119 124 126 147 149 **S** QHR, Brentwood, TN
Primary Contact: Tate J. Kreitinger, Chief Executive Officer
CFO: Charles T Pearce, Chief Financial and Information Officer
CIO: Charles T Pearce, Chief Financial and Information Officer
CHR: Susan Stevens, Director Human Resources
CNO: Victoria Johnson, R.N., Nursing Director of Surgical and Medical Services
Web address: www.krmc.org
Control: Corporation, Investor-owned (for-profit) **Service**: General medical and surgical

Staffed Beds: 28 **Admissions**: 820 **Census**: 10 **Outpatient Visits**: 74910
Births: 0 **Total Expense ($000)**: 72183 **Payroll Expense ($000)**: 17394
Personnel: 247

LEWISTOWN—Fergus County

★ **CENTRAL MONTANA MEDICAL CENTER (271345)**, 408 Wendell Avenue,
Zip 59457-2261; tel. 406/535-7711, **A**5 10 18 **F**3 7 11 13 15 28 29 31 34 35
40 43 45 50 53 59 62 63 64 65 75 76 77 81 84 85 86 87 89 91 92 93 97 107
108 110 111 115 119 129 130 131 132 133 146 148 156
Primary Contact: Laura Bennett, Interim Chief Executive Officer
CFO: Alan Aldrich, Chief Financial Officer
CHR: Torie A Lynch, Manager Human Resources
CNO: Karen White, Chief Nursing Officer
Web address: www.cmmccares.com
Control: Other not-for-profit (including NFP Corporation) **Service**: General
medical and surgical

Staffed Beds: 25 **Admissions**: 712 **Census**: 5 **Outpatient Visits**: 51336
Births: 76 **Total Expense ($000)**: 34221 **Payroll Expense ($000)**: 16713
Personnel: 276

LIBBY—Lincoln County

★ **CABINET PEAKS MEDICAL CENTER (271320)**, 209 Health Park Drive,
Zip 59923-2130; tel. 406/283-7000, **A**5 10 18 **F**3 11 13 15 17 28 29 30 31
34 35 40 45 50 54 56 57 59 64 70 75 76 77 79 81 84 85 86 87 89 93 97 102
107 110 111 114 119 128 129 130 131 132 133 135 144 146 147 148 154
156 **S** QHR, Brentwood, TN
Primary Contact: Bruce Whitfield, CPA, Chief Executive Officer and Chief Financial
Officer
CFO: Bruce Whitfield, CPA, Chief Executive Officer and Chief Financial Officer
CMO: Jay Maloney, M.D., Chief of Staff
Web address: www.sjlh.com
Control: Other not-for-profit (including NFP Corporation) **Service**: General
medical and surgical

Staffed Beds: 25 **Admissions**: 925 **Census**: 7 **Outpatient Visits**: 43064
Births: 93 **Total Expense ($000)**: 35135 **Payroll Expense ($000)**: 14382
Personnel: 226

LIVINGSTON—Park County

★ **LIVINGSTON HEALTHCARE (271317)**, 320 Alpenglow Lane, Zip 59047-8506;
tel. 406/222-3541, **A**5 10 18 **F**3 13 15 17 28 29 30 31 34 35 38 40 41 43 45
46 50 55 56 57 59 62 63 64 65 66 67 70 75 76 77 78 79 81 84 85 86 87 89
93 100 101 102 104 107 108 110 111 114 119 124 127 128 129 130 131
133 144 146 147 148 149 150 154 156
Primary Contact: Deb Anczak, Interim Chief Executive Officer
CFO: Ryan Speas, Director Finance
CMO: D. Scott Coleman, M.D., Medical Director
CIO: Jody Duran, Manager Information Systems
CHR: Vicki Axtell, Director Human Resources
CNO: Dave Noble, Director of Nursing
Web address: www.livingstonhealthcare.org
Control: Other not-for-profit (including NFP Corporation) **Service**: General
medical and surgical

Staffed Beds: 25 **Admissions**: 1176 **Census**: 12 **Outpatient Visits**: 34500
Births: 136 **Total Expense ($000)**: 48727 **Payroll Expense ($000)**: 22022
Personnel: 312

MALTA—Phillips County

★ **PHILLIPS COUNTY HOSPITAL (271312)**, 311 South 8th Avenue East,
Zip 59538-0640, Mailing Address: P.O. Box 640, Zip 59538-0640; tel. 406/654-
1100, **A**10 18 **F**3 29 31 34 40 41 56 57 59 62 66 68 82 84 90 93 107 115
119 127 130 132 133 156
Primary Contact: Ward C. VanWichen, Chief Executive Officer
CFO: Stephanie Denham, Chief Financial Officer and Human Resources Officer
CMO: Ed Medina, M.D., Medical Director
CHR: Stephanie Denham, Chief Financial Officer and Human Resources Officer
CNO: Lonna Crowder, Director of Nursing
Web address: www.pchospital.us/
Control: Other not-for-profit (including NFP Corporation) **Service**: General
medical and surgical

Staffed Beds: 8 **Admissions**: 171 **Census**: 1 **Outpatient Visits**: 6765
Births: 0 **Total Expense ($000)**: 6675 **Payroll Expense ($000)**: 3351
Personnel: 60

MILES CITY—Custer County

⊠ **HOLY ROSARY HEALTHCARE (271347)**, 2600 Wilson Street, Zip 59301-5094;
tel. 406/233-2600, (Total facility includes 75 beds in nursing home-type unit) **A**1
10 18 **F**3 13 15 27 28 29 30 31 32 34 35 40 47 50 56 57 59 63 64 65 68 70
75 76 77 78 79 81 84 85 87 89 93 94 97 107 108 110 111 115 119 124 127
130 131 132 133 135 146 147 149 154 156 157 **S** SCL Health, Broomfield, CO
Primary Contact: Paul Lewis, Chief Executive Officer
CFO: Travis Scheving, Chief Financial Officer
CMO: Michael Bush, M.D., Chief Medical Officer
CHR: Cathy Rodenbaugh, Director Human Resources
CNO: Lisa Sanford, VP Patient Care/CNO
Web address: www.holyrosaryhealthcare.org
Control: Other not-for-profit (including NFP Corporation) **Service**: General
medical and surgical

Staffed Beds: 90 **Admissions**: 1212 **Census**: 57 **Outpatient Visits**: 30626
Births: 196 **Total Expense ($000)**: 40702 **Payroll Expense ($000)**: 15264
Personnel: 213

MISSOULA—Missoula County

⊠ △ **COMMUNITY MEDICAL CENTER (270023)**, 2827 Fort Missoula Road,
Zip 59804-7408; tel. 406/728-4100, **A**1 3 5 7 10 19 **F**3 11 13 15 17 18 20
22 26 28 29 30 31 34 35 37 40 43 46 47 48 49 51 54 55 57 59 64 65 68 70
72 74 75 76 78 79 81 82 83 84 85 87 88 90 91 92 93 94 96 97 106 107 108
110 111 114 115 116 117 118 119 120 121 123 124 126 130 132 134 135
141 143 144 145 146 147 148 149 154 156 **S** LifePoint Health, Brentwood, TN
Primary Contact: Dean French, M.D., Chief Executive Officer
CMO: David Lechner, M.D., Chief Medical Officer and Vice President Innovation
CNO: Jan Perry, R.N., Vice President Patient Care Services
Web address: www.communitymed.org
Control: Corporation, Investor-owned (for-profit) **Service**: General medical and surgical

Staffed Beds: 135 **Admissions**: 4682 **Census**: 62 **Outpatient
Visits**: 140579 **Births**: 1039 **Total Expense ($000)**: 161289 **Payroll
Expense ($000)**: 61437 **Personnel**: 1023

MT

Many Facility Codes have changed. Please refer to the AHA Guide Code Chart. © 2019 AHA Guide

⊞ **PROVIDENCE ST. PATRICK HOSPITAL (270014)**, 500 West Broadway, Zip 59802–4096, Mailing Address: P.O. Box 4587, Zip 59806–4587; tel. 406/543–7271, **A**1 2 3 5 10 19 **F**3 11 12 13 15 18 20 22 24 26 28 29 30 31 34 35 38 40 43 50 51 53 57 58 59 60 61 64 68 70 72 74 75 76 77 78 79 81 82 83 84 85 86 87 89 92 93 96 97 98 99 100 101 102 103 104 105 107 108 109 110 111 113 114 115 116 117 118 119 120 121 123 124 126 127 129 130 131 132 141 146 148 149 154 156 157 **S** Providence St. Joseph Health, Renton, WA
Primary Contact: Joyce Dombrouski, R.N., Chief Executive Officer
CFO: Kirk Bodlovic, WMSA Chief Financial Officer
CHR: Karyn Trainor, Director Human Resources
CNO: Carol Bensen, MSN, R.N., Chief Nursing Officer
Web address: www.https://montana.providence.org/locations-directory/s/st-patrick-hospital
Control: Church operated, Nongovernment, not–for–profit **Service**: General medical and surgical

Staffed Beds: 183 **Admissions**: 10688 **Census**: 130 **Outpatient Visits**: 336086 **Births**: 477 **Total Expense ($000)**: 249000 **Payroll Expense ($000)**: 78648 **Personnel**: 1652

PHILIPSBURG—Granite County

★ **GRANITE COUNTY MEDICAL CENTER (271303)**, 310 Sansome Street, Zip 59858–0729, Mailing Address: P.O. Box 729, Zip 59858–0729; tel. 406/859–3271, **A**10 18 **F**2 32 34 35 40 41 56 57 59 64 67 68 89 90 93 97 100 102 104 105 119 127 128 130 133 135 143 146 147 148 154 **S** Providence St. Joseph Health, Renton, WA
Primary Contact: Maria Stoppler, Chief Executive Officer
CFO: Susan Ossello, Chief Financial Officer
CMO: John Moore, M.D., Medical Director
Web address: www.gcmedcenter.org/
Control: Hospital district or authority, Government, nonfederal **Service**: General medical and surgical

Staffed Beds: 25 **Admissions**: 25 **Census**: 1 **Outpatient Visits**: 4537 **Births**: 0 **Total Expense ($000)**: 4132 **Payroll Expense ($000)**: 1713

PLAINS—Sanders County

★ **CLARK FORK VALLEY HOSPITAL (271323)**, 10 Kruger Road, Zip 59859, Mailing Address: P.O. Box 768, Zip 59859–0768; tel. 406/826–4800, (Total facility includes 28 beds in nursing home–type unit) **A**10 18 **F**3 11 13 15 28 29 30 32 34 35 36 40 43 44 45 50 57 58 59 62 63 64 65 70 75 76 77 79 81 82 83 84 85 86 87 89 91 93 97 107 110 114 115 118 119 127 128 129 130 132 133 135 143 146 147 148 149 154 156
Primary Contact: Gregory S. Hanson, M.D., Chief Executive Officer
CFO: Carla A Neiman, Chief Financial Officer
CMO: Ronald Black, M.D., Chief Medical Officer
CIO: Carla A Neiman, Chief Financial Officer
CHR: Barry Fowler, Director Human and System Resources
CNO: Lisa Eberhardt, Chief Nursing Officer
Web address: www.cfvh.org
Control: Other not–for–profit (including NFP Corporation) **Service**: General medical and surgical

Staffed Beds: 44 **Admissions**: 522 **Census**: 35 **Outpatient Visits**: 20589 **Births**: 28 **Total Expense ($000)**: 21546 **Payroll Expense ($000)**: 9737 **Personnel**: 205

PLENTYWOOD—Sheridan County

SHERIDAN MEMORIAL HOSPITAL (271322), 440 West Laurel Avenue, Zip 59254–1596; tel. 406/765–3700, (Nonreporting) **A**10 18
Primary Contact: Gregory L. Maurer, Chief Executive Officer
CIO: Troy McClymont, Chief Information Technology Officer
Web address: www.sheridanmemorial.net/
Control: Other not–for–profit (including NFP Corporation) **Service**: General medical and surgical

Staffed Beds: 97

POLSON—Lake County

⊞ **PROVIDENCE ST. JOSEPH MEDICAL CENTER (271343)**, 6 Thirteenth Avenue East, Zip 59860–5315, Mailing Address: P.O. Box 1010, Zip 59860–1010; tel. 406/883–5377, **A**1 10 18 **F**3 10 13 15 28 29 30 31 34 35 40 43 45 50 57 59 64 68 75 76 77 79 81 82 85 87 89 93 97 107 110 111 115 119 125 127 129 130 131 133 146 147 148 149 154 **S** Providence St. Joseph Health, Renton, WA
Primary Contact: Devin Huntley, Chief Operating Officer
COO: Devin Huntley, Chief Operating Officer
CFO: Kirk Bodlovic, Vice President and Chief Financial Officer
CMO: Kelly Bagnell, M.D., Chief of Staff
Web address: www.saintjoes.org
Control: Church operated, Nongovernment, not–for–profit **Service**: General medical and surgical

Staffed Beds: 22 **Admissions**: 697 **Census**: 6 **Outpatient Visits**: 97783 **Births**: 135 **Total Expense ($000)**: 28325 **Payroll Expense ($000)**: 17790 **Personnel**: 194

POPLAR—Richland County

★ **POPLAR COMMUNITY HOSPITAL (271300)**, 211 H Street, Zip 59255–9519, Mailing Address: P.O. Box 38, Zip 59255–0038; tel. 406/768–6100, **A**10 18 **F**3 7 31 40 43 50 57 59 75 87 97 101 102 104 107 115 127 130 133 143 147
Primary Contact: Margaret B. Norgaard, Chief Executive Officer
CHR: Annie Block, Director Human Resources
Web address: www.nemhs.net
Control: Other not–for–profit (including NFP Corporation) **Service**: General medical and surgical

Staffed Beds: 20 **Admissions**: 165 **Census**: 5 **Outpatient Visits**: 7044 **Births**: 5 **Total Expense ($000)**: 8008 **Payroll Expense ($000)**: 3337 **Personnel**: 83

RED LODGE—Carbon County

★ **BEARTOOTH BILLINGS CLINIC (271326)**, 2525 North Broadway Avenue, Zip 59068–9222, Mailing Address: P.O. Box 590, Zip 59068–0590; tel. 406/446–2345, **A**5 10 18 **F**3 11 15 18 28 29 34 35 40 43 44 45 50 56 57 59 62 63 64 65 68 75 77 81 84 85 86 87 91 93 94 96 97 107 110 114 119 130 131 133 135 146 147 148 149 154 156
Primary Contact: Kelley Evans, Chief Administrative Officer
CFO: Kyle Gee, Chief Financial Officer
CMO: William George, M.D., Chief of Staff
CHR: Katie Murray, Director Human Resources
CNO: Bridgett Chartier, Director of Nursing
Web address: www.beartoothbillingsclinic.org
Control: Other not–for–profit (including NFP Corporation) **Service**: General medical and surgical

Staffed Beds: 10 **Admissions**: 178 **Census**: 2 **Outpatient Visits**: 63479 **Births**: 0 **Total Expense ($000)**: 14677 **Payroll Expense ($000)**: 5416 **Personnel**: 109

RONAN—Lake County

★ **ST. LUKE COMMUNITY HEALTHCARE (271325)**, 107 Sixth Avenue SW, Zip 59864–2634; tel. 406/676–4441, (Total facility includes 75 beds in nursing home–type unit) **A**10 18 **F**2 13 15 28 29 31 34 40 43 45 53 54 56 57 59 61 64 65 68 75 76 78 79 81 85 93 97 107 108 110 111 115 119 127 128 129 130 131 132 133 135 144 145 147 154
Primary Contact: Steve J. Todd, Chief Executive Officer
COO: Sarah Teaff, Chief Operating Officer
CFO: Paul Soukup, Chief Financial Officer
CMO: Edred T. Vizcarra, M.D., Chief of Staff
CHR: Theresa L. Jones, Manager Human Resources
CNO: Leah Emerson, Director of Nursing
Web address: www.stlukehealthcare.org
Control: Other not–for–profit (including NFP Corporation) **Service**: General medical and surgical

Staffed Beds: 100 **Admissions**: 939 **Census**: 52 **Outpatient Visits**: 68750 **Births**: 83 **Total Expense ($000)**: 39818 **Payroll Expense ($000)**: 20800 **Personnel**: 353

MT

Hospital, Medicare Provider Number, Address, Telephone, Approval, Facility, and Physician Codes, Health Care System

★ American Hospital Association (AHA) membership ○ Healthcare Facilities Accreditation Program ⇑ Center for Improvement in Healthcare Quality Accreditation
□ The Joint Commission accreditation ◇ DNV Healthcare Inc. accreditation △ Commission on Accreditation of Rehabilitation Facilities (CARF) accreditation

© 2019 AHA Guide · *Many Facility Codes have changed. Please refer to the AHA Guide Code Chart.* · Hospitals **A379**

ROUNDUP—Musselshell County

★ **ROUNDUP MEMORIAL HEALTHCARE (271346)**, 1202 Third Street West, Zip 59072–1816, Mailing Address: P.O. Box 40, Zip 59072–0040; tel. 406/323–2301, **A**10 18 **F**3 11 29 30 34 35 40 57 59 65 66 67 87 93 97 102 107 119 127 130 132 133 146 147 148 156
Primary Contact: Randy Anderson, Interim Chief Executive Officer
CFO: Kyle Gee, Regional Vice President Financial Operations
CMO: Mark Ward, M.D., Chief of Staff
CHR: Michelle Clement, Executive Assistant/Human Resources Director
CNO: Emily Shoup, Director Nursing Services
Web address: www.rmhmt.org/
Control: Other not–for–profit (including NFP Corporation) **Service**: General medical and surgical

Staffed Beds: 25 **Admissions:** 222 **Census:** 19 **Outpatient Visits:** 10001
Births: 0 **Total Expense ($000):** 8249 **Payroll Expense ($000):** 3415
Personnel: 84

SAINT MARY—Glacier County

BLACKFEET COMMUNITY HOSPITAL (270074), 760 New Hospital Circle, Zip 59417–0760, Mailing Address: P.O. Box 760, Browning, Zip 59417–0760; tel. 406/338–6100, (Nonreporting) **A**10 **S** U. S. Indian Health Service, Rockville, MD
Primary Contact: Garland Stiffarm, Chief Executive Officer
CFO: Cleo Main, Finance Officer
CMO: Neil Sun Rhodes, M.D., Chief Medical Officer
CNO: Susan Head, Director Nursing Services
Web address: www.ihs.gov
Control: PHS, Indian Service, Government, federal **Service**: General medical and surgical

Staffed Beds: 25

SCOBEY—Daniels County

DANIELS MEMORIAL HEALTHCARE CENTER (271342), 105 Fifth Avenue East, Zip 59263, Mailing Address: P.O. Box 400, Zip 59263–0400; tel. 406/487–2296, **A**10 18 **F**2 11 29 40 44 50 56 59 64 65 67 69 75 85 91 93 97 107 114 119 127 130 133 143 146 148
Primary Contact: Eric Connell, Chief Executive Officer
CMO: Don Sawdey, M.D., Medical Director
CHR: Edith Huda, Director Human Resources
CNO: Kathy Ware, Director of Nursing
Web address: www.danielsmemorialhealthcare.org
Control: Hospital district or authority, Government, nonfederal **Service**: General medical and surgical

Staffed Beds: 25 **Admissions:** 117 **Census:** 21 **Outpatient Visits:** 4101
Births: 0 **Total Expense ($000):** 7548 **Payroll Expense ($000):** 3508
Personnel: 92

SHELBY—Toole County

MARIAS MEDICAL CENTER (271328), 640 Park Drive, Zip 59474–1663, Mailing Address: P.O. Box 915, Zip 59474–0915; tel. 406/434–3200, **A**10 18 **F**3 11 13 15 17 28 29 34 40 41 53 56 57 59 65 70 77 81 83 85 87 93 102 107 110 114 119 129 130 133 146 154 **S** QHR, Brentwood, TN
Primary Contact: Jessica Brusven, Chief Executive Officer
CFO: Melissa Ostberg, Chief Financial Officer
CMO: Melanie Hardy, D.O., Chief of Staff
CIO: Jayce Yarn, Director Information Technology
CHR: Cindy Lamb, Director Human Resources
CNO: Tamra Fender, Chief Nursing Officer
Web address: www.mmcmt.org
Control: County, Government, nonfederal **Service**: General medical and surgical

Staffed Beds: 21 **Admissions:** 143 **Census:** 2 **Outpatient Visits:** 21154
Births: 36 **Total Expense ($000):** 11350 **Payroll Expense ($000):** 3928
Personnel: 73

SHERIDAN—Madison County

RUBY VALLEY MEDICAL CENTER (271319), 220 East Crofoot Street, Zip 59749–7714, Mailing Address: 321 Madison Street, Zip 59749–0336; tel. 406/842–5453, **A**10 18 **F**3 7 11 29 33 34 35 38 40 43 55 56 57 65 66 75 82 86 87 91 93 97 100 104 107 111 114 127 130 133 135 147 148 149
Primary Contact: John H. Semingson, Chief Executive Officer
CFO: Dennis Holschbach, Chief Financial Officer
CMO: Roman Hendrickson, M.D., Medical Director
CHR: Jenny Rohrback, Director Human Resource
CNO: Brenda Green, Director of Nursing
Web address: www.rubyvalleyhospital.com/
Control: Hospital district or authority, Government, nonfederal **Service**: General medical and surgical

Staffed Beds: 5 **Admissions:** 106 **Census:** 1 **Outpatient Visits:** 8711
Births: 0 **Total Expense ($000):** 7015 **Payroll Expense ($000):** 3870
Personnel: 43

SIDNEY—Richland County

★ **SIDNEY HEALTH CENTER (271344)**, 216 14th Avenue SW, Zip 59270–3586; tel. 406/488–2100, (Total facility includes 56 beds in nursing home–type unit) **A**10 18 **F**2 3 11 13 15 17 28 30 31 34 35 40 41 45 50 55 56 58 59 62 63 64 70 75 76 78 79 81 82 84 85 86 87 89 93 96 97 107 108 110 111 115 119 120 121 122 123 124 128 129 130 132 133 144 145 146 147 148 149 154
Primary Contact: Jennifer Doty, Chief Executive Officer
CFO: Tina Montgomery, Chief Financial Officer
CMO: Rajohn Karanjai, M.D., Chief Medical Officer
CIO: Brian Fay, Director Information Systems
CHR: Lisa Aisenbrey, Administrator Human Resources and Support Services
Web address: www.sidneyhealth.org
Control: Other not–for–profit (including NFP Corporation) **Service**: General medical and surgical

Staffed Beds: 81 **Admissions:** 1150 **Census:** 56 **Outpatient Visits:** 42189
Births: 197 **Total Expense ($000):** 63437 **Payroll Expense ($000):** 22320
Personnel: 354

SUPERIOR—Mineral County

MINERAL COMMUNITY HOSPITAL (271331), 1208 6th Avenue East, Zip 59872–9618; tel. 406/822–4841, (Nonreporting) **A**10 18
Primary Contact: Steve McNeece, Interim Chief Executive Officer
CFO: Cliff Case, Chief Financial Officer
CMO: Roger Pafford, M.D., Medical Director
CHR: Stacy Conrow-Ververis, Director Human Resources
CNO: Jenifer Mitchell, R.N., Director of Nursing Services
Web address: www.mineralcommunityhospital.com/
Control: Other not–for–profit (including NFP Corporation) **Service**: General medical and surgical

Staffed Beds: 25

TERRY—Prairie County

PRAIRIE COMMUNITY HEALTH CENTER See Prairie Community Hospital

★ **PRAIRIE COMMUNITY HOSPITAL (271309)**, 312 South Adams Avenue, Zip 59349–0156, Mailing Address: P.O. Box 156, Zip 59349–0156; tel. 406/635–5511, **A**10 18 **F**2 34 40 41 57 59 64 65 69 75 87 93 127 133 135 146 148 154
Primary Contact: Burt Keltner, Administrator
CFO: Laurie Chandler, Financial Officer
CIO: Laurie Chandler, Chairman
CNO: Susan Morgan, Director of Nursing Services
Web address: www.prairiecommunityhospital.org/
Control: Hospital district or authority, Government, nonfederal **Service**: General medical and surgical

Staffed Beds: 22 **Admissions:** 50 **Census:** 20 **Outpatient Visits:** 3683
Births: 0 **Total Expense ($000):** 3183 **Payroll Expense ($000):** 1219
Personnel: 38

TOWNSEND—Broadwater County

BROADWATER HEALTH CENTER (271333), 110 North Oak Street, Zip 59644–2306; tel. 406/266–3186, (Nonreporting) **A**10 18
Primary Contact: Kyle Hopstad, Chief Executive Officer
CFO: Jennifer Clowes, Chief Financial Officer
CMO: Carol Bridges, M.D., Medical Director
CHR: April Campbell, Director Human Resources
CNO: Fran Wright, Director of Nursing
Web address: www.broadwaterhealthcenter.com
Control: County, Government, nonfederal **Service**: General medical and surgical

Staffed Beds: 41

WARM SPRINGS—Deer Lodge County

MONTANA STATE HOSPITAL (274086), 100 Garnet Way, Zip 59756–9705, Mailing Address: P.O. Box 300, tel. 406/693–7000, (Nonreporting) **A**10
Primary Contact: Kyle Fouts, Interim Administrator
CFO: Tracey Thun, Director Business and Support Services
CMO: Thomas Gray, M.D., Medical Director
CIO: Melinda Bridgewater, Director, Information Services
CHR: Todd Thun, Director Human Resources
CNO: Dave Olson, Director of Nursing
Web address: www.msh.mt.gov
Control: State, Government, nonfederal **Service**: Psychiatric

Staffed Beds: 288

MT

Many Facility Codes have changed. Please refer to the AHA Guide Code Chart. © 2019 AHA Guide

WHITE SULPHUR SPRINGS—Meagher County

MOUNTAINVIEW MEDICAL CENTER (271306), 16 West Main Street,
Zip 59645–9036, Mailing Address: P.O. Box 'Q', Zip 59645–0817;
tel. 406/547–3321, **A**10 18 **F**3 14 29 30 33 34 35 40 41 43 50 55 56 57 59 63
64 65 70 75 77 82 84 86 87 90 91 93 97 100 102 104 106 107 114 119 130
133 135 147 148 154
Primary Contact: Rob Brandt, Chief Executive Officer
Web address: www.mvmc.org
Control: Other not–for–profit (including NFP Corporation) **Service**: General
medical and surgical

Staffed Beds: 25 **Admissions:** 60 **Census:** 1 **Outpatient Visits:** 3500
Births: 0

WHITEFISH—Flathead County

★ **NORTH VALLEY HOSPITAL (271336)**, 1600 Hospital Way, Zip 59937–7849;
tel. 406/863–3500, **A**10 18 **F**3 11 13 15 28 29 30 31 34 35 37 40 43 50 51
54 56 59 64 65 68 70 75 76 79 81 85 86 87 97 104 107 110 111 114 119
126 127 129 131 132 133 135 144 146 148 156 **S** QHR, Brentwood, TN
Primary Contact: Kevin Abel, Chief Executive Officer
COO: Christina Bogers, Chief Clinical Officer
CFO: David Richhart, Chief Financial Officer
CMO: Jason Cohen, M.D., Chief Medical Officer
CIO: Michael Barnes, Chief Information Officer
CHR: Joseph Schmier, Interim Director Human Resources
Web address: www.nvhosp.org
Control: Other not–for–profit (including NFP Corporation) **Service**: General
medical and surgical

Staffed Beds: 25 **Admissions:** 1671 **Census:** 13 **Outpatient Visits:** 96919
Births: 566 **Total Expense ($000):** 62097 **Payroll Expense ($000):** 25160
Personnel: 361

WOLF POINT—Roosevelt County

★ **TRINITY HOSPITAL (271341)**, 315 Knapp Street, Zip 59201–1826;
tel. 406/653–6500, (Total facility includes 60 beds in nursing home–type unit) **A**10
18 **F**2 3 6 7 8 13 15 29 31 32 34 40 43 45 50 56 57 59 64 70 75 76 78 81 92
93 110 119 120 125 127 128 130 133 143 145 154
Primary Contact: Margaret B. Norgaard, Chief Executive Officer
Web address: www.nemhs.net
Control: Other not–for–profit (including NFP Corporation) **Service**: General
medical and surgical

Staffed Beds: 82 **Admissions:** 366 **Census:** 53 **Outpatient Visits:** 11961
Births: 90 **Total Expense ($000):** 18509 **Payroll Expense ($000):** 9133
Personnel: 212

MT

Hospital, Medicare Provider Number, Address, Telephone, Approval, Facility, and Physician Codes, Health Care System

★ American Hospital Association (AHA) membership ○ Healthcare Facilities Accreditation Program ⇑ Center for Improvement in Healthcare Quality Accreditation
☐ The Joint Commission accreditation ◇ DNV Healthcare Inc. accreditation △ Commission on Accreditation of Rehabilitation Facilities (CARF) accreditation

© 2019 AHA Guide *Many Facility Codes have changed. Please refer to the AHA Guide Code Chart.* Hospitals **A381**

NEBRASKA

AINSWORTH—Brown County

BROWN COUNTY HOSPITAL (281325), 945 East Zero Street, Zip 69210–1547; tel. 402/387–2800, (Nonreporting) **A**10 18
Primary Contact: John W. Werner, Chief Executive Officer
CFO: Tom Wiedell, Chief Financial Officer
CMO: Melvin Campbell, M.D., Medical Staff Chairman
CIO: Mike Depko, Director Information Technology
CHR: Lisa Fischer, Director Human Resources
CNO: Matt Lentz, R.N., Director of Patient Services
Web address: www.browncountyhospital.org
Control: County, Government, nonfederal **Service:** General medical and surgical

Staffed Beds: 18

ALBION—Boone County

★ **BOONE COUNTY HEALTH CENTER (281334)**, 723 West Fairview Street, Zip 68620–1725, Mailing Address: P.O. Box 151, Zip 68620–0151; tel. 402/395–2191, (Nonreporting) **A**3 5 10 18
Primary Contact: Tanya Sharp, President and Chief Executive Officer
CFO: Rita Liss, Vice President Fiscal Services and Chief Financial Officer
CMO: Lynette Kramer, M.D., Chief Medical Officer
CIO: Larry Zoucha, Chief Information Officer
CHR: Jennifer Beierman, Director Human Resources
CNO: Cindy Lesiak, Vice President Patient Care Services and Director of Nursing
Web address: www.boonecohealth.org
Control: County, Government, nonfederal **Service:** General medical and surgical

Staffed Beds: 25

ALLIANCE—Box Butte County

✉ **BOX BUTTE GENERAL HOSPITAL (281360)**, 2101 Box Butte Avenue, Zip 69301–4445, Mailing Address: P.O. Box 810, Zip 69301–0810; tel. 308/762–6660, **A**1 10 18 **F**3 5 11 13 15 28 29 32 34 35 36 38 40 43 47 48 50 51 53 57 59 60 64 68 69 75 77 78 79 81 82 85 86 87 92 93 97 100 101 104 107 108 111 114 116 118 119 127 129 130 131 132 133 134 135 146 148 154 156
Primary Contact: Lori Mazanec, Chief Executive Officer
COO: Lori Mazanec, Chief Operating Officer
CFO: Tracy E Jatczak, CPA, Chief Financial Officer
CHR: Lisa L Hillyer, Human Resources Manager
CNO: Carolyn Jones, R.N., MSN, Chief Nursing Officer
Web address: www.bbgh.org
Control: County, Government, nonfederal **Service:** General medical and surgical

Staffed Beds: 25 Admissions: 874 Census: 8 Outpatient Visits: 47597 Births: 83 Total Expense ($000): 44225 Payroll Expense ($000): 15850 Personnel: 276

ALMA—Harlan County

★ **HARLAN COUNTY HEALTH SYSTEM (281300)**, 717 North Brown Street, Zip 68920–2132, Mailing Address: P.O. Box 836, Zip 68920–0836; tel. 308/928–2151, **A**10 18 **F**1 3 4 11 15 16 17 29 31 40 45 50 57 59 64 67 70 72 73 80 81 85 88 89 90 93 97 98 107 110 114 119 127 128 130 133 135 146 156 **S** Great Plains Health Alliance, Inc., Wichita, KS
Primary Contact: Mark A. Miller, FACHE, Chief Executive Officer
CFO: Heidi Cushing, Chief Financial Officer
CMO: Cameron Knackstedt, D.O., Chief Medical Staff
CIO: Michael Andrews, Coordinator Information Systems
CHR: Ana Schluntz, Director of Human Resources
CNO: Elizabeth Miller, Director of Nursing
Web address: www.harlancountyhealth.com
Control: County, Government, nonfederal **Service:** General medical and surgical

Staffed Beds: 19 Admissions: 109 Census: 2 Outpatient Visits: 17697 Births: 0 Total Expense ($000): 9583 Payroll Expense ($000): 3991 Personnel: 70

ATKINSON—Holt County

WEST HOLT MEDICAL SERVICES (281343), 406 West Neely Street, Zip 68713–4801; tel. 402/925–2811, (Nonreporting) **A**10 18 **S** Faith Regional Health Services, Norfolk, NE
Primary Contact: Jeremy Bauer, Interim Chief Executive Officer
CFO: Jeremy Bauer, Director of Finance
CMO: John Tubbs, M.D., Chief of Staff
CIO: Mark Johnson, Chief Information Officer
CHR: Margaret Linse, Administrative Secretary and Director Human Resources
CNO: Jennifer Rystrom, R.N., Chief Nursing Officer
Web address: www.westholtmed.org
Control: Other not–for–profit (including NFP Corporation) **Service:** General medical and surgical

Staffed Beds: 17

AUBURN—Nemaha County

★ ⇑ **NEMAHA COUNTY HOSPITAL (281324)**, 2022 13th Street, Zip 68305–1799; tel. 402/274–4366, **A**10 18 21 **F**3 7 12 15 28 29 30 31 34 35 40 43 62 64 68 74 75 77 78 79 81 85 86 87 93 94 107 110 111 114 117 119 128 129 130 131 133 135 141 148 149 154 156
Primary Contact: Marty Fattig, Chief Executive Officer
COO: Kermit Moore, R.N., Chief Operating Officer and Chief Nursing Officer
CFO: Stacy Taylor, Chief Financial Officer
CIO: Kathy McNaughton, Chief Information Officer
CHR: Susan Shupp, Chief Human Resources Officer
Web address: www.nchnet.org
Control: County, Government, nonfederal **Service:** General medical and surgical

Staffed Beds: 16 Admissions: 212 Census: 3 Outpatient Visits: 20235 Births: 0 Total Expense ($000): 10364 Payroll Expense ($000): 5202 Personnel: 90

AURORA—Hamilton County

★ **MEMORIAL COMMUNITY HEALTH (281320)**, 1423 Seventh Street, Zip 68818–1197; tel. 402/694–3171, (Total facility includes 47 beds in nursing home–type unit) **A**10 18 **F**10 11 13 15 28 29 31 34 35 40 41 43 45 50 51 57 59 64 65 67 75 76 77 78 79 81 82 85 86 87 93 94 97 107 108 110 114 119 130 131 132 133 146 154 156
Primary Contact: Diane R. Keller, Chief Executive Officer
CFO: Phil Fendt, Chief Financial Officer
CMO: Jeff Muilenburg, Chief of Staff
CIO: Brad Tiede, Director Information Systems
CHR: Laura Teichmeier, Director Human Resources
CNO: Lindy Mosel, Director of Nursing
Web address: www.memorialcommunityhealth.org
Control: Other not–for–profit (including NFP Corporation) **Service:** General medical and surgical

Staffed Beds: 63 Admissions: 338 Census: 45 Outpatient Visits: 25954 Births: 20 Total Expense ($000): 22762 Payroll Expense ($000): 11379 Personnel: 217

MEMORIAL HOSPITAL See Memorial Community Health

BASSETT—Rock County

ROCK COUNTY HOSPITAL (281333), 102 East South Street, Zip 68714–5508; tel. 402/684–3366, (Total facility includes 30 beds in nursing home–type unit) **A**10 18 **F**7 11 15 28 40 53 81 84 107 110 119 127 128 133 154
Primary Contact: Stacey A. Knox, Administrator
CMO: John Tubbs, M.D., Chief of Staff
CIO: Cal Alder, Director Information Technology
CHR: Jackie Carpenter, Office Manager
CNO: Katie Ogier, Director of Nursing
Web address: www.rockcountyhospital.com
Control: County, Government, nonfederal **Service:** General medical and surgical

Staffed Beds: 54 Admissions: 122 Census: 24 Outpatient Visits: 5680 Births: 0 Total Expense ($000): 11542 Payroll Expense ($000): 4298 Personnel: 92

NE

Many Facility Codes have changed. Please refer to the AHA Guide Code Chart.
© 2019 AHA Guide

BEATRICE—Gage County

★ **BEATRICE COMMUNITY HOSPITAL AND HEALTH CENTER (281364)**, 4800 Hospital Parkway, Zip 68310–6906, Mailing Address: P.O. Box 278, Zip 68310–0278; tel. 402/228–3344, **A**10 18 **F**3 13 15 28 29 31 34 35 40 45 57 62 63 64 65 68 69 70 75 76 78 79 81 82 84 85 87 93 104 107 108 110 111 114 119 127 129 130 131 132 133 135 146 147 149 156
Primary Contact: Richard Haraldson, CPA, FACHE, Chief Executive Officer
CFO: Alan W Streeter, Chief Financial Officer
CMO: John T Findley, M.D., Chief Medical Officer
CHR: Kathryn G. Humble, Chief Human Resources Officer
CNO: Arlinda K Ament, R.N., Interim Chief Nursing Officer
Web address: www.beatricecommunityhospital.com
Control: Other not–for–profit (including NFP Corporation) **Service**: General medical and surgical

Staffed Beds: 25 **Admissions**: 1063 **Census**: 10 **Outpatient Visits**: 197565 **Births**: 208 **Total Expense ($000)**: 75575 **Payroll Expense ($000)**: 36047 **Personnel**: 504

BELLEVUE—Sarpy County

☐ **NEBRASKA MEDICINE - BELLEVUE (280132)**, 2500 Bellevue Medical Center Drive, Zip 68123–1591; tel. 402/763–3000, **A**1 3 5 10 **F**3 13 15 18 20 22 28 29 30 31 34 35 40 41 44 45 47 48 49 50 51 53 55 57 58 59 60 63 64 65 68 70 74 75 76 77 78 79 81 82 84 85 86 87 91 92 93 96 97 107 108 110 111 114 119 130 131 132 135 141 143 145 146 147 148 149 150 154
Primary Contact: Matt E. Pospisil, Vice President Perioperative Services
CFO: Stephanie Daubert, Chief Financial Officer
CMO: Jeffrey D. Akerson, M.D., Chief Medical Officer
CIO: Brian Lancaster, Executive Director Information Management
CNO: Ray D. Dial, Director of Nursing
Web address: www.nebraskamed.com
Control: Other not–for–profit (including NFP Corporation) **Service**: General medical and surgical

Staffed Beds: 64 **Admissions**: 4649 **Census**: 41 **Outpatient Visits**: 116459 **Births**: 529 **Total Expense ($000)**: 66772 **Payroll Expense ($000)**: 28120 **Personnel**: 406

BENKELMAN—Dundy County

▲ **DUNDY COUNTY HOSPITAL (281340)**, 1313 North Cheyenne Street, Zip 69021–3074, Mailing Address: P.O. Box 626, Zip 69021–0626; tel. 308/423–2204, **A**10 18 **F**3 29 31 32 33 34 40 43 50 56 57 59 65 78 79 81 82 87 93 107 110 114 119 127 130 131 133 154
Primary Contact: Rita A. Jones, Chief Executive Officer
COO: Wendy Elkins, Director Operations
CFO: Renee Fink, CPA, Chief Financial Officer
CMO: Jose Garcia, M.D., Chief Medical Staff
CIO: David Craw, Coordinator Information Technology
CHR: Dundy Noffsinger, Executive Assistant, Risk Manager and Director Marketing
CNO: Laken Vrbas, R.N., Director of Nursing
Web address: www.dchbenkelman.com
Control: County, Government, nonfederal **Service**: General medical and surgical

Staffed Beds: 14 **Admissions**: 136 **Census**: 1 **Outpatient Visits**: 6653 **Births**: 0 **Total Expense ($000)**: 9454 **Payroll Expense ($000)**: 4779 **Personnel**: 87

BLAIR—Washington County

★ **MEMORIAL COMMUNITY HOSPITAL AND HEALTH SYSTEM (281359)**, 810 North 22nd Street, Zip 68008–1199, Mailing Address: P.O. Box 250, Zip 68008–0250; tel. 402/426–2182, (Nonreporting) **A**10 18
Primary Contact: Manuela Wolf, R.N., President and Chief Executive Officer
CFO: Jennifer Newby, Operations Director Support Services and Finance
CMO: John F Simonson, M.D., President Medical Staff
CHR: Kristine Nielsen, Manager Human Resources
CNO: Christinia Jepsen, R.N., Chief Nursing Executive
Web address: www.mchhs.org
Control: Other not–for–profit (including NFP Corporation) **Service**: General medical and surgical

Staffed Beds: 25

BRIDGEPORT—Morrill County

MORRILL COUNTY COMMUNITY HOSPITAL (281318), 1313 'S' Street, Zip 69336–0579; tel. 308/262–1616, (Nonreporting) **A**10 18
Primary Contact: Robin Stuart, Chief Executive Officer
CFO: Connie Christensen, Chief Financial Officer
CMO: John Post, M.D., Medical Director
CIO: Lori Shengle, Director Information Technology
CHR: Rhea Basa, Director Human Resources
CNO: Sylvia Marie Lichius, R.N., Chief Nursing Officer
Web address: www.morrillcountyhospital.com
Control: County, Government, nonfederal **Service**: General medical and surgical

Staffed Beds: 20

BROKEN BOW—Custer County

★ **JENNIE M. MELHAM MEMORIAL MEDICAL CENTER (281365)**, 145 Memorial Drive, Zip 68822–1378, Mailing Address: P.O. Box 250, Zip 68822–0250; tel. 308/872–4100, (Nonreporting) **A**10 18
Primary Contact: Veronica Schmidt, President and Chief Executive Officer
CFO: Tim Schuckman, Chief Financial Officer
CIO: Tim Schuckman, Chief Financial Officer
CHR: Teri Sell, Payroll and Personnel Coordinator
CNO: Shelly Amsberry, Director of Nursing
Web address: www.https://www.melham.org
Control: Other not–for–profit (including NFP Corporation) **Service**: General medical and surgical

Staffed Beds: 73

CALLAWAY—Custer County

★ **CALLAWAY DISTRICT HOSPITAL (281335)**, 211 East Kimball, Zip 68825–2589, Mailing Address: P.O. Box 100, Zip 68825–0100; tel. 308/836–2228, (Nonreporting) **A**10 18
Primary Contact: Brett Eggleston, Chief Executive Officer
CFO: Caleb Poore, Chief Financial Officer
CHR: Toni French, Manager Human Resources
Web address: www.callawayhospital.org
Control: Hospital district or authority, Government, nonfederal **Service**: General medical and surgical

Staffed Beds: 12

CAMBRIDGE—Furnas County

★ **TRI VALLEY HEALTH SYSTEM (281348)**, 1305 West Highway 6 and 34, Zip 69022–0488, Mailing Address: P.O. Box 488, Zip 69022–0488; tel. 308/697–3329, (Nonreporting) **A**10 18
Primary Contact: Jessica Marie. Fisher, Chief Executive Officer
COO: Keith Luedders, Chief Operations Officer
CFO: Diana Swindler, Chief Financial Officer
CMO: Shiuvaun Jaeger, M.D., Chief of Staff
CIO: Ciprian Galarneau, Director Information Systems
CHR: Tammy Claussen, Chief Human Resource Officer
CNO: Jessica Roth, R.N., Chief Clinical Officer
Web address: www.trivalleyhealth.com
Control: Other not–for–profit (including NFP Corporation) **Service**: General medical and surgical

Staffed Beds: 52

CENTRAL CITY—Merrick County

★ **MERRICK MEDICAL CENTER (281328)**, 1715 26th Street, Zip 68826–9620; tel. 308/946–3015, (Nonreporting) **A**10 18 **S** Bryan Health, Lincoln, NE
Primary Contact: Paul A. Clark, President and Chief Executive Officer
CHR: Shauna Graham, Director of Professional Services Human Resources, Marketing Foundation
Web address: www.https://www.bryanhealth.com
Control: County, Government, nonfederal **Service**: General medical and surgical

Staffed Beds: 20

NE

CHADRON—Dawes County

★ **CHADRON COMMUNITY HOSPITAL AND HEALTH SERVICES (281341)**, 825 Centennial Drive, Zip 69337–9400; tel. 308/432-5586, **A**10 18 **F**3 7 10 11 12 13 15 28 29 31 34 35 38 39 40 43 44 45 57 59 60 61 62 63 64 65 66 68 70 75 77 78 79 81 82 84 86 87 91 93 96 107 110 111 114 119 125 127 130 131 132 133 134 135 143 146 148 149 156
Primary Contact: Allen J. Gamble, Interim Chief Executive Officer
CFO: Russ Bohnenkamp, Chief Financial Officer
CMO: Ed Pelton, Chief of Staff
CHR: Ellen Krueger, Director Human Resources
CNO: Alisha Obando, Director of Nursing
Web address: www.chadronhospital.com
Control: Other not–for–profit (including NFP Corporation) **Service**: General medical and surgical

Staffed Beds: 25 Admissions: 456 Census: 4 Outpatient Visits: 16775
Births: 92 Total Expense ($000): 25580 **Payroll Expense ($000):** 9556
Personnel: 170

COLUMBUS—Platte County

✉ **COLUMBUS COMMUNITY HOSPITAL (280111)**, 4600 38th Street, Zip 68601–1664, Mailing Address: P.O. Box 1800, Zip 68602–1800; tel. 402/564-7118, (Nonreporting) **A**1 10 20
Primary Contact: Michael T. Hansen, FACHE, President and Chief Executive Officer
COO: James P Goulet, Vice President Operations
CFO: Chad Van Cleave, Chief Financial Officer
CMO: Mark Howerter, M.D., President Medical Staff
CIO: Cheryl Tira, Director Information Systems
CHR: Scott E Messersmith, Director Human Resources
CNO: Linda K Walline, R.N., Ph.D., MSN, Vice President Nursing
Web address: www.columbushosp.org
Control: Other not–for–profit (including NFP Corporation) **Service**: General medical and surgical

Staffed Beds: 51

COZAD—Dawson County

★ **COZAD COMMUNITY HEALTH SYSTEM (281327)**, 300 East 12th Street, Zip 69130–1505, Mailing Address: P.O. Box 108, Zip 69130–0108; tel. 308/784-2261, **A**5 10 18 **F**3 10 13 15 28 30 31 34 35 40 43 50 53 57 59 62 63 68 70 75 76 77 81 84 86 87 93 94 97 107 114 119 127 128 129 130 131 132 133 135 146 148 149 154 157
Primary Contact: Lyle E. Davis, Administrator
Web address: www.cozadhealthcare.com
Control: Hospital district or authority, Government, nonfederal **Service**: General medical and surgical

Staffed Beds: 20 Admissions: 259 Census: 3 Outpatient Visits: 8831
Births: 19 Total Expense ($000): 15103 **Payroll Expense ($000):** 7319
Personnel: 149

CREIGHTON—Knox County

★ **AVERA CREIGHTON HOSPITAL (281331)**, 1503 Main Street, Zip 68729–3007, Mailing Address: P.O. Box 126, Zip 68729–0186; tel. 402/358-5700, (Total facility includes 47 beds in nursing home–type unit) **A**10 18 **F**7 15 18 28 29 34 35 40 41 43 45 47 50 53 56 59 65 67 77 79 81 82 89 93 94 97 100 104 107 108 110 115 127 128 129 131 133 143 146 149 154 **S** Avera Health, Sioux Falls, SD
Primary Contact: Todd Consbruck, Chief Executive Officer
CHR: Jane E. Miller, Director Human Resources
CNO: Jean M. Henes, MSN, R.N., Director of Nursing
Web address: www.avera.org/creighton/
Control: Other not–for–profit (including NFP Corporation) **Service**: General medical and surgical

Staffed Beds: 70 Admissions: 249 Census: 46 Outpatient Visits: 14414
Births: 0 Total Expense ($000): 14662 **Payroll Expense ($000):** 7542
Personnel: 52

CRETE—Saline County

★ **CRETE AREA MEDICAL CENTER (281354)**, 2910 Betten Drive, Zip 68333–3084, Mailing Address: P.O. Box 220, Zip 68333–0220; tel. 402/826-2102, **A**10 18 **F**13 15 28 29 31 34 40 43 45 57 59 64 65 68 78 79 81 93 97 107 111 114 117 119 127 129 130 131 133 143 146 147 148 154 156 **S** Bryan Health, Lincoln, NE
Primary Contact: Rebekah Mussman, President and Chief Executive Officer
CFO: Julie Lacy, Chief Financial Officer
CMO: Amy Vertin, M.D., Chief of Staff
CIO: Drew Kotil, Director Information Technology
CHR: Bobbie Wilson, Director Human Resources
CNO: Jeaniffr P. Snide, Chief Nursing Officer
Web address: www.creteareamedicalcenter.com
Control: Other not–for–profit (including NFP Corporation) **Service**: General medical and surgical

Staffed Beds: 24 Admissions: 256 Census: 2 Outpatient Visits: 107494
Births: 74 Total Expense ($000): 22766 **Payroll Expense ($000):** 9816
Personnel: 142

DAVID CITY—Butler County

★ **BUTLER COUNTY HEALTH CARE CENTER (281332)**, 372 South Ninth Street, Zip 68632–2116; tel. 402/367-1200, (Nonreporting) **A**10 18
Primary Contact: Donald T. Naiberk, Administrator and Chief Executive Officer
CFO: Jodi Prochaska, Chief Financial Officer
CMO: Victor Thoendel, M.D., Chief Medical Officer
CIO: Cindy Neesen, Director of Information Technology
CHR: Andra Vandenberg, Director Human Resources
CNO: Sue M Birkel, R.N., Director of Nursing
Web address: www.bchccnet.org
Control: County, Government, nonfederal **Service**: General medical and surgical

Staffed Beds: 20

ELKHORN—Douglas County

METHODIST WOMEN'S HOSPITAL See Nebraska Methodist Hospital, Omaha

FAIRBURY—Jefferson County

★ **JEFFERSON COMMUNITY HEALTH AND LIFE (281319)**, 2200 'H' Street, Zip 68352–1119, Mailing Address: P.O. Box 277, Zip 68352–0277; tel. 402/729-3351, (Total facility includes 40 beds in nursing home–type unit) **A**10 18 **F**2 3 15 28 29 30 31 34 35 40 45 50 53 57 59 62 64 75 77 78 79 81 85 86 87 93 107 110 114 119 127 128 130 131 132 133 135 146 149 156
Primary Contact: Chad Jurgens, Chief Executive Officer
CFO: Chance Klasek, CPA, Chief Financial Officer
CIO: Dennis Ahl, Director Information Technology
CHR: Sandra A. Bauer, Director Human Resources
CNO: Erin L. Starr, Chief Nursing Officer
Web address: www.jchealthandlife.org
Control: Other not–for–profit (including NFP Corporation) **Service**: General medical and surgical

Staffed Beds: 57 Admissions: 338 Census: 39 Outpatient Visits: 28152
Births: 7 Total Expense ($000): 21955 **Payroll Expense ($000):** 10520
Personnel: 201

FALLS CITY—Richardson County

★ **COMMUNITY MEDICAL CENTER, INC. (281352)**, 3307 Barada Street, Zip 68355–2470, Mailing Address: P.O. Box 399, Zip 68355–0399; tel. 402/245-2428, **A**10 18 **F**3 13 15 28 31 34 35 40 43 45 59 75 76 78 79 81 82 85 93 97 107 111 114 119 127 130 133 135 154
Primary Contact: Ryan C. Larsen, FACHE, Chief Executive Officer
CFO: Scott Sawyer, Chief Financial Officer
CMO: David E. Borg, Chief of Medical Staff
CIO: Joe Buckminster, Manager Information Technology
CHR: Shannon Weinmann, Human Resources Manager
CNO: Ivy Campbell, Director of Nursing
Web address: www.cmcfc.org
Control: Other not–for–profit (including NFP Corporation) **Service**: General medical and surgical

Staffed Beds: 24 Admissions: 759 Census: 8 Outpatient Visits: 22445
Births: 53 Total Expense ($000): 27545 **Payroll Expense ($000):** 9305
Personnel: 178

FRANKLIN—Franklin County

★ **FRANKLIN COUNTY MEMORIAL HOSPITAL (281311)**, 1406 'Q' Street, Zip 68939–0315, Mailing Address: 1406 Q Street, Zip 68939–0315; tel. 308/425-6221, (Nonreporting) **A**10 18
Primary Contact: Theresa Rizzo, Administrator
CFO: Amy Kahrs, Director of Finance
CMO: Linda Mazour, M.D., President
CIO: Cathy Webber, Director of Health Information Management
CNO: Kari Yelken, R.N., Director of Nursing
Web address: www.fcmh.com
Control: County, Government, nonfederal **Service**: General medical and surgical

Staffed Beds: 14

FREMONT—Dodge County

⊞ **METHODIST FREMONT HEALTH (280077)**, 450 East 23rd Street, Zip 68025–2387; tel. 402/721–1610, (Total facility includes 106 beds in nursing home–type unit) **A**1 2 3 5 10 20 **F**3 8 11 13 15 17 18 20 22 26 28 29 30 31 34 35 37 40 44 45 56 57 59 62 63 64 68 70 75 76 77 78 81 85 86 87 89 93 98 100 103 104 107 108 110 111 114 119 120 121 123 124 126 128 129 130 131 132 135 143 144 146 156 **S** Nebraska Methodist Health System, Inc., Omaha, NE
Primary Contact: Brett M. Richmond, President and Chief Executive Officer
CFO: Michael Sindelar, Vice President and Chief Financial Officer
CIO: Matt Sakalosky, Director Information Services and Chief Information Officer
CHR: Bethany Childers, Director Human Resources
CNO: Melinda Johanna Kentfield, R.N., Director of Nursing and Interim Chief Nursing Officer
Web address: www.fremonthealth.com
Control: County, Government, nonfederal **Service**: General medical and surgical

Staffed Beds: 181 Admissions: 4158 Census: 116 Outpatient Visits: 84379 Births: 299 Total Expense ($000): 120833 Payroll Expense ($000): 53391 Personnel: 748

FRIEND—Saline County

FRIEND COMMUNITY HEALTHCARE SYSTEM (281330), 905 Second Street, Zip 68359–1133; tel. 402/947–2541, **A**10 18 **F**1 11 34 35 40 53 57 59 64 67 69 81 87 91 97 107 119 128 130 133 143 146 157
Primary Contact: John W. Wilson, Chief Executive Officer
CFO: Mackenzie Svarc, Finance Director
CMO: Roger Meyer, M.D., Chief of Staff
CHR: Shyanne Scholl, Interim Human Resources Director
CNO: Dayna Pulver, Director of Nursing
Web address: www.friendmed.org/
Control: City, Government, nonfederal **Service**: General medical and surgical

Staffed Beds: 17 Admissions: 89 Census: 3 Outpatient Visits: 2408 Births: 0 Total Expense ($000): 5204 Payroll Expense ($000): 2292

GENEVA—Fillmore County

FILLMORE COUNTY HOSPITAL (281301), 1900 'F' Street, Zip 68361–1325, Mailing Address: P.O. Box 193, Zip 68361–0193; tel. 402/759–3167, **A**10 18 **F**7 11 13 15 18 28 29 31 34 40 41 45 46 47 48 49 50 56 57 59 64 67 68 74 75 76 77 78 79 81 82 85 87 92 93 94 98 101 102 103 104 107 110 111 114 119 128 130 131 132 133 143 148 153 154
Primary Contact: Christopher Nichols, Chief Executive Officer
COO: Debbie Domann, Director of Operations
CFO: Jeanne Ackland, Director of Finance
CMO: Jason Bespaloc, M.D., Chief of Staff
CIO: Tyler Gewecke, Information Technology Technician
CHR: Abby Tuberville, Human Resource Manager
Web address: www.fhsofgeneva.org
Control: County, Government, nonfederal **Service**: General medical and surgical

Staffed Beds: 30 Admissions: 438 Census: 8 Outpatient Visits: 25539 Births: 27 Total Expense ($000): 19721 Payroll Expense ($000): 7655 Personnel: 160

GENOA—Nance County

GENOA MEDICAL FACILITIES (281312), 706 Ewing Avenue, Zip 68640–3035, Mailing Address: P.O. Box 310, Zip 68640–0310; tel. 402/993–2283, (Nonreporting) **A**10 18 **S** Faith Regional Health Services, Norfolk, NE
Primary Contact: Amanda Roebuck, Chief Executive Officer
CFO: Angie Sutton, Chief Financial Officer
CMO: Brian Buhlke, M.D., Medical Director
CHR: Brianna Molt, Human Resources Director
Web address: www.genoamedical.org/
Control: City–county, Government, nonfederal **Service**: General medical and surgical

Staffed Beds: 58

GORDON—Sheridan County

GORDON MEMORIAL HEALTH SERVICES (281358), 300 East Eighth Street, Zip 69343–1123; tel. 308/282–0401, (Nonreporting) **A**10 18
Primary Contact: Doris Brown, Chief Executive Officer
CMO: Christopher P. Costa, M.D., Chief of Staff
CIO: Ray Waldron, Director Information Technology
CNO: Megan Heath, Chief Nursing Officer
Web address: www.gordonmemorial.org
Control: Hospital district or authority, Government, nonfederal **Service**: General medical and surgical

Staffed Beds: 25

GOTHENBURG—Dawson County

★ **GOTHENBURG HEALTH (281313)**, 910 20th Street, Zip 69138–1237, Mailing Address: P.O. Box 469, Zip 69138–0469; tel. 308/537–3661, **A**10 18 **F**3 13 15 28 29 30 31 34 35 36 37 38 40 41 43 45 50 53 56 57 59 64 65 75 76 77 78 79 81 85 97 107 110 111 115 119 127 129 133 147
Primary Contact: Mick Brant, FACHE, Chief Executive Officer
CFO: Michael Pracheil, Chief Financial Officer
CMO: Carol Shackleton, M.D., Medical Director
CIO: Tinna Therrien, R.N., Chief Information Officer and Senior Director Ancillary Services
CHR: Jim Imler, Director Human Resources
CNO: Susan Moore, MS, R.N., Chief Nursing Officer
Web address: www.gothenburghealth.org
Control: Hospital district or authority, Government, nonfederal **Service**: General medical and surgical

Staffed Beds: 7 Admissions: 227 Census: 1

GRAND ISLAND—Hall County

⊞ **CHI HEALTH SAINT FRANCIS (280023)**, 2620 West Faidley Avenue, Zip 68803–4297, Mailing Address: P.O. Box 9804, Zip 68802–9804; tel. 308/384–4600, (Includes ST. FRANCIS MEDICAL PLAZA, 2116 West Faidley Avenue, Grand Island, Nebraska, Zip 68803, Mailing Address: P O Box 9804, Zip 68802, tel. 308/384–4600) **A**1 2 3 5 10 19 **F**3 5 11 12 13 15 17 18 19 20 22 28 30 31 34 35 40 43 45 47 50 51 53 59 60 62 63 64 65 68 70 72 74 75 76 77 78 79 81 82 84 85 89 90 91 97 110 120 121 123 128 129 130 132 135 145 146 148 **S** CommonSpirit Health, Chicago, IL
Primary Contact: Edward J. Hannon, FACHE, President
CFO: Lisa Webb, Vice President Operational Finance
CMO: Shu–Ming Wang, MD, Vice President Medical Affairs
CHR: Nancy Wallace, Vice President Human Resources, CHI Health
CNO: Beth Bartlett, MSN, R.N., Vice President Nursing
Web address: www.saintfrancisgi.org
Control: Church operated, Nongovernment, not–for–profit **Service**: General medical and surgical

Staffed Beds: 159 Admissions: 5925 Census: 83 Outpatient Visits: 82348 Births: 880 Total Expense ($000): 140236 Payroll Expense ($000): 34186 Personnel: 586

GRANT—Perkins County

★ **PERKINS COUNTY HEALTH SERVICES (281356)**, 900 Lincoln Avenue, Zip 69140–3095; tel. 308/352–7200, (Nonreporting) **A**10 18
Primary Contact: Neil A. Hilton, FACHE, President and Chief Executive Officer
CMO: Ruth Demmel, M.D., Chief Medical Officer
CIO: Jennifer Baumgartner, Chief Information Officer
CHR: Julie Bevard, Vice President Human Resources
CNO: Dana McArtor, R.N., Director of Nursing
Web address: www.pchsgrant.com
Control: Hospital district or authority, Government, nonfederal **Service**: General medical and surgical

Staffed Beds: 20

HASTINGS—Adams County

⊞ **MARY LANNING HEALTHCARE (280032)**, 715 North St Joseph Avenue, Zip 68901–4497; tel. 402/463–4521, (Nonreporting) **A**1 2 3 5 10
Primary Contact: Eric A. Barber, President and Chief Executive Officer
COO: Mark Callahan, Chief Operating Officer
CFO: Shawn A Nordby, Chief Financial Officer
CMO: Donald R. Snodgrass, M.D., Chief Medical Officer
CIO: Lisa Nonneman, Director Information Technology Services
CHR: Bruce E Cutright, MS, Vice President Human Resources
CNO: Ronda S Ehly, R.N., Chief Nursing Officer
Web address: www.marylanning.org
Control: Other not–for–profit (including NFP Corporation) **Service**: General medical and surgical

Staffed Beds: 148

NE

HEBRON—Thayer County

★ **THAYER COUNTY HEALTH SERVICES (281304)**, 120 Park Avenue, Zip 68370–2019, Mailing Address: P.O. Box 49, Zip 68370–0049; tel. 402/768–6041, (Nonreporting) **A**10 18
Primary Contact: David Burd, Chief Executive Officer
COO: Stephanie Boldt, Chief Operating Officer
CFO: Doug Wismer, Chief Financial Officer
CMO: Leann Heinrichs, M.D., Chief of Staff
CIO: Randy Levendofsky, Director Information Technology
CHR: Tamara Brose, Director Human Resources
CNO: Jamie Koch, R.N., Chief Nursing Officer
Web address: www.thayercountyhealth.com
Control: County, Government, nonfederal **Service:** General medical and surgical

Staffed Beds: 19

HENDERSON—York County

HENDERSON HEALTH CARE SERVICES (281308), 1621 Front Street, Zip 68371–8902; tel. 402/723–4512, (Nonreporting) **A**10 18
Primary Contact: Cheryl Brown, Chief Executive Officer
CMO: James M Ohrt, M.D., Director Medical Staff
CHR: Lynette Friesen, Manager Human Resources
CNO: Carrie Peterson, Director of Nursing
Web address: www.hendersonhealthcare.org/getpage.php?name=message
Control: Other not–for–profit (including NFP Corporation) **Service:** General medical and surgical

Staffed Beds: 56

HOLDREGE—Phelps County

★ ⇑ **PHELPS MEMORIAL HEALTH CENTER (281362)**, 1215 Tibbals Street, Zip 68949–1255; tel. 308/995–2211, (Nonreporting) **A**10 18 21 **S** QHR, Brentwood, TN
Primary Contact: Mark Harrel, Chief Executive Officer
CFO: Loren D Schroder, Chief Financial Officer
CMO: Stuart Embury, M.D., Chief Medical Officer
CIO: Leora Smith, Information System and Health Information Management Team Leader
CHR: Cindy Jackson, Director Human Resources
Web address: www.phelpsmemorial.com
Control: Other not–for–profit (including NFP Corporation) **Service:** General medical and surgical

Staffed Beds: 25

IMPERIAL—Chase County

★ **CHASE COUNTY COMMUNITY HOSPITAL (281351)**, 600 West 12th Street, Zip 69033–3130, Mailing Address: P.O. Box 819, Zip 69033–0819; tel. 308/882–7111, **A**10 18 **F**11 13 15 28 29 30 31 34 35 40 41 43 45 57 59 64 75 76 81 91 93 107 110 114 127 133 156
Primary Contact: Stephen Lewis, Chief Executive Officer
CFO: Abigail Cyboron, Chief Financial Officer
CMO: Jonathan Richman, M.D., Chief of Staff
CIO: Jen Harris, Director Health Information Management
CHR: Julie Sharp, Supervisor Human Resources
CNO: Kathy Geier, Director of Nursing
Web address: www.chasecountyhospital.com
Control: County, Government, nonfederal **Service:** General medical and surgical

Staffed Beds: 20 **Admissions:** 151 **Census:** 2 **Outpatient Visits:** 15397 **Births:** 12 **Total Expense ($000):** 12286 **Payroll Expense ($000):** 5017 **Personnel:** 92

KEARNEY—Buffalo County

⊞ **CHI HEALTH GOOD SAMARITAN (280009)**, 10 East 31st Street, Zip 68847–2926, Mailing Address: P.O. Box 1990, Zip 68848–1990; tel. 308/865–7100, (Includes RICHARD H. YOUNG BEHAVIORAL HEALTH CENTER, 1755 Prairie View Place, Kearney, Nebraska, Zip 68848, Mailing Address: P O Box 1750, Zip 68848–1705, tel. 308/865–2000; Michelle Hansen, Director) **A**1 2 3 5 10 19 **F**3 7 11 13 15 18 20 22 24 28 29 30 31 34 35 37 40 41 43 45 46 49 50 51 53 54 55 56 57 58 59 60 62 67 68 70 72 74 75 76 77 78 79 81 82 84 85 89 90 91 93 97 100 101 102 104 107 108 110 111 112 113 114 115 117 119 124 126 129 130 131 132 134 135 146 148 149 150 154 155 **S** CommonSpirit Health, Chicago, IL
Primary Contact: Michael H. Schnieders, FACHE, President
CFO: Lisa Webb, Vice President for Operational Finance
CMO: Dennis Edwards, M.D., Vice President Medical Affairs
CIO: Katie Gartner, Director Health Information Management
CNO: Kimber Bonner, R.N., Vice President Patient Care Services
Web address: www.chihealthgoodsamaritan.org
Control: Church operated, Nongovernment, not–for–profit **Service:** General medical and surgical

Staffed Beds: 218 **Admissions:** 6980 **Census:** 95 **Outpatient Visits:** 50517 **Births:** 479 **Total Expense ($000):** 161039 **Payroll Expense ($000):** 43542 **Personnel:** 678

GOOD SAMARITAN HEALTH SYSTEMS See Chi Health Good Samaritan

★ ○ **KEARNEY REGIONAL MEDICAL CENTER (280134)**, 804 22nd Avenue, Zip 68845–2206; tel. 855/404–5762, (Nonreporting) **A**10 11
Primary Contact: William Calhoun, Chief Executive Officer
COO: John Lanning, Chief Operating Officer
CFO: Steve Regier, Chief Financial Officer
CIO: Travis Gregg, Director of Strategy and Business Development
CHR: Steve Beck, MS, Chief Human Resource Officer
CNO: Adrienne Carney, R.N., Director Nursing and Surgical Services
Web address: www.kearneyregional.com
Control: Partnership, Investor–owned (for–profit) **Service:** General medical and surgical

Staffed Beds: 92

KIMBALL—Kimball County

★ **KIMBALL HEALTH SERVICES (281305)**, 505 South Burg Street, Zip 69145–1398; tel. 308/235–1952, (Nonreporting) **A**10 18
Primary Contact: Ken Hunter, R.N., Chief Executive Officer
CFO: Melissa Prante, Chief Financial Officer
CMO: James Plate, M.D., Chief of Staff
CIO: Charles Walker, Director Information Technology
CHR: Jim Imler, Director Human Resources
CNO: Richard Harriger, Director of Emergency Services
Web address: www.kimballhealth.org
Control: County, Government, nonfederal **Service:** General medical and surgical

Staffed Beds: 10

LEXINGTON—Dawson County

★ ⇑ **LEXINGTON REGIONAL HEALTH CENTER (281361)**, 1201 North Erie Street, Zip 68850–1560, Mailing Address: P.O. Box 980, Zip 68850–0980; tel. 308/324–5651, (Nonreporting) **A**3 5 10 18 21
Primary Contact: Leslie Marsh, Chief Executive Officer
COO: Jim Hain, Chief Operating Officer
CFO: Wade Eschenbrenner, Chief Financial Officer
CMO: Francisca Acosta–Carlson, M.D., Chief of Staff
CIO: Robb Hanna, Executive Director Information Technology
CHR: Jill Denker, Executive Director Human Resources
CNO: Nicole Thorell, R.N., MSN, Chief Nursing Officer
Web address: www.lexingtonregional.org
Control: Hospital district or authority, Government, nonfederal **Service:** General medical and surgical

Staffed Beds: 25

LINCOLN—Lancaster County

⊞ △ **BRYAN MEDICAL CENTER (280003)**, 1600 South 48th Street, Zip 68506–1299; tel. 402/481–1111, (Includes BRYAN MEDICAL CENTER-EAST, 1600 South 48th Street, Lincoln, Nebraska, Zip 68506–1299; tel. 402/481–1111; BRYAN MEDICAL CENTER-WEST, 2300 South 16th Street, Lincoln, Nebraska, Zip 68502–3781; tel. 402/475–1011) **A**1 2 3 7 10 **F**3 4 5 12 13 15 17 18 19 20 22 24 26 28 29 30 31 34 35 37 38 39 40 43 45 46 47 48 49 50 54 56 57 58 59 61 64 70 71 72 74 75 76 77 78 79 81 82 84 85 86 87 89 90 92 93 96 98 99 100 101 102 103 104 105 107 108 110 111 114 115 116 117 118 119 121 123 126 129 130 131 132 135 145 146 147 148 149 151 152 153 156 **S** Bryan Health, Lincoln, NE
Primary Contact: John T. Woodrich, President and Chief Operating Officer
CFO: Russell Gronewold, Chief Financial Officer
CMO: John Trapp, Vice President Medical Affairs
CIO: George Carr, Chief Information Officer
CHR: Jan Garvin, Vice President Human Resources
CNO: Lisa M Vail, R.N., Chief Nursing Officer and Vice President of Patient Care Services
Web address: www.bryanhealth.com
Control: Other not–for–profit (including NFP Corporation) **Service:** General medical and surgical

Staffed Beds: 551 **Admissions:** 29199 **Census:** 376 **Outpatient Visits:** 205392 **Births:** 3479 **Total Expense ($000):** 561720 **Payroll Expense ($000):** 211120 **Personnel:** 3266

★ **CHI HEALTH NEBRASKA HEART (280128)**, 7500 South 91st Street, Zip 68526–9437; tel. 402/327–2700, **A**10 **F**17 18 20 22 24 26 29 30 34 45 57 58 59 64 81 107 115 119 130 **S** CommonSpirit Health, Chicago, IL
Primary Contact: Derek Vance, President
Web address: www.CHIhealthNebraskaHeart.com
Control: Church operated, Nongovernment, not–for–profit **Service:** Heart

Staffed Beds: 54 **Admissions:** 2001 **Census:** 19 **Outpatient Visits:** 12547 **Births:** 0 **Total Expense ($000):** 65612 **Payroll Expense ($000):** 16685 **Personnel:** 223

NE

⊞ **CHI HEALTH ST ELIZABETH (280020)**, 555 South 70th Street, Zip 68510–2494; tel. 402/219–8000, **A**1 2 3 5 10 **F**3 8 11 12 13 15 16 29 30 31 34 35 37 39 40 44 45 46 47 48 49 50 51 53 55 58 59 60 61 64 65 68 70 72 74 75 76 78 79 80 81 84 85 86 87 89 92 107 108 110 111 114 115 116 117 118 119 120 121 123 124 126 129 130 131 132 144 145 146 147 148 154 **S** CommonSpirit Health, Chicago, IL
Primary Contact: Derek Vance, President
CFO: Tyler DeJong, Vice President, Operational Finance
CMO: Michael Ferris, M.D., Chief Medical Officer
CIO: Richard Bohaty, Director Information Technology
CHR: Nancy Wallace, Senior Vice President, Chief Human Resources Officer
CNO: Elizabeth A Raetz, R.N., MSN, Vice President Nursing and Chief Nursing Officer
Web address: www.saintelizabethonline.com
Control: Church operated, Nongovernment, not–for–profit **Service**: General medical and surgical

Staffed Beds: 258 Admissions: 7790 Census: 94 Outpatient Visits: 88696 Births: 1130 Total Expense ($000): 188459 Payroll Expense ($000): 48527 Personnel: 687

LINCOLN DIVISION See Veterans Affairs Nebraska-Western Iowa Health Care System - Lincoln, Lincoln

☐ **LINCOLN REGIONAL CENTER (284003)**, West Prospector Place and South Folsom, Zip 68522–2299, Mailing Address: P.O. Box 94949, Zip 68509–4949; tel. 402/471–4444, (Nonreporting) **A**1 10
Primary Contact: Mark LaBouchardiere, Interim Facility Administrator
COO: Stacey Werth-Sweeney, Facility Operating Officer
CFO: Randy Willey, Business Manager
CMO: Vijay Dewan, M.D., Clinical Director
CHR: Scott Rasmussen, Director Human Resources
Web address: www.hhs.state.ne.us/beh/rc
Control: State, Government, nonfederal **Service**: Psychiatric

Staffed Beds: 244

LINCOLN SURGICAL HOSPITAL (280127), 1710 South 70th Street, Suite 200, Zip 68506–1677; tel. 402/484–9090, (Nonreporting) **A**10
Primary Contact: Robb Linafelter, Chief Executive Officer
Web address: www.lincolnsurgery.com
Control: Corporation, Investor–owned (for–profit) **Service**: Surgical

Staffed Beds: 7

△ **MADONNA REHABILITATION HOSPITAL (283025)**, 5401 South Street, Zip 68506–2134; tel. 402/489–7102, (Nonreporting) **A**3 5 7 10
Primary Contact: Paul Dongilli Jr, Ph.D., FACHE, President and Chief Executive Officer
CFO: Victor J Witkowicz, Senior Vice President and Chief Financial Officer
CMO: Thomas Stadler, M.D., Vice President Medical Affairs and Chief Medical Officer
CIO: David Rolfe, Chief Information Officer
CHR: Lou Ann Manske, Vice President Human Resources
Web address: www.madonna.org
Control: Church operated **Service**: Rehabilitation

Staffed Beds: 308

MADONNA REHABILITATION HOSPITAL (282000), 5401 South Street, Zip 68506–2150; tel. 402/413–3000, (Nonreporting) **A**3 5 10
Primary Contact: Paul Dongilli Jr, Ph.D., FACHE, President and Chief Executive Officer
Web address: www.madonna.org/
Control: Other not–for–profit (including NFP Corporation) **Service**: Acute long–term care hospital

Staffed Beds: 300

NEBRASKA PENAL AND CORRECTIONAL HOSPITAL, 14th and Pioneer Streets, Zip 68501, Mailing Address: P.O. Box 94661, Zip 94661; tel. 402/471–3161, (Nonreporting)
Primary Contact: Randy T. Kohl, M.D., Deputy Director, Health Services
Web address: www.corrections.nebraska.gov
Control: State, Government, nonfederal **Service**: Hospital unit of an institution (prison hospital, college infirmary, etc.)

Staffed Beds: 12

⊞ **SELECT SPECIALTY HOSPITAL - LINCOLN (282002)**, 2300 South 16th Street, 7th Floor, Zip 68502–3704; tel. 402/483–8444, (Nonreporting) **A**1 10 **S** Select Medical Corporation, Mechanicsburg, PA
Primary Contact: Connie K. Siffring, Chief Executive Officer
CHR: Bob Dorsey, Human Resources Coordinator
CNO: Trisha Smolik, R.N., MSN, Chief Nursing Officer
Web address: www.selectmedical.com
Control: Corporation, Investor–owned (for–profit) **Service**: Acute long–term care hospital

Staffed Beds: 24

★ **VETERANS AFFAIRS NEBRASKA-WESTERN IOWA HEALTH CARE SYSTEM - LINCOLN**, 600 South 70th Street, Zip 68510–2493; tel. 402/489–3802, (Includes LINCOLN DIVISION, 600 South 70th Street, Lincoln, Nebraska, Zip 68510–2493; tel. 402/489–3802), (Non-reporting) **S** Department of Veterans Affairs, Washington, DC
Primary Contact: Don Burman, Director
CIO: David Daiker, Chief Information Resource Management
CHR: Dave Peters, Chief Human Resources Officer
Web address: www.nebraska.va.gov/
Control: Veterans Affairs, Government, federal **Service**: General medical and surgical

Staffed Beds: 132

LYNCH—Boyd County

NIOBRARA VALLEY HOSPITAL (281303), 401 South Fifth Street, Zip 68746–0118, Mailing Address: P.O. Box 118, Zip 68746–0118; tel. 402/569–2451, (Nonreporting) **A**10 18 **S** Faith Regional Health Services, Norfolk, NE
Primary Contact: Kelly Kalkowski, Chief Executive Officer
CFO: Martha Nelson, Chief Financial Officer
CMO: James Keil, M.D., Chief Medical Officer
CHR: Trudy Nelson, Chief Human Resource Officer
CNO: Debra Dawn Hanzlik, R.N., Director of Nursing
Web address: www.nvhcares.org
Control: Other not–for–profit (including NFP Corporation) **Service**: General medical and surgical

Staffed Beds: 20

MCCOOK—Red Willow County

★ ⇑ **COMMUNITY HOSPITAL (281363)**, 1301 East 'H' Street, Zip 69001-1328, Mailing Address: P.O. Box 1328, Zip 69001–1328; tel. 308/344–2650, **A**3 5 10 18 21 **F**3 11 13 15 28 29 31 34 35 40 41 45 48 50 51 57 62 63 64 75 77 78 79 81 85 93 96 107 110 111 114 119 120 121 127 129 130 131 132 133 135 146 148 154 156
Primary Contact: Troy Bruntz, President and Chief Executive Officer
CFO: Sean Wolfe, Vice President Finance and Chief Financial Officer
CMO: Jason Blomstedt, Chief of Staff
CIO: Lori Beeby, Director Information Systems
CHR: Leanne R Miller, Director Human Resources
Web address: www.chmccook.org
Control: Other not–for–profit (including NFP Corporation) **Service**: General medical and surgical

Staffed Beds: 25 Admissions: 1020 Census: 9 Outpatient Visits: 28952 Births: 132 Total Expense ($000): 44816 Payroll Expense ($000): 16132 Personnel: 249

MINDEN—Kearney County

KEARNEY COUNTY HEALTH SERVICES (281306), 727 East First Street, Zip 68959–1705; tel. 308/832–3400, **A**10 18 **F**3 15 28 29 34 40 41 55 57 59 64 65 68 75 81 87 89 97 104 107 110 114 115 119 127 128 129 130 132 133 135 145 146 147 148 149 154 156
Primary Contact: Luke David. Poore, Chief Executive Officer
CFO: Kayla Rhynalds, Interim Chief Financial Officer
CMO: Douglas Althouse, Chief Medical Staff
CHR: Rebecca L Cooke, Director Human Resources
CNO: Kendra Brown, MSN, R.N., Director of Nursing
Web address: www.kchs.org
Control: County, Government, nonfederal **Service**: General medical and surgical

Staffed Beds: 10 Admissions: 129 Census: 2 Outpatient Visits: 5123 Births: 0 Total Expense ($000): 12021 Payroll Expense ($000): 5477 Personnel: 80

NE

NEBRASKA CITY—Otoe County

★ **CHI HEALTH ST. MARY'S (281342)**, 1301 Grundman Boulevard, Zip 68410; tel. 402/873–3321, **A**10 18 **F**3 13 15 18 28 31 34 35 40 43 45 57 59 64 66 68 69 75 76 77 78 79 81 82 85 87 97 107 108 110 111 114 115 118 119 127 129 130 132 133 135 144 146 147 148 154 156 **S** CommonSpirit Health, Chicago, IL
Primary Contact: Daniel DeFreece, M.D., Interim President
CFO: Tim H. Schnack, Vice President Operations Finance
CMO: Jonathan Stelling, M.D., Vice President Medical Affairs
CNO: Brenda Jean Sebek, R.N., Administrator
Web address: www.chihealthstmarys.com
Control: Church operated, Nongovernment, not–for–profit **Service**: General medical and surgical

Staffed Beds: 18 **Admissions**: 378 **Census**: 3 **Outpatient Visits**: 34558 **Births**: 120 **Total Expense ($000)**: 24338 **Payroll Expense ($000)**: 6509 **Personnel**: 136

NELIGH—Antelope County

★ **ANTELOPE MEMORIAL HOSPITAL (281326)**, 102 West Ninth Street, Zip 68756–1114, Mailing Address: P.O. Box 229, Zip 68756–0229; tel. 402/887–4151, **A**10 18 **F**7 13 15 28 34 35 36 40 41 45 53 56 57 59 62 63 64 67 68 75 76 77 79 81 82 87 89 93 94 107 115 119 127 128 129 130 131 133 147 154
Primary Contact: Diane Carlin, FACHE, Chief Executive Officer
CFO: Martha Nelson, Chief Financial Officer
CMO: Troy Dawson, M.D., President Medical Staff
CIO: Kevin Trease, Chief Information Officer
CHR: Mary A Schwager, Director Human Resources
CNO: Merry Sprout, R.N., Chief Nursing Officer
Web address: www.amhne.org/
Control: Other not–for–profit (including NFP Corporation) **Service**: General medical and surgical

Staffed Beds: 23 **Admissions**: 232 **Census**: 3

NORFOLK—Madison County

✠ **FAITH REGIONAL HEALTH SERVICES (280125)**, 2700 West Norfolk Avenue, Zip 68701–4438, Mailing Address: P.O. Box 869, Zip 68702–0869; tel. 402/371–4880, (Includes EAST CAMPUS, 1500 Koenigstein Avenue, Norfolk, Nebraska, Zip 68701; tel. 402/371–3402; WEST CAMPUS, 2700 Norfolk Avenue, Norfolk, Nebraska, Zip 68701, Mailing Address: P O Box 869, Zip 68702–0869, tel. 402/371–4880) (Total facility includes 63 beds in nursing home–type unit) **A**1 2 3 5 10 20 **F**3 8 10 11 13 15 17 18 20 22 24 26 28 29 30 31 34 35 40 41 43 44 45 46 47 49 50 53 57 58 59 61 62 63 64 67 70 71 73 74 75 76 77 78 79 80 81 82 84 85 86 87 89 90 91 92 93 96 98 100 101 102 107 108 110 111 114 115 119 120 121 123 128 129 130 131 132 135 141 146 147 148 149 154 157 **S** Faith Regional Health Services, Norfolk, NE
Primary Contact: Kelly Driscoll, R.N., FACHE, President and Chief Executive Officer
CFO: Johnathan Wilker, Vice President Finance and Chief Financial Officer
CMO: Dean O French, M.D., Chief of Staff
CIO: Brian Sterud, Chief Information Officer
CHR: Janet M Pinkelman, Director Human Resources
Web address: www.frhs.org
Control: Other not–for–profit (including NFP Corporation) **Service**: General medical and surgical

Staffed Beds: 194 **Admissions**: 5258 **Census**: 194 **Outpatient Visits**: 80218 **Births**: 834 **Total Expense ($000)**: 150783 **Payroll Expense ($000)**: 53541 **Personnel**: 1112

NORTH PLATTE—Lincoln County

✠ **GREAT PLAINS HEALTH (280065)**, 601 West Leota Street, Zip 69101–6598, Mailing Address: P.O. Box 1167, Zip 69103–1167; tel. 308/568–8000, **A**1 2 3 5 10 **F**3 11 12 13 15 17 18 20 22 28 29 30 31 34 35 40 41 43 45 46 48 50 51 54 55 57 58 59 60 62 63 64 65 68 70 72 73 74 75 76 78 79 81 82 84 85 86 87 89 93 94 96 97 98 100 102 104 107 108 109 110 111 115 116 117 118 119 120 121 122 123 124 129 130 131 132 135 143 145 146 147 148 154 156 157 158
Primary Contact: Melvin McNea, Chief Executive Officer
COO: Ivan Mitchell, Chief Operating Officer
CFO: Krystal Claymore, Chief Financial Officer
CIO: Brandon Kelliher, Chief Information Officer
CHR: Jayne Johnson, Director Human Resources
CNO: Tamara Martin-Linnard, R.N., Chief Clinical Officer
Web address: www.gphealth.org
Control: Other not–for–profit (including NFP Corporation) **Service**: General medical and surgical

Staffed Beds: 116 **Admissions**: 5951 **Census**: 61 **Outpatient Visits**: 186261 **Births**: 554 **Total Expense ($000)**: 207554 **Payroll Expense ($000)**: 81137 **Personnel**: 1013

OAKLAND—Burt County

★ **MERCYONE OAKLAND MEDICAL CENTER (281321)**, 601 East Second Street, Zip 68045–1499; tel. 402/685–5601, (Nonreporting) **A**10 18 **S** Trinity Health, Livonia, MI
Primary Contact: Rita Going, Director of Critical Access Hospitals
CFO: Terri Mentink, Chief Financial Officer
CMO: Tracie Martin, M.D., Chief Medical Officer
CNO: Jayma Brown, R.N., Director of Nursing
Web address: www.oaklandhospital.org
Control: Church operated **Service**: General medical and surgical

Staffed Beds: 18

OGALLALA—Keith County

★ **OGALLALA COMMUNITY HOSPITAL (281355)**, 2601 North Spruce Street, Zip 69153–2465; tel. 308/284–4011, **A**10 18 **F**3 13 15 29 31 34 40 43 45 59 65 68 75 76 77 79 81 85 87 93 97 107 110 111 115 119 127 128 130 132 133 148 149 154 **S** Banner Health, Phoenix, AZ
Primary Contact: Drew H. Dostal, R.N., FACHE, Chief Executive Officer
CFO: Dena Klockman, Chief Financial Officer
CMO: Gabriel Godina, M.D., Chief of Staff
CHR: Gracie Ramos, Chief Human Resources Officer
CNO: Linda Baldwin, Chief Nursing Officer
Web address: www.https://www.bannerhealth.com/locations/ogallala/ogallala-community-hospital
Control: Other not–for–profit (including NFP Corporation) **Service**: General medical and surgical

Staffed Beds: 18 **Admissions**: 268 **Census**: 2 **Outpatient Visits**: 31376 **Births**: 55 **Total Expense ($000)**: 23098 **Payroll Expense ($000)**: 9244 **Personnel**: 114

OMAHA—Douglas County

☐ **BOYS TOWN NATIONAL RESEARCH HOSPITAL (283300)**, 555 North 30th Street, Zip 68131–2198; tel. 402/498–6511, (Nonreporting) **A**1 3 5 10
Primary Contact: John K. Arch, FACHE, Director
CFO: Leigh Jean Koinzan, Director Finance
CMO: Edward Kolb, M.D., Medical Director
CIO: Ann Ducey, Chief Information Officer
CHR: Michael Gell, Director Human Resources
CNO: Patricia Allgeier, R.N., Chief Nursing Officer
Web address: www.boystownhospital.org
Control: Other not–for–profit (including NFP Corporation) **Service**: Children's general medical and surgical

Staffed Beds: 129

✠ **CHI HEALTH CREIGHTON UNIVERSITY MEDICAL CENTER - BERGAN MERCY (280060)**, 7500 Mercy Road, Zip 68124–2319; tel. 402/398–6060, (Includes LASTING HOPE RECOVERY CENTER, 415 South 25th Avenue, Omaha, Nebraska, Zip 68131; tel. 402/717–5300; Robin Conyers, Administrator) **A**1 2 3 5 8 10 **F**3 8 11 13 15 17 18 20 22 24 26 28 29 30 31 32 34 35 37 38 40 42 43 44 45 46 47 48 49 50 51 53 54 55 56 57 58 59 60 61 64 65 68 70 72 74 75 76 77 78 79 81 82 83 84 85 86 87 89 92 93 97 98 100 107 108 109 110 111 114 115 116 117 118 119 120 121 123 124 126 130 131 132 134 145 146 147 148 150 154 156 **S** CommonSpirit Health, Chicago, IL
Primary Contact: Marie E. Knedler, R.N., FACHE, Interim President
COO: Patricia Townley, Director Operations
CFO: Tim H. Schnack, Vice President Financial Services
CMO: Devin Fox, M.D., Vice President Medical Operations
CIO: Thomas Haley, Division Assistant Vice President Business Relationship Management
CHR: Nancy Wallace, Vice President Human Resources
Web address: www.chihealth.com/chi-health-bergan-mercy
Control: Church operated, Nongovernment, not–for–profit **Service**: General medical and surgical

Staffed Beds: 361 **Admissions**: 17096 **Census**: 225 **Outpatient Visits**: 159667 **Births**: 4030 **Total Expense ($000)**: 433528 **Payroll Expense ($000)**: 107673 **Personnel**: 1602

NE

Many Facility Codes have changed. Please refer to the AHA Guide Code Chart. © 2019 AHA Guide

★ △ **CHI HEALTH IMMANUEL (280081)**, 6901 North 72nd Street, Zip 68122–1799; tel. 402/572–2121, **A2** 3 5 7 10 **F3** 5 11 12 13 15 17 18 20 22 26 28 29 30 31 32 34 35 36 37 38 40 43 45 46 49 50 51 53 55 56 57 58 59 64 65 67 68 70 74 75 76 77 78 79 81 82 84 85 86 87 90 91 92 93 94 95 96 97 98 99 100 101 102 103 104 105 106 107 108 110 111 114 115 117 118 119 120 121 123 124 126 129 130 131 132 136 141 142 146 147 149 154 157 **S** CommonSpirit Health, Chicago, IL
Primary Contact: Ann Schumacher, R.N., MSN, FACHE, President
CFO: Tim H. Schnack, Chief Financial Officer
CMO: Joseph Hoagbin, M.D., Chief Medical Officer
CHR: Nancy Wallace, Vice President Human Resources
Web address: www.alegent.com/immanuel
Control: Church operated, Nongovernment, not–for–profit **Service**: General medical and surgical

Staffed Beds: 269 **Admissions**: 10594 **Census**: 165 **Outpatient Visits**: 117598 **Births**: 552 **Total Expense ($000)**: 163487 **Payroll Expense ($000)**: 54370 **Personnel**: 893

✠ **CHI HEALTH LAKESIDE (280130)**, 6901 N 72nd St, Zip 68122, Mailing Address: 16901 Lakeside Hills Court, Zip 68130–2318; tel. 402/717–8000, **A1** 2 3 10 **F3** 13 15 17 18 20 22 26 28 29 30 31 34 35 36 40 45 46 49 50 53 55 59 60 62 63 64 68 69 70 72 74 75 76 77 78 79 81 82 83 84 85 87 93 94 97 100 102 106 107 108 110 111 114 115 116 117 119 120 124 126 129 130 131 132 135 143 146 147 148 149 154 157 **S** CommonSpirit Health, Chicago, IL
Primary Contact: Kevin Miller, President
COO: Kathy Bressler, Division Senior Vice President and Chief Operating Officer
CFO: Nick O'Tool, Vice President Operational Finance
CMO: Patricia Murdock-Langan, M.D., Chief Medical Officer
CIO: Thomas Haley, Information Technology Systems Site Director
CHR: Nancy Wallace, Division Senior Vice President, Chief Human Resource Officer
CNO: Linda K. Chase, Ph.D., R.N., Division Senior Vice President and Chief Nursing Officer
Web address: www.CHIhealth.com
Control: Church operated, Nongovernment, not–for–profit **Service**: General medical and surgical

Staffed Beds: 137 **Admissions**: 6326 **Census**: 66 **Outpatient Visits**: 96475 **Births**: 930 **Total Expense ($000)**: 120736 **Payroll Expense ($000)**: 35726 **Personnel**: 540

✠ **CHILDREN'S HOSPITAL AND MEDICAL CENTER (283301)**, 8200 Dodge St, Zip 68114–4113; tel. 402/955–5400, **A1** 3 5 10 **F3** 7 8 11 12 13 19 21 23 25 27 29 30 31 32 34 35 40 41 43 45 46 47 48 49 53 54 55 58 59 60 62 64 65 68 71 72 74 75 76 77 78 79 81 82 84 85 87 88 89 92 93 97 104 107 108 111 115 119 129 130 131 132 137 144 145 146 148 149 154 156
Primary Contact: Rodrigo Lopez, Interim President and Chief Executive Officer
COO: Kathy L English, R.N., MSN, Executive Vice President and Chief Operating Officer
CFO: Amy Hatcher, Senior Vice President and Chief Financial Officer
CMO: Christopher Maloney, M.D., Senior Vice President, Medical Affairs and Chief Medical Officer
CIO: Mark Stastny, Vice President and Chief Information Officer
CHR: Suzanne Nocita, Senior Vice President and Chief Human Resource Officer
Web address: www.childrensomaha.org
Control: Other not–for–profit (including NFP Corporation) **Service**: Children's general medical and surgical

Staffed Beds: 145 **Admissions**: 4852 **Census**: 102 **Outpatient Visits**: 406786 **Births**: 10 **Total Expense ($000)**: 429418 **Payroll Expense ($000)**: 198145 **Personnel**: 2137

★ ○ **DOUGLAS COUNTY COMMUNITY MENTAL HEALTH CENTER (284009)**, 4102 Woolworth Avenue, Zip 68105–1899; tel. 402/444–7449, (Nonreporting) **A3** 5 10 11
Primary Contact: Sherry L. Glasnapp, Director
CFO: DeDe Will, Director Finance
CMO: Sidney A. Kauzlarich, M.D., Medical Director
CIO: Dianne Wallace, County Information Manager
CHR: Karen Buche, Chief Human Resource Officer
CNO: Marti Christensen, Director of Psychiatric Nursing
Web address: www.co.douglas.ne.us
Control: County, Government, nonfederal **Service**: Psychiatric

Staffed Beds: 16

☐ △ **MADONNA REHABILITATION HOSPITAL (283026)**, 17500 Burke Street, Zip 68118–2244; tel. 844/403–3131, (Nonreporting) **A1** 3 5 7 10
Primary Contact: Paul Dongilli Jr, Ph.D., FACHE, President and Chief Executive Officer
Web address: www.https://www.madonna.org
Control: Other not–for–profit (including NFP Corporation) **Service**: Rehabilitation

Staffed Beds: 57

☐ **MADONNA REHABILITATION SPECIALTY HOSPITAL (282003)**, 17500 Burke Street, Zip 68118–2244; tel. 844/403–3131, (Nonreporting) **A1** 5 10
Primary Contact: Paul Dongilli Jr, Ph.D., FACHE, President and Chief Executive Officer
Web address: www.https://www.madonna.org
Control: Other not–for–profit (including NFP Corporation) **Service**: Acute long–term care hospital

Staffed Beds: 48

MIDWEST SURGICAL HOSPITAL (280131), 7915 Farnam Drive, Zip 68114–4504; tel. 402/399–1900, (Nonreporting) **A3** 10
Primary Contact: Charles Livingston, Chief Executive Officer
Web address: www.mwsurgicalhospital.com
Control: Corporation, Investor–owned (for–profit) **Service**: Surgical

Staffed Beds: 19

✠ **NEBRASKA MEDICINE - NEBRASKA MEDICAL CENTER (280013)**, 987400 Nebraska Medical Center, Zip 68198–7400; tel. 402/552–2000, **A1** 2 3 5 8 10 **F3** 5 6 8 9 11 12 13 15 16 17 18 20 22 24 26 28 29 30 31 32 34 35 36 37 38 39 40 41 43 44 45 46 47 48 49 50 51 53 54 55 56 57 58 59 60 61 62 63 64 65 66 68 70 71 72 74 75 76 77 78 79 80 81 82 84 85 86 87 88 89 91 92 93 94 96 97 98 100 102 104 107 108 110 111 113 114 115 116 117 118 119 120 121 123 124 126 127 129 130 131 132 134 135 136 137 138 139 140 141 142 143 144 145 146 147 148 149 150 154 156
Primary Contact: James Linder, M.D., Chief Executive Officer
COO: Dennis Bierle, Chief Operating Officer
CFO: Stephanie Daubert, Chief Financial Officer
CMO: Harris Frankel, M.D., Interim Chief Medical Officer
CIO: Michael A Ash, Chief Transformation Officer
CHR: Frank Venuto, Chief Human Capital Officer
CNO: Suzanne Langan Nuss, Ph.D., R.N., Chief Nursing Officer
Web address: www.nebraskamed.com
Control: Other not–for–profit (including NFP Corporation) **Service**: General medical and surgical

Staffed Beds: 571 **Admissions**: 28276 **Census**: 452 **Outpatient Visits**: 1028205 **Births**: 1638 **Total Expense ($000)**: 1365814 **Payroll Expense ($000)**: 614917 **Personnel**: 7222

✠ △ **NEBRASKA METHODIST HOSPITAL (280040)**, 8303 Dodge Street, Zip 68114–4199; tel. 402/354–4000, (Includes METHODIST WOMEN'S HOSPITAL, 707 North 190th Plaza, Elkhorn, Nebraska, Zip 68022–3974; tel. 402/815–4000; Josie Abboud, President and Chief Executive Officer) **A1** 2 3 5 7 10 **F3** 8 11 12 13 15 18 20 22 24 26 28 29 30 31 34 35 40 45 46 47 48 49 50 51 52 53 54 55 56 57 58 59 65 66 68 70 71 72 74 75 76 77 78 79 80 81 82 83 84 85 86 87 90 91 92 93 96 100 101 102 107 108 110 111 114 115 116 117 118 119 120 121 123 124 126 127 129 130 132 135 142 143 146 147 148 154 156 157 **S** Nebraska Methodist Health System, Inc., Omaha, NE
Primary Contact: Josie Abboud, President and Chief Executive Officer
CFO: Linda K Burt, Corporate Vice President Finance
CMO: William Shiffermiller, M.D., Vice President Medical Affairs
CHR: Holly Huerter, Vice President Human Resources
CNO: Teri Tipton Bruening, MSN, Chief Nursing Officer and Vice President Patient Care Services
Web address: www.bestcare.org
Control: Other not–for–profit (including NFP Corporation) **Service**: General medical and surgical

Staffed Beds: 402 **Admissions**: 18938 **Census**: 266 **Outpatient Visits**: 158924 **Births**: 5000 **Total Expense ($000)**: 486775 **Payroll Expense ($000)**: 186302 **Personnel**: 2778

✠ **NEBRASKA SPINE HOSPITAL (280133)**, 6901 North 72nd Street, Suite 20300, Zip 68122–1755, Mailing Address: 6901 North 72nd Street, Zip 68122–1709; tel. 402/572–3000, (Nonreporting) **A1** 10
Primary Contact: Christopher M. Palumbo, Chief Executive Officer
Web address: www.nebraskaspinehospital.com
Control: Partnership, Investor–owned (for–profit) **Service**: Orthopedic

Staffed Beds: 34

NE

Hospital, Medicare Provider Number, Address, Telephone, Approval, Facility, and Physician Codes, Health Care System

★ American Hospital Association (AHA) membership
☐ The Joint Commission accreditation
○ Healthcare Facilities Accreditation Program
◇ DNV Healthcare Inc. accreditation
⇧ Center for Improvement in Healthcare Quality Accreditation
△ Commission on Accreditation of Rehabilitation Facilities (CARF) accreditation

© 2019 AHA Guide   *Many Facility Codes have changed. Please refer to the AHA Guide Code Chart.*   Hospitals **A389**

☐ **ORTHONEBRASKA HOSPITAL (280129)**, 2808 South 143rd Plaza, Zip 68144–5611; tel. 402/609–1600, **A**1 3 5 10 **F**3 29 34 37 40 57 59 64 68 74 75 77 79 81 82 85 87 93 94 96 107 111 114 119 131 141
Primary Contact: Levi Scheppers, Chief Executive Officer
COO: Mark E Longacre, FACHE, Chief Operating Officer
CFO: Anna McCaslin, Chief Financial Officer
CMO: Ian Crabb, M.D., Chief Medical Officer
CIO: Tim Pugsley, Chief Information Officer
CHR: Lori L Thompson, Manager Human Resources
Web address: www.neorthohospital.com
Control: Partnership, Investor–owned (for–profit) **Service**: Orthopedic

Staffed Beds: 24 **Admissions**: 1885 **Census**: 8 **Outpatient Visits**: 57152 **Births**: 0 **Total Expense ($000)**: 68121 **Payroll Expense ($000)**: 22932 **Personnel**: 365	

✉ **SELECT SPECIALTY HOSPITAL-OMAHA (282001)**, 1870 South 75th Street, Zip 68124–1700; tel. 402/361–5700, (Nonreporting) **A**1 10 **S** Select Medical Corporation, Mechanicsburg, PA
Primary Contact: Kerry McLane, Interim Chief Executive Officer
COO: Joel White, Chief Operating Officer
CMO: Guillermo Huerta, M.D., Chief Medical Officer
CHR: Laurna Hoss, Human Resource Coordinator
CNO: Amanda Wellman, MSN, R.N., Chief Nursing Officer
Web address: www.https://omaha.selectspecialtyhospitals.com
Control: Corporation, Investor–owned (for–profit) **Service**: Acute long–term care hospital

Staffed Beds: 52

✉ **VETERANS AFFAIRS NEBRASKA-WESTERN IOWA HEALTH CARE SYSTEM**, 4101 Woolworth Avenue, Zip 68105–1873; tel. 402/346–8800, (Nonreporting) **A**1 2 3 5 8 **S** Department of Veterans Affairs, Washington, DC
Primary Contact: Don Burman, Director
COO: Denise Harrison, Associate Director
CFO: Kirk Kay, Chief Financial Officer
CMO: Grace Stringfellow, M.D., Chief of Staff
CIO: Jennifer Rosenbalm, Manager Business Office
CHR: Cheryl M DeWispelare, Chief Human Resources Officer
CNO: Eileen M Kingston, R.N., Nurse Executive, Associate Director Patient Care
Web address: www.nebraska.va.gov/
Control: Veterans Affairs, Government, federal **Service**: General medical and surgical

Staffed Beds: 137

O'NEILL—Holt County

★ **AVERA ST. ANTHONY'S HOSPITAL (281329)**, 300 North Second Street, Zip 68763–1514, Mailing Address: P.O. Box 270, Oneill, Zip 68763–0270; tel. 402/336–2611, (Nonreporting) **A**10 18 **S** Avera Health, Sioux Falls, SD
Primary Contact: Todd Consbruck, President and Chief Executive Officer
CFO: Michael Garman, Chief Financial Officer
CIO: Michael Garman, Chief Financial Officer
CHR: Kathryn Benson, Human Resources Partner
Web address: www.avera.org/st-anthonys
Control: Church operated **Service**: General medical and surgical

Staffed Beds: 25

ORD—Valley County

★ **VALLEY COUNTY HEALTH SYSTEM (281353)**, 2707 L Street, Zip 68862–1275; tel. 308/728–4200, **A**10 18 **F**3 7 15 28 29 31 34 35 40 41 43 45 46 50 56 57 59 62 63 64 65 68 74 75 77 78 79 81 82 84 87 90 93 94 97 103 107 110 111 119 127 128 129 130 131 132 133 148 154 156
Primary Contact: Nancy Glaubke, Chief Executive Officer
CFO: Ashley Woodward, Director Financial Services
CMO: Jennifer Bengston, M.D., Chief Medical Officer
CIO: Shane Molacek, Chief Information Officer
CHR: Danielle Proskocil, Director Human Resources
CNO: Vicki Bredthauer, R.N., Director of Nursing
Web address: www.valleycountyhealthsystem.org
Control: County, Government, nonfederal **Service**: General medical and surgical

Staffed Beds: 16 **Admissions**: 326 **Census**: 2 **Outpatient Visits**: 25000 **Births**: 0 **Total Expense ($000)**: 21195 **Payroll Expense ($000)**: 9168 **Personnel**: 156

OSCEOLA—Polk County

ANNIE JEFFREY MEMORIAL COUNTY HEALTH CENTER (281314), 531 Beebe Street, Zip 68651–5537, Mailing Address: P.O. Box 428, Zip 68651–0428; tel. 402/747–2031, (Nonreporting) **A**10 18
Primary Contact: Joseph W. Lohrman, Chief Executive Officer
CFO: Joseph W Lohrman, Chief Executive Officer
CMO: David Jameson, M.D., Chief of Staff
CIO: Frank Vrba, Chief Information Officer
CHR: Sue Leif, R.N., Director Human Resources
Web address: www.ajhc.org
Control: County, Government, nonfederal **Service**: General medical and surgical

Staffed Beds: 16

OSHKOSH—Garden County

★ **REGIONAL WEST GARDEN COUNTY (281310)**, 1100 West Second Street, Zip 69154–6152; tel. 308/772–3283, (Nonreporting) **A**10 18
Primary Contact: Donald Weidemann, Acting Administrator
CFO: Jennifer Moffat, Staff Accountant
CMO: Steve Boyer, M.D., Chief Medical Officer
CHR: Ricca Sanford, Director Human Resources
CNO: Trish Davison, R.N., Chief Nursing Officer
Web address: www.gchealth.org
Control: County, Government, nonfederal **Service**: General medical and surgical

Staffed Beds: 10

OSMOND—Pierce County

★ **OSMOND GENERAL HOSPITAL (281347)**, 402 North Maple Street, Zip 68765–5726, Mailing Address: P.O. Box 429, Zip 68765–0429; tel. 402/748–3393, **A**10 18 **F**3 28 34 40 57 59 64 67 69 81 90 97 107 115 127 128 133 143
Primary Contact: Lon Knievel, Chief Executive Officer
CFO: Jodi Aschoff, Chief Financial Officer
CMO: David Mwebe, M.D., Chief of Staff
CNO: Kristen Colsden, Director of Nursing
Web address: www.osmondhospital.com
Control: Other not–for–profit (including NFP Corporation) **Service**: General medical and surgical

Staffed Beds: 20 **Admissions**: 152 **Census**: 2 **Outpatient Visits**: 63186 **Births**: 0 **Total Expense ($000)**: 7603 **Payroll Expense ($000)**: 3237 **Personnel**: 60

PAPILLION—Sarpy County

✉ **CHI HEALTH MIDLANDS (280105)**, 11111 South 84th Street, Zip 68046–4122; tel. 402/593–3000, **A**1 2 5 10 **F**3 11 15 18 26 28 29 30 34 35 36 38 40 43 44 45 46 49 50 51 53 56 57 59 61 62 63 64 65 68 77 79 81 84 85 86 87 93 97 107 110 111 114 115 117 118 119 129 130 131 132 135 143 146 147 154 **S** CommonSpirit Health, Chicago, IL
Primary Contact: Kevin Miller, President
CFO: Tyler DeJong, Vice President, Operational Finance
CMO: Patricia Murdock-Langan, M.D., Chief Medical Officer
CIO: Thomas Haley, Information Technology Systems Site Director
CHR: Nancy Wallace, Division Senior Vice President, Chief Human Resource Officer
CNO: Brenda Bergman-Evans, Chief Nursing Officer
Web address: www.CHIhealth.com
Control: Church operated, Nongovernment, not–for–profit **Service**: General medical and surgical

Staffed Beds: 28 **Admissions**: 870 **Census**: 7 **Outpatient Visits**: 40829 **Births**: 0 **Total Expense ($000)**: 35575 **Payroll Expense ($000)**: 9841 **Personnel**: 158

PAWNEE CITY—Pawnee County

★ **PAWNEE COUNTY MEMORIAL HOSPITAL AND RURAL HEALTH CLINIC (281302)**, 600 'I' Street, Zip 68420–3001, Mailing Address: P.O. Box 433, Zip 68420–0433; tel. 402/852–2231, **A**10 18 **F**3 7 15 28 29 30 40 43 45 59 81 107 110 119 127 128 130 133 147 154
Primary Contact: Ruth M. Stephens, MSN, R.N., Chief Executive Officer
CFO: Dawn Friesel, Director of Finance
CHR: Jennifer Bartels, Director Human Resources
CNO: Kelly Findlay, Director of Nurses
Web address: www.pawneehospital.com
Control: County, Government, nonfederal **Service**: General medical and surgical

Staffed Beds: 11 **Admissions**: 53 **Census**: 1 **Births**: 0

NE

Many Facility Codes have changed. Please refer to the AHA Guide Code Chart. © 2019 AHA Guide

PENDER—Thurston County

★ **PENDER COMMUNITY HOSPITAL (281349)**, 100 Hospital Drive, Zip 68047–0100, Mailing Address: P.O. Box 100, Zip 68047–0100; tel. 402/385–3083, (Nonreporting) **A**10 18 **S** Trinity Health, Livonia, MI
Primary Contact: Melissa Kelly, Chief Executive Officer and Chief Financial Officer
CFO: Melissa Kelly, Chief Executive Officer and Chief Financial Officer
CMO: Matt Timm, M.D., Medical Director
CIO: Teresa Heise, Coordinator Management Information Systems
CHR: Nancy Suhr, Manager Human Resources
CNO: Katie Peterson, R.N., Chief Nursing Officer
Web address: www.pendercommunityhospital.com
Control: Hospital district or authority, Government, nonfederal **Service:** General medical and surgical

Staffed Beds: 67

PLAINVIEW—Pierce County

★ **CHI HEALTH PLAINVIEW (281346)**, 704 North Third Street, Zip 68769–2047, Mailing Address: P.O. Box 489, Zip 68769–0489; tel. 402/582–4245, (Nonreporting) **A**10 18 **S** CommonSpirit Health, Chicago, IL
Primary Contact: Gregory Beckmann, Regional President
CFO: Tim H. Schnack, Chief Financial Officer
CMO: Steve Peterson, M.D., Chief of Staff
CHR: Diane Blair, Human Resources and Admissions
CNO: Debra K Rutledge, R.N., Vice President Nursing Services
Web address: www.alegentcreighton.com/plainview-hospital
Control: Church operated, Nongovernment, not–for–profit **Service:** General medical and surgical

Staffed Beds: 15

RED CLOUD—Webster County

★ **WEBSTER COUNTY COMMUNITY HOSPITAL (281316)**, Sixth Avenue and Franklin Street, Zip 68970–0465, Mailing Address: P.O. Box 465, Zip 68970–0465; tel. 402/746–5600, **A**10 18 **F**3 15 18 28 29 30 32 34 35 40 41 45 50 56 57 59 64 65 68 70 75 77 78 79 81 82 83 84 90 93 94 96 97 107 110 111 112 115 119 127 128 129 130 133 135 145 146 147 148 149 150 154
Primary Contact: Mirya Hallock, Administrator
CFO: Marcia Olson, Business Office Manager
CMO: Amy Springer, Medical Director
CHR: Marcia Olson, Business Office Manager
CNO: Candace Peters, R.N., Director of Nursing
Web address: www.websterhospital.org
Control: County, Government, nonfederal **Service:** General medical and surgical

Staffed Beds: 13 **Admissions:** 72 **Census:** 1 **Outpatient Visits:** 619
Births: 0 **Total Expense ($000):** 6629 **Payroll Expense ($000):** 2298
Personnel: 47

SAINT PAUL—Howard County

HOWARD COUNTY COMMUNITY HOSPITAL See Howard County Medical Center

★ **HOWARD COUNTY MEDICAL CENTER (281338)**, 1113 Sherman Street, Zip 68873–1546, Mailing Address: P.O. Box 406, Zip 68873–0406; tel. 308/754–4421, (Nonreporting) **A**5 10 18
Primary Contact: Arlan D. Johnson, Chief Executive Officer
COO: Jillyn Klein, Chief Operating Officer
CFO: Morgan Meyer, Chief Financial Officer
CMO: Angela Brennan, M.D., Chief of Staff
CIO: Cheryl Watson, Chief Information Officer
CHR: Leslie Belzer, Director Human Resources
CNO: Janelle Morgan, Interim Director of Nursing
Web address: www.hcmc.us.com
Control: County, Government, nonfederal **Service:** General medical and surgical

Staffed Beds: 25

SCHUYLER—Colfax County

★ **CHI HEALTH SCHUYLER (281323)**, 104 West 17th Street, Zip 68661–1304; tel. 402/352–2441, (Nonreporting) **A**10 18 **S** CommonSpirit Health, Chicago, IL
Primary Contact: Connie Peters, R.N., President
CFO: Tim H. Schnack, Chief Financial Officer
CIO: Kenneth Lawonn, Senior Vice President and Chief Information Officer
CHR: Nancy Wallace, Vice President Human Resources
Web address: www.alegent.org
Control: Church operated, Nongovernment, not–for–profit **Service:** General medical and surgical

Staffed Beds: 25

SCOTTSBLUFF—Scotts Bluff County

✉ △ **REGIONAL WEST MEDICAL CENTER (280061)**, 4021 Avenue 'B', Zip 69361–4695; tel. 308/635–3711, (Nonreporting) **A**1 2 3 5 7 10
Primary Contact: John Mentgen, FACHE, President and Chief Executive Officer
COO: Tadd Greenfield, Executive Vice President and Chief Operating Officer
CFO: Michael F Ickowski, Vice President and Chief Financial Officer
CMO: Lisa Scheppers, Chief Medical Officer
CIO: Montie Hodge, Vice President Information Technology and Chief Information Officer
CHR: Brenda J Forge, Vice President, Human Resources
CNO: Connie Rupp, MSN, R.N., Executive Vice President and Chief Nursing Officer
Web address: www.rwhs.org
Control: Other not–for–profit (including NFP Corporation) **Service:** General medical and surgical

Staffed Beds: 122

SEWARD—Seward County

★ **MEMORIAL HEALTH CARE SYSTEMS (281339)**, 300 North Columbia Avenue, Zip 68434–2228; tel. 402/643–2971, (Nonreporting) **A**10 18
Primary Contact: Roger J. Reamer, Chief Executive Officer
CFO: Greg Jerger, Chief Financial Officer
CMO: James Plasek, M.D., Chief of Staff
CIO: Mark Criner, Director Information Technology
CHR: Corey Mann, Director Human Resources
Web address: www.mhcs.us
Control: Other not–for–profit (including NFP Corporation) **Service:** General medical and surgical

Staffed Beds: 25

SIDNEY—Cheyenne County

★ **SIDNEY REGIONAL MEDICAL CENTER (281357)**, 1000 Pole Creek Crossing, Zip 69162–1799; tel. 308/254–5825, (Total facility includes 63 beds in nursing home–type unit) **A**10 18 **F**2 10 11 12 13 15 18 26 27 28 29 30 31 34 35 40 41 45 46 47 40 50 56 57 59 62 63 64 65 68 70 76 77 78 79 81 85 86 87 91 92 93 94 97 107 111 115 119 127 129 130 131 132 133 135 143 144 148 154 156 157
Primary Contact: Jason Petik, Chief Executive Officer
CMO: Mandy Shaw, M.D., Chief of Staff
CIO: Jennifer Brockhaus, Chief Information Officer
CHR: Catherine T Arterburn, R.N., Vice President Human Resources
CNO: Julie A Slagle, R.N., MSN, Vice President Patient Care Services
Web address: www.sidneyrmc.com
Control: Other not–for–profit (including NFP Corporation) **Service:** General medical and surgical

Staffed Beds: 88 **Admissions:** 602 **Census:** 53 **Outpatient Visits:** 44506
Births: 56 **Total Expense ($000):** 53940 **Payroll Expense ($000):** 22810
Personnel: 363

NE

Hospital, Medicare Provider Number, Address, Telephone, Approval, Facility, and Physician Codes, Health Care System

★ American Hospital Association (AHA) membership ◯ Healthcare Facilities Accreditation Program ⇑ Center for Improvement in Healthcare Quality Accreditation
☐ The Joint Commission accreditation ◇ DNV Healthcare Inc. accreditation △ Commission on Accreditation of Rehabilitation Facilities (CARF) accreditation

© 2019 AHA Guide *Many Facility Codes have changed. Please refer to the AHA Guide Code Chart.* Hospitals **A391**

SUPERIOR—Nuckolls County

★ **BRODSTONE MEMORIAL HOSPITAL (281315)**, 520 East Tenth Street, Zip 68978–1225, Mailing Address: P.O. Box 187, Zip 68978–0187; tel. 402/879–3281, **A**10 18 **F**3 8 11 13 15 28 29 30 34 35 40 41 45 50 57 59 64 65 70 74 75 77 79 81 82 85 86 87 93 94 97 107 110 111 115 119 127 129 130 131 132 133 135 146 148 154 156
Primary Contact: Treg Vyzourek, Chief Executive Officer
COO: Dena C Alvarez, R.N., COO & Chief Compliance Officer
CFO: Sandy Borden, Chief Financial Officer
CMO: Timothy Blecha, M.D., Medical Director
CIO: Tim Hiatt, Chief Information Officer
CHR: Beth A Schlichtman, Manager Human Resources
CNO: Kori Field, Director of Nursing
Web address: www.brodstonehospital.org
Control: Other not–for–profit (including NFP Corporation) **Service**: General medical and surgical

Staffed Beds: 25 **Admissions**: 617 **Census**: 4 **Outpatient Visits**: 18000 **Births**: 30 **Total Expense ($000)**: 25195 **Payroll Expense ($000)**: 10322 **Personnel**: 178

SYRACUSE—Otoe County

★ **SYRACUSE AREA HEALTH (281309)**, 2731 Healthcare Drive, Zip 68446, Mailing Address: P.O. Box N, Zip 68446–0518; tel. 402/269–2011, **A**10 18 **F**3 8 11 15 28 29 34 35 37 40 41 43 45 47 48 50 53 57 59 65 74 75 78 79 81 82 85 87 89 91 92 93 94 96 97 107 110 115 119 126 127 128 129 130 131 133 146 148 154 156 157
Primary Contact: Michael Harvey, FACHE, President and Chief Executive Officer
CFO: Karrie Beach, Vice President Finance
CMO: Zak Tempelmeyer, M.D., Chief Medical Staff
CIO: Matthew Steinblock, Director Information Systems
CHR: Nancy R Brack, Vice President Human Resources
CNO: Pat Howell, Chief Nursing Officer
Web address: www.syracusecmh.org
Control: Hospital district or authority, Government, nonfederal **Service**: General medical and surgical

Staffed Beds: 10 **Admissions**: 175 **Census**: 1 **Outpatient Visits**: 12981 **Births**: 0 **Total Expense ($000)**: 16884 **Payroll Expense ($000)**: 7880 **Personnel**: 129

TECUMSEH—Johnson County

★ **JOHNSON COUNTY HOSPITAL (281350)**, 202 High Street, Zip 68450–2443, Mailing Address: P.O. Box 599, Zip 68450–0599; tel. 402/335–3361, (Nonreporting) **A**10 18
Primary Contact: Mary Kent, Administrator
CMO: Benjamin Biehl, M.D., Chief Medical Officer
CIO: Joseph Randall Stollar, Chief Information Officer
CHR: Susan Hessheimer, Director Human Resources
CNO: Matthew Snyder, R.N., Director of Nursing
Web address: www.jchosp.com
Control: County, Government, nonfederal **Service**: General medical and surgical

Staffed Beds: 25

VALENTINE—Cherry County

★ **CHERRY COUNTY HOSPITAL (281344)**, 510 North Green Street, Zip 69201–1932, Mailing Address: P.O. Box 410, Zip 69201–0410; tel. 402/376–2525, (Nonreporting) **A**3 5 10 18
Primary Contact: Brent A. Peterson, Administrator
CFO: Peggy Snell, Chief Finance Officer
CNO: Kathryn Renning, Director of Nursing
Web address: www.cherrycountyhospital.org
Control: County, Government, nonfederal **Service**: General medical and surgical

Staffed Beds: 25

WAHOO—Saunders County

★ **SAUNDERS MEDICAL CENTER (281307)**, 1760 County Road J, Zip 68066–4152; tel. 402/443–4191, (Nonreporting) **A**10 18 **S** Bryan Health, Lincoln, NE
Primary Contact: Tyler Toline, FACHE, Chief Executive Officer
COO: Julie A Rezac, R.N., Chief Operating Officer
CFO: Chase Manstedt, Chief Financial Officer
CMO: Lorance Newburn, M.D., Medical Chief of Staff
CIO: Carrie Stephens, Director Information Technology
CNO: Lalah Landers, R.N., Director of Nursing
Web address: www.saundersmedicalcenter.com
Control: County, Government, nonfederal **Service**: General medical and surgical

Staffed Beds: 16

WAYNE—Wayne County

★ **PROVIDENCE MEDICAL CENTER (281345)**, 1200 Providence Road, Zip 68787–1299; tel. 402/375–3800, **A**10 18 **F**3 7 13 15 28 29 30 31 34 35 36 40 50 53 57 59 62 63 64 68 75 76 81 82 84 85 93 107 110 111 115 119 128 130 132 133 135 154
Primary Contact: James Frank, CPA, Chief Executive Officer
COO: Kristine A Giese, Chief Operating Officer
CFO: Kim Hixson, Vice President of Financial Officer and Chief Financial Officer
CNO: Nicole Haglund, Vice President of Nursing Services
Web address: www.providencemedical.com
Control: Other not–for–profit (including NFP Corporation) **Service**: General medical and surgical

Staffed Beds: 21 **Admissions**: 407 **Census**: 4 **Outpatient Visits**: 14791 **Births**: 67 **Total Expense ($000)**: 21613 **Payroll Expense ($000)**: 8454 **Personnel**: 158

WEST POINT—Cuming County

★ **ST. FRANCIS MEMORIAL HOSPITAL (281322)**, 430 North Monitor Street, Zip 68788–1555; tel. 402/372–2404, **A**10 18 **F**3 6 11 13 15 28 29 30 31 34 35 40 43 45 50 53 57 59 62 63 64 68 75 76 77 78 79 81 82 85 86 90 92 93 94 98 99 100 103 107 111 114 119 127 128 129 130 131 132 133 135 146 147 148 154 156 **S** Franciscan Sisters of Christian Charity Sponsored Ministries, Inc., Manitowoc, WI
Primary Contact: David J. Ameen, Interim President and Chief Executive Officer
CFO: Alisa A. Brunsing, Chief Financial Officer
CMO: Kenneth Pitz, M.D., Chief of Staff
CIO: Jean Meiergerd, Chief Information Officer
CHR: Terri Ridder, Director Human Resources
CNO: Carol Kampschnieder, Vice President Clinical and Regulatory Services
Web address: www.fcswp.org
Control: Church operated, Nongovernment, not–for–profit **Service**: General medical and surgical

Staffed Beds: 25 **Admissions**: 427 **Census**: 5 **Outpatient Visits**: 72910 **Births**: 45 **Total Expense ($000)**: 32267 **Payroll Expense ($000)**: 15825 **Personnel**: 215

WINNEBAGO—Thurston County

TWELVE CLANS UNITY HOSPITAL (280119), Highway 7577, Zip 68071; tel. 402/878–2231, (Nonreporting) **A**10
Primary Contact: Danelle Smith, Chief Executive Officer
CFO: Audrey Parker, Budget Analyst
Control: PHS, Indian Service, Government, federal **Service**: General medical and surgical

Staffed Beds: 30

YORK—York County

★ **YORK GENERAL (281336)**, 2222 North Lincoln Avenue, Zip 68467–1095; tel. 402/362–6671, (Total facility includes 129 beds in nursing home–type unit) **A**10 18 **F**3 10 11 12 13 15 28 29 31 34 35 40 45 53 56 57 59 60 62 64 68 70 75 76 77 78 79 81 82 85 86 87 89 93 96 107 108 110 111 115 117 118 119 125 128 129 130 131 132 133 145 146 148 149
Primary Contact: James P. Ulrich Jr, Chief Executive Officer
COO: Jenny Obermier, Senior Vice President, Chief Operating Officer and Chief Nursing Officer
CFO: Bob McQuistan, Vice President Finance
CMO: Patrick Hotovy, M.D., Chief of Staff
CIO: Chris Kraft, Director Information Systems
CHR: Cathy Norquest, Director Human Resources
CNO: Jenny Obermier, Senior Vice President, Chief Operating Officer and Chief Nursing Officer
Web address: www.yorkgeneral.org
Control: Other not–for–profit (including NFP Corporation) **Service**: General medical and surgical

Staffed Beds: 154 **Admissions**: 967 **Census**: 115 **Outpatient Visits**: 41290 **Births**: 92 **Total Expense ($000)**: 43998 **Payroll Expense ($000)**: 20298 **Personnel**: 402

NE

Many Facility Codes have changed. Please refer to the AHA Guide Code Chart. © 2019 AHA Guide

NEVADA

BATTLE MOUNTAIN—Lander County

BATTLE MOUNTAIN GENERAL HOSPITAL (291303), 535 South Humboldt Street, Zip 89820–1988; tel. 775/635–2550, (Nonreporting) **A**10 18
Primary Contact: Jason Bleak, Chief Executive Officer
CFO: Cindy Fagg, Fiscal Officer
CMO: Mark S. Meyers, M.D., Chief of Staff
CIO: Terry Dunn, Director Information Technology
CHR: Lori Sherbondy, Director Human Resources
CNO: Kelley Price, R.N., Chief Nursing Officer
Web address: www.bmgh.org
Control: Hospital district or authority, Government, nonfederal **Service:** General medical and surgical

Staffed Beds: 7

BOULDER CITY—Clark County

BOULDER CITY HOSPITAL (291309), 901 Adams Boulevard, Zip 89005–2213; tel. 702/293–4111, (Nonreporting) **A**10 18
Primary Contact: Thomas Maher, Chief Executive Officer and Administrator
CFO: Douglas Lewis, Chief Financial Officer
CMO: Herve Bezard, M.D., Chief of Staff
CHR: Belinda McGraw, Director Human Resources
CNO: Andre Pastian, R.N., MSN, Chief Nursing Officer
Web address: www.bouldercityhospital.org
Control: Other not-for-profit (including NFP Corporation) **Service:** General medical and surgical

Staffed Beds: 25

CALIENTE—Lincoln County

GROVER C. DILS MEDICAL CENTER (291312), 700 North Spring Street, Zip 89008, Mailing Address: P.O. Box 1010, Zip 89008–1010; tel. 775/726–3171, (Nonreporting) **A**10 18
Primary Contact: Melissa O. Rowe, Chief Executive Officer
CFO: Sherlyn Fackrell, Finance Controller
CMO: R William Kalschke, M.D., Jr Medical Director
CHR: Rozanne Mangum, Administrative Assistant and Director Human Resources
Web address: www.gcdmc.org
Control: Other not-for-profit (including NFP Corporation) **Service:** Other specialty treatment

Staffed Beds: 20

CARSON CITY—Carson City County

CARSON TAHOE CONTINUING CARE HOSPITAL (292008), 775 Fleischmann Way, 2nd Floor, Zip 89703–2995; tel. 775/445–7795, **A**10 22 **F**1 3 29 68 85 130 148
Primary Contact: Michelle L. Joy, FACHE, Chief Executive Officer
CFO: Ann Beck, Vice President and Chief Financial Officer
CMO: Jose Aguirre, M.D., Medical Director
CHR: Larry Fagerhaug
CNO: Cynthia Parker, R.N., Administrator and Director of Nursing
Web address: www.carsontahoe.com
Control: Other not-for-profit (including NFP Corporation) **Service:** Acute long-term care hospital

Staffed Beds: 29 Admissions: 252 Census: 14 Outpatient Visits: 0 Births: 0 Total Expense ($000): 9434 Payroll Expense ($000): 3574 Personnel: 47

★ **CARSON TAHOE HEALTH (290019)**, 1600 Medical Parkway, Zip 89703–4625, Mailing Address: P.O. Box 2168, Zip 89702–2168; tel. 775/445–8672, (Includes SIERRA SURGERY HOSPITAL, 1400 Medical Parkway, Carson City, Nevada, Zip 89703–4624; tel. 775/883–1700; Ken Doran, Interim Chief Executive Officer) **A**2 10 22 **F**3 4 5 8 11 13 15 17 18 20 22 24 26 28 29 30 31 34 35 38 40 46 47 49 50 51 54 56 57 59 64 65 68 70 74 75 76 77 78 79 81 82 84 85 86 87 89 93 96 98 100 101 102 103 104 105 107 108 110 111 115 116 117 118 119 126 130 132 135 144 146 147 148 149 152 153 154 156
Primary Contact: Alan H. Garrett, Chief Executive Officer
COO: Michelle L Joy, FACHE, Chief Operating Officer
CFO: Ann Beck, Vice President Finance
CMO: Jeffrey Sanders, M.D., Chief of Staff
CHR: Jim Lewandowski, Interim Director of Human Resources
CNO: Anna Anders, R.N., MSN, Vice President and Chief Nursing Officer
Web address: www.carsontahoe.com
Control: Other not-for-profit (including NFP Corporation) **Service:** General medical and surgical

Staffed Beds: 211 Admissions: 12774 Census: 154 Outpatient Visits: 363062 Births: 961 Total Expense ($000): 270095 Payroll Expense ($000): 90278 Personnel: 1555

ELKO—Elko County

▣ **NORTHEASTERN NEVADA REGIONAL HOSPITAL (290008)**, 2001 Errecart Boulevard, Zip 89801–8333; tel. 775/738–5151, **A**1 3 10 20 **F**3 11 13 15 18 20 22 28 29 30 31 34 38 40 41 45 46 50 51 57 59 60 68 70 75 76 77 79 81 85 89 93 102 107 108 111 114 115 119 129 148 155 **S** LifePoint Health, Brentwood, TN
Primary Contact: Steve Simpson, Chief Executive Officer
CFO: Grant Trollope, Chief Financial Officer
CIO: Jeff Morgan, Director Information Systems
CHR: Laura Elliott, Director Human Resources
Web address: www.nnrhospital.com
Control: Corporation, Investor-owned (for-profit) **Service:** General medical and surgical

Staffed Beds: 75 Admissions: 1923 Census: 14 Outpatient Visits: 46519 Births: 511 Total Expense ($000): 57206 Payroll Expense ($000): 23017 Personnel: 247

ELY—White Pine County

▣ **WILLIAM BEE RIRIE HOSPITAL (291302)**, 1500 Avenue 'H', Zip 89301–2699; tel. 775/289–3001, (Nonreporting) **A**1 10 18
Primary Contact: Matthew Walker, Chief Executive Officer and Administrator
CMO: G N Christensen, M.D., Chief Medical Officer
CIO: Destin Brandis, Chief Information Officer
CHR: Vicki Pereace, Manager Human Resources
Web address: www.wbrhely.org/getpage.php?name=index
Control: Hospital district or authority, Government, nonfederal **Service:** General medical and surgical

Staffed Beds: 15

FALLON—Churchill County

▣ **BANNER CHURCHILL COMMUNITY HOSPITAL (291313)**, 801 East Williams Avenue, Zip 89406–3052; tel. 775/423–3151, **A**1 10 18 **F**3 7 11 13 15 29 31 34 35 40 41 45 47 50 59 64 65 68 70 75 76 79 81 85 86 87 93 97 107 110 111 115 119 127 129 130 146 149 154 **S** Banner Health, Phoenix, AZ
Primary Contact: Robert H. Carnahan II, R.N., Chief Executive Officer
CFO: Steve Fraker, Chief Financial Officer
CMO: Tedd McDonald, M.D., Chief Medical Officer
CHR: Darlene Hanefeld, Chief Human Resources Officer
Web address: www.bannerhealth.com/churchill
Control: Other not-for-profit (including NFP Corporation) **Service:** General medical and surgical

Staffed Beds: 25 Admissions: 1434 Census: 13 Births: 344 Total Expense ($000): 48275 Payroll Expense ($000): 23090 Personnel: 246

NV

GARDNERVILLE—Douglas County

★ **CARSON VALLEY MEDICAL CENTER (291306)**, 1107 Hwy 395, Zip 89410,
Mailing Address: 1107 Highway 395, Zip 89410; tel. 775/782–1500, **A**3 10 18
F3 15 26 29 30 31 34 35 38 39 40 45 50 54 56 57 59 61 64 65 66 70 74 75
77 79 81 82 85 87 93 97 100 104 107 108 110 111 114 119 127 128 129
130 131 132 133 144 146 147 148 149 153 154 156 157
Primary Contact: Jeffrey Prater, Chief Executive Officer
COO: Linda Lilleboe, R.N., MSN, Director Operations
CMO: Evan Easley, M.D., Chief Medical Officer
CIO: Jason Roberts, Director Information System
CHR: Lisa Tremaine, Manager Human Resources
CNO: Kathy Cocking, R.N., Director of Clinical Services
Web address: www.cvmchospital.org
Control: Other not–for–profit (including NFP Corporation) **Service**: General
medical and surgical

Staffed Beds: 23 **Admissions**: 1203 **Census**: 12 **Outpatient Visits**: 160099
Births: 0 **Total Expense ($000)**: 54834 **Payroll Expense ($000)**: 20016
Personnel: 421

HAWTHORNE—Mineral County

MOUNT GRANT GENERAL HOSPITAL (291300), First and 'A' Street,
Zip 89415, Mailing Address: P.O. Box 1510, Zip 89415–1510; tel. 775/945–
2461, (Nonreporting) **A**10 18
Primary Contact: Hugh Qualls, Administrator
Web address: www.mtgrantgenhospital.org/
Control: Other not–for–profit (including NFP Corporation) **Service**: General
medical and surgical

Staffed Beds: 11

HENDERSON—Clark County

⊠ **ENCOMPASS HEALTH REHABILITATION HOSPITAL OF HENDERSON
(293032)**, 10301 Jeffreys Street, Zip 89052–3922; tel. 702/939–9400,
(Nonreporting) **A**1 10 **S** Encompass Health Corporation, Birmingham, AL
Primary Contact: Samantha Billig, Chief Executive Officer
CFO: Robert Bollard, Chief Financial Officer
Web address: www.hendersonrehabhospital.com
Control: Corporation, Investor–owned (for–profit) **Service**: Rehabilitation

Staffed Beds: 90

☐ **HENDERSON HOSPITAL (290057)**, 1050 West Galleria Drive, Zip 89011;
tel. 702/963–7000, (Nonreporting) **A**1 3 10 **S** Universal Health Services, Inc.,
King of Prussia, PA
Primary Contact: Samuel Kaufman, Chief Executive Officer
CNO: Tina Coker, MSN, Chief Nursing Officer
Web address: www.hendersonhospital.com/
Control: Corporation, Investor–owned (for–profit) **Service**: General medical and
surgical

Staffed Beds: 145

★ **KINDRED HOSPITAL LAS VEGAS-SAHARA (292002)**, 102 East Mead
Parkway, 3rd Floor, Zip 89015; tel. 702/871–1418, (Includes KINDRED
HOSPITAL-FLAMINGO, 2250 East Flamingo Road, Las Vegas, Nevada, Zip 89119;
tel. 702/871–1418), (Non-reporting) **A**10 **S** Kindred Healthcare, Louisville, KY
Primary Contact: Doug McCoy, Chief Executive Officer
CFO: William Lysaght, Chief Financial Officer
CMO: Paul Stewart, M.D., Medical Director
CHR: Jim Sturgeon, Area Director Human Resources
Web address: www.kindredhospitallvs.com/
Control: Corporation, Investor–owned (for–profit) **Service**: Acute long–term care
hospital

Staffed Beds: 238

SEVEN HILLS HOSPITAL (294012), 3021 West Horizon Ridge Parkway,
Zip 89052–3990; tel. 702/646–5000, (Nonreporting) **A**3 10 **S** Acadia Healthcare
Company, Inc., Franklin, TN
Primary Contact: Christopher West, Chief Executive Officer
CFO: Mars Patricio Jr Chief Financial Officer
CMO: Jonathan Wirjo, M.D., Medical Director
CIO: Jessica Raub, Director Health Information Management
CHR: Teresa Sulit, Director of Human Resources
CNO: Rustin Park, Director of Nursing
Web address: www.sevenhillsbi.com
Control: Corporation, Investor–owned (for–profit) **Service**: Psychiatric

Staffed Beds: 134

⊠ **ST. ROSE DOMINICAN HOSPITALS - ROSE DE LIMA CAMPUS (290012)**, 102
East Lake Mead Parkway, Zip 89015–5524; tel. 702/616–5000, **A**1 10 **F**3 8 15
18 20 29 30 31 32 34 35 38 40 44 45 49 50 57 59 61 62 64 65 68 70 74 75
77 78 79 80 81 82 84 85 86 87 90 91 95 96 102 107 110 111 115 119 130
131 132 135 143 146 147 148 149 **S** CommonSpirit Health, Chicago, IL
Primary Contact: Teressa Conley, President and Chief Executive Officer
COO: Teressa Conley, Vice President and Chief Operating Officer
CFO: Kevin Walters, Chief Financial Officer
CMO: Stephen K Jones, M.D., Vice President Medical Staff Affairs
Web address: www.strosehospitals.org
Control: Church operated, Nongovernment, not–for–profit **Service**: General
medical and surgical

Staffed Beds: 110 **Admissions**: 3906 **Census**: 53 **Outpatient Visits**: 33357
Births: 0 **Total Expense ($000)**: 130587 **Payroll Expense ($000)**: 55061
Personnel: 401

⊠ **ST. ROSE DOMINICAN HOSPITALS - SIENA CAMPUS (290045)**, 3001 St
Rose Parkway, Zip 89052; tel. 702/616–5000, **A**1 3 5 10 **F**3 7 8 12 13 15 17
18 19 20 22 24 26 28 29 30 31 32 34 35 37 38 40 41 42 43 44 45 46 47 48
49 50 51 57 59 61 63 64 68 70 72 74 75 78 79 80 81 82 84 85 87 88 93 102
107 108 110 111 115 116 117 119 126 130 131 132 135 146 147 148 149
154 156 **S** CommonSpirit Health, Chicago, IL
Primary Contact: Eugene Bassett, President and Chief Executive Officer
COO: Kimberly Shaw, Chief Operating Officer
CFO: Brian Kleven, Chief Financial Officer
CMO: Robert Pretzlaff, M.D., Chief Medical Officer
CIO: Russ Patterson, Director Information Technology
CHR: Linda Gerstenberger, Vice President Human Resources
CNO: Cathleen Hamel, Chief Nurse Executive
Web address: www.strosehospitals.com
Control: Church operated, Nongovernment, not–for–profit **Service**: General
medical and surgical

Staffed Beds: 326 **Admissions**: 19912 **Census**: 252 **Outpatient
Visits**: 95328 **Births**: 3473 **Total Expense ($000)**: 443728 **Payroll Expense
($000)**: 175360 **Personnel**: 1935

INCLINE VILLAGE—Washoe County

★ ○ **INCLINE VILLAGE COMMUNITY HOSPITAL (291301)**, 880 Alder Avenue,
Zip 89451–8335; tel. 775/833–4100, (Nonreporting) **A**5 10 11 18 **S** Tahoe
Forest Health System, Truckee, CA
Primary Contact: Judy Newland, R.N., Chief Nursing Officer
CFO: Crystal Betts, Chief Financial Officer
CIO: Mark Griffiths, Director Management Information Systems
CHR: Jayne O'Flanagan, Director Human Resources
Web address: www.tfhd.com
Control: Hospital district or authority, Government, nonfederal **Service**: General
medical and surgical

Staffed Beds: 6

LAS VEGAS—Clark County

AMG SPECIALTY HOSPITAL - LAS VEGAS (292007), 4015 Mcleod Drive,
Zip 89121–4305; tel. 702/433–2200, (Nonreporting) **A**10 **S** AMG Integrated
Healthcare Management, Lafayette, LA
Primary Contact: Kenneth D'Amico, Chief Executive Officer
CMO: Anthony Pollard, D.O., Chief Medical Officer
Web address: www.amgihm.com/locations/#map_top
Control: Partnership, Investor–owned (for–profit) **Service**: Acute long–term care
hospital

Staffed Beds: 24

☐ **CENTENNIAL HILLS HOSPITAL MEDICAL CENTER (290054)**, 6900 North
Durango Drive, Zip 89149–4409; tel. 702/835–9700, (Nonreporting) **A**1 10 **S**
Universal Health Services, Inc., King of Prussia, PA
Primary Contact: Sajit Pullarkat, Chief Executive Officer and Managing Director
Web address: www.centennialhillshospital.com
Control: Corporation, Investor–owned (for–profit) **Service**: General medical and
surgical

Staffed Beds: 165

⊠ **COMPLEX CARE HOSPITAL AT TENAYA (292006)**, 2500 North Tenaya,
Zip 89128–0482; tel. 702/562–2021, (Nonreporting) **A**1 3 10 **S** LifeCare
Management Services, Plano, TX
Primary Contact: Matt Archer, Chief Executive Officer
COO: Robin Hager, Chief Operating Officer
CFO: Anna Rich, Chief Financial Officer
CMO: C Dean Milne, D.O., Medical Director
CIO: Lynn Tunson, Manager Medical Records
CHR: Belinda McGraw, Director Human Resources
CNO: Robin Wolf, Chief Nursing Officer
Web address: www.lifecare-hospitals.com
Control: Corporation, Investor–owned (for–profit) **Service**: Acute long–term care
hospital

Staffed Beds: 70

☐ **DESERT PARKWAY BEHAVIORAL HEALTHCARE HOSPITAL (294013)**, 3247 South Maryland Parkway, Zip 89109–2412; tel. 702/776–3500, (Nonreporting) **A1 S** Signature Healthcare Services, Corona, CA
Primary Contact: Allison Zednicek, Chief Executive Officer
Web address: www.https://www.desertparkway.com/
Control: Other not–for–profit (including NFP Corporation) **Service:** Psychiatric

Staffed Beds: 83

☐ **DESERT SPRINGS HOSPITAL MEDICAL CENTER (290022)**, 2075 East Flamingo Road, Zip 89119–5121; tel. 702/733–8800, **A1** 3 10 **F3** 12 17 18 20 22 24 26 28 29 30 31 40 45 46 47 48 49 50 54 58 60 64 68 70 74 75 77 78 79 81 85 86 87 90 93 96 98 102 103 107 108 110 111 112 114 115 116 117 119 120 121 122 123 124 126 130 132 135 146 148 149 154 155 156 **S** Universal Health Services, Inc., King of Prussia, PA
Primary Contact: Ryan Jensen, Chief Executive Officer
CFO: George Wiley, Chief Financial Officer
CMO: Golam Choudhury, Chief of Staff
CIO: Alan Woratschek, System Director of Information Services
CNO: Elena McNutt, Chief Nursing Officer
Web address: www.desertspringshospital.com
Control: Corporation, Investor–owned (for–profit) **Service:** General medical and surgical

Staffed Beds: 293 **Admissions:** 13673 **Census:** 192 **Outpatient Visits:** 62013

DESERT WILLOW TREATMENT CENTER, 6171 West Charleston Boulevard, Zip 89146–1126; tel. 702/486–8900, **A5 F29** 98 106
Primary Contact: Jacqueline Wade, Ph.D., Director
Web address: www.dcfs.nv.gov/
Control: State, Government, nonfederal **Service:** Children's general medical and surgical

Staffed Beds: 20 **Admissions:** 121 **Census:** 15 **Outpatient Visits:** 0 **Births:** 0

⊞ **ENCOMPASS HEALTH REHABILITATION HOSPITAL OF DESERT CANYON (293033)**, 9175 West Oquendo Road, Zip 89148–1234; tel. 702/252–7342, (Nonreporting) **A1** 10 **S** Encompass Health Corporation, Birmingham, AL
Primary Contact: Peggy Nelson, Chief Executive Officer
CMO: Bevins Chue, M.D., Medical Director
CNO: Timothy Murphy, R.N., Chief Nursing Officer
Web address: www.healthsouthdesertcanyon.com
Control: Corporation, Investor–owned (for–profit) **Service:** Rehabilitation

Staffed Beds: 50

⊞ **ENCOMPASS HEALTH REHABILITATION HOSPITAL OF LAS VEGAS (293026)**, 1250 South Valley View Boulevard, Zip 89102–1861; tel. 702/877–8898, (Nonreporting) **A1** 10 **S** Encompass Health Corporation, Birmingham, AL
Primary Contact: Michael Ward, Chief Executive Officer
CFO: Raymond Hardy, Controller
CMO: John D. Reneau, Medical Director
CHR: Cheryl Ballew, Human Resources Director
CNO: Susan Ramirez, Chief Nursing Officer
Web address: www.healthsouthlasvegas.com
Control: Corporation, Investor–owned (for–profit) **Service:** Rehabilitation

Staffed Beds: 79

HARMON MEDICAL AND REHABILITATION HOSPITAL (290042), 2170 East Harmon Avenue, Zip 89119–7840; tel. 702/794–0100, **A10 S** Fundamental Long Term Care Holdings, LLC, Sparks Glencoe, MD
Primary Contact: Bonnie Essex. Hillegass, Chief Executive Officer
Control: Corporation, Investor–owned (for–profit) **Service:** Rehabilitation

Staffed Beds: 118

HORIZON SPECIALTY HOSPITAL (292003), 640 Desert Lane, Zip 89106–4207; tel. 702/382–3155, (Nonreporting) **A10 S** Fundamental Long Term Care Holdings, LLC, Sparks Glencoe, MD
Primary Contact: Darrin Cook, Chief Executive Officer and Administrator
CFO: Darnell Bennett, Director Finance
CMO: Syed Rahman, M.D., Chief of Staff
CIO: Azena Ansi, Manager Health Information Management
CHR: Melvin Layugan, Director Human Resources
Web address: www.horizonspecialtyhosp.com/
Control: Corporation, Investor–owned (for–profit) **Service:** Acute long–term care hospital

Staffed Beds: 49

☐ **MONTEVISTA HOSPITAL (294009)**, 5900 West Rochelle Avenue, Zip 89103–3327; tel. 702/364–1111, (Includes RED ROCK BEHAVIORAL HOSPITAL, 5900 West Rochelle Avenue, Las Vegas, Nevada, Zip 89103–3304, Mailing Address: 5900 W Rochelle Ave, Zip 89103–3304, tel. 702/214–8099; Richard Failla, Chief Executive Officer) **A1** 10 **F4** 5 38 98 99 100 103 104 105 106 130 151 152 153 154 **S** Strategic Behavioral Health, LLC, Memphis, TN
Primary Contact: Curtis Ohashi, Chief Executive Officer
CMO: William Bauer, M.D., Medical Director
CHR: Carol Nelson, Director Human Resources
Web address: www.montevistahospital.com
Control: Partnership, Investor–owned (for–profit) **Service:** Psychiatric

Staffed Beds: 202 **Admissions:** 6729 **Census:** 136

☐ **MOUNTAIN'S EDGE HOSPITAL (290056)**, 8656 West Patrick Lane, Zip 89148–5043; tel. 702/777–7100, (Nonreporting) **A1** 10
Primary Contact: Melissa War, Chief Executive Officer
Web address: www.mountainsedgehospital.com/
Control: Other not–for–profit (including NFP Corporation) **Service:** General medical and surgical

Staffed Beds: 130

⊞ **MOUNTAINVIEW HOSPITAL (290039)**, 3100 North Tenaya Way, Zip 89128–0436; tel. 702/255–5000, (Nonreporting) **A1** 3 5 10 **S** HCA Healthcare, Nashville, TN
Primary Contact: Jeremy Bradshaw, Chief Executive Officer
CFO: Lana Arad, Chief Financial Officer
CMO: Jack Collier, M.D., Chief of Staff
CHR: Robert Nettles, Director Human Resources
CNO: Natalie Ransom, Chief Nursing Officer
Web address: www.mountainview-hospital.com
Control: Corporation, Investor–owned (for–profit) **Service:** General medical and surgical

Staffed Beds: 340

☐ **PAM REHABILITATION HOSPITAL OF CENTENNIAL HILLS (293034)**, 6166 North Durango Drive, Zip 89149; tel. 725/223–4100, (Nonreporting) **A1** 10 **S** Post Acute Medical, LLC, Enola, PA
Primary Contact: Jeanette Williams, Chief Executive Officer
Web address: www.postacutemedical.com/facilities/find-facility/rehabilitation-hospitals/pam-rehabilitation-hospital-centennial-hills
Control: Partnership, Investor–owned (for–profit) **Service:** Rehabilitation

Staffed Beds: 44

⊞ **SOUTHERN HILLS HOSPITAL AND MEDICAL CENTER (290047)**, 9300 West Sunset Road, Zip 89148–4844; tel. 702/880–2100, (Nonreporting) **A1** 3 10 **S** HCA Healthcare, Nashville, TN
Primary Contact: Alexis Mussi, Interim Chief Executive Officer
COO: Alexis Mussi, Chief Operating Officer
CFO: Jennifer Le, Chief Financial Officer
CMO: Eric Ramos, M.D., Division Chief Medical Officer
CIO: Joe Grandiosi, Director Information Technology
CHR: Brian Wood, Director Human Resources
CNO: Maura Wright, Chief Nursing Officer
Web address: www.southernhillshospital.com
Control: Corporation, Investor–owned (for–profit) **Service:** General medical and surgical

Staffed Beds: 134

☐ **SOUTHERN NEVADA ADULT MENTAL HEALTH SERVICES (294002)**, 6161 West Charleston Boulevard, Zip 89146–1126; tel. 702/486–6000, (Nonreporting) **A1** 3 5 10
Primary Contact: Chelsea Szklany, Hospital Administrator
Web address: www.mhds.state.nv.us
Control: State, Government, nonfederal **Service:** Psychiatric

Staffed Beds: 289

☐ **SPRING MOUNTAIN SAHARA (294010)**, 5460 West Sahara, Zip 89146–3307; tel. 702/216–8900, **A1** 10 **F29** 56 98 103 130 153 **S** Universal Health Services, Inc., King of Prussia, PA
Primary Contact: Darryl S. Dubroca, Chief Executive Officer and Managing Director
Web address: www.springmountainsahara.com
Control: Corporation, Investor–owned (for–profit) **Service:** Psychiatric

Staffed Beds: 30 **Admissions:** 927 **Census:** 24 **Outpatient Visits:** 2440 **Births:** 0 **Total Expense ($000):** 6627 **Payroll Expense ($000):** 3336 **Personnel:** 59

NV

Hospital, Medicare Provider Number, Address, Telephone, Approval, Facility, and Physician Codes, Health Care System

★ American Hospital Association (AHA) membership   ○ Healthcare Facilities Accreditation Program   ⇑ Center for Improvement in Healthcare Quality Accreditation
☐ The Joint Commission accreditation   ◇ DNV Healthcare Inc. accreditation   △ Commission on Accreditation of Rehabilitation Facilities (CARF) accreditation

☐ **SPRING MOUNTAIN TREATMENT CENTER (294011)**, 7000 West Spring Mountain Road, Zip 89117–3816; tel. 702/873–2400, **A1** 10 **F**29 98 130 143 149 153 **S** Universal Health Services, Inc., King of Prussia, PA
Primary Contact: C. Alan. Eaks, Chief Executive Officer and Managing Director
CFO: Sherilene DeLeon, Chief Financial Officer
CMO: Jerome Nwokike, M.D., Medical Director
CNO: Norma Ferris, R.N., MS, Chief Nursing Officer
Web address: www.springmountaintreatmentcenter.com/
Control: Corporation, Investor–owned (for–profit) **Service**: Psychiatric

Staffed Beds: 110 **Admissions**: 5687 **Census**: 86 **Outpatient Visits**: 482
Births: 0 **Total Expense ($000)**: 21203 **Payroll Expense ($000)**: 9927
Personnel: 178

☐ **SPRING VALLEY HOSPITAL MEDICAL CENTER (290046)**, 5400 South Rainbow Boulevard, Zip 89118–1859; tel. 702/853–3000, (Nonreporting) **A1** 3 10 **S** Universal Health Services, Inc., King of Prussia, PA
Primary Contact: Leonard Freehof, Chief Executive Officer and Managing Director
COO: Matthew Wheelus, Chief Operating Officer
CFO: Carl Caley, Chief Financial Officer
CMO: S. Daniel, M.D., Chief Medical Officer
CHR: Angelique Ford, Administrator Human Resources
CNO: Margaret Covelli, R.N., Chief Nursing Officer
Web address: www.springvalleyhospital.com
Control: Corporation, Investor–owned (for–profit) **Service**: General medical and surgical

Staffed Beds: 169

⊠ **ST. ROSE DOMINICAN HOSPITALS - SAN MARTIN CAMPUS (290053)**, 8280 West Warm Springs Road, Zip 89113–3612; tel. 702/492–8000, **A1** 10 **F**3 8 13 15 18 19 20 22 24 26 28 29 30 31 35 38 40 44 45 47 49 50 57 59 61 62 64 68 70 72 74 75 76 77 78 79 80 81 85 86 87 93 102 107 108 110 111 115 119 126 130 131 132 135 146 148 149 **S** CommonSpirit Health, Chicago, IL
Primary Contact: Lawrence Barnard, President and Chief Executive Officer
CFO: Dev Ramsamy, Chief Financial Officer
CMO: Robert Pretzlaff, M.D., Chief Medical Officer
CIO: Russ Patterson, Site Manager Information Technology
CHR: Linda Gerstenberger, Vice President Human Resources
CNO: Katherine Raymond, Chief Nursing Officer
Web address: www.strosehospitals.org
Control: Church operated, Nongovernment, not–for–profit **Service**: General medical and surgical

Staffed Beds: 147 **Admissions**: 7955 **Census**: 92 **Outpatient Visits**: 35764
Births: 1221 **Total Expense ($000)**: 194293 **Payroll Expense ($000)**: 67655 **Personnel**: 671

☐ **SUMMERLIN HOSPITAL MEDICAL CENTER (290041)**, 657 Town Center Drive, Zip 89144–6367; tel. 702/233–7000, (Nonreporting) **A1** 3 10 **S** Universal Health Services, Inc., King of Prussia, PA
Primary Contact: Robert S. Freymuller, Chief Executive Officer
Web address: www.summerlinhospital.com
Control: Corporation, Investor–owned (for–profit) **Service**: General medical and surgical

Staffed Beds: 148

⊠ △ **SUNRISE HOSPITAL AND MEDICAL CENTER (290003)**, 3186 South Maryland Parkway, Zip 89109–2306, Mailing Address: P.O. Box 98530, Zip 89193; tel. 702/731–8000, (Nonreporting) **A1** 2 3 5 7 10 **S** HCA Healthcare, Nashville, TN
Primary Contact: Todd Sklamberg, President
COO: Mark J. Amox, Chief Operating Officer
CFO: Daniel Perritt, Chief Financial Officer
CMO: Katherine Keeley, M.D., Chief of Staff
CIO: Alan Burt, Director Information Services
Web address: www.sunrisehospital.com
Control: Corporation, Investor–owned (for–profit) **Service**: General medical and surgical

Staffed Beds: 668

⊠ **UNIVERSITY MEDICAL CENTER (290007)**, 1800 West Charleston Boulevard, Zip 89102–2386; tel. 702/383–2000, (Includes CHILDREN'S HOSPITAL OF NEVADA AT UMC, 800 Hope Place, Las Vegas, Nevada, Zip 89106; tel. 702/383–2000) **A1** 2 3 5 10 **F**3 8 11 13 15 16 17 18 19 20 22 24 26 28 29 31 34 35 36 40 41 42 43 45 46 47 48 49 50 57 58 59 60 61 65 68 70 72 73 74 75 76 77 78 79 80 81 83 84 85 86 87 88 89 93 97 100 102 107 108 111 114 115 116 117 119 126 130 131 132 138 141 142 143 144 146 148
Primary Contact: Mason VanHouweling, Chief Executive Officer
COO: Anthony Marinello, Chief Operating Officer
CFO: Jennifer Wakem, Chief Financial Officer
CHR: John Espinoza, Chief Human Resources Officer
CNO: Debra Fox, Chief Nursing Officer
Web address: www.umcsn.com
Control: County, Government, nonfederal **Service**: General medical and surgical

Staffed Beds: 497 **Admissions**: 22906 **Census**: 359 **Outpatient Visits**: 455422 **Births**: 2069 **Total Expense ($000)**: 656200 **Payroll Expense ($000)**: 267671 **Personnel**: 3693

☐ **VALLEY HOSPITAL MEDICAL CENTER (290021)**, 620 Shadow Lane, Zip 89106–4119; tel. 702/388–4000, (Nonreporting) **A1** 3 5 10 12 13 **S** Universal Health Services, Inc., King of Prussia, PA
Primary Contact: Claude Wise, Chief Executive Officer
CFO: Betsy A Sponsler, Chief Financial Officer
CMO: Dost Wattoo, M.D., Chief of Staff
CIO: Tom Schoenig, Regional Director Information Services
CHR: Dana Thorne, Administrator Human Resources
Web address: www.valleyhospital.net
Control: Corporation, Investor–owned (for–profit) **Service**: General medical and surgical

Staffed Beds: 365

LOVELOCK—Pershing County

★ **PERSHING GENERAL HOSPITAL (291304)**, 855 Sixth Street, Zip 89419, Mailing Address: P.O. Box 661, Zip 89419–0661; tel. 775/273–2621, (Nonreporting) **A**10 18
Primary Contact: Patty Bianchi, Chief Executive Officer
CFO: Marjorie Skinner, Director Finance
CMO: Yousri Gadallah, M.D., Chief Medical Officer
CIO: Jim Weeldreyer, Manager Information Technology
CHR: Cynthia Hixenbaugh, Director Human Resources
Web address: www.pershinghospital.org
Control: Hospital district or authority, Government, nonfederal **Service**: General medical and surgical

Staffed Beds: 38

MESQUITE—Clark County

⊠ **MESA VIEW REGIONAL HOSPITAL (291307)**, 1299 Bertha Howe Avenue, Zip 89027–7500; tel. 702/346–8040, **A1** 10 18 **F**11 13 15 18 29 30 34 35 40 45 46 51 56 57 59 63 64 70 75 79 81 85 87 107 108 110 111 114 119 130 132 133 135 146 147 148 **S** Quorum Health, Brentwood, TN
Primary Contact: Ned Hill, Chief Executive Officer
CFO: Mitchell Fransen, Chief Financial Officer
CHR: Steve Siegrist, Director of Human Resources
CNO: Leslie Woodson, Chief Nursing Officer
Web address: www.mesaviewhospital.com
Control: Corporation, Investor–owned (for–profit) **Service**: General medical and surgical

Staffed Beds: 25 **Admissions**: 713 **Census**: 6 **Outpatient Visits**: 37312
Births: 61 **Total Expense ($000)**: 24418 **Payroll Expense ($000)**: 9891
Personnel: 176

NELLIS AFB—Clark County

⊠ **MIKE O'CALLAGHAN FEDERAL HOSPITAL**, 4700 Las Vegas Boulevard North, Suite 2419, Zip 89191–6600; tel. 702/653–2000, (Nonreporting) **A1** 3 5 **S** Department of the Air Force, Washington, DC
Primary Contact: Colonel Christian Benjamin, USAF, MC, Commander
COO: Colonel Linnes L Chester, USAF, MSC, Administrator
CFO: Major Kari Turkal-Barrett, Flight Commander Resource Management Officer
CMO: Lieutenant Colonel Markham Brown, M.D., Chief Medical Staff
CIO: Major Kevin Seeley, Chief Information Officer
Web address: www.nellis.af.mil/
Control: Department of Defense, Government, federal **Service**: General medical and surgical

Staffed Beds: 46

NORTH LAS VEGAS—Clark County

★ ⇑ **NORTH VISTA HOSPITAL (290005)**, 1409 East Lake Mead Boulevard, Zip 89030–7197; tel. 702/649–7711, (Nonreporting) **A**10 21 **S** Prime Healthcare, Ontario, CA
Primary Contact: Vincenzo Variale, Chief Executive Officer
CFO: Peter S Miller, Chief Financial Officer
CHR: Abayomi Fibiyi, Chief Human Resources Officer
Web address: www.northvistahospital.com
Control: Corporation, Investor–owned (for–profit) **Service**: General medical and surgical

Staffed Beds: 177

⊠ **VETERANS AFFAIRS SOUTHERN NEVADA HEALTHCARE SYSTEM**, 6900 North Pecos Road, Zip 89086–4400; tel. 702/791–9000, (Nonreporting) **A1** 3 5 **S** Department of Veterans Affairs, Washington, DC
Primary Contact: William J. Caron, Chief Executive Officer
CFO: Richard O Hays, Chief Fiscal Service
CMO: Ramanujam Komanduri, M.D., Chief of Staff
Web address: www.lasvegas.va.gov/
Control: Veterans Affairs, Government, federal **Service**: General medical and surgical

Staffed Beds: 90

NV

PAHRUMP—Nye County

★ **DESERT VIEW HOSPITAL (291311)**, 360 South Lola Lane, Zip 89048–0884; tel. 775/751–7500, **A**3 10 18 **F**3 15 29 34 37 40 45 46 56 57 59 81 85 107 108 110 111 114 119 133 148 154 **S** Universal Health Services, Inc., King of Prussia, PA
Primary Contact: Susan Davila, Chief Executive Officer
CFO: Ryan Eggleston, Chief Financial Officer
CMO: Fredric Siegel, M.D., Chief of Staff
CIO: Chad Andres, Chief Information Officer
CHR: Lisa Doty, Manager Human Resources
CNO: Markeeta Araujo, Chief Nursing Officer
Web address: www.desertviewhospital.com
Control: Corporation, Investor–owned (for–profit) **Service**: General medical and surgical

Staffed Beds: 25 **Admissions**: 1353 **Census**: 10 **Outpatient Visits**: 50531 **Births**: 0 **Personnel**: 211

DESERT VIEW REGIONAL MEDICAL CENTER See Desert View Hospital

RENO—Washoe County

☐ **RENO BEHAVIORAL HEALTHCARE HOSPITAL**, 6940 Sierra Center Parkway, Zip 89511; tel. 877/787–8518, (Nonreporting) **A**1 **S** Signature Healthcare Services, Corona, CA
Primary Contact: Steve Shell, Chief Executive Officer
Web address: www.renobehavioral.com
Control: Corporation, Investor–owned (for–profit) **Service**: Rehabilitation

Staffed Beds: 124

⊞ **RENOWN REGIONAL MEDICAL CENTER (290001)**, 1155 Mill Street, Zip 89502–1576; tel. 775/982–4100, (Includes RENOWN CHILDREN'S HOSPITAL, 1155 Mill Street, Reno, Nevada, Zip 89502–1576; tel. 775/982–5437) **A**1 2 3 5 8 10 **F**3 5 11 13 15 17 18 19 20 21 22 23 24 25 26 27 29 30 31 32 34 35 40 41 43 44 45 46 48 49 54 56 57 58 59 61 62 63 65 66 68 70 72 73 74 75 76 77 78 79 80 81 84 85 86 87 88 89 92 100 101 102 107 108 111 114 115 118 119 120 121 123 124 126 130 132 135 146 148 149 **S** Renown Health, Reno, NV
Primary Contact: Erik Olson, Chief Executive Officer
COO: Sy Johnson, Executive Vice President, Chief Operating Officer
CFO: Sam King, Chief Financial Officer
CMO: Charles Johnson, M.D., Chief of Staff
CIO: Charles Scully, Chief Information Officer
CHR: Michelle Sanchez-Bickley, Chief Human Resources Officer
Web address: www.renown.org
Control: Other not–for–profit (including NFP Corporation) **Service**: General medical and surgical

Staffed Beds: 667 **Admissions**: 33538 **Census**: 501 **Outpatient Visits**: 582021 **Births**: 4487 **Total Expense ($000)**: 692925 **Payroll Expense ($000)**: 248046 **Personnel**: 4431

★ △ **RENOWN REHABILITATION HOSPITAL**, 1495 Mill Street, Zip 89502–1479; tel. 775/982–3500, **A**7 **F**29 54 77 82 90 93 95 96 148 149 **S** Renown Health, Reno, NV
Primary Contact: Chris Nicholas, Administrator of Rehabilitation Hospital
CFO: Dawn Ahner, Chief Financial Officer
CMO: Doug Merrill, Executive Vice President Chief Medical and Academic Officer
CIO: Ronald Fuschillo, Chief Information Officer
CHR: Michelle Sanchez-Bickley, Vice President Human Resources
CNO: Melodie Osborn, Vice President and Chief Nursing Officer, Transitional Care Services
Web address: www.renown.org
Control: Other not–for–profit (including NFP Corporation) **Service**: Rehabilitation

Staffed Beds: 62 **Admissions**: 824 **Census**: 34 **Outpatient Visits**: 25660 **Births**: 0 **Total Expense ($000)**: 23716 **Payroll Expense ($000)**: 11293 **Personnel**: 158

⊞ **RENOWN SOUTH MEADOWS MEDICAL CENTER (290049)**, 10101 Double 'R' Boulevard, Zip 89521–5931; tel. 775/982–7000, **A**1 10 **F**10 12 28 29 30 35 38 40 44 46 68 70 74 75 79 81 82 85 87 92 93 97 107 108 111 119 130 131 146 157 **S** Renown Health, Reno, NV
Primary Contact: Siri Nelson, Chief Executive Officer
COO: Sy Johnson, Executive Vice President, Chief Operating Officer
CFO: Gina Nelson, Chief Financial Officer
CMO: Dennis Rochier, Chief Medical Officer
CIO: Ronald Fuschillo, Chief Information Officer
CHR: Michelle Sanchez-Bickley, Vice President Human Resources
CNO: Melodie Osborn, Vice President and Chief Nursing Officer, Transitional Care Services
Web address: www.renown.org
Control: Other not–for–profit (including NFP Corporation) **Service**: General medical and surgical

Staffed Beds: 76 **Admissions**: 4358 **Census**: 34 **Outpatient Visits**: 73053 **Births**: 0 **Total Expense ($000)**: 81669 **Payroll Expense ($000)**: 26179 **Personnel**: 352

⊞ **SAINT MARY'S REGIONAL MEDICAL CENTER (290009)**, 235 West Sixth Street, Zip 89503–4548; tel. 775/770–3000, (Nonreporting) **A**1 2 3 5 10 **S** Prime Healthcare, Ontario, CA
Primary Contact: Helen Lidholm, Chief Executive Officer
CFO: John R Deakyne, Chief Financial Officer
CIO: Cindy Mullins, Director Information Technology
CHR: David Milovich, Vice President Human Resources
Web address: www.saintmarysreno.org
Control: Corporation, Investor–owned (for–profit) **Service**: General medical and surgical

Staffed Beds: 293

⊞ **VETERANS AFFAIRS SIERRA NEVADA HEALTH CARE SYSTEM**, 975 Kirman Avenue, Zip 89502–0993; tel. 775/786–7200, **A**1 3 5 **F**3 5 8 18 20 22 28 29 30 31 33 34 35 36 38 39 40 45 46 47 48 51 56 57 58 59 60 61 62 63 65 68 70 71 74 75 77 78 79 81 82 83 84 85 86 87 93 94 96 97 98 100 101 102 103 104 107 108 109 118 119 127 128 129 130 132 135 143 146 147 148 149 152 153 154 156 **S** Department of Veterans Affairs, Washington, DC
Primary Contact: Lisa M. Howard, Director
COO: Lisa M Howard, Associate Director
CFO: Kelly Manson, Chief Financial Officer
CMO: Steven Brilliant, M.D., Chief of Staff
CIO: Jack Smith, Acting Chief Information Resources Management Service
CHR: Debbie Jenkins, Chief Human Resources Management Service
Web address: www.reno.va.gov/
Control: Veterans Affairs, Government, federal **Service**: General medical and surgical

Staffed Beds: 124 **Admissions**: 3512 **Census**: 104 **Outpatient Visits**: 457674 **Births**: 0 **Total Expense ($000)**: 334254 **Personnel**: 1612

☐ **WEST HILLS HOSPITAL (294003)**, 1240 East Ninth Street, Zip 89512–2964; tel. 775/323–0478, (Nonreporting) **A**1 3 10 **S** Universal Health Services, Inc., King of Prussia, PA
Primary Contact: Nadine Dexter, Chief Executive Officer
CMO: Philip Rich, M.D., Chief Medical Officer
CHR: Don Gay, Director Human Resources
Web address: www.westhillshospital.net
Control: Corporation, Investor–owned (for–profit) **Service**: Psychiatric

Staffed Beds: 190

WILLOW SPRINGS CENTER, 690 Edison Way, Zip 89502–4135; tel. 775/858–3303, **A**3 5 **F**98 99 104 106
Primary Contact: Ann Schaack, Chief Executive Officer
CFO: Chris Farley, Chief Financial Officer
CMO: Dana Arlien, M.D., Chief Medical Officer
CIO: Wallace Marsh, Director of Information Technology
CHR: Kristine Anglin, Human Resources Manager
CNO: Laurie MacAffee, Director of Nursing
Web address: www.willowspringscenter.com
Control: Corporation, Investor–owned (for–profit) **Service**: Children's hospital psychiatric

Staffed Beds: 116 **Admissions**: 345 **Census**: 76 **Outpatient Visits**: 2113 **Births**: 0 **Total Expense ($000)**: 15888 **Payroll Expense ($000)**: 8515 **Personnel**: 143

NV

Hospital, Medicare Provider Number, Address, Telephone, Approval, Facility, and Physician Codes, Health Care System

★ American Hospital Association (AHA) membership   ○ Healthcare Facilities Accreditation Program   ⇑ Center for Improvement in Healthcare Quality Accreditation
☐ The Joint Commission accreditation   ◇ DNV Healthcare Inc. accreditation   △ Commission on Accreditation of Rehabilitation Facilities (CARF) accreditation

SPARKS—Washoe County

☐ **NORTHERN NEVADA ADULT MENTAL HEALTH SERVICES (294000)**, 480 Galletti Way, Zip 89431–5564; tel. 775/688–2001, **A**1 3 5 10 **F**29 50 98 104 130 149 158
Primary Contact: Cody Phinney, Administrator
CFO: Elizabeth O'Brien, Chief Financial Officer
CIO: Lois Repass, Quality Assurance Specialist and Coordinator Performance Improvement
Web address: www.mhds.state.nv.us/
Control: State, Government, nonfederal **Service:** Psychiatric

Staffed Beds: 30 **Admissions:** 659 **Census:** 26 **Outpatient Visits:** 29682
Births: 0

☐ ○ **NORTHERN NEVADA MEDICAL CENTER (290032)**, 2375 East Prater Way, Zip 89434–9641; tel. 775/331–7000, (Nonreporting) **A**1 10 11 **S** Universal Health Services, Inc., King of Prussia, PA
Primary Contact: Alan C. Olive, Chief Executive Officer
COO: Tiffany Coury, Chief Operating Officer
CFO: Ryan Heit, Chief Financial Officer
CHR: Patricia Downs, Director Human Resources
CNO: Carla Adams, Chief Nursing Officer
Web address: www.nnmc.com
Control: Corporation, Investor–owned (for–profit) **Service:** General medical and surgical

Staffed Beds: 108

✠ **TAHOE PACIFIC HOSPITALS (292004)**, 2375 East Prater Way, Zip 89434; tel. 775/355–5600, (Includes TAHOE PACIFIC HOSPITALS - WEST, 235 West Sixth Street, 5th Floor, Reno, Nevada, Zip 89503–4548; tel. 775/982–5437; TAHOE PACIFIC HOSPITALS, 10101 Double R Boulevard, Reno, Nevada, Zip 89521–5931; tel. 775/331–1044), (Non-reporting) **A**1 10 **S** LifeCare Management Services, Plano, TX
Primary Contact: Matt Archer, Chief Executive Officer
COO: Gary Brooks, Chief Operating Officer
CFO: Nena Swenson, Financial Manager
CMO: T Brian Callister, M.D., Chief Medical Officer
CIO: Kaylene Reeves, Director
CHR: Nelson Coy, Director Human Resources
Web address: www.lifecare-hospitals.com
Control: Corporation, Investor–owned (for–profit) **Service:** Acute long–term care hospital

Staffed Beds: 60

WINNEMUCCA—Humboldt County

★ **HUMBOLDT GENERAL HOSPITAL (291308)**, 118 East Haskell Street, Zip 89445–3299; tel. 775/623–5222, (Nonreporting) **A**3 5 10 18
Primary Contact: Arthur H. Frable, Chief Executive Officer
CFO: Sandi Lehman, Chief Financial Officer
CMO: Brad Granath, M.D., Chief of Staff
CHR: Rose Marie Green, Director Human Resources
CNO: Darlene Bryan, R.N., Chief Nursing Officer
Web address: www.hghospital.org
Control: Hospital district or authority, Government, nonfederal **Service:** General medical and surgical

Staffed Beds: 67

YERINGTON—Lyon County

SOUTH LYON MEDICAL CENTER (290002), 213 South Whitacre, Zip 89447–2561, Mailing Address: P.O. Box 940, Zip 89447–0940; tel. 775/463–2301, (Nonreporting) **A**10 18
Primary Contact: Toni A. Inserra, Interim Administrator
Web address: www.southlyonmedicalcenter.org
Control: Other not–for–profit (including NFP Corporation) **Service:** General medical and surgical

Staffed Beds: 63

NV

Many Facility Codes have changed. Please refer to the AHA Guide Code Chart. © 2019 AHA Guide

NEW HAMPSHIRE

BERLIN—Coos County

★ **ANDROSCOGGIN VALLEY HOSPITAL (301310)**, 59 Page Hill Road,
Zip 03570–3531; tel. 603/752–2200, **A**10 18 **F**3 8 11 12 13 15 17 28 29 30 34 40
41 45 47 57 59 61 64 67 68 70 74 75 76 77 79 81 82 85 89 92 93 102 107 108
110 115 119 128 129 130 131 132 133 146 147 149 156 **S** QHR, Brentwood, TN
Primary Contact: Michael Peterson, FACHE, President
CFO: Jeremy Roberge, Director Reimbursement
CMO: Keith M Shute, M.D., Senior Vice President Medical Affairs and Clinical Services
CIO: Linda M Laperle, Vice President Administrative Services
CHR: James A Wheeler, Vice President Human Relations and Community
Development
Web address: www.avhnh.org
Control: Other not–for–profit (including NFP Corporation) **Service**: General
medical and surgical

> **Staffed Beds: 25 Admissions: 1157 Census: 12 Outpatient Visits:** 66352
> **Births:** 88 **Total Expense ($000):** 57082 **Payroll Expense ($000):** 24418
> **Personnel:** 302

CLAREMONT—Sullivan County

★ **VALLEY REGIONAL HOSPITAL (301308)**, 243 Elm Street, Zip 03743–4921;
tel. 603/542–7771, **A**10 18 **F**3 11 14 15 28 29 31 34 35 38 40 43 45 49 50
54 57 59 64 68 75 77 79 81 83 84 85 87 93 97 107 110 114 118 119 130
131 132 133 135 144 146 147 149 154 156 157
Primary Contact: Deanna S. Howard, Interim President and Chief Executive Officer
CFO: Jean Shaw, Chief Financial Officer
CMO: Oliver Herfort, M.D., Chief Medical Officer
CIO: Patricia Witthaus, Director Information Services
CHR: Cheryl Cavanaugh, Senior Director Human Resources
Web address: www.vrh.org
Control: Other not–for–profit (including NFP Corporation) **Service**: General
medical and surgical

> **Staffed Beds: 25 Admissions:** 708 **Census:** 9 **Outpatient Visits:** 81782 **Births:** 0
> **Total Expense ($000):** 43078 **Payroll Expense ($000):** 17072 **Personnel:** 274

COLEBROOK—Coos County

★ **UPPER CONNECTICUT VALLEY HOSPITAL (301300)**, 181 Corliss Lane,
Zip 03576–3207; tel. 603/237–4971, (Nonreporting) **A**10 18 **S** QHR,
Brentwood, TN
Primary Contact: Scott Colby, President
CFO: Celeste Pitts, Chief Financial Officer
CMO: Robert Rose, M.D., Chief Medical Officer
CIO: Heather Leighton, Director, Revenue Cycle and Privacy Officer
CHR: Heidi L Saari, Director, Human Resources
CNO: Lindsay Rancourt, Director of Nursing
Web address: www.ucvh.org
Control: Other not–for–profit (including NFP Corporation) **Service**: General
medical and surgical

> **Staffed Beds:** 12

CONCORD—Merrimack County

★ ⇧ **CONCORD HOSPITAL (300001)**, 250 Pleasant Street, Zip 03301–2598;
tel. 603/225–2711, **A**2 3 5 10 21 **F**3 8 12 13 14 15 17 18 20 22 24 26 28 29 30
31 33 34 35 37 38 39 40 43 44 45 46 47 49 50 51 53 54 55 56 57 58 59 61 64
65 66 68 69 70 71 73 74 75 76 77 78 79 80 81 82 83 84 85 86 87 89 92 93 97
98 100 101 102 104 105 107 108 110 111 114 115 118 119 120 121 123 124
126 129 130 132 134 135 144 145 146 147 148 149 150 152 153 154 156 157
Primary Contact: Robert P. Steigmeyer, President and Chief Executive Officer
COO: Timothy P. Jones, Chief Operating Officer
CFO: Bruce R. Burns, Chief Financial Officer
CMO: David F. Green, M.D., Chief Medical Officer
CIO: Deane Morrison, Chief Information Officer
CHR: Robin A. Moore, Chief Human Resources Officer
CNO: Amy Dumont, MSN, R.N., FACHE, Chief Nursing Officer
Web address: www.concordhospital.org
Control: Other not–for–profit (including NFP Corporation) **Service**: General
medical and surgical

> **Staffed Beds: 245 Admissions: 13355 Census: 153 Outpatient**
> **Visits:** 511157 **Births:** 1338 **Total Expense ($000):** 485879 **Payroll**
> **Expense ($000):** 232432 **Personnel:** 3113

⊞ **ENCOMPASS HEALTH REHABILITATION HOSPITAL OF CONCORD (303027)**,
254 Pleasant Street, Zip 03301–2508; tel. 603/226–9800, (Nonreporting) **A**1 10
S Encompass Health Corporation, Birmingham, AL
Primary Contact: Diana Lachapelle, CPA, Chief Executive Officer
CMO: Muhammad Salmanullah, Chief Medical Director
CHR: Myra Nixon, Director Human Resources
CNO: Joseph Adamski, Chief Nursing Officer
Web address: www.healthsouthrehabconcordnh.com
Control: Corporation, Investor–owned (for–profit) **Service**: Rehabilitation

> **Staffed Beds:** 50

☐ **NEW HAMPSHIRE HOSPITAL (304000)**, 36 Clinton Street, Zip 03301–2359;
tel. 603/271–5300, **A**1 3 5 10 **F**3 29 30 32 35 44 50 53 56 57 58 59 65 68 74
75 77 86 87 91 98 99 101 103 130 132 135 146 149
Primary Contact: Lori Shibinette, Chief Executive Officer
COO: Geoffrey C Souther, Chief Operating Officer
CFO: Jamie Dall, Chief Financial Officer
CIO: David Levesque, Director, Information Systems
CHR: Mark Bussiere, Administrator Human Resources
CNO: Roberta A Vitale-Nolen, Administrator, Patient Care Services
Web address: www.dhhs.nh.gov/dcbcs/nhh/
Control: State, Government, nonfederal **Service**: Psychiatric

> **Staffed Beds: 168 Admissions: 1369 Census: 161 Outpatient Visits:** 0
> **Births:** 0 **Total Expense ($000):** 69151 **Payroll Expense ($000):** 31178
> **Personnel:** 608

DERRY—Rockingham County

⊞ **PARKLAND MEDICAL CENTER (300017)**, One Parkland Drive,
Zip 03038–2750; tel. 603/432–1500, (Nonreporting) **A**1 2 10 **S** HCA Healthcare,
Nashville, TN
Primary Contact: Jeff Scionti, Chief Executive Officer
CFO: Jacob Wisemann, Chief Financial Officer
CMO: Edward Yourtee, M.D., Chief Medical Officer
CIO: Brad George, Director Information Systems
CHR: Molly Lahti, Director Human Resources
CNO: Eileen Keefe, Chief Nursing Officer
Web address: www.parklandmedicalcenter.com
Control: Corporation, Investor–owned (for–profit) **Service**: General medical and
surgical

> **Staffed Beds:** 82

DOVER—Strafford County

⊞ **WENTWORTH-DOUGLASS HOSPITAL (300018)**, 789 Central Avenue,
Zip 03820; tel. 603/742–5252, **A**1 2 10 **F**3 5 8 12 13 18 19 20 22 26 28 29
30 31 32 34 35 36 38 39 40 41 43 44 45 46 47 48 49 50 51 52 53 54 55 57
58 59 61 63 64 65 68 70 73 74 75 76 77 78 79 81 82 84 85 86 87 89 91 92
93 94 96 97 100 101 102 104 107 108 111 114 115 118 119 120 121 123
124 126 129 130 131 132 134 135 143 144 145 146 147 148 149 154 156 **S**
Partners HealthCare System, Inc., Boston, MA
Primary Contact: Gregory J. Walker, Chief Executive Officer
COO: Daniel N Dunn, Vice President Operations
CFO: Peter Walcek, Vice President Finance
CMO: Paul Cass, D.O., Chief Medical & Clinical Integration Officer
CIO: Jeffrey Pollock, Chief Information Officer
CHR: Erin Flanigan, Vice President Human Resources
CNO: Sheila Woolley, R.N., M.P.H., Vice President, Patient Care Services
Web address: www.wdhospital.com
Control: Other not–for–profit (including NFP Corporation) **Service**: General
medical and surgical

> **Staffed Beds: 142 Admissions: 6880 Census: 82 Outpatient**
> **Visits:** 331225 **Births:** 1253 **Total Expense ($000):** 304326 **Payroll**
> **Expense ($000):** 123731 **Personnel:** 2388

NH

Hospital, Medicare Provider Number, Address, Telephone, Approval, Facility, and Physician Codes, Health Care System

★ American Hospital Association (AHA) membership   ○ Healthcare Facilities Accreditation Program   ⇧ Center for Improvement in Healthcare Quality Accreditation
☐ The Joint Commission accreditation   ◇ DNV Healthcare Inc. accreditation   △ Commission on Accreditation of Rehabilitation Facilities (CARF) accreditation

EXETER—Rockingham County

★ ⊞ **EXETER HOSPITAL (300023)**, 5 Alumni Drive, Zip 03833–2128;
tel. 603/778–7311, **A**2 5 10 21 **F**3 8 13 14 15 18 20 22 26 28 29 30 31 34 35
37 38 40 44 45 46 47 48 49 50 51 52 54 55 57 58 59 64 70 74 75 76 77 78
79 80 81 84 85 86 87 89 93 107 108 110 111 114 115 117 118 119 120 121
123 124 126 129 130 131 132 135 143 144 145 146 147 148 149 156
Primary Contact: Kevin J. Callahan, President and Chief Executive Officer
CFO: Kevin J O'Leary, Senior Vice President and Chief Financial Officer
CMO: Richard Hollister, President of Medical Staff
CIO: David Briden, Chief Information Officer
CHR: Christopher M Callahan, Vice President Human Resources
CNO: Susan Burns-Tisdale, Senior Vice President Clinical Operations, Interim CNO
Web address: www.ehr.org
Control: Other not–for–profit (including NFP Corporation) **Service:** General
medical and surgical

Staffed Beds: 99 **Admissions:** 5312 **Census:** 59 **Outpatient Visits:** 223572 **Births:** 615 **Total Expense ($000):** 226238 **Payroll Expense ($000):** 81669 **Personnel:** 1037	

FRANKLIN—Merrimack County

★ ⊞ **FRANKLIN REGIONAL HOSPITAL (301306)**, 15 Aiken Avenue, Zip 03235–
1299; tel. 603/934–2060, **A**10 18 21 **F**3 5 11 15 18 29 30 32 34 35 39 40
44 50 59 61 64 65 68 74 75 77 79 84 85 87 93 97 98 100 101 102 107 110
119 127 130 132 133 135 146 147 148 149 154 156 157 **S** LRGHealthcare,
Laconia, NH
Primary Contact: Kevin Donovan, FACHE, President and Chief Executive Officer
CFO: Henry D Lipman, Senior Vice President, Financial Strategy and External
Relations
CMO: Peter Doane, M.D., Chief Medical Officer
CIO: Kevin Irish, Chief Information Officer
CHR: Cass Walker, Vice President Administrative & Support Services
CNO: Patti Strohla, R.N., Chief Nursing Officer
Web address: www.lrgh.org
Control: Other not–for–profit (including NFP Corporation) **Service:** General
medical and surgical

Staffed Beds: 31 **Admissions:** 890 **Census:** 17 **Outpatient Visits:** 66330 **Births:** 0 **Total Expense ($000):** 23504 **Payroll Expense ($000):** 10287 **Personnel:** 114	

HAMPSTEAD—Rockingham County

☐ **HAMPSTEAD HOSPITAL (304001)**, 218 East Road, Zip 03841–2305;
tel. 603/329–5311, (Nonreporting) **A**1 10
Primary Contact: Phillip J. Kubiak, President
COO: Cynthia A Gove, Chief Operating Officer
CFO: Cherie Clough-Berry, Vice President, Finance
CMO: Michael Knight, M.D., Medical Director
CIO: Sandra J Lucia, Director Health Information and Corporate Compliance Officer
CHR: Lisa M Ryan, Coordinator Human Resources
CNO: Julie D'Apollo, R.N., Director of Nursing
Web address: www.hampsteadhospital.com
Control: Corporation, Investor–owned (for–profit) **Service:** Psychiatric

Staffed Beds: 60	

KEENE—Cheshire County

⊞ **CHESHIRE MEDICAL CENTER (300019)**, 580 Court Street, Zip 03431–1718,
Mailing Address: 82 Westport Village Rd, Swanzey, Zip 3446; tel. 603/354–5400,
A1 2 3 10 **F**3 13 15 18 28 29 30 31 34 35 36 40 41 44 45 46 49 50 54 55 56
58 59 64 65 68 70 74 75 76 78 79 80 81 82 84 85 86 87 89 90 91 92 93 96
97 100 104 107 108 110 111 115 118 119 120 121 123 130 131 132 133
135 146 147 148 149 156
Primary Contact: Don Caruso, M.D., Chief Executive Officer and President
CMO: Don Caruso, M.D., Chief Medical Officer
CIO: Peter Malloy, Chief Information Officer
CHR: Julie Green, Vice President Human Resources
CNO: Cynthia Coughlin, MS, R.N., Chief Nursing Officer
Web address: www.cheshire-med.com
Control: Other not–for–profit (including NFP Corporation) **Service:** General
medical and surgical

Staffed Beds: 94 **Admissions:** 4341 **Census:** 59 **Outpatient Visits:** 429044 **Births:** 385 **Total Expense ($000):** 218119 **Payroll Expense ($000):** 105607 **Personnel:** 1180	

LACONIA—Belknap County

★ ⊞ **LAKES REGION GENERAL HOSPITAL (300005)**, 80 Highland Street,
Zip 03246–3298; tel. 603/524–3211, **A**10 21 **F**3 5 8 11 12 13 15 28 29 30
31 32 33 34 35 37 39 40 44 45 46 47 49 50 53 54 56 59 61 64 65 68 70
74 75 76 77 78 79 81 84 85 87 93 94 97 98 100 102 103 107 108 110 115
118 119 126 129 131 132 133 135 146 147 148 149 154 156 157 **S**
LRGHealthcare, Laconia, NH
Primary Contact: Kevin Donovan, FACHE, President and Chief Executive Officer
CFO: Henry D Lipman, Senior Vice President, Financial Strategy and External
Relations
CMO: Peter Doane, M.D., Chief Medical Officer
CIO: Kevin Irish, Chief Information Officer
CHR: Cass Walker, Vice President Administrative & Support Services
CNO: Jacqueline Dawe, R.N., Chief Nursing Officer
Web address: www.lrgh.org
Control: Other not–for–profit (including NFP Corporation) **Service:** General
medical and surgical

Staffed Beds: 90 **Admissions:** 5232 **Census:** 63 **Outpatient Visits:** 305747 **Births:** 175 **Total Expense ($000):** 206176 **Payroll Expense ($000):** 94901 **Personnel:** 773	

LANCASTER—Coos County

★ **WEEKS MEDICAL CENTER (301303)**, 173 Middle Street, Zip 03584–3508;
tel. 603/788–4911, **A**10 18 **F**11 15 18 28 29 31 32 34 35 36 40 45 50 51 56
57 59 61 62 63 64 65 66 68 70 75 77 78 79 81 85 86 87 91 92 93 94 97 100
104 107 108 110 111 114 116 117 118 119 127 130 131 132 133 134 135
146 147 148 154 156 **S** QHR, Brentwood, TN
Primary Contact: Michael Lee, President
CMO: Lars Nielson, M.D., Chief Medical Officer
CIO: Darrell Bodnar, Director Information
CHR: Linda Rexford, Director Human Resources
CNO: Donna Walker, Chief Nurse Executive
Web address: www.weeksmedical.org
Control: Other not–for–profit (including NFP Corporation) **Service:** General
medical and surgical

Staffed Beds: 25 **Admissions:** 747 **Census:** 9 **Outpatient Visits:** 92006 **Births:** 0 **Total Expense ($000):** 47781 **Payroll Expense ($000):** 23079 **Personnel:** 268	

LEBANON—Grafton County

★ **ALICE PECK DAY MEMORIAL HOSPITAL (301305)**, 10 Alice Peck Day Drive,
Zip 03766–2650; tel. 603/448–3121, **A**5 10 18 **F**3 10 11 15 29 34 35 36 39
40 41 44 45 50 54 56 57 59 64 65 75 77 79 81 82 85 93 97 107 110 119
125 128 129 130 133 135 146 147 148
Primary Contact: Susan E. Mooney, M.D., MS, President and Chief Executive
Officer
CFO: Evalie M Crosby, CPA, Vice President Finance and Chief Financial Officer
CMO: Michael T. Lynch, M.D., Chief Medical Officer
CIO: Kristin Kneisel, Interim Director, Information Services
CNO: Barbra Brown, MS, R.N., Interim Chief Nursing Officer and Vice President of
Nursing
Web address: www.alicepeckday.org
Control: Other not–for–profit (including NFP Corporation) **Service:** General
medical and surgical

Staffed Beds: 25 **Admissions:** 1196 **Census:** 15 **Outpatient Visits:** 126230 **Births:** 237 **Total Expense ($000):** 69307 **Payroll Expense ($000):** 29215 **Personnel:** 374	

⊞ **DARTMOUTH-HITCHCOCK MEDICAL CENTER (300003)**, One Medical Center
Drive, Zip 03756–0001; tel. 603/650–5000, (Includes CHILDREN'S HOSPITAL AT
DARTMOUTH-HITCHCOCK, One Medical Center Drive, Lebanon, New Hampshire,
Zip 3756; tel. 603/650–5000) **A**1 3 5 8 10 **F**3 5 6 7 8 9 11 12 13 14 15 17 18
19 20 21 22 23 24 25 26 27 28 29 30 31 32 33 34 35 36 37 38 39 40 41 43
44 45 46 47 48 49 50 51 52 53 54 55 56 57 58 59 60 61 63 64 65 66 68 70
71 72 74 75 76 77 78 79 80 81 82 83 84 85 86 87 88 89 91 92 93 94 96 97
98 99 100 101 102 103 104 107 108 110 111 112 114 115 116 117 118 119
120 121 123 124 126 129 130 131 132 134 135 136 138 141 142 143 145
146 147 148 149 150 153 154 155 156 157
Primary Contact: Joanne M. Conroy, M.D., President and Chief Executive Officer
COO: Patrick Jordan III Chief Operating Officer
CFO: Daniel Jantzen, Chief Financial Officer
CMO: Alexander de Nesherea, M.D., Chief Medical Officer
CHR: Aimee M. Giglio, Chief Human Resources Officer
CNO: Susan A Reeves, Chief Nursing Executive
Web address: www.hitchcock.org
Control: Other not–for–profit (including NFP Corporation) **Service:** General
medical and surgical

Staffed Beds: 406 **Admissions:** 18660 **Census:** 321 **Outpatient Visits:** 810012 **Births:** 1143 **Total Expense ($000):** 1371141 **Payroll Expense ($000):** 630710 **Personnel:** 6751	

NH

Many Facility Codes have changed. Please refer to the AHA Guide Code Chart. © 2019 AHA Guide

LITTLETON—Grafton County

★ **LITTLETON REGIONAL HEALTHCARE (301302)**, 600 Saint Johnsbury Road, Zip 03561–3442; tel. 603/444–9000, **A**10 18 **F**3 11 13 15 18 26 28 29 31 32 34 35 36 38 40 44 45 50 56 57 59 64 65 67 70 74 75 76 77 78 79 81 82 84 85 86 87 89 90 92 93 96 97 107 108 110 111 114 115 118 119 127 128 129 130 131 133 143 146 147 148 154 **S** QHR, Brentwood, TN
Primary Contact: Robert Nutter, President
CFO: Robert L Fotter, Chief Financial Officer
CIO: Scott Vachon, Director Information Technology
CHR: Georgene Novak, Director Human Resources
Web address: www.littletonhospital.org
Control: Other not–for–profit (including NFP Corporation) **Service**: General medical and surgical

Staffed Beds: 25 Admissions: 1641 Census: 14 Outpatient Visits: 58038 Births: 335 Total Expense ($000): 88664 Payroll Expense ($000): 37992 Personnel: 405

MANCHESTER—Hillsborough County

⊠ **CATHOLIC MEDICAL CENTER (300034)**, 100 McGregor Street, Zip 03102–3770; tel. 603/668–3545, **A**1 2 3 10 **F**3 5 9 12 13 15 18 20 22 24 26 28 29 30 31 34 35 36 37 38 39 40 41 43 44 45 46 47 48 49 50 51 53 57 58 59 60 63 64 65 66 68 70 71 73 74 75 76 77 78 79 80 81 82 84 85 90 92 93 94 97 100 102 104 107 110 111 114 115 118 119 126 129 130 131 132 135 143 144 146 147 148 149 154 156
Primary Contact: Joseph Pepe, M.D., President and Chief Executive Officer
COO: Alexander J. Walker, Executive Vice President Operations and Strategic Development
CFO: Edward L Dudley III Executive Vice President and Chief Financial Officer
CMO: William H. Goodman, Vice President Medical Affairs, Chief Medical Officer
CIO: Thomas Della Flora, Vice President and Chief Information Officer
CHR: Merryll Rosenfeld, Vice President, Human Resources
CNO: Robert A Duhaime, R.N., Senior Vice President Clinical Operations and Chief Nursing Officer
Web address: www.catholicmedicalcenter.org
Control: Other not–for–profit (including NFP Corporation) **Service**: General medical and surgical

Staffed Beds: 251 Admissions: 12394 Census: 188 Births: 1137 Total Expense ($000): 410270 Payroll Expense ($000): 180786 Personnel: 2357

△ ⋔ **ELLIOT HOSPITAL (300012)**, One Elliot Way, Zip 03103–3502; tel. 603/669–5300, **A**2 3 5 7 10 21 **F**3 5 8 9 11 12 13 15 18 20 22 26 28 29 30 31 32 34 35 36 37 38 39 40 41 43 44 45 46 47 48 49 50 51 53 54 55 56 57 59 62 64 65 68 70 72 74 75 76 77 78 79 81 82 83 84 85 86 87 89 91 93 97 98 100 101 102 103 104 105 107 108 110 111 114 115 118 119 120 121 123 124 126 129 130 131 132 134 135 144 146 147 148 149 154 156 **S** SolutioNHealth, Manchester, NH
Primary Contact: Douglas P. Dean Jr, Chief Executive Officer
COO: Joseph Tate Curti, Chief Operating Officer
CFO: Richard Elwell, Senior Vice President and Chief Financial Officer
CMO: Greg Baxter, M.D., Senior Vice President Medical Affairs and Chief Medical Officer
CIO: Denise Purington, Vice President and Chief Information Officer
CHR: Catherine Bardier, Vice President, Human Resources
CNO: Martha Leighton, Senior Vice President and Chief Nursing Officer
Web address: www.elliothospital.org
Control: Other not–for–profit (including NFP Corporation) **Service**: General medical and surgical

Staffed Beds: 268 Admissions: 12764 Census: 180 Outpatient Visits: 502206 Births: 1770 Total Expense ($000): 416875 Payroll Expense ($000): 151525 Personnel: 3365

★ **MANCHESTER VETERANS AFFAIRS MEDICAL CENTER**, 718 Smyth Road, Zip 03104–4098; tel. 603/624–4366, (Nonreporting) **A**5 **S** Department of Veterans Affairs, Washington, DC
Primary Contact: Alfred Montoya, Director
COO: Richard T Rose, Associate Director
CFO: Frank Ryan, Chief Financial Officer
CMO: Andrew Breuder, M.D., Chief of Staff
CIO: John Foote, Chief Information Officer
CHR: Mary Ellen Kenney, Chief Human Services
Web address: www.manchester.va.gov/
Control: Veterans Affairs, Government, federal **Service**: Rehabilitation

Staffed Beds: 90

VETERANS AFFAIRS MEDICAL CENTER See Manchester Veterans Affairs Medical Center

NASHUA—Hillsborough County

★ △ ⋔ **SOUTHERN NEW HAMPSHIRE MEDICAL CENTER (300020)**, 8 Prospect Street, Zip 03060–3925, Mailing Address: P.O. Box 2014, Zip 03061–2014; tel. 603/577–2000, **A**2 3 5 7 10 21 **F**3 11 13 15 18 20 22 26 28 29 30 31 34 35 40 43 45 49 50 51 52 57 59 61 65 68 70 72 74 75 77 78 79 81 84 85 86 87 93 96 98 100 102 104 105 107 110 111 115 118 119 126 129 130 131 132 135 143 146 147 148 149 150 153 154 156 **S** SolutioNHealth, Manchester, NH
Primary Contact: Michael S. Rose, President and Chief Executive Officer
COO: Tate Curti, Senior Vice President and Chief Operating Officer
CFO: Paul Trainor, Senior Vice President Finance and Chief Financial Officer
CMO: Timothy Scherer, M.D., Chief Medical Officer
CIO: Andrew Watt, M.D., Vice President, Information Technology & Services, Chief Information Officer, Chief Medical Information Officer
CHR: Jacqueline Woolley, Vice President Human Resources
CNO: Cheryl Gagne I Vice President Patient Care Services and Chief Nursing Officer
Web address: www.snhhs.org
Control: Other not–for–profit (including NFP Corporation) **Service**: General medical and surgical

Staffed Beds: 162 Admissions: 8765 Census: 107 Outpatient Visits: 236097 Births: 1230 Total Expense ($000): 209581 Payroll Expense ($000): 101062 Personnel: 1532

★ ⋔ **ST. JOSEPH HOSPITAL (300011)**, 172 Kinsley Street, Zip 03060–3648; tel. 603/882–3000, **A**2 10 21 **F**3 13 15 18 20 22 28 29 30 31 32 34 35 36 37 40 43 44 45 46 47 48 49 50 51 54 55 56 57 58 59 61 63 64 65 68 70 71 74 75 76 77 78 79 81 82 83 84 85 86 87 89 90 91 92 93 94 96 97 102 107 108 109 110 111 115 116 117 118 119 126 129 130 131 132 135 144 145 146 147 148 149 157 **S** Covenant Health, Tewksbury, MA
Primary Contact: John A. Jurczyk, FACHE, Senior Vice President and President
COO: Pam Duchene, R.N., Vice President Patient Care Services
CFO: Richard Plamondon, Vice President Finance and Chief Financial Officer
CIO: Keith A Choinka, Vice President Information Systems and Chief Information Officer
CHR: Jacqueline Woolley, Vice President Human Resources
Web address: www.stjosephhospital.com
Control: Church operated, Nongovernment, not for profit **Service**: General medical and surgical

Staffed Beds: 135 Admissions: 4887 Census: 76 Outpatient Visits: 165120 Births: 396 Total Expense ($000): 229324 Payroll Expense ($000): 79946 Personnel: 954

NEW LONDON—Merrimack County

★ **NEW LONDON HOSPITAL (301304)**, 273 County Road, Zip 03257–6726; tel. 603/526–2911, **A**3 10 18 **F**3 7 11 15 18 29 30 31 32 34 35 36 38 40 41 44 45 50 53 54 55 56 57 59 64 70 71 74 75 77 78 79 81 82 84 85 86 87 93 94 97 100 102 104 107 110 111 114 115 119 127 128 130 131 133 146 147 149 150 154 156
Primary Contact: Bruce King, President and Chief Executive Officer
CFO: Lisa Cohen, Chief Financial Officer
CMO: James M. Murphy, M.D., Chief Medical Officer Regional Development and Outpatient Services
CIO: David Foss, Chief Information Officer
CHR: Shari Bostwick, Director Human Resources
CNO: Sally K Patton, R.N., MS, Chief Nursing Officer
Web address: www.newlondonhospital.org
Control: Other not–for–profit (including NFP Corporation) **Service**: General medical and surgical

Staffed Beds: 25 Admissions: 1168 Census: 8 Outpatient Visits: 234904 Births: 0 Total Expense ($000): 64933 Payroll Expense ($000): 30360 Personnel: 427

NH

NORTH CONWAY—Carroll County

★ **MEMORIAL HOSPITAL (301307)**, 3073 White Mountain Highway, Zip 03860–7101; tel. 603/356–5461, (Total facility includes 45 beds in nursing home–type unit) **A**10 18 **F**3 13 15 28 29 30 31 32 34 35 36 40 41 44 45 57 59 64 67 68 70 75 76 77 78 79 81 85 86 87 90 93 94 96 97 100 101 104 107 110 115 119 127 128 129 130 131 132 133 146 147 148 156 **S** MaineHealth, Portland, ME
Primary Contact: Arthur Mathisen, FACHE, President
CFO: Diane Maheux, Vice President Finance
CMO: Ray Rabideau, M.D., Senior Vice President and Chief Medical Officer
CIO: Curtis Kerbs, Regional Chief Information Officer
CHR: Melanie Sleime, Director Human Resources
CNO: Kristine Dascoulias, Interim Chief Nursing Officer
Web address: www.memorialhospitalnh.org
Control: Other not–for–profit (including NFP Corporation) **Service**: General medical and surgical

Staffed Beds: 70 **Admissions**: 1389 **Census**: 51 **Outpatient Visits**: 58595 **Births**: 210 **Total Expense ($000)**: 74089 **Payroll Expense ($000)**: 29121 **Personnel**: 319

PETERBOROUGH—Hillsborough County

★ **MONADNOCK COMMUNITY HOSPITAL (301309)**, 452 Old Street Road, Zip 03458–1295; tel. 603/924–7191, **A**5 10 18 **F**3 11 13 15 28 29 31 34 35 36 38 40 41 44 50 53 59 64 65 70 75 76 77 78 79 81 82 85 86 90 91 92 93 96 97 98 99 100 101 102 103 104 107 108 110 114 118 119 124 127 128 130 131 132 133 134 135 146 147 148 149 156
Primary Contact: Cynthia McGuire, FACHE, President and Chief Executive Officer
CFO: Richard Scheinblum, Chief Financial Officer
CMO: Michael Lindberg, M.D., Chief Medical Officer
CIO: Peter A Johnson, Interim Chief Information Officer
CHR: John Sansone, Vice President, Human Resources
CNO: Vicki Loughery, R.N., MS, Chief Nursing Officer
Web address: www.monadnockhospital.org
Control: Other not–for–profit (including NFP Corporation) **Service**: General medical and surgical

Staffed Beds: 25 **Admissions**: 1451 **Census**: 12 **Outpatient Visits**: 79385 **Births**: 311 **Total Expense ($000)**: 88006 **Payroll Expense ($000)**: 35935 **Personnel**: 476

PLYMOUTH—Grafton County

★ **SPEARE MEMORIAL HOSPITAL (301311)**, 16 Hospital Road, Zip 03264–1199; tel. 603/536–1120, **A**5 10 18 **F**3 13 15 28 29 30 31 32 34 35 40 45 47 50 53 54 57 59 64 65 70 75 76 77 79 81 83 84 85 87 89 93 97 107 110 111 113 114 119 127 130 131 132 133 146 147 148 156
Primary Contact: Michelle McEwen, President and Chief Executive Officer
CFO: Travis Boucher, Chief Financial Officer
CMO: Joseph Ebner, M.D., Chief Medical Officer
CHR: Laurie Bolognani, Human Resources Officer
CNO: Kristine Hering, R.N., Chief Nursing Officer
Web address: www.spearehospital.com
Control: Other not–for–profit (including NFP Corporation) **Service**: General medical and surgical

Staffed Beds: 25 **Admissions**: 1483 **Census**: 14 **Outpatient Visits**: 45098 **Births**: 182 **Total Expense ($000)**: 61751 **Payroll Expense ($000)**: 28666 **Personnel**: 337

PORTSMOUTH—Rockingham County

⊠ **PORTSMOUTH REGIONAL HOSPITAL (300029)**, 333 Borthwick Avenue, Zip 03801–7128; tel. 603/436–5110, (Nonreporting) **A**1 2 10 **S** HCA Healthcare, Nashville, TN
Primary Contact: Dean Carucci, Chief Executive Officer
COO: Stuart Hemming, Chief Operating Officer
CFO: Richard Senger, Chief Financial Officer
CMO: Tim Pike, M.D., Chief Medical Officer
CIO: Ed Sovetskhy, Director Information Services
CHR: Jackie Brayton, Vice President Human Resources
Web address: www.portsmouthhospital.com
Control: Corporation, Investor–owned (for–profit) **Service**: General medical and surgical

Staffed Beds: 165

ROCHESTER—Strafford County

★ **FRISBIE MEMORIAL HOSPITAL (300014)**, 11 Whitehall Road, Zip 03867–3297; tel. 603/332–5211, **A**10 **F**1 7 11 13 17 18 20 29 31 34 40 45 46 49 50 55 59 60 61 67 68 70 71 75 76 77 78 79 81 82 85 86 89 91 92 93 97 98 103 104 107 108 111 115 118 119 128 129 130 135 143 146 149
Primary Contact: Jocelyn Caple, M.D., Interim President and Chief Executive Officer
CFO: Robert K. Cochrane, Vice President Finance and Chief Financial Officer
CMO: Jocelyn Caple, M.D., Chief Medical Officer
CHR: Christi Green, R.N., MS, Vice President, Human Resources
CNO: John Levitow, Vice President Patient Care Services and Chief Nursing Officer
Web address: www.frisbiehospital.com
Control: Other not–for–profit (including NFP Corporation) **Service**: General medical and surgical

Staffed Beds: 96 **Admissions**: 3126 **Census**: 45 **Outpatient Visits**: 155697 **Births**: 314 **Total Expense ($000)**: 161671 **Payroll Expense ($000)**: 67496 **Personnel**: 872

SALEM—Rockingham County

☐ △ **NORTHEAST REHABILITATION HOSPITAL (303026)**, 70 Butler Street, Zip 03079–3925; tel. 603/893–2900, (Nonreporting) **A**1 7 10
Primary Contact: John F. Prochilo Jr, Chief Executive Officer
CFO: Charles D. Champagne, Chief Financial Officer
CMO: A Deniz Ozel, M.D., Chief Medical Officer
CHR: Shirley G Lussier, Vice President Human Resources
CNO: Helene Thibodeau, R.N., MSN, Vice President Patient Care Services
Web address: www.northeastrehab.com
Control: Corporation, Investor–owned (for–profit) **Service**: Rehabilitation

Staffed Beds: 135

WOLFEBORO—Carroll County

★ **HUGGINS HOSPITAL (301312)**, 240 South Main Street, Zip 03894–4455, Mailing Address: P.O. Box 912, Zip 03894–0912; tel. 603/569–7500, **A**10 18 **F**2 3 10 15 28 29 34 35 36 40 45 50 53 57 59 64 65 68 70 75 79 81 85 86 87 93 96 97 107 108 110 115 119 130 131 132 133 135 146 147 148 149 156
Primary Contact: Jeremy Roberge, President and Chief Executive Officer
CFO: Jeremy Roberge, Chief Financial Officer
CMO: John Boornazian, M.D., Chief Medical Officer
CIO: Pam McGovern, Director Technology
CHR: Laura Stauss, Director of Human Resources
Web address: www.hugginshospital.org
Control: Other not–for–profit (including NFP Corporation) **Service**: General medical and surgical

Staffed Beds: 25 **Admissions**: 915 **Census**: 12 **Outpatient Visits**: 74403 **Births**: 0 **Total Expense ($000)**: 59810 **Payroll Expense ($000)**: 27099 **Personnel**: 373

WOODSVILLE—Grafton County

★ **COTTAGE HOSPITAL (301301)**, 90 Swiftwater Road, Zip 03785–1421, Mailing Address: P.O. Box 2001, Zip 03785–2001; tel. 603/747–9000, (Nonreporting) **A**5 10 18
Primary Contact: Maria Ryan, Ph.D., Chief Executive Officer
COO: Lori Hughes, R.N., MSN, Chief Nursing Officer, Vice President Operations and Patient Care Services
CFO: Steven L Plant, Chief Financial Officer
CIO: Rick Fredrick, Director Information Technology
CNO: Lori Hughes, R.N., MSN, Chief Nursing Officer, Vice President Operations & Patient Care Services
Web address: www.cottagehospital.org
Control: Other not–for–profit (including NFP Corporation) **Service**: General medical and surgical

Staffed Beds: 25

NH

Many Facility Codes have changed. Please refer to the AHA Guide Code Chart. © 2019 AHA Guide

NEW JERSEY

ATLANTIC CITY—Atlantic County

★ ⇑ **ACUITY SPECIALTY HOSPITAL OF NEW JERSEY (312023)**, 1925 Pacific Avenue, 7th Floor, Zip 08401–6713; tel. 609/441–2122, (Nonreporting) **A**10 21 **S** AcuityHealthcare, LP, Charlotte, NC
Primary Contact: Monica B. Titus, R.N., Chief Executive Officer
CFO: Cheryl Lambert, Chief Financial Officer
CHR: Maria Ciro, Director Human Resources
CNO: Kathleen Kerstetter, R.N., MSN, Chief Clinical Officer
Web address: www.acuityhealthcare.net
Control: Corporation, Investor–owned (for–profit) **Service**: Acute long–term care hospital

Staffed Beds: 30

⊠ **ATLANTICARE REGIONAL MEDICAL CENTER (310064)**, 1925 Pacific Avenue, Zip 08401–6713; tel. 609/441–8994, (Includes ATLANTICARE REGIONAL MEDICAL CENTER-MAINLAND DIVISION, Jimmie Leeds Road, Pomona, New Jersey, Zip 8240, Mailing Address: 65 West Jimmie Leeds Road, Zip 8240, tel. 609/652–1000; Lori Herdon, President and Chief Executive Officer) **A**1 2 3 5 10 **F**3 7 11 12 13 15 17 18 20 22 24 26 28 29 30 31 34 35 36 37 38 40 41 42 43 44 45 46 47 48 49 50 54 55 56 57 58 59 60 61 64 66 68 70 71 72 73 74 75 76 78 79 81 82 83 84 85 86 87 89 97 98 100 102 104 105 107 108 110 111 114 115 116 117 118 119 120 121 123 124 126 130 132 135 143 146 147 148 149 150 153 154 155 156 157 **S** Geisinger, Danville, PA
Primary Contact: Lori S. Herndon, R.N., President and Chief Executive Officer
CFO: Walter Greiner, Chief Financial Officer
CMO: Marilouise Vendetti, M.D., Chief Medical Officer
CIO: Christopher A Scanzera, Vice President and Chief Information Officer
CHR: Richard Lovering, Corporate Vice President Human Resources and Organizational Development
CNO: Robyn Begley, R.N., Chief Nursing Officer
Web address: www.atlanticare.org
Control: Other not–for–profit (including NFP Corporation) **Service**: General medical and surgical

Starred Beds: 633 **Admissions:** 29070 **Census:** 351 **Outpatient Visits:** 305545 **Births:** 1310 **Total Expense ($000):** 673378 **Payroll Expense ($000):** 304498 **Personnel:** 3177

BAYONNE—Hudson County

☐ **CAREPOINT HEALTH BAYONNE MEDICAL CENTER (310025)**, 29th Street & Avenue E, Zip 07002–4699, Mailing Address: 29 East 29 Street, Zip 07002–4699; tel. 201/858–5000, (Nonreporting) **A**1 2 3 10 12 13 **S** CarePoint Health, Jersey City, NJ
Primary Contact: W. Peter Daniels, FACHE, Executive Vice President and Chief Operating Officer
CFO: Gary Bryant, Chief Financial Officer
CMO: Vijayant Singh, M.D., Chief Medical Officer
CIO: Joel Taylor, Chief Information Officer
CHR: Jennifer Dobin, Executive Vice President Human Resources
Web address: www.carepointhealth.org
Control: Corporation, Investor–owned (for–profit) **Service**: General medical and surgical

Staffed Beds: 178

BELLE MEAD—Somerset County

⊠ **HACKENSACK MERIDIAN HEALTH CARRIER CLINIC (314012)**, 252 County Route 601, Zip 08502–0147, Mailing Address: P.O. Box 147, Zip 08502–0147; tel. 908/281–1000, **A**1 3 5 10 **F**4 5 29 30 38 75 98 99 100 101 102 103 104 106 130 132 149 151 154 **S** Hackensack Meridian Health, Edison, NJ
Primary Contact: Donald J. Parker, President and Chief Executive Officer
CFO: Randolph Jacobson, Chief Financial Officer
CMO: Umesh Mehta, M.D., Interim Chief Medical Officer
CIO: Peter Schwartz, Director of Information Systems
CHR: Trish Toole, Vice President Administrative Services
CNO: Shaun Sweeney, Vice President Patient Care Services
Web address: www.carrierclinic.org
Control: Other not–for–profit (including NFP Corporation) **Service**: Psychiatric

Staffed Beds: 328 **Admissions:** 6453 **Census:** 257 **Outpatient Visits:** 3436 **Births:** 0 **Total Expense ($000):** 82007 **Payroll Expense ($000):** 49365 **Personnel:** 807

BELLEVILLE—Essex County

⊠ **CLARA MAASS MEDICAL CENTER (310009)**, One Clara Maass Drive, Zip 07109–3557; tel. 973/450–2000, **A**1 3 10 **F**1 3 8 11 12 13 15 18 19 20 22 26 28 29 30 31 34 35 36 38 40 41 46 47 49 50 51 53 55 56 57 59 60 61 63 64 65 66 68 70 71 73 74 75 76 77 78 79 81 82 83 84 85 86 87 89 92 93 94 98 100 101 102 103 107 108 110 114 115 119 120 121 123 126 129 130 131 132 135 143 146 147 148 149 154 156 157 **S** RWJBarnabas Health, West Orange, NJ
Primary Contact: Mary Ellen Clyne, Ph.D., President and Chief Executive Officer
COO: Domenic Segalla, Chief Operating Officer and Chief Financial Officer
CFO: Domenic Segalla, Chief Operating Officer and Chief Financial Officer
CMO: Frank Mazzarella, M.D., Chief Medical Officer
CIO: Michael McTigue, Chief Information Officer
CHR: Jim Rolek, Chief Human Resources Officer, Vice President
CNO: Bonnie Geissler, R.N., Chief Nursing Officer, Vice President Patient Care Services
Web address: www.barnabashealth.org/hospitals/clara_maass/index.html
Control: Other not–for–profit (including NFP Corporation) **Service**: General medical and surgical

Staffed Beds: 352 **Admissions:** 14395 **Census:** 214 **Outpatient Visits:** 144693 **Births:** 1697 **Total Expense ($000):** 268487 **Payroll Expense ($000):** 114289 **Personnel:** 1298

BERKELEY HEIGHTS—Union County

CORNERSTONE BEHAVIORAL HEALTH HOSPITAL OF UNION COUNTY (314027), 40 Watchung Way, Zip 07922–2600; tel. 908/790–5300, (Nonreporting)
Primary Contact: Michael Flemming, Administrator
Control: County, Government, nonfederal **Service**: Psychiatric

Staffed Beds: 44

BLACKWOOD—Camden County

☐ **NORTHBROOK BEHAVIORAL HEALTH HOSPITAL (314018)**, 425 Woodbury Turnersville Road, Zip 08012–2960; tel. 856/374–6500, (Nonreporting) **A**1
Primary Contact: Avi Feigenbaum, Chief Executive Officer
Web address: www.northbrookbhh.com
Control: Corporation, Investor–owned (for–profit) **Service**: Psychiatric

Staffed Beds: 153

BOONTON TOWNSHIP—Morris County

SAINT CLARE'S HOSPITAL/BOONTON TOWNSHIP See Saint Clare's Denville Hospital, Denville

BRICK—Ocean County

⊠ △ **HACKENSACK MERIDIAN HEALTH SHORE REHABILITATION INSTITUTE (313033)**, 425 Jack Martin Boulevard, Zip 08724–7732; tel. 732/836–4500, **A**1 5 7 10 **F**29 36 50 75 90 91 93 94 95 96 130 132 148 149 **S** Hackensack Meridian Health, Edison, NJ
Primary Contact: Kerri Fitzgerald, Executive Director
CFO: Richard C. Smith, Senior Vice President Finance
CMO: Lisa Luciano, D.O., Medical Director
CNO: Maria Clohsey, Director of Nursing
Web address: www.shorerehabilitationinstitute.com
Control: Other not–for–profit (including NFP Corporation) **Service**: Rehabilitation

Staffed Beds: 40 **Admissions:** 827 **Census:** 29 **Outpatient Visits:** 6448 **Births:** 0 **Total Expense ($000):** 16888 **Payroll Expense ($000):** 8807 **Personnel:** 137

NJ

BRICK TOWNSHIP—Ocean County

★ **HACKENSACK MERIDIAN HEALTH OCEAN MEDICAL CENTER (310052)**, 425 Jack Martin Boulevard, Zip 08724–7732; tel. 732/840–2200, **A2** 10 22 **F3** 5 11 12 13 15 17 18 20 22 28 29 30 31 32 34 35 36 38 40 41 42 43 44 45 46 47 48 49 50 54 55 56 57 58 59 60 61 63 64 65 66 68 70 71 73 74 75 76 77 78 79 80 81 82 84 85 86 87 91 92 93 94 96 97 100 101 102 104 107 108 109 110 111 114 115 116 117 118 119 120 121 123 124 126 129 130 131 132 134 135 141 144 146 147 148 149 154 **S** Hackensack Meridian Health, Edison, NJ
Primary Contact: Dean Q. Lin, FACHE, Regional President
COO: Regina Foley, R.N., FACHE, Vice President Nursing and Operations
CFO: Robert Palermo, Vice President Finance
CMO: James Clarke, M.D., Vice President Medical Affairs and Clinical Effectiveness
CIO: Rebecca Weber, Senior Vice President and Chief Information Officer
CHR: Sherrie String, Senior Vice President Human Resources
Web address: www.meridianhealth.com
Control: Other not–for–profit (including NFP Corporation) **Service:** General medical and surgical

Staffed Beds: 324 **Admissions:** 28680 **Census:** 204 **Outpatient Visits:** 164732 **Births:** 823 **Total Expense ($000):** 333681 **Payroll Expense ($000):** 130071 **Personnel:** 1562

BRIDGETON—Cumberland County

BRIDGETON HEALTH CENTER See Inspira Medical Center-Vineland, Vineland

BROWNS MILLS—Burlington County

☐ **DEBORAH HEART AND LUNG CENTER (310031)**, 200 Trenton Road, Zip 08015–1705; tel. 609/893–6611, (Nonreporting) **A1** 3 5 10 13
Primary Contact: Joseph Chirichella, President and Chief Executive Officer
COO: Joseph Manni, Executive Vice President and Chief Operating Officer
CFO: R. Grant Leidy, Chief Financial Officer
CMO: Lynn McGrath, M.D., Vice President Medical Affairs
CIO: Richard Temple, Chief Information Officer
CHR: Marion Stamopoulos, Vice President Human Resources
CNO: Rita Zenna, R.N., Vice President Patient Care Services
Web address: www.deborah.org
Control: Other not–for–profit (including NFP Corporation) **Service:** Other specialty treatment

Staffed Beds: 89

CAMDEN—Camden County

☐ **COOPER UNIVERSITY HEALTH CARE (310014)**, One Cooper Plaza, Zip 08103–1489; tel. 856/342–2000, (Includes CHILDEN'S REGIONAL HOSPITAL AT COOPER, Three Cooper Plaza, Camden, New Jersey, Zip 8103; tel. 800/826–6737) **A1** 2 3 5 8 10 13 **F3** 5 7 8 9 11 12 13 15 17 18 19 20 22 24 26 29 30 31 32 34 35 36 37 38 39 40 41 43 44 45 46 47 48 49 51 52 54 55 56 57 58 59 60 61 63 64 65 66 68 70 72 73 74 75 76 77 78 79 80 81 82 84 85 86 87 88 89 92 93 96 97 98 99 100 101 102 103 104 107 108 110 111 114 115 119 120 121 123 124 126 130 131 132 135 144 146 147 148 149 150 153 154 155 157
Primary Contact: Adrienne Kirby, Ph.D., FACHE, President and Executive Chair
CFO: Douglas E. Shirley, Senior Executive Vice President and Chief Financial Officer
CMO: Anthony J Mazzarelli, JD, M.D., Co-President
CIO: Stephanie Conners, Senior Executive Vice President Chief Operating Officer and Chief Nursing Officer
CHR: Elizabeth Green, Chief Human Resources Officer
Web address: www.cooperhealth.org
Control: Other not–for–profit (including NFP Corporation) **Service:** General medical and surgical

Staffed Beds: 594 **Admissions:** 26832 **Census:** 428 **Outpatient Visits:** 363996 **Births:** 2113 **Total Expense ($000):** 956917 **Payroll Expense ($000):** 329365 **Personnel:** 6684

⊞ **OUR LADY OF LOURDES MEDICAL CENTER (310029)**, 1600 Haddon Avenue, Zip 08103–3117; tel. 856/757–3500, **A1** 2 3 10 **F3** 7 11 12 13 15 17 18 20 22 24 26 28 29 30 31 32 34 35 36 37 38 40 44 47 49 50 55 56 57 58 59 60 61 64 65 66 68 70 73 74 75 76 78 79 81 82 84 85 86 87 90 95 96 107 108 110 111 114 115 118 119 126 130 132 134 135 138 139 142 146 147 148 149 **S** Virtua Health, Marlton, NJ
Primary Contact: Reginald Blaber, M.D., FACC, President
COO: Mark Nessel, Chief Operating Officer
CFO: Michael Hammond, Chief Financial Officer
CMO: Alan R Pope, M.D., Chief Medical Officer
CIO: Maureen Hetu, Chief Information Officer
CHR: Jennifer L Moughan, Chief Human Resources Officer
CNO: Audrey Jadczak, R.N., FACHE, Vice President Chief Nursing Officer
Web address: www.lourdesnet.org
Control: Other not–for–profit (including NFP Corporation) **Service:** General medical and surgical

Staffed Beds: 340 **Admissions:** 11888 **Census:** 161 **Outpatient Visits:** 143016 **Births:** 905 **Total Expense ($000):** 365872 **Payroll Expense ($000):** 112422 **Personnel:** 1440

CAPE MAY COURT HOUSE—Cape May County

⊞ **CAPE REGIONAL HEALTH SYSTEM (310011)**, Two Stone Harbor Boulevard, Zip 08210–9990; tel. 609/463–2000, **A1** 2 10 **F3** 8 11 12 13 15 18 20 28 29 30 31 34 35 40 44 45 46 49 50 57 59 64 70 74 75 76 77 78 79 81 82 85 86 87 89 93 97 107 111 114 118 119 120 121 123 124 129 130 132 135 143 146 149 156
Primary Contact: Joanne Carrocino, FACHE, President and Chief Executive Officer
CFO: Mark Gill, Vice President Finance and Chief Financial Officer
CMO: Andrea C.S. McCoy, M.D., Chief Medical Officer
CIO: Richard Wheatley, Chief Information Officer
CHR: Byron Hunter, Vice President Human Resources
CNO: Rosemary Dunn, R.N., Chief Nursing Officer
Web address: www.caperegional.com
Control: Other not–for–profit (including NFP Corporation) **Service:** General medical and surgical

Staffed Beds: 178 **Admissions:** 6206 **Census:** 75 **Outpatient Visits:** 207674 **Births:** 326 **Total Expense ($000):** 125992 **Payroll Expense ($000):** 54842 **Personnel:** 904

CEDAR GROVE—Essex County

☐ **ESSEX COUNTY HOSPITAL CENTER (314020)**, 204 Grove Avenue, Zip 07009–1436; tel. 973/571–2800, (Nonreporting) **A1** 10
Primary Contact: Frank J. Del Gaudio, Director and Chief Executive Officer
CFO: Jacqueline Campoverde, Business Manager
CMO: Bolivar Pascual, M.D., Medical Director
CIO: Vijay Prakash, Information Technology Officer
CHR: Marlon Brown, Human Resources
CNO: Fern Papalia, Director of Nursing
Web address: www.essexcountynj.org
Control: County, Government, nonfederal **Service:** Psychiatric

Staffed Beds: 180

CHESTER—Morris County

KESSLER INSTITUTE FOR REHABILITATION See Kessler Institute for Rehabilitation, West Orange

DENVILLE—Morris County

⊞ **SAINT CLARE'S DENVILLE HOSPITAL (310050)**, 25 Pocono Road, Zip 07834–2954; tel. 973/625–6000, (Includes SAINT CLARE'S HEALTH CENTER AT SUSSEX, 20 Walnut Street, Sussex, New Jersey, Zip 7461; tel. 973/702–2200; SAINT CLARE'S HOSPITAL/BOONTON TOWNSHIP, 130 Powerville Road, Boonton Township, New Jersey, Zip 7005; tel. 973/316–1800; SAINT CLARE'S HOSPITAL/DENVILLE, 25 Pocono Road, Denville, New Jersey, Zip 7834; tel. 973/625–6000; SAINT CLARE'S HOSPITAL/DOVER, 400 West Blackwell Street, Dover, New Jersey, Zip 07801–3311; tel. 973/989–3000), (Non-reporting) **A1** 2 10 **S** Prime Healthcare, Ontario, CA
Primary Contact: Brian Finestein, Chief Executive Officer
COO: Joe Nolan, Chief Operating Officer
CFO: Dianne Halford, Chief Financial Officer
CMO: Alma Ratcliffe, M.D., Executive Vice President Medical Staff and Business Development
CIO: Tero Caamano, Director Information Technology
CHR: Kay Bryant, Executive Director Human Resources
Web address: www.saintclares.org
Service: General medical and surgical

Staffed Beds: 412

SAINT CLARE'S HOSPITAL/DENVILLE See Saint Clare's Denville Hospital, Denville

DOVER—Morris County

⊞ **KINDRED HOSPITAL-NEW JERSEY MORRIS COUNTY (312020)**, 400 West Blackwell Street, Zip 07801–2525; tel. 973/537–3818, (Includes KINDRED HOSPITAL NEW JERSEY - RAHWAY, 865 Stone Street, Rahway, New Jersey, Zip 7065; tel. 732/669–8200; Christopher Cannara, Chief Executive Officer; KINDRED HOSPITAL NEW JERSEY - WAYNE, 224 Hamburg Turnpike, Wayne, New Jersey, Zip 7470; tel. 973/636–7200; Alice M O'Connor, Chief Executive Officer), (Non-reporting) **A1** 10 **S** Kindred Healthcare, Louisville, KY
Primary Contact: Tarra Washington, Chief Executive Officer
CFO: Stephen D. Farber, Chief Financial Officer
CMO: Sean R Muldoon, M.D., Chief Medical Officer
Web address: www.khmorriscounty.com/
Control: Corporation, Investor–owned (for–profit) **Service:** Acute long–term care hospital

Staffed Beds: 117

Many Facility Codes have changed. Please refer to the AHA Guide Code Chart. © 2019 AHA Guide

NJ

EAST ORANGE—Essex County

☐ **EAST ORANGE GENERAL HOSPITAL (310083)**, 300 Central Avenue,
Zip 07018–2897; tel. 973/672–8400, **A**1 10 **F**3 12 15 17 18 28 29 30 34 35
38 40 44 45 48 49 50 51 53 57 59 60 64 65 66 70 74 75 77 79 81 82 84 85
86 87 92 93 94 97 98 100 101 104 107 108 110 111 119 130 132 135 143
147 149 150 156 157 158 **S** Prospect Medical Holdings, Los Angeles, CA
Primary Contact: Paige Dworak, FACHE, Chief Executive Officer
CMO: Valentine Burroughs, M.D., Chief Medical Officer
CIO: Thomas Ciccarelli, Chief Information Officer
CHR: Chester Banks, Director Human Resources
Web address: www.evh.org
Control: Corporation, Investor–owned (for–profit) **Service**: General medical and
surgical

> **Staffed Beds:** 143 **Admissions:** 6220 **Census:** 102 **Outpatient**
> **Visits:** 46996 **Births:** 0 **Total Expense ($000):** 101441 **Payroll Expense**
> **($000):** 43182 **Personnel:** 758

⊞ **VETERANS AFFAIRS NEW JERSEY HEALTH CARE SYSTEM**, 385 Tremont
Avenue, Zip 07018–1095; tel. 973/676–1000, (Includes EAST ORANGE
DIVISION, 385 Tremont Avenue, East Orange, New Jersey, Zip 07018–1095;
tel. 973/676–1000; LYONS DIVISION, 151 Knollcroft Road, Lyons, New Jersey,
Zip 07939–9998; tel. 908/647–0180), (Non-reporting) **A**1 2 5 **S** Department of
Veterans Affairs, Washington, DC
Primary Contact: Vincent F. Immiti, FACHE, Director
CFO: Tyrone Taylor, Chief Financial Officer
CMO: Steven L Lieberman, M.D., Chief of Staff
CIO: Kamesha Scarlett, Chief Information Resource Management
CHR: Nancy Hamilton, Chief Human and Learning Resources
CNO: Patrick J Troy, R.N., MSN, Associate Director Patient Care Services
Web address: www.newjersey.va.gov/
Control: Veterans Affairs, Government, federal **Service**: General medical and
surgical

> **Staffed Beds:** 439

EDISON—Middlesex County

★ △ **HACKENSACK MERIDIAN HEALTH JFK JOHNSON REHABILITATION
INSTITUTE**, 65 James Street, Zip 08818; tel. 732/321–7050, **A**5 7 **F**3 9 28 29
30 35 36 44 50 53 54 82 87 90 91 92 93 94 96 130 131 132 143 149 150
157 **S** Hackensack Meridian Health, Edison, NJ
Primary Contact: Anthony Cuzzola, Vice President and Administrator
COO: Scott Gebhard, Chief Operating Officer
CFO: Richard C. Smith, Chief Financial Officer
CMO: William F. Oser, M.D., Chief Medical Officer
CIO: Neal Ganguly, Chief Information Officer
CNO: James Lindquist, Chief Nursing Officer
Web address: www.njrehab.org
Control: Other not–for–profit (including NFP Corporation) **Service**: Rehabilitation

> **Staffed Beds:** 94 **Admissions:** 1514 **Census:** 71 **Outpatient Visits:** 171174
> **Births:** 0 **Total Expense ($000):** 74946 **Payroll Expense ($000):** 49948
> **Personnel:** 579

⊞ **HACKENSACK MERIDIAN HEALTH JFK MEDICAL CENTER (310108)**, 65
James Street, Zip 08818; tel. 732/321–7000, **A**1 2 3 5 10 **F**2 3 5 6 7 8 11 12
13 14 15 17 18 20 22 26 28 29 30 31 34 35 36 37 38 39 40 41 42 44 45 47
49 50 51 53 54 56 57 58 59 60 61 63 64 66 68 69 70 71 73 74 75 76 77 78
79 80 81 82 84 85 86 87 89 90 91 92 93 94 96 97 100 101 102 104 107 108
109 110 111 113 114 115 116 117 118 119 120 121 123 124 126 129 130
131 132 135 141 143 144 145 146 147 148 149 153 154 156 **S** Hackensack
Meridian Health, Edison, NJ
Primary Contact: Raymond F. Fredericks, Central Regional President
COO: Scott Gebhard, Executive VP and Chief Operating Officer
CFO: Richard C. Smith, Senior Vice President and Chief Financial Officer
CMO: William F. Oser, M.D., Senior Vice President and Chief Medical Officer
CIO: Indranil Ganguly, Vice President and Chief Information Officer
CHR: Shirley Higgins Bowers, Senior Vice President Human Resources
CNO: James Lindquist, Chief Nursing Officer
Web address: www.jfkmc.org
Control: Other not–for–profit (including NFP Corporation) **Service**: General
medical and surgical

> **Staffed Beds:** 360 **Admissions:** 18117 **Census:** 250 **Outpatient**
> **Visits:** 438421 **Births:** 2223 **Total Expense ($000):** 476614 **Payroll**
> **Expense ($000):** 213250 **Personnel:** 3048

ELIZABETH—Union County

CAREONE AT TRINITAS REGIONAL MEDICAL CENTER, 225 Williamson Street,
Zip 07202–3625; tel. 908/994–5288, (Nonreporting)
Primary Contact: Sharon Bready, R.N., Chief Executive Officer
Web address: www.care-one.com/locations/ltach-careone-at-trinitas-regional-
medical-center/
Control: Other not–for–profit (including NFP Corporation) **Service**: Acute long–
term care hospital

> **Staffed Beds:** 25

⊞ **TRINITAS REGIONAL MEDICAL CENTER (310027)**, 225 Williamson Street,
Zip 07202–3625; tel. 908/994–5000, (Includes TRINITAS HOSPITAL, 225
Williamson Street, Elizabeth, New Jersey, Zip 7207; tel. 908/994–5000; Gary
S Horan, FACHE, President and Chief Executive Officer; TRINITAS REGIONAL
MEDICAL CENTER - NEW POINT CAMPUS, 655 East Jersey Street, Elizabeth, New
Jersey, Zip 7206; tel. 908/994–5000; Gary S Horan, FACHE, President and Chief
Executive Officer) (Total facility includes 124 beds in nursing home–type unit) **A**1 2
3 5 10 **F**3 5 7 8 11 13 15 17 18 20 22 28 29 30 31 32 34 35 36 38 40 44 45
46 48 49 53 55 56 57 58 59 60 61 64 65 66 68 70 73 74 75 77 78 79 81 82
84 85 86 87 91 93 97 98 99 100 101 102 103 104 105 106 107 108 110 111
115 117 118 119 120 121 123 124 126 128 129 130 132 134 135 141 143
146 147 148 149 153 154 157
Primary Contact: Gary S. Horan, FACHE, President and Chief Executive Officer
CFO: Karen Lumpp, Senior Vice President and Chief Financial Officer
CMO: William McHugh, M.D., Medical Director and Chief Medical Officer
CIO: Judy Comitto, Vice President Information Services and Chief Information
Officer
CHR: Glenn Nacion, Vice President Human Resources
CNO: Mary McTigue, Vice President Patient Care Services and Chief Nursing
Officer
Web address: www.trinitasrmc.com
Control: Other not–for–profit (including NFP Corporation) **Service**: General
medical and surgical

> **Staffed Beds:** 464 **Admissions:** 12402 **Census:** 352 **Outpatient**
> **Visits:** 429768 **Births:** 1454 **Total Expense ($000):** 297171 **Payroll**
> **Expense ($000):** 139467 **Personnel:** 2295

ELMER—Salem County

★ ⇑ **INSPIRA MEDICAL CENTER-ELMER (310069)**, 501 West Front Street,
Zip 08318–2101; tel. 856/363–1000, **A**10 21 **F**3 7 8 11 12 13 15 18 20 22 28
29 30 34 37 38 40 42 44 50 57 59 64 68 70 74 75 76 77 78 79 81 82 85 86
07 93 107 100 110 111 114 115 116 117 118 119 120 121 122 124 126 130
131 132 134 146 147 148 154 **S** Inspira Health Network, Mullica Hill, NJ
Primary Contact: John A. DiAngelo, President and Chief Executive Officer
COO: David Yhlen, Chief Operating Officer
CFO: Thomas Baldosaro, Chief Financial Officer
CMO: Steven C Linn, M.D., Chief Medical Officer
CIO: Thomas Pacek, Vice President Information Systems and Chief Information
Officer
CHR: Erich Florentine, Chief People Officer
CNO: Elizabeth Sheridan, Chief Operating Officer and Chief Nursing Executive
Web address: www.inspirahealthnetwork.org/?id=5281&sid=1
Control: Other not–for–profit (including NFP Corporation) **Service**: General
medical and surgical

> **Staffed Beds:** 96 **Admissions:** 2930 **Census:** 31 **Outpatient Visits:** 51530
> **Births:** 265 **Total Expense ($000):** 62328 **Payroll Expense ($000):** 28171
> **Personnel:** 278

ENGLEWOOD—Bergen County

⊞ **ENGLEWOOD HOSPITAL AND MEDICAL CENTER (310045)**, 350 Engle Street,
Zip 07631–1898; tel. 201/894–3000, **A**1 2 3 5 10 **F**3 5 6 7 8 9 11 12 13 15
17 18 19 20 22 24 26 28 29 30 31 32 34 35 36 37 38 39 40 41 44 45 46 47
48 49 50 51 53 54 55 56 57 58 59 60 61 62 63 64 65 68 70 71 72 73 74 75
76 77 78 79 80 81 82 83 84 85 86 87 89 91 92 93 94 96 97 98 100 101 102
103 104 107 108 110 111 114 115 116 117 118 119 120 121 123 124 126
129 130 131 132 133 134 135 141 143 144 145 146 147 148 149 150 153
154 156 157
Primary Contact: Warren Geller, President and Chief Executive Officer
CFO: Anthony T Orlando, Senior Vice President Finance
CMO: Michael Harris, M.D., Chief Medical Officer
CHR: Patricia Wilson, Senior Vice President Human Resources
CNO: MaryAnn Donohue-Ryan, Ph.D., Vice President Patient Care Services
Web address: www.englewoodhealth.org
Control: Other not–for–profit (including NFP Corporation) **Service**: General
medical and surgical

> **Staffed Beds:** 295 **Admissions:** 15281 **Census:** 199 **Outpatient**
> **Visits:** 1266308 **Births:** 2881 **Total Expense ($000):** 651343 **Payroll**
> **Expense ($000):** 166588 **Personnel:** 2897

NJ

Hospital, Medicare Provider Number, Address, Telephone, Approval, Facility, and Physician Codes, Health Care System

★ American Hospital Association (AHA) membership   ○ Healthcare Facilities Accreditation Program   ⇑ Center for Improvement in Healthcare Quality Accreditation
☐ The Joint Commission accreditation   ◇ DNV Healthcare Inc. accreditation   △ Commission on Accreditation of Rehabilitation Facilities (CARF) accreditation

© 2019 AHA Guide   *Many Facility Codes have changed. Please refer to the AHA Guide Code Chart.*   Hospitals **A405**

FLEMINGTON—Hunterdon County

☒ **HUNTERDON HEALTHCARE (310005)**, 2100 Wescott Drive, Zip 08822–4604;
tel. 908/788–6100, (Nonreporting) **A**1 2 3 5 10 13
Primary Contact: Patrick J. Gavin, President and Chief Executive Officer
COO: Lawrence N Grand, MS, R.N., Chief Operating Officer
CFO: Gail Kosyla, Chief Financial Officer and Senior Vice President Strategy
CMO: Robert Coates, M.D., Vice President, Medical Affairs
CIO: Daniel Morreale, Chief Information Officer
CHR: Violet Kocsis, Chief Human Resources Officer
CNO: Patricia Steingall, MS, R.N., R.N., MS, Vice President, Patient Care Services
Web address: www.hunterdonhealthcare.org
Control: Other not–for–profit (including NFP Corporation) **Service:** General
medical and surgical

Staffed Beds: 178

FREEHOLD—Monmouth County

☒ **CENTRASTATE HEALTHCARE SYSTEM (310111)**, 901 West Main Street,
Zip 07728–2549; tel. 732/431–2000, **A**1 2 3 5 10 **F**3 11 12 13 15 18 19 20 28
29 30 31 32 34 35 36 37 38 40 41 45 46 47 49 56 57 58 59 61 64 65 66 70
73 74 75 76 77 78 79 81 82 84 86 87 89 92 93 97 98 100 101 102 107 108
110 114 118 119 120 121 123 124 126 129 130 131 132 134 135 146 147
148 149 154 156
Primary Contact: John Gribbin, FACHE, President and Chief Executive Officer
COO: Thomas W. Scott, Senior Vice President and Chief Operating Officer
CFO: John Dellocono, Senior Vice President and Chief Financial Officer
CMO: Jack H Dworkin, M.D., Vice President Medical Affairs and Chief Medical
Officer
CIO: John Ulett, Vice President and Chief Information Officer
CHR: Fran Keane, Vice President Human Resources
CNO: Linda W Geisler, R.N., FACHE, Vice President Patient Services
Web address: www.centrastate.com
Control: Other not–for–profit (including NFP Corporation) **Service:** General
medical and surgical

Staffed Beds: 263 **Admissions:** 11940 **Census:** 151 **Outpatient**
Visits: 251883 **Births:** 726 **Total Expense ($000):** 283487 **Payroll Expense**
($000): 113493 **Personnel:** 1525

HACKENSACK—Bergen County

☒ **HACKENSACK MERIDIAN HEALTH HACKENSACK UNIVERSITY MEDICAL
CENTER (310001)**, 30 Prospect Avenue, Zip 07601–1914; tel. 201/996–2000,
(Includes THE JOSEPH M. SANZARI CHILDREN'S HOSPITAL, 30 Prospect Avenue,
Hackensack, New Jersey, Zip 07601–1914; tel. 201/996–2000) **A**1 2 3 5 8 10
F2 3 4 5 6 7 8 9 11 12 13 14 15 16 17 18 19 20 22 24 26 28 29 30 31 32 33
34 35 36 37 38 39 40 41 43 44 45 46 47 48 49 50 51 52 53 54 55 56 57 58
59 60 61 63 64 65 66 68 69 70 71 72 73 74 75 76 77 78 79 80 81 82 84 85
86 87 88 89 91 92 93 94 96 97 98 99 100 101 102 103 104 107 108 109
110 111 112 113 114 115 116 117 118 119 120 121 123 124 126 129 130
131 132 134 135 136 138 141 142 143 145 146 147 148 149 150 153 154
155 156 157 158 **S** Hackensack Meridian Health, Edison, NJ
Primary Contact: Mark Sparta, President
CFO: Robert Glenning, Executive Vice President Finance and Chief Financial Officer
CMO: Peter A Gross, M.D., Senior Vice President and Chief Medical Officer
CHR: Nancy R Corcoran, Senior Vice President Human Resources and Quality
Service
Web address: www.hackensackumc.org
Control: Other not–for–profit (including NFP Corporation) **Service:** General
medical and surgical

Staffed Beds: 691 **Admissions:** 73598 **Census:** 647 **Outpatient**
Visits: 499195 **Births:** 6054 **Total Expense ($000):** 1620719 **Payroll**
Expense ($000): 579877 **Personnel:** 7703

HACKETTSTOWN—Warren County

☒ **HACKETTSTOWN MEDICAL CENTER (310115)**, 651 Willow Grove Street,
Zip 07840–1799; tel. 908/852–5100, **A**1 10 **F**3 5 8 11 12 15 18 28 29 30 31
32 34 35 36 38 39 40 41 44 45 47 49 50 53 54 56 57 59 60 61 62 63 84 85
68 70 74 75 77 78 79 81 82 84 85 86 87 92 93 94 100 101 102 104 107 108
110 111 114 116 117 118 119 120 129 130 131 132 135 141 146 148 149
154 156 **S** Atlantic Health System, Morristown, NJ
Primary Contact: Joseph DiPaolo, FACHE, President
COO: Donna Watridge, R.N., Director of Operations
CFO: Robert Peterson, CPA, Chief Financial Officer
CMO: Paul Owens, M.D., Chief Medical Officer
CIO: Dorothy Cox, Manager Information Systems
CHR: Kimberly McGovern, Manager Human Resources
CNO: Donna Watridge, R.N., Chief Nursing Officer
Web address: www.atlantichealth.org
Control: Other not–for–profit (including NFP Corporation) **Service:** General
medical and surgical

Staffed Beds: 80 **Admissions:** 3211 **Census:** 37 **Outpatient Visits:** 57439
Births: 0 **Total Expense ($000):** 84088 **Payroll Expense ($000):** 37423
Personnel: 590

HAMILTON—Mercer County

☒ **ROBERT WOOD JOHNSON UNIVERSITY HOSPITAL AT HAMILTON (310110)**,
One Hamilton Health Place, Zip 08690–3599; tel. 609/586–7900, **A**1 2 5 10
F11 12 15 18 20 22 26 28 29 30 31 32 34 35 36 37 40 41 45 46 47 48 49
50 51 54 55 56 57 58 59 64 65 66 68 69 70 74 75 77 78 79 81 82 84 85 86
87 92 93 94 95 96 97 100 107 108 110 111 114 115 116 117 119 121 124
126 130 131 132 134 135 143 144 145 146 147 148 149 150 154 156 **S**
RWJBarnabas Health, West Orange, NJ
Primary Contact: Richard Freeman, President and Chief Executive Officer
COO: Barbara H Smith, Senior Vice President & Chief Operating Officer
CMO: Ronald Ryder, D.O., President of the Medical Staff
CIO: L. Gill Gottle, Senior Vice President and Chief Financial Officer
CNO: Lisa Breza, R.N., Vice President and Chief Nursing Officer
Web address: www.rwjhamilton.org
Control: Other not–for–profit (including NFP Corporation) **Service:** General
medical and surgical

Staffed Beds: 164 **Admissions:** 7150 **Census:** 99 **Outpatient**
Visits: 143409 **Births:** 0 **Total Expense ($000):** 190309 **Payroll Expense**
($000): 64829 **Personnel:** 914

HAMMONTON—Camden County

☐ **ANCORA PSYCHIATRIC HOSPITAL (314005)**, 301 Spring Garden Road,
Zip 08037–9699; tel. 609/561–1700, (Nonreporting) **A**1 3 10 **S** Division of
Mental Health and Addiction Services, Department of Human Services, State of
New Jersey, Trenton, NJ
Primary Contact: Joseph Canale, Acting Chief Executive Officer
CFO: John Holmes, Business Manager
CIO: Charlene Ruberti, Director Information Technology Development
CHR: Alfred Filipini, Manager Human Resources
Web address: www.https://www.state.nj.us/humanservices/dmhas/resources/
services/treatment/aph.html
Control: State, Government, nonfederal **Service:** Psychiatric

Staffed Beds: 449

HOBOKEN—Hudson County

☐ **CAREPOINT HEALTH HOBOKEN UNIVERSITY MEDICAL CENTER (310040)**,
308 Willow Avenue, Zip 07030–3889; tel. 201/418–1000, (Nonreporting) **A**1 3 5
10 **S** CarePoint Health, Jersey City, NJ
Primary Contact: Ann P. Logan, R.N., Ph.D., Chief Operating Officer
COO: Ann P. Logan, R.N., Ph.D., Chief Operating Officer
CMO: Meika Roberson, M.D., Chief Medical Officer
CIO: Joel Taylor, Chief Information Officer
CHR: Roberto Gonzalez, Executive Director Human Resources
CNO: Neena S. Philip, R.N., Vice President of Patient Care Services and Chief
Nursing Officer
Web address: www.hobokenumc.com
Control: Corporation, Investor–owned (for–profit) **Service:** General medical and
surgical

Staffed Beds: 333

HOLMDEL—Monmouth County

☒ **HACKENSACK MERIDIAN HEALTH BAYSHORE COMMUNITY HOSPITAL
(310112)**, 727 North Beers Street, Zip 07733–1598; tel. 732/739–5900, **A**1 2
5 10 **F**3 11 12 15 18 20 22 28 29 30 31 32 34 35 36 38 39 40 41 44 45 46
49 50 51 54 55 56 57 58 59 60 61 63 64 65 66 68 69 70 71 74 75 77 78 79
81 82 84 85 86 87 92 93 94 96 97 100 101 102 103 107 108 110 111 114
116 117 118 119 126 129 130 131 132 134 135 141 144 146 147 148 149
150 154 **S** Hackensack Meridian Health, Edison, NJ
Primary Contact: Timothy J. Hogan, FACHE, President, RMC and BMC
CFO: Joseph M Lemaire, Executive Vice President Finance and Partner Company
Operations
CMO: Ian Leber, M.D., Chief Medical Officer
CIO: Rebecca Weber, Senior Vice President and Chief Information Officer
CHR: Sherrie String, Senior Vice President Human Resources
CNO: Linda Walsh, R.N., MSN, Vice President Chief Nursing Executive
Web address: www.bchs.com
Control: Other not–for–profit (including NFP Corporation) **Service:** General
medical and surgical

Staffed Beds: 160 **Admissions:** 17526 **Census:** 103 **Outpatient**
Visits: 79220 **Births:** 0 **Total Expense ($000):** 152914 **Payroll Expense**
($000): 66147 **Personnel:** 826

NJ

Many Facility Codes have changed. Please refer to the AHA Guide Code Chart. © 2019 AHA Guide

JERSEY CITY—Hudson County

☐ **CAREPOINT HEALTH CHRIST HOSPITAL (310016)**, 176 Palisade Avenue, Zip 07306–1196, Mailing Address: 176 Palisades Avenue, Zip 07306–1196; tel. 201/795–8200, (Nonreporting) **A**1 3 10 12 13 **S** CarePoint Health, Jersey City, NJ
Primary Contact: Marie Theresa Duffy, Chief Hospital Executive
COO: Marie Theresa Duffy, Chief Operating Officer
CFO: Gary Bryant, Executive Vice President and Chief Financial Officer
CMO: William Holubek, M.D., Chief Medical Officer
CHR: Josiane Deroncerey, Director Human Resources
CNO: Denise Cimmino, MSN, R.N., Assistant Vice President, Nursing and Patient Care Services
Web address: www.carepointhealth.org
Control: Other not–for–profit (including NFP Corporation) **Service:** General medical and surgical

Staffed Beds: 376

★ ⇑ **JERSEY CITY MEDICAL CENTER (310074)**, 355 Grand Street, Zip 07302–4321; tel. 201/915–2000, **A**3 5 10 13 21 **F**3 5 7 8 11 13 15 17 18 20 22 24 26 29 31 34 35 38 39 40 41 42 43 45 46 47 48 49 50 54 55 56 57 59 60 61 64 65 66 68 70 71 72 73 74 75 76 77 78 79 81 84 85 87 89 91 92 93 96 97 98 100 101 102 104 105 107 108 110 111 112 114 115 119 130 132 143 146 147 148 149 153 154 156 157 **S** RWJBarnabas Health, West Orange, NJ
Primary Contact: Michael Prilutsky, President and Chief Executive Officer
CFO: Paul R Goldberg, Chief Financial Officer
CMO: Kenneth Garay, M.D., Chief Medical Officer
CIO: Stephen Li, Vice President Management Information Systems
CHR: Mary Cataudella, Corporate Director Human Resources
CNO: Joanne Reich, R.N., Chief Nursing Officer
Web address: www.barnabashealth.org/Jersey-City-Medical-Center.aspx
Control: Other not–for–profit (including NFP Corporation) **Service:** General medical and surgical

Staffed Beds: 316 Admissions: 14448 Census: 215 Outpatient Visits: 240460 Births: 1996 Total Expense ($000): 391206 Payroll Expense ($000): 168569 Personnel: 2179

LAKEWOOD—Ocean County

⊞ **MONMOUTH MEDICAL CENTER, SOUTHERN CAMPUS (310084)**, 600 River Avenue, Zip 08701–5237; tel. 732/363–1900, **A**1 2 10 **F**3 11 12 15 18 28 29 30 31 34 35 36 38 40 41 44 45 49 50 51 56 57 58 59 60 61 64 65 66 68 70 74 75 77 78 79 81 82 84 85 86 87 92 93 97 98 100 101 102 103 104 107 108 110 111 114 116 117 119 130 131 132 135 143 146 148 149 154 156 157 **S** RWJBarnabas Health, West Orange, NJ
Primary Contact: Frank J Vozos, M.D. FACS, Chief Executive Officer, MMC Southern Campus
CFO: Joanna Zimmerman, Regional Chief Financial Officer
CMO: Rajesh Mohan, M.D., Chief Medical Officer
CIO: Ray Duarte, Director, Information Technology and Services
CHR: Richard Kiernan, Regional Chief Human Resources Officer
CNO: Judy Colorado, R.N., Chief Nursing Officer
Web address: www.rwjbarnabashealth.org/monmouth-medical-center-southern-campus.aspx
Control: Other not–for–profit (including NFP Corporation) **Service:** General medical and surgical

Staffed Beds: 124 Admissions: 6101 Census: 98 Outpatient Visits: 79683 Births: 0 Total Expense ($000): 121001 Payroll Expense ($000): 49687 Personnel: 614

☐ **SPECIALTY HOSPITAL OF CENTRAL JERSEY (312017)**, 600 River Avenue, 4 and 5 West, Zip 08701–5237; tel. 732/942–3588, (Nonreporting) **A**1 10
Primary Contact: Violeta Peters, R.N., Chief Executive Officer and Interim Center Director
CFO: Kristin Prentiss, Chief Financial Officer
CMO: Howard Lebowitz, M.D., Chief Medical Officer
CHR: Mary Pat Napolitano, Director Human Resources
CNO: Judy Boccellato, R.N., MSN, Chief Nursing Officer
Web address: www.acutecarehs.com
Control: Corporation, Investor–owned (for–profit) **Service:** Acute long–term care hospital

Staffed Beds: 50

LAWRENCEVILLE—Mercer County

⊞ **ST. LAWRENCE REHABILITATION CENTER (313027)**, 2381 Lawrenceville Road, Zip 08648–2025; tel. 609/896–9500, (Total facility includes 56 beds in nursing home–type unit) **A**1 10 **F**34 57 64 90 91 93 96 104 108 119 128 130 132 135 143 146 148 149 154
Primary Contact: Darlene S. Hanley, R.N., President and Chief Executive Officer
COO: Shirley Pukala, R.N., Assistant Administrator Operations
CFO: Thomas W Boyle, Chief Financial Officer
CMO: Kevin McGuigan, M.D., Medical Director
CIO: Joseph Castronuevo, Director Information Management
CHR: John Levi, Director Human Resources
CNO: Hsiu-chin Brix, R.N., Director of Nursing
Web address: www.slrc.org
Control: Church operated, Nongovernment, not–for–profit **Service:** Rehabilitation

Staffed Beds: 116 Admissions: 2066 Census: 87 Outpatient Visits: 23312 Births: 0 Total Expense ($000): 33083 Payroll Expense ($000): 19977 Personnel: 305

LIVINGSTON—Essex County

⊞ **SAINT BARNABAS MEDICAL CENTER (310076)**, 94 Old Short Hills Rd, Zip 07039–5672; tel. 973/322–5000, **A**1 2 3 5 8 10 13 **F**3 7 8 11 12 13 16 17 18 20 22 24 26 28 29 30 31 32 34 35 36 37 38 39 40 41 44 45 46 47 48 49 50 53 54 55 56 57 58 59 60 61 63 64 65 66 68 69 70 71 72 73 74 75 76 77 78 79 81 82 84 85 86 87 88 89 91 92 93 94 96 97 100 101 102 107 108 111 114 115 118 119 120 121 123 124 126 129 130 131 132 134 135 138 141 142 143 144 146 147 148 149 150 154 156 157 **S** RWJBarnabas Health, West Orange, NJ
Primary Contact: Stephen P. Zieniewicz, FACHE, President and Chief Executive Officer
COO: Patrick Ahearn, Chief Operating Officer and Senior Vice President
CFO: Richard Davis, Chief Financial Officer
CMO: Gregory Rokosz, D.O., Senior Vice President Medical and Academic Affairs
CIO: Michael McTigue, Chief Information Officer
CHR: Arnold D Manzo, Vice President Human Resources
CNO: Jennifer A O'Neill, R.N., Chief Nursing Officer, Vice President Patient Care Services
Web address: www.barnabashealth.org/hospitals/saint_barnabas/index.html
Control: Other not–for–profit (including NFP Corporation) **Service:** General medical and surgical

Staffed Beds: 561 Admissions: 29164 Census: 431 Outpatient Visits: 338057 Births: 5943 Total Expense ($000): 808314 Payroll Expense ($000): 280617 Personnel: 3619

LONG BRANCH—Monmouth County

⊞ **MONMOUTH MEDICAL CENTER, LONG BRANCH CAMPUS (310075)**, 300 Second Avenue, Zip 07740–6303; tel. 732/222–5200, (Includes CHILDREN'S HOSPITAL AT MONMOUTH MEDICAL CENTER, 300 Second Avenue, Long Branch, New Jersey, Zip 07740–6303; tel. 732/222–5200) **A**1 2 3 5 10 **F**3 9 11 12 13 15 18 20 22 28 29 30 31 34 35 37 38 39 40 41 43 44 45 46 47 48 49 50 51 54 55 56 57 58 59 60 61 63 64 66 68 70 72 73 74 75 76 77 78 79 81 82 84 85 86 87 88 89 96 97 98 99 100 101 102 104 105 107 108 109 110 111 114 115 117 118 119 120 121 123 124 126 129 130 132 135 141 143 145 146 147 148 149 153 154 156 157 **S** RWJBarnabas Health, West Orange, NJ
Primary Contact: Eric Carney, Chief Executive Officer
CMO: Eric Burkett, M.D., Vice President Medical Affairs
CIO: Chris Butler, Chief Information Officer
CHR: Richard Kiernan, Vice President Human Resources
CNO: Diann Johnston, R.N., MSN, Vice President of Patient Care Services
Web address: www.barnabashealth.org/hospitals/monmouth_medical/index.html
Control: Other not–for–profit (including NFP Corporation) **Service:** General medical and surgical

Staffed Beds: 296 Admissions: 18280 Census: 213 Outpatient Visits: 222590 Births: 5903 Total Expense ($000): 381308 Payroll Expense ($000): 146527 Personnel: 2055

LYONS—Somerset County

LYONS DIVISION See Veterans Affairs New Jersey Health Care System, East Orange

NJ

MANAHAWKIN—Ocean County

☒ **HACKENSACK MERIDIAN HEALTH SOUTHERN OCEAN MEDICAL CENTER (310113)**, 1140 Route 72 West, Zip 08050–2499; tel. 609/597–6011, **A**1 2 5 10 **F**3 11 12 13 15 18 20 28 29 30 31 32 34 35 36 38 39 41 44 45 46 48 49 50 51 54 55 56 57 58 59 60 61 63 64 65 66 68 70 71 74 75 76 77 78 79 80 81 82 84 85 86 87 92 93 94 96 97 100 101 102 107 108 110 111 114 115 116 117 118 119 120 121 123 128 129 130 131 132 134 135 141 144 145 146 147 148 149 154 156 **S** Hackensack Meridian Health, Edison, NJ
Primary Contact: Regina Foley, R.N., FACHE, Chief Operating Officer
CFO: Joseph M Lemaire, Executive Vice President
CMO: Theodore Zaleski, M.D., Vice President Clinical Effectiveness
CIO: Rebecca Weber, Senior Vice President and Chief Information Officer
CHR: Susan Tillman-Taylor, Manager Human Resources
CNO: Donna Ciufo, R.N., Vice President and Chief Nurse Executive
Web address: www.soch.com
Control: Other not–for–profit (including NFP Corporation) **Service**: General medical and surgical

Staffed Beds: 174 **Admissions:** 16971 **Census:** 90 **Outpatient Visits:** 109644 **Births:** 363 **Total Expense ($000):** 189027 **Payroll Expense ($000):** 71534 **Personnel:** 834

MARLTON—Burlington County

☒ △ **KESSLER MARLTON REHABILITATION (313032)**, 92 Brick Road, Zip 08053–2177; tel. 856/988–8778, **A**1 7 10 **F**3 29 85 90 130 132 157 **S** Select Medical Corporation, Mechanicsburg, PA
Primary Contact: Phyllis J. Schlichtmann, R.N., Chief Executive Officer
CFO: Stuart Moss, Chief Financial Officer
CMO: Kenneth Wu, M.D., Medical Director
CHR: Joanne Cernava, Director Human Resources
CNO: Chris Kreeley, Director Nursing
Web address: www.marltonrehab.com
Control: Corporation, Investor–owned (for–profit) **Service**: Rehabilitation

Staffed Beds: 61 **Admissions:** 1480 **Census:** 55 **Outpatient Visits:** 12190 **Births:** 0 **Personnel:** 187

☒ **VIRTUA MARLTON**, 90 Brick Road, Zip 08053–2177; tel. 856/355–6000, **A**1 2 5 **F**3 12 18 20 22 29 30 31 40 45 46 47 49 56 60 64 70 75 77 78 79 81 82 84 85 87 91 92 107 108 111 114 115 118 119 130 141 146 149 157 **S** Virtua Health, Marlton, NJ
Primary Contact: Dennis W. Pullin, FACHE, President and Chief Executive Officer
COO: Lisa Ferraro, Senior Vice President and Chief Operating Officer
CFO: Robert Segin, Executive Vice President & Chief Financial Officer
CMO: John Matsinger, D.O., Chief Medical Officer
CIO: Thomas Gordon, Chief Information Officer
CHR: Rhonda R Jordan, Chief Human Resources Officer
CNO: Tracy Carlino, R.N., Chief Nursing Officer
Web address: www.virtua.org
Control: Other not–for–profit (including NFP Corporation) **Service**: General medical and surgical

Staffed Beds: 185 **Admissions:** 7675 **Census:** 104 **Outpatient Visits:** 46447 **Births:** 0 **Total Expense ($000):** 161541 **Payroll Expense ($000):** 52465 **Personnel:** 628

☐ **WEISMAN CHILDREN'S REHABILITATION HOSPITAL (313302)**, 92 Brick Road 3rd Floor, Zip 08053–2177; tel. 856/489–4520, (Nonreporting) **A**1 10
Primary Contact: Kathy Hall-Olsen, Administrator
CMO: Connie Domingo, M.D., Medical Director
CIO: Darren Pedersen, Coordinator Information Technology
CHR: Jill Koerner, Manager Employee Relations
CNO: Daniel William Pfeffer, Chief Nurse Executive
Web address: www.weismanchildrens.com
Control: Corporation, Investor–owned (for–profit) **Service**: Children's rehabilitation

Staffed Beds: 24

MONTCLAIR—Essex County

☒ **HACKENSACK MERIDIAN HEALTH MOUNTAINSIDE MEDICAL CENTER (310054)**, 1 Bay Avenue, Zip 07042–4898; tel. 973/429–6000, **A**1 2 3 5 10 **F**3 12 13 15 17 18 20 22 28 29 30 31 32 34 35 38 39 40 44 45 46 47 48 49 50 51 52 54 55 56 57 58 59 60 64 66 67 68 70 73 74 75 76 77 78 79 80 81 82 84 85 86 87 93 94 96 97 98 100 101 102 103 104 105 107 108 110 111 114 115 116 117 118 119 121 126 129 130 131 132 135 141 146 147 148 149 153 157 **S** Ardent Health Services, Nashville, TN
Primary Contact: John A. Fromhold, FACHE, President and Chief Executive Officer
CFO: Al Aboud, CPA, Chief Financial Officer
CMO: Valerie Alluson, M.D., Chief Medical Officer
CIO: Max Siu, Chief Information Officer
CNO: Debbie Regen, R.N., Chief Nursing Officer
Web address: www.mountainsidenow.com
Control: Partnership, Investor–owned (for–profit) **Service**: General medical and surgical

Staffed Beds: 202 **Admissions:** 11435 **Census:** 141 **Outpatient Visits:** 98703 **Births:** 721 **Total Expense ($000):** 217999 **Payroll Expense ($000):** 87452 **Personnel:** 1278

MORRIS PLAINS—Morris County

☐ **GREYSTONE PARK PSYCHIATRIC HOSPITAL (314016)**, 59 Koch Avenue, Zip 07950–4400; tel. 973/538–1800, (Nonreporting) **A**1 3 10 **S** Division of Mental Health and Addiction Services, Department of Human Services, State of New Jersey, Trenton, NJ
Primary Contact: Tomika Carter, Chief Executive Officer
COO: Stacey Provenzano, Chief Operating Officer
CFO: Jack Frey, Acting Business Manager
CMO: Cherry Monroy-Miller, M.D., Acting Medical Director
CIO: David Saleem, Director Information Technology
CHR: James Frey Jr Acting Manager Human Resources
Web address: www.https://www.state.nj.us/humanservices/dmhas/resources/services/treatment/gpph.html
Control: State, Government, nonfederal **Service**: Psychiatric

Staffed Beds: 542

MORRISTOWN—Morris County

☒ **MORRISTOWN MEDICAL CENTER (310015)**, 100 Madison Avenue, Zip 07960–6136; tel. 973/971–5000, (Includes GORYEB CHILDREN'S HOSPITAL, 100 Madison Avenue, Morristown, New Jersey, Zip 07960–6136; tel. 973/971–5000) **A**1 2 3 5 8 10 **F**3 5 6 8 9 11 12 13 15 17 18 19 20 22 24 26 28 29 30 31 32 33 34 35 36 37 38 39 40 41 43 44 45 46 47 48 49 50 51 52 53 54 55 56 57 58 59 60 61 64 65 66 68 69 70 71 72 73 74 75 76 77 78 79 81 82 83 84 85 86 87 88 89 90 91 92 93 94 95 96 97 98 100 101 102 103 104 107 108 110 111 115 117 118 119 120 121 123 124 126 129 130 131 132 134 135 141 143 145 146 147 148 149 150 153 154 156 157 **S** Atlantic Health System, Morristown, NJ
Primary Contact: Trish O'Keefe, Ph.D., R.N., President
CFO: Joseph D'Auria, Director Finance
CMO: Louis Brusco, M.D., Chief Medical Officer
CNO: Carol S. Jones, MSN, R.N., Interim Chief Nursing Officer
Web address: www.atlantichealth.org/Morristown/
Control: Other not–for–profit (including NFP Corporation) **Service**: General medical and surgical

Staffed Beds: 695 **Admissions:** 38672 **Census:** 557 **Outpatient Visits:** 617510 **Births:** 4519 **Total Expense ($000):** 1421613 **Payroll Expense ($000):** 583282 **Personnel:** 6549

MOUNT HOLLY—Burlington County

☒ **VIRTUA MEMORIAL (310057)**, 175 Madison Avenue, Zip 08060–2099; tel. 609/267–0700, **A**1 3 5 10 **F**3 11 12 13 15 18 20 22 28 29 30 31 40 41 45 46 48 60 64 70 73 74 75 76 77 78 79 81 84 85 86 87 89 92 98 100 102 107 108 110 111 114 115 119 120 121 123 126 129 130 143 146 149 154 **S** Virtua Health, Marlton, NJ
Primary Contact: Dennis W. Pullin, FACHE, President and Chief Executive Officer
COO: John Kirby, Senior Vice President and Chief Financial Officer
CFO: Robert Segin, Chief Financial Officer
CMO: James P Dwyer, D.O., Executive Vice President and Chief Medical Officer
CHR: E D Dunn, Vice President Human Resources
Web address: www.virtua.org
Control: Other not–for–profit (including NFP Corporation) **Service**: General medical and surgical

Staffed Beds: 334 **Admissions:** 16077 **Census:** 206 **Outpatient Visits:** 150521 **Births:** 2184 **Total Expense ($000):** 314902 **Payroll Expense ($000):** 97811 **Personnel:** 1296

VIRTUA MEMORIAL HOSPITAL BURLINGTON COUNTY See Virtua Memorial

NEPTUNE—Monmouth County

☒ **HACKENSACK MERIDIAN HEALTH JERSEY SHORE UNIVERSITY MEDICAL CENTER (310073)**, 1945 Route 33, Zip 07754–0397; tel. 732/775–5500, (Includes K. HOVNANIAN CHILDREN'S HOSPITAL, 1945 State Route 33, Neptune, New Jersey, Zip 07753–4859; tel. 800/560–9990) **A**1 2 3 5 8 10 **F**3 5 9 11 12 13 15 16 17 18 19 20 22 24 26 28 29 30 31 32 34 35 36 37 38 39 40 41 43 44 45 46 47 48 49 50 52 54 55 56 57 58 59 60 61 63 64 65 66 68 70 71 72 73 74 75 76 77 78 79 80 81 82 84 85 86 87 88 89 92 93 94 96 97 98 99 100 101 102 103 104 105 107 108 111 114 115 116 117 118 119 120 121 123 124 126 129 130 131 132 134 135 141 144 145 146 147 148 149 150 152 153 154 156 157 **S** Hackensack Meridian Health, Edison, NJ
Primary Contact: Vito Buccellato, Chief Executive Officer
COO: Robert H Adams, Vice President Operations
CMO: David Kountz, M.D., Senior Vice President Medical Affairs
CIO: Rebecca Weber, Senior Vice President and Chief Information Officer
Web address: www.meridianhealth.com
Control: Other not–for–profit (including NFP Corporation) **Service**: General medical and surgical

Staffed Beds: 583 **Admissions:** 62293 **Census:** 381 **Outpatient Visits:** 190782 **Births:** 2771 **Total Expense ($000):** 790614 **Payroll Expense ($000):** 290346 **Personnel:** 3460

NJ

NEW BRUNSWICK—Middlesex County

☐ **CHILDREN'S SPECIALIZED HOSPITAL (313300)**, 200 Somerset Street, Zip 08901–1942; tel. 732/258–7000, (Includes CHILDREN'S SPECIALIZED HOSPITAL, 200 Somerset Street, New Brunswick, New Jersey, Zip 08901–1942; tel. 732/258–7134; Warren E. Moore, FACHE, President and Chief Executive Officer) (Total facility includes 72 beds in nursing home–type unit) **A**1 3 5 10 **F**29 32 35 54 64 65 74 75 82 90 91 93 94 97 104 130 131 132 146 154 **S** RWJBarnabas Health, West Orange, NJ
Primary Contact: Warren E. Moore, FACHE, President and Chief Executive Officer
COO: Charles Chianese, Vice President, Chief Operating Officer
CFO: Joseph J Dobosh Jr Vice President and Chief Financial Officer
CMO: Christopher Haines, D.O., Vice President and Chief Medical Officer
CHR: William Dwyer, Vice President and Chief Human Resources Officer
CNO: Bonnie Baloga-Altieri, Ph.D., R.N., Vice President Patient Care Services and Chief Nursing Officer
Web address: www.childrens-specialized.org
Control: Other not–for–profit (including NFP Corporation) **Service:** Children's rehabilitation

Staffed Beds: 140 **Admissions:** 697 **Census:** 119 **Outpatient Visits:** 216126 **Births:** 0 **Total Expense ($000):** 142085 **Payroll Expense ($000):** 84356 **Personnel:** 1128

⊞ **ROBERT WOOD JOHNSON UNIVERSITY HOSPITAL (310038)**, 1 Robert Wood Johnson Place, Zip 08901–1928; tel. 732/828–3000, (Includes BRISTOL-MYERS SQUIBB CHILDREN'S HOSPITAL, One Robert Wood Johnson Place, New Brunswick, New Jersey, Zip 8901, Mailing Address: P.O. Box 2601, Zip 08903–2601, tel. 732/828–3000) **A**1 2 3 5 8 10 **F**3 6 7 8 9 11 12 13 14 17 18 19 20 22 24 26 28 29 30 31 32 34 35 37 38 39 40 41 43 44 45 46 47 48 49 50 51 52 53 54 55 56 57 58 59 60 61 62 63 64 65 66 68 70 71 72 73 74 75 76 77 78 79 81 82 84 85 86 87 88 89 91 92 93 94 96 97 100 101 102 104 107 108 109 111 114 115 116 117 118 119 120 121 122 123 124 126 129 130 131 132 134 135 136 137 138 141 142 143 144 145 146 147 148 149 150 154 156 157 **S** RWJBarnabas Health, West Orange, NJ
Primary Contact: John J. Gantner, President and Chief Executive Officer
CFO: Brian M Reilly, Chief Financial Officer
CMO: Joshua M Bershad, M.D., Senior Vice President Medical Affairs and Chief Medical Officer
CIO: Robert G Irwin, Vice President Information Systems
CHR: Martin S Everhart, Senior Vice President Human Resources
CNO: Lori Colineri, R.N., Senior Vice President Nursing and Chief Nursing Officer
Web address: www.rwjuh.edu
Control: Other not–for–profit (including NFP Corporation) **Service:** General medical and surgical

Staffed Beds: 599 **Admissions:** 29491 **Census:** 488 **Outpatient Visits:** 227281 **Births:** 2641 **Total Expense ($000):** 1071491 **Payroll Expense ($000):** 357288 **Personnel:** 4791

⊞ **SAINT PETER'S UNIVERSITY HOSPITAL (310070)**, 254 Easton Avenue, Zip 08901–1780; tel. 732/745–8600, (Includes THE CHILDREN'S HOSPITAL AT SAINT PETER'S UNIVERSITY, 254 Easton Avenue, New Brunswick, New Jersey, Zip 08901–1766; tel. 732/565–5437) **A**1 2 3 5 8 10 **F**3 12 13 15 18 19 20 22 26 27 29 30 31 32 34 35 37 38 39 40 41 44 45 48 50 51 54 55 56 57 58 59 60 61 63 64 65 66 67 68 70 71 72 73 74 75 76 77 78 79 81 82 83 84 85 86 87 88 89 91 92 93 94 96 97 100 101 102 104 105 107 108 110 111 113 114 115 118 119 120 121 123 124 126 129 130 131 132 134 135 143 145 146 147 148 149 150 153 154 156 157
Primary Contact: Leslie D. Hirsch, FACHE, Interim Chief Executive Officer and President
CFO: Garrick J Stoldt, Vice President and Chief Financial Officer
CHR: Susan Ballestero, Vice President and Chief Human Resources Officer
CNO: Elizabeth Wise, R.N., MS, Chief Nursing Officer and Vice President, Patient Care Services
Web address: www.saintpetersuh.com
Control: Church operated, Nongovernment, not–for–profit **Service:** General medical and surgical

Staffed Beds: 353 **Admissions:** 19424 **Census:** 221 **Outpatient Visits:** 267512 **Births:** 5443 **Total Expense ($000):** 458454 **Payroll Expense ($000):** 216757 **Personnel:** 2311

NEWARK—Essex County

⇑ **COLUMBUS HOSPITAL LTACH (312024)**, 495 North Thirteenth Street, Zip 07107–1317; tel. 973/587–7777, (Nonreporting) **A**10 21
Primary Contact: Peter Callaghan, President and Chief Executive Officer
CFO: Alexey Gololobov, Chief Financial Officer
CHR: Patrice Ricciardi, Director Human Resources
CNO: Arthur Kharonov, Vice President Nursing
Web address: www.columbusltach.org
Control: Corporation, Investor–owned (for–profit) **Service:** Acute long–term care hospital

Staffed Beds: 66

⊞ **NEWARK BETH ISRAEL MEDICAL CENTER (310002)**, 201 Lyons Avenue at Osborne Terrace, Zip 07112–2027; tel. 973/926–7000, (Includes CHILDREN'S HOSPITAL OF NEW JERSEY, 201 Lyons Avenue, Newark, New Jersey, Zip 07112–2027; tel. 973/926–7000; Darrell K. Terry Sr, M.P.H., FACHE, President and Chief Executive Officer) **A**1 2 3 5 8 10 12 13 **F**3 15 17 18 19 20 21 22 23 24 25 26 27 28 29 30 31 32 34 35 38 39 40 41 44 45 46 47 48 49 50 51 53 55 56 57 58 59 60 61 64 65 66 68 70 71 72 74 75 76 77 78 79 81 82 84 85 86 87 88 89 91 92 93 94 97 98 99 100 101 102 104 107 108 109 110 111 114 115 117 118 119 120 121 123 126 129 130 131 132 135 137 140 141 143 145 146 147 148 149 153 156 157 **S** RWJBarnabas Health, West Orange, NJ
Primary Contact: Darrell K. Terry Sr, M.P.H., FACHE, President and Chief Executive Officer
CFO: Douglas A Zehner, Chief Financial Officer
CMO: Jeremias Murillo, M.D., Chief Medical Officer
CHR: Zach Lipner, Vice President Human Resources
CNO: Mary Fuhro, Chief Nursing Officer
Web address: www.barnabashealth.org/hospitals/newark_beth_israel/index.html
Control: Other not–for–profit (including NFP Corporation) **Service:** General medical and surgical

Staffed Beds: 372 **Admissions:** 21183 **Census:** 369 **Outpatient Visits:** 295043 **Births:** 3128 **Total Expense ($000):** 623999 **Payroll Expense ($000):** 271746 **Personnel:** 3158

⊞ **SAINT MICHAEL'S MEDICAL CENTER (310096)**, 111 Central Avenue, Zip 07102–1909; tel. 973/877–5350, **A**1 3 5 10 13 **F**3 5 12 15 17 18 20 22 24 26 29 30 31 34 37 40 45 47 49 50 57 58 59 61 64 66 68 70 71 74 75 77 78 79 81 85 87 97 98 100 107 108 109 110 111 114 115 119 121 122 123 126 129 130 132 143 147 148 149 154 **S** Prime Healthcare, Ontario, CA
Primary Contact: Robert C. Iannaccone, JD, Chief Executive Officer
COO: Dennis Pettigrew, Chief Operating Officer
CFO: Carolyn Allen, Chief Financial Officer
CMO: Joseph DePasquale, M.D., Interim Chief Medical Officer
CIO: Tom Addington, Chief Information Officer
CHR: Dennis W. Sparks, Vice President Human Resources
CNO: Johanna Magner, Interim Chief Nursing Officer
Web address: www.smmcnj.org
Control: Corporation, Investor–owned (for–profit) **Service:** General medical and surgical

Staffed Beds: 162 **Admissions:** 8367 **Census:** 96 **Outpatient Visits:** 93430 **Births:** 0 **Total Expense ($000):** 177055 **Payroll Expense ($000):** 76969 **Personnel:** 900

⊞ **UNIVERSITY HOSPITAL (310119)**, 150 Bergen Street, Zip 07103–2496; tel. 973/972–4300, **A**1 2 3 8 10 **F**3 7 8 11 15 17 18 20 24 26 29 30 31 34 35 38 39 40 41 43 45 48 49 50 52 54 55 56 57 58 59 60 61 64 65 66 67 68 70 71 72 73 74 75 76 77 78 79 81 82 84 85 86 87 88 89 93 96 97 98 100 102 107 108 111 116 119 121 124 126 130 131 132 134 135 139 146 147 148 150 155 156 157
Primary Contact: Judith M. Persichilli, Acting President and Chief Executive Officer
COO: Nancy Hamstra, Chief Operating Officer
CFO: Thomas M Daly, CPA, Chief Financial Officer
CMO: Suzanne Atkin, M.D., Chief Medical Officer
CIO: Richard Tunnell, Chief Information Officer
CHR: Gerard Garcia, Chief Human Resource Officer
CNO: Carl Kirton, Ph.D., Chief Nursing Officer
Web address: www.uhnj.org
Control: Other not–for–profit (including NFP Corporation) **Service:** General medical and surgical

Staffed Beds: 404 **Admissions:** 16180 **Census:** 281 **Outpatient Visits:** 262058 **Births:** 1552 **Total Expense ($000):** 718450 **Payroll Expense ($000):** 337311 **Personnel:** 3443

NJ

NEWTON—Sussex County

⊞ **NEWTON MEDICAL CENTER (310028)**, 175 High Street, Zip 07860–1004;
tel. 973/383–2121, **A**1 2 10 **F**3 5 8 11 12 13 15 18 19 20 28 29 30 31 32 34
35 36 38 39 40 41 44 45 47 49 50 53 54 56 57 59 60 61 64 65 68 69 70 71
73 74 75 76 77 78 79 81 82 84 85 86 87 91 92 93 94 96 98 100 101 102
104 105 106 107 108 110 111 114 115 118 119 130 131 132 134 135 141
146 148 149 153 154 156 **S** Atlantic Health System, Morristown, NJ
Primary Contact: Joseph DiPaolo, FACHE, President
CFO: Kevin Lenahan, Director Corporate Accounting, Budgets, Grants and
Reimbursements
CMO: David Lazarus, M.D., Medical Director Clinical Affairs
CIO: Linda Reed, Vice President Information Systems and Chief Information Officer
CHR: Andrew L Kovach, Vice President Human Resources and Chief Administrative
Officer
Web address: www.atlantichealth.org/newton/
Control: Other not–for–profit (including NFP Corporation) **Service**: General
medical and surgical

Staffed Beds: 148 **Admissions**: 8053 **Census**: 108 **Outpatient
Visits**: 95872 **Births**: 572 **Total Expense ($000)**: 182306 **Payroll Expense
($000)**: 85043 **Personnel**: 1267

NORTH BERGEN—Hudson County

⊞ **HACKENSACK MERIDIAN HEALTH PALISADES MEDICAL CENTER (310003)**,
7600 River Road, Zip 07047–6217; tel. 201/854–5000, **A**1 3 5 10 12 13 **F**3 7
11 12 13 15 17 18 20 28 29 30 31 34 35 38 40 43 44 45 46 49 50 56 57 59
60 63 64 65 68 70 72 73 74 75 76 77 78 79 80 81 82 84 85 86 87 89 90 92
93 97 100 101 102 104 107 108 110 111 114 115 119 129 130 132 141 143
146 147 148 149 154 **S** Hackensack Meridian Health, Edison, NJ
Primary Contact: Anthony Passannante Jr, M.D., FACC, President
COO: David J Berkowitz, Vice President and Chief Operating Officer
CFO: John Calandriello, Vice President and Chief Financial Officer
CMO: Suresh Raina, M.D., Vice President Medical Staff and Chief Medical Officer
CIO: Albert Porco, Director Management Information Systems
CNO: Ruben D Fernandez, R.N., Vice President and Chief Nursing Officer
Web address: www.palisadesmedical.org
Control: Other not–for–profit (including NFP Corporation) **Service**: General
medical and surgical

Staffed Beds: 182 **Admissions**: 14446 **Census**: 109 **Outpatient
Visits**: 95359 **Births**: 1264 **Total Expense ($000)**: 177033 **Payroll Expense
($000)**: 84473 **Personnel**: 1145

PARAMUS—Bergen County

⊞ **NEW BRIDGE MEDICAL CENTER (310058)**, 230 East Ridgewood Avenue,
Zip 07652–4142; tel. 201/967–4000, (Total facility includes 574 beds in nursing
home–type unit) **A**1 3 10 **F**4 5 12 15 17 18 26 29 30 31 34 35 40 45 46 47 48
49 50 57 60 61 64 65 66 68 70 74 75 77 78 79 81 82 85 87 92 93 94 97 98
99 100 101 102 103 104 105 107 108 110 111 115 119 124 128 130 131
132 134 143 146 147 148 149 152 153 154
Primary Contact: Deborah D. Visconi, President and Chief Executive Officer
COO: Susan Mendelowitz, R.N., FACHE, Executive Vice President and Chief
Operating Officer
CFO: Connie Magdangal, Executive Vice President and Chief Financial Officer
CMO: Robert M Harris, M.D., President Medical and Dental Staff
CIO: Ronald Li, Vice President Management Information Systems
CHR: Guy Mennonna, Senior Vice President Human Resources
Web address: www.bergenregional.com
Control: County, Government, nonfederal **Service**: General medical and surgical

Staffed Beds: 1070 **Admissions**: 13085 **Census**: 894 **Outpatient
Visits**: 153010 **Births**: 0 **Total Expense ($000)**: 210155 **Payroll Expense
($000)**: 114750 **Personnel**: 1699

PASSAIC—Passaic County

⊞ **ST. MARY'S GENERAL HOSPITAL (310006)**, 350 Boulevard, Zip 07055–2840;
tel. 973/365–4300, (Nonreporting) **A**1 10 **S** Prime Healthcare, Ontario, CA
Primary Contact: Edward Condit, President and Chief Executive Officer
CFO: Nicholas Lanza, Controller
CMO: Ronald Poblete, M.D., President Medical and Dental Staff
CHR: Cathy Lynch-Kilic, Vice President Human Resources
Web address: www.smh-passaic.org
Control: Other not–for–profit (including NFP Corporation) **Service**: General
medical and surgical

Staffed Beds: 287

PATERSON—Passaic County

★ ⇑ **ST. JOSEPH'S UNIVERSITY MEDICAL CENTER (310019)**, 703 Main
Street, Zip 07503–2691; tel. 973/754–2000, (Includes ST. JOSEPH'S
CHILDREN'S HOSPITAL, 703 Main Street, Paterson, New Jersey, Zip 07503–2621;
tel. 973/754–2500; Kevin J Slavin, FACHE, President and Chief Executive Officer;
ST. JOSEPH'S WAYNE HOSPITAL, 224 Hamburg Turnpike, Wayne, New Jersey,
Zip 07470–2100; tel. 973/942–6900; Daniel B Kline, Vice President, Site
Administrator) (Total facility includes 151 beds in nursing home–type unit) **A**2 3 5
10 13 21 **F**3 8 11 12 13 15 17 18 19 20 21 22 23 24 25 26 27 28 29 30 31
32 34 35 36 37 38 39 40 41 43 44 45 47 48 49 50 51 54 55 56 57 58 59
60 61 62 63 64 65 66 68 70 72 73 74 75 76 77 78 79 81 82 84 85 86 87 88
89 90 92 93 94 96 97 98 100 101 102 104 105 106 107 108 110 111 114
115 116 117 118 119 121 123 126 128 129 130 131 132 133 134 135 146
147 148 149 150 153 154 155 156 157 158
Primary Contact: Kevin J. Slavin, FACHE, President and Chief Executive Officer
COO: Lisa Brady, Senior Vice President and Chief Operating Officer
CFO: David Alexander, Senior Vice President and Chief Financial Officer
CMO: James Labagnara, M.D., Vice President Medical Affairs
CIO: Linda Reed, Vice President and Chief Information Officer
CHR: John P Bruno, Senior Vice President Human Resources
CNO: Judy Padula, MSN, R.N., Vice President Patient Care Services and Chief
Nursing Officer
Web address: www.stjosephshealth.org
Control: Church operated, Nongovernment, not–for–profit **Service**: General
medical and surgical

Staffed Beds: 1031 **Admissions**: 29519 **Census**: 531 **Outpatient
Visits**: 361424 **Births**: 3326 **Total Expense ($000)**: 781005 **Payroll
Expense ($000)**: 377290 **Personnel**: 4831

PEAPACK—Somerset County

☐ **MATHENY MEDICAL AND EDUCATIONAL CENTER (312014)**, 65 Highland
Avenue, Zip 07977, Mailing Address: P.O. Box 339, Zip 07977–0339;
tel. 908/234–0011, (Nonreporting) **A**1 10
Primary Contact: Kendell R. Sprott, M.D., JD, Chief Executive Officer
COO: Christopher King, Director Operations and Administrative Services
CFO: Wayne Guberman, Director Finance
CMO: Gary E Eddey, M.D., Medical Director
CIO: Ron Daniel, Manager Information Systems
CHR: Nancy Petrillo, Director Human Resources
Web address: www.matheny.org
Control: Other not–for–profit (including NFP Corporation) **Service**: Acute long–
term care hospital

Staffed Beds: 101

PENNINGTON—Mercer County

⊞ ⇑ **CAPITAL HEALTH MEDICAL CENTER-HOPEWELL (310044)**, 1 Capital Way,
Zip 08534–2520; tel. 609/303–4000, **A**1 2 10 21 **F**3 8 11 12 13 15 18 20 22
28 29 30 31 32 34 35 36 40 41 44 45 46 47 48 49 50 51 52 55 57 58 59 60
61 64 65 68 70 72 73 74 75 76 78 79 81 82 84 85 86 87 89 93 96 97 107
108 109 110 111 112 114 115 117 118 119 120 121 123 124 126 130 132
135 143 145 146 147 148 154 156 **S** Capital Health, Trenton, NJ
Primary Contact: Al Maghazehe, Ph.D., FACHE, President and Chief Executive
Officer
CFO: Shane Fleming, Chief Financial Officer
CMO: Eugene McMahon, Senior Vice President and Chief Medical Officer
CIO: Eugene Grochala, Vice President Information Systems
CHR: Scott Clemmensen, Vice President Human Resources and Leadership
Enhancement
CNO: Deborah Mican, R.N., Chief Nursing Officer
Web address: www.capitalhealth.org
Control: Other not–for–profit (including NFP Corporation) **Service**: General
medical and surgical

Staffed Beds: 171 **Admissions**: 14362 **Census**: 165 **Outpatient
Visits**: 176351 **Births**: 3301 **Personnel**: 1639

PERTH AMBOY—Middlesex County

☐ **CAREONE AT RARITAN BAY MEDICAL CENTER (312018)**, 530 New
Brunswick Avenue, Zip 08861–3654; tel. 732/324–6090, (Nonreporting) **A**1 10
Primary Contact: Sharon Bready, R.N., Chief Executive Officer
CFO: Richard Burguillos, Chief Financial Officer
Web address: www.care-one.com
Control: Corporation, Investor–owned (for–profit) **Service**: Acute long–term care
hospital

Staffed Beds: 30

Many Facility Codes have changed. Please refer to the AHA Guide Code Chart. © 2019 AHA Guide

✠ **HACKENSACK MERIDIAN HEALTH RARITAN BAY MEDICAL CENTER (310039)**, 530 New Brunswick Avenue, Zip 08861–3654; tel. 732/442–3700, (Includes OLD BRIDGE DIVISION, One Hospital Plaza, Old Bridge, New Jersey, Zip 8857; tel. 732/360–1000; PERTH AMBOY DIVISION, 530 New Brunswick Avenue, Perth Amboy, New Jersey, Zip 08861–3685; tel. 732/442–3700) **A**1 3 5 10 **F**3 4 7 8 11 12 13 15 17 18 20 22 29 30 31 32 34 35 36 38 39 40 44 45 46 47 48 49 50 51 54 56 57 58 59 60 61 63 64 65 66 68 70 73 74 75 76 77 78 79 80 81 82 84 85 86 87 89 91 92 93 94 96 97 98 99 100 101 102 103 104 107 108 110 111 114 115 116 117 119 126 129 130 131 132 135 141 143 144 145 146 147 148 149 150 154 156 157 **S** Hackensack Meridian Health, Edison, NJ
Primary Contact: Thomas Shanahan, Chief Operating Officer
CFO: Thomas Shanahan, Chief Financial Officer and Senior Vice President
CMO: Michael Ciencewicki, M.D., Vice President Medical Affairs
CHR: Vincent Costantino, Vice President Operations and Human Resources
Web address: www.rbmc.org
Control: Other not–for–profit (including NFP Corporation) **Service:** General medical and surgical

Staffed Beds: 282 **Admissions:** 24503 **Census:** 159 **Outpatient Visits:** 122592 **Births:** 1140 **Total Expense ($000):** 247020 **Payroll Expense ($000):** 113887 **Personnel:** 1514

PHILLIPSBURG—Warren County

☐ **ST. LUKE'S HOSPITAL - WARREN CAMPUS (310060)**, 185 Roseberry Street, Zip 08865–1690; tel. 908/859–6700, **A**1 2 3 5 10 13 **F**3 8 11 15 18 20 28 29 30 31 34 35 39 40 44 45 47 48 49 50 51 53 54 56 59 60 61 63 64 65 66 70 74 75 77 78 79 81 82 85 86 87 89 91 92 93 97 100 101 102 104 107 108 110 111 115 118 119 124 129 130 131 132 134 146 147 148 149 154 **S** St. Luke's University Health Network, Bethlehem, PA
Primary Contact: Scott R. Wolfe, CPA, President
COO: Alice Wilson, FACHE, Vice President Administration
CMO: Edward Gilkey, M.D., Vice President Medical Affairs
CHR: Morgan G Mahl, Director Human Resources
CNO: Gail Newton, R.N., MSN, Vice President Patient Care Services
Web address: www.slhn.org
Control: Other not–for–profit (including NFP Corporation) **Service:** General medical and surgical

Staffed Beds: 92 **Admissions:** 4248 **Census:** 51 **Outpatient Visits:** 95885 **Births:** 0 **Total Expense ($000):** 106691 **Payroll Expense ($000):** 43353 **Personnel:** 514

PISCATAWAY—Middlesex County

RUTGERS UNIVERSITY BEHAVIORAL HEALTHCARE (314011), 671 Hoes Lane West, Zip 08854–8021; tel. 732/235–5900, (Nonreporting) **A**3 5 10
Primary Contact: Frank A. Ghinassi, Ph.D., President and Chief Executive Officer
COO: Rosemarie Rosati, Chief Operating Officer
CFO: Alan Weinkrantz, Chief Financial Officer, Finance
CMO: Theresa Miskimen, M.D., Vice President Medical Services
CIO: Adam Levinson, Associate Director, Information Services
CNO: Michele A Miller, R.N., MSN, Vice President, Acute and Nursing Services
Web address: www.ubhc.rutgers.edu
Control: State, Government, nonfederal **Service:** Psychiatric

Staffed Beds: 48

PLAINSBORO—Middlesex County

✠ **PENN MEDICINE PRINCETON MEDICAL CENTER (310010)**, One Plainsboro Road, Zip 08536–1913; tel. 609/853–7100, **A**1 2 3 5 10 **F**3 4 5 8 11 12 13 14 15 18 19 20 22 26 28 29 30 31 34 35 36 37 38 39 40 41 45 46 47 48 49 50 51 53 54 55 56 57 58 59 60 61 62 63 64 65 66 71 72 73 74 76 77 78 79 81 82 84 85 86 87 89 90 91 92 93 96 97 98 100 101 102 103 104 105 107 108 110 111 114 115 116 117 118 119 120 121 123 124 126 129 130 131 132 134 135 143 144 146 150 153 154 155 156 **S** University of Pennsylvania Health System, Philadelphia, PA
Primary Contact: Barry S. Rabner, President and Chief Executive Officer, Princeton Healthcare System
COO: James Demetriades, Vice President, Operations
CMO: Donald Denny, M.D., Senior Vice President, Medical Affairs
CIO: Anne Searle, Chief Information Officer
CHR: Marcia M Telthorster, M.Ed, Vice President Human Resources
CNO: Barbara Christiano, Vice President, Patient Care Services and Chief Nursing Officer
Web address: www.princetonhcs.org
Control: Other not–for–profit (including NFP Corporation) **Service:** General medical and surgical

Staffed Beds: 355 **Admissions:** 18337 **Census:** 273 **Outpatient Visits:** 386145 **Births:** 2220 **Total Expense ($000):** 431211 **Payroll Expense ($000):** 170697 **Personnel:** 2878

UNIVERSITY MEDICAL CENTER AT PRINCETON See Penn Medicine Princeton Medical Center, Plainsboro

POMONA—Atlantic County

ATLANTICARE REGIONAL MEDICAL CENTER-MAINLAND DIVISION See Atlanticare Regional Medical Center, Atlantic City

✠ △ **BACHARACH INSTITUTE FOR REHABILITATION (313030)**, 61 West Jimmie Leeds Road, Zip 08240–9102, Mailing Address: P.O. Box 723, Zip 08240–0723; tel. 609/652–7000, (Total facility includes 30 beds in nursing home–type unit) **A**1 7 10 **F**11 28 29 30 33 34 35 36 44 56 57 58 59 64 74 77 79 82 90 91 92 93 95 96 128 129 130 131 132 143 148
Primary Contact: Richard J. Kathrins, Ph.D., President and Chief Executive Officer
CFO: Jeanne Vuksta, Chief Financial Officer
CMO: Craig Anmuth, M.D., Medical Director
CIO: Jeff Rees, Director Information Systems
CHR: Diane S Croshaw, Vice President Human Resources
Web address: www.bacharach.org
Control: Other not–for–profit (including NFP Corporation) **Service:** Rehabilitation

Staffed Beds: 80 **Admissions:** 1695 **Census:** 66 **Outpatient Visits:** 140199 **Births:** 0 **Total Expense ($000):** 52544 **Payroll Expense ($000):** 31127 **Personnel:** 458

POMPTON PLAINS—Morris County

✠ **CHILTON MEDICAL CENTER (310017)**, 97 West Parkway, Zip 07444–1696; tel. 973/831–5000, **A**1 2 10 **F**3 9 11 12 13 15 18 20 22 26 28 29 30 31 32 34 35 36 38 39 40 41 44 45 46 47 49 50 53 54 55 56 57 58 59 60 61 62 63 64 65 66 68 70 73 74 75 76 77 78 79 81 82 84 85 86 87 89 93 96 97 100 101 102 104 107 108 110 111 114 115 116 118 119 120 121 123 124 126 129 130 131 132 134 135 141 143 146 147 148 149 150 154 156 **S** Atlantic Health System, Morristown, NJ
Primary Contact: Stephanie L. Schwartz, FACHE, Vice President AHS and President CMC
CFO: Michael Richetti, Chief Financial Officer
CMO: Charles Ross, M.D., Vice President Medical Affairs
CIO: Karen S Smith, Director Information Services
CHR: Julia McGovern, Vice President Human Resources
Web address: www.chiltonmemorial.org
Control: Other not–for–profit (including NFP Corporation) **Service:** General medical and surgical

Staffed Beds: 133 **Admissions:** 8481 **Census:** 107 **Outpatient Visits:** 118078 **Births:** 627 **Total Expense ($000):** 206476 **Payroll Expense ($000):** 96139 **Personnel:** 1178

RAHWAY—Union County

KINDRED HOSPITAL NEW JERSEY - RAHWAY See Kindred Hospital-New Jersey Morris County, Dover

✠ **ROBERT WOOD JOHNSON UNIVERSITY HOSPITAL RAHWAY (310024)**, 865 Stone Street, Zip 07065–2797; tel. 732/381–4200, **A**1 10 **F**3 11 12 15 17 20 22 29 30 31 34 35 38 40 46 47 49 50 51 53 56 57 59 60 64 65 66 68 70 74 75 77 78 79 81 86 87 92 93 97 100 101 102 107 108 110 111 114 117 118 119 129 130 132 143 146 147 148 149 154 156 **S** RWJBarnabas Health, West Orange, NJ
Primary Contact: Kirk C. Tice, President and Chief Executive Officer
CFO: Peter Bihuniak, Vice President Finance
CMO: Juan Baez, M.D., President Medical Staff
CIO: Denine Izzi, Senior Director Information Technology
CHR: Barbara M Mullery CHHR, Vice President Administration
CNO: Ann Marie Shears, Vice President Patient Care Services
Web address: www.rwjuhr.com
Control: Other not–for–profit (including NFP Corporation) **Service:** General medical and surgical

Staffed Beds: 106 **Admissions:** 4798 **Census:** 69 **Outpatient Visits:** 69045 **Births:** 0 **Total Expense ($000):** 113934 **Payroll Expense ($000):** 46766 **Personnel:** 642

NJ

Hospital, Medicare Provider Number, Address, Telephone, Approval, Facility, and Physician Codes, Health Care System

★ American Hospital Association (AHA) membership
☐ The Joint Commission accreditation
○ Healthcare Facilities Accreditation Program
◇ DNV Healthcare Inc. accreditation
⇑ Center for Improvement in Healthcare Quality Accreditation
△ Commission on Accreditation of Rehabilitation Facilities (CARF) accreditation

---

RED BANK—Monmouth County

✠ △ **HACKENSACK MERIDIAN HEALTH RIVERVIEW MEDICAL CENTER (310034)**, 1 Riverview Plaza, Zip 07701–1864; tel. 732/741–2700, **A**1 2 5 7 10 **F**3 4 5 9 11 13 15 17 18 20 22 28 29 30 31 32 34 35 36 37 38 39 40 41 44 45 46 47 49 50 51 54 55 56 57 58 59 60 61 63 64 65 66 68 70 71 73 74 75 76 77 78 79 81 82 84 85 86 87 90 91 92 93 94 96 97 98 99 100 101 102 103 104 105 107 108 110 111 114 115 116 117 118 119 120 121 123 124 126 130 131 132 134 135 141 144 145 146 147 148 149 150 152 153 154 157 **S** Hackensack Meridian Health, Edison, NJ
Primary Contact: Timothy J. Hogan, FACHE, President, RMC and BMC
COO: Kelly O'Brien, Chief Operating Officer
CFO: Joseph M Lemaire, Executive Vice President Finance
CMO: Joseph Reichman, M.D., Vice President Medical Affairs and Clinical Effectiveness
CIO: Rebecca Weber, Senior Vice President Information Technology
CHR: Sherrie String, Senior Vice President Human Resources
CNO: Rebecca Graboso, Vice President and Chief Nurse Executive
Web address: www.riverviewmedicalcenter.com
Control: Other not–for–profit (including NFP Corporation) **Service**: General medical and surgical

Staffed Beds: 324 **Admissions**: 27218 **Census**: 181 **Outpatient Visits**: 129246 **Births**: 1321 **Total Expense ($000)**: 286596 **Payroll Expense ($000)**: 114936 **Personnel**: 1319

RIDGEWOOD—Bergen County

✠ **VALLEY HOSPITAL (310012)**, 223 North Van Dien Avenue, Zip 07450–2726; tel. 201/447–8000, **A**1 2 10 **F**3 7 8 11 12 13 19 20 22 24 26 28 29 30 31 32 34 35 36 37 38 40 41 44 45 46 47 48 49 50 51 52 53 54 55 56 57 58 59 60 61 64 65 66 68 69 70 71 72 73 74 75 76 77 78 79 80 81 82 83 84 85 86 87 88 89 91 92 93 94 96 97 100 101 102 107 108 109 110 111 114 115 117 118 119 120 121 123 124 126 129 130 131 132 134 135 141 143 145 146 147 148 149 150 156
Primary Contact: Audrey Meyers, FACHE, President and Chief Executive Officer
COO: Peter Diestel, Senior Vice President and Chief Operating Officer
CFO: Richard Keenan, Senior Vice President Finance and Chief Financial Officer
CMO: Joseph Yallowitz, M.D., Vice President and Chief Medical Officer
CIO: Eric R Carey, Vice President Information Systems and Chief Information Officer
CHR: Jose Balderrama, Vice President Human Resources
CNO: Ann Marie Leichman, MSN, R.N., Esq Senior Vice President Patient Care Services and Chief Nursing Officer
Web address: www.valleyhealth.com
Control: Other not–for–profit (including NFP Corporation) **Service**: General medical and surgical

Staffed Beds: 446 **Admissions**: 27097 **Census**: 285 **Outpatient Visits**: 308097 **Births**: 3243 **Total Expense ($000)**: 578262 **Payroll Expense ($000)**: 248271 **Personnel**: 3408

ROCHELLE PARK—Bergen County

✠ **SELECT SPECIALTY HOSPITAL-NORTHEAST NEW JERSEY (312019)**, 96 Parkway, Zip 07662–4200; tel. 201/221–2352, (Nonreporting) **A**1 10 **S** Select Medical Corporation, Mechanicsburg, PA
Primary Contact: Patrick T. Swift, Ph.D., FACHE, Chief Executive Officer
Web address: www.northeastnewjersey.selectspecialtyhospitals.com/about/
Control: Corporation, Investor–owned (for–profit) **Service**: Acute long–term care hospital

Staffed Beds: 62

SADDLE BROOK—Bergen County

KESSLER INSTITUTE FOR REHABILITATION See Kessler Institute for Rehabilitation, West Orange

SALEM—Salem County

✠ **SALEM MEDICAL CENTER (310091)**, 310 Woodstown Road, Zip 08079–2080; tel. 856/935–1000, **A**1 10 **F**3 70 81
Primary Contact: Tammy Torres, R.N., MSN, Chief Executive Officer
CFO: Donald Bevers, Chief Financial Officer
CIO: Brian McCarthy, Director Information Systems
CHR: Victoria A. Bates, Director Human Resources
Web address: www.salemhospitalnj.org
Control: Corporation, Investor–owned (for–profit) **Service**: General medical and surgical

Staffed Beds: 126 **Admissions**: 2633 **Census**: 24 **Outpatient Visits**: 42835 **Births**: 0 **Total Expense ($000)**: 66095 **Payroll Expense ($000)**: 18421 **Personnel**: 330

SECAUCUS—Hudson County

☐ **HUDSON COUNTY MEADOWVIEW PSYCHIATRIC HOSPITAL (314024)**, 595 County Avenue, Zip 07094–2605; tel. 201/369–5252, **A**1 **F**98 100
Primary Contact: Joanne Reilly, Administrator
Web address: www.hudsoncountynj.org
Control: County, Government, nonfederal **Service**: Psychiatric

Staffed Beds: 84 **Admissions**: 186 **Census**: 79 **Outpatient Visits**: 0 **Births**: 0 **Total Expense ($000)**: 29720 **Payroll Expense ($000)**: 11957 **Personnel**: 157

⇑ **HUDSON REGIONAL HOSPITAL (310118)**, 55 Meadowlands Parkway, Zip 07094–2977; tel. 201/392–3100, (Nonreporting) **A**3 5 10 21
Primary Contact: Felicia Karsos, R.N., President and Chief Executive Officer
COO: Lynn McVey, Chief Operating Officer
CMO: Michael Sciarra, M.D., Chief Medical Officer
CHR: Elizabeth Garrity, Director Human Resources
CNO: Felicia Karsos, R.N., Chief Nursing Officer
Web address: www.hudsonregionalhospital.com/
Control: Partnership, Investor–owned (for–profit) **Service**: General medical and surgical

Staffed Beds: 230

⇑ **LIBERTYHEALTH-MEADOWLANDS HOSPITAL MEDICAL CENTER** See Hudson Regional Hospital

SOMERS POINT—Atlantic County

☐ **SHORE MEDICAL CENTER (310047)**, 100 Medical Center Way, Zip 08244; tel. 609/653–3500, (Nonreporting) **A**1 2 10
Primary Contact: Ronald W. Johnson, FACHE, President and Chief Executive Officer
COO: Linda S Kenwood, R.N., MSN, Chief Nursing Officer and Chief Operating Officer
CFO: James T Foley, CPA, Vice President and Chief Financial Officer
CMO: Jeanne M Rowe, M.D., Chief Medical Officer
CIO: Fred Banner, Chief Information Officer
CHR: Alan L Beatty, Vice President Human Resources
CNO: Linda S Kenwood, R.N., MSN, Chief Nursing Officer and Chief Operating Officer
Web address: www.shoremedicalcenter.org
Control: Other not–for–profit (including NFP Corporation) **Service**: General medical and surgical

Staffed Beds: 198

SOMERVILLE—Somerset County

✠ **ROBERT WOOD JOHNSON UNIVERSITY HOSPITAL SOMERSET (310048)**, 110 Rehill Avenue, Zip 08876–2598; tel. 908/685–2200, **A**1 2 3 5 10 **F**3 5 7 8 9 11 12 13 14 15 18 20 22 26 28 29 30 31 34 35 36 38 40 44 45 46 47 48 49 50 51 52 53 55 56 57 58 59 61 62 63 65 66 68 70 71 73 74 75 76 77 78 79 81 82 84 85 86 87 92 93 97 98 100 101 102 104 105 107 108 109 110 111 114 115 116 117 118 119 120 121 123 124 126 129 130 131 132 134 135 143 144 145 146 149 150 152 153 154 156 **S** RWJBarnabas Health, West Orange, NJ
Primary Contact: Anthony V. Cava, MS, FACHE, President
COO: Patrick Delaney, Administrative Director, Operations
CMO: Salvatore Moffa, M.D., Vice President, Medical Affairs and Chief Medical Officer
CIO: Jordan Ruch, Vice President and Chief Information Officer
CHR: Anastasia Jacobs, Chief Human Resources Officer
CNO: Lynn Kearney, Vice President Nursing
Web address: www.rwjuh.edu
Control: Other not–for–profit (including NFP Corporation) **Service**: General medical and surgical

Staffed Beds: 228 **Admissions**: 12622 **Census**: 171 **Outpatient Visits**: 177603 **Births**: 825 **Total Expense ($000)**: 265805 **Payroll Expense ($000)**: 112317 **Personnel**: 1569

STRATFORD—Camden County

JEFFERSON STRATFORD HOSPITAL See Jefferson Stratford Hospital, Stratford

⊞ **JEFFERSON STRATFORD HOSPITAL (310086)**, 18 East Laurel Road, Zip 08084–1327; tel. 856/346–6000, (Includes JEFFERSON STRATFORD HOSPITAL, 18 East Laurel Road, Stratford, New Jersey, Zip 8084; tel. 609/346–6000; JEFFERSON WASHINGTON TOWNSHIP HOSPITAL, 435 Hurffville-Cross Keys Road, Turnersville, New Jersey, Zip 8012; tel. 856/582–2500; John W Graham, FACHE, Chief Administrative Officer) (Total facility includes 190 beds in nursing home–type unit) **A**1 2 3 5 10 12 **F**3 5 7 8 11 12 13 15 18 20 22 24 29 30 31 32 34 35 38 39 40 41 44 45 46 49 50 51 53 54 55 56 57 59 60 61 62 63 64 65 66 70 72 73 74 75 76 77 78 79 81 82 84 85 86 87 89 92 93 97 98 99 100 101 102 103 104 105 107 108 110 111 114 115 116 119 120 121 123 124 126 128 129 130 131 132 134 143 144 146 147 148 149 154 155 156 157 **S** Jefferson Health, Philadelphia, PA
Primary Contact: Jill Ostrem, Senior Vice President and Chief Operating Officer
CFO: Glenn Zirbser, Senior Vice President Finance and Chief Financial Officer
CMO: David Condoluci, M.D., Senior Vice President and Chief Medical Officer
CIO: Thomas Balcavage, Vice President Chief Patient Safety and Quality Officer
CHR: Anneliese McMenamin, Senior Vice President Information Technology and Program Services
CNO: Helene M Burns, MSN, R.N., Chief Nursing Executive
Web address: www.kennedyhealth.org
Control: Other not–for–profit (including NFP Corporation) **Service:** General medical and surgical

Staffed Beds: 716 Admissions: 27131 Census: 494 Outpatient Visits: 420338 Births: 1015 Total Expense ($000): 564030 Payroll Expense ($000): 237573 Personnel: 4313

KENNEDY MEMORIAL HOSPITALS-UNIVERSITY MEDICAL CENTER See Jefferson Stratford Hospital

SUMMIT—Union County

⊞ **OVERLOOK MEDICAL CENTER (310051)**, 99 Beauvoir Avenue, Zip 07901–3533; tel. 908/522-2000, **A**1 2 3 5 8 10 **F**3 5 6 8 9 11 12 13 15 17 18 20 22 28 29 30 31 32 34 35 36 37 38 39 40 41 42 44 45 46 47 48 49 50 51 52 53 54 55 56 57 58 59 60 61 64 65 66 68 69 70 71 72 74 75 76 77 78 79 81 82 84 85 86 87 89 91 92 93 94 95 96 97 98 100 101 102 103 104 105 107 108 110 111 113 115 117 118 119 120 121 123 124 126 129 130 131 132 134 135 141 143 144 145 146 147 148 149 150 153 154 156 157 **S** Atlantic Health System, Morristown, NJ
Primary Contact: Alan R. Lieber, President
CFO: Kevin Lenahan, Vice President Finance and Chief Financial Officer
CMO: John R Audett, M.D., Medical Director Clinical Affairs
CIO: Elizabeth Lindsay-Wood, Interim Chief Information Officer
CNO: Mary Patricia Sullivan, R.N., MSN, Chief Nursing Officer
Web address: www.atlantichealth.org/Overlook
Control: Other not–for–profit (including NFP Corporation) **Service:** General medical and surgical

Staffed Beds: 384 Admissions: 21878 Census: 272 Outpatient Visits: 273900 Births: 2734 Total Expense ($000): 781561 Payroll Expense ($000): 352970 Personnel: 3388

☐ **SUMMIT OAKS HOSPITAL (314001)**, 19 Prospect Street, Zip 07901–2530; tel. 908/522–7000, (Nonreporting) **A**1 10 **S** Universal Health Services, Inc., King of Prussia, PA
Primary Contact: Ross Friedman, Chief Executive Officer
Web address: www.summitoakshospital.com/
Control: Corporation, Investor–owned (for–profit) **Service:** Psychiatric

Staffed Beds: 90

SUSSEX—Sussex County

SAINT CLARE'S HEALTH CENTER AT SUSSEX See Saint Clare's Denville Hospital, Denville

TEANECK—Bergen County

HOLY NAME HOSPITAL See Holy Name Medical Center

⊞ **HOLY NAME MEDICAL CENTER (310008)**, 718 Teaneck Road, Zip 07666–4281; tel. 201/833–3000, **A**1 2 3 10 **F**3 7 11 12 13 15 18 20 22 28 29 30 31 32 34 35 36 37 38 39 40 44 45 46 47 48 49 50 51 53 54 55 56 57 58 59 60 62 63 64 65 66 68 70 71 73 74 75 76 77 78 79 80 81 82 83 84 85 86 87 89 91 92 93 94 96 97 98 100 101 102 103 107 108 110 111 114 115 116 117 118 119 120 121 123 124 126 129 130 131 132 133 135 143 144 145 146 147 148 149 154 156
Primary Contact: Michael Maron, President and Chief Executive Officer
CFO: Ryan Kennedy, Chief Financial Officer
CMO: Adam D Jarrett, M.D., Executive Vice President and Chief Medical Officer
CIO: Michael Skvarenina, Assistant Vice President Information Systems
CHR: April Rodgers, Vice President, Human Resources
CNO: Sheryl A Slonim, Executive Vice President and Chief Nursing Officer
Web address: www.holyname.org
Control: Other not–for–profit (including NFP Corporation) **Service:** General medical and surgical

Staffed Beds: 318 Admissions: 19867 Census: 204 Outpatient Visits: 354919 Births: 1301 Total Expense ($000): 373741 Payroll Expense ($000): 154231 Personnel: 2278

TINTON FALLS—Monmouth County

⊞ **ENCOMPASS HEALTH REHABILITATION HOSPITAL OF TINTON FALLS (313035)**, 2 Centre Plaza, Zip 07724–9744; tel. 732/460–5320, (Nonreporting) **A**1 10 **S** Encompass Health Corporation, Birmingham, AL
Primary Contact: Jason Dan. Hudson, R.N., Chief Executive Officer
CFO: Lynne Traister, Controller
CMO: Todd Cooperman, M.D., Medical Director
CHR: Anita Saum, Director Human Resources
Web address: www.rehabnjtintonfalls.com/
Control: Corporation, Investor–owned (for–profit) **Service:** Rehabilitation

Staffed Beds: 60

TOMS RIVER—Ocean County

⊞ **COMMUNITY MEDICAL CENTER (310041)**, 99 Route 37 West, Zip 08755–6423; tel. 732/557–8000, **A**1 2 3 10 **F**3 11 12 13 15 18 20 22 26 28 29 30 31 32 34 35 36 37 38 39 40 41 43 44 49 50 54 55 56 57 58 59 60 61 63 64 68 70 73 74 75 76 77 78 79 81 82 83 84 85 86 87 89 93 96 97 100 102 107 108 109 110 111 114 115 118 119 120 121 123 124 126 129 130 131 132 133 134 135 143 146 147 148 149 154 156 157 **S** RWJBarnabas Health, West Orange, NJ
Primary Contact: Patrick Ahearn, Chief Executive Officer
COO: Patrick Ahearn, Chief Operating Officer
CFO: Thomas Percello, Chief Financial Officer
CMO: Yeshavanth Nayak, M.D., Interim Chief Medical Officer
CIO: Shaun Fitzsimmons, Director Information Technology Services
CHR: Vanessa Smith, Chief Human Resources Officer
CNO: Donna Bonacorso, Interim Chief Nursing Officer
Web address: www.barnabashealth.org/hospitals/community_medical/index.html
Control: Other not–for–profit (including NFP Corporation) **Service:** General medical and surgical

Staffed Beds: 295 Admissions: 20201 Census: 289 Outpatient Visits: 234392 Births: 2037 Total Expense ($000): 371105 Payroll Expense ($000): 143238 Personnel: 2183

⊞ **HEALTHSOUTH REHABILITATION HOSPITAL OF TOMS RIVER (313029)**, 14 Hospital Drive, Zip 08755–6470; tel. 732/244–3100, (Nonreporting) **A**1 10 **S** Encompass Health Corporation, Birmingham, AL
Primary Contact: Patricia Ostaszewski, MS, Chief Executive Officer
COO: Patricia Ostaszewski, MS, Chief Executive Officer
CFO: Janet Turso, Controller
CMO: Carol Sonatore, D.O., Medical Director
CIO: Coleen Rossi, Director Quality Services
CHR: Lori Munyan, Director, Human Resources
CNO: Susan Castor, Chief Nursing Officer
Web address: www.rehabnjtomsriver.com/
Control: Corporation, Investor–owned (for–profit) **Service:** Rehabilitation

Staffed Beds: 92

NJ

Hospital, Medicare Provider Number, Address, Telephone, Approval, Facility, and Physician Codes, Health Care System

★ American Hospital Association (AHA) membership
☐ The Joint Commission accreditation
○ Healthcare Facilities Accreditation Program
◇ DNV Healthcare Inc. accreditation
⇑ Center for Improvement in Healthcare Quality Accreditation
△ Commission on Accreditation of Rehabilitation Facilities (CARF) accreditation

✠ **RWJBARNABAS HEALTH BEHAVIORAL HEALTH CENTER AND NETWORK (314022)**, 1691 Highway 9, Zip 08754; tel. 732/914–1688, **A**1 10 **F**35 68 98 100 101 103 104 153 **S** RWJBarnabas Health, West Orange, NJ
Primary Contact: Deanna Sperling, R.N., President and Chief Executive Officer
Web address: www.https://www.rwjbh.org/our-locations/behavioral-health-center/barnabas-health-behavioral-health-center/
Control: Other not–for–profit (including NFP Corporation) **Service**: Psychiatric

Staffed Beds: 40 Admissions: 1406 Census: 30 Outpatient Visits: 5825 Births: 0 Total Expense ($000): 9996 Payroll Expense ($000): 5431 Personnel: 391	

SAINT BARNABAS BEHAVIORAL HEALTH CENTER See Rwjbarnabas Health Behavioral Health Center and Network

TRENTON—Mercer County

✠ **CAPITAL HEALTH REGIONAL MEDICAL CENTER (310092)**, 750 Brunswick Avenue, Zip 08638–4143; tel. 609/394–6000, **A**1 3 5 10 **F**3 7 15 18 29 30 34 35 40 43 44 45 46 47 48 50 54 57 58 59 60 61 64 65 66 68 70 74 75 78 79 81 82 84 85 87 89 93 96 97 98 100 101 102 104 107 108 109 111 112 114 115 118 119 129 130 132 135 143 145 146 147 148 154 156 **S** Capital Health, Trenton, NJ
Primary Contact: Al Maghazehe, Ph.D., FACHE, President and Chief Executive Officer
CFO: Shane Fleming, Chief Financial Officer
CMO: Eugene McMahon, Senior Vice President and Chief Medical Officer
CIO: Eugene Grochala, Vice President Information Systems
CHR: Scott Clemmensen, Vice President Human Resources and Leadership Enhancement
CNO: Gina Mumolie, Senior Vice President Hospital Administration
Web address: www.capitalhealth.org
Control: Other not–for–profit (including NFP Corporation) **Service**: General medical and surgical

Staffed Beds: 162 Admissions: 7254 Census: 128 Outpatient Visits: 150717 Births: 0 Personnel: 1435	

✠ **ST. FRANCIS MEDICAL CENTER (310021)**, 601 Hamilton Avenue, Zip 08629–1986; tel. 609/599–5000, **A**1 3 10 **F**2 3 10 11 12 15 17 18 20 22 24 26 29 30 31 34 35 40 43 45 46 50 56 57 58 59 60 61 62 64 65 66 70 74 77 78 79 81 82 84 85 86 87 92 93 98 100 101 102 104 107 108 110 111 114 115 118 119 121 123 124 126 129 130 132 135 143 144 146 147 148 149 154 156 157 **S** Trinity Health, Livonia, MI
Primary Contact: Daniel P. Moen, President
CFO: Mark Kelly, Vice President Finance
CMO: C. James Romano, M.D., Chief Medical Officer
CIO: Richard Dowgun, Chief Information Officer
CHR: Laura James, Director Human Resources
CNO: Mary Anne Suttles, Chief Nursing Officer
Web address: www.stfrancismedical.org/
Control: Church operated, Nongovernment, not–for–profit **Service**: General medical and surgical

Staffed Beds: 142 Admissions: 4141 Census: 59 Outpatient Visits: 85832 Births: 0 Total Expense ($000): 131960 Payroll Expense ($000): 48394 Personnel: 751	

☐ **TRENTON PSYCHIATRIC HOSPITAL (314013)**, Route 29 and Sullivan Way, Zip 08628–3425, Mailing Address: P.O. Box 7500, West Trenton, Zip 08628–0500; tel. 609/633–1500, (Nonreporting) **A**1 10 **S** Division of Mental Health and Addiction Services, Department of Human Services, State of New Jersey, Trenton, NJ
Primary Contact: Robyn Caporoso, Chief Executive Officer
CFO: Joseph Canale, Business Manager
CMO: Lawrence Rossi, M.D., Clinical Director
CIO: Scott Eustace, Director Health Information Technology
CHR: Marybeth Longo, Manager Human Resources
CNO: Colleen Birkhofer, Chief Nursing Officer
Web address: www.state.nj.us/humanservices/dmhs/oshm/tph/
Control: State, Government, nonfederal **Service**: Psychiatric

Staffed Beds: 431	

TURNERSVILLE—Camden County

JEFFERSON WASHINGTON TOWNSHIP HOSPITAL See Jefferson Stratford Hospital, Stratford

VINELAND—Cumberland County

✠ **HEALTHSOUTH REHABILITATION HOSPITAL OF VINELAND (313036)**, 1237 West Sherman Avenue, Zip 08360–6920; tel. 856/696–7100, **A**1 10 **F**29 30 65 75 90 130 132 148 149 **S** Encompass Health Corporation, Birmingham, AL
Primary Contact: Tammy Feuer, Chief Executive Officer
CHR: Dawn Pearson, Director Human Resources
Web address: www.healthsouthvineland.com
Control: Corporation, Investor–owned (for–profit) **Service**: Rehabilitation

Staffed Beds: 41 Admissions: 1028 Census: 37 Outpatient Visits: 0 Births: 0 Total Expense ($000): 14489 Payroll Expense ($000): 8077 Personnel: 102	

★ ⇧ **INSPIRA MEDICAL CENTER-VINELAND (310032)**, 1505 West Sherman Avenue, Zip 08360–6912; tel. 856/641–8000, (Includes BRIDGETON HEALTH CENTER, 333 Irving Avenue, Bridgeton, New Jersey, Zip 08302–2100; tel. 856/575–4500) **A**2 3 10 12 13 21 **F**3 7 8 11 12 13 15 17 18 20 22 28 29 30 34 35 37 38 40 41 42 44 49 50 54 57 59 64 68 70 72 73 74 75 76 77 78 79 81 82 85 86 87 89 93 98 99 100 104 105 107 108 110 111 114 115 116 117 118 119 120 121 123 124 126 130 131 132 134 144 146 147 148 153 154 **S** Inspira Health Network, Mullica Hill, NJ
Primary Contact: John A. DiAngelo, President and Chief Executive Officer
COO: Elizabeth Sheridan, Chief Operating Officer and Chief Nursing Executive
CFO: Thomas Baldosaro, Chief Financial Officer
CMO: Steven C Linn, M.D., Chief Medical Officer
CIO: Thomas Pacek, Vice President Information Systems and Chief Information Officer
CHR: Erich Florentine, Chief People Officer
CNO: Elizabeth Sheridan, Chief Operating Officer and Chief Nursing Executive
Web address: www.inspirahealthnetwork.org/?id=5280&sid=1
Control: Other not–for–profit (including NFP Corporation) **Service**: General medical and surgical

Staffed Beds: 335 Admissions: 17427 Census: 232 Outpatient Visits: 272342 Births: 1900 Total Expense ($000): 367294 Payroll Expense ($000): 161100 Personnel: 1705	

VOORHEES—Camden County

✠ **VIRTUA VOORHEES (310022)**, 100 Bowman Drive, Zip 08043–9612; tel. 856/325–3000, (Includes VOORHEES PEDIATRIC FACILITY, 1304 Laurel Oak Road, Voorhees, New Jersey, Zip 08043–4310; tel. 888/873–5437) **A**1 3 5 10 **F**3 11 13 15 28 29 30 31 34 37 39 40 41 45 46 48 49 50 55 64 68 70 72 73 74 75 76 78 79 81 84 85 87 88 89 92 93 107 108 111 115 116 117 119 126 129 130 132 146 147 148 149 157 **S** Virtua Health, Marlton, NJ
Primary Contact: Dennis W. Pullin, FACHE, President and Chief Executive Officer
COO: Paul E Minnick, R.N., MSN, Senior Vice President and Chief Operating Officer
CFO: Robert Rosvold, Director Finance
CMO: James P Dwyer, D.O., Executive Vice President and Chief Medical Officer
CIO: Alfred Campanella, Chief Information Officer
Web address: www.virtua.org
Control: Other not–for–profit (including NFP Corporation) **Service**: General medical and surgical

Staffed Beds: 402 Admissions: 22875 Census: 276 Outpatient Visits: 285946 Births: 4749 Total Expense ($000): 542190 Payroll Expense ($000): 156204 Personnel: 1886	

WAYNE—Passaic County

KINDRED HOSPITAL NEW JERSEY - WAYNE See Kindred Hospital-New Jersey Morris County, Dover

WEST ORANGE—Essex County

KESSLER INSTITUTE FOR REHABILITATION See Kessler Institute for Rehabilitation, West Orange

✠ △ **KESSLER INSTITUTE FOR REHABILITATION (313025)**, 1199 Pleasant Valley Way, Zip 07052–1424; tel. 973/731–3600, (Includes KESSLER INSTITUTE FOR REHABILITATION, 1199 Pleasant Valley Way, West Orange, New Jersey, Zip 07052–1424; tel. 973/731–3600; Bonnie A. Evans, Chief Executive Officer; KESSLER INSTITUTE FOR REHABILITATION, 201 Pleasant Hill Road, Chester, New Jersey, Zip 07930–2141; tel. 973/252–6300; Sue Kida, Chief Executive Officer; KESSLER INSTITUTE FOR REHABILITATION, 300 Market Street, Saddle Brook, New Jersey, Zip 07663–5309; tel. 201/368–6000; Philip J Driscoll Jr, Chief Executive Officer) **A**1 3 5 7 10 **F**3 29 34 57 58 74 75 78 79 86 87 90 91 92 93 94 95 96 119 130 131 132 146 148 149 **S** Select Medical Corporation, Mechanicsburg, PA
Primary Contact: Bonnie A. Evans, Chief Executive Officer
CMO: Bruce M Gans, M.D., Executive Vice President and Chief Medical Officer
CHR: Ken Caldera, Director Human Resources
Web address: www.kessler-rehab.com
Control: Corporation, Investor–owned (for–profit) **Service**: Rehabilitation

Staffed Beds: 336 Admissions: 5987 Census: 272 Outpatient Visits: 111468 Births: 0 Personnel: 1448	

Many Facility Codes have changed. Please refer to the AHA Guide Code Chart. © 2019 AHA Guide

WESTAMPTON—Burlington County

☐ **HAMPTON BEHAVIORAL HEALTH CENTER (314021)**, 650 Rancocas Road, Zip 08060–5613; tel. 609/267–7000, **A**1 3 10 **F**30 35 98 99 100 103 104 105 130 132 143 149 153 **S** Universal Health Services, Inc., King of Prussia, PA
Primary Contact: Craig Hilton, Chief Executive Officer and Managing Director
COO: Joanne Wijaya, MSN, R.N., Chief Operating Officer and Risk Manager
CFO: Melissa Zinni, Chief Financial Officer
CMO: Anusuya Balasundaram, M.D., Medical Director
CHR: Lori DeCelis, Director Human Resources
CNO: Kathleena Cohen, MSN, R.N., Director of Nursing
Web address: www.hamptonhospital.com
Control: Corporation, Investor–owned (for–profit) **Service:** Psychiatric

Staffed Beds: 120 **Admissions:** 2533 **Census:** 105 **Outpatient Visits:** 19356 **Births:** 0 **Total Expense ($000):** 28398 **Payroll Expense ($000):** 17313 **Personnel:** 215

WESTWOOD—Bergen County

CAREONE AT HACKENSACK UNIVERSITY MEDICAL CENTER AT PASCACK VALLEY, 250 Old Hook Road, Zip 07675–3123, Mailing Address: 250 Old Hook Road, 4 Central, Zip 07675–3123; tel. 201/781–1555, (Nonreporting)
Primary Contact: Sharon Bready, R.N., Chief Executive Officer
Web address: www.care-one.com/locations/ltach-careone-at-hackensack-university-medical-center-pascack-valley/
Control: Other not–for–profit (including NFP Corporation) **Service:** Acute long–term care hospital

Staffed Beds: 25

⊞ **HACKENSACK MERIDIAN HEALTH PASCACK VALLEY MEDICAL CENTER (310130)**, 250 Old Hook Road, Zip 07675–3123; tel. 201/383–1035, **A**1 5 **F**3 12 13 15 18 20 28 29 30 34 35 40 44 45 46 47 49 50 51 57 59 60 64 68 70 73 74 75 76 77 78 79 81 82 85 87 93 107 108 110 111 115 119 126 129 130 135 141 146 147 148 149 156 157 **S** Ardent Health Services, Nashville, TN
Primary Contact: Emily L. Holliman, Chief Executive Officer
COO: Colleen Smorra, Assistant Administrator
CFO: Jason Pritchard, Chief Financial Officer
CMO: George Lin, M.D., Physician Advisor
CIO: Anthony Teri, Director Information Technology
CNO: Susan Giordano, Chief Nursing Officer
Web address: www.hackensackumcpv.com/
Control: Partnership, Investor–owned (for–profit) **Service:** General medical and surgical

Staffed Beds: 128 **Admissions:** 5160 **Census:** 50 **Outpatient Visits:** 33107 **Births:** 1350 **Total Expense ($000):** 104694 **Payroll Expense ($000):** 36209 **Personnel:** 510

WILLINGBORO—Burlington County

⊞ **ACUITY SPECIALTY HOSPITAL OF SOUTHERN NEW JERSEY (312022)**, 218 A Sunset Road, Zip 08046–1110, Mailing Address: 220 Sunset Road, Zip 08046–1110; tel. 609/835–3650, (Nonreporting) **A**1 10 **S** AcuityHealthcare, LP, Charlotte, NC
Primary Contact: Garrett Arneson, FACHE, R.N., Chief Executive Officer
CMO: Edward G. Hamaty, D.O., Chief Medical Officer
CHR: Lisa M Sinnott, Director Human Resources
CNO: Kim Fetterolf, R.N., Chief Clinical Officer
Web address: www.willingboro.acuityhealthcare.net
Control: Corporation, Investor–owned (for–profit) **Service:** Acute long–term care hospital

Staffed Beds: 53

⊞ **LOURDES MEDICAL CENTER OF BURLINGTON COUNTY (310061)**, 218-A Sunset Road, Zip 08046–1162; tel. 609/835–2900, **A**1 2 3 10 **F**3 7 11 12 15 17 18 29 30 31 34 35 36 38 40 42 44 45 46 47 49 50 55 56 57 59 60 61 64 66 68 70 74 75 78 79 81 82 85 86 87 93 98 100 103 107 108 109 110 111 114 118 119 121 129 130 131 132 135 146 147 148 149 **S** Virtua Health, Marlton, NJ
Primary Contact: Mark Nessel, Executive Vice President and Chief Operating Officer
CFO: Michael Hammond, Chief Financial Officer
CMO: Alan R Pope, M.D., Vice President, Medical Affairs
CIO: Mike Elfert, Director Information Services
CNO: Audrey Jadczak, R.N., FACHE, Vice President/Chief Nursing Officer
Web address: www.lourdesnet.org
Control: Other not–for–profit (including NFP Corporation) **Service:** General medical and surgical

Staffed Beds: 169 **Admissions:** 6180 **Census:** 95 **Outpatient Visits:** 107657 **Births:** 0 **Total Expense ($000):** 141763 **Payroll Expense ($000):** 48441 **Personnel:** 686

WOODBURY—Gloucester County

★ ⇑ **INSPIRA MEDICAL CENTER-WOODBURY (310081)**, 509 North Broad Street, Zip 08096–1697; tel. 856/845–0100, **A**3 5 10 21 **F**3 5 11 12 13 15 18 20 22 24 26 28 29 30 31 34 37 40 41 42 45 46 47 48 49 56 57 58 59 64 66 70 73 74 75 76 78 79 81 84 85 86 87 89 91 92 93 94 96 97 98 100 101 102 104 105 107 110 111 114 115 118 119 126 129 133 135 144 146 147 148 149 152 153 154 156 **S** Inspira Health Network, Mullica Hill, NJ
Primary Contact: John A. DiAngelo, President and Chief Executive Officer
COO: Patrick B Nolan, Chief Operating Officer
CIO: Robert Mizia, Director Information Systems and Chief Information Officer
CHR: Robert Manestrina, Vice President Human Resources
CNO: Gina Mumolie, Senior Vice President and Chief Nurse Executive
Web address: www.inspirahealthnetwork.org/?id=5282&sid=1
Control: Other not–for–profit (including NFP Corporation) **Service:** General medical and surgical

Staffed Beds: 311 **Admissions:** 8847 **Census:** 118 **Outpatient Visits:** 168714 **Births:** 811 **Total Expense ($000):** 204891 **Payroll Expense ($000):** 96289 **Personnel:** 994

WYCKOFF—Bergen County

⊞ **CHRISTIAN HEALTH CARE CENTER (314019)**, 301 Sicomac Avenue, Zip 07481–2194; tel. 201/848–5200, (Total facility includes 294 beds in nursing home–type unit) **A**1 10 **F**2 10 35 63 69 93 98 100 104 105 106 128 131 153
Primary Contact: Douglas A. Struyk, CPA, President and Chief Executive Officer
COO: Steve Durnke, FACHE, Executive Vice President and Chief Operating Officer
CFO: Kevin Stagg, Executive Vice President Finance and Chief Financial Officer
CMO: Howard Gilman, M.D., Medical Executive
CIO: Jennifer D'Angelo, Vice President Information Services
CHR: Bob Zierold, Senior Vice President Human Resources
CNO: Marianne Guerriero, Nurse Executive
Web address: www.chccnj.org
Control: Church operated, Nongovernment, not–for–profit **Service:** Rehabilitation

Staffed Beds: 857 **Admissions:** 2185 **Census:** 495 **Outpatient Visits:** 57174 **Births:** 0 **Total Expense ($000):** 82642 **Payroll Expense ($000):** 45199 **Personnel:** 741

NJ

NEW MEXICO

ACOMA—Bergen County

☐ **ACOMA-CANONCITO-LAGUNA HOSPITAL (320070)**, 80B Veterans Boulevard, Zip 87034, Mailing Address: P.O. Box 130, San Fidel, Zip 87049–0130; tel. 505/552–5300, (Nonreporting) **A**1 10 **S** U. S. Indian Health Service, Rockville, MD
Primary Contact: Melody Price-Yonts, Chief Executive Officer
Web address: www.ihs.gov/albuquerque/index.cfm?module=dsp_abq_acoma_canoncito_laguna
Control: PHS, Indian Service, Government, federal **Service:** General medical and surgical

Staffed Beds: 6

ALAMOGORDO—Otero County

★ △ ⇑ **GERALD CHAMPION REGIONAL MEDICAL CENTER (320004)**, 2669 North Scenic Drive, Zip 88310–8799; tel. 575/439–6100, **A**3 7 10 13 20 21 **F**3 8 11 12 13 18 20 22 26 28 29 30 31 34 35 38 40 43 44 45 50 51 54 57 59 64 70 74 75 76 77 78 79 81 82 85 86 87 90 97 98 100 101 102 103 104 107 108 111 114 115 117 119 120 121 123 129 130 131 132 144 145 146 147 148 149 156
Primary Contact: Robert J. Heckert Jr, Chief Executive Officer
CFO: Bashar Naser, Chief Financial Officer
CMO: Lee Saltzgaber, Chief Medical Officer
CIO: Ana Castro, Director Information Technology
CHR: Karen O'Brien, Director Human Resources
CNO: Robert Eldon Middleton, MSN, R.N., III Chief Nursing Officer
Web address: www.gcrmc.org
Control: Other not–for–profit (including NFP Corporation) **Service:** General medical and surgical

Staffed Beds: 100 **Admissions:** 3913 **Census:** 53 **Outpatient Visits:** 103778 **Births:** 520 **Total Expense ($000):** 146366 **Payroll Expense ($000):** 54591 **Personnel:** 858

ALBUQUERQUE—Bernalillo County

☐ **AMG SPECIALTY HOSPITAL-ALBUQUERQUE (322003)**, 235 Elm Street NE, Zip 87102–3672; tel. 505/842–5550, (Nonreporting) **A**1 10 **S** AMG Integrated Healthcare Management, Lafayette, LA
Primary Contact: Kendra Camp, R.N., Chief Executive Officer
CFO: Julie Lenzo, Director Business Office
CMO: Jeffrey Ross, M.D., Medical Director
CHR: Robin Stendel-Freels, Coordinator Human Resources
Web address: www.amgalbuquerque.com/
Control: Partnership, Investor–owned (for–profit) **Service:** Acute long–term care hospital

Staffed Beds: 24

☐ **HAVEN BEHAVIORAL SENIOR CARE OF ALBUQUERQUE (324013)**, 5400 Gibson Boulevard SE, 4th Floor, Zip 87108–4729; tel. 505/336–1247, (Nonreporting) **A**1 10
Primary Contact: Sheila McDermott-Lord, Chief Executive Officer
Web address: www.https://albuquerque.havenbehavioral.com/
Control: Corporation, Investor–owned (for–profit) **Service:** Psychiatric

Staffed Beds: 32

 HEALTHSOUTH REHABILITATION HOSPITAL OF NEW MEXICO (323027), 7000 Jefferson Street NE, Zip 87109–4313; tel. 505/344–9478, **A**1 10 **F**28 29 34 35 56 57 59 60 62 64 74 75 77 79 90 91 93 94 95 96 130 132 143 148 **S** Encompass Health Corporation, Birmingham, AL
Primary Contact: Rachelle Spencer, Chief Executive Officer
CFO: Michelle Martinez, Controller
CMO: Angela Walker, M.D., Medical Director
CHR: Kristen Hernandez, Director Human Resources
CNO: Karin Jones, Interim Chief Nursing Officer
Web address: www.healthsouthnewmexico.com
Control: Corporation, Investor–owned (for–profit) **Service:** Rehabilitation

Staffed Beds: 87 **Admissions:** 1842 **Census:** 60 **Births:** 0

⊠ **KINDRED HOSPITAL-ALBUQUERQUE (322002)**, 700 High Street NE, Zip 87102–2565; tel. 505/242–4444, (Nonreporting) **A**1 10 **S** Kindred Healthcare, Louisville, KY
Primary Contact: Bud Schawl, Chief Executive Officer
CFO: Sheila Bova, Chief Financial Officer
CMO: Jon Marinaro, M.D., Chief Medical Officer
CHR: Donald Whitney, Director Human Resources
CNO: Diane Nelson, R.N., Chief Nursing Officer
Web address: www.kindredalbuquerque.com/
Control: Corporation, Investor–owned (for–profit) **Service:** Acute long–term care hospital

Staffed Beds: 61

★ **LOVELACE MEDICAL CENTER (320009)**, 601 Martin Luther King Avenue NE, Zip 87102–3619; tel. 505/727–8000, (Includes HEART HOSPITAL OF NEW MEXICO, 504 Elm Street, Albuquerque, New Mexico, Zip 87102; tel. 505/724–2000; Denzil Ross, Administrator) **A**3 5 10 21 **F**3 17 18 20 22 24 26 28 29 30 31 34 35 36 38 40 45 46 50 51 56 57 58 59 60 65 68 70 74 75 77 78 79 81 82 87 98 100 105 106 107 108 109 111 114 115 117 118 119 120 121 124 126 130 132 146 148 154 157 **S** Ardent Health Services, Nashville, TN
Primary Contact: Troy Greer, Chief Executive Officer
COO: Denzil Ross, Chief Operating Officer
CHR: Helen V Nielsen, Director Human Resources
CNO: Nancye Cole, MS, R.N., FACHE, Chief Nursing Officer
Web address: www.lovelace.com/albuquerque-hospital/lovelace-medical-center#.UDZ1IaDhf48
Control: Corporation, Investor–owned (for–profit) **Service:** General medical and surgical

Staffed Beds: 247 **Admissions:** 12441 **Census:** 171 **Outpatient Visits:** 33700

★ △ **LOVELACE UNM REHABILITATION HOSPITAL (323028)**, 505 Elm Street NE, Zip 87102–2500; tel. 505/727–4700, **A**7 10 **F**3 29 30 90 143 148 **S** Ardent Health Services, Nashville, TN
Primary Contact: Derrick Jones, Chief Executive Officer
CFO: Andrea Solin, Chief Financial Officer
CHR: Helen V Nielsen, Director Human Resources
CNO: Cynthia Rankin, Chief Nursing Officer
Web address: www.lovelace.com
Control: Corporation, Investor–owned (for–profit) **Service:** Rehabilitation

Staffed Beds: 52 **Admissions:** 1180 **Census:** 39 **Births:** 0

★ ⇑ **LOVELACE WESTSIDE HOSPITAL (320074)**, 10501 Golf Course Road NW, Zip 87114–5000, Mailing Address: P.O. Box 25555, Zip 87125–0555; tel. 505/727–8000, **A**10 21 **F**3 12 13 15 29 30 34 39 40 41 49 51 57 59 68 70 75 76 79 81 85 93 107 110 111 115 119 130 133 135 146 148 **S** Ardent Health Services, Nashville, TN
Primary Contact: Amy Blasing, Chief Executive Officer
CFO: Andrea Solin, Chief Financial Officer
CNO: Brenda Holley, Chief Nursing Officer
Web address: www.lovelace.com/albuquerque-hospital/lovelace-westside-hospital#.UDZ1t6Dhf48
Control: Corporation, Investor–owned (for–profit) **Service:** General medical and surgical

Staffed Beds: 80 **Admissions:** 3172 **Census:** 26

★ ⇑ **LOVELACE WOMEN'S HOSPITAL (320017)**, 4701 Montgomery Boulevard NE, Zip 87109–1251, Mailing Address: P.O. Box 25555, Zip 87125–0555; tel. 505/727–7800, **A**10 21 **F**8 11 15 34 35 42 43 46 49 57 59 64 70 72 73 76 78 79 81 85 91 93 107 108 110 111 114 115 116 117 119 126 130 132 146 147 **S** Ardent Health Services, Nashville, TN
Primary Contact: Sheri Milone, Chief Executive Officer and Administrator
COO: Janelle Raborn, Chief Operating Officer
CFO: Joseph Sereno, Chief Financial Officer
CHR: Carol Shelton, Director Human Resources
Web address: www.lovelace.com/albuquerque-hospital/lovelace-womens-hospital#.UDZ17KDhf48
Control: Corporation, Investor–owned (for–profit) **Service:** General medical and surgical

Staffed Beds: 78 **Admissions:** 6167 **Census:** 55

NM

Many Facility Codes have changed. Please refer to the AHA Guide Code Chart. © 2019 AHA Guide

☒ △ **NEW MEXICO VETERANS AFFAIRS HEALTH CARE SYSTEM - RAYMOND G. MURPHY MEDICAL CENTER**, 1501 San Pedro SE, Zip 87108–5153; tel. 505/265–1711, (Nonreporting) **A**1 2 3 5 7 8 **S** Department of Veterans Affairs, Washington, DC
Primary Contact: Andrew Welch, Director
CFO: Michael McNeill, Chief Financial Management
CMO: Meghan Gerety, M.D., Chief of Staff
CIO: Ronald Ferrell, Chief Information Officer
CHR: Melvin Hooker, Chief Human Resources
Web address: www.albuquerque.va.gov/
Control: Veterans Affairs, Government, federal **Service**: General medical and surgical

Staffed Beds: 203

☒ **PRESBYTERIAN HOSPITAL (320021)**, 1100 Central Avenue SE, Zip 87106–4934, Mailing Address: P.O. Box 26666, Zip 87125–6666; tel. 505/841–1234, (Includes PRESBYTERIAN KASEMAN HOSPITAL, 8300 Constitution Avenue NE, Albuquerque, New Mexico, Zip 87110–7624, Mailing Address: P O Box 26666, Zip 87125–6666, tel. 505/291–2000; Doyle Boykin, R.N., MSN, Administrator; PRESBYTERIAN RUST MEDICAL CENTER, 2400 Unser Boulevard SE, Rio Rancho, New Mexico, Zip 87124–4740; tel. 505/253–7878; Jeff McBee, Administrator) **A**1 2 3 5 10 **F**7 8 11 12 13 17 18 19 20 21 22 23 24 25 26 27 28 29 30 31 32 34 35 38 40 45 47 48 49 50 51 53 55 56 57 58 59 61 62 63 64 65 68 70 72 74 75 76 77 78 79 80 81 82 84 85 86 87 88 89 91 92 93 96 97 98 99 100 102 104 107 108 111 112 114 115 116 117 118 119 121 126 127 129 130 131 132 135 138 144 146 147 148 149 153 154 **S** Presbyterian Healthcare Services, Albuquerque, NM
Primary Contact: Devon Hyde, Vice President, Chief Administrative Officer
COO: Paul Briggs, Executive Vice President and Chief Operating Officer
CFO: Dale Maxwell, Executive Vice President and Chief Financial Officer
CMO: Jayne McCormick, M.D., Chief Medical Officer CDS
CIO: Lee Marley, VP/Information Services Chief Application Officer
CHR: Lee Patchell, Lead Human Resources Business Partner
CNO: Ann L Wright, R.N., MSN, Assistant Central Delivery System CNO
Web address: www.phs.org
Control: Other not–for–profit (including NFP Corporation) **Service**: General medical and surgical

Staffed Beds: 644 Admissions: 43882 Census: 534 Births: 4043
Total Expense ($000): 1590192 Payroll Expense ($000): 538560
Personnel: 7258

TURQUOISE LODGE HOSPITAL, 5901 Zuni Road SE, Zip 87108–3073; tel. 505/841–8978, **F**4 5 152
Primary Contact: Shauna Hartley, Administrator
CFO: Juliette Aragon, Finance Director
CIO: Eric Gurule, Chief Information Officer
CHR: Mario Lechuga, Director Human Resources
CNO: Debra Jane Green, R.N., Director of Nursing
Web address: www.health.state.nm.us
Control: State, Government, nonfederal **Service**: Alcoholism and other chemical dependency

Staffed Beds: 36 Admissions: 1307 Census: 26 Births: 0 Personnel: 76

☒ **UNIVERSITY OF NEW MEXICO HOSPITALS (320001)**, 2211 Lomas Boulevard NE, Zip 87106–2745; tel. 505/272–2111, (Includes CARRIE TINGLEY HOSPITAL, 1127 University Boulevard NE, Albuquerque, New Mexico, Zip 87102–1715; tel. 505/272–5200; Doris Tinagero, Executive Director; MENTAL HEALTH CENTER, 2600 Marble NE, Albuquerque, New Mexico, Zip 87131–2600; tel. 505/272–2800; UNIVERSITY OF NEW MEXICO CHILDREN'S PSYCHIATRIC HOSPITAL, 1001 Yale Boulevard NE, Albuquerque, New Mexico, Zip 87131–3830; tel. 505/272–2890; UNM CHILDREN'S HOSPITAL, 2211 Lomas Boulevard, NE, 3rd Floor of UNM Hospital, Albuquerque, New Mexico, Zip 87106–2745; tel. 505/272–2111) **A**1 2 3 5 8 10 19 **F**3 8 9 11 13 15 16 17 18 19 20 21 22 23 24 25 26 27 28 29 30 31 32 34 35 38 40 41 43 44 45 46 47 48 49 50 51 54 55 57 59 60 61 62 63 64 65 68 70 72 73 74 75 76 77 78 79 81 82 84 85 86 87 88 89 92 93 94 95 96 97 107 108 110 111 113 114 115 116 117 118 119 126 129 130 131 132 135 136 138 144 146 147 148 155 156 **S** University of New Mexico Hospitals, Albuquerque, NM
Primary Contact: Kathleen R. Becker, M.P.H., JD, Chief Executive Officer
CFO: Ella Watt, Chief Financial Officer
CMO: Irene Agostini, M.D., Chief Medical Officer
CIO: Dawn Harrington, Chief Information Officer
CHR: Sara Frasch, Chief Human Resource Officer
Web address: www.unm.edu
Control: State, Government, nonfederal **Service**: General medical and surgical

Staffed Beds: 537 Admissions: 33338 Census: 415 Outpatient
Visits: 674763 Births: 2987 Total Expense ($000): 1027797 Payroll
Expense ($000): 383771 Personnel: 6492

ARTESIA—Eddy County

★ **ARTESIA GENERAL HOSPITAL (320030)**, 702 North 13th Street, Zip 88210–1199; tel. 575/748–3333, (Nonreporting) **A**10 20
Primary Contact: Robert C. Tyk, Interim Chief Executive Officer
CFO: Carl Hollingsworth, Chief Financial Officer
CMO: Joe Salgado, M.D., Chief of Staff
CHR: Bruce Hinshaw, Director Human Resources
CNO: Wendi Hulett, Chief Nursing Officer
Web address: www.artesiageneral.com
Control: Other not–for–profit (including NFP Corporation) **Service**: General medical and surgical

Staffed Beds: 30

CARLSBAD—Eddy County

☒ **CARLSBAD MEDICAL CENTER (320063)**, 2430 West Pierce Street, Zip 88220–3597; tel. 575/887–4100, (Total facility includes 15 beds in nursing home–type unit) **A**1 10 **F**3 11 13 15 18 20 22 28 29 30 34 35 40 41 43 45 46 50 51 54 57 59 64 65 66 70 76 77 78 79 81 82 83 85 86 87 90 91 92 93 107 108 110 111 115 119 120 121 122 123 128 129 135 144 146 147 148 149 **S** Community Health Systems, Inc., Franklin, TN
Primary Contact: Cathy Hibbs, Chief Executive Officer
CFO: Craig Morse, Chief Financial Officer
CIO: Thomas Motejzik, Director Information Systems
CNO: Connie Shofner, Chief Nursing Officer
Web address: www.carlsbadmedicalcenter.com
Control: Corporation, Investor–owned (for–profit) **Service**: General medical and surgical

Staffed Beds: 114 Admissions: 2318 Census: 28 Outpatient Visits: 63692
Births: 306 Personnel: 358

CLAYTON—Union County

★ **UNION COUNTY GENERAL HOSPITAL (321304)**, 300 Wilson Street, Zip 88415–3304, Mailing Address: P.O. Box 489, Zip 88415–0489; tel. 575/374–2585, (Nonreporting) **A**10 18 **S** Community Hospital Corporation, Plano, TX
Primary Contact: Tammie Stump, R.N., Chief Executive Officer
CFO: Alexander B Altman III Chief Financial Officer
CMO: Daniel Radunsky, M.D., Medical Staff President
CIO: Kelsey Lawrence, Manager Information Technology
CHR: Jill Swagerty, Director Human Resources
CNO: Stacye Bradley, R.N., Chief Nursing Officer
Web address: www.ucgh.net/
Control: Other not–for–profit (including NFP Corporation) **Service**: General medical and surgical

Staffed Beds: 21

CLOVIS Curry County

☒ **PLAINS REGIONAL MEDICAL CENTER (320022)**, 2100 North Doctor Martin Luther King Boulevard, Zip 88101 9412, Mailing Address: P.O. Box 1688, Zip 88102–1688; tel. 575/769–2141 **A**1 10 **F**3 11 13 15 18 20 22 28 29 30 31 35 40 43 45 50 51 53 56 57 61 62 63 64 65 68 69 70 75 76 77 78 79 80 81 84 85 87 89 93 97 107 108 110 111 112 114 115 116 119 120 121 123 129 130 135 146 148 149 150 154 **S** Presbyterian Healthcare Services, Albuquerque, NM
Primary Contact: Richard Smith, Administrator
CMO: Brian Willmon, M.D., Medical Director
CHR: Cindy Duncan, Manager Human Resources
CNO: Terri A Marney, R.N., Director of Nursing
Web address: www.phs.org
Control: Other not–for–profit (including NFP Corporation) **Service**: General medical and surgical

Staffed Beds: 80 Admissions: 3650 Census: 30 Outpatient Visits: 117121
Births: 1129 Total Expense ($000): 96364 Payroll Expense ($000): 34751
Personnel: 495

CROWNPOINT—McKinley County

U. S. PUBLIC HEALTH SERVICE INDIAN HOSPITAL (320062), Route 9 and State Road 371, Zip 87313, Mailing Address: P.O. Box 358, Zip 87313–0358; tel. 505/786–5291, (Nonreporting) **A**10 **S** U. S. Indian Health Service, Rockville, MD
Primary Contact: Anslem Roanhorse, Chief Executive Officer
CFO: Darlene Kirk, Manager Finance
CMO: John Johnson, M.D., Clinical Director
CIO: Jimmy Burbank, Chief Information Officer
CHR: Christina Bitsilly, Human Resource Specialist
CNO: Alex Daniels, Chief Nurse Executive
Web address: www.ihs.gov
Control: PHS, Indian Service, Government, federal **Service**: General medical and surgical

Staffed Beds: 12

NM

Hospital, Medicare Provider Number, Address, Telephone, Approval, Facility, and Physician Codes, Health Care System

★ American Hospital Association (AHA) membership
□ The Joint Commission accreditation
○ Healthcare Facilities Accreditation Program
◇ DNV Healthcare Inc. accreditation
⇑ Center for Improvement in Healthcare Quality Accreditation
△ Commission on Accreditation of Rehabilitation Facilities (CARF) accreditation

---

DEMING—Luna County

✉ **MIMBRES MEMORIAL HOSPITAL (321309)**, 900 West Ash Street, Zip 88030–4098, Mailing Address: P.O. Box 710, Zip 88031–0710; tel. 575/546–5800, (Nonreporting) **A**1 10 18 **S** Quorum Health, Brentwood, TN
Primary Contact: Gary R. Poquette, FACHE, Chief Executive Officer
CFO: Trisha Smith, Chief Financial Officer
CHR: Johanna Gramer, Director Human Resources
CNO: Joy Harrell, R.N., Chief Nursing Officer
Web address: www.mimbresmemorial.com
Control: Corporation, Investor–owned (for–profit) **Service**: General medical and surgical

Staffed Beds: 75

ESPANOLA—Rio Arriba County

✉ **PRESBYTERIAN ESPANOLA HOSPITAL (320011)**, 1010 Spruce Street, Zip 87532–2746; tel. 505/753–7111, **A**1 10 20 **F**3 7 8 11 13 15 29 30 34 35 40 45 50 51 53 57 59 62 64 68 70 76 79 81 85 89 93 97 107 108 110 115 119 129 130 146 **S** Presbyterian Healthcare Services, Albuquerque, NM
Primary Contact: Brenda Romero, Hospital Chief
CFO: Lupe Lucero, Manager Business Office
CMO: Fernando Bayardo, M.D., Chief Medical Officer
CHR: Joshua Griffith, Manager Human Resources
CNO: Nancy Santiesteban, Director Patient Care Services
Web address: www.phs.org
Control: Other not–for–profit (including NFP Corporation) **Service**: General medical and surgical

Staffed Beds: 46 Admissions: 2358 Census: 23 Outpatient Visits: 85045 Births: 262 Total Expense ($000): 70378 Payroll Expense ($000): 32389 Personnel: 315

FARMINGTON—San Juan County

★ ⇑ **SAN JUAN REGIONAL MEDICAL CENTER (323029)**, 801 West Maple Street, Zip 87401–5630; tel. 505/609–2000, (Includes SAN JUAN REGIONAL MEDICAL CENTER REHABILITATION HOSPITAL, 525 South Schwartz Avenue, Farmington, New Mexico, Zip 87401–5955; tel. 505/609–2625; Jeff A. Bourgeois, President and Chief Executive Officer) **A**10 21 **F**3 7 8 11 13 15 18 20 22 26 28 29 30 31 32 34 35 39 40 43 45 46 47 48 49 50 53 54 57 59 60 61 64 65 68 70 74 75 76 77 78 79 81 82 85 86 87 89 90 92 93 96 97 98 100 102 104 107 108 110 111 112 114 115 117 119 121 130 132 135 143 144 146 147 148 154 155 156
Primary Contact: Jeff A. Bourgeois, President and Chief Executive Officer
COO: John Buffington, Chief Operating Officer
CFO: Karen Miller, Chief Financial Officer
CMO: Melania Yeats, M.D., Chief Medical Officer
CIO: Sheri Rawlings, Chief Information Officer
CHR: Elizabeth Volkerding, Director Workforce Excellence
CNO: Suzanne E Smith, R.N., MSN, Chief Nursing Officer
Web address: www.sanjuanregional.com
Control: Other not–for–profit (including NFP Corporation) **Service**: General medical and surgical

Staffed Beds: 198 Admissions: 9515 Census: 115 Outpatient Visits: 782841 Total Expense ($000): 298448 Payroll Expense ($000): 143367 Personnel: 1675

GALLUP—Mckinley County

✉ **GALLUP INDIAN MEDICAL CENTER (320061)**, 516 East Nizhoni Boulevard, Zip 87301–5748, Mailing Address: P.O. Box 1337, Zip 87301; tel. 505/722–1000, (Nonreporting) **A**1 5 10 **S** U. S. Indian Health Service, Rockville, MD
Primary Contact: John Meese, Acting Director
CFO: Agnes Kee, Financial Manager
CMO: Douglas G Peter, M.D., Chief Medical Officer
CIO: Adrian C Haven, Site Manager
CHR: Karen Lee, Director Human Resources
CNO: Selva Thompson, R.N., Chief Nurse Executive
Web address: www.ihs.gov/navajo/index.cfm?module=nao_hcc_gallup
Control: PHS, Indian Service, Government, federal **Service**: General medical and surgical

Staffed Beds: 58

GALLUP—McKinley County

★ ⇑ **REHOBOTH MCKINLEY CHRISTIAN HEALTH CARE SERVICES (320038)**, 1901 Red Rock Drive, Zip 87301–5683; tel. 505/863–7000, (Nonreporting) **A**5 10 20 21
Primary Contact: David Conejo, Chief Executive Officer
COO: William Kiefer, Chief Operating Officer
CFO: John McMullin, Chief Financial Officer
CIO: Randy Myers, Chief Information Officer
CHR: Ronnye Etcitty, Director Human Resources
CNO: Bill Norton, Chief Nursing Officer
Web address: www.rmch.org
Control: Other not–for–profit (including NFP Corporation) **Service**: General medical and surgical

Staffed Beds: 60

GRANTS—Cibola County

✉ **CIBOLA GENERAL HOSPITAL (321308)**, 1016 East Roosevelt Avenue, Zip 87020–2118; tel. 505/287–4446, **A**1 10 18 **F**3 13 15 29 30 34 40 45 46 50 56 57 59 64 65 66 68 70 75 76 77 81 85 93 97 107 110 115 119 129 130 133 135 147 148 **S** QHR, Brentwood, TN
Primary Contact: Thomas Whelan, Chief Executive Officer
CFO: Ed Brown, Chief Financial Officer
CMO: Janice Shipley, M.D., Chief Medical Officer
CIO: Rick Smith, Director Information Services
CHR: Sheila Cox, Director Human Resources
CNO: Glenna Losito, R.N., MSN, Chief Nursing Officer
Web address: www.cibolahospital.com
Control: Other not–for–profit (including NFP Corporation) **Service**: General medical and surgical

Staffed Beds: 25 Admissions: 902 Census: 8

HOBBS—Lea County

✉ **LEA REGIONAL MEDICAL CENTER (320065)**, 5419 North Lovington Highway, Zip 88240–9125, Mailing Address: P.O. Box 3000, Zip 88241–9501; tel. 575/492–5000, **A**1 10 **F**3 8 11 13 15 18 20 22 29 30 35 37 40 44 45 54 57 59 60 64 65 68 70 75 76 77 79 80 81 82 86 87 89 91 93 100 102 104 107 108 110 111 112 128 130 131 133 135 146 147 148 154 **S** Community Health Systems, Inc., Franklin, TN
Primary Contact: Timothy Thornell, FACHE, Chief Executive Officer
CFO: Jorge Latibeaudiere, Chief Financial Officer
CMO: Ali Sherif, M.D., Chief of Staff
CIO: Terrance J. Purcell, Director Information Services
CHR: Laurie Russell, Director Human Resources
CNO: Patrick A Dunn, R.N., Chief Nursing Officer
Web address: www.learegionalmedical.com
Control: Corporation, Investor–owned (for–profit) **Service**: General medical and surgical

Staffed Beds: 99 Admissions: 2600 Census: 26 Outpatient Visits: 74000 Births: 537 Total Expense ($000): 48140 Payroll Expense ($000): 14672 Personnel: 251

LAS CRUCES—Dona Ana County

☐ **ADVANCED CARE HOSPITAL OF SOUTHERN NEW MEXICO (322004)**, 4451 East Lohman Avenue, Zip 88011–8267; tel. 575/521–6600, (Nonreporting) **A**1 10 **S** Ernest Health, Inc., Albuquerque, NM
Primary Contact: Claudia Saiz, Chief Executive Officer
Web address: www.achsnm.ernesthealth.com
Control: Corporation, Investor–owned (for–profit) **Service**: Acute long–term care hospital

Staffed Beds: 40

✉ **MEMORIAL MEDICAL CENTER (320018)**, 2450 South Telshor Boulevard, Zip 88011–5076; tel. 575/522–8641, **A**1 2 3 10 **F**3 8 11 12 13 15 17 18 20 22 24 28 29 30 31 34 35 40 45 49 50 51 54 57 60 64 65 66 68 70 72 73 74 75 76 78 79 81 84 85 88 89 98 102 107 108 109 110 111 114 115 118 119 120 121 123 144 146 147 148 149 **S** LifePoint Health, Brentwood, TN
Primary Contact: John Harris, Chief Executive Officer
COO: Steven T Ruwoldt, Chief Operating Officer
CFO: Raymond Grenier, Chief Financial Officer
CMO: Bruce San Filippo, M.D., Chief Medical Officer
CHR: Laura Pierce, Director Human Resources
CNO: Caryn Iverson, MSN, Chief Nursing Officer
Web address: www.mmclc.org
Control: Corporation, Investor–owned (for–profit) **Service**: General medical and surgical

Staffed Beds: 173 Admissions: 10132 Census: 114 Outpatient Visits: 142626 Births: 1120 Total Expense ($000): 245830 Payroll Expense ($000): 92808 Personnel: 1316

✉ **MESILLA VALLEY HOSPITAL (324010)**, 3751 Del Rey Boulevard, Zip 88012–8526; tel. 575/382–3500, (Nonreporting) **A**1 10 **S** Universal Health Services, Inc., King of Prussia, PA
Primary Contact: Anna Laliotis, Chief Executive Officer
CFO: Dana McRimmon, Chief Financial Officer
CMO: Arthur L. Ramirez, M.D., Medical Director
CIO: Rebecca Mumpower, Director Marketing
CHR: Linda Moya, Director Human Resources
CNO: Veronica Hughes, Chief Nursing Officer
Web address: www.mesillavalleyhospital.com
Control: Corporation, Investor–owned (for–profit) **Service**: Psychiatric

Staffed Beds: 105

NM

Many Facility Codes have changed. Please refer to the AHA Guide Code Chart. © 2019 AHA Guide

✠ **MOUNTAINVIEW REGIONAL MEDICAL CENTER (320085)**, 4311 East Lohman Avenue, Zip 88011–8255; tel. 575/556–7600, (Nonreporting) **A**1 3 5 10 12 13 **S** Community Health Systems, Inc., Franklin, TN
Primary Contact: Derrick Cuenca, Chief Executive Officer
CIO: Donald Harlow, Director of Information Services
CHR: Delilah Doss, Director, Human Resources
CNO: Gayle Nash, R.N., M.P.H., Chief Nursing Officer
Web address: www.mountainviewregional.com
Control: Corporation, Investor–owned (for–profit) **Service:** General medical and surgical

Staffed Beds: 142

✠ **REHABILITATION HOSPITAL OF SOUTHERN NEW MEXICO (323032)**, 4441 East Lohman Avenue, Zip 88011–8267; tel. 575/521–6400, (Nonreporting) **A**1 10 **S** Ernest Health, Inc., Albuquerque, NM
Primary Contact: Sabrina Martin, Chief Executive Officer
CFO: Elizabeth Striplin, Chief Financial Officer
CMO: Kimberly Encapera, M.D., Medical Director
CHR: Yolanda Mendoza, Director Human Resources
CNO: Carole Carson, Director of Nursing Operations
Web address: www.rhsnm.ernesthealth.com
Control: Corporation, Investor–owned (for–profit) **Service:** Rehabilitation

Staffed Beds: 40

LAS VEGAS—San Miguel County

✠ **ALTA VISTA REGIONAL HOSPITAL (320003)**, 104 Legion Drive, Zip 87701–4804; tel. 505/426–3500, (Nonreporting) **A**1 10 20 **S** Quorum Health, Brentwood, TN
Primary Contact: Caleb F. O'Rear, Chief Executive Officer
CMO: Nancy Wright, M.D., Chief Medical Staff
CIO: Laird Thornton, Director Information Systems
CHR: Michael Freeman, Director Human Resources
CNO: Rhonda Clark, Interim Chief Nursing Officer
Web address: www.altavistaregionalhospital.com
Control: Corporation, Investor–owned (for–profit) **Service:** General medical and surgical

Staffed Beds: 54

☐ **NEW MEXICO BEHAVIORAL HEALTH INSTITUTE AT LAS VEGAS**, 3695 Hot Springs Boulevard, Zip 87701–9549; tel. 505/454–2100, (Nonreporting) **A**1
Primary Contact: Frances Tweed, R.N., Executive Director and Administrator
COO: Charles Jaramillo, Chief Operating Officer
CFO: Darlene Martinez, Director Finance
CMO: Daniel Collins, M.D., Clinical Director
CNO: Mabel Arguello-Vasquez, R.N., Executive Nurse Administrator
Web address: www.nmbhi.org
Control: State, Government, nonfederal **Service:** Psychiatric

Staffed Beds: 257

LOS ALAMOS—Los Alamos County

✠ **LOS ALAMOS MEDICAL CENTER (320033)**, 3917 West Road, Zip 87544–2293; tel. 505/661–9500, **A**1 10 20 **F**3 8 11 13 15 28 29 31 34 35 40 45 46 47 49 50 57 59 64 65 68 70 73 75 76 78 81 85 87 90 93 107 108 110 111 114 119 123 129 130 146 147 149 **S** LifePoint Health, Brentwood, TN
Primary Contact: John Whiteside, Chief Executive Officer
CFO: Steve Weingart, Chief Financial Officer
CMO: Barbara Van Eeckhout, M.D., Chief of Staff
CIO: Kevin Vigil, Director Information Systems
CHR: Jacqueline Carroll, Director Human Resources
Web address: www.losalamosmedicalcenter.com
Control: Corporation, Investor–owned (for–profit) **Service:** General medical and surgical

Staffed Beds: 29 Admissions: 758 Census: 6 Outpatient Visits: 49644 Births: 175 Total Expense ($000): 40961 Payroll Expense ($000): 12599

LOVINGTON—Lea County

★ ⇑ **NOR-LEA HOSPITAL DISTRICT (321305)**, 1600 North Main Avenue, Zip 88260–2871; tel. 575/396–6611, **A**10 18 21 **F**3 8 9 15 18 26 28 29 30 31 32 34 35 39 40 43 45 46 49 50 54 57 59 64 65 66 68 69 74 75 77 78 81 82 89 92 93 97 100 101 102 104 107 108 110 111 115 119 127 129 130 132 133 135 146 147 148 149 154
Primary Contact: David B. Shaw, Chief Executive Officer and Administrator
COO: Dan Hamilton, Chief Operating Officer
CFO: Allyson Roberts, CPA, Chief Financial Officer
CMO: Ronald Hopkins, D.O., Chief of Staff
CIO: Brent Kelley, Director Information Technology
CHR: Angela Carrejo, Director Human Resources
CNO: Marcia Patterson, MSN, R.N., Chief Nursing Officer
Web address: www.norlea.org/
Control: Hospital district or authority, Government, nonfederal **Service:** General medical and surgical

Staffed Beds: 25 Admissions: 477 Census: 4

MESCALERO—Otero County

☐ **MESCALERO PUBLIC HEALTH SERVICE INDIAN HOSPITAL (320058)**, 318 Abalone Loop, Zip 88340, Mailing Address: Box 210, Zip 88340–0210; tel. 505/464–3801, (Nonreporting) **A**1 10 **S** U. S. Indian Health Service, Rockville, MD
Primary Contact: Dorlynn Simmons, Chief Executive Officer
CFO: Rainey Enjady, Administrative Officer
CIO: Kathy Murphy, Site Manager
Web address: www.ihs.gov
Control: PHS, Indian Service, Government, federal **Service:** General medical and surgical

Staffed Beds: 13

PORTALES—Roosevelt County

⇑ **ROOSEVELT GENERAL HOSPITAL (320084)**, 42121 U S Highway 70, Zip 88130, Mailing Address: P.O. Box 868, Zip 88130–0868; tel. 575/359–1800, (Nonreporting) **A**10 21
Primary Contact: Kaye Green, FACHE, Chief Executive Officer
CFO: Eva Steven, Chief Financial Officer
CMO: Les Donaldson, M.D., Chief of Staff
CHR: Cindy Duncan, Director Human Resources
Web address: www.myrgh.org
Control: Hospital district or authority, Government, nonfederal **Service:** General medical and surgical

Staffed Beds: 22

RATON—Colfax County

△ **MINERS' COLFAX MEDICAL CENTER (321307)**, 200 Hospital Drive, Zip 87740–2099; tel. 575/445–7700, (Includes MINERS' COLFAX MEDICAL CENTER, 203 Hospital Drive, Raton, New Mexico, Zip 87740, Mailing Address: Box 1067, Zip 87740, tel. 575/445–3661; Bo Beames, Chief Executive Officer) **A**10 10 **F**11 13 16 18 34 40 45 46 50 53 54 56 57 58 59 65 70 71 75 77 78 81 82 85 86 87 97 107 115 119 127 129 130 132 133 135 146 147 148 154
Primary Contact: Bo Beames, Interim Chief Executive Officer
CFO: Albino Martinez, Director Budget and Finance
CIO: Richard Laner Jr Manager Information Systems
CHR: Jamie Johnson, Director Human Resources
Web address: www.minershosp.com
Control: State, Government, nonfederal **Service:** General medical and surgical

Staffed Beds: 25 Admissions: 817 Census: 9 Outpatient Visits: 25551 Births: 103 Total Expense ($000): 32879 Payroll Expense ($000): 12479 Personnel: 213

RIO RANCHO—Sandoval County

☐ **UNM SANDOVAL REGIONAL MEDICAL CENTER, INC. (320089)**, 3001 Broadmoor Boulevard NE, Zip 87131; tel. 505/994–7000, **A**1 3 5 18 29 30 34 35 40 45 46 47 48 49 50 57 59 70 74 79 81 87 93 94 97 100 107 108 110 111 114 115 119 126 129 130 131 143 146 148 154 **S** University of New Mexico Hospitals, Albuquerque, NM
Primary Contact: Jamie A. Silva-Steele, FACHE, R.N., President and Chief Executive Officer
CFO: Darlene Fernandez, Chief Financial Officer
CMO: Robb McLean, M.D., Chief Medical Officer
CIO: Matthew Braun, Chief Information Officer
CHR: Correen Bales, Executive Director Human Resources
CNO: Pamela Demarest, MSN, R.N., Chief Nursing Officer
Web address: www.hsc.unm.edu/health/locations/sandoval-regional-medical-center.html
Control: Other not–for–profit (including NFP Corporation) **Service:** General medical and surgical

Staffed Beds: 60 Admissions: 3126 Census: 40 Outpatient Visits: 44048 Births: 0 Total Expense ($000): 87246 Payroll Expense ($000): 33392 Personnel: 473

NM

Hospital, Medicare Provider Number, Address, Telephone, Approval, Facility, and Physician Codes, Health Care System

★ American Hospital Association (AHA) membership
☐ The Joint Commission accreditation
○ Healthcare Facilities Accreditation Program
◇ DNV Healthcare Inc. accreditation
⇑ Center for Improvement in Healthcare Quality Accreditation
△ Commission on Accreditation of Rehabilitation Facilities (CARF) accreditation

ROSWELL—Chaves County

EASTERN NEW MEXICO MEDICAL CENTER (320006), 405 West Country Club Road, Zip 88201–5209; tel. 575/622–8170, (Nonreporting) **A**1 10 19 **S** Community Health Systems, Inc., Franklin, TN
Primary Contact: Warren Yehl, Chief Executive Officer
CFO: Leanne Hacker, Chief Financial Officer
CMO: Richard Pinon, Chief Medical Officer
CIO: Deepak Surl, Chief Information Officer
CHR: Sheila Nunez, Director Human Resources
CNO: Kathy Williams, Chief Nursing Officer
Web address: www.enmmc.com
Control: Corporation, Investor–owned (for–profit) **Service**: General medical and surgical

Staffed Beds: 149

★ **LOVELACE REGIONAL HOSPITAL - ROSWELL (320086)**, 117 East 19th Street, Zip 88201–5151; tel. 575/627–7000, **A**10 **F**3 13 17 18 22 29 34 40 45 57 59 70 76 79 81 82 85 89 90 91 93 111 119 130 146 147 **S** Ardent Health Services, Nashville, TN
Primary Contact: Heather L. Harper, FACHE, Chief Executive Officer
CFO: Veronica Galaviz, Chief Financial Officer
CNO: Rhonda Rauch, Chief Nursing Officer
Web address: www.lovelace.com
Control: Corporation, Investor–owned (for–profit) **Service**: General medical and surgical

Staffed Beds: 26 **Admissions:** 2046 **Census:** 15 **Outpatient Visits:** 31700 **Births:** 795 **Total Expense ($000):** 35785 **Personnel:** 144

NEW MEXICO REHABILITATION CENTER (323026), 72 Gail Harris Street, Zip 88203–8116; tel. 575/347–3400, (Includes PECOS VALLEY LODGE, 31 Gail Harris Avenue, Roswell, New Mexico, Zip 88201; tel. 505/347–5491), (Non-reporting) **A**1 10
Primary Contact: Jose Gurrola, Administrator
CFO: Shirley Donaldson, Chief Financial Officer
CMO: Stephen Dorman, M.D., Chief Medical Officer
CIO: Dennis Hoefs, Manager Information Technology
CHR: Teresa Casarez, Director Human Resources
CNO: William Chaltry, Chief Nursing Officer
Control: State, Government, nonfederal **Service**: Rehabilitation

Staffed Beds: 41

RUIDOSO—Lincoln County

LINCOLN COUNTY MEDICAL CENTER (321306), 211 Sudderth Drive, Zip 88345–6043, Mailing Address: P.O. Box 8000, Zip 88355–8000; tel. 575/257–8200, **A**1 10 18 **F**3 7 11 13 15 18 29 34 35 39 40 45 46 48 50 53 56 57 59 64 65 68 70 76 77 79 81 85 87 91 93 97 107 110 111 115 119 127 130 131 132 135 144 146 148 **S** Presbyterian Healthcare Services, Albuquerque, NM
Primary Contact: Todd Oberheu, Administrator
CFO: Dudley McCauley, Controller
CMO: Gary Jackson, D.O., Medical Director
CHR: Susanne Johnston, Manager Human Resources
Web address: www.phs.org
Control: Other not–for–profit (including NFP Corporation) **Service**: General medical and surgical

Staffed Beds: 25 **Admissions:** 1017 **Census:** 10 **Outpatient Visits:** 47576 **Births:** 262 **Total Expense ($000):** 46824 **Payroll Expense ($000):** 19895 **Personnel:** 249

SANTA FE—Santa Fe County

△ **CHRISTUS ST. VINCENT REGIONAL MEDICAL CENTER (320002)**, 455 Saint Michaels Drive, Zip 87505–7601, Mailing Address: P.O. Box 2107, Zip 87505; tel. 505/983–3361, (Includes CHRISTUS ST. VINCENT PHYSICIANS MEDICAL CENTER, 2990 Rodeo Park Drive East, Santa Fe, New Mexico, Zip 87505; tel. 505/428–5400; J. Alex Valdez, JD, President and Chief Executive Officer) **A**1 2 3 7 10 20 **F**8 12 13 15 17 18 19 20 21 22 24 26 28 29 30 31 32 34 35 36 37 38 39 40 41 43 45 46 47 48 49 50 51 53 54 56 57 64 65 66 68 70 73 74 75 76 77 78 79 81 82 83 84 85 86 87 88 89 90 91 92 93 97 98 100 101 102 104 107 108 109 110 111 112 113 114 115 119 120 121 122 124 126 129 130 131 132 135 143 144 146 147 148 149 150 154 **S** CHRISTUS Health, Irving, TX
Primary Contact: Lillian Montoya, President and Chief Executive Officer
COO: Hope Wade, Chief Operating Officer
CFO: Bob Moon, Chief Financial Officer
CMO: John C Beeson, M.D., Chief Medical Officer
CIO: Ron Dekeyzer, Regional Director Information Systems
CHR: Pearl Mohnkern, Vice President and Director Human Resources
Web address: www.stvin.org
Control: Other not–for–profit (including NFP Corporation) **Service**: General medical and surgical

Staffed Beds: 219 **Admissions:** 11770 **Census:** 141

PHS SANTA FE INDIAN HOSPITAL (320057), 1700 Cerrillos Road, Zip 87505–3554; tel. 505/988–9821, (Nonreporting) **A**1 5 10 **S** U. S. Indian Health Service, Rockville, MD
Primary Contact: Leslie Dye, Chief Executive Officer
CMO: Bret Smoker, M.D., Clinical Director
CIO: Vernita Jones, Site Manager
Control: PHS, Indian Service, Government, federal **Service**: General medical and surgical

Staffed Beds: 4

PRESBYTERIAN SANTA FE MEDICAL CENTER (320090), 4801 Beckner Road, Zip 87507; tel. 505/772–1234, (Nonreporting)
Primary Contact: Helen M. Brooks, Chief Executive Officer
Web address: www.https://santa-fe-medical-center.phs.org/Pages/default.aspx
Control: Corporation, Investor–owned (for–profit) **Service**: General medical and surgical

Staffed Beds: 30

SANTA ROSA—Guadalupe County

★ **GUADALUPE COUNTY HOSPITAL (320067)**, 117 Camino de Vida, Zip 88435–2267; tel. 575/472–3417, **A**10 20 **F**3 29 34 35 40 50 57 59 64 65 81 82 87 107 114 119 148
Primary Contact: Christina Campos, Administrator
CFO: Bret Goebel, Chief Financial Officer
CMO: Randal Brown, M.D., Chief of Medical Staff
CIO: Emilio Campos, Department Head Information Technology
CHR: Colleen Gallegos, Director Human Resources
CNO: Mandelyn Cordova, R.N., Director of Nurses
Web address: www.gchnm.org
Control: County, Government, nonfederal **Service**: General medical and surgical

Staffed Beds: 10 **Admissions:** 192 **Census:** 2 **Outpatient Visits:** 8066 **Births:** 2 **Total Expense ($000):** 10011 **Payroll Expense ($000):** 1987 **Personnel:** 46

SANTA TERESA—Dona Ana County

PEAK BEHAVIORAL HEALTH SERVICES (324012), 5065 McNutt Road, Zip 88008–9442; tel. 575/589–3000, (Nonreporting) **A**10 **S** Strategic Behavioral Health, LLC, Memphis, TN
Primary Contact: Peggy Cunningham, Chief Executive Officer
COO: Doug Ginn, Executive Vice President Operations
CFO: Espie Herrara, Chief Financial Officer
CHR: Norma Oaxaca, Director Human Resources
Web address: www.peakbehavioral.com/
Control: Corporation, Investor–owned (for–profit) **Service**: Psychiatric

Staffed Beds: 120

SHIPROCK—San Juan County

NORTHERN NAVAJO MEDICAL CENTER (320059), Highway 491 North, Zip 87420–0160, Mailing Address: P.O. Box 160, Zip 87420–0160; tel. 505/368–6001, (Nonreporting) **A**1 10 **S** U. S. Indian Health Service, Rockville, MD
Primary Contact: Fannessa Comer, Chief Executive Officer
CFO: Shawn Morgan, Finance Officer
CMO: Ira Salom, M.D., Clinical Director
CIO: Roland Chapman, Chief Information Officer
CHR: Gloria Redhorse-Charley, Director Human Resources
CNO: Lavenia Diswood, R.N., Chief Nurse Executive
Web address: www.ihs.gov/
Control: PHS, Indian Service, Government, federal **Service**: General medical and surgical

Staffed Beds: 68

SILVER CITY—Grant County

GILA REGIONAL MEDICAL CENTER (320016), 1313 East 32nd Street, Zip 88061–7251; tel. 575/538–4000, **A**1 3 10 20 **F**3 7 8 11 13 15 18 29 30 31 35 40 45 50 51 53 64 68 70 75 76 78 79 81 85 87 89 93 98 100 102 103 107 108 110 111 115 119 120 121 123 129 130 132 146 149 157
Primary Contact: Taffy J. Arias, Chief Executive Officer
CFO: Richard W Stokes, CPA, Jr Chief Financial Officer
CIO: David Furnas, Chief Information Officer
CHR: Barbara Barela, Director Human Resources
CNO: Patricia Sheyka, Chief Nursing Officer
Web address: www.grmc.org
Control: County, Government, nonfederal **Service**: General medical and surgical

Staffed Beds: 47 **Admissions:** 1903 **Census:** 17 **Outpatient Visits:** 18050 **Total Expense ($000):** 68942 **Payroll Expense ($000):** 28352

NM

Many Facility Codes have changed. Please refer to the AHA Guide Code Chart. © 2019 AHA Guide

SOCORRO—Socorro County

☒ **SOCORRO GENERAL HOSPITAL (321301)**, 1202 Highway 60 West,
Zip 87801–3914, Mailing Address: P.O. Box 1009, Zip 87801–1009;
tel. 575/835–1140, **A**1 10 18 **F**3 62 63 64 81 107 115 119 130 132 133 134
135 146 147 **S** Presbyterian Healthcare Services, Albuquerque, NM
Primary Contact: Veronica Pound, R.N., Administrator
CFO: Scott Shannon, Director Finance
CMO: Darla Bejnar, M.D., Chief Medical Officer
CHR: Pam Miller-Balfour, Director Human Resources
CNO: Veronica Pound, R.N., Interim Administrator and Director of Patient Care
Web address: www.phs.org
Control: Other not–for–profit (including NFP Corporation) **Service:** General
medical and surgical

Staffed Beds: 24 **Admissions:** 399 **Census:** 5 **Outpatient Visits:** 10900
Births: 107 **Total Expense ($000):** 29525 **Payroll Expense ($000):** 15096
Personnel: 167

TAOS—Taos County

★ ⇑ **HOLY CROSS HOSPITAL (321310)**, 1397 Weimer Road, Zip 87571–6253;
tel. 575/758–8883, **A**3 10 18 21 **F**3 11 13 15 18 29 30 32 34 35 40 45 46 50
59 64 68 75 77 79 80 81 85 86 87 91 93 97 100 102 107 110 114 115 118
119 130 132 133 145 146 147 148 149 156 **S** QHR, Brentwood, TN
Primary Contact: William D. Patten Jr, Chief Executive Officer
CFO: Steve Rozenboom, Chief Financial Officer
CHR: Judy Marshall, Director Human Resources
CNO: Denise Clark, Chief Nursing Officer
Web address: www.taoshospital.com
Control: Other not–for–profit (including NFP Corporation) **Service:** General
medical and surgical

Staffed Beds: 25 **Admissions:** 1514 **Census:** 14 **Outpatient Visits:** 69959
Births: 218 **Total Expense ($000):** 62396 **Payroll Expense ($000):** 26223
Personnel: 357

TRUTH OR CONSEQUENCES—Sierra County

★ **SIERRA VISTA HOSPITAL (321300)**, 800 East Ninth Avenue, Zip 87901–1961;
tel. 575/894–2111, **A**10 18 **F**7 11 15 16 30 34 40 54 57 59 65 67 93 99 102
104 107 110 127 128 130 133 **S** QHR, Brentwood, TN
Primary Contact: David Faulkner, Interim Chief Executive Officer
CFO: Bret Gobel, Chief Financial Officer
CMO: James F Malcolmson, M.D., Chief of Staff
CIO: Dan Morrell, Manager Information Systems
CHR: Mindee Holguin, Manager Human Resources
CNO: Palmer Greene, R.N., Chief Nursing Officer
Web address: www.svhnm.org
Control: City–county, Government, nonfederal **Service:** General medical and
surgical

Staffed Beds: 15 **Admissions:** 372 **Census:** 3

TUCUMCARI—Quay County

★ **DR. DAN C. TRIGG MEMORIAL HOSPITAL (321302)**, 301 East Miel De Luna
Avenue, Zip 88401–3810, Mailing Address: P.O. Box 608, Zip 88401–0608;
tel. 575/461–7000, **A**10 18 **F**11 15 29 35 40 59 62 63 64 65 68 85 87 97
107 110 114 119 130 133 135 146 148 **S** Presbyterian Healthcare Services,
Albuquerque, NM
Primary Contact: Troy Clark, Interim Administrator
CMO: Darrell Willis, M.D., Chief of Staff
CNO: Vickie Gutierrez, Director of Patient Care
Web address: www.phs.org
Control: Other not–for–profit (including NFP Corporation) **Service:** General
medical and surgical

Staffed Beds: 10 **Admissions:** 146 **Census:** 2 **Outpatient Visits:** 14732
Births: 0 **Total Expense ($000):** 15812 **Payroll Expense ($000):** 4869
Personnel: 75

ZUNI—McKinley County

☐ **U. S. PUBLIC HEALTH SERVICE INDIAN HOSPITAL (320060)**, Route 301
North B Street, Zip 87327, Mailing Address: P.O. Box 467, Zip 87327–0467;
tel. 505/782–4431, (Nonreporting) **A**1 10 **S** U. S. Indian Health Service,
Rockville, MD
Primary Contact: Jean Othole, Chief Executive Officer
CFO: Clyde Yatsattie, Administrative Officer
CMO: David Kessler, M.D., Clinical Director
CHR: Cynthia Tsalate, Human Resource Specialist
Web address: www.ihs.gov
Control: PHS, Indian Service, Government, federal **Service:** General medical and
surgical

Staffed Beds: 32

NM

Hospital, Medicare Provider Number, Address, Telephone, Approval, Facility, and Physician Codes, Health Care System

★ American Hospital Association (AHA) membership   ◯ Healthcare Facilities Accreditation Program   ⇑ Center for Improvement in Healthcare Quality Accreditation
☐ The Joint Commission accreditation   ◇ DNV Healthcare Inc. accreditation   △ Commission on Accreditation of Rehabilitation Facilities (CARF) accreditation

NEW YORK

ALBANY—Albany County

☐ **ALBANY MEDICAL CENTER (330013)**, 43 New Scotland Avenue, Zip 12208–3478; tel. 518/262–3125, (Includes ALBANY MEDICAL CENTER SOUTH-CLINICAL CAMPUS, 25 Hackett Boulevard, Albany, New York, Zip 12208–3499; tel. 518/242–1200; Timothy W Duffy, General Director) **A**1 2 3 5 8 10 **F**3 6 7 8 11 12 13 15 17 18 19 20 21 22 23 24 25 26 27 28 29 30 31 32 34 35 38 39 40 41 43 44 45 46 47 49 50 51 52 53 54 55 56 57 58 59 60 61 64 65 68 70 72 73 74 75 76 77 78 79 81 82 84 85 86 87 88 89 90 92 93 96 97 98 100 102 103 104 105 107 108 109 110 111 114 115 116 117 118 119 120 121 122 123 124 126 130 131 132 135 138 142 145 146 148 155 156
Primary Contact: James J. Barba, President and Chief Executive Officer
COO: Bernadette R Pedlow, Senior Vice President Business and Chief Operating Officer
CFO: Frances Spreer-Albert, Chief Financial Officer and Executive Vice President
CMO: Dennis McKenna, M.D., Interim Vice President Medical Affairs
CIO: George Hickman, Executive Vice President and Chief Information Officer
Web address: www.amc.edu
Control: Other not–for–profit (including NFP Corporation) **Service**: General medical and surgical

> **Staffed Beds**: 793 **Admissions**: 40651 **Census**: 616 **Outpatient Visits**: 484105 **Births**: 2000 **Total Expense ($000)**: 1057090 **Payroll Expense ($000)**: 329180 **Personnel**: 6212

★ **ALBANY MEMORIAL HOSPITAL (330003)**, 600 Northern Boulevard, Zip 12204–1083; tel. 518/471–3221, **A**5 10 **F**3 8 11 15 17 18 29 30 34 35 39 40 44 45 50 51 54 57 59 60 63 64 68 70 75 77 79 81 84 85 86 87 93 107 111 119 130 146 147 148 **S** Trinity Health, Livonia, MI
Primary Contact: James K. Reed, M.D., Chief Executive Officer
CFO: Lori Santos, Vice President Finance
CMO: Robert Cella, M.D., Chief Medical Officer
CHR: Judy Gray, Vice President Human Resources
Web address: www.nehealth.com
Control: Other not–for–profit (including NFP Corporation) **Service**: General medical and surgical

> **Staffed Beds**: 74 **Admissions**: 2469 **Census**: 28 **Outpatient Visits**: 147939 **Births**: 0 **Total Expense ($000)**: 90137 **Payroll Expense ($000)**: 35518

⊞ **ALBANY STRATTON VETERANS AFFAIRS MEDICAL CENTER**, 113 Holland Avenue, Zip 12208–3473; tel. 518/626–5000, (Total facility includes 50 beds in nursing home–type unit) **A**1 2 3 5 8 **F**2 3 4 5 15 17 18 20 22 28 29 30 31 33 34 35 38 39 40 44 45 46 47 49 50 54 55 56 57 58 59 60 61 62 63 64 65 68 70 71 74 75 77 78 79 81 82 83 84 85 86 87 91 92 93 94 95 96 97 98 100 101 102 103 104 105 106 107 108 110 111 115 117 118 119 120 121 122 123 126 127 128 129 130 131 132 133 135 143 144 146 147 148 149 150 152 153 154 156 157 158 **S** Department of Veterans Affairs, Washington, DC
Primary Contact: Darlene DeLancey, Interim Director
CFO: Gerard Scorzelli, Chief Financial Officer
CMO: Lourdes Irizarry, M.D., Chief of Staff
CIO: Ron Diaz, Manager Operations
CHR: Kenneth Kio, Manager Human Resources
CNO: Deborah Spath, R.N., MSN, Associate Director Patient and Nurses Services
Web address: www.albany.va.gov/
Control: Veterans Affairs, Government, federal **Service**: General medical and surgical

> **Staffed Beds**: 121 **Admissions**: 3400 **Census**: 97 **Outpatient Visits**: 375000 **Births**: 0

☐ **CAPITAL DISTRICT PSYCHIATRIC CENTER (334046)**, 75 New Scotland Avenue, Zip 12208–3474; tel. 518/549–6000, (Nonreporting) **A**1 3 5 10 **S** New York State Office of Mental Health, Albany, NY
Primary Contact: William Dickson, Executive Director
COO: Catherine McGregor, Deputy Director Facility and Administrative Services
CMO: Kren K Shriver, M.D., Clinical Director
CNO: Charlene Puorto, Chief Nursing Officer
Web address: www.omh.ny.gov/omhweb/facilities/cdpc/facility.htm
Control: State, Government, nonfederal **Service**: Psychiatric

> **Staffed Beds**: 200

⊞ **ST. PETER'S HOSPITAL (330057)**, 315 South Manning Boulevard, Zip 12208–1789; tel. 518/525–1550, **A**1 2 3 5 10 **F**3 4 5 8 11 12 13 15 17 18 19 20 22 24 26 27 28 29 30 31 34 35 36 37 38 39 40 44 45 46 47 48 49 50 51 53 54 55 56 57 59 60 61 63 64 65 66 68 70 71 72 73 74 75 76 77 78 79 80 81 84 85 86 87 89 92 93 97 100 107 108 109 110 111 114 115 116 117 118 119 120 121 123 124 126 129 130 132 133 135 143 145 146 147 148 152 156 **S** Trinity Health, Livonia, MI
Primary Contact: James K. Reed, M.D., Chief Executive Officer
CFO: Lori Santos, Chief Financial Officer
CMO: Robert Cella, M.D., Chief Medical Officer
CHR: Judy Gray, Vice President Human Resources
CNO: Jane O'Rourke, R.N., Chief Nursing Officer, Vice President Operations
Web address: www.sphcs.org
Control: Other not–for–profit (including NFP Corporation) **Service**: General medical and surgical

> **Staffed Beds**: 442 **Admissions**: 26493 **Census**: 358 **Outpatient Visits**: 473227 **Births**: 2806 **Total Expense ($000)**: 569904 **Payroll Expense ($000)**: 201308 **Personnel**: 2999

ALEXANDRIA BAY—Jefferson County

RIVER HOSPITAL (331309), 4 Fuller Street, Zip 13607–1316; tel. 315/482–2511, (Nonreporting) **A**10 18
Primary Contact: Ben Moore III, President and Chief Executive Officer
COO: William Connor, Assistant Administrator and Director Human Resources
CFO: Traci Mintonye, Chief Financial Officer
CMO: Prasad Yitta, M.D., Medical Director
CIO: John Smithers, Network Specialist
CHR: William Connor, Assistant Administrator and Director Human Resources
CNO: Ann Narrow, Director of Nursing
Web address: www.riverhospital.org
Control: Other not–for–profit (including NFP Corporation) **Service**: General medical and surgical

> **Staffed Beds**: 11

AMITYVILLE—Suffolk County

☐ **BRUNSWICK PSYCH CENTER (334026)**, 81 Louden Avenue, Zip 11701–2736; tel. 631/789–7421, (Nonreporting) **A**1 10
Primary Contact: Amarjit Singh, M.D., President and Chief Executive Officer
Control: Corporation, Investor–owned (for–profit) **Service**: Psychiatric

> **Staffed Beds**: 124

⊞ **SOUTH OAKS HOSPITAL (334027)**, 400 Sunrise Highway, Zip 11701–2508; tel. 631/264–4000, **A**1 3 10 **F**4 5 53 68 98 99 101 102 103 104 105 135 153 154 **S** Northwell Health, New Hyde Park, NY
Primary Contact: Carolyn Sweetapple, Ph.D., CPA, R.N., Executive Director
CMO: Tina Walch, M.D., Medical Director
CHR: Irene Calvin, Vice President Human Resources
Web address: www.longislandhome.org
Control: Other not–for–profit (including NFP Corporation) **Service**: Psychiatric

> **Staffed Beds**: 202 **Admissions**: 5190 **Census**: 168 **Outpatient Visits**: 108373 **Births**: 0 **Total Expense ($000)**: 97777 **Payroll Expense ($000)**: 59214 **Personnel**: 805

AMSTERDAM—Montgomery County

⊞ **ST. MARY'S HEALTHCARE (330047)**, 427 Guy Park Avenue, Zip 12010–1054; tel. 518/842–1900, (Includes ST. MARY'S HEALTHCARE, 427 Guy Park Avenue, Amsterdam, New York, Zip 12010–1054; tel. 518/842–1900; Victor Giulianelli, FACHE, President and Chief Executive Officer) (Total facility includes 160 beds in nursing home–type unit) **A**1 10 **F**2 3 4 5 8 11 13 15 17 28 29 30 31 34 35 36 38 40 45 46 49 50 51 54 56 57 59 60 61 65 66 68 70 71 74 75 76 77 78 79 81 83 84 85 86 87 89 90 93 94 96 97 98 99 100 101 102 103 104 107 108 110 111 115 118 119 126 127 128 130 131 132 135 144 145 146 147 149 150 154 156 **S** Ascension Healthcare, Saint Louis, MO
Primary Contact: Victor Giulianelli, FACHE, President and Chief Executive Officer
COO: Scott Bruce, Vice President Operations
CFO: Rick Henze, Chief Financial Officer
CMO: William Mayer, M.D., Vice President Medical Staff Services
CHR: Albert Turo, Vice President Human Resources
CNO: Michele M Walsh, Chief Nursing Officer
Web address: www.smha.org
Control: Other not–for–profit (including NFP Corporation) **Service**: General medical and surgical

> **Staffed Beds**: 290 **Admissions**: 6103 **Census**: 232 **Outpatient Visits**: 437835 **Births**: 469 **Total Expense ($000)**: 174844 **Payroll Expense ($000)**: 88212 **Personnel**: 1453

NY

Many Facility Codes have changed. Please refer to the AHA Guide Code Chart.

ST. MARY'S HEALTHCARE See St. Mary's Healthcare, Amsterdam

AUBURN—Cayuga County

✠ **AUBURN COMMUNITY HOSPITAL (330235)**, 17 Lansing Street, Zip 13021–1943; tel. 315/255–7011, (Total facility includes 80 beds in nursing home–type unit) **A**1 10 20 **F**1 3 8 11 12 13 15 17 18 26 28 29 30 31 34 35 40 44 45 50 51 53 54 55 57 59 60 64 68 70 74 76 77 79 81 82 84 85 86 87 89 92 93 94 97 98 102 104 107 108 110 111 114 115 119 129 130 131 132 135 144 146 147 148 149 152 154 157
Primary Contact: Scott A. Berlucchi, FACHE, President and Chief Executive Officer
CFO: Jason Lesch, Chief Financial Officer
CMO: John A. Riccio, M.D., Chief Medical Officer
CIO: Chris Ryan, Chief Information Officer
CHR: Linda Daly, Vice President Human Resources
CNO: Tammy Sunderlin, Director of Nursing
Web address: www.auburnhospital.org
Control: Other not–for–profit (including NFP Corporation) **Service**: General medical and surgical

Staffed Beds: 179 **Admissions**: 5136 **Census**: 131 **Outpatient Visits**: 154004 **Births**: 362 **Total Expense ($000)**: 138275 **Payroll Expense ($000)**: 67070 **Personnel**: 671

BATAVIA—Genesee County

✠ **UNITED MEMORIAL MEDICAL CENTER (330073)**, 127 North Street, Zip 14020–1631; tel. 585/343–6030, (Includes UNITED MEMORIAL MEDICAL CENTER-BANK STREET, 16 Bank Street, Batavia, New York, Zip 14020–2260; tel. 585/343–6030; UNITED MEMORIAL MEDICAL CENTER-NORTH STREET, 127 North Street, Batavia, New York, Zip 14020–1697; tel. 585/343–6030) **A**1 3 10 13 **F**3 4 8 13 15 17 18 28 29 30 31 34 35 40 49 50 54 57 59 64 65 68 70 75 76 77 78 79 81 82 84 85 86 87 89 93 97 107 111 114 115 119 120 121 122 127 129 130 131 132 135 144 146 147 148 149 154 156 157 **S** Rochester Regional Health, Rochester, NY
Primary Contact: Daniel P. Ireland, FACHE, President
CFO: Robert Chiavetta, Vice President Finance
CMO: Tara L Gellasch, Chief Medical Officer
CIO: Chad Caccamise, Director Information Services
CHR: Eileen Herkimer, Director Human Resources
CNO: Marilyn Almeter, Chief Nursing Officer
Web address: www.ummc.org
Control: Other not–for–profit (including NFP Corporation) **Service**: General medical and surgical

Staffed Beds: 133 **Admissions**: 4364 **Census**: 51 **Outpatient Visits**: 243187 **Births**: 523 **Total Expense ($000)**: 103600 **Payroll Expense ($000)**: 44730 **Personnel**: 726

★ **VETERANS AFFAIRS WESTERN NEW YORK HEALTHCARE SYSTEM-BATAVIA DIVISION**, 222 Richmond Avenue, Zip 14020–1288; tel. 585/297–1000, (Nonreporting) **S** Department of Veterans Affairs, Washington, DC
Primary Contact: Michael J. Swartz, FACHE, Interim Director
Web address: www.buffalo.va.gov/batavia.asp
Control: Veterans Affairs, Government, federal **Service**: General medical and surgical

Staffed Beds: 128

BATH—Steuben County

✠ **BATH VETERANS AFFAIRS MEDICAL CENTER**, 76 Veterans Avenue, Zip 14810–0842; tel. 607/664–4000, (Total facility includes 94 beds in nursing home–type unit) **A**1 **F**3 4 5 7 11 12 18 29 30 33 34 35 36 38 39 44 50 53 54 56 57 59 61 62 63 64 65 66 68 71 74 75 77 79 82 83 84 86 87 90 91 93 94 97 100 101 103 104 107 119 127 128 130 132 133 135 143 144 146 147 148 149 154 156 157 158 **S** Department of Veterans Affairs, Washington, DC
Primary Contact: Kenneth P. Piazza, Medical Center Director
CFO: Jill Haynes, Financial Coach
CMO: Robert Babcock, M.D., Interim Chief of Staff
CHR: Susan DeSalvo, Manager Human Resources
Web address: www.bath.va.gov
Control: Veterans Affairs, Government, federal **Service**: General medical and surgical

Staffed Beds: 274 **Admissions**: 1255 **Census**: 213 **Outpatient Visits**: 164320 **Births**: 0 **Total Expense ($000)**: 116201 **Payroll Expense ($000)**: 67424 **Personnel**: 708

IRA DAVENPORT MEMORIAL HOSPITAL (330144), 7571 State Route 54, Zip 14810–9590; tel. 607/776–8500, (Total facility includes 120 beds in nursing home–type unit) **A**10 **F**2 11 29 40 45 81 93 107 111 119 128 130 133 146 154 **S** Arnot Health, Elmira, NY
Primary Contact: Elizabeth Weir, MSN, R.N., Site Administrator and Vice President of Nursing
CFO: Ronald J Kintz, Chief Financial Officer
CMO: Dennis O'Connor, M.D., Medical Director
CIO: Gregg Martin, Chief Information Officer
CHR: Dave Stanbro, Director Human Resources
CNO: Linda Donley, Vice President Operations
Web address: www.arnothealth.org
Control: Other not–for–profit (including NFP Corporation) **Service**: General medical and surgical

Staffed Beds: 135 **Admissions**: 555 **Census**: 101 **Outpatient Visits**: 43545 **Total Expense ($000)**: 25003 **Payroll Expense ($000)**: 10079 **Personnel**: 222

BAY SHORE—Suffolk County

✠ △ **SOUTHSIDE HOSPITAL (330043)**, 301 East Main Street, Zip 11706–8458; tel. 631/968–3000, **A**1 2 3 5 7 10 **F**3 5 8 11 13 15 17 18 20 22 24 26 28 29 30 31 32 34 35 36 38 40 41 43 44 45 46 49 50 51 54 56 57 58 59 60 61 62 63 64 65 66 68 70 73 74 75 76 77 78 79 80 81 82 84 85 86 87 89 92 93 95 96 97 100 101 102 107 108 111 115 119 126 129 130 131 132 135 145 146 147 148 149 152 154 157 **S** Northwell Health, New Hyde Park, NY
Primary Contact: Donna Moravick, R.N., MSN, Executive Director
CFO: Michele Cusack, Senior Vice President and Chief Financial Officer
CMO: Jay Enden, M.D., Medical Director
CHR: Anne J Barrett, Associate Executive Director Human Resources
Web address: www.https://www.northwell.edu/find-care/locations/southside-hospital
Control: Other not–for–profit (including NFP Corporation) **Service**: General medical and surgical

Staffed Beds: 278 **Admissions**: 21739 **Census**: 264 **Outpatient Visits**: 149346 **Births**: 2551 **Total Expense ($000)**: 648591 **Payroll Expense ($000)**: 324489 **Personnel**: 3017

BETHPAGE—Nassau County

☐ **ST. JOSEPH HOSPITAL (330332)**, 4295 Hempstead Turnpike, Zip 11714–5769; tel. 516/579–6000, **A**1 10 **F**3 8 15 18 29 30 31 34 35 39 40 45 46 47 49 50 51 56 57 59 60 64 65 68 70 74 75 78 79 80 81 82 84 85 86 87 93 107 108 110 111 114 115 119 129 130 131 132 141 146 148 149 154 156 **S** Catholic Health Services of Long Island, Rockville Centre, NY
Primary Contact: Peter Scaminaci, President
CFO: John Moranon, Vice President Finance
CMO: Howard Sussman, M.D., Chief Medical Officer
CHR: Peter Chiacchiaro, Vice President Human Resources
CNO: Barbara Gibbons, Vice President Patient Care Services
Web address: www.stjosephhospital.chsli.org/
Control: Church operated, Nongovernment, not–for–profit **Service**: General medical and surgical

Staffed Beds: 128 **Admissions**: 6135 **Census**: 81 **Outpatient Visits**: 44249 **Births**: 0 **Total Expense ($000)**: 129716 **Payroll Expense ($000)**: 50728 **Personnel**: 676

BINGHAMTON—Broome County

BINGHAMTON GENERAL HOSPITAL See United Health Services Hospitals-Binghamton, Binghamton

☐ **GREATER BINGHAMTON HEALTH CENTER (334012)**, 425 Robinson Street, Zip 13904–1735; tel. 607/724–1391, **A**1 3 10 **F**29 30 50 54 59 65 66 68 86 98 99 100 101 103 104 106 130 132 135 143 146 149 153 **S** New York State Office of Mental Health, Albany, NY
Primary Contact: David Peppel, Executive Director
CFO: Cherry Randall, Business Officer
CHR: Renee O'Brien, Director Human Resources
Web address: www.omh.ny.gov/omhweb/facilities/bipc/facility.htm
Control: State, Government, nonfederal **Service**: Psychiatric

Staffed Beds: 86 **Admissions**: 309 **Census**: 83 **Outpatient Visits**: 39030 **Births**: 0 **Total Expense ($000)**: 56431 **Payroll Expense ($000)**: 26185 **Personnel**: 393

NY

Hospital, Medicare Provider Number, Address, Telephone, Approval, Facility, and Physician Codes, Health Care System

★ American Hospital Association (AHA) membership
☐ The Joint Commission accreditation
○ Healthcare Facilities Accreditation Program
◇ DNV Healthcare Inc. accreditation
⇧ Center for Improvement in Healthcare Quality Accreditation
△ Commission on Accreditation of Rehabilitation Facilities (CARF) accreditation

✉ **OUR LADY OF LOURDES MEMORIAL HOSPITAL, INC. (330011)**, 169 Riverside Drive, Zip 13905–4246; tel. 607/798–5111, **A**1 2 3 10 13 19 **F**3 11 12 13 15 18 19 28 29 30 31 32 33 34 35 36 39 40 44 45 46 47 49 50 51 53 54 56 57 59 60 62 63 64 65 66 68 70 71 74 75 76 77 78 79 81 84 87 89 93 97 100 101 104 107 108 110 111 114 115 118 119 120 121 123 124 126 127 129 130 131 132 134 135 143 144 145 146 147 148 149 154 156 157 **S** Ascension Healthcare, Saint Louis, MO
Primary Contact: Kathryn Connerton, President and Chief Executive Officer
CFO: Sean Mills, Chief Financial Officer
CMO: Richard Blansky, M.D., Chief Medical Officer
CIO: Thomas Ellerson, Chief Information Officer
CHR: Mary Hughs, Chief Human Resources Officer
Web address: www.lourdes.com
Control: Church operated, Nongovernment, not–for–profit **Service**: General medical and surgical

Staffed Beds: 154 **Admissions**: 9577 **Census**: 100 **Outpatient Visits**: 1602837 **Births**: 858 **Total Expense ($000)**: 367512 **Payroll Expense ($000)**: 154723 **Personnel**: 2115

UNITED HEALTH SERVICES HOSPITALS-BINGHAMTON (330394), 10–42 Mitchell Avenue, Zip 13903–1678; tel. 607/763–6000, (Includes BINGHAMTON GENERAL HOSPITAL, 10–42 Mitchell Avenue, Binghamton, New York, Zip 13903; tel. 607/762–2200; John M. Carrigg, President and Chief Executive Officer; WILSON MEMORIAL REGIONAL MEDICAL CENTER, 33–57 Harrison Street, Johnson City, New York, Zip 13790; tel. 607/763–6000; John M. Carrigg, President and Chief Executive Officer) **A**8 10 **F**1 3 4 5 8 11 12 13 15 17 18 20 22 24 26 28 29 30 31 32 33 34 35 38 39 40 43 45 46 47 48 49 50 51 54 56 57 58 59 61 64 65 68 70 72 74 75 76 77 78 79 81 82 84 85 86 87 89 90 92 93 96 97 98 100 101 102 103 104 106 107 108 110 114 115 118 119 120 121 123 124 127 129 130 131 132 135 144 145 146 147 148 149 154 156 **S** United Health Services, Binghamton, NY
Primary Contact: John M. Carrigg, President and Chief Executive Officer
COO: John M. Carrigg, Executive Vice President and Chief Operating Officer
CFO: David MacDougall, Chief Financial Officer
CMO: Rajesh J Dave', M.D., Executive Vice President and Chief Medical Officer
CIO: Susan Carman, Chief Information Officer
CNO: E. Kay Boland, R.N., MS, Vice President and Chief Nursing Officer
Web address: www.uhs.net
Control: Other not–for–profit (including NFP Corporation) **Service**: General medical and surgical

Staffed Beds: 464 **Admissions**: 18010 **Census**: 296 **Outpatient Visits**: 1137268 **Births**: 1369 **Total Expense ($000)**: 676570 **Payroll Expense ($000)**: 243047 **Personnel**: 4342

BRENTWOOD—Suffolk County

☐ **PILGRIM PSYCHIATRIC CENTER (334013)**, 998 Crooked Hill Road, Zip 11717–1019; tel. 631/761–3500, (Nonreporting) **A**1 5 10 **S** New York State Office of Mental Health, Albany, NY
Primary Contact: Kathy O'Keefe, Executive Director
Web address: www.omh.ny.gov/omhweb/facilities/pgpc/facility.htm
Control: State, Government, nonfederal **Service**: Psychiatric

Staffed Beds: 569

BRONX—Bronx County, See New York City

BROOKLYN—Kings County, See New York City

BUFFALO—Erie County

BRYLIN HOSPITALS (334022), 1263 Delaware Avenue, Zip 14209–2402; tel. 716/886–8200, (Nonreporting) **A**10
Primary Contact: Eric D. Pleskow, President and Chief Executive Officer
CFO: E Paul Hettich, Chief Financial Officer
CMO: Maria Cartagena, M.D., Chief Medical Officer
CIO: Pawel Wieczorek, Director Information Technology
CHR: Pamela Nicastro, Director Human Resources
Web address: www.brylin.com
Control: Corporation, Investor–owned (for–profit) **Service**: Psychiatric

Staffed Beds: 88

☐ **BUFFALO PSYCHIATRIC CENTER (334052)**, 400 Forest Avenue, Zip 14213–1298; tel. 716/885–2261, (Nonreporting) **A**1 3 5 10 **S** New York State Office of Mental Health, Albany, NY
Primary Contact: Beatrix Souza, Chief Executive Officer
COO: Celia Spacone, M.D., Director Operations
CFO: Pamela Esposito, Director Administration
CMO: Jeffery Grace, M.D., Clinical Director
CIO: Anne Buchheit, Coordinator Mental Health Local Information Systems
CHR: Charles Siewert, Director Human Resources
CNO: Susan Fallis, Chief Nursing Officer
Web address: www.omh.ny.gov
Control: State, Government, nonfederal **Service**: Psychiatric

Staffed Beds: 240

✉ △ **ERIE COUNTY MEDICAL CENTER (330219)**, 462 Grider Street, Zip 14215–3098; tel. 716/898–3000, (Total facility includes 390 beds in nursing home–type unit) **A**1 3 5 7 10 **F**3 4 5 12 16 18 20 29 30 31 33 34 35 38 39 40 43 45 49 50 51 53 54 56 57 58 59 60 61 65 66 70 71 74 75 77 78 79 81 82 83 84 85 87 90 91 93 94 96 97 98 99 100 101 102 103 104 105 107 111 115 119 128 130 131 132 135 138 146 148 149
Primary Contact: Thomas J. Quatroche Jr, President and Chief Executive Officer
COO: Andrew L Davis Jr Chief Operating Officer
CFO: Michael Sammarco, M.D., Chief Financial Officer
CMO: Brian Murray, M.D., Medical Director
CIO: Leslie Feidt, Chief Information Officer
CHR: Kathleen O'Hara, Vice President Human Resources
CNO: Karen Ziemianski, R.N., MS, Senior Vice President Nursing
Web address: www.ecmc.edu
Control: Hospital district or authority, Government, nonfederal **Service**: General medical and surgical

Staffed Beds: 912 **Admissions**: 21347 **Census**: 814 **Outpatient Visits**: 321661 **Births**: 0 **Total Expense ($000)**: 657195 **Payroll Expense ($000)**: 239957 **Personnel**: 3482

⇈ **KALEIDA HEALTH (330005)**, 100 High Street, Zip 14203–1154; tel. 716/859–5600, (Includes DE GRAFF MEMORIAL HOSPITAL, 445 Tremont Street, North Tonawanda, New York, Zip 14120–0750, Mailing Address: P O Box 0750, Zip 14120–0750, tel. 716/694–4500; Darcy Craven, President; MILLARD FILLMORE SUBURBAN HOSPITAL, 1540 Maple Road, Williamsville, New York, Zip 14221; tel. 716/688–3100; Darcy Craven, President; WOMEN AND CHILDREN'S HOSPITAL, 219 Bryant Street, Buffalo, New York, Zip 14222–2099; tel. 716/878–7000; Cheryl Klass, President) (Total facility includes 380 beds in nursing home–type unit) **A**3 5 10 21 **F**1 2 3 6 8 9 11 12 13 15 17 18 19 20 21 22 24 26 27 28 29 30 31 32 34 35 36 37 38 39 40 41 43 44 45 46 47 48 49 50 51 54 55 56 57 58 59 60 61 62 63 64 65 66 67 68 70 71 72 73 74 75 76 77 78 79 80 81 82 83 84 85 86 87 88 89 90 91 92 93 94 96 97 99 100 101 102 103 104 107 108 109 110 111 114 115 118 119 120 124 126 128 130 131 132 134 135 136 143 146 147 148 154 156
Primary Contact: Jody Lomeo, Chief Executive Officer
COO: Donald Boyd, Executive Vice President and Chief Operating Officer
CFO: Joseph Kessler, Executive Vice President and Chief Financial Officer
CMO: Margaret Paroski, M.D., Executive Vice President and Chief Medical Officer
CIO: Francis Meyer, Vice President Information Systems Technology
Web address: www.kaleidahealth.org
Control: Other not–for–profit (including NFP Corporation) **Service**: General medical and surgical

Staffed Beds: 1409 **Admissions**: 56390 **Census**: 733 **Outpatient Visits**: 305796 **Births**: 5774 **Total Expense ($000)**: 1440486 **Payroll Expense ($000)**: 601863 **Personnel**: 8061

✉ **MERCY HOSPITAL (330279)**, 565 Abbott Road, Zip 14220–2095; tel. 716/826–7000, (Total facility includes 84 beds in nursing home–type unit) **A**1 3 5 10 **F**3 13 15 17 18 19 20 22 26 28 29 30 34 31 40 41 42 44 45 46 48 49 50 53 54 56 57 58 59 60 63 64 65 66 68 70 72 74 75 76 77 79 81 84 85 87 90 92 93 95 97 100 107 108 110 111 114 115 118 119 124 126 128 129 130 131 132 141 146 147 148 149 154 156 **S** Catholic Health System, Buffalo, NY
Primary Contact: Charles J. Urlaub, President and Chief Executive Officer
COO: Eddie Bratko, Chief Operating Officer
CFO: James H Dunlop, CPA, Jr Senior Vice President Finance and Chief Financial Officer
CMO: Timothy Gabryel, M.D., Vice President Medical Affairs and Medical Director
CIO: Michael Galang, M.D., Chief Information Officer
CHR: Joseph A Scrivo Jr Director Human Resources
CNO: Shari McDonald, Vice President Patient Care Services
Web address: www.chsbuffalo.org
Control: Church operated, Nongovernment, not–for–profit **Service**: General medical and surgical

Staffed Beds: 436 **Admissions**: 19423 **Census**: 342 **Outpatient Visits**: 289023 **Births**: 2121 **Total Expense ($000)**: 427505 **Payroll Expense ($000)**: 180778 **Personnel**: 2177

☐ **ROSWELL PARK COMPREHENSIVE CANCER CENTER (330354)**, Elm and Carlton Streets, Zip 14263–0001; tel. 716/845–2300, **A**1 2 3 5 10 **F**3 14 15 29 30 31 32 34 35 36 38 39 44 45 46 47 49 50 54 55 57 58 59 63 64 65 66 67 70 74 75 77 78 79 80 81 82 84 85 86 87 89 90 92 93 94 96 98 100 104 107 108 110 111 112 114 115 116 117 118 119 120 121 123 124 126 130 132 134 135 136 141 145 146 147 148 149
Primary Contact: Candace Johnson, Ph.D., President and Chief Executive Officer
COO: Victor A Filadora, M.D., MS, II Chief Clinical Services
CFO: Gregory McDonald, Vice President Finance and Chief Financial Officer
CMO: Boris Kuvshinoff, M.D., II Chief Medical Officer
CIO: Kerry Kerlin, Chief Information Officer
CHR: Errol A. Douglas, MS, Vice President, Human Resources
CNO: Shirley Johnson, MS, R.N., Senior Vice President Nursing and Patient Care Services, Chief Nursing Officer
Web address: www.roswellpark.org
Control: Hospital district or authority, Government, nonfederal **Service**: Cancer

Staffed Beds: 133 **Admissions**: 5068 **Census**: 105 **Outpatient Visits**: 248798 **Births**: 0 **Total Expense ($000)**: 656546 **Payroll Expense ($000)**: 216773 **Personnel**: 3167

NY

Many Facility Codes have changed. Please refer to the AHA Guide Code Chart. © 2019 AHA Guide

☒ **SISTERS OF CHARITY HOSPITAL OF BUFFALO (330078)**, 2157 Main Street, Zip 14214–2692; tel. 716/862–1000, (Includes ELIZABETH SETON PEDIATRIC CENTER, 300 Corporate Boulevard South, Yonkers, New York, Zip 10701–6862; tel. 914/294–6300; ST. JOSEPH HOSPITAL, 2605 Harlem Road, Cheektowaga, New York, Zip 14225–4097; tel. 716/891–2400) (Total facility includes 80 beds in nursing home–type unit) **A**1 2 3 5 10 12 **F**2 3 5 11 12 13 15 18 19 28 29 30 31 32 34 35 36 37 38 40 41 44 45 46 47 49 50 53 54 55 57 58 59 60 64 65 66 68 70 72 73 74 75 76 77 78 79 81 82 84 85 87 92 93 97 100 107 108 110 111 114 115 118 119 126 128 129 130 131 132 141 146 147 148 149 154 156 **S** Catholic Health System, Buffalo, NY
Primary Contact: Martin Boryszak, President and Chief Executive Officer
COO: John Sperrazza, Chief Operating Officer
CFO: James H Dunlop, CPA, Jr Chief Financial Officer
CMO: Nady Shehata, M.D., Vice President Medical Affairs
CIO: Michael Galang, M.D., Chief Information Officer
CHR: David DeLorenzo, Senior Director Human Resources
CNO: Mary E Dillon, MS, R.N., Vice President Patient Care Services
Web address: www.chsbuffalo.org
Control: Church operated, Nongovernment, not–for–profit **Service**: General medical and surgical

Staffed Beds: 388 **Admissions**: 15261 **Census**: 275 **Outpatient Visits**: 776880 **Births**: 3425 **Total Expense ($000)**: 335677 **Payroll Expense ($000)**: 152257 **Personnel**: 1922

☒ **VETERANS AFFAIRS WESTERN NEW YORK HEALTHCARE SYSTEM–BUFFALO DIVISION**, 3495 Bailey Avenue, Zip 14215–1129; tel. 716/834–9200, (Nonreporting) **A**1 3 5 **S** Department of Veterans Affairs, Washington, DC
Primary Contact: Brian G. Stiller, Director Medical Center
CFO: Susan Gage, Financial Manager
CMO: Ali El-Solh, M.D., Interim Chief of Staff
CIO: Margaret Senker, Chief Information Officer
Web address: www.buffalo.va.gov/index.asp
Control: Veterans Affairs, Government, federal **Service**: General medical and surgical

Staffed Beds: 113

WOMEN AND CHILDREN'S HOSPITAL See Kaleida Health, Buffalo

CALLICOON—Sullivan County

★ ⇑ **GROVER M. HERMANN HOSPITAL (331303)**, 8881 Route 97, Zip 12723; tel. 845/887–5530, **A**10 19 21 **F**3 11 15 29 30 34 35 40 50 57 59 64 75 85 93 97 107 130 132 133 146 149 **S** Greater Hudson Valley Health System, Middletown, NY
Primary Contact: Rolland Bojo, R.N., Administrator
Web address: www.crmcny.org
Control: Other not–for–profit (including NFP Corporation) **Service**: General medical and surgical

Staffed Beds: 15 **Admissions**: 104 **Census**: 3 **Outpatient Visits**: 9335 **Births**: 0 **Total Expense ($000)**: 5813 **Payroll Expense ($000)**: 2761 **Personnel**: 29

CANANDAIGUA—Ontario County

★ **CANANDAIGUA VETERANS AFFAIRS MEDICAL CENTER**, 400 Fort Hill Avenue, Zip 14424–1159; tel. 585/394–2000, (Total facility includes 116 beds in nursing home–type unit) **A**3 5 **F**2 4 5 7 21 29 30 33 34 35 38 39 42 53 54 56 57 58 59 62 63 64 65 66 68 74 75 77 79 82 84 86 87 91 93 94 97 100 104 128 130 132 135 143 146 147 148 149 153 154 156 157 **S** Department of Veterans Affairs, Washington, DC
Primary Contact: Bruce Tucker, Acting Director
CIO: Bob Corrado, Chief Information Officer
Web address: www.canandaigua.va.gov/
Control: Veterans Affairs, Government, federal **Service**: Psychiatric

Staffed Beds: 164 **Admissions**: 419 **Census**: 120 **Outpatient Visits**: 239286 **Births**: 0 **Total Expense ($000)**: 137012 **Payroll Expense ($000)**: 82200 **Personnel**: 1046

☒ **F. F. THOMPSON HOSPITAL (330074)**, 350 Parrish Street, Zip 14424–1731; tel. 585/396–6000, (Total facility includes 178 beds in nursing home–type unit) **A**1 3 5 10 **F**3 8 11 13 15 17 18 28 29 30 32 33 34 35 38 40 43 44 45 46 49 50 51 54 56 57 59 60 64 68 70 75 76 77 79 81 84 85 86 87 89 91 93 95 96 97 107 108 110 111 115 118 119 125 126 128 129 130 131 132 135 144 145 146 147 148 149 154 **S** University of Rochester Medical Center, Rochester, NY
Primary Contact: Michael Stapleton, President and Chief Executive Officer
COO: Kurt Koczent, Executive Vice President and Chief Operating Officer
CFO: Mark Prunoske, Chief Financial Officer and Senior Vice President Finance
CMO: David Baum, M.D., Senior Vice President Medical Services
CHR: Jennifer DeVault, Vice President Associate Services
CNO: Hazel Robertshaw, R.N., Ph.D., Chief Nursing Officer, Vice President Patient Services
Web address: www.thompsonhealth.com
Control: Other not–for–profit (including NFP Corporation) **Service**: General medical and surgical

Staffed Beds: 291 **Admissions**: 5430 **Census**: 228 **Outpatient Visits**: 343974 **Total Expense ($000)**: 162151 **Payroll Expense ($000)**: 76962 **Personnel**: 1525

THOMPSON HEALTH See F. F. Thompson Hospital

CARMEL—Putnam County

ARMS ACRES, 75 Seminary Hill Road, Zip 10512–1921; tel. 845/225–3400, **F**4 5 34 35 39 54 68 75 86 87 100 101 133 135
Primary Contact: Patrice Wallace-Moore, Chief Executive Officer and Executive Director
CFO: Jason Burczeuski, Controller
CMO: Fred Hesse, M.D., Medical Director
CIO: Dolores Watson, Director Health Information Management
CHR: Kim Halpin, Director Human Resources
CNO: Barbara Klein, R.N., Director of Nursing
Web address: www.armsacres.com
Control: State, Government, nonfederal **Service**: Alcoholism and other chemical dependency

Staffed Beds: 191 **Admissions**: 5714 **Census**: 208 **Outpatient Visits**: 7493 **Births**: 0 **Personnel**: 324

☐ **PUTNAM HOSPITAL CENTER (330273)**, 670 Stoneleigh Avenue, Zip 10512–3997; tel. 845/279–5711, **A**1 2 3 10 **F**3 7 8 11 12 18 28 29 30 31 34 35 36 37 38 40 45 46 49 51 54 55 56 57 58 59 64 65 68 70 74 75 76 77 78 79 81 82 83 84 85 87 89 91 92 93 94 98 100 101 102 104 105 107 108 110 111 114 118 119 120 121 126 129 130 131 132 135 146 147 148 149 154 156 157 **S** Health Quest Systems, Inc., LaGrangeville, NY
Primary Contact: Peter Kelly, President
CFO: Joseph Hart, Director Finance and Support Services
CNO: Luanne Convery, Vice President Patient Care Services
Web address: www.healthquest.org/carmel/putnam-hospital-center.aspx
Control: Other not–for–profit (including NFP Corporation) **Service**: General medical and surgical

Staffed Beds: 140 **Admissions**: 5566 **Census**: 53 **Outpatient Visits**: 120542 **Births**: 389 **Total Expense ($000)**: 155300 **Payroll Expense ($000)**: 52811 **Personnel**: 660

CARTHAGE—Jefferson County

☒ **CARTHAGE AREA HOSPITAL (331318)**, 1001 West Street, Zip 13619–9703; tel. 315/493–1000, (Nonreporting) **A**1 10 18
Primary Contact: Richard Duvall, Chief Executive Officer
CFO: Rob Bloom, Chief Financial Officer
CMO: Mirza Ashraf, M.D., Medical Director
CIO: Joe Virkler, Chief Information Officer
CHR: Cathy Siedlecki, Director Human Resources
CNO: Susan Kellogg, Administrator Patient Care Services
Web address: www.carthagehospital.com
Control: Other not–for–profit (including NFP Corporation) **Service**: General medical and surgical

Staffed Beds: 55

NY

CLIFTON SPRINGS—Ontario County

★ ⋔ **CLIFTON SPRINGS HOSPITAL AND CLINIC (330265)**, 2 Coulter Road, Zip 14432–1189; tel. 315/462–9561, (Total facility includes 108 beds in nursing home–type unit) **A**10 21 **F**3 4 5 11 15 28 29 30 31 32 34 35 36 38 39 40 44 45 48 49 50 51 54 56 57 59 60 64 68 70 71 75 77 78 79 81 82 85 87 90 93 96 97 98 99 100 101 102 103 104 107 108 110 111 114 117 118 119 120 121 123 128 130 132 141 146 147 148 149 150 151 154 156 **S** Rochester Regional Health, Rochester, NY
Primary Contact: Dustin Riccio, M.D., President
CFO: Sharon Kelley, Chief Financial Officer
CIO: Joel Majauskas, Chief Information Officer
CHR: Kathy Babb, Manager Human Resources
CNO: Donna P Smith, R.N., Vice President Chief Operating Officer and Chief Nursing Officer
Web address: www.cliftonspringshospital.org
Control: Other not–for–profit (including NFP Corporation) **Service:** General medical and surgical

Staffed Beds: 179 **Admissions:** 2652 **Census:** 153 **Outpatient Visits:** 120577 **Births:** 0 **Total Expense ($000):** 66897 **Payroll Expense ($000):** 35548 **Personnel:** 522

COBLESKILL—Schoharie County

⊞ **COBLESKILL REGIONAL HOSPITAL (331320)**, 178 Grandview Drive, Zip 12043–5144; tel. 518/254–3456, (Nonreporting) **A**1 10 20 **S** Bassett Healthcare Network, Cooperstown, NY
Primary Contact: Eric H. Stein, FACHE, President
CFO: James Vielkind, Chief Financial Officer
CMO: Roy Korn, M.D., Medical Director
CIO: Bridgette West, Director Patient Access Services
CNO: Susan Oakes Ferrucci, MS, Vice President Patient Services and Chief Nursing Officer
Web address: www.bassett.org
Control: Other not–for–profit (including NFP Corporation) **Service:** General medical and surgical

Staffed Beds: 40

COOPERSTOWN—Otsego County

⊞ **BASSETT MEDICAL CENTER (330136)**, One Atwell Road, Zip 13326–1394; tel. 607/547–3456, (Nonreporting) **A**1 2 3 5 8 10 **S** Bassett Healthcare Network, Cooperstown, NY
Primary Contact: William W. LeCates, M.D., President
COO: Ronette Wiley, R.N., Executive Vice President and Chief Operating Officer
CFO: Michael A. Tengeres, Corporate Vice President and Chief Financial Officer
CMO: William W LeCates, M.D., Vice President Medical Affairs and Medical Director
CHR: Sara Z Albright, Vice President Human Resources
CNO: Judi Brendle, Vice President Clinical Support and Chief Nursing Officer
Web address: www.bassett.org
Control: Other not–for–profit (including NFP Corporation) **Service:** General medical and surgical

Staffed Beds: 152

CORNING—Steuben County

⊞ **GUTHRIE CORNING HOSPITAL (330277)**, One Guthrie Drive, Zip 14830–3696; tel. 607/937–7200, **A**1 3 10 **F**8 11 13 15 18 20 22 24 26 28 29 30 31 34 37 38 40 45 46 47 48 49 50 51 53 57 59 64 68 70 76 77 78 79 81 85 86 87 91 93 107 108 110 111 112 114 115 116 117 118 119 120 121 123 126 129 130 131 146 148 156 **S** Guthrie Clinic, Sayre, PA
Primary Contact: Garrett W. Hoover, FACHE, President
CFO: Francis M Macafee, Vice President Finance and Chief Financial Officer
CMO: Chris Wentzel, M.D., Interim Medical Director
CHR: Laura Manning, Administrative Director
CNO: Deb Raupers, MSN, R.N., Chief Nursing Officer
Web address: www.corninghospital.com
Control: Other not–for–profit (including NFP Corporation) **Service:** General medical and surgical

Staffed Beds: 65 **Admissions:** 4470 **Census:** 39 **Outpatient Visits:** 118598 **Births:** 560 **Total Expense ($000):** 105687 **Payroll Expense ($000):** 30724 **Personnel:** 652

CORNWALL—Orange County

ST. LUKE'S CORNWALL HOSPITAL - CORNWALL CAMPUS See Montefiore St. Luke's Cornwall, Newburgh

CORTLAND—Cortland County

⊞ **CORTLAND REGIONAL MEDICAL CENTER (330175)**, 134 Homer Avenue, Zip 13045–1206; tel. 607/756–3500, (Total facility includes 82 beds in nursing home–type unit) **A**1 10 20 **F**2 3 8 11 13 15 18 28 29 30 31 34 35 38 40 44 45 49 50 51 54 56 57 59 62 64 70 75 76 77 78 79 81 85 86 87 91 93 96 98 100 102 103 107 108 110 111 118 119 128 130 131 132 133 135 146 147 148 149 150 154 156
Primary Contact: Mark Webster, President and Chief Executive Officer
COO: Tracy Gates, Vice President Operations and Chief Operating Officer
CFO: Denise Wrinn, Vice President Finance and Chief Financial Officer
CMO: Russell Firman, M.D., Chief Medical Officer
CIO: Robert J Duthe, Director Information Systems and Chief Information Officer
CNO: Mary Wright, Vice President Nursing Services and Chief Nursing Officer
Web address: www.cortlandregional.org
Control: Other not–for–profit (including NFP Corporation) **Service:** General medical and surgical

Staffed Beds: 149 **Admissions:** 4040 **Census:** 114 **Outpatient Visits:** 116839 **Births:** 383 **Total Expense ($000):** 92163 **Payroll Expense ($000):** 39770 **Personnel:** 715

CORTLANDT MANOR—Westchester County

⊞ **NEW YORK-PRESBYTERIAN/HUDSON VALLEY HOSPITAL (330267)**, 1980 Crompond Road, Zip 10567–4182; tel. 914/737–9000, **A**1 10 **F**3 8 11 12 13 15 18 28 29 30 31 34 35 36 37 40 41 45 46 47 49 53 54 56 57 59 64 70 73 74 75 76 77 78 79 81 82 84 85 87 89 93 94 102 107 108 110 111 114 115 116 117 119 120 124 129 131 132 145 146 147 148 149 154 156 **S** NewYork-Presbyterian, New York, NY
Primary Contact: Stacey Petrower, President
COO: Deborah Neuendorf, Vice President Administration
CFO: Mark Webster, Vice President Finance
CMO: William Higgins, M.D., Vice President Medical Affairs
CIO: Bud Sorbello, Director Management Information Systems
CHR: Jeane L Costella, Vice President
CNO: Kathleen Webster, R.N., MSN, Vice President Patient Services
Web address: www.hvhc.org
Control: Other not–for–profit (including NFP Corporation) **Service:** General medical and surgical

Staffed Beds: 128 **Admissions:** 7870 **Census:** 90 **Outpatient Visits:** 164445 **Births:** 633 **Total Expense ($000):** 222214 **Payroll Expense ($000):** 86783 **Personnel:** 1027

CUBA—Allegany County

CUBA MEMORIAL HOSPITAL (331301), 140 West Main Street, Zip 14727–1398; tel. 585/968–2000, (Nonreporting) **A**10 18
Primary Contact: Andrew Boser, Chief Executive Officer
CFO: Jack Ormond, Chief Financial Officer
Web address: www.cubamemorialhospital.com
Control: Other not–for–profit (including NFP Corporation) **Service:** General medical and surgical

Staffed Beds: 81

DANSVILLE—Livingston County

⊞ **NICHOLAS H. NOYES MEMORIAL HOSPITAL (330238)**, 111 Clara Barton Street, Zip 14437–9503; tel. 585/335–6001, **A**1 10 **F**3 8 11 13 15 29 30 32 34 35 38 40 45 47 49 50 51 53 54 57 59 60 64 68 70 75 76 78 79 81 82 84 85 87 89 93 100 102 104 107 110 111 115 119 120 121 123 130 131 132 133 144 146 149 154 156 **S** University of Rochester Medical Center, Rochester, NY
Primary Contact: Amy Pollard, R.N., President and Chief Executive Officer
CMO: Douglas Mayhle, M.D., Medical Director
CNO: Tamara West, R.N., MSN, Vice President Patient Care
Web address: www.noyes-health.org
Control: Other not–for–profit (including NFP Corporation) **Service:** General medical and surgical

Staffed Beds: 48 **Admissions:** 2030 **Census:** 21 **Outpatient Visits:** 201277 **Births:** 331 **Total Expense ($000):** 59587 **Payroll Expense ($000):** 27918 **Personnel:** 483

DELHI—Delaware County

⊞ **O'CONNOR HOSPITAL (331305)**, 460 Andes Road, State Route 28, Zip 13753–7407; tel. 607/746–0300, (Nonreporting) **A**1 10 18 **S** Bassett Healthcare Network, Cooperstown, NY
Primary Contact: Scott Bonderoff, President
CFO: Sue E. Andrews, Chief Financial Officer
CMO: Peter L Sosnow, Medical Director
CHR: Barbara Green, Director Human Resources
CNO: Debra Neale, R.N., Chief Nursing Officer
Web address: www.bassett.org/oconnor
Control: Other not–for–profit (including NFP Corporation) **Service:** General medical and surgical

Staffed Beds: 16

NY

DIX HILLS—Suffolk County

☐ **SAGAMORE CHILDREN'S PSYCHIATRIC CENTER (334064)**, 197 Half Hollow Road, Zip 11746–5861; tel. 631/370–1700, (Nonreporting) **A**1 **S** New York State Office of Mental Health, Albany, NY
Primary Contact: Kathy O'Keefe, Interim Executive Director
COO: Cathy Stein, Chief Inpatient Services
CFO: Jane Alexander, Director Facility Administrative Services
CIO: Bryan Doherty, Management Information Technology Services I
CHR: Nancy Angell, Associate Administrator Personnel
CNO: Sandra King, Chief Nursing Officer
Web address: www.omh.ny.gov
Control: State, Government, nonfederal **Service**: Children's hospital psychiatric

Staffed Beds: 54

DUNKIRK—Chautauqua County

⇑ **BROOKS MEMORIAL HOSPITAL (330229)**, 529 Central Avenue, Zip 14048–2599; tel. 716/366–1111, (Includes TLC HEALTH NETWORK - LAKE SHORE HOSPITAL, 845 Route 5 and 20, Irving, New York, Zip 14081–9716; tel. 716/951–7000; John P Galati, Chief Executive Officer), (Non-reporting) **A**10 21
Primary Contact: Mary E. LaRowe, FACHE, President and Chief Executive Officer
CFO: Jeffrey H. Morgan, Vice President Finance and Chief Financial Officer
CIO: Kevin Kimball, Director Information Technology
CHR: Tracie Luther, Director Employee and Labor Relations
CNO: Jodi Witherell, Vice President Patient Care and Quality
Web address: www.brookshospital.org
Control: Other not–for–profit (including NFP Corporation) **Service**: General medical and surgical

Staffed Beds: 65

EAST MEADOW—Nassau County

⊞ **NASSAU UNIVERSITY MEDICAL CENTER (330027)**, 2201 Hempstead Turnpike, Zip 11554–1859; tel. 516/572–0123, (Nonreporting) **A**1 3 5 10 12 13
Primary Contact: Winnie Mack, Interim President and Chief Executive Officer
COO: Donald L Ashkenase, Executive Vice President and Chief Operating Officer
CFO: John P Maher, Executive Vice President and Chief Financial Officer
CMO: Victor Scarmato, M.D., Acting Medical Director
CIO: Farooq Ajmal, Vice President and Chief Information Officer
CHR: Maureen Roarty, Executive Vice President Human Resources
CNO: Kathy Okurka, MON, R.N., Executive Vice President Patient Care Services
Web address: www.nuhealth.net
Control: Hospital district or authority, Government, nonfederal **Service**: General medical and surgical

Staffed Beds: 481

ELIZABETHTOWN—Essex County

⊞ **THE UNIVERSITY OF VERMONT HEALTH NETWORK ELIZABETHTOWN COMMUNITY HOSPITAL (331302)**, 75 Park Street, Zip 12932, Mailing Address: P.O. Box 277, Zip 12932–0277; tel. 518/873–6377, (Includes MOSES LUDINGTON HOSPITAL, 1019 Wicker Street, Ticonderoga, New York, Zip 12883–1097; tel. 518/585–2831; John R Remillard, President and Chief Executive Officer), (Non-reporting) **A**1 10 18
Primary Contact: John R. Remillard, President and Chief Executive Officer
COO: Matthew Nolan, Chief Operating Officer
CFO: Alan Chardavoyne, Chief Financial Officer
CMO: Rob DeMuro, M.D., Chief Medical Officer
CIO: Darrin Goodrow, Chief Information Officer
CHR: Michelle Meachem, Director Human Resources
CNO: Julie Tromblee, R.N., Chief Nursing Officer
Web address: www.ech.org
Control: Other not–for–profit (including NFP Corporation) **Service**: General medical and surgical

Staffed Beds: 40

ELLENVILLE—Ulster County

★ **ELLENVILLE REGIONAL HOSPITAL (331310)**, 10 Healthy Way, Zip 12428–5612; tel. 845/647–6400, **A**10 18 **F**3 11 15 28 29 30 34 35 40 41 45 46 47 48 50 57 59 63 64 68 75 77 79 81 85 87 93 94 107 108 110 111 115 119 132 133 135 146 147 148 149 152 156
Primary Contact: Steven L. Kelley, President and Chief Executive Officer
CFO: Robert Rue, Chief Financial Officer
CMO: Walter Sperling, M.D., Medical Director
CHR: Deborah Briggs, Vice President Human Resources, Marketing, Volunteer Services and Community Relations
CNO: Ann Marie Guntlow, Chief Nursing Officer
Web address: www.ellenvilleregional.org
Control: Other not–for–profit (including NFP Corporation) **Service**: General medical and surgical

Staffed Beds: 25 **Admissions**: 419 **Census**: 13 **Outpatient Visits**: 28559 **Births**: 0 **Total Expense ($000)**: 18890 **Payroll Expense ($000)**: 9894 **Personnel**: 175

ELMHURST—Queens County, See New York City

ELMIRA—Chemung County

★ **ARNOT OGDEN MEDICAL CENTER (330090)**, 600 Roe Avenue, Zip 14905–1629; tel. 607/737–4100, **A**2 3 5 10 12 13 **F**3 8 11 12 13 15 17 18 19 20 22 24 26 28 29 30 31 34 35 40 41 43 51 57 65 68 70 71 72 73 75 76 77 79 89 102 107 108 110 111 114 115 118 119 120 121 124 129 130 132 135 143 144 146 147 148 154 **S** Arnot Health, Elmira, NY
Primary Contact: Jonathan I. Lawrence, System Chief Operating Officer
CFO: Ronald J Kintz, Vice President and Treasurer
CMO: Kenneth Herzl-Betz, M.D., Chief Medical Officer
CIO: Gregg Martin, Chief Information Officer
CHR: Dave Stanbro, Director Human Resources
CNO: Sandra Mac"" McCarthy, Chief Nursing Officer
Web address: www.arnothealth.org
Control: Other not–for–profit (including NFP Corporation) **Service**: General medical and surgical

Staffed Beds: 266 **Admissions**: 11761 **Census**: 125

☐ **ELMIRA PSYCHIATRIC CENTER (334045)**, 100 Washington Street, Zip 14901–2898; tel. 607/737–4739, **A**1 3 10 **F**29 30 35 38 39 54 57 59 62 68 71 77 87 98 99 100 101 103 151 157 158 **S** New York State Office of Mental Health, Albany, NY
Primary Contact: David Peppel, Executive Director
COO: Karen Patterson, Deputy Director Operations
CFO: J. Paul Bedzyk, Deputy Director Administration
CMO: Kurt Hahn, M.D., Acting Clinical Director
CIO: Jeremy Newcomer, Director Information Services
CHR: Patricia Santulli, Director Human Resources
CNO: Pam Seeley, Chief Nursing Officer
Web address: www.omh.ny.gov/omhweb/facilities/elpc/facility.htm
Control: State, Government, nonfederal **Service**: Psychiatric

Staffed Beds: 61 **Admissions**: 237 **Census**: 62 **Outpatient Visits**: 0 **Births**: 0 **Personnel**: 362

ST. JOSEPH'S HOSPITAL (330108), 555 St. Joseph's Boulevard, Zip 14901–3223; tel. 607/733–6541, (Nonreporting) **A**10 **S** Arnot Health, Elmira, NY
Primary Contact: Jonathan I. Lawrence, President and Chief Executive Officer
CFO: Ronald J Kintz, Senior Vice President Finance and Chief Financial Officer
CMO: Kenneth Herzl-Betz, M.D., Chief Medical Officer and Senior Vice President Medical Affairs
CIO: Gregg Martin, Chief Information Officer
CHR: Dave Stanbro, Director Human Resources
CNO: Sandra Mac"" McCarthy, Chief Nursing Officer
Web address: www.arnothealth.org
Service: General medical and surgical

Staffed Beds: 141

NY

FAR ROCKAWAY—Queens County, See New York City

FLUSHING—Queens County, See New York City

FRESH MEADOWS—Queens County

☒ **CORNERSTONE OF MEDICAL ARTS CENTER HOSPITAL**, 159–05 Union Turnpike, Zip 11366–1950; tel. 212/755–0200, (Nonreporting)
Primary Contact: Thomas C. Puzo, President and Chief Executive Officer
CFO: Jeff OniFather, Chief Financial Officer
CMO: Sami Kaddouri, M.D., Medical Director
CHR: Gloria Burtch, Director Human Resources
Web address: www.cornerstoneny.com
Control: Corporation, Investor–owned (for–profit) **Service**: Alcoholism and other chemical dependency

> **Staffed Beds**: 162

GENEVA—Ontario County

☒ **FINGER LAKES HOSPITAL (330058)**, 196 North Street, Zip 14456–1694; tel. 315/787–4000, **A**1 3 10 **F**3 8 11 15 17 18 28 29 31 32 34 35 40 45 50 54 57 59 60 61 64 66 70 74 75 76 77 79 81 85 86 87 90 92 93 96 97 107 108 110 115 118 119 128 129 130 131 132 135 146 147 156 **S** Finger Lakes Health, Geneva, NY
Primary Contact: Frank Korich, FACHE, Senior Vice President, Operations
COO: Frank Korich, FACHE, Senior Vice President, Operations
CFO: Pamela Johnson, Treasurer and Chief Financial Officer
CMO: Jason Feinberg, M.D., Vice President Medical Affairs and Chief Medical Officer
CIO: Guy W Mosher III Manager Information Systems
CHR: Patrick R Boyle, Vice President Human Resources
CNO: Eileen Gage, R.N., Vice President Nursing
Web address: www.flhealth.org
Control: Other not–for–profit (including NFP Corporation) **Service**: General medical and surgical

> **Staffed Beds**: 132 **Admissions**: 3706 **Census**: 44 **Outpatient Visits**: 510304 **Births**: 0 **Total Expense ($000)**: 92167 **Payroll Expense ($000)**: 53929 **Personnel**: 748

GLEN COVE—Nassau County

☒ **GLEN COVE HOSPITAL (330181)**, 101 St Andrews Lane, Zip 11542–2254; tel. 516/674–7300, **A**1 2 3 5 10 **F**3 5 7 8 11 15 17 18 28 29 30 32 33 34 35 36 38 39 40 43 45 46 47 48 49 50 51 54 55 56 57 58 59 60 61 63 64 65 66 68 69 70 74 75 77 78 81 84 85 86 87 90 91 92 93 94 95 96 97 100 102 104 107 110 111 115 118 119 121 130 131 132 135 143 146 147 149 152 154 156 **S** Northwell Health, New Hyde Park, NY
Primary Contact: Susan Kwiatek, R.N., Executive Director
COO: Michele Frankel, Associate Executive Director Finance
CFO: Michele Frankel, Associate Executive Director Finance
Web address: www.northshorelij.com
Control: Other not–for–profit (including NFP Corporation) **Service**: General medical and surgical

> **Staffed Beds**: 119 **Admissions**: 4732 **Census**: 96 **Outpatient Visits**: 74672 **Births**: 0 **Total Expense ($000)**: 151491 **Payroll Expense ($000)**: 83878 **Personnel**: 791

GLEN OAKS—Queens County, See New York City

GLENS FALLS—Warren County

☒ ⇑ **GLENS FALLS HOSPITAL (330191)**, 100 Park Street, Zip 12801–4413; tel. 518/926–1000, **A**1 2 5 10 19 21 **F**3 5 8 11 13 15 17 18 20 22 26 28 29 30 31 32 34 35 36 37 38 40 43 44 45 46 47 49 50 53 54 57 59 64 68 70 71 73 74 75 76 77 78 79 81 82 84 85 86 87 89 90 92 93 96 97 98 100 102 104 107 108 110 111 114 115 118 119 120 121 123 124 126 127 129 130 132 135 144 145 146 147 148
Primary Contact: Dianne Shugrue, President and Chief Executive Officer
COO: Paul Scimeca, Senior Vice President Operations and Chief Operating Officer
CFO: Mitchell Amado, Senior Vice President Finance and Chief Financial Officer
CMO: Howard P Fritz, M.D., Vice President, Medical Affairs and Chief Medical Officer
CHR: Kyle Brock, Vice President Human Resources
CNO: Donna Kirker, R.N., MS, Vice President Patient Services and Chief Nursing Officer
Web address: www.glensfallshospital.org
Control: Other not–for–profit (including NFP Corporation) **Service**: General medical and surgical

> **Staffed Beds**: 349 **Admissions**: 12150 **Census**: 153 **Outpatient Visits**: 711593 **Births**: 1175 **Total Expense ($000)**: 356554 **Payroll Expense ($000)**: 157998 **Personnel**: 2154

GLENVILLE—Schenectady County

CONIFER PARK, 79 Glenridge Road, Zip 12302–4523; tel. 518/399–6446, (Nonreporting)
Primary Contact: Jeanne Gluchowski, Executive Director
COO: Jeanne Gluchowski, Executive Director
CFO: Jason Burczeuski, Controller
CMO: John Melbourne, M.D., Medical Director
CIO: Amy Kentera, Chief Information Officer
CHR: Maureen Fowler, Director Human Resources
Web address: www.coniferpark.com/
Control: Corporation, Investor–owned (for–profit) **Service**: Alcoholism and other chemical dependency

> **Staffed Beds**: 225

GLOVERSVILLE—Fulton County

★ ⇑ **NATHAN LITTAUER HOSPITAL AND NURSING HOME (330276)**, 99 East State Street, Zip 12078–1203; tel. 518/725–8621, (Total facility includes 84 beds in nursing home–type unit) **A**10 21 **F**3 8 11 13 15 18 28 29 30 31 32 34 35 36 37 40 45 50 53 54 57 59 61 64 65 70 74 75 76 77 78 79 81 82 85 86 87 89 93 96 97 107 108 110 115 118 119 128 129 130 131 132 135 144 145 146 147 149 156
Primary Contact: Laurence E. Kelly, President and Chief Executive Officer
CMO: Frederick Goldberg, M.D., Vice President Medical Affairs and Chief Medical Officer
CIO: Martin Brown, Vice President Information Services and Chief Information Officer
CHR: Lana Wydra, Vice President Human Resources
CNO: Stephanie Fishel, Vice President Patient Care Services and Chief Nursing Officer
Web address: www.nlh.org
Control: Other not–for–profit (including NFP Corporation) **Service**: General medical and surgical

> **Staffed Beds**: 137 **Admissions**: 2617 **Census**: 103 **Outpatient Visits**: 263972 **Births**: 363 **Total Expense ($000)**: 105639 **Payroll Expense ($000)**: 54052 **Personnel**: 810

GOUVERNEUR—St. Lawrence County

★ ⇑ **GOUVERNEUR HOSPITAL (331315)**, 77 West Barney Street, Zip 13642–1040; tel. 315/287–1000, **A**10 18 21 **F**3 11 15 29 34 35 39 40 44 45 50 57 59 64 68 75 77 80 81 85 87 89 93 97 100 107 110 111 115 116 119 127 129 130 132 133 135 146 149 154 **S** St. Lawrence Health System, Potsdam, NY
Primary Contact: David Bender, Chief Executive Officer
CFO: Richard T Lang, Chief Financial Officer
CMO: George Dodds, M.D., Medical Director
CNO: Jennifer Shaver, Director of Nursing
Web address: www.gvnrhospital.org
Control: Other not–for–profit (including NFP Corporation) **Service**: General medical and surgical

> **Staffed Beds**: 25 **Admissions**: 720 **Census**: 12 **Outpatient Visits**: 39482 **Births**: 0 **Total Expense ($000)**: 22821 **Payroll Expense ($000)**: 10134 **Personnel**: 189

GREENPORT—Suffolk County

☒ **EASTERN LONG ISLAND HOSPITAL (330088)**, 201 Manor Place, Zip 11944–1298; tel. 631/477–1000, **A**1 3 10 **F**3 4 5 7 8 11 14 15 17 18 28 29 30 34 35 38 40 45 47 49 50 53 56 57 59 62 65 68 70 75 77 79 81 82 84 85 86 87 93 98 100 102 103 104 106 107 110 111 114 115 119 130 131 132 135 143 146 147 148 149 154 156 157
Primary Contact: Paul J. Connor III, President and Chief Executive Officer
CFO: Robert A Ragona, Senior Vice President Finance and Chief Financial Officer
CMO: Lloyd Simon, M.D., Medical Director
CIO: Dan Scotto, Director Information Technology
CHR: Frank Dumont, Assistant Vice President Human Resources and Corporate Compliance
CNO: D. Patricia Pispisa, Senior Vice President, Patient Care Services and Chief Nursing Officer
Web address: www.elih.org
Control: Other not–for–profit (including NFP Corporation) **Service**: General medical and surgical

> **Staffed Beds**: 90 **Admissions**: 2659 **Census**: 51 **Outpatient Visits**: 44993 **Births**: 0 **Total Expense ($000)**: 53863 **Payroll Expense ($000)**: 26578 **Personnel**: 355

NY

Many Facility Codes have changed. Please refer to the AHA Guide Code Chart. © 2019 AHA Guide

HAMILTON—Madison County

☒ **COMMUNITY MEMORIAL HOSPITAL (331316)**, 150 Broad Street, Zip 13346–9518; tel. 315/824–1100, (Nonreporting) **A**1 10 18
Primary Contact: Sean Fadale, President and Chief Executive Officer
CFO: Christopher W Graham, Chief Financial Officer
CMO: Robert Delorme, Vice President Medical Affairs
CHR: Jennifer Montana, Manager Human Resources
CNO: Denise Hummer, R.N., Vice President Administrative Services
Web address: www.communitymemorial.org
Control: Other not–for–profit (including NFP Corporation) **Service**: General medical and surgical

Staffed Beds: 25

HARRIS—Sullivan County

★ ⇑ **CATSKILL REGIONAL MEDICAL CENTER (330386)**, 68 Harris Bushville Road, Zip 12742–5030, Mailing Address: P.O. Box 800, Zip 12742–0800; tel. 845/794–3300, (Total facility includes 58 beds in nursing home–type unit) **A**2 10 21 **F**2 3 13 15 17 18 28 29 30 31 32 34 35 40 45 57 59 64 66 70 74 75 76 77 78 79 81 85 87 89 93 97 98 100 102 104 107 108 110 111 115 119 127 128 130 132 133 135 144 146 147 148 149 153 154 **S** Greater Hudson Valley Health System, Middletown, NY
Primary Contact: Jonathan Schiller, Chief Executive Officer
CFO: Rick Caprico, Chief Financial Officer
CMO: Gerard Galarneau, M.D., Regional Chief Medical Officer
CIO: Brian Tew, Chief Information Officer
CNO: Rolland Bojo, R.N., Chief Nursing Officer, Administrator Patient Care and Services
Web address: www.crmcny.org
Control: Other not–for–profit (including NFP Corporation) **Service**: General medical and surgical

Staffed Beds: 119 Admissions: 4193 Census: 112 Outpatient Visits: 64370 **Births:** 587 **Total Expense ($000):** 91375 **Payroll Expense ($000):** 36722 **Personnel:** 636

HORNELL—Steuben County

☒ **ST. JAMES MERCY HOSPITAL (330151)**, 411 Canisteo Street, Zip 14843–2197; tel. 607/324–8000, (Nonreporting) **A**1 10 20 **S** University of Rochester Medical Center, Rochester, NY
Primary Contact: Leo P. Brideau, FACHE, Interim President and Chief Executive Officer
CMO: John Carroll, M.D., Chief Medical Officer
CIO: Jason Soles, Manager Information Systems
CHR: Jennifer Spike, Director Human Resources
CNO: Kathleen Brodbeck MSN, RN-D Chief Nursing Officer
Web address: www.stjamesmercy.org
Control: Other not–for–profit (Including NFP Corporation) **Service**: General medical and surgical

Staffed Beds: 127

HUDSON—Columbia County

★ **COLUMBIA MEMORIAL HOSPITAL (330094)**, 71 Prospect Avenue, Zip 12534–2907; tel. 518/828–7601, (Nonreporting) **A**10 19
Primary Contact: Jay P. Cahalan, Chief Executive Officer
COO: Karen Tassey, FACHE, Chief Operating Officer
CFO: Bryan Mahoney, Chief Financial Officer
CMO: Lawrence Perl, M.D., Chief Medical Officer
CIO: Bonnie Ratliff, Chief Information Officer
CNO: Mary Ellen Plass, MS, R.N., Senior Vice President and Chief Nursing Officer
Web address: www.columbiamemorialhealth.org
Control: Other not–for–profit (including NFP Corporation) **Service**: General medical and surgical

Staffed Beds: 192

HUNTINGTON—Suffolk County

☒ **HUNTINGTON HOSPITAL (330045)**, 270 Park Avenue, Zip 11743–2799; tel. 631/351–2000, **A**1 2 3 10 **F**3 8 11 12 13 17 18 20 26 29 30 31 32 34 35 36 37 38 40 41 43 44 45 46 47 48 49 50 51 54 55 56 57 58 59 60 61 63 64 65 66 68 69 70 73 74 75 76 78 79 81 82 84 85 86 87 89 97 98 100 101 102 103 107 108 110 111 115 118 119 126 130 132 146 147 148 149 150 154 **S** Northwell Health, New Hyde Park, NY
Primary Contact: Nick Fitterman, M.D., Executive Director
CMO: Michael Grosso, M.D., Senior Vice President Medical Affairs
CIO: Scott C Groom, Senior Vice President and Chief Information Officer
CHR: Lisa Khavkin, Vice President Human Resources
CNO: Susan Knoepffler, R.N., Vice President Nursing
Web address: www.https://huntington.northwell.edu
Control: Other not–for–profit (including NFP Corporation) **Service**: General medical and surgical

Staffed Beds: 280 Admissions: 16885 Census: 204 Outpatient Visits: 109992 **Births:** 1198 **Total Expense ($000):** 434088 **Payroll Expense ($000):** 213872 **Personnel:** 1959

ITHACA—Tompkins County

☒ **CAYUGA MEDICAL CENTER AT ITHACA (330307)**, 101 Dates Drive, Zip 14850–1342; tel. 607/274–4011, **A**1 2 3 5 10 20 **F**3 8 11 12 13 15 18 20 22 26 28 29 30 31 34 35 38 40 41 44 45 46 48 49 51 54 55 56 57 58 59 61 64 65 66 70 72 74 75 76 77 78 79 81 82 84 85 86 87 90 92 93 98 99 100 101 102 103 107 108 110 111 114 115 116 117 118 119 121 129 130 131 132 133 135 144 145 146 147 148 149 154 156 **S** Cayuga Health System, Ithaca, NY
Primary Contact: John B. Rudd, President and Chief Executive Officer
CFO: John Collett, Vice President and Chief Financial Officer
CMO: David M Evelyn, M.D., Vice President Medical Affairs
CIO: Brett Mello, Chief Information Officer
CHR: Brian Forrest, Vice President Human Resources
CNO: Deb Raupers, MSN, R.N., Vice President Patient Services and Chief Nursing Officer
Web address: www.cayugamed.org
Control: Other not–for–profit (including NFP Corporation) **Service**: General medical and surgical

Staffed Beds: 159 Admissions: 6617 Census: 82 Outpatient Visits: 270826 **Births:** 881 **Total Expense ($000):** 222777 **Payroll Expense ($000):** 78478 **Personnel:** 1445

JAMAICA   Queens County, See New York City

JAMESTOWN—Chautauqua County

☒ **UPMC CHAUTAUQUA WCA (330239)**, 207 Foote Avenue, Zip 14701–7077, Mailing Address: P.O. Box 840, Zip 14702–0840; tel. 716/487–0141, **A**1 2 10 **F**3 4 5 11 12 13 15 17 18 20 28 29 34 35 38 40 45 50 57 59 64 70 74 75 76 77 78 79 81 82 84 87 89 90 93 96 98 99 100 102 104 107 108 109 110 115 119 120 124 126 129 130 131 132 135 146 147 148 149 154 155 156 157 **S** UPMC, Pittsburgh, PA
Primary Contact: Brian Durniok, Interim President and Chief Executive Officer
CMO: Marlene Garone, M.D., Vice President Medical Affairs and Medical Director
CIO: Keith Robison, Chief Information Officer
CHR: Karen Bohall, Director Human Resources
Web address: www.wcahospital.org
Control: Other not–for–profit (including NFP Corporation) **Service**: General medical and surgical

Staffed Beds: 111 Admissions: 6879 Census: 104 Outpatient Visits: 224114 **Births:** 672 **Total Expense ($000):** 116797 **Payroll Expense ($000):** 43912 **Personnel:** 948

JOHNSON CITY—Broome County

WILSON MEMORIAL REGIONAL MEDICAL CENTER See United Health Services Hospitals-Binghamton, Binghamton

KATONAH—Westchester County

☐ **FOUR WINDS HOSPITAL (334002)**, 800 Cross River Road, Zip 10536–3549; tel. 914/763–8151, (Nonreporting) **A**1 10
Primary Contact: Martin A. Buccolo, Ph.D., Chief Executive Officer
COO: Moira Morrissey, Chief Operating Officer and General Counsel
CFO: Barry S Weinstein, Chief Financial Officer
CMO: Jonathan Bauman, M.D., Chief Medical Officer
CIO: Barry S Weinstein, Chief Financial Officer
CHR: Susan Cusano, Director Human Resources
Web address: www.fourwindshospital.com
Control: Partnership, Investor–owned (for–profit) **Service**: Psychiatric

Staffed Beds: 181

NY

Hospital, Medicare Provider Number, Address, Telephone, Approval, Facility, and Physician Codes, Health Care System

★ American Hospital Association (AHA) membership
☐ The Joint Commission accreditation
○ Healthcare Facilities Accreditation Program
◇ DNV Healthcare Inc. accreditation
⇑ Center for Improvement in Healthcare Quality Accreditation
△ Commission on Accreditation of Rehabilitation Facilities (CARF) accreditation

KENMORE—Erie County

⊞ **KENMORE MERCY HOSPITAL (330102)**, 2950 Elmwood Avenue, Zip 14217–1390, Mailing Address: 2950 Elmwood Avenue, Room 4024, Zip 14217–1390; tel. 716/447–6100, (Total facility includes 160 beds in nursing home–type unit) **A**1 10 **F**3 11 15 18 29 30 34 35 37 38 40 41 44 45 46 49 50 53 54 57 58 59 63 64 65 66 68 70 74 75 77 79 81 84 85 87 90 92 93 97 100 107 108 110 111 115 118 119 126 128 129 130 131 132 141 146 147 148 149 156 **S** Catholic Health System, Buffalo, NY
Primary Contact: Walter Ludwig, President and Chief Executive Officer
CFO: James H Dunlop, CPA, Jr Executive Vice President and Chief Financial Officer
CMO: James Fitzpatrick, M.D., Vice President Medical Affairs
CHR: Laura Cianflone, Director Human Resources
Web address: www.chsbuffalo.org
Control: Church operated, Nongovernment, not–for–profit **Service**: General medical and surgical

Staffed Beds: 321 **Admissions:** 9361 **Census:** 232 **Outpatient Visits:** 120310 **Births:** 0 **Total Expense ($000):** 173662 **Payroll Expense ($000):** 74135 **Personnel:** 1009

KINGSTON—Ulster County

⇧ **BENEDICTINE HOSPITAL** See Health Alliance Hospital - Mary's Avenue Campus

⇧ **HEALTH ALLIANCE HOSPITAL - BROADWAY CAMPUS (330004)**, 396 Broadway, Zip 12401–4692; tel. 845/331–3131, (Nonreporting) **A**3 10 19 21 **S** WMCHealth, Valhalla, NY
Primary Contact: David Scarpino, President and Chief Executive Officer
COO: Robert Seidman, Chief Operating Officer
CFO: Steven J Haas, Chief Financial Officer
CMO: Frank Ehrlich, M.D., Chief Medical Officer
CIO: John Finch, Vice President Information Services
CHR: Greg M Howard, Director Human Resource
Web address: www.hahv.org
Control: Other not–for–profit (including NFP Corporation) **Service**: General medical and surgical

Staffed Beds: 150

⇧ **HEALTH ALLIANCE HOSPITAL - MARY'S AVENUE CAMPUS (330224)**, 105 Marys Avenue, Zip 12401–5894; tel. 845/338–2500, (Nonreporting) **A**2 10 19 21 **S** WMCHealth, Valhalla, NY
Primary Contact: David Scarpino, President and Chief Executive Officer
COO: Robert Seidman, Chief Operating Officer
CFO: Steven J Haas, Chief Financial Officer
CMO: Frank Ehrlich, M.D., Chief Medical Officer
CIO: John Finch, Chief Information and Community Officer
CHR: Greg M Howard, Vice President Human Resources
Web address: www.hahv.org
Control: Other not–for–profit (including NFP Corporation) **Service**: General medical and surgical

Staffed Beds: 120

⇧ **KINGSTON HOSPITAL** See Health Alliance Hospital - Broadway Campus

LEWISTON—Niagara County

⊞ **MOUNT ST. MARY'S HOSPITAL AND HEALTH CENTER (330188)**, 5300 Military Road, Zip 14092–1903; tel. 716/297–4800, **A**1 10 **F**3 4 11 13 15 18 28 29 30 34 35 38 40 41 44 45 46 49 50 51 54 56 57 58 59 64 65 66 68 70 74 75 76 77 79 81 84 85 87 90 97 100 107 108 110 111 114 115 118 119 124 130 131 132 141 143 146 147 148 149 156 **S** Catholic Health System, Buffalo, NY
Primary Contact: Gary C. Tucker, President and Chief Executive Officer
CFO: Stephen Franko, Vice President Finance and Chief Financial Officer
CNO: Jessica Visser, R.N., Vice President Patient Care Services and Chief Nursing Officer
Web address: www.msmh.org
Control: Church operated, Nongovernment, not–for–profit **Service**: General medical and surgical

Staffed Beds: 152 **Admissions:** 4226 **Census:** 86 **Outpatient Visits:** 166435 **Births:** 318 **Total Expense ($000):** 100703 **Payroll Expense ($000):** 50179 **Personnel:** 637

LITTLE FALLS—Herkimer County

⊞ **LITTLE FALLS HOSPITAL (331311)**, 140 Burwell Street, Zip 13365–1725; tel. 315/823–1000, (Nonreporting) **A**1 10 18 **S** Bassett Healthcare Network, Cooperstown, NY
Primary Contact: Michael L. Ogden, President and Chief Executive Officer
CFO: James Vielkind, Chief Financial Officer
CMO: Louis Oceguera, M.D., Medical Director
CIO: Duane Merry, Chief Information Officer
CHR: Christine Pirri, Vice President Human Resources
CNO: Heidi Camardello, Vice President Patient Care Services and Chief Nursing Officer
Web address: www.bassett.org
Control: Other not–for–profit (including NFP Corporation) **Service**: General medical and surgical

Staffed Beds: 25

LOCKPORT—Niagara County

★ **EASTERN NIAGARA HOSPITAL (330163)**, 521 East Avenue, Zip 14094–3299; tel. 716/514–5700, (Includes EASTERN NIAGARA HOSPITAL LOCKPORT, 521 East Avenue, Lockport, New York, Zip 14094–3299; tel. 716/514–5700; EASTERN NIAGARA HOSPITAL NEWFANE, 2600 William Street, Newfane, New York, Zip 14108–1093; tel. 716/778–5111) **A**10 13 **F**3 4 8 13 15 18 19 28 29 30 31 34 40 45 46 47 48 49 50 51 54 57 59 60 63 65 68 70 74 75 76 77 79 81 82 83 84 85 87 89 93 94 97 98 99 100 102 107 108 110 111 115 119 126 130 132 135 144 146 147 148
Primary Contact: Anne E. McCaffrey, President and Chief Executive Officer
CMO: Bruce J Cusenz, M.D., Medical Director
CHR: Joseph Farrauto, Director Human Resources
CNO: Mary Beth Campo, MS, R.N., Director of Nursing
Web address: www.enhs.org
Control: Other not–for–profit (including NFP Corporation) **Service**: General medical and surgical

Staffed Beds: 125 **Admissions:** 4052 **Census:** 73 **Outpatient Visits:** 103812 **Births:** 322 **Total Expense ($000):** 65333 **Payroll Expense ($000):** 29557 **Personnel:** 523

LOWVILLE—Lewis County

⊞ **LEWIS COUNTY GENERAL HOSPITAL (331317)**, 7785 North State Street, Zip 13367–1297; tel. 315/376–5200, (Total facility includes 160 beds in nursing home–type unit) **A**1 10 18 **F**2 3 11 13 15 29 30 34 35 36 40 45 50 56 57 59 62 63 70 75 76 77 79 81 82 93 96 97 107 110 111 115 119 128 129 130 132 133 141 143 145 146 147 154
Primary Contact: Gerald Cayer, Chief Executive Officer
COO: Michele Prince, Chief Operating Officer
CMO: Catherine Williams, M.D., Medical Director
CIO: Rob Uttendorfsky, Director Information Management
CNO: Jennifer Shaver, Director of Nursing
Web address: www.lcgh.net
Control: County, Government, nonfederal **Service**: General medical and surgical

Staffed Beds: 185 **Admissions:** 1319 **Census:** 164 **Outpatient Visits:** 145223 **Births:** 208 **Total Expense ($000):** 77689 **Payroll Expense ($000):** 29676 **Personnel:** 550

MALONE—Franklin County

⊞ **THE UNIVERSITY OF VERMONT HEALTH NETWORK - ALICE HYDE MEDICAL CENTER (330084)**, 133 Park Street, Zip 12953–1243, Mailing Address: P.O. Box 729, Zip 12953–0729; tel. 518/483–3000, (Total facility includes 165 beds in nursing home–type unit) **A**1 10 20 **F**3 10 11 13 15 17 18 28 29 31 34 35 39 40 45 57 59 64 67 70 75 76 77 78 79 81 82 84 85 86 87 90 92 93 96 97 107 108 110 111 115 117 119 121 127 128 129 130 131 132 135 141 146 147 149 154 156
Primary Contact: Michelle Lebeau, President
COO: Matthew Jones, Vice President Support Services and Facilities
CFO: Sean Curtin, Chief Financial Officer
CMO: William Latreille, M.D., Chief Medical Officer
CIO: Darrin Goodrow, Chief Information Officer
CHR: Emily Campbell, Vice President Human Resources
CNO: Julie Marshall, Assistant Vice President Quality and Risk Management
Web address: www.UVMHealth.org/AHMC
Control: Other not–for–profit (including NFP Corporation) **Service**: General medical and surgical

Staffed Beds: 206 **Admissions:** 1700 **Census:** 174 **Outpatient Visits:** 213697 **Births:** 260 **Total Expense ($000):** 93259 **Payroll Expense ($000):** 46154 **Personnel:** 672

MANHASSET—Nassau County

⊞ **NORTH SHORE UNIVERSITY HOSPITAL (330106)**, 300 Community Drive, Zip 11030–3816; tel. 516/562–0100, (Includes SYOSSET HOSPITAL, 221 Jericho Turnpike, Syosset, New York, Zip 11791–4515; tel. 516/496–6500; Michael Fener, Executive Director) **A**1 2 3 5 8 10 **F**3 5 6 7 8 9 11 12 13 14 15 17 18 20 22 24 26 28 29 30 31 34 35 36 37 38 39 40 41 43 44 45 46 47 48 49 50 51 52 53 54 55 56 57 58 59 60 61 62 63 64 65 66 68 69 70 71 72 73 74 75 76 77 78 79 80 81 82 83 84 85 86 87 91 92 93 94 96 97 98 100 101 102 104 107 108 110 111 112 114 115 117 118 119 126 129 130 131 132 134 135 136 137 138 139 141 142 143 144 145 146 147 148 149 150 152 154 156 157 **S** Northwell Health, New Hyde Park, NY
Primary Contact: Alessandro Bellucci, M.D., Executive Director
CFO: Frank Rizzo, Chief Financial Officer, Central Region
CMO: Michael Gitman, M.D., Medical Director
CIO: Nympha Meindel, R.N., Chief Information Officer
CHR: Debra Bierman, Associate Executive Director Human Resources
CNO: Kerri Scanlon, MSN, Chief Nursing Officer
Web address: www.https://www.northwell.edu/find-care/locations/north-shore-university-hospital
Control: Other not–for–profit (including NFP Corporation) **Service**: General medical and surgical

Staffed Beds: 813 **Admissions:** 49758 **Census:** 785 **Outpatient Visits:** 1117720 **Births:** 6569 **Total Expense ($000):** 2595195 **Payroll Expense ($000):** 1328466 **Personnel:** 12833

NY

Many Facility Codes have changed. Please refer to the AHA Guide Code Chart. © 2019 AHA Guide

MARCY—Oneida County

☐ **CENTRAL NEW YORK PSYCHIATRIC CENTER**, 9005 Old River Road,
Zip 13403–3000, Mailing Address: P.O. Box 300, Zip 13403–0300; tel. 315/765–
3600, (Nonreporting) **A**1 3 **S** New York State Office of Mental Health, Albany, NY
Primary Contact: Maureen Bosco, Executive Director
Web address: www.omh.ny.gov
Control: State, Government, nonfederal **Service:** Psychiatric

Staffed Beds: 226

MARGARETVILLE—Delaware County

⇑ **MARGARETVILLE HOSPITAL (331304)**, 42084 State Highway 28, Zip 12455–
2820; tel. 845/586–2631, (Nonreporting) **A**10 18 21 **S** WMCHealth, Valhalla, NY
Primary Contact: Mark Pohar, Executive Director
CHR: Linda Mead, Director Human Resources
Web address: www.margaretvillehospital.org
Control: Other not–for–profit (including NFP Corporation) **Service:** General
medical and surgical

Staffed Beds: 15

MASSENA—St. Lawrence County

☐ **MASSENA MEMORIAL HOSPITAL (330223)**, One Hospital Drive, Zip 13662–
1097; tel. 315/764–1711, (Nonreporting) **A**1 10 20
Primary Contact: Charles Gijanto, Interim Chief Executive Officer
CFO: Patrick M. Facteau, Chief Financial Officer
CMO: Nimesh Desai, M.D., Medical Director
CHR: Jonnie Dorothy, Senior Director Human Resources
CNO: Ralene North, Chief Nurse Executive
Web address: www.massenahospital.org
Control: City, Government, nonfederal **Service:** General medical and surgical

Staffed Beds: 50

MEDINA—Orleans County

⇑ **MEDINA MEMORIAL HOSPITAL (331319)**, 200 Ohio Street, Zip 14103–1095;
tel. 585/798–2000, (Nonreporting) **A**10 18 21
Primary Contact: Mark Cye, Chief Executive Officer
CFO: David Britton, Interim Chief Financial Officer
CMO: Joseph Misiti, M.D., President Medical Staff
CHR: Mary Williams, Director Human Resources
Web address: www.medinamemorial.org
Control: State, Government, nonfederal **Service:** General medical and surgical

Staffed Beds: 64

MIDDLETOWN—Orange County

★ △ ⇑ **ORANGE REGIONAL MEDICAL CENTER (000120)**, 707 East Main
Street, Zip 10940–2650; tel. 845/333–1000, **A**2 3 5 7 10 12 13 21 **F**3 5 8 11
12 13 15 17 18 20 22 26 28 29 30 31 34 35 36 40 41 43 45 46 47 48 49 50
51 54 55 59 63 64 66 70 72 74 75 76 77 78 79 81 82 84 85 86 87 89 90
91 93 96 97 98 100 101 102 104 107 108 110 111 114 115 116 117 119
120 121 122 123 124 126 129 130 132 135 144 146 148 149 156 **S** Greater
Hudson Valley Health System, Middletown, NY
Primary Contact: Scott Batulis, President and Chief Executive Officer
COO: Timothy P Selz, Vice President
CFO: Mitch Amodo, Vice President and Chief Financial Officer
CMO: James Oxley, D.O., Vice President Medical Affairs
CHR: Deborah Carr, Vice President Human Resources
Web address: www.ormc.org
Control: Other not–for–profit (including NFP Corporation) **Service:** General
medical and surgical

Staffed Beds: 340 **Admissions:** 22855 **Census:** 311 **Outpatient
Visits:** 263399 **Births:** 2001 **Total Expense ($000):** 486453 **Payroll
Expense ($000):** 184962 **Personnel:** 2560

MINEOLA—Nassau County

⊞ **NYU WINTHROP HOSPITAL (330167)**, 259 First Street, Zip 11501–3957;
tel. 516/663–0333, (Includes CHILDREN'S MEDICAL CENTER, 259 First Street,
Mineola, New York, Zip 11501–3957; tel. 516/663–0333) **A**1 2 3 5 8 10 **F**3 5 6
8 9 11 12 13 15 17 18 19 20 22 24 26 28 29 30 31 32 34 35 36 37 38 39 40
41 43 44 45 46 47 48 49 50 51 52 54 55 56 57 58 59 60 61 62 63 64 65 66
68 70 72 73 74 75 76 77 78 79 81 82 84 85 86 87 88 89 92 93 94 96 97 100
101 102 104 107 108 110 111 114 115 116 117 118 119 120 121 123 124
126 129 130 131 132 134 135 136 141 142 144 145 146 147 148 149 150
154 156 157 **S** NYU Langone Health, New York, NY
Primary Contact: John F. Collins, President and Chief Executive Officer
COO: Garry Schwall, Chief Operating Officer
CFO: Palmira Cataliotti, Senior Vice President, Chief Financial Officer and Treasurer
CMO: Michael Ammazzalorso, M.D., Chief Medical Officer
CIO: Nicholas Casabona, Chief Information Officer
CHR: Stacey Pfeffer, Senior Vice President Human Resources
CNO: Valerie Terzano, MSN, R.N., Senior Vice President Nursing
Web address: www.winthrop.org
Control: Other not–for–profit (including NFP Corporation) **Service:** General
medical and surgical

Staffed Beds: 511 **Admissions:** 33607 **Census:** 463 **Outpatient
Visits:** 462147 **Births:** 4915 **Total Expense ($000):** 1208892 **Payroll
Expense ($000):** 519479 **Personnel:** 8962

MONTOUR FALLS—Schuyler County

⊞ **SCHUYLER HOSPITAL (331313)**, 220 Steuben Street, Zip 14865–9709;
tel. 607/535–7121, (Total facility includes 120 beds in nursing home–type unit) **A**1
3 10 18 **F**3 11 14 15 29 30 34 35 40 50 59 64 70 74 75 77 81 82 85 87 91
92 93 94 97 107 110 111 114 119 128 129 130 133 135 146 149 **S** Cayuga
Health System, Ithaca, NY
Primary Contact: James B. Watson, President
CMO: Michael Eisman, M.D., Medical Director
Web address: www.schuylerhospital.org
Control: Other not–for–profit (including NFP Corporation) **Service:** General
medical and surgical

Staffed Beds: 145 **Admissions:** 876 **Census:** 121 **Outpatient Visits:** 54473
Births: 0 **Total Expense ($000):** 34375 **Payroll Expense ($000):** 18398
Personnel: 355

MONTROSE—Westchester County

⊞ **VETERANS AFFAIRS HUDSON VALLEY HEALTH CARE SYSTEM**, 2094
Albany Post Road, Zip 10548–1454, Mailing Address: P.O. Box 100,
Zip 10548–0100; tel. 914/737–4400, (Includes VETERAN AFFAIRS HUDSON
VALLEY HEALTH CARE SYSTEM–CASTLE POINT CAMPUS, 41 Castle Point
Road, Wappingers, New York, Zip 12590; tel. 914/831–2000; VETERANS
AFFAIRS HUDSON VALLEY HEALTH CARE SYSTEM–MONTROSE CAMPUS, 2094
Albany Post Road, Montrose, New York, Zip 10548; tel. 914/737–4400)
(Total facility includes 121 beds in nursing home–type unit) **A**1 3 5 **F**3 4 6
7 8 12 18 29 30 31 34 35 36 38 39 44 45 46 47 48 49 53 54 56 57 58
59 61 63 65 66 71 74 75 77 78 79 82 83 84 86 87 90 93 94 97 98 100
101 103 104 106 107 108 111 115 118 119 127 128 129 130 132 135
143 144 146 147 148 149 153 154 156 **S** Department of Veterans Affairs,
Washington, DC
Primary Contact: Margaret B. Caplan, Director
COO: John M Grady, Associate Director
CFO: John Walsh, Chief Fiscal Services
CMO: Joanne J Malina, M.D., Chief of Staff
CIO: Thomas Rooney, Chief Information Resource Management
CHR: Dardanella Russell, Chief Human Resources Management Service
Web address: www.hudsonvalley.va.gov/
Control: Veterans Affairs, Government, federal **Service:** Psychiatric

Staffed Beds: 270 **Admissions:** 1337 **Census:** 222 **Outpatient
Visits:** 370230 **Births:** 0 **Total Expense ($000):** 268985 **Payroll Expense
($000):** 126337 **Personnel:** 1804

NY

Hospital, Medicare Provider Number, Address, Telephone, Approval, Facility, and Physician Codes, Health Care System

★ American Hospital Association (AHA) membership   ○ Healthcare Facilities Accreditation Program   ⇑ Center for Improvement in Healthcare Quality Accreditation
☐ The Joint Commission accreditation   ◇ DNV Healthcare Inc. accreditation   △ Commission on Accreditation of Rehabilitation Facilities (CARF) accreditation

MOUNT KISCO—Westchester County

☒ **NORTHERN WESTCHESTER HOSPITAL (330162)**, 400 East Main Street, Zip 10549–3477, Mailing Address: 400 East Main Street, G-02, Zip 10549–3477; tel. 914/666–1200, **A**1 2 10 **F**3 5 7 8 12 13 15 17 18 28 29 30 31 32 34 35 36 37 40 46 47 48 49 50 51 54 55 56 57 59 60 61 64 65 68 70 72 73 74 75 76 78 79 81 82 84 85 86 87 89 91 92 93 97 98 100 101 102 107 108 109 110 111 114 115 118 119 120 121 123 124 126 129 130 131 132 135 146 147 148 152 **S** Northwell Health, New Hyde Park, NY
Primary Contact: Joel Seligman, President and Chief Executive Officer
CFO: John Partenza, Vice President and Treasurer
CMO: Marla Koroly, M.D., Chief Medical Officer and Senior Vice President Medical Affairs
CIO: Sue Prince, Director Information Systems
CHR: Kerry Flynn Barrett, Vice President Human Resources
CNO: Lauraine Szekely, R.N., Senior Vice President, Patient Care
Web address: www.nwhc.net
Control: Other not–for–profit (including NFP Corporation) **Service**: General medical and surgical

Staffed Beds: 195 **Admissions:** 9211 **Census:** 109 **Outpatient Visits:** 136380 **Births:** 1591 **Total Expense ($000):** 264073 **Payroll Expense ($000):** 128565 **Personnel:** 1420

MOUNT VERNON—Westchester County

☐ **MONTEFIORE MOUNT VERNON (330086)**, 12 North Seventh Avenue, Zip 10550–2098; tel. 914/664–8000, **A**1 3 10 **F**3 14 15 18 29 30 31 34 35 40 45 50 59 60 61 64 65 66 68 70 74 75 77 78 79 81 84 85 86 87 92 93 97 98 100 102 104 107 110 111 114 119 130 146 147 148 156 **S** Montefiore Health System, Bronx, NY
Primary Contact: Jaccel Kouns, R.N., MS, Vice President and Executive Director
CFO: Albert M Farina, Chief Financial Officer
CMO: Gary Ishkanian, M.D., Vice President Medical Affairs
CIO: Barbara Cooke, Director Health Information Systems
CHR: Dennis H Ashley, Vice President Human Resources
Web address: www.montefiorehealthsystem.org/landing.cfm?id=17
Control: Other not–for–profit (including NFP Corporation) **Service**: General medical and surgical

Staffed Beds: 62 **Admissions:** 3459 **Census:** 58 **Outpatient Visits:** 136618 **Births:** 0 **Total Expense ($000):** 93910 **Payroll Expense ($000):** 38971 **Personnel:** 530

NEW HAMPTON—Orange County

☐ **MID-HUDSON FORENSIC PSYCHIATRIC CENTER (334061)**, Route 17M, Zip 10958, Mailing Address: P.O. Box 158, Zip 10958–0158; tel. 845/374–8700, (Nonreporting) **A**1 3 10 **S** New York State Office of Mental Health, Albany, NY
Primary Contact: Joseph Freebern, Executive Director
COO: Kristin Orlando, Director Operations
Web address: www.omh.ny.gov
Control: State, Government, nonfederal **Service**: Psychiatric

Staffed Beds: 285

NEW HYDE PARK—Queens County, See New York City

NEW HYDE PARK—Nassau County

STEVEN AND ALEXANDRA COHEN CHILDREN'S MEDICAL CENTER OF NEW YORK See Long Island Jewish Medical Center, New Hyde Park

NEW ROCHELLE—Westchester County

☒ **MONTEFIORE NEW ROCHELLE (330184)**, 16 Guion Place, Zip 10801–5502; tel. 914/632–5000, (Total facility includes 150 beds in nursing home–type unit) **A**1 2 3 5 10 19 **F**3 12 13 14 15 18 28 29 30 31 32 34 35 37 40 45 50 55 59 64 65 66 68 70 72 74 75 77 78 79 81 82 84 85 86 87 90 92 93 100 107 108 110 114 119 128 130 135 146 156 **S** Montefiore Health System, Bronx, NY
Primary Contact: Anthony Alfano, Vice President Executive Director
CMO: Richard Barone, M.D., Medical Director
CHR: Dennis H Ashley, Vice President Human Resources
CNO: Pamela M Dupuis, R.N., Senior Vice President Patient Care Services
Web address: www.montefiorehealthsystem.org
Control: Other not–for–profit (including NFP Corporation) **Service**: General medical and surgical

Staffed Beds: 301 **Admissions:** 7048 **Census:** 222 **Outpatient Visits:** 87937 **Total Expense ($000):** 196258 **Payroll Expense ($000):** 90075 **Personnel:** 1129

NEW YORK—Kings County

☐ **BROOKDALE HOSPITAL MEDICAL CENTER (330233)**, 125 Worth Street, 4th Fl Ste 418, Zip 10013, Mailing Address: One Brookdale Plaza, Brooklyn, Zip 11212–3139; tel. 718/240–5000, (Total facility includes 448 beds in nursing home–type unit) **A**1 3 5 10 **F**2 6 12 13 15 17 18 19 20 22 26 29 30 31 34 35 39 40 43 45 47 49 50 51 54 55 56 57 58 59 60 61 63 64 65 66 68 70 72 74 75 76 77 78 79 81 82 83 84 85 86 87 88 89 92 93 97 98 99 100 102 104 107 108 109 110 111 114 115 119 120 121 123 126 128 129 130 131 132 134 135 144 146 147 148 149 150 154 156 157
Primary Contact: Dominick Stanzione, President and Chief Executive Officer
CFO: James Porter, Chief Financial Officer
CIO: David Reitzel, Chief Information Officer
CHR: Margaret M Brubaker, Senior Vice President Human Resources
Web address: www.brookdalehospital.org
Control: Other not–for–profit (including NFP Corporation) **Service**: General medical and surgical

Staffed Beds: 808 **Admissions:** 14731 **Census:** 663 **Outpatient Visits:** 262720 **Births:** 898 **Total Expense ($000):** 611734 **Payroll Expense ($000):** 309782 **Personnel:** 3663

NEW YORK (Includes all hospitals located within the five boroughs)
BRONX—Bronx County (Mailing Address – Bronx)
BROOKLYN—Kings County (Mailing Address – Brooklyn)
MANHATTAN—New York County (Mailing Address – New York)
QUEENS—Queens County (Mailing Addresses – Bellerose, Elmhurst, Far Rockaway, Flushing, Forest Hills, Glen Oaks, Holliswood, Jackson Heights, Jamaica, Little Neck, Long Island City, New Hyde Park, and Queens Village)
RICHMOND VALLEY—Richmond County (Mailing Address – Staten Island)

BETH ISRAEL MEDICAL CENTER See Mount Sinai Beth Israel

BETH ISRAEL MEDICAL CENTER-KINGS HIGHWAY DIVISION See Mount Sinai Beth Israel Brooklyn

☐ **BRONX PSYCHIATRIC CENTER (334053)**, 1500 Waters Place, Zip 10461–2796; tel. 718/931–0600, (Nonreporting) **A**1 3 5 10 **S** New York State Office of Mental Health, Albany, NY
Primary Contact: Anita Daniels, Director
CFO: Robert Erway, Director for Administration
Web address: www.omh.ny.gov
Control: State, Government, nonfederal **Service**: Psychiatric

Staffed Beds: 450

☒ **BRONXCARE HEALTH SYSTEM (330009)**, 1276 Fulton Avenue, Zip 10456–3499; tel. 718/590–1800, (Includes BRONX-LEBANON SPECIAL CARE CENTER, 1265 Fulton Avenue, Bronx, New York, Zip 10465; tel. 718/579–7000; Octavio Marin, Vice President Long Term Care and Ambulatory Care Services; CONCOURSE DIVISION, 1650 Grand Concourse, Bronx, New York, Zip 10457, Mailing Address: 1276 Fulton Ave, Zip 10456–3402, tel. 718/590–1800; Miguel A Fuentes Jr, President and Chief Executive Officer; FULTON DIVISION, 1276 Fulton Avenue, Bronx, New York, Zip 10456, Mailing Address: 1650 Grand Concourse, Zip 10457–7606, tel. 718/590–1800; Miguel A Fuentes Jr, President and Chief Executive Officer; HIGHBRIDGE WOODYCREST CENTER, 936 Woodycrest Avenue, Bronx, New York, Zip 10452; tel. 718/579–8875; Leonardo Vicent III, Executive Director) (Total facility includes 240 beds in nursing home–type unit) **A**1 3 5 10 **F**3 4 5 6 7 8 11 12 13 15 17 18 19 20 21 22 23 27 28 29 30 31 32 34 35 36 37 38 39 40 41 42 43 44 45 46 47 48 49 50 51 52 54 55 56 57 58 59 60 61 64 65 66 68 70 71 72 73 74 75 76 77 78 79 81 82 83 84 85 86 87 88 89 91 92 93 95 96 97 98 99 100 101 102 103 104 105 106 107 108 110 111 114 115 118 119 126 128 129 130 131 132 133 134 135 143 144 146 147 148 149 150 151 152 153 156 157
Primary Contact: Miguel A. Fuentes Jr, President and Chief Executive Officer
CFO: Victor DeMarco, Chief Financial Officer
CMO: Milton A Gumbs, M.D., Vice President and Medical Director
CIO: Ivan Durbak, Chief Information Officer
CHR: Selena Griffin-Mahon, Assistant Vice President Human Resources
CNO: Patricia Cahill, Vice President, Patient Care Services and Chief Nursing Officer
Web address: www.bronxcare.org
Control: Other not–for–profit (including NFP Corporation) **Service**: General medical and surgical

Staffed Beds: 859 **Admissions:** 30380 **Census:** 684 **Outpatient Visits:** 1084011 **Births:** 1948 **Total Expense ($000):** 858004 **Payroll Expense ($000):** 405665 **Personnel:** 4170

NY

Many Facility Codes have changed. Please refer to the AHA Guide Code Chart.

© 2019 AHA Guide

☐ **BROOKLYN HOSPITAL CENTER (330056)**, 121 DeKalb Avenue, Zip 11201–5425; tel. 718/250–8000, **A**1 3 5 10 F3 4 7 8 12 13 15 17 18 19 20 26 29 30 31 32 34 35 39 40 41 45 46 47 48 49 50 52 54 55 56 57 58 59 60 61 63 64 65 68 70 72 74 75 76 77 78 79 81 82 83 84 85 86 87 88 90 93 94 97 100 101 103 107 109 110 111 112 114 115 116 117 119 120 121 122 123 129 130 131 132 133 134 135 143 144 145 146 147 148 149 150 156 157
Primary Contact: Gary G. Terrinoni, President and Chief Executive Officer
COO: John Gupta, Executive Vice President and Chief Operating Officer
CIO: Irene Farrelly, Vice President and Chief Information Officer
CHR: Ira Warm, Senior Vice President Human Resources
Web address: www.tbh.org
Control: Other not–for–profit (including NFP Corporation) **Service:** General medical and surgical

Staffed Beds: 282 Admissions: 17416 Census: 224 Outpatient Visits: 306293 Births: 2516 Total Expense ($000): 447426 Payroll Expense ($000): 221183 Personnel: 4538

✉ **CALVARY HOSPITAL (332006)**, 1740 Eastchester Road, Zip 10461–2392; tel. 718/863–6900, **A**1 3 5 10 F1 29 30 35 39 62 63 64 68 74 78 82 84 87 119 121 130 132 134 146 148 149
Primary Contact: Frank A. Calamari, President and Chief Executive Officer
COO: Richard J Kutilek, Chief Operating Officer
CFO: Andrew Greco, Chief Financial Officer
CMO: Michael J Brescia, M.D., Executive Medical Director
CIO: Patrick Martin, Director Information Systems
CHR: Michael T Troncone, Chief Human Resources Officer
CNO: Margaret Pelkowski, R.N., Vice President Patient Care Services
Web address: www.calvaryhospital.org
Control: Church operated, Nongovernment, not–for–profit **Service:** Other specialty treatment

Staffed Beds: 225 Admissions: 2947 Census: 213 Births: 0

COLER–GOLDWATER SPECIALTY HOSPITAL AND NURSING FACILITY See Nyc Health + Hospitals / Henry J Carter Specialty Hospital and Medical Center

CONCOURSE DIVISION See Bronxcare Health System, Bronx

☐ **CREEDMOOR PSYCHIATRIC CENTER (334004)**, 79–25 Winchester Boulevard, Zip 11427–2128; tel. 718/264–3600, (Nonreporting) **A**1 3 10 **S** New York State Office of Mental Health, Albany, NY
Primary Contact: Ann Marie. Barbarotta, Executive Director
CFO: Viodelda Ho-Shing, Deputy Director Administration
CIO: Ed Yunusov, Chief Information Officer
CHR: Adrienne Jones, Director Human Resources
CNO: Marie S Jean-Louis, R.N., Chief Nursing Officer
Web address: www.omh.ny.gov
Control: State, Government, nonfederal **Service:** Psychiatric

Staffed Beds: 322

✉ **FLUSHING HOSPITAL MEDICAL CENTER (330193)**, 4500 Parsons Boulevard, Zip 11355–2205; tel. 718/670–5000, **A**1 3 5 10 F3 4 5 7 8 12 13 15 18 19 29 30 31 32 34 35 36 39 40 41 45 49 50 51 55 56 57 59 60 61 64 65 68 70 71 72 73 74 75 76 77 78 79 81 82 84 85 87 89 91 92 93 97 98 100 101 104 107 110 111 114 119 126 128 130 132 135 146 147 148 149 150 154 156 **S** MediSys Health Network, Jamaica, NY
Primary Contact: Bruce J. Flanz, President and Chief Executive Officer
COO: Robert V Levine, Executive Vice President and Chief Operating Officer
CFO: Mounir F Doss, Executive Vice President and Chief Financial Officer
CIO: Tony Gatto, Director Management Information Systems
Web address: www.flushinghospital.org
Control: Other not–for–profit (including NFP Corporation) **Service:** General medical and surgical

Staffed Beds: 299 Admissions: 14056 Census: 188 Outpatient Visits: 173604 Births: 2617 Total Expense ($000): 749253 Payroll Expense ($000): 129838 Personnel: 1942

FULTON DIVISION See Bronxcare Health System, Bronx

☐ **GRACIE SQUARE HOSPITAL (334048)**, 420 East 76th Street, Zip 10021–3396; tel. 212/988–4400, (Nonreporting) **A**1 10
Primary Contact: David Wyman, President and Chief Executive Officer
Web address: www.nygsh.org
Control: Other not–for–profit (including NFP Corporation) **Service:** Psychiatric

Staffed Beds: 157

HENRY J. CARTER SPECIALTY HOSPITAL & NURSING FACILITY See Nyc Health + Hospitals / Henry J Carter Specialty Hospital and Medical Center, New York

⊞ **HOSPITAL FOR SPECIAL SURGERY (330270)**, 535 East 70th Street, Zip 10021–4898, Mailing Address: 535 East 70th Street, Belaire 10–08, Zip 10021–4898; tel. 212/606–1000, **A**1 3 5 8 10 19 F3 8 9 29 30 32 33 34 35 36 37 38 43 44 50 53 54 56 57 58 59 64 66 68 70 74 75 77 79 80 81 82 84 85 86 87 89 91 92 93 94 97 100 107 109 111 114 115 116 117 119 121 123 126 130 131 132 134 141 142 143 146 147 148 149 154
Primary Contact: Louis A. Shapiro, President and Chief Executive Officer
COO: Lisa Goldstein, Executive Vice President and Chief Operating Officer
CFO: Stacey Malakoff, Executive Vice President and Chief Financial Officer
CMO: Todd Albert, M.D., Surgeon-in-Chief and Medical Director
CIO: Jamie Nelson, Vice President and Chief Information Officer
CHR: Bruce Slawitsky, Vice President Human Resources
CNO: Stephanie J Goldberg, MSN, R.N., Senior Vice President and Chief Nursing Officer
Web address: www.hss.edu
Control: Other not–for–profit (including NFP Corporation) **Service:** Orthopedic

Staffed Beds: 215 Admissions: 15765 Census: 130 Outpatient Visits: 484588 Births: 0 Total Expense ($000): 1134925 Payroll Expense ($000): 519749 Personnel: 4772

☐ **INTERFAITH MEDICAL CENTER (330397)**, 1545 Atlantic Avenue, Zip 11213–1122; tel. 718/613–4000, **A**1 3 5 10 F4 5 8 15 18 20 22 26 29 30 34 35 38 39 40 41 43 44 45 46 50 54 56 57 59 60 61 64 68 70 75 77 79 81 82 84 89 93 94 97 98 100 101 102 104 105 107 108 109 110 111 114 115 119 130 132 135 143 146 148 152 154 156
Primary Contact: LaRay Brown, President and Chief Executive Officer
CMO: Jochanan Weisenfreund, M.D., Senior Vice President Academic and Medical Affairs
CIO: Mark Lederman, Chief Information Officer
CHR: Venra Mathurin, Vice President Human Resources
Web address: www.interfaithmedical.com
Control: Other not–for–profit (including NFP Corporation) **Service:** General medical and surgical

Staffed Beds: 243 Admissions: 9119 Census: 183 Outpatient Visits: 105281 Births: 0 Total Expense ($000): 243879 Payroll Expense ($000): 124781 Personnel: 1405

JACK D WEILER HOSPITAL OF ALBERT EINSTEIN COLLEGE OF MEDICINE See Montefiore Medical Center, Bronx

⊞ **JAMAICA HOSPITAL MEDICAL CENTER (330014)**, 8900 Van Wyck Expressway, Zip 11418–2832; tel. 718/206–6000, (Nonreporting) **A**1 3 5 10 13 **S** MediSys Health Network, Jamaica, NY
Primary Contact: Bruce J. Flanz, President and Chief Executive Officer
COO: William Lynch, Executive Vice President and Chief Operating Officer
CFO: Mounir F Doss, Executive Vice President and Chief Financial Officer
CMO: Antonietta Morisco, M.D., Medical Director, Chairman Anesthesiology
CIO: Sunil Dashut, Chief Information Officer
CHR: Trina Cornet, JD, Vice President Human Resources
CNO: Kathleen Scher, Ed.D., R.N., Chief Nursing Officer
Web address: www.Jamaicahospital.org
Control: Other not–for–profit (including NFP Corporation) **Service:** General medical and surgical

Staffed Beds: 668

⊞ △ **JAMES J. PETERS VETERANS AFFAIRS MEDICAL CENTER**, 130 West Kingsbridge Road, Zip 10468–3904; tel. 718/584–9000, (Total facility includes 80 beds in nursing home–type unit) **A**1 2 3 5 7 8 F1 3 5 8 12 15 17 18 26 29 30 31 34 35 39 40 46 47 48 49 51 53 54 56 57 58 59 60 61 63 64 65 70 71 74 75 77 78 79 80 81 82 83 84 85 86 87 90 91 92 93 95 97 98 100 101 102 104 105 107 108 110 111 112 114 116 117 118 119 120 121 122 123 126 129 130 132 135 138 143 145 146 147 148 149 152 153 154 156 **S** Department of Veterans Affairs, Washington, DC
Primary Contact: Erik Langhoff, M.D., Ph.D., Director
CFO: Gregory Angelo, Chief Fiscal Program
CIO: Linda Bund, Chief Information Officer and Director Education
CNO: Kathleen Capitulo, Ph.D., R.N., Chief Nurse Executive
Web address: www.bronx.va.gov/
Control: Veterans Affairs, Government, federal **Service:** General medical and surgical

Staffed Beds: 378 Admissions: 3711 Census: 156 Outpatient Visits: 350594 Births: 0 Total Expense ($000): 485909 Payroll Expense ($000): 169193 Personnel: 1857

Hospital, Medicare Provider Number, Address, Telephone, Approval, Facility, and Physician Codes, Health Care System

★ American Hospital Association (AHA) membership
☐ The Joint Commission accreditation
○ Healthcare Facilities Accreditation Program
◇ DNV Healthcare Inc. accreditation
⇑ Center for Improvement in Healthcare Quality Accreditation
△ Commission on Accreditation of Rehabilitation Facilities (CARF) accreditation

☐ **KINGSBORO PSYCHIATRIC CENTER (334063)**, 681 Clarkson Avenue, Zip 11203–2125; tel. 718/221–7395, (Nonreporting) **A**1 3 5 10 **S** New York State Office of Mental Health, Albany, NY
Primary Contact: Deborah Parchment, Executive Director
CFO: Yinusa Awolowo, Business Officer
CMO: Jeffery Lucey, M.D., Clinical Director
CIO: George Gavora, Director Program Evaluation
CHR: Vera Thompson, Director Human Resources
CNO: Deborah Denigris, Chief Nursing Officer
Web address: www.omh.ny.gov/omhweb/facilities/kbpc/facility/htm
Control: State, Government, nonfederal **Service**: Psychiatric

Staffed Beds: 290

☐ △ **KINGSBROOK JEWISH MEDICAL CENTER (330201)**, 585 Schenectady Avenue, Zip 11203–1891; tel. 718/604–5000, (Total facility includes 438 beds in nursing home–type unit) **A**1 3 5 7 10 **F**3 8 14 15 17 18 28 29 30 31 34 35 39 40 45 46 48 49 50 54 56 57 59 60 61 64 65 68 70 74 75 77 78 79 80 81 82 84 85 87 90 91 92 93 96 97 98 100 101 103 104 107 108 110 111 115 119 128 130 131 132 135 146 147 148 149 156
Primary Contact: Kurt Kodroff, M.D., Chief Executive Officer
COO: Robert Dubicki, Executive Vice President and Chief Operating Officer
CFO: John Schmitt, Senior Vice President and Chief Financial Officer
CMO: Sibte Burney, M.D., Senior Vice President Medical Affairs and Chief Medical Officer
CIO: Daniel Morreale, Vice President and Chief Information Officer
CHR: John McKeon, Vice President Human Resources
CNO: Jane Lederer, R.N., Ed.D., Vice President and Chief Nursing Officer
Web address: www.kingsbrook.org
Control: Other not-for-profit (including NFP Corporation) **Service**: General medical and surgical

Staffed Beds: 647 **Admissions**: 9058 **Census**: 623 **Outpatient Visits**: 124468 **Births**: 0 **Total Expense ($000)**: 315555 **Payroll Expense ($000)**: 156033 **Personnel**: 1664

☐ **KIRBY FORENSIC PSYCHIATRIC CENTER (334060)**, 600 East 125th Street, Zip 10035–6000; tel. 646/672–5800, (Nonreporting) **A**1 3 5 **S** New York State Office of Mental Health, Albany, NY
Primary Contact: Vincent Miccoli, Executive Director
Web address: www.https://www.omh.ny.gov/omhweb/facilities/krpc/
Control: Other not-for-profit (including NFP Corporation) **Service**: Psychiatric

Staffed Beds: 193

⊞ **LENOX HILL HOSPITAL (330119)**, 100 East 77th Street, Zip 10075–1850; tel. 212/434–2000, (Includes MANHATTAN EYE, EAR AND THROAT HOSPITAL, 210 East 64th Street, New York, New York, Zip 10021–9885; tel. 212/838–9200; Philip P Rosenthal, Executive Director) **A**1 3 5 8 10 19 **F**3 5 7 8 9 11 12 13 14 15 17 18 20 22 24 26 29 30 31 32 34 35 36 37 39 40 42 43 44 45 46 47 48 49 50 51 52 54 55 56 57 58 59 60 61 62 63 64 65 66 68 70 72 74 75 76 77 78 79 81 82 84 85 86 87 89 91 92 93 94 97 98 100 101 102 103 104 107 108 110 111 114 115 116 117 118 119 120 121 123 124 126 129 130 131 132 135 141 143 146 147 148 149 150 152 154 **S** Northwell Health, New Hyde Park, NY
Primary Contact: Jill Kalman, M.D., Executive Director
CIO: Beth Dituro, Divisional Chief Information Officer
Web address: www.lenoxhillhospital.org
Control: Other not-for-profit (including NFP Corporation) **Service**: General medical and surgical

Staffed Beds: 440 **Admissions**: 29485 **Census**: 339 **Outpatient Visits**: 258540 **Births**: 3862 **Total Expense ($000)**: 1349416 **Payroll Expense ($000)**: 674253 **Personnel**: 5455

⊞ **LONG ISLAND JEWISH MEDICAL CENTER (330195)**, 270–05 76th Avenue, Zip 11040–1496; tel. 718/470–7000, (Includes LONG ISLAND JEWISH FOREST HILLS, 102–01 66th Road, Forest Hills, New York, Zip 11375–2029; tel. 718/830–4000; Susan Browning, Executive Director; LONG ISLAND JEWISH VALLEY STREAM, 900 Franklin Avenue, Valley Stream, New York, Zip 11580–2190; tel. 516/256–6000; Stephen Bello, Executive Director; MANHASSET AMBULATORY CARE PAVILION, 1554 Northern Boulevard, Manhasset, New York, Zip 11030; tel. 516/365–2070; STEVEN AND ALEXANDRA COHEN CHILDREN'S MEDICAL CENTER OF NEW YORK, 270–05 76th Avenue, New Hyde Park, New York, Zip 11040; tel. 718/470–3000; ZUCKER HILLSIDE HOSPITAL, 75–59 263rd Street, Glen Oaks, New York, Zip 11004; tel. 718/470–8000) **A**1 2 3 5 8 10 **F**2 3 4 5 6 7 8 9 11 12 13 14 18 19 20 21 22 23 24 25 26 27 28 29 30 31 32 34 35 38 39 40 41 43 44 45 46 47 48 49 50 51 52 53 54 55 56 57 58 59 60 61 62 63 64 65 66 67 68 70 71 72 73 74 75 76 77 78 79 80 81 82 84 85 86 87 88 89 92 93 97 98 99 100 101 102 103 104 105 107 108 109 110 111 114 115 116 117 118 119 120 121 123 124 126 128 129 130 131 132 134 135 136 138 141 142 143 144 145 146 147 148 149 151 152 153 154 158 **S** Northwell Health, New Hyde Park, NY
Primary Contact: Michael Goldberg, Executive Director
CIO: John Bosco, Senior Vice President and Chief Information Officer
CHR: Ronald W Stone, Regional Chief Human Resource Officer
Web address: www.lij.edu
Control: Other not-for-profit (including NFP Corporation) **Service**: General medical and surgical

Staffed Beds: 1522 **Admissions**: 84479 **Census**: 1339 **Outpatient Visits**: 1069240 **Births**: 11041 **Total Expense ($000)**: 2981635 **Payroll Expense ($000)**: 1446993 **Personnel**: 14281

⊞ **MAIMONIDES MEDICAL CENTER (330194)**, 4802 Tenth Avenue, Zip 11219–2916; tel. 718/283–6000, (Includes MAIMONIDES INFANTS AND CHILDREN'S HOSPITAL OF BROOKLYN, 4802 Tenth Avenue, Brooklyn, New York, Zip 11219–2916; tel. 718/283–6000) **A**1 2 3 5 8 10 13 **F**3 7 8 9 11 12 13 14 15 17 18 19 20 22 24 26 28 29 30 31 32 34 35 38 39 40 41 43 44 45 46 47 48 49 50 51 52 54 55 56 57 58 59 60 61 64 65 66 68 70 72 73 74 75 76 77 78 79 81 82 84 85 86 87 88 89 91 92 93 96 97 98 99 100 101 102 103 104 107 108 110 111 114 115 117 118 119 120 121 123 124 126 129 130 131 132 135 144 145 146 147 148 149 150 154
Primary Contact: Kenneth Gibbs, President and Chief Executive Officer
COO: Mark McDougle, Executive Vice President and Chief Operating Officer
CFO: Robert Naldi, Chief Financial Officer
CMO: Samuel Kopel, M.D., Medical Director
CIO: Walter Fahey, Chief Information Officer
Web address: www.maimonidesmed.org/
Control: Other not-for-profit (including NFP Corporation) **Service**: General medical and surgical

Staffed Beds: 598 **Admissions**: 35928 **Census**: 568 **Outpatient Visits**: 534005 **Births**: 8009 **Total Expense ($000)**: 1285450 **Payroll Expense ($000)**: 614169 **Personnel**: 5759

☐ **MANHATTAN PSYCHIATRIC CENTER-WARD'S ISLAND (334054)**, 600 East 125th Street, Zip 10035–6000; tel. 646/672–6767, (Nonreporting) **A**1 3 5 10 **S** New York State Office of Mental Health, Albany, NY
Primary Contact: Vincent Miccoli, Executive Director
Web address: www.omh.ny.gov
Control: State, Government, nonfederal **Service**: Psychiatric

Staffed Beds: 745

⊞ **MEMORIAL SLOAN-KETTERING CANCER CENTER (330154)**, 1275 York Avenue, Zip 10065–6007; tel. 212/639–2000, **A**1 2 3 5 8 10 **F**3 8 11 14 15 29 31 32 34 35 36 37 39 44 45 46 47 48 49 50 54 55 56 59 60 61 64 66 68 70 74 75 77 78 79 81 82 84 85 86 87 88 89 92 93 94 96 98 99 100 103 104 107 108 110 111 112 114 115 117 118 119 120 121 123 124 126 130 132 135 136 142 143 144 145 146 147 148 149 154 157
Primary Contact: Craig B. Thompson, M.D., President and Chief Executive Officer
COO: Ned Groves, Executive Vice President and Administrator
CFO: Michael Gutnick, Executive Vice President and Chief Financial Officer
CMO: Lisa DeAngelis, M.D., Acting Physician-in-Chief
CIO: Patricia Skarulis, Senior Vice President and Chief Information Systems Officer
CHR: Kerry Bessey, Senior Vice President and Chief Human Resources Officer
CNO: Elizabeth Nelkin McCormick, MSN, R.N., Senior Vice President and Chief Nursing Officer
Web address: www.mskcc.org
Control: Other not-for-profit (including NFP Corporation) **Service**: Cancer

Staffed Beds: 498 **Admissions**: 24243 **Census**: 471 **Outpatient Visits**: 1883786 **Births**: 0 **Total Expense ($000)**: 3879673 **Payroll Expense ($000)**: 1479452 **Personnel**: 17838

NY

Many Facility Codes have changed. Please refer to the AHA Guide Code Chart.

✠ **MONTEFIORE MEDICAL CENTER (330059)**, 111 East 210th Street, Zip 10467–2401; tel. 718/920–4321, (Includes CHILDREN'S HOSPITAL OF MONTEFIORE, 3415 Bainbridge Avenue, Bronx, New York, Zip 10467–2403; tel. 718/741–2426; JACK D WEILER HOSPITAL OF ALBERT EINSTEIN COLLEGE OF MEDICINE, 1825 Eastchester Road, Bronx, New York, Zip 10461–2373; tel. 718/904–2000; MONTEFIORE MEDICAL CENTER - NORTH DIVISION, 600 East 233rd Street, Bronx, New York, Zip 10466–2697; tel. 718/920–9000) **A**1 2 3 5 8 10 19 **F**3 5 6 7 8 9 12 13 14 15 17 18 20 21 22 23 24 25 26 27 28 29 30 31 32 34 35 36 37 38 39 40 41 42 43 44 45 46 47 48 49 50 51 52 54 55 56 57 58 59 60 61 62 63 64 65 66 68 70 71 72 73 74 75 76 77 78 79 80 81 82 83 84 85 86 87 88 89 90 91 92 93 94 96 97 98 99 100 101 102 103 104 107 108 110 111 114 115 116 117 118 119 120 121 124 126 129 130 131 132 134 135 136 137 138 139 140 141 142 143 144 145 146 147 148 149 150 154 156 157 **S** Montefiore Health System, Bronx, NY
Primary Contact: Steven M. Safyer, M.D., President and Chief Executive Officer
COO: Philip O. Ozuah, M.D., Ph.D., Executive Vice President and Chief Operating Officer
CFO: Colleen M Blye, Executive Vice President and Chief Financial Officer
CMO: Gary Kalkut, M.D., Senior Vice President and Chief Medical Officer
CIO: Jack Wolf, Vice President Information Systems
Web address: www.montefiore.org
Control: Other not–for–profit (including NFP Corporation) **Service**: General medical and surgical

Staffed Beds: 1553 **Admissions**: 89785 **Census**: 1371 **Outpatient Visits**: 2767819 **Births**: 5699 **Total Expense ($000)**: 3876900 **Payroll Expense ($000)**: 1849552 **Personnel**: 19804

MORGAN STANLEY CHILDREN'S HOSPITAL OF NEW YORK-PRESBYTERIAN
See New York-Presbyterian Hospital, New York

✠ **MOUNT SINAI BETH ISRAEL (330169)**, First Avenue and 16th Street, Zip 10003–3803; tel. 212/420–2000, (Includes MOUNT SINAI BETH ISRAEL BROOKLYN, 3201 Kings Highway, Brooklyn, New York, Zip 11234; tel. 718/252–3000; Lin H Mo, M.P.H., President) **A**1 2 3 5 8 10 19 **F**3 4 5 7 8 9 11 12 14 15 17 18 20 22 26 29 30 31 34 35 36 38 39 40 41 44 45 46 47 48 49 50 51 53 54 55 56 57 58 59 60 61 63 64 65 68 70 74 75 77 78 79 81 82 84 85 86 87 92 93 94 97 98 100 101 102 103 104 107 108 110 111 114 115 117 118 119 120 121 123 124 126 130 131 132 134 135 141 143 144 146 147 148 149 150 154 156 157 **S** Mount Sinai Health System, New York, NY
Primary Contact: Jeremy Boal, M.D., President
COO: Kevin Molloy, Senior Vice President and Chief Operating Officer
CFO: Donald Scanlon, Chief Corporate Services, Mount Sinai Health System
CIO: Kumar Chatani, Senior Vice President and Chief Information Officer Mount Sinai Health System
CHR: Jane Maksoud, R.N., Senior Vice President Human Resources and Labor Relations, Mount Sinai Health System
CNO: Mary Walsh, R.N., MSN, Vice President Patient Care Services and Chief Nursing Officer
Web address: www.bethisraelny.org
Control: Other not–for–profit (including NFP Corporation) **Service**: General medical and surgical

Staffed Beds: 537 **Admissions**: 25689 **Census**: 428 **Outpatient Visits**: 398528 **Births**: 0 **Total Expense ($000)**: 1009455 **Payroll Expense ($000)**: 383133 **Personnel**: 5622

✠ **MOUNT SINAI HOSPITAL (330024)**, One Gustave L Levy Place, Zip 10029–0310; tel. 212/241–6500, (Includes KRAVIS CHILDREN'S HOSPITAL, 1184 Fifth Avenue, New York, New York, Zip 10029–6503, Mailing Address: One Gustave L Levy Place, Zip 10029–0312, tel. 212/241–9500; MOUNT SINAI QUEENS, 25–10 30th Avenue, Long Island City, New York, Zip 11102–2448; tel. 718/932–1000; Caryn A Schwab, Executive Director) **A**1 2 5 8 10 **F**3 4 5 6 7 8 9 11 12 13 14 15 17 18 19 20 21 22 23 24 25 26 27 28 29 30 31 32 33 34 35 36 37 38 39 40 41 43 44 45 46 47 48 49 50 51 52 54 55 56 57 58 59 60 61 62 63 64 65 66 68 70 71 72 73 74 75 76 77 78 79 80 81 82 83 84 85 86 89 90 91 92 93 94 95 96 97 98 100 101 102 103 104 105 107 108 110 111 115 117 118 119 120 121 123 124 126 129 130 131 132 134 135 136 137 138 139 141 142 143 144 145 146 147 148 149 150 153 154 156 157 **S** Mount Sinai Health System, New York, NY
Primary Contact: David L. Reich, M.D., President and Chief Operating Officer
COO: David L Reich, M.D., President and Chief Operating Officer
CFO: Donald Scanlon, Chief Financial Officer
CMO: Vicki LoPachin, M.D., Chief Medical Officer
CIO: Kumar Chatani, Senior Vice President and Chief Information Officer Mount Sinai Health System
CHR: Jane Maksoud, R.N., Senior Vice President Human Resources and Labor Relations
Web address: www.mountsinai.org
Control: Other not–for–profit (including NFP Corporation) **Service**: General medical and surgical

Staffed Beds: 1181 **Admissions**: 58465 **Census**: 1005 **Outpatient Visits**: 1081165 **Births**: 8079 **Total Expense ($000)**: 2687468 **Payroll Expense ($000)**: 1051151 **Personnel**: 11355

✠ **MOUNT SINAI WEST (330046)**, 1111 Amsterdam Avenue, Zip 10025–1716; tel. 212/523–4000, (Includes MOUNT SINAI WEST HOSPITAL, 1000 Tenth Avenue, New York, New York, Zip 10019; tel. 212/523–4000; Evan Flatow, M.D., President) **A**1 2 3 5 8 10 19 **F**3 4 5 7 8 9 11 12 13 15 17 18 20 22 24 26 29 30 31 32 34 36 37 38 39 40 41 43 44 45 46 47 48 49 50 51 52 54 55 56 57 58 59 60 61 63 64 65 66 68 70 72 74 75 76 77 78 79 81 82 84 85 86 87 90 93 96 97 98 99 100 101 102 103 104 107 108 110 111 112 114 115 117 118 119 120 121 123 124 126 130 131 132 134 135 141 143 144 145 146 147 148 149 150 153 154 156 157 **S** Mount Sinai Health System, New York, NY
Primary Contact: Arthur A. Gianelli, M.P.H., President
COO: Kevin Molloy, Senior Vice President and Chief Operating Officer
CFO: Donald Scanlon, Chief Corporate Services, Mount Sinai Health System
CIO: Kumar Chatani, Chief Information Officer, Mount Sinai Health System
CHR: Jane Maksoud, R.N., Senior Vice President Human Resources and Labor Relations, Mount Sinai Health System
CNO: Mary Walsh, R.N., MSN, Vice President Patient Care Services and Chief Nursing Officer
Web address: www.stlukeshospitalnyc.org
Control: Other not–for–profit (including NFP Corporation) **Service**: General medical and surgical

Staffed Beds: 763 **Admissions**: 34991 **Census**: 544 **Outpatient Visits**: 463571 **Births**: 5411 **Total Expense ($000)**: 1271580 **Payroll Expense ($000)**: 519350 **Personnel**: 5774

MOUNT SINAI WEST HOSPITAL See Mount Sinai West, New York

NEW YORK CITY CHILDREN'S CENTER, 74–03 Commonwealth Boulevard, Zip 11426–1890; tel. 718/264–4506, (Includes BRONX CHILDREN'S PSYCHIATRIC CENTER, 1000 Waters Place, Bronx, New York, Zip 10461–2799; tel. 718/239–3600; BROOKLYN CHILDREN'S PSYCHIATRIC CENTER, 1819 Bergen Street, Brooklyn, New York, Zip 11233–4513; tel. 718/221–4500) **A**3 **F**29 32 35 39 57 58 59 68 75 87 98 99 104 105 130 135 146 149 **S** New York State Office of Mental Health, Albany, NY
Primary Contact: Kanika Jefferies, Executive Director
CMO: David M Rube, M.D., Clinical Director
CIO: Ed Yunusov, Coordinator Facility Information Center
Web address: www.omh.ny.gov/omhweb/facilities/nyccc/
Control: State, Government, nonfederal **Service**: Children's hospital psychiatric

Staffed Beds: 97 **Admissions**: 248 **Census**: 123 **Outpatient Visits**: 0 **Births**: 0

☐ **NEW YORK COMMUNITY HOSPITAL (330019)**, 2525 Kings Highway, Zip 11229–1705; tel. 718/692–5300, (Nonreporting) **A**1 3 10
Primary Contact: Barry Stern, President and Chief Executive Officer
COO: Una E Morrissey, R.N., MSN, Senior Vice President Operations, Chief Operating Officer and Chief Nursing Officer
CFO: Leonardo Tamburello, Chief Financial Officer
CMO: Herbert Rader, M.D., Advisor for Medical Affairs
CIO: Edward B. Stolyar, D.O., Divisional Chief Informational Officer
CHR: Raquel Collado, Vice President Human Resources
CNO: Una E Morrissey, R.N., MSN, Senior Vice President Operations, Chief Operating Officer and Chief Nursing Officer
Web address: www.nych.com
Control: Other not–for–profit (including NFP Corporation) **Service**: General medical and surgical

Staffed Beds: 134

✠ **NEW YORK EYE AND EAR INFIRMARY OF MOUNT SINAI (330100)**, 310 East 14th Street, Zip 10003–4201; tel. 212/979–4000, **A**1 3 5 8 10 **F**3 8 29 30 34 35 44 50 57 58 59 64 66 68 75 81 82 87 107 115 119 129 130 141 143 146 149 157 **S** Mount Sinai Health System, New York, NY
Primary Contact: James Tsai, M.D., President
CFO: Donald Scanlon, Chief Corporate Services, Mount Sinai Health System
CIO: Kumar Chatani, Chief Information Officer, Mount Sinai Health System
CHR: Jane Maksoud, R.N., Senior Vice President Human Resources and Labor Relations, Mount Sinai Health System
Web address: www.nyee.edu
Control: Other not–for–profit (including NFP Corporation) **Service**: Eye, ear, nose and throat

Staffed Beds: 16 **Admissions**: 322 **Census**: 2 **Outpatient Visits**: 158959 **Births**: 0 **Total Expense ($000)**: 144957 **Payroll Expense ($000)**: 54673 **Personnel**: 740

NY

Hospital, Medicare Provider Number, Address, Telephone, Approval, Facility, and Physician Codes, Health Care System

★ American Hospital Association (AHA) membership ○ Healthcare Facilities Accreditation Program ⇑ Center for Improvement in Healthcare Quality Accreditation
☐ The Joint Commission accreditation ◇ DNV Healthcare Inc. accreditation △ Commission on Accreditation of Rehabilitation Facilities (CARF) accreditation

© 2019 AHA Guide   Many Facility Codes have changed. Please refer to the AHA Guide Code Chart.   Hospitals   **A435**

☐ **NEW YORK STATE PSYCHIATRIC INSTITUTE (334009)**, 1051 Riverside Drive, Zip 10032–1007; tel. 646/774–5000, (Nonreporting) **A**1 3 5 10 **S** New York State Office of Mental Health, Albany, NY
Primary Contact: Jeffrey A. Lieberman, M.D., Executive Director
COO: Janelle Dierkens, Chief Administration Officer
CFO: Jonathan Segal, Chief Financial Officer
CMO: David Lowenthal, M.D., Clinical Director
CIO: Joseph Grun, Chief Information Officer
CHR: Rebecca Dechabert, Acting Director Personnel
Web address: www.nyspi.org
Control: State, Government, nonfederal **Service**: Psychiatric

Staffed Beds: 58

⊞ **NEW YORK-PRESBYTERIAN HOSPITAL (330101)**, 525 East 68th Street, Zip 10065–4870; tel. 212/746–5454, (Includes MORGAN STANLEY CHILDREN'S HOSPITAL OF NEW YORK-PRESBYTERIAN, 3959 Broadway, New York, New York, Zip 10032–3784; tel. 212/305–2500; NEW YORK PRESBYTERIAN LOWER MANHATTAN HOSPITAL, 170 William Street, New York, New York, Zip 10038–2649; tel. 212/312–5000; Robert E Kelly, M.D., President; NEW YORK-PRESBYTERIAN HOSPITAL, WESTCHESTER DIVISION, 21 Bloomingdale Road, White Plains, New York, Zip 10605; tel. 914/682–9100; NEW YORK-PRESBYTERIAN HOSPITAL/WEILL CORNELL MEDICAL CENTER, 525 East 68th Street, New York, New York, Zip 10021–4885; tel. 212/746–5454; NEW YORK-PRESBYTERIAN/COLUMBIA UNIVERSITY MEDICAL CENTER, 161 Fort Washington Avenue, New York, New York, Zip 10032; tel. 212/305–2500; NEW YORK-PRESBYTERIAN/LAWRENCE HOSPITAL, 55 Palmer Avenue, Bronxville, New York, Zip 10708–3403; tel. 914/787–1000; Michael Fosina, M.P.H., FACHE, President; PAYNE WHITNEY PSYCHIATRIC CLINIC, 525 East 68th Street, New York, New York, Zip 10021; tel. 212/746–3800; PHYLLIS AND DAVID KOMANSKY CENTER FOR CHILDREN'S HEALTH, 525 East 68th Street, New York, New York, Zip 10065–4870; tel. 212/746–5454; THE ALLEN PAVILION, 5141 Broadway, New York, New York, Zip 10032; tel. 212/932–5000) **A**1 2 3 5 8 10 19 **F**3 4 5 6 7 8 11 12 13 14 15 16 17 18 19 20 21 22 23 24 25 26 27 28 29 30 31 32 34 35 36 37 38 39 40 41 43 44 45 46 47 48 49 50 51 52 53 54 55 56 57 58 59 61 62 63 64 65 66 68 69 70 71 72 73 74 75 76 77 78 79 80 81 82 84 85 86 87 88 89 90 91 92 93 94 96 97 98 99 100 101 102 103 104 105 107 108 110 111 112 114 115 116 117 118 119 120 121 123 124 126 129 130 131 132 133 134 135 136 137 138 139 140 141 142 143 144 145 146 147 148 149 150 153 154 155 156 157 **S** NewYork-Presbyterian, New York, NY
Primary Contact: Steven J. Corwin, M.D., President and Chief Executive Officer
CFO: Phyllis R Lantos, Executive Vice President, Corporate Chief Financial Officer and Treasurer
CMO: Laura Forese, M.D., M.P.H., Executive Vice President and Chief Medical Officer
CIO: Aurelia Boyer, Senior Vice President and Chief Information Officer
CHR: G Thomas Ferguson, Senior Vice President and Chief Human Resources Officer
CNO: Rosemary Ventura, M.D., Chief Nursing Informatics Officer
Web address: www.nyp.org
Control: Other not–for–profit (including NFP Corporation) **Service**: General medical and surgical

Staffed Beds: 2586 Admissions: 121296 Census: 2104 Outpatient Visits: 2524848 Births: 16829 Total Expense ($000): 6004751 Payroll Expense ($000): 2834445 Personnel: 26304

⊞ **NEW YORK-PRESBYTERIAN QUEENS (330055)**, 56–45 Main Street, Zip 11355–5045; tel. 718/670–1231, **A**1 2 3 5 10 19 **F**3 7 11 12 13 15 17 18 19 20 22 24 26 28 29 30 31 32 34 35 39 40 41 43 44 45 46 47 48 49 50 51 54 55 56 57 58 59 60 61 63 64 65 66 68 70 72 73 74 75 76 77 78 79 80 81 82 83 84 85 87 89 91 92 93 96 97 100 101 107 108 110 111 114 115 118 119 120 121 123 124 126 130 131 141 145 146 147 148 149 154 **S** NewYork-Presbyterian, New York, NY
Primary Contact: Jaclyn Mucaria, President
COO: Robert Blenderman, Senior Vice President and Chief Operating Officer
CFO: Kevin J Ward, Vice President and Chief Financial Officer
CMO: Amir Jaffer, M.D., Senior Vice President Medical Affairs
CIO: Mark Greaker, Chief Information Officer
CHR: Lorraine Orlando, Vice President Human Resources
CNO: Alan M. Levin, MSN, R.N., Chief Nursing Officer
Web address: www.nyhq.org
Control: Other not–for–profit (including NFP Corporation) **Service**: General medical and surgical

Staffed Beds: 491 Admissions: 31895 Census: 463 Outpatient Visits: 503859 Births: 3779 Total Expense ($000): 866007 Payroll Expense ($000): 437615 Personnel: 4061

⊞ **NEWYORK-PRESBYTERIAN BROOKLYN METHODIST HOSPITAL (330236)**, 506 Sixth Street, Zip 11215–3609; tel. 718/780–3000, **A**1 2 3 5 8 10 **F**3 6 7 9 11 12 13 15 17 18 19 20 22 24 26 29 30 31 32 34 35 36 39 40 41 43 44 45 46 47 48 50 51 52 54 55 56 57 58 59 61 64 65 66 68 70 71 72 73 74 75 76 77 78 79 81 82 84 85 87 88 89 90 91 92 93 95 96 97 98 100 102 103 107 108 109 110 111 112 114 115 118 119 120 121 123 124 126 129 130 131 132 145 146 147 148 149 154 156 **S** NewYork-Presbyterian, New York, NY
Primary Contact: Robert Guimento, President
CFO: Michael Fagan, Senior Vice President Finance
CMO: Steven Silber, M.D., Senior Vice President Medical Affairs
CHR: Rick Pogue, Vice President, Human Resources
CNO: Ernesto Perez-Mir, Vice President, Chief Nursing Officer
Web address: www.nym.org
Control: Other not–for–profit (including NFP Corporation) **Service**: General medical and surgical

Staffed Beds: 591 Admissions: 34675 Census: 517 Outpatient Visits: 565943 Births: 5133 Total Expense ($000): 1016228 Payroll Expense ($000): 453194 Personnel: 4192

⊞ **NYC HEALTH + HOSPITALS / BELLEVUE (330204)**, 462 First Avenue, Zip 10016–9198; tel. 212/562–4141, **A**1 3 5 10 **F**3 4 5 8 11 12 13 15 17 18 19 20 22 24 26 28 29 30 31 34 35 36 37 38 39 40 41 43 45 46 47 48 49 50 52 53 55 56 57 58 59 61 64 65 66 68 70 71 72 74 75 76 77 78 79 81 82 83 84 85 86 87 88 89 90 91 92 93 94 96 97 98 99 100 101 102 103 104 105 107 108 110 111 114 115 118 119 126 130 132 134 135 143 144 146 147 148 149 152 153 154 156 **S** NYC Health + Hospitals, New York, NY
Primary Contact: William Hicks, Chief Executive Officer
COO: Michael Rawlings, Interim Chief Operating Officer
CFO: Rebecca J Fischer, Chief Financial Officer
CMO: Nathan Link, M.D., Medical Director
CIO: James Carr, Chief Information Officer
CNO: Kim K Mendez, Ed.D., R.N., Chief Nurse Officer
Web address: www.nyc.gov/bellevue
Control: City, Government, nonfederal **Service**: General medical and surgical

Staffed Beds: 722 Admissions: 26532 Census: 584 Outpatient Visits: 543474 Births: 1407 Total Expense ($000): 1013664 Payroll Expense ($000): 387206 Personnel: 4391

⊞ **NYC HEALTH + HOSPITALS / CONEY ISLAND (330196)**, 2601 Ocean Parkway, Zip 11235–7795; tel. 718/616–3000, **A**1 3 5 10 12 13 **F**3 4 5 13 15 17 18 20 29 30 31 34 39 40 41 44 45 49 50 51 54 55 56 57 58 59 60 61 64 65 66 68 70 72 73 74 75 76 77 78 79 81 82 83 84 85 87 89 90 91 92 93 94 96 97 98 100 102 104 107 108 110 111 114 115 118 119 130 132 135 146 147 148 149 150 **S** NYC Health + Hospitals, New York, NY
Primary Contact: William A. Brown, FACHE, Chief Executive Officer
COO: Mei Kong, Chief Operating Officer
CMO: Wehbeh Wehbeh, M.D., Chief Medical Officer
CIO: Robert Kee, Chief Information Officer
CHR: Andrew Campbell, Associate Executive Director
CNO: Patricia Ruiz, R.N., Chief Nursing Officer
Web address: www.nyc.gov/html/hhc/html/facilities/coneyisland.shtml
Control: City, Government, nonfederal **Service**: General medical and surgical

Staffed Beds: 381 Admissions: 13653 Census: 283 Outpatient Visits: 305173 Births: 1111 Total Expense ($000): 526002 Payroll Expense ($000): 207763 Personnel: 2386

⊞ **NYC HEALTH + HOSPITALS / ELMHURST (330128)**, 79–01 Broadway, Zip 11373–1329; tel. 718/334–4000, **A**1 2 3 5 10 **F**2 3 5 8 9 11 13 14 15 17 18 19 20 22 26 29 30 31 34 35 37 38 39 40 41 43 45 46 49 50 51 52 53 54 55 56 57 58 59 60 61 64 65 66 68 70 71 72 73 74 75 76 77 78 79 80 81 82 83 84 85 86 87 89 90 91 92 93 94 96 97 98 99 100 101 102 104 105 107 108 109 110 111 115 118 119 121 123 126 130 132 135 141 143 144 145 146 147 148 149 152 153 154 156 157 **S** NYC Health + Hospitals, New York, NY
Primary Contact: Israel Rocha Jr, Chief Executive Officer
COO: Wayne Zimmermann, Chief Operating Officer
CFO: David Guzman, Chief Financial Officer
CMO: Jasmin Moshirpur, M.D., Dean and Medical Director
CIO: Jeannith Michelen, Chief Implementation Officer
CHR: Peter Maris, Director Human Resources
CNO: Joann Bernadette Gull, Chief Nursing Officer
Web address: www.nyc.gov/html/hhc/ehc/html/home/home.shtml
Control: City, Government, nonfederal **Service**: General medical and surgical

Staffed Beds: 506 Admissions: 18881 Census: 366 Outpatient Visits: 574969 Births: 2430 Total Expense ($000): 718861 Payroll Expense ($000): 281612 Personnel: 3075

NY

Many Facility Codes have changed. Please refer to the AHA Guide Code Chart.   © 2019 AHA Guide

☒ **NYC HEALTH + HOSPITALS / HARLEM (330240)**, 506 Lenox Avenue, Zip 10037–1802; tel. 212/939–1000, **A**1 3 5 10 **F**3 4 5 8 11 12 13 15 16 17 18 19 20 29 30 32 34 35 38 39 40 41 43 44 45 46 47 48 49 50 52 53 55 57 58 59 60 61 64 65 68 70 71 72 74 75 76 77 79 81 82 84 85 86 87 88 89 90 93 94 96 97 98 99 100 102 103 104 107 108 110 111 114 115 118 119 130 132 134 135 141 144 146 147 148 149 154 156 **S** NYC Health + Hospitals, New York, NY
Primary Contact: Ebone' Carrington, Chief Executive Officer and Chief Operating Officer
COO: Ebone' Carrington, Chief Executive Officer and Chief Operating Officer
Web address: www.nyc.gov/html/hhc/harlem
Control: City, Government, nonfederal **Service**: General medical and surgical

Staffed Beds: 258 **Admissions**: 12207 **Census**: 212 **Outpatient Visits**: 293270 **Births**: 878 **Total Expense ($000)**: 501618 **Payroll Expense ($000)**: 188975 **Personnel**: 2239

☒ **NYC HEALTH + HOSPITALS / HENRY J CARTER SPECIALTY HOSPITAL AND MEDICAL CENTER (332008)**, 1752 Park Avenue, Zip 10035; tel. 646/686–0000, (Includes COLER REHABILITATION AND NURSING CARE CENTER, 900 Main Street, Roosevelt Island, New York, New York, Zip 10044; tel. 212/848–6300; Robert K. Hughes, Chief Executive Officer; HENRY J. CARTER SPECIALTY HOSPITAL & NURSING FACILITY, 1752 Park Avenue, New York, New York, Zip 10035; tel. 646/686–0000; Floyd R Long, Chief Executive Officer) (Total facility includes 164 beds in nursing home–type unit) **A**1 10 **F**1 3 11 28 29 30 39 56 58 68 74 75 77 79 84 85 87 100 107 114 119 128 130 132 135 146 148 149 **S** NYC Health + Hospitals, New York, NY
Primary Contact: Robert K. Hughes, Executive Director
CFO: Manuela Brito, Chief Financial Officer Post Acute Care
CMO: Vasudeva Raju, M.D., Suffix Chief, Long Term Acute Care Medicine
CIO: Steve ONeill, Chief Information Officer
CHR: Jamie Grecco, Director Human Resources Post Acute
CNO: Stanlee Richards, R.N., MS, Chief Nurse Executive
Web address: www.nychealthandhospitals.org/Carter
Control: City, Government, nonfederal **Service**: Acute long–term care hospital

Staffed Beds: 365 **Admissions**: 376 **Census**: 303 **Outpatient Visits**: 0 **Births**: 0 **Total Expense ($000)**: 163040 **Payroll Expense ($000)**: 59668 **Personnel**: 799

☒ **NYC HEALTH + HOSPITALS / JACOBI (330127)**, 1400 Pelham Parkway South, Zip 10461–1197; tel. 718/918–5000, **A**1 3 5 10 **F**3 4 5 8 11 12 13 15 18 20 26 29 30 31 32 34 35 30 39 40 41 43 44 45 16 17 19 50 51 52 55 56 57 58 59 60 61 64 65 66 68 70 73 74 75 76 77 78 79 81 82 84 85 86 87 89 90 92 93 94 96 97 98 100 101 102 104 107 108 110 111 114 115 118 119 130 132 134 135 141 144 146 147 148 149 150 154 156 157 **S** NYC Health + Hospitals, New York, NY
Primary Contact: Christopher Mastromanno, Interim Chief Executive Officer
COO: Christopher Mastromanno, Chief Operating Officer
CFO: Ellen Barlis, Chief Financial Officer
CMO: Michael Zinaman, M.D., Acting Chief Medical Officer
CIO: Md Alam, Chief Information Officer
CHR: Jamie Grecco, Chief Human Resource Executive
CNO: Suzanne Pennacchio, MSN, R.N., Chief Nursing Officer
Web address: www.nyc.gov/html/hhc/jacobi/home.html
Control: City, Government, nonfederal **Service**: General medical and surgical

Staffed Beds: 388 **Admissions**: 18743 **Census**: 326 **Outpatient Visits**: 385711 **Births**: 1819 **Total Expense ($000)**: 716579 **Payroll Expense ($000)**: 293410 **Personnel**: 3300

☒ **NYC HEALTH + HOSPITALS / KINGS COUNTY (330202)**, 451 Clarkson Avenue, Zip 11203–2054; tel. 718/245–3131, **A**1 3 5 10 **F**3 4 5 8 9 11 12 13 15 17 18 19 20 24 26 28 29 30 31 32 34 35 38 39 40 41 43 45 46 47 49 50 51 52 53 56 57 58 59 60 61 64 65 66 68 69 70 71 72 73 74 75 76 77 78 79 81 82 84 85 86 87 88 89 90 91 92 93 94 97 98 99 100 101 102 103 104 105 106 107 108 110 111 114 115 116 119 120 121 123 129 130 131 132 134 135 143 144 145 146 147 148 149 153 154 156 157 **S** NYC Health + Hospitals, New York, NY
Primary Contact: Sheldon Mcleod, Chief Executive Officer
CNO: Opal Sinclair-Chung, R.N., MS, Chief Nursing Officer, Deputy Executive Director
Web address: www.nyc.gov/html/hhc/kchc/html/home/home.shtml
Control: City, Government, nonfederal **Service**: General medical and surgical

Staffed Beds: 544 **Admissions**: 19913 **Census**: 415 **Outpatient Visits**: 655784 **Births**: 1865 **Total Expense ($000)**: 923662 **Payroll Expense ($000)**: 424050 **Personnel**: 4492

☒ **NYC HEALTH + HOSPITALS / LINCOLN (330080)**, 234 East 149th Street, Zip 10451–5504, Mailing Address: 234 East 149th Street, Room 923, Zip 10451–5504; tel. 718/579–5700, **A**1 2 5 10 **F**3 5 8 11 13 15 18 19 29 30 31 32 34 35 38 39 40 41 43 45 50 55 56 57 58 59 60 61 64 65 66 68 70 71 73 74 75 76 77 78 79 81 82 84 85 86 87 89 93 97 98 100 102 107 108 110 111 114 115 119 121 123 130 132 134 135 143 144 146 147 148 151 157 **S** NYC Health + Hospitals, New York, NY
Primary Contact: Milton Nunez, Executive Director
CFO: Caswell Samms, Network Chief Financial Officer
CMO: Anita Soni, M.D., Chief Medical Officer
CIO: James Carr, Chief Information Officer
CHR: Jeannith Michelen, Senior Associate Executive Director
Web address: www.nyc.gov/html/hhc/lincoln/
Control: City, Government, nonfederal **Service**: General medical and surgical

Staffed Beds: 347 **Admissions**: 20208 **Census**: 279 **Outpatient Visits**: 512919 **Births**: 1970 **Total Expense ($000)**: 626726 **Payroll Expense ($000)**: 263181 **Personnel**: 3218

☒ **NYC HEALTH + HOSPITALS / METROPOLITAN (330199)**, 1901 First Avenue, Zip 10029–7404; tel. 212/423–6262, **A**1 3 5 10 **F**3 4 8 11 13 15 17 18 28 29 30 31 32 34 35 38 39 40 41 44 45 47 48 50 51 52 53 60 61 64 65 66 68 70 71 72 73 74 75 76 77 78 79 81 82 84 85 86 87 89 90 92 93 94 96 97 98 99 100 101 102 104 107 108 110 111 114 119 130 131 132 134 135 144 146 147 149 153 156 157 **S** NYC Health + Hospitals, New York, NY
Primary Contact: Alina Moran, Chief Executive Officer
COO: William Norberto Wang, M.D., Chief Operating Officer
CFO: Tracy V. Green, Chief Financial Officer
CMO: John T Pellicone, M.D., Chief Medical Officer
CIO: Md Alam, Chief Information Officer
CHR: April Alexander, Director Human Resources
CNO: Noreen Brennan, Chief Nursing Officer
Web address: www.nyc.gov/html/hhc/mhc/html/home/home.shtml
Control: City, Government, nonfederal **Service**: General medical and surgical

Staffed Beds: 273 **Admissions**: 9498 **Census**: 201 **Outpatient Visits**: 359083 **Births**: 957 **Total Expense ($000)**: 398090 **Payroll Expense ($000)**: 158099 **Personnel**: 1781

☒ **NYC HEALTH + HOSPITALS / NORTH CENTRAL BRONX (330385)**, 3424 Kossuth Avenue, Zip 10467–2489; tel. 718/519–3500, **A**1 5 10 **F**3 5 8 11 12 13 15 18 28 29 30 32 34 35 38 39 40 41 43 44 45 46 48 50 51 55 56 57 58 59 60 61 64 65 66 68 70 72 74 75 76 77 79 81 82 84 85 87 92 93 94 96 97 98 100 101 102 103 104 107 108 110 111 115 119 130 131 132 135 146 147 148 152 154 **S** NYC Health + Hospitals, New York, NY
Primary Contact: Maureen Pode, Co-Interim Executive Director
COO: Sheldon McLeod, Chief Operating Officer
CMO: Joseph Skarzynski, M.D., Medical Director
CIO: Diane Carr, Chief Information Officer
CNO: Elizabeth Gerdts, Chief Nursing Officer
Web address: www.nyc.gov/html/hhc/ncbh/html/home/home.shtml
Control: City, Government, nonfederal **Service**: General medical and surgical

Staffed Beds: 142 **Admissions**: 6987 **Census**: 111 **Outpatient Visits**: 200221 **Births**: 1718 **Total Expense ($000)**: 232514 **Payroll Expense ($000)**: 94857 **Personnel**: 1102

☒ **NYC HEALTH + HOSPITALS / QUEENS (330231)**, 82–68 164th Street, Zip 11432–1104; tel. 718/883–3000, **A**1 2 3 5 10 **F**3 5 8 9 11 13 15 18 19 28 29 30 31 32 34 35 38 39 40 41 45 46 47 49 50 52 53 54 55 56 58 59 60 61 64 65 66 68 70 71 72 73 74 75 76 77 78 81 82 84 85 86 87 97 98 100 101 102 104 105 107 108 110 111 114 116 117 118 119 120 121 123 129 130 132 141 143 144 146 147 148 149 152 153 154 156 **S** NYC Health + Hospitals, New York, NY
Primary Contact: Christopher Roker, Chief Executive Officer
COO: Dean Milhaltses, Chief Operating Officer
CFO: Brian Stacey, Chief Financial Officer
CMO: Jasmin Moshirpur, M.D., Chief Medical Officer
CIO: Vincent Smith, Chief Information Officer
CHR: Jeannith Michelen, Senior Associate Executive Director
CNO: Joan Gabriele, Deputy Executive Director
Web address: www.nyc.gov/html/hhc/qhc/html/home/home.shtml
Control: City, Government, nonfederal **Service**: General medical and surgical

Staffed Beds: 259 **Admissions**: 13511 **Census**: 193 **Outpatient Visits**: 398551 **Births**: 1556 **Total Expense ($000)**: 476611 **Payroll Expense ($000)**: 172970 **Personnel**: 1764

NY

Hospital, Medicare Provider Number, Address, Telephone, Approval, Facility, and Physician Codes, Health Care System

★ American Hospital Association (AHA) membership
☐ The Joint Commission accreditation
○ Healthcare Facilities Accreditation Program
◇ DNV Healthcare Inc. accreditation
⇑ Center for Improvement in Healthcare Quality Accreditation
△ Commission on Accreditation of Rehabilitation Facilities (CARF) accreditation

☒ **NYC HEALTH + HOSPITALS / WOODHULL (330396)**, 760 Broadway, Zip 11206–5383; tel. 718/963–8000, **A**1 3 5 10 **F**3 4 5 11 13 15 18 19 26 27 29 30 31 32 34 35 36 38 39 40 41 43 44 45 46 49 50 55 56 57 58 59 60 61 62 64 65 66 70 71 72 73 74 75 76 77 78 79 81 82 84 85 87 89 92 93 94 97 98 100 102 104 106 107 108 110 111 115 118 119 124 130 131 132 134 135 141 142 143 145 146 147 148 149 154 156 **S** NYC Health + Hospitals, New York, NY
Primary Contact: Gregory Calliste, Ph.D., FACHE, Chief Executive Officer
COO: Eve Borzon, R.N., Chief Operating Officer
CFO: Erika Soiman, CPA, Chief Financial Officer
CMO: Edward Fishkin, M.D., Medical Director
CHR: Irma Suarez, Deputy Executive Director
CNO: Angela Imelda Edwards, R.N., Chief Nurse Executive
Web address: www.nyc.gov/html/hhc
Control: City–county, Government, nonfederal **Service**: General medical and surgical

Staffed Beds: 274 **Admissions**: 10331 **Census**: 211 **Outpatient Visits**: 402999 **Births**: 1499 **Total Expense ($000)**: 481784 **Payroll Expense ($000)**: 192490 **Personnel**: 2090

NYU HOSPITAL FOR JOINT DISEASES See Nyu Langone Orthopedic Hospital

☒ **NYU LANGONE HOSPITALS (330214)**, 550 First Avenue, Zip 10016–6402; tel. 212/263–7300, (Includes HASSENFELD CHILDRENS HOSPITAL OF NEW YORK AT NYU LANGONE MEDICAL CENTER, 550 First Avenue, New York, New York, Zip 10016–6401; tel. 212/263–7300; NYU LANGONE HOSPITAL-BROOKLYN, 150 55th Street, Brooklyn, New York, Zip 11220–2559; tel. 718/630–7000; Bret Rudy, M.D., Executive Director and Senior Vice President; NYU LANGONE ORTHOPEDIC HOSPITAL, 301 East 17th Street, New York, New York, Zip 10003–3890; tel. 212/598–6000; David A Dibner, FACHE, Senior Vice President Hospital Operations and Musculoskeletal Strategic Areas; RUSK INSTITUTE AT NYU-HJD, 301 E 17th ST, New York, New York, Zip 10003–3804; tel. 212/598–6000; David A Dibner, FACHE, Senior Vice President Hospital Operations and Musculoskeletal Strategic Areas) **A**1 2 3 5 8 10 13 **F**3 5 6 7 8 9 11 12 13 15 17 18 19 20 21 22 23 24 25 26 27 28 29 30 31 32 33 34 35 36 37 38 39 40 41 42 43 44 45 46 47 48 49 50 51 52 53 54 55 56 57 58 59 60 61 62 64 65 66 68 70 72 73 74 75 76 77 78 79 81 82 84 85 86 87 88 89 90 91 92 93 94 95 96 97 98 100 101 102 103 104 107 108 110 111 112 113 114 115 117 118 119 120 121 123 124 126 129 130 131 132 134 135 136 137 138 139 140 141 142 143 145 146 147 148 149 150 153 154 156 157 **S** NYU Langone Health, New York, NY
Primary Contact: Robert I. Grossman, M.D., Chief Executive Officer
COO: Robert Press, M.D., Senior Vice President, Vice Dean and Chief Hospital Operations
CFO: Michael Burke, Senior Vice President and Corporate Chief Financial Officer
CMO: Fritz Francois, M.D., Chief Medical Officer
CIO: Nader Mherabi, Senior Vice President and Vice Dean, Chief Information Officer
CHR: Nancy Sanchez, Senior Vice President and Vice Dean Human Resources
CNO: Kimberly S Glassman, Ph.D., R.N., Chief Nursing Officer
Web address: www.nyumedicalcenter.org
Control: Other not–for–profit (including NFP Corporation) **Service**: General medical and surgical

Staffed Beds: 1152 **Admissions**: 62386 **Census**: 829 **Outpatient Visits**: 1827890 **Births**: 10571 **Total Expense ($000)**: 4307329 **Payroll Expense ($000)**: 1461472 **Personnel**: 18120

PAYNE WHITNEY PSYCHIATRIC CLINIC See New York-Presbyterian Hospital, New York

QUEENS CHILDREN'S PSYCHIATRIC CENTER See New York City Children's Center

☒ **RICHMOND UNIVERSITY MEDICAL CENTER (330028)**, 355 Bard Avenue, Zip 10310–1664; tel. 718/818–1234, **A**1 2 3 5 10 **F**3 4 5 7 11 12 13 14 15 17 18 20 22 26 28 29 30 31 32 34 35 38 40 41 43 45 46 47 48 49 50 51 54 56 57 58 59 60 61 64 65 66 68 70 71 72 74 75 76 78 79 80 81 82 84 85 87 88 89 90 92 93 94 97 98 99 100 101 102 103 104 105 107 108 110 111 114 115 116 117 118 119 120 121 122 123 124 126 129 130 131 132 134 135 144 146 147 148 149 150 152 153 156
Primary Contact: Daniel J. Messina, Ph.D., FACHE, President and Chief Executive Officer
CMO: Edward Arsura, M.D., Chief Medical Officer
CHR: Patricia Caldari, Vice President
Web address: www.rumcsi.org
Control: Other not–for–profit (including NFP Corporation) **Service**: General medical and surgical

Staffed Beds: 448 **Admissions**: 11942 **Census**: 201 **Outpatient Visits**: 259752 **Total Expense ($000)**: 355037 **Payroll Expense ($000)**: 181766 **Personnel**: 1825

☐ **ROCKEFELLER UNIVERSITY HOSPITAL (330387)**, 1230 York Avenue, Zip 10065–6399; tel. 212/327–8000, (Nonreporting) **A**1 10
Primary Contact: James G. Krueger, M.D., Ph.D., Chief Executive Officer
CMO: Barbara O'Sullivan, M.D., M.P.H., Medical Director
Web address: www.rucares.org
Control: Other not–for–profit (including NFP Corporation) **Service**: Other specialty treatment

Staffed Beds: 17

ROOSEVELT HOSPITAL See Mount Sinai West Hospital

☐ **SOUTH BEACH PSYCHIATRIC CENTER (334043)**, 777 Seaview Avenue, Zip 10305–3409; tel. 718/667–2300, **A**1 3 10 **F**98 101 104 105 106 153 **S** New York State Office of Mental Health, Albany, NY
Primary Contact: Doreen Piazza, Acting Executive Director
CHR: George Bouquio, Director Human Resources
Web address: www.omh.ny.gov/omhweb/facilities/sbpc/facility.htm
Control: State, Government, nonfederal **Service**: Psychiatric

Staffed Beds: 248 **Admissions**: 330 **Census**: 236 **Outpatient Visits**: 169839 **Births**: 0 **Personnel**: 740

☒ △ **STATEN ISLAND UNIVERSITY HOSPITAL (330160)**, 475 Seaview Avenue, Zip 10305–3436; tel. 718/226–9000, **A**1 2 3 5 7 8 10 **F**3 4 5 7 8 11 12 13 14 15 16 17 18 19 20 22 24 26 28 30 31 32 33 35 38 39 40 41 43 44 45 46 47 48 49 50 51 52 54 55 56 57 58 59 60 61 63 64 65 66 68 70 71 72 73 74 75 76 77 78 79 81 82 84 85 86 87 88 89 90 92 93 94 95 96 97 98 100 101 102 104 105 107 108 110 111 114 115 116 117 118 119 120 121 123 124 126 129 130 131 132 134 135 145 146 147 148 152 153 154 **S** Northwell Health, New Hyde Park, NY
Primary Contact: Brahim Ardolic, M.D., Chief Executive Officer
CFO: Thomas Reca Sr Deputy Executive Director and Chief Financial Officer
CMO: Theodore Maniatis, M.D., Medical Director
CIO: Kathy Kania, Associate Executive Director and Chief Information Officer
CHR: Margaret DiAlto, Regional Chief Human Resource Officer
CNO: Terry Pando, R.N., Associate Executive Director and Chief Nursing Officer
Web address: www.siuh.edu
Control: Other not–for–profit (including NFP Corporation) **Service**: General medical and surgical

Staffed Beds: 627 **Admissions**: 38382 **Census**: 581 **Outpatient Visits**: 926349 **Births**: 2722 **Total Expense ($000)**: 949967 **Payroll Expense ($000)**: 480829 **Personnel**: 5721

☒ **ST. BARNABAS HOSPITAL (330399)**, 4422 Third Avenue, Zip 10457–2545; tel. 718/960–9000, **A**1 3 5 10 12 13 19 **F**3 4 5 11 12 13 15 17 18 19 20 22 26 29 30 31 32 34 35 36 38 39 40 41 43 44 45 46 47 49 50 51 54 55 56 57 58 59 60 61 64 65 66 68 70 71 72 74 75 76 77 78 79 81 82 83 84 85 86 87 89 91 92 93 94 97 98 100 101 102 104 107 108 109 110 111 114 115 117 118 119 123 129 130 131 132 134 135 143 146 147 148 149 150 156 157
Primary Contact: David A. Perlstein, M.D., President and Chief Executive Officer
COO: Len Walsh, Executive Vice President and Chief Operating Officer
CFO: Todd Gorlewski, Senior Vice President and Chief Financial Officer
CIO: Jitendra Barmecha, M.D., M.P.H., Senior Vice President and Chief Information Officer
CHR: Marc Wolf, Assistant Vice President Human Resources
CNO: Denise Richardson, R.N., MSN, Senior Vice President and Chief Nursing Officer
Web address: www.sbhny.org
Control: Other not–for–profit (including NFP Corporation) **Service**: General medical and surgical

Staffed Beds: 422 **Admissions**: 14515 **Census**: 212 **Outpatient Visits**: 558898 **Births**: 871 **Total Expense ($000)**: 455113 **Payroll Expense ($000)**: 205783 **Personnel**: 2675

☐ **ST. JOHN'S EPISCOPAL HOSPITAL-SOUTH SHORE (330395)**, 327 Beach 19th Street, Zip 11691–4423; tel. 718/869–7000, **A**1 3 5 10 12 13 19 **F**3 13 15 17 18 19 29 30 31 32 34 35 38 40 41 45 49 50 54 55 56 57 59 60 61 64 65 68 70 73 74 75 76 77 78 79 81 82 84 85 87 89 92 93 97 98 100 101 102 103 104 107 108 110 111 114 119 130 132 134 135 141 146 148 149 153 156
Primary Contact: Gerard W. Walsh, Chief Executive Officer
COO: Patrick L Sullivan, Chief Operating Officer
CFO: Kathleen Garcia, Controller
CMO: Raymond Pastore, M.D., Chief Medical Officer
CIO: Michael J Piro, Chief Information Officer
CHR: Roger Franco, Director Human Resources
Web address: www.ehs.org
Control: State, Government, nonfederal **Service**: General medical and surgical

Staffed Beds: 213 **Admissions**: 7719 **Census**: 155 **Outpatient Visits**: 123230 **Births**: 650 **Total Expense ($000)**: 236301 **Payroll Expense ($000)**: 126955 **Personnel**: 1385

NY

Many Facility Codes have changed. Please refer to the AHA Guide Code Chart. © 2019 AHA Guide

☒ **SUNY DOWNSTATE MEDICAL CENTER UNIVERSITY HOSPITAL (330350)**, 450 Clarkson Avenue, Zip 11203–2012, Mailing Address: 450 Clarkson Avenue, MSC#75, Zip 11203–2012; tel. 718/270–1000, (Includes UNIVERSITY HOSPITAL OF BROOKLYN AT LONG ISLAND COLLEGE HOSPITAL, 339 Hicks Street, Brooklyn, New York, Zip 11201–5509; tel. 718/780–1000; George P Caralis, Interim Chief Executive Officer) **A**1 3 5 8 10 **F**8 13 14 15 17 18 19 20 22 24 26 29 30 31 34 35 36 38 40 41 42 44 45 46 47 48 49 50 51 54 55 56 57 58 59 60 61 64 65 66 68 70 72 73 74 75 76 77 78 79 80 81 82 84 86 87 88 89 90 92 93 94 95 96 97 104 107 108 110 111 114 115 118 119 126 129 130 131 138 143 144 146 147 149 150 156
Primary Contact: Wayne J. Riley, M.D., M.P.H., President
COO: Patricia A Winston, FACHE, MS, R.N., Vice President, Chief Administrative Officer and Chief Operating Officer
CFO: Richard B. Miller, Ph.D., Vice President Hospital Affairs and Chief Financial Officer
CMO: Michael Lucchesi, M.D., Chief Medical Officer; Chair, Emergency Medicine
CIO: Dilip Nath, Sc.D., Associate Chief Information Officer
CHR: Maria Silas, Manager Human Resources
CNO: Margaret G. Jackson, R.N., Vice President Patient Care Services and Chief Nursing Officer
Web address: www.downstate.edu
Control: State, Government, nonfederal **Service**: General medical and surgical

Staffed Beds: 323 Admissions: 10838 Census: 191 Outpatient Visits: 299974 Births: 931 Total Expense ($000): 497486 Payroll Expense ($000): 264049 Personnel: 2606

TERENCE CARDINAL COOKE HEALTH CARE CENTER (332022), 1249 Fifth Avenue, Zip 10029–4413; tel. 212/360–1000, (Nonreporting) **A**5 10
Primary Contact: Mitch Marsh, Interim Executive Director
COO: Neil Pollack, Senior Administrator
CFO: Ann Marie Covone, Senior Vice President and Chief Financial Officer
CMO: Anthony Lechich, M.D., Chief Medical Officer
CIO: Mitze Amoroso, Chief Information Officer
CHR: Hugo A Pizarro, Vice President Human Resources
CNO: Monica McGibbon, Chief Nursing Officer
Web address: www.tcchcc.org/
Control: Church operated, Nongovernment, not–for–profit **Service**: Acute long–term care hospital

Staffed Beds: 28

THE ALLEN PAVILION See New York Presbyterian Hospital, New York

VETERANS AFFAIRS MEDICAL CENTER See James J. Peters Veterans Affairs Medical Center

☒ **VETERANS AFFAIRS NEW YORK HARBOR HEALTHCARE SYSTEM**, 800 Poly Place, Zip 11209–7104; tel. 718/630–3500, (Includes VETERANS AFFAIRS NEW YORK HARBOR HEALTHCARE SYSTEM - MANHATTAN CAMPUS, 423 East 23rd Street, New York, New York, Zip 10010–5050, tel. 212/686–7500; Martina A Parauda, Director), (Non-reporting) **A**1 2 3 5 **S** Department of Veterans Affairs, Washington, DC
Primary Contact: Martina A. Parauda, Director
COO: Jodie A. Jackson, Associate Director
CFO: Andre Chance, Chief Financial Officer
CMO: Patrick C. Malloy, M D , Chief of Staff
CIO: Luis Barrios, Chief Information Officer
CHR: Kevin Grundig, Chief Human Resource Officer
CNO: Cynthia A. Caroselli, R.N., Ph.D., Chief Nursing Officer
Web address: www.nyharbor.va.gov
Control: Veterans Affairs, Government, federal **Service**: General medical and surgical

Staffed Beds: 522

☐ **WYCKOFF HEIGHTS MEDICAL CENTER (330221)**, 374 Stockholm Street, Zip 11237–4006; tel. 718/963–7272, (Nonreporting) **A**1 3 5 10 13
Primary Contact: Ramon J. Rodriguez, President and Chief Executive Officer
COO: David Rock, Executive Vice President and Chief Operating Officer
CFO: Frank A Vutrano, Chief Financial Officer
CMO: Gustavo Del Toro, M.D., Chief Medical Officer
CIO: Jebashini Jesurasa, Vice President, Chief Information Technology Officer
CHR: Margaret E Cornelius, Vice President Human Resources
CNO: Catherine A Gallogly-Simon, R.N., MS, Chief Nursing Officer
Web address: www.wyckoffhospital.org
Control: Other not–for–profit (including NFP Corporation) **Service**: General medical and surgical

Staffed Beds: 276

ZUCKER HILLSIDE HOSPITAL See Long Island Jewish Medical Center, New Hyde Park

NEWARK—Wayne County

☒ **NEWARK-WAYNE COMMUNITY HOSPITAL (330030)**, 1200 Driving Park Avenue, Zip 14513–1057, Mailing Address: P.O. Box 111, Zip 14513–0111; tel. 315/332–2022, (Total facility includes 180 beds in nursing home–type unit) **A**1 10 **F**2 3 5 6 11 12 13 15 28 29 30 34 35 38 40 44 45 46 50 51 54 56 57 59 64 68 70 75 76 77 79 80 81 85 86 87 90 93 96 97 98 100 101 102 103 107 108 110 111 115 119 126 127 128 130 131 132 135 141 146 147 148 149 150 154 156 **S** Rochester Regional Health, Rochester, NY
Primary Contact: Dustin Riccio, M.D., President Eastern Region
CFO: Tom Crilly, Executive Vice President, Chief Financial Officer, Rochester Regional Health
CMO: Robert Mayo, M.D., Executive Vice President, Chief Medical Officer, Rochester Regional Health
CIO: John Glynn, Executive Vice President, Chief Information Officer, Rochester Regional Health
CHR: Janine Schue, Executive Vice President, Chief Human Resources Officer, Rochester Regional Health
CNO: Theresa Glessner, Chief Nursing Officer, Eastern Region
Web address: www.rochesterregional.org
Control: Other not-for-profit (including NFP Corporation) **Service**: General medical and surgical

Staffed Beds: 289 Admissions: 6049 Census: 226 Outpatient Visits: 113593 Births: 693 Total Expense ($000): 103718 Payroll Expense ($000): 51344 Personnel: 747

NEWBURGH—Orange County

☒ **MONTEFIORE ST. LUKE'S CORNWALL (330264)**, 70 Dubois Street, Zip 12550–4851; tel. 845/561–4400, (Includes ST. LUKE'S CORNWALL HOSPITAL - CORNWALL CAMPUS, 19 Laurel Avenue, Cornwall, New York, Zip 12518–1499; tel. 845/534–7711; ST. LUKE'S CORNWALL HOSPITAL - NEWBURGH CAMPUS, 70 Dubois Street, Newburgh, New York, Zip 12550–4898; tel. 845/561–4400; Joan Cusack-McGuirk, President and Chief Executive Officer), (Non-reporting) **A**1 2 10 **S** Montefiore Health System, Bronx, NY
Primary Contact: Joan Cusack-McGuirk, President and Chief Executive Officer
CFO: Thomas Gibney, Senior Vice President and Chief Financial Officer
CMO: Christine Jelalian, M.D., Medical Director
CIO: Dwayne Simmons, Interim Chief Information Officer
CHR: Daniel Bengyak, Vice President, Administrative Services
CNO: Margaret Deyo-Allers, Vice President, Chief Nursing Officer
Web address: www.stlukescornwallhospital.org
Control: Other not–for–profit (including NFP Corporation) **Service**: General medical and surgical

Staffed Beds: 128

NIAGARA FALLS—Niagara County

○ **NIAGARA FALLS MEMORIAL MEDICAL CENTER (330065)**, 621 Tenth Street, Zip 14301–1813, Mailing Address: P.O. Box 708, Zip 14302–0708; tel. 716/278–4000, (Nonreporting) **A**3 5 10 11 13
Primary Contact: Joseph A. Ruffolo, President and Chief Executive Officer
CMO: Fatma Patel, M.D., Vice President Medical Affairs
CIO: Diane Martin-Pratt, Director Information Systems
Web address: www.nfmmc.org
Control: Other not-for-profit (including NFP Corporation) **Service**: General medical and surgical

Staffed Beds: 288

NORTH TONAWANDA—Niagara County

DE GRAFF MEMORIAL HOSPITAL See Kaleida Health, Buffalo

NORTHPORT—Suffolk County

☒ **NORTHPORT VETERANS AFFAIRS MEDICAL CENTER**, 79 Middleville Road, Zip 11768–2200; tel. 631/261–4400, (Nonreporting) **A**1 2 3 5 **S** Department of Veterans Affairs, Washington, DC
Primary Contact: Antonio Sanchez, M.D., Executive Director
COO: Michael McCully, Chief Operating Officer
CFO: Mary Pat Hessman, Chief Fiscal
CIO: Robert Ziskin, Chief Information Officer
CHR: Wilmino Sainbert, Chief Human Resources Management Service
Web address: www.northport.va.gov/index.asp
Control: Veterans Affairs, Government, federal **Service**: General medical and surgical

Staffed Beds: 254

NY

NORWICH—Chenango County

★ ○ **UHS CHENANGO MEMORIAL HOSPITAL (330033)**, 179 North Broad Street, Zip 13815–1097; tel. 607/337–4111, (Total facility includes 80 beds in nursing home–type unit) **A**10 11 20 **F**3 8 11 13 15 17 18 29 32 34 35 38 40 45 47 50 54 56 57 59 61 64 65 68 70 75 76 77 79 81 82 85 86 87 89 93 97 107 108 110 111 115 119 127 128 130 132 133 146 147 148 156 **S** United Health Services, Binghamton, NY
Primary Contact: Drake M. Lamen, M.D., President, Chief Executive Officer and Chief Medical Officer
COO: Christina A Kisacky, Vice President, Operations
CFO: Peggy Swartwood, Assistant Vice President, Finance and Controller
CIO: Richard Stone, Manager, Technical Services
CHR: Anne L English, Director Human Resources
CNO: David Finney, R.N., Vice President Nursing
Web address: www.uhs.net/cmh
Control: Other not–for–profit (including NFP Corporation) **Service**: General medical and surgical

Staffed Beds: 138 **Admissions**: 1353 **Census**: 73 **Outpatient Visits**: 265223 **Births**: 253 **Total Expense ($000)**: 70316 **Payroll Expense ($000)**: 21521 **Personnel**: 341

NYACK—Rockland County

☐ **NYACK HOSPITAL (330104)**, 160 North Midland Avenue, Zip 10960–1998; tel. 845/348–2000, **A**1 2 10 **F**4 5 8 11 12 13 14 15 17 20 29 30 31 34 35 40 41 43 45 46 50 51 54 55 57 58 59 62 64 65 66 68 70 72 74 75 76 77 78 79 81 82 85 86 87 89 91 97 98 100 102 107 108 111 112 114 115 119 129 130 145 146 147 148 151 154 156 157 **S** Montefiore Health System, Bronx, NY
Primary Contact: Mark Geller, M.D., President and Chief Executive Officer
COO: Michael Novak, Vice President and Chief Operating Officer
CFO: John Burke, Chief Financial Officer
CMO: Anthony Matejicka, D.O., M.P.H., Vice President, Chief Medical Officer
CHR: Mary K Shinick, Vice President Human Resources
CNO: Kathleen Lunney, MS, R.N., Vice President Patient Care Services and Chief Nursing Officer
Web address: www.nyackhospital.org
Control: Other not–for–profit (including NFP Corporation) **Service**: General medical and surgical

Staffed Beds: 235 **Admissions**: 10983 **Census**: 175 **Outpatient Visits**: 165745 **Births**: 1381 **Total Expense ($000)**: 268212 **Payroll Expense ($000)**: 108908 **Personnel**: 1446

OCEANSIDE—Nassau County

⊞ **SOUTH NASSAU COMMUNITIES HOSPITAL (330198)**, One Healthy Way, Zip 11572–1551; tel. 516/632–3000, **A**1 2 3 5 10 12 13 **F**3 5 11 12 13 15 17 18 20 22 26 28 29 30 31 34 35 37 38 40 42 43 44 45 46 47 49 50 54 55 56 57 58 59 60 62 64 66 68 70 73 74 75 76 77 78 79 81 82 83 84 85 86 87 89 91 92 93 97 98 99 100 102 103 104 105 107 108 110 111 114 115 117 118 119 120 121 123 124 126 128 129 130 131 132 135 145 146 148 149 153 154 156 157
Primary Contact: Richard J. Murphy, President and Chief Executive Officer
COO: William E. Allison, Senior Vice President and Chief Operating Officer, Administration
CFO: Mark A. Bogen, CPA, Senior Vice President, Finance
CMO: Adhi Sharma, M.D., Senior Vice President, Medical Affairs and Chief Medical Officer
CIO: Noah Caldwell, Vice President and Chief Information Officer
CHR: Paul D. Giordano, Senior Vice President, Human Resources
CNO: Stacey A Conklin, Chief Nursing Officer
Web address: www.southnassau.org
Control: Other not–for–profit (including NFP Corporation) **Service**: General medical and surgical

Staffed Beds: 381 **Admissions**: 19973 **Census**: 356 **Outpatient Visits**: 329836 **Births**: 1839 **Total Expense ($000)**: 569454 **Payroll Expense ($000)**: 280204 **Personnel**: 2913

OGDENSBURG—St. Lawrence County

★ ⇑ **CLAXTON-HEPBURN MEDICAL CENTER (330211)**, 214 King Street, Zip 13669–1142; tel. 315/393–3600, (Nonreporting) **A**2 10 20 21
Primary Contact: Charles Gijanto, Interim Chief Executive Officer
COO: Vicki Perrine, FACHE, Chief Operating Officer
CFO: Kelley Tiernan, Chief Financial Officer
CIO: James Flood, Director Information Systems
CHR: Lou-Ann McNally, Executive Director Human Resources and Staff Development
CNO: David Ferris, Chief Nursing Officer and Vice President Patient Care Services
Web address: www.claxtonhepburn.org
Control: Other not–for–profit (including NFP Corporation) **Service**: General medical and surgical

Staffed Beds: 97

☐ **ST. LAWRENCE PSYCHIATRIC CENTER (334003)**, 1 Chimney Point Drive, Zip 13669–2291; tel. 315/541–2001, (Nonreporting) **A**1 3 10 **S** New York State Office of Mental Health, Albany, NY
Primary Contact: Timothy Farrell, Executive Director
CMO: Harishankar Sanghi, M.D., Clinical Director
CHR: Rosie Turnbull, Director Human Resources
Web address: www.omh.ny.gov/omhweb/facilities/slpc/facility.htm
Control: State, Government, nonfederal **Service**: Psychiatric

Staffed Beds: 146

OLEAN—Cattaraugus County

⊞ **OLEAN GENERAL HOSPITAL (330103)**, 515 Main Street, Zip 14760–1513; tel. 716/373–2600, (Nonreporting) **A**1 3 5 10 19 **S** Upper Allegheny Health System, Olean, NY
Primary Contact: Timothy J. Finan, FACHE, President and Chief Executive Officer
COO: Jeff S Zewe, R.N., Senior Vice President, Chief Operating Officer
CFO: Richard G Braun, CPA, Jr Senior Vice President and Chief Financial Officer
CMO: William Mills, M.D., Senior Vice President Quality and Professional Affairs
CIO: Jason Yaworsky, Senior Vice President Information Systems and Chief Information Officer
CHR: Timothy M McNamara, Senior Vice President Human Resources
Web address: www.ogh.org
Control: Other not–for–profit (including NFP Corporation) **Service**: General medical and surgical

Staffed Beds: 186

ONEIDA—Madison County

⊞ **ONEIDA HEALTHCARE (330115)**, 321 Genesee Street, Zip 13421–2611; tel. 315/363–6000, (Total facility includes 160 beds in nursing home–type unit) **A**1 10 **F**3 10 11 13 15 18 29 30 34 35 40 45 49 50 54 57 59 64 65 68 70 74 75 76 77 78 79 81 85 86 87 89 92 93 97 107 108 110 111 115 117 118 119 126 128 129 130 135 146 149 156
Primary Contact: Gene Morreale, President and Chief Executive Officer
COO: Mary Parry, Vice President Operations and Chief Operating Officer
CMO: Dan J. Vick, M.D., Vice President of Medical Affairs and Chief Medical Officer
CIO: Mary McGuirl, Director Information Systems
CHR: Michael Fifield, Vice President Human Resources
Web address: www.oneidahealthcare.org
Control: Other not–for–profit (including NFP Corporation) **Service**: General medical and surgical

Staffed Beds: 231 **Admissions**: 2872 **Census**: 177 **Outpatient Visits**: 240354 **Births**: 507 **Total Expense ($000)**: 103078 **Payroll Expense ($000)**: 49767 **Personnel**: 910

ONEONTA—Otsego County

★ ⇑ **AURELIA OSBORN FOX MEMORIAL HOSPITAL (330085)**, 1 Norton Avenue, Zip 13820–2629; tel. 607/432–2000, (Total facility includes 131 beds in nursing home–type unit) **A**10 21 **F**2 3 11 15 18 26 28 29 30 34 35 37 39 40 42 45 51 53 54 56 57 59 64 65 68 75 77 81 85 86 87 93 96 97 104 107 108 110 111 115 118 119 120 121 123 128 129 130 135 146 147 154 **S** Bassett Healthcare Network, Cooperstown, NY
Primary Contact: Jeff Joyner, President
COO: Gary Smith, Chief Operating Officer
CFO: Mark J. Wright, Chief Financial Officer
CMO: Reginald Q. Knight, Chief Medical Officer
CHR: Jennie Gliha, Chief Human Resource Officer
CNO: Joan MacDonald, R.N., MSN, Chief Nursing Officer
Web address: www.bassett.org/ao-fox-hospital/
Control: Other not–for–profit (including NFP Corporation) **Service**: General medical and surgical

Staffed Beds: 184 **Admissions**: 2423 **Census**: 150 **Outpatient Visits**: 123302 **Births**: 0 **Total Expense ($000)**: 83403 **Payroll Expense ($000)**: 31897 **Personnel**: 688

ORANGEBURG—Rockland County

☐ **ROCKLAND CHILDREN'S PSYCHIATRIC CENTER (334066)**, 599 Convent Road, Zip 10962–1162; tel. 845/359–7400, (Nonreporting) **A**1 3 5 **S** New York State Office of Mental Health, Albany, NY
Primary Contact: Christopher Tavella, Acting Executive Director
COO: Kenneth Perrotte, Director Operations
CFO: Peter Gorey, Administrative Coordinator
CMO: Sadhana Sardana, M.D., Clinical Director
CIO: Mary Pivonka, Director Quality Management
Web address: www.omh.ny.gov/
Control: State, Government, nonfederal **Service**: Children's hospital psychiatric

Staffed Beds: 54

Many Facility Codes have changed. Please refer to the AHA Guide Code Chart. © 2019 AHA Guide

☐ **ROCKLAND PSYCHIATRIC CENTER (334015)**, 140 Old Orangeburg Road, Zip 10962–1157; tel. 845/359–1000, (Nonreporting) **A**1 3 5 10 **S** New York State Office of Mental Health, Albany, NY
Primary Contact: Christopher Tavella, Executive Director
Web address: www.omh.ny.gov/
Control: State, Government, nonfederal **Service**: Psychiatric

Staffed Beds: 525

OSSINING—Westchester County

OSSINING CORRECTIONAL FACILITIES HOSPITAL, 354 Hunter Street, Zip 10562–5498; tel. 914/941–0108, (Nonreporting) **A**3
Primary Contact: Riza Ferdous, Health Services Director
Control: State, Government, nonfederal **Service**: Hospital unit of an institution (prison hospital, college infirmary, etc.)

Staffed Beds: 25

OSWEGO—Oswego County

⊞ **OSWEGO HOSPITAL (330218)**, 110 West Sixth Street, Zip 13126–2507; tel. 315/349–5511, **A**1 3 10 20 **F**2 3 8 11 12 13 15 18 29 34 38 40 41 45 49 50 51 57 59 62 70 75 77 79 81 85 86 87 93 97 98 100 101 102 104 107 108 110 111 114 115 118 119 130 131 132 135 144 146 156
Primary Contact: Michael Harlovic, R.N., President and Chief Executive Officer
COO: Jeff Coakley, Executive Vice President and Chief Operating Officer
CFO: Eric Campbell, Chief Financial Officer
CMO: Renato Mandanas, M.D., Chief Medical Officer
CIO: Barry W. Ryle, Chief Information Officer
CHR: James E Marco Jr Interim Vice President, Human Resources
CNO: Valerie Favata, R.N., MS, Chief Nursing Officer
Web address: www.oswegohealth.org
Control: Other not–for–profit (including NFP Corporation) **Service**: General medical and surgical

Staffed Beds: 99 **Admissions:** 4661 **Census:** 55 **Outpatient Visits:** 319388 **Births:** 484

PATCHOGUE—Suffolk County

★ ⇧ **LONG ISLAND COMMUNITY HOSPITAL (330141)**, 101 Hospital Road, Zip 11772–4897; tel. 631/654–7100, (Nonreporting) **A**3 5 10 13 21
Primary Contact: Richard T. Margulis, President and Chief Executive Officer
COO: Ron Stephenson, Chief Operating Officer
CFO: Brenda Farrell, Vice President Finance
CMO: Nejat Zeyneloglu, Vice President and Chief Quality Medical Officer
CIO: Joseph Wood, Vice President and Chief Information Officer
CNO: Debra Grimm, MS, R.N., Vice President and Chief Nursing Officer
Web address: www.bmhmc.org
Control: Other not–for–profit (including NFP Corporation) **Service**: General medical and surgical

Staffed Beds: 247

PENN YAN—Yates County

SOLDIERS AND SAILORS MEMORIAL HOSPITAL OF YATES COUNTY (331314), 418 North Main Street, Zip 14527–1085; tel. 315/531–2000, **A**10 18 **F**2 3 11 15 18 28 29 34 35 38 40 54 56 57 59 64 65 66 68 70 75 87 93 97 98 100 101 104 107 110 114 119 128 130 132 133 135 146 147 **S** Finger Lakes Health, Geneva, NY
Primary Contact: Frank Korich, FACHE, Senior Vice President, Operations
COO: Lina Brennan, Site Administrator
CFO: Pamela Johnson, Treasurer and Chief Financial Officer
CMO: Jason Feinberg, M.D., Vice President Medical Affairs and Chief Medical Officer
CIO: Guy W Mosher III Manager Information Systems
CHR: Patrick R Boyle, Vice President Human Resources
CNO: Eileen Gage, R.N., Vice President Nursing
Web address: www.flhealth.org
Control: Other not–for–profit (including NFP Corporation) **Service**: General medical and surgical

Staffed Beds: 189 **Admissions:** 903 **Census:** 143 **Outpatient Visits:** 149650 **Births:** 0 **Total Expense ($000):** 28172 **Payroll Expense ($000):** 16466 **Personnel:** 310

PLAINVIEW—Nassau County

⊞ **PLAINVIEW HOSPITAL (330331)**, 888 Old Country Road, Zip 11803–4978; tel. 516/719–3000, **A**1 3 5 10 12 13 **F**3 5 8 9 15 17 18 29 30 31 34 35 36 38 40 43 44 45 46 49 50 51 57 58 59 60 63 64 65 68 69 70 71 74 75 78 79 81 84 85 86 87 97 100 101 102 107 108 110 111 114 115 119 130 132 135 146 148 152 154 157 **S** Northwell Health, New Hyde Park, NY
Primary Contact: Michael Fener, Executive Director
CMO: Alan Mensch, M.D., Senior Vice President Medical Affairs
Web address: www.https://www.planview.com/
Control: Other not–for–profit (including NFP Corporation) **Service**: General medical and surgical

Staffed Beds: 150 **Admissions:** 8400 **Census:** 109 **Outpatient Visits:** 60494 **Births:** 0 **Total Expense ($000):** 224135 **Payroll Expense ($000):** 110317 **Personnel:** 1203

PLATTSBURGH—Clinton County

⊞ **THE UNIVERSITY OF VERMONT HEALTH NETWORK-CHAMPLAIN VALLEY PHYSICIANS HOSPITAL (330250)**, 75 Beekman Street, Zip 12901–1438; tel. 518/561–2000, (Total facility includes 35 beds in nursing home–type unit) **A**1 2 3 5 10 **F**1 3 7 8 13 14 15 17 18 20 22 26 28 29 30 31 34 35 36 37 38 40 41 43 45 46 47 48 49 50 51 53 54 57 59 60 64 68 70 75 76 77 78 79 81 82 84 85 86 87 89 90 91 92 93 97 98 99 100 101 102 107 108 109 110 111 112 113 114 115 116 117 118 119 120 121 122 123 124 126 128 129 130 131 132 135 144 146 147 148 149 154 156 157
Primary Contact: Michelle Lebeau, President and Chief Operating Officer
COO: Michelle Lebeau, President and Chief Operating Officer
CFO: Joyce Rafferty, Vice President Finance
CMO: Kent Hall, M.D., Vice President and Chief Medical Officer
CIO: Wouter Rietsema, M.D., Chief Quality and Information Officer
CHR: Dean Civitello, Vice President, Human Resources, Public Relations and Development
Web address: www.https://profiles.health.ny.gov/hospital/view/103048
Control: Other not–for–profit (including NFP Corporation) **Service**: General medical and surgical

Staffed Beds: 264 **Admissions:** 8551 **Census:** 167 **Outpatient Visits:** 310978 **Births:** 803 **Total Expense ($000):** 351832 **Payroll Expense ($000):** 188994 **Personnel:** 2027

PORT JEFFERSON—Suffolk County

⊞ **JOHN T. MATHER MEMORIAL HOSPITAL (330185)**, 75 North Country Road, Zip 11777–2190; tel. 631/473–1320, **A**1 2 3 10 **F**5 8 11 12 14 15 17 18 29 31 34 35 36 37 38 40 44 45 46 49 51 55 56 57 59 64 65 69 70 74 75 77 78 79 81 82 84 85 86 87 93 98 99 100 101 102 103 104 105 107 108 110 111 114 115 118 119 124 126 129 130 132 146 147 148 152 **S** Northwell Health, New Hyde Park, NY
Primary Contact: Kenneth D. Roberts, President
COO: Kevin J Murray, Senior Vice President
CFO: Joseph Wisnoski, Chief Financial Officer
CMO: Joan Faro, M.D., Chief Medical Officer
CIO: Thomas Hoiman, Vice President Information Services and Chief Information Officer
CHR: Diane Marotta, Vice President Human Resources
CNO: Marie Mulligan, R.N., MSN, Vice President Nursing
Web address: www.matherhospital.com
Control: Other not–for–profit (Including NFP Corporation) **Service**: General medical and surgical

Staffed Beds: 248 **Admissions:** 12170 **Census:** 206 **Outpatient Visits:** 175682 **Births:** 0 **Total Expense ($000):** 373614 **Payroll Expense ($000):** 178194 **Personnel:** 2320

☐ △ **ST. CHARLES HOSPITAL (330246)**, 200 Belle Terre Road, Zip 11777–1928; tel. 631/474–6000, **A**1 2 3 7 10 **F**3 4 5 8 11 12 13 15 17 28 29 30 31 32 34 35 37 39 40 41 44 45 46 47 48 49 50 54 57 58 59 64 65 66 68 70 72 73 74 75 76 77 78 79 80 81 82 84 85 86 87 89 90 91 92 93 96 97 100 107 108 110 111 114 115 119 126 129 130 131 132 134 135 141 142 146 148 149 151 153 157 **S** Catholic Health Services of Long Island, Rockville Centre, NY
Primary Contact: James O'Connor, President
COO: Ronald Weingartner, Vice President Administration
CFO: Kathleen Vasil, Vice President Finance
CMO: Michael Sauter, M.D., Chief Medical Officer
CIO: Felix Pabon-Ramirez, Chief Information Officer
CNO: Nicolette Fiore-Lopez, R.N., Chief Nursing Officer
Web address: www.stcharleshospital.chsli.org
Control: Church operated, Nongovernment, not–for–profit **Service**: General medical and surgical

Staffed Beds: 243 **Admissions:** 10516 **Census:** 171 **Outpatient Visits:** 31241 **Births:** 1170 **Total Expense ($000):** 235360 **Payroll Expense ($000):** 95264 **Personnel:** 1275

NY

PORT JERVIS—Orange County

☒ **BON SECOURS COMMUNITY HOSPITAL (330135)**, 160 East Main Street, Zip 12771–2245, Mailing Address: P.O. Box 1014, Zip 12771–0268; tel. 845/858–7000, (Nonreporting) **A**1 10 **S** WMCHealth, Valhalla, NY
Primary Contact: Mary Leahy, M.D., Chief Executive Officer
COO: Gaynor Rosenstein, Vice President Operations
CHR: Kim Hirkaler, Director Human Resources
Web address: www.bonsecourscommunityhosp.org
Service: General medical and surgical

Staffed Beds: 143

POTSDAM—St. Lawrence County

★ ⇑ **CANTON-POTSDAM HOSPITAL (330197)**, 50 Leroy Street, Zip 13676–1799; tel. 315/265–3300, **A**10 20 21 **F**1 3 4 5 11 13 15 16 17 18 26 28 29 30 31 34 35 36 38 40 43 46 51 54 57 58 59 64 65 67 68 70 72 73 74 75 76 77 78 79 80 81 82 85 86 87 88 89 90 92 93 94 95 96 97 98 100 101 102 104 107 108 110 111 115 116 117 118 119 120 121 123 127 128 129 130 131 132 133 135 144 145 146 147 149 150 152 156 **S** St. Lawrence Health System, Potsdam, NY
Primary Contact: David B. Acker, FACHE, President and Chief Executive Officer
CFO: Richard Jacobs, Vice President Finance and Chief Financial Officer
CMO: Robert T Rogers, M.D., II Medical Director
CIO: Jorge C Grillo, Chief Information Officer
CHR: Darlene Lewis, Vice President Human Resources
CNO: Jan Carroll, MSN, M.P.H., R.N., Chief Nursing Officer
Web address: www.cphospital.org
Control: Other not–for–profit (including NFP Corporation) **Service:** General medical and surgical

Staffed Beds: 87 Admissions: 4899 Census: 63 Outpatient Visits: 346979 Births: 502 Total Expense ($000): 192864 Payroll Expense ($000): 100270 Personnel: 1125

POUGHKEEPSIE—Dutchess County

☐ **VASSAR BROTHERS MEDICAL CENTER (330023)**, 45 Reade Place, Zip 12601–3947; tel. 845/454–8500, **A**1 2 3 10 **F**3 7 8 11 13 15 17 18 20 22 24 26 28 29 30 31 34 35 36 37 40 43 44 45 46 47 48 49 50 51 54 55 57 58 59 60 64 65 68 70 72 73 74 75 76 77 78 79 81 82 84 85 87 89 92 93 97 100 102 104 107 108 109 110 111 114 115 117 118 119 120 121 123 124 126 129 130 131 132 135 143 146 147 148 149 154 156 157 **S** Health Quest Systems, Inc., LaGrangeville, NY
Primary Contact: Ann McMackin, President
COO: Robert Rosenbaum, Vice President Operations
CFO: Tony Perugino, Assistant Vice President Decision Support
CMO: Michael Doyle, M.D., Vice President Medical Affairs
CNO: Lore Bogolin, MSN, R.N., Chief Nursing Officer and Vice President Care Services
Web address: www.health-quest.org
Control: Other not–for–profit (including NFP Corporation) **Service:** General medical and surgical

Staffed Beds: 365 Admissions: 21256 Census: 263 Outpatient Visits: 313577 Births: 2540 Total Expense ($000): 573620 Payroll Expense ($000): 162208 Personnel: 1950

RHINEBECK—Dutchess County

☐ **NORTHERN DUTCHESS HOSPITAL (330049)**, 6511 Springbrook Avenue, Zip 12572–3709, Mailing Address: P.O. Box 5002, Zip 12572–5002; tel. 845/876–3001, **A**1 3 10 **F**3 7 11 12 13 15 18 28 29 30 31 34 35 36 37 40 44 45 47 48 50 53 56 57 58 59 64 65 68 70 74 75 76 77 78 79 81 82 84 85 87 90 93 100 107 108 110 111 115 118 119 125 126 129 130 131 132 146 147 148 149 154 156 157 158 **S** Health Quest Systems, Inc., LaGrangeville, NY
Primary Contact: Denise George, R.N., President
CMO: John Sabia, M.D., Vice President Medical Affairs
Web address: www.health-quest.org/home_nd.cfm?id=9
Control: Other not–for–profit (including NFP Corporation) **Service:** General medical and surgical

Staffed Beds: 84 Admissions: 5197 Census: 50 Outpatient Visits: 95077 Births: 875 Total Expense ($000): 119147 Payroll Expense ($000): 40148 Personnel: 582

RIVERHEAD—Suffolk County

☒ **PECONIC BAY MEDICAL CENTER (330107)**, 1300 Roanoke Avenue, Zip 11901–2031; tel. 631/548–6000, **A**1 3 5 10 12 13 **F**3 5 7 11 12 13 15 18 20 22 28 29 30 31 33 34 35 40 41 43 44 45 46 49 50 51 53 54 56 57 59 62 64 67 68 70 74 75 76 77 78 79 80 81 82 83 84 85 86 87 93 96 100 102 107 108 110 111 115 118 119 129 130 131 132 143 144 146 147 148 149 152 154 157 **S** Northwell Health, New Hyde Park, NY
Primary Contact: Andrew J. Mitchell, President and Chief Executive Officer
COO: Ronald McManus, Senior Vice President Clinical Services and Business Entities
CFO: Michael F. O'Donnell, CPA, Chief Financial Officer
CIO: Arthur Crowe, Director Information Systems
CHR: Monica Chestnut-Rauls, Vice President Human Resources
CNO: Amy E Loeb, Ed.D., R.N., Chief Nursing Officer
Web address: www.pbmchealth.org
Control: Other not–for–profit (including NFP Corporation) **Service:** General medical and surgical

Staffed Beds: 110 Admissions: 8517 Census: 101 Outpatient Visits: 98904 Births: 306 Total Expense ($000): 201953 Payroll Expense ($000): 86904 Personnel: 1181

ROCHESTER—Monroe County

☒ **HIGHLAND HOSPITAL (330164)**, 1000 South Avenue, Zip 14620–2733; tel. 585/473–2200, **A**1 3 5 10 19 **F**3 12 13 15 18 26 29 30 31 34 35 36 37 40 44 45 46 47 49 50 54 55 56 57 58 59 60 63 64 65 66 68 70 74 75 76 77 78 79 81 83 84 85 86 87 91 93 97 100 107 108 110 114 115 118 119 120 121 122 123 126 130 132 135 141 145 146 147 148 149 154 **S** University of Rochester Medical Center, Rochester, NY
Primary Contact: Steven I. Goldstein, President and Chief Executive Officer
COO: Cindy Becker, Vice President and Chief Operating Officer
CFO: Adam Anolik, Chief Financial Officer
CMO: Raymond Mayewski, M.D., Chief Medical Officer
CIO: Tom Barnett, Chief Information Officer
CHR: Amy Taney, Chief Human Resource Officer
Web address: www.https://www.urmc.rochester.edu/highland
Control: Other not–for–profit (including NFP Corporation) **Service:** General medical and surgical

Staffed Beds: 261 Admissions: 16858 Census: 213 Outpatient Visits: 480296 Births: 3117 Total Expense ($000): 378013 Payroll Expense ($000): 178313 Personnel: 2413

☒ **ROCHESTER GENERAL HOSPITAL (330125)**, 1425 Portland Avenue, Zip 14621–3099; tel. 585/922–4000, **A**1 2 3 5 10 **F**3 5 8 9 11 12 13 15 17 18 20 22 24 26 29 30 31 32 34 35 38 39 40 41 44 45 47 49 50 51 54 55 56 57 58 59 60 61 63 64 65 66 68 70 71 73 74 75 76 77 78 79 80 81 82 84 85 86 87 89 92 93 96 97 98 100 101 102 103 104 107 108 110 111 114 115 116 117 118 119 120 121 123 124 126 127 129 130 131 132 134 135 141 144 145 146 147 148 149 150 154 156 157 158 **S** Rochester Regional Health, Rochester, NY
Primary Contact: Kevin John. Casey, President
CMO: Robert Mayo, M.D., Chief Medical Officer
CIO: John Glynn, Chief Information Officer
CHR: Janine Schue, Senior Vice President Human Resources
CNO: Cheryl Sheridan, R.N., Senior Vice President Patient Care Services
Web address: www.https://www.rochesterregional.org/
Control: Other not–for–profit (including NFP Corporation) **Service:** General medical and surgical

Staffed Beds: 528 Admissions: 31342 Census: 402 Outpatient Visits: 2083022 Births: 2070 Total Expense ($000): 1079039 Payroll Expense ($000): 517502 Personnel: 7041

☐ **ROCHESTER PSYCHIATRIC CENTER (334020)**, 1111 Elmwood Avenue, Zip 14620–3005; tel. 585/241–1200, (Nonreporting) **A**1 3 5 10 **S** New York State Office of Mental Health, Albany, NY
Primary Contact: Philip Griffin, Director of Operations
COO: Joseph Coffey, Director Facility Administration
CFO: Rosanne Minnis, Business Officer
CMO: Laurence Guttmacher, M.D., Clinical Director
CIO: Lori Hintz, Coordinator Information Systems
CHR: Colomba Misseritti, Director Human Resources
CNO: Christopher Kirisits, Chief Nursing Officer
Web address: www.omh.ny.gov/omhweb/facilities/ropc/facility.htm
Control: State, Government, nonfederal **Service:** Psychiatric

Staffed Beds: 180

NY

Many Facility Codes have changed. Please refer to the AHA Guide Code Chart. © 2019 AHA Guide

☒ △ **STRONG MEMORIAL HOSPITAL OF THE UNIVERSITY OF ROCHESTER (330285)**, 601 Elmwood Avenue, Zip 14642–0002, Mailing Address: 601 Elmwood Avenue, Box 612, Zip 14642–0002; tel. 585/275–2100, (Includes GOLISANO CHILDREN'S HOSPITAL, 601 Elmwood Avenue, Rochester, New York, Zip 14610; tel. 585/275–2182) **A**1 2 3 5 7 8 10 19 **F**3 5 6 8 9 11 12 13 14 15 16 17 18 19 20 21 22 23 24 25 26 27 28 29 30 31 32 33 34 35 36 38 39 40 41 42 43 44 45 46 47 48 49 50 51 52 53 54 55 56 57 58 59 60 61 63 64 65 66 68 70 71 72 73 74 75 76 77 78 79 80 81 82 83 84 85 86 87 88 89 90 91 92 93 94 95 96 97 98 99 100 101 102 103 104 105 107 108 110 111 114 115 116 117 118 119 120 121 123 124 126 127 129 130 131 132 134 135 136 137 138 139 141 142 143 144 145 146 147 148 149 150 152 153 154 157 **S** University of Rochester Medical Center, Rochester, NY
Primary Contact: Steven I. Goldstein, President and Chief Executive Officer
COO: Kathleen M Parrinello, Ph.D., Chief Operating Officer
CFO: David L. Kirshner, Chief Financial Officer
CMO: Raymond Mayewski, M.D., Chief Medical Officer
CIO: D Jerome Powell, M.D., Chief Information Officer
CHR: Charles J Murphy, Associate Vice President Human Resources
Web address: www.urmc.rochester.edu
Control: Other not–for–profit (including NFP Corporation) **Service**: General medical and surgical

> **Staffed Beds: 869 Admissions: 41222 Census: 804 Outpatient Visits: 1849201 Births: 2849 Total Expense ($000): 1908332 Payroll Expense ($000): 719516 Personnel: 11951**

☒ **UNITY HOSPITAL (330226)**, 1555 Long Pond Road, Zip 14626–4182; tel. 585/723–7000, (Total facility includes 120 beds in nursing home–type unit) **A**1 3 5 10 **F**3 4 5 11 12 13 15 18 20 22 26 28 29 30 31 33 34 35 38 39 40 44 45 46 47 48 49 50 52 55 56 57 59 60 61 63 64 65 66 68 70 71 73 74 75 76 77 78 79 80 81 82 84 85 86 87 90 91 92 93 96 97 98 100 101 102 103 104 107 108 114 118 119 121 126 128 129 130 133 135 141 144 146 147 148 149 150 151 156 157 158 **S** Rochester Regional Health, Rochester, NY
Primary Contact: Douglas Stewart, PsyD, President
COO: Stewart C Putnam, Executive Vice President and Chief Operating Officer
CFO: Tom Crilly, Executive Vice President and Chief Financial Officer
CMO: James Haley, M.D., Senior Vice President and Chief Medical Officer
CIO: John Glynn, Senior Vice President and Chief Information Officer
CHR: Maryalice Keller, Vice President Brand and Talent Management
CNO: Jane McCormack, R.N., MSN, Vice President, Chief Nursing Officer and Nursing and Patient Care Services
Web address: www.unityhealth.org
Control: Other not–for–profit (including NFP Corporation) **Service**: General medical and surgical

> **Staffed Beds: 451 Admissions: 18916 Census: 404 Outpatient Visits: 886317 Births: 1558 Total Expense ($000): 490655 Payroll Expense ($000): 243398 Personnel: 4039**

ROCKVILLE CENTRE—Nassau County

☐ **MERCY MEDICAL CENTER (330259)**, 1000 North Village Avenue, Zip 11570–1000; tel. 516/705–2525, **A**1 2 3 10 13 **F**3 5 8 12 13 15 18 20 26 29 30 31 34 35 38 40 45 46 48 49 50 51 56 57 59 60 61 64 68 70 72 74 75 76 77 78 79 81 82 84 85 87 90 92 93 94 96 97 98 100 102 104 105 107 108 110 111 114 115 118 119 129 130 131 132 135 143 146 147 148 149 152 153 **S** Catholic Health Services of Long Island, Rockville Centre, NY
Primary Contact: Peter Scaminaci, President
CFO: William C Armstrong, Senior Vice President and Chief Financial Officer
CMO: John Reilly, M.D., Vice President Medical Affairs and Chief Medical Officer
CIO: Marcy Dunn, Vice President Information Services and Chief Information Officer
CHR: Allison Cianciotto Croyle, Vice President of Human Resources
CNO: Beth Vlahavas, R.N., MSN, Vice President Patient Care Services and Chief Nursing Officer
Web address: www.mercymedicalcenter.chsli.org
Control: Church operated, Nongovernment, not–for–profit **Service**: General medical and surgical

> **Staffed Beds: 191 Admissions: 10688 Census: 185 Outpatient Visits: 113341 Births: 902 Total Expense ($000): 243487 Payroll Expense ($000): 98994 Personnel: 1140**

ROME—Oneida County

★ ○ **ROME MEMORIAL HOSPITAL (330215)**, 1500 North James Street, Zip 13440–2844; tel. 315/338–7000, (Total facility includes 82 beds in nursing home–type unit) **A**5 10 11 **F**3 5 8 13 15 18 26 29 30 34 35 37 38 40 45 49 50 51 54 55 56 57 59 64 70 74 75 76 77 78 79 80 81 82 85 87 89 90 93 97 98 102 103 107 108 109 110 111 112 113 114 115 116 117 119 120 121 122 123 124 127 128 129 130 132 135 144 146 147 148 149 154 157
Primary Contact: David W. Lundquist, President and Chief Executive Officer
CFO: Dewey R Rowlands, Vice President and Chief Financial Officer
CMO: Andrew Bushnell, M.D., Interim Chief Medical Officer
CIO: Mark Rowan, Interim Chief Information Officer
CHR: Regina Chambers, Vice President Human Resource
CNO: Durinda Durr, Vice President and Chief Nursing Officer
Web address: www.romehospital.org
Control: Other not–for–profit (including NFP Corporation) **Service**: General medical and surgical

> **Staffed Beds: 203 Admissions: 4459 Census: 119 Outpatient Visits: 160358 Births: 540 Total Expense ($000): 87296 Payroll Expense ($000): 40422 Personnel: 798**

ROSLYN—Nassau County

☒ **ST. FRANCIS HOSPITAL, THE HEART CENTER (330182)**, 100 Port Washington Boulevard, Zip 11576–1353; tel. 516/562–6000, **A**1 3 10 **F**3 7 8 11 12 14 15 17 18 20 21 22 23 24 25 26 27 28 29 30 31 34 35 36 37 38 39 40 44 45 46 47 49 50 51 53 54 55 56 57 58 59 60 61 62 63 64 65 66 68 70 71 74 75 77 78 79 81 82 84 85 86 87 93 97 100 102 107 108 109 110 111 114 115 116 117 118 119 120 121 123 126 130 131 132 135 146 147 148 149 154 156 **S** Catholic Health Services of Long Island, Rockville Centre, NY
Primary Contact: Charles Lucore, M.D., President
CFO: William C Armstrong, Vice President and Chief Financial Officer
CMO: Jack Soterakis, M.D., Executive Vice President Medical Affairs
CIO: Marcy Dunn, Vice President Information Services and Chief Information Officer
CHR: Barbara Fierro, Director, Human Resources
CNO: Ann S Cella, R.N., Senior Vice President, Patient Care Services
Web address: www.stfrancisheartcenter.com/index.html
Control: Church operated, Nongovernment, not–for–profit **Service**: General medical and surgical

> **Staffed Beds: 320 Admissions: 18554 Census: 266 Outpatient Visits: 223862 Births: 0 Total Expense ($000): 660589 Payroll Expense ($000): 277925 Personnel: 2973**

SARANAC LAKE—Franklin County

★ ○ **ADIRONDACK HEALTH (330079)**, 2233 State Route 86, Zip 12983–5644, Mailing Address: P.O. Box 471, Zip 12983–0471; tel. 518/891–4141, (Total facility includes 60 beds in nursing home–type unit) **A**10 11 **F**3 8 9 12 13 15 18 28 29 30 31 34 35 37 38 39 40 41 42 43 45 46 49 50 53 54 56 57 59 60 64 70 71 74 75 76 77 78 79 81 82 84 85 86 89 90 92 93 94 97 98 102 103 104 107 108 110 111 114 116 119 127 128 129 130 131 132 135 146 147 148 153 154 156 **S** QHR, Brentwood, TN
Primary Contact: Sylvia Getman, President and Chief Executive Officer
COO: Patti Hammond, Chief Operating Officer
CFO: Tristan Glanville, Chief Financial Officer
CMO: Joahd Toure', M.D., Chief Medical Officer
CHR: Michael D Lee, Chief Human Resources Officer
CNO: Linda McClarigan, R.N., Chief Nursing Officer
Web address: www.adirondackhealth.org
Control: Other not–for–profit (including NFP Corporation) **Service**: General medical and surgical

> **Staffed Beds: 120 Admissions: 2353 Census: 79 Outpatient Visits: 150721 Births: 165 Total Expense ($000): 111329 Payroll Expense ($000): 52267 Personnel: 1036**

SARATOGA SPRINGS—Saratoga County

☐ **FOUR WINDS HOSPITAL (334049)**, 30 Crescent Avenue, Zip 12866–5142; tel. 518/584–3600, **A**1 10 **F**30 35 98 99 100 101 103 104 105 153
Primary Contact: Samuel A. Bastien IV, Ph.D., Chief Executive Officer
CFO: Juanita Wheeler-Moore, Director Financial Services
CMO: Kevin P. Martin, M.D., Chief Medical Officer
CIO: Susan Snowdon, Director Information Technology
CHR: Susan M Kirchner, Director Human Resources
CNO: James Colamaria, Director of Nursing
Web address: www.fourwindshospital.com
Control: Individual, Investor–owned (for–profit) **Service**: Psychiatric

> **Staffed Beds: 88 Admissions: 2677 Census: 87 Outpatient Visits: 20722 Births: 0 Total Expense ($000): 33444**

NY

Hospital, Medicare Provider Number, Address, Telephone, Approval, Facility, and Physician Codes, Health Care System

★ American Hospital Association (AHA) membership
☐ The Joint Commission accreditation
○ Healthcare Facilities Accreditation Program
◇ DNV Healthcare Inc. accreditation
⇧ Center for Improvement in Healthcare Quality Accreditation
△ Commission on Accreditation of Rehabilitation Facilities (CARF) accreditation

SARATOGA HOSPITAL (330222), 211 Church Street, Zip 12866–1003; tel. 518/587–3222, **A**1 2 3 10 19 **F**3 5 8 11 12 13 15 17 18 20 22 28 29 30 31 34 35 36 38 39 40 45 46 47 48 49 50 51 53 54 55 57 59 60 63 64 65 66 70 74 75 76 77 78 79 81 82 84 85 86 87 89 92 93 96 97 98 100 101 102 104 107 108 110 111 114 115 116 117 119 120 121 123 126 129 130 131 132 135 144 145 146 147 149 157
Primary Contact: Angelo G. Calbone, President and Chief Executive Officer
CFO: Gary Foster, Vice President and Chief Financial Officer
CMO: Richard Falivena, D.O., M.P.H., Vice President and Chief Medical Officer
CIO: John Mangona, Vice President, Chief Information Officer and Compliance Officer
CHR: Jeffrey M Methven, Vice President Ambulatory Services and Chief Human Resources Officer
CNO: Mary Jo LaPosta, Ph.D., R.N., Senior Vice President Patient Care and Organizational Excellence
Web address: www.saratogacare.org
Control: Other not–for–profit (including NFP Corporation) **Service**: General medical and surgical

Staffed Beds: 171 **Admissions**: 10348 **Census**: 139 **Outpatient Visits**: 529905 **Births**: 731 **Total Expense ($000)**: 347647 **Payroll Expense ($000)**: 171928 **Personnel**: 2376

SCHENECTADY—Schenectady County

ELLIS HOSPITAL (330153), 1101 Nott Street, Zip 12308–2425; tel. 518/243–4000, (Includes BELLEVUE WOMAN'S CARE CENTER, 2210 Troy Road, Schenectady, New York, Zip 12309–4797; tel. 518/346–9400; ELLIS HOSPITAL HEALTH CENTER, 600 McClellan Street, Schenectady, New York, Zip 12304–1090; tel. 518/382–2000) (Total facility includes 82 beds in nursing home–type unit) **A**1 3 5 10 13 **F**8 11 12 13 15 17 18 20 22 24 26 28 29 30 31 34 35 38 39 40 44 45 46 47 48 49 50 51 54 59 60 61 62 64 65 68 70 72 74 75 76 77 78 79 81 82 84 85 87 89 93 97 98 100 102 103 104 105 107 108 109 110 111 112 113 114 115 116 119 120 121 126 128 129 130 131 132 133 135 143 144 146 147 148 156
Primary Contact: Paul A. Milton, President and Chief Executive Officer
COO: Paul A Milton, Executive Vice President and Chief Operating Officer
CFO: Marc Mesick, Vice President and Chief Financial Officer
CMO: David Liebers, M.D., Chief Medical Officer and Vice President Medical Affairs
CIO: Ron McKinnon, Chief Information Officer
CHR: Joseph Giansante, Vice President Human Resources
Web address: www.ellismedicine.org
Control: Other not–for–profit (including NFP Corporation) **Service**: General medical and surgical

Staffed Beds: 541 **Admissions**: 19506 **Census**: 315 **Outpatient Visits**: 550985 **Births**: 2293 **Total Expense ($000)**: 422284 **Payroll Expense ($000)**: 217465 **Personnel**: 2917

ELLIS HOSPITAL HEALTH CENTER See Ellis Hospital, Schenectady

ELLIS HOSPITAL MCCLELLAN CAMPUS See Ellis Hospital Health Center

△ **SUNNYVIEW REHABILITATION HOSPITAL (330406)**, 1270 Belmont Avenue, Zip 12308–2104; tel. 518/382–4500, (Nonreporting) **A**1 3 7 10 **S** Trinity Health, Livonia, MI
Primary Contact: Edward Eisenman, Chief Executive Officer
CFO: Kristin Signor, Director Finance
CMO: Lynne T Nicolson, M.D., Medical Director
CIO: Patrick Clark, Manager Information Technology
CHR: Meghan Glowa, Director Human Resources
Web address: www.sunnyview.org
Control: Other not–for–profit (including NFP Corporation) **Service**: Rehabilitation

Staffed Beds: 115

SLEEPY HOLLOW—Westchester County

PHELPS MEMORIAL HOSPITAL CENTER (330261), 701 North Broadway, Zip 10591–1020; tel. 914/366–3000, **A**1 2 3 5 10 **F**3 4 5 8 9 11 12 13 15 17 18 28 29 30 31 34 35 36 39 40 41 45 46 47 48 49 50 51 53 55 56 57 59 60 61 63 64 65 68 70 74 75 76 77 78 79 81 82 84 85 86 87 89 90 91 92 93 94 96 97 98 100 101 102 104 105 106 107 108 110 111 114 115 118 119 120 121 124 126 129 130 131 132 135 143 145 146 147 148 149 152 153 154 156 158 **S** Northwell Health, New Hyde Park, NY
Primary Contact: Daniel Blum, President
CFO: Vincent DeSantis, Vice President Finance
CHR: Jussi Maijala, Vice President, Human Resources
CNO: Mary McDermott, MS, MSN, R.N., Senior Vice President Patient Care Services and Chief Nursing Officer
Web address: www.phelpshospital.org
Control: Other not–for–profit (including NFP Corporation) **Service**: General medical and surgical

Staffed Beds: 153 **Admissions**: 7637 **Census**: 131 **Outpatient Visits**: 189812 **Births**: 1011 **Total Expense ($000)**: 272512 **Payroll Expense ($000)**: 152345 **Personnel**: 1758

SMITHTOWN—Suffolk County

☐ **ST. CATHERINE OF SIENA MEDICAL CENTER (330401)**, 50 Route 25-A, Zip 11787–1348; tel. 631/862–3000, (Total facility includes 240 beds in nursing home–type unit) **A**1 3 10 **F**3 13 15 17 18 20 22 26 29 30 31 34 35 40 41 45 49 57 59 60 70 72 74 75 76 78 79 81 84 85 87 94 98 100 102 103 107 108 110 111 114 115 119 126 129 130 132 146 147 148 149 154 **S** Catholic Health Services of Long Island, Rockville Centre, NY
Primary Contact: James O'Connor, Chief Administrative Officer
CFO: John Pohlman, Vice President Finance and Administration
CMO: Jason Golbin, M.D., Chief Medical Officer
CNO: Mary Jane Finnegan, Chief Nursing Officer
Web address: www.stcatherines.chsli.org/
Control: Church operated, Nongovernment, not–for–profit **Service**: General medical and surgical

Staffed Beds: 281 **Admissions**: 13334 **Census**: 389 **Outpatient Visits**: 37059 **Births**: 523 **Total Expense ($000)**: 268369 **Payroll Expense ($000)**: 117593 **Personnel**: 1513

SPRINGVILLE—Erie County

BERTRAND CHAFFEE HOSPITAL (330111), 224 East Main Street, Zip 14141–1497; tel. 716/592–2871, (Nonreporting) **A**10
Primary Contact: Nils Gunnersen, Administrator
CMO: J Matthew Baker, M.D., President Medical Staff
CHR: Mary Beth Brown, Director Human Resources
Web address: www.chaffeehospitalandhome.com
Control: Other not–for–profit (including NFP Corporation) **Service**: General medical and surgical

Staffed Beds: 24

STAR LAKE—St. Lawrence County

★ **CLIFTON-FINE HOSPITAL (331307)**, 1014 Oswegatchie Trail, Zip 13690–3143; tel. 315/848–3351, (Nonreporting) **A**10 18
Primary Contact: Dierdra Sorrell, R.N., MSN, Chief Executive Officer
COO: Cathy Rice, Director Support Services
CFO: Heather Cockayne, Chief Financial Officer
CMO: David Welch, M.D., Medical Director
CIO: Joe Deeter, MS, Director Information Systems
CNO: John Schaffer, R.N., Director of Nursing
Web address: www.cliftonfinehospital.org
Control: Other not–for–profit (including NFP Corporation) **Service**: General medical and surgical

Staffed Beds: 20

STATEN ISLAND—Richmond County, See New York City

STONY BROOK—Suffolk County

STONY BROOK UNIVERSITY HOSPITAL (330393), 101 Nicolls Road, Zip 11794–8410; tel. 631/444–1077, (Includes STONY BROOK CHILDREN'S HOSPITAL, 100 Nicolls Road, Stony Brook, New York, Zip 11794–0001; tel. 631/444–4000; STONY BROOK SOUTHAMPTON HOSPITAL, 240 Meeting House Lane, Southampton, New York, Zip 11968–5090; tel. 631/726–8200; Robert S Chaloner, Chief Administrative Officer) **A**1 2 5 8 10 **F**1 3 4 6 7 8 9 11 12 13 14 15 16 17 18 19 20 22 24 26 28 29 30 31 32 34 35 36 37 38 39 40 41 43 44 45 46 47 48 49 50 51 52 53 54 59 60 61 63 64 65 66 67 68 70 71 72 73 74 75 76 77 78 79 80 81 82 83 84 85 86 87 88 89 90 91 92 93 96 97 98 99 100 101 102 103 104 107 108 110 111 114 115 116 117 118 119 120 121 122 123 124 126 129 130 131 132 134 135 136 138 141 143 145 146 147 148 149 150 154 156 157
Primary Contact: Lewis Reuven. Pasternak, M.D., M.P.H., Chief Executive Officer
COO: Carol Gomes, FACHE, Chief Operating Officer
CFO: Gary E Bie, CPA, Chief Financial Officer
CMO: Mark Sands, M.D., Chief Medical Officer
CIO: Jim Murry, Chief Information Officer
CHR: Luis de Onis, Interim Chief Human Resources Officer
CNO: Mary Ann T Donohue, Ph.D., R.N., Chief Patient Care Services Officer
Web address: www.https://www.stonybrookmedicine.edu/sbuh
Control: State, Government, nonfederal **Service**: General medical and surgical

Staffed Beds: 687 **Admissions**: 37914 **Census**: 591 **Outpatient Visits**: 542685 **Births**: 3338 **Total Expense ($000)**: 1491436 **Payroll Expense ($000)**: 647843 **Personnel**: 6919

SUFFERN—Rockland County

☒ **GOOD SAMARITAN REGIONAL MEDICAL CENTER (330158)**, 255 Lafayette Avenue, Zip 10901–4869; tel. 845/368–5000, (Nonreporting) **A**1 2 5 10 **S** WMCHealth, Valhalla, NY
Primary Contact: Mary Leahy, M.D., Chief Executive Officer
COO: Gerry Durney, Chief Operating Officer
CMO: Rodney W Williams, M.D., JD, MS, Vice President Medical Affairs
CIO: Deborah K Marshall, Vice President Public Relations
CHR: Pamela Tarulli, Senior Vice President Human Resources
Web address: www.goodsamhosp.org
Service: General medical and surgical

Staffed Beds: 308

SYRACUSE—Onondaga County

COMMUNITY-GENERAL HOSPITAL OF GREATER SYRACUSE See Upstate University Hospital at Community General

★ ⇑ **CROUSE HEALTH (330203)**, 736 Irving Avenue, Zip 13210–1690; tel. 315/470–7375, **A**3 5 10 21 **F**3 4 5 8 11 12 13 15 18 19 20 21 22 23 26 27 29 31 34 35 36 37 40 49 50 53 58 59 60 64 66 68 70 72 73 74 75 76 77 78 79 81 83 84 86 87 89 91 93 96 107 108 110 112 114 115 116 117 118 119 126 129 130 131 132 135 144 145 146 147 148 149 150 157
Primary Contact: Kimberly Boynton, President and Chief Executive Officer
CFO: Michael A. Tengeres, Chief Financial Officer
CMO: Seth Kronenberg, M.D., Chief Medical Officer
CIO: Kim Rose, Chief Information Technology
CHR: John Bergemann, Director Human Resources
CNO: Betty O'Connor, Chief Nursing Officer
Web address: www.crouse.org
Control: Other not-for-profit (including NFP Corporation) **Service:** General medical and surgical

Staffed Beds: 487 **Admissions:** 19522 **Census:** 298 **Outpatient Visits:** 454787 **Births:** 3893 **Total Expense ($000):** 444302 **Payroll Expense ($000):** 176815 **Personnel:** 2167

☐ **RICHARD H. HUTCHINGS PSYCHIATRIC CENTER (334001)**, 620 Madison Street, Zip 13210–2319; tel. 315/426–3632, (Nonreporting) **A**1 3 5 10 **S** New York State Office of Mental Health, Albany, NY
Primary Contact: Colleen A. Sawyer, R.N., MSN, Executive Director
CFO: Robert Stapleton, Director Administration
CMO: Mark Cattalani, M.D., Clinical Director
CIO: Neil Nemi, Administrator Facility Information Center
CHR: Katherine Herron, Director Human Resources
Web address: www.omh.ny.gov
Control: State, Government, nonfederal **Service:** Psychiatric

Staffed Beds: 131

★ ⇑ **ST. JOSEPH'S HOSPITAL HEALTH CENTER (330140)**, 301 Prospect Avenue, Zip 13203–1807; tel. 315/448–5111, **A**3 5 10 21 **F**3 8 11 12 13 14 15 17 18 20 22 24 26 28 29 30 31 34 35 37 38 39 40 45 46 47 48 49 50 51 54 57 58 59 60 61 62 64 65 66 68 70 72 73 74 75 76 77 78 79 81 82 83 84 85 87 90 92 93 94 97 98 100 101 102 103 104 106 107 108 110 111 114 115 118 119 126 129 130 131 132 135 144 146 147 148 149 154 **S** Trinity Health, Livonia, MI
Primary Contact: Leslie Paul. Luke, President and Chief Executive Officer
COO: Mary W Brown, Senior Vice President Operations
CFO: Meredith Price, Vice President Fiscal Services and Chief Financial Officer
CMO: Joseph W Spinale, D.O., Chief Medical Officer
CIO: Charles Fennell, Vice President Information Management
CHR: Erika Duncan, Vice President Human Resources
CNO: AnneMarie Czyz, R.N., Ed.D., Chief Operating Officer and Chief Nursing Officer
Web address: www.sjhsyr.org
Control: Other not-for-profit (including NFP Corporation) **Service:** General medical and surgical

Staffed Beds: 451 **Admissions:** 25739 **Census:** 316 **Outpatient Visits:** 519877 **Births:** 1948 **Total Expense ($000):** 576754 **Payroll Expense ($000):** 242655 **Personnel:** 4235

☒ △ **SYRACUSE VETERANS AFFAIRS MEDICAL CENTER**, 800 Irving Avenue, Zip 13210–2716; tel. 315/425–4400, **A**1 3 5 7 8 **F**1 2 3 4 5 8 12 18 20 22 26 28 29 30 31 33 34 35 36 38 39 40 45 46 47 49 50 53 54 56 57 58 59 60 61 62 63 64 65 67 70 71 74 75 77 78 79 81 82 84 85 86 87 90 91 92 94 95 97 98 100 101 104 105 106 107 108 111 126 128 132 135 146 147 148 152 153 154 156 157 **S** Department of Veterans Affairs, Washington, DC
Primary Contact: Judy A. Hayman, Ph.D., Director
CFO: Deborah Angell, Chief Financial Officer
CMO: Syed Asif Ali, M.D., Chief of Staff
CIO: James Stenson, Chief Information Officer
CHR: Mark Antinelli, Manager Human Resources
CNO: Cheryl Czajkowski, Associate Director Patient and Nursing Services
Web address: www.syracuse.va.gov/
Control: Veterans Affairs, Government, federal **Service:** General medical and surgical

Staffed Beds: 160 **Admissions:** 5050 **Census:** 124 **Outpatient Visits:** 560530 **Births:** 0 **Personnel:** 1857

★ ⇑ **UPSTATE UNIVERSITY HOSPITAL (330241)**, 750 East Adams Street, Zip 13210–2342; tel. 315/464–5540, (Includes GOLISANO CHILDREN'S HOSPITAL, 750 East Adams Street, Syracuse, New York, Zip 13210–2342; tel. 315/464–4570; UPSTATE UNIVERSITY HOSPITAL AT COMMUNITY GENERAL, 4900 Broad Road, Syracuse, New York, Zip 13215–2293; tel. 315/492–5011) **A**2 3 5 8 10 21 **F**3 5 6 9 12 13 15 16 17 18 19 20 22 24 25 26 28 29 30 31 33 34 35 36 37 38 39 40 41 43 44 45 46 47 48 49 50 51 52 53 54 55 56 57 58 59 61 64 65 66 68 70 74 76 78 79 81 82 84 85 86 87 88 89 90 92 93 95 96 97 98 100 101 102 104 107 108 109 110 111 112 114 115 118 119 120 121 123 124 126 128 129 130 131 132 135 136 138 141 142 145 146 147 148 149 150 154 156 157
Primary Contact: Robert J Corona Jr., D.O., Chief Executive Officer
COO: Robert Marzella, Chief Operations Officer
CFO: Stuart M Wright, CPA, Chief Financial Officer
CMO: Amy Tucker, M.D., Chief Medical Officer
CIO: Terry Wagner, Chief Information Officer
CHR: Eric Frost, Associate Vice President Human Resources
CNO: Nancy E. Page, MS, R.N., Chief Nursing Officer
Web address: www.upstate.edu/hospital
Control: State, Government, nonfederal **Service:** General medical and surgical

Staffed Beds: 650 **Admissions:** 33647 **Census:** 514 **Outpatient Visits:** 825284 **Births:** 1125 **Total Expense ($000):** 1120913 **Payroll Expense ($000):** 392153 **Personnel:** 5629

VETERANS AFFAIRS MEDICAL CENTER See Syracuse Veterans Affairs Medical Center

TROY—Rensselaer County

BURDETT BIRTH CENTER (330409), 2215 Burdett Avenue, Suite 200, Zip 12180–2466; tel. 518/271–3393, (Nonreporting) **S** Trinity Health, Livonia, MI
Primary Contact: , MS, R.N.
Web address: www.burdettbirthcenter.org/
Control: Church operated, Nongovernment, not-for-profit **Service:** Obstetrics and gynecology

Staffed Beds: 15

★ **SAMARITAN HOSPITAL - MAIN CAMPUS (330180)**, 2215 Burdett Avenue, Zip 12180–2475; tel. 518/271–3300, (Includes SAMARITAN HOSPITAL - ST. MARY'S CAMPUS, 1300 Massachusetts Avenue, Troy, New York, Zip 12180–1695; tel. 518/268–5000; James K. Reed, M.D., Chief Executive Officer) **A**3 10 19 **F**3 4 8 11 12 15 17 18 20 22 26 28 29 30 31 32 34 35 36 38 40 44 45 46 47 48 49 50 51 55 56 57 59 60 63 64 65 66 68 70 74 75 77 78 79 80 81 84 85 87 93 94 97 98 100 101 102 103 104 107 108 109 111 114 119 120 121 123 126 130 132 135 145 146 147 148 149 150 153 154 **S** Trinity Health, Livonia, MI
Primary Contact: James K. Reed, M.D., Chief Executive Officer
CFO: Daniel A Kochie, CPA, Chief Financial Officer
CMO: Daniel C Silverman, M.D., Chief Medical Officer, Acute Care Troy
CIO: Karen LeBlanc, Director, Applications
CNO: Jacqueline Priore, Chief Nursing Officer
Web address: www.nehealth.com
Control: Other not-for-profit (including NFP Corporation) **Service:** General medical and surgical

Staffed Beds: 277 **Admissions:** 9251 **Census:** 159 **Outpatient Visits:** 491602 **Births:** 0 **Total Expense ($000):** 265656 **Payroll Expense ($000):** 121659 **Personnel:** 1632

NY

UTICA—Oneida County

★ △ ⇑ **FAXTON ST. LUKE'S HEALTHCARE (330044)**, 1656 Champlin Avenue, Zip 13502–4830, Mailing Address: P.O. Box 479, Zip 13503–0479; tel. 315/624–6000, (Includes FAXTON CAMPUS, 1676 Sunset Avenue, Utica, New York, Zip 13502–5475; tel. 315/624–6000; ST. LUKE'S CAMPUS, 1656 Champlin Avenue, Utica, New York, Zip 13502–4830, Mailing Address: P O Box 479, Zip 13503–0479, tel. 315/624–6000) **A**2 3 7 10 21 **F**2 3 8 11 12 13 15 28 29 30 31 34 35 36 39 40 45 46 47 48 49 50 51 53 54 56 57 58 59 60 62 64 65 66 68 70 73 74 75 76 77 78 79 80 81 84 85 86 87 89 90 92 93 97 98 100 101 102 104 107 108 109 110 114 115 116 117 118 119 120 121 123 124 127 130 132 135 143 144 146 147 149 150 154 156
Primary Contact: Scott H. Perra, FACHE, President and Chief Executive Officer
COO: Robert Scholefield, MS, R.N., Executive Vice President and Chief Operating Officer
CFO: Louis Aiello, Senior Vice President and Chief Financial Officer
CMO: Michael F Trevisani, M.D., Senior Vice President and Chief Medical Officer
CIO: John Lynch, Vice President and Chief Information Officer
CHR: Jack Davis, Vice President Human Resources
CNO: Linda McCormack-Miller, Chief Nursing Officer
Web address: www.mvhealthsystem.org
Control: Other not–for–profit (including NFP Corporation) **Service:** General medical and surgical

Staffed Beds: 278 **Admissions:** 12810 **Census:** 168 **Outpatient Visits:** 347308 **Births:** 1776 **Total Expense ($000):** 305347 **Payroll Expense ($000):** 146046 **Personnel:** 1946

☐ **MOHAWK VALLEY PSYCHIATRIC CENTER (334021)**, 1400 Noyes Street, Zip 13502–3854; tel. 315/738–3800, (Nonreporting) **A**1 10 **S** New York State Office of Mental Health, Albany, NY
Primary Contact: Colleen A. Sawyer, R.N., MSN, Executive Director
Web address: www.omh.ny.gov/omhweb/facilities/mvpc/facility.htm
Control: State, Government, nonfederal **Service:** Psychiatric

Staffed Beds: 614

★ ⇑ **ST. ELIZABETH MEDICAL CENTER (330245)**, 2209 Genesee Street, Zip 13501–5999; tel. 315/798–8100, **A**3 10 13 21 **F**3 11 15 17 18 20 22 24 26 29 30 32 34 35 36 37 40 43 45 50 54 57 58 59 61 64 65 66 68 70 74 75 77 79 80 81 84 85 87 89 92 93 97 98 100 101 102 104 107 108 110 114 115 119 126 127 129 130 131 132 135 146 147 148 149 150
Primary Contact: Scott H. Perra, FACHE, Chief Executive Officer
CFO: Louis Aiello, Chief Financial Officer
CMO: Albert D'Accurzio, M.D., Medical Director
CIO: Robert Gillette, Chief Information Officer
CNO: Varinya Sheppard, R.N., Chief Nursing Officer
Web address: www.stemc.org
Control: Church operated, Nongovernment, not–for–profit **Service:** General medical and surgical

Staffed Beds: 181 **Admissions:** 9873 **Census:** 145 **Outpatient Visits:** 425003 **Births:** 0 **Total Expense ($000):** 217106 **Payroll Expense ($000):** 104337 **Personnel:** 1620

ST. LUKE'S CAMPUS See Faxton St. Luke's Healthcare, Utica

VALHALLA—Westchester County

⊞ **BLYTHEDALE CHILDREN'S HOSPITAL (333301)**, 95 Bradhurst Avenue, Zip 10595–1697; tel. 914/592–7555, (Nonreporting) **A**1 3 10
Primary Contact: Larry L. Levine, President and Chief Executive Officer
COO: Maureen Desimone, Chief Operating Officer
CFO: John Canning, Chief Financial Officer
CMO: Joelle Mast, Ph.D., M.D., Chief Medical Officer
CHR: Ronald Gallo, Director Human Resources
Web address: www.blythedale.org
Control: Other not–for–profit (including NFP Corporation) **Service:** Children's rehabilitation

Staffed Beds: 92

⇑ **WESTCHESTER MEDICAL CENTER (330234)**, 100 Woods Road, Zip 10595–1530; tel. 914/493–7000, (Includes MARIA FARERI CHILDREN'S HOSPITAL, 100 Woods Road, Valhalla, New York, Zip 10595–1652; tel. 866/962–7337; MIDHUDSON REGIONAL HOSPITAL OF WESTCHESTER MEDICAL CENTER, 241 North Road, Poughkeepsie, New York, Zip 12601–1154; tel. 845/483–5000; Paul S Hochenberg, Executive Director) **A**2 3 5 8 10 21 **F**3 4 5 8 12 13 14 15 16 17 18 19 20 21 22 23 24 25 26 27 28 29 30 31 32 34 35 36 37 38 39 40 41 43 44 45 46 47 48 49 50 51 52 54 55 56 57 58 59 60 61 62 64 65 66 68 70 71 72 73 74 75 76 77 78 79 80 81 82 84 85 86 87 88 89 90 91 92 93 94 97 98 99 100 101 102 103 104 107 108 110 111 114 115 116 117 118 119 120 121 123 124 126 129 130 131 132 134 135 136 137 138 139 141 142 145 146 147 148 149 151 154 156 157 **S** WMCHealth, Valhalla, NY
Primary Contact: Michael D. Israel, President and Chief Executive Officer
COO: Gary F Brudnicki, Senior Executive Vice President, Chief Operating Officer and Chief Financial Officer
CFO: Gary F Brudnicki, Senior Executive Vice President, Chief Operating Officer and Chief Financial Officer
CMO: Renee Garrick, M.D., Executive Medical Director
CIO: John Moustakakis, Senior Vice President Information Systems and Chief Information Officer
CHR: Jordy Rabinowitz, Senior Vice President Human Resources Operations
CNO: Paula Fessler, MSN, R.N., Chief Nursing Executive
Web address: www.wmchealth.org
Control: Hospital district or authority, Government, nonfederal **Service:** General medical and surgical

Staffed Beds: 872 **Admissions:** 27323 **Census:** 665 **Outpatient Visits:** 267834 **Births:** 945 **Total Expense ($000):** 1270152 **Payroll Expense ($000):** 330359 **Personnel:** 5173

WALTON—Delaware County

UHS DELAWARE VALLEY HOSPITAL (331312), 1 Titus Place, Zip 13856–1498; tel. 607/865–2100, **A**10 18 **F**3 4 5 11 15 18 28 29 30 34 35 40 45 50 57 59 64 75 77 82 85 87 93 97 107 110 115 119 130 131 133 146 147 148 154 **S** United Health Services, Binghamton, NY
Primary Contact: Paul Summers, President and Chief Executive Officer
CFO: Paul Summers, Interim Chief Financial Officer
CMO: John Giannone, M.D., Delaware Valley Hospital Medical Director
CHR: Cynthia Gardepe, Director, Human Resources
CNO: Victoria Conkling, Vice President, Patient Services and Chief Nursing Officer
Web address: www.uhs.net/locations/
Control: Other not–for–profit (including NFP Corporation) **Service:** General medical and surgical

Staffed Beds: 25 **Admissions:** 441 **Census:** 11 **Outpatient Visits:** 169463 **Births:** 0 **Total Expense ($000):** 23478 **Payroll Expense ($000):** 7600 **Personnel:** 175

WAPPINGERS—Dutchess County

VETERAN AFFAIRS HUDSON VALLEY HEALTH CARE SYSTEM-CASTLE POINT CAMPUS See Veterans Affairs Hudson Valley Health Care System, Montrose

WARSAW—Wyoming County

☐ **WYOMING COUNTY COMMUNITY HOSPITAL (330008)**, 400 North Main Street, Zip 14569–1025; tel. 585/786–2233, (Nonreporting) **A**1 10 20
Primary Contact: Donald T. Eichenauer, Chief Executive Officer
COO: Michael Corcimiglia, Chief Operating Officer
CFO: John (Jack) T. Ormond, Director Finance and Revenue
CMO: Bilal Ahmed, M.D., Medical Director
CIO: Jane Beechler, Director Healthcare Information Systems
CHR: Peter J. Bendyna, Director Human Resources and Civil Service Administrator
CNO: Connie Almeter, Director of Nursing (Acute)
Web address: www.wcchs.net
Control: County, Government, nonfederal **Service:** General medical and surgical

Staffed Beds: 75

WARWICK—Orange County

⊞ **ST. ANTHONY COMMUNITY HOSPITAL (330205)**, 15 Maple Avenue, Zip 10990–1028; tel. 845/986–2276, (Nonreporting) **A**1 10 **S** WMCHealth, Valhalla, NY
Primary Contact: Mary Leahy, M.D., Chief Executive Officer
Web address: www.stanthonycommunityhosp.org
Service: General medical and surgical

Staffed Beds: 60

NY

Many Facility Codes have changed. Please refer to the AHA Guide Code Chart. © 2019 AHA Guide

WATERTOWN—Jefferson County

SAMARITAN MEDICAL CENTER (330157), 830 Washington Street, Zip 13601–4034; tel. 315/785–4000, **A**1 3 10 12 13 20 **F**3 5 8 13 15 18 28 29 30 31 35 40 47 49 50 51 57 60 62 64 68 70 73 75 76 77 78 81 82 87 89 90 93 94 97 98 100 102 104 107 108 111 114 115 116 119 120 121 126 129 130 135 146 147 148 154
Primary Contact: Thomas H. Carman, President and Chief Executive Officer
CFO: Sean Mills, Chief Financial Officer
CMO: Mario Victoria, M.D., Vice President, Medical Affairs
CIO: M Andrew Short, Vice President Information Services
CHR: Thomas Shatraw, Director Human Resources
CNO: Kimberly Thibert, R.N., MSN, Vice President Patient Care Services and Chief Nursing Officer
Web address: www.samaritanhealth.com
Control: Other not–for–profit (including NFP Corporation) **Service**: General medical and surgical

Staffed Beds: 195 Admissions: 8674 Census: 115 Outpatient Visits: 287110 Births: 1637 Total Expense ($000): 231663 Payroll Expense ($000): 104185 Personnel: 1760

WELLSVILLE—Allegany County

JONES MEMORIAL HOSPITAL (330096), 191 North Main Street, Zip 14895–1150, Mailing Address: P.O. Box 72, Zip 14895–0072; tel. 585/593–1100, **A**1 10 20 **F**3 8 11 13 15 17 28 29 30 31 34 35 36 40 43 50 57 59 61 64 68 70 75 76 77 78 79 81 85 89 93 97 107 110 114 119 129 131 132 133 146 147 149 156 157 **S** University of Rochester Medical Center, Rochester, NY
Primary Contact: Eva Benedict, R.N., President and Chief Executive Officer
CFO: James Helms, Vice President Finance
CMO: William Coch, M.D., Medical Director
CIO: James Helms, Vice President Finance
CHR: Brenda Sobeck, Director of Human Resources
CNO: Donna Bliven, Vice President Patient Care Services and Chief Nursing Officer
Web address: www.jmhny.org
Control: Other not–for–profit (including NFP Corporation) **Service**: General medical and surgical

Staffed Beds: 33 Admissions: 1870 Census: 20 Outpatient Visits: 139292 Births: 417 Total Expense ($000): 41796 Payroll Expense ($000): 19154 Personnel: 373

WEST HAVERSTRAW—Rockland County

△ **HELEN HAYES HOSPITAL (330405)**, Route 9W, Zip 10993–1127; tel. 845/786–4000, (Nonreporting) **A**1 3 5 7 10
Primary Contact: Edmund Coletti, Chief Executive Officer
COO: Kathleen Martucci, Chief Operating Officer
CFO: Lori A. Meszler, Chief Financial Officer
CIO: Virgil Ennis, Chief Information Officer
CHR: Patrick J. Ryan, Chief Human Resources Officer
Web address: www.helenhayeshospital.org
Control: State, Government, nonfederal **Service**: Rehabilitation

Staffed Beds: 155

WEST ISLIP—Suffolk County

GOOD SAMARITAN HOSPITAL MEDICAL CENTER (330286), 1000 Montauk Highway, Zip 11795–4927; tel. 631/376–3000, (Total facility includes 100 beds in nursing home–type unit) **A**1 2 3 10 13 **F**3 8 11 12 13 15 17 18 20 22 24 26 28 29 30 31 32 34 35 40 41 43 45 46 47 48 49 50 51 54 55 56 57 58 59 64 65 66 68 70 72 73 74 75 76 77 78 79 80 81 82 84 85 86 87 88 89 91 93 94 96 97 99 100 102 107 108 110 111 115 117 119 120 121 123 124 126 128 129 130 131 132 142 146 147 149 154 **S** Catholic Health Services of Long Island, Rockville Centre, NY
Primary Contact: Ruth E Hennessey, President
CFO: Dan Macksood, Regional Senior Vice President and Chief Financial Officer
CMO: Jerome Weiner, M.D., Senior Vice President Medical Affairs
CIO: Marcy Dunn, Vice President Information Services and Chief Information Officer
CHR: Lori Spina, Vice President Human Resources
Web address: www.good-samaritan-hospital.org
Control: Church operated, Nongovernment, not–for–profit **Service**: General medical and surgical

Staffed Beds: 417 Admissions: 24418 Census: 334 Outpatient Visits: 224050 Births: 2621 Total Expense ($000): 737806 Payroll Expense ($000): 328612 Personnel: 3043

WEST POINT—Orange County

KELLER ARMY COMMUNITY HOSPITAL, 900 Washington Road, Zip 10996–1197, Mailing Address: U S Military Academy, Building 900, Zip 10996–1197; tel. 845/938–5169, **A**1 3 5 **F**3 5 7 8 15 29 34 36 38 39 40 45 50 54 57 58 59 64 65 68 75 77 79 81 82 87 91 93 97 100 101 102 104 107 110 111 115 119 130 131 135 146 147 149 154 156 **S** Department of the Army, Office of the Surgeon General, Falls Church, VA
Primary Contact: Brett Venable, Commander
CIO: Patrick McGuinness, Chief Information Management
CHR: Margaret Greco, Chief Human Resources
Web address: www.kach.amedd.army.mil/SitePages/Home.aspx
Control: Department of Defense, Government, federal **Service**: General medical and surgical

Staffed Beds: 12 Admissions: 783 Census: 4 Outpatient Visits: 143821 Births: 54 Total Expense ($000): 49323 Payroll Expense ($000): 24682 Personnel: 507

WEST SENECA—Erie County

☐ **WESTERN NEW YORK CHILDREN'S PSYCHIATRIC CENTER (334065)**, 1010 East and West Road, Zip 14224–3602; tel. 716/677–7000, **A**1 3 5 **F**32 34 38 54 59 64 75 77 99 100 101 104 130 132 134 135 146 149 **S** New York State Office of Mental Health, Albany, NY
Primary Contact: Kathe Hayes, Executive Director
COO: David Privett, Deputy Director
CMO: Patrick Stein, M.D., Clinical Director
CIO: Dan Hrubiak, Associate Computer Program Analyst
CHR: Charles Siewert, Director Human Resources
Web address: www.omh.ny.gov
Control: State, Government, nonfederal **Service**: Children's hospital psychiatric

Staffed Beds: 46 Admissions: 145 Census: 39 Births: 0

WESTFIELD—Chautauqua County

★ **WESTFIELD MEMORIAL HOSPITAL (330166)**, 189 East Main Street, Zip 14787–1195; tel. 716/326–4921, **A**10 **F**11 15 28 29 34 35 40 44 45 50 57 59 64 68 75 79 81 85 86 87 93 97 102 107 108 110 115 118 119 130 131 132 146 147 155 156 **S** Allegheny Health Network, Pittsburgh, PA
Primary Contact: Henry J. Ward, Interim President
COO: Patricia Ballman, Director
CFO: Tina Gowan, System Controller
CMO: Russell Elwell, M.D., Medical Director
CIO: Cindy Harper, Manager Patient Data
Web address: www.wmhinc.org
Control: Other not–for–profit (including NFP Corporation) **Service**: General medical and surgical

Staffed Beds: 4 Admissions: 11 Census: 1 Outpatient Visits: 22275 Births: 0 Total Expense ($000): 10670 Payroll Expense ($000): 4743 Personnel: 76

WHITE PLAINS—Westchester County

△ **BURKE REHABILITATION HOSPITAL (333030)**, 785 Mamaroneck Avenue, Zip 10605–2523; tel. 914/597–2500, **A**1 3 5 7 10 **F**11 28 29 30 34 35 53 54 57 58 59 74 75 77 87 90 92 93 94 95 96 100 104 130 131 132 146 148 149 **S** Montefiore Health System, Bronx, NY
Primary Contact: Jeffrey Menkes, President and Chief Executive Officer
COO: Brian M Swift, Senior Administrator Plant Operations
CFO: John Stewart, Director Finance
CIO: Cathy Dwyer, Senior Administrator Information Systems
CHR: Annette Bucci, Vice President Human Resources
CNO: Marie Spencer, Chief Nursing Officer and Senior Administrator
Web address: www.burke.org
Control: Other not–for–profit (including NFP Corporation) **Service**: Rehabilitation

Staffed Beds: 150 Admissions: 2793 Census: 134 Outpatient Visits: 125544 Births: 0 Total Expense ($000): 90053 Payroll Expense ($000): 49748 Personnel: 708

NEW YORK-PRESBYTERIAN HOSPITAL, WESTCHESTER DIVISION See New York-Presbyterian Hospital, New York

NY

Hospital, Medicare Provider Number, Address, Telephone, Approval, Facility, and Physician Codes, Health Care System

★ American Hospital Association (AHA) membership
☐ The Joint Commission accreditation
○ Healthcare Facilities Accreditation Program
◇ DNV Healthcare Inc. accreditation
⇧ Center for Improvement in Healthcare Quality Accreditation
△ Commission on Accreditation of Rehabilitation Facilities (CARF) accreditation

✠ **WHITE PLAINS HOSPITAL CENTER (330304)**, 41 East Post Road, Zip 10601–4699; tel. 914/681–0600, **A**1 2 3 10 19 **F**3 8 9 11 12 13 15 17 18 19 20 22 26 29 30 31 32 34 35 36 37 38 39 40 41 42 44 45 46 47 49 50 51 53 54 55 56 57 58 59 60 61 63 64 65 66 68 70 72 74 75 76 77 78 79 80 81 82 84 85 86 87 89 92 93 97 100 101 102 104 107 108 109 110 111 114 115 116 117 118 119 120 121 122 123 124 126 129 130 131 132 134 135 144 146 147 148 149 150 154 155 156 157 **S** Montefiore Health System, Bronx, NY
Primary Contact: Susan Fox, President and Chief Executive Officer
COO: Edward F Leonard, Executive Vice President and Chief Operating Officer
CFO: Joseph Guarracino, Senior Vice President and Chief Financial Officer
CMO: Michael Palumbo, M.D., Executive Vice President and Medical Director
CIO: Rick McCarthy, Chief Information Officer
CHR: John Sanchez, Vice President Human Resources
CNO: Leigh McMahon, MS, R.N., Senior Vice President Patient Care Services and Chief Nursing Officer
Web address: www.wphospital.org
Control: Other not–for–profit (including NFP Corporation) **Service:** General medical and surgical

Staffed Beds: 246 **Admissions:** 19230 **Census:** 240 **Outpatient Visits:** 380937 **Births:** 1868 **Total Expense ($000):** 696357 **Payroll Expense ($000):** 339828 **Personnel:** 3114

WILLIAMSVILLE—Erie County

MILLARD FILLMORE SUBURBAN HOSPITAL See Kaleida Health, Buffalo

YONKERS—Westchester County

ANDRUS PAVILION See St. John's Riverside Hospital, Yonkers

✠ **SAINT JOSEPH'S MEDICAL CENTER (330006)**, 127 South Broadway, Zip 10701–4006; tel. 914/378–7000, (Nonreporting) **A**1 3 10
Primary Contact: Michael J. Spicer, President and Chief Executive Officer
COO: Frances Casola, Senior Vice President Operations
CFO: Frank Hagan, Senior Vice President Finance
CMO: James Neuendorf, M.D., Medical Director
CIO: Deborah Di Bernardo, Chief Information Officer
CHR: Dean Civitello, Vice President Human Resources
CNO: Margaret M Cusumano, R.N., MSN, Vice President Patient Care Services and Chief Nursing Officer
Web address: www.saintjosephs.org
Service: General medical and surgical

Staffed Beds: 473

☐ **ST. JOHN'S RIVERSIDE HOSPITAL (330208)**, 967 North Broadway, Zip 10701–1399; tel. 914/964–4444, (Includes ANDRUS PAVILION, 967 North Broadway, Yonkers, New York, Zip 10701–1399; tel. 914/964–4444; ST. JOHN'S RIVERSIDE HOSPITAL - PARK CARE PAVILION, Two Park Avenue, Yonkers, New York, Zip 10703–3497; tel. 914/964–7300; ST. JOHN'S RIVERSIDE HOSPITAL - DOBBS FERRY PAVILION, 128 Ashford Avenue, Dobbs Ferry, New York, Zip 10522–1896; tel. 914/693–0700) **A**1 2 3 10 19 **F**3 4 5 8 11 12 13 15 18 29 30 31 34 35 36 37 40 41 45 49 50 51 55 56 57 59 60 61 64 68 70 72 74 76 77 78 79 81 82 83 84 85 93 97 107 108 110 111 114 115 118 119 124 126 129 130 131 132 135 141 142 143 146 147 148 149 152 154
Primary Contact: Ronald J. Corti, President and Chief Executive Officer
COO: Lynn M. Nelson, R.N., R.N., Chief Nursing Officer and Chief Operating Officer
CFO: Dennis M. Keane, Vice President Finance and Chief Financial Officer
CMO: Paul Antonecchia, M.D., Vice President Medical Affairs and Chief Medical Officer
CIO: Peter Weidner, Director Information Technology
CHR: Marc Leff, Vice President Human Resources
CNO: Lynn M. Nelson, R.N., R.N., Chief Nursing Officer and Chief Operating Officer
Web address: www.riversidehealth.org
Control: Other not–for–profit (including NFP Corporation) **Service:** General medical and surgical

Staffed Beds: 376 **Admissions:** 17069 **Census:** 249 **Outpatient Visits:** 229089 **Births:** 1069 **Total Expense ($000):** 279445 **Payroll Expense ($000):** 123591 **Personnel:** 1509

NY

Many Facility Codes have changed. Please refer to the AHA Guide Code Chart. © 2019 AHA Guide

NORTH CAROLINA

AHOSKIE—Hertford County

⊞ **VIDANT ROANOKE-CHOWAN HOSPITAL (340099)**, 500 South Academy Street, Zip 27910–3261, Mailing Address. P.O. Box 1385, Zip 27910–1385; tel. 252/209–3000, **A**1 10 20 **F**3 11 13 15 29 30 31 34 35 40 43 44 45 56 57 59 64 68 70 75 76 77 78 79 81 82 85 86 87 89 92 93 98 100 101 102 103 107 108 110 111 114 118 119 120 121 123 129 130 132 146 148 149 154 156 **S** Vidant Health, Greenville, NC
Primary Contact: Judy Bruno, President
CFO: Jon Graham, Chief Finance Officer
CMO: David Lingle, Directors Council Chairman and Chief of Staff
CHR: Debbie Sisler, Director, Human Resource
Web address: www.vidanthealth.com
Control: Other not–for–profit (including NFP Corporation) **Service:** General medical and surgical

Staffed Beds: 71 **Admissions:** 4766 **Census:** 57 **Outpatient Visits:** 67094 **Births:** 321 **Total Expense ($000):** 74366 **Payroll Expense ($000):** 28125 **Personnel:** 590

ALBEMARLE—Stanly County

⊞ **ATRIUM HEALTH STANLY (340119)**, 301 Yadkin Street, Zip 28001–3441, Mailing Address: P.O. Box 1489, Zip 28002–1489; tel. 704/984–4000, **A**1 2 10 **F**3 13 15 28 29 30 31 32 34 35 39 40 45 46 49 59 68 75 76 77 78 79 81 82 85 86 87 93 98 100 101 102 107 108 110 111 114 115 118 119 120 121 123 129 130 131 132 146 147 148 149 154 **S** Atrium Health, Charlotte, NC
Primary Contact: Brian Freeman, President
CFO: Nick Samilo, Vice President Fiscal Services and Chief Financial Officer
CMO: Paul D'Amico, M.D., Chief of Staff
CNO: Judy Doran, Vice President of Hospital Services and Chief Nurse Executive
Web address: www.stanly.org
Control: Hospital district or authority, Government, nonfederal **Service:** General medical and surgical

Staffed Beds: 109 **Admissions:** 3774 **Census:** 42 **Outpatient Visits:** 73725 **Births:** 454 **Total Expense ($000):** 79818 **Payroll Expense ($000):** 28347 **Personnel:** 453

ASHEBORO—Randolph County

⊞ **RANDOLPH HOSPITAL (340123)**, 364 White Oak Street, Zip 27203–5400, Mailing Address: P.O. Box 1048, Zip 27204–1048; tel. 336/625–5151, **A**1 2 10 19 **F**3 8 13 15 18 28 29 30 31 34 35 40 45 49 53 56 57 58 59 62 64 68 70 75 76 77 79 80 81 85 86 87 89 91 92 93 94 96 97 107 110 111 114 115 118 119 120 121 123 130 131 132 135 143 146 148 **S** Atrium Health, Charlotte, NC
Primary Contact: Angela P. Orth, Executive Officer
CMO: Charles West, M.D., Chief Medical Officer
CIO: Angela Burgess, Chief Information Officer
Web address: www.randolphhospital.org
Control: Other not–for–profit (including NFP Corporation) **Service:** General medical and surgical

Staffed Beds: 85 **Admissions:** 4611 **Census:** 41 **Outpatient Visits:** 88565 **Births:** 664 **Total Expense ($000):** 94719 **Payroll Expense ($000):** 37281 **Personnel:** 773

ASHEVILLE—Buncombe County

⊞ **ASHEVILLE SPECIALTY HOSPITAL (342017)**, 428 Biltmore Avenue, 4th Floor, Zip 28801–4502; tel. 828/213–5400, (Nonreporting) **A**1 3 10 **S** HCA Healthcare, Nashville, TN
Primary Contact: Julie A. Dikos, President and Chief Executive Officer
CFO: Gregg Dixon, Chief Financial Officer
CMO: Ronnie Jacobs, M.D., Chief Medical Officer
CIO: Megan Serzan, Director of Quality, Compliance, Risk & Safety
CNO: Josephine Picker, MSN, R.N., Director of Nursing
Web address: www.missionhospitals.org/acute-care
Control: Partnership, Investor–owned (for–profit) **Service:** Acute long–term care hospital

Staffed Beds: 34

⊞ △ **CAREPARTNERS HEALTH SERVICES (343025)**, 68 Sweeten Creek Road, Zip 28803–2318, Mailing Address: P.O. Box 15025, Zip 28813–0025; tel. 828/277–4800, (Nonreporting) **A**1 3 7 10 **S** HCA Healthcare, Nashville, TN
Primary Contact: Tracy Buchanan, Chief Executive Officer and President
CFO: Gregg Dixon, Chief Financial Officer
CMO: Michael Parmer, Chief Medical Officer
CIO: Jennifer Scott, Director of Informatics
CHR: Katy Pless, Director of Human Resources
CNO: Cathleen Adams, Chief Nursing Officer
Web address: www.carepartners.org
Control: Other not–for–profit (including NFP Corporation) **Service:** Rehabilitation

Staffed Beds: 80

⊞ **CHARLES GEORGE VETERANS AFFAIRS MEDICAL CENTER**, 1100 Tunnel Road, Zip 28805–2087; tel. 828/298–7911, (Total facility includes 73 beds in nursing home–type unit) **A**1 3 5 **F**3 4 5 12 18 20 22 24 26 28 29 30 31 34 35 36 38 39 40 45 49 50 54 56 57 58 59 61 63 64 65 68 70 74 75 77 78 79 81 82 83 84 85 86 87 91 92 93 94 97 98 100 101 102 104 107 108 111 114 115 119 128 129 130 132 135 143 145 146 147 148 149 151 153 154 156 157 158 **S** Department of Veterans Affairs, Washington, DC
Primary Contact: Cynthia Breyfogle, FACHE, Director
CFO: Margaret Wilkes, Chief Fiscal Officer
CIO: Carla McLendon, Director Information Resource Management Services
CHR: James Sitlinger, Chief Human Resources Management
CNO: David Przestrzelski, Associate Director, Patient Care Services and Chief Nursing Executive
Web address: www.asheville.va.gov/
Control: Veterans Affairs, Government, federal **Service:** General medical and surgical

Staffed Beds: 170 **Admissions:** 5028 **Census:** 134 **Outpatient Visits:** 576269 **Births:** 0 **Total Expense ($000):** 336086 **Payroll Expense ($000):** 168848 **Personnel:** 2172

⊞ **MISSION HOSPITAL (340002)**, 509 Biltmore Avenue, Zip 28801–4690; tel. 828/213–1111, (Includes MISSION CHILDREN'S HOSPITAL, 509 Biltmore Avenue, Asheville, North Carolina, Zip 28801–4601; tel. 828/213–1111; MISSION HOSPITAL - ST. JOSEPH'S CAMPUS, 428 Biltmore Avenue, Asheville, North Carolina, Zip 28801–9839; tel. 828/213–1111; MISSION HOSPITAL, 509 Biltmore Avenue, Asheville, North Carolina, Zip 28801–4690; tel. 828/213–1111; Jill Hoggard Green, Ph.D., R.N., President), (Nonreporting) **A**1 2 3 5 10 19 **S** HCA Healthcare, Nashville, TN
Primary Contact: Jill Hoggard Green, Ph.D., R.N., President
CFO: Paul L McDowell, Deputy Chief Financial Officer
CMO: William Hathaway, M.D., Chief Medical Officer
CIO: Jon Brown, Chief Information Officer
CHR: Sheila M Meadows, Chief Human Resources Officer
CNO: Karen M Olsen, R.N., Chief Nursing Officer
Web address: www.mission-health.org
Control: Other not–for–profit (including NFP Corporation) **Service:** General medical and surgical

Staffed Beds: 763

BERMUDA RUN—Davie County

⊞ **WAKE FOREST BAPTIST HEALTH-DAVIE MEDICAL CENTER (340187)**, 329 NC Highway 801 North, Zip 27006; tel. 336/998–1300, **A**1 10 **F**3 15 18 28 29 30 34 35 40 45 50 56 57 59 64 68 74 75 77 81 85 87 93 102 107 110 115 119 129 130 131 146 154 **S** Wake Forest Baptist Health, Winston-Salem, NC
Primary Contact: Chad J. Brown, M.P.H., President
CFO: Danny Squires, Chief Financial Officer
CMO: Bret Nicks, M.D., Chief Medical Officer and Chief of Staff
CIO: William Showalter, Senior Vice President and Chief Information Officer, Information Technology Services
CHR: Jennifer Bandy, Human Resource Business Partner
CNO: Susan T. Bachmeier, MSN, R.N., Chief Nursing Officer
Web address: www.wakehealth.edu/Davie-Medical-Center
Control: Other not–for–profit (including NFP Corporation) **Service:** General medical and surgical

Staffed Beds: 25 **Admissions:** 1504 **Census:** 8 **Outpatient Visits:** 57503 **Births:** 0 **Total Expense ($000):** 56473 **Payroll Expense ($000):** 20047 **Personnel:** 253

Hospital, Medicare Provider Number, Address, Telephone, Approval, Facility, and Physician Codes, Health Care System

★ American Hospital Association (AHA) membership   ○ Healthcare Facilities Accreditation Program   ⇑ Center for Improvement in Healthcare Quality Accreditation
□ The Joint Commission accreditation   ◇ DNV Healthcare Inc. accreditation   △ Commission on Accreditation of Rehabilitation Facilities (CARF) accreditation

NC

BLACK MOUNTAIN—Buncombe County

JULIAN F. KEITH ALCOHOL AND DRUG ABUSE TREATMENT CENTER (344023), 201 Tabernacle Road, Zip 28711–2599; tel. 828/669–3400, (Nonreporting) **A**10
Primary Contact: W Douglas. Baker, Director
CFO: Jackie Maurer, Fiscal Officer
CMO: Anthony Burnett, M.D., Medical Director
CHR: Faye Hamlin, Manager Human Resources
Web address: www.jfkadatc.net
Control: State, Government, nonfederal **Service**: Alcoholism and other chemical dependency

Staffed Beds: 80

BOLIVIA—Brunswick County

☒ **NOVANT HEALTH BRUNSWICK MEDICAL CENTER (340158)**, 240 Hospital Drive NE, Zip 28422–8346; tel. 910/721–1000, (Nonreporting) **A**1 10 **S** Novant Health, Winston Salem, NC
Primary Contact: Shelbourn Stevens, President and Chief Operating Officer
CFO: Fred M Hargett, Executive Vice President and Chief Financial Officer
CMO: Thomas Zweng, Executive Vice President and Chief Medical Officer
CIO: David B Garrett, Senior Vice President and Chief Information Officer
CHR: Janet Smith-Hill, Executive Vice President and Chief Human Resources Officer
CNO: Lorna J Ward, MSN, R.N., Chief Nursing Officer
Web address: www.https://www.novanthealth.org
Control: Other not–for–profit (including NFP Corporation) **Service**: General medical and surgical

Staffed Beds: 54

BOONE—Watauga County

☒ **WATAUGA MEDICAL CENTER (340051)**, 336 Deerfield Road, Zip 28607–5008, Mailing Address: P.O. Box 2600, Zip 28607–2600; tel. 828/262–4100, **A**1 2 10 **F**3 5 13 15 17 18 20 22 26 28 29 30 31 32 34 35 38 40 44 45 46 47 48 49 50 53 54 57 59 64 70 73 75 76 77 78 81 82 84 85 86 87 91 92 93 96 107 108 110 111 114 115 118 119 120 121 122 123 124 129 130 131 132 135 144 145 146 147 148 149 154 156 **S** Appalachian Regional Healthcare System, Boone, NC
Primary Contact: Charles Mantooth, President and Chief Executive Officer
CFO: Kevin B May, Chief Financial Officer
CMO: Herman A Godwin, M.D., Jr Senior Vice President and Medical Director
CIO: Mike Quinto, Chief Information Officer
CHR: Amy J. Crabbe, Senior Vice President Human Resources
Web address: www.https://apprhs.org/contact-us
Control: Other not–for–profit (including NFP Corporation) **Service**: General medical and surgical

Staffed Beds: 99 Admissions: 4225 Census: 39 Outpatient Visits: 127543 Births: 624 Total Expense ($000): 122359 Payroll Expense ($000): 39423 Personnel: 678

BREVARD—Transylvania County

☒ **TRANSYLVANIA REGIONAL HOSPITAL (341319)**, 260 Hospital Drive, Zip 28712–3378; tel. 828/884–9111, (Nonreporting) **A**1 10 18 **S** HCA Healthcare, Nashville, TN
Primary Contact: Michele Pilon, President and Chief Nursing Officer
CFO: Theresa M Parker, Regional Finance Director
CMO: Mark Lemel, Chief of Staff
CIO: Ed Coye, Director Information Technology
CHR: Susan Stevens, Human Resources Strategic Business Partner
CNO: Melina Arrowood, Interim President and Chief Nursing Officer
Web address: www.trhospital.org
Control: Other not–for–profit (including NFP Corporation) **Service**: General medical and surgical

Staffed Beds: 40

BRYSON CITY—Swain County

★ **SWAIN COMMUNITY HOSPITAL (341305)**, 45 Plateau Street, Zip 28713–4200; tel. 828/488–2155, (Nonreporting) **A**10 18 **S** Duke LifePoint Healthcare, Brentwood, TN
Primary Contact: Steve Heatherly, Chief Executive Officer
CMO: David Zimmerman, M.D., Chief of Staff
Web address: www.westcare.org
Control: Other not–for–profit (including NFP Corporation) **Service**: General medical and surgical

Staffed Beds: 25

BURGAW—Pender County

★ ⓕ **PENDER MEMORIAL HOSPITAL (341307)**, 507 East Freemont Street, Zip 28425–5131; tel. 910/259–5451, (Total facility includes 43 beds in nursing home–type unit) **A**10 18 21 **F**3 11 15 29 34 35 40 45 54 56 57 59 62 64 81 85 87 93 96 107 110 114 119 128 130 133 143 146 148 149 **S** New Hanover Regional Medical Center, Wilmington, NC
Primary Contact: Ruth Glaser, President
CFO: Morrison Hall, Chief Financial Officer
CMO: Heather Davis, M.D., Chief of Staff
CIO: Ashley Hernandez, Chief Information Technology Officer
CHR: Lori McKoy, Business Partner
CNO: Cynthia Faulkner, R.N., Chief Nursing Executive
Web address: www.pendermemorial.org
Control: County, Government, nonfederal **Service**: General medical and surgical

Staffed Beds: 59 Admissions: 717 Census: 40 Outpatient Visits: 43415 Births: 0 Total Expense ($000): 27353 Payroll Expense ($000): 7550 Personnel: 166

BURLINGTON—Alamance County

☒ **ALAMANCE REGIONAL MEDICAL CENTER (340070)**, 1240 Huffman Mill Road, Zip 27215–8700, Mailing Address: P.O. Box 202, Zip 27216–0202; tel. 336/538–7000, **A**1 2 10 **F**3 8 9 12 13 15 18 20 22 24 26 28 29 30 31 32 34 35 36 38 39 40 44 45 47 49 50 53 54 56 57 58 59 60 64 66 68 70 73 74 75 76 77 78 79 81 82 84 85 86 87 89 91 93 94 96 97 98 100 101 102 103 107 108 110 111 115 117 118 119 120 121 123 126 130 131 132 135 144 145 146 147 148 154 155 **S** Cone Health, Greensboro, NC
Primary Contact: Preston W. Hammock, President
CFO: Rex Street, Senior Vice President and Chief Financial Officer
CMO: Andrew Lamb, M.D., Chief of Staff
CIO: Terri Andrews, Director Information Technology
Web address: www.armc.com
Control: Other not–for–profit (including NFP Corporation) **Service**: General medical and surgical

Staffed Beds: 197 Admissions: 10338 Census: 109 Outpatient Visits: 292799 Births: 1349 Total Expense ($000): 232914 Payroll Expense ($000): 70650 Personnel: 1473

BUTNER—Granville County

☐ **CENTRAL REGIONAL HOSPITAL (344004)**, 300 Veazey Road, Zip 27509–1668; tel. 919/764–2000, **A**1 3 5 10 **F**3 30 39 40 41 50 53 56 57 59 61 65 68 74 75 77 86 87 91 92 96 97 98 99 103 119 130 132 135 143 146 149 154 157
Primary Contact: Walter Edwin. Beal, Chief Executive Officer
COO: Cliff Hood, Chief Operating Officer
CFO: Pamela Richardson, Business Manager
CMO: Alan Cook, Chief Medical Officer
CIO: Joe Thurber, Director Information Technology
CHR: Kathleen Tardif, Director of Human Resources
CNO: Diana Holmes, Chief Nursing Officer
Control: State, Government, nonfederal **Service**: Psychiatric

Staffed Beds: 398 Admissions: 919 Census: 368 Outpatient Visits: 0 Births: 0 Total Expense ($000): 218104 Payroll Expense ($000): 91984

CAMP LEJEUNE—Onslow County

☒ **NAVAL HOSPITAL CAMP LEJEUNE**, 100 Brewster Boulevard, Zip 28547–2538, Mailing Address: P.O. Box 10100, Zip 28547–0100; tel. 910/450–4300, (Nonreporting) **A**1 3 5 **S** Bureau of Medicine and Surgery, Department of the Navy, Falls Church, VA
Primary Contact: Captain Rick Freedman, Commanding Officer
Web address: www.med.navy.mil/sites/nhcl/Pages/default.aspx
Control: Department of Defense, Government, federal **Service**: General medical and surgical

Staffed Beds: 117

CARY—Wake County

☒ **WAKEMED CARY HOSPITAL (340173)**, 1900 Kildaire Farm Road, Zip 27518–6616; tel. 919/350–8000, **A**1 10 **F**3 7 12 13 15 18 20 26 28 29 30 31 35 40 42 44 45 46 48 49 50 54 61 64 68 70 73 74 75 76 77 79 81 82 85 86 92 100 101 102 107 110 111 114 115 118 119 126 129 130 132 146 147 149 154 **S** WakeMed Health & Hospitals, Raleigh, NC
Primary Contact: Donald R. Gintzig, President and Chief Executive Officer
COO: Denise Wilder Warren, R.N., Executive Vice President and Chief Operating Officer
CMO: West Paul, M.D., Ph.D., Senior Vice President, Chief Quality and Medical Staff Officer
CIO: Denton Arledge, Vice President and Chief Information Officer
CHR: Jeanene R Martin, M.P.H., Senior Vice President Human Resources and Chief People Officer
CNO: Cindy Boily, MSN, R.N., Senior Vice President and Chief Nursing Officer
Web address: www.wakemed.org
Control: Other not–for–profit (including NFP Corporation) **Service**: General medical and surgical

Staffed Beds: 178 Admissions: 11475 Census: 125 Outpatient Visits: 262004 Births: 2495 Total Expense ($000): 197490 Payroll Expense ($000): 71347 Personnel: 1055

CHAPEL HILL—Orange County

☒ △ **UNIVERSITY OF NORTH CAROLINA HOSPITALS (340061)**, 101 Manning Drive, Zip 27514–4220; tel. 984/974–1000, (Includes N.C. WOMEN'S HOSPITAL, 101 Manning Drive, Chapel Hill, North Carolina, Zip 27514–4220; tel. 984/974–1000; Gary L Park, President; NORTH CAROLINA CHILDREN'S HOSPITAL, 101 Manning Drive, Chapel Hill, North Carolina, Zip 27514–4220; tel. 984/974–1000; UNC HEALTH CARE HILLSBOROUGH CAMPUS, 430 Waterstone Drive, Hillsborough, North Carolina, Zip 27278–9078; tel. 984/215–2000; Gary L Park, Chief Executive Officer; UNC LINEBERGER COMPREHENSIVE CANCER CENTER, 450 West Drive, Chapel Hill, North Carolina, Zip 27599–5020; tel. 919/966–3036) **A**1 2 3 5 7 8 10 **F**3 4 5 7 8 9 11 12 13 14 15 16 17 18 19 20 21 22 23 24 25 26 27 28 29 30 31 32 34 35 36 38 39 40 41 43 44 45 46 47 48 49 50 51 52 53 54 55 56 57 58 59 60 61 62 63 64 65 66 68 70 72 73 74 75 76 77 78 79 80 81 82 83 84 85 86 87 88 89 90 92 93 94 97 98 99 100 101 102 103 104 106 107 108 110 111 114 115 116 117 118 119 120 121 123 124 126 129 130 131 132 134 135 136 137 138 139 140 141 142 143 144 145 146 147 148 149 150 153 154 155 156 157 **S** UNC Health Care, Chapel Hill, NC
Primary Contact: Gary L. Park, President
CFO: Christopher Ellington, Executive Vice President and Chief Financial Officer
CMO: Tony Lindsey, M.D., Chief of Staff
CIO: Tracy Parham
CHR: Scott Doak, System Vice President, Human Resources
CNO: Catherine Madigan, Chief Nursing Officer
Web address: www.unchealthcare.org
Control: State, Government, nonfederal **Service:** General medical and surgical

Staffed Beds: 949 **Admissions:** 43320 **Census:** 774 **Outpatient Visits:** 1570793 **Births:** 3995 **Total Expense ($000):** 1714077 **Payroll Expense ($000):** 562252 **Personnel:** 10152

CHARLOTTE—Mecklenburg County

☒ △ **ATRIUM HEALTH PINEVILLE (340098)**, 10628 Park Road, Zip 28210–8407; tel. 704/667–1000, **A**1 2 3 7 10 **F**3 5 7 10 13 17 18 20 22 24 26 28 29 30 31 40 42 45 49 50 64 68 70 73 74 75 76 77 78 79 81 82 84 85 86 87 90 91 92 93 100 107 108 111 114 115 119 120 121 123 126 129 130 132 135 146 147 148 149 154 157 **S** Atrium Health, Charlotte, NC
Primary Contact: Michael Lutes, Senior Vice President, Market President South
Web address: www.carolinashealthcare.org/pineville
Control: Hospital district or authority, Government, nonfederal **Service:** General medical and surgical

Staffed Beds: 250 **Admissions:** 17283 **Census:** 213 **Outpatient Visits:** 160156 **Births:** 2356 **Total Expense ($000):** 307182 **Payroll Expense ($000):** 96991 **Personnel:** 1539

☒ **ATRIUM HEALTH UNIVERSITY CITY (340166)**, 8800 North Tryon Street, Zip 28262–3300, Mailing Address: P.O. Box 560727, Zip 28256–0727; tel. 704/863–6000, **A**1 2 3 10 **F**3 8 13 15 18 20 26 29 30 31 34 40 42 43 44 45 46 49 50 51 57 59 60 64 65 68 70 72 74 75 76 78 79 81 82 84 85 86 87 93 107 111 114 115 118 119 126 129 130 145 146 148 149 150 154 **S** Atrium Health, Charlotte, NC
Primary Contact: William H. Leonard, President
CFO: Greg A Gombar, Chief Financial Officer
CIO: John Knox, Senior Vice President and Chief Information Officer
Web address: www.carolinashealthcare.org/university
Control: Hospital district or authority, Government, nonfederal **Service:** General medical and surgical

Staffed Beds: 100 **Admissions:** 6968 **Census:** 75 **Outpatient Visits:** 156277 **Births:** 1550 **Total Expense ($000):** 158114 **Payroll Expense ($000):** 52578 **Personnel:** 817

☒ **ATRIUM HEALTH'S CAROLINAS MEDICAL CENTER (340113)**, 1000 Blythe Boulevard, Zip 28203–5871, Mailing Address: P.O. Box 32861, Zip 28232–2861; tel. 704/355–2000, (Includes CAROLINAS MEDICAL CENTER-MERCY, 2001 Vail Avenue, Charlotte, North Carolina, Zip 28207–1289; tel. 704/304–5000; Scott Jones, Senior Vice President and Facility Executive; LEVINE CHILDREN'S HOSPITAL, 1000 Blythe Boulevard, Charlotte, North Carolina, Zip 28203; tel. 704/381–2000) **A**1 2 3 5 8 10 **F**3 4 6 8 13 15 17 18 19 20 21 22 23 24 25 26 27 28 29 30 31 32 34 35 36 37 38 39 40 41 42 43 44 45 46 47 48 49 50 51 52 56 57 59 60 61 62 64 65 66 68 70 71 72 73 74 75 76 77 78 79 80 81 82 84 85 86 87 88 89 90 93 96 97 98 99 100 101 102 103 104 105 107 108 111 114 115 117 118 119 120 121 123 124 126 130 131 133 136 137 138 139 141 142 145 146 147 148 151 153 154 156 **S** Atrium Health, Charlotte, NC
Primary Contact: Christopher Bowe, FACHE, Interim Chief Executive Officer
CFO: Anthony C DeFurio, Executive Vice President Chief Financial Officer
CMO: Roger A Ray, M.D., Executive Vice President and Chief Medical Officer
CHR: Jim Dunn, Ph.D., Chief Human Resource Officer
Web address: www.carolinashealthcare.org/cmc
Control: Hospital district or authority, Government, nonfederal **Service:** General medical and surgical

Staffed Beds: 1291 **Admissions:** 61393 **Census:** 1004 **Outpatient Visits:** 1065679 **Births:** 7018 **Total Expense ($000):** 2183931 **Payroll Expense ($000):** 630858 **Personnel:** 9546

☒ △ **ATRIUM HEALTH'S CAROLINAS REHABILITATION (343026)**, 1100 Blythe Boulevard, Zip 28203–5864; tel. 704/355–4300, **A**1 3 7 10 **F**29 30 64 68 82 90 91 93 95 96 119 130 143 144 146 147 148 149 **S** Atrium Health, Charlotte, NC
Primary Contact: Robert G. Larrison Jr, President
CFO: William Hopkins, Director Finance
CMO: William Bockenek, M.D., Chief Medical Officer
CHR: Deonca Leach, Director, Human Resources
CNO: Susan Chase, Vice President
Web address: www.carolinashealthcare.org/rehabilitation
Control: Other not-for-profit (including NFP Corporation) **Service:** Rehabilitation

Staffed Beds: 150 **Admissions:** 2714 **Census:** 118 **Outpatient Visits:** 83163 **Births:** 0 **Total Expense ($000):** 89735 **Payroll Expense ($000):** 37909 **Personnel:** 642

☒ **CAROLINAS CONTINUECARE HOSPITAL AT PINEVILLE (342015)**, 10648 Park Road, Zip 28210; tel. 704/667–8050, **A**1 10 22 **F**1 3 18 20 29 34 35 45 46 59 65 68 74 75 77 82 85 91 96 130 148 154 **S** Community Hospital Corporation, Plano, TX
Primary Contact: Derek Murzyn, Market Chief Executive Officer
CFO: Joanne Tyo, Chief Financial Officer
CMO: Joseph Lang, M.D., Chief of Staff
CHR: Doug Gallagher, Director Human Resources
CNO: Teshia Davis, Chief Clinical Officer
Web address: www.continuecare.org/pineville/
Control: Other not-for-profit (including NFP Corporation) **Service:** Acute long-term care hospital

Staffed Beds: 40 **Admissions:** 350 **Census:** 24 **Outpatient Visits:** 0 **Births:** 0 **Total Expense ($000):** 15253 **Payroll Expense ($000):** 6090 **Personnel:** 114

★ **CAROLINAS CONTINUECARE HOSPITAL AT UNIVERSITY (342021)**, 8800 North Tryon Street, Zip 28262–3300; tel. 704/863–8300, **A**10 22 **F**1 3 18 20 29 34 35 45 46 59 65 68 74 75 77 82 84 85 91 96 148 154 **S** Community Hospital Corporation, Plano, TX
Primary Contact: Derek Murzyn, Chief Executive Officer
Web address: www.continuecare.org/charlotte//
Control: Other not-for-profit (including NFP Corporation) **Service:** Acute long-term care hospital

Staffed Beds: 35 **Admissions:** 147 **Census:** 11 **Outpatient Visits:** 0 **Births:** 0 **Total Expense ($000):** 6809 **Payroll Expense ($000):** 2925 **Personnel:** 56

★ **NOVANT HEALTH CHARLOTTE ORTHOPAEDIC HOSPITAL (340153)**, 1901 Randolph Road, Zip 28207–1195; tel. 704/316–2000, (Nonreporting) **S** Novant Health, Winston Salem, NC
Primary Contact: Jason Bernd, President and Chief Operating Officer
CFO: Fred M Hargett, Executive Vice President and Chief Financial Officer
CMO: Thomas Zweng, Executive Vice President and Chief Medical Officer
CIO: David B Garrett, Senior Vice President and Chief Information Officer
CHR: Janet Smith-Hill, Executive Vice President and Chief Human Resource Officer
CNO: Kelli S Sadler Bell, R.N., Vice President, Chief Nursing Officer
Web address: www.novanthealth.org
Control: Other not-for-profit (including NFP Corporation) **Service:** Orthopedic

Staffed Beds: 31

☒ **NOVANT HEALTH PRESBYTERIAN MEDICAL CENTER (340053)**, 200 Hawthorne Lane, Zip 28204–2528, Mailing Address: P.O. Box 33549, Zip 28233–3549; tel. 704/384–4000, (Includes PRESBYTERIAN HEMBY CHILDREN'S HOSPITAL, 200 Hawthorne Lane, Charlotte, North Carolina, Zip 28204–2515; tel. 704/384–5134), (Nonreporting) **A**1 2 3 10 **S** Novant Health, Winston Salem, NC
Primary Contact: Paula Vincent, MSN, President and Chief Operating Officer
CFO: Fred M Hargett, Executive Vice President and Chief Financial Officer
CMO: Thomas Zweng, Executive Vice President and Chief Medical Officer
CIO: David B Garrett, Senior Vice President Information Technology
CHR: Janet Smith-Hill, Senior Vice President Human Resources
CNO: Kelli S Sadler Bell, R.N., Vice President, Chief Nursing Officer
Web address: www.novanthealth.org
Control: Other not-for-profit (including NFP Corporation) **Service:** General medical and surgical

Staffed Beds: 440

PRESBYTERIAN HOSPITAL See Novant Health Presbyterian Medical Center

PRESBYTERIAN-ORTHOPAEDIC HOSPITAL See Novant Health Charlotte Orthopaedic Hospital

---

STRATEGIC BEHAVIORAL HEALTH - CHARLOTTE (344031), 1715 Sharon Road West, Zip 28210–5663; tel. 704/944–0650, (Nonreporting) **A**10 **S** Strategic Behavioral Health, LLC, Memphis, TN
Primary Contact: George G. Boykin, Chief Executive Officer
Web address: www.sbccharlotte.com/
Control: Corporation, Investor–owned (for–profit) **Service**: Children's hospital psychiatric

Staffed Beds: 60	

CHEROKEE—Swain County

CHEROKEE INDIAN HOSPITAL (340156), 1 Hospital Road, Zip 28719; tel. 828/497–9163, (Nonreporting) **A**1 3 10
Primary Contact: Casey Cooper, Chief Executive Officer
COO: Beth Greene, Chief Operating Officer
CFO: Chrissy Arch, Chief Financial Officer
CMO: Michael E Toedt, M.D., Director Clinical Services
CIO: Anthony Taylor, Manager Information Technology
Web address: www.cherokeehospital.org
Control: Other not–for–profit (including NFP Corporation) **Service**: General medical and surgical

Staffed Beds: 15	

CLINTON—Sampson County

SAMPSON REGIONAL MEDICAL CENTER (340024), 607 Beaman Street, Zip 28328–2697, Mailing Address: P.O. Box 260, Zip 28329–0260; tel. 910/592–8511, **A**1 3 5 10 12 13 **F**3 13 14 15 29 34 35 40 45 46 47 50 51 53 57 59 62 64 68 70 75 76 77 79 81 82 85 86 89 91 93 107 110 111 114 119 130 132 133 144 146 156
Primary Contact: Shawn Howerton, M.D., Chief Executive Officer and President, Medical Staff
COO: Geraldine H Shipp, Director of Risk Management
CFO: Jerry Heinzman, Senior Vice President and Chief Financial Officer
CMO: Shawn Howerton, M.D., Chief Executive Officer and President, Medical Staff
CIO: Kelly Lucas, Chief Information Officer
CHR: Michael W. Gilpin, Vice President Human Resources
CNO: Allison H Taylor, R.N., Chief Nursing Officer and Vice President Clinical Services
Web address: www.sampsonrmc.org
Control: County, Government, nonfederal **Service**: General medical and surgical

Staffed Beds: 83 **Admissions**: 2958 **Census**: 28 **Outpatient Visits**: 75867 **Births**: 454 **Total Expense ($000)**: 63339 **Payroll Expense ($000)**: 28028 **Personnel**: 482	

CLYDE—Haywood County

HAYWOOD REGIONAL MEDICAL CENTER (340184), 262 Leroy George Drive, Zip 28721–7430; tel. 828/456–7311, (Nonreporting) **A**1 3 10 **S** Duke LifePoint Healthcare, Brentwood, TN
Primary Contact: Rod Harkleroad, R.N., Chief Executive Officer
COO: Teresa Reynolds, Chief Operating Officer
CFO: Rose Coyne, Interim CFO
CMO: Tyson Smith, M.D., Chief Medical Officer
CIO: Greg Copen, Chief Information Officer
CHR: Janet Millsaps, Vice President Human Resources
Web address: www.haymed.org
Control: Hospital district or authority, Government, nonfederal **Service**: General medical and surgical

Staffed Beds: 146	

COLUMBUS—Polk County

ST. LUKE'S HOSPITAL (341322), 101 Hospital Drive, Zip 28722–6418; tel. 828/894–3311, **A**1 10 18 **F**3 11 15 29 30 31 34 35 40 45 56 57 59 64 70 75 77 78 79 81 82 85 87 93 98 103 107 108 110 115 119 127 130 133 135 146 148 149 153 154 **S** Atrium Health, Charlotte, NC
Primary Contact: Michelle Fortune, R.N., Chief Executive Officer
CFO: Elizabeth Presnell, Assistant Vice President of Finance
CMO: James Holleman, M.D., Chief of Staff
CIO: Nick Whichard, Chief Information Officer
CHR: Amy Norville, Vice President Support Services
CNO: Katherine Hefner, MSN, Chief Nursing Officer
Web address: www.saintlukeshospital.com
Control: Other not–for–profit (including NFP Corporation) **Service**: General medical and surgical

Staffed Beds: 35 **Admissions**: 1556 **Census**: 19 **Outpatient Visits**: 26036 **Births**: 0 **Total Expense ($000)**: 36282 **Payroll Expense ($000)**: 13795 **Personnel**: 331	

CONCORD—Cabarrus County

ATRIUM HEALTH CABARRUS (340001), 920 Church Street North, Zip 28025–2983; tel. 704/403–3000, **A**1 2 3 10 **F**3 5 6 8 9 11 12 13 15 17 18 20 22 24 26 28 29 30 32 34 35 36 38 40 42 43 44 45 46 47 48 49 50 53 54 55 56 57 58 59 60 61 64 65 68 70 71 72 73 74 75 76 78 79 81 82 84 85 86 87 88 89 92 93 94 97 98 100 102 103 104 107 108 110 111 114 115 117 118 119 120 121 123 124 126 129 130 131 132 135 145 146 147 148 149 150 154 156 **S** Atrium Health, Charlotte, NC
Primary Contact: Phyllis A. Wingate, FACHE, President
COO: Bill Hubbard, Vice President, Operations
CFO: Rodney Ball, Vice President Finance
CMO: Dan Hagler, M.D., Vice President and Chief Medical Officer
CIO: Lisa Sykes, Manager, Information Services
CHR: Lesley Chambless, Assistant Vice President Workforce Relations
CNO: Kate Grew, MSN, R.N., Vice President/Chief Nurse Executive
Web address: www.carolinashealthcare.org/northeast
Control: Hospital district or authority, Government, nonfederal **Service**: General medical and surgical

Staffed Beds: 455 **Admissions**: 23064 **Census**: 305 **Outpatient Visits**: 321486 **Births**: 2785 **Total Expense ($000)**: 481335 **Payroll Expense ($000)**: 158921 **Personnel**: 2714	

DANBURY—Stokes County

★ 🏥 **LIFEBRITE COMMUNITY HOSPITAL OF STOKES (341317)**, 1570 NC 8 & 89 Highway North, Zip 27016, Mailing Address: P.O. Box 10, Zip 27016–0010; tel. 336/593–2831, (Nonreporting) **A**10 18 21 **S** LifeBrite Hospital Group, LLC, Lilburn, GA
Primary Contact: Pamela P. Tillman, Administrator
CFO: Warren S. Binderman, Chief Financial Officer
CMO: Samuel C Newsome, M.D., Chief of Staff
CIO: Ada Ashley, HIM Director
CHR: Lee Sykes, Human Resources Director
CNO: Amanda Parks, Chief Nursing Officer
Web address: www.lifebritestokes.com
Control: Corporation, Investor–owned (for–profit) **Service**: General medical and surgical

Staffed Beds: 65	

DUNN—Harnett County

☐ **HARNETT HEALTH SYSTEM (340071)**, 800 Tilghman Drive, Zip 28334–5599, Mailing Address: P.O. Box 1706, Zip 28335–1706; tel. 910/892–1000, (Includes CENTRAL HARTNETT HOSPITAL, 215 Brightwater Drive, Lillington, North Carolina, Zip 27546; tel. 910/892–1000) **A**1 3 5 10 12 13 **F**3 11 13 15 18 20 28 29 30 34 35 39 40 45 50 56 57 59 70 73 75 76 77 79 81 85 86 87 89 92 93 96 102 107 108 110 111 114 118 119 130 146 148 **S** Cape Fear Valley Health System, Fayetteville, NC
Primary Contact: Kevin Jackson, Interim Chief Executive Officer
COO: Kenneth E Bryan, FACHE, President and Chief Executive Officer
CFO: Lynn Lambert, Chief Financial Officer
CIO: Tim Krieger, Director Information Systems
CHR: Sondra Davis, Vice President Human Resources & System Development
CNO: Vicki Allen, R.N., MS, Vice President Patient Care Services and Chief Nursing Officer
Web address: www.myharnetthealth.org/
Control: Other not–for–profit (including NFP Corporation) **Service**: General medical and surgical

Staffed Beds: 105 **Admissions**: 5093 **Census**: 49 **Outpatient Visits**: 114788 **Births**: 512 **Total Expense ($000)**: 94817 **Payroll Expense ($000)**: 41354 **Personnel**: 739	

DURHAM—Durham County

DUKE REGIONAL HOSPITAL (340155), 3643 North Roxboro Street, Zip 27704–2763; tel. 919/470–4000, **A**1 3 5 10 **F**3 8 11 12 13 15 17 18 20 22 24 26 29 30 31 34 35 40 44 45 47 50 51 57 58 59 60 64 66 68 70 73 74 75 76 77 78 79 80 81 82 84 85 86 87 90 96 98 100 101 102 107 108 110 111 115 118 119 120 121 123 124 126 131 132 135 146 147 148 149 154 **S** Duke University Health System, Durham, NC
Primary Contact: Kathleen B. Galbraith, FACHE, President
COO: A. Mitch Babb, Vice President, Operations
CFO: Jonathan B Hoy, Chief Financial Officer
CMO: Barbara Griffith, M.D., Chief Medical Officer
CIO: Terry Mears, Director Information Systems
CHR: Dexter Nolley, Chief Human Resources Officer
CNO: Victoria K Orto, R.N., Chief Nursing and Patient Care Services Officer
Web address: www.dukehealth.org
Control: Other not–for–profit (including NFP Corporation) **Service**: General medical and surgical

Staffed Beds: 214 **Admissions**: 16356 **Census**: 214 **Outpatient Visits**: 195071 **Births**: 2272 **Total Expense ($000)**: 355486 **Payroll Expense ($000)**: 152241 **Personnel**: 2072	

NC

Many Facility Codes have changed. Please refer to the AHA Guide Code Chart. © 2019 AHA Guide

☒ **DUKE UNIVERSITY HOSPITAL (340030)**, 2301 Erwin Road, Zip 27705–4699, Mailing Address: P.O. Box 3814, Zip 27710–3708; tel. 919/684–8111, (Includes DUKE CHILDREN'S HOSPITAL & HEALTH CENTER, 2301 Erwin Road, Durham, North Carolina, Zip 27710–0001, Mailing Address: P.O. Box 3708, Zip 27702, tel. 919/684–8111) **A**1 2 3 5 8 10 **F**3 5 6 7 9 11 12 13 15 17 18 19 20 21 22 23 24 25 26 27 28 29 30 31 32 34 35 37 39 40 41 43 44 45 46 47 48 49 50 53 54 55 56 57 58 59 60 61 64 65 66 68 70 72 73 74 75 76 77 78 79 80 81 82 84 85 86 87 88 89 91 92 93 94 96 97 98 99 100 101 102 103 104 107 108 110 111 112 114 115 116 117 118 119 120 121 123 124 126 129 130 131 132 134 135 136 137 138 139 140 141 142 145 146 147 148 149 154 155 156 **S** Duke University Health System, Durham, NC
Primary Contact: Thomas Owens, M.D., President
CFO: Sabrina Olsen, Chief Financial Officer
CMO: Lisa C Pickett, M.D., Chief Medical Officer
CIO: Jeffrey Ferranti, M.D., Chief Information Officer
CHR: Deborah Page, Chief Human Resources Officer
CNO: Mary Ann Fuchs, R.N., Vice President Patient Care and System Chief Nurse Executive
Web address: www.dukehealth.org
Control: Other not-for-profit (including NFP Corporation) **Service:** General medical and surgical

Staffed Beds: 970 **Admissions:** 43283 **Census:** 815 **Outpatient Visits:** 1087262 **Births:** 3428 **Total Expense ($000):** 2227816 **Payroll Expense ($000):** 625300 **Personnel:** 11185

DURHAM REGIONAL HOSPITAL See Duke Regional Hospital

☒ **DURHAM VETERANS AFFAIRS MEDICAL CENTER**, 508 Fulton Street, Zip 27705–3897; tel. 919/286–0411, (Total facility includes 66 beds in nursing home–type unit) **A**1 3 5 **F**3 5 6 8 9 10 11 12 15 17 18 20 22 24 26 28 29 30 31 34 35 36 38 39 40 44 45 46 47 48 49 50 51 52 53 54 55 56 57 58 59 60 61 62 63 64 65 66 70 71 74 75 77 78 79 81 82 83 84 85 86 87 91 92 93 94 96 97 98 100 101 102 103 104 105 107 108 110 111 114 115 116 117 118 119 120 121 126 127 128 129 130 131 132 133 135 143 144 146 147 148 149 150 152 153 154 156 157 158 **S** Department of Veterans Affairs, Washington, DC
Primary Contact: Paul Crews, Director
COO: Sara Haigh, Associate Director
CFO: David Kuboushek, Chief, Fiscal Service
CMO: John D Shelburne, M.D., Chief of Staff
CIO: Toby Dickerson, Chief Information Resources Management Services
CHR: Jerry Freeman, Chief, Human Resources Management Services
Web address: www.durham.va.gov/
Control: Veterans Affairs, Government, federal **Service:** General medical and surgical

Staffed Beds: 251 **Admissions:** 7405 **Census:** 226 **Outpatient Visits:** 778319 **Births:** 0 **Total Expense ($000):** 726705 **Payroll Expense ($000):** 301949 **Personnel:** 3710

☐ **NORTH CAROLINA SPECIALTY HOSPITAL (340049)**, 3916 Ben Franklin Boulevard, Zip 27704 2383, Mailing Address: P.O. Box 15819, Zip 27704–2383; tel. 919/956–9300, **A**1 10 **F**3 29 30 51 64 79 81 82 85 86 87 89 107 119 126 130 131 148 154 **S** National Surgical Healthcare, Chicago, IL
Primary Contact: Randi L. Shults, Chief Executive Officer
CFO: Bill Wilson, Chief Financial Officer
CMO: David Musante, M.D., Medical Director
CHR: Sarah Bohlin, Human Resources Director
CNO: John Medlin, Chief Nursing Officer
Web address: www.ncspecialty.com
Control: Partnership, Investor–owned (for–profit) **Service:** Surgical

Staffed Beds: 18 **Admissions:** 1606 **Census:** 9 **Outpatient Visits:** 7501 **Births:** 0 **Total Expense ($000):** 46050 **Payroll Expense ($000):** 11910 **Personnel:** 204

☒ **SELECT SPECIALTY HOSPITAL-DURHAM (342018)**, 3643 North Roxboro Road, 6th Floor, Zip 27704–2702; tel. 919/470–9159, (Nonreporting) **A**1 10 **S** Select Medical Corporation, Mechanicsburg, PA
Primary Contact: Jennifer Rawley, PharmD, Chief Executive Officer
CHR: Michael Stinson, Human Resources Coordinator
CNO: Cole Oren, R.N., Chief Nursing Officer
Web address: www.selectspecialtyhospitals.com/company/locations/durham.aspx
Control: Corporation, Investor–owned (for–profit) **Service:** Acute long–term care hospital

Staffed Beds: 30

VERITAS COLLABORATIVE, 615 Douglas Street, Suite 500, Zip 27705–6616; tel. 919/908–9730, (Nonreporting) **S** Veritas Collaborative, Durham, NC
Primary Contact: Becca Eckstein, Executive Director
Web address: www.https://veritascollaborative.com
Control: Partnership, Investor–owned (for–profit) **Service:** Psychiatric

Staffed Beds: 25

VERITAS COLLABORATIVE, 4024 Stirrup Creek Drive, Zip 27703–9464; tel. 919/908–9730, (Nonreporting) **S** Veritas Collaborative, Durham, NC
Primary Contact: Sara Hofmeier, Executive Director
Web address: www.https://veritascollaborative.com
Control: Partnership, Investor–owned (for–profit) **Service:** Psychiatric

Staffed Beds: 40

EDEN—Rockingham County

★ ⇑ **UNC ROCKINGHAM HEALTH CARE (340060)**, 117 East King's Highway, Zip 27288–5201; tel. 336/623–9711, (Total facility includes 121 beds in nursing home–type unit) (Data for 181 days) **A**2 10 21 **F**3 11 13 15 26 29 30 34 35 40 45 47 48 49 50 57 59 64 68 70 74 76 77 81 85 87 89 90 93 107 108 110 111 114 118 119 128 129 130 132 143 144 146 147 148 154 **S** UNC Health Care, Chapel Hill, NC
Primary Contact: Dana Weston, Chief Executive Officer
CFO: Raymond C. Owings, Interim Chief Financial Officer
CIO: Wade Williams, Chief Information Officer
CHR: Tom Stevens, Director Personnel
CNO: JoAnn P. Smith, R.N., Chief Nursing Officer, and Vice President Patient Care Services
Web address: www.morehead.org
Control: Other not-for-profit (including NFP Corporation) **Service:** General medical and surgical

Staffed Beds: 188 **Admissions:** 1576 **Census:** 126 **Outpatient Visits:** 73435 **Births:** 232 **Total Expense ($000):** 33790 **Payroll Expense ($000):** 14572 **Personnel:** 505

EDENTON—Chowan County

☒ **VIDANT CHOWAN HOSPITAL (341318)**, 211 Virginia Road, Zip 27932–9668, Mailing Address: P.O. Box 629, Zip 27932–0629; tel. 252/482–8451, **A**1 3 10 18 **F**3 11 13 15 28 29 30 31 34 35 40 45 46 57 59 64 70 74 75 76 77 78 79 81 82 84 85 93 107 108 110 111 114 119 130 132 135 146 147 148 156 **S** Vidant Health, Greenville, NC
Primary Contact: Jeffrey Sackrison, President
CFO: Brian Harvill, Vice President Financial Services
CMO: William Hope IV Chief of Medical Staff
CIO: Brian White, Director Strategic Operations
CHR: Nicole Spell, Director Human Resources
CNO: Cindy Coker, Vice President, Patient Care Services
Web address: www.vidanthealth.com
Control: Other not-for-profit (including NFP Corporation) **Service:** General medical and surgical

Staffed Beds: 19 **Admissions:** 1488 **Census:** 15 **Outpatient Visits:** 39250 **Total Expense ($000):** 44726 **Payroll Expense ($000):** 16104 **Personnel:** 305

ELIZABETH CITY—Pasquotank County

★ ⇑ **SENTARA ALBEMARLE MEDICAL CENTER (340109)**, 1144 North Road Street, Zip 27909–3473, Mailing Address: P.O. Box 1587, Zip 27906–1587; tel. 252/335–0531, **A**10 21 **F**3 11 13 15 18 22 28 29 30 31 34 35 36 37 38 39 40 41 44 45 46 47 48 49 50 51 56 57 58 59 60 61 64 65 68 70 74 75 76 77 78 79 81 84 85 86 87 91 92 93 94 96 97 102 107 108 110 111 114 116 117 118 119 121 130 131 132 135 141 146 147 148 149 154 **S** Sentara Healthcare, Norfolk, VA
Primary Contact: Coleen F. Santa Ana, President
CFO: Craig Lewis, Chief Financial Officer
CMO: Charles Nicholson, Vice President, Medical Affairs
CHR: Deborah Ferguson, Director, Human Resources
CNO: Jaime Carroll, R.N., Vice President Nursing
Web address: www.albemarlehealth.org
Control: Other not-for-profit (including NFP Corporation) **Service:** General medical and surgical

Staffed Beds: 109 **Admissions:** 4818 **Census:** 54 **Outpatient Visits:** 247514 **Births:** 444 **Total Expense ($000):** 103045 **Payroll Expense ($000):** 42291 **Personnel:** 763

Hospital, Medicare Provider Number, Address, Telephone, Approval, Facility, and Physician Codes, Health Care System

★ American Hospital Association (AHA) membership
☐ The Joint Commission accreditation
○ Healthcare Facilities Accreditation Program
◇ DNV Healthcare Inc. accreditation
⇑ Center for Improvement in Healthcare Quality Accreditation
△ Commission on Accreditation of Rehabilitation Facilities (CARF) accreditation

NC

ELIZABETHTOWN—Bladen County

BLADEN COUNTY HOSPITAL See Cape Fear Valley - Bladen County Hospital

☒ **CAPE FEAR VALLEY - BLADEN COUNTY HOSPITAL (341315)**, 501 South Poplar Street, Zip 28337–9375, Mailing Address: P.O. Box 398, Zip 28337–0398; tel. 910/862–5100, (Nonreporting) **A**1 10 18 **S** Cape Fear Valley Health System, Fayetteville, NC
Primary Contact: Mark Cobb, Chief Executive Officer
CFO: Stephen Fife, Chief Financial Officer
CIO: Craig Kellum, Director Management Information Systems
CHR: Ginger Parks, Director Human Resources
CNO: Diana Harris, Chief Nursing Officer
Web address: www.bchn.org
Control: County, Government, nonfederal **Service**: General medical and surgical

Staffed Beds: 25

ELKIN—Surry County

☒ **HUGH CHATHAM MEMORIAL HOSPITAL (340097)**, 180 Parkwood Drive, Zip 28621–2430, Mailing Address: P.O. Box 560, Zip 28621–0560; tel. 336/527–7000, **A**1 10 **F**3 11 13 15 28 29 30 34 40 45 49 53 57 59 62 64 70 74 75 76 77 79 81 85 87 93 96 107 108 110 111 118 119 120 121 125 127 130 131 132 133 135 144 146 147 148 149
Primary Contact: Paul Hammes, Chief Executive Officer
COO: Mary Blackburn, Vice President Operations and Chief Practice Officer
CFO: Donald E Trippel, Chief Financial Officer
CMO: Dominick Carbone, M.D., Chief of Staff
CIO: Lee Powe, Director Management Information Systems
CHR: Kathy Poteate, Interim Director Human Resources
CNO: Paula Moore, R.N., Chief Clinical Officer
Web address: www.hughchatham.org
Control: Other not–for–profit (including NFP Corporation) **Service**: General medical and surgical

Staffed Beds: 81 **Admissions:** 3760 **Census:** 35 **Outpatient Visits:** 70651 **Births:** 560 **Total Expense ($000):** 66406 **Payroll Expense ($000):** 23834 **Personnel:** 681

FAYETTEVILLE—Cumberland County

☒ △ **CAPE FEAR VALLEY MEDICAL CENTER (340028)**, 1638 Owen Drive, Zip 28304–3431, Mailing Address: P.O. Box 2000, Zip 28302–2000; tel. 910/615–4000, (Includes BEHAVIORAL HEALTH CARE OF CAPE FEAR VALLEY HEALTH SYSTEM, 711 Executive Place, Fayetteville, North Carolina, Zip 28301; tel. 910/615–3700; CAPE FEAR VALLEY REHABILITATION CENTER, 1638 Owen Drive, Fayetteville, North Carolina, Zip 28304; tel. 910/615–4000) **A**1 2 3 5 7 8 10 12 13 19 **F**3 4 5 7 12 13 14 15 17 18 20 22 24 26 28 29 30 31 34 35 38 39 40 41 43 44 45 46 47 48 49 53 54 55 56 57 58 59 60 61 64 65 68 70 72 73 74 75 76 77 78 79 81 82 84 85 86 87 88 89 90 91 92 93 96 97 98 100 101 102 103 104 105 107 108 109 110 111 114 115 116 117 118 119 120 121 122 123 124 126 127 129 130 132 135 143 144 146 147 148 149 150 152 153 154 155 156 **S** Cape Fear Valley Health System, Fayetteville, NC
Primary Contact: Michael Nagowski, Chief Executive Officer
COO: Daniel R Weatherly, Chief Operating Officer
CFO: Sandra Williams, Chief Financial Officer
CMO: Samuel A Fleishman, M.D., Chief Medical Officer
CIO: Phillip E. Wood Jr Chief Information Officer
CNO: Deborah Marshburn, Chief Nursing Executive
Web address: www.capefearvalley.com
Control: Other not–for–profit (including NFP Corporation) **Service**: General medical and surgical

Staffed Beds: 620 **Admissions:** 33157 **Census:** 454 **Outpatient Visits:** 255604 **Births:** 4570 **Total Expense ($000):** 759430 **Payroll Expense ($000):** 366784 **Personnel:** 5116

☒ **FAYETTEVILLE VETERANS AFFAIRS MEDICAL CENTER**, 2300 Ramsey Street, Zip 28301–3899; tel. 910/488–2120, (Nonreporting) **A**1 3 5 **S** Department of Veterans Affairs, Washington, DC
Primary Contact: Webster Carl. Bazemore, M.D., Interim Medical Director
COO: James Galkowski, Associate Director for Operations
CFO: Patrick Bullard, Chief Financial Officer
CMO: Greg Antoine, M.D., Chief of Staff
CIO: Kenneth Williams, Chief Information Officer
CHR: Joseph Whaley, Chief, Human Resources Management Service
CNO: Joyce Alexander-Hines, R.N., MSN, Associate Director, Patient Care Services
Web address: www.fayettevillenc.va.gov
Control: Veterans Affairs, Government, federal **Service**: General medical and surgical

Staffed Beds: 58

☐ **HIGHSMITH-RAINEY SPECIALTY HOSPITAL (342014)**, 150 Robeson Street, Zip 28301–5570; tel. 910/615–1000, **A**1 10 **F**1 3 11 29 30 35 39 50 51 58 68 70 81 85 107 114 119 130 144 146 148 149 150 **S** Cape Fear Valley Health System, Fayetteville, NC
Primary Contact: Kevin Jackson, On Site Administrator
Web address: www.capefearvalley.com
Control: Other not–for–profit (including NFP Corporation) **Service**: Acute long–term care hospital

Staffed Beds: 66 **Admissions:** 367 **Census:** 57 **Outpatient Visits:** 32767 **Births:** 0 **Total Expense ($000):** 41575 **Payroll Expense ($000):** 23435 **Personnel:** 312

VETERANS AFFAIRS MEDICAL CENTER See Fayetteville Veterans Affairs Medical Center

FORT BRAGG—Cumberland County

☒ **WOMACK ARMY MEDICAL CENTER**, 2817 Reilly Road, Zip 28310–7302; tel. 910/907–6000, (Nonreporting) **A**1 3 5 **S** Department of the Army, Office of the Surgeon General, Falls Church, VA
Primary Contact: Colonel Lance C. Raney, Commander
CIO: Mary Peters, Chief Information Officer
Web address: www.wamc.amedd.army.mil/
Control: Department of Defense, Government, federal **Service**: General medical and surgical

Staffed Beds: 156

FRANKLIN—Macon County

☒ **ANGEL MEDICAL CENTER (341326)**, 120 Riverview Street, Zip 28734–2612, Mailing Address: P.O. Box 1209, Zip 28744–0569; tel. 828/524–8411, **A**1 3 10 18 **F**3 11 15 18 28 29 30 31 34 35 40 44 45 47 49 50 54 57 59 64 70 77 78 79 81 85 86 87 93 96 97 107 108 110 111 114 119 127 131 132 133 135 144 146 147 148 **S** HCA Healthcare, Nashville, TN
Primary Contact: Karen S. Gorby, R.N., MSN, FACHE, Chief Executive Officer and Chief Nursing Officer
COO: Martin Wadewitz, Chief Operations Officer/ Vice President, Operations
CFO: George Kimbro, Vice President Finance
CIO: Ed Coye, Director Information Technology Mission Health System Hospitals
CHR: Teresa Mallonee, Director Human Resources
Web address: www.angelmed.org
Control: Other not–for–profit (including NFP Corporation) **Service**: General medical and surgical

Staffed Beds: 36 **Admissions:** 1610 **Census:** 14 **Outpatient Visits:** 98909 **Births:** 0 **Total Expense ($000):** 54516 **Payroll Expense ($000):** 13987 **Personnel:** 272

GARNER—Wake County

☐ **STRATEGIC BEHAVIORAL HEALTH - RALEIGH (344028)**, 3200 Waterfield Drive, Zip 27529–7727; tel. 919/800–4400, (Nonreporting) **A**1 10 **S** Strategic Behavioral Health, LLC, Memphis, TN
Primary Contact: Matt Doyle, Chief Executive Officer
CMO: Karen Miles, M.D., Medical Director
CHR: Christina Meeker, Director Human Resources
CNO: Shawanna Royal, R.N., Director Nursing
Web address: www.sbcraleigh.com/
Control: Corporation, Investor–owned (for–profit) **Service**: Children's hospital psychiatric

Staffed Beds: 50

GASTONIA—Gaston County

☒ **CAROMONT REGIONAL MEDICAL CENTER (340032)**, 2525 Court Drive, Zip 28054–2140, Mailing Address: P.O. Box 1747, Zip 28053–1747; tel. 704/834–2000, **A**1 2 10 **F**3 13 15 17 18 20 22 24 26 28 29 30 31 34 35 40 41 42 43 44 45 46 47 49 50 53 54 57 58 59 60 64 68 70 71 72 73 74 75 76 78 79 81 82 83 87 89 92 93 94 96 98 99 100 102 107 108 110 111 114 115 117 118 119 120 121 123 124 126 129 130 131 132 135 146 148 149
Primary Contact: Chris Peek, Chief Executive Officer
COO: Kathleen Besson, Executive Vice President and Chief Operating Officer
CFO: David O'Connor, Executive Vice President and Chief Financial Officer
CMO: Todd Davis, M.D., Vice President Medical Affairs, Patient Safety Officer
CIO: Mike Johnson, Vice President, Chief Information Officer
CHR: Elizabeth McCraw, Vice President, Human Resources
CNO: Scott E Wells, MSN, R.N., Vice President Patient Care Services
Web address: www.caromont.org
Control: Other not–for–profit (including NFP Corporation) **Service**: General medical and surgical

Staffed Beds: 417 **Admissions:** 22780 **Census:** 288 **Outpatient Visits:** 453731 **Births:** 1938 **Total Expense ($000):** 420139 **Payroll Expense ($000):** 170215 **Personnel:** 3079

GASTON MEMORIAL HOSPITAL See Caromont Regional Medical Center

NC

Many Facility Codes have changed. Please refer to the AHA Guide Code Chart. © 2019 AHA Guide

GOLDSBORO—Wayne County

☐ **CHERRY HOSPITAL (344026)**, 1401 West Ash Street, Zip 27530–1057; tel. 919/947–7000, **A**1 3 10 **F**30 39 98 103 106 119 130 143 146 149
Primary Contact: J. Luckey. Welsh Jr, Chief Executive Officer
CFO: Susie Sherrod Sanders, Chief Financial Officer
CMO: Jim Mayo, M.D., Clinical Director
CIO: Mike Letchworth, Manager Information Systems
CHR: Carol Thornton, Director Human Resources
CNO: Debbie Wall, Chief Nursing Officer
Web address: www.cherryhospital.org
Control: State, Government, nonfederal **Service**: Psychiatric

Staffed Beds: 243 **Admissions**: 859 **Census**: 223 **Outpatient Visits**: 0 **Births**: 0 **Total Expense ($000)**: 101712 **Payroll Expense ($000)**: 59865 **Personnel**: 1114

⊞ **WAYNE UNC HEALTH CARE (340010)**, 2700 Wayne Memorial Drive, Zip 27534–9494, Mailing Address: P.O. Box 8001, Zip 27533–8001; tel. 919/736–1110, **A**1 5 10 **F**3 8 13 15 18 20 22 28 29 30 31 34 35 39 40 45 47 49 50 57 58 59 60 64 66 68 70 73 74 75 76 77 78 79 80 81 85 86 87 89 92 93 96 98 100 101 102 107 108 110 111 114 118 119 126 129 130 132 145 146 147 148 156 **S** UNC Health Care, Chapel Hill, NC
Primary Contact: Janie Jaberg, FACHE, President and Chief Executive Officer
COO: Thomas A Bradshaw, Vice President Operations
CFO: Rebecca W Craig, Vice President and Chief Financial Officer
CIO: Lori Cole, Director Information Technology
Web address: www.waynehealth.org
Control: Other not–for–profit (including NFP Corporation) **Service**: General medical and surgical

Staffed Beds: 274 **Admissions**: 10444 **Census**: 137 **Outpatient Visits**: 145047 **Births**: 1333 **Total Expense ($000)**: 239628 **Payroll Expense ($000)**: 95280 **Personnel**: 1538

GREENSBORO—Guilford County

⊞ **KINDRED HOSPITAL-GREENSBORO (342012)**, 2401 Southside Boulevard, Zip 27406–3311; tel. 336/271–2800, (Nonreporting) **A**1 10 **S** Kindred Healthcare, Louisville, KY
Primary Contact: Chad Lovett, Chief Executive Officer
CFO: Anthony Grate, Controller
CMO: Saad Amin, Medical Director Hospital
CIO: Little Shuford, Health Information Manager
CNO: Anne Correll, Chief Clinical Officer
Web address: www.khgreensboro.com
Control: Corporation, Investor–owned (for–profit) **Service**: Acute long–term care hospital

Staffed Beds: 101

⊞ △ **MOSES H. CONE MEMORIAL HOSPITAL (340091)**, 1200 North Elm Street, Zip 27401–1020; tel. 336/832–7000, (Includes ANNIE PENN HOSPITAL, 618 South Main Street, Reidsville, North Carolina, Zip 27320–5094; tel. 336/951–4000; Cynthia B Farrand, President; BEHAVIORAL HEALTH CENTER, 700 Walter Reed Drive, Greensboro, North Carolina, Zip 27403–1129; tel. 336/832–9600; Debbie Cunningham, R.N., Senior Vice President, Cone Health and President, Maternal, Child and Behavioral Health Services; CONE HEALTH, 1200 North Elm Street, Greensboro, North Carolina, Zip 27401; tel. 336/832–7000; Judith A Schanel, R.N., MSN, FACHE, Chief Operating Officer; WESLEY LONG COMMUNITY HOSPITAL, 501 North Elam Avenue, Greensboro, North Carolina, Zip 27403; tel. 336/832–1000; Paul A Jeffrey, President; WOMEN'S HOSPITAL OF GREENSBORO, 801 Green Valley Road, Greensboro, North Carolina, Zip 27408; tel. 336/832–6500; Debbie Cunningham, R.N., President), (Non-reporting) **A**1 2 3 5 7 10 19 **S** Cone Health, Greensboro, NC
Primary Contact: Terry Akin, Chief Executive Officer
CFO: Jeffrey Jones, Chief Financial Officer
CMO: William Bowman, M.D., Vice President Medical Affairs
CIO: Steve Horsley, Vice President and Chief Information Officer
CHR: Noel F Burt, Ph.D., Chief Human Resources Officer
CNO: Ann Marie Madden, MS, R.N., Vice President of Patient Care Services and Chief Nursing Officer
Web address: www.conehealth.com/locations/moses-cone-hospital/
Control: Other not–for–profit (including NFP Corporation) **Service**: General medical and surgical

Staffed Beds: 935

⊞ **SELECT SPECIALTY HOSPITAL-GREENSBORO (342020)**, 1200 North Elm Street, 5th Floor, Zip 27401–1004; tel. 336/832–8571, (Nonreporting) **A**1 10 **S** Select Medical Corporation, Mechanicsburg, PA
Primary Contact: Deana Knight, Chief Executive Officer
CHR: Karen Tracey, Chief Human Resources
CNO: Robin Clark, Chief Nursing Officer
Web address: www.selectspecialtyhospitals.com/company/locations/greensboro. aspx
Control: Corporation, Investor–owned (for–profit) **Service**: Acute long–term care hospital

Staffed Beds: 30

GREENVILLE—Pitt County

PITT COUNTY MEMORIAL HOSPITAL See Vidant Medical Center

⊞ △ **VIDANT MEDICAL CENTER (340040)**, 2100 Stantonsburg Road, Zip 27834–2818, Mailing Address: P.O. Box 6028, Zip 27835–6028; tel. 252/847–4100, (Includes JAMES AND CONNIE MAYNARD CHILDREN'S HOSPITAL, 2101 Stantonsburg Road, Greenville, North Carolina, Zip 27834–2817; tel. 252/847–5712; UNIVERSITY HEALTH SYSTEMS CHILDREN'S HOSPITAL, 2100 Stantonsburg Road, Greenville, North Carolina, Zip 27834–2818, Mailing Address: P.O. Box 6028, Zip 27835–6028, tel. 252/847–4100) **A**1 2 3 5 7 8 10 **F**3 7 12 13 14 15 17 18 19 20 21 22 23 24 25 26 27 28 29 30 34 35 38 40 41 43 44 45 46 47 48 49 50 51 52 55 56 57 58 59 60 61 64 65 68 70 71 72 73 74 75 76 77 78 79 80 81 82 83 84 85 86 87 88 89 90 92 93 94 95 96 97 98 100 101 102 104 107 108 110 111 114 115 117 118 119 124 126 129 130 131 132 134 135 138 139 143 145 146 147 148 149 150 155 156 157 **S** Vidant Health, Greenville, NC
Primary Contact: William Brian. Floyd, President
CFO: David S Hughes, Chief Financial Officer
CMO: Paul Shackelford, M.D., Chief Medical Officer
CIO: Donnette Herring, Chief Information Officer
CHR: Tyree Walker, Chief Human Resources Officer
CNO: Linda D Hofler, Ph.D., R.N., FACHE, Senior Vice President, Nurse Executive
Web address: https://www.vidanthealth.com/
Control: Other not–for–profit (including NFP Corporation) **Service**: General medical and surgical

Staffed Beds: 974 **Admissions**: 38357 **Census**: 702 **Outpatient Visits**: 271878 **Births**: 3527 **Total Expense ($000)**: 1081942 **Payroll Expense ($000)**: 358135 **Personnel**: 7361

WALTER B. JONES ALCOHOL AND DRUG ABUSE TREATMENT CENTER (344024), 2577 West Fifth Street, Zip 27834–7813; tel. 252/830–3426, (Nonreporting) **A**3
Primary Contact: Ben Gregory, Chief Executive Officer
CFO: Roy Carlton, Chief Financial Officer
CMO: Sonya Longest, M.D., Chief Medical Officer
CIO: Jed Hayn, Chief Information Officer
CHR: Amy Marion, Chief Human Resource Officer
CNO: Linda Roy, R.N., Chief Nursing Officer
Web address: www.ncdhhs.gov
Control: State, Government, nonfederal **Service**: Alcoholism and other chemical dependency

Staffed Beds: 80

HENDERSON—Vance County

⊞ **MARIA PARHAM MEDICAL CENTER (340132)**, 566 Ruin Creek Road, Zip 27536–2927; tel. 252/438–4143, (Nonreporting) **A**1 2 3 5 10 **S** Duke LifePoint Healthcare, Brentwood, TN
Primary Contact: Bert Beard, Chief Executive Officer
CFO: Jim Chatman, Chief Financial Officer
CIO: Randy Williams, Director Management Information Systems
Web address: www.mariaparham.com
Control: Other not–for–profit (including NFP Corporation) **Service**: General medical and surgical

Staffed Beds: 102

Hospital, Medicare Provider Number, Address, Telephone, Approval, Facility, and Physician Codes, Health Care System

★ American Hospital Association (AHA) membership
☐ The Joint Commission accreditation
○ Healthcare Facilities Accreditation Program
◇ DNV Healthcare Inc. accreditation
⇑ Center for Improvement in Healthcare Quality Accreditation
△ Commission on Accreditation of Rehabilitation Facilities (CARF) accreditation

NC

© 2019 AHA Guide   *Many Facility Codes have changed. Please refer to the AHA Guide Code Chart.*   Hospitals **A455**

HENDERSONVILLE—Henderson County

☒ ○ **ADVENTHEALTH HENDERSONVILLE (340023)**, 100 Hospital Drive, Zip 28792–5272; tel. 828/684–8501, **A**1 2 3 10 11 19 **F**3 11 13 15 18 26 28 29 30 31 34 35 40 50 54 59 62 64 65 68 70 71 74 75 76 77 78 79 80 81 85 87 93 97 98 100 101 102 103 104 105 107 108 110 111 114 115 118 119 126 129 130 131 135 142 146 147 148 153 154 157 **S** AdventHealth, Altamonte Springs, FL
Primary Contact: Jimm Bunch, President and Chief Executive Officer
CFO: Wendi Barber, Vice President Finance and Chief Financial Officer
CMO: Teresa Herbert, M.D., Chief Medical Officer
CIO: Lee Strickland, Regional Director Information Technology
CHR: Sharon J Campbell, Director, Human Resources
CNO: Roland Eugene Joy Jr Vice President and Chief Nursing Officer
Web address: www.parkridgehealth.org
Control: Other not–for–profit (including NFP Corporation) **Service**: General medical and surgical

Staffed Beds: 86 **Admissions**: 3976 **Census**: 46 **Outpatient Visits**: 369334 **Births**: 620 **Total Expense ($000)**: 181008 **Payroll Expense ($000)**: 71210 **Personnel**: 1051

★ ⇧ **MARGARET R. PARDEE MEMORIAL HOSPITAL (340017)**, 800 North Justice Street, Zip 28791–3410; tel. 828/696–1000, **A**2 3 10 21 **F**3 4 5 11 12 13 15 18 20 22 26 28 29 30 31 34 35 36 38 39 40 44 45 46 47 48 49 50 54 56 57 58 59 62 63 64 65 68 69 70 74 75 76 77 78 79 81 82 85 86 87 89 93 94 97 98 100 101 102 103 104 107 108 110 111 114 115 118 119 121 123 129 130 131 132 135 143 144 146 147 148 149 150 156 157 **S** UNC Health Care, Chapel Hill, NC
Primary Contact: James M. Kirby II, President and Chief Executive Officer
CFO: Andrew Wampler, Chief Financial Officer
CMO: Robert Kiskaddon, M.D., Chief Medical Officer
CNO: Denise Lucas, R.N., MSN, Vice President Clinical Services and Chief Nursing Officer
Web address: www.pardeehospital.org
Control: County, Government, nonfederal **Service**: General medical and surgical

Staffed Beds: 158 **Admissions**: 8090 **Census**: 85 **Outpatient Visits**: 283805 **Births**: 358 **Total Expense ($000)**: 237917 **Payroll Expense ($000)**: 85834 **Personnel**: 1242

HICKORY—Catawba County

☒ △ **CATAWBA VALLEY MEDICAL CENTER (340143)**, 810 Fairgrove Church Road SE, Zip 28602–9643; tel. 828/326–3000, **A**1 2 7 10 **F**3 11 12 13 15 18 20 22 26 28 29 30 31 34 35 37 39 40 44 49 50 51 53 54 56 57 58 59 61 64 65 68 70 71 72 74 75 76 77 78 79 81 84 85 86 87 89 90 91 92 93 96 97 98 100 101 102 103 104 107 108 109 110 111 114 115 117 118 119 120 121 122 123 124 126 129 130 131 132 135 143 144 145 146 147 148 149 154 156
Primary Contact: Edward L. Beard, R.N., President and Chief Executive Officer
CFO: Kimberly Crews, Vice President and Chief Financial Officer
CMO: Andrew Chesson, Chief Medical Officer
CIO: Tim Blanchat, Chief Information Officer
CHR: Phyllis M. Johnston, Vice President
Web address: www.catawbavalleymc.org
Control: County, Government, nonfederal **Service**: General medical and surgical

Staffed Beds: 250 **Admissions**: 11654 **Census**: 145 **Outpatient Visits**: 502732 **Births**: 1964 **Total Expense ($000)**: 285523 **Payroll Expense ($000)**: 124726 **Personnel**: 1730

☒ **FRYE REGIONAL MEDICAL CENTER (340116)**, 420 North Center Street, Zip 28601–5049, Mailing Address: 1950 11th Street Crt. NW, Zip 28601; tel. 828/315–5000, (Includes FRYE REGIONAL MEDICAL CENTER-SOUTH CAMPUS, One Third Avenue NW, Hickory, North Carolina, Zip 28601, Mailing Address: 420 North Center St., Zip 28603, tel. 828/315–5777) **A**1 2 10 19 **F**3 11 12 13 15 17 18 20 22 24 26 28 29 30 31 34 35 37 40 44 45 46 49 54 57 59 64 70 72 74 75 76 77 78 79 81 82 85 86 87 89 90 93 96 98 101 103 107 108 110 111 114 115 118 119 128 129 130 131 132 144 146 147 148 156 **S** Duke LifePoint Healthcare, Brentwood, TN
Primary Contact: Garfield Atchison, Chief Executive Officer
COO: Chris Fensterle, Chief Operating Officer
CFO: Jamey Stoner, Chief Financial Officer
CNO: Michelle Dickerson, Chief Nursing Officer
Web address: www.fryemedctr.com
Control: Corporation, Investor–owned (for–profit) **Service**: General medical and surgical

Staffed Beds: 271 **Admissions**: 10313 **Census**: 154 **Outpatient Visits**: 141055 **Births**: 412 **Personnel**: 1297

HIGH POINT—Guilford County

☒ △ **HIGH POINT MEDICAL CENTER (340004)**, 601 North Elm Street, Zip 27262–4398, Mailing Address: P.O. Box HP-5, Zip 27261–1899; tel. 336/878–6000, **A**1 7 10 19 **F**3 4 8 12 13 15 17 18 20 22 24 26 28 29 30 31 32 34 35 36 38 39 40 44 45 47 48 49 50 53 54 55 57 58 59 60 61 64 66 67 68 70 73 74 75 76 77 78 79 81 82 84 85 86 87 89 90 91 92 93 96 98 100 101 102 104 107 108 109 110 111 114 115 116 117 118 119 120 121 123 124 126 130 131 132 135 145 146 147 148 149 151 154 **S** Wake Forest Baptist Health, Winston-Salem, NC
Primary Contact: James Hoekstra, M.D., President
COO: Gregory W Taylor, M.D., Vice President and Chief Operating Officer
CMO: L Dale Williams, M.D., Vice President and Chief Medical Director
CIO: Nancy Waters, Interim Chief Information Officer
CHR: Katherine Burns, Vice President Human Resources
CNO: Tammi Erving-Mengel, R.N., MSN, Vice President, Chief Nursing Officer
Web address: www.highpointregional.com
Control: Other not–for–profit (including NFP Corporation) **Service**: General medical and surgical

Staffed Beds: 311 **Admissions**: 13211 **Census**: 154 **Outpatient Visits**: 224431 **Births**: 1152 **Total Expense ($000)**: 251742 **Payroll Expense ($000)**: 98252 **Personnel**: 1570

HIGHLANDS—Macon County

☒ **HIGHLANDS-CASHIERS HOSPITAL (341316)**, 190 Hospital Drive, Zip 28741–7600, Mailing Address: P O Drawer 190, Zip 28741–0190; tel. 828/526–1200, (Total facility includes 80 beds in nursing home–type unit) **A**1 10 18 **F**3 11 15 28 29 30 34 35 40 45 46 47 48 53 56 57 59 64 65 74 75 77 79 81 91 93 96 107 108 110 111 119 128 130 131 133 146 **S** HCA Healthcare, Nashville, TN
Primary Contact: Jacqueline Medland, MS, Ph.D., President and Chief Nursing Officer
CFO: Lena Cochran, Director of Finance
CHR: Ruby Rowland, Strategic Partner
CNO: Cindy Pierson, Interim Chief Nursing Officer
Web address: www.hchospital.org
Control: Other not–for–profit (including NFP Corporation) **Service**: General medical and surgical

Staffed Beds: 104 **Admissions**: 552 **Census**: 65 **Outpatient Visits**: 43853 **Births**: 0 **Total Expense ($000)**: 21812 **Payroll Expense ($000)**: 5644 **Personnel**: 101

HUNTERSVILLE—Mecklenburg County

☒ **NOVANT HEALTH HUNTERSVILLE MEDICAL CENTER (340183)**, 10030 Gilead Road, Zip 28078–7545, Mailing Address: P.O. Box 3508, Zip 28070–3508; tel. 704/316–4000, (Nonreporting) **A**1 2 3 10 **S** Novant Health, Winston Salem, NC
Primary Contact: Mike Riley, President and Chief Operating Officer
CFO: Fred M Hargett, Executive Vice President and Chief Financial Officer
CMO: Thomas Zweng, Executive Vice President and Chief Medical Officer
CIO: David B Garrett, Senior Vice President and Chief Information Officer
CHR: Janet Smith-Hill, Executive Vice President and Chief Human Resources
CNO: Katrina King, R.N., Senior Director, Nursing
Web address: www.novanthealth.org
Control: Other not–for–profit (including NFP Corporation) **Service**: General medical and surgical

Staffed Beds: 91

JACKSONVILLE—Onslow County

☐ **BRYNN MARR HOSPITAL (344016)**, 192 Village Drive, Zip 28546–7299; tel. 910/577–1400, (Nonreporting) **A**1 10 **S** Universal Health Services, Inc., King of Prussia, PA
Primary Contact: Colin Weaver, Chief Executive Officer
CFO: David Warmerdam, Chief Financial Officer
CMO: Ashraf Mikhail, M.D., Medical Director
CIO: Amy Black, Risk Manager/PI Director
CHR: Jennifer Gier, Director Human Resources
CNO: Sheila Maraan, Director of Nursing
Web address: www.brynnmarr.org
Control: Corporation, Investor–owned (for–profit) **Service**: Psychiatric

Staffed Beds: 99

NC

Many Facility Codes have changed. Please refer to the AHA Guide Code Chart.

✠ **ONSLOW MEMORIAL HOSPITAL (340042)**, 317 Western Boulevard, Zip 28546–6379, Mailing Address: P.O. Box 1358, Zip 28541–1358; tel. 910/577–2345, **A**1 2 10 20 **F**3 8 11 13 15 18 19 20 28 29 34 35 40 45 46 47 48 49 54 57 59 60 64 68 70 72 73 75 76 77 79 81 82 84 85 86 87 89 93 96 107 108 110 111 114 115 117 118 119 126 131 132 135 146 147 148 154
Primary Contact: Penney Burlingame Deal, FACHE, R.N., Chief Executive Officer
CMO: Scott Johnston, Chief of Staff
CIO: Rob Lowe, Director, Healthcare Information Management
CHR: Taylor Flowers, Senior Vice President Human Resources
CNO: Regina Lanier, MSN, R.N., Senior Vice President and Chief Nursing Officer
Web address: www.onslow.org
Control: Hospital district or authority, Government, nonfederal **Service:** General medical and surgical

Staffed Beds: 149 **Admissions:** 6714 **Census:** 84 **Outpatient Visits:** 130128 **Births:** 1325 **Total Expense ($000):** 149670 **Payroll Expense ($000):** 53721 **Personnel:** 930

JEFFERSON—Ashe County

✠ **ASHE MEMORIAL HOSPITAL (341325)**, 200 Hospital Avenue, Zip 28640–9244; tel. 336/846–7101, **A**1 10 18 **F**3 11 13 15 28 30 31 34 35 40 45 48 56 57 59 64 75 76 77 78 79 80 81 85 86 89 91 93 102 107 108 110 111 114 118 119 127 130 132 133 135 141 142 146 147 154 156 **S** Novant Health, Winston Salem, NC
Primary Contact: Laura Lambeth, Chief Executive Officer
COO: Joe Thore, Chief Operating Officer
CFO: Charles Wright, Chief Financial Officer
CMO: Jayne Leonard, M.D., Family Medicine
CIO: William Baldwin, Chief Information Officer
CHR: Lana Smith, Human Resources Director
CNO: Sara Houser, Chief Nursing Officer
Web address: www.ashememorial.org
Control: Other not–for–profit (including NFP Corporation) **Service:** General medical and surgical

Staffed Beds: 25 **Admissions:** 1359 **Census:** 12 **Outpatient Visits:** 73195 **Births:** 109 **Total Expense ($000):** 31194 **Payroll Expense ($000):** 14228 **Personnel:** 327

KENANSVILLE—Duplin County

✠ **VIDANT DUPLIN HOSPITAL (340120)**, 401 North Main Street, Zip 28349–8801, Mailing Address: P.O. Box 278, Zip 28349–0278; tel. 910/296–0941, **A**1 10 **F**3 11 13 15 18 19 29 30 31 34 35 39 40 45 56 57 59 68 70 75 76 77 79 81 91 93 97 98 101 102 103 107 108 110 111 115 116 119 129 130 131 132 135 146 147 154 **S** Vidant Health, Greenville, NC
Primary Contact: Jay Briley, President
COO: Matthew Gitzinger, Director of Operations
CFO: Lucinda Crawford, Vice President Financial Services
CMO: Dyrek Miller, M.D., Chief Medical Staff
CIO: Lucinda Crawford, Vice President Financial Services
CHR: Pansy Chase, Director Human Resources
CNO: Sue O. Taylor, Vice President Nursing
Web address: www.vidanthealth.com
Control: Other not–for–profit (including NFP Corporation) **Service:** General medical and surgical

Staffed Beds: 47 **Admissions:** 3513 **Census:** 48 **Outpatient Visits:** 52661 **Births:** 407 **Total Expense ($000):** 51309 **Payroll Expense ($000):** 21362 **Personnel:** 445

KINGS MOUNTAIN—Cleveland County

✠ **ATRIUM HEALTH KINGS MOUNTAIN (340037)**, 706 West King Street, Zip 28086–2708; tel. 980/487–5000, **A**1 10 **F**3 4 15 29 30 34 39 40 44 45 49 50 59 64 75 79 81 82 85 86 87 93 98 100 107 110 111 115 119 130 146 148 149 154 **S** Atrium Health, Charlotte, NC
Primary Contact: Brian Gwyn, President and Chief Executive Officer
CFO: Terry Edwards, Controller
CHR: Debra Kale, Director Human Resources
Web address: www.clevelandregional.org/kings-mountain-hospital.html
Control: Hospital district or authority, Government, nonfederal **Service:** General medical and surgical

Staffed Beds: 53 **Admissions:** 2593 **Census:** 34 **Outpatient Visits:** 55517 **Births:** 0 **Total Expense ($000):** 42311 **Payroll Expense ($000):** 14756 **Personnel:** 248

KINSTON—Lenoir County

✠ **UNC LENOIR HEALTHCARE (340027)**, 100 Airport Road, Zip 28501–1634, Mailing Address: P.O. Box 1678, Zip 28503–1678; tel. 252/522–7000, **A**1 10 **F**3 8 11 12 13 18 20 22 28 29 30 31 34 35 38 40 43 45 47 48 49 50 53 56 57 59 60 61 64 65 68 70 74 75 76 77 78 79 81 85 86 87 89 90 93 102 107 108 111 115 118 119 120 123 129 130 132 134 135 143 145 146 147 148 154 156 **S** UNC Health Care, Chapel Hill, NC
Primary Contact: Gary E. Black, President and Chief Executive Officer
CFO: Sarah Mayo, Vice President Financial Services
CMO: John Herlong, Medical Staff President
CIO: Karl Vanderstouw, Vice President Information Systems
CHR: Jim Dobbins, Vice President Human Resources
CNO: Shirley S. Harkey, R.N., FACHE, Interim Vice President and Chief Nursing Officer
Web address: www.lenoirmemorial.org
Control: Other not–for–profit (including NFP Corporation) **Service:** General medical and surgical

Staffed Beds: 176 **Admissions:** 5342 **Census:** 69 **Outpatient Visits:** 96272 **Births:** 402 **Total Expense ($000):** 110284 **Payroll Expense ($000):** 48361 **Personnel:** 761

LAURINBURG—Scotland County

✠ **SCOTLAND HEALTH CARE SYSTEM (340008)**, 500 Lauchwood Drive, Zip 28352–5599; tel. 910/291–7000, **A**1 2 3 5 10 **F**3 11 13 15 18 28 29 31 34 37 40 45 54 57 59 63 64 70 71 73 74 75 76 77 78 79 81 83 84 85 86 87 89 90 92 93 96 97 107 110 111 114 115 119 120 121 123 126 127 130 132 135 143 144 145 146 147 148 149 156 **S** Atrium Health, Charlotte, NC
Primary Contact: Gregory C. Wood, President and Chief Executive Officer
CFO: Matthew Pracht, Vice President Finance
CMO: Cheryl Davis, M.D., Chief Medical Officer
CIO: Gary Liuzzo, Director Information Systems
CHR: Ann Locklear, Vice President, Human Resources
CNO: Camille Utter, R.N., Chief Nursing Officer
Web address: www.scotlandhealth.org
Control: Other not–for–profit (including NFP Corporation) **Service:** General medical and surgical

Staffed Beds: 104 **Admissions:** 5523 **Census:** 54 **Outpatient Visits:** 132111 **Births:** 754 **Total Expense ($000):** 141333 **Payroll Expense ($000):** 50017 **Personnel:** 1021

LELAND—Brunswick County

☐ **STRATEGIC BEHAVIORAL HEALTH - WILMINGTON (344030)**, 2050 Mercantile Drive, Zip 28451–4053; tel. 910/371–2500, **A**1 10 **F**56 98 99 101 103 **S** Strategic Behavioral Health, LLC, Memphis, TN
Primary Contact: Daniel Kern, Chief Executive Officer
CHR: Kelly Pace, Director Human Resource
CNO: Brooke Cook, Director of Nursing
Web address: www.sbcwilmington.com/
Control: Corporation, Investor–owned (for–profit) **Service:** Psychiatric

Staffed Beds: 112 **Admissions:** 814 **Census:** 15 **Outpatient Visits:** 0 **Births:** 0 **Total Expense ($000):** 15266 **Payroll Expense ($000):** 9231 **Personnel:** 274

LENOIR—Caldwell County

✠ **CALDWELL UNC HEALTH CARE (340041)**, 321 Mulberry Street SW, Zip 28645–5720, Mailing Address: P.O. Box 1890, Zip 28645–1890; tel. 828/757–5100, **A**1 10 **F**3 8 11 13 15 18 20 22 29 30 31 34 35 37 40 45 46 48 49 50 53 54 55 57 59 64 65 70 75 76 77 78 79 81 82 85 86 87 93 97 107 108 109 110 111 114 119 120 121 122 123 129 132 135 145 146 147 148 149 154 156 **S** UNC Health Care, Chapel Hill, NC
Primary Contact: Laura J. Easton, President and Chief Executive Officer
COO: Rebecca T Smith, Chief Operating Officer and Chief Nursing Officer
CFO: Shawn Hartley, Chief Financial Officer
CMO: David Lowry, M.D., Chief Medical Officer
CIO: Deborah Purcell, Director of Information Technology
CHR: Laura J Easton, President and Chief Executive Officer
CNO: Rebecca T Smith, Chief Operating Officer and Chief Nursing Officer
Web address: www.caldwellmemorial.org
Control: Other not–for–profit (including NFP Corporation) **Service:** General medical and surgical

Staffed Beds: 82 **Admissions:** 4270 **Census:** 52 **Outpatient Visits:** 100133 **Births:** 346 **Total Expense ($000):** 111199 **Payroll Expense ($000):** 51599 **Personnel:** 810

LEXINGTON—Davidson County

LEXINGTON MEMORIAL HOSPITAL See Wake Forest Baptist Health-Lexington Medical Center

☒ **WAKE FOREST BAPTIST HEALTH-LEXINGTON MEDICAL CENTER (340096)**, 250 Hospital Drive, Zip 27292–6728, Mailing Address: P.O. Box 1817, Zip 27293–1817; tel. 336/248–5161, **A**1 3 5 10 **F**3 13 15 18 28 29 30 31 34 35 39 40 45 46 50 57 58 59 61 64 65 68 70 74 75 76 78 79 81 82 85 87 89 91 92 93 97 102 107 108 110 111 115 119 120 121 123 129 130 131 146 147 148 154 156 **S** Wake Forest Baptist Health, Winston-Salem, NC
Primary Contact: William B. James, FACHE, President
CFO: Danny Squires, Vice President and Chief Financial Officer
CMO: Raghava Nagaraj, Chief Medical Officer
CIO: Dee Emon, R.N., Chief Information Officer
CNO: Clyde A. Bristow, R.N., III Senior Director Nursing and Clinical Services, Chief Nursing Officer
Web address: www.lexington.wakehealth.edu
Control: Other not–for–profit (including NFP Corporation) **Service:** General medical and surgical

Staffed Beds: 75 **Admissions:** 3043 **Census:** 27 **Outpatient Visits:** 117161 **Births:** 368 **Total Expense ($000):** 90110 **Payroll Expense ($000):** 38300 **Personnel:** 533

LINCOLNTON—Lincoln County

☒ **ATRIUM HEALTH LINCOLN (340145)**, 433 McAlister Road, Zip 28092–4147, Mailing Address: P.O. Box 677, Zip 28093–0677; tel. 980/212–2000, **A**1 10 **F**3 8 11 13 15 18 28 29 30 31 34 40 44 45 50 51 57 59 64 70 73 74 75 76 77 78 79 81 82 84 85 87 91 93 94 96 107 108 114 115 118 119 129 130 131 132 135 146 148 149 150 154 **S** Atrium Health, Charlotte, NC
Primary Contact: Peter W. Acker, President and Chief Executive Officer
COO: Teresa C Watson, Vice President Administration
CFO: Jarrett L Morris, Controller
CMO: Vineet Goel, Chief Medical Officer
CIO: Jarrett L Morris, Controller and Chief Information Officer
CHR: Lesley Chambless, Assistant Vice President Human Resources
CNO: Elaine S Haynes, R.N., MSN, Vice President Patient Services and Chief Nursing Executive
Web address: www.carolinashealthcare.org/lincoln
Control: Hospital district or authority, Government, nonfederal **Service:** General medical and surgical

Staffed Beds: 101 **Admissions:** 4571 **Census:** 53 **Outpatient Visits:** 89070 **Births:** 464 **Total Expense ($000):** 105190 **Payroll Expense ($000):** 31948 **Personnel:** 569

LUMBERTON—Robeson County

★ ⇑ **SOUTHEASTERN HEALTH (340050)**, 300 West 27th Street, Zip 28358–3075, Mailing Address: P.O. Box 1408, Zip 28359–1408; tel. 910/671–5000, (Nonreporting) **A**2 3 5 10 12 13 21
Primary Contact: Joann Anderson, President and Chief Executive Officer
CFO: C Thomas Johnson III Vice President Finance and Chief Financial Officer
CMO: Barry Williamson, President Medical Staff
CIO: Eric Harper, Chief Information Officer
CHR: Susan Hayes, Director Human Resources
CNO: Renae Taylor, Chief Nursing Officer
Web address: www.srmc.org
Control: Other not–for–profit (including NFP Corporation) **Service:** General medical and surgical

Staffed Beds: 385

MARION—Mcdowell County

☒ **MCDOWELL HOSPITAL (340087)**, 430 Rankin Drive, Zip 28752–6568, Mailing Address: P.O. Box 730, Zip 28752–0730; tel. 828/659–5000, **A**1 10 **F**3 13 15 18 28 29 30 31 34 35 40 45 57 59 64 70 76 77 78 79 81 85 87 93 97 107 108 110 111 115 119 127 129 130 131 132 135 144 146 147 148 149 156 **S** HCA Healthcare, Nashville, TN
Primary Contact: Carol C. Wolfenbarger, FACHE, MSN, President
CFO: Clint Stewart, Regional Director of Finance East
CMO: Rex Henderson, M.D., Chief of Staff
CIO: Pam Blevins, R.N., Director Information Technology Member Hospitals Mission
CHR: Tonya Revels, Senior Strategic Business Partner
CNO: Kathy Hefner, Chief Nursing Officer
Web address: www.mission-health.org
Control: Other not–for–profit (including NFP Corporation) **Service:** General medical and surgical

Staffed Beds: 30 **Admissions:** 2147 **Census:** 21 **Outpatient Visits:** 173604 **Births:** 268 **Total Expense ($000):** 70806 **Payroll Expense ($000):** 29817 **Personnel:** 359

MATTHEWS—Mecklenburg County

☒ **NOVANT HEALTH MATTHEWS MEDICAL CENTER (340171)**, 1500 Matthews Township Parkway, Zip 28105–4656; tel. 704/384–6500, (Nonreporting) **A**1 2 10 **S** Novant Health, Winston Salem, NC
Primary Contact: Roland R. Bibeau, President and Chief Operating Officer
CFO: Fred M Hargett, Executive Vice President and Chief Financial Officer
CMO: Thomas Zweng, Executive Vice President and Chief Medical Officer
CIO: David B Garrett, Senior Vice President and Chief Information Officer
CHR: Janet Smith-Hill, Executive Vice President and Chief HR Officer
CNO: Tracy B Forster, R.N., Senior Director of Nursing
Web address: www.https://www.novanthealth.org
Control: Other not–for–profit (including NFP Corporation) **Service:** General medical and surgical

Staffed Beds: 117

MONROE—Union County

☒ **ATRIUM HEALTH UNION (340130)**, 600 Hospital Drive, Zip 28112–6000, Mailing Address: P.O. Box 5003, Zip 28111–5003; tel. 980/993–3100, (Total facility includes 70 beds in nursing home–type unit) **A**1 2 3 10 **F**3 8 13 18 20 22 26 27 28 29 30 31 34 35 39 40 42 45 49 53 56 57 59 60 64 66 68 70 72 74 75 76 77 78 79 81 82 84 86 87 89 93 97 102 107 108 111 114 117 118 119 120 121 123 126 128 129 130 131 132 135 143 146 147 148 154 156 157 **S** Atrium Health, Charlotte, NC
Primary Contact: Michael Lutes, President
COO: Dave Anderson, FACHE, Vice President Administration
CFO: John G Moore, Vice President and Chief Financial Officer
CMO: Craig M Slater, M.D., Chief Medical Officer
CIO: Lisa Sykes, Director Information Services
CHR: Rhonda McFarland, Director Human Resources
CNO: Denise White, MSN, Chief Nurse Executive
Web address: www.carolinashealthcare.org/union
Control: Hospital district or authority, Government, nonfederal **Service:** General medical and surgical

Staffed Beds: 231 **Admissions:** 9265 **Census:** 149 **Outpatient Visits:** 176839 **Births:** 990 **Total Expense ($000):** 204230 **Payroll Expense ($000):** 60897 **Personnel:** 1032

MOORESVILLE—Iredell County

☒ **LAKE NORMAN REGIONAL MEDICAL CENTER (340129)**, 171 Fairview Road, Zip 28117–9500, Mailing Address: P.O. Box 3250, Zip 28117–3250; tel. 704/660–4000, (Nonreporting) **A**1 2 10 19 **S** Community Health Systems, Inc., Franklin, TN
Primary Contact: Stephen L. Midkiff, Chief Executive Officer
CFO: Claire Polk, Chief Financial Officer
CHR: Stephanie Williams, Market Director Human Resources
CNO: Marie Marks, Chief Nursing Officer
Web address: www.lnrmc.com
Control: Corporation, Investor–owned (for–profit) **Service:** General medical and surgical

Staffed Beds: 123

MOREHEAD CITY—Carteret County

☒ **CARTERET HEALTH CARE (340142)**, 3500 Arendell Street, Zip 28557–2901, Mailing Address: P.O. Box 1619, Zip 28557–1619; tel. 252/499–6000, **A**1 2 10 **F**3 7 11 12 13 15 18 20 22 28 29 30 31 34 35 37 40 45 46 54 57 59 62 63 64 65 68 70 74 75 76 77 78 79 81 82 84 85 86 87 89 91 93 97 107 108 110 111 114 115 118 119 120 121 123 129 130 132 135 143 145 146 148 154 156
Primary Contact: Richard A. Brvenik, President
CFO: Joanie King, Chief Financial Officer
CMO: Donald Pocock, Vice-President Medical Affairs
CIO: Kyle Marek, Chief Information Officer
CHR: Elizabeth Beswick, Vice President Human Resources and Public Relations
Web address: www.carterethealth.org
Control: County, Government, nonfederal **Service:** General medical and surgical

Staffed Beds: 104 **Admissions:** 6082 **Census:** 70 **Outpatient Visits:** 168884 **Births:** 772 **Total Expense ($000):** 138997 **Payroll Expense ($000):** 56850 **Personnel:** 947

MORGANTON—Burke County

☐ **BROUGHTON HOSPITAL (344025)**, 1000 South Sterling Street, Zip 28655–3999; tel. 828/433–2111, (Nonreporting) **A**1 3 5 10
Primary Contact: Vivian Streater, Co-Acting Chief Executive Officer
CFO: Bea Tullis, Chief Financial Officer and Budget Officer
CMO: George Krebs, M.D., Chief Medical Officer
CIO: Darin Kiracofe, Director Information Resource Management
CHR: Jean Buchanan, Director Human Resources
CNO: Vivian Streater, Chief Nursing Officer and Co-Acting Chief Executive Officer
Web address: www.ncdhhs.gov/dsohf/broughton
Control: State, Government, nonfederal **Service:** Psychiatric

Staffed Beds: 297

NC

Many Facility Codes have changed. Please refer to the AHA Guide Code Chart. © 2019 AHA Guide

⊞ **CAROLINAS HEALTHCARE SYSTEM BLUE RIDGE (340075)**, 2201 South Sterling Street, Zip 28655–4058; tel. 828/580–5000, (Includes CAROLINAS HEALTHCARE SYSTEM - BLUE RIDGE - MORGANTON, 2201 South Sterling Street, Morganton, North Carolina, Zip 28655–4058; tel. 828/580–5000; VALDESE GENERAL HOSPITAL, 720 Malcolm Boulevard, Valdese, North Carolina, Zip 28690–2872, Mailing Address: P O Box 700, Zip 28690–0700, tel. 828/874–2251) **A1** 2 3 10 13 **F**3 8 13 15 18 20 22 28 29 30 31 34 35 40 45 49 50 53 56 57 59 64 68 69 70 71 72 77 78 81 82 85 86 87 93 96 97 98 107 108 110 111 114 115 119 120 121 123 126 130 131 132 146 147 148 **S** Atrium Health, Charlotte, NC
Primary Contact: Kathy C. Bailey, Ph.D., FACHE, President and Chief Executive Officer
CFO: Robert G Fritts, Chief Financial Officer and Senior Vice President
CMO: Joe Mazzola, D.O., Senior Vice President Medical Affairs and Chief Medical Officer
CHR: Thomas Eure, Vice President Administration
Web address: www.blueridgehealth.org
Control: Other not–for–profit (including NFP Corporation) **Service:** General medical and surgical

Staffed Beds: 156 **Admissions:** 6994 **Census:** 80 **Outpatient Visits:** 108634 **Births:** 793 **Total Expense ($000):** 204477 **Payroll Expense ($000):** 88997 **Personnel:** 1046

MOUNT AIRY—Surry County

⊞ **NORTHERN HOSPITAL OF SURRY COUNTY (340003)**, 830 Rockford Street, Zip 27030–5365, Mailing Address: P.O. Box 1101, Zip 27030–1101; tel. 336/719–7000, (Total facility includes 33 beds in nursing home–type unit) **A1** 10 **F**3 5 11 12 13 15 18 28 29 30 31 34 35 40 45 50 53 54 55 56 57 59 64 65 67 70 75 76 77 79 80 81 82 85 86 87 89 97 107 108 110 111 114 115 118 119 128 130 131 132 133 135 145 146 147 148 149
Primary Contact: Chris A. Lumsden, President and Chief Executive Officer
CFO: Andrea Hickling, Vice President of Finance and Chief Financial Officer
CMO: Druery DeVore, Chief of Medical Staff
CIO: Rodney Bond, Director of Information Technology
CHR: Julia Nelson, Vice President of Human Resources
CNO: Robin Hodgin, R.N., Vice President of Patient Services and Chief Nursing Officer
Web address: www.northernhospital.com
Control: Hospital district or authority, Government, nonfederal **Service:** General medical and surgical

Staffed Beds: 108 **Admissions:** 4234 **Census:** 68 **Outpatient Visits:** 122286 **Births:** 293 **Total Expense ($000):** 92106 **Payroll Expense ($000):** 41007 **Personnel:** 790

MURPHY—Cherokee County

⊞ **ERLANGER WESTERN CAROLINA HOSPITAL (341328)**, 3990 U S Highway 64 East Alt. Zip 28906–7917; tel. 828/837–8161, **A1** 10 18 **F**3 13 28 29 30 34 35 40 45 50 53 62 63 64 68 70 76 77 79 81 84 87 93 102 107 110 111 114 115 119 127 130 133 144 146 148 157 **S** Erlanger Health System, Chattanooga, TN
Primary Contact: Mark E. Kimball, Chief Executive Officer
COO: Toni Lovingood, Chief Operating Officer
CFO: Steve Gilgen, Chief Financial Officer
CMO: Jeffrey H Martin, M.D., Chief of Staff
CIO: Connie Stalcup, Manager Information Systems
CHR: Russ Paine, Human Resources Officer
CNO: Teresa Bowleg, R.N., Chief Nursing Officer
Web address: www.https://www.erlanger.org
Control: Hospital district or authority, Government, nonfederal **Service:** General medical and surgical

Staffed Beds: 25 **Admissions:** 1799 **Census:** 17 **Outpatient Visits:** 253894 **Births:** 127 **Total Expense ($000):** 63910 **Payroll Expense ($000):** 26149 **Personnel:** 394

NAGS HEAD—Dare County

⊞ **THE OUTER BANKS HOSPITAL (341324)**, 4800 South Croatan Highway, Zip 27959–9704; tel. 252/449–4500, (Nonreporting) **A1** 2 10 18 **S** Vidant Health, Greenville, NC
Primary Contact: Ronald A. Sloan, FACHE, President
CFO: Todd Warlitner, Vice President Business Operations
CMO: Roger Lever, M.D., President Medical Staff
CHR: Mary Kelley, Director Human Resources
CNO: Marcia Bryant, R.N., Vice President, Clinical Operations
Web address: www.theouterbankshospital.com
Control: Other not–for–profit (including NFP Corporation) **Service:** General medical and surgical

Staffed Beds: 21

NEW BERN—Craven County

⊞ △ **CAROLINAEAST HEALTH SYSTEM (340131)**, 2000 Neuse Boulevard, Zip 28560–3499, Mailing Address: P.O. Box 12157, Zip 28561–2157; tel. 252/633–8111, **A1** 2 7 10 **F**3 7 11 13 15 17 18 20 22 24 26 28 29 30 31 34 35 36 39 40 45 46 47 48 49 53 54 57 58 59 62 64 67 70 74 75 76 77 78 79 81 84 85 86 87 89 90 91 92 93 94 96 98 100 101 102 104 107 108 110 111 114 115 117 118 119 120 121 123 126 130 132 135 141 142 146 147 148 149
Primary Contact: G Raymond. Leggett III, President and Chief Executive Officer
CFO: Tammy M. Sherron, Vice President Finance
CMO: Ronald B May, M.D., Vice President Medical Affairs
CIO: Ronald B May, M.D., Vice President Medical Affairs
CHR: Bruce A Martin, Vice President Human Resources
CNO: Rosanne Leahy, Vice President Nursing Services
Web address: www.carolinaeasthealth.com
Control: Hospital district or authority, Government, nonfederal **Service:** General medical and surgical

Staffed Beds: 208 **Admissions:** 14255 **Census:** 180 **Outpatient Visits:** 160025 **Births:** 1047 **Total Expense ($000):** 289223 **Payroll Expense ($000):** 104953 **Personnel:** 2020

NEWLAND—Avery County

⊞ **CHARLES A. CANNON MEMORIAL HOSPITAL (341323)**, 434 Hospital Drive, Zip 28646, Mailing Address: P.O. Box 767, Linville, Zip 28646–0767; tel. 828/737–7000, **A1** 10 18 **F**3 11 15 28 29 30 40 45 64 68 81 85 93 98 100 101 102 104 107 110 115 119 130 133 135 146 149 154 **S** Appalachian Regional Healthcare System, Boone, NC
Primary Contact: Carmen Lacey, MSN, R.N., President
CFO: Kevin B May, System Director Finance
CMO: Thomas M Haizlip, M.D., Jr Chief of Staff
CIO: Nathan White, Chief Information Officer
CHR: Amy J. Crabbe, Vice President People Services
CNO: Carmen Lacey, MSN, R.N., President and Director of Patient Care Services
Web address: www.https://apprhs.org/locations/cannon-memorial-hospital
Control: Other not–for–profit (including NFP Corporation) **Service:** General medical and surgical

Staffed Beds: 31 **Admissions:** 1080 **Census:** 14 **Outpatient Visits:** 29280 **Births:** 0 **Total Expense ($000):** 23385 **Payroll Expense ($000):** 8851 **Personnel:** 148

NORTH WILKESBORO—Wilkes County

⊞ **WAKE FOREST BAPTIST HEALTH - WILKES MEDICAL CENTER (340064)**, 1370 West 'D' Street, Zip 28659–3506, Mailing Address: P.O. Box 609, Zip 28659–0609; tel. 336/651–8100, (Total facility includes 10 beds in nursing home–type unit) **A1** 10 **F**3 11 13 15 18 28 29 30 34 35 40 45 49 57 59 60 64 67 68 70 74 76 77 79 81 85 87 92 93 107 108 110 111 114 115 119 124 128 129 130 131 133 146 148 154 **S** Wake Forest Baptist Health, Winston-Salem, NC
Primary Contact: J Gene. Faile, Chief Executive Officer and President
CFO: Barry Wald, Chief Financial Officer
CMO: Richard Barber, M.D., Chief Medical Officer
CIO: William Hofman, Manager Information Technology
CHR: Vanya Baker, Director
CNO: Sandy Sheppard, Vice President Patient Services
Web address: www.wilkesregional.com/
Control: Other not–for–profit (including NFP Corporation) **Service:** General medical and surgical

Staffed Beds: 92 **Admissions:** 3466 **Census:** 40 **Outpatient Visits:** 74713 **Births:** 365 **Total Expense ($000):** 73125 **Payroll Expense ($000):** 33423 **Personnel:** 586

Hospital, Medicare Provider Number, Address, Telephone, Approval, Facility, and Physician Codes, Health Care System

★ American Hospital Association (AHA) membership
□ The Joint Commission accreditation
○ Healthcare Facilities Accreditation Program
◇ DNV Healthcare Inc. accreditation
⇧ Center for Improvement in Healthcare Quality Accreditation
△ Commission on Accreditation of Rehabilitation Facilities (CARF) accreditation

NC

OXFORD—Granville County

✠ **GRANVILLE HEALTH SYSTEM (340127)**, 1010 College Street, Zip 27565–2507, Mailing Address: P.O. Box 947, Zip 27565–0947; tel. 919/690–3000, (Total facility includes 80 beds in nursing home–type unit) **A**1 3 10 **F**2 3 7 11 13 15 18 19 29 30 34 35 38 39 40 45 50 54 55 56 57 59 64 66 70 75 76 77 79 81 82 85 86 93 100 101 104 107 108 110 111 114 115 118 119 124 127 128 129 130 132 133 143 144 146 147 148
Primary Contact: John Snow, Chief Executive Officer
COO: Cristina Rigsbee Carroll, Chief Operating Officer
CFO: Jeffery Armstrong, CPA, Chief Financial Officer
CMO: Richard Pacca, M.D., Chief of Staff
CIO: Geoff Tanthorey, Director, Information Systems
CHR: Scott Thomas, Administrative Director Human Resources and Communications
CNO: Bill Hughes, Chief Nursing Officer
Web address: www.ghshospital.org
Control: County, Government, nonfederal **Service**: General medical and surgical

Staffed Beds: 142 Admissions: 2620 Census: 86 Outpatient Visits: 61517 **Births:** 291 **Total Expense ($000):** 63918 **Payroll Expense ($000):** 28530 **Personnel:** 549

PINEHURST—Moore County

✠ △ **FIRSTHEALTH MOORE REGIONAL HOSPITAL (340115)**, 155 Memorial Drive, Zip 28374–8710, Mailing Address: P.O. Box 3000, Zip 28374–3000; tel. 910/715–1000, (Includes FIRSTHEALTH MOORE REGIONAL HOSPITAL - HOKE, 6408 Fayetteville Road, Raeford, North Carolina, Zip 28376–7977; tel. 910/878–6000; Susan R Beaty, R.N., Administrator; FIRSTHEALTH MOORE REGIONAL HOSPITAL - RICHMOND, 925 Long Drive, Rockingham, North Carolina, Zip 28379–4835; tel. 910/417–3000; John J Jackson, President) **A**1 2 7 10 19 **F**3 4 5 11 12 13 15 17 18 20 22 24 26 28 29 30 31 34 35 40 44 45 46 47 48 49 50 51 54 55 56 57 58 59 60 64 65 68 70 72 74 75 76 77 78 79 81 82 86 87 89 90 91 93 96 98 99 100 101 102 103 104 105 108 111 114 115 118 119 120 121 124 126 129 130 132 134 135 143 146 147 153 154 155 **S** FirstHealth of the Carolinas, Pinehurst, NC
Primary Contact: David J. Kilarski, FACHE, Chief Executive Officer
COO: Brian Canfield, Chief Operating Officer
CFO: Lynn S DeJaco, Chief Financial Officer
CMO: John F Krahnert, M.D., Chief Medical Officer
CIO: David B Dillehunt, Chief Information Officer
CHR: Daniel F Biediger, Vice President Human Resources
CNO: Karen Robeano, R.N., Chief Nursing Officer and Vice President Patient Care Services
Web address: www.firsthealth.org
Control: Other not–for–profit (including NFP Corporation) **Service**: General medical and surgical

Staffed Beds: 362 Admissions: 22589 Census: 273 Outpatient Visits: 195084 **Births:** 2053 **Total Expense ($000):** 398116 **Payroll Expense ($000):** 180888 **Personnel:** 3504

PLYMOUTH—Washington County

WASHINGTON COUNTY HOSPITAL (341314), 958 U S Highway 64 East, Zip 27962–9591, Mailing Address: P.O. Box 707, Zip 27962–9591; tel. 252/793–4135, (Nonreporting) **A**10 18 **S** Rural Community Hospitals of America, Kansas City, MO
Primary Contact: Melanie A. Perry, Chief Executive Officer
CMO: Robert Venable, M.D., Chief Medical Staff
CIO: Christina Craft, Director Information Systems
CNO: Kimberly Manning, Chief Nursing Officer
Control: County, Government, nonfederal **Service**: General medical and surgical

Staffed Beds: 25

RAEFORD—Hoke County

✠ **HOKE HOSPITAL (340188)**, 210 Medical Pavilion Drive, Zip 28376–9111; tel. 910/904–8000, **A**1 10 **F**3 15 28 29 35 40 44 50 68 70 79 81 85 87 93 97 107 108 110 114 115 118 119 149 150 154 **S** Cape Fear Valley Health System, Fayetteville, NC
Primary Contact: Roxie Cannon. Wells, M.D., President
Web address: www.capefearvalley.com
Control: Other not–for–profit (including NFP Corporation) **Service**: General medical and surgical

Staffed Beds: 29 Admissions: 1310 Census: 8 Outpatient Visits: 41984 **Total Expense ($000):** 39344 **Payroll Expense ($000):** 16574 **Personnel:** 270

RALEIGH—Wake County

CENTRAL PRISON HOSPITAL, 1300 Western Boulevard, Zip 27606–2148; tel. 919/743–2440, (Nonreporting) **A**3
Primary Contact: Dean Doering, Chief Executive Officer
CMO: Olushola Metiko, M.D., Medical Director
CHR: Bruce McKinney, Business Officer, Administrative Services
CNO: Cindy J McLean, R.N., MSN, Director of Nursing
Web address: www.https://www.ncdps.gov/index2.cfm?a=000003,002240,002381,002252
Control: State, Government, nonfederal **Service**: Hospital unit of an institution (prison hospital, college infirmary, etc.)

Staffed Beds: 230

✠ **DUKE RALEIGH HOSPITAL (340073)**, 3400 Wake Forest Road, Zip 27609–7373; tel. 919/954–3000, **A**1 2 3 5 10 **F**3 11 12 15 18 20 22 24 26 29 30 31 34 35 36 37 39 40 44 46 47 49 50 51 55 57 58 59 60 64 68 70 74 75 77 78 79 80 81 82 84 85 86 87 92 93 94 96 100 102 103 107 108 110 111 114 115 117 118 119 120 121 123 124 126 129 130 131 132 135 142 146 147 148 149 154 **S** Duke University Health System, Durham, NC
Primary Contact: David William. Zaas, M.D., Chief Executive Officer
COO: Brian Sloan, Chief Operating Officer
CMO: Ted Kunstling, M.D., Chief Medical Officer
CIO: Janis Curtis, Interim Director Information Technology
CHR: Donald K Barnes, Chief Human Resources Officer
Web address: www.dukehealthraleigh.org
Control: Other not–for–profit (including NFP Corporation) **Service**: General medical and surgical

Staffed Beds: 175 Admissions: 9436 Census: 117 Outpatient Visits: 252221 **Births:** 0 **Total Expense ($000):** 428600 **Payroll Expense ($000):** 108827 **Personnel:** 1792

☐ **HOLLY HILL HOSPITAL (344014)**, 3019 Falstaff Road, Zip 27610–1812; tel. 919/250–7000, (Nonreporting) **A**1 10 **S** Universal Health Services, Inc., King of Prussia, PA
Primary Contact: Amanda Johanson, Chief Executive Officer
COO: Jessica Knudsen, Chief Operating Officer and Director Performance Improvement and Risk Management
CFO: Ron Howard, Chief Financial Officer
CMO: Thomas Cornwall, M.D., Medical Director
CHR: Ebuni McFall-Roberts, Director Human Resources
CNO: Michael Hartley, MS, Chief Nursing Officer
Web address: www.hollyhillhospital.com
Control: Corporation, Investor–owned (for–profit) **Service**: Psychiatric

Staffed Beds: 228

LARRY B. ZIEVERINK, SR. ALCOHOLISM TREATMENT CENTER, 3000 Falstaff Road, Zip 27610–1897; tel. 919/250–1500, (Nonreporting)
Primary Contact: Martin D. Woodward, Director Acute Care Services
COO: Martin D Woodward, Director Acute Care Services
CFO: Paul Gross, Human Services and Finance Officer
CMO: Enrique Lopez, M.D., Medical Director
CIO: Wil A Glenn, Director Communications
Web address: www.wakegov.com/county/family/atc
Control: County, Government, nonfederal **Service**: Alcoholism and other chemical dependency

Staffed Beds: 34

☐ **TRIANGLE SPRINGS HOSPITAL**, 10901 World Trade Boulevard, Zip 27617–4203; tel. 919/372–4408, (Nonreporting) **A**1 **S** Springstone, Louisville, KY
Primary Contact: Carla Hollis, Chief Executive Officer
Web address: www.https://www.trianglesprings.com
Control: Corporation, Investor–owned (for–profit) **Service**: Psychiatric

Staffed Beds: 77

UNC REX HEALTH CARE (340114), 4420 Lake Boone Trail, Zip 27607–6599; tel. 919/784–3100, (Total facility includes 227 beds in nursing home–type unit) **A**1 2 3 5 10 **F**3 7 8 11 12 13 15 17 18 20 22 24 26 28 29 30 31 34 35 36 40 44 45 46 47 48 49 50 53 54 56 57 58 59 60 62 64 65 66 68 70 71 72 73 74 75 76 77 78 79 81 82 84 85 86 87 89 92 93 96 97 100 102 107 108 110 111 114 115 116 117 118 119 120 121 123 126 128 129 130 131 132 135 142 143 144 145 146 147 148 149 154 156 157 **S** UNC Health Care, Chapel Hill, NC
Primary Contact: Stephen W. Burriss, President
COO: Ernest L. Bovio Jr Chief Operating Officer
CFO: Andrew Zukowski, Chief Financial Officer
CMO: Linda H. Butler, M.D., Chief Medical Officer
CIO: Tracy Parham, Health Care System Chief Information Officer
CHR: Scott Doak, Vice President, Human Resources
CNO: Colonel Joel Ray, MSN, Vice President and Chief Nursing Officer
Web address: www.rexhealth.com
Control: Other not–for–profit (including NFP Corporation) **Service**: General medical and surgical

Staffed Beds: 666 Admissions: 30640 Census: 527 Outpatient Visits: 1006503 **Births:** 5047 **Total Expense ($000):** 1051317 **Payroll Expense ($000):** 409128 **Personnel:** 5429

NC

☒ △ **WAKEMED RALEIGH CAMPUS (340069)**, 3000 New Bern Avenue, Zip 27610–1295; tel. 919/350–8000, (Includes WAKEMED NORTH FAMILY HEALTH AND WOMEN'S HOSPITAL, 10000 Falls of Neuse Road, Raleigh, North Carolina, Zip 27614–7838; tel. 919/350–8000; Sheri De Shazo, R.N., Senior Vice President and Hospital Administrator) **A**1 3 5 7 10 **F**3 7 8 12 13 15 17 18 19 20 22 24 25 28 29 30 32 34 35 37 38 40 41 42 43 44 45 46 48 49 50 53 54 56 57 58 59 60 61 62 64 65 66 68 70 71 72 73 74 75 76 77 78 79 80 81 82 85 86 87 88 89 90 91 92 93 94 95 96 97 100 101 102 107 110 111 114 115 118 119 126 129 130 131 132 135 143 144 145 146 147 148 149 154 156 **S** WakeMed Health & Hospitals, Raleigh, NC
Primary Contact: Donald R. Gintzig, President and Chief Executive Officer
COO: Denise Wilder Warren, R.N., Executive Vice President and Chief Operating Officer
CMO: West Paul, M.D., Ph.D., Senior Vice President and Chief Quality and Medical Staff Officer
CIO: Peter Marks, Vice President & Chief Information Officer
CHR: Jeanene R Martin, M.P.H., Senior Vice President Human Resources
CNO: Cindy Boily, MSN, R.N., Senior Vice President and Chief Nursing Officer
Web address: www.wakemed.com
Control: Other not–for–profit (including NFP Corporation) **Service:** General medical and surgical

Staffed Beds: 695 **Admissions:** 32538 **Census:** 513 **Outpatient Visits:** 1522940 **Births:** 5642 **Total Expense ($000):** 1072288 **Payroll Expense ($000):** 595079 **Personnel:** 7076

REIDSVILLE—Rockingham County

ANNIE PENN HOSPITAL See Moses H. Cone Memorial Hospital, Greensboro

ROANOKE RAPIDS—Halifax County

☒ **HALIFAX REGIONAL MEDICAL CENTER (340151)**, 250 Smith Church Road, Zip 27870–4914, Mailing Address: P.O. Box 1089, Zip 27870–1089; tel. 252/535–8011, (Nonreporting) **A**1 10 20 **S** Novant Health, Winston Salem, NC
Primary Contact: William Mahone, President and Chief Executive Officer
CFO: Sherry Jensen, Chief Financial Officer
CIO: Robert Gordon, Manager Information Systems
CHR: Thomas Mastroianni, Administrative Director of Human Resources
CNO: Karen Daniels, MSN, R.N., Chief Nursing Officer
Web address: www.halifaxmedicalcenter.org
Control: Other not–for–profit (including NFP Corporation) **Service:** General medical and surgical

Staffed Beds: 142

ROCKY MOUNT—Nash County

☒ **LIFECARE HOSPITALS OF NORTH CAROLINA (342013)**, 1051 Noell Lane, Zip 27804–1761; tel. 252/451–2300, **A**1 10 **F**1 3 29 30 77 91 148 **S** LifeCare Management Services, Plano, TX
Primary Contact: Robyn Perkerson, R.N., Administrator
COO: Robyn Perkerson, R.N., Administrator
CMO: Daniel Crocker, M.D., Chief Medical Officer
CHR: Vicky Goode, Director Human Resources
CNO: Brandee Chappell, Director of Nursing
Web address: www.lifecare-hospitals.com
Control: Corporation, Investor–owned (for–profit) **Service:** Acute long–term care hospital

Staffed Beds: 43 **Admissions:** 495 **Census:** 41 **Outpatient Visits:** 0 **Births:** 0 **Personnel:** 187

☒ **NASH UNC HEALTH CARE (340147)**, 2460 Curtis Ellis Drive, Zip 27804–2237; tel. 252/962–8000, **A**1 2 10 **F**3 4 8 11 12 13 15 18 20 22 28 29 30 31 34 35 38 40 41 44 45 48 49 50 54 55 57 59 60 63 64 70 73 74 75 76 77 78 79 81 82 84 85 86 87 90 93 96 98 100 101 102 107 108 110 111 114 115 117 118 119 120 121 123 126 127 129 130 131 132 135 146 147 148 **S** UNC Health Care, Chapel Hill, NC
Primary Contact: L Lee. Isley, FACHE, Ph.D., President and Chief Executive Officer
COO: Brad Weisner, Executive Vice President and Chief Operating Officer
CFO: Shawn Hartley, Chief Financial Officer
CHR: Katie Davison, Executive Director, Human Resources
CNO: Crystal Hayden, MSN, R.N., Senior Vice President and Chief Nursing Officer
Web address: www.nhcs.org
Control: Hospital district or authority, Government, nonfederal **Service:** General medical and surgical

Staffed Beds: 249 **Admissions:** 11466 **Census:** 165 **Outpatient Visits:** 178864 **Births:** 1108 **Total Expense ($000):** 236718 **Payroll Expense ($000):** 102912 **Personnel:** 1532

ROXBORO—Person County

☒ **PERSON MEMORIAL HOSPITAL (340159)**, 615 Ridge Road, Zip 27573–4629; tel. 336/599–2121, (Total facility includes 60 beds in nursing home–type unit) **A**1 10 **F**3 11 15 18 28 29 34 40 45 57 59 64 70 75 77 79 81 85 87 93 96 97 107 108 110 111 114 119 124 128 130 132 146 149 154 **S** Duke LifePoint Healthcare, Brentwood, TN
Primary Contact: David Ziolkowski, Chief Executive Officer
CFO: Jessi Ayers, Chief Financial Officer
CIO: Rhonda M. Elliott, Director Information Technology and Meaningful Use
CHR: Mary Barksdale, Director Human Resources
CNO: Lynn Peoples, Interim Chief Nursing Officer
Web address: www.personhospital.com
Control: Partnership, Investor–owned (for–profit) **Service:** General medical and surgical

Staffed Beds: 77 **Admissions:** 1256 **Census:** 55 **Outpatient Visits:** 37259 **Births:** 0 **Total Expense ($000):** 33760 **Payroll Expense ($000):** 9051

RUTHERFORDTON—Rutherford County

☒ **RUTHERFORD REGIONAL HEALTH SYSTEM (340013)**, 288 South Ridgecrest Avenue, Zip 28139–2838; tel. 828/286–5000, **A**1 2 10 **F**3 13 15 18 20 28 29 30 31 34 35 40 45 48 49 50 57 59 64 70 75 76 77 78 79 81 85 86 87 89 93 97 98 100 101 102 104 107 108 110 111 114 115 118 119 130 131 132 135 146 147 149 **S** Duke LifePoint Healthcare, Brentwood, TN
Primary Contact: Rebecca Segal, Chief Executive Officer
COO: John Domansky, Vice President Operations
CFO: Jeff Rush, Chief Financial Officer
CIO: Tommy Finley, Chief Information Officer
CHR: Robin B Callas, R.N., Vice President Human Resources
Web address: www.rutherfordhosp.org
Control: Partnership, Investor–owned (for–profit) **Service:** General medical and surgical

Staffed Beds: 112 **Admissions:** 3982 **Census:** 47 **Outpatient Visits:** 71426 **Births:** 384 **Total Expense ($000):** 75499 **Payroll Expense ($000):** 30852 **Personnel:** 457

SALISBURY—Rowan County

☒ **NOVANT HEALTH ROWAN MEDICAL CENTER (340015)**, 612 Mocksville Avenue, Zip 28144–2799; tel. 704/210–5000, (Nonreporting) **A**1 2 10 19 **S** Novant Health, Winston Salem, NC
Primary Contact: Dari Caldwell, R.N., Ph.D., FACHE, President and Chief Operating Officer
CFO: Fred M Hargett, Executive Vice President and Chief Financial Officer
CMO: Thomas Zwong, Executive Vice President and Chief Medical Officer
CIO: David B Garrett, Senior Vice President and Chief Information Officer
CHR: Janet Smith-Hill, Executive Vice President and Chief Human Resource Officer
CNO: Cora Greene, Senior Director, Chief Nursing Officer
Web address: www.https://www.novanthealth.org/rowan-medical-center.aspx
Control: Other not–for–profit (including NFP Corporation) **Service:** General medical and surgical

Staffed Beds: 149

VETERANS AFFAIRS MEDICAL CENTER See W. G. (Bill) Heffner Veterans Affairs Medical Center

☒ **W. G. (BILL) HEFFNER VETERANS AFFAIRS MEDICAL CENTER**, 1601 Brenner Avenue, Zip 28144–2559; tel. 704/638–9000, **A**1 3 5 **F**1 3 4 5 8 9 11 12 15 18 20 26 27 28 29 30 31 33 34 35 36 38 39 40 45 46 47 48 49 50 53 54 56 57 58 59 60 61 62 63 64 65 66 70 74 75 77 78 79 81 82 83 84 85 86 87 91 92 93 94 96 97 98 100 101 102 103 104 105 106 107 108 110 111 114 115 116 117 118 119 126 129 130 132 135 143 146 147 148 149 152 153 154 156 157 158 **S** Department of Veterans Affairs, Washington, DC
Primary Contact: Joseph Vaughn, Director
CFO: Steve Patil, Chief Financial Officer
CIO: Deborah Gunn, Chief Information Officer
CHR: Sandra Fischer, Director Human Resources
Web address: www.salisbury.va.gov
Control: Veterans Affairs, Government, federal **Service:** General medical and surgical

Staffed Beds: 218 **Admissions:** 4345 **Census:** 208 **Outpatient Visits:** 1375004 **Births:** 0 **Personnel:** 2337

Hospital, Medicare Provider Number, Address, Telephone, Approval, Facility, and Physician Codes, Health Care System

★ American Hospital Association (AHA) membership
□ The Joint Commission accreditation
○ Healthcare Facilities Accreditation Program
◇ DNV Healthcare Inc. accreditation
⇧ Center for Improvement in Healthcare Quality Accreditation
△ Commission on Accreditation of Rehabilitation Facilities (CARF) accreditation

NC

SANFORD—Lee County

⊞ **CENTRAL CAROLINA HOSPITAL (340020)**, 1135 Carthage Street, Zip 27330–4162; tel. 919/774–2100, **A**1 10 **F**3 7 11 13 15 18 20 22 28 29 30 34 35 37 40 45 46 48 49 50 57 59 60 64 65 68 70 73 76 77 79 81 85 87 93 94 96 107 108 110 111 115 119 126 129 130 132 135 146 147 148 149 156 **S** Duke LifePoint Healthcare, Brentwood, TN
Primary Contact: Spencer Thomas, Chief Executive Officer
CFO: Jared Stimpson, Chief Financial Officer
CIO: Jimmy Whitaker, Director Information Systems
CHR: Deanna Lamb, Director Human Resources
CNO: Jan P. Phillips, R.N., Chief Nursing Officer
Web address: www.centralcarolinahosp.com
Control: Corporation, Investor–owned (for–profit) **Service**: General medical and surgical

> **Staffed Beds:** 127 **Admissions:** 4581 **Census:** 43 **Outpatient Visits:** 74338 **Births:** 985 **Total Expense ($000):** 68470 **Payroll Expense ($000):** 25747 **Personnel:** 565

SHELBY—Cleveland County

⊞ **ATRIUM HEALTH CLEVELAND (340021)**, 201 East Grover Street, Zip 28150–3917; tel. 980/487–3000, **A**1 2 10 19 **F**3 8 13 15 18 20 28 29 30 31 32 34 35 39 40 43 44 45 47 48 49 50 53 55 56 57 59 64 65 70 71 74 75 76 77 78 79 80 81 85 86 87 89 93 100 107 108 110 111 115 118 119 120 121 123 126 129 130 131 132 135 145 146 147 148 149 154 156 **S** Atrium Health, Charlotte, NC
Primary Contact: Brian Gwyn, President and Chief Executive Officer
COO: Brian Gwyn, President Chief Operating Officer
CFO: Christine M Martin, Vice President and Chief Financial Officer
CMO: Charles M Tomlinson, M.D., Chief Medical Officer
CHR: Debra Kale, Vice President Human Resources
CNO: Veronica Poole-Adams, R.N., Vice President, Chief Operating Officer and Chief Nursing Executive
Web address: www.clevelandregional.org
Control: Hospital district or authority, Government, nonfederal **Service**: General medical and surgical

> **Staffed Beds:** 177 **Admissions:** 8572 **Census:** 93 **Outpatient Visits:** 177238 **Births:** 1099 **Total Expense ($000):** 189389 **Payroll Expense ($000):** 56352 **Personnel:** 922

SILER CITY—Chatham County

⊞ **CHATHAM HOSPITAL (341311)**, 475 Progress Boulevard, Zip 27344–6787, Mailing Address: P.O. Box 649, Zip 27344–0649; tel. 919/799–4000, **A**1 10 18 **F**3 15 18 26 28 29 30 34 35 39 40 45 46 57 59 68 70 75 77 79 81 85 92 93 107 110 111 114 119 130 133 135 154 156 **S** UNC Health Care, Chapel Hill, NC
Primary Contact: Robert A. Enders Jr, President
CFO: Jeff LeGay, Chief Financial Officer
CMO: Andrew Hannapel, Chief Medical Officer
CIO: Deborah Taylor, Chief Information Officer
CHR: Jodie Sartor Solow, Director of Human Resources
CNO: Tammy Needham, Chief Nursing Officer
Web address: www.chathamhospital.org
Control: Other not–for–profit (including NFP Corporation) **Service**: General medical and surgical

> **Staffed Beds:** 25 **Admissions:** 866 **Census:** 12 **Outpatient Visits:** 48629 **Births:** 0 **Total Expense ($000):** 35197 **Payroll Expense ($000):** 10777 **Personnel:** 186

SMITHFIELD—Johnston County

⊞ **JOHNSTON HEALTH (340090)**, 509 North Bright Leaf Blvd, Zip 27577–4407, Mailing Address: P.O. Box 1376, Zip 27577–1376; tel. 919/934–8171, **A**1 2 10 **F**3 11 13 15 17 18 20 22 26 28 29 30 31 32 34 35 38 40 45 49 50 53 57 59 61 62 63 64 66 68 70 73 74 75 76 79 81 82 85 86 87 89 92 93 98 100 107 108 110 111 114 115 119 120 121 126 130 132 144 146 147 148 149 154 156 **S** UNC Health Care, Chapel Hill, NC
Primary Contact: Charles W. Elliott Jr, Chief Executive Officer
COO: Ruth Marler, Chief Nursing Officer and Chief Operating Officer
CFO: Edward A Klein, Chief Financial Officer
CIO: Teresa Chappell, Chief Information Officer
CHR: Timothy A Hays, Vice President Human Resources
CNO: Ruth Marler, Chief Nursing Officer and Chief Operating Officer
Web address: www.johnstonhealth.org
Control: Hospital district or authority, Government, nonfederal **Service**: General medical and surgical

> **Staffed Beds:** 153 **Admissions:** 10286 **Census:** 102 **Outpatient Visits:** 173013 **Births:** 1545 **Total Expense ($000):** 211425 **Payroll Expense ($000):** 84127 **Personnel:** 1384

SOUTHPORT—Brunswick County

★ **J. ARTHUR DOSHER MEMORIAL HOSPITAL (341327)**, 924 North Howe Street, Zip 28461–3099; tel. 910/457–3800, **A**10 18 **F**3 11 12 15 28 30 34 35 40 45 47 50 54 57 59 64 68 75 77 79 81 91 93 97 107 110 111 114 115 118 119 127 129 130 131 132 133 144 146 148 149 154 156
Primary Contact: Thomas R. Siemers, Chief Executive Officer
COO: Carol Northup, R.N., Chief Nursing Officer and Chief Operating Officer
CFO: Daniel J. Porter, Senior Vice President and Chief Financial Officer
CMO: Brad L Hilaman, M.D., Chief Medical Officer
CIO: Susan Shomaker, Director Information Management Systems
CHR: Deanna Parker, Director Human Resources
CNO: Carol Northup, R.N., Chief Nursing Officer and Chief Operating Officer
Web address: www.dosher.org
Control: Hospital district or authority, Government, nonfederal **Service**: General medical and surgical

> **Staffed Beds:** 25 **Admissions:** 988 **Census:** 7 **Outpatient Visits:** 68643 **Births:** 0 **Total Expense ($000):** 44905 **Payroll Expense ($000):** 16759 **Personnel:** 253

SPARTA—Alleghany County

⊞ **ALLEGHANY MEMORIAL HOSPITAL (341320)**, 233 Doctors Street, Zip 28675–9247; tel. 336/372–5511, **A**1 10 18 **F**3 15 18 28 29 30 34 35 40 43 45 59 64 67 70 77 78 79 81 82 87 90 93 97 107 111 114 119 129 130 131 133 135 146 154
Primary Contact: Craig James, President
CFO: Brett Liverman, Chief Financial Officer
CMO: Joe Arocha, Chief of Staff
CIO: Darlene Keith, Chief Information Systems
CHR: Courtney Bennett, Human Resource Manager
CNO: Wendy Orton, Chief Nursing Officer
Web address: www.amhsparta.org
Control: Other not–for–profit (including NFP Corporation) **Service**: General medical and surgical

> **Staffed Beds:** 25 **Admissions:** 331 **Census:** 3 **Outpatient Visits:** 25346 **Births:** 0 **Total Expense ($000):** 11834 **Payroll Expense ($000):** 5051 **Personnel:** 122

SPRUCE PINE—Mitchell County

⊞ **BLUE RIDGE REGIONAL HOSPITAL (341329)**, 125 Hospital Drive, Zip 28777–3035; tel. 828/765–4201, (Includes BLUE RIDGE MEDICAL CENTER - YANCEY CAMPUS, 800 Medical Campus Drive, Burnsville, North Carolina, Zip 28714–9010; tel. 828/682–0200) **A**1 10 18 **F**3 15 17 28 29 30 31 32 34 35 40 42 45 50 54 59 64 66 70 75 77 78 79 81 82 85 87 90 93 96 97 107 108 111 114 118 119 127 128 129 130 131 132 133 135 146 147 148 154 157 **S** HCA Healthcare, Nashville, TN
Primary Contact: Rebecca W. Carter, MSN, R.N., FACHE, President and Chief Nursing Officer
CFO: Clint Stewart, Chief Financial Officer
CMO: Jennifer Larson, M.D., Chief of Staff
CIO: Pam Blevins, R.N., Director, Clinical Informatics
CNO: Rebecca W. Carter, MSN, R.N., FACHE, President and Chief Nursing Officer
Web address: www.spchospital.org
Control: Other not–for–profit (including NFP Corporation) **Service**: General medical and surgical

> **Staffed Beds:** 21 **Admissions:** 1376 **Census:** 12 **Outpatient Visits:** 123708 **Births:** 0 **Total Expense ($000):** 44930 **Payroll Expense ($000):** 21374 **Personnel:** 250

STATESVILLE—Iredell County

⊞ **DAVIS REGIONAL MEDICAL CENTER (340144)**, 218 Old Mocksville Road, Zip 28625–1930, Mailing Address: P.O. Box 1823, Zip 28687–1823; tel. 704/873–0281, (Nonreporting) **A**1 10 19 **S** Community Health Systems, Inc., Franklin, TN
Primary Contact: Matthew Banks, Chief Executive Officer
CFO: Hugh Tobin, Chief Financial Officer
CMO: Christopher Lariscy, M.D., Chief of Staff
CIO: Janie Stikeleather, Director Marketing and Community Relations
CHR: Christine McKenzie, Director Human Resources
CNO: Janice S Martin, R.N., Chief Nursing Officer
Web address: www.davisregional.com
Control: Corporation, Investor–owned (for–profit) **Service**: General medical and surgical

> **Staffed Beds:** 130

NC

Many Facility Codes have changed. Please refer to the AHA Guide Code Chart.   © 2019 AHA Guide

IREDELL HEALTH SYSTEM (340039), 557 Brookdale Drive, Zip 28677–4107, Mailing Address: P.O. Box 1828, Zip 28687–1828; tel. 704/873–5661, (Total facility includes 48 beds in nursing home–type unit) **A**1 2 10 **F**3 11 13 15 17 18 20 22 28 29 30 31 32 34 35 40 41 44 45 47 49 50 56 57 58 59 60 62 64 68 70 74 75 76 77 78 79 81 82 85 86 87 89 91 93 97 107 108 110 111 114 115 116 117 118 119 120 121 123 127 128 129 130 132 135 146 147 148 156 Primary Contact: Ed Rush, President and Chief Executive Officer COO: John Green, Chief Operating Officer CFO: Skip Smith, Vice President Finance CMO: Brent Warren, President Medical Staff CIO: Kyle Smith, Director Information Systems CHR: Cindy Smale, Director, Human Resources CNO: Becky Quate, Vice President Nursing and Patient Care Services Web address: www.iredellhealth.org **Control:** Other not–for–profit (including NFP Corporation) **Service:** General medical and surgical

Staffed Beds: 199 **Admissions:** 7363 **Census:** 117 **Outpatient Visits:** 116331 **Births:** 517 **Total Expense ($000):** 169304 **Payroll Expense ($000):** 70313 **Personnel:** 1453

SYLVA—Jackson County

HARRIS REGIONAL HOSPITAL (340016), 68 Hospital Road, Zip 28779–2722; tel. 828/586–7000, (Nonreporting) **A**1 10 **S** Duke LifePoint Healthcare, Brentwood, TN Primary Contact: Steve Heatherly, Chief Executive Officer CHR: Janet Millsaps, Chief Human Resources Officer Web address: www.westcare.org **Control:** Other not–for–profit (including NFP Corporation) **Service:** General medical and surgical

Staffed Beds: 86

TARBORO—Edgecombe County

VIDANT EDGECOMBE HOSPITAL (340107), 111 Hospital Drive, Zip 27886–2011; tel. 252/641–7700, **A**1 2 3 10 **F**3 11 13 15 28 29 30 31 34 35 40 45 50 57 59 60 64 70 73 75 76 78 79 81 82 85 87 90 92 96 107 110 111 119 127 130 131 132 145 146 149 154 **S** Vidant Health, Greenville, NC Primary Contact: Patrick Heins, President CFO: Charles Alford, Vice President Financial Services CMO: Barry Bunn, M.D., Chief of Staff CHR: David Prafka, Ed.D., Director of Human Resources Web address: www.https://www.vidanthealth.com/edgecombe/default.aspx **Control:** Other not–for–profit (including NFP Corporation) **Service:** General medical and surgical

Staffed Beds: 65 **Admissions:** 3508 **Census:** 46 **Outpatient Visits:** 87359 **Births:** 401 **Total Expense ($000):** 78469 **Payroll Expense ($000):** 27146 **Personnel:** 448

THOMASVILLE—Davidson County

NOVANT HEALTH THOMASVILLE MEDICAL CENTER (340085), 207 Old Lexington Road, Zip 27360–3428, Mailing Address: P.O. Box 789, Zip 27361–0789; tel. 336/472–2000, (Nonreporting) **A**1 3 10 **S** Novant Health, Winston Salem, NC Primary Contact: Jon D. Applebaum, President and Chief Operating Officer CFO: Fred M Hargett, Executive Vice President and Chief Financial Officer CMO: Thomas Zweng, Executive Vice President and Chief Medical Officer CIO: David B Garrett, Senior Vice President and Chief Information Officer CHR: Janet Smith-Hill, Executive Vice President and Chief Human Resource Officer CNO: Nancy Pearson, MSN, R.N., Director, Nursing Web address: www.thomasvillemedicalcenter.org **Control:** Other not–for–profit (including NFP Corporation) **Service:** General medical and surgical

Staffed Beds: 87

TROY—Montgomery County

FIRSTHEALTH MONTGOMERY MEMORIAL HOSPITAL (341303), 520 Allen Street, Zip 27371–2802; tel. 910/571–5000, **A**1 10 18 **F**3 11 15 40 45 47 49 59 64 81 85 87 93 97 107 110 114 119 127 129 133 135 146 154 **S** FirstHealth of the Carolinas, Pinehurst, NC Primary Contact: Beth Walker, R.N., President CFO: Bryan Hawkins, Controller CIO: David B Dillehunt, Chief Information Officer CHR: Tina H Thompson, Coordinator Human Resources CNO: Pam Gaddy, Director, Patient Care Services and Chief Nursing Officer Web address: www.firsthealth.org **Control:** Other not–for–profit (including NFP Corporation) **Service:** General medical and surgical

Staffed Beds: 5 **Admissions:** 144 **Census:** 1 **Outpatient Visits:** 23518 **Births:** 0 **Total Expense ($000):** 11384 **Payroll Expense ($000):** 5843 **Personnel:** 106

WADESBORO—Anson County

ATRIUM HEALTH ANSON (340084), 2301 US Highway 74 W, Zip 28170–7554, Mailing Address: 2301 U.S Highway 74 West, Zip 28170; tel. 704/994–4500, **A**1 10 **F**15 18 29 34 35 40 57 59 64 71 75 77 81 86 87 93 97 100 107 110 114 119 129 130 131 132 135 143 146 154 **S** Atrium Health, Charlotte, NC Primary Contact: Dave Anderson, FACHE, Vice President and Administrator CFO: Jeff Griffin, Assistant Vice President Finance CMO: Edward Blasko, Chief of Staff CIO: Lisa Sykes, IS/Communications Director CHR: Rhonda McFarland, Director Human Resources CNO: Denise White, MSN, Chief Nurse Executive Web address: www.carolinashealthcare.org/anson **Control:** Hospital district or authority, Government, nonfederal **Service:** General medical and surgical

Staffed Beds: 15 **Admissions:** 343 **Census:** 2 **Outpatient Visits:** 33131 **Births:** 0 **Total Expense ($000):** 17411 **Payroll Expense ($000):** 6733 **Personnel:** 105

WASHINGTON—Beaufort County

BEAUFORT COUNTY HOSPITAL See Vidant Beaufort Hospital

VIDANT BEAUFORT HOSPITAL (340186), 628 East 12th Street, Zip 27889–3409; tel. 252/975–4100, (Nonreporting) **A**1 3 10 **S** Vidant Health, Greenville, NC Primary Contact: Harvey Case, President CFO: Lucinda Crawford, Vice President of Patient Care Services CMO: James Egbert, Chief of Staff CHR: Jenny Brown, Director of Human Resources CNO: Lou Montana-Rhodes, Vice President of Patient Care Services Web address: www.vidanthealth.com **Control:** Hospital district or authority, Government, nonfederal **Service:** General medical and surgical

Staffed Beds: 84

WHITEVILLE—Columbus County

★ ⇧ **COLUMBUS REGIONAL HEALTHCARE SYSTEM (340068)**, 500 Jefferson Street, Zip 28472–3634; tel. 910/642–8011, **A**10 19 21 **F**3 11 12 13 15 28 29 30 31 34 35 40 45 46 47 48 50 54 55 57 59 64 65 68 70 75 77 78 79 81 85 86 87 91 92 93 94 107 108 110 111 114 115 118 119 126 129 130 132 145 146 148 149 156 **S** Atrium Health, Charlotte, NC Primary Contact: John F. Young, Interim Chief Executive Officer CFO: Carl Biber, Chief Financial Officer CMO: Samuel N Wheatley, Chief Medical Officer CIO: Lisa Ward, Director Information Systems CHR: Andrea West, MS, Vice President of Human Resources CNO: Terri Veneziano, Interim Chief Nursing Officer Web address: www.crhealthcare.org/ **Control:** Other not–for–profit (including NFP Corporation) **Service:** General medical and surgical

Staffed Beds: 85 **Admissions:** 3839 **Census:** 46 **Outpatient Visits:** 112576 **Births:** 349 **Total Expense ($000):** 78833 **Payroll Expense ($000):** 27418 **Personnel:** 573

WILLIAMSTON—Martin County

MARTIN GENERAL HOSPITAL (340133), 310 South McCaskey Road, Zip 27892–2150, Mailing Address: P.O. Box 1128, Zip 27892–1128; tel. 252/809–6300, (Nonreporting) **A**1 10 **S** Quorum Health, Brentwood, TN Primary Contact: Joanie White Wagner, Chief Executive Officer CFO: John Jacobson, Chief Financial Officer CIO: James Griffin, Manager Information Systems CHR: Rebecca Edwards, Director Human Resources CNO: Gregory Hornick, MSN, Chief Nursing Officer Web address: www.martingeneral.com **Control:** Corporation, Investor–owned (for–profit) **Service:** General medical and surgical

Staffed Beds: 49

WILMINGTON—New Hanover County

★ △ ⭡ **NEW HANOVER REGIONAL MEDICAL CENTER (340141)**, 2131 South 17th Street, Zip 28401–7483, Mailing Address: P.O. Box 9000, Zip 28402–9000; tel. 910/343–7000, (Includes CAPE FEAR HOSPITAL, 5301 Wrightsville Avenue, Wilmington, North Carolina, Zip 28403–6599; tel. 910/452–8100) **A**2 3 5 7 10 21 **F**3 7 8 11 12 13 18 20 22 24 26 28 29 30 31 34 35 36 37 39 40 42 43 44 45 46 47 48 49 50 53 54 56 57 58 59 60 61 64 65 66 68 70 72 73 74 75 76 77 78 79 80 81 82 84 85 86 87 88 89 90 92 93 94 96 97 98 100 101 102 107 108 110 111 114 115 117 118 119 121 123 126 130 131 132 135 144 146 147 148 149 154 155 **S** New Hanover Regional Medical Center, Wilmington, NC
Primary Contact: Andre Boyd Sr, Executive Vice President, Hospital Division
CFO: Edwin J Ollie, Executive Vice President and Chief Financial Officer
CMO: Sam Spicer, M.D., Vice President Medical Affairs
CIO: Avery Cloud, Vice President and Chief Information Officer
CHR: Keith A Strawn, Vice President Human Resources
CNO: Mary Ellen Bonczek, R.N., Chief Nursing Executive
Web address: www.nhrmc.org
Control: County, Government, nonfederal **Service**: General medical and surgical

Staffed Beds: 713 **Admissions:** 40009 **Census:** 580 **Outpatient Visits:** 454500 **Births:** 4063 **Total Expense ($000):** 971271 **Payroll Expense ($000):** 350367 **Personnel:** 6120

WILMINGTON TREATMENT CENTER (340168), 2520 Troy Drive, Zip 28401–7643; tel. 910/762–2727, (Nonreporting) **A**10 **S** CRC Health Group, Inc., Cupertino, CA
Primary Contact: Robert Pitts, Executive Director
COO: Paige Bottom, Director Operations
CFO: Virginia Powell, Director Finance
CMO: Patrick Martin, M.D., Medical Director
Web address: www.wilmtreatment.com
Control: Corporation, Investor–owned (for–profit) **Service**: Alcoholism and other chemical dependency

Staffed Beds: 44

WILSON—Wilson County

TRIANGLE EAST NURSING CARE CENTER See Wilmed Nursing Care Center

⊞ **WILSON MEDICAL CENTER (340126)**, 1705 Tarboro Street, SW, Zip 27893–3428; tel. 252/399–8040, (Total facility includes 90 beds in nursing home–type unit) **A**1 2 10 19 **F**3 11 13 15 18 20 22 26 28 29 30 31 34 35 39 40 45 47 48 50 54 57 60 64 68 70 73 74 75 76 77 78 79 81 82 85 86 87 89 92 93 94 97 98 102 103 107 108 110 111 114 115 118 119 120 121 123 128 129 130 132 135 146 148 154 156 **S** Duke LifePoint Healthcare, Brentwood, TN
Primary Contact: William E. Caldwell Jr, FACHE, Chief Executive Officer
CMO: Rick Guarino, M.D., Vice President Medical Affairs
CIO: Brian Dietrick, Director Information Systems
CHR: Denise O'Hara, Vice President Human Resources
Web address: www.wilmed.org
Control: Corporation, Investor–owned (for–profit) **Service**: General medical and surgical

Staffed Beds: 220 **Admissions:** 6889 **Census:** 145 **Outpatient Visits:** 92199 **Births:** 838 **Total Expense ($000):** 113902 **Payroll Expense ($000):** 43434 **Personnel:** 787

WINDSOR—Bertie County

⊞ **VIDANT BERTIE HOSPITAL (341304)**, 1403 South King Street, Zip 27983–9666, Mailing Address: P.O. Box 40, Zip 27983–0040; tel. 252/794–6600, **A**1 10 18 **F**3 15 29 30 34 35 40 45 46 47 48 49 57 59 64 77 79 81 82 93 94 97 107 110 114 119 127 132 135 146 148 154 156 **S** Vidant Health, Greenville, NC
Primary Contact: Jeffrey Sackrison, President
CFO: Brian Harvill, Vice President Financial Services
CMO: William Ballance, Chief of Medical Staff
CIO: Brian White, Director Strategic Planning
CHR: Nicole Spell, Director Human Resources
CNO: Silvia Rose, Director Patient Care Services
Web address: www.vidanthealth.com
Control: Other not–for–profit (including NFP Corporation) **Service**: General medical and surgical

Staffed Beds: 6 **Admissions:** 380 **Census:** 4 **Outpatient Visits:** 25082 **Births:** 0 **Total Expense ($000):** 18126 **Payroll Expense ($000):** 7962 **Personnel:** 104

WINSTON—SALEM-Forsyth County

BRENNER CHILDREN'S HOSPITAL & HEALTH SERVICES See Wake Forest Baptist Medical Center, Winston-Salem

MEDICAL PARK HOSPITAL See Novant Health Medical Park Hospital

⊞ **NOVANT HEALTH FORSYTH MEDICAL CENTER (340014)**, 3333 Silas Creek Parkway, Zip 27103–3090; tel. 336/718–5000, (Includes KERNERSVILLE MEDICAL CENTER, 2911 750 Kernersville Medical Parkway, Kernersville, North Carolina, Zip 27284–2932, Mailing Address: 1750 Kernersville Medical Parkway, Zip 27284–2932, tel. 336/564–4000; Chad Setliff, President and Chief Operating Officer; NOVANT HEALTH CLEMMONS MEDICAL CENTER, 6915 Village Medical Circle, Clemmons, North Carolina, Zip 27012–8002; tel. 336/893–1000; Chad Setliff, President and Chief Operating Officer), (Non-reporting) **A**1 2 3 5 10 **S** Novant Health, Winston Salem, NC
Primary Contact: Chad Setliff, President and Chief Operating Officer
CFO: Fred M Hargett, Executive Vice President and Chief Financial Officer
CMO: Thomas Zweng, Executive Vice President and Chief Medical Officer
CIO: David B Garrett, Senior Vice President and Chief Information Officer
CHR: Janet Smith-Hill, Senior Vice President Human Resources
CNO: Janet L Bright, Vice President, Chief Nursing Officer
Web address: www.https://www.novanthealth.org
Control: Other not–for–profit (including NFP Corporation) **Service**: General medical and surgical

Staffed Beds: 740

⊞ **NOVANT HEALTH MEDICAL PARK HOSPITAL (340148)**, 1950 South Hawthorne Road, Zip 27103–3993; tel. 336/718–0600, (Nonreporting) **A**1 2 10 **S** Novant Health, Winston Salem, NC
Primary Contact: Kirsten Royster, President and Chief Operating Officer
CFO: Fred M Hargett, Executive Vice President and Chief Financial Officer
CMO: Thomas Zweng, Executive Vice President and Chief Medical Officer
CIO: David B Garrett, Senior Vice President and Chief Information Officer
CHR: Janet Smith-Hill, Executive Vice President and Chief Human Resource Officer
CNO: Carol A Smith, R.N., Director Operations and Nursing
Web address: www.novanthealth.org
Control: Other not–for–profit (including NFP Corporation) **Service**: General medical and surgical

Staffed Beds: 21

☐ **OLD VINEYARD BEHAVIORAL HEALTH SERVICES (344007)**, 3637 Old Vineyard Road, Zip 27104–4842; tel. 336/794–3550, **A**1 10 **F**4 29 50 75 87 98 99 101 102 103 104 105 130 149 153 154 **S** Universal Health Services, Inc., King of Prussia, PA
Primary Contact: Kevin Patton, Chief Executive Officer
CFO: Ernest C Priddy III Chief Financial Officer
CMO: Raj Thotakura, M.D., Medical Director
CHR: Jackie Pennino, Director Human Resources
CNO: Susan Evans, Chief Nursing Officer
Web address: www.oldvineyardbhs.com
Control: Corporation, Investor–owned (for–profit) **Service**: Psychiatric

Staffed Beds: 158 **Admissions:** 6069 **Census:** 139 **Outpatient Visits:** 5662 **Births:** 0 **Total Expense ($000):** 25273 **Payroll Expense ($000):** 15028 **Personnel:** 271

⊞ △ **WAKE FOREST BAPTIST MEDICAL CENTER (340047)**, Medical Center Boulevard, Zip 27157–0001; tel. 336/716–2011, (Includes BRENNER CHILDREN'S HOSPITAL & HEALTH SERVICES, Medical Center Boulevard, Winston Salem, North Carolina, Zip 27157, Mailing Address: One Medical Center Boulevard, Zip 27157, tel. 336/716–2255) **A**1 2 3 5 7 8 10 **F**3 5 6 7 9 11 12 15 16 17 18 19 20 21 22 23 24 25 26 27 28 29 30 31 32 34 35 36 37 38 40 41 43 44 45 46 47 48 49 50 52 53 54 55 56 57 58 59 60 61 62 64 65 66 67 68 70 72 73 74 75 77 78 79 80 81 82 84 85 86 87 88 89 90 91 92 93 96 97 98 99 100 101 102 103 104 107 108 110 111 113 114 115 116 117 118 119 120 121 123 124 126 127 129 130 131 132 134 135 136 137 138 141 142 143 145 146 147 148 149 150 153 154 155 156 157 **S** Wake Forest Baptist Health, Winston-Salem, NC
Primary Contact: Julie Ann Freischlag, M.D., Chief Executive Officer
CMO: Russell M Howerton, M.D., Chief Medical Officer
CHR: Cheryl Locke, Vice President and Chief Human Resource Officer
Web address: www.wakehealth.edu
Control: Other not–for–profit (including NFP Corporation) **Service**: General medical and surgical

Staffed Beds: 800 **Admissions:** 38390 **Census:** 680 **Outpatient Visits:** 969919 **Births:** 24 **Total Expense ($000):** 1633451 **Payroll Expense ($000):** 553400 **Personnel:** 9258

NC

NORTH DAKOTA

ASHLEY—McIntosh County

★ **ASHLEY MEDICAL CENTER (351322)**, 612 North Center Avenue,
Zip 58413–7013, Mailing Address: P.O. Box 450, Zip 58413–0450;
tel. 701/288–3433, (Nonreporting) **A**10 18
Primary Contact: Holly Wolff, Chief Executive Officer
CMO: Udom Tinsa, M.D., Medical Director
Web address: www.amctoday.org
Control: Other not-for-profit (including NFP Corporation) **Service:** General
medical and surgical

Staffed Beds: 64

BELCOURT—Rolette County

☐ **INDIAN HEALTH SERVICE - QUENTIN N. BURDICK MEMORIAL HEALTH CARE
FACILITY (350063)**, 1300 Hospital Loop, Zip 58316, Mailing Address: P.O. Box
160, Zip 58316–0160; tel. 701/477–6111, (Nonreporting) **A**1 10 **S** U. S. Indian
Health Service, Rockville, MD
Primary Contact: Shelly Harris, Chief Executive Officer
CFO: Deland Davis, Chief Financial Officer
CMO: Vernon Azure, Clinical Director
CIO: Chance Wilkie, Information Technology Specialist
CHR: Donna Belgarde, Human Resources Specialist
CNO: Lynelle Hunt, Director of Nursing
Web address: www.ihs.gov
Control: PHS, Indian Service, Government, federal **Service:** General medical and
surgical

Staffed Beds: 27

BISMARCK—Burleigh County

⊞ **CHI ST. ALEXIUS HEALTH (350002)**, 900 East Broadway, Zip 58501–4586,
Mailing Address: P.O. Box 5510, Zip 58506–5510; tel. 701/530–7000, (Total
facility includes 19 beds in nursing home–type unit) **A**1 2 3 10 **F**3 5 8 9 11 12 13
15 17 18 19 20 21 22 23 24 25 26 28 29 30 31 32 34 35 38 39 40 42 45 46 49
53 54 56 57 58 59 60 64 68 70 72 73 74 75 76 77 78 79 81 82 84 85 87 88
89 92 93 94 96 97 98 99 100 101 102 103 104 105 107 110 111 114 115
118 119 126 128 129 130 131 132 135 146 147 148 149 150 152 154 **S**
CommonSpirit Health, Chicago, IL
Primary Contact: Kurt Gahley, Market Chief Executive Officer
CFO: Susan Sisk, Chief Financial Officer
CMO: Shiraz Hyder, M.D., Director Medical Affairs
CIO: Todd Bortke, Director Information Systems
CHR: Tom Gregg, Vice President Human Resources
CNO: Rosanne Schmidt, R.N., Chief Nursing Officer
Web address: www.st.alexius.org
Control: Church operated, Nongovernment, not-for-profit **Service:** General
medical and surgical

Staffed Beds: 237 **Admissions:** 9274 **Census:** 116 **Outpatient
Visits:** 147718 **Births:** 1224 **Total Expense ($000):** 303327 **Payroll
Expense ($000):** 132388 **Personnel:** 1493

⊞ **SANFORD BISMARCK (350015)**, 300 North Seventh Street, Zip 58501–4439,
Mailing Address: P.O. Box 5525, Zip 58506–5525; tel. 701/323–6000, **A**1 2 3
5 10 19 **F**3 8 9 11 12 13 15 17 18 20 22 24 26 28 29 30 31 32 33 34 35 36
37 38 40 43 44 45 49 51 53 54 55 56 57 58 59 60 61 62 63 64 65 66 68 69
70 71 72 73 74 75 76 77 78 79 81 82 84 85 86 87 88 89 92 93 96 97 98
100 101 102 104 107 108 110 111 115 118 119 126 129 130 131 132 134
135 138 141 142 146 147 148 149 150 154 156 157 **S** Sanford Health, Sioux
Falls, SD
Primary Contact: Michael LeBeau, President
CFO: Kirk Cristy, Chief Financial Officer
CMO: Chris Meeker, M.D., Chief Medical Officer
CHR: Scott D Boehm, Executive Vice President Human Resources and Facilities
CNO: Jan Kamphuis, Ph.D., R.N., Executive Vice President and Chief Nurse
Executive
Web address: www.bismarck.sanfordhealth.org/
Control: Other not-for-profit (including NFP Corporation) **Service:** General
medical and surgical

Staffed Beds: 227 **Admissions:** 12493 **Census:** 153 **Outpatient
Visits:** 206538 **Births:** 1357 **Total Expense ($000):** 505321 **Payroll
Expense ($000):** 236840 **Personnel:** 2591

SANFORD HEALTH See Sanford Bismarck

BOTTINEAU—Bottineau County

ST. ANDREW'S HEALTH CENTER (351307), 316 Ohmer Street,
Zip 58318–1045; tel. 701/228–9300, (Nonreporting) **A**10 18 **S** Sisters of Mary
of the Presentation Health System, Fargo, ND
Primary Contact: Alfred Sams, President and Chief Executive Officer
CFO: Sean Rinkenberger, Chief Financial Officer
CMO: Jessica Skjolden, M.D., Chief of Staff
CHR: Brenda Arneson, Administrative Assistant
CNO: Karla Spence, Director of Nursing
Web address: www.standrewshealth.com
Control: Church operated **Service:** General medical and surgical

Staffed Beds: 25

BOWMAN—Bowman County

SOUTHWEST HEALTHCARE SERVICES (351313), 802 2nd Street Northwest,
Zip 58623–4483, Mailing Address: P O Drawer 'C', Zip 58623;
tel. 701/523–5265, (Nonreporting) **A**10 18
Primary Contact: Jerry Wiesner, Administrator and Chief Executive Officer
Web address: www.swhealthcare.net
Control: Other not-for-profit (including NFP Corporation) **Service:** General
medical and surgical

Staffed Beds: 55

CANDO—Towner County

★ **TOWNER COUNTY MEDICAL CENTER (351331)**, State Highway 281 North,
Zip 58324, Mailing Address: P.O. Box 688, Zip 58324–0688; tel. 701/968–4411,
(Nonreporting) **A**10 18
Primary Contact: Ben Bucher, Chief Executive Officer
CFO: Tammy Larson, Chief Financial Officer
CMO: Russ Petty, M.D., Chief of Staff
CIO: David Fite, Director Information Technology
CHR: Pat Klingenberg, Director Human Resources
Web address: www.tcmedcenter.org
Control: Other not-for-profit (including NFP Corporation) **Service:** General
medical and surgical

Staffed Beds: 50

CARRINGTON—Foster County

★ **CHI ST ALEXIUS HEALTH CARRINGTON MEDICAL CENTER (351318)**,
800 North Fourth Street, Zip 58421–1217, Mailing Address: P.O. Box 461,
Zip 58421 0461; tel. 701/652–3141, **A**10 18 **F**3 7 11 15 28 34 40 45 46 64
75 81 87 107 108 110 114 119 127 132 133 143 146 154 **S** CommonSpirit
Health, Chicago, IL
Primary Contact: Mariann Doeling, R.N., President
COO: Brenda Rask, Vice President Operations
CFO: Kurt Sargent, CPA, Vice President, Operational Finance
CIO: Keith Stauffer, Regional Chief Information Officer
CHR: Carol Risovi, Human Resources
CNO: Jodi Lynn Hovdenes, R.N., Vice President Patient Care
Web address: www.carringtonhealthcenter.org
Control: Other not-for-profit (including NFP Corporation) **Service:** General
medical and surgical

Staffed Beds: 25 **Admissions:** 369 **Census:** 5 **Outpatient Visits:** 21801
Births: 0 **Total Expense ($000):** 11705 **Payroll Expense ($000):** 3388
Personnel: 50

Hospital, Medicare Provider Number, Address, Telephone, Approval, Facility, and Physician Codes, Health Care System

★ American Hospital Association (AHA) membership   ○ Healthcare Facilities Accreditation Program   ⇑ Center for Improvement in Healthcare Quality Accreditation
☐ The Joint Commission accreditation   ◇ DNV Healthcare Inc. accreditation   △ Commission on Accreditation of Rehabilitation Facilities (CARF) accreditation

CAVALIER—Pembina County

★ **PEMBINA COUNTY MEMORIAL HOSPITAL AND WEDGEWOOD MANOR (351319)**, 301 Mountain Street East, Zip 58220–4015, Mailing Address: P.O. Box 380, Zip 58220–0380; tel. 701/265–8461, (Nonreporting) **A**10 18
Primary Contact: Lisa LeTexier, Interim Chief Executive Officer
CMO: K S Sumra, M.D., Chief of Staff
CIO: Robert Heidt, Director Information Systems
Web address: www.cavalierhospital.com
Control: Other not–for–profit (including NFP Corporation) **Service:** General medical and surgical

> **Staffed Beds:** 70

COOPERSTOWN—Griggs County

★ **COOPERSTOWN MEDICAL CENTER (351306)**, 1200 Roberts Avenue NorthEast, Zip 58425–7101; tel. 701/797–2221, (Nonreporting) **A**10 18
Primary Contact: Nikki Johnson, Interim Chief Executive Officer
CMO: Jeffrey Peterson, M.D., Medical Director
CHR: Pamela VenHuizen, Chief Human Resources Officer
Web address: www.coopermc.com
Control: Other not–for–profit (including NFP Corporation) **Service:** General medical and surgical

> **Staffed Beds:** 62

CROSBY—Divide County

★ **ST. LUKE'S MEDICAL CENTER (351325)**, 702 First Street Southwest, Zip 58730–3329, Mailing Address: P.O. Box 10, Zip 58730–0010; tel. 701/965–6384, (Total facility includes 44 beds in nursing home–type unit) **A**10 18 **F**3 29 30 32 34 40 41 43 45 50 59 64 69 77 81 82 83 84 86 87 92 93 94 96 97 119 127 128 130 132 133 148 149 150 154
Primary Contact: Jodi Nelson, Interim Chief Executive Officer
Web address: www.dcstlukes.org/
Control: Other not–for–profit (including NFP Corporation) **Service:** General medical and surgical

> **Staffed Beds:** 60 **Admissions:** 85 **Census:** 60 **Outpatient Visits:** 807 **Births:** 0 **Total Expense ($000):** 10850 **Payroll Expense ($000):** 2404 **Personnel:** 111

DEVILS LAKE—Ramsey County

⊞ **CHI ST. ALEXIUS HEALTH DEVILS LAKE HOSPITAL (351333)**, 1031 Seventh Street NE, Zip 58301–2798; tel. 701/662–2131, **A**1 10 18 **F**3 11 13 28 29 34 40 45 54 57 64 70 75 77 81 85 87 93 97 107 108 111 115 119 131 132 133 148 149 150 **S** CommonSpirit Health, Chicago, IL
Primary Contact: Andrew Lankowicz, FACHE, President
CFO: Kurt Sargent, CPA, Vice President Operational Finance
CMO: Richard Johnson, M.D., Chief of Medical Staff
CHR: Bonnie Mattern, Director Human Resources
CNO: Aaron Johnson, Vice President Patient Care Services and Chief Nursing Officer
Web address: www.mercyhospitaldl.com
Control: Other not–for–profit (including NFP Corporation) **Service:** General medical and surgical

> **Staffed Beds:** 25 **Admissions:** 827 **Census:** 9 **Outpatient Visits:** 21725 **Births:** 278 **Total Expense ($000):** 20741 **Payroll Expense ($000):** 8353 **Personnel:** 130

DICKINSON—Stark County

⊞ **CHI ST. ALEXIUS HEALTH - DICKINSON MEDICAL CENTER (351336)**, 2500 Fairway Street, Zip 58601–4399; tel. 701/456–4000, **A**1 10 18 **F**3 8 11 13 15 28 29 30 34 35 40 53 57 59 64 70 75 76 79 81 84 85 86 87 89 97 107 108 111 114 119 127 129 130 132 133 146 149 **S** CommonSpirit Health, Chicago, IL
Primary Contact: Reed Reyman, President
CFO: Stephanie Franken, Vice President Operational Finance
CHR: Denise Lutz, Chief Human Resources Officer
CNO: DeeAnna Opstedahl, R.N., Vice President Patient Care Services
Web address: www.stjoeshospital.org
Control: Church operated, Nongovernment, not–for–profit **Service:** General medical and surgical

> **Staffed Beds:** 25 **Admissions:** 1749 **Census:** 12

ELGIN—Grant County

★ **JACOBSON MEMORIAL HOSPITAL CARE CENTER (351314)**, 601 East Street North, Zip 58533–7105, Mailing Address: P.O. Box 367, Zip 58533–0367; tel. 701/584–2792, (Nonreporting) **A**10 18
Primary Contact: Theo Stoller, Chief Executive Officer
CFO: Scott Ostenson, Chief Financial Officer
CMO: Deepak Goyal, M.D., Chief of Staff
CHR: Rynae Golke, Director Human Resources
CNO: Connie Gustafson, Director of Nursing
Web address: www.jacobsonhospital.org
Control: Other not–for–profit (including NFP Corporation) **Service:** General medical and surgical

> **Staffed Beds:** 30

FARGO—Cass County

⊞ **ESSENTIA HEALTH FARGO (350070)**, 3000 32nd Avenue South, Zip 58103–6132; tel. 701/364–8000, **A**1 2 3 5 10 **F**3 9 11 12 13 15 17 18 20 22 24 25 26 28 29 30 31 32 33 34 35 38 40 41 43 44 45 46 47 48 49 50 51 56 57 58 59 60 61 64 65 70 72 74 75 76 77 78 79 81 82 83 84 85 86 87 89 91 92 93 97 107 108 109 110 111 112 113 114 115 116 117 118 119 120 121 122 123 124 126 129 130 131 132 135 144 145 146 147 148 154 156 157 **S** Essentia Health, Duluth, MN
Primary Contact: Al Hurley, Chief Operating Officer
COO: Al Hurley, Chief Operating Officer
CFO: Dennis Fuhrman, Vice President Finance
CMO: Michael Briggs, M.D., Chief Medical Officer
CIO: Ken Gilles, Chief Information Officer
CHR: Keith Wahlund, Vice President Human Resources
Web address: www.essentiahealth.com
Control: Other not–for–profit (including NFP Corporation) **Service:** General medical and surgical

> **Staffed Beds:** 137 **Admissions:** 8718 **Census:** 95 **Outpatient Visits:** 114223 **Births:** 1228 **Total Expense ($000):** 399019 **Payroll Expense ($000):** 166970 **Personnel:** 1598

⊞ **FARGO VETERANS AFFAIRS HEALTH CARE SYSTEM**, 2101 Elm Street North, Zip 58102; tel. 701/232–3241, (Nonreporting) **A**1 3 5 **S** Department of Veterans Affairs, Washington, DC
Primary Contact: Lavonne Liversage, Director
COO: Dale DeKrey, MS, Associate Director Operations and Resources
CFO: Roger Sayler, Finance Officer
CMO: J Brian Hancock, M.D., Chief of Staff
CIO: Raymond Nelson, Acting Chief Information Resource Management
CHR: Jason Wells, Chief Human Resources Management Service
CNO: Julie Bruhn, R.N., MS, Associate Director Patient Care and Nurse Executive
Web address: www.fargo.va.gov/
Control: Veterans Affairs, Government, federal **Service:** General medical and surgical

> **Staffed Beds:** 65

INNOVIS HEALTH See Essentia Health Fargo

KINDRED HOSPITAL FARGO See Vibra Hospital of Fargo

MERITCARE MEDICAL CENTER See Sanford Medical Center Fargo

☐ **PRAIRIE ST. JOHN'S (354004)**, 510 4th Street South, Zip 58103–1914; tel. 701/476–7200, (Nonreporting) **A**1 3 10 **S** Universal Health Services, Inc., King of Prussia, PA
Primary Contact: Jeff Herman, Chief Executive Officer
COO: Jennifer Faul, Chief Operating Officer
CFO: Tom Eide, Chief Financial Officer
CMO: Eduardo Meza, M.D., Medical Director
CHR: Michelle A Parkinson, Director Human Resources
CNO: Jacki Toppen, Director of Nursing
Web address: www.prairie-stjohns.com
Control: Partnership, Investor–owned (for–profit) **Service:** Psychiatric

> **Staffed Beds:** 94

☒ △ **SANFORD MEDICAL CENTER FARGO (350011)**, 801 Broadway North, Zip 58122–3641; tel. 701/234–2000, (Includes SANFORD SOUTH UNIVERSITY, 1720 South University Drive, Fargo, North Dakota, Zip 58103–4994; tel. 701/234–2000; Nate White, Executive Vice President) **A**1 2 3 5 7 10 19 **F**3 7 8 9 11 12 13 15 17 18 19 20 21 22 23 24 25 26 27 28 29 30 31 32 33 34 35 36 37 38 39 40 43 44 45 46 47 48 49 50 51 52 53 54 55 56 57 58 59 60 61 62 63 64 65 66 67 68 70 71 72 74 75 76 78 79 80 81 82 83 84 85 86 87 88 89 90 91 92 93 94 96 97 98 99 100 101 102 103 104 105 107 108 110 111 112 114 115 116 117 118 119 120 121 123 124 126 129 130 131 132 135 138 141 142 143 144 145 146 147 148 149 150 153 154 155 156 157 **S** Sanford Health, Sioux Falls, SD
Primary Contact: Nate White, Executive Vice President
COO: Susan Jarvis, Vice President Operations
CFO: Tiffany Lawrence, Vice President of Finance
CMO: Douglas Griffin, M.D., Vice President Medical Officer
CIO: Arlyn Broekhuis, Chief Information Officer
CNO: Roberta Young, Vice President Nursing
Web address: www.sanfordhealth.org
Control: Other not-for-profit (including NFP Corporation) **Service:** General medical and surgical

Staffed Beds: 540 **Admissions:** 26352 **Census:** 353 **Outpatient Visits:** 353846 **Births:** 2769 **Total Expense ($000):** 1193438 **Payroll Expense ($000):** 502526 **Personnel:** 5224

VETERANS AFFAIRS HEALTH CARE SYSTEM See Fargo Veterans Affairs Health Care System

★ **VIBRA HOSPITAL OF FARGO (352004)**, 1720 University Drive South, Zip 58103–4940; tel. 701/241–9099, (Nonreporting) **A**10 **S** Vibra Healthcare, Mechanicsburg, PA
Primary Contact: Custer Huseby, Chief Executive Officer
Web address: www.vhfargo.com
Control: Corporation, Investor-owned (for-profit) **Service:** Acute long-term care hospital

Staffed Beds: 31

FORT YATES—Sioux County

☐ ⇑ **STANDING ROCK SERVICE UNIT, FORT YATES HOSPITAL, INDIAN HEALTH SERVICE, DHHS (350064)**, 10 North River Road, Zip 58538, Mailing Address: P.O. Box 'J', Zip 58538; tel. 701/854–3831, (Nonreporting) **A**1 10 21 **S** U. S. Indian Health Service, Rockville, MD
Primary Contact: Jana Gipp, Chief Executive Officer
CFO: Byron Wilcox, Chief Financial Management Officer
CMO: Sara Jumping Eagle, Clinical Director
CNO: Joelle Keepseagle, Director of Nursing
Web address: www.ihs.gov
Control: IHS, Indian Service, Government, federal **Service:** General medical and surgical

Staffed Beds: 14

GARRISON—Mclean County

★ **CHI ST. ALEXIUS HEALTH GARRISON (351303)**, 407 Third Avenue SE, Zip 58540–7235; tel. 701/463–2275, (Total facility includes 28 beds in nursing home-type unit) **A**10 18 **F**2 15 28 29 30 34 35 40 56 57 59 64 65 66 68 71 77 93 97 107 110 115 127 128 130 131 132 133 154 **S** CommonSpirit Health, Chicago, IL
Primary Contact: Tod Graeber, Administrator
CMO: Vern Harchenko, M.D., Chief of Staff
CNO: Beth Hetletved, Director of Nurses
Web address: www.garrisonmh.com
Control: Church operated, Nongovernment, not-for-profit **Service:** General medical and surgical

Staffed Beds: 50 **Admissions:** 144 **Census:** 33 **Births:** 0

GRAFTON—Walsh County

★ **UNITY MEDICAL CENTER (351320)**, 164 West 13th Street, Zip 58237–1896; tel. 701/352–1620, (Nonreporting) **A**10 18
Primary Contact: Alan O'Neil, Chief Executive Officer
CFO: Rachel Ray, Chief Financial Officer
Web address: www.unitymedcenter.com
Control: Other not-for-profit (including NFP Corporation) **Service:** General medical and surgical

Staffed Beds: 14

GRAND FORKS—Grand Forks County

☒ △ **ALTRU HEALTH SYSTEM (350019)**, 1200 South Columbia Road, Zip 58201–4036, Mailing Address: P.O. Box 6002, Zip 58206–6002; tel. 701/780–5000, (Includes ALTRU HOSPITAL, 1200 South Columbia Road, Grand Forks, North Dakota, Zip 58201, Mailing Address: P.O. Box 6002, Zip 58206–6002, tel. 701/780–5000; Brad Wehe, Chief Executive Officer; ALTRU REHABILITATION CENTER, 1300 South Columbia Road, Grand Forks, North Dakota, Zip 58201; tel. 701/780–2311; Brad Wehe, Chief Executive Officer) **A**1 2 3 5 7 10 20 **F**3 7 11 12 13 14 15 18 20 22 24 26 28 29 30 31 32 33 34 35 36 37 38 40 43 44 45 48 49 50 52 53 55 56 57 58 59 60 61 62 63 64 65 68 69 70 71 72 74 75 76 77 78 79 81 82 83 84 85 86 87 90 91 92 93 94 96 97 98 99 100 101 102 103 104 105 107 108 110 111 114 115 116 117 119 120 121 123 124 126 129 130 131 132 133 135 143 144 146 147 148 149 153 154 155 156 157
Primary Contact: Brad Wehe, Chief Executive Officer
COO: Brad Wehe, Chief Operating Officer
CFO: Dwight Thompson, Chief Financial Officer
CMO: Colleen Swank, Chief Medical Officer
CIO: Mark Waind, Chief Information Officer
CHR: Kellee J. Fisk, Chief People and Strategy Officer
CNO: Margaret M Reed, R.N., Chief Nursing Officer
Web address: www.altru.org
Control: Other not-for-profit (including NFP Corporation) **Service:** General medical and surgical

Staffed Beds: 305 **Admissions:** 10792 **Census:** 169 **Outpatient Visits:** 968947 **Births:** 1731 **Total Expense ($000):** 584883 **Payroll Expense ($000):** 289547 **Personnel:** 2905

⇑ **RED RIVER BEHAVIORAL HEALTH SYSTEM (354005)**, 1451 44th Avenue South Unit A, Zip 58201–3434; tel. 701/772–2500, **A**10 21 **F**4 98 102 106 151
Primary Contact: Susan Tabor, Interim Chief Executive Officer
CFO: Michelle Currie, Chief Financial Officer
CHR: Amanda Altendorf, Chief Human Resources and Quality Management
Web address: www.redriverbhs.com
Control: Corporation, Investor-owned (for-profit) **Service:** Psychiatric

Staffed Beds: 70 **Admissions:** 1538 **Census:** 42 **Outpatient Visits:** 0 **Births:** 0

HARVEY—Wells County

★ **ST. ALOISIUS MEDICAL CENTER (351327)**, 325 East Brewster Street, Zip 58341–1653; tel. 701/324–4651, (Total facility includes 85 beds in nursing home-type unit) **A**10 18 **F**16 28 30 40 45 53 56 57 59 77 81 93 107 110 114 125 128 130 131 132 133 146 147 156 **S** Sisters of Mary of the Presentation Health System, Fargo, ND
Primary Contact: Mike Zwicker, Chief Executive Officer
CFO: Sandra Teubner, Chief Financial Officer
Web address: www.staloisius.com
Control: Church operated, Nongovernment, not-for-profit **Service:** General medical and surgical

Staffed Beds: 110 **Admissions:** 262 **Census:** 80 **Outpatient Visits:** 7715 **Births:** 0 **Total Expense ($000):** 16165 **Payroll Expense ($000):** 7330 **Personnel:** 203

HAZEN—Mercer County

★ **SAKAKAWEA MEDICAL CENTER (351310)**, 510 Eighth Avenue NE, Zip 58545–4637; tel. 701/748–2225, (Nonreporting) **A**10 18
Primary Contact: Darrold Bertsch, Chief Executive Officer
CFO: Renae Snyder, Chief Financial Officer
CHR: Laurie Miller, Administrative Assistant
CNO: Marcie Schulz, Director Patient Care
Web address: www.smcnd.org
Control: Other not-for-profit (including NFP Corporation) **Service:** General medical and surgical

Staffed Beds: 18

HETTINGER—Adams County

WEST RIVER REGIONAL MEDICAL CENTER (351330), 1000 Highway 12, Zip 58639–7530; tel. 701/567–4561, (Nonreporting) **A**3 5 10 18
Primary Contact: Matthew Shahan, Chief Executive Officer
CFO: Nathan Stadheim, Chief Financial Officer
CMO: Jennifer Shefield, M.D., Chief of Staff
CIO: Julia Gochenour, Manager Information Systems
CHR: Tera Fried, Manager Human Resources
CNO: Barbara Stadheim, Chief Nursing Officer
Web address: www.wrhs.com
Control: Other not–for–profit (including NFP Corporation) **Service**: General medical and surgical

Staffed Beds: 25

HILLSBORO—Traill County

★ **SANFORD HILLSBORO MEDICAL CENTER (351329)**, 12 Third Street SE, Zip 58045–4840, Mailing Address: P.O. Box 609, Zip 58045–0609; tel. 701/636–3200, (Total facility includes 36 beds in nursing home–type unit) **A**10 18 **F**7 10 11 34 35 40 64 65 68 75 93 97 103 125 128 130 131 133 143 146 148 156 158 **S** Sanford Health, Sioux Falls, SD
Primary Contact: Jac McTaggart, Chief Executive Officer
CFO: Scott Awalt, Chief Financial Officer
CMO: Charles J Breen, M.D., Medical Director
CHR: Jenny Jacobson, Manager Human Resources
Web address: www.hillsboromedicalcenter.com
Control: Other not–for–profit (including NFP Corporation) **Service**: General medical and surgical

Staffed Beds: 46 Admissions: 169 Census: 37 Outpatient Visits: 13599 Births: 0 Total Expense ($000): 13220 Payroll Expense ($000): 5567 Personnel: 87

JAMESTOWN—Stutsman County

⊞ **JAMESTOWN REGIONAL MEDICAL CENTER (351335)**, 2422 20th Street SW, Zip 58401–6201; tel. 701/252–1050, **A**1 10 18 **F**3 11 13 15 28 29 31 34 35 40 43 45 50 52 53 57 59 62 63 64 68 70 75 77 78 79 81 82 84 85 86 87 93 107 108 110 111 115 118 119 130 131 132 133 135 146 148 149 156
Primary Contact: Michael Delfs, President and Chief Executive Officer
COO: Ricki Ramlo, Chief Operating Officer and Human Resources
CFO: Brandon Vaughan, Chief Financial Officer and Vice President Finance
CMO: Derek Brickner, President Medical Staff
CIO: Jeff Gunkel, Chief Information Officer
CHR: Ricki Ramlo, Chief Operating Officer and Human Resources
CNO: Trisha Jungels, R.N., Chief Nursing Officer and Vice President Clinical Services
Web address: www.jamestownhospital.com
Control: Other not–for–profit (including NFP Corporation) **Service**: General medical and surgical

Staffed Beds: 25 Admissions: 914 Census: 9 Outpatient Visits: 35596 Births: 356 Total Expense ($000): 47921 Payroll Expense ($000): 19751 Personnel: 308

☐ **NORTH DAKOTA STATE HOSPITAL (354003)**, 2605 Circle Drive SE, Zip 58401–6905; tel. 701/253–3964, (Nonreporting) **A**1 3 5 10
Primary Contact: Rosalie Etherington, Superintendent and Chief Executive Officer
COO: Ken Schulz, Chief Operating Officer
CMO: Eduardo Yabut, M.D., Medical Director
CIO: Amy Shape, Information Technology
CNO: Leah Schulz, Director of Nursing
Web address: www.nd.gov/
Control: State, Government, nonfederal **Service**: Psychiatric

Staffed Beds: 100

KENMARE—Ward County

★ **KENMARE COMMUNITY HOSPITAL (351305)**, 317 First Avenue NW, Zip 58746–7104, Mailing Address: P.O. Box 697, Zip 58746–0697; tel. 701/385–4296, (Nonreporting) **A**10 18
Primary Contact: Danielle Alsadon, Clinic/Hospital Manager
COO: Bev Heninger, Director of Nursing
CFO: Dennis Empey, Chief Financial Officer
CMO: Buki Oni, M.D., Chief Medical Officer
CIO: David Wanner, Director Information Technology
CHR: Ranae Ehlke, Administrative Secretary and Coordinator Risk Management and Human Resources
CNO: Bev Heninger, Director of Nursing
Web address: www.kenmarend.net/hospital.htm
Control: Corporation, Investor–owned (for–profit) **Service**: General medical and surgical

Staffed Beds: 25

LANGDON—Cavalier County

★ **CAVALIER COUNTY MEMORIAL HOSPITAL AND CLINICS (351323)**, 909 Second Street, Zip 58249–2407; tel. 701/256–6100, (Nonreporting) **A**10 18
Primary Contact: Jeff Stanley, Chief Executive Officer
COO: Darla Roder, Chief Operating Officer
CFO: Richard Fromme, Chief Financial Officer
CMO: Lynne Didrikson, M.D., Chief Medical Officer
CHR: Linda Benoit, Human Resource Officer
CNO: Jamie Nienhuis, Chief Nursing Officer
Web address: www.cavaliercountyhospital.com
Control: Other not–for–profit (including NFP Corporation) **Service**: General medical and surgical

Staffed Beds: 20

LINTON—Emmons County

★ **LINTON HOSPITAL (351328)**, 518 North Broadway, Zip 58552–7308, Mailing Address: P.O. Box 850, Zip 58552–0850; tel. 701/254–4511, (Nonreporting) **A**10 18
Primary Contact: Robert O. Black, Chief Executive Officer
CMO: John Knecht, Chief Medical Staff
CHR: Sue Meidinger, Manager Business Office
Web address: www.lintonhospital.com
Control: Other not–for–profit (including NFP Corporation) **Service**: General medical and surgical

Staffed Beds: 14

LISBON—Ransom County

★ **CHI LISBON HEALTH (351311)**, 905 Main Street, Zip 58054–4334, Mailing Address: P.O. Box 353, Zip 58054–0353; tel. 701/683–6400, (Nonreporting) **A**10 18 **S** CommonSpirit Health, Chicago, IL
Primary Contact: Peggy Reinke, R.N., Administrator
COO: Sheri Heinisch, Compliance Officer
CFO: Amber Stowman, Controller
CHR: Janet Froemke, Human Resources Officer
Web address: www.lisbonhospital.com
Control: Church operated **Service**: General medical and surgical

Staffed Beds: 25

MANDAN—Morton County

TRIUMPH HOSPITAL - CENTRAL DAKOTAS See Vibra Hospital of Central Dakotas

⊞ **VIBRA HOSPITAL OF CENTRAL DAKOTAS (352005)**, 1000 18th Street NW, Zip 58554–1612; tel. 701/667–2000, (Nonreporting) **A**1 10 **S** Vibra Healthcare, Mechanicsburg, PA
Primary Contact: Glynda Troyo-Sauviac, Chief Executive Officer
Web address: www.vhcentraldakotas.com
Control: Corporation, Investor–owned (for–profit) **Service**: Acute long–term care hospital

Staffed Beds: 41

MAYVILLE—Traill County

MERITCARE MAYVILLE UNION HOSPITAL See Sanford Mayville Medical Center

★ **SANFORD MAYVILLE MEDICAL CENTER (351309)**, 42 Sixth Avenue SE, Zip 58257–1598; tel. 701/786–3800, **A**10 18 **F**7 40 43 45 50 65 77 81 93 97 107 119 128 129 130 133 156 **S** Sanford Health, Sioux Falls, SD
Primary Contact: Jac McTaggart, Chief Executive Officer
CFO: Shauna Slabik, Chief Financial Officer
CMO: Jane Ostlig, Chief Medical Officer
Web address: www.unionhospital.com
Control: Other not–for–profit (including NFP Corporation) **Service**: General medical and surgical

Staffed Beds: 10 Admissions: 197 Census: 4 Outpatient Visits: 18337 Births: 0 Total Expense ($000): 8604 Payroll Expense ($000): 4446 Personnel: 62

MCVILLE—Nelson County

NELSON COUNTY HEALTH SYSTEM (351308), 200 Main Street, Zip 58254, Mailing Address: P.O. Box 367, Zip 58254–0367; tel. 701/322–4328, (Total facility includes 39 beds in nursing home–type unit) **A**10 18 **F**10 40 59 65 71 75 97 107 110 119 127 133 143 147 156
Primary Contact: Steve Forde, Chief Executive Officer
CMO: Erling Martinson, M.D., Medical Director
Web address: www.nelsoncountyhealthsystem.org
Control: Other not–for–profit (including NFP Corporation) **Service**: General medical and surgical

Staffed Beds: 49 Admissions: 148 Census: 37 Outpatient Visits: 508 Births: 0

Many Facility Codes have changed. Please refer to the AHA Guide Code Chart.
© 2019 AHA Guide

MINOT—Ward County

⊠ △ **TRINITY HEALTH (350006)**, One Burdick Expressway West, Zip 58701–4406, Mailing Address: P.O. Box 5020, Zip 58702–5020; tel. 701/857–5766, (Includes TRINITY HOSPITAL-ST. JOSEPH'S, 407 3rd Street SE, Minot, North Dakota, Zip 58702–5001; tel. 701/857–2000) (Total facility includes 215 beds in nursing home–type unit) **A**1 2 3 5 7 10 **F**3 4 5 7 8 11 13 15 18 20 22 24 28 29 30 31 33 34 35 38 39 40 43 45 46 50 54 55 56 57 59 60 62 63 64 65 68 70 72 73 74 75 76 77 78 79 81 82 84 85 86 87 89 90 92 93 94 97 98 99 100 101 103 104 105 107 108 110 111 114 115 116 117 118 119 120 121 124 126 127 128 129 130 131 132 133 143 144 146 147 148 151 152 154 155 156
Primary Contact: John M. Kutch, President
CFO: Dennis Empey, Chief Financial Officer
CIO: David Wanner, Chief Information Officer
CHR: Paul Simonson, Vice President
Web address: www.trinityhealth.org
Control: Other not-for-profit (including NFP Corporation) **Service**: General medical and surgical

Staffed Beds: 580 **Admissions**: 8903 **Census**: 310 **Outpatient Visits**: 417115 **Births**: 1577 **Total Expense ($000)**: 438580 **Payroll Expense ($000)**: 220937 **Personnel**: 2499

NORTHWOOD—Grand Forks County

★ **NORTHWOOD DEACONESS HEALTH CENTER (351312)**, 4 North Park Street, Zip 58267–4102, Mailing Address: P.O. Box 190, Zip 58267–0190; tel. 701/587–6060, (Nonreporting) **A**10 18 **S** Sanford Health, Sioux Falls, SD
Primary Contact: Pete Antonson, Chief Executive Officer
CMO: Jon Berg, M.D., Chief of Staff
CIO: Chad Peterson, Chief Information Officer
Web address: www.ndhc.net
Control: Church operated, Nongovernment, not-for-profit **Service**: General medical and surgical

Staffed Beds: 57

OAKES—Dickey County

⊠ **CHI OAKES HOSPITAL (351315)**, 1200 North Seventh Street, Zip 58474–2502; tel. 701/742–3291, (Nonreporting) **A**1 10 18 **S** CommonSpirit Health, Chicago, IL
Primary Contact: Becki Thompson, President
CFO: Bethany Smith, Director of Finance
CMO: Katie O'Brien-Paradis, M.D., Chief Medical Officer
CHR: Julie Entzminger, Manager Human Resources
CNO: Kimberly A. Ketterling, R.N., Vice President Patient Care Services
Web address: www.oakeshospital.com
Control: Church operated **Service**: General medical and surgical

Staffed Beds: 20

PARK RIVER—Walsh County

★ **FIRST CARE HEALTH CENTER (351326)**, 115 Vivian Street, Zip 58270–4540, Mailing Address: P.O. Box I, Zip 58270–0708; tel. 701/284–7500, **A**10 18 **F**11 15 28 29 31 33 34 35 40 45 50 57 59 64 65 68 75 77 78 79 81 82 86 87 93 104 107 108 110 111 115 119 127 129 130 133 135 146 147 148 154 156
Primary Contact: Marcus Lewis, Chief Executive Officer and Administrator
CFO: Layne Encrude, Chief Financial Officer
CMO: Joel Johnson, M.D., Chief Medical Staff
CNO: Lori Seim, R.N., Director Nursing Services
Web address: www.firstcarehc.com
Control: Other not-for-profit (including NFP Corporation) **Service**: General medical and surgical

Staffed Beds: 14 **Admissions**: 384 **Census**: 7 **Outpatient Visits**: 29876 **Births**: 0 **Total Expense ($000)**: 11869 **Payroll Expense ($000)**: 4694 **Personnel**: 87

ROLLA—Rolette County

PRESENTATION MEDICAL CENTER (351316), 213 Second Avenue NE, Zip 58367–7153, Mailing Address: P.O. Box 759, Zip 58367–0759; tel. 701/477–3161, (Nonreporting) **A**10 18 **S** Sisters of Mary of the Presentation Health System, Fargo, ND
Primary Contact: Chris Albertson, Chief Executive Officer
CFO: Paula Wilkie, Chief Financial Officer
CMO: Roy Cordy, M.D., President Medical Staff
CHR: Chris Albertson, Director Human Resources
Web address: www.pmc-rolla.com
Control: Church operated **Service**: General medical and surgical

Staffed Beds: 25

RUGBY—Pierce County

★ **HEART OF AMERICA MEDICAL CENTER (351332)**, 800 Main Avenue South, Zip 58368–2198; tel. 701/776–5261, (Nonreporting) **A**10 18
Primary Contact: Patrick J. Branco, Chief Executive Officer
CFO: Lee H. Holter, Chief Financial Officer
CIO: Jeremy Schonebery, Director Information Technology
Web address: www.hamc.com
Control: Other not-for-profit (including NFP Corporation) **Service**: General medical and surgical

Staffed Beds: 85

STANLEY—Mountrail County

★ **MOUNTRAIL COUNTY MEDICAL CENTER (351301)**, 615 6th Street SE, Zip 58784–4444, Mailing Address: P.O. Box 399, Zip 58784–0399; tel. 701/628–2424, (Nonreporting) **A**10 18
Primary Contact: Ben Bucher, Interim Chief Executive Officer
CFO: Susan Weston, CPA, Chief Financial Officer
CMO: Marla Longmuir, M.D., Chief Medical Officer
CIO: Kathy Janssen, Director Medical Records
CHR: Alisha McMahon, Director Human Resources
CNO: Belinda Moen, R.N., MSN, Interim Director of Nursing
Web address: www.stanleyhealth.org
Control: Other not-for-profit (including NFP Corporation) **Service**: General medical and surgical

Staffed Beds: 11

TIOGA—Williams County

★ **TIOGA MEDICAL CENTER (351300)**, 810 North Welo Street, Zip 58852–7157, Mailing Address: P.O. Box 159, Zip 58852–0159; tel. 701/664–3305, (Nonreporting) **A**5 10 18
Primary Contact: Randall K. Pederson, Chief Executive Officer
CMO: Swami P Gade, M.D., Medical Director
CHR: Mary Ann Holm, Office Clerk
Web address: www.tiogahealth.org
Control: Other not-for-profit (including NFP Corporation) **Service**: General medical and surgical

Staffed Beds: 55

TURTLE LAKE—McLean County

★ **COMMUNITY MEMORIAL HOSPITAL (351304)**, 220 Fifth Avenue, Zip 58575–4005, Mailing Address: P.O. Box 280, Zip 58575–0280; tel. 701/448–2331, (Nonreporting) **A**10 18 **S** CommonSpirit Health, Chicago, IL
Primary Contact: Tod Graeber, Administrator
CFO: Tom Spain, Director Operations Finance
CNO: Jessie Martin, R.N., Chief Nursing Executive
Web address: www.wrtc.com/cullum/hospital
Control: Church operated, Nongovernment, not-for-profit **Service**: General medical and surgical

Staffed Beds: 25

VALLEY CITY—Barnes County

★ **CHI MERCY HEALTH (351324)**, 570 Chautauqua Boulevard, Zip 58072–3199; tel. 701/845–6400, (Nonreporting) **A**10 18 **S** CommonSpirit Health, Chicago, IL
Primary Contact: Keith E. Heuser, Market President
CFO: Joshua Senger, Vice President, Operational Finance
CHR: Nicole Nestler, Division Director Human Resources
Web address: www.mercyhospitalvalleycity.org
Control: Church operated **Service**: General medical and surgical

Staffed Beds: 19

Hospital, Medicare Provider Number, Address, Telephone, Approval, Facility, and Physician Codes, Health Care System

★ American Hospital Association (AHA) membership ○ Healthcare Facilities Accreditation Program ⇧ Center for Improvement in Healthcare Quality Accreditation
☐ The Joint Commission accreditation ◇ DNV Healthcare Inc. accreditation △ Commission on Accreditation of Rehabilitation Facilities (CARF) accreditation

WATFORD CITY—Mckenzie County

★ **MCKENZIE COUNTY HEALTHCARE SYSTEM (351302)**, 516 North Main Street, Zip 58854–7310; tel. 701/842–3000, **A**10 18 **F**3 11 28 29 34 40 43 45 57 59 64 65 68 75 81 86 87 93 94 107 119 127 129 133 144 154 156
Primary Contact: Daniel R. Kelly, Chief Executive Officer
COO: Michael Curtis, Chief Administrative Officer
CFO: Kenneth Cox, Interim Chief Financial Officer
CMO: Gary Ramage, M.D., Chief Medical Officer
CIO: Karn Pederson, Manager Health Information Management
CHR: Amy Gonzales, Director of Human Resources
CNO: Cheryl Faulkner, Director of Nursing
Web address: www.mckenziehealth.com
Control: Other not–for–profit (including NFP Corporation) **Service**: General medical and surgical

Staffed Beds: 24 **Admissions:** 152 **Census:** 2 **Outpatient Visits:** 13755 **Births:** 0 **Total Expense ($000):** 18082 **Payroll Expense ($000):** 7492 **Personnel:** 71

WILLISTON—Williams County

☒ **CHI ST. ALEXIUS HEALTH - WILLISTON MEDICAL CENTER (351334)**, 1301 15th Avenue West, Zip 58801–3896; tel. 701/774–7400, (Nonreporting) **A**1 3 10 18 **S** CommonSpirit Health, Chicago, IL
Primary Contact: Dan Bjerknes, Market Leader
CMO: Brett Vibeto, M.D., Chief of Staff
CIO: Jeff Rust, Information Technology Systems Site Manager
CHR: Dan Bjerknes, Director Human Resources
CNO: Lori Hahn, Vice President Nursing Services
Web address: www.mercy-williston.org
Control: Church operated **Service**: General medical and surgical

Staffed Beds: 25

WISHEK—Mcintosh County

★ **WISHEK COMMUNITY HOSPITAL AND CLINICS (351321)**, 1007 Fourth Avenue South, Zip 58495–7527, Mailing Address: P.O. Box 647, Zip 58495–0647; tel. 701/452–2326, **A**10 18 **F**3 7 11 15 17 18 28 29 32 34 35 36 40 44 45 50 53 56 57 59 64 65 68 75 81 82 83 87 91 92 93 97 107 114 127 128 130 131 133 143 146 147 148 149 156
Primary Contact: Beverly Vilhauer, Chief Executive Officer
CFO: Megan Rath, Chief Financial Officer
CMO: Joseph Thirumalareddy, M.D., Chief of Staff
CIO: Kari Buchholz, Director Health Information Management
CHR: Shar Bauer, Executive Secretary
Web address: www.wishekhospital.com
Control: Other not–for–profit (including NFP Corporation) **Service**: General medical and surgical

Staffed Beds: 19 **Admissions:** 182 **Census:** 2 **Outpatient Visits:** 8580 **Births:** 0 **Total Expense ($000):** 7914 **Payroll Expense ($000):** 3766 **Personnel:** 79

Many Facility Codes have changed. Please refer to the AHA Guide Code Chart. © 2019 AHA Guide

OHIO

AKRON—Summit County

AKRON CHILDREN'S HOSPITAL (363303), One Perkins Square, Zip 44308–1063; tel. 330/543–1000, **A**1 2 3 5 8 10 **F**3 7 11 13 16 18 19 20 21 22 23 25 26 27 29 30 31 32 33 34 35 36 38 39 40 41 43 44 48 50 54 55 57 58 59 60 61 62 63 64 65 66 68 72 73 74 75 76 77 78 79 81 82 84 85 86 87 88 89 91 92 93 94 96 97 98 99 100 101 102 104 105 106 107 108 111 112 114 115 116 117 118 119 120 126 129 130 131 132 134 135 136 141 143 144 146 148 149 153 154 155 156
Primary Contact: William H. Considine, President
COO: Lisa Aurilio, R.N., MSN, Chief Operating Officer
CFO: Michael Trainer, Chief Financial Officer
CMO: Robert McGregor, M.D., Chief Medical Officer
CIO: Harun Rashid, Vice President and Chief Information Officer
CHR: Bernett Williams, Interim Chief Human Resource Officer
CNO: Christine Young, MSN, R.N., Vice President of Patient Services and Chief Nursing Officer
Web address: www.akronchildrens.org
Control: Other not-for-profit (including NFP Corporation) **Service:** Children's general medical and surgical

Staffed Beds: 434 **Admissions:** 9835 **Census:** 215 **Outpatient Visits:** 1141071 **Births:** 1 **Total Expense ($000):** 839089 **Payroll Expense ($000):** 424033 **Personnel:** 5194

CLEVELAND CLINIC AKRON GENERAL (360027), 1 Akron General Avenue, Zip 44307–2433; tel. 330/344–6000, **A**1 2 3 5 8 10 **F**3 5 8 11 12 13 15 17 18 20 22 24 26 28 29 30 31 34 35 36 37 38 40 42 43 44 45 46 47 48 49 50 51 52 53 54 58 59 60 61 62 63 64 65 66 68 70 71 72 74 75 76 77 78 79 81 82 84 85 87 93 94 96 97 98 100 101 102 103 104 105 107 108 110 111 112 114 115 117 118 119 120 121 123 124 126 129 130 131 132 135 138 144 146 147 148 149 152 153 154 155 156 **S** Cleveland Clinic Health System, Cleveland, OH
Primary Contact: Brian J. Harte, M.D., President
CFO: Dave Frigo, Vice President Financial Planning and Treasury
CMO: David Peter, M.D., Senior Vice President Medical Affairs and Chief Medical Director
CIO: David Fiser, Vice President and Chief Information Officer
CHR: Don Corpora, Executive Vice President and Chief Human Resources Officer
CNO: Cherie M Guster, R.N., MSN, Senior Vice President and Chief Nursing Officer
Web address: www.akrongeneral.org
Control: Other not-for-profit (including NFP Corporation) **Service:** General medical and surgical

Staffed Beds: 482 **Admissions:** 24321 **Census:** 314 **Outpatient Visits:** 530776 **Births:** 2629 **Total Expense ($000):** 547864 **Payroll Expense ($000):** 235479 **Personnel:** 4267

SELECT SPECIALTY HOSPITAL–AKRON (362027), 200 East Market Street, Zip 44308–2015; tel. 330/761–7500, (Nonreporting) **A**1 10 **S** Select Medical Corporation, Mechanicsburg, PA
Primary Contact: Dawne Wheeler, Chief Executive Officer
Web address: www.selectspecialtyhospitals.com/company/locations/akron.aspx
Control: Corporation, Investor–owned (for-profit) **Service:** Acute long-term care hospital

Staffed Beds: 60

SUMMA AKRON CITY HOSPITAL See Summa Health System, Akron

SUMMA HEALTH SYSTEM See Summa Health System

SUMMA HEALTH SYSTEM (360020), 525 East Market Street, Zip 44304–1619; tel. 330/375–3000, (Includes SUMMA AKRON CITY HOSPITAL, 525 East Market Street, Akron, Ohio, Zip 44309–2090, tel. 330/375–3000; SUMMA HEALTH SYSTEM BARBERTON HOSPITAL, 155 Fifth Street NE, Barberton, Ohio, Zip 44203–3332; tel. 330/615–3000; Michael Hughes, M.D., President, Summa Health System Barberton; SUMMA SAINT THOMAS HOSPITAL, 444 North Main Street, Akron, Ohio, Zip 44310; tel. 330/375–3000) **A**1 2 5 8 10 19 **F**3 4 5 8 11 12 13 15 17 18 20 22 24 26 28 29 30 31 34 35 36 37 38 39 40 42 43 44 45 46 47 48 49 51 53 54 56 57 58 59 61 64 65 66 70 71 74 75 76 77 78 79 80 81 82 83 84 85 86 87 90 92 93 96 97 98 100 101 102 103 104 105 107 108 110 111 114 115 116 117 119 120 121 123 124 126 129 130 131 132 133 135 144 146 147 148 149 152 153 154 156 157 **S** Summa Health, Akron, OH
Primary Contact: David Custodio, M.D., President Summa Health System Akron
CMO: Erik N Steele, D.O., Senior Vice President and Chief Medical Officer
CIO: Greg Kall, Chief Information Officer
CHR: Kyle Klawitter, Vice President Human Resources
Web address: www.summahealth.org
Control: Other not-for-profit (including NFP Corporation) **Service:** General medical and surgical

Staffed Beds: 623 **Admissions:** 31724 **Census:** 393 **Outpatient Visits:** 471166 **Births:** 4134 **Total Expense ($000):** 802504 **Payroll Expense ($000):** 240649 **Personnel:** 6409

SUMMA REHAB HOSPITAL (363035), 29 North Adams Street, Zip 44304–1641; tel. 330/572–7300, **A**1 7 10 **F**3 29 30 34 35 60 61 66 68 74 75 78 79 82 85 87 90 91 94 96 100 119 132 148 154 156 **S** Summa Health, Akron, OH
Primary Contact: Cheryl Henthorn, Chief Executive Officer
Web address: www.summarehabhospital.com/
Control: Partnership, Investor–owned (for-profit) **Service:** Rehabilitation

Staffed Beds: 60 **Admissions:** 1732 **Census:** 52 **Outpatient Visits:** 0 **Births:** 0

SUMMA SAINT THOMAS HOSPITAL See Summa Health System, Akron

ALLIANCE—Stark County

ALLIANCE COMMUNITY HOSPITAL (360131), 200 East State Street, Zip 44601–4926; tel. 330/596–6000 (Total facility includes 78 beds in nursing home–type unit) **A**2 5 10 11 **F**3 11 15 28 29 30 34 35 36 37 40 44 45 50 51 56 57 59 60 63 64 68 69 70 71 74 75 77 79 81 82 84 85 86 87 90 92 93 96 98 103 107 108 110 111 114 115 118 119 128 130 131 132 135 143 144 146 147 148 154 156 157 **G** Aultman Health Foundation, Canton, OH
Primary Contact: Ryan Jones, Chief Executive Officer
COO: Dale W. Wells, Chief Financial and Operating Officer
CFO: Dale W. Wells, Chief Financial and Operating Officer
CMO: Ashraf Ahmed, M.D., Senior Vice President Physician and Hospital Services
CIO: David W Shroades, Vice President Technology Services
CHR: Nicole L Russ, Director Colleague Relations
CNO: Amy Antonacci, MSN, R.N., Vice President Nursing Services
Web address: www.achosp.org
Control: Other not-for-profit (including NFP Corporation) **Service:** General medical and surgical

Staffed Beds: 202 **Admissions:** 2734 **Census:** 99 **Outpatient Visits:** 180714 **Births:** 0 **Total Expense ($000):** 85467 **Payroll Expense ($000):** 36156 **Personnel:** 733

AMHERST—Lorain County

SPECIALTY HOSPITAL OF LORAIN (362025), 254 Cleveland Avenue, Zip 44001–1620; tel. 440/988–6260, (Nonreporting) **A**1 10
Primary Contact: Rajive Khanna, Chief Executive Officer
COO: Susan Adams, Chief Nursing Officer and Chief Operating Officer
CNO: Susan Adams, Chief Nursing Officer and Chief Operating Officer
Control: Church operated **Service:** Acute long-term care hospital

Staffed Beds: 30

Hospital, Medicare Provider Number, Address, Telephone, Approval, Facility, and Physician Codes, Health Care System

★ American Hospital Association (AHA) membership
□ The Joint Commission accreditation
○ Healthcare Facilities Accreditation Program
◇ DNV Healthcare Inc. accreditation
⇑ Center for Improvement in Healthcare Quality Accreditation
△ Commission on Accreditation of Rehabilitation Facilities (CARF) accreditation

OH

ARCHBOLD—Fulton County

ARCHBOLD HOSPITAL See Community Hospitals and Wellness Centers, Bryan

ASHLAND—Ashland County

⊞ **UNIVERSITY HOSPITALS SAMARITAN MEDICAL CENTER (360002)**, 1025 Center Street, Zip 44805–4011; tel. 419/289–0491, **A**1 10 **F**3 11 13 15 18 20 28 29 30 31 34 35 40 45 50 51 57 59 60 62 64 68 70 75 76 77 78 79 81 82 85 86 87 93 96 102 107 111 114 115 119 129 130 131 132 135 144 146 147 148 149 154 **S** University Hospitals, Cleveland, OH
Primary Contact: Karen McNeil, President
CFO: Mary Griest, Vice President Finance and Chief Financial Officer
CMO: Philip Myers, M.D., Vice President Medical Affairs
CIO: Kathleen Metcalf, Chief Information Officer
CHR: Alyce Legg, Vice President Human Resources
CNO: Karin Schwan, Chief Nursing Officer, Vice President Patient Care Services
Web address: www.samaritanhospital.org
Control: Other not–for–profit (including NFP Corporation) **Service**: General medical and surgical

Staffed Beds: 39 **Admissions:** 2433 **Census:** 20 **Outpatient Visits:** 142246 **Births:** 299 **Total Expense ($000):** 66678 **Payroll Expense ($000):** 21533 **Personnel:** 407

ASHTABULA—Ashtabula County

⊞ **ASHTABULA COUNTY MEDICAL CENTER (360125)**, 2420 Lake Avenue, Zip 44004–4954; tel. 440/997–2262, (Total facility includes 15 beds in nursing home–type unit) **A**1 5 10 20 **F**3 11 13 15 18 19 20 26 28 29 30 31 34 35 40 44 45 49 51 53 54 57 59 61 62 63 64 68 70 74 76 78 79 81 82 85 87 89 92 93 97 98 100 102 103 104 107 108 110 111 114 115 116 117 118 119 128 129 130 131 132 135 144 146 147 148 149 153 154
Primary Contact: Michael J. Habowski, President and Chief Executive Officer
COO: Lewis Hutchison, Vice President Operations and Quality
CFO: Donald L Kepner, Chief Financial Officer
CMO: Jude Cauwenberg, M.D., Chief of Staff
CIO: Jared Swiger, Director Information Systems
CHR: Jonathan Forbes, Director Human Resources
CNO: Ken Frame, Chief Nursing Officer
Web address: www.acmchealth.org
Control: Other not–for–profit (including NFP Corporation) **Service**: General medical and surgical

Staffed Beds: 151 **Admissions:** 5767 **Census:** 69 **Outpatient Visits:** 258094 **Births:** 359 **Total Expense ($000):** 136519 **Payroll Expense ($000):** 64026 **Personnel:** 915

ATHENS—Athens County

☐ **APPALACHIAN BEHAVIORAL HEALTHCARE (364015)**, 100 Hospital Drive, Zip 45701–2301; tel. 740/594–5000, (Nonreporting) **A**1 3 10 **S** Ohio Department of Mental Health, Columbus, OH
Primary Contact: Jane E. Krason, R.N., Chief Executive Officer
COO: Kelly Sole, Chief Operating Officer
CMO: Mark F McGee, M.D., Chief Clinical Officer
CHR: Donovan Workman, Director Human Capital Management
CNO: Karen Durniat-Sushrstedt, Nurse Executive
Web address: www.mh.state.oh.us
Control: State, Government, nonfederal **Service**: Psychiatric

Staffed Beds: 224

⊞ **O'BLENESS MEMORIAL HOSPITAL (360014)**, 55 Hospital Drive, Zip 45701–2302; tel. 740/593–5551, (Nonreporting) **A**1 3 10 12 13 **S** OhioHealth, Columbus, OH
Primary Contact: Mark R. Seckinger, President
CFO: Robert Melaragno, Vice President Finance
CIO: Kristine Barr, Vice President Communication Services
CHR: Sandie Leasure, Senior Vice President Human Resources
CNO: Sandy Wood, MSN, R.N., Vice President Patient Services and Chief Nursing Officer
Web address: www.obleness.org
Control: Other not–for–profit (including NFP Corporation) **Service**: General medical and surgical

Staffed Beds: 76

AVON—Lorain County

⊞ **CLEVELAND CLINIC AVON HOSPITAL (360364)**, 33300 Cleveland Clinic Boulevard, Zip 44011; tel. 440/695–5000, **A**1 10 **F**3 15 18 20 29 30 34 35 40 45 49 51 64 68 70 74 75 77 79 80 81 82 85 87 92 100 107 108 110 111 114 115 119 130 146 147 148 154 155 156 **S** Cleveland Clinic Health System, Cleveland, OH
Primary Contact: Rebecca Starck, M.D., President
COO: John Mills, Chief Operating Officer
CFO: Lori Koenig, Assistant Finance Director
CNO: Mary R Sauer, R.N., Chief Nursing Officer
Web address: www.my.clevelandclinic.org
Control: Other not–for–profit (including NFP Corporation) **Service**: General medical and surgical

Staffed Beds: 126 **Admissions:** 6465 **Census:** 64 **Outpatient Visits:** 94770 **Births:** 0 **Total Expense ($000):** 114873 **Payroll Expense ($000):** 41042 **Personnel:** 580

⊞ **CLEVELAND CLINIC REHABILITATION HOSPITAL (363038)**, 33355 Health Campus Boulevard, Zip 44011; tel. 440/937–9099, (Includes CLEVELAND CLINIC REHABILITATION HOSPITAL, 3025 Science Park Drive, Beachwood, Ohio, Zip 44122; tel. 216/455–6400; R David Richer, Chief Executive Officer) **A**1 3 10 **F**3 34 60 68 69 75 90 91 92 94 96 119 130 132 135 143 148 149 157 **S** Select Medical Corporation, Mechanicsburg, PA
Primary Contact: Sam Bayoumy, Chief Executive Officer
Web address: www.my.clevelandclinic.org
Control: Partnership, Investor–owned (for–profit) **Service**: Rehabilitation

Staffed Beds: 180 **Admissions:** 2739 **Census:** 105 **Outpatient Visits:** 0 **Births:** 0 **Personnel:** 470

☐ **UH AVON REHABILITATION HOSPITAL (363039)**, 37900 Chester Road, Zip 44011–1044; tel. 440/695–7100, (Nonreporting) **A**1 10 **S** Kindred Healthcare, Louisville, KY
Primary Contact: Andrew Goldfrach, Chief Executive Officer
CFO: Jason DiGiulio, Controller
CHR: Abby Hoag, Director, Human Resources
CNO: Katie Kasper, Chief Clinical Officer
Web address: www.uhhospitals.org/uh-avon-rehabilitation-hospital
Control: Corporation, Investor–owned (for–profit) **Service**: Rehabilitation

Staffed Beds: 50

BARNESVILLE—Belmont County

⊞ **BARNESVILLE HOSPITAL (361321)**, 639 West Main Street, Zip 43713–1039, Mailing Address: P.O. Box 309, Zip 43713–0309; tel. 740/425–3941, **A**1 10 18 **F**3 11 15 28 29 30 34 35 40 46 57 59 65 68 69 70 75 77 81 89 93 97 107 111 119 128 129 130 133 146
Primary Contact: David D. Phillips, Chief Executive Officer and Administrator
CFO: Willie Cooper-Lohr, Chief Financial Officer
CMO: David J Hilliard, D.O., Chief of Staff
CHR: Beth K. Brill, Senior Director Human Resources
CNO: Cynthia Touvelle, R.N., Senior Director Care Management and Chief Nursing Officer
Web address: www.barnesvillehospital.com
Control: Other not–for–profit (including NFP Corporation) **Service**: General medical and surgical

Staffed Beds: 65 **Admissions:** 648 **Census:** 6

BATAVIA—Clermont County

☐ **MERCY HEALTH - CLERMONT HOSPITAL (360236)**, 3000 Hospital Drive, Zip 45103–1921; tel. 513/732–8200, **A**1 2 10 **F**3 4 8 11 15 16 17 18 19 20 21 22 23 24 25 26 27 28 29 30 34 35 36 37 38 40 41 44 45 46 49 50 51 56 57 59 60 61 64 67 68 70 74 75 77 79 81 83 84 86 87 88 89 90 92 93 94 95 98 99 100 101 102 103 105 107 110 111 115 118 119 126 130 131 132 134 146 148 149 152 153 154 **S** Mercy Health, Cincinnati, OH
Primary Contact: Justin Krueger, FACHE, President
CFO: Philip Wheeler, Director Finance
CMO: Parma Hariharan, M.D., Chief of Staff
CHR: Angie Ferrell, Director Human Resources
CNO: Melissa A Samuelson, R.N., Vice President and Chief Nursing Officer
Web address: www.e-mercy.com
Control: Church operated, Nongovernment, not–for–profit **Service**: General medical and surgical

Staffed Beds: 147 **Admissions:** 7309 **Census:** 79

Many Facility Codes have changed. Please refer to the AHA Guide Code Chart. © 2019 AHA Guide

BEACHWOOD—Cuyahoga County

☐ **UH REHABILITATION HOSPITAL (363036)**, 23333 Harvard Road,
Zip 44122–6232; tel. 216/593–2200, (Nonreporting) **A**1 3 **S** Kindred Healthcare,
Louisville, KY
Primary Contact: Mirza Baig, M.D., Medical Director
Web address: www.uhhospitals.org
Control: Corporation, Investor–owned (for–profit) **Service:** Rehabilitation

Staffed Beds: 50

⊞ **UNIVERSITY HOSPITALS AHUJA MEDICAL CENTER (360359)**, 3999
Richmond Road, Zip 44122–6046; tel. 216/593–5500, **A**1 3 10 **F**3 5 9 14 15 17
18 19 20 22 24 26 28 29 30 31 34 35 36 37 40 41 42 45 46 47 48 49 50 51
56 57 58 59 60 61 63 64 65 68 70 74 75 77 78 79 80 81 82 84 85 87 91 92
93 97 100 102 107 108 109 110 111 115 119 126 130 131 132 144 145 146
148 149 152 154 156 **S** University Hospitals, Cleveland, OH
Primary Contact: Susan V. Juris, President
Web address: www.uhhospitals.org/ahuja/tabid/7051/uhahujamedicalcenter.aspx
Control: Other not–for–profit (including NFP Corporation) **Service:** General
medical and surgical

Staffed Beds: 144 **Admissions:** 8672 **Census:** 93 **Outpatient
Visits:** 165470 **Births:** 0 **Total Expense ($000):** 185864 **Payroll Expense
($000):** 55393 **Personnel:** 930

BEAVERCREEK—Greene County

★ ○ **SOIN MEDICAL CENTER (360360)**, 3535 Pentagon Boulevard,
Zip 45431–1705; tel. 937/702–4000, **A**2 3 10 11 **F**3 11 13 15 18 20 22 29
30 34 35 40 43 44 45 46 47 48 50 51 53 54 57 59 64 68 70 73 74 75 76 77
79 81 82 87 92 96 102 107 108 110 111 115 116 117 118 119 126 130 131
132 135 146 147 148 149 154 157 **S** Kettering Health Network, Dayton, OH
Primary Contact: Rick A. Dodds, President
COO: Ron D Connovich, Chief Financial Officer and Chief Operating Officer
CFO: Ron D Connovich, Chief Financial Officer and Chief Operating Officer
CMO: Michael Caccamo, M.D., Chief Medical Officer
CIO: Andy Lehman, Vice President Information Systems
CNO: Belinda Mallett, R.N., MS, Vice President, Patient Care and Clinical Services
Web address: www.khnetwork.org/soin
Control: Church operated, Nongovernment, not–for–profit **Service:** General
medical and surgical

Staffed Beds: 133 **Admissions:** 7355 **Census:** 74 **Outpatient
Visits:** 102411 **Births:** 754 **Total Expense ($000):** 188789 **Payroll Expense
($000):** 68427 **Personnel:** 1099

BELLEFONTAINE—Logan County

★ ↑ **MARY RUTAN HOSPITAL (360197)**, 205 Palmer Avenue, Zip 43311–2281;
tel. 937/592–4015, **A**5 10 20 21 **F**3 11 12 13 14 15 18 20 28 29 30 31 32 34
50 51 57 59 64 68 70 75 76 77 79 81 82 85 86 87 89 97 107 108 110 111
115 118 119 129 130 132 133 135 144 146 147 149 154 156
Primary Contact: Mandy C. Goble, President and Chief Executive Officer
CFO: Steven Brown, Vice President Fiscal Affairs
CMO: Grant Varian, M.D., Medical Director
CIO: Robert Reynolds, Director Information Systems
CHR: Vickie L Crumley, Chief Human Resources Officer
CNO: Frank Gliha, Vice President of Patient Care
Web address: www.maryrutan.org
Control: Other not–for–profit (including NFP Corporation) **Service:** General
medical and surgical

Staffed Beds: 46 **Admissions:** 1381 **Census:** 10 **Outpatient Visits:** 123407
Births: 344 **Total Expense ($000):** 99532 **Payroll Expense ($000):** 48265
Personnel: 607

BELLEVUE—Sandusky County

⊞ **BELLEVUE HOSPITAL (360107)**, 1400 West Main Street, Zip 44811–9088,
Mailing Address: P.O. Box 8004, Zip 44811–8004; tel. 419/483–4040, **A**1 3 5
10 **F**3 11 13 15 18 25 29 30 31 34 35 40 41 45 46 50 53 56 57 59 61 68 70 74
75 76 77 79 81 82 85 87 89 91 93 107 110 111 115 118 119 127 129 130
131 132 133 135 143 144 146 147 148 149 154 156
Primary Contact: Michael Winthrop, President
CFO: Timothy Buit, Executive Vice President and Chief Financial Officer
CMO: Donald Smith, President Medical Staff
CIO: Kim Stults, Director, Information Systems
CHR: Lisa M. Sartain, Vice President, Human Resources
CNO: Sara Brokaw, Vice President Patient Care Services
Web address: www.bellevuehospital.com
Control: Other not–for–profit (including NFP Corporation) **Service:** General
medical and surgical

Staffed Beds: 50 **Admissions:** 1428 **Census:** 12 **Outpatient Visits:** 84681
Births: 402 **Total Expense ($000):** 51027 **Payroll Expense ($000):** 18689
Personnel: 357

BLUFFTON—Allen County

★ **BLUFFTON HOSPITAL (361322)**, 139 Garau Street, Zip 45817–1027;
tel. 419/358–9010, **A**10 18 **F**3 8 11 13 15 18 30 35 40 45 59 63 64 68 70 75
76 77 79 81 82 89 91 93 107 110 114 119 126 127 146 147 154 **S** Blanchard
Valley Health System, Findlay, OH
Primary Contact: Christine Keller, Chief Administrative Officer
CFO: David Cytlak, Vice President Finance
CMO: William H Kose, M.D., Vice President Quality and Medical Affairs
CIO: David Cytlak, Vice President Finance
CHR: Ryan Fisher, Director Human Resources
CNO: Barbara J. Pasztor, R.N., Vice President Nursing and Patient Care Services
Web address: www.bvhealthsystem.org/
Control: Other not–for–profit (including NFP Corporation) **Service:** General
medical and surgical

Staffed Beds: 25 **Admissions:** 307 **Census:** 2 **Outpatient Visits:** 22112
Births: 179 **Total Expense ($000):** 15564 **Payroll Expense ($000):** 7692
Personnel: 115

BOARDMAN—Mahoning County

MAHONING VALLEY HOSPITAL See Vibra Hospital of Mahoning Valley

☐ **MERCY HEALTH - ST. ELIZABETH BOARDMAN HOSPITAL (360276)**, 8401
Market Street, Zip 44512–6777; tel. 330/729–2929, **A**1 3 5 10 13 **F**3 8 11 13
15 18 29 30 31 34 35 37 40 45 46 49 59 60 68 70 74 75 76 77 78 79 81 84
87 93 107 108 110 111 114 115 116 117 118 119 120 121 123 126 129 130
146 147 148 149 154 **S** Mercy Health, Cincinnati, OH
Primary Contact: Eugenia Aubel, President, St. Elizabeth Boardman Hospital
CFO: Anthony J. Seminaro, Chief Financial Youngstown
CMO: Heath Dorion, Physician Administrator
CIO: Maureen Kordupel, Director Information Technology Relationship Manager
CNO: Stacie Call, Chief Nursing Officer
Web address: www.https://www.mercy.com/youngstown
Control: Church operated, Nongovernment, not–for–profit **Service:** General
medical and surgical

Staffed Beds: 217 **Admissions:** 14937 **Census:** 145 **Outpatient
Visits:** 125731 **Births:** 3047 **Personnel:** 942

★ **SELECT SPECIALTY HOSPITAL - BOARDMAN (360363)**, 8401 Market Street,
7 South, Zip 44512–6725; tel. 330/729–1750, (Nonreporting) **S** Select Medical
Corporation, Mechanicsburg, PA
Primary Contact: Jodi Costello, Chief Executive Officer
Web address: www.selectspecialtyhospitals.com/
Control: Corporation, Investor–owned (for–profit) **Service:** Acute long–term care
hospital

Staffed Beds: 24

⊞ **VIBRA HOSPITAL OF MAHONING VALLEY (362023)**, 8049 South Avenue,
Zip 44512–6154; tel. 330/726–5000, (Includes VIBRA HOSPITAL OF MAHONING
VALLEY-TRUMBULL CAMPUS, 1350 E Market Street, 9th Floor, Warren, Ohio,
Zip 44483–6608; tel. 330/675–5555; Nathan Mast, Chief Executive Officer),
(Nonreporting) **A**1 10 **S** Vibra Healthcare, Mechanicsburg, PA
Primary Contact: Nathan Mast, Chief Executive Officer
CMO: Lawrence Goldstein, M.D., Chief Medical Officer
Web address: www.vhmvalley.com
Control: Corporation, Investor–owned (for–profit) **Service:** Acute long–term care
hospital

Staffed Beds: 42

BOWLING GREEN—Wood County

⊞ **WOOD COUNTY HOSPITAL (360029)**, 950 West Wooster Street, Zip 43402–
2603; tel. 419/354–8900, **A**1 5 10 **F**3 11 12 13 15 17 28 29 30 31 32 33 34
35 36 40 44 45 50 54 56 57 59 64 65 68 69 70 74 75 76 77 78 79 81 82 85
87 89 93 107 108 110 111 114 115 118 119 120 121 123 124 126 129 130
131 132 135 144 146 147 148 149 154 156
Primary Contact: Stanley R. Korducki, President
CFO: Karol Bortel, Vice President Financial Services
CMO: Shawn Stansbery, M.D., Chief of Staff
CIO: Joanne White, Chief Information Officer
CHR: Michael Ford, Vice President Patient Services
CNO: Sandra Beidelschies, MSN, R.N., Vice President Patient Services
Web address: www.woodcountyhospital.org
Control: Other not–for–profit (including NFP Corporation) **Service:** General
medical and surgical

Staffed Beds: 108 **Admissions:** 2500 **Census:** 22 **Outpatient Visits:** 99705
Births: 363 **Total Expense ($000):** 88854 **Payroll Expense ($000):** 33858
Personnel: 813

Hospital, Medicare Provider Number, Address, Telephone, Approval, Facility, and Physician Codes, Health Care System

★ American Hospital Association (AHA) membership   ○ Healthcare Facilities Accreditation Program   ↑ Center for Improvement in Healthcare Quality Accreditation
☐ The Joint Commission accreditation   ◇ DNV Healthcare Inc. accreditation   △ Commission on Accreditation of Rehabilitation Facilities (CARF) accreditation

BRYAN—Williams County

☐ **COMMUNITY HOSPITALS AND WELLNESS CENTERS (360121)**, 433 West High Street, Zip 43506–1679; tel. 419/636–1131, (Includes ARCHBOLD HOSPITAL, 121 Westfield Drive, Archbold, Ohio, Zip 43502; tel. 419/445–4415; BRYAN HOSPITAL, 433 West High Street, Bryan, Ohio, Zip 43506; tel. 419/636–1131; MONTPELIER HOSPITAL, 909 East Snyder Avenue, Montpelier, Ohio, Zip 43543; tel. 419/485–3154), (Non-reporting) **A**1 2 5 10
Primary Contact: Philip L. Ennen, Vice President and Chief Executive Officer
CFO: Leroy P Feather, Vice President Finance
CIO: Greg Slattery, Vice President Information
CHR: Mary Ann Potts, Director Personnel
Web address: www.chwchospital.com
Control: Other not–for–profit (including NFP Corporation) **Service**: General medical and surgical

Staffed Beds: 113

BUCYRUS—Crawford County

★ ⑂ **BUCYRUS HOSPITAL (361316)**, 629 North Sandusky Avenue, Zip 44820–1821; tel. 419/562–4677, (Nonreporting) **A**5 10 18 21 **S** Avita Health System, Galion, OH
Primary Contact: Jerome Morasko, Chief Executive Officer
COO: Andy Daniels, Chief Operating Officer
CMO: Michael A Johnson, M.D., Chief of Staff
CIO: Joann Riedlinger, Vice President Nursing and Manager Information Systems
CHR: Jeanne Perkins, Vice President Nursing and Interim Manager Human Resources
Web address: www.bchonline.org
Control: Other not–for–profit (including NFP Corporation) **Service**: General medical and surgical

Staffed Beds: 25

CADIZ—Harrison County

☐ **HARRISON COMMUNITY HOSPITAL (361311)**, 951 East Market Street, Zip 43907–9799; tel. 740/942–4631, (Nonreporting) **A**1 10 18
Primary Contact: John DeBlasis, Vice President
CFO: Donald Huelskamp, Interim Chief Financial Officer
CMO: Anandhi Murthy, Chief Medical Officer
CIO: Will Combs, Director Information Technology
CHR: Peter Giordano, Senior Director Human Resources
CNO: Janis Olinski, R.N., Vice President Clinical Services
Web address: www.harrisoncommunity.com
Control: Other not–for–profit (including NFP Corporation) **Service**: General medical and surgical

Staffed Beds: 25

CAMBRIDGE—Guernsey County

☐ **CAMBRIDGE BEHAVIORAL HOSPITAL (364027)**, 66755 State Street, Zip 43725–8757; tel. 740/432–4906, (Nonreporting) **A**1 10
Primary Contact: Pamela Braden, Administrator
Web address: www.cbhohio.com
Control: Corporation, Investor–owned (for–profit) **Service**: Psychiatric

Staffed Beds: 66

⊞ **SOUTHEASTERN OHIO REGIONAL MEDICAL CENTER (360203)**, 1341 North Clark Street, Zip 43725–9614, Mailing Address: P.O. Box 610, Zip 43725–0610; tel. 740/439–8000, **A**1 2 3 10 20 **F**3 11 13 15 17 28 29 30 31 32 34 35 40 43 44 45 48 49 50 51 57 59 60 62 64 68 70 75 76 77 78 79 81 83 84 85 86 87 91 93 96 107 108 110 111 114 115 118 119 120 121 123 130 131 132 135 146 147 148 149 156
Primary Contact: Raymond M. Chorey, President and Chief Executive Officer
CFO: Timothy R. Evancho, Chief Financial Officer
CMO: E Edwin Conaway, M.D., Vice President Medical Affairs and Chief Medical Officer
CIO: Kevin Ludwigsen, Chief Information Officer
CHR: Steven Michael Brooks, Vice President Human Resources
CNO: Angela S Long, Vice President Clinical Services and Chief Nursing Officer
Web address: www.seormc.org
Control: Other not–for–profit (including NFP Corporation) **Service**: General medical and surgical

Staffed Beds: 90 **Admissions**: 3384 **Census**: 30 **Outpatient Visits**: 133358 **Births**: 395 **Total Expense ($000)**: 89424 **Payroll Expense ($000)**: 31493 **Personnel**: 621

CANAL WINCHESTER—Fairfield County

☐ **DILEY RIDGE MEDICAL CENTER (360358)**, 7911 Diley Road, Zip 43110–9653; tel. 614/838–7911, **A**1 10 **F**3 15 29 35 40 50 54 64 68 85 87 107 110 111 114 119 130 147
Primary Contact: Jodi Wilson, President and Chief Operating Officer
COO: Jodi Wilson, President and Chief Operating Officer
Web address: www.dileyridgemedicalcenter.com
Control: Other not–for–profit (including NFP Corporation) **Service**: General medical and surgical

Staffed Beds: 10 **Admissions**: 44 **Census**: 1 **Outpatient Visits**: 50431 **Births**: 0 **Total Expense ($000)**: 13263 **Payroll Expense ($000)**: 5227 **Personnel**: 85

CANTON—Stark County

⊞ △ **AULTMAN HOSPITAL (360084)**, 2600 Sixth Street SW, Zip 44710–1702; tel. 330/452–9911, (Includes AULTMAN HOSPITAL PEDIATRIC SERVICES, 2600 Sixth Street, SW, Canton, Ohio, Zip 44710–1702; tel. 330/363–5455) (Total facility includes 60 beds in nursing home–type unit) **A**1 2 3 5 7 10 13 19 **F**3 7 8 11 12 13 15 17 18 20 22 24 26 28 29 30 31 34 35 39 40 42 43 44 45 48 49 50 51 53 54 55 56 57 58 59 60 61 62 63 64 68 70 71 72 74 75 76 77 78 79 81 82 83 84 85 86 87 89 90 93 96 97 102 104 105 107 108 109 110 111 114 115 116 117 118 119 120 121 123 126 127 128 129 130 131 132 133 134 135 143 144 145 146 147 148 149 150 154 155 156 157 **S** Aultman Health Foundation, Canton, OH
Primary Contact: Edward J. Roth III, President and Chief Executive Officer
CFO: Mark Wright, Vice President
CMO: Allison Oprandi, M.D., Chief Medical Officer
CIO: Liz Getz, Chief Information Officer
CHR: Sue Olivera, Vice President
CNO: Nicole Kolacz, Chief Nursing Officer
Web address: www.aultman.com
Control: Other not–for–profit (including NFP Corporation) **Service**: General medical and surgical

Staffed Beds: 532 **Admissions**: 24091 **Census**: 306 **Outpatient Visits**: 446503 **Births**: 2910 **Total Expense ($000)**: 501043 **Payroll Expense ($000)**: 186939 **Personnel**: 6400

☐ **AULTMAN SPECIALTY HOSPITAL (362032)**, 2600 Sixth Street, SW, Zip 44710–1702; tel. 330/363–4000, (Nonreporting) **A**1 10 **S** Aultman Health Foundation, Canton, OH
Primary Contact: Ryan Kuharich, Chief Executive Officer
CFO: Mark Wright, Chief Financial Officer
CMO: George Kefalas, Chief Medical Officer
Web address: www.aultman.org
Control: Other not–for–profit (including NFP Corporation) **Service**: Acute long–term care hospital

Staffed Beds: 30

⊞ **MERCY MEDICAL CENTER (360070)**, 1320 Mercy Drive NW, Zip 44708–2641; tel. 330/489–1000, **A**1 2 3 5 10 19 **F**3 11 12 13 15 17 18 20 22 24 26 28 29 30 31 34 35 39 40 43 44 46 48 49 50 51 53 54 57 58 59 60 61 62 63 64 66 68 70 72 74 75 76 77 78 79 80 81 82 84 85 86 87 89 90 91 92 93 96 97 107 108 110 111 114 115 116 117 118 119 120 121 123 124 126 129 130 131 132 135 144 146 147 148 149 150 155 156 **S** Sisters of Charity Health System, Cleveland, OH
Primary Contact: Paul C. Hiltz, FACHE, President and Chief Executive Officer
COO: David D Cemate, FACHE, Senior Vice President and Chief Operating Officer
CFO: David K Stewart, Senior Vice President and Chief Financial Officer
CMO: David Gormsen, D.O., Vice President and Chief Medical Officer
CIO: Trevor Clere, Director Information Technology
CHR: Patti Bresnahan, Director Human Resources
CNO: Barbara Yingling, R.N., Vice President Patient Care Services and Chief Nursing Officer
Web address: www.cantonmercy.org
Control: Other not–for–profit (including NFP Corporation) **Service**: General medical and surgical

Staffed Beds: 338 **Admissions**: 15962 **Census**: 200 **Outpatient Visits**: 713678 **Births**: 1357 **Total Expense ($000)**: 344119 **Payroll Expense ($000)**: 139636 **Personnel**: 2222

⊞ **SELECT SPECIALTY HOSPITAL-CANTON (362016)**, 1320 Mercy Drive NW, 6th Floor, Zip 44708–2614; tel. 330/489–8189, (Nonreporting) **A**1 10 **S** Select Medical Corporation, Mechanicsburg, PA
Primary Contact: Sherri Becker, Chief Executive Officer
Web address: www.selectspecialtyhospitals.com/company/locations/canton.aspx
Control: Corporation, Investor–owned (for–profit) **Service**: Acute long–term care hospital

Staffed Beds: 30

Many Facility Codes have changed. Please refer to the AHA Guide Code Chart. © 2019 AHA Guide

CHARDON—Geauga County

HEATHERHILL CARE COMMUNITIES (362014), 12340 Bass Lake Road, Zip 44024–8327; tel. 440/285–4040, (Nonreporting)
Primary Contact: Jim Homa, Chief Executive Officer
COO: Lisa Deering, Administrator
CFO: Valerie Love, Manager Business Office
CMO: Beejadi Makunda, M.D., Chief Medical Officer
CHR: Pam McCall, Director Human Resources
CNO: Alice Harvey, Director of Nursing
Web address: www.heatherhill.com
Control: Other not–for–profit (including NFP Corporation) **Service:** Acute long–term care hospital

Staffed Beds: 214

UNIVERSITY HOSPITALS GEAUGA MEDICAL CENTER (360192), 13207 Ravenna Road, Zip 44024–7032; tel. 440/269–6000, **A**1 2 3 10 **F**3 8 11 12 13 15 18 20 22 26 28 29 30 31 32 34 35 36 38 39 40 41 42 43 44 47 49 50 51 54 56 57 58 59 60 62 63 64 65 68 70 74 75 76 77 78 79 81 82 84 85 86 87 91 92 93 96 97 98 100 101 102 103 107 108 109 110 111 114 115 116 117 118 119 120 121 123 124 129 130 131 132 134 135 143 144 145 146 147 148 149 154 **S** University Hospitals, Cleveland, OH
Primary Contact: M Steven. Jones, President
COO: M Steven Jones, President
CFO: Paul Amantea, Director Finance
CMO: David Kosnosky, M.D., Chief Medical Officer
CIO: Lou Ciraldo, Information Services Representative
CHR: Danialle Lynce, Manager Human Resources
CNO: Peggy A Kuhar, R.N., MSN, Chief Nursing Officer
Web address: www.uhhospitals.org/geauga/
Control: Other not–for–profit (including NFP Corporation) **Service:** General medical and surgical

Staffed Beds: 142 **Admissions:** 7870 **Census:** 84 **Outpatient Visits:** 159638 **Births:** 1011 **Total Expense ($000):** 159787 **Payroll Expense ($000):** 44237 **Personnel:** 792

CHILLICOTHE—Ross County

ADENA MEDICAL CENTER (360159), 272 Hospital Road, Zip 45601–9031; tel. 740/779–7500, **A**1 2 3 5 10 19 **F**3 5 8 13 15 18 20 22 24 26 28 29 30 31 32 34 35 37 38 40 41 45 46 48 49 51 54 57 59 62 63 64 66 70 73 74 75 76 77 78 79 81 82 83 84 85 86 87 89 91 93 96 97 98 100 101 102 104 107 108 111 114 115 119 120 121 123 126 127 129 130 131 132 135 144 146 147 148 154 156 **S** Adena Health System, Chillicothe, OH
Primary Contact: Jeff Graham, President and Chief Executive Officer
COO: Eric Cecava, Chief Operating Officer
CFO: Robert Rosenberger, Chief Financial Officer
CMO: John Fortney, Senior System Medical Advisor
CIO: Linn Weimer, Chief Information Officer
CHR: Jay D. Justice, Chief Human Resource Officer
Web address: www.adena.org
Control: Other not–for–profit (including NFP Corporation) **Service:** General medical and surgical

Staffed Beds: 236 **Admissions:** 10756 **Census:** 109 **Outpatient Visits:** 681805 **Births:** 1070 **Total Expense ($000):** 347195 **Payroll Expense ($000):** 129459 **Personnel:** 2644

CHILLICOTHE VETERANS AFFAIRS MEDICAL CENTER, 17273 State Route 104, Zip 45601–9718; tel. 740/773–1141, (Nonreporting) **A**1 3 5 **S** Department of Veterans Affairs, Washington, DC
Primary Contact: Beth A. Lumia, Acting Medical Center Director
CFO: Rick Deckard, Chief Fiscal Service
CMO: Deborah Meesig, M.D., Chief of Staff
CIO: William Gawler, Chief Information Officer
CHR: Angela Young, Human Resources Officer
Web address: www.chillicothe.va.gov/
Control: Veterans Affairs, Government, federal **Service:** Psychiatric

Staffed Beds: 295

VETERANS AFFAIRS MEDICAL CENTER See Chillicothe Veterans Affairs Medical Center

CINCINNATI—Hamilton County

BETHESDA NORTH HOSPITAL (360179), 10500 Montgomery Road, Zip 45242–4402; tel. 513/865–1111, (Includes BETHESDA BUTLER HOSPITAL, 3125 Hamilton Mason Road, Hamilton, Ohio, Zip 45011–5307; tel. 513/894–8888; Chuck Brown, Administrator) **A**1 3 5 10 **F**3 5 8 9 11 12 13 15 17 18 20 22 24 26 28 29 30 31 34 35 36 37 38 39 40 41 42 43 44 45 46 47 48 49 50 53 54 55 56 57 58 59 61 63 64 65 66 68 70 71 73 74 75 76 77 79 81 82 83 84 85 86 87 91 92 93 94 96 97 100 101 102 104 107 108 109 110 111 114 115 116 117 118 119 120 121 123 124 126 129 130 131 132 134 135 141 143 144 145 146 147 148 149 153 154 156
Primary Contact: Mark C. Clement, President
COO: Jenny Oliphant, Executive Vice President and Chief Operating Officer
CFO: Michael Crofton, Senior Vice President and Chief Financial Officer
CMO: Georges Feghali, M.D., Senior Vice President Quality and Chief Medical Officer
CIO: Rick Moore, Chief Information Officer
CHR: Walter L McLarty, Chief Human Resources Officer
CNO: Mary Irvin, R.N., MSN, Senior Vice President and Chief Nursing Officer
Web address: www.trihealth.com
Control: Other not–for–profit (including NFP Corporation) **Service:** General medical and surgical

Staffed Beds: 370 **Admissions:** 24219 **Census:** 272 **Outpatient Visits:** 364684 **Births:** 3941 **Total Expense ($000):** 556728 **Payroll Expense ($000):** 176404 **Personnel:** 3198

△ **CHRIST HOSPITAL (360163)**, 2139 Auburn Avenue, Zip 45219–2906; tel. 513/585–2000, **A**1 2 3 5 7 10 **F**1 3 6 8 9 12 13 15 17 18 20 22 24 26 28 29 30 31 34 35 36 37 38 39 40 42 44 45 46 47 48 49 50 51 53 54 55 56 57 58 59 60 64 65 66 68 70 73 74 75 76 77 78 79 80 81 82 83 84 85 86 87 90 92 93 94 96 97 98 100 103 107 108 109 110 111 114 115 116 117 118 119 120 121 123 124 126 129 130 131 132 135 138 141 144 145 146 147 148 149 154 156
Primary Contact: Arturo Polizzi, President and Chief Executive Officer
COO: Deborah Marie Hayes, R.N., MS, MSN, Chief Operating Officer
CMO: Bernard B Gawne, M.D., Vice President and Chief Medical Officer
CIO: Alex Vaillancourt, Chief Information Officer
CHR: Rick Tolson, Chief Administrative Officer and Chief Human Resources Officer
Web address: www.thechristhospital.com
Control: Other not–for–profit (including NFP Corporation) **Service:** General medical and surgical

Staffed Beds: 594 **Admissions:** 25276 **Census:** 303 **Outpatient Visits:** 624125 **Births:** 3345 **Total Expense ($000):** 714888 **Payroll Expense ($000):** 247088 **Personnel:** 3956

△ **CINCINNATI CHILDREN'S HOSPITAL MEDICAL CENTER (363300)**, 3333 Burnet Avenue MLC 8006, Zip 45229–3039, Mailing Address: 3333 Burnet Avenue, Zip 45229–3039; tel. 513/636–4200, (Includes CHILDREN'S HOSPITAL, 3300 Elland Avenue, Cincinnati, Ohio, Zip 45229–2804; tel. 513/894–8888) **A**1 2 3 5 7 8 10 **F**3 7 9 11 12 17 18 19 20 21 22 23 24 25 26 27 28 29 30 31 32 34 35 36 37 38 39 40 41 42 43 44 45 46 48 49 50 51 54 55 57 58 59 60 61 62 63 64 65 66 68 72 74 75 76 77 78 79 81 82 84 85 86 87 88 89 90 91 92 93 94 95 96 97 98 99 100 101 102 104 105 106 107 108 111 112 113 115 117 118 119 120 122 126 129 130 131 132 134 135 136 137 138 139 140 141 142 144 146 148 149 150 154 155 157
Primary Contact: Michael Fisher, President and Chief Executive Officer
CIO: Marianne Speight, Vice President Information System and Chief Information Officer
CHR: Nerissa E. Morris, Senior Vice President and Chief Human Resource Officer
CNO: Barbara F. Tofani, R.N., MSN, Senior Vice President and Chief Nursing Officer
Web address: www.cincinnatichildrens.org
Control: Other not–for–profit (including NFP Corporation) **Service:** Children's general medical and surgical

Staffed Beds: 634 **Admissions:** 18822 **Census:** 439 **Outpatient Visits:** 1263080 **Births:** 31 **Total Expense ($000):** 2259931 **Payroll Expense ($000):** 1125097 **Personnel:** 13270

CINCINNATI VETERANS AFFAIRS MEDICAL CENTER, 3200 Vine Street, Zip 45220–2288; tel. 513/475–6300, (Nonreporting) **A**1 2 3 5 **S** Department of Veterans Affairs, Washington, DC
Primary Contact: Mark Murdock, FACHE, Medical Center Director
COO: David Ninneman, Associate Director
CFO: Sandra Selvidge, Chief Fiscal Service
CIO: Vique Caro, Chief Information Officer
CHR: Sandra Stenger, Acting Chief Human Resources
CNO: Katheryn Cook, R.N., Nurse Executive
Web address: www.cincinnati.va.gov/
Control: Veterans Affairs, Government, federal **Service**: General medical and surgical

Staffed Beds: 268

DANIEL DRAKE CENTER FOR POST ACUTE CARE (362004), 151 West Galbraith Road, Zip 45216–1015; tel. 513/418–2500, (Nonreporting) **A**1 3 5 10 **S** UC Health, Cincinnati, OH
Primary Contact: Lafe Bauer, Vice President, Post Acute Care Services and Chief Administrative Officer
CFO: Duane Pifko, Interim Director Financial Services
Web address: www.uchealth.com/danieldrakecenter/
Control: Other not–for–profit (including NFP Corporation) **Service**: Acute long–term care hospital

Staffed Beds: 202

GOOD SAMARITAN HOSPITAL (360134), 375 Dixmyth Avenue, Zip 45220–2489; tel. 513/862–1400, **A**1 2 3 5 8 10 **F**3 5 6 8 9 11 12 13 15 17 18 20 22 24 26 28 29 30 31 34 35 36 37 38 39 40 41 42 44 45 46 47 48 49 50 53 54 55 56 57 58 59 61 63 64 65 66 68 70 71 72 74 75 76 77 78 79 81 82 83 84 85 86 87 91 92 93 94 96 97 98 100 101 102 103 104 105 107 108 109 110 111 114 115 116 117 118 119 120 121 123 124 126 129 130 131 132 134 135 141 143 144 145 146 147 148 149 152 153 154 156 **S** CommonSpirit Health, Chicago, IL
Primary Contact: Jamie Easterling, Executive Director, Operations
COO: Gerald P Oliphant, Executive Vice President and Chief Operating Officer
CFO: Michael Crofton, Chief Financial Officer
CMO: Georges Feghali, M.D., Senior Vice President Quality and Chief Medical Officer
CIO: Rick Moore, Chief Information Officer
CHR: Walter L McLarty, Chief Human Resources Officer
Web address: www.trihealth.com
Control: Church operated, Nongovernment, not–for–profit **Service**: General medical and surgical

Staffed Beds: 423 Admissions: 22693 Census: 294 Outpatient Visits: 295076 Births: 5237 Total Expense ($000): 544539 Payroll Expense ($000): 175629 Personnel: 2704

HEALTHSOUTH REHABILITATION HOSPITAL AT DRAKE (363034), 151 West Galbraith Road, Zip 45216–1015; tel. 513/418–5600, (Includes HEALTHSOUTH REHABILITATION HOSPITAL OF CINCINNATI AT NORWOOD, 4953 Section Avenue, Cincinnati, Ohio, Zip 45212–2120; tel. 513/712–9200; Ryan Smokovitz, Chief Executive Officer) **A**1 3 10 **F**29 34 35 56 57 74 90 91 130 148 **S** Encompass Health Corporation, Birmingham, AL
Primary Contact: Ryan Smokovitz, Chief Executive Officer
CFO: Scott Corder, Controller
CMO: Mark Goddard, M.D., Medical Director
CHR: Jason Sparks, Director, Human Resources
CNO: Kathy McNally, Chief Nursing Officer
Web address: www.healthsouthatdrake.com
Control: Corporation, Investor–owned (for–profit) **Service**: Rehabilitation

Staffed Beds: 100 Admissions: 1739 Census: 67 Outpatient Visits: 0 Births: 0 Total Expense ($000): 27011 Payroll Expense ($000): 13175 Personnel: 177

MERCY HEALTH - ANDERSON HOSPITAL (360001), 7500 State Road, Zip 45255–2492; tel. 513/624–4500, **A**1 2 3 10 **F**3 8 9 11 12 13 14 15 17 18 20 22 24 26 28 29 30 31 34 35 37 38 39 40 44 45 46 47 48 49 50 51 53 54 55 56 57 58 59 61 63 64 65 68 70 71 74 75 76 77 78 79 81 82 84 85 86 87 90 93 96 97 107 110 111 114 115 116 117 118 119 120 121 123 126 127 129 130 131 132 134 135 144 146 147 148 154 **S** Mercy Health, Cincinnati, OH
Primary Contact: Ken James, President and Chief Executive Officer of East Market
COO: Robert Maloney Jr Chief Operating Officer
CFO: Patrick A Kowalski, Chief Financial Officer
CMO: Dan Roth, M.D., Vice President Medical Affairs
CIO: Matt Eversole, Regional Vice President Information Services
CHR: Angie Ferrell, Director Human Resources
CNO: Melissa A Samuelson, R.N., Vice President and Chief Nursing Officer
Web address: www.e-mercy.com
Control: Church operated, Nongovernment, not–for–profit **Service**: General medical and surgical

Staffed Beds: 281 Admissions: 13419 Census: 149

MERCY HEALTH - WEST HOSPITAL (360234), 3300 Mercy Health Boulevard, Zip 45211–1103; tel. 513/215–5000, (Nonreporting) **A**1 2 10 **S** Mercy Health, Cincinnati, OH
Primary Contact: Michael Kramer, Chief Executive Officer
COO: Jason Asic, Chief Operating Officer
CFO: Kyle Klein, Assistant Chief Financial Officer
CMO: Creighton Wright, M.D., Vice President Medical Administration
CHR: Bridget Mentzel, Director Human Resources
CNO: Stephanie Meade, R.N., Chief Nursing Officer
Web address: www.e-mercy.com/west-hospital
Control: Church operated **Service**: General medical and surgical

Staffed Beds: 250

★ **SELECT SPECIALTY HOSPITAL - CINCINNATI NORTH (362034)**, 10500 Montgomery Road, Zip 45242–4402; tel. 513/865–5300, (Nonreporting) **A**10 **S** Select Medical Corporation, Mechanicsburg, PA
Primary Contact: David D. Muggli, FACHE, Interim Chief Executive Officer
CMO: Sunil Dama, M.D., Medical Director
CHR: Elizabeth M Wilson, Coordinator Human Resources
Web address: www.cincinnatinorth.selectspecialtyhospitals.com/
Control: Corporation, Investor–owned (for–profit) **Service**: Acute long–term care hospital

Staffed Beds: 41

SELECT SPECIALTY HOSPITAL-CINCINNATI (362019), 375 Dixmyth Avenue, 15th Floor, Zip 45220–2475; tel. 513/862–4444, (Nonreporting) **A**1 10 **S** Select Medical Corporation, Mechanicsburg, PA
Primary Contact: David D. Muggli, FACHE, Chief Executive Officer
CMO: Brian Boster, M.D., Medical Director
CNO: Bobbi Schmidt, Chief Nursing Officer
Web address: www.selectspecialtyhospitals.com/company/locations/cincinnati.aspx
Control: Corporation, Investor–owned (for–profit) **Service**: Acute long–term care hospital

Staffed Beds: 36

SHRINERS HOSPITALS FOR CHILDREN - CINCINNATI (363308), 3229 Burnet Avenue, Zip 45229–3095; tel. 513/872–6000, (Nonreporting) **A**1 3 5 10 **S** Shriners Hospitals for Children, Tampa, FL
Primary Contact: Mark D. Shugarman, Administrator
CFO: Susan Harris, Director Fiscal Services
CMO: Petra Warner, Chief of Staff
CIO: David Brian, Chief Information Officer
CHR: Gretchen Long, Manager Human Resources
Web address: www.shrinershospitalsforchildren.org/Hospitals/Locations/Cincinnati.aspx
Control: Other not–for–profit (including NFP Corporation) **Service**: Children's other specialty

Staffed Beds: 30

SUMMIT BEHAVIORAL HEALTHCARE (364035), 1101 Summit Road, Zip 45237–2652; tel. 513/948–3600, (Nonreporting) **A**1 3 5 10 **S** Ohio Department of Mental Health, Columbus, OH
Primary Contact: Elizabeth Banks, Chief Executive Officer
COO: Steven Burns, Director Fiscal Services
CFO: Steven Burns, Director Fiscal Services
CMO: Patrick McCullough, M.D., Chief Medical Services
CIO: Eric Bradley, Director Computer Information Services
CHR: Bobbie Carrelli, Director Human Resources
CNO: Kathy A. Smith, MSN, R.N., Nurse Executive
Web address: www.mh.state.oh.us/
Control: State, Government, nonfederal **Service**: Psychiatric

Staffed Beds: 291

THE JEWISH HOSPITAL - MERCY HEALTH (360016), 4777 East Galbraith Road, Zip 45236–2725; tel. 513/686–3000, (Nonreporting) **A**1 2 3 5 10 **S** Mercy Health, Cincinnati, OH
Primary Contact: Patricia Davis-Hagens, R.N., Central Market Leader and President
COO: Jack Hill, Chief Operating Officer and Administrator
Web address: www.jewishhospitalcincinnati.com/
Control: Other not–for–profit (including NFP Corporation) **Service**: General medical and surgical

Staffed Beds: 209

TRIHEALTH EVENDALE HOSPITAL (360362), 3155 Glendale Milford Road, Zip 45241–3134; tel. 513/454–2222, **A**1 2 10 **F**3 8 29 30 34 35 44 46 50 57 59 64 68 70 75 79 81 82 85 86 87 107 111 115 119 130 131 143 146 149 156
Primary Contact: Kelvin Hanger, Chief Executive Officer
CFO: Michael Crofton, Chief Financial Officer
Web address: www.evendalemedical.com
Control: Other not–for–profit (including NFP Corporation) **Service**: Surgical

Staffed Beds: 19 Admissions: 648 Census: 3 Outpatient Visits: 36525 Births: 0 Total Expense ($000): 50537 Payroll Expense ($000): 14652 Personnel: 185

⊞ **TRIHEALTH REHABILITATION HOSPITAL (363041)**, 2155 Dana Avenue, Zip 45207; tel. 513/601–0600, (Nonreporting) **A**1 10 **S** Select Medical Corporation, Mechanicsburg, PA
Primary Contact: Daphne Glenn, Chief Executive Officer
Web address: www.trihealthrehab.com
Control: Corporation, Investor–owned (for–profit) **Service:** Rehabilitation

Staffed Beds: 60

⊞ **UNIVERSITY OF CINCINNATI MEDICAL CENTER (360003)**, 234 Goodman Street, Zip 45219–2316; tel. 513/584–1000, **A**1 2 3 5 8 10 **F**3 7 9 11 12 13 15 16 17 18 20 22 24 26 29 30 31 34 38 39 40 41 43 44 45 46 47 48 49 50 51 54 55 56 57 58 59 60 61 63 64 66 68 70 71 72 74 75 76 77 78 79 80 81 82 84 85 86 87 91 92 97 98 100 101 102 103 104 107 108 110 111 112 114 115 116 117 118 119 120 121 122 123 124 126 129 130 131 132 134 135 136 137 138 139 141 142 143 145 146 147 148 149 150 154 155 156 157 **S** UC Health, Cincinnati, OH
Primary Contact: Ann Smith, Senior Vice President, Inpatient Services and Interim Chief Administrative Officer
CFO: Matthew Nealon, Vice President, Chief Financial Officer
CMO: Bill Hurford, Chief Medical Officer
CIO: Jay Brown, Vice President and Chief Information Officer
CHR: Clarence Pauley, Senior Vice President and Chief Human Resources Officer
CNO: Beverly A Bokovitz, R.N., Chief Nursing Officer
Web address: www.uchealth.com/university-of-cincinnati-medical-center/
Control: Other not–for–profit (including NFP Corporation) **Service:** General medical and surgical

Staffed Beds: 579 **Admissions:** 25838 **Census:** 440 **Outpatient Visits:** 721269 **Births:** 2406 **Total Expense ($000):** 951635 **Payroll Expense ($000):** 279483 **Personnel:** 4548

VETERANS AFFAIRS MEDICAL CENTER See Cincinnati Veterans Affairs Medical Center

CIRCLEVILLE—Pickaway County

⊞ **BERGER HEALTH SYSTEM (360170)**, 600 North Pickaway Street, Zip 43113–1447; tel. 740/474–2126, **A**1 10 **F**3 13 15 18 20 28 29 30 31 34 35 40 45 46 50 53 54 59 63 64 70 76 77 78 81 85 87 92 93 96 107 108 110 111 115 119 124 129 130 131 132 135 146 148 **S** OhioHealth, Columbus, OH
Primary Contact: Tim A. Colburn, President and Chief Executive Officer
CFO: Richard Filler, Chief Financial Officer
CMO: Jill Barno, M.D., Chief Medical Officer
CIO: Andy Chileski, Chief Information Officer and Vice President Facilities
CHR: Diane Guglielmi, Vice President, Human Resources
CNO: Kristin Day Gardner, Chief Nursing Officer
Web address: www.bergerhealth.com
Control: City–county, Government, nonfederal **Service:** General medical and surgical

Staffed Beds: 56 **Admissions:** 2022 **Census:** 17 **Outpatient Visits:** 101261 **Births:** 435 **Total Expense ($000):** 78871 **Payroll Expense ($000):** 24182

CLEVELAND—Cuyahoga County

⊞ **CLEVELAND CLINIC (360180)**, 9500 Euclid Avenue, Zip 44195–5108; tel. 216/444–2200, (Includes CLEVELAND CLINIC CHILDREN'S HOSPITAL, 9500 Euclid Avenue, Cleveland, Ohio, Zip 44103; tel. 800/223–2273) **A**1 3 5 8 10 **F**3 6 7 8 9 11 12 13 14 15 17 18 19 20 21 22 23 24 25 26 27 28 29 30 31 32 33 34 35 36 37 38 39 40 44 45 46 47 48 49 50 51 52 53 54 55 56 57 58 59 60 61 63 64 65 66 68 70 71 72 74 75 76 77 78 79 80 81 82 83 84 85 86 87 88 89 90 91 92 93 94 95 96 97 100 101 104 107 108 109 110 111 112 113 114 115 116 117 118 119 120 121 123 124 126 129 130 131 132 134 135 136 137 138 139 140 141 142 143 144 145 146 147 148 149 150 154 **S** Cleveland Clinic Health System, Cleveland, OH
Primary Contact: Tomislav Mihaljevic, M.D., President and Chief Executive Officer
CFO: Steven Glass, Chief Financial Officer
CMO: Joseph Hahn, M.D., Chief of Staff
CIO: Edward Marx, Chief Information Officer
CNO: Katherine Hancock, R.N., Executive Chief Nursing Officer
Web address: www.clevelandclinic.org
Control: Other not–for–profit (including NFP Corporation) **Service:** General medical and surgical

Staffed Beds: 1294 **Admissions:** 51514 **Census:** 1025 **Outpatient Visits:** 6615600 **Births:** 109 **Total Expense ($000):** 5775458 **Payroll Expense ($000):** 2841140 **Personnel:** 30152

⊞ △ **CLEVELAND CLINIC CHILDREN'S HOSPITAL FOR REHABILITATION (363304)**, 2801 Martin Luther King Jr Drive, Zip 44104–3865; tel. 216/448–6400, **A**1 3 7 10 **F**28 29 30 32 34 35 36 44 50 60 68 74 75 79 80 82 84 90 91 93 94 96 99 100 130 131 132 143 146 148 154 **S** Cleveland Clinic Health System, Cleveland, OH
Primary Contact: Michelle Marks, D.O., Medical Director
COO: Alec G Kulik, Administrator
CFO: Debra Nyikes, Director Finance and Chief Financial Officer
CMO: Roberta Bauer, M.D., Acting Chair Medical Staff
CIO: C Martin Harris, M.D., Chief Information Officer
CHR: Jan Hlahol, Manager Human Resources
Web address: www.my.clevelandclinic.org/childrens-hospital/default.aspx
Control: Other not–for–profit (including NFP Corporation) **Service:** Children's rehabilitation

Staffed Beds: 25 **Admissions:** 219 **Census:** 14 **Outpatient Visits:** 42590 **Births:** 0 **Total Expense ($000):** 48377 **Payroll Expense ($000):** 28349 **Personnel:** 423

⊞ **CLEVELAND CLINIC FAIRVIEW HOSPITAL (360077)**, 18101 Lorain Avenue, Zip 44111–5656; tel. 216/476–7000, **A**1 2 3 10 **F**3 8 11 12 13 15 17 18 19 20 22 24 26 28 29 30 31 32 34 35 36 40 41 43 45 46 47 49 50 51 53 55 57 58 59 60 64 65 66 68 69 70 71 72 73 74 75 76 77 78 79 80 81 82 84 85 86 87 89 92 93 97 98 99 100 107 108 110 111 114 115 117 118 119 120 121 123 124 126 130 131 132 135 143 146 147 148 149 150 154 155 156 **S** Cleveland Clinic Health System, Cleveland, OH
Primary Contact: Neil Smith, D.O., President
COO: John C Mills, Senior Vice President Operations
CFO: Ankit Chhabra, Director Finance
CIO: C Martin Harris, M.D., Chief Information Officer
CHR: Ann Beatty, Director Human Resources
Web address: www.fairviewhospital.org
Control: Other not–for–profit (including NFP Corporation) **Service:** General medical and surgical

Staffed Beds: 460 **Admissions:** 26629 **Census:** 302 **Outpatient Visits:** 216991 **Births:** 5203 **Total Expense ($000):** 408245 **Payroll Expense ($000):** 155408 **Personnel:** 2335

☐ **GRACE HOSPITAL (362015)**, 2307 West 14th Street, Zip 44113–3698; tel. 216/687–1500, (Nonreporting) **A**1 10
Primary Contact: Rajive Khanna, Chief Executive Officer
COO: Rajive Khanna, Chief Executive Officer
CFO: Michelle Hennis, Administrative Director Financial Services
CMO: John Nickels, M.D., President Medical Staff
Web address: www.gracehospital.org
Control: Other not–for–profit (including NFP Corporation) **Service:** Acute long–term care hospital

Staffed Beds: 87

△ **HILLCREST HOSPITAL (360230)**, 6780 Mayfield Road, Zip 44124–2203; tel. 440/312–4500, **A**1 2 3 10 **F**3 8 12 13 15 17 18 20 22 24 26 28 29 30 31 34 35 36 37 38 40 41 43 46 49 50 51 53 54 55 56 57 59 60 62 63 64 65 68 70 72 74 75 76 77 78 79 81 82 84 85 86 89 93 97 99 100 107 108 110 111 114 115 116 117 118 119 120 121 123 124 129 130 131 132 135 143 145 146 147 148 149 154 155 156 **S** Cleveland Clinic Health System, Cleveland, OH
Primary Contact: Richard Parker, M.D., President, Hillcrest Hospital
Web address: www.hillcresthospital.org
Control: Other not–for–profit (including NFP Corporation) **Service:** General medical and surgical

Staffed Beds: 440 **Admissions:** 24830 **Census:** 310 **Outpatient Visits:** 215460 **Births:** 4383 **Total Expense ($000):** 410908 **Payroll Expense ($000):** 141375 **Personnel:** 2123

△ **LOUIS STOKES CLEVELAND VETERANS AFFAIRS MEDICAL CENTER**, 10701 East Boulevard, Zip 44106–1702; tel. 216/791–3800, (Total facility includes 123 beds in nursing home–type unit) **A**1 2 3 5 7 8 **F**3 4 5 8 9 10 12 15 17 18 20 22 24 26 28 29 30 31 33 34 35 36 38 39 40 44 45 46 47 48 49 50 51 53 54 55 56 57 58 59 60 61 62 63 64 65 67 68 70 71 74 75 77 78 79 80 81 82 83 84 85 86 87 90 91 92 93 94 95 96 97 98 100 101 102 103 104 105 106 107 110 111 113 116 117 119 120 121 126 127 128 129 130 132 135 143 144 146 147 148 149 150 152 153 154 156 157 158 **S** Department of Veterans Affairs, Washington, DC
Primary Contact: Susan Fuehrer, Director
COO: Andrew Pacyna, Deputy Director
CFO: Michael Pappas, Chief Fiscal Service Officer
CMO: Murray Altose, M.D., Chief of Staff
CIO: Steve Gaj, Facility Chief Information Officer
CHR: Charles Franks, Chief Human Resources
CNO: Innette Mary Sarduy, M.P.H., R.N., Associate Director Patient Care Services and Nurse Executive
Web address: www.cleveland.va.gov/
Control: Veterans Affairs, Government, federal **Service:** General medical and surgical

Staffed Beds: 578 **Admissions:** 12342 **Census:** 500 **Outpatient Visits:** 1515656 **Births:** 0 **Personnel:** 4962

LUTHERAN HOSPITAL (360087), 1730 West 25th Street, Zip 44113–3170; tel. 216/696–4300, **A**1 3 10 **F**3 4 5 12 15 29 30 34 35 37 40 45 50 56 57 58 59 60 64 65 68 70 74 75 77 79 81 82 85 86 87 93 94 98 100 102 103 104 107 108 110 111 114 115 119 126 130 132 135 143 146 148 149 152 153 154 156 **S** Cleveland Clinic Health System, Cleveland, OH
Primary Contact: Donald A. Malone Jr, President
COO: Matthew Mattner, Chief Operating Officer
CFO: Don Urbancsik, Director Finance
CMO: Ronald Golovan, M.D., Vice President Medical Operations
CIO: C Martin Harris, M.D., Chief Information Officer
CHR: Judith Santora, Chief Human Resource Officer
CNO: Janet Schuster, Chief Nursing Officer
Web address: www.lutheranhospital.org
Control: Other not–for–profit (including NFP Corporation) **Service:** General medical and surgical

Staffed Beds: 194 **Admissions:** 8254 **Census:** 104 **Outpatient Visits:** 74829 **Births:** 0 **Total Expense ($000):** 114879 **Payroll Expense ($000):** 45407 **Personnel:** 655

△ **METROHEALTH MEDICAL CENTER (360059)**, 2500 MetroHealth Drive, Zip 44109–1998; tel. 216/778–7800, (Total facility includes 133 beds in nursing home–type unit) **A**1 2 3 5 7 8 10 **F**3 5 6 7 8 9 11 12 13 15 16 17 18 19 20 22 24 26 27 28 29 30 31 32 34 35 36 38 39 40 41 42 43 44 45 46 47 48 49 50 51 52 53 54 55 56 57 58 59 60 61 63 64 65 66 68 70 71 72 74 75 76 77 78 79 80 81 82 83 84 85 86 87 88 89 90 91 92 93 94 95 96 97 98 100 101 102 104 105 107 108 110 111 114 115 116 117 118 119 120 121 123 124 126 128 129 130 131 132 134 135 143 144 146 147 148 149 150 153 154 155 156 157
Primary Contact: Akram Boutros, M.D., FACHE, President and Chief Executive Officer
COO: Daniel Lewis, Executive Vice President and Chief Operating Officer
CFO: Craig Richmond, Senior Vice President and Chief Financial Officer
CMO: Alfred Connors, M.D., Executive Vice President and Chief Quality Officer and Interim Chief Medical Officer
CIO: Don Reichert, Vice President Associate Chief Information Officer
CHR: Debbie Warman, Vice President Human Resources
CNO: Melissa Kline, Chief Nursing Officer
Web address: www.metrohealth.org
Control: County, Government, nonfederal **Service:** General medical and surgical

Staffed Beds: 721 **Admissions:** 23398 **Census:** 487 **Outpatient Visits:** 1393416 **Births:** 2992 **Total Expense ($000):** 1150354 **Payroll Expense ($000):** 608117 **Personnel:** 6832

SELECT SPECIALTY HOSPITAL - CLEVELAND FAIRHILL See Select Specialty Hospital - Cleveland Gateway, Cleveland

★ **SELECT SPECIALTY HOSPITAL - CLEVELAND GATEWAY (362026)**, 2351 East 22nd Street, 7th Floor, Zip 44115–3111; tel. 216/363–2671, (Includes SELECT SPECIALTY HOSPITAL - CLEVELAND FAIRHILL, 11900 Fairhill Road, Cleveland, Ohio, Zip 44120–1062; tel. 216/983–8030; Julie Idoine-Fries, Chief Executive Officer), (Non-reporting) **A**10 **S** Select Medical Corporation, Mechanicsburg, PA
Primary Contact: Julie Idoine-Fries, Chief Executive Officer
Web address: www.selectspecialtyhospitals.com/
Control: Corporation, Investor–owned (for–profit) **Service:** Acute long–term care hospital

Staffed Beds: 143

VETERANS AFFAIRS MEDICAL CENTER See Louis Stokes Cleveland Veterans Affairs Medical Center

☐ **ST. VINCENT CHARITY MEDICAL CENTER (360037)**, 2351 East 22nd Street, Zip 44115–3111; tel. 216/861–6200, (Nonreporting) **A**1 2 3 5 10 **S** Sisters of Charity Health System, Cleveland, OH
Primary Contact: David F. Perse, M.D., President and Chief Executive Officer
COO: Joan Ross, Senior Vice President and Chief Operating Officer
CFO: John Rusnaczyk, Senior Vice President and Chief Financial Officer
CMO: Joseph A. Sopko, M.D., Chief Medical Officer
CIO: Robin Stursa, Chief Information Officer
CHR: Ted Monczewski, Vice President Human Resources
CNO: Beverly Lozar, Chief Nursing Executive
Web address: www.stvincentcharity.com/
Control: Church operated **Service:** General medical and surgical

Staffed Beds: 208

UH REGIONAL HOSPITALS (360075), 27100 Chardon Road, Zip 44143–1116; tel. 440/585–6500, (Includes UNIVERSITY HOSPITALS BEDFORD MEDICAL CENTER, 44 Blaine Avenue, Cleveland, Ohio, Zip 44146–2709; tel. 440/735–3900; UNIVERSITY HOSPITALS RICHMOND MEDICAL CENTER, 27100 Chardon Road, Cleveland, Ohio, Zip 44143–1116; tel. 440/585–6500) **A**1 10 12 13 **F**8 14 15 18 20 26 29 30 34 35 39 40 50 56 57 59 60 64 65 66 68 70 74 75 77 78 79 81 82 84 85 86 87 91 92 93 96 97 100 107 108 109 110 111 114 116 117 118 119 130 131 132 133 135 143 146 147 148 149 154 **S** University Hospitals, Cleveland, OH
Primary Contact: Brian Monter, MSN, R.N., President
CFO: Scott Platz, Director Finance
CMO: Rosemary Leeming, M.D., Chief Medical Officer
CHR: Stephanie W Neonakis, Manager Human Resources
CNO: Michelle Giltner, Interim Chief Nursing Officer
Web address: www.uhhospitals.org
Control: Other not–for–profit (including NFP Corporation) **Service:** General medical and surgical

Staffed Beds: 101 **Admissions:** 4507 **Census:** 47 **Outpatient Visits:** 121143 **Births:** 0 **Total Expense ($000):** 114987 **Payroll Expense ($000):** 43172 **Personnel:** 768

UNIVERSITY HOSPITALS CLEVELAND MEDICAL CENTER (360137), 11100 Euclid Avenue, Zip 44106–1716; tel. 216/844–1000, (Includes HANNA HOUSE SKILLED NURSING FACILITY, 11100 Euclid Avenue, Cleveland, Ohio, Zip 44106; tel. 216/844–3911; RAINBOW BABIES AND CHILDREN'S HOSPITAL, 2101 Adelbert Road, Cleveland, Ohio, Zip 44106–2624; tel. 216/844–3911; Patricia DePompei, President; UNIVERSITY MACDONALD WOMEN'S HOSPITAL, 2101 Adelbert Road, Cleveland, Ohio, Zip 44106–2624; tel. 216/844–3911; Patricia DePompei, President) (Total facility includes 26 beds in nursing home–type unit) **A**1 2 3 5 8 10 **F**3 5 6 8 9 11 12 13 14 15 17 18 19 20 21 22 23 24 25 26 27 28 29 30 31 32 34 35 36 37 38 39 40 41 42 43 44 45 46 47 48 49 50 51 52 53 54 55 56 57 58 59 60 61 62 63 64 65 68 70 71 72 73 74 75 76 77 78 79 80 81 82 83 84 85 86 87 88 89 91 92 93 94 96 97 98 99 100 101 102 104 105 107 108 109 110 111 112 113 114 115 116 117 118 119 120 121 122 123 124 126 128 129 130 131 132 134 135 136 137 138 139 140 141 142 144 145 146 147 148 149 150 151 152 153 154 156 157 **S** University Hospitals, Cleveland, OH
Primary Contact: Daniel I. Simon, M.D., President
COO: Ron Dziedzicki, R.N., Chief Operating Officer
CFO: Sonia Salvino, Vice President Finance
CIO: Sue Schade, Interim Chief Information Officer
CHR: Julie Chester, Vice President Human Resources
CNO: Jean Blake, Chief Nursing Officer
Web address: www.UHhospitals.org
Control: Other not–for–profit (including NFP Corporation) **Service:** General medical and surgical

Staffed Beds: 938 **Admissions:** 41428 **Census:** 691 **Outpatient Visits:** 898594 **Births:** 4053 **Total Expense ($000):** 1620962 **Payroll Expense ($000):** 493175 **Personnel:** 8874

COLDWATER—Mercer County

MERCER HEALTH (360058), 800 West Main Street, Zip 45828–1698; tel. 419/678–2341, **A**1 10 **F**3 7 11 12 13 15 18 28 29 30 31 34 35 40 44 45 47 50 51 54 57 59 61 62 64 65 70 75 76 77 78 79 81 82 85 87 92 93 94 95 97 107 108 110 111 114 118 119 130 131 132 133 134 135 143 144 145 146 147 148 149 150 156
Primary Contact: Lisa R. Klenke, R.N., Chief Executive Officer
CFO: George Boyles, Senior Vice President of Finance and Chief Financial Officer
CMO: James Reichert, Chief Medical Officer
CIO: DeWayne Marsee, Director Information Systems
CHR: Jon Dingledine, Senior Director Human Resources and Support Services
CNO: Cindy Liette, Vice President Patient Care Services
Web address: www.mercer-health.com
Control: Hospital district or authority, Government, nonfederal **Service:** General medical and surgical

Staffed Beds: 60 **Admissions:** 1929 **Census:** 16 **Outpatient Visits:** 11002 **Births:** 356 **Total Expense ($000):** 59112 **Payroll Expense ($000):** 19185 **Personnel:** 357

COLUMBUS—Franklin County

✠ **JAMES CANCER HOSPITAL AND SOLOVE RESEARCH INSTITUTE (360242)**, 460 West Tenth Avenue, Zip 43210–1240; tel. 614/293–3300, **A**1 2 3 5 10 **F**3 15 29 30 31 32 34 35 36 37 38 39 44 46 47 48 49 50 52 54 55 57 58 59 61 64 65 66 68 70 71 74 75 77 78 79 80 81 82 84 85 86 87 93 97 100 107 108 110 111 112 114 115 116 117 118 119 120 121 123 124 126 130 132 134 135 136 141 143 144 145 146 147 148 149 154 157 **S** Ohio State University Health System, Columbus, OH
Primary Contact: William Farrar, M.D., Interim Chief Executive Officer
CFO: Bell Julian, Associate Executive Director and Chief Financial Officer
CIO: Michael Townsend, Chief Information Officer
CHR: Jill Hannah, Director Human Resources
CNO: Kris M Kipp, Executive Director, Patient Services and Chief Nursing Officer
Web address: www.https://cancer.osu.edu/
Control: State, Government, nonfederal **Service**: Cancer

Staffed Beds: 308 **Admissions**: 14967 **Census**: 266 **Outpatient Visits**: 430209 **Births**: 0 **Total Expense ($000)**: 1054348 **Payroll Expense ($000)**: 251559 **Personnel**: 4451

✠ **MOUNT CARMEL (360035)**, 793 West State Street, Zip 43222–1551; tel. 614/234–5000, (Includes MOUNT CARMEL EAST HOSPITAL, 6001 East Broad Street, Columbus, Ohio, Zip 43213; tel. 614/234–6000; Michael Wilkins, President; MOUNT CARMEL WEST HOSPITAL, 793 West State Street, Columbus, Ohio, Zip 43222; tel. 614/234–5000) **A**1 2 3 5 10 **F**3 11 12 13 15 17 18 20 22 24 26 28 29 30 31 34 35 37 40 43 44 45 46 47 48 49 50 51 54 55 57 58 59 61 63 64 65 66 68 70 72 74 75 76 77 78 79 81 82 83 84 85 86 87 90 93 97 98 100 101 102 103 104 107 108 109 110 111 114 115 116 117 118 119 120 121 123 126 130 131 132 141 146 147 148 149 154 **S** Trinity Health, Livonia, MI
Primary Contact: Sean McKibben, President and Chief Operating Officer
COO: Mary R Trimmer, Interim Chief Operating Officer
Web address: www.mountcarmelhealth.com
Control: Church operated, Nongovernment, not-for-profit **Service**: General medical and surgical

Staffed Beds: 612 **Admissions**: 37834 **Census**: 438 **Outpatient Visits**: 360409 **Births**: 3322 **Total Expense ($000)**: 733288 **Payroll Expense ($000)**: 250154 **Personnel**: 3690

✠ △ **NATIONWIDE CHILDREN'S HOSPITAL (363305)**, 700 Children's Drive, Zip 43205–2664; tel. 614/722–2000, **A**1 2 3 5 7 8 10 18 **F**3 5 7 8 12 16 17 18 19 20 21 22 23 24 25 26 27 28 29 30 31 32 34 35 36 38 39 40 41 42 43 44 45 47 48 50 51 52 53 54 55 57 58 59 60 61 62 63 64 65 66 68 71 72 74 75 77 78 79 81 82 83 84 85 86 87 88 89 90 92 93 94 96 97 98 99 100 101 102 104 105 107 108 111 112 114 115 116 117 118 119 126 127 129 130 131 132 133 134 135 136 137 138 139 140 141 143 144 145 146 148 149 150 153 154 155 156 157 158
Primary Contact: Tim Robinson, Chief Executive Officer
COO: Rick Miller, President and Chief Operating Officer
CMO: Richard Brilli, M.D., Chief Medical Officer
CIO: Denise Zabawski, Vice President Information Services and Chief Information Officer
Web address: www.nationwidechildrens.org
Control: Other not-for-profit (including NFP Corporation) **Service**: Children's general medical and surgical

Staffed Beds: 673 **Admissions**: 17734 **Census**: 430 **Outpatient Visits**: 1519642 **Births**: 0 **Total Expense ($000)**: 1280639 **Payroll Expense ($000)**: 588901 **Personnel**: 10486

☐ **OHIO HOSPITAL FOR PSYCHIATRY (364041)**, 880 Greenlawn Avenue, Zip 43223–2616; tel. 614/449–9664, **A**1 10 **F**64 98 103 130 153 **S** Acadia Healthcare Company, Inc., Franklin, TN
Primary Contact: Angel Piper, Chief Executive Officer
COO: Shannon Robbins, Chief Operating Officer
CFO: Steve Snyder, Chief Financial Officer
CMO: Richard Nockowitz, M.D., Medical Director
CNO: Jayne Zink, Director of Nursing
Web address: www.ohiohospitalforpsychiatry.com/
Control: Corporation, Investor-owned (for-profit) **Service**: Psychiatric

Staffed Beds: 130 **Admissions**: 3316 **Census**: 66 **Outpatient Visits**: 5059 **Births**: 0 **Total Expense ($000)**: 18429 **Payroll Expense ($000)**: 8865 **Personnel**: 155

✠ △ **OHIO STATE UNIVERSITY WEXNER MEDICAL CENTER (360085)**, 410 West 10th Avenue, Zip 43210–1240; tel. 614/293–8000, (Includes OHIO STATE UNIVERSITY HOSPITALS EAST, 1492 East Broad Street, Columbus, Ohio, Zip 43205–1546; tel. 614/257–3000) **A**1 3 5 7 8 10 **F**3 4 5 6 8 9 11 12 13 15 16 17 18 20 22 24 26 28 29 30 31 34 35 36 37 38 39 40 42 43 44 45 46 47 48 49 50 51 52 53 54 55 56 57 58 59 60 61 64 65 66 68 70 72 73 74 75 76 77 78 79 80 81 82 84 85 86 87 90 91 92 93 95 96 97 98 99 100 101 102 103 104 105 107 108 110 111 112 113 114 115 118 119 126 129 130 131 132 134 135 137 138 139 140 141 142 143 144 145 146 147 148 149 152 153 154 156 157 **S** Ohio State University Health System, Columbus, OH
Primary Contact: David P. McQuaid, FACHE, Chief Operating Officer
COO: David P. McQuaid, FACHE, Chief Operating Officer
CFO: Mark Larmore, Chief Financial Officer
CMO: Andrew Thomas, M.D., Chief Medical Officer
CIO: Phyllis Teater, Chief Information Officer
CHR: Kim Shumate, Human Resources Officer
CNO: Mary G Nash, Ph.D., R.N., Chief Nursing Officer
Web address: www.medicalcenter.osu.edu
Control: State, Government, nonfederal **Service**: General medical and surgical

Staffed Beds: 1091 **Admissions**: 49562 **Census**: 830 **Outpatient Visits**: 1384861 **Births**: 5264 **Total Expense ($000)**: 1618254 **Payroll Expense ($000)**: 488421 **Personnel**: 11524

✠ **OHIOHEALTH DOCTORS HOSPITAL (360152)**, 5100 West Broad Street, Zip 43228–1607; tel. 614/544–1000, **A**1 2 3 5 10 12 13 **F**3 15 17 18 20 22 26 28 29 30 31 34 35 36 40 45 46 47 48 49 50 57 58 59 64 65 66 68 70 72 74 75 76 77 78 79 81 82 84 85 87 90 92 93 97 100 107 109 110 111 114 115 116 117 119 120 121 123 126 130 131 135 145 146 147 148 149 154 **S** OhioHealth, Columbus, OH
Primary Contact: Michael L. Reichfield, President
CMO: Dean Colwell, D.O., Vice President Medical Affairs
CIO: Michael Krouse, Chief Information Officer
CHR: David Sullivan, Director Human Resources
Web address: www.ohiohealth.com
Control: Church operated, Nongovernment, not-for-profit **Service**: General medical and surgical

Staffed Beds: 195 **Admissions**: 8359 **Census**: 91

✠ **OHIOHEALTH GRANT MEDICAL CENTER (360017)**, 111 South Grant Avenue, Zip 43215–1898; tel. 614/566–9000, **A**1 2 3 5 8 10 **F**3 7 8 11 13 15 17 18 20 22 24 26 28 29 30 31 35 36 37 40 42 43 45 46 47 48 49 50 53 56 57 58 59 60 61 64 66 67 69 70 72 74 75 76 78 79 81 82 83 84 85 86 87 97 100 102 107 108 109 110 111 114 115 116 117 119 120 121 123 124 126 130 131 132 135 143 144 146 147 148 149 150 154 155 156 157 **S** OhioHealth, Columbus, OH
Primary Contact: Michael Lawson, President and Chief Operating Officer
COO: Kevin Lutz, DPM, Chief Operating Officer, Grant
CFO: Heather Brandon, Vice President of Finance, Grant
CMO: Michael Ezzie, Director of Medical Education and Interim Vice President of Medical Affairs
CIO: Michael Krouse, Chief Information Officer
CHR: Qiana Williams, Director, Human Resource Business Partner, Grant
CNO: Sharon Neenan, Interim Chief Nursing Officer, Grant
Web address: www.ohiohealth.com
Control: Church operated, Nongovernment, not-for-profit **Service**: General medical and surgical

Staffed Beds: 471 **Admissions**: 19231 **Census**: 262 **Outpatient Visits**: 189376 **Births**: 2258 **Personnel**: 2620

✠ **OHIOHEALTH REHABILITATION HOSPITAL (363037)**, 1087 Dennison Avenue, 4th Floor, Zip 43201–3201; tel. 614/484–9600, **A**1 10 **F**3 29 30 34 35 50 57 90 95 96 130 132 135 146 148 149 **S** Select Medical Corporation, Mechanicsburg, PA
Primary Contact: Eric Yap, Chief Executive Officer
CFO: Ted Bolcavage, Vice President Division Controller, Inpatient
CMO: Lisa Lombard, Chief Medical Officer
CHR: Josette Alexander, Director, Human Resources
CNO: Graydon Todd Auckerman, Chief Nursing Officer
Web address: www.ohiohealth-rehab.com
Control: Corporation, Investor-owned (for-profit) **Service**: Rehabilitation

Staffed Beds: 74 **Admissions**: 1801 **Census**: 66 **Outpatient Visits**: 0 **Births**: 0 **Total Expense ($000)**: 19993 **Payroll Expense ($000)**: 8835 **Personnel**: 186

Hospital, Medicare Provider Number, Address, Telephone, Approval, Facility, and Physician Codes, Health Care System

★ American Hospital Association (AHA) membership
☐ The Joint Commission accreditation
○ Healthcare Facilities Accreditation Program
◇ DNV Healthcare Inc. accreditation
⇑ Center for Improvement in Healthcare Quality Accreditation
△ Commission on Accreditation of Rehabilitation Facilities (CARF) accreditation

OH

⊞ **OHIOHEALTH RIVERSIDE METHODIST HOSPITAL (360006)**, 3535 Olentangy River Road, Zip 43214–3998; tel. 614/566–5000, **A**1 2 3 5 8 10 **F**3 5 7 8 12 13 14 15 17 18 20 22 24 26 28 29 30 31 34 35 36 37 38 39 40 43 44 45 46 47 48 49 50 51 53 54 55 56 57 58 59 60 61 62 63 64 65 66 67 68 69 70 71 72 73 74 75 76 77 78 79 80 81 82 83 84 85 86 87 91 92 93 94 96 97 98 100 102 103 104 105 106 107 108 109 110 111 112 114 115 116 117 118 119 120 121 123 124 126 130 131 132 133 135 143 144 145 146 147 148 152 153 154 156 **S** OhioHealth, Columbus, OH
Primary Contact: Brian Jepson, President
COO: Elizabeth Brill, M.D., Chief Operating Officer
CFO: Peter Bury, Vice President Finance
CMO: Thomas Harmon, M.D., Vice President Medical Affairs
CIO: Michael Krouse, Chief Information Officer
CHR: Shereen Solaiman, Vice President Human Resources
CNO: Lisa Gossett, MSN, R.N., Chief Nursing Officer
Web address: www.ohiohealth.com
Control: Church operated, Nongovernment, not–for–profit **Service**: General medical and surgical

Staffed Beds: 753 **Admissions:** 43690 **Census:** 550 **Outpatient Visits:** 1035723 **Births:** 6069 **Total Expense ($000):** 1189810 **Payroll Expense ($000):** 452478 **Personnel:** 5934

⊞ **REGENCY HOSPITAL OF COLUMBUS (362037)**, 1430 South High Street, Zip 43207–1045; tel. 614/456–0300, (Includes SELECT SPECIALTY HOSPITAL - COLUMBUS EAST, 1492 East Broad Street, 6th Floor, Columbus, Ohio, Zip 43205–1546; tel. 614/685–1703; Nabarun Kundu, Chief Executive Officer), (Non-reporting) **A**1 10 **S** Select Medical Corporation, Mechanicsburg, PA
Primary Contact: Kindra Marks, Chief Executive Officer
Web address: www.regencyhospital.com/
Control: Corporation, Investor–owned (for–profit) **Service**: Acute long–term care hospital

Staffed Beds: 66

⊞ **SELECT SPECIALTY HOSPITAL-COLUMBUS (362022)**, 1087 Dennison Avenue, Zip 43201–3201; tel. 614/458–9000, (Nonreporting) **A**1 10 **S** Select Medical Corporation, Mechanicsburg, PA
Primary Contact: Lisa J. Pettrey, MSN, R.N., Chief Executive Officer
CMO: Victoria Ruff, M.D., Medical Director
CHR: Charles Pankowski, Manager Human Resources
Web address: www.selectspecialtyhospitals.com/company/locations/columbus.aspx
Control: Corporation, Investor–owned (for–profit) **Service**: Acute long–term care hospital

Staffed Beds: 162

SEQUEL POMEGRANATE HEALTH SYSTEMS (364045), 765 Pierce Drive, Zip 43223, Mailing Address: 975 Pierce Avenue, Zip 43227; tel. 614/223–1650, (Nonreporting) **A**10
Primary Contact: Angela Nickell, Executive Director
Web address: www.pomegranatehealthsystems.com
Control: Other not–for–profit (including NFP Corporation) **Service**: Psychiatric

Staffed Beds: 90

☐ **SUN BEHAVIORAL COLUMBUS (364058)**, 900 Dublin Granville Road, Zip 43229–2452; tel. 614/706–2786, **A**1 10 **F**4 5 98 101 102 104 105 106 130 135 151 152 153
Primary Contact: Lance Folske, Chief Executive Officer
Web address: www.https://www.suncolumbus.com
Control: Corporation, Investor–owned (for–profit) **Service**: Psychiatric

Staffed Beds: 80 **Admissions:** 2758 **Census:** 58 **Outpatient Visits:** 2659 **Births:** 0

☐ **TWIN VALLEY BEHAVIORAL HEALTHCARE (364007)**, 2200 West Broad Street, Zip 43223–1297; tel. 614/752–0333, **A**1 3 10 **F**29 30 54 59 98 104 130 **S** Ohio Department of Mental Health, Columbus, OH
Primary Contact: Veronica Lofton, Acting Chief Executive Officer
COO: David Blahnik, Chief Operating Officer
CFO: Tracy Gladen, Chief Financial Officer
CMO: R Alan Freeland, M.D., Chief Clinical Officer
CIO: Missy McGarvey, Chief Information Officer
CHR: Marcia McKeen, Director Human Resources
CNO: Michael Breakwell, R.N., Nurse Executive
Web address: www.mh.state.oh.us/ibhs/bhos/tvbh.html
Control: State, Government, nonfederal **Service**: Psychiatric

Staffed Beds: 178 **Admissions:** 1600 **Census:** 174 **Outpatient Visits:** 28536 **Births:** 0 **Personnel:** 444

CONCORD TOWNSHIP—Lake County

⊞ **LAKE HEALTH (360098)**, 7590 Auburn Road, Zip 44077–9176; tel. 440/953–9600, (Includes TRIPOINT MEDICAL CENTER, 7590 Auburn Road, Concord Township, Ohio, Zip 44077; tel. 614/685–1703; Cynthia Moore-Hardy, FACHE, President and Chief Executive Officer) **A**1 10 **F**3 5 11 12 13 15 18 20 22 24 26 28 29 30 32 33 34 35 36 40 42 44 45 50 51 53 54 56 57 58 59 60 62 63 64 65 68 70 75 76 77 79 81 82 84 85 86 87 90 93 97 98 103 107 108 110 111 112 113 114 115 116 117 119 120 121 122 123 124 126 129 130 131 132 133 135 143 144 146 147 148 154 156
Primary Contact: Cynthia Moore-Hardy, FACHE, President and Chief Executive Officer
CFO: Robert B Tracz, CPA, Senior Vice President and Chief Financial Officer
CMO: John Baniewicz, M.D., Chief Medical Officer
CIO: Gerald Peters, Vice President Information Technologies and Chief Information Officer
CHR: Craig J Ghidotti, Vice President Human Resources
CNO: Mary L Ogrinc, R.N., MS, Chief Nursing Officer, Senior Vice President Patient Care Services
Web address: www.lakehealth.org
Control: Other not–for–profit (including NFP Corporation) **Service**: General medical and surgical

Staffed Beds: 352 **Admissions:** 16981 **Census:** 183 **Outpatient Visits:** 499124 **Births:** 1742 **Total Expense ($000):** 372222 **Payroll Expense ($000):** 127486 **Personnel:** 2393

CONNEAUT—Ashtabula County

⊞ **UNIVERSITY HOSPITALS CONNEAUT MEDICAL CENTER (361308)**, 158 West Main Street, Zip 44030–2039; tel. 440/593–1131, **A**1 10 18 **F**3 11 15 18 28 29 31 34 35 37 40 45 56 57 59 64 68 70 75 77 78 79 81 82 85 86 87 93 107 110 111 115 119 130 132 133 135 143 144 146 147 148 149 154 **S** University Hospitals, Cleveland, OH
Primary Contact: M Steven. Jones, President
COO: Jason Glowczewski, Chief Operating Officer
CFO: Lara Eggleston, Finance Manager
CMO: Abirammy Sundaramoorthy, M.D., Chief Medical Officer
CIO: Kirsten Hale, Coordinator Health Information Services
CHR: Danialle Lynce, Business Partner Human Resources
CNO: Ashley Fertig, Chief Nursing Officer
Web address: www.uhhospitals.org
Control: Other not–for–profit (including NFP Corporation) **Service**: General medical and surgical

Staffed Beds: 25 **Admissions:** 595 **Census:** 5 **Outpatient Visits:** 29225 **Births:** 0 **Total Expense ($000):** 27157 **Payroll Expense ($000):** 8665 **Personnel:** 153

COSHOCTON—Coshocton County

⊞ **COSHOCTON REGIONAL MEDICAL CENTER (360109)**, 1460 Orange Street, Zip 43812–2229, Mailing Address: P.O. Box 1330, Zip 43812–6330; tel. 740/622–6411, **A**1 10 20 **F**3 15 20 28 29 30 31 34 35 40 45 46 47 57 59 64 68 70 75 77 79 81 82 85 86 87 92 93 96 97 107 111 115 119 132 144 147 149 154 **S** Prime Healthcare, Ontario, CA
Primary Contact: Stephanie Conn, Administrator and Chief Nursing Officer
CFO: Dennis Lockard, FACHE, Chief Financial Officer
CMO: Gary J. Carver, M.D., Chief Medical Officer
CIO: Seth Peterson, Director Information Services
CHR: Rick Davis, Chief Operating Officer and Support Services
Web address: www.https://www.coshoctonhospital.org
Control: Other not–for–profit (including NFP Corporation) **Service**: General medical and surgical

Staffed Beds: 44 **Admissions:** 1837 **Census:** 18 **Outpatient Visits:** 80266 **Births:** 0 **Total Expense ($000):** 41889 **Payroll Expense ($000):** 15486 **Personnel:** 304

CUYAHOGA FALLS—Summit County

CUYAHOGA FALLS GENERAL HOSPITAL See Western Reserve Hospital

★ **EDWIN SHAW REHAB (360241)**, 330 Broadway Street East, Zip 44221–3312; tel. 330/436–0910, (Nonreporting) **A**5 10 **S** Cleveland Clinic Health System, Cleveland, OH
Primary Contact: Geoffrey Hall, Chief Executive Officer
CFO: Dave Frigo, Chief Financial Officer
CMO: Anthony Hayek, D.O., Medical Director
CHR: Heather Saus, Human Resource Generalist
Web address: www.edwinshaw.com
Control: County, Government, nonfederal **Service**: Rehabilitation

Staffed Beds: 35

Many Facility Codes have changed. Please refer to the AHA Guide Code Chart. © 2019 AHA Guide

○ **WESTERN RESERVE HOSPITAL (360150)**, 1900 23rd Street, Zip 44223–1499; tel. 330/971–7000, **A**3 5 10 11 **F**3 12 26 29 30 31 33 34 35 36 38 40 44 45 47 49 50 51 54 57 58 59 60 64 65 66 68 70 74 75 77 78 79 81 82 84 85 86 87 92 93 94 96 97 107 108 111 114 115 119 129 130 132 135 144 146 148
Primary Contact: Robert Kent, D.O., President and Chief Executive Officer
CFO: Jill Hiner, Vice President and Chief Financial Officer
CMO: Charles Feunning, M.D., Chief Medical Officer
CIO: Pamela Banchy, Chief Information Officer
CHR: Heather Milicevic, Director Human Resources
CNO: Carrie Gallo, Chief Nursing Officer
Web address: www.westernreservehospital.org
Control: Partnership, Investor–owned (for–profit) **Service**: General medical and surgical

Staffed Beds: 83 **Admissions**: 3558 **Census**: 35 **Outpatient Visits**: 128434 **Births**: 0 **Total Expense ($000)**: 116145 **Payroll Expense ($000)**: 40764 **Personnel**: 726

DAYTON—Montgomery County

□ **ACCESS HOSPITAL DAYTON (364050)**, 2611 Wayne Avenue, Zip 45420–1833; tel. 937/256–7801, (Nonreporting) **A**1 10
Primary Contact: Lauren Biles, Administrator
Web address: www.accesshospital.com/
Control: Corporation, Investor–owned (for–profit) **Service**: Psychiatric

Staffed Beds: 28

□ **DAYTON CHILDREN'S HOSPITAL (363306)**, One Children's Plaza, Zip 45404–1815; tel. 937/641–3000, **A**1 2 3 5 10 **F**3 7 8 11 19 21 29 30 31 32 34 35 39 40 41 42 43 44 45 50 54 55 57 58 59 60 61 62 63 64 65 66 68 72 74 75 77 78 79 81 82 84 85 86 87 88 89 93 97 100 101 102 104 107 111 115 119 129 130 131 132 134 135 144 146 156
Primary Contact: Deborah A. Feldman, President and Chief Executive Officer
COO: Matthew P Graybill, Vice President, Human Resources and Chief Administrative Officer
CFO: Chris Bergman, Chief Financial Officer
CMO: Adam Mezoff, M.D., Vice President and Chief Medical Officer
CIO: Beth Fredette, Chief Information Officer
Web address: www.childrensdayton.org
Control: Other not–for–profit (including NFP Corporation) **Service**: Children's general medical and surgical

Staffed Beds: 170 **Admissions**: 4576 **Census**: 72 **Outpatient Visits**: 381035 **Births**: 0 **Total Expense ($000)**: 387840 **Payroll Expense ($000)**: 174778 **Personnel**: 2937

☒ △ **DAYTON VETERANS AFFAIRS MEDICAL CENTER**, 4100 West Third Street, Zip 45428–9000; tel. 937/268–6511, (Nonreporting) **A**1 3 5 7 8 **S** Department of Veterans Affairs, Washington, DC
Primary Contact: Jill Dietrich, JD, FACHE, Medical Center Director
CFO: Shannon Rappach, Chief Fiscal Services
CMO: James Hardy, D.O., Chief of Staff
CIO: Susan Sherer, Chief Information Resource Management
CHR: Rolanda Watkins, Chief Human Resources Management Service
CNO: Penelope Franklin Gorsuch, Associate Director Patient Care Services
Web address: www.dayton.va.gov/
Control: Veterans Affairs, Government, federal **Service**: General medical and surgical

Staffed Beds: 486

★ ○ **GRANDVIEW MEDICAL CENTER (360133)**, 405 West Grand Avenue, Zip 45405–4796; tel. 937/723–3200, (Includes SOUTHVIEW MEDICAL CENTER, 1997 Miamisburg-Centerville Road, Dayton, Ohio, Zip 45459–3800; tel. 937/439–6000; Richard Manchur, President) **A**2 3 5 10 11 12 13 19 **F**3 11 12 13 15 18 20 22 24 26 28 29 30 31 34 35 36 38 40 42 43 44 45 47 48 49 50 51 53 54 56 57 58 59 60 61 64 65 66 68 70 73 74 75 76 77 78 79 81 82 85 86 87 93 96 97 98 100 101 102 104 106 107 108 110 111 114 115 116 117 118 119 120 121 123 124 129 130 131 132 135 141 144 145 146 147 148 149 157 **S** Kettering Health Network, Dayton, OH
Primary Contact: Rebecca Lewis, President
CFO: Luis Chanaga, Chief Financial Officer
CMO: Paul Martin, Chief Medical Officer
CIO: Andy Lehman, Senior Vice President Technology and Analytics
CHR: Keith Jenkins, Director, Human Resources
CNO: Ronda Brandstater, Vice President Patient Care
Web address: www.ketteringhealth.org/grandview/
Control: Church operated, Nongovernment, not–for–profit **Service**: General medical and surgical

Staffed Beds: 297 **Admissions**: 15128 **Census**: 175 **Outpatient Visits**: 433793 **Births**: 2129 **Total Expense ($000)**: 448114 **Payroll Expense ($000)**: 137733 **Personnel**: 2375

□ **HAVEN BEHAVIORAL SENIOR CARE OF DAYTON (364048)**, One Elizabeth Place, 4th Floor Southwest Tower, Zip 45417–3445; tel. 937/234–0100, (Nonreporting) **A**1 10 **S** Haven Behavioral Healthcare, Nashville, TN
Primary Contact: Keith Kuhn, Chief Executive Officer
CMO: Amita Patel, M.D., Medical Director
CNO: Cheryl Meyer, MSN, Director of Nursing
Web address: www.havenbehavioraldayton.com/
Control: Corporation, Investor–owned (for–profit) **Service**: Psychiatric

Staffed Beds: 32

☒ **HEALTHSOUTH REHABILITATION HOSPITAL OF DAYTON (363033)**, One Elizabeth Place, Zip 45417–3445; tel. 937/424–8200, **A**1 10 **F**29 57 90 148 **S** Encompass Health Corporation, Birmingham, AL
Primary Contact: Lynne Blinco, Chief Executive Officer
Web address: www.reliantdayton.com
Control: Corporation, Investor–owned (for–profit) **Service**: Rehabilitation

Staffed Beds: 50 **Admissions**: 702 **Census**: 25 **Outpatient Visits**: 0 **Births**: 0 **Total Expense ($000)**: 10140 **Payroll Expense ($000)**: 5690 **Personnel**: 64

☒ **KINDRED HOSPITAL-DAYTON (362033)**, 707 South Edwin C Moses Boulevard, Zip 45417–3462; tel. 937/222–5963, (Nonreporting) **A**1 10 **S** Kindred Healthcare, Louisville, KY
Primary Contact: Phillip Underwood, Chief Executive Officer
CMO: Felipe Rubio, M.D., Medical Director
Web address: www.khdayton.com
Control: Corporation, Investor–owned (for–profit) **Service**: Acute long–term care hospital

Staffed Beds: 67

☒ △ **MIAMI VALLEY HOSPITAL (360051)**, One Wyoming Street, Zip 45409–2793; tel. 937/208–8000, (Includes MIAMI VALLEY HOSPITAL SOUTH, 2400 Miami Valley Drive, Centerville, Ohio, Zip 45459–4774; tel. 937/438–2400) **A**1 2 3 5 7 10 19 **F**3 4 5 7 11 12 13 15 16 17 18 20 22 24 26 28 29 30 31 34 35 37 38 39 40 41 42 43 44 45 46 47 48 49 50 53 54 55 56 57 58 59 60 61 63 64 68 70 71 72 73 74 75 77 78 79 80 81 82 84 85 86 87 90 91 92 93 95 96 98 100 101 102 103 104 107 108 110 111 114 115 116 117 118 119 120 121 123 124 126 129 130 131 132 134 135 141 143 145 146 147 148 149 153 154 155 156 **S** Premier Health, Dayton, OH
Primary Contact: Michael J. Maiberger, President
COO: Mikki Clancy, Chief Operating Officer
CFO: Thomas M Duncan, Executive Vice President and Chief Financial Officer
CMO: Marc Belcastro, D.O., Chief Medical Officer
CIO: Gary Ginter, System Vice President and Chief Information Officer
CNO: Jolyn M Angus, R.N., Chief Nursing Officer
Web address: www.miamivalleyhospital.org
Control: Other not–for–profit (including NFP Corporation) **Service**: General medical and surgical

Staffed Beds: 516 **Admissions**: 35717 **Census**: 452 **Outpatient Visits**: 452509 **Births**: 4037 **Total Expense ($000)**: 921518 **Payroll Expense ($000)**: 361629 **Personnel**: 6686

VETERANS AFFAIRS MEDICAL CENTER See Dayton Veterans Affairs Medical Center

DEFIANCE—Defiance County

□ **MERCY HOSPITAL OF DEFIANCE (360270)**, 1404 East Second Street, Zip 43512–2440; tel. 419/782–8444, (Nonreporting) **A**1 10 **S** Mercy Health, Cincinnati, OH
Primary Contact: B Lynn. Detterman, President and Chief Executive Officer
COO: Kerry Knuth, Chief Operating Officer
CFO: James Puffenberger, Vice President and Chief Financial Officer
CMO: Jeffrey Pruitt, M.D., Chief of Staff
CHR: Susan Pscodna, Director Human Resources
CNO: Sonya Selhorst, R.N., Administrator and Chief Nursing Officer
Web address: www.ehealthconnection.com/regions/toledo/
Control: Church operated **Service**: General medical and surgical

Staffed Beds: 23

Hospital, Medicare Provider Number, Address, Telephone, Approval, Facility, and Physician Codes, Health Care System

★ American Hospital Association (AHA) membership ○ Healthcare Facilities Accreditation Program ⇑ Center for Improvement in Healthcare Quality Accreditation
□ The Joint Commission accreditation ◇ DNV Healthcare Inc. accreditation △ Commission on Accreditation of Rehabilitation Facilities (CARF) accreditation

OH

⊞ **PROMEDICA DEFIANCE REGIONAL HOSPITAL (361328)**, 1200 Ralston Avenue, Zip 43512–1396; tel. 419/783–6955, **A**1 5 10 18 **F**3 11 13 15 18 20 28 31 32 34 40 43 55 57 59 64 66 68 70 75 76 77 78 79 81 82 85 86 87 93 98 100 101 102 104 105 107 108 110 111 114 118 119 129 130 132 135 144 146 147 148 153 156 157 **S** ProMedica Health System, Toledo, OH
Primary Contact: Doug Bush, President
CFO: Ken Swint, Director Finance
CMO: Stanislaw Dajczak, M.D., Chief of Staff
CIO: Patricia Swint, Director Information Management Systems
CHR: Carrie Miller, Director Human Resources
Web address: www.promedica.org
Control: Other not–for–profit (including NFP Corporation) **Service**: General medical and surgical

Staffed Beds: 35 **Admissions**: 1756 **Census**: 14 **Outpatient Visits**: 94488 **Births**: 436 **Total Expense ($000)**: 53451 **Payroll Expense ($000)**: 15334 **Personnel**: 271

DELAWARE—Delaware County

⊞ **OHIOHEALTH GRADY MEMORIAL HOSPITAL (360210)**, 561 West Central Avenue, Zip 43015–1410; tel. 740/615–1000, **A**1 2 10 **F**3 13 15 18 20 28 29 30 31 34 35 40 42 45 50 51 54 55 57 58 59 64 70 74 76 78 79 81 82 84 85 86 87 96 97 102 107 108 109 110 111 114 119 126 131 132 146 147 148 149 154 **S** OhioHealth, Columbus, OH
Primary Contact: Steve Bunyard, President
COO: Anna Hensley, Chief Operating Officer
CFO: David Hensel, Director Financial Operations
CMO: Barbara Evert, M.D., Vice President Medical Affairs
CIO: Michael Krouse, Chief Information Officer Information Services
CHR: Victoria L. Matlack, Director and Human Resources Business Partner
CNO: Elizabeth Anne Biegler, R.N., Chief Nursing Officer
Web address: www.ohiohealth.com
Control: Church operated, Nongovernment, not–for–profit **Service**: General medical and surgical

Staffed Beds: 61 **Admissions**: 1969 **Census**: 26 **Outpatient Visits**: 76832 **Births**: 298

DENNISON—Tuscarawas County

☐ **TEN LAKES CENTER (364042)**, 819 North First Street, 3rd Floor, Zip 44621–1003; tel. 740/922–7499, (Nonreporting) **A**1 10 **S** Acadia Healthcare Company, Inc., Franklin, TN
Primary Contact: Debra C. Gardner, R.N., MSN, Administrator
Web address: www.tenlakescenter.com/
Control: Corporation, Investor–owned (for–profit) **Service**: Psychiatric

Staffed Beds: 16

⊞ **TRINITY HOSPITAL TWIN CITY (361302)**, 819 North First Street, Zip 44621–1098; tel. 740/922–2800, **A**1 10 18 **F**11 15 18 29 30 34 35 40 45 50 57 59 64 70 75 77 81 85 86 87 93 97 107 114 119 127 128 129 130 132 133 146 147 148 **S** CommonSpirit Health, Chicago, IL
Primary Contact: Teresa Gagliardi, R.N., Vice President of Hospital Operations and Site Administrator
CMO: Tim McKnight, M.D., Chief of Staff
CHR: Bianca Love, Assistant Administrator Human Resources
CNO: Teresa Gagliardi, R.N., Chief Nursing Officer
Web address: www.trinitytwincity.org
Control: Church operated, Nongovernment, not–for–profit **Service**: General medical and surgical

Staffed Beds: 12 **Admissions**: 153 **Census**: 2 **Outpatient Visits**: 44403 **Births**: 0 **Total Expense ($000)**: 23039 **Payroll Expense ($000)**: 9761 **Personnel**: 202

DOVER—Tuscarawas County

★ △ ⇑ **CLEVELAND CLINIC UNION HOSPITAL (360010)**, 659 Boulevard, Zip 44622–2077; tel. 330/343–3311, **A**5 7 10 19 21 **F**3 8 11 13 15 18 28 29 34 35 36 40 48 50 53 54 57 59 62 64 65 70 74 75 76 77 79 81 82 85 86 90 93 100 102 104 105 107 108 110 111 115 119 124 129 130 131 132 135 144 146 148 149 153 154 156 157 **S** Cleveland Clinic Health System, Cleveland, OH
Primary Contact: Bruce James, President and Chief Executive Officer
CFO: Eugene A Thorn III Vice President Finance and Chief Financial Officer
CMO: Todd Meyerhoefer, M.D., Vice President Medical Affairs
CIO: David Baumgardner, Director Information Management
CHR: Darwin K Smith, Vice President Human Resources
CNO: Diana Boyd, Vice President Nursing
Web address: www.unionhospital.org
Control: Other not–for–profit (including NFP Corporation) **Service**: General medical and surgical

Staffed Beds: 139 **Admissions**: 4172 **Census**: 44 **Outpatient Visits**: 255669 **Births**: 581 **Total Expense ($000)**: 138108 **Payroll Expense ($000)**: 78449 **Personnel**: 987

DUBLIN—Franklin County

☐ **COLUMBUS DUBLIN SPRINGS (364049)**, 7625 Hospital Drive, Zip 43016–9649; tel. 614/717–1800, (Includes COLUMBUS SPRINGS EAST HOSPITAL, 2085 Citygate Drive, Columbus, Ohio, Zip 43219–3656; tel. 614/412–1772; Garry W Hoyes, Chief Executive Officer), (Non-reporting) **A**1 10 **S** Springstone, Louisville, KY
Primary Contact: Garry W. Hoyes, Chief Executive Officer
COO: Merissa McKinstry, Chief Operating Officer
CFO: Alexis Barbour, Director Finance
CMO: Mark Blair, M.D., Medical Director
CHR: Tam Wisler, Director Human Resources
CNO: Melissa Patton, MSN, Director of Nursing
Web address: www.dublinsprings.com
Control: Corporation, Investor–owned (for–profit) **Service**: Psychiatric

Staffed Beds: 144

⊞ **OHIOHEALTH DUBLIN METHODIST HOSPITAL (360348)**, 7500 Hospital Drive, Zip 43016–8518; tel. 614/544–8000, **A**1 2 3 5 10 **F**3 13 15 18 20 28 29 30 34 40 45 50 51 57 59 60 68 70 73 76 79 81 84 85 87 97 100 102 107 108 109 110 111 113 114 115 118 119 126 130 131 132 141 146 147 148 149 **S** OhioHealth, Columbus, OH
Primary Contact: Steve Bunyard, President
COO: Anna Hensley, Chief Operating Officer
CFO: Keely Pummel, Director, Financial Operations
CMO: Barbara Evert, M.D., Vice President Medical Affairs
CIO: Michael Krouse, Senior Vice President Chief Information Officer
CHR: Victoria L. Matlack, Director and Human Resources Business Partner
CNO: Elizabeth Anne Biegler, R.N., Chief Nursing Officer
Web address: www.ohiohealth.com
Control: Church operated, Nongovernment, not–for–profit **Service**: General medical and surgical

Staffed Beds: 114 **Admissions**: 6439 **Census**: 45 **Outpatient Visits**: 72708 **Births**: 2573

EAST LIVERPOOL—Columbiana County

⊞ **EAST LIVERPOOL CITY HOSPITAL (360096)**, 425 West Fifth Street, Zip 43920–2498; tel. 330/385–7200, (Nonreporting) **A**1 10 **S** Prime Healthcare, Ontario, CA
Primary Contact: Keith Richardson, President and Chief Executive Officer
CFO: Kyle Johnson, Vice President Finance
CMO: Steve LaTulippe, President Medical Staff
CIO: Frank Mader, Director Information Services
CHR: Teri Pasco, Director Human Resources
CNO: Stacie Call, R.N., Vice President Patient Care and Chief Nursing Officer
Web address: www.elch.org
Control: Other not–for–profit (including NFP Corporation) **Service**: General medical and surgical

Staffed Beds: 120

ELYRIA—Lorain County

⊞ **UNIVERSITY HOSPITALS ELYRIA MEDICAL CENTER (360145)**, 630 East River Street, Zip 44035–5902; tel. 440/329–7500, **A**1 2 5 10 **F**3 11 12 13 15 17 18 20 22 24 26 28 29 30 31 32 34 35 36 37 40 41 42 44 45 46 49 50 53 54 57 59 60 64 68 70 73 74 75 76 77 78 79 81 82 84 85 86 87 89 91 92 93 94 98 100 102 107 108 110 111 114 115 116 117 118 119 126 129 130 131 132 133 135 146 147 148 149 154 **S** University Hospitals, Cleveland, OH
Primary Contact: Kristi M. Sink, President
CFO: David A Cook, Vice President and Chief Financial Officer
CHR: Daniel Miller, Vice President Human Resources
CNO: Sandra Jean Kantelas, Chief Nursing Officer
Web address: www.uhhospitals.org/elyria
Control: Other not–for–profit (including NFP Corporation) **Service**: General medical and surgical

Staffed Beds: 202 **Admissions**: 9796 **Census**: 107 **Outpatient Visits**: 301205 **Births**: 672 **Total Expense ($000)**: 199553 **Payroll Expense ($000)**: 63872 **Personnel**: 1194

EUCLID—Cuyahoga County

⊞ **EUCLID HOSPITAL (360082)**, 18901 Lake Shore Boulevard, Zip 44119–1090; tel. 216/531–9000, (Total facility includes 40 beds in nursing home–type unit) **A**1 3 10 **F**3 8 15 17 18 28 29 30 34 35 40 45 50 56 57 59 60 64 70 74 75 77 79 81 82 85 87 91 93 94 96 98 100 102 103 107 108 111 114 118 119 128 130 131 135 146 148 154 155 156 **S** Cleveland Clinic Health System, Cleveland, OH
Primary Contact: Daniel Napierkowski, M.D., President
COO: Rich Lea, Vice President Operations
CFO: Don Urbancsik, Director Finance
CMO: John Bertsch, M.D., Chief of Staff
CNO: Dawn A Bailey, R.N., Vice President Nursing and Chief Nursing Officer
Web address: www.euclidhospital.org
Control: Other not–for–profit (including NFP Corporation) **Service**: General medical and surgical

Staffed Beds: 165 **Admissions**: 6451 **Census**: 91 **Outpatient Visits**: 88659 **Births**: 0 **Total Expense ($000)**: 111747 **Payroll Expense ($000)**: 45233 **Personnel**: 615

Many Facility Codes have changed. Please refer to the AHA Guide Code Chart. © 2019 AHA Guide

FAIRFIELD—Butler County

□ △ **MERCY HEALTH - FAIRFIELD HOSPITAL (360056)**, 3000 Mack Road, Zip 45014–5335; tel. 513/870–7000, (Nonreporting) **A**1 2 7 10 **S** Mercy Health, Cincinnati, OH
Primary Contact: Thomas S. Urban, FACHE, President and Chief Executive Officer
COO: Shane Knisley, Chief Operating Officer
CFO: Liz Mohr, Assistant Chief Financial Officer
CMO: John Kennedy, M.D., Vice President of Medical Affairs
CIO: Rebecca S Sykes, Chief Information Officer
CNO: Ramona Cheek, MS, R.N., Chief Nursing Officer
Web address: www.e-mercy.com
Control: Church operated **Service:** General medical and surgical

Staffed Beds: 236

FINDLAY—Hancock County

⊞ **BLANCHARD VALLEY HOSPITAL (360095)**, 1900 South Main Street, Zip 45840–1214; tel. 419/423–4500, (Includes BLANCHARD VALLEY HOSPITAL, 1900 South Main Street, Findlay, Ohio, Zip 45840; tel. 419/423–4500) **A**1 2 5 10 19 **F**3 11 13 15 17 18 20 22 24 26 28 29 30 31 34 40 41 43 44 45 48 49 50 54 55 57 58 59 60 64 65 68 70 73 74 76 77 78 79 81 82 83 84 85 87 91 93 96 97 98 100 102 104 107 108 110 111 114 115 117 118 119 120 121 124 126 129 130 131 132 135 146 147 148 149 154 **S** Blanchard Valley Health System, Findlay, OH
Primary Contact: Scott C. Malaney, FACHE, President and Chief Executive Officer
CFO: David Cytlak, Chief Financial Officer
CMO: Michael Denike, D.O., Vice President, Medical Affairs
CIO: David Cytlak, Chief Financial Officer
CHR: Ryan Fisher, Director of Human Resources
CNO: Barbara J. Pasztor, R.N., Vice President Patient Care Services and Chief Nursing Officer
Web address: www.bvhealthsystem.org
Control: Other not-for-profit (including NFP Corporation) **Service:** General medical and surgical

Staffed Beds: 159 **Admissions:** 7056 **Census:** 65 **Outpatient Visits:** 147719 **Births:** 1230 **Total Expense ($000):** 211956 **Payroll Expense ($000):** 86554 **Personnel:** 1318

FOSTORIA—Hancock County

⊞ **PROMEDICA FOSTORIA COMMUNITY HOSPITAL (361318)**, 501 Van Buren Street, Zip 44830–1534, Mailing Address: P.O. Box 907, Zip 44830–0907; tel. 419/435–7734, **A**1 10 18 **F**3 11 15 28 29 30 31 34 35 40 45 46 57 59 60 64 70 75 78 79 81 82 85 87 89 93 96 104 107 108 110 111 115 119 128 129 130 131 132 133 135 146 147 148 149 156 157 **S** ProMedica Health System, Toledo, OH
Primary Contact: Pamela M. Jensen, FACHE, President
COO: Tom Borer, Vice President Operations
CFO: Ken Swint, Vice President Finance and Chief Financial Officer
CMO: Terrence Fondessy, M.D., Vice President Medical Affairs
CIO: Rose Ann Laureto, Chief Information Officer
Web address: www.promedica.org
Control: Other not-for-profit (including NFP Corporation) **Service:** General medical and surgical

Staffed Beds: 25 **Admissions:** 410 **Census:** 3 **Outpatient Visits:** 66289 **Births:** 0 **Total Expense ($000):** 32997 **Payroll Expense ($000):** 8816 **Personnel:** 154

FREMONT—Sandusky County

⊞ **PROMEDICA MEMORIAL HOSPITAL (360156)**, 715 South Taft Avenue, Zip 43420–3237; tel. 419/332–7321, **A**1 3 10 **F**3 11 13 15 18 19 28 29 30 31 34 35 38 40 44 45 46 47 48 51 53 56 57 59 64 65 70 74 75 76 77 78 79 80 81 82 84 85 87 89 93 96 97 107 108 110 111 114 115 119 123 124 129 130 131 132 135 141 142 146 147 148 149 156 157 **S** ProMedica Health System, Toledo, OH
Primary Contact: Pamela M. Jensen, FACHE, President
CFO: David Brewer, Associate Vice President Finance and Operations
CMO: Scott Farrell, M.D., Vice President Medical Affairs
CHR: Warrenette Parthemore, Director Human Resources
CNO: Jodi Rucker, MSN, R.N., Vice President Patient Care Services and Chief Nursing Officer
Web address: www.https://www.promedica.org
Control: Other not-for-profit (including NFP Corporation) **Service:** General medical and surgical

Staffed Beds: 76 **Admissions:** 1234 **Census:** 9 **Outpatient Visits:** 61496 **Births:** 143 **Total Expense ($000):** 59851 **Payroll Expense ($000):** 14373 **Personnel:** 290

GAHANNA—Franklin County

□ **THE WOODS AT PARKSIDE (360247)**, 349 Olde Ridenour Road, Zip 43230–2528; tel. 614/471–2552, (Nonreporting) **A**1 10
Primary Contact: Harry Nguyen, M.D., Medical Director
Web address: www.thewoodsatparkside.com
Control: Partnership, Investor–owned (for–profit) **Service:** Alcoholism and other chemical dependency

Staffed Beds: 50

GALION—Crawford County

★ ⇑ **GALION HOSPITAL (361325)**, 269 Portland Way South, Zip 44833–2399; tel. 419/468–4841, (Nonreporting) **A**10 18 21 **S** Avita Health System, Galion, OH
Primary Contact: Jerome Morasko, President and Chief Executive Officer
CFO: D. Eric Draime, Vice President and Chief Financial Officer
CIO: Alex Reed, Chief Information Officer
CHR: Traci L Oswald, Vice President of Human Resources
CNO: Kathy Durflinger, Vice President and Chief Nursing Officer
Web address: www.avitahs.org
Control: Other not-for-profit (including NFP Corporation) **Service:** General medical and surgical

Staffed Beds: 35

GALLIPOLIS—Gallia County

□ △ **HOLZER MEDICAL CENTER (360054)**, 100 Jackson Pike, Zip 45631–1563; tel. 740/446–5000, **A**1 2 3 5 7 10 19 **F**3 12 13 15 18 20 22 26 28 29 30 31 33 34 35 37 40 42 45 49 55 57 59 60 62 63 64 70 74 76 77 78 79 81 82 85 87 89 90 93 96 97 98 103 107 108 110 111 114 115 118 119 120 121 123 126 129 130 131 132 144 146 149 **S** Holzer Health System, Jackson, OH
Primary Contact: Michael R. Canady, M.D., Interim Chief Executive Officer
CFO: Kenneth G Payne, Chief Financial Officer
CMO: John Viall, M.D., Vice President Medical Affairs
CIO: John Allen, Chief Information Officer
CHR: Lisa B Halley, Vice President Human Resources
Web address: www.holzer.org
Control: Other not-for-profit (including NFP Corporation) **Service:** General medical and surgical

Staffed Beds: 195 **Admissions:** 5219 **Census:** 63 **Outpatient Visits:** 704687 **Births:** 724 **Total Expense ($000):** 136270 **Payroll Expense ($000):** 51110 **Personnel:** 588

GARFIELD HEIGHTS—Cuyahoga County

⊞ **MARYMOUNT HOSPITAL (360143)**, 12300 McCracken Road, Zip 44125–2975; tel. 216/581–0500, **A**1 2 3 10 **F**3 7 8 10 11 15 18 28 29 30 31 34 35 38 40 44 50 51 53 54 56 57 59 60 62 63 64 65 68 70 74 75 77 78 79 81 82 85 86 87 92 93 96 97 98 100 102 103 104 107 108 110 111 114 115 116 118 119 124 125 130 131 132 135 140 141 146 147 148 162 154 155 157 158 **S** Cleveland Clinic Health System, Cleveland, OH
Primary Contact: Daniel Napierkowski, M.D., President
COO: Mark Nussbaum, Vice President Operations
CFO: Mike Stilgenbauer, Director Finance
CMO: Douglas Kohler, M.D., Vice President Medical Operations
CIO: Ralph A Cagna, Director Information Technology Operations, Cleveland Clinic Health System South Market
CHR: Judith Santora, Human Resources Business Partner
CNO: Barbara Zinner, Chief Nursing Officer
Web address: www.marymount.org
Control: Other not-for-profit (including NFP Corporation) **Service:** General medical and surgical

Staffed Beds: 277 **Admissions:** 8980 **Census:** 130 **Outpatient Visits:** 73840 **Births:** 0 **Total Expense ($000):** 159660 **Payroll Expense ($000):** 56839 **Personnel:** 855

OH

GENEVA—Ashtabula County

⌧ **UNIVERSITY HOSPITALS GENEVA MEDICAL CENTER (361307)**, 870 West Main Street, Zip 44041–1295; tel. 440/466–1141, **A**1 3 10 18 **F**3 5 7 11 15 18 29 34 35 40 46 51 56 57 59 60 64 68 70 75 77 78 79 81 82 85 86 87 91 93 107 110 111 115 116 119 129 130 132 133 135 143 146 147 148 149 154 **S** University Hospitals, Cleveland, OH
Primary Contact: M Steven. Jones, President
COO: Jason Glowczewski, Chief Operating Officer
CFO: Lara Eggleston, Finance Manager
CMO: Amitabh Goel, M.D., Chief Medical Officer
CIO: Kirsten Hale, Coordinator Health Information Systems and Coding
CHR: Danialle Lynce, Business Partner Human Resources
CNO: Ashley Fertig, Chief Nursing Officer
Web address: www.uhhs.com
Control: Other not–for–profit (including NFP Corporation) **Service:** General medical and surgical

Staffed Beds: 25 **Admissions:** 1598 **Census:** 16 **Outpatient Visits:** 53817 **Births:** 0 **Total Expense ($000):** 42068 **Payroll Expense ($000):** 13735 **Personnel:** 243

GREEN SPRINGS—Sandusky County

☐ **EDEN SPRINGS HEALTH CARE CENTER (362007)**, 401 North Broadway, Zip 44836–9653; tel. 419/639–2626, (Nonreporting) **A**1 10
Primary Contact: Kathy Hunt, Chief Executive Officer
CFO: Douglas Morris, Chief Financial Officer
CMO: John Yuhas, D.O., Medical Director
CHR: Joan E Schmidt, Director Human Resources
Control: Church operated, Nongovernment, not–for–profit **Service:** Acute long–term care hospital

Staffed Beds: 186

GREENFIELD—Highland County

☐ △ **ADENA GREENFIELD MEDICAL CENTER (361304)**, 550 Mirabeau Street, Zip 45123–1617; tel. 937/981–9400, **A**1 7 10 18 **F**3 15 18 29 30 34 35 40 41 45 50 54 57 59 68 74 75 77 79 81 82 93 107 110 111 114 119 130 131 132 133 135 146 147 148 154 **S** Adena Health System, Chillicothe, OH
Primary Contact: Josh McCoy, Administrator
CFO: Ralph W Sorrell Sr Chief Financial Officer
CIO: Marcus Bost, Director Information Services and Chief Information Officer
CHR: Brandt Lippert, Vice President Human Resources
Web address: www.adena.org
Control: Other not–for–profit (including NFP Corporation) **Service:** General medical and surgical

Staffed Beds: 25 **Admissions:** 366 **Census:** 8 **Outpatient Visits:** 39834 **Births:** 0 **Total Expense ($000):** 15250 **Payroll Expense ($000):** 6325 **Personnel:** 108

GREENVILLE—Darke County

★ ○ **WAYNE HEALTHCARE (360044)**, 835 Sweitzer Street, Zip 45331–1077; tel. 937/548–1141, **A**2 10 11 **F**3 8 11 13 18 29 30 31 34 35 39 40 41 45 57 59 64 65 70 75 76 77 78 79 81 82 84 85 86 87 89 93 98 103 107 108 110 111 114 117 118 119 124 126 129 130 131 132 135 141 146 147 148 149 154 156
Primary Contact: Wayne G. Deschambeau, President and Chief Executive Officer
COO: Jeffrey R. Subler, Vice President Support Services
CMO: Tom Brown, M.D., President Medical Staff
CIO: Shelton Monger, Director Information Technology
CHR: Peggy Schwartz, Vice President Human Resources
CNO: Kimberlee Freeman, Vice President Patient Care Services and Chief Nursing Officer
Web address: www.waynehealthcare.org
Control: Other not–for–profit (including NFP Corporation) **Service:** General medical and surgical

Staffed Beds: 53 **Admissions:** 1566 **Census:** 16 **Outpatient Visits:** 77396 **Births:** 269 **Total Expense ($000):** 55415 **Payroll Expense ($000):** 19188 **Personnel:** 335

HAMILTON—Butler County

★ ○ **FORT HAMILTON HOSPITAL (360132)**, 630 Eaton Avenue, Zip 45013–2770; tel. 513/867–2000, **A**2 10 11 **F**3 11 13 15 18 20 22 24 28 29 30 31 34 35 40 45 49 50 54 59 60 64 68 70 73 74 75 76 77 78 79 81 85 86 87 93 98 100 107 108 110 111 115 116 117 119 120 121 124 129 130 131 135 144 146 147 148 154 **S** Kettering Health Network, Dayton, OH
Primary Contact: Michael Mewhirter, President
CFO: William Villegas, Vice President Finance
CMO: Marcus Romanello, Chief Medical Officer
CIO: Andy Lehman, Senior Vice President Technology and Analytics
CHR: Joseph Geigle, Director Human Resources
CNO: Carol Applegeet, MSN, R.N., Vice President and Chief Nursing Officer
Web address: www.khnetwork.org/forthamilton
Control: Church operated, Nongovernment, not–for–profit **Service:** General medical and surgical

Staffed Beds: 164 **Admissions:** 7071 **Census:** 81 **Outpatient Visits:** 109906 **Births:** 549 **Total Expense ($000):** 162084 **Payroll Expense ($000):** 69367 **Personnel:** 1081

HICKSVILLE—Defiance County

☐ **COMMUNITY MEMORIAL HOSPITAL (361301)**, 208 North Columbus Street, Zip 43526–1299; tel. 419/542–6692, (Nonreporting) **A**1 10 18
Primary Contact: Michelle Waggoner, Chief Executive Officer
CFO: Steve Caryer, Chief Financial Officer
CNO: Betty Clevinger, Chief Nursing Officer
Web address: www.cmhosp.com
Control: Hospital district or authority, Government, nonfederal **Service:** General medical and surgical

Staffed Beds: 25

HIGHLAND HILLS—Cuyahoga County

☐ **HIGHLAND SPRINGS HOSPITAL (364053)**, 4199 Mill Pond Drive, Zip 44122–5731; tel. 602/314–7800, (Nonreporting) **A**1 **S** Springstone, Louisville, KY
Primary Contact: Matthew Winchester, Chief Executive Officer
Web address: www.https://www.highlandspringshealth.com
Control: Corporation, Investor–owned (for–profit) **Service:** Psychiatric

Staffed Beds: 72

HILLSBORO—Highland County

⌧ **HIGHLAND DISTRICT HOSPITAL (361332)**, 1275 North High Street, Zip 45133–8273; tel. 937/393–6100, **A**1 10 18 **F**3 11 13 15 29 30 31 34 35 40 44 45 47 49 50 57 59 62 64 74 76 77 78 79 81 82 85 86 87 92 93 94 96 98 103 107 108 110 111 115 118 119 127 130 131 132 133 135 146 148 149 156
Primary Contact: Randal P. Lennartz, CPA, President and Chief Executive Officer
COO: Timothy Parry, R.N., Chief Operating Officer
CMO: Ron Zile, M.D., Chief of Staff
CIO: Tim Bogard, Manager Information Technology
CHR: Melanie Wymer, Director Human Resources
CNO: Pam Barnett, R.N., Director of Nursing
Web address: www.hdh.org
Control: Hospital district or authority, Government, nonfederal **Service:** General medical and surgical

Staffed Beds: 35 **Admissions:** 1501 **Census:** 12 **Outpatient Visits:** 78360 **Births:** 265 **Total Expense ($000):** 44494 **Payroll Expense ($000):** 17121 **Personnel:** 337

JACKSON—Jackson County

⌧ **HOLZER MEDICAL CENTER - JACKSON (361320)**, 500 Burlington Road, Zip 45640–9360; tel. 740/288–4625, **A**1 10 18 **F**15 18 29 30 40 64 68 75 77 79 82 85 87 97 107 108 114 118 119 130 131 133 146 148 149 154 **S** Holzer Health System, Jackson, OH
Primary Contact: Michael R. Canady, M.D., Chief Executive Officer
CFO: Kevin Yeager, Vice President Fiscal Services
CMO: Nimal Dutla, M.D., Chief Medical Staff
CHR: Sandy Carlisle, Manager Human Resources
Web address: www.holzer.org
Control: Other not–for–profit (including NFP Corporation) **Service:** General medical and surgical

Staffed Beds: 24 **Admissions:** 705 **Census:** 6 **Outpatient Visits:** 63595 **Births:** 0 **Total Expense ($000):** 18849 **Payroll Expense ($000):** 7146 **Personnel:** 186

Many Facility Codes have changed. Please refer to the AHA Guide Code Chart. © 2019 AHA Guide

KENTON—Hardin County

☒ **OHIOHEALTH HARDIN MEMORIAL HOSPITAL (361315)**, 921 East Franklin Street, Zip 43326–2099; tel. 419/673–0761, **A**1 10 18 **F**11 15 29 30 34 40 45 50 57 59 61 68 75 77 78 79 81 86 87 93 97 102 107 108 110 111 114 115 116 119 129 130 131 132 133 135 146 147 154 **S** OhioHealth, Columbus, OH
Primary Contact: Ron Snyder, Chief Operating Officer
Web address: www.hardinmemorial.org
Control: Other not–for–profit (including NFP Corporation) **Service:** General medical and surgical

Staffed Beds: 25 **Admissions:** 421 **Census:** 4

KETTERING—Montgomery County

★ ○ △ **KETTERING MEDICAL CENTER (360079)**, 3535 Southern Boulevard, Zip 45429–1221; tel. 937/298–4331, **A**2 3 5 7 8 10 11 19 **F**3 8 11 13 17 18 20 22 24 26 28 29 30 31 34 35 36 37 38 39 40 42 43 44 45 46 47 48 49 50 51 52 53 54 55 56 57 58 59 60 61 62 64 65 66 68 70 71 72 74 75 76 77 78 79 81 82 84 85 86 87 90 91 92 93 96 97 102 107 108 110 111 114 115 116 117 118 119 120 121 123 124 126 129 130 131 132 135 141 145 146 147 148 149 154 157 **S** Kettering Health Network, Dayton, OH
Primary Contact: Terry M. Burns, President
CFO: Steven Chavez, Vice President Finance and Operations
CMO: Robert T. Smith, M.D., Chief Medical Officer
CIO: Andy Lehman, Senior Vice President Technology and Analytics
CHR: Derek Morgan, Vice President Human Resources
CNO: Brenda Kuhn, Ph.D., R.N., FACHE, Chief Nursing Officer
Web address: www.ketteringhealth.org/kettering
Control: Church operated, Nongovernment, not–for–profit **Service:** General medical and surgical

Staffed Beds: 422 **Admissions:** 23190 **Census:** 287 **Outpatient Visits:** 294363 **Births:** 2636 **Total Expense ($000):** 754226 **Payroll Expense ($000):** 290366 **Personnel:** 3410

LANCASTER—Fairfield County

☐ **FAIRFIELD MEDICAL CENTER (360072)**, 401 North Ewing Street, Zip 43130–3371; tel. 740/687–8000, **A**1 2 3 5 10 13 **F**3 8 11 12 13 15 18 20 22 24 26 28 29 30 31 34 35 38 40 44 45 48 49 50 53 54 57 59 64 70 74 75 76 77 78 79 81 82 83 84 85 87 89 93 96 97 98 102 104 105 107 108 110 111 114 115 118 119 120 121 123 124 129 130 131 132 135 144 145 146 147 148 149 152 154 156
Primary Contact: John R. Janoso, Chief Executive Officer
CFO: Sky Gettys, Chief Financial Officer
CMO: Renee Wagner, M.D., Chief Medical Officer
CIO: Martha Buckley, Chief Medical Informatics Officer
CHR: Debra L Palmer, MS, R.N., Chief Human Resources Officer and Corporate Compliance Officer
CNO: Helen Harding, Chief Nursing Officer
Web address: www.fmchealth.org
Control: Other not–for–profit (including NFP Corporation) **Service:** General medical and surgical

Staffed Beds: 222 **Admissions:** 11210 **Census:** 116 **Outpatient Visits:** 227382 **Births:** 896 **Total Expense ($000):** 252652 **Payroll Expense ($000):** 94954 **Personnel:** 1867

LIMA—Allen County

☐ **INSTITUTE FOR ORTHOPAEDIC SURGERY (360263)**, 801 Medical Drive, Suite B, Zip 45804–4030; tel. 419/224–7586, (Nonreporting) **A**1 10 **S** Mercy Health, Cincinnati, OH
Primary Contact: Mark McDonald, M.D., President and Chief Executive Officer
CMO: Mark McDonald, M.D., President and Chief Executive Officer
CHR: Pat Farmer, Coordinator Human Resources and Safety Officer
Web address: www.ioshospital.com
Control: Partnership, Investor–owned (for–profit) **Service:** Orthopedic

Staffed Beds: 3

☒ **KINDRED HOSPITAL LIMA (362020)**, 730 West Market Street, 6th Floor, Zip 45801–4602; tel. 419/224–1888, (Nonreporting) **A**1 10 **S** Kindred Healthcare, Louisville, KY
Primary Contact: Susan Krinke, Chief Executive Officer
Web address: www.khlima.com
Control: Corporation, Investor–owned (for–profit) **Service:** Acute long–term care hospital

Staffed Beds: 26

☒ △ **LIMA MEMORIAL HEALTH SYSTEM (360009)**, 1001 Bellefontaine Avenue, Zip 45804–2899; tel. 419/228–3335, **A**1 2 7 10 **F**3 11 13 15 17 18 20 22 24 26 28 29 30 31 34 35 36 40 41 43 45 46 47 48 49 50 54 57 59 60 62 63 64 68 70 73 74 75 76 77 78 79 81 84 85 86 87 89 90 93 96 107 108 110 111 114 115 116 119 121 126 129 130 131 132 135 146 147 148 149 154 156
Primary Contact: Michael D. Swick, President and Chief Executive Officer
COO: Robert E. Armstrong, Senior Vice President and Chief Operating Officer
CFO: John T. Fischbach, Vice President of Finance, Chief Financial Officer
CIO: Mathew P. Gaug, Executive Director of Information Technology
CHR: Denise G Kiraly, Director, Human Resources and Organization Development
CNO: Ann-Marie J Pohl, Vice President and Chief Nursing Officer
Web address: www.limamemorial.org
Control: Other not–for–profit (including NFP Corporation) **Service:** General medical and surgical

Staffed Beds: 183 **Admissions:** 6097 **Census:** 68 **Outpatient Visits:** 202425 **Births:** 571 **Total Expense ($000):** 166442 **Payroll Expense ($000):** 63336 **Personnel:** 1204

☐ △ **MERCY HEALTH - ST. RITA'S MEDICAL CENTER (360066)**, 730 West Market Street, Zip 45801–4602; tel. 419/227–3361, **A**1 2 7 10 **F**3 5 7 8 11 12 13 15 17 18 20 22 24 26 28 29 30 31 34 35 36 38 40 42 43 45 46 47 48 49 50 53 54 57 58 59 60 61 62 63 64 65 67 68 70 73 74 75 76 77 78 79 81 82 84 85 86 87 89 90 92 93 94 96 97 98 100 102 104 105 107 108 110 111 114 115 117 118 119 120 121 123 126 128 129 130 132 135 143 144 146 147 148 149 153 154 156 **S** Mercy Health, Cincinnati, OH
Primary Contact: Dale Gisi, President
COO: Ronda Lehman, PharmD, Chief Operating Officer, SRPS
CFO: Tim Rieger, Chief Financial Officer
CMO: Kevin Casey, M.D., Chief Clinical Officer
CHR: Will Cason, Vice President Human Resources
CNO: Jodi Pahl, Chief Nurse Executive
Web address: www.stritas.org
Control: Other not–for–profit (including NFP Corporation) **Service:** General medical and surgical

Staffed Beds: 271 **Admissions:** 18499 **Census:** 218 **Outpatient Visits:** 254008 **Births:** 1567 **Personnel:** 1546

TRIUMPH HOSPITAL LIMA See Kindred Hospital Lima

LODI—Medina County

☒ **CLEVELAND CLINIC AKRON GENERAL LODI HOSPITAL (361303)**, 225 Elyria Street, Zip 44254–1096; tel. 330/948–1222, **A**1 10 18 **F**3 15 18 28 29 30 34 35 40 45 57 59 64 65 75 81 90 93 96 97 107 111 114 119 128 129 130 133 135 146 147 154 **S** Cleveland Clinic Health System, Cleveland, OH
Primary Contact: Dana Kocsis, Vice President, Nursing and Operations
COO: Dana Kocsis, Vice President Nursing and Operations
CFO: Dave Frigo, Director Finance and Controller
CMO: David Peter, M.D., Senior Vice President Medical Affairs and Chief Medical Officer
CIO: Robb Baldauf, Coordinator Information Systems
CHR: Lynn Moraca, Director Human Resources
CNO: Dana Kocsis, Vice President, Nursing and Operations
Web address: www.lodihospital.org
Control: Other not–for–profit (including NFP Corporation) **Service:** General medical and surgical

Staffed Beds: 20 **Admissions:** 228 **Census:** 5 **Outpatient Visits:** 24497 **Births:** 0 **Total Expense ($000):** 15584 **Payroll Expense ($000):** 7411 **Personnel:** 97

LOGAN—Hocking County

☒ **HOCKING VALLEY COMMUNITY HOSPITAL (361330)**, 601 State Route 664 North, Zip 43138–8541, Mailing Address: P.O. Box 966, Zip 43138–0966; tel. 740/380–8000, **A**1 10 18 **F**3 8 11 15 28 29 31 34 40 56 57 59 64 70 75 77 79 81 82 85 86 87 93 98 103 107 111 114 118 119 129 130 133 135 144 146 147 148 152 154 156
Primary Contact: Stacey Gabriel, R.N., President and Chief Executive Officer
CFO: Julie E Grow, Chief Financial Officer
CMO: Duane Mast, M.D., Medical Director
CIO: John Burgess, Director Information Services
CHR: Robert F Schmidt, Director Human Resources
CNO: Janelle Hicks, R.N., Vice President Patient Services
Web address: www.hvch.org
Control: County, Government, nonfederal **Service:** General medical and surgical

Staffed Beds: 35 **Admissions:** 859 **Census:** 16 **Outpatient Visits:** 193405 **Births:** 0 **Total Expense ($000):** 39651 **Payroll Expense ($000):** 12549 **Personnel:** 271

Hospital, Medicare Provider Number, Address, Telephone, Approval, Facility, and Physician Codes, Health Care System

★ American Hospital Association (AHA) membership
☐ The Joint Commission accreditation
○ Healthcare Facilities Accreditation Program
◇ DNV Healthcare Inc. accreditation
⇑ Center for Improvement in Healthcare Quality Accreditation
△ Commission on Accreditation of Rehabilitation Facilities (CARF) accreditation

OH

LONDON—Madison County

☒ **MADISON HEALTH (360189)**, 210 North Main Street, Zip 43140–1115; tel. 740/845–7000, **A**1 10 **F**3 11 13 15 18 29 30 31 34 35 40 45 50 53 57 59 64 68 70 75 76 77 78 79 81 85 89 93 97 107 108 110 111 114 118 119 129 130 131 132 135 146
Primary Contact: Dana E. Engle, Chief Executive Officer
CFO: Michael Browning, Chief Financial Officer
CMO: Bernard Oppong, D.O., Chief of Staff
CIO: Dennis Vogt, Director Information Technology
CHR: Becky Rozell, Vice President, Human Resources
CNO: Jennifer Piccione, Chief Nursing and Clinical Services Officer
Web address: www.madison-health.com
Control: Other not–for–profit (including NFP Corporation) **Service**: General medical and surgical

Staffed Beds: 53 **Admissions**: 1335 **Census**: 11 **Outpatient Visits**: 53486 **Births**: 235 **Total Expense ($000)**: 41955 **Payroll Expense ($000)**: 16639 **Personnel**: 322

LORAIN—Lorain County

CLEARVISTA HEALTH AND WELLNESS (364052), 3364 Kolbe Road, Zip 44053–1628; tel. 440/960–7960, (Nonreporting)
Primary Contact: John Sannuto, Chief Executive Officer
Web address: www.clearvistahealth.com
Control: Corporation, Investor–owned (for–profit) **Service**: Psychiatric

Staffed Beds: 30

☐ △ **MERCY REGIONAL MEDICAL CENTER (360172)**, 3700 Kolbe Road, Zip 44053–1697; tel. 440/960–4000, **A**1 2 7 10 **F**3 5 8 11 13 15 18 20 22 26 28 29 30 31 34 35 37 38 39 40 41 44 45 46 47 49 50 51 53 54 55 56 57 58 59 60 61 62 63 64 65 68 70 74 75 76 77 78 79 81 82 84 85 86 87 90 92 93 96 97 98 100 101 102 104 105 107 108 109 110 111 112 114 115 116 117 119 120 121 123 124 129 130 131 132 134 135 141 146 147 148 149 152 153 154 156 157 **S** Mercy Health, Cincinnati, OH
Primary Contact: Edwin M. Oley, President and Chief Executive Officer
CMO: Sam El-Dalati, M.D., Chief Medical Officer
CHR: JC Fischer, Director Human Resources
CNO: Catherine Walsh, Interim Nursing Executive
Web address: www.community-health-partners.com
Control: Church operated, Nongovernment, not–for–profit **Service**: General medical and surgical

Staffed Beds: 251 **Admissions**: 11253 **Census**: 132 **Outpatient Visits**: 132130 **Births**: 722 **Personnel**: 962

MANSFIELD—Richland County

MEDCENTRAL - MANSFIELD HOSPITAL See Ohiohealth Medcentral Mansfield Hospital

☒ **OHIOHEALTH MEDCENTRAL MANSFIELD HOSPITAL (360118)**, 335 Glessner Avenue, Zip 44903–2265; tel. 419/526–8000, (Includes MANSFIELD HOSPITAL, 335 Glessner Avenue, Mansfield, Ohio, Zip 44903–2265; tel. 419/526–8000) **A**1 2 3 10 **F**3 8 11 13 15 17 18 20 22 24 26 28 29 31 34 35 40 42 43 45 46 47 48 50 51 53 54 57 58 59 61 62 63 64 65 67 68 70 74 75 76 77 78 79 80 81 84 85 86 87 89 90 93 96 97 98 99 100 101 102 107 108 110 111 114 115 116 117 119 120 121 123 126 129 130 131 132 135 144 146 147 148 149 153 154 156 **S** OhioHealth, Columbus, OH
Primary Contact: Vinson Yates, President
CFO: Joseph Lyren, Chief Financial Officer
CMO: Terry Weston, M.D., Vice President Physician Services
CIO: Cindy Sheets, Vice President Information Systems and Chief Information Officer
CHR: Beth Hildreth, Vice President Human Resources
CNO: Pam Crawford, R.N., Ph.D., Vice President of Nursing and Chief Nursing Officer
Web address: www.medcentral.org
Control: Other not–for–profit (including NFP Corporation) **Service**: General medical and surgical

Staffed Beds: 249 **Admissions**: 11442 **Census**: 145 **Outpatient Visits**: 332500 **Births**: 930 **Total Expense ($000)**: 252582 **Payroll Expense ($000)**: 97477 **Personnel**: 1513

MARIETTA—Washington County

★ ○ **MARIETTA MEMORIAL HOSPITAL (360147)**, 401 Matthew Street, Zip 45750–1699; tel. 740/374–1400, (Nonreporting) **A**2 3 5 10 11 19 **S** Memorial Health System, Marietta, OH
Primary Contact: J Scott. Cantley, President and Chief Executive Officer
CFO: Eric L Young, Vice President Finance and Chief Financial Officer
CMO: Matthew Macatol, M.D., President Medical Staff
CIO: Andy Altenburger, Chief Information Officer
CHR: Dee Ann Gehlauf, Senior Vice President Business and Organization Development
Web address: www.mhsystem.org
Control: Other not–for–profit (including NFP Corporation) **Service**: General medical and surgical

Staffed Beds: 152

★ ○ △ **SELBY GENERAL HOSPITAL (361319)**, 1106 Colegate Drive, Zip 45750–1323; tel. 740/568–2000, **A**7 10 11 18 **F**3 11 29 30 34 40 42 59 69 79 81 87 90 107 116 117 119 133 147 148 **S** Memorial Health System, Marietta, OH
Primary Contact: Stephen Smith, President
CFO: Eric L Young, Chief Financial Officer
CMO: David Spears, D.O., Chief of Staff
CHR: Tricia A Engfehr, Chief Human Resources
CNO: Misti Spencer, Director Inpatient Services
Web address: www.selbygeneral.org
Control: Other not–for–profit (including NFP Corporation) **Service**: General medical and surgical

Staffed Beds: 35 **Admissions**: 1294 **Census**: 17 **Outpatient Visits**: 23518 **Births**: 0 **Total Expense ($000)**: 42832 **Payroll Expense ($000)**: 11807 **Personnel**: 156

MARION—Marion County

☒ **OHIOHEALTH MARION GENERAL HOSPITAL (360011)**, 1000 McKinley Park Drive, Zip 43302–6397; tel. 740/383–8400, **A**1 2 10 19 **F**3 8 13 15 18 20 22 24 26 28 29 30 31 35 40 53 54 56 59 60 63 64 65 67 68 70 74 75 76 77 78 79 80 81 84 87 89 91 93 94 98 103 104 105 107 110 111 114 115 116 117 118 119 126 129 130 132 135 144 146 147 148 149 153 154 **S** OhioHealth, Columbus, OH
Primary Contact: Curtis Gingrich, M.D., Chief Operating Officer
CIO: Chris King, Director Information Services
CHR: Gianna Ferrarotti, Director Human Resources North Region
Web address: www.ohiohealth.com/mariongeneral
Control: Church operated, Nongovernment, not–for–profit **Service**: General medical and surgical

Staffed Beds: 174 **Admissions**: 7368 **Census**: 89 **Outpatient Visits**: 233874 **Births**: 880 **Total Expense ($000)**: 198502 **Payroll Expense ($000)**: 76267 **Personnel**: 1053

MARTINS FERRY—Belmont County

☐ **EAST OHIO REGIONAL HOSPITAL (360080)**, 90 North Fourth Street, Zip 43935–1648; tel. 740/633–1100, (Nonreporting) **A**1 3 10 **S** Alecto Healthcare, Irvine, CA
Primary Contact: Jennifer Coello, Chief Operating Officer
COO: Jennifer Coello, Chief Operating Officer
CHR: Robert Wright, Senior Human Resource Advisor
CNO: Christine Kerwood, Chief Nursing Officer
Web address: www.ovmc-eorh.com
Control: Corporation, Investor–owned (for–profit) **Service**: General medical and surgical

Staffed Beds: 120

MARYSVILLE—Union County

★ ⇑ **MEMORIAL HEALTH (360092)**, 500 London Avenue, Zip 43040–1594; tel. 937/644–6115, **A**5 10 21 **F**3 8 11 13 15 18 20 28 29 30 31 32 34 35 38 40 45 48 49 50 51 53 54 56 57 59 60 62 64 69 74 75 76 77 78 79 80 81 82 85 86 87 91 92 93 96 100 107 108 110 111 114 115 116 118 119 120 124 129 130 131 132 135 144 145 146 148 149 150 152 156
Primary Contact: Olas A. Hubbs III, FACHE, President and Chief Executive Officer
COO: Laurie A Whittington, Chief Operating Officer
CFO: Jeffrey Ehlers, Chief Financial Officer
CMO: Matthew Hazelbaker, M.D., President Medical Staff
CIO: Carl Zani, Chief Technology Director
CHR: Larry C Schleeter, Chief Human Resources Officer
CNO: Robin Slattman, Chief Nursing Officer
Web address: www.memorialhosp.org
Control: County, Government, nonfederal **Service**: General medical and surgical

Staffed Beds: 74 **Admissions**: 2030 **Census**: 15 **Outpatient Visits**: 137636 **Births**: 615 **Total Expense ($000)**: 108120 **Payroll Expense ($000)**: 40234 **Personnel**: 554

Many Facility Codes have changed. Please refer to the AHA Guide Code Chart. © 2019 AHA Guide

MASON—Warren County

☐ **LINDNER CENTER OF HOPE (364044)**, 4075 Old Western Row Road, Zip 45040–3104; tel. 513/536–0311, (Nonreporting) **A**1 2 3 10
Primary Contact: Paul Keck, M.D., President and Chief Executive Officer
COO: Brian Owens, Chief Operating Officer
CFO: David McAdams, Chief Financial Officer
CIO: Cliff McClintick, Chief Information Officer
CHR: Debbie A Strawser, Director Human Resources
Web address: www.lindnercenterofhope.org
Control: Other not–for–profit (including NFP Corporation) **Service**: Psychiatric

Staffed Beds: 48

MASSILLON—Stark County

☐ **HEARTLAND BEHAVIORAL HEALTHCARE (364031)**, 3000 Erie Stree South, Zip 44646–7993, Mailing Address: 3000 Erie Street South, Zip 44646–7976; tel. 330/833–3135, (Nonreporting) **A**1 5 10 **S** Ohio Department of Mental Health, Columbus, OH
Primary Contact: Jeffrey Sims, Chief Executive Officer
CFO: Patricia Eddleman, Fiscal Officer
CMO: Steven Thomson, M.D., Medical Director
CIO: Robert Hobart, Director Management Information Systems
CHR: Jerald Wilhite, Administrator Human Resources
Web address: www.mh.state.oh.us/ibhs/bhos/hoh.html
Control: State, Government, nonfederal **Service**: Psychiatric

Staffed Beds: 152

MAUMEE—Lucas County

☐ **ARROWHEAD BEHAVIORAL HEALTH HOSPITAL (364036)**, 1725 Timber Line Road, Zip 43537–4015; tel. 419/891–9333, (Nonreporting) **A**1 10 **S** Universal Health Services, Inc., King of Prussia, PA
Primary Contact: Theresa Contreras, Chief Executive Officer
CFO: Allison Duncan, Chief Financial Officer
CMO: Kenneth Adler, M.D., Medical Director
CIO: Peggy Montgomery, Director Medical Records
CHR: Dawn Bosworth, Director Human Resources
CNO: Anita Zych, Director of Nursing
Web address: www.arrowheadbehavioral.com
Control: Corporation, Investor–owned (for–profit) **Service**: Psychiatric

Staffed Beds: 48

★ ⇧ **ST. LUKE'S HOSPITAL (360090)**, 5901 Monclova Road, Zip 43537–1899; tel. 419/893–5911, (Nonreporting) **A**3 10 21
Primary Contact: Daniel L. Wakeman, President
CMO: Stephen Bazeley, M.D., Vice President Medical Affairs
CIO: Patricia Swint, Director Information Technology
CHR: Connie Sessler, Director Human Resources
CNO: Jill A. Trosin, R.N., MSN, Vice President Patient Care Services, Chief Nursing Officer
Web address: www.stlukeshospital.com
Control: Other not–for–profit (including NFP Corporation) **Service**: General medical and surgical

Staffed Beds: 170

MEDINA—Medina County

⊞ **CLEVELAND CLINIC, MEDINA HOSPITAL (360091)**, 1000 East Washington Street, Zip 44256–2170; tel. 330/725–1000, **A**1 2 3 5 10 **F**3 7 8 15 18 20 28 29 30 31 34 35 40 47 49 50 51 57 59 60 64 70 74 75 77 78 79 81 82 85 86 93 96 107 111 115 117 119 129 130 131 132 133 135 146 148 154 **S** Cleveland Clinic Health System, Cleveland, OH
Primary Contact: Richard K. Shewbridge, President
COO: Vicky Snyder, Chief Operating Officer
CFO: Becky Molnar, Director of Finance
CMO: Matthew Vrobel, Vice President, Medical Operations
CIO: Frank Longley, Business Partner Information Technology
CHR: Tracie Curtis, Business Partner Human Resources
CNO: Julie Fetto, R.N., Chief Nursing Officer
Web address: www.medinahospital.org
Control: Other not–for–profit (including NFP Corporation) **Service**: General medical and surgical

Staffed Beds: 143 Admissions: 6286 Census: 72 Outpatient Visits: 74429 Births: 0 Total Expense ($000): 114592 Payroll Expense ($000): 41240 Personnel: 653

MIAMISBURG—Montgomery County

⊞ **LIFECARE HOSPITAL OF DAYTON (362028)**, 4000 Miamisburg-Centerville Road, Zip 45342–7615; tel. 937/384–8300, (Nonreporting) **A**1 10 **S** LifeCare Management Services, Plano, TX
Primary Contact: William Bryant, Chief Executive Officer
CMO: Richard Gregg, M.D., Medical Director
CHR: Pam Fannin, Coordinator Human Resources
Web address: www.lifecare-hospitals.com
Control: Corporation, Investor–owned (for–profit) **Service**: Acute long–term care hospital

Staffed Beds: 44

★ ◯ **SYCAMORE MEDICAL CENTER (360239)**, 4000 Miamisburg-Centerville Road, Zip 45342–7615; tel. 937/866–0551, (Includes KETTERING BEHAVIORAL MEDICAL CENTER, 5350 Lamme Road, Dayton, Ohio, Zip 45439; tel. 937/534–4600; Jason Brown, Director) **A**10 11 **F**3 10 11 12 15 18 20 28 29 30 35 36 38 40 42 44 45 47 48 49 50 53 54 56 57 58 59 60 63 64 65 66 68 70 71 74 75 77 78 79 81 82 84 85 86 87 91 92 93 97 98 99 100 101 102 103 104 107 108 110 111 114 115 118 119 125 129 130 131 132 134 135 141 145 146 147 148 149 150 157 158 **S** Kettering Health Network, Dayton, OH
Primary Contact: Walter Sackett, President
CMO: Robert T. Smith, M.D., Chief Medical Officer
CIO: Andy Lehman, Senior Vice President Technology and Analytics
CHR: Derek Morgan, Vice President Human Resources
CNO: Julie S. Vincent, R.N., MSN, Chief Nursing Officer
Web address: www.khnetwork.org/sycamore
Control: Church operated, Nongovernment, not–for–profit **Service**: General medical and surgical

Staffed Beds: 168 Admissions: 9198 Census: 97 Outpatient Visits: 155467 Births: 0 Total Expense ($000): 184438 Payroll Expense ($000): 69755 Personnel: 924

MIDDLE POINT—Van Wert County

☐ **RIDGEVIEW BEHAVIORAL HOSPITAL (364047)**, 17872 Lincoln Highway, Zip 45863–9700; tel. 419/968–2950, (Nonreporting) **A**1 10
Primary Contact: Pat Tracy, Administrator
Web address: www.ridgeviewhospital.net/
Control: Corporation, Investor–owned (for–profit) **Service**: Psychiatric

Staffed Beds: 40

MIDDLEBURG HEIGHTS—Cuyahoga County

☐ **SOUTHWEST GENERAL HEALTH CENTER (360155)**, 18697 Bagley Road, Zip 44130–3497; tel. 440/816–8000, (Nonreporting) **A**1 2 3 5 10
Primary Contact: William A. Young Jr, President and Chief Executive Officer
COO: Bradley W. Rauh, Vice President, Chief Operating Officer
CFO: Mary Ann Freas, Senior Vice President and Chief Financial Officer
CMO: Marilyn McNamara, M.D., Chief Medical Officer
CIO: Alec Williams, Chief Information Officer
CHR: Dee Murphy, Vice President Human Resources
CNO: Martha F. Bauschka, R.N., Vice President and Chief Nursing Officer
Web address: www.swgeneral.com
Control: Other not–for–profit (including NFP Corporation) **Service**: General medical and surgical

Staffed Beds: 252

MIDDLETOWN—Warren County

⊞ △ **ATRIUM MEDICAL CENTER (360076)**, One Medical Center Drive, Zip 45005–1066; tel. 513/424–2111, **A**1 2 3 7 10 **F**3 8 11 13 15 17 18 20 22 24 26 28 29 30 31 32 34 35 36 38 40 41 42 43 44 45 46 47 48 49 50 53 54 55 56 57 58 59 63 64 65 66 68 70 71 73 74 75 76 77 78 79 80 81 82 84 85 86 87 90 91 92 93 96 98 100 101 102 103 107 108 110 111 114 115 117 118 119 124 126 130 131 132 135 141 143 145 146 147 148 149 154 156 157 **S** Premier Health, Dayton, OH
Primary Contact: Michael Uhl, President
CMO: Matthew Reeves, D.O., Esq Chief Medical Officer
CHR: Ted Ripperger, Administrative Director Human Resources
CNO: Marquita Turner, Chief Operating Officer and Chief Nursing Officer
Web address: www.PremierHealth.com
Control: Other not–for–profit (including NFP Corporation) **Service**: General medical and surgical

Staffed Beds: 284 Admissions: 9064 Census: 102 Outpatient Visits: 237650 Births: 946 Total Expense ($000): 229248 Payroll Expense ($000): 88954 Personnel: 1302

OH

MILLERSBURG—Holmes County

POMERENE HOSPITAL (360148), 981 Wooster Road, Zip 44654–1094; tel. 330/674–1015, **A**10 22 **F**3 11 13 15 18 28 29 30 34 35 40 50 53 55 57 59 70 75 76 77 79 81 85 86 87 89 93 107 108 110 115 119 130 131 132 135 143 144 146 147 149
Primary Contact: Tony Snyder, Administrator and Chief Executive Officer
CFO: Jason Justus, Vice President Finance and Chief Financial Officer
CMO: Yasser Omran, M.D., President Medical Staff
CIO: Brent Edington, Director Information Services
CHR: Kim Croft, R.N., Executive Director Human Resources
Web address: www.pomerenehospital.org
Control: Other not–for–profit (including NFP Corporation) **Service**: General medical and surgical

Staffed Beds: 41 **Admissions:** 1523 **Census:** 14 **Outpatient Visits:** 40320
Births: 466 **Total Expense ($000):** 29264 **Payroll Expense ($000):** 11177
Personnel: 330

MONTPELIER—Williams County

COMMUNITY HOSPITALS AND WELLNESS CENTERS-MONTPELIER (361327), 909 East Snyder Avenue, Zip 43543–1251; tel. 419/636–1131, (Nonreporting) **A**10 18
Primary Contact: Philip L. Ennen, President and Chief Executive Officer
Web address: www.chwchospital.com
Control: Corporation, Investor–owned (for–profit) **Service**: General medical and surgical

Staffed Beds: 35

MONTPELIER HOSPITAL See Community Hospitals and Wellness Centers, Bryan

MOUNT GILEAD—Morrow County

MORROW COUNTY HOSPITAL (361313), 651 West Marion Road, Zip 43338–1027; tel. 419/946–5015, (Nonreporting) **A**1 10 18 **S** OhioHealth, Columbus, OH
Primary Contact: Chad J. Miller, President and Chief Executive Officer
CFO: Joe Schueler, Chief Financial Officer
Web address: www.morrowcountyhospital.com
Control: County, Government, nonfederal **Service**: General medical and surgical

Staffed Beds: 23

MOUNT VERNON—Knox County

KNOX COMMUNITY HOSPITAL (360040), 1330 Coshocton Road, Zip 43050–1495; tel. 740/393–9000, **A**1 2 10 20 **F**3 5 11 12 13 15 18 20 22 26 28 29 31 34 35 36 40 41 44 45 46 48 49 50 53 57 59 62 64 69 70 74 75 76 77 78 79 81 82 83 84 85 86 87 93 94 96 97 104 107 108 110 111 112 113 114 115 118 119 120 121 123 129 130 131 132 144 146 147 149 150 154 156 157 **S** QHR, Brentwood, TN
Primary Contact: Bruce D. White, Chief Executive Officer
COO: Bruce M Behner, Chief Operating Officer
CFO: Michael Ambrosiani, Chief Financial Officer
CMO: Jeffrey Northup, D.O., Chief Medical Officer
CIO: Kwi Holland, Vice President Information Services
CHR: Lisa Bragg, Vice President Human Resources
CNO: James Middleton, MSN, R.N., Chief Nursing Officer
Web address: www.kch.org
Control: Other not–for–profit (including NFP Corporation) **Service**: General medical and surgical

Staffed Beds: 71 **Admissions:** 3556 **Census:** 33 **Outpatient Visits:** 141865
Births: 431 **Total Expense ($000):** 163640 **Payroll Expense ($000):** 74180
Personnel: 1047

NAPOLEON—Henry County

★ ⇑ **HENRY COUNTY HOSPITAL (361309)**, 1600 East Riverview Avenue, Zip 43545–9399; tel. 419/592–4015, **A**5 10 18 21 **F**3 5 11 13 15 28 29 30 31 34 35 36 40 45 50 53 57 59 64 65 68 70 75 76 77 78 79 81 82 85 86 87 93 100 101 104 107 108 110 114 119 130 132 133 135 146 148 149 156
Primary Contact: Kimberly Hupp. Bordenkircher, Chief Executive Officer
CFO: Diane Walther, Controller
CIO: William Grimm, Chief Information Officer
CHR: Jennifer A Fisher, Manager Human Resources
CNO: Patricia Frank, Chief Nursing Officer
Web address: www.henrycountyhospital.org
Control: Other not–for–profit (including NFP Corporation) **Service**: General medical and surgical

Staffed Beds: 25 **Admissions:** 737 **Census:** 7 **Outpatient Visits:** 60354
Births: 202 **Total Expense ($000):** 31760 **Payroll Expense ($000):** 12809
Personnel: 202

NEW ALBANY—Franklin County

⊠ **MOUNT CARMEL NEW ALBANY SURGICAL HOSPITAL (360266)**, 7333 Smith's Mill Road, Zip 43054–9291; tel. 614/775–6600, **A**1 5 10 **F**3 29 34 35 44 57 58 59 64 65 68 74 75 79 81 85 86 87 107 111 114 119 141 146 **S** Trinity Health, Livonia, MI
Primary Contact: Diane Doucette, R.N., President
Web address: www.mountcarmelhealth.com
Control: Church operated, Nongovernment, not–for–profit **Service**: Surgical

Staffed Beds: 60 **Admissions:** 3967 **Census:** 17 **Outpatient Visits:** 15793
Births: 0 **Total Expense ($000):** 83244 **Payroll Expense ($000):** 15303
Personnel: 246

NEWARK—Licking County

☐ **LICKING MEMORIAL HOSPITAL (360218)**, 1320 West Main Street, Zip 43055–3699; tel. 740/348–4000, **A**1 2 10 **F**3 4 5 13 15 18 20 22 28 29 30 31 32 34 35 40 41 45 46 48 49 50 53 57 59 62 64 65 68 70 72 74 75 76 77 78 79 81 82 84 85 86 89 90 92 93 97 98 100 101 102 104 107 108 110 111 114 115 116 117 118 119 129 130 131 132 135 144 146 147 148 152 154
Primary Contact: Robert A. Montagnese, President and Chief Executive Officer
CFO: Cindy Webster, Vice President Financial Services
CMO: Craig Cairns, M.D., Vice President Medical Affairs
CIO: Sallie Arnett, Vice President Information Systems
CHR: Anne Peterson, Vice President Human Resources and Support Services
Web address: www.lmhealth.org
Control: Other not–for–profit (including NFP Corporation) **Service**: General medical and surgical

Staffed Beds: 227 **Admissions:** 7973 **Census:** 77 **Outpatient Visits:** 313541 **Births:** 1041 **Total Expense ($000):** 192852 **Payroll Expense ($000):** 78623 **Personnel:** 1471

⊠ **SELECT SPECIALTY HOSPITAL OF SOUTHEAST OHIO (362031)**, 2000 Tamarack Road, Zip 43055; tel. 740/588–7888, (Nonreporting) **A**1 10 **S** Select Medical Corporation, Mechanicsburg, PA
Primary Contact: Linda Supplee, Chief Executive Officer
CMO: Armand Bermudez, M.D., Medical Director
CHR: Jacqueline Nezbeth, Human Resources Officer
CNO: Taryn Vierling, Chief Nursing Officer
Web address: www.selectspecialtyhospitals.com/company/locations/zanesville.aspx
Control: Corporation, Investor–owned (for–profit) **Service**: Acute long–term care hospital

Staffed Beds: 35

NORTHFIELD—Summit County

☐ **NORTHCOAST BEHAVIORAL HEALTHCARE (364011)**, 1756 Sagamore Road, Zip 44067–1086; tel. 330/467–7131, (Nonreporting) **A**1 5 10 **S** Ohio Department of Mental Health, Columbus, OH
Primary Contact: Douglas W. Kern, Chief Executive Officer
CIO: Karl Donenwirth, Vice President Information Services
Web address: www.mha.ohio.gov
Control: State, Government, nonfederal **Service**: Psychiatric

Staffed Beds: 258

NORWALK—Huron County

★ ○ **FISHER-TITUS MEDICAL CENTER (360065)**, 272 Benedict Avenue, Zip 44857–2374; tel. 419/668–8101, (Total facility includes 69 beds in nursing home–type unit) **A**2 3 5 10 11 19 **F**3 10 11 13 15 18 20 22 26 28 29 31 34 35 36 38 40 43 44 45 48 49 50 51 54 55 56 57 59 61 62 64 68 70 74 75 76 77 78 79 81 82 84 85 86 87 92 93 94 96 107 108 110 111 115 118 119 126 128 129 130 131 132 135 143 146 147 148 149 154
Primary Contact: Brent Burkey, M.D., President and Chief Executive Officer
COO: Jeffrey A Hayes, Vice President System Operations
CFO: Duane L Woods Jr Chief Financial Officer
CMO: Shankar Kurra, M.D., Senior Vice President Medical Affairs
CIO: John Britton, Vice President Information Services
CHR: Phillip Annarino, Vice President Human Resources
CNO: Suzanne Inglis, MSN, FACHE, Senior Vice President Nursing Services
Web address: www.fisher-titus.org
Control: Other not–for–profit (including NFP Corporation) **Service**: General medical and surgical

Staffed Beds: 147 **Admissions:** 3817 **Census:** 91 **Outpatient Visits:** 173380 **Births:** 528 **Total Expense ($000):** 122200 **Payroll Expense ($000):** 48439 **Personnel:** 820

Many Facility Codes have changed. Please refer to the AHA Guide Code Chart.

OBERLIN—Lorain County

☐ **MERCY ALLEN HOSPITAL (361306)**, 200 West Lorain Street, Zip 44074–1077; tel. 440/775–1211, (Nonreporting) **A**1 10 18 **S** Mercy Health, Cincinnati, OH
Primary Contact: Ed Ruth, President
COO: Ken Hale, Executive Director of Operations
CFO: Cynthia Dennison, Chief Financial Officer
CMO: Rafik Massouh, M.D., Chief of Staff
CHR: Kathy Dolbin, Director of Human Resources
CNO: Cheryl Rieves, Chief Nurse Executive Lorain Region
Web address: www.mercyonline.org/mercy_allen_hospital.aspx
Control: Church operated **Service:** General medical and surgical

Staffed Beds: 25

ONTARIO—Richland County

★ ⇑ **AVITA ONTARIO HOSPITAL (360365)**, 715 Richland Mall, Zip 44906–3802; tel. 567/307–7666, (Nonreporting) **A**10 21 **S** Avita Health System, Galion, OH
Primary Contact: Jerome Morasko, President and Chief Executive Officer
CFO: D. Eric Draime, Vice President and Chief Financial Officer
CIO: Alex Reed, Chief Information Officer
CHR: Traci L Oswald, Vice President, Chief Human Resources
CNO: Kathy Durflinger, Vice President and Chief Nursing Officer
Web address: www.avitahealth.org
Control: Other not–for–profit (including NFP Corporation) **Service:** General medical and surgical

Staffed Beds: 26

OREGON—Lucas County

☐ △ **MERCY HEALTH - ST. CHARLES HOSPITAL (360081)**, 2600 Navarre Avenue, Zip 43616–3297; tel. 419/696–7200, **A**1 2 3 7 10 **F**3 11 13 15 18 28 29 30 31 34 35 40 43 44 46 47 48 49 51 56 57 59 60 64 66 68 70 74 75 76 77 78 79 81 82 85 86 87 90 91 92 93 97 98 100 101 102 103 104 107 108 110 111 114 115 118 119 120 121 123 126 129 130 132 135 146 147 148 149 154 **S** Mercy Health, Cincinnati, OH
Primary Contact: Craig Albers, President and Chief Operating Officer
COO: Craig Albers, President and Chief Operating Officer
CFO: Mark Thompson, Market Chief Financial Officer Northern Region and Chief Financial Officer
CMO: Riaz Chaudhry, M.D., Chief Medical Officer
CIO: Rebecca S Sykes, Senior Vice President Resource Management, Chief Information Officer
Web address: www.mercyweb.org
Control: Church operated, Nongovernment, not–for–profit **Service:** General medical and surgical

Staffed Beds: 279 Admissions: 10603 Census: 139 Outpatient Visits: 117723 Births: 461 Personnel: 751

☒ **PROMEDICA BAY PARK HOSPITAL (360259)**, 2801 Bay Park Drive, Zip 43616–4920; tel. 419/690–7900, **A**1 10 **F**3 11 13 15 18 28 29 30 31 34 35 40 45 49 50 54 57 59 64 68 70 74 75 76 77 78 79 81 82 85 86 92 93 97 107 108 110 111 114 118 119 124 126 129 130 131 132 134 135 143 146 147 148 149 154 155 156 **S** ProMedica Health System, Toledo, OH
Primary Contact: Neeraj Kanwal, M.D., Interim President, Metro Region
COO: Darrell Wachowiak, Associate Vice President Operations
CFO: Scott Fought, Vice President Finance
CMO: David Lindstrom, M.D., Vice President Medical Affairs
CIO: Rose Ann Laureto, Corporate Vice President Information Resources
CHR: Kara Zimmerly, Manager Human Resources
Web address: www.promedica.org
Control: Other not–for–profit (including NFP Corporation) **Service:** General medical and surgical

Staffed Beds: 44 Admissions: 3282 Census: 33 Outpatient Visits: 105135 Births: 545 Total Expense ($000): 68136 Payroll Expense ($000): 23034 Personnel: 396

ST. CHARLES MERCY HOSPITAL See Mercy Health - St. Charles Hospital

ORRVILLE—Wayne County

☒ **AULTMAN ORRVILLE HOSPITAL (361323)**, 832 South Main Street, Zip 44667–2208; tel. 330/682–3010, **A**1 10 18 **F**3 8 9 11 12 13 14 15 28 29 30 34 35 40 45 49 50 51 53 55 57 59 68 71 75 76 77 79 81 82 85 86 87 93 107 108 110 111 112 114 115 118 119 126 127 129 130 131 132 133 135 143 146 147 152 154 156 **S** Aultman Health Foundation, Canton, OH
Primary Contact: Jennifer Kessel, Chief Executive Officer
CFO: Adam Luntz, Chief Financial Officer
CIO: Vince Logozzo, Director Information Technology
CNO: Angela McGee, Vice President Nursing Services
Web address: www.aultmanorrville.org
Control: Other not–for–profit (including NFP Corporation) **Service:** General medical and surgical

Staffed Beds: 25 Admissions: 990 Census: 7 Outpatient Visits: 39429 Births: 479 Total Expense ($000): 25806 Payroll Expense ($000): 10931 Personnel: 211

OXFORD—Butler County

★ ○ **MCCULLOUGH-HYDE MEMORIAL HOSPITAL/TRIHEALTH (360046)**, 110 North Poplar Street, Zip 45056–1292; tel. 513/523–2111, **A**1 10 18 **F**3 8 9 11 13 15 18 28 29 30 31 34 35 36 40 45 47 50 54 57 59 64 68 69 70 75 76 77 78 79 81 82 84 85 86 87 93 102 107 108 110 111 114 119 129 130 131 132 144 146 147 149 154 156
Primary Contact: Brett Kirkpatrick, Executive Director
CFO: John R Clements, Chief Financial Officer
CMO: Amy Spivey, Chief Medical Officer
CHR: Sharon Hancock, Chief Human Resources Officer
CNO: Pamela Collins, Vice President Chief Patient Services Officer
Web address: www.mhmh.org
Control: Other not–for–profit (including NFP Corporation) **Service:** General medical and surgical

Staffed Beds: 48 Admissions: 1943 Census: 16 Outpatient Visits: 57795 Births: 396 Total Expense ($000): 53141 Payroll Expense ($000): 18899 Personnel: 319

PARMA—Cuyahoga County

☒ △ **UNIVERSITY HOSPITALS PARMA MEDICAL CENTER (360041)**, 7007 Powers Boulevard, Zip 44129–5495; tel. 440/743–3000, **A**1 2 3 7 10 13 **F**3 11 12 13 15 17 18 20 22 24 26 28 29 30 31 34 35 36 40 44 45 49 50 51 53 54 56 57 58 59 60 62 63 64 65 68 69 70 71 74 75 76 77 78 79 81 82 84 85 86 87 90 93 94 96 97 98 100 101 103 107 108 111 114 115 116 117 119 120 121 126 129 130 131 132 135 143 146 147 148 149 154 **S** University Hospitals, Cleveland, OH
Primary Contact: Peter U. Bergmann, President
CMO: Christopher Loyke, Chief Medical Officer
CHR: Daniel Miller, Human Resources Business Partner
Web address: www.uhhospitals.org/parma
Control: Other not–for–profit (including NFP Corporation) **Service:** General medical and surgical

Staffed Beds: 271 Admissions: 9861 Census: 118 Outpatient Visits: 165022 Births: 265 Total Expense ($000): 178505 Payroll Expense ($000): 58786 Personnel: 1046

PAULDING—Paulding County

☐ **PAULDING COUNTY HOSPITAL (361300)**, 1035 West Wayne Street, Zip 45879–1544; tel. 419/399–4080, (Nonreporting) **A**1 10 18
Primary Contact: Randy Ruge, Chief Executive Officer
COO: Randy Ruge, Chief Operating Officer
CFO: Rob Goshia, Chief Financial Officer
CMO: Wendell J Spangler, M.D., Chief of Staff
CIO: Dan Kaufman, Director Information Services
CHR: Melanie Rittenour, Director Human Resources
Web address: www.pauldingcountyhospital.com
Control: County, Government, nonfederal **Service:** General medical and surgical

Staffed Beds: 25

OH

PORT CLINTON—Ottawa County

⊞ **MAGRUDER MEMORIAL HOSPITAL (361314)**, 615 Fulton Street, Zip 43452–2001; tel. 419/734–3131, **A**1 5 10 18 **F**3 11 15 18 28 29 31 34 35 40 44 45 46 48 50 53 57 59 64 65 70 75 77 78 79 81 82 85 86 87 89 93 107 108 110 115 118 119 129 130 131 132 133 135 144 146 147 148 149
Primary Contact: J Todd. Almendinger, President and Chief Executive Officer
COO: Nick Marsico, Vice President and Chief Operating Officer
CFO: Julie Georgoff, Vice President of Finance and Chief Financial Officer
CHR: Jason Kraus, Director Human Resources
Web address: www.magruderhospital.com
Control: Other not–for–profit (including NFP Corporation) **Service:** General medical and surgical

Staffed Beds: 25 **Admissions:** 368 **Census:** 3 **Outpatient Visits:** 84991 **Births:** 0 **Total Expense ($000):** 54075 **Payroll Expense ($000):** 20568 **Personnel:** 365

PORTSMOUTH—Scioto County

KING'S DAUGHTERS MEDICAL CENTER OHIO (360361), 2001 Scioto Trail, Zip 45662–2845; tel. 740/991–4000, (Nonreporting) **A**10
Primary Contact: Kim Grooms, Administrator
Web address: www.kdmcohio.com/
Control: Other not–for–profit (including NFP Corporation) **Service:** General medical and surgical

Staffed Beds: 10

⊞ △ **SOUTHERN OHIO MEDICAL CENTER (360008)**, 1805 27th Street, Zip 45662–2640, Mailing Address: 1805 27th Street,Waller Building Suite B01, Zip 45662–2640; tel. 740/356–5000, **A**1 2 3 5 7 10 **F**3 11 13 15 17 18 20 22 24 26 28 29 30 31 34 35 37 38 40 41 44 45 46 47 48 49 50 53 54 57 59 62 63 64 65 70 74 75 77 78 79 81 82 83 84 85 86 87 90 92 97 98 100 101 102 103 104 105 107 108 109 110 111 114 115 116 117 118 119 120 121 122 123 124 129 130 131 132 135 144 146 147 149 152 154 156 157
Primary Contact: Randal M. Arnett, President and Chief Executive Officer
CFO: Dean Wray, Vice President Finance
CMO: Kendall Stewart, M.D., Chief Medical Officer
CIO: Brent Richard, Administrative Director Information Systems
CHR: Vicki Noel, Vice President Human Resources
CNO: Claudia L Burchett, R.N., Vice President of Patient Services
Web address: www.somc.org
Control: Other not–for–profit (including NFP Corporation) **Service:** General medical and surgical

Staffed Beds: 248 **Admissions:** 12534 **Census:** 169 **Outpatient Visits:** 569975 **Births:** 1158 **Total Expense ($000):** 319530 **Payroll Expense ($000):** 121604 **Personnel:** 2581

PROCTORVILLE—Lawrence County

☐ **THREE GABLES SURGERY CENTER (360261)**, 5897 County Road 107, Zip 45669–8852, Mailing Address: P.O. Box 490, Zip 45669–0490; tel. 740/886–9911, (Nonreporting) **A**1 10
Primary Contact: Tony Aluise, Chief Executive Officer
Web address: www.threegablessurgery.com
Control: Partnership, Investor–owned (for–profit) **Service:** Surgical

Staffed Beds: 8

RAVENNA—Portage County

⊞ **UH PORTAGE MEDICAL CENTER (360078)**, 6847 North Chestnut Street, Zip 44266–3929, Mailing Address: P.O. Box 1204, Zip 44266–1204; tel. 330/297–0811, **A**1 2 5 10 **F**3 4 11 13 15 18 20 22 26 28 29 30 31 34 35 36 40 42 43 44 45 46 47 48 49 50 51 54 56 57 58 59 60 64 65 68 70 74 75 76 77 78 79 81 82 84 85 87 92 93 100 107 108 109 110 111 115 117 119 129 130 131 132 135 143 144 145 146 147 148 149 154 156 **S** University Hospitals, Cleveland, OH
Primary Contact: M Steven. Jones, President
CFO: Jen Hahn, Finance Manager
CMO: Benjamin Prestegaard, Chief Medical Officer
CIO: Rhonda Smith, Applications Support Manager
CHR: Neil Everett, Vice President Human Resources
Web address: www.uhportage.org
Control: Other not–for–profit (including NFP Corporation) **Service:** General medical and surgical

Staffed Beds: 135 **Admissions:** 7093 **Census:** 78 **Outpatient Visits:** 229720 **Births:** 658 **Total Expense ($000):** 126855 **Payroll Expense ($000):** 42794 **Personnel:** 844

ROCK CREEK—Ashtabula County

GLENBEIGH HOSPITAL AND OUTPATIENT CENTERS (360245), 2863 Route 45, Zip 44084, Mailing Address: P.O. Box 298, Zip 44084–0298; tel. 440/563–3400, **A**10 **F**4 5 29 30 34 36 53 54 57 75 86 87 100 130 132 135 149 152
Primary Contact: Patricia Weston-Hall, Chief Executive Officer
CFO: Phil Pawlowski, Chief Financial Officer
CIO: Linda Advey, Manager Information Systems
CHR: Shirley Deary, Director Human Resources
Web address: www.glenbeigh.com
Control: Other not–for–profit (including NFP Corporation) **Service:** Alcoholism and other chemical dependency

Staffed Beds: 114 **Admissions:** 3309 **Census:** 121 **Outpatient Visits:** 75166 **Births:** 0 **Total Expense ($000):** 23388 **Payroll Expense ($000):** 10954 **Personnel:** 270

SAINT MARYS—Auglaize County

⇑ **JOINT TOWNSHIP DISTRICT MEMORIAL HOSPITAL (360032)**, 200 St Clair Street, Zip 45885–2400; tel. 419/394–3335, (Total facility includes 12 beds in nursing home–type unit) **A**10 21 **F**3 7 8 12 13 15 28 29 30 34 35 36 40 41 45 46 47 51 53 56 57 59 62 63 64 67 70 74 75 76 77 79 81 82 83 84 85 87 89 90 93 98 103 107 108 110 115 119 124 128 129 130 131 132 143 144 146 147 148 156
Primary Contact: Kevin W. Harlan, President
CFO: Jeffrey W Vossler, Chief Financial Officer
CIO: Joshua Miller, Director Information Systems
CHR: Art Swain, Vice President Support Services
CNO: Debra McKee, R.N., Chief Clinical Officer and Chief Nursing Officer
Web address: www.grandlakehealth.org
Control: Other not–for–profit (including NFP Corporation) **Service:** General medical and surgical

Staffed Beds: 72 **Admissions:** 2109 **Census:** 17 **Outpatient Visits:** 89968 **Births:** 338 **Total Expense ($000):** 78917 **Payroll Expense ($000):** 21400 **Personnel:** 515

SALEM—Columbiana County

⊞ **SALEM REGIONAL MEDICAL CENTER (360185)**, 1995 East State Street, Zip 44460–2423; tel. 330/332–1551, (Nonreporting) **A**1 3 5 10
Primary Contact: Anita Hackstedde, M.D., President and Chief Executive Officer
COO: Keith Meredith, Chief Operating Officer
CFO: Mike Giangardella, Vice President Finance and Administration
CMO: Anita Hackstedde, M.D., Vice President Medical Affairs
CIO: Mark L'Italien, Director Information Services
CHR: Barb Hirst, R.N., Vice President Human Resources and Chief Nursing Officer
CNO: Barb Hirst, R.N., Vice President Human Resources and Chief Nursing Officer
Web address: www.salemregional.com
Control: Other not–for–profit (including NFP Corporation) **Service:** General medical and surgical

Staffed Beds: 116

SANDUSKY—Erie County

○ **FIRELANDS REGIONAL HEALTH SYSTEM (360025)**, 1111 Hayes Avenue, Zip 44870–3323; tel. 419/557–7400, (Includes FIRELANDS REGIONAL MEDICAL CENTER - MAIN CAMPUS, 1111 Hayes Avenue, Sandusky, Ohio, Zip 44870; tel. 419/557–7400; FIRELANDS REGIONAL MEDICAL CENTER SOUTH CAMPUS, 1912 Hayes Avenue, Sandusky, Ohio, Zip 44870–4736; tel. 419/557–7000), (Non-reporting) **A**2 3 5 10 11 19
Primary Contact: Daniel J. Moncher, Interim President and Chief Executive Officer
CFO: Daniel J Moncher, Vice President and Chief Financial Officer
CMO: Brenda Violette, M.D., Director Medical Staff
CIO: Robert Ayres, Director Information Systems
CHR: James Sennish, Vice President Human Resources
Web address: www.firelands.com
Control: Other not–for–profit (including NFP Corporation) **Service:** General medical and surgical

Staffed Beds: 239

SEAMAN—Adams County

☐ **ADAMS COUNTY REGIONAL MEDICAL CENTER (361326)**, 230 Medical Center Drive, Zip 45679–8002; tel. 937/386–3400, (Nonreporting) **A**1 10 18
Primary Contact: Alan Bird, Chief Executive Officer
CFO: Pete Dagenbach, Chief Financial Officer
CHR: Heather Hoop, Human Resources Generalist
CNO: Sharon Ashley, MSN, Chief Nursing Officer
Web address: www.acrmc.com
Control: County, Government, nonfederal **Service:** General medical and surgical

Staffed Beds: 25

Many Facility Codes have changed. Please refer to the AHA Guide Code Chart. © 2019 AHA Guide

SHELBY—Richland County

★ **OHIOHEALTH MEDCENTRAL SHELBY HOSPITAL (361324)**, 199 West Main Street, Zip 44875–1490; tel. 419/342–5015, **A**10 18 **F**3 11 13 15 18 29 30 31 34 35 40 45 50 59 64 65 68 76 78 79 81 85 89 93 96 107 108 110 115 119 128 130 133 135 146 149 154 156 **S** OhioHealth, Columbus, OH
Primary Contact: Vinson Yates, President
CNO: Trish DelGreco, Director of Nursing
Web address: www.medcentral.org/body.cfm?id=153
Control: Other not–for–profit (including NFP Corporation) **Service**: General medical and surgical

Staffed Beds: 25 **Admissions**: 950 **Census**: 12 **Outpatient Visits**: 43855 **Births**: 156 **Total Expense ($000)**: 27874 **Payroll Expense ($000)**: 9077

SIDNEY—Shelby County

★ ○ **WILSON MEMORIAL HOSPITAL (360013)**, 915 West Michigan Street, Zip 45365–2491; tel. 937/498–2311, **A**10 11 **F**3 7 11 12 13 15 18 20 28 29 30 34 40 45 49 51 56 57 59 62 63 64 68 70 75 76 77 79 81 82 85 86 87 89 93 97 98 103 107 108 111 115 118 119 129 130 131 132 135 146 147 156 157
Primary Contact: Duane Francis, Interim Chief Executive Officer
COO: Craig Lannoye, Vice President Operations
CFO: Julie Covault, Vice President Finance
CMO: Robert J McDevitt, M.D., Chief of Staff
CIO: Larry Meyers, Chief Information Officer
CHR: John Eve, Vice President Human Resources and Education
CNO: Linda Maurer, Vice President Patient Care Services
Web address: www.wilsonhospital.com
Control: Other not–for–profit (including NFP Corporation) **Service**: General medical and surgical

Staffed Beds: 71 **Admissions**: 2487 **Census**: 24 **Outpatient Visits**: 204944 **Births**: 708 **Total Expense ($000)**: 79950 **Payroll Expense ($000)**: 30541 **Personnel**: 552

SPRINGFIELD—Clark County

☐ **MENTAL HEALTH SERVICES FOR CLARK AND MADISON COUNTIES (364040)**, 474 North Yellow Springs Street, Zip 45504–2463; tel. 937/399–9500, (Nonreporting) **A**1
Primary Contact: Curt Gillespie, Chief Executive Officer
Web address: www.mhscc.org
Control: County, Government, nonfederal **Service**: Psychiatric

Staffed Beds: 16

☐ **OHIO VALLEY SURGICAL HOSPITAL (360355)**, 100 West Main Street, Zip 45502–1312; tel. 937/521–3900, (Nonreporting) **A**1 10
Primary Contact: Steve Eisentrager, President
CFO: Amanda martin, Manager Human Resources
CMO: Thales Pavlatos, Medical Director
CIO: Jonathan Bisdorf, Director Information Technology
CNO: Beth Lizza, Chief Nursing Officer
Web address: www.ovsurgical.com/
Control: Partnership, Investor–owned (for–profit) **Service**: Surgical

Staffed Beds: 24

☐ **SPRINGFIELD REGIONAL MEDICAL CENTER (360086)**, 100 Medical Center Drive, Zip 45504–2687; tel. 937/523–1000, (Nonreporting) **A**1 2 3 10 **S** Mercy Health, Cincinnati, OH
Primary Contact: Adam Groshans, President
CFO: William J. Kusnierz, Vice President and Chief Financial Officer
CNO: Elaine Storrs, Chief Nursing Officer
Web address: www.community-mercy.org
Control: Church operated **Service**: General medical and surgical

Staffed Beds: 259

STEUBENVILLE—Jefferson County

★ **ACUITY SPECIALTY HOSPITALS OHIO VALLEY (362035)**, 380 Summit Avenue, 3rd Floor, Zip 43952–2667; tel. 740/283–7600, (Includes ACUITY SPECIALTY HOSPITALS OHIO VALLEY AT BELMONT, 4697 Harrison Street, Bellaire, Ohio, Zip 43906–1338; tel. 740/671–2086) **F**1 3 29 34 57 85 91 148 **S** AcuityHealthcare, LP, Charlotte, NC
Primary Contact: Judy K. Weaver, MS, Chief Executive Officer
Web address: www.acuityhealthcare.net
Control: Partnership, Investor–owned (for–profit) **Service**: Acute long–term care hospital

Staffed Beds: 52 **Admissions**: 546 **Census**: 40 **Outpatient Visits**: 0 **Births**: 0 **Total Expense ($000)**: 22520 **Payroll Expense ($000)**: 10494 **Personnel**: 175

LIFE LINE HOSPITAL (362039), 200 School Street, Zip 43953–9610; tel. 740/346–2600, (Nonreporting) **A**10
Primary Contact: Patricia Cross, Chief Executive Officer
Web address: www.llhospital.com
Control: Partnership, Investor–owned (for–profit) **Service**: Acute long–term care hospital

Staffed Beds: 30

⊞ **TRINITY HEALTH SYSTEM (360211)**, 380 Summit Avenue, Zip 43952–2699; tel. 740/283–7000, (Includes TRINITY MEDICAL CENTER EAST, 380 Summit Avenue, Steubenville, Ohio, Zip 43952–2699; tel. 740/283–7000; TRINITY MEDICAL CENTER WEST, 4000 Johnson Road, Steubenville, Ohio, Zip 43952–2393; tel. 740/264–8000) **A**1 2 10 **F**3 4 5 12 13 15 17 18 20 22 24 26 28 29 30 31 32 33 34 35 38 40 44 45 46 47 48 49 51 54 56 57 59 62 64 65 69 70 71 74 75 77 78 79 81 82 85 86 87 90 91 92 93 94 96 97 98 100 101 102 104 105 106 107 108 110 111 115 117 118 119 120 121 123 124 126 128 129 130 131 132 135 144 146 147 148 149 152 153 156 **S** CommonSpirit Health, Chicago, IL
Primary Contact: Matthew Grimshaw, Market Chief Executive Officer
COO: JoAnn M Mulrooney, R.N., Chief Operating Officer
CFO: Dave Werkin, Vice President Finance and Chief Financial Officer
CMO: Gray Goncz, Vice President of Medical Affairs
CIO: Tom Kiger, Director Information Systems
CHR: Lewis C Musso, Vice President Human Resources
Web address: www.trinityhealth.com
Control: Other not–for–profit (including NFP Corporation) **Service**: General medical and surgical

Staffed Beds: 277 **Admissions**: 8440 **Census**: 121 **Outpatient Visits**: 270256 **Births**: 490 **Total Expense ($000)**: 226584 **Payroll Expense ($000)**: 81814 **Personnel**: 1616

SYLVANIA—Lucas County

⊞ △ **PROMEDICA FLOWER HOSPITAL (360074)**, 5200 Harroun Road, Zip 43560–2196; tel. 419/824–1444, **A**1 2 3 5 7 10 **F**3 11 12 13 15 18 28 29 30 31 34 35 36 38 40 45 47 48 49 50 53 54 57 59 64 65 67 68 75 76 77 78 79 81 82 84 85 86 87 90 91 92 93 96 97 98 100 101 102 103 107 108 109 110 111 114 116 117 118 119 120 121 123 124 126 129 130 131 132 143 146 147 149 150 154 **S** ProMedica Health System, Toledo, OH
Primary Contact: Neeraj Kanwal, M.D., Interim President, Metro Region
CFO: Michael Browning, Chief Financial Officer
CMO: John Evanoff, M.D., Vice President Medical Affairs
CIO: Lori Johnston, Chief Information Officer
CHR: Karen Strauss, Chief Human Resources Officer
CNO: Maurine Weis, MSN, R.N., Vice President Nursing and Chief Nursing Officer
Web address: www.promedica.org
Control: Other not–for–profit (including NFP Corporation) **Service**: General medical and surgical

Staffed Beds: 245 **Admissions**: 9778 **Census**: 145 **Outpatient Visits**: 169046 **Births**: 923 **Total Expense ($000)**: 200414 **Payroll Expense ($000)**: 67273 **Personnel**: 1122

⊞ **REGENCY HOSPITAL OF TOLEDO (362036)**, 5220 Alexis Road, Zip 43560–2504; tel. 419/318–5700, (Nonreporting) **A**1 5 10 **S** Select Medical Corporation, Mechanicsburg, PA
Primary Contact: Gary Zaciewski, Chief Executive Officer
Web address: www.regencyhospital.com
Control: Corporation, Investor–owned (for–profit) **Service**: Acute long–term care hospital

Staffed Beds: 45

TIFFIN—Seneca County

☐ **MERCY TIFFIN HOSPITAL (360089)**, 45 St Lawrence Drive, Zip 44883–8310; tel. 419/455–7000, (Nonreporting) **A**1 2 10 **S** Mercy Health, Cincinnati, OH
Primary Contact: B Lynn. Detterman, President and Chief Executive Officer
CMO: Steven Bruhl, Chief Medical Officer
CHR: Diana Olson, Director Human Resources
CNO: Anne Zimmerman, Senior Director Patient Care Services and Chief Nursing Officer
Web address: www.mercyweb.org
Control: Church operated **Service**: General medical and surgical

Staffed Beds: 46

Hospital, Medicare Provider Number, Address, Telephone, Approval, Facility, and Physician Codes, Health Care System

★ American Hospital Association (AHA) membership ○ Healthcare Facilities Accreditation Program ⇑ Center for Improvement in Healthcare Quality Accreditation
☐ The Joint Commission accreditation ◇ DNV Healthcare Inc. accreditation △ Commission on Accreditation of Rehabilitation Facilities (CARF) accreditation

TOLEDO—Lucas County

☐ **ADVANCED SPECIALTY HOSPITAL OF TOLEDO (362038)**, 1015 Garden Lake Parkway, Zip 43614–2779; tel. 419/381–0037, (Nonreporting) **A**1 3 10
Primary Contact: Troy Holmes, Interim Chief Executive Officer and Chief Financial Officer
CFO: Troy Holmes, Chief Financial Officer
CMO: B Sarroui, M.D., Chief of Staff
CHR: Lauren Avigdor, Director Human Resources
CNO: Bridgett Mitchell, Chief Clinical Officer
Web address: www.advancedspecialtyhospitals.com
Control: Corporation, Investor–owned (for–profit) **Service**: Acute long–term care hospital

Staffed Beds: 25

☐ **MERCY ST. ANNE HOSPITAL (360262)**, 3404 West Sylvania Avenue, Zip 43623–4467; tel. 419/407–2663, **A**1 2 3 10 **F**3 15 17 18 20 22 24 28 29 30 31 34 35 36 37 38 40 42 45 49 54 56 57 59 64 65 68 70 74 75 78 79 81 82 84 85 86 87 92 102 107 108 110 111 115 119 124 126 129 130 132 135 146 147 148 149 154 **S** Mercy Health, Cincinnati, OH
Primary Contact: Bradley J. Bertke, President and Chief Operating Officer
CFO: Michael Whipple, Chief Financial Officer
CMO: Herbert Stockard, M.D., Chief Medical Officer
CIO: Rebecca S Sykes, Chief Information Officer
CNO: Barb Dianda-Martin, Chief Nursing Officer
Web address: www.mercyweb.org
Control: Church operated, Nongovernment, not–for–profit **Service**: General medical and surgical

Staffed Beds: 96 Admissions: 5976 Census: 58 Outpatient Visits: 129776 Births: 0 Personnel: 484

☐ **MERCY ST. VINCENT MEDICAL CENTER (360112)**, 2213 Cherry Street, Zip 43608–2691; tel. 419/251–3232, (Includes MERCY CHILDREN'S HOSPITAL, 2213 Cherry Street, Toledo, Ohio, Zip 43608–2691; tel. 419/251–8000) **A**1 2 3 5 10 13 **F**3 7 8 11 12 13 15 16 17 18 19 20 22 24 26 29 30 31 32 34 35 37 38 39 40 41 42 43 44 45 46 47 48 49 50 51 53 54 55 56 57 58 59 60 61 64 65 66 68 70 72 74 75 76 77 78 79 81 82 83 84 85 86 87 88 89 92 93 97 107 108 110 111 114 115 118 119 126 129 130 131 132 134 135 146 147 154 155 157 **S** Mercy Health, Cincinnati, OH
Primary Contact: Jeffrey Dempsey, President
CMO: Thomas Welch, M.D., Chief Medical Officer
CHR: Gary George, Senior Vice President Human Resources
CNO: Barbara Martin, Chief Nursing Officer
Web address: www.mercyweb.org
Control: Church operated, Nongovernment, not–for–profit **Service**: General medical and surgical

Staffed Beds: 370 Admissions: 19053 Census: 204 Outpatient Visits: 246704 Births: 1426 Personnel: 1697

☐ **NORTHWEST OHIO PSYCHIATRIC HOSPITAL (364014)**, 930 Detroit Avenue, Zip 43614–2701; tel. 419/381–1881, **A**1 3 10 **F**30 50 53 75 87 98 130 146 149 154 **S** Ohio Department of Mental Health, Columbus, OH
Primary Contact: Brett M. Johnson, Chief Executive Officer
COO: Kyle Hurst, Chief Operations Officer
CIO: Michael Carter, Administrator Information Technology
CHR: Ursula Barrera-Richards, Human Resource Director
CNO: Deb Duris, Director of Nursing
Web address: www.mh.state.oh.us/
Control: State, Government, nonfederal **Service**: Psychiatric

Staffed Beds: 112 Admissions: 641 Census: 107 Outpatient Visits: 0 Births: 0 Total Expense ($000): 25700 Payroll Expense ($000): 14502 Personnel: 212

⊞ **PROMEDICA TOLEDO HOSPITAL (360068)**, 2142 North Cove Boulevard, Zip 43606–3896; tel. 419/291–4000, (Includes PROMEDICA WILDWOOD ORTHOPAEDIC AND SPINE HOSPITAL, 2901 North Reynolds Road, Toledo, Ohio, Zip 43615; tel. 419/578–7700; Neeraj Kanwal, M.D., Interim President, Metro Region; TOLEDO CHILDREN'S HOSPITAL, 2142 North Cove Boulevard, Toledo, Ohio, Zip 43606; tel. 419/291–4000; Arturo Polizzi, President and Chief Executive Officer) **A**1 2 3 5 10 **F**3 7 8 11 12 13 15 17 18 20 22 24 26 29 30 31 32 34 36 38 39 40 41 43 45 46 47 48 49 50 51 53 54 55 57 58 59 60 64 65 67 68 70 72 74 76 77 78 79 81 82 84 85 86 87 88 89 91 92 93 94 96 97 98 99 100 101 102 104 105 107 108 109 110 111 113 114 115 118 119 126 129 130 131 132 134 135 143 144 146 147 148 150 153 154 155 157 **S** ProMedica Health System, Toledo, OH
Primary Contact: Neeraj Kanwal, M.D., Interim President, Metro Region
CMO: Khurram Kamran, M.D., Vice President Medical Affairs
CIO: Rose Ann Laureto, Chief Information Officer
CNO: Deana Sievert, MSN, R.N., Chief Nursing Officer
Web address: www.promedica.org
Control: Other not–for–profit (including NFP Corporation) **Service**: General medical and surgical

Staffed Beds: 560 Admissions: 33833 Census: 450 Outpatient Visits: 663675 Births: 3596 Total Expense ($000): 760743 Payroll Expense ($000): 237777 Personnel: 3983

☐ **REHABILITATION HOSPITAL OF NORTHWEST OHIO (363040)**, 1455 West Medical Loop, Zip 43614; tel. 419/214–6600, (Nonreporting) **A**1 3 10 **S** Ernest Health, Inc., Albuquerque, NM
Primary Contact: Scott Williams, Chief Executive Officer
Control: Corporation, Investor–owned (for–profit) **Service**: Rehabilitation

Staffed Beds: 40

⊞ **THE UNIVERSITY OF TOLEDO MEDICAL CENTER (360048)**, 3000 Arlington Avenue, Zip 43614–2595; tel. 419/383–4000, **A**1 2 3 5 8 10 **F**3 4 5 8 11 12 15 17 18 20 22 24 26 28 29 30 31 32 34 35 36 37 38 39 40 43 44 45 46 47 48 49 50 51 53 54 55 56 57 68 70 74 75 77 78 79 81 82 84 85 86 87 91 92 93 94 96 97 98 99 100 101 102 103 104 107 108 110 111 114 115 116 117 118 119 120 121 123 124 126 129 130 131 132 134 135 138 146 147 148 149 153 154 156 157
Primary Contact: Daniel Barbee, Chief Executive Officer
CMO: Michael Ellis, M.D., Chief Medical Officer
CIO: William McCreary, Vice President and Chief Information Officer
CHR: Wendy Davis, Associate Vice President and Chief Human Resource Officer
CNO: Moneca Smith, Chief Nursing Officer
Web address: www.utoledo.edu
Control: State, Government, nonfederal **Service**: General medical and surgical

Staffed Beds: 246 Admissions: 11650 Census: 155 Outpatient Visits: 471020 Births: 0 Total Expense ($000): 304272 Payroll Expense ($000): 117903 Personnel: 2033

TROY—Miami County

⊞ △ **UPPER VALLEY MEDICAL CENTER (360174)**, 3130 North County Road 25A, Zip 45373–1309; tel. 937/440–4000, **A**1 2 3 5 7 10 **F**3 8 11 15 18 20 22 26 28 29 30 31 34 35 36 38 40 41 44 45 46 48 49 50 54 55 56 57 58 59 60 63 64 68 70 73 74 75 76 77 78 79 80 81 84 85 86 87 90 91 92 93 96 98 100 101 102 103 104 107 108 110 111 114 115 118 119 124 126 129 130 131 132 135 141 143 145 146 147 148 149 154 156 157 **S** Premier Health, Dayton, OH
Primary Contact: Thomas Parker, President
CFO: Tim Snider, Senior Vice President for Finance
CMO: Jennifer Hauler, D.O., Chief Medical Officer
CIO: James Kaiser, Site Director Information Technology
CHR: Kathy Boerger, Director Human Resources
CNO: Terry Fry, R.N., Chief Nursing Officer
Web address: www.uvmc.com
Control: Other not–for–profit (including NFP Corporation) **Service**: General medical and surgical

Staffed Beds: 78 Admissions: 6394 Census: 63 Outpatient Visits: 258598 Births: 623 Total Expense ($000): 141278 Payroll Expense ($000): 61046 Personnel: 997

UPPER SANDUSKY—Wyandot County

★ **WYANDOT MEMORIAL HOSPITAL (361329)**, 885 North Sandusky Avenue, Zip 43351–1098; tel. 419/294–4991, **A**10 18 **F**3 11 13 15 17 18 28 29 30 31 34 35 40 45 46 50 53 57 59 64 74 75 76 77 78 79 81 82 85 86 87 89 92 93 97 107 108 110 111 115 116 117 118 119 124 129 130 131 132 133 135 144 146 148 149
Primary Contact: Ty Shaull, President and Chief Executive Officer
CFO: Alan H Yeates, Vice President Fiscal Services
CHR: Vickie Underwood, Director Human Resources
CNO: Marty Gray, R.N., Director of Nursing
Web address: www.wyandotmemorial.org
Control: Hospital district or authority, Government, nonfederal **Service**: General medical and surgical

Staffed Beds: 25 Admissions: 736 Census: 7 Outpatient Visits: 68695 Births: 125 Total Expense ($000): 45988 Payroll Expense ($000): 17107 Personnel: 237

URBANA—Champaign County

MERCY MEMORIAL HOSPITAL (361312), 904 Scioto Street, Zip 43078–2200; tel. 937/653–5231, (Nonreporting) **A**10 18 **S** Mercy Health, Cincinnati, OH
Primary Contact: Matthew T. Caldwell, President and Chief Executive Officer
Web address: www.health-partners.org
Control: Church operated **Service**: General medical and surgical

Staffed Beds: 25

VAN WERT—Van Wert County

⊞ **VAN WERT COUNTY HOSPITAL (360071)**, 1250 South Washington Street, Zip 45891–2599; tel. 419/238–2390, **A**1 5 10 **F**3 8 13 15 18 28 29 32 34 35 36 40 44 48 50 53 54 57 59 62 64 65 68 70 75 76 77 79 81 82 85 87 89 93 94 97 107 108 110 113 119 129 130 131 135 146 147 148 154 157
Primary Contact: James W. Pope, FACHE, President and Chief Executive Officer
CMO: Charles Hoehn, President, Medical Staff
CIO: Brett Taylor, Manager Information
CNO: Shelia Kay Brokenshire, Vice President of Nursing
Web address: www.vanwerthospital.org
Control: Other not–for–profit (including NFP Corporation) **Service**: General medical and surgical

Staffed Beds: 27 **Admissions**: 904 **Census**: 8 **Outpatient Visits**: 64159 **Births**: 160 **Total Expense ($000)**: 62479 **Payroll Expense ($000)**: 23593 **Personnel**: 298

WARREN—Trumbull County

⊞ △ **HILLSIDE REHABILITATION HOSPITAL (363026)**, 8747 Squires Lane NE, Zip 44484–1649; tel. 330/841–3700, (Nonreporting) **A**1 5 7 10 **S** Steward Health Care System, LLC, Dallas, TX
Primary Contact: Krista McFadden, Interim Chief Executive Officer
CMO: Joseph Cerimele, D.O., Medical Director
CIO: Barry Fitts, Chief Information Officer
CHR: Jody Roman, Chief Human Resource Officer
CNO: Susan Joy, Chief Nursing Officer
Web address: www.https://valleycareofohio.steward.org
Control: Corporation, Investor–owned (for–profit) **Service**: Rehabilitation

Staffed Beds: 65

☐ **MERCY HEALTH - ST. JOSEPH WARREN HOSPITAL (360161)**, 667 Eastland Avenue SE, Zip 44484–4531, Mailing Address: 627 Eastland Avenue, Zip 44484–4531; tel. 330/841–4000, **A**1 2 3 5 10 13 **F**3 5 8 11 12 13 15 28 29 30 31 32 34 35 37 40 42 43 45 46 48 49 50 51 54 58 59 64 66 67 68 70 74 75 76 77 78 79 81 82 83 84 85 87 91 92 93 97 100 102 107 108 109 110 111 114 115 116 117 118 119 120 121 123 124 126 129 130 135 144 146 147 148 149 154 **S** Mercy Health, Cincinnati, OH
Primary Contact: Kathy Cook, FACHE, MSN, President
COO: Donald E. Koenig Jr Chief Operating Officer
CMO: Nicholas Kreatsoulas, Vice President Medical Affairs
Web address: www.hmpartners.org
Control: Church operated, Nongovernment, not–for–profit **Service**: General medical and surgical

Staffed Beds: 140 **Admissions**: 8850 **Census**: 92 **Outpatient Visits**: 165238 **Births**: 1134 **Personnel**: 633

⊞ **TRUMBULL MEMORIAL HOSPITAL (360055)**, 1350 East Market Street, Zip 44400–0020, tel. 330/841–9011, (Nonreporting) **A**1 2 3 5 10 **S** Steward Health Care System, LLC, Dallas, TX
Primary Contact: Ronald L. Bierman, Chief Executive Officer
CMO: Thomas L James, M.D., Chief Medical Officer
CIO: Barry Fitts, Chief Information Officer
CHR: Robert Sincich, Vice President Human Resources
CNO: Melissa Bennett, Chief Nursing Officer
Web address: www.https://trumbullmemorial.org/?_ga=2.209137234.1564767671.1497292183–315051339.1497292183
Control: Corporation, Investor–owned (for–profit) **Service**: General medical and surgical

Staffed Beds: 292

WARRENSVILLE HEIGHTS—Cuyahoga County

⊞ **REGENCY HOSPITAL CLEVELAND EAST (362029)**, 4200 Interchange Corporate Center Road, Zip 44128–5631; tel. 216/910–3800, (Includes REGENCY HOSPITAL OF CLEVELAND - WEST, 6990 Engle Road, Middleburg Heights, Ohio, Zip 44130–3420; tel. 440/202–4200; Timothy Rolsen, Chief Executive Officer), (Nonreporting) **A**1 10 **S** Select Medical Corporation, Mechanicsburg, PA
Primary Contact: Lisa Deering, Chief Executive Officer
Web address: www.regencyhospital.com/
Control: Corporation, Investor–owned (for–profit) **Service**: Acute long–term care hospital

Staffed Beds: 87

⊞ **SOUTH POINTE HOSPITAL (360144)**, 20000 Harvard Road, Zip 44122–6805; tel. 216/491–6000, **A**1 2 3 5 10 13 **F**3 15 18 26 28 29 30 34 35 36 38 39 40 44 50 51 55 56 57 58 59 60 61 64 65 66 68 70 74 75 77 78 79 81 82 84 85 86 87 93 97 100 102 107 108 110 111 114 117 119 143 144 146 148 154 156 **S** Cleveland Clinic Health System, Cleveland, OH
Primary Contact: Margaret McKenzie, M.D., President
COO: Andrea Jacobs, Chief Operating Officer
CFO: Lindsay Bird, Director Finance
CMO: Arun Gupta, M.D., Vice President Medical Affairs
CIO: Ralph A Cagna, Director Information Technology
CHR: Doris A. Zajec, Director Human Resources
Web address: www.southpointehospital.org
Control: Other not–for–profit (including NFP Corporation) **Service**: General medical and surgical

Staffed Beds: 172 **Admissions**: 6517 **Census**: 84 **Outpatient Visits**: 99777 **Births**: 0 **Total Expense ($000)**: 131115 **Payroll Expense ($000)**: 49880 **Personnel**: 762

WASHINGTON COURT HOUSE—Fayette County

⊞ **FAYETTE COUNTY MEMORIAL HOSPITAL (361331)**, 1430 Columbus Avenue, Zip 43160–1791; tel. 740/335–1210, **A**1 10 18 **F**3 7 8 11 15 18 29 34 35 40 41 44 45 51 57 59 64 68 70 75 77 79 81 82 85 87 89 91 92 93 97 107 108 110 114 119 127 128 130 131 132 133 135 144 146 147 148 149 154 156
Primary Contact: D Michael. Diener, Chief Executive Officer
CFO: Trent Lemle, Chief Financial Officer
CNO: Tammie Wilson, R.N., MSN, Chief Nursing Officer
Web address: www.fcmh.org
Control: County, Government, nonfederal **Service**: General medical and surgical

Staffed Beds: 25 **Admissions**: 767 **Census**: 7 **Outpatient Visits**: 155831 **Births**: 0 **Total Expense ($000)**: 47268 **Payroll Expense ($000)**: 20515 **Personnel**: 374

WAUSEON—Fulton County

⊞ **FULTON COUNTY HEALTH CENTER (361333)**, 725 South Shoop Avenue, Zip 43567–1701; tel. 419/335–2015, (Total facility includes 71 beds in nursing home–type unit) **A**1 2 5 10 18 **F**3 8 11 12 13 15 18 26 28 29 31 34 40 53 57 59 67 69 70 75 76 77 78 79 81 87 89 93 98 101 102 103 104 105 107 108 111 115 118 119 128 129 130 131 132 135 146 148 149 153
Primary Contact: Patricia Finn, Chief Executive Officer
COO: Kristine Snyder, Chief Operating Officer
CFO: Jenee Seibert, Chief Finance Officer
CIO: Larry Hefflinger, Chief Information Officer
CHR: Rachel Geckle, Chief Human Resource Officer
CNO: Tiffany Siegel, Chief Nursing Officer
Web address: www.fultoncountyhealthcenter.org
Control: Other not–for–profit (including NFP Corporation) **Service**: General medical and surgical

Staffed Beds: 100 **Admissions**: 1418 **Census**: 76 **Outpatient Visits**: 185154 **Births**: 184 **Total Expense ($000)**: 66215 **Payroll Expense ($000)**: 24639 **Personnel**: 667

WAVERLY—Pike County

☐ **ADENA PIKE MEDICAL CENTER (361334)**, 100 Dawn Lane, Zip 45690–9138; tel. 740/947–2186, **A**1 10 18 **F**3 11 18 29 30 34 35 40 43 45 50 57 59 62 63 64 65 78 79 81 82 85 86 91 93 96 104 105 107 110 111 114 115 118 120 121 123 130 131 133 135 146 148 149 154 156 **S** Adena Health System, Chillicothe, OH
Primary Contact: David M. Zanni, Administrator
COO: Eric Cecava, Chief Operating Officer
CFO: Lisa Carlson, Chief Financial Officer
CMO: John Fortney, Chief Medical Officer
CIO: Tom Bialorucki, Chief Information Officer
CHR: Jay D. Justice, Chief Human Resources Officer
Web address: www.adena.org
Control: Other not–for–profit (including NFP Corporation) **Service**: General medical and surgical

Staffed Beds: 25 **Admissions**: 478 **Census**: 7 **Outpatient Visits**: 34786 **Births**: 0 **Total Expense ($000)**: 17868 **Payroll Expense ($000)**: 6903 **Personnel**: 127

Hospital, Medicare Provider Number, Address, Telephone, Approval, Facility, and Physician Codes, Health Care System

★ American Hospital Association (AHA) membership
☐ The Joint Commission accreditation
○ Healthcare Facilities Accreditation Program
◇ DNV Healthcare Inc. accreditation
⇑ Center for Improvement in Healthcare Quality Accreditation
△ Commission on Accreditation of Rehabilitation Facilities (CARF) accreditation

WEST CHESTER—Butler County

☐ **BECKETT SPRINGS (364051)**, 8614 Shepherd Farm Drive, Zip 45069; tel. 513/942–9500, **A**1 10 **F**4 5 98 105 152 153 **S** Springstone, Louisville, KY
Primary Contact: Jeff Pritchard, Chief Executive Officer
Web address: www.springstone.com/hospitals.stmhl
Control: Corporation, Investor–owned (for–profit) **Service**: Psychiatric

Staffed Beds: 96 **Admissions**: 2880 **Census**: 83 **Outpatient Visits**: 27044
Births: 0 **Total Expense ($000)**: 23395 **Payroll Expense ($000)**: 12819
Personnel: 162

⊞ **WEST CHESTER HOSPITAL (360354)**, 7700 University Drive, Zip 45069–2505; tel. 513/298–3000, (Includes WEST CHESTER HOSPITAL SURGICAL CENTER, 7750 University Court, West Chester, Ohio, Zip 45069; tel. 513/475–8300; Tom G Daskalakis, Chief Administrative Officer) **A**1 3 5 10 **F**3 9 12 13 15 18 20 22 26 29 30 31 34 35 37 38 40 41 43 44 45 46 47 48 49 50 51 54 57 58 59 60 61 63 64 70 73 74 75 76 77 78 79 80 81 82 84 85 86 87 91 92 100 107 108 110 111 114 115 119 126 129 130 131 132 134 135 141 145 146 147 148 149 150 154 155 156 157 **S** UC Health, Cincinnati, OH
Primary Contact: Tom G. Daskalakis, Chief Administrative Officer
CFO: Karen Shadowens, Director Finance and Chief Financial Officer
CIO: Jay Brown, Senior Vice President, Chief Information Officer
CHR: Jack Talbot, Director, Human Resources
CNO: Kathie Hays, MSN, R.N., Chief Nursing Officer
Web address: www.uchealth.com/westchesterhospital
Control: Other not–for–profit (including NFP Corporation) **Service**: General medical and surgical

Staffed Beds: 174 **Admissions**: 9124 **Census**: 92 **Outpatient Visits**: 211616 **Births**: 970 **Total Expense ($000)**: 254386 **Payroll Expense ($000)**: 66029 **Personnel**: 1087

WESTERVILLE—Franklin County

⊞ **MOUNT CARMEL ST. ANN'S (360012)**, 500 South Cleveland Avenue, Zip 43081–8998; tel. 614/898–4000, **A**1 2 3 5 10 **F**3 11 13 15 18 20 22 24 26 28 29 30 31 34 35 37 40 44 45 47 48 49 50 51 54 55 57 58 59 61 63 64 65 66 68 70 74 75 76 77 78 79 81 82 83 84 85 86 87 93 97 100 107 108 109 110 111 114 115 116 118 119 120 121 123 124 126 130 131 132 141 146 147 148 154 **S** Trinity Health, Livonia, MI
Primary Contact: Kim Unhee, President
Web address: www.mountcarmelhealth.com
Control: Church operated, Nongovernment, not–for–profit **Service**: General medical and surgical

Staffed Beds: 294 **Admissions**: 21537 **Census**: 184 **Outpatient Visits**: 166311 **Births**: 4062 **Total Expense ($000)**: 325197 **Payroll Expense ($000)**: 106592 **Personnel**: 1623

WESTLAKE—Cuyahoga County

⊞ **ST. JOHN MEDICAL CENTER (360123)**, 29000 Center Ridge Road, Zip 44145–5293; tel. 440/835–8000, **A**1 2 3 10 13 **F**3 8 11 13 15 17 18 19 20 22 24 26 28 29 30 31 34 35 36 39 40 41 43 44 45 46 47 49 50 51 54 55 56 57 58 59 60 63 64 65 67 68 69 70 71 74 75 76 78 79 81 82 83 84 85 86 87 89 92 93 100 102 107 108 110 111 114 115 119 126 130 131 132 135 143 144 146 147 148 149 154 **S** University Hospitals, Cleveland, OH
Primary Contact: Robert G. David, President
CFO: Allen R Tracy, Senior Vice President and Chief Financial Officer
CMO: Michael Dobrovich, M.D., Chief Medical Officer
CIO: James H Carroll, Chief Information Officer
CHR: Gary Lazroff, Vice President Human Resources
Web address: www.sjws.net
Control: Other not–for–profit (including NFP Corporation) **Service**: General medical and surgical

Staffed Beds: 176 **Admissions**: 9356 **Census**: 85 **Outpatient Visits**: 145413 **Births**: 845 **Total Expense ($000)**: 164914 **Payroll Expense ($000)**: 51561 **Personnel**: 888

ST. JOHN WEST SHORE HOSPITAL See St. John Medical Center

WILLARD—Huron County

☐ **MERCY HEALTH - WILLARD HOSPITAL (361310)**, 1100 Neal Zick Road, Zip 44890–9287; tel. 419/964–5000, **A**1 10 18 **F**3 5 7 15 18 28 29 30 31 34 35 40 45 46 57 59 68 70 74 75 77 78 79 81 84 85 87 89 93 97 107 111 114 119 129 130 131 132 133 135 143 145 146 147 149 154 **S** Mercy Health, Cincinnati, OH
Primary Contact: B Lynn. Detterman, President and Chief Executive Officer
CMO: Christopher Bohach, DPM, Chief of Staff
CHR: Diana Olson, Chief Human Resources Officer
Web address: www.mercyweb.org
Control: Church operated, Nongovernment, not–for–profit **Service**: General medical and surgical

Staffed Beds: 20 **Admissions**: 584 **Census**: 6

WILLOUGHBY—Lake County

☐ **WINDSOR-LAURELWOOD CENTER FOR BEHAVIORAL MEDICINE (364029)**, 35900 Euclid Avenue, Zip 44094–4648; tel. 440/953–3000, (Nonreporting) **A**1 10 **S** Universal Health Services, Inc., King of Prussia, PA
Primary Contact: Ric McAllister, Chief Executive Officer
COO: Brenda Bailey, Assistant Administrator
CFO: Leanne Smith, Chief Financial Officer
CMO: Leonard Barley, M.D., Chief Medical Officer
CHR: Pam Connell, Manager Human Resources
CNO: Debra Schaefer, Chief Nursing Officer
Web address: www.windsorlaurelwood.com
Control: Individual, Investor–owned (for–profit) **Service**: Psychiatric

Staffed Beds: 159

WILMINGTON—Clinton County

⊞ **CMH REGIONAL HEALTH SYSTEM (360175)**, 610 West Main Street, Zip 45177–2125; tel. 937/382–6611, (Nonreporting) **A**1 2 5 10 **S** LifePoint Health, Brentwood, TN
Primary Contact: Lance Beus, Chief Executive Officer
CFO: Bradley Boggus, Chief Financial Officer
CIO: Ray Doherty, Director Information Technology
CHR: Jan Blair, Director Human Resources
CNO: Sheila Martin, Chief Nursing Officer
Web address: www.cmhregional.com
Control: Corporation, Investor–owned (for–profit) **Service**: General medical and surgical

Staffed Beds: 165

WOOSTER—Wayne County

⇑ **WOOSTER COMMUNITY HOSPITAL (360036)**, 1761 Beall Avenue, Zip 44691–2342; tel. 330/263–8100, (Nonreporting) **A**2 10 19 21 **S** QHR, Brentwood, TN
Primary Contact: William E. Sheron, Chief Executive Officer
Web address: www.woosterhospital.org
Control: City, Government, nonfederal **Service**: General medical and surgical

Staffed Beds: 152

WRIGHT—PATTERSON AFB-Greene County

⊞ **WRIGHT PATTERSON MEDICAL CENTER**, 4881 Sugar Maple Drive, Zip 45433–5529; tel. 937/257–0837, (Nonreporting) **A**1 2 3 5 **S** Department of the Air Force, Washington, DC
Primary Contact: Colonel Freddie Jenkins, Administrator
COO: Colonel Brent J Erickson, Administrator
CFO: Major Kelly Lesnick, Resource Manager Flight Commander
CMO: Gregory Sweitzer, Chief Medical Officer
CIO: John Beighle, Flight Chief Medical Information Systems
CHR: Hubert Chatman, Chief Civilian Personnel
CNO: Colonel Daniel Gerke, Chief Nursing Officer
Web address: www.wpafb.af.mil/units/wpmc/
Control: Department of Defense, Government, federal **Service**: General medical and surgical

Staffed Beds: 62

XENIA—Greene County

★ ○ **GREENE MEMORIAL HOSPITAL (360026)**, 1141 North Monroe Drive, Zip 45385–1600; tel. 937/352–2000, **A**2 5 10 11 **F**3 11 15 18 28 29 30 34 35 36 38 40 43 44 45 46 48 50 51 54 57 59 61 64 68 70 74 75 77 79 81 86 87 93 96 102 107 108 110 114 117 118 119 127 129 130 132 135 146 147 148 157 **S** Kettering Health Network, Dayton, OH
Primary Contact: Rick A. Dodds, President
CFO: Ron D Connovich, Chief Financial Officer
CMO: Michael Caccamo, M.D., Chief Medical Officer
CIO: Andy Lehman, Senior Vice President Technology & Analytics
CHR: Jeff Jones, Director Human Resources
CNO: Brenda Kuhn, Ph.D., R.N., FACHE, Chief Nursing Officer
Web address: www.ketteringhealth.org/greene
Control: Church operated, Nongovernment, not–for–profit **Service**: General medical and surgical

Staffed Beds: 49 **Admissions**: 2284 **Census**: 25 **Outpatient Visits**: 106728 **Births**: 0 **Total Expense ($000)**: 106237 **Payroll Expense ($000)**: 52899 **Personnel**: 402

Many Facility Codes have changed. Please refer to the AHA Guide Code Chart.

YOUNGSTOWN—Trumbull County

☐ **BELMONT PINES HOSPITAL (364038)**, 615 Churchill-Hubbard Road, Zip 44505–1379; tel. 330/759–2700, (Nonreporting) **A**1 10 **S** Universal Health Services, Inc., King of Prussia, PA
Primary Contact: Lisa Cocca, Chief Executive Officer
CFO: Sylvia Kupper, Chief Financial Officer
CMO: Phillip G Maiden, M.D., Medical Director
CHR: Deidre L Watson, Director Human Resources
CNO: Tammy Shells, Chief Nursing Officer
Web address: www.belmontpines.com
Control: Corporation, Investor–owned (for–profit) **Service**: Psychiatric

Staffed Beds: 96

YOUNGSTOWN—Mahoning County

☐ △ **MERCY HEALTH - ST. ELIZABETH YOUNGSTOWN HOSPITAL (360064)**, 1044 Belmont Avenue, Zip 44504–1096, Mailing Address: P.O. Box 1790, Zip 44501–1790; tel. 330/746–7211, **A**1 2 3 5 7 10 19 **F**3 7 8 11 15 17 18 20 22 24 26 28 29 30 31 34 35 37 39 40 43 44 45 46 50 51 53 54 56 57 58 59 60 61 64 66 67 68 70 71 74 75 77 78 79 81 84 85 86 87 88 89 90 91 92 93 96 97 98 100 101 102 103 104 105 107 110 111 114 115 116 117 118 119 120 121 123 126 130 131 132 135 143 146 147 148 149 153 154 156 **S** Mercy Health, Cincinnati, OH
Primary Contact: Donald E. Kline, President and Chief Executive Officer
COO: Donald E. Koenig Jr Executive Vice President and Regional Chief Operating Officer, President, St. Elizabeth Youngstown Hospital
CFO: Anthony J. Seminaro, Chief Financial Officer
CIO: Maureen Kordupel, Director Relationship Manager
CNO: Lori DeNiro, Regional Chief Nursing Officer
Web address: www.mercy.com
Control: Church operated, Nongovernment, not–for–profit **Service**: General medical and surgical

Staffed Beds: 387 **Admissions**: 19948 **Census**: 265 **Outpatient Visits**: 306971 **Births**: 0 **Personnel**: 1702

⊞ **SELECT SPECIALTY HOSPITAL-YOUNGSTOWN (362024)**, 1044 Belmont Avenue, Zip 44504–1006; tel. 330/480–2349, (Includes SELECT SPECIALTY HOSPITAL-YOUNGSTOWN, BOARDMAN CAMPUS, 667 Eastland Avenue SE, Warren, Ohio, Zip 44484–4503; tel. 330/729–1700), (Non-reporting) **A**1 10 **S** Select Medical Corporation, Mechanicsburg, PA
Primary Contact: Jodi Costello, Chief Executive Officer
Web address: www.selectspecialtyhospitals.com/company/locations/youngstown.aspx
Control: Corporation, Investor–owned (for–profit) **Service**: Acute long–term care hospital

Staffed Beds: 56

☐ **SURGICAL HOSPITAL AT SOUTHWOODS (360352)**, 7630 Southern Boulevard, Zip 44512–5633; tel. 330/729–8000, (Nonreporting) **A**1 10
Primary Contact: Ed Muransky, Owner
Web address: www.surgeryatsouthwoods.com/
Control: Individual, Investor–owned (for–profit) **Service**: Surgical

Staffed Beds: 12

ZANESVILLE—Muskingum County

★ ○ **GENESIS HEALTHCARE SYSTEM (360039)**, 2951 Maple Avenue, Zip 43701–1406; tel. 740/454–5000, (Includes BETHESDA HOSPITAL, 2951 Maple Avenue, Zanesville, Ohio, Zip 43701–1465; tel. 614/454–4000; GOOD SAMARITAN MEDICAL AND REHABILITATION CENTER, 800 Forest Avenue, Zanesville, Ohio, Zip 43701–2881; tel. 614/454–5000) **A**2 3 10 11 **F**3 5 8 9 11 13 15 17 18 20 22 24 26 28 29 30 31 32 34 35 40 42 43 44 45 46 47 48 50 51 54 57 58 59 60 63 64 65 68 70 73 74 75 76 77 78 79 81 82 84 85 86 87 89 91 92 93 94 96 98 99 100 101 102 104 105 106 107 108 109 110 111 114 115 116 117 118 119 120 121 123 124 126 129 130 131 132 135 144 146 147 148 151 154 156 157 **S** Franciscan Sisters of Christian Charity Sponsored Ministries, Inc., Manitowoc, WI
Primary Contact: Matthew J. Perry, President and Chief Executive Officer
COO: Richard S Helsper, Chief Operating Officer
CFO: Paul Masterson, Chief Financial Officer
CMO: Dan Scheerer, M.D., Chief Medical Officer
CIO: Edmund J Romito, Chief Information Officer
CHR: Dianna LeVeck, Chief Human Resources Officer
CNO: Abby Nguyen, R.N., Chief Nursing Officer
Web address: www.genesishcs.org
Control: Other not–for–profit (including NFP Corporation) **Service**: General medical and surgical

Staffed Beds: 321 **Admissions**: 13923 **Census**: 159 **Outpatient Visits**: 432223 **Births**: 1539 **Total Expense ($000)**: 375475 **Payroll Expense ($000)**: 127168 **Personnel**: 3054

Hospital, Medicare Provider Number, Address, Telephone, Approval, Facility, and Physician Codes, Health Care System

★ American Hospital Association (AHA) membership   ○ Healthcare Facilities Accreditation Program   ⇑ Center for Improvement in Healthcare Quality Accreditation
☐ The Joint Commission accreditation   ◇ DNV Healthcare Inc. accreditation   △ Commission on Accreditation of Rehabilitation Facilities (CARF) accreditation

OKLAHOMA

ADA—Pontotoc County

☒ **CHICKASAW NATION MEDICAL CENTER (370180)**, 1921 Stonecipher Boulevard, Zip 74820–3439; tel. 580/436–3980, **A**1 3 10 13 **F**3 5 7 8 13 15 18 29 30 34 35 38 39 40 43 45 50 53 54 57 58 59 60 64 65 68 69 70 71 75 76 79 81 85 86 87 89 91 93 97 100 104 107 110 111 115 119 127 130 133 135 143 144 145 146 147 148 149 154
Primary Contact: Chris Anoatubby, Deputy Secretary of Health
CFO: Marty Wafford, Under Secretary of Support and Programs
CMO: Richard McClain, M.D., Chief Medical Officer
CIO: Desiree Traylor, Chief Information Officer
CHR: Jalinda Kelley, Secretary of Interior Services
CNO: Jerod Waters, Chief Nursing Officer
Web address: www.chickasaw.net
Control: PHS, Indian Service, Government, federal **Service**: General medical and surgical

Staffed Beds: 72 Admissions: 2788 Census: 26 Outpatient Visits: 362016 Births: 932 Total Expense ($000): 241574 Payroll Expense ($000): 104714 Personnel: 1401

☒ **MERCY HOSPITAL ADA (370020)**, 430 North Monte Vista, Zip 74820–4610; tel. 580/332–2323, **A**1 2 10 **F**3 7 11 13 15 18 29 30 31 34 35 40 43 44 45 49 50 59 64 68 69 70 72 75 76 77 78 79 81 85 86 87 89 90 93 98 100 101 102 103 107 108 110 111 114 116 117 119 120 121 124 127 130 131 132 146 148 149 156 **S** Mercy, Chesterfield, MO
Primary Contact: Terence Farrell, President
CFO: Mary Garber, Vice President Finance
CMO: Imtiaz Ahmed, Chief of Staff
CHR: Katrina Godfrey, Director Human Resources
CNO: Karen Sweeney, Vice President, Chief Nursing Officer
Web address: www.https://www.mercy.net/practice/mercy-hospital-ada/
Control: Church operated, Nongovernment, not–for–profit **Service**: General medical and surgical

Staffed Beds: 156 Admissions: 3688 Census: 54 Outpatient Visits: 130805 Births: 468 Total Expense ($000): 91446 Payroll Expense ($000): 38420 Personnel: 493

☐ **ROLLING HILLS HOSPITAL (374016)**, 1000 Rolling Hills Lane, Zip 74820–9415; tel. 580/436–3600, **A**1 3 10 **F**34 35 38 98 100 101 103 106 130 135 154 **S** Acadia Healthcare Company, Inc., Franklin, TN
Primary Contact: Dennis Gober, Interim Chief Executive Officer
CMO: Robert Morton, M.D., Medical Director
CIO: Sherry Barnes, Director Health Information and Quality Management
CHR: Timothy Blackwell, Manager Human Resources
Web address: www.rollinghillshospital.com
Control: Corporation, Investor–owned (for–profit) **Service**: Psychiatric

Staffed Beds: 108 Admissions: 1135 Census: 71 Outpatient Visits: 0 Births: 0 Total Expense ($000): 14048 Payroll Expense ($000): 7181 Personnel: 150

ALTUS—Jackson County

☒ **JACKSON COUNTY MEMORIAL HOSPITAL (370022)**, 1200 East Pecan Street, Zip 73521–6192, Mailing Address: P.O. Box 8190, Zip 73522–8190; tel. 580/379–5000, **A**1 3 10 **F**3 10 11 13 15 29 30 34 35 40 43 45 49 56 57 59 62 63 64 65 70 75 76 77 79 81 85 86 87 93 100 101 104 107 110 111 114 119 127 129 130 131 132 133 135 145 146 147 148 149
Primary Contact: Steve L. Hartgraves, President and Chief Executive Officer
COO: Casey D. Miranda, Executive Vice President and Chief Operating Officer
CFO: Nancy Davidson, Senior Vice President and Chief Financial Officer
CMO: M. George Zakhary, M.D., Chief of Staff
CIO: Dena Daniel, Director Information Systems
CHR: Richard Pope, Vice President Human Resources
Web address: www.jcmh.com
Control: Hospital district or authority, Government, nonfederal **Service**: General medical and surgical

Staffed Beds: 49 Admissions: 3170 Census: 25 Outpatient Visits: 161667 Births: 361 Total Expense ($000): 70856 Payroll Expense ($000): 37171 Personnel: 722

ALVA—Woods County

☒ **SHARE MEDICAL CENTER (371341)**, 800 Share Drive, Zip 73717–3618, Mailing Address: P.O. Box 727, Zip 73717–0727; tel. 580/327–2800, **A**10 20 **F**3 15 29 40 43 45 59 64 65 68 69 77 81 93 96 97 107 110 114 127 129 130 133 144 149
Primary Contact: Kandice K. Allen, R.N., Chief Executive Officer
CFO: Kevin O'Brien, Chief Financial Officer
CMO: Elizabeth Kinzic, M.D., Chief of Staff
CIO: Alan Vaughan, Director Information Technology
CHR: Mary Herold, Director Human Resources
CNO: Regina Wilson, R.N., Director of Nursing
Web address: www.smcok.com
Control: Hospital district or authority, Government, nonfederal **Service**: General medical and surgical

Staffed Beds: 12 Admissions: 268 Census: 3 Outpatient Visits: 17321 Births: 0 Total Expense ($000): 10466 Payroll Expense ($000): 4206 Personnel: 91

ANADARKO—Caddo County

PHYSICIANS' HOSPITAL IN ANADARKO (371314), 1002 Central Boulevard East, Zip 73005–4496; tel. 405/247–2551, (Nonreporting) **A**10 18 **S** First Physicians Capital Group, Inc., Oklahoma City, OK
Primary Contact: Travis A. Villani, FACHE, Chief Executive Officer and Administrator
Web address: www.anadarkohospital.com
Control: Partnership, Investor–owned (for–profit) **Service**: General medical and surgical

Staffed Beds: 25

ANTLERS—Pushmataha County

PUSHMATAHA HOSPITAL (370083), 510 East Main Street, Zip 74523–3262, Mailing Address: P.O. Box 518, Zip 74523–0518; tel. 580/298–3341, (Nonreporting) **A**10
Primary Contact: Nick Rowland, Chief Executive Officer
COO: Nick Rowland, Chief Operating Officer
CFO: Rory Ward, Chief Financial Officer
CMO: G Wayne Flatt, D.O., Chief Medical Director
CHR: Paula Schalski, Director Human Resources
CNO: Marla Barnes, Director of Nursing
Web address: www.pushhospital.com
Control: State, Government, nonfederal **Service**: General medical and surgical

Staffed Beds: 23

ARDMORE—Carter County

☒ **MERCY HOSPITAL ARDMORE (370047)**, 1011 14th Avenue NW, Zip 73401–1828; tel. 580/223–5400, **A**1 10 **F**3 13 15 18 20 22 28 29 30 31 34 35 40 43 45 47 48 49 50 57 59 62 64 67 68 70 74 75 76 77 78 79 81 82 84 85 87 89 90 93 98 103 107 108 110 111 114 115 117 119 120 121 123 126 129 130 146 148 149 156 **S** Mercy, Chesterfield, MO
Primary Contact: Daryle Voss, FACHE, President and Chief Executive Officer
CMO: Pam Kimbrough, M.D., Vice President Medical Affairs
CHR: Melinda Sharum, Director Human Resources
CNO: Debra Pender, MS, R.N., Vice President Nursing
Web address: www.mercyok.net
Control: Church operated, Nongovernment, not–for–profit **Service**: General medical and surgical

Staffed Beds: 190 Admissions: 6418 Census: 78 Outpatient Visits: 198597 Births: 839 Total Expense ($000): 139755 Payroll Expense ($000): 51748 Personnel: 724

ATOKA—Atoka County

ATOKA COUNTY MEDICAL CENTER (371300), 1590 West Liberty Road, Zip 74525–1621, Mailing Address: P.O. Box 1107, Zip 74525–1621; tel. 580/889–3333, **A**10 18 **F**3 29 34 40 45 46 53 56 57 59 64 77 81 91 93 107 119 128 133 146 154
Primary Contact: Shawn Howard, Interim Chief Executive Officer
CMO: Ted Rowland, Chief of Medical Staff
CHR: Stacy Sharp, Coordinator Human Resources
CNO: David Lively, Chief Nursing Officer
Web address: www.atokamedicalcenter.org
Control: Hospital district or authority, Government, nonfederal **Service**: General medical and surgical

Staffed Beds: 25 Admissions: 480 Census: 8 Outpatient Visits: 6799 Births: 0 Total Expense ($000): 8368 Payroll Expense ($000): 3436 Personnel: 112

Many Facility Codes have changed. Please refer to the AHA Guide Code Chart. © 2019 AHA Guide

OK

BARTLESVILLE—Washington County

★ ⇑ **JANE PHILLIPS MEDICAL CENTER (370018)**, 3500 East Frank Phillips Boulevard, Zip 74006–2411; tel. 918/333–7200, **A**3 5 10 21 **F**8 11 13 15 17 18 20 22 24 28 29 30 31 34 35 40 46 49 50 51 53 57 58 59 60 61 64 68 74 75 76 77 78 79 81 82 84 85 86 87 90 92 93 96 98 102 105 107 111 114 115 116 117 118 119 121 123 127 129 130 131 135 143 145 146 147 148 154 156 **S** Ascension Healthcare, Saint Louis, MO
Primary Contact: Mike Moore, President and Chief Operating Officer
CFO: James Brasel, Chief Financial Officer
CMO: Paul McQuillen, M.D., Chief Medical Officer
CNO: Angie Bidleman, Chief Nursing Officer
Web address: www.jpmc.org
Control: Church operated, Nongovernment, not–for–profit **Service:** General medical and surgical

Staffed Beds: 114 **Admissions:** 4631 **Census:** 54 **Outpatient Visits:** 88787
Births: 503 **Total Expense ($000):** 101530 **Payroll Expense ($000):** 33662
Personnel: 526

BEAVER—Beaver County

BEAVER COUNTY MEMORIAL HOSPITAL (371322), 212 East Eighth Street, Zip 73932, Mailing Address: P.O. Box 640, Zip 73932–0640; tel. 580/625–4551, (Nonreporting) **A**10 18
Primary Contact: Alissa Schlessman, Administrator
CMO: Gary Mathews, M.D., Medical Doctor
CHR: Karla Leisher, Business Office Manager
Web address: www.beavercountyhospitalauthority.com
Control: Hospital district or authority, Government, nonfederal **Service:** General medical and surgical

Staffed Beds: 24

BETHANY—Oklahoma County

△ **THE CHILDREN'S CENTER REHABILITATION HOSPITAL (373302)**, 6800 NW 39th Expressway, Zip 73008–2513; tel. 405/789–6711, **A**3 5 7 10 **F**1 29 30 34 35 39 53 58 59 68 74 75 79 84 87 90 91 93 96 107 130 132 146 148 149
Primary Contact: Albert Gray, Chief Executive Officer
Web address: www.tccokc.org
Control: Other not–for–profit (including NFP Corporation) **Service:** Children's general medical and surgical

Staffed Beds: 160 **Admissions:** 184 **Census:** 105 **Outpatient Visits:** 18234
Births: 0 **Total Expense ($000):** 45198 **Payroll Expense ($000):** 27236
Personnel: 578

BLACKWELL—Kay County

★ ⇑ **BLACKWELL REGIONAL HOSPITAL (370030)**, 710 South 13th Street, Zip 74631–3700; tel. 580/363–2311, **A**10 21 **F**3 15 29 34 40 43 65 67 68 87 89 107 110 119 130 146 149 154
Primary Contact: Steven E. Taylor, Chief Executive Officer
CFO: Jacob Easson, Chief Financial Officer
CMO: Jeffery Shuart, M.D., Chief of Staff
CHR: Tonya Criner, Human Resource Lead
CNO: Joyce Daniel, Chief Nursing Officer
Web address: www.blackwellregional.org
Control: Hospital district or authority, Government, nonfederal **Service:** General medical and surgical

Staffed Beds: 28 **Admissions:** 475 **Census:** 4 **Outpatient Visits:** 17232
Births: 0 **Total Expense ($000):** 9604 **Payroll Expense ($000):** 3476
Personnel: 76

BOISE CITY—Cimarron County

CIMARRON MEMORIAL HOSPITAL (371307), 100 South Ellis Street, Zip 73933, Mailing Address: P.O. Box 1059, Zip 73933–1059; tel. 580/544–2501, (Nonreporting) **A**10 18
Primary Contact: Tim Beard, Chief Executive Officer
CFO: Jamie Jacoby, Chief Financial Officer
CIO: Tim Beard, Director, Information Technology
CNO: Barbara Carter, Chief Nursing Officer
Web address: www.cimarronmemorialhospital.org
Control: County, Government, nonfederal **Service:** General medical and surgical

Staffed Beds: 25

BRISTOW—Creek County

BRISTOW MEDICAL CENTER (370041), 700 West 7th Avenue, Suite 6, Zip 74010–2302; tel. 918/367–2215, (Nonreporting) **A**10
Primary Contact: Jan Winter-Clark, Chief Executive Officer
CFO: Robin Van Vickle, Chief Financial Officer
Web address: www.bristowmedcenter.com
Control: Corporation, Investor–owned (for–profit) **Service:** General medical and surgical

Staffed Beds: 30

BROKEN ARROW—Tulsa County

⊠ **ST. JOHN BROKEN ARROW (370235)**, 1000 West Boise Circle, Zip 74012–4900; tel. 918/994–8100, **A**1 10 **F**3 11 14 15 18 29 30 34 35 37 40 43 45 50 57 59 64 65 68 74 79 81 84 85 87 94 107 108 110 111 114 115 119 130 132 135 143 146 **S** Ascension Healthcare, Saint Louis, MO
Primary Contact: David L. Phillips, Chief Operating Officer
CFO: Katie Caughman, Chief Financial Officer
CMO: Jason Lepak, M.D., Medical Director
CNO: Dwan Borens, Chief Nursing Officer
Web address: www.stjohnbrokenarrow.com
Control: Church operated, Nongovernment, not–for–profit **Service:** General medical and surgical

Staffed Beds: 44 **Admissions:** 2292 **Census:** 14 **Outpatient Visits:** 116031
Births: 0 **Total Expense ($000):** 52992 **Payroll Expense ($000):** 11762
Personnel: 205

☐ **ST. JOHN REHABILITATION HOSPITAL**, 1200 West Albany Drive, Zip 74012–8146; tel. 918/744–2338, **A**1 **F**3 90 91 95 96 148 **S** Encompass Health Corporation, Birmingham, AL
Primary Contact: David Nicholas, Chief Executive Officer
Web address: www.stjohnrehab.com
Control: Corporation, Investor–owned (for–profit) **Service:** Rehabilitation

Staffed Beds: 40 **Admissions:** 1207 **Census:** 38 **Outpatient Visits:** 0
Births: 0

BUFFALO—Harper County

★ **HARPER COUNTY COMMUNITY HOSPITAL (371324)**, Highway 64 North, Zip 73834, Mailing Address: P.O. Box 60, Zip 73834–0060; tel. 580/735–2555, (Nonreporting) **A**10 18
Primary Contact: Melissa Headlee, Interim Chief Executive Officer
COO: Pam Dodd, Chief Operating Officer
CFO: Lisa Oakley, Chief Financial Officer
CNO: Melissa Madrid, R.N., Chief Nursing Officer
Web address: www.hcchospital.com/
Control: County, Government, nonfederal **Service:** General medical and surgical

Staffed Beds: 16

CARNEGIE—Caddo County

CARNEGIE TRI-COUNTY MUNICIPAL HOSPITAL (371334), 102 North Broadway, Zip 73015, Mailing Address: P.O. Box 97, Zip 73015–0097; tel. 580/654–1050, **A**10 18 **F**29 30 40 41 56 68 75 84 91 93 97 104 107 119 128 130 133 149 154 **S** First Physicians Capital Group, Inc., Oklahoma City, OK
Primary Contact: Thomas Henton, Chief Executive Officer
Web address: www.carnegiehospital.org/
Control: Other not–for–profit (including NFP Corporation) **Service:** General medical and surgical

Staffed Beds: 17 **Admissions:** 351 **Census:** 3 **Outpatient Visits:** 5280
Births: 0 **Total Expense ($000):** 12630 **Personnel:** 83

CHEYENNE—Roger Mills County

★ **ROGER MILLS MEMORIAL HOSPITAL (371303)**, 501 South L.L. Males, Zip 73628, Mailing Address: P.O. Box 219, Zip 73628; tel. 580/497–3336, **A**10 18 **F**3 7 34 40 57 59 64 65 93 107 115 119 127 133
Primary Contact: Cynthia Duncan, Chief Executive Officer
Web address: www.rmmhonline.com
Control: Hospital district or authority, Government, nonfederal **Service:** General medical and surgical

Staffed Beds: 15 **Admissions:** 151 **Census:** 2 **Outpatient Visits:** 5360
Births: 0 **Total Expense ($000):** 6061 **Payroll Expense ($000):** 3054
Personnel: 43

Hospital, Medicare Provider Number, Address, Telephone, Approval, Facility, and Physician Codes, Health Care System

★ American Hospital Association (AHA) membership
☐ The Joint Commission accreditation
○ Healthcare Facilities Accreditation Program
◇ DNV Healthcare Inc. accreditation
⇑ Center for Improvement in Healthcare Quality Accreditation
△ Commission on Accreditation of Rehabilitation Facilities (CARF) accreditation

OK

CHICKASHA—Grady County

★ **GRADY MEMORIAL HOSPITAL (370054)**, 2220 West Iowa Avenue, Zip 73018–2738; tel. 405/224–2300, **A**10 **F**3 8 11 15 17 29 30 34 35 40 43 45 50 51 54 57 59 65 66 70 76 79 81 82 85 87 89 91 93 107 110 111 114 115 119 127 128 130 131 132 133 144 146 147 148 149 155
Primary Contact: Warren K. Spellman, Chief Executive Officer
CFO: Jackie McAdoo, Chief Financial Officer
CMO: Mitch Coppedge, M.D., Chief Medical Officer
CIO: Mike Townsend, Interim Director Health Information Systems
CHR: Rebel Rutledge, Director Human Resources
CNO: Cathy Groseclose, Vice President Patient Care Services
Web address: www.gradymem.org
Control: Hospital district or authority, Government, nonfederal **Service**: General medical and surgical

Staffed Beds: 39 Admissions: 927 Census: 10 Outpatient Visits: 66666 Births: 0 Total Expense ($000): 32956 Payroll Expense ($000): 17393 Personnel: 289

CLAREMORE—Rogers County

☐ **CLAREMORE INDIAN HOSPITAL (370173)**, 101 South Moore Avenue, Zip 74017–5091; tel. 918/342–6200, (Nonreporting) **A**1 10 **S** U. S. Indian Health Service, Rockville, MD
Primary Contact: George Valliere, Chief Executive Officer
CFO: LaLana Spears, Supervisor Accounting
CMO: Gary Lang, M.D., Clinical Director
CIO: David Ponder, Information Technology Officer
CHR: Quinn Proctor, Director Human Resources
CNO: Alonna Adair-Triplett, Chief Nurse Executive
Web address: www.ihs.gov
Control: PHS, Indian Service, Government, federal **Service**: General medical and surgical

Staffed Beds: 44

★ ⇑ **HILLCREST HOSPITAL CLAREMORE (370039)**, 1202 North Muskogee Place, Zip 74017–3036; tel. 918/341–2556, **A**10 21 **F**3 6 11 13 15 18 20 22 26 28 29 30 34 35 37 40 45 49 51 59 64 70 74 76 77 79 81 82 85 86 87 93 98 103 107 108 110 111 119 126 129 130 131 133 135 145 146 147 148 156 **S** Ardent Health Services, Nashville, TN
Primary Contact: David Chaussard, Chief Executive Officer
CFO: Brandon Bullard, Chief Financial Officer
CIO: Celeste Rodden, Chief Information Officer
CHR: Pat Goad, Director Human Resources
CNO: Randy Walker, Chief Nursing Officer
Web address: www.hillcrestclaremore.com
Control: Corporation, Investor-owned (for-profit) **Service**: General medical and surgical

Staffed Beds: 67 Admissions: 2636 Census: 27 Outpatient Visits: 43116 Births: 673 Total Expense ($000): 49578 Payroll Expense ($000): 16571 Personnel: 296

CLEVELAND—Pawnee County

CLEVELAND AREA HOSPITAL (371320), 1401 West Pawnee Street, Zip 74020–3019; tel. 918/358–2501, **A**10 18 **F**3 11 15 28 29 32 34 35 40 41 43 57 59 64 65 75 77 82 87 90 91 93 96 97 107 110 115 119 128 130 131 133 135 148 156
Primary Contact: Edred Benton, Chief Executive Officer and Chief Operating Officer
COO: Edred Benton, Chief Executive Officer and Chief Operating Officer
CMO: Jason Sims, M.D., Chief Medical Officer
CHR: Sherry Brown, Director Human Resources
Web address: www.clevelandareahospital.com
Control: Hospital district or authority, Government, nonfederal **Service**: General medical and surgical

Staffed Beds: 14 Admissions: 201 Census: 6 Outpatient Visits: 22810 Births: 0 Total Expense ($000): 13957 Payroll Expense ($000): 9274 Personnel: 145

CLINTON—Custer County

⊞ **ALLIANCEHEALTH CLINTON (370029)**, 100 North 30th Street, Zip 73601–3117; tel. 580/323–2363, (Nonreporting) **A**1 10 20 **S** Community Health Systems, Inc., Franklin, TN
Primary Contact: Landon E. Hise, Chief Executive Officer
CFO: Jay Johnson, Chief Financial Officer
CHR: Julie Graumann, Director
CNO: Kimberly Todd, Chief Nursing Officer
Web address: www.alliancehealthclinton.com
Control: Partnership, Investor-owned (for-profit) **Service**: General medical and surgical

Staffed Beds: 49

COALGATE—Coal County

★ **COAL COUNTY GENERAL HOSPITAL (371319)**, 6 North Covington Street, Zip 74538–2002, Mailing Address: P.O. Box 326, Zip 74538–0326; tel. 580/927–2327, (Nonreporting) **A**10 18
Primary Contact: Billy Johnson, Chief Executive Officer
CFO: Diane Downard, Chief Financial Officer
CMO: R.J Helton, D.O., Chief of Staff
CIO: Matt Balliett, Chief Information Officer
CHR: Cyndie Martin, Director
CNO: Farra Ybarra, R.N., Chief Nursing Officer
Web address: www.hillcrest.com
Control: Other not-for-profit (including NFP Corporation) **Service**: General medical and surgical

Staffed Beds: 95

CORDELL—Washita County

★ ⇑ **CORDELL MEMORIAL HOSPITAL (371325)**, 1220 North Glenn English Street, Zip 73632–2010; tel. 580/832–3339, (Nonreporting) **A**10 18 21
Primary Contact: Kenny Downs, Chief Executive Officer
CFO: Sue Kelley, Chief Financial Officer
Web address: www.cordellmemorialhospital.com
Control: City, Government, nonfederal **Service**: General medical and surgical

Staffed Beds: 14

CUSHING—Payne County

★ **HILLCREST HOSPITAL CUSHING (370099)**, 1027 East Cherry Street, Zip 74023–4101; tel. 918/225–2915, **A**10 **F**11 13 15 18 29 34 35 40 43 44 45 46 50 51 56 57 59 64 68 70 71 75 76 77 79 81 86 87 93 94 97 98 100 101 102 103 107 110 111 114 115 119 128 129 130 131 143 145 146 147 148 154 **S** Ardent Health Services, Nashville, TN
Primary Contact: Kevin Hawk, Chief Executive Officer
CFO: Joseph Mendoza, Chief Financial Officer
CHR: Bethany Leininger, Manager Human Resource
CNO: Tina Petersen, Chief Nursing Officer
Web address: www.hillcrestcushing.com/
Control: Corporation, Investor-owned (for-profit) **Service**: General medical and surgical

Staffed Beds: 99 Admissions: 1227 Census: 14 Outpatient Visits: 19429 Births: 17 Total Expense ($000): 20858 Payroll Expense ($000): 7481 Personnel: 160

DRUMRIGHT—Creek County

DRUMRIGHT REGIONAL HOSPITAL (371331), 610 West Bypass, Zip 74030–5957; tel. 918/382–2300, (Nonreporting) **A**10 18 **S** Rural Community Hospitals of America, Kansas City, MO
Primary Contact: Micheal Christensen, Interim Chief Executive Officer
CFO: Mark Conrath, Chief Financial Officer
Web address: www.drumrighthospital.com/
Control: Corporation, Investor-owned (for-profit) **Service**: General medical and surgical

Staffed Beds: 15

DUNCAN—Stephens County

⊞ **DUNCAN REGIONAL HOSPITAL (370023)**, 1407 North Whisenant Drive, Zip 73533–1650, Mailing Address: P.O. Box 2000, Zip 73534–2000; tel. 580/252–5300, (Nonreporting) **A**1 3 5 10 20 **S** Duncan Regional Hospital, Duncan, OK
Primary Contact: Jay R. Johnson, FACHE, President and Chief Executive Officer
COO: Roger Neal, Chief Operating Officer
CFO: Douglas R Volinski, Vice President and Chief Financial Officer
CMO: Che' Miller, M.D., Chief of Staff
CHR: Mark Rhoades, Vice President and Chief Human Resources Officer
CNO: Cindy Rauh, R.N., Vice President and Chief Nursing Officer
Web address: www.duncanregional.com
Control: Other not-for-profit (including NFP Corporation) **Service**: General medical and surgical

Staffed Beds: 117

Many Facility Codes have changed. Please refer to the AHA Guide Code Chart. © 2019 AHA Guide

DURANT—Bryan County

⊞ **ALLIANCEHEALTH DURANT (370014)**, 1800 University Boulevard, Zip 74701–3006, Mailing Address: P.O. Box 1207, Zip 74702–1207; tel. 580/924–3080, **A**1 3 5 10 13 19 **F**3 8 11 12 13 15 17 18 20 22 28 29 30 34 35 39 40 43 45 50 51 56 57 59 70 74 75 76 77 79 80 81 82 85 86 89 97 102 107 110 111 114 115 119 126 130 131 135 145 146 147 148 154 **S** Community Health Systems, Inc., Franklin, TN
Primary Contact: Charles Hall, Interim Chief Executive Officer
CFO: Cindy Rios, Chief Financial Officer
CMO: Kevin Gordon, M.D., Chief of Staff
CIO: Katy Stinson, Director Information Services
Web address: www.alliancehealthdurant.com/
Control: Corporation, Investor–owned (for–profit) **Service**: General medical and surgical

Staffed Beds: 140 **Admissions**: 5051 **Census**: 45 **Outpatient Visits**: 53525 **Births**: 894 **Total Expense ($000)**: 68325 **Payroll Expense ($000)**: 24278 **Personnel**: 475

EDMOND—Oklahoma County

EDMOND MEDICAL CENTER See Ou Medical Center Edmond

⊞ **INTEGRIS HEALTH EDMOND (370236)**, 4801 Integris Parkway, Zip 73034–8864; tel. 405/657–3000, **A**1 3 5 10 **F**3 8 11 20 22 29 30 34 35 40 43 45 46 47 49 53 54 57 59 60 64 68 70 73 74 76 77 78 79 81 82 85 87 93 97 100 102 107 108 110 111 114 115 118 119 130 131 132 135 146 147 148 149 154 155 **S** INTEGRIS Health, Oklahoma City, OK
Primary Contact: Avilla Williams, MS, President
CNO: Angela K Kamermayer, MS, Chief Nursing Officer
Web address: www.integrisok.com/edmond
Control: Other not–for–profit (including NFP Corporation) **Service**: General medical and surgical

Staffed Beds: 40 **Admissions**: 2699 **Census**: 25 **Outpatient Visits**: 50990 **Births**: 673 **Total Expense ($000)**: 62089 **Payroll Expense ($000)**: 17668 **Personnel**: 236

OU MEDICAL CENTER EDMOND See Ou Medical Center, Oklahoma City

☆ **SUMMIT MEDICAL CENTER (370225)**, 1800 S Renaissance Boulevard, Zip 73013–3023; tel. 405/359–2400, **A**10 **F**3 12 29 40 41 45 54 64 70 75 79 81 82 85 107 111 119 129 148 149 156
Primary Contact: Curtis Summers, Chief Executive Officer
Web address: www.summitmedcenter.com/
Control: Individual, Investor–owned (for–profit) **Service**: General medical and surgical

Staffed Beds: 9 **Admissions**: 556 **Census**: 3 **Outpatient Visits**: 22896 **Births**: 0 **Total Expense ($000)**: 46747 **Payroll Expense ($000)**: 10703 **Personnel**: 187

ELK CITY—Beckham County

★ **GREAT PLAINS REGIONAL MEDICAL CENTER (370019)**, 1801 West Third Street, Zip 73644–5145, Mailing Address: P.O. Box 2339, Zip 73648–2339; tel. 580/225–2511, **A**3 10 20 **F**3 11 12 13 15 18 28 29 30 31 34 35 40 43 50 56 57 59 62 64 68 70 74 75 76 77 78 79 81 82 85 87 89 91 93 96 98 100 101 103 107 108 110 111 115 118 119 120 121 123 129 130 131 132 133 146 147 148 149 156
Primary Contact: Corey Lively, Chief Executive Officer
CFO: Monica Scott, Chief Financial Officer
CMO: Craig Phelps, M.D., Chief of Staff
CIO: Terry Price, Director Information Technology
CHR: Misty Carter, Vice President Human Resources and Ancillary Services
CNO: Debra D. Morris, R.N., MSN, Chief Nursing Officer
Web address: www.gprmc-ok.com
Control: Other not–for–profit (including NFP Corporation) **Service**: General medical and surgical

Staffed Beds: 60 **Admissions**: 1486 **Census**: 16 **Outpatient Visits**: 54759 **Births**: 330 **Total Expense ($000)**: 48855 **Payroll Expense ($000)**: 16810 **Personnel**: 378

ENID—Garfield County

INTEGRIS BASS BEHAVIORAL HEALTH SYSTEM See Integris Bass Meadowlake

⊞ **INTEGRIS BASS BAPTIST HEALTH CENTER (370016)**, 600 South Monroe Street, Zip 73701–7211, Mailing Address: P.O. Box 3168, Zip 73702–3168; tel. 580/233–2300, (Includes INTEGRIS BASS MEADOWLAKE, 2216 South Van Buren Street, Enid, Oklahoma, Zip 73703–8299; tel. 580/234–2220) **A**1 10 **F**3 11 13 15 17 18 20 22 28 30 31 35 40 43 45 49 51 56 57 59 62 64 65 70 74 75 76 78 79 81 85 97 98 99 107 108 109 110 111 114 118 119 120 121 126 127 128 129 130 131 132 146 147 148 149 154 156 **S** INTEGRIS Health, Oklahoma City, OK
Primary Contact: Finny Mathew, President
CFO: Duane Miller, Chief Financial Officer
CNO: Cynthia Leathers, R.N., Chief Nursing Officer
Web address: www.integris-health.com
Control: Other not–for–profit (including NFP Corporation) **Service**: General medical and surgical

Staffed Beds: 152 **Admissions**: 3701 **Census**: 73 **Outpatient Visits**: 60977 **Births**: 905 **Total Expense ($000)**: 99294 **Payroll Expense ($000)**: 29975 **Personnel**: 477

☐ **INTEGRIS BASS PAVILION (372016)**, 401 South Third Street, Zip 73701–5737; tel. 580/249–4260, **A**1 10 **F**11 77 93 119 132 148 154 156
Primary Contact: Finny Mathew, President
CHR: Kerri Johnson, Human Resources Operations Consultant
CNO: Sherry Dunlay, R.N., MSN, Vice President Chief Nursing Officer
Web address: www.integris-health.com/integris/en-us/locations/bass-enid
Control: Other not–for–profit (including NFP Corporation) **Service**: General medical and surgical

Staffed Beds: 24 **Admissions**: 124 **Census**: 8 **Outpatient Visits**: 5095 **Births**: 0 **Total Expense ($000)**: 6747 **Payroll Expense ($000)**: 2826 **Personnel**: 37

☐ △ **ST. MARY'S REGIONAL MEDICAL CENTER (370026)**, 305 South Fifth Street, Zip 73701–5899, Mailing Address: P.O. Box 232, Zip 73702–0232; tel. 580/233–6100, **A**1 7 10 **F**3 11 13 15 18 20 22 28 29 30 31 34 35 39 40 43 45 51 56 57 59 60 64 68 70 73 74 75 76 78 79 80 81 82 85 86 87 89 90 92 93 96 98 100 101 107 108 110 111 114 115 118 119 125 128 130 131 132 135 146 147 149 **S** Universal Health Services, Inc., King of Prussia, PA
Primary Contact: Krista Roberts, Chief Executive Officer
COO: Anthony Rodebush, Chief Operating Officer
CFO: David Jamin, Chief Financial Officer
CMO: Michael Pontious, M.D., Chief of Staff
CIO: Tracy Andersen, Chief Information Officer
CHR: David Camp, Director Human Resources
CNO: Douglas W Coffey, R.N., MSN, Chief Nursing Officer
Web address: www.stmarysregional.com
Control: Corporation, Investor–owned (for–profit) **Service**: General medical and surgical

Staffed Beds: 124 **Admissions**: 5210 **Census**: 63 **Outpatient Visits**: 92391 **Births**: 321 **Total Expense ($000)**: 83306 **Payroll Expense ($000)**: 33083 **Personnel**: 495

FAIRFAX—Osage County

FAIRFAX COMMUNITY HOSPITAL (371318), 40 Hospital Road, Zip 74637–5084; tel. 918/642–3291, (Nonreporting) **A**10 18 **S** Rural Community Hospitals of America, Kansas City, MO
Primary Contact: Tina Steele, Chief Executive Officer and Chief Financial Officer
COO: Linda Thompson, Chief Operating Officer
CFO: Tina Steele, Chief Executive Officer and Chief Financial Officer
CMO: Arman Janloo, M.D., Chief Medical Staff
CIO: Lisa Drymon, Manager
CHR: Sharon Binkley, Director Human Resources
Control: Corporation, Investor–owned (for–profit) **Service**: General medical and surgical

Staffed Beds: 15

FAIRFAX MEMORIAL HOSPITAL See Fairfax Community Hospital

Hospital, Medicare Provider Number, Address, Telephone, Approval, Facility, and Physician Codes, Health Care System

★ American Hospital Association (AHA) membership
☐ The Joint Commission accreditation
○ Healthcare Facilities Accreditation Program
◇ DNV Healthcare Inc. accreditation
⇑ Center for Improvement in Healthcare Quality Accreditation
△ Commission on Accreditation of Rehabilitation Facilities (CARF) accreditation

OK

FAIRVIEW—Major County

FAIRVIEW REGIONAL MEDICAL CENTER (371329), 523 East State Road, Zip 73737–1453, Mailing Address: P.O. Box 548, Zip 73737–0548; tel. 580/227–3721, **A**10 18 **F**3 28 34 35 38 40 43 45 57 59 64 65 68 69 75 77 81 84 85 91 93 100 107 114 127 128 130 131 132 133 135 146 148 149 154 156
Primary Contact: Roger Knak, Administrator and Chief Executive Officer
CMO: John Stephen Price, M.D., Chief of Staff
CIO: Bob Maynard, Chief Information Officer
CHR: Elisabeth Hughes, Director Human Resources and Community Relations
CNO: Tamara Eitzen, Chief Nursing Officer
Web address: www.fairviewregionalmedicalcenter.com
Control: Hospital district or authority, Government, nonfederal **Service**: General medical and surgical

Staffed Beds: 25 **Admissions**: 167 **Census**: 2 **Outpatient Visits**: 11947
Births: 0 **Total Expense ($000)**: 6396 **Payroll Expense ($000)**: 3307
Personnel: 67

FORT SUPPLY—Major County

NORTHWEST CENTER FOR BEHAVIORAL HEALTH (374001), 1 Mi East Highway 270, Zip 73841, Mailing Address: 1222 10th Street, Suite 211, Woodward, Zip 73801–3156; tel. 580/766–2311, **A**3 10 **F**98 104 130 132 135 149 154 **S** Oklahoma Department of Mental Health and Substance Abuse Services, Oklahoma City, OK
Primary Contact: Cathy Billings, Interim Executive Director
Web address: www.ncbhok.org/
Control: State, Government, nonfederal **Service**: Psychiatric

Staffed Beds: 24 **Admissions**: 565 **Census**: 15 **Outpatient Visits**: 61780
Births: 0 **Total Expense ($000)**: 12234 **Payroll Expense ($000)**: 6177
Personnel: 179

GROVE—Delaware County

INTEGRIS GROVE HOSPITAL (370113), 1001 East 18th Street, Zip 74344–2907; tel. 918/786–2243, **A**1 10 20 **F**3 7 11 13 15 18 20 22 29 30 31 34 35 40 43 45 51 54 57 59 62 64 70 77 78 79 81 85 93 107 108 109 110 111 115 119 129 146 147 148 154 **S** INTEGRIS Health, Oklahoma City, OK
Primary Contact: Robert Rupp, President
CFO: Stacie Mason, Vice President and Chief Financial Officer
CMO: Kyle Schauf, M.D., President Medical Staff
CNO: Brandi Stewart, R.N., Vice President and Chief Nursing Officer
Web address: www.integris-health.com
Control: Other not–for–profit (including NFP Corporation) **Service**: General medical and surgical

Staffed Beds: 58 **Admissions**: 1835 **Census**: 15 **Outpatient Visits**: 39972
Births: 341 **Total Expense ($000)**: 45878 **Payroll Expense ($000)**: 13103
Personnel: 195

GUTHRIE—Logan County

★ **MERCY HOSPITAL LOGAN COUNTY (371317)**, 200 South Academy Road, Zip 73044–8727, Mailing Address: P.O. Box 1017, Zip 73044–1017; tel. 405/282–6700, **A**10 18 **F**3 15 29 30 34 35 40 44 50 57 59 68 75 77 87 93 107 110 111 114 119 127 129 130 131 133 144 146 148 149 **S** Mercy, Chesterfield, MO
Primary Contact: Bobby Stitt, R.N., Administrator
CMO: Jignesh Veragiwala, Chief of Staff
CHR: Mary Jo Messelt, Senior Human Resources Manager
Web address: www.mercy.net
Control: Church operated, Nongovernment, not–for–profit **Service**: General medical and surgical

Staffed Beds: 25 **Admissions**: 506 **Census**: 7 **Outpatient Visits**: 82947
Births: 0 **Total Expense ($000)**: 17698 **Payroll Expense ($000)**: 10611
Personnel: 135

GUYMON—Texas County

⚕ **MEMORIAL HOSPITAL OF TEXAS COUNTY (371340)**, 520 Medical Drive, Zip 73942–4438; tel. 580/338–6515, (Nonreporting) **A**10 18 21
Primary Contact: Emmanuel Barias, M.D., Interim Chief Executive Officer
CFO: Michele Reust, Controller
CIO: Sheldon Spence, Director of Revenue Cycle, IT
CHR: Sarah Wagner, Human Resources Officer
CNO: Dondie Rodgers, Interim Chief Nursing Officer
Web address: www.mhtcguymon.org
Control: County, Government, nonfederal **Service**: General medical and surgical

Staffed Beds: 14

HEALDTON—Carter County

★ **MERCY HOSPITAL HEALDTON (371310)**, 3462 Hospital Road, Zip 73438–6124, Mailing Address: P.O. Box 928, Zip 73438–0928; tel. 580/229–0701, **A**10 18 **F**3 29 34 35 40 43 44 57 64 68 107 114 127 133 146 149 154 157 **S** Mercy, Chesterfield, MO
Primary Contact: Nichole Barrett, R.N., Interim Administrator
CMO: Mark Newey, D.O., Chief of Staff
CHR: Melinda Sharum, Director Human Resources
Web address: www.mercyok.com
Control: Church operated, Nongovernment, not–for–profit **Service**: General medical and surgical

Staffed Beds: 22 **Admissions**: 217 **Census**: 6 **Outpatient Visits**: 11249
Births: 0 **Total Expense ($000)**: 6016 **Payroll Expense ($000)**: 3405
Personnel: 49

HENRYETTA—Okmulgee County

★ **HILLCREST HOSPITAL HENRYETTA (370183)**, 2401 West Main Street, Zip 74437–3893, Mailing Address: P.O. Box 1269, Zip 74437–1269; tel. 918/650–1100, **A**10 **F**3 15 18 29 40 45 54 56 64 65 75 79 81 85 87 91 93 102 107 108 110 111 114 119 129 130 131 133 143 148 **S** Ardent Health Services, Nashville, TN
Primary Contact: Dee Renshaw, Chief Executive Officer
CFO: Joseph Mendoza, Chief Financial Officer
CHR: Sheree Snyder, Manager Human Resources
CNO: April Secor, R.N., Chief Nursing Officer
Web address: www.hillcresthenryetta.com/
Control: Corporation, Investor–owned (for–profit) **Service**: General medical and surgical

Staffed Beds: 37 **Admissions**: 737 **Census**: 11 **Outpatient Visits**: 27789
Births: 0 **Total Expense ($000)**: 16323 **Payroll Expense ($000)**: 6603
Personnel: 100

HOBART—Kiowa County

★ **ELKVIEW GENERAL HOSPITAL (370153)**, 429 West Elm Street, Zip 73651–1615; tel. 580/726–1900, **A**10 20 **F**3 15 29 34 40 51 57 59 79 81 85 89 93 107 108 110 111 115 119 129 133 146 148 154
Primary Contact: Lisa Hart, Chief Executive Officer
CFO: Amy Harmon, Chief Financial Officer
CMO: William Sims, M.D., Medical Director
CIO: Dennis Tarver, Director Information Technology
CHR: Sharon Moad, Human Resources Director Health Information Management
CNO: Debbie Norman, MSN, R.N., Chief Nursing Officer
Web address: www.elkviewhospital.com
Control: Hospital district or authority, Government, nonfederal **Service**: General medical and surgical

Staffed Beds: 25 **Admissions**: 698 **Census**: 7 **Outpatient Visits**: 20269
Births: 0 **Total Expense ($000)**: 13054 **Payroll Expense ($000)**: 6071
Personnel: 121

HOLDENVILLE—Hughes County

★ **HOLDENVILLE GENERAL HOSPITAL (371321)**, 100 McDougal Drive, Zip 74848–2822; tel. 405/379–4200, **A**10 18 **F**3 11 29 30 34 40 45 46 57 59 64 65 79 81 97 107 111 115 119 127 128 133 146
Primary Contact: Stephen C. Stewart, Chief Executive Officer
CFO: Drew Johnson, Chief Financial Officer
CMO: Tom Osborn, D.O., Chief Medical Staff
CIO: Mike Combs, Manager Information Technology
CHR: Heather Heard, Director Human Resources
CNO: Jackie Smith, R.N., Chief Nursing Officer
Web address: www.holdenvillehospital.com/
Control: City, Government, nonfederal **Service**: General medical and surgical

Staffed Beds: 25 **Admissions**: 356 **Census**: 5 **Outpatient Visits**: 39601
Births: 0 **Total Expense ($000)**: 11756 **Payroll Expense ($000)**: 5620
Personnel: 101

HOLLIS—Harmon County

HARMON MEMORIAL HOSPITAL (371338), 400 East Chestnut Street, Zip 73550–2030, Mailing Address: P.O. Box 791, Zip 73550–0791; tel. 580/688–3363, (Nonreporting) **A**10 18
Primary Contact: Sheila Lewis, Administrator
CFO: Willie Mae Copeland, Chief Financial Officer
CMO: Akram Abraham, M.D., Chief of Staff
CHR: Abbey Welch, Director Human Resources
Control: Hospital district or authority, Government, nonfederal **Service**: General medical and surgical

Staffed Beds: 31

HUGO—Choctaw County

CHOCTAW MEMORIAL HOSPITAL (370100), 1405 East Kirk Street,
Zip 74743–3603; tel. 580/317–9500, (Nonreporting) **A**10
Primary Contact: Nick Rowland, Interim Chief Executive Officer
CIO: Andy Richmond, Director Information Technology
CHR: Darlene Galyon, Director Human Resources
Web address: www.choctawmemorial.com
Control: Hospital district or authority, Government, nonfederal **Service:** General
medical and surgical

Staffed Beds: 32

IDABEL—McCurtain County

MCCURTAIN MEMORIAL HOSPITAL (370048), 1301 Lincoln Road, Zip 74745–
7341; tel. 580/286–7623, (Nonreporting) **A**10 20
Primary Contact: Brad S. Morse, FACHE, Interim Chief Executive Officer
CFO: Ray B Whitmore, Chief Financial Officer
CMO: Michael C West, M.D., Chief of Staff
CIO: Dana A Stowell, Chief Information Officer
CNO: Pamela Johnson, R.N., Chief Nursing Officer
Web address: www.mmhok.com
Control: Other not–for–profit (including NFP Corporation) **Service:** General
medical and surgical

Staffed Beds: 77

KINGFISHER—Kingfisher County

⊞ **MERCY HOSPITAL KINGFISHER (371313)**, 1000 Hospital Cirle, Zip 73750–
5002, Mailing Address: P.O. Box 59, Zip 73750–0059; tel. 405/375–3141, **A**1
10 18 **F**3 11 15 29 30 34 35 40 41 43 45 50 59 64 68 75 77 79 81 82 85
87 89 93 107 110 111 115 119 128 129 133 146 148 149 154 157 **S** Mercy,
Chesterfield, MO
Primary Contact: Brian Denton, Administrator
CMO: Brett Krablin, M.D., Chief of Staff
CIO: Chad Kliewer, Information Technology Specialist
CHR: Carolyn Bjerke, Director Human Resources
CNO: Hannah Powell, Chief Nursing Officer
Web address: www.https://www.mercy.net/practice/mercy-hospital-kingfisher/
Control: Church operated, Nongovernment, not–for–profit **Service:** General
medical and surgical

Staffed Beds: 25 **Admissions:** 317 **Census:** 9 **Outpatient Visits:** 19632
Births: 0 **Total Expense ($000):** 11612 **Payroll Expense ($000):** 5781
Personnel: 82

LAWTON—Comanche County

⊞ △ **COMANCHE COUNTY MEMORIAL HOSPITAL (370056)**, 3401 West Gore
Boulevard, Zip 73505–6332, Mailing Address: P.O. Box 129, Zip 73502–0129;
tel. 580/355–8620, (Total facility includes 146 beds in nursing home–type unit) **A**1
2 3 5 7 10 13 **F**3 6 7 8 10 11 12 13 15 17 18 20 22 24 26 28 29 30 31 32 34 35
40 43 45 46 47 48 49 50 51 54 56 57 58 59 62 63 64 65 66 68 70 72 74 75
76 77 78 79 80 81 82 84 85 86 89 90 91 92 93 96 97 98 103 104 107 108
110 111 114 115 116 117 118 119 120 121 127 129 130 131 132 134 135
143 146 147 148 156
Primary Contact: Brent Smith, Chief Executive Officer
CFO: George Kruger, CPA, Chief Financial Officer
CMO: Scott Michener, M.D., Chief Medical Officer
CIO: James Wellman, Senior Director Information Services
CHR: Donna Wade, Senior Director Human Resources
CNO: Chris Ward, Chief Nursing Officer
Web address: www.ccmhonline.com
Control: Hospital district or authority, Government, nonfederal **Service:** General
medical and surgical

Staffed Beds: 352 **Admissions:** 9863 **Census:** 252 **Outpatient
Visits:** 178009 **Births:** 1416 **Total Expense ($000):** 257666 **Payroll
Expense ($000):** 110170 **Personnel:** 1463

JIM TALIAFERRO COMMUNITY MENTAL HEALTH (374008), 602 SW 38th
Street, Zip 73505; tel. 580/248–5780, **A**3 10 **F**4 5 29 35 38 66 68 98 101 102
104 135 149 153 154
Primary Contact: Debbie Moran, Executive Director
Web address: www.odmhsas.org
Control: State, Government, nonfederal **Service:** Psychiatric

Staffed Beds: 22 **Admissions:** 4767 **Census:** 15 **Outpatient Visits:** 85446
Births: 0

☐ **LAWTON INDIAN HOSPITAL (370170)**, 1515 Lawrie Tatum Road, Zip 73507–
3099; tel. 580/353–0350, (Nonreporting) **A**1 5 10 **S** U. S. Indian Health Service,
Rockville, MD
Primary Contact: Travis Scott, Chief Executive Officer
COO: John Bear, Hospital Administrator Officer and Supervisor Human Resources
CFO: Sarabeth Sahmaunt, Supervisory Accountant
CMO: Richard Chadek, M.D., Clinical Director
CIO: William R Harris, Chief Information Officer
CHR: John Bear, Hospital Administrator Officer and Supervisor Human Resources
CNO: Lenora Littledeer, R.N., Director of Nursing
Web address: www.ihs.gov
Control: PHS, Indian Service, Government, federal **Service:** General medical and
surgical

Staffed Beds: 26

⊞ △ **SOUTHWESTERN MEDICAL CENTER (370097)**, 5602 SW Lee Boulevard,
Zip 73505–9635; tel. 580/531–4700, **A**1 3 5 7 10 19 **F**3 8 13 29 30 34 38 40
41 45 47 49 50 51 57 59 60 64 65 67 68 70 74 76 77 79 81 85 87 89 90 91
92 93 98 99 100 101 102 104 106 107 108 111 114 118 119 129 130 131
133 135 146 147 148 **S** LifePoint Health, Brentwood, TN
Primary Contact: Elizabeth Jones, Chief Executive Officer
CFO: Wayne Colson, Chief Financial Officer
CMO: Aryan Kadivar, M.D., Chief Medical Officer
CIO: Kent Lewis, Director Information Services
CHR: Danny Hale, Director Human Resources
CNO: Jayne Thomas, Chief Nursing Officer
Web address: www.swmconline.com
Control: Corporation, Investor–owned (for–profit) **Service:** General medical and
surgical

Staffed Beds: 178 **Admissions:** 4744 **Census:** 72 **Outpatient Visits:** 58684
Births: 657 **Total Expense ($000):** 82671 **Payroll Expense ($000):** 37901
Personnel: 516

LINDSAY—Garvin County

LINDSAY MUNICIPAL HOSPITAL (370214), Highway 19 West, Zip 73052,
Mailing Address: P.O. Box 888, Zip 73052–0888; tel. 405/756–1404,
(Nonreporting) **A**10
Primary Contact: Jeff Walraven, Chief Executive Officer
Control: City, Government, nonfederal **Service:** General medical and surgical

Staffed Beds: 26

MADILL—Marshall County

⊞ **ALLIANCEHEALTH MADILL (371326)**, 901 South Fifth Avenue, Zip 73446–
3640, Mailing Address: P.O. Box 827, Zip 73446–0827; tel. 580/795–3384,
A1 10 18 **F**29 35 40 43 45 75 81 93 107 111 114 119 127 133 146 157 **S**
Community Health Systems, Inc., Franklin, TN
Primary Contact: Charles Hall, Interim Chief Executive Officer
CFO: Thomas Driggs, Chief Financial Officer
CMO: Heidi Haislip, M.D., Chief of Staff
CHR: D.J. Shawn, Director Human Resources
CNO: Carol Wright, Chief Nursing Officer
Web address: www.myalliancehealth.com
Control: Corporation, Investor–owned (for–profit) **Service:** General medical and
surgical

Staffed Beds: 25 **Admissions:** 263 **Census:** 4 **Outpatient Visits:** 28044
Births: 0 **Total Expense ($000):** 11376 **Payroll Expense ($000):** 5241
Personnel: 99

MANGUM—Greer County

⇑ **MANGUM REGIONAL MEDICAL CENTER (371330)**, One Wickersham Drive,
Zip 73554–9116, Mailing Address: P.O. Box 280, Zip 73554–0280; tel. 580/782–
3353, (Nonreporting) **A**10 18 21
Primary Contact: Godwin Feh, Interim Chief Executive Officer
COO: Danny Avery, Chief Financial Officer and Chief Operating Officer
CIO: Gregg Burnam, Chief Information Officer and Manager Business Office
Web address: www.qmhealth.org/
Control: City, Government, nonfederal **Service:** General medical and surgical

Staffed Beds: 25

Hospital, Medicare Provider Number, Address, Telephone, Approval, Facility, and Physician Codes, Health Care System

★ American Hospital Association (AHA) membership ○ Healthcare Facilities Accreditation Program ⇑ Center for Improvement in Healthcare Quality Accreditation
☐ The Joint Commission accreditation ◇ DNV Healthcare Inc. accreditation △ Commission on Accreditation of Rehabilitation Facilities (CARF) accreditation

© 2019 AHA Guide *Many Facility Codes have changed. Please refer to the AHA Guide Code Chart.* Hospitals **A501**

OK

MARIETTA—Love County

★ **MERCY HEALTH LOVE COUNTY (371306)**, 300 Wanda Street, Zip 73448–1200; tel. 580/276–3347, (Nonreporting) **A**10 18 **S** Mercy, Chesterfield, MO
Primary Contact: Richard Barker, Administrator and Chief Executive Officer
CIO: Connie Graham, Public Information Officer
Web address: www.mercyhealthlovecounty.com
Control: Church operated, Nongovernment, not–for–profit **Service**: General medical and surgical

Staffed Beds: 25

MCALESTER—Pittsburg County

CARL ALBERT COMMUNITY MENTAL HEALTH CENTER (374006), 1101 East Monroe Avenue, Zip 74501–4826; tel. 918/426–7800, **A**3 10 **F**29 38 59 98 100 101 102 104 130 132 135 149 153 154
Primary Contact: Debbie Moran, Executive Director
CFO: Konnie Taylor, Chief Financial Officer
CMO: William Mings, M.D., Medical Director
CHR: Judy Allen, Human Resource Specialist
Web address: www.odmhsas.org
Control: State, Government, nonfederal **Service**: Psychiatric

Staffed Beds: 15 Admissions: 361 Census: 6 Outpatient Visits: 0 Births: 0 Personnel: 38

★ ⇑ **MCALESTER REGIONAL HEALTH CENTER (370034)**, One East Clark Bass Boulevard, Zip 74501–4267, Mailing Address: 3473 E Hereford LN, Zip 74501; tel. 918/426–1800, (Total facility includes 60 beds in nursing home–type unit) **A**3 5 10 13 21 **F**3 8 10 11 13 15 18 20 22 26 29 30 34 40 43 45 49 50 51 53 54 56 57 59 61 62 63 64 66 68 69 70 75 76 77 79 81 82 85 86 87 90 91 92 93 98 101 102 103 104 107 108 109 110 111 114 115 116 117 118 119 125 129 130 131 132 135 144 146 147 148 154 158
Primary Contact: David N. Keith, FACHE, President and Chief Executive Officer
CFO: Darryl Linnington, Chief Financial Officer
CIO: Jason Bray, Chief Information Officer
CHR: Scott Lowe, Director Human Resource
CNO: Kimberly Dawn Stout, Chief Nursing Officer and Chief Operating Officer
Web address: www.mrhcok.com
Control: City, Government, nonfederal **Service**: General medical and surgical

Staffed Beds: 209 Admissions: 4336 Census: 87 Outpatient Visits: 80335 Births: 504 Total Expense ($000): 84638 Payroll Expense ($000): 38686 Personnel: 660

MIAMI—Ottawa County

⊞ **INTEGRIS MIAMI HOSPITAL (370004)**, 200 Second Avenue SW, Zip 74354–6830; tel. 918/542–6611, **A**1 10 **F**7 11 13 15 18 20 22 26 29 30 34 35 40 43 45 56 57 59 62 63 70 75 76 77 79 81 85 89 93 98 103 107 108 109 110 111 115 119 125 129 130 131 132 135 144 146 147 148 154 **S** INTEGRIS Health, Oklahoma City, OK
Primary Contact: Jonas Rabel, President
CFO: Valerie Reeves, Chief Financial Officer
CMO: Elaine Mader, M.D., Chief of Staff
CHR: Jamil Haynes, Regional Director Human Resources
CNO: Lisa Halstead, Chief Nursing Officer
Web address: www.integrisok.com/miami-hospital
Control: Other not–for–profit (including NFP Corporation) **Service**: General medical and surgical

Staffed Beds: 57 Admissions: 1970 Census: 22 Outpatient Visits: 48366 Births: 267 Total Expense ($000): 45751 Payroll Expense ($000): 15480 Personnel: 264

★ **WILLOW CREST HOSPITAL (374017)**, 130 'A' Street SW, Zip 74354–6800; tel. 918/542–1836, (Nonreporting) **A**10
Primary Contact: Shari Murphree, Chief Executive Officer
COO: Steven Goodman, Chief Operating Officer
CFO: Cindy Bell, Director Finance
CMO: Mark Elkington, M.D., Chief Medical Officer
CIO: Steven Goodman, Chief Operating Officer
CHR: Kathy Henderson, Director Human Resources
CNO: Kassi Davis, Director Patient Care Services
Web address: www.willowcresthospital.com
Control: Corporation, Investor–owned (for–profit) **Service**: Children's hospital psychiatric

Staffed Beds: 75

MIDWEST CITY—Oklahoma County

⊞ **ALLIANCEHEALTH MIDWEST (370094)**, 2825 Parklawn Drive, Zip 73110–4258; tel. 405/610–4411, (Nonreporting) **A**1 5 10 **S** Community Health Systems, Inc., Franklin, TN
Primary Contact: Clay Franklin, Chief Executive Officer
COO: Lisa Ellis, Chief Operating Officer
CFO: Cynthia Gray, Interim Chief Financial Officer
CMO: Rockey Talley, M.D., Chief Medical Officer
CHR: Dana Leach, Director Human Resources
CNO: Jaconna Joni"" Tiller, Chief Nursing Officer
Web address: www.myalliancehealth.com
Control: Corporation, Investor–owned (for–profit) **Service**: General medical and surgical

Staffed Beds: 255

☐ **INSPIRE SPECIALTY HOSPITAL (372012)**, 8210 National Avenue, Zip 73110–8518; tel. 405/739–0800, (Nonreporting) **A**1 10 **S** Concord Healthcare Group, Lakewood, NJ
Primary Contact: Bobby Snyder, Chief Executive Officer
CFO: Veronica Scott, Business Office Manager
CHR: Anna Emamghoraishi, Human Resources
CNO: Jason Farris, Chief Nursing Officer
Web address: www.inspirehospital.com
Control: Corporation, Investor–owned (for–profit) **Service**: Acute long–term care hospital

Staffed Beds: 31

MOORE—Cleveland County

NORMAN REGIONAL MOORE See Norman Regional Health System, Norman

MUSKOGEE—Muskogee County

CORNERSTONE HOSPITAL OF OKLAHOMA-MUSKOGEE (372022), 351 South 40th Street, Zip 74401–4916; tel. 918/682–6161, (Includes CORNERSTONE HOSPITAL OF OKLAHOMA-BROKEN ARROW, 1000 West Boise Circle, Third Floor, Broken Arrow, Oklahoma, Zip 74012–4900, Mailing Address: 1000 West Boise Circle, Zip 74012–4900, tel. 918/994–8300; Craig Koele, Chief Executive Officer), (Non-reporting) **A**10 22 **S** Cornerstone Healthcare Group, Dallas, TX
Primary Contact: Elizabeth Waytula, Chief Executive Officer
CMO: Jeremiah Rutherford, Chief Medical Officer
Web address: www.chghospitals.com/muskogee/
Control: Corporation, Investor–owned (for–profit) **Service**: Acute long–term care hospital

Staffed Beds: 41

EASTAR HEALTH SYSTEM, EAST CAMPUS See Saint Francis Hospital Muskogee, Muskogee

⊞ △ **JACK C. MONTGOMERY VETERANS AFFAIRS MEDICAL CENTER**, 1011 Honor Heights Drive, Zip 74401–1318; tel. 918/577–3000, (Nonreporting) **A**1 2 3 5 7 **S** Department of Veterans Affairs, Washington, DC
Primary Contact: Mark E. Morgan, Medical Center Director
CFO: Dwight Beal, Chief Fiscal Services
CMO: Thomas D Schneider, D.O., Chief of Staff
CNO: Bonnie Pierce, MSN, R.N., Associate Director for Patient Care Services
Web address: www.muskogee.va.gov
Control: Veterans Affairs, Government, federal **Service**: General medical and surgical

Staffed Beds: 89

MUSKOGEE REGIONAL MEDICAL CENTER See Saint Francis Hospital Muskogee

⊞ **SAINT FRANCIS HOSPITAL MUSKOGEE (370025)**, 300 Rockefeller Drive, Zip 74401–5081; tel. 918/682–5501, (Includes EASTAR HEALTH SYSTEM, EAST CAMPUS, 2900 North Main Street, Muskogee, Oklahoma, Zip 74401–4078; tel. 918/687–7777) **A**1 2 3 10 19 **F**3 8 11 13 15 18 20 22 28 29 30 31 35 37 40 43 45 53 54 56 57 60 64 68 70 74 75 76 78 79 81 82 85 86 87 89 90 92 96 98 100 102 103 107 108 110 111 114 115 119 120 121 123 124 126 129 130 131 141 143 146 147 148 **S** Saint Francis Health System, Tulsa, OK
Primary Contact: Michele A. Keeling, Vice President and Administrator
COO: Tony Capuano, Chief Operating Officer
CFO: Scott Bailey, Chief Financial Officer
CMO: Jay Gregory, M.D., Chief Medical Officer
CIO: James Tolbert, Director Information Systems
CHR: Bill Peterson, Director Human Resources
Web address: www.https://www.saintfrancis.com/muskogee/Pages/default.aspx
Control: Church operated, Nongovernment, not–for–profit **Service**: General medical and surgical

Staffed Beds: 160 Admissions: 7548 Census: 117 Outpatient Visits: 74613 Births: 601 Total Expense ($000): 125893 Payroll Expense ($000): 44270 Personnel: 604

Many Facility Codes have changed. Please refer to the AHA Guide Code Chart.

NORMAN—Cleveland County

☐ **GRIFFIN MEMORIAL HOSPITAL (374000)**, 900 East Main Street, Zip 73071–5305, Mailing Address: P.O. Box 151, Zip 73070–0151; tel. 405/573–6600, **A**1 3 5 10 **F**29 58 75 87 98 100 102 103 130 132 135 143 149 154 **S** Oklahoma Department of Mental Health and Substance Abuse Services, Oklahoma City, OK
Primary Contact: Henry Hartsell, Ph.D., Executive Director
CFO: Cheryl Cupps, Director Finance
CMO: Clayton Morris, Medical Director
CNO: Mike Abla, Director of Nursing
Web address: www.odmhsas.org
Control: State, Government, nonfederal **Service**: Psychiatric

Staffed Beds: 120 **Admissions:** 1552 **Census:** 113 **Outpatient Visits:** 312 **Births:** 0 **Total Expense ($000):** 23315 **Payroll Expense ($000):** 10649 **Personnel:** 311

J. D. MCCARTY CENTER FOR CHILDREN WITH DEVELOPMENTAL DISABILITIES (373300), 2002 East Robinson, Zip 73071–7420; tel. 405/307–2800, (Nonreporting) **A**10
Primary Contact: Vicki Kuerstersteffen, Director and Chief Executive Officer
CFO: Erik Paulson, Director of Finance
CMO: Thomas Thurston, M.D., Medical Director
CIO: Jeffery Setzer, Administrator Information Systems
CHR: Tina Martinez, Director Human Resources
Web address: www.jdmc.org
Control: State, Government, nonfederal **Service**: Children's rehabilitation

Staffed Beds: 36

⊠ **NORMAN REGIONAL HEALTH SYSTEM (370008)**, 901 North Porter Avenue, Zip 73071–6404, Mailing Address: P.O. Box 1308, Zip 73070–1308; tel. 405/515–1000, (Includes NORMAN REGIONAL HOSPITAL, 901 North Porter Street, Norman, Oklahoma, Zip 73071–6482, Mailing Address: P O Box 1308, Zip 73070–1308, tel. 405/307–1000; Richie Splitt, FACHE, President and Chief Executive Office; NORMAN REGIONAL MOORE, 700 South Telephone Road, Moore, Oklahoma, Zip 73160; tel. 405/793–9355; Richie Splitt, FACHE, President and Chief Executive Officer) **A**1 3 5 10 13 **F**3 7 11 12 13 15 17 18 20 22 24 28 29 30 31 32 34 35 36 37 39 40 43 44 45 47 48 49 50 53 54 55 56 57 58 59 63 64 65 69 70 72 74 75 76 77 78 79 80 81 82 83 84 85 86 87 89 90 93 94 96 97 98 100 101 102 103 104 107 110 111 114 115 117 118 119 120 123 126 127 129 130 131 132 135 143 145 146 147 148 154 156 157
Primary Contact: Richie Splitt, FACHE, President and Chief Executive Officer
COO: John Manfredo, Chief Operating Officer
CFO: Ken Hopkins, Vice President Finance and Chief Financial Officer
CMO: Aaron Boyd, M.D., Chief Medical Officer
CIO: Danny Kelley, Administrative Director, Health Information Technology
CHR: Jim Beyer, Administrative Director Human Resources
CNO: Brittini McGill, MSN, R.N., Chief Nursing Officer
Web address: www.normanregional.com
Control: Hospital district or authority, Government, nonfederal **Service**: General medical and surgical

Staffed Beds: 387 **Admissions:** 16849 **Census:** 199 **Outpatient Visits:** 373387 **Births:** 2515 **Total Expense ($000):** 406808 **Payroll Expense ($000):** 184044 **Personnel:** 2733

NOWATA—Nowata County

★ **JANE PHILLIPS NOWATA HEALTH CENTER (371305)**, 237 South Locust Street, Zip 74048–3660; tel. 918/273–3102, **A**10 18 **F**3 29 30 34 35 40 50 57 64 68 107 114 119 128 133 146 154 **S** Ascension Healthcare, Saint Louis, MO
Primary Contact: Jason McCauley, Administrator
CMO: David Caughell, M.D., Chief of Staff
Web address: www.jpmc.org
Control: Church operated, Nongovernment, not-for-profit **Service**: General medical and surgical

Staffed Beds: 15 **Admissions:** 172 **Census:** 5 **Outpatient Visits:** 9759 **Births:** 0 **Total Expense ($000):** 4959 **Payroll Expense ($000):** 2560 **Personnel:** 37

OKEENE—Blaine County

★ **OKEENE MUNICIPAL HOSPITAL (371327)**, 207 East 'F' Street, Zip 73763–9441, Mailing Address: P.O. Box 489, Zip 73763–0489; tel. 580/822–4417, **A**10 18 **F**3 29 34 40 45 59 64 65 68 77 81 85 93 97 107 119 130 133 135 148 149 154
Primary Contact: Shelly Dunham, Chief Executive Officer
COO: Tammi Jantzen, Chief Operating Officer
CFO: Sandra Lamle, Chief Financial Officer
CMO: George S. Stenger, D.O., Chief of Staff
CHR: Barbara Creps, Director Human Resources and Accounting
CNO: Tamara Fischer, Chief Nursing Officer
Web address: www.okeenehospital.com
Control: Hospital district or authority, Government, nonfederal **Service**: General medical and surgical

Staffed Beds: 17 **Admissions:** 144 **Census:** 4 **Outpatient Visits:** 22323 **Births:** 0 **Total Expense ($000):** 6703 **Payroll Expense ($000):** 2784 **Personnel:** 57

OKEMAH—Okfuskee County

★ ⇑ **CREEK NATION COMMUNITY HOSPITAL (371333)**, 1800 East Coplin Street, Zip 74859–4642; tel. 918/623–1424, **A**10 18 21 **F**3 7 29 35 40 64 65 81 107 119 133
Primary Contact: Karen Lee, Interim Administrator
COO: Rhonda Beaver, Chief Operating Officer
CFO: Tyler McIntosh, Chief Financial Officer
CMO: Lawrence Vark, M.D., Chief Medical Officer
CIO: Robert Coffee, Chief Information Officer
CHR: Russell B Torbett, Director Human Resources
CNO: Annette James, R.N., MSN, Chief Nursing Officer
Web address: www.creekhealth.org
Control: Other not-for-profit (including NFP Corporation) **Service**: General medical and surgical

Staffed Beds: 25 **Admissions:** 191 **Census:** 1 **Outpatient Visits:** 20086 **Births:** 0 **Total Expense ($000):** 8891 **Payroll Expense ($000):** 4639 **Personnel:** 94

OKLAHOMA CITY—Oklahoma County

AMG MERCY (372005), 4300 West Memorial Road, 2nd Floor, Zip 73120–8304; tel. 405/936–5822, (Nonreporting) **3** AMG Integrated Healthcare Management, Lafayette, LA
Primary Contact: Eric Heflin, Chief Executive Officer
Web address: www.https://amgmercy.com/
Control: General Investor-owned, for-profit **Service**: Acute long-term care hospital

Staffed Beds: 30

☐ **CEDAR RIDGE HOSPITAL (374023)**, 6501 NE 50th Street, Zip 73141–9118; tel. 405/605–6111, (Includes BETHANY BEHAVIORAL HEALTH, 7600 NW 23rd Street, Bethany, Oklahoma, Zip 73008–4944; tel. 405/792 5360; Heather Joseph, Chief Executive Officer) **A**1 10 **F**98 99 103 105 106 130 149 153 **S** Universal Health Services, Inc., King of Prussia, PA
Primary Contact: Heather Joseph, Chief Executive Officer
Web address: www.cedarridgebhs.com
Control: Corporation, Investor-owned (for–profit) **Service**: Psychiatric

Staffed Beds: 172 **Admissions:** 4117 **Census:** 109 **Outpatient Visits:** 1219 **Births:** 0 **Total Expense ($000):** 20595 **Payroll Expense ($000):** 11240 **Personnel:** 213

CHILDREN'S HOSPITAL OF OKLAHOMA See Ou Medical Center, Oklahoma City

☐ **CURAHEALTH HOSPITAL OKLAHOMA CITY (372004)**, 1407 North Robinson Avenue, Zip 73103–4823; tel. 405/232–8000, (Includes CURAHEALTH OKLAHOMA, 2129 SW 59th Street, Oklahoma City, Oklahoma, Zip 73119; tel. 405/713–5955; Brenda Hood, Chief Executive Officer), (Non-reporting) **A**1 10 **S** Curahealth Hospitals, Garland, TX
Primary Contact: Brenda Hood, Chief Executive Officer
Web address: www.curahealth.com
Control: Corporation, Investor-owned (for-profit) **Service**: Acute long-term care hospital

Staffed Beds: 93

EVERETT TOWER See Ou Medical Center, Oklahoma City

Hospital, Medicare Provider Number, Address, Telephone, Approval, Facility, and Physician Codes, Health Care System

★ American Hospital Association (AHA) membership   ○ Healthcare Facilities Accreditation Program   ⇑ Center for Improvement in Healthcare Quality Accreditation
☐ The Joint Commission accreditation   ◇ DNV Healthcare Inc. accreditation   △ Commission on Accreditation of Rehabilitation Facilities (CARF) accreditation

OK

✠ **INTEGRIS BAPTIST MEDICAL CENTER (370028)**, 3300 NW Expressway, Zip 73112–4418; tel. 405/949–3011, (Includes INTEGRIS MENTAL HEALTH SYSTEM–SPENCER, 2601 North Spencer Road, Spencer, Oklahoma, Zip 73084–3699, Mailing Address: P O Box 11137, Oklahoma City, Zip 73136–0137, tel. 405/717–9800) **A**1 2 3 5 10 **F**3 8 11 12 13 15 16 17 18 19 20 22 24 26 28 29 30 31 32 34 35 38 39 40 43 44 45 46 47 49 50 51 54 55 57 58 59 60 62 63 64 68 70 71 72 73 74 75 76 77 78 79 80 81 82 84 85 86 87 88 89 92 93 96 97 98 99 100 101 102 104 105 106 107 108 109 110 111 114 115 116 118 119 120 121 123 124 126 129 130 131 132 135 137 138 139 140 141 142 146 147 148 149 153 154 156 157 **S** INTEGRIS Health, Oklahoma City, OK
Primary Contact: Timothy J. Johnsen, MS, President
CFO: Cheryl Perry, Chief Financial Officer
CIO: Mark Pasquale, Chief Information Officer
CHR: Jason L Eliot, Vice President Human Resources
CNO: Lewis L. Perkins, R.N., MSN, Jr Chief Nursing Officer
Web address: www.integrisok.com
Control: Other not–for–profit (including NFP Corporation) **Service:** General medical and surgical

Staffed Beds: 597 **Admissions:** 25403 **Census:** 466 **Outpatient Visits:** 222571 **Births:** 2604 **Total Expense ($000):** 771721 **Payroll Expense ($000):** 217971 **Personnel:** 2234

★ △ **INTEGRIS DEACONESS (370032)**, 5501 North Portland Avenue, Zip 73112–2099; tel. 405/604–6000, **A**3 5 7 10 **F**3 13 15 17 18 20 22 24 28 29 30 31 34 39 40 43 44 45 46 47 48 49 50 51 54 56 57 59 60 61 64 68 70 72 74 75 77 78 79 81 82 84 85 86 87 90 93 96 97 102 107 111 112 114 115 119 124 126 129 130 131 135 146 147 148 154 **S** INTEGRIS Health, Oklahoma City, OK
Primary Contact: Rex Van Meter, President
COO: Brett Kirkham, Chief Operating Officer
CIO: Don Bandy, Director Information Technology
CHR: Ellen Gifford, Director Human Resources
CNO: Jayne Thomas, Chief Nursing Officer
Web address: www.https://integrisok.com/locations/hospital/integris-deaconess
Control: Corporation, Investor–owned (for–profit) **Service:** General medical and surgical

Staffed Beds: 155 **Admissions:** 5240 **Census:** 64 **Outpatient Visits:** 29600 **Births:** 700 **Personnel:** 380

✠ **INTEGRIS SOUTHWEST MEDICAL CENTER (370106)**, 4401 South Western, Zip 73109–3413; tel. 405/636–7000, **A**1 2 3 5 10 13 **F**3 11 13 15 18 20 22 24 26 28 29 30 31 34 35 40 43 44 45 47 49 50 51 53 57 58 59 60 64 68 70 74 75 76 77 78 79 80 81 82 85 86 87 90 91 92 93 95 96 97 98 100 102 107 108 110 111 114 115 118 119 120 121 123 124 126 129 130 131 132 135 146 147 148 149 154 156 157 **S** INTEGRIS Health, Oklahoma City, OK
Primary Contact: Jordan Cash, President
CFO: Dan Davis, Managing Director and Chief Financial Officer
CMO: Philip Mosca, M.D., President, Medical Staff
CIO: Mark Pasquale, Chief Information Officer
CHR: Lynn Ketch, Regional Director Integris Southwest Medical Center
CNO: Marva Harrison, R.N., Vice President and Chief Nursing Officer
Web address: www.integrisok.com
Control: Other not–for–profit (including NFP Corporation) **Service:** General medical and surgical

Staffed Beds: 275 **Admissions:** 11904 **Census:** 184 **Outpatient Visits:** 167866 **Births:** 1136 **Total Expense ($000):** 242085 **Payroll Expense ($000):** 73613 **Personnel:** 1037

✠ **LAKESIDE WOMEN'S HOSPITAL (370199)**, 11200 North Portland Avenue, Zip 73120–5045; tel. 405/936–1500, **A**1 10 **F**3 12 13 15 30 35 36 40 45 59 64 73 76 81 85 87 110 119 126 130 132 147 **S** INTEGRIS Health, Oklahoma City, OK
Primary Contact: Kelley Brewer, R.N., MSN, President
CFO: Darla McCallister, Chief Financial Officer
CMO: Margaret Hall, M.D., Chief Medical Officer
Web address: www.lakeside-wh.net
Control: Corporation, Investor–owned (for–profit) **Service:** Obstetrics and gynecology

Staffed Beds: 23 **Admissions:** 1497 **Census:** 9 **Outpatient Visits:** 22085 **Births:** 1395 **Total Expense ($000):** 22434 **Payroll Expense ($000):** 8609 **Personnel:** 107

⇑ **MCBRIDE ORTHOPEDIC HOSPITAL (370222)**, 9600 Broadway Extension, Zip 73114–7408; tel. 405/486–2100, **A**3 5 10 21 **F**3 29 34 40 64 68 77 79 81 82 85 86 87 93 97 107 111 114 119 126 130 131 146 149
Primary Contact: Mark Galliart, Chief Executive Officer
CFO: Greg Gisler, Chief Financial Officer
CNO: Krista Reyna, Chief Nursing Officer
Web address: www.mcboh.com
Control: Corporation, Investor–owned (for–profit) **Service:** Orthopedic

Staffed Beds: 60 **Admissions:** 3528 **Census:** 26 **Outpatient Visits:** 165862 **Births:** 0 **Total Expense ($000):** 141321 **Payroll Expense ($000):** 56474 **Personnel:** 734

✠ **MERCY HOSPITAL OKLAHOMA CITY (370013)**, 4300 West Memorial Road, Zip 73120–8362; tel. 405/755–1515, **A**1 2 3 10 **F**3 11 13 15 28 29 30 31 32 34 35 40 43 44 45 46 47 48 49 50 53 55 57 58 59 60 61 62 63 64 65 68 69 70 72 74 75 76 77 78 79 81 82 83 84 85 86 87 89 91 92 93 94 96 100 101 107 108 110 111 114 115 117 118 119 120 121 124 126 129 130 131 132 134 135 143 146 147 148 149 154 156 **S** Mercy, Chesterfield, MO
Primary Contact: Jim Gebhart Jr, FACHE, President
COO: Aaron Steffens, Chief Operating Officer
CFO: Jon Vitiello, Senior Vice President, Finance Operations and Analytics
CIO: Ellen Stephens, Vice President Information Services
CHR: Becky J Payton, Vice President Human Resources
Web address: www.mercyok.net
Control: Church operated, Nongovernment, not–for–profit **Service:** General medical and surgical

Staffed Beds: 349 **Admissions:** 16840 **Census:** 223 **Outpatient Visits:** 514106 **Births:** 3910 **Total Expense ($000):** 453803 **Payroll Expense ($000):** 152711 **Personnel:** 2118

☐ △ **MERCY REHABILITATION HOSPITAL OKLAHOMA CITY (373033)**, 5401 West Memorial Rd, Zip 73142–2026; tel. 405/752–3935, (Nonreporting) **A**1 7 10
Primary Contact: Thomas Elliott, President
Web address: www.https://www.mercy.net/practice/mercy-rehabilitation-hospital-oklahoma-city/
Control: Church operated **Service:** Rehabilitation

Staffed Beds: 50

⇑ **NORTHWEST SURGICAL HOSPITAL (370192)**, 9204 North May Avenue, Zip 73120–4419; tel. 405/848–1918, **A**3 5 10 21 **F**3 15 29 40 75 79 81 85 107 111 119 149 154
Primary Contact: Debbie Kearns, Chief Executive Officer
CFO: Cindy Thompson, Chief Financial Officer
CMO: Jimmy Conway, M.D., President Medical Staff
Web address: www.nwsurgicalokc.com/
Control: Partnership, Investor–owned (for–profit) **Service:** Surgical

Staffed Beds: 9 **Admissions:** 182 **Census:** 1 **Outpatient Visits:** 6831 **Births:** 0 **Total Expense ($000):** 12652 **Payroll Expense ($000):** 2508 **Personnel:** 33

☐ **OAKWOOD SPRINGS (374025)**, 13101 Memorial Springs Court, Zip 73114–2226; tel. 405/438–3000, **A**1 10 **F**4 5 29 34 38 53 68 98 100 101 102 104 105 132 135 143 144 148 149 152 153 **S** Springstone, Louisville, KY
Primary Contact: Karen Walker, Chief Executive Officer
Web address: www.oakwoodsprings.com/
Control: Corporation, Investor–owned (for–profit) **Service:** Psychiatric

Staffed Beds: 72 **Admissions:** 2017 **Census:** 47 **Outpatient Visits:** 7092 **Births:** 0 **Total Expense ($000):** 13309 **Payroll Expense ($000):** 7362 **Personnel:** 152

☐ **OKLAHOMA CENTER FOR ORTHOPEDIC AND MULTI-SPECIALTY SURGERY (370212)**, 8100 South Walker, Suite C, Zip 73139–9402, Mailing Address: P.O. Box 890609, Zip 73189–0609; tel. 405/602–6500, **A**1 10 **F**3 12 29 34 35 37 39 40 45 47 48 54 57 59 64 74 79 81 82 85 86 93 94 97 107 111 131 148 149 **S** United Surgical Partners International, Addison, TX
Primary Contact: Daniel J. Coats, Chief Executive Officer
COO: Jeff Bibb, Chief Operating Officer
CFO: Amy Taylor, Chief Financial Officer
CHR: Emily Phipps, Director Human Resources
CNO: Jolena Wyer, R.N., Chief Nursing Officer
Web address: www.ocomhospital.com
Control: Partnership, Investor–owned (for–profit) **Service:** Surgical

Staffed Beds: 10 **Admissions:** 779 **Census:** 4 **Outpatient Visits:** 37028 **Births:** 0 **Total Expense ($000):** 50651 **Payroll Expense ($000):** 14782 **Personnel:** 225

✠ △ **OKLAHOMA CITY VETERANS AFFAIRS MEDICAL CENTER**, 921 NE 13th Street, Zip 73104–5028; tel. 405/456–1000, (Nonreporting) **A**1 2 3 5 7 8 **S** Department of Veterans Affairs, Washington, DC
Primary Contact: Kristopher Wade. Vlosich, Director
CFO: Michele Pipgrass, Chief Fiscal Service
CIO: David Buckley, Acting Chief Information Management Services
CHR: Kyle Inhofe, Chief Human Resources Officer
Web address: www.oklahoma.va.gov
Control: Veterans Affairs, Government, federal **Service:** General medical and surgical

Staffed Beds: 192

Many Facility Codes have changed. Please refer to the AHA Guide Code Chart. © 2019 AHA Guide

⇑ **OKLAHOMA HEART HOSPITAL (370215)**, 4050 West Memorial Road, Zip 73120–8382; tel. 405/608–3200, **A**10 21 **F**17 18 20 22 24 26 28 29 30 34 35 40 50 59 64 68 75 81 82 85 86 87 100 102 107 108 111 114 115 117 118 119 126 127 129 130 135 146 154
Primary Contact: John Harvey, M.D., Chief Executive Officer
COO: Peggy Tipton, Chief Operating Officer and Chief Nursing Officer
CFO: Carol Walker, Chief Financial Officer
CMO: John Harvey, M.D., Chief Executive Officer
CIO: Michelle Mullins, Chief Information Officer
CHR: Katherine Wynn, Director Human Resource
Web address: www.okheart.com
Control: Corporation, Investor–owned (for–profit) **Service:** Heart

Staffed Beds: 98 **Admissions:** 6588 **Census:** 72 **Outpatient Visits:** 282580 **Births:** 0 **Total Expense ($000):** 226635 **Payroll Expense ($000):** 95396 **Personnel:** 1973

⇑ **OKLAHOMA HEART HOSPITAL SOUTH CAMPUS (370234)**, 5200 East I-240 Service Road, Zip 73135; tel. 405/628–6000, **A**10 21 **F**17 18 20 22 24 26 28 29 30 34 35 40 50 59 64 68 75 81 82 85 86 87 100 107 111 115 117 118 119 126 129 130 135 146 154
Primary Contact: John Harvey, M.D., Chief Executive Officer
Web address: www.okheart.com
Control: Corporation, Investor–owned (for–profit) **Service:** Heart

Staffed Beds: 44 **Admissions:** 3904 **Census:** 42 **Outpatient Visits:** 76798 **Births:** 0 **Total Expense ($000):** 134684 **Payroll Expense ($000):** 49891 **Personnel:** 694

OKLAHOMA SPINE HOSPITAL (370206), 14101 Parkway Commons Drive, Zip 73134–6012; tel. 405/749–2700, (Nonreporting) **A**10
Primary Contact: Kevin Blaylock, Chief Executive Officer
Web address: www.oklahomaspine.com
Control: Corporation, Investor–owned (for–profit) **Service:** Surgical

Staffed Beds: 12

ONECORE HEALTH (370220), 1044 SW 44th Street, Suite 350, Zip 73109–3609; tel. 405/631–3085, (Nonreporting) **A**10
Primary Contact: Mike Kimzey, Chief Executive Officer
CMO: Joel L Frazier, M.D., Medical Director
CNO: Teresa Carter, Vice President Patient Care Services
Web address: www.onecorehealth.com
Control: Corporation, Investor–owned (for–profit) **Service:** Orthopedic

Staffed Beds: 8

⊞ **OU MEDICAL CENTER (370093)**, 1200 Everett Drive, Zip 73104–5047, Mailing Address: P.O. Box 26307, Zip 73126–0307; tel. 405/271–3636, (Includes CHILDREN'S HOSPITAL OF OKLAHOMA, 940 NE 13th Street, Oklahoma City, Oklahoma, Zip 73104, Mailing Address: P O Box 26307, Zip 73126, tel. 405/271–6165; EVERETT TOWER, 1200 Everett Drive, Oklahoma City, Oklahoma, Zip 73104; tel. 405/271–4700; OU MEDICAL CENTER EDMOND, 1 South Bryant Avenue, Edmond, Oklahoma, Zip 73034–6309; tel. 405/341–6100; PRESBYTERIAN TOWER, 700 NE 13th Street, Oklahoma City, Oklahoma, Zip 73104–5070; tel. 405/271–5100) (Data for 150 days)**A**1 2 3 5 8 10 **F**3 5 6 11 12 13 15 17 18 19 20 21 22 23 24 25 26 27 28 29 30 31 32 34 35 36 37 38 39 40 41 43 44 45 46 47 48 49 50 51 52 54 55 56 57 58 59 60 61 63 64 65 66 68 70 71 72 74 75 76 77 78 79 80 81 82 83 84 85 86 87 88 89 91 92 93 94 96 97 98 99 100 101 102 103 107 108 110 111 114 115 116 117 118 119 120 121 122 123 124 126 129 130 131 132 134 135 136 138 139 141 142 145 146 147 148 149 150 154
Primary Contact: Kristina Wallace, R.N., Chief Executive Officer
CFO: Mike Reese, Chief Financial Officer
CMO: Curt Steinhart, M.D., Chief Medical Officer
CIO: Larry Forsyth, Director Information Services
CHR: Jed M Liuzza, Chief Human Resources Officer
Web address: www.oumedicine.com/oumedicalcenter
Control: Other not–for–profit (including NFP Corporation) **Service:** General medical and surgical

Staffed Beds: 727 **Admissions:** 13834 **Census:** 580 **Outpatient Visits:** 104802 **Births:** 1465 **Total Expense ($000):** 422347 **Payroll Expense ($000):** 111570 **Personnel:** 3951

PRESBYTERIAN TOWER See Ou Medical Center, Oklahoma City

⊞ **SELECT SPECIALTY HOSPITAL-OKLAHOMA CITY (372009)**, 3524 NW 56th Street, Zip 73112–4518; tel. 405/606–6700, (Nonreporting) **A**1 10 **S** Select Medical Corporation, Mechanicsburg, PA
Primary Contact: Judy Webb-Hapgood, Chief Executive Officer
Web address: www.https://oklahomacity.selectspecialtyhospitals.com/
Control: Corporation, Investor–owned (for–profit) **Service:** Acute long–term care hospital

Staffed Beds: 72

⊞ **SSM HEALTH ST. ANTHONY HOSPITAL - OKLAHOMA CITY (370037)**, 1000 North Lee Street, Zip 73102–1080, Mailing Address: P.O. Box 205, Zip 73101–0205; tel. 405/272–7000, (Includes SSM HEALTH BONE AND JOINT HOSPITAL AT ST. ANTHONY, 1111 North Dewey Avenue, Oklahoma City, Oklahoma, Zip 73103–2609; tel. 405/272–9671; Tammy Powell, FACHE, M.P.H., President; SSM HEALTH ST. ANTHONY SOUTH, 2129 SW 59th Street, Oklahoma City, Oklahoma, Zip 73119–7001; tel. 405/713–5700)**A**1 2 3 10 12 13 **F**1 3 4 5 7 8 11 12 13 15 17 18 20 22 24 26 28 29 30 31 34 35 36 37 38 40 42 43 45 46 47 48 49 50 54 56 57 58 59 64 67 70 71 72 73 74 76 77 78 79 81 82 84 85 86 87 89 90 91 92 93 96 97 98 99 100 101 102 103 104 105 106 107 108 110 111 114 115 117 118 119 120 121 123 124 126 127 129 130 131 132 144 146 147 148 149 152 153 154 **S** SSM Health, Saint Louis, MO
Primary Contact: Tammy Powell, FACHE, M.P.H., President
COO: Marti Jourden, FACHE, Chief Quality Officer
CFO: Shasta Manuel, Executive Director Finance
CMO: Kersey Winfree, M.D., Chief Medical Officer
CIO: Kevin Olson, Director Information Systems
CHR: Cynthia Brundise, Vice President Human Resources
Web address: www.saintsok.com
Control: Church operated, Nongovernment, not–for–profit **Service:** General medical and surgical

Staffed Beds: 625 **Admissions:** 23615 **Census:** 446 **Outpatient Visits:** 356612 **Births:** 1136 **Total Expense ($000):** 511836 **Payroll Expense ($000):** 149987 **Personnel:** 2595

☐ **SURGICAL HOSPITAL OF OKLAHOMA (370201)**, 100 SE 59th Street, Zip 73129–3616; tel. 405/634–9300, (Nonreporting) **A**1 3 10
Primary Contact: Phil Ross, Chief Executive Officer
CNO: Cindy Ridge Braly, MAAL, R.N., Chief Nursing Officer
Web address: www.sh-ok.com/
Control: Partnership, Investor–owned (for–profit) **Service:** Other specialty treatment

Staffed Beds: 12

★ **VALIR REHABILITATION HOSPITAL (373025)**, 700 NW Seventh Street, Zip 73102–1212; tel. 405/236–3131, **A**10 **F**3 28 29 30 34 40 50 53 54 56 57 59 64 77 82 85 86 87 90 91 93 96 100 130 131 132 135 143 148 156
Primary Contact: Meaghan Skelton, Chief Executive Officer
COO: Ginger Castleberry, Corporate Risk Manager, Quality and Patient Safety
CFO: Scott Brown, Chief Financial Officer
CMO: Tonya Washburn, M.D., Medical Director
CIO: Mark Dickey, Director Business Development
CHR: Bill Turner, Vice President Human Resources
Web address: www.valir.com
Control: Partnership, Investor–owned (for–profit) **Service:** Rehabilitation

Staffed Beds: 49 **Admissions:** 943 **Census:** 31 **Outpatient Visits:** 4231 **Births:** 0 **Total Expense ($000):** 14968 **Payroll Expense ($000):** 8542 **Personnel:** 185

VETERANS AFFAIRS MEDICAL CENTER See Oklahoma City Veterans Affairs Medical Center

OKLAHOMA CITY—Cleveland County

⇑ **COMMUNITY HOSPITAL (370203)**, 3100 SW 89th Street, Zip 73159–7900, Mailing Address: 3125 SW 89th Street, Zip 73159–7900; tel. 405/602–8100, **A**10 21 **F**3 15 29 40 45 70 79 81 82 85 89 93 107 111 114 115 119 126 146 149
Primary Contact: Debbie Kearns, Chief Executive Officer
Web address: www.communityhospitalokc.com
Control: Partnership, Investor–owned (for–profit) **Service:** Surgical

Staffed Beds: 45 **Admissions:** 2334 **Census:** 13 **Outpatient Visits:** 91767 **Births:** 0 **Total Expense ($000):** 109124 **Payroll Expense ($000):** 27963 **Personnel:** 442

Hospital, Medicare Provider Number, Address, Telephone, Approval, Facility, and Physician Codes, Health Care System

★ American Hospital Association (AHA) membership
☐ The Joint Commission accreditation
○ Healthcare Facilities Accreditation Program
◇ DNV Healthcare Inc. accreditation
⇑ Center for Improvement in Healthcare Quality Accreditation
△ Commission on Accreditation of Rehabilitation Facilities (CARF) accreditation

OK

OKMULGEE—Okmulgee County

MUSCOGEE CREEK NATION MEDICAL CENTER (370057), 1401 Morris Drive, Zip 74447–6429, Mailing Address: P.O. Box 1038, Zip 74447–1038; tel. 918/756–4233, (Nonreporting) **A**10
Primary Contact: Tim Hicks, Administrator
CFO: John W Crawford, Chief Financial Officer
CMO: Michael Sandlin, M.D., Chief of Staff
CHR: Stacey R. Burton, Director Human Resources
Web address: www.creekhealth.org/medical-center/
Control: Other not–for–profit (including NFP Corporation) **Service**: General medical and surgical

Staffed Beds: 45

MUSCOGEE CREEK NATION PHYSICAL REHABILITATION CENTER (372023), 1401 Morris Drive, Zip 74447–6429, Mailing Address: P.O. Box 1038, Zip 74447–1938; tel. 918/756–4233, (Nonreporting)
Primary Contact: Tim Hicks, Administrator
Control: Other not–for–profit (including NFP Corporation) **Service**: Acute long–term care hospital

Staffed Beds: 12

OWASSO—Tulsa County

★ ⋔ **BAILEY MEDICAL CENTER (370228)**, 10502 North 110th East Avenue, Zip 74055–6655; tel. 918/376–8000, **A**10 21 **F**3 12 13 15 18 29 34 40 45 51 57 70 75 76 77 79 81 85 91 93 107 108 110 111 115 119 129 132 146 147 149 **S** Ardent Health Services, Nashville, TN
Primary Contact: Keith Mason, Chief Executive Officer
CFO: Brandon Bullard, Chief Financial Officer
CHR: Tandy Groves, Coordinator Human Resources
Web address: www.baileymedicalcenter.com
Control: Corporation, Investor–owned (for–profit) **Service**: General medical and surgical

Staffed Beds: 37 **Admissions:** 1625 **Census:** 9 **Outpatient Visits:** 36276 **Births:** 320 **Total Expense ($000):** 38592 **Payroll Expense ($000):** 13568 **Personnel:** 209

★ **ST. JOHN OWASSO (370227)**, 12451 East 100th Street North, Zip 74055–4600; tel. 918/274–5000, **A**10 **F**3 11 13 15 18 29 30 34 35 40 43 45 57 59 64 68 76 79 81 85 87 93 107 108 110 111 114 115 119 130 131 132 146 147 149 156 **S** Ascension Healthcare, Saint Louis, MO
Primary Contact: David L. Phillips, President and Chief Operating Officer
CFO: Katie Caughman, Chief Financial Officer
CMO: Tim Hepner, M.D., Chief Medical Officer
CIO: Mike Reeves, Chief Information Officer
CNO: Dan Hall, R.N., Chief Operating Officer
Web address: www.stjohnowasso.com
Control: Church operated, Nongovernment, not–for–profit **Service**: General medical and surgical

Staffed Beds: 36 **Admissions:** 1728 **Census:** 11 **Outpatient Visits:** 158344 **Births:** 503 **Total Expense ($000):** 26701 **Payroll Expense ($000):** 9437 **Personnel:** 156

PAWHUSKA—Osage County

★ **PAWHUSKA HOSPITAL (371309)**, 1101 East 15th Street, Zip 74056–1920; tel. 918/287–3232, (Nonreporting) **A**10 18
Primary Contact: Godwin Feh, Interim Administrator
CMO: Mike Priest, M.D., Chief of Staff
Web address: www.https://pawhuskahospital.com/
Control: City, Government, nonfederal **Service**: General medical and surgical

Staffed Beds: 15

PERRY—Noble County

★ ⋔ **STILLWATER MEDICAL PERRY (370139)**, 501 North 14th Street, Zip 73077–5099; tel. 580/336–3541, (Data for 274 days) **A**10 20 21 **F**3 11 15 28 29 34 35 40 59 62 64 65 67 81 85 90 93 97 107 114 127 128 131 133 146 148 149 154
Primary Contact: Steven E. Taylor, Chief Executive Officer
CFO: Courtney Kozikuski, Chief Financial Officer
CMO: Michael Hartwig, M.D., Chief of Staff
CIO: Randy Taylor, Chief Information Technology Officer
CHR: Deb Ellis, Director Human Resources
CNO: Jeannie Carey, R.N., Director Patient Care
Web address: www.pmh-ok.org
Control: Hospital district or authority, Government, nonfederal **Service**: General medical and surgical

Staffed Beds: 23 **Admissions:** 171 **Census:** 2 **Outpatient Visits:** 10522 **Births:** 1 **Total Expense ($000):** 6537 **Payroll Expense ($000):** 2962 **Personnel:** 65

PONCA CITY—Kay County

✉ **ALLIANCEHEALTH PONCA CITY (370006)**, 1900 North 14th Street, Zip 74601–2099; tel. 580/765–3321, **A**1 10 19 **F**3 13 15 18 28 29 30 34 35 40 43 45 46 50 51 53 55 57 59 64 65 66 68 69 70 75 76 77 79 81 82 85 89 90 93 97 107 108 110 111 115 119 127 130 131 132 133 145 146 147 148 149 154 156 **S** Community Health Systems, Inc., Franklin, TN
Primary Contact: Christopher Mendoza, Chief Executive Officer
CFO: Sheryl Schmidtberger, Chief Financial Officer
CIO: William Gazaway, Information Technology Security Officer
CHR: Calvin Hodges, Director Human Resources
CNO: Jeanne Stara, R.N., MSN, Chief Nursing Officer
Web address: www.AllianceHealthPoncaCity.com
Control: Corporation, Investor–owned (for–profit) **Service**: General medical and surgical

Staffed Beds: 74 **Admissions:** 2303 **Census:** 22 **Outpatient Visits:** 60131 **Births:** 474 **Total Expense ($000):** 53836 **Payroll Expense ($000):** 22039 **Personnel:** 410

POTEAU—Le Flore County

⋔ **EASTERN OKLAHOMA MEDICAL CENTER (371337)**, 105 Wall Street, Zip 74953–4433, Mailing Address: P.O. Box 1148, Zip 74953–1148; tel. 918/647–8161, (Nonreporting) **A**10 18 21
Primary Contact: Bob Carter, Interim Chief Executive Officer
CFO: Shaun Keef, Chief Financial Officer
CMO: Dennis Carter, M.D., Chief of Staff
CIO: Michael C Huggins, Administrator Network System
Web address: www.eomchospital.com
Control: County, Government, nonfederal **Service**: General medical and surgical

Staffed Beds: 45

PRAGUE—Lincoln County

PRAGUE COMMUNITY HOSPITAL (371301), 1322 Klabzuba Avenue, Zip 74864–9005, Mailing Address: P.O. Box S, Zip 74864–1090; tel. 405/567–4922, (Nonreporting) **A**10 18 **S** Rural Community Hospitals of America, Kansas City, MO
Primary Contact: Shelly Dyer, Interim Chief Executive Officer
CFO: Doug Erickson, Chief Financial Officer
CMO: Darryl Jackson, D.O., Chief of Staff
CIO: Rhonda Whitnum, Director Health Improvement Management
CHR: Angie Brezny, Director Human Resources
Web address: www.praguehospital.com
Control: Corporation, Investor–owned (for–profit) **Service**: General medical and surgical

Staffed Beds: 15

PRYOR—Mayes County

★ ⋔ **HILLCREST HOSPITAL PRYOR (370015)**, 111 North Bailey Street, Zip 74361–4201; tel. 918/825–1600, **A**10 21 **F**3 11 15 18 26 29 30 34 35 45 50 57 59 64 65 79 81 93 107 108 110 111 114 119 147 **S** Ardent Health Services, Nashville, TN
Primary Contact: Douglas K. Weaver, FACHE, Chief Executive Officer
CMO: Jason Joice, M.D., Chief Medical Staff
CHR: Pamela A Guthrie, Chief Human Resources Officer
CNO: Mary Ozment, Chief Nursing Officer
Web address: www.hillcrestpryor.com/
Control: Corporation, Investor–owned (for–profit) **Service**: General medical and surgical

Staffed Beds: 22 **Admissions:** 696 **Census:** 3 **Outpatient Visits:** 28205 **Births:** 0 **Total Expense ($000):** 20555 **Payroll Expense ($000):** 8036 **Personnel:** 138

PURCELL—McClain County

PURCELL MUNICIPAL HOSPITAL (370158), 1500 North Green Avenue, Zip 73080–1699, Mailing Address: P.O. Box 511, Zip 73080–0511; tel. 405/527–6524, **A**10 **F**3 11 18 29 30 34 35 40 45 48 57 59 64 65 75 79 81 82 86 87 89 107 119 133 135 154
Primary Contact: Kem Scully, Chief Executive Officer and Chief Nursing Officer
CFO: Mary Morris, Chief Financial Officer
CMO: David Bryan Dye, M.D., Chief Medical Officer
CIO: Jennifer Coates, Coordinator Information Technology
CHR: Tara Selfridge, Manager Human Resources
CNO: Kem Scully, Chief Executive Officer and Chief Nursing Officer
Web address: www.purcellhospital.com
Control: City, Government, nonfederal **Service**: General medical and surgical

Staffed Beds: 28 **Admissions:** 523 **Census:** 4 **Outpatient Visits:** 47326 **Births:** 0 **Total Expense ($000):** 11064 **Payroll Expense ($000):** 4910 **Personnel:** 103

Many Facility Codes have changed. Please refer to the AHA Guide Code Chart. © 2019 AHA Guide

OK

SALLISAW—Sequoyah County

NORTHEASTERN HEALTH SYSTEM SEQUOYAH (370112), 213 East Redwood Street, Zip 74955–2811, Mailing Address: P.O. Box 505, Zip 74955–0505; tel. 918/774–1100, **A**10 **F**3 15 18 29 30 34 40 43 45 50 59 62 63 64 81 82 83 84 87 97 102 107 110 111 112 114 115 119 128 129 133 146 147 148 149 154 157
Primary Contact: Stephanie Six, Chief Executive Officer
CMO: Jennifer Scoufos, M.D., Chief of Staff
CIO: Gary McClanahan, Chief Information Officer
CHR: Shayna Brooke Roberts, Director Human Resources
CNO: Ozalina Martinez, R.N., Director of Nursing
Web address: www.pmtc.ok.gov/sequoyah-memorial-hospital-sallisaw-ok
Control: Hospital district or authority, Government, nonfederal **Service**: General medical and surgical

Staffed Beds: 26 **Admissions**: 479 **Census**: 8 **Outpatient Visits**: 23700 **Births**: 0 **Total Expense ($000)**: 11307 **Payroll Expense ($000)**: 4879 **Personnel**: 200

SAPULPA—Creek County

★ **ST. JOHN SAPULPA (371312)**, 1004 East Bryan Avenue, Zip 74066–4513, Mailing Address: P.O. Box 1368, Zip 74067–1368; tel. 918/224–4280, **A**10 18 **F**3 8 11 14 29 30 34 35 40 45 57 59 64 68 79 81 85 86 87 107 111 119 130 132 133 135 143 149 154 **S** Ascension Healthcare, Saint Louis, MO
Primary Contact: Michael Christian, Chief Operating Officer
COO: Michael Christian, Chief Operating Officer
CFO: John W Crawford, Chief Financial Officer
CMO: Jason Lepak, M.D., Medical Director
CNO: Kelly Johnson, R.N., Chief Nursing Officer
Web address: www.stjohnhealthsystem.com/sapulpa
Control: Church operated, Nongovernment, not–for–profit **Service**: General medical and surgical

Staffed Beds: 25 **Admissions**: 714 **Census**: 16 **Outpatient Visits**: 59308 **Births**: 0 **Total Expense ($000)**: 18479 **Payroll Expense ($000)**: 6774 **Personnel**: 107

SEILING—Dewey County

⇑ **SEILING REGIONAL MEDICAL CENTER (371332)**, Highway 60 NE, Zip 73663, Mailing Address: P.O. Box 720, Zip 73663–0720; tel. 580/377–1005, **A**10 10 21 **F**11 29 34 40 57 59 64 65 75 77 79 84 86 87 92 93 97 114 127 133 148 154 156
Primary Contact: Rachel Farrow, Interim Chief Executive Officer
CFO: Nancy Freed, Chief Financial Officer
CMO: Kenneth Duffy, M.D., Medical Director
CHR: Sandy Landreth, Director Human Resources
Web address: www.seilingmunicipalhospital.org/
Control: City, Government, nonfederal **Service**: General medical and surgical

Staffed Beds: 18 **Admissions**: 201 **Census**: 4 **Outpatient Visits**: 4651 **Births**: 0 **Total Expense ($000)**: 4748 **Payroll Expense ($000)**: 2496

SEMINOLE—Seminole County

⊞ **ALLIANCEHEALTH SEMINOLE (370229)**, 2401 Wrangler Boulevard, Zip 74868–1917; tel. 405/303–4000, **A**1 10 **F**3 11 15 18 29 30 34 40 41 43 44 45 46 47 48 49 50 51 57 59 64 65 68 79 81 87 91 92 93 96 97 100 107 108 109 110 111 114 119 127 129 133 146 147 148 154 **S** Community Health Systems, Inc., Franklin, TN
Primary Contact: Damon Brown, Interim Chief Executive Officer
CMO: Nikki Chawla, M.D., Medical Director
CHR: Lori Friend, Human Resources Director
CNO: Barbara Lewis, Chief Nursing Officer
Web address: www.alliancehealthseminole.com/
Control: Corporation, Investor–owned (for–profit) **Service**: General medical and surgical

Staffed Beds: 32 **Admissions**: 529 **Census**: 5 **Outpatient Visits**: 37818 **Births**: 0

SHATTUCK—Ellis County

★ ○ **NEWMAN MEMORIAL HOSPITAL (371336)**, 905 South Main Street, Zip 73858–9205; tel. 580/938–2551, **A**10 11 18 **F**3 8 11 15 18 19 29 32 34 35 40 41 43 45 57 64 65 69 81 85 93 107 110 114 119 128 133 149
Primary Contact: Ed Majors, Chief Executive Officer
CFO: Kellcie Skinner, Controller
CMO: Danna Stuart, M.D., Chief Medical Officer
CIO: Robert Neal, Manager Information Technology Services
Web address: www.newmanmemorialhospital.org
Control: City, Government, nonfederal **Service**: General medical and surgical

Staffed Beds: 25 **Admissions**: 145 **Census**: 1 **Outpatient Visits**: 9712 **Births**: 0 **Total Expense ($000)**: 8308 **Payroll Expense ($000)**: 1553 **Personnel**: 72

SHAWNEE—Pottawatomie County

CORNERSTONE HOSPITAL OF OKLAHOMA-SHAWNEE (372019), 1900 Gordon Cooper Drive, 2nd Floor, Zip 74801–8603, Mailing Address: P.O. Box 1245, Zip 74802–1245; tel. 405/395–5800, (Nonreporting) **A**10 **S** Cornerstone Healthcare Group, Dallas, TX
Primary Contact: Kristopher Karns, Chief Executive Officer
COO: Cindy Linck, Chief Nursing Officer
CMO: Rakesh Shrivastava, M.D., Chief Medical Officer
Web address: www.chghospitals.com/shawnee/
Control: Corporation, Investor–owned (for–profit) **Service**: Acute long–term care hospital

Staffed Beds: 34

⊞ **SSM HEALTH ST. ANTHONY HOSPITAL - SHAWNEE (370149)**, 1102 West MacArthur Street, Zip 74804–1744; tel. 405/273–2270, **A**1 10 19 **F**3 11 13 15 18 20 22 29 30 31 34 35 40 43 45 50 57 59 60 64 65 68 69 70 75 76 77 78 79 81 82 84 87 94 107 110 111 114 115 116 117 119 120 121 123 129 130 131 132 135 146 147 148 **S** SSM Health, Saint Louis, MO
Primary Contact: Charles E. Skillings, President and Chief Executive Officer
COO: Angela Mohr, R.N., MS, Vice President Nursing and Chief Operating Officer
CFO: Jennifer Pierce, Administrative Director of Finance
CMO: Gaynell Anderson, M.D., Medical Director
CHR: Michael Spears, Human Resource Leader
CNO: Angela Mohr, R.N., MS, Vice President Nursing and Chief Operating Officer
Web address: www.stanthonyshawnee.com
Control: Other not–for–profit (including NFP Corporation) **Service**: General medical and surgical

Staffed Beds: 70 **Admissions**: 4040 **Census**: 33 **Outpatient Visits**: 123652 **Births**: 876 **Total Expense ($000)**: 80596 **Payroll Expense ($000)**: 25870 **Personnel**: 503

UNITY HEALTH CENTER See Ssm Health St. Anthony Hospital - Shawnee

SPENCER—Oklahoma County

INTEGRIS MENTAL HEALTH SYSTEM-SPENCER See Integris Baptist Medical Center, Oklahoma City

STIGLER—Haskell County

HASKELL COUNTY COMMUNITY HOSPITAL (371335), 401 Northwest 'H' Street, Zip 74462–1625; tel. 918/967–4682, (Nonreporting) **A**10 18 **S** Rural Community Hospitals of America, Kansas City, MO
Primary Contact: Andrea Randall, Interim Chief Executive Officer
CMO: Stephen Woodson, D.O., Chief of Staff
CIO: Steve Hurst, Information Technology Specialist
Web address: www.haskellhospital.com
Control: Corporation, Investor–owned (for–profit) **Service**: General medical and surgical

Staffed Beds: 20

HASKELL COUNTY HEALTHCARE SYSTEM See Haskell County Community Hospital

STILLWATER—Payne County

★ ⇑ **STILLWATER MEDICAL CENTER (370049)**, 1323 West Sixth Avenue, Zip 74074–4399, Mailing Address: P.O. Box 2408, Zip 74076–2408; tel. 405/372–1480, **A**10 21 **F**3 11 13 15 18 20 22 28 29 30 31 34 35 40 43 44 45 46 47 48 49 50 51 53 54 55 57 59 62 63 64 65 66 68 70 75 76 77 78 79 81 82 85 86 87 89 90 93 94 97 104 107 108 110 111 115 116 119 120 121 124 126 127 130 131 132 133 135 144 145 146 147 148 149 154 156
Primary Contact: Denise Webber, President and Chief Executive Officer
CFO: Alan Lovelace, Vice President and Chief Financial Officer
CMO: Steve Cummings, M.D., Chief of Medical Staff
CIO: Chris Roark, Chief Information Officer
CHR: Keith Hufnagel, Director Human Resources
CNO: Elizabeth Michael, R.N., MS, Vice President Patient Care Services and Chief Nursing Officer
Web address: www.stillwater-medical.org
Control: Hospital district or authority, Government, nonfederal **Service**: General medical and surgical

Staffed Beds: 100 **Admissions**: 3662 **Census**: 35 **Outpatient Visits**: 140939 **Births**: 816 **Total Expense ($000)**: 194804 **Payroll Expense ($000)**: 84066 **Personnel**: 1606

Hospital, Medicare Provider Number, Address, Telephone, Approval, Facility, and Physician Codes, Health Care System

★ American Hospital Association (AHA) membership ○ Healthcare Facilities Accreditation Program ⇑ Center for Improvement in Healthcare Quality Accreditation
□ The Joint Commission accreditation ◇ DNV Healthcare Inc. accreditation △ Commission on Accreditation of Rehabilitation Facilities (CARF) accreditation

OK

STILWELL—Adair County

MEMORIAL HOSPITAL OF STILWELL (370178), 1401 West Locust, Zip 74960–3275, Mailing Address: P.O. Box 272, Zip 74960–0272; tel. 918/696–3101, (Nonreporting) **A**10
Primary Contact: Alan L. Adams, Administrator
Web address: www.stilwellmemorialhospital.com
Control: Corporation, Investor–owned (for–profit) **Service**: General medical and surgical

Staffed Beds: 34

STROUD—Lincoln County

STROUD REGIONAL MEDICAL CENTER (371316), Highway 66 West, Zip 74079, Mailing Address: P.O. Box 530, Zip 74079–0530; tel. 918/968–3571, (Nonreporting) **A**10 18 **S** First Physicians Capital Group, Inc., Oklahoma City, OK
Primary Contact: Ed Dyer, Chief Executive Officer
CFO: Richard E Rentsch, President
CMO: Ken Darvin, M.D., Chief of Staff
CIO: Donna Buchanan, Director Nursing
CHR: Leannette Raffety, Administrative Generalist
Web address: www.stroudhospital.com/
Control: Other not–for–profit (including NFP Corporation) **Service**: General medical and surgical

Staffed Beds: 25

SULPHUR—Murray County

★ **ARBUCKLE MEMORIAL HOSPITAL (371328)**, 2011 West Broadway Street, Zip 73086–4221, Mailing Address: P.O. Box 1109, Zip 73086–8109; tel. 580/622–2161, (Nonreporting) **A**10 18 **S** Preferred Management Corporation, Shawnee, OK
Primary Contact: Jeremy A. Jones, Chief Executive Officer
CFO: Denise Welch, Chief Financial Officer
CMO: Ryan Oden, D.O., Chief of Staff
CIO: Tiffany Sands, Manager Health Information
CHR: Sallie Tomlinson, Manager Human Resources
CNO: Sarah Freehill, Chief Nursing Officer
Web address: www.arbucklehospital.com/
Control: County, Government, nonfederal **Service**: General medical and surgical

Staffed Beds: 13

TAHLEQUAH—Cherokee County

★ ⋔ **CHEROKEE NATION W.W. HASTINGS INDIAN HOSPITAL (370171)**, 100 South Bliss Avenue, Zip 74464–2512; tel. 918/458–3100, (Nonreporting) **A**3 10 21
Primary Contact: Brian Hail, Chief Executive Officer
COO: Mitchell Thornbrugh, Administrative Officer
CMO: Douglas Nolan, M.D., Medical Director
CIO: Mitchell Thornbrugh, Acting Chief Information Officer
CNO: Valerie J Rogers, Director of Nursing
Web address: www.cherokee.org
Control: Public Health Service other than 47, Government, federal **Service**: General medical and surgical

Staffed Beds: 58

★ **NORTHEASTERN HEALTH SYSTEM (370089)**, 1400 East Downing Street, Zip 74464–3324, Mailing Address: P.O. Box 1008, Zip 74465–1008; tel. 918/456–0641, (Nonreporting) **A**3 5 10 13 20
Primary Contact: James T. Berry, FACHE, Executive Vice President and Administrator
COO: Mark McCroskey, Vice President Operations
CFO: Julie Ward, Vice President Finance
CIO: Julie Ward, Vice President Finance
CHR: Phyllis Smith, Vice President Human Resources
CNO: Donna Dallis, R.N., Vice President Patient Care
Web address: www.nhs-ok.org/
Control: City, Government, nonfederal **Service**: General medical and surgical

Staffed Beds: 90

TALIHINA—Latimer County

⊞ **CHOCTAW NATION HEALTH CARE CENTER (370172)**, One Choctaw Way, Zip 74571–2022; tel. 918/567–7000, (Nonreporting) **A**1 10 13
Primary Contact: Todd Hallmark, Chief Executive Officer
COO: Todd Hallmark, Chief Operating Officer
CMO: Jason Hill, M.D., Chief Medical Officer
CIO: Dwane Sorrells, Chief Information Officer
CHR: Jami Beckwith, Director Human Resources
CNO: Lisa Isaac, Chief Nursing Officer
Web address: www.cnhsa.com
Control: Other not–for–profit (including NFP Corporation) **Service**: General medical and surgical

Staffed Beds: 44

TISHOMINGO—Johnston County

JOHNSTON MEMORIAL HOSPITAL See Mercy Hospital Tishomingo

★ **MERCY HOSPITAL TISHOMINGO (371304)**, 1000 South Byrd Street, Zip 73460–3299; tel. 580/371–2327, **A**10 18 **F**3 29 34 40 43 44 50 59 64 68 75 84 107 114 119 133 143 146 148 149 154 156 **S** Mercy, Chesterfield, MO
Primary Contact: Lori McMillin, Administrator
CFO: Lisa Dowling, Manager Finance
CHR: Arlita Hummelke, Manager Human Resources
Web address: www.mercy.net/
Control: Church operated, Nongovernment, not–for–profit **Service**: General medical and surgical

Staffed Beds: 12 Admissions: 260 Census: 5 Outpatient Visits: 5686 Births: 0 Total Expense ($000): 7470 Payroll Expense ($000): 4133 Personnel: 59

TULSA—Tulsa County

△ **BROOKHAVEN HOSPITAL (374012)**, 201 South Garnett Road, Zip 74128–1805; tel. 918/438–4257, **A**7 10 **F**4 5 29 30 54 64 74 75 77 98 101 102 104 106 130 132 154
Primary Contact: Rolf B. Gainer, Ph.D., Chief Executive Officer
CFO: Kenneth Pierce, Chief Financial Officer
CMO: Mark Gage, D.O., Medical Director
CHR: Heather Dudley, Director Administrative Services
CNO: Debbie Jones, Director of Nursing
Web address: www.brookhavenhospital.com
Control: Corporation, Investor–owned (for–profit) **Service**: Psychiatric

Staffed Beds: 64 Admissions: 745 Census: 49 Outpatient Visits: 1430 Births: 0 Total Expense ($000): 18715 Payroll Expense ($000): 7166 Personnel: 187

★ ⋔ **HILLCREST HOSPITAL - SOUTH (370202)**, 8801 South 101st East Avenue, Zip 74133–5716; tel. 918/294–4000, **A**10 21 **F**3 13 15 18 20 22 24 26 28 29 34 35 40 43 45 46 47 48 49 51 57 70 73 74 76 79 81 85 86 87 91 93 107 108 110 111 115 119 126 129 130 146 147 148 **S** Ardent Health Services, Nashville, TN
Primary Contact: Bennett Geister, Chief Executive Officer
COO: Matthew Morgan, Associate Administrator
CFO: James Washecka, Chief Financial Officer
CMO: David L. Pohl, M.D., Chief of Staff
CIO: David Graser, Vice President and Chief Information Officer
CHR: Rachel Steward, Director Human Resources
CNO: Dava Baldridge, R.N., Chief Nursing Officer
Web address: www.southcresthospital.com
Control: Corporation, Investor–owned (for–profit) **Service**: General medical and surgical

Staffed Beds: 164 Admissions: 9701 Census: 118 Outpatient Visits: 97259 Births: 1499 Total Expense ($000): 148467 Payroll Expense ($000): 47340 Personnel: 813

★ ⋔ **HILLCREST MEDICAL CENTER (370001)**, 1120 South Utica Avenue, Zip 74104–4090; tel. 918/579–1000, **A**3 5 10 19 21 **F**3 10 11 13 15 16 17 18 20 22 24 26 28 29 30 31 34 37 39 40 43 45 46 49 50 51 53 58 59 60 64 68 70 72 74 75 76 77 78 79 80 81 83 84 85 86 87 89 90 93 98 100 107 108 110 111 114 115 116 117 118 119 120 121 123 124 126 129 130 131 135 145 146 147 148 154 156 **S** Ardent Health Services, Nashville, TN
Primary Contact: Xavier Villarreal, FACHE, Chief Executive Officer
COO: Farron Sneed, Chief Operating Officer
CFO: Joseph Mendoza, Chief Financial Officer
CIO: Richard Gomez, Assistant Vice President Information Technology Division
CHR: Donald Morris, Vice President Human Resources
CNO: Jodi Simmons, Chief Nursing Officer
Web address: www.hillcrestmedicalcenter.com
Control: Corporation, Investor–owned (for–profit) **Service**: General medical and surgical

Staffed Beds: 510 Admissions: 24108 Census: 356 Outpatient Visits: 81204 Births: 2685 Total Expense ($000): 427384 Payroll Expense ($000): 125700 Personnel: 2097

⊞ **LAUREATE PSYCHIATRIC CLINIC AND HOSPITAL (374020)**, 6655 South Yale Avenue, Zip 74136–3329; tel. 918/481–4000, **A**1 3 5 10 **F**4 5 98 99 100 101 102 103 104 105 106 146 151 152 153 **S** Saint Francis Health System, Tulsa, OK
Primary Contact: Brandon Keppner, Administrator
CFO: Eric Schick, Senior Vice President, Chief Administrative Officer and Chief Financial Officer
CMO: Mark I Frost, M.D., Senior Vice President Medical Affairs
CNO: Lynn A. Sund, Senior Vice President, Administrator and Chief Nursing Executive
Web address: www.laureate.com
Control: Other not–for–profit (including NFP Corporation) **Service**: Psychiatric

Staffed Beds: 106 Admissions: 3526 Census: 80 Outpatient Visits: 11115 Births: 0 Total Expense ($000): 36129 Payroll Expense ($000): 21290 Personnel: 345

OK

MEADOWBROOK SPECIALTY HOSPITAL OF TULSA See Post Acute Medical Specialty Hospital of Tulsa

○ **OKLAHOMA STATE UNIVERSITY MEDICAL CENTER (370078)**, 744 West Ninth Street, Zip 74127–9020; tel. 918/599–1000, (Nonreporting) **A**3 5 10 11 12 13 19 **S** Saint Francis Health System, Tulsa, OK
Primary Contact: Matthew Adams, Administrator
COO: Jeff Stroup, Chief Operating Officer
CFO: Sara Bradley, Chief Financial Officer
CMO: Damon Baker, D.O., Chief Medical Officer
CIO: Heidi Holmes, Chief Information Officer
CNO: Joy Upshaw, Chief Nursing Officer
Web address: www.osumc.net
Control: City, Government, nonfederal **Service**: General medical and surgical

Staffed Beds: 191

○ **OKLAHOMA SURGICAL HOSPITAL (370210)**, 2408 East 81st Street, Suite 300, Zip 74137–4215; tel. 918/477–5000, **A**3 5 10 11 **F**3 12 18 20 22 24 26 29 30 34 37 40 44 45 49 50 51 57 58 64 65 68 70 74 75 77 79 81 82 85 86 87 93 94 107 108 111 115 118 119 120 121 126 129 130 131 148 149
Primary Contact: Rick Ferguson, Chief Executive Officer
CFO: Dub Cleland, Chief Financial Officer
Web address: www.oklahomasurgicalhospital.com
Control: Partnership, Investor–owned (for–profit) **Service**: Surgical

Staffed Beds: 55 Admissions: 4019 Census: 25 Outpatient Visits: 30869 Births: 0 Total Expense ($000): 111964 Payroll Expense ($000): 24926 Personnel: 449

☒ **PAM REHABILITATION HOSPITAL OF TULSA (373035)**, 10020 East 91st Street, Zip 74133; tel. 918/893–2400, (Nonreporting) **A**1 10 **S** Post Acute Medical, LLC, Enola, PA
Primary Contact: Thomas Biby, Chief Executive Officer
CNO: Angelia Sylsberry, Chief Nursing Officer
Web address: www.warmsprings.org/our-facilities/outpatient-rehabilitation
Control: Corporation, Investor–owned (for–profit) **Service**: Rehabilitation

Staffed Beds: 41

PARKSIDE PSYCHIATRIC HOSPITAL AND CLINIC (374021), 1619 East 13th Street, Zip 74120–5407; tel. 918/582–2131, **A**10 **F**3 4 5 29 31 35 38 40 41 44 50 56 57 59 64 87 98 99 100 101 102 103 104 106 130 132 143 146 149 151 153 154
Primary Contact: Debra Moore-Jones, Chief Executive Officer
CFO: Saunya Moore, Chief Financial Officer
CMO: Marvin Jin, M.D., Medical Director
CIO: Joe Vitali, Director Information Technology
CHR: David Patterson, Director Human Resources
Web address: www.parksideinc.org
Control: Other not–for–profit (including NFP Corporation) **Service**: Psychiatric

Staffed Beds: 71 Admissions: 2056 Census: 60 Outpatient Visits: 11308 Births: 0 Total Expense ($000): 15283 Payroll Expense ($000): 9263 Personnel: 178

☒ **POST ACUTE MEDICAL SPECIALTY HOSPITAL OF TULSA (372018)**, 3219 South 79th East Avenue, Zip 74145–1343; tel. 918/663–8183, (Nonreporting) **A**1 10 **S** Post Acute Medical, LLC, Enola, PA
Primary Contact: Ian Cooper, Chief Executive Officer
Web address: www.postacutetulsa.com
Control: Corporation, Investor–owned (for–profit) **Service**: Acute long–term care hospital

Staffed Beds: 60

SAINT FRANCIS HEART HOSPITAL See Saint Francis Hospital, Tulsa

☒ **SAINT FRANCIS HOSPITAL (370091)**, 6161 South Yale Avenue, Zip 74136–1902; tel. 918/494–2200, (Includes CHILDREN'S HOSPITAL AT SAINT FRANCIS, 6161 South Yale Avenue, Tulsa, Oklahoma, Zip 74136–1902; tel. 918/502–6714; Shannon M. Filosa, Executive Director Women's and Children; SAINT FRANCIS HEART HOSPITAL, 6151 South Yale Avenue, Tulsa, Oklahoma, Zip 74136–1902; tel. 918/494–1817; Douglas Williams, Vice President, Saint Francis Heart Hospital) **A**1 2 3 5 10 **F**3 7 8 11 12 13 15 17 18 19 20 21 22 23 24 25 26 27 28 29 30 31 32 35 37 39 40 41 43 44 45 46 47 48 49 50 51 54 55 56 57 58 59 60 61 64 66 68 70 72 73 74 75 76 77 78 79 80 81 82 83 84 85 86 87 88 89 90 92 93 100 102 107 108 110 111 114 115 116 117 118 119 120 121 123 124 126 129 130 131 132 135 136 138 141 146 147 148 154 **S** Saint Francis Health System, Tulsa, OK
Primary Contact: Douglas Williams, Senior Vice President, Administrator
COO: Barry L Steichen, Executive Vice President and Chief Operating Officer, Saint Francis Health System
CFO: Eric Schick, Senior Vice President and Chief Financial Officer, Saint Francis Health System
CMO: Mark I Frost, M.D., Senior Vice President Medical Affairs, Saint Francis Health System
CIO: Meridith Coburn, Vice President Information Services
CHR: Maria E. Isquierdo, Executive Director, Human Resources
CNO: Lynn A. Sund, Senior Vice President, Chief Nurse Executive, Saint Francis Health System and Administrator, Saint Francis Hospital
Web address: www.saintfrancis.com
Control: Other not–for–profit (including NFP Corporation) **Service**: General medical and surgical

Staffed Beds: 865 Admissions: 45460 Census: 642 Outpatient Visits: 456252 Births: 4201 Total Expense ($000): 864305 Payroll Expense ($000): 333264 Personnel: 4599

☒ **SAINT FRANCIS HOSPITAL SOUTH (370218)**, 10501 East 91st Street, Zip 74133–5790; tel. 918/307–6010, **A**1 10 **F**11 13 15 18 20 22 26 29 30 34 35 37 39 40 42 44 48 49 50 51 57 58 60 61 64 68 70 72 75 76 79 80 81 82 85 87 107 108 110 111 114 115 118 119 130 146 148 **S** Saint Francis Health System, Tulsa, OK
Primary Contact: David S. Weil, Senior Vice President and Administrator
COO: Barry L Steichen, Executive Vice President and Chief Operating Officer
CFO: Eric Schick, Chief Financial Officer
CMO: Mark I Frost, M.D., Senior Vice President Medical Affairs
CIO: Meridith Coburn, Vice President, Information Systems
CHR: Maria E. Isquierdo, Executive Director, Human Resources
CNO: Lynn A. Sund, Chief Nursing Executive
Web address: www.saintfrancis.com/south/
Control: Other not–for–profit (including NFP Corporation) **Service**: General medical and surgical

Staffed Beds: 90 Admissions: 5206 Census: 52 Outpatient Visits: 80510 Births: 907 Total Expense ($000): 75267 Payroll Expense ($000): 31866 Personnel: 371

☒ **SELECT SPECIALTY HOSPITAL-TULSA MIDTOWN (372007)**, 1125 South Trenton Avenue, 3rd Floor, Zip 74120–5418; tel. 918/579–7300, (Nonreporting) **A**1 10 **S** Select Medical Corporation, Mechanicsburg, PA
Primary Contact: Charles D. Nasem, FACHE, Chief Executive Officer
CMO: E Joe Schelbar, M.D., Medical Director
CNO: Connie Ryan, Chief Nursing Officer
Web address: www.tulsa.selectspecialtyhospitals.com/
Control: Corporation, Investor–owned (for–profit) **Service**: Acute long–term care hospital

Staffed Beds: 56

☐ **SOUTHWESTERN REGIONAL MEDICAL CENTER (370190)**, 10109 East 79th Street, Zip 74133–4564; tel. 918/286–5000, **A**1 2 3 10 13 **F**3 15 29 30 31 34 35 36 40 44 45 46 47 49 53 57 58 59 64 70 75 77 78 81 82 84 85 86 87 93 97 107 108 110 111 115 116 117 118 119 120 121 123 124 126 130 132 135 145 146 148 **S** Cancer Treatment Centers of America, Schaumburg, IL
Primary Contact: Jay Foley, President and Chief Executive Officer
CFO: David Hedges, Chief Financial Officer
CMO: Daniel Nader, D.O., Chief of Staff
CIO: Craig Olson, Director Information Technology
CHR: Ryan Crawford, Director Talent
CNO: Denise Geuder, Vice President Patient Care Service and Chief Nursing Officer
Web address: www.cancercenter.com
Control: Corporation, Investor–owned (for–profit) **Service**: Cancer

Staffed Beds: 40 Admissions: 726 Census: 12 Outpatient Visits: 45175 Births: 0 Personnel: 533

Hospital, Medicare Provider Number, Address, Telephone, Approval, Facility, and Physician Codes, Health Care System

★ American Hospital Association (AHA) membership ○ Healthcare Facilities Accreditation Program ⇧ Center for Improvement in Healthcare Quality Accreditation
☐ The Joint Commission accreditation ◇ DNV Healthcare Inc. accreditation △ Commission on Accreditation of Rehabilitation Facilities (CARF) accreditation

OK

⊞ **ST. JOHN MEDICAL CENTER (370114)**, 1923 South Utica Avenue, Zip 74104–6502; tel. 918/744–2345, **A**1 2 3 5 10 19 **F**3 8 9 11 12 13 14 15 17 18 19 20 22 24 26 28 29 30 31 34 35 37 38 39 40 43 45 46 47 48 49 50 51 53 54 56 57 58 59 60 61 63 64 65 66 68 70 72 73 74 75 76 77 78 79 80 81 82 83 84 85 86 87 88 89 90 92 93 94 96 97 100 104 107 108 110 111 114 115 116 117 118 119 120 121 123 124 126 129 130 131 132 135 138 141 143 145 146 147 148 149 154 156 **S** Ascension Healthcare, Saint Louis, MO
Primary Contact: Jeffrey D. Nowlin, President and Chief Operating Officer
COO: Jeffrey D. Nowlin, President and Chief Operating Officer
CFO: Wayne Walthall, Vice President and Chief Financial Officer
CMO: William Allred, M.D., Vice President Medical Affairs
CIO: Mike Reeves, Vice President
CHR: John Page Bachman, Corporate Vice President
CNO: Pamela Kiser, R.N., MS, Chief Nursing Executive and Vice President of Nursing
Web address: www.sjmc.org
Control: Church operated, Nongovernment, not–for–profit **Service**: General medical and surgical

Staffed Beds: 523 **Admissions**: 29028 **Census**: 420 **Outpatient Visits**: 236666 **Births**: 2249 **Total Expense ($000)**: 507605 **Payroll Expense ($000)**: 160517 **Personnel**: 2375

⊞ **TULSA SPINE AND SPECIALTY HOSPITAL (370216)**, 6901 South Olympia Avenue, Zip 74132–1843; tel. 918/388–5701, (Nonreporting) **A**1 3 10 **S** Ardent Health Services, Nashville, TN
Primary Contact: Trent Gastineau, Chief Executive Officer
CMO: David Fell, M.D., Chief Medical Officer
Web address: www.tulsaspinehospital.com
Control: Corporation, Investor–owned (for–profit) **Service**: General medical and surgical

Staffed Beds: 21

VINITA—Craig County

OKLAHOMA FORENSIC CENTER, 24800 South 4420 Road, Zip 74301–5544, Mailing Address: P.O. Box 69, Zip 74301–0069; tel. 918/256–7841, (Nonreporting) **A**3 **S** Oklahoma Department of Mental Health and Substance Abuse Services, Oklahoma City, OK
Primary Contact: Kevan Finley, Chief Executive Officer
CFO: Miriam Harris, Director Finance
CMO: Satwant Tandon, M.D., Director of Clinical Services
CIO: Kevin Marble, Director Information Technology
CHR: Julie Jacobs, Director Human Resources
CNO: Glenda Satterwhite, Director of Nursing
Web address: www.odmhsas.org
Control: State, Government, nonfederal **Service**: Psychiatric

Staffed Beds: 200

★ ⇑ **SAINT FRANCIS HOSPITAL VINITA (370237)**, 735 North Foreman Street, Zip 74301–1418, Mailing Address: P.O. Box 326, Zip 74301–0326; tel. 918/256–7551, **A**10 20 21 **F**3 11 15 18 29 30 34 35 36 40 45 50 53 57 59 68 74 75 77 79 80 82 86 87 93 94 98 100 102 103 104 107 108 111 114 115 119 127 129 130 133 143 146 147 148 154 **S** Saint Francis Health System, Tulsa, OK
Primary Contact: Todd Schuster, Administrator
CMO: Ed Allensworth, M.D., Medical Director
CHR: Darlene R Nolte, Chief Human Resource Officer
CNO: Ann Carr, R.N., Chief Nursing Officer
Web address: www.https://www.saintfrancis.com/vinita/Pages/default.aspx
Control: Other not–for–profit (including NFP Corporation) **Service**: General medical and surgical

Staffed Beds: 70 **Admissions**: 854 **Census**: 15 **Outpatient Visits**: 29321 **Births**: 0 **Total Expense ($000)**: 15435 **Payroll Expense ($000)**: 7051 **Personnel**: 106

WAGONER—Wagoner County

WAGONER COMMUNITY HOSPITAL (370166), 1200 West Cherokee Street, Zip 74467–4624, Mailing Address: P.O. Box 407, Zip 74477–0407; tel. 918/485–5514, **A**10 **F**3 11 15 18 28 29 30 34 39 40 41 45 50 51 57 59 60 64 65 68 70 75 79 81 82 85 87 93 97 98 102 107 108 110 111 115 118 119 129 130 131 132 135 146 147 148 149 154 156 157
Primary Contact: Jimmy Leopard, FACHE, Chief Executive Officer
COO: Louise Dodson, R.N., Chief Operating Officer and Chief Nursing Officer
CFO: Rebecca Sharp, Chief Financial Officer
CMO: Casey Hanna, M.D., Chief of Staff
CIO: Jim Riley, Director Information Technology
CHR: Barnetta Pofahl, Director Human Resources
CNO: Louise Dodson, R.N., Chief Nursing Officer
Web address: www.wagonerhospital.com
Control: Hospital district or authority, Government, nonfederal **Service**: General medical and surgical

Staffed Beds: 100 **Admissions**: 2330 **Census**: 35 **Outpatient Visits**: 30231 **Births**: 0 **Total Expense ($000)**: 21947 **Payroll Expense ($000)**: 9482 **Personnel**: 170

WATONGA—Blaine County

★ **MERCY HOSPITAL WATONGA (371302)**, 500 North Clarence Nash Boulevard, Zip 73772–2845, Mailing Address: P.O. Box 370, Zip 73772–0370; tel. 580/623–7211, **A**10 18 **F**3 11 29 30 34 40 43 50 57 59 64 68 75 85 87 93 107 114 119 128 130 132 133 135 149 154 **S** Mercy, Chesterfield, MO
Primary Contact: Bobby Stitt, R.N., Administrator
CHR: Mary Jo Messelt, Manager Human Resources
Web address: www.mercy.net/watongaok/practice/mercy-hospital-watonga
Control: Church operated, Nongovernment, not–for–profit **Service**: General medical and surgical

Staffed Beds: 25 **Admissions**: 195 **Census**: 3 **Outpatient Visits**: 9175 **Births**: 0 **Total Expense ($000)**: 6996 **Payroll Expense ($000)**: 3926 **Personnel**: 56

WAURIKA—Jefferson County

JEFFERSON COUNTY HOSPITAL (371311), Highway 70 and 81, Zip 73573–3075, Mailing Address: P.O. Box 90, Zip 73573–0090; tel. 580/228–2344, (Nonreporting) **A**10 18 **S** Duncan Regional Hospital, Duncan, OK
Primary Contact: Richard Gillespie, Chief Executive Officer
CFO: Richard Tallon, Chief Financial Officer
CMO: Rob Linzman, D.O., Chief of Staff
CIO: Nikki McGahey, Information Officer
Web address: www.jeffersoncountyhospital.net
Control: Hospital district or authority, Government, nonfederal **Service**: General medical and surgical

Staffed Beds: 25

WEATHERFORD—Custer County

★ **WEATHERFORD REGIONAL HOSPITAL (371323)**, 3701 East Main Street, Zip 73096–3309; tel. 580/772–5551, **A**10 18 **F**3 11 13 15 29 34 40 43 45 59 64 68 75 76 77 79 81 86 87 93 97 107 108 110 111 115 119 129 130 133 135 144 146 147 148 149
Primary Contact: Debbie Howe, Chief Executive Officer
CFO: Stephanie Helton, Chief Financial Officer
CMO: Jonathan Ray Long, M.D., Chief of Staff
CIO: Amy Outhier, Director Health Information Management
CHR: Tawnya Paden, Director Human Resources
CNO: Delvin Mast, R.N., Director of Nursing
Web address: www.weatherfordhospital.com
Control: Hospital district or authority, Government, nonfederal **Service**: General medical and surgical

Staffed Beds: 22 **Admissions**: 604 **Census**: 6 **Outpatient Visits**: 54472 **Births**: 133 **Total Expense ($000)**: 17140 **Payroll Expense ($000)**: 6860 **Personnel**: 142

WOODWARD—Woodward County

⊞ **ALLIANCEHEALTH WOODWARD (370002)**, 900 17th Street, Zip 73801–2448; tel. 580/256–5511, (Nonreporting) **A**1 10 20 **S** Community Health Systems, Inc., Franklin, TN
Primary Contact: Landon E. Hise, Interim Chief Executive Officer
CFO: Tom Earley, Chief Financial Officer
CIO: Larry Churchill, Director Information Services
CHR: Melinda Brock, Director Human Resources
CNO: Kimberly N Arnold, R.N., Chief Nursing Officer and Interim Chief Quality Officer
Web address: www.woodwardhospital.com
Control: Corporation, Investor–owned (for–profit) **Service**: General medical and surgical

Staffed Beds: 40

YUKON—Canadian County

⊞ **INTEGRIS CANADIAN VALLEY HOSPITAL (370211)**, 1201 Health Center Parkway, Zip 73099–6381; tel. 405/717–6800, **A**1 3 10 **F**3 11 13 15 18 20 22 29 30 39 40 43 44 45 46 49 52 57 60 64 68 70 76 77 79 81 85 87 93 96 107 108 110 111 115 118 119 130 135 146 147 156 **S** INTEGRIS Health, Oklahoma City, OK
Primary Contact: Teresa Gray, President
COO: Cindy White, CPA, Vice President of Operations
CFO: Errol Mitchell, Chief Financial Officer
CHR: Lynn Ketch, Human Resources Recruiter Generalist
Web address: www.integris-health.com
Control: Other not–for–profit (including NFP Corporation) **Service**: General medical and surgical

Staffed Beds: 59 **Admissions**: 3150 **Census**: 28 **Outpatient Visits**: 62205 **Births**: 761 **Total Expense ($000)**: 59315 **Payroll Expense ($000)**: 17505 **Personnel**: 250

Many Facility Codes have changed. Please refer to the AHA Guide Code Chart. © 2019 AHA Guide

OREGON

ALBANY—Linn County

★ ⸙ **SAMARITAN ALBANY GENERAL HOSPITAL (380022)**, 1046 Sixth Avenue, SW, Zip 97321–1999; tel. 541/812–4000, **A**3 10 21 **F**3 5 11 13 15 18 28 29 30 31 34 35 36 37 40 43 45 47 49 53 54 57 59 61 63 64 67 68 70 73 74 76 77 78 79 81 84 85 86 87 89 92 93 97 104 107 108 110 111 114 116 117 119 129 130 131 132 135 144 145 146 147 148 149 150 156 **S** Samaritan Health Services, Corvallis, OR
Primary Contact: David G. Triebes, Chief Executive Officer
CFO: Daniel B Smith, Vice President Finance
Web address: www.samhealth.org
Control: Other not-for-profit (including NFP Corporation) **Service**: General medical and surgical

Staffed Beds: 70 Admissions: 2557 Census: 22 Outpatient Visits: 303035 Births: 565 Total Expense ($000): 196699 Payroll Expense ($000): 80010 Personnel: 892

ASHLAND—Jackson County

★ ⸙ **ASANTE ASHLAND COMMUNITY HOSPITAL (380005)**, 280 Maple Street, Zip 97520–1593; tel. 541/201–4000, **A**10 21 **F**3 15 29 30 34 35 36 40 45 46 48 50 57 59 64 65 70 75 76 79 81 85 87 93 107 110 114 119 130 131 132 143 145 146 147 148 **S** Asante Health System, Medford, OR
Primary Contact: Sheila Clough, Chief Executive Officer
CFO: Patrick Hocking, Chief Financial Officer
CMO: Bill Steinsick, M.D., Chief Medical Staff
CIO: Mark Hetz, Chief Information Officer
CHR: Gregg Edwards, Vice President Human Resources
CNO: Susan Montgomery, Chief Nursing Officer
Web address: www.ashlandhospital.org
Control: Other not-for-profit (including NFP Corporation) **Service**: General medical and surgical

Staffed Beds: 38 Admissions: 1294 Census: 12 Outpatient Visits: 37855 Births: 261 Total Expense ($000): 50301 Payroll Expense ($000): 18831 Personnel: 225

ASTORIA—Clatsop County

★ ○ **COLUMBIA MEMORIAL HOSPITAL (381320)**, 2111 Exchange Street, Zip 97103–3329; tel. 503/325–4321, **A**3 5 10 11 18 **F**3 11 13 15 18 26 28 29 30 31 32 34 35 36 40 41 43 44 45 50 51 57 58 59 63 64 65 68 70 75 76 77 78 79 81 85 86 87 89 91 93 97 107 108 110 111 114 115 116 117 119 127 130 131 132 133 134 135 143 144 146 147 148 149 154
Primary Contact: Erik Thorsen, Chief Executive Officer
COO: Nicole Williams, Chief Operating Officer
CFO: Stephanie D Drenden, Vice President Finance
CMO: Bruce Bobek, President Professional Staff
CIO: Galina Gandy, Vice President Information Technology
CHR: Lucy G Dupree, Director Human Resources
CNO: Trece Gurrad, Vice President Patient Care Services
Web address: www.columbiamemorial.org
Control: Other not-for-profit (including NFP Corporation) **Service**: General medical and surgical

Staffed Beds: 25 Admissions: 1697 Census: 14 Outpatient Visits: 214920 Births: 311 Total Expense ($000): 121616 Payroll Expense ($000): 43807 Personnel: 648

BAKER CITY—Baker County

⊞ **SAINT ALPHONSUS MEDICAL CENTER - BAKER CITY (381315)**, 3325 Pocahontas Road, Zip 97814–1464; tel. 541/523–6461, **A**1 10 18 **F**3 11 13 15 29 30 31 34 35 37 40 43 44 45 50 59 64 68 70 75 76 77 78 79 81 82 83 85 91 93 97 107 110 111 115 119 127 128 129 131 133 143 146 147 148 154 **S** Trinity Health, Livonia, MI
Primary Contact: Priscilla Lynn, President
CFO: Robert D Wehling, Interim Chief Financial Officer
CHR: Jerry Nickell, Vice President Human Resource and Mission
Web address: www.https://www.saintalphonsus.org/bakercity
Control: Other not-for-profit (including NFP Corporation) **Service**: General medical and surgical

Staffed Beds: 25 Admissions: 828 Census: 7 Outpatient Visits: 40534 Births: 120 Total Expense ($000): 32239 Payroll Expense ($000): 14189 Personnel: 192

ST. ELIZABETH HEALTH SERVICES See Saint Alphonsus Medical Center - Baker City

BANDON—Coos County

★ **SOUTHERN COOS HOSPITAL AND HEALTH CENTER (381304)**, 900 11th Street SE, Zip 97411–9114; tel. 541/347–2426, **A**10 18 **F**3 11 15 29 34 35 40 45 50 57 59 64 65 75 81 82 85 87 97 107 110 111 115 119 130 132 133 135 146 148 149 154 156
Primary Contact: Amy Fine, Chief Executive Officer
CFO: Alan Dow, Chief Financial Officer
CMO: Megan Holland, Chief Medical Officer and Family Practitioner
CIO: Mandy Calvert, Director Information Systems
CHR: Kalen M Mills, Director Human Resources
CNO: Rachel Beissel, Chief Nursing Officer
Web address: www.southerncoos.org
Control: Hospital district or authority, Government, nonfederal **Service**: General medical and surgical

Staffed Beds: 19 Admissions: 303 Census: 3 Outpatient Visits: 67883 Births: 0 Total Expense ($000): 20347 Payroll Expense ($000): 8861 Personnel: 117

BEND—Deschutes County

⊞ **ST. CHARLES BEND (380047)**, 2500 NE Neff Road, Zip 97701–6015; tel. 541/382–4321, **A**1 2 3 5 10 19 **F**3 8 11 12 13 15 18 19 20 21 22 24 26 28 29 30 31 34 35 36 37 38 40 43 44 45 47 49 50 51 54 57 58 59 60 62 63 64 65 67 68 70 72 74 75 76 77 78 79 81 82 84 85 86 87 89 90 91 92 93 97 98 100 101 102 104 107 108 111 114 115 119 120 121 123 124 126 129 130 132 135 144 146 147 148 149 154 **S** St. Charles Health System, Inc., Bend, OR
Primary Contact: Aaron Adams, President
CFO: Jennifer Wolander, CPA, Senior Vice President Finance and Chief Financial Officer
CMO: Jeffrey Absalon, M.D., Chief Physician Officer
CIO: Jerimiah Brickhouse, Chief Information Officer
CHR: Rebecca Berry, Vice President Human Resources
Web address: www.stcharleshealthcare.org
Control: Other not-for-profit (including NFP Corporation) **Service**: General medical and surgical

Staffed Beds: 259 Admissions: 16499 Census: 178 Outpatient Visits: 155958 Births: 1685 Total Expense ($000): 340467 Payroll Expense ($000): 161682 Personnel: 3015

BURNS—Harney County

★ **HARNEY DISTRICT HOSPITAL (381307)**, 557 West Washington Street, Zip 97720–1497; tel. 541/573–7281, **A**10 18 **F**3 7 12 13 15 29 31 34 35 40 43 45 50 53 57 59 64 65 70 75 76 78 81 82 85 93 97 107 111 114 119 127 131 132 133 146 149 156
Primary Contact: Dan Grigg, Chief Executive Officer
CFO: Catherine White, Chief Financial Officer
CMO: Sarah Laiosa, M.D., Chief Medical Staff
CIO: Tanya Strong, Manager Information Technology
CHR: Sammie Masterson, Director Human Resources
CNO: Deana Altman, Interim Chief Nursing Officer
Web address: www.harneydh.com
Control: Hospital district or authority, Government, nonfederal **Service**: General medical and surgical

Staffed Beds: 21 Admissions: 342 Census: 2 Outpatient Visits: 33424 Births: 53 Total Expense ($000): 24933 Payroll Expense ($000): 11207 Personnel: 182

Hospital, Medicare Provider Number, Address, Telephone, Approval, Facility, and Physician Codes, Health Care System

★ American Hospital Association (AHA) membership
□ The Joint Commission accreditation
○ Healthcare Facilities Accreditation Program
◇ DNV Healthcare Inc. accreditation
⸙ Center for Improvement in Healthcare Quality Accreditation
△ Commission on Accreditation of Rehabilitation Facilities (CARF) accreditation

CLACKAMAS—Clackamas County

✉ ⇑ **KAISER SUNNYSIDE MEDICAL CENTER (380091)**, 10180 SE Sunnyside Road, Zip 97015–8970; tel. 503/652–2880, **A**1 2 3 5 10 21 **F**3 11 12 13 15 17 18 20 22 24 26 29 30 31 34 35 40 45 46 47 49 51 60 61 64 65 68 70 72 74 75 76 77 78 79 81 85 86 87 93 94 97 102 107 108 110 111 114 115 118 119 130 135 141 146 147 148 154 **S** Kaiser Foundation Hospitals, Oakland, CA
Primary Contact: Justin N. Evander, Administrator and Chief Operating Officer
CFO: Justin N. Evander, Chief Financial Officer
CMO: Richard Hunt, M.D., Chief Operating Officer
CIO: Mark A Burmester, Vice President Strategy and Communications
CHR: Rich Smith, Vice President Human Resources
CNO: Lauren M Bridge, R.N., Chief Nursing Officer
Web address: www.kaiserpermanente.org
Control: Other not–for–profit (including NFP Corporation) **Service:** General medical and surgical

Staffed Beds: 301 **Admissions:** 19863 **Census:** 199 **Outpatient Visits:** 72019 **Births:** 2395 **Total Expense ($000):** 400059 **Payroll Expense ($000):** 173811 **Personnel:** 2217

COOS BAY—Coos County

✉ **BAY AREA HOSPITAL (380090)**, 1775 Thompson Road, Zip 97420–2198; tel. 541/269–8111, **A**1 2 3 5 10 **F**3 11 12 13 15 18 20 22 26 28 29 31 34 35 40 43 45 46 48 50 51 57 59 62 68 70 73 74 75 76 77 78 79 81 84 85 89 91 92 93 98 100 101 102 107 108 110 111 115 118 119 120 121 123 126 129 130 132 135 146 147 148 149 156 157
Primary Contact: Brian Moore, President and Chief Executive Officer
COO: Ben Pfau, Chief Facility and Information Officer
CFO: Sam Patterson, Chief Financial Officer
CMO: Michael van Duren, M.D., Chief Medical Officer
CIO: Bob Adams, Director Information Services
CHR: Suzie Q McDaniel, Chief Human Resource Officer
Web address: www.bayareahospital.org
Control: Hospital district or authority, Government, nonfederal **Service:** General medical and surgical

Staffed Beds: 130 **Admissions:** 6211 **Census:** 65 **Outpatient Visits:** 97848 **Births:** 672 **Total Expense ($000):** 177236 **Payroll Expense ($000):** 69346 **Personnel:** 890

COQUILLE—Coos County

★ **COQUILLE VALLEY HOSPITAL (381312)**, 940 East Fifth Street, Zip 97423–1699; tel. 541/396–3101, **A**10 18 **F**11 15 29 30 34 40 43 57 68 77 79 81 107 108 111 114 119 133 135 146 148
Primary Contact: Jeff Lang, Chief Executive Officer
CFO: Robert E Fisher, Chief Financial Officer
CMO: James Sinnott, M.D., Chief Medical Staff
CIO: Curt Carpenter, Manager Information Technology
CHR: Monte Johnston, Manager Human Resources
Web address: www.cvhospital.org
Control: Hospital district or authority, Government, nonfederal **Service:** General medical and surgical

Staffed Beds: 17 **Admissions:** 571 **Census:** 7 **Outpatient Visits:** 29298 **Births:** 0 **Total Expense ($000):** 27158 **Payroll Expense ($000):** 12984 **Personnel:** 258

CORVALLIS—Benton County

★ ⇑ **GOOD SAMARITAN REGIONAL MEDICAL CENTER (380014)**, 3600 NW Samaritan Drive, Zip 97330–3737, Mailing Address: P.O. Box 1068, Zip 97339–1068; tel. 541/768–5111, **A**2 3 5 10 12 13 19 21 **F**3 11 12 13 15 17 18 20 22 24 26 28 29 30 31 34 35 36 37 40 43 53 54 56 57 58 59 61 62 64 68 70 71 73 74 76 77 78 79 81 82 85 86 87 89 92 93 97 98 100 101 102 104 107 108 110 111 114 115 116 117 118 119 120 121 123 124 126 130 131 132 135 144 146 147 148 149 153 154 156 **S** Samaritan Health Services, Corvallis, OR
Primary Contact: Becky A. Pape, R.N., Chief Executive Officer
CFO: Daniel B Smith, Vice President Finance
CIO: Bob Power, Vice President Information Services
CHR: Doug Boysen, Chief Legal Counsel and Vice President Human Resources
CNO: William Howden, Vice President Nursing
Web address: www.samhealth.org
Control: Other not–for–profit (including NFP Corporation) **Service:** General medical and surgical

Staffed Beds: 168 **Admissions:** 8182 **Census:** 109 **Outpatient Visits:** 440017 **Births:** 949 **Total Expense ($000):** 450168 **Payroll Expense ($000):** 174305 **Personnel:** 1863

COTTAGE GROVE—Lane County

★ **PEACEHEALTH COTTAGE GROVE COMMUNITY MEDICAL CENTER (381301)**, 1515 Village Drive, Zip 97424–9700; tel. 541/942–0511, **A**10 18 **F**3 11 15 29 30 34 35 40 59 64 65 93 97 100 107 110 115 119 127 130 132 133 146 148 149 154 **S** PeaceHealth, Vancouver, WA
Primary Contact: Tim Herrmann, R.N., Administrator
Control: Church operated, Nongovernment, not–for–profit **Service:** General medical and surgical

Staffed Beds: 14 **Admissions:** 381 **Census:** 4 **Outpatient Visits:** 37435 **Births:** 0 **Total Expense ($000):** 16499 **Payroll Expense ($000):** 6333 **Personnel:** 75

DALLAS—Polk County

SALEM HEALTH WEST VALLEY (381308), 525 SE Washington Street, Zip 97338–2834, Mailing Address: P.O. Box 378, Zip 97338–0378; tel. 503/623–8301, **A**10 18 **F**3 15 35 40 50 59 64 75 79 81 85 93 97 107 108 110 111 114 119 131 132 133 143 146 148 **S** Salem Health, Salem, OR
Primary Contact: Bruce C. Rodgers, Chief Administrative Officer
CFO: James Parr, Chief Financial Officer
CMO: Ralph Yates, D.O., Chief Medical Officer
CNO: Sarah Horn, Chief Nursing Officer
Web address: www.salemhealth.org/wvh/
Control: Other not–for–profit (including NFP Corporation) **Service:** General medical and surgical

Staffed Beds: 6 **Admissions:** 162 **Census:** 1 **Outpatient Visits:** 70957 **Births:** 0 **Total Expense ($000):** 26231 **Payroll Expense ($000):** 12187 **Personnel:** 130

ENTERPRISE—Wallowa County

★ ⇑ **WALLOWA MEMORIAL HOSPITAL (381306)**, 601 Medical Parkway, Zip 97828–5124; tel. 541/426–3111, **A**3 5 10 18 21 **F**3 7 10 11 13 15 29 30 31 34 35 40 43 45 46 56 57 59 64 68 75 76 77 78 79 81 82 85 87 93 97 102 107 110 115 119 127 128 131 132 133 134 135 143 145 148 149
Primary Contact: Larry Davy, Chief Executive Officer
CFO: Daniel Jessup, Chief Financial Officer
CMO: Keith DeYoung, M.D., Chief Medical Staff
CIO: John Straughan, Director Information Technology
CHR: Linda Childers, Director Human Resources
CNO: Jenni Word, R.N., Chief Nursing Officer
Web address: www.wchcd.org
Control: Hospital district or authority, Government, nonfederal **Service:** General medical and surgical

Staffed Beds: 25 **Admissions:** 563 **Census:** 7 **Outpatient Visits:** 33670 **Births:** 42 **Total Expense ($000):** 22401 **Payroll Expense ($000):** 9818 **Personnel:** 148

EUGENE—Lane County

★ △ ⇑ **PEACEHEALTH SACRED HEART MEDICAL CENTER UNIVERSITY DISTRICT (380033)**, 1255 Hilyard Street, Zip 97401–3700, Mailing Address: P.O. Box 10905, Zip 97440–2905; tel. 541/686–7300, **A**5 7 10 21 **F**3 29 30 31 38 40 43 56 62 63 68 84 90 93 98 102 105 107 115 130 146 148 153 154 **S** PeaceHealth, Vancouver, WA
Primary Contact: Mary Anne McMurren, R.N., Chief Administrative Officer
CFO: Wendy Apland, Interim Chief Financial Officer
CMO: Bill Moshofsky, M.D., Chief of Staff
CIO: Donn McMillan, Chief Information Officer
CHR: Craig Mills, Vice President Human Resources
Web address: www.peacehealth.org
Control: Church operated, Nongovernment, not–for–profit **Service:** General medical and surgical

Staffed Beds: 93 **Admissions:** 2834 **Census:** 63 **Outpatient Visits:** 48174 **Births:** 0 **Total Expense ($000):** 116491 **Payroll Expense ($000):** 48071 **Personnel:** 506

FLORENCE—Lane County

★ ⇑ **PEACEHEALTH PEACE HARBOR MEDICAL CENTER (381316)**, 400 Ninth Street, Zip 97439–7398; tel. 541/997–8412, **A**10 18 21 **F**3 8 13 15 18 28 29 30 34 38 40 43 45 50 57 59 62 63 68 70 75 76 79 81 82 84 93 97 100 104 107 110 111 115 118 119 130 133 135 144 147 148 149 154 156 **S** PeaceHealth, Vancouver, WA
Primary Contact: Jason F. Hawkins, Chief Administrative Officer
CMO: Ron Shearer, M.D., Regional Medical Director
CIO: Ginni Boughal, Director Health Information and Information Technology
CHR: Don Bourland, Vice President Human Resources
Web address: www.peacehealth.org
Control: Church operated, Nongovernment, not–for–profit **Service:** General medical and surgical

Staffed Beds: 21 **Admissions:** 1061 **Census:** 10 **Outpatient Visits:** 54253 **Births:** 61 **Personnel:** 413

Many Facility Codes have changed. Please refer to the AHA Guide Code Chart. © 2019 AHA Guide

FOREST GROVE—Washington County

TUALITY FOREST GROVE HOSPITAL See Tuality Healthcare, Hillsboro

GOLD BEACH—Curry County

★ ⮝ **CURRY GENERAL HOSPITAL (381322)**, 94220 Fourth Street, Zip 97444–7756; tel. 541/247–3000, **A**10 18 21 **F**3 11 15 18 28 29 34 40 43 50 51 54 59 64 75 79 81 82 85 87 90 97 107 110 111 114 119 127 128 130 133 135 144 148 149
Primary Contact: Virginia Razo, Chief Executive Officer
CFO: Carl Gerlach, Chief Financial Officer
CMO: Reginald Williams, M.D., Medical Staff President
CIO: Kristina Martin, Chief Information Officer
Web address: www.curryhealthnetwork.com
Control: Hospital district or authority, Government, nonfederal **Service**: General medical and surgical

Staffed Beds: 18 **Admissions**: 526 **Census**: 6 **Outpatient Visits**: 108021 **Births**: 0 **Total Expense ($000)**: 44467 **Payroll Expense ($000)**: 22693 **Personnel**: 274

GRANTS PASS—Josephine County

★ ⮝ **ASANTE THREE RIVERS MEDICAL CENTER (380002)**, 500 SW Ramsey Avenue, Zip 97527–5554; tel. 541/472–7000, **A**3 10 21 **F**3 11 13 15 28 29 30 31 34 35 36 40 43 45 46 48 49 50 53 54 57 59 64 65 70 75 76 78 79 81 85 87 93 94 107 108 110 111 114 115 118 119 120 129 130 132 143 144 145 146 147 148 154 **S** Asante Health System, Medford, OR
Primary Contact: Win Howard, Chief Executive Officer
COO: David Kinyon, Vice President of Operations and Outpatient Services
CFO: Patrick Hocking, Chief Financial Officer
CMO: Eric Loeliger, Vice President of Medical Affairs
CIO: Mark Hetz, Chief Information Officer
CHR: Gregg Edwards, Chief People Officer
Web address: www.asante.org/trmc/
Control: Other not-for-profit (including NFP Corporation) **Service**: General medical and surgical

Staffed Beds: 121 **Admissions**: 7294 **Census**: 72 **Outpatient Visits**: 291130 **Births**: 776 **Total Expense ($000)**: 172303 **Payroll Expense ($000)**: 65857 **Personnel**: 893

GRESHAM—Multnomah County

✉ **LEGACY MOUNT HOOD MEDICAL CENTER (380025)**, 24800 SE Stark, Zip 97030–3378; tel 503/667–1122, **A**1 2 10 **F**3 11 13 15 18 20 26 28 29 30 31 32 34 35 38 40 44 45 46 48 49 50 51 57 59 60 64 68 70 74 75 76 77 78 79 81 85 86 87 93 100 101 102 107 108 110 111 114 115 118 119 120 121 123 126 129 130 132 146 147 148 149 156 **S** Legacy Health, Portland, OR
Primary Contact: Gretchen Nichols, R N, President
COO: Michael Newcomb, D.O., Senior Vice President and Chief Operating Officer
CFO: Linda Hoff, Senior Vice President and Chief Financial Officer
CMO: Lewis Low, M.D., Chief Medical Officer
CIO: John Jay Kenagy, Ph.D., Senior Vice President and Chief Information Officer
CHR: Sonja Steves, Senior Vice President Human Resources
CNO: Marcia Soderling, R.N., Hospital Nurse Executive
Web address: www.legacyhealth.org
Control: Other not-for-profit (including NFP Corporation) **Service**: General medical and surgical

Staffed Beds: 98 **Admissions**: 5928 **Census**: 61 **Outpatient Visits**: 166049 **Births**: 871 **Total Expense ($000)**: 144684 **Payroll Expense ($000)**: 55711 **Personnel**: 601

HEPPNER—Morrow County

PIONEER MEMORIAL HOSPITAL (381310), 564 East Pioneer Drive, Zip 97836–7318, Mailing Address: P.O. Box 9, Zip 97836–0009; tel. 541/676–9133, **A**10 18 **F**3 7 17 34 35 40 43 45 50 57 59 62 63 64 66 68 75 81 97 107 119 127 133 135 146 147 148 154
Primary Contact: Robert Houser, FACHE, Chief Executive Officer
CFO: Nicole Mahoney, Chief Financial Officer
CIO: Shawn Cutsforth, Information Systems Officer
CHR: Patti Allstott, Administrative Coordinator Human Resources and Grant Writer
Web address: www.morrowcountyhealthdistrict.org
Control: Hospital district or authority, Government, nonfederal **Service**: General medical and surgical

Staffed Beds: 21 **Admissions**: 107 **Census**: 7 **Outpatient Visits**: 6261 **Births**: 0 **Total Expense ($000)**: 12298 **Payroll Expense ($000)**: 6507 **Personnel**: 109

HERMISTON—Umatilla County

★ ⮝ **GOOD SHEPHERD HEALTH CARE SYSTEM (381325)**, 610 NW 11th Street, Zip 97838–6601; tel. 541/667–3400, **A**5 10 18 21 **F**3 11 13 15 28 29 30 33 34 35 40 43 45 46 50 53 54 57 59 62 63 64 65 68 70 75 79 81 85 86 87 97 107 108 110 111 115 119 126 127 132 133 135 143 144 146 147 148 149 154 156
Primary Contact: Dennis E. Burke, President and Chief Executive Officer
COO: Jim Schlenker, Chief Operating Officer
CFO: Jan D Peter, Vice President Fiscal Services and Chief Financial Officer
CMO: Thomas Holt, M.D., Medical Staff President
CIO: Rob Rizk, Director Information Technology
CHR: Kelly B. Sanders, Vice President Human Resources
CNO: Theresa Brock, Vice President Nursing
Web address: www.gshealth.org
Control: Other not-for-profit (including NFP Corporation) **Service**: General medical and surgical

Staffed Beds: 25 **Admissions**: 1578 **Census**: 12 **Outpatient Visits**: 67381 **Births**: 400 **Total Expense ($000)**: 80698 **Payroll Expense ($000)**: 34265 **Personnel**: 651

HILLSBORO—Washington County

✉ **KAISER WESTSIDE MEDICAL CENTER (380103)**, 2875 NE Stucki Avenue, Zip 97124–5806; tel. 971/310–1000, **A**1 10 **F**3 13 15 29 30 31 34 35 40 45 46 47 49 51 59 60 61 64 65 68 70 74 75 76 77 79 81 85 86 87 93 94 96 97 102 107 108 110 111 115 118 119 126 130 135 141 146 147 148 149 154 **S** Kaiser Foundation Hospitals, Oakland, CA
Primary Contact: Brantley Dettmer, Administrator and Chief Operating Officer
CMO: Carol Unitan, M.D., Chief Medical Officer
CIO: Charles Stearns, Area Information Officer
CHR: Rich Smith, Vice President Human Resources
CNO: Janet Lee Reeder, MSN, Chief Nurse Executive
Web address: www.kp.org
Control: Other not-for-profit (including NFP Corporation) **Service**: General medical and surgical

Staffed Beds: 122 **Admissions**: 8674 **Census**: 69 **Outpatient Visits**: 47114 **Births**: 1531 **Total Expense ($000)**: 169085 **Payroll Expense ($000)**: 72936 **Personnel**: 883

✉ **TUALITY HEALTHCARE (380021)**, 335 SE Eighth Avenue, Zip 97123–4246; tel. 503/681–1111, (Includes TUALITY COMMUNITY HOSPITAL, 335 SE Eighth Avenue, Hillsboro, Oregon, Zip 97123, Mailing Address: P O Box 309, Zip 97123, tel. 503/681–1111; Manuel S Berman, FACHE, President and Chief Executive Officer; TUALITY FOREST GROVE HOSPITAL, 1809 Maple Street, Forest Grove, Oregon, Zip 97116–1995; tel. 503/357–2173; Manuel S Berman, FACHE, President and Chief Executive Officer) **A**1 3 5 10 **F**3 11 13 15 18 20 22 24 26 28 29 30 31 32 34 35 40 44 45 47 49 50 53 54 56 57 59 62 64 68 70 71 74 75 77 78 79 80 81 82 85 86 87 92 93 97 98 100 103 104 107 108 110 111 114 115 118 119 126 129 130 131 132 135 143 144 145 146 147 148
Primary Contact: Lori James-Nielsen, President
COO: Steven P Krautscheid, Ancillary Services Administrator
CFO: Tim Fleischmann, Chief Financial Officer
CMO: Joe Hardman, M.D., Chief Medical Officer
CHR: Cheryl Gebhart, Chief Human Resources Officer
Web address: www.tuality.org
Control: Other not-for-profit (including NFP Corporation) **Service**: General medical and surgical

Staffed Beds: 122 **Admissions**: 4670 **Census**: 55 **Outpatient Visits**: 229603 **Births**: 619 **Total Expense ($000)**: 194070 **Payroll Expense ($000)**: 86997 **Personnel**: 983

HOOD RIVER—Hood River County

✉ **PROVIDENCE HOOD RIVER MEMORIAL HOSPITAL (381318)**, 810 12th Street, Zip 97031–1587, Mailing Address: P.O. Box 149, Zip 97031–0055; tel. 541/386–3911, **A**1 3 10 18 **F**3 5 9 10 11 12 13 15 18 28 29 30 31 34 35 36 40 43 45 47 48 53 54 56 57 59 60 64 65 68 70 75 76 77 78 79 81 82 84 85 86 89 90 92 97 100 101 102 104 107 108 110 111 114 118 119 125 130 131 132 133 134 135 143 146 147 148 149 154 156 **S** Providence St. Joseph Health, Renton, WA
Primary Contact: Jeanette Vieira, Chief Executive
CHR: Jami McCaslin, Director Human Resources
Web address: www.providence.org/hoodriver
Control: Church operated, Nongovernment, not-for-profit **Service**: General medical and surgical

Staffed Beds: 25 **Admissions**: 1569 **Census**: 11 **Outpatient Visits**: 173261 **Births**: 430 **Total Expense ($000)**: 99442 **Payroll Expense ($000)**: 32762 **Personnel**: 421

OR

Hospital, Medicare Provider Number, Address, Telephone, Approval, Facility, and Physician Codes, Health Care System

★ American Hospital Association (AHA) membership ○ Healthcare Facilities Accreditation Program ⮝ Center for Improvement in Healthcare Quality Accreditation
☐ The Joint Commission accreditation ◇ DNV Healthcare Inc. accreditation △ Commission on Accreditation of Rehabilitation Facilities (CARF) accreditation

JOHN DAY—Grant County

★ **BLUE MOUNTAIN HOSPITAL DISTRICT (381305)**, 170 Ford Road, Zip 97845–2009; tel. 541/575–1311, (Total facility includes 40 beds in nursing home–type unit) **A**3 5 10 18 **F**1 3 4 7 8 11 13 15 16 17 29 30 34 35 36 40 41 43 45 50 57 59 62 63 64 65 67 68 70 72 73 75 76 77 80 81 82 85 86 87 88 89 90 93 97 98 107 110 111 114 116 117 127 128 130 132 133 134 135 143 145 146 148 149 155 156 158 **S** HealthTech Management Services, Brentwood, TN
Primary Contact: Derek Daly, Chief Executive Officer
CMO: Keith Thomas, M.D., Chief of Staff
CIO: Sean Tsao, Director Information Technology
CHR: Verlene Davis, Director Human Resources
CNO: Les McLeod, Director of Nursing Services
Web address: www.bluemountainhospital.org
Control: Hospital district or authority, Government, nonfederal **Service**: General medical and surgical

Staffed Beds: 62 **Admissions:** 410 **Census:** 22 **Outpatient Visits:** 22511
Births: 34 **Total Expense ($000):** 26008 **Payroll Expense ($000):** 13271
Personnel: 261

KLAMATH FALLS—Klamath County

★ ⇑ **SKY LAKES MEDICAL CENTER (380050)**, 2865 Daggett Avenue, Zip 97601–1106; tel. 541/882–6311, **A**2 3 5 10 21 **F**3 8 11 13 15 18 20 22 29 31 34 35 37 40 43 44 45 46 47 48 50 51 53 54 56 57 59 61 62 64 68 70 71 75 76 77 78 79 81 84 85 86 87 92 93 94 96 97 100 102 107 108 110 111 114 115 116 117 118 119 120 121 123 130 131 132 134 135 141 142 143 144 145 146 147 148 149 156 157
Primary Contact: Paul R. Stewart, President and Chief Executive Officer
CFO: Richard Rico, Vice President and Chief Financial Officer
CMO: Grant Niskanen, M.D., Vice President Medical Affairs
CHR: Don York, Vice President and Chief Human Resource Officer
CNO: Annette E. Cole, R.N., MSN, Vice President and Chief Nursing Officer
Web address: www.skylakes.org
Control: Other not–for–profit (including NFP Corporation) **Service**: General medical and surgical

Staffed Beds: 105 **Admissions:** 5071 **Census:** 49 **Outpatient Visits:** 268985 **Births:** 732 **Total Expense ($000):** 243654 **Payroll Expense ($000):** 93185 **Personnel:** 1267

LA GRANDE—Union County

✉ **GRANDE RONDE HOSPITAL (381321)**, 900 Sunset Drive, Zip 97850–1387, Mailing Address: P.O. Box 3290, Zip 97850–7290; tel. 541/963–8421, **A**1 5 10 18 **F**3 8 11 13 15 17 18 29 30 31 34 35 37 39 40 41 44 45 50 54 59 62 63 64 66 70 74 75 76 78 79 81 82 84 85 86 87 89 91 92 93 96 97 107 108 110 111 114 115 118 119 127 128 129 130 131 132 133 135 144 146 147 148 149 154
Primary Contact: Jeremy P. Davis, President and Chief Executive Officer
CFO: Robert Seymour, Chief Financial Officer/Senior Director Finance
CMO: Mary Porter, M.D., Medical Staff President
CIO: Parhez Sattar, Senior Director Information Technology
CHR: Kristi Puckett, Director Human Resources
CNO: Douglas Romer, Executive Director Patient Care Services
Web address: www.grh.org
Control: Other not–for–profit (including NFP Corporation) **Service**: General medical and surgical

Staffed Beds: 25 **Admissions:** 1572 **Census:** 11 **Outpatient Visits:** 120804
Births: 258 **Total Expense ($000):** 102622 **Payroll Expense ($000):** 53920
Personnel: 636

LAKEVIEW—Lake County

★ **LAKE DISTRICT HOSPITAL (381309)**, 700 South 'J' Street, Zip 97630–1679; tel. 541/947–2114, **A**5 10 18 **F**3 13 15 29 30 31 32 34 35 37 40 45 46 57 59 62 63 64 68 75 76 77 78 79 81 82 84 85 87 90 93 97 107 111 115 119 127 129 130 132 133 134 135 146 148 149
Primary Contact: Charles B. Tveit, Chief Executive Officer
CFO: Cheryl J Cornwell, Chief Financial Officer
CMO: Stephen Hussey, M.D., Chief of Staff
CIO: Steven Vance, Information Technology Director
CHR: Lesley Hanson, Director Human Resources
CNO: Teresa Squires, R.N., Chief Nursing Officer
Web address: www.lakehealthdistrict.org
Control: Hospital district or authority, Government, nonfederal **Service**: General medical and surgical

Staffed Beds: 24 **Admissions:** 378 **Census:** 3 **Outpatient Visits:** 53967
Births: 51 **Total Expense ($000):** 28334 **Payroll Expense ($000):** 13547
Personnel: 266

LEBANON—Linn County

★ ⇑ **SAMARITAN LEBANON COMMUNITY HOSPITAL (381323)**, 525 North Santiam Highway, Zip 97355–4363, Mailing Address: P.O. Box 739, Zip 97355–0739; tel. 541/258–2101, **A**3 10 18 21 **F**3 10 11 13 15 28 29 30 31 34 35 40 43 44 45 46 47 53 59 64 68 70 75 76 78 79 81 85 86 87 89 92 93 97 107 108 110 111 114 116 117 118 119 125 127 130 131 132 135 144 146 147 148 149 156 **S** Samaritan Health Services, Corvallis, OR
Primary Contact: Marty Cahill, Chief Executive Officer
CFO: Daniel B Smith, Vice President Finance
CMO: Alan Blake, M.D., President Medical Staff
CIO: Robert Power, Vice President Information Services
CHR: Connie Erwin, Manager
CNO: Wendie Wunderwald, R.N., Vice President Patient Care Services
Web address: www.samhealth.org
Control: Other not–for–profit (including NFP Corporation) **Service**: General medical and surgical

Staffed Beds: 25 **Admissions:** 1524 **Census:** 16 **Outpatient Visits:** 235638
Births: 306 **Total Expense ($000):** 131223 **Payroll Expense ($000):** 54542
Personnel: 651

LINCOLN CITY—Lincoln County

★ ⇑ **SAMARITAN NORTH LINCOLN HOSPITAL (381302)**, 3043 NE 28th Street, Zip 97367–4518, Mailing Address: P.O. Box 767, Zip 97367–0767; tel. 541/994–3661, **A**3 5 10 18 21 **F**3 8 11 13 15 26 29 30 31 34 35 40 43 44 45 51 57 58 59 62 63 64 65 68 70 75 76 77 78 79 81 85 87 93 97 104 107 108 110 111 115 116 117 118 119 127 130 132 133 135 144 146 147 148 149 156 **S** Samaritan Health Services, Corvallis, OR
Primary Contact: Lesley Ogden, M.D., Chief Executive Officer
CFO: Kathryn Doksum, Director Finance
CMO: Raj Baman, D.O., President Medical Staff
CHR: Gina Tapp, Director Human Resources
CNO: Virginia Riffle, Vice President Patient Care Services
Web address: www.samhealth.org
Control: Other not–for–profit (including NFP Corporation) **Service**: General medical and surgical

Staffed Beds: 25 **Admissions:** 951 **Census:** 11 **Outpatient Visits:** 107370
Births: 102 **Total Expense ($000):** 65359 **Payroll Expense ($000):** 30190
Personnel: 318

MADRAS—Jefferson County

★ **ST. CHARLES MADRAS (381324)**, 470 NE 'A' Street, Zip 97741–1844; tel. 541/475–3882, **A**10 18 **F**3 13 15 29 34 35 40 43 45 57 59 62 63 64 70 75 76 77 81 83 84 85 89 90 93 97 107 110 115 119 130 132 133 135 156 **S** St. Charles Health System, Inc., Bend, OR
Primary Contact: David Golda, Administrator and Vice President
Web address: www.stcharleshealthcare.org/Our-Locations/Madras
Control: Other not–for–profit (including NFP Corporation) **Service**: General medical and surgical

Staffed Beds: 25 **Admissions:** 698 **Census:** 8 **Outpatient Visits:** 24142
Births: 149 **Total Expense ($000):** 23558 **Payroll Expense ($000):** 14519
Personnel: 142

MCMINNVILLE—Yamhill County

✉ **WILLAMETTE VALLEY MEDICAL CENTER (380071)**, 2700 SE Stratus Avenue, Zip 97128–6255; tel. 503/472–6131, **A**1 2 3 10 **F**3 11 12 13 15 18 20 24 26 27 28 29 30 31 34 35 40 41 43 45 46 48 50 51 56 57 58 59 60 64 65 70 74 75 76 78 79 80 81 82 84 85 86 87 91 92 93 98 103 107 108 110 111 114 115 118 119 120 123 124 130 131 132 135 146 147 148 154 156 **S** LifePoint Health, Brentwood, TN
Primary Contact: Peter A. Hofstetter, Chief Executive Officer
CFO: Meredith Nelson, Chief Financial Officer
CMO: Jeanne Savage, M.D., Chief Medical Officer
CIO: Diane Farrow, Manager Information Technology and Systems
CHR: Lisa Clark, Director Human Resources
CNO: Connie Pullen, R.N., Chief Nursing Officer
Web address: www.willamettevalleymedical.com/
Control: Corporation, Investor–owned (for–profit) **Service**: General medical and surgical

Staffed Beds: 60 **Admissions:** 3523 **Census:** 37 **Outpatient Visits:** 115059
Births: 427 **Total Expense ($000):** 87725 **Payroll Expense ($000):** 33180
Personnel: 523

Many Facility Codes have changed. Please refer to the AHA Guide Code Chart. © 2019 AHA Guide

OR

MEDFORD—Jackson County

★ ⇑ **ASANTE ROGUE REGIONAL MEDICAL CENTER (380018)**, 2825 East Barnett Road, Zip 97504–8332; tel. 541/789–7000, **A**2 3 10 19 21 **F**3 11 12 13 15 17 18 20 22 24 26 28 29 30 31 32 34 35 36 37 40 43 45 46 48 49 50 57 58 59 60 63 64 65 70 72 74 75 76 78 79 81 85 86 87 89 90 93 94 96 98 100 101 102 107 108 110 111 112 115 119 120 121 122 126 129 130 132 143 145 146 147 148 154 **S** Asante Health System, Medford, OR
Primary Contact: Mick Zdeblick, Chief Executive Officer
COO: Kristi Blackhurst, Interim Vice President Operations
CFO: Patrick Hocking, Chief Financial Officer
CMO: Jamie Grebosky, M.D., Vice President of Medical Affairs
CIO: Mark Hetz, Chief Information Officer
CHR: Gregg Edwards, Chief People Officer
Web address: www.asante.org
Control: Other not–for–profit (Including NFP Corporation) **Service:** General medical and surgical

Staffed Beds: 337 **Admissions:** 16121 **Census:** 235 **Outpatient Visits:** 507519 **Births:** 1576 **Total Expense ($000):** 502061 **Payroll Expense ($000):** 165499 **Personnel:** 2281

⊞ **PROVIDENCE MEDFORD MEDICAL CENTER (380075)**, 1111 Crater Lake Avenue, Zip 97504–6241; tel. 541/732–5000, **A**1 2 10 19 **F**3 11 13 15 18 19 20 21 22 28 29 30 31 32 34 35 40 43 45 49 50 55 56 57 59 61 64 68 70 74 75 76 77 78 79 81 82 84 85 86 87 90 91 92 93 96 97 102 107 110 114 115 118 119 120 121 123 124 126 129 130 131 132 146 147 148 **S** Providence St. Joseph Health, Renton, WA
Primary Contact: Tom Lorish, M.D., Interim Chief Executive
COO: Chris Pizzi, Chief Operating Officer and Chief Financial Officer
CFO: Chris Pizzi, Chief Operating Officer and Chief Financial Officer
CHR: Julie Levison, Director Human Resources
CNO: Sherri Steele, Chief Nursing Officer
Web address: www.providence.org
Control: Church operated, Nongovernment, not–for–profit **Service:** General medical and surgical

Staffed Beds: 138 **Admissions:** 6429 **Census:** 73 **Outpatient Visits:** 368502 **Births:** 479 **Total Expense ($000):** 249709 **Payroll Expense ($000):** 69352 **Personnel:** 961

MILWAUKIE—Clackamas County

⊞ **PROVIDENCE MILWAUKIE HOSPITAL (380082)**, 10150 SE 32nd Avenue, Zip 97222–6516; tel. 503/513–8300, **A**1 3 5 10 **F**3 15 18 29 30 34 35 36 40 44 45 46 50 53 54 56 57 59 63 64 68 70 71 74 75 77 79 81 82 84 85 87 91 92 93 97 98 100 102 103 104 107 108 110 111 114 115 119 129 130 131 132 133 135 146 147 148 154 **S** Providence St. Joseph Health, Renton, WA
Primary Contact: Keith Hyde, Chief Executive
COO: Sherri Paris, Chief Operating Officer
CFO: Sheila Waldron, Finance Manager
CHR: Julie Smith, Senior Human Resources Strategic Partner
CNO: Lisa Halvorsen, Chief Nurse Executive
Web address: www.providence.org
Control: Church operated, Nongovernment, not–for–profit **Service:** General medical and surgical

Staffed Beds: 60 **Admissions:** 2760 **Census:** 41 **Outpatient Visits:** 272490 **Births:** 0 **Total Expense ($000):** 117522 **Payroll Expense ($000):** 40234 **Personnel:** 494

NEWBERG—Yamhill County

⊞ **PROVIDENCE NEWBERG MEDICAL CENTER (380037)**, 1001 Providence Drive, Zip 97132–7485; tel. 503/537–1555, **A**1 10 **F**3 11 13 15 18 20 29 30 34 35 40 45 46 47 49 50 51 57 59 60 64 68 70 74 75 76 77 79 81 84 85 87 92 93 100 107 108 110 111 114 118 119 129 130 132 135 146 147 148 149 **S** Providence St. Joseph Health, Renton, WA
Primary Contact: Lorinda Van Zanten, MSN, Chief Executive
CFO: Jack R Sumner, Assistant Administrator Finance
CMO: George Weghorst, M.D., Chief Medical Officer
CIO: Laureen O'Brien, Chief Information Officer
CHR: Cheryl Gebhart, Director Human Resources Providence Health Plan and Providence Medical Group
Web address: www.phsor.org
Control: Church operated, Nongovernment, not–for–profit **Service:** General medical and surgical

Staffed Beds: 40 **Admissions:** 2387 **Census:** 22 **Outpatient Visits:** 248443 **Births:** 495 **Total Expense ($000):** 112435 **Payroll Expense ($000):** 32911 **Personnel:** 397

NEWPORT—Lincoln County

★ ⇑ **SAMARITAN PACIFIC COMMUNITIES HOSPITAL (381314)**, 930 SW Abbey Street, Zip 97365–4820, Mailing Address: P.O. Box 945, Zip 97365–0072; tel. 541/265–2244, **A**10 18 21 **F**3 8 11 13 15 26 28 29 30 31 34 35 40 43 44 45 47 53 54 59 62 63 64 65 68 70 75 76 77 78 79 81 82 85 86 87 92 93 97 107 110 111 114 119 127 129 130 132 133 135 144 146 147 148 149 156 **S** Samaritan Health Services, Corvallis, OR
Primary Contact: Lesley Ogden, M.D., Chief Executive Officer
CFO: Daniel B Smith, Chief Financial Officer
CIO: Robert Power, Chief Information Officer
CHR: Gina Tapp, Director Human Resources
CNO: Lorie Williams, R.N., Vice President Nursing
Web address: www.samhealth.org
Control: Other not–for–profit (including NFP Corporation) **Service:** General medical and surgical

Staffed Beds: 25 **Admissions:** 1167 **Census:** 11 **Outpatient Visits:** 149833 **Births:** 184 **Total Expense ($000):** 98338 **Payroll Expense ($000):** 39158 **Personnel:** 406

ONTARIO—Malheur County

HOLY ROSARY MEDICAL CENTER See Saint Alphonsus Medical Center - Ontario

⊞ **SAINT ALPHONSUS MEDICAL CENTER - ONTARIO (380052)**, 351 SW Ninth Street, Zip 97914–2693; tel. 541/881–7000, **A**1 3 10 20 **F**3 11 13 15 28 29 30 31 34 35 39 40 42 43 44 45 46 50 54 56 57 59 64 65 68 70 75 76 77 78 79 81 83 85 87 93 97 107 108 110 111 114 118 119 127 129 130 131 132 135 144 146 147 148 149 154 **S** Trinity Health, Livonia, MI
Primary Contact: Kenneth Hart, President
CFO: Lannie Checketts, Chief Financial Officer
CMO: Paul Gering, M.D., Vice President Medical Affairs
CHR: Stefanie Thiel, Senior Human Resources Business Partner
Web address: www.saintalphonsus.org/ontario
Control: Other not–for–profit (including NFP Corporation) **Service:** General medical and surgical

Staffed Beds: 37 **Admissions:** 2082 **Census:** 15 **Outpatient Visits:** 72596 **Births:** 438 **Total Expense ($000):** 76051 **Payroll Expense ($000):** 25687 **Personnel:** 396

OREGON CITY—Clackamas County

⊞ **PROVIDENCE WILLAMETTE FALLS MEDICAL CENTER (380038)**, 1500 Division Street, Zip 97045–1597; tel. 503/656–1631, **A**1 10 **F**13 15 29 30 34 35 36 40 44 45 46 50 53 54 57 59 63 64 68 70 74 75 76 77 78 79 81 82 84 85 87 91 92 93 97 98 100 107 108 111 114 119 130 131 132 133 135 146 147 **S** Providence St. Joseph Health, Renton, WA
Primary Contact: Russ Reinhard, Chief Executive
COO: Patricia A Markesino, FACHE, Chief Nurse Executive and Chief Operating Officer
CFO: Elizabeth Oublette, Director Finance
CMO: James Watkins, M.D., President Medical Staff
CHR: Joann M Pfister, Director Human Resources
CNO: Jessica Bailey-Oetker, Director Quality and Medical Staff
Web address: www.providence.org/pwfmc
Control: Church operated, Nongovernment, not–for–profit **Service:** General medical and surgical

Staffed Beds: 111 **Admissions:** 4178 **Census:** 45 **Outpatient Visits:** 184059 **Births:** 861 **Total Expense ($000):** 135878 **Payroll Expense ($000):** 44095 **Personnel:** 509

PENDLETON—Umatilla County

⊞ **CHI ST. ANTHONY HOSPITAL (381319)**, 2801 St Anthony Way, Zip 97801–3800; tel. 541/276–5121, **A**1 10 18 **F**3 11 13 15 18 29 30 31 35 40 43 45 50 53 54 57 59 64 65 68 70 75 77 78 79 81 85 86 87 91 93 97 107 108 110 111 114 118 119 127 129 130 131 132 133 134 135 146 147 148 149 156 157 **S** CommonSpirit Health, Chicago, IL
Primary Contact: Harold S. Geller, Chief Executive Officer
CFO: Scott Attridge, Chief Financial Officer
CMO: John McBee, Chief of Staff
CHR: Janeen K. Reding, Ed.D., Market Vice President of Human Resources
CNO: Joyce Bailey, Vice President Patient Care
Web address: www.sahpendleton.org
Control: Church operated, Nongovernment, not–for–profit **Service:** General medical and surgical

Staffed Beds: 25 **Admissions:** 1464 **Census:** 13 **Outpatient Visits:** 70597 **Births:** 326 **Total Expense ($000):** 67173 **Payroll Expense ($000):** 25617 **Personnel:** 272

Hospital, Medicare Provider Number, Address, Telephone, Approval, Facility, and Physician Codes, Health Care System

★ American Hospital Association (AHA) membership ◯ Healthcare Facilities Accreditation Program ⇑ Center for Improvement in Healthcare Quality Accreditation
☐ The Joint Commission accreditation ◇ DNV Healthcare Inc. accreditation △ Commission on Accreditation of Rehabilitation Facilities (CARF) accreditation

PORTLAND—Multnomah County

ADVENTIST HEALTH PORTLAND (380060), 10123 SE Market Street, Zip 97216–2599; tel. 503/257–2500, **A**1 2 5 10 **F**3 9 11 13 15 17 18 20 22 24 26 28 29 30 31 34 35 36 37 40 44 45 46 49 53 54 57 58 59 64 68 70 71 74 75 76 77 78 79 81 82 84 85 86 93 97 100 102 104 105 107 108 110 111 114 115 117 118 119 120 121 123 126 129 130 131 132 135 143 144 146 147 148 149 153 154 157 **S** Adventist Health, Roseville, CA
Primary Contact: David Russell, President and Chief Executive Officer
CFO: V Mark Perry, Chief Financial Officer
CMO: Wesley E Rippey, M.D., Chief Medical Officer
CHR: Shane Voshell, Director Human Resources
CNO: Ellen Tryon, R.N., Chief Nursing Officer
Web address: www.adventisthealthnw.com
Control: Church operated, Nongovernment, not–for–profit **Service**: General medical and surgical

Staffed Beds: 169 Admissions: 9489 Census: 83 Outpatient Visits: 482066 Births: 783 Total Expense ($000): 342935 Payroll Expense ($000): 127957 Personnel: 1464

GOOD SAMARITAN HOSPITAL AND MEDICAL CENTER See Legacy Good Samaritan Medical Center, Portland

△ **LEGACY EMANUEL MEDICAL CENTER (380007)**, 2801 North Gantenbein Avenue, Zip 97227–1674; tel. 503/413–2200, (Includes RANDALL CHILDREN'S HOSPITAL, 2801 North Gantenbein Avenue, Portland, Oregon, Zip 97227–1623; tel. 503/413–2200) **A**1 2 3 5 7 8 10 **F**3 7 11 13 15 16 17 18 19 20 21 22 23 24 25 26 27 29 30 31 32 34 35 37 38 39 40 41 43 44 45 46 47 48 49 50 51 54 55 56 57 59 60 61 64 65 66 68 72 74 75 76 77 78 79 80 81 83 84 85 86 87 88 89 91 93 97 98 99 100 101 102 103 107 108 110 111 114 115 118 119 126 127 130 131 132 135 144 146 147 148 149 154 **S** Legacy Health, Portland, OR
Primary Contact: Trent Green, President
CHR: Sonja Steves, Senior Vice President Human Resources and Marketing
Web address: www.legacyhealth.org
Control: Other not–for–profit (including NFP Corporation) **Service**: General medical and surgical

Staffed Beds: 532 Admissions: 21017 Census: 394 Outpatient Visits: 428127 Births: 1850 Total Expense ($000): 939194 Payroll Expense ($000): 457422 Personnel: 3466

LEGACY GOOD SAMARITAN MEDICAL CENTER (380017), 1015 NW 22nd Avenue, Zip 97210–3099; tel. 503/413–7711, (Includes GOOD SAMARITAN HOSPITAL AND MEDICAL CENTER, 1015 NW 22nd Avenue, Portland, Oregon, Zip 97210; tel. 503/229–7711; REHABILITATION INSTITUTE OF OREGON, 2010 NW Kearney Street, Portland, Oregon, Zip 97209; tel. 503/226–3774) **A**1 2 3 5 10 **F**3 8 11 12 15 18 20 22 26 28 29 30 31 34 35 38 40 44 45 46 47 48 49 50 51 55 56 57 58 59 60 61 64 65 69 70 71 74 75 76 77 78 79 80 81 82 83 84 85 86 87 90 91 93 94 95 96 97 107 108 110 111 114 115 116 117 118 119 120 121 123 124 126 129 130 132 135 138 142 143 144 145 146 147 148 149 154 **S** Legacy Health, Portland, OR
Primary Contact: Jonathan Avery, Chief Administrative Officer
CIO: C Matthew Calais, Senior Vice President and Chief Information Officer
CHR: Sonja Steves, Vice President Marketing
CNO: Cindy Evans, R.N., MS, Chief Nursing Officer
Web address: www.legacyhealth.org
Control: Other not–for–profit (including NFP Corporation) **Service**: General medical and surgical

Staffed Beds: 222 Admissions: 9817 Census: 136 Outpatient Visits: 195482 Births: 1035 Total Expense ($000): 321798 Payroll Expense ($000): 123946 Personnel: 1316

★ ⇑ **OHSU HOSPITAL (380009)**, 3181 SW Sam Jackson Park Road, Zip 97239–3098; tel. 503/494–8311, (Includes DOERNBECHER CHILDREN'S HOSPITAL, 700 SW Campus Drive, Portland, Oregon, Zip 97239; tel. 503/494–8811; Timothy Goldfarb, Interim Chief Executive Officer) **A**2 3 5 8 10 21 **F**3 6 8 9 12 13 15 17 18 19 20 21 22 23 24 25 26 27 28 29 30 31 32 33 34 35 36 37 38 39 40 41 43 44 45 46 47 48 49 50 51 52 53 54 55 56 57 58 59 60 61 64 66 67 68 70 71 72 74 75 76 77 78 79 81 82 84 85 86 87 88 89 90 91 92 93 95 96 97 100 101 104 107 108 109 110 111 112 114 115 116 117 118 119 120 121 123 124 126 127 129 130 131 132 134 135 136 137 138 139 141 142 145 146 147 148 149 153 154 156
Primary Contact: John G. Hunter, M.D., FACS, Chief Executive Officer
COO: Joe Ness, Chief Operating Officer
CFO: Diana Gernhart, Senior Vice President and Hospital Chief Financial Officer
CMO: Michael Bonazzola, M.D., Interim Chief Medical Officer
CIO: Bridget Barnes, Vice President and Chief Information Officer
CHR: Dan Forbes, Vice President Human Resources
CNO: Dana Bjarnason, Ph.D., R.N., Vice President and Chief Nursing Officer
Web address: www.ohsu.edu
Control: Hospital district or authority, Government, nonfederal **Service**: General medical and surgical

Staffed Beds: 556 Admissions: 29213 Census: 463 Outpatient Visits: 955857 Births: 2264 Total Expense ($000): 1604129 Payroll Expense ($000): 603976 Personnel: 7978

PROVIDENCE PORTLAND MEDICAL CENTER (380061), 4805 NE Glisan Street, Zip 97213–2933; tel. 503/215–5526, **A**1 2 3 5 10 **F**3 5 13 15 18 20 22 24 26 29 30 31 34 35 36 37 38 40 44 45 46 49 50 51 54 55 56 57 58 59 60 61 64 66 68 70 72 74 75 76 77 78 79 81 82 84 85 86 87 90 92 93 98 100 101 102 104 105 106 107 108 109 110 111 114 116 117 118 119 121 123 124 126 129 130 131 132 133 135 136 145 146 147 148 153 154 156 **S** Providence St. Joseph Health, Renton, WA
Primary Contact: Krista Farnham, Chief Executive
COO: Kendall Sawa, R.N., Chief Operating Officer
CFO: Eric Olson, Chief Financial Officer
CMO: Robert Wells, M.D., Chief Medical Officer
CIO: Mark Premo, Senior Director HC Intelligence
CHR: Jeannie Mikulic, Director Human Resources
Web address: www.providence.org
Control: Church operated, Nongovernment, not–for–profit **Service**: General medical and surgical

Staffed Beds: 407 Admissions: 19813 Census: 301 Outpatient Visits: 1413014 Births: 2889 Total Expense ($000): 873016 Payroll Expense ($000): 248294 Personnel: 2979

REHABILITATION INSTITUTE OF OREGON See Legacy Good Samaritan Medical Center, Portland

☐ **SHRINERS HOSPITALS FOR CHILDREN-PORTLAND (383300)**, 3101 SW Sam Jackson Park Road, Zip 97239–3009; tel. 503/241–5090, **A**1 3 5 10 **F**3 29 34 35 37 50 58 64 68 75 77 79 81 85 86 87 91 93 94 130 131 132 134 146 148 **S** Shriners Hospitals for Children, Tampa, FL
Primary Contact: Dereesa Reid, Administrator
CFO: Mark Knudsen, Director Fiscal Services
CMO: Michael Aiona, M.D., Chief of Staff
CIO: Carl Montante, Director Information Systems and Information Technology
CHR: Rhonda Smith, Director Human Resources
CNO: Suzanne Diers, R.N., Director Patient Care Services
Web address: www.shrinershospitalsforchildren.org/portland
Control: Other not–for–profit (including NFP Corporation) **Service**: Children's general medical and surgical

Staffed Beds: 12 Admissions: 317 Census: 6 Outpatient Visits: 15180 Births: 0 Total Expense ($000): 43482 Payroll Expense ($000): 24549 Personnel: 263

VA PORTLAND HEALTHCARE SYSTEM, 3710 SW U S Veterans Hospital Road, Zip 97239–2964, Mailing Address: 3710 SW US Veterans Hospital Road, Zip 97207–1034; tel. 503/220–8262, (Nonreporting) **A**1 2 3 5 8 **S** Department of Veterans Affairs, Washington, DC
Primary Contact: Michael W. Fisher, Director
CFO: Josh Wiseman, Chief Financial Officer
CMO: Sahana Misra, Acting Chief of Staff
CHR: Karla Azcuy, Acting Chief Human Resources Officer
CNO: Kathleen Chapman Esq Deputy Director, Patient Care Services
Web address: www.portland.va.gov/
Control: Veterans Affairs, Government, federal **Service**: General medical and surgical

Staffed Beds: 176

VETERANS AFFAIRS MEDICAL CENTER See Va Portland Healthcare System

VIBRA SPECIALTY HOSPITAL OF PORTLAND (382004), 10300 NE Hancock Street, Zip 97220–3831; tel. 503/257–5500, (Nonreporting) **A**1 10 **S** Vibra Healthcare, Mechanicsburg, PA
Primary Contact: Victor Jackson, Chief Executive Officer
CFO: Stephanie Lawrence, Chief Financial Officer
CMO: Cynthia Wallace, M.D., Medical Director
CIO: Marie Roof, Executive Vice President Information Systems
CHR: Kellie Bernert-Yap, Director Human Resources
CNO: Susan E Brooker, R.N., Chief Clinical Officer
Web address: www.vshportland.com
Control: Corporation, Investor–owned (for–profit) **Service**: Acute long–term care hospital

Staffed Beds: 68

PORTLAND—Washington County

☐ **CEDAR HILLS HOSPITAL (384012)**, 10300 SW Eastridge Street, Zip 97225–5004; tel. 503/944–5000, (Nonreporting) **A**1 10 **S** Universal Health Services, Inc., King of Prussia, PA
Primary Contact: Elizabeth Hutter, Chief Executive Officer
Web address: www.cedarhillshospital.com
Control: Corporation, Investor–owned (for–profit) **Service**: Psychiatric

Staffed Beds: 78

Many Facility Codes have changed. Please refer to the AHA Guide Code Chart. © 2019 AHA Guide

OR

PORTLAND—Washington County

☒ **PROVIDENCE ST. VINCENT MEDICAL CENTER (380004)**, 9205 SW Barnes Road, Zip 97225–6661; tel. 503/216–1234, (Includes CHILDREN AI PROVIDENCE ST. VINCENT, 9205 SW Barnes Road, Portland, Oregon, Zip 97225–6603; tel. 503/216–4400) **A**1 2 3 5 10 **F**3 5 13 15 17 18 20 22 24 26 28 29 30 31 34 35 36 37 38 40 41 44 45 46 47 48 49 50 53 54 56 57 58 59 60 61 64 65 70 72 74 75 76 77 78 79 81 82 84 85 86 87 88 89 91 92 93 97 98 100 102 104 105 106 107 108 109 110 111 112 114 115 116 117 118 119 120 121 123 126 129 130 131 132 135 146 147 148 149 153 156 **S** Providence St. Joseph Health, Renton, WA
Primary Contact: Janice Burger, Chief Executive
COO: Nancy Roberts, Chief Operating Officer
CFO: Scott Pfister, Director Finance
Web address: www.providence.org/portland/hospitals
Control: Church operated, Nongovernment, not–for–profit **Service**: General medical and surgical

Staffed Beds: 528 Admissions: 24190 Census: 326 Outpatient Visits: 949978 Births: 3643 Total Expense ($000): 877580 Payroll Expense ($000): 256759 Personnel: 3055

PRINEVILLE—Crook County

★ **ST. CHARLES PRINEVILLE (381313)**, 384 SE Combs Flat Road, Zip 97754–1206; tel. 541/447–6254, **A**10 18 **F**3 11 15 29 30 34 35 40 43 45 50 59 64 65 75 77 79 80 81 82 84 85 86 87 89 93 97 107 110 115 119 127 130 132 133 **S** St. Charles Health System, Inc., Bend, OR
Primary Contact: Todd Shields, Administrator
CFO: Karen Shepard, Senior Vice President and Chief Financial Officer
CMO: Michel Boileau, M.D., Chief Clinical Officer
CHR: Rebecca Berry, Senior Director Human Resources
Web address: www.stcharleshealthcare.org
Control: Other not–for–profit (including NFP Corporation) **Service**: General medical and surgical

Staffed Beds: 20 Admissions: 625 Census: 7 Outpatient Visits: 42405 Births: 0 Total Expense ($000): 22586 Payroll Expense ($000): 13638 Personnel: 156

REDMOND—Deschutes County

☒ **ST. CHARLES REDMOND (380040)**, 1253 NW Canal Boulevard, Zip 97766–1395; tel. 541/548–8131, **A**1 10 20 **F**3 11 13 15 18 20 22 24 26 28 29 30 31 32 34 35 37 38 40 44 45 46 47 48 49 50 51 53 59 64 65 68 70 75 76 77 78 79 81 84 85 87 97 107 111 115 119 130 132 135 146 147 149 154 156 **S** St. Charles Health System, Inc., Bend, OR
Primary Contact: Aaron Adams, President
CFO: Jennifer Welander, CPA, Senior Vice President Finance and Chief Financial Officer
CMO: Jeffrey Absalon, M.D., Chief Physician Officer
CIO: Jerimiah Brickhouse, Chief Information Officer
CHR: Rebecca Berry, Vice President Human Resources
Web address: www.stcharleshealthcare.org
Control: Other not–for–profit (including NFP Corporation) **Service**: General medical and surgical

Staffed Beds: 48 Admissions: 2750 Census: 23 Outpatient Visits: 54408 Births: 495 Total Expense ($000): 55930 Payroll Expense ($000): 34326 Personnel: 412

REEDSPORT—Douglas County

LOWER UMPQUA HOSPITAL DISTRICT (381311), 600 Ranch Road, Zip 97467–1795; tel. 541/271–2171, **A**5 10 18 **F**3 7 11 15 29 34 35 40 43 45 46 50 57 59 64 65 70 75 77 79 81 82 85 87 93 97 104 107 108 115 119 127 130 131 132 133 135 143 144 148 153
Primary Contact: Ryan Fowler, Chief Administrative Officer
CMO: Ronald Vail, M.D., Chief of Staff
CIO: Timothy Picou, Manager Information Technology
Web address: www.lowerumpquahospital.com
Control: Hospital district or authority, Government, nonfederal **Service**: General medical and surgical

Staffed Beds: 20 Admissions: 430 Census: 5 Outpatient Visits: 18987 Births: 0 Total Expense ($000): 27355 Payroll Expense ($000): 10750 Personnel: 166

ROSEBURG—Douglas County

☒ **MERCY MEDICAL CENTER (380027)**, 2700 Stewart Parkway, Zip 97471–1281; tel. 541/673–0611, **A**1 3 10 **F**3 8 11 13 15 17 18 19 20 22 24 26 28 29 30 31 35 37 40 43 45 47 50 51 56 57 59 60 62 63 70 73 76 81 84 85 87 89 93 102 107 108 110 111 115 118 119 126 129 130 146 148 149 154 **S** CommonSpirit Health, Chicago, IL
Primary Contact: Kelly C. Morgan, President and Chief Executive Officer
COO: Debbie Boswell, Chief Operating Officer and Chief Nursing Officer
CFO: Grant L Glines, Vice President Operation Finance
CMO: Jason Gray, M.D., Chief Medical Officer
CIO: Kathleen Nickel, Director Communications
CHR: Debora Lightcap, Director Human Resources
CNO: Debbie Boswell, Chief Operating Officer and Chief Nursing Officer
Web address: www.mercyrose.org
Control: Church operated, Nongovernment, not–for–profit **Service**: General medical and surgical

Staffed Beds: 140 Admissions: 7037 Census: 71 Outpatient Visits: 428620 Births: 895 Total Expense ($000): 175361 Payroll Expense ($000): 64535 Personnel: 824

☒ **VETERANS AFFAIRS ROSEBURG HEALTHCARE SYSTEM**, 913 NW Garden Valley Boulevard, Zip 97471–6513; tel. 541/440–1000, (Nonreporting) **A**1 3 10 **S** Department of Veterans Affairs, Washington, DC
Primary Contact: Douglas V. Paxton, Director
CHR: Larry Mentzer, Chief Human Resources Officer
CNO: Tracy Weistreich, Ph.D., R.N., Associate Director Patient Care Services/ Nurse Executive
Web address: www.roseburg.va.gov/
Control: Veterans Affairs, Government, federal **Service**: General medical and surgical

Staffed Beds: 88

SALEM—Marion County

☐ **OREGON STATE HOSPITAL (384008)**, 2600 Center Street NE, Zip 97301–2682; tel. 503/945–2870, (Nonreporting) **A**1 3 5 10
Primary Contact: Dolly Matteucci, Superintendent
Web address: www.oregon.gov/OHA/amh/osh/
Control: State, Government, nonfederal **Service**: Psychiatric

Staffed Beds: 669

☒ **SALEM HOSPITAL (380051)**, 890 Oak Street SE, Zip 97301–3959, Mailing Address: P.O. Box 14001, Zip 97309–5014; tel. 503/561–5200, (Includes PSYCHIATRIC MEDICINE CENTER, 1127 Oak Street SE, Salem, Oregon, Zip 97301, Mailing Address: P O Box 14001, Zip 97309–5014, tel. 503/561–5761; SALEM HEALTH REHABILITATION CENTER, 755 Mission St SE, Salem, Oregon, Zip 97301, Mailing Address: P O Box 14001, Zip 97309–5014, tel. 503/561–5986) **A**1 2 10 **F**3 11 12 13 15 17 18 20 22 24 26 28 29 30 31 34 35 36 37 38 40 43 44 45 46 47 48 49 50 53 54 55 56 57 58 59 64 67 68 70 72 74 75 76 77 78 79 81 82 84 85 86 87 89 90 91 92 93 94 95 96 97 98 102 105 106 107 108 109 110 111 112 113 114 115 116 117 118 119 120 121 122 123 124 126 129 130 131 132 135 144 145 146 147 148 156 **S** Salem Health, Salem, OR
Primary Contact: Cheryl R. Nester Wolfe, President and Chief Executive Officer
COO: Bahaa Wanly, Interim Chief Operating Officer
CFO: James Parr, Chief Financial Officer
CMO: Ralph Yates, D.O., Chief Medical Officer
CIO: Leah Mitchell, R.N., Interim Chief Information Officer
CNO: Sarah Horn, Chief Nursing Officer
Web address: www.salemhealth.org
Control: Other not–for–profit (including NFP Corporation) **Service**: General medical and surgical

Staffed Beds: 441 Admissions: 26392 Census: 323 Outpatient Visits: 425680 Births: 3443 Total Expense ($000): 721754 Payroll Expense ($000): 325532 Personnel: 3724

OR

Hospital, Medicare Provider Number, Address, Telephone, Approval, Facility, and Physician Codes, Health Care System

★ American Hospital Association (AHA) membership
☐ The Joint Commission accreditation
○ Healthcare Facilities Accreditation Program
◇ DNV Healthcare Inc. accreditation
⇑ Center for Improvement in Healthcare Quality Accreditation
△ Commission on Accreditation of Rehabilitation Facilities (CARF) accreditation

© 2019 AHA Guide   *Many Facility Codes have changed. Please refer to the AHA Guide Code Chart.*   Hospitals **A517**

OR

SEASIDE—Clatsop County

☒ **PROVIDENCE SEASIDE HOSPITAL (381303)**, 725 South Wahanna Road,
Zip 97138–7735; tel. 503/717–7000, **A**1 10 18 **F**3 12 13 15 18 29 30 31 32
34 35 40 45 46 56 57 59 61 64 65 66 70 75 76 78 79 81 82 83 84 85 86 87
91 92 93 97 107 108 110 111 114 119 127 130 132 133 135 143 146 147
148 149 154 **S** Providence St. Joseph Health, Renton, WA
Primary Contact: Don Lemmon, Chief Executive Officer
COO: Janiece Zauner, Chief Operating Officer
CFO: Pamela Cooper, Director Finance
CMO: Julie Paquette, M.D., Chief Medical Officer
CHR: John Anglim, Human Resources Client Manager
CNO: Janiece Zauner, Chief Nursing Officer
Web address: www.providence.org
Control: Church operated, Nongovernment, not–for–profit **Service**: General
medical and surgical

Staffed Beds: 25 **Admissions**: 821 **Census**: 9 **Outpatient Visits**: 158581
Births: 95 **Total Expense ($000)**: 73847 **Payroll Expense ($000)**: 30891
Personnel: 345

SILVERTON—Marion County

☒ **LEGACY SILVERTON MEDICAL CENTER (380029)**, 139 Breyonna Way,
Zip 97381, Mailing Address: 342 Fairview Street, Zip 97381–1993; tel. 503/873–
1500, **A**1 5 10 **F**3 11 13 15 28 29 30 34 35 40 43 45 47 50 54 59 64 65 68
70 75 76 77 79 81 85 86 87 93 96 107 108 110 111 114 115 119 124 127
130 131 132 135 143 144 146 147 148 149 154 **S** Legacy Health, Portland, OR
Primary Contact: Sarah Fronza, President
COO: Karen Brady, R.N., MSN, Vice President, Chief Nursing Officer
CFO: Daniel Jessup, Chief Financial Officer
CMO: Joseph Huang, M.D., Chief Medical and Quality Officer
CIO: Karen Brady, R.N., MSN, Vice President, Chief Nursing Officer
CHR: Natalie Britton, Manager Employee Relations
CNO: Karen Brady, R.N., MSN, Vice President, Chief Nursing Officer
Web address: www.legacyhealth.org/locations/hospitals/legacy-silverton-medical-
center.aspx
Control: Other not–for–profit (including NFP Corporation) **Service**: General
medical and surgical

Staffed Beds: 47 **Admissions**: 3129 **Census**: 23 **Outpatient Visits**: 242823
Births: 1192 **Total Expense ($000)**: 143418 **Payroll Expense**
($000): 49583 **Personnel**: 545

SPRINGFIELD—Lane County

☒ **MCKENZIE-WILLAMETTE MEDICAL CENTER (380020)**, 1460 'G' Street,
Zip 97477–4197; tel. 541/726–4400, **A**1 10 **F**3 11 13 18 20 22 24 26 28 29
34 35 39 40 41 43 45 46 47 49 50 57 59 70 73 79 81 82 85 87 107 108 111
115 118 119 126 130 132 146 147 148 154 **S** Quorum Health, Brentwood, TN
Primary Contact: David Elgarico, Chief Executive Officer
CFO: Rosanne Devault, Chief Financial Officer
CIO: David Blomquist, Director Information Technology
CHR: Megan A O'Leary, Vice President Human Resources and Rehabilitation
Services
Web address: www.mckweb.com
Control: Corporation, Investor–owned (for–profit) **Service**: General medical and
surgical

Staffed Beds: 112 **Admissions**: 8468 **Census**: 77 **Outpatient Visits**: 94953
Births: 1243 **Total Expense ($000)**: 198389 **Payroll Expense**
($000): 71697 **Personnel**: 777

★ ⇑ **PEACEHEALTH SACRED HEART MEDICAL CENTER AT RIVERBEND**
(380102), 3333 Riverbend Drive, Zip 97477–8800; tel. 541/222–7300, **A**10 21
F3 11 12 13 19 20 21 22 24 26 28 29 30 31 37 38 40 43 45 46 47 48 49 51
53 57 58 59 60 68 70 72 74 75 76 77 78 79 81 84 85 89 107 108 111 112
114 115 118 119 124 126 129 130 132 135 145 146 147 148 149 154 **S**
PeaceHealth, Vancouver, WA
Primary Contact: Mary E. Kingston, FACHE, R.N., Chief Executive
COO: Shannon Surber, Chief Operating Officer
CHR: Marie F Stehmer, Senior Director of Human Resources
CNO: Heather Wall, Chief Nursing Officer
Web address: www.peacehealth.org
Control: Church operated, Nongovernment, not–for–profit **Service**: General
medical and surgical

Staffed Beds: 379 **Admissions**: 25945 **Census**: 341 **Outpatient**
Visits: 103102 **Births**: 2453 **Total Expense ($000)**: 598656 **Payroll**
Expense ($000): 220304 **Personnel**: 2471

STAYTON—Marion County

☒ **SANTIAM HOSPITAL (380056)**, 1401 North 10th Avenue, Zip 97383–1399;
tel. 503/769–2175, **A**1 10 **F**3 7 11 13 15 16 17 29 30 40 41 43 50 65 70
72 73 76 79 80 81 85 87 88 89 90 98 107 111 115 119 128 130 133 135
143 154
Primary Contact: Terry L. Fletchall, President and Chief Executive Officer
COO: Maggie Hudson, Chief Financial and Operations Officer
CFO: Rachael Seeder, Controller
CMO: Amy Sutkus, M.D., Medical Staff President
CIO: Trace Jacobs, Director Information Technology
CNO: Janet Dow, R.N., Chief Nursing Officer
Web address: www.santiamhospital.org
Control: Other not–for–profit (including NFP Corporation) **Service**: General
medical and surgical

Staffed Beds: 40 **Admissions**: 922 **Census**: 9 **Outpatient Visits**: 46783
Births: 124 **Total Expense ($000)**: 55052 **Payroll Expense ($000)**: 25589
Personnel: 292

THE DALLES—Wasco County

☒ △ **MID-COLUMBIA MEDICAL CENTER (380001)**, 1700 East 19th Street,
Zip 97058–3317; tel. 541/296–1111, **A**1 2 7 10 **F**3 11 13 15 18 20 28 29 30
31 32 34 35 36 40 43 45 46 50 53 54 57 59 62 64 65 66 68 70 75 76 77 78
79 81 82 83 84 85 87 89 90 91 92 93 97 100 101 104 107 108 110 111 114
118 119 120 121 123 126 127 129 130 131 132 133 134 135 146 147 148
149 154 156 157
Primary Contact: Dennis M. Knox, Chief Executive Officer
COO: Larry Kahl, Chief Operating Officer
CFO: Edwin J Bode, Chief Financial Officer
CMO: Judy Richardson, M.D., President Medical Staff
CIO: Erick Larson, Vice President and Chief Information Officer
CHR: Christine Espy, Division Director
CNO: Felicia M Adams, MS, Chief Nursing Officer
Web address: www.mcmc.net
Control: Other not–for–profit (including NFP Corporation) **Service**: General
medical and surgical

Staffed Beds: 46 **Admissions**: 1815 **Census**: 16 **Outpatient Visits**: 105551
Births: 260 **Total Expense ($000)**: 99639 **Payroll Expense ($000)**: 43630
Personnel: 690

TILLAMOOK—Tillamook County

☒ **ADVENTIST HEALTHTILLAMOOK (381317)**, 1000 Third Street, Zip 97141–
3430; tel. 503/842–4444, **A**1 10 18 **F**2 3 7 13 15 17 18 29 30 31 33 34 35 37
40 43 45 50 57 59 64 65 68 75 76 77 78 79 81 82 85 87 93 94 97 102 107
108 110 111 115 119 127 129 130 131 132 133 134 135 144 146 147 148
149 154 156 **S** Adventist Health, Roseville, CA
Primary Contact: David Butler, President and Chief Executive Officer
CFO: Walt Larson, Vice President Finance
CMO: Mark Bowman, M.D., President Medical Staff
CNO: Kathy Saxon, R.N., Vice President Patient Care Services
Web address: www.https://www.adventisthealth.org/tillamook/
Control: Church operated, Nongovernment, not–for–profit **Service**: General
medical and surgical

Staffed Beds: 25 **Admissions**: 1300 **Census**: 12 **Outpatient Visits**: 192670
Births: 176 **Total Expense ($000)**: 85098 **Payroll Expense ($000)**: 31346
Personnel: 385

TUALATIN—Clackamas County

☒ **LEGACY MERIDIAN PARK MEDICAL CENTER (380089)**, 19300 SW 65th
Avenue, Zip 97062–9741; tel. 503/692–1212, **A**1 2 10 **F**3 13 15 18 20 22 28
29 30 31 32 34 35 38 40 44 45 46 49 50 51 56 57 59 60 64 68 70 74 75 76
77 78 79 80 81 85 86 87 91 93 97 107 108 110 111 114 115 116 117 118
119 120 121 126 129 130 132 145 146 147 148 149 154 **S** Legacy Health,
Portland, OR
Primary Contact: Allyson Anderson, President
COO: Michael Newcomb, D.O., Senior Vice President and Chief Operating Officer
CMO: Lewis Low, M.D., Senior Vice President and Chief Medical Officer
CIO: John Jay Kenagy, Ph.D., Senior Vice President and Chief Information Officer
CHR: Sonja Steves, Vice President Human Resources and Marketing
CNO: Carol Bradley, MSN, R.N., Senior Vice President and Chief Nursing Officer
Web address: www.legacyhealth.org
Control: Other not–for–profit (including NFP Corporation) **Service**: General
medical and surgical

Staffed Beds: 144 **Admissions**: 9102 **Census**: 89 **Outpatient**
Visits: 275799 **Births**: 1000 **Total Expense ($000)**: 208590 **Payroll**
Expense ($000): 77667 **Personnel**: 825

Many Facility Codes have changed. Please refer to the AHA Guide Code Chart. © 2019 AHA Guide

PENNSYLVANIA

ABINGTON—Montgomery County

✠ **ABINGTON HOSPITAL (390231)**, 1200 Old York Road, Zip 19001–3720;
tel. 215/481–2000, **A**1 2 3 5 10 13 **F**3 6 8 9 11 12 13 15 17 18 20 22 24 26
28 29 30 31 32 34 35 36 37 38 39 40 43 44 45 46 47 48 49 50 52 53 54 55
56 57 58 59 61 62 63 64 65 66 68 70 72 73 74 75 76 77 78 79 80 81 82 84
85 86 87 88 89 90 91 93 96 97 98 100 101 102 103 104 107 108 110 111 114
115 118 119 120 121 123 124 126 129 130 131 132 135 144 145 146 147
148 149 150 154 156 **S** Jefferson Health, Philadelphia, PA
Primary Contact: Margaret M. McGoldrick, President
COO: Eileen Jameson, Chief Operating Officer
CFO: Michael Walsh, Senior Vice President Finance and Chief Financial Officer
CMO: Gerard M. Cleary, M.D., Senior Vice President, Chief of Staff and Chief
Medical Officer
CIO: Daniel P. Walsh, Vice President, Information Systems and Technology Northern
Division
CHR: Meghan Patton, Vice President Human Resources
CNO: Theresa Reilly, MSN, R.N., Senior Vice President Patient Services and Chief
Nursing Officer
Web address: www.abingtonhealth.org
Control: Other not–for–profit (including NFP Corporation) **Service:** General
medical and surgical

Staffed Beds: 611 **Admissions:** 30353 **Census:** 374 **Outpatient
Visits:** 572856 **Births:** 4521 **Total Expense ($000):** 817029 **Payroll
Expense ($000):** 386517 **Personnel:** 4280

ALLENTOWN—Lehigh County

☐ △ **GOOD SHEPHERD REHABILITATION HOSPITAL (393035)**, 850 South
5th Street, Zip 18103–3308; tel. 610/776–3299, **A**1 3 5 7 10 **F**1 28 29 30 32
34 35 36 53 54 56 57 58 59 64 65 66 68 74 75 82 86 87 90 91 92 93 94
95 96 100 107 119 130 131 132 146 147 148 154 157 **S** Good Shepherd
Rehabilitation Network, Allentown, PA
Primary Contact: John Kristel, President and Chief Executive Officer
CFO: Ronald J. Petula, Chief Financial Officer
Web address: www.goodshepherdrehab.org
Control: Other not–for–profit (including NFP Corporation) **Service:** Rehabilitation

Staffed Beds: 106 **Admissions:** 1248 **Census:** 72 **Outpatient
Visits:** 247319 **Births:** 0 **Total Expense ($000):** 90515 **Payroll Expense
($000):** 37256 **Personnel:** 926

✠ **LEHIGH VALLEY HOSPITAL (390133)**, 1200 South Cedar Crest Boulevard,
Zip 18103–6248, Mailing Address: P.O. Box 689, Zip 18105–1556,
tel. 610/402–8000, (Includes LEHIGH VALLEY HEALTH NETWORK PEDITRICS,
1200 South Cedar Crest Boulevard, Allentown, Pennsylvania, Zip 18103–6202,
Mailing Address: P.O. Box 689, Zip 18105, tel. 484/862–3131; LEHIGH VALLEY
HOSPITAL-MUHLENBERG, 2545 Schoenersville Road, Bethlehem, Pennsylvania,
Zip 18017–7300; tel. 484/884–2200; Brian A. Nester, D.O., President and Chief
Executive Officer) **A**1 2 3 5 8 10 13 **F**3 6 7 8 9 12 13 15 16 17 18 20 22 24
26 28 29 30 31 32 33 34 35 36 37 38 39 40 41 43 44 45 46 47 48 49 50 51
53 54 55 56 57 58 59 60 61 62 63 64 65 66 68 70 71 72 74 76 77 78 79 80
81 82 84 85 86 87 88 89 90 92 93 96 97 98 99 100 101 102 104 105 106
107 108 110 111 114 115 116 117 118 119 120 121 123 124 126 128 129
130 131 132 134 135 138 142 143 144 145 146 147 148 149 154 155 157 **S**
Lehigh Valley Health Network, Allentown, PA
Primary Contact: Brian A. Nester, D.O., President and Chief Executive Officer
COO: Terry Ann Capuano, R.N., MSN, FACHE, Executive Vice President and Chief
Operating Officer
CFO: Edward O'Dea, Executive Vice President and Chief Financial Officer
CMO: Thomas V. Whalen, M.D., Chief Medical Officer
CIO: Michael N. Minear, Senior Vice President and Chief Information Officer
CNO: Marie Kim Jordan, R.N., Senior Vice President and Chief Nursing Officer
Web address: www.lvhn.org
Control: Other not–for–profit (including NFP Corporation) **Service:** General
medical and surgical

Staffed Beds: 1052 **Admissions:** 54991 **Census:** 822 **Outpatient
Visits:** 783086 **Births:** 4773 **Total Expense ($000):** 1857042 **Payroll
Expense ($000):** 564318 **Personnel:** 8855

ST LUKE'S HOSPITAL - ALLENTOWN CAMPUS See St. Luke's University
Hospital - Bethlehem Campus, Bethlehem

☐ △ **ST. LUKE'S SACRED HEART CAMPUS (390197)**, 421 West Chew Street,
Zip 18102–3490; tel. 610/776–4500, (Total facility includes 22 beds in nursing
home–type unit) **A**1 3 5 7 10 **F**3 11 12 15 18 29 30 31 34 35 38 40 44 45 49
50 54 56 57 59 60 64 70 74 75 78 79 81 85 86 87 92 93 97 98 100 101 102
103 107 108 110 111 114 115 117 118 119 128 129 130 132 134 135 146
147 149 154 **S** St. Luke's University Health Network, Bethlehem, PA
Primary Contact: Frank Ford, President
CMO: Farrokh Sadr, M.D., Chief Medical Officer
CIO: Tracy Burkhart, Vice President Information Services
CHR: Joseph Mikitka, Vice President Human Resources
Web address: www.shh.org
Control: Other not–for–profit (including NFP Corporation) **Service:** General
medical and surgical

Staffed Beds: 155 **Admissions:** 723 **Census:** 19 **Outpatient Visits:** 43064
Births: 0 **Total Expense ($000):** 26372 **Payroll Expense ($000):** 12014
Personnel: 605

☐ **SURGICAL SPECIALTY CENTER AT COORDINATED HEALTH (390321)**,
1503 North Cedar Crest Boulevard, Zip 18104–2302; tel. 610/861–8080,
(Nonreporting) **A**1 10
Primary Contact: Emil Dilorio, M.D., Chief Executive Officer
Web address: www.coordinatedhealth.com
Control: Other not–for–profit (including NFP Corporation) **Service:** Surgical

Staffed Beds: 20

ALTOONA—Blair County

ALTOONA REGIONAL HEALTH SYSTEM See Upmc Altoona

✠ **ENCOMPASS HEALTH REHABILITATION HOSPITAL OF ALTOONA (393040)**,
2005 Valley View Boulevard, Zip 16602–4598; tel. 814/944–3535, (Nonreporting)
A1 10 **S** Encompass Health Corporation, Birmingham, AL
Primary Contact: Scott Filler, Chief Executive Officer
CFO: George Berger, Controller
CMO: Rakesh Patel, D.O., Medical Director
CIO: Kathleen Edwards, Manager Information Systems Operation
CHR: Christine Filer, Director Human Resources
CNO: Mary Gen Boyles, Chief Nursing Officer
Web address: www.healthsouthaltoona.com
Control: Corporation, Investor–owned (for–profit) **Service:** Rehabilitation

Staffed Beds: 80

✠ **JAMES E. VAN ZANDT VETERANS AFFAIRS MEDICAL CENTER**, 2907
Pleasant Valley Boulevard, Zip 16602–4305; tel. 877/626–2500, (Nonreporting)
A1 **S** Department of Veterans Affairs, Washington, DC
Primary Contact: Sigrid Andrew, Director
CFO: Carl Parrish, Chief Fiscal Service
CIO: Michael Hynoski, Chief Information Resource Management
CHR: Gina Dunio, Chief Human Resources
Web address: www.altoona.va.gov/
Control: Veterans Affairs, Government, federal **Service:** General medical and
surgical

Staffed Beds: 68

PA

☐ **UPMC ALTOONA (390073)**, 620 Howard Avenue, Zip 16601–4804; tel. 814/889–2011, **A**1 2 3 5 10 12 13 **F**3 8 11 12 13 15 17 18 20 22 24 26 28 29 30 31 34 35 37 38 39 40 43 44 45 47 48 49 50 51 56 57 59 60 61 64 65 66 68 70 73 74 75 76 77 78 79 81 83 84 85 86 87 89 97 98 100 103 107 108 110 111 114 115 116 117 118 119 120 121 123 124 126 129 130 131 132 135 146 147 148 149 154 155 156 **S** UPMC, Pittsburgh, PA
Primary Contact: Jan E. Fisher, President
COO: Ron McConnell, Chief Operating Officer
CFO: Betsy Kreuz, Chief Financial Officer
CMO: Linnane Batzel, M.D., Senior Vice President Quality and Medical Affairs and Chief Medical Officer
CIO: Dale Fuller, Vice President and Chief Information Officer
CHR: Michelle A Speck, Vice President Human Resources
CNO: Chris Rickens, R.N., MS, Senior Vice President and Chief Nursing Officer
Web address: www.altoonaregional.org
Control: Other not–for–profit (including NFP Corporation) **Service**: General medical and surgical

> **Staffed Beds: 346 Admissions: 18956 Census: 244 Outpatient Visits: 340547 Births: 1125 Total Expense ($000): 453590 Payroll Expense ($000): 138292 Personnel: 1980**

AMBLER—Montgomery County

☐ **HORSHAM CLINIC (394034)**, 722 East Butler Pike, Zip 19002–2310; tel. 215/643–7800, **A**1 3 5 10 **F**4 98 99 105 154 **S** Universal Health Services, Inc., King of Prussia, PA
Primary Contact: Phyllis Weisfield, Chief Executive Officer and Managing Director
CFO: Jeffrey Beiler, Chief Operating Officer
CMO: James B Congdon, M.D., Medical Director
CIO: Suzanne Scholz, Director Medical Records
CHR: Kathleen Nichelson, Director Human Resources
CNO: Calvin Litka, R.N., Director of Nursing
Web address: www.horshamclinic.com
Control: Corporation, Investor–owned (for–profit) **Service**: Psychiatric

> **Staffed Beds: 206 Admissions: 5397 Census: 188 Outpatient Visits: 0 Births: 0**

BEAVER—Beaver County

☐ **CURAHEALTH HERITAGE VALLEY (392043)**, 1000 Dutch Ridge Road, Zip 15009–9727; tel. 724/773–8480, (Nonreporting) **A**1 10 **S** Curahealth Hospitals, Garland, TX
Primary Contact: Janie Rosenberger-Slampack, Chief Executive Officer
CFO: Kevin Varley, Chief Financial Officer
CMO: Jeffrey Erukhimou, M.D., Medical Director
Web address: www.curahealth.com
Control: Corporation, Investor–owned (for–profit) **Service**: Acute long–term care hospital

> **Staffed Beds: 35**

☐ **HERITAGE VALLEY HEALTH SYSTEM (390036)**, 1000 Dutch Ridge Road, Zip 15009–9727; tel. 724/728–7000, (Nonreporting) **A**1 3 5 10 13 **S** Heritage Valley Health System, Beaver, PA
Primary Contact: Norman F. Mitry, President and Chief Executive Officer
COO: John Luellen, M.D., Chief Operating Officer
CFO: Bryan J Randall, Vice President Finance and Chief Financial Officer
CMO: Michael Cratty, M.D., Chief Medical Officer
CIO: David Carleton, Chief Information Officer
CHR: Bruce Edwards, Vice President Human Resources
CNO: Linda Homyk, Chief Nursing Officer
Web address: www.heritagevalley.org
Control: Other not–for–profit (including NFP Corporation) **Service**: General medical and surgical

> **Staffed Beds: 271**

BENSALEM—Bucks County

LIVENGRIN FOUNDATION, 4833 Hulmeville Road, Zip 19020–3099; tel. 215/638–5200, (Nonreporting)
Primary Contact: Richard M. Pine, President and Chief Executive Officer
CFO: James D Flis, Chief Financial Officer
CMO: William J Lorman, Ph.D., Clinical Director
CIO: William Miller, Coordinator Management Information Systems
Web address: www.livengrin.org
Control: Other not–for–profit (including NFP Corporation) **Service**: Alcoholism and other chemical dependency

> **Staffed Beds: 76**

☐ **ROTHMAN SPECIALTY HOSPITAL (390322)**, 3300 Tillman Drive, Zip 19020–2071; tel. 215/244–7400, (Nonreporting) **A**1 3 10
Primary Contact: Kelly Doyle, Chief Executive Officer
Web address: www.rothmanspecialtyhospital.com/
Control: Partnership, Investor–owned (for–profit) **Service**: Orthopedic

> **Staffed Beds: 24**

BERWICK—Columbia County

⊠ **BERWICK HOSPITAL CENTER (390072)**, 701 East 16th Street, Zip 18603–2397; tel. 570/759–5000, (Nonreporting) **A**1 10 **S** Community Health Systems, Inc., Franklin, TN
Primary Contact: Thomas Neal, Chief Executive Officer
CFO: Whitney Holloway, Chief Financial Officer
CMO: John A. Guerriero, Chief of Staff
CIO: Kerry Yeager, Director Information Technology
CHR: Jackie Ridall, Director Human Resources
CNO: Maribeth Angeli, Chief Nursing Officer
Web address: www.berwick-hospital.com
Control: Corporation, Investor–owned (for–profit) **Service**: General medical and surgical

> **Staffed Beds: 101**

BETHLEHEM—Northampton County

☐ **COORDINATED HEALTH-BETHLEHEM (390314)**, 2310 Highland Avenue, Zip 18020–8920, Mailing Address: 2300 Highland Avenue, Zip 18020; tel. 610/861–8080, **A**1 3 10 **F**3 29 34 79 81 82 85 119 130 141 148 149
Primary Contact: Laurie H. Gombert, Administrator
Web address: www.coordinatedhealth.com
Control: Corporation, Investor–owned (for–profit) **Service**: Orthopedic

> **Staffed Beds: 20 Admissions: 1177 Census: 7 Outpatient Visits: 6897 Births: 0 Total Expense ($000): 30684 Payroll Expense ($000): 5313 Personnel: 105**

BETHLEHEM—Lehigh County

☐ △ **GOOD SHEPHERD SPECIALTY HOSPITAL (392033)**, 2545 Schoenersville Road, 4th Floor, Zip 18017–7300; tel. 484/884–5051, **A**1 7 10 **F**1 3 29 30 36 77 85 87 91 95 130 148 **S** Good Shepherd Rehabilitation Network, Allentown, PA
Primary Contact: Andrew Shane. Martin, Administrator
CFO: Ronald J. Petula, Chief Financial Officer
CIO: Michael Cirba, Chief Information Officer
CHR: Kristen Melan, Director Human Resources Administration
CNO: Samuel Miranda Jr Chief Nursing Officer
Web address: www.goodshepherdrehab.org
Control: Other not–for–profit (including NFP Corporation) **Service**: Acute long–term care hospital

> **Staffed Beds: 32 Admissions: 382 Census: 26 Outpatient Visits: 0 Births: 0 Total Expense ($000): 16494 Payroll Expense ($000): 5069 Personnel: 92**

☐ △ **ST. LUKE'S UNIVERSITY HOSPITAL - BETHLEHEM CAMPUS (390049)**, 801 Ostrum Street, Zip 18015–1065; tel. 484/526–4000, (Includes ST LUKE'S HOSPITAL - ALLENTOWN CAMPUS, 1736 Hamilton Street, Allentown, Pennsylvania, Zip 18104–5656; tel. 610/628–8300; William Moyer, President) **A**1 2 3 7 8 10 12 13 **F**3 9 11 12 13 15 17 18 19 20 22 24 26 27 28 29 30 31 32 34 35 36 37 38 39 40 43 44 45 46 47 48 49 50 51 52 53 54 55 56 57 58 59 60 61 63 64 65 68 70 71 72 73 74 75 76 77 78 79 81 82 84 85 86 87 89 90 92 93 96 97 98 100 101 102 103 104 105 107 108 109 110 111 115 117 118 119 120 121 123 124 126 129 130 131 132 134 135 144 145 146 147 148 149 153 154 **S** St. Luke's University Health Network, Bethlehem, PA
Primary Contact: Carol Kuplen, R.N., MSN, President and Chief Executive Officer
CFO: Tom Lichtenwalner, Vice President Finance
CMO: Jeffrey Jahre, M.D., Vice President Medical and Academic Affairs
CIO: Chad Brisendine, Chief Information Officer
CHR: Robert Zimmel, Senior Vice President Human Resources
Web address: www.slhn-lehighvalley.org
Control: Other not–for–profit (including NFP Corporation) **Service**: General medical and surgical

> **Staffed Beds: 572 Admissions: 30052 Census: 415 Outpatient Visits: 608925 Births: 4217 Total Expense ($000): 650595 Payroll Expense ($000): 280537 Personnel: 5423**

BLOOMSBURG—Columbia County

★ **GEISINGER-BLOOMSBURG HOSPITAL (390003)**, 549 Fair Street, Zip 17815–1419; tel. 570/387–2100, **A**3 10 **F**3 8 11 12 13 15 26 27 28 29 30 32 34 35 36 38 40 41 44 45 46 50 51 53 55 56 57 59 62 63 65 68 70 74 75 76 81 85 86 87 91 92 93 97 98 100 101 102 103 104 107 108 110 111 115 119 130 131 132 135 144 145 146 147 148 149 150 153 154 156 **S** Geisinger, Danville, PA
Primary Contact: Lissa Bryan-Smith, Chief Administrative Officer
COO: Joseph M DeVito, Vice President Finance and Chief Operating Officer
CFO: Joseph M DeVito, Vice President Finance and Chief Operating Officer
CMO: James Joseph, M.D., President Medical Staff
CIO: Thomas Wray, Director Information
Web address: www.bloomhealth.net
Control: Other not–for–profit (including NFP Corporation) **Service:** General medical and surgical

Staffed Beds: 76 **Admissions:** 2457 **Census:** 26 **Outpatient Visits:** 89468 **Births:** 435 **Total Expense ($000):** 50688 **Payroll Expense ($000):** 18009 **Personnel:** 362

BRADFORD—Mckean County

☐ **BRADFORD REGIONAL MEDICAL CENTER (390118)**, 116 Interstate Parkway, Zip 16701–1036; tel. 814/368–4143, (Total facility includes 95 beds in nursing home–type unit) **A**1 10 **F**3 5 11 16 18 20 28 29 30 31 34 35 38 39 40 45 47 49 50 53 54 56 57 59 64 65 69 70 75 76 77 78 79 81 82 83 84 85 86 87 93 94 96 97 98 100 101 102 105 107 108 110 111 114 117 118 119 127 128 129 130 131 132 135 146 147 148 149 156 **S** Upper Allegheny Health System, Olean, NY
Primary Contact: Timothy J. Finan, FACHE, President and Chief Executive Officer
COO: Jeff S Zewe, R.N., Chief Operating Officer
CFO: Richard G Braun, CPA, Jr Senior Vice President and Chief Financial Officer
CMO: William Mills, M.D., Senior Vice President Quality and Professional Affairs
CIO: Jason Yaworsky, Chief Information Officer
CHR: Timothy M McNamara, Senior Vice President Human Resources
Web address: www.brmc.com
Control: Other not–for–profit (including NFP Corporation) **Service:** General medical and surgical

Staffed Beds: 202 **Admissions:** 2873 **Census:** 120 **Outpatient Visits:** 147547 **Births:** 161 **Total Expense ($000):** 67956 **Payroll Expense ($000):** 28201 **Personnel:** 389

BRISTOL—Bucks County

☒ **LOWER BUCKS HOSPITAL (390070)**, 501 Bath Road, Zip 19007–3190; tel. 215/785–9200, (Nonreporting) **A**1 3 10 13 **S** Prime Healthcare, Ontario, CA
Primary Contact: Kelly M. Lorah, FACHE, Chief Executive Officer
CMO: Sanjay Bhatia, Chief Medical Officer
CIO: Steve Kane, Director Information Technology
CNO: Pat Bain, Chief Nursing Officer
Web address: www.lowerbuckshosp.com
Control: Other not–for–profit (including NFP Corporation) **Service:** General medical and surgical

Staffed Beds: 104

BROOKVILLE—Jefferson County

PENN HIGHLANDS BROOKVILLE (391312), 100 Hospital Road, Zip 15825–1367; tel. 814/849–2312, (Nonreporting) **A**3 10 18
Primary Contact: Julianne Peer, President
CFO: Jessica Park, Director Accounting
CMO: Timothy Pendleton, M.D., President Medical Staff
CIO: Thomas Johnson, Director Information Systems
CHR: Rebecca Edwards, Chief Human Resources Officer
CNO: Debra A. Thomas, Vice President of Patient Care Services and Chief Nursing Officer
Web address: www.phhealthcare.org/
Control: Other not–for–profit (including NFP Corporation) **Service:** General medical and surgical

Staffed Beds: 35

BRYN MAWR—Montgomery County

☒ **BRYN MAWR HOSPITAL (390139)**, 130 South Bryn Mawr Avenue, Zip 19010–3160; tel. 484/337–3000, **A**1 2 3 5 10 13 **F**3 5 11 12 13 15 17 18 20 22 24 26 28 29 30 31 34 35 36 37 38 39 40 41 44 45 46 48 49 50 54 55 56 57 58 59 63 64 65 70 72 74 75 76 78 79 80 81 82 84 85 86 87 89 92 97 98 100 102 103 104 107 108 110 111 114 115 118 119 120 124 126 129 130 131 134 135 141 146 147 148 149 154 156 **S** Main Line Health, Ontario, CA
Primary Contact: Andrea F. Gilbert, FACHE, President
CFO: Michael J Buongiorno, Executive Vice President Finance and Chief Financial Officer
CMO: Andrew J Norton, M.D., Chief Medical Officer
CIO: Kay Carr, Chief Information Officer
CHR: Terry Dougherty, Director Human Resources
CNO: Barbara A Wadsworth, MSN, R.N., FACHE, Chief Nursing Officer
Web address: www.brynmawrhospital.org
Control: Other not–for–profit (including NFP Corporation) **Service:** General medical and surgical

Staffed Beds: 287 **Admissions:** 15092 **Census:** 156 **Outpatient Visits:** 214359 **Births:** 1599 **Total Expense ($000):** 327066 **Payroll Expense ($000):** 105058 **Personnel:** 1449

BUTLER—Butler County

★ **BUTLER HEALTH SYSTEM (390168)**, 1 Hospital Way, Zip 16001–4697; tel. 724/283–6666, (Nonreporting) **A**2 10
Primary Contact: Ken DeFurio, President and Chief Executive Officer
COO: Stephanie Roskovski, Chief Operating Officer
CFO: Michael Deitschmann, Chief Financial Officer
CMO: John C Reefer, M.D., Director
CIO: Thomas McGill, M.D., Chief Information Officer
CHR: Thomas A Genevro, Vice President Human Resources
CNO: Karen A Allen, R.N., Chief Nursing Officer
Web address: www.butlerhealthsystem.org
Control: Other not–for–profit (including NFP Corporation) **Service:** General medical and surgical

Staffed Beds: 288

CAMP HILL—Cumberland County

☒ **GEISINGER HOLY SPIRIT (390004)**, 503 North 21st Street, Zip 17011–2204; tel. 717/763–2100, **A**1 2 10 **F**3 6 11 13 14 15 17 18 20 22 24 26 28 29 30 31 34 35 38 40 43 44 45 46 47 48 49 50 54 57 59 64 65 70 72 74 75 76 77 78 79 81 82 84 85 86 87 89 93 98 100 101 102 104 105 107 108 110 111 114 115 118 119 120 121 123 124 126 129 130 132 134 135 143 146 147 148 149 153 154 156 **S** Geisinger, Danville, PA
Primary Contact: Kyle C. Snyder, Chief Administrative Officer
CNO: Lisa F Torchia NEA-BC, MSN, R.N., Vice President and Chief Nursing Officer
Web address: www.hsh.org
Control: Other not–for–profit (including NFP Corporation) **Service:** General medical and surgical

Staffed Beds: 311 **Admissions:** 11262 **Census:** 158 **Outpatient Visits:** 206863 **Births:** 1125 **Total Expense ($000):** 431518 **Payroll Expense ($000):** 107323 **Personnel:** 2142

★ **SELECT SPECIALTY HOSPITAL-CAMP HILL (392039)**, 503 North 21st Street, 5th Floor, Zip 17011–2204; tel. 717/972–4575, (Includes SELECT SPECIALTY HOSPITAL-HARRISBURG, 111 South Front Street, Alex Grass Building, 5th Floor, Harrisburg, Pennsylvania, Zip 17101; tel. 717/724–6610; John E Simodejka, Marketing Chief Executive Officer; SELECT SPECIALTY HOSPITAL-YORK, 1001 South George Street, York, Pennsylvania, Zip 17403–3676; tel. 717/851–2661; Marcia Medlin, Chief Executive Officer), (Non-reporting) **A**10 **S** Select Medical Corporation, Mechanicsburg, PA
Primary Contact: John E. Simodejka, Chief Executive Officer
Web address: www.camphill.selectspecialtyhospitals.com/
Control: Corporation, Investor–owned (for–profit) **Service:** Acute long–term care hospital

Staffed Beds: 92

STATE CORRECTIONAL INSTITUTION AT CAMP HILL, 2500 Lisburn Road, Zip 17011–8005, Mailing Address: P.O. Box 200, Zip 17001–0200; tel. 717/737–4531, (Nonreporting)
Primary Contact: Beth Herb, Administrator
Web address: www.cor.state.pa.us
Control: State, Government, nonfederal **Service:** Hospital unit of an institution (prison hospital, college infirmary, etc.)

Staffed Beds: 34

Hospital, Medicare Provider Number, Address, Telephone, Approval, Facility, and Physician Codes, Health Care System

★ American Hospital Association (AHA) membership
☐ The Joint Commission accreditation
○ Healthcare Facilities Accreditation Program
◇ DNV Healthcare Inc. accreditation
⇧ Center for Improvement in Healthcare Quality Accreditation
△ Commission on Accreditation of Rehabilitation Facilities (CARF) accreditation

PA

CANONSBURG—Washington County

☒ **CANONSBURG HOSPITAL (390160)**, 100 Medical Boulevard, Zip 15317–9762; tel. 724/745–6100, **A**1 10 **F**3 7 11 15 18 28 29 30 34 35 40 44 45 46 47 49 50 54 57 59 64 70 74 75 77 79 81 84 85 86 87 90 92 93 96 102 107 108 110 111 115 118 119 129 130 131 132 135 141 143 146 148 149 154 **S** Allegheny Health Network, Pittsburgh, PA
Primary Contact: Louise Urban, R.N., President and Chief Executive Officer
CMO: Thomas B Corkery, D.O., Chief Medical Officer
CIO: David Vincent, Director Information Systems
CHR: Martha L Clister, Director Human Resources
Web address: www.wpahs.org
Control: Other not–for–profit (including NFP Corporation) **Service**: General medical and surgical

Staffed Beds: 42 Admissions: 1982 Census: 24 Outpatient Visits: 64405
Births: 0 **Total Expense ($000):** 47940 **Payroll Expense ($000):** 18625
Personnel: 322

CARLISLE—Cumberland County

☐ **UPMC CARLISLE (390058)**, 361 Alexander Spring Road, Zip 17015–6940; tel. 717/249–1212, **A**1 10 **F**3 8 12 13 14 15 18 20 29 30 31 34 36 40 45 46 48 49 50 54 55 57 59 60 64 65 68 70 73 74 75 76 77 78 79 81 85 86 87 90 96 107 108 109 110 111 114 115 116 117 118 119 120 121 123 126 129 130 141 146 147 148 149 154 156 **S** UPMC, Pittsburgh, PA
Primary Contact: Christian H. Caicedo, M.D., President
CFO: Mark Reyngoudt, Chief Financial Officer
CMO: Ivan' Sola', President Medical Staff
CIO: Sherry Aby, Director Information Management
CHR: Sylvia Rockwood, Director Human Resources
Web address: www.https://www.pinnaclehealth.org/carlisle/
Control: Other not–for–profit (including NFP Corporation) **Service**: General medical and surgical

Staffed Beds: 165 Admissions: 4145 Census: 42 Outpatient Visits: 90562
Births: 396 **Total Expense ($000):** 115628 **Payroll Expense ($000):** 35469
Personnel: 571

CENTRE HALL—Centre County

☒ **MEADOWS PSYCHIATRIC CENTER (394040)**, 132 The Meadows Drive, Zip 16828–9231; tel. 814/364–2161, **A**1 10 **F**29 38 40 59 98 99 100 103 130 135 **S** Universal Health Services, Inc., King of Prussia, PA
Primary Contact: David Grabowski, Chief Executive Officer
CFO: David Witt, Chief Financial Officer
CMO: Craig Richman, M.D., Medical Director
CHR: Mary Jane Schreffler, Director Human Resources
CNO: Dana Thies, Director of Nursing
Web address: www.themeadows.net
Control: Corporation, Investor–owned (for–profit) **Service**: Psychiatric

Staffed Beds: 119 Admissions: 2494 Census: 96 Outpatient Visits: 224
Births: 0 **Personnel:** 200

CHAMBERSBURG—Franklin County

☒ **CHAMBERSBURG HOSPITAL (390151)**, 112 North Seventh Street, Zip 17201–1720; tel. 717/267–3000, **A**1 2 3 5 10 19 **F**3 13 15 17 18 20 22 26 29 30 40 44 45 49 50 58 68 70 72 75 76 81 85 86 87 90 98 100 102 104 107 108 110 111 114 115 119 126 129 130 146 148 149 154 **S** WellSpan Health, York, PA
Primary Contact: Patrick W. O'Donnell, CPA, President and Chief Executive Officer
COO: John P Massimilla, FACHE, Vice President and Chief Operating Officer
CFO: Kimberly Rzomp, Vice President and Chief Financial Officer
CMO: Thomas Anderson, M.D., Vice President Medical Affairs
CIO: Michele Zeigler, Vice President and Chief Information Officer
CHR: Cathy A. Puhl, Vice President Human Resources
CNO: Sherri Stahl, R.N., Senior Vice President Hospital Services
Web address: www.summithealth.org
Control: Other not–for–profit (including NFP Corporation) **Service**: General medical and surgical

Staffed Beds: 273 Admissions: 12463 Census: 145 Outpatient Visits: 431878 **Births:** 1349 **Total Expense ($000):** 305889 **Payroll Expense ($000):** 127812 **Personnel:** 1688

CLARION—Clarion County

★ ○ **CLARION HOSPITAL (390093)**, One Hospital Drive, Zip 16214–8501; tel. 814/226–9500, **A**3 5 10 11 12 13 **F**3 7 11 13 15 29 30 31 35 40 48 51 57 59 64 70 76 77 78 79 81 82 84 85 90 107 108 110 111 115 118 119 120 121 122 129 130 132 133 135 145 146 148 156 **S** QHR, Brentwood, TN
Primary Contact: Steven T. Davis, Chief Executive Officer
CFO: Vincent M Lamorella, Chief Financial Officer
CMO: Janice Semeyn, D.O., President, Medical Staff
CIO: James Confer, Manager Information Systems
CNO: Leslie Walters, MSN, Chief Nursing Officer
Web address: www.clarionhospital.org
Control: Other not–for–profit (including NFP Corporation) **Service**: General medical and surgical

Staffed Beds: 66 Admissions: 1576 Census: 18 Outpatient Visits: 153002
Births: 95 **Total Expense ($000):** 51450 **Payroll Expense ($000):** 17779
Personnel: 376

☐ **CLARION PSYCHIATRIC CENTER (394043)**, 2 Hospital Drive, Zip 16214–8502; tel. 814/226–9545, (Nonreporting) **A**1 10 **S** Universal Health Services, Inc., King of Prussia, PA
Primary Contact: Michael Post, Chief Executive Officer
CFO: Shelly Rhoades, Chief Financial Officer
CMO: Jeffrey Moll, M.D., Medical Director
CHR: Dianne C Bilunka, Director Human Resources
CNO: Rhonda Massa, Director of Nursing
Web address: www.clarioncenter.com
Control: Corporation, Investor–owned (for–profit) **Service**: Psychiatric

Staffed Beds: 74

CLARKS SUMMIT—Lackawanna County

CLARKS SUMMIT STATE HOSPITAL (394012), 1451 Hillside Drive, Zip 18411–9504; tel. 570/586–2011, (Nonreporting) **A**10
Primary Contact: Monica Bradbury, Chief Executive Officer
COO: Gordon Weber, Chief Operating Officer
CMO: David Waibel, M.D., Medical Director
CHR: William Abda, Chief Human Resources Officer
Web address: www.dpw.state.pa.us/
Control: State, Government, nonfederal **Service**: Psychiatric

Staffed Beds: 210

CLEARFIELD—Clearfield County

PENN HIGHLANDS CLEARFIELD (390052), 809 Turnpike Avenue, Zip 16830–1232, Mailing Address: P.O. Box 992, Zip 16830–0992; tel. 814/765–5341, **A**3 10 **F**3 8 11 14 15 18 28 29 30 32 34 40 45 50 57 59 62 63 68 75 77 79 81 82 84 85 86 87 93 97 98 103 104 107 108 110 111 115 118 119 130 131 132 133 146 148
Primary Contact: Rhonda Halstead, President
CFO: William Cain, Controller
CMO: Kevin L Tyler, M.D., President Medical Staff
CNO: Kathy Bedger, Chief Nursing Officer
Web address: www.phhealthcare.org
Control: Other not–for–profit (including NFP Corporation) **Service**: General medical and surgical

Staffed Beds: 50 Admissions: 1477 Census: 19 Births: 0

COALDALE—Schuylkill County

☐ **ST. LUKE'S HOSPITAL - MINERS CAMPUS (390183)**, 360 West Ruddle Street, Zip 18218–1027; tel. 570/645–2131, (Total facility includes 48 beds in nursing home–type unit) **A**1 2 10 **F**3 15 18 28 29 31 34 35 38 40 43 44 45 50 51 53 54 56 57 58 59 60 63 64 65 70 74 75 77 78 79 81 82 85 86 93 102 107 108 110 111 115 118 119 127 128 129 130 131 132 144 145 146 148 149 154 **S** St. Luke's University Health Network, Bethlehem, PA
Primary Contact: Wendy Lazo, President
COO: Joel Fagerstrom, Executive Vice President and Chief Operating Officer
CFO: Michele Levitz, Director Finance
CIO: Chad Brisendine, Vice President and Chief Information Officer
CHR: Susan Van Why, Director Human Resources
CNO: Kimberly Sargent, Vice President Patient Services
Web address: www.slhn.org
Control: Other not–for–profit (including NFP Corporation) **Service**: General medical and surgical

Staffed Beds: 97 Admissions: 2666 Census: 69 Outpatient Visits: 114876
Births: 0 **Total Expense ($000):** 62622 **Payroll Expense ($000):** 27885
Personnel: 359

Many Facility Codes have changed. Please refer to the AHA Guide Code Chart.
© 2019 AHA Guide

COATESVILLE—Chester County

⊞ **BRANDYWINE HOSPITAL (390076)**, 201 Reeceville Road, Zip 19320–1536; tel. 610/383–8000, (Data for 273 days) **A**1 10 **F**3 15 18 20 22 24 26 27 28 29 30 34 35 38 40 45 49 50 51 55 56 57 59 60 63 64 68 70 74 75 77 79 81 82 85 87 91 92 93 98 99 100 101 102 103 107 108 110 111 115 117 119 126 129 130 131 132 146 147 148 149 154 156 157 **S** Tower Health, West Reading, PA
Primary Contact: W. Jeffrey. Hunt, Chief Executive Officer
COO: Jill Tillman, Assistant Chief Executive Officer
CFO: Mark Reyngoudt, Chief Financial Officer
Web address: www.https://brandywine.towerhealth.org/
Control: Other not-for-profit (including NFP Corporation) **Service**: General medical and surgical

Staffed Beds: 171 **Admissions**: 4784 **Census**: 102 **Outpatient Visits**: 46644 **Births**: 0 **Total Expense ($000)**: 89182 **Payroll Expense ($000)**: 31055 **Personnel**: 532

⊞ **COATESVILLE VETERANS AFFAIRS MEDICAL CENTER**, 1400 Black Horse Hill Road, Zip 19320–2040; tel. 610/384–7711, (Nonreporting) **A**1 3 5 **S** Department of Veterans Affairs, Washington, DC
Primary Contact: Carla Sivek, Director
CFO: Tony Wolfgang, Chief Financial Officer
CMO: Sheila Chellappa, M.D., Chief of Staff
CIO: Ryan McGettigan, Chief Information Officer
CHR: Andrew Sutton, Chief Human Resources Officer
CNO: Nancy A Schmid, R.N., MS, Associate Director Patient Care Services
Web address: www.coatesville.va.gov/
Control: Veterans Affairs, Government, federal **Service**: Alcoholism and other chemical dependency

Staffed Beds: 118

VETERANS AFFAIRS MEDICAL CENTER See Coatesville Veterans Affairs Medical Center

CONNELLSVILLE—Fayette County

HIGHLANDS HOSPITAL (390184), 401 East Murphy Avenue, Zip 15425–2700; tel. 724/628–1500, (Nonreporting) **A**10
Primary Contact: John S. Andursky, President and Chief Executive Officer
CMO: Paul Means, M.D., President Medical Staff
CHR: Mary June Krosoff, Chief Human Resources Officer
CNO: Vicki Rough, Chief Nursing Officer
Web address: www.highlandshospital.org
Control: Other not-for-profit (including NFP Corporation) **Service**: General medical and surgical

Staffed Beds: 64

CORRY—Erie County

LECOM CORRY MEMORIAL HOSPITAL (391308), 965 Shamrock Lane, Zip 16407; tel. 814/664–4641, (Nonreporting) **A**10 18
Primary Contact: Barbara Nichols, R.N., President and Chief Executive Officer
CFO: Michael Heller, Chief Financial Officer
CMO: Paul McGeehan, M.D., Chief Medical Staff
CHR: Brenda Cooper, Director Quality and Human Resources
CNO: Patty White, R.N., Director Patient Care Services
Web address: www.corryhospital.com
Control: Other not-for-profit (including NFP Corporation) **Service**: General medical and surgical

Staffed Beds: 25

COUDERSPORT—Potter County

⊞ **UPMC COLE (391313)**, 1001 East Second Street, Zip 16915–8161; tel. 814/274–9300, (Total facility includes 44 beds in nursing home–type unit) **A**1 10 18 **F**70 76 81 128
Primary Contact: Janie Hilfiger, President
CFO: Ron Rapp, Vice President Finance
CMO: Brenda Wahlers, M.D., Chief of Staff
CHR: James Evens, Executive Director, Human Resources and General Services
CNO: Emily Ann Bunnell, Chief Nurse Executive, Senior Director of Acute Care
Web address: www.colememorial.org/
Control: Other not-for-profit (including NFP Corporation) **Service**: General medical and surgical

Staffed Beds: 69 **Admissions**: 1945 **Census**: 55 **Outpatient Visits**: 253564 **Births**: 215 **Total Expense ($000)**: 92984 **Payroll Expense ($000)**: 32298 **Personnel**: 503

CRANBERRY—Butler County

UPMC PASSAVANT CRANBERRY See Upmc Passavant, Pittsburgh

DANVILLE—Montour County

DANVILLE STATE HOSPITAL (394004), 200 State Hospital Drive, Zip 17821–9198; tel. 570/271–4500, **A**3 10 **F**30 39 65 75 77 98 106 130 135 154 156 157
Primary Contact: Theresa Long, Chief Executive Officer
COO: Thomas J Burk, Chief Operating Officer
CFO: Patricia Riegert, Director Fiscal Services
CMO: Vikrant Mittal, M.D., Chief Medical Officer
CHR: Thomas J Burk, Chief Operating Officer
CNO: Brenda Lahout, Chief Nurse Executive
Web address: www.dpw.state.pa.us/foradults/statehospitals/danvillestatehospital/index.htm
Control: State, Government, nonfederal **Service**: Psychiatric

Staffed Beds: 161 **Admissions**: 76 **Census**: 155 **Outpatient Visits**: 0 **Births**: 0 **Total Expense ($000)**: 34639 **Personnel**: 354

⊞ **GEISINGER ENCOMPASS HEALTH REHABILITATION HOSPITAL (393047)**, 2 Rehab Lane, Zip 17821–8498; tel. 570/271–6733, (Nonreporting) **A**1 3 10 **S** Encompass Health Corporation, Birmingham, AL
Primary Contact: Lorie Dillon, Chief Executive Officer
CMO: Greg Burke, M.D., Medical Director
CHR: Christian Shirley, Director Human Resources
Web address: www.geisingerhealthsouth.com
Control: Corporation, Investor–owned (for–profit) **Service**: Rehabilitation

Staffed Beds: 42

⊞ **GEISINGER MEDICAL CENTER (390006)**, 100 North Academy Avenue, Zip 17822–2201; tel. 570/271–6211, (Includes GEISINGER-SHAMOKIN AREA COMMUNITY HOSPITAL, 4200 Hospital Road, Coal Township, Pennsylvania, Zip 17866–9697; tel. 570/644–4200; Sam Balukoff, Interim Administrator) **A**1 2 3 5 8 10 13 19 **F**3 4 7 8 9 11 12 13 14 15 17 18 19 20 21 22 23 24 25 26 27 28 29 30 31 32 34 35 36 37 39 40 41 43 44 45 46 47 48 49 50 51 52 53 54 55 56 57 58 59 60 61 62 63 64 65 66 67 68 69 70 71 72 73 74 75 76 77 78 79 80 81 82 83 84 85 86 87 88 89 91 92 93 94 96 97 98 99 100 101 102 104 107 108 110 111 114 115 117 118 119 120 121 123 124 126 129 130 131 132 134 135 136 138 139 141 143 145 146 147 148 149 150 153 154 155 156 **S** Geisinger, Danville, PA
Primary Contact: Thomas P. Sokola, Chief Administrative Officer
CFO: Kevin F Brennan, CPA, Executive Vice President and Chief Financial Officer
CIO: Frank Richards, Chief Information Officer
CHR: Amy Brayford, Chief Human Resources Officer
CNO: Susan M Robel, R.N., Executive Vice President and Chief Nursing Officer
Web address: www.geisinger.org
Control: Other not-for-profit (including NFP Corporation) **Service**: General medical and surgical

Staffed Beds: 540 **Admissions**: 30759 **Census**: 431 **Outpatient Visits**: 1393426 **Births**: 1830 **Total Expense ($000)**: 1118123 **Payroll Expense ($000)**: 324925 **Personnel**: 7162

⊞ **SELECT SPECIALTY HOSPITAL-DANVILLE (392047)**, 100 North Academy Avenue, 3rd Floor, Zip 17822–3050; tel. 570/214–9653, (Nonreporting) **A**1 10 **S** Select Medical Corporation, Mechanicsburg, PA
Primary Contact: Brian Mann, Chief Executive Officer
Web address: www.https://danville.selectspecialtyhospitals.com
Control: Corporation, Investor–owned (for–profit) **Service**: Acute long–term care hospital

Staffed Beds: 30

PA

PA

DARBY—Delaware County

⊞ **MERCY FITZGERALD HOSPITAL (390156)**, 1500 Lansdowne Avenue, Zip 19023–1200; tel. 610/237–4000, (Includes MERCY FITZGERALD HOSPITAL, 1500 South Lansdowne Avenue, Darby, Pennsylvania, Zip 19023; tel. 610/237–4000; MERCY PHILADELPHIA HOSPITAL, 501 South 54th Street, Philadelphia, Pennsylvania, Zip 19143; tel. 215/748–9000; Susan Cusack, Executive Director) **A**1 2 3 5 10 **F**3 4 11 12 15 18 20 22 24 26 28 29 30 31 34 35 38 40 45 46 49 50 51 54 57 59 61 64 66 70 74 75 77 78 79 81 82 85 86 87 90 91 92 93 97 98 100 101 102 107 108 110 111 114 115 118 119 120 121 123 124 130 131 132 135 145 146 147 148 149 150 154 **S** Trinity Health, Livonia, MI
Primary Contact: Susan Cusack, Executive Director
COO: Ruth Thomas, Chief Operating Officer
CFO: Don Snenk, Chief Financial Officer
CMO: Jeff Komins, M.D., Chief Medical Officer
CIO: Jeff Byda, Vice President Information Technology
Web address: www.mercyhealth.org
Control: Other not–for–profit (including NFP Corporation) **Service**: General medical and surgical

Staffed Beds: 340 **Admissions:** 15499 **Census:** 211 **Outpatient Visits:** 302218 **Births:** 0 **Total Expense ($000):** 310058 **Payroll Expense ($000):** 121480 **Personnel:** 2057

DOWNINGTOWN—Chester County

★ **ST. JOHN VIANNEY HOSPITAL**, 151 Woodbine Road, Zip 19335–3057; tel. 610/269–2600, **F**4 12 29 30 90 98 154
Primary Contact: David Shellenberger, President
CMO: James MacFadyen, M.D., Medical Director
CNO: Diana Karanja, R.N., Director of Nursing
Web address: www.sjvcenter.org
Control: Church operated, Nongovernment, not–for–profit **Service**: Psychiatric

Staffed Beds: 47 **Admissions:** 119 **Census:** 40 **Outpatient Visits:** 0 **Births:** 0 **Total Expense ($000):** 8927 **Payroll Expense ($000):** 7331 **Personnel:** 64

DOYLESTOWN—Bucks County

⊞ △ **DOYLESTOWN HOSPITAL (390203)**, 595 West State Street, Zip 18901–2597; tel. 215/345–2200, **A**1 2 3 5 7 10 **F**3 8 13 15 17 18 20 22 24 26 28 29 30 31 32 34 35 40 45 46 49 50 51 54 55 56 57 58 59 62 63 64 70 73 74 75 76 77 78 79 81 85 86 87 89 92 93 94 96 107 108 110 111 114 115 118 119 124 126 129 130 131 132 141 146 147 149 154
Primary Contact: James L. Brexler, President and Chief Executive Officer
COO: Eleanor Wilson, R.N., MSN, Vice President and Chief Operating Officer
CFO: Daniel Upton, Vice President and Chief Financial Officer
CMO: Scott S Levy, M.D., Vice President and Chief Medical Officer
CIO: Richard Lang, Ed.D., Vice President and Chief Information Officer
CHR: Barbara Hebel, Vice President Human Resources
CNO: Patricia A Stover, Administrator Nursing
Web address: www.doylestownhealth.org
Control: Other not–for–profit (including NFP Corporation) **Service**: General medical and surgical

Staffed Beds: 217 **Admissions:** 12346 **Census:** 133 **Outpatient Visits:** 260488 **Births:** 1290 **Total Expense ($000):** 268039 **Payroll Expense ($000):** 111085 **Personnel:** 2057

◻ **FOUNDATIONS BEHAVIORAL HEALTH (394038)**, 833 East Butler Avenue, Zip 18901–2280; tel. 215/345–0444, (Nonreporting) **A**1 10 **S** Universal Health Services, Inc., King of Prussia, PA
Primary Contact: Gina Fusco, Chief Executive Officer
Web address: www.fbh.com
Control: Other not–for–profit (including NFP Corporation) **Service**: Children's hospital psychiatric

Staffed Beds: 58

DREXEL HILL—Delaware County

◻ **DELAWARE COUNTY MEMORIAL HOSPITAL (390081)**, 501 North Lansdowne Avenue, Zip 19026–1114; tel. 610/284–8100, (Nonreporting) **A**1 2 3 5 10 **S** Prospect Medical Holdings, Los Angeles, CA
Primary Contact: Robert Haffey, R.N., President
CFO: Richard I Bennett, Senior Vice President and Chief Financial Officer
CMO: Seth Malin, M.D., President Medical and Dental Staff
CIO: Robert E Wilson, Vice President and Chief Information Officer
Web address: www.crozer.org
Control: Other not–for–profit (including NFP Corporation) **Service**: General medical and surgical

Staffed Beds: 168

DUBOIS—Clearfield County

⇑ **PENN HIGHLANDS DUBOIS (390086)**, 100 Hospital Avenue, Zip 15801–1440, Mailing Address: P.O. Box 447, Zip 15801–0447; tel. 814/371–2200, (Nonreporting) **A**5 10 13 19 21
Primary Contact: John Sutika, President
CFO: Brian S Kline, Vice President and Chief Financial Officer
CMO: Gary Dugan, M.D., Vice President Medical Affairs
CHR: Robert J McKee, Vice President Human Resources
Web address: www.drmc.org
Control: Other not–for–profit (including NFP Corporation) **Service**: General medical and surgical

Staffed Beds: 219

EAGLEVILLE—Montgomery County

★ **EAGLEVILLE HOSPITAL (390278)**, 100 Eagleville Road, Zip 19403–1829, Mailing Address: P.O. Box 45, Zip 19408–0045; tel. 610/539–6000, (Nonreporting) **A**5 10
Primary Contact: Eugene J. Ott Jr, Chief Executive Officer
CFO: Alfred P Salvitti, Chief Financial Officer
CMO: Robert Wilson, D.O., Director Medical Services
CIO: Richard R Mitchell, Director Information Technology
CHR: Zoe Yousaitis, Director Human Resources
Web address: www.eaglevillehospital.org
Control: Other not–for–profit (including NFP Corporation) **Service**: Alcoholism and other chemical dependency

Staffed Beds: 83

EAST NORRITON—Montgomery County

◻ **EINSTEIN MEDICAL CENTER MONTGOMERY (390329)**, 559 West Germantown Pike, Zip 19403–4250; tel. 484/622–1000, **A**1 2 3 10 **F**3 8 11 12 13 15 18 20 22 24 26 29 30 31 34 35 40 45 46 49 55 57 59 62 63 64 68 70 72 74 75 76 78 79 80 81 82 84 85 87 92 100 107 108 110 111 115 117 119 120 121 123 126 129 130 131 132 135 146 147 149 **S** Einstein Healthcare Network, Philadelphia, PA
Primary Contact: Beth Duffy, Chief Operating Officer
COO: Beth Duffy, Chief Operating Officer
CFO: Gerard Blaney, Vice President, Finance
CMO: Angela Nicholas, Vice President, Medical Affairs
CIO: Mary Carroll Ford, Chief Information Officer
CHR: Kenneth Levitan, Chief Administrative Officer
CNO: AnnMarie Papa, R.N., Vice President and Chief Nursing Officer
Control: Other not–for–profit (including NFP Corporation) **Service**: General medical and surgical

Staffed Beds: 171 **Admissions:** 10574 **Census:** 123 **Outpatient Visits:** 211089 **Births:** 2060 **Total Expense ($000):** 223865 **Payroll Expense ($000):** 78211 **Personnel:** 1103

EAST STROUDSBURG—Monroe County

⊞ **LEHIGH VALLEY HOSPITAL - POCONO (390201)**, 206 East Brown Street, Zip 18301–3006; tel. 570/421–4000, (Nonreporting) **A**1 2 10 **S** Lehigh Valley Health Network, Allentown, PA
Primary Contact: Elizabeth Wise, President and Chief Executive Officer
CMO: William K. Cors, M.D., Senior Medical Director
CIO: Ferd Feola, Chief Information Officer
CHR: Lynn Lansdowne, Administrator Human Resources
Web address: www.pmchealthsystem.org
Control: Other not–for–profit (including NFP Corporation) **Service**: General medical and surgical

Staffed Beds: 239

EASTON—Northampton County

◻ **EASTON HOSPITAL (390162)**, 250 South 21st Street, Zip 18042–3892; tel. 610/250–4000, (Nonreporting) **A**1 2 3 5 10 **S** Steward Health Care System, LLC, Dallas, TX
Primary Contact: Linda J. Grass, President
COO: Ronald Ziobro, Chief Operating Officer
CFO: Arthur Comito, Chief Financial Officer
CMO: Roman Tuma, Chief Medical Officer
CIO: Don Lutz, Director Information Technology
CHR: Tanya Segal, Director
CNO: Karen Vadyak, Chief Nursing Officer
Web address: www.easton-hospital.com
Control: Other not–for–profit (including NFP Corporation) **Service**: General medical and surgical

Staffed Beds: 196

Many Facility Codes have changed. Please refer to the AHA Guide Code Chart. © 2019 AHA Guide

PA

☐ **ST. LUKE'S HOSPITAL - ANDERSON CAMPUS (390326)**, 1872 Riverside Circle, Zip 18045–5669; tel. 484/503–3000, **A**1 2 3 10 **F**3 8 11 15 18 20 22 24 26 28 29 30 31 34 35 38 40 44 45 46 49 50 51 53 54 55 57 59 60 63 64 68 70 71 74 75 77 78 79 81 82 84 85 86 87 92 93 96 100 102 107 108 110 111 115 118 119 120 121 123 124 126 130 132 144 145 146 148 149 154 **S** St. Luke's University Health Network, Bethlehem, PA
Primary Contact: Edward Nawrocki, President
CMO: Justin P Psaila, M.D., Vice President Medical Affairs
CNO: Darla Frack, R.N., RN Vice President, Patient Services
Web address: www.mystlukesonline.org
Control: Other not–for–profit (including NFP Corporation) **Service**: General medical and surgical

Staffed Beds: 108 **Admissions**: 7213 **Census**: 77 **Outpatient Visits**: 212404 **Births**: 0 **Total Expense ($000)**: 164464 **Payroll Expense ($000)**: 57795 **Personnel**: 655

ELLWOOD CITY—Lawrence County

☒ **ELLWOOD CITY MEDICAL CENTER, LLC (390008)**, 724 Pershing Street, Zip 16117–1474; tel. 724/752–0081, (Nonreporting) **A**10
Primary Contact: Beverly Annarumo, R.N., MSN, President
CFO: Christopher M Little, Vice President and Chief Financial Officer
CIO: Connie Cunningham, Chief Information Officer
CHR: Paul Landman, Director Human Resources
CNO: Della Stabryla, Director of Nursing
Web address: www.TheEllwoodCityHospital.org
Control: Other not–for–profit (including NFP Corporation) **Service**: General medical and surgical

Staffed Beds: 95

EPHRATA—Lancaster County

☒ **WELLSPAN EPHRATA COMMUNITY HOSPITAL (390225)**, 169 Martin Avenue, Zip 17522–1724, Mailing Address: P.O. Box 1002, Zip 17522–1002; tel. 717/733–0311, (Nonreporting) **A**1 2 10 **S** WellSpan Health, York, PA
CFO: David Kreider, Controller
CMO: Mark Jacobson, D.O., Vice President Medical Affairs
CIO: Leon John Jabour, Regional Chief Information Officer
CHR: Jana Salaki, Regional Director Human Resources
CNO: Tina Citro, R.N., Chief Nursing Officer, Vice President, Patient Services
Web address: www.wellspan.org
Control: Other not–for–profit (including NFP Corporation) **Service**: General medical and surgical

Staffed Beds: 130

ERIE—Erie County

☒ **ENCOMPASS HEALTH REHABILITATION HOSPITAL OF ERIE (393046)**, 143 East Second Street, Zip 16507–1501; tel. 814/878–1200, (Nonreporting) **A**1 10 **S** Encompass Health Corporation, Birmingham, AL
Primary Contact: John Papalia, Chief Executive Officer
CFO: Lori Gibbens, Controller
CMO: Douglas Grisier, D.O., Medical Director
CIO: Sharon Zielinski, Manager Health Information
CHR: William Robinson, Director Human Resources
Web address: www.healthsoutherie.com
Control: Corporation, Investor–owned (for–profit) **Service**: Rehabilitation

Staffed Beds: 100

☒ **ERIE VETERANS AFFAIRS MEDICAL CENTER**, 135 East 38th Street, Zip 16504–1559; tel. 814/860–2576, (Total facility includes 45 beds in nursing home–type unit) **A**1 **F**3 5 8 29 30 31 33 34 35 36 38 39 45 54 55 56 57 59 61 62 63 64 65 68 74 75 77 78 79 81 82 83 84 85 86 87 91 93 94 96 97 100 101 102 104 107 114 119 127 128 130 132 135 143 144 146 147 148 149 153 154 156 157 158 **S** Department of Veterans Affairs, Washington, DC
Primary Contact: John Gennaro, FACHE, Director
CFO: Joann Pritchard, Chief Financial Officer
CMO: Anthony Behm, D.O., Chief of Staff
CIO: Jonathan Seale, Chief Information Officer
CHR: Lynn Nies, Human Resources Officer
CNO: Dorene M. Sommers, Associate Director Patient Care Services
Web address: www.erie.va.gov/
Control: Veterans Affairs, Government, federal **Service**: General medical and surgical

Staffed Beds: 52 **Admissions**: 359 **Census**: 46 **Outpatient Visits**: 255963 **Births**: 0 **Total Expense ($000)**: 148026 **Personnel**: 851

HAMOT MEDICAL CENTER See Upmc Hamot

○ **LECOM HEALTH MILLCREEK COMMUNITY HOSPITAL (390198)**, 5515 Peach Street, Zip 16509–2695; tel. 814/864–4031, (Nonreporting) **A**3 5 10 11 12 13
Primary Contact: Mary L. Eckert, President and Chief Executive Officer
CFO: Richard P Olinger, Chief Financial Officer
CMO: James Y Lin, D.O., Chief of Staff
CIO: Cheryl Girardier, Director Information Technology
CHR: Polly Momeyer, Manager Human Resources
CNO: Katie Agresti, R.N., Director Patient Care Services
Web address: www.millcreekcommunityhospital.com
Control: Other not–for–profit (including NFP Corporation) **Service**: General medical and surgical

Staffed Beds: 168

☒ **SAINT VINCENT HOSPITAL (390009)**, 232 West 25th Street, Zip 16544–0002; tel. 814/452–5000, **A**1 2 3 5 10 12 13 19 **F**3 7 8 11 12 13 15 17 18 20 22 24 26 28 29 30 31 34 35 37 39 40 44 45 46 47 48 49 50 54 56 57 58 59 60 61 64 65 68 70 71 72 74 75 76 77 78 79 80 81 84 85 86 87 89 90 92 96 98 100 101 102 103 107 108 110 111 115 118 119 121 123 124 128 130 132 135 141 146 147 148 149 154 **S** Allegheny Health Network, Pittsburgh, PA
Primary Contact: Christopher Clark, D.O., President and Chief Executive Officer
COO: Jason Roeback, Chief Operating Officer
CFO: Randolph Levis, Chief Financial Officer
CIO: Richard B Ong, Chief Information Officer
CHR: Johnie M Atkinson, Chief Human Resources Officer
Web address: www.svhs.org
Control: Other not–for–profit (including NFP Corporation) **Service**: General medical and surgical

Staffed Beds: 251 **Admissions**: 13111 **Census**: 179 **Outpatient Visits**: 159471 **Births**: 883 **Total Expense ($000)**: 272426 **Payroll Expense ($000)**: 86727 **Personnel**: 1659

☒ **SELECT SPECIALTY HOSPITAL-ERIE (392037)**, 252 West 11th Street, Zip 16501–1702; tel. 814/874–5300, (Nonreporting) **A**1 10 **S** Select Medical Corporation, Mechanicsburg, PA
Primary Contact: Karen Surkala, Chief Executive Officer
CNO: Keith Christiansen, Chief Nursing Officer
Web address: www.erie.selectspecialtyhospitals.com/
Control: Corporation, Investor–owned (for–profit) **Service**: Acute long–term care hospital

Staffed Beds: 50

☐ **UPMC HAMOT (390063)**, 201 State Street, Zip 16550–0002; tel. 814/877–6000, **A**1 2 3 5 10 19 **F**3 5 9 10 11 13 15 17 18 20 22 24 26 28 29 30 31 34 35 36 37 38 39 40 43 44 45 46 47 48 49 50 51 54 56 57 58 59 60 61 64 65 66 68 70 72 74 75 76 77 78 79 80 81 82 84 85 86 87 89 91 92 93 96 97 100 101 102 104 106 107 108 109 110 111 114 115 118 119 124 126 129 130 131 132 134 135 138 141 147 148 149 150 154 **S** UPMC, Pittsburgh, PA
Primary Contact: David Gibbons, President
CFO: Bradley Dinger, Chief Financial Officer
CMO: Richard Long, M.D., Chief Medical Officer
CIO: Lisa D McChesney, R.N., Senior Director Information Systems
CNO: James E Donnelly, Chief Nursing Officer and Vice President Patient Care Services
Web address: www.upmc.com/locations/hospitals/hamot
Control: Other not–for–profit (including NFP Corporation) **Service**: General medical and surgical

Staffed Beds: 365 **Admissions**: 20053 **Census**: 250 **Outpatient Visits**: 229992 **Births**: 2294 **Total Expense ($000)**: 373601 **Payroll Expense ($000)**: 104257 **Personnel**: 1954

VETERANS AFFAIRS MEDICAL CENTER See Erie Veterans Affairs Medical Center

---

Hospital, Medicare Provider Number, Address, Telephone, Approval, Facility, and Physician Codes, Health Care System
★ American Hospital Association (AHA) membership   ○ Healthcare Facilities Accreditation Program   ⇑ Center for Improvement in Healthcare Quality Accreditation
☐ The Joint Commission accreditation   ◇ DNV Healthcare Inc. accreditation   △ Commission on Accreditation of Rehabilitation Facilities (CARF) accreditation

PA

EVERETT—Bedford County

☐ **UPMC BEDFORD MEMORIAL (390117)**, 10455 Lincoln Highway, Zip 15537–7046; tel. 814/623–6161, **A**1 10 20 **F**3 8 11 15 18 28 29 30 31 34 35 36 38 40 45 50 51 56 57 59 61 64 65 68 70 74 75 77 78 79 81 85 86 87 89 102 107 108 110 111 114 119 129 130 131 132 135 146 147 148 149 154 156 **S** UPMC, Pittsburgh, PA
Primary Contact: Jan E. Fisher, President
CFO: Mario Wilfong, Vice President Finance and Administration
CIO: Mark Wiley, Manager Information Systems Development
CHR: Michelle A Speck, Vice President Human Resources
CNO: Paula Thomas, Vice President Patient Services
Web address: www.upmcbedfordmemorial.com
Control: Other not–for–profit (including NFP Corporation) **Service**: General medical and surgical

Staffed Beds: 27 **Admissions**: 1500 **Census**: 13 **Outpatient Visits**: 110750 **Births**: 126 **Total Expense ($000)**: 59381 **Payroll Expense ($000)**: 13735 **Personnel**: 239

FARRELL—Mercer County

SHENANGO VALLEY CAMPUS See Upmc Horizon, Farrell

☐ **UPMC HORIZON (390178)**, 2200 Memorial Drive, Zip 16121–1357; tel. 724/588–2100, (Includes GREENVILLE CAMPUS, 110 North Main Street, Greenville, Pennsylvania, Zip 16125–1795; tel. 724/588–2100; SHENANGO VALLEY CAMPUS, 2200 Memorial Drive, Farrell, Pennsylvania, Zip 16121–1398; tel. 724/981–3500) **A**1 3 10 13 **F**3 11 12 13 15 18 26 28 29 30 31 32 34 35 40 43 44 45 46 49 50 51 53 54 56 57 59 61 64 65 68 70 73 74 75 76 77 78 79 81 82 85 86 87 92 93 97 100 107 110 111 114 115 118 119 120 129 130 131 132 133 135 146 147 148 149 154 156 157 **S** UPMC, Pittsburgh, PA
Primary Contact: Donald R. Owrey, President
CFO: David Shulik, Vice President and Chief Financial Officer
CMO: Samuel Daisley, D.O., Vice President Medical Affairs
CHR: Connie Mayle, Vice President Administrative Services
Web address: www.upmc.com
Control: Other not–for–profit (including NFP Corporation) **Service**: General medical and surgical

Staffed Beds: 77 **Admissions**: 4845 **Census**: 49 **Outpatient Visits**: 212890 **Births**: 1022 **Total Expense ($000)**: 138726 **Payroll Expense ($000)**: 36225 **Personnel**: 619

FORT WASHINGTON—Montgomery County

☐ **BROOKE GLEN BEHAVIORAL HOSPITAL (394049)**, 7170 Lafayette Avenue, Zip 19034–2301; tel. 215/641–5300, (Nonreporting) **A**1 10 **S** Universal Health Services, Inc., King of Prussia, PA
Primary Contact: Neil Callahan, Chief Executive Officer
COO: William R Mason, Chief Operating Officer
CFO: Robert Zagerman, Chief Financial Officer
CMO: Chand Nair, M.D., Medical Director
CHR: Dawn Kownacki, Director Human Resources
Web address: www.brookeglenhospital.com
Control: Corporation, Investor–owned (for–profit) **Service**: Psychiatric

Staffed Beds: 146

GETTYSBURG—Adams County

⊞ ⇑ **WELLSPAN GETTYSBURG HOSPITAL (390065)**, 147 Gettys Street, Zip 17325–2534; tel. 717/334–2121, **A**1 3 10 21 **F**3 8 11 13 15 18 20 22 26 28 29 30 31 35 40 46 49 50 51 54 56 59 64 68 70 74 75 76 77 78 79 81 82 84 85 87 91 93 94 95 96 102 107 108 110 111 114 119 120 121 123 129 130 131 132 134 135 146 147 148 149 154 157 **S** WellSpan Health, York, PA
Primary Contact: Jane E. Hyde, President
COO: Joseph H Edgar, Senior Vice President Operations
CMO: Charles Marley, D.O., Vice President Medical Affairs
CIO: Robin Kimple, Director Information Services
CHR: Kim Brister, Director Human Resources
Web address: www.wellspan.org
Control: Other not–for–profit (including NFP Corporation) **Service**: General medical and surgical

Staffed Beds: 76 **Admissions**: 4175 **Census**: 46 **Outpatient Visits**: 191579 **Births**: 483 **Total Expense ($000)**: 169553 **Payroll Expense ($000)**: 43017 **Personnel**: 686

GREENSBURG—Westmoreland County

☐ **EXCELA HEALTH WESTMORELAND HOSPITAL (390145)**, 532 West Pittsburgh Street, Zip 15601–2282; tel. 724/832–4000, (Nonreporting) **A**1 3 5 10 **S** Excela Health, Greensburg, PA
Primary Contact: Robert Rogalski, Chief Executive Officer
COO: Michael D Busch, Executive Vice President and Chief Operating Officer
CFO: Jeffrey T Curry, Executive Vice President and Chief Financial Officer
CMO: Jerome Granato, M.D., Senior Vice President and Chief Medical Officer
CIO: David Gawaluck, Vice President and Chief Information Officer
CHR: John Caverno, Chief Human Resources Officer
CNO: Helen K Burns, Ph.D., R.N., Senior Vice President and Chief Nursing Officer
Web address: www.excelahealth.org
Control: Other not–for–profit (including NFP Corporation) **Service**: General medical and surgical

Staffed Beds: 270

GROVE CITY—Mercer County

GROVE CITY MEDICAL CENTER (390266), 631 North Broad Street Extension, Zip 16127–4603; tel. 724/450–7000, **A**10 **F**3 15 20 26 28 29 31 34 35 40 45 46 49 51 57 59 64 70 75 78 79 81 82 87 91 92 93 107 108 110 111 115 117 119 129 130 132 146 148 149
Primary Contact: Robert Jackson Jr, Chief Executive Officer
CFO: David Poland, Chief Financial Officer
CMO: Daniel Ferguson, Chief of Staff
CIO: Philip Swartwood, Director Information Systems
CHR: Donald Henley, Vice President Human Resources
CNO: Anthony Bono Jr Chief Nursing Officer
Web address: www.gcmcpa.org
Control: Other not–for–profit (including NFP Corporation) **Service**: General medical and surgical

Staffed Beds: 35 **Admissions**: 1411 **Census**: 13 **Outpatient Visits**: 101982 **Births**: 0 **Total Expense ($000)**: 44248 **Payroll Expense ($000)**: 16425 **Personnel**: 330

HANOVER—York County

☐ **UPMC HANOVER (390233)**, 300 Highland Avenue, Zip 17331–2297; tel. 717/316–3711, **A**1 10 **F**3 11 13 15 18 20 22 26 28 29 30 31 35 36 40 44 45 47 49 50 53 54 57 59 61 62 64 65 75 76 77 78 79 81 84 85 86 87 89 93 94 96 107 108 110 111 115 117 118 119 126 129 130 131 132 134 135 144 146 147 148 149 150 157 **S** UPMC, Pittsburgh, PA
Primary Contact: Michael W. Gaskins, President
COO: Michael A. Hockenberry, Senior Vice President and Chief Operating Officer
CFO: Donna L. Muller, Interim Chief Financial Officer
CMO: Michael H Ader, M.D., Vice President Medical Affairs
CIO: William C. Tandy, Chief Information Officer
CHR: Christine Miller, General Counsel and Vice President Human Resources
CNO: M Patricia Saunders, R.N., MS, Vice President Nursing
Web address: www.hanoverhospital.org
Control: Other not–for–profit (including NFP Corporation) **Service**: General medical and surgical

Staffed Beds: 93 **Admissions**: 5294 **Census**: 56 **Outpatient Visits**: 208054 **Births**: 505 **Total Expense ($000)**: 155412 **Payroll Expense ($000)**: 60359 **Personnel**: 950

HARRISBURG—Dauphin County

⊞ **HELEN M. SIMPSON REHABILITATION HOSPITAL (393056)**, 4300 Londonderry Road, Zip 17109–5317; tel. 717/920–4300, **A**1 13 **F**28 29 74 77 86 90 91 96 130 132 135 148 149 156 **S** Select Medical Corporation, Mechanicsburg, PA
Primary Contact: Mark Freeburn, Chief Executive Officer
Web address: www.simpson-rehab.com/
Control: Partnership, Investor–owned (for–profit) **Service**: Rehabilitation

Staffed Beds: 50 **Admissions**: 1173 **Census**: 39 **Outpatient Visits**: 0 **Births**: 0 **Personnel**: 157

⊞ **PENNSYLVANIA PSYCHIATRIC INSTITUTE (394051)**, 2501 North Third Street, Zip 17110–1904; tel. 717/782–6420, (Nonreporting) **A**1 3 5 10
Primary Contact: Kimberly Feeman, Interim Chief Executive Officer
CFO: Robert Fotter, Chief Financial Officer
CMO: Elisabeth J. Kunkel, M.D., Professor, Pennsylvania State College of Medicine
CHR: Wanda Geesey, Director Human Resources
CNO: Teresa Terry-Williams, R.N., Chief Nursing Officer
Web address: www.ppimhs.org/
Control: Other not–for–profit (including NFP Corporation) **Service**: Psychiatric

Staffed Beds: 72

Many Facility Codes have changed. Please refer to the AHA Guide Code Chart. © 2019 AHA Guide

PINNACLEHEALTH AT COMMUNITY GENERAL OSTEOPATHIC HOSPITAL See Upmc Pinnacle Harrisburg, Harrisburg

SELECT SPECIALTY HOSPITAL-HARRISBURG See Select Specialty Hospital-Camp Hill, Camp Hill

☐ **UPMC PINNACLE HARRISBURG (390067)**, 111 South Front Street, Zip 17101–2010, Mailing Address: P.O. Box 8700, Zip 17105–8700; tel. 717/231–8900, (Includes PINNACLEHEALTH AT COMMUNITY GENERAL OSTEOPATHIC HOSPITAL, 4300 Londonderry Road, Harrisburg, Pennsylvania, Zip 17109–5397, Mailing Address: P O Box 3000, Zip 17105–3000, tel. 717/652–3000; PINNACLEHEALTH AT HARRISBURG HOSPITAL, 111 South Front Street, Harrisburg, Pennsylvania, Zip 17101–2099; tel. 717/782–3131; PINNACLEHEALTH WEST SHORE HOSPITAL, 1995 Technology Parkway, Mechanicsburg, Pennsylvania, Zip 17050–8522; tel. 717/791–2600) **A**1 2 3 5 10 12 19 **F**3 7 8 11 12 13 14 15 17 18 19 20 22 24 26 27 28 29 30 31 32 34 35 36 37 38 40 44 45 46 47 48 49 50 52 54 55 56 57 58 59 60 61 64 65 66 68 70 72 74 75 76 77 78 79 81 84 85 86 87 89 93 97 100 107 108 109 110 111 114 115 116 117 118 119 120 121 123 124 126 129 130 131 132 134 138 141 142 143 144 145 146 147 148 149 154 156 157 **S** UPMC, Pittsburgh, PA
Primary Contact: Philip Guarneschelli, Interim Chief Executive Officer
COO: Mark Sevco, Chief Operating Officer
CFO: William H Pugh, Senior Vice President Corporate Finance and Chief Financial Officer
CMO: Nirmal Joshi, M.D., Senior Vice President Medical Affairs and Chief Medical Officer
CHR: Ann H Gormley, Senior Vice President Human Resources
CNO: Susan Comp, Senior Vice President and Chief Nursing Officer
Web address: www.pinnaclehealth.org
Control: Other not–for–profit (including NFP Corporation) **Service:** General medical and surgical

Staffed Beds: 655 **Admissions:** 35835 **Census:** 422 **Outpatient Visits:** 862488 **Births:** 3706 **Total Expense ($000):** 864635 **Payroll Expense ($000):** 302347 **Personnel:** 4427

HASTINGS—Cambria County

⊞ **CONEMAUGH MINERS MEDICAL CENTER (390130)**, 290 Haida Avenue, Zip 16646–5610, Mailing Address: P.O. Box 689, Zip 16646–0689; tel. 814/247–3100, **A**1 10 20 **F**3 15 18 29 30 31 35 36 40 45 48 50 56 59 64 70 75 78 79 81 86 92 93 96 97 102 107 108 110 119 129 133 148 **S** Duke LifePoint Healthcare, Brentwood, TN
Primary Contact: Timothy Harclerode, Chief Executive Officer
COO: Debbie Spells-Wilson, R.N., Chief Operating Officer and Chief Nursing Officer
CFO: Linda Fanale, Chief Financial Officer
CMO: Susan Williams, M.D., Chief Medical Officer
CIO: Joe Dado, Chief Information Officer
CNO: Debbie Spells-Wilson, R.N., Chief Operating Officer and Chief Nursing Officer
Web address: www.conemaugh.org
Control: Corporation, Investor–owned (for–profit) **Service:** General medical and surgical

Staffed Beds: 30 **Admissions:** 342 **Census:** 4 **Outpatient Visits:** 37518 **Births:** 0 **Total Expense ($000):** 17331 **Payroll Expense ($000):** 5265 **Personnel:** 105

HAZLETON—Luzerne County

★ ○ **LEHIGH VALLEY HOSPITAL - HAZLETON (390185)**, 700 East Broad Street, Zip 18201–6897; tel. 570/501–4000, **A**10 11 **F**3 8 9 11 12 13 15 18 28 29 31 33 34 35 40 43 44 50 53 54 57 59 60 62 64 68 69 70 75 76 77 78 79 81 82 85 86 87 89 90 93 107 108 110 111 114 118 119 129 130 131 132 135 143 144 146 147 148 154 **S** Lehigh Valley Health Network, Allentown, PA
Primary Contact: John R. Fletcher, President
CFO: William Bauer, Vice President Finance and Chief Financial Officer
CMO: Anthony Valente, M.D., Vice President Medical Affairs
CIO: Carl Shoener, Chief Information Officer
Web address: www.lvhn.org/hazleton/
Control: Other not–for–profit (including NFP Corporation) **Service:** General medical and surgical

Staffed Beds: 120 **Admissions:** 6002 **Census:** 71 **Outpatient Visits:** 156434 **Births:** 797 **Total Expense ($000):** 111169 **Payroll Expense ($000):** 37510 **Personnel:** 794

HERSHEY—Dauphin County

⊞ **PENN STATE MILTON S. HERSHEY MEDICAL CENTER (390256)**, 500 University Drive, Zip 17033–2360, Mailing Address: P.O. Box 850, Zip 17033–0850; tel. 717/531–8521, (Includes PENN STATE CHILDREN'S HOSPITAL, 500 University Drive, Hershey, Pennsylvania, Zip 17033–2360; tel. 717/531–8521) **A**1 2 3 5 8 9 10 19 **F**3 5 6 7 8 9 11 12 13 14 15 17 18 19 20 21 22 23 24 25 26 27 28 29 30 31 32 34 35 36 37 38 40 41 43 44 45 46 47 48 49 50 51 52 53 54 55 56 57 58 59 60 61 64 65 66 68 70 71 72 73 74 75 76 77 78 79 80 81 82 84 85 86 87 88 89 91 92 93 95 96 97 100 101 102 104 105 107 108 110 111 114 115 116 117 118 119 120 121 123 124 126 129 130 131 132 134 135 136 137 138 139 141 142 143 144 145 146 147 148 149 150 151 153 154 155 156 157 **S** Penn State Hershey Health System, Hershey, PA
Primary Contact: Stephen M. Massini, Chief Executive Officer
CMO: Thomas Tracy Jr Chief Medical Officer
CIO: Rod Dykehouse, Chief Information Officer
CHR: David Swift, Chief Human Resources Officer
CNO: Judy N. Himes, MSN, R.N., Chief Nursing Officer
Web address: www.pennstatehershey.org/
Control: Other not–for–profit (including NFP Corporation) **Service:** General medical and surgical

Staffed Beds: 528 **Admissions:** 27243 **Census:** 455 **Outpatient Visits:** 1074825 **Births:** 2154 **Total Expense ($000):** 1485219 **Payroll Expense ($000):** 424044 **Personnel:** 9185

HONESDALE—Wayne County

★ **WAYNE MEMORIAL HOSPITAL (390125)**, 601 Park Street, Zip 18431–1498; tel. 570/253–8100, **A**10 20 **F**3 13 15 18 20 22 26 28 29 31 34 35 39 40 43 46 49 57 59 62 63 70 74 75 76 77 78 81 85 86 90 92 93 100 107 108 110 111 119 128 129 130 132 133 135 146 148 149 154
Primary Contact: David L. Hoff, Chief Executive Officer
COO: John Conte, Director Facility Services and Real Estate
CFO: Michael J Clifford, Director Finance
CMO: William Dewar, M.D., Chief of Staff
CIO: Tom Hoffman, Manager Information Systems
CHR: Elizabeth McDonald, Director Human Resources
CNO: Jim Pettinato, Director Patient Care Services
Web address: www.wmh.org
Control: Other not–for–profit (including NFP Corporation) **Service:** General medical and surgical

Staffed Beds: 87 **Admissions:** 3299 **Census:** 36 **Outpatient Visits:** 157674 **Births:** 437 **Total Expense ($000):** 90330 **Payroll Expense ($000):** 35166 **Personnel:** 638

HUMMELSTOWN—Dauphin County

Ⓐ △ **PENN STATE HERSHEY REHABILITATION HOSPITAL (393053)**, 1135 Old West Chocolate Avenue, Zip 17036; tel. 717/832–2600, (Total facility includes 22 beds in nursing home–type unit) **A**1 3 5 7 10 **F**3 29 60 90 93 96 128 130 132 148 149 **S** Select Medical Corporation, Mechanicsburg, PA
Primary Contact: Michelle Von Arx, Chief Executive Officer
CMO: Brenda Mallory, M.D., Medical Director
Web address: www.psh-rehab.com
Control: Corporation, Investor–owned (for–profit) **Service:** Rehabilitation

Staffed Beds: 98 **Admissions:** 1771 **Census:** 66 **Outpatient Visits:** 0 **Births:** 0 **Personnel:** 237

HUNTINGDON—Huntingdon County

⊞ **J. C. BLAIR MEMORIAL HOSPITAL (390056)**, 1225 Warm Springs Avenue, Zip 16652–2398; tel. 814/643–2290, **A**1 10 20 **F**3 11 13 15 18 20 22 26 28 29 34 43 45 50 53 55 56 59 64 70 75 76 77 79 81 84 85 86 87 89 96 98 100 103 107 108 110 111 115 118 119 129 130 132 133 135 144 146 148 154 156
Primary Contact: Joseph Myers, Interim Administrator
COO: Adam Dimm, Chief Executive Officer
CMO: James Hayden, M.D., Chief Medical Officer
CIO: Armen Arakelian, Chief Information Officer
CHR: Susan Hess, Director Human Resources
CNO: Joye Gingrich, Director Patient Care Services and Chief Nursing Officer
Web address: www.jcblair.org
Control: Other not–for–profit (including NFP Corporation) **Service:** General medical and surgical

Staffed Beds: 62 **Admissions:** 2372 **Census:** 30 **Outpatient Visits:** 108563 **Births:** 212 **Total Expense ($000):** 53454 **Payroll Expense ($000):** 22654 **Personnel:** 398

PA

Hospital, Medicare Provider Number, Address, Telephone, Approval, Facility, and Physician Codes, Health Care System

★ American Hospital Association (AHA) membership
☐ The Joint Commission accreditation
○ Healthcare Facilities Accreditation Program
◇ DNV Healthcare Inc. accreditation
⇑ Center for Improvement in Healthcare Quality Accreditation
△ Commission on Accreditation of Rehabilitation Facilities (CARF) accreditation

INDIANA—Indiana County

★ **INDIANA REGIONAL MEDICAL CENTER (390173)**, 835 Hospital Road, Zip 15701–3629, Mailing Address: P.O. Box 788, Zip 15701–0788; tel. 724/357–7000, **A**2 10 20 22 **F**3 11 15 18 20 22 28 29 31 34 35 40 44 45 46 47 49 53 56 57 59 64 65 70 71 74 75 76 77 78 79 81 82 83 84 85 90 91 96 98 102 103 107 108 111 114 115 118 119 120 121 123 124 126 129 130 132 144 145 146 147 148 149 154 156 157
Primary Contact: Stephen A. Wolfe, President and Chief Executive Officer
COO: Dominic Paccapaniccia, Chief Operating Officer
CFO: Robert Gongaware, Senior Vice President Finance
CMO: Bruce A Bush, M.D., Senior Vice President Medical Affairs
CIO: Mark Volovic, Vice President and Chief Information Officer
CHR: James W Kinneer, Vice President Organizational Development
CNO: Cindy L Virgil, MSN, R.N., Senior Vice President Patient Care Services
Web address: www.indianarmc.org
Control: Other not–for–profit (including NFP Corporation) **Service**: General medical and surgical

Staffed Beds: 166 **Admissions**: 6596 **Census**: 75 **Outpatient Visits**: 255284 **Births**: 525 **Total Expense ($000)**: 153546 **Payroll Expense ($000)**: 63503 **Personnel**: 939

JEFFERSON HILLS—Allegheny County

✉ **JEFFERSON HOSPITAL (390265)**, 565 Coal Valley Road, Zip 15025–3703, Mailing Address: Box 18119, Pittsburgh, Zip 15236–0119; tel. 412/469–5000, **A**1 2 3 10 **F**3 11 12 13 15 17 18 20 22 24 26 28 29 30 31 34 35 36 40 44 45 46 47 48 49 50 54 57 59 60 64 70 73 74 75 76 77 78 79 81 82 84 85 86 87 89 90 92 93 96 98 100 101 102 104 107 108 110 111 114 115 117 118 119 126 129 130 131 132 135 141 146 147 148 149 153 154 **S** Allegheny Health Network, Pittsburgh, PA
Primary Contact: Louise Urban, R.N., President and Chief Executive Officer
CMO: Richard F Collins, M.D., Executive Vice President and Chief Medical Officer
CIO: James Witenske, Chief Information Officer
CNO: Kimberley Finnerty, MSN, R.N., Chief Nursing Officer
Web address: www.jeffersonregional.com
Control: Other not–for–profit (including NFP Corporation) **Service**: General medical and surgical

Staffed Beds: 242 **Admissions**: 13967 **Census**: 176 **Outpatient Visits**: 275280 **Births**: 1041 **Total Expense ($000)**: 246305 **Payroll Expense ($000)**: 81920 **Personnel**: 1451

JERSEY SHORE—Lycoming County

✉ **GEISINGER JERSEY SHORE HOSPITAL (391300)**, 1020 Thompson Street, Zip 17740–1794; tel. 570/398–0100, **A**1 10 18 **F**3 7 12 15 18 28 29 30 34 35 40 45 50 54 57 59 65 68 75 81 85 93 107 108 110 111 115 119 129 130 133 135 144 155 156 **S** Geisinger, Danville, PA
Primary Contact: Tammy Anderer, Acting President
CFO: Mark Rice, CPA, Chief Financial Officer
CMO: Stephen Goykovich, D.O., Chief Medical Officer
CIO: Christine Haas, Chief Information Officer
CHR: Joan Rounsley, Director Human Resources
CNO: Paulette Nish, Chief Nursing Officer
Web address: www.jsh.org
Control: Other not–for–profit (including NFP Corporation) **Service**: General medical and surgical

Staffed Beds: 25 **Admissions**: 671 **Census**: 6 **Outpatient Visits**: 71212 **Births**: 0 **Total Expense ($000)**: 24684 **Payroll Expense ($000)**: 12398 **Personnel**: 211

JOHNSTOWN—Cambria County

✉ **CONEMAUGH MEMORIAL MEDICAL CENTER (390110)**, 1086 Franklin Street, Zip 15905–4398; tel. 814/534–9000, (Includes MEMORIAL MEDICAL CENTER - LEE CAMPUS, 320 Main Street, Johnstown, Pennsylvania, Zip 15901–1601; tel. 814/533–0123) **A**1 3 5 10 13 **F**3 5 7 8 12 13 14 15 17 18 20 22 24 26 28 29 30 31 32 34 35 36 37 40 43 44 45 46 49 50 53 54 55 56 57 58 59 60 61 64 65 68 70 72 74 75 76 77 78 79 81 82 83 84 85 86 87 89 90 92 93 96 97 98 99 100 101 102 103 104 107 108 109 110 111 114 115 117 118 119 120 121 122 123 124 126 128 129 130 131 132 134 144 145 146 147 148 149 150 154 155 156 **S** Duke LifePoint Healthcare, Brentwood, TN
Primary Contact: William E. Caldwell Jr, FACHE, Chief Executive Officer
CMO: Susan Williams, M.D., Chief Medical Officer
CIO: Joe Dado, Chief Information Officer
CNO: Claudia Rager, R.N., Vice President Patient Care Services
Web address: www.conemaugh.org
Control: Corporation, Investor–owned (for–profit) **Service**: General medical and surgical

Staffed Beds: 539 **Admissions**: 18738 **Census**: 264 **Outpatient Visits**: 493230 **Births**: 1864 **Total Expense ($000)**: 363898 **Payroll Expense ($000)**: 137243 **Personnel**: 2356

MEMORIAL MEDICAL CENTER - LEE CAMPUS See Conemaugh Memorial Medical Center, Johnstown

✉ **SELECT SPECIALTY HOSPITAL-JOHNSTOWN (392031)**, 320 Main Street, 3rd Floor, Zip 15901–1601; tel. 814/534–7300, (Nonreporting) **A**1 10 **S** Select Medical Corporation, Mechanicsburg, PA
Primary Contact: Kelly Blake, Chief Executive Officer
CMO: Gary Davidson, M.D., Medical Director
Web address: www.selectspecialtyhospitals.com/company/locations/johnstown.aspx
Control: Corporation, Investor–owned (for–profit) **Service**: Acute long–term care hospital

Staffed Beds: 39

KANE—Mckean County

UPMC KANE (390104), 4372 Route 6, Zip 16735–3060; tel. 814/837–8585, **A**10 20 **F**3 11 15 17 18 28 29 30 34 35 40 41 45 46 50 53 57 59 64 65 70 75 77 78 79 81 82 85 89 107 108 110 111 115 117 118 128 130 131 132 133 135 145 146 147 149 156 **S** UPMC, Pittsburgh, PA
Primary Contact: Mark Papalia, President
CFO: Angela Hadzega, Chief Financial Officer
CMO: Linda Rettger, M.D., President Medical Staff
CIO: Deano Cherry, Chief Information Officer
CHR: Marsha Keller, Director Human Resources
CNO: Pam Bray, Director of Nursing and Director Inpatient Services
Web address: www.kanehosp.com
Control: Other not–for–profit (including NFP Corporation) **Service**: General medical and surgical

Staffed Beds: 31 **Admissions**: 441 **Census**: 5 **Outpatient Visits**: 76945 **Births**: 0 **Total Expense ($000)**: 22462 **Payroll Expense ($000)**: 10726 **Personnel**: 125

KINGSTON—Luzerne County

✉ **FIRST HOSPITAL WYOMING VALLEY (394039)**, 562 Wyoming Avenue, Zip 18704–3721; tel. 570/552–3900, (Nonreporting) **A**1 3 10 **S** Community Health Systems, Inc., Franklin, TN
Primary Contact: Greg Shannon, Chief Executive Officer
CFO: Kelly Knorr, Chief Financial Officer
CMO: David Liskov, M.D., Medical Director
CNO: Rhonda Moffitt Sod, Chief Nursing Officer
Web address: www.commonwealthhealth.net/locations/first-hospital
Control: Corporation, Investor–owned (for–profit) **Service**: Psychiatric

Staffed Beds: 149

KITTANNING—Armstrong County

⇑ **ACMH HOSPITAL (390163)**, One Nolte Drive, Zip 16201–7111; tel. 724/543–8500, (Total facility includes 17 beds in nursing home–type unit) **A**2 10 19 21 **F**3 4 11 13 15 17 18 20 22 26 28 29 30 34 35 40 45 47 49 59 70 74 75 76 77 78 79 81 82 85 90 93 98 100 102 107 108 110 111 112 114 119 120 126 127 128 129 130 131 132 135 136 141 142 146 148 149 151 154 156
Primary Contact: John I. Lewis, President and Chief Executive Officer
CFO: Patrick Burns, Vice President Finance
CMO: Harold Altman, M.D., Chief Medical Officer
CIO: Dianne Emminger, Vice President Information Services
CHR: Anne Remaley, Vice President Human Resources
Web address: www.acmh.org
Control: Other not–for–profit (including NFP Corporation) **Service**: General medical and surgical

Staffed Beds: 164 **Admissions**: 4773 **Census**: 63 **Outpatient Visits**: 257149 **Births**: 397 **Total Expense ($000)**: 97124 **Payroll Expense ($000)**: 43177 **Personnel**: 817

LANCASTER—Lancaster County

☐ **LANCASTER REHABILITATION HOSPITAL (393054)**, 675 Good Drive, Zip 17601–2426; tel. 717/406–3000, (Nonreporting) **A**1 10
Primary Contact: Tammy Derk, Chief Executive Officer
CFO: David Stark, Chief Financial Officer
CHR: Lisa Andrews, Director Human Resources
Web address: www.lancastergeneral.org
Control: Corporation, Investor–owned (for–profit) **Service**: Rehabilitation

Staffed Beds: 10

Many Facility Codes have changed. Please refer to the AHA Guide Code Chart. © 2019 AHA Guide

⊞ PENN MEDICINE LANCASTER GENERAL HOSPITAL (390100), 555 North Duke Street, Zip 17602–2250; tel. 717/544–5511, **A**1 2 3 5 10 **F**3 11 12 13 14 15 17 18 20 22 24 26 28 29 30 31 32 34 35 36 38 39 40 43 44 45 46 47 48 49 50 54 55 56 57 58 59 60 61 64 65 66 68 70 72 73 74 75 76 77 78 79 80 81 82 84 85 86 87 89 91 92 93 94 95 96 97 98 100 101 102 107 108 110 114 115 118 119 120 121 123 124 126 129 130 132 135 141 142 145 146 147 148 149 150 154 156 157 **S** University of Pennsylvania Health System, Philadelphia, PA
Primary Contact: Jan L. Bergen, President and Chief Executive Officer
CFO: Joseph Byorick, Senior Vice President and Chief Financial Officer
CMO: Lee M Duke, M.D., II Senior Vice President and Chief Physician Executive
CIO: Gary Davidson, Senior Vice President and Chief Information Officer
CHR: Regina Mingle, Senior Vice President and Chief Leadership Officer
CNO: Lanyce Roldan, Chief Nursing Officer
Web address: www.lancastergeneralhealth.org
Control: Other not–for–profit (including NFP Corporation) **Service:** General medical and surgical

Staffed Beds: 616 Admissions: 33797 Census: 418 Outpatient Visits: 1626983 Births: 4310 Total Expense ($000): 948276 Payroll Expense ($000): 364085 Personnel: 5314

LANGHORNE—Bucks County

☐ BARIX CLINICS OF PENNSYLVANIA (390302), 280 Middletown Boulevard, Zip 19047–1816; tel. 267/572–3100, (Nonreporting) **A**1 10
Primary Contact: Tony Adams, President
Web address: www.barixclinics.com
Control: Partnership, Investor–owned (for–profit) **Service:** Surgical

Staffed Beds: 40

BUCKS COUNTY CAMPUS See Jefferson Health Northeast, Philadelphia

⊞ ST. MARY MEDICAL CENTER (390258), 1201 Langhorne-Newtown Road, Zip 19047–1201; tel. 215/710–2000, **A**1 2 3 5 10 19 **F**3 7 12 15 17 18 20 22 24 26 29 30 31 32 34 35 36 37 39 40 43 44 45 46 49 50 51 53 54 56 57 58 59 63 64 70 72 74 76 77 78 79 80 81 82 84 85 86 87 89 91 92 93 94 96 107 108 110 111 112 114 115 117 118 119 120 121 123 124 126 129 130 131 132 135 146 147 149 154 156 **S** Trinity Health, Livonia, MI
Primary Contact: Lawrence Brilliant, M.D., Vice President and Chief Medical Officer
COO: Jeffrey N Yarmel, Chief Operating Officer
CFO: Daniel Confalone, Chief Financial Officer and Vice President Finance
CMO: Lawrence Brilliant, M.D., Vice President and Chief Medical Officer
CIO: Bonnie Buehler, Chief Information Officer
CNO: Sharon Brown, Vice President Patient Care and Chief Nursing Officer
Web address: www.stmaryhealthcare.org
Control: Church operated, Nongovernment, not–for–profit **Service:** General medical and surgical

Staffed Beds: 353 Admissions: 20526 Census: 227 Outpatient Visits: 298610 Births: 2090 Total Expense ($000): 374857 Payroll Expense ($000): 137639

☐ ST. MARY REHABILITATION HOSPITAL (393055), 1201 Langhorne Newtown Road, Zip 19047–1201, Mailing Address: 1208 Langhorne Newtown Road, Zip 19047–1234; tel. 267/560–1111, (Nonreporting) **A**1 **S** Kindred Healthcare, Louisville, KY
Primary Contact: Lisa Haney, Chief Executive Officer
Web address: www.stmaryhealthcare.org
Control: Church operated, Nongovernment, not–for–profit **Service:** Rehabilitation

Staffed Beds: 50

LANSDALE—Montgomery County

⊞ ABINGTON-LANSDALE HOSPITAL JEFFERSON HEALTH (390012), 100 Medical Campus Drive, Zip 19446–1200; tel. 215/368–2100, **A**1 3 10 **F**2 3 11 15 18 28 29 30 32 34 35 36 37 40 44 45 49 50 53 56 57 59 63 64 65 66 68 70 74 75 77 79 81 82 84 85 86 87 93 96 97 107 108 110 111 114 115 119 129 130 131 132 135 146 147 148 149 150 154 156 **S** Jefferson Health, Philadelphia, PA
Primary Contact: Kathleen Farrell, Chief Administrative Officer
CFO: Michael Walsh, Senior Vice President Finance and Chief Financial Officer
CMO: Michel Taupin, M.D., Chief Medical Officer
CIO: Alison Ferren, Vice President Information Technology and Chief Information Officer
CHR: Meghan Patton, Vice President Human Resources
CNO: Kelly Cummings, Chief Nursing Officer
Web address: www.abingtonhealth.org/find-a-location/abington-lansdale-hospital/#.V5dyVVL9yk4
Control: Other not–for–profit (including NFP Corporation) **Service:** General medical and surgical

Staffed Beds: 127 Admissions: 5876 Census: 53 Outpatient Visits: 78332 Births: 0 Total Expense ($000): 83922 Payroll Expense ($000): 30765 Personnel: 336

LATROBE—Westmoreland County

☐ EXCELA LATROBE AREA HOSPITAL (390219), One Mellon Way, Zip 15650–1096; tel. 724/537–1000, (Nonreporting) **A**1 2 3 5 10 13 **S** Excela Health, Greensburg, PA
Primary Contact: Michael D. Busch, Executive Vice President and Chief Operating Officer
COO: Michael D Busch, Executive Vice President and Chief Operating Officer
CMO: Carol J. Fox, M.D., Senior Vice President and Chief Medical Officer
CIO: David Gawaluck, Vice President and Chief Information Officer
CHR: Laurie English, Senior Vice President and Chief Human Resource Officer
CNO: Helen K Burns, Ph.D., R.N., Senior Vice President and Chief Nursing Officer
Web address: www.excelahealth.org
Control: Other not–for–profit (including NFP Corporation) **Service:** General medical and surgical

Staffed Beds: 114

⊞ SELECT SPECIALTY HOSPITAL-LAUREL HIGHLANDS (392036), One Mellon Way, 3rd Floor, Zip 15650–1197; tel. 724/539–3870, (Nonreporting) **A**1 10 **S** Select Medical Corporation, Mechanicsburg, PA
Primary Contact: Eric Schwab, Chief Executive Officer
Web address: www.laurelhighlands.selectspecialtyhospitals.com/
Control: Corporation, Investor–owned (for–profit) **Service:** Acute long–term care hospital

Staffed Beds: 40

LEBANON—Lebanon County

⊞ LEBANON VETERANS AFFAIRS MEDICAL CENTER, 1700 South Lincoln Avenue, Zip 17042–7529; tel. 717/272–6621, (Nonreporting) **A**1 3 5 **S** Department of Veterans Affairs, Washington, DC
Primary Contact: Margaret G. Wilson, R.N., MSN, Acting Director
CFO: Geoffrey Smith, Chief Financial Officer
CMO: Kanan Chatterjee, M.D., Chief of Staff
CIO: Andru Ditzler, Chief Information Officer
CHR: Cindy Shiner, Manager Human Resources
Web address: www.lebanon.va.gov
Control: Veterans Affairs, Government, federal **Service:** General medical and surgical

Staffed Beds: 213

VETERANS AFFAIRS MEDICAL CENTER See Lebanon Veterans Affairs Medical Center

---

Hospital, Medicare Provider Number, Address, Telephone, Approval, Facility, and Physician Codes, Health Care System

★ American Hospital Association (AHA) membership
☐ The Joint Commission accreditation
○ Healthcare Facilities Accreditation Program
◇ DNV Healthcare Inc. accreditation
⇑ Center for Improvement in Healthcare Quality Accreditation
△ Commission on Accreditation of Rehabilitation Facilities (CARF) accreditation

PA

⊞ **WELLSPAN GOOD SAMARITAN HOSPITAL (390066)**, Fourth and Walnut Streets, Zip 17042–1281, Mailing Address: P.O. Box 1281, Zip 17042–1281; tel. 717/270–7500, **A**1 3 10 13 **F**3 8 11 13 14 15 17 18 20 22 24 26 28 29 30 31 34 35 40 45 49 50 55 57 58 59 62 63 64 68 70 74 75 76 77 78 79 80 81 82 85 87 90 91 92 93 94 96 97 107 110 111 114 115 116 117 118 119 120 121 124 126 129 130 132 135 146 148 149 156 **S** WellSpan Health, York, PA
Primary Contact: Thomas R. Harlow, FACHE, President
COO: Kimberly Feeman, Senior Vice President and Chief Operating Officer
CMO: Robert D Shaver, M.D., Vice President Medical Affairs
CIO: Leon John Jabour, Regional Chief Information Officer
CHR: Denise M Garman, Director Human Resources
CNO: Jacquelyn M Gould, MS, R.N., Vice President Patient Care Services and Chief Nursing Officer
Web address: www.gshleb.org
Control: Other not–for–profit (including NFP Corporation) **Service**: General medical and surgical

Staffed Beds: 151 **Admissions**: 7283 **Census**: 83 **Outpatient Visits**: 282563 **Births**: 751 **Total Expense ($000)**: 213609 **Payroll Expense ($000)**: 60383 **Personnel**: 884

LEHIGHTON—Carbon County

⊞ △ **ST. LUKE'S - GNADEN HUETTEN CAMPUS (390194)**, 211 North 12th Street, Zip 18235–1138; tel. 610/377–1300, (Includes ST. LUKE'S - PALMERTON CAMPUS, 135 Lafayette Avenue, Palmerton, Pennsylvania, Zip 18071–1596; tel. 610/826–3141; John L Nespoli, President) (Total facility includes 91 beds in nursing home–type unit) **A**1 7 10 **F**2 3 11 15 16 17 18 28 29 30 34 35 38 40 46 49 50 54 56 57 59 60 64 68 70 72 73 74 75 79 80 81 85 87 88 90 93 98 100 102 103 104 105 107 108 110 111 114 119 128 130 132 134 135 146 148 149 153 154 **S** St. Luke's University Health Network, Bethlehem, PA
Primary Contact: John L. Nespoli, President
CFO: Andrea Andrae, Chief Financial Officer
CMO: Patrick Hanley, D.O., Interim Vice President Medical Affairs
CIO: Steve Kinkaid, Director Information Systems
Web address: www.blmtn.org
Control: Other not–for–profit (including NFP Corporation) **Service**: General medical and surgical

Staffed Beds: 250 **Admissions**: 1441 **Census**: 13 **Outpatient Visits**: 33268 **Births**: 0 **Total Expense ($000)**: 36185 **Payroll Expense ($000)**: 16099 **Personnel**: 754

LEWISBURG—Union County

EVANGELICAL COMMUNITY HOSPITAL (390013), One Hospital Drive, Zip 17837–9350; tel. 570/522–2000, **A**10 19 **F**3 8 12 13 15 18 20 22 28 29 30 31 34 35 40 43 45 49 50 51 54 57 59 63 64 65 68 71 74 75 76 77 78 79 80 81 82 84 85 86 87 90 91 92 93 94 96 97 107 108 110 111 114 115 116 117 118 119 129 130 131 132 135 144 146 147 148 156 157
Primary Contact: Kendra A. Aucker, President and Chief Executive Officer
COO: Kendra A. Aucker, Vice President Operations
CFO: Jim Stopper, CPA, Chief Financial Officer
CMO: J Lawrence Ginsburg, M.D., Vice President Medical Affairs
CIO: Dale Moyer, Vice President Information Systems
CHR: Angela Hummel, Vice President Human Resources
CNO: Tamara F. Persing MHA, BSN, Chief Nursing Officer
Web address: www.evanhospital.com
Control: Other not–for–profit (including NFP Corporation) **Service**: General medical and surgical

Staffed Beds: 132 **Admissions**: 5682 **Census**: 49 **Outpatient Visits**: 245775 **Births**: 870 **Total Expense ($000)**: 166213 **Payroll Expense ($000)**: 67100 **Personnel**: 1403

U. S. PENITENTIARY INFIRMARY, Route 7, Zip 17837–9303; tel. 570/523–1251, (Nonreporting)
Primary Contact: Steve Brown, Health Services Director
Control: Department of Justice, Government, federal **Service**: Hospital unit of an institution (prison hospital, college infirmary, etc.)

Staffed Beds: 17

LEWISTOWN—Mifflin County

⊞ **GEISINGER-LEWISTOWN HOSPITAL (390048)**, 400 Highland Avenue, Zip 17044–1198; tel. 717/248–5411, **A**1 2 3 10 **F**3 11 13 15 17 18 28 29 30 31 34 35 40 41 45 46 49 50 51 57 59 64 70 71 74 75 76 78 79 81 82 84 85 86 87 98 100 101 102 103 107 108 110 111 114 115 116 117 118 119 120 121 123 124 129 130 131 132 135 146 147 148 149 154 156 157 **S** Geisinger, Danville, PA
Primary Contact: Kirk E. Thomas, Chief Administrative Officer
COO: Kirk E Thomas, Chief Administrative Officer
CFO: Kristy Hine, Associate Vice President Finance
CMO: Michael T Hegstrom, M.D., Chief Medical Officer
CIO: Ronald M Cowan, Vice President Information Systems
CHR: N Sue Reinke, Vice President Human Resources
CNO: Christine Mathews, R.N., MSN, Vice President Nursing Services
Web address: www.geisinger.org
Control: Other not–for–profit (including NFP Corporation) **Service**: General medical and surgical

Staffed Beds: 123 **Admissions**: 4902 **Census**: 53 **Outpatient Visits**: 191526 **Births**: 570 **Total Expense ($000)**: 112078 **Payroll Expense ($000)**: 41530 **Personnel**: 953

LITITZ—Lancaster County

☐ **UPMC LITITZ (390068)**, 1500 Highlands Drive, Zip 17543–7694; tel. 717/625–5000, (Nonreporting) **A**1 3 5 10 13 **S** UPMC, Pittsburgh, PA
Primary Contact: Deborah J. Willwerth, R.N., MSN, Chief Executive Officer
CIO: David Fisher, Director Information Systems
Web address: www.heartoflancaster.com
Control: Other not–for–profit (including NFP Corporation) **Service**: General medical and surgical

Staffed Beds: 148

LOCK HAVEN—Clinton County

⊞ **UPMC SUSQUEHANNA LOCK HAVEN (390071)**, 24 Cree Drive, Zip 17745–2699; tel. 570/893–5000, (Total facility includes 90 beds in nursing home–type unit) (Data for 273 days) **A**1 10 **F**3 6 11 15 29 30 34 35 40 45 46 50 54 56 57 59 62 67 68 70 77 79 81 82 85 86 87 90 93 96 97 107 108 110 111 114 118 119 128 130 131 132 146 150 154 157 **S** UPMC Susquehanna, Williamsport, PA
Primary Contact: Ronald J. Reynolds, President
CFO: Jennifer Lesher, Chief Financial Officer
CMO: Rajesh Patel, M.D., Chief of Staff
CIO: Judy Chapman, Interim Director Information Systems
CHR: Courtney Kunes, Director Human Resources
Web address: www.lockhavenhospital.com
Control: Other not–for–profit (including NFP Corporation) **Service**: General medical and surgical

Staffed Beds: 102 **Admissions**: 868 **Census**: 105 **Outpatient Visits**: 22179 **Births**: 0 **Total Expense ($000)**: 22268 **Payroll Expense ($000)**: 9138 **Personnel**: 182

MALVERN—Chester County

⊞ △ **BRYN MAWR REHABILITATION HOSPITAL (393025)**, 414 Paoli Pike, Zip 19355–3300, Mailing Address: P.O. Box 3007, Zip 19355–0707; tel. 484/596–5400, **A**1 3 7 10 **F**3 11 28 29 30 34 35 36 60 65 71 75 82 86 87 90 91 92 93 95 96 119 130 131 132 143 146 157 **S** Main Line Health, Williamsport, PA
Primary Contact: Donna Phillips, President
CFO: Dave Schmotzer, Chief Financial Officer
CMO: John Kraus, M.D., Chief Medical Officer
CIO: Kay Carr, Chief Information Officer
Web address: www.brynmawrrehab.org
Control: Other not–for–profit (including NFP Corporation) **Service**: Rehabilitation

Staffed Beds: 148 **Admissions**: 1984 **Census**: 91 **Outpatient Visits**: 79177 **Births**: 0 **Total Expense ($000)**: 69654 **Payroll Expense ($000)**: 36602 **Personnel**: 512

DEVEREUX CHILDREN'S BEHAVIORAL HEALTH CENTER, 655 Sugartown Road, Zip 19355–3303, Mailing Address: 655 Sugartown Rd, Zip 19355–3303; tel. 800/345–1292, (Nonreporting) **S** Devereux, Villanova, PA
Primary Contact: Patricia Hillis-Clark, Executive Director
CFO: Tim Evans, Assistant Financial Director
CMO: Jacquelyn Zavodnick, M.D., Medical Director
CIO: MaryLou Hettinger, Director Quality Management
CHR: Sean Maher, Director Human Resources
CNO: Deanna Reiss, Hospital Director of Nursing
Web address: www.devereux.org
Control: Other not–for–profit (including NFP Corporation) **Service**: Children's hospital psychiatric

Staffed Beds: 49

MALVERN INSTITUTE, 940 King Road, Zip 19355–3166; tel. 610/647–0330, **F**4 5 38 152 154
Primary Contact: Geoff Botak, Chief Executive Officer
CFO: Janet Corley, Accountant
Web address: www.malverninstitute.com
Control: Corporation, Investor–owned (for–profit) **Service**: Alcoholism and other chemical dependency

Staffed Beds: 175 **Admissions**: 3057 **Census**: 139 **Outpatient Visits**: 0 **Births**: 0

MC CONNELLSBURG—Fulton County

★ **FULTON COUNTY MEDICAL CENTER (391303)**, 214 Peach Orchard Road, Zip 17233–8559, Mailing Address: McConnellsburg, tel. 717/485–3155, (Total facility includes 67 beds in nursing home–type unit) **A**10 18 **F**3 11 15 18 28 29 30 34 35 40 45 46 50 53 57 59 62 64 70 75 77 78 79 81 87 91 93 97 107 108 110 111 115 118 119 128 129 130 132 133 135 144 146 147 148 149 154 156
Primary Contact: Michael D. Makosky, Chief Executive Officer
COO: Kim Slee, Chief Operating Officer
CFO: Deborah A Shughart, Chief Financial Officer
CMO: Sharon E Martin, M.D., Ph.D., President Medical Staff
CIO: Armen Arakelian, Chief Information Officer
CHR: Cheryl Rose, Human Resources Director
Web address: www.fcmcpa.org
Control: Other not–for–profit (including NFP Corporation) **Service**: General medical and surgical

Staffed Beds: 88 **Admissions**: 767 **Census**: 74 **Outpatient Visits**: 63596 **Births**: 0 **Total Expense ($000)**: 49632 **Payroll Expense ($000)**: 22222 **Personnel**: 355

MCKEES ROCKS—Allegheny County

⌧ **OHIO VALLEY HOSPITAL (390157)**, 25 Heckel Road, Zip 15136–1694; tel. 412/777–6161, **A**1 10 **F**3 7 10 15 18 20 29 30 40 45 46 49 51 59 65 70 74 75 77 79 81 82 85 87 90 92 93 98 103 104 107 108 110 111 115 119 126 129 130 143 146 148 149 154
Primary Contact: David W. Scott, President and Chief Executive Officer
CFO: Jack Nelson, Vice President Finance and Chief Financial Officer
CHR: Erin J Frohnhofer, Vice President Human Resources
CNO: Paulette Bingham, Director Nursing Services
Web address: www.ohiovalleyhospital.org
Control: Other not–for–profit (including NFP Corporation) **Service**: General medical and surgical

Staffed Beds: 124 **Admissions**: 3448 **Census**: 55 **Outpatient Visits**: 99732 **Births**: 0 **Total Expense ($000)**: 65804 **Payroll Expense ($000)**: 23463 **Personnel**: 501

MCKEESPORT—Allegheny County

⌧ **SELECT SPECIALTY HOSPITAL–MCKEESPORT (392045)**, 1500 Fifth Avenue, 6th Floor, Zip 15132–2422; tel. 412/664–2900, (Nonreporting) **A**1 10 **S** Select Medical Corporation, Mechanicsburg, PA
Primary Contact: Patrick Tuer, Interim Chief Executive Officer
Web address: www.mckeesport.selectspecialtyhospitals.com/
Control: Corporation, Investor–owned (for–profit) **Service**: Acute long–term care hospital

Staffed Beds: 30

☐ **UPMC MCKEESPORT (390002)**, 1500 Fifth Avenue, Zip 15132–2422; tel. 412/664–2000, (Total facility includes 24 beds in nursing home–type unit) **A**1 3 5 10 13 **F**3 4 15 18 20 28 29 30 31 34 35 40 46 49 50 54 56 57 59 60 61 62 64 65 66 68 70 74 75 77 78 79 81 82 85 86 87 90 97 98 100 101 102 103 107 111 114 115 119 120 121 128 130 131 132 135 143 146 148 154 156 157 **S** UPMC, Pittsburgh, PA
Primary Contact: Mark O'Hern, President
COO: Amy Bush, Vice President Operations
CFO: Christopher Stockhausen, Chief Financial Officer
CMO: R Curtis Waligura, D.O., Vice President Medical Affairs, Chief Medical Officer
CIO: Terri Keeling, Vice President Information Systems
CHR: Kelli Reale, Vice President Human Resources
CNO: Leeanna McKibben, R.N., MSN, Vice President Patient Services and Chief Nursing Officer
Web address: www.mckeesport.upmc.com
Control: Other not–for–profit (including NFP Corporation) **Service**: General medical and surgical

Staffed Beds: 190 **Admissions**: 7589 **Census**: 130 **Outpatient Visits**: 117121 **Births**: 0 **Total Expense ($000)**: 138553 **Payroll Expense ($000)**: 42422 **Personnel**: 671

MEADOWBROOK—Montgomery County

⇑ **HOLY REDEEMER HOSPITAL (390097)**, 1648 Huntingdon Pike, Zip 19046–8001; tel. 215/947–3000, (Nonreporting) **A**2 3 5 10 21
Primary Contact: Michael B. Laign, President and Chief Executive Officer
CFO: Russell R Wagner, Executive Vice President and Chief Financial Officer
CMO: Henry D. Unger, M.D., Senior Vice President and Chief Medical Officer
CIO: Donald F. Friel, Executive Vice President
CHR: Joseph J Cassidy, Vice President
CNO: Anne Catino, MS, R.N., Vice President and Chief Nursing Officer
Web address: www.holyredeemer.com
Service: General medical and surgical

Staffed Beds: 250

MEADVILLE—Crawford County

★ ⇑ **MEADVILLE MEDICAL CENTER (390113)**, 751 Liberty Street, Zip 16335–2559; tel. 814/333–5000, (Total facility includes 32 beds in nursing home–type unit) **A**2 5 10 12 13 21 **F**3 4 5 8 11 13 15 18 20 22 26 28 29 30 31 34 35 36 38 39 40 43 45 49 50 54 56 57 58 59 63 64 68 70 71 74 75 76 77 78 79 81 82 84 85 86 87 89 90 93 96 98 100 101 102 103 104 107 108 110 111 114 115 118 119 120 121 123 127 128 129 130 131 132 135 143 146 147 148 149 154 **S** Meadville Medical Center, Meadville, PA
Primary Contact: Philip E. Pandolph, FACHE, Chief Executive Officer
CFO: Renato Suntay, Chief Financial Officer
CMO: Denise Johnson, M.D., Medical Director
CHR: Greg Maras, Vice President Human Resources
CNO: MaryAnn Hewston, R.N., Chief Nurse Executive
Web address: www.mmchs.org
Control: Other not–for–profit (including NFP Corporation) **Service**: General medical and surgical

Staffed Beds: 232 **Admissions**: 7130 **Census**: 100 **Outpatient Visits**: 256998 **Births**: 575 **Total Expense ($000)**: 197803 **Payroll Expense ($000)**: 78403 **Personnel**: 1386

MECHANICSBURG—Cumberland County

⌧ **ENCOMPASS HEALTH REHABILITATION HOSPITAL OF MECHANICSBURG (393031)**, 175 Lancaster Boulevard, Zip 17055–3562; tel. 717/691–3700, (Nonreporting) **A**1 10 **S** Encompass Health Corporation, Birmingham, AL
Primary Contact: Josette M. Myers, Chief Executive Officer
CMO: Michael Lupinacci, M.D., Medical Director
CHR: David Staskin, Director Human Resources
Web address: www.healthsouthpa.com
Control: Corporation, Investor–owned (for–profit) **Service**: Rehabilitation

Staffed Beds: 75

MEDIA—Delaware County

⌧ **RIDDLE HOSPITAL (390222)**, 1068 West Baltimore Pike, Zip 19063–5177; tel. 484/227–9400, (Total facility includes 23 beds in nursing home–type unit) **A**1 2 3 10 **F**3 7 11 13 15 18 20 22 26 28 29 30 31 34 35 36 37 38 40 41 44 45 46 49 50 51 53 54 55 56 57 58 59 63 64 65 70 72 74 75 76 78 79 80 81 82 84 85 86 87 92 97 100 102 107 108 110 111 114 115 118 119 120 124 126 128 129 130 131 132 135 141 143 145 146 147 148 149 156 **S** Main Line Health, Washington, DC
Primary Contact: Gary L. Perecko, President
CFO: Ed McKillip, Vice President Finance
CMO: David Thomas, President Medical Staff
CHR: Mary Louise Ciciretti, Director Human Resources
Web address: www.riddlehospital.org
Control: Other not–for–profit (including NFP Corporation) **Service**: General medical and surgical

Staffed Beds: 227 **Admissions**: 10709 **Census**: 123 **Outpatient Visits**: 120155 **Births**: 968 **Total Expense ($000)**: 192547 **Payroll Expense ($000)**: 66208 **Personnel**: 944

RIDDLE MEMORIAL HOSPITAL See Riddle Hospital

Hospital, Medicare Provider Number, Address, Telephone, Approval, Facility, and Physician Codes, Health Care System

★ American Hospital Association (AHA) membership
☐ The Joint Commission accreditation
○ Healthcare Facilities Accreditation Program
◇ DNV Healthcare Inc. accreditation
⇑ Center for Improvement in Healthcare Quality Accreditation
△ Commission on Accreditation of Rehabilitation Facilities (CARF) accreditation

MEYERSDALE—Somerset County

⊞ **CONEMAUGH MEYERSDALE MEDICAL CENTER (391302)**, 200 Hospital Drive, Zip 15552–1249; tel. 814/634–5911, **A**1 10 18 **F**29 34 40 45 50 59 64 75 81 107 111 114 119 127 130 132 133 146 148 154 **S** Duke LifePoint Healthcare, Brentwood, TN
Primary Contact: Heather Smith, President
CMO: Dwayne Platt, M.D., Chief Medical Officer
CNO: Pam Swansboro, R.N., Chief Nursing Officer
Web address: www.conemaugh.org
Control: Corporation, Investor–owned (for–profit) **Service:** General medical and surgical

Staffed Beds: 20 **Admissions:** 280 **Census:** 4 **Outpatient Visits:** 47047 **Births:** 0 **Total Expense ($000):** 14810 **Payroll Expense ($000):** 4808 **Personnel:** 106

MONONGAHELA—Washington County

⊞ **MONONGAHELA VALLEY HOSPITAL (390147)**, 1163 Country Club Road, Zip 15063–1095; tel. 724/258–1000, **A**1 2 10 **F**3 8 9 11 12 15 17 18 20 22 28 29 30 31 32 34 35 40 45 48 49 51 54 55 56 57 59 61 64 70 74 75 77 78 79 80 81 82 85 86 87 89 90 92 93 96 98 100 101 102 103 107 108 110 111 114 115 118 119 120 121 123 124 129 130 131 132 134 135 146 147 148 149 154 156
Primary Contact: Louis J. Panza Jr, President and Chief Executive Officer
COO: Patrick J Alberts, Senior Vice President.and Chief Operating Officer
CFO: Daniel F Simmons, Senior Vice President and Treasurer
CMO: L. Douglas Pepper, M.D., President, Medical Staff
CIO: Matt Rashilla, Chief Information and Application Officer
CHR: Louis Goodman, Senior Vice President Human Resources
CNO: Mary Lou Murt, R.N., Senior Vice President Nursing
Web address: www.monvalleyhospital.com
Control: Other not–for–profit (including NFP Corporation) **Service:** General medical and surgical

Staffed Beds: 200 **Admissions:** 6814 **Census:** 98 **Outpatient Visits:** 289050 **Births:** 0 **Total Expense ($000):** 133884 **Payroll Expense ($000):** 57002 **Personnel:** 1021

MONROEVILLE—Allegheny County

⊞ **FORBES HOSPITAL (390267)**, 2570 Haymaker Road, Zip 15146–3513; tel. 412/858–2000, **A**1 2 3 5 10 **F**3 8 11 13 15 17 18 20 22 24 26 28 29 30 31 34 35 36 40 43 44 45 46 48 49 50 54 55 57 58 59 64 65 69 70 73 74 75 76 77 78 79 80 81 82 84 85 86 87 90 92 96 98 100 102 107 108 110 111 115 117 118 119 126 130 132 135 141 145 146 147 148 149 154 155 **S** Allegheny Health Network, Pittsburgh, PA
Primary Contact: Mark Rubino, M.D., President
COO: Krista A. Bragg, MSN, Chief Operating Officer
CFO: Tom Hipkiss, Vice President Finance
CMO: Mark Rubino, M.D., Chief Medical Officer
CIO: Sharon Lewis, Director Information Systems
CHR: Georgia Redding, Director Human Resources
Web address: www.ahn.org
Control: Other not–for–profit (including NFP Corporation) **Service:** General medical and surgical

Staffed Beds: 285 **Admissions:** 14467 **Census:** 208 **Outpatient Visits:** 151731 **Births:** 1356 **Total Expense ($000):** 240741 **Payroll Expense ($000):** 79517 **Personnel:** 1391

☐ **UPMC EAST (390328)**, 2775 Mosside Boulevard, Zip 15146–2760; tel. 412/357–3000, **A**1 3 10 **F**3 18 20 22 26 29 30 34 35 40 45 46 49 50 57 59 60 62 65 68 70 74 75 77 78 79 81 82 84 85 87 90 91 92 96 100 107 108 111 115 119 120 121 122 123 130 132 135 146 148 154 157 **S** UPMC, Pittsburgh, PA
Primary Contact: Mark O'Hern, President
CNO: Tamra Minton, R.N., MSN, Vice President Patient Care Services and Chief Nursing Officer
Web address: www.upmc.com/locations/hospitals/east/Pages/default.aspx
Control: Other not–for–profit (including NFP Corporation) **Service:** General medical and surgical

Staffed Beds: 155 **Admissions:** 8307 **Census:** 117 **Outpatient Visits:** 94293 **Births:** 0 **Total Expense ($000):** 151237 **Payroll Expense ($000):** 41337 **Personnel:** 629

WESTERN PENNSYLVANIA HOSPITAL - FORBES REGIONAL CAMPUS See Forbes Hospital

MONTROSE—Susquehanna County

ENDLESS MOUNTAIN HEALTH SYSTEMS (391306), 100 Hospital Drive, Zip 18801–6402; tel. 570/278–3801, **A**10 18 **F**3 15 29 30 34 35 40 44 45 53 56 57 59 65 66 68 75 79 81 84 85 87 93 102 107 110 111 114 119 130 132 133 135 146 149 156
Primary Contact: Loren Stone, Chief Executive Officer
CIO: Gary Passmore, Chief Information Officer
CHR: Paula Anderson, Administrative Director Human Resources
Web address: www.endlesscare.org
Control: Other not–for–profit (including NFP Corporation) **Service:** General medical and surgical

Staffed Beds: 25 **Admissions:** 703 **Census:** 6 **Outpatient Visits:** 28090 **Births:** 0 **Total Expense ($000):** 21772 **Payroll Expense ($000):** 6960

MOUNT GRETNA—Lebanon County

⊞ **WELLSPAN PHILHAVEN (394020)**, 283 South Butler Road, Zip 17064–6085; Mailing Address: P.O. Box 550, Zip 17064–0550; tel. 717/273–8871, (Nonreporting) **A**1 10 **S** WellSpan Health, York, PA
Primary Contact: Phil Hess, Chief Executive Officer
COO: Phil Hess, Chief Executive Officer
CFO: Matt Rogers, Chief Financial Officer
CMO: Francis D Sparrow, M.D., Medical Director
CIO: Lori Nolt, Director Information Technology
CHR: Denis Orthaus, Director Human Resources
CNO: Heidi McMullan, R.N., Chief Nursing Officer
Web address: www.philhaven.org
Control: Church operated, Nongovernment, not–for–profit **Service:** Psychiatric

Staffed Beds: 103

MOUNT PLEASANT—Westmoreland County

☐ **EXCELA FRICK HOSPITAL (390217)**, 508 South Church Street, Zip 15666–1790; tel. 724/547–1500, (Nonreporting) **A**1 10 **S** Excela Health, Greensburg, PA
Primary Contact: Michael D. Busch, Executive Vice President and Chief Operating Officer
COO: Michael D Busch, Executive Vice President and Chief Operating Officer
CFO: Jeffrey T Curry, Executive Vice President and Chief Financial Officer
CMO: Jerome Granato, M.D., Senior Vice President and Chief Medical Officer
CIO: David Gawaluck, Vice President and Chief Information Officer
CHR: John Caverno, Chief Human Resources Officer
CNO: Helen K Burns, Ph.D., R.N., Senior Vice President and Chief Nursing Officer
Web address: www.excelahealth.org/PatientsandVisitors/HospitalsFacilities/Hospitals/Frick.aspx
Control: Other not–for–profit (including NFP Corporation) **Service:** General medical and surgical

Staffed Beds: 33

MUNCY—Lycoming County

★ **UPMC SUSQUEHANNA MUNCY (391301)**, 215 East Water Street, Zip 17756–8700; tel. 570/546–8282, (Total facility includes 125 beds in nursing home–type unit) **A**3 10 18 **F**6 11 15 29 30 34 35 40 44 45 46 50 56 57 59 62 67 68 77 81 86 87 90 93 96 97 107 108 110 111 114 118 119 128 130 131 132 133 146 154 157 **S** UPMC Susquehanna, Williamsport, PA
Primary Contact: Christine Ballard, President
CFO: Eric Pohjala, Executive Vice President and Chief Financial Officer
CIO: Timothy E Schoener, Chief Information Officer
CHR: Donald Wilver Jr Vice President Human Resources
CNO: C Cynthia Whipple, Director of Nursing
Web address: www.susquehannahealth.org
Control: Other not–for–profit (including NFP Corporation) **Service:** General medical and surgical

Staffed Beds: 145 **Admissions:** 717 **Census:** 136 **Outpatient Visits:** 46839 **Births:** 0 **Total Expense ($000):** 44906 **Payroll Expense ($000):** 15461 **Personnel:** 251

Many Facility Codes have changed. Please refer to the AHA Guide Code Chart. © 2019 AHA Guide

NATRONA HEIGHTS—Allegheny County

⊞ **ALLEGHENY VALLEY HOSPITAL (390032)**, 1301 Carlisle Street, Zip 15065–1152; tel. 724/224–5100, **A**1 2 3 10 **F**3 11 15 17 18 24 28 29 30 31 34 35 39 40 44 45 47 49 50 54 56 57 58 59 64 65 70 74 75 77 78 79 80 81 84 85 86 87 90 92 93 96 98 100 102 103 107 108 110 111 114 115 118 119 120 121 123 126 129 130 132 135 144 146 149 154 **S** Allegheny Health Network, Pittsburgh, PA
Primary Contact: Jeffrey Carlson, Interim Chief Executive Officer
CFO: James A Kanuch, Vice President Finance
CMO: Suzanne M. Labriola, D.O., Chief Medical Officer
CIO: Linda Fergus, Manager Information Technology
CHR: Cindy Moser, Director Human Resources
Web address: www.wpahs.org
Control: Other not–for–profit (including NFP Corporation) **Service:** General medical and surgical

Staffed Beds: 77 **Admissions:** 5066 **Census:** 67 **Outpatient Visits:** 175244 **Births:** 0 **Total Expense ($000):** 111754 **Payroll Expense ($000):** 41778 **Personnel:** 735

NEW CASTLE—Lawrence County

☐ **UPMC JAMESON (390016)**, 1211 Wilmington Avenue, Zip 16105–2516; tel. 724/658–9001, **A**1 3 10 19 **F**3 11 12 15 18 20 22 28 29 30 32 34 35 40 43 45 46 49 50 57 59 61 64 65 68 70 74 75 77 78 79 81 82 85 86 87 90 92 93 96 100 107 108 110 111 114 115 118 119 130 135 146 147 149 154 156 157 **S** UPMC, Pittsburgh, PA
Primary Contact: Donald R. Owrey, President
COO: Albert Boland, Vice President Operations
CMO: Elizabeth Piccione, M.D., Chief Medical Officer
CIO: Charles M. Rudek, Chief Information Officer
CHR: Eric D. McIntosh, Vice President Human Resources
CNO: Marianna Stoneburner, R.N., Chief Nursing Officer
Web address: www.upmcjameson.com
Control: Other not–for–profit (including NFP Corporation) **Service:** General medical and surgical

Staffed Beds: 96 **Admissions:** 5459 **Census:** 72 **Outpatient Visits:** 140093 **Births:** 0 **Total Expense ($000):** 102494 **Payroll Expense ($000):** 35367 **Personnel:** 742

NORRISTOWN—Montgomery County

☐ **MONTGOMERY COUNTY EMERGENCY SERVICE (394033)**, 50 Beech Drive, Zip 19403–5421; tel. 610/279–6100, **A**1 10 **F**4 7 29 35 38 50 64 98 100 101 102 103 104 130 151
Primary Contact: William Myers, Chief Executive Officer
CFO: Wendy Walt, Chief Financial Officer
CMO: Marina Cooney, Medical Director
CHR: Byanka Meacham, Director Human Resources
CNO: Naomi Finkel, Nurse Executive
Web address: www.mces.org
Control: Other not–for–profit (including NFP Corporation) **Service:** Psychiatric

Staffed Beds: 81 **Admissions:** 1610 **Census:** 54 **Outpatient Visits:** 2209 **Births:** 0 **Total Expense ($000):** 16381 **Payroll Expense ($000):** 10342 **Personnel:** 199

NORRISTOWN STATE HOSPITAL (394001), 1001 Sterigere Street, Zip 19401–5300; tel. 610/270–1000, **A**10 **F**30 35 38 39 53 59 65 75 77 98 101 102 103 130 135 146 149
Primary Contact: Edna I. McCutcheon, Chief Executive Officer
COO: Gary Raisner, Chief Operating Officer
CMO: Mia Marcovici, M.D., Chief Medical Officer
CHR: Richard Szczurowski, Director Human Resources
CNO: Taryn Mason-Jones, Chief Nurse Executive
Control: State, Government, nonfederal **Service:** Psychiatric

Staffed Beds: 306 **Admissions:** 162 **Census:** 263 **Outpatient Visits:** 118 **Births:** 0 **Total Expense ($000):** 90365 **Payroll Expense ($000):** 42776 **Personnel:** 651

⊞ **SUBURBAN COMMUNITY HOSPITAL (390116)**, 2701 DeKalb Pike, Zip 19401–1820; tel. 610/278–2000, (Nonreporting) **A**1 2 5 10 12 13 **S** Prime Healthcare, Ontario, CA
Primary Contact: Mark McLoone, Chief Executive Officer
COO: Joseph Schofield, Chief Operating Officer
CFO: Joseph Marino, Chief Financial Officer
CMO: Andrea D Pedano, D.O., Chief Medical Officer
CIO: Jason Wayne, Network Administrator
CHR: Gretchen Pendleton, Director Human Resources
CNO: Mary Ellen Rauner, R.N., Chief Nursing Officer
Web address: www.suburbanhosp.org
Control: Corporation, Investor–owned (for–profit) **Service:** General medical and surgical

Staffed Beds: 126

☐ **VALLEY FORGE MEDICAL CENTER AND HOSPITAL (390272)**, 1033 West Germantown Pike, Zip 19403–3905; tel. 610/539–8500, **A**1 10 **F**4 154
Primary Contact: Marian W. Colcher, President and Chief Executive Officer
CFO: Gregg Y Slocum, Chief Financial Officer
CMO: Robert E Colcher, M.D., Medical Director
CHR: Frederick D Jackes, Assistant Administrator and Director Human Resources
Web address: www.vfmc.net
Control: Corporation, Investor–owned (for–profit) **Service:** Alcoholism and other chemical dependency

Staffed Beds: 86 **Admissions:** 1073 **Census:** 39 **Outpatient Visits:** 0 **Births:** 0 **Total Expense ($000):** 14797 **Payroll Expense ($000):** 9243 **Personnel:** 89

OAKDALE—Allegheny County

☐ **CURAHEALTH PITTSBURGH (392028)**, 7777 Steubenville Pike, Zip 15071–3409; tel. 412/494–5500, (Nonreporting) **A**1 10 **S** Curahealth Hospitals, Garland, TX
Primary Contact: Carol Falo, R.N., Chief Executive Officer
CFO: Kevin Varley, Chief Financial Officer
CMO: Ravi Alagar, M.D., Medical Director
Web address: www.curahealth.com
Control: Corporation, Investor–owned (for–profit) **Service:** Acute long–term care hospital

Staffed Beds: 63

OREFIELD—Lehigh County

KIDSPEACE CHILDREN'S HOSPITAL (394047), 5300 Kids Peace Drive, Zip 18069–2044; tel. 610/799–7900, (Nonreporting) **A**3
Primary Contact: William R. Isemann, President and Chief Executive Officer
CFO: Michael Callan, Executive Vice President and Chief Financial Officer
CMO: Matthew Koval, M.D., Vice President Medical Affairs
CIO: Joan Lesko, Director Technical Support and Services
CHR: Sheila Rulli, Director Human Resources
CNO: Tamara Wasilick, Director Operations
Web address: www.kidspeace.org
Control: Other not–for–profit (including NFP Corporation) **Service:** Children's hospital psychiatric

Staffed Beds: 120

PAOLI—Chester County

⊞ **PAOLI HOSPITAL (390153)**, 255 West Lancaster Avenue, Zip 19301–1763; tel. 484/565–1000, **A**1 2 3 10 **F**3 11 13 15 18 20 22 24 26 28 29 30 31 32 34 35 36 38 39 40 41 43 44 45 46 47 48 49 50 55 56 57 59 63 64 65 70 72 74 75 76 78 79 80 81 82 84 85 86 87 92 97 102 107 108 110 111 114 115 118 119 120 121 123 124 126 129 130 131 132 134 135 141 146 147 148 149 150 154 156 **S** Main Line Health, Garland, TX
Primary Contact: James Paradis, President
CFO: John Doyle, Vice President Finance
CMO: Andrew J Norton, M.D., Chief Medical Officer
CIO: Kay Carr, Senior Vice President and Chief Information Officer
CHR: Deborah Fedora, Director Human Resources
Web address: www.mainlinehealth.org
Control: Other not–for–profit (including NFP Corporation) **Service:** General medical and surgical

Staffed Beds: 231 **Admissions:** 13598 **Census:** 139 **Outpatient Visits:** 289280 **Births:** 2070 **Total Expense ($000):** 286331 **Payroll Expense ($000):** 86232 **Personnel:** 1132

Hospital, Medicare Provider Number, Address, Telephone, Approval, Facility, and Physician Codes, Health Care System

★ American Hospital Association (AHA) membership
☐ The Joint Commission accreditation
○ Healthcare Facilities Accreditation Program
◇ DNV Healthcare Inc. accreditation
⇑ Center for Improvement in Healthcare Quality Accreditation
△ Commission on Accreditation of Rehabilitation Facilities (CARF) accreditation

PA

PHILADELPHIA—Philadelphia County

ALBERT EINSTEIN MEDICAL CENTER See Einstein Medical Center Philadelphia

☐ **BELMONT BEHAVIORAL HOSPITAL (394023)**, 4200 Monument Road, Zip 19131–1625; tel. 215/877–2000, (Nonreporting) **A**1 3 5 10 **S** Acadia Healthcare Company, Inc., Franklin, TN
Primary Contact: Mark Schor, Chief Executive Officer
CFO: Guy Romaniello, Director Fiscal Services
CMO: Richard Jaffe, M.D., Medical Director
CHR: Jenna Pacini, Human Resources Specialist
CNO: Nona Fain, Ph.D., R.N., Director of Nursing
Web address: www.einstein.edu/locations/belmont-behavioral-health/
Control: Corporation, Investor–owned (for–profit) **Service:** Psychiatric

Staffed Beds: 171

☐ **CANCER TREATMENT CENTERS OF AMERICA-EASTERN REGIONAL MEDICAL CENTER (390312)**, 1331 East Wyoming Avenue, Zip 19124–3808; tel. 215/537–7400, (Nonreporting) **A**1 2 3 5 10 **S** Cancer Treatment Centers of America, Schaumburg, IL
Primary Contact: Nancy Hesse, MSN, R.N., President and Chief Executive Officer
COO: Jeffrey Ryan, Chief Operating Officer
CFO: Jeffrey Ryan, Senior Vice President, Finance and Business Development
CMO: Steven B. Standiford, M.D., Chief of Staff
CIO: Kristin Darby, Chief Information Officer
CHR: Ronald Gilg, Assistant Vice President Talent
CNO: Joanne McGovern, MSN, R.N., Chief Nursing Officer
Web address: www.cancercenter.com
Control: Corporation, Investor–owned (for–profit) **Service:** Cancer

Staffed Beds: 56

☒ **CHESTNUT HILL HOSPITAL (390026)**, 8835 Germantown Avenue, Zip 19118–2718; tel. 215/248–8200, (Nonreporting) **A**1 3 5 10 **S** Tower Health, West Reading, PA
Primary Contact: John D. Cacciamani, M.D., Chief Executive Officer
CFO: Marc Costner, Chief Financial Officer
CMO: John Scanlon, DPM, Chief Medical Officer
CHR: Marilyn DiCicco, Director Human Resources
CNO: Teresa M Kelly, MSN, R.N., Chief Nursing Officer
Web address: www.chhealthsystem.com
Control: Other not–for–profit (including NFP Corporation) **Service:** General medical and surgical

Staffed Beds: 212

☐ **CHILDREN'S HOSPITAL OF PHILADELPHIA (393303)**, 3401 Civic Center Boulevard, Zip 19104–4319; tel. 215/590–1000, (Nonreporting) **A**1 3 5 8 10
Primary Contact: Madeline Bell, President and Chief Executive Officer
COO: Douglas G Hock, Executive Vice President and Chief Operating Officer
CFO: Thomas Todorow, Chief Financial Officer and Executive Vice President
CMO: Jan Boswinkel, M.D., Vice President Medical Operations and Chief Safety Officer
CHR: Robert Croner, Senior Vice President and Chief Human Resources Officer
CNO: Paula M Agosto, R.N., MSN, Senior Vice President and Chief Nursing Officer
Web address: www.chop.edu
Control: Other not–for–profit (including NFP Corporation) **Service:** Children's general medical and surgical

Staffed Beds: 546

☐ **EINSTEIN MEDICAL CENTER PHILADELPHIA (390142)**, 5501 Old York Road, Zip 19141–3098; tel. 215/456–7890, (Includes EINSTEIN MEDICAL CENTER ELKINS PARK, 60 Township Line Road, Elkins Park, Pennsylvania, Zip 19027–2220; tel. 215/663–6000; Barry R Freedman, President and Chief Executive Officer) (Total facility includes 44 beds in nursing home–type unit) **A**1 2 3 5 8 10 **F**3 8 11 12 13 15 17 18 20 22 24 26 28 29 30 31 32 34 35 36 37 38 39 40 43 44 45 46 47 48 49 54 55 56 57 58 59 61 64 65 66 68 70 72 73 74 75 76 77 78 79 81 82 84 85 86 87 90 91 92 93 94 95 97 98 100 101 102 103 104 106 107 108 110 111 114 115 119 120 121 123 124 126 128 129 130 131 132 138 139 142 143 145 146 147 148 149 150 154 156 157 158 **S** Einstein Healthcare Network, Philadelphia, PA
Primary Contact: Barry R. Freedman, President and Chief Executive Officer
COO: Ruth Lefton, Chief Operating Officer
CFO: Gerard Blaney, Vice President Finance and Interim Chief Financial Officer
CMO: Steven Sivak, M.D., Chief Medical Officer, Einstein Physicians Philadelphia
CIO: Brenda West, Vice President, Information Services and Interim Chief Information Officer
CHR: Lynne R Kornblatt, Chief Human Resources Officer
CNO: Jill Stunkard, R.N., MSN, Associate Chief Nurse Executive and Interim Chief Nursing Officer
Web address: www.einstein.edu
Control: Other not–for–profit (including NFP Corporation) **Service:** General medical and surgical

Staffed Beds: 499 **Admissions:** 27174 **Census:** 476 **Outpatient Visits:** 572121 **Births:** 2826 **Total Expense ($000):** 816115 **Payroll Expense ($000):** 388373 **Personnel:** 4884

☐ **FAIRMOUNT BEHAVIORAL HEALTH SYSTEM (394027)**, 561 Fairthorne Avenue, Zip 19128–2499; tel. 215/487–4000, (Nonreporting) **A**1 10 **S** Universal Health Services, Inc., King of Prussia, PA
Primary Contact: Mark L. Howard, Chief Executive Officer
CFO: Anthony Tortella, Chief Financial Officer
CMO: Silvia Gratz, D.O., Chief Medical Officer
CIO: Anthony Tortella, Chief Financial Officer
CHR: Brendan Aurand, Director, Human Resources
CNO: Wanda Nolasco, Chief Nursing Officer
Web address: www.fairmountbhs.com
Control: Corporation, Investor–owned (for–profit) **Service:** Psychiatric

Staffed Beds: 235

☒ **FOX CHASE CANCER CENTER-AMERICAN ONCOLOGIC HOSPITAL (390196)**, 333 Cottman Avenue, Zip 19111–2434; tel. 215/728–6900, **A**1 2 3 5 10 **F**11 15 29 30 31 34 35 36 45 46 47 49 50 55 57 58 59 60 63 64 68 70 71 75 77 78 79 81 82 84 85 86 87 93 100 104 107 108 109 110 111 114 115 116 117 118 119 120 121 123 124 126 130 132 135 136 145 146 147 148 149 157 **S** Temple University Health System, Philadelphia, PA
Primary Contact: Richard Fisher, M.D., President and Chief Executive Officer
COO: Judith Lynn Bachman, Chief Operating Officer
CFO: Anthony J Diasio, Chief Financial Officer
CMO: James Helstrom, Chief Medical Officer
CIO: Michael Sweeney, Chief Information Officer
CNO: Anne Jadwin, R.N., MSN, Chief Nursing Officer
Web address: www.fccc.org
Control: Other not–for–profit (including NFP Corporation) **Service:** Cancer

Staffed Beds: 67 **Admissions:** 4304 **Census:** 65 **Outpatient Visits:** 113546 **Births:** 0 **Total Expense ($000):** 336047 **Payroll Expense ($000):** 92194 **Personnel:** 1571

☐ **FRIENDS HOSPITAL (394008)**, 4641 Roosevelt Boulevard, Zip 19124–2343; tel. 215/831–4600, (Nonreporting) **A**1 3 5 10 **S** Universal Health Services, Inc., King of Prussia, PA
Primary Contact: Michael S. McDonald Jr, Chief Executive Officer
COO: Diane Carugati, Chief Operating Officer
CFO: Michael Terwilliger, Chief Financial Officer
CMO: Marc Rothman, M.D., Medical Director
CIO: John Healy, Manager Information Technology
CHR: Paul Cavanaugh, Director Human Resources
Web address: www.friendshospital.com
Control: Corporation, Investor–owned (for–profit) **Service:** Psychiatric

Staffed Beds: 192

☒ **GOOD SHEPHERD PENN PARTNERS SPECIALTY HOSPITAL AT RITTENHOUSE (392050)**, 1800 Lombard Street, Zip 19146–1414; tel. 877/969–7342, **A**1 10 **F**1 3 28 29 30 34 35 44 50 56 57 58 59 60 64 68 74 75 77 79 82 84 85 86 87 90 91 93 94 95 96 100 130 131 132 143 146 148 149 154
Primary Contact: Laura Porter, Executive Director
CFO: Ronald J. Petula, Vice President Finance
CMO: Michael Grippi, M.D., Chief Medical Officer
CHR: Mark Sneff, Vice President Human Resources
CNO: Jean Romano, Chief Nursing Officer
Web address: www.phillyrehab.com
Control: Other not–for–profit (including NFP Corporation) **Service:** Acute long–term care hospital

Staffed Beds: 38 **Admissions:** 273 **Census:** 28 **Outpatient Visits:** 205969 **Births:** 0 **Total Expense ($000):** 52752 **Payroll Expense ($000):** 25194 **Personnel:** 411

☒ **HAHNEMANN UNIVERSITY HOSPITAL (390290)**, 230 North Broad Street, Zip 19102–1192; tel. 215/762–7000, (Nonreporting) **A**1 2 3 5 8 10 **S** American Academic Health System, Philadelphia, PA
Primary Contact: Suzanne Richards, R.N., M.P.H., FACHE, Chief Executive Officer
COO: Barbara Boston, Interim Chief Operating Officer
CFO: Richard Imbimbo, Chief Financial Officer
CIO: Irvin Fisher, Director, Information Services
Web address: www.hahnemannhospital.com
Control: Corporation, Investor–owned (for–profit) **Service:** General medical and surgical

Staffed Beds: 496

HAVEN BEHAVIORAL HOSPITAL OF PHILADELPHIA (394053), Four Falls Building, Zip 19129–1121; tel. 215/791–6821, (Nonreporting) **A**3 5 **S** Haven Behavioral Healthcare, Nashville, TN
Primary Contact: Abigail Halloran, Chief Executive Officer
Web address: www.https://philadelphia.havenbehavioral.com
Control: Corporation, Investor–owned (for–profit) **Service:** Psychiatric

Staffed Beds: 36

Many Facility Codes have changed. Please refer to the AHA Guide Code Chart. © 2019 AHA Guide

PA

⊞ **HOSPITAL OF THE UNIVERSITY OF PENNSYLVANIA (390111)**, 3400 Spruce Street, Zip 19104–4206; tel. 215/662–4000, (Includes SCHEIE EYE INSTITUTE OF THE HOSPITAL OF THE UNIVERSITY OF PENNSYLVANIA, 3400 Civic Center Blvd FL 3, West Pavilion, 3rd Floor, Philadelphia, Pennsylvania, Zip 19104–5127; tel. 215/662–8100; Sheara Hollin, Chief Operating Officer) **A**1 2 5 8 10 **F**3 6 7 8 9 11 12 13 15 17 18 20 22 24 26 29 30 31 34 35 36 38 39 40 44 45 46 47 48 49 51 52 54 55 56 57 58 59 60 61 62 63 64 65 66 68 70 72 73 74 75 76 77 78 79 80 81 82 84 85 86 87 90 91 92 93 94 95 96 97 100 104 107 108 110 111 114 115 116 117 118 119 120 121 122 123 124 126 129 130 131 132 135 136 137 138 139 140 141 142 145 146 147 148 149 150 154 155 156 **S** University of Pennsylvania Health System, Philadelphia, PA
Primary Contact: Regina Cunningham, Ph.D., R.N., Chief Executive Officer
CFO: Joseph M Huber, Chief Financial Officer
CMO: Patrick J Brennan, M.D., Senior Vice President and Chief Medical Officer
CIO: Michael Restuccia, Chief Information Officer
CHR: Denise J. Mariotti, Chief Human Resource Officer
Web address: www.pennmedicine.org
Control: Other not–for–profit (including NFP Corporation) **Service:** General medical and surgical

Staffed Beds: 805 **Admissions:** 35182 **Census:** 707 **Outpatient Visits:** 1881270 **Births:** 4421 **Total Expense ($000):** 2786172 **Payroll Expense ($000):** 1084920 **Personnel:** 14784

⊞ **JEANES HOSPITAL (390080)**, 7600 Central Avenue, Zip 19111–2499; tel. 215/728–2000, **A**1 3 5 10 **F**3 11 12 15 17 18 20 22 24 26 28 29 30 31 34 35 40 44 45 49 50 51 56 57 59 60 61 62 65 68 70 74 75 77 78 79 81 82 84 85 86 87 91 92 93 96 107 108 110 111 115 118 119 129 130 132 135 146 148 149 154 **S** Temple University Health System, Philadelphia, PA
Primary Contact: Marc P. Hurowitz, D.O., President and Chief Executive Officer
COO: Judith Lynn Bachman, Chief Operating Officer
CFO: Ray Lefton, Chief Financial Officer
CMO: Rebecca Armbruster, M.D., Chief Medical Officer
CIO: Michael Sweeney, Chief Informatics Officer
CHR: Beverly Sherbondy, Assistant Vice President, Human Resources
CNO: Denise Anne Lavery Frasca, MSN, R.N., Vice President Patient Care Services and Chief Nursing Officer
Web address: www.jeanes.com
Control: Other not–for–profit (including NFP Corporation) **Service:** General medical and surgical

Staffed Beds: 146 **Admissions:** 6840 **Census:** 85 **Outpatient Visits:** 125704 **Births:** 0 **Total Expense ($000):** 161790 **Payroll Expense ($000):** 65027 **Personnel:** 917

⊞ **JEFFERSON HEALTH NORTHEAST (390115)**, 10800 Knights Road, Zip 19114–4200; tel. 215/612–4000, (Includes BUCKS COUNTY CAMPUS, 380 North Oxford Valley Road, Langhorne, Pennsylvania, Zip 19047–8399; tel. 215/949–5000; FRANKFORD CAMPUS, Frankford Avenue and Wakeling Street, Philadelphia, Pennsylvania, Zip 19124; tel. 215/831–2000) **A**1 3 5 10 **F**3 11 12 15 17 18 20 22 24 26 28 29 30 31 34 35 39 40 43 44 45 46 49 50 53 54 57 58 59 61 64 65 66 68 70 74 75 77 78 79 80 81 82 84 85 86 87 92 93 94 96 100 107 108 110 111 114 115 117 118 119 120 121 123 124 126 129 130 131 132 135 144 145 146 147 148 149 154 **S** Jefferson Health, Philadelphia, PA
Primary Contact: Kathleen Kinslow, Ed.D., President
COO: Sandra Gomberg, Chief Operating Officer
CFO: William Degnan, Vice President Finance
CMO: Stanton Segal, M.D., Chief Medical Officer
CHR: Dorinda Carolina, Chief Human Resources Officer
CNO: Michelle E Conley, R.N., Chief Nursing Officer
Web address: www.ariahealth.org
Control: Other not–for–profit (including NFP Corporation) **Service:** General medical and surgical

Staffed Beds: 450 **Admissions:** 23489 **Census:** 289 **Outpatient Visits:** 230946 **Births:** 0 **Total Expense ($000):** 443286 **Payroll Expense ($000):** 195169 **Personnel:** 2700

JEFFERSON METHODIST HOSPITAL See Thomas Jefferson University Hospitals, Philadelphia

☐ **KENSINGTON HOSPITAL (390025)**, 136 West Diamond Street, Zip 19122–1721; tel. 215/426–8100, (Nonreporting) **A**1 10
Primary Contact: Eileen Hause, Chief Executive Officer
CFO: Kenneth Biddle, Controller
CMO: Luis F Vera, M.D., Medical Director
CHR: Maria Dimichele, Administrative Assistant
CNO: Aleyamma John, R.N., Director of Nursing
Control: State, Government, nonfederal **Service:** General medical and surgical

Staffed Beds: 33

⊞ **KINDRED HOSPITAL-PHILADELPHIA (392027)**, 6129 Palmetto Street, Zip 19111–5729; tel. 215/722–8555, (Includes KINDRED HOSPITAL PHILADELPHIA - HAVERTOWN, 2000 Old West Chester Pike, Havertown, Pennsylvania, Zip 19083–2712; tel. 610/536–2100; Margaret M Murphy, Chief Executive Officer), (Non-reporting) **A**1 10 **S** Kindred Healthcare, Louisville, KY
Primary Contact: Michele S. Basile, Interim Chief Executive Officer
CFO: Kathy Andrews, Chief Financial Officer
CNO: Erin McCullough, Chief Clinical Officer
Web address: www.kindredphila.com/
Control: Corporation, Investor–owned (for–profit) **Service:** Acute long–term care hospital

Staffed Beds: 52

⊞ **KINDRED HOSPITAL SOUTH PHILADELPHIA (392046)**, 1930 South Broad Street, Zip 19145–2328; tel. 267/570–5200, (Nonreporting) **A**1 10 **S** Kindred Healthcare, Louisville, KY
Primary Contact: Michele S. Basile, Chief Executive Officer
COO: Diane K. White, MSN, R.N., Chief Clinical Officer
CFO: Kevin Varley, Chief Financial Officer
CMO: James Dovnarsky, M.D., Director Pulmonary Medical
CHR: Amy Cain, District Director Human Resources
CNO: Diane K. White, MSN, R.N., Chief Clinical Officer
Web address: www.khsouthphilly.com
Control: Corporation, Investor–owned (for–profit) **Service:** Acute long–term care hospital

Staffed Beds: 58

☐ **KIRKBRIDE CENTER (394007)**, 111 North 49th Street, Zip 19139–2718; tel. 215/471–2600, (Nonreporting) **A**1 10
Primary Contact: Marlene Douglas-Walsh, Chief Executive Officer
CFO: Robert Anthony, Chief Financial Officer
CMO: Mark Novitsky, M.D., Sr Corporate Medical Director
CHR: Arend Boersema, Director Human Resources
CNO: Abbie Lampie, Director of Nursing
Web address: www.kirkbridecenter.com
Control: Partnership, Investor–owned (for–profit) **Service:** Psychiatric

Staffed Beds: 205

⊞ △ **MAGEE REHABILITATION HOSPITAL (393038)**, 1513 Race Street, Zip 19102–1177; tel. 215/587–3000, **A**1 3 5 7 10 **F**18 28 29 30 34 35 50 60 64 68 74 75 77 79 82 86 90 91 92 93 94 95 96 130 132 146 148
Primary Contact: Jack A. Carroll, Ph.D., President and Chief Executive Officer
CFO: Stephen DeStefano, Chief Financial Officer
CMO: Guy Fried, M.D., Chief Medical Officer
CIO: Shawna White, Chief Information Officer
CHR: Cindy Tobin-Payne, Director
Web address: www.mageerehab.org
Control: Other not–for–profit (including NFP Corporation) **Service:** Rehabilitation

Staffed Beds: 83 **Admissions:** 930 **Census:** 67 **Outpatient Visits:** 63717 **Births:** 0 **Total Expense ($000):** 66055 **Payroll Expense ($000):** 37808 **Personnel:** 599

MERCY PHILADELPHIA HOSPITAL See Mercy Fitzgerald Hospital, Darby

⊞ △ **NAZARETH HOSPITAL (390204)**, 2601 Holme Avenue, Zip 19152–2096; tel. 215/335–6000, (Total facility includes 19 beds in nursing home–type unit) **A**1 3 5 7 10 **F**3 12 15 18 20 22 29 30 31 34 35 37 39 40 44 45 46 49 50 53 56 57 58 59 64 65 70 74 75 77 78 79 81 82 84 85 86 87 90 93 96 97 100 107 108 110 111 114 118 119 120 121 128 130 131 132 146 147 148 149 154 **S** Trinity Health, Livonia, MI
Primary Contact: Nancy Cherone, Executive Director and Administrator
CFO: David Wajda, Chief Financial Officer
CMO: Mathew Matthew, M.D., Chief Medical Officer
CIO: Terry O'Neil, Chief Information Technology
CHR: Kathleen M Pries, Director Human Resources
CNO: Michael Beshel, R.N., Vice President Patient Care and Chief Nursing Officer
Web address: www.nazarethhospital.org
Control: Other not–for–profit (including NFP Corporation) **Service:** General medical and surgical

Staffed Beds: 147 **Admissions:** 7720 **Census:** 109 **Outpatient Visits:** 107057 **Births:** 0 **Total Expense ($000):** 145909 **Payroll Expense ($000):** 57704 **Personnel:** 944

PA

NORTH PHILADELPHIA HEALTH SYSTEM (390132), 801 West Girard Ave, Zip 19122–4212, Mailing Address: 801 West Girard Avenue, Zip 19122–4212; tel. 215/787–9000, (Includes GIRARD MEDICAL CENTER, Girard Avenue at Eighth Street, Philadelphia, Pennsylvania, Zip 19122; tel. 215/787–2000; Gerri H. Walker, President and Chief Executive Officer), (Non-reporting) **A**10
Primary Contact: Gerri H. Walker, President and Chief Executive Officer
CFO: Ronald Kaplan, Chief Financial Officer
CIO: Tony Iero, Director Management Information Systems
CHR: James Gloner, Senior Vice President
Web address: www.nphs.com
Control: Other not–for–profit (including NFP Corporation) **Service:** General medical and surgical

Staffed Beds: 315

PENN PRESBYTERIAN MEDICAL CENTER (390223), 51 North 39th Street, Zip 19104–2699; tel. 215/662–8000, (Total facility includes 25 beds in nursing home–type unit) **A**1 2 3 5 10 **F**3 4 5 7 8 9 11 12 15 17 18 20 22 24 26 29 30 31 32 34 35 36 37 38 39 40 43 44 45 46 49 50 51 52 54 56 57 58 59 60 61 62 63 64 65 66 68 70 74 75 77 78 79 81 82 84 85 86 87 92 94 96 97 98 100 101 104 107 108 110 111 114 115 118 119 120 121 126 128 130 131 132 134 135 141 142 146 147 148 149 150 154 155 **S** University of Pennsylvania Health System, Philadelphia, PA
Primary Contact: Michele M. Volpe, Chief Executive Officer
COO: Robert J Russell, Associate Executive Director Operations
CFO: Anthony Zumpano, Chief Financial Officer
CMO: Kevin Fosnocht, M.D., Chief Medical Officer and Associate Executive Director
CIO: Theresa Hiltunen, Entity Information Officer
CHR: Margorie Michele, Chief Human Resources Officer
CNO: James R Ballinghoff, MSN, R.N., Chief Nursing Officer and Associate Executive Director
Web address: www.pennmedicine.org/pmc/
Control: Other not–for–profit (including NFP Corporation) **Service:** General medical and surgical

Staffed Beds: 375 Admissions: 17601 Census: 270 Outpatient Visits: 300780 Births: 0 Total Expense ($000): 669488 Payroll Expense ($000): 242959 Personnel: 2517

PENNSYLVANIA HOSPITAL (390226), 800 Spruce Street, Zip 19107–6192; tel. 215/829–3000, **A**1 2 3 5 10 13 **F**3 8 12 13 15 17 18 20 22 24 26 29 30 31 34 35 36 37 38 39 40 44 45 46 49 50 51 52 54 55 56 57 58 59 60 61 62 63 64 68 70 72 74 75 76 77 78 79 80 81 82 84 85 86 87 92 96 97 98 100 101 102 103 104 107 108 110 111 114 115 116 117 118 119 120 121 123 124 126 129 130 131 132 135 136 141 142 145 146 147 148 149 150 154 **S** University of Pennsylvania Health System, Philadelphia, PA
Primary Contact: Theresa M. Larivee, Chief Executive Officer
CFO: Frank Anastasi, Chief Financial Officer
CMO: Daniel Feinberg, M.D., Chief Medical Officer
CIO: Kwon Lee, Chief Information Officer
CNO: Joanne Ruggiero, Interim Chief Nursing Officer
Web address: www.pahosp.com
Control: Other not–for–profit (including NFP Corporation) **Service:** General medical and surgical

Staffed Beds: 475 Admissions: 18498 Census: 259 Outpatient Visits: 327451 Births: 5231 Total Expense ($000): 638270 Payroll Expense ($000): 217429 Personnel: 2526

△ **PHILADELPHIA VETERANS AFFAIRS MEDICAL CENTER**, 3900 Woodland Avenue, Zip 19104–4594; tel. 215/823–5800, (Nonreporting) **A**1 2 3 5 7 **S** Department of Veterans Affairs, Washington, DC
Primary Contact: Daniel Hendee, Director
CMO: Dave Oslin, M.D., Chief of Staff
CIO: Adrienne Ficchi, Vice President Information Management
CHR: Gerald Morelli, Director Human Resources
Web address: www.philadelphia.va.gov/
Control: Veterans Affairs, Government, federal **Service:** General medical and surgical

Staffed Beds: 291

ROXBOROUGH MEMORIAL HOSPITAL (390304), 5800 Ridge Avenue, Zip 19128–1737; tel. 215/483–9900, (Nonreporting) **A**1 3 5 10 **S** Prime Healthcare, Ontario, CA
Primary Contact: Matt Shelak, Chief Executive Officer
CFO: Thomas Reinboth, Chief Financial Officer
CHR: Michael Henrici, Associate Administrator
Web address: www.roxboroughmemorial.com
Control: Corporation, Investor–owned (for–profit) **Service:** General medical and surgical

Staffed Beds: 140

SHRINERS HOSPITALS FOR CHILDREN-PHILADELPHIA (393309), 3551 North Broad Street, Zip 19140–4160; tel. 215/430–4000, (Nonreporting) **A**1 3 5 10 **S** Shriners Hospitals for Children, Tampa, FL
Primary Contact: Ed Myers, Administrator
CFO: Mario Salvati, Director Fiscal Services
CMO: Scott Kozin, M.D., Chief of Staff
CHR: Megan Hauser, Director Human Resources
CNO: Krista Miller, R.N., Chief Nursing Officer
Web address: www.shrinershospitalsforchildren.org/Hospitals/Locations/Philadelphia.aspx
Control: Other not–for–profit (including NFP Corporation) **Service:** Children's orthopedic

Staffed Beds: 39

ST. CHRISTOPHER'S HOSPITAL FOR CHILDREN (393307), 3601 A Street, Zip 19134–1043, Mailing Address: 160 E. Erie Avenue, Zip 19134–1011; tel. 215/427–5000, **A**1 3 5 8 10 **F**3 7 16 17 19 21 23 25 27 29 30 31 32 34 35 39 40 41 43 44 48 49 50 54 55 58 59 60 61 64 68 70 71 72 73 74 75 77 78 79 80 81 82 83 84 87 88 89 93 97 99 100 101 102 107 111 119 129 130 131 132 134 136 138 143 144 146 **S** American Academic Health System, Philadelphia, PA
Primary Contact: Suzanne Richards, R.N., M.P.H., FACHE, Chief Executive Officer
COO: Thomas Runkle, MS, Ph.D., Chief Operating Officer
CMO: Mary Moran, M.D., Pediatrician In Chief
CIO: Robert Taylor, Director Information Services
CHR: Kellie T. Pearson, Chief Human Resource Officer
CNO: Joanna Horst, MSN, R.N., Chief Nursing Officer
Web address: www.stchristophershospital.com
Control: Corporation, Investor–owned (for–profit) **Service:** Children's general medical and surgical

Staffed Beds: 121 Admissions: 6733 Census: 89 Births: 0

TEMPLE UNIVERSITY HOSPITAL (390027), 3401 North Broad Street, Zip 19140–5103; tel. 215/707–2000, (Includes TEMPLE UNIVERSITY HOSPITAL - EPISCOPAL DIVISION, 100 East Lehigh Avenue, Philadelphia, Pennsylvania, Zip 19125–1098; tel. 215/427–7000; Kathleen Barron, Executive Director) **A**1 2 3 5 8 10 **F**3 4 8 12 13 15 16 17 20 22 24 26 28 29 30 31 34 35 38 40 43 44 45 46 47 48 49 50 53 54 55 56 57 58 59 60 61 64 68 70 72 73 74 75 76 77 78 79 80 81 82 83 84 85 86 87 90 92 93 94 96 97 98 100 101 102 104 107 108 109 110 111 112 114 115 118 119 120 121 124 126 129 130 131 132 135 136 137 138 139 140 141 142 145 146 147 149 154 156 157 **S** Temple University Health System, Philadelphia, PA
Primary Contact: Michael A. Young, FACHE, Chief Executive Officer
COO: Rosemary Nolan, R.N., MSN, JD, Chief Operating Officer
CFO: Gerald P Oetzel, Chief Financial Officer
CMO: Herbert Cushing, M.D., Chief Medical Officer
CIO: David Kamowski, Vice President and Chief Information Officer
CHR: John Lasky Jr Vice President, Chief Human Resources Officer
CNO: Elizabeth J Craig, MSN, Chief Nursing Officer and Vice President Patient Services
Web address: www.tuh.templehealth.org/content/default.htm
Control: Other not–for–profit (including NFP Corporation) **Service:** General medical and surgical

Staffed Beds: 732 Admissions: 34382 Census: 580 Outpatient Visits: 330400 Births: 2488 Total Expense ($000): 1154510 Payroll Expense ($000): 383798 Personnel: 4902

THOMAS JEFFERSON UNIVERSITY HOSPITALS (390174), 111 South 11th Street, Zip 19107–5084; tel. 215/955–6000, (Includes JEFFERSON METHODIST HOSPITAL, 2301 South Broad Street, Philadelphia, Pennsylvania, Zip 19148; tel. 215/952–9000; Stephen K Klasko, M.D., President) **A**1 2 3 5 8 10 **F**3 5 6 7 8 9 11 12 13 14 15 16 17 18 20 22 24 26 28 29 30 31 34 35 36 37 38 39 40 43 44 45 46 47 48 49 50 52 53 54 55 56 57 58 59 61 64 65 66 68 70 72 74 75 76 77 78 79 80 81 82 84 85 86 87 89 90 92 93 94 96 97 98 100 101 103 104 107 108 110 111 114 115 116 117 118 119 120 121 123 124 126 129 130 131 132 134 135 136 137 138 139 141 142 144 145 146 147 148 149 150 153 154 155 156 **S** Jefferson Health, Philadelphia, PA
Primary Contact: Richard Webster, R.N., President
CFO: Neil Lubarsky, Senior Vice President, Finance and Chief Financial Officer
CMO: Edmund A. Pribitkin, M.D., Chief Medical Officer
CIO: Nassar Nizami, Chief Information Officer
CHR: Jeffrey Stevens, Executive Vice President and Chief Human Resource Officer
CNO: Mary Ann McGinley, Ph.D., Senior Vice President, Patient Services and Chief Nursing Officer
Web address: www.jefferson.edu
Control: Other not–for–profit (including NFP Corporation) **Service:** General medical and surgical

Staffed Beds: 888 Admissions: 39969 Census: 610 Outpatient Visits: 449098 Births: 1861 Total Expense ($000): 1666775 Payroll Expense ($000): 505770 Personnel: 7060

TRIUMPH HOSPITAL PHILADELPHIA See Kindred Hospital South Philadelphia

VETERANS AFFAIRS MEDICAL CENTER See Philadelphia Veterans Affairs Medical Center

PHOENIXVILLE—Chester County

☒ △ **PHOENIXVILLE HOSPITAL (390127)**, 140 Nutt Road, Zip 19460–3900, Mailing Address: P.O. Box 3001, Zip 19460–0916; tel. 610/983–1000, **A**1 2 3 7 10 **F**3 8 13 15 18 20 22 24 26 28 29 31 32 34 35 36 38 39 40 45 49 50 51 55 56 57 59 61 64 68 69 70 72 74 75 76 77 78 79 81 82 85 86 87 93 102 107 108 111 114 115 117 118 119 126 130 132 134 135 146 147 154 156 **S** Tower Health, West Reading, PA
Primary Contact: Stephen M. Tullman, Chief Executive Officer
CFO: Edward Chabalowski, Chief Financial Officer
CMO: David Stepansky, M.D., Chief Medical Officer
CIO: Terry Murphy, Director Information Services
CHR: Denise Chiolo, Chief Human Resources Officer
CNO: Sarah Strzelecki, Ed.D., R.N., Chief Nursing Officer
Web address: www.https://phoenixville.towerhealth.org
Control: Other not–for–profit (including NFP Corporation) **Service**: General medical and surgical

Staffed Beds: 139 **Admissions**: 6431 **Census**: 81 **Outpatient Visits**: 85059 **Births**: 814 **Total Expense ($000)**: 167559 **Payroll Expense ($000)**: 50814 **Personnel**: 816

PITTSBURGH—Allegheny County

☒ **ALLEGHENY GENERAL HOSPITAL (390050)**, 320 East North Avenue, Zip 15212–4756; tel. 412/359–3131, **A**1 2 3 5 8 10 12 **F**3 6 11 12 15 17 18 20 22 24 26 28 29 30 31 34 35 36 37 39 40 43 44 45 46 47 48 49 50 53 54 57 58 59 64 65 66 70 74 75 77 78 79 80 81 82 84 85 86 87 89 92 93 96 100 102 104 105 107 108 110 111 114 115 117 118 119 121 123 124 126 130 131 132 135 137 138 139 141 146 147 148 149 153 154 155 **S** Allegheny Health Network, Pittsburgh, PA
Primary Contact: Jeffrey Cohen, M.D., President
COO: Duke Rupert, Chief Operating Officer
CFO: Richard W Fries, Vice President Finance
CMO: Tony Farah, M.D., President Medical Staff
CIO: John Foley, Chief Information Officer
Web address: www.wpahs.org/locations/allegheny-general-hospital
Control: Other not–for–profit (including NFP Corporation) **Service**: General medical and surgical

Staffed Beds: 384 **Admissions**: 23467 **Census**: 348 **Outpatient Visits**: 317923 **Births**: 0 **Total Expense ($000)**: 777261 **Payroll Expense ($000)**: 216600 **Personnel**: 3478

☒ **ENCOMPASS HEALTH HARMARVILLE REHABILITATION HOSPITAL (393027)**, 320 Guys Run Road, Zip 15238–0460, Mailing Address: P.O. Box 11460, Zip 15238–0460; tel. 412/828–1300, **A**1 10 **F**28 29 30 34 56 64 75 77 79 82 86 87 90 91 93 94 95 96 131 132 146 148 149 154 156 157 **S** Encompass Health Corporation, Birmingham, AL
Primary Contact: Mark Van Volkenburg, Chief Executive Officer
CFO: Daniel A Vrana, Controller
CMO: James Kreshon, M.D., Medical Director
CHR: Kathy Grills, Director Human Resources
CNO: Eileen Skalski, Chief Nursing Officer
Web address: www.healthsouthharmarville.com
Control: Corporation, Investor–owned (for–profit) **Service**: Rehabilitation

Staffed Beds: 60 **Admissions**: 1248 **Census**: 52 **Outpatient Visits**: 7792 **Births**: 0 **Total Expense ($000)**: 25659 **Payroll Expense ($000)**: 11574 **Personnel**: 186

EYE AND EAR HOSPITAL OF PITTSBURGH See Upmc Presbyterian, Pittsburgh

☒ **LIFECARE HOSPITALS OF PITTSBURGH (392024)**, 225 Penn Avenue, Zip 15221–2148; tel. 469/241–2100, (Includes LIFECARE HOSPITALS OF PITTSBURGH - SUBURBAN, 100 South Jackson Avenue, Pittsburgh, Pennsylvania, Zip 15202–3428, Mailing Address: 100 South Jackson Avenue, 4th Floor, Zip 15202–3428, tel. 412/734–7600; Trisha Niemuth, Market Chief Executive Officer), (Non-reporting) **A**1 10 **S** LifeCare Management Services, Plano, TX
Primary Contact: Jennifer Malko, Market Chief Executive Officer
CFO: Asia Holyfield, Manager Business Office
CMO: Steven Sotos, M.D., President Medical Staff
CIO: Mike Wattenbarger, Chief Information Officer
CHR: Robin F. Arslanpay, Director Human Resources
CNO: Paula Pawloski, Chief Nursing Officer
Web address: www.lifecare-hospitals.com
Control: Corporation, Investor–owned (for–profit) **Service**: Acute long–term care hospital

Staffed Beds: 196

☒ **SELECT SPECIALTY HOSPITAL-PITTSBURGH/UPMC (392044)**, 200 Lothrop Street, E824, Zip 15213–2536; tel. 412/586–9800, (Nonreporting) **A**1 10 **S** Select Medical Corporation, Mechanicsburg, PA
Primary Contact: Darrell Jones, Chief Executive Officer
CMO: Michael Donahue, M.D., Medical Director
CHR: Prudence Sloan, Coordinator Human Resources
CNO: Eli Babich, Chief Nursing Officer
Web address: www.pittsburghupmc.selectspecialtyhospitals.com/
Control: Corporation, Investor–owned (for–profit) **Service**: Acute long–term care hospital

Staffed Beds: 32

☐ **SOUTHWOOD PSYCHIATRIC HOSPITAL**, 2575 Boyce Plaza Road, Zip 15241–3925; tel. 412/257–2290, (Nonreporting) **A**1 **S** Acadia Healthcare Company, Inc., Franklin, TN
Primary Contact: Stephen J. Quigley, Chief Executive Officer
CFO: Frank Urban, Chief Financial Officer
CMO: Allan W Clark, M.D., Medical Director
CHR: Erin J Frohnhofer, Director Human Resources
Web address: www.southwoodhospital.com
Control: Corporation, Investor–owned (for–profit) **Service**: Children's hospital psychiatric

Staffed Beds: 156

☒ **ST. CLAIR HOSPITAL (390228)**, 1000 Bower Hill Road, Zip 15243–1873; tel. 412/942–4000, **A**1 2 3 10 **F**3 8 13 15 17 18 20 22 24 26 28 29 30 31 34 35 40 45 46 47 48 49 51 53 54 57 59 60 64 67 70 73 74 75 76 77 78 79 81 84 85 86 87 89 92 93 96 97 98 100 102 105 107 108 110 111 114 115 117 119 120 121 126 129 130 131 132 134 135 142 143 144 146 147 148 149 153 156
Primary Contact: James M. Collins, President and Chief Executive Officer
COO: Michael J Flanagan, Senior Vice President and Chief Operating Officer
CFO: Richard C Chesnos, Senior Vice President Finance and Chief Financial Officer
CMO: John Sullivan, M.D., Chief Medical Officer
CIO: Richard Schaeffer, Vice President Information Systems and Chief Information Officer
CHR: Andrea Kalina, Vice President External Affairs and Chief Human Resources Officer
CNO: Joan Massella, Administrative Vice President and Chief Nursing Officer
Web address: www.stclair.org
Control: Other not–for–profit (including NFP Corporation) **Service**: General medical and surgical

Staffed Beds: 302 **Admissions**: 15662 **Census**: 176 **Outpatient Visits**: 324160 **Births**: 1525 **Total Expense ($000)**: 269637 **Payroll Expense ($000)**: 103273 **Personnel**: 1771

★ **THE CHILDREN'S HOME OF PITTSBURGH (393304)**, 5324 Penn Avenue, Zip 15224–1733; tel. 412/441–4884, (Nonreporting) **A**10
Primary Contact: Pamela R. Schanwald, Chief Executive Officer
COO: Kimberly Reblock, M.D., Chief Operating Officer
CFO: Kimberly A Phillips, Chief Financial Officer
CMO: Frederick C Sherman, M.D., Chief Medical Officer
Web address: www.childrenshomepgh.org
Control: Other not–for–profit (including NFP Corporation) **Service**: Children's general medical and surgical

Staffed Beds: 30

THE CHILDREN'S INSTITUTE OF PITTSBURGH (393308), 1405 Shady Avenue, Zip 15217–1350; tel. 412/420–2400, (Nonreporting) **A**10
Primary Contact: Wendy Ann. Pardee, President and Chief Executive Officer
COO: Stacey Vaccaro, Chief Operating Officer
CFO: John Jubas, Vice President Finance
CMO: Matthew Masiello, M.D., Chief Medical Officer
CIO: Sharon Dorogy, Chief Information Officer
CHR: Linda M Allen, Vice President Human Resources
Web address: www.amazingkids.org
Control: Other not–for–profit (including NFP Corporation) **Service**: Children's rehabilitation

Staffed Beds: 62

PA

| Hospital, Medicare Provider Number, Address, Telephone, Approval, Facility, and Physician Codes, Health Care System |

★ American Hospital Association (AHA) membership
☐ The Joint Commission accreditation
○ Healthcare Facilities Accreditation Program
◇ DNV Healthcare Inc. accreditation
⇧ Center for Improvement in Healthcare Quality Accreditation
△ Commission on Accreditation of Rehabilitation Facilities (CARF) accreditation

© 2019 AHA Guide   *Many Facility Codes have changed. Please refer to the AHA Guide Code Chart.*   Hospitals **A537**

PA

☐ **UPMC CHILDREN'S HOSPITAL OF PITTSBURGH (393302)**, One Children's Hospital Drive, Zip 15224–1334; tel. 412/692–5325, **A**1 3 5 10 **F**3 8 12 17 19 21 22 23 24 25 27 28 29 30 31 32 34 35 36 38 39 40 41 43 45 46 48 49 50 53 54 55 57 58 59 60 61 64 65 66 68 71 72 74 75 77 78 79 81 82 84 86 87 88 89 90 91 92 93 94 97 100 107 108 109 111 112 114 115 116 117 118 119 120 121 123 124 126 127 129 130 131 132 134 135 136 137 138 139 140 141 142 143 144 146 148 150 154 **S** UPMC, Pittsburgh, PA
Primary Contact: Mark Sevco, President
CFO: Nicholas J. Barcellona, Chief Financial Officer
CMO: Brian Martin, Vice President Medical Affairs
CIO: Srinivasan Suresh, M.D., Chief Medical Information Officer
CHR: Rhonda Larimore, Vice President, Human Resources
CNO: Diane Hupp, R.N., Vice President Support Services and Patient Care Services
Web address: www.chp.edu
Control: Other not–for–profit (including NFP Corporation) **Service**: Children's general medical and surgical

> **Staffed Beds:** 305 **Admissions:** 12192 **Census:** 228 **Outpatient Visits:** 345494 **Births:** 1 **Total Expense ($000):** 695850 **Payroll Expense ($000):** 170467 **Personnel:** 2776

⊞ **UPMC MAGEE-WOMENS HOSPITAL (390114)**, 300 Halket Street, Zip 15213–3108; tel. 412/641–1000, (Total facility includes 20 beds in nursing home–type unit) **A**1 2 3 5 10 **F**3 11 12 13 15 18 29 30 31 35 40 44 45 46 49 52 54 55 56 57 58 59 64 65 66 68 70 72 74 75 76 77 78 79 80 81 82 84 85 86 87 91 97 100 107 108 110 111 115 117 119 120 121 123 126 128 130 132 134 135 146 147 148 149 150 154 **S** UPMC, Pittsburgh, PA
Primary Contact: Richard Beigi, M.D., President
COO: Lou Baverso, Vice President Operations
CFO: Eileen Simmons, Chief Financial Officer
CMO: Dennis English, M.D., Vice President Medical Affairs
CHR: Rhonda Larimore, Vice President Human Resources
CNO: Maribeth McLaughlin, R.N., Vice President Patient Care Services
Web address: www.magee.edu
Control: Other not–for–profit (including NFP Corporation) **Service**: Obstetrics and gynecology

> **Staffed Beds:** 321 **Admissions:** 18264 **Census:** 229 **Outpatient Visits:** 584685 **Births:** 8671 **Total Expense ($000):** 870188 **Payroll Expense ($000):** 142194 **Personnel:** 2841

☐ **UPMC MERCY (390028)**, 1400 Locust Street, Zip 15219–5166; tel. 412/232–8111, **A**1 3 5 10 13 **F**3 4 7 8 9 10 11 12 13 14 15 18 20 22 24 26 28 29 30 31 32 34 35 36 39 40 43 44 45 46 47 48 49 50 51 54 56 57 58 59 60 61 64 65 66 68 70 72 74 75 76 77 78 79 81 82 84 85 86 87 90 91 92 93 94 95 96 97 100 101 102 107 108 111 114 115 116 118 119 126 129 130 131 132 135 141 142 146 147 148 154 156 157 **S** UPMC, Pittsburgh, PA
Primary Contact: Michael A. Grace, President
COO: Julie Hecker, Vice President, Operations
CFO: Eileen Simmons, Chief Financial Officer, UPMC Hospital Network
CIO: Kevin Conway, Chief Information Officer
CHR: Tracey Stange Kolo, Vice President, Human Resources
CNO: Leeanna McKibben, R.N., MSN, Vice President Patient Services and Chief Nursing Officer
Web address: www.upmc.com/HospitalsFacilities/HFHome/Hospitals/Mercy/
Control: Other not–for–profit (including NFP Corporation) **Service**: General medical and surgical

> **Staffed Beds:** 419 **Admissions:** 18720 **Census:** 327 **Outpatient Visits:** 178284 **Births:** 1071 **Total Expense ($000):** 402522 **Payroll Expense ($000):** 127450 **Personnel:** 2179

UPMC MONTEFIORE See Upmc Presbyterian, Pittsburgh

☐ **UPMC PASSAVANT (390107)**, 9100 Babcock Boulevard, Zip 15237–5815; tel. 412/748–6700, (Includes UPMC PASSAVANT CRANBERRY, One St Francis Way, Cranberry, Pennsylvania, Zip 16066; tel. 724/772–5300; Teresa G Petrick, President) **A**1 2 3 5 10 **F**3 8 11 15 17 18 20 22 24 26 28 29 30 31 34 35 40 45 46 47 48 49 51 54 56 57 58 59 64 68 70 74 75 77 78 79 81 82 84 85 86 87 90 92 96 100 107 108 109 110 111 114 115 117 118 119 120 121 123 126 129 130 132 135 143 146 147 148 154 156 157 **S** UPMC, Pittsburgh, PA
Primary Contact: Susan E. Hoolahan, R.N., MSN, President
CFO: Thomas M Newman, Chief Financial Officer
CMO: James W Boyle, M.D., Chief Medical Officer
CNO: Susan E Hoolahan, R.N., MSN, Vice President Patient Care Services and Chief Nursing Officer
Web address: www.upmc.edu/passavant
Control: Other not–for–profit (including NFP Corporation) **Service**: General medical and surgical

> **Staffed Beds:** 306 **Admissions:** 15985 **Census:** 218 **Outpatient Visits:** 291672 **Births:** 0 **Total Expense ($000):** 365629 **Payroll Expense ($000):** 95997 **Personnel:** 1780

☐ **UPMC PRESBYTERIAN (390164)**, 200 Lothrop Street, Zip 15213–2536; tel. 412/647–2345, (Includes EYE AND EAR HOSPITAL OF PITTSBURGH, 200 Lothrop Street, Pittsburgh, Pennsylvania, Zip 15213–2592; tel. 412/647–2345; UPMC MONTEFIORE, 3459 Fifth Avenue, Pittsburgh, Pennsylvania, Zip 15213; tel. 412/647–2345; John Innocenti Sr, President and Chief Executive Officer; UPMC PRESBYTERIAN HOSPITAL, 200 Lothrop Street, Pittsburgh, Pennsylvania, Zip 15213; tel. 412/647–2345; UPMC SHADYSIDE, 5230 Centre Avenue, Pittsburgh, Pennsylvania, Zip 15232–1381; tel. 412/623–2121; WESTERN PSYCHIATRIC INSTITUTE AND CLINIC, 3811 O'Hara Street, Pittsburgh, Pennsylvania, Zip 15213–2593; tel. 412/624–2100) **A**1 2 3 5 8 10 **F**3 5 6 8 9 11 12 14 17 18 20 22 24 29 30 31 34 35 36 37 38 39 40 43 44 45 46 47 48 49 50 51 53 54 55 56 57 58 59 60 61 63 64 65 66 68 70 71 74 75 77 78 79 81 82 84 85 86 87 90 91 92 93 94 95 96 97 98 99 100 101 102 103 104 105 106 107 108 111 113 114 115 116 117 118 119 120 121 123 124 126 129 130 131 132 135 139 140 141 142 145 146 148 149 152 153 154 156 157 158 **S** UPMC, Pittsburgh, PA
Primary Contact: John Innocenti Sr, President and Chief Executive Officer
CFO: Eileen Simmons, Chief Financial Officer
CMO: Margaret Reidy, M.D., Vice President Medical Affairs
CHR: Kathryn Devine, Vice President Human Resources
Web address: www.upmc.edu
Control: Other not–for–profit (including NFP Corporation) **Service**: General medical and surgical

> **Staffed Beds:** 1398 **Admissions:** 58467 **Census:** 1151 **Outpatient Visits:** 1037204 **Births:** 0 **Total Expense ($000):** 2102883 **Payroll Expense ($000):** 519047 **Personnel:** 9471

☐ **UPMC ST. MARGARET (390102)**, 815 Freeport Road, Zip 15215–3301; tel. 412/784–4000, **A**1 2 3 5 10 13 **F**3 6 8 9 11 15 18 20 29 30 31 34 35 40 44 45 49 51 54 56 57 58 59 60 61 63 64 65 68 70 74 75 77 78 79 81 82 84 85 86 87 90 96 97 102 104 107 108 111 114 115 119 120 121 123 129 130 131 132 134 135 144 146 148 154 156 157 **S** UPMC, Pittsburgh, PA
Primary Contact: David J. Patton, President
COO: Merle Taylor, Vice President Operations
CFO: Thomas M Newman, Vice President Finance
CMO: John Lagnese, M.D., Vice President Medical Affairs
CIO: Charles M. Rudek, Chief Information Officer
CHR: Tracey Stange Kolo, Vice President Human Resources
CNO: Mary C Barkhymer, R.N., MSN, Vice President Patient Care Services and Chief Nursing Officer
Web address: www.upmc.com/locations/hospitals/st-margaret/Pages/default.aspx
Control: Other not–for–profit (including NFP Corporation) **Service**: General medical and surgical

> **Staffed Beds:** 208 **Admissions:** 10961 **Census:** 144 **Outpatient Visits:** 159543 **Births:** 0 **Total Expense ($000):** 235259 **Payroll Expense ($000):** 64426 **Personnel:** 1403

⊞ **VETERANS AFFAIRS PITTSBURGH HEALTHCARE SYSTEM**, University Drive, Zip 15240–1001; tel. 866/482–7488, (Includes VETERANS AFFAIRS MEDICAL CENTER, 7180 Highland Drive, Pittsburgh, Pennsylvania, Zip 15206–1297; tel. 412/365–4900; VETERANS AFFAIRS MEDICAL CENTER, University Drive 'C', Pittsburgh, Pennsylvania, Zip 15240–1001; tel. 412/688–6000), (Non-reporting) **A**1 3 5 8 **S** Department of Veterans Affairs, Washington, DC
Primary Contact: Karin L. McGraw, MSN, FACHE, Director
CMO: Ali Sonel, M.D., Chief of Staff
CIO: John Kovac, Facility Chief Information Officer
CHR: Amber Mesoras, Chief Human Resources Officer
CNO: Ira Richmond, Associate Director Patient Care Services
Web address: www.pittsburgh.va.gov/
Control: Veterans Affairs, Government, federal **Service**: Psychiatric

> **Staffed Beds:** 549

⊞ **WEST PENN HOSPITAL (390090)**, 4800 Friendship Avenue, Zip 15224–1722; tel. 412/578–5000, **A**1 2 3 5 8 10 **F**3 11 12 13 15 16 17 18 20 22 24 26 29 30 31 34 35 36 37 40 44 45 46 47 48 49 50 51 54 55 57 58 59 64 66 70 72 73 74 75 76 77 78 79 80 81 82 84 85 86 87 90 96 102 107 108 110 111 115 118 119 120 121 123 126 129 130 132 135 136 141 142 145 146 147 148 149 154 **S** Allegheny Health Network, Pittsburgh, PA
Primary Contact: Ronald J. Andro, R.N., MS, President and Chief Executive Officer
CFO: James A Kanuch, Vice President Finance
CMO: I William Goldfarb, Chief Medical Officer
CIO: Jacqueline Dailey, Chief Information Officer
CHR: Sally Carozza, Director Human Resources
CNO: Paula A Lacher, MSN, R.N., Chief Nursing Officer
Web address: www.wpahs.org
Control: Other not–for–profit (including NFP Corporation) **Service**: General medical and surgical

> **Staffed Beds:** 238 **Admissions:** 13918 **Census:** 207 **Outpatient Visits:** 112591 **Births:** 4392 **Total Expense ($000):** 433906 **Payroll Expense ($000):** 102661 **Personnel:** 1753

WESTERN PSYCHIATRIC INSTITUTE AND CLINIC See Upmc Presbyterian, Pittsburgh

PLEASANT GAP—Centre County

⊠ **ENCOMPASS HEALTH NITTANY VALLEY REHABILITATION HOSPITAL (393039)**, 550 West College Avenue, Zip 16823–7401; tel. 814/359–3421, (Nonreporting) **A**1 10 **S** Encompass Health Corporation, Birmingham, AL
Primary Contact: Susan Hartman, Chief Executive Officer
CFO: Alan M Phillips, Controller
CMO: Richard Allatt, M.D., Medical Director
CHR: Michelle Katz, Director Human Resources
CNO: Penny Frownfelter, Chief Nursing Officer
Web address: www.nittanyvalleyrehab.com
Control: Corporation, Investor–owned (for–profit) **Service:** Rehabilitation

Staffed Beds: 73

POTTSTOWN—Montgomery County

⊠ **POTTSTOWN HOSPITAL (390123)**, 1600 East High Street, Zip 19464–5093; tel. 610/327–7000, (Nonreporting) **A**1 2 10 **S** Tower Health, West Reading, PA
Primary Contact: Richard Newell, Chief Executive Officer
COO: Bryce Sillyman, Chief Operating Officer
CFO: Debbie Konarski, Interim Chief Financial Officer
CMO: Richard F Saylor, M.D., Chief Medical Officer
CIO: Ron Peterson, Chief Information Officer
CHR: Ruta Ore, Director Human Resources
Web address: www.https://pottstown.towerhealth.org/
Control: Other not–for–profit (including NFP Corporation) **Service:** General medical and surgical

Staffed Beds: 232

POTTSVILLE—Schuylkill County

⊠ **LEHIGH VALLEY HOSPITAL - SCHUYLKILL (390030)**, 420 South Jackson Street, Zip 17901–3625; tel. 570/621–5000, (Includes LEHIGH VALLEY HOSPITAL - SCHUYLKILL EAST NORWEGIAN STREET, 700 East Norwegian Street, Pottsville, Pennsylvania, Zip 17901–2710; tel. 570/621–4000; William Reppy, President), (Non-reporting) **A**1 10 19 **S** Lehigh Valley Health Network, Allentown, PA
Primary Contact: William Reppy, President
CFO: Diane Borls, Chief Financial Officer
CIO: Tina Zanis, Director Information Systems
CHR: Martin Treasure, Director Human Resources
CNO: Darnell F Furer, MS, R.N., Vice President Patient Care Services and Chief Nursing Officer
Web address: www.schuylkillhealth.com
Control: Other not–for–profit (including NFP Corporation) **Service:** General medical and surgical

Staffed Beds: 211

PUNXSUTAWNEY—Jefferson County

PUNXSUTAWNEY AREA HOSPITAL (390199), 81 Hillcrest Drive, Zip 15767–2616; tel. 814/938–1800, **A**10 20 **F**3 13 15 26 29 30 34 35 40 44 45 46 48 50 51 57 59 62 64 70 74 75 76 77 78 79 81 82 85 86 87 92 93 97 100 104 107 108 110 111 115 118 119 124 130 132 133 146 147 148 149 154
Primary Contact: Daniel D. Blough Jr, Chief Executive Officer
CFO: Jack Sisk, Chief Financial Officer
CMO: Dajani Zuhd, M.D., President Medical Staff
CIO: Chuck States, Director Information Systems
CHR: Barbara Kostok, Manager Human Resources
CNO: Paula Spack, R.N., MSN, Vice President Nursing
Web address: www.pah.org
Control: Other not–for–profit (including NFP Corporation) **Service:** General medical and surgical

Staffed Beds: 49 **Admissions:** 1449 **Census:** 17 **Outpatient Visits:** 95024 **Births:** 135 **Total Expense ($000):** 36593 **Payroll Expense ($000):** 20220 **Personnel:** 341

QUAKERTOWN—Bucks County

☐ **ST. LUKE'S HOSPITAL - QUAKERTOWN CAMPUS (390035)**, 1021 Park Avenue, Zip 18951–1573; tel. 215/538–4500, **A**1 2 3 10 **F**3 11 15 18 28 29 30 31 34 35 38 40 43 44 45 49 50 51 54 56 57 59 60 63 64 65 70 71 74 75 77 78 79 81 82 85 86 87 92 93 98 100 102 107 108 109 110 111 115 118 119 129 130 131 132 135 144 146 148 149 154 **S** St. Luke's University Health Network, Bethlehem, PA
Primary Contact: Dennis Pfleiger, President and Chief Operating Officer
CFO: Theresa Corrado, Director Finance
CMO: Thomas Filipowicz, M.D., Medical Director
CIO: Chad Brisendine, Chief Information Officer
CHR: Shelley Maley, Director Human Resources
Web address: www.slhhn.org
Control: Other not–for–profit (including NFP Corporation) **Service:** General medical and surgical

Staffed Beds: 62 **Admissions:** 3329 **Census:** 42 **Outpatient Visits:** 91334 **Births:** 0 **Total Expense ($000):** 71839 **Payroll Expense ($000):** 28137 **Personnel:** 319

READING—Berks County

⊠ **ENCOMPASS HEALTH READING REHABILITATION HOSPITAL (393026)**, 1623 Morgantown Road, Zip 19607–9455; tel. 610/796–6000, (Nonreporting) **A**1 10 19 **S** Encompass Health Corporation, Birmingham, AL
Primary Contact: Mathew Gooch, Area Chief Executive Officer
CFO: Jason Pulaski, Controller
CMO: Suzanne Adam, D.O., Medical Director
CHR: Kelly Kozik, Director Human Resources
Web address: www.healthsouthreading.com
Control: Corporation, Investor–owned (for–profit) **Service:** Rehabilitation

Staffed Beds: 60

☐ **HAVEN BEHAVIORAL HOSPITAL OF EASTERN PENNSYLVANIA (394052)**, 145 North 6th Street, 3rd Floor, Zip 19601–3096; tel. 610/406–4340, (Nonreporting) **A**1 10 **S** Haven Behavioral Healthcare, Nashville, TN
Primary Contact: Robert Scheffler, Chief Executive Officer
CMO: Mark Putnam, M.D., Medical Director
CHR: Kathy Copenhaver, Director Human Resources
Web address: www.https://havenbehavioral.com/
Control: Corporation, Investor–owned (for–profit) **Service:** Psychiatric

Staffed Beds: 48

⊠ **PENN STATE HEALTH ST. JOSEPH (390096)**, 2500 Bernville Road, Zip 19605–9453, Mailing Address: P.O. Box 316, Zip 19603–0316; tel. 610/378–2000, (Includes PENN STATE HEALTH ST. JOSEPH - DOWNTOWN CAMPUS, 145 North Sixth Street, Reading, Pennsylvania, Zip 19601, Mailing Address: P O Box 316, Zip 19603–0316, tel. 610/378–2000; John R Morahan, President and Chief Executive Officer) **A**1 2 10 13 19 **F**3 13 15 18 20 22 24 26 28 29 30 31 32 34 35 39 40 44 45 46 49 50 51 53 54 57 58 59 64 66 68 70 71 72 74 75 76 77 78 79 81 82 84 85 87 89 93 97 100 108 111 113 114 115 116 117 118 119 120 121 130 131 132 135 144 146 147 148 149 156 157 **S** Penn State Hershey Health System, Hershey, PA
Primary Contact: John R. Morahan, President and Chief Executive Officer
CFO: Courtney Coffman, Vice President, Finance and Chief Financial Officer
CMO: Christopher Newman, M.D., Vice President Medical Affairs and Chief Medical Officer
CIO: Amanda Klopp, Director, Innovation and Clinical Integration
CHR: Scott Mengle, Vice President Human Resources
CNO: Sharon Strohecker, R.N., MSN, Vice President Clinical Operations and Chief Nursing Officer
Web address: www.thefutureofhealthcare.org
Control: Other not–for–profit (including NFP Corporation) **Service:** General medical and surgical

Staffed Beds: 180 **Admissions:** 7345 **Census:** 89 **Outpatient Visits:** 256103 **Births:** 699 **Total Expense ($000):** 207493 **Payroll Expense ($000):** 66445 **Personnel:** 1466

PA

REGIONAL HOSPITAL OF SCRANTON (390237), 746 Jefferson Avenue, Zip 18510–1624; tel. 570/348–7100, **A**1 2 3 5 10 19 **F**7 8 11 12 15 17 18 20 22 24 26 28 29 31 34 35 39 40 44 45 46 47 48 49 50 51 53 54 57 58 59 60 61 64 65 66 68 70 74 75 77 78 79 81 85 86 87 91 92 93 97 107 108 109 110 111 112 113 114 115 116 117 118 119 120 121 122 123 124 126 130 132 143 144 145 146 147 148 149 157 **S** Community Health Systems, Inc., Franklin, TNPrimary Contact: Ronald Ziobro, Interim Chief Executive OfficerCFO: Stephen Franko, Vice President Finance and Chief Financial OfficerCMO: Anthony Yanni, M.D., Vice President Medical AffairsCIO: Jorge Coronel, Chief Information OfficerWeb address: www.regionalhospitalofscranton.net**Control**: Corporation, Investor–owned (for–profit) **Service**: General medical and surgical

Staffed Beds: 186**Admissions:** 7914**Census:** 108**Outpatient Visits:** 80360**Births:** 0**Total Expense ($000):** 167344**Payroll Expense ($000):** 50039**Personnel:** 787

RENOVO—Clinton County

BUCKTAIL MEDICAL CENTER (391304), 1001 Pine Street, Zip 17764–1620; tel. 570/923–1000, (Total facility includes 43 beds in nursing home–type unit) **A**10 18 **F**3 7 52 53 54 55 56 57 65 66 69 97 128 130 143 146 154
Primary Contact: Timothy Reeves, Administrator
CFO: Wendy Janerella, Controller
CMO: Alvin Berlot, M.D., Medical Director
Web address: www.bucktailmed.org
Control: Other not–for–profit (including NFP Corporation) **Service**: General medical and surgical

Staffed Beds: 59 **Admissions:** 146 **Census:** 40 **Outpatient Visits:** 8101 **Births:** 0 **Total Expense ($000):** 7315 **Payroll Expense ($000):** 2835 **Personnel:** 60

RIDLEY PARK—Delaware County

TAYLOR HOSPITAL See Crozer-Chester Medical Center, Upland

ROARING SPRING—Blair County

CONEMAUGH NASON MEDICAL CENTER (390062), 105 Nason Drive, Zip 16673–1202; tel. 814/224–2141, **A**1 10 **F**3 5 8 11 13 15 17 18 19 24 26 29 30 34 35 39 40 45 50 56 57 59 64 65 70 74 75 76 77 79 81 85 87 89 91 107 108 110 111 114 119 124 127 130 141 146 147 148 149 152 154 **S** LifePoint Health, Brentwood, TN
Primary Contact: Timothy Harclerode, Chief Executive Officer
CFO: Kimberly Semelsberger, CPA, Chief Financial Officer
CHR: Lorie Smith, Director Human Resources
Web address: www.nasonhospital.com
Control: Corporation, Investor–owned (for–profit) **Service**: General medical and surgical

Staffed Beds: 45 **Admissions:** 1588 **Census:** 12 **Outpatient Visits:** 72789 **Births:** 315 **Total Expense ($000):** 31396 **Payroll Expense ($000):** 12331 **Personnel:** 256

ROYERSFORD—Montgomery County

PHYSICIANS CARE SURGICAL HOSPITAL (390324), 454 Enterprise Drive, Zip 19468–1200; tel. 610/495–3330, (Nonreporting) **A**10 21
Primary Contact: Christopher Doyle, Chief Executive Officer
Web address: www.phycarehospital.com
Control: Partnership, Investor–owned (for–profit) **Service**: Surgical

Staffed Beds: 12

SAINT MARYS—Elk County

PENN HIGHLANDS ELK (391315), 763 Johnsonburg Road, Zip 15857–3498; tel. 814/788–8000, (Nonreporting) **A**10 18
Primary Contact: Bradley Chapman, President
CFO: Laurie MacDonald, Vice President Finance
CMO: David Johe, M.D., President Medical Staff
CIO: Mary Ann Schwabenbauer, Director Information Technology
CHR: Seanna D'Amore, Director Human Resources
Web address: www.phhealthcare.org
Control: Other not–for–profit (including NFP Corporation) **Service**: General medical and surgical

Staffed Beds: 173

SAYRE—Bradford County

GUTHRIE ROBERT PACKER HOSPITAL (390079), 1 Guthrie Square, Zip 18840–1698; tel. 570/888–6666, **A**1 2 3 5 10 13 19 **F**3 11 12 13 15 18 20 22 24 26 28 29 30 31 34 37 38 40 43 45 46 47 48 49 50 57 58 59 61 64 70 73 74 75 76 78 79 81 82 84 85 86 87 89 91 92 93 96 98 100 102 105 107 108 110 111 114 115 116 117 118 119 120 121 123 126 129 130 132 141 142 145 146 148 149 150 154 **S** Guthrie Clinic, Sayre, PA
Primary Contact: Joseph T. Sawyer Jr, President
CFO: Scott Silvestri, Chief Financial Officer, Hospital Financial Operations
CMO: Brian Fillipo, M.D., Chief Medical Officer
CIO: Burt Robles, Vice President Information Services
CHR: Frank Pinkosky, Senior Vice President
CNO: Catherine Mohr, R.N., MSN, Chief Nursing Officer
Web address: www.https://www.guthrie.org/location/robert-packer-hospital
Control: Other not–for–profit (including NFP Corporation) **Service**: General medical and surgical

Staffed Beds: 237 **Admissions:** 14291 **Census:** 169 **Outpatient Visits:** 144887 **Births:** 763 **Total Expense ($000):** 308939 **Payroll Expense ($000):** 83993 **Personnel:** 1400

SCRANTON—Lackawanna County

☐ △ **ALLIED SERVICES REHABILITATION HOSPITAL (393030)**, 475 Morgan Highway, Zip 18508–2605, Mailing Address: P.O. Box 1103, Zip 18501–1103; tel. 570/348–1300, (Nonreporting) **A**1 7 10
Primary Contact: Karen Kearney, Vice President Inpatient Rehabilitation Services
CFO: Michael Avvisato, Senior Vice President and Chief Financial Officer
CMO: Gregory Basting, M.D., Vice President Medical Affairs
CIO: John Regula, Chief Information Officer
CHR: Judy P Oprisko, Vice President
CNO: Jeana Sluck, R.N., Executive Director Nursing Clinical Inpatient Departments
Web address: www.allied-services.org
Control: Other not–for–profit (including NFP Corporation) **Service**: Rehabilitation

Staffed Beds: 117

COMMUNITY MEDICAL CENTER HEALTHCARE SYSTEM See Geisinger-Community Medical Center

GEISINGER-COMMUNITY MEDICAL CENTER (390001), 1800 Mulberry Street, Zip 18510–2369; tel. 570/703–8000, **A**1 2 3 5 10 19 **F**3 11 12 15 18 20 22 24 26 28 29 30 31 34 35 37 39 40 43 44 45 46 47 49 53 54 56 58 59 61 64 65 68 70 74 75 77 78 79 80 81 82 84 85 86 87 89 91 92 93 94 97 98 100 102 107 108 110 111 114 115 117 118 119 126 129 130 131 132 135 145 146 147 148 149 154 156 **S** Geisinger, Danville, PA
Primary Contact: Ronald R. Beer, FACHE, Chief Administrative Officer
CMO: Anthony Aquilina, D.O., Chief Medical Officer
CHR: Lois Wolfe, Director Human Resources
Web address: www.geisinger.org/for-patients/locations-directions/gcmc/
Control: Other not–for–profit (including NFP Corporation) **Service**: General medical and surgical

Staffed Beds: 213 **Admissions:** 12645 **Census:** 158 **Outpatient Visits:** 382790 **Births:** 0 **Total Expense ($000):** 293780 **Payroll Expense ($000):** 106707 **Personnel:** 1521

MERCY HOSPITAL OF SCRANTON See Regional Hospital of Scranton

MOSES TAYLOR HOSPITAL (390119), 700 Quincy Avenue, Zip 18510–1724; tel. 570/770–5000, **A**1 3 5 10 **F**3 7 13 15 18 29 30 31 34 40 44 45 49 50 51 54 56 57 59 60 61 64 65 66 68 70 72 74 75 76 77 78 79 81 85 86 87 89 92 93 98 103 107 108 110 111 114 115 116 117 119 124 129 130 132 135 146 147 154 **S** Community Health Systems, Inc., Franklin, TN
Primary Contact: Ronald Ziobro, Interim Chief Executive Officer
CFO: Thomas Bisignani, Chief Financial Officer
CMO: Mary Sewatsky, M.D., Chief Medical Officer
CHR: Elizabeth Leo, Chief Human Resources Officer
CNO: Patricia Seliga, R.N., Chief Nursing Officer
Web address: www.mth.org
Control: Corporation, Investor–owned (for–profit) **Service**: General medical and surgical

Staffed Beds: 213 **Admissions:** 8229 **Census:** 107 **Outpatient Visits:** 180135 **Births:** 2254 **Total Expense ($000):** 151472 **Payroll Expense ($000):** 42263 **Personnel:** 833

Many Facility Codes have changed. Please refer to the AHA Guide Code Chart. © 2019 AHA Guide

PA

SELLERSVILLE—Bucks County

✠ **GRAND VIEW HEALTH (390057)**, 700 Lawn Avenue, Zip 18960–1548, Mailing Address: P.O. Box 902, Zip 18960–0902; tel. 215/453–4000, **A**1 2 10 **F**3 7 11 12 13 15 18 28 29 31 34 35 37 40 44 45 46 50 54 56 57 59 62 63 64 68 70 72 74 75 76 77 78 79 81 84 85 86 87 89 90 93 96 107 108 110 111 114 115 117 118 119 120 121 123 130 132 135 146 149 156 157
Primary Contact: Jean M. Keeler, President and Chief Executive Officer
COO: J Mark Horne, Senior Vice President, Ambulatory Services and Chief Operating Officer
CFO: Michael Keen, Senior Vice President and Chief Financial Officer
CMO: Jane Ferry, M.D., Vice President Medical Affairs
CIO: Jane Doll Loveless, Vice President, Chief Information Officer
CNO: Kathleen Burkey, R.N., MSN, Vice President, Patient Care Service and Chief Nursing Officer
Web address: www.gvh.org
Control: Other not–for–profit (including NFP Corporation) **Service**: General medical and surgical

Staffed Beds: 194 Admissions: 8205 Census: 93 Outpatient Visits: 330669 Births: 1182 Total Expense ($000): 196837 Payroll Expense ($000): 102273 Personnel: 1410

SENECA—Venango County

☐ **UPMC NORTHWEST (390091)**, 100 Fairfield Drive, Zip 16346–2130; tel. 814/676–7600, (Total facility includes 16 beds in nursing home–type unit) **A**1 2 3 10 19 **F**3 11 13 15 18 20 28 29 31 34 35 40 44 45 46 47 50 51 56 57 59 63 64 65 68 70 74 75 76 77 78 79 81 82 84 85 86 87 90 93 96 98 100 101 102 103 107 108 110 111 115 119 121 123 128 130 131 132 135 141 142 146 147 148 149 154 155 157 **S** UPMC, Pittsburgh, PA
Primary Contact: Brian Durniok, President
COO: Brian Durniok, Vice President Operations
CFO: Bradley Dinger, Financial Representative
CMO: David McCandless, Vice President Medical Affairs
CHR: Brian Durniok, President
Web address: www.upmc.com/locations/hospitals/northwest/Pages/default.aspx
Control: Other not–for–profit (including NFP Corporation) **Service**: General medical and surgical

Staffed Beds: 128 Admissions: 6038 Census: 92 Outpatient Visits: 142055 Births: 589 Total Expense ($000): 110215 Payroll Expense ($000): 29301 Personnel: 655

SEWICKLEY—Allegheny County

✠ **ENCOMPASS HEALTH REHABILITATION HOSPITAL OF SEWICKLEY (393045)**, 303 Camp Meeting Road, Zip 15143–8322; tel. 412/741–9500, (Nonreporting) **A**1 10 **S** Encompass Health Corporation, Birmingham, AL
Primary Contact: Leah Laffey, R.N., Chief Executive Officer
CFO: Daniel A Vrana, Area Controller
CMO: Shelana Gibbs-McElvy, M.D., Medical Director
CIO: Jamie Smith, Supervisor Health Information Management Systems
CHR: Melissa Coleman, Director Human Resources
CNO: Christie Ryan, Chief Nursing Officer
Web address: www.healthsouthsewickley.com
Control: Corporation, Investor–owned (for–profit) **Service**: Rehabilitation

Staffed Beds: 44

☐ **SEWICKLEY VALLEY HOSPITAL, (A DIVISION OF VALLEY MEDICAL FACILITIES) (390037)**, 720 Blackburn Road, Zip 15143–1459; tel. 412/741–6600, (Nonreporting) **A**1 10 **S** Heritage Valley Health System, Beaver, PA
Primary Contact: Norman F. Mitry, President and Chief Executive Officer
COO: John Luellen, M.D., Chief Operating Officer
CFO: Bryan J Randall, Vice President Finance and Chief Financial Officer
CMO: Michael Cratty, M.D., Chief Medical Officer
CIO: David Carleton, Chief Information Officer
CHR: Bruce Edwards, Vice President Human Resources
CNO: Linda Homyk, Chief Nursing Officer
Web address: www.heritagevalley.org
Control: Other not–for–profit (including NFP Corporation) **Service**: General medical and surgical

Staffed Beds: 179

SHARON—Mercer County

☐ **SHARON REGIONAL MEDICAL CENTER (390211)**, 740 East State Street, Zip 16146–3395; tel. 724/983–3911, (Nonreporting) **A**1 3 10 **S** Steward Health Care System, LLC, Dallas, TX
Primary Contact: Joseph G. Hugar, President
Web address: www.https://www.sharonregionalmedical.org
Control: Corporation, Investor–owned (for–profit) **Service**: General medical and surgical

Staffed Beds: 218

SHICKSHINNY—Luzerne County

HUNTINGTON CREEK RECOVERY CENTER, 890 Bethel Road, Zip 18655; tel. 570/864–3116, (Nonreporting)
Primary Contact: Robert Norris, Chief Executive Officer
Web address: www.clearbrookinc.com
Control: Other not–for–profit (including NFP Corporation) **Service**: Alcoholism and other chemical dependency

Staffed Beds: 65

SHIPPENSBURG—Franklin County

☐ **ROXBURY TREATMENT CENTER (394050)**, 601 Roxbury Road, Zip 17257–9302; tel. 800/648–4673, (Nonreporting) **A**1 10 **S** Universal Health Services, Inc., King of Prussia, PA
Primary Contact: Shauna Mogerman, Chief Executive Officer
Web address: www.roxburyhospital.com
Control: Corporation, Investor–owned (for–profit) **Service**: Psychiatric

Staffed Beds: 94

SOMERSET—Somerset County

✠ **UPMC SOMERSET HOSPITAL (390039)**, 225 South Center Avenue, Zip 15501–2088; tel. 814/443–5000, **A**1 10 20 **F**3 8 11 15 17 18 20 22 26 28 29 30 32 34 35 40 45 49 50 53 57 59 62 63 64 68 77 79 80 81 82 84 85 86 87 89 93 97 98 100 103 104 107 108 110 111 115 119 129 130 131 132 133 135 141 146 148 149 154 **S** UPMC, Pittsburgh, PA
Primary Contact: Andrew G. Rush, Chief Executive Officer
CFO: Matthew Kociola, Senior Vice President and Chief Financial Officer
CIO: Jonathan Bauer, Director Information Systems
CHR: Mark P Frick, Senior Vice President Human Resources
CNO: Suellen Lichtenfels, Vice President and Chief Nursing Officer
Web address: www.somersethospital.com
Control: Other not–for–profit (including NFP Corporation) **Service**: General medical and surgical

Staffed Beds: 98 Admissions: 2713 Census: 35 Outpatient Visits: 131732 Births: 0 Total Expense ($000): 65444 Payroll Expense ($000): 26109 Personnel: 557

SPRINGFIELD—Delaware County

SPRINGFIELD HOSPITAL See Crozer-Chester Medical Center, Upland

STATE COLLEGE—Centre County

✠ **MOUNT NITTANY MEDICAL CENTER (390268)**, 1800 East Park Avenue, Zip 16803–6797; tel. 814/231–7000, **A**1 2 3 5 10 20 **F**3 7 8 13 15 17 20 22 26 28 29 30 31 35 40 46 49 51 57 59 64 68 70 73 74 75 76 77 78 79 80 81 82 84 85 87 89 93 98 100 101 102 107 108 111 114 115 118 119 121 126 129 130 132 135 143 146 148 149 154
Primary Contact: Kathleen Rhine, President and Chief Executive Officer
CFO: Randy E Tewksbury, Senior Vice President Finance and Chief Financial Officer
CIO: Wayne Thompson, Executive Vice President and Chief Information Officer
Web address: www.mountnittany.org
Control: Other not–for–profit (including NFP Corporation) **Service**: General medical and surgical

Staffed Beds: 260 Admissions: 13345 Census: 134 Outpatient Visits: 311512 Births: 1341 Total Expense ($000): 396994 Payroll Expense ($000): 178717 Personnel: 1638

PA

Hospital, Medicare Provider Number, Address, Telephone, Approval, Facility, and Physician Codes, Health Care System

★ American Hospital Association (AHA) membership
☐ The Joint Commission accreditation
○ Healthcare Facilities Accreditation Program
◇ DNV Healthcare Inc. accreditation
⇈ Center for Improvement in Healthcare Quality Accreditation
△ Commission on Accreditation of Rehabilitation Facilities (CARF) accreditation

PA

STROUDSBURG—Centre County

☐ **ST. LUKE'S MONROE (390330)**, 100 St. Luke's Lane, Zip 18360; tel. 484/526–2116, **A1** 10 **F3** 7 12 15 18 20 22 26 29 30 31 34 35 38 40 44 45 46 47 49 50 51 54 56 57 59 60 63 64 70 74 75 77 78 79 81 85 86 87 93 100 102 107 108 109 110 111 115 118 119 129 130 132 145 146 147 149 154 155
Primary Contact: Donald Seiple, President
Web address: www.slhn.org/Choose/choose-monroe
Control: Other not–for–profit (including NFP Corporation) **Service**: General medical and surgical

Staffed Beds: 90 **Admissions**: 5744 **Census**: 61 **Outpatient Visits**: 78683 **Births**: 0 **Total Expense ($000)**: 88600 **Payroll Expense ($000)**: 33154 **Personnel**: 529	

SUNBURY—Northumberland County

⊞ **UPMC SUSQUEHANNA SUNBURY (390084)**, 350 North Eleventh Street, Zip 17801–1611; tel. 570/286–3333, (Data for 273 days) **A1** 10 **F11** 15 18 29 30 34 35 40 45 46 50 57 59 62 68 77 79 81 85 86 87 90 93 96 97 106 107 108 110 111 114 118 119 130 146 154 **S** UPMC Susquehanna, Williamsport, PA
Primary Contact: Robert E. Kane, Chief Executive Officer
CFO: James J. Pachucki Jr Chief Financial Officer
CMO: Charles C Pagana, M.D., Chief Medical Officer
CIO: Fax Rector III Director Information Technology
CHR: Talia Beatty, Director Human Resources
CNO: Catharine L Keister, Chief Nursing Officer
Web address: www.sunburyhospital.com
Control: Other not–for–profit (including NFP Corporation) **Service**: General medical and surgical

Staffed Beds: 16 **Admissions**: 688 **Census**: 15 **Outpatient Visits**: 23995 **Births**: 0 **Total Expense ($000)**: 14422 **Payroll Expense ($000)**: 6525 **Personnel**: 110	

SUSQUEHANNA—Susquehanna County

BARNES-KASSON COUNTY HOSPITAL (391309), 2872 Turnpike Street, Zip 18847–2771; tel. 570/853–3135, (Nonreporting) **A10** 18
Primary Contact: Sara F. Adornato, Executive Director
CFO: Kelli R Kane, Director of Finance
CMO: Pravinchandra Patel, M.D., Chief Medical Officer
CIO: Eric Detwiler, Director Information Technology
Web address: www.barnes-kasson.org
Control: Other not–for–profit (including NFP Corporation) **Service**: General medical and surgical

Staffed Beds: 83	

TITUSVILLE—Crawford County

★ **TITUSVILLE AREA HOSPITAL (391314)**, 406 West Oak Street, Zip 16354–1404; tel. 814/827–1851, (Nonreporting) **A10** 18 **S** Meadville Medical Center, Meadville, PA
Primary Contact: Lee Clinton, FACHE, Chief Executive Officer
CFO: Jill Neely, Chief Financial Officer
CMO: William Sonnenberg, M.D., President Medical Staff
CIO: Karen Humes, Chief Information Officer
CHR: Jeffrey Saintz, Vice President Human Resources
CNO: Brenda Burnett, R.N., Vice President Patient Care Services and Chief Nursing Officer
Web address: www.titusvillehospital.org
Control: Other not–for–profit (including NFP Corporation) **Service**: General medical and surgical

Staffed Beds: 25	

TORRANCE—Westmoreland County

TORRANCE STATE HOSPITAL (394026), Torrance Road, Zip 15779–0111, Mailing Address: P.O. Box 111, Zip 15779–0111; tel. 724/459–8000, **A10** **F39** 53 65 75 77 97 98 100 101 130 135 143 146 147 148 154
Primary Contact: Edna I. McCutcheon, Chief Executive Officer
COO: R Brad Snyder, Chief Operating Officer
CFO: Michael Yahner, Chief Financial Officer
CMO: Herbert G Chissell, M.D., Chief Medical Officer
Web address: www.dpw.state.pa.us
Control: State, Government, nonfederal **Service**: Psychiatric

Staffed Beds: 353 **Admissions**: 256 **Census**: 318 **Outpatient Visits**: 0 **Births**: 0 **Total Expense ($000)**: 87492 **Payroll Expense ($000)**: 40825 **Personnel**: 699	

TOWANDA—Bradford County

★ **GUTHRIE TOWANDA MEMORIAL HOSPITAL (390236)**, 91 Hospital Drive, Zip 18848–9702; tel. 570/265–2191, (Total facility includes 160 beds in nursing home–type unit) **A10** **F7** 10 11 28 29 35 36 40 50 57 59 64 75 77 79 81 82 84 85 87 93 107 115 119 129 130 133 135 143 146 154 157 **S** Guthrie Clinic, Sayre, PA
Primary Contact: Felissa Koernig, President and Chief Operating Officer
CIO: Karen Brown, Manager Information Technology
CHR: Linda Berry, Vice President Human Resources
CNO: Lynn Dibble, Vice President Patient Care Services
Web address: www.https://www.guthrie.org/location/guthrie-towanda-memorial-hospital
Control: Other not–for–profit (including NFP Corporation) **Service**: General medical and surgical

Staffed Beds: 195 **Admissions**: 985 **Census**: 11 **Outpatient Visits**: 36491 **Births**: 0	

TRANSFER—Mercer County

EDGEWOOD SURGICAL HOSPITAL (390307), 239 Edgewood Drive Extension, Zip 16154–1817; tel. 724/646–0400, (Nonreporting) **A10**
Primary Contact: Lloyd Scarrow, FACHE, Chief Executive Officer
Web address: www.edgewoodsurgical.com
Control: Corporation, Investor–owned (for–profit) **Service**: Surgical

Staffed Beds: 10	

TROY—Bradford County

★ ○ **GUTHRIE TROY COMMUNITY HOSPITAL (391305)**, 275 Guthrie Drive, Zip 16947; tel. 570/297–2121, **A10** 11 18 **F3** 11 15 28 29 30 40 107 110 111 119 129 130 133 135 146 148 **S** Guthrie Clinic, Sayre, PA
Primary Contact: Lori Barnett, R.N., MSN, President and Chief Operating Officer
CFO: Bernie Smith, Chief Financial Officer
CMO: Vance A Good, M.D., Chief Medical Staff
CIO: Dale Swingle, Vice President Information Services
CHR: Frank Pinkosky, Executive Vice President
Web address: www.guthrie.org
Control: Other not–for–profit (including NFP Corporation) **Service**: General medical and surgical

Staffed Beds: 25 **Admissions**: 659 **Census**: 7 **Births**: 0	

TUNKHANNOCK—Bradford County

⊞ **TYLER MEMORIAL HOSPITAL (390192)**, 5950 State Route 6, Zip 18657–7905; tel. 570/836–2161, (Nonreporting) **A1** 10 **S** Community Health Systems, Inc., Franklin, TN
Primary Contact: Ann Marie. Stevens, R.N., Chief Executive Officer
CMO: Terrance Chilson, Chief of Staff
CNO: Judith Ragukas, Interim Chief Nursing Officer
Web address: www.tylermemorialhospital.net
Control: Corporation, Investor–owned (for–profit) **Service**: General medical and surgical

Staffed Beds: 44	

TYRONE—Blair County

TYRONE HOSPITAL (391307), 187 Hospital Drive, Zip 16686–1808; tel. 814/684–1255, (Nonreporting) **A10** 18
Primary Contact: Joseph J. Peluso, Chief Executive Officer
CMO: Kelly Biggs, M.D., Chief Medical Officer
CHR: Rosemary Jorden Best, Director Human Resources
CNO: Sharon Fisher, R.N., Chief Nursing Officer
Web address: www.tyronehospital.org
Control: Other not–for–profit (including NFP Corporation) **Service**: General medical and surgical

Staffed Beds: 25	

UNIONTOWN—Fayette County

✠ **UNIONTOWN HOSPITAL (390041)**, 500 West Berkeley Street, Zip 15401–5596; tel. 724/430–5000, **A**1 10 **F**3 11 13 15 18 20 22 28 29 30 34 35 40 45 49 51 54 57 59 64 70 73 74 75 76 77 78 79 81 89 90 92 96 102 107 108 110 111 114 115 118 119 130 132 146 148 149 154
Primary Contact: Steven P. Handy, CPA, Chief Executive Officer
CHR: James Proud, Vice President Human Resources and Marketing
CNO: Betty Ann Rock, Vice President Nursing and Chief Nursing Officer
Web address: www.uniontownhospital.com
Control: Other not–for–profit (including NFP Corporation) **Service**: General medical and surgical

Staffed Beds: 142 Admissions: 8357 **Census:** 96 **Outpatient Visits:** 222315 **Births:** 841 **Total Expense ($000):** 139607 **Payroll Expense ($000):** 45791 **Personnel:** 1038

UPLAND—Delaware County

☐ **CROZER-CHESTER MEDICAL CENTER (390180)**, One Medical Center Boulevard, Zip 19013–3995; tel. 610/447–2000, (Includes SPRINGFIELD HOSPITAL, 190 West Sproul Road, Springfield, Pennsylvania, Zip 19064–2097; tel. 610/328–8700; TAYLOR HOSPITAL, 175 East Chester Pike, Ridley Park, Pennsylvania, Zip 19078–2212; tel. 610/595–6000), (Non-reporting) **A**1 2 3 5 10 12 13 **S** Prospect Medical Holdings, Los Angeles, CA
Primary Contact: Michael Curran, President
CMO: Sat Arora, M.D., President Medical and Dental Staff
CIO: Robert E Wilson, Vice President and Chief Information Officer
Web address: www.crozer.org
Control: Other not–for–profit (including NFP Corporation) **Service**: General medical and surgical

Staffed Beds: 384

WARREN—Warren County

WARREN GENERAL HOSPITAL (390146), Two Crescent Park West, Zip 16365–0068, Mailing Address: P.O. Box 68, Zip 16365–0068; tel. 814/723–4973, **A**10 **F**3 4 11 13 15 18 26 27 28 29 31 34 35 40 41 44 45 47 48 50 51 57 59 62 64 68 70 75 76 77 78 79 81 85 87 89 90 92 93 97 98 99 100 101 102 103 107 108 109 110 111 114 115 116 117 118 119 120 121 123 130 133 145 146 148 154 157
Primary Contact: Richard Allen, Chief Executive Officer
COO: Randy California, Chief Operating Officer
CFO: Julie Jacobs, Chief Financial Officer
CMO: John Maljovec, M.D., Medical Director
CIO: Helen Rosequist, Manager Information Systems
CHR: Matthew Franklin, Director Human Resources
CNO: Joe Akif, Chief Clinical Officer and Chief Nursing Officer
Web address: www.wgh.org
Control: Other not–for–profit (including NFP Corporation) **Service**: General medical and surgical

Staffed Beds: 85 Admissions: 2994 **Census:** 31 **Outpatient Visits:** 104810 **Births:** 279 **Total Expense ($000):** 75372 **Payroll Expense ($000):** 31998 **Personnel:** 385

WARREN STATE HOSPITAL (394016), 33 Main Drive, Zip 16365–5001; tel. 814/723–5500, **A**10 **F**39 50 56 75 77 82 98 100 128 130 132 135 146 149
Primary Contact: Charlotte M. Uber, Chief Executive Officer
COO: Ronnie Cropper, Chief Operating Officer
CFO: Terry Crambes, Manager Finance
CMO: Andrea J. Richard, M.D., Chief Medical Officer
CIO: Karen Byler, Information Technology Generalist
CNO: Sara Flasher, Chief Nurse Executive
Web address: www.dpw.pa.gov
Control: State, Government, nonfederal **Service**: Psychiatric

Staffed Beds: 152 Admissions: 80 **Census:** 138 **Outpatient Visits:** 0 **Births:** 0 **Total Expense ($000):** 47657 **Payroll Expense ($000):** 20666 **Personnel:** 382

WASHINGTON—Washington County

☐ **ADVANCED SURGICAL HOSPITAL (390323)**, 100 Trich Drive Suite 1, Zip 15301–5990; tel. 724/884–0710, (Nonreporting) **A**1 10
Primary Contact: Anne S. Hast, R.N., Chief Executive Officer
CFO: Diane Hritz, Chief Financial Officer
CNO: Anne S Hast, R.N., Director of Nursing
Web address: www.ashospital.net
Control: Partnership, Investor–owned (for–profit) **Service**: Orthopedic

Staffed Beds: 14

✠ **WASHINGTON HOSPITAL (390042)**, 155 Wilson Avenue, Zip 15301–3398; tel. 724/225–7000, **A**1 3 5 10 13 **F**3 5 11 12 13 15 18 20 22 24 26 28 29 30 31 32 34 35 36 38 39 40 44 45 46 49 50 53 54 56 57 59 60 61 64 65 70 74 75 76 77 78 79 81 82 84 85 86 87 89 90 91 92 93 94 96 97 98 100 101 102 103 107 108 110 111 114 115 118 119 126 127 130 131 132 134 135 146 147 148 154 156 **S** Washington Health System, Washington, PA
Primary Contact: Gary B. Weinstein, President and Chief Executive Officer
COO: Brook Ward, Executive Vice President
CFO: Alisa Rucker, Vice President Finance and Chief Financial Officer
CMO: Paul T Cullen, M.D., Vice President Medical Affairs
CIO: Rodney Louk, Vice President Information Systems
CHR: Barbara A McCullough, Vice President Human Resources
CNO: Karen A Bray, R.N., MSN, Vice President Patient Care Services
Web address: www.washingtonhospital.org
Control: Other not–for–profit (including NFP Corporation) **Service**: General medical and surgical

Staffed Beds: 206 Admissions: 10593 **Census:** 126 **Outpatient Visits:** 735800 **Births:** 839 **Total Expense ($000):** 232417 **Payroll Expense ($000):** 102843 **Personnel:** 1621

WAYNESBORO—Franklin County

✠ **WAYNESBORO HOSPITAL (390138)**, 501 East Main Street, Zip 17268–2394; tel. 717/765–4000, **A**1 10 **F**3 11 13 15 29 30 34 40 44 45 49 50 54 56 57 59 61 64 65 68 74 75 76 77 79 81 85 86 87 93 94 100 107 108 110 111 115 118 119 130 131 132 133 135 146 147 148 149 150 154 157 **S** WellSpan Health, York, PA
Primary Contact: Melissa Dubrow, Chief Operating Officer
COO: Melissa Dubrow, Vice President and Chief Operating Officer
CFO: Kimberly Rzomp, Vice President Finance
CMO: Thomas Anderson, M.D., Vice President Medical Affairs
CIO: Michele Zeigler, Vice President Information Services
CHR: Jennifer Knight, Manager Human Resources
CNO: Jill Keller, R.N., MSN, Vice President for Nursing Services, Quality and Risk Management
Web address: www.summithealth.org
Control: Other not–for–profit (including NFP Corporation) **Service**: General medical and surgical

Staffed Beds: 56 Admissions: 2353 **Census:** 20 **Outpatient Visits:** 94373 **Births:** 378 **Total Expense ($000):** 62960 **Payroll Expense ($000):** 28688 **Personnel:** 435

WAYNESBURG—Greene County

✠ **WASHINGTON HEALTH SYSTEM GREENE (390150)**, 350 Bonar Avenue, Zip 15370–1608; tel. 724/627–3101, **A**1 3 10 **F**3 11 15 29 30 34 35 40 44 57 59 64 81 85 87 98 104 107 108 110 111 114 119 130 133 135 146 **S** Washington Health System, Washington, PA
Primary Contact: Terry Wiltrout, President
COO: Janel Mudry, Chief Operating Officer
CMO: Jamie Boris, M.D., President Medical Staff
CIO: Leslie Hayhurst, Director Information Systems
CHR: Patricia Marshall, Assistant Administrator Human Resources
Web address: www.southwestregionalmedical.com/
Control: Other not–for–profit (including NFP Corporation) **Service**: General medical and surgical

Staffed Beds: 49 Admissions: 1559 **Census:** 20 **Outpatient Visits:** 48403 **Births:** 0 **Total Expense ($000):** 23029 **Payroll Expense ($000):** 11339 **Personnel:** 185

PA

Hospital, Medicare Provider Number, Address, Telephone, Approval, Facility, and Physician Codes, Health Care System

★ American Hospital Association (AHA) membership
☐ The Joint Commission accreditation
○ Healthcare Facilities Accreditation Program
◇ DNV Healthcare Inc. accreditation
⇑ Center for Improvement in Healthcare Quality Accreditation
△ Commission on Accreditation of Rehabilitation Facilities (CARF) accreditation

WELLSBORO—Tioga County

☒ **UPMC SUSQUEHANNA SOLDIERS + SAILORS (391316)**, 32–36 Central Avenue, Zip 16901–1899; tel. 570/724–1631, **A**1 10 18 **F**3 10 11 13 15 28 29 30 31 32 34 35 40 44 45 46 50 54 56 57 59 62 63 67 68 70 75 76 77 78 79 81 84 86 87 90 91 93 96 97 107 108 110 111 115 118 119 120 128 129 130 131 132 146 147 150 154 157 **S** UPMC Susquehanna, Williamsport, PA
Primary Contact: Janie Hilfiger, Chief Administrative Officer
CFO: Eric Pohjala, Chief Financial Officer
CMO: Walter Laibinis, M.D., Chief Medical Officer
CIO: Timothy E Schoener, Senior Vice President and Chief Information Officer
CHR: Christine Ballard, Vice President Human Resources
CNO: Matt Romania, Director of Nursing
Web address: www.susquehannahealth.org
Control: Other not–for–profit (including NFP Corporation) **Service**: General medical and surgical

Staffed Beds: 25 **Admissions:** 1707 **Census:** 16 **Outpatient Visits:** 81657 **Births:** 206 **Total Expense ($000):** 57697 **Payroll Expense ($000):** 20879 **Personnel:** 457

WERNERSVILLE—Berks County

WERNERSVILLE STATE HOSPITAL (394014), 160 Main Street, Zip 19565–9490; tel. 610/678–3411, **A**10 **F**30 39 75 77 98 103 130 135 146
Primary Contact: Shirley Sowizral, Chief Executive Officer
COO: Cheryl Benson, Chief Operating Officer
CMO: Dale K Adair, M.D., Chief Medical Officer
CIO: William Edwards, Information Technology Generalist
CHR: Melvin McMinn, Director Human Resources
Web address: www.dhs.pa.gov/citizens/statehospitals/wernersvillestatehospital/
Control: State, Government, nonfederal **Service**: Psychiatric

Staffed Beds: 266 **Admissions:** 55 **Census:** 246 **Outpatient Visits:** 0 **Births:** 0 **Total Expense ($000):** 69879 **Payroll Expense ($000):** 32934 **Personnel:** 578

WEST CHESTER—Chester County

☒ **LIFECARE HOSPITALS OF CHESTER COUNTY (392048)**, 400 East Marshall Street, Zip 19380–5412; tel. 484/826–0400, (Nonreporting) **A**1 10 **S** LifeCare Management Services, Plano, TX
Primary Contact: Janet Biedron, R.N., Chief Executive Officer
CMO: Raj Patel, M.D., Medical Director
CHR: Evan Ganley, Manager Human Resources
CNO: Bonnie Barclay, Chief Nursing Officer
Web address: www.lifecare-hospitals.com
Control: Corporation, Investor–owned (for–profit) **Service**: Acute long–term care hospital

Staffed Beds: 39

☒ **PENN MEDICINE CHESTER COUNTY HOSPITAL (390179)**, 701 East Marshall Street, Zip 19380–4412; tel. 610/431–5000, **A**1 2 5 10 **F**3 11 13 15 18 20 22 24 26 28 29 30 31 34 35 36 40 44 45 46 49 50 51 54 55 56 57 58 59 60 62 64 65 68 70 72 74 75 76 77 78 79 81 84 85 86 87 89 92 93 96 107 108 110 111 114 115 117 118 119 120 121 126 130 131 132 135 146 147 148 149 154 156 **S** University of Pennsylvania Health System, Philadelphia, PA
Primary Contact: Michael J. Duncan, President and Chief Executive Officer
COO: Michael Barber, Chief Operating Officer
CFO: Kenneth E Flickinger, Chief Financial Officer
CMO: Richard D Donze, D.O., Senior Vice President Medical Affairs
CIO: Karen Pinsky, M.D., Chief Medical Information Officer
CHR: Jacqueline Felicetti, Chief Human Resource Officer
CNO: Angela R. Coladonato, R.N., MSN, Chief Nursing Officer
Web address: www.chestercountyhospital.org
Control: Other not–for–profit (including NFP Corporation) **Service**: General medical and surgical

Staffed Beds: 224 **Admissions:** 14071 **Census:** 154 **Outpatient Visits:** 264375 **Births:** 2775 **Total Expense ($000):** 338689 **Payroll Expense ($000):** 123535 **Personnel:** 1809

WEST GROVE—Chester County

☒ **JENNERSVILLE HOSPITAL (390220)**, 1015 West Baltimore Pike, Zip 19390–9459; tel. 610/869–1000, **A**1 2 10 **F**3 15 18 34 40 45 49 50 51 57 59 65 70 74 75 79 81 85 87 92 93 107 108 110 111 115 119 129 130 146 149 154 **S** Tower Health, West Reading, PA
Primary Contact: Claire Bradley. Mooney, R.N., President and Chief Executive Officer
CFO: Tracey Claxton, Chief Financial Officer
CMO: Tracy Carmellini, M.D., Chief of Staff
CHR: Debra Basquill, Director Human Resources
CNO: Claire Bradley Mooney, R.N., Vice President and Chief Nursing Officer
Web address: www.jennersville.com
Control: Other not–for–profit (including NFP Corporation) **Service**: General medical and surgical

Staffed Beds: 63 **Admissions:** 1977 **Census:** 17 **Outpatient Visits:** 26037 **Births:** 0 **Total Expense ($000):** 33128 **Payroll Expense ($000):** 10871 **Personnel:** 307

WEST READING—Berks County

☒ **READING HOSPITAL (390044)**, Sixth Avenue and Spruce Street, Zip 19611–1428, Mailing Address: P.O. Box 16052, Zip 19612–6052; tel. 610/988–8000, **A**1 2 3 5 8 10 13 **F**3 5 11 12 13 15 18 20 22 24 26 28 29 30 31 32 34 35 40 41 43 44 45 46 47 48 49 50 52 54 55 56 57 58 59 60 61 64 65 66 68 70 71 72 73 74 75 76 77 78 79 80 81 82 84 85 87 89 92 93 94 96 97 98 100 101 102 103 104 105 107 108 110 111 114 115 116 117 118 119 120 121 123 124 126 128 129 130 131 132 135 146 147 148 149 150 154 156 157 **S** Tower Health, West Reading, PA
Primary Contact: William Jennings, President and Chief Executive Officer
COO: Dawn Anuszkiewicz, Chief Operating Officer
CFO: Richard W Jones, Chief Financial Officer
CMO: M. Joseph Grennan, M.D., Jr Senior Vice President and Chief Medical Officer
CIO: Jayashree Raman, Vice President and Chief Information Officer
CNO: Mary Christine Agnew, R.N., Senior Vice President and Chief Nursing Officer
Web address: www.readinghospital.org
Control: Other not–for–profit (including NFP Corporation) **Service**: General medical and surgical

Staffed Beds: 713 **Admissions:** 33047 **Census:** 451 **Outpatient Visits:** 1183563 **Births:** 3442 **Total Expense ($000):** 877276 **Payroll Expense ($000):** 345240 **Personnel:** 5261

WILKES BARRE—Luzerne County

☒ **GEISINGER WYOMING VALLEY MEDICAL CENTER (390270)**, 1000 East Mountain Boulevard, Zip 18711–0027; tel. 570/808–7300, **A**1 2 5 10 13 19 **F**3 6 9 11 12 13 15 18 19 20 22 24 26 28 29 30 31 32 34 35 37 39 40 43 44 45 46 47 48 49 52 53 54 56 57 58 59 61 64 65 68 70 71 72 74 75 76 77 78 79 80 81 82 84 85 86 87 89 90 91 92 93 94 96 97 100 102 107 108 110 111 114 115 116 117 118 119 120 121 123 124 126 129 130 131 132 135 144 145 146 147 148 149 154 156 **S** Geisinger, Danville, PA
Primary Contact: Ronald R. Beer, FACHE, Chief Administrative Officer
CFO: Thomas A Bielecki, Chief Financial Officer
CMO: Steven Pierdon, M.D., Executive Vice President and Chief Medical Officer
CIO: Frank Richards, Chief Information Officer
CHR: Margaret Heffers, Assistant Vice President Human Resources
Web address: www.geisinger.org
Control: Other not–for–profit (including NFP Corporation) **Service**: General medical and surgical

Staffed Beds: 277 **Admissions:** 17382 **Census:** 207 **Outpatient Visits:** 834671 **Births:** 1633 **Total Expense ($000):** 481780 **Payroll Expense ($000):** 131207 **Personnel:** 2630

★ **PAM SPECIALTY HOSPITAL OF WILKES-BARRE (392025)**, 575 North River Street, 7th Floor, Zip 18702–2634; tel. 570/208–3310, (Nonreporting) **S** Post Acute Medical, LLC, Enola, PA
Primary Contact: Cindy Miller, Chief Executive Officer
Web address: www.warmsprings.org/our-facilities/hospitals/post-acute-medical-specialty-hospital-wilkes-barre/
Control: Corporation, Investor–owned (for–profit) **Service**: Acute long–term care hospital

Staffed Beds: 36

WILKES—BARRE-Luzerne County

☐ **JOHN HEINZ INSTITUTE OF REHABILITATION MEDICINE (393036)**, 150 Mundy Street, Zip 18702–6830; tel. 570/826–3800, (Nonreporting) **A**1 10
Primary Contact: Karen Kearney, Vice President Inpatient Rehabilitation Services
CFO: Mike Avvisato, Vice President and Chief Financial Officer
CMO: Gregory Basting, M.D., Vice President Medical Affairs
CIO: John Regula, Chief Information Officer
CHR: Judy P Oprisko, Vice President Human Resources
CNO: Maria Berlyn, Assistant Vice President Nursing Services
Web address: www.allied-services.org
Control: Other not–for–profit (including NFP Corporation) **Service**: Rehabilitation

Staffed Beds: 71

VETERANS AFFAIRS MEDICAL CENTER See Wilkes-Barre Veterans Affairs Medical Center

★ △ **WILKES-BARRE GENERAL HOSPITAL (390137)**, 575 North River Street, Zip 18764–0001; tel. 570/829–8111, (Includes WILKES-BARRE GENERAL HOSPITAL, 575 North River Street, Wilkes-Barre, Pennsylvania, Zip 18764; tel. 570/829–8111) **A**2 3 5 7 10 19 **F**3 8 12 13 15 17 18 20 22 24 26 28 29 30 31 34 37 40 43 44 45 46 47 48 49 50 51 54 56 57 59 61 64 66 70 73 74 75 76 78 79 81 82 83 84 85 86 87 89 90 92 93 96 107 108 110 111 112 114 115 116 117 118 119 120 121 123 124 126 129 130 132 145 146 147 149 154 **S** Community Health Systems, Inc., Franklin, TN
Primary Contact: Cornelio R. Catena, President and Chief Executive Officer
COO: Robert Stiekes, Chief Operating Officer
CFO: Roy Boyd, Chief Financial Officer
CIO: Denis Tucker, Chief Information Officer
CHR: James Carmody, Vice President Human Resources
CNO: Robert P Hoffman, R.N., Chief Nursing Officer
Web address: www.wvhc.org
Control: Corporation, Investor–owned (for–profit) **Service**: General medical and surgical

Staffed Beds: 374 Admissions: 12993 Census: 181 Outpatient Visits: 512019 Births: 1052 Total Expense ($000): 306946 Payroll Expense ($000): 81924 Personnel: 1306

⊞ **WILKES-BARRE VETERANS AFFAIRS MEDICAL CENTER**, 1111 East End Boulevard, Zip 18711–0030; tel. 570/824–3521, (Nonreporting) **A**1 2 3 5 **S** Department of Veterans Affairs, Washington, DC
Primary Contact: Russell E. Lloyd, Director
COO: Joesph P. Sharon, Associate Director
CFO: Donald E Foote, Fiscal Officer
CMO: Mirza Z Ali, M.D., Chief of Staff
CIO: David Longmore, Chief Information Officer
CHR: Dawn P DeMorrow, Chief Human Resources Service
Web address: www.va.gov/vamcwb
Control: Veterans Affairs, Government, federal **Service**: General medical and surgical

Staffed Beds: 165

WYOMING VALLEY HEALTH CARE SYSTEM See Wilkes-Barre General Hospital

WILLIAMSPORT—Lycoming County

★ **UPMC SUSQUEHANNA DIVINE PROVIDENCE CAMPUS (394048)**, 1100 Grampian Boulevard, Zip 17701–1995; tel. 570/326–8000, **A**3 10 **F**11 15 31 35 38 44 50 55 56 59 62 63 64 68 75 77 78 79 81 82 84 86 87 91 93 98 99 100 103 104 107 108 110 115 120 121 129 130 131 132 134 146 147 148 150 151 152 154 156 157 **S** UPMC Susquehanna, Williamsport, PA
Primary Contact: Robert E. Kane, Chief Administrative Officer
COO: Neil G Armstrong, FACHE, Vice President and Chief Operating Officer
Web address: www.susquehannahealth.org
Control: Other not–for–profit (including NFP Corporation) **Service**: Psychiatric

Staffed Beds: 31 Admissions: 609 Census: 14 Outpatient Visits: 130750 Births: 0 Total Expense ($000): 95656 Payroll Expense ($000): 25462 Personnel: 368

⊞ **UPMC SUSQUEHANNA WILLIAMSPORT (390045)**, 700 High Street, Zip 17701–3100; tel. 570/321–1000, **A**1 2 5 10 13 19 **F**3 4 5 7 11 13 15 17 18 20 22 24 26 28 29 30 31 32 34 35 38 40 44 45 46 47 48 49 50 54 55 56 57 59 60 61 62 63 64 68 70 73 74 75 76 77 78 79 81 82 84 85 86 87 89 90 91 92 93 96 97 98 99 100 103 104 107 108 110 111 114 115 117 118 119 120 121 123 124 126 129 130 131 132 134 135 138 139 143 146 147 148 150 151 152 154 156 157 **S** UPMC Susquehanna, Williamsport, PA
Primary Contact: Steven P. Johnson, FACHE, President
COO: Jan E Fisher, Executive Vice President, Chief Operating Officer and Chief Administrative Officer
CFO: Eric Pohjala, Executive Vice President and Chief Financial Officer
CIO: Timothy E Schoener, Vice President and Chief Information Officer
CHR: Donald Wilver Jr Vice President Human Resources
CNO: Lori A Beucler, MSN, RN, BS-NE, FACHE, R.N., Vice President and Chief Nursing Officer
Web address: www.susquehannahealth.org
Control: Other not–for–profit (including NFP Corporation) **Service**: General medical and surgical

Staffed Beds: 224 Admissions: 11450 Census: 145 Outpatient Visits: 224355 Births: 1105 Total Expense ($000): 314028 Payroll Expense ($000): 118598 Personnel: 1633

WILLIAMSPORT HOSPITAL AND MEDICAL CENTER See Upmc Susquehanna Williamsport

WINDBER—Somerset County

★ **CHAN SOON-SHIONG MEDICAL CENTER (390112)**, 600 Somerset Avenue, Zip 15963–1331; tel. 814/467–3000, **A**10 **F**3 11 12 15 18 20 22 28 29 30 34 35 36 40 45 48 53 55 56 57 58 59 62 63 70 75 79 81 83 84 85 93 107 108 110 111 114 118 119 129 130 131 132 135 145 146 147
Primary Contact: Thomas M. Kurtz, President and Chief Executive Officer
CFO: Richard Sukenik, CPA, Vice President Finance and Chief Financial Officer
CIO: Renee Adams, Director Information Technology
CHR: Jamie Brock, Vice President Human Resources
CNO: Michelle Hamula, Director of Nursing and Quality
Web address: www.windbercare.org
Control: Other not–for–profit (including NFP Corporation) **Service**: General medical and surgical

Staffed Beds: 54 Admissions: 1144 Census: 8 Outpatient Visits: 100413 Births: 0 Total Expense ($000): 43414 Payroll Expense ($000): 19450 Personnel: 340

WYOMISSING—Berks County

☐ △ **READING HOSPITAL REHABILITATION AT WYOMISSING**, 2802 Papermill Road, Zip 19610–1065; tel. 484/628–2388, (Nonreporting) **A**1 /
Primary Contact: Clinton Matthews, President and Chief Executive Officer
Web address: www.https://www.readinghealth.org/locations/locations-module/reading-health-rehabilitation-hospital-2802-papermill-road-wyomissing-pa-19610–889615952/
Control: Other not–for–profit (including NFP Corporation) **Service**: Rehabilitation

Staffed Beds: 112

⊞ **SURGICAL INSTITUTE OF READING (390316)**, 2752 Century Boulevard, Zip 19610–3345; tel. 610/378–8800, (Nonreporting) **A**1 10
Primary Contact: James Bennett, Chief Executive Officer
CFO: Cheryl Peterson, Business Office Manager
CHR: Megan Schaffer, Administrative Assistant
Web address: www.sireading.com
Control: Partnership, Investor–owned (for–profit) **Service**: Surgical

Staffed Beds: 15

PA

WYNNEWOOD—Montgomery County

LANKENAU HOSPITAL See Lankenau Medical Center

☒ **LANKENAU MEDICAL CENTER (390195)**, 100 East Lancaster Avenue,
Zip 19096–3411; tel. 484/476–2000, **A**1 2 3 5 8 10 12 13 **F**3 11 13 15 17 18
20 22 24 26 28 29 30 31 34 35 36 37 38 39 40 41 43 44 45 46 47 48 49 50
54 55 56 57 58 59 63 64 65 66 68 70 72 73 74 75 76 78 79 80 81 82 84 85
86 87 92 97 100 102 107 108 110 111 114 115 119 120 121 124 126 129
130 131 132 135 138 146 148 149 154 **S** Main Line Health, Williamsport, PA
Primary Contact: Phillip D. Robinson, President
COO: John Schwarz, Vice President Administration
CFO: Michael J Buongiorno, Vice President Finance
CMO: Robert Benz, M.D., Chief Medical Officer
CIO: Kay Carr, Chief Information Officer
CHR: Paul Yakulis, MS, R.N., Senior Vice President Human Resources
Web address: www.https://www.mainlinehealth.org/
Control: Other not–for–profit (including NFP Corporation) **Service**: General
medical and surgical

Staffed Beds: 370 **Admissions:** 19284 **Census:** 244 **Outpatient
Visits:** 315589 **Births:** 2892 **Total Expense ($000):** 516612 **Payroll
Expense ($000):** 143440 **Personnel:** 2410

YORK—York County

☒ **ENCOMPASS HEALTH REHABILITATION HOSPITAL OF YORK (393037)**,
1850 Normandie Drive, Zip 17408–1534; tel. 717/767–6941, (Nonreporting) **A**1
10 **S** Encompass Health Corporation, Birmingham, AL
Primary Contact: Steven Alwine, Chief Executive Officer
CFO: Joyce Henry, Controller
CMO: Bruce Sicilia, M.D., Medical Director
CIO: Laura Emig, Director Marketing Operations
CHR: Bradley Teahl, Director Human Resources
CNO: Julie Scott, Chief Nursing Officer
Web address: www.healthsouthyork.com
Control: Corporation, Investor–owned (for–profit) **Service**: Rehabilitation

Staffed Beds: 90

☒ **OSS ORTHOPAEDIC HOSPITAL (390325)**, 1861 Powder Mill Road, Zip 17402–
4723; tel. 717/718–2000, (Nonreporting) **A**1 10
Primary Contact: Joseph Alhadeff, M.D., President
COO: Cynthia Page, FACHE, Chief Operating Officer
CFO: Dale Bushey, Chief Financial Officer
CMO: Todd A. Curran, M.D., President Medical Staff
CIO: Tricia Wolf, Director Information Technology
CHR: Maureen M Putnam, Director Human Resources
CNO: Debra Garton, R.N., Chief Nursing Officer
Web address: www.osshealth.com
Control: Partnership, Investor–owned (for–profit) **Service**: Orthopedic

Staffed Beds: 30

SELECT SPECIALTY HOSPITAL-YORK See Select Specialty Hospital-Camp Hill,
Camp Hill

○ **UPMC MEMORIAL (390101)**, 325 South Belmont Street, Zip 17403–2609,
Mailing Address: P.O. Box 15118, Zip 17405–7118; tel. 717/843–8623, **A**10
11 13 **F**3 13 15 18 20 22 26 34 35 36 37 40 44 45 47 48 49 50 51 54 55
56 57 58 59 60 64 65 66 68 70 74 75 76 77 78 79 81 84 85 92 93 97 107
108 111 116 117 118 119 126 129 130 132 135 146 147 154 156 **S** UPMC,
Pittsburgh, PA
Primary Contact: Curtis Herrin, Chief Financial Officer
CIO: James Mahoney, Chief Information Officer
CHR: Corey Hudak, Director Human Resources
CNO: Susan Gordon, R.N., Chief Nursing Officer
Web address: www.mhyork.org
Control: Other not–for–profit (including NFP Corporation) **Service**: General
medical and surgical

Staffed Beds: 100 **Admissions:** 3999 **Census:** 38 **Outpatient Visits:** 99309
Births: 551 **Total Expense ($000):** 83774 **Payroll Expense ($000):** 35543
Personnel: 525

⇑ **WELLSPAN SURGERY AND REHABILLITATION HOSPITAL (390327)**, 55
Monument Road, Zip 17403–5023; tel. 717/812–6100, (Nonreporting) **A**3 21 **S**
WellSpan Health, York, PA
Primary Contact: Barbara Yarrish, R.N., President
Web address: www.wellspan.org
Control: Other not–for–profit (including NFP Corporation) **Service**: Rehabilitation

Staffed Beds: 73

☒ △ **WELLSPAN YORK HOSPITAL (390046)**, 1001 South George Street,
Zip 17403–3645; tel. 717/851–2345, **A**1 2 3 5 7 8 10 12 13 **F**3 11 12 13 14
15 17 18 20 22 24 26 28 29 30 31 34 35 39 40 43 44 45 46 47 48 49 50 54
55 56 57 58 59 60 61 64 65 66 68 70 72 74 75 76 77 78 79 81 82 84 85 86
87 89 92 93 96 97 98 101 102 104 105 107 108 110 111 114 115 117 118
119 120 121 123 124 126 129 130 131 132 135 146 147 148 149 154 **S**
WellSpan Health, York, PA
Primary Contact: Keith D. Noll, President
COO: Raymond Rosen, FACHE, Vice President Operations
CFO: Michael F O'Connor, Senior Vice President Finance
CMO: Peter M Hartmann, M.D., Vice President Medical Affairs
CIO: R Hal Baker, M.D., Vice President and Chief Information Officer
CHR: Robert J Batory, Vice President Human Resources
CNO: Astrid Davis, R.N., Chief Nursing Officer
Web address: www.wellspan.org
Control: Other not–for–profit (including NFP Corporation) **Service**: General
medical and surgical

Staffed Beds: 573 **Admissions:** 30544 **Census:** 450 **Outpatient
Visits:** 888888 **Births:** 3082 **Total Expense ($000):** 954450 **Payroll
Expense ($000):** 263946 **Personnel:** 3929

Many Facility Codes have changed. Please refer to the AHA Guide Code Chart.   © 2019 AHA Guide

RHODE ISLAND

RI

CRANSTON—Providence County

☐ **ELEANOR SLATER HOSPITAL (412001)**, 111 Howard Avenue, Zip 02920–0269, Mailing Address: P.O. Box 8269, Zip 02920–0269; tel. 401/462–3085, (Nonreporting) **A**1 3 10
Primary Contact: Paul J. Despres, Chief Executive Officer
CMO: Charlene Tate, M.D., Chief Medical Staff and Clinical Services
Web address: www.bhddh.ri.gov/esh/
Control: State, Government, nonfederal **Service**: Acute long–term care hospital

Staffed Beds: 284

EAST PROVIDENCE—Providence County

☐ **EMMA PENDLETON BRADLEY HOSPITAL (414003)**, 1011 Veterans Memorial Parkway, Zip 02915–5099; tel. 401/432–1000, **A**1 3 5 10 **F**5 29 30 35 55 75 98 99 101 104 105 106 130 132 153 **S** Lifespan Corporation, Providence, RI
Primary Contact: Daniel J. Wall, President and Chief Executive Officer
CFO: Mamie Wakefield, Vice President Finance and Chief Financial Officer
CMO: Henry T Sachs, M.D., III Medical Director
CIO: Carole Cotter, Senior Vice President and Chief Information Officer
CHR: Rob Duval, Chief Human Resources Officer
CNO: Vareen O'Keefe Domaleski, MS, R.N., Vice Patient Care Services and Chief Nursing Officer
Web address: www.lifespan.org
Control: Other not–for–profit (including NFP Corporation) **Service**: Children's hospital psychiatric

Staffed Beds: 70 Admissions: 1137 Census: 66 Outpatient Visits: 3104 Births: 0 Total Expense ($000): 75852 Payroll Expense ($000): 44417 Personnel: 618

NEWPORT—Newport County

☐ △ **NEWPORT HOSPITAL (410006)**, 11 Friendship Street, Zip 02840–2299; tel. 401/846–6400, **A**1 2 3 5 7 10 **F**3 8 11 13 15 18 28 29 30 31 34 35 40 45 50 51 53 54 56 57 59 60 64 68 70 74 75 76 77 78 79 81 82 85 86 87 89 90 91 92 93 94 96 97 98 100 102 107 108 111 114 118 119 129 130 132 135 146 147 148 154 156 157 **S** Lifespan Corporation, Providence, RI
Primary Contact: Crista F. Durand, President
CFO: Frank J Byrne, Vice President Finance
CMO: Jeffrey Gaines, M.D., Vice President and Chief Medical Officer
CHR: Barbara J. Arcangeli, Vice President Human Resources
CNO: Orla Brandos, Vice President of Patient Care Services and Chief Nursing Officer
Web address: www.newporthospital.org
Control: Other not–for–profit (including NFP Corporation) **Service**: General medical and surgical

Staffed Beds: 104 Admissions: 5055 Census: 68 Outpatient Visits: 85504 Births: 503 Total Expense ($000): 113404 Payroll Expense ($000): 50728 Personnel: 674

NORTH PROVIDENCE—Providence County

☐ **ST. JOSEPH HEALTH SERVICES OF RHODE ISLAND (410005)**, 200 High Service Avenue, Zip 02904–5199; tel. 401/456–3000, (Includes OUR LADY OF FATIMA HOSPITAL, 200 High Service Avenue, North Providence, Rhode Island, Zip 2904; tel. 401/456–3000; Thomas Hughes, President; ST. JOSEPH HOSPITAL FOR SPECIALTY CARE, 21 Peace Street, Providence, Rhode Island, Zip 2907; tel. 401/456–3000), (Non-reporting) **A**1 5 10 **S** Prospect Medical Holdings, Los Angeles, CA
Primary Contact: John J. Holiver, Chief Executive Officer
CFO: Michael E Conklin Jr Chief Financial Officer
CIO: Susan Cerrone Abely, Chief Information Officer
CHR: Darlene Souza, Vice President
CNO: Patricia A Nadle, R.N., Chief Nursing Officer
Web address: www.saintjosephri.com
Control: Church operated **Service**: General medical and surgical

Staffed Beds: 125

NORTH SMITHFIELD—Providence County

LANDMARK MEDICAL CENTER-FOGARTY UNIT See Landmark Medical Center, Woonsocket

⊞ **REHABILITATION HOSPITAL OF RHODE ISLAND (413025)**, 116 Eddie Dowling Highway, Zip 02896–7327; tel. 401/766–0800, (Nonreporting) **A**1 10 **S** Prime Healthcare, Ontario, CA
Primary Contact: Michael Souza, Chief Executive Officer
COO: Demetra Ouellette, Chief Operating Officer
CFO: Thomas Klessens, Chief Financial Officer
CMO: Khin Yin, Medical Director
CIO: Vincent Larosa, Director of Information Technology Services
CHR: Gail Gosselin, Director Human Resources
CNO: Kathy Keeling, Director of Nursing
Web address: www.rhri.net
Control: Corporation, Investor–owned (for–profit) **Service**: Rehabilitation

Staffed Beds: 70

PROVIDENCE—Providence County

⊞ **BUTLER HOSPITAL (414000)**, 345 Blackstone Boulevard, Zip 02906–4829; tel. 401/455–6200, (Nonreporting) **A**1 3 5 10 **S** Care New England Health System, Providence, RI
Primary Contact: Mary Marran, MS, President and Chief Operating Officer
CFO: Bonnie Baker, Vice President Finance and Chief Financial Officer
CMO: James Sullivan, M.D., Chief Medical Officer
CIO: Summa Gaddam, Chief Information Officer
CHR: Timothy Bigelow, Director Human Resources
CNO: Mary Leveillee, Senior Vice President Patient Care Services and Chief Nursing Officer
Web address: www.butler.org
Control: Other not–for–profit (including NFP Corporation) **Service**: Psychiatric

Staffed Beds: 143

☐ **MIRIAM HOSPITAL (410012)**, 164 Summit Avenue, Zip 02906–2853; tel. 401/793–2500, **A**1 2 3 5 8 10 **F**3 8 11 12 15 18 20 22 26 28 29 30 31 34 35 40 44 45 46 49 50 51 53 54 56 57 58 59 60 61 64 67 68 70 74 75 77 78 79 81 82 84 85 87 91 92 93 97 100 107 108 110 111 114 115 118 119 126 130 132 135 146 147 148 149 156 157 **S** Lifespan Corporation, Providence, RI
Primary Contact: Arthur J. Sampson, FACHE, President
COO: Maria Ducharme, R.N., Senior Vice President Patient Care Services and Chief Nursing Officer
CFO: Mamie Wakefield, Chief Financial Officer
CMO: G. Dean Roye, M.D., Senior Vice President of Medical Affairs and Chief Medical Officer
CIO: Carole Cotter, Vice President and Chief Information Officer
CHR: Nancy McMahon, Vice President Human Resources
Web address: www.lifespan.org
Control: Other not–for–profit (including NFP Corporation) **Service**: General medical and surgical

Staffed Beds: 247 Admissions: 19264 Census: 202 Outpatient Visits: 224145 Births: 0 Total Expense ($000): 467746 Payroll Expense ($000): 200289 Personnel: 2693

⊞ **PROVIDENCE VETERANS AFFAIRS MEDICAL CENTER**, 830 Chalkstone Avenue, Zip 02908–4799; tel. 401/273–7100, (Nonreporting) **A**1 2 3 5 **S** Department of Veterans Affairs, Washington, DC
Primary Contact: Susan Mackenzie, Ph.D., Medical Center Director
COO: Erin Clare Sears, Associate Director of Operations
CMO: Satish C Sharma, M.D., Chief of Staff
Web address: www.providence.va.gov/
Control: Veterans Affairs, Government, federal **Service**: General medical and surgical

Staffed Beds: 73

Hospital, Medicare Provider Number, Address, Telephone, Approval, Facility, and Physician Codes, Health Care System

★ American Hospital Association (AHA) membership ☐ The Joint Commission accreditation ○ Healthcare Facilities Accreditation Program ◇ DNV Healthcare Inc. accreditation ⇑ Center for Improvement in Healthcare Quality Accreditation △ Commission on Accreditation of Rehabilitation Facilities (CARF) accreditation

☐ **RHODE ISLAND HOSPITAL (410007)**, 593 Eddy Street, Zip 02903–4900; tel. 401/444–4000, (Includes HASBRO CHILDREN'S HOSPITAL, 593 Eddy Street, Providence, Rhode Island, Zip 02903–4923; tel. 401/444–4000) **A**1 2 3 5 8 10 **F**3 6 7 8 11 15 16 17 18 19 20 21 22 23 24 29 30 31 32 34 35 38 39 40 41 43 44 45 46 47 48 49 50 51 53 54 55 56 57 58 59 60 61 64 67 68 70 74 75 77 78 79 81 82 84 85 86 87 88 89 90 91 92 93 94 97 98 99 100 101 102 103 104 105 107 108 110 111 114 115 116 117 118 119 120 121 122 123 124 126 129 130 131 134 135 138 143 145 146 147 148 149 156 157 **S** Lifespan Corporation, Providence, RI
Primary Contact: Margaret M. Van Bree, Dr.PH, President
COO: Fredrick Macri, Executive Vice President
CFO: Mamie Wakefield, Senior Vice President and Chief Financial Officer
CMO: John B Murphy, M.D., Vice President Medical Affairs and Chief Medical Officer
CIO: Carole Cotter, Senior Vice President and Chief Information Officer
CHR: Louis J Sperling, Vice President Human Resources
Web address: www.rhodeislandhospital.org/
Control: Other not–for–profit (including NFP Corporation) **Service**: General medical and surgical

Staffed Beds: 682 **Admissions:** 36912 **Census:** 569 **Outpatient Visits:** 499559 **Births:** 0 **Total Expense ($000):** 1402698 **Payroll Expense ($000):** 577011 **Personnel:** 6346

☐ **ROGER WILLIAMS MEDICAL CENTER (410004)**, 825 Chalkstone Avenue, Zip 02908–4735; tel. 401/456–2000, (Nonreporting) **A**1 2 3 5 10 **S** Prospect Medical Holdings, Los Angeles, CA
Primary Contact: Jeffrey H. Liebman, Chief Executive Officer
CFO: Addy Kane, Chief Financial Officer
CMO: Elaine Jones, M.D., President Medical Staff
CIO: Susan Cerrone Abely, Vice President and Chief Information Officer
Web address: www.rwmc.org/
Control: Other not–for–profit (including NFP Corporation) **Service**: General medical and surgical

Staffed Beds: 86

ST. JOSEPH HOSPITAL FOR SPECIALTY CARE See St. Joseph Health Services of Rhode Island, North Providence

VETERANS AFFAIRS MEDICAL CENTER See Providence Veterans Affairs Medical Center

☒ **WOMEN & INFANTS HOSPITAL OF RHODE ISLAND (410010)**, 101 Dudley Street, Zip 02905–2499; tel. 401/274–1100, (Nonreporting) **A**1 2 3 5 8 10 **S** Care New England Health System, Providence, RI
Primary Contact: Matt Quin, Interim Chief Operating Officer
CFO: Robert W Pacheco, Vice President Finance
CMO: Raymond Powrie, M.D., Senior Vice President Quality and Clinical Effectiveness
CHR: Paul F Heffernan, Vice President Human Resources
Web address: www.womenandinfants.org
Control: Other not–for–profit (including NFP Corporation) **Service**: Obstetrics and gynecology

Staffed Beds: 247

☐ **SOUTH COUNTY HOSPITAL (410008)**, 100 Kenyon Avenue, Zip 02879–4299; tel. 401/782–8000, **A**1 2 10 **F**11 13 15 18 20 26 28 29 30 31 34 35 36 37 39 40 44 45 46 47 49 50 51 53 54 56 57 59 60 61 64 65 68 70 74 77 78 79 81 85 86 87 107 108 110 111 114 119 126 129 130 131 135 141 145 146 149 154 156 157
Primary Contact: Aaron Robinson, President and Chief Executive Officer
CFO: Thomas Breen, Vice President and Chief Financial Officer
CMO: John Russell Corcoran, Vice President Medical Affairs
CIO: Gary Croteau, Assistant Vice President and Chief Information Officer
CHR: Maggie Thomas, Vice President Human Resources and Practice Management
CNO: Anne Schmidt, Vice President of Patient Care Services and Chief Nursing Officer
Web address: www.https://www.southcountyhealth.org/
Control: Other not–for–profit (including NFP Corporation) **Service**: General medical and surgical

Staffed Beds: 91 **Admissions:** 5243 **Census:** 50 **Outpatient Visits:** 219634 **Births:** 677 **Total Expense ($000):** 169765 **Payroll Expense ($000):** 74653 **Personnel:** 1103

☒ △ **KENT COUNTY MEMORIAL HOSPITAL (410009)**, 455 Tollgate Road, Zip 02886–2770; tel. 401/737–7000, **A**1 3 5 7 10 13 **F**3 4 8 11 12 13 15 18 20 22 26 29 30 31 34 35 36 40 44 45 46 47 48 49 50 51 55 56 57 58 59 60 61 63 64 65 68 70 73 74 75 76 77 78 79 80 81 82 84 85 86 87 90 93 94 96 97 100 102 107 108 110 111 114 115 116 117 118 119 126 129 130 131 132 143 146 147 148 149 154 156 **S** Care New England Health System, Providence, RI
Primary Contact: Robert Haffey, R.N., President and Chief Operating Officer
CFO: James M. Burke, Vice President Finance, Chief Nursing Executive Medical Surgical Hospitals
CMO: Paari Gopalakrishnan, M.D., Chief Medical Officer
CIO: Sumalatha Gaddam, Senior Vice President and Chief Information Officer
CHR: Marilyn J Walsh, Vice President Human Resources
CNO: Rebecca Burke, R.N., MS, Senior Vice President and Chief Nursing Officer
Web address: www.kentri.org
Control: Other not–for–profit (including NFP Corporation) **Service**: General medical and surgical

Staffed Beds: 320 **Admissions:** 13102 **Census:** 153 **Outpatient Visits:** 306734 **Births:** 782 **Total Expense ($000):** 340941 **Payroll Expense ($000):** 108385 **Personnel:** 2021

☒ **WESTERLY HOSPITAL (410013)**, 25 Wells Street, Zip 02891–2934; tel. 401/596–6000, **A**1 2 10 **F**3 11 15 18 20 26 34 35 40 44 49 51 57 59 64 68 70 75 79 81 85 86 87 93 94 101 107 108 110 111 115 118 119 130 132 135 146 149 **S** Yale New Haven Health, New Haven, CT
Primary Contact: Patrick Green, FACHE, President and Chief Executive Officer
CFO: Seth Van Essendelft, Vice President and Chief Financial Officer
CMO: Oliver Mayorga, M.D., Chief Medical Officer
CIO: Kimberly Kalajainen, Vice President, Operations and Information Technology, Chief Information Officer
CHR: Donna Epps, Vice President, Chief Human Resource Officer
Web address: www.westerlyhospital.org
Control: Other not–for–profit (including NFP Corporation) **Service**: General medical and surgical

Staffed Beds: 75 **Admissions:** 2700 **Census:** 31 **Outpatient Visits:** 101436 **Births:** 0 **Total Expense ($000):** 69765 **Payroll Expense ($000):** 29800 **Personnel:** 296

☒ **LANDMARK MEDICAL CENTER (410011)**, 115 Cass Avenue, Zip 02895–4731; tel. 401/769–4100, (Includes LANDMARK MEDICAL CENTER-FOGARTY UNIT, 116 Eddie Dowling Highway, North Smithfield, Rhode Island, Zip 02896–7327; tel. 401/766–0800; LANDMARK MEDICAL CENTER-WOONSOCKET UNIT, 115 Cass Avenue, Woonsocket, Rhode Island, Zip 2895; tel. 401/769–4100), (Nonreporting) **A**1 2 10 **S** Prime Healthcare, Ontario, CA
Primary Contact: Michael Souza, Chief Executive Officer
CFO: Thomas Klessens, Chief Financial Officer
CMO: Glenn Fort, Chief Medical Officer
CIO: Vincent Larosa, Director of Information Systems
CHR: Gail Gosselin, Director Human Resources
Web address: www.landmarkmedcenter.com
Control: Corporation, Investor–owned (for–profit) **Service**: General medical and surgical

Staffed Beds: 140

SOUTH CAROLINA

ABBEVILLE—Abbeville County

★ ⚕ **ABBEVILLE AREA MEDICAL CENTER (421301)**, 420 Thomson Circle, Zip 29620–5656, Mailing Address: P.O. Box 887, Zip 29620–0887; tel. 864/366–5011, **A**10 18 21 **F**3 15 29 30 35 40 51 53 56 57 59 62 67 70 74 75 77 81 85 87 89 90 94 107 108 110 114 119 127 128 129 130 132 133 135 146 147 148 149 **S** QHR, Brentwood, TN
Primary Contact: Howard D. Turner, Chief Executive Officer
CFO: Timothy Wren, Chief Financial Officer
CMO: Christopher Ceraldi, M.D., Chief of Staff
CIO: Tim Stewart, Chief Information Officer
CHR: Alice Rigney, Chief Human Resources Officer
CNO: Ernest Shock, Chief Nursing Officer
Web address: www.abbevilleareamc.com
Control: County, Government, nonfederal **Service**: General medical and surgical

Staffed Beds: 25 Admissions: 559 Census: 8 Outpatient Visits: 28198 Births: 0 Total Expense ($000): 44198 Payroll Expense ($000): 21874 Personnel: 402

AIKEN—Aiken County

☐ **AIKEN REGIONAL MEDICAL CENTERS (420082)**, 302 University Parkway, Zip 29801–6302; tel. 803/641–5000, (Includes AURORA PAVILION, 655 Medical Park Drive, Aiken, South Carolina, Zip 29801; tel. 803/641–5900) **A**1 3 5 10 **F**3 4 11 15 18 20 22 24 29 30 31 34 35 40 46 49 56 57 58 59 64 70 73 74 75 77 78 79 80 81 85 86 87 89 90 94 98 99 100 101 102 103 104 107 108 110 111 114 115 119 121 123 126 129 130 131 132 135 146 147 148 149 **S** Universal Health Services, Inc., King of Prussia, PA
Primary Contact: James F. O'Loughlin, Chief Executive Officer
COO: Matt Merrifield, Chief Operating Officer
Web address: www.aikenregional.com
Control: Corporation, Investor–owned (for–profit) **Service**: General medical and surgical

Staffed Beds: 299 Admissions: 12360 Census: 161 Outpatient Visits: 142363 Births: 1071 Total Expense ($000): 167309 Payroll Expense ($000): 59605 Personnel: 832

ANDERSON—Anderson County

★ ⚕ **ANMED HEALTH MEDICAL CENTER (420027)**, 800 North Fant Street, Zip 29621–5793; tel. 864/512–1000, (Includes ANMED HEALTH WOMEN'S AND CHILDREN'S HOSPITAL, 2000 East Greenville Street, Anderson, South Carolina, Zip 29621; tel. 864/512–1000; William T Manson III, FACHE, Chief Executive Officer) **A**2 3 5 10 21 **F**3 4 5 8 11 12 13 14 15 17 18 20 22 24 26 28 29 30 31 34 35 37 39 40 43 45 46 48 49 50 51 53 54 56 57 58 59 60 61 62 64 65 68 70 71 73 74 75 76 77 78 79 80 81 84 85 86 87 89 90 91 97 98 100 101 102 103 104 107 108 110 111 114 115 117 118 119 121 123 126 127 129 130 131 132 135 146 147 148 149 156 **S** AnMed Health, Anderson, SC
Primary Contact: William T. Manson III, FACHE, Chief Executive Officer
CFO: Christine Pearson, Chief Financial Officer
CMO: Thomas Kayrouz, M.D., Chief Medical Officer
CIO: Marty Stewart, Chief Information Officer
CHR: Richard Walter Grooms Jr Chief Human Resources Officer
CNO: Tina M. Jury, MSN, Chief Nursing Officer
Web address: www.anmedhealth.org
Control: Other not–for–profit (including NFP Corporation) **Service**: General medical and surgical

Staffed Beds: 376 Admissions: 24222 Census: 259 Outpatient Visits: 737755 Births: 1669 Total Expense ($000): 535481 Payroll Expense ($000): 223135 Personnel: 3389

⊞ **ANMED HEALTH REHABILITATION HOSPITAL (423029)**, 1 Spring Back Way, Zip 29621–2676; tel. 864/716–2600, **A**1 10 **F**3 29 30 56 57 60 68 74 75 79 90 91 93 94 95 96 **S** Encompass Health Corporation, Birmingham, AL
Primary Contact: Denise R. Murray, Chief Executive Officer
CFO: Julie Harris, Controller
CMO: William Vogentiz, M.D., Medical Director
CHR: Morgan Clements, Director of Human Resources
CNO: Kelly Davis, Chief Nursing Officer
Web address: www.anmedrehab.com
Control: Corporation, Investor–owned (for–profit) **Service**: Rehabilitation

Staffed Beds: 60 Admissions: 1437 Census: 47 Births: 0 Total Expense ($000): 15919 Payroll Expense ($000): 9180 Personnel: 162

☐ **PATRICK B. HARRIS PSYCHIATRIC HOSPITAL (424011)**, 130 Highway 252, Zip 29621–5054; tel. 864/231–2600, **A**1 3 5 10 **F**98 100 101 102 103 130 143 146
Primary Contact: John Fletcher, Chief Executive Officer
Web address: www.patrickbharris.com/
Control: State, Government, nonfederal **Service**: Psychiatric

Staffed Beds: 131 Admissions: 301 Census: 127 Outpatient Visits: 0 Births: 0 Personnel: 269

BEAUFORT—Beaufort County

⊞ **BEAUFORT MEMORIAL HOSPITAL (420067)**, 955 Ribaut Road, Zip 29902–5441; tel. 843/522–5200, **A**1 2 10 **F**3 11 12 13 15 18 20 22 28 29 30 31 32 34 35 40 45 46 49 50 51 53 54 57 59 60 64 65 69 70 71 73 74 75 76 77 78 79 81 85 86 87 89 90 91 93 94 96 97 98 100 101 102 103 104 107 108 110 111 114 115 118 119 120 121 126 127 130 132 134 145 146 147 148 149 154
Primary Contact: Edmond Russell. Baxley III, President and Chief Executive Officer
CFO: Ken Miller, Chief Financial Officer
CMO: Kurt Gambla, D.O., Chief Medical Officer
CIO: Edward Ricks, Vice President and Chief Information Officer
CHR: Doug Douglas, Interim Vice President Human Resources
CNO: Karen Manuel Carroll, R.N., Vice President Patient Care Services
Web address: www.bmhsc.org
Control: County, Government, nonfederal **Service**: General medical and surgical

Staffed Beds: 203 Admissions: 8908 Census: 109 Outpatient Visits: 169430 Births: 943

⊞ **NAVAL HOSPITAL BEAUFORT**, 1 Pinckney Boulevard, Zip 29902–6122; tel. 843/228–5301, (Nonreporting) **A**1 5 **S** Bureau of Medicine and Surgery, Department of the Navy, Falls Church, VA
Primary Contact: Lieutenant Commander Willie Brown, Director Administration
Web address: www.med.navy.mil/sites/nhbeaufort/Pages/Welcome_Page.aspx
Control: Department of Defense, Government, federal **Service**: General medical and surgical

Staffed Beds: 20

CAMDEN—Kershaw County

⊞ **KERSHAWHEALTH (420048)**, 1315 Roberts Street, Zip 29020–3737, Mailing Address: P.O. Box 7003, Zip 29021–7003; tel. 803/432–4311, **A**1 10 **F**3 11 13 15 18 20 24 28 29 30 31 32 34 35 40 44 45 49 50 51 54 57 59 61 62 63 64 66 68 70 75 76 77 78 79 81 85 86 87 89 90 94 97 98 103 107 108 110 111 114 115 118 119 127 129 130 132 144 146 147 148 154 **S** LifePoint Health, Brentwood, TN
Primary Contact: Susan C. Shugart, Chief Executive Officer
COO: Susan R Burroughs, FACHE, Chief Operating Officer
CFO: Mike Bunch, Executive Vice President, Chief Operating Officer and Chief Financial Officer
CMO: Tallulah Holmstrom, M.D., Chief Medical Officer
CIO: Diane Arrants, Chief Information Officer
CHR: Angela F Nettles, Vice President, Human Resources and Support Services
Web address: www.kershawhealth.com
Control: Corporation, Investor–owned (for–profit) **Service**: General medical and surgical

Staffed Beds: 110 Admissions: 3960 Census: 48 Outpatient Visits: 122864 Births: 247 Personnel: 765

CHARLESTON—Charleston County

⊞ **BON SECOURS ST. FRANCIS HOSPITAL (420065)**, 2095 Henry Tecklenburg Drive, Zip 29414–5733; tel. 843/402–1000, **A**1 10 **F**3 7 12 13 14 15 28 29 30 31 34 35 40 45 46 47 48 49 50 51 56 57 59 64 68 70 73 74 75 76 77 78 79 80 81 82 84 85 86 87 89 93 94 100 102 107 108 110 111 114 115 117 118 119 120 121 123 124 130 131 132 145 146 147 148 149 154 **S** Roper St. Francis Healthcare, Charleston, SC
Primary Contact: W. Anthony. Jackson, Chief Executive Officer
CFO: Bret Johnson, Chief Financial Officer
CMO: Steven D Shapiro, M.D., Chief Medical Officer
CIO: Michael Taylor, Chief Information Officer
CNO: Pennie Peralta, R.N., VP, Nursing & Chief Nursing Officer
Web address: www.rsfh.com/
Control: Other not–for–profit (including NFP Corporation) **Service**: General medical and surgical

Staffed Beds: 160 Admissions: 8990 Census: 95 Outpatient Visits: 164006 Births: 2428 Total Expense ($000): 195225 Payroll Expense ($000): 58102 Personnel: 1005

SC

Hospital, Medicare Provider Number, Address, Telephone, Approval, Facility, and Physician Codes, Health Care System

★ American Hospital Association (AHA) membership
☐ The Joint Commission accreditation
○ Healthcare Facilities Accreditation Program
◇ DNV Healthcare Inc. accreditation
⚕ Center for Improvement in Healthcare Quality Accreditation
△ Commission on Accreditation of Rehabilitation Facilities (CARF) accreditation

⊞ **ENCOMPASS HEALTH REHABILITATION HOSPITAL OF CHARLESTON (423027)**, 9181 Medcom Street, Zip 29406–9168; tel. 843/820–7777, (Nonreporting) **A**1 10 **S** Encompass Health Corporation, Birmingham, AL
Primary Contact: Michele M. Skripps, R.N., Chief Executive Officer
CFO: Beckye Lariviere, Controller
CMO: William Livesay, D.O., Jr Medical Director
CHR: Traxler Littlejohn, Human Resources Director
CNO: Patricia Simon, Chief Nursing Officer
Web address: www.healthsouthcharleston.com
Control: Corporation, Investor–owned (for–profit) **Service**: Rehabilitation

Staffed Beds: 49

⊞ **MUSC HEALTH OF MEDICAL UNIVERSITY OF SOUTH CAROLINA (420004)**, 169 Ashley Avenue, Zip 29425–8905; tel. 843/792–2300, (Includes CHILDREN'S HOSPITAL OF SOUTH CAROLINA AT MUSC, 171 Ashley Avenue, Charleston, South Carolina, Zip 29425–8908; tel. 843/792–1414; Patrick J Cawley, Chief Executive Officer, MUSC Health and Vice President for Health Affairs, University) **A**1 2 3 5 8 10 **F**3 4 5 6 7 8 9 11 12 13 14 15 16 17 18 19 20 21 22 23 24 25 26 27 28 29 30 31 32 34 35 36 37 38 39 40 41 43 44 45 46 47 48 49 50 51 52 53 54 55 56 57 58 59 60 61 64 65 66 67 68 70 71 72 73 74 75 76 77 78 79 80 81 82 84 85 86 87 88 89 91 92 93 94 97 98 99 100 101 102 103 104 105 107 108 109 110 111 114 115 116 117 118 119 120 121 123 124 126 129 130 131 132 134 135 136 137 138 139 140 141 142 144 145 146 147 148 149 150 151 153 154 155 156
Primary Contact: Patrick J. Cawley, Chief Executive Officer, MUSC Health and Vice President for Health Affairs, University
COO: Matthew Wain, Chief Operating Officer
CFO: Lisa Goodlett, Administrator Finance and Support Services
CMO: Daniel Handel, M.D., Chief Medical Officer
CIO: Michael Caputo, Chief Information Officer
CHR: Darrick Paul, Chief People Officer
CNO: Jerry A Mansfield, Ph.D., R.N., Executive Chief Nursing Officer & Chief Patient Experience Officer
Web address: www.muschealth.com
Control: State, Government, nonfederal **Service**: General medical and surgical

Staffed Beds: 779 **Admissions:** 37650 **Census:** 689 **Outpatient Visits:** 963194 **Births:** 2687 **Total Expense ($000):** 1510271 **Payroll Expense ($000):** 491807 **Personnel:** 7231

☐ **PALMETTO LOWCOUNTRY BEHAVIORAL HEALTH (424006)**, 2777 Speissegger Drive, Zip 29405–8229; tel. 843/747–5830, **A**1 10 **F**4 5 98 99 102 103 104 105 152 153 **S** Universal Health Services, Inc., King of Prussia, PA
Primary Contact: Clint Hauger, Chief Executive Officer
CFO: Stan Markowski, Chief Financial Officer
CMO: Steven Lopez, M.D., Chief Medical Officer
CHR: Sheila Simpson, Vice President Human Resources
CNO: Jo Good, Director of Nursing
Web address: www.palmettobehavioralhealth.com
Control: Corporation, Investor–owned (for–profit) **Service**: Psychiatric

Staffed Beds: 100 **Admissions:** 3025 **Census:** 65 **Outpatient Visits:** 4053 **Births:** 0 **Total Expense ($000):** 17216 **Payroll Expense ($000):** 9114 **Personnel:** 175

⊞ **RALPH H. JOHNSON VETERANS AFFAIRS MEDICAL CENTER**, 109 Bee Street, Zip 29401–5799; tel. 843/577–5011, (Nonreporting) **A**1 2 3 5 8 **S** Department of Veterans Affairs, Washington, DC
Primary Contact: Scott R. Isaacks, FACHE, Director and Chief Executive Officer
CFO: Cassandra Helfer, Chief Financial Officer
CMO: Florence N. Hutchison, M.D., Chief of Staff
CIO: LaBon Hardy, Chief Information Officer
CHR: Renae A. Jacobson, Human Resources Officer
CNO: Garett E. Schreier, R.N., Associate Director, Nursing and Patient Care Services
Web address: www.charleston.va.gov/
Control: Veterans Affairs, Government, federal **Service**: General medical and surgical

Staffed Beds: 98

⊞ △ **ROPER HOSPITAL (420087)**, 316 Calhoun Street, Zip 29401–1125; tel. 843/724–2000, **A**1 2 3 5 7 10 **F**3 7 8 9 14 15 17 18 20 22 24 26 28 29 30 31 34 35 37 40 42 45 49 50 51 53 54 55 56 57 58 59 60 61 62 63 64 65 67 68 70 74 75 77 78 79 80 81 82 84 85 86 87 90 92 93 94 95 96 102 107 108 110 111 115 118 119 120 121 123 124 126 129 130 131 132 135 136 143 146 147 148 149 154 **S** Roper St. Francis Healthcare, Charleston, SC
Primary Contact: W. Anthony. Jackson, Chief Executive Officer
CFO: Bret Johnson, Chief Financial Officer
CMO: Steven D Shapiro, M.D., Vice President Medical Affairs
CIO: Melinda H. Cardell, Interim Vice President and Chief Information Officer
CHR: Melanie Stith, Vice President Human Resources
Web address: www.rsfh.com/
Control: Other not–for–profit (including NFP Corporation) **Service**: General medical and surgical

Staffed Beds: 305 **Admissions:** 12234 **Census:** 192 **Outpatient Visits:** 187211 **Births:** 0 **Total Expense ($000):** 349101 **Payroll Expense ($000):** 96915 **Personnel:** 1863

⊞ **TRIDENT MEDICAL CENTER (420079)**, 9330 Medical Plaza Drive, Zip 29406–9195; tel. 843/797–7000, (Includes MONCKS CORNER MEDICAL CENTER, 401 North Live Oak Drive, Highway 17A, Moncks Corner, South Carolina, Zip 29461–5603; tel. 843/761–8721; SUMMERVILLE MEDICAL CENTER, 295 Midland Parkway, Summerville, South Carolina, Zip 29485–8104; tel. 843/832–5000; Lisa R Valentine, Chief Executive Officer) **A**1 2 3 5 10 **F**3 8 12 13 15 16 18 20 22 24 26 28 29 30 31 34 35 37 40 41 42 43 45 46 47 48 49 50 54 55 56 57 59 60 61 64 70 72 73 74 75 76 77 78 79 80 81 84 85 86 87 88 89 90 93 94 98 100 102 107 108 110 111 114 115 116 117 118 119 120 121 123 126 130 131 132 135 145 146 147 148 154 156 **S** HCA Healthcare, Nashville, TN
Primary Contact: Todd Gallati, FACHE, President and Chief Executive Officer
COO: Scott Weiskittel, Chief Operating Officer
CFO: Teresa Finch, Chief Financial Officer
CMO: Lee Biggs, M.D., Chief Medical Officer
CIO: Susan Murray, Director Information Services
CHR: Joe B Hill Jr Vice President Human Resources
Web address: www.tridenthealthsystem.com
Control: Corporation, Investor–owned (for–profit) **Service**: General medical and surgical

Staffed Beds: 451 **Admissions:** 26374 **Census:** 330 **Outpatient Visits:** 436617 **Births:** 2794 **Personnel:** 2156

CHERAW—Chesterfield County

⇑ **MCLEOD HEALTH CHERAW (420107)**, 711 Chesterfield Highway, Zip 29520–7002; tel. 843/537–7881, **A**10 21 **F**3 13 15 18 28 29 30 34 35 40 45 56 57 59 68 70 76 79 81 85 86 87 89 107 108 111 114 118 119 130 132 133 135 **S** McLeod Health, Florence, SC
Primary Contact: Mib Scoggins, Chief Executive Officer
CFO: Louis Anderson, Chief Financial Officer
CMO: David Bersinger, M.D., Chief of Staff
CIO: Jim Spencer, Director Information System
Web address: www.chesterfieldgeneral.com
Control: Other not–for–profit (including NFP Corporation) **Service**: General medical and surgical

Staffed Beds: 40 **Admissions:** 2271 **Census:** 23 **Outpatient Visits:** 39082 **Births:** 166 **Total Expense ($000):** 39366 **Payroll Expense ($000):** 14833 **Personnel:** 204

CHESTER—Chester County

⊞ **MUSC HEALTH CHESTER MEDICAL CENTER (420019)**, 1 Medical Park Drive, Zip 29706–9769; tel. 803/581–3151, **A**1 10 **F**15 28 29 34 35 40 50 56 57 59 70 75 77 79 81 85 86 87 89 90 94 107 108 110 111 119 128 130 131 132 135 **S** Community Health Systems, Inc., Franklin, TN
Primary Contact: Page H. Vaughan, Chief Executive Officer
CFO: Tracey Claxton, Chief Financial Officer
CMO: Terry Dodge, M.D., Chief of Staff
CIO: Shaw Laird, Chief Information Officer
CHR: Karen Chapman, Director Human Resources
CNO: Betty Griffin, Interim Chief Nursing Officer
Web address: www.chesterregional.com
Control: Corporation, Investor–owned (for–profit) **Service**: General medical and surgical

Staffed Beds: 36 **Admissions:** 827 **Census:** 3 **Outpatient Visits:** 47584 **Births:** 0 **Total Expense ($000):** 25927 **Payroll Expense ($000):** 9024

CLINTON—Laurens County

⊞ **PRISMA HEALTH LAURENS COUNTY HOSPITAL (420038)**, 22725 Highway 76 East, Zip 29325–7527, Mailing Address: P O Drawer 976, Zip 29325–0976; tel. 864/833–9100, (Includes GHS - LAURENS COUNTY MEMORIAL HOSPITAL, 22725 Highway 76 E, PO Drawer 976, Clinton, South Carolina, Zip 29325–7527, Mailing Address: P.O. Box 976, Zip 29325–0976, tel. 803/833–9100; Justin Benfield, Southern Region Chief Operating Officer) (Total facility includes 14 beds in nursing home–type unit) **A**1 10 20 **F**3 13 15 18 28 30 40 45 46 59 70 76 79 80 81 87 107 110 111 114 115 119 127 128 132 146 147 **S** Prisma Health - Upstate, Greenville, SC
Primary Contact: Justin Benfield, Southern Region Chief Operating Officer
CFO: Michael Norrick, Director of Campus Operations
CMO: Vincent Green, Medical Director
CIO: Kathleen Anderson, Director, Acute Clinical Systems
CHR: Cathy M Rogers, Manager Human Resources
CNO: Kay Swisher, Chief Nursing Officer
Web address: www.ghs.org/laurens
Control: Other not–for–profit (including NFP Corporation) **Service**: General medical and surgical

Staffed Beds: 71 **Admissions:** 2577 **Census:** 29 **Outpatient Visits:** 134014 **Births:** 363 **Total Expense ($000):** 58885 **Payroll Expense ($000):** 17640 **Personnel:** 315

SC

COLUMBIA—Laurens County

★ **CONTINUECARE HOSPITAL AT PALMETTO HEALTH BAPTIST (422006)**, Taylor at Marion Street, Zip 29220, Mailing Address: P.O. Box 11069, Zip 29211–1069; tel. 803/296–3757, (Nonreporting) **A**10 22 **S** Community Hospital Corporation, Plano, TX
Primary Contact: Thomas P. Harlan, Chief Executive Officer
Web address: www.continuecare.org/palmetto//
Control: Other not–for–profit (including NFP Corporation) **Service:** Acute long–term care hospital

Staffed Beds: 35

COLUMBIA—Richland County

EARLE E. MORRIS ALCOHOL AND DRUG TREATMENT CENTER, 610 Faison Drive, Zip 29203–3218; tel. 803/935–7100, **F**4 29 39 53 61 67 74 75 87 98 130 132 146
Primary Contact: George McConnell, Director
Web address: www.state.sc.us/dmh/morris_village/
Control: State, Government, nonfederal **Service:** Alcoholism and other chemical dependency

Staffed Beds: 103 **Admissions:** 1384 **Census:** 96 **Outpatient Visits:** 0 **Births:** 0 **Personnel:** 146

☒ **ENCOMPASS HEALTH REHABILITATION HOSPITAL OF COLUMBIA (423025)**, 2935 Colonial Drive, Zip 29203–6811; tel. 803/254–7777, **A**1 10 **F**29 50 53 60 64 77 90 91 92 93 94 95 96 97 119 149 **S** Encompass Health Corporation, Birmingham, AL
Primary Contact: Chris Daughtry, Chief Executive Officer
CFO: Jessica Burriss, Chief Financial Officer
CMO: Devin Troyer, M.D., Medical Director
CHR: Luanne Burton, Director Human Resources
CNO: April Brooks, Chief Nursing Officer
Web address: www.healthsouthcolumbia.com
Control: Corporation, Investor–owned (for–profit) **Service:** Rehabilitation

Staffed Beds: 96 **Admissions:** 1970 **Census:** 70 **Outpatient Visits:** 11811 **Births:** 0 **Total Expense ($000):** 22235 **Payroll Expense ($000):** 12650 **Personnel:** 221

☐ **G. WERBER BRYAN PSYCHIATRIC HOSPITAL (424005)**, 220 Faison Drive, Zip 29203–3210; tel. 803/935–7140, **A**1 3 10 **F**4 30 50 74 75 97 98 99 101 103 130 132 135 146
Primary Contact: Stuart Shields, Director
COO: Jaclyn Upfield, Chief Operating Officer
CIO: Sam Livingston, Information Resource Consultant
CHR: Kim Church, Manager Human Resources
Web address: www.scdmh.org
Control: State, Government, nonfederal **Service:** Psychiatric

Staffed Beds: 236 **Admissions:** 610 **Census:** 106 **Outpatient Visits:** 0 **Births:** 0 **Personnel:** 513

☒ **PRISMA HEALTH BAPTIST HOSPITAL (420086)**, Taylor at Marion Street, Zip 29220–0001; tel. 803/296–5010, **A**1 2 3 5 10 **F**1 3 4 5 11 12 13 15 18 20 29 30 31 34 35 38 40 45 47 48 49 51 53 54 57 59 61 62 63 64 65 66 67 70 72 73 74 75 76 77 78 79 80 81 82 84 85 86 87 89 90 93 94 97 98 99 100 101 102 103 104 105 107 108 110 111 114 115 117 118 119 126 130 132 146 147 148 151 153 **S** Prisma Health - Midlands, Columbia, SC
Primary Contact: Michael N. Bundy, Chief Operating Officer
COO: James M Bridges, Executive Vice President and Chief Operating Officer
CFO: Paul K Duane, Chief Financial Officer and Office of Health Reform
CMO: Mark J Mayson, M.D., Medical Director
CIO: Michelle Edwards, Executive Vice President Information Technology
CHR: Trip Gregory, Senior Vice President Human Resources
Web address: www.palmettohealth.org
Control: Other not–for–profit (including NFP Corporation) **Service:** General medical and surgical

Staffed Beds: 401 **Admissions:** 20671 **Census:** 251 **Outpatient Visits:** 191562 **Births:** 2906 **Total Expense ($000):** 349771 **Payroll Expense ($000):** 132240 **Personnel:** 2248

COLUMBIA—Lexington County

☒ **PRISMA HEALTH BAPTIST PARKRIDGE HOSPITAL (420106)**, 400 Palmetto Health Parkway, Zip 29212–1760, Mailing Address: P.O. Box 2266, Zip 29202–2266; tel. 803/907–7000, **A**1 3 10 **F**3 8 11 13 15 29 30 34 35 40 45 46 50 57 59 64 70 75 76 77 79 81 85 86 87 90 93 94 97 107 110 111 115 119 130 132 144 146 147 **S** Prisma Health - Midlands, Columbia, SC
Primary Contact: Michael N. Bundy, Chief Operating Officer
COO: Emilie Keene, FACHE, Interim Chief Operating Officer
Web address: www.palmettohealth.org
Control: Other not–for–profit (including NFP Corporation) **Service:** General medical and surgical

Staffed Beds: 76 **Admissions:** 4620 **Census:** 55 **Outpatient Visits:** 116057 **Total Expense ($000):** 134620 **Payroll Expense ($000):** 44236 **Personnel:** 896

COLUMBIA—Richland County

☒ **PRISMA HEALTH RICHLAND HOSPITAL (420018)**, Five Richland Medical Park Drive, Zip 29203–6897; tel. 803/434–7000, (Includes PRISMA HEALTH CHILDREN'S HOSPITAL, Five Richland Medical Park Dr, Columbia, South Carolina, Zip 29203–6863; tel. 803/434–6882) **A**1 2 3 5 8 10 19 **F**3 4 7 11 13 15 17 18 19 20 22 24 26 28 29 30 31 32 34 35 38 39 40 41 43 45 46 50 53 54 56 57 59 61 64 65 66 68 70 72 73 74 75 76 77 78 79 81 85 86 87 88 89 90 93 94 97 98 99 100 101 102 103 104 107 110 111 114 115 119 124 126 129 130 132 146 147 148 154 **S** Prisma Health - Midlands, Columbia, SC
Primary Contact: Jay Hamm, R.N., FACHE, Chief Operating Officer
CFO: Paul K Duane, Chief Financial Officer and Office of Health Reform
CMO: Eric Brown, M.D., Physician Executive
CNO: Carole A Siegfried, MSN, R.N., Campus Nurse Executive
Web address: www.palmettohealth.org
Control: Other not–for–profit (including NFP Corporation) **Service:** General medical and surgical

Staffed Beds: 674 **Admissions:** 32659 **Census:** 591 **Outpatient Visits:** 605489 **Total Expense ($000):** 832995 **Payroll Expense ($000):** 300035 **Personnel:** 2772

★ **PROVIDENCE HOSPITAL (420026)**, 2435 Forest Drive, Zip 29204–2098; tel. 803/865–4500, (Includes PROVIDENCE HOSPITAL NORTHEAST, 120 Gateway Corporate Boulevard, Columbia, South Carolina, Zip 29203–9611; tel. 803/865–4500; Ryan Hall, Vice President) **A**5 10 19 **F**3 11 15 17 18 20 22 24 26 28 29 30 34 35 38 40 42 44 45 49 50 53 54 57 58 59 60 63 64 70 74 75 77 79 81 84 85 86 87 90 93 94 100 107 108 110 111 115 119 129 130 132 135 141 146 148 **S** LifePoint Health, Brentwood, TN
Primary Contact: Stephen R. Selzer, Market Chief Executive Officer
COO: W. Carl Martin, Chief Operating Officer
CFO: Pamela Gallagher, Chief Financial Officer
CMO: Wayne Sribnick, M.D., Senior Vice President and Chief Medical Officer
CIO: Lib Cumbee, Director Information Systems
CHR: Justin A Lofurno, Director Human Resources
Web address: www.sistersofcharityhealth.org/health–care/providence–hospitals/
Control: Corporation, Investor–owned (for–profit) **Service:** General medical and surgical

Staffed Beds: 216 **Admissions:** 10180 **Census:** 116 **Outpatient Visits:** 177432 **Births:** 0 **Total Expense ($000):** 198230 **Payroll Expense ($000):** 57937 **Personnel:** 797

PROVIDENCE HOSPITAL NORTHEAST See Providence Hospital, Columbia

SOUTH CAROLINA DEPARTMENT OF CORRECTIONS HOSPITAL, 4344 Broad River Road, Zip 29210–4098; tel. 803/896–8567, (Nonreporting) **A**3
Primary Contact: John Solomon, M.D., Director
Web address: www.doc.sc.gov/
Control: State, Government, nonfederal **Service:** Hospital unit of an institution (prison hospital, college infirmary, etc.)

Staffed Beds: 70

WILLIAM S. HALL PSYCHIATRIC INSTITUTE (424003), 1800 Colonial Drive, Zip 29203–6827; tel. 803/898–1693, (Nonreporting) **A**3
Primary Contact: Angela Forand, Director
COO: Doug Glover, Controller
CFO: Doug Glover, Controller
CMO: Phyllis Bryant-Mobley, M.D., Director Medical Services
CIO: Mesa Foard, Director Information technology
CHR: Kim Church, Manager Human Resources
Web address: www.scdmh.org
Control: State, Government, nonfederal **Service:** Psychiatric

Staffed Beds: 37

SC

☒ △ **WM. JENNINGS BRYAN DORN VETERANS AFFAIRS MEDICAL CENTER**,
6439 Garners Ferry Road, Zip 29209–1639; tel. 803/776–4000, (Nonreporting)
A1 2 3 5 7 8 **S** Department of Veterans Affairs, Washington, DC
Primary Contact: David Omura, Director
CMO: Bernard L. DeKoning, M.D., Chief of Staff
CIO: Steve Chalphant, Director Information Management Service Line
CHR: Phyllis Jones, Chief Human Resources
CNO: Ruth W. Mustard, R.N., MSN, Associate Director Nursing and Patient Services
Web address: www.columbiasc.va.gov/
Control: Veterans Affairs, Government, federal **Service**: General medical and
surgical

Staffed Beds: 216

CONWAY—Horry County

★ ⭧ **CONWAY MEDICAL CENTER (420049)**, 300 Singleton Ridge Road,
Zip 29526–9142, Mailing Address: P.O. Box 829, Zip 29528–0829; tel. 843/347–
7111, (Total facility includes 88 beds in nursing home–type unit) **A**10 21 **F**1 3 8
11 12 13 15 18 20 26 28 29 30 34 35 37 40 43 45 46 49 50 51 57 59 60 61
68 70 71 73 74 75 76 77 79 81 84 85 86 87 89 90 93 94 100 102 107 108
110 111 114 115 118 119 128 129 130 132 135 145 146 147 148 149 150
154 156
Primary Contact: Bret A. Barr, President and Chief Executive Officer
CMO: Paul McKinley Richardson Jr Chief Medical Officer
CIO: David Crutchfield, Vice President, Information Services & Chief Information
Officer
CHR: Matthew J. Securro, Vice President, Human Resources
CNO: Tony L. Minshew, Vice President, Patient Care Services
Web address: www.conwaymedicalcenter.com
Control: Other not–for–profit (including NFP Corporation) **Service**: General
medical and surgical

Staffed Beds: 266 Admissions: 9549 Census: 177 Outpatient
Visits: 162160 Births: 1366 Total Expense ($000): 169667 Payroll
Expense ($000): 57808 Personnel: 1147

☐ **LIGHTHOUSE BEHAVIORAL HEALTH HOSPITAL (424002)**, 152 Waccamaw
Medical Park Drive, Zip 29526–8901; tel. 843/347–8871, **A**1 10 **F**4 98 99 101
102 103 130 **S** Universal Health Services, Inc., King of Prussia, PA
Primary Contact: Thomas L. Ryba, Chief Executive Officer
CFO: Gabrielle Gale, Chief Financial Officer
CMO: Adedapo Oduwole, M.D., Medical Director
CIO: Gabrielle Gale, Chief Financial Officer
CHR: Lois Woodall, Director Human Resources
Web address: www.lighthousecarecenterofconway.com/
Control: Corporation, Investor–owned (for–profit) **Service**: Psychiatric

Staffed Beds: 96 Admissions: 3281 Census: 79 Outpatient Visits: 0
Births: 0 Total Expense ($000): 13560 Payroll Expense ($000): 7402
Personnel: 158

DARLINGTON—Darlington County

⭧ **MCLEOD MEDICAL CENTER DARLINGTON (420057)**, 701 Cashua Ferry Road,
Zip 29532–8488, Mailing Address: P.O. Box 1859, Zip 29540; tel. 843/395–
1100, **A**10 21 **F**3 4 15 34 35 38 56 57 59 64 68 77 85 97 98 100 101
103 104 107 110 119 127 128 130 133 135 147 148 **S** McLeod Health,
Florence, SC
Primary Contact: Tim Smoak, Administrator
Web address: www.mcleodhealth.org
Control: Other not–for–profit (including NFP Corporation) **Service**: General
medical and surgical

Staffed Beds: 41 Admissions: 1154 Census: 37 Outpatient Visits: 8264
Births: 0 Total Expense ($000): 13415 Payroll Expense ($000): 6868
Personnel: 142

DILLON—Dillon County

⭧ **MCLEOD MEDICAL CENTER DILLON (420005)**, 301 East Jackson
Street, Zip 29536–2509, Mailing Address: P.O. Box 1327, Zip 29536–1327;
tel. 843/774–4111, **A**10 21 **F**3 11 13 15 28 29 30 34 35 40 50 57 59 64 68
70 75 76 79 81 85 87 89 90 94 107 111 114 119 128 130 132 133 134 135
146 147 148 149 **S** McLeod Health, Florence, SC
Primary Contact: Joan Ervin, Administrator
CFO: Fulton Ervin, Senior Vice President and Chief Financial Officer
CMO: Walter B Blum, M.D., Chief of Staff
CIO: Jenean Blackmon, Assistant Vice President and Chief Information Officer
CHR: Cynthia Causey, Associate Administrator Human and Mission Services
Web address: www.mcleodhealth.org
Control: Other not–for–profit (including NFP Corporation) **Service**: General
medical and surgical

Staffed Beds: 34 Admissions: 2416 Census: 22 Outpatient Visits: 85544
Births: 274 Total Expense ($000): 39449 Payroll Expense ($000): 17435
Personnel: 272

EASLEY—Pickens County

☒ **PRISMA HEALTH BAPTIST EASLEY HOSPITAL (420015)**, 200 Fleetwood
Drive, Zip 29640–2022, Mailing Address: P.O. Box 2129, Zip 29641–2129;
tel. 864/442–7200, **A**1 5 10 **F**3 11 13 15 18 28 29 30 34 35 40 56 57 59 64
70 74 75 76 79 81 85 87 89 107 108 111 114 115 119 124 129 130 132
146 147
Primary Contact: Todd Walker, President
CFO: Kathleen Stapleton, Chief Financial Officer
CIO: Cynthia Ellenburg, Director Health Information Services
CHR: Richard B Posey, Director Human Resources
CNO: Mary Ann Hunter, Director Nursing Services
Web address: www.baptisteasley.org
Control: Other not–for–profit (including NFP Corporation) **Service**: General
medical and surgical

Staffed Beds: 89 Admissions: 3289 Census: 40 Outpatient Visits: 99381
Births: 385 Total Expense ($000): 106537 Payroll Expense ($000): 37492
Personnel: 593

EDGEFIELD—Edgefield County

★ **EDGEFIELD COUNTY HEALTHCARE (421304)**, 300 Ridge Medical Plaza,
Zip 29824–4525, Mailing Address: P.O. Box 590, Zip 29824–4525; tel. 803/637–
3174, **A**10 18 **F**3 28 29 34 35 40 45 59 65 68 77 79 81 84 93 94 107 119
127 128 130 133 146
Primary Contact: Carlos Milanes, Chief Executive Officer
CFO: Lori Jacobs, Chief Financial Officer
CMO: Tami Massey, M.D., Chief of Medical Staff
CIO: Juli Corley, Chief Information Officer
CHR: Theresa Stover, Chief Human Resource Officer
CNO: Cheryl Faust, Chief Nursing Officer
Web address: www.myech.org
Control: County, Government, nonfederal **Service**: General medical and surgical

Staffed Beds: 25 Admissions: 372 Census: 9 Outpatient Visits: 14357
Births: 0 Personnel: 187

FAIRFAX—Allendale County

★ **ALLENDALE COUNTY HOSPITAL (421300)**, 1787 Allendale Fairfax Highway,
Zip 29827–9133, Mailing Address: P.O. Box 218, Zip 29827–0218; tel. 803/632–
3311, (Total facility includes 44 beds in nursing home–type unit) **A**10 18 **F**3 15 34
35 40 56 57 59 61 64 67 68 90 97 107 110 114 119 127 128 133 147
Primary Contact: Lari Gooding, Chief Executive Officer
Web address: www.achospital.org
Control: County, Government, nonfederal **Service**: General medical and surgical

Staffed Beds: 69 Admissions: 245 Census: 38 Outpatient Visits: 22671
Births: 0 Personnel: 138

FLORENCE—Florence County

☒ **ENCOMPASS HEALTH REHABILITATION HOSPITAL OF FLORENCE (423026)**,
900 East Cheves Street, Zip 29506–2704; tel. 843/679–9000, **A**1 10 **F**9 28 29
34 35 56 57 59 75 77 82 86 87 90 91 92 93 94 95 96 130 131 132 148 149
S Encompass Health Corporation, Birmingham, AL
Primary Contact: Brian Nunn, R.N., Chief Executive Officer
CFO: Robert Wheeler, Controller
CMO: Adora Matthews, M.D., Medical Director
CHR: Susan Trantham, Director Human Resources
Web address: www.healthsouthflorence.com
Control: Corporation, Investor–owned (for–profit) **Service**: Rehabilitation

Staffed Beds: 88 Admissions: 1200 Census: 44 Outpatient Visits: 0
Births: 0 Personnel: 168

★ ⭧ **MCLEOD REGIONAL MEDICAL CENTER (420051)**, 555 East Cheves
Street, Zip 29506–2617, Mailing Address: P.O. Box 100551, Zip 29502–0551;
tel. 843/777–2000, **A**2 3 5 10 21 **F**3 7 8 11 13 15 17 18 19 20 22 24 26 28
29 30 31 32 34 35 37 40 43 44 45 46 47 48 49 50 51 53 54 56 57 58 59 60
61 62 63 64 65 66 68 70 71 72 73 74 75 76 77 78 79 80 81 82 84 85 86 87
88 89 92 94 96 97 100 102 107 108 110 111 115 117 118 119 120 121 123
124 126 129 130 131 132 135 143 145 146 147 148 149 150 154 **S** McLeod
Health, Florence, SC
Primary Contact: Robert L. Colones, President and Chief Executive Officer
COO: Ron Boring, Senior Vice President and Chief Operating Officer
CFO: Fulton Ervin, Chief Financial Officer
CMO: Alva W Whitehead, M.D., Vice President Medical Services
CIO: Jenean Blackmon, Associate Vice President and Chief Information Officer
CHR: Jeannette Glenn, Vice President Human Resources, Education and Training
Web address: www.mcleodhealth.org
Control: Other not–for–profit (including NFP Corporation) **Service**: General
medical and surgical

Staffed Beds: 488 Admissions: 26090 Census: 353 Outpatient
Visits: 240031 Births: 2116 Total Expense ($000): 636791 Payroll
Expense ($000): 215163 Personnel: 3473

SC

☒ △ **MUSC HEALTH FLORENCE MEDICAL CENTER (420091)**, 805 Pamplico Highway, Zip 29505–6050, Mailing Address: P.O. Box 100550, Zip 29502–0550; tel. 843/674–5000, **A**1 7 10 **F**8 15 17 18 20 22 24 26 28 29 30 31 34 35 40 41 43 45 56 57 59 60 64 67 70 74 75 77 78 79 81 87 88 89 90 94 107 110 111 114 115 116 117 119 129 132 135 145 146 148 **S** Community Health Systems, Inc., Franklin, TN
Primary Contact: Vance V. Reynolds, FACHE, CPA, Chief Executive Officer
COO: Kyle Baxter, Chief Operating Officer
CFO: Loren Rials, Chief Financial Officer
CIO: Lynn Northcutt, Chief Information Officer
CHR: Kay Douglas, Human Resources Director
CNO: Costa Cockfield, Chief Nursing Officer
Web address: www.carolinashospital.com
Control: Corporation, Investor–owned (for–profit) **Service**: General medical and surgical

Staffed Beds: 310 **Admissions**: 10312 **Census**: 153 **Outpatient Visits**: 120832 **Births**: 0 **Total Expense ($000)**: 173883 **Payroll Expense ($000)**: 48093

☒ **REGENCY HOSPITAL OF FLORENCE (422007)**, 121 East Cedar Street, 4th Floor, Zip 29506–2576; tel. 843/661–3471, **A**1 10 **F**1 3 29 34 35 57 58 77 80 85 90 100 130 148 **S** Select Medical Corporation, Mechanicsburg, PA
Primary Contact: Amy Metz, Chief Executive Officer
CMO: Stephen Dersch, M.D., President Medical Staff
CHR: Tina Stokes, Manager Human Resources
Web address: www.regencyhospital.com
Control: Corporation, Investor–owned (for–profit) **Service**: Acute long–term care hospital

Staffed Beds: 40 **Admissions**: 485 **Census**: 38 **Outpatient Visits**: 0 **Births**: 0 **Personnel**: 92

FORT JACKSON—Richland County

★ **MONCRIEF ARMY COMMUNITY HOSPITAL**, 4500 Stuart Street, Zip 29207–5700; tel. 803/751–2160, (Nonreporting) **A**5 **S** Department of the Army, Office of the Surgeon General, Falls Church, VA
Primary Contact: Colonel Traci Crawford, R.N., Commander
Web address: www.moncrief.amedd.army.mil
Control: Department of Defense, Government, federal **Service**: General medical and surgical

Staffed Beds: 60

GAFFNEY—Cherokee County

☒ **CHEROKEE MEDICAL CENTER (420043)**, 1530 North Limestone Street, Zip 29340 4738; tel. 864/487–4271, **A**1 10 **F**3 11 15 18 19 29 34 35 40 45 46 51 57 59 64 65 67 70 75 79 81 82 85 86 87 89 107 108 110 111 113 115 119 129 130 131 132 135 145 146 147 140 **O** Spartanburg Regional Healthcare System, Spartanburg, SC
Primary Contact: Cody Butts, President
COO: Leslie Glover, Director Operations
CFO: Christine Poplawski, Chief Financial Officer
CMO: Frank Phillips, M.D., Chief of Staff
CIO: Richard Bledsoe, Director Information Systems
CHR: Connie Gibson, R.N., Director Human Resources
Web address: www.maryblackgaffney.com/mary-black-gaffney/home.aspx
Control: Corporation, Investor–owned (for–profit) **Service**: General medical and surgical

Staffed Beds: 45 **Admissions**: 1590 **Census**: 18 **Outpatient Visits**: 49023 **Births**: 66 **Total Expense ($000)**: 36585 **Payroll Expense ($000)**: 12045 **Personnel**: 210

GEORGETOWN—Georgetown County

☒ **TIDELANDS GEORGETOWN MEMORIAL HOSPITAL (420020)**, 606 Black River Road, Zip 29440–3368, Mailing Address: Drawer 421718, Zip 29442–4203; tel. 843/527–7000, **A**1 3 5 10 19 **F**3 8 11 12 13 15 17 18 20 22 26 28 29 30 31 32 34 35 39 40 45 46 49 50 51 53 54 56 57 59 60 61 64 65 68 70 73 74 75 76 77 78 79 80 81 82 84 85 86 87 89 90 93 94 97 100 102 107 108 110 111 115 118 119 130 131 132 135 146 147 148 **S** QHR, Brentwood, TN
Primary Contact: Bruce P. Bailey, Chief Executive Officer
COO: Gayle L Resetar, Vice President and Chief Operating Officer
CFO: Elizabeth S. Ward, Chief Financial Officer
CHR: James F Harper, Senior Vice President and Chief Human Resources Officer
Web address: www.tidelandshealth.org
Control: Other not–for–profit (including NFP Corporation) **Service**: General medical and surgical

Staffed Beds: 136 **Admissions**: 3963 **Census**: 42 **Outpatient Visits**: 191019 **Births**: 244 **Total Expense ($000)**: 139490 **Payroll Expense ($000)**: 55586 **Personnel**: 961

GREENVILLE—Greenville County

☐ △ **BON SECOURS ST. FRANCIS HEALTH SYSTEM (420023)**, One St Francis Drive, Zip 29601–3207; tel. 864/255–1000, (Includes ST. FRANCIS EASTSIDE, 125 Commonwealth Drive, Greenville, South Carolina, Zip 29615–4812; tel. 864/675–4000) **A**1 2 7 10 **F**3 8 11 12 13 15 17 18 20 22 24 26 28 29 30 31 34 35 36 39 40 44 45 46 47 48 49 50 51 53 54 57 58 59 60 61 62 63 64 66 68 69 70 71 73 74 75 76 77 78 79 80 81 82 83 84 85 86 87 89 90 94 96 97 107 108 110 111 114 115 118 119 124 126 129 130 132 135 136 141 146 147 **S** Bon Secours Mercy Health, Marriottsville, MD
Primary Contact: Matthew T. Caldwell, President
CFO: Ronnie Hyatt, Senior Vice President Finance and Chief Financial Officer
CMO: Thomas H. Cummins, M.D., Chief Medical Officer
CIO: Rita Hooker, Administrative Director Information Services
CHR: Fernando Fleites, Senior Vice President Human Resources
CNO: Teri Ficicchy, R.N., MSN, Chief Nursing Officer
Web address: www.stfrancishealth.org
Control: Other not–for–profit (including NFP Corporation) **Service**: General medical and surgical

Staffed Beds: 352 **Admissions**: 19505 **Census**: 248 **Outpatient Visits**: 200244 **Births**: 2098 **Total Expense ($000)**: 429724 **Payroll Expense ($000)**: 138987 **Personnel**: 2537

☒ △ **PRISMA HEALTH GREENVILLE MEMORIAL HOSPITAL (420078)**, 701 Grove Road, Zip 29605–4295; tel. 864/455–7000, (Includes GHS CHILDREN'S HOSPITAL, 701 Grove Road, Greenville, South Carolina, Zip 29605–5611; tel. 864/455–7000; MARSHALL I. PICKENS HOSPITAL, 701 Grove Road, Greenville, South Carolina, Zip 29605–5601; tel. 864/455–8988; ROGER C. PEACE REHABILITATION HOSPITAL, 701 Grove Road, Greenville, South Carolina, Zip 29605–4295; tel. 864/455–7000) **A**1 2 3 5 7 8 10 **F**3 4 11 13 15 17 18 19 20 22 24 26 27 28 29 30 31 32 34 35 36 38 39 40 41 43 44 45 46 47 48 49 50 51 52 53 54 56 57 58 59 61 64 65 66 68 70 72 73 74 75 76 77 78 79 80 81 82 83 84 85 86 87 88 89 90 92 93 94 96 97 98 99 100 101 102 103 104 105 106 107 108 110 111 114 115 116 117 118 119 120 121 123 124 126 129 130 132 134 136 141 142 145 146 147 148 153 154 156 **S** Prisma Health - Upstate, Greenville, SC
Primary Contact: Ric A. Ransom, Chief Operating Officer
COO: Greg Rusnak, Executive Vice President and Chief Operating Officer
CFO: Terri T. Newsom, Vice President of Finance and Chief Financial Officer
CMO: Angelo Sinopoli, M.D., Vice President Clinical Integration and Chief Medical Officer
CIO: Rich Rogers, Vice President Information Services
CHR: Doug Dorman, Vice President Human Resources
CNO: Michelle T Smith, R.N., MSN, FACHE, Vice President Nursing Chief Nursing Officer Chief Experience Officer
Web address: www.ghs.org
Control: Other not–for–profit (including NFP Corporation) **Service**: General medical and surgical

Staffed Beds: 814 **Admissions**: 35355 **Census**: 586 **Outpatient Visits**: 793187 **Births**: 3913 **Total Expense ($000)**: 1034219 **Payroll Expense ($000)**: 284870 **Personnel**: 4604

☒ **PRISMA HEALTH PATEWOOD HOSPITAL (420102)**, 175 Patewood Drive, Zip 29615–3570; tel. 864/797–1000, **A**1 5 10 **F**3 11 13 29 30 37 45 50 64 74 76 77 79 80 81 85 86 130 146 147 **S** Prisma Health - Upstate, Greenville, SC
Primary Contact: Tim Brookshire, Chief Operating Officer
Web address: www.ghs.org/patewood
Control: Other not–for–profit (including NFP Corporation) **Service**: Surgical

Staffed Beds: 72 **Admissions**: 3519 **Census**: 18 **Outpatient Visits**: 28742 **Births**: 1747 **Total Expense ($000)**: 109060 **Payroll Expense ($000)**: 30729 **Personnel**: 275

☒ **REGENCY HOSPITAL OF GREENVILLE (422009)**, One St Francis Drive, 4th Floor, Zip 29601–3955; tel. 864/255–1438, **A**1 10 **F**1 3 29 75 77 85 97 **S** Select Medical Corporation, Mechanicsburg, PA
Primary Contact: Tammy Ratliff, Chief Executive Officer
Web address: www.regencyhospital.com
Control: Corporation, Investor–owned (for–profit) **Service**: Acute long–term care hospital

Staffed Beds: 32 **Admissions**: 32 **Census**: 25 **Outpatient Visits**: 0 **Births**: 0 **Total Expense ($000)**: 12926 **Payroll Expense ($000)**: 7340 **Personnel**: 97

SC

SC

☐ **SHRINERS HOSPITALS FOR CHILDREN-GREENVILLE (423300)**, 950 West Faris Road, Zip 29605–4277; tel. 864/271–3444, **A**1 3 10 **F**29 59 64 68 75 77 79 81 85 87 89 90 93 94 130 131 146 148 154 **S** Shriners Hospitals for Children, Tampa, FL
Primary Contact: William Munley, Administrator
CFO: John Conti, Director Finance
CMO: J. Michael Wattenbarger, M.D., Chief of Staff
CHR: Willis E Tisdale, Director Human Resources
CNO: Allison Leigh Windas, Director of Patient Care Services-Nurse Executive
Web address: www.greenvilleshrinershospital.org
Control: Other not–for–profit (including NFP Corporation) **Service**: Children's orthopedic

Staffed Beds: 15 Admissions: 240 **Census:** 3 **Outpatient Visits:** 20810
Births: 0 **Total Expense ($000):** 28393 **Payroll Expense ($000):** 14457
Personnel: 179

GREENWOOD—Greenwood County

☐ **GREENWOOD REGIONAL REHABILITATION HOSPITAL (423030)**, 1530 Parkway, Zip 29646–4027; tel. 864/330–1800, (Total facility includes 12 beds in nursing home–type unit) **A**1 10 **F**3 75 90 128 130 132 143 148 **S** Ernest Health, Inc., Albuquerque, NM
Primary Contact: Kristin Manske, Chief Executive Officer
CFO: Charity Martin, Controller and Regional Business Officer Manager
CMO: Cam Monda, D.O., Medical Director
CHR: Michelle Watkins, Human Resources Manager
CNO: Jessica Lawson, Director of Nursing
Web address: www.grrh.ernesthealth.com
Control: Corporation, Investor–owned (for–profit) **Service**: Rehabilitation

Staffed Beds: 54 Admissions: 1018 **Census:** 38 **Outpatient Visits:** 0
Births: 0 **Total Expense ($000):** 16373 **Payroll Expense ($000):** 6944
Personnel: 139

★ ⍦ **SELF REGIONAL HEALTHCARE (420071)**, 1325 Spring Street, Zip 29646–3860; tel. 864/725–4111, **A**2 3 5 10 21 **F**3 8 11 13 15 17 18 19 20 22 24 26 28 29 30 31 32 34 35 39 40 43 44 45 46 48 49 50 53 55 57 58 59 60 61 62 64 68 70 71 72 73 74 75 76 77 78 79 80 81 82 85 86 87 89 90 91 94 96 97 98 102 103 107 108 110 111 114 115 119 120 121 123 124 129 130 131 132 134 135 146 147 148 149 156
Primary Contact: James A. Pfeiffer, FACHE, President and Chief Executive Officer
CFO: Timothy Evans, Vice President and Chief Financial Officer
CMO: F Gregory Mappin, M.D., Vice President Medical Affairs and Chief Medical Officer
CIO: Andy Hartung, Director Information Systems
CHR: Michael Dixon, Director Human Resources
CNO: Linda Russell, Vice President and Chief Nursing Officer
Web address: www.selfregional.org
Control: State, Government, nonfederal **Service**: General medical and surgical

Staffed Beds: 322 Admissions: 11203 **Census:** 152 **Outpatient Visits:** 167539 **Births:** 1321 **Total Expense ($000):** 329256 **Payroll Expense ($000):** 110983 **Personnel:** 2443

GREER—Greenville County

☐ **CAROLINA CENTER FOR BEHAVIORAL HEALTH (424010)**, 2700 East Phillips Road, Zip 29650–4816; tel. 864/235–2335, **A**1 3 10 **F**4 5 98 99 100 101 102 103 104 105 151 153 **S** Universal Health Services, Inc., King of Prussia, PA
Primary Contact: John Willingham, Chief Executive Officer and Managing Director
COO: Greg Schlangen, R.N., Chief Operating Officer
CFO: James P Boynton Jr Chief Financial Officer
CMO: Gergana Dimitrova, M.D., Medical Director
CHR: Ginny Savage, Director of Human Resources
CNO: Jennifer Daigle, R.N., Director of Nursing and Utilization Review
Web address: www.thecarolinacenter.com
Control: Corporation, Investor–owned (for–profit) **Service**: Psychiatric

Staffed Beds: 138 Admissions: 4170 **Census:** 112 **Births:** 0
Personnel: 279

GREER—Spartanburg County

★ ⍦ **PELHAM MEDICAL CENTER (420103)**, 250 Westmoreland Road, Zip 29651–9013; tel. 864/530–6000, **A**10 21 **F**3 11 15 18 20 26 29 30 34 35 37 40 45 49 50 54 57 59 64 68 70 74 75 77 79 81 82 84 85 86 87 90 94 107 108 110 111 114 115 118 119 130 146 148 149 154 **S** Spartanburg Regional Healthcare System, Spartanburg, SC
Primary Contact: Anthony Kouskolekas, FACHE, President
CNO: Connie Spykerman, Chief Nursing Officer
Web address: www.pelhammedicalcenter.com
Control: Hospital district or authority, Government, nonfederal **Service**: General medical and surgical

Staffed Beds: 48 Admissions: 2703 **Census:** 33 **Outpatient Visits:** 54846
Births: 0 **Total Expense ($000):** 73737 **Payroll Expense ($000):** 24033
Personnel: 630

GREER—Greenville County

⊞ **PRISMA HEALTH GREER MEMORIAL HOSPITAL (420033)**, 830 South Buncombe Road, Zip 29650–2400; tel. 864/797–8000, **A**1 3 5 10 **F**3 11 13 15 18 28 29 30 34 35 40 44 45 49 50 51 57 59 64 65 68 70 76 77 79 81 85 87 89 94 107 110 111 114 115 119 126 129 130 146 147 148 **S** Prisma Health - Upstate, Greenville, SC
Primary Contact: John F. Mansure, FACHE, President
Web address: www.ghs.org
Control: Other not–for–profit (including NFP Corporation) **Service**: General medical and surgical

Staffed Beds: 70 Admissions: 2886 **Census:** 23 **Outpatient Visits:** 96285
Births: 728 **Total Expense ($000):** 78324 **Payroll Expense ($000):** 25182
Personnel: 388

HARDEEVILLE—Jasper County

⊞ **COASTAL CAROLINA HOSPITAL (420101)**, 1000 Medical Center Drive, Zip 29927–3446; tel. 843/784–8000, **A**1 10 **F**3 11 13 15 28 29 34 35 40 45 46 47 48 49 57 59 64 70 74 75 76 77 79 81 85 90 93 94 107 108 110 111 115 117 119 126 132 146 147 148 **S** TENET Healthcare Corporation, Dallas, TX
Primary Contact: Joel Taylor, Chief Executive Officer
COO: Christopher Borgstrom, Associate Administrator
CFO: Ronald J. Groteluschen, Chief Financial Officer
CIO: Cheryl Grant, Director Information Systems
CHR: Darlene E. Nester, Market Chief Human Resources Officer
CNO: Christina Brzezinski, Chief Nursing Officer
Web address: www.coastalhospital.com
Control: Corporation, Investor–owned (for–profit) **Service**: General medical and surgical

Staffed Beds: 35 Admissions: 2917 **Census:** 26 **Outpatient Visits:** 42653
Births: 716 **Total Expense ($000):** 52109 **Payroll Expense ($000):** 16345
Personnel: 388

HARTSVILLE—Darlington County

⊞ ○ **CAROLINA PINES REGIONAL MEDICAL CENTER (420010)**, 1304 West Bobo Newsom Highway, Zip 29550–4710; tel. 843/339–2100, **A**1 10 11 19 **F**3 11 13 15 20 28 29 30 34 35 40 43 46 49 57 64 70 73 75 76 79 81 82 85 86 87 89 90 93 107 108 110 111 114 115 118 119 129 130 131 132 135 146 147 148 **S** LifePoint Health, Brentwood, TN
Primary Contact: William Little, Chief Executive Officer
COO: Susan C Shugart, Chief Operating Officer
CFO: Rodney VanDonkelaar, Chief Financial Officer
CMO: Tallulah Holmstrom, M.D., Chief Medical Officer
CIO: Denise Barefoot, Director of Information Technology
CHR: Charlotte Adams, Director of Human Resources
CNO: Christy Moody, R.N., Chief Nursing Officer
Web address: www.cprmc.com
Control: Corporation, Investor–owned (for–profit) **Service**: General medical and surgical

Staffed Beds: 105 Admissions: 4135 **Census:** 39 **Outpatient Visits:** 91992
Births: 584 **Total Expense ($000):** 69519 **Payroll Expense ($000):** 25426
Personnel: 404

HILTON HEAD ISLAND—Beaufort County

⊞ **HILTON HEAD HOSPITAL (420080)**, 25 Hospital Center Boulevard, Zip 29926–2738; tel. 843/681–6122, **A**1 10 20 **F**3 11 13 15 17 18 20 22 24 28 29 30 34 35 37 40 45 46 48 49 50 51 54 57 59 60 61 64 65 68 70 74 76 77 78 79 81 85 86 89 94 96 107 108 110 111 114 115 119 126 130 131 132 135 146 147 148 **S** TENET Healthcare Corporation, Dallas, TX
Primary Contact: Jeremy L. Clark, Market Chief Executive Officer
CMO: Glenn Neil Love, M.D., Medical Director
CIO: Stephen Brendler, Director Information Systems
CHR: Darlene E. Nester, Chief Human Resources Officer
Web address: www.hiltonheadregional.com
Control: Partnership, Investor–owned (for–profit) **Service**: General medical and surgical

Staffed Beds: 93 Admissions: 6266 **Census:** 61 **Outpatient Visits:** 82977
Births: 505 **Total Expense ($000):** 101784 **Payroll Expense ($000):** 26974
Personnel: 485

KINGSTREE—Williamsburg County

⊞ **WILLIAMSBURG REGIONAL HOSPITAL (421303)**, 500 Nelson Boulevard, Zip 29556–4027; tel. 843/355–8888, (Nonreporting) **A**1 10 18
Primary Contact: Sharon Poston, President and Chief Executive Officer
COO: Dan Harrington, Chief Operating Officer and Director Human Resources
CMO: Troy B Gamble, M.D., Jr Chief Medical Staff
CIO: David Slenszak, Director, Information Services
CHR: Dan Harrington, Chief Operating Officer and Director Human Resources
CNO: Kelly Lawson, Chief Nursing Officer
Web address: www.wmbgrh.com/
Control: Other not–for–profit (including NFP Corporation) **Service**: General medical and surgical

Staffed Beds: 25

Many Facility Codes have changed. Please refer to the AHA Guide Code Chart.   © 2019 AHA Guide

LAKE CITY—Florence County

★ **LAKE CITY COMMUNITY HOSPITAL (420066)**, 258 N Ron McNair Boulevard, Zip 29560–2462, Mailing Address: P.O. Box 1479, Zip 29560–1479; tel. 843/374–2036, **A**10 **F**3 11 15 28 29 34 35 40 45 50 53 56 57 59 64 65 68 69 75 77 79 81 85 86 87 90 93 94 107 108 110 111 113 114 119 127 130 132 146 149
Primary Contact: Michael Faucett, Chief Operating Officer
COO: Michael Faucett, Chief Operating Officer
CMO: Stephen Askins, M.D., Chief of Staff
CIO: David Moon Jr Director Information Systems
CHR: Anne Poston, Director of Human Resources/Compliance
CNO: Renate Browder, R.N., Director of Nursing
Web address: www.lcchospital.org
Control: Hospital district or authority, Government, nonfederal **Service**: General medical and surgical

Staffed Beds: 26 **Admissions**: 480 **Census**: 10 **Outpatient Visits**: 37462
Births: 0

LANCASTER—Lancaster County

✉ **MUSC HEALTH LANCASTER MEDICAL CENTER (420036)**, 800 West Meeting Street, Zip 29720–2298; tel. 803/286–1214, (Total facility includes 14 beds in nursing home–type unit) **A**1 5 10 **F**3 8 11 13 15 17 18 20 28 29 30 31 34 35 40 45 46 47 48 49 57 59 60 64 70 73 74 75 76 77 78 79 81 82 85 89 90 93 94 98 102 103 107 108 110 111 114 115 118 119 128 129 130 131 132 135 146 147 148 149 **S** Community Health Systems, Inc., Franklin, TN
Primary Contact: Page H. Vaughan, Chief Executive Officer
COO: Richard Warrin, Chief Operating Officer
CFO: Holt Smith, Chief Financial Officer
CMO: Douglas Tiedt, M.D., Chief of Staff
CIO: Chrys Steele, Director Information Systems
CHR: Karen Chapman, Human Resources Director
CNO: Karen Martin, Chief Nursing Officer
Web address: www.springsmemorial.com
Control: Corporation, Investor–owned (for–profit) **Service**: General medical and surgical

Staffed Beds: 176 **Admissions**: 5691 **Census**: 89 **Outpatient Visits**: 67776
Births: 492 **Total Expense ($000)**: 109187 **Payroll Expense ($000)**: 31863
Personnel: 590

☐ **REBOUND BEHAVIORAL HEALTH (424014)**, 134 East Rebound Road, Zip 29720–7712; tel. 877/959–5063, **A**1 10 **F**4 98 102 105 152 **S** Acadia Healthcare Company, Inc., Franklin, TN
Primary Contact: Patricia Hamilton, Chief Executive Officer
Web address: www.reboundbehavioralhealth.com
Control: Corporation, Investor–owned (for–profit) **Service**: Psychiatric

Staffed Beds: 42 **Admissions**: 1867 **Census**: 37 **Outpatient Visits**: 0
Births: 0

LORIS—Horry County

⇑ **MCLEOD LORIS SEACOAST HOSPITAL (420105)**, 3655 Mitchell Street, Zip 29569–2827; tel. 843/716–7000, (Includes MCLEOD SEACOAST, 4000 Highway 9 East, Little River, South Carolina, Zip 29566–7833; tel. 843/390–8100) **A**10 21 **F**3 11 13 15 18 20 28 29 30 31 32 34 35 40 44 45 50 51 53 57 59 63 64 68 70 74 75 76 77 78 79 81 82 85 86 87 90 94 96 102 107 108 110 111 114 115 116 119 130 131 132 134 135 143 146 148 149 156 **S** McLeod Health, Florence, SC
Primary Contact: Edward D. Tinsley III, Regional Administrator
CMO: John Charles, M.D., Chief Medical Officer
CNO: Amanda Mills, Chief Nursing Officer
Web address: www.mcleodhealth.org
Control: Other not–for–profit (including NFP Corporation) **Service**: General medical and surgical

Staffed Beds: 100 **Admissions**: 5939 **Census**: 66 **Outpatient Visits**: 108112 **Births**: 431 **Total Expense ($000)**: 130382 **Payroll Expense ($000)**: 47584 **Personnel**: 303

MANNING—Clarendon County

⇑ **MCLEOD HEALTH CLARENDON (420109)**, 10 Hospital Street, Zip 29102–3153, Mailing Address: P.O. Box 550, Zip 29102–0550; tel. 803/433–3000, **A**10 21 **F**3 13 15 28 29 34 35 40 45 53 59 62 64 68 70 75 76 79 81 85 86 87 90 94 97 107 108 111 114 119 127 130 133 135 143 146 149 154 **S** McLeod Health, Florence, SC
Primary Contact: Rachel Gainey, Administrator
COO: Paul Schumacher, Chief Operating Officer
CFO: John Shaughnessy, Chief Financial Officer
CMO: Catherine Rabon, M.D., Chief Medical Officer
CIO: Pat Kolb, Manager Information Technology
CHR: Gail A Richbourg, Director Human Resources
CNO: Natalie Davis, R.N., Interim Chief Nursing Officer
Web address: www.clarendonhealth.com
Control: Other not–for–profit (including NFP Corporation) **Service**: General medical and surgical

Staffed Beds: 49 **Admissions**: 1861 **Census**: 25 **Outpatient Visits**: 209389
Births: 288 **Total Expense ($000)**: 39873 **Payroll Expense ($000)**: 18055
Personnel: 305

MOUNT PLEASANT—Charleston County

✉ **EAST COOPER MEDICAL CENTER (420089)**, 2000 Hospital Drive, Zip 29464–3764; tel. 843/881–0100, **A**1 3 5 10 **F**3 13 15 18 20 29 31 34 35 40 43 46 51 57 59 60 64 68 70 73 74 75 76 77 78 79 80 81 82 84 85 86 90 92 93 94 100 107 108 110 111 114 115 119 126 129 130 131 132 146 147 148 **S** TENET Healthcare Corporation, Dallas, TX
Primary Contact: Patrick Downes, Chief Executive Officer
COO: Ramona Pickens, Chief Operating Officer
CFO: Patrick C Bolander, Chief Financial Officer
CMO: Kevin Keenan, M.D., Physician Advisor
CIO: Michael Foster, Director Information Systems
CHR: Tracy Hunter, Chief Human Resources Officer
CNO: Patrick Beaver, MSN, R.N., Chief Nursing Officer
Web address: www.eastcoopermedctr.com
Control: Corporation, Investor–owned (for–profit) **Service**: General medical and surgical

Staffed Beds: 140 **Admissions**: 4990 **Census**: 41 **Outpatient Visits**: 51481
Births: 1481 **Total Expense ($000)**: 120942 **Payroll Expense ($000)**: 32156 **Personnel**: 506

EAST COOPER REGIONAL MEDICAL CENTER See East Cooper Medical Center

✉ **ROPER ST. FRANCIS MOUNT PLEASANT HOSPITAL (420104)**, 3500 Highway 17 North, Zip 29466–9123, Mailing Address: 3500 North Highway 17, Zip 29466–9123; tel. 843/606–7000, **A**1 10 **F**3 7 13 15 29 30 34 40 45 54 59 67 68 70 75 76 79 81 84 85 86 87 89 94 102 107 108 110 111 115 118 119 129 143 146 147 148 149 156 **S** Roper St. Francis Healthcare, Charleston, SC
Primary Contact: W. Anthony. Jackson, Chief Executive Officer
CFO: Bret Johnson, Chief Financial Officer
CMO: Steven D Shapiro, M.D., Chief Medical Officer
CIO: Melinda H. Cardell, Interim Chief Information Officer
CHR: Melanie Stith, Vice President Human Resources
CNO: Tavia Buck, Chief Nursing Officer
Web address: www.rsfh.com/mount-pleasant-hospital
Control: Other not–for–profit (including NFP Corporation) **Service**: General medical and surgical

Staffed Beds: 73 **Admissions**: 2740 **Census**: 22 **Outpatient Visits**: 45352
Births: 542 **Total Expense ($000)**: 74512 **Payroll Expense ($000)**: 17543
Personnel: 337

MT. PLEASANT—Mt. Pleasant County

KINDRED HOSPITAL-CHARLESTON See Vibra Hospital of Charleston

✉ **VIBRA HOSPITAL OF CHARLESTON (422005)**, 1200 Hospital Drive, Zip 29464; tel. 843/375–4000, **A**1 10 **F**1 3 29 85 90 107 114 119 148 **S** Vibra Healthcare, Mechanicsburg, PA
Primary Contact: J. Scott Broome, Chief Executive Officer
CFO: Julia Smith, Chief Financial Officer
CMO: Athena Beldecos, M.D., Medical Director
CHR: Julia Taylor, Area Director Human Resources
Web address: www.vhcharleston.com
Control: Corporation, Investor–owned (for–profit) **Service**: Acute long–term care hospital

Staffed Beds: 59 **Admissions**: 435 **Census**: 39 **Outpatient Visits**: 0
Births: 0

SC

Hospital, Medicare Provider Number, Address, Telephone, Approval, Facility, and Physician Codes, Health Care System

★ American Hospital Association (AHA) membership   ○ Healthcare Facilities Accreditation Program   ⇑ Center for Improvement in Healthcare Quality Accreditation
☐ The Joint Commission accreditation   ◇ DNV Healthcare Inc. accreditation   △ Commission on Accreditation of Rehabilitation Facilities (CARF) accreditation

MULLINS—Marion County

MARION COUNTY MEDICAL CENTER See Musc Health Marion Medical Center

⊞ **MUSC HEALTH MARION MEDICAL CENTER (420055)**, 2829 East Highway 76, Zip 29574–6035, Mailing Address: P O Drawer 1150, Marion, Zip 29571–1150; tel. 843/431–2000, (Total facility includes 92 beds in nursing home–type unit) **A**1 10 **F**3 15 18 28 29 34 40 45 46 53 57 59 60 67 70 73 75 76 77 79 81 82 85 86 89 90 94 107 111 119 128 130 131 133 146 148 **S** Community Health Systems, Inc., Franklin, TN
Primary Contact: Spencer Twigg, Chief Executive Officer
CFO: Loren Rials, Chief Financial Officer
CMO: Robert DeGrood, M.D., Chief Medical Staff
CIO: Charlie Grantham, Manager Information Systems
CHR: Christi Meggs, Director
CNO: Linda Parnell, Chief Nursing Officer
Web address: www.carolinashospitalmarion.com
Control: Corporation, Investor–owned (for–profit) **Service:** General medical and surgical

Staffed Beds: 209 **Admissions:** 1775 **Census:** 103 **Outpatient Visits:** 47312 **Births:** 33 **Total Expense ($000):** 63411 **Payroll Expense ($000):** 14741 **Personnel:** 346

MURRELLS INLET—Georgetown County

⊞ △ **TIDELANDS WACCAMAW COMMUNITY HOSPITAL (420098)**, 4070 Highway 17 Bypass, Zip 29576–5033, Mailing Address: P O Drawer 3350, Zip 29576–2673; tel. 843/652–1000, **A**1 2 3 7 10 **F**3 8 11 13 15 17 18 28 29 30 31 32 35 37 39 40 45 50 51 56 60 61 64 65 68 70 73 74 75 76 77 78 79 81 82 84 85 86 87 89 90 93 94 96 97 100 102 107 108 110 111 114 115 118 119 130 131 146 147 148 **S** QHR, Brentwood, TN
Primary Contact: Bruce P. Bailey, Chief Executive Officer
CFO: Elizabeth S. Ward, Chief Financial Officer
Web address: www.tidelandswaccamawcommunity.org
Control: Other not–for–profit (including NFP Corporation) **Service:** General medical and surgical

Staffed Beds: 169 **Admissions:** 7662 **Census:** 94 **Outpatient Visits:** 121684 **Births:** 569 **Total Expense ($000):** 158788 **Payroll Expense ($000):** 34089 **Personnel:** 601

MYRTLE BEACH—Horry County

⊞ **GRAND STRAND REGIONAL MEDICAL CENTER (420085)**, 809 82nd Parkway, Zip 29572–4607; tel. 843/692–1000, **A**1 2 3 5 10 19 **F**3 11 13 15 17 18 20 22 24 26 28 29 30 31 34 35 37 39 40 41 42 43 46 47 49 50 54 57 58 59 60 64 70 73 74 75 76 77 78 79 81 82 84 85 86 87 88 89 90 94 96 98 101 102 107 108 109 110 111 114 115 118 119 120 121 123 126 130 132 135 146 147 153 **S** HCA Healthcare, Nashville, TN
Primary Contact: Mark E. Sims, Chief Executive Officer
CFO: Turner Wortham, Chief Financial Officer
Web address: www.grandstrandmed.com
Control: Corporation, Investor–owned (for–profit) **Service:** General medical and surgical

Staffed Beds: 371 **Admissions:** 23068 **Census:** 292 **Outpatient Visits:** 189681 **Births:** 906 **Personnel:** 1413

NEWBERRY—Newberry County

⊞ **NEWBERRY COUNTY MEMORIAL HOSPITAL (420053)**, 2669 Kinard Street, Zip 29108–2911, Mailing Address: P.O. Box 497, Zip 29108–0497; tel. 803/276–7570, **A**1 10 20 **F**3 7 11 13 15 17 28 29 30 31 32 34 35 37 40 45 47 53 56 57 59 64 68 70 75 76 77 78 79 81 82 85 86 87 89 90 93 94 107 108 109 110 111 115 119 128 130 133 135 143 146 147 148 149 **S** QHR, Brentwood, TN
Primary Contact: Bruce A. Baldwin, Chief Executive Officer
CFO: Mike Reynolds, Chief Financial Officer
CMO: Mark Davis, M.D., Chief of Staff
CIO: David Wolff, Director Information Technology
CHR: Dyan Bowman, Director Human Resources
Web address: www.newberryhospital.org
Control: County, Government, nonfederal **Service:** General medical and surgical

Staffed Beds: 54 **Admissions:** 1918 **Census:** 19 **Outpatient Visits:** 43709 **Births:** 264 **Total Expense ($000):** 49394 **Payroll Expense ($000):** 18172 **Personnel:** 351

ORANGEBURG—Orangeburg County

⊞ **REGIONAL MEDICAL CENTER (420068)**, 3000 St Matthews Road, Zip 29118–1442; tel. 803/395–2200, **A**1 10 **F**3 11 12 13 14 15 17 18 20 28 29 30 31 34 35 40 43 44 45 46 47 48 49 50 53 57 58 59 60 61 62 64 65 66 68 70 71 73 76 77 78 79 81 82 84 85 86 87 89 90 93 94 97 100 101 102 103 104 107 108 110 111 114 115 119 121 127 129 130 131 132 135 144 146 147 149 **S** QHR, Brentwood, TN
Primary Contact: Charles E. Williams, FACHE, President and Chief Executive Officer
COO: Nicole Smith Hendricks, Chief Operating Officer
CFO: Liza Porterfield, Chief Financial Officer
CIO: James Albin, Chief Information Officer
CHR: Howard Harris, Vice President Human Resources
CNO: Mickey Whisenhunt, Interim Chief Nursing Officer
Web address: www.trmchealth.org
Control: County, Government, nonfederal **Service:** General medical and surgical

Staffed Beds: 283 **Admissions:** 10981 **Census:** 150 **Outpatient Visits:** 193485 **Births:** 878 **Total Expense ($000):** 222477 **Payroll Expense ($000):** 92348 **Personnel:** 1194

☐ **WILLIAM J. MCCORD ADOLESCENT TREATMENT FACILITY (424013)**, 910 Cook Road, Zip 29118–2124, Mailing Address: P.O. Box 1166, Zip 29116–1166; tel. 803/534–2328, **A**1 10 **F**4 29 34 38 57 61 98 99 130 132 134 135 151
Primary Contact: Michael Dennis, Director
CFO: Laura Murdaugh, Finance Director
CMO: Dorothy Kendall, Medical Director
CNO: Linda Mitchum, Director of Nursing
Web address: www.tccada.com
Control: Other not–for–profit (including NFP Corporation) **Service:** Children's hospital psychiatric

Staffed Beds: 15 **Admissions:** 96 **Census:** 8 **Outpatient Visits:** 0 **Births:** 0 **Total Expense ($000):** 2254 **Payroll Expense ($000):** 1129 **Personnel:** 30

PICKENS—Pickens County

★ ⇑ **ANMED HEALTH CANNON (420011)**, 123 W G Acker Drive, Zip 29671–2739, Mailing Address: P.O. Box 188, Zip 29671–0188; tel. 864/878–4791, **A**10 21 **F**3 11 15 29 34 40 45 50 56 57 59 64 70 75 79 81 85 97 107 108 110 111 114 119 127 135 146 149 **S** AnMed Health, Anderson, SC
Primary Contact: Brandon Clary, President and Chief Executive Officer
CFO: Will Grant, Chief Financial Officer
CMO: Daniel J Dahlhausen, M.D., President of Medical Staff/Chief Medical Officer
CIO: Robert Furr, Director Information Services
CHR: Lisa G Bryant, Director Human Resources
CNO: Donna K Anderson, R.N., Chief Nursing Officer
Web address: www.cannonhospital.org
Control: Other not–for–profit (including NFP Corporation) **Service:** General medical and surgical

Staffed Beds: 26 **Admissions:** 731 **Census:** 7 **Outpatient Visits:** 50977 **Births:** 0 **Personnel:** 182

ROCK HILL—York County

⊞ **ENCOMPASS HEALTH REHABILITATION HOSPITAL OF ROCK HILL (423028)**, 1795 Dr. Frank Gaston Boulevard, Zip 29732–1190; tel. 803/326–3500, (Nonreporting) **A**1 10 **S** Encompass Health Corporation, Birmingham, AL
Primary Contact: Deanna Martin, Chief Executive Officer
Web address: www.healthsouthrockhill.com
Control: Corporation, Investor–owned (for–profit) **Service:** Rehabilitation

Staffed Beds: 50

⊞ **PIEDMONT MEDICAL CENTER (420002)**, 222 Herlong Avenue, Zip 29732; tel. 803/329–1234, **A**1 2 10 **F**3 7 11 12 13 15 17 18 20 22 24 26 28 29 30 31 34 35 40 43 45 49 50 57 59 60 64 67 70 72 73 74 75 76 77 78 79 81 82 85 86 89 90 91 93 98 100 102 103 107 108 110 111 114 115 118 119 126 130 132 135 146 147 148 154 **S** TENET Healthcare Corporation, Dallas, TX
Primary Contact: Mark Nosacka, Chief Executive Officer
COO: James Riley, Chief Operating Officer
CFO: Stephen Gilmore, Chief Financial Officer
CIO: Joel Dean, Director Information Services
CHR: Elizabeth Elich, Chief Human Resources Officer
CNO: Patricia A. Feilmeier, R.N., Chief Nursing Officer
Web address: www.piedmontmedicalcenter.com
Control: Corporation, Investor–owned (for–profit) **Service:** General medical and surgical

Staffed Beds: 279 **Admissions:** 14969 **Census:** 192 **Outpatient Visits:** 140218 **Births:** 1600 **Total Expense ($000):** 248228 **Payroll Expense ($000):** 82216 **Personnel:** 2003

SC

SENECA—Oconee County

PRISMA HEALTH OCONEE MEMORIAL HOSPITAL (420009), 298 Memorial Drive, Zip 29672-9499; tel. 864/882-3351, (Total facility includes 120 beds in nursing home–type unit) **A**1 3 5 10 20 **F**3 7 11 13 15 17 18 20 28 29 30 31 34 35 39 40 51 54 56 57 59 63 64 67 70 75 76 77 78 79 80 81 82 84 85 86 87 89 90 94 97 107 108 111 114 115 119 128 130 132 143 146 **S** Prisma Health - Upstate, Greenville, SC
Primary Contact: Hunter Kome, Campus President
CMO: Conrad K Shuler, M.D., Chief Medical Officer
CIO: Jay Hansen, Director Information Services
CNO: Patricia Smith, Chief Nursing Officer
Web address: www.oconeemed.org
Control: Other not–for–profit (including NFP Corporation) **Service:** General medical and surgical

Staffed Beds: 256 **Admissions:** 5783 **Census:** 164 **Outpatient Visits:** 131701 **Births:** 457 **Total Expense ($000):** 113229 **Payroll Expense ($000):** 38963 **Personnel:** 795

SIMPSONVILLE—Greenville County

PRISMA HEALTH HILLCREST HOSPITAL (420037), 729 SE Main Street, Zip 29681-3280; tel. 864/454-6100, **A**1 5 10 **F**3 11 12 15 18 29 34 35 40 44 45 50 57 59 64 68 70 79 81 85 86 90 107 110 111 114 115 119 129 130 132 146 **S** Prisma Health - Upstate, Greenville, SC
Primary Contact: Scott R. Jones, FACHE, Chief Operating Officer
Web address: www.ghs.org
Control: Other not–for–profit (including NFP Corporation) **Service:** General medical and surgical

Staffed Beds: 43 **Admissions:** 1530 **Census:** 11 **Outpatient Visits:** 79743 **Births:** 0 **Total Expense ($000):** 56154 **Payroll Expense ($000):** 17175 **Personnel:** 244

SPARTANBURG—Spartanburg County

★ **SPARTANBURG HOSPITAL FOR RESTORATIVE CARE (422004)**, 389 Serpentine Drive, Zip 29303-3026; tel. 864/560-3280, (Total facility includes 25 beds in nursing home–type unit) **A**10 **F**1 3 29 30 31 35 70 75 77 79 82 85 87 90 119 128 130 148 149 **S** Spartanburg Regional Healthcare System, Spartanburg, SC
Primary Contact: Anita M. Butler, Chief Executive Officer
Web address: www.srhs.com
Control: Hospital district or authority, Government, nonfederal **Service:** Acute long–term care hospital

Staffed Beds: 116 **Admissions:** 708 **Census:** 42 **Outpatient Visits:** 0 **Births:** 0 **Total Expense ($000):** 23557 **Payroll Expense ($000):** 12024 **Personnel:** 175

★ ⇑ **SPARTANBURG MEDICAL CENTER - CHURCH STREET CAMPUS (420007)**, 101 East Wood Street, Zip 29303-3040; tel. 864/560-6000, **A**2 3 5 10 21 **F**3 7 11 12 13 15 17 18 20 22 24 26 28 29 30 31 34 35 36 37 38 39 40 43 44 45 46 47 48 49 50 53 54 56 57 58 59 60 61 62 63 64 65 66 68 70 71 72 73 74 75 76 77 78 79 81 82 83 84 85 86 87 88 89 90 94 97 98 99 100 101 102 103 104 107 108 110 111 114 115 117 118 119 120 123 124 126 129 130 131 132 135 143 144 145 146 147 148 149 154 **S** Spartanburg Regional Healthcare System, Spartanburg, SC
Primary Contact: J Philip. Feisal, President and Chief Executive Officer
COO: Mark Aycock, Chief Operating Officer
CFO: Kenneth Meinke, Senior Vice President Administrative Services, Finance and Chief Financial Officer
CMO: Charles Morrow, M.D., Chief Medical Officer
CIO: Harold Moore, Chief Information Technology Officer
CHR: Kathy Sinclair, Vice President Human Resources
CNO: Susan Duggar, MSN, Vice President Nursing
Web address: www.spartanburgregional.com
Control: Hospital district or authority, Government, nonfederal **Service:** General medical and surgical

Staffed Beds: 519 **Admissions:** 26079 **Census:** 414 **Outpatient Visits:** 443786 **Births:** 2786 **Total Expense ($000):** 723251 **Payroll Expense ($000):** 233430 **Personnel:** 4597

⊠ △ **SPARTANBURG MEDICAL CENTER - MARY BLACK (420083)**, 1700 Skylyn Drive, Zip 29307-1061, Mailing Address: P.O. Box 3217, Zip 29304-3217; tel. 864/573-3000, **A**1 5 7 10 **F**3 11 13 15 18 20 29 30 31 34 35 40 45 47 49 50 51 56 57 59 60 64 68 70 73 74 75 76 77 78 79 81 85 87 89 90 93 94 96 98 100 102 103 107 108 110 111 114 115 119 126 129 130 132 135 145 146 147 148 154 **S** Spartanburg Regional Healthcare System, Spartanburg, SC
Primary Contact: Parkes Coggins, Vice President Hospital Integration
CFO: Brett English, Chief Financial Officer
CMO: Howard Bean, M.D., Chief Medical Officer
CIO: John O'Donnell, Director of Information Technology Services
CHR: Lee Ann Roque, Director of Human Resources
CNO: Chanda Flynn, R.N., MSN, Chief Nursing Officer
Web address: www.maryblackhealthsystem.com
Control: Corporation, Investor–owned (for–profit) **Service:** General medical and surgical

Staffed Beds: 160 **Admissions:** 5896 **Census:** 72 **Outpatient Visits:** 100319 **Births:** 1172 **Total Expense ($000):** 108590 **Payroll Expense ($000):** 36091 **Personnel:** 630

SUMTER—Sumter County

⊠ **PRISMA HEALTH TUOMEY HOSPITAL (420070)**, 129 North Washington Street, Zip 29150-4983; tel. 803/774-9000, **A**1 3 10 19 **F**3 11 13 15 20 28 29 30 31 32 34 35 40 48 49 50 51 54 56 59 62 63 64 68 70 71 73 75 76 77 78 79 80 81 84 85 86 87 89 90 94 102 107 108 110 111 114 119 120 121 128 129 130 131 132 135 146 147 148 **S** Prisma Health - Midlands, Columbia, SC
Primary Contact: Michelle Logan-Owens, Ph.D., R.N., Chief Operating Officer
CFO: Mark Lovell, Vice President and Chief Financial Officer
CMO: Gene Dickerson, M.D., Vice President Medical Affairs
CIO: Cheryl Martin, Chief Information Officer
CHR: Letitia Pringle-Miller, Administrative Director
CNO: Terrie Carlton, R.N., Vice President & Chief Nursing Officer
Web address: www.tuomey.com
Control: Other not–for–profit (including NFP Corporation) **Service:** General medical and surgical

Staffed Beds: 219 **Admissions:** 9317 **Census:** 138 **Outpatient Visits:** 152019 **Births:** 1296 **Total Expense ($000):** 174320 **Payroll Expense ($000):** 68485 **Personnel:** 1384

TRAVELERS REST—Greenville County

⊠ △ **PRISMA HEALTH NORTH GREENVILLE LTACH (420008)**, 807 North Main Street, Zip 29690-1551; tel. 864/455-9206, **A**1 5 7 10 **F**1 3 15 29 30 34 35 40 44 50 64 75 79 85 86 87 107 110 111 114 119 130 146 148
Primary Contact: Adrienne Talbert, Interim Administrator
CMO: Amy Treece, M.D., Medical Director
CHR: Carol Bish, Human Resources Coordinator
CNO: Marian Lorraine McVey, Chief Nursing Officer
Web address: www.ghs.org
Control: Other not–for–profit (including NFP Corporation) **Service:** Acute long–term care hospital

Staffed Beds: 28 **Admissions:** 224 **Census:** 21 **Outpatient Visits:** 26152 **Births:** 0 **Total Expense ($000):** 28827 **Payroll Expense ($000):** 8837 **Personnel:** 148

☐ **SPRINGBROOK BEHAVIORAL HEALTH SYSTEM (424007)**, One Havenwood Lane, Zip 29690-9447, Mailing Address: P.O. Box 1005, Zip 29690-1005; tel. 864/834-8013, **A**1 10 **F**4 98 99 103 104
Primary Contact: Mike Rowley, Chief Executive Officer
COO: Mary Ann Bennett, R.N., Chief Operating Officer and Chief Nursing Officer
CFO: Bart Bennett, Chief Financial Officer
CMO: Mathew Fisher, M.D., Medical Director
CIO: Bart Bennett, Chief Information Technology Officer
CHR: Teresa Lipscomb, Director Human Resources
CNO: Marylynn Johnson, Director of Nursing
Web address: www.springbookbehavioral.com
Control: Corporation, Investor–owned (for–profit) **Service:** Psychiatric

Staffed Beds: 44 **Admissions:** 1049 **Census:** 28 **Outpatient Visits:** 0 **Births:** 0 **Personnel:** 256

SC

Hospital, Medicare Provider Number, Address, Telephone, Approval, Facility, and Physician Codes, Health Care System

★ American Hospital Association (AHA) membership
☐ The Joint Commission accreditation
○ Healthcare Facilities Accreditation Program
◇ DNV Healthcare Inc. accreditation
⇑ Center for Improvement in Healthcare Quality Accreditation
△ Commission on Accreditation of Rehabilitation Facilities (CARF) accreditation

© 2019 AHA Guide   *Many Facility Codes have changed. Please refer to the AHA Guide Code Chart.*   Hospitals **A557**

UNION—Union County

★ ⇑ **UNION MEDICAL CENTER (420108)**, 322 West South Street, Zip 29379–2857, Mailing Address: P.O. Box 789, Zip 29379–0789; tel. 864/301–2000, **A**10 21 **F**3 7 11 15 29 30 34 35 40 57 59 64 75 89 107 111 115 119 130 135 146 147 149 **S** Spartanburg Regional Healthcare System, Spartanburg, SC
Primary Contact: Paul R. Newhouse, President
CFO: Cindy L. Gault, Chief Financial Officer
CHR: Angie Benfield, Human Resources Generalist
CNO: Beth Lawson, Chief Nursing Officer
Web address: www.https://www.spartanburgregional.com/locations/union-medical-center/
Control: Hospital district or authority, Government, nonfederal **Service:** General medical and surgical

Staffed Beds: 50 **Admissions:** 412 **Census:** 6 **Births:** 0 **Total Expense ($000):** 18366 **Payroll Expense ($000):** 8777 **Personnel:** 176

VARNVILLE—Hampton County

★ **HAMPTON REGIONAL MEDICAL CENTER (420072)**, 503 West Carolina Avenue, Zip 29944–4735, Mailing Address: P.O. Box 338, Zip 29944–0338; tel. 803/943–2771, **A**10 20 **F**15 17 18 24 28 29 31 34 40 57 59 65 67 70 75 78 79 81 90 93 94 102 107 108 110 111 115 119 127 128 129 133 146
Primary Contact: Dave H. Hamill, President and Chief Executive Officer
Web address: www.hamptonregional.com
Control: Other not–for–profit (including NFP Corporation) **Service:** General medical and surgical

Staffed Beds: 32 **Admissions:** 683 **Census:** 7 **Outpatient Visits:** 25698 **Births:** 0 **Total Expense ($000):** 22203 **Payroll Expense ($000):** 9840 **Personnel:** 200

WALTERBORO—Colleton County

⊠ **COLLETON MEDICAL CENTER (420030)**, 501 Robertson Boulevard, Zip 29488–5714; tel. 843/782–2000, **A**1 10 20 **F**3 11 13 15 18 26 29 30 32 34 35 36 40 41 45 47 49 56 57 59 60 64 65 68 70 75 76 77 79 81 82 85 86 87 89 90 93 94 96 98 102 107 108 110 111 114 115 119 129 130 131 132 146 147 148 149 **S** HCA Healthcare, Nashville, TN
Primary Contact: Jimmy O. Hiott III, Chief Executive Officer
CFO: Cassie Ball, Chief Financial Officer
CMO: Kim Rakes-Stephens, M.D., Chief Medical Staff
CIO: Damien Noble, Director Information Technology and System
CHR: Wendy Glass, Director Human Resources
CNO: Anna Jonason, Ph.D., R.N., Chief Nursing Officer
Web address: www.colletonmedical.com
Control: Corporation, Investor–owned (for–profit) **Service:** General medical and surgical

Staffed Beds: 131 **Admissions:** 4449 **Census:** 56 **Outpatient Visits:** 74855 **Births:** 279 **Total Expense ($000):** 72277 **Payroll Expense ($000):** 22493 **Personnel:** 348

WEST COLUMBIA—Lexington County

★ ⇑ **LEXINGTON MEDICAL CENTER (420073)**, 2720 Sunset Boulevard, Zip 29169–4810; tel. 803/791–2000, **A**2 3 10 21 **F**3 8 11 12 13 15 18 20 22 24 26 28 29 30 31 32 34 35 38 39 40 43 44 45 46 48 49 50 53 54 57 58 59 60 61 64 68 70 72 73 74 75 76 77 78 79 80 81 82 84 85 86 87 90 92 93 94 96 107 108 110 111 114 115 117 118 119 120 121 123 124 126 127 129 130 131 132 135 141 142 144 145 146 147 148
Primary Contact: Tod Augsburger, FACHE, President and Chief Executive Officer
COO: Tod Augsburger, FACHE, Senior Vice President and Chief Operating Officer
CFO: Melinda Kruzner, Chief Financial Officer
CMO: Brent Powers, M.D., Vice President/Chief Medical Officer
CIO: Kathleen R Herald, Vice President and Chief Information Officer
CHR: Kathy A Howell, Vice President Human Resources
CNO: Cindy Rohman, R.N., MS, Vice President/Chief Nursing Officer
Web address: www.lexmed.com
Control: Hospital district or authority, Government, nonfederal **Service:** General medical and surgical

Staffed Beds: 456 **Admissions:** 29312 **Census:** 373 **Outpatient Visits:** 290108 **Births:** 3340 **Total Expense ($000):** 665758 **Payroll Expense ($000):** 243364 **Personnel:** 3757

□ **THREE RIVERS BEHAVIORAL HEALTH (424008)**, 2900 Sunset Boulevard, Zip 29169–3422; tel. 803/796–9911, **A**1 10 **F**4 5 98 99 100 101 103 104 105 152 153 **S** Universal Health Services, Inc., King of Prussia, PA
Primary Contact: Shannon Marcus, Chief Executive Officer
CFO: Christopher Jensen, Chief Financial Officer
CMO: Christina Lynn, M.D., Medical Director
CHR: Nita Sundberg, Director Human Resources
CNO: Lilly Wing, Chief Nursing Officer
Web address: www.threeriversbehavioral.org
Control: Corporation, Investor–owned (for–profit) **Service:** Psychiatric

Staffed Beds: 122 **Admissions:** 3677 **Census:** 88 **Outpatient Visits:** 5630 **Births:** 0 **Total Expense ($000):** 22160 **Payroll Expense ($000):** 10563 **Personnel:** 175

SC

Many Facility Codes have changed. Please refer to the AHA Guide Code Chart. © 2019 AHA Guide

SOUTH DAKOTA

ABERDEEN—Brown County

⊞ **AVERA ST. LUKE'S HOSPITAL (430014)**, 305 South State Street, Zip 57401–4527; tel. 605/622–5000, (Nonreporting) **A**1 2 5 10 19 **S** Avera Health, Sioux Falls, SD
Primary Contact: Todd Forkel, President and Chief Executive Officer
CFO: Geoff Durst, Vice President Finance
CMO: Shahid Chaudhary, M.D., Chief Medical Officer
CIO: Julie Kusler, Manager Information Services
CHR: Tracy L Olson, Human Resource Officer
CNO: Jan Patterson, Chief Nursing Officer
Web address: www.avera.org/st-lukes-hospital/
Control: Church operated **Service:** General medical and surgical

Staffed Beds: 212

DAKOTA PLAINS SURGICAL CENTER (430092), 701 8th Avenue NW, Suite C, Zip 57401–1865; tel. 605/225–3300, (Nonreporting)
Primary Contact: Charles Livingston, Administrator
Control: Corporation, Investor–owned (for–profit) **Service:** Surgical

Staffed Beds: 15

★ **SANFORD ABERDEEN MEDICAL CENTER (430097)**, 2905 3rd Avenue SE, Zip 57401–5420; tel. 605/626–4200, **A**10 **F**3 13 15 18 20 22 26 28 29 31 32 34 35 40 43 45 46 50 56 57 59 61 64 65 70 75 76 77 78 79 81 85 89 90 93 94 97 107 110 111 115 119 130 131 132 144 146 147 148 156 **S** Sanford Health, Sioux Falls, SD
Primary Contact: Ashley M. Erickson, Chief Executive Officer
CFO: Jeffrey Poppen, Chief Financial Officer
CMO: Samuel Nyamu, M.D., Chief Medical Officer
CHR: Katie Palmer, Manager Human Resources
CNO: Kila Legrand, Chief Nursing Officer
Web address: www.sanfordaberdeen.org/
Control: Other not–for–profit (including NFP Corporation) **Service:** General medical and surgical

Staffed Beds: 48 **Admissions:** 1429 **Census:** 10 **Outpatient Visits:** 78299
Births: 226 **Total Expense ($000):** 68538 **Payroll Expense ($000):** 31302
Personnel: 384

ARMOUR—Douglas County

DOUGLAS COUNTY MEMORIAL HOSPITAL (431305), 708 Eighth Street, Zip 57313–2102; tel. 605/724–2159, **A**10 18 **F**3 8 10 28 31 34 40 41 43 46 53 57 59 62 64 65 78 81 91 100 102 107 114 119 127 133 154
Primary Contact: Heath Brouwer, Administrator
CFO: Dorothy Spease, Manager Business Office
Web address: www.dcmhsd.org
Control: Other not–for–profit (including NFP Corporation) **Service:** General medical and surgical

Staffed Beds: 11 **Admissions:** 161 **Census:** 2 **Outpatient Visits:** 8827
Births: 0 **Total Expense ($000):** 9254 **Payroll Expense ($000):** 4205
Personnel: 79

BOWDLE—Douglas County

★ **BOWDLE HOSPITAL (431318)**, 8001 West Fifth Street, Zip 57428, Mailing Address: P.O. Box 556, Zip 57428–0556; tel. 605/285–6146, (Nonreporting) **A**10 18
Primary Contact: Sandy Schlechter, Chief Executive Officer
CFO: Brooke Heilman, Chief Financial Officer
CMO: John Ottenbacher, Chief of Staff
CNO: Bobbi Noess, Director of Nursing
Web address: www.bowdlehc.com
Control: City, Government, nonfederal **Service:** General medical and surgical

Staffed Beds: 50

BRITTON—Marshall County

★ **MARSHALL COUNTY HEALTHCARE CENTER AVERA (431312)**, 413 Ninth Street, Zip 57430–2274; tel. 605/448–2253, (Nonreporting) **A**10 18 **S** Avera Health, Sioux Falls, SD
Primary Contact: Nick Fosness, Chief Executive Officer
Web address: www.avera.org
Control: Other not–for–profit (including NFP Corporation) **Service:** General medical and surgical

Staffed Beds: 18

BROOKINGS—Brookings County

★ **BROOKINGS HEALTH SYSTEM (430008)**, 300 22nd Avenue, Zip 57006–2496; tel. 605/696–9000, (Total facility includes 79 beds in nursing home–type unit) **A**10 20 **F**3 7 8 11 13 28 29 30 31 32 34 37 40 41 45 51 53 57 59 62 63 64 65 70 74 75 76 77 79 81 82 85 86 87 89 92 93 102 107 108 111 114 118 119 125 126 127 128 129 130 133 135 146 147 148 149 154
Primary Contact: Jason R. Merkley, Chief Executive Officer
CFO: Steve Lindemann, Chief Financial Officer
CMO: Shelby Eischens, Chief Medical Officer
CHR: September Bessler, Director, Human Resources
CNO: Tammy Hillestad, Chief Nursing Officer
Web address: www.brookingshealth.org
Control: City, Government, nonfederal **Service:** General medical and surgical

Staffed Beds: 128 **Admissions:** 1358 **Census:** 87 **Outpatient Visits:** 72476
Births: 356 **Total Expense ($000):** 69885 **Payroll Expense ($000):** 30410
Personnel: 341

BURKE—Gregory County

★ **COMMUNITY MEMORIAL HOSPITAL (431309)**, 809 Jackson Street, Zip 57523–2065, Mailing Address: P.O. Box 319, Zip 57523–0319; tel. 605/775–2621, (Nonreporting) **A**10 18 **S** Sanford Health, Sioux Falls, SD
Primary Contact: Mistie Sachtien, Chief Executive Officer
CMO: Megan Smith, M.D., Chief Medical Staff
CHR: Tami Lyon, Director Human Resources
Web address: www.sanfordhealth.org
Control: Other not–for–profit (including NFP Corporation) **Service:** General medical and surgical

Staffed Beds: 16

CANTON—Lincoln County

★ **SANFORD CANTON-INWOOD MEDICAL CENTER (431333)**, 440 North Hiawatha Drive, Zip 57013–5800; tel. 605/764–1400, **A**10 18 **F**7 10 15 28 34 40 45 59 65 71 75 77 81 93 97 104 107 114 119 128 130 133 143 149 150 156 **S** Sanford Health, Sioux Falls, SD
Primary Contact: Scott C. Larson, Chief Executive Officer
CFO: Paul Gerhart, Chief Financial Officer
Web address: www.sanfordcantoninwood.org
Control: Other not–for–profit (including NFP Corporation) **Service:** General medical and surgical

Staffed Beds: 11 **Admissions:** 220 **Census:** 4 **Outpatient Visits:** 19420
Births: 0 **Total Expense ($000):** 10255 **Payroll Expense ($000):** 5122
Personnel: 78

SD

Hospital, Medicare Provider Number, Address, Telephone, Approval, Facility, and Physician Codes, Health Care System
★ American Hospital Association (AHA) membership ○ Healthcare Facilities Accreditation Program ⇑ Center for Improvement in Healthcare Quality Accreditation
☐ The Joint Commission accreditation ◇ DNV Healthcare Inc. accreditation △ Commission on Accreditation of Rehabilitation Facilities (CARF) accreditation

© 2019 AHA Guide *Many Facility Codes have changed. Please refer to the AHA Guide Code Chart.* Hospitals **A559**

CHAMBERLAIN—Brule County

★ **SANFORD CHAMBERLAIN MEDICAL CENTER (431329)**, 300 South Byron Boulevard, Zip 57325–9741; tel. 605/234–5511, (Total facility includes 44 beds in nursing home–type unit) **A**10 18 **F**3 13 15 18 19 28 29 31 34 35 40 43 45 50 57 59 64 65 68 75 76 77 78 81 85 86 87 89 93 100 101 102 104 107 110 115 119 130 131 132 133 148 149 154 156 157 **S** Sanford Health, Sioux Falls, SD
Primary Contact: Erica Peterson, Chief Executive Officer
COO: Paul Miller, Director of Operations
CFO: Erica Peterson, Chief Executive Officer and Chief Financial Officer
CMO: Lacey Olson, M.D., Chief Medical Staff
CHR: Dorothy Hieb, Director Human Resources
CNO: Sarah Talbott, Chief Nursing Officer
Web address: www.sanfordchamberlain.org
Control: Other not–for–profit (including NFP Corporation) **Service**: General medical and surgical

Staffed Beds: 69 **Admissions**: 437 **Census**: 48 **Outpatient Visits**: 27019
Births: 40 **Total Expense ($000)**: 21258 **Payroll Expense ($000)**: 10483
Personnel: 178

SANFORD MID DAKOTA MEDICAL CENTER See Sanford Chamberlain Medical Center

CLEAR LAKE—Deuel County

★ **SANFORD CLEAR LAKE MEDICAL CENTER (431307)**, 701 Third Avenue South, Zip 57226–2016; tel. 605/874–2141, **A**10 18 **F**3 28 29 34 35 40 43 45 50 53 57 59 62 64 65 68 75 81 92 93 97 107 115 119 127 128 133 135 144 149 **S** Sanford Health, Sioux Falls, SD
Primary Contact: Lori Sisk, R.N., Chief Executive Officer
CFO: Allison Nelson, Chief Financial Officer
CMO: Terrance Smith, M.D., Chairman Medical Staff
CNO: Stephanie Dobbs, Chief Nursing Officer
Web address: www.sanforddeuelcounty.org
Control: Other not–for–profit (including NFP Corporation) **Service**: General medical and surgical

Staffed Beds: 10 **Admissions**: 168 **Census**: 2 **Outpatient Visits**: 8795
Births: 0 **Total Expense ($000)**: 6392 **Payroll Expense ($000)**: 3191
Personnel: 48

CUSTER—Custer County

★ **CUSTER REGIONAL HOSPITAL (431323)**, 1039 Montgomery Street, Zip 57730–1397; tel. 605/673–2229, (Total facility includes 60 beds in nursing home–type unit) **A**10 18 **F**3 10 12 15 29 34 35 40 43 53 54 56 57 59 64 65 67 68 75 77 79 84 87 89 90 93 97 102 104 107 108 110 111 114 119 127 128 132 133 134 135 144 147 148 149 154 156 **S** Regional Health, Rapid City, SD
Primary Contact: Mark C. Schmidt, President
Web address: www.regionalhealth.com
Control: Other not–for–profit (including NFP Corporation) **Service**: General medical and surgical

Staffed Beds: 87 **Admissions**: 385 **Census**: 56 **Births**: 0 **Total Expense ($000)**: 23939 **Payroll Expense ($000)**: 10583

DAKOTA DUNES—Union County

DUNES SURGICAL HOSPITAL (430089), 600 North Sioux Point Road, Zip 57049–5000; tel. 605/232–3332, (Nonreporting) **A**10
Primary Contact: Greg Miner, Administrator
Web address: www.dunessurgicalhospital.com
Control: Corporation, Investor–owned (for–profit) **Service**: Surgical

Staffed Beds: 40

DE SMET—Kingsbury County

★ **AVERA DE SMET MEMORIAL HOSPITAL (431332)**, 306 Prairie Avenue SW, Zip 57231–2285, Mailing Address: P.O. Box 160, Zip 57231–0160; tel. 605/854–6100, **A**10 18 **F**3 15 28 34 35 40 59 68 93 107 133 154 **S** Avera Health, Sioux Falls, SD
Primary Contact: Stephanie Reasy, Administrator and Chief Executive Officer
Web address: www.avera.org
Control: Other not–for–profit (including NFP Corporation) **Service**: General medical and surgical

Staffed Beds: 6 **Admissions**: 59 **Census**: 1 **Outpatient Visits**: 11075
Births: 0 **Total Expense ($000)**: 4273 **Payroll Expense ($000)**: 1914
Personnel: 26

DEADWOOD—Lawrence County

★ **LEAD-DEADWOOD REGIONAL HOSPITAL (431320)**, 61 Charles Street, Zip 57732–1303; tel. 605/717–6000, **A**10 18 **F**3 7 15 28 29 30 34 40 43 45 59 64 68 69 70 71 75 77 87 93 94 97 107 110 115 119 132 133 144 148 154 **S** Regional Health, Rapid City, SD
Primary Contact: Mark C. Schmidt, President
CMO: Elizabeth Sayler, M.D., Chief of Staff
CHR: Kathryn L Shockey, Director Human Resources
Web address: www.regionalhealth.com
Control: State, Government, nonfederal **Service**: General medical and surgical

Staffed Beds: 8 **Admissions**: 292 **Census**: 8 **Outpatient Visits**: 12528
Births: 0 **Personnel**: 101

DELL RAPIDS—Minnehaha County

AVERA DELLS AREA HEALTH CENTER See Avera Dells Area Hospital

★ **AVERA DELLS AREA HOSPITAL (431331)**, 909 North Iowa Avenue, Zip 57022–1231; tel. 605/428–5431, **A**10 18 **F**3 15 28 34 35 40 41 45 53 57 59 64 65 75 81 86 92 93 94 97 107 110 128 132 133 144 148 154 **S** Avera Health, Sioux Falls, SD
Primary Contact: Scott James. Hargens, Administrator and Chief Executive Officer
CFO: Kory Holt, Division Controller Network Operations
CMO: Demetre Skliris, Chief Medical Officer
CIO: Val Witham, Director of Health Information
CHR: Amy Aukes, Regional Manager of Human Resources
CNO: Karla Carstensen, Director Patient Care
Web address: www.avera.org/dell-rapids/
Control: Other not–for–profit (including NFP Corporation) **Service**: General medical and surgical

Staffed Beds: 23 **Admissions**: 190 **Census**: 3 **Outpatient Visits**: 16606
Births: 0 **Total Expense ($000)**: 5762 **Payroll Expense ($000)**: 2422
Personnel: 50

EAGLE BUTTE—Dewey County

☐ **U. S. PUBLIC HEALTH SERVICE INDIAN HOSPITAL (430083)**, 317 Main Street, Zip 57625–1012, Mailing Address: P.O. Box 1012, Zip 57625–1012; tel. 605/964–7724, (Nonreporting) **A**1 10 **S** U. S. Indian Health Service, Rockville, MD
Primary Contact: Charles Fisher, Chief Executive Officer
CFO: Lisa Deal, Budget Analyst
Web address: www.ihs.gov
Control: PHS, Indian Service, Government, federal **Service**: General medical and surgical

Staffed Beds: 8

EUREKA—Mcpherson County

★ **EUREKA COMMUNITY HEALTH SERVICES AVERA (431308)**, 410 Ninth Street, Zip 57437–2182, Mailing Address: P.O. Box 517, Zip 57437–0517; tel. 605/284–2661, **A**10 18 **F**10 28 34 35 40 41 45 59 65 81 93 107 133 154 156 **S** Avera Health, Sioux Falls, SD
Primary Contact: Carmen Weber, Administrator
CFO: Joyce Schwingler, Chief Financial Officer
Web address: www.avera.org
Control: Other not–for–profit (including NFP Corporation) **Service**: General medical and surgical

Staffed Beds: 4 **Admissions**: 57 **Census**: 1 **Outpatient Visits**: 6450
Births: 0 **Total Expense ($000)**: 3084 **Payroll Expense ($000)**: 1352
Personnel: 33

FAULKTON—Faulk County

FAULKTON AREA MEDICAL CENTER (431301), 1300 Oak Street, Zip 57438–2149, Mailing Address: P.O. Box 100, Zip 57438–0100; tel. 605/598–6262, **A**10 18 **F**3 17 28 29 31 40 45 59 64 77 78 82 93 97 107 115 127 128 133
Primary Contact: Dirkland T. Smith, Chief Executive Officer
COO: Jay A Jahnig, Chief Executive Officer
CFO: Susan Miller, Financial Administrator
CMO: K A Bartholomew, M.D., Medical Director
CIO: Cheryl Bue, Health Information Transcriptionist
CHR: Blythe Smith, Administrative Assistant
CNO: Shannon Stuwe, Director of Nursing
Web address: www.faulktonmedical.org
Control: Other not–for–profit (including NFP Corporation) **Service**: General medical and surgical

Staffed Beds: 12 **Admissions**: 215 **Census**: 3 **Outpatient Visits**: 11872
Births: 0 **Total Expense ($000)**: 9858 **Payroll Expense ($000)**: 4571
Personnel: 77

Many Facility Codes have changed. Please refer to the AHA Guide Code Chart.

FLANDREAU—Moody County

★ **AVERA FLANDREAU HOSPITAL (431310)**, 214 North Prairie Street, Zip 57028–1243; tel. 605/997-2433, **A**10 18 **F**3 28 34 35 40 41 45 57 59 64 65 75 81 86 92 93 97 107 127 128 133 144 146 148 154 **S** Avera Health, Sioux Falls, SD
Primary Contact: Scott James. Hargens, Administrator and Chief Executive Officer
CFO: Kory Holt, Assistant Vice President for Financial Integration
CMO: Scott Peterson, M.D., President Medical Staff
CIO: Val Witham, Director Health Information
CHR: Amy Aukes, Human Resources Analyst
Web address: www.avera.org/flandreau-medical/
Control: Other not–for–profit (including NFP Corporation) **Service:** General medical and surgical

Staffed Beds: 18 **Admissions:** 153 **Census:** 1 **Outpatient Visits:** 14157
Births: 0 **Total Expense ($000):** 5984 **Payroll Expense ($000):** 2351
Personnel: 46

AVERA FLANDREAU MEDICAL CENTER See Avera Flandreau Hospital

FORT MEADE—Meade County

⊞ **VETERANS AFFAIRS BLACK HILLS HEALTH CARE SYSTEM**, 113 Comanche Road, Zip 57741–1099; tel. 605/347-2511, (Includes VETERANS AFFAIRS MEDICAL CENTER HOT SPRINGS CAMPUS, 500 North Fifth Street, Hot Springs, South Dakota, Zip 57747; tel. 605/745-2052), (Non-reporting) **A**1 5 **S** Department of Veterans Affairs, Washington, DC
Primary Contact: Sandra Horsman, Director
CFO: Joseph Ferris, Chief Financial Officer
CHR: Denis Sullivan, Chief Human Resources Management
Web address: www.blackhills.va.gov/
Control: Veterans Affairs, Government, federal **Service:** General medical and surgical

Staffed Beds: 243

FREEMAN—Hutchinson County

★ **FREEMAN REGIONAL HEALTH SERVICES (431313)**, 510 East Eighth Street, Zip 57029–2086, Mailing Address: P.O. Box 370, Zip 57029–0370; tel. 605/925-4000, (Nonreporting) **A**10 18
Primary Contact: Nicholas R. Brandner, Chief Executive Officer
CFO: Mark Miller, Chief Financial Officer
Web address: www.freemanregional.com
Control: Other not–for–profit (including NFP Corporation) **Service:** General medical and surgical

Staffed Beds: 81

GETTYSBURG—Potter County

★ **AVERA GETTYSBURG HOSPITAL (431302)**, 606 East Garfield Avenue, Zip 57442–1398; tel. 605/765-2480, (Nonreporting) **A**10 18 **S** Avera Health, Sioux Falls, SD
Primary Contact: Robert L. Sheckler, Administrator
Web address: www.avera.org/st-marys-pierre/gellysburg-hospital/
Control: Church operated **Service:** General medical and surgical

Staffed Beds: 55

GREGORY—Gregory County

★ **AVERA GREGORY HOSPITAL (431338)**, 400 Park Avenue, Zip 57533–1302, Mailing Address: P.O. Box 408, Zip 57533–0408; tel. 605/835-8394, (Nonreporting) **A**10 18 **S** Avera Health, Sioux Falls, SD
Primary Contact: Anthony Timanus, Chief Executive Officer
CFO: Trish Keiser, Comptroller
CMO: Rich Kafka, M.D., Chief Medical Officer
CIO: Justin Keegan, Director Support Services
CHR: Carol Postulka, Administrative Coordinator
Web address: www.gregoryhealthcare.org
Control: Church operated **Service:** General medical and surgical

Staffed Beds: 65

HOT SPRINGS—Fall River County

★ **FALL RIVER HOSPITAL (431322)**, 1201 Highway 71 South, Zip 57747–8800; tel. 605/745-3159, (Total facility includes 48 beds in nursing home–type unit) **A**10 18 **F**3 28 29 34 40 56 57 59 64 65 74 77 81 89 93 104 107 119 127 128 129 132 133 146 148 154
Primary Contact: Tricia Uhlir, Chief Executive Officer
CFO: Jesse Naze, Chief Financial Officer
CMO: Rodney Larson, M.D., Medical Director
CIO: Dustin Kleinsasser, Information Technology and BioMed
CHR: Cindy Trent, Manager Personnel
Web address: www.frhssd.org
Control: Other not–for–profit (including NFP Corporation) **Service:** General medical and surgical

Staffed Beds: 73 **Admissions:** 199 **Census:** 54 **Outpatient Visits:** 13065
Births: 0 **Total Expense ($000):** 21733 **Payroll Expense ($000):** 9892
Personnel: 116

VETERANS AFFAIRS MEDICAL CENTER HOT SPRINGS CAMPUS See Veterans Affairs Black Hills Health Care System, Fort Meade

HURON—Beadle County

★ **HURON REGIONAL MEDICAL CENTER (431335)**, 172 Fourth Street SE, Zip 57350–2590; tel. 605/353-6200, **A**10 18 **F**3 11 13 14 15 28 29 31 34 35 40 43 45 57 59 60 62 63 64 68 70 75 77 78 79 81 85 86 93 102 107 108 110 111 115 118 119 130 132 133 146 148 **S** QHR, Brentwood, TN
Primary Contact: David Dick, Chief Executive Officer
CFO: Marcia Zwanziger, Vice President Finance
CMO: Bill Miner, M.D., Chief of Staff
CHR: Rhonda Hanson, Director Human Resources
CNO: Gail Robeson, Vice President Patient Services
Web address: www.huronregional.org
Control: Other not–for–profit (including NFP Corporation) **Service:** General medical and surgical

Staffed Beds: 30 **Admissions:** 1326 **Census:** 13 **Outpatient Visits:** 60721
Births: 279 **Total Expense ($000):** 37901 **Payroll Expense ($000):** 16244
Personnel: 262

MADISON—Lake County

★ **MADISON REGIONAL HEALTH SYSTEM (431300)**, 323 SW 10th Street, Zip 57042–3200; tel. 605/256-6551, **A**10 18 **F**7 13 15 28 31 34 35 40 41 43 50 57 59 62 64 65 70 75 76 77 81 82 85 87 89 93 97 107 110 111 114 119 129 132 133 135 143 144 145 146 148 156
Primary Contact: Tamara Miller, FACHE, Chief Executive Officer and Administrator
CFO: Teresa Mallett, Chief Financial Officer
CNO: Charlotte Charles, Director Acute Patient Services
Web address: www.madisonregionalhealth.org
Control: Other not–for–profit (including NFP Corporation) **Service:** General medical and surgical

Staffed Beds: 22 **Admissions:** 644 **Census:** 11 **Outpatient Visits:** 26824
Births: 45 **Total Expense ($000):** 26837 **Payroll Expense ($000):** 12610
Personnel: 259

MARTIN—Bennett County

★ **BENNETT COUNTY HOSPITAL AND NURSING HOME (431314)**, 102 Major Allen Street, Zip 57551–6005, Mailing Address: P.O. Box 70, Zip 57551–0070; tel. 605/685-6622, (Total facility includes 48 beds in nursing home–type unit) **A**10 18 **F**7 34 40 50 53 57 59 62 65 66 67 68 77 84 93 107 119 130 133 143 154
Primary Contact: Andrew Riggin, Chief Executive Officer
CFO: Jean Kirk, Chief Financial Officer
CMO: Peter Knowles-Smith, M.D., Medical Director
CIO: Jean Kirk, Chief Financial Officer
CHR: T J Porter, Director Human Resources
Web address: www.bennettcountyhospital.com/
Control: Other not–for–profit (including NFP Corporation) **Service:** General medical and surgical

Staffed Beds: 62 **Admissions:** 158 **Census:** 48 **Births:** 0

SD

MILBANK—Grant County

★ **MILBANK AREA HOSPITAL AVERA (431326)**, 301 Flynn Drive, Zip 57252–1508; tel. 605/432–4538, (Nonreporting) **A**10 18 **S** Avera Health, Sioux Falls, SD
Primary Contact: Natalie Gauer, Administrator
CMO: Kevin Bjordahl, M.D., Chief Medical Officer
CHR: Mona Schafer, Regional Manager Human Resources
Web address: www.averamilbank.org
Control: Church operated **Service**: General medical and surgical

Staffed Beds: 25

MILLER—Hand County

★ **AVERA HAND COUNTY MEMORIAL HOSPITAL (431337)**, 300 West Fifth Street, Zip 57362–1238; tel. 605/853–2421, **A**10 18 **F**1 3 4 8 11 15 16 17 28 29 34 35 40 43 45 46 50 53 57 59 64 67 70 73 77 79 80 81 86 87 88 89 90 93 98 107 115 119 128 129 132 133 146 148 154 **S** Avera Health, Sioux Falls, SD
Primary Contact: Bryan Breitling, Administrator
CFO: Debbie Pullman, Director Finance
CMO: John Hopkins, M.D., Chief of Staff
CIO: Janice Purrington, Coordinator Medical Records
CNO: Sarah DeHaai, R.N., Director of Nursing
Web address: www.avera.org
Control: Other not–for–profit (including NFP Corporation) **Service**: General medical and surgical

Staffed Beds: 15 Admissions: 280 Census: 3 Outpatient Visits: 12089
Births: 0 Total Expense ($000): 7540 Payroll Expense ($000): 3449
Personnel: 65

MITCHELL—Davison County

⊞ **AVERA QUEEN OF PEACE HOSPITAL (430013)**, 525 North Foster, Zip 57301–2999; tel. 605/995–2000, (Total facility includes 109 beds in nursing home–type unit) **A**1 2 10 **F**3 10 13 15 28 29 30 31 34 40 43 45 48 50 51 53 54 57 59 64 69 70 71 75 76 77 78 79 81 82 84 85 86 89 93 94 96 104 107 108 110 111 114 117 118 119 121 123 127 128 129 130 131 132 133 135 146 147 148 154 155 156 **S** Avera Health, Sioux Falls, SD
Primary Contact: Thomas A. Clark, Regional President and Chief Executive Officer
CFO: Will Flett, Vice President Finance and Chief Financial Officer
CMO: David Balt, D.O., Chief Medical Officer
CIO: Jim Hanson, Director Information Systems
CHR: Rita Lemon, Director Human Resources
CNO: Rochelle Reider, Vice President Patient Care
Web address: www.averaqueenofpeace.org
Control: Church operated, Nongovernment, not–for–profit **Service**: General medical and surgical

Staffed Beds: 159 Admissions: 1992 Census: 118 Outpatient
Visits: 125985 Births: 514 Total Expense ($000): 97868 Payroll Expense ($000): 44772 Personnel: 436

MOBRIDGE—Walworth County

★ **MOBRIDGE REGIONAL HOSPITAL (431325)**, 1401 Tenth Avenue West, Zip 57601–1106, Mailing Address: P.O. Box 580, Zip 57601–0580; tel. 605/845–3692, **A**10 18 **F**3 7 10 11 13 15 28 29 32 34 35 40 43 45 50 56 57 59 62 64 65 66 70 76 77 79 81 82 83 84 85 89 93 97 101 102 107 110 114 119 125 127 128 129 130 131 132 133 147 148 154 156
Primary Contact: John J. Ayoub, FACHE, Chief Executive Officer
COO: Beth Jensen, Director Clinic Operations
CFO: Renae Tisdall, Chief Financial Officer
CMO: Travis Henderson, M.D., Chief of Staff
CIO: Josiah Barton, Director Information Technology
CHR: Keri Wientjes, Director Human Resources
CNO: Kristi Voller, Director of Nursing
Web address: www.mobridgehospital.org
Control: Other not–for–profit (including NFP Corporation) **Service**: General medical and surgical

Staffed Beds: 25 Admissions: 685 Census: 7 Outpatient Visits: 56730
Births: 55 Total Expense ($000): 20749 Payroll Expense ($000): 10068
Personnel: 168

PARKSTON—Hutchinson County

★ **AVERA ST. BENEDICT HEALTH CENTER (431330)**, 401 West Glynn Drive, Zip 57366–9605; tel. 605/928–3311, (Total facility includes 74 beds in nursing home–type unit) **A**10 18 **F**2 3 8 10 13 15 28 29 30 31 32 34 35 38 40 45 53 56 57 59 62 64 65 69 71 75 76 81 82 83 85 86 87 89 107 110 111 115 116 119 127 128 129 130 131 132 133 135 146 147 148 154 156 **S** Avera Health, Sioux Falls, SD
Primary Contact: Rita Blasius, President and Chief Executive Officer
CFO: Rita Blasius, Assistant Administrator and Chief Financial Officer
CMO: Antoinette VanderPol, Chief of Staff
CIO: Adam Popp, Director Information Systems
CHR: Phyllis Ehler, Director Human Resources
CNO: Denise Muntefering, Vice President Patient Care Services
Web address: www.averastbenedict.org
Control: Church operated, Nongovernment, not–for–profit **Service**: General medical and surgical

Staffed Beds: 99 Admissions: 620 Census: 77 Outpatient Visits: 21303
Births: 55 Total Expense ($000): 21826 Payroll Expense ($000): 10887
Personnel: 176

PHILIP—Haakon County

HANS P. PETERSON MEMORIAL HOSPITAL See Philip Health Services

★ **PHILIP HEALTH SERVICES (431319)**, 503 West Pine Street, Zip 57567–3300, Mailing Address: P.O. Box 790, Zip 57567–0790; tel. 605/859–2511, (Total facility includes 30 beds in nursing home–type unit) **A**10 18 **F**10 40 43 57 59 62 67 85 90 93 107 114 127 128 130 131 133 147 148 149 150 **S** Regional Health, Rapid City, SD
Primary Contact: Jeremy Schultes, Administrator and Chief Executive Officer
Web address: www.philiphealthservices.com/
Control: Other not–for–profit (including NFP Corporation) **Service**: General medical and surgical

Staffed Beds: 48 Admissions: 203 Census: 31 Outpatient Visits: 20540
Total Expense ($000): 12416 Payroll Expense ($000): 6922
Personnel: 132

PIERRE—Hughes County

⊞ **AVERA ST. MARY'S HOSPITAL (430015)**, 801 East Sioux Avenue, Zip 57501–3323; tel. 605/224–3100, (Nonreporting) **A**1 3 10 20 **S** Avera Health, Sioux Falls, SD
Primary Contact: Todd Forkel, Interim Chief Executive Officer
CFO: Tom Wagner, Interim Vice President Finance
CMO: Denise Hanisch, M.D., Chief of Staff
CIO: Jamie Raske, Information Technology Lead
CHR: Paul Marso, Vice President Human Resources
Web address: www.avera.org/st-marys-pierre/
Control: Church operated **Service**: General medical and surgical

Staffed Beds: 110

PINE RIDGE—Shannon County

U. S. PUBLIC HEALTH SERVICE INDIAN HOSPITAL (430081), East Highway 18, Zip 57770, Mailing Address: P.O. Box 1201, Zip 57770–1201; tel. 605/867–5131, (Nonreporting) **A**10 **S** U. S. Indian Health Service, Rockville, MD
Primary Contact: Travis Scott, Service Unit Director
CFO: Sophia Conny, Deputy Administrative Officer
CMO: Jan Colton, M.D., Acting Clinical Director
CHR: Annabelle Blackbear, Human Resources Specialist
Web address: www.ihs.gov
Control: PHS, Indian Service, Government, federal **Service**: General medical and surgical

Staffed Beds: 45

PLATTE—Charles Mix County

★ **PLATTE HEALTH CENTER AVERA (431306)**, 601 East Seventh, Zip 57369–2123, Mailing Address: P.O. Box 200, Zip 57369–0200; tel. 605/337–3364, (Total facility includes 44 beds in nursing home–type unit) **A**10 18 **F**3 11 15 28 29 30 31 34 35 40 41 45 56 57 59 62 64 65 66 67 68 69 75 77 78 79 81 87 91 93 97 107 110 115 119 127 128 129 130 131 132 133 146 148 154 **S** Avera Health, Sioux Falls, SD
Primary Contact: Mark Burket, Chief Executive Officer
CFO: Jerry Hoffman, Chief Financial Officer
Web address: www.phcavera.org
Control: Other not–for–profit (including NFP Corporation) **Service**: General medical and surgical

Staffed Beds: 61 Admissions: 143 Census: 45 Outpatient Visits: 9019
Births: 0 Total Expense ($000): 14037 Payroll Expense ($000): 7694
Personnel: 133

SD

Many Facility Codes have changed. Please refer to the AHA Guide Code Chart.

RAPID CITY—Pennington County

BLACK HILLS SURGICAL HOSPITAL (430091), 216 Anamaria Drive, Zip 57701–7366, Mailing Address: 1868 Lombardy Drive, Zip 57703–4130; tel. 605/721–4900, (Nonreporting) **A**10
Primary Contact: Franklin Shobe, Administrator and Chief Executive Officer
Web address: www.bhsc.com
Control: Partnership, Investor–owned (for–profit) **Service**: Surgical

Staffed Beds: 26

INDIAN HEALTH SERVICE HOSPITAL (430082), 3200 Canyon Lake Drive, Zip 57702–8197; tel. 605/355–2280, (Nonreporting) **A**10 **S** U. S. Indian Health Service, Rockville, MD
Primary Contact: Kevin J. Stiffarm, Chief Executive Officer
Web address: www.ihs.gov
Control: PHS, Indian Service, Government, federal **Service**: General medical and surgical

Staffed Beds: 9

☒ **RAPID CITY REGIONAL HOSPITAL (430077)**, 353 Fairmont Boulevard, Zip 57701–7393, Mailing Address: P.O. Box 6000, Zip 57709–6000; tel. 605/755–1000, **A**1 3 5 10 **F**3 12 13 15 17 18 20 22 24 26 28 29 30 31 34 40 43 45 46 48 49 51 56 58 59 60 61 64 70 72 74 77 78 79 81 82 84 85 87 90 92 93 97 98 99 102 104 107 108 111 115 118 119 120 121 124 126 129 130 131 144 146 148 149 154 **S** Regional Health, Rapid City, SD
Primary Contact: John Pierce, Acting President
CFO: Mark Thompson, Vice President Financial Services
CMO: David Houser, M.D., Vice President Medical Affairs
CIO: Richard Latuchie, Vice President Business Development
CHR: Maureen Henson, Vice President Human Resources
Web address: www.regionalhealth.com
Control: Other not–for–profit (including NFP Corporation) **Service**: General medical and surgical

Staffed Beds: 375 Admissions: 17899 Census: 242 Outpatient Visits: 564900 Births: 2164 Total Expense ($000): 497678 Payroll Expense ($000): 210126 Personnel: 2784

SAME DAY SURGERY CENTER (430093), 651 Cathedral Drive, Zip 57701–7368; tel. 605/755–9900, (Nonreporting) **A**10
Primary Contact: Doris Fritts, R.N., Executive Director
Web address: www.samedaysurgerycenter.org
Control: Corporation, Investor–owned (for–profit) **Service**: Surgical

Staffed Beds: 8

REDFIELD—Spink County

COMMUNITY MEMORIAL HOSPITAL (431316), 110 West Tenth Avenue, Zip 57469–1520, Mailing Address: P.O. Box 420, Zip 57469–0420; tel. 605/472–1110, (Nonreporting) **A**10 18
Primary Contact: Tom Snyder, Interim Chief Executive Officer
CFO: William Boyer, Chief Financial Officer
CHR: Rhonda Stroh, Chief Human Resources Officer
CNO: Julene J Cass, R.N., Director of Nursing
Web address: www.redfieldcmh.org/
Control: City, Government, nonfederal **Service**: General medical and surgical

Staffed Beds: 18

ROSEBUD—Todd County

U. S. PUBLIC HEALTH SERVICE INDIAN HOSPITAL (430084), Highway 18, Soldier Creek Road, Zip 57570; tel. 605/747–2231, (Nonreporting) **A**10 **S** U. S. Indian Health Service, Rockville, MD
Primary Contact: Kathey Wilson, Acting Chief Executive Officer
COO: Romeo Vivit, Chief Surgeon
CMO: Valerie Parker, M.D., Clinical Director
CHR: Michelle Zephier, Human Resource Specialist
Web address: www.ihs.gov
Control: PHS, Indian Service, Government, federal **Service**: General medical and surgical

Staffed Beds: 35

SCOTLAND—Bon Homme County

★ **LANDMANN-JUNGMAN MEMORIAL HOSPITAL AVERA (431317)**, 600 Billars Street, Zip 57059–2026; tel. 605/583–2226, **A**10 18 **F**27 28 32 34 35 38 40 41 43 53 55 56 57 58 59 64 65 67 68 71 81 84 89 93 97 107 114 125 128 131 132 133 134 135 147 148 149 150 154 **S** Avera Health, Sioux Falls, SD
Primary Contact: Melissa Gale, Chief Executive Officer
CFO: Darcy Permann, Manager Business Office
Web address: www.ljmh.org
Control: Other not–for–profit (including NFP Corporation) **Service**: General medical and surgical

Staffed Beds: 12 Admissions: 57 Census: 1 Outpatient Visits: 3726 Births: 0 Total Expense ($000): 4733 Payroll Expense ($000): 2116 Personnel: 37

SIOUX FALLS—Lincoln County

☐ **AVERA HEART HOSPITAL OF SOUTH DAKOTA (430095)**, 4500 West 69th Street, Zip 57108–8148; tel. 605/977–7000, **A**1 5 10 **F**3 17 18 19 20 21 22 23 24 26 28 29 30 34 35 40 41 43 50 57 58 59 60 64 68 74 75 81 84 85 87 102 107 108 114 119 130 146 154 **S** Avera Health, Sioux Falls, SD
Primary Contact: Michael Gibbs, President
CFO: Jean White, Vice President Finance
Web address: www.avera.org/heart-hospital
Control: Corporation, Investor–owned (for–profit) **Service**: Heart

Staffed Beds: 53 Admissions: 2069 Census: 22 Outpatient Visits: 6820 Births: 0 Total Expense ($000): 95098 Payroll Expense ($000): 29407 Personnel: 488

SIOUX FALLS—Minnehaha County

☒ △ **AVERA MCKENNAN HOSPITAL AND UNIVERSITY HEALTH CENTER (430016)**, 1325 South Cliff Avenue, Zip 57105–1007, Mailing Address: P.O. Box 5045, Zip 57117–5045; tel. 605/322–8000, (Includes AVERA BEHAVIORAL HEALTH CENTER, 440 West 69th Street, Sioux Falls, South Dakota, Zip 57108; tel. 605/322–4065; Steve Lindquist, Assistant Vice President, Behavioral Health; AVERA CHILDREN'S HOSPITAL, 1325 South Cliff Avenue, Sioux Falls, South Dakota, Zip 57105–1016, Mailing Address: P.O. Box 5045, Zip 57117–5045, tel. 605/322–5437) (Total facility includes 114 beds in nursing home–type unit) **A**1 2 3 5 7 10 **F**3 5 7 8 11 12 13 15 18 19 20 21 22 23 24 28 29 31 32 34 35 36 38 39 40 41 42 43 44 45 46 47 48 49 50 53 54 55 56 57 58 59 60 61 64 65 66 68 70 71 72 74 75 76 77 78 79 81 82 83 84 85 86 87 88 89 90 91 92 93 94 96 97 98 99 100 101 102 103 104 105 107 108 109 110 111 112 114 115 116 117 118 119 120 121 123 124 126 127 128 129 130 131 132 134 135 136 138 139 141 142 143 144 145 146 147 148 149 152 153 154 155 156 157 **S** Avera Health, Sioux Falls, SD
Primary Contact: David Flicek, President and Chief Executive Officer
COO: Judy Blauwet, M.P.H., R.N., Senior Vice President Operations and Chief Nursing Officer
CFO: Julie Norton, Vice President, Operational Finance
CMO: Michael Elliott, M.D., Chief Medical Officer and Senior Vice President of Medical Affairs
CIO: Kristin Gross, Director Information Technology Center
CHR: Lynne D Hagen, Human Resources Officer
CNO: Judy Blauwet, M.P.H., R.N., Senior Vice President of Hospital Operations and Chief Nursing Officer
Web address: www.averamckennan.org
Control: Church operated, Nongovernment, not–for–profit **Service**: General medical and surgical

Staffed Beds: 500 Admissions: 23837 Census: 350 Outpatient Visits: 325970 Births: 2354 Total Expense ($000): 966303 Payroll Expense ($000): 404399 Personnel: 6860

LIFESCAPE (433300), 2501 West 26th Street, Zip 57105–2498; tel. 605/444–9500, (Nonreporting) **A**10
Primary Contact: Steve Watkins, Chief Executive Officer
CFO: Stephan A. Wilson, Chief Financial Officer
CMO: Christiane Maroun, M.D., Chief of Staff
CHR: Tiffany Reilly, Director Human Resources
Web address: www.cchs.org
Control: Other not–for–profit (including NFP Corporation) **Service**: Children's rehabilitation

Staffed Beds: 114

SD

Hospital, Medicare Provider Number, Address, Telephone, Approval, Facility, and Physician Codes, Health Care System

★ American Hospital Association (AHA) membership   ○ Healthcare Facilities Accreditation Program   ⇑ Center for Improvement in Healthcare Quality Accreditation
☐ The Joint Commission accreditation   ◇ DNV Healthcare Inc. accreditation   △ Commission on Accreditation of Rehabilitation Facilities (CARF) accreditation

⊞ △ **SANFORD USD MEDICAL CENTER (430027)**, 1305 West 18th Street, Zip 57105–0496, Mailing Address: P.O. Box 5039, Zip 57117–5039; tel. 605/333–1000, (Includes SANFORD CHILDREN'S HOSPITAL, 1600 West 22nd Street, Sioux Falls, South Dakota, Zip 57105, Mailing Address: P.O. Box 5039, Zip 57117–5039, tel. 605/333–1000) **A**1 2 3 5 7 8 10 **F**3 7 8 9 11 12 13 14 15 17 18 19 20 21 22 23 24 25 26 27 28 29 30 31 32 34 35 36 37 38 40 43 44 45 46 47 48 49 50 51 52 53 54 55 56 57 58 59 60 61 62 63 64 65 66 67 68 69 70 71 72 73 74 75 76 77 78 79 80 81 82 83 84 85 86 87 88 89 90 91 92 93 94 96 97 99 100 101 102 103 104 105 106 107 108 110 111 114 115 116 117 118 119 120 121 123 124 125 126 129 130 131 132 134 135 138 141 142 143 144 146 147 148 149 150 153 154 155 156 157 **S** Sanford Health, Sioux Falls, SD
Primary Contact: Paul A. Hanson, FACHE, President
COO: Brad J. Schipper, Chief Operating Officer
CFO: Merrilee Schultz, Chief Finance
CIO: Arlyn Broekhuis, Vice President and Chief Information Officer
CHR: Evan Burkett, Chief Human Resource Officer
Web address: www.sanfordhealth.org
Control: Other not–for–profit (including NFP Corporation) **Service**: General medical and surgical

Staffed Beds: 500 **Admissions**: 26433 **Census**: 306 **Outpatient Visits**: 523424 **Births**: 3119 **Total Expense ($000)**: 902917 **Payroll Expense ($000)**: 391524 **Personnel**: 5190

⊞ **SELECT SPECIALTY HOSPITAL-SIOUX FALLS (432002)**, 1305 West 18th Street, Zip 57105–0401; tel. 605/312–9500, (Nonreporting) **A**1 10 **S** Select Medical Corporation, Mechanicsburg, PA
Primary Contact: Carol Ulmer, Chief Executive Officer
CNO: Alison Anderson, Chief Nursing Officer
Web address: www.selectspecialtyhospitals.com/company/locations/siouxfalls.aspx
Control: Corporation, Investor–owned (for–profit) **Service**: Acute long–term care hospital

Staffed Beds: 24

◯ **SIOUX FALLS SPECIALTY HOSPITAL (430090)**, 910 East 20th Street, Zip 57105–1012; tel. 605/334–5123, (Nonreporting) **A**10 11
Primary Contact: R Blake. Curd, M.D., Chief Executive Officer
CFO: Kyle Goldammer, Chief Financial Officer
Web address: www.sfsurgical.com
Control: Partnership, Investor–owned (for–profit) **Service**: Surgical

Staffed Beds: 35

⊞ **SIOUX FALLS VETERANS AFFAIRS HEALTH CARE SYSTEM**, 2501 West 22nd Street, Zip 57105–1305, Mailing Address: P.O. Box 5046, Zip 57117–5046; tel. 605/336–3230, (Total facility includes 58 beds in nursing home–type unit) **A**1 3 5 **F**3 5 8 18 28 29 30 31 33 34 35 36 38 39 40 44 45 46 47 50 51 53 54 55 56 57 58 59 60 61 62 63 64 65 68 70 71 74 75 77 78 79 81 82 83 84 85 86 87 91 92 93 94 97 98 100 101 102 103 104 105 107 108 111 119 130 132 135 143 146 147 148 149 152 153 154 156 157 158 **S** Department of Veterans Affairs, Washington, DC
Primary Contact: Darwin Goodspeed, Director
COO: Sara Ackert, Associate Director
CFO: Daniel Hubbard, Chief Financial Officer
CMO: John M Wempe, M.D., Chief of Staff
CIO: Eric Heiser, Chief Information Resource Management
CHR: Betsy Geiver, Chief Human Resources Officer
CNO: Barbara Teal, R.N., Associate Director Patient Care Services and Nurse Executive
Web address: www.siouxfalls.va.gov
Control: Veterans Affairs, Government, federal **Service**: General medical and surgical

Staffed Beds: 92 **Admissions**: 2934 **Census**: 78 **Outpatient Visits**: 324000 **Births**: 0 **Total Expense ($000)**: 208752 **Payroll Expense ($000)**: 76794 **Personnel**: 1215

★ **COTEAU DES PRAIRIES HOSPITAL (431339)**, 205 Orchard Drive, Zip 57262–2398; tel. 605/698–7647, (Nonreporting) **A**10 18 **S** Sanford Health, Sioux Falls, SD
Primary Contact: Craig A. Kantos, Chief Executive Officer
COO: Greg Weaver, Chief Operating Officer
CFO: Larry Moen, Chief Financial Officer
CMO: David Staub, M.D., Chief of Staff
CIO: Cheryl Kaufman, Information Technology Technician
CHR: Leslie Hendrickson, Director Human Resources
CNO: Brenda Bostrom, Director of Nursing
Web address: www.cdphospital.com
Control: Other not–for–profit (including NFP Corporation) **Service**: General medical and surgical

Staffed Beds: 25

★ **SPEARFISH REGIONAL HOSPITAL (430048)**, 1440 North Main Street, Zip 57783–1504; tel. 605/644–4000, (Includes SPEARFISH REGIONAL SURGERY CENTER, 1316 N 10th St, Spearfish, South Dakota, Zip 57783–1530, Mailing Address: 1316 North 10th Street, Zip 57783–1530, tel. 605/642–3113) **A**10 20 **F**3 12 13 15 18 28 29 34 40 56 57 59 64 68 70 75 76 79 81 82 85 89 93 97 107 108 110 111 115 119 127 129 131 132 144 147 148 154 156 **S** Regional Health, Rapid City, SD
Primary Contact: Thomas Worsley, Chief Executive Officer
CFO: Marcia Olson, Director Finance and Controller
CMO: Christopher Gasbarre, D.O., Community Medical Director
CIO: Richard Latuchie, Chief Information Officer
CHR: Patsy Aiken, Coordinator Human Resource
CNO: Suzanne Campbell, R.N., Director Patient Services
Web address: www.regionalhealth.com/Our-Locations/Regional-Hospitals/Spearfish-Regional-Hospital.aspx
Control: Other not–for–profit (including NFP Corporation) **Service**: General medical and surgical

Staffed Beds: 35 **Admissions**: 1496 **Census**: 8 **Outpatient Visits**: 149578 **Births**: 462 **Total Expense ($000)**: 86299 **Payroll Expense ($000)**: 38994 **Personnel**: 445

★ **STURGIS REGIONAL HOSPITAL (431321)**, 949 Harmon Street, Zip 57785–2452; tel. 605/720–2400, (Total facility includes 84 beds in nursing home–type unit) **A**10 18 **F**15 28 29 40 43 70 77 81 82 93 107 111 115 119 128 130 133 144 148 149 156 **S** Regional Health, Rapid City, SD
Primary Contact: Mark Schulte, FACHE, President
CFO: Jodie Mitchell, Facility Financial Director
CMO: Constance Stock, M.D., Chief Medical Officer
CHR: Ginger Chord, Coordinator Human Resources
CNO: Rikki Plaggemeyer, Director Acute Care Nursing
Web address: www.regionalhealth.org/Our-Locations/Regional-Hospitals/Sturgis-Regional-Hospital.aspx
Control: Other not–for–profit (including NFP Corporation) **Service**: General medical and surgical

Staffed Beds: 109 **Admissions**: 709 **Census**: 81 **Births**: 0 **Total Expense ($000)**: 26450 **Payroll Expense ($000)**: 11702 **Personnel**: 208

★ **ST. MICHAEL'S HOSPITAL AVERA (431327)**, 410 West 16th Avenue, Zip 57066–2318; tel. 605/589–2152, **A**10 18 **F**3 15 28 31 34 40 43 45 53 57 59 64 65 67 70 75 77 81 86 89 92 93 94 107 110 114 119 127 128 129 131 133 148 154 **S** Avera Health, Sioux Falls, SD
Primary Contact: Carol Deurmier, Chief Executive Officer
CFO: Lisa Ronke, Director Finance
CMO: Melvin Wallinga, M.D., Medical Director
Web address: www.stmichaels-bhfp.org
Control: Church operated, Nongovernment, not–for–profit **Service**: General medical and surgical

Staffed Beds: 25 **Admissions**: 212 **Census**: 5 **Births**: 0

★ **SANFORD VERMILLION MEDICAL CENTER (431336)**, 20 South Plum Street, Zip 57069–3346; tel. 605/677–3500, (Total facility includes 95 beds in nursing home–type unit) **A**10 18 **F**10 15 28 29 31 34 35 40 43 45 57 59 67 76 81 91 92 93 97 107 110 111 114 116 119 129 130 131 132 133 135 148 149 156 **S** Sanford Health, Sioux Falls, SD
Primary Contact: Timothy J. Tracy, Senior Director
CFO: Valerie Osterberg, Chief Financial Officer
CMO: Roy Mortinsen, M.D., Chief of Staff
CIO: Mary C Merrigan, Manager Public Relations
CHR: Cindy Benzel, Manager Human Resources
CNO: Jeff Berens, MS, Chief Nursing Officer
Web address: www.sanfordvermillion.org
Control: Other not–for–profit (including NFP Corporation) **Service**: General medical and surgical

Staffed Beds: 120 **Admissions**: 462 **Census**: 68 **Outpatient Visits**: 38580 **Births**: 76 **Total Expense ($000)**: 23150 **Payroll Expense ($000)**: 11247 **Personnel**: 210

SD

VIBORG—Turner County

★ **PIONEER MEMORIAL HOSPITAL AND HEALTH SERVICES (431328)**, 315 North Washington Street, Zip 57070–2002, Mailing Address: P.O. Box 368, Zip 57070–0368; tel. 605/326–5161, (Total facility includes 52 beds in nursing home–type unit) **A**10 18 **F**6 10 15 28 30 34 40 43 45 53 56 57 59 63 65 69 75 79 81 87 97 107 111 119 125 127 128 130 132 133 154 156 158 **S** Sanford Health, Sioux Falls, SD
Primary Contact: Thomas V. Richter, Chief Executive Officer
CFO: Anne Christiansen, Chief Financial Officer
CMO: Syed Shah, M.D., Chief of Staff
Web address: www.pioneermemorial.org
Control: Other not–for–profit (including NFP Corporation) **Service:** General medical and surgical

> **Staffed Beds: 64 Admissions: 155 Census: 44 Outpatient Visits: 20007 Births: 0 Total Expense ($000): 10806 Payroll Expense ($000): 6165 Personnel: 136**

WAGNER—Charles Mix County

★ **WAGNER COMMUNITY MEMORIAL HOSPITAL AVERA (431315)**, 513 Third Street SW, Zip 57380–9675, Mailing Address: P.O. Box 280, Zip 57380–0280; tel. 605/384–3611, **A**10 18 **F**3 11 28 31 34 40 43 45 57 59 64 67 70 77 81 93 97 107 114 119 128 130 133 148 154 **S** Avera Health, Sioux Falls, SD
Primary Contact: Bryan Slaba, Chief Executive Officer
CFO: Lisa Weisser, Supervisor Finance
CHR: Marcia Podzimek, Chief Human Resources Officer
Web address: www.avera.org/wagnerhospital
Control: Other not–for–profit (including NFP Corporation) **Service:** General medical and surgical

> **Staffed Beds: 20 Admissions: 116 Census: 1 Outpatient Visits: 8454 Births: 0 Total Expense ($000): 8684 Payroll Expense ($000): 3795 Personnel: 72**

WATERTOWN—Codington County

★ **PRAIRIE LAKES HEALTHCARE SYSTEM (430005)**, 401 9th Avenue NW, Zip 57201–1548, Mailing Address: P.O. Box 1210, Zip 57201–6210; tel. 605/882–7000, **A**10 20 **F**3 8 12 13 18 20 22 28 29 30 31 34 35 38 40 43 48 50 57 58 59 60 62 63 64 75 76 77 78 79 80 81 82 83 84 85 87 89 93 107 111 114 115 118 119 120 121 123 130 132 133 146 148 154
Primary Contact: K. C. DeBoer, President and Chief Executive Officer
COO: Traci Rabine, Vice President Clinic Operations
CFO: Adam Paul, Chief Financial Officer
CMO: Henri Lanctin, M.D., Chief of Staff
CIO: Grant Tillett, Chief Information Officer
CHR: Nathan Lake, Vice President Human Resources
CNO: Shelly Turbak, R.N., Chief Nursing Officer
Web address: www.prairielakes.com
Control: Other not–for–profit (including NFP Corporation) **Service:** General medical and surgical

> **Staffed Beds: 79 Admissions: 2674 Census: 22 Outpatient Visits: 97051 Births: 632 Total Expense ($000): 92470 Payroll Expense ($000): 42226 Personnel: 801**

WEBSTER—Day County

★ **SANFORD WEBSTER MEDICAL CENTER (431311)**, 1401 West 1st Street, Zip 57274–1054, Mailing Address: P.O. Box 489, Zip 57274–0489; tel. 605/345–3336, **A**10 18 **F**28 29 31 32 34 35 40 43 53 56 57 59 61 64 65 67 75 81 85 89 90 93 94 97 107 110 115 119 127 128 130 132 133 144 146 **S** Sanford Health, Sioux Falls, SD
Primary Contact: Isaac Gerdes, Chief Executive Officer
CFO: Sheryl L Pappas, Chief Financial Officer
Web address: www.sanfordhealth.org
Control: Other not–for–profit (including NFP Corporation) **Service:** General medical and surgical

> **Staffed Beds: 20 Admissions: 161 Census: 2 Outpatient Visits: 14260 Births: 0 Total Expense ($000): 7718 Payroll Expense ($000): 3769 Personnel: 61**

SANFORD WEBSTER MEDICAL CENTER See Sanford Webster Medical Center

WESSINGTON SPRINGS—Jerauld County

★ **AVERA WESKOTA MEMORIAL HOSPITAL (431324)**, 604 First Street NE, Zip 57382–2166; tel. 605/539–1201, **A**10 18 **F**3 15 28 34 35 40 53 57 59 64 75 77 85 93 107 114 119 128 130 131 133 **S** Avera Health, Sioux Falls, SD
Primary Contact: Stephanie Reasy, Administrator and Chief Executive Officer
CFO: Linda Jager, Director Finance
CMO: Thomas Dean, M.D., Chief of Staff
CNO: JoAnn Hettinger, R.N., Director of Patient Care Services
Web address: www.averaweskota.org
Control: Other not–for–profit (including NFP Corporation) **Service:** General medical and surgical

> **Staffed Beds: 23 Admissions: 82 Census: 1 Outpatient Visits: 4297 Births: 0 Total Expense ($000): 3721 Payroll Expense ($000): 1582 Personnel: 21**

WINNER—Tripp County

★ **WINNER REGIONAL HEALTHCARE CENTER (431334)**, 745 East Eighth Street, Zip 57580–2631; tel. 605/842–7100, (Nonreporting) **A**10 18 **S** Sanford Health, Sioux Falls, SD
Primary Contact: Kevin Coffey, Chief Executive Officer
COO: Debra K. Davis, Director of Operations
CFO: Phil Husher, Chief Financial Officer
CMO: Tony L. Berg, M.D., Chief of Staff
CIO: Gary Burrus, Director Information Technology
CHR: Susan Hughes, Interim Director Human Resources
CNO: Julie Hennebold, R.N., Interim Chief Nursing Officer
Web address: www.winnerregional.org
Control: Other not–for–profit (including NFP Corporation) **Service:** General medical and surgical

> **Staffed Beds: 104**

YANKTON—Yankton County

⊠ **AVERA SACRED HEART HOSPITAL (430012)**, 501 Summit Avenue, Zip 57078–3855; tel. 605/668–8000, (Total facility includes 187 beds in nursing home–type unit) **A**1 2 3 5 10 **F**2 3 6 8 10 13 15 18 20 28 29 30 31 34 35 39 40 43 45 46 47 48 53 57 59 60 63 64 70 71 73 75 76 77 78 79 81 82 84 85 86 87 89 91 93 96 97 100 104 107 108 110 111 114 115 118 119 120 121 125 128 129 130 131 132 133 146 147 148 154 156 **S** Avera Health, Sioux Falls, SD
Primary Contact: Douglas R. Ekeren, Regional President and Chief Executive Officer
CFO: Jamie Schaefer, Vice President Finance
CIO: Kathy Quinlivan, Director Management Information Systems
CHR: Jane E. Miller, Human Resources Officer
CNO: Lindsay Flannery, R.N., Vice President Patient Care Services
Web address: www.averasacredheart.com
Control: Church operated, Nongovernment, not–for–profit **Service:** General medical and surgical

> **Staffed Beds: 286 Admissions: 3548 Census: 210 Outpatient Visits: 79731 Births: 638 Total Expense ($000): 84358 Payroll Expense ($000): 38648 Personnel: 670**

LEWIS AND CLARK SPECIALTY HOSPITAL (430096), 2601 Fox Run Parkway, Zip 57078–5341; tel. 605/665–5100, (Nonreporting) **A**10
Primary Contact: Douglas Doorn, Chief Executive Officer
CFO: Terry Steichen, Business Officer
CHR: Elizabeth Steichen, Human Resources
Web address: www.lewisandclarkspecialty.com
Control: Corporation, Investor–owned (for–profit) **Service:** Surgical

> **Staffed Beds: 6**

TENNESSEE

TN

ASHLAND CITY—Cheatham County

⊞ **TRISTAR ASHLAND CITY MEDICAL CENTER (441311)**, 313 North Main Street, Zip 37015–1347; tel. 615/792–3030, (Nonreporting) **A**1 10 18 **S** HCA Healthcare, Nashville, TN
Primary Contact: Darrell White, R.N., Administrator and Chief Nursing Officer
CFO: Joe Bowman, Chief Financial Officer
CMO: Divya Shroff, Chief Medical Officer
CIO: David Archer, Director Information Systems
CNO: Darrell White, R.N., Administrator and Chief Nursing Officer
Web address: www.tristarashlandcity.com/
Control: Corporation, Investor–owned (for–profit) **Service**: General medical and surgical

Staffed Beds: 12

ATHENS—Mcminn County

⊞ **STARR REGIONAL MEDICAL CENTER (440068)**, 1114 West Madison Avenue, Zip 37303–4150, Mailing Address: P.O. Box 250, Zip 37371–0250; tel. 423/745–1411, (Nonreporting) **A**1 3 5 10 **S** LifePoint Health, Brentwood, TN
Primary Contact: John R. McLain, Chief Executive Officer
COO: Michael Herr, Chief Operating Officer
CFO: David Alley, Chief Financial Officer
Web address: www.starrregional.com
Control: Corporation, Investor–owned (for–profit) **Service**: General medical and surgical

Staffed Beds: 63

BARTLETT—Shelby County

⊞ **SAINT FRANCIS HOSPITAL-BARTLETT (440228)**, 2986 Kate Bond Road, Zip 38133–4003; tel. 901/820–7000, **A**1 10 **F**3 11 13 15 18 20 22 29 30 31 34 35 38 40 45 46 49 50 54 57 59 64 70 72 74 75 76 77 78 79 81 85 86 87 93 102 107 108 110 111 115 118 119 126 130 131 132 142 146 147 148 149 **S** TENET Healthcare Corporation, Dallas, TX
Primary Contact: Christopher Locke, Chief Executive Officer
COO: Gwen Bonner, Chief Operating Officer
CFO: Tina Kovacs, Chief Financial Officer
CMO: David Schwartz, M.D., Chief Medical Officer
CIO: Mark Lawrence, Director Information Systems
CHR: Adrienne Huntley, Chief Human Resources Officer
CNO: Kris Cherry, Ph.D., R.N., Chief Nursing Officer
Web address: www.saintfrancisbartlett.com
Control: Corporation, Investor–owned (for–profit) **Service**: General medical and surgical

Staffed Beds: 156 Admissions: 7950 Census: 99 Outpatient Visits: 67287 Births: 334 Total Expense ($000): 111501 Payroll Expense ($000): 37440 Personnel: 584

BOLIVAR—Hardeman County

⊞ **BOLIVAR GENERAL HOSPITAL (440181)**, 650 Nuckolls Road, Zip 38008–1532, Mailing Address: P.O. Box 509, Zip 38008–0509; tel. 731/658–3100, **A**1 **F**3 15 29 30 35 40 44 45 57 59 64 75 81 87 93 107 119 130 132 133 146 149 **S** West Tennessee Healthcare, Jackson, TN
Primary Contact: Ruby Kirby, Administrator
CFO: Terry Swindell, Controller
CMO: Felix Nnaji, Chief Medical Staff
CNO: Angela Lacy, Director of Nursing
Web address: www.wth.net
Control: Hospital district or authority, Government, nonfederal **Service**: General medical and surgical

Staffed Beds: 25 Admissions: 203 Census: 2 Outpatient Visits: 15043 Births: 0 Total Expense ($000): 6929 Payroll Expense ($000): 2774 Personnel: 51

☐ **WESTERN MENTAL HEALTH INSTITUTE (444008)**, 11100 Old Highway 64, West, Zip 38008–1554; tel. 731/228–2000, (Nonreporting) **A**1 10
Primary Contact: Roger Pursley, Chief Executive Officer
CFO: Richard Taylor, Chief Financial Officer
CMO: Doug King, M.D., Director Clinical Services
CIO: Earl Bates, Director Information Technology
CHR: Barry Young, Director Human Resources
Control: State, Government, nonfederal **Service**: Psychiatric

Staffed Beds: 247

BRISTOL—Sullivan County

⊞ **BRISTOL REGIONAL MEDICAL CENTER (440012)**, 1 Medical Park Boulevard, Zip 37620–7430; tel. 423/844–1121, **A**1 2 3 5 10 19 **F**3 8 11 13 15 17 18 20 22 24 28 29 30 31 34 35 37 38 39 40 43 44 45 46 47 48 49 51 54 56 57 58 59 60 61 62 63 64 70 73 74 75 76 77 78 79 81 82 83 84 85 86 87 91 92 93 94 96 97 98 100 102 107 108 110 111 114 115 117 118 119 120 121 123 124 126 129 130 131 132 135 144 145 146 147 148 149 154 157 **S** Ballad Health, Johnson City, TN
Primary Contact: Greg Neal, FACHE, President
COO: Christopher Brian Hobson, Chief Operating Officer
CFO: Bob Bender, Vice-President Hospital Finance and Operations
CMO: Chad Couch, Chief Medical Officer
CIO: Martha O'Regan Chill, Chief Information Officer
CHR: Hamlin J Wilson, Senior Vice President Human Resources
CNO: Timothy Craig Anderson Jr Chief Nursing Officer
Web address: www.wellmont.org
Control: Other not–for–profit (including NFP Corporation) **Service**: General medical and surgical

Staffed Beds: 306 Admissions: 16884 Census: 200 Outpatient Visits: 320238 Births: 825 Total Expense ($000): 236099 Payroll Expense ($000): 76455 Personnel: 1575

⊞ **SELECT SPECIALTY HOSPITAL-TRI CITIES (442016)**, One Medical Park Boulevard, 5th Floor, Zip 37620–8964; tel. 423/844–5900, (Nonreporting) **A**1 10 **S** Select Medical Corporation, Mechanicsburg, PA
Primary Contact: Jeffrey Radford, Chief Executive Officer
CMO: John Byers, M.D., Medical Director
CHR: William G Ison, Human Resources Manager
CNO: Valerie Anderson, Chief Nursing Officer
Web address: www.tricities.selectspecialtyhospitals.com/
Control: Corporation, Investor–owned (for–profit) **Service**: Acute long–term care hospital

Staffed Beds: 33

CAMDEN—Benton County

⊞ **CAMDEN GENERAL HOSPITAL (441316)**, 175 Hospital Drive, Zip 38320–1617; tel. 731/593–6300, **A**1 10 18 **F**3 15 29 30 35 40 44 57 59 64 75 79 81 85 87 93 107 111 119 130 132 133 146 149 **S** West Tennessee Healthcare, Jackson, TN
Primary Contact: Scott Barber, Vice President
CFO: Terry Swindell, Chief Financial Officer
CMO: Jon R. Winter, D.O., Chief of Staff
CIO: Jeff Frieling, Vice President Information Systems
CHR: Barry Phillips, Executive Director Human Resources
Web address: www.wth.net
Control: Hospital district or authority, Government, nonfederal **Service**: General medical and surgical

Staffed Beds: 25 Admissions: 321 Census: 4 Outpatient Visits: 12051 Births: 0 Total Expense ($000): 8001 Payroll Expense ($000): 3191 Personnel: 62

CARTHAGE—Smith County

⊞ **RIVERVIEW REGIONAL MEDICAL CENTER (441307)**, 158 Hospital Drive, Zip 37030–1096; tel. 615/735–1560, (Nonreporting) **A**1 10 18 **S** LifePoint Health, Brentwood, TN
Primary Contact: Michael Herman, Chief Executive Officer
CHR: Gina Anderson, Human Resources Officer
CNO: Patricia Anderson, Chief Nursing Officer
Web address: www.myriverviewmedical.com/
Control: Corporation, Investor–owned (for–profit) **Service**: General medical and surgical

Staffed Beds: 35

CENTERVILLE—Hickman County

☒ **SAINT THOMAS HICKMAN HOSPITAL (441300)**, 135 East Swan Street,
Zip 37033–1417; tel. 931/729–4271, (Nonreporting) **A**1 10 18 **S** Ascension
Healthcare, Saint Louis, MO
Primary Contact: Kevin Campbell, Chief Executive Officer
COO: Robin Crowell, Chief Nursing Officer and Chief Operating Officer
CMO: Zachary Hutchens, M.D., Chief Medical Officer
CHR: Patty Matney, Human Resources Consultant
CNO: Robin Crowell, Chief Nursing Officer and Chief Operating Officer
Web address: www.sths.com/hickman
Control: Church operated **Service:** General medical and surgical

Staffed Beds: 65

CHATTANOOGA—Hamilton County

☒ **CHI MEMORIAL (440091)**, 2525 De Sales Avenue, Zip 37404–1161;
tel. 423/495–2525, (Includes MEMORIAL HOSPITAL HIXSON, 2051 Hamill Road,
Hixson, Tennessee, Zip 37343–4026; tel. 423/495–7100; Larry P Schumacher,
R.N., MSN, Chief Executive Officer) **A**1 2 3 10 **F**3 7 8 11 12 15 17 18 20 22 24
26 28 29 30 31 34 35 36 37 40 44 45 46 47 48 49 50 53 54 55 56 57 58 59
60 61 64 67 68 70 71 74 75 77 78 79 80 82 84 85 86 87 93 107 108 109
110 111 114 115 116 117 118 119 120 121 124 126 129 130 132 135 145
146 147 148 149 150 154 156 **S** CommonSpirit Health, Chicago, IL
Primary Contact: Janelle Reilly, Chief Executive Officer
COO: Anthony Houston, FACHE, Chief Operating Officer
CFO: Michael Sutton, Chief Financial Officer
CMO: Helen Kuroki, Senior Vice President and Chief Medical Officer
CHR: Brad W Pope, Vice President Human Resources
CNO: Rhonda Poulson, Chief Nursing Officer and Vice President of Clinical Operations
Web address: www.memorial.org
Control: Church operated, Nongovernment, not–for–profit **Service:** General
medical and surgical

Staffed Beds: 405 Admissions: 23214 Census: 307 Outpatient
Visits: 396585 Births: 0 Total Expense ($000): 508267 Payroll Expense
($000): 147907 Personnel: 2672

☒ **ENCOMPASS HEALTH REHABILITATION HOSPITAL OF CHATTANOOGA
(443032)**, 2412 McCallie Avenue, Zip 37404–3398; tel. 423/698–0221,
(Nonreporting) **A**1 10 **S** Encompass Health Corporation, Birmingham, AL
Primary Contact: Scott Rowe, Chief Executive Officer
COO: Scott Rowe, Chief Executive Officer
CFO: Karen Klassen, Controller
CMO: Amjad Munir, M.D., Medical Director
CIO: Denise Smith, Director Health Information
CHR: Rebekah McNair, Director Human Resources
CNO: Cinthia Campbell, Chief Nursing Officer
Web address: www.healthsouthchattanooga.com
Control: Corporation, Investor–owned (for–profit) **Service:** Rehabilitation

Staffed Beds: 69

★ ⇑ **ERLANGER MEDICAL CENTER (440104)**, 975 East Third Street,
Zip 37403–2147; tel. 423/778–7000, (Includes ERLANGER EAST HOSPITAL,
1755 Gunbarrel Road, Chattanooga, Tennessee, Zip 37421; tel. 423/778–8700;
Phillip E. Jackson, Vice President & CEO; ERLANGER NORTH HOSPITAL, 632
Morrison Springs Road, Chattanooga, Tennessee, Zip 37415; tel. 615/778–3300;
Phillip E. Jackson, Vice President and CEO; T. C. THOMPSON CHILDREN'S
HOSPITAL, 910 Blackford Street, Chattanooga, Tennessee, Zip 37403;
tel. 615/778–6011; Donald Mueller, Vice President and CEO; WILLIE D. MILLER
EYE CENTER, 975 East Third Street, Chattanooga, Tennessee, Zip 37403;
tel. 615/778–6011) **A**2 5 8 10 21 **F**3 8 9 11 12 13 14 15 17 18 19 20 21 22
23 24 25 26 27 28 29 30 31 32 34 35 37 38 39 40 41 42 43 44 45 46 47 48
49 50 51 52 53 54 55 56 57 58 59 60 61 62 64 65 66 68 70 71 72 73 74 75
76 77 78 79 80 81 82 83 84 85 86 87 88 89 92 93 96 97 98 99 100 101 102
103 107 108 109 110 111 112 114 116 117 118 119 120 121 123 124 126
127 129 130 131 132 133 134 135 136 138 141 142 144 145 146 147 148
149 150 154 155 156 157 **S** Erlanger Health System, Chattanooga, TN
Primary Contact: Kevin M. Spiegel, Chief Executive Officer
CFO: J. Britton Tabor, Executive Vice President, Chief Financial Officer
CMO: William L. Jackson, M.D., Jr Executive Vice President, Chief Medical Officer
CIO: David Peterson, Senior Vice President, Chief Technology Officer
CHR: Floyd Chasse, Vice President Human Resources
CNO: Janice C. Keys, Senior Vice President, Chief Nurse Executive
Web address: www.erlanger.org
Control: Hospital district or authority, Government, nonfederal **Service:** General
medical and surgical

Staffed Beds: 788 Admissions: 39282 Census: 521 Outpatient
Visits: 824117 Births: 5436 Total Expense ($000): 931354 Payroll
Expense ($000): 383548 Personnel: 5904

ERLANGER WOMEN'S EAST HOSPITAL See Erlanger East Hospital

☒ **KINDRED HOSPITAL-CHATTANOOGA (442007)**, 709 Walnut Street,
Zip 37402–1916; tel. 423/266–7721, (Nonreporting) **A**1 10 **S** Kindred
Healthcare, Louisville, KY
Primary Contact: Andrea White, Chief Executive Officer
COO: Rick Rheinheimer, Chief Clinical Officer
CFO: Julia Smith, Chief Financial Officer
CMO: Randy Heisser, M.D., Medical Director
CHR: Kellie McCampbell, Coordinator Human Resources
CNO: Gigi Johnson, Chief Nursing Officer
Web address: www.kindredchattanooga.com/
Control: Corporation, Investor–owned (for–profit) **Service:** Acute long–term care
hospital

Staffed Beds: 39

☐ **MOCCASIN BEND MENTAL HEALTH INSTITUTE (444002)**, 100 Moccasin
Bend Road, Zip 37405–4415; tel. 423/265–2271, **A**1 10 **F**34 57 59 65 75 77
86 98 101 102 130 135
Primary Contact: Mary C. Young, Chief Executive Officer
CFO: Sylvia Harris, Fiscal Director
CMO: Terry R Holmes, M.D., Clinical Director
CIO: Mickey Williams, Manager Information Technology
CHR: Cynthia Honeycutt, Director Human Resources
CNO: Charlynne Parson, Nurse Executive
Web address: www.state.tn.us/mental/mhs/mbhmhi/moc.htm
Control: State, Government, nonfederal **Service:** Psychiatric

Staffed Beds: 165 Admissions: 2866 Census: 139 Outpatient Visits: 0
Births: 0 Total Expense ($000): 39778 Payroll Expense ($000): 20699
Personnel: 482

☒ **PARKRIDGE MEDICAL CENTER (440156)**, 2333 McCallie Avenue,
Zip 37404–3258; tel. 423/698–6061, (Includes EAST RIDGE HOSPITAL, 941
Spring Creek Road, East Ridge, Tennessee, Zip 37412, Mailing Address: P
O Box 91229, Zip 37412–6229, tel. 423/855–3500; Jarrett B. Millsaps Jr,
FACHE, Chief Executive Officer; PARKRIDGE EAST HOSPITAL, 941 Spring Creek
Road, Chattanooga, Tennessee, Zip 37412–3909; tel. 423/894–7870; Jarrett
B. Millsaps Jr, FACHE, Chief Executive Officer; PARKRIDGE VALLEY CHILD AND
ADOLESCENT CAMPUS, 2200 Morris Hill Road, Chattanooga, Tennessee,
Zip 37421; tel. 423/894–4220; Melissa Arkin, Chief Executive Officer; PARKRIDGE
WEST HOSPITAL, 1000 Highway 28, Jasper, Tennessee, Zip 37347–3000,
tel. 423/837–9500; Shirley K Scarlatti, Associate Chief Nursing Officer), (Non-
reporting) **A**1 2 3 5 10 **S** HCA Healthcare, Nashville, TN
Primary Contact: Thomas H. Ozburn, Chief Executive Officer
COO: Jim L Coleman Jr Chief Operating Officer
CMO: Timothy M. Grant, M.D., Chief Medical Officer
CIO: David Cornelius, Director Information Systems
CHR: Carole Hoffman, Vice President
CNO: Jerri C Underwood, R.N., Chief Nursing Officer
Web address: www.parkridgemedicalcenter.com
Control: Corporation, Investor–owned (for–profit) **Service:** General medical and
surgical

Staffed Beds: 464

☒ △ **SISKIN HOSPITAL FOR PHYSICAL REHABILITATION (443025)**, One
Siskin Plaza, Zip 37403–1306; tel. 423/634–1200, (Nonreporting) **A**1 7 10
Primary Contact: Carol Sim, President and Chief Executive Officer
CFO: Carol Arnhart, Vice President Finance and Chief Financial Officer
CMO: David N Bowers, M.D., Medical Director
CIO: Shane Pilcher, Administrative Director Information Systems
CHR: Kristi Delaney, Director, Human Resources
CNO: Tracy Collings Reed, Vice President Patient Care Services, Chief Nursing Officer
Web address: www.siskinrehab.org
Control: Other not–for–profit (including NFP Corporation) **Service:** Rehabilitation

Staffed Beds: 195

T. C. THOMPSON CHILDREN'S HOSPITAL See Erlanger Medical Center,
Chattanooga

Hospital, Medicare Provider Number, Address, Telephone, Approval, Facility, and Physician Codes, Health Care System

★ American Hospital Association (AHA) membership   ○ Healthcare Facilities Accreditation Program   ⇑ Center for Improvement in Healthcare Quality Accreditation
☐ The Joint Commission accreditation   ◇ DNV Healthcare Inc. accreditation   △ Commission on Accreditation of Rehabilitation Facilities (CARF) accreditation

CLARKSVILLE—Montgomery County

⊠ **TENNOVA HEALTHCARE-CLARKSVILLE (440035)**, 651 Dunlop Lane, Zip 37040–5015, Mailing Address: P.O. Box 31629, Zip 37040–0028; tel. 931/502–1000, (Nonreporting) **A**1 10 19 **S** Community Health Systems, Inc., Franklin, TN
Primary Contact: Alex Villa, Chief Executive Officer
CFO: George Sprinkel, Chief Financial Officer
CMO: Thomas L Ely, D.O., Chief Medical Officer
CIO: Scott Greene, Chief Information Officer
CHR: Liza Edmunds, Director Human Resources
CNO: Faye Perry, Chief Nursing Officer
Web address: www.tennova.com/
Control: Partnership, Investor–owned (for–profit) **Service**: General medical and surgical

Staffed Beds: 247

UNITY PSYCHIATRIC CARE-CLARKSVILLE (444019), 930 Professional Park Drive, Zip 37040–5136; tel. 931/538–6420, (Nonreporting) **A**10 **S** Tennessee Health Management, Parsons, TN
Primary Contact: Jennifer Robinson, Administrator
CMO: Michael McGhee, M.D., Medical Director
CNO: Chrissy Myers, R.N., Director of Nursing
Web address: www.unitypsych.com
Control: Partnership, Investor–owned (for–profit) **Service**: Psychiatric

Staffed Beds: 26

CLEVELAND—Bradley County

⊠ **TENNOVA HEALTHCARE - CLEVELAND (440185)**, 2305 Chambliss Avenue NW, Zip 37311–3847, Mailing Address: P.O. Box 3060, Zip 37320–3060; tel. 423/559–6000, (Includes SKYRIDGE MEDICAL CENTER - WESTSIDE CAMPUS, 2800 Westside Drive NW, Cleveland, Tennessee, Zip 37312–3599; tel. 423/339–4100; R Coleman Foss, Chief Executive Officer) **A**1 3 10 **F**3 5 13 15 18 20 22 28 29 30 31 34 35 39 40 41 44 45 46 49 50 51 57 59 60 68 70 73 74 75 76 77 78 79 81 82 85 87 89 93 98 100 101 102 104 107 108 110 111 114 115 119 126 129 135 136 141 146 148 149 153 154 **S** Community Health Systems, Inc., Franklin, TN
Primary Contact: J. T. Barnhart, Chief Executive Officer
CFO: H. Wes Griffith, Chief Financial Officer
CMO: William F Johnson, Chief Medical Officer
CHR: Kristine Godfrey, Director Human Resources
Web address: www.skyridgemedicalcenter.net
Control: Corporation, Investor–owned (for–profit) **Service**: General medical and surgical

Staffed Beds: 186 **Admissions**: 9156 **Census**: 108 **Outpatient Visits**: 94252 **Births**: 1095 **Total Expense ($000)**: 130703 **Payroll Expense ($000)**: 47004 **Personnel**: 841

COLLIERVILLE—Shelby County

★ **BAPTIST MEMORIAL HOSPITAL-COLLIERVILLE (440217)**, 1500 West Poplar Avenue, Zip 38017–0601; tel. 901/861–9400, **A**5 **F**3 7 8 12 15 18 29 30 34 35 36 38 40 41 45 46 47 48 49 50 53 57 58 59 60 61 64 65 68 70 74 75 77 79 80 81 84 85 87 91 92 93 96 107 108 109 110 111 114 115 119 120 129 130 132 135 146 147 148 149 154 **S** Baptist Memorial Health Care Corporation, Memphis, TN
Primary Contact: Lindsay Stencel, Chief Administrative Officer
CFO: Terri Seago, Chief Financial Officer
CIO: Doug Reiselt, Vice President and Chief Information Officer
CHR: Brenda Johnson, Director Human Resources
CNO: Denise Ferguson, Chief Nursing Officer
Web address: www.baptistonline.org/collierville/
Control: Other not–for–profit (including NFP Corporation) **Service**: General medical and surgical

Staffed Beds: 51 **Admissions**: 3127 **Census**: 24 **Outpatient Visits**: 37077 **Births**: 0 **Total Expense ($000)**: 55541 **Payroll Expense ($000)**: 17847 **Personnel**: 271

COLUMBIA—Maury County

⊠ **MAURY REGIONAL HOSPITAL (440073)**, 1224 Trotwood Avenue, Zip 38401–4802; tel. 931/381–1111, **A**1 2 10 19 **F**3 7 8 11 13 15 18 20 22 26 28 29 30 31 34 35 37 38 40 41 44 45 46 47 48 49 50 51 53 54 55 57 58 59 60 62 64 68 70 71 73 74 75 76 77 78 79 80 81 82 84 85 86 87 89 91 92 93 96 102 107 108 110 111 114 115 116 117 118 119 120 121 123 124 126 129 130 131 132 135 146 147 149 154 **S** Maury Regional Health System, Columbia, TN
Primary Contact: H Alan. Watson, FACHE, Chief Executive Officer
COO: Kenneth Boyd, Chief Operating Officer
CFO: Nick Swift, Chief Financial Officer
CIO: Jim Parcel, Director Information Technology
CHR: Kaye Brewer, Chief Human Resources Officer
CNO: Deborah Lumpkins, MSN, Chief Nursing Officer
Web address: www.mauryregional.com
Control: County, Government, nonfederal **Service**: General medical and surgical

Staffed Beds: 219 **Admissions**: 12640 **Census**: 138 **Outpatient Visits**: 256235 **Births**: 1493 **Total Expense ($000)**: 291074 **Payroll Expense ($000)**: 111774 **Personnel**: 2293

UNITY PSYCHIATRIC CARE-COLUMBIA (440230), 1400 Rosewood Drive, Zip 38401–4878; tel. 931/388–6573, (Nonreporting) **S** Tennessee Health Management, Parsons, TN
Primary Contact: Paula Chennault, Administrator
CMO: Rodney Poling, M.D., Medical Director
CHR: Pam Brown, Human Resources Manager
CNO: Sheila Ridner, R.N., Director of Nursing
Web address: www.unitypsych.com
Control: Partnership, Investor–owned (for–profit) **Service**: Psychiatric

Staffed Beds: 16

COOKEVILLE—Putnam County

⊠ **COOKEVILLE REGIONAL MEDICAL CENTER (440059)**, 1 Medical Center Boulevard, Zip 38501–4294; tel. 931/783–2000, (Nonreporting) **A**1 2 10 19
Primary Contact: Paul Korth, Chief Executive Officer
COO: Scott Williams, Chief Operating Officer
CFO: Paul Korth, Chief Financial Officer
CMO: Jeffrey J Gleason, M.D., Chief Medical Officer
CIO: Les Bernstein, Chief Information Officer
CHR: Angela Lewis, Senior Vice President Administration
CNO: Linda Crawford, R.N., MSN, Chief Nursing Officer
Web address: www.crmhealth.org
Control: City, Government, nonfederal **Service**: General medical and surgical

Staffed Beds: 243

⇑ **TEN BROECK TENNESSEE TREATMENT FACILITY (444022)**, 1 Medical Center Boulevard, 5 West, Zip 38501; tel. 931/783–2570, **A**10 21 **F**4 5 98 101 103 104 105 151 152 153 **S** United Medical Corporation, Windermere, FL
Primary Contact: Kelly Tripp, Chief Executive Officer
CFO: David Corddry, Chief Financial Officer
CMO: Glenn T. Webb, M.D., Medical Director
CHR: Glenda Guy, Director, Health Information Management
CNO: Annasue Collins, Chief Nursing Officer
Web address: www.tenbroeck.com
Control: Corporation, Investor–owned (for–profit) **Service**: Psychiatric

Staffed Beds: 38 **Admissions**: 1708 **Census**: 25 **Outpatient Visits**: 335 **Births**: 0

COVINGTON—Tipton County

⊠ **BAPTIST MEMORIAL HOSPITAL-TIPTON (440131)**, 1995 Highway 51 South, Zip 38019–3635; tel. 901/476–2621, **A**1 10 **F**3 11 15 29 30 31 34 35 40 45 55 57 58 59 65 70 74 75 76 78 79 81 85 87 89 93 100 107 108 110 111 114 115 119 120 121 130 146 148 154 **S** Baptist Memorial Health Care Corporation, Memphis, TN
Primary Contact: Samuel Lynd, Administrator and Chief Executive Officer
CFO: Monique Hart, Chief Financial Officer
CMO: Kenneth Afenya, M.D., Chief of Staff
CHR: Myra Cousar, Director Human Resources
Web address: www.baptistonline.org/tipton/
Control: Other not–for–profit (including NFP Corporation) **Service**: General medical and surgical

Staffed Beds: 50 **Admissions**: 1058 **Census**: 8 **Outpatient Visits**: 56635 **Births**: 348 **Total Expense ($000)**: 95878 **Payroll Expense ($000)**: 16490 **Personnel**: 255

CROSSVILLE—Cumberland County

☐ **CUMBERLAND MEDICAL CENTER (440009)**, 421 South Main Street, Zip 38555–5031; tel. 931/484–9511, **A**1 2 10 20 **F**3 11 13 15 18 20 22 28 29 30 31 34 35 40 44 45 47 48 51 53 57 58 59 61 64 68 70 74 75 76 77 78 79 81 82 85 86 87 93 94 102 107 108 110 111 114 115 119 121 129 130 132 135 146 147 148 154 156 **S** Covenant Health, Knoxville, TN
Primary Contact: David V. Bunch, President and Chief Administrative Officer
CFO: April VonAchen, Chief Financial Officer and Vice President Financial Services
CIO: Joe Lowe, Director Management Information Systems
CHR: Charles Sexton, Manager Human Resources
CNO: Rebecca Foster, MSN, R.N., Chief Nursing Officer
Web address: www.cmchealthcare.org
Control: Other not–for–profit (including NFP Corporation) **Service**: General medical and surgical

Staffed Beds: 85 **Admissions**: 4794 **Census**: 47 **Outpatient Visits**: 91803 **Births**: 699 **Total Expense ($000)**: 77698 **Payroll Expense ($000)**: 29112 **Personnel**: 786

TN

Many Facility Codes have changed. Please refer to the AHA Guide Code Chart. © 2019 AHA Guide

DAYTON—Rhea County

☒ **RHEA MEDICAL CENTER (441310)**, 9400 Rhea County Highway, Zip 37321–7922; tel. 423/775–1121, (Nonreporting) **A**1 10 18 **S** QHR, Brentwood, TN
Primary Contact: David Bixler, Chief Executive Officer
CFO: Harv Sanders, Chief Financial Officer
CMO: Benjamin Kellogg, M.D., Chief of Staff
CNO: Samantha Bryant, Chief Nursing Officer
Web address: www.rheamedical.org
Control: County, Government, nonfederal **Service:** General medical and surgical

Staffed Beds: 25

DICKSON—Dickson County

☒ **TRISTAR HORIZON MEDICAL CENTER (440046)**, 111 Highway 70 East, Zip 37055–2080; tel. 615/446–0446, (Nonreporting) **A**1 2 10 **S** HCA Healthcare, Nashville, TN
Primary Contact: Dustin Greene, Chief Executive Officer
CFO: Clarence Gray, Chief Financial Officer
CIO: Rick Stoker, Director Management Information Systems
CHR: Sheila Kight, Director Human Resources
CNO: Gina Bullington, Chief Nursing Officer
Web address: www.horizonmedicalcenter.com
Control: Corporation, Investor–owned (for–profit) **Service:** General medical and surgical

Staffed Beds: 130

DYERSBURG—Dyer County

☒ **WEST TENNESSEE HEALTHCARE DYERSBURG HOSPITAL (440072)**, 400 East Tickle Street, Zip 38024–3120; tel. 731/285–2410, **A**1 10 20 **F**3 8 11 13 15 18 20 22 26 29 30 34 35 39 40 44 45 46 47 48 49 50 51 57 59 60 70 76 79 81 82 85 87 92 93 97 107 108 110 111 115 119 120 121 124 127 129 130 145 146 147 149 157 **S** West Tennessee Healthcare, Jackson, TN
Primary Contact: Reba Celsor, Chief Executive Officer
CFO: Meredith Malone, Chief Financial Officer
CMO: Darren Johnson, M.D., Chief of Staff
CIO: Russ Shephard, Senior Systems Analyst
CHR: Beverly Ray, Director Human Resources
CNO: Jan Zimmer, R.N., MSN, R.N., MS, Chief Nursing Officer
Web address: www.wth.org/locations/west-tennessee-healthcare-dyersburg-hospital
Control: Hospital district or authority, Government, nonfederal **Service:** General medical and surgical

Staffed Beds: 124 **Admissions:** 4365 **Census:** 43 **Outpatient Visits:** 55875
Births: 491 **Total Expense ($000):** 78874 **Payroll Expense ($000):** 19241
Personnel: 293

EAST RIDGE—Hamilton County

EAST RIDGE HOSPITAL See Parkridge Medical Center, Chattanooga

ELIZABETHTON—Carter County

☐ **SYCAMORE SHOALS HOSPITAL (440018)**, 1501 West Elk Avenue, Zip 37643–2874; tel. 423/542–1300, **A**1 10 **F**3 11 15 18 29 30 34 35 40 41 44 45 48 50 53 54 56 57 59 62 63 64 68 70 75 77 79 81 84 85 87 93 97 98 103 107 110 111 115 118 119 130 144 146 147 148 154 **S** Ballad Health, Johnson City, TN
Primary Contact: Dwayne Taylor, Chief Executive Officer
COO: Melanie Stanton, R.N., Chief Nursing Officer
CFO: Chase Wilson, Chief Financial Officer
CMO: Morris H Seligman, M.D., Chief Medical Officer and Chief Medical Information Officer
CIO: Paul Merrywell, Chief Information Officer
CHR: Sharon Sheppard, Manager Human Resources
Web address: www.msha.com
Control: Other not–for–profit (including NFP Corporation) **Service:** General medical and surgical

Staffed Beds: 74 **Admissions:** 3516 **Census:** 42 **Outpatient Visits:** 65904
Births: 0 **Total Expense ($000):** 42956 **Payroll Expense ($000):** 17364
Personnel: 1144

ERIN—Houston County

☐ **HOUSTON COUNTY COMMUNITY HOSPITAL (441320)**, 5001 East Main Street, Zip 37061–4115, Mailing Address: P.O. Box 489, Zip 37061–0489; tel. 931/289–4211, **A**1 10 18 **F**29 34 40 91 93 107 115 133 146
Primary Contact: Doug Martin, Chief Executive Officer
CFO: Kim Pridgen, Chief Financial Officer
CMO: Michael Carter, M.D., Chief Medical Officer
CNO: Angie Beard, R.N.
Control: County, Government, nonfederal **Service:** General medical and surgical

Staffed Beds: 15 **Admissions:** 230 **Census:** 4 **Outpatient Visits:** 9940
Births: 0

ERWIN—Unicoi County

☒ **UNICOI COUNTY MEMORIAL HOSPITAL (440001)**, 2030 Temple Hill Road, Zip 37650, Mailing Address: P.O. Box 802, Zip 37650–0802; tel. 423/743–3141, (Total facility includes 46 beds in nursing home–type unit) **A**1 10 **F**11 15 29 30 34 35 40 50 64 67 68 75 77 85 93 107 110 111 115 119 130 131 146 154 **S** Ballad Health, Johnson City, TN
Primary Contact: Eric Carroll, Chief Executive Officer
CFO: Toni Buchanan, Chief Financial Officer
CMO: Jose Picaza, M.D., Chief of Staff
CIO: Maggie Tipton, Chief Information Officer
CHR: Susan Broyles, Director Human Resources and Safety
CNO: Melanie Stanton, R.N., Chief Nursing Officer
Web address: www.msha.com
Control: Other not–for–profit (including NFP Corporation) **Service:** General medical and surgical

Staffed Beds: 94 **Admissions:** 468 **Census:** 47 **Outpatient Visits:** 22643
Births: 0 **Total Expense ($000):** 11690 **Payroll Expense ($000):** 4809
Personnel: 225

FAYETTEVILLE—Lincoln County

☐ **LINCOLN COUNTY HEALTH SYSTEM (440102)**, 106 Medical Center Boulevard, Zip 37334–2684, Mailing Address: P.O. Box 637, Zip 37334–2684; tel. 931/438–1100, (Nonreporting) **A**1 10
Primary Contact: Robert M. Lonis, CPA, Interim Chief Executive Officer
CFO: Robert M Lonis, CPA, Chief Financial Officer
CIO: John Kenneth Lavender, Chief Information Officer
CHR: Wendy Naglor, Director Human Resources
CNO: Vicky Groce, Chief Nursing Officer
Web address: www.lchealthsystem.com
Control: County, Government, nonfederal **Service:** General medical and surgical

Staffed Beds: 313

FRANKLIN—Williamson County

☒ **ENCOMPASS HEALTH REHABILITATION HOSPITAL OF FRANKLIN (443035)**, 1000 Physicians Way, Zip 37067–1471; tel. 615/721–4000, **A**1 10 **F**28 29 34 35 68 75 90 91 96 148 154 **S** Encompass Health Corporation, Birmingham, AL
Primary Contact: Scott J. Peterson, Chief Executive Officer
CMO: Scott Craig, M.D., Medical Director
Web address: www.healthsouthfranklin.com
Control: Corporation, Investor–owned (for–profit) **Service:** Rehabilitation

Staffed Beds: 40 **Admissions:** 681 **Census:** 23 **Outpatient Visits:** 0
Births: 0

☐ **ROLLING HILLS HOSPITAL (444007)**, 2014 Quail Hollow Circle, Zip 37067–5967; tel. 615/628–5700, (Nonreporting) **A**1 10 **S** Universal Health Services, Inc., King of Prussia, PA
Primary Contact: Laurel Roberts, R.N., MSN, Interim Chief Executive Officer
CFO: Ray Brocato, Chief Financial Officer
CMO: James Hart, M.D., Medical Director
CHR: Lisa Hodge, Director, Human Resources
CNO: Laurel Roberts, R.N., MSN, Chief Nursing Officer
Web address: www.RollingHillsHospital.org/
Control: Corporation, Investor–owned (for–profit) **Service:** Psychiatric

Staffed Beds: 120

☐ **WILLIAMSON MEDICAL CENTER (440029)**, 4321 Carothers Parkway,
Zip 37067–8542; tel. 615/435–5000, (Nonreporting) **A**1 2 3 5 10
Primary Contact: Donald Webb, Chief Executive Officer
COO: Julie Miller, Chief Operating Officer
CMO: Starling C Evins, M.D., Chief of Staff
CIO: Steve Dycus, Director Marketing and Public Relations
CHR: Phyllis Molyneux, Associate Administrator Human Resources and Education
Web address: www.williamsonmedicalcenter.org
Control: County, Government, nonfederal **Service**: General medical and surgical

Staffed Beds: 185

GALLATIN—Sumner County

⌖ **SUMNER REGIONAL MEDICAL CENTER (440003)**, 555 Hartsville Pike,
Zip 37066–2400, Mailing Address: P.O. Box 1558, Zip 37066–1558;
tel. 615/452–4210, (Nonreporting) **A**1 2 3 10 **S** LifePoint Health, Brentwood, TN
Primary Contact: Susan M. Peach, R.N., Chief Executive Officer
CMO: Geoffrey Lifferth, M.D., Chief Medical Officer
CIO: Vickie Carter, Information Systems Director
CNO: Anne Melton, Chief Nursing Officer
Web address: www.mysumnermedical.com
Control: Corporation, Investor–owned (for–profit) **Service**: General medical and surgical

Staffed Beds: 110

GERMANTOWN—Shelby County

☐ **BAPTIST MEMORIAL REHABILITATION HOSPITAL (443034)**, 1240 South
Germantown Road, Zip 38138–2226; tel. 901/275–3300, **A**1 10 **F**3 90 148 **S**
Baptist Memorial Health Care Corporation, Memphis, TN
Primary Contact: Christopher L. Bariola, Chief Executive Officer
CFO: Carlos Mendoza, Controller
CHR: Stacie Schroeppel, Director of Human Resources
CNO: Donna Hale, Director of Nursing
Web address: www.baptistrehab.com
Control: Corporation, Investor–owned (for–profit) **Service**: Rehabilitation

Staffed Beds: 49 Admissions: 1177 Census: 39 Outpatient Visits: 0
Births: 0 Total Expense ($000): 16839 Payroll Expense ($000): 7813
Personnel: 192

METHODIST LE BONHEUR GERMANTOWN HOSPITAL See Methodist
Healthcare Memphis Hospitals, Memphis

GREENEVILLE—Greene County

⌖ **GREENEVILLE COMMUNITY HOSPITAL EAST (440025)**, 1420 Tusculum
Boulevard, Zip 37745–5825; tel. 423/787–5000, (Total facility includes 90 beds
in nursing home–type unit) **A**1 2 10 19 **F**3 11 12 13 15 18 20 28 29 31 34 35
37 40 44 45 46 47 48 49 56 57 59 62 64 66 68 70 73 75 76 77 78 79 81 85
87 88 89 93 94 97 107 108 110 111 114 115 118 119 120 121 123 128 129
130 131 132 134 146 147 148 149 156 **S** Ballad Health, Johnson City, TN
Primary Contact: Tammy Albright, Chief Executive Officer
CFO: Mark Compton, Chief Financial Officer
CMO: Mark Patterson, M.D., Chief Medical Officer
CIO: Eric L Garrison, Chief Information Officer
CHR: Robert R Roark, Director Human Resources
CNO: Brenda Cannon, R.N., Director of Nursing
Web address: www.balladhealth.org/hospitals/laughlin-memorial-greeneville
Control: Other not–for–profit (including NFP Corporation) **Service**: General
medical and surgical

Staffed Beds: 121 Admissions: 3295 Census: 108 Outpatient
Visits: 98637 Births: 156 Total Expense ($000): 61754 Payroll Expense
($000): 25202 Personnel: 573

⌖ **GREENEVILLE COMMUNITY HOSPITAL WEST (440050)**, 401 Takoma Avenue,
Zip 37743–4647; tel. 423/639–3151, **A**1 10 **F**3 6 11 12 13 15 18 29 30 32 34
35 40 44 45 46 49 50 54 56 57 59 64 65 68 70 74 75 76 77 81 85 87 90 97
98 100 102 103 104 107 108 110 111 115 119 129 130 131 132 135 144
146 147 149 154 156 **S** Ballad Health, Johnson City, TN
Primary Contact: Tammy Albright, President
CFO: Judith Clark, Chief Financial Officer
CMO: Daniel Lewis, Chief Medical Officer
CHR: Jack Lister, Director Human Resources
CNO: Robin Roberts, Executive Director of Patient Services
Web address: www.takoma.org
Control: Other not–for–profit (including NFP Corporation) **Service**: General
medical and surgical

Staffed Beds: 92 Admissions: 2460 Census: 25 Outpatient Visits: 160011
Births: 421 Total Expense ($000): 64718 Payroll Expense ($000): 29125
Personnel: 466

HARRIMAN—Roane County

☐ **ROANE MEDICAL CENTER (440031)**, 8045 Roane Medical Center Dr,
Zip 37748–8333; tel. 865/316–1000, **A**1 3 10 **F**3 11 15 18 20 28 29 30 34 35
40 44 45 50 57 58 59 61 64 68 69 70 75 78 79 81 82 85 87 93 94 102 107
108 110 111 114 118 119 129 130 132 135 143 146 147 148 154 156 **S**
Covenant Health, Knoxville, TN
Primary Contact: Jason B. Pilant, President and Chief Administrative Officer
CFO: Julie Utterback, Chief Financial Officer
CMO: Mark Browne, M.D., Chief Medical Officer
CIO: Mike Ward, Senior Vice President Chief Information Officer
CHR: Randall Carr, Director Human Resources
CNO: Carolyn Shipley, R.N., Chief Nursing Officer
Web address: www.roanemedical.com
Control: Other not–for–profit (including NFP Corporation) **Service**: General
medical and surgical

Staffed Beds: 52 Admissions: 2698 Census: 28 Outpatient Visits: 63050
Births: 0 Total Expense ($000): 35015 Payroll Expense ($000): 13220
Personnel: 225

HARTSVILLE—Trousdale County

⌖ **TROUSDALE MEDICAL CENTER (441301)**, 500 Church Street, Zip 37074–
1744; tel. 615/374–2221, (Nonreporting) **A**1 10 18 **S** LifePoint Health,
Brentwood, TN
Primary Contact: Michael Herman, Chief Executive Officer
COO: William D Mize, Chief Operating Officer
CFO: David Wilhoite, CPA, Senior Vice President Finance and Chief Financial Officer
CIO: David Young, Senior Vice President Planning and Technology
CHR: Amy Overstreet, Director Human Resources
CNO: Jennifer Holder, Chief Nursing Officer
Web address: www.mytrousdalemedical.com
Control: Corporation, Investor–owned (for–profit) **Service**: General medical and
surgical

Staffed Beds: 25

HENDERSONVILLE—Sumner County

⌖ **TRISTAR HENDERSONVILLE MEDICAL CENTER (440194)**, 355 New Shackle
Island Road, Zip 37075–2479; tel. 615/338–1000, **A**1 3 10 **F**3 7 11 13 14 15
18 20 22 24 26 28 29 30 34 35 38 40 42 44 45 46 47 48 49 50 51 54 56 57
60 63 64 65 68 70 72 74 75 76 77 78 79 81 82 84 85 86 87 93 96 97 102
107 108 110 111 112 114 115 116 117 119 126 130 135 146 147 148 149
154 155 157 **S** HCA Healthcare, Nashville, TN
Primary Contact: Regina Bartlett, Chief Executive Officer
CFO: Stephen Bearden, Chief Financial Officer
CMO: Brett Branson, M.D., Chief Medical Officer
CIO: Hal Schultheis, Director Information Systems
CHR: Matt Gilday, Vice President of Human Resources
CNO: Lisa Gann, R.N., Chief Nursing Officer
Web address: www.hendersonvillemedicalcenter.com
Control: Corporation, Investor–owned (for–profit) **Service**: General medical and
surgical

Staffed Beds: 125 Admissions: 7380 Census: 70 Outpatient Visits: 90429
Births: 1122

HERMITAGE—Davidson County

⌖ **TRISTAR SUMMIT MEDICAL CENTER (440150)**, 5655 Frist Boulevard,
Zip 37076–2053; tel. 615/316–3000, (Nonreporting) **A**1 2 10 **S** HCA Healthcare,
Nashville, TN
Primary Contact: Brian Marger, Chief Executive Officer
CFO: Bryan Shephard, Chief Financial Officer
CMO: Kevin M. Hamilton, M.D., Chief Medical Officer
CIO: Joel Bain, Director Information Services
CHR: Emily Dye, Vice President Human Resources
CNO: Mary Ann Angle, R.N., FACHE, Chief Nursing Officer
Web address: www.summitmedctr.com
Control: Corporation, Investor–owned (for–profit) **Service**: General medical and
surgical

Staffed Beds: 196

TN

HUNTINGDON—Carroll County

✠ **BAPTIST MEMORIAL HOSPITAL-CARROLL COUNTY (440016)**, 631 R.B. Wilson Drive, Zip 38344–1727; tel. 731/986–4461, **A**1 10 **F**3 11 15 18 28 29 30 32 34 35 38 39 40 44 50 56 57 59 64 65 66 70 75 77 79 81 85 86 87 93 97 98 101 102 103 107 108 111 115 118 119 130 132 133 134 135 146 148 149 154 156 **S** Baptist Memorial Health Care Corporation, Memphis, TN
Primary Contact: Susan M. Breeden, Administrator and Chief Executive Officer
CFO: Sharron Holland, Chief Financial Officer
CHR: Kim King, Director Human Resources and Public Relations
CNO: Kimberly Sanders, Chief Nursing Officer
Web address: www.baptistonline.org/huntingdon/
Control: Other not–for–profit (including NFP Corporation) **Service:** General medical and surgical

Staffed Beds: 35 **Admissions:** 885 **Census:** 15 **Outpatient Visits:** 13152 **Births:** 0 **Total Expense ($000):** 17698 **Payroll Expense ($000):** 6731 **Personnel:** 190

JACKSON—Madison County

✠ **JACKSON-MADISON COUNTY GENERAL HOSPITAL (440002)**, 620 Skyline Drive, Zip 38301–3923; tel. 731/541–5000, (Includes WEST TENNESSEE HEALTHCARE NORTH HOSPITAL, 367 Hospital Boulevard, Jackson, Tennessee, Zip 38305–2080; tel. 731/661–2000; Kevin Rinks, Chief Executive Officer) **A**1 2 3 5 10 19 **F**3 7 8 11 13 15 17 18 20 22 24 26 28 29 30 31 34 35 40 42 44 45 46 47 48 49 51 55 56 57 58 59 60 63 64 65 68 70 72 73 74 75 76 77 78 79 80 81 82 83 84 85 86 87 89 92 93 94 96 97 107 108 109 110 111 112 114 115 116 117 118 119 120 121 124 126 129 130 131 132 135 145 146 147 148 149 **S** West Tennessee Healthcare, Jackson, TN
Primary Contact: Deann Thelen, Chief Executive Officer
CFO: Jeff Blankenship, CPA, Vice President and Chief Financial Officer
CMO: David Roberts, M.D., Chief Medical Officer
CIO: Jeff Frieling, Vice President and Chief Information Officer
CHR: Wendie Carlson, Chief Human Resources Officer
CNO: Tina Prescott, Vice President, Hospital Services
Web address: www.wth.org
Control: Hospital district or authority, Government, nonfederal **Service:** General medical and surgical

Staffed Beds: 672 **Admissions:** 30814 **Census:** 462 **Outpatient Visits:** 245034 **Births:** 3400 **Total Expense ($000):** 727662 **Payroll Expense ($000):** 256096 **Personnel:** 4299

★ **PATHWAYS OF TENNESSEE (444010)**, 238 Summar Drive, Zip 38301–3906; tel. 731/541–8200, **A**10 **F**4 5 29 35 38 44 57 59 98 99 100 101 102 103 104 132 134 135 149 150 153 154 157 **S** West Tennessee Healthcare, Jackson, TN
Primary Contact: Pam Henson, Executive Director
CFO: Jeff Blankenship, CPA, Chief Financial Officer
CMO: Kevin Turner, M.D., Medical Director
CIO: Jeff Fricling, Chief Information Officer
CHR: Wendy Carlson, Director Human Resources
CNO: Angela Hensley, Director of Nursing
Web address: www.wth.net/pathways
Control: Hospital district or authority, Government, nonfederal **Service:** Psychiatric

Staffed Beds: 25 **Admissions:** 1050 **Census:** 12 **Outpatient Visits:** 97001 **Births:** 0 **Total Expense ($000):** 17336 **Payroll Expense ($000):** 9824 **Personnel:** 204

JEFFERSON CITY—Jefferson County

ST. MARY'S JEFFERSON MEMORIAL HOSPITAL See Tennova Healthcare-Jefferson Memorial Hospital

✠ **TENNOVA HEALTHCARE-JEFFERSON MEMORIAL HOSPITAL (440056)**, 110 Hospital Drive, Zip 37760–5281; tel. 865/471–2500, (Nonreporting) **A**1 10 **S** Community Health Systems, Inc., Franklin, TN
Primary Contact: Colin McRae, Chief Executive Officer
CFO: Roseann M Devault, Chief Financial Officer
CMO: Richard Carter, M.D., Chief of Staff
Web address: www.tennova.com/
Control: Corporation, Investor–owned (for–profit) **Service:** General medical and surgical

Staffed Beds: 54

JELLICO—Campbell County

★ **JELLICO COMMUNITY HOSPITAL (440180)**, 188 Hospital Lane, Zip 37762–4400; tel. 423/784–7252, (Nonreporting) **A**10 22 **S** Community Hospital Corporation, Plano, TX
Primary Contact: Gene Miller, Interim Chief Executive Officer
COO: Pamela Hodge, R.N., Chief Nursing Officer and Coordinator Performance Improvement
CFO: Evelyn Ghulum, Chief Financial Officer
CMO: Gregory Wilkens, M.D., Chief of Staff
CIO: Derek Brown, Chief Information Officer
CHR: Vince Vannett, Director Human Resources
Web address: www.jellicohospital.com
Control: Other not–for–profit (including NFP Corporation) **Service:** General medical and surgical

Staffed Beds: 31

JOHNSON CITY—Washington County

✠ **FRANKLIN WOODS COMMUNITY HOSPITAL (440184)**, 300 MedTech Parkway, Zip 37604–2277; tel. 423/302–1000, (Total facility includes 34 beds in nursing home–type unit) **A**1 10 **F**3 11 13 29 30 34 35 36 38 40 44 45 50 51 56 57 63 65 68 70 74 75 76 77 81 85 87 100 107 108 111 114 115 118 119 126 128 130 146 147 148 149 154 157 **S** Ballad Health, Johnson City, TN
Primary Contact: Patricia Baise, R.N., FACHE, Chief Executive Officer
CFO: Andrew Wampler, Chief Financial Officer
CHR: Brooke Graham, Human Resources Manager
CNO: Rhonda Mann, Chief Nursing Officer
Web address: www.msha.com
Control: Other not–for–profit (including NFP Corporation) **Service:** General medical and surgical

Staffed Beds: 102 **Admissions:** 6238 **Census:** 80 **Outpatient Visits:** 51050 **Births:** 1187 **Total Expense ($000):** 66051 **Payroll Expense ($000):** 21577 **Personnel:** 945

✠ **JOHNSON CITY MEDICAL CENTER (440063)**, 400 North State of Franklin Road, Zip 37604–6094; tel. 423/431–6111, (Includes NISWONGER CHILDREN'S HOSPITAL, 400 North State of Franklin Road, Johnson City, Tennessee, Zip 37604–6035; tel. 423/431–6111; Lisa Carter, Chief Executive Officer; WOODRIDGE HOSPITAL, 403 State of Franklin Road, Johnson City, Tennessee, Zip 37604–6034; tel. 423/431–7111; Patricia Baise, R.N., FACHE, Chief Executive Officer) **A**1 2 3 5 8 10 19 **F**3 4 5 7 11 12 13 15 17 18 19 20 21 22 24 26 28 29 30 31 32 34 35 38 39 40 41 43 44 45 46 47 48 49 50 51 52 53 54 55 56 57 58 59 60 61 62 63 64 68 70 72 74 75 76 77 78 79 81 82 84 85 86 87 88 89 91 93 97 98 99 100 101 102 103 104 107 108 110 111 114 115 117 118 119 120 121 123 124 129 130 131 132 134 135 143 146 147 148 153 154 **S** Ballad Health, Johnson City, TN
Primary Contact: Stan Hickson, FACHE, Chief Executive Officer
COO: Kenny Shafer, Chief Operating Officer
CFO: Richard Boone, Chief Financial Officer
CMO: Clay Runnels, Vice President Chief Medical Officer Washington County
CHR: Barry Tourigny, Human Resources Director
CNO: Dru Malcolm, Vice President and Chief Nursing Officer
Web address: www.msha.com
Control: Other not–for–profit (including NFP Corporation) **Service:** General medical and surgical

Staffed Beds: 585 **Admissions:** 29375 **Census:** 405 **Outpatient Visits:** 267175 **Births:** 1255 **Total Expense ($000):** 382279 **Payroll Expense ($000):** 130527 **Personnel:** 9447

NORTH SIDE HOSPITAL See Franklin Woods Community Hospital

✠ **QUILLEN REHABILITATION HOSPITAL (443033)**, 2511 Wesley Street, Zip 37601–1723; tel. 423/952–1700, **A**1 10 **F**29 75 90 132 148 149 154 **S** Encompass Health Corporation, Birmingham, AL
Primary Contact: Brian Luff, Chief Executive Officer
CFO: Debbie Wyse, Controller
CHR: Penny Lawson, Human Resource Director
CNO: Lynn Langan, Chief Nursing Officer
Web address: www.quillenrehabilitationhospital.com/
Control: Corporation, Investor–owned (for–profit) **Service:** Rehabilitation

Staffed Beds: 31 **Admissions:** 657 **Census:** 27 **Outpatient Visits:** 0 **Births:** 0 **Total Expense ($000):** 10781 **Payroll Expense ($000):** 5504 **Personnel:** 89

TN

Hospital, Medicare Provider Number, Address, Telephone, Approval, Facility, and Physician Codes, Health Care System

★ American Hospital Association (AHA) membership
□ The Joint Commission accreditation
○ Healthcare Facilities Accreditation Program
◇ DNV Healthcare Inc. accreditation
⇑ Center for Improvement in Healthcare Quality Accreditation
△ Commission on Accreditation of Rehabilitation Facilities (CARF) accreditation

KINGSPORT—Sullivan County

ENCOMPASS HEALTH REHABILITATION HOSPITAL OF KINGSPORT (443027), 113 Cassel Drive, Zip 37660–3775; tel. 423/246–7240, (Nonreporting) **A**1 10 **S** Encompass Health Corporation, Birmingham, AL
Primary Contact: Troy Clark, Chief Executive Officer
CFO: Natalie Tilson, Controller
CMO: James P Little, M.D., Medical Director
CIO: Natalie Tilson, Controller
CHR: Joyce Jones, Director Human Resources
CNO: Debra Smith, Chief Nursing Officer
Web address: www.healthsouthkingsport.com
Control: Corporation, Investor–owned (for–profit) **Service**: Rehabilitation

Staffed Beds: 50

HOLSTON VALLEY MEDICAL CENTER (440017), 130 West Ravine Street, Zip 37660–3837, Mailing Address: P.O. Box 238, Zip 37662–0238; tel. 423/224–4000, (Nonreporting) **A**1 2 3 5 10 13 19 **S** Ballad Health, Johnson City, TN
Primary Contact: Lindy P. White, Vice President and Chief Executive Officer
COO: Dale Clark, Chief Operating Officer
CFO: Dale Poe, Vice President Finance and Operations
CMO: Daniel Carlson, M.D., Chief Medical Officer
CIO: Will Showalter, Senior Vice President Information Technology
CHR: Hamlin J Wilson, Senior Vice President Human Resources
CNO: Kathy Campbell, Interim Chief Nursing Officer
Web address: www.wellmont.org
Control: Other not–for–profit (including NFP Corporation) **Service**: General medical and surgical

Staffed Beds: 345

INDIAN PATH MEDICAL CENTER (440176), 2000 Brookside Drive, Zip 37660–4627; tel. 423/857–7000, **A**1 10 **F**3 8 11 13 15 18 29 30 31 34 35 40 45 46 47 49 50 51 54 55 57 59 60 64 65 68 70 73 74 75 76 77 78 79 81 84 85 86 87 93 97 107 108 110 111 114 116 117 118 119 123 129 130 132 135 146 147 149 154 156 157 **S** Ballad Health, Johnson City, TN
Primary Contact: Monty E. McLaurin, Chief Executive Officer, Northwest Market
CFO: Steve Sawyer, Chief Financial Officer
CMO: Mark Wilkinson, M.D., Chief Medical Officer
CIO: Jackson Dale, Site Manager Information Systems
CHR: Kevin M Smith, Director Human Resources
CNO: Susan Fannon, Chief Nursing Officer
Web address: www.msha.com
Control: Other not–for–profit (including NFP Corporation) **Service**: General medical and surgical

Staffed Beds: 160 Admissions: 4903 Census: 54 Outpatient Visits: 121340 Births: 710 Total Expense ($000): 87573 Payroll Expense ($000): 30983 Personnel: 2201

KNOXVILLE—Knox County

EAST TENNESSEE CHILDREN'S HOSPITAL (443303), 2018 Clinch Avenue, Zip 37916–2393, Mailing Address: P.O. Box 15010, Zip 37901–5010; tel. 865/541–8000, (Nonreporting) **A**1 3 5 10
Primary Contact: Keith D. Goodwin, President and Chief Executive Officer
COO: Steven Godbold, Vice President Operations and Chief Operating Officer
CFO: Caryn Hawthorne, Vice President Finance and Chief Finance Officer
CMO: Joe Childs, M.D., Vice President Medical Services
CIO: John Hanks, Director Information Systems
CHR: Sue Wilburn, Vice President Human Resources and Organizational Development
CNO: Hella Ewing, Vice President Patient Care Services and Chief Nursing Officer
Web address: www.etch.com
Control: Other not–for–profit (including NFP Corporation) **Service**: Children's general medical and surgical

Staffed Beds: 152

FORT SANDERS REGIONAL MEDICAL CENTER (440125), 1901 West Clinch Avenue, Zip 37916–2307; tel. 865/541–1111, (Total facility includes 24 beds in nursing home–type unit) **A**1 2 10 19 **F**3 11 12 13 15 17 18 20 22 24 26 28 29 30 31 34 35 39 40 44 45 46 47 49 50 51 54 55 57 58 59 60 61 64 68 70 74 75 76 77 78 79 80 81 82 84 85 86 87 90 91 92 93 94 96 100 102 107 108 110 111 114 115 116 117 118 119 120 121 123 124 126 128 129 130 131 132 135 146 147 148 149 154 156 157 **S** Covenant Health, Knoxville, TN
Primary Contact: Keith Altshuler, President and Chief Administrative Officer
CNO: Lynda Watts, Vice President, Chief Nursing Officer
Web address: www.covenanthealth.com
Control: Other not–for–profit (including NFP Corporation) **Service**: General medical and surgical

Staffed Beds: 384 Admissions: 17385 Census: 260 Outpatient Visits: 226542 Births: 2637 Total Expense ($000): 286635 Payroll Expense ($000): 98195 Personnel: 1610

MERCY MEDICAL CENTER WEST See Tennova Turkey Creek Medical Center

PARKWEST MEDICAL CENTER (440173), 9352 Park West Boulevard, Zip 37923–4325, Mailing Address: P.O. Box 22993, Zip 37933–0993; tel. 865/373–1000, (Includes PENINSULA HOSPITAL, 2347 Jones Bend Road, Louisville, Tennessee, Zip 37777–5213, Mailing Address: P O Box 2000, Zip 37777–2000, tel. 865/970–9800; Elizabeth P Clary, R.N., Vice President Behavioral Health) **A**1 2 10 **F**3 11 13 15 17 18 20 22 24 26 28 29 30 31 34 35 37 38 39 40 44 45 46 48 49 50 51 56 57 58 59 60 61 64 68 70 74 75 76 77 78 79 80 81 82 84 85 86 87 92 93 94 96 98 99 100 101 102 103 104 107 108 110 111 115 116 117 118 119 122 123 129 130 131 132 135 146 147 148 153 154 **S** Covenant Health, Knoxville, TN
Primary Contact: James VanderSteeg, Chief Executive Officer
COO: Emlyn Cobble, Vice President and Chief Support Officer
CFO: Scott Hamilton, Vice President and Chief Financial Officer
CHR: Randall Carr, Director Human Resources
CNO: Diane Oliver, R.N., MSN, Chief Nursing Officer
Web address: www.treatedwell.com/
Control: Other not–for–profit (including NFP Corporation) **Service**: General medical and surgical

Staffed Beds: 434 Admissions: 23039 Census: 307 Outpatient Visits: 265871 Births: 1799 Total Expense ($000): 314874 Payroll Expense ($000): 107845 Personnel: 1830

UNIVERSITY OF TENNESSEE MEDICAL CENTER (440015), 1924 Alcoa Highway, Zip 37920–6900; tel. 865/305–9000, **A**1 2 3 5 8 10 19 **F**3 6 8 9 11 12 13 15 17 18 20 22 24 26 28 29 30 31 34 35 36 37 39 40 41 43 44 45 46 47 48 49 50 51 52 53 54 55 56 57 58 59 60 61 64 65 70 71 72 74 75 76 77 78 79 81 82 84 85 86 87 88 91 92 93 94 96 97 100 102 103 105 107 108 109 110 111 114 115 116 117 118 119 120 121 123 124 126 129 130 131 132 135 138 141 142 144 145 146 147 148 149 150 153 154 155 156
Primary Contact: Joseph Landsman, President and Chief Executive Officer
COO: David Hall, Senior Vice President and Chief Operating Officer
CFO: Thomas Fisher, Senior Vice President and Chief Financial Officer
CMO: Jerry Epps, M.D., Senior Vice President and Chief Medical Officer
CIO: Michael Saad, Vice President and Chief Information Officer
CHR: Julie Simpson, Vice President Human Resources
CNO: Janell Cecil, R.N., MSN, Senior Vice President and Chief Nursing Officer
Web address: www.utmedicalcenter.org
Control: Other not–for–profit (including NFP Corporation) **Service**: General medical and surgical

Staffed Beds: 609 Admissions: 30769 Census: 459 Outpatient Visits: 308581 Births: 3256 Total Expense ($000): 888813 Payroll Expense ($000): 314706 Personnel: 4229

LA FOLLETTE—Campbell County

TENNOVA HEALTHCARE-LAFOLLETTE MEDICAL CENTER (440033), 923 East Central Avenue, Zip 37766–2768, Mailing Address: P.O. Box 1301, Zip 37766–1301; tel. 423/907–1200, **A**1 10 20 **F**1 3 11 15 18 29 30 34 35 40 41 45 47 48 50 51 56 64 68 70 77 78 79 81 85 97 98 100 103 107 110 111 119 120 121 123 127 129 131 146 154 **S** Community Health Systems, Inc., Franklin, TN
Primary Contact: Mark Cain, Chief Executive Officer
COO: Sara Heatherly-Lloyd, Chief Operating Officer
CFO: Michael Cherry, Chief Financial Officer
CMO: George O'Neal Vinsant, M.D., Chief Medical Officer
CIO: Dillon Ward, Management Information Systems Specialist
CHR: Bess Stout, Director Human Resources
CNO: Kathy R Myers, MS, R.N., Chief Nursing Officer
Web address: www.tennova.com
Control: Corporation, Investor–owned (for–profit) **Service**: General medical and surgical

Staffed Beds: 164 Admissions: 2060 Census: 42

LAFAYETTE—Macon County

★ ⇑ **MACON COMMUNITY HOSPITAL (441305)**, 204 Medical Drive, Zip 37083–1799, Mailing Address: P.O. Box 378, Zip 37083–0378; tel. 615/666–2147, (Nonreporting) **A**10 18 21 **S** QHR, Brentwood, TN
Primary Contact: Thomas J. Kidd, CPA, Chief Executive Officer
CFO: Scott A. Tongate, Chief Financial Officer
Web address: www.mcgh.net
Control: Other not–for–profit (including NFP Corporation) **Service**: General medical and surgical

Staffed Beds: 25

Many Facility Codes have changed. Please refer to the AHA Guide Code Chart.   © 2019 AHA Guide

TN

LAWRENCEBURG—Lawrence County

⊠ **SOUTHERN TENNESSEE REGIONAL HEALTH SYSTEM-LAWRENCEBURG (440175)**, 1607 South Locust Avenue, Zip 38464–4011, Mailing Address: P.O. Box 847, Zip 38464–0847; tel. 931/762–6571, (Nonreporting) **A**1 10 **S** LifePoint Health, Brentwood, TN
Primary Contact: Adam Martin, Chief Executive Officer
CFO: Kristie Taylor, Chief Financial Officer
CIO: Jason Weaver, Director Information Systems
CHR: Robert Augustin, Director Human Resources
CNO: Carrie Rogers, Chief Nursing Officer
Web address: www.crocketthospital.com
Control: Corporation, Investor–owned (for–profit) **Service**: General medical and surgical

Staffed Beds: 99

LEBANON—Wilson County

⊠ **VANDERBILT WILSON COUNTY HOSPITAL (440193)**, 1411 Baddour Parkway, Zip 37087–2513; tel. 615/444–8262, (Includes VANDERBILT WILSON COUNTY HOSPITAL-MCFARLAND HOSPITAL, 500 Park Avenue, Lebanon, Tennessee, Zip 37087–3720; tel. 615/449–0500), (Non-reporting) **A**1 10 **S** Vanderbilt Health, Nashville, TN
Primary Contact: Jay Hinesley, FACHE, Chief Executive Officer
CMO: Andrew Jordan, M.D., Chief of Staff
CIO: Adrian Fung, Director Information Systems
Web address: www.universitymedicalcenter.com
Control: Other not–for–profit (including NFP Corporation) **Service**: General medical and surgical

Staffed Beds: 245

LENOIR CITY—Loudon County

☐ **FORT LOUDOUN MEDICAL CENTER (440110)**, 550 Fort Loudoun Medical Center Drive, Zip 37772–5673; tel. 865/271–6000, **A**1 10 **F**3 11 15 18 28 29 30 34 35 39 40 44 45 50 57 58 59 61 64 68 70 75 77 78 79 81 85 86 87 93 94 102 107 108 110 111 115 118 119 130 132 135 143 146 147 148 154 156 **S** Covenant Health, Knoxville, TN
Primary Contact: Jeffrey Feike, President and Chief Administrative Officer
CNO: Teresa Fisher, R.N., Chief Nursing Officer
Web address: www.covenanthealth.com
Control: Other not–for–profit (including NFP Corporation) **Service**: General medical and surgical

Staffed Beds: 30 **Admissions:** 2205 **Census:** 26 **Outpatient Visits:** 67349 **Births:** 0 **Total Expense ($000):** 30894 **Payroll Expense ($000):** 13090 **Personnel:** 217

LEWISBURG—Marshall County

⊠ **MARSHALL MEDICAL CENTER (441309)**, 1080 North Ellington Parkway, Zip 37091–2227, Mailing Address: P.O. Box 1609, Zip 37091–1609; tel. 931/359–6241, **A**1 10 18 **F**3 11 15 29 30 34 40 45 50 56 57 59 68 75 77 81 85 86 92 93 102 104 107 108 110 111 114 119 129 131 132 133 135 146 149 **S** Maury Regional Health System, Columbia, TN
Primary Contact: Phyllis Brown, Chief Executive Officer
CFO: Kyle Jones, Chief Financial Officer
CMO: Tim Nash, M.D., Chief of Staff, Board Vice Chairman
CHR: Jeff M Pierce, Chief Human Resource Officer
CNO: Karen Martin, R.N., MSN, Chief Nursing Officer
Web address: www.mauryregional.com
Control: County, Government, nonfederal **Service**: General medical and surgical

Staffed Beds: 12 **Admissions:** 163 **Census:** 1 **Outpatient Visits:** 33727 **Births:** 0 **Total Expense ($000):** 15272 **Payroll Expense ($000):** 7310 **Personnel:** 177

LEXINGTON—Henderson County

⊠ **HENDERSON COUNTY COMMUNITY HOSPITAL (440008)**, 200 West Church Street, Zip 38351–2038; tel. 731/968–3646, (Nonreporting) **A**1 10 **S** Quorum Health, Brentwood, TN
Primary Contact: Pamela W. Roberts, Chief Executive Officer
CFO: John Bostwick, Interim Chief Financial Officer
CHR: Linda Durham, Director Human Resources
CNO: Charlene Morgan, Chief Nursing Officer
Web address: www.hendersoncchospital.com
Control: Corporation, Investor–owned (for–profit) **Service**: General medical and surgical

Staffed Beds: 45

LINDEN—Perry County

PERRY COMMUNITY HOSPITAL (440040), 2718 Squirrel Hollow Drive, Zip 37096–3526; tel. 931/589–2121, (Nonreporting) **A**10
Primary Contact: John B. Avery III, Administrator
Web address: www.3riverscommunityhealth.com/
Control: Other not–for–profit (including NFP Corporation) **Service**: General medical and surgical

Staffed Beds: 53

LIVINGSTON—Overton County

⊠ **LIVINGSTON REGIONAL HOSPITAL (440187)**, 315 Oak Street, Zip 38570–1728, Mailing Address: P.O. Box 550, Zip 38570–0550; tel. 931/823–5611, (Nonreporting) **A**1 10 **S** LifePoint Health, Brentwood, TN
Primary Contact: Timothy W. McGill, Chief Executive Officer
CMO: Christopher Nahm, M.D., Chief Medical Officer
CIO: Mark Hambridge, Director Information Systems
CNO: Penny V Kirby, MSN, Chief Nursing Officer
Web address: www.MyLivingstonHospital.com
Control: Corporation, Investor–owned (for–profit) **Service**: General medical and surgical

Staffed Beds: 82

MANCHESTER—Coffee County

UNITY MEDICAL CENTER (440007), 1001 McArthur Drive, Zip 37355–2455, Mailing Address: P.O. Box 1079, Zip 37349–1079; tel. 931/728–3586, (Nonreporting) **A**10
Primary Contact: Martha McCormick, Chief Executive Officer
CFO: Pam Jernigan, Chief Financial Officer
CMO: James Van Winkle, M.D., Chief of Staff
CIO: Matt Burks, Director Information Technology
CHR: Sherry Holt, Director Human Resources
CNO: Stephanie Byars, Chief Nursing Officer
Web address: www.urmchealthcare.com
Control: Corporation, Investor–owned (for–profit) **Service**: General medical and surgical

Staffed Beds: 36

MARTIN—Weakley County

⊠ **SPIRE CANE CREEK REHABILITATION HOSPITAL (443030)**, 180 Mount Pelia Road, Zip 38237–3812; tel. 731/587–4231, (Nonreporting) **A**1 10 **S** Encompass Health Corporation, Birmingham, AL
Primary Contact: Rick Johnson, Chief Executive Officer
CFO: Bethany Smith, Controller
CMO: Belinda Merritt, M.D., Medical Director
CIO: Jan Trowhill, Director Health Information Management Systems
CHR: Sharon Shihady, Director Human Resources
CNO: Lindsey Rotger, Chief Nursing Officer
Web address: www.healthsouthcanecreek.com
Control: Corporation, Investor–owned (for–profit) **Service**: Rehabilitation

Staffed Beds: 40

UNITY PSYCHIATRIC CARE-MARTIN (444005), 458 Hannings Lane, Zip 38237–3308; tel. 731/588–2830, (Nonreporting) **A**10 **S** Tennessee Health Management, Parsons, TN
Primary Contact: Carrie Brawley, Administrator
Web address: www.unitypsych.com
Control: Partnership, Investor–owned (for–profit) **Service**: Psychiatric

Staffed Beds: 16

TN

☒ **WEST TENNESSEE HEALTHCARE VOLUNTEER HOSPITAL (440061)**, 161 Mount Pelia Road, Zip 38237–3811; tel. 731/587–4261, **A**1 10 **F**3 11 13 15 18 28 29 34 35 40 45 53 57 59 60 70 76 81 91 108 110 111 115 119 127 129 133 135 **S** West Tennessee Healthcare, Jackson, TN
Primary Contact: Darrell Blaylock, Chief Executive Officer
CFO: Jason Draper, Chief Financial Officer
CMO: Elizabeth Lund, M.D., Chief of Staff
CHR: Tammie Bell, Director Human Resources
CNO: Donna Barfield, Chief Nursing Officer
Web address: www.wth.org/locations/west-tennessee-healthcare-volunteer-hospital
Control: Hospital district or authority, Government, nonfederal **Service**: General medical and surgical

Staffed Beds: 41 **Admissions:** 654 **Census:** 5 **Outpatient Visits:** 18851 **Births:** 320 **Total Expense ($000):** 32088 **Payroll Expense ($000):** 11195 **Personnel:** 171	

MARYVILLE—Blount County

☒ **BLOUNT MEMORIAL HOSPITAL (440011)**, 907 East Lamar Alexander Parkway, Zip 37804–5016; tel. 865/983–7211, (Total facility includes 76 beds in nursing home–type unit) **A**1 2 10 19 **F**3 4 10 11 12 13 15 17 18 20 22 26 28 29 30 31 35 38 40 45 46 48 49 53 54 56 57 59 62 63 64 67 70 74 75 76 77 78 79 80 81 82 84 85 86 87 90 93 96 97 98 100 101 102 103 104 105 107 108 110 111 115 116 119 120 121 123 125 126 128 129 130 131 132 135 144 146 147 148 153 154 156
Primary Contact: Don Heinemann, Administrator and Chief Executive Officer
CFO: Jonathan Smith, Assistant Administrator and Chief Financial Officer
CMO: G Harold Naramore, M.D., Chief Medical Officer and In house Legal Counsel
CIO: Clay Puckett, Assistant Administrator and Chief Information Officer
CHR: Chris Wilkes, MS, Executive Director, Human Resources
CNO: Sonya Newman, R.N., Chief Nursing Officer
Web address: www.blountmemorial.org
Control: County, Government, nonfederal **Service**: General medical and surgical

Staffed Beds: 275 **Admissions:** 12875 **Census:** 204 **Outpatient Visits:** 364897 **Births:** 722 **Total Expense ($000):** 276181 **Payroll Expense ($000):** 135836 **Personnel:** 1931	

MC MINNVILLE—Warren County

☒ **SAINT THOMAS RIVER PARK HOSPITAL (440151)**, 1559 Sparta Street, Zip 37110–1316; tel. 931/815–4000, (Nonreporting) **A**1 10 **S** Ascension Healthcare, Saint Louis, MO
Primary Contact: Dale Humphrey, Chief Executive Officer
CFO: Christina Patterson, Chief Financial Officer
CMO: Randal D Rampp, M.D., Chief Medical Officer
CIO: Jeff Johnson, Director Information Systems
CHR: Deeann Johnson, Director Human Resources
Web address: www.riverparkhospital.com
Control: Church operated, Nongovernment, not–for–profit **Service**: General medical and surgical

Staffed Beds: 85	

MEMPHIS—Shelby County

☒ **BAPTIST MEMORIAL HOSPITAL - MEMPHIS (440048)**, 6019 Walnut Grove Road, Zip 38120–2173; tel. 901/226–5000, **A**1 2 10 **F**3 6 8 12 17 18 20 22 26 27 28 29 30 31 34 35 36 40 41 45 46 47 48 49 50 53 54 56 57 58 59 60 63 64 65 68 70 74 75 77 78 79 80 81 82 84 85 86 87 91 92 93 102 107 108 109 111 112 114 115 116 118 119 120 121 122 123 124 126 130 132 135 136 137 143 146 148 154 157 **S** Baptist Memorial Health Care Corporation, Memphis, TN
Primary Contact: Dana Dye, R.N., Vice President, Administrator and Chief Executive Officer
CFO: Cyndi Pittman, Chief Financial Officer
CMO: Christian C Patrick, M.D., Chief Medical Officer
CIO: Doug Reiselt, Vice President and Chief Information Officer
CHR: Jerry Barbaree, Director Human Resources
Web address: www.baptistonline.org/memphis/
Control: Other not–for–profit (including NFP Corporation) **Service**: General medical and surgical

Staffed Beds: 571 **Admissions:** 26661 **Census:** 445 **Outpatient Visits:** 137891 **Births:** 0 **Total Expense ($000):** 511038 **Payroll Expense ($000):** 159996 **Personnel:** 2701	

★ **BAPTIST MEMORIAL HOSPITAL FOR WOMEN (440222)**, 6225 Humphreys Boulevard, Zip 38120–2373; tel. 901/227–9000, **A**3 **F**3 7 8 12 13 15 19 25 29 30 32 34 35 38 41 45 46 47 48 49 54 55 56 57 58 59 64 65 68 70 71 72 73 74 75 76 77 78 79 81 82 85 86 87 88 89 107 108 109 110 111 112 114 115 119 124 126 130 132 135 146 147 148 154 **S** Baptist Memorial Health Care Corporation, Memphis, TN
Primary Contact: Kevin R. Hammeran, Chief Executive Officer and Administrator
CFO: Margaret Williams, Chief Financial Officer
CMO: Judi Carney, M.D., President Medical Staff
CIO: Melissa Nelson, Assistant Administrator
CHR: Karen Ingram, Director Human Resources
CNO: Carol Thetford, Chief Nursing Officer
Web address: www.baptistonline.org/womens/
Control: Other not–for–profit (including NFP Corporation) **Service**: Obstetrics and gynecology

Staffed Beds: 140 **Admissions:** 7392 **Census:** 51 **Outpatient Visits:** 70237 **Births:** 6091 **Total Expense ($000):** 97466 **Payroll Expense ($000):** 42046 **Personnel:** 638	

☒ **BAPTIST MEMORIAL RESTORATIVE CARE HOSPITAL (442010)**, 6019 Walnut Grove Road, Zip 38120–2113; tel. 901/226–4200, **A**1 10 **F**1 3 29 68 75 77 130 148 **S** Baptist Memorial Health Care Corporation, Memphis, TN
Primary Contact: Janice Hill, R.N., Administrator
Web address: www.baptistonline.org/restorative-care/
Control: Other not–for–profit (including NFP Corporation) **Service**: Acute long–term care hospital

Staffed Beds: 30 **Admissions:** 198 **Census:** 17 **Outpatient Visits:** 0 **Births:** 0 **Total Expense ($000):** 12311 **Payroll Expense ($000):** 4614 **Personnel:** 69	

☐ **CRESTWYN BEHAVIORAL HEALTH (444025)**, 9485 Crestwyn Hills Cove, Zip 38125–8515; tel. 901/248–1500, (Nonreporting) **A**1 10 **S** Acadia Healthcare Company, Inc., Franklin, TN
Primary Contact: Debby Willis, Chief Executive Officer
Web address: www.crestwynbh.com
Control: Corporation, Investor–owned (for–profit) **Service**: Psychiatric

Staffed Beds: 60	

☐ **DELTA MEDICAL CENTER (440159)**, 3000 Getwell Road, Zip 38118–2299; tel. 901/369–8100, (Nonreporting) **A**1 10 **S** Acadia Healthcare Company, Inc., Franklin, TN
Primary Contact: Phil Willcoxon, Chief Executive Officer
CFO: Mike Reynolds, Chief Financial Officer
CMO: David Richardson, M.D., Chief of Staff
CIO: Patrick Duffee, Director Medical Information Systems
CHR: Karyn Erickson, Director Human Resources
CNO: Donna Lanier, R.N., Chief Nursing Officer
Web address: www.deltamedcenter.com
Control: Corporation, Investor–owned (for–profit) **Service**: General medical and surgical

Staffed Beds: 167	

☒ **ENCOMPASS HEALTH REHABILITATION HOSPITAL OF MEMPHIS (443029)**, 1282 Union Avenue, Zip 38104–3414; tel. 901/722–2000, (Nonreporting) **A**1 3 5 10 **S** Encompass Health Corporation, Birmingham, AL
Primary Contact: Stephanie Bridges, Chief Executive Officer
CFO: Eric Gray, Chief Financial Officer
CMO: Jonathan D Ellen, M.D., Medical Director
CHR: Sandra Milburn, Director Human Resources
CNO: Jennifer Ferrell, Chief Nursing Officer
Web address: www.healthsouthmemphis.com
Control: Partnership, Investor–owned (for–profit) **Service**: Rehabilitation

Staffed Beds: 72	

☒ **ENCOMPASS HEALTH REHABILITATION HOSPITAL OF NORTH MEMPHIS (443031)**, 4100 Austin Peay Highway, Zip 38128–2502; tel. 901/213–5400, **A**1 10 **F**3 28 29 34 35 57 59 75 77 82 87 90 91 96 130 132 148 157 **S** Encompass Health Corporation, Birmingham, AL
Primary Contact: Adam Yoe, Chief Executive Officer
CFO: Thaddeus Williams, Controller
CMO: Donald Sullivan, M.D., Medical Director
CHR: Adrienne Huntley, Director Human Resources
CNO: Charlotte Boyce, Chief Nursing Officer
Web address: www.healthsouthnorthmemphis.com
Control: Corporation, Investor–owned (for–profit) **Service**: Rehabilitation

Staffed Beds: 50 **Admissions:** 1126 **Census:** 37 **Outpatient Visits:** 0 **Births:** 0 **Total Expense ($000):** 14085 **Payroll Expense ($000):** 7313 **Personnel:** 117	

TN

Many Facility Codes have changed. Please refer to the AHA Guide Code Chart. © 2019 AHA Guide

☐ **LAKESIDE BEHAVIORAL HEALTH SYSTEM (444004)**, 2911 Brunswick Road, Zip 38133–4199; tel. 901/377–4700, **A**1 3 5 10 **F**4 5 34 38 54 56 98 99 100 101 102 103 104 105 106 130 132 149 152 153 154 **S** Universal Health Services, Inc., King of Prussia, PA
Primary Contact: Joy Golden, Chief Executive Officer
CFO: Thomas Joyner, Chief Financial Officer
CMO: C Hal Brunt, M.D., Medical Director
CIO: Jacob Arnett, Chief Information Technology Officer
CHR: Lori Deason, Director
CNO: Scott Thomason, Chief Nursing Officer
Web address: www.lakesidebhs.com
Control: Corporation, Investor–owned (for–profit) **Service**: Psychiatric

> **Staffed Beds: 345 Admissions: 9207 Census: 261 Outpatient Visits: 21373 Births: 0 Total Expense ($000): 48321 Payroll Expense ($000): 24218 Personnel: 517**

LE BONHEUR CHILDREN'S HOSPITAL See Methodist Healthcare Memphis Hospitals, Memphis

☐ **MEMPHIS MENTAL HEALTH INSTITUTE (444001)**, 951 Court Ave, Zip 38103–2813, Mailing Address: P.O. Box 63656, Zip 38163–3656; tel. 901/577–1800, **A**1 3 5 10 **F**29 38 50 98 100 101 130 154
Primary Contact: Josh Carter, Chief Executive Officer
CFO: Donny Hornsby, Director Fiscal Services
CHR: Claudette Seymour, Director Personnel
Web address: www.tn.gov/mental/mhs/mhs2.html
Control: State, Government, nonfederal **Service**: Psychiatric

> **Staffed Beds: 55 Admissions: 1436 Census: 48 Outpatient Visits: 0 Births: 0 Total Expense ($000): 19385 Payroll Expense ($000): 9949 Personnel: 153**

⊞ △ **MEMPHIS VETERANS AFFAIRS MEDICAL CENTER**, 1030 Jefferson Avenue, Zip 38104–2193; tel. 901/523–8990, (Nonreporting) **A**1 3 5 7 **S** Department of Veterans Affairs, Washington, DC
Primary Contact: David K. Dunning, Medical Center Director and Chief Executive Officer
CFO: Kristi Depperman, Chief Financial Officer
CMO: Christopher Marino, M.D., Chief of Staff
CIO: Robert Page III Chief Information and Technology Officer
CHR: Natalie Brown, Chief Human Resources Management Services
CNO: Karen Gillette, Associate Director Patient Care Services
Web address: www.memphis.va.gov/
Control: Veterans Affairs, Government, federal **Service**: General medical and surgical

> **Staffed Beds: 261**

⊞ **METHODIST HEALTHCARE MEMPHIS HOSPITALS (440049)**, 1265 Union Avenue, Zip 38104–3415; tel. 901/516–7000, (Includes LE BONHEUR CHILDREN'S HOSPITAL, 848 Adams Avenue, Memphis, Tennessee, Zip 38103; tel. 901/287–5437; Michael Wiggins, President; METHODIST HEALTHCARE–NORTH HOSPITAL, 3960 New Covington Pike, Memphis, Tennessee, Zip 38128; tel. 901/516–5200; Florence Jones, President; METHODIST HEALTHCARE–SOUTH HOSPITAL, 1300 Wesley Drive, Memphis, Tennessee, Zip 38116, tel. 901/516–3700; Jessie Lee Tucker III, Ph.D., Chief Executive Officer; METHODIST LE BONHEUR GERMANTOWN HOSPITAL, 7691 Poplar Avenue, Germantown, Tennessee, Zip 38138; tel. 901/516–6000; Rebecca Cullison, President) **A**1 2 3 5 8 10 **F**3 7 8 9 11 12 13 15 17 18 19 20 21 22 23 24 25 26 27 28 29 30 31 32 34 35 37 38 39 40 41 43 44 45 46 47 48 49 50 54 55 56 57 58 59 60 61 64 65 68 70 71 72 73 74 75 76 78 79 80 81 82 84 85 86 87 88 89 91 92 93 94 96 97 98 100 101 102 103 104 107 108 110 111 112 113 114 115 116 117 118 119 120 121 123 126 129 130 131 132 134 135 136 137 138 139 141 142 143 144 146 147 148 149 150 154 156 **S** Methodist Le Bonheur Healthcare, Memphis, TN
Primary Contact: Michael Ugwueke, President and Chief Executive Officer
CFO: Chris McLean, Chief Administrative Officer
CIO: Mark W McMath, Chief Information Officer
CHR: Carol Ross-Spang, Chief Human Resources Officer
CNO: Nikki S Polis, Ph.D., Chief Nurse Executive
Web address: www.methodisthealth.org
Control: Other not–for–profit (including NFP Corporation) **Service**: General medical and surgical

> **Staffed Beds: 1362 Admissions: 62200 Census: 970 Outpatient Visits: 1122681 Births: 4902 Total Expense ($000): 1710683 Payroll Expense ($000): 514330 Personnel: 7708**

★ △ **REGIONAL ONE HEALTH (440152)**, 877 Jefferson Avenue, Zip 38103–2897; tel. 901/545–7100, (Total facility includes 16 beds in nursing home–type unit) **A**3 5 7 10 **F**1 3 8 11 13 15 16 18 20 22 29 30 32 34 35 38 40 43 44 45 46 48 49 50 52 54 55 56 57 58 59 61 64 65 66 68 70 72 74 75 76 77 79 80 81 82 85 86 87 90 91 92 93 94 96 97 100 107 108 110 111 115 119 128 130 131 132 135 141 146 147 148 149 150 154 158
Primary Contact: Reginald W. Coopwood, M.D., President and Chief Executive Officer
COO: Rob Sumter, Executive Vice President and Chief Operating Officer
CFO: Rick Wagers, Senior Executive Vice President and Chief Financial Officer
CMO: Martin Croce, M.D., Senior Vice President and Chief Medical Officer
CIO: Rob Sumter, Executive Vice President and Chief Operation Officer
CHR: Sarah Colley, Senior Vice President Human Resources
CNO: Pam Castleman, MSN, Chief Nursing Officer
Web address: www.regionalonehealth.org
Control: Other not–for–profit (including NFP Corporation) **Service**: General medical and surgical

> **Staffed Beds: 382 Admissions: 14209 Census: 287 Outpatient Visits: 239759 Births: 3208 Total Expense ($000): 475992 Payroll Expense ($000): 170002 Personnel: 397**

REGIONAL ONE HEALTH EXTENDED CARE HOSPITAL (442017), 890 Madison Avenue, Turner Tower, Zip 38103–3409; tel. 901/515–3000, (Nonreporting) **A**10
Primary Contact: Mark Kelly, Administrator
CNO: Paula Harrell, Chief Nursing Officer
Web address: www.regionalonehealth.org/extended-care-hospital/
Control: Other not–for–profit (including NFP Corporation) **Service**: Acute long–term care hospital

> **Staffed Beds: 21**

⊞ **SAINT FRANCIS HOSPITAL (440183)**, 5959 Park Avenue, Zip 38119–5198; tel. 901/765–1000, **A**1 3 10 **F**3 8 11 12 13 15 17 18 20 22 24 26 28 29 30 31 34 35 37 38 40 45 46 47 48 49 50 54 57 58 59 64 70 72 74 75 76 77 78 79 81 85 86 87 90 93 98 99 100 101 102 103 106 107 108 110 111 114 115 118 119 121 123 124 126 130 131 132 142 146 147 148 149 **S** TENET Healthcare Corporation, Dallas, TX
Primary Contact: Audrey Gregory, R.N., MSN, Chief Executive Officer
COO: Samuel Pieh, Chief Operating Officer
CFO: Steven Frantz, Chief Financial Officer
CMO: David Schwartz, M.D., Chief Medical Officer
CIO: Keith Scarbrough, Director, Information Systems
CHR: Keith Stanhill, Chief Human Resources Officer
CNO: Jennifer Chiusano, R.N., Chief Nursing Officer
Web address: www.saintfrancishosp.com
Control: Corporation, Investor–owned (for–profit) **Service**: General medical and surgical

> **Staffed Beds: 415 Admissions: 15382 Census: 212 Outpatient Visits: 118221 Births: 1255 Total Expense ($000): 268691 Payroll Expense ($000): 80273 Personnel: 1129**

⊞ **SELECT SPECIALTY HOSPITAL-MEMPHIS (442014)**, 5959 Park Avenue, 12th Floor, Zip 38119–5200; tel. 901/765–1245, (Nonreporting) **A**1 10 **S** Select Medical Corporation, Mechanicsburg, PA
Primary Contact: Marcia Taylor, Chief Executive Officer
Web address: www.selectspecialtyhospitals.com/company/locations/memphis.aspx
Control: Corporation, Investor–owned (for–profit) **Service**: Acute long–term care hospital

> **Staffed Beds: 39**

⊞ **ST. JUDE CHILDREN'S RESEARCH HOSPITAL (443302)**, 262 Danny Thomas Place, Zip 38105–3678; tel. 901/595–3300, **A**1 3 5 10 **F**31 39 53 78 81 86 88 89 100 104 120 121 122 124
Primary Contact: James R. Downing, M.D., Chief Executive Officer
COO: Mary Anna Quinn, Executive Vice President, Chief Administrative Officer
CFO: Patricia Keel, Senior Vice President and Chief Financial Officer
CMO: Ellis Neufeld, M.D., Chief Medical Officer
CIO: Darrin Keith Perry, Chief Information Officer and Senior Vice President
CHR: Dana Bottenfield, Vice President Human Resources
Web address: www.stjude.org
Control: Other not–for–profit (including NFP Corporation) **Service**: Children's Cancer

> **Staffed Beds: 69 Admissions: 3412 Census: 54 Outpatient Visits: 79024 Births: 0 Total Expense ($000): 950716 Payroll Expense ($000): 393559**

VETERANS AFFAIRS MEDICAL CENTER See Memphis Veterans Affairs Medical Center

MILAN—Gibson County

⊞ **MILAN GENERAL HOSPITAL (440060)**, 4039 Highland Street, Zip 38358–3483; tel. 731/686–1591, **A**1 10 **F**3 15 29 30 35 40 44 45 57 59 64 68 70 81 87 107 110 114 119 130 132 133 135 146 149 **S** West Tennessee Healthcare, Jackson, TN
Primary Contact: Sherry Scruggs, Administrator
CMO: Joe Appleton, M.D., Chief of Surgery
CNO: Carolyn Drake, Director of Nursing
Web address: www.wth.org
Control: Hospital district or authority, Government, nonfederal **Service:** General medical and surgical

Staffed Beds: 28 **Admissions:** 486 **Census:** 5 **Outpatient Visits:** 13604
Births: 0 **Total Expense ($000):** 9664 **Payroll Expense ($000):** 4038
Personnel: 77

MORRISTOWN—Hamblen County

☐ **MORRISTOWN-HAMBLEN HEALTHCARE SYSTEM (440030)**, 908 West Fourth North Street, Zip 37814–3894, Mailing Address: P.O. Box 1178, Zip 37816–1178; tel. 423/492–9000, **A**1 2 3 5 10 **F**3 11 13 15 18 20 22 26 28 29 30 31 34 35 39 40 41 44 45 46 47 49 50 51 56 57 58 59 60 61 64 68 74 75 76 78 79 80 81 82 85 86 87 93 94 96 98 101 102 103 107 108 110 111 114 115 117 118 119 120 121 123 129 130 131 132 135 146 147 148 154 156 **S** Covenant Health, Knoxville, TN
Primary Contact: Gordon Lintz, President and Chief Administrative Officer
CFO: Amy Herndon, Chief Finance Officer
CIO: Mike Ward, Chief Information Officer
CNO: Wilma Hart-Flynn, Ph.D., R.N., Chief Nursing Officer
Web address: www.morristownhamblen.com
Control: Other not–for–profit (including NFP Corporation) **Service:** General medical and surgical

Staffed Beds: 131 **Admissions:** 6389 **Census:** 75 **Outpatient Visits:** 104233 **Births:** 859 **Total Expense ($000):** 81573 **Payroll Expense ($000):** 31721 **Personnel:** 560

MOUNTAIN CITY—Johnson County

JOHNSON COUNTY COMMUNITY HOSPITAL (441304), 1901 South Shady Street, Zip 37683–2271; tel. 423/727–1100, **A**5 10 18 **F**3 15 18 28 30 34 35 40 44 50 56 57 62 64 68 87 93 97 107 108 110 114 119 127 154 **S** Ballad Health, Johnson City, TN
Primary Contact: Chastity Trivette, Chief Executive Officer
CNO: Helen Pardue, Interim Chief Nursing Officer
Web address: www.msha.com
Control: Other not–for–profit (including NFP Corporation) **Service:** General medical and surgical

Staffed Beds: 2 **Admissions:** 33 **Census:** 1 **Outpatient Visits:** 39707
Births: 0 **Total Expense ($000):** 8952 **Payroll Expense ($000):** 4236
Personnel: 163

MOUNTAIN HOME—Johnson County

⊞ **JAMES H. QUILLEN VETERANS AFFAIRS MEDICAL CENTER**, Corner of Lamont & Veterans Way, Zip 37684, Mailing Address: P.O. Box 4000, Zip 37684–4000; tel. 423/926–1171, (Nonreporting) **A**1 3 5 **S** Department of Veterans Affairs, Washington, DC
Primary Contact: Dean B. Borsos, Medical Center Director
CFO: Sandra Nash, Chief Fiscal Service
CMO: David Hecht, M.D., Chief of Staff
CIO: Karen Perry, Chief Information Resource Management Services
CHR: John Henderson, Chief Human Resources Management
CNO: Linda M McConnell, R.N., MSN, FACHE, Associate Medical Center Director Patient Care Services
Web address: www.mountainhome.va.gov/
Control: Veterans Affairs, Government, federal **Service:** General medical and surgical

Staffed Beds: 98

MURFREESBORO—Rutherford County

ALVIN C. YORK CAMPUS See Tennessee Valley Healthcare System, Nashville

⊞ **SAINT THOMAS RUTHERFORD HOSPITAL (440053)**, 1700 Medical Center Parkway, Zip 37129–2245; tel. 615/396–4100, (Nonreporting) **A**1 2 3 5 10 **S** Ascension Healthcare, Saint Louis, MO
Primary Contact: Gordon B. Ferguson, President and Chief Executive Officer
COO: Thomas Roddy, Chief Operating Officer
CFO: Bailey Pratt, Chief Financial Officer
CMO: Richard Rogers, M.D., Chief Medical Officer
CHR: Carol Bragdon, Director Human Resources
CNO: Stacey Beaven, R.N., Chief Nursing Officer
Web address: www.mtmc.org
Control: Church operated **Service:** General medical and surgical

Staffed Beds: 286

☐ **TRUSTPOINT HOSPITAL (440231)**, 1009 North Thompson Lane, Zip 37129–4351; tel. 615/867–1111, **A**1 10 **F**3 29 34 59 64 77 90 93 98 99 100 101 102 103 104 130 132 135 148 149 150 153 154 **S** Acadia Healthcare Company, Inc., Franklin, TN
Primary Contact: Beth Goodner, Chief Executive Officer
Web address: www.trustpointhospital.com
Control: Corporation, Investor–owned (for–profit) **Service:** General medical and surgical

Staffed Beds: 101 **Admissions:** 229 **Census:** 59 **Outpatient Visits:** 15407
Births: 0 **Total Expense ($000):** 30501 **Payroll Expense ($000):** 16046

NASHVILLE—Davidson County

CENTENNIAL MEDICAL CENTER See Tristar Centennial Medical Center

☐ **CURAHEALTH NASHVILLE (442006)**, 1412 County Hospital Road, Zip 37218–3007; tel. 615/687–2600, **A**1 10 **F**1 3 29 75 130 148 **S** Curahealth Hospitals, Garland, TX
Primary Contact: Timothy C. Deaton, Chief Executive Officer
CFO: Philip L Jones, Chief Financial Officer
CMO: Clyde Heflin, M.D., Chief Medical Officer
Web address: www.curahealth.com
Control: Corporation, Investor–owned (for–profit) **Service:** Acute long–term care hospital

Staffed Beds: 60 **Admissions:** 110 **Census:** 8 **Outpatient Visits:** 0
Births: 0 **Total Expense ($000):** 5411 **Payroll Expense ($000):** 1664
Personnel: 207

☐ **MIDDLE TENNESSEE MENTAL HEALTH INSTITUTE (444014)**, 221 Stewarts Ferry Pike, Zip 37214–3325; tel. 615/902–7535, **A**1 3 5 10 **F**3 29 30 75 98 101 102 103 130
Primary Contact: Rob Cotterman, Chief Executive Officer
CFO: Mark Stanley, Director Fiscal Services
CMO: Mohammad S Jahan, M.D., Clinical Director
CHR: Margie Dunn, Director Human Resources
Web address: www.tn.gov/mental/mhs/mhs2.html
Control: State, Government, nonfederal **Service:** Psychiatric

Staffed Beds: 207 **Admissions:** 3054 **Census:** 157 **Outpatient Visits:** 0
Births: 0 **Total Expense ($000):** 53206 **Payroll Expense ($000):** 28435
Personnel: 566

MONROE CARELL JR. CHILDREN'S HOSPITAL AT VANDERBILT See Vanderbilt University Medical Center, Nashville

☐ **NASHVILLE GENERAL HOSPITAL (440111)**, 1818 Albion Street, Zip 37208–2918; tel. 615/341–4000, **A**1 2 3 5 10 **F**3 9 11 13 14 15 18 20 22 26 29 30 31 34 35 39 40 44 45 49 50 55 57 58 59 60 64 66 68 70 73 74 75 76 77 78 79 80 81 85 86 87 92 93 96 97 102 107 108 110 111 114 118 119 124 130 131 135 141 144 146 147 148 149
Primary Contact: Joseph Webb, Chief Executive Officer
CMO: Deann Bullock, M.D., Chief Medical Officer
CIO: Chris Whorley, Chief Information Officer
CHR: Diana Wohlfardt, Director Human Resources
CNO: Leonora Collins, Chief Nursing Officer
Web address: www.nashvillegeneral.org/
Control: Hospital district or authority, Government, nonfederal **Service:** General medical and surgical

Staffed Beds: 114 **Admissions:** 2450 **Census:** 29 **Outpatient Visits:** 86237
Births: 317 **Total Expense ($000):** 103721 **Payroll Expense ($000):** 33939
Personnel: 551

⊞ **SAINT THOMAS HOSPITAL FOR SPINAL SURGERY (440218)**, 2011 Murphy Avenue, Suite 400, Zip 37203–2065; tel. 615/341–7500, (Nonreporting) **A**1 10 **S** Ascension Healthcare, Saint Louis, MO
Primary Contact: Kathy Watson, R.N., Administrator and Chief Nursing Officer
CFO: Angie Crow, Director Finance
CMO: Carl Hampf, M.D., Chief Medical Officer
Web address: www.hospitalforspinalsurgery.com
Control: Partnership, Investor–owned (for–profit) **Service:** General medical and surgical

Staffed Beds: 23

TN

Many Facility Codes have changed. Please refer to the AHA Guide Code Chart. © 2019 AHA Guide

✠ **SAINT THOMAS MIDTOWN HOSPITAL (440133)**, 2000 Church Street, Zip 37236–0002; tel. 615/284–5555, (Nonreporting) **A**1 2 3 5 10 **S** Ascension Healthcare, Saint Louis, MO
Primary Contact: Fahad Tahir, Chief Executive Officer
COO: Jeremy Gray, Chief Operating Officer
CFO: Pamela Hess, Chief Financial Officer
CMO: William Thompson, M.D., Chief Medical Officer
CIO: Jim Drew, Chief Information Officer
CHR: Martha Underwood, Chief Human Resources Officer
CNO: Marco Fernandez, R.N., MSN, Chief Nursing Officer
Web address: www.sths.com
Control: Church operated **Service**: General medical and surgical

Staffed Beds: 425

✠ **SAINT THOMAS WEST HOSPITAL (440082)**, 4220 Harding Road, Zip 37205–2095, Mailing Address: P.O. Box 380, Zip 37202–0380; tel. 615/222–2111, (Nonreporting) **A**1 2 3 5 10 **S** Ascension Healthcare, Saint Louis, MO
Primary Contact: Fahad Tahir, Chief Executive Officer
COO: Harrison Kiser, Chief Operating Officer
CFO: Pamela Hess, Chief Financial Officer
CMO: Dale Batchelor, M.D., Chief Medical Officer
CHR: Bud Wood, Chief Human Resources Officer
CNO: Sam Straton, Chief Nursing Officer
Web address: www.stthomas.org
Control: Church operated **Service**: General medical and surgical

Staffed Beds: 395

✠ **SELECT SPECIALTY HOSPITAL-NASHVILLE (442011)**, 2000 Hayes Street, Zip 37203–2318; tel. 615/284–4599, (Nonreporting) **A**1 10 **S** Select Medical Corporation, Mechanicsburg, PA
Primary Contact: Jennifer Causey, Chief Executive Officer
CNO: Karen Cagle, Chief Nursing Officer
Web address: www.selectspecialtyhospitals.com/company/locations/nashville.aspx
Control: Corporation, Investor–owned (for–profit) **Service**: Acute long–term care hospital

Staffed Beds: 70

✠ **TENNESSEE VALLEY HEALTHCARE SYSTEM**, 1310 24th Avenue South, Zip 37212–2637; tel. 615/327–4751, (Includes ALVIN C. YORK CAMPUS, 3400 Lebanon Pike, Murfreesboro, Tennessee, Zip 37129–1236; tel. 615/867–6000; NASHVILLE CAMPUS, 1310 24th Avenue South, Nashville, Tennessee, Zip 37212–2637; tel. 615/327–4751) (Total facility includes 178 beds in nursing home–type unit) **A**1 3 5 F1 2 3 4 6 6 7 8 9 10 12 15 18 20 22 24 26 28 29 30 31 33 34 35 36 38 39 40 44 45 46 47 48 49 50 51 53 54 55 56 57 58 59 60 61 62 63 64 65 66 67 70 74 75 77 78 79 80 81 82 83 84 85 86 87 91 92 93 94 95 96 97 98 100 101 102 103 104 105 106 107 109 111 113 114 115 116 117 118 119 120 121 125 126 127 128 129 130 131 132 133 135 136 137 138 139 140 143 144 145 146 147 148 149 150 152 153 154 156 157 158 **S** Department of Veterans Affairs, Washington, DC
Primary Contact: Jennifer Vedral-Baron, Health System Director
COO: Suzanne L. Jene, Chief Operating Officer
CFO: Lynn Menthcoast, Chief Fiscal Service
CMO: Roger Jones, M.D., Interim Chief of Staff
CIO: Paul Mardy, Chief Information Technology Officer
CHR: Shirley F Pettite, Chief Human Resources Officer
CNO: Janice M Cobb, R.N., Chief Nursing Officer
Web address: www.tennesseevalley.va.gov
Control: Veterans Affairs, Government, federal **Service**: General medical and surgical

Staffed Beds: 437 **Admissions**: 9313 **Census**: 301 **Outpatient Visits**: 1278792 **Births**: 0 **Total Expense ($000)**: 918616 **Payroll Expense ($000)**: 351740 **Personnel**: 4500

✠ **TRISTAR CENTENNIAL MEDICAL CENTER (440161)**, 2300 Patterson Street, Zip 37203–1528; tel. 615/342–1000, (Includes TRISTAR CENTENNIAL WOMEN'S & CHILDREN'S, 2221 Murphy Avenue, Nashville, Tennessee, Zip 37203; tel. 615/342–1000), (Nonreporting) **A**1 2 5 10 **S** HCA Healthcare, Nashville, TN
Primary Contact: Scott A. Cihak, President and Chief Executive Officer
COO: Justin Coury, Chief Operating Officer
CFO: Tom Jackson, Chief Financial Officer
CHR: Jennifer Burden, Human Resources Director
Web address: www.tristarcentennial.com
Control: Corporation, Investor–owned (for–profit) **Service**: General medical and surgical

Staffed Beds: 650

△ **TRISTAR SKYLINE MEDICAL CENTER (440006)**, 3441 Dickerson Pike, Zip 37207–2539; tel. 615/769–2000, (Includes TRISTAR SKYLINE MADISON CAMPUS, 500 Hospital Drive, Madison, Tennessee, Zip 37115–5032; tel. 615/769–5000; Steve Otto, Chief Executive Officer), (Non-reporting) **A**1 2 7 10 **S** HCA Healthcare, Nashville, TN
Primary Contact: Steve Otto, Chief Executive Officer
COO: Jason E Boyd, Chief Operating Officer
CFO: Michael Morrison, Chief Financial Officer
CMO: Christopher Conley, M.D., President of the Medical Staff
CIO: Troy Sypien, Director Information Technology and Systems
CHR: Robert A Hooper, Director Human Resources
CNO: Christine Staigl, Chief Nursing Officer
Web address: www.tristarskyline.com
Control: Corporation, Investor–owned (for–profit) **Service**: General medical and surgical

Staffed Beds: 579

✠ **TRISTAR SOUTHERN HILLS MEDICAL CENTER (440197)**, 391 Wallace Road, Zip 37211–4859, Mailing Address: 3441 Dickerson Pike, Zip 37207; tel. 615/781–4000, (Nonreporting) **A**1 2 10 **S** HCA Healthcare, Nashville, TN
Primary Contact: Joanna J. Conley, FACHE, Chief Executive Officer
CFO: John Porada, Chief Financial Officer
CMO: Eric Schuck, M.D., Chief Medical Officer
CIO: Ronnie Gannon, Director Information Services
CHR: Gary Briggs, Vice President Human Resources
Web address: www.tristarsouthernhills.com
Control: Corporation, Investor–owned (for–profit) **Service**: General medical and surgical

Staffed Beds: 87

VANDERBILT PSYCHIATRIC HOSPITAL See Vanderbilt University Medical Center, Nashville

✠ **VANDERBILT STALLWORTH REHABILITATION HOSPITAL (443028)**, 2201 Childrens Way, Zip 37212–3165; tel. 615/320–7600, (Nonreporting) **A**1 3 5 10 **S** Encompass Health Corporation, Birmingham, AL
Primary Contact: Jeffrey Palmucci, Chief Executive Officer
CFO: Christine Campbell, Controller
CMO: Jeffery Johns, M.D., Medical Director
CHR: Ruth Beasley, Director Human Resources
CNO: Karen Lasher, Chief Nursing Officer
Web address: www.vanderbiltstallworthrehab.com
Control: Corporation, Investor–owned (for–profit) **Service**: Rehabilitation

Staffed Beds: 80

✠ **VANDERBILT UNIVERSITY MEDICAL CENTER (440039)**, 1211 Medical Center Drive, Zip 37232–2102; tel. 615/322–5000, (Includes MONROE CARELL JR. CHILDREN'S HOSPITAL AT VANDERBILT, 2200 Children's Way, Nashville, Tennessee, Zip 37232; tel. 615/936–1000; Luke Gregory, Chief Executive Officer; VANDERBILT PSYCHIATRIC HOSPITAL, 1001 23rd Avenue South, Nashville, Tennessee, Zip 37212–3198; tel. 615/320 7770) **A**1 2 3 5 8 10 **F**3 4 5 6 7 8 9 12 13 15 16 17 18 19 20 21 22 23 24 25 26 27 28 29 30 31 32 34 35 36 37 38 39 40 41 43 44 45 46 47 48 49 50 51 52 53 54 55 56 57 58 59 60 61 62 63 64 65 66 68 70 71 72 74 75 76 77 78 79 80 81 82 83 84 85 86 87 88 89 91 92 93 94 96 97 98 99 100 101 102 103 104 105 107 108 109 110 111 114 115 116 117 118 119 120 121 123 124 126 129 130 131 132 134 135 136 137 138 139 140 141 142 144 146 147 148 149 150 151 152 153 154 156 157 158 **S** Vanderbilt Health, Nashville, TN
Primary Contact: Jeffrey R. Balsar, President and Chief Executive Officer Vanderbilt Medical Center and Dean, Vanderbilt University Scho
CFO: Cecelia B Moore, CPA, Associate Vice Chancellor Finance
CMO: Paul Sternberg, M.D., Professor and Chairman
CIO: William Stead, Associate Vice Chancellor Health Affairs, Director Informatics Center and Chief Strategy and Information Officer
CHR: Traci Nordberg, Chief Human Resources Officer
CNO: Pam Jones, MSN, R.N., Associate Hospital Director and Chief Nursing Officer
Web address: www.mc.vanderbilt.edu
Control: Other not-for-profit (including NFP Corporation) **Service**: General medical and surgical

Staffed Beds: 1051 **Admissions**: 57511 **Census**: 889 **Outpatient Visits**: 2187533 **Births**: 4409 **Total Expense ($000)**: 3280990 **Payroll Expense ($000)**: 1207461 **Personnel**: 24377

VETERANS AFFAIRS TENNESSEE VALLEY HEALTHCARE SYSTEM See Tennessee Valley Healthcare System

TN

NEWPORT—Cocke County

BAPTIST HOSPITAL OF COCKE COUNTY See Tennova Newport Medical Center

☒ **TENNOVA NEWPORT MEDICAL CENTER (440153)**, 435 Second Street, Zip 37821–3799; tel. 423/625–2200, (Nonreporting) **A**1 10 **S** Community Health Systems, Inc., Franklin, TN
Primary Contact: Matthew Littlejohn, Chief Executive Officer
CFO: Jon Richards, Chief Financial Officer
CMO: Larry Mathers, M.D., Chief of Staff
CNO: Tonia Hale, Chief Nursing Officer
Web address: www.tennova.com
Control: Corporation, Investor–owned (for–profit) **Service:** General medical and surgical

Staffed Beds: 47

OAK RIDGE—Anderson County

☐ **METHODIST MEDICAL CENTER OF OAK RIDGE (440034)**, 990 Oak Ridge Turnpike, Zip 37830–6976, Mailing Address: P.O. Box 2529, Zip 37831–2529; tel. 865/835–1000, **A**1 2 3 5 10 **F**3 11 13 15 17 18 20 22 24 26 28 29 30 31 34 35 39 40 44 45 49 50 51 54 57 58 59 60 61 64 68 70 74 75 76 78 79 80 81 84 85 86 87 92 93 94 96 102 107 108 110 111 114 115 118 119 120 121 123 126 129 130 132 135 146 148 154 156 **S** Covenant Health, Knoxville, TN
Primary Contact: Jeremy Biggs, President and Chief Administrative Officer
COO: Connie Martin, Vice President and Chief Support Officer
CFO: Rick Carringer, Vice President and Chief Financial Officer
CMO: Mark Browne, M.D., Covenant Health, Senior Vice President and Chief Medical Officer
CIO: Mike Ward, Covenant Health, Senior Vice President and Chief Information Officer
CHR: Rick Akens, Director Human Resources and Labor Relations
CNO: Sue Harris, Vice President and Chief Nursing Officer
Web address: www.mmcoakridge.com
Control: Other not–for–profit (including NFP Corporation) **Service:** General medical and surgical

Staffed Beds: 210 **Admissions:** 10106 **Census:** 124 **Outpatient Visits:** 156826 **Births:** 458 **Total Expense ($000):** 154474 **Payroll Expense ($000):** 57391 **Personnel:** 878

RIDGEVIEW PSYCHIATRIC HOSPITAL AND CENTER (444003), 240 West Tyrone Road, Zip 37830–6571; tel. 865/482–1076, (Nonreporting) **A**10
Primary Contact: Brian Buuck, Chief Executive Officer
CFO: Mary Claire Duff, CPA, Chief Financial Officer
CMO: Renu Bhateja, M.D., President Medical Staff
CHR: Julie M Wright, Director Human Resources
Web address: www.ridgeviewresources.com
Control: Other not–for–profit (including NFP Corporation) **Service:** Psychiatric

Staffed Beds: 20

ONEIDA—Scott County

⇑ **BIG SOUTH FORK MEDICAL CENTER (440235)**, 18797 Alberta Street, Zip 37841–2127; tel. 423/286–5500, **A**10 21 **F**3 29 34 40 107 114 135 149 154
Primary Contact: Hal W. Leftwich, FACHE, Chief Executive Officer
Web address: www.bsfmedical.com
Control: Corporation, Investor–owned (for–profit) **Service:** General medical and surgical

Staffed Beds: 25 **Admissions:** 531 **Census:** 4

PARIS—Henry County

☒ **HENRY COUNTY MEDICAL CENTER (440132)**, 301 Tyson Avenue, Zip 38242–4544, Mailing Address: P.O. Box 1030, Zip 38242–1030; tel. 731/642–1220, (Total facility includes 116 beds in nursing home–type unit) **A**1 10 **F**3 7 11 13 15 18 20 28 29 30 32 34 35 37 40 44 50 51 53 56 57 59 62 63 64 65 67 68 70 71 76 77 79 81 85 86 87 89 93 98 100 102 103 107 108 110 111 114 115 118 119 126 127 128 129 130 131 132 133 135 143 146 147 148 154 156
Primary Contact: Lisa Casteel, Chief Executive Officer
CIO: Pam Ridley, Director Information Systems
CHR: Edwin L Ledden, Assistant Administrator and Director Human Resources
CNO: Cynthia Whitaker, Chief Nursing Officer
Web address: www.hcmc-tn.org
Control: Hospital district or authority, Government, nonfederal **Service:** General medical and surgical

Staffed Beds: 202 **Admissions:** 3838 **Census:** 120 **Outpatient Visits:** 136619 **Births:** 286 **Total Expense ($000):** 90084 **Payroll Expense ($000):** 41853 **Personnel:** 652

PARSONS—Decatur County

☐ **DECATUR COUNTY GENERAL HOSPITAL (440070)**, 969 Tennessee Avenue South, Zip 38363–3700, Mailing Address: P.O. Box 250, Zip 38363–0250; tel. 731/847–3031, (Nonreporting) **A**1 10
Primary Contact: Mike Creasy, Chief Executive Officer
CFO: Donna Hayes, Controller
CMO: Tom Hamilton, M.D., Chief of Staff
CHR: Shelley Bartholomew, Director Human Resources
Web address: www.dcgh.org
Control: Corporation, Investor–owned (for–profit) **Service:** General medical and surgical

Staffed Beds: 40

PIKEVILLE—Bledsoe County

⇑ **ERLANGER BLEDSOE HOSPITAL (441306)**, 71 Wheeler Avenue, Zip 37367, Mailing Address: P.O. Box 699, Zip 37367–0699; tel. 423/447–2112, **A**10 18 21 **F**3 11 18 28 29 30 34 35 38 40 42 44 50 53 54 56 57 58 59 61 63 64 65 66 68 74 75 79 82 84 86 87 92 93 96 97 102 107 119 127 130 132 133 135 145 146 147 148 154 156 157 **S** Erlanger Health System, Chattanooga, TN
Primary Contact: Stephanie Boynton, Administrator
CMO: Arturo L Quito, M.D., Chief of Staff
CIO: Debbie Rains, Coordinator Health Information Management
CHR: Patsy Brown, Site Coordinator Human Resources
Web address: www.erlanger.org
Control: Hospital district or authority, Government, nonfederal **Service:** General medical and surgical

Staffed Beds: 25 **Admissions:** 360 **Census:** 7 **Outpatient Visits:** 25257 **Births:** 0 **Total Expense ($000):** 13593 **Payroll Expense ($000):** 6249 **Personnel:** 128

POWELL—Knox County

MERCY MEDICAL CENTER NORTH See Tennova North Knoxville Medical Center

☒ **SELECT SPECIALTY HOSPITAL-NORTH KNOXVILLE (442015)**, 7557B Dannaher Drive, Suite 145, Zip 37849–3568; tel. 865/512–2450, (Includes SELECT SPECIALTY HOSPITAL-KNOXVILLE, 1901 Clinch Avenue, 4th Floor North, Knoxville, Tennessee, Zip 37916–2307; tel. 865/541–2615; Andrew Howard, Chief Executive Officer), (Non-reporting) **A**1 10 **S** Select Medical Corporation, Mechanicsburg, PA
Primary Contact: Steve Plumlee, Chief Executive Officer
CFO: David Elledge, Controller
CMO: Jeff Summers, M.D., Medical Director
CIO: Steve Plumlee, Chief Executive Officer
CHR: Mallory Wilson, Administrative Assistant and Human Resources Coordinator
CNO: Nancy Johnson, Chief Nursing Officer
Web address: www.northknoxville.selectspecialtyhospitals.com/
Control: Corporation, Investor–owned (for–profit) **Service:** Acute long–term care hospital

Staffed Beds: 33

☒ **TENNOVA NORTH KNOXVILLE MEDICAL CENTER (440120)**, 7565 Dannaher Way, Zip 37849–4029; tel. 865/859–8000, (Includes TENNOVA TURKEY CREEK MEDICAL CENTER, 10820 Parkside Drive, Knoxville, Tennessee, Zip 37934–1956; tel. 865/218–7092; Ben Youree, Chief Executive Officer), (Nonreporting) **A**1 **S** Community Health Systems, Inc., Franklin, TN
Primary Contact: Clyde Wood, Chief Executive Officer
Control: General Investor-owned, for-profit **Service:** General medical and surgical

Staffed Beds: 220

PULASKI—Giles County

☒ **SOUTHERN TENNESSEE REGIONAL HEALTH SYSTEM-PULASKI (440020)**, 1265 East College Street, Zip 38478–4541; tel. 931/363–7531, **A**1 10 **F**3 4 13 15 17 28 29 30 34 39 40 41 44 45 50 51 56 57 59 63 65 66 68 70 74 75 76 77 79 81 82 83 85 87 89 91 93 98 103 107 111 115 116 117 119 129 130 133 146 147 148 154 **S** LifePoint Health, Brentwood, TN
Primary Contact: James H. Edmondson, Chief Executive Officer
CFO: Donald Gavin, Chief Financial Officer
CMO: J Michael Windland, M.D., Chief of Staff
CIO: Mitzi Foster, Director Information Services
CHR: Jane Petty, Director Human Resources
CNO: Sherry Sands, R.N., Chief Nursing Officer
Web address: www.southerntnpulaski.com/
Control: Corporation, Investor–owned (for–profit) **Service:** General medical and surgical

Staffed Beds: 56 **Admissions:** 1898 **Census:** 24 **Outpatient Visits:** 34044 **Births:** 136 **Total Expense ($000):** 32030 **Payroll Expense ($000):** 11842 **Personnel:** 188

Many Facility Codes have changed. Please refer to the AHA Guide Code Chart. © 2019 AHA Guide

ROGERSVILLE—Hawkins County

⊠ **HAWKINS COUNTY MEMORIAL HOSPITAL (440032)**, 851 Locust Street, Zip 37857–2407, Mailing Address: P.O. Box 130, Zip 37857–0130; tel. 423/921–7000, **A**1 5 10 **F**3 15 29 30 34 40 45 50 57 59 64 70 75 80 81 82 85 87 93 107 108 114 119 129 130 133 135 146 154 **S** Ballad Health, Johnson City, TN
Primary Contact: Regina Day, Chief Executive Officer
CFO: Dale Poe, Vice President and Chief Financial Officer
CHR: Robin Poteete, Manager Human Resources
Web address: www.wellmont.org
Control: Other not–for–profit (including NFP Corporation) **Service:** General medical and surgical

Staffed Beds: 22 **Admissions:** 929 **Census:** 9 **Outpatient Visits:** 46159 **Births:** 0 **Total Expense ($000):** 18814 **Payroll Expense ($000):** 5891 **Personnel:** 130

SAVANNAH—Hardin County

★ ⋔ **HARDIN MEDICAL CENTER (440109)**, 935 Wayne Road, Zip 38372–1904; tel. 731/926–8000, (Total facility includes 73 beds in nursing home–type unit) **A**10 21 **F**2 3 7 11 13 15 18 19 28 29 31 34 40 45 57 59 62 65 68 69 75 76 77 78 79 80 81 89 93 107 110 111 115 119 124 128 129 130 133 144 148
Primary Contact: Nicholas P. Lewis, Chief Executive Officer
CFO: Leigh Ann Hughes, Chief Financial Officer
CMO: Gilbert M. Thayer, M.D., Chief Medical Staff
CIO: Jacob Bomar, Director Information Technology
CNO: Jesse Wint, Director of Nursing
Web address: www.hardinmedicalcenter.org
Control: County, Government, nonfederal **Service:** General medical and surgical

Staffed Beds: 122 **Admissions:** 1757 **Census:** 78 **Outpatient Visits:** 62440 **Births:** 361 **Total Expense ($000):** 39470 **Payroll Expense ($000):** 16702 **Personnel:** 392

SEVIERVILLE—Sevier County

☐ **LECONTE MEDICAL CENTER (440081)**, 742 Middle Creek Road, Zip 37862–5019, Mailing Address: P.O. Box 8005, Zip 37864–8005; tel. 865/446–7000, (Total facility includes 51 beds in nursing home–type unit) **A**1 5 10 **F**3 11 13 15 18 20 28 29 30 31 34 35 39 40 44 45 46 50 51 53 57 58 59 61 64 67 68 70 75 76 77 78 79 80 81 82 85 86 87 90 93 94 102 107 108 110 111 114 115 116 117 119 120 121 123 128 130 131 132 133 135 143 146 147 148 149 154 156 **S** Covenant Health, Knoxville, TN
Primary Contact: Gaye Jolly, FACHE, President and Chief Administrative Officer
COO: Michael Hatmaker, Vice President Support Services and Admin Nursing Home
CFO: Jacqueline Hounshell, Chief Financial Officer
CMO: William Clifford Cole, M.D., Chief of Staff
CHR: Tami McClain, Human Resources Operations Specialist
Web address: www.lecontemedicalcenter.com
Control: Other not–for–profit (including NFP Corporation) **Service:** General medical and surgical

Staffed Beds: 128 **Admissions:** 4592 **Census:** 76 **Outpatient Visits:** 132975 **Births:** 1074 **Total Expense ($000):** 94896 **Payroll Expense ($000):** 30137 **Personnel:** 494

SEWANEE—Franklin County

SOUTHERN TENNESSEE REGIONAL HEALTH SYSTEM-SEWANEE See Southern Tennessee Regional Health System-Winchester, Winchester

SHELBYVILLE—Bedford County

⊠ **TENNOVA HEALTHCARE-SHELBYVILLE (440137)**, 2835 Highway 231 North, Zip 37160–7327; tel. 931/685–5433, **A**1 10 **F**3 12 13 15 18 29 34 40 45 57 59 60 64 68 70 76 79 81 85 87 89 93 96 102 107 108 111 115 119 124 129 130 131 132 148 154 **S** Community Health Systems, Inc., Franklin, TN
Primary Contact: Bill Rich, Chief Executive Officer
CFO: Tammy Cobb, Chief Financial Officer
CIO: Jonathon Willis, Director Information Services
CHR: Charisse Parker, Director Human Resources
CNO: Vickie Vaughn, Chief Nursing Officer
Web address: www.Tennova.com
Control: Corporation, Investor–owned (for–profit) **Service:** General medical and surgical

Staffed Beds: 49 **Admissions:** 1400 **Census:** 11 **Births:** 0

SMITHVILLE—Dekalb County

⊠ **SAINT THOMAS DEKALB HOSPITAL (440148)**, 520 West Main Street, Zip 37166–1138, Mailing Address: P.O. Box 640, Zip 37166–0640; tel. 615/215–5000, (Nonreporting) **A**1 10 **S** Ascension Healthcare, Saint Louis, MO
Primary Contact: Bradley Mullinax, Chief Administrative Officer
CFO: Alan Sharp, Chief Financial Officer
CMO: Kimberly Collins, M.D., Chief of Staff
CNO: Emily Elrod, R.N., Chief Nursing Officer
Web address: www.dekalbcommunityhospital.com
Control: Church operated, Nongovernment, not–for–profit **Service:** General medical and surgical

Staffed Beds: 56

SMYRNA—Rutherford County

⊠ **TRISTAR STONECREST MEDICAL CENTER (440227)**, 200 StoneCrest Boulevard, Zip 37167–6810; tel. 615/768–2000, (Nonreporting) **A**1 2 10 **S** HCA Healthcare, Nashville, TN
Primary Contact: Louis Caputo, Chief Executive Officer
COO: Joe Gleason, Chief Operating Officer
CFO: Joseph E Bowman, Chief Financial Officer
CMO: William Mayfield, M.D., Chief of Staff
CHR: Cynthia Adams, Vice President Human Resources
CNO: Amy Cason, MSN, Chief Nursing Officer
Web address: www.stonecrestmedical.com
Control: Corporation, Investor–owned (for–profit) **Service:** General medical and surgical

Staffed Beds: 101

SNEEDVILLE—Hancock County

★ **HANCOCK COUNTY HOSPITAL (441313)**, 1519 Main Street, Zip 37869–3657; tel. 423/733–5000, **A**10 18 **F**3 29 30 34 40 50 57 59 85 87 107 108 119 127 133 135 154 **S** Ballad Health, Johnson City, TN
Primary Contact: Rebecca Beck, President
COO: Eric Deaton, Executive Vice President, Chief Operating Officer and Corporate Operating
CFO: Regina Day, Director of Finance
CIO: Martha O'Regan Chill, Interim Chief Information Officer
CHR: Denise Adams, Human Resources Generalist
CNO: Phyllis Dossett, Director of Clinical Services
Web address: www.wellmont.org/Hospitals/Hancock County Hospital.aspx
Control: Other not–for–profit (including NFP Corporation) **Service:** General medical and surgical

Staffed Beds: 10 **Admissions:** 211 **Census:** 2 **Outpatient Visits:** 22285 **Births:** 0 **Total Expense ($000):** 7027 **Payroll Expense ($000):** 2305 **Personnel:** 43

SPARTA—White County

⊠ **SAINT THOMAS HIGHLANDS HOSPITAL (440192)**, 401 Sewell Road, Zip 38583–1299; tel. 931/738–9211, (Nonreporting) **A**1 10 **S** Ascension Healthcare, Saint Louis, MO
Primary Contact: Richard Tumlin, Chief Administrative Officer
CFO: Rodney VanDonkelaar, Chief Financial Officer
CMO: Robert Knowles, M.D., Chief of Staff
CIO: Glenn Wade, Director Information Systems
CHR: Kent Frisbee, Director Human Resources
CNO: Gearline Copeland, R.N., Chief Nursing Officer
Web address: www.whitecountyhospital.com
Control: Church operated, Nongovernment, not–for–profit **Service:** General medical and surgical

Staffed Beds: 60

SPRINGFIELD—Robertson County

⊠ **NORTHCREST MEDICAL CENTER (440065)**, 100 North Crest Drive, Zip 37172–3961; tel. 615/384–2411, **A**1 10 **F**3 13 18 20 22 28 29 30 34 40 46 57 59 63 64 68 70 75 76 78 79 81 84 85 87 89 107 111 115 116 117 119 128 129 130 131 133 135 146 147 148 149 154 156
Primary Contact: Randy Davis, Chief Executive Officer
CFO: Kim Pridgen, Chief Financial Officer
CHR: Kimberly Walker, Director of Human Resources
CNO: Angie Beard, R.N., Chief Nursing Officer
Web address: www.northcrest.com
Control: Other not–for–profit (including NFP Corporation) **Service:** General medical and surgical

Staffed Beds: 80 **Admissions:** 2756 **Census:** 30 **Outpatient Visits:** 77477

TN

SWEETWATER—Monroe County

⊞ **SWEETWATER HOSPITAL (440084)**, 304 Wright Street, Zip 37874–2823; tel. 865/213–8200, (Nonreporting) **A**1 10
Primary Contact: Scott Bowman, Administrator
CFO: Debbie Thompson, Chief Financial Officer
CMO: David Norris, Chief Medical Staff
CIO: Tony Sharp, Supervisor Information System
CHR: Lucretia Allen, Director Human Resources
CNO: Andrea Henry, Director of Nursing
Web address: www.sweetwaterhospital.org
Control: Other not–for–profit (including NFP Corporation) **Service:** General medical and surgical

Staffed Beds: 59

TAZEWELL—Claiborne County

☐ **CLAIBORNE MEDICAL CENTER (440057)**, 1850 Old Knoxville Road, Zip 37879–3625; tel. 423/626–4211, (Total facility includes 72 beds in nursing home–type unit) **A**1 10 **F**7 11 15 18 28 29 30 34 35 39 40 44 45 50 57 58 59 61 64 67 68 70 75 79 81 85 86 87 93 94 101 102 107 108 115 119 128 130 131 132 135 143 146 148 154 **S** Covenant Health, Knoxville, TN
Primary Contact: Patricia P. Ketterman, R.N., President and Chief Administrative Officer
CFO: Tracee McFarland, Chief Financial Officer
CHR: Susan Stone, Director Human Resources
Web address: www.claibornehospital.org
Control: Other not–for–profit (including NFP Corporation) **Service:** General medical and surgical

Staffed Beds: 105 **Admissions:** 1348 **Census:** 82 **Outpatient Visits:** 37989 **Births:** 0 **Total Expense ($000):** 28841 **Payroll Expense ($000):** 13977 **Personnel:** 309

TULLAHOMA—Coffee County

⊞ **TENNOVA HEALTHCARE-HARTON (440144)**, 1801 North Jackson Street, Zip 37388–8259; tel. 931/393–3000, (Nonreporting) **A**1 10 **S** Community Health Systems, Inc., Franklin, TN
Primary Contact: Richard Ellis, Chief Executive Officer
CFO: Shaun Adams, Chief Financial Officer
CMO: John D Crabtree, M.D., Chief of Staff
CIO: Donald Cooper, Director Information Systems
CHR: Lenore Blackwell, Director Human Resources
Web address: www.hartonmedicalcenter.com
Control: Corporation, Investor–owned (for–profit) **Service:** General medical and surgical

Staffed Beds: 135

UNION CITY—Obion County

⊞ **BAPTIST MEMORIAL HOSPITAL-UNION CITY (440130)**, 1201 Bishop Street, Zip 38261–5403, Mailing Address: P.O. Box 310, Zip 38281–0310; tel. 731/885–2410, **A**1 10 **F**11 13 15 18 20 26 28 29 30 34 35 40 45 48 50 51 53 57 59 63 64 70 75 76 78 79 81 82 84 85 86 87 89 91 93 107 108 109 110 111 115 118 119 121 124 130 132 135 146 156 **S** Baptist Memorial Health Care Corporation, Memphis, TN
Primary Contact: Barry Bondurant, Administrator and Chief Executive Officer
CFO: Mike Perryman, Chief Financial Officer
CMO: Kofi Nuako, M.D., President Medical Staff
CIO: David Mercer, Coordinator Information Systems
CHR: Nicky Thomas, Director Human Resources
CNO: Lori Brown, Chief Nursing Officer
Web address: www.baptistonline.org/union-city/
Control: Other not–for–profit (including NFP Corporation) **Service:** General medical and surgical

Staffed Beds: 63 **Admissions:** 2368 **Census:** 20 **Outpatient Visits:** 51797 **Births:** 280 **Total Expense ($000):** 46822 **Payroll Expense ($000):** 14516 **Personnel:** 244

WAVERLY—Humphreys County

THREE RIVERS HOSPITAL (441303), 451 Highway 13 South, Zip 37185–2109, Mailing Address: P.O. Box 437, Zip 37185–0437; tel. 931/296–4203, (Nonreporting) **A**10 18
Primary Contact: Freda Russell, R.N., Chief Executive Officer and Chief Nursing Officer
CFO: Sandra Patrick, Chief Financial Officer
CMO: George Mathai, M.D., Chief of Staff
CIO: Joe Hildreth, Director Information Technology
CHR: Linda Rawlings, Director Human Resources and Personnel
CNO: Freda Russell, R.N., Chief Executive Officer and Chief Nursing Officer
Web address: www.threerivershospital.org
Control: Other not–for–profit (including NFP Corporation) **Service:** General medical and surgical

Staffed Beds: 25

WAYNESBORO—Wayne County

⊞ **WAYNE MEDICAL CENTER (440010)**, 103 J V Mangubat Drive, Zip 38485–2440, Mailing Address: P.O. Box 580, Zip 38485–0580; tel. 931/722–5411, **A**1 10 20 **F**3 7 15 29 34 35 40 41 45 57 59 68 75 77 81 82 85 86 93 102 107 110 111 114 119 129 130 133 135 149 **S** Maury Regional Health System, Columbia, TN
Primary Contact: Tyler Taylor, Chief Executive Officer
CMO: Harish Veeramachaneni, M.D., Chief of Staff
CHR: Jeff M Pierce, Manager Human Resources
Web address: www.mauryregional.com
Control: County, Government, nonfederal **Service:** General medical and surgical

Staffed Beds: 25 **Admissions:** 355 **Census:** 6 **Outpatient Visits:** 25111 **Births:** 0 **Total Expense ($000):** 13112 **Payroll Expense ($000):** 6090 **Personnel:** 174

WINCHESTER—Franklin County

⊞ **SOUTHERN TENNESSEE REGIONAL HEALTH SYSTEM-WINCHESTER (440058)**, 185 Hospital Road, Zip 37398–2404; tel. 931/967–8200, (Includes SOUTHERN TENNESSEE REGIONAL HEALTH SYSTEM-SEWANEE, 1260 University Avenue, Sewanee, Tennessee, Zip 37375–2303; tel. 931/598–5691; William R Spray, Interim Chief Executive Officer), (Non-reporting) **A**1 10 **S** LifePoint Health, Brentwood, TN
Primary Contact: William R. Spray, Chief Executive Officer
COO: Clifford Wilson, Chief Operating Officer
CFO: Steve Moore, Chief Financial Officer
CIO: James Payne, Director Information Systems
CHR: Linda Tipps, Director Human Resources
CNO: Jean Ann McMurrey, R.N., MSN, Chief Nursing Officer
Web address: www.southerntennessee.com
Control: Corporation, Investor–owned (for–profit) **Service:** General medical and surgical

Staffed Beds: 190

WOODBURY—Cannon County

⊞ **SAINT THOMAS STONES RIVER HOSPITAL (440200)**, 324 Doolittle Road, Zip 37190–1139; tel. 615/563–4001, (Nonreporting) **A**1 10 **S** Ascension Healthcare, Saint Louis, MO
Primary Contact: Robert Peglow, Interim Chief Administrative Officer
CFO: Alan Sharp, Chief Financial Officer
CMO: James Spurlock, D.O., Chief of Staff
CNO: Emily Elrod, R.N., Director of Nursing
Web address: www.stonesriverhospital.com
Control: Church operated, Nongovernment, not–for–profit **Service:** General medical and surgical

Staffed Beds: 60

TN

Many Facility Codes have changed. Please refer to the AHA Guide Code Chart.

TEXAS

ABILENE—Taylor County

✠ **ABILENE REGIONAL MEDICAL CENTER (450558)**, 6250 US Highway 83, Zip 79606–5299; tel. 325/428–1000, **A**1 10 **F**8 11 13 15 17 18 20 22 24 26 28 29 30 31 34 35 40 41 43 45 46 49 50 53 56 57 59 64 68 70 72 75 76 77 78 79 81 85 86 87 89 91 93 107 108 110 111 114 115 118 119 126 128 130 132 135 146 147 148 149 154 **S** Community Health Systems, Inc., Franklin, TN
Primary Contact: Michael D. Murphy, FACHE, Chief Executive Officer
COO: Matthew van Leeuwe, Chief Operating Officer
CFO: Ron Bennett, Chief Financial Officer
CMO: Tim Bumann, D.O., Chief of Staff
CIO: Dennis Newquist, Director Information Systems
CHR: John J Jeziorske, Director Human Resources
CNO: Jessica Kiehle, R.N., Chief Nursing Officer
Web address: www.abileneregional.com
Control: Partnership, Investor–owned (for–profit) **Service**: General medical and surgical

Staffed Beds: 205 **Admissions**: 5673 **Census**: 63 **Outpatient Visits**: 72375
Total Expense ($000): 99331 **Payroll Expense ($000)**: 34500
Personnel: 548

★ **CONTINUECARE HOSPITAL AT HENDRICK MEDICAL CENTER (452029)**, 1900 Pine Street, Zip 79601–2432; tel. 325/670–6251, **A**10 **F**1 3 29 34 35 68 85 87 148 149 **S** Community Hospital Corporation, Plano, TX
Primary Contact: Billy Blasingame, Chief Executive Officer
CFO: Lisa Young, CPA, Chief Financial Officer
CHR: Trisha Kane, Director Human Resources
CNO: Sherry Hendricksen, R.N., MSN, Chief Nursing Officer
Web address: www.continuecare.org/hendrick/
Control: Other not–for–profit (including NFP Corporation)
Service: Acute long–term care hospital

Staffed Beds: 23 **Admissions**: 202 **Census**: 14 **Outpatient Visits**: 0
Births: 0 **Total Expense ($000)**: 7203 **Payroll Expense ($000)**: 3394
Personnel: 41

✠ **ENCOMPASS HEALTH REHABILITATION HOSPITAL OF ABILENE (673039)**, 6401 Directors Parkway, Zip 79606–5869; tel. 325/691–1600, **A**1 10 **F**3 29 57 59 74 75 77 90 96 130 143 148 **S** Encompass Health Corporation, Birmingham, AL
Primary Contact: Joe Roberson, Chief Executive Officer
Web address: www.reliantabilene.com
Control: Corporation, Investor–owned (for–profit) **Service**: Rehabilitation

Staffed Beds: 60 **Admissions**: 1201 **Census**: 42 **Outpatient Visits**: 0
Births: 0 **Total Expense ($000)**: 18999 **Payroll Expense ($000)**: 9308
Personnel: 152

✠ **HENDRICK HEALTH SYSTEM (450229)**, 1900 Pine Street, Zip 79601–2432; tel. 325/670–2000, (Total facility includes 20 beds in nursing home–type unit) **A**1 10 **F**3 11 12 13 14 15 17 18 20 22 24 26 28 29 30 31 34 35 36 39 40 42 43 44 45 46 48 49 50 51 53 54 56 57 58 59 60 61 62 63 64 68 70 72 74 75 77 78 79 80 81 82 84 85 86 87 88 90 91 92 93 96 97 102 107 108 110 111 114 115 118 119 120 121 123 124 126 128 129 130 131 132 135 143 146 147 148 149 154 156
Primary Contact: Brad D. Holland, President and Chief Executive Officer
CFO: Jeremy Tyler Walker, Vice President and Chief Financial Officer
CIO: Duane Donaway, Director Information Technology
CHR: Susan Wade, Vice President
CNO: Susie Cassle, R.N., MSN, Vice President Nursing Services
Web address: www.ehendrick.org
Control: Church operated, Nongovernment, not–for–profit **Service**: General medical and surgical

Staffed Beds: 407 **Admissions**: 16891 **Census**: 277 **Outpatient Visits**: 331114 **Births**: 1734 **Total Expense ($000)**: 382108 **Payroll Expense ($000)**: 140721 **Personnel**: 2922

☐ **OCEANS BEHAVIORAL HOSPITAL ABILENE (454122)**, 4225 Woods Place, Zip 79602–7991; tel. 325/691–0030, **A**1 10 **F**29 34 35 98 99 100 101 103 104 130 132 149 153 154 **S** Oceans Healthcare, Lake Charles, LA
Primary Contact: Stacy Sanford, Chief Executive Officer
Web address: www.oceansabilene.com
Control: Corporation, Investor–owned (for–profit) **Service**: Psychiatric

Staffed Beds: 90 **Admissions**: 2300 **Census**: 66 **Outpatient Visits**: 26812
Births: 0 **Total Expense ($000)**: 14764 **Payroll Expense ($000)**: 7867
Personnel: 292

ADDISON—Dallas County

⇑ **METHODIST HOSPITAL FOR SURGERY (670073)**, 17101 North Dallas Parkway, Zip 75001–7103; tel. 469/248–3900, **A**10 21 **F**3 29 37 40 64 68 70 75 81 85 93 107 111 114 119 129 146 148 149
Primary Contact: Lynn Warren, Interim Chief Executive Officer, Group Vice President NueHealth
CFO: Kelly Hayes, Chief Financial Officer
CMO: Robert Fischer, M.D., Medical Director
CHR: Erik Leopard, Manager Human Resource
CNO: Patti Griffith, R.N., MS, Chief Nursing Officer
Web address: www.methodisthospitalforsurgery.com/
Control: Partnership, Investor–owned (for–profit) **Service**: Surgical

Staffed Beds: 32 **Admissions**: 2500 **Census**: 19 **Outpatient Visits**: 20427
Births: 0 **Total Expense ($000)**: 143747 **Payroll Expense ($000)**: 17657
Personnel: 208

ALICE—Jim Wells County

✠ **CHRISTUS SPOHN HOSPITAL ALICE (450828)**, 2500 East Main Street, Zip 78332–4169; tel. 361/661–8000, **A**1 10 20 **F**3 13 18 20 22 24 28 29 40 43 70 76 77 78 81 93 98 107 111 115 127 146 **S** CHRISTUS Health, Irving, TX
Primary Contact: Thomas McKinney, President
CFO: Michael Guajardo, Director Finance
CMO: Jerry Liles, D.O., Chief Medical Officer
CHR: Mindy Soliz, Director Human Resources
CNO: Margot Rios, R.N., Chief Nursing Officer
Web address: www.christusspohn.org/locations_alice.htm
Control: Church operated, Nongovernment, not–for–profit **Service**: General medical and surgical

Staffed Beds: 74 **Admissions**: 2482 **Census**: 23 **Outpatient Visits**: 65411
Births: 110 **Total Expense ($000)**: 42983 **Payroll Expense ($000)**: 13129
Personnel: 195

ALLEN—Collin County

✠ **POST ACUTE REHABILITATION HOSPITAL OF ALLEN (673025)**, 1001 Raintree Circle, Zip 75013–4912; tel. 972/908–2015, **A**1 10 **F**3 29 34 35 40 54 56 59 60 64 68 74 75 77 82 87 90 91 92 93 94 96 100 130 132 146 148 153 **S** Post Acute Medical, LLC, Enola, PA
Primary Contact: Jennifer Beuerlein, Chief Executive Officer
Web address: www.warmsprings.org
Control: Partnership, Investor–owned (for–profit) **Service**: Rehabilitation

Staffed Beds: 40 **Admissions**: 1102 **Census**: 29 **Outpatient Visits**: 1646
Births: 0 **Total Expense ($000)**: 15697 **Payroll Expense ($000)**: 7905
Personnel: 125

Hospital, Medicare Provider Number, Address, Telephone, Approval, Facility, and Physician Codes, Health Care System

★ American Hospital Association (AHA) membership   ○ Healthcare Facilities Accreditation Program   ⇑ Center for Improvement in Healthcare Quality Accreditation
☐ The Joint Commission accreditation   ◇ DNV Healthcare Inc. accreditation   △ Commission on Accreditation of Rehabilitation Facilities (CARF) accreditation

TX

⊠ **TEXAS HEALTH PRESBYTERIAN HOSPITAL ALLEN (450840)**, 1105 Central Expressway North, Suite 140, Zip 75013–6103; tel. 972/747–1000, **A**1 10 **F**3 13 15 18 20 22 28 29 30 34 35 38 40 43 44 45 47 49 51 55 57 59 64 65 70 72 73 74 75 76 78 79 81 84 85 89 90 91 93 102 104 105 107 108 110 111 115 118 119 126 130 132 135 146 147 148 149 153 154 **S** Texas Health Resources, Arlington, TX
Primary Contact: Jared Shelton, Chief Executive Officer
COO: Crispin P Hocate, Professional and Support Services Officer
CFO: Lisa Gildon, Group Financial Officer
CMO: Bob Schwab, M.D., Chief Medical Officer
CHR: Sharon Chisholm, Entity Human Resource Officer
Web address: www.texashealth.org
Control: Other not–for–profit (including NFP Corporation) **Service**: General medical and surgical

Staffed Beds: 52 **Admissions**: 3034 **Census**: 27 **Outpatient Visits**: 43006
Births: 341 **Total Expense ($000)**: 86489 **Payroll Expense ($000)**: 31612
Personnel: 348

ALPINE—Brewster County

⊠ **BIG BEND REGIONAL MEDICAL CENTER (451378)**, 2600 Highway 118 North, Zip 79830–2002; tel. 432/837–3447, **A**1 3 10 18 **F**3 11 13 29 34 35 40 43 45 50 57 64 65 70 75 76 77 81 93 107 115 119 127 132 133 146 147 148 **S** Quorum Health, Brentwood, TN
Primary Contact: Rick Flores, Interim Chief Executive Officer
CNO: Keith Ellison, Chief Nursing Officer
Web address: www.bigbendhealthcare.com
Control: Corporation, Investor–owned (for–profit) **Service**: General medical and surgical

Staffed Beds: 25 **Admissions**: 665 **Census**: 8 **Outpatient Visits**: 16155
Births: 175 **Total Expense ($000)**: 19822 **Payroll Expense ($000)**: 7795
Personnel: 137

ALVIN—Brazoria County

ALVIN DIAGNOSTIC AND URGENT CARE CENTER See Hca Houston Healthcare Clear Lake, League City

AMARILLO—Potter County

⊠ **AMARILLO VETERANS AFFAIRS HEALTH CARE SYSTEM**, 6010 West Amarillo Boulevard, Zip 79106–1992; tel. 806/355–9703, (Nonreporting) **A**1 2 3 5 **S** Department of Veterans Affairs, Washington, DC
Primary Contact: Elizabeth Lowery, Interim Director
CIO: Modesto Baca, Chief Information Officer
CHR: Ken Creamer, Chief Human Resource
Web address: www.amarillo.va.gov/
Control: Veterans Affairs, Government, federal **Service**: General medical and surgical

Staffed Beds: 55

★ ⇑ **BSA HOSPITAL, LLC (450231)**, 1600 Wallace Boulevard, Zip 79106–1799; tel. 806/212–2000, **A**2 3 5 10 21 **F**3 7 8 11 12 13 15 17 18 20 22 24 26 28 29 30 31 34 35 40 43 45 46 48 49 51 53 54 56 57 58 59 64 70 71 72 74 75 76 77 78 79 81 82 84 85 86 87 88 89 90 91 92 93 96 107 108 109 110 111 114 115 116 117 118 119 120 121 123 124 126 129 130 143 145 146 147 148 **S** Ardent Health Services, Nashville, TN
Primary Contact: Bob Williams, President and Chief Executive Officer
COO: Michael Cruz, Senior Vice President Operations
CFO: Lorenzo Olivarez, Senior Vice President and Chief Financial Officer
CMO: Mike Lamanteer, M.D., Senior Vice President Medical Affairs
CIO: Lewis Brown, Director Information Technology
CHR: Mona Tucker, Vice President Human Resources
CNO: Belinda D Gibson, R.N., Senior Vice President Patient Services
Web address: www.bsahs.org
Control: Corporation, Investor–owned (for–profit) **Service**: General medical and surgical

Staffed Beds: 355 **Admissions**: 20367 **Census**: 224 **Outpatient Visits**: 134934 **Births**: 1953 **Total Expense ($000)**: 332748 **Payroll Expense ($000)**: 125545 **Personnel**: 1965

KINDRED HOSPITAL-AMARILLO See Vibra Hospital of Amarillo

KINDRED REHABILITATION HOSPITAL AMARILLO See Vibra Rehabilitation Hospital of Amarillo

▫ **NORTHWEST TEXAS HEALTHCARE SYSTEM (450209)**, 1501 South Coulter Avenue, Zip 79106–1770, Mailing Address: P.O. Box 1110, Zip 79105–1110; tel. 806/354–1000, (Includes NORTHWEST CHILDREN'S HOSPITAL, 1501 South Coulter Street, Amarillo, Texas, Zip 79106–1770; tel. 806/354–1000; NORTHWEST PAVILION, 7201 Evans, Amarillo, Texas, Zip 79106, Mailing Address: P O Box 1110, Zip 79105–1110, tel. 806/354–1000; NORTHWEST TEXAS SURGERY CENTER, 3501 South Soncy Road Suite 118, Amarillo, Texas, Zip 79119–6405; tel. 806/359–7999; Ryan Chandler, Chief Executive Officer) **A**1 2 3 5 10 19 **F**3 4 5 8 11 12 13 15 17 18 20 22 24 26 28 29 30 31 32 34 35 37 38 39 40 42 43 44 45 46 48 49 50 54 56 57 59 60 61 64 65 66 68 70 72 74 75 76 77 78 79 81 82 84 85 86 87 88 89 90 92 93 94 96 97 98 99 100 101 102 103 104 105 107 108 110 111 115 118 119 126 129 130 132 135 144 146 147 148 152 153 154 **S** Universal Health Services, Inc., King of Prussia, PA
Primary Contact: Ryan Chandler, Chief Executive Officer
COO: John McDonald, Chief Operating Officer
CFO: Divya Matai, Chief Financial Officer
CMO: Brian Weis, M.D., Chief Medical Officer
CIO: Bach Nguyen, Director Information Systems
CHR: Samuel Lynn, Director Human Resources
Web address: www.nwtexashealthcare.com
Control: Corporation, Investor–owned (for–profit) **Service**: General medical and surgical

Staffed Beds: 430 **Admissions**: 18544 **Census**: 237 **Outpatient Visits**: 232287 **Births**: 2138 **Total Expense ($000)**: 287522 **Payroll Expense ($000)**: 95675 **Personnel**: 1679

★ **PHYSICIANS SURGICAL HOSPITAL - QUAIL CREEK (450875)**, 6819 Plum Creek, Zip 79124–1602; tel. 806/354–6100, (Includes PHYSICIANS SURGICAL HOSPITAL - PANHANDLE CAMPUS, 7100 West 9th Avenue, Amarillo, Texas, Zip 79106–1704; tel. 806/212–0247; Todd Greene, Chief Executive Officer) **A**10 **F**3 29 30 40 64 68 79 81 82 93 130 131 **S** Ardent Health Services, Nashville, TN
Primary Contact: Todd Greene, Chief Executive Officer
CFO: Austin Jones, CPA, Chief Financial Officer
CMO: Robert Crabtree, M.D., Chief of Staff and Medical Director
CNO: Debbie Inman, Chief Nursing Officer
Web address: www.physurg.com
Control: Partnership, Investor–owned (for–profit) **Service**: Surgical

Staffed Beds: 41 **Admissions**: 2268 **Census**: 11 **Outpatient Visits**: 9634
Births: 0 **Total Expense ($000)**: 51269 **Payroll Expense ($000)**: 12706
Personnel: 196

⊠ **VIBRA HOSPITAL OF AMARILLO (452060)**, 7501 Wallace Boulevard, Zip 79124–2150; tel. 806/467–7000, **A**1 10 **F**1 3 29 45 46 56 59 60 61 70 74 75 77 79 82 84 85 86 87 91 96 107 114 130 148 154 **S** Vibra Healthcare, Mechanicsburg, PA
Primary Contact: Eric Mueller, Chief Executive Officer and Market Chief Executive Officer
CFO: Carlene Wright, Chief Financial Officer
CMO: Pablo Rodrigues, M.D., Medical Director
CNO: Melany McCarty, R.N., Chief Clinical Officer
Web address: www.vhamarillo.com
Control: Corporation, Investor–owned (for–profit) **Service**: Acute long–term care hospital

Staffed Beds: 72 **Admissions**: 739 **Census**: 46 **Outpatient Visits**: 0
Births: 0 **Total Expense ($000)**: 20602 **Payroll Expense ($000)**: 9304
Personnel: 155

⊠ △ **VIBRA REHABILITATION HOSPITAL OF AMARILLO (453096)**, 7200 West 9th Avenue, Zip 79106–1703; tel. 806/468–2900, **A**1 7 10 **F**3 28 29 34 56 57 75 77 79 82 87 90 91 96 130 132 143 148 154 **S** Vibra Healthcare, Mechanicsburg, PA
Primary Contact: Tammie Tabor, Chief Executive Officer
Web address: www.vrhamarillo.com
Control: Corporation, Investor–owned (for–profit) **Service**: Rehabilitation

Staffed Beds: 44 **Admissions**: 643 **Census**: 20 **Outpatient Visits**: 0
Births: 0 **Total Expense ($000)**: 8081 **Payroll Expense ($000)**: 5613
Personnel: 127

TX

ANAHUAC—Chambers County

★ **BAYSIDE COMMUNITY HOSPITAL (451320)**, 200 Hospital Drive, Zip 77514, Mailing Address: P.O. Box 398, Zip 77514–0398; tel. 409/267–3143, **A**5 10 18 **F**3 11 29 34 35 40 41 45 50 53 54 56 57 59 64 81 86 107 111 114 119 130 133
Primary Contact: Steven Gularte, Chief Executive Officer
CFO: Peggy Hamilton, Chief Financial Officer
CMO: Anthony Capili, M.D., Chief of Staff
CNO: Christi Morris, Director of Nursing
Web address: www.chambershealth.org/html/bayside_hospital.html
Control: Hospital district or authority, Government, nonfederal **Service:** General medical and surgical

Staffed Beds: 10 **Admissions:** 101 **Census:** 1 **Outpatient Visits:** 15525 **Births:** 0 **Total Expense ($000):** 24794 **Payroll Expense ($000):** 6720 **Personnel:** 110

ANDREWS—Andrews County

★ ⇑ **PERMIAN REGIONAL MEDICAL CENTER (450144)**, Northeast By-Pass, Zip 79714, Mailing Address: P.O. Box 2108, Zip 79714–2108; tel. 432/523–2200, **A**3 10 20 21 **F**3 11 13 15 29 34 35 36 38 40 43 44 50 53 56 57 59 62 63 64 65 68 70 75 76 77 81 82 84 85 86 87 93 97 107 108 110 111 115 119 127 129 130 131 132 133 135 145 146 148
Primary Contact: Russell Tippin, Chief Executive Officer and Administrator
CFO: Sandra Cox, Controller
CIO: Dan Smart, Chief Information Management Officer
CHR: Pam McCormick, Director Human Resources
Web address: www.permianregional.com
Control: Hospital district or authority, Government, nonfederal **Service:** General medical and surgical

Staffed Beds: 34 **Admissions:** 764 **Census:** 4 **Outpatient Visits:** 31343 **Births:** 310 **Total Expense ($000):** 53277 **Payroll Expense ($000):** 21553 **Personnel:** 248

ANSON—Jones County

ANSON GENERAL HOSPITAL (450078), 101 Avenue 'J', Zip 79501–2198; tel. 325/823–3231, **A**10 **F**11 29 40 75 77 81 93 107 127 133
Primary Contact: Nathan Staggs, Interim Chief Executive Officer
CIO: Lynna B Cox, Director Health Information Services
Control: Hospital district or authority, Government, nonfederal **Service:** General medical and surgical

Staffed Beds: 13 **Admissions:** 271 **Census:** 5 **Outpatient Visits:** 6648 **Births:** 0 **Total Expense ($000):** 6147 **Payroll Expense ($000):** 3285 **Personnel:** 67

ARLINGTON—Tarrant County

☐ **BAYLOR ORTHOPEDIC AND SPINE HOSPITAL AT ARLINGTON (670067)**, 707 Highlander Boulevard, Zip 76015–4319; tel. 817/583–7100, **A**1 10 **F**3 29 40 79 81 82 85 97 107 111 119
Primary Contact: Allan Beck, Chief Executive Officer
Web address: www.baylorarlington.com/
Control: Partnership, Investor–owned (for–profit) **Service:** General medical and surgical

Staffed Beds: 20 **Admissions:** 1691 **Census:** 11 **Outpatient Visits:** 12327 **Births:** 0 **Total Expense ($000):** 63138 **Payroll Expense ($000):** 12285 **Personnel:** 152

⊞ **ENCOMPASS HEALTH REHABILITATION HOSPITAL OF ARLINGTON (453040)**, 3200 Matlock Road, Zip 76015–2911; tel. 817/468–4000, **A**1 10 **F**3 29 74 75 77 79 90 91 95 96 130 148 154 **S** Encompass Health Corporation, Birmingham, AL
Primary Contact: Tyrrell Taplin, Chief Executive Officer
CFO: Kathy Dickerson, Chief Financial Officer
CMO: Todd Daniels, M.D., Medical Director
CHR: Nancy Rosiles, Director Human Resources
Web address: www.healthsoutharlington.com
Control: Corporation, Investor–owned (for–profit) **Service:** Rehabilitation

Staffed Beds: 85 **Admissions:** 1622 **Census:** 57 **Outpatient Visits:** 0 **Births:** 0 **Total Expense ($000):** 25976 **Payroll Expense ($000):** 12479 **Personnel:** 159

⊞ **KINDRED HOSPITAL TARRANT COUNTY-ARLINGTON (452028)**, 1000 North Cooper Street, Zip 76011–5540; tel. 817/548–3400, (Includes KINDRED HOSPITAL TARRANT COUNTY-FORT WORTH SOUTHWEST, 7800 Oakmont Boulevard, Fort Worth, Texas, Zip 76132–4299; tel. 817/346–0094; Susan Schaetti, Chief Executive Officer) **A**1 10 **F**1 3 29 30 40 45 56 57 64 70 77 80 82 93 107 130 148 **S** Kindred Healthcare, Louisville, KY
Primary Contact: Christina Richard, Market Chief Executive Officer
CFO: Jennifer Penland, Controller
CMO: Bernard A McGowen, M.D., Medical Director
Web address: www.kindredhospitalarl.com/
Control: Corporation, Investor–owned (for–profit) **Service:** Acute long–term care hospital

Staffed Beds: 147 **Admissions:** 1336 **Census:** 95 **Outpatient Visits:** 7481 **Births:** 0 **Total Expense ($000):** 42848 **Payroll Expense ($000):** 22840 **Personnel:** 343

⊞ **MEDICAL CITY ARLINGTON (450675)**, 3301 Matlock Road, Zip 76015–2908; tel. 817/465–3241, **A**1 2 3 10 **F**3 11 12 13 17 18 20 22 24 26 28 29 31 34 35 39 40 41 42 43 45 47 49 50 57 59 64 70 72 74 75 76 78 79 81 85 86 87 90 93 96 107 108 111 114 115 118 119 126 130 131 132 135 146 147 148 149 154 **S** HCA Healthcare, Nashville, TN
Primary Contact: Keith Zimmerman, Chief Executive Officer
COO: Ben Coogan, Chief Operating Officer
CFO: Jeff Ardemagni, Chief Financial Officer
CMO: Eric Benink, M.D., Chief Medical Officer
CIO: Craig Santangelo, Director Information Services
CNO: Cathy McLaughlin, R.N., MSN, Chief Nursing Officer
Web address: www.medicalcenterarlington.com
Control: Partnership, Investor–owned (for–profit) **Service:** General medical and surgical

Staffed Beds: 324 **Admissions:** 18124 **Census:** 241 **Outpatient Visits:** 135240 **Births:** 3910 **Total Expense ($000):** 232828 **Payroll Expense ($000):** 95578 **Personnel:** 1272

☐ **MILLWOOD HOSPITAL (454012)**, 1011 North Cooper Street, Zip 76011–5517; tel. 817/261–3121, **A**1 10 **F**4 5 29 30 35 54 56 71 75 87 98 99 100 101 102 103 104 105 130 132 135 143 148 152 153 154 **S** Universal Health Services, Inc., King of Prussia, PA
Primary Contact: Brian Gill, Chief Executive Officer
CFO: Jeff Epperson, Chief Financial Officer
CMO: Robert Bennett, M.D., Medical Director
CIO: William Jackson, Director Medical Records
CHR: Betty Nuru, Director Human Resources
Web address: www.millwoodhospital.com
Control: Partnership, Investor–owned (for–profit) **Service:** Psychiatric

Staffed Beds: 134 **Admissions:** 4269 **Census:** 110 **Outpatient Visits:** 27847 **Births:** 0 **Total Expense ($000):** 31112 **Payroll Expense ($000):** 14970 **Personnel:** 294

☐ **SUNDANCE HOSPITAL ARLINGTON (454113)**, 7000 US Highway 287 South, Zip 76001; tel. 817/583–8080, (Includes SUNDANCE HOSPITAL DALLAS, 2696 West Walnut Street, Garland, Texas, Zip 75042–6441; tel. 469/440–5566; Scott Blakeley, Chief Executive Officer), (Non–reporting) **A**1 10
Primary Contact: Scott Blakeley, Chief Executive Officer
Web address: www.sunbhc.com/
Control: Corporation, Investor–owned (for–profit) **Service:** Psychiatric

Staffed Beds: 232

⊞ **TEXAS HEALTH ARLINGTON MEMORIAL HOSPITAL (450064)**, 800 West Randol Mill Road, Zip 76012–2503; tel. 817/548–6100, **A**1 2 10 **F**3 5 11 13 15 18 28 29 30 31 34 35 37 40 43 45 46 47 48 49 51 53 54 57 59 60 64 65 66 68 70 72 74 75 76 77 78 79 80 81 85 86 87 93 98 100 101 102 103 104 105 106 107 108 110 111 114 115 118 119 120 123 124 126 130 131 132 135 145 146 147 148 149 152 153 156 **S** Texas Health Resources, Arlington, TX
Primary Contact: Blake Kretz, FACHE, President
CMO: Robert N Cluck, M.D., Vice President and Medical Director
CHR: Yvonne Kyler, Director Human Resources
Web address: www.arlingtonmemorial.org
Control: Other not–for–profit (including NFP Corporation) **Service:** General medical and surgical

Staffed Beds: 252 **Admissions:** 13035 **Census:** 180 **Outpatient Visits:** 109169 **Births:** 1886 **Total Expense ($000):** 294199 **Payroll Expense ($000):** 109999 **Personnel:** 1520

TX

Hospital, Medicare Provider Number, Address, Telephone, Approval, Facility, and Physician Codes, Health Care System

★ American Hospital Association (AHA) membership
☐ The Joint Commission accreditation
○ Healthcare Facilities Accreditation Program
◇ DNV Healthcare Inc. accreditation
⇑ Center for Improvement in Healthcare Quality Accreditation
△ Commission on Accreditation of Rehabilitation Facilities (CARF) accreditation

© 2019 AHA Guide   *Many Facility Codes have changed. Please refer to the AHA Guide Code Chart.*   Hospitals **A583**

☐ **TEXAS HEALTH HEART & VASCULAR HOSPITAL ARLINGTON (670071)**, 811 Wright Street, Zip 76012–4708; tel. 817/960–3500, **A**1 10 **F**3 17 18 20 22 24 26 29 30 58 64 65 68 81 85 130
Primary Contact: William Nesbitt, M.D., President
COO: Sherri Leigh Emerson, Chief Operating Officer
CFO: Kay Mason, Chief Financial Officer
CMO: Baron L Hamman, M.D., Chief Medical Officer
CHR: Yvonne Kyler, Director Human Resources
Web address: www.texashealthheartandvascular.org/
Control: Partnership, Investor–owned (for–profit) **Service**: Heart

Staffed Beds: 26 **Admissions:** 1015 **Census:** 13 **Outpatient Visits:** 2970 **Births:** 0 **Total Expense ($000):** 47887 **Payroll Expense ($000):** 13174 **Personnel:** 119

☐ **TEXAS REHABILITATION HOSPITAL OF ARLINGTON (673060)**, 900 W Arbrook Blvd, Zip 76015; tel. 682/304–6000, **A**1 **F**3 28 29 34 35 90 95 96 130 132 135 148 149 156
Primary Contact: Teresa Huffman, Chief Executive Officer
CFO: Debbie Horn, Controller
CMO: Camelia Mitchell, M.D., Medical Director
CHR: Stanley Coleman, Director Human Resources
Web address: www.texasrehabarlington.com
Control: Partnership, Investor–owned (for–profit) **Service**: Rehabilitation

Staffed Beds: 40 **Admissions:** 985 **Census:** 33 **Outpatient Visits:** 0 **Births:** 0 **Total Expense ($000):** 14460 **Payroll Expense ($000):** 7423 **Personnel:** 124

⊞ **USMD HOSPITAL AT ARLINGTON (450872)**, 801 West Interstate 20, Zip 76017–5851; tel. 817/472–3400, **A**1 10 **F**3 12 29 34 35 36 39 40 45 46 49 50 51 57 59 64 70 74 75 78 79 81 82 85 86 87 107 108 111 114 115 119 126 132 **S** USMD Health System, Irving, TX
Primary Contact: Marcia Crim, R.N., MSN, Chief Executive Officer
CFO: Tonya Smith, Chief Financial Officer
CMO: M. Patrick Collini, M.D., President Medical Staff
CIO: Bob Rick, Vice President Information Technology
CHR: Bernardo Valle, Vice President Human Resources
CNO: Marcia Crim, R.N., MSN, Chief Nursing Officer and Chief Executive Officer
Web address: www.usmdarlington.com
Control: Partnership, Investor–owned (for–profit) **Service**: General medical and surgical

Staffed Beds: 34 **Admissions:** 1348 **Census:** 12 **Outpatient Visits:** 22474 **Births:** 0 **Total Expense ($000):** 77855 **Payroll Expense ($000):** 18116 **Personnel:** 280

ASPERMONT—Stonewall County

STONEWALL MEMORIAL HOSPITAL (451318), 821 North Broadway, Zip 79502–2029, Mailing Address: P.O. Box 'C', Zip 79502–0902; tel. 940/989–3551, **A**10 18 **F**3 29 34 35 40 41 56 57 59 64 93 97 103 107 114 119 127 133 148
Primary Contact: Billie Carter, Chief Executive Officer
CMO: Frederic K Passmann, M.D., Chief of Staff
CNO: Jan Harris, R.N., Director of Nursing
Web address: www.smhdhealth.org/
Control: Hospital district or authority, Government, nonfederal **Service**: General medical and surgical

Staffed Beds: 20 **Admissions:** 100 **Census:** 3 **Outpatient Visits:** 4763 **Births:** 0 **Total Expense ($000):** 10209 **Payroll Expense ($000):** 4837 **Personnel:** 54

ATHENS—Henderson County

⊞ **UT HEALTH ATHENS (450389)**, 2000 South Palestine Street, Zip 75751–5610; tel. 903/676–1000, (Data for 306 days) **A**1 10 **F**3 11 13 15 18 29 34 40 42 43 45 49 50 57 68 70 74 75 76 78 79 81 82 85 89 107 108 110 111 114 115 118 119 130 132 145 146 148 156 **S** Ardent Health Services, Nashville, TN
Primary Contact: Scott Campbell, Interim Chief Executive Officer
CFO: David A Travis, Chief Financial Officer
CHR: Jennifer Rummel, Director Human Resources
CNO: Kevin M Jablonski, Chief Nursing Officer
Web address: www.https://uthealthathens.com/
Control: Individual, Investor–owned (for–profit) **Service**: General medical and surgical

Staffed Beds: 127 **Admissions:** 4023 **Census:** 44 **Outpatient Visits:** 65641 **Births:** 756 **Total Expense ($000):** 63007 **Payroll Expense ($000):** 22352 **Personnel:** 440

AUBREY—Denton County

★ ⤊ **BAYLOR SCOTT & WHITE EMERGENCY HOSPITAL–AUBREY (670062)**, 26791 Highway 380, Zip 76227; tel. 972/347–2525, (Includes BAYLOR EMERGENCY MEDICAL CENTER MURPHY, 511 FM 544, Suite 100, Plano, Texas, Zip 75094; tel. 214/294–6150; Kyle Kirkpatrick, Chief Executive Officer; BAYLOR EMERGENCY MEDICAL CENTERS - COLLEYVILLE, 5500 Colleyville Boulevard, Colleyville, Texas, Zip 76034–5835; tel. 214/294–6350; Kyle Kirkpatrick, Chief Executive Officer; BAYLOR EMERGENCY MEDICAL CENTERS - KELLER, 620 S Main Street, Suite 100, Keller, Texas, Zip 76248–4960; tel. 214/294–6100; Kyle Kirkpatrick, Chief Executive Officer) **A**10 21 **F**3 29 40 75 87 107 119 149 **S** Emerus, The Woodlands, TX
Primary Contact: Kyle Kirkpatrick, Chief Executive Officer
CMO: Amynah Kara, M.D., Chief Medical Officer
CIO: Trang Dawson, Chief Information Officer
CHR: Larry Guillory, Chief Human Resources Officer
Web address: www.bemcataubrey.com
Control: Corporation, Investor–owned (for–profit) **Service**: General medical and surgical

Staffed Beds: 40 **Admissions:** 553 **Census:** 3 **Outpatient Visits:** 35135 **Births:** 0 **Total Expense ($000):** 34873 **Payroll Expense ($000):** 10248 **Personnel:** 170

AUSTIN—Travis County

☐ **ARISE AUSTIN MEDICAL CENTER (450871)**, 3003 Bee Caves Road, Zip 78746–5542; tel. 512/314–3800, **A**1 10 **F**3 29 40 64 68 70 75 79 81 82 85 107 111 114 119 126 149
Primary Contact: Tammy Smittle, R.N., Chief Executive Officer
CFO: Lawrence Oldham, Chief Financial Officer
CMO: Robert Wills, M.D., Chief Medical Officer
CHR: Marilyn Jennings, Director Human Resources
Web address: www.austinsurgicalhospital.com
Control: Corporation, Investor–owned (for–profit) **Service**: General medical and surgical

Staffed Beds: 19 **Admissions:** 572 **Census:** 3 **Outpatient Visits:** 1913 **Births:** 0 **Total Expense ($000):** 31179 **Payroll Expense ($000):** 5367 **Personnel:** 105

⊞ ⤊ **ASCENSION SETON MEDICAL CENTER AUSTIN (450056)**, 1201 West 38th Street, Zip 78705–1006; tel. 512/324–1000, **A**1 2 3 5 10 21 **F**3 12 13 15 18 20 22 24 26 28 29 30 31 34 35 40 43 44 45 46 49 50 51 57 58 59 60 61 64 68 70 72 74 75 76 77 78 79 80 81 82 84 85 86 87 93 107 108 110 111 114 115 118 119 124 126 130 131 132 135 137 145 146 147 148 149 154 **S** Ascension Healthcare, Saint Louis, MO
Primary Contact: Christann Vasquez, President and Chief Executive Officer
COO: Tad Hatton, Vice President Chief Operating Officer
CFO: Robert Scott Herndon, Vice President Chief Financial Officer
CMO: David W Martin, M.D., Vice President Chief Medical Officer
CIO: Michael H. Minks, Chief Information Officer VI
CHR: Joe Canales, Vice President Human Resources
CNO: Elizabeth Steger, FACHE, R.N., Chief Nursing Officer
Web address: www.seton.net/locations/smc/
Control: Church operated, Nongovernment, not–for–profit **Service**: General medical and surgical

Staffed Beds: 382 **Admissions:** 19113 **Census:** 251 **Outpatient Visits:** 88397 **Births:** 4780 **Total Expense ($000):** 460891 **Payroll Expense ($000):** 104605 **Personnel:** 2764

⊞ **ASCENSION SETON NORTHWEST (450867)**, 11113 Research Boulevard, Zip 78759–5236; tel. 512/324–6000, **A**1 2 3 5 10 **F**3 11 12 13 15 29 30 34 35 40 41 45 47 49 57 59 60 70 72 76 77 79 80 81 85 87 107 108 111 114 115 119 126 130 146 147 **S** Ascension Healthcare, Saint Louis, MO
Primary Contact: Katherine Henderson, President and Chief Executive Officer
COO: Margaret E Butler, Vice President Chief Operating Officer, Seton Northwest Hospital
CFO: Scott Herndon, FACHE, Chief Financial Officer, Texas Market
CMO: Jason Martin, M.D., Medical Director
CIO: Michael H. Minks, Chief Information Officer
CHR: Joe Canales, Vice President, Ascension and Human Resources Officer, Texas Market
CNO: Yvonne VanDyke, R.N., MSN, Chief Nursing Officer, Texas Market
Web address: www.seton.net
Control: Church operated, Nongovernment, not–for–profit **Service**: General medical and surgical

Staffed Beds: 117 **Admissions:** 4564 **Census:** 41 **Outpatient Visits:** 44734 **Births:** 1267 **Total Expense ($000):** 85278 **Payroll Expense ($000):** 23297 **Personnel:** 533

TX

Many Facility Codes have changed. Please refer to the AHA Guide Code Chart.
© 2019 AHA Guide

ASCENSION SETON SHOAL CREEK (454029), 3501 Mills Avenue, Zip 78731–6391; tel. 512/324–2000, **A**1 3 5 10 **F**4 29 30 68 98 100 101 130 132 135 154 **S** Ascension Healthcare, Saint Louis, MO
Primary Contact: Christann Vasquez, President and Chief Executive Officer
COO: William Henricks, Ph.D., Vice President and Chief Operating Officer
CFO: Robert Scott Herndon, Chief Financial Officer
CMO: Amy E. Walton, M.D., Chief Medical Officer
CIO: Michael H. Minks, Chief Information Officer
CHR: Joe Canales, Director Human Resources
Web address: www.seton.net
Control: Church operated, Nongovernment, not–for–profit **Service:** Psychiatric

> **Staffed Beds:** 94 **Admissions:** 3325 **Census:** 54 **Outpatient Visits:** 21213
> **Births:** 0 **Total Expense ($000):** 24856 **Payroll Expense ($000):** 11610
> **Personnel:** 213

ASCENSION SETON SOUTHWEST (450865), 7900 F M 1826, Building 1, Zip 78737–1407; tel. 512/324–9000, **A**1 10 **F**3 11 28 29 30 40 41 45 50 57 64 68 79 81 85 87 107 110 111 119 126 130 135 146 **S** Ascension Healthcare, Saint Louis, MO
Primary Contact: Katherine Henderson, President and Chief Executive Officer
Web address: www.seton.net
Control: Church operated, Nongovernment, not–for–profit **Service:** General medical and surgical

> **Staffed Beds:** 11 **Admissions:** 230 **Census:** 2 **Outpatient Visits:** 24875
> **Births:** 45 **Total Expense ($000):** 25071 **Payroll Expense ($000):** 6486
> **Personnel:** 142

AUSTIN LAKES HOSPITAL (454069), 1025 East 32nd Street, Zip 78705–2714; tel. 512/544–5253, **A**1 10 **F**98 103 104 105 130 153 **S** Universal Health Services, Inc., King of Prussia, PA
Primary Contact: Robert J. Lerma, MS, Chief Executive Officer
CFO: Greg Wysocki, Chief Financial Officer
CMO: Shiva Lam, M.D., Executive Medical Director
CHR: Dan Smith, Director Human Resources
CNO: Barbara Powers, R.N., Chief Nursing Officer
Web address: www.austinlakeshospital.com
Control: Corporation, Investor–owned (for–profit) **Service:** Psychiatric

> **Staffed Beds:** 58 **Admissions:** 2673 **Census:** 48 **Outpatient Visits:** 5733
> **Births:** 0 **Total Expense ($000):** 12811 **Payroll Expense ($000):** 6994
> **Personnel:** 122

AUSTIN OAKS HOSPITAL (454121), 1407 West Stassney Lane, Zip 78745–2047; tel. 512/440–4800, **A**1 10 **F**29 38 64 98 99 100 101 103 104 105 130 153 154 **S** Universal Health Services, Inc., King of Prussia, PA
Primary Contact: Steve Kelly, Interim Chief Executive Officer
Web address: www.austinoakshospital.com
Control: Partnership, Investor–owned (for–profit) **Service:** Psychiatric

> **Staffed Beds:** 80 **Admissions:** 2781 **Census:** 55 **Outpatient Visits:** 6079 **Births:** 0
> **Total Expense ($000):** 13485 **Payroll Expense ($000):** 7246 **Personnel:** 160

AUSTIN STATE HOSPITAL (454084), 4110 Guadalupe Street, Zip 78751–4296; tel. 512/452–0381, **A**1 3 5 10 **F**29 30 39 50 56 59 65 68 75 86 98 99 101 103 106 130 132 143 146 149 154 157 **S** Texas Department of State Health Services, Austin, TX
Primary Contact: Stacey Thompson, Superintendent
CMO: Ross Taylor, M.D., Clinical Director
CIO: Cindy Reed, Director Community Relations
Web address: www.dshs.state.tx.us/mhhospitals/austinsh/default.shtm
Control: State, Government, nonfederal **Service:** Psychiatric

> **Staffed Beds:** 252 **Admissions:** 1133 **Census:** 247 **Outpatient Visits:** 0
> **Births:** 0 **Total Expense ($000):** 70102 **Payroll Expense ($000):** 52366
> **Personnel:** 899

CENTRAL TEXAS REHABILITATION HOSPITAL (673027), 700 West 45th Street, Zip 78751–2800; tel. 512/407–2111, **A**1 3 5 10 **F**3 29 44 60 68 90 91 94 95 96 100 132 148 152 154 156 157
Primary Contact: John Wood, Chief Executive Officer
CFO: Lisa Donnely, Controller II
CMO: Christopher Garrison, M.D., Medical Director
CHR: Trena Robinson, Director, Human Resources
CNO: Lauren Brandt, Chief Clinical Officer
Web address: www.khrehabcentraltexas.com/
Control: Corporation, Investor–owned (for–profit) **Service:** Rehabilitation

> **Staffed Beds:** 50 **Admissions:** 1024 **Census:** 33 **Outpatient Visits:** 0 **Births:** 0
> **Total Expense ($000):** 14524 **Payroll Expense ($000):** 6706 **Personnel:** 98

CORNERSTONE HOSPITAL OF AUSTIN (452034), 4207 Burnet Road, Zip 78756–3396; tel. 512/706–1900, (Includes CORNERSTONE HOSPITAL OF AUSTIN, 1005 East 32nd Street, Austin, Texas, Zip 78705; tel. 512/867–5822; Edward J Sherwood, M.D., Chief Executive Officer; CORNERSTONE HOSPITAL OF ROUND ROCK, 4681 College Park Drive, Round Rock, Texas, Zip 78665; tel. 512/533–2525; Edward L Dyer, Chief Executive Officer) **A**10 22 **F**1 3 29 30 45 64 70 75 77 87 107 148 **S** Cornerstone Healthcare Group, Dallas, TX
Primary Contact: Curt L. Roberts, Chief Executive Officer
CMO: David F. Pohl, M.D., Chief of Staff
Web address: www.chghospitals.com/austin/
Control: Corporation, Investor–owned (for–profit) **Service:** Acute long–term care hospital

> **Staffed Beds:** 86 **Admissions:** 798 **Census:** 58 **Outpatient Visits:** 2025
> **Births:** 0 **Total Expense ($000):** 28188 **Payroll Expense ($000):** 13835
> **Personnel:** 167

CROSS CREEK HOSPITAL (454133), 8402 Cross Park Drive, Zip 78754; tel. 512/215–3900, (Nonreporting) **S** Acadia Healthcare Company, Inc., Franklin, TN
Primary Contact: Coleby Wright, Chief Executive Officer
Web address: www.cornerstonehealthcaregroup.com
Control: Corporation, Investor–owned (for–profit) **Service:** Psychiatric

> **Staffed Beds:** 90

DELL CHILDREN'S MEDICAL CENTER OF CENTRAL TEXAS (453310), 4900 Mueller Boulevard, Zip 78723–3079; tel. 512/324–0000, **A**1 2 3 5 10 **F**3 11 12 21 23 25 27 29 30 31 34 35 39 40 41 43 44 46 49 50 53 54 55 57 58 59 60 64 68 71 72 74 75 78 79 81 82 84 85 86 87 88 89 90 92 93 94 96 98 99 100 102 104 107 108 111 112 113 114 115 119 129 130 131 132 133 143 146 148 149 154 **S** Ascension Healthcare, Saint Louis, MO
Primary Contact: Debra M. Brown, Vice President, Chief Nursing Officer and Chief Operating Officer
CNO: Elizabeth E. Fredeboelling, Chief Nursing Officer
Web address: www.dellchildrens.net
Control: Church operated, Nongovernment, not–for–profit **Service:** Children's general medical and surgical

> **Staffed Beds:** 189 **Admissions:** 9638 **Census:** 106 **Outpatient Visits:** 117769 **Births:** 0 **Total Expense ($000):** 477252 **Payroll Expense ($000):** 134681 **Personnel:** 2892

DELL SETON MEDICAL CENTER AT THE UNIVERSITY OF TEXAS (450124), 1500 Red River Street, Zip 78701; tel. 512/324 7000, **A**1 3 **F**3 11 16 18 20 22 24 26 29 30 31 34 35 37 39 40 43 44 45 47 48 49 51 57 58 59 64 65 66 68 70 71 74 75 77 78 79 81 82 84 85 87 91 97 100 102 107 108 111 114 115 118 119 124 126 130 132 135 140 146 148 154 166 **S** Ascension Healthcare, Saint Louis, MO
Primary Contact: Christann Vasquez, President
COO: Debra T. Hernandez, Vice President, Chief Operation Officer and Chief Nursing Officer
CFO: Scott Herndon, FACHE, Chief Financial Officer, Ministry Market Texas
CMO: Tom Caven, M.D., Vice President, Medical Director
CIO: Michael H. Minks, Chief Information Officer VI
CHR: Joe Canales, Vice President Human Resources, Ministry Market Texas
CNO: Debra T. Hernandez, Vice President, Chief Operating Officer and Chief Nursing Officer
Web address: www.seton.net/locations/dell-seton/
Control: Church operated, Nongovernment, not–for–profit **Service:** General medical and surgical

> **Staffed Beds:** 195 **Admissions:** 12062 **Census:** 174 **Outpatient Visits:** 108551 **Births:** 0 **Total Expense ($000):** 676649 **Payroll Expense ($000):** 209786 **Personnel:** 3370

ENCOMPASS HEALTH REHABILITATION HOSPITAL OF AUSTIN (673054), 330 West Ben White Boulevard, Zip 78704; tel. 512/730–4800, (Nonreporting) **A**1 10 **S** Encompass Health Corporation, Birmingham, AL
Primary Contact: Lauren Suarez, Chief Executive Officer
CFO: Pamela McLaughlin, Chief Financial Officer
CMO: Johnny Shane Ross, Executive Medical Director
Web address: www.healthsouthaustin.com
Control: Corporation, Investor–owned (for–profit) **Service:** Rehabilitation

> **Staffed Beds:** 40

Hospital, Medicare Provider Number, Address, Telephone, Approval, Facility, and Physician Codes, Health Care System

★ American Hospital Association (AHA) membership
□ The Joint Commission accreditation
○ Healthcare Facilities Accreditation Program
◇ DNV Healthcare Inc. accreditation
⇑ Center for Improvement in Healthcare Quality Accreditation
△ Commission on Accreditation of Rehabilitation Facilities (CARF) accreditation

☐ **NORTHWEST HILLS SURGICAL HOSPITAL (450808)**, 6818 Austin Center Boulevard, Suite 100, Zip 78731–3199; tel. 512/346–1994, **A**1 5 10 **F**3 18 40 45 64 74 75 79 81 157
Primary Contact: Cullen Scott, Chief Executive Officer
CFO: Jenny Salome, Chief Financial Officer and Assistant Administrator
Web address: www.northwesthillssurgical.com
Control: Partnership, Investor–owned (for–profit) **Service**: General medical and surgical

Staffed Beds: 8 **Admissions**: 509 **Census**: 2 **Outpatient Visits**: 5667 **Births**: 0 **Total Expense ($000)**: 33964 **Payroll Expense ($000)**: 6736 **Personnel**: 117

⊞ **ST. DAVID'S MEDICAL CENTER (450431)**, 919 East 32nd Street, Zip 78705–2709, Mailing Address: P.O. Box 4039, Zip 78765–4039; tel. 512/476–7111, (Includes HEART HOSPITAL OF AUSTIN, 3801 North Lamar Boulevard, Austin, Texas, Zip 78756–4080; tel. 512/407–7000; David Laird, Chief Executive Officer; ST. DAVID'S GEORGETOWN HOSPITAL, 2000 Scenic Drive, Georgetown, Texas, Zip 78626–7726; tel. 512/943–3000; Hugh Brown, Chief Executive Officer; ST. DAVID'S REHABILITATION CENTER, 1005 East 32nd Street, Austin, Texas, Zip 78705–2713, Mailing Address: P O Box 4270, Zip 78765–4270, tel. 512/544–5100; Diane Owens, Assistant Administrator) **A**1 2 3 5 10 **F**3 8 11 12 13 15 17 18 20 22 24 26 28 29 30 31 34 35 36 37 39 40 43 45 46 47 48 49 53 57 58 59 60 61 64 67 70 72 73 74 75 76 77 78 79 81 82 84 85 86 87 90 93 95 96 107 108 110 111 114 115 116 119 126 129 130 131 132 135 146 147 148 149 154 **S** HCA Healthcare, Nashville, TN
Primary Contact: Todd E. Steward, FACHE, Chief Executive Officer
COO: Esther Chung, Chief Operating Officer
CFO: Daniel Huffine, Chief Financial Officer
CMO: John Marietta, M.D., Chief Medical Officer
CIO: Richard Lear, Director Information Systems
CHR: Julie Hajek, Director Human Resources
Web address: www.stdavids.com
Control: Other not–for–profit (including NFP Corporation) **Service**: General medical and surgical

Staffed Beds: 591 **Admissions**: 28215 **Census**: 405 **Outpatient Visits**: 179992 **Births**: 4884 **Total Expense ($000)**: 535616 **Payroll Expense ($000)**: 171141 **Personnel**: 2689

⊞ **ST. DAVID'S NORTH AUSTIN MEDICAL CENTER (450809)**, 12221 North MoPac Expressway, Zip 78758–2496; tel. 512/901–1000, **A**1 2 3 10 **F**3 8 12 13 15 18 20 22 24 28 29 30 31 34 35 37 40 41 42 43 45 46 47 49 52 53 54 55 57 58 59 60 64 70 72 73 74 75 76 77 78 79 81 84 85 86 87 88 89 90 91 92 93 96 107 108 110 111 114 115 118 119 124 126 129 130 138 146 147 148 149 154 157 **S** HCA Healthcare, Nashville, TN
Primary Contact: Thomas W. Jackson, Chief Executive Officer
COO: Becky Barnes, Chief Operating Officer
CFO: Natalie Pack, Chief Financial Officer
CMO: Ryan Charbeneau, M.D., Chief Medical Officer
CIO: Marshall Pearson, Director Management Information Systems
CHR: Laura Light, Director Human Resources
Web address: www.northaustin.com
Control: Other not–for–profit (including NFP Corporation) **Service**: General medical and surgical

Staffed Beds: 398 **Admissions**: 22509 **Census**: 291 **Outpatient Visits**: 159582 **Births**: 7194 **Total Expense ($000)**: 329466 **Payroll Expense ($000)**: 115765 **Personnel**: 1292

⊞ **ST. DAVID'S SOUTH AUSTIN MEDICAL CENTER (450713)**, 901 West Ben White Boulevard, Zip 78704–6903; tel. 512/447–2211, **A**1 2 3 5 10 **F**3 11 12 13 15 17 18 20 22 24 26 28 29 30 31 34 35 37 40 42 43 45 46 48 49 54 56 58 59 60 64 70 73 74 76 77 78 79 80 81 82 84 85 87 93 102 107 108 110 111 114 115 119 126 129 130 132 136 145 146 147 148 154 **S** HCA Healthcare, Nashville, TN
Primary Contact: Todd E. Steward, FACHE, Acting Chief Executive Officer
CFO: Wesley D Fountain, Chief Financial Officer
CMO: Albert Gros, M.D., Chief Medical Officer
CIO: Richard Lear, Director Information Systems
CHR: Lisa Talbot, Director Human Resources
CNO: Sally A Gillam, R.N., Chief Nursing Officer
Web address: www.southaustinmc.com
Control: Other not–for–profit (including NFP Corporation) **Service**: General medical and surgical

Staffed Beds: 290 **Admissions**: 19447 **Census**: 259 **Outpatient Visits**: 145836 **Births**: 2455 **Total Expense ($000)**: 298619 **Payroll Expense ($000)**: 101906 **Personnel**: 1561

⊞ **TEXAS NEUROREHAB CENTER (452038)**, 1106 West Dittmar Road, Building 9, Zip 78745–6328, Mailing Address: P.O. Box 150459, Zip 78715–0459; tel. 512/444–4835, **A**1 10 **F**1 3 29 30 54 74 75 77 79 93 108 130 148 154 **S** Universal Health Services, Inc., King of Prussia, PA
Primary Contact: Edgar E. Prettyman, PsyD, Chief Executive Officer
COO: Janet Bitner, Chief Operating Officer
CFO: Omar Correa, Chief Financial Officer
CMO: James Boysen, M.D., Executive Medical Director
CHR: Colleen Lewis, Director Human Resources
Web address: www.texasneurorehab.com
Control: Partnership, Investor–owned (for–profit) **Service**: Acute long–term care hospital

Staffed Beds: 47 **Admissions**: 479 **Census**: 40 **Outpatient Visits**: 6591 **Births**: 0 **Total Expense ($000)**: 19768 **Payroll Expense ($000)**: 11577 **Personnel**: 311

☐ **TEXAS STAR RECOVERY (454111)**, 1106 West Dittmar Road, Zip 78745–6328; tel. 512/462–6729, (Nonreporting) **A**1 10
Primary Contact: Craig Franke, M.D., Medical Director
Web address: www.texasstarrecovery.com
Control: Partnership, Investor–owned (for–profit) **Service**: Psychiatric

Staffed Beds: 28

THE HOSPITAL AT WESTLAKE MEDICAL CENTER (670006), 5656 Bee Caves Road, Suite M302, Zip 78746–5280; tel. 512/327–0000, **A**10 **F**3 18 29 37 39 40 45 48 51 53 58 59 64 70 75 77 79 81 82 85 93 96 107 108 111 114 119 130 131 148 149
Primary Contact: Tammy Smittle, R.N., Chief Executive Officer
CFO: Devon Culbert, Controller
CMO: Tom Burns, M.D., Chief of Staff
CHR: Kellie Bryson, Director Human Resources
Web address: www.westlakemedical.com
Control: Partnership, Investor–owned (for–profit) **Service**: General medical and surgical

Staffed Beds: 23 **Admissions**: 818 **Census**: 5 **Outpatient Visits**: 5758 **Births**: 0 **Total Expense ($000)**: 35257 **Payroll Expense ($000)**: 7823 **Personnel**: 168

AZLE—Tarrant County

⊞ **TEXAS HEALTH HARRIS METHODIST HOSPITAL AZLE (450419)**, 108 Denver Trail, Zip 76020–3614; tel. 817/444–8600, **A**1 10 **F**3 11 15 18 29 30 34 35 40 43 45 56 57 59 64 70 75 77 79 81 85 93 107 110 114 119 130 135 146 147 148 149 154 156 157 **S** Texas Health Resources, Arlington, TX
Primary Contact: Tonya Sosebee, MSN, R.N., Chief Operating and Nursing Officer
COO: Tonya Sosebee, MSN, R.N., Chief Operating and Nursing Officer
CFO: Brian Blessing, Chief Financial Officer
CMO: Judy Laviolette, M.D., Chief Medical Officer
CIO: Patricia Johnston, Vice President Information Services
CHR: Lance Waring, Director Human Resources
CNO: Tonya Sosebee, MSN, R.N., Chief Operating and Nursing Officer
Web address: www.texashealth.org/Azle
Control: Other not–for–profit (including NFP Corporation) **Service**: General medical and surgical

Staffed Beds: 31 **Admissions**: 1548 **Census**: 14 **Outpatient Visits**: 30135 **Births**: 0 **Total Expense ($000)**: 36490 **Payroll Expense ($000)**: 15436 **Personnel**: 191

BALLINGER—Runnels County

★ **BALLINGER MEMORIAL HOSPITAL (451310)**, 608 Avenue 'B', Zip 76821–2499, Mailing Address: P.O. Box 617, Zip 76821–0617; tel. 325/365–2531, **A**10 18 **F**3 7 11 29 34 40 43 53 64 65 68 77 93 107 114 127 130 133 135 154 156
Primary Contact: Rhett D. Fricke, Chief Executive Officer
CFO: Josilyn Peterson, Chief Financial Officer
CHR: Roselyn Hudgens, Director Human Resources
Web address: www.ballingerhospital.org
Control: Hospital district or authority, Government, nonfederal **Service**: General medical and surgical

Staffed Beds: 16 **Admissions**: 171 **Census**: 3 **Outpatient Visits**: 24834 **Births**: 0 **Total Expense ($000)**: 11530 **Payroll Expense ($000)**: 4713 **Personnel**: 96

TX

BAY CITY—Matagorda County

☒ **MATAGORDA REGIONAL MEDICAL CENTER (450465)**, 104 7th Street, Zip 77414–4853; tel. 979/245–6383, **A**1 10 20 **F**3 11 13 15 18 20 22 28 29 30 34 38 39 40 43 45 46 47 50 51 53 56 57 59 64 65 66 68 70 75 76 77 79 81 82 85 86 89 93 98 103 107 108 110 111 114 119 130 132 135 144 146 147 148 154 156 **S** QHR, Brentwood, TN
Primary Contact: James Warren. Robicheaux, FACHE, Chief Executive Officer
CFO: Bryan Prochnow, Chief Financial Officer
CIO: Beverly Trombatore, R.N., Director Managed Information Systems
CHR: Cindy Krebs, District Director Human Resources
CNO: Mike Lee, R.N., Chief Nursing Officer
Web address: www.matagordaregional.org
Control: Hospital district or authority, Government, nonfederal **Service:** General medical and surgical

Staffed Beds: 58 **Admissions:** 2013 **Census:** 24 **Outpatient Visits:** 63707 **Births:** 459 **Total Expense ($000):** 60394 **Payroll Expense ($000):** 22372 **Personnel:** 322

BAYTOWN—Harris County

ALTUS BAYTOWN HOSPITAL (670109), 1626 West Baker Road, Zip 77521–2271; tel. 281/837–7600, **F**3 12 29 40 44 45 49 77 79 81 82 85 87 107 108 111 114 116 117 119 124 130 149
Primary Contact: Sourabh Sanduja, Administrator
Web address: www.altusbaytownhospital.org
Control: Partnership, Investor–owned (for–profit) **Service:** Surgical

Staffed Beds: 10 **Admissions:** 264 **Census:** 2 **Outpatient Visits:** 7824 **Births:** 0 **Total Expense ($000):** 22940 **Payroll Expense ($000):** 7463 **Personnel:** 83

★ ⇑ **HOUSTON METHODIST BAYTOWN HOSPITAL (450424)**, 4401 Garth Road, Zip 77521–2122; tel. 281/420–8600, (Includes HOUSTON METHODIST SAN JACINTO HOSPITAL - ALEXANDER, 1700 James Bowie Drive, Baytown, Texas, Zip 77520–3386, Mailing Address: 4401 Garth Road, Zip 77520–1451, tel. 281/420–6100; David P. Bernard, FACHE, Chief Executive Officer) (Total facility includes 1 beds in nursing home–type unit) **A**2 3 10 21 **F**3 8 11 12 13 15 18 20 22 24 26 28 29 30 31 34 35 38 40 41 44 45 49 50 51 53 55 56 57 59 60 61 63 64 65 68 70 73 74 75 77 78 79 81 82 84 85 86 87 90 91 93 94 96 102 107 108 110 111 115 116 117 118 119 120 121 123 126 129 130 131 132 145 146 147 148 149 154 156 **S** Houston Methodist, Houston, TX
Primary Contact: David P. Bernard, FACHE, Chief Executive Officer
CFO: Jonathan Sturgis, Chief Financial Officer
CMO: Klaus Thaler, FACS, M.D., Chief Medical Officer
CHR: Courtney Lewis, Director Human Resources
CNO: Rebecca Chalupa, MSN, R.N., Chief Nursing Officer
Web address: www.houstonmethodist.org
Control: Other not–for–profit (including NFP Corporation) **Service:** General medical and surgical

Staffed Beds: 227 **Admissions:** 13374 **Census:** 177 **Outpatient Visits:** 164758 **Births:** 1731 **Total Expense ($000):** 250973 **Payroll Expense ($000):** 100342 **Personnel:** 1466

BEAUMONT—Jefferson County

★ **BAPTIST HOSPITALS OF SOUTHEAST TEXAS (450346)**, 3080 College Street, Zip 77701–4689, Mailing Address: P.O. Box 1591, Zip 77704–1591; tel. 409/212–5000, (Includes BAPTIST HOSPITALS OF SOUTHEAST TEXAS FANNIN BEHAVIORAL HEALTH CENTER, 3250 Fannin Street, Beaumont, Texas, Zip 77701; tel. 409/212–7000; David N Parmer, FACHE, Chief Executive Officer) **A**2 10 19 22 **F**3 11 12 13 15 17 18 20 22 24 26 28 29 30 31 34 35 40 41 43 45 46 49 50 51 54 57 59 60 61 64 68 70 72 73 74 75 76 77 78 79 81 85 88 89 90 93 98 99 103 104 105 107 108 110 111 114 115 116 117 118 119 120 121 123 129 130 144 146 148 153 154 **S** Community Hospital Corporation, Plano, TX
Primary Contact: David N. Parmer, FACHE, Chief Executive Officer
COO: Patrick Shannon, Chief Operating Officer
CFO: Gary Troutman, CPA, Chief Financial Officer
CMO: Shariq Ahmad, M.D., Chief of Staff
CIO: William Toon, Chief Information Officer
CHR: Hannah Schiesler, Interim Assistant Director Human Resources
CNO: Karen Tomsu, MSN, R.N., Chief Nursing Officer
Web address: www.bhset.net
Control: Other not–for–profit (including NFP Corporation) **Service:** General medical and surgical

Staffed Beds: 317 **Admissions:** 15600 **Census:** 189 **Outpatient Visits:** 161650 **Births:** 1556 **Total Expense ($000):** 257214 **Payroll Expense ($000):** 90292 **Personnel:** 1521

☐ **CHRISTUS DUBUIS HOSPITAL OF BEAUMONT (452042)**, 2830 Calder Avenue, 4th Floor, Zip 77702–1809; tel. 409/899–7680, (Includes CHRISTUS DUBUIS HOSPITAL OF PORT ARTHUR, 3600 Gates Boulevard, 3rd Floor West, Port Arthur, Texas, Zip 77642–3858; tel. 409/989–5300; Tuan Le, Chief Executive Officer) **A**1 10 **F**1 3 18 29 31 154 **S** LHC Group, Lafayette, LA
Primary Contact: Jason Baker, Administrator
Web address: www.christusdubuis.org/BeaumontandPortArthurSystem-CHRISTUSDubuisHospitalofBeaumont
Control: Corporation, Investor–owned (for–profit) **Service:** Acute long–term care hospital

Staffed Beds: 33 **Admissions:** 375 **Census:** 27 **Outpatient Visits:** 0 **Births:** 0 **Total Expense ($000):** 9600 **Payroll Expense ($000):** 4225 **Personnel:** 79

☒ **CHRISTUS SOUTHEAST TEXAS HOSPITAL - ST. ELIZABETH (450034)**, 2830 Calder Avenue, Zip 77702–1809, Mailing Address: P.O. Box 5405, Zip 77726–5405; tel. 409/892–7171, (Includes CHRISTUS SOUTHEAST TEXAS HOSPITAL-ST. MARY, 3600 Gates Boulevard, Port Arthur, Texas, Zip 77642–3601, Mailing Address: P O Box 3696, Zip 77643–3696, tel. 409/985–7431; Ryan Miller, FACHE, Administrator) **A**1 2 3 10 19 **F**3 11 12 13 15 17 18 20 22 24 26 28 29 30 31 34 35 36 38 40 42 43 44 45 46 49 50 51 54 57 59 60 63 64 70 72 74 75 76 77 78 79 81 82 84 85 86 87 89 93 94 107 108 110 111 114 118 119 126 130 131 132 144 146 147 148 149 156 **S** CHRISTUS Health, Irving, TX
Primary Contact: Paul Trevino, Chief Executive Officer
CFO: Shawn Adams, Chief Financial Officer
CMO: Rick Tyler, M.D., Vice President Medical Affairs
CIO: Robert Jacobs, Regional Director Information Management
CHR: Charles Foster, Regional Director Human Resources
Web address: www.christushospital.org
Control: Church operated, Nongovernment, not–for–profit **Service:** General medical and surgical

Staffed Beds: 370 **Admissions:** 16020 **Census:** 179 **Outpatient Visits:** 388011 **Births:** 1875 **Total Expense ($000):** 308792 **Payroll Expense ($000):** 97130 **Personnel:** 1693

CHRISTUS SOUTHEAST TEXAS ORTHOPEDIC SPECIALTY CENTER (670007), 3650 Laurel Street, Zip 77707–2216; tel. 409/838–0346, (Nonreporting) **A**10
Primary Contact: William Klamfoth, Administrator
Web address: www.orthodoc.aaos.org/bbji/
Control: Partnership, Investor–owned (for–profit) **Service:** General medical and surgical

Staffed Beds: 6

KATE DISHMAN REHABILITATION HOSPITAL (673030), 2830 Calder Street, 6th Floor, Zip 77702–1809, tel. 409/899–0300, **F**29 06 87 90 96 97 100 **S** CHRISTUS Health, Irving, TX
Primary Contact: David Pipkins, Chief Executive Officer and Administrator
Web address: www.christushospital.org
Control: Partnership, Investor–owned (for–profit) **Service:** Rehabilitation

Staffed Beds: 27 **Admissions:** 396 **Census:** 14 **Outpatient Visits:** 0 **Births:** 0 **Total Expense ($000):** 5856 **Payroll Expense ($000):** 3436 **Personnel:** 59

☐ **MEDICAL CENTER OF SOUTHEAST TEXAS**, 6025 Metropolitan Drive, Zip 77706–2407; tel. 409/617–7700, (Nonreporting) **A**1 **S** Steward Health Care System, LLC, Dallas, TX
Primary Contact: Becky Ames, Chief Executive Officer
Web address: www.medicalcentersetexas.com/
Control: Other not–for–profit (including NFP Corporation) **Service:** Surgical

Staffed Beds: 17

MEMORIAL HERMANN BAPTIST FANNIN BEHAVIORAL HEALTH CENTER See Baptist Hospitals of Southeast Texas Fannin Behavioral Health Center

☒ **PAM REHABILITATION HOSPITAL OF BEAUMONT (453048)**, 3340 Plaza 10 Boulevard, Zip 77707–2551; tel. 409/835–0835, **A**1 10 **F**3 29 34 35 57 74 75 90 93 96 148 **S** Post Acute Medical, LLC, Enola, PA
Primary Contact: Todd Lorenz, Chief Executive Officer
CMO: Linda C Smith, M.D., Medical Director
CHR: Joanna Donica, Director Human Resource
CNO: Barbara Morris, R.N., Chief Nursing Officer
Web address: www.postacutemedical.com/our-facilities/outpatient-rehabilitation/rehabilitation-hospital-beaumont/
Control: Partnership, Investor–owned (for–profit) **Service:** Rehabilitation

Staffed Beds: 61 **Admissions:** 642 **Census:** 21 **Outpatient Visits:** 2136 **Births:** 0 **Total Expense ($000):** 10477 **Payroll Expense ($000):** 5592 **Personnel:** 86

TX

Hospital, Medicare Provider Number, Address, Telephone, Approval, Facility, and Physician Codes, Health Care System

★ American Hospital Association (AHA) membership ○ Healthcare Facilities Accreditation Program ⇑ Center for Improvement in Healthcare Quality Accreditation
☐ The Joint Commission accreditation ◇ DNV Healthcare Inc. accreditation △ Commission on Accreditation of Rehabilitation Facilities (CARF) accreditation

BEDFORD—Tarrant County

⊞ **ENCOMPASS HEALTH REHABILITATION HOSPITAL OF THE MID-CITIES (673044)**, 2304 State Highway 121, Zip 76021–5985; tel. 817/684–2000, **A**1 10 **F**3 29 90 96 148 **S** Encompass Health Corporation, Birmingham, AL
Primary Contact: Robert M. Smart, Chief Executive Officer
CFO: Mary Mwaniki, Chief Financial Officer
CMO: Toni Willis, M.D., Medical Director
CHR: Christie Moore, Director Human Resources
Web address: www.relianthcp.com
Control: Partnership, Investor–owned (for–profit) **Service**: Rehabilitation

> **Staffed Beds**: 60 **Admissions**: 1230 **Census**: 41 **Outpatient Visits**: 0
> **Births**: 0 **Total Expense ($000)**: 21065 **Payroll Expense ($000)**: 8766
> **Personnel**: 171

⊞ **TEXAS HEALTH HARRIS METHODIST HOSPITAL HURST-EULESS-BEDFORD (450639)**, 1600 Hospital Parkway, Zip 76022–6913; tel. 817/685–4000, (Includes TEXAS HEALTH SPRINGWOOD, 1608 Hospital Parkway, Bedford, Texas, Zip 76022; tel. 817/355–7700) **A**1 2 10 **F**9 11 12 13 15 18 20 22 24 26 28 29 30 31 34 35 40 43 45 46 47 48 49 50 53 57 59 60 64 70 72 74 75 76 78 79 80 81 82 84 86 87 93 98 107 108 111 114 118 119 126 130 131 132 134 135 146 147 148 154 157 **S** Texas Health Resources, Arlington, TX
Primary Contact: Fraser Hay, President
COO: Alice Landers, Administrative Director Operations
CFO: Jaime James, Entity Finance Officer
CMO: Susann Land, M.D., Chief Medical Officer
CHR: Lee Mulvey, Human Resource Officer
CNO: Ray Kelly, R.N., MSN, Vice President Chief Nursing Officer
Web address: www.texashealth.org
Control: Other not–for–profit (including NFP Corporation) **Service**: General medical and surgical

> **Staffed Beds**: 285 **Admissions**: 12452 **Census**: 137 **Outpatient Visits**: 80456 **Births**: 2189 **Total Expense ($000)**: 245258 **Payroll Expense ($000)**: 95536 **Personnel**: 1208

BEEVILLE—Bee County

⊞ **CHRISTUS SPOHN HOSPITAL BEEVILLE (450082)**, 1500 East Houston Street, Zip 78102–5312; tel. 361/354–2000, **A**1 10 20 **F**3 11 13 29 30 32 34 35 40 43 45 50 53 57 59 63 64 68 70 75 76 79 81 85 87 93 97 107 108 111 114 115 119 127 130 146 147 148 154 **S** CHRISTUS Health, Irving, TX
Primary Contact: Genifer Rucker, President
Web address: www.christusspohn.org
Control: Church operated, Nongovernment, not–for–profit **Service**: General medical and surgical

> **Staffed Beds**: 49 **Admissions**: 2110 **Census**: 16 **Outpatient Visits**: 48524 **Births**: 229 **Total Expense ($000)**: 29440 **Payroll Expense ($000)**: 10091 **Personnel**: 147

BELLAIRE—Harris County

⫟ **FIRST SURGICAL HOSPITAL (670029)**, 4801 Bissonnet, Zip 77401–4028; tel. 713/275–1111, **A**10 21 **F**40 45 77 78 79 81 85 107 149 **S** Nobilis Health Corporation, Houston, TX
Primary Contact: Nicole Walker, Chief Executive Officer
Web address: www.firststreethospital.com
Control: Corporation, Investor–owned (for–profit) **Service**: General medical and surgical

> **Staffed Beds**: 19 **Admissions**: 357 **Census**: 1 **Outpatient Visits**: 4500
> **Births**: 0 **Total Expense ($000)**: 51883 **Payroll Expense ($000)**: 9918
> **Personnel**: 36

BELLVILLE—Austin County

BELLVILLE GENERAL HOSPITAL See Chi St. Joseph Health Bellville Hospital

⊞ **CHI ST. JOSEPH HEALTH BELLVILLE HOSPITAL (450253)**, 44 North Cummings Street, Zip 77418–1347, Mailing Address: P.O. Box 977, Zip 77418–0977; tel. 979/413–7400, **A**1 10 **F**3 11 15 29 34 35 40 43 45 50 53 57 59 64 65 68 75 81 87 93 107 110 111 114 119 133 146 **S** CommonSpirit Health, Chicago, IL
Primary Contact: Theron Park, Chief Executive Officer
CMO: Christophe Gay, M.D., Chief of Staff
CHR: Jacqueline McEuen, Coordinator Human Resources
Web address: www.chistjoseph.org/
Control: Other not–for–profit (including NFP Corporation) **Service**: General medical and surgical

> **Staffed Beds**: 10 **Admissions**: 81 **Census**: 2 **Outpatient Visits**: 16069
> **Births**: 0 **Total Expense ($000)**: 12730 **Payroll Expense ($000)**: 3991
> **Personnel**: 49

BELTON—Bell County

☐ **CEDAR CREST HOSPITAL AND RESIDENTIAL TREATMENT CENTER (454114)**, 3500 I-35 South, Zip 76513; tel. 254/939–2100, **A**1 10 **F**4 29 34 35 59 68 86 87 98 99 100 101 103 104 105 106 130 143 151 152 153
Primary Contact: Joshua Woodson, Chief Executive Officer
CFO: Melissa West, Chief Financial Officer
CMO: Alejandro Munoz, M.D., Chief Medical Officer
CIO: Cesar Osorio, Specialist Information Technology
CHR: Allison Liston, Director, Human Resources
CNO: Catherine Reed, MSN, R.N., Chief Nursing Officer
Web address: www.cedarcresthospital.com
Control: Corporation, Investor–owned (for–profit) **Service**: Psychiatric

> **Staffed Beds**: 88 **Admissions**: 2601 **Census**: 54 **Outpatient Visits**: 3398
> **Births**: 0 **Total Expense ($000)**: 10657 **Payroll Expense ($000)**: 6066
> **Personnel**: 190

BIG LAKE—Reagan County

★ **REAGAN MEMORIAL HOSPITAL (451301)**, 805 North Main Avenue, Zip 76932–3938; tel. 325/884–2561, **A**10 18 **F**3 40 43 53 57 89 93 107 114 115 128 130 133 143 154 156 157
Primary Contact: Jonathon Voelkel, Chief Executive Officer
CMO: Joseph Sudolcan, M.D., Medical Director
Web address: www.reaganhealth.com/getpage.php?name=index
Control: Hospital district or authority, Government, nonfederal **Service**: General medical and surgical

> **Staffed Beds**: 7 **Admissions**: 20 **Census**: 1 **Outpatient Visits**: 10468
> **Births**: 0 **Total Expense ($000)**: 14997 **Payroll Expense ($000)**: 5348
> **Personnel**: 40

BIG SPRING—Howard County

☐ **BIG SPRING STATE HOSPITAL (454000)**, 1901 North Highway 87, Zip 79720–0283; tel. 432/267–8216, **A**1 3 5 10 **F**30 39 50 56 59 61 74 75 77 86 87 97 98 101 103 106 130 132 135 146 154 158 **S** Texas Department of State Health Services, Austin, TX
Primary Contact: Traci Phillips, Superintendent
CFO: Adrienne Bides, Assistant Chief Financial Officer and Budget Analyst
CMO: Guido Spangher, M.D., Clinical Director
CIO: Elizabeth Correa, Director Information Management
CNO: Stormy Ward, Chief Nurse Executive
Web address: www.dshs.state.tx.us/mhhospitals/BigSpringSH/default.shtm
Control: State, Government, nonfederal **Service**: Psychiatric

> **Staffed Beds**: 180 **Admissions**: 185 **Census**: 170 **Outpatient Visits**: 0
> **Births**: 0 **Total Expense ($000)**: 50918 **Payroll Expense ($000)**: 30630
> **Personnel**: 501

⊞ **SCENIC MOUNTAIN MEDICAL CENTER (450653)**, 1601 West 11th Place, Zip 79720–4198; tel. 432/263–1211, **A**1 10 20 **F**3 13 15 18 20 29 30 34 35 40 43 47 50 57 59 64 65 69 70 75 76 77 79 81 85 86 87 93 98 100 105 107 108 110 111 115 119 129 130 146 147 148 156 **S** Steward Health Care System, LLC, Dallas, TX
Primary Contact: Emma Krabill, Chief Executive Officer
CFO: Rodger W Bowen, M.P.H., Chief Financial Officer
CMO: Keith Ledford, M.D., Chief of Staff
CIO: Gene Mills, Director Information Technology
CHR: Deborah Elder, Director Human Resources
CNO: Judy Roever, MSN, R.N., Chief Nursing Officer
Web address: www.smmccares.com
Control: Corporation, Investor–owned (for–profit) **Service**: General medical and surgical

> **Staffed Beds**: 82 **Admissions**: 2673 **Census**: 28 **Outpatient Visits**: 37109
> **Births**: 188 **Total Expense ($000)**: 46124 **Payroll Expense ($000)**: 17725
> **Personnel**: 275

★ **WEST TEXAS VETERANS AFFAIRS HEALTH CARE SYSTEM**, 300 Veterans Boulevard, Zip 79720–5500, Mailing Address: Big Springs, tel. 432/263–7361, (Nonreporting) **A**3 5 **S** Department of Veterans Affairs, Washington, DC
Primary Contact: Kalautie JangDhari, Director
CFO: Ray Olivas, Chief Fiscal Service
CMO: Martin Schnier, D.O., Chief of Staff
CIO: Mike McKinley, Information Security Officer
CHR: Anna Osborne, Chief Human Resources Management Service
Web address: www.bigspring.va.gov/about/
Control: Veterans Affairs, Government, federal **Service**: General medical and surgical

> **Staffed Beds**: 149

Many Facility Codes have changed. Please refer to the AHA Guide Code Chart. © 2019 AHA Guide

BONHAM—Fannin County

SAM RAYBURN MEMORIAL VETERANS CENTER See Veterans Affairs North Texas Health Care System, Dallas

TMC BONHAM HOSPITAL (451370), 504 Lipscomb Street, Zip 75418–4028; tel. 903/583–8585, **A**10 18 **F**3 11 15 29 30 34 35 40 43 46 50 57 59 64 65 70 75 81 87 93 107 108 110 111 118 119 130 133 135 148 154
Primary Contact: Harley Smith, Chief Executive Officer
CFO: Jay Hodges, Chief Financial Officer
CMO: Michael Brown, D.O., Chief of Staff
CIO: Jack Farguson, Director Information Technology
CHR: Brenda Bagley, Director Human Resources
CNO: William Kiefer, Chief Nursing Officer
Web address: www.redriverregional.com/
Control: Hospital district or authority, Government, nonfederal **Service**: General medical and surgical

Staffed Beds: 25 **Admissions**: 704 **Census**: 12 **Outpatient Visits**: 21475
Births: 1 **Total Expense ($000)**: 18609 **Payroll Expense ($000)**: 9001
Personnel: 128

BORGER—Hutchinson County

GOLDEN PLAINS COMMUNITY HOSPITAL (451369), 100 Medical Drive, Zip 79007–7579; tel. 806/467–5700, **A**10 18 **F**11 13 15 29 30 34 35 40 43 45 50 54 56 57 59 62 64 65 66 68 70 75 76 77 79 81 85 86 87 89 93 107 108 110 115 119 127 130 131 132 133 143 146 147 148 153 154 156
Primary Contact: Don Bates, Chief Executive Officer
COO: Melody Henderson, Ph.D., R.N., Chief Operating Officer and Chief Nursing Officer
CFO: Dina Hermes, Chief Financial Officer
CMO: Tanay M. Patel, M.D., Chief of Staff
CHR: Jennifer Harvey, Director Human Resources
Web address: www.goldenplains.org
Control: Corporation, Investor–owned (for–profit) **Service**: General medical and surgical

Staffed Beds: 17 **Admissions**: 706 **Census**: 6 **Outpatient Visits**: 34115
Births: 249 **Total Expense ($000)**: 27964 **Payroll Expense ($000)**: 7953
Personnel: 175

BOWIE—Montague County

CENTRAL HOSPITAL OF BOWIE (450497), 705 East Greenwood Avenue, Zip 76230–3135; tel. 940/872–1126, (Nonreporting)
Primary Contact: Faraz Hashmi, Chief Executive Officer
CNO: Jeannia Case, Chief Nursing Officer
Web address: www.bowiehospital.com
Control: Individual, Investor–owned (for–profit) **Service**: General medical and surgical

Staffed Beds: 49

BRADY—Mcculloch County

HEART OF TEXAS MEMORIAL HOSPITAL (451348), 2008 Nine Road, Zip 76825–7210, Mailing Address: P.O. Box 1150, Zip 76825–1150; tel. 325/597–2901, **A**10 18 **F**15 28 40 43 45 64 81 93 107 111 114 119 127 133 152 154 156 157
Primary Contact: Tim Jones, Chief Executive Officer
CFO: Brad Burnett, Chief Financial Officer
CMO: Pete Castro, D.O., Chief of Staff
Web address: www.bradyhospital.com/
Control: Other not–for–profit (including NFP Corporation) **Service**: General medical and surgical

Staffed Beds: 25 **Admissions**: 235 **Census**: 2 **Outpatient Visits**: 10413
Births: 0 **Total Expense ($000)**: 14661 **Payroll Expense ($000)**: 3689
Personnel: 97

BRECKENRIDGE—Stephens County

STEPHENS MEMORIAL HOSPITAL (450498), 200 South Geneva Street, Zip 76424–4799; tel. 254/559–2242, **A**10 20 **F**3 8 11 15 28 30 34 35 40 43 45 50 53 54 56 57 59 63 64 68 69 81 85 87 89 93 97 107 114 127 130 133 144 146
Primary Contact: Matthew Kempton, Chief Executive Officer and Administrator
CFO: Samuel Grant, Chief Financial Officer
CMO: Cynthia Perry, M.D., Chief of Staff
CIO: Bobby Thompson, Director Information Technology
CHR: Michelle Funderburg, Director Human Resources
CNO: Alicia Whitt, R.N., Chief Nursing Officer
Web address: www.smhtx.com
Control: Hospital district or authority, Government, nonfederal **Service**: General medical and surgical

Staffed Beds: 14 **Admissions**: 290 **Census**: 3 **Outpatient Visits**: 13590
Births: 0 **Total Expense ($000)**: 12490 **Payroll Expense ($000)**: 5507
Personnel: 119

BRENHAM—Washington County

⊞ **BAYLOR SCOTT & WHITE HOSPITAL MEDICAL CENTER - BRENHAM (450187)**, 700 Medical Parkway, Zip 77833–5498; tel. 979/337–5000, **A**1 10 **F**3 11 13 15 18 28 29 30 34 35 40 50 51 57 58 59 64 65 66 68 70 74 75 76 77 79 81 82 85 86 87 92 93 97 100 102 107 108 110 114 119 127 130 132 135 146 147 148 149 150 154 156 157 **S** Baylor Scott & White Health, Dallas, TX
Primary Contact: Jason Jennings, FACHE, President
CFO: Jane Wellmann, Chief Financial Officer
CMO: Michael Schlabach, M.D., Chief Medical Officer
CIO: Sharon Schwartz, Director Medical Records
CHR: Virginia Counts, Manager Human Resources
Web address: www.swbrenham.org
Control: Other not–for–profit (including NFP Corporation) **Service**: General medical and surgical

Staffed Beds: 53 **Admissions**: 1471 **Census**: 12 **Outpatient Visits**: 41285
Births: 353 **Total Expense ($000)**: 34106 **Payroll Expense ($000)**: 13408
Personnel: 167

BROWNFIELD—Terry County

★ **BROWNFIELD REGIONAL MEDICAL CENTER (450399)**, 705 East Felt Street, Zip 79316–3439; tel. 806/637–3551, **A**10 20 **F**3 7 13 28 29 30 34 40 43 45 50 53 57 59 62 64 65 68 75 76 80 81 85 86 87 93 97 102 107 111 114 119 127 129 130 133 135 148 149
Primary Contact: Jerry Jasper, Chief Executive Officer
CFO: Grady Paul Gafford, Chief Financial Officer
CIO: Edgar Rivera, Chief Information Officer
CHR: Kelly Barnett, Human Resource Officer
CNO: Olivia Deard, Chief Nursing Officer
Web address: www.brownfield-rmc.org
Control: Hospital district or authority, Government, nonfederal **Service**: General medical and surgical

Staffed Beds: 26 **Admissions**: 549 **Census**: 4 **Outpatient Visits**: 40812
Births: 93 **Total Expense ($000)**: 15477 **Payroll Expense ($000)**: 7244
Personnel: 158

BROWNSVILLE—Cameron County

☐ **SOUTH TEXAS REHABILITATION HOSPITAL (453092)**, 425 East Alton Gloor Boulevard, Zip 78526–3361; tel. 956/554–6000, **A**1 10 **F**3 28 29 34 35 59 64 75 77 86 87 90 93 94 96 130 132 148 149 **S** Ernest Health, Inc., Albuquerque, NM
Primary Contact: Leo Garza, Chief Executive Officer
CFO: Ernest Nash, Chief Financial Officer
CMO: Christopher Wilson, M.D., Inpatient Medical Director
CIO: Deborah Alcocer, Chief Information Officer
CHR: Tony Rodriguez, Director Human Resources
CNO: Aaron Cepeda, Director Nursing Operations
Web address: www.strh.ernesthealth.com
Control: Partnership, Investor–owned (for–profit) **Service**: Rehabilitation

Staffed Beds: 40 **Admissions**: 743 **Census**: 30 **Outpatient Visits**: 5472
Births: 0 **Total Expense ($000)**: 15394 **Payroll Expense ($000)**: 6565
Personnel: 141

TX

✉ **VALLEY REGIONAL MEDICAL CENTER (450662)**, 100A Alton Gloor Boulevard, Zip 78526–3354; tel. 956/350–7101, **A**1 3 5 10 **F**3 11 12 13 15 18 20 22 24 26 29 30 31 32 34 35 40 43 44 45 47 49 50 53 57 59 60 61 64 65 68 70 72 74 75 76 77 78 79 81 82 84 85 86 87 89 93 107 108 110 111 114 115 118 119 124 126 130 132 135 146 147 148 149 156 **S** HCA Healthcare, Nashville, TN
Primary Contact: Art Garza, FACHE, Chief Executive Officer
COO: Steven C Hoelscher, Chief Operating Officer
CFO: Marcia Patterson, Chief Financial Officer
CIO: Carlos Leal, Director Information Technology
CHR: Vicky Kahl, Director Human Resources
Web address: www.valleyregionalmedicalcenter.com
Control: Partnership, Investor–owned (for–profit) **Service**: General medical and surgical

Staffed Beds: 214 Admissions: 9154 Census: 125 Outpatient Visits: 72678 Births: 2337 Total Expense ($000): 135597 Payroll Expense ($000): 57598 Personnel: 686

BROWNWOOD—Brown County

✉ **BROWNWOOD REGIONAL MEDICAL CENTER (450587)**, 1501 Burnet Road, Zip 76801–8520, Mailing Address: P.O. Box 760, Zip 76804–0760; tel. 325/646–8541, **A**1 10 20 **F**3 11 13 15 18 20 22 28 29 30 31 34 35 39 40 43 45 50 51 54 57 59 64 68 70 74 75 76 77 78 79 81 85 86 87 89 93 97 107 108 111 114 115 119 120 121 123 127 129 130 135 146 147 148 **S** Community Health Systems, Inc., Franklin, TN
Primary Contact: Jace Jones, Interim Chief Executive Officer
CFO: Joseph Wooldridge, Chief Financial Officer
CMO: Sammy Horton, Chief of Staff
CIO: Jay Smith, Director Information Systems
CHR: Mikeana Bailey, Director Human Resources
CNO: Alicia R. Kayga, R.N., Chief Nursing Officer
Web address: www.brmc-cares.com
Control: Partnership, Investor–owned (for–profit) **Service**: General medical and surgical

Staffed Beds: 153 Admissions: 2744 Census: 28 Outpatient Visits: 62478 Births: 545 Total Expense ($000): 67820 Payroll Expense ($000): 20653 Personnel: 371

BRYAN—Brazos County

CAPROCK HOSPITAL, 3134 Briarcrest Drive, Zip 77802–3014; tel. 979/314–2323, **A**22 **F**3 40 41 42 89 107 114 115
Primary Contact: Braden Anderson, Chief Executive Officer
Control: Partnership, Investor–owned (for–profit) **Service**: General medical and surgical

Staffed Beds: 10 Admissions: 92 Census: 1 Outpatient Visits: 5558 Births: 0 Total Expense ($000): 26403 Payroll Expense ($000): 2236 Personnel: 55

☐ **CHI ST. JOSEPH HEALTH REHABILITATION HOSPITAL, AN AFFILIATE OF ENCOMPASS HEALTH (673065)**, 1600 Joseph Drive, Suite 2000, Zip 77802–1502; tel. 979/213–4300, (Nonreporting) **A**1 **S** Encompass Health Corporation, Birmingham, AL
Primary Contact: Amy Gray, Chief Executive Officer
CFO: Kris Smith, Controller
Web address: www.encompasshealth.com/locations/stjrehab
Control: Corporation, Investor–owned (for–profit) **Service**: Rehabilitation

Staffed Beds: 49

✉ **CHI ST. JOSEPH REGIONAL HEALTH CENTER (450011)**, 2801 Franciscan Drive, Zip 77802–2599; tel. 979/776–3777, **A**1 2 3 5 10 **F**3 7 11 12 13 15 17 18 20 22 24 28 29 30 31 32 33 34 35 37 40 42 43 44 45 46 48 49 50 53 54 57 59 64 65 67 68 70 72 74 75 76 77 78 79 80 81 82 84 85 86 87 89 93 96 107 110 111 114 118 119 121 123 124 126 127 129 130 131 132 135 143 144 146 148 **S** CommonSpirit Health, Chicago, IL
Primary Contact: Theron Park, Chief Executive Officer
CFO: Lisa McNair, CPA, Senior Vice President and Chief Financial Officer
CMO: Kia Parsi, M.D., Chief Medical Officer
CIO: John Phillips, Vice President Information Services
CHR: Michael G Costa, Vice President Human Resources
Web address: www.st-joseph.org
Control: Church operated, Nongovernment, not–for–profit **Service**: General medical and surgical

Staffed Beds: 222 Admissions: 13087 Census: 141 Outpatient Visits: 275456 Births: 1383 Total Expense ($000): 247683 Payroll Expense ($000): 86152 Personnel: 1433

☐ **THE PHYSICIANS CENTRE HOSPITAL (450834)**, 3131 University Drive East, Zip 77802–3473; tel. 979/731–3100, **A**1 3 10 **F**3 12 15 29 34 35 37 40 44 45 51 59 64 74 75 77 79 81 82 85 86 87 107 111 114 119 126 130 131 135 157
Primary Contact: Kori Rich, Chief Executive Officer
CFO: Paul Tannos, Chief Financial Officer
CMO: Barry Solcher, M.D., Chief of Staff
CIO: Shawn Clark, Director Information Systems
CHR: LeeAnn Ford, Director Human Resources and Imaging
CNO: Robert Raymond Lemay, R.N., Chief Nursing Officer
Web address: www.thephysicianscentre.com
Control: Corporation, Investor–owned (for–profit) **Service**: Surgical

Staffed Beds: 16 Admissions: 263 Census: 1 Outpatient Visits: 11154 Births: 0 Total Expense ($000): 15707 Payroll Expense ($000): 4361 Personnel: 101

BURLESON—Tarrant County

⇑ **BAYLOR SCOTT & WHITE EMERGENCY HOSPITAL – BURLESON (670107)**, 12500 South Freeway Suite 100, Zip 76028–7128; tel. 214/294–6250, (Includes BAYLOR EMERGENCY MEDICAL CENTERS - MANSFIELD, 1776 US 287, Suite 100, Mansfield, Texas, Zip 76063; tel. 214/294–6300; Kyle Kirkpatrick, Chief Executive Officer) **A**10 21 **F**3 40 107 119 149 **S** Emerus, The Woodlands, TX
Primary Contact: Kyle Kirkpatrick, Chief Executive Officer
Web address: www.baylormc.com/burleson
Control: Corporation, Investor–owned (for–profit) **Service**: General medical and surgical

Staffed Beds: 24 Admissions: 421 Census: 2 Outpatient Visits: 32588 Births: 0 Total Expense ($000): 24140 Payroll Expense ($000): 6871 Personnel: 76

✉ **TEXAS HEALTH HUGULEY HOSPITAL FORT WORTH SOUTH (450677)**, 11801 South Freeway, Zip 76028–7021, Mailing Address: P.O. Box 6337, Fort Worth, Zip 76115–0337; tel. 817/293–9110, **A**1 10 **F**3 5 11 13 15 17 18 20 22 24 26 28 29 30 31 32 34 35 37 38 40 41 43 45 46 48 49 50 51 53 54 56 57 59 60 64 65 68 70 71 73 74 75 76 77 78 79 80 81 84 85 86 87 91 93 98 100 101 102 103 104 105 107 108 110 111 114 115 118 119 126 130 131 132 135 146 147 148 152 153 154 156 **S** AdventHealth, Altamonte Springs, FL
Primary Contact: Kenneth A. Finch, President and Chief Executive Officer
CFO: Jesse Sutton, Senior Vice President and Chief Financial Officer
CMO: Edward Laue, M.D., Chief Medical Officer
CIO: Thomas Schoenig, Regional Chief Information Officer
CHR: Laura Shepherd, Director Human Resources
CNO: Tammy Ellis, FACHE, R.N., Vice President Patient Services
Web address: www.TexasHealthHuguley.org
Control: Church operated, Nongovernment, not–for–profit **Service**: General medical and surgical

Staffed Beds: 193 Admissions: 10694 Census: 128 Outpatient Visits: 126093 Births: 1247 Total Expense ($000): 186154 Payroll Expense ($000): 70981 Personnel: 1124

BURNET—Burnet County

✉ **ASCENSION SETON HIGHLAND LAKES (451365)**, 3201 South Water Street, Zip 78611–4510, Mailing Address: P.O. Box 1219, Zip 78611–7219; tel. 512/715–3000, **A**1 3 5 10 18 **F**3 11 15 28 29 34 35 40 43 45 50 51 57 59 64 67 68 71 74 79 81 85 87 92 93 97 107 108 110 111 115 119 126 127 130 132 133 146 154 **S** Ascension Healthcare, Saint Louis, MO
Primary Contact: Scott O. Fuller, President and Chief Executive Officer
COO: Karen Litterer, R.N., MSN, Administrator and Chief Operating Officer
CFO: Douglas D Waite, Senior Vice President and Chief Financial Officer
CIO: Gerry Lewis, Chief Information Officer
Web address: www.seton.net
Control: Church operated, Nongovernment, not–for–profit **Service**: General medical and surgical

Staffed Beds: 19 Admissions: 795 Census: 8 Outpatient Visits: 95708 Births: 0 Total Expense ($000): 46775 Payroll Expense ($000): 12339 Personnel: 313

TX

Many Facility Codes have changed. Please refer to the AHA Guide Code Chart. © 2019 AHA Guide

CALDWELL—Burleson County

CHI ST. JOSEPH HEALTH BURLESON HOSPITAL (451305), 1101 Woodson Drive, Zip 77836–1052, Mailing Address: P.O. Box 360, Zip 77836–0360; tel. 979/567–3245, **A**1 10 18 **F**3 7 11 28 29 30 34 35 40 43 57 59 64 93 119 130 133 135 143 **S** CommonSpirit Health, Chicago, IL
Primary Contact: Theron Park, Chief Executive Officer
CFO: Daniel Goggin, Senior Vice President and Chief Financial Officer
CMO: Kristel Leubner, D.O., Chief of Staff
CHR: Jackie Stradtman, Director Human Resources
CNO: Heather Page, MSN, Director of Nursing
Web address: www.chistjoseph.org/
Control: Church operated, Nongovernment, not–for–profit **Service:** General medical and surgical

Staffed Beds: 12 **Admissions:** 190 **Census:** 5 **Outpatient Visits:** 7768
Births: 0 **Total Expense ($000):** 9981 **Payroll Expense ($000):** 3793
Personnel: 53

CAMERON—Milam County

CAMERON HOSPITAL (670094), 806 North Crockett Avenue, Zip 76520–2553; tel. 254/605–1300, (Nonreporting) **A**21
Primary Contact: Troy Zinn, Chief Executive Officer
Web address: www.lrhealthcare.com/cameronhospital
Control: Corporation, Investor–owned (for–profit) **Service:** General medical and surgical

Staffed Beds: 10

CANADIAN—Hemphill County

HEMPHILL COUNTY HOSPITAL (450578), 1020 South Fourth Street, Zip 79014–3315; tel. 806/323–6422, **A**10 20 **F**2 7 29 35 40 45 56 57 62 63 64 68 69 87 89 93 97 102 107 108 130 133 146 148
Primary Contact: Christy Francis, Chief Executive Officer
CFO: Bob Ericson, Chief Financial Officer
CMO: G. Anthony Cook, M.D., Medical Director
CIO: Brian Goza, Chief Information Officer
CHR: David C Troublefield, Director, Human Resources
CNO: Debra Sappenfield, R.N., Chief Nursing Officer
Web address: www.hchdst.org
Control: Hospital district or authority, Government, nonfederal **Service:** General medical and surgical

Staffed Beds: 19 **Admissions:** 231 **Census:** 2 **Outpatient Visits:** 13751
Births: 0 **Total Expense ($000):** 11831 **Payroll Expense ($000):** 6560
Personnel: 93

CARRIZO SPRINGS—Dimmit County

★ DIMMIT REGIONAL HOSPITAL (450620), 704 Hospital Drive, Zip 78834–3836, Mailing Address: P.O. Box 1016, Zip 78834–7016; tel. 830/876–2424, **A**10 18 **F**11 13 15 40 43 57 64 70 76 81 89 93 107 115 119 133 154
Primary Contact: John A. Graves, Chief Executive Officer
CFO: Alma Melendez, Controller
Web address: www.dimmitregionalhospital.com/
Control: Other not–for–profit (including NFP Corporation) **Service:** General medical and surgical

Staffed Beds: 35 **Admissions:** 503 **Census:** 7 **Outpatient Visits:** 21983
Births: 155 **Total Expense ($000):** 17798 **Payroll Expense ($000):** 7611
Personnel: 162

CARROLLTON—Denton County

BAYLOR SCOTT & WHITE MEDICAL CENTER - CARROLLTON (450730), 4343 North Josey Lane, Zip 75010–4691; tel. 972/394–1010, **A**1 2 10 **F**3 11 12 15 18 20 22 26 29 30 31 34 35 40 45 46 47 48 49 51 54 57 59 64 66 70 74 78 79 80 81 84 85 107 108 109 110 111 114 115 119 120 121 126 129 130 132 135 148 154 **S** Baylor Scott & White Health, Dallas, TX
Primary Contact: Beth O'Brien, R.N., Chief Executive Officer
COO: Jerri Garison, R.N., Interim Chief Executive Officer and Chief Operating Officer
CFO: James McNatt, Chief Financial Officer
CMO: Matthew Smith, M.D., Vice President Medical Affairs and Chief Medical Officer
CIO: Paul Ratcliff, Director Information Services
CHR: Erica Calime, Director Human Resources
CNO: Barbara Vaughn, R.N., Chief Nursing Officer
Web address: www.baylorhealth.com
Control: Other not–for–profit (including NFP Corporation) **Service:** General medical and surgical

Staffed Beds: 89 **Admissions:** 5344 **Census:** 62 **Outpatient Visits:** 51800
Births: 266 **Total Expense ($000):** 177134 **Payroll Expense ($000):** 40666
Personnel: 422

CARROLLTON SPRINGS (454119), 2225 Parker Road, Zip 75010–4711; tel. 972/242–4114, **A**1 10 **F**4 98 102 103 104 105 151 152 153 154 **S** Springstone, Louisville, KY
Primary Contact: Samantha Castle, Chief Executive Officer
Web address: www.carrolltonsprings.com
Control: Corporation, Investor–owned (for–profit) **Service:** Psychiatric

Staffed Beds: 78 **Admissions:** 2298 **Census:** 62 **Outpatient Visits:** 34780
Births: 0 **Total Expense ($000):** 20196 **Payroll Expense ($000):** 12472
Personnel: 191

SELECT SPECIALTY HOSPITAL-DALLAS (452022), 2329 West Parker Road, Zip 75010–4713; tel. 469/892–1400, **A**1 10 **F**1 3 29 56 74 75 77 85 91 107 114 119 130 135 148 **S** Select Medical Corporation, Mechanicsburg, PA
Primary Contact: Jerome M. Brooks, Chief Executive Officer
Web address: www.firsttexashospital.com/
Control: Corporation, Investor–owned (for–profit) **Service:** Acute long–term care hospital

Staffed Beds: 60 **Admissions:** 347 **Census:** 27 **Outpatient Visits:** 0
Births: 0 **Total Expense ($000):** 17493 **Payroll Expense ($000):** 7829
Personnel: 110

TEXAS HEALTH HOSPITAL (670110), 1401 East Trinity Mills Road, Zip 75006; tel. 972/810–0700, **A**10 **F**3 29 40 42 45 46 49 50 68 70 75 79 81 82 85 87 101 107 119 130 148 149
Primary Contact: Ashley Anson, Chief Executive Officer
Web address: www.firsttexashospital.com/
Control: Corporation, Investor–owned (for–profit) **Service:** General medical and surgical

Staffed Beds: 50 **Admissions:** 571 **Census:** 5 **Outpatient Visits:** 169867
Births: 4 **Total Expense ($000):** 158505 **Payroll Expense ($000):** 80668
Personnel: 861

CARTHAGE—Panola County

UT HEALTH CARTHAGE (450210), 409 Cottage Road, Zip 75633–1466; tel. 903/693–3841, (Data for 306 days) **A**1 10 20 **F**3 8 11 15 28 29 30 34 35 40 43 45 50 57 59 64 65 75 81 85 107 108 110 111 115 119 127 129 145 146 149 150 155 157 **S** Ardent Health Services, Nashville, TN
Primary Contact: Gary Mikeal. Hudson, Administrator
COO: Gary Mikeal Hudson, Administrator
CMO: Salah Almohammed, Chief of Staff
CIO: Renee Lawhorn, Director Medical Records
CHR: Amber Cox, Director Human Resources
CNO: Judy Peterson, R.N., Chief Nursing Officer
Web address: www.https://uthealthcarthage.com/
Control: Corporation, Investor–owned (for–profit) **Service:** General medical and surgical

Staffed Beds: 23 **Admissions:** 616 **Census:** 6 **Outpatient Visits:** 55615
Births: 0 **Total Expense ($000):** 16723 **Payroll Expense ($000):** 5607
Personnel: 126

TX

CEDAR PARK—Williamson County

★ ⚕ **BAYLOR SCOTT & WHITE EMERGENCY MEDICAL CENTER- CEDAR PARK (670087)**, 900 East Whitestone Boulevard, Zip 78613–9093; tel. 512/684–4911, **A**10 21 **F**3 29 40 75 87 107 119 149
Primary Contact: Kyle Kirkpatrick, Chief Executive Officer
Web address: www.sweh.org
Control: Corporation, Investor–owned (for–profit) **Service:** General medical and surgical

Staffed Beds: 8 **Admissions:** 29 **Census:** 1 **Outpatient Visits:** 6892 **Births:** 0 **Total Expense ($000):** 5804 **Payroll Expense ($000):** 1997 **Personnel:** 39	

⊠ **CEDAR PARK REGIONAL MEDICAL CENTER (670043)**, 1401 Medical Parkway, Zip 78613–7763; tel. 512/528–7000, **A**1 5 10 **F**3 12 13 15 18 20 22 28 29 34 35 37 39 40 42 43 45 46 47 49 50 54 57 59 64 70 73 74 75 76 77 78 79 81 82 85 87 89 93 107 108 110 111 114 115 118 119 126 129 130 132 135 146 147 148 **S** Community Health Systems, Inc., Franklin, TN
Primary Contact: Carl Bo"". Beaudry, Chief Executive Officer
CFO: Erich Wallschlaeger, Chief Financial Officer
CIO: Brad Hoar, Director Information and Technology
CHR: Jeffery Ward, Director Human Resources
CNO: Krista Baty, R.N., Chief Nursing Officer
Web address: www.cedarparkregional.com
Control: Corporation, Investor–owned (for–profit) **Service:** General medical and surgical

Staffed Beds: 108 **Admissions:** 5133 **Census:** 49 **Outpatient Visits:** 52386 **Births:** 863 **Total Expense ($000):** 99362 **Payroll Expense ($000):** 34860 **Personnel:** 574	

CHILDRESS—Childress County

★ **CHILDRESS REGIONAL MEDICAL CENTER (450369)**, Highway 83 North, Zip 79201–5800, Mailing Address: P.O. Box 1030, Zip 79201–1030; tel. 940/937–6371, **A**10 20 **F**3 7 8 13 15 29 31 32 34 35 40 43 45 50 56 57 59 60 61 62 63 64 65 66 68 76 77 78 79 81 84 91 92 93 107 108 111 114 119 126 127 129 130 133 154 157
Primary Contact: Kevin Latimer, Chief Executive Officer
COO: Holly Holcomb, R.N., Chief Operating Officer
CMO: Dustin Pratt, M.D., Chief of Staff
CIO: Holly Holcomb, R.N., Chie Operating Officer
CHR: Gayle Cannon, Director Human Resources
CNO: Sulynn Mester, R.N., Chief Nursing Officer
Web address: www.childresshospital.com
Control: Hospital district or authority, Government, nonfederal **Service:** General medical and surgical

Staffed Beds: 35 **Admissions:** 676 **Census:** 6 **Outpatient Visits:** 207510 **Births:** 166 **Total Expense ($000):** 28941 **Payroll Expense ($000):** 14909 **Personnel:** 235	

CLEBURNE—Johnson County

⊠ **TEXAS HEALTH HARRIS METHODIST HOSPITAL CLEBURNE (450148)**, 201 Walls Drive, Zip 76033–4007; tel. 817/641–2551, **A**1 10 **F**3 11 13 15 18 29 30 34 35 40 43 47 48 57 59 64 65 68 70 75 76 77 79 81 85 87 93 107 108 110 111 114 119 124 126 132 135 146 147 148 149 154 **S** Texas Health Resources, Arlington, TX
Primary Contact: Ajith Pai, PharmD, FACHE, President
CFO: Shelly Miland, Group Finance Officer
CMO: Judy Laviolette, M.D., Chief Medical Officer
CIO: Brenda Taylor, Director Information Systems
CHR: Marsha Adams, Interim Director Human Resources
CNO: Vicki Brockman, R.N., Chief Nursing Officer
Web address: www.texashealth.org
Control: Other not–for–profit (including NFP Corporation) **Service:** General medical and surgical

Staffed Beds: 92 **Admissions:** 3294 **Census:** 30 **Outpatient Visits:** 44872 **Births:** 411 **Total Expense ($000):** 71305 **Payroll Expense ($000):** 26730 **Personnel:** 313	

CLEVELAND—Liberty County

CLEVELAND EMERGENCY HOSPITAL (670115), 1017 South Travis Avenue, Zip 77327–5152; tel. 281/592–5400, (Nonreporting) **A**10
Primary Contact: Don Vickers, Chief Executive Officer
Control: Other not–for–profit (including NFP Corporation) **Service:** General medical and surgical

Staffed Beds: 40	

CLIFTON—Bosque County

★ ⚕ **GOODALL-WITCHER HOSPITAL AUTHORITY (451385)**, 101 South Avenue 'T', Zip 76634–1897, Mailing Address: P.O. Box 549, Zip 76634–0549; tel. 254/675–8322, **A**10 18 21 **F**3 11 13 15 28 29 30 34 35 36 40 43 45 50 53 57 59 62 64 65 68 76 77 81 93 107 108 114 119 127 129 130 133 146 147 148
Primary Contact: Adam Willmann, President and Chief Executive Officer
CFO: Vicki Gloff, Chief Financial Officer
CMO: Kevin Blanton, D.O., Chief of Staff
CHR: Jennie Oldham, Director Human Resources
CNO: Donna Nichols, R.N., Chief Nursing Officer
Web address: www.gwhf.org
Control: Hospital district or authority, Government, nonfederal **Service:** General medical and surgical

Staffed Beds: 25 **Admissions:** 516 **Census:** 8 **Outpatient Visits:** 56108 **Births:** 81 **Total Expense ($000):** 20962 **Payroll Expense ($000):** 8726 **Personnel:** 184	

COLEMAN—Coleman County

COLEMAN COUNTY MEDICAL CENTER (451347), 310 South Pecos Street, Zip 76834–4159; tel. 325/625–2135, **A**10 18 **F**3 11 13 28 29 32 34 40 43 44 45 50 54 56 57 59 62 63 64 65 68 81 84 86 87 93 97 107 114 127 130 132 133 147 148 149 150 154 **S** Preferred Management Corporation, Shawnee, OK
Primary Contact: Clay Vogel, Administrator and Chief Executive Officer
CMO: Paul Reynolds, M.D., Medical Director
CIO: Harvey Ramirez, Chief Information Officer
CHR: Sue Titsworth, Director Human Resources
CNO: Melissa Ereman, R.N., Chief Nursing Officer
Web address: www.colemantexas.org/hospital.html
Control: Corporation, Investor–owned (for–profit) **Service:** General medical and surgical

Staffed Beds: 25 **Admissions:** 666 **Census:** 8 **Outpatient Visits:** 24239 **Births:** 23 **Total Expense ($000):** 11101 **Payroll Expense ($000):** 5068 **Personnel:** 110	

COLLEGE STATION—Brazos County

⊠ **BAYLOR SCOTT & WHITE HOSPITAL MEDICAL CENTER - COLLEGE STATION (670088)**, 700 Scott & White Drive, Zip 77845; tel. 979/207–0100, **A**1 5 10 **F**3 10 12 13 14 15 18 20 22 24 26 28 29 30 31 34 35 40 43 45 46 47 48 49 50 51 56 57 59 61 63 64 65 67 68 70 72 73 74 75 76 77 78 79 81 82 83 84 85 87 89 93 94 97 101 102 104 107 108 110 111 114 115 118 119 120 121 122 123 124 125 127 129 130 131 145 146 147 148 153 156 157 158 **S** Baylor Scott & White Health, Dallas, TX
Primary Contact: Jason Jennings, FACHE, President
Web address: www.sw.org/location/college-station-hospital
Control: Other not–for–profit (including NFP Corporation) **Service:** General medical and surgical

Staffed Beds: 119 **Admissions:** 6564 **Census:** 63 **Outpatient Visits:** 265751 **Births:** 1201 **Total Expense ($000):** 165067 **Payroll Expense ($000):** 43281 **Personnel:** 905	

⊠ **COLLEGE STATION MEDICAL CENTER (450299)**, 1604 Rock Prairie Road, Zip 77845–8345; tel. 979/764–5100, **A**1 3 5 10 **F**3 11 12 15 18 20 22 24 26 28 29 30 34 40 43 45 46 57 72 74 76 79 80 81 85 87 93 107 110 111 114 119 124 126 129 130 146 148 157 **S** Community Health Systems, Inc., Franklin, TN
Primary Contact: America S. Farrell, FACHE, Chief Executive Officer
COO: Vicky Cha Bridier, Chief Operating Officer
CFO: Kenneth Pannell, Chief Financial Officer
CIO: Daphane Hartman, Director Information Systems
CHR: Sharon Bond, Director Human Resources
CNO: Sherri Welch, R.N., Chief Nursing Officer
Web address: www.csmedcenter.com
Control: Corporation, Investor–owned (for–profit) **Service:** General medical and surgical

Staffed Beds: 167 **Admissions:** 3402 **Census:** 34 **Outpatient Visits:** 45624 **Births:** 945 **Total Expense ($000):** 76137 **Payroll Expense ($000):** 25411 **Personnel:** 291	

TX

Many Facility Codes have changed. Please refer to the AHA Guide Code Chart. © 2019 AHA Guide

☐ **ROCK PRAIRIE BEHAVIORAL HEALTH (454125)**, 3550 Normand Drive, Zip 77845–6399; tel. 979/703–8848, **A**1 10 **F**5 29 34 35 38 40 56 57 98 99 101 102 103 105 130 135 149 151 152 153 **S** Strategic Behavioral Health, LLC, Memphis, TN
Primary Contact: Orvin Fillman, Dr.PH, Chief Executive Officer
CMO: Jason Boley, M.D., Medical Director
CHR: MaxAnne Jones, Director Human Resources
Web address: www.rockprairiebh.com
Control: Partnership, Investor–owned (for–profit) **Service**: Psychiatric

Staffed Beds: 72 **Admissions**: 2082 **Census**: 46 **Outpatient Visits**: 3730 **Births**: 0 **Total Expense ($000)**: 11759 **Payroll Expense ($000)**: 6406 **Personnel**: 126

COLORADO CITY—Mitchell County

★ **MITCHELL COUNTY HOSPITAL (451342)**, 997 West Interstate 20, Zip 79512–2685; tel. 325/728–3431, **A**10 18 **F**3 7 11 28 29 34 35 40 43 45 50 53 57 59 64 65 68 71 81 86 87 93 107 108 109 114 119 127 133 135 146
Primary Contact: Robbie Dewberry, Chief Executive Officer
CFO: Joe Wright, Chief Financial Officer
CMO: Dee A Roach, M.D., Chief of Staff
CHR: Deana Overton, Director Human Resources
CNO: Donna Goebel, M.D., Chief Nursing Officer
Web address: www.mitchellcountyhospital.com
Control: Hospital district or authority, Government, nonfederal **Service**: General medical and surgical

Staffed Beds: 17 **Admissions**: 466 **Census**: 8 **Outpatient Visits**: 14766 **Births**: 0 **Total Expense ($000)**: 18589 **Payroll Expense ($000)**: 8625 **Personnel**: 203

COLUMBUS—Colorado County

COLUMBUS COMMUNITY HOSPITAL (450370), 110 Shult Drive, Zip 78934–3010; tel. 979/732–2371, **A**5 10 20 **F**11 13 15 29 35 40 43 57 68 76 79 81 107 110 111 114 119 127 130 133 135 149 154 156
Primary Contact: James Vanek, Chief Executive Officer
CFO: Regina Wicke, Chief Financial Officer
CMO: Robert Katz, M.D., Chief of Staff
CIO: Ashley Mathis, Privacy Officer
CHR: Janie Hammonds, Human Resources Officer
CNO: Jeno Hargrove, R.N., Director of Nursing
Web address: www.columbusch.com
Control: Other not–for–profit (Including NFP Corporation) **Service**: General medical and surgical

Staffed Beds: 40 **Admissions**: 981 **Census**: 9 **Outpatient Visits**: 88171 **Births**: 314 **Total Expense ($000)**: 27602 **Payroll Expense ($000)**: 9008 **Personnel**: 165

COMANCHE—Comanche County

★ **COMANCHE COUNTY MEDICAL CENTER (451382)**, 10201 Highway 16 North, Zip 76442–4462; tel. 254/879–4900, **A**10 18 **F**3 11 15 28 29 30 34 35 40 43 45 50 53 57 59 64 65 75 77 79 81 85 86 87 93 97 107 108 110 111 115 119 127 129 130 131 133 145 146 147 148 156
Primary Contact: Larry Troxell, Chief Executive Officer
CMO: Guyle Donham, M.D., Chief of Staff
CIO: Ismelda Garza, Director Information Systems
CHR: Karen DeLavan, Interim Director Human Resources
CNO: Colleen Jedlicka, R.N., JD, Chief Nursing Officer
Web address: www.comanchecmc.org
Control: Other not–for–profit (including NFP Corporation) **Service**: General medical and surgical

Staffed Beds: 23 **Admissions**: 580 **Census**: 7 **Outpatient Visits**: 30716 **Births**: 0 **Total Expense ($000)**: 23068 **Payroll Expense ($000)**: 8217 **Personnel**: 148

CONROE—Montgomery County

⊞ **ASPIRE HOSPITAL (670093)**, 2006 South Loop 336 West, Suite 500, Zip 77304–3315; tel. 936/647–3500, **A**1 10 **F**3 34 57 59 93 98 100 101 103 105 107 108 111 112 113 114 115 118 119 120 121 123 124 129 130 131 153
Primary Contact: Kostas Gotsoulias, Interim Chief Executive Officer
CFO: Bob Gray, Chief Financial Officer
CIO: John Heemann, Vice President and Chief Information Officer
CHR: Angela Walker, Manager Human Resources
Web address: www.aspirehospital.com
Control: Partnership, Investor–owned (for–profit) **Service**: Psychiatric

Staffed Beds: 30 **Admissions**: 784 **Census**: 19 **Outpatient Visits**: 30449 **Births**: 0 **Total Expense ($000)**: 10912 **Payroll Expense ($000)**: 4689 **Personnel**: 103

☐ **CHG CORNERSTONE HOSPITAL CONROE (452107)**, 1500 Grand Lake Drive, Zip 77304–2891; tel. 936/523–1800, **A**1 10 22 **F**1 3 29 40 70 75 77 79 85 86 87 91 119 130 148 149 **S** Cornerstone Healthcare Group, Dallas, TX
Primary Contact: Suzanne Kretschmer, Chief Executive Officer
Web address: www.chghospitals.com/conroe/
Control: Partnership, Investor–owned (for–profit) **Service**: Acute long–term care hospital

Staffed Beds: 41 **Admissions**: 438 **Census**: 31 **Outpatient Visits**: 0 **Births**: 0 **Total Expense ($000)**: 15029 **Payroll Expense ($000)**: 6620 **Personnel**: 92

⊞ **ENCOMPASS HEALTH REHABILITATION HOSPITAL THE WOODLANDS (453059)**, 18550 'IH' 45 South, Zip 77384; tel. 281/364–2000, **A**1 10 **F**3 28 29 34 35 44 57 59 65 68 74 75 77 78 79 82 86 87 90 91 95 96 130 132 148 149 **S** Encompass Health Corporation, Birmingham, AL
Primary Contact: Jennifer Brewer, Chief Executive Officer
CMO: Ben Agana, M.D., Medical Director
CHR: Valerie Wells, Manager Human Resources
Web address: www.healthsouththewoodlands.com
Control: Corporation, Investor–owned (for–profit) **Service**: Rehabilitation

Staffed Beds: 84 **Admissions**: 637 **Census**: 21 **Outpatient Visits**: 0 **Births**: 0 **Total Expense ($000)**: 12998 **Payroll Expense ($000)**: 5788 **Personnel**: 103

⊞ **HCA HOUSTON HEALTHCARE CONROE (450222)**, 504 Medical Boulevard, Zip 77304, Mailing Address: P.O. Box 1538, Zip 77305–1538; tel. 936/539–1111, **A**1 3 10 **F**11 12 13 17 18 20 22 24 26 28 29 31 33 34 40 43 45 46 47 48 49 51 53 54 56 57 59 60 64 68 70 72 73 74 75 76 77 78 79 81 82 85 89 90 91 93 107 100 111 112 114 115 116 117 118 119 121 123 126 129 130 131 132 135 142 144 146 147 148 154 156 157 **S** HCA Healthcare, Nashville, TN
Primary Contact: Matt Davis, FACHE, Chief Executive Officer
COO: Reed Hammond, Chief Operating Officer
CFO: Thomas A Holt, Chief Financial Officer
CMO: Mujtaba Ali-Khan, D.O., Chief Medical Officer
CIO: Jeremy Fuller, Director Information Systems
CHR: Diana Howell, Director Human Resources
Web address: www.conroeregional.com/
Control: Partnership, Investor–owned (for–profit) **Service**: General medical and surgical

Staffed Beds: 301 **Admissions**: 14802 **Census**: 183 **Outpatient Visits**: 112965 **Births**: 1432 **Total Expense ($000)**: 209962 **Payroll Expense ($000)**: 76926 **Personnel**: 973

☐ **WOODLAND SPRINGS HOSPITAL (454144)**, 15680 Old Conroe Road, Zip 77384; tel. 936/270–7520, **A**1 **F**5 87 98 99 100 101 102 104 105 152 153 **S** Springstone, Louisville, KY
Primary Contact: Dustin Davis, Chief Executive Officer
Web address: www.https://www.woodlandspringshealth.com/
Control: State, Government, nonfederal **Service**: Psychiatric

Staffed Beds: 96 **Admissions**: 817 **Census**: 20 **Outpatient Visits**: 1313 **Births**: 0 **Total Expense ($000)**: 7585 **Payroll Expense ($000)**: 4638 **Personnel**: 134

TX

Hospital, Medicare Provider Number, Address, Telephone, Approval, Facility, and Physician Codes, Health Care System

★ American Hospital Association (AHA) membership ☐ The Joint Commission accreditation ○ Healthcare Facilities Accreditation Program ◇ DNV Healthcare Inc. accreditation ⇑ Center for Improvement in Healthcare Quality Accreditation △ Commission on Accreditation of Rehabilitation Facilities (CARF) accreditation

CORINTH—Denton County

ATRIUM MEDICAL CENTER OF CORINTH (452111), 3305 Corinth Parkway, Zip 76208–5380; tel. 940/270–4100, **A**10 **F**1 3 8 29 64 75 81 129 148
Primary Contact: Andrew Carlton, Administrator
COO: Kathy Mason, Chief Operating Officer
CFO: Anbu Nachimuthu, Chief Financial Officer
CMO: Jalil Kahn, M.D., Chief of Staff
CIO: Wendy Keller, Director Health Information Management
CHR: Melissa Dovel, Manager Human Resources
CNO: Michelle Gray, Nurse Executive
Web address: www.atriumhealthcare.net
Control: Partnership, Investor–owned (for–profit) **Service:** Acute long–term care hospital

Staffed Beds: 18 **Admissions:** 126 **Census:** 8 **Outpatient Visits:** 2486 **Births:** 0 **Total Expense ($000):** 23785 **Payroll Expense ($000):** 3733 **Personnel:** 104

CORPUS CHRISTI—Nueces County

☒ **CHRISTUS SPOHN HOSPITAL CORPUS CHRISTI MEMORIAL (450046)**, 2606 Hospital Boulevard, Zip 78405–1804, Mailing Address: P.O. Box 5280, Zip 78405; tel. 361/902–4000, (Includes CHRISTUS SPOHN HOSPITAL CORPUS CHRISTI SHORELINE, 600 Elizabeth Street, Corpus Christi, Texas, Zip 78404–2235; tel. 361/881–3000; Brian Connor, FACHE, President; CHRISTUS SPOHN HOSPITAL CORPUS CHRISTUS SOUTH, 5950 Saratoga, Corpus Christi, Texas, Zip 78414–4100; tel. 361/985–5000) (Total facility includes 22 beds in nursing home–type unit) **A**1 2 3 5 8 10 **F**3 4 11 13 17 18 20 22 24 26 28 29 30 31 34 35 37 38 39 40 43 45 46 47 48 49 50 51 53 54 56 57 59 60 64 65 66 68 70 71 72 74 75 76 77 78 79 81 84 85 87 90 91 92 93 94 96 98 101 102 103 107 108 111 114 115 118 119 120 121 123 124 126 127 128 130 131 141 142 145 146 147 148 154 156 **S** CHRISTUS Health, Irving, TX
Primary Contact: Osbert Blow, M.D., Ph.D., FACS, President and Chief Medical Officer
CFO: Brower Pam, Chief Financial Officer
CMO: Charles T. Volk, M.D., Regional Chief Medical Officer
CHR: Mary LaFrancois, Vice President Human Resources
CNO: Jennifer Gentry, R.N., Chief Nursing Officer
Web address: www.christusspohn.org
Control: Church operated, Nongovernment, not–for–profit **Service:** General medical and surgical

Staffed Beds: 518 **Admissions:** 28002 **Census:** 416 **Outpatient Visits:** 311219 **Births:** 2511 **Total Expense ($000):** 578820 **Payroll Expense ($000):** 162625 **Personnel:** 2498

☒ **CORPUS CHRISTI MEDICAL CENTER (450788)**, 3315 South Alameda Street, Zip 78411–1883, Mailing Address: P.O. Box 8991, Zip 78468–8991; tel. 361/761–1400, (Includes BAYVIEW BEHAVIORAL HOSPITAL, 6629 Wooldridge Road, Corpus Christi, Texas, Zip 78414; tel. 361/986–9444; CORPUS CHRISTI MEDICAL CENTER BAY AREA, 7101 South Padre Island Drive, Corpus Christi, Texas, Zip 78412–4999; tel. 361/985–1200) **A**1 5 10 13 **F**3 4 5 11 12 13 15 17 18 20 22 24 26 28 29 31 34 35 37 38 40 42 44 47 49 50 53 57 58 59 64 67 68 70 72 73 74 75 76 77 78 79 81 82 85 86 87 90 93 97 98 99 103 104 105 107 108 110 111 114 115 118 119 120 121 123 124 126 130 131 132 146 147 148 149 150 153 156 157 **S** HCA Healthcare, Nashville, TN
Primary Contact: Jay Woodall, FACHE, Chief Executive Officer
CFO: Chris Nicosia, Chief Financial Officer
CHR: Michael Conwill, Director Human Resources
CNO: Kathleen A Rubano, MSN, R.N., Chief Nursing Officer
Web address: www.ccmedicalcenter.com
Control: Partnership, Investor–owned (for–profit) **Service:** General medical and surgical

Staffed Beds: 424 **Admissions:** 22419 **Census:** 286 **Outpatient Visits:** 138553 **Births:** 4243 **Total Expense ($000):** 324056 **Payroll Expense ($000):** 97345 **Personnel:** 1501

☒ △ **DRISCOLL CHILDREN'S HOSPITAL (453301)**, 3533 South Alameda Street, Zip 78411–1785, Mailing Address: P.O. Box 6530, Zip 78466–6530; tel. 361/694–5000, **A**1 3 5 7 10 **F**3 7 11 12 19 21 23 25 27 29 30 31 32 34 35 38 39 40 41 43 49 50 54 55 57 58 59 60 61 64 65 68 72 74 75 77 78 79 81 82 85 86 87 88 89 92 93 97 104 107 108 111 115 118 119 130 131 132 134 138 143 144 146 148 149 150 153 155 156
Primary Contact: Eric Hamon, Interim President and Chief Executive Officer
COO: Donna Quinn, Vice President Operations
CFO: Eric Hamon, Executive Vice President and Chief Financial Officer
CIO: Miguel Perez, III, Chief Information Officer
CHR: Bill Larsen, Vice President Human Resources
CNO: Julie A. Pina, Assistant Vice President Patient Care Services and Chief Nursing Officer
Web address: www.driscollchildrens.org
Control: Other not–for–profit (including NFP Corporation) **Service:** Children's general medical and surgical

Staffed Beds: 162 **Admissions:** 3639 **Census:** 75 **Outpatient Visits:** 190625 **Births:** 0 **Total Expense ($000):** 278853 **Payroll Expense ($000):** 107617 **Personnel:** 1948

KINDRED HOSPITAL-CORPUS CHRISTI See Pam Specialty Hospital of Corpus Christi South

☒ **PAM SPECIALTY HOSPITAL OF CORPUS CHRISTI SOUTH (452092)**, 6226 Saratoga Boulevard, Zip 78414–3421; tel. 361/986–1600, **A**1 10 **F**1 3 29 34 35 45 59 74 75 77 79 82 86 87 107 130 148 **S** Post Acute Medical, LLC, Enola, PA
Primary Contact: Hector Bernal, Chief Executive Officer
CHR: Kasey Parkey, Coordinator Payroll and Benefits
Web address: www.postacutemedical.com
Control: Corporation, Investor–owned (for–profit) **Service:** Acute long–term care hospital

Staffed Beds: 74 **Admissions:** 566 **Census:** 34 **Outpatient Visits:** 0 **Births:** 0 **Total Expense ($000):** 18164 **Payroll Expense ($000):** 8436 **Personnel:** 132

☒ **POST ACUTE MEDICAL SPECIALTY HOSPITAL OF CORPUS CHRISTI - NORTH (452086)**, 600 Elizabeth Street, 3rd Floor, Zip 78404–2235; tel. 361/881–3223, **A**1 10 **F**1 3 29 75 85 87 91 148 **S** Post Acute Medical, LLC, Enola, PA
Primary Contact: Hector Bernal, Chief Executive Officer
Web address: www.postacutemedical.com/our-facilities/hospitals/post-acute-medical-specialty-hospital-corpus-christi/
Control: Corporation, Investor–owned (for–profit) **Service:** Acute long–term care hospital

Staffed Beds: 41 **Admissions:** 516 **Census:** 29 **Outpatient Visits:** 0 **Births:** 0 **Total Expense ($000):** 14489 **Payroll Expense ($000):** 5965 **Personnel:** 105

☐ **SOUTH TEXAS SURGICAL HOSPITAL (670061)**, 6130 Parkway Drive, Zip 78414–2455; tel. 361/993–2000, **A**1 3 10 **F**3 12 29 40 45 54 64 68 75 79 81 82 85 119 126 130 149 **S** National Surgical Healthcare, Chicago, IL
Primary Contact: David G. Covert, Chief Executive Officer
CFO: Julie Wittwer, Chief Financial Officer
CMO: Michael Mintz, M.D., Chief Medical Officer
CHR: Lory Beth Smith, Manager Human Resource
CNO: Jan O'Donnell, Chief Nursing Officer
Web address: www.southtexassurgicalhospital.com
Control: Partnership, Investor–owned (for–profit) **Service:** General medical and surgical

Staffed Beds: 20 **Admissions:** 868 **Census:** 5 **Outpatient Visits:** 15787 **Births:** 0 **Total Expense ($000):** 37139 **Payroll Expense ($000):** 9646 **Personnel:** 187

CORSICANA—Navarro County

☒ **NAVARRO REGIONAL HOSPITAL (450447)**, 3201 West State Highway 22, Zip 75110–2469; tel. 903/654–6800, **A**1 10 19 **F**3 11 13 15 18 20 28 29 30 34 35 39 40 43 46 49 50 51 54 57 60 64 68 70 75 76 79 81 82 85 93 107 108 110 111 114 115 119 129 132 135 146 148 149 154 **S** Community Health Systems, Inc., Franklin, TN
Primary Contact: Curt M. Junkins, Chief Executive Officer
CFO: Shea C. Brock, Chief Financial Officer
CIO: Bryan Chilton, Director Information Systems
CHR: Melodee Pugh, Director Human Resources
CNO: Dona E Townsend, Chief Nursing Officer
Web address: www.navarrohospital.com
Control: Partnership, Investor–owned (for–profit) **Service:** General medical and surgical

Staffed Beds: 49 **Admissions:** 2356 **Census:** 21 **Outpatient Visits:** 44605 **Births:** 543 **Total Expense ($000):** 46298 **Payroll Expense ($000):** 14967 **Personnel:** 219

TX

Many Facility Codes have changed. Please refer to the AHA Guide Code Chart. © 2019 AHA Guide

CRANE—Crane County

★ **CRANE MEMORIAL HOSPITAL (451353)**, 1310 South Alford Street,
Zip 79731–3899; tel. 432/558–3555, **A**10 18 **F**3 29 32 34 40 57 59 64 65 68
75 81 86 97 107 114 119 127 133 145 147 148
Primary Contact: Dianne Yeager, Chief Executive Officer
CFO: Daniel Ibarra, Chief Financial Officer
CMO: Sixta Gumato, M.D., Chief Medical Officer
CHR: Becky Esparza, Human Resources
CNO: Pat Touchstone, Chief Nursing Officer
Web address: www.cranememorial.org
Control: Hospital district or authority, Government, nonfederal **Service:** General
medical and surgical

Staffed Beds: 10 **Admissions:** 88 **Census:** 2 **Outpatient Visits:** 11191
Births: 0 **Total Expense ($000):** 7840 **Payroll Expense ($000):** 3367
Personnel: 51

CROCKETT—Houston County

CROCKETT MEDICAL CENTER (670126), 1100 East Loop 304,
Zip 75835–1810; tel. 936/546–3891, (Nonreporting)
Primary Contact: Subir Chhikara, M.D., President and Founder
Web address: www.crockettmedicalcenter.com
Control: Corporation, Investor–owned (for–profit) **Service:** General medical and
surgical

Staffed Beds: 25

CROSBYTON—Crosby County

CROSBYTON CLINIC HOSPITAL (451345), 710 West Main Street,
Zip 79322–2143; tel. 806/675–2382, **A**10 18 **F**7 10 29 40 50 57 59 64 68 87
93 119 127 130 133 148
Primary Contact: Debra Miller, Administrator
CFO: Cherie Parkhill, Chief Financial Officer
CMO: Steve B Alley, M.D., Chief of Staff
CHR: Janie Cantu, Director Human Resources
CNO: Freda Bartlett, Director of Nursing
Web address: www.crosbytonclinichospital.com
Control: Other not–for–profit (including NFP Corporation) **Service:** General
medical and surgical

Staffed Beds: 7 **Admissions:** 141 **Census:** 2 **Outpatient Visits:** 14937
Births: 0 **Total Expense ($000):** 5964 **Payroll Expense ($000):** 2680
Personnel: 77

CUERO—Dewitt County

★ **CUERO COMMUNITY HOSPITAL (450597)**, 2550 North Esplanade Street,
Zip 77954–4716; tel. 361/275–6191, **A**10 **F**3 7 11 13 15 29 34 40 43 45 53
57 59 62 64 68 70 75 76 77 79 81 85 86 93 107 108 110 111 115 118 119
127 129 130 131 154
Primary Contact: Lynn Falcone, Chief Executive Officer
CFO: Greg Pritchett, Chief Financial Officer
CMO: Michael McLeod, M.D., Chief Medical Officer
CIO: Arthur Mueller, Director Management Information Systems
CHR: Wanda S Kolodziejcyk, Director Human Resources
CNO: Judith Krupala, R.N., Chief Nursing Officer
Web address: www.cuerohospital.org
Control: Hospital district or authority, Government, nonfederal **Service:** General
medical and surgical

Staffed Beds: 24 **Admissions:** 1022 **Census:** 9 **Outpatient Visits:** 118206
Births: 145 **Total Expense ($000):** 38753 **Payroll Expense ($000):** 15707
Personnel: 296

CYPRESS—Harris County

☐ **LONE STAR BEHAVIORAL HEALTH (454118)**, 16303 Grant Road,
Zip 77429–1253; tel. 281/516–6200, **A**1 10 **F**98 105 149 153
Primary Contact: Nathan Daniel. Ingram, Chief Executive Officer and Owner
Web address: www.lonestarbehavioralhealth.com
Control: Corporation, Investor–owned (for–profit) **Service:** Psychiatric

Staffed Beds: 24 **Admissions:** 421 **Census:** 14 **Outpatient Visits:** 34982
Births: 0 **Total Expense ($000):** 5987 **Payroll Expense ($000):** 3678
Personnel: 78

DALHART—Hartley County

COON MEMORIAL HOSPITAL (451331), 1411 Denver Avenue,
Zip 79022–4809, Mailing Address: P.O. Box 2014, Zip 79022–6014;
tel. 806/244–4571, **A**10 18 **F**3 7 10 11 13 30 34 35 40 43 45 50 53 57 59 62
63 64 65 68 69 71 77 79 81 82 83 85 87 93 97 103 107 114 119 125 127
131 133 143 144 146 148
Primary Contact: Loree Tamayo, Chief Executive Officer
CFO: Donny Pettit, Chief Financial Officer
CMO: Randy Herring, M.D., Chief of Staff
CIO: Anthony Lovato, Director Information Technology
CHR: Dee Dawn McCormick, Director Personnel and Human Resources
Web address: www.dhchd.org/
Control: Hospital district or authority, Government, nonfederal **Service:** General
medical and surgical

Staffed Beds: 21 **Admissions:** 334 **Census:** 5 **Outpatient Visits:** 24365
Births: 165 **Total Expense ($000):** 22762 **Payroll Expense ($000):** 10846
Personnel: 192

DALLAS—Dallas County

⊞ **BAYLOR SCOTT & WHITE HEART & VASCULAR HOSPITAL-DALLAS
(450851)**, 621 North Hall Street, Suite 150, Zip 75226–1339;
tel. 214/820–0600, **A**1 5 10 **F**3 18 20 22 26 28 29 30 34 35 44 50 57 58 59
60 64 68 75 77 81 85 86 87 93 96 107 115 119 130 131 132 135 146 149
156
Primary Contact: Nancy Vish, Ph.D., FACHE, R.N., President
CFO: Julius Wicke III Vice President Finance and Hospital Financial Officer
CMO: Kevin Wheelan, M.D., Medical Director
CHR: Kim Krause, Director Human Resources
Web address: www.baylorhearthospital.com
Control: Partnership, Investor–owned (for–profit) **Service:** Heart

Staffed Beds: 54 **Admissions:** 2539 **Census:** 23 **Outpatient Visits:** 39205
Births: 0 **Total Expense ($000):** 138288 **Payroll Expense ($000):** 35878
Personnel: 420

⊞ **BAYLOR SCOTT & WHITE INSTITUTE FOR REHABILITATION - DALLAS
(453036)**, 909 North Washington Avenue, Zip 75246–1520; tel. 214/820–9300,
A1 3 10 **F**3 29 30 34 35 44 62 64 65 68 74 75 77 85 86 87 90 92 93 94 95
96 130 131 132 135 143 148 149 156
Primary Contact: David Smith, Chief Executive Officer
CMO: Amy Wilson, M.D., Medical Director
CHR: Karen Hill, Director Human Resources
CNO: Beth Hudson, Chief Nursing Officer
Web address: www.baylorhealth.com/PhysiciansLocations/BIR/Pages/Default.aspx
Control: Partnership, Investor–owned (for–profit) **Service:** Rehabilitation

Staffed Beds: 89 **Admissions:** 1478 **Census:** 79 **Outpatient Visits:** 912
Births: 0 **Total Expense ($000):** 75198 **Payroll Expense ($000):** 47313
Personnel: 356

⊞ **BAYLOR SCOTT & WHITE MEDICAL CENTER-UPTOWN (450422)**, 2727 East
Lemmon Avenue, Zip 75204–2895; tel. 214/443–3000, **A**1 5 10 **F**29 40 68 77
79 81 82 85 107 111 **S** United Surgical Partners International, Addison, TX
Primary Contact: Nick Taylor, Chief Executive Officer
CFO: Colene Fielding, Manager Business Office
CMO: Mark Armstrong, M.D., Medical Director
CIO: Javier Vela, Director Information Technology
CHR: Emalie Sanchez, Director Human Resources
CNO: Verette Neeb, R.N., MSN, Chief Nursing Officer
Web address: www.bmcuptown.com
Control: Partnership, Investor–owned (for–profit) **Service:** Surgical

Staffed Beds: 24 **Admissions:** 1078 **Census:** 6 **Outpatient Visits:** 11087
Births: 0 **Total Expense ($000):** 56737 **Payroll Expense ($000):** 13698
Personnel: 187

TX

⊞ **BAYLOR UNIVERSITY MEDICAL CENTER (450021)**, 3500 Gaston Avenue, Zip 75246–2088; tel. 214/820–0111, (Includes A. WEBB ROBERTS HOSPITAL, 3500 Gaston Avenue, Dallas, Texas, Zip 75246–2017; tel. 361/986–9444; ERIK AND MARGARET JONSSON HOSPITAL, 3500 Gaston Avenue, Dallas, Texas, Zip 75246–2017; tel. 361/986–9444; GEORGE W. TRUETT MEMORIAL HOSPITAL, 3500 Gaston Avenue, Dallas, Texas, Zip 75246; tel. 361/986–9444; KARL AND ESTHER HOBLITZELLE MEMORIAL HOSPITAL, 3500 Gaston Avenue, Dallas, Texas, Zip 75246; tel. 361/986–9444) **A1** 2 3 5 8 10 **F3** 6 8 11 12 13 14 15 17 18 19 20 21 22 24 26 29 30 31 34 35 36 37 38 39 40 41 42 43 44 45 46 47 48 49 50 51 52 53 54 55 56 57 58 59 60 61 64 65 66 68 70 71 72 74 75 76 77 78 79 80 81 82 84 85 86 87 100 101 102 107 108 110 111 112 114 115 116 117 119 120 121 122 123 124 126 129 130 132 133 135 136 137 138 139 140 141 142 144 145 146 147 148 149 150 154 156 157 **S** Baylor Scott & White Health, Dallas, TX
Primary Contact: Steven R. Newton, FACHE, President
COO: Scott Peek, FACHE, Chief Operating Officer
CFO: Jay Whitfield, Chief Financial Officer
CMO: Brad Lembcke, M.D., Vice President Medical Staff Affairs
CHR: Julie Strittmatter, Director Human Resources
Web address: www.baylorhealth.com/PhysiciansLocations/Dallas/Pages/Default.aspx
Control: Other not–for–profit (including NFP Corporation) **Service:** General medical and surgical

Staffed Beds: 857 **Admissions:** 37895 **Census:** 625 **Outpatient Visits:** 227901 **Births:** 4539 **Total Expense ($000):** 1011614 **Payroll Expense ($000):** 311709 **Personnel:** 3966

⊞ **CHILDREN'S MEDICAL CENTER DALLAS (453302)**, 1935 Medical District Drive, Zip 75235–7701; tel. 214/456–7000, **A1** 3 5 8 10 **F3** 7 8 11 12 17 19 21 22 23 24 25 27 29 30 31 32 34 35 36 38 39 40 41 43 44 45 46 48 49 50 51 54 55 57 58 59 60 61 62 64 65 66 68 72 74 75 77 78 79 81 82 84 85 86 87 88 89 91 92 93 94 97 98 99 100 101 102 104 105 107 108 111 115 116 117 118 119 126 127 129 130 131 132 134 136 137 138 139 140 141 142 143 145 146 148 153 154 155 **S** Children's Health, Dallas, TX
Primary Contact: Christopher J. Durovich, President and Chief Executive Officer
CFO: Richard P. Goode, Executive Vice President and Chief Financial Officer
CMO: W. Robert Morrow, M.D., Executive Vice President and Chief Medical Officer
CIO: Pamela Arora, Senior Vice President Information Systems
CHR: Kim Besse, Executive Vice President and Chief Human Resource Officer
CNO: Mary Stowe, Senior Vice President and Chief Nursing Officer
Web address: www.childrens.com
Control: Other not–for–profit (including NFP Corporation) **Service:** Children's general medical and surgical

Staffed Beds: 385 **Admissions:** 11718 **Census:** 241 **Outpatient Visits:** 564757 **Births:** 0 **Total Expense ($000):** 1046873 **Payroll Expense ($000):** 327245 **Personnel:** 4530

⊞ **CITY HOSPITAL AT WHITE ROCK (450678)**, 9440 Poppy Drive, Zip 75218–3694; tel. 214/324–6100, **A1** 10 **F3** 11 12 13 15 17 18 20 22 24 26 28 29 30 31 34 35 37 40 42 45 47 49 50 51 53 56 57 59 64 70 72 74 75 76 77 78 79 81 85 93 107 108 110 111 114 115 119 120 124 126 129 130 132 135 146 147 148
Primary Contact: Jorge Trevino, Chief Executive Officer
COO: Jorge Trevino, Chief Executive Officer
CFO: Drew Shea, Chief Financial Officer
CMO: William Jones, M.D., II Chief Medical Officer
CHR: David Olmstead, Director, Human Resources
CNO: Cheryl Nail, R.N., Chief Nursing Officer
Web address: www.https://cityhospital.co/
Control: Partnership, Investor–owned (for–profit) **Service:** General medical and surgical

Staffed Beds: 151 **Admissions:** 7000 **Census:** 74 **Outpatient Visits:** 62805 **Births:** 1256 **Total Expense ($000):** 90630 **Payroll Expense ($000):** 37804 **Personnel:** 559

⊞ **DALLAS MEDICAL CENTER (450379)**, Seven Medical Parkway, Zip 75234–7823, Mailing Address: P.O. Box 819094, Zip 75381–9094; tel. 972/247–1000, **A1** 10 **F3** 12 15 18 20 22 26 29 34 40 43 44 45 46 49 50 51 54 57 59 64 68 70 74 75 77 78 79 81 82 84 85 86 93 97 107 108 111 114 116 119 130 131 141 142 146 147 148 149 **S** Prime Healthcare, Ontario, CA
Primary Contact: J. T. Barnhart, Chief Executive Officer
CFO: Nicholas Geer, Chief Financial Officer
CHR: Sheila K Richards, Human Resources Director
Web address: www.dallasmedcenter.com
Control: Corporation, Investor–owned (for–profit) **Service:** General medical and surgical

Staffed Beds: 71 **Admissions:** 2611 **Census:** 28 **Outpatient Visits:** 32684 **Births:** 0 **Total Expense ($000):** 67997 **Payroll Expense ($000):** 21990 **Personnel:** 349

⊞ **ENCOMPASS HEALTH REHABILITATION HOSPITAL OF DALLAS (673043)**, 7930 Northaven Road, Zip 75230–3331; tel. 214/706–8200, **A1** 10 **F3** 29 90 96 130 148 149 **S** Encompass Health Corporation, Birmingham, AL
Primary Contact: Daniel MacNicol, Chief Executive Officer
CFO: Elizabeth Robertson, Area Controller
CMO: Anna Freed-Sigurdsson, M.D., Medical Director
CHR: Lindsay Battles, Director Human Resources
CNO: Elysia Clay, Chief Nursing Officer
Web address: www.healthsouthdallas.com
Control: Corporation, Investor–owned (for–profit) **Service:** Rehabilitation

Staffed Beds: 40 **Admissions:** 943 **Census:** 31 **Outpatient Visits:** 0 **Births:** 0 **Total Expense ($000):** 20255 **Payroll Expense ($000):** 8047 **Personnel:** 135

★ **FIRST BAPTIST MEDICAL CENTER**, 8111 Meadow Road, Zip 75231; tel. 469/329–3700, **F3** 12 29 37 40 45 49 64 70 79 81 82 85 86 87 107 114 119 126 130 149
Primary Contact: Harold Gaskill III, M.D., Chief Executive Officer
Web address: www.fbmcdallas.com
Control: Corporation, Investor–owned (for–profit) **Service:** Surgical

Staffed Beds: 18 **Admissions:** 514 **Census:** 4 **Outpatient Visits:** 1616 **Births:** 0 **Total Expense ($000):** 31138 **Payroll Expense ($000):** 8874 **Personnel:** 135

⊞ **KINDRED HOSPITAL DALLAS CENTRAL (452108)**, 8050 Meadow Road, Zip 75231–3406; tel. 469/232–6500, **A1** 10 **F1** 3 29 75 77 85 87 96 107 114 148 **S** Kindred Healthcare, Louisville, KY
Primary Contact: Kyron J. Kooken, MS, Chief Executive Officer
CFO: Robin Fry, CPA, Market Controller
CNO: Traci Brewer, R.N., Chief Clinical Officer
Web address: www.khdallascentral.com/
Control: Partnership, Investor–owned (for–profit) **Service:** Acute long–term care hospital

Staffed Beds: 60 **Admissions:** 618 **Census:** 42 **Outpatient Visits:** 7 **Births:** 0 **Total Expense ($000):** 25335 **Payroll Expense ($000):** 9675 **Personnel:** 162

⊞ **KINDRED HOSPITAL-DALLAS (452015)**, 9525 Greenville Avenue, Zip 75243–4116; tel. 214/355–2600, **A1** 10 **F1** 3 16 17 29 67 70 80 90 107 114 130 148 156 **S** Kindred Healthcare, Louisville, KY
Primary Contact: Misti Varnell, Chief Executive Officer
CFO: Jean McDowell, Chief Financial Officer
Web address: www.khdallas.com
Control: Corporation, Investor–owned (for–profit) **Service:** Acute long–term care hospital

Staffed Beds: 66 **Admissions:** 528 **Census:** 36 **Outpatient Visits:** 2178 **Births:** 0 **Total Expense ($000):** 23769 **Payroll Expense ($000):** 8993 **Personnel:** 124

⊞ **LIFECARE HOSPITALS OF DALLAS (452044)**, 1950 Record Crossing Road, Zip 75235–6223; tel. 214/640–9600, (Includes LIFECARE HOSPITALS OF NORTH TEXAS-FORT WORTH, 6201 Overton Ridge Boulevard, Fort Worth, Texas, Zip 76132–3613; tel. 817/370–6078; Phillip B Douglas, Chairman and Chief Executive Officer; LIFECARE HOSPITALS OF NORTH TEXAS-PLANO, 6800 Preston Road, Plano, Texas, Zip 75024–2505; tel. 214/473–8822; Kathleen Wallace, R.N., MSN, Administrator and Chief Executive Officer) **A1** 10 **F1** 3 29 30 74 75 77 81 82 84 91 96 107 114 115 119 130 135 146 148 **S** LifeCare Management Services, Plano, TX
Primary Contact: Deborah Paganelli, FACHE, Chief Executive Officer
CFO: Amie Gratch, Director Financial Services
CMO: Jonathan Weissler, M.D., Chief Medical Officer
CHR: Linzie Riley, Interim Human Resource Manager
CNO: Kathy Mason, R.N., MSN, Chief Nursing Officer
Web address: www.lifecare-hospitals.com/hospital/dallas
Control: Corporation, Investor–owned (for–profit) **Service:** Acute long–term care hospital

Staffed Beds: 156 **Admissions:** 1504 **Census:** 104 **Outpatient Visits:** 31244 **Births:** 0 **Total Expense ($000):** 75944 **Payroll Expense ($000):** 30431 **Personnel:** 535

LIFECARE HOSPITALS OF NORTH TEXAS See Lifecare Hospitals of Dallas

MARY SHIELS HOSPITAL See Baylor Scott & White Medical Center-Uptown

TX

✠ **MEDICAL CITY DALLAS (450647)**, 7777 Forest Lane, Zip 75230–2598; tel. 972/566–7000, (Includes MEDICAL CITY CHILDREN'S HOSPITAL, 7777 Forest Lane, Dallas, Texas, Zip 75230–2505; tel. 972/566–7000; Jessica O'Neal, Chief Executive Officer) **A**1 2 3 5 10 **F**3 4 11 12 13 17 18 19 20 21 22 23 24 25 26 27 28 29 31 35 37 40 41 42 43 44 45 46 47 48 49 50 51 55 56 57 58 59 60 64 65 68 70 72 73 74 75 76 77 78 79 81 82 84 85 86 87 88 89 90 91 93 96 107 108 111 114 115 116 117 118 119 124 126 130 132 135 136 137 138 141 142 143 146 147 148 149 157 **S** HCA Healthcare, Nashville, TN
Primary Contact: Chris Mowan, Chief Executive Officer
CFO: Mark Atchley, Vice President and Chief Financial Officer
CMO: Kenneth Rothfield, M.D., Chief Medical Officer
CIO: Troy Sypien, Director Information Technology and Systems
CHR: Jenifer K Tertel, Director Human Resources
CNO: Joyce Soule, R.N., MSN, Chief Nursing Officer
Web address: www.medicalcityhospital.com
Control: Corporation, Investor–owned (for–profit) **Service**: General medical and surgical

Staffed Beds: **711** Admissions: **29736** Census: **520** Outpatient Visits: **195540** Births: **4176** Total Expense ($000): **592259** Payroll Expense ($000): **216056** Personnel: **2531**

✠ **MEDICAL CITY GREEN OAKS HOSPITAL (454094)**, 7808 Clodus Fields Drive, Zip 75251–2206; tel. 972/991–9504, **A**1 5 10 **F**4 5 29 30 50 68 87 98 99 101 102 103 104 105 130 132 135 149 151 152 153 154 **S** HCA Healthcare, Nashville, TN
Primary Contact: Thomas M. Collins, President, Chairman and Chief Executive Officer
COO: Pam Whitley, R.N., Chief Operating Officer and Chief Nursing Officer
CMO: Joel Holiner, M.D., Executive Medical Director
CIO: Richard Fontenault, Director Information Systems
CHR: Kevin Adkins, Director Human Resources
CNO: Pam Whitley, R.N., Chief Nursing Officer and Chief Operating Officer
Web address: www.greenoakspsych.com
Control: Corporation, Investor–owned (for–profit) **Service**: Psychiatric

Staffed Beds: **124** Admissions: **4533** Census: **105** Outpatient Visits: **21392** Births: **0** Total Expense ($000): **39641** Payroll Expense ($000): **17670** Personnel: **286**

✠ **METHODIST CHARLTON MEDICAL CENTER (450723)**, 3500 West Wheatland Road, Zip 75237–3460, Mailing Address: P.O. Box 225357, Zip 75222–5357; tel. 214/947–7777, **A**1 3 10 **F**3 11 13 15 18 20 22 24 28 29 30 31 34 35 40 45 46 47 49 50 53 58 59 60 64 66 68 70 74 76 78 79 81 82 84 85 86 87 97 107 108 110 111 114 115 118 119 126 130 131 132 146 148 156 **S** Methodist Health System, Dallas, TX
Primary Contact: Fran Laukaitis, R.N., FACHE, President
COO: Pamela Stoyanoff, Executive Vice President and Chief Operating Officer
CFO: Michael J Schaefer, Executive Vice President and Chief Financial Officer
CIO: Pamela McNutt, Vice President Information Systems
CHR: Cheryl Flynn, Senior Vice President Chief Human Resources Officer
Web address: www.methodisthealthsystem.org/charlton
Control: Other not–for–profit (including NFP Corporation) **Service**: General medical and surgical

Staffed Beds: **292** Admissions: **14423** Census: **198** Outpatient Visits: **145036** Births: **1832** Total Expense ($000): **254583** Payroll Expense ($000): **119005** Personnel: **1617**

✠ **METHODIST DALLAS MEDICAL CENTER (450051)**, 1441 North Beckley Avenue, Zip 75203–1201, Mailing Address: P.O. Box 655999, Zip 75265–5999; tel. 214/947–8181, **A**1 2 5 10 **F**3 11 12 13 15 18 20 22 24 26 28 29 30 31 34 35 37 40 43 45 46 47 48 49 50 53 54 58 59 60 64 66 68 70 72 74 76 78 79 81 82 84 85 87 92 93 97 107 108 110 111 114 115 118 119 126 130 132 138 139 142 146 148 149 150 156 **S** Methodist Health System, Dallas, TX
Primary Contact: John E. Phillips, FACHE, President
COO: Pamela Stoyanoff, Executive Vice President and Chief Operating Officer
CFO: Randy Walker, Vice President
CMO: Leslie Cler, M.D., Chief Medical Officer
CIO: Pamela McNutt, Senior Vice President and Chief Information Officer
CHR: Jackie Middleton, Vice President Human Resources
Web address: www.methodisthealthsystem.org/Dallas
Control: Other not–for–profit (including NFP Corporation) **Service**: General medical and surgical

Staffed Beds: **390** Admissions: **15561** Census: **250** Outpatient Visits: **153614** Births: **2277** Total Expense ($000): **445250** Payroll Expense ($000): **169594** Personnel: **2329**

□ △ **METHODIST REHABILITATION HOSPITAL (673031)**, 3020 West Wheatland Road, Zip 75237–3537; tel. 972/708–8600, **A**1 7 10 **F**29 30 60 90 91 93 95 96
Primary Contact: Shari Moore, Chief Executive Officer
CFO: Darline Kennemer, Controller
Web address: www.methodist-rehab.com
Control: Partnership, Investor–owned (for–profit) **Service**: Rehabilitation

Staffed Beds: **40** Admissions: **1043** Census: **32** Outpatient Visits: **10264** Births: **0** Total Expense ($000): **15409** Payroll Expense ($000): **7930** Personnel: **153**

□ **NORTH CENTRAL SURGICAL CENTER (670049)**, 9301 North Central Expressway, Suite 100, Zip 75231–0802; tel. 214/265–2810, **A**1 3 10 **F**3 8 29 40 45 68 79 81 82 85 93 96 107 111 115 119 146
Primary Contact: Thanh Tran, FACHE, Chief Executive Officer
COO: Ben Magestro, Chief Operating Officer
CFO: Mike Quaglieri, Chief Financial Officer
CMO: Stuart Simon, M.D., Medical Director
CNO: Katherine Martinez, Chief Nursing Officer
Web address: www.northcentralsurgical.com
Control: Partnership, Investor–owned (for–profit) **Service**: Surgical

Staffed Beds: **23** Admissions: **1434** Census: **8** Outpatient Visits: **19617** Births: **0** Total Expense ($000): **70337** Payroll Expense ($000): **17742** Personnel: **265**

★ **OUR CHILDREN'S HOUSE (453308)**, 1340 Empire Central Drive, Zip 75247–4022; tel. 214/867–6700, **A**3 5 10 **F**3 29 30 35 89 129 130 132 146 154 **S** Children's Health, Dallas, TX
Primary Contact: David T. Berry, President, Children's Health Clinical Operations
CMO: Andrew Gelfand, M.D., Medical Director
CNO: Kelli Terpstra, R.N., Senior Director
Web address: www.https://www.childrens.com/och
Control: Other not–for–profit (including NFP Corporation) **Service**: Children's general medical and surgical

Staffed Beds: **39** Admissions: **423** Census: **26** Outpatient Visits: **22194** Births: **0** Total Expense ($000): **29230** Payroll Expense ($000): **12292** Personnel: **195**

✠ **PARKLAND HEALTH & HOSPITAL SYSTEM (450015)**, 2070 Victory Avenue, Zip 75219, Mailing Address: 5200 Harry Hines Boulevard, Zip 75235–7708; tel. 214/590–8000, **A**1 2 3 5 8 10 **F**3 8 9 11 13 15 16 18 20 22 26 28 29 30 31 34 36 38 39 40 43 45 46 47 48 49 50 51 54 55 56 57 58 59 60 61 64 65 66 68 70 72 74 75 76 77 78 79 81 82 84 85 87 90 93 96 97 98 100 101 102 104 105 107 108 110 111 113 114 115 117 118 119 126 129 130 132 135 138 141 144 145 146 147 148 149 154 156 157
Primary Contact: Fred Cerise, M.D., Chief Executive Officer
COO: David S Lopez, FACHE, Executive Vice President and Chief Operating Officer
CFO: Richard Humphrey, Executive Vice President and Chief Financial Officer
CIO: Joseph Longo, Chief Information Officer
CHR: Corey D. Jackson, Executive Vice President and Chief Talent Officer
CNO: Mary K Eagen, R.N., MS, Executive Vice President, Chief Nursing Officer
Web address: www.parklandhospital.com
Control: Hospital district or authority, Government, nonfederal **Service**: General medical and surgical

Staffed Beds: **841** Admissions: **39944** Census: **657** Outpatient Visits: **1322746** Births: **12615** Total Expense ($000): **1873517** Payroll Expense ($000): **821943** Personnel: **11868**

□ **PINE CREEK MEDICAL CENTER (450894)**, 9032 Harry Hines Boulevard, Zip 75235–1720; tel. 214/231–2273, (Nonreporting) **A**1 10
Primary Contact: Daniel L. Gideon, FACHE, Chief Executive Officer
CFO: Michael Conroy, Chief Financial Officer
CIO: Kevin Carney, Senior Information Systems Analyst
Web address: www.pinecreekmedicalcenter.com
Control: Partnership, Investor–owned (for–profit) **Service**: Surgical

Staffed Beds: **15**

TX

☐ **PROMISE HOSPITAL OF DALLAS (452067)**, 7955 Harry Hines Boulevard, Zip 75235–3305; tel. 214/637–0000, **A**1 10 **F**1 3 29 30 40 64 75 77 91 148 **S** Promise Healthcare, Boca Raton, FL
Primary Contact: Louis P. Bradley Jr, Chief Executive Officer
CFO: Diana B Smith, Chief Financial Officer
CMO: Gary E. Goff, M.D., Medical Director
CHR: Ginger Davenport, Director Human Resources
Web address: www.promise-dallas.com/
Control: Corporation, Investor–owned (for–profit) **Service**: Acute long–term care hospital

Staffed Beds: 66 **Admissions:** 143 **Census:** 10 **Outpatient Visits:** 88 **Births:** 0 **Total Expense ($000):** 7818 **Payroll Expense ($000):** 4206 **Personnel:** 77

★ **SELECT SPECIALTY HOSPITAL - DALLAS DOWNTOWN (452119)**, 3500 Gaston Avenue, Floors 3&4 Jonsson, Zip 75246–2017; tel. 469/801–4500, **F**1 3 29 74 77 85 86 87 91 96 148 **S** Select Medical Corporation, Mechanicsburg, PA
Primary Contact: Michael McAlister, Chief Executive Officer
Web address: www.dallasdowntown.selectspecialtyhospitals.com/
Control: Corporation, Investor–owned (for–profit) **Service**: Acute long–term care hospital

Staffed Beds: 26 **Admissions:** 310 **Census:** 24 **Outpatient Visits:** 0 **Births:** 0 **Total Expense ($000):** 16027 **Payroll Expense ($000):** 6509 **Personnel:** 91

⊞ △ **TEXAS HEALTH PRESBYTERIAN HOSPITAL DALLAS (450462)**, 8200 Walnut Hill Lane, Zip 75231–4426; tel. 214/345–6789, **A**1 2 3 5 7 10 **F**3 5 11 12 13 15 17 18 20 22 24 26 28 29 30 31 34 35 37 38 40 43 44 45 46 47 49 50 51 53 54 56 57 58 59 60 61 64 65 66 68 70 72 73 74 75 76 77 78 79 81 84 85 86 87 90 91 92 93 94 95 96 97 98 100 101 102 104 105 106 107 108 110 111 112 114 115 118 119 124 126 129 131 132 135 141 143 144 146 148 151 152 153 **S** Texas Health Resources, Arlington, TX
Primary Contact: James Berg, FACHE, President
CFO: Brian Craft, Group Finance Officer
CMO: Aurora Estevez, M.D., Chief Medical Officer
CIO: Tammy Phillips, Director, Information Systems
CHR: Stacy Miller, Entity Human Resources Officer
Web address: www.texashealth.org
Control: Other not–for–profit (including NFP Corporation) **Service**: General medical and surgical

Staffed Beds: 553 **Admissions:** 26618 **Census:** 385 **Outpatient Visits:** 138784 **Births:** 5015 **Total Expense ($000):** 619151 **Payroll Expense ($000):** 217793 **Personnel:** 2404

TEXAS HOSPITAL FOR ADVANCED MEDICINE See Dallas Medical Center

☐ **TEXAS INSTITUTE FOR SURGERY AT TEXAS HEALTH PRESBYTERIAN DALLAS (450889)**, 7115 Greenville Avenue, Suite 100, Zip 75231–5100; tel. 214/647–5300, **A**1 10 22 **F**40 51 64 79 81 82 107 114 115 119
Primary Contact: John S. Croley, Chief Executive Officer and Chief Financial Officer
CFO: John S. Croley, Chief Executive Officer and Chief Financial Officer
CMO: Presley Mock, M.D., Chief of Staff
CHR: Jennifer C. Levy, Director Human Resources
CNO: Tammy Jarvis, Vice President Clinical Services and Chief Nursing Officer
Web address: www.texasinstituteforsurgery.com
Control: Partnership, Investor–owned (for–profit) **Service**: General medical and surgical

Staffed Beds: 9 **Admissions:** 573 **Census:** 3 **Outpatient Visits:** 10144 **Births:** 0 **Total Expense ($000):** 57714 **Payroll Expense ($000):** 13029 **Personnel:** 175

⊞ **TEXAS SCOTTISH RITE HOSPITAL FOR CHILDREN (453314)**, 2222 Welborn Street, Zip 75219–3924, Mailing Address: P.O. Box 190567, Zip 75219–0567; tel. 214/559–5000, **A**1 3 5 10 **F**3 9 11 29 34 35 39 50 53 54 57 58 64 68 74 75 77 79 81 82 85 86 87 89 92 93 94 107 111 115 119 130 131 132 146 157
Primary Contact: Robert L. Walker, FACHE, President and Chief Executive Officer
CFO: William R Huston, Senior Vice President and Chief Financial Officer
CMO: Daniel J Sucato, M.D., MS, Chief of Staff
CIO: Les Clonch, Chief Information Officer
CHR: Connie Wright, Vice President Human Resources
CNO: Debbie A Sayles, R.N., Vice President and Chief Nursing Officer
Web address: www.tsrhc.org
Control: Other not–for–profit (including NFP Corporation) **Service**: Children's orthopedic

Staffed Beds: 30 **Admissions:** 634 **Census:** 11 **Outpatient Visits:** 55571 **Births:** 0 **Total Expense ($000):** 142512 **Payroll Expense ($000):** 73677 **Personnel:** 830

⊞ **UNIVERSITY OF TEXAS SOUTHWESTERN MEDICAL CENTER (450766)**, 5323 Harry Hines Boulevard, Zip 75390–9265; tel. 214/648–3111, (Includes UNIVERSITY OF TEXAS SOUTHWESTERN MEDICAL CENTER - ZALE LIPSHY, 5151 Harry Hines Boulevard, Dallas, Texas, Zip 75390–9265; tel. 214/645–8300; Daniel Podolsky, M.D., President) **A**1 2 3 5 8 10 19 **F**3 5 6 7 8 9 11 12 13 14 15 17 18 19 20 21 22 23 24 25 26 27 28 29 30 31 32 34 35 36 37 38 39 40 41 44 45 46 47 48 49 50 52 53 54 55 56 57 58 59 60 61 62 63 64 65 66 70 71 72 74 75 76 77 78 79 80 81 82 83 84 85 86 87 90 91 92 93 94 95 96 97 98 99 100 101 102 103 104 107 108 109 110 111 113 114 115 116 117 118 119 120 121 123 124 126 127 129 130 131 132 134 135 136 137 138 139 140 141 142 143 145 146 147 148 149 150 151 152 153 154 155 156
Primary Contact: John Warner, M.D., Chief Executive Officer
COO: Becky McCulley, Chief Operations Officer
CMO: John Warner, M.D., Chief Executive Officer, Interim Chief Medical Officer
CIO: Marc E. Milstein, Vice President Information Resources
CHR: Ivan Thompson, Vice President, Chief Human Resource Officer
CNO: Susan Hernandez, R.N., Chief Nurse Executive
Web address: www.utsouthwestern.edu
Control: State, Government, nonfederal **Service**: General medical and surgical

Staffed Beds: 608 **Admissions:** 27107 **Census:** 452 **Outpatient Visits:** 524738 **Births:** 2014 **Total Expense ($000):** 1256897 **Payroll Expense ($000):** 473363 **Personnel:** 5765

⊞ △ **VETERANS AFFAIRS NORTH TEXAS HEALTH CARE SYSTEM**, 4500 South Lancaster Road, Zip 75216–7167; tel. 214/742–8387, (Includes SAM RAYBURN MEMORIAL VETERANS CENTER, 1201 East Ninth Street, Bonham, Texas, Zip 75418–2111; Angela Nix, Administrator), (Non-reporting) **A**1 2 3 5 7 **S** Department of Veterans Affairs, Washington, DC
Primary Contact: Stephen R. Holt, M.D., Director
CFO: Alton McKinley, Chief Financial Officer
CIO: Lucy Rogers, Chief Information Resource Management Systems
Web address: www.northtexas.va.gov/
Control: Veterans Affairs, Government, federal **Service**: General medical and surgical

Staffed Beds: 875

WILLIAM P. CLEMENTS, JR. UNIVERSITY HOSPITAL (450044), 6201 Harry Hines Boulevard, Zip 75235–5202; tel. 214/633–5555, (Nonreporting) **A**3 5
Primary Contact: Daniel Podolsky, M.D., President
Web address: www.utswmedicine.org/hospitals-clinics/clements/about/faqs/
Control: State, Government, nonfederal **Service**: General medical and surgical

Staffed Beds: 460

DECATUR—Wise County

⊞ **WISE HEALTH SYSTEM (450271)**, 609 Medical Center Drive, Zip 76234–3836; tel. 940/627–5921, (Includes WISE HEALTH SURGICAL HOSPITAL AT ARGYLE, 7218 Crawford Road, Argyle, Texas, Zip 76226; tel. 940/293–2885; Jason Wren, President and Chief Executive Officer; WISE HEALTH SURGICAL HOSPITAL AT PARKWAY, 3200 North Tarrant Parkway, Fort Worth, Texas, Zip 76177–8611; tel. 817/502–7300; Jason Wren, President and Chief Executive Officer; WISE REGIONAL HEALTH SYSTEM, WEST CAMPUS DECATUR, 2000 South Fm 51, Decatur, Texas, Zip 76234–3702; tel. 940/627–5921; Jason Wren, Chief Executive Officer) **A**1 2 10 **F**3 11 12 13 15 17 18 20 22 24 26 28 29 30 31 32 34 40 43 45 47 49 51 53 54 56 57 59 60 64 70 74 75 76 77 78 79 81 85 87 89 90 93 96 97 98 103 104 107 108 110 111 114 115 117 119 121 124 129 130 131 132 135 144 147 148 149 154 156
Primary Contact: Jason Wren, President and Chief Executive Officer
COO: Leon Fuqua, Chief Operating Officer
CFO: Todd Scroggins, Chief Financial Officer
CMO: Jon W. Walker, M.D., Chief Medical Officer
CIO: Joe Arispe, Director Information Systems
CHR: Mike McQuiston, Administrative Director Human Resources
CNO: Lee Ann Jennings, R.N., Vice President, Nursing Services
Web address: www.wiseregional.com
Control: Hospital district or authority, Government, nonfederal **Service**: General medical and surgical

Staffed Beds: 133 **Admissions:** 5720 **Census:** 74 **Outpatient Visits:** 465955 **Births:** 631 **Total Expense ($000):** 348031 **Payroll Expense ($000):** 88200 **Personnel:** 1410

TX

DEL RIO—Val Verde County

⊞ **VAL VERDE REGIONAL MEDICAL CENTER (450154)**, 801 Bedell Avenue, Zip 78840–4112, Mailing Address: 801 North Bedell Avenue, Zip 78840–4112; tel. 830/775–8566, **A**1 10 20 22 **F**3 7 11 13 15 18 20 28 29 30 34 35 40 43 46 48 54 56 57 59 63 64 73 75 76 77 79 81 82 84 85 87 89 93 96 101 104 107 108 110 111 114 119 127 129 130 131 132 133 146 147 149 153 154 155 156
Primary Contact: Linda Walker, Chief Executive Officer
CFO: Eddie Read, Interim Chief Financial Officer
CMO: Mohamed Shafiu, M.D., Chief of Staff
CIO: Val King, Chief Information Officer
CNO: Kathy Fletcher, R.N., MSN, Interim Chief Nursing Officer
Web address: www.vvrmc.org
Control: Hospital district or authority, Government, nonfederal **Service**: General medical and surgical

Staffed Beds: 80 **Admissions**: 2339 **Census**: 20 **Outpatient Visits**: 72344 **Births**: 824 **Total Expense ($000)**: 69402 **Payroll Expense ($000)**: 22509 **Personnel**: 519

DENISON—Grayson County

☐ **TEXOMA MEDICAL CENTER (450324)**, 5016 South US Highway 75, Zip 75020–4584, Mailing Address: P.O. Box 890, Zip 75021–0890; tel. 903/416–4000, (Includes TMC BEHAVIORAL HEALTH CENTER, 2601 North Cornerstone Drive, Sherman, Texas, Zip 75092–2551; tel. 903/416–3000; Ryan Tatu, Chief Executive Officer) **A**1 10 13 **F**3 11 12 13 15 17 18 20 22 24 28 29 30 31 34 35 40 43 45 46 47 48 49 50 53 54 57 59 62 64 70 72 74 75 76 77 78 79 80 81 82 85 86 87 89 90 91 93 96 98 99 100 101 102 103 104 107 108 110 111 115 118 119 126 129 130 132 144 145 146 147 148 149 150 153 156 **S** Universal Health Services, Inc., King of Prussia, PA
Primary Contact: Ronald T. Seal, Chief Executive Officer
CFO: Gerard Hebert, Chief Financial Officer
CMO: Robert Sanders, M.D., Chief Medical Officer
CIO: Lisa Engle, Director Information Technology
CHR: Bill Heinzmann, Director Human Resources
CNO: Andrea Brenn, R.N., Chief Nursing Officer
Web address: www.texomamedicalcenter.net
Control: Corporation, Investor–owned (for–profit) **Service**: General medical and surgical

Staffed Beds: 378 **Admissions**: 20580 **Census**: 268 **Outpatient Visits**: 136538 **Births**: 1234 **Total Expense ($000)**: 265557 **Payroll Expense ($000)**: 110233 **Personnel**: 2018

DENTON—Denton County

★ **BAYLOR SCOTT & WHITE THE HEART HOSPITAL–DENTON (450893)**, 2801 South Mayhill Road, Zip 76208–5910, Mailing Address: 2891 South Mayhill Road, Zip 76208, tel. 469/014–3270, **A**10 **F**3 17 18 20 22 24 26 28 29 30 34 35 40 53 54 57 59 60 64 68 74 75 77 81 82 84 85 87 90 107 111 115 119 130 132 135 146 148 149 154 157
Primary Contact: Mark Valentine, President
COO: Bradley Morgan, Vice President of Operations
CFO: Bryan Nichols, Chief Financial Officer
CMO: Trent Pettijohn, M.D., Esq Chief Medical Officer
CHR: Tracy Stanford, Director Human Resources
CNO: Susan K. Moats, R.N., Vice President Patient Care Services and Chief Nursing Officer
Web address: www.https://denton.thehearthospitalbaylor.com
Control: Partnership, Investor–owned (for–profit) **Service**: Heart

Staffed Beds: 22 **Admissions**: 666 **Census**: 8 **Outpatient Visits**: 6755 **Births**: 0 **Total Expense ($000)**: 41627 **Payroll Expense ($000)**: 12882 **Personnel**: 133

⊞ **MAYHILL HOSPITAL (670010)**, 2809 South Mayhill Road, Zip 76208–5910; tel. 940/239–3000, **A**1 10 **F**4 5 29 34 40 44 56 57 59 64 82 86 87 98 100 101 102 103 104 105 106 130 132 135 148 149 151 152 153 154 156 157 **S** Universal Health Services, Inc., King of Prussia, PA
Primary Contact: Loren Fouch, Chief Executive Officer
CFO: Emmy Adams, Chief Financial Officer
CMO: Asad Islam, M.D., Chief Medical Officer
CIO: Kyle Murphy, Director Information Technology
CHR: Patricia Gloria-Barraza, Coordinator Human Resources
Web address: www.mayhillhospital.com
Control: Partnership, Investor–owned (for–profit) **Service**: Psychiatric

Staffed Beds: 59 **Admissions**: 2129 **Census**: 47 **Outpatient Visits**: 2706 **Births**: 0 **Total Expense ($000)**: 11843 **Payroll Expense ($000)**: 5877 **Personnel**: 99

⊞ **MEDICAL CITY DENTON (450634)**, 3535 South I–35 East, Zip 76210; tel. 940/384–3535, **A**1 10 **F**3 15 18 20 22 24 26 28 29 30 34 35 40 43 45 46 47 49 50 57 64 70 74 75 77 79 80 81 82 84 85 86 87 93 107 108 110 111 114 115 118 119 126 130 132 144 146 148 149 154 **S** HCA Healthcare, Nashville, TN
Primary Contact: Steven Edgar, FACHE, President and Chief Executive Officer
COO: John Walker, Chief Operating Officer
CFO: Todd Gibson, Chief Financial Officer
CMO: Howard Shaw, M.D., Chief Medical Officer
CHR: Stacey Bravo, Vice President Human Resources
CNO: Brandy H Farrer, R.N., Chief Nursing Officer
Web address: www.dentonregional.com
Control: Partnership, Investor–owned (for–profit) **Service**: General medical and surgical

Staffed Beds: 185 **Admissions**: 8269 **Census**: 126 **Outpatient Visits**: 78546 **Births**: 0 **Total Expense ($000)**: 158433 **Payroll Expense ($000)**: 54624 **Personnel**: 805

⊞ **SELECT REHABILITATION HOSPITAL OF DENTON (673036)**, 2620 Scripture Street, Zip 76201–4315; tel. 940/297–6500, **A**1 10 **F**3 29 64 68 74 75 77 79 86 87 90 93 96 132 135 148 149 **S** Select Medical Corporation, Mechanicsburg, PA
Primary Contact: Michelle Powell, Chief Executive Officer
CFO: Doug Selsor, Director Finance
CHR: Patsy Martin, Manager Human Resources
CNO: Lee Ann Elliott, R.N., Director of Nursing
Web address: www.selectrehab-denton.com/
Control: Partnership, Investor–owned (for–profit) **Service**: Rehabilitation

Staffed Beds: 44 **Admissions**: 742 **Census**: 24 **Outpatient Visits**: 13254 **Births**: 0 **Total Expense ($000)**: 14885 **Payroll Expense ($000)**: 8050 **Personnel**: 91

⊞ **TEXAS HEALTH PRESBYTERIAN HOSPITAL DENTON (450743)**, 3000 North I-35, Zip 76201; tel. 940/898–7000, **A**1 10 **F**3 12 13 15 18 20 22 24 26 28 29 30 31 34 35 39 40 45 46 47 48 49 57 59 65 66 68 70 72 74 75 76 78 79 81 82 83 84 85 86 87 93 107 108 110 111 115 118 119 126 129 130 132 135 146 147 148 149 156 **S** Texas Health Resources, Arlington, TX
Primary Contact: Jeff Reecer, FACHE, Chief Executive Officer
CFO: David B Meltzer, Chief Financial Officer
CMO: Timothy Harris, M.D., Chief Quality Officer
CIO: Melissa Smart, Communication ad Public Relations Specialist
CHR: Kathy Hardcastle, Director Human Resources
CNO: Deborah Bostic, R.N., Chief Nursing Officer
Web address: www.dentonhocpital.com
Control: Other not for profit (including NFP Corporation) **Service**: General medical and surgical

Staffed Beds: 197 **Admissions**: 10590 **Census**: 124 **Outpatient Visits**: 73200 **Births**: 2214 **Total Expense ($000)**: 200155 **Payroll Expense ($000)**: 73398 **Personnel**: 935

⊞ **UNIVERSITY BEHAVIORAL HEALTH OF DENTON (454104)**, 2026 West University Drive, Zip 76201–0644; tel. 940/320–8100, **A**1 10 **F**4 5 59 68 75 98 99 100 101 102 103 104 105 106 132 134 135 144 151 152 153 154 **S** Universal Health Services, Inc., King of Prussia, PA
Primary Contact: Ronald Rains, Chief Executive Officer
CFO: Ed Sopiarz, Chief Financial Officer
CMO: Atique Khan, M.D., Medical Director
CIO: Marsh Smith, Manager Health Information
CHR: Dorie Atherton, Manager Human Resources
CNO: Vicki Stoker, Chief Nursing Officer
Web address: www.ubhdenton.com
Control: Partnership, Investor–owned (for–profit) **Service**: Psychiatric

Staffed Beds: 104 **Admissions**: 2868 **Census**: 73 **Outpatient Visits**: 8520 **Births**: 0 **Total Expense ($000)**: 24549 **Payroll Expense ($000)**: 10547 **Personnel**: 169

TX

DENVER CITY—Yoakum County

★ **YOAKUM COUNTY HOSPITAL (451308)**, 412 Mustang Avenue, Zip 79323–2762, Mailing Address: P.O. Box 1130, Zip 79323–1130; tel. 806/592–2121, **A**10 18 **F**3 11 13 28 34 35 40 41 43 50 53 57 59 60 62 64 76 81 87 89 93 107 114 119 127 129 133 149 154
Primary Contact: Jerry Osburn, Chief Executive Officer
CFO: Suann Parrish, Chief Financial Officer
CMO: Dan Khan, M.D., Chief Medical Officer
CIO: Todd Carrillo, Chief Information Officer
CHR: Teresa Howard, Manager Human Resources
Web address: www.ych.us
Control: County, Government, nonfederal **Service**: General medical and surgical

Staffed Beds: 22 **Admissions:** 501 **Census:** 4 **Outpatient Visits:** 55521
Births: 283 **Total Expense ($000):** 26654 **Payroll Expense ($000):** 8938
Personnel: 177

DESOTO—Dallas County

☐ **DALLAS BEHAVIORAL HEALTHCARE HOSPITAL (454126)**, 800 Kirnwood Drive, Zip 75115–2000; tel. 855/982–0897, **A**1 **F**4 5 56 87 98 99 100 101 103 104 105 130 151 152 153 154 **S** Signature Healthcare Services, Corona, CA
Primary Contact: Terrance O'Reilly, Chief Executive Officer
CMO: Rahim Haqqani, M.D., Medical Director
CHR: Henry In, Director Human Resources
CNO: Susie Edler, R.N., Chief Nursing Officer
Web address: www.dallasbehavioral.com
Control: Individual, Investor–owned (for–profit) **Service**: Psychiatric

Staffed Beds: 116 **Admissions:** 4301 **Census:** 96 **Outpatient Visits:** 9183
Births: 0 **Total Expense ($000):** 23524 **Payroll Expense ($000):** 12819
Personnel: 259

☐ **HICKORY TRAIL HOSPITAL (454065)**, 2000 Old Hickory Trail, Zip 75115–2242; tel. 972/298–7323, **A**1 10 **F**4 5 29 38 98 99 100 101 103 105 130 152 153 **S** Universal Health Services, Inc., King of Prussia, PA
Primary Contact: Kay McKennery, Interim Chief Executive Officer
CFO: Terri Logsdon, Chief Financial Officer
CMO: Manoochehr Khatami, M.D., Medical Director
CHR: Sarah Warren, Coordinator Human Resources
Web address: www.hickorytrail.com
Control: Corporation, Investor–owned (for–profit) **Service**: Psychiatric

Staffed Beds: 86 **Admissions:** 3055 **Census:** 65 **Outpatient Visits:** 8703
Births: 0 **Total Expense ($000):** 17920 **Payroll Expense ($000):** 9053
Personnel: 171

⊞ **VIBRA SPECIALTY HOSPITAL AT DESOTO (452097)**, 2700 Walker Way, Zip 75115–2088; tel. 972/298–1100, **A**1 10 **F**1 3 29 70 75 77 87 91 107 130 148 **S** Vibra Healthcare, Mechanicsburg, PA
Primary Contact: Thomas Alexander, Chief Executive Officer
CFO: Donald Trimble, CPA, Chief Financial Officer
CMO: Ed Dominguez, President Medical Staff
CHR: Tim Lozier, Director Human Resources
CNO: Mae C Weathersby, R.N., Chief Clinical Officer
Web address: www.vshdesoto.com
Control: Corporation, Investor–owned (for–profit) **Service**: Acute long–term care hospital

Staffed Beds: 60 **Admissions:** 651 **Census:** 46 **Outpatient Visits:** 0
Births: 0 **Total Expense ($000):** 22801 **Payroll Expense ($000):** 11787
Personnel: 169

DIMMITT—Castro County

★ **PLAINS MEMORIAL HOSPITAL (451350)**, 310 West Halsell Street, Zip 79027–1846, Mailing Address: P.O. Box 278, Zip 79027–0278; tel. 806/647–2191, **A**10 18 **F**3 7 32 34 35 40 43 53 57 59 64 65 69 75 77 85 86 87 93 97 107 114 115 119 127 130 133 135 149 156
Primary Contact: Linda Rasor, R.N., Chief Executive Officer
CFO: Terri Martinez, Chief Financial Officer
CMO: Gary R Hardee, M.D., Medical Director
CIO: Terry Young, Chief Information Officer
CHR: Debbie Underwood, Manager Human Resources
CNO: Renee Castillo, Chief Nursing Officer
Web address: www.plainsmemorial.com
Control: Hospital district or authority, Government, nonfederal **Service**: General medical and surgical

Staffed Beds: 17 **Admissions:** 135 **Census:** 3 **Outpatient Visits:** 21243
Births: 0 **Total Expense ($000):** 11715 **Payroll Expense ($000):** 4781
Personnel: 103

DUMAS—Moore County

☐ **MOORE COUNTY HOSPITAL DISTRICT (451386)**, 224 East Second Street, Zip 79029–3808; tel. 806/935–7171, **A**1 10 18 **F**3 7 11 13 15 28 34 35 40 43 46 50 51 57 59 62 63 70 75 76 79 81 85 86 89 91 93 107 110 111 115 119 130 131 132 133 135 146 147 148 154
Primary Contact: Jeff Turner, FACHE, Chief Executive Officer
COO: Ashleigh Wiswell, Chief Operations Officer
CFO: John E. Bailey, Chief Financial Officer
CHR: Kathie Fuston, Director Human Resources
CNO: Ronda Crow, Chief Nursing Officer
Web address: www.mchd.net
Control: Hospital district or authority, Government, nonfederal **Service**: General medical and surgical

Staffed Beds: 25 **Admissions:** 1454 **Census:** 10 **Outpatient Visits:** 25336
Births: 353 **Total Expense ($000):** 40558 **Payroll Expense ($000):** 18352
Personnel: 337

EAGLE LAKE—Colorado County

RICE MEDICAL CENTER (451312), 600 South Austin Road, Zip 77434–3298, Mailing Address: P.O. Box 277, Zip 77434–0277; tel. 979/234–5571, **A**10 18 **F**3 11 13 15 29 34 35 40 43 56 59 64 65 75 76 77 79 80 81 85 101 104 107 114 119 127 133 153 154 156
Primary Contact: James D. Janek, Chief Executive Officer
CMO: Russell Thomas, M.D., Chief of Staff
CHR: Velma Loya, Administrative Human Resource Coordinator
CNO: Susan Hernandez, R.N., Chief Nursing Officer
Web address: www.ricemedicalcenter.net/
Control: Corporation, Investor–owned (for–profit) **Service**: General medical and surgical

Staffed Beds: 13 **Admissions:** 166 **Census:** 2 **Outpatient Visits:** 24175
Births: 9 **Total Expense ($000):** 13401 **Payroll Expense ($000):** 3645
Personnel: 96

EAGLE PASS—Maverick County

☐ **FORT DUNCAN REGIONAL MEDICAL CENTER (450092)**, 3333 North Foster Maldonado Boulevard, Zip 78852–5893; tel. 830/773–5321, **A**1 10 20 **F**11 13 15 18 20 22 29 40 43 45 57 60 65 68 70 75 76 77 79 81 85 87 89 90 91 93 107 108 110 111 114 115 118 119 129 130 146 147 148 149 **S** Universal Health Services, Inc., King of Prussia, PA
Primary Contact: Eladio Montalvo, Chief Executive Officer
COO: Alan Gonzalez, Chief Operating Officer
CFO: Joel Morales, Chief Financial Officer
CMO: Ruben de los Santos, M.D., Chief Medical Officer
CIO: Jose Elias, Director Information Technology
CHR: Daisy Rodriquez, Director Human Resources
CNO: Scott Lethi, R.N., FACHE, Chief Nursing Officer
Web address: www.fortduncanmedicalcenter.com
Control: Partnership, Investor–owned (for–profit) **Service**: General medical and surgical

Staffed Beds: 101 **Admissions:** 4445 **Census:** 48 **Outpatient Visits:** 49088
Births: 1038 **Total Expense ($000):** 53173 **Payroll Expense ($000):** 21737
Personnel: 349

EASTLAND—Eastland County

EASTLAND MEMORIAL HOSPITAL (450411), 304 South Daugherty Street, Zip 76448–2609, Mailing Address: P.O. Box 897, Zip 76448–0897; tel. 254/629–2601, **A**10 20 **F**7 11 12 15 28 29 30 34 35 40 43 45 50 53 57 59 60 64 68 77 81 85 86 87 89 93 107 110 114 128 130 131 133 146 148
Primary Contact: Ted Matthews, Chief Executive Officer
CFO: Jamie Hayden, Chief Financial Officer
CHR: Leisha Hodges, Human Resources Officer
Web address: www.eastlandmemorial.com
Control: Hospital district or authority, Government, nonfederal **Service**: General medical and surgical

Staffed Beds: 34 **Admissions:** 466 **Census:** 7 **Outpatient Visits:** 34120
Births: 0 **Total Expense ($000):** 14313 **Payroll Expense ($000):** 6245
Personnel: 146

Many Facility Codes have changed. Please refer to the AHA Guide Code Chart. © 2019 AHA Guide

EDEN—Concho County

CONCHO COUNTY HOSPITAL (451325), 614 Eaker Street, Zip 76837–0359, Mailing Address: P.O. Box 987, Zip 76837–0987; tel. 325/869–5911, **A**10 18 **F**3 34 40 43 50 53 59 77 87 107 115 129 133 146
Primary Contact: Brian Lady, Administrator and Chief Executive Officer
CFO: Melanie Lozano, Chief Financial Officer
CNO: Toby Lehn, Director of Nurses
Web address: www.conchocountyhospital.com/
Control: Hospital district or authority, Government, nonfederal **Service**: General medical and surgical

Staffed Beds: 16 **Admissions**: 97 **Census**: 1 **Outpatient Visits**: 3705 **Births**: 0 **Total Expense ($000)**: 7595 **Payroll Expense ($000)**: 2835 **Personnel**: 53	

EDINBURG—Hidalgo County

⊞ **CORNERSTONE REGIONAL HOSPITAL (450825)**, 2302 Cornerstone Boulevard, Zip 78539–8471; tel. 956/618–4444, **A**1 10 **F**3 8 29 34 35 37 39 40 45 46 47 51 57 59 68 74 79 81 82 85 119 126 145 **S** Universal Health Services, Inc., King of Prussia, PA
Primary Contact: Roxanna M. Godinez, Chief Executive Officer
CFO: Janie Alvarez, Accounting Director
CMO: Omar Gomez, M.D., Chief of Staff
CHR: Erika Betancourt, Coordinator Human Resources
CNO: Roxanne Reyes, Director of Nursing
Web address: www.cornerstoneregional.com
Control: Partnership, Investor–owned (for–profit) **Service**: General medical and surgical

Staffed Beds: 14 **Admissions**: 489 **Census**: 3 **Outpatient Visits**: 2838 **Births**: 0 **Total Expense ($000)**: 13905 **Payroll Expense ($000)**: 4069 **Personnel**: 74	

☐ △ **DOCTOR'S HOSPITAL AT RENAISSANCE (450869)**, 5501 South McColl Road, Zip 78539–9152; tel. 956/362–7360, **A**1 2 3 5 7 8 10 **F**1 3 4 5 8 9 12 13 15 16 17 18 19 20 21 22 24 25 26 28 29 30 31 34 35 38 39 40 41 43 45 46 47 48 49 50 51 53 54 55 56 57 58 59 60 63 64 65 66 67 68 70 71 72 73 74 75 76 77 78 79 80 81 82 83 84 85 86 87 88 89 90 91 92 93 95 96 97 98 99 100 101 102 103 104 107 108 109 110 111 112 113 114 115 116 117 118 119 120 121 123 124 126 127 128 130 131 132 135 138 139 144 145 146 147 148 149 151 154 155 156 157
Primary Contact: Manish Singh, M.D., Chief Executive Officer
COO: Marissa Castaneda, Chief Operating Officer and Director Marketing
Web address: www.dhr-rgv.com
Control: Partnership, Investor–owned (for–profit) **Service**: General medical and surgical

Staffed Beds: 519 **Admissions**: 30208 **Census**: 408 **Outpatient Visits**: 422992 **Births**: 8472 **Total Expense ($000)**: 580489 **Payroll Expense ($000)**: 200930 **Personnel**: 4666	

☐ **SOUTH TEXAS HEALTH SYSTEM (450119)**, 1400 West Trenton Road, Zip 78539–9105, Mailing Address: 1102 West Trenton Road, Zip 78539–9105; tel. 956/388–6000, (Includes EDINBURG CHILDREN'S HOSPITAL, 1400 West Trenton Road, Edinburg, Texas, Zip 78539; tel. 956/388–8000; EDINBURG REGIONAL MEDICAL CENTER, 1102 West Trenton Road, Edinburg, Texas, Zip 78539–6199; tel. 956/388–6000; Lance Ames, Interim Chief Executive Officer; MCALLEN HEART HOSPITAL, 1900 South D Street, McAllen, Texas, Zip 78503; tel. 956/994–2000; Dan Caldwell, Chief Executive Officer; MCALLEN MEDICAL CENTER, 301 West Expressway 83, McAllen, Texas, Zip 78503–3045; tel. 956/632–4000; Todd Mann, Chief Executive Officer; SOUTH TEXAS BEHAVIORAL HEALTH CENTER, 2101 West Trenton Road, Edinburg, Texas, Zip 78539; tel. 956/388–1300; Joe Rodriguez, Chief Executive Officer) **A**1 10 19 **F**3 4 5 11 12 13 15 17 18 19 20 22 24 26 29 30 31 34 35 38 40 41 42 43 45 46 47 48 49 50 56 57 58 59 64 68 70 72 74 75 76 77 78 79 81 85 86 87 88 89 90 93 96 97 98 99 100 101 102 103 104 105 107 108 110 111 114 115 119 126 130 132 133 135 146 148 149 150 153 **S** Universal Health Services, Inc., King of Prussia, PA
Primary Contact: Brenda Ivory, MSN, Chief Executive Officer
CFO: Carlos Guajardo, Chief Financial Officer
CMO: Yuri Bermudez, M.D., Chief of Staff
CIO: Rosie L Mendiola-Balderas, Director Information Systems
CHR: Patricia Mcclelland, Director Human Resources
CNO: Candida Constantine-Castillo, MSN, R.N., Chief Nursing Officer
Web address: www.southtexashealthsystem.com
Control: Partnership, Investor–owned (for–profit) **Service**: General medical and surgical

Staffed Beds: 810 **Admissions**: 27159 **Census**: 369 **Outpatient Visits**: 221078 **Births**: 1620 **Total Expense ($000)**: 365221 **Payroll Expense ($000)**: 131922 **Personnel**: 2408	

EDNA—Jackson County

★ **JACKSON COUNTY HOSPITAL DISTRICT (451363)**, 1013 South Wells Street, Zip 77957–4098; tel. 361/782–7800, **A**10 18 **F**3 7 15 29 34 35 40 43 44 45 50 53 57 59 62 64 65 68 75 81 87 97 102 107 110 114 119 127 130 133 143 146 156 157
Primary Contact: Bill Jones, Chief Executive Officer
CFO: Lance Smiga, Chief Financial Officer
CMO: Francisco Ortiz, M.D., Chief of Staff
CIO: Jeff Prukop, Director Professional Services
CHR: Donna Coleman, Coordinator Human Resources
CNO: Tammy Zajicek, Director of Nursing
Web address: www.jchd.org
Control: Hospital district or authority, Government, nonfederal **Service**: General medical and surgical

Staffed Beds: 17 **Admissions**: 213 **Census**: 3 **Outpatient Visits**: 19078 **Births**: 0 **Total Expense ($000)**: 18795 **Payroll Expense ($000)**: 7805 **Personnel**: 124	

EL CAMPO—Wharton County

EL CAMPO MEMORIAL HOSPITAL (450694), 303 Sandy Corner Road, Zip 77437–9535; tel. 979/543–6251, **A**10 20 **F**3 11 15 18 28 29 30 34 35 40 45 54 57 59 60 64 65 66 68 70 77 79 81 85 86 91 92 93 97 107 108 110 111 112 114 119 127 129 130 133 135 148 154
Primary Contact: Nathan Tudor, Chief Executive Officer
CFO: David Mak, Chief Financial Officer
CMO: Thai Huynh, M.D., Chief of Medical Staff
CIO: Bill Eller, Director Information Technology
CHR: Ginger Andreas, Coordinator Personnel and Credentialing
CNO: Desiree Cernoch, Director of Nurses
Web address: www.ecmh.org
Control: Other not–for–profit (including NFP Corporation) **Service**: General medical and surgical

Staffed Beds: 26 **Admissions**: 710 **Census**: 7 **Outpatient Visits**: 72785 **Births**: 0 **Total Expense ($000)**: 19941 **Payroll Expense ($000)**: 8024 **Personnel**: 285	

EL PASO—El Paso County

EAST EL PASO PHYSICIANS MEDICAL CENTER See Foundation Surgical Hospital of El Paso

☐ **EL PASO BEHAVIORAL HEALTH SYSTEM (154109)**, 1900 Denver Avenue, Zip 79902–3000, tel. 915/544–4000, **A**1 10 **F**4 5 66 67 75 86 87 98 99 101 102 103 104 105 130 135 149 150 152 153 154 **S** Universal Health Services, Inc., King of Prussia, PA
Primary Contact: Phillip Sosa, Interim Chief Executive Officer
CFO: Phillip Sosa, Chief Financial Officer
CMO: Arthur L. Ramirez, M.D., Medical Director
CIO: Victor Torres, Information Technology Specialist Administrator
CHR: Brenda Holguin, Manager Human Resources
CNO: Susan Brown, Chief Nursing Officer
Web address: www.ubhelpaso.com/
Control: Corporation, Investor–owned (for–profit) **Service**: Psychiatric

Staffed Beds: 166 **Admissions**: 6073 **Census**: 142 **Outpatient Visits**: 32801 **Births**: 0 **Total Expense ($000)**: 44923 **Payroll Expense ($000)**: 16931 **Personnel**: 279	

☐ **EL PASO CHILDREN'S HOSPITAL (453313)**, 4845 Alameda Avenue, Zip 79905–2705; tel. 915/242–8614, **A**1 3 5 10 **F**3 19 29 30 31 34 35 38 39 40 41 42 44 45 48 49 50 57 58 59 61 64 68 72 73 74 75 78 79 81 82 85 86 87 88 89 93 96 111 119 130 132 146 148 149 150 156
Primary Contact: Cindy Stout, R.N., Chief Executive Officer
COO: Ellen Pitcher, Chief Nursing Officer and Chief Operating Officer
CFO: Andrew Rybolt, Chief Financial Officer
CMO: Bradley Fuhrman, M.D., Physician in Chief
CIO: Janina Prada, Director Information Technology
CHR: Marina Estrada, Director Human Resources
CNO: Ellen Pitcher, Chief Nursing Officer and Chief Operating Officer
Web address: www.elpasochildrens.org
Control: Other not–for–profit (including NFP Corporation) **Service**: Children's general medical and surgical

Staffed Beds: 122 **Admissions**: 3592 **Census**: 55 **Outpatient Visits**: 62059 **Births**: 0 **Total Expense ($000)**: 97010 **Payroll Expense ($000)**: 30374 **Personnel**: 584	

TX

EL PASO LTAC HOSPITAL (452103), 1221 North Cotton Street, Zip 79902–3015; tel. 915/546–5822, **A**10 **F**1 3 29 30 34 57 60 75 77 82 84 85 86 87 100 103 119 130 148
Primary Contact: Skylier Blake, R.N., Chief Executive Officer
CFO: Eddie Martinez, Chief Financial Officer
Control: Partnership, Investor–owned (for–profit) **Service**: Acute long–term care hospital

Staffed Beds: 33 **Admissions**: 228 **Census**: 12 **Outpatient Visits**: 4968 **Births**: 0 **Total Expense ($000)**: 6431 **Payroll Expense ($000)**: 2753 **Personnel**: 51

EL PASO PSYCHIATRIC CENTER (454100), 4615 Alameda Avenue, Zip 79905–2702; tel. 915/532–2202, **A**1 3 5 10 **F**29 98 99 103 130 135 **S** Texas Department of State Health Services, Austin, TX
Primary Contact: Zulema Carrillo, Superintendent
CFO: David Osterhout, Assistant Superintendent and Chief Financial Officer
CNO: Raul D. Luna, Chief Nurse Executive
Web address: www.dshs.state.tx.us/mhhospitals/ElPasoPC/default.shtm
Control: State, Government, nonfederal **Service**: Psychiatric

Staffed Beds: 74 **Admissions**: 758 **Census**: 68 **Outpatient Visits**: 0 **Births**: 0 **Total Expense ($000)**: 32057 **Payroll Expense ($000)**: 13726 **Personnel**: 211

FOUNDATION SURGICAL HOSPITAL OF EL PASO (450877), 1416 George Dieter Drive, Zip 79936–7601; tel. 915/598–4240, **A**3 10 11 **F**3 29 40 45 49 79 81 82 85 86 93 107 111 114 119 126 **S** Foundation Surgical Hospital Affiliates, Oklahoma City, OK
Primary Contact: Don Burris, Chief Executive Officer
COO: Marta Contreras, Chief Nursing Officer and Chief Operating Officer
CIO: Louie Aguilera, Director Information Technology
CHR: Grace Beltran, Director Human Resources
CNO: Marta Contreras, Chief Nursing Officer and Chief Operating Officer
Control: Partnership, Investor–owned (for–profit) **Service**: Surgical

Staffed Beds: 20 **Admissions**: 567 **Census**: 4 **Outpatient Visits**: 41016 **Births**: 0 **Total Expense ($000)**: 46357 **Payroll Expense ($000)**: 8533 **Personnel**: 152

HIGHLANDS REHABILITATION HOSPITAL (453086), 1395 George Dieter Drive, Zip 79936–7410; tel. 915/298–7222, **A**1 10 **F**3 29 30 34 57 59 64 74 75 79 86 87 90 93 96 100 130 132 143 146 148 149 **S** Vibra Healthcare, Mechanicsburg, PA
Primary Contact: Travis Rich, Chief Executive Officer
CHR: Janet Straughan, Manager Human Resources
CNO: Oscar Mendizabal, Chief Nursing Officer
Web address: www.vrhhighlands.com/
Control: Partnership, Investor–owned (for–profit) **Service**: Rehabilitation

Staffed Beds: 41 **Admissions**: 716 **Census**: 25 **Outpatient Visits**: 5500 **Births**: 0 **Total Expense ($000)**: 13451 **Payroll Expense ($000)**: 7942 **Personnel**: 131

KINDRED HOSPITAL EL PASO (452079), 1740 Curie Drive, Zip 79902–2901; tel. 915/351–9044, **A**1 10 **F**1 3 29 45 46 70 75 148 149 **S** Kindred Healthcare, Louisville, KY
Primary Contact: America Jones, R.N., Chief Executive Officer
CFO: Melissa Campa, Controller
CMO: Edward Juarez, M.D., Chief Medical Officer
CHR: Laura Anchondo, Administrator Human Resources
Web address: www.khelpaso.com
Control: Corporation, Investor–owned (for–profit) **Service**: Acute long–term care hospital

Staffed Beds: 52 **Admissions**: 521 **Census**: 36 **Outpatient Visits**: 8 **Births**: 0 **Total Expense ($000)**: 16326 **Payroll Expense ($000)**: 8038 **Personnel**: 117

LAS PALMAS MEDICAL CENTER (450107), 1801 North Oregon Street, Zip 79902–3591; tel. 915/521–1200, (Includes DEL SOL MEDICAL CENTER, 10301 West Gateway Boulevard, El Paso, Texas, Zip 79925–7798; tel. 915/595–9000; David Shimp, Chief Executive Officer; LAS PALMAS REHABILITATION HOSPITAL, 300 Waymore Drive, El Paso, Texas, Zip 79902–1628; tel. 915/577–2600; Don Karl, Interim Chief Executive Officer) **A**1 3 5 10 **F**3 8 9 11 12 13 15 17 18 19 20 22 24 26 28 29 30 31 34 35 37 38 39 40 41 42 43 45 46 47 48 49 50 51 53 54 56 57 58 59 60 64 68 70 72 73 74 75 76 77 78 79 81 82 85 86 87 88 89 90 91 92 93 96 102 107 108 110 111 112 114 115 119 120 121 122 124 126 127 129 130 132 134 135 138 143 144 145 146 147 148 149 154 157 **S** HCA Healthcare, Nashville, TN
Primary Contact: Don Karl, Interim Chief Executive Officer
COO: Don Karl, Chief Operating Officer
CMO: Oscar Vega, M.D., Chief Medical Officer
CNO: Jerry Gonzalez, Interim Chief Nursing Officer
Web address: www.laspalmashealth.com
Control: Partnership, Investor–owned (for–profit) **Service**: General medical and surgical

Staffed Beds: 546 **Admissions**: 26390 **Census**: 356 **Outpatient Visits**: 125804 **Births**: 4763 **Total Expense ($000)**: 338893 **Payroll Expense ($000)**: 137567 **Personnel**: 2228

MESA HILLS SPECIALTY HOSPITAL (452035), 2311 North Oregon Street, 5th Floor, Zip 79902–3216; tel. 915/545–1823, **A**1 10 **F**1 3 8 29 64 75 81 148 **S** Concord Healthcare Group, Lakewood, NJ
Primary Contact: Jose Huerta, Chief Executive Officer
COO: Elena Pino, Chief Operating Officer and Chief Nursing Officer
CFO: Priscilla Carter, Chief Financial Officer
Web address: www.specialtyhospitalmesahills.com/
Control: Corporation, Investor–owned (for–profit) **Service**: Acute long–term care hospital

Staffed Beds: 32 **Admissions**: 147 **Census**: 9 **Outpatient Visits**: 13890 **Births**: 0 **Total Expense ($000)**: 19756 **Payroll Expense ($000)**: 3734 **Personnel**: 124

THE HOSPITALS OF PROVIDENCE EAST CAMPUS (670047), 3280 Joe Battle Boulevard, Zip 79938–2622; tel. 915/832–2000, **A**1 10 **F**3 13 15 18 20 22 26 29 30 31 34 35 39 40 41 42 45 49 50 51 57 58 59 60 64 68 70 72 73 74 75 76 77 78 79 81 84 85 86 87 93 107 108 110 111 114 115 119 126 130 134 146 147 148 149 154 **S** TENET Healthcare Corporation, Dallas, TX
Primary Contact: Monica Vargas-Mahar, FACHE, Chief Executive Officer
COO: Brandon May, Chief Operating Officer
Web address: www.sphn.com
Control: Individual, Investor–owned (for–profit) **Service**: General medical and surgical

Staffed Beds: 182 **Admissions**: 12905 **Census**: 154 **Outpatient Visits**: 99456 **Births**: 2248 **Total Expense ($000)**: 187950 **Payroll Expense ($000)**: 57544 **Personnel**: 733

THE HOSPITALS OF PROVIDENCE MEMORIAL CAMPUS (450002), 2001 North Oregon Street, Zip 79902–3368; tel. 915/577–6625, (Includes PROVIDENCE CHILDREN'S HOSPITAL, 2001 North Oregon Street, El Paso, Texas, Zip 79902–3320; tel. 915/577–7746; Nicholas R Tejeda, FACHE, Market Chief Executive Officer) **A**1 10 **F**3 8 11 12 13 14 15 17 18 19 20 21 22 23 26 29 30 31 32 34 35 37 40 41 42 43 45 46 48 49 50 54 55 56 57 58 59 60 63 64 65 67 70 71 72 74 75 76 77 78 79 81 84 85 86 88 89 93 97 98 100 101 102 103 105 107 110 111 115 119 125 126 130 132 133 134 141 143 145 146 147 148 149 150 154 157 **S** TENET Healthcare Corporation, Dallas, TX
Primary Contact: Nicholas R. Tejeda, FACHE, Market Chief Executive Officer
COO: Roddex Barlow, Chief Operating Officer
CFO: Charles Handley, Chief Financial Officer
CIO: Ray Davis, Administrative Director
CHR: Stephanie S. Talley, Market Chief Human Resource Officer
CNO: Barbara Vazquez, Chief Nursing Officer
Web address: www.thehospitalsofprovidence.com
Control: Partnership, Investor–owned (for–profit) **Service**: General medical and surgical

Staffed Beds: 332 **Admissions**: 15453 **Census**: 173 **Outpatient Visits**: 130744 **Births**: 3018 **Total Expense ($000)**: 250463 **Payroll Expense ($000)**: 80446 **Personnel**: 1123

THE HOSPITALS OF PROVIDENCE SIERRA CAMPUS (450668), 1625 Medical Center Drive, Zip 79902–5005; tel. 915/747–4000, **A**1 5 10 **F**11 13 15 17 18 20 22 24 26 28 29 34 40 43 46 47 49 50 54 57 59 60 61 64 70 72 74 76 77 78 79 81 85 90 92 93 96 107 108 109 110 111 114 115 119 126 130 132 146 148 149 154 157 **S** TENET Healthcare Corporation, Dallas, TX
Primary Contact: Rob Anderson, Chief Executive Officer
COO: Benson Chacko, Chief Operating Officer
CFO: Victoria Gonzalez, Chief Financial Officer
CIO: Ray Davis, Administrative Director Information Systems
CHR: Stephanie S. Talley, Chief Human Resource Officer
CNO: Erik Cazares, Chief Operating Officer
Web address: www.thehospitalsofprovidence.com
Control: Partnership, Investor–owned (for–profit) **Service:** General medical and surgical

Staffed Beds: 180 **Admissions:** 10125 **Census:** 117 **Outpatient Visits:** 90731 **Births:** 287 **Total Expense ($000):** 173870 **Payroll Expense ($000):** 51689 **Personnel:** 701

★ **THE HOSPITALS OF PROVIDENCE TRANSMOUNTAIN CAMPUS (670120)**, 2000 Transmountain Road, Zip 79911; tel. 915/877–8300, **A**10 **F**3 11 13 18 20 22 26 29 30 34 35 40 41 43 44 45 46 48 49 50 51 57 59 60 64 68 70 73 74 75 76 77 78 79 81 85 93 107 108 111 115 118 119 126 130 146 148 149 154 **S** TENET Healthcare Corporation, Dallas, TX
Primary Contact: Tasha Hopper, Chief Executive Officer
COO: Tasha Hopper, Chief Operating Officer
CFO: David Byrd, Chief Financial Officer
CMO: Gustavo Martell, M.D., Chief Medical Officer
CIO: Ray Davis, Chief Information Officer
CHR: Stephanie S. Talley, Chief Human Resource Officer
CNO: Linda B. Lawson, Chief Nursing Officer
Web address: www.https://www.thehospitalsofprovidence.com/our-locations/transmountain
Control: Corporation, Investor–owned (for–profit) **Service:** General medical and surgical

Staffed Beds: 106 **Admissions:** 4399 **Census:** 47 **Outpatient Visits:** 34969 **Births:** 487 **Total Expense ($000):** 81157 **Payroll Expense ($000):** 27489 **Personnel:** 732

TRIUMPH HOSPITAL EL PASO See Kindred Hospital El Paso

UNIVERSITY MEDICAL CENTER OF EL PASO (450024), 4815 Alameda Avenue, Zip 79905–2794; tel. 915/544–1200, **A**1 2 3 5 10 **F**3 8 11 13 15 18 20 22 24 26 28 29 30 31 34 35 37 40 43 45 46 47 48 49 50 51 53 54 56 57 59 60 61 64 65 68 74 75 77 78 79 81 82 85 86 87 91 92 93 94 96 97 100 102 107 108 110 111 112 113 114 115 118 119 126 127 130 131 134 143 144 145 146 147 148 149 150 157
Primary Contact: Jacob Cintron, FACHE, President and Chief Executive Officer
COO: Maria Zampini, Chief Operating Officer
CFO: Michael Nunez, Chief Financial Officer
CMO: Joel Hendryx, M.D., Chief Medical Officer
CIO: Janina Prada, Director Information Services
CHR: Janice M Harris, Director Human Resources
Web address: www.thomasoncares.org
Control: Hospital district or authority, Government, nonfederal **Service:** General medical and surgical

Staffed Beds: 251 **Admissions:** 16042 **Census:** 206 **Outpatient Visits:** 811880 **Births:** 2783 **Total Expense ($000):** 663931 **Payroll Expense ($000):** 164176

WILLIAM BEAUMONT ARMY MEDICAL CENTER, 5005 North Piedras Street, Zip 79920–5001; tel. 915/742–2121, (Nonreporting) **A**1 2 3 5 **S** Department of the Army, Office of the Surgeon General, Falls Church, VA
Primary Contact: Colonel Erik G. Rude, Commander
CIO: Major Rion Koon, Chief Information Management Division
Web address: www.https://www.wbamc.amedd.army.mil/NewPersonnel/CDR.aspx
Control: Department of Defense, Government, federal **Service:** General medical and surgical

Staffed Beds: 209

★ **SCHLEICHER COUNTY MEDICAL CENTER (451304)**, 102 North US Highway 277, Zip 76936–4010; tel. 325/853–2507, **A**10 18 **F**34 40 57 59 64 65 68 87 93 107 127 133 154 **S** Preferred Management Corporation, Shawnee, OK
Primary Contact: Paul Burke, Administrator
CFO: Larry Stephens, Chief Financial Officer
CMO: Gordy Day, M.D., Medical Director
CHR: Beverly Minor, Chief Human Resources
Web address: www.scmc.us
Control: Corporation, Investor–owned (for–profit) **Service:** General medical and surgical

Staffed Beds: 14 **Admissions:** 73 **Census:** 1 **Outpatient Visits:** 8177 **Births:** 0 **Total Expense ($000):** 5249 **Payroll Expense ($000):** 2422 **Personnel:** 51

★ **ELECTRA MEMORIAL HOSPITAL (451343)**, 1207 South Bailey Street, Zip 76360–3221, Mailing Address: P.O. Box 1112, Zip 76360–1112; tel. 940/495–3981, **A**10 18 **F**3 7 11 28 29 32 34 35 40 43 53 57 59 62 64 65 66 75 77 86 93 97 107 114 119 127 129 130 131 133 148
Primary Contact: Rebecca J. McCain, Chief Executive Officer
CFO: Ginnie Holmes, Chief Financial Officer
CIO: Brandon Huffstutler, Chief Information Officer
CNO: Kim Gilbert, R.N., Chief Nursing Officer
Web address: www.electrahospital.com
Control: Hospital district or authority, Government, nonfederal **Service:** General medical and surgical

Staffed Beds: 19 **Admissions:** 361 **Census:** 5 **Outpatient Visits:** 31370 **Births:** 0 **Total Expense ($000):** 18818 **Payroll Expense ($000):** 9302 **Personnel:** 99

ENNIS REGIONAL MEDICAL CENTER (450833), 2201 West Lampasas Street, Zip 75119–5644; tel. 972/875–0900, **A**1 11 15 18 29 30 34 35 40 43 45 50 51 57 59 64 65 70 75 77 79 81 82 85 91 93 107 108 110 111 115 119 146 147 149 157 **S** LifePoint Health, Brentwood, TN
Primary Contact: Robert C. Honeycutt, Chief Executive Officer
CFO: Jack Wilcox, Chief Financial Officer
CMO: Raymond W Blair, M.D., Jr Chief of Staff
CHR: Selena Cryer, Director Human Resources
CNO: Edwina A Miner, R.N., Chief Nursing Officer
Web address: www.ennisregional.com
Control: Partnership, Investor–owned (for–profit) **Service:** General medical and surgical

Staffed Beds: 58 **Admissions:** 635 **Census:** 5 **Outpatient Visits:** 30035 **Births:** 0 **Total Expense ($000):** 22442 **Payroll Expense ($000):** 8210 **Personnel:** 143

★ **FREESTONE MEDICAL CENTER (450658)**, 125 Newman Street, Zip 75840–1499; tel. 903/389–2121, **A**10 **F**3 11 15 28 29 34 35 40 43 45 57 59 64 65 75 81 97 107 108 110 115 119 127 **S** Community Hospital Corporation, Plano, TX
Primary Contact: John M. Yeary, FACHE, Chief Executive Officer
CFO: David A Travis, Chief Financial Officer
CMO: Darryl White, M.D., Chief of Staff
CHR: Jennifer Rummel, Director Human Resources
CNO: Tonya Basque, Chief Nursing Officer
Web address: www.freestonemc.com/
Control: Hospital district or authority, Government, nonfederal **Service:** General medical and surgical

Staffed Beds: 14 **Admissions:** 493 **Census:** 4 **Outpatient Visits:** 31077 **Births:** 0 **Total Expense ($000):** 13878 **Payroll Expense ($000):** 5824 **Personnel:** 107

TX

Hospital, Medicare Provider Number, Address, Telephone, Approval, Facility, and Physician Codes, Health Care System

★ American Hospital Association (AHA) membership   ○ Healthcare Facilities Accreditation Program   ⇑ Center for Improvement in Healthcare Quality Accreditation
□ The Joint Commission accreditation   ◇ DNV Healthcare Inc. accreditation   △ Commission on Accreditation of Rehabilitation Facilities (CARF) accreditation

© 2019 AHA Guide   *Many Facility Codes have changed. Please refer to the AHA Guide Code Chart.*   Hospitals **A603**

FLORESVILLE—Wilson County

CONNALLY MEMORIAL MEDICAL CENTER (450108), 499 10th Street,
Zip 78114–3175; tel. 830/393–1300, **A**10 **F**15 18 29 34 35 40 45 47 49 54 57
59 62 64 70 75 81 82 85 86 87 107 108 110 111 114 119 130 132 133 144
146 148 154 156
Primary Contact: Bob Gillespie, Chief Executive Officer
COO: Bob Gillespie, Chief Operating Officer
CFO: Curtis Rojas, Interim Chief Financial Officer
CMO: Wade Krause, M.D., Chief Medical Officer
CHR: Loretta Y Morgan, Director Human Resources
CNO: Sue Tackitt, Chief Nursing Officer
Web address: www.connallymmc.org
Control: Hospital district or authority, Government, nonfederal **Service**: General
medical and surgical

**Staffed Beds: 26 Admissions: 859 Census: 9 Outpatient Visits: 126265
Births: 1 Total Expense ($000): 36556 Payroll Expense ($000): 14917
Personnel: 288**

FLOWER MOUND—Denton County

ICARE REHABILITATION HOSPITAL (673064), 3100 Peters Colony Road,
Zip 75022–2949; tel. 214/513–0310, **A**10 22 **F**3 29 90 93
Primary Contact: Gina Tomaseski, Chief Executive Officer
Web address: www.https://www.icarerehabilitation.com/
Control: Corporation, Investor–owned (for–profit) **Service**: Rehabilitation

**Staffed Beds: 41 Admissions: 306 Census: 9 Outpatient Visits: 2148
Births: 0 Total Expense ($000): 6337 Payroll Expense ($000): 3449
Personnel: 60**

☐ **TEXAS HEALTH PRESBYTERIAN HOSPITAL FLOWER MOUND (670068)**,
4400 Long Prairie Road, Zip 75028–1892; tel. 469/322–7000, **A**1 10 **F**3 12 13
15 18 20 29 30 31 34 40 45 49 51 54 57 59 64 70 73 74 75 76 77 78 79 81
82 85 87 89 93 107 108 110 111 114 115 119 126 130 132 146 147 149
157
Primary Contact: Spencer Turner, FACHE, President
COO: Shelley R Tobey, R.N., MS, Chief Operating Officer and Chief Nursing Officer
CFO: Tom Howard, Chief Financial Officer
CHR: Nicole Schweigert, Director Human Resources
CNO: Shelley R Tobey, R.N., MS, Chief Operating Officer and Chief Nursing Officer
Web address: www.texashealthflowermound.com/
Control: Partnership, Investor–owned (for–profit) **Service**: General medical and
surgical

**Staffed Beds: 99 Admissions: 6507 Census: 45 Outpatient Visits: 37430
Births: 1810 Total Expense ($000): 125818 Payroll Expense
($000): 44045 Personnel: 630**

FORT HOOD—Bell County

⊠ **CARL R. DARNALL ARMY MEDICAL CENTER**, 36000 Darnall Loop,
Zip 76544–5095; tel. 254/288–8000, (Nonreporting) **A**1 2 3 5 **S** Department of
the Army, Office of the Surgeon General, Falls Church, VA
Primary Contact: Colonel David R. Gibson, Chief Executive Officer
CHR: Charles Burton, Chief Human Resources
Web address: www.crdamc.amedd.army.mil
Control: Department of Defense, Government, federal **Service**: General medical
and surgical

Staffed Beds: 109

FORT SAM HOUSTON—Bexar County

BROOKE ARMY MEDICAL CENTER See Brooke Army Medical Center

⊠ **BROOKE ARMY MEDICAL CENTER**, 3851 Roger Brookes Drive,
Zip 78234–4501; tel. 210/916–4141, (Nonreporting) **A**1 2 3 5 **S** Department of
the Army, Office of the Surgeon General, Falls Church, VA
Primary Contact: Brigadier General Jeffrey Johnson, Commander
CMO: Colonel Joseph P Chozinski, M.D., Deputy Commander Clinical Services
CHR: Rose Juarez, Chief Civilian Personnel Branch
CNO: Colonel Sheri Howell, Deputy Commander Nursing
Web address: www.bamc.amedd.army.mil
Control: Department of Defense, Government, federal **Service**: General medical
and surgical

Staffed Beds: 226

FORT STOCKTON—Pecos County

PECOS COUNTY MEMORIAL HOSPITAL (451389), 387 West I H-10,
Zip 79735–8912, Mailing Address: P.O. Box 1648, Zip 79735–1648;
tel. 432/336–2004, **A**3 10 18 **F**3 11 13 28 29 30 34 35 40 43 45 46 50 53 57
59 62 63 64 65 75 76 81 93 107 111 119 127 130 133 144 146 148
Primary Contact: Betsy Briscoe, Chief Executive Officer
COO: Margaret Davis, Chief Operating Officer
CFO: Sharon Hunt, Interim Chief Financial Officer
CMO: Subodh Mallik, M.D., Chief of Staff
CHR: Malissa Trevino, Director Human Resources
CNO: Gina Kalka, R.N., Chief Nursing Officer
Web address: www.pcmhfs.com
Control: County, Government, nonfederal **Service**: General medical and surgical

**Staffed Beds: 25 Admissions: 545 Census: 5 Outpatient Visits: 57033
Births: 156 Total Expense ($000): 29260 Payroll Expense ($000): 13583
Personnel: 280**

FORT WORTH—Tarrant County

⊠ **BAYLOR SCOTT & WHITE ALL SAINTS MEDICAL CENTER - FORT WORTH
(450137)**, 1400 Eighth Avenue, Zip 76104–4192; tel. 817/926–2544, **A**1 2 3 5
10 **F**3 11 13 17 18 24 26 28 29 30 31 34 35 38 40 43 45 46 47 49 53 55 59
64 70 72 73 74 75 76 77 78 79 80 81 84 86 87 96 97 102 107 108 111 114
115 119 124 126 130 131 132 138 139 142 146 147 148 149 154 **S** Baylor
Scott & White Health, Dallas, TX
Primary Contact: Michael Sanborn, FACHE, MS, President
COO: Janice L Walker, R.N., System Chief Nursing Executive, Senior Vice President
CFO: Lucy Catala, Vice President Finance
CMO: Dahlia Hassani, Vice President of Medical Affairs
CIO: Sandy Vaughn, Director Information Services
CHR: Tracy Stanford, Director Human Resources
Web address: www.baylorhealth.com/PhysiciansLocations/AllSaints/Pages/Default.aspx
Control: Other not–for–profit (including NFP Corporation) **Service**: General
medical and surgical

**Staffed Beds: 377 Admissions: 17913 Census: 240 Outpatient
Visits: 65294 Births: 5665 Total Expense ($000): 350276 Payroll Expense
($000): 122912 Personnel: 1446**

⊠ **BAYLOR SCOTT & WHITE INSTITUTE FOR REHABILITATION-FORT WORTH
(673035)**, 6601 Harris Parkway, Zip 76132–6108; tel. 817/433–9600,
A1 10 **F**3 28 29 30 64 75 90 93 130 149 **S** Select Medical Corporation,
Mechanicsburg, PA
Primary Contact: Ryan Seymour, Chief Executive Officer
CMO: Asher Light, M.D., Medical Director
CHR: Nissi Dalton, Manager Human Resources
CNO: Catherine Ewing, M.D., Chief Nursing Officer
Web address: www.baylorhealth.com/PhysiciansLocations/BIR/Pages/Default.aspx
Control: Partnership, Investor–owned (for–profit) **Service**: Rehabilitation

**Staffed Beds: 42 Admissions: 610 Census: 20 Outpatient Visits: 6794
Births: 0 Total Expense ($000): 14300 Payroll Expense ($000): 7325
Personnel: 106**

☐ **BAYLOR SCOTT & WHITE SURGICAL HOSPITAL FORT WORTH (450880)**,
1800 Park Place Avenue, Zip 76110–1302; tel. 682/703–5600, **A**1 10 **F**3 8 12
40 51 64 70 79 81 82 85 87 107 111 119 126 131
Primary Contact: Paul Debona, Chief Executive Officer
CFO: Jane Mathis, Chief Financial Officer
CMO: Bruce Bollinger, M.D., Medical Director
CNO: Stacie Merrill, Chief Nursing Officer
Web address: www.mcsh-hospital.com
Control: Partnership, Investor–owned (for–profit) **Service**: Surgical

**Staffed Beds: 30 Admissions: 1670 Census: 10 Outpatient Visits: 10396
Births: 0 Total Expense ($000): 87766 Payroll Expense ($000): 17170
Personnel: 255**

⊠ **COOK CHILDREN'S MEDICAL CENTER (453300)**, 801 Seventh Avenue,
Zip 76104–2796; tel. 682/885–4000, **A**1 3 5 10 **F**3 7 8 9 17 19 21 23 25 27
29 30 31 32 34 35 37 38 39 40 41 43 44 45 46 47 48 49 50 54 55 57 58 59
60 61 62 64 65 68 72 74 75 77 78 79 80 81 82 84 85 86 87 88 89 90 91 92
93 94 98 99 100 101 102 104 105 107 108 111 112 113 114 115 118
119 126 129 130 131 132 136 138 143 144 146 148 149 150 154 155
Primary Contact: Rick W. Merrill, System President and Chief Executive Officer
CFO: Stephen Kimmel, Chief Financial Officer
CMO: James C Cunningham, M.D., Chief Medical Officer
CIO: Theresa Meadows, Chief Information Officer
CNO: Teresa J Clark, R.N., MS, Chief Nursing Officer
Web address: www.cookchildrens.org
Control: Other not–for–profit (including NFP Corporation) **Service**: Children's
general medical and surgical

**Staffed Beds: 391 Admissions: 13453 Census: 227 Outpatient
Visits: 286062 Births: 0 Total Expense ($000): 866020 Payroll Expense
($000): 271419 Personnel: 4568**

TX

☒ **ENCOMPASS HEALTH REHABILITATION HOSPITAL OF CITY VIEW (453042)**, 6701 Oakmont Boulevard, Zip 76132–2957; tel. 817/370–4700, **A**1 10 **F**3 29 75 77 90 91 94 95 96 130 148 154 **S** Encompass Health Corporation, Birmingham, AL
Primary Contact: Janell Briscoe, Chief Executive Officer
Web address: www.healthsouthcityview.com
Control: Corporation, Investor–owned (for–profit) **Service:** Rehabilitation

Staffed Beds: 62 **Admissions:** 1316 **Census:** 44 **Outpatient Visits:** 0 **Births:** 0 **Total Expense ($000):** 19350 **Payroll Expense ($000):** 10263 **Personnel:** 162

☒ **ENCOMPASS HEALTH REHABILITATION HOSPITAL OF FORT WORTH (453041)**, 1212 West Lancaster Avenue, Zip 76102–4510; tel. 817/870–2336, (Nonreporting) **A**1 10 **S** Encompass Health Corporation, Birmingham, AL
Primary Contact: Janell Briscoe, Chief Executive Officer
CFO: Sherry Hapney, Chief Financial Officer
CMO: Patrick Donovan, M.D., Director Medical Staff
CHR: Tara Kleas, Area Director Human Resources
Web address: www.healthsouthfortworth.com
Control: Corporation, Investor–owned (for–profit) **Service:** Rehabilitation

Staffed Beds: 60

JOHN PETER SMITH HOSPITAL See Jps Health Network, Fort Worth

★ **JPS HEALTH NETWORK (450039)**, 1500 South Main Street, Zip 76104–4917; tel. 817/921–3431, (Includes JOHN PETER SMITH HOSPITAL, 1500 South Main Street, Fort Worth, Texas, Zip 76104; tel. 817/921–3431; TRINITY SPRINGS PAVILION, 1500 South Main Street, Fort Worth, Texas, Zip 76104–4917; tel. 817/927–3636; Lily Wong, Director Psychiatry) **A**2 3 5 8 10 **F**3 4 8 11 13 18 20 22 24 26 28 29 30 31 32 34 35 36 39 40 43 44 45 46 47 49 50 54 56 57 58 59 60 61 64 65 66 68 70 71 72 74 75 76 77 78 79 80 81 82 84 85 86 87 91 92 93 97 98 100 101 102 104 105 107 108 110 111 114 115 118 119 121 123 124 126 130 131 132 135 141 143 144 146 147 148 153 154 156
Primary Contact: Robert Earley, President and Chief Executive Officer
CFO: Alan Townsend, Interim Chief Financial Officer
CIO: Melinda Custin, Chief Information Officer
CHR: Nikki Sumpter, Senior Vice President Human Resources
CNO: Wanda V. Peebles, Chief Nursing Officer
Web address: www.jpshealthnet.org
Control: Hospital district or authority, Government, nonfederal **Service:** General medical and surgical

Staffed Beds: 540 **Admissions:** 31642 **Census:** 489 **Outpatient Visits:** 1044637 **Births:** 4302 **Total Expense ($000):** 959926 **Payroll Expense ($000):** 391046 **Personnel:** 6258

☒ **KINDRED HOSPITAL-FORT WORTH (452088)**, 815 Eighth Avenue, Zip 76104–2609; tel. 817/332–4812, **A**1 10 **F**3 29 46 48 70 77 79 82 85 107 114 119 130 148 154 **S** Kindred Healthcare, Louisville, KY
Primary Contact: Susan Schaetti, Chief Executive Officer
CFO: Susan Popp, Controller
CMO: Stuart McDonald, M.D., President Medical Staff
CIO: Norma Warner, Area Director Health Information Management
CHR: Nicole Newpower, Coordinator Human Resources
Web address: www.kindredfortworth.com/
Control: Corporation, Investor–owned (for–profit) **Service:** Acute long–term care hospital

Staffed Beds: 67 **Admissions:** 571 **Census:** 41 **Outpatient Visits:** 0 **Births:** 0 **Total Expense ($000):** 25430 **Payroll Expense ($000):** 10665 **Personnel:** 163

★ **MEDICAL CITY ALLIANCE (670103)**, 3101 North Tarrant Parkway, Zip 76177; tel. 817/639–1000, **F**3 11 12 13 15 18 20 22 24 26 29 30 34 35 40 42 45 46 47 48 49 50 54 56 57 59 64 70 72 74 75 76 77 79 81 82 85 86 87 92 107 108 110 111 114 119 126 130 132 135 145 146 147 148 149 154 156 **S** HCA Healthcare, Nashville, TN
Primary Contact: Glenn Wallace, Chief Executive Officer
Web address: www.baylorhealth.com/PhysiciansLocations/BIR/Pages/Default.aspx
Control: Corporation, Investor–owned (for–profit) **Service:** General medical and surgical

Staffed Beds: 75 **Admissions:** 4170 **Census:** 43 **Outpatient Visits:** 51163 **Births:** 866 **Total Expense ($000):** 81486 **Payroll Expense ($000):** 27867 **Personnel:** 371

☒ **MEDICAL CITY FORT WORTH (450672)**, 900 Eighth Avenue, Zip 76104–3902; tel. 817/336–2100, **A**1 2 3 5 10 **F**3 12 17 18 20 22 24 26 28 29 30 31 40 42 45 46 47 48 49 56 58 64 67 70 74 77 78 79 81 85 87 90 91 93 107 108 111 114 115 119 126 130 138 139 145 146 148 **S** HCA Healthcare, Nashville, TN
Primary Contact: Jyric Sims, FACHE, Chief Executive Officer
COO: JW Newman, Chief Operating Officer
CFO: Andrew Lane, Chief Financial Officer
CMO: Terry Loftus, M.D., Chief Medical Officer
CIO: Kelley Fredrickson, Director Information Services
CHR: Cyndi Roberts, Director Human Resources
CNO: Damita Williams, Ed.D., R.N., MSN, Chief Nursing Officer
Web address: www.medicalcityfortworth.com/about/
Control: Partnership, Investor–owned (for–profit) **Service:** General medical and surgical

Staffed Beds: 218 **Admissions:** 9825 **Census:** 149 **Outpatient Visits:** 44986 **Births:** 0 **Total Expense ($000):** 256136 **Payroll Expense ($000):** 77679 **Personnel:** 898

☐ **MESA SPRINGS (454124)**, 5560 Mesa Springs Drive, Zip 76123; tel. 817/292–4600, **A**1 10 **F**1 4 5 16 17 29 54 67 70 72 73 80 88 89 90 98 99 101 103 104 105 128 135 153 **S** Springstone, Louisville, KY
Primary Contact: Barbara Schmidt, Chief Executive Officer
CFO: Kent Ashley, Chief Financial Officer
CMO: Stewart Keller, M.D., Medical Director
CHR: Jill Housand, Director Human Resources
CNO: Ana Ramirez, Director of Nursing
Web address: www.springstone.com/hospitals.stmnl
Control: Corporation, Investor–owned (for–profit) **Service:** Psychiatric

Staffed Beds: 72 **Admissions:** 3053 **Census:** 65 **Outpatient Visits:** 36892 **Births:** 0 **Total Expense ($000):** 20508 **Payroll Expense ($000):** 13015 **Personnel:** 269

☒ **TEXAS HEALTH HARRIS METHODIST HOSPITAL ALLIANCE (670085)**, 10864 Texas Health Trail, Zip 76244–4897; tel. 682/212–2000, **A**1 10 **F**3 11 12 13 15 18 20 22 24 26 28 29 30 34 35 40 45 48 49 50 57 59 64 70 72 74 75 76 77 79 80 81 82 85 86 91 93 107 108 110 111 113 114 115 118 119 126 130 131 132 135 146 147 148 **S** Texas Health Resources, Arlington, TX
Primary Contact: Clint Abernathy, President and Chief Operating Officer
Web address: www.https://www.texashealth.org/alliance/Pages/default.aspx
Control: Other not-for-profit (including NFP Corporation) **Service:** General medical and surgical

Staffed Beds: 101 **Admissions:** 6706 **Census:** 63 **Outpatient Visits:** 59765 **Births:** 1963 **Total Expense ($000):** 108245 **Payroll Expense ($000):** 42552 **Personnel:** 535

☒ △ **TEXAS HEALTH HARRIS METHODIST HOSPITAL FORT WORTH (450135)**, 1301 Pennsylvania Avenue, Zip 76104–2122; tel. 817/250–2000, **A**1 2 3 5 7 10 **F**3 11 13 15 17 18 20 22 24 26 28 29 30 31 34 35 36 38 40 42 43 45 46 47 48 49 51 53 54 56 57 58 59 60 64 65 66 67 68 70 71 72 74 75 76 77 78 79 81 83 84 85 86 87 91 92 93 94 95 96 100 107 108 110 111 112 113 114 115 116 117 118 119 120 126 130 131 132 135 138 145 146 147 148 149 150 154 156 **S** Texas Health Resources, Arlington, TX
Primary Contact: Joseph DeLeon, President
CFO: Shelly Miland, Group Financial Officer
CMO: Joseph Prosser, M.D., Chief Medical Officer
CHR: Joseph Condon, Entity Human Resources Officer
CNO: Elaine Nelson, R.N., MSN, Chief Nursing Officer
Web address: www.texashealth.org
Control: Other not-for-profit (including NFP Corporation) **Service:** General medical and surgical

Staffed Beds: 650 **Admissions:** 34532 **Census:** 538 **Outpatient Visits:** 210797 **Births:** 2885 **Total Expense ($000):** 806351 **Payroll Expense ($000):** 294975 **Personnel:** 4251

TX

⊞ **TEXAS HEALTH HARRIS METHODIST HOSPITAL SOUTHWEST FORT WORTH (450779)**, 6100 Harris Parkway, Zip 76132–4199; tel. 817/433–5000, (Includes TEXAS HEALTH HOSPITAL CLEARFORK, 5400 Clearfork Main Street, Fort Worth, Texas, Zip 76109–3553; tel. 682/703–5000; Rebecca Tucker, President) **A**1 2 10 **F**3 8 11 13 15 18 20 28 29 34 35 36 37 40 45 46 47 48 49 50 53 57 59 60 64 68 70 72 75 76 77 78 79 80 81 84 85 86 87 93 102 107 110 111 114 115 119 126 130 131 146 147 148 149 **S** Texas Health Resources, Arlington, TX
Primary Contact: Rebecca Tucker, President
CFO: Charlotte Ward, Entity Financial Officer
CMO: Mark Montgomery, M.D., Chief Medical Officer
CHR: Leanna W Nalley, Director Human Resources
CNO: Mary Robinson, Chief Nursing Officer and Vice President Patient Care Services
Web address: www.texashealth.org
Control: Other not–for–profit (including NFP Corporation) **Service**: General medical and surgical

Staffed Beds: 235 **Admissions:** 14315 **Census:** 137 **Outpatient Visits:** 100440 **Births:** 3068 **Total Expense ($000):** 288339 **Payroll Expense ($000):** 89211 **Personnel:** 1121

⊞ **TEXAS HEALTH SPECIALTY HOSPITAL (452018)**, 1301 Pennsylvania Avenue, 4th Floor, Zip 76104–2190; tel. 817/250–5500, **A**1 10 **F**1 3 87 130 148 **S** Texas Health Resources, Arlington, TX
Primary Contact: Pamela Duffey, DNP, RN, NEA-BC, MSN, R.N., Chief Executive Officer
CFO: Shelly Miland, Chief Financial Officer
CMO: Michael Thornsberry, M.D., Chief Medical Officer
CHR: Joseph Condon, Director Human Resources
CNO: Pamela Duffey, DNP, RN, NEA-BC, MSN, R.N., Chief Nursing Officer
Web address: www.https://www.texashealth.org/texas-health-specialty-hospital/
Control: Other not–for–profit (including NFP Corporation) **Service**: Acute long–term care hospital

Staffed Beds: 10 **Admissions:** 92 **Census:** 9 **Outpatient Visits:** 0 **Births:** 0 **Total Expense ($000):** 7712 **Payroll Expense ($000):** 3471 **Personnel:** 35

☐ △ **TEXAS REHABILITATION HOSPITAL OF FORT WORTH (673048)**, 425 Alabama Avenue, Zip 76104–1022; tel. 817/820–3400, **A**1 7 10 **F**3 29 34 57 68 74 79 90 91 96 130 132 148 156 **S** Kindred Healthcare, Louisville, KY
Primary Contact: Jake Daggett, Chief Executive Officer
Web address: www.texasrehabhospital.com/
Control: Corporation, Investor–owned (for–profit) **Service**: Rehabilitation

Staffed Beds: 66 **Admissions:** 1272 **Census:** 46 **Outpatient Visits:** 0 **Births:** 0 **Total Expense ($000):** 17340 **Payroll Expense ($000):** 9201 **Personnel:** 178

☐ **USMD HOSPITAL AT FORT WORTH (670046)**, 5900 Altamesa Boulevard, Zip 76132–5473; tel. 817/433–9100, **A**1 10 **F**3 29 39 40 51 64 68 81 85 89 107 114 119 130 **S** USMD Health System, Irving, TX
Primary Contact: Kathy Early, Chief Executive Officer and Chief Nursing Officer
CHR: Michelle Speck, Senior Vice President Human Resources
Web address: www.usmdfortworth.com/
Control: Partnership, Investor–owned (for–profit) **Service**: General medical and surgical

Staffed Beds: 8 **Admissions:** 201 **Census:** 1 **Outpatient Visits:** 4079 **Births:** 0 **Total Expense ($000):** 24298 **Payroll Expense ($000):** 4780 **Personnel:** 73

WELLBRIDGE HEALTHCARE OF FORT WORTH (454128), 6200 Overton Ridge Boulevard, Zip 76132–3614; tel. 817/361–1991, (Nonreporting)
Primary Contact: Soni Helmicki, Chief Executive Officer
Web address: www.oceanshealthcare.com
Control: Corporation, Investor–owned (for–profit) **Service**: Psychiatric

Staffed Beds: 48

⊞ **HILL COUNTRY MEMORIAL HOSPITAL (450604)**, 1020 South State Highway 16, Zip 78624–4471, Mailing Address: P.O. Box 835, Zip 78624–0835; tel. 830/997–4353, **A**1 10 **F**3 11 13 15 18 20 28 29 30 31 32 34 35 37 40 43 45 49 50 51 53 57 59 62 63 64 68 70 74 75 76 77 78 79 81 82 84 85 86 87 93 96 97 107 108 110 111 114 115 119 124 126 129 130 131 132 135 144 146 148 149
Primary Contact: Jayne E. Pope, R.N., FACHE, Chief Executive Officer
COO: Mike Reno, Chief Operating Officer
CFO: Mark Jones, Chief Financial Officer
CMO: James R Partin, M.D., Chief Medical Director
CIO: John Mason, Chief Information Officer
CHR: Alysha Metzger, Director Human Resources
CNO: Maureen Polivka, Chief Nursing Officer
Web address: www.hillcountrymemorial.org
Control: Other not–for–profit (including NFP Corporation) **Service**: General medical and surgical

Staffed Beds: 57 **Admissions:** 2384 **Census:** 19 **Outpatient Visits:** 89198 **Births:** 442 **Total Expense ($000):** 78299 **Payroll Expense ($000):** 29464 **Personnel:** 428

PARMER COUNTY COMMUNITY HOSPITAL See Parmer Medical Center

★ **PARMER MEDICAL CENTER (451300)**, 1307 Cleveland Street, Zip 79035–1121; tel. 806/250–2754, **A**10 18 **F**11 30 34 35 40 57 64 75 77 93 107 119 127 130 133 148 **S** Preferred Management Corporation, Shawnee, OK
Primary Contact: Gayla Quillin, Administrator
Web address: www.parmermedicalcenter.com
Control: Other not–for–profit (including NFP Corporation) **Service**: General medical and surgical

Staffed Beds: 15 **Admissions:** 126 **Census:** 3 **Outpatient Visits:** 18193 **Births:** 1 **Total Expense ($000):** 9371 **Payroll Expense ($000):** 4338 **Personnel:** 93

⊞ **BAYLOR SCOTT & WHITE INSTITUTE FOR REHABILITATION-FRISCO (673046)**, 2990 Legacy Drive, Zip 75034–6066; tel. 469/888–5100, **A**1 10 **F**3 29 30 34 35 36 64 75 90 91 92 93 96 130 132 148 149 **S** Select Medical Corporation, Mechanicsburg, PA
Primary Contact: Ryan Seymour, Chief Executive Officer
Web address: www.baylorhealth.org/bir
Control: Partnership, Investor–owned (for–profit) **Service**: Rehabilitation

Staffed Beds: 44 **Admissions:** 813 **Census:** 30 **Outpatient Visits:** 15509 **Births:** 0 **Total Expense ($000):** 21133 **Payroll Expense ($000):** 10968 **Personnel:** 104

⊞ **BAYLOR SCOTT & WHITE MEDICAL CENTER - CENTENNIAL (450885)**, 12505 Lebanon Road, Zip 75035–8298; tel. 972/963–3333, **A**1 10 **F**3 13 15 17 18 20 22 26 29 30 34 35 40 41 45 46 47 48 49 50 51 57 59 64 65 70 72 74 75 76 77 78 79 81 82 85 89 93 107 110 111 114 115 119 126 132 146 154 **S** Baylor Scott & White Health, Dallas, TX
Primary Contact: Jaikumar Krishnaswamy, President
CFO: Blaise Bondi, Chief Financial Officer
CIO: Dianne Yarborough, Director of Information Technology
CHR: Stephanie S. Talley, Director Human Resources
CNO: Calee Travis, R.N., Chief Nursing Officer
Web address: www.centennialmedcenter.com
Control: Other not–for–profit (including NFP Corporation) **Service**: General medical and surgical

Staffed Beds: 106 **Admissions:** 4216 **Census:** 46 **Outpatient Visits:** 37442 **Births:** 1134 **Total Expense ($000):** 103608 **Payroll Expense ($000):** 31987 **Personnel:** 401

☐ **BAYLOR SCOTT & WHITE MEDICAL CENTER–FRISCO (450853)**, 5601 Warren Parkway, Zip 75034–4069; tel. 214/407–5000, **A**1 3 5 10 **F**3 13 29 34 40 45 51 54 57 64 68 72 75 76 79 81 85 86 87 107 111 115 119 126 129 130 131 144 **S** United Surgical Partners International, Addison, TX
Primary Contact: Trevor Castaneda, Chief Executive Officer
COO: Kevin Coats, Chief Operating Officer and Chief Financial Officer
CFO: Kevin Coats, Chief Financial Officer
CMO: Jimmy Laferney, M.D., Vice President Medical Staff Affairs
CIO: Rick Barry, Director Information Systems
CHR: Margaret Garcia, Manager Human Resources
CNO: Randi Elliott, MSN, Chief Nursing Officer
Web address: www.bmcf.com
Control: Partnership, Investor–owned (for–profit) **Service**: Surgical

Staffed Beds: 68 **Admissions:** 4126 **Census:** 31 **Outpatient Visits:** 27165 **Births:** 2360 **Total Expense ($000):** 133305 **Payroll Expense ($000):** 46977 **Personnel:** 553

☐ **HAVEN BEHAVIORAL HOSPITAL OF FRISCO (454134)**, 5680 Frisco Square Boulevard, Suite 3000, Zip 75034–3300; tel. 469/353–2219, **A**1 **F**98 130
Primary Contact: William W. Brattvet, Chief Executive Officer
Web address: www.frisco.havenbehavioral.com/
Control: Corporation, Investor–owned (for–profit) **Service**: Psychiatric

Staffed Beds: 70 **Admissions:** 1051 **Census:** 26 **Outpatient Visits:** 0 **Births:** 0 **Total Expense ($000):** 9984 **Payroll Expense ($000):** 4450 **Personnel:** 74

TX

Many Facility Codes have changed. Please refer to the AHA Guide Code Chart. © 2019 AHA Guide

GAINESVILLE—Cooke County

NORTH TEXAS MEDICAL CENTER (450090), 1900 Hospital Boulevard, Zip 76240–2002; tel. 940/665–1751, **A**10 20 **F**3 11 13 15 28 29 34 35 40 43 45 50 59 62 64 65 66 68 70 75 76 77 79 81 82 85 86 87 93 107 108 110 111 115 119 127 129 130 132 133 135 146 147 149 154 156
Primary Contact: Thomas Sledge, Chief Executive Officer
CFO: Melissa Walker, CPA, Chief Financial Officer
CHR: Teresa Westover, Director Human Resources
CNO: Becky Small, Chief Nursing Officer
Web address: www.ntmconline.net
Control: Hospital district or authority, Government, nonfederal **Service:** General medical and surgical

Staffed Beds: 48 **Admissions:** 1596 **Census:** 16 **Outpatient Visits:** 79579 **Births:** 314 **Total Expense ($000):** 45950 **Payroll Expense ($000):** 14768 **Personnel:** 238

GALVESTON—Galveston County

☐ **SHRINERS HOSPITALS FOR CHILDREN-GALVESTON (453311)**, 815 Market Street, Zip 77550–2725; tel. 409/770–6600, **A**1 3 5 10 **F**3 11 16 29 30 32 34 35 50 64 68 75 77 81 82 85 86 89 93 100 104 119 130 132 146 148 154 **S** Shriners Hospitals for Children, Tampa, FL
Primary Contact: Mary Jaco, Administrator
CFO: Michael B Schimming, Director Financial Services
CMO: David N Herndon, M.D., Chief of Staff
CIO: Michael Lyons, Regional Director Information Services
CHR: Robert A Magee, Director Human Resources
CNO: Angel Martinez, R.N., RN, BSN, Director Patient Care Services
Web address: www.shrinershospitalsforchildren.org/Hospitals/Locations/Galveston.aspx
Control: Other not–for–profit (including NFP Corporation) **Service:** Children's other specialty

Staffed Beds: 20 **Admissions:** 193 **Census:** 9 **Outpatient Visits:** 8501 **Births:** 0 **Total Expense ($000):** 40499 **Payroll Expense ($000):** 15804 **Personnel:** 244

UNIVERSITY OF TEXAS MEDICAL BRANCH (450018), 301 University Boulevard, Zip 77555–0128; tel. 409/772–1011, (Includes ANGLETON DANBURY CAMPUS, 132 East Hospital Drive, Angleton, Texas, Zip 77515–4112; tel. 979/849–7721, Donna K Sollenberger, Executive Vice President and Chief Executive Officer) **A**1 2 3 5 10 **F**3 11 12 13 15 16 17 18 19 20 22 24 26 28 29 30 31 34 35 36 38 39 40 41 43 44 45 46 49 50 51 52 53 54 55 56 57 58 59 60 61 63 64 65 68 70 71 72 73 74 75 76 77 78 79 81 82 84 85 86 87 88 89 92 93 94 96 97 100 101 102 104 107 108 110 111 112 114 115 116 117 118 119 120 121 123 124 126 129 130 131 132 134 135 137 138 139 141 142 144 145 146 147 148 149 150 154 156 **S** University of Texas System, Austin, TX
Primary Contact: Donna K. Sollenberger, Executive Vice President and Chief Executive Officer
COO: Deborah A McGrew, Vice President and Chief Operating Officer
CFO: Cheryl A Sadro, Executive Vice President Chief Business and Finance Officer
CIO: Todd Leach, Vice President and Chief Information Officer
CHR: Ronald McKinley, Ph.D., Vice President Human Resources and Employee Services
CNO: Annette Macias-Hoag, R.N., Vice President, Health System and Service Line Operations Interim Associate Chief Nursing & Patient Care Services Office
Web address: www.utmb.edu
Control: State, Government, nonfederal **Service:** General medical and surgical

Staffed Beds: 480 **Admissions:** 32323 **Census:** 399 **Outpatient Visits:** 1164470 **Births:** 6443 **Total Expense ($000):** 1009273 **Payroll Expense ($000):** 340815 **Personnel:** 4627

GARLAND—Dallas County

GARLAND BEHAVIORAL HOSPITAL (454138), 2300 Marie Curie Boulevard, 5th Floor, Zip 75402; tel. 972/487–5309, **F**98 101 103 104 105 153 **S** Universal Health Services, Inc., King of Prussia, PA
Primary Contact: Kristin Harris, Chief Executive Officer
CFO: Scott Cook, Chief Financial Officer
Web address: www.garlandbehavioralhospital.com/
Control: Corporation, Investor–owned (for–profit) **Service:** Psychiatric

Staffed Beds: 72 **Admissions:** 1953 **Census:** 50 **Outpatient Visits:** 63 **Births:** 0 **Total Expense ($000):** 14309 **Payroll Expense ($000):** 6628 **Personnel:** 101

GATESVILLE—Coryell County

☐ **CORYELL HEALTH (451379)**, 1507 West Main Street, Zip 76528–1098; tel. 254/865–8251, **A**1 **F**3 7 10 11 12 15 18 20 28 34 35 40 43 45 50 57 58 59 60 62 64 65 70 74 79 81 82 84 86 87 93 97 102 104 107 108 110 111 115 116 117 119 125 127 129 130 131 133 146 148 154
Primary Contact: David Byrom, Chief Executive Officer
COO: David Byrom, Chief Executive Officer
CFO: Carol Jones, Controller and Manager Business Office
CMO: Diedra Wuenschel, D.O., President Medical Staff
CIO: Mike Huckabee, Network Administrator
CHR: Paula Smithhart, Director Human Resources
CNO: Jeanne Griffith, Chief Nursing Officer
Web address: www.cmhos.org
Control: Hospital district or authority, Government, nonfederal **Service:** General medical and surgical

Staffed Beds: 25 **Admissions:** 804 **Census:** 7 **Outpatient Visits:** 72275 **Births:** 0 **Total Expense ($000):** 51883 **Payroll Expense ($000):** 17465 **Personnel:** 499

GEORGETOWN—Williamson County

☐ **GEORGETOWN BEHAVIORAL HEALTH INSTITUTE (454129)**, 3101 South Austin Avenue, Zip 78626–7541; tel. 512/819–1100, **A**1 **F**4 5 56 98 99 100 102 103 104 105 130 132 135 151 152 153 154 **S** Signature Healthcare Services, Corona, CA
Primary Contact: Monica Ochoa, Chief Executive Officer
COO: Ellen Payne, Chief Operating Officer
CFO: Shelli Surcouf, Chief Financial Officer
CHR: Kristi Hynes, Director Human Resources
CNO: Nini Perry, Chief Nursing Officer
Web address: www.georgetownbehavioral.com
Control: Corporation, Investor–owned (for–profit) **Service:** Psychiatric

Staffed Beds: 118 **Admissions:** 3426 **Census:** 65 **Outpatient Visits:** 7241 **Births:** 0 **Total Expense ($000):** 20978 **Payroll Expense ($000):** 9069 **Personnel:** 167

★ **ROCK SPRINGS (454127)**, 700 Southeast Inner Loop, Zip 78626; tel. 512/819–9400, **F**4 5 54 98 100 102 104 105 152 153 **S** Springstone, Louisville, KY
Primary Contact: Jason McPherson, Chief Executive Officer
CFO: Jason Guzak, Chief Financial Officer
CHR: Sharon McMurray, Director, Human Resources
CNO: Randall Luce, R.N., Director of Nursing
Web address: www.rockspringshealth.com/
Control: Corporation, Investor–owned (for–profit) **Service:** Psychiatric

Staffed Beds: 72 **Admissions:** 2285 **Census:** 56 **Outpatient Visits:** 8096 **Births:** 0 **Total Expense ($000):** 16423 **Payroll Expense ($000):** 8434 **Personnel:** 168

GLEN ROSE—Somervell County

☐ **GLEN ROSE MEDICAL CENTER (450451)**, 1021 Holden Street, Zip 76043–4937, Mailing Address: P.O. Box 2099, Zip 76043–2099; tel. 254/897–2215, **A**1 10 **F**2 3 4 15 29 34 40 43 45 48 51 53 54 56 57 59 65 68 81 93 97 98 100 103 104 107 110 116 129 141 143 146 148 153
Primary Contact: Ray Reynolds, Chief Executive Officer
CFO: Michael Honea, Chief Financial Officer
CHR: Ladonna Green, Director Human Resources
CNO: Laura Hodnett, Interim Chief Nursing Officer
Web address: www.glenrosemedicalcenter.com
Control: Hospital district or authority, Government, nonfederal **Service:** General medical and surgical

Staffed Beds: 10 **Admissions:** 314 **Census:** 2 **Outpatient Visits:** 34485 **Births:** 0 **Total Expense ($000):** 20546 **Payroll Expense ($000):** 6434 **Personnel:** 169

GONZALES—Gonzales County

★ **GONZALES HEALTHCARE SYSTEMS (450235)**, 1110 Sarah Dewitt Drive, Zip 78629–3311, Mailing Address: P.O. Box 587, Zip 78629–0587; tel. 830/672–7581, **A**10 20 **F**3 11 13 15 29 34 35 38 40 43 53 57 59 62 64 65 66 68 75 76 77 79 81 85 87 93 97 107 110 111 115 119 127 130 **S** QHR, Brentwood, TN
Primary Contact: Patty Stewart, Interim Chief Executive Officer
CFO: Patty Stewart, Chief Financial Officer
CMO: Commie Hisey, D.O., Chief of Staff
CHR: Joni Leland, Director Human Resources
CNO: Valerie Hohenshell, Director of Clinical Services
Web address: www.gonzaleshealthcare.com
Control: Hospital district or authority, Government, nonfederal **Service:** General medical and surgical

Staffed Beds: 33 **Admissions:** 684 **Census:** 5 **Outpatient Visits:** 30378 **Births:** 138 **Total Expense ($000):** 49907 **Payroll Expense ($000):** 11075 **Personnel:** 296

GRAHAM—Young County

GRAHAM REGIONAL MEDICAL CENTER (450085), 1301 Montgomery Road, Zip 76450–4240, Mailing Address: P.O. Box 1390, Zip 76450–1390; tel. 940/549–3400, **A**10 20 **F**3 7 11 15 28 29 40 43 45 50 53 57 59 62 63 75 77 79 81 85 89 93 104 107 111 115 119 127 130 133 135
Primary Contact: Shane Kernell, Chief Executive Officer
CIO: Jeff Clark, Director Information Systems
Web address: www.grahamrmc.com
Control: Hospital district or authority, Government, nonfederal **Service:** General medical and surgical

Staffed Beds: 17 **Admissions:** 630 **Census:** 6 **Outpatient Visits:** 34609 **Births:** 0 **Total Expense ($000):** 19715 **Payroll Expense ($000):** 7529 **Personnel:** 163

GRANBURY—Hood County

✠ **LAKE GRANBURY MEDICAL CENTER (450596)**, 1310 Paluxy Road, Zip 76048–5655; tel. 817/573–2273, **A**1 3 10 **F**3 8 11 12 13 15 18 20 22 26 28 29 30 34 37 40 43 45 49 53 57 59 64 68 70 74 75 76 77 79 81 82 85 86 93 107 108 110 111 114 118 119 126 129 146 147 149 154 157 **S** Community Health Systems, Inc., Franklin, TN
Primary Contact: David Orcutt, Chief Executive Officer
CFO: Noe Gutierrez, Chief Financial Officer
CIO: Kevin Myers, Director Information Systems
CHR: Brooke Montoya, Director Human Resources
CNO: Abigail Kendall, Chief Nursing Officer
Web address: www.lakegranburymedicalcenter.com
Control: Corporation, Investor–owned (for–profit) **Service:** General medical and surgical

Staffed Beds: 73 **Admissions:** 3206 **Census:** 30 **Outpatient Visits:** 77422 **Births:** 553 **Total Expense ($000):** 78764 **Payroll Expense ($000):** 25642 **Personnel:** 389

GRAND PRAIRIE—Dallas County

⇧ **TEXAS GENERAL HOSPITAL (670083)**, 2709 Hospital Boulevard, Zip 75051–1017; tel. 469/557–9430, (Nonreporting) **A**10 21
Primary Contact: Suleman Hashmi, President and Chief Executive Officer
Web address: www.texasgeneralhospital.com
Control: Partnership, Investor–owned (for–profit) **Service:** General medical and surgical

Staffed Beds: 41

GRAPEVINE—Tarrant County

✠ **BAYLOR SCOTT & WHITE MEDICAL CENTER - GRAPEVINE (450563)**, 1650 West College Street, Zip 76051–3565; tel. 817/481–1588, **A**1 2 3 5 10 **F**3 5 8 12 13 15 18 20 22 24 26 28 29 30 31 34 35 40 43 45 46 47 48 49 56 57 59 64 65 70 72 74 75 76 77 78 79 80 81 82 84 86 87 90 107 108 110 111 114 115 119 126 130 131 132 135 145 146 147 148 149 152 **S** Baylor Scott & White Health, Dallas, TX
Primary Contact: Christopher York, FACHE, President
CFO: Terri Foster, Hospital Finance Officer
CMO: Ron Jensen, D.O., Chief Medical Officer and Vice President
CIO: Sandy Vaughn, Director Information Systems
CHR: Donna Stark, Director Human Resources
Web address: www.https://www.baylorhealth.com/PhysiciansLocations/Grapevine/Pages/Default.aspx
Control: Other not–for–profit (including NFP Corporation) **Service:** General medical and surgical

Staffed Beds: 270 **Admissions:** 13730 **Census:** 170 **Outpatient Visits:** 62000 **Births:** 2184 **Total Expense ($000):** 214945 **Payroll Expense ($000):** 76548 **Personnel:** 863

☐ **SAGECREST HOSPITAL OF GRAPEVINE (452110)**, 4201 William D Tate Avenue, Zip 76051–5736; tel. 817/288–1300, **A**1 10 **F**1 3 29 64 75 77 82 85 93 96 107 115 119 130 135 148
Primary Contact: Krystal Mims, Chief Executive Officer
Web address: www.ethicusgrapevine.com
Control: Partnership, Investor–owned (for–profit) **Service:** Acute long–term care hospital

Staffed Beds: 60 **Admissions:** 56 **Census:** 4 **Outpatient Visits:** 1217 **Births:** 0 **Total Expense ($000):** 12386 **Payroll Expense ($000):** 4755 **Personnel:** 34

GREENVILLE—Hunt County

⊠ **GLEN OAKS HOSPITAL (454050)**, 301 Division Street, Zip 75401–4101; tel. 903/454–6000, **A**1 10 **F**4 5 29 34 35 75 86 87 98 100 101 102 104 105 132 152 153 **S** Universal Health Services, Inc., King of Prussia, PA
Primary Contact: James Miller, Chief Executive Officer
Web address: www.glenoakshospital.com
Control: Corporation, Investor–owned (for–profit) **Service:** Psychiatric

Staffed Beds: 54 **Admissions:** 2115 **Census:** 41 **Outpatient Visits:** 2506 **Births:** 0 **Total Expense ($000):** 11640 **Payroll Expense ($000):** 5956 **Personnel:** 103

☐ **HUNT REGIONAL MEDICAL CENTER (450352)**, 4215 Joe Ramsey Boulevard, Zip 75401–7899, Mailing Address: P.O. Box 1059, Zip 75403–1059; tel. 903/408–5000, **A**1 10 **F**3 11 12 13 15 28 29 30 34 37 40 42 43 44 45 46 49 50 53 56 57 59 62 64 65 68 70 71 72 73 74 75 76 77 78 79 81 82 84 85 86 87 90 91 92 93 94 96 98 102 103 104 107 108 110 111 114 115 118 119 120 121 123 129 130 132 135 141 143 144 146 147 148 149 154 156 157 **S** Hunt Regional Healthcare, Greenville, TX
Primary Contact: Richard Carter, District Chief Executive Officer
COO: Michael R Klepin, Administrator
CFO: Lee Boles, Assistant Administrator and Chief Financial Officer
CMO: James H Sandin, M.D., Assistant Administrator Medical Affairs
CIO: Richard Montanye, Director Information Systems
CNO: Deborah Clack, Chief Nursing Officer
Web address: www.huntregional.org
Control: Hospital district or authority, Government, nonfederal **Service:** General medical and surgical

Staffed Beds: 167 **Admissions:** 5766 **Census:** 82 **Outpatient Visits:** 141848 **Births:** 1226 **Total Expense ($000):** 152900 **Payroll Expense ($000):** 64059 **Personnel:** 1040

GROESBECK—Limestone County

LIMESTONE MEDICAL CENTER (451303), 701 McClintic Drive, Zip 76642–2128; tel. 254/729–3281, **A**10 18 **F**3 7 11 28 29 30 32 34 35 40 41 43 45 57 64 65 68 75 77 84 85 90 93 96 97 104 107 111 115 119 127 129 130 133 135 146 148 153
Primary Contact: Larry Price, Chief Executive Officer
CFO: Michael F. Williams, Chief Financial Officer
CMO: Jeffrey Rettig, D.O., Chief of Staff
CIO: Byong Lee, Chief Information Officer
CHR: Jean Koester, Manager Human Resources
CNO: Jean Wragge, Chief Nursing Officer
Web address: www.lmchospital.com
Control: Hospital district or authority, Government, nonfederal **Service:** General medical and surgical

Staffed Beds: 20 **Admissions:** 338 **Census:** 6 **Outpatient Visits:** 12857 **Births:** 0 **Total Expense ($000):** 19826 **Payroll Expense ($000):** 10185 **Personnel:** 231

HALLETTSVILLE—Lavaca County

LAVACA MEDICAL CENTER (451376), 1400 North Texana Street, Zip 77964–2099; tel. 361/798–3671, **A**10 18 **F**3 11 15 18 29 34 40 41 43 45 47 53 56 57 59 64 65 68 75 77 81 85 86 87 93 107 108 110 111 114 118 119 127 133 135 146 148 149
Primary Contact: Stephen Bowen, Administrator
Control: Hospital district or authority, Government, nonfederal **Service:** General medical and surgical

Staffed Beds: 25 **Admissions:** 413 **Census:** 6 **Outpatient Visits:** 43098 **Births:** 0 **Total Expense ($000):** 18811 **Payroll Expense ($000):** 6707 **Personnel:** 156

Many Facility Codes have changed. Please refer to the AHA Guide Code Chart. © 2019 AHA Guide

TX

HAMILTON—Hamilton County

★ ⇑ **HAMILTON GENERAL HOSPITAL (450754)**, 400 North Brown Street, Zip 76531–1518; tel. 254/386–1600, **A**10 20 21 **F**3 5 7 11 15 28 29 34 35 40 43 44 45 50 53 57 59 64 65 68 75 79 81 82 85 86 87 93 97 100 104 107 108 110 111 115 119 127 129 130 131 132 133 148 149 153 154
Primary Contact: Grady A. Hooper, Chief Executive Officer
CMO: James R Lee, M.D., Chief of Staff
CIO: Chad Reinert, Chief Information Officer
CHR: Keela Payne, Director Human Resources
CNO: Debra Martin, Chief Nursing Officer
Web address: www.hamiltonhospital.org
Control: Hospital district or authority, Government, nonfederal **Service**: General medical and surgical

Staffed Beds: 25 **Admissions**: 811 **Census**: 8 **Outpatient Visits**: 73765
Births: 0 **Total Expense ($000)**: 27690 **Payroll Expense ($000)**: 12598
Personnel: 284

HARKER HEIGHTS—Bell County

⊞ **SETON MEDICAL CENTER HARKER HEIGHTS (670080)**, 850 West Central Texas Expressway, Zip 76548–1890; tel. 254/690–0900, **A**1 10 **F**3 13 15 18 20 22 26 28 29 30 34 35 40 43 45 49 50 51 57 59 60 66 70 74 75 76 79 81 91 93 107 108 110 111 115 119 129 130 146 147 148 **S** Ardent Health Services, Nashville, TN
Primary Contact: Zachary K. Dietze, Chief Executive Officer
CFO: John K Sharp, Chief Financial Officer
CNO: Pamela Craig, R.N., Chief Nursing Officer
Web address: www.setonharkerheights.net
Control: Partnership, Investor–owned (for–profit) **Service**: General medical and surgical

Staffed Beds: 83 **Admissions**: 4057 **Census**: 26 **Outpatient Visits**: 79184
Births: 910 **Total Expense ($000)**: 73960 **Payroll Expense ($000)**: 23806
Personnel: 392

HARLINGEN—Cameron County

⊞ **HARLINGEN MEDICAL CENTER (450855)**, 5501 South Expressway 77, Zip 78550–3213; tel. 956/365–1000, **A**1 3 5 10 **F**3 12 13 15 17 18 20 22 24 29 30 40 43 49 50 51 57 59 64 68 70 74 75 76 79 81 85 86 107 108 110 111 114 115 118 119 129 130 146 147 148 **S** Prime Healthcare, Ontario, CA
Primary Contact: Matt Wolthoff, Chief Executive Officer
CFO: David Glassburn, Vice President Finance and Chief Financial Officer
CMO: Elizabeth Juarez, M.D., Chief Medical Officer
CHR: Emmett Craig, Director Human Resources
CNO: Deborah Meeks, Chief Nursing Officer
Web address: www.harlingenmedicalcenter.com
Control: Partnership, Investor–owned (for–profit) **Service**: General medical and surgical

Staffed Beds: 88 **Admissions**: 6584 **Census**: 66 **Outpatient Visits**: 72504
Births: 931 **Total Expense ($000)**: 98950 **Payroll Expense ($000)**: 34526
Personnel: 577

☐ **RIO GRANDE STATE CENTER/SOUTH TEXAS HEALTH CARE SYSTEM (454088)**, 1401 South Rangerville Road, Zip 78552–7638; tel. 956/364–8000, (Includes RIO GRANDE STATE CENTER, 1401 South Rangerville Road, Harlingen, Texas, Zip 78552–7638; tel. 956/364–8000; SOUTH TEXAS HEALTH CARE SYSTEM, 1401 Rangerville Road, Harlingen, Texas, Zip 78552–7609; tel. 956/364–8000) **A**1 3 10 **F**30 53 57 65 66 68 75 87 97 98 101 107 119 130 132 135 143 146 147 154 156 **S** Texas Department of State Health Services, Austin, TX
Primary Contact: Sonia Hernandez-Keeble, Superintendent
CFO: Tom Garza, Director Fiscal and Support
CMO: David Moron, M.D., Clinical Director
CIO: Blas Ortiz Jr Assistant Superintendent and Public Information Officer
CHR: Irma Garcia, Job Coordinator
CNO: Maia Baker, MSN, Chief Nurse Executive
Web address: www.dshs.state.tx.us/mhhospitals/RioGrandeSC/default.shtm
Control: State, Government, nonfederal **Service**: Psychiatric

Staffed Beds: 55 **Admissions**: 833 **Census**: 52 **Outpatient Visits**: 0
Births: 0 **Total Expense ($000)**: 18274 **Payroll Expense ($000)**: 12619
Personnel: 232

SOLARA HOSPITAL HARLINGEN (452101), 508 Victoria Lane, Zip 78550–3225; tel. 956/425–9600, (Includes SOLARA HOSPITAL - BROWNSVILLE CAMPUS, 333 Lorenaly Drive, Brownsville, Texas, Zip 78526–4333; tel. 956/546–0808; Cynthia Issacs, Chief Executive Officer) **A**10 22 **F**1 3 29 35 40 57 70 85 86 130 148 **S** Cornerstone Healthcare Group, Dallas, TX
Primary Contact: Cynthia Isaacs, Chief Executive Officer
CFO: Kurt Schultz, Chief Financial Officer
CHR: Dan Perkins, Vice President of Human Resources
CNO: Nesa Caldwell, Chief Nursing Officer
Web address: www.chghospitals.com/harlingen/
Control: Partnership, Investor–owned (for–profit) **Service**: Acute long–term care hospital

Staffed Beds: 82 **Admissions**: 852 **Census**: 58 **Outpatient Visits**: 0
Births: 0 **Total Expense ($000)**: 21796 **Payroll Expense ($000)**: 10596
Personnel: 152

⊞ **VALLEY BAPTIST MEDICAL CENTER-HARLINGEN (450033)**, 2101 Pease Street, Zip 78550–8307, Mailing Address: P O Drawer 2588, Zip 78551–2588; tel. 956/389–1100, **A**1 3 5 10 **F**3 11 12 13 14 15 17 18 20 22 24 26 28 29 30 31 34 35 39 40 41 43 44 45 46 47 48 49 50 53 54 56 57 58 59 60 63 64 65 68 70 72 73 74 75 76 77 78 79 80 81 82 84 85 86 87 88 89 90 92 93 94 98 100 101 102 103 104 105 107 108 110 111 112 114 115 119 126 129 130 132 144 146 147 148 153 156 157 **S** TENET Healthcare Corporation, Dallas, TX
Primary Contact: Manuel Vela, President and Chief Executive Officer
CFO: Marco Rodriguez, Chief Financial Officer
CNO: Stephen Hill, Vice President and Chief Nursing Officer
Web address: www.valleybaptist.net/harlingen/index.htm
Control: Corporation, Investor–owned (for–profit) **Service**: General medical and surgical

Staffed Beds: 432 **Admissions**: 17444 **Census**: 227 **Outpatient Visits**: 124437 **Births**: 1774 **Total Expense ($000)**: 257941 **Payroll Expense ($000)**: 90114 **Personnel**: 1428

HASKELL—Haskell County

HASKELL MEMORIAL HOSPITAL (451341), 1 North Avenue 'N', Zip 79521–5499, Mailing Address: P.O. Box 1117, Zip 79521–1117; tel. 940/864–2621, **A**10 18 **F**11 28 29 34 35 40 53 54 57 59 64 68 75 77 86 87 93 97 107 119 130 131 133 146
Primary Contact: Fran McCown, Administrator
CHR: Emily Moore, Director Human Resources and Information Technology
CNO: Teri Turner, Chief Nursing Officer
Web address: www.haskellmemorialhospital.com/
Control: Hospital district or authority, Government, nonfederal **Service**: General medical and surgical

Staffed Beds: 15 **Admissions**: 203 **Census**: 2 **Outpatient Visits**: 24350
Births: 0 **Total Expense ($000)**: 7277 **Payroll Expense ($000)**: 3342
Personnel: 80

HEMPHILL—Sabine County

☐ **SABINE COUNTY HOSPITAL (451361)**, 2301 Worth Street, Zip 75948–7216, Mailing Address: P.O. Box 750, Zip 75948–0750; tel. 409/787–3300, **A**1 10 18 **F**3 29 40 43 93 97 107 114 119 127 133 154 **S** Preferred Management Corporation, Shawnee, OK
Primary Contact: Jerry Howell, Administrator
COO: Mike Easley, Vice President and Chief Operating Officer
CFO: Larry Stephens, Chief Financial Officer
CMO: Vera Luther, M.D., Chief of Staff
CIO: Margaret Moore, Director Business Office
CHR: Laura Simpson, Director Human Resources
CNO: Margie Watson MSN, RN-B Chief Nursing Officer
Web address: www.sabinecountyhospital.com/
Control: Corporation, Investor–owned (for–profit) **Service**: General medical and surgical

Staffed Beds: 25 **Admissions**: 278 **Census**: 4 **Outpatient Visits**: 18350
Births: 0 **Total Expense ($000)**: 9485 **Payroll Expense ($000)**: 4072
Personnel: 85

TX

Hospital, Medicare Provider Number, Address, Telephone, Approval, Facility, and Physician Codes, Health Care System

★ American Hospital Association (AHA) membership ☐ The Joint Commission accreditation ○ Healthcare Facilities Accreditation Program ◇ DNV Healthcare Inc. accreditation ⇑ Center for Improvement in Healthcare Quality Accreditation △ Commission on Accreditation of Rehabilitation Facilities (CARF) accreditation

© 2019 AHA Guide — *Many Facility Codes have changed. Please refer to the AHA Guide Code Chart.* — Hospitals **A609**

HENDERSON—Rusk County

⊞ **UT HEALTH HENDERSON (450475)**, 300 Wilson Street, Zip 75652–5956; tel. 903/657–7541, (Data for 306 days) **A**1 10 **F**3 8 11 13 15 28 29 30 34 35 37 40 43 45 50 57 59 64 65 75 76 79 81 87 107 108 110 111 115 119 127 129 135 145 146 147 148 149 156 **S** Ardent Health Services, Nashville, TN
Primary Contact: Mark Leitner, FACHE, Administrator
CFO: Wesley Knight, Chief Financial Officer
CHR: William Henry, Director Human Resources
CNO: Donna K Stanley, R.N., Chief Nursing Officer
Web address: www.https://uthealthhenderson.com/
Control: Corporation, Investor–owned (for–profit) **Service**: General medical and surgical

Staffed Beds: 41 **Admissions**: 1182 **Census**: 12 **Outpatient Visits**: 46032 **Births**: 196 **Total Expense ($000)**: 24993 **Payroll Expense ($000)**: 6982 **Personnel**: 161

HENRIETTA—Clay County

CLAY COUNTY MEMORIAL HOSPITAL (451362), 310 West South Street, Zip 76365–3346; tel. 940/538–5621, **A**10 18 **F**7 8 11 28 34 35 40 50 53 57 62 68 80 81 90 93 107 111 119 130 132 133 144 146 148
Primary Contact: Jeff Huskey, Chief Executive Officer and Administrator
CFO: Debra Haehn, Chief Financial Officer
CMO: Lexi Mitchell Sanchez, D.O., Chief of Staff
CHR: Linda Burleson, Administrative Secretary
CNO: Kelley McMillion, Chief Nursing Officer
Web address: www.ccmhospital.com
Control: County, Government, nonfederal **Service**: General medical and surgical

Staffed Beds: 25 **Admissions**: 151 **Census**: 1 **Outpatient Visits**: 8367 **Births**: 0 **Total Expense ($000)**: 7994 **Payroll Expense ($000)**: 3400 **Personnel**: 83

HEREFORD—Deaf Smith County

HEREFORD REGIONAL MEDICAL CENTER (450155), 540 West 15th Street, Zip 79045–2820; tel. 806/364–2141, **A**10 **F**3 7 11 13 15 29 35 40 43 50 57 59 62 65 70 76 77 81 85 93 107 111 114 119 127 130 133 147 154
Primary Contact: Jeff Barnhart, Chief Executive Officer
COO: Meri Killingsworth, Chief Operating Officer
CNO: Anthony T. Jerina, Chief Nursing Officer
Web address: www.dschd.org/
Control: Hospital district or authority, Government, nonfederal **Service**: General medical and surgical

Staffed Beds: 39 **Admissions**: 610 **Census**: 4 **Outpatient Visits**: 72469 **Births**: 312 **Total Expense ($000)**: 25387 **Payroll Expense ($000)**: 9009 **Personnel**: 172

HILLSBORO—Hill County

⊞ **HILL REGIONAL HOSPITAL (450192)**, 101 Circle Drive, Zip 76645–2670; tel. 254/580–8500, (Nonreporting) **A**1 10 20 **S** Community Health Systems, Inc., Franklin, TN
Primary Contact: Michael J. Ellis, FACHE, Chief Executive Officer
CFO: Judy Culp, Chief Financial Officer
CHR: Becky Hale, Director Human Resources
Web address: www.chs.net
Control: Corporation, Investor–owned (for–profit) **Service**: General medical and surgical

Staffed Beds: 66

HONDO—Medina County

MEDINA COMMUNITY HOSPITAL See Medina Regional Hospital

MEDINA REGIONAL HOSPITAL (451330), 3100 Avenue E, Zip 78861–3599; tel. 830/426–7700, **A**10 18 **F**3 11 13 15 28 29 34 35 40 43 45 50 57 59 64 65 66 68 75 76 77 81 82 84 85 93 107 110 111 114 115 119 127 130 132 133 134 135 146 147 148 154 156
Primary Contact: Janice Simons, FACHE, Chief Executive Officer
CFO: Kevin Frosch, Chief Financial Officer
CMO: Matthew Windrow, M.D., Chief of Staff
CIO: Ken Gallegos, Director Support Services and Information Technology
CHR: Sharon Garcia, Human Resources Representative
CNO: Billie Bell, Chief Nursing Officer
Web address: www.medinahospital.net
Control: Hospital district or authority, Government, nonfederal **Service**: General medical and surgical

Staffed Beds: 25 **Admissions**: 727 **Census**: 9 **Outpatient Visits**: 111085 **Births**: 138 **Total Expense ($000)**: 27894 **Payroll Expense ($000)**: 11232 **Personnel**: 243

HOUSTON—Harris County

AD HOSPITAL EAST (670102), 12950 East Freeway, Zip 77015–5710; tel. 713/330–3887, (Nonreporting)
Primary Contact: Robert A. Turner, Chief Executive Officer
Control: Other not–for–profit (including NFP Corporation) **Service**: General medical and surgical

Staffed Beds: 25

☐ **ADVANCED DIAGNOSTICS HOSPITAL (670203)**, 12950 East Freeway, Zip 77015–5710; tel. 713/330–3887, **A**1 **F**3 12 15 29 35 40 44 45 54 64 68 75 79 81 82 85 87 92 107 110 111 115 119 131 148 149 156
Primary Contact: Steve Winnett, Chief Executive Officer
CFO: Carol Files, Chief Financial Officer
CMO: Ian Reynolds, Chief Medical Officer
CIO: Yobi Kasper, Chief Information Officer
CHR: Gabby Myers, Human Resources Director
CNO: David Gonzalez, Chief Clinical Officer
Control: Individual, Investor–owned (for–profit) **Service**: General medical and surgical

Staffed Beds: 4 **Admissions**: 402 **Census**: 3 **Outpatient Visits**: 8678 **Births**: 0 **Total Expense ($000)**: 19141 **Payroll Expense ($000)**: 5410 **Personnel**: 78

ALTUS HOUSTON HOSPITAL, 6011 West Sam Houston Parkway South, Zip 77072–1646; tel. 713/773–0556, (Nonreporting)
Primary Contact: Kris Jenkins, Administrator
Web address: www.https://altushospital.org
Control: Partnership, Investor–owned (for–profit) **Service**: General medical and surgical

Staffed Beds: 10

★ ⇑ **BAYLOR ST. LUKE'S MEDICAL CENTER (450193)**, 6720 Bertner Avenue, Zip 77030–2697, Mailing Address: P.O. Box 20269, Zip 77225–0269; tel. 832/355–1000, **A**2 3 5 8 10 21 **F**3 8 11 12 14 15 17 18 20 22 24 26 28 29 30 31 34 35 36 37 39 40 42 45 46 47 48 49 50 51 54 55 56 57 58 59 60 61 63 64 65 66 68 70 74 75 77 78 79 81 82 84 85 86 87 90 91 92 93 100 107 108 109 110 111 112 113 114 115 116 117 118 119 120 121 122 123 124 126 129 130 131 132 137 138 139 140 146 148 149 154 156 **S** CommonSpirit Health, Chicago, IL
Primary Contact: T Douglas. Lawson, Ph.D., FACHE, Chief Executive Officer
CMO: John Byrne, M.D., Vice President and Chief Medical Officer
CIO: James Albin, Chief Information Officer
CHR: Susan Bailey-Newell, Vice President Human Resources
CNO: Loretta Lee, Acting Chief Nursing Officer
Web address: www.stlukestexas.com
Control: Church operated, Nongovernment, not–for–profit **Service**: General medical and surgical

Staffed Beds: 615 **Admissions**: 23334 **Census**: 434 **Outpatient Visits**: 165737 **Births**: 0 **Total Expense ($000)**: 882630 **Payroll Expense ($000)**: 288069 **Personnel**: 3278

⊞ **BAYLOR ST. LUKE'S MEDICAL CENTER MCNAIR CAMPUS**, One Baylor Plaza, BCM 100, Zip 77030–3411; tel. 713/798–4951, (Nonreporting) **A**1 **S** CommonSpirit Health, Chicago, IL
Primary Contact: Gay Nord, President
Web address: www.bcm.edu
Control: Other not–for–profit (including NFP Corporation) **Service**: General medical and surgical

Staffed Beds: 256

☐ **BEHAVIORAL HOSPITAL OF BELLAIRE (454107)**, 5314 Dashwood Drive, Zip 77081–4603; tel. 713/600–9500, **A**1 10 **F**4 5 29 98 99 100 101 103 105 130 152 153 154 **S** Universal Health Services, Inc., King of Prussia, PA
Primary Contact: Eric Amoh, Chief Executive Officer
CFO: Autumn Crouse, Chief Financial Officer
Web address: www.bhbhospital.com
Control: Corporation, Investor–owned (for–profit) **Service**: Psychiatric

Staffed Beds: 122 **Admissions**: 3834 **Census**: 94 **Outpatient Visits**: 5102 **Births**: 0 **Total Expense ($000)**: 19817 **Payroll Expense ($000)**: 11469 **Personnel**: 198

TX

Many Facility Codes have changed. Please refer to the AHA Guide Code Chart. © 2019 AHA Guide

★ ⇧ **CHI ST. LUKE'S HOSPITAL - THE VINTAGE HOSPITAL (670075)**, 20171 Chasewood Park Drive, Zip 77070–1437; tel. 832/534–5000, **A**10 21 **F**3 13 15 18 20 22 24 26 29 30 34 35 40 44 45 46 49 50 57 59 60 64 68 70 72 74 75 76 77 79 81 85 87 107 108 110 111 114 115 118 119 130 146 147 149 **S** CommonSpirit Health, Chicago, IL
Primary Contact: Mario J. Garner, Ed.D., FACHE, Chief Executive Officer
Web address: www.https://www.chistlukeshealth.org/locations/vintage-hospital
Control: Church operated, Nongovernment, not–for–profit **Service**: General medical and surgical

Staffed Beds: 78 **Admissions**: 3644 **Census**: 37 **Outpatient Visits**: 28325 **Births**: 742 **Total Expense ($000)**: 73403 **Payroll Expense ($000)**: 29434 **Personnel**: 412

CORNERSTONE HOSPITAL-MEDICAL CENTER OF HOUSTON (452055), 2001 Hermann Drive, Zip 77004; tel. 832/649–6200, **A**10 22 **F**1 3 29 70 85 86 87 91 119 130 148 149 **S** Cornerstone Healthcare Group, Dallas, TX
Primary Contact: Guido J. Cubellis, Chief Executive Officer
Web address: www.chghospitals.com
Control: Corporation, Investor–owned (for–profit) **Service**: Acute long–term care hospital

Staffed Beds: 35 **Admissions**: 414 **Census**: 27 **Outpatient Visits**: 0 **Births**: 0 **Total Expense ($000)**: 15409 **Payroll Expense ($000)**: 6864 **Personnel**: 78

☐ **CYPRESS CREEK HOSPITAL (454108)**, 17750 Cali Drive, Zip 77090–2700; tel. 281/586–7600, **A**1 10 **F**4 5 29 64 75 87 98 100 102 104 105 130 132 153 154 **S** Universal Health Services, Inc., King of Prussia, PA
Primary Contact: Phuong Cardoza, Interim Chief Executive Officer
CFO: Stephen Copeland, Chief Financial Officer
CMO: Marshall Lucas, M.D., Medical Director
CIO: James Harmon, Information Technology
CHR: Brenda Dominguez, Director Human Resources
CNO: Michael Smith, Director of Nursing
Web address: www.cypresscreekhospital.com
Control: Corporation, Investor–owned (for–profit) **Service**: Psychiatric

Staffed Beds: 128 **Admissions**: 4193 **Census**: 97 **Outpatient Visits**: 8812 **Births**: 0 **Total Expense ($000)**: 26131 **Payroll Expense ($000)**: 12516 **Personnel**: 228

DUBUIS HOSPITAL OF HOUSTON See Cornerstone Hospital-Medical Center of Houston

⊠ **ENCOMPASS HEALTH REHABILITATION HOSPITAL OF CYPRESS (673050)**, 13031 Wortham Center Drive, Zip 77065–5662; tel. 832/280–2500, **A**1 10 **F**3 29 34 57 59 62 75 77 82 86 87 90 91 95 96 130 132 148 149 156 **S** Encompass Health Corporation, Birmingham, AL
Primary Contact: Sheila A. Bollier, Chief Executive Officer
CFO: Melissa Haddox, Controller
CMO: Ignazio LaChina, M.D., Medical Director
CNO: Roshonda Henry, Chief Nursing Officer
Web address: www.healthsouthcypress.com
Control: Corporation, Investor–owned (for–profit) **Service**: Rehabilitation

Staffed Beds: 60 **Admissions**: 1388 **Census**: 51 **Outpatient Visits**: 3930 **Births**: 0 **Total Expense ($000)**: 19880 **Payroll Expense ($000)**: 10742 **Personnel**: 185

⊠ **ENCOMPASS HEALTH REHABILITATION HOSPITAL THE VINTAGE (673052)**, 20180 Chasewood Park Drive, Zip 77070–1436; tel. 281/205–5100, **A**1 10 **F**3 29 63 65 90 91 96 130 148 149 154 **S** Encompass Health Corporation, Birmingham, AL
Primary Contact: Krista Uselman, Chief Executive Officer
CNO: Stanley F Kiebzak, R.N., Chief Nursing Officer
Web address: www.reliantnwhouston.com
Control: Corporation, Investor–owned (for–profit) **Service**: Rehabilitation

Staffed Beds: 60 **Admissions**: 1251 **Census**: 37 **Outpatient Visits**: 4514 **Births**: 0 **Total Expense ($000)**: 17578 **Payroll Expense ($000)**: 9745 **Personnel**: 139

☐ **FIRST TEXAS HOSPITAL (670118)**, 9922 Louetta Road, Zip 77070–1468, Mailing Address: 2941 Lake Vista Drive, Lewisville, Zip 75067–3801; tel. 346/206–2300, **A**1 **F**3 12 18 29 40 42 45 51 68 70 75 77 79 81 85 94 97 100 107 108 115 119 130
Primary Contact: Maridel Acosta-Cruz, Chief Executive Officer
Control: Corporation, Investor–owned (for–profit) **Service**: General medical and surgical

Staffed Beds: 12 **Admissions**: 232 **Census**: 2 **Outpatient Visits**: 77215 **Births**: 1 **Total Expense ($000)**: 109878 **Payroll Expense ($000)**: 63234 **Personnel**: 153

⇧ **HARRIS HEALTH SYSTEM (450289)**, 2525 Holly Hall Street, Zip 77054–4108, Mailing Address: P.O. Box 66769, Zip 77266–6769; tel. 713/566–6403, (Includes BEN TAUB GENERAL HOSPITAL, 1504 Taub Loop, Houston, Texas, Zip 77030; tel. 713/873–2300; LYNDON B JOHNSON GENERAL HOSPITAL, 5656 Kelley, Houston, Texas, Zip 77026; tel. 713/566–5000; QUENTIN MEASE HOSPITAL, 3601 North MacGregor, Houston, Texas, Zip 77004; tel. 713/873–3700; Jeffrey Webster, Administrator) (Total facility includes 24 beds in nursing home–type unit) **A**2 5 10 21 **F**3 5 7 8 13 15 17 18 20 22 29 30 31 32 34 35 39 40 41 43 45 46 49 50 51 54 55 56 57 58 59 60 61 64 65 68 70 71 72 73 74 75 76 77 78 79 81 82 84 87 89 90 91 92 93 94 97 98 100 101 102 104 107 110 111 112 114 115 118 119 120 121 124 128 129 130 132 134 135 143 144 146 147 148 149 150 153 156
Primary Contact: George V. Masi, Chief Executive Officer
CFO: Michael Norby, Chief Financial Officer
CMO: Fred Sutton, M.D., Chief Medical Officer
CIO: Tim Tindle, Chief Information Officer
CHR: Diane Poirot, Vice President Human Resources
CNO: Toni Cotton, R.N., Chief Nursing Officer
Web address: www.https://www.harrishealth.org
Control: Hospital district or authority, Government, nonfederal **Service**: General medical and surgical

Staffed Beds: 716 **Admissions**: 30998 **Census**: 477 **Outpatient Visits**: 1764181 **Births**: 5369 **Total Expense ($000)**: 1456493 **Payroll Expense ($000)**: 541325 **Personnel**: 8790

⊠ **HCA HOUSTON HEALTHCARE NORTHWEST (450638)**, 710 Cypress Creek Parkway, Zip 77090–3402; tel. 281/440–1000, **A**1 3 5 10 **F**3 11 12 13 15 18 20 22 24 26 28 29 30 31 34 35 40 43 45 46 49 50 57 59 64 65 70 72 74 75 76 77 78 79 81 82 84 85 86 87 90 91 92 93 96 102 107 108 109 110 111 114 115 117 118 119 126 129 130 132 135 144 145 146 147 148 149 **S** HCA Healthcare, Nashville, TN
Primary Contact: Scott Davis, Chief Executive Officer
COO: Michael Adkins, Chief Operating Officer
CFO: Cameron Pophan, Chief Financial Officer
CIO: Ed Roberson, Director Information Systems
CHR: Melanie R Webb, Vice President Human Resources
CNO: Cindy Henning, R.N., Chief Nursing Officer
Web address: www.hnmc.com
Control: Partnership, Investor–owned (for–profit) **Service**: General medical and surgical

Staffed Beds: 254 **Admissions**: 15095 **Census**: 188 **Outpatient Visits**: 140196 **Births**: 3492 **Total Expense ($000)**: 285384 **Payroll Expense ($000)**: 105437 **Personnel**: 1078

⇧ **HEALTHBRIDGE CHILDREN'S HOSPITAL OF HOUSTON (453309)**, 2929 Woodland Park Drive, Zip 77082–2687; tel. 281/293–7774, **A**3 5 10 **F**3 29 74 75 79 85 87 89 91 93 100 130 146 148 **S** Nexus Health Systems, Houston, TX
Primary Contact: Joel Telly, Chief Executive Officer
CMO: Robert Yetman, M.D., Medical Director
CHR: Guy Murdock, Vice President Human Resources
Web address: www.healthbridgehouston.com/
Control: Partnership, Investor–owned (for–profit) **Service**: Children's general medical and surgical

Staffed Beds: 40 **Admissions**: 152 **Census**: 17 **Outpatient Visits**: 485 **Births**: 0 **Total Expense ($000)**: 11230 **Payroll Expense ($000)**: 4472 **Personnel**: 71

☐ ⇧ **HERMANN DRIVE SURGICAL HOSPITAL**, 2001 Hermann Drive, Zip 77004–7643; tel. 713/285–5500, **A**1 21 **F**3 12 29 40 45 46 64 68 73 74 75 77 81 85 86 107 114 119 **S** Nobilis Health Corporation, Houston, TX
Primary Contact: Nicole Walker, Chief Executive Officer
Web address: www.nobilishealth.com/our-facilities/houston/
Control: Corporation, Investor–owned (for–profit) **Service**: General medical and surgical

Staffed Beds: 25 **Admissions**: 605 **Census**: 4 **Outpatient Visits**: 2144 **Births**: 0 **Personnel**: 34

HOUSTON BEHAVIORAL HEALTHCARE HOSPITAL (454135), 2801 Gessner Road, Zip 77080–2503; tel. 832/834–7710, (Nonreporting) **S** Signature Healthcare Services, Corona, CA
Primary Contact: Roy Hollis, Chief Executive Officer
Web address: www.houstonbehavioralhealth.com/
Control: Individual, Investor–owned (for–profit) **Service**: Psychiatric

Staffed Beds: 25

TX

Hospital, Medicare Provider Number, Address, Telephone, Approval, Facility, and Physician Codes, Health Care System

★ American Hospital Association (AHA) membership   ○ Healthcare Facilities Accreditation Program   ⇧ Center for Improvement in Healthcare Quality Accreditation
☐ The Joint Commission accreditation   ◇ DNV Healthcare Inc. accreditation   △ Commission on Accreditation of Rehabilitation Facilities (CARF) accreditation

© 2019 AHA Guide   *Many Facility Codes have changed. Please refer to the AHA Guide Code Chart.*   Hospitals **A611**

★ ⊞ **HOUSTON METHODIST HOSPITAL (450358)**, 6565 Fannin Street, D200, Zip 77030–2707; tel. 713/790–3311, (Total facility includes 18 beds in nursing home–type unit) **A**2 3 5 8 10 21 **F**3 5 6 8 9 11 12 13 14 15 17 18 20 22 24 26 28 29 30 31 34 35 36 37 38 39 40 41 42 44 45 46 47 48 49 50 51 53 54 55 56 57 58 59 60 61 62 63 64 65 66 68 70 73 74 75 76 77 78 79 80 81 82 84 85 86 87 90 91 92 93 95 96 97 98 99 100 101 103 104 105 107 108 110 111 112 114 115 117 118 119 120 121 123 124 126 128 129 130 131 132 135 136 137 138 139 140 141 142 145 146 147 148 149 150 153 154 156 **S** Houston Methodist, Houston, TX
Primary Contact: Roberta Schwartz, Ph.D., Executive Vice President
CMO: Robert Phillips, M.D., Ph.D., FACC, Executive Vice President and Chief Medical Officer
CIO: Robert K Eardley, Senior Vice President and Chief Information Officer
CNO: Katherine Walsh, MS, R.N., Dr.PH, Vice President and Chief Nursing Officer
Web address: www.methodisthealth.com
Control: Other not–for–profit (including NFP Corporation) **Service**: General medical and surgical

Staffed Beds: 948 **Admissions:** 38867 **Census:** 728 **Outpatient Visits:** 453071 **Births:** 1132 **Total Expense ($000):** 1787247 **Payroll Expense ($000):** 499693 **Personnel:** 10126

★ ⊞ **HOUSTON METHODIST WEST HOSPITAL (670077)**, 18500 Katy Freeway, Zip 77094–1110; tel. 832/522–1000, **A**10 21 **F**3 11 12 13 15 18 20 22 24 26 28 29 30 31 34 35 36 39 40 42 44 45 49 50 51 53 54 57 59 60 61 63 64 68 70 72 74 75 76 77 78 79 81 82 84 85 86 87 93 107 108 109 110 111 114 115 116 117 118 119 120 121 123 124 126 130 131 132 135 146 147 148 149 156 **S** Houston Methodist, Houston, TX
Primary Contact: Wayne M. Voss, Chief Executive Officer
CNO: Victoria Brownewell, Chief Nursing Officer
Web address: www.methodisthealth.com
Control: Other not–for–profit (including NFP Corporation) **Service**: General medical and surgical

Staffed Beds: 212 **Admissions:** 11888 **Census:** 123 **Outpatient Visits:** 169531 **Births:** 2305 **Total Expense ($000):** 274115 **Payroll Expense ($000):** 96258 **Personnel:** 1398

★ ⊞ **HOUSTON METHODIST WILLOWBROOK HOSPITAL (450844)**, 18220 State Highway 249, Zip 77070–4347; tel. 281/477–1000, **A**3 10 21 **F**3 8 11 12 13 15 17 18 20 22 24 26 28 29 30 31 34 35 36 37 40 42 44 45 49 50 53 54 57 59 64 65 70 72 73 74 75 76 77 78 79 81 85 86 87 93 97 100 102 107 108 110 111 112 115 119 120 121 123 126 129 130 131 132 135 146 147 149 156 **S** Houston Methodist, Houston, TX
Primary Contact: Keith Barber, CPA, Chief Executive Officer
CHR: Elizabeth Acevedo, Director Human Resources
CNO: Nancy C Keenan, R.N., Senior Vice President and Chief Nursing Officer
Web address: www.houstonmethodist.org/locations/willowbrook/
Control: Other not–for–profit (including NFP Corporation) **Service**: General medical and surgical

Staffed Beds: 312 **Admissions:** 18333 **Census:** 218 **Outpatient Visits:** 250961 **Births:** 3428 **Total Expense ($000):** 373015 **Payroll Expense ($000):** 134158 **Personnel:** 1843

☐ **INTRACARE NORTH HOSPITAL (454083)**, 1120 Cypress Station Drive, Zip 77090–3031; tel. 281/893–7200, **A**1 10 **F**98 99 100 101 103 104 105 153
Primary Contact: Terry Scovill, Chief Executive Officer
CFO: Fred Chan, Chief Financial Officer
CMO: Javier Ruiz, M.D., Medical Director
Web address: www.intracare.org
Control: Other not–for–profit (including NFP Corporation) **Service**: Psychiatric

Staffed Beds: 90 **Admissions:** 2298 **Census:** 56 **Outpatient Visits:** 30030 **Births:** 0 **Total Expense ($000):** 17381 **Payroll Expense ($000):** 8239 **Personnel:** 191

⊞ **KINDRED HOSPITAL HOUSTON MEDICAL CENTER (452023)**, 6441 Main Street, Zip 77030–1596; tel. 713/790–0500, **A**1 3 5 10 **F**1 3 29 30 70 75 77 85 107 130 148 **S** Kindred Healthcare, Louisville, KY
Primary Contact: Robert Stein, Chief Executive Officer
CFO: Sara Langlitz, Controller
Web address: www.khhouston.com/
Control: Corporation, Investor–owned (for–profit) **Service**: Acute long–term care hospital

Staffed Beds: 105 **Admissions:** 845 **Census:** 76 **Outpatient Visits:** 0 **Births:** 0 **Total Expense ($000):** 42651 **Payroll Expense ($000):** 20850 **Personnel:** 276

⊞ **KINDRED HOSPITAL-HOUSTON NORTHWEST (452039)**, 11297 Fallbrook Drive, Zip 77065–4292; tel. 281/897–8114, (Includes KINDRED HOSPITAL-BAY AREA, 4801 East Sam Houston Parkway South, Pasadena, Texas, Zip 77505–3955; tel. 281/991–5463) **A**1 10 **F**1 3 29 49 57 64 70 77 85 87 107 114 130 148 **S** Kindred Healthcare, Louisville, KY
Primary Contact: Tracy Kohler, Chief Executive Officer
Web address: www.khhoustonnw.com/
Control: Corporation, Investor–owned (for–profit) **Service**: Acute long–term care hospital

Staffed Beds: 84 **Admissions:** 622 **Census:** 48 **Outpatient Visits:** 320 **Births:** 0 **Total Expense ($000):** 27769 **Payroll Expense ($000):** 11392 **Personnel:** 156

LYNDON B JOHNSON GENERAL HOSPITAL See Harris Health System, Houston

⊞ **MEMORIAL HERMANN - TEXAS MEDICAL CENTER (450068)**, 6411 Fannin Street, Zip 77030–1501; tel. 713/704–4000, (Includes CHILDREN'S MEMORIAL HERMANN HOSPITAL, 6411 Fannin, Houston, Texas, Zip 77030; tel. 713/704–5437; MEMORIAL HERMAN CYPRESS, 27700 NW Freeway, Suite 380, Cypress, Texas, Zip 77433; tel. 832/658–3102; Heath Rushing, Senior Vice President and Chief Executive Officer; MEMORIAL HERMANN ORTHOPEDIC AND SPINE HOSPITAL, 5410 West Loop South, Bellaire, Texas, Zip 77401–2103; tel. 713/314–4500; Gregory Haralson, FACHE, Senior Vice President and Chief Executive Officer) (Total facility includes 8 beds in nursing home–type unit) **A**1 2 3 5 8 10 **F**3 7 8 11 12 13 15 16 17 18 19 20 21 22 23 24 25 26 27 28 29 30 31 32 34 35 36 37 39 40 41 43 44 45 46 47 48 49 50 53 54 55 56 57 58 59 60 61 63 64 65 68 70 71 72 73 74 76 77 78 80 81 82 83 84 85 86 87 88 89 90 92 93 97 102 107 108 109 110 111 113 114 115 116 117 118 119 120 121 123 124 126 128 129 130 131 132 135 136 137 138 139 140 141 142 144 146 147 148 149 150 154 155 **S** Memorial Hermann Health System, Houston, TX
Primary Contact: Gregory Haralson, FACHE, Senior Vice President and Chief Executive Officer
COO: Shawn Cloonan, Executive Vice President and Chief Operating Officer
CFO: William Pack, Chief Financial Officer
CMO: Jeffrey Katz, M.D., Chief Medical Officer
CIO: David Bradshaw, Chief Information Officer
CHR: Vivian Kardow, Chief Human Resources Officer
Web address: www.mhhs.org
Control: Other not–for–profit (including NFP Corporation) **Service**: General medical and surgical

Staffed Beds: 1075 **Admissions:** 43218 **Census:** 748 **Outpatient Visits:** 274107 **Births:** 5883 **Total Expense ($000):** 1578634 **Payroll Expense ($000):** 454349 **Personnel:** 5295

⊞ **MEMORIAL HERMANN GREATER HEIGHTS HOSPITAL (450184)**, 1635 North Loop West, Zip 77008–1532; tel. 713/867–3380, (Includes MEMORIAL HERMANN PEARLAND MEDICAL CENTER, 16100 South Freeway, Pearland, Texas, Zip 77584–1895; tel. 713/413–5000; Kyle Price, Chief Executive Officer; MEMORIAL HERMANN SOUTHEAST HOSPITAL, 11800 Astoria Boulevard, Houston, Texas, Zip 77089–6041; tel. 281/929–6100; Kyle Price, Chief Executive Officer; MEMORIAL HERMANN SOUTHWEST HOSPITAL, 7600 Beechnut, Houston, Texas, Zip 77074–1850; tel. 713/456–5000; Malisha Patel, Senior Vice President and Chief Executive Officer; MEMORIAL HERMANN THE WOODLANDS HOSPITAL, 9250 Pinecroft Drive, The Woodlands, Texas, Zip 77380–3225; tel. 281/364–2300) **A**1 2 3 5 10 **F**3 8 11 12 13 15 17 18 20 22 24 26 28 29 30 31 34 35 37 40 41 42 43 44 45 46 47 48 49 50 51 54 56 57 58 59 60 62 64 65 69 70 72 73 74 75 77 78 79 80 81 82 84 85 86 87 90 91 92 93 94 96 100 102 107 108 109 110 111 112 114 115 116 117 119 120 121 122 123 124 126 129 130 131 132 135 143 144 146 147 148 149 154 **S** Memorial Hermann Health System, Houston, TX
Primary Contact: Paul O'Sullivan, FACHE, Chief Executive Officer
COO: Wesley Tidwell, Chief Operating Officer
CFO: James R Shallock, Chief Financial Officer
CMO: Maurice Leibman, M.D., Chief Medical Officer
CIO: David Bradshaw, Chief Information Officer
CNO: Ann Szapor, Vice President and Chief Nursing Officer
Web address: www.memorialhermann.org
Control: Other not–for–profit (including NFP Corporation) **Service**: General medical and surgical

Staffed Beds: 1380 **Admissions:** 68847 **Census:** 909 **Outpatient Visits:** 637896 **Births:** 9533 **Total Expense ($000):** 1383452 **Payroll Expense ($000):** 453992 **Personnel:** 5352

TX

Many Facility Codes have changed. Please refer to the AHA Guide Code Chart. © 2019 AHA Guide

⊞ **MEMORIAL HERMANN MEMORIAL CITY MEDICAL CENTER (450610)**, 1760 Barker Cypress Rd, Zip 77084, Mailing Address: 921 Gessner Road, Zip 77024–2501; tel. 713/242–3000, **A**1 2 3 5 10 **F**3 12 13 15 18 20 22 24 26 28 29 30 31 34 35 37 40 41 43 45 46 47 49 50 51 56 57 59 60 65 70 72 74 75 76 77 78 79 80 81 82 84 85 86 87 89 107 108 110 111 114 115 117 118 119 120 121 123 124 126 129 130 131 132 135 146 147 148 149 156 **S** Memorial Hermann Health System, Houston, TX
Primary Contact: Paul O'Sullivan, FACHE, Chief Executive Officer
COO: Allen Tseng, Chief Operations Officer
CFO: Lisa Kendler, Chief Financial Officer
CMO: Harold Gottlieb, M.D., Chief Medical Officer
CIO: David Bradshaw, Chief Information, Planning and Marketing Officer
CHR: Suzanne S Meier, System Director, Compensation and Human Resources Technology
CNO: Dan Kelly, R.N., Chief Nursing Officer
Web address: www.memorialhermann.org
Control: Other not–for–profit (including NFP Corporation) **Service**: General medical and surgical

Staffed Beds: 421 **Admissions**: 21454 **Census**: 240 **Outpatient Visits**: 199686 **Births**: 3816 **Total Expense ($000)**: 488581 **Payroll Expense ($000)**: 125375 **Personnel**: 1436

MEMORIAL HERMANN SOUTHEAST HOSPITAL See Memorial Hermann Greater Heights Hospital, Houston

MEMORIAL HERMANN SOUTHWEST HOSPITAL See Memorial Hermann Greater Heights Hospital, Houston

☐ **MENNINGER CLINIC**, 12301 Main Street, Zip 77035–6207; tel. 713/275–5000, **A**1 3 5 **F**30 35 74 98 101 104 106 130 132 154
Primary Contact: Anthony Gaglio, CPA, Interim President and Chief Executive Officer
CFO: Anthony Gaglio, CPA, Senior Vice President and Chief Financial Officer
CIO: M. Justin Coffey, Vice President and Chief Information Officer, Medical Director Center for Brain Stimulation
CHR: Andrea Preisinger, Director Human Resources
Web address: www.menningerclinic.com
Control: Other not–for–profit (including NFP Corporation) **Service**: Psychiatric

Staffed Beds: 102 **Admissions**: 711 **Census**: 63 **Outpatient Visits**: 9828 **Births**: 0 **Total Expense ($000)**: 61558 **Payroll Expense ($000)**: 26917 **Personnel**: 394

⇑ **METHODIST WEST HOUSTON HOSPITAL** See Houston Methodist West Hospital

⇑ **METHODIST WILLOWBROOK HOSPITAL** See Houston Methodist Willowbrook Hospital

⊞ **MICHAEL E. DEBAKEY VETERANS AFFAIRS MEDICAL CENTER**, 2002 Holcombe Boulevard, Zip 77030–4298; tel. 713/791–1414, (Nonreporting) **A**1 3 5 **S** Department of Veterans Affairs, Washington, DC
Primary Contact: Francisco Vazquez, Director
CFO: Alisa Cooper, Manager Financial Resources
CMO: Jagadeesh S Kalavar, M.D., Chief of Staff
CIO: Kevin Lenamond, Information Management Service Line Executive
CHR: Mark Muhammad, Manager Human Resources
CNO: Kelly Ann Irving MSN, RN-B Associate Director for Patient Care Services
Web address: www.houston.va.gov
Control: Veterans Affairs, Government, federal **Service**: General medical and surgical

Staffed Beds: 479

⊞ **PARK PLAZA HOSPITAL (450659)**, 1313 Hermann Drive, Zip 77004–7092; tel. 713/527–5000, **A**1 2 5 10 **F**3 12 15 18 20 22 29 30 34 35 40 45 49 50 57 59 70 74 79 81 85 92 107 108 110 111 114 115 118 119 120 121 123 129 130 132 146 147 148 **S** HCA Healthcare, Nashville, TN
Primary Contact: Peyton Elliott, Chief Executive Officer
COO: Mary Jo Goodman, Chief Operating Officer
CIO: Terry Janis, Assistant Vice President
CHR: Melanie R Webb, Vice President Human Resources
Web address: www.parkplazahospital.com
Control: Corporation, Investor–owned (for–profit) **Service**: General medical and surgical

Staffed Beds: 139 **Admissions**: 3203 **Census**: 52 **Outpatient Visits**: 27896 **Births**: 0 **Total Expense ($000)**: 89342 **Payroll Expense ($000)**: 31163 **Personnel**: 416

⊞ **PLAZA SPECIALTY HOSPITAL (452046)**, 1300 Binz Street, Zip 77004–7016; tel. 713/285–1000, **A**1 10 **F**1 3 70 85 87 **S** HCA Healthcare, Nashville, TN
Primary Contact: Peyton Elliott, Chief Executive Officer
CFO: Charles Handley, Chief Financial Officer
CMO: Wasae S Tabibi, M.D., President Medical Staff
CIO: Michael Turner, Chief Information Officer
Web address: www.plazaspecialtyhospital.com
Control: Corporation, Investor–owned (for–profit) **Service**: Acute long–term care hospital

Staffed Beds: 46 **Admissions**: 326 **Census**: 24 **Outpatient Visits**: 0 **Births**: 0 **Total Expense ($000)**: 19018 **Payroll Expense ($000)**: 7076 **Personnel**: 76

PROVIDENCE HOSPITAL OF NORTH HOUSTON (670119), 16750 Red Oak Drive, Zip 77090; tel. 281/453–7110, (Nonreporting) **A**10 22
Primary Contact: Stephen Myers, Chief Executive Officer
Control: Individual, Investor–owned (for–profit) **Service**: General medical and surgical

Staffed Beds: 16

SACRED OAK MEDICAL CENTER (454142), 11500 Space Center Boulevard, Zip 77059–3603; tel. 281/241–6460, **A**10 **F**5 98 104 105 152 153 156
Primary Contact: Raquel Diati, Chief Executive Officer
Web address: www.sacredoakmedical.com/
Control: Partnership, Investor–owned (for–profit) **Service**: Psychiatric

Staffed Beds: 20 **Admissions**: 824 **Census**: 14 **Outpatient Visits**: 1092 **Births**: 0 **Total Expense ($000)**: 11168 **Payroll Expense ($000)**: 5321 **Personnel**: 106

☐ **SCA HOUSTON HOSPITAL FOR SPECIALIZED SURGERY (450797)**, 5445 La Branch Street, Zip 77004–6835; tel. 713/528–6800, (Nonreporting) **A**1 10
Primary Contact: Mary Whitmeyer, Chief Executive Officer
CFO: Deborah Jones, Controller
Web address: www.scasurgery.com
Control: Partnership, Investor–owned (for–profit) **Service**: General medical and surgical

Staffed Beds: 7

☐ **SHRINERS HOSPITALS FOR CHILDREN-HOUSTON (453312)**, 6977 Main Street, Zip 77030–3701; tel. 713/797–1616, **A**1 3 5 10 **F**3 29 30 35 50 59 64 68 74 75 77 79 81 86 87 89 93 94 96 130 131 132 134 143 146 148 154 **S** Shriners Hospitals for Children, Tampa, FL
Primary Contact: Cathy Moniaci, Administrator
COO: Cathy Moniaci, Administrator
CFO: Michael B Schimming, Director Fiscal Services
CMO: Douglas A Barnes, M.D., Chief of Staff
CHR: Robert A Magee, Director Human Resources
CNO: Jeannie Keith, Director Patient Care Services and Nurse Executive
Web address: www.shrinershospitalsforchildren.org/Locations/houston
Control: Other not–for–profit (including NFP Corporation) **Service**: Children's orthopedic

Staffed Beds: 40 **Admissions**: 449 **Census**: 10 **Outpatient Visits**: 7841 **Births**: 0 **Total Expense ($000)**: 29234 **Payroll Expense ($000)**: 16164 **Personnel**: 173

⇑ **ST. JOSEPH MEDICAL CENTER (450035)**, 1401 St Joseph Parkway, Zip 77002–8301; tel. 713/757–1000, (Includes ST. JOSEPH MEDICAL CENTER IN THE HEIGHTS, 1917 Ashland Street, Houston, Texas, Zip 77008–3907; tel. 713/969–5400; Kimberly S. Bassett, R.N., Chief Executive Officer) **A**3 5 10 21 **F**3 11 12 13 15 18 20 22 24 26 29 30 34 35 40 43 45 49 50 51 53 55 57 59 60 64 68 70 72 74 75 76 77 78 79 81 82 84 85 86 87 90 93 98 101 102 107 108 110 111 114 115 116 117 118 119 121 123 124 126 130 131 132 135 143 146 147 148 149 156 **S** Steward Health Care System, LLC, Dallas, TX
Primary Contact: Kimberly S. Bassett, R.N., President
COO: Laura Fortin, R.N., Chief Operating Officer
CFO: Mark Hartman, Interim Chief Financial Officer
CIO: Robin Brown, Chief Information Officer and Compliance Officer
CHR: Kris Clatanoff, Director Human Resources
Web address: www.sjmctx.com
Control: Partnership, Investor–owned (for–profit) **Service**: General medical and surgical

Staffed Beds: 463 **Admissions**: 13528 **Census**: 183 **Outpatient Visits**: 100512 **Births**: 4436 **Total Expense ($000)**: 254166 **Payroll Expense ($000)**: 93028 **Personnel**: 1352

Hospital, Medicare Provider Number, Address, Telephone, Approval, Facility, and Physician Codes, Health Care System

★ American Hospital Association (AHA) membership
☐ The Joint Commission accreditation
○ Healthcare Facilities Accreditation Program
◇ DNV Healthcare Inc. accreditation
⇑ Center for Improvement in Healthcare Quality Accreditation
△ Commission on Accreditation of Rehabilitation Facilities (CARF) accreditation

SUN BEHAVIORAL HOUSTON (454139), 7601 Fannin Street, Zip 77054–1905; tel. 713/796–2273, **A**3 **F**98 99 100 101 103 104 105 106 153
Primary Contact: Laura Brown, Chief Executive Officer
CFO: Doug Smith, Chief Financial Officer
CMO: Vernon Walling, M.D., Chief Medical Officer
Web address: www.sunhouston.com
Control: Corporation, Investor–owned (for–profit) **Service:** Psychiatric

Staffed Beds: 148 **Admissions:** 3404 **Census:** 84 **Outpatient Visits:** 7208 **Births:** 0 **Total Expense ($000):** 21313 **Payroll Expense ($000):** 11781 **Personnel:** 199

☐ **TEXAS CHILDREN'S HOSPITAL (453304)**, 6621 Fannin Street, Zip 77030–2399, Mailing Address: Box 300630, Zip 77230–0630; tel. 832/824–1000, (Includes TEXAS CHILDREN'S HOSPITAL THE WOODLANDS, 17600 Interstate 45 South, The Woodlands, Texas, Zip 77384–5148; tel. 936/267–5000; Michelle Riley–Brown, President; TEXAS CHILDREN'S HOSPITAL WEST CAMPUS, 18200 Katy Freeway, Houston, Texas, Zip 77094–1285; tel. 832/227–1000; Michelle Riley–Brown, President) **A**1 3 5 8 10 **F**3 7 11 12 13 17 19 21 23 25 27 29 30 31 32 34 35 38 39 40 41 42 43 46 48 49 50 52 54 55 57 58 59 60 61 64 65 66 68 71 72 73 74 75 76 77 78 79 80 81 82 84 85 86 87 88 89 90 92 93 94 95 96 97 100 101 102 104 107 108 111 113 114 115 116 117 118 119 124 126 129 130 131 132 134 136 137 138 139 140 143 146 147 148 149 150 154 155
Primary Contact: Mark A. Wallace, FACHE, President and Chief Executive Officer
CMO: Mark W Kline, M.D., Physician in Chief
CIO: Myra Davis, Senior Vice President and Chief Information Officer
CHR: Linda W Aldred, Senior Vice President
Web address: www.texaschildrens.org
Control: Other not–for–profit (including NFP Corporation) **Service:** Children's general medical and surgical

Staffed Beds: 795 **Admissions:** 29397 **Census:** 482 **Outpatient Visits:** 1590213 **Births:** 6403 **Total Expense ($000):** 2157179 **Payroll Expense ($000):** 836082 **Personnel:** 9210

⊞ **TEXAS ORTHOPEDIC HOSPITAL (450804)**, 7401 South Main Street, Zip 77030–4509; tel. 713/799–8600, **A**1 3 5 10 **F**3 29 30 40 59 64 68 70 79 81 82 85 86 87 93 94 97 107 111 119 146 149 **S** HCA Healthcare, Nashville, TN
Primary Contact: Eric Becker, Chief Executive Officer
CFO: Blair Callaway, Chief Financial Officer
CMO: Gregory Stocks, M.D., Chief of Staff
CNO: Troy Sarver, R.N., Chief Nursing Officer
Web address: www.texasorthopedic.com
Control: Partnership, Investor–owned (for–profit) **Service:** Orthopedic

Staffed Beds: 49 **Admissions:** 3722 **Census:** 20 **Outpatient Visits:** 40695 **Births:** 0 **Total Expense ($000):** 95026 **Payroll Expense ($000):** 25855 **Personnel:** 400

⇑ **THE METHODIST HOSPITAL** See Houston Methodist Hospital

⊞ **TIRR MEMORIAL HERMANN (453025)**, 1333 Moursund Street, Zip 77030–3405; tel. 713/799–5000, **A**1 3 5 10 **F**3 11 29 30 34 35 44 50 54 58 59 60 64 68 74 75 77 79 82 86 87 90 91 93 95 96 97 100 104 107 114 119 129 130 131 132 146 148 149 157 **S** Memorial Hermann Health System, Houston, TX
Primary Contact: Jerry Ashworth, Senior Vice President and Chief Executive Officer
COO: Jerry Ashworth, Senior Vice President and Chief Executive Officer
CFO: Wayne Gordon, Chief Financial Officer
CMO: Gerard E Francisco, M.D., Chief Medical Officer
CIO: Gina Tripp, Director Information Systems
CHR: Vivian Kardow, Chief Human Resources Officer
Web address: www.memorialhermann.org/locations/tirr.html
Control: Other not–for–profit (including NFP Corporation) **Service:** Rehabilitation

Staffed Beds: 134 **Admissions:** 1474 **Census:** 101 **Outpatient Visits:** 34929 **Births:** 0 **Total Expense ($000):** 125920 **Payroll Expense ($000):** 59435 **Personnel:** 807

☐ **TOPS SURGICAL SPECIALTY HOSPITAL (450774)**, 17080 Red Oak Drive, Zip 77090–2602; tel. 281/539–2900, **A**1 10 **F**3 15 29 40 45 47 64 78 79 81 82 85 86 87 107 110 114 119 148 **S** United Surgical Partners International, Addison, TX
Primary Contact: Samuel H. Rossmann, Chief Executive Officer
CFO: Daniel Smith, Chief Financial Officer
CMO: Thomas Barton, M.D., Medical Director
CIO: Maud Jones, Manager Medical Records
CHR: Ashley Monzingo, Human Resources, Accounts Payable and Payroll
CNO: Andrea Wappelhorst, Chief Nursing Officer
Web address: www.tops-hospital.com
Control: Partnership, Investor–owned (for–profit) **Service:** Surgical

Staffed Beds: 15 **Admissions:** 645 **Census:** 3 **Outpatient Visits:** 45256 **Births:** 0 **Total Expense ($000):** 33910 **Payroll Expense ($000):** 9213 **Personnel:** 207

TRIUMPH HOSPITAL NORTHWEST See Kindred Hospital Spring

UNITED MEMORIAL MEDICAL CARE (450803), 510 West Tidwell Road, Zip 77091–4399; tel. 281/618–8500, (Includes DOCTORS HOSPITAL PARKWAY, 233 West Parker Road, Houston, Texas, Zip 77076–2999; tel. 281/765–2600) **A**10 22 **F**20 22 29 40 43 50 64 70 75 79 81 92 107 114 119 130
Primary Contact: Farida Moeen, M.D., Chief Executive Officer
COO: Farida Moeen, M.D., Chief Executive Officer
CFO: Theresa Eatherly, Chief Financial Officer
CMO: Cesar Ortega, M.D., Chief of Staff
CIO: Dell Davis, Director Information Systems
CHR: Carolyn Washington, Director of Human Resources
Web address: www.ummc.care/
Control: Partnership, Investor–owned (for–profit) **Service:** General medical and surgical

Staffed Beds: 42 **Admissions:** 4468 **Census:** 18 **Outpatient Visits:** 9136 **Births:** 0 **Total Expense ($000):** 32519 **Payroll Expense ($000):** 12352 **Personnel:** 271

★ **UNIVERSITY OF TEXAS HARRIS COUNTY PSYCHIATRIC CENTER (454076)**, 2800 South MacGregor Way, Zip 77021–1000, Mailing Address: P.O. Box 20249, Zip 77225–0249; tel. 713/741–7870, **A**5 10 **F**29 30 34 35 57 58 68 75 86 87 98 99 100 101 103 104 130 146 **S** University of Texas System, Austin, TX
Primary Contact: Jair C. Soares, M.D., Executive Director
COO: Stephen Glazier, Chief Operating Officer
CFO: Lois K. Pierson, Chief Financial Officer
CMO: R Andrew Harper, M.D., Medical Director
CNO: Margaret Pung, R.N., Chief Nursing Officer
Web address: www.hcpc.uth.tmc.edu
Control: State, Government, nonfederal **Service:** Psychiatric

Staffed Beds: 216 **Admissions:** 8417 **Census:** 188 **Outpatient Visits:** 502 **Births:** 0 **Total Expense ($000):** 52046 **Payroll Expense ($000):** 33909 **Personnel:** 454

⊞ **UNIVERSITY OF TEXAS M.D. ANDERSON CANCER CENTER (450076)**, 1515 Holcombe Boulevard, Unit 1491, Zip 77030–4000; tel. 713/792–2121, **A**1 2 3 5 8 10 **F**3 8 11 14 15 18 20 22 26 29 30 31 32 34 35 36 37 38 39 40 41 44 45 46 47 48 49 50 54 55 56 57 58 59 64 66 68 70 71 74 75 77 78 79 80 81 82 83 84 85 86 87 88 89 92 93 96 97 100 101 102 104 107 108 110 111 112 114 115 116 117 118 119 120 121 122 123 124 126 129 130 132 134 135 136 141 142 145 146 147 148 149 150 157 **S** University of Texas System, Austin, TX
Primary Contact: Peter Pisters, M.D., President
COO: Stephen Hahn, Deputy to the President and Chief Operating Officer
CFO: Weldon Gage, Chief Financial Officer
CIO: Chris Belmont, Chief Information Officer and Vice President
CHR: Shibu Varghese, Vice President Human Resources
CNO: Barbara L. Summers, Ph.D., R.N., Vice President Nursing Practice and Chief Nursing Officer
Web address: www.mdanderson.org
Control: State, Government, nonfederal **Service:** Cancer

Staffed Beds: 658 **Admissions:** 29118 **Census:** 567 **Outpatient Visits:** 1469760 **Births:** 0 **Total Expense ($000):** 4583815 **Payroll Expense ($000):** 1853383 **Personnel:** 19860

⊞ **WEST HOUSTON MEDICAL CENTER (450644)**, 12141 Richmond Avenue, Zip 77082–2499; tel. 281/558–3444, **A**1 10 **F**3 11 12 13 15 18 20 22 24 26 28 29 31 39 40 45 46 47 48 49 50 51 56 57 59 60 64 70 73 74 75 76 77 78 79 80 81 82 85 90 93 96 98 102 103 107 110 111 115 116 117 118 119 121 124 126 129 130 132 145 146 147 148 149 **S** HCA Healthcare, Nashville, TN
Primary Contact: Megan Marietta, Chief Executive Officer
COO: Philip Morris, Chief Operating Officer
CFO: Stanley K Nord, Chief Financial Officer
CMO: Magdy Rizk, M.D., Chief of Staff
CIO: Sergio Almeida, Director Information Systems
CHR: Carol Melville, Director Human Resources
Web address: www.westhoustonmedical.com
Control: Partnership, Investor–owned (for–profit) **Service:** General medical and surgical

Staffed Beds: 264 **Admissions:** 12389 **Census:** 175 **Outpatient Visits:** 107566 **Births:** 2426 **Total Expense ($000):** 192487 **Payroll Expense ($000):** 78616 **Personnel:** 976

TX

☐ **WEST OAKS HOSPITAL (454026)**, 6500 Hornwood Drive, Zip 77074–5095; tel. 713/995–0909, **A**1 5 10 **F**5 29 54 56 64 68 98 99 101 104 105 132 152 153 **S** Universal Health Services, Inc., King of Prussia, PA
Primary Contact: Mandy Westerman, Chief Executive Officer
CFO: Rob Tyler, Chief Financial Officer
CMO: Vernon Walling, M.D., Executive Medical Director
CIO: James Harmon, Network Administrator
CHR: Janice Webster, Director Human Resources
CNO: Israel Ahaine, Chief Nursing Officer
Web address: www.westoakshospital.com
Control: Corporation, Investor–owned (for–profit) **Service**: Psychiatric

Staffed Beds: 144 **Admissions**: 5924 **Census**: 137 **Outpatient Visits**: 14909 **Births**: 0 **Total Expense ($000)**: 27547 **Payroll Expense ($000)**: 17121 **Personnel**: 282

⇑ **WESTSIDE SURGICAL HOSPITAL**, 4200 Twelve Oaks Drive, Zip 77027; tel. 713/621–5010, (Nonreporting) **A**21
Primary Contact: Chad Baldwin, Interim Chief Executive Officer
CNO: Jimmy Wells, Chief Nursing and Administrative Officer
Web address: www.westsidesurgical.net
Control: Partnership, Investor–owned (for–profit) **Service**: Surgical

Staffed Beds: 12

✠ **WOMAN'S HOSPITAL OF TEXAS (450674)**, 7600 Fannin Street, Zip 77054–1906; tel. 713/790–1234, **A**1 3 5 10 **F**3 7 8 13 15 19 29 30 34 35 40 41 45 46 50 53 54 55 58 64 65 68 70 71 72 73 75 76 77 78 81 85 86 87 88 89 90 93 100 107 108 110 111 114 119 126 130 132 146 147 155 156 **S** HCA Healthcare, Nashville, TN
Primary Contact: Ashley McClellan, FACHE, Chief Executive Officer
CFO: Scott Bentley, Chief Financial Officer
CMO: Eberhard Lotze, M.D., Chief Medical Officer
CIO: Emily Le, Director Information Technology and Services
CHR: Arnita Crawford, Director Human Resources
CNO: Holley Tyler, R.N., Chief Nursing Officer
Web address: www.womanshospital.com
Control: Partnership, Investor–owned (for–profit) **Service**: Obstetrics and gynecology

Staffed Beds: 367 **Admissions**: 16237 **Census**: 257 **Outpatient Visits**: 55174 **Births**: 10727 **Total Expense ($000)**: 227578 **Payroll Expense ($000)**: 107088 **Personnel**: 1112

HUMBLE—Harris County

✠ **ENCOMPASS HEALTH REHABILITATION HOSPITAL OF HUMBLE (453029)**, 19002 McKay Drive, Zip 77338–5701; tel. 281/446–6148, **A**1 10 **F**29 56 75 77 78 79 82 86 87 90 91 92 95 96 130 132 143 148 149 **S** Encompass Health Corporation, Birmingham, AL
Primary Contact: Angela L. Simmons, Chief Executive Officer
CFO: Sheila Shepard, Controller
CMO: Emile Mathurin, M.D., Jr Medical Director
CHR: Christy Dixon, Chief Human Resources Officer
CNO: Christie Griffin-Jones, R.N., Chief Nursing Officer
Web address: www.healthsouthhumble.com
Control: Corporation, Investor–owned (for–profit) **Service**: Rehabilitation

Staffed Beds: 60 **Admissions**: 1083 **Census**: 38 **Outpatient Visits**: 0 **Births**: 0 **Total Expense ($000)**: 15172 **Payroll Expense ($000)**: 9479 **Personnel**: 161

☐ **KINDRED REHABILITATION HOSPITAL NORTHEAST HOUSTON (673051)**, 18839 McKay Boulevard, Zip 77338–5721; tel. 281/964–6600, **A**1 10 **F**3 29 77 90 91 93 148 149
Primary Contact: Tracy Wilson, Chief Executive Officer
CFO: Cheryl Csepke, Controller
CMO: Helen Schilling, M.D., Medical Director
CHR: Stephanie Williams, Coordinator Human Resources
CNO: Albert J. Chapple, R.N., Chief Clinical Officer
Web address: www.khrehabnortheasthouston.com
Control: Corporation, Investor–owned (for–profit) **Service**: Rehabilitation

Staffed Beds: 25 **Admissions**: 459 **Census**: 15 **Outpatient Visits**: 4355 **Births**: 0 **Total Expense ($000)**: 8328 **Payroll Expense ($000)**: 4638 **Personnel**: 104

✠ **MEMORIAL HERMANN NORTHEAST (450684)**, 18951 North Memorial Drive, Zip 77338–4297; tel. 281/540–7700, **A**1 2 3 5 10 **F**3 11 13 15 18 20 22 24 26 29 30 31 34 35 40 42 44 45 46 49 53 54 57 59 64 65 68 70 72 73 74 75 76 77 78 79 80 81 84 85 87 91 93 100 107 108 109 111 114 115 119 120 121 126 129 130 131 132 135 146 147 148 154 157 **S** Memorial Hermann Health System, Houston, TX
Primary Contact: Josh Urban, Chief Executive Officer
CFO: Rebecca Tucker, Chief Financial Officer
CMO: Susan Curling, M.D., Chief Medical Officer
CHR: Monica Baisden, Director Human Resources
CNO: Linda Stephens, R.N., Chief Nursing Officer
Web address: www.memorialhermann.org/locations/northeast/
Control: Other not–for–profit (including NFP Corporation) **Service**: General medical and surgical

Staffed Beds: 217 **Admissions**: 12863 **Census**: 160 **Outpatient Visits**: 138250 **Births**: 1256 **Total Expense ($000)**: 249114 **Payroll Expense ($000)**: 81869 **Personnel**: 972

★ **SE TEXAS ER & HOSPITAL (452112)**, 19211 McKay Boulevard, Zip 77338–5502; tel. 281/883–5500, (Nonreporting) **A**10
Primary Contact: DR. Michelle Heinrich, Interim Chief Executive Officer
Web address: www.iconhospitalonline.com/
Control: Partnership, Investor–owned (for–profit) **Service**: Acute long–term care hospital

Staffed Beds: 32

HUNTSVILLE—Walker County

✠ **HUNTSVILLE MEMORIAL HOSPITAL (450347)**, 110 Memorial Hospital Drive, Zip 77340–4940, Mailing Address: P.O. Box 4001, Zip 77342–4001; tel. 936/291–3411, **A**1 10 **F**3 8 11 12 13 15 18 20 22 26 28 29 32 34 35 40 43 46 47 49 50 53 54 57 59 60 64 65 66 67 68 70 74 75 76 77 79 81 82 85 86 87 89 90 91 92 93 96 97 102 107 108 110 111 114 115 119 126 127 130 131 132 135 146 147 148 149 150 154
Primary Contact: Steven L. Smith, Chief Executive Officer
CFO: Maxwell Owens, FACHE, Chief Financial Officer
CIO: Raul Velez, Director Information Systems
CHR: Brenda Ray, Director Human Resources
CNO: Sheila Ard, Chief Nursing Officer
Web address: www.huntsvillememorial.com
Control: Other not–for–profit (including NFP Corporation) **Service**: General medical and surgical

Staffed Beds: 98 **Admissions**: 4902 **Census**: 57 **Outpatient Visits**: 123317 **Births**: 370 **Total Expense ($000)**: 96011 **Payroll Expense ($000)**: 36191 **Personnel**: 513

HURST—Tarrant County

⇑ **SAINT CAMILLUS MEDICAL CENTER (670121)**, 1612 Hurst Town Center Drive, Zip 76054–6236; tel. 817/519–3700, **A**21 **F**3 12 29 40 45 64 74 75 79 81 82 85 87 107 135 149
Primary Contact: Corazon Ramirez, M.D., Chief Executive Officer
COO: Karen Sperduti, Chief Operating Officer
Web address: www.https://saintcamillusmedicalcenter.com/
Control: Corporation, Investor–owned (for–profit) **Service**: Surgical

Staffed Beds: 23 **Admissions**: 162 **Census**: 1 **Outpatient Visits**: 931 **Births**: 0 **Total Expense ($000)**: 20159 **Payroll Expense ($000)**: 2549 **Personnel**: 27

IRAAN—Pecos County

IRAAN GENERAL HOSPITAL (451307), 600 349 North, Zip 79744, Mailing Address: P.O. Box 665, Zip 79744–0665; tel. 432/639–2871, **A**10 18 **F**28 40 43 56 57 59 64 65 75 82 86 93 107 119 127 130 133 154
Primary Contact: Keith L. Butler, Chief Executive Officer
CFO: Tami Burks, Chief Fiscal Services
CMO: Robert W Garcia, M.D., Chief Medical Officer
CHR: Cathy Tucker, Director Human Resources
Web address: www.igh-hospital.com
Control: Hospital district or authority, Government, nonfederal **Service**: General medical and surgical

Staffed Beds: 14 **Admissions**: 47 **Census**: 1 **Outpatient Visits**: 7250 **Births**: 0 **Total Expense ($000)**: 10075 **Payroll Expense ($000)**: 4898 **Personnel**: 82

TX

Hospital, Medicare Provider Number, Address, Telephone, Approval, Facility, and Physician Codes, Health Care System

★ American Hospital Association (AHA) membership ○ Healthcare Facilities Accreditation Program ⇑ Center for Improvement in Healthcare Quality Accreditation
☐ The Joint Commission accreditation ◇ DNV Healthcare Inc. accreditation △ Commission on Accreditation of Rehabilitation Facilities (CARF) accreditation

IRVING—Dallas County

☒ **BAYLOR SCOTT & WHITE MEDICAL CENTER-IRVING (450079)**, 1901 North MacArthur Boulevard, Zip 75061–2220; tel. 972/579–8100, **A**1 2 3 5 10 **F**3 8 11 13 15 17 18 20 22 24 26 28 29 30 31 34 35 40 45 46 47 49 54 55 57 58 59 64 65 66 70 73 74 75 76 77 78 79 80 81 82 84 85 86 87 90 93 94 100 107 108 110 111 114 115 116 117 118 119 120 121 122 126 129 130 141 143 146 147 148 149 150 156 **S** Baylor Scott & White Health, Dallas, TX
Primary Contact: Cindy K. Schamp, FACHE, President
CFO: Steve Roussel, Vice President Finance
CMO: Jeffrey Embrey, M.D., Chief Medical Officer
CIO: Tim Huffman, Western Region Director, Information Systems Business Relationships
CHR: Vonetta Fuller-Williams, Director Human Resources Strategic and Business Services
Web address: www.bswhealth.com
Control: Other not–for–profit (including NFP Corporation) **Service**: General medical and surgical

Staffed Beds: 233 **Admissions**: 11351 **Census**: 139 **Outpatient Visits**: 96142 **Births**: 1507 **Total Expense ($000)**: 217432 **Payroll Expense ($000)**: 72315 **Personnel**: 847

☐ **BAYLOR SURGICAL HOSPITAL AT LAS COLINAS (450874)**, 400 West Interstate 635, Zip 75063; tel. 972/868–4000, **A**1 10 **F**3 29 30 40 51 79 81 107 111 119 126 130 **S** United Surgical Partners International, Addison, TX
Primary Contact: Deonna Unell, Chief Executive Officer
CFO: Gabrielle Holland, Chief Financial Officer
CMO: Scott McGraw, M.D., Medical Director
Web address: www.baylorhealth.com/About/Community/Assessments/West/ICSH/Pages/Default.aspx
Control: Partnership, Investor–owned (for–profit) **Service**: General medical and surgical

Staffed Beds: 12 **Admissions**: 763 **Census**: 4 **Outpatient Visits**: 7505 **Births**: 0 **Total Expense ($000)**: 44554 **Payroll Expense ($000)**: 10347 **Personnel**: 138

☒ **MEDICAL CITY LAS COLINAS (450822)**, 6800 North MacArthur Boulevard, Zip 75039–2422; tel. 972/969–2000, **A**1 10 **F**8 12 13 15 18 20 22 24 29 30 34 35 37 40 45 46 47 48 49 50 57 59 60 63 64 68 70 72 74 75 76 77 78 79 80 81 87 93 100 102 107 108 110 111 114 118 119 126 130 147 148 149 **S** HCA Healthcare, Nashville, TN
Primary Contact: Daniela Decell, Chief Executive Officer
COO: Chip Zahn, Chief Operating Officer
CFO: Nick Galt, Chief Financial Officer
CMO: Miguel Benet, M.D., Chief Medical Officer
Web address: www.lascolinasmedical.com
Control: Corporation, Investor–owned (for–profit) **Service**: General medical and surgical

Staffed Beds: 72 **Admissions**: 5967 **Census**: 53 **Outpatient Visits**: 57995 **Births**: 2188 **Total Expense ($000)**: 89082 **Payroll Expense ($000)**: 28399 **Personnel**: 365

JACKSBORO—Jack County

FAITH COMMUNITY HOSPITAL (450241), 215 Chisholm Trail, Zip 76458–1111; tel. 940/567–6633, **A**10 20 **F**7 11 13 15 28 34 35 40 43 45 57 59 65 66 68 75 76 77 81 93 97 107 110 114 119 127 130 133 135 148 149 156
Primary Contact: Frank Beaman, Chief Executive Officer
COO: Kim Lee, Chief Operating Officer
CFO: Bonnie Blevins, R.N., Chief Financial Officer
CMO: Sushil Chokshi, M.D., Chief Medical Officer
CIO: Troy McKenzie, Chief Information Officer
CHR: Deborah White, Human Resource Coordinator
CNO: Joy Henry, R.N., Chief of Nursing
Web address: www.fchtexas.com
Control: Hospital district or authority, Government, nonfederal **Service**: General medical and surgical

Staffed Beds: 17 **Admissions**: 260 **Census**: 3 **Outpatient Visits**: 51253 **Births**: 48 **Total Expense ($000)**: 40278 **Payroll Expense ($000)**: 8322 **Personnel**: 163

JACKSONVILLE—Cherokee County

☒ **CHRISTUS MOTHER FRANCES HOSPITAL - JACKSONVILLE (451319)**, 2026 South Jackson, Zip 75766–5822; tel. 903/541–4500, **A**1 10 18 **F**3 15 18 29 30 32 34 35 40 43 45 50 53 56 57 59 64 65 68 79 81 82 85 93 97 107 108 110 111 114 119 129 130 133 145 147 **S** CHRISTUS Health, Irving, TX
Primary Contact: Anne Pileggi, Administrator and Associate Vice President
CFO: Elizabeth Pulliam, Chief Financial Officer
CMO: Jane Ragland, President Medical Staff
CIO: Jeff Pearson, Chief Information Officer
CHR: Marsha Ballard, Human Resources
CNO: Jamie Maddox, Chief Nursing Officer
Web address: www.tmfhs.org/jacksonville
Control: Other not–for–profit (including NFP Corporation) **Service**: General medical and surgical

Staffed Beds: 23 **Admissions**: 779 **Census**: 12 **Outpatient Visits**: 69076 **Births**: 0 **Total Expense ($000)**: 31494 **Payroll Expense ($000)**: 9729 **Personnel**: 196

☒ **UT HEALTH JACKSONVILLE (450194)**, 501 South Ragsdale Street, Zip 75766–2413; tel. 903/541–5000, (Data for 306 days) **A**1 3 10 20 **F**3 8 11 13 15 18 26 29 34 35 39 40 43 45 50 57 59 64 65 70 75 76 79 81 82 85 97 107 108 110 111 115 119 127 129 145 146 147 148 155 156 **S** Ardent Health Services, Nashville, TN
Primary Contact: DeLeigh Haley, Chief Executive Officer
CMO: Todd Parrish, M.D., Chief of Staff
CHR: Elysia Epperson, Director Human Resources
CNO: Jana Bateman, R.N., Chief Nursing Officer
Web address: www.https://uthealthjacksonville.com/
Control: Corporation, Investor–owned (for–profit) **Service**: General medical and surgical

Staffed Beds: 38 **Admissions**: 918 **Census**: 8 **Outpatient Visits**: 76416 **Births**: 249 **Total Expense ($000)**: 26540 **Payroll Expense ($000)**: 7909 **Personnel**: 191

JASPER—Jasper County

☒ **CHRISTUS SOUTHEAST TEXAS JASPER MEMORIAL (450573)**, 1275 Marvin Hancock Drive, Zip 75951–4995; tel. 409/384–5461, **A**1 10 **F**3 11 13 15 29 30 34 40 43 50 51 57 59 64 70 76 77 79 81 82 107 110 111 114 119 127 130 135 146 **S** CHRISTUS Health, Irving, TX
Primary Contact: Wayne Moore, Interim Administrator
COO: Mark Durand, Assistant Administrator Operations
CFO: Nikki Martin, Chief Financial Officer
CIO: Robert Jacobs, Regional Information Management Executive
CHR: Kay Powell, Director Human Resources
Web address: www.christusjasper.org
Control: Hospital district or authority, Government, nonfederal **Service**: General medical and surgical

Staffed Beds: 40 **Admissions**: 1037 **Census**: 8 **Outpatient Visits**: 73667 **Births**: 236 **Total Expense ($000)**: 26744 **Payroll Expense ($000)**: 8844 **Personnel**: 150

JOURDANTON—Atascosa County

☒ **METHODIST HOSPITAL SOUTH (450165)**, 1905 Highway 97 East, Zip 78026–1504; tel. 830/769–3515, **A**1 10 20 **F**3 11 13 15 18 29 30 34 35 39 40 45 49 57 59 63 64 68 70 74 75 76 77 79 81 85 93 107 108 110 111 114 119 129 130 132 133 146 147 154 **S** HCA Healthcare, Nashville, TN
Primary Contact: Pamela Guillory, Interim Chief Executive Officer
CFO: Gary Redmon, Chief Financial Officer
CIO: Rita S Castillo, R.N., Vice President, Quality, Risk and Safety
CNO: Pamela Guillory, Chief Nursing Officer
Web address: www.https://sahealth.com/locations/methodisthospitalsouth/
Control: Partnership, Investor–owned (for–profit) **Service**: General medical and surgical

Staffed Beds: 51 **Admissions**: 1606 **Census**: 13 **Outpatient Visits**: 40683 **Births**: 214 **Total Expense ($000)**: 30691 **Payroll Expense ($000)**: 11653 **Personnel**: 163

Many Facility Codes have changed. Please refer to the AHA Guide Code Chart.

JUNCTION—Kimble County

KIMBLE HOSPITAL (451306), 349 Reid Road, Zip 76849–3049;
tel. 325/446–3321, **A**10 18 **F**3 34 40 43 45 57 59 65 68 93 97 107 119 127
133 146 148 154 **S** Preferred Management Corporation, Shawnee, OK
Primary Contact: Duke Young, Chief Executive Officer
COO: Teena Hagood, Chief Nursing Officer
CFO: Larry Stephens, Chief Financial Officer
CMO: Ben Udall, M.D., Chief of Staff
CIO: Anna Henry, Chief Information Officer
CHR: Hope Lamb, Manager Human Resources
Web address: www.kimblehospital.org/
Control: Corporation, Investor–owned (for–profit) **Service**: General medical and
surgical

Staffed Beds: 15 **Admissions:** 102 **Census:** 1 **Outpatient Visits:** 14841
Births: 0 **Total Expense ($000):** 7362 **Payroll Expense ($000):** 3062
Personnel: 70

KATY—Harris County

⇑ **CHRISTUS ST. CATHERINE HOSPITAL** See Houston Methodist Continuing Care
Hospital

★ ⇑ **HOUSTON METHODIST CONTINUING CARE HOSPITAL (452118)**, 701 Fry
Road, Zip 77450–2255; tel. 281/599–5700, **A**10 21 **F**1 75 82 84 86 87 130
132 149 150 **S** Houston Methodist, Houston, TX
Primary Contact: Gary L. Kempf, R.N., Administrator
CFO: Nancy Brock, Chief Financial Officer
CHR: James A Fitch, Director Human Resources
Web address: www.houstonmethodist.org/katy-st-catherine-hospital
Control: Other not–for–profit (including NFP Corporation) **Service**: Acute long–
term care hospital

Staffed Beds: 58 **Admissions:** 473 **Census:** 43 **Outpatient Visits:** 0
Births: 0 **Total Expense ($000):** 39512 **Payroll Expense ($000):** 15802
Personnel: 232

✦ **MEMORIAL HERMANN KATY HOSPITAL (450847)**, 23900 Katy Freeway,
Zip 77494–1323; tel. 281/644–7000, **A**1 2 3 5 10 **F**3 8 11 13 15 18 20 22 26
29 30 34 35 37 39 40 42 43 45 46 49 50 51 54 57 59 61 64 65 68 70 72 73
74 75 77 78 79 80 81 85 87 93 102 107 108 110 111 114 119 126 130 131
132 144 145 146 147 149 154 **S** Memorial Hermann Health System, Houston, TX
Primary Contact: Heath Rushing, Senior Vice President and Chief Executive Officer
CFO: Linda Kulhanek, Chief Financial Officer
Web address: www.memorialhermann.org/locations/katy/
Control: Other not–for–profit (including NFP Corporation) **Service**: General
medical and surgical

Staffed Beds: 199 **Admissions:** 11345 **Census:** 115 **Outpatient
Visits:** 113833 **Births:** 2959 **Total Expense ($000):** 213106 **Payroll
Expense ($000):** 73204 **Personnel:** 815

✦ **MEMORIAL HERMANN REHABILITATION HOSPITAL - KATY (673038)**, 21720
Kingsland Boulevard, 2nd Floor, Zip 77450–2550; tel. 800/447–3422, **A**1 2 10
F3 29 30 64 74 75 77 79 90 92 93 96 107 111 114 119 129 130 131 146
148 **S** Memorial Hermann Health System, Houston, TX
Primary Contact: Jerry Ashworth, Senior Vice President and Chief Executive Officer
COO: Mary Ann Euliarte, R.N., Chief Operating Officer
CFO: Wayne Gordon, Chief Financial Officer
CMO: Shalin Patel, M.D., Chief Medical Officer
CHR: Joyce Williams, Consultant Human Resources and Organizational
Development
CNO: Mary Ann Euliarte, R.N., Chief Nursing Officer
Web address: www.memorialhermann.org/locations/katy-rehab/
Control: Partnership, Investor–owned (for–profit) **Service**: Rehabilitation

Staffed Beds: 35 **Admissions:** 659 **Census:** 25 **Outpatient Visits:** 13593
Births: 0 **Total Expense ($000):** 22202 **Payroll Expense ($000):** 10045
Personnel: 109

OCEANS BEHAVIORAL HOSPITAL KATY (454136), 455 Park Grove Lane,
Zip 77450–1572; tel. 281/492–8888, **F**29 34 35 64 98 100 101 103 104 149
153 154 **S** Oceans Healthcare, Lake Charles, LA
Primary Contact: Stuart Archer, Chief Executive Officer
Web address: www.memorialhermann.org/locations/katy-rehab/
Control: Corporation, Investor–owned (for–profit) **Service**: Psychiatric

Staffed Beds: 48 **Admissions:** 953 **Census:** 38 **Outpatient Visits:** 13092
Births: 0 **Total Expense ($000):** 10224 **Payroll Expense ($000):** 4833
Personnel: 158

KAUFMAN—Kaufman County

✦ **TEXAS HEALTH PRESBYTERIAN HOSPITAL KAUFMAN (450292)**, 850 Ed
Hall Drive, Zip 75142–1861, Mailing Address: P.O. Box 1108, Zip 75142–5401;
tel. 972/932–7200, **A**1 10 **F**3 11 15 18 29 30 34 35 40 43 45 53 57 59 64 65
70 75 79 81 82 85 86 87 93 102 107 108 111 115 118 119 130 132 146 149
S Texas Health Resources, Arlington, TX
Primary Contact: Patsy Youngs, President
CMO: Benjamin Bradshaw, M.D., President Medical Staff
CHR: Mark J Rainey, Director Human Resources
CNO: Denise Claussen, R.N., MSN, Chief Nursing Officer
Web address: www.texashealth.org/Kaufman
Control: Other not–for–profit (including NFP Corporation) **Service**: General
medical and surgical

Staffed Beds: 37 **Admissions:** 1319 **Census:** 10 **Outpatient Visits:** 33152
Births: 0 **Total Expense ($000):** 36196 **Payroll Expense ($000):** 13485
Personnel: 172

KENEDY—Karnes County

★ **OTTO KAISER MEMORIAL HOSPITAL (451364)**, 3349 South Highway 181,
Zip 78119–5247; tel. 830/583–3401, **A**10 18 **F**3 11 15 29 30 34 40 43 45 46
53 57 59 62 64 68 77 81 93 107 111 115 119 132 133 135 148 154
Primary Contact: David Lee, Chief Executive Officer
CIO: Joseph Wiatrek, Director Information Technology
CHR: Christina Benavides, Director Employee Services
CNO: Vincent Sowell, Chief Nursing Officer
Web address: www.okmh.org/
Control: Hospital district or authority, Government, nonfederal **Service**: General
medical and surgical

Staffed Beds: 25 **Admissions:** 201 **Census:** 4 **Outpatient Visits:** 22126
Births: 0 **Total Expense ($000):** 22540 **Payroll Expense ($000):** 8990
Personnel: 154

KERMIT—Winkler County

WINKLER COUNTY MEMORIAL HOSPITAL (451314), 821 Jeffee
Drive, Zip 79745–4696, Mailing Address: P.O. Box H, Zip 79745–6008;
tel. 432/586–5864, **A**10 18 **F**3 32 34 36 40 57 59 64 65 69 93 107 119 127
133
Primary Contact: Lorenzo Serrano, Chief Executive Officer
CFO: Wannah Hartley, Controller
CMO: K Pham, M.D., Chief of Staff
CIO: Keith Palmer, Assistant Administrator
Control: County, Government, nonfederal **Service**: General medical and surgical

Staffed Beds: 19 **Admissions:** 89 **Census:** 1 **Births:** 0 **Total Expense
($000):** 8907 **Payroll Expense ($000):** 3664 **Personnel:** 77

KERRVILLE—Kerr County

KERRVILLE DIVISION See South Texas Veterans Health Care System, San
Antonio

☐ **KERRVILLE STATE HOSPITAL (454014)**, 721 Thompson Drive,
Zip 78028–5154; tel. 830/896–2211, **A**1 10 **F**11 30 34 39 44 50 56 65 68 75
86 87 97 98 101 103 130 132 135 146 149 157 **S** Texas Department of State
Health Services, Austin, TX
Primary Contact: Leigh Ann Fitzpatrick, Superintendent
CFO: Laurie Harris, Chief Accountant
CMO: Matthew Faubion, M.D., Clinical Director
CNO: Amanda McDonald, MSN, Chief Nurse Executive
Web address: www.dshs.state.tx.us/mhhospitals/KerrvilleSH/default.shtm
Control: State, Government, nonfederal **Service**: Psychiatric

Staffed Beds: 218 **Admissions:** 82 **Census:** 200 **Outpatient Visits:** 0
Births: 0 **Total Expense ($000):** 57671 **Payroll Expense ($000):** 22909
Personnel: 591

TX

Hospital, Medicare Provider Number, Address, Telephone, Approval, Facility, and Physician Codes, Health Care System

★ American Hospital Association (AHA) membership ◯ Healthcare Facilities Accreditation Program ⇑ Center for Improvement in Healthcare Quality Accreditation
☐ The Joint Commission accreditation ◇ DNV Healthcare Inc. accreditation △ Commission on Accreditation of Rehabilitation Facilities (CARF) accreditation

⊞ **PETERSON REGIONAL MEDICAL CENTER (450007)**, 551 Hill Country Drive, Zip 78028–6085; tel. 830/896–4200, **A**1 10 **F**3 8 11 13 15 18 20 22 28 29 30 31 34 35 39 40 44 45 47 49 51 54 57 59 62 63 64 65 68 70 74 75 76 77 78 79 81 82 85 86 87 90 93 96 97 107 108 109 110 111 114 115 118 119 126 130 131 132 135 145 146 147 148 149 154 156 157
Primary Contact: Cory Edmondson, President and Chief Executive Officer
COO: J. Stephen Pautler, FACHE, Chief Operating Officer
CFO: Lisa Medovich, Chief Financial Officer
CMO: Thomas Ducker, M.D., Chief of Staff
CIO: Richard Cruthirds, Director Information Systems
CHR: Buddy Volpe, Director Human Resources
CNO: Kaeli Dressler, R.N., MSN, Chief Nursing Officer
Web address: www.petersonhealth.com
Control: Other not–for–profit (including NFP Corporation) **Service**: General medical and surgical

> **Staffed Beds**: 124 **Admissions**: 4532 **Census**: 52 **Outpatient Visits**: 149315 **Births**: 392 **Total Expense ($000)**: 132086 **Payroll Expense ($000)**: 53349 **Personnel**: 920

KILGORE—Gregg County

★ ⇑ **ALLEGIANCE SPECIALTY HOSPITAL OF KILGORE (450488)**, 1612 South Henderson Boulevard, Zip 75662–3594; tel. 903/984–3505, (Nonreporting) **A**10 21 **S** Allegiance Health Management, Shreveport, LA
Primary Contact: Karen Ross, Chief Executive Officer
CHR: Michelle Yarbrough, Coordinator Human Resources
Web address: www.ahmgt.com
Control: Corporation, Investor–owned (for–profit) **Service**: Psychiatric

> **Staffed Beds**: 60

KILLEEN—Bell County

⊞ **ADVENTHEALTH CENTRAL TEXAS (450152)**, 2201 South Clear Creek Road, Zip 76549–4110; tel. 254/526–7523, (Includes METROPLEX BEHAVIORAL HEALTH CENTER, 2201 South Clear Creek Road, Killeen, Texas, Zip 76549–4110; tel. 254/628–1000; Kevin A. Roberts, FACHE, President and Chief Executive Officer) **A**1 10 **F**3 8 11 12 13 15 18 20 22 26 28 29 30 34 35 39 40 43 45 46 48 49 54 57 59 62 65 68 70 71 74 75 76 77 78 79 81 82 83 85 86 87 89 91 93 98 100 101 102 104 107 108 110 111 114 115 118 119 129 130 131 132 135 146 147 148 154 156 **S** AdventHealth, Altamonte Springs, FL
Primary Contact: Kevin A. Roberts, FACHE, President and Chief Executive Officer
CFO: Penny Johnson, Chief Financial Officer
CMO: Frederick Barnett, M.D., Chief of Staff
CHR: Brenda Coley, Executive Director
Web address: www.mplex.org
Control: Church operated, Nongovernment, not–for–profit **Service**: General medical and surgical

> **Staffed Beds**: 177 **Admissions**: 6645 **Census**: 65 **Outpatient Visits**: 95111 **Births**: 1327 **Total Expense ($000)**: 113201 **Payroll Expense ($000)**: 46285 **Personnel**: 800

KINGSVILLE—Kleberg County

⊞ **CHRISTUS SPOHN HOSPITAL KLEBERG (450163)**, 1311 General Cavazos Boulevard, Zip 78363–7130; tel. 361/595–1661, **A**1 10 20 **F**3 11 13 15 28 29 30 34 35 40 43 53 54 57 59 64 65 76 77 79 81 85 86 87 89 93 102 107 108 110 111 115 119 130 146 **S** CHRISTUS Health, Irving, TX
Primary Contact: Thomas McKinney, President
COO: David LeMonte, Vice President and Chief Operating Officer
CFO: Jessica Pena, Manager Finance
CHR: Mindy Soliz, Director Human Resource Strategy
CNO: Lieutenant Laci Lasater, R.N., Chief Nursing Officer
Web address: www.christusspohn.org
Control: Church operated, Nongovernment, not–for–profit **Service**: General medical and surgical

> **Staffed Beds**: 50 **Admissions**: 2797 **Census**: 31 **Outpatient Visits**: 57769 **Births**: 336 **Total Expense ($000)**: 37119 **Payroll Expense ($000)**: 13696 **Personnel**: 198

KINGWOOD—Harris County

KINGWOOD EMERGENCY HOSPITAL, 23330 US 59 North, Zip 77339–3043; tel. 832/777–6165, (Data for 338 days) **F**3 34 40 57 64 75 87 107 115
Primary Contact: Jeremy M. Byrnes, Chief Executive Officer
Control: Partnership, Investor–owned (for–profit) **Service**: General medical and surgical

> **Staffed Beds**: 3 **Admissions**: 21 **Census**: 1 **Outpatient Visits**: 3106 **Births**: 0 **Total Expense ($000)**: 6922 **Payroll Expense ($000)**: 1619 **Personnel**: 28

KINGWOOD—Montgomery County

⊞ **KINGWOOD MEDICAL CENTER (450775)**, 22999 U S Highway 59 North, Zip 77339; tel. 281/348–8000, (Includes HCA HOUSTON HEALTHCARE NORTH CYPRESS, 21214 Northwest Freeway, Cypress, Texas, Zip 77429–3373; tel. 832/912–3500; Jim Brown, Chief Executive Officer) (Data for 122 days)**A**1 3 10 **F**3 12 13 18 19 20 22 24 26 28 29 30 31 34 35 40 41 42 45 46 47 48 49 57 70 72 74 76 77 78 79 81 82 84 85 89 90 96 107 108 110 111 114 115 118 119 126 130 132 146 147 154 **S** HCA Healthcare, Nashville, TN
Primary Contact: John Corbeil, Chief Executive Officer
CFO: Daniel E Davis, Chief Financial Officer
CMO: Eugene Ogrod, M.D., Chief Medical Officer
CNO: Kevin Manning, Chief Nursing Officer
Web address: www.kingwoodmedical.com
Control: Corporation, Investor–owned (for–profit) **Service**: General medical and surgical

> **Staffed Beds**: 559 **Admissions**: 9493 **Census**: 364 **Outpatient Visits**: 98475 **Births**: 936 **Total Expense ($000)**: 163707 **Payroll Expense ($000)**: 55569 **Personnel**: 2668

KINGWOOD SPECIALTY HOSPITAL See Memorial Hermann Surgical Hospital Kingwood

☐ **MEMORIAL HERMANN SURGICAL HOSPITAL KINGWOOD (670005)**, 300 Kingwood Medical Drive, Zip 77339–6400; tel. 281/312–4000, **A**1 10 **F**3 45 51 79 81 82 111 119 154
Primary Contact: Teal A. Holden, Chief Executive Officer
CFO: Jay Michael Gomez, Chief Financial Officer
CNO: Shawna Fugler, R.N., Chief Nursing Officer
Web address: www.memorialhermannkingwood.com
Control: Partnership, Investor–owned (for–profit) **Service**: Surgical

> **Staffed Beds**: 10 **Admissions**: 354 **Census**: 2 **Outpatient Visits**: 8879 **Births**: 0 **Total Expense ($000)**: 25322 **Payroll Expense ($000)**: 5732 **Personnel**: 104

KINGWOOD—Harris County

☐ **KINGWOOD PINES HOSPITAL (454103)**, 2001 Ladbrook Drive, Zip 77339–3004; tel. 281/404–1001, **A**1 10 **F**4 5 75 86 87 98 99 101 102 103 104 105 130 149 153 **S** Universal Health Services, Inc., King of Prussia, PA
Primary Contact: Shanti Carter, Chief Executive Officer
COO: Grey Mc Kellar, Chief Operating Officer and Director of Performance Improvement and Risk
CFO: Sharon Corum, Chief Financial Officer
CMO: Javier Ruiz, M.D., Medical Director
CNO: Kim Wheeler, R.N., Director of Nursing
Web address: www.kingwoodpines.com
Control: Corporation, Investor–owned (for–profit) **Service**: Psychiatric

> **Staffed Beds**: 55 **Admissions**: 3461 **Census**: 90 **Outpatient Visits**: 4081 **Births**: 0 **Total Expense ($000)**: 23054 **Payroll Expense ($000)**: 11716 **Personnel**: 194

KNOX CITY—Knox County

KNOX COUNTY HOSPITAL (450746), 701 South Fifth Street, Zip 79529–2107; Mailing Address: P.O. Box 608, Zip 79529–0608; tel. 940/657–3535, **A**10 20 **F**7 11 28 33 34 35 40 43 57 59 62 127 130 133 149
Primary Contact: Stephen A. Kuehler, Administrator
CFO: Dan Offutt, Manager Finance
CMO: Ezekiel Duke, M.D., Chief of Staff
CNO: Sheila Kuehler, R.N., Director of Nursing
Web address: www.knoxcountyhospital-texas.com
Control: Hospital district or authority, Government, nonfederal **Service**: General medical and surgical

> **Staffed Beds**: 14 **Admissions**: 59 **Census**: 1 **Outpatient Visits**: 34551 **Births**: 0 **Total Expense ($000)**: 19577 **Payroll Expense ($000)**: 5204 **Personnel**: 83

KYLE—Hays County

⊞ **ASCENSION SETON HAYS (670056)**, 6001 Kyle Parkway, Zip 78640–6112; tel. 512/504–5000, **A**1 3 5 10 **F**3 11 13 15 17 18 20 22 24 28 29 30 31 34 40 41 43 45 46 47 48 49 50 57 59 64 68 70 72 76 78 79 81 82 84 85 93 107 108 110 111 115 119 126 129 130 131 132 135 146 147 148 154 **S** Ascension Healthcare, Saint Louis, MO
Primary Contact: Katherine Henderson, President and Chief Executive Officer
COO: Neal Kelley, Vice President and Chief Operating Officer
CNO: Nikki Rivers, R.N., Regional Chief Nursing Officer, South Market
Web address: www.seton.net/locations/seton_medical_center_hays/
Control: Church operated, Nongovernment, not–for–profit **Service**: General medical and surgical

> **Staffed Beds**: 142 **Admissions**: 7175 **Census**: 77 **Outpatient Visits**: 66505 **Births**: 1120 **Total Expense ($000)**: 137293 **Payroll Expense ($000)**: 35333 **Personnel**: 944

TX

Many Facility Codes have changed. Please refer to the AHA Guide Code Chart. © 2019 AHA Guide

★ **WARM SPRINGS REHABILITATION HOSPITAL OF KYLE (673057)**, 5980 Kyle Parkway, Zip 78640–2400; tel. 512/262–0821, (Nonreporting) **S** Post Acute Medical, LLC, Enola, PA
Primary Contact: Duke Saldivar, FACHE, Chief Executive Officer
Web address: www.warmsprings.org/our-facilities/outpatient-rehabilitation/warm-springs-rehabilitation-center-kyle/
Control: Corporation, Investor–owned (for–profit) **Service:** Rehabilitation

> **Staffed Beds:** 36

LA GRANGE—Fayette County

★ **ST. MARK'S MEDICAL CENTER (670004)**, One St Mark's Place, Zip 78945; tel. 979/242–2200, **A**5 10 **F**3 11 15 28 29 34 40 45 50 57 59 64 70 74 75 77 79 81 85 89 93 107 108 110 111 114 119 130 133 145 147 **S** Community Hospital Corporation, Plano, TX
Primary Contact: Rick J. Montelongo, Chief Executive Officer
COO: Carol Drozd, Chief Operating Officer
CFO: Barbara Brooks, Interim Chief Financial Officer
CMO: Russell Juno, M.D., Chief of Staff
CHR: Tammy Oehlke, Director Human Resources
Web address: www.smmctx.org
Control: Other not–for–profit (including NFP Corporation) **Service:** General medical and surgical

> **Staffed Beds:** 38 **Admissions:** 1158 **Census:** 12 **Outpatient Visits:** 40550
> **Births:** 49 **Total Expense ($000):** 28733 **Payroll Expense ($000):** 10347
> **Personnel:** 146

LAKE JACKSON—Brazoria County

✠ **CHI ST. LUKE'S HEALTH BRAZOSPORT (450072)**, 100 Medical Drive, Zip 77566–5674; tel. 979/297–4411, **A**1 10 **F**3 11 13 15 18 20 22 28 29 30 31 34 37 40 41 43 45 47 48 49 51 54 59 60 62 64 65 70 74 75 76 78 79 81 82 85 86 87 90 91 93 94 107 108 110 111 114 115 117 118 119 120 121 123 129 130 131 132 146 147 148 149 154 **S** CommonSpirit Health, Chicago, IL
Primary Contact: Al Guevara Jr, FACHE, President
CFO: Chuck Jeffress, Vice President Fiscal Services
CMO: Michael Gilliand, M.D., Chief of Staff
CIO: Todd Edwards, Director Information Management Systems
CHR: Christopher Calia, Vice President Human Resources
CNO: Shannon Haltom, Vice President, Patient Care Services
Web address: www.chistlukesbrazosport.org
Control: Other not–for–profit (including NFP Corporation) **Service:** General medical and surgical

> **Staffed Beds:** 103 **Admissions:** 4074 **Census:** 41 **Outpatient Visits:** 95150
> **Births:** 461 **Total Expense ($000):** 78280 **Payroll Expense ($000):** 28947
> **Personnel:** 558

LAKEWAY—Travis County

✠ △ **BAYLOR SCOTT & WHITE INSTITUTE FOR REHABILITATION - LAKEWAY (673058)**, 2000 Medical Drive, Zip 78734–4200; tel. 512/263–4500, (Data for 189 days) **A**1 7 **F**3 29 30 60 68 90 91 96 119 148 **S** Select Medical Corporation, Mechanicsburg, PA
Primary Contact: Deborah Hopps, R.N., FACHE, Chief Executive Officer
CMO: Maria Elena Arizmendez, M.D., Medical Director
CHR: Debbie Belcher, Director Human Resource
CNO: Ramon Austria, R.N., Chief Nursing Officer
Web address: www.vrhlaketravis.com
Control: Partnership, Investor–owned (for–profit) **Service:** Rehabilitation

> **Staffed Beds:** 25 **Admissions:** 315 **Census:** 35 **Outpatient Visits:** 0
> **Births:** 0 **Total Expense ($000):** 7821 **Payroll Expense ($000):** 3424
> **Personnel:** 101

LAMESA—Dawson County

✠ **MEDICAL ARTS HOSPITAL (450489)**, 2200 North Bryan Avenue, Zip 79331–2451; tel. 806/872–2183, **A**10 20 **F**3 7 11 13 29 30 35 40 43 45 50 57 59 62 63 64 75 76 81 87 97 107 111 115 119 127 128 130 133 146 148
Primary Contact: Letha Stokes, Chief Executive Officer
COO: Jo Beth Smith, Chief Operating Officer
CFO: Jeff Weaver, Chief Financial Officer
CMO: Michael Sprys, D.O., Chief of Staff
CHR: Traci Brown, Human Resources Generalist
CNO: Heidi Cobb, R.N., Chief Nursing Officer
Web address: www.medicalartshospital.org
Control: Hospital district or authority, Government, nonfederal **Service:** General medical and surgical

> **Staffed Beds:** 22 **Admissions:** 311 **Census:** 3 **Outpatient Visits:** 77553
> **Births:** 136 **Total Expense ($000):** 21772 **Payroll Expense ($000):** 7983
> **Personnel:** 139

LAMPASAS—Lampasas County

✠ **ADVENTHEALTH ROLLINS BROOK (451323)**, 608 North Key Avenue, Zip 76550–1106, Mailing Address: P.O. Box 589, Zip 76550–0032; tel. 512/556–3682, **A**1 10 18 **F**3 8 15 29 35 40 43 45 46 61 81 85 87 93 97 107 110 111 114 119 130 131 133 146 **S** AdventHealth, Altamonte Springs, FL
Primary Contact: Kevin A. Roberts, FACHE, President and Chief Executive Officer
CFO: Robert Brock, Chief Financial Officer and Vice President
CMO: Don Daniels, M.D., Chief Medical Officer
CIO: Carl Elkins, Director Information Technology
CHR: Brenda Coley, Executive Director
CNO: Tammy Rodriguez, Vice President of Patient Care Services
Web address: www.mplex.org
Control: Church operated, Nongovernment, not–for–profit **Service:** General medical and surgical

> **Staffed Beds:** 35 **Admissions:** 585 **Census:** 8 **Outpatient Visits:** 12876
> **Births:** 0 **Total Expense ($000):** 15975 **Payroll Expense ($000):** 4829
> **Personnel:** 39

LANCASTER—Dallas County

⇧ **CRESCENT MEDICAL CENTER LANCASTER (670090)**, 2600 West Pleasant Run Road, Zip 75146–1114; tel. 972/230–8888, **A**10 21 **F**3 29 30 34 40 51 57 59 60 64 68 70 77 79 81 82 85 107 108 111 114 119 129 130 143 148
Primary Contact: Khalid Mahmood, M.D., President and Chairman
Web address: www.cmcl.us/
Control: Partnership, Investor–owned (for–profit) **Service:** General medical and surgical

> **Staffed Beds:** 23 **Admissions:** 696 **Census:** 6 **Outpatient Visits:** 22228
> **Births:** 0 **Total Expense ($000):** 36918 **Payroll Expense ($000):** 12508
> **Personnel:** 259

LAREDO—Webb County

☐ **DOCTORS HOSPITAL OF LAREDO (450643)**, 10700 McPherson Road, Zip 78045–6268; tel. 956/523–2000, **A**1 2 10 **F**3 11 12 13 15 18 20 22 24 26 28 29 31 32 34 35 37 39 40 42 43 45 48 49 50 54 57 59 60 63 64 70 71 72 74 75 76 77 78 79 81 85 87 89 90 91 107 108 111 115 118 119 121 126 129 130 132 146 147 148 154 156 **S** Universal Health Services, Inc., King of Prussia, PA
Primary Contact: James R. Resendez, Chief Executive Officer
COO: Raymond Ramos, FACHE, Chief Operating Officer
CFO: Faraz Khan, Chief Financial Officer
CMO: Santiago Gutierrez, M.D., Chief Medical Officer
CIO: Maribel Mata, Director Information Services
CHR: Roseann Figueroa, Director Human Resources
CNO: Daman Mott, MSN, Chief Nursing Officer
Web address: www.doctorshoslaredo.com
Control: Partnership, Investor–owned (for–profit) **Service:** General medical and surgical

> **Staffed Beds:** 183 **Admissions:** 7489 **Census:** 105 **Outpatient Visits:** 124338 **Births:** 1834 **Total Expense ($000):** 123934 **Payroll Expense ($000):** 48893 **Personnel:** 742

TX

Hospital, Medicare Provider Number, Address, Telephone, Approval, Facility, and Physician Codes, Health Care System

★ American Hospital Association (AHA) membership
☐ The Joint Commission accreditation
○ Healthcare Facilities Accreditation Program
◇ DNV Healthcare Inc. accreditation
⇧ Center for Improvement in Healthcare Quality Accreditation
△ Commission on Accreditation of Rehabilitation Facilities (CARF) accreditation

⊞ **LAREDO MEDICAL CENTER (450029)**, 1700 East Saunders Avenue, Zip 78041–5474, Mailing Address: P.O. Box 2068, Zip 78044–2068; tel. 956/796–5000, (Total facility includes 18 beds in nursing home–type unit) **A**1 10 19 **F**3 8 11 12 13 15 18 20 24 26 28 29 30 31 34 35 40 43 45 46 49 50 51 53 54 57 59 60 64 65 68 70 72 74 75 76 77 78 79 81 85 86 87 89 91 92 93 107 108 110 111 114 119 120 121 123 126 128 132 135 144 146 147 148 149 **S** Community Health Systems, Inc., Franklin, TN
Primary Contact: Enrique Gallegos, Chief Executive Officer
CIO: Joe Rivera, Chief Information Technology Officer
Web address: www.laredomedical.com
Control: Corporation, Investor–owned (for–profit) **Service**: General medical and surgical

Staffed Beds: 326 **Admissions**: 13794 **Census**: 204 **Outpatient Visits**: 134398 **Births**: 3435 **Total Expense ($000)**: 172632 **Payroll Expense ($000)**: 59588 **Personnel**: 1073

LAREDO REHABILITATION HOSPITAL (673059), 2005a East Bustamante Street, Zip 78041; tel. 956/764–8555, **F**3 29 75 90 91 96 **S** Ernest Health, Inc., Albuquerque, NM
Primary Contact: Larisa Higgins, Administrator and Chief Operating Officer
Web address: www.lrh.ernesthealth.com
Control: Corporation, Investor–owned (for–profit) **Service**: Rehabilitation

Staffed Beds: 20 **Admissions**: 426 **Census**: 18 **Outpatient Visits**: 0 **Births**: 0 **Total Expense ($000)**: 6296 **Payroll Expense ($000)**: 3327 **Personnel**: 57

☐ **LAREDO SPECIALTY HOSPITAL (452096)**, 2005 Bustamante Street, Zip 78041–5470; tel. 956/753–5353, **A**1 10 **F**1 3 29 75 85 91 96 130 **S** Ernest Health, Inc., Albuquerque, NM
Primary Contact: Hanna Huang, Chief Executive Officer
CFO: Robert Voss, Chief Financial Officer
CMO: Marisa Guerrero, Director Human Resources
Web address: www.lsh.ernesthealth.com
Control: Partnership, Investor–owned (for–profit) **Service**: Acute long–term care hospital

Staffed Beds: 40 **Admissions**: 375 **Census**: 24 **Outpatient Visits**: 0 **Births**: 0 **Total Expense ($000)**: 15593 **Payroll Expense ($000)**: 5419 **Personnel**: 150

LEAGUE CITY—Galveston County

☐ **DEVEREUX TEXAS TREATMENT NETWORK (454085)**, 1150 Devereux Drive, Zip 77573–2043; tel. 281/335–1000, **A**1 10 **F**4 29 32 35 38 53 59 75 86 87 98 101 106 130 132 134 **S** Devereux, Villanova, PA
Primary Contact: Pamela E. Helm, Executive Director
Web address: www.devereux.org
Control: Other not–for–profit (including NFP Corporation) **Service**: Children's hospital psychiatric

Staffed Beds: 30 **Admissions**: 40 **Census**: 33 **Outpatient Visits**: 0 **Births**: 0 **Total Expense ($000)**: 6742 **Payroll Expense ($000)**: 2336 **Personnel**: 49

LEAGUE CITY—Harris County

⊞ **HCA HOUSTON HEALTHCARE CLEAR LAKE (450617)**, 620 Power St., Zip 77598–4220, Mailing Address: 500 Medical Center Boulevard, Webster, Zip 77598–4220; tel. 281/332–2511, (Includes ALVIN DIAGNOSTIC AND URGENT CARE CENTER, 301 Medic Lane, Alvin, Texas, Zip 77511–5597; tel. 281/331–6141; MAINLAND MEDICAL CENTER, 6801 'E' 'F' Lowry Expressway, Texas City, Texas, Zip 77591; tel. 409/938–5000; Tripp Montalbo, Chief Executive Officer) **A**1 2 3 5 10 **F**3 11 12 13 17 18 19 20 22 24 26 28 29 31 34 35 40 41 43 44 45 46 47 49 50 51 56 57 59 60 64 70 72 74 75 76 78 79 81 85 86 87 88 89 90 91 93 94 96 98 100 105 107 108 110 111 114 115 119 124 126 129 130 132 135 146 147 148 149 153 **S** HCA Healthcare, Nashville, TN
Primary Contact: Todd Caliva, FACHE, Chief Executive Officer
CFO: Jeff Sliwinski, Chief Financial Officer
CMO: Richard Marietta, M.D., Medical Director
CIO: Ley Samson, Director Management Information Systems
CHR: Brad Horst, Director Human Resources
Web address: www.clearlakermc.com
Control: Partnership, Investor–owned (for–profit) **Service**: General medical and surgical

Staffed Beds: 584 **Admissions**: 31503 **Census**: 445 **Outpatient Visits**: 178279 **Births**: 3123 **Total Expense ($000)**: 433190 **Payroll Expense ($000)**: 184118 **Personnel**: 2250

LEVELLAND—Hockley County

★ **COVENANT HOSPITAL-LEVELLAND (450755)**, 1900 South College Avenue, Zip 79336–6508; tel. 806/894–4963, **A**10 **F**7 11 13 15 29 30 34 40 43 45 50 57 59 64 65 68 75 76 77 81 85 87 93 97 107 110 111 114 115 119 127 133 149 **S** Providence St. Joseph Health, Renton, WA
Primary Contact: Bruce White, Administrator
CFO: Newman Wheeler, Chief Financial Officer and Chief Operating Officer
CMO: Harry Weaver, M.D., Chief of Staff
CIO: Kevin Elmore, Chief Information Officer
CHR: Tammy Franklin, Manager Personnel and Marketing
CNO: Connie Thomman, Director of Nursing
Web address: www.covenanthospitallevelland.com/
Control: Church operated, Nongovernment, not–for–profit **Service**: General medical and surgical

Staffed Beds: 26 **Admissions**: 681 **Census**: 5 **Outpatient Visits**: 33681 **Births**: 241 **Total Expense ($000)**: 22970 **Payroll Expense ($000)**: 10156 **Personnel**: 189

LEWISVILLE—Denton County

⊞ **MEDICAL CITY LEWISVILLE (450669)**, 500 West Main, Zip 75057–3699; tel. 972/420–1000, **A**1 2 10 **F**3 12 13 18 20 22 24 26 27 28 29 30 31 34 35 36 37 40 41 42 43 45 46 47 49 50 55 56 57 58 59 60 61 63 64 68 70 72 74 75 76 77 78 79 81 84 85 87 89 90 91 92 93 96 107 108 110 111 114 118 119 126 129 130 132 135 143 146 147 148 149 150 154 **S** HCA Healthcare, Nashville, TN
Primary Contact: LaSharndra Barbarin, Chief Executive Officer
CFO: Lisa Brodbeck, Chief Financial Officer
CIO: Shirley Archambault, Chief Information Officer
CHR: Dara Biegert, Vice President Human Resources
CNO: Lynn O'Neill, R.N., Chief Nursing Officer
Web address: www.lewisvillemedical.com
Control: Corporation, Investor–owned (for–profit) **Service**: General medical and surgical

Staffed Beds: 156 **Admissions**: 7051 **Census**: 89 **Outpatient Visits**: 86517 **Births**: 1414 **Total Expense ($000)**: 137226 **Payroll Expense ($000)**: 52980 **Personnel**: 667

LIBERTY—Liberty County

☐ **LIBERTY DAYTON REGIONAL MEDICAL CENTER (451375)**, 1353 North Travis, Zip 77575–3549; tel. 936/336–7316, **A**1 10 18 **F**3 29 40 45 59 64 89 107 115 119 127 128 130 133
Primary Contact: Matt Thornton, Chief Executive Officer
CFO: Hal Mayo, Chief Financial Officer
CMO: Don Callens, M.D., Chief Medical Officer
CNO: Cindy Griffin, Chief Nursing Officer
Web address: www.libertydaytonrmc.com
Control: Hospital district or authority, Government, nonfederal **Service**: General medical and surgical

Staffed Beds: 15 **Admissions**: 136 **Census**: 1 **Outpatient Visits**: 22444 **Births**: 0 **Total Expense ($000)**: 6647 **Payroll Expense ($000)**: 4609 **Personnel**: 92

LITTLEFIELD—Lamb County

★ **LAMB HEALTHCARE CENTER (450698)**, 1500 South Sunset, Zip 79339–4899; tel. 806/385–6411, **A**10 20 **F**13 35 40 43 50 57 59 64 66 75 81 86 87 107 114 119 127 132 133 134 146 147 149 156
Primary Contact: Cindy Klein, Chief Executive Officer
CMO: Isabel Molina, M.D., Chief Medical Officer
CHR: Joan Williams, Administrative Assistant/Human Resources
CNO: Stacie Styron, Chief Nursing Officer
Web address: www.littlefieldtexas.net/index.php/our-community/lamb-healthcare-center
Control: County, Government, nonfederal **Service**: General medical and surgical

Staffed Beds: 41 **Admissions**: 344 **Census**: 5 **Outpatient Visits**: 28075 **Births**: 94 **Total Expense ($000)**: 10684 **Payroll Expense ($000)**: 4264 **Personnel**: 116

TX

Many Facility Codes have changed. Please refer to the AHA Guide Code Chart. © 2019 AHA Guide

LIVINGSTON—Polk County

✠ **CHI ST. LUKE'S HEALTH MEMORIAL LIVINGSTON (450395)**, 1717 Highway 59 Bypass, Zip 77351–1257, Mailing Address: P.O. Box 1257, Zip 77351–0022; tel. 936/329–8700, **A**1 10 **F**3 11 13 15 29 34 35 40 42 43 45 46 50 57 59 62 64 68 70 74 75 76 79 81 85 87 89 107 108 110 111 114 119 129 130 132 146 149 156 **S** CommonSpirit Health, Chicago, IL
Primary Contact: Kristi Froese, R.N., Vice President Clinical Operations
CFO: Duane Miller, Chief Financial Officer
CMO: Verner Nellsch, M.D., Chief of Staff
CIO: Kathy DeFiguieredo, Director, Information Technology
CHR: Heather Jordan, Director Human Resources
CNO: Kristi Froese, R.N., Chief Nursing Officer
Web address: www.memorialhealth.org
Control: Other not–for–profit (including NFP Corporation) **Service:** General medical and surgical

Staffed Beds: 66 **Admissions:** 2092 **Census:** 19 **Outpatient Visits:** 51439 **Births:** 405 **Total Expense ($000):** 39137 **Payroll Expense ($000):** 14561 **Personnel:** 218

LLANO—Llano County

★ **BAYLOR SCOTT & WHITE MEDICAL CENTER - LLANO (450219)**, 200 West Ollie Street, Zip 78643–2628; tel. 325/247–5040, **A**10 20 **F**3 7 29 40 45 68 75 85 87 93 97 107 114 127 129 149 **S** Baylor Scott & White Health, Dallas, TX
Primary Contact: Timothy A. Ols, FACHE, Chief Executive Officer
COO: Royce Bramer Owens, Chief Operating Officer
CFO: Jennie Campbell, Chief Financial Officer
CMO: Paul Cook, M.D., Chief Medical Officer
CIO: Rodney Lott, Director Management Information Systems and Facility Operations
CHR: Jane Frasure, Human Resources
CNO: Betsy B Patterson, MSN, R.N., Chief Nursing Officer
Web address: www.bwshealth.com
Control: Other not–for–profit (including NFP Corporation) **Service:** General medical and surgical

Staffed Beds: 10 **Admissions:** 185 **Census:** 1 **Outpatient Visits:** 6139 **Births:** 0 **Total Expense ($000):** 25725 **Payroll Expense ($000):** 12663 **Personnel:** 127

LOCKNEY—Floyd County

▲ **W. J. MANGOLD MEMORIAL HOSPITAL (451337)**, 320 North Main Street, Zip 79241–0037, Mailing Address: Box 37, Zip 79241–0037; tel. 806/652–3373, **A**10 18 **F**3 35 40 43 45 53 57 59 62 64 65 81 85 93 97 107 111 119 127 130 133 148 157
Primary Contact: James F. Heitzenrater, FACHE, Chief Executive Officer
CFO: Alyssa McCarter, Chief Financial Officer
CMO: Kevin T Stennett, M.D., Chief of Staff
CIO: Sam Vanderbeek, Chief Information Officer
CNO: Billie Hendrix, R.N., Director of Nursing
Web address: www.mangoldmemorial.org
Control: Hospital district or authority, Government, nonfederal **Service:** General medical and surgical

Staffed Beds: 25 **Admissions:** 323 **Census:** 3 **Outpatient Visits:** 23883 **Births:** 1 **Total Expense ($000):** 11345 **Payroll Expense ($000):** 4646 **Personnel:** 104

LONGVIEW—Gregg County

✠ **LONGVIEW REGIONAL MEDICAL CENTER (450702)**, 2901 North Fourth Street, Zip 75605–5191, Mailing Address: P.O. Box 14000, Zip 75607–4000; tel. 903/758–1818, **A**1 3 10 **F**3 8 11 12 13 15 18 20 22 24 26 28 29 30 31 34 35 37 39 40 43 45 46 47 49 50 57 59 61 64 65 67 70 72 74 75 76 77 78 79 81 85 86 87 89 91 93 107 108 110 111 114 115 118 119 120 126 130 146 148 **S** Community Health Systems, Inc., Franklin, TN
Primary Contact: Casey Robertson, Chief Executive Officer
COO: Roy Finch, Chief Operating Officer
CFO: Todd Johnson, Chief Financial Officer
CMO: Kenneth McClure, M.D., Chief of Staff
CIO: Keith Jarvis, Director Information Systems
CHR: Terry Hardan, Director Human Resources
CNO: Stephanie Foster, MSN, R.N., Chief Nursing Officer
Web address: www.longviewregional.com
Control: Partnership, Investor–owned (for–profit) **Service:** General medical and surgical

Staffed Beds: 224 **Admissions:** 10115 **Census:** 126 **Outpatient Visits:** 107320 **Births:** 1804 **Total Expense ($000):** 177792 **Payroll Expense ($000):** 57703 **Personnel:** 970

□ **MAGNOLIA BEHAVIORAL HOSPITAL OF EAST TEXAS (454143)**, 22 Bermuda Lane, Zip 75605–2902; tel. 903/291–3456, (Nonreporting) **A**1
Primary Contact: Allison Debruycker, Administrator
Web address: www.magnoliabehavioralhospital.com/
Control: Corporation, Investor–owned (for–profit) **Service:** Psychiatric

Staffed Beds: 76

□ **OCEANS BEHAVIORAL HOSPITAL LONGVIEW (454117)**, 615 Clinic Drive, Zip 75605–5172; tel. 903/212–3105, **A**1 10 **F**29 64 98 100 101 103 104 130 132 149 153 154 **S** Oceans Healthcare, Lake Charles, LA
Primary Contact: Lauren Weber, Administrator
Web address: www.oceanslongview.com/
Control: Corporation, Investor–owned (for–profit) **Service:** Psychiatric

Staffed Beds: 24 **Admissions:** 597 **Census:** 21 **Outpatient Visits:** 21768 **Births:** 0 **Total Expense ($000):** 5765 **Payroll Expense ($000):** 2720 **Personnel:** 113

✠ **SELECT SPECIALTY HOSPITAL-LONGVIEW (452087)**, 700 East Marshall Avenue, 1st Floor, Zip 75601–5580; tel. 903/315–1100, **A**1 10 **F**1 3 28 29 75 77 85 91 92 130 148 **S** Select Medical Corporation, Mechanicsburg, PA
Primary Contact: Andrew Meade, Chief Executive Officer
Web address: www.longview.selectspecialtyhospitals.com/
Control: Corporation, Investor–owned (for–profit) **Service:** Acute long–term care hospital

Staffed Beds: 32 **Admissions:** 311 **Census:** 21 **Outpatient Visits:** 0 **Births:** 0 **Total Expense ($000):** 12006 **Payroll Expense ($000):** 5369 **Personnel:** 76

LUBBOCK—Lubbock County

✠ **COVENANT CHILDREN'S HOSPITAL (453306)**, 4015 22nd Place, Zip 79410; tel. 806/725–1011, **A**1 3 5 10 **F**3 4 19 21 23 25 27 30 31 32 40 41 43 50 59 70 72 73 76 81 88 89 98 102 104 154 **S** Providence St. Joseph Health, Renton, WA
Primary Contact: Amy Thompson, M.D., Chief Executive Officer
COO: Clay Thomas, Chief Operating Officer
CMO: Craig Rhyne, M.D., FACS, Chief Medical Officer
CIO: Jim Reid, Vice President and Chief Information Officer
CHR: Chris Shaver, Vice President Human Resources
Web address: www.covenanthealth.org/About-Us/Tacilities/Childrens-Hospital.aspx
Control: Other not–for–profit (including NFP Corporation) **Service:** Obstetrics and gynecology

Staffed Beds: 201 **Admissions:** 5055 **Census:** 76 **Outpatient Visits:** 109107 **Births:** 3356 **Total Expense ($000):** 216464 **Payroll Expense ($000):** 55083 **Personnel:** 780

✠ **COVENANT MEDICAL CENTER (450040)**, 3615 19th Street, Zip 79410–1203, Mailing Address: P.O. Box 1201, Zip 79408–1201; tel. 806/725–0000, (Includes COVENANT MEDICAL CENTER-LAKESIDE, 4000 24th Street, Lubbock, Texas, Zip 79410–1894; tel. 806/725–0000) **A**1 3 10 **F**7 8 15 17 18 19 20 22 23 26 27 28 30 34 35 37 39 40 42 43 46 47 48 49 50 51 53 54 55 57 58 59 60 61 63 64 65 68 70 71 74 75 77 78 79 80 81 82 83 84 85 86 87 91 92 93 94 107 108 109 111 114 115 116 117 119 120 121 123 129 130 131 132 135 143 144 146 147 148 **S** Providence St. Joseph Health, Renton, WA
Primary Contact: Walt Cathey, Chief Executive Officer
CFO: John A Grigson, Vice President and Chief Financial Officer
CMO: Craig Rhyne, M.D., FACS, Chief Medical Officer
CIO: Troy Pratt, Information Technology Site Director
CHR: Chris Shaver, Vice President Human Resources
CNO: Karen Baggerly, Chief Nursing Officer and Vice President
Web address: www.covenanthealth.org
Control: Other not–for–profit (including NFP Corporation) **Service:** General medical and surgical

Staffed Beds: 380 **Admissions:** 17516 **Census:** 262 **Outpatient Visits:** 253389 **Births:** 1 **Total Expense ($000):** 485473 **Payroll Expense ($000):** 139693 **Personnel:** 2521

★ **COVENANT SPECIALTY HOSPITAL (452102)**, 3815 20th Street, Zip 79410–1235; tel. 806/725–9200, **A**10 **F**1 3 29 30 31 60 63 68 75 77 78 79 87 119 130 143 148 **S** Providence St. Joseph Health, Renton, WA
Primary Contact: Ely Perea, Director and Chief Executive Officer
CFO: John Carigson, Chief Financial Officer
CMO: Naidu Chekuru, M.D., Chief Medical Officer
CHR: Chris Shaver, Vice President Human Resources
Web address: www.covenanthealth.org/view/Facilities/Specialty_Hospital
Control: Partnership, Investor–owned (for–profit) **Service:** Acute long–term care hospital

Staffed Beds: 56 **Admissions:** 453 **Census:** 32 **Outpatient Visits:** 0 **Births:** 0 **Total Expense ($000):** 19876 **Payroll Expense ($000):** 8213 **Personnel:** 116

TX

Hospital, Medicare Provider Number, Address, Telephone, Approval, Facility, and Physician Codes, Health Care System

★ American Hospital Association (AHA) membership
□ The Joint Commission accreditation
○ Healthcare Facilities Accreditation Program
◇ DNV Healthcare Inc. accreditation
⇑ Center for Improvement in Healthcare Quality Accreditation
△ Commission on Accreditation of Rehabilitation Facilities (CARF) accreditation

⊞ **GRACE MEDICAL CENTER (450162)**, 2412 50th Street, Zip 79412–2494;
tel. 806/788–4100, (Nonreporting) **A**1 5 10 **S** Providence St. Joseph Health,
Renton, WA
Primary Contact: Vanessa Reasoner, Chief Executive Officer
CMO: Howard Beck, M.D., Chief of Staff
CIO: Jason Derouen, Director Management Information Systems
CHR: Sally Charles, Coordinator Human Resources
Web address: www.gracehealthsystem.com
Control: Partnership, Investor–owned (for–profit) **Service**: General medical and
surgical

Staffed Beds: 43

LUBBOCK HEART & SURGICAL HOSPITAL (450876), 4810 North Loop 289,
Zip 79416–3025; tel. 806/687–7777, **A**3 5 10 **F**3 17 18 20 22 24 26 28 29 34
37 40 45 57 59 75 77 79 81 82 85 107 108 115 119 130 131 148 149
Primary Contact: Charles Powell, Interim Chief Executive Officer
Web address: www.lubbockhsns.com/lubbock-heart/
Control: Partnership, Investor–owned (for–profit) **Service**: Heart

Staffed Beds: 73 **Admissions**: 2590 **Census**: 24 **Outpatient Visits**: 73153
Births: 0 **Total Expense ($000)**: 77056 **Payroll Expense ($000)**: 21540
Personnel: 393

☐ **SUNRISE CANYON HOSPITAL (454093)**, 1950 Aspen Ave, Zip 79404–1211,
Mailing Address: P.O. Box 2828, Zip 79408–2828; tel. 806/740–1420, **A**1 10 **F**4
35 38 98 101 130 135 154
Primary Contact: Leonard Valderaz, Administrator
CFO: Jerome Flores, Chief Financial Officer
CMO: Dana Butler, M.D., Medical Director
CIO: Wendy Potitadkul, Chief Information Officer
CHR: Barbara McCann, Director Human Resources
Web address: www.starcarelubbock.org
Control: Other not–for–profit (including NFP Corporation) **Service**: Psychiatric

Staffed Beds: 30 **Admissions**: 669 **Census**: 28 **Outpatient Visits**: 0
Births: 0 **Total Expense ($000)**: 7508 **Payroll Expense ($000)**: 2282
Personnel: 50

☐ **TRUSTPOINT REHABILITATION HOSPITAL OF LUBBOCK (673063)**, 4302A
Princeton Street, Zip 79415–1304; tel. 806/749–2222, **A**1 5 10 **F**3 29 34
35 56 57 74 75 77 79 85 86 87 90 91 96 130 132 **S** Ernest Health, Inc.,
Albuquerque, NM
Primary Contact: Craig Bragg, Chief Executive Officer
CFO: Crystal Roach, Chief Financial Officer
CNO: John Parsons, R.N., Chief Nursing Officer
Web address: www.trustpointhospital.com/
Control: Partnership, Investor–owned (for–profit) **Service**: Rehabilitation

Staffed Beds: 72 **Admissions**: 1345 **Census**: 60 **Outpatient Visits**: 0
Births: 0 **Total Expense ($000)**: 24005 **Payroll Expense ($000)**: 11546
Personnel: 197

⇑ **UNIVERSITY MEDICAL CENTER (450686)**, 602 Indiana Avenue,
Zip 79415–3364, Mailing Address: P.O. Box 5980, Zip 79408–5980;
tel. 806/775–8200, **A**2 3 5 8 10 21 **F**3 7 9 11 12 13 15 16 17 18 19 20 22 24
26 28 29 30 31 34 35 38 40 41 43 45 46 47 48 49 50 54 55 57 58 59 62 64
65 66 68 70 72 74 75 76 77 78 79 81 83 84 85 86 87 88 89 93 94 96 97 107
108 110 111 114 115 116 117 118 119 120 121 122 123 124 126 130 131
132 135 141 142 143 144 146 147 148 149 150
Primary Contact: Mark Funderburk, President and Chief Executive Officer
CFO: Jeff Dane, Executive Vice President and Chief Financial Officer
CMO: Michael Ragain, M.D., Chief Medical Officer and Senior Vice President
CIO: Bill Eubanks, Senior Vice President and Chief Information Officer
CHR: Adrienne Cozart, Senior Vice President Human Resources
CNO: Timothy W. Howell, R.N., Senior Vice President and Chief Nursing Officer
Web address: www.umchealthsystem.com
Control: Hospital district or authority, Government, nonfederal **Service**: General
medical and surgical

Staffed Beds: 476 **Admissions**: 31897 **Census**: 391 **Outpatient
Visits**: 192201 **Births**: 2986 **Total Expense ($000)**: 588422 **Payroll
Expense ($000)**: 227998 **Personnel**: 3418

★ **CHI ST. LUKE'S HEALTH MEMORIAL LUFKIN (450211)**, 1201 West Frank
Avenue, Zip 75904–3357, Mailing Address: P.O. Box 1447, Zip 75902–1447;
tel. 936/634–8111, **A**2 10 19 **F**3 11 12 13 14 15 17 18 20 21 22 23 24 26 28
29 30 31 34 35 37 38 40 42 43 44 45 46 47 48 49 50 51 56 57 59 60 61 62
63 64 68 70 71 74 75 76 77 78 79 81 82 83 84 85 86 87 90 91 92 93 97 100
101 102 107 108 110 111 112 114 115 116 117 119 121 126 129 130 132
135 143 144 146 147 148 149 156 **S** CommonSpirit Health, Chicago, IL
Primary Contact: Monte J. Bostwick, Market Chief Executive Officer
CFO: Kristi Gay, Chief Financial Officer
CHR: Tanya Tyler, Vice President Human Resources
Web address: www.memorialhealth.us/centers/lufkin
Control: Other not–for–profit (including NFP Corporation) **Service**: General
medical and surgical

Staffed Beds: 194 **Admissions**: 6563 **Census**: 82 **Outpatient Visits**: 91545
Births: 315 **Total Expense ($000)**: 149925 **Payroll Expense ($000)**: 45370
Personnel: 719

☐ **OCEANS BEHAVIORAL HOSPITAL LUFKIN (454123)**, 302 Gobblers Knob
Road, Zip 75904–5419; tel. 936/632–2276, **A**1 10 **F**29 35 64 98 100 101 103
104 130 153 154 **S** Oceans Healthcare, Lake Charles, LA
Primary Contact: Laci Laird, Chief Executive Officer
Web address: www.oceanslufkin.com/
Control: Corporation, Investor–owned (for–profit) **Service**: Psychiatric

Staffed Beds: 24 **Admissions**: 497 **Census**: 19 **Outpatient Visits**: 19934
Births: 0 **Total Expense ($000)**: 5390 **Payroll Expense ($000)**: 2546
Personnel: 103

★ **PAM SPECIALTY HOSPITAL OF LUFKIN (452031)**, 1201 West Frank Avenue,
D5, Zip 75904–3357, Mailing Address: P.O. Box 1447, Zip 75902–1447;
tel. 936/639–7530, **A**10 **F**1 3 29 31 50 61 68 74 75 86 149 **S** Post Acute
Medical, LLC, Enola, PA
Primary Contact: Leslie Leach, Administrator
CFO: Duane Miller, Chief Financial Officer
CMO: David Todd, M.D., President Medical Staff
CNO: Deborah Burgess, R.N., Chief Nursing Officer
Web address: www.postacutemedical.com/facilities/find-facility/specialty-hospitals/
PAM-Specialty-Hospital-Lufkin
Control: Other not–for–profit (including NFP Corporation) **Service**: Acute long–
term care hospital

Staffed Beds: 26 **Admissions**: 144 **Census**: 9 **Outpatient Visits**: 0 **Births**: 0
Total Expense ($000): 6492 **Payroll Expense ($000)**: 2214 **Personnel**: 39

⊞ **WOODLAND HEIGHTS MEDICAL CENTER (450484)**, 505 South John
Redditt Drive, Zip 75904–3157, Mailing Address: P.O. Box 150610, Zip 75904;
tel. 936/634–8311, **A**1 10 19 **F**8 11 12 13 15 18 20 22 24 26 28 29 30 34 35
40 41 46 49 50 51 53 57 59 64 68 70 72 74 75 76 77 78 79 81 82 85 86 87
93 102 107 108 111 114 115 118 119 126 129 130 131 146 147 148 156 **S**
Community Health Systems, Inc., Franklin, TN
Primary Contact: Kyle Swift, Chief Executive Officer
COO: Conner Hickey, Chief Operating Officer
CFO: William Whiddon, Chief Financial Officer
CMO: Imran Nazeer, M.D., Chief of Staff
CIO: Kalvin Buckley, Director Information Systems
CHR: Emilie Hobbs, Director Human Resources
Web address: www.woodlandheights.net
Control: Partnership, Investor–owned (for–profit) **Service**: General medical and
surgical

Staffed Beds: 124 **Admissions**: 5627 **Census**: 64 **Outpatient Visits**: 53816
Births: 1050 **Total Expense ($000)**: 88571 **Payroll Expense ($000)**: 31708
Personnel: 497

⊞ **ASCENSION SETON EDGAR B. DAVIS HOSPITAL (451371)**, 130 Hays Street,
Zip 78648–3207; tel. 830/875–7000, **A**1 10 18 **F**3 11 15 29 30 31 35 40 45
46 50 56 57 59 64 65 66 67 68 71 81 85 97 104 107 110 115 119 127 128
130 133 135 146 150 **S** Ascension Healthcare, Saint Louis, MO
Primary Contact: Scott O. Fuller, President and Chief Executive Officer
CMO: Arjun Mohandas, M.D., Chief of Staff
CIO: Michael H. Minks, Chief Information Officer
CHR: Joe Canales, Director Human Resources
Web address: www.seton.net/locations/edgar_davis/
Control: Church operated, Nongovernment, not–for–profit **Service**: General
medical and surgical

Staffed Beds: 25 **Admissions**: 729 **Census**: 8 **Outpatient Visits**: 57536
Births: 0 **Total Expense ($000)**: 24620 **Payroll Expense ($000)**: 8232
Personnel: 228

TX

✠ **POST ACUTE/WARM SPRINGS SPECIALTY HOSPITAL OF LULING (452062)**, 200 Memorial Drive, Zip 78648–3213; tel. 830/875–8400, **A**1 10 **F**1 3 29 53 64 93 96 130 133 148 **S** Post Acute Medical, LLC, Enola, PA
Primary Contact: Jana Kuykendall, Chief Executive Officer
Web address: www.warmsprings.org
Control: Partnership, Investor–owned (for–profit) **Service:** Acute long–term care hospital

Staffed Beds: 34 **Admissions:** 602 **Census:** 28 **Outpatient Visits:** 10994
Births: 0 **Total Expense ($000):** 15353 **Payroll Expense ($000):** 6944
Personnel: 129

WARM SPRINGS SPECIALTY HOSPITAL OF LULING See Post Acute/Warm Springs Specialty Hospital of Luling

MADISONVILLE—Madison County

✠ **CHI ST. JOSEPH HEALTH MADISON HOSPITAL (451316)**, 100 West Cross Street, Zip 77864–2432, Mailing Address: Box 698, Zip 77864–0698; tel. 936/348–2631, **A**1 10 18 **F**3 7 11 15 30 34 40 43 50 56 57 59 64 68 75 77 93 102 107 110 119 130 133 146 148 **S** CommonSpirit Health, Chicago, IL
Primary Contact: Theron Park, Chief Executive Officer
CMO: Grover Hubley, M.D., President Medical Staff
CIO: Maurita Turner, Team Leader Health Information Systems Services
CNO: Roxanne Hass, Director of Nursing
Web address: www.st-joseph.org
Control: Church operated, Nongovernment, not–for–profit **Service:** General medical and surgical

Staffed Beds: 25 **Admissions:** 209 **Census:** 10 **Outpatient Visits:** 8799
Births: 0 **Total Expense ($000):** 10831 **Payroll Expense ($000):** 4452
Personnel: 67

MANSFIELD—Tarrant County

✠ **KINDRED HOSPITAL-MANSFIELD (452019)**, 1802 Highway 157 North, Zip 76063–3923; tel. 817/473–6101, **A**1 10 **F**1 3 29 30 45 46 64 70 75 82 85 107 130 132 148 **S** Kindred Healthcare, Louisville, KY
Primary Contact: Blake Peart, Administrator
CFO: Judy Baker, Chief Financial Officer
Web address: www.kindredmansfield.com
Control: Corporation, Investor–owned (for–profit) **Service:** Acute long–term care hospital

Staffed Beds: 55 **Admissions:** 376 **Census:** 26 **Outpatient Visits:** 339
Births: 0 **Total Expense ($000):** 12565 **Payroll Expense ($000):** 6742
Personnel: 95

✠ **METHODIST MANSFIELD MEDICAL CENTER (670023)**, 2700 East Broad Street, Zip 76063–5899; tel. 682/622–2000, **A**1 10 **F**3 11 13 15 18 20 22 24 29 30 31 34 35 37 40 45 46 48 49 50 58 59 60 64 68 70 72 74 76 78 79 81 82 85 87 93 97 107 108 110 111 115 118 119 126 130 132 146 148 156 **S** Methodist Health System, Dallas, TX
Primary Contact: Juan Fresquez, President
CFO: Jary Ganske, Chief Financial Officer
CIO: Pamela McNutt, Senior Vice President and Chief Information Officer
CHR: Judy K Laister, Director, Human Resources
CNO: Nora Frasier, R.N., FACHE, Chief Nursing Officer
Web address: www.methodisthealthsystem.org/mansfield
Control: Other not–for–profit (including NFP Corporation) **Service:** General medical and surgical

Staffed Beds: 254 **Admissions:** 11492 **Census:** 155 **Outpatient Visits:** 84471 **Births:** 2008 **Total Expense ($000):** 199772 **Payroll Expense ($000):** 85997 **Personnel:** 1046

MARBLE FALLS—Burnet County

★ **BAYLOR SCOTT & WHITE MEDICAL CENTER - MARBLE FALLS (670108)**, 800 West Highway 71, Zip 78654; tel. 830/201–8000, **F**3 13 15 18 20 22 29 31 34 40 45 50 57 59 70 74 75 76 77 78 79 81 82 85 87 93 107 110 111 119 130 131 132 146 147 149 154 **S** Baylor Scott & White Health, Dallas, TX
Primary Contact: Timothy A. Ols, FACHE, President
Web address: www.sw.org/location/marble-falls-hospital
Control: Other not–for–profit (including NFP Corporation) **Service:** General medical and surgical

Staffed Beds: 46 **Admissions:** 2391 **Census:** 19 **Outpatient Visits:** 110075
Births: 342 **Total Expense ($000):** 78895 **Payroll Expense ($000):** 23776
Personnel: 312

MARLIN—Falls County

★ **FALLS COMMUNITY HOSPITAL AND CLINIC (450348)**, 322 Coleman Street, Zip 76661–2358, Mailing Address: P.O. Box 60, Zip 76661–0060; tel. 254/803–3561, **A**10 20 **F**3 11 32 33 34 35 36 40 43 53 56 57 59 64 65 66 68 75 82 87 91 93 97 99 103 104 107 114 119 127 129 131 135 146 148
Primary Contact: Jeffrey Lyle, Chief Executive Officer
COO: Becca Brewer, Chief Operations Officer
CMO: James Scott Crockett, M.D., Chief of Staff
CIO: Chris Smith, Chief Information Officer
CHR: Peggy Polster, Manager Personnel and Administrative Assistant
CNO: Tasha Burnett, Director of Nursing
Web address: www.fallshospital.com
Control: Other not–for–profit (including NFP Corporation) **Service:** General medical and surgical

Staffed Beds: 32 **Admissions:** 378 **Census:** 3 **Outpatient Visits:** 66796
Births: 0 **Total Expense ($000):** 19722 **Payroll Expense ($000):** 6324
Personnel: 121

MARSHALL—Harrison County

✠ **CHRISTUS GOOD SHEPHERD MEDICAL CENTER-MARSHALL (450032)**, 811 South Washington Avenue, Zip 75670–5336, Mailing Address: P.O. Box 1599, Zip 75671–1599; tel. 903/927–6000, (Includes CHRISTUS GOOD SHEPHERD MEDICAL CENTER, 700 East Marshall Avenue, Longview, Texas, Zip 75601–5580; tel. 903/315–1800; Todd Hancock, President and Chief Executive Officer) **A**1 3 10 **F**3 8 11 13 15 18 20 22 24 28 29 30 31 34 35 38 40 42 43 45 46 49 50 53 54 56 57 59 60 61 64 65 68 70 71 72 73 74 75 76 77 78 79 80 81 82 85 86 87 89 90 93 97 102 107 110 111 114 115 117 119 127 129 130 131 132 135 143 144 145 146 147 148 149 150 154 156 **S** CHRISTUS Health, Irving, TX
Primary Contact: Todd Hancock, President and Chief Executive Officer
COO: Keith Creel, Vice President Operations
CFO: Michael Cheek, Chief Financial Officer
CMO: Larry Verfurth, D.O., Executive Vice President and Chief Medical Officer
CIO: Walter Grimes, Director Information Technology
CHR: Ginger Morrow, Executive Vice President Human Resources
CNO: Keith Kirbow, R.N., Vice President and Chief Nursing Officer
Web address: www.https://www.christushealth.org/good-shepherd/marshall
Control: Church operated, Nongovernment, not–for–profit **Service:** General medical and surgical

Staffed Beds: 438 **Admissions:** 23789 **Census:** 217 **Outpatient Visits:** 225607 **Births:** 1553 **Total Expense ($000):** 320750 **Payroll Expense ($000):** 119506 **Personnel:** 1818

MCALLEN—Hidalgo County

✠ **RIO GRANDE REGIONAL HOSPITAL (450711)**, 101 East Ridge Road, Zip 78503–1299; tel. 956/632–6000, **A**1 10 19 **F**3 8 11 12 13 15 18 19 20 21 22 23 24 25 26 27 29 30 31 34 35 39 40 42 43 45 46 49 50 54 56 57 59 60 64 66 68 70 71 72 73 74 75 76 77 78 79 81 85 87 88 89 93 107 108 110 111 114 118 119 126 130 132 146 147 148 149 154 156 157 **S** HCA Healthcare, Nashville, TN
Primary Contact: Cristina Rivera, Chief Executive Officer
CFO: William Saller, Chief Financial Officer
CHR: Marjorie Whittemore, Director Human Resources
Web address: www.riohealth.com
Control: Partnership, Investor–owned (for–profit) **Service:** General medical and surgical

Staffed Beds: 320 **Admissions:** 15484 **Census:** 182 **Outpatient Visits:** 126942 **Births:** 2196 **Total Expense ($000):** 172767 **Payroll Expense ($000):** 67859 **Personnel:** 856

SOLARA HOSPITAL MCALLEN (452095), 301 West Expressway 83, 8th Floor, Zip 78503–3045; tel. 956/632–4880, **A**10 22 **F**1 3 29 30 56 70 75 77 85 86 87 91 130 148 **S** Cornerstone Healthcare Group, Dallas, TX
Primary Contact: David Tupper, Chief Executive Officer
Web address: www.chghospitals.com/mcallen/
Control: Corporation, Investor–owned (for–profit) **Service:** Acute long–term care hospital

Staffed Beds: 78 **Admissions:** 635 **Census:** 50 **Outpatient Visits:** 0
Births: 0 **Total Expense ($000):** 19804 **Payroll Expense ($000):** 9808
Personnel: 128

TX

Hospital, Medicare Provider Number, Address, Telephone, Approval, Facility, and Physician Codes, Health Care System

★ American Hospital Association (AHA) membership   ○ Healthcare Facilities Accreditation Program   ⇑ Center for Improvement in Healthcare Quality Accreditation
□ The Joint Commission accreditation   ◇ DNV Healthcare Inc. accreditation   △ Commission on Accreditation of Rehabilitation Facilities (CARF) accreditation

© 2019 AHA Guide   *Many Facility Codes have changed. Please refer to the AHA Guide Code Chart.*   Hospitals **A623**

MCCAMEY—Upton County

★ **MCCAMEY COUNTY HOSPITAL DISTRICT (451309)**, 2500 Highway 305 South, Zip 79752, Mailing Address: P.O. Box 1200, Zip 79752–1200; tel. 432/652–8626, (Total facility includes 30 beds in nursing home–type unit) **A**10 18 **F**3 40 53 59 64 65 66 93 127 128 133
Primary Contact: Jaime Ramirez, Chief Executive Officer
CFO: Jason J Menefee, Chief Financial Officer
CMO: John Bruce Addison, D.O., Chief Medical Officer
CIO: Larry Rollins, Supervisor Information Technology
CHR: Ashley Johnson, Director Human Resource
CNO: Erin Mann, R.N., Chief Nursing Officer
Web address: www.mccameyhospitaldistrict.org
Control: Hospital district or authority, Government, nonfederal **Service:** General medical and surgical

Staffed Beds: 41 **Admissions:** 84 **Census:** 26 **Outpatient Visits:** 9013 **Births:** 0 **Total Expense ($000):** 13982 **Payroll Expense ($000):** 4779 **Personnel:** 71

MCKINNEY—Collin County

⊞ **BAYLOR SCOTT & WHITE MEDICAL CENTER AT - MCKINNEY (670082)**, 5252 West University Drive, Zip 75071–7822; tel. 469/764–1000, **A**1 2 10 **F**3 13 15 18 20 22 26 29 30 31 34 35 40 43 45 46 47 49 50 51 57 59 60 70 72 73 74 75 76 77 78 79 81 84 85 87 107 110 111 114 115 116 119 126 130 131 132 146 147 148 **S** Baylor Scott & White Health, Dallas, TX
Primary Contact: Kyle Armstrong, President
COO: Melissa Winter, R.N., MSN, Chief Operating Officer and Chief Nursing Officer
CFO: Steve Roussel, Chief Financial Officer
CMO: Jeff Kerr, M.D., Chief Medical Officer
CNO: Melissa Winter, R.N., MSN, Chief Operating Officer and Chief Nursing Officer
Web address: www.baylorhealth.com/PhysiciansLocations/McKinney/Pages/Default.aspx
Control: Other not–for–profit (including NFP Corporation) **Service:** General medical and surgical

Staffed Beds: 143 **Admissions:** 8396 **Census:** 86 **Outpatient Visits:** 59433 **Births:** 1832 **Total Expense ($000):** 156641 **Payroll Expense ($000):** 51473 **Personnel:** 589

⊞ **MEDICAL CITY MCKINNEY (450403)**, 4500 Medical Center Drive, Zip 75069–1650; tel. 972/547–8000, (Includes WYSONG CAMPUS, 130 South Central Expressway, McKinney, Texas, Zip 75070; tel. 972/548–5300) **A**1 10 **F**3 4 11 13 18 20 22 24 26 28 29 30 34 37 40 42 43 45 49 50 56 57 59 60 64 68 70 72 74 75 76 77 78 79 81 82 85 87 90 91 92 93 94 96 97 98 102 103 107 108 109 111 114 115 119 126 130 131 132 146 147 148 149 **S** HCA Healthcare, Nashville, TN
Primary Contact: Ernest C. Lynch III, FACHE, President and Chief Executive Officer
COO: Andrew Zenger, Chief Operating Officer
CFO: Brad Stein, Chief Financial Officer
CMO: Jaya Kumar, M.D., Chief Medical Officer
CIO: Kevin Fletcher, Director Information Systems
CHR: Alayne Sewick, Vice President Human Resources
CNO: Cassidi Roberts, R.N., Chief Nursing Officer
Web address: www.medicalcenterofmckinney.com
Control: Partnership, Investor–owned (for–profit) **Service:** General medical and surgical

Staffed Beds: 222 **Admissions:** 12398 **Census:** 170 **Outpatient Visits:** 83974 **Births:** 1421 **Total Expense ($000):** 151030 **Payroll Expense ($000):** 64862 **Personnel:** 840

☐ **METHODIST MCKINNEY HOSPITAL (670069)**, 8000 West Eldorado Parkway, Zip 75070–5940; tel. 972/569–2700, (Nonreporting) **A**1 10
Primary Contact: Joseph Minissale, President
CFO: Mike Conroy, Chief Financial Officer
CIO: Sharon Stark, R.N., Manager Clinical Information Systems
CHR: Diana Hume, Manager Human Resources
CNO: Staci Jones, R.N., Chief Nursing Officer
Web address: www.methodistmckinneyhospital.com
Control: Partnership, Investor–owned (for–profit) **Service:** Surgical

Staffed Beds: 21

MESQUITE—Dallas County

⊞ **DALLAS REGIONAL MEDICAL CENTER (450688)**, 1011 North Galloway Avenue, Zip 75149–2433; tel. 214/320–7000, **A**1 10 **F**3 12 13 15 18 20 22 24 26 29 30 34 35 37 39 40 41 43 45 46 49 50 56 57 59 65 67 70 74 75 76 78 79 81 85 86 87 102 105 107 108 110 111 115 118 119 126 129 130 134 135 146 147 148 149 154 157 **S** Prime Healthcare, Ontario, CA
Primary Contact: Glenda Newby, Chief Executive Officer
CMO: Srinivas Gunukula, M.D., Chief of Staff
Web address: www.dallasregionalmedicalcenter.com
Control: Individual, Investor–owned (for–profit) **Service:** General medical and surgical

Staffed Beds: 127 **Admissions:** 7468 **Census:** 79 **Outpatient Visits:** 55221 **Births:** 843 **Total Expense ($000):** 85366 **Payroll Expense ($000):** 38798 **Personnel:** 480

☐ **MESQUITE REHABILITATION INSTITUTE (673045)**, 1023 North Belt Line Road, Zip 75149–1788; tel. 972/216–2400, **A**1 10 **F**3 28 29 34 90 93 96 130 132 148 149 **S** Ernest Health, Inc., Albuquerque, NM
Primary Contact: Brian Abraham, Chief Executive Officer
Web address: www.mesquiterehab.ernesthealth.com/
Control: Corporation, Investor–owned (for–profit) **Service:** Rehabilitation

Staffed Beds: 30 **Admissions:** 641 **Census:** 25 **Outpatient Visits:** 3608 **Births:** 0 **Total Expense ($000):** 8716 **Payroll Expense ($000):** 5437 **Personnel:** 86

☐ **MESQUITE SPECIALTY HOSPITAL (452100)**, 1024 North Galloway Avenue, Zip 75149–2434; tel. 972/216–2300, **A**1 10 **F**1 3 29 75 148 149 **S** Ernest Health, Inc., Albuquerque, NM
Primary Contact: Louis Bradley, Chief Executive Officer
Web address: www.msh.ernesthealth.com
Control: Partnership, Investor–owned (for–profit) **Service:** Acute long–term care hospital

Staffed Beds: 40 **Admissions:** 354 **Census:** 23 **Outpatient Visits:** 0 **Births:** 0 **Total Expense ($000):** 15066 **Payroll Expense ($000):** 5550 **Personnel:** 105

MEXIA—Limestone County

⊞ **PARKVIEW REGIONAL HOSPITAL (450400)**, 600 South Bonham, Zip 76667–3603; tel. 254/562–5332, **A**1 10 **F**3 11 15 29 30 34 35 40 43 45 51 53 56 57 59 64 65 70 75 77 78 79 81 85 86 87 90 93 97 98 103 107 108 110 111 114 119 127 130 132 133 146 **S** LifePoint Health, Brentwood, TN
Primary Contact: Robert C. Honeycutt, Chief Executive Officer
COO: R. Austin Wratchford, Chief Operating Officer
CFO: Jack Wilcox, Chief Financial Officer
CNO: Edwina J Henry, Assistant Chief Nursing Officer
Web address: www.parkviewregional.com
Control: Partnership, Investor–owned (for–profit) **Service:** General medical and surgical

Staffed Beds: 58 **Admissions:** 527 **Census:** 6 **Outpatient Visits:** 23108 **Births:** 0 **Total Expense ($000):** 21357 **Payroll Expense ($000):** 7279 **Personnel:** 137

MIDLAND—Midland County

⊞ **ENCOMPASS HEALTH REHABILITATION HOSPITAL MIDLAND ODESSA (453057)**, 1800 Heritage Boulevard, Zip 79707–9750; tel. 432/520–1600, **A**1 10 **F**3 29 57 59 65 75 77 82 90 91 96 130 143 148 154 **S** Encompass Health Corporation, Birmingham, AL
Primary Contact: Christopher Wortham, Chief Executive Officer
CFO: Vivian Irwin, Chief Financial Officer and Controller
CMO: Mark A Fredrickson, M.D., Medical Director
CHR: Tina Parker, Director Human Resources
Web address: www.healthsouthmidland.com
Control: Corporation, Investor–owned (for–profit) **Service:** Rehabilitation

Staffed Beds: 80 **Admissions:** 1647 **Census:** 60 **Outpatient Visits:** 0 **Births:** 0 **Total Expense ($000):** 27621 **Payroll Expense ($000):** 13688 **Personnel:** 173

★ ⇑ **MIDLAND MEMORIAL HOSPITAL (450133)**, 400 Rosalind Redfern Grover Parkway, Zip 79701–6499; tel. 432/221–1111, (Includes MIDLAND MEMORIAL HOSPITAL, 400 Rosalind Redfern Grover Pkwy, Midland, Texas, Zip 79701–5846; tel. 432/221–1111) **A**3 5 10 21 **F**3 8 11 12 13 15 17 18 20 22 24 26 28 29 30 32 34 35 37 40 43 45 49 50 53 56 57 59 61 64 68 70 73 74 75 76 77 78 79 80 81 82 83 84 85 86 87 88 89 93 97 107 108 111 114 115 116 117 118 119 124 126 129 130 131 135 145 146 147 148 156 157
Primary Contact: Russell Meyers, FACHE, President and Chief Executive Officer
CFO: Stephen Bowerman, Senior Vice President, Chief Financial Officer
CMO: Lawrence Wilson, M.D., Vice President, Chief Medical Officer
CIO: Taylor Weems, Vice President, Chief Information Officer
CHR: Roberta SoloRio, Vice President, Chief Human Resource Officer
Web address: www.https://www.midlandhealth.org/
Control: Hospital district or authority, Government, nonfederal **Service:** General medical and surgical

Staffed Beds: 245 **Admissions:** 10562 **Census:** 129 **Outpatient Visits:** 160841 **Births:** 2535 **Total Expense ($000):** 269847 **Payroll Expense ($000):** 105542 **Personnel:** 1672

☐ **OCEANS BEHAVIORAL HEALTH CENTER PERMIAN BASIN (454110)**, 3300 South FM 1788, Zip 79706–2601; tel. 432/561–5915, **A**1 3 10 **F**29 34 35 64 68 98 99 100 101 103 104 130 132 153 154 **S** Oceans Healthcare, Lake Charles, LA
Primary Contact: Lorie Dunnam, Chief Executive Officer
Web address: www.oceanspermianbasin.com/
Control: Corporation, Investor–owned (for–profit) **Service:** Psychiatric

Staffed Beds: 58 **Admissions:** 1904 **Census:** 44 **Outpatient Visits:** 7747 **Births:** 0 **Total Expense ($000):** 10978 **Payroll Expense ($000):** 5771 **Personnel:** 221

TX

MINERAL WELLS—Palo Pinto County

⊠ **PALO PINTO GENERAL HOSPITAL (450565)**, 400 SW 25th Avenue, Zip 76067–8246; tel. 940/325–7891, **A**1 10 F11 13 15 18 28 29 34 40 43 45 46 51 53 54 57 59 64 65 66 68 69 70 71 74 75 76 77 78 79 81 82 86 87 91 93 100 107 108 110 111 114 119 127 129 130 131 133 135 146 147 154
Primary Contact: Ross Korkmas, Chief Executive Officer
CFO: Daniel Smith, Chief Financial Officer
CMO: George Thomas, M.D., Chief of Staff
CIO: Shane Coleman, Chief Information Officer
CHR: Mary B Braddock, Director Human Resources
CNO: James Fesser, Chief Nursing Officer
Web address: www.ppgh.com
Control: Hospital district or authority, Government, nonfederal **Service:** General medical and surgical

Staffed Beds: 54 **Admissions:** 1829 **Census:** 11 **Outpatient Visits:** 58490
Births: 307 **Total Expense ($000):** 44437 **Payroll Expense ($000):** 18394
Personnel: 350

MISSION—Hidalgo County

⊠ △ **MISSION REGIONAL MEDICAL CENTER (450176)**, 900 South Bryan Road, Zip 78572–6613; tel. 956/323–9103, **A**1 7 10 F3 11 12 13 15 18 20 22 29 34 35 40 43 45 46 49 50 51 57 59 60 64 65 66 68 70 72 74 75 76 77 79 81 85 87 89 90 93 96 107 108 110 111 115 118 119 130 132 146 147 148 149 154 **S** Prime Healthcare, Ontario, CA
Primary Contact: Kane A. Dawson, Chief Executive Officer
CFO: Lester Surrock, Chief Financial Officer
CMO: Humberto F. Nunez, M.D., Chief Medical Officer
CNO: Kennetha Foster, Chief Nursing Officer
Web address: www.missionrmc.org
Control: Other not-for-profit (including NFP Corporation) **Service:** General medical and surgical

Staffed Beds: 228 **Admissions:** 9170 **Census:** 117 **Outpatient Visits:** 76506 **Births:** 1784 **Total Expense ($000):** 102106 **Payroll Expense ($000):** 43676 **Personnel:** 782

MONAHANS—Ward County

★ **WARD MEMORIAL HOSPITAL (451373)**, 406 South Gary Street, Zip 79756–4798, Mailing Address: P.O. Box 40, Zip 79756–0040; tel. 432/943–2511, **A**10 18 F3 40 43 45 64 65 66 81 82 89 93 107 114 119 127 131 133 148
Primary Contact: Leticia Rodriguez, Chief Executive Officer
CFO: Alison Cooper, Chief Financial Officer
CMO: Htin Thaung, M.D., Chief Medical Officer
CIO: David Hargrave, Chief Information Officer
CHR: Corina Subia, Director Human Resources
CNO: Jason Harbin, Director of Nursing
Web address: www.wardmemorial.com
Control: County, Government, nonfederal **Service:** General medical and surgical

Staffed Beds: 25 **Admissions:** 464 **Census:** 4 **Outpatient Visits:** 55577
Births: 0 **Total Expense ($000):** 16665 **Payroll Expense ($000):** 7532
Personnel: 105

MORTON—Cochran County

COCHRAN MEMORIAL HOSPITAL (451366), 201 East Grant Street, Zip 79346–3444; tel. 806/266–5565, **A**10 18 F7 34 40 57 59 65 127 149
Primary Contact: Larry Turney, Administrator
CFO: Maggie Ramon, Chief Financial Officer
CIO: David Turney, Chief Information Officer
CHR: Amanda Turney, Director Human Resources
CNO: Rosemary Franco, Chief Nursing Officer
Control: Hospital district or authority, Government, nonfederal **Service:** General medical and surgical

Staffed Beds: 13 **Admissions:** 14 **Census:** 1 **Outpatient Visits:** 5228
Births: 0 **Total Expense ($000):** 4124 **Payroll Expense ($000):** 2036
Personnel: 51

MOUNT PLEASANT—Titus County

⊠ **TITUS REGIONAL MEDICAL CENTER (450080)**, 2001 North Jefferson Avenue, Zip 75455–2398; tel. 903/577–6000, **A**1 10 F3 7 11 12 13 15 18 20 22 24 28 29 30 34 35 39 40 43 45 47 50 51 53 54 56 57 58 59 64 68 70 73 74 75 76 77 78 79 81 82 85 87 89 90 93 97 98 103 107 108 110 111 114 115 117 118 119 121 123 127 129 130 132 135 147 148 149 154 156
Primary Contact: Terry Scoggin, Chief Executive Officer
CFO: Terry Scoggin, Chief Financial Officer
CMO: Chris Burling, M.D., Chief of Staff
CIO: Kevin Harris, Director Information Systems
CHR: Tony Piazza, Director Human Resources
CNO: Carol Slider, Chief Nursing Officer
Web address: www.titusregional.com
Control: Hospital district or authority, Government, nonfederal **Service:** General medical and surgical

Staffed Beds: 73 **Admissions:** 4393 **Census:** 44 **Outpatient Visits:** 236615
Births: 974 **Total Expense ($000):** 90094 **Payroll Expense ($000):** 30155
Personnel: 631

MUENSTER—Cooke County

MUENSTER MEMORIAL HOSPITAL (451335), 605 North Maple Street, Zip 76252–2424, Mailing Address: P.O. Box 370, Zip 76252–0370; tel. 940/759–2271, **A**10 18 F11 35 40 43 45 53 57 59 62 64 65 75 77 81 93 107 114 119 127 130 133 146
Primary Contact: Brian Roland, Chief Executive Officer
CFO: Julie Williams, Chief Financial Officer
CNO: Tiffany Lutkenhaus, Chief Nursing Officer
Web address: www.muensterhospital.com
Control: Hospital district or authority, Government, nonfederal **Service:** General medical and surgical

Staffed Beds: 18 **Admissions:** 110 **Census:** 10 **Outpatient Visits:** 4503
Births: 0 **Total Expense ($000):** 12395 **Payroll Expense ($000):** 5718
Personnel: 94

MULESHOE—Bailey County

MULESHOE AREA MEDICAL CENTER (451372), 708 South First Street, Zip 79347–3627; tel. 806/272–4524, **A**10 18 F34 40 57 59 64 93 97 107 119 127 133 154 **S** Preferred Management Corporation, Shawnee, OK
Primary Contact: Dennis Fleenor, R.N., Administrator
CMO: Bruce Purdy, M.D., Chief of Staff
CHR: Suzanne Nichols, Director Human Resources
Web address: www.mahdtx.org
Control: Corporation, Investor-owned (for-profit) **Service:** General medical and surgical

Staffed Beds: 25 **Admissions:** 187 **Census:** 2 **Outpatient Visits:** 19075
Births: 0 **Total Expense ($000):** 6577 **Payroll Expense ($000):** 3410
Personnel: 85

NACOGDOCHES—Nacogdoches County

⊠ **NACOGDOCHES MEDICAL CENTER (450656)**, 4920 NE Stallings Drive, Zip 75965–1200; tel. 936/569–9481, **A**1 2 10 19 F3 13 15 17 18 20 22 24 26 29 30 31 34 35 40 42 43 45 46 49 50 54 56 57 59 64 65 68 70 72 74 75 76 77 78 79 81 82 84 85 86 87 89 93 96 97 100 102 107 108 110 111 114 115 118 119 120 121 122 123 126 129 130 131 132 135 141 146 147 154 **S** TENET Healthcare Corporation, Dallas, TX
Primary Contact: Philip Koovakada, Chief Executive Officer
CFO: Randy Slack, Chief Financial Officer
CMO: Charles Thompson, M.D., Chief Medical Officer
CIO: Teresa Simon, Director Information Systems
CHR: Teresa Farrell, Chief Human Resources Officer
CNO: Mario B Estrella, Chief Nursing Officer
Web address: www.nacmedicalcenter.com
Control: Partnership, Investor-owned (for-profit) **Service:** General medical and surgical

Staffed Beds: 117 **Admissions:** 4290 **Census:** 42 **Outpatient Visits:** 63836
Births: 616 **Total Expense ($000):** 78176 **Payroll Expense ($000):** 25053
Personnel: 411

TX

☐ **NACOGDOCHES MEMORIAL HOSPITAL (450508)**, 1204 North Mound Street, Zip 75961–4061; tel. 936/564–4611, **A**1 10 19 **F**3 7 11 13 15 18 20 22 26 28 29 30 31 38 40 43 45 50 59 64 65 66 70 72 73 74 75 76 77 78 79 80 81 85 89 90 93 96 97 107 108 110 111 114 115 119 130 135 146 147 148 149 155
Primary Contact: Gary L. Stokes, Interim Chief Executive Officer
CFO: Jane Ann Bridges, Chief Financial Officer
CNO: Beth Knight, Chief Nursing Officer
Web address: www.nacmem.org
Control: Hospital district or authority, Government, nonfederal **Service**: General medical and surgical

Staffed Beds: 115 **Admissions**: 3976 **Census**: 54 **Outpatient Visits**: 97306 **Births**: 737 **Total Expense ($000)**: 83978 **Payroll Expense ($000)**: 29635 **Personnel**: 633

NASSAU BAY—Harris County

★ **HOUSTON METHODIST CLEAR LAKE HOSPITAL (450709)**, 18300 St John Drive, Zip 77058–6302; tel. 281/333–5503, **A**3 5 10 **F**3 8 11 12 13 15 18 20 22 24 26 28 29 30 31 34 35 39 40 41 44 45 47 49 50 51 53 54 57 59 60 63 64 65 68 70 72 73 74 75 76 77 78 79 81 82 84 85 86 87 93 94 96 102 107 108 110 111 115 118 119 126 130 131 132 135 146 147 148 149 150 **S** Houston Methodist, Houston, TX
Primary Contact: Dan Newman, Chief Executive Officer
CFO: David A Witt, Vice President Finances
CHR: Becky A Merritt, Director Human Resources
Web address: www.houstonmethodist.org/st-john-clear-lake
Control: Other not–for–profit (including NFP Corporation) **Service**: General medical and surgical

Staffed Beds: 129 **Admissions**: 6714 **Census**: 75 **Outpatient Visits**: 151871 **Births**: 743 **Total Expense ($000)**: 146435 **Payroll Expense ($000)**: 57540 **Personnel**: 776

NAVASOTA—Grimes County

⊞ **CHI ST. JOSEPH HEALTH GRIMES HOSPITAL (451322)**, 210 South Judson Street, Zip 77868–3704; tel. 936/825–6585, **A**1 10 18 **F**3 28 29 34 40 43 56 57 59 75 77 93 104 107 111 119 130 132 133 135 146 **S** CommonSpirit Health, Chicago, IL
Primary Contact: Theron Park, Chief Executive Officer
CFO: Daniel Goggin, Senior Vice President and Chief Financial Officer
CMO: Luke P Scamardo, M.D., II Chief of Staff
CIO: Mike Russo, Vice President Information Systems
CHR: Kristina Lee, Director Human Resources
CNO: Cesar Lopez, R.N., Director of Nurses
Web address: www.st-joseph.org
Control: Church operated, Nongovernment, not–for–profit **Service**: General medical and surgical

Staffed Beds: 18 **Admissions**: 188 **Census**: 7 **Outpatient Visits**: 13179 **Births**: 0 **Total Expense ($000)**: 10068 **Payroll Expense ($000)**: 4354 **Personnel**: 71

NEDERLAND—Jefferson County

MID-JEFFERSON EXTENDED CARE HOSPITAL (452083), 2600 Highway 365, Zip 77627–6237; tel. 409/726–8700, **A**10 **F**1 3 29 30 34 35 40 70 74 75 77 79 85 148
Primary Contact: Wade K. Lester, Administrator
CIO: Nikki Robin, Chief Operating Officer
Web address: www.midjeffextendedcare.com/index.php
Control: Corporation, Investor–owned (for–profit) **Service**: Acute long–term care hospital

Staffed Beds: 48 **Admissions**: 647 **Census**: 43 **Outpatient Visits**: 0 **Births**: 0 **Total Expense ($000)**: 14465 **Payroll Expense ($000)**: 8872 **Personnel**: 166

NEW BRAUNFELS—Comal County

GULF STATES LONG TERM ACUTE CARE OF NEW BRAUNFELS See Post Acute/Warm Springs Specialty Hospital of New Braunfels

☐ **NEW BRAUNFELS REGIONAL REHABILITATION HOSPITAL (673049)**, 2041 Sundance Parkway, Zip 78130–2779; tel. 830/625–6700, **A**1 10 **F**3 29 34 57 64 90 93 96 130 132 148 **S** Ernest Health, Inc., Albuquerque, NM
Primary Contact: Mario Rodriguez, Chief Executive Officer
CFO: Sue Thomsen, Chief Financial Officer
CMO: Maria R Lomba, Medical Director
CHR: Cheryl Smith, Manager Human Resources
CNO: Peggy Schmits, Director, Nursing Operations
Web address: www.nbrrh.ernesthealth.com
Control: Corporation, Investor–owned (for–profit) **Service**: Rehabilitation

Staffed Beds: 40 **Admissions**: 816 **Census**: 32 **Outpatient Visits**: 8005 **Births**: 0 **Total Expense ($000)**: 14229 **Payroll Expense ($000)**: 6908 **Personnel**: 156

⊞ **POST ACUTE/WARM SPRINGS SPECIALTY HOSPITAL OF NEW BRAUNFELS (452106)**, 1445 Hanz Drive, Zip 78130–2567; tel. 830/627–7600, **A**1 10 **F**1 3 29 30 34 85 130 148 **S** Post Acute Medical, LLC, Enola, PA
Primary Contact: Ashley Ondrusek, Chief Executive Officer
Web address: www.warmsprings.org/locations/hos/h1/
Control: Partnership, Investor–owned (for–profit) **Service**: Acute long–term care hospital

Staffed Beds: 40 **Admissions**: 751 **Census**: 27 **Outpatient Visits**: 0 **Births**: 0 **Total Expense ($000)**: 14096 **Payroll Expense ($000)**: 5576 **Personnel**: 71

⊞ **RESOLUTE HEALTH (670098)**, 555 Creekside Crossing, Zip 78130–2594; tel. 830/500–6000, **A**1 10 **F**3 13 15 18 20 22 29 30 34 35 40 45 48 49 50 53 60 64 65 70 72 74 75 76 77 79 81 85 87 107 108 111 114 115 119 126 130 146 147 149 150 156 **S** TENET Healthcare Corporation, Dallas, TX
Primary Contact: Mark L. Bernard, Chief Executive Officer
Web address: www.resolutehealth.com
Control: Corporation, Investor–owned (for–profit) **Service**: General medical and surgical

Staffed Beds: 70 **Admissions**: 4158 **Census**: 41 **Outpatient Visits**: 37924 **Births**: 684 **Total Expense ($000)**: 84902 **Payroll Expense ($000)**: 24353 **Personnel**: 373

NOCONA—Montague County

NOCONA GENERAL HOSPITAL (450641), 100 Park Road, Zip 76255–3616; tel. 940/825–3235, **A**10 **F**3 7 11 28 29 30 34 35 40 43 45 50 53 57 59 62 64 68 75 81 82 86 87 93 107 108 114 119 130 133 146 148
Primary Contact: Lance Meekins, Chief Executive Officer
CFO: Lance Meekins, Chief Executive Officer
CMO: Chance Dingler, M.D., Chief Medical Officer
CHR: Paula Monkres, Administrative Assistant and Director Human Resources
Web address: www.noconageneral.com/
Control: Hospital district or authority, Government, nonfederal **Service**: General medical and surgical

Staffed Beds: 14 **Admissions**: 412 **Census**: 4 **Outpatient Visits**: 7670 **Births**: 0 **Total Expense ($000)**: 8025 **Payroll Expense ($000)**: 4032 **Personnel**: 104

NORTH RICHLAND HILLS—Tarrant County

⊞ **MEDICAL CITY NORTH HILLS (450087)**, 4401 Booth Calloway Road, Zip 76180–7399; tel. 817/255–1000, **A**1 10 **F**3 12 15 17 18 20 22 24 26 28 29 31 34 35 37 39 40 41 43 45 49 50 56 57 64 67 70 74 75 77 78 79 81 85 86 87 93 98 103 107 108 110 111 115 118 119 126 130 132 135 146 148 149 **S** HCA Healthcare, Nashville, TN
Primary Contact: Nancy L. Hill, R.N., MSN, Chief Operating Officer
COO: Nancy L Hill, R.N., MSN, Chief Operating Officer
CFO: Nick Galt, Chief Financial Officer
CMO: John McDonald, M.D., Chief Medical Officer
CIO: Jason Sims, Facility Information Security Officer
CHR: Cynthia Dang, Vice President Human Resources
CNO: John Marker, MSN, R.N., Chief Nursing Officer
Web address: www.northhillshospital.com
Control: Partnership, Investor–owned (for–profit) **Service**: General medical and surgical

Staffed Beds: 140 **Admissions**: 6779 **Census**: 91 **Outpatient Visits**: 78134 **Births**: 0 **Total Expense ($000)**: 113145 **Payroll Expense ($000)**: 43282 **Personnel**: 589

ODESSA—Ector County

★ **CONTINUECARE HOSPITAL AT MEDICAL CENTER (ODESSA) (452121)**, 500 West Fourth Street, 4th Floor, Zip 79761–5001; tel. 432/640–4380, (Nonreporting) **A**10 22 **S** Community Hospital Corporation, Plano, TX
Primary Contact: Holly Powell, Administrator
Web address: www.continuecare.org/odessa//
Control: Other not–for–profit (including NFP Corporation) **Service**: Acute long–term care hospital

Staffed Beds: 25

Many Facility Codes have changed. Please refer to the AHA Guide Code Chart. © 2019 AHA Guide

TX

⇑ **ODESSA REGIONAL MEDICAL CENTER (450661)**, 520 East Sixth Street, Zip 79761–4565, Mailing Address: P.O. Box 4859, Zip 79760–4859; tel. 432/582–8000, **A**3 5 10 21 **F**3 12 13 15 17 18 20 22 23 24 25 29 34 35 40 43 46 49 50 51 52 55 57 59 60 64 66 72 74 75 76 79 81 82 85 86 87 89 90 91 107 108 111 115 119 124 130 132 146 147 148 154 **S** Steward Health Care System, LLC, Dallas, TX
Primary Contact: Stacey L. Gerig, Chief Executive Officer
CIO: Jimmy Diaz, Director Information Technology
CHR: Jill Sparkman, Director Human Resources
CNO: Levi Ross Stone, R.N., Chief Nursing Officer and Chief Operating Officer
Web address: www.odessaregionalmedicalcenter.com
Control: Partnership, Investor–owned (for–profit) **Service**: General medical and surgical

> **Staffed Beds**: 213 **Admissions**: 6414 **Census**: 87 **Outpatient Visits**: 50393 **Births**: 2366 **Total Expense ($000)**: 127898 **Payroll Expense ($000)**: 42304 **Personnel**: 650

☐ **ODESSA REGIONAL MEDICAL CENTER SOUTH CAMPUS (670066)**, 900 East 4th Street, Zip 79761–5255; tel. 432/362–9900, (Nonreporting) **A**1 10
Primary Contact: Stacey L. Gerig, Chief Executive Officer
CMO: Richard Bartlett, M.D., Chief Medical Officer
Web address: www.bhcodessa.com/
Control: Partnership, Investor–owned (for–profit) **Service**: General medical and surgical

> **Staffed Beds**: 14

⊞ **MEDICAL CENTER HEALTH SYSTEM (450132)**, 500 West Fourth Street, Zip 79761–5059, Mailing Address: P O Drawer 7239, Zip 79760–7239; tel. 432/640–4000, **A**1 2 3 5 10 **F**3 11 12 13 15 17 18 20 22 24 26 28 29 30 31 34 35 40 42 43 45 46 47 48 49 50 53 54 57 59 64 65 66 68 70 71 72 74 75 76 77 78 79 81 85 87 89 90 93 107 111 114 115 116 117 118 119 126 129 130 131 132 135 144 146 147 148 155 157
Primary Contact: Rick D. Napper, Chief Executive Officer
COO: Tony Ruiz, Senior Vice President, Chief Operating Officer
CFO: Robert Abernethy, Interim Chief Financial Officer
CMO: Sari A. Nabulshi, M.D., Chief Medical Officer
CIO: Gary Barnes, Senior Vice President, Chief Information Officer
CHR: Robbi Banks, Vice President, Human Resources
CNO: Chad Dunavan, R.N., Vice President, Chief Nursing Officer
Web address: www.mchodessa.com
Control: Hospital district or authority, Government, nonfederal **Service**: General medical and surgical

> **Staffed Beds**: 368 **Admissions**: 15265 **Census**: 195 **Outpatient Visits**: 333442 **Births**: 1886 **Total Expense ($000)**: 298486 **Payroll Expense ($000)**: 100249 **Personnel**: 1500

MEDICAL CENTER HOSPITAL See Medical Center Health System

OLNEY—Young County

★ **HAMILTON HOSPITAL (451354)**, 901 West Hamilton Street, Zip 76374–1725, Mailing Address: P.O. Box 158, Zip 76374–0158; tel. 940/564–5521, **A**10 18 **F**1 4 7 11 13 16 17 28 29 30 34 40 43 53 57 67 70 72 73 76 77 80 81 86 88 89 90 93 98 107 114 127 128 129 130 133 146 148
Primary Contact: Michael H. Huff, Chief Executive Officer
CFO: Coy Noles, Chief Financial Officer Consultant
CMO: Mark L Mankins, M.D., Chief of Staff
CIO: Rick Oliver, Information Technology
CHR: Amy Moore, Human Resources
CNO: Samantha Isbell, R.N., Chief Nursing Officer
Web address: www.olneyhamiltonhospital.com
Control: Hospital district or authority, Government, nonfederal **Service**: General medical and surgical

> **Staffed Beds**: 25 **Admissions**: 526 **Census**: 9 **Outpatient Visits**: 23651 **Births**: 45 **Total Expense ($000)**: 15488 **Payroll Expense ($000)**: 5709 **Personnel**: 133

PALACIOS—Matagorda County

PALACIOS COMMUNITY MEDICAL CENTER (451332), 311 Green Street, Zip 77465–3213; tel. 361/972–2511, **A**10 18 **F**3 29 32 34 40 41 50 57 59 64 65 87 91 93 96 97 107 119 127 128 133 146 148
Primary Contact: Robert A. Pascasio, FACHE, Chief Executive Officer
COO: Lisa Henderson, Chief Operating Officer
CFO: Claude Manning, Chief Financial Officer
CIO: Angela Yeager, Director Information Technology
CHR: Lisa Henderson, Chief Operations Officer
CNO: Susan Easter, Chief Nursing Officer
Web address: www.palacioshospital.net/
Control: Other not–for–profit (including NFP Corporation) **Service**: General medical and surgical

> **Staffed Beds**: 17 **Admissions**: 95 **Census**: 1 **Outpatient Visits**: 12025 **Births**: 0 **Total Expense ($000)**: 4658 **Payroll Expense ($000)**: 2405 **Personnel**: 60

PALESTINE—Anderson County

⊞ **PALESTINE REGIONAL MEDICAL CENTER-EAST (450747)**, 2900 South Loop 256, Zip 75801–6958; tel. 903/731–1000, (Includes PALESTINE REGIONAL MEDICAL CENTER, 2900 S Loop 256, Palestine, Texas, Zip 75801–6958; tel. 903/731–1000; Roy Finch, Chief Executive Officer) **A**1 5 10 **F**3 7 13 15 18 20 26 28 29 31 34 40 43 44 47 48 49 50 51 56 57 59 60 62 63 70 76 79 81 82 85 86 87 89 90 93 96 97 98 100 101 102 103 104 107 108 110 111 114 118 119 129 130 131 146 147 148 154 **S** LifePoint Health, Brentwood, TN
Primary Contact: Roy Finch, Chief Executive Officer
CFO: Celena Brim, Chief Financial Officer
CIO: Rebecca Chou, Director Information Systems
CHR: Rhonda Beard, Director Human Resources
Web address: www.palestineregional.com
Control: Partnership, Investor–owned (for–profit) **Service**: General medical and surgical

> **Staffed Beds**: 120 **Admissions**: 3677 **Census**: 57 **Outpatient Visits**: 57721 **Births**: 641 **Total Expense ($000)**: 66892 **Payroll Expense ($000)**: 28310 **Personnel**: 488

PAMPA—Gray County

⊞ **PAMPA REGIONAL MEDICAL CENTER (450099)**, One Medical Plaza, Zip 79065; tel. 806/665–3721, **A**1 10 20 **F**3 11 12 13 15 18 20 22 29 30 34 40 43 45 46 47 48 49 50 51 52 54 56 57 58 59 60 61 63 64 65 66 68 70 75 77 79 81 83 84 85 86 87 91 92 93 96 97 98 100 101 103 104 105 107 108 110 111 114 115 119 130 132 134 135 146 147 148 153 154 **S** Prime Healthcare, Ontario, CA
Primary Contact: Edwin Leon, Chief Executive Officer
CFO: Ronald Collins, Chief Financial Officer
CMO: James Hall, M.D., Chief Medical Officer
CIO: Joy Patton, Director Information Technology
CHR: Debbie Dixon, Director Human Resources
CNO: Twilla Thomas, Chief Nursing Officer
Web address: www.prmctx.com
Control: Other not–for–profit (including NFP Corporation) **Service**: General medical and surgical

> **Staffed Beds**: 72 **Admissions**: 1658 **Census**: 17 **Outpatient Visits**: 36692 **Births**: 165 **Total Expense ($000)**: 38616 **Payroll Expense ($000)**: 12645 **Personnel**: 225

PARIS—Lamar County

★ **CHRISTUS DUBUIS HOSPITAL OF PARIS (452082)**, 820 Clarksville Street, 6th Floor, Zip 75460–6027; tel. 903/737–3600, (Nonreporting) **A**10 **S** LHC Group, Lafayette, LA
Primary Contact: Kathie Reese, R.N., Regional Administrator and Chief Executive Officer
CFO: Michael Murray, Chief Financial Officer
CMO: Devabrata Ganguly, M.D., Medical Director
CNO: Janice Cochran, R.N., Director Patient Care
Web address: www.christusdubuis.org
Service: Acute long–term care hospital

> **Staffed Beds**: 25

TX

⊠ **PARIS REGIONAL MEDICAL CENTER (450196)**, 865 Deshong Drive, Zip 75460–9313, Mailing Address: P.O. Box 9070, Zip 75461–9070; tel. 903/785–4521, (Includes PARIS REGIONAL MEDICAL CENTER, 865 Deshong Drive, Paris, Texas, Zip 75462–2097; tel. 903/785–4521) **A**1 10 **F**3 8 11 13 15 17 18 20 22 24 26 28 29 30 31 34 35 36 39 40 43 44 45 49 50 51 55 57 59 60 64 65 66 68 70 74 75 76 77 78 79 81 82 85 86 87 89 90 91 93 97 102 107 108 110 111 115 118 119 126 127 129 130 132 135 145 146 147 148 149 **S** LifePoint Health, Brentwood, TN
Primary Contact: Steve Hyde, Chief Executive Officer
COO: Scott B. Avery, Chief Operating Officer
CFO: Donald E McDaniel III Chief Financial Officer
CMO: Richard Bercher, M.D., Chief Medical Officer
CHR: Cheryl Perry, Executive Director Human Resources
CNO: Debra Taylor, Chief Nursing Officer
Web address: www.https://parisregionalmedical.com/
Control: Partnership, Investor–owned (for–profit) **Service**: General medical and surgical

Staffed Beds: 171 Admissions: 7331 Census: 77 Outpatient Visits: 78775 Births: 785 Total Expense ($000): 122398 Payroll Expense ($000): 38251 Personnel: 668

PASADENA—Harris County

⊠ **BAYSHORE MEDICAL CENTER (450097)**, 4000 Spencer Highway, Zip 77504–1202; tel. 713/359–2000, **A**1 2 10 **F**3 8 11 12 13 15 17 18 20 22 24 26 28 29 31 34 35 40 42 43 45 46 49 50 51 54 56 57 59 60 64 67 70 72 74 75 76 77 78 79 81 82 84 85 90 93 96 98 100 102 103 107 108 110 111 114 115 118 119 121 123 124 126 129 130 131 132 146 147 154 **S** HCA Healthcare, Nashville, TN
Primary Contact: Jeanna Bamburg, FACHE, Chief Executive Officer
CFO: John Armour, Chief Financial Officer
CIO: Clifford Ferguson, Director Information Technology and Systems
Web address: www.bayshoremedical.com
Control: Partnership, Investor–owned (for–profit) **Service**: General medical and surgical

Staffed Beds: 286 Admissions: 12817 Census: 189 Outpatient Visits: 130903 Births: 2454 Total Expense ($000): 223032 Payroll Expense ($000): 81151 Personnel: 1044

★ ⇧ **CHI ST. LUKE'S HEALTH - PATIENTS MEDICAL CENTER (670031)**, 4600 East Sam Houston Parkway South, Zip 77505–3948; tel. 713/948–7000, **A**10 21 **F**12 15 17 18 20 22 24 26 28 29 30 35 40 42 45 46 51 54 64 70 74 77 79 81 82 86 87 91 93 94 107 111 114 115 116 117 119 129 130 146 147 148 157 **S** CommonSpirit Health, Chicago, IL
Primary Contact: Steven Foster, Chief Executive Officer
Web address: www.stlukestexas.com
Control: Partnership, Investor–owned (for–profit) **Service**: General medical and surgical

Staffed Beds: 61 Admissions: 3728 Census: 52 Outpatient Visits: 37988 Births: 0 Total Expense ($000): 67449 Payroll Expense ($000): 28215 Personnel: 409

⇧ **PATIENTS MEDICAL CENTER** See Chi St. Luke's Health - Patients Medical Center

○ **SURGERY SPECIALTY HOSPITALS OF AMERICA (450831)**, 4301B Vista Road, Zip 77504; tel. 713/378–3000, **A**10 11 **F**3 12 29 40 68 70 75 79 81 85 107 111 119 132
Primary Contact: Eric Chan, M.D., Chief Executive Officer
COO: Hemant Khemka, Chief Operating Officer
CFO: Hemant Khemka, Chief Financial Officer
CMO: Xiao H. Li, M.D., Chief of Staff
CIO: Ringo Cheng, Director Information Technology
Web address: www.surgeryspecialty.com/
Control: Partnership, Investor–owned (for–profit) **Service**: General medical and surgical

Staffed Beds: 37 Admissions: 106 Census: 1 Outpatient Visits: 1314 Births: 0 Total Expense ($000): 12976 Payroll Expense ($000): 3269 Personnel: 87

PEARLAND—Brazoria County

ENCOMPASS HEALTH REHABILITATION HOSPITAL OF PEARLAND (673066), 2121 Business Center Drive, Zip 77584–2153; tel. 346/907–3000, **A**10 **F**3 29 90 96 130 **S** Encompass Health Corporation, Birmingham, AL
Primary Contact: Michael Cabiro, Chief Executive Officer
Web address: www.https://www.encompasshealth.com/locations/pearlandrehab
Control: Corporation, Investor–owned (for–profit) **Service**: Rehabilitation

Staffed Beds: 40 Admissions: 927 Census: 31 Outpatient Visits: 0 Births: 0 Total Expense ($000): 14308 Payroll Expense ($000): 8377 Personnel: 101

⊠ **PEARLAND MEDICAL CENTER (670106)**, 11100 Shadow Creek Parkway, Zip 77584–7285; tel. 713/770–7000, **A**1 **F**3 18 20 22 26 29 31 34 35 37 40 41 45 49 50 51 57 59 68 74 75 77 78 79 81 82 85 86 87 107 108 110 111 114 119 126 130 143 146 148 **S** HCA Healthcare, Nashville, TN
Primary Contact: David S. Wagner, Chief Executive Officer
Web address: www.pearlandmc.com
Control: Partnership, Investor–owned (for–profit) **Service**: General medical and surgical

Staffed Beds: 53 Admissions: 2526 Census: 25 Outpatient Visits: 28349 Births: 0 Total Expense ($000): 58896 Payroll Expense ($000): 16197 Personnel: 190

PEARSALL—Frio County

★ **FRIO REGIONAL HOSPITAL (450293)**, 200 South I H 35, Zip 78061–3998; tel. 830/334–3617, **A**10 18 **F**3 13 15 29 34 35 40 43 45 57 59 62 64 68 76 77 81 87 96 107 110 114 115 119 130 133 146 148 154
Primary Contact: John R. Hughson, Chief Executive Officer
CMO: Oscar Garza, M.D., Chief Medical Staff
CIO: Jacob Flores, Chief Information Officer
CHR: Nancy Ortiz, Director Human Resource and Marketing
CNO: Louisa Martinez, Director of Nursing
Web address: www.frioregionalhospital.com
Control: Other not–for–profit (including NFP Corporation) **Service**: General medical and surgical

Staffed Beds: 22 Admissions: 361 Census: 5 Outpatient Visits: 26302 Births: 131 Total Expense ($000): 17163 Payroll Expense ($000): 7052 Personnel: 129

PECOS—Reeves County

REEVES COUNTY HOSPITAL (451377), 2323 Texas Street, Zip 79772–7338; tel. 432/447–3551, **A**10 18 **F**3 11 13 15 35 40 43 57 60 64 68 70 76 81 87 89 93 107 110 114 119 127 130 131 133 146 147 148
Primary Contact: Brenda McKinney, Chief Executive Officer
CFO: Bomi Bharucha, Chief Financial Officer
CMO: W J Bang, M.D., Chief of Staff
CHR: Nadine Smith, Director Human Resources
CNO: Faye Lease, Director of Nursing
Web address: www.reevescountyhospital.com
Control: Hospital district or authority, Government, nonfederal **Service**: General medical and surgical

Staffed Beds: 25 Admissions: 808 Census: 8 Outpatient Visits: 74669 Births: 133 Total Expense ($000): 30328 Payroll Expense ($000): 15471 Personnel: 253

PERRYTON—Ochiltree County

★ **OCHILTREE GENERAL HOSPITAL (451359)**, 3101 Garrett Drive, Zip 79070–5323; tel. 806/435–3606, **A**10 18 **F**10 11 13 15 30 35 40 43 57 59 62 63 64 69 76 81 85 89 93 104 107 108 114 119 127 130 133 143 146 147
Primary Contact: Leroy Schaffner, Interim Chief Executive Officer
CFO: Debbie Blodgett, Director Fiscal Services
CMO: Rex Mann, M.D., Chief Medical Officer
CIO: Dyan Harrison, Manager Health Information
CHR: Debbie Beck, Manager Human Resource and Payroll
Web address: www.ochiltreehospital.com
Control: Hospital district or authority, Government, nonfederal **Service**: General medical and surgical

Staffed Beds: 25 Admissions: 420 Census: 6 Outpatient Visits: 35954 Births: 120 Total Expense ($000): 18280 Payroll Expense ($000): 8130 Personnel: 138

PITTSBURG—Camp County

★ **UT HEALTH PITTSBURG (451367)**, 2701 Highway 271 North, Zip 75686–1032; tel. 903/946–5000, (Data for 306 days) **A**3 10 18 **F**3 11 12 28 29 34 35 40 43 45 50 57 59 64 65 75 77 79 81 82 84 85 87 92 93 97 107 108 111 115 119 127 129 130 133 **S** Ardent Health Services, Nashville, TN
Primary Contact: Patrick Swindle, Interim Chief Executive Officer
CFO: Janet Andersen, Chief Financial Officer
CMO: W R Christensen, M.D., Chief of Staff
CIO: Paula Anthony, Vice President Information Services
CHR: Kathy Shelton, Director Human Resources
CNO: Casey Mayben, Chief Nursing Officer
Web address: www.https://uthealthpittsburg.com/
Control: Partnership, Investor–owned (for–profit) **Service**: General medical and surgical

Staffed Beds: 25 Admissions: 608 Census: 8 Outpatient Visits: 68121 Births: 0 Total Expense ($000): 22874 Payroll Expense ($000): 7607 Personnel: 143

TX

Many Facility Codes have changed. Please refer to the AHA Guide Code Chart. © 2019 AHA Guide

PLAINVIEW—Hale County

ALLEGIANCE BEHAVIORAL HEALTH CENTER OF PLAINVIEW (454101), 2601 Dimmit Road, Suite 400, Zip 79072–1833; tel. 806/296–9191, **A**10 **F**29 35 56 64 98 101 103 104 149 **S** Allegiance Health Management, Shreveport, LA
Primary Contact: Angie Alexander, Chief Executive Officer
COO: Don Cameron, Chief Operating Officer
CMO: Victor A Gutierrez, M.D., Medical Director
CIO: Richard Merk, Executive Vice President
CHR: Richard Merk, Director Human Resources
Web address: www.ahmgt.com
Control: Corporation, Investor–owned (for–profit) **Service**: Psychiatric

Staffed Beds: 20 **Admissions:** 278 **Census:** 11 **Outpatient Visits:** 30195 **Births:** 0 **Total Expense ($000):** 7447 **Payroll Expense ($000):** 2166 **Personnel:** 40

☒ **COVENANT HOSPITAL PLAINVIEW (450539)**, 2601 Dimmitt Road, Zip 79072–1833; tel. 806/296–5531, **A**1 3 10 20 **F**3 11 13 15 18 29 30 32 34 35 38 40 41 43 44 45 46 48 50 51 54 57 59 61 64 65 68 70 75 76 77 79 80 81 85 86 87 97 107 108 110 111 114 119 127 129 130 131 132 135 146 147 148 149 156 **S** Providence St. Joseph Health, Renton, WA
Primary Contact: Robert Copeland, Interim Chief Executive Officer
COO: Mike McNutt, Assistant Administrator
CFO: Cassie Mogg, Chief Financial Officer
CMO: Sergio Lara, M.D., Chief Medical Officer
CNO: Leslie Hackett, Chief Nursing Officer
Web address: www.covenantplainview.org
Control: Other not–for–profit (including NFP Corporation) **Service**: General medical and surgical

Staffed Beds: 68 **Admissions:** 1877 **Census:** 16 **Outpatient Visits:** 80191 **Births:** 427 **Total Expense ($000):** 41592 **Payroll Expense ($000):** 14443 **Personnel:** 281

PLANO—Denton County

ACCEL REHABILITATION HOSPITAL OF PLANO (673055), 2301 Marsh Lane, #200, Zip 75093–8497; tel. 972/899–5510, **F**3 29 90 96 130 132
Primary Contact: Rick Tichenor, Chief Executive Officer
Web address: www.accelrehab.com
Control: Partnership, Investor–owned (for–profit) **Service**: Rehabilitation

Staffed Beds: 28 **Admissions:** 470 **Census:** 16 **Outpatient Visits:** 1282 **Births:** 0 **Total Expense ($000):** 8277 **Payroll Expense ($000):** 2813 **Personnel:** 70

PLANO—Collin County

☒ **BAYLOR SCOTT & WHITE MEDICAL CENTER - PLANO (450890)**, 4700 Alliance Boulevard, Zip 75093–5323; tel. 469/814–2000, **A**1 2 3 5 10 **F**3 12 15 29 30 31 34 35 40 45 46 47 48 49 51 54 55 57 58 59 60 64 70 75 77 78 79 80 81 82 84 85 86 87 107 108 110 111 114 115 118 119 126 130 131 132 133 135 145 146 147 148 149 154 **S** Baylor Scott & White Health, Dallas, TX
Primary Contact: Jerri Garison, R.N., President
COO: Joseph C. Brown, Vice President Operations
CFO: Deanne Kindred, Vice President Finance
CMO: John Marcucci, M.D., Vice President Medical Affairs
CHR: Kriss Gamez, Director Human Resources
Web address: www.baylorhealth.com/PhysiciansLocations/Plano/Pages/Default.aspx
Control: Other not–for–profit (including NFP Corporation) **Service**: General medical and surgical

Staffed Beds: 124 **Admissions:** 7227 **Census:** 90 **Outpatient Visits:** 57922 **Births:** 0 **Total Expense ($000):** 187546 **Payroll Expense ($000):** 56549 **Personnel:** 633

☒ **BAYLOR SCOTT & WHITE THE HEART HOSPITAL PLANO (670025)**, 1100 Allied Drive, Zip 75093–5348; tel. 469/814–3278, **A**1 3 5 10 **F**3 17 18 20 22 24 26 28 29 30 34 35 40 46 49 53 54 55 57 58 59 60 64 68 74 75 77 81 84 85 86 87 90 107 108 111 114 115 119 126 130 132 135 146 148 149 154 157
Primary Contact: Mark Valentine, President
CFO: Bryan Nichols, Chief Financial Officer
CMO: Trent Pettijohn, M.D., Esq Chief Medical Officer
CHR: Tracy Stanford, Director Human Resources
CNO: Susan K. Moats, R.N., Vice President Patient Care Services and Chief Nursing Officer
Web address: www.https://www.thehearthospitalbaylor.com
Control: Partnership, Investor–owned (for–profit) **Service**: Heart

Staffed Beds: 114 **Admissions:** 5117 **Census:** 79 **Outpatient Visits:** 31142 **Births:** 0 **Total Expense ($000):** 238476 **Payroll Expense ($000):** 69803 **Personnel:** 842

CHILDREN'S MEDICAL CENTER PLANO (453316), 7601 Preston Road, Zip 75024–3214; tel. 469/303–7000, **A**3 5 **F**3 19 29 31 34 40 41 43 54 59 64 68 74 75 77 78 79 81 85 86 87 88 89 93 98 99 107 111 119 126 129 130 131 146 148 154 **S** Children's Health, Dallas, TX
Primary Contact: Jeremiah Radandt, President
CIO: Pamela Arora, Senior Vice President and Chief Information Officer
CHR: Kim Besse, Executive Vice President and Chief Human Resource Officer
CNO: Mary Stowe, Senior Vice President and Chief Nursing Officer
Web address: www.https://www.childrens.com/location-landing/locations-and-directions/childrens-health-plano
Control: Other not–for–profit (including NFP Corporation) **Service**: Children's general medical and surgical

Staffed Beds: 72 **Admissions:** 2393 **Census:** 22 **Outpatient Visits:** 142944 **Births:** 0 **Total Expense ($000):** 170998 **Payroll Expense ($000):** 52940 **Personnel:** 758

☒ **ENCOMPASS HEALTH REHABILITATION HOSPITAL OF PLANO (453047)**, 2800 West 15th Street, Zip 75075–7526; tel. 972/612–9000, **A**1 10 **F**34 57 59 90 93 95 96 130 132 148 **S** Encompass Health Corporation, Birmingham, AL
Primary Contact: Brandon Tudor, Chief Executive Officer
CFO: Catrina Madkins, Controller and Chief Financial Officer
CMO: Omar Colon, M.D., Medical Director
Web address: www.healthsouthplano.com
Control: Corporation, Investor–owned (for–profit) **Service**: Rehabilitation

Staffed Beds: 83 **Admissions:** 1490 **Census:** 49 **Outpatient Visits:** 0 **Births:** 0 **Total Expense ($000):** 20313 **Payroll Expense ($000):** 10960 **Personnel:** 197

☒ **MEDICAL CITY PLANO (450651)**, 3901 West 15th Street, Zip 75075–7738; tel. 972/596–6800, (Includes MEDICAL CITY FRISCO, 5500 Frisco Square Boulevard, Frisco, Texas, Zip 75034–3305; tel. 214/618–0500; Carlton Ulmer, Chief Executive Officer) **A**1 2 3 10 **F**3 12 13 15 16 18 19 20 22 24 26 28 29 30 31 34 35 40 41 42 43 45 46 47 48 49 51 54 55 57 58 59 60 64 70 72 74 75 76 78 79 81 82 84 85 86 87 90 93 107 108 110 111 112 114 115 117 118 119 124 126 130 132 135 145 146 147 148 157 **S** HCA Healthcare, Nashville, TN
Primary Contact: Carlton Ulmer, Chief Executive Officer
CFO: Jon Alford, Chief Financial Officer
CMO: Ann Arnold, M.D., Medical Director
CIO: Michael Gfeller, Director Information Systems
CHR: Shanna Warren, Director Human Resources
Web address: www.medicalcenterplano.com
Control: Partnership, Investor–owned (for–profit) **Service**: General medical and surgical

Staffed Beds: 472 **Admissions:** 23279 **Census:** 359 **Outpatient Visits:** 161627 **Births:** 2746 **Total Expense ($000):** 405783 **Payroll Expense ($000):** 144434 **Personnel:** 2217

PLANO—Denton County

☐ ⇧ **PLANO SURGICAL HOSPITAL**, 2301 Marsh Lane, Zip 75093–8497; tel. 972/820–2600, **A**1 21 **F**3 29 40 41 45 49 79 81 82 85 87 107 114 149 157 **S** Nobilis Health Corporation, Houston, TX
Primary Contact: Jay Lindsey, Chief Executive Officer
Web address: www.nobilishealth.com/our-facilities/dallas/
Control: Corporation, Investor–owned (for–profit) **Service**: Surgical

Staffed Beds: 26 **Admissions:** 238 **Census:** 2 **Births:** 0 **Personnel:** 61

PLANO—Collin County

⇧ **STAR MEDICAL CENTER**, 4100 Mapleshade Lane, Zip 75093–0012; tel. 972/265–1050, **A**21 **F**3 29 40 45 46 64 68 74 75 77 79 81 82 85
Primary Contact: Jeffrey VanHorn, Chief Executive Officer
CNO: Joyce O. Winbush, Chief Nursing Officer
Web address: www.https://starmedicalcenter.com/
Control: Partnership, Investor–owned (for–profit) **Service**: General medical and surgical

Staffed Beds: 7 **Admissions:** 83 **Census:** 1 **Outpatient Visits:** 1158 **Births:** 0 **Personnel:** 72

TX

Hospital, Medicare Provider Number, Address, Telephone, Approval, Facility, and Physician Codes, Health Care System

★ American Hospital Association (AHA) membership   ◯ Healthcare Facilities Accreditation Program   ⇧ Center for Improvement in Healthcare Quality Accreditation
☐ The Joint Commission accreditation   ◇ DNV Healthcare Inc. accreditation   △ Commission on Accreditation of Rehabilitation Facilities (CARF) accreditation

☐ **TEXAS HEALTH CENTER FOR DIAGNOSTIC & SURGERY (450891)**, 6020 West Parker Road, Suite 100, Zip 75093–8171; tel. 972/403–2700, **A**1 2 10 **F**3 29 40 45 51 54 64 79 81 82 85 87 107 111 115 119 126 129 149
Primary Contact: Larry Robertson, President
CFO: Douglas Browning, Chief Financial Officer
CHR: Cookie Tedder, Human Resources Manager
CNO: Ellen Baldwin, R.N., Chief Nursing Officer
Web address: www.thcds.com
Control: Partnership, Investor–owned (for–profit) **Service**: General medical and surgical

Staffed Beds: 18 **Admissions:** 600 **Census:** 3 **Outpatient Visits:** 15070 **Births:** 0 **Total Expense ($000):** 57767 **Payroll Expense ($000):** 14026 **Personnel:** 173

⊠ **TEXAS HEALTH PRESBYTERIAN HOSPITAL PLANO (450771)**, 6200 West Parker Road, Zip 75093–8185; tel. 972/981–8000, **A**1 3 10 **F**3 12 13 15 18 20 22 24 26 28 29 30 31 32 34 35 37 38 40 42 43 44 45 46 49 50 52 53 54 55 57 58 59 60 64 65 68 70 72 74 75 76 77 78 79 81 84 85 86 87 89 93 98 104 105 107 108 110 111 114 115 118 119 126 130 131 132 134 135 141 145 146 147 148 149 150 153 157 **S** Texas Health Resources, Arlington, TX
Primary Contact: Joshua Floren, President
CFO: Lisa Gildon, Vice President and Chief Financial Officer
CMO: Gwen Webster, M.D., President Medical Staff
CIO: Susan Anderson, Director Information Systems
CHR: Kelly K Martin, Human Resource Officer
Web address: www.texashealth.org
Control: Other not–for–profit (including NFP Corporation) **Service**: General medical and surgical

Staffed Beds: 308 **Admissions:** 18734 **Census:** 235 **Outpatient Visits:** 98400 **Births:** 4353 **Total Expense ($000):** 360632 **Payroll Expense ($000):** 123370 **Personnel:** 1684

WELLBRIDGE HEALTHCARE GREATER DALLAS (454130), 4301 Mapleshade Lane, Zip 75093–0010; tel. 972/596–5445, (Nonreporting)
Primary Contact: John Sannuto, Chief Executive Officer
Web address: www.wellbridgedallas.com/
Control: Corporation, Investor–owned (for–profit) **Service**: Psychiatric

Staffed Beds: 25

PORT ARTHUR—Jefferson County

DUBUIS HOSPITAL OF PORT ARTHUR See Christus Dubuis Hospital of Port Arthur

⇑ **THE MEDICAL CENTER OF SOUTHEAST TEXAS (450518)**, 2555 Jimmy Johnson Boulevard, Zip 77640–2007; tel. 409/724–7389, **A**10 21 **F**3 8 11 12 13 15 17 18 20 22 24 26 28 29 30 34 35 40 43 44 45 47 49 50 56 57 59 64 70 72 74 76 77 78 79 81 82 85 86 87 89 90 91 92 93 94 98 101 102 103 104 105 107 108 110 111 114 115 119 121 129 130 132 135 146 147 148 153 154 **S** Steward Health Care System, LLC, Dallas, TX
Primary Contact: Carl Bo"". Beaudry, President
COO: Chris McMahon, Chief Operating Officer
CFO: Jason R. Miller, Chief Financial Officer
CMO: Ryan McHugh, M.D., Chief of Staff
CIO: Bryan Hebert, Director Information Systems
CHR: Carol Hebert, Director Human Resources
CNO: Debbie Vaughn, Chief Nursing Officer
Web address: www.medicalcentersetexas.com
Control: Partnership, Investor–owned (for–profit) **Service**: General medical and surgical

Staffed Beds: 156 **Admissions:** 8337 **Census:** 107 **Outpatient Visits:** 80209 **Births:** 1121 **Total Expense ($000):** 150435 **Payroll Expense ($000):** 50557 **Personnel:** 791

PORT LAVACA—Calhoun County

★ **MEMORIAL MEDICAL CENTER (451356)**, 815 North Virginia Street, Zip 77979–3025, Mailing Address: P.O. Box 25, Zip 77979–0025; tel. 361/552–6713, **A**10 18 **F**3 11 13 15 18 29 30 32 34 35 40 43 44 45 46 49 50 57 59 64 65 68 70 75 77 78 79 81 82 84 85 86 87 93 97 104 107 108 111 115 118 119 127 129 130 132 133 134 135 146 147 148
Primary Contact: Jason Anglin, Chief Executive Officer
COO: Roshanda Gray, Assistant Administrator
CFO: Diane C. Moore, Chief Financial Officer
CMO: Jeannine Griffin, M.D., Chief of Staff
CIO: Adam Besio, Chief Information Officer
CNO: Erin R Clevenger, Chief Nursing Officer and Director of Quality
Web address: www.mmcportlavaca.com
Control: County, Government, nonfederal **Service**: General medical and surgical

Staffed Beds: 25 **Admissions:** 1020 **Census:** 9 **Outpatient Visits:** 62711 **Births:** 122 **Total Expense ($000):** 27699 **Payroll Expense ($000):** 10383 **Personnel:** 214

QUANAH—Hardeman County

HARDEMAN COUNTY MEMORIAL HOSPITAL (451352), 402 Mercer Street, Zip 79252–4026, Mailing Address: P.O. Box 90, Zip 79252–0090; tel. 940/663–2795, **A**10 18 **F**28 29 34 40 43 50 56 57 59 64 75 93 94 100 101 104 107 127 130 133 148 149 153
Primary Contact: Dave Clark, FACHE, Interim Chief Executive Officer
CFO: Tracy Betts, Chief Financial Officer
CMO: Kevin Lane, D.O., Chief of Staff
CNO: Dennis Thomas, Chief Nursing Officer
Web address: www.hcmhosp.com/
Control: Hospital district or authority, Government, nonfederal **Service**: General medical and surgical

Staffed Beds: 18 **Admissions:** 192 **Census:** 3 **Outpatient Visits:** 19065 **Births:** 0 **Total Expense ($000):** 7940 **Payroll Expense ($000):** 3613 **Personnel:** 74

QUITMAN—Wood County

★ **UT HEALTH QUITMAN (451380)**, 117 Winnsboro Street, Zip 75783–2144, Mailing Address: P.O. Box 1000, Zip 75783–1000; tel. 903/763–6300, (Data for 306 days) **A**10 18 **F**3 11 28 29 30 34 35 40 43 45 50 57 59 64 65 77 79 81 82 84 85 87 107 108 111 115 119 127 129 130 133 144 148 149 **S** Ardent Health Services, Nashville, TN
Primary Contact: Patrick Swindle, Administrator
CFO: Janet Andersen, Chief Financial Officer
CHR: William Henry, Director Human Resources
CNO: Allicia Settles, Chief Nursing Officer
Web address: www.https://uthealthquitman.com/
Control: Partnership, Investor–owned (for–profit) **Service**: General medical and surgical

Staffed Beds: 25 **Admissions:** 731 **Census:** 9 **Outpatient Visits:** 49147 **Births:** 0 **Total Expense ($000):** 20521 **Payroll Expense ($000):** 7040 **Personnel:** 139

RANKIN—Upton County

★ **RANKIN COUNTY HOSPITAL DISTRICT (451329)**, 1105 Elizabeth Street, Zip 79778, Mailing Address: P.O. Box 327, Zip 79778–0327; tel. 432/693–2443, **A**10 18 **F**3 7 34 35 40 50 53 54 55 56 57 59 64 65 66 68 75 86 87 93 97 102 107 119 130 131 133 135 147 148 156
Primary Contact: Jim Horton, Chief Executive Officer
CFO: Tami Burks, Comptroller
CMO: Thomas J Curvin, M.D., Chief of Staff
Web address: www.rankincountyhospital.com/
Control: Hospital district or authority, Government, nonfederal **Service**: General medical and surgical

Staffed Beds: 14 **Admissions:** 59 **Census:** 1 **Outpatient Visits:** 10209 **Births:** 0 **Total Expense ($000):** 12127 **Payroll Expense ($000):** 5983 **Personnel:** 78

REFUGIO—Refugio County

REFUGIO COUNTY MEMORIAL HOSPITAL (451317), 107 Swift Street, Zip 78377–2425; tel. 361/526–2321, **A**10 18 **F**3 7 29 40 43 57 61 64 75 81 86 87 93 97 107 119 127 133 155
Primary Contact: Horace Whitt, Chief Executive Officer and Chief Operating Officer
Web address: www.refugiohospital.com/
Control: Hospital district or authority, Government, nonfederal **Service**: General medical and surgical

Staffed Beds: 20 **Admissions:** 72 **Census:** 2 **Outpatient Visits:** 20319 **Births:** 0 **Total Expense ($000):** 13748 **Payroll Expense ($000):** 5443 **Personnel:** 121

RICHARDSON—Collin County

⇑ **EMINENT MEDICAL CENTER**, 1351 West President George Bush Hwy, Zip 75080; tel. 469/910–8800, **A**21 **F**3 29 40 75 77 79 81 85 92 149
Primary Contact: Ryan Gehrke, Chief Executive Officer
CNO: Erin Baker, Chief Nursing Officer
Web address: www.eminentmedicalcenter.com
Control: Partnership, Investor–owned (for–profit) **Service**: Surgical

Staffed Beds: 5 **Admissions:** 59 **Census:** 1 **Outpatient Visits:** 1973 **Births:** 0 **Total Expense ($000):** 14306 **Payroll Expense ($000):** 2609 **Personnel:** 38

TX

⊞ **ENCOMPASS HEALTH REHABILITATION HOSPITAL OF RICHARDSON (673029)**, 3351 Waterview Parkway, Zip 75080–1449; tel. 972/398–5700, **A**1 10 **F**3 29 90 96 132 148 149 156 **S** Encompass Health Corporation, Birmingham, AL
Primary Contact: Brent Yates, Chief Executive Officer
CMO: Richard Jones, M.D., Medical Director
CNO: Pam Smith, Chief Nursing Officer
Web address: www.relianthcp.com
Control: Corporation, Investor–owned (for–profit) **Service:** Rehabilitation

Staffed Beds: 50 **Admissions:** 1892 **Census:** 44 **Outpatient Visits:** 0
Births: 0 **Total Expense ($000):** 21568 **Payroll Expense ($000):** 10129
Personnel: 146

⊞ **METHODIST RICHARDSON MEDICAL CENTER (450537)**, 2831 East President George Bush Highway, Zip 75082–3561; tel. 469/204–1000, **A**1 2 3 10 **F**3 5 11 13 15 18 20 22 24 29 30 31 34 35 38 40 45 46 49 54 55 56 57 59 64 65 68 70 72 74 75 76 77 78 79 81 82 85 86 87 93 97 98 100 101 102 103 104 105 107 108 109 110 111 112 115 116 117 119 120 121 123 124 126 129 130 131 132 135 146 147 148 153 156 **S** Methodist Health System, Dallas, TX
Primary Contact: E. Kenneth. Hutchenrider Jr, FACHE, President
COO: Robert Simpson, Vice President Operations
CFO: Amy Bodwell, Vice President Finance
CMO: Mark Smith, M.D., Chief Medical Officer
CIO: Pamela McNutt, Senior Vice President and Chief Information Officer
CHR: Chris Loyd, Director Human Resources
CNO: Irene T Strejc, M.P.H., R.N., Vice President, Nursing
Web address: www.methodisthealthsystem.org/richardson
Control: Other not–for–profit (including NFP Corporation) **Service:** General medical and surgical

Staffed Beds: 226 **Admissions:** 12983 **Census:** 185 **Outpatient Visits:** 99287 **Births:** 1797 **Total Expense ($000):** 246166 **Payroll Expense ($000):** 98330 **Personnel:** 1093

RICHMOND—Fort Bend County

☐ **OAKBEND MEDICAL CENTER (450330)**, 1705 Jackson Street, Zip 77469–3289; tel. 281/341–3000, (Includes HOSPITAL FOR SURGICAL EXCELLENCE, 1211 Highway 6, Suite 70, Sugar Land, Texas, Zip 77478–4940; tel. 281/238–3900; Joe Freudenberger, Chief Executive Officer; OAKBEND MEDICAL CENTER WILLIAMS WAY CAMPUS, 22003 Southwest Freeway, Richmond, Texas, Zip 77469–7003; tel. 281/341–2000; Joe Freudenberger, Chief Executive Officer) (Total facility includes 36 beds in nursing home–type unit) **A**1 10 **F**3 8 13 15 18 20 22 24 26 28 29 30 34 35 40 42 43 45 46 48 49 50 51 53 56 57 59 70 72 74 75 76 77 78 79 81 85 87 93 97 98 103 107 108 110 111 114 115 119 128 129 130 131 146 147 148
Primary Contact: Joe Freudenberger, Chief Executive Officer
CFO: Rodney Lenfant, Chief Financial Officer
CMO: Douglas Thibodeaux, M.D., Chief Medical Officer
CIO: Tim McCarly, Chief Information Officer
CHR: Eileen Gamboa, Director Human Resources
Web address: www.oakbendmedcenter.org
Control: Hospital district or authority, Government, nonfederal **Service:** General medical and surgical

Staffed Beds: 207 **Admissions:** 6518 **Census:** 85 **Outpatient Visits:** 84834 **Births:** 1433 **Total Expense ($000):** 184371 **Payroll Expense ($000):** 55937 **Personnel:** 764

WESTPARK SPRINGS (454131), 6902 South Peek Road, Zip 77407; tel. 832/532–8107, **F**4 5 54 64 68 75 86 87 98 99 101 102 104 105 106 130 151 152 153 154 **S** Springstone, Louisville, KY
Primary Contact: Colleen McCammon, Chief Executive Officer
Web address: www.westparksprings.com/why-westpark-springs/
Control: Corporation, Investor–owned (for–profit) **Service:** Psychiatric

Staffed Beds: 72 **Admissions:** 3064 **Census:** 60 **Outpatient Visits:** 10212 **Births:** 0 **Total Expense ($000):** 17326 **Payroll Expense ($000):** 9416 **Personnel:** 180

RIO GRANDE CITY—Starr County

★ **STARR COUNTY MEMORIAL HOSPITAL (450654)**, 2753 Hospital Court, Zip 78582–6859, Mailing Address: P.O. Box 78, Zip 78582–0078; tel. 956/487–5561, **A**10 20 **F**7 11 13 15 29 34 35 39 40 43 45 46 50 57 59 64 65 66 68 75 76 81 89 97 107 111 115 119 127 130 135 145 146 148
Primary Contact: Thalia H. Munoz, R.N., MS, Chief Executive Officer
CFO: Rafael Olivares, Controller
CHR: Amaro Salinas, Assistant Administrator and Human Resource Officer
CNO: Mario Segura, Director of Nursing
Web address: www.starrcountyhospital.com
Control: Hospital district or authority, Government, nonfederal **Service:** General medical and surgical

Staffed Beds: 47 **Admissions:** 1009 **Census:** 9 **Outpatient Visits:** 40422 **Births:** 141 **Total Expense ($000):** 32716 **Payroll Expense ($000):** 14068 **Personnel:** 276

RIO HONDO—Cameron County

⊞ **VALLEY BAPTIST MEDICAL CENTER-BROWNSVILLE (450028)**, P O Box 708, Zip 78583, Mailing Address: P.O. Box 3590, Brownsville, Zip 78523–3590; tel. 956/698–5400, **A**1 5 10 **F**3 11 12 13 15 18 20 22 24 26 29 30 34 35 37 40 42 43 44 45 49 50 51 54 56 57 59 60 63 64 65 68 70 72 74 75 76 77 79 81 82 84 85 87 89 93 101 102 103 104 107 108 110 111 112 114 115 119 126 129 130 132 146 147 148 149 153 154 157 **S** TENET Healthcare Corporation, Dallas, TX
Primary Contact: Leslie Bingham, Senior Vice President and Chief Executive Officer
COO: Marisa Aguilar, Chief Operating Officer
CFO: Edwin Cordero, Chief Financial Officer
CMO: Jose L Ayala, M.D., Chief Medical Officer
CNO: Marisa Aguilar, Interim Chief Nursing Officer
Web address: www.valleybaptist.net/brownsville/index.htm
Control: Corporation, Investor–owned (for–profit) **Service:** General medical and surgical

Staffed Beds: 225 **Admissions:** 9090 **Census:** 102 **Outpatient Visits:** 74565 **Births:** 1975 **Total Expense ($000):** 125143 **Payroll Expense ($000):** 48860 **Personnel:** 715

ROCKWALL—Rockwall County

BAYLOR SCOTT & WHITE EMERGENCY HOSPITAL - ROCKWALL (670097), 1975 Alpha Drive Suite 100, Zip 75087–4951; tel. 214/294–6200, (Data for 100 days) **A**10 **F**3 40 107 119 149 **S** Emerus, The Woodlands, TX
Primary Contact: Kyle Kirkpatrick, Chief Executive Officer
Web address: www.bayloremc.com/rockwall
Control: Corporation, Investor–owned (for–profit) **Service:** General medical and surgical

Staffed Beds: 8 **Admissions:** 51 **Census:** 1 **Outpatient Visits:** 3489 **Births:** 0 **Total Expense ($000):** 2294 **Payroll Expense ($000):** 676 **Personnel:** 43

⊞ **TEXAS HEALTH PRESBYTERIAN HOSPITAL OF ROCKWALL (670044)**, 3150 Horizon Road, Zip 75032–7805; tel. 469/698–1000, **A**1 3 10 **F**3 4 12 13 15 16 17 29 30 34 35 40 42 45 46 47 49 50 54 67 68 70 72 73 75 76 77 79 80 81 82 84 85 87 88 90 98 107 108 110 111 115 119 126 128 130 131 146 147
Primary Contact: Cynthia K. Perrin, FACHE, R.N., President and Chief Executive Officer
CFO: Jason Linscott, CPA, Chief Financial Officer
CMO: Gary Bonacquisti, M.D., Chief Medical Officer
CNO: Tami Hawkins, R.N., MSN, Vice President Patient Care and Chief Nursing Officer
Web address: www.phrtexas.com
Control: Corporation, Investor–owned (for–profit) **Service:** General medical and surgical

Staffed Beds: 61 **Admissions:** 3725 **Census:** 30 **Outpatient Visits:** 57448 **Births:** 722 **Total Expense ($000):** 106182 **Payroll Expense ($000):** 36493 **Personnel:** 494

TX

ROTAN—Fisher County

FISHER COUNTY HOSPITAL DISTRICT (451313), 774 State Highway 70
North, Zip 79546–6918, Mailing Address: P O Drawer 'F', Zip 79546–4019;
tel. 325/735–2256, **A**10 18 **F**7 28 32 34 35 40 43 50 53 56 57 59 64 66 75
93 97 107 119 127 133 155
Primary Contact: Leanne Martinez, Chief Executive Officer and Administrator
CFO: Debbie Hull, Chief Financial Officer
CMO: Joseph Lampley, D.O., Chief of Staff
CHR: Teresa Terry, Director Human Resource, Payroll
CNO: D'Linda Benham, Director of Nursing
Web address: www.fishercountyhospital.com
Control: Hospital district or authority, Government, nonfederal **Service:** General
medical and surgical

Staffed Beds: 14 **Admissions:** 96 **Census:** 2 **Outpatient Visits:** 15030
Births: 0 **Total Expense ($000):** 7996 **Payroll Expense ($000):** 3932
Personnel: 64

ROUND ROCK—Williamson County

☒ **ASCENSION SETON WILLIAMSON (670041)**, 201 Seton Parkway,
Zip 78665–8000; tel. 512/324–4000, **A**1 2 3 5 10 **F**3 11 12 13 18 20 22 24
26 28 29 30 35 37 40 41 43 45 46 47 48 49 60 64 68 70 74 76 77 79 81 85
87 92 100 107 108 109 111 114 115 116 117 118 119 120 126 130 131 132
146 147 148 149 154 **S** Ascension Healthcare, Saint Louis, MO
Primary Contact: Katherine Henderson, President and Chief Executive Officer
CFO: Douglas D Waite, Senior Vice President and Chief Financial Officer
CMO: Hugh V Gilmore, M.D., Vice President Medical Affairs
CIO: Gerry Lewis, Chief Information Officer
CHR: Thomas Wilken, Vice President Human Resources
Web address: www.seton.net/williamson
Control: Church operated, Nongovernment, not–for–profit **Service:** General
medical and surgical

Staffed Beds: 126 **Admissions:** 7304 **Census:** 91 **Outpatient Visits:** 43039
Births: 324 **Total Expense ($000):** 151994 **Payroll Expense ($000):** 39038
Personnel: 960

☒ **BAYLOR SCOTT & WHITE MEDICAL CENTER - ROUND ROCK (670034)**, 300
University Boulevard, Zip 78665–1032; tel. 512/509–0100, (Includes BAYLOR
SCOTT & WHITE MEDICAL CENTER - LAKEWAY, 100 Medical Parkway, Lakeway,
Texas, Zip 78738–5621; tel. 512/571–5000; Philippe Bochaton, President) **A**1 3
10 **F**3 11 13 15 18 20 22 24 28 29 30 34 36 40 45 46 47 49 50 51 54 56 58
60 62 63 65 68 72 74 75 76 78 79 81 82 84 85 87 89 91 92 93 97 100 107
108 110 111 114 115 116 117 119 126 129 130 132 133 135 143 146 147
148 149 154 156 **S** Baylor Scott & White Health, Dallas, TX
Primary Contact: Jay Fox, President
COO: Joseph C. Brown, Vice President Operations
CFO: Jason Cole, Regional Chief Financial Officer
CMO: Rob Watson, M.D., Chief Medical Officer
CIO: Matthew Chambers, Chief Information Officer
CHR: Mark A. Sherry, Regional Director Human Resource Strategic Services,
Austin/Round Rock Region
CNO: Leslie Gembol, MSN, R.N., Chief Nursing Officer
Web address: www.sw.org
Control: Other not–for–profit (including NFP Corporation) **Service:** General
medical and surgical

Staffed Beds: 173 **Admissions:** 9674 **Census:** 93 **Outpatient
Visits:** 642356 **Births:** 796 **Total Expense ($000):** 313586 **Payroll Expense
($000):** 81145 **Personnel:** 1368

☒ **ENCOMPASS HEALTH REHABILITATION HOSPITAL OF ROUND ROCK
(673032)**, 1400 Hester's Crossing, Zip 78681–8025; tel. 512/244–4400, (Total
facility includes 1 beds in nursing home–type unit) **A**1 10 **F**3 29 90 95 96 128
130 132 148 149 **S** Encompass Health Corporation, Birmingham, AL
Primary Contact: David Jones, Chief Executive Officer
CFO: Joe Griffin, Controller
CHR: Amelia Leudecke, Director Human Resources
CNO: Stephanie Guerin, Chief Nursing Officer
Web address: www.https://www.encompasshealth.com/roundrockrehab
Control: Corporation, Investor–owned (for–profit) **Service:** Rehabilitation

Staffed Beds: 51 **Admissions:** 1991 **Census:** 70 **Outpatient Visits:** 0
Births: 0 **Total Expense ($000):** 25481 **Payroll Expense ($000):** 13483
Personnel: 150

☒ **ST. DAVID'S ROUND ROCK MEDICAL CENTER (450718)**, 2400 Round Rock
Avenue, Zip 78681–4097; tel. 512/341–1000, **A**1 2 10 **F**3 12 13 15 18 20 22
24 26 28 29 30 31 34 35 37 40 42 43 45 49 54 64 67 69 70 72 74 75 76 77
78 79 81 85 87 93 102 107 108 110 111 115 116 117 119 124 126 129 130
132 135 146 147 149 152 154 157 **S** HCA Healthcare, Nashville, TN
Primary Contact: Jeremy Barclay, Chief Executive Officer
COO: Katie Lattanzi, Chief Operating Officer
CFO: Cindy Sexton, Chief Financial Officer
CHR: Amy Noak, Director Human Resources
Web address: www.stdavids.com
Control: Other not–for–profit (including NFP Corporation) **Service:** General
medical and surgical

Staffed Beds: 171 **Admissions:** 10038 **Census:** 122 **Outpatient
Visits:** 70332 **Births:** 1630 **Total Expense ($000):** 172249 **Payroll Expense
($000):** 58255 **Personnel:** 847

ROWLETT—Rockwall County

☒ **BAYLOR SCOTT & WHITE MEDICAL CENTER - LAKE POINTE (450742)**,
6800 Scenic Drive, Zip 75088–4552, Mailing Address: P.O. Box 1550,
Zip 75030–1550; tel. 972/412–2273, **A**1 10 **F**3 13 15 18 20 22 28 29 30 34
35 40 42 43 45 46 49 50 59 64 68 70 72 73 74 75 76 77 79 81 82 85 86 87
93 97 100 107 108 110 111 114 115 119 126 129 146 147 148 149 156 **S**
Baylor Scott & White Health, Dallas, TX
Primary Contact: Donas Cole, FACHE, President
COO: Benson Chacko, Vice President, Operations
CMO: Larry Dencklau, D.O., Chief of Staff
CIO: Mark Slater, Director Information Systems
Web address: www.lakepointemedical.com
Control: Corporation, Investor–owned (for–profit) **Service:** General medical and
surgical

Staffed Beds: 112 **Admissions:** 7405 **Census:** 77 **Outpatient
Visits:** 103787 **Births:** 1789 **Total Expense ($000):** 171436 **Payroll
Expense ($000):** 49874 **Personnel:** 667

RUSK—Cherokee County

☐ **RUSK STATE HOSPITAL (454009)**, 805 North Dickinson, Zip 75785–2333,
Mailing Address: P.O. Box 318, Zip 75785–0318; tel. 903/683–3421,
(Nonreporting) **A**1 3 5 10 **S** Texas Department of State Health Services, Austin, TX
Primary Contact: Brenda Slaton, Superintendent
COO: Lynda Roberson, Senior Program Director
CFO: Rhonda Transier, Financial Officer
CMO: Joe Bates, M.D., Clinical Director
CHR: Kendra Brown, Job Requisition Coordinator
Web address: www.dshs.state.tx.us/mhhospitals/RuskSH/default.shtm
Control: State, Government, nonfederal **Service:** Psychiatric

Staffed Beds: 249

SAN ANGELO—Tom Green County

☐ **RIVER CREST HOSPITAL (454064)**, 1636 Hunters Glen Road, Zip 76901–5016;
tel. 325/949–5722, **A**1 10 **F**4 5 29 64 87 98 99 100 101 102 103 104 105
130 132 151 152 153 **S** Universal Health Services, Inc., King of Prussia, PA
Primary Contact: Juana Giralt, Interim Chief Executive Officer
CFO: Juana Giralt, Chief Financial Officer
CMO: Raymond Mays, M.D., Medical Director
CHR: Lydia Cardenas, Director Human Resources
CNO: Debra Millsap, Director of Nursing
Web address: www.rivercresthospital.com
Control: Corporation, Investor–owned (for–profit) **Service:** Psychiatric

Staffed Beds: 80 **Admissions:** 2997 **Census:** 48 **Outpatient Visits:** 4059
Births: 0 **Total Expense ($000):** 12858 **Payroll Expense ($000):** 6533
Personnel: 141

☒ **SAN ANGELO COMMUNITY MEDICAL CENTER (450340)**, 3501
Knickerbocker Road, Zip 76904–7698; tel. 325/949–9511, **A**1 10 **F**3 8 11 12
13 15 18 20 22 24 26 28 29 30 34 35 37 40 43 45 49 51 53 54 57 59 60 63
64 68 70 72 74 75 76 77 78 79 81 85 89 93 107 108 110 111 115 118 119
126 129 130 131 135 144 145 146 147 148 **S** Community Health Systems,
Inc., Franklin, TN
Primary Contact: Rodney Schumacher, Interim Chief Executive Officer
CFO: Steven Ewing, Chief Financial Officer
CHR: Lisa Bibb, Director Human Resources
Web address: www.sacmc.com
Control: Partnership, Investor–owned (for–profit) **Service:** General medical and
surgical

Staffed Beds: 131 **Admissions:** 4110 **Census:** 51 **Outpatient Visits:** 70538
Births: 730 **Total Expense ($000):** 92487 **Payroll Expense ($000):** 29608
Personnel: 447

Many Facility Codes have changed. Please refer to the AHA Guide Code Chart. © 2019 AHA Guide

TX

★ **SHANNON MEDICAL CENTER (450571)**, 120 East Harris Street,
Zip 76903–5976, Mailing Address: P.O. Box 1879, Zip 76902–1879;
tel. 325/653–6741, (Includes SHANNON MEDICAL CENTER- ST. JOHN'S CAMPUS,
2018 Pulliam Street, San Angelo, Texas, Zip 76905–5197; tel. 325/659–7100;
Bryan Horner, President and Chief Executive Officer) (Total facility includes 21 beds
in nursing home–type unit) **A**3 5 10 22 **F**3 8 11 12 13 15 18 20 22 24 26 28 29
30 31 32 34 35 37 38 40 43 44 45 47 48 49 50 51 53 54 56 57 58 59 60 61
62 64 68 70 71 72 73 74 75 76 77 78 79 80 81 82 84 85 86 87 89 90 92 93
94 96 98 100 101 102 107 108 110 111 114 115 117 119 126 128 130 132
145 146 147 148 149 155
Primary Contact: Shane Plymell, Chief Executive Officer
COO: Pamela Bradshaw, Vice President, Chief Operating Officer and Chief Nursing
Officer
CFO: Staci Wetz, Chief Financial Officer
CMO: Irvin Zeitler, D.O., Vice President Medical Affairs
CIO: Tom Perkins, Chief Information Officer
CHR: Teresa Morgan, Assistant Vice President Human Resources
CNO: Pamela Bradshaw, Vice President, Chief Operating Officer and Chief Nursing
Officer
Web address: www.shannonhealth.com
Control: Other not–for–profit (including NFP Corporation) **Service:** General
medical and surgical

Staffed Beds: 314 **Admissions:** 13913 **Census:** 199 **Outpatient
Visits:** 120368 **Births:** 1203 **Total Expense ($000):** 294176 **Payroll
Expense ($000):** 102719 **Personnel:** 1679

SAN ANTONIO—Bexar County

☐ **LEGENT ORTHOPEDIC + SPINE (670112)**, 5330 N. Loop 1604 W, Zip 78249;
tel. 210/877–8000, (Nonreporting) **A**1 10
Primary Contact: Donald Plummer, Senior Vice President, Operations
CNO: Lisa Kuopus, Chief Nursing Officer
Web address: www.cumberlandsh.com/
Control: Partnership, Investor–owned (for–profit) **Service:** General medical and
surgical

Staffed Beds: 9

☐ **AMG SPECIALTY HOSPITAL (452040)**, 718 Lexington Avenue,
Zip 78212–4768; tel. 210/572–4600, (Data for 208 days) **A**1 10 22 **F**1 3
29 40 75 85 87 91 119 148 149 **S** AMG Integrated Healthcare Management,
Lafayette, LA
Primary Contact: Melissa Low, Chief Executive Officer
Web address: www.southtexas.acuityhealthcare.net/
Control: Partnership, Investor–owned (for–profit) **Service:** Acute long–term care
hospital

Staffed Beds: 30 **Admissions:** 48 **Census:** 5 **Outpatient Visits:** 0 **Births:** 0
Total Expense ($000): 3106 **Payroll Expense ($000):** 1604 **Personnel:** 70

⇑ **BAPTIST EMERGENCY HOSPITAL (670078)**, 16088 San Pedro,
Zip 78232–2249; tel. 210/402–4092, (Includes BAPTIST EMERGENCY
HOSPITAL - HAUSMAN, 8230 North 1604 West, San Antonio, Texas, Zip 78249;
tel. 210/572–8885; David Mitchell, Chief Executive Officer; BAPTIST EMERGENCY
HOSPITAL - OVERLOOK, 25615 US Highway 281 North, San Antonio, Texas,
Zip 78258–7135; tel. 210/572–2911; David Mitchell, Chief Executive Officer;
BAPTIST EMERGENCY HOSPITAL - SCHERTZ, 16977 Interstate 35 North, Schertz,
Texas, Zip 78154–1466; tel. 210/572–8400; Sandra Diaz, Administrator;
BAPTIST EMERGENCY HOSPITAL - WESTOVER HILLS, 10811 Town Center Drive,
San Antonio, Texas, Zip 78251–4585; tel. 210/572–0911; David Mitchell, Chief
Executive Officer) **A**10 21 **F**3 40 41 **S** Emerus, The Woodlands, TX
Primary Contact: David Mitchell, Interim Chief Executive Officer
Web address: www.baptistemergencyhospital.com
Control: Corporation, Investor–owned (for–profit) **Service:** General medical and
surgical

Staffed Beds: 30 **Admissions:** 1246 **Census:** 7 **Outpatient Visits:** 109451
Births: 0 **Total Expense ($000):** 61901 **Payroll Expense ($000):** 18374
Personnel: 285

★ △ ⇑ **BAPTIST MEDICAL CENTER (450058)**, 111 Dallas Street,
Zip 78205–1230; tel. 210/297–7000, (Includes MISSION TRAIL BAPTIST
HOSPITAL, 3333 Research Plaza, San Antonio, Texas, Zip 78235–5154;
tel. 210/297–3000; Gina Temple, Chief Executive Officer; NORTH
CENTRAL BAPTIST HOSPITAL, 520 Madison Oak Drive, San Antonio, Texas,
Zip 78258–3912; tel. 210/297–4000; NORTHEAST BAPTIST HOSPITAL, 8811
Village Drive, San Antonio, Texas, Zip 78217–5440; tel. 210/297–2000; J Phillip
Young, FACHE, Chief Executive Officer; ST. LUKE'S BAPTIST HOSPITAL, 7930
Floyd Curl Drive, San Antonio, Texas, Zip 78229–0100; tel. 210/297–5000; Eric
Schmacker, Chief Executive Officer) **A**2 3 5 7 10 21 **F**3 11 12 13 14 15 17 18 19
20 22 24 26 28 29 30 31 35 37 38 40 41 43 44 45 46 47 50 54 55 56 57 59
60 64 65 68 70 72 73 74 75 76 77 78 79 80 81 82 85 86 87 88 89 90 91 92
93 95 96 98 101 102 103 107 108 111 114 115 116 117 119 124 126 129
130 132 135 145 146 147 148 149 **S** TENET Healthcare Corporation, Dallas, TX
Primary Contact: Matt Stone, President and Chief Executive Officer
COO: Sandy Ethridge, Interim Chief Operating Officer
CIO: Gary Davis, Vice President Information Systems
Web address: www.baptisthealthsystem.com
Control: Partnership, Investor–owned (for–profit) **Service:** General medical and
surgical

Staffed Beds: 1531 **Admissions:** 64004 **Census:** 773 **Outpatient
Visits:** 443670 **Births:** 10833 **Total Expense ($000):** 890716 **Payroll
Expense ($000):** 334054 **Personnel:** 5424

⊞ **CHILDREN'S HOSPITAL OF SAN ANTONIO (453315)**, 333 North Santa Rosa
Street, Zip 78207; tel. 210/704–2011, (Nonreporting) **A**1 3 5 10 **S** CHRISTUS
Health, Irving, TX
Primary Contact: Cris Daskevich, Chief Executive Officer
Web address: www.chofsa.org/
Control: Church operated, Nongovernment, not–for–profit **Service:** Children's
general medical and surgical

Staffed Beds: 196

⊞ **CHRISTUS SANTA ROSA HEALTH SYSTEM (450237)**, 333 North Santa
Rosa Street, Zip 78207–3108, Mailing Address: 100 NE Loop 410 Suite 800,
Zip 78216–4749; tel. 210/704–2000, (Includes CHRISTUS SANTA ROSA
HOSPITAL - ALAMO HEIGHTS, 403 Treeline Park Building, San Antonio, Texas,
Zip 78209–2042; tel. 210/294–8000; Lanell Scott, Chief Executive Officer;
CHRISTUS SANTA ROSA HOSPITAL - NEW BRAUNFELS, 600 North Union Avenue,
New Braunfels, Texas, Zip 78130–4191; tel. 830/606–9111; Jim D Wesson,
President and Administrator; CHRISTUS SANTA ROSA-MEDICAL CENTER, 2827
Babcock Road, San Antonio, Texas, Zip 78229 4813; tel. 210/705–6300; Ian
Thompson Jr, M.D., President) **A**1 3 5 10 **F**3 8 11 12 13 15 18 19 20 21 22 23
24 25 26 27 28 29 30 31 32 34 35 37 39 40 41 42 43 45 46 48 49 54 56 57
58 59 60 62 63 64 65 68 70 71 72 74 75 76 77 78 79 81 82 83 84 85 86
87 88 89 92 93 95 97 107 108 110 111 112 113 114 115 116 117 118 119
124 126 130 131 132 134 138 141 144 146 147 149 154 **S** CHRISTUS Health,
Irving, TX
Primary Contact: Dean Alexander, President and Chief Executive Officer
CFO: Linda Kirks, Vice President and Chief Financial Officer
CMO: Kenneth Davis, M.D., Chief Medical Officer
CHR: Crystal H Kohanke, Group Vice President, Human Resources
CNO: Patty Toney, R.N., MSN, Chief Nurse Executive
Web address: www.christussantarosa.org
Control: Church operated, Nongovernment, not–for–profit **Service:** General
medical and surgical

Staffed Beds: 572 **Admissions:** 26720 **Census:** 359 **Outpatient
Visits:** 616291 **Births:** 2773 **Total Expense ($000):** 638995 **Payroll
Expense ($000):** 195272 **Personnel:** 2614

☐ **CLARITY CHILD GUIDANCE CENTER**, 8535 Tom Slick, Zip 78229–3363;
tel. 210/616–0300, **A**1 3 5 **F**29 34 50 75 98 99 101 102 104 105 106 130
Primary Contact: Frederick W. Hines, President and Chief Executive Officer
CFO: Michael Bernick, Executive Vice President and Chief Financial Officer
CMO: Soad Michelson, M.D., Senior Medical Director
CHR: Gina Massey, Vice President Human Resources
CNO: Carol Carver, MSN, R.N., Vice President Patient Services
Web address: www.claritycgc.org
Control: Other not–for–profit (including NFP Corporation) **Service:** Children's
hospital psychiatric

Staffed Beds: 66 **Admissions:** 3136 **Census:** 66 **Outpatient Visits:** 21013
Births: 0 **Total Expense ($000):** 27600 **Payroll Expense ($000):** 15244
Personnel: 293

Hospital, Medicare Provider Number, Address, Telephone, Approval, Facility, and Physician Codes, Health Care System

★ American Hospital Association (AHA) membership   ○ Healthcare Facilities Accreditation Program   ⇑ Center for Improvement in Healthcare Quality Accreditation
☐ The Joint Commission accreditation   ◇ DNV Healthcare Inc. accreditation   △ Commission on Accreditation of Rehabilitation Facilities (CARF) accreditation

© 2019 AHA Guide   *Many Facility Codes have changed. Please refer to the AHA Guide Code Chart.*   Hospitals **A633**

ENCOMPASS HEALTH REHABILITATION HOSPITAL OF SAN ANTONIO (453031), 9119 Cinnamon Hill, Zip 78240–5401; tel. 210/691–0737, **A**1 10 **F**29 90 91 96 130 132 148 **S** Encompass Health Corporation, Birmingham, AL
Primary Contact: Michael Thomas, Chief Executive Officer
CFO: Larry Floyd Spriggs, CPA, Controller
CMO: Chaula Rana, M.D., Medical Director
CHR: Vanessa Tejada, Director Human Resources
CNO: Matthew D'Ambrosio, MSN, R.N., Chief Nursing Officer
Web address: www.hsriosa.com
Control: Corporation, Investor–owned (for–profit) **Service:** Rehabilitation

> **Staffed Beds:** 96 **Admissions:** 1162 **Census:** 41 **Outpatient Visits:** 0
> **Births:** 0 **Total Expense ($000):** 19581 **Payroll Expense ($000):** 9893
> **Personnel:** 162

FOUNDATION SURGICAL HOSPITAL OF SAN ANTONIO (670054), 9522 Huebner Road, Zip 78240–1548; tel. 210/478–5400, **A**3 5 10 21 **F**3 12 29 35 37 40 44 45 51 53 68 74 75 79 81 85 86 87 107 114 126 130 132 135 148 149
Primary Contact: Blake W. Hubbard, FACHE, Chief Executive Officer
CNO: Beckie Leonard, R.N., Chief Nursing Officer
Web address: www.https://www.fshsanantonio.com/
Control: Corporation, Investor–owned (for–profit) **Service:** Surgical

> **Staffed Beds:** 20 **Admissions:** 1331 **Census:** 6 **Outpatient Visits:** 3794
> **Births:** 0 **Total Expense ($000):** 39404 **Payroll Expense ($000):** 6757
> **Personnel:** 106

KINDRED HOSPITAL SAN ANTONIO CENTRAL (452073), 111 Dallas Street, 4th Floor, Zip 78205–1201; tel. 210/297–7185, **A**1 10 **F**1 29 75 77 87 91 130 148 157 **S** Kindred Healthcare, Louisville, KY
Primary Contact: Abiola Anyebe, Interim Chief Executive Officer
Web address: www.kindredsanantoniocentral.com/
Control: Corporation, Investor–owned (for–profit) **Service:** Acute long–term care hospital

> **Staffed Beds:** 44 **Admissions:** 452 **Census:** 30 **Outpatient Visits:** 0
> **Births:** 0 **Total Expense ($000):** 17904 **Payroll Expense ($000):** 7493
> **Personnel:** 84

KINDRED HOSPITAL-SAN ANTONIO (452016), 3636 Medical Drive, Zip 78229–2183; tel. 210/616–0616, **A**1 10 **F**1 3 29 30 70 75 77 85 87 91 107 130 148 157 **S** Kindred Healthcare, Louisville, KY
Primary Contact: Abiola Anyebe, Interim Chief Executive Officer
CFO: Erin Russell, Controller
CMO: Charles Duncan, M.D., Medical Director
CHR: Stanley Richardson, Coordinator Human Resources and Payroll Benefits
Web address: www.khsanantonio.com/
Control: Corporation, Investor–owned (for–profit) **Service:** Acute long–term care hospital

> **Staffed Beds:** 59 **Admissions:** 435 **Census:** 32 **Outpatient Visits:** 0
> **Births:** 0 **Total Expense ($000):** 18988 **Payroll Expense ($000):** 8219
> **Personnel:** 107

LAUREL RIDGE TREATMENT CENTER (454060), 17720 Corporate Woods Drive, Zip 78259–3500; tel. 210/491–9400, **A**1 3 5 10 **F**4 5 29 35 38 75 87 98 99 100 101 102 103 105 106 130 132 135 151 152 153 **S** Universal Health Services, Inc., King of Prussia, PA
Primary Contact: Jacob Cuellar, M.D., Chief Executive Officer
CFO: Linda Maenius, Chief Financial Officer
CMO: Benigno J Fernandez, M.D., Executive Medical Director
CHR: Brenda Frederick, Director Human Resources
CNO: Kathy Rosetta, Chief Nursing Officer
Web address: www.laurelridgetc.com
Control: Partnership, Investor–owned (for–profit) **Service:** Psychiatric

> **Staffed Beds:** 208 **Admissions:** 7751 **Census:** 185 **Outpatient Visits:** 20432 **Births:** 0 **Total Expense ($000):** 56602 **Payroll Expense ($000):** 23224 **Personnel:** 361

LIFECARE HOSPITALS OF SAN ANTONIO (452059), 8902 Floyd Curl Drive, Zip 78240–1681; tel. 210/690–7000, **A**1 10 **F**1 3 29 45 70 75 77 85 86 87 96 97 107 114 130 148 149 **S** LifeCare Management Services, Plano, TX
Primary Contact: Michelle Lozano, Chief Executive Officer
CMO: Randall C Bell, M.D., Medical Director
CIO: Mike Wattenbarger, Chief Information Officer
Web address: www.lifecare-hospitals.com
Control: Corporation, Investor–owned (for–profit) **Service:** Acute long–term care hospital

> **Staffed Beds:** 62 **Admissions:** 638 **Census:** 45 **Outpatient Visits:** 0
> **Births:** 0

METHODIST AMBULATORY SURGERY HOSPITAL - NORTHWEST (450780), 9150 Huebner Road, Suite 100, Zip 78240–1545; tel. 210/575–5000, **A**1 3 10 **F**3 29 40 50 65 68 79 81 85 87 107 114 **S** HCA Healthcare, Nashville, TN
Primary Contact: Cathy Bump, R.N., Interim Chief Executive Officer
CFO: Tim Carr, Chief Financial Officer
CHR: Barry Burns, Vice President
CNO: Cathy Bump, R.N., Chief Nursing Officer
Web address: www.sahealth.com
Control: Partnership, Investor–owned (for–profit) **Service:** Surgical

> **Staffed Beds:** 21 **Admissions:** 460 **Census:** 3 **Outpatient Visits:** 6231
> **Births:** 0 **Total Expense ($000):** 22626 **Payroll Expense ($000):** 6703
> **Personnel:** 101

★ **METHODIST HOSPITAL (450388)**, 7700 Floyd Curl Drive, Zip 78229–3993; tel. 210/575–4000, (Includes METHODIST CHILDREN'S HOSPITAL, 7700 Floyd Curl Drive, San Antonio, Texas, Zip 78229–3383; tel. 210/575–7000; Robert Lenza, Chief Executive Officer; METHODIST SPECIALTY AND TRANSPLANT HOSPITAL, 8026 Floyd Curl Drive, San Antonio, Texas, Zip 78229–3915; tel. 210/575–8090; Jeffrey Wilson, Chief Executive Officer; METHODIST TEXSAN HOSPITAL, 6700 IH-10 West, San Antonio, Texas, Zip 78201; tel. 210/736–6700; Megan Cool, Interim Chief Executive Officer and Chief Operating Officer; METROPOLITAN METHODIST HOSPITAL, 1310 McCullough Avenue, San Antonio, Texas, Zip 78212–2617; tel. 210/757–2909; Gregory A Seiler, Chief Executive Officer; NORTHEAST METHODIST HOSPITAL, 12412 Judson Road, Live Oak, Texas, Zip 78233–3255; tel. 210/757–5000; Michael D Beaver, Chief Executive Officer) **A**2 3 5 10 **F**3 5 8 11 12 13 15 18 19 20 21 22 23 24 25 26 27 28 29 30 31 34 35 38 40 41 42 43 44 45 46 47 48 49 51 53 54 56 57 58 59 60 64 65 68 70 72 74 75 76 77 78 79 80 81 82 84 85 86 87 88 89 90 93 95 96 98 100 101 102 103 104 105 107 108 111 112 114 115 118 119 120 121 124 126 127 129 130 132 135 136 137 138 139 142 143 144 145 146 147 148 152 153 154 156 **S** HCA Healthcare, Nashville, TN
Primary Contact: Daniel Miller, FACHE, Chief Executive Officer
CFO: Nancy Meadows, Chief Financial Officer
CMO: Russell Woodward, M.D., Chief Medical Officer
CIO: Eddie Cuellar, Vice President Information Systems
CHR: Nancy Edgar, Vice President Human Resources
Web address: www.sahealth.com
Control: Partnership, Investor–owned (for–profit) **Service:** General medical and surgical

> **Staffed Beds:** 1631 **Admissions:** 83777 **Census:** 1216 **Outpatient Visits:** 471495 **Births:** 8935 **Total Expense ($000):** 1358637 **Payroll Expense ($000):** 477453 **Personnel:** 6313

METHODIST STONE OAK HOSPITAL (670055), 1139 E Sonterra Boulevard, Zip 78258–4347, Mailing Address: 1139 East Sonterra Boulevard, Zip 78258–4347; tel. 210/638–2100, **A**1 3 5 10 **F**3 13 15 18 20 22 24 28 29 30 31 34 35 38 40 41 44 45 46 47 49 52 56 57 59 60 65 68 70 72 74 75 76 77 78 79 80 81 82 85 87 90 102 107 108 114 119 126 130 145 146 147 148 149 154 **S** HCA Healthcare, Nashville, TN
Primary Contact: Marc Strode, Chief Executive Officer
CFO: Gabriel Marrufo, Chief Financial Officer
CNO: Ann M Winn, M.D., R.N., FACHE, Chief Nursing Officer
Web address: www.sahealth.com/locations/methodist-stone-oak-hospital/
Control: Partnership, Investor–owned (for–profit) **Service:** General medical and surgical

> **Staffed Beds:** 242 **Admissions:** 13190 **Census:** 170 **Outpatient Visits:** 48785 **Births:** 1858 **Total Expense ($000):** 192361 **Payroll Expense ($000):** 62395 **Personnel:** 862

NIX HEALTH CARE SYSTEM (450130), 414 Navarro Street, Zip 78205–2516; tel. 210/271–1800, **A**3 5 10 21 **F**5 12 15 18 20 22 24 26 29 30 31 34 35 40 44 45 49 50 54 56 57 59 60 62 64 68 70 74 75 78 79 81 82 85 87 93 97 98 99 102 103 104 107 108 110 111 114 118 119 129 130 132 142 143 146 147 148 153 154 **S** Prospect Medical Holdings, Los Angeles, CA
Primary Contact: Jesse Peralez, Chief Executive Officer
CMO: Dina Goytia-Leos, M.D., Chief of Staff
CIO: Adrian Dickreiter, Vice President Technology
CNO: Maria Rose Lopez, R.N., Chief of Nursing
Web address: www.nixhealth.com
Control: Corporation, Investor–owned (for–profit) **Service:** General medical and surgical

> **Staffed Beds:** 228 **Admissions:** 8711 **Census:** 145 **Outpatient Visits:** 41159 **Births:** 0 **Total Expense ($000):** 122333 **Payroll Expense ($000):** 45446 **Personnel:** 907

TX

Many Facility Codes have changed. Please refer to the AHA Guide Code Chart. © 2019 AHA Guide

⊠ POST ACUTE/WARM SPRINGS SPECIALTY HOSPITAL OF SAN ANTONIO (452090), 5418 N Loop 1604 W, Zip 78247; tel. 210/921–3550, **A**1 10 **F**1 3 29 30 148 **S** Post Acute Medical, LLC, Enola, PA
Primary Contact: Kristen Lowe, Chief Executive Officer
CNO: Carrie Nims, Director of Nursing
Web address: www.postacutemedical.com
Control: Partnership, Investor–owned (for–profit) **Service:** Acute long–term care hospital

Staffed Beds: 26 **Admissions:** 364 **Census:** 21 **Outpatient Visits:** 0 **Births:** 0
Total Expense ($000): 13354 **Payroll Expense ($000):** 5015 **Personnel:** 87

SAN ANTONIO BEHAVIORAL HEALTHCARE HOSPITAL (454132), 8550 Huebner Road, Zip 78240–1803; tel. 877/514–0010, **F**5 87 98 99 100 101 103 104 105 132 152 153 **S** Signature Healthcare Services, Corona, CA
Primary Contact: Aleen D. Arabit, Chief Executive Officer
Web address: www.sanantoniobehavioral.com
Control: Individual, Investor–owned (for–profit) **Service:** Psychiatric

Staffed Beds: 198 **Admissions:** 4725 **Census:** 88 **Outpatient Visits:** 5958
Births: 0 **Total Expense ($000):** 20905 **Payroll Expense ($000):** 10807
Personnel: 203

☐ SAN ANTONIO STATE HOSPITAL (454011), 6711 South New Braunfels, Suite 100, Zip 78223–3006; tel. 210/531–7711, **A**1 3 5 10 **F**30 39 53 56 57 59 68 75 77 86 87 91 98 99 100 101 103 130 132 135 146 **S** Texas Department of State Health Services, Austin, TX
Primary Contact: Robert C. Arizpe, Superintendent
CFO: Janie Rabago, Chief Accountant
CMO: Terresa Stallworth, M.D., Clinical Director
CIO: Chris Stanush, Director Information Management
CHR: Renee Bourland, Human Resources Specialist
CNO: Maria DC Ostrander, R.N., MSN, Chief Nurse Executive
Web address: www.dshs.state.tx.us/mhhospitals/SanAntonioSH/default.shtm
Control: State, Government, nonfederal **Service:** Psychiatric

Staffed Beds: 282 **Admissions:** 715 **Census:** 245 **Outpatient Visits:** 0
Births: 0 **Total Expense ($000):** 107781 **Payroll Expense ($000):** 35873
Personnel: 823

★ SELECT REHABILITATION HOSPITAL OF SAN ANTONIO (673040), 19126 Stonehue Road, Zip 78258–3490; tel. 210/482–3400, **A**10 **F**3 29 30 34 35 75 90 91 96 130 148 149 156 **S** Select Medical Corporation, Mechanicsburg, PA
Primary Contact: John Deleon, Chief Executive Officer
Web address: www.sanantonio-rehab.com/
Control: Partnership, Investor–owned (for–profit) **Service:** Rehabilitation

Staffed Beds: 42 **Admissions:** 746 **Census:** 28 **Outpatient Visits:** 0
Births: 0 **Total Expense ($000):** 14795 **Payroll Expense ($000):** 8082
Personnel: 156

☐ SOUTH TEXAS SPINE AND SURGICAL HOSPITAL (450856), 18600 Hardy Oak Boulevard, Zip 78258–4206; tel. 210/507–4090, **A**1 3 5 10 **F**3 29 40 41 70 75 77 79 81 82 85 86 87 126 **S** National Surgical Healthcare, Chicago, IL
Primary Contact: Angie Kauffman, Chief Executive Officer
CFO: Sylvia Garcia, Chief Accounting Officer
CHR: Sally Hall, Manager Human Resources
CNO: Jennifer West, R.N., Chief Nursing Officer
Web address: www.southtexassurgical.com
Control: Partnership, Investor–owned (for–profit) **Service:** Orthopedic

Staffed Beds: 30 **Admissions:** 1472 **Census:** 8 **Outpatient Visits:** 2223
Births: 0 **Total Expense ($000):** 42035 **Payroll Expense ($000):** 8111
Personnel: 132

⊠ △ SOUTH TEXAS VETERANS HEALTH CARE SYSTEM, 7400 Merton Minter Boulevard, Zip 78229–4404; tel. 210/617–5300, (Includes KERRVILLE DIVISION, 3600 Memorial Boulevard, Kerrville, Texas, Zip 78028; tel. 210/896–2020; SAN ANTONIO DIVISION, 7400 Merton Minter Boulevard, San Antonio, Texas, Zip 78284–5799; tel. 210/617–5300), (Non-reporting) **A**1 3 5 7 8 **S** Department of Veterans Affairs, Washington, DC
Primary Contact: Christopher R. Sandles, FACHE, Medical Center Director
COO: Joe Perez, Associate Director
CFO: Eloisa Salazar, Chief Financial Officer
CMO: Julianne Flynn, M.D., Chief of Staff
CIO: Simon Willett, Director Administrative Operations
CHR: Jeffrey Young, Chief Human Resource Officer
CNO: Sharon Millican, Associate Director, Patient Care Services
Web address: www.southtexas.va.gov/
Control: Veterans Affairs, Government, federal **Service:** General medical and surgical

Staffed Beds: 838

⇑ SOUTHWEST GENERAL HOSPITAL (450697), 7400 Barlite Boulevard, Zip 78224–1399; tel. 210/921–2000, **A**10 21 **F**3 12 13 18 20 22 24 26 29 30 35 37 40 43 44 45 46 49 50 51 56 57 59 60 64 65 70 71 72 74 75 76 77 79 80 81 85 87 90 96 98 100 102 103 104 107 108 111 114 115 119 130 132 135 146 147 148 149 153 **S** Steward Health Care System, LLC, Dallas, TX
Primary Contact: P Craig. Desmond, Chief Executive Officer
COO: Sarah Humme, MSN, R.N., Chief Operating Officer
CFO: Colin B. Brooks, Chief Financial Officer
CIO: Debbie Mora, Director
CHR: Christina Rivera, Director Human Resources
CNO: Sarah Humme, MSN, R.N., Chief Nursing Officer
Web address: www.swgeneralhospital.com
Control: Corporation, Investor–owned (for–profit) **Service:** General medical and surgical

Staffed Beds: 242 **Admissions:** 9159 **Census:** 128 **Outpatient Visits:** 50396 **Births:** 1385 **Total Expense ($000):** 115484 **Payroll Expense ($000):** 46526 **Personnel:** 660

ST. LUKE'S BAPTIST HOSPITAL See Baptist Medical Center, San Antonio

☐ TEXAS CENTER FOR INFECTIOUS DISEASE (452033), 2303 SE Military Drive, Zip 78223–3597; tel. 210/534–8857, **A**1 3 5 10 **F**3 29 30 50 53 58 59 61 65 68 75 80 86 87 130 132 135 143 146 149 **S** Texas Department of State Health Services, Austin, TX
Primary Contact: James N. Elkins, FACHE, Director
CFO: Glenda Armstrong-Huff, Assistant Superintendent
CMO: David Griffith, M.D., Medical Director
CIO: Andre Avant, Facility Automation Manager
CHR: Gerald Shackelford, Staff Support Specialist
CNO: Rebecca Sanchez, R.N., M.P.H., Director of Nursing
Web address: www.dshs.state.tx.us/tcid/default.shtm
Control: State, Government, nonfederal **Service:** Tuberculosis and other respiratory diseases

Staffed Beds: 37 **Admissions:** 84 **Census:** 37 **Outpatient Visits:** 135 **Births:** 0
Total Expense ($000): 15286 **Payroll Expense ($000):** 6302 **Personnel:** 161

⊠ UNIVERSITY HEALTH SYSTEM (450213), 4502 Medical Drive, Zip 78229–4493; tel. 210/358–2000, (Includes UNIVERSITY HEALTH CENTER - DOWNTOWN, 4502 Medical Drive, San Antonio, Texas, Zip 78229–4493; tel. 210/358–3400; UNIVERSITY HOSPITAL, 4502 Medical Drive, San Antonio, Texas, Zip 78229 4493; tel. 210/358–4000; Michael Roussos, Administrator) **A**1 2 3 5 8 10 19 **F**3 4 11 12 13 14 15 16 17 18 19 20 21 22 23 24 25 26 27 28 29 30 31 32 34 35 38 40 41 43 44 45 46 47 48 49 50 51 52 54 55 56 57 58 59 60 61 64 65 66 68 70 72 73 74 75 76 77 79 81 82 84 85 86 87 88 89 90 92 93 95 98 100 101 102 107 108 110 111 115 118 119 126 129 130 132 135 138 139 140 141 142 143 144 145 146 147 148 149 154
Primary Contact: George B. Hernandez Jr, President and Chief Executive Officer
COO: Christann Vasquez, Executive Vice President and Chief Operating Officer
CFO: Peggy Deming, Executive Vice President and Chief Financial Officer
CMO: Bryan Alsip, M.D., Executive Vice President, Chief Medical Officer
CIO: Bill Phillips, Vice President Information Services
CHR: Theresa Scepanski, Vice President People and Organizational Development
CNO: Tommye Austin, Ph.D., R.N., MSN, Chief Nursing Executive
Web address: www.universityhealthsystem.com
Control: Hospital district or authority, Government, nonfederal **Service:** General medical and surgical

Staffed Beds: 659 **Admissions:** 30482 **Census:** 499 **Outpatient Visits:** 1788364 **Births:** 3248 **Total Expense ($000):** 1295253 **Payroll Expense ($000):** 470948 **Personnel:** 7414

⊠ WARM SPRINGS REHABILITATION HOSPITAL OF SAN ANTONIO (453035), 5101 Medical Drive, Zip 78229–4801; tel. 210/616–0100, (Includes WARM SPRINGS REHABILITATION HOSPITAL OF THOUSAND OAKS, 14747 Jones Maltsberger Road, San Antonio, Texas, Zip 78247–3713; tel. 210/581–5300; Kasondra Kistner, R.N., Chief Executive Officer; WARM SPRINGS REHABILITATION HOSPITAL OF WESTOVER HILLS, 10323 State Highway 151, San Antonio, Texas, Zip 78251–4557; tel. 210/581–5306; Steve Flaherty, Chief Executive Officer) **A**1 3 5 10 **F**3 11 29 30 34 57 64 68 74 75 79 82 90 93 94 95 96 100 130 132 146 148 154 **S** Post Acute Medical, LLC, Enola, PA
Primary Contact: Debra Bornmann, Chief Executive Officer
CIO: Rick Marek, Vice President Medical Information Systems
CHR: Waynea Finley, System Director Human Resources
Web address: www.postacutemedical.com/our-facilities/hospitals/warm-springs-rehabilitation-hospital-san-antonio/
Control: Partnership, Investor–owned (for–profit) **Service:** Rehabilitation

Staffed Beds: 139 **Admissions:** 2892 **Census:** 104 **Outpatient Visits:** 28742
Births: 0 **Total Expense ($000):** 52387 **Payroll Expense ($000):** 25542
Personnel: 535

TX

SAN AUGUSTINE—San Augustine County

★ **CHI ST. LUKE'S HEALTH MEMORIAL SAN AUGUSTINE (451360)**, 511 East Hospital Street, Zip 75972–2121, Mailing Address: P.O. Box 658, Zip 75972–0658; tel. 936/275–3446, **A**10 18 **F**29 35 40 57 59 64 102 107 119 132 133 149 **S** CommonSpirit Health, Chicago, IL
Primary Contact: Darlene Williams, R.N., Administrator
CFO: Kristi Gay, Chief Financial Officer
Web address: www.memorialhealth.org
Control: Other not–for–profit (including NFP Corporation) **Service**: General medical and surgical

Staffed Beds: 9 **Admissions**: 208 **Census**: 2 **Outpatient Visits**: 10459
Births: 0 **Total Expense ($000)**: 6402 **Payroll Expense ($000)**: 2592
Personnel: 39

SAN MARCOS—Hays County

⊞ **CENTRAL TEXAS MEDICAL CENTER (450272)**, 1301 Wonder World Drive, Zip 78666–7544; tel. 512/353–8979, **A**1 10 **F**3 11 13 15 18 20 29 30 32 34 35 39 40 43 44 45 49 50 51 56 57 59 60 62 63 64 65 66 68 70 72 75 76 77 79 80 81 82 85 86 87 92 93 94 98 107 108 109 110 111 114 116 117 118 119 126 129 130 131 132 146 147 148 152 157 **S** AdventHealth, Altamonte Springs, FL
Primary Contact: Anthony Stahl, Ph.D., FACHE, Chief Executive Officer
CFO: Parker Pridgen, Chief Financial Officer
CMO: Lee Johannsen, M.D., Chief Medical Officer
CHR: Debbie D Cox, Administrative Director Human Resources
CNO: Elsie Graves, Chief Nursing Officer
Web address: www.ctmc.org
Control: Church operated, Nongovernment, not–for–profit **Service**: General medical and surgical

Staffed Beds: 111 **Admissions**: 3871 **Census**: 42 **Outpatient Visits**: 77801
Births: 753 **Total Expense ($000)**: 88458 **Payroll Expense ($000)**: 31760
Personnel: 466

WELLBRIDGE HEATLHCARE OF SAN MARCOS (454137), 1106 North Interstate 35, Zip 78666–7030; tel. 512/353–0194, **F**29 98 100 101 103 130 135 149 153 154
Primary Contact: Gregory Drummond, Chief Executive Officer
Web address: www.oceanssanmarcos.com
Control: Partnership, Investor–owned (for–profit) **Service**: Psychiatric

Staffed Beds: 24 **Admissions**: 212 **Census**: 9 **Outpatient Visits**: 125
Births: 0 **Total Expense ($000)**: 4641 **Payroll Expense ($000)**: 2038
Personnel: 45

SEGUIN—Guadalupe County

⊞ **GUADALUPE REGIONAL MEDICAL CENTER (450104)**, 1215 East Court Street, Zip 78155–5189; tel. 830/379–2411, **A**1 10 **F**3 5 11 13 15 18 20 22 24 28 29 30 31 34 35 38 39 40 43 45 46 49 50 51 53 57 58 59 60 63 66 68 70 73 74 75 76 77 78 79 81 82 84 85 90 93 96 104 107 108 110 111 112 114 115 118 119 126 129 132 135 143 146 148 149 150 154 156
Primary Contact: Robert Gerard. Haynes, FACHE, Chief Executive Officer
COO: Sheri Williams, Chief Operating Officer
CFO: Penny Wallace, Chief Financial Officer
CMO: Robert Ryan, M.D., Chief Medical Officer
CIO: Steve Ratliff, Director Information Technology
CHR: Fay Bennett, Vice President Employee Services
CNO: Daphne Blake, R.N., MSN, Chief Nursing Officer
Web address: www.grmedcenter.com
Control: City–county, Government, nonfederal **Service**: General medical and surgical

Staffed Beds: 90 **Admissions**: 3937 **Census**: 41 **Outpatient Visits**: 140601
Births: 834 **Total Expense ($000)**: 95869 **Payroll Expense ($000)**: 35630
Personnel: 702

SEMINOLE—Gaines County

★ **MEMORIAL HOSPITAL (451358)**, 209 NW Eighth Street, Zip 79360–3447; tel. 432/758–5811, **A**10 18 **F**3 10 11 13 28 29 30 32 34 35 40 43 45 53 56 57 59 62 63 64 65 75 76 81 87 93 97 102 107 111 114 119 127 130 131 132 133 143 146 147 148
Primary Contact: Joe Wright, Interim Chief Executive Officer
COO: Heath Mitchell, Chief Operating Officer
CFO: Traci Anderson, Chief Financial Officer
CMO: Michael Watson, M.D., Chief of Staff
Web address: www.seminolehospitaldistrict.com
Control: Hospital district or authority, Government, nonfederal **Service**: General medical and surgical

Staffed Beds: 25 **Admissions**: 898 **Census**: 9 **Outpatient Visits**: 89555
Births: 488 **Total Expense ($000)**: 42444 **Payroll Expense ($000)**: 10481
Personnel: 203

SEYMOUR—Baylor County

SEYMOUR HOSPITAL (450586), 200 Stadium Drive, Zip 76380–2344; tel. 940/889–5572, **A**10 20 **F**3 7 8 11 13 14 28 29 34 36 40 43 45 50 53 56 57 59 62 64 65 66 68 70 75 76 81 85 86 87 89 93 94 100 102 103 104 107 119 127 130 133 135 146 147 148 154
Primary Contact: Leslie Hardin, Chief Executive Officer and Chief Financial Officer
CFO: Leslie Hardin, Chief Executive Officer and Chief Financial Officer
CMO: Kory Lann Martin, M.D., Chief of Staff
CHR: Linda Moore, Manager Human Resources
CNO: Julie Smajstrla, Director Nursing
Web address: www.seymourhospital.com/
Control: Hospital district or authority, Government, nonfederal **Service**: General medical and surgical

Staffed Beds: 40 **Admissions**: 379 **Census**: 3 **Outpatient Visits**: 38862
Births: 25 **Total Expense ($000)**: 38081 **Payroll Expense ($000)**: 5697
Personnel: 132

SHAMROCK—Wheeler County

SHAMROCK GENERAL HOSPITAL (451340), 1000 South Main Street, Zip 79079–2896, Mailing Address: P O Box 511, Zip 79079–0511; tel. 806/256–2114, **A**10 18 **F**7 11 29 32 34 35 40 43 63 65 68 93 107 119 127 130 133
Primary Contact: Wiley M. Fires, Administrator
CFO: Wiley M Fires, Administrator
CHR: Cecille Williams, Assistant Administrator
CNO: Jeanne Crossland, Director of Nursing
Control: Hospital district or authority, Government, nonfederal **Service**: General medical and surgical

Staffed Beds: 13 **Admissions**: 101 **Census**: 2 **Outpatient Visits**: 9647
Births: 0 **Total Expense ($000)**: 6682 **Payroll Expense ($000)**: 3390
Personnel: 71

SHENANDOAH—Montgomery County

⊞ **ENCOMPASS HEALTH REHABILITATION HOSPITAL VISION PARK (673034)**, 117 Vision Park Boulevard, Zip 77384–3001; tel. 936/444–1700, **A**1 10 **F**3 28 29 34 35 44 57 59 65 68 71 74 75 77 78 79 82 86 87 90 91 95 96 130 132 148 149 **S** Encompass Health Corporation, Birmingham, AL
Primary Contact: Jennifer Brewer, Chief Executive Officer
CFO: Terri Weiss, Chief Financial Officer
Web address: www.healthsouthvisionpark.com/
Control: Corporation, Investor–owned (for–profit) **Service**: Rehabilitation

Staffed Beds: 60 **Admissions**: 1385 **Census**: 46 **Outpatient Visits**: 0
Births: 0 **Total Expense ($000)**: 20540 **Payroll Expense ($000)**: 10202
Personnel: 155

⇑ **NEXUS SPECIALTY HOSPITAL**, 123 Vision Park Boulevard, Zip 77384–3001; tel. 281/364–0317, **A**21 **F**1 3 70 74 75 77 82 84 85 91 92 93 100 101 107 119 130 132 135 148 **S** Nexus Health Systems, Houston, TX
Primary Contact: Eric Cantrell, Chief Executive Officer
CFO: David Strickler, Chief Financial Officer
CMO: Ather Siddiqi, M.D., Medical Director
CIO: Noe Salinas, Vice President Information Technology
CHR: Kevin McAndrews, Vice President Human Resources
CNO: Rhena Anderson, Chief Nursing Officer
Web address: www.nexusspecialty.com
Control: Partnership, Investor–owned (for–profit) **Service**: Acute long–term care hospital

Staffed Beds: 76 **Admissions**: 505 **Census**: 37 **Outpatient Visits**: 561
Births: 0 **Total Expense ($000)**: 22725 **Payroll Expense ($000)**: 8458
Personnel: 152

SHERMAN—Grayson County

⇑ **BAYLOR SCOTT & WHITE SURGICAL HOSPITAL-SHERMAN (670076)**, 3601 North Calais Street, Zip 75090–1785; tel. 903/870–0999, **A**10 21 **F**3 29 37 40 45 47 77 81 85 107 111 119 126 131 145 **S** Foundation Surgical Hospital Affiliates, Oklahoma City, OK
Primary Contact: Marc Devorsetz, Chief Executive Officer
CMO: Curtis Holbrook, M.D., Chief Medical Officer
CIO: Grant Hulsey, Director Information Technology
CHR: Terrie Langford, Director Human Resources
CNO: Teresa Dutton, R.N., Chief Nursing Officer
Web address: www.heritageparksurgicalhospital.com
Control: Partnership, Investor–owned (for–profit) **Service**: General medical and surgical

Staffed Beds: 12 **Admissions**: 494 **Census**: 3 **Outpatient Visits**: 24520
Births: 0 **Total Expense ($000)**: 40410 **Payroll Expense ($000)**: 11534
Personnel: 206

TX

☐ **CARRUS REHABILITATION HOSPITAL (673041)**, 1810 West US Highway 82, Suite 100, Zip 75092-7069; tel. 903/870-2600, **A**1 10 **F**3 29 40 41 44 65 74 75 77 79 85 86 87 90 91 96 130 **S** Carrus Hospitals, Sherman, TX
Primary Contact: Jon-Michael Rains, Chief Executive Officer
CFO: Michael Exline, Chief Financial Officer
CMO: Jose Matus, M.D., Director Medical
CIO: Gary Glenn, Director Information Technology
CHR: Charlene Shupert, Director Staff Services
CNO: Marie Johnson, Chief Nursing Officer
Web address: www.carrushospital.com
Control: Corporation, Investor-owned (for-profit) **Service**: Rehabilitation

Staffed Beds: 24 **Admissions**: 731 **Census**: 24 **Outpatient Visits**: 0
Births: 0 **Total Expense ($000)**: 10402 **Payroll Expense ($000)**: 4121
Personnel: 89

☐ **CARRUS SPECIALTY HOSPITAL (452041)**, 1810 West US Highway 82, Zip 75092-7069; tel. 903/870-2600, **A**10 **F**1 3 29 40 41 44 56 65 74 75 77 78 79 82 83 85 86 87 91 107 114 119 129 130 148 **S** Carrus Hospitals, Sherman, TX
Primary Contact: Jon-Michael Rains, Chief Executive Officer
CFO: Michael Exline, Chief Financial Officer
CMO: Nathan Watson, M.D., Jr Chief of Staff
CIO: Gary Glenn, Director Information Technology
CHR: Charlene Shupert, Director Staff Services
CNO: Marie Johnson, Chief Nursing Officer
Web address: www.carrushospital.com
Control: Corporation, Investor-owned (for-profit) **Service**: Acute long-term care hospital

Staffed Beds: 33 **Admissions**: 391 **Census**: 19 **Outpatient Visits**: 1789
Births: 0 **Total Expense ($000)**: 13647 **Payroll Expense ($000)**: 6178
Personnel: 128

WILSON N. JONES MEDICAL CENTER See Wilson N. Jones Regional Medical Center

☐ **WILSON N. JONES REGIONAL MEDICAL CENTER (450469)**, 500 North Highland Avenue, Zip 75092-7354; tel. 903/870-4611, **A**1 10 **F**3 12 13 15 17 18 20 22 24 28 29 30 34 35 40 41 43 45 47 49 53 56 57 58 59 64 70 74 75 76 79 81 84 85 86 87 91 92 93 96 98 103 107 108 110 111 118 119 129 130 132 135 146 147 148 149 154 156 157 **S** Alecto Healthcare, Irvine, CA
Primary Contact: Glenn Carney, Chief Executive Officer
CFO: Chuck Cave, CPA, Chief Financial Officer
CMO: Kenton Schrank, M.D., President Medical Staff
CIO: Prabhu Bollu, Director Information Technology
CHR: Bill Barrell, Manager Human Resources
CNO: Tonya Price, Chief Nursing Officer
Web address: www.wnj.org
Control: Corporation, Investor-owned (for-profit) **Service**: General medical and surgical

Staffed Beds: 109 **Admissions**: 5435 **Census**: 65 **Outpatient Visits**: 39030
Births: 390 **Total Expense ($000)**: 78682 **Payroll Expense ($000)**: 30280
Personnel: 499

SMITHVILLE—Bastrop County

⊠ **ASCENSION SETON SMITHVILLE (450143)**, 1201 Hill Road, Zip 78957; tel. 512/237-3214, **A**1 10 **F**3 11 15 29 30 35 40 45 46 47 50 53 57 77 79 81 82 85 87 92 93 97 107 110 111 114 119 127 130 143 146 147 148 149 **S** Ascension Healthcare, Saint Louis, MO
Primary Contact: Scott O. Fuller, President and Chief Executive Officer
CFO: Melissa Nordyke, Chief Financial Officer
CHR: Sara Rodriguez, Human Resources
CNO: Christine Laflamme, R.N., MSN, Chief Nursing Officer
Web address: www.seton.org
Control: Church operated, Nongovernment, not-for-profit **Service**: General medical and surgical

Staffed Beds: 5 **Admissions**: 186 **Census**: 2 **Outpatient Visits**: 26991
Births: 0 **Total Expense ($000)**: 13809 **Payroll Expense ($000)**: 4762
Personnel: 132

SNYDER—Scurry County

COGDELL MEMORIAL HOSPITAL (451384), 1700 Cogdell Boulevard, Zip 79549-6198; tel. 325/573-6374, **A**10 18 **F**3 8 11 12 13 15 18 19 29 30 34 35 40 43 45 46 47 48 49 50 53 56 57 59 62 63 64 65 66 68 75 76 77 79 81 83 84 85 86 87 91 92 93 97 107 110 111 115 119 127 130 131 132 133 145 146 147 148 149 154 156 157
Primary Contact: Ella Raye. Helms, Chief Executive Officer
CFO: John Everett, Chief Financial Officer
CMO: Robert Rakov, M.D., Chief Medical Officer
CHR: Linda Warren, Director Human Resources
Web address: www.cogdellhospital.com
Control: Hospital district or authority, Government, nonfederal **Service**: General medical and surgical

Staffed Beds: 25 **Admissions**: 776 **Census**: 6 **Outpatient Visits**: 90144
Births: 148 **Total Expense ($000)**: 51546 **Payroll Expense ($000)**: 15787
Personnel: 286

SONORA—Sutton County

★ **LILLIAN M. HUDSPETH MEMORIAL HOSPITAL (451324)**, 308 Hudspeth Avenue, Zip 76950-8003, Mailing Address: P.O. Box 455, Zip 76950-0455; tel. 325/387-2521, **A**10 18 **F**3 7 15 26 28 29 30 34 35 40 41 43 50 53 57 59 63 64 65 66 68 75 79 86 87 90 93 96 97 107 110 111 115 119 127 128 131 133 135 154
Primary Contact: Andy Kolb, Chief Executive Officer
COO: Joe Marshall, Chief Operating Officer
CFO: Michelle Schaefer, Chief Financial Officer
CNO: Lara Ellen Teague, R.N., Chief Nursing Officer
Web address: www.sonora-hospital.org
Control: Hospital district or authority, Government, nonfederal **Service**: General medical and surgical

Staffed Beds: 12 **Admissions**: 101 **Census**: 1 **Outpatient Visits**: 7938 **Births**: 0
Total Expense ($000): 9317 **Payroll Expense ($000)**: 3920 **Personnel**: 80

SOUTHLAKE—Tarrant County

★ **METHODIST SOUTHLAKE HOSPITAL**, 421 East State Highway 114, Zip 76092; tel. 817/865-4400, **F**3 12 29 40 45 49 50 51 68 70 75 79 81 82 85 107 111 115 119 124 126 130 135 149 **S** Methodist Health System, Dallas, TX
Primary Contact: John McGreevy, FACHE, President
Web address: www.https://methodistsouthlake.com/
Control: Partnership, Investor-owned (for-profit) **Service**: General medical and surgical

Staffed Beds: 12 **Admissions**: 473 **Census**: 3 **Outpatient Visits**: 5559
Births: 0 **Total Expense ($000)**: 53899 **Payroll Expense ($000)**: 11548
Personnel: 148

☐ **TEXAS HEALTH HARRIS METHODIST HOSPITAL SOUTHLAKE (450888)**, 1545 East Southlake Boulevard, Zip 76092-6422; tel. 817/748-8700, **A**1 10 **F**3 29 30 40 64 74 79 81 85 107 111 115 119 130
Primary Contact: Traci Bernard, R.N., President, Chief Executive Officer and Chief Operating Officer
CFO: Mitchell Mulvehill, Group Financial Officer
CMO: David Taunton, M.D., Chief of Staff
CHR: Tasha Sledge, Director Human Resources
CNO: Debra Ennis, Vice President and Chief Nursing Officer
Web address: www.texashealthsouthlake.com
Control: Corporation, Investor-owned (for-profit) **Service**: Surgical

Staffed Beds: 23 **Admissions**: 790 **Census**: 4 **Outpatient Visits**: 14470
Births: 0 **Total Expense ($000)**: 57564 **Payroll Expense ($000)**: 10983
Personnel: 144

SPEARMAN—Hansford County

★ **HANSFORD HOSPITAL (451344)**, 707 South Roland Street, Zip 79081-3441; tel. 806/659-2535, **A**10 18 **F**3 7 11 32 34 35 40 43 56 57 59 62 63 64 65 68 69 77 78 93 107 114 127 130 133 148 158
Primary Contact: Jonathan D. Bailey, Chief Executive Officer and Administrator
CFO: Scott Beedy, Chief Financial Officer
CMO: Mark Garnett, M.D., Chief of Staff
CHR: Jackie Nelson, Director Human Resources
Web address: www.hchd.net
Control: Hospital district or authority, Government, nonfederal **Service**: General medical and surgical

Staffed Beds: 14 **Admissions**: 106 **Census**: 2 **Outpatient Visits**: 22096
Births: 0 **Total Expense ($000)**: 11853 **Payroll Expense ($000)**: 4856
Personnel: 109

TX

STAFFORD—Fort Bend County

ATRIUM MEDICAL CENTER (452114), 11929 West Airport Boulevard, Zip 77477–2451; tel. 281/207–8200, **A**10 22 **F**1 3 18 28 29 45 46 56 59 60 64 65 68 70 74 77 82 83 85 90 91 107 114 119 130 148
Primary Contact: Ahmad Zaid, Chief Executive Officer
CFO: Ana Urbina, Chief Financial Officer
CMO: Shatish Patel, M.D., Chief Medical Officer
CNO: Ava Hearing, Chief Nursing Officer
Web address: www.atriummedicalcenter.com
Control: Partnership, Investor–owned (for–profit) **Service:** Acute long–term care hospital

Staffed Beds: 68 **Admissions:** 232 **Census:** 17 **Outpatient Visits:** 28 **Births:** 0 **Total Expense ($000):** 12891 **Payroll Expense ($000):** 3281 **Personnel:** 97

STANTON—Martin County

MARTIN COUNTY HOSPITAL DISTRICT (451333), 600 Interstate 20E, Zip 79782, Mailing Address: P.O. Box 640, Zip 79782–0640; tel. 432/607–3200, **A**10 18 **F**3 7 29 34 35 39 40 45 57 59 64 65 75 81 87 93 107 114 119 127 133 157
Primary Contact: Rance Ramsey, Chief Executive Officer
CFO: Michele Cathey, Interim Chief Financial officer
CIO: Freddy Oliveras, Chief Information Officer
CHR: Paula Dority, Director Human Resources
CNO: Brandi Avila, Chief Nursing Officer
Web address: www.martincountyhospital.org/
Control: Hospital district or authority, Government, nonfederal **Service:** General medical and surgical

Staffed Beds: 18 **Admissions:** 195 **Census:** 6 **Outpatient Visits:** 7433 **Births:** 0 **Total Expense ($000):** 23396 **Payroll Expense ($000):** 10396 **Personnel:** 171

STEPHENVILLE—Erath County

TEXAS HEALTH HARRIS METHODIST HOSPITAL STEPHENVILLE (450351), 411 North Belknap Street, Zip 76401–3415; tel. 254/965–1500, **A**1 10 20 **F**3 13 15 28 29 30 34 35 39 40 41 43 45 50 51 57 59 64 65 68 70 75 76 77 79 81 85 86 89 107 108 110 111 114 118 119 130 146 147 148 149 154 156 **S** Texas Health Resources, Arlington, TX
Primary Contact: Christopher Leu, President
CMO: Marilyn Brister, M.D., Chief of Staff
CHR: Kimberly Leondar, Director Human Resources
CNO: Cynthia L McCarthy, Chief Nursing Officer
Web address: www.texashealth.org/landing.cfm?id=108
Control: Other not–for–profit (including NFP Corporation) **Service:** General medical and surgical

Staffed Beds: 50 **Admissions:** 1681 **Census:** 13 **Outpatient Visits:** 28849 **Births:** 365 **Total Expense ($000):** 49075 **Payroll Expense ($000):** 16657 **Personnel:** 220

SUGAR LAND—Fort Bend County

ENCOMPASS HEALTH REHABILITATION HOSPITAL OF SUGAR LAND (673042), 1325 Highway 6, Zip 77478–4906; tel. 281/276–7574, **A**1 10 **F**3 29 30 34 75 87 90 91 95 96 130 132 146 148 149 154 **S** Encompass Health Corporation, Birmingham, AL
Primary Contact: Nicholas Hardin, FACHE, Chief Executive Officer
CFO: Carol Neilson, CPA, Controller
CNO: Steve Midgett, R.N., Chief Nursing Officer
Web address: www.healthsouthsugarland.com
Control: Corporation, Investor–owned (for–profit) **Service:** Rehabilitation

Staffed Beds: 50 **Admissions:** 1358 **Census:** 46 **Outpatient Visits:** 0 **Births:** 0 **Total Expense ($000):** 20139 **Payroll Expense ($000):** 10488 **Personnel:** 193

★ ⇑ **HOUSTON METHODIST SUGAR LAND HOSPITAL (450820)**, 16655 SW Freeway, Zip 77479–2329; tel. 281/274–7000, **A**2 3 10 21 **F**3 12 13 15 18 20 22 24 26 29 30 31 33 34 35 36 37 38 40 41 44 45 49 50 51 53 55 57 59 60 61 64 65 68 70 73 74 75 77 78 79 81 82 84 85 86 87 91 92 93 94 96 100 102 107 108 110 111 114 115 118 119 120 121 123 124 126 130 131 132 135 145 146 147 148 149 150 154 156 **S** Houston Methodist, Houston, TX
Primary Contact: Christopher Siebenaler, Regional Senior Vice President and Chief Executive Officer
CFO: Lowell Stanton, Chief Financial Officer
CMO: Jeffrey Jackson, M.D., Medical Director
CHR: Luis Mario Garcia Jr Director Human Resources
Web address: www.methodisthealth.com
Control: Other not–for–profit (including NFP Corporation) **Service:** General medical and surgical

Staffed Beds: 321 **Admissions:** 17066 **Census:** 213 **Outpatient Visits:** 255405 **Births:** 2860 **Total Expense ($000):** 405904 **Payroll Expense ($000):** 141568 **Personnel:** 2120

KINDRED HOSPITAL SUGAR LAND (452080), 1550 First Colony Boulevard, Zip 77479–4000; tel. 281/275–6000, **A**1 10 **F**1 3 29 30 64 75 77 81 82 84 87 107 130 146 148 149 154 **S** Kindred Healthcare, Louisville, KY
Primary Contact: John D. Cross, Chief Executive Officer
CFO: Sara Rodriguez, Chief Financial Officer
CMO: Subodh Bhuchar, M.D., Chief of Staff
CIO: Feisal Ndomea, Director Case Management
CHR: Lupe Delgado, Coordinator Human Resources
CNO: Hala Alameddine, Chief Nursing Executive
Web address: www.kindred.com
Control: Corporation, Investor–owned (for–profit) **Service:** Acute long–term care hospital

Staffed Beds: 105 **Admissions:** 934 **Census:** 66 **Outpatient Visits:** 97 **Births:** 0 **Total Expense ($000):** 40067 **Payroll Expense ($000):** 14954 **Personnel:** 216

⇑ **METHODIST SUGAR LAND HOSPITAL** See Houston Methodist Sugar Land Hospital

⇑ **MEMORIAL HERMANN FIRST COLONY HOSPITAL (670058)**, 16000 Southwest Freeway, Suite 100, Zip 77479–2674; tel. 281/277–0911, (Data for 151 days) **A**10 21 **F**3 40 75 107 114 119 149 152 **S** Emerus, The Woodlands, TX
Primary Contact: Brenda Villafranco, Administrator
Web address: www.emerus.com
Control: Corporation, Investor–owned (for–profit) **Service:** General medical and surgical

Staffed Beds: 7 **Admissions:** 49 **Census:** 1 **Outpatient Visits:** 2797 **Births:** 0 **Total Expense ($000):** 2165 **Payroll Expense ($000):** 706 **Personnel:** 29

MEMORIAL HERMANN SUGAR LAND HOSPITAL (450848), 17500 West Grand Parkway South, Zip 77479–2562; tel. 281/725–5000, **A**1 10 **F**3 8 11 12 13 15 18 20 22 26 29 30 34 35 37 40 41 43 44 45 46 47 48 49 50 51 55 56 57 58 59 64 68 70 72 74 75 76 77 78 79 80 81 82 85 86 87 89 91 107 108 109 110 111 112 114 119 126 129 130 146 147 148 154 **S** Memorial Hermann Health System, Houston, TX
Primary Contact: Malisha Patel, Senior Vice President and Chief Executive Officer
CFO: Lisa Kendler, Chief Financial Officer
CMO: William Riley, M.D., Jr Chief of Staff
CHR: Robert Blake, Chief Human Resources Officer Southwest Market
Web address: www.memorialhermann.org
Control: Other not–for–profit (including NFP Corporation) **Service:** General medical and surgical

Staffed Beds: 149 **Admissions:** 8119 **Census:** 72 **Outpatient Visits:** 108249 **Births:** 2004 **Total Expense ($000):** 163531 **Payroll Expense ($000):** 53302 **Personnel:** 590

★ ⇑ **ST. LUKE'S SUGAR LAND HOSPITAL (670053)**, 1317 Lake Pointe Parkway, Zip 77478–3997; tel. 281/637–7000, **A**10 21 **F**3 13 15 18 20 22 26 29 30 35 37 39 40 41 44 45 46 49 50 57 60 64 68 70 72 74 75 76 79 81 82 85 107 108 110 111 115 119 126 130 146 147 148 **S** CommonSpirit Health, Chicago, IL
Primary Contact: Robert A. Heifner, FACHE, Chief Executive Officer
CFO: Bill Beauchamp, Chief Financial Officer
CNO: Wes Garrison
Web address: www.stlukessugarland.com
Control: Church operated, Nongovernment, not–for–profit **Service:** General medical and surgical

Staffed Beds: 96 **Admissions:** 4394 **Census:** 52 **Outpatient Visits:** 23861 **Births:** 1099 **Total Expense ($000):** 72343 **Payroll Expense ($000):** 29785 **Personnel:** 369

SUGAR LAND REHABILITATION HOSPITAL See Encompass Health Rehabilitation Hospital of Sugar Land

TRIUMPH HOSPITAL SOUTHWEST See Kindred Hospital Sugar Land

SULPHUR SPRINGS—Hopkins County

★ **CHRISTUS MOTHER FRANCES HOSPITAL - SULPHUR SPRINGS (450236)**, 115 Airport Road, Zip 75482–2105; tel. 903/885–7671, **A**10 **F**1 3 11 13 15 18 29 30 34 35 40 43 45 57 59 64 66 70 72 76 79 80 81 82 85 93 96 97 107 108 110 111 115 119 130 146 148 **S** CHRISTUS Health, Irving, TX
Primary Contact: Paul Harvey, President and Chief Executive Officer
COO: Donna Geiken Wallace, Chief Operating Officer and Chief Financial Officer
CFO: Donna Geiken Wallace, Chief Operating Officer and Chief Financial Officer
CMO: Chris Gallagher, M.D., Chief Medical Officer
CHR: Donna Rudzik, Director Human Resources
Web address: www.tmfhc.org/maps-and-locations/locations-profile/?id=72&searchId=8bcb329f-a152-e611-b37f-2c768a4e1b84&sort=11&page=1&pageSize=10
Control: Other not–for–profit (including NFP Corporation) **Service:** General medical and surgical

Staffed Beds: 56 **Admissions:** 3280 **Census:** 33 **Outpatient Visits:** 134086 **Births:** 613 **Total Expense ($000):** 62036 **Payroll Expense ($000):** 17772 **Personnel:** 295

TX

Many Facility Codes have changed. Please refer to the AHA Guide Code Chart. © 2019 AHA Guide

SUNNYVALE—Dallas County

⊞ **BAYLOR SCOTT & WHITE MEDICAL CENTER - SUNNYVALE (670060)**, 231 South Collins Road, Zip 75182–4624; tel. 972/892–3000, **A**1 10 **F**15 18 20 22 24 28 29 40 45 49 64 70 77 79 80 81 82 85 93 107 108 110 111 115 119 130 **S** TENET Healthcare Corporation, Dallas, TX
Primary Contact: Jon Duckert, FACHE, Chief Executive Officer
COO: Josiah De La Garza, Chief Operating Officer
CMO: William G. Jones, M.D., Chief Medical Officer
CNO: Deborah A Moeller, R.N., MS, Interim Chief Nursing Officer
Web address: www.BaylorScottandWhite.com/Sunnyvale
Control: Partnership, Investor–owned (for–profit) **Service:** General medical and surgical

Staffed Beds: 70 **Admissions:** 4564 **Census:** 54 **Outpatient Visits:** 42616 **Births:** 0 **Total Expense ($000):** 87368 **Payroll Expense ($000):** 27943 **Personnel:** 369

SWEENY—Brazoria County

★ **SWEENY COMMUNITY HOSPITAL (451311)**, 305 North McKinney Street, Zip 77480–2895; tel. 979/548–1500, **A**10 18 **F**3 7 10 11 15 29 34 35 40 43 53 57 59 64 65 69 70 75 81 85 93 104 107 110 114 119 127 132 133 143 145 148 149 153 156
Primary Contact: Scott Briner, Chief Executive Officer
CFO: Hong Wade, Chief Financial Officer
CMO: Enrique A Leal, M.D., III Chief of Staff
CIO: Stuart Butler, Director Information Technology
CHR: Rebecca McKay, Director Human Resources
CNO: Sherri Pierce, R.N., Chief Nursing Officer
Web address: www.sweenyhospital.org
Control: Hospital district or authority, Government, nonfederal **Service:** General medical and surgical

Staffed Beds: 14 **Admissions:** 248 **Census:** 3 **Outpatient Visits:** 21141 **Births:** 0 **Total Expense ($000):** 50168 **Payroll Expense ($000):** 9258 **Personnel:** 176

SWEETWATER—Nolan County

★ ⇧ **ROLLING PLAINS MEMORIAL HOSPITAL (450055)**, 200 East Arizona Street, Zip 79556–7199, Mailing Address: P.O. Box 690, Zip 79556–0690; tel. 325/235–1701, **A**10 20 21 **F**3 11 13 15 28 29 34 40 43 45 53 57 59 62 70 76 77 79 81 85 89 93 107 108 114 119 127 130 133 135 146 148 156
Primary Contact: Donna Boatright, R.N., MSN, Chief Executive Officer
COO: Rhonda Guelker, Senior Director Finance
CFO: Rhonda Guelker, Senior Director Finance
CIO: Rhonda Guelker, Senior Director Finance
CHR: Ame Monroe, Director Human Resources
CNO: Maxine Montano, R.N., Chief Nursing Officer
Web address: www.rpmh.net
Control: Hospital district or authority, Government, nonfederal **Service:** General medical and surgical

Staffed Beds: 57 **Admissions:** 1216 **Census:** 11 **Outpatient Visits:** 67070 **Births:** 230 **Total Expense ($000):** 37964 **Payroll Expense ($000):** 17019 **Personnel:** 292

TAHOKA—Lynn County

★ **LYNN COUNTY HOSPITAL DISTRICT (451351)**, 2600 Lockwood, Zip 79373–4118; tel. 806/998–4533, **A**10 18 **F**3 7 10 28 29 30 32 34 35 40 43 44 53 54 56 57 59 64 65 66 75 84 86 87 93 97 107 119 133 135 147 148 149 154
Primary Contact: Melanie Richburg, Chief Executive Officer
CFO: Steve Brock, Chief Financial Officer
CMO: Donald Freitag, M.D., Chief Medical Officer
CIO: Jim Brown, Director Information Technology
CHR: Jill Stone, Manager Human Resources
CNO: Angie Jalomo, Chief Nursing Officer
Web address: www.lchdhealthcare.org
Control: Hospital district or authority, Government, nonfederal **Service:** General medical and surgical

Staffed Beds: 24 **Admissions:** 93 **Census:** 5 **Outpatient Visits:** 7105 **Births:** 0 **Total Expense ($000):** 21404 **Payroll Expense ($000):** 6228 **Personnel:** 137

TAYLOR—Williamson County

⊞ **BAYLOR SCOTT & WHITE MEDICAL CENTER - TAYLOR (451374)**, 305 Mallard Lane, Zip 76574–1208; tel. 512/352–7611, **A**1 10 18 **F**3 18 29 34 35 40 45 50 56 57 59 62 64 65 68 75 77 81 82 85 87 91 92 93 97 107 108 111 119 127 129 130 132 133 135 146 148 149 **S** Baylor Scott & White Health, Dallas, TX
Primary Contact: Jay Fox, Chief Executive Officer
Web address: www.https://www.bswhealth.com/locations/taylor/pages/default.aspx?utm_source=BSWHealth.com-Taylor&utm_medium=offline&utm_campaign=BSWHealth.com&utm_term=BSWHealth.com-Taylor&utm_content=redirect
Control: Other not-for-profit (including NFP Corporation) **Service:** General medical and surgical

Staffed Beds: 25 **Admissions:** 311 **Census:** 6 **Outpatient Visits:** 57353 **Births:** 0 **Total Expense ($000):** 19577 **Payroll Expense ($000):** 10063 **Personnel:** 118

JOHNS COMMUNITY HOSPITAL See Baylor Scott & White Medical Center - Taylor

TEMPLE—Bell County

★ **BAYLOR SCOTT & WHITE CONTINUING CARE HOSPITAL-TEMPLE (452105)**, 546 North Kegley Road, Zip 76502–4069; tel. 254/215–0900, (Total facility includes 23 beds in nursing home–type unit) **A**10 **F**1 3 29 30 60 68 85 87 107 119 128 148 **S** Baylor Scott & White Health, Dallas, TX
Primary Contact: Shahin Motakef, President
CMO: David P Ciceri, M.D., Chief Medical Officer
CNO: Robert Pisicotta, Chief Nursing Officer
Web address: www.sw.org/location/temple-cch
Control: Other not-for-profit (including NFP Corporation) **Service:** Acute long–term care hospital

Staffed Beds: 48 **Admissions:** 451 **Census:** 40 **Outpatient Visits:** 41 **Births:** 0 **Total Expense ($000):** 21224 **Payroll Expense ($000):** 9482 **Personnel:** 70

⊞ **BAYLOR SCOTT & WHITE MEDICAL CENTER - TEMPLE (450054)**, 2401 South 31st Street, Zip 76508–0002; tel. 254/724–2111, (Includes MCLANE CHILDREN'S HOSPITAL SCOTT & WHITE, 1901 SW H K Dodgen Loop, Temple, Texas, Zip 76502–1896; tel. 254/771–8600; John Boyd III, M.D., Chief Executive Officer; MCLANE CHILDREN'S HOSPITAL SCOTT & WHITE, 2401 South 31st Street, Temple, Texas, Zip 76508–0001; tel. 877/724–5437; John Boyd III, M.D., Chief Executive Officer and Chief Medical Officer) **A**1 2 5 8 10 **F**3 4 5 8 9 11 12 13 14 15 17 18 19 20 22 24 25 26 27 28 29 30 31 32 34 35 36 37 38 39 40 41 43 46 46 47 48 49 50 51 52 54 55 56 57 58 59 60 61 63 64 65 66 68 70 71 72 73 74 75 76 77 78 79 81 82 83 84 85 86 87 88 89 91 92 93 94 95 97 98 99 100 101 102 103 104 107 108 109 110 111 112 113 114 115 116 117 118 119 120 121 124 126 127 129 130 131 132 133 134 135 136 137 138 141 142 143 144 146 147 148 149 150 154 156 157 **S** Baylor Scott & White Health, Dallas, TX
Primary Contact: Shahin Motakef, FACHE, President
CFO: Alita Prosser, Chief Financial Officer
CMO: Stephen Sibbitt, M.D., Chief Medical Officer
CIO: Matthew Chambers, Chief Information Officer
CHR: Pat Balz, Vice President Operations Human Resources
CNO: Gerald W Bryant, R.N., Chief Nursing Officer
Web address: www.sw.org/location/temple-hospital
Control: Other not-for-profit (including NFP Corporation) **Service:** General medical and surgical

Staffed Beds: 640 **Admissions:** 36537 **Census:** 482 **Outpatient Visits:** 1812613 **Births:** 2497 **Total Expense ($000):** 1012378 **Payroll Expense ($000):** 307821 **Personnel:** 5572

CENTRAL TEXAS VETERANS AFFAIRS HEALTH CARE SYSTEM, OLIN E. TEAGUE VETERANS MEDICAL CENTER See Central Texas Veterans Health Care System, Temple

TX

Hospital, Medicare Provider Number, Address, Telephone, Approval, Facility, and Physician Codes, Health Care System

★ American Hospital Association (AHA) membership   ○ Healthcare Facilities Accreditation Program   ⇧ Center for Improvement in Healthcare Quality Accreditation
□ The Joint Commission accreditation   ◇ DNV Healthcare Inc. accreditation   △ Commission on Accreditation of Rehabilitation Facilities (CARF) accreditation

© 2019 AHA Guide   *Many Facility Codes have changed. Please refer to the AHA Guide Code Chart.*   Hospitals **A639**

△ **CENTRAL TEXAS VETERANS HEALTH CARE SYSTEM**, 1901 Veterans Memorial Drive, Zip 76504–7493; tel. 254/778–4811, (Includes CENTRAL TEXAS VETERANS AFFAIRS HEALTH CARE SYSTEM, OLIN E. TEAGUE VETERANS MEDICAL CENTER, 1901 Veterans Memorial Drive, Temple, Texas, Zip 76504; tel. 254/778–4811; Andrew T. Garcia, Interim Director; CENTRAL TEXAS VETERANS HEALTH CARE SYSTEM, DORIS MILLER VETERANS MEDICAL CENTER, 4800 Memorial Drive, Waco, Texas, Zip 76711–1397; tel. 254/752–6581; Andrew T. Garcia, Interim Director), (Non-reporting) **A**1 3 5 7 8 **S** Department of Veterans Affairs, Washington, DC
Primary Contact: Andrew T. Garcia, Interim Director
CFO: Rosey Anzures, Acting Chief Financial Officer
CMO: Olawale Fashina, M.D., Chief of Staff
CIO: Victor Vitolas, Acting Chief Information Technology Services
CHR: Mary P. Doerfler, Chief Human Resources Officer
CNO: Bryan W. Sisk, Associate Director Patient and Nursing Services
Web address: www.centraltexas.va.gov/
Control: Veterans Affairs, Government, federal **Service**: General medical and surgical

Staffed Beds: 1532	

MCLANE CHILDREN'S HOSPITAL SCOTT & WHITE See Baylor Scott & White Medical Center - Temple, Temple

TERRELL—Kaufman County

☐ **TERRELL STATE HOSPITAL (454006)**, 1200 East Brin Street, Zip 75160–2938, Mailing Address: P.O. Box 70, Zip 75160–9000; tel. 972/524–6452, **A**1 3 5 10 **F**30 34 39 57 68 75 86 87 98 99 100 101 103 130 132 135 146 **S** Texas Department of State Health Services, Austin, TX
Primary Contact: Dorothy Floyd, Ph.D., Superintendent
CFO: David R. Teel, Financial Officer
CMO: Mark Messer, D.O., Clinical Director
CIO: Sims Anderson, Manager Facility Automation
CNO: Kathryn Griffin, Chief Nurse Executive
Web address: www.dshs.state.tx.us/mhhospitals/terrellsh
Control: State, Government, nonfederal **Service**: Psychiatric

Staffed Beds: 288 **Admissions:** 1359 **Census:** 271 **Outpatient Visits:** 0 **Births:** 0 **Total Expense ($000):** 59314 **Payroll Expense ($000):** 37382 **Personnel:** 835

TEXARKANA—Bowie County

CHRISTUS ST. MICHAEL HEALTH SYSTEM (450801), 2600 St Michael Drive, Zip 75503–5220; tel. 903/614–1000, (Includes CHRISTUS ST. MICHAEL HOSPITAL-ATLANTA, 1007 South William Street, Atlanta, Texas, Zip 75551–3245; tel. 903/799–3000; William Micah Johnson, Administrator and Chief Nursing Officer) **A**1 2 10 19 **F**3 11 13 15 17 18 20 22 24 26 28 29 30 31 34 35 37 40 41 43 45 48 49 51 53 55 56 57 59 60 64 65 68 70 71 72 73 74 75 76 77 78 79 80 81 82 84 85 86 87 89 92 93 102 107 108 109 110 111 114 115 118 119 120 121 122 123 124 126 129 130 131 132 135 143 146 147 148 149 154 156 **S** CHRISTUS Health, Irving, TX
Primary Contact: Jason Rounds, Chief Executive Officer
COO: Jason Rounds, Chief Operating Officer and Administrator
CFO: Glen Boles, Vice President and Chief Financial Officer
CMO: Mike Finley, M.D., Chief Medical Officer
CIO: Alana Higgins, Regional Information Management Executive
CHR: Jennifer Wright, Vice President Regional Human Resources
CNO: Louise Thornell, Chief Nursing Officer
Web address: www.christusstmichael.org
Control: Church operated, Nongovernment, not-for-profit **Service**: General medical and surgical

Staffed Beds: 354 **Admissions:** 13938 **Census:** 170 **Outpatient Visits:** 281308 **Births:** 1512 **Total Expense ($000):** 261865 **Payroll Expense ($000):** 79551 **Personnel:** 1221

△ **CHRISTUS ST. MICHAEL REHABILITATION HOSPITAL (453065)**, 2400 St Michael Drive, Zip 75503–2374; tel. 903/614–4000, **A**1 7 10 **F**11 18 28 29 30 34 35 57 59 65 68 75 77 79 82 87 90 93 96 132 135 143 148 149 154 **S** CHRISTUS Health, Irving, TX
Primary Contact: Patrick Flannery, Administrator
CFO: Glen Boles, Vice President and Chief Financial Officer
CMO: Richard Sharp, M.D., Medical Director
CIO: Alana Higgins, Regional Information Management Executive
CHR: Jennifer Wright, Vice President Human Resources
CNO: Stacey Breedlove, Chief Nursing Officer
Web address: www.christusstmichael.org/rehab
Control: Church operated, Nongovernment, not-for-profit **Service**: Rehabilitation

Staffed Beds: 50 **Admissions:** 992 **Census:** 31 **Outpatient Visits:** 50745 **Births:** 0 **Total Expense ($000):** 22686 **Payroll Expense ($000):** 10633 **Personnel:** 168

ENCOMPASS HEALTH REHABILITATION HOSPITAL OF TEXARKANA (453053), 515 West 12th Street, Zip 75501–4416; tel. 903/735–5000, **A**1 10 **F**3 28 29 64 74 77 79 90 91 93 96 130 131 132 143 148 154 **S** Encompass Health Corporation, Birmingham, AL
Primary Contact: Harlo McCall, Chief Executive Officer
CFO: Phylis Buck, Controller
CMO: Mark A Wren, M.D., Medical Director
CHR: Ann R Clapp, Director Human Resources
CNO: Lorri Oglesby, Chief Nursing Officer
Web address: www.healthsouthtexarkana.com
Control: Corporation, Investor–owned (for–profit) **Service**: Rehabilitation

Staffed Beds: 60 **Admissions:** 1175 **Census:** 43 **Outpatient Visits:** 8679 **Births:** 0 **Total Expense ($000):** 19419 **Payroll Expense ($000):** 10230 **Personnel:** 149

POST ACUTE MEDICAL SPECIALTY HOSPITAL OF TEXARKANA - NORTH (452061), 2400 St Michael Drive, 2nd Floor, Zip 75503–2372; tel. 903/614–7600, **A**1 10 **F**1 3 29 68 85 148 154 **S** Post Acute Medical, LLC, Enola, PA
Primary Contact: Lorraine Murray, Chief Executive Officer
Web address: www.postacutemedical.com
Control: Corporation, Investor–owned (for–profit) **Service**: Acute long–term care hospital

Staffed Beds: 30 **Admissions:** 357 **Census:** 22 **Outpatient Visits:** 0 **Births:** 0 **Total Expense ($000):** 12787 **Payroll Expense ($000):** 4497 **Personnel:** 74

☐ **WADLEY REGIONAL MEDICAL CENTER (450200)**, 1000 Pine Street, Zip 75501–5170; tel. 903/798–8000, **A**1 3 10 19 **F**3 11 13 15 18 20 22 28 29 30 31 34 35 40 43 45 49 50 56 57 59 60 64 65 70 71 72 74 75 76 77 78 79 81 85 86 87 89 98 103 107 108 110 111 114 115 119 121 123 126 130 146 147 148 149 154 **S** Steward Health Care System, LLC, Dallas, TX
Primary Contact: Thomas D. Gilbert, FACHE, Chief Executive Officer
CFO: Bonny Sorensen, Chief Financial Officer
CIO: Matt Kesterson, Director Information Services
CHR: Debby Butler, Director Human Resources
CNO: Shelly Strayhorn, R.N., Chief Nursing Officer
Web address: www.wadleyhealth.com
Control: Corporation, Investor–owned (for–profit) **Service**: General medical and surgical

Staffed Beds: 178 **Admissions:** 6308 **Census:** 82 **Outpatient Visits:** 81014 **Births:** 927 **Total Expense ($000):** 97904 **Payroll Expense ($000):** 38865 **Personnel:** 678

THE COLONY—Denton County

THE COLONY ER HOSPITAL, 4780 State Highway 121, Zip 75056–2913; tel. 214/469–1119, (Nonreporting)
Primary Contact: Russell Kaiser, Interim Chief Executive Officer and Chief Nursing Officer
Web address: www.https://thecolonyer.com/
Control: Individual, Investor–owned (for–profit) **Service**: General medical and surgical

Staffed Beds: 13	

THE WOODLANDS—Montgomery County

★ ⇑ **CHI ST. LUKE'S HEALTH-LAKESIDE HOSPITAL (670059)**, 17400 St. Luke's Way, Zip 77384–8036; tel. 936/266–9000, **A**10 21 **F**3 18 20 22 26 29 30 34 35 40 50 57 59 64 68 75 79 81 87 94 107 111 115 119 130 131 135 157 **S** CommonSpirit Health, Chicago, IL
Primary Contact: James Parisi, Chief Executive Officer
CHR: Debra Roberts, Director of Human Resources
CNO: Diane Freeman, R.N., Assistant Vice President and Chief Nursing Officer
Web address: www.stlukeslakeside.com/
Control: Corporation, Investor–owned (for–profit) **Service**: Surgical

Staffed Beds: 30 **Admissions:** 636 **Census:** 4 **Outpatient Visits:** 14282 **Births:** 0 **Total Expense ($000):** 34822 **Payroll Expense ($000):** 7155 **Personnel:** 116

CHI ST. LUKE'S HEALTH-THE WOODLANDS HOSPITAL (450862), 17200 St. Luke's Way, Zip 77384–8007; tel. 936/266–2000, **A**1 5 10 **F**3 11 12 13 15 18 20 22 24 26 28 29 30 34 35 38 40 41 42 45 49 50 57 58 59 64 68 70 72 74 75 78 79 81 82 85 86 87 89 90 93 107 108 109 110 111 114 118 119 124 126 129 130 131 135 145 146 147 148 **S** CommonSpirit Health, Chicago, IL
Primary Contact: James Parisi, Chief Executive Officer
CMO: Charles Sims, M.D., Chief of Staff
Web address: www.stlukeswoodlands.com
Control: Church operated, Nongovernment, not-for-profit **Service**: General medical and surgical

Staffed Beds: 201 **Admissions:** 11069 **Census:** 137 **Outpatient Visits:** 85809 **Births:** 1729 **Total Expense ($000):** 213702 **Payroll Expense ($000):** 73049 **Personnel:** 1021

Many Facility Codes have changed. Please refer to the AHA Guide Code Chart. © 2019 AHA Guide

TX

★ **HOUSTON METHODIST THE WOODLANDS HOSPITAL (670122)**, 17201 Interstate 45 South, Zip 77385; tel. 713/790–3333, **A**10 **F**3 4 11 12 13 15 18 20 22 24 26 28 29 30 31 34 35 36 37 40 41 42 44 45 46 48 49 50 51 53 57 59 64 65 68 70 72 74 75 76 77 78 79 81 85 86 87 93 96 97 102 107 108 110 111 115 117 118 119 120 121 123 124 126 130 131 132 135 146 147 149 154 **S** Houston Methodist, Houston, TX
Primary Contact: Debra F. Sukin, Ph.D., Regional Senior Vice President and Chief Executive Officer
CNO: Kerrie Guerrero, R.N., MSN, Vice President and Chief Nursing Officer
Web address: www.houstonmethodist.org/locations/the-woodlands/
Control: Other not–for–profit (including NFP Corporation) **Service:** General medical and surgical

Staffed Beds: 146 **Admissions:** 7871 **Census:** 76 **Outpatient Visits:** 113760 **Births:** 1598 **Total Expense ($000):** 204302 **Payroll Expense ($000):** 64738 **Personnel:** 957

MEMORIAL HERMANN THE WOODLANDS HOSPITAL See Memorial Hermann Greater Heights Hospital, Houston

NEXUS SPECIALTY HOSPITAL THE WOODLANDS (452057), 9182 Six Pines Drive, Zip 77380–3670; tel. 281/364–0317, (Nonreporting) **A**10
Primary Contact: Eric Cantrell, Chief Executive Officer
CFO: David Strickler, Chief Financial Officer
CMO: Ather Siddiqi, M.D., Medical Director
CIO: Noe Salinas, Vice President Information Technology
CHR: Kevin McAndrews, Vice President, Human Resources
CNO: Rhena Anderson, Chief Nursing Officer
Web address: www.nexusspecialty.com
Control: Partnership, Investor–owned (for–profit) **Service:** Acute long–term care hospital

Staffed Beds: 21

★ **WOODLANDS SPECIALTY HOSPITAL**, 9182 Six Pines Drive, Zip 77380–3670, Mailing Address: 25540 I-45 North, Suite 100, Spring, Zip 77380–3670; tel. 281/602–8160, **F**3 18 20 22 24 26 29 40 45 46 47 48 49 79 80 81 92 107 108 109 111 115 118 119 120 149 156
Primary Contact: Jody Randall, MSN, R.N., Chief Executive Officer/Chief Nursing Officer
CFO: Virginia de Bond, Chief Financial Officer
Web address: www.woodlandsspecialtyhospital.com/
Control: Individual, Investor–owned (for–profit) **Service:** General medical and surgical

Staffed Beds: 8 **Admissions:** 119 **Census:** 1 **Outpatient Visits:** 6164 **Births:** 0 **Total Expense ($000):** 29322 **Payroll Expense ($000):** 6366 **Personnel:** 164

THROCKMORTON COUNTY MEMORIAL HOSPITAL (451339), 802 North Minter Street, Zip 76483–5357, Mailing Address: P.O. Box 729, Zip 76483–0729; tel. 940/849–2151, **A**10 18 **F**1 4 7 34 40 41 42 43 44 50 59 61 64 65 67 68 79 8/ 97 102 127 128 130 133 148
Primary Contact: Kirby Gober, Chief Executive Officer
CFO: Cindy Parker, Chief Financial Officer and Director Human Resources
CMO: Ruth Ebangit, M.D., Chief of Staff and Medical Officer
CIO: Amber Myer, Director Medical Technology
CHR: Cindy Parker, Chief Financial Officer and Director Human Resources
CNO: Pam Stamm, Chief Nursing Officer
Web address: www.throckmortonhospital.com/index.html
Control: County, Government, nonfederal **Service:** General medical and surgical

Staffed Beds: 14 **Admissions:** 60 **Census:** 1 **Outpatient Visits:** 8559 **Births:** 0 **Total Expense ($000):** 4234 **Payroll Expense ($000):** 1866 **Personnel:** 52

⊞ **HCA HOUSTON HEALTHCARE TOMBALL (450670)**, 605 Holderrieth Street, Zip 77375–6445; tel. 281/401–7500, (Includes HCA HOUSTON HEALTHCARE CYPRESS FAIRBANKS, 10655 Steepletop Drive, Houston, Texas, Zip 77065–4297; tel. 281/890–4285; Eric Evans, Chief Executive Officer) **A**1 10 **F**3 8 12 13 15 18 20 22 24 26 28 29 30 31 34 35 40 42 43 44 45 46 47 48 49 50 51 53 54 57 59 64 65 70 72 74 75 76 77 78 79 80 81 82 85 86 87 89 90 91 93 94 96 98 103 107 108 110 111 114 115 119 120 121 124 126 129 130 131 132 144 145 146 147 148 149 154 **S** HCA Healthcare, Nashville, TN
Primary Contact: Saumya Sutaria, M.D., Chief Operating Officer
COO: Saumya Sutaria, M.D., Chief Operating Officer
CFO: Richard Ervin, Chief Financial Officer
CMO: Ian Glass, M.D., Chief Medical Officer
CIO: Marisa Smith, Director
CHR: Vanessa Hunt, Director Human Resources
Web address: www.tomballregionalmedicalcenter.com
Control: Corporation, Investor–owned (for–profit) **Service:** General medical and surgical

Staffed Beds: 346 **Admissions:** 17160 **Census:** 214 **Outpatient Visits:** 152348 **Births:** 3479 **Total Expense ($000):** 367922 **Payroll Expense ($000):** 107291 **Personnel:** 1334

⊞ **KINDRED HOSPITAL TOMBALL (452074)**, 505 Graham Drive, Zip 77375–3368; tel. 281/255–5600, (Includes KINDRED HOSPITAL SPRING, 205 Hollow Tree Lane, Houston, Texas, Zip 77090; tel. 832/249–2700; Randy Briones, Chief Executive Officer; KINDRED HOSPITAL THE HEIGHTS, 1800 West 26th Street, Houston, Texas, Zip 77008–1450; tel. 832/673–4200; William Elsesser, Chief Executive Officer) **A**1 10 **F**1 3 18 29 30 31 49 64 70 74 75 78 79 84 85 86 87 93 94 107 119 130 **S** Kindred Healthcare, Louisville, KY
Primary Contact: Tracy Kohler, Chief Executive Officer
Web address: www.khtomball.com/
Control: Partnership, Investor–owned (for–profit) **Service:** Acute long–term care hospital

Staffed Beds: 258 **Admissions:** 1861 **Census:** 135 **Outpatient Visits:** 2195 **Births:** 0 **Total Expense ($000):** 86820 **Payroll Expense ($000):** 33315 **Personnel:** 425

⇑ **MEMORIAL HERMANN TOMBALL HOSPITAL (670095)**, 24429 State Highway 249, Zip 77375–8214; tel. 281/516–0911, **A**21 **F**3 40 68 75 107 114 119 149 **S** Emerus, The Woodlands, TX
Primary Contact: Brenda Villafranco, Administrator
Web address: www.emerus.com/tomball/
Control: Corporation, Investor–owned (for–profit) **Service:** General medical and surgical

Staffed Beds: 15 **Admissions:** 140 **Census:** 1 **Outpatient Visits:** 9655 **Births:** 0 **Total Expense ($000):** 8971 **Payroll Expense ($000):** 2881 **Personnel:** 52

☐ **BAYLOR SCOTT & WHITE MEDICAL CENTER - TROPHY CLUB (450883)**, 2850 East State Highway 114, Zip 76262–5302; tel. 817/837–4600, **A**1 10 **F**3 29 40 70 75 79 81 85 87 107 108 111 114 118 121 123 141
Primary Contact: Melanie Chick, Chief Executive Officer
CFO: Jonathan Saunders, Chief Financial Officer
CMO: Mike Stanton, D.O., Medical Director
CIO: Scot Bradford, Chief Information Officer
CHR: Donna Irvin, Director Human Resources
CNO: Tina Huddleston, R.N., Chief Nursing Officer
Web address: www.baylortrophyclub.com
Control: Partnership, Investor–owned (for–profit) **Service:** General medical and surgical

Staffed Beds: 22 **Admissions:** 1116 **Census:** 7 **Outpatient Visits:** 7620 **Births:** 0 **Total Expense ($000):** 57893 **Payroll Expense ($000):** 12013 **Personnel:** 172

TX

TULIA—Swisher County

★ **SWISHER MEMORIAL HEALTHCARE SYSTEM (451349)**, 539 Southeast Second, Zip 79088-2400, Mailing Address: P.O. Box 808, Zip 79088-0808; tel. 806/995-3581, **A**3 10 18 **F**3 7 10 11 29 33 34 35 36 40 43 50 53 57 59 64 65 68 75 77 93 104 107 114 127 130 132 133
Primary Contact: Luke Brewer, Acting Chief Executive Officer
CFO: Connie Wilhelm, Chief Financial Officer
CIO: Brad Roberts, Network Administrator
Web address: www.swisherhospital.com
Control: Other not-for-profit (including NFP Corporation) **Service:** General medical and surgical

Staffed Beds: 20 **Admissions:** 211 **Census:** 4 **Outpatient Visits:** 22824 **Births:** 0 **Total Expense ($000):** 11634 **Payroll Expense ($000):** 4298 **Personnel:** 83

TYLER—Smith County

⊞ **BAYLOR SCOTT & WHITE TEXAS SPINE & JOINT HOSPITAL-TYLER (450864)**, 1814 Roseland Boulevard, Suite 100, Zip 75701-4262; tel. 903/525-3300, **A**1 10 **F**8 29 39 40 53 77 79 81 82 107 111 114 119 131 144
Primary Contact: Tony Wahl, Chief Executive Officer
CFO: Greg Cummings, Chief Financial Officer
CMO: Kim Foreman, M.D., Chief of Staff
CNO: Aaron Fleet, R.N., Chief Nursing Officer
Web address: www.tsjh.org
Control: Partnership, Investor-owned (for-profit) **Service:** Orthopedic

Staffed Beds: 20 **Admissions:** 2142 **Census:** 14 **Outpatient Visits:** 44995 **Births:** 0 **Total Expense ($000):** 92064 **Payroll Expense ($000):** 21288 **Personnel:** 414

⊞ **CHRISTUS MOTHER FRANCES HOSPITAL - TYLER (450102)**, 800 East Dawson Street, Zip 75701-2036; tel. 903/593-8441, (Includes LOUIS & PEACHES OWEN HEART HOSPITAL, 703 South Fleishel Avenue, Tyler, Texas, Zip 75701-2015; tel. 903/606-3000; John McGreevy, FACHE, Chief Executive Officer) **A**1 2 3 10 **F**3 8 11 12 13 15 17 18 20 22 24 26 28 29 30 31 34 37 40 42 43 45 46 47 48 49 50 51 53 54 55 57 58 59 60 64 68 70 71 72 73 74 75 76 78 79 80 81 82 84 85 86 87 89 93 97 107 108 109 110 111 113 114 115 119 126 127 129 130 131 132 144 145 146 147 148 156 157 **S** CHRISTUS Health, Irving, TX
Primary Contact: Jason J. Proctor, Chief Operating Officer
CFO: Joyce Hester, CPA, Senior Vice President and Chief Financial Officer
CMO: Fadi Nasrallah, M.D., Vice President Medical Affairs
CIO: Jeff Pearson, Vice President and Chief Information Officer
CHR: Thomas Wilken, Senior Vice President and Chief Human Resources Officer
Web address: www.tmfhc.org
Control: Other not-for-profit (including NFP Corporation) **Service:** General medical and surgical

Staffed Beds: 446 **Admissions:** 25319 **Census:** 316 **Outpatient Visits:** 656791 **Births:** 2814 **Total Expense ($000):** 574630 **Payroll Expense ($000):** 197783 **Personnel:** 3653

⊞ **CHRISTUS TRINITY MOTHER FRANCES REHABILITATION HOSPITAL, A PARTNER OF ENCOMPASS HEALTH (453056)**, 3131 Troup Highway, Zip 75701-8352; tel. 903/510-7000, **A**1 10 **F**3 9 28 29 56 60 74 75 77 79 82 87 90 91 95 96 130 132 143 148 149 154 156 157 **S** Encompass Health Corporation, Birmingham, AL
Primary Contact: Sharla Anderson, Chief Executive Officer
CFO: Michael G Treadway, Controller
CMO: Bradley Merritt, M.D., Medical Director
Web address: www.tmfrehabhospital.com
Control: Partnership, Investor-owned (for-profit) **Service:** Rehabilitation

Staffed Beds: 94 **Admissions:** 2159 **Census:** 72 **Outpatient Visits:** 364 **Births:** 0 **Total Expense ($000):** 26904 **Payroll Expense ($000):** 12611 **Personnel:** 221

★ **TYLER CONTINUECARE HOSPITAL (452091)**, 800 East Dawson, 4th Floor, Zip 75701-2036; tel. 903/531-4080, **A**10 22 **F**1 3 29 34 57 59 85 86 130 148 **S** Community Hospital Corporation, Plano, TX
Primary Contact: Stephanie Hyde, R.N., MSN, Chief Executive Officer
Web address: www.continuecare.org
Control: Other not-for-profit (including NFP Corporation) **Service:** Acute long-term care hospital

Staffed Beds: 51 **Admissions:** 545 **Census:** 40 **Outpatient Visits:** 0 **Births:** 0 **Total Expense ($000):** 22757 **Payroll Expense ($000):** 8390 **Personnel:** 122

⊞ **UT HEALTH NORTH CAMPUS TYLER (450690)**, 11937 Highway 271, Zip 75708-3154; tel. 903/877-7777, **A**1 2 8 10 **F**3 8 11 15 18 20 22 24 26 28 29 30 31 32 34 35 40 43 45 46 47 49 50 53 54 55 56 57 58 59 64 65 68 70 71 75 77 78 79 81 84 85 86 87 93 97 98 100 101 102 103 104 105 107 108 110 111 114 115 116 117 118 119 120 121 123 124 129 130 132 135 143 146 147 148 153 156 **S** University of Texas System, Austin, TX
Primary Contact: Kirk A. Calhoun, M.D., President
COO: Joe Woelkers, Executive Vice President and Chief Staff
CFO: Vernon Moore, Senior Vice President Chief Business and Finance
CMO: Steven Cox, M.D., Chief Medical Officer
CIO: Vernon Moore, Senior Vice President Chief Business and Finance
CHR: Jesse Gomez, Vice President Human Resources
CNO: Don Hunt, M.D., Vice President Patient Centered Care and Chief Nursing Officer
Web address: www.https://uthealthnorth.com/
Control: State, Government, nonfederal **Service:** General medical and surgical

Staffed Beds: 114 **Admissions:** 1385 **Census:** 22 **Outpatient Visits:** 308037 **Births:** 0 **Total Expense ($000):** 214511 **Payroll Expense ($000):** 78972 **Personnel:** 1192

⊞ **UT HEALTH REHABILITATION HOSPITAL (453072)**, 701 Olympic Plaza Circle, Zip 75701-1950, Mailing Address: P.O. Box 7530, Zip 75711-7530; tel. 903/596-3000, (Data for 306 days) **A**1 10 **F**3 28 29 30 34 53 57 75 86 90 91 93 96 130 131 132 148 149 **S** Ardent Health Services, Nashville, TN
Primary Contact: Laurie Lehnhof-Watts, Administrator and Chief Nursing Officer
CFO: James Blanton, Chief Financial Officer
CMO: Jerry Schwarzbach, M.D., Medical Director
CIO: Paula Anthony, Vice President Information Services
CHR: David L Langston, Corporate Vice President Human Resources
CNO: Laurie Lehnhof-Watts, Administrator and Chief Nursing Officer
Web address: www.https://uthealthrehab.com/
Control: Corporation, Investor-owned (for-profit) **Service:** Rehabilitation

Staffed Beds: 49 **Admissions:** 825 **Census:** 35 **Outpatient Visits:** 70100 **Births:** 0 **Total Expense ($000):** 21510 **Payroll Expense ($000):** 11449 **Personnel:** 200

⊞ **UT HEALTH SPECIALTY HOSPITAL (452051)**, 1000 South Beckham, 5th Floor, Zip 75701-1908, Mailing Address: P.O. Box 7018, Zip 75711-7018; tel. 903/596-3600, (Data for 306 days) **A**1 10 **F**1 3 29 30 75 84 130 148 149 **S** Ardent Health Services, Nashville, TN
Primary Contact: Laurie Lehnhof-Watts, Administrator and Chief Nursing Officer
CFO: James Blanton, Chief Financial Officer
CMO: J David Johnson, M.D., Chief of Staff
CIO: Paula Anthony, Vice President Information Services
CHR: David L Langston, Corporate Vice President Human Resources
CNO: Laurie Lehnhof-Watts, Administrator and Chief Nursing Officer
Web address: www.https://uthealtheasttexas.com/locations/ut-health-east-texas-specialty-hospital
Control: Corporation, Investor-owned (for-profit) **Service:** Acute long-term care hospital

Staffed Beds: 36 **Admissions:** 307 **Census:** 25 **Outpatient Visits:** 0 **Births:** 0 **Total Expense ($000):** 9742 **Payroll Expense ($000):** 3666 **Personnel:** 61

⊞ **UT HEALTH TYLER (450083)**, 1000 South Beckham Street, Zip 75701-1908, Mailing Address: Box 6400, Zip 75711-6400; tel. 903/597-0351, (Includes UT HEALTH BEHAVIORAL HEALTH CENTER, 4101 University Boulevard, Tyler, Texas, Zip 75701-6600; tel. 903/566-8668; Marcey Davis, Chief Executive Officer) (Data for 306 days) **A**1 2 3 5 10 **F**3 5 8 11 12 13 15 17 18 20 22 24 26 28 29 30 31 34 35 37 38 40 42 43 44 45 46 47 48 49 51 56 58 59 60 61 64 65 68 70 71 73 74 75 76 78 79 80 81 82 84 85 86 87 89 93 98 99 100 101 102 104 107 110 111 115 117 118 119 126 129 130 132 141 145 146 147 148 149 150 152 153 156 **S** Ardent Health Services, Nashville, TN
Primary Contact: Vicki R. Briggs, Chief Executive Officer
CFO: Byron Hale, Chief Financial Officer
CMO: John Andrews, M.D., Chief of Staff
CIO: Paula Anthony, Vice President Information Services
CHR: Mike Gray, Corporate Vice President Human Resources
CNO: Mariarose Kulma, R.N., Vice President Patient Services
Web address: www.https://uthealthtylerhospital.com/
Control: Individual, Investor-owned (for-profit) **Service:** General medical and surgical

Staffed Beds: 399 **Admissions:** 18646 **Census:** 307 **Outpatient Visits:** 101724 **Births:** 615 **Total Expense ($000):** 296656 **Payroll Expense ($000):** 98092 **Personnel:** 2011

UVALDE—Uvalde County

⊠ **UVALDE MEMORIAL HOSPITAL (451387)**, 1025 Garner Field Road,
Zip 78801–4809; tel. 830/278–6251, **A**1 10 18 **F**3 11 13 15 18 29 30 34 39
40 43 45 50 57 59 63 64 70 76 79 81 84 85 86 87 88 89 93 104 107 108
110 111 115 118 119 127 130 132 133 146 147 148 149
Primary Contact: Thomas Nordwick, FACHE, Chief Executive Officer
CFO: Valerie Lopez, CPA, Chief Financial Officer
CMO: Jared Reading, M.D., Chief of Staff
CIO: Blake Eaker, Interim Director Information Services
CHR: Charla Carter, Human Resource Officer
CNO: Adam Apolinar, Chief Nursing Officer
Web address: www.umhtx.org
Control: Hospital district or authority, Government, nonfederal **Service**: General
medical and surgical

> **Staffed Beds**: 25 **Admissions**: 1257 **Census**: 12 **Outpatient Visits**: 168965
> **Births**: 408 **Total Expense ($000)**: 57586 **Payroll Expense ($000)**: 24984
> **Personnel**: 436

VAN HORN—Culberson County

CULBERSON HOSPITAL (451338), Eisenhower-Farm Market Road 2185,
Zip 79855, Mailing Address: P.O. Box 609, Zip 79855–0609; tel. 432/283–2760,
A10 18 **F**3 7 34 40 43 50 57 59 64 65 68 74 75 93 107 114 119 127 133 **S**
Preferred Management Corporation, Shawnee, OK
Primary Contact: Rick Gray, Chief Executive Officer
CMO: John A. Thomas, M.D., Chief Medical Staff
Web address: www.culbersonhospital.org
Control: Corporation, Investor–owned (for–profit) **Service**: General medical and
surgical

> **Staffed Beds**: 14 **Admissions**: 143 **Census**: 2 **Outpatient Visits**: 9082
> **Births**: 0 **Total Expense ($000)**: 6833 **Payroll Expense ($000)**: 3290
> **Personnel**: 62

VERNON—Wilbarger County

☐ **NORTH TEXAS STATE HOSPITAL**, Highway 70 Northwest, Zip 76384, Mailing
Address: P.O. Box 2231, Zip 76385–2231; tel. 940/552–9901, **A**1 **F**30 39 50
56 57 68 75 87 96 97 98 99 100 101 103 130 132 135 143 146 149 154 **S**
Texas Department of State Health Services, Austin, TX
Primary Contact: James E. Smith, Superintendent
CFO: Robin Moreno, Financial Officer
CIO: Chad Hughes, Information Officer
Web address: www.online.dshs.state.tx.us/northtexassh/default.htm
Control: State, Government, nonfederal **Service**: Psychiatric

> **Staffed Beds**: 562 **Admissions**: 1696 **Census**: 517 **Outpatient Visits**: 0
> **Births**: 0 **Personnel**: 2032

★ **WILBARGER GENERAL HOSPITAL (450584)**, 920 Hillcrest Drive,
Zip 76384–3196; tel. 940/552–9351, **A**10 20 **F**3 11 15 28 29 34 35 40 43 45
55 57 60 62 75 77 81 85 86 87 93 107 108 110 111 115 119 124 130 132
133 146 148 153 **S** QHR, Brentwood, TN
Primary Contact: Dennis D. Jack, FACHE, Chief Executive Officer
CMO: Travis Lehman, M.D., Medical Director
CIO: Ken Mikos, Director Information Technology
CHR: Alisha Nix, Director Human Resources
CNO: Kim Pierson, R.N., Chief Nursing Officer
Web address: www.wghospital.com
Control: Hospital district or authority, Government, nonfederal **Service**: General
medical and surgical

> **Staffed Beds**: 27 **Admissions**: 711 **Census**: 9 **Outpatient Visits**: 18365
> **Births**: 2 **Total Expense ($000)**: 22051 **Payroll Expense ($000)**: 10602
> **Personnel**: 152

VICTORIA—Victoria County

★ ⇑ **CITIZENS MEDICAL CENTER (450023)**, 2701 Hospital Drive,
Zip 77901–5749; tel. 361/573–9181, (Total facility includes 20 beds in
nursing home–type unit) **A**2 10 19 21 **F**3 11 12 13 15 18 20 22 24 28 29
30 31 34 35 40 41 43 45 46 49 50 51 53 54 56 57 59 62 64 65 70 72 74
75 76 78 79 81 82 85 86 87 89 93 97 107 108 109 110 111 113 114 115
116 117 118 119 120 121 123 126 128 129 130 131 132 135 146 147
148 149 154
Primary Contact: Michael R. Olson, Chief Executive Officer
CFO: Carolyn Zafereo, Chief Accounting Officer
CMO: Daniel Cano, M.D., Chief Medical Officer
CIO: Russell Witte, Director Information Technology
CHR: Kathleen C Mosmeyer, Director Human Resources
Web address: www.citizensmedicalcenter.org
Control: County, Government, nonfederal **Service**: General medical and
surgical

> **Staffed Beds**: 265 **Admissions**: 7406 **Census**: 99 **Outpatient
> Visits**: 125479 **Births**: 769 **Total Expense ($000)**: 162331 **Payroll Expense
> ($000)**: 70681 **Personnel**: 1084

⊠ **DETAR HEALTHCARE SYSTEM (450147)**, 506 East San Antonio Street,
Zip 77901–6060, Mailing Address: P.O. Box 2089, Zip 77902–2089;
tel. 361/575–7441, (Includes DETAR HOSPITAL NORTH, 101 Medical Drive,
Victoria, Texas, Zip 77904–3198; tel. 361/573–6100; Gary Malaer, Chief
Executive Officer) **A**1 3 10 **F**3 12 13 15 18 20 22 24 26 28 29 30 31 34 39 40
41 43 45 47 49 50 51 53 56 64 70 72 74 75 76 77 78 79 81 82 85 86 87 89
90 93 107 108 110 111 114 118 119 126 130 132 146 147 148 149 156 **S**
Community Health Systems, Inc., Franklin, TN
Primary Contact: Gary Malaer, Chief Executive Officer
COO: George N Parsley, Chief Operating Officer
CFO: Donald E Hagan, Chief Financial Officer
CMO: Conde Nevin Anderson, M.D., Chief of Staff
CIO: Kim Tompkins, Director Information Services
CHR: Dwight Linton, Director Human Resources
CNO: Sammie Drehr, Chief Nursing Officer
Web address: www.detar.com
Control: Corporation, Investor–owned (for–profit) **Service**: General medical and
surgical

> **Staffed Beds**: 225 **Admissions**: 8742 **Census**: 101 **Outpatient
> Visits**: 97129 **Births**: 1201 **Total Expense ($000)**: 153699 **Payroll Expense
> ($000)**: 53929 **Personnel**: 964

★ **PAM REHABILITATION HOSPITAL OF VICTORIA (673056)**, 101 James
Coleman Drive, Zip 77904–3147; tel. 361/220–7900, (Nonreporting) **S** Post
Acute Medical, LLC, Enola, PA
Primary Contact: Jennifer Nickel, Chief Executive Officer
Web address: www.warmsprings.org/our-facilities/outpatient-rehabilitation/warm-
springs-rehabilitation-center-victoria/
Control: Partnership, Investor–owned (for–profit) **Service**: Rehabilitation

> **Staffed Beds**: 26

⊠ **PAM SPECIALTY HOSPITAL OF VICTORIA NORTH (452094)**, 102 Medical
Drive, Zip 77904–3101; tel. 361/576–6200, **A**1 10 **F**1 3 29 64 75 77 85 93 94
148 157 **S** Post Acute Medical, LLC, Enola, PA
Primary Contact: Christina Adrean, Chief Executive Officer
CMO: Adam Burick, M.D., Chief Medical Officer
CHR: Waynea Finley, Corporate Director Human Resources
CNO: Chris Reed, Director of Nursing
Web address: www.warmsprings.org
Control: Partnership, Investor–owned (for–profit) **Service**: Acute long–term care
hospital

> **Staffed Beds**: 26 **Admissions**: 510 **Census**: 25 **Outpatient Visits**: 10248
> **Births**: 0 **Total Expense ($000)**: 14115 **Payroll Expense ($000)**: 5129
> **Personnel**: 112

TX

Hospital, Medicare Provider Number, Address, Telephone, Approval, Facility, and Physician Codes, Health Care System

★ American Hospital Association (AHA) membership   ○ Healthcare Facilities Accreditation Program   ⇑ Center for Improvement in Healthcare Quality Accreditation
☐ The Joint Commission accreditation   ◇ DNV Healthcare Inc. accreditation   △ Commission on Accreditation of Rehabilitation Facilities (CARF) accreditation

⊞ **PAM SPECIALTY HOSPITAL OF VICTORIA SOUTH (452056)**, 506 East San Antonio Street, 3rd Floor, Zip 77901–6060; tel. 361/575–1445, **A**1 10 **F**1 3 29 82 85 86 87 97 130 148 **S** Post Acute Medical, LLC, Enola, PA
Primary Contact: Christina Adrean, Chief Executive Officer
CMO: Adam Burick, M.D., Chief Medical Officer
CHR: Waynea Finley, Manager Human Resources
CNO: Pamella Barrett, Director of Nursing
Web address: www.warmsprings.org/our-facilities/hospitals/post-acute-medical-specialty-hospital-victoria/
Control: Partnership, Investor–owned (for–profit) **Service**: Acute long–term care hospital

Staffed Beds: 23 **Admissions**: 353 **Census**: 22 **Outpatient Visits**: 0
Births: 0 **Total Expense ($000)**: 10945 **Payroll Expense ($000)**: 4692
Personnel: 73

WACO—McLennan County

⊞ △ **BAYLOR SCOTT & WHITE MEDICAL CENTER - HILLCREST (450101)**, 100 Hillcrest Medical Boulevard, Zip 76712–8897; tel. 254/202–2000, **A**1 2 3 7 10 19 **F**3 8 11 13 15 18 20 22 24 26 28 29 30 31 34 40 43 45 46 49 50 53 54 56 57 59 60 63 64 68 70 72 74 75 76 77 78 79 81 82 84 85 86 87 89 90 93 96 97 107 108 110 111 115 118 119 120 121 123 129 130 131 132 135 145 146 148 150 154 **S** Baylor Scott & White Health, Dallas, TX
Primary Contact: Glenn A. Robinson, FACHE, President
COO: David Blackwell, Vice President Operations
CFO: Richard Perkins, Chief Financial Officer
CMO: J. E. Morrison, M.D., M.P.H., Chief Medical Officer
CNO: Rebecca Kay Hardie, Chief Nursing Officer
Web address: www.sw.org/hillcrest-medical-center
Control: Other not–for–profit (including NFP Corporation) **Service**: General medical and surgical

Staffed Beds: 226 **Admissions**: 14220 **Census**: 167 **Outpatient Visits**: 180501 **Births**: 2913 **Total Expense ($000)**: 282378 **Payroll Expense ($000)**: 79761 **Personnel**: 1523

WACO—McLennan County

CENTRAL TEXAS VETERANS HEALTH CARE SYSTEM, DORIS MILLER VETERANS MEDICAL CENTER See Central Texas Veterans Health Care System, Temple

⊞ **PROVIDENCE HEALTHCARE NETWORK (450042)**, 6901 Medical Parkway, Zip 76712–7998, Mailing Address: P.O. Box 2589, Zip 76702–2589; tel. 254/751–4000, (Includes DEPAUL CENTER, 301 Londonderry Drive, Waco, Texas, Zip 76712; tel. 254/776–5970; Vicky Campbell, Vice President Mental Health and Support Services), (Non-reporting) **A**1 2 3 10 **S** Ascension Healthcare, Saint Louis, MO
Primary Contact: Philip A. Patterson, President
CFO: Karen K. Richardson, Senior Vice President and Chief Financial Officer
CMO: Brian Becker, Vice President Medical Affairs and Chief Medical Officer
CIO: Jay Scherler, Vice President Finance and Chief Information Officer
CNO: Cyndy Dunlap, R.N., FACHE, Chief Nursing Officer
Web address: www.providence.net
Service: General medical and surgical

Staffed Beds: 284

WAXAHACHIE—Ellis County

⊞ **BAYLOR SCOTT & WHITE MEDICAL CENTER-WAXAHACHIE (450372)**, 2400 North I-35E, Zip 75165; tel. 469/843–4000, **A**1 2 3 10 **F**3 8 11 12 13 14 15 18 28 29 30 31 34 35 37 39 40 41 44 45 47 48 49 50 51 56 57 58 59 60 61 63 64 68 70 74 75 76 77 78 79 80 81 84 85 86 87 96 100 102 107 108 109 110 111 114 115 116 117 118 119 120 121 123 126 129 130 131 132 135 143 145 146 147 148 149 154 156 **S** Baylor Scott & White Health, Dallas, TX
Primary Contact: Will Turner, President
COO: Cindy Murray, R.N., Chief Nursing Officer and Chief Operating Officer
CFO: Cheryl McMullan, Chief Financial Officer
CMO: Thomas Glenn Ledbetter, M.D., Chief Medical Officer
CNO: Cindy Murray, R.N., Chief Nursing Officer and Chief Operating Officer
Web address: www.baylorhealth.com/PhysiciansLocations/Waxahachie/Pages/Default.aspx
Control: Other not–for–profit (including NFP Corporation) **Service**: General medical and surgical

Staffed Beds: 129 **Admissions**: 7551 **Census**: 73 **Outpatient Visits**: 96237 **Births**: 926 **Total Expense ($000)**: 157508 **Payroll Expense ($000)**: 51511 **Personnel**: 646

WEATHERFORD—Parker County

⊞ **MEDICAL CITY WEATHERFORD (450203)**, 713 East Anderson Street, Zip 76086–5705; tel. 682/582–1000, **A**1 3 5 10 **F**3 13 15 17 18 20 22 28 29 30 40 43 48 57 59 60 68 70 74 75 76 79 81 82 85 93 107 110 111 114 115 119 130 146 148 154 **S** HCA Healthcare, Nashville, TN
Primary Contact: Sean Kamber, Chief Executive Officer
CFO: Nancy Cooke, Chief Financial Officer
CMO: Sanjeeb Shrestha, M.D., Chief Medical Staff
CIO: Brett Cates, Director Information Services
CNO: Donna Boone, MS, R.N., Chief Nursing Officer
Web address: www.weatherfordregional.com
Control: Corporation, Investor–owned (for–profit) **Service**: General medical and surgical

Staffed Beds: 82 **Admissions**: 5206 **Census**: 51 **Outpatient Visits**: 70684
Births: 803 **Total Expense ($000)**: 91405 **Payroll Expense ($000)**: 24261
Personnel: 369

WEATHERFORD REHABILITATION HOSPITAL (673062), 703 Eureka Street, Zip 76086–6547; tel. 682/803–0100, **F**3 28 29 30 34 35 50 56 57 59 68 74 75 77 82 86 87 90 91 96 130 131 148 156
Primary Contact: Tina Densley, R.N., Chief Executive Officer
Web address: www.weatherfordrehab.com
Control: Corporation, Investor–owned (for–profit) **Service**: Rehabilitation

Staffed Beds: 26 **Admissions**: 504 **Census**: 15 **Outpatient Visits**: 0
Births: 0 **Total Expense ($000)**: 6548 **Payroll Expense ($000)**: 3274
Personnel: 77

WEBSTER—Harris County

CLEAR LAKE REHABILITATION HOSPITAL See Kindred Rehabilitation Hospital Clear Lake

CORNERSTONE HOSPITAL OF HOUSTON AT CLEARLAKE (452032), 709 Medical Center Boulevard, Zip 77598; tel. 281/332–3322, (Includes CORNERSTONE HOSPITAL OF HOUSTON - BELLAIRE, 5314 Dashwood, Houston, Texas, Zip 77081–4603; tel. 713/295–5300; Colin O'Sullivan, Interim Chief Executive Officer) **A**10 22 **F**1 3 29 75 82 85 86 87 130 148 149 **S** Cornerstone Healthcare Group, Dallas, TX
Primary Contact: Amy Stasney, R.N., Chief Executive Officer
COO: Brenda Lucero, Chief Clinical Officer
CFO: A Shane Wells, Chief Financial Officer
CMO: Mark Barlow, M.D., Chief Medical Officer and President Medical Staff
CIO: Jerald Harris, Chief Information Officer
CHR: Yolanda Jacobs, Coordinator Human Resources
Web address: www.cornerstonehealthcaregroup.com
Control: Partnership, Investor–owned (for–profit) **Service**: Acute long–term care hospital

Staffed Beds: 148 **Admissions**: 995 **Census**: 75 **Outpatient Visits**: 0
Births: 0 **Total Expense ($000)**: 39005 **Payroll Expense ($000)**: 16484
Personnel: 173

⇧ **HOUSTON PHYSICIANS HOSPITAL (670008)**, 333 North Texas Avenue, Suite 100, Zip 77598–4966; tel. 281/557–5620, **A**10 21 **F**3 29 37 40 51 64 74 79 81 82 85 86 91 93 107 111 114 141 149
Primary Contact: Nicholas Crafts, Chief Executive Officer
Web address: www.houstonphysicianshospital.com
Control: Corporation, Investor–owned (for–profit) **Service**: Surgical

Staffed Beds: 21 **Admissions**: 884 **Census**: 4 **Outpatient Visits**: 83111
Births: 0 **Total Expense ($000)**: 53091 **Payroll Expense ($000)**: 13664
Personnel: 222

⊞ **KINDRED HOSPITAL CLEAR LAKE (452075)**, 350 Blossom Street, Zip 77598; tel. 281/316–7800, **A**1 **F**1 3 29 45 57 60 64 75 77 85 91 93 96 107 130 148 **S** Kindred Healthcare, Louisville, KY
Primary Contact: Angel Gradney, Chief Executive Officer
Web address: www.khclearlake.com
Control: Corporation, Investor–owned (for–profit) **Service**: Acute long–term care hospital

Staffed Beds: 110 **Admissions**: 853 **Census**: 58 **Outpatient Visits**: 3504
Births: 0 **Total Expense ($000)**: 42561 **Payroll Expense ($000)**: 13634
Personnel: 214

TX

☐ **KINDRED REHABILITATION HOSPITAL CLEAR LAKE (453052)**, 655 East Medical Center Boulevard, Zip 77598–4328; tel. 281/286–1500, **A**1 10 **F**3 29 64 74 75 79 90 93 95 130 131 132 143 146 148 149
Primary Contact: Mikael Simpson, Chief Executive Officer
CFO: Michael McFall, Chief Financial Officer
CMO: Michael Rosenblatt, M.D., Medical Director
CHR: Monica Little, Coordinator Human Resources
CNO: Kathy Hutchins-Otero, Chief Clinical Officer
Web address: www.khrehabclearlake.com/
Control: Corporation, Investor–owned (for–profit) **Service:** Rehabilitation

Staffed Beds: 60 **Admissions:** 774 **Census:** 25 **Outpatient Visits:** 2175
Births: 0 **Total Expense ($000):** 11753 **Payroll Expense ($000):** 8557
Personnel: 172

WELLINGTON—Collingsworth County

COLLINGSWORTH GENERAL HOSPITAL (451355), 1013 15th Street, Zip 79095–3703, Mailing Address: P.O. Box 1112, Zip 79095–1112; tel. 806/447–2521, **A**10 18 **F**3 40 43 57 59 64 65 68 93 97 107 114 127 130 133 **S** Preferred Management Corporation, Shawnee, OK
Primary Contact: Candy Powell, Administrator
CFO: Larry Stephens, Chief Financial Officer
CMO: Wesley Nickens, M.D., Chief of Staff
CIO: Thomas T. Ng, Chief Information Officer
CHR: April Wright, Human Resources Officer
CNO: Vikki Barton, R.N., Chief Nursing Officer
Web address: www.collingsworthgeneral.net
Control: Corporation, Investor–owned (for–profit) **Service:** General medical and surgical

Staffed Beds: 13 **Admissions:** 187 **Census:** 3 **Outpatient Visits:** 10141
Births: 0 **Total Expense ($000):** 6997 **Payroll Expense ($000):** 3052
Personnel: 61

WESLACO—Hidalgo County

⊠ **KNAPP MEDICAL CENTER (450128)**, 1401 East Eighth Street, Zip 78596–6640, Mailing Address: P.O. Box 1110, Zip 78599–1110; tel. 956/968–8567, **A**1 3 5 10 **F**3 8 11 12 13 15 20 22 29 30 31 34 35 39 40 43 44 46 49 50 51 56 57 59 60 64 70 73 74 75 76 77 78 79 81 82 84 85 86 87 89 93 107 108 110 111 114 115 119 130 131 132 134 135 143 146 147 148 149 154 156 **S** Prime Healthcare, Ontario, CA
Primary Contact: Rene Lopez, Chief Executive Officer
CFO: Dinah L. Gonzalez, Chief Financial Officer
CIO: Teri Garza, Director Health Information Services
CHR: Emmett Craig, Chief Human Resources Officer
CNO: Anna Hinojosa, MSN, R.N., Interim Chief Nursing Officer
Web address: www.knappmed.org
Control: Other not–for–profit (including NFP Corporation) **Service:** General medical and surgical

Staffed Beds: 186 **Admissions:** 8526 **Census:** 89 **Outpatient Visits:** 73482
Births: 1511 **Total Expense ($000):** 98576 **Payroll Expense ($000):** 39232
Personnel: 592

WESLACO REGIONAL REHABILITATION HOSPITAL (453091), 906 South James Street, Zip 78596–9840; tel. 956/969–2222, **A**10 **F**3 29 34 35 68 82 86 87 90 96 130 132 148 149 154
Primary Contact: Corina Humphreys, Chief Executive Officer
CFO: Ernest Nash, Chief Financial Officer
CMO: Daisy Arce, President Medical Staff
CHR: Debbie Pemelton, Director Human Resources
CNO: Rita Mata-Guerrero, Director of Nursing
Web address: www.wrrh.ernesthealth.com
Control: Corporation, Investor–owned (for–profit) **Service:** Rehabilitation

Staffed Beds: 32 **Admissions:** 557 **Census:** 22 **Outpatient Visits:** 0
Births: 0 **Total Expense ($000):** 10885 **Payroll Expense ($000):** 4943
Personnel: 81

WHEELER—Wheeler County

PARKVIEW HOSPITAL (451334), 901 Sweetwater Street, Zip 79096–2421, Mailing Address: P.O. Box 1030, Zip 79096–1030; tel. 806/826–5581, **A**10 18 **F**3 7 10 40 43 59 62 64 65 68 91 93 107 114 127 128 130 133 148
Primary Contact: Monica Kidd, R.N., MSN, Administrator
CFO: Jace Henderson, Chief Financial Officer
CMO: John P. Lavelle, M.D., Chief Medical Officer
CNO: Melisa Scales, Director of Nursing
Web address: www.parkviewhosp.org
Control: Hospital district or authority, Government, nonfederal **Service:** General medical and surgical

Staffed Beds: 15 **Admissions:** 79 **Census:** 3 **Outpatient Visits:** 4136
Births: 0 **Total Expense ($000):** 8467 **Payroll Expense ($000):** 4104
Personnel: 112

WICHITA FALLS—Wichita County

⊠ **ENCOMPASS HEALTH REHABILITATION HOSPITAL OF WICHITA FALLS (453054)**, 3901 Armory Road, Zip 76302–2204; tel. 940/720–5700, **A**1 10 **F**3 28 29 68 74 75 77 79 86 87 90 91 94 95 96 130 132 **S** Encompass Health Corporation, Birmingham, AL
Primary Contact: Robbi Hudson, Chief Executive Officer
CMO: Virgil Frardo, M.D., Medical Director
CIO: Mary Walker, Manager Information Technology
CHR: Kathleen Pirtle, Director Human Resources
CNO: Jody S Gregory, R.N., Chief Nursing Officer
Web address: www.healthsouthwichitafalls.com
Control: Partnership, Investor–owned (for–profit) **Service:** Rehabilitation

Staffed Beds: 63 **Admissions:** 1624 **Census:** 53 **Outpatient Visits:** 0
Births: 0 **Total Expense ($000):** 17006 **Payroll Expense ($000):** 10433
Personnel: 176

☐ **KELL WEST REGIONAL HOSPITAL (450827)**, 5420 Kell West Boulevard, Zip 76310–1610; tel. 940/692–5888, **A**1 10 **F**3 37 39 40 49 51 59 65 74 75 78 79 81 85 97 107 108 114 119 126 129 130 135 149
Primary Contact: Jerry Myers, M.D., Chief Executive Officer and Medical Director
CFO: Fran Lindemann, Director Finance
Web address: www.kellwest.com
Control: Partnership, Investor–owned (for–profit) **Service:** General medical and surgical

Staffed Beds: 41 **Admissions:** 1166 **Census:** 9 **Outpatient Visits:** 22719
Births: 0 **Total Expense ($000):** 33614 **Payroll Expense ($000):** 10245
Personnel: 242

☐ **NORTH TEXAS STATE HOSPITAL, WICHITA FALLS CAMPUS (454008)**, 6515 Lake Road, Zip 76308–5419, Mailing Address: Box 300, Zip 76307–0300; tel. 940/692–1220, (Nonreporting) **A**1 10
Primary Contact: James E. Smith, Superintendent
CFO: Robin Moreno, Chief Financial Officer
CMO: Eulon Ross Taylor, Clinical Director
CIO: Chad Hughes, Chief Information Officer
Web address: www.online.dshs.state.tx.us/northtexassh/default.htm
Control: State, Government, nonfederal **Service:** Psychiatric

Staffed Beds: 381

☐ **PROMISE HOSPITAL OF WICHITA FALLS (452068)**, 1103 Grace Street, Zip 76301–4414; tel. 940/720–6633, **A**1 10 **F**1 3 29 30 68 75 77 85 86 87 91 100 130 143 148 **S** Promise Healthcare, Boca Raton, FL
Primary Contact: Louis P. Bradley Jr, Chief Executive Officer
CFO: Debbie Herder, Controller
CMO: Robert McBroom, M.D., Medical Director
CIO: Gail McIlroy, Director Medical Records
CNO: Deanna Dowling, R.N., Chief Nursing Officer
Web address: www.promise-wichitafalls.com
Control: Corporation, Investor–owned (for–profit) **Service:** Acute long–term care hospital

Staffed Beds: 31 **Admissions:** 332 **Census:** 22 **Outpatient Visits:** 0
Births: 0 **Total Expense ($000):** 9036 **Payroll Expense ($000):** 4323
Personnel: 85

TX

☐ **RED RIVER HOSPITAL, LLC (454018)**, 1505 Eighth Street, Zip 76301–3106; tel. 940/322–3171, **A**1 10 **F**4 5 29 38 50 86 87 98 99 100 101 102 103 104 105 130 135 143 152 153 157 **S** Acadia Healthcare Company, Inc., Franklin, TN
Primary Contact: James Wilfer, Chief Executive Officer
CFO: Bruce Porter, Chief Financial Officer
CMO: Harvey C Martin, M.D., Medical Director
CIO: Fay Helton, Director Medical Records
CHR: Kimberley Pellegrin, Director, Human Resources
CNO: Glenda Lawrence, R.N., Chief Nursing Officer
Web address: www.redriverhospital.com
Control: Corporation, Investor–owned (for–profit) **Service**: Psychiatric

Staffed Beds: 96 Admissions: 2154 Census: 67 Outpatient Visits: 4472 Births: 0 Total Expense ($000): 12457 Payroll Expense ($000): 6880 Personnel: 232

⊞ **UNITED REGIONAL HEALTH CARE SYSTEM (450010)**, 1600 11th Street, Zip 76301–4300; tel. 940/764–7000, (Includes UNITED REGIONAL HEALTH CARE SYSTEM-ELEVENTH STREET CAMPUS, 1600 11th Street, Wichita Falls, Texas, Zip 76301–9988; tel. 940/764–7000) **A**1 10 20 **F**3 11 12 13 15 17 18 20 21 22 24 26 28 29 30 31 32 34 35 37 39 40 43 44 45 46 47 48 49 50 51 53 57 59 60 61 64 65 68 70 73 74 75 76 77 78 79 80 81 82 84 85 86 87 89 92 93 102 107 110 111 114 115 116 117 118 119 126 130 131 132 134 146 147 148 149
Primary Contact: Phyllis A. Cowling, CPA, President and Chief Executive Officer
COO: Nancy Townley, R.N., Senior Vice President Operations
CFO: Robert M Pert, Vice President Finance and Chief Financial Officer
CMO: Lee Rodgers, M.D., Vice President Quality
CIO: Jerry Marshall, Director Information Services, Information Technology Security Officer
CHR: Kristi Faulkner, Vice President Organizational Growth
CNO: Jane Ritter, R.N., Vice President, Patient Care and Clinical Services
Web address: www.unitedregional.org
Control: Other not–for–profit (including NFP Corporation) **Service**: General medical and surgical

Staffed Beds: 277 Admissions: 15000 Census: 173 Outpatient Visits: 136168 Births: 1946 Total Expense ($000): 313927 Payroll Expense ($000): 119505 Personnel: 2005

WINNIE—Chambers County

RICELAND MEDICAL CENTER (451328), 538 Broadway, Zip 77665–7600; tel. 409/296–6000, **A**10 18 **F**3 8 29 34 40 57 59 65 81 93 105 107 119 127 133 146
Primary Contact: Saad Javed, Administrator
CFO: Julie Harris, Chief Financial Officer
CMO: Leonidas Andres, M.D., Chief of Staff
CHR: Anha Simon, Director Human Resources
Web address: www.energis.in/index.html
Control: Partnership, Investor–owned (for–profit) **Service**: General medical and surgical

Staffed Beds: 25 Admissions: 306 Census: 3 Outpatient Visits: 76269 Births: 0 Total Expense ($000): 30027 Payroll Expense ($000): 11895 Personnel: 248

WINNSBORO—Wood County

⊞ **CHRISTUS MOTHER FRANCES HOSPITAL - WINNSBORO (451381)**, 719 West Coke Road, Zip 75494–3011; tel. 903/342–5227, **A**1 10 18 **F**3 11 29 30 35 40 43 50 56 57 64 77 81 82 85 86 87 89 102 107 114 119 127 128 129 130 132 133 146 148 154 156 **S** CHRISTUS Health, Irving, TX
Primary Contact: Paul Harvey, Chief Executive Officer
CFO: Glenn Peltier, Chief Financial Officer
CNO: Kevin Jablonski, Chief Nursing Officer
Web address: www.tmfhs.org
Control: Other not–for–profit (including NFP Corporation) **Service**: General medical and surgical

Staffed Beds: 14 Admissions: 426 Census: 6 Outpatient Visits: 21349 Births: 0 Total Expense ($000): 17973 Payroll Expense ($000): 5337 Personnel: 109

TEXAS HEALTH PRESBYTERIAN HOSPITAL WINNSBORO See Christus Mother Frances Hospital - Winnsboro

WINTERS—Runnels County

★ **NORTH RUNNELS HOSPITAL (451315)**, 7821 State Highway 153, Zip 79567–7345, Mailing Address: P.O. Box 185, Zip 79567–0185; tel. 325/754–1317, (Nonreporting) **A**10 18
Primary Contact: Richard C. Mathis, Chief Executive Officer
CMO: Mark McKinnon, M.D., Chief of Staff
CNO: Bobbie Collom, Nursing Director
Control: Hospital district or authority, Government, nonfederal **Service**: General medical and surgical

Staffed Beds: 21

WOODVILLE—Tyler County

★ **TYLER COUNTY HOSPITAL (450460)**, 1100 West Bluff Street, Zip 75979–4799, Mailing Address: P.O. Box 549, Zip 75979–0549; tel. 409/283–8141, **A**10 20 **F**3 11 30 35 40 43 57 59 64 75 107 114 119 127 146
Primary Contact: Sondra Dianne. Wilson, R.N., MSN, Chief Executive Officer
CFO: Scott Elton McCluskey, Chief Financial Officer
CMO: Paula Lajean Denson, M.D., President
CIO: Rachel Joy Haygood, Director Information Technology
CHR: Kenneth Lynn Jobe, Director Human Resources
Web address: www.tchospital.us
Control: County, Government, nonfederal **Service**: General medical and surgical

Staffed Beds: 25 Admissions: 371 Census: 3 Outpatient Visits: 25184 Births: 0 Total Expense ($000): 11531 Payroll Expense ($000): 4391 Personnel: 109

YOAKUM—Lavaca County

★ **YOAKUM COMMUNITY HOSPITAL (451346)**, 1200 Carl Ramert Drive, Zip 77995–4868; tel. 361/293–2321, **A**10 18 **F**3 11 15 29 34 35 40 43 56 57 59 64 70 79 81 85 86 93 104 107 108 111 114 119 129 132 133 134 146 148 153 **S** Community Hospital Corporation, Plano, TX
Primary Contact: Karen Barber, R.N., Chief Executive Officer
CFO: Robert Foret, Chief Financial Officer
CMO: Timothy Wagner, M.D., Chief Medical Staff
CIO: Barbara Vasek, Director Information Technology
CHR: Karen Roznovsky, Director Human Resources
CNO: Jennifer Franklin, R.N., Chief Clinical Officer
Web address: www.yoakumhospital.org
Control: Other not–for–profit (including NFP Corporation) **Service**: General medical and surgical

Staffed Beds: 23 Admissions: 739 Census: 9 Outpatient Visits: 23395 Births: 52 Total Expense ($000): 18625 Payroll Expense ($000): 7965 Personnel: 125

TX

UTAH

AMERICAN FORK—Utah County

⊞ **AMERICAN FORK HOSPITAL (460023)**, 170 North 1100 East, Zip 84003–2096; tel. 801/855–3300, **A**1 10 **F**3 13 15 29 31 34 35 38 40 43 44 50 53 54 57 62 63 68 70 72 75 76 77 78 79 81 84 85 87 92 93 97 100 107 108 110 111 115 118 119 120 121 123 124 129 130 131 132 135 141 144 146 147 148 149 154 **S** Intermountain Healthcare, Inc., Salt Lake City, UT
Primary Contact: Jason Wilson, Administrator and Chief Executive Officer
CMO: Paul H Robinson, M.D., Medical Director
CIO: Mary Gathers, Manager Information Systems
CHR: Luke P Morris, Assistant Vice President Talent
CNO: Terri Lynn Hunter, R.N., Nurse Administrator
Web address: www.intermountainhealthcare.org
Control: Other not–for–profit (including NFP Corporation) **Service**: General medical and surgical

Staffed Beds: 78 **Admissions**: 7864 **Census**: 51 **Outpatient Visits**: 64576 **Births**: 2793 **Total Expense ($000)**: 126014 **Payroll Expense ($000)**: 36664 **Personnel**: 611

BEAVER—Beaver County

BEAVER VALLEY HOSPITAL (461335), 1109 North 100 West, Zip 84713, Mailing Address: P.O. Box 1670, Zip 84713–1670; tel. 435/438–7100, (Total facility includes 17 beds in nursing home–type unit) **A**10 18 **F**13 34 40 41 43 44 45 50 56 57 59 62 63 64 68 75 76 77 79 81 84 87 89 90 91 101 102 104 107 111 119 128 130 133 146 147 148 149 150 154
Primary Contact: Scott Langford, Administrator
Web address: www.bvhospital.com/
Control: City–county, Government, nonfederal **Service**: General medical and surgical

Staffed Beds: 27 **Admissions**: 251 **Census**: 17

BLANDING—San Juan County

⊞ **BLUE MOUNTAIN HOSPITAL (461310)**, 802 South 200 West, Suite A, Zip 84511–3910; tel. 435/678–3993, **A**1 10 18 **F**3 8 15 29 34 35 40 41 45 50 59 60 65 68 70 75 76 79 81 83 87 107 111 119 133 145 146 154
Primary Contact: Jeremy Lyman, Chief Executive Officer
CFO: Jimmy Johnson, Chief Financial Officer
CMO: Mahana Fisher, M.D., Medical Director
CIO: Anthony Torres, Manager Information Technology
CHR: Gail M. Northern, Director Human Resources
CNO: Derrill Kent Turek, R.N., Chief Nursing Officer
Web address: www.bmhutah.org/
Control: Other not–for–profit (including NFP Corporation) **Service**: General medical and surgical

Staffed Beds: 11 **Admissions**: 503 **Census**: 5 **Outpatient Visits**: 8378 **Births**: 113 **Total Expense ($000)**: 12117 **Payroll Expense ($000)**: 4299

BOUNTIFUL—Davis County

⊞ **LAKEVIEW HOSPITAL (460042)**, 630 East Medical Drive, Zip 84010–4908; tel. 801/299–2200, **A**1 5 10 **F**3 8 11 13 15 18 20 22 26 28 29 30 34 37 38 40 43 44 45 49 50 51 53 56 57 59 60 64 65 67 68 70 72 74 75 76 77 79 81 82 85 86 87 93 96 97 98 100 101 102 107 108 110 111 114 115 118 119 129 130 132 135 146 147 148 **S** HCA Healthcare, Nashville, TN
Primary Contact: Troy Wood, Chief Executive Officer
CFO: Wayne Dalton, Chief Financial Officer
CMO: Michael Hess, M.D., Chief Medical Officer
CIO: Mark Ellis, Director Information Technology
CHR: Julie Isom, Director Human Resources
CNO: Marilyn Mariani, R.N., Chief Nursing Officer
Web address: www.lakeviewhospital.com
Control: Corporation, Investor–owned (for–profit) **Service**: General medical and surgical

Staffed Beds: 119 **Admissions**: 3926 **Census**: 40

SOUTH DAVIS COMMUNITY HOSPITAL (462003), 401 South 400 East, Zip 84010–4933; tel. 801/295–2361, (Nonreporting) **A**10
Primary Contact: David Bland, Chief Executive Officer
CMO: Scott Southworth, M.D., Medical Director
CHR: Jamey Sulser, Director Human Resources
Web address: www.sdch.com
Control: Other not–for–profit (including NFP Corporation) **Service**: Acute long–term care hospital

Staffed Beds: 176

BRIGHAM CITY—Box Elder County

⊞ **BRIGHAM CITY COMMUNITY HOSPITAL (460017)**, 950 South Medical Drive, Zip 84302–4724; tel. 435/734–9471, (Nonreporting) **A**1 10 **S** HCA Healthcare, Nashville, TN
Primary Contact: Richard Spuhler, Chief Executive Officer
CMO: Joel Gardner, D.O., Chief Medical Officer
CIO: Steve Reichard, Manager Information Systems
CHR: Tracie Greene, Director Human Resources
CNO: Jerry Bushman, Chief Nursing Officer
Web address: www.brighamcityhospital.com
Control: Corporation, Investor–owned (for–profit) **Service**: General medical and surgical

Staffed Beds: 39

CEDAR CITY—Iron County

⊞ **CEDAR CITY HOSPITAL (460007)**, 1303 North Main Street, Zip 84721–9746; tel. 435/868–5000, **A**1 10 20 **F**3 13 15 26 28 29 31 34 35 38 39 40 43 45 50 57 60 64 68 70 74 75 76 77 78 79 81 85 86 87 92 93 100 102 107 108 110 111 115 118 119 120 121 123 124 130 132 135 141 146 147 148 149 154 157 **S** Intermountain Healthcare, Inc., Salt Lake City, UT
Primary Contact: Eric Packer, Chief Executive Officer
CFO: Reed Sargent, Assistant Administrator Finance
Web address: www.https://intermountainhealthcare.org/locations/cedar-city-hospital/
Control: Other not–for–profit (including NFP Corporation) **Service**: General medical and surgical

Staffed Beds: 48 **Admissions**: 3221 **Census**: 18 **Outpatient Visits**: 40202 **Births**: 836 **Total Expense ($000)**: 76306 **Payroll Expense ($000)**: 21763 **Personnel**: 381

DELTA—Millard County

★ **DELTA COMMUNITY MEDICAL CENTER (461300)**, 126 South White Sage Avenue, Zip 84624–8937; tel. 435/864–5591, (Total facility includes 16 beds in nursing home–type unit) **A**10 18 **F**3 15 29 34 35 38 40 43 45 50 59 64 65 68 71 75 76 77 81 85 87 89 97 100 102 107 110 111 114 119 128 133 146 147 148 149 150 154 157 **S** Intermountain Healthcare, Inc., Salt Lake City, UT
Primary Contact: Lenny Lyons, Administrator
CFO: Chris Thompson, Chief Financial Officer
Web address: www.ihc.com
Control: Other not–for–profit (including NFP Corporation) **Service**: General medical and surgical

Staffed Beds: 31 **Admissions**: 332 **Census**: 3 **Outpatient Visits**: 4555 **Births**: 80 **Total Expense ($000)**: 10167 **Payroll Expense ($000)**: 3314 **Personnel**: 48

DRAPER—Salt Lake County

⊞ **LONE PEAK HOSPITAL (460060)**, 1925 South State Street, Zip 84020; tel. 801/545–8000, (Nonreporting) **A**1 10 **S** HCA Healthcare, Nashville, TN
Primary Contact: Brian Lines, Chief Executive Officer
Web address: www.lonepeakhospital.com
Control: Corporation, Investor–owned (for–profit) **Service**: General medical and surgical

Staffed Beds: 32

UT

FILLMORE—Millard County

★ **FILLMORE COMMUNITY HOSPITAL (461301)**, 674 South Highway 99, Zip 84631–5013; tel. 435/743–5591, **A**10 18 **F**3 15 29 34 35 38 40 44 50 75 76 77 81 85 86 87 96 97 100 102 107 110 111 114 119 127 130 132 133 146 147 148 149 154 **S** Intermountain Healthcare, Inc., Salt Lake City, UT
Primary Contact: Lenny Lyons, Administrator
CFO: Chris Thompson, Chief Financial Officer
Web address: www.ihc.com
Control: Other not–for–profit (including NFP Corporation) **Service:** General medical and surgical

Staffed Beds: 19 **Admissions:** 216 **Census:** 12 **Outpatient Visits:** 3060 **Births:** 38 **Total Expense ($000):** 10103 **Payroll Expense ($000):** 3770 **Personnel:** 46

GUNNISON—Sanpete County

★ **GUNNISON VALLEY HOSPITAL (461306)**, 64 East 100 North, Zip 84634, Mailing Address: P.O. Box 759, Zip 84634–0759; tel. 435/528–7246, (Nonreporting) **A**10 18
Primary Contact: Mark F. Dalley, Administrator
CFO: Brian Murray, Chief Financial Officer
CIO: Mike Ryan, Director of Information Services
CHR: Liz Brown, Manager Human Resources
CNO: Brenda Bartholomew, Chief Nursing Officer
Web address: www.gvhospital.org
Control: County, Government, nonfederal **Service:** General medical and surgical

Staffed Beds: 124

HEBER CITY—Wasatch County

★ **HEBER VALLEY HOSPITAL (461307)**, 1485 South Highway 40, Zip 84032–3522; tel. 435/654–2500, **A**3 10 18 **F**3 13 15 29 34 35 38 40 43 44 45 51 53 57 59 64 68 75 76 77 79 81 85 86 87 92 93 102 107 110 111 115 119 128 129 130 133 135 141 144 146 148 149 154 **S** Intermountain Healthcare, Inc., Salt Lake City, UT
Primary Contact: Si William. Hutt, Administrator
CFO: Craig Mills, Chief Financial Officer
CMO: Stanton B McDonald, M.D., Medical Director
CHR: Bruce Dent, Human Resources Director
CNO: Gayle Sturgis, R.N., Nurse Administrator
Web address: www.https://intermountainhealthcare.org/locations/heber-valley-hospital/
Control: Other not–for–profit (including NFP Corporation) **Service:** General medical and surgical

Staffed Beds: 19 **Admissions:** 826 **Census:** 5 **Outpatient Visits:** 13103 **Births:** 180 **Total Expense ($000):** 33491 **Payroll Expense ($000):** 11259 **Personnel:** 139

KANAB—Kane County

KANE COUNTY HOSPITAL (461309), 355 North Main Street, Zip 84741–3260; tel. 435/644–5811, (Nonreporting) **A**10 18
Primary Contact: Sherrie Pandya, Administrator
CFO: Stephen Howells, Chief Financial Officer
CMO: Darin Ott, D.O., Chief of Staff
CHR: Laurali Noteman, Director Human Resources
CNO: Charlene Kelly, Chief Nursing Officer
Web address: www.kanecountyhospital.net
Control: Hospital district or authority, Government, nonfederal **Service:** General medical and surgical

Staffed Beds: 25

LAYTON—Davis County

★ ⇑ **DAVIS HOSPITAL AND MEDICAL CENTER (460041)**, 1600 West Antelope Drive, Zip 84041–1142; tel. 801/807–1000, (Nonreporting) **A**3 10 21 **S** Steward Health Care System, LLC, Dallas, TX
Primary Contact: Michael Jensen, Chief Executive Officer
COO: Jared Spackman, Chief Operating Officer
CFO: Jared Spackman, Chief Financial Officer
CMO: Les Greenwood, M.D., President, Medical Staff
CIO: Shane Williams, Director Information Systems
CHR: Tara Figgins, Director Human Resources
CNO: Chris Johnson, Chief Nursing Officer
Web address: www.davishospital.com
Control: Partnership, Investor–owned (for–profit) **Service:** General medical and surgical

Staffed Beds: 221

LAYTON HOSPITAL, 201 West Layton Parkway, Zip 84041–3692; tel. 801/543–6000, (Data for 77 days) **A**1 **F**3 13 18 29 30 31 35 38 40 45 50 60 68 70 73 75 76 77 79 81 85 86 87 92 93 100 102 107 108 110 111 115 118 119 120 121 123 124 130 131 141 144 146 147 148 149 154 **S** Intermountain Healthcare, Inc., Salt Lake City, UT
Primary Contact: Judy Williamson, R.N., Administrator
Web address: www.https://intermountainhealthcare.org/locations/layton-hospital/medical-services/
Control: Other not–for–profit (including NFP Corporation) **Service:** General medical and surgical

Staffed Beds: 43 **Admissions:** 345 **Census:** 10 **Outpatient Visits:** 4328 **Births:** 76 **Personnel:** 311

LOGAN—Cache County

LOGAN REGIONAL HOSPITAL (460015), 1400 North 500 East, Zip 84341–2455; tel. 435/716–1000, (Total facility includes 11 beds in nursing home–type unit) **A**1 10 **F**3 13 15 18 20 22 29 31 34 35 38 39 40 43 44 45 46 48 49 50 56 57 59 60 64 68 70 73 75 76 77 78 79 81 85 86 87 98 100 102 107 108 110 111 115 116 117 118 119 120 121 123 124 126 128 129 130 131 132 141 144 146 147 148 149 154 157 **S** Intermountain Healthcare, Inc., Salt Lake City, UT
Primary Contact: Kyle A. Hansen, Chief Executive Officer
COO: Brandon McBride, Operations Officer
CFO: Alan Robinson, Chief Financial Officer
CMO: Todd A Brown, M.D., Medical Director
CIO: Dave Felts, Chief Information Systems
CHR: Jolene Clonts, Director Human Resources
CNO: Neil C Perkes, Operations Officer
Web address: www.loganregionalhospital.org
Control: Other not–for–profit (including NFP Corporation) **Service:** General medical and surgical

Staffed Beds: 137 **Admissions:** 8480 **Census:** 60 **Outpatient Visits:** 55060 **Births:** 2240 **Total Expense ($000):** 182642 **Payroll Expense ($000):** 50953 **Personnel:** 894

MIDVALE—Salt Lake County

☐ **HIGHLAND RIDGE HOSPITAL (464015)**, 7309 South 180 West, Zip 84047–3769; tel. 801/569–2153, (Nonreporting) **A**1 **S** Acadia Healthcare Company, Inc., Franklin, TN
Primary Contact: Michelle Neville, Chief Executive Officer
COO: Robert Beatty, Chief Operating Officer
CFO: Sheri Sorenson, Manager Business Office
CHR: Carol Cunningham, Administrative Assistant
Web address: www.highlandridgehospital.com
Control: Corporation, Investor–owned (for–profit) **Service:** Psychiatric

Staffed Beds: 83

MILFORD—Beaver County

★ **MILFORD VALLEY MEMORIAL HOSPITAL (461305)**, 850 North Main Street, Zip 84751–0640, Mailing Address: P.O. Box 640, Zip 84751–0640; tel. 435/387–2411, (Nonreporting) **A**10 18
Primary Contact: Scott Langford, Administrator
COO: Michelle Barton, Chief Operating Officer
CFO: Tyler Moss, Chief Financial Officer
CNO: Amy Contreras Esq Chief Nursing Officer
Web address: www.milfordmemorialhospital.org
Control: Hospital district or authority, Government, nonfederal **Service:** General medical and surgical

Staffed Beds: 25

MOAB—Grand County

★ **MOAB REGIONAL HOSPITAL (461302)**, 450 West Williams Way, Zip 84532–2065, Mailing Address: P.O. Box 998, Zip 84532–0998; tel. 435/719–3500, (Nonreporting) **A**10 18
Primary Contact: Jennifer Sadoff, Chief Executive Officer
COO: Vicki Gigliotti, Chief Clinical Officer
CFO: Craig M Daniels, Chief Financial Officer
CMO: Dylan Cole, Chief Medical Officer
CIO: Mike Foster, Manager Information Systems
CHR: Katherine Sullivan, Director, Human Resources
Web address: www.mrhmoab.org
Control: Other not–for–profit (including NFP Corporation) **Service:** General medical and surgical

Staffed Beds: 17

Many Facility Codes have changed. Please refer to the AHA Guide Code Chart.

MONTICELLO—San Juan County

SAN JUAN HEALTH SERVICE DISTRICT (461308), 380 West 100 North, Zip 84535, Mailing Address: P.O. Box 308, Zip 84535–0308; tel. 435/587–2116, **A**10 18 **F**3 13 15 29 31 32 34 35 38 39 40 41 44 45 47 50 56 57 59 64 65 66 68 76 79 80 81 82 87 107 110 114 119 127 128 133 145 148
Primary Contact: Clayton Holt, Chief Executive Officer
CFO: Lyman Duncan, Chief Financial Officer
CMO: Kelly Jeppesen, Chief Medical Officer
CIO: Julie Bingham, IT Supervisor
CHR: Deana Dalton, Human Resources
CNO: Laurie Schafer, Chief Nursing Officer
Web address: www.sanjuanhealthservices.org/
Control: Hospital district or authority, Government, nonfederal **Service**: General medical and surgical

Staffed Beds: 25 **Admissions**: 257 **Census**: 2 **Outpatient Visits**: 5000 **Births**: 47 **Total Expense ($000)**: 15625 **Payroll Expense ($000)**: 6448 **Personnel**: 108

MOUNT PLEASANT—Sanpete County

★ **SANPETE VALLEY HOSPITAL (461303)**, 1100 South Medical Drive, Zip 84647–2222; tel. 435/462–2441, **A**10 18 **F**3 15 29 34 35 38 40 43 44 50 67 68 75 76 77 81 85 86 87 90 97 100 102 107 110 111 115 119 127 128 130 132 149 154 157 **S** Intermountain Healthcare, Inc., Salt Lake City, UT
Primary Contact: Aaron C. Wood, Chief Executive Officer and Administrator
COO: Kristina Skinner, Director Quality
CFO: Chris Thompson, Chief Financial Officer
CMO: David Krzymowski, M.D., Chief of Staff
CIO: Michael Ence, Computer Specialist
CHR: Brett Gray, Director Human Resource
CNO: Ryan Robison, Chief Nursing Officer
Web address: www.intermountainhealthcare.com
Control: Other not–for–profit (including NFP Corporation) **Service**: General medical and surgical

Staffed Beds: 18 **Admissions**: 549 **Census**: 4 **Outpatient Visits**: 9022 **Births**: 111 **Total Expense ($000)**: 20256 **Payroll Expense ($000)**: 7079 **Personnel**: 99

MURRAY—Salt Lake County

□ △ **INTERMOUNTAIN MEDICAL CENTER (460010)**, 5121 South Cottonwood Street, Zip 84107–5701; tel. 801/507–7000, **A**1 2 3 5 7 10 **F**3 8 11 13 15 17 18 20 22 24 26 28 29 30 31 34 35 37 38 39 40 43 44 45 46 47 48 49 50 51 52 53 54 55 56 57 58 59 60 61 64 66 68 70 71 72 74 75 76 77 78 79 80 81 82 84 85 86 87 90 91 92 93 94 96 97 100 102 107 108 110 111 115 116 117 118 119 120 121 123 124 126 129 130 131 132 135 137 138 139 141 142 146 147 148 149 150 154 155 156 157 **S** Intermountain Healthcare, Inc., Salt Lake City, UT
Primary Contact: Joseph Mott, Chief Executive Officer
COO: Kelly L Duffin, Operations Officer
CFO: Royce Stephens, Director Finance
CMO: Mark Ott, M.D., Regional Chief Medical Director
CIO: David Baird, Director of Information Systems
CHR: Tiffiny J Lipscomb, Manager Human Resources
CNO: Suzanne P. Anderson, Nurse Administrator
Web address: www.intermountainhealthcare.org
Control: Other not–for–profit (including NFP Corporation) **Service**: General medical and surgical

Staffed Beds: 502 **Admissions**: 30174 **Census**: 348 **Outpatient Visits**: 219320 **Births**: 4292 **Total Expense ($000)**: 893294 **Payroll Expense ($000)**: 260728 **Personnel**: 3955

LANDMARK HOSPITAL OF SALT LAKE CITY (462006), 4252 South Birkhill Boulevard, Zip 84107–5715; tel. 801/268–5400, (Nonreporting) **A**10 22 **S** Landmark Hospitals, Cape Girardeau, MO
Primary Contact: Gina Herchenhahn, Chief Executive Officer
Web address: www.https://landmarkhospitalsaltlake.com/
Control: Partnership, Investor–owned (for–profit) **Service**: Acute long–term care hospital

Staffed Beds: 38

⊞ **THE ORTHOPEDIC SPECIALTY HOSPITAL (460049)**, 5848 South 300 East, Zip 84107–6121; tel. 801/314–4100, **A**1 10 **F**9 29 34 35 37 44 50 53 57 58 59 64 68 75 77 79 81 82 84 85 86 87 92 93 94 96 97 107 111 115 119 129 130 131 132 141 144 146 149 154 **S** Intermountain Healthcare, Inc., Salt Lake City, UT
Primary Contact: Adam Chandio, Administrator
CFO: Sherlyn Lewis, Manager Finance
CMO: Jon Sundin, M.D., Medical Director
CIO: David Baird, Chief Information Officer
CHR: Tina Tasso, Manager Human Resources
Web address: www.intermountainhealthcare.org
Control: Other not–for–profit (including NFP Corporation) **Service**: Orthopedic

Staffed Beds: 40 **Admissions**: 1739 **Census**: 8 **Births**: 0 **Total Expense ($000)**: 71456 **Payroll Expense ($000)**: 20134 **Personnel**: 324

NEPHI—Juab County

★ **CENTRAL VALLEY MEDICAL CENTER (461304)**, 48 West 1500 North, Zip 84648–8900; tel. 435/623–3000, **A**10 18 **F**3 13 15 29 34 35 40 41 43 45 50 57 59 62 63 64 65 75 76 77 79 81 82 85 86 87 89 93 94 97 99 100 101 102 103 104 107 110 111 115 119 128 129 130 131 133 146 147 148 154 156 **S** Rural Health Group, Nephi, UT
Primary Contact: Mark R. Stoddard, Chief Executive Officer
COO: Randy Cuff, Chief Operating Officer
CFO: Brent Davis, Chief Financial Officer
CMO: Mark Oveson, M.D., Chief Medical Staff
CIO: Ken Richens, Chief Information Officer
CHR: Brian Allsop, Director Human Resources
CNO: Randy Allinson, R.N., Chief Nursing Officer
Web address: www.cvmed.net
Control: Other not–for–profit (including NFP Corporation) **Service**: General medical and surgical

Staffed Beds: 27 **Admissions**: 934 **Census**: 12 **Outpatient Visits**: 32154 **Births**: 115 **Total Expense ($000)**: 39021 **Payroll Expense ($000)**: 11830 **Personnel**: 293

NORTH LOGAN—Cache County

⊞ **CACHE VALLEY HOSPITAL (460054)**, 2380 North 400 East, Zip 84341–6000; tel. 435/713–9700, (Nonreporting) **A**1 10 **S** HCA Healthcare, Nashville, TN
Primary Contact: Daren Wells, Chief Executive Officer
CFO: David S Geary, Chief Financial Officer
CMO: Jona Jowett, Chief Medical Officer
Web address: www.cachevalleyhospital.com/
Control: Corporation, Investor–owned (for profit) **Service**: General medical and surgical

Staffed Beds: 22

OGDEN—Weber County

⊞ **MCKAY-DEE HOSPITAL (460004)**, 4401 Harrison Boulevard, Zip 84403–3195; tel. 801/387–2800, **A**1 2 3 5 10 **F**3 8 11 12 13 15 18 20 22 24 26 28 29 30 31 34 35 36 38 39 40 43 44 45 46 49 50 51 53 54 57 58 59 60 64 68 70 72 74 75 76 77 78 79 80 81 82 85 86 87 89 90 91 92 93 96 97 98 99 100 102 104 107 108 110 111 115 116 117 118 119 120 121 123 124 126 129 130 131 132 134 135 141 146 147 148 149 154 156 157 **S** Intermountain Healthcare, Inc., Salt Lake City, UT
Primary Contact: Michael A. Clark, Administrator
COO: Michael A Clark, Chief Operating Officer
CFO: Doug Smith, Chief Financial Officer
CMO: Christine Nefcy, Chief Medical Officer
CIO: Mary Gathers, Director Information Systems
CHR: Lee Lorimer IV Regional Director Human Resources
CNO: Bonnie Jacklin, R.N., MSN, Chief Nursing Officer
Web address: www.mckay-dee.org
Control: Other not–for–profit (including NFP Corporation) **Service**: General medical and surgical

Staffed Beds: 310 **Admissions**: 21648 **Census**: 194 **Outpatient Visits**: 146016 **Births**: 3628 **Total Expense ($000)**: 462622 **Payroll Expense ($000)**: 131411 **Personnel**: 2173

UT

⊞ **OGDEN REGIONAL MEDICAL CENTER (460005)**, 5475 South 500 East, Zip 84405–6905; tel. 801/479–2111, (Nonreporting) **A**1 3 5 10 13 **S** HCA Healthcare, Nashville, TN
Primary Contact: Mark B. Adams, Chief Executive Officer
COO: Brian Lines, Chief Operating Officer
CFO: Judd Taylor, Chief Financial Officer
CMO: Jeffrey Abel, M.D., Chief Medical Officer
CIO: Eric Peterson, Director
CHR: Chris Bissenden, Director Human Resources
CNO: Elizabeth B. Later, R.N., Chief Nursing Officer
Web address: www.ogdenregional.com
Control: Corporation, Investor–owned (for–profit) **Service**: General medical and surgical

Staffed Beds: 167

OREM—Utah County

⊞ **OREM COMMUNITY HOSPITAL (460043)**, 331 North 400 West, Zip 84057–1999; tel. 801/224–4080, **A**1 10 **F**3 13 15 29 34 35 38 40 44 50 64 68 75 76 77 81 85 86 87 96 97 100 102 107 111 115 119 130 132 141 146 147 149 154 **S** Intermountain Healthcare, Inc., Salt Lake City, UT
Primary Contact: J. Francis. Gibson, Administrator and Chief Executive Officer
CMO: Neil Whitaker, M.D., Chief Medical Director
CIO: Diane Rindlisbacher, Manager Information Systems
CHR: Pamela S Niece, Director Human Resources
Web address: www.intermountainhealthcare.org
Control: Other not–for–profit (including NFP Corporation) **Service**: General medical and surgical

Staffed Beds: 24 **Admissions:** 1828 **Census:** 10 **Outpatient Visits:** 24272
Births: 895 **Total Expense ($000):** 28567 **Payroll Expense ($000):** 10042
Personnel: 153

☐ **PROVO CANYON BEHAVIORAL HOSPITAL (464014)**, 1350 East 750 North, Zip 84097–4345; tel. 801/852–2273, **A**1 10 **F**4 5 29 35 36 38 56 57 59 75 86 87 98 99 101 103 104 149 153 **S** Universal Health Services, Inc., King of Prussia, PA
Primary Contact: Jeremy Cottle, Ph.D., Chief Executive Officer
CFO: Emmy Adams, Chief Financial Officer
CHR: Diann Decker, Chief Human Resource Officer
Web address: www.pcbh.com
Control: Corporation, Investor–owned (for–profit) **Service**: Psychiatric

Staffed Beds: 80 **Admissions:** 2301 **Census:** 57 **Outpatient Visits:** 2820
Births: 0 **Total Expense ($000):** 12717 **Payroll Expense ($000):** 7110
Personnel: 143

⊞ **TIMPANOGOS REGIONAL HOSPITAL (460052)**, 750 West 800 North, Zip 84057–3660; tel. 801/714–6000, **A**1 5 10 **F**3 11 12 13 15 17 18 19 20 22 24 26 28 29 30 34 35 39 40 41 45 46 47 48 49 50 68 70 72 73 74 76 78 79 81 82 85 88 89 93 97 107 108 109 110 111 115 116 117 119 120 121 123 126 130 131 135 146 147 149 154 156 **S** HCA Healthcare, Nashville, TN
Primary Contact: Kimball S. Anderson, FACHE, Chief Executive Officer
COO: Ryan LeMasters, Chief Operating Officer
CFO: Jody S Dial, Chief Financial Officer
CMO: Randle L Likes, M.D., Chief Medical Officer
CIO: Richard Neilson, Director of Information Services
CHR: Tim Black, Director Human Resources
CNO: Sandy Ewell, Chief Nursing Officer
Web address: www.timpanogosregionalhospital.com
Control: Corporation, Investor–owned (for–profit) **Service**: General medical and surgical

Staffed Beds: 106 **Admissions:** 4242 **Census:** 46 **Outpatient Visits:** 22615
Births: 1598

PANGUITCH—Garfield County

★ **GARFIELD MEMORIAL HOSPITAL (461333)**, 200 North 400 East, Zip 84759, Mailing Address: P.O. Box 389, Zip 84759–0389; tel. 435/676–8811, **A**10 18 **F**3 15 29 34 38 40 44 50 68 71 75 81 83 85 86 87 96 97 100 102 107 110 115 119 127 128 130 132 133 149 154 **S** Intermountain Healthcare, Inc., Salt Lake City, UT
Primary Contact: Alberto Vasquez, Administrator
CFO: Reed Sargent, Assistant Administrator Finance
Web address: www.ihc.com/hospitals/garfield
Control: County, Government, nonfederal **Service**: General medical and surgical

Staffed Beds: 15 **Admissions:** 308 **Census:** 3 **Outpatient Visits:** 12541
Births: 21 **Total Expense ($000):** 11372 **Payroll Expense ($000):** 5833
Personnel: 93

PARK CITY—Summit County

⊞ **PARK CITY HOSPITAL (460057)**, 900 Round Valley Drive, Zip 84060–7552; tel. 435/658–7000, **A**1 10 **F**3 13 15 29 34 35 36 38 40 43 44 50 53 57 59 64 68 70 75 76 77 79 81 85 86 87 92 93 97 100 102 107 108 110 111 115 118 119 129 130 131 132 141 146 147 149 154 157 **S** Intermountain Healthcare, Inc., Salt Lake City, UT
Primary Contact: Lori Weston, Administrator
CFO: Lori Nielson, Regional Finance Director
CMO: Wain Allen, M.D., Medical Director
CHR: Christopher Saling, Manager Human Resources
CNO: Dan Davis, MSN, R.N., Nurse Administrator
Web address: www.intermountainhealthcare.org
Control: Other not–for–profit (including NFP Corporation) **Service**: General medical and surgical

Staffed Beds: 37 **Admissions:** 2124 **Census:** 12 **Outpatient Visits:** 25700
Births: 327 **Total Expense ($000):** 88664 **Payroll Expense ($000):** 23615
Personnel: 329

PAYSON—Utah County

⊞ **MOUNTAIN VIEW HOSPITAL (460013)**, 1000 East 100 North, Zip 84651–1600; tel. 801/465–7000, (Nonreporting) **A**1 10 **S** HCA Healthcare, Nashville, TN
Primary Contact: Kevin Johnson, Chief Executive Officer
COO: Ric Johnson, Associate Administrator
CFO: Steven R Schramm, Chief Financial Officer
CMO: Jeffrey Wallentine, Chief of Staff
CIO: Cindy Mecham, Health Information Director
CHR: Wally Trotter, Director Human Resources
CNO: Katie King, R.N., Chief Nursing Officer
Web address: www.mvhpayson.com
Control: Corporation, Investor–owned (for–profit) **Service**: General medical and surgical

Staffed Beds: 114

PRICE—Carbon County

⊞ **CASTLEVIEW HOSPITAL (460011)**, 300 North Hospital Drive, Zip 84501–4200; tel. 435/637–4800, **A**1 10 20 **F**3 8 11 12 13 15 18 29 31 34 39 40 41 45 50 51 54 56 57 59 64 65 68 70 75 76 77 78 79 81 82 84 86 87 89 92 93 97 107 108 110 111 115 119 127 130 131 144 146 147 148 149 154 156 157 **S** LifePoint Health, Brentwood, TN
Primary Contact: Greg Cook, Chief Executive Officer
CMO: Glen T. Etzel, M.D., Chief of Staff
CIO: Fiore Wilson, Director Information Systems
CHR: Misty Birch, Director Human Resources
CNO: Grant Barraclough, R.N., Chief Nursing Officer
Web address: www.castleviewhospital.net
Control: Corporation, Investor–owned (for–profit) **Service**: General medical and surgical

Staffed Beds: 49 **Admissions:** 1649 **Census:** 12 **Outpatient Visits:** 42678
Births: 287 **Total Expense ($000):** 39633 **Payroll Expense ($000):** 14026
Personnel: 355

PROVO—Utah County

☐ **UTAH STATE HOSPITAL (464001)**, 1300 East Center Street, Zip 84606–3554, Mailing Address: P.O. Box 270, Zip 84603–0270; tel. 801/344–4400, **A**1 3 10 **F**30 34 56 59 75 77 86 87 91 98 99 100 101 103 106 130 135 143 146 149 150 157
Primary Contact: Dallas Earnshaw, Superintendent
COO: Dallas Earnshaw, Superintendent
CFO: Robert Burton, Manager Finance
CMO: Madhu Gundlapalli, M.D., Clinical Director
CIO: Jill Hill, Director Information Technology
CHR: Devin Patrick, Manager Human Resources
CNO: Chris Metcalf, Director of Nursing
Web address: www.ush.utah.gov
Control: State, Government, nonfederal **Service**: Psychiatric

Staffed Beds: 384 **Admissions:** 280 **Census:** 293 **Outpatient Visits:** 0
Births: 0 **Total Expense ($000):** 66224 **Payroll Expense ($000):** 37088

UT

Many Facility Codes have changed. Please refer to the AHA Guide Code Chart. © 2019 AHA Guide

⊞ △ **UTAH VALLEY HOSPITAL (460001)**, 1034 North 500 West, Zip 84604–3337; tel. 801/357–7850, **A**1 2 3 5 7 10 **F**3 12 13 15 17 18 20 22 24 26 28 29 30 31 32 34 35 37 38 39 40 43 44 45 46 48 49 50 51 53 54 56 57 59 64 68 70 72 74 75 76 77 78 79 80 81 82 84 85 86 87 88 89 90 93 94 97 98 100 102 107 108 110 111 115 116 117 118 119 120 121 123 124 130 131 132 141 146 147 148 149 154 156 157 **S** Intermountain Healthcare, Inc., Salt Lake City, UT
Primary Contact: Maria Black, Interim Administrator
CFO: Rod Lisonbee, Chief Financial Officer
CIO: Mary Gathers, Director Information Systems
CHR: Luke P Morris, Assistant Vice President Talent
CNO: Lisa A. Paletta, R.N., FACHE, Chief Nursing Officer
Web address: www.https://intermountainhealthcare.org/locations/utah-valley-hospital/
Control: Other not–for–profit (including NFP Corporation) **Service**: General medical and surgical

Staffed Beds: 359 **Admissions**: 22839 **Census**: 243 **Outpatient Visits**: 213016 **Births**: 4112 **Total Expense ($000)**: 511834 **Payroll Expense ($000)**: 154743 **Personnel**: 2635

☐ **UTAH VALLEY SPECIALTY HOSPITAL (462005)**, 306 River Bend Lane, Zip 84604–5625; tel. 801/226–8880, (Nonreporting) **A**1 10 **S** Ernest Health, Inc., Albuquerque, NM
Primary Contact: Brynn Beck, Chief Executive Officer
Web address: www.uvsh.ernesthealth.com
Control: Corporation, Investor–owned (for–profit) **Service**: Acute long–term care hospital

Staffed Beds: 40

RICHFIELD—Sevier County

⊞ **SEVIER VALLEY HOSPITAL (460026)**, 1000 North Main Street, Zip 84701–1857; tel. 435/893–4100, **A**1 10 20 **F**3 15 29 31 34 35 38 40 44 50 64 68 75 76 77 79 81 85 86 87 97 100 102 107 110 111 115 119 127 130 132 141 146 147 149 154 **S** Intermountain Healthcare, Inc., Salt Lake City, UT
Primary Contact: Gary E. Beck, Administrator
CFO: Chris Thompson, Chief Financial Officer
CMO: Justin Abbott, M.D., Medical Director
CHR: Katey Nelson, Director Human Resources
CNO: Cami Blackham, R.N., Nurse Administrator
Web address: www.sevierhospital.org
Control: Other not–for–profit (including NFP Corporation) **Service**: General medical and surgical

Staffed Beds: 24 **Admissions**: 1139 **Census**: 7 **Outpatient Visits**: 14319 **Births**: 250 **Total Expense ($000)**: 41678 **Payroll Expense ($000)**: 10288 **Personnel**: 165

RIVERTON—Salt Lake County

⊞ **RIVERTON HOSPITAL (460058)**, 3741 West 12600 South, Zip 84065–7215; tel. 801/285–4000, **A**1 3 10 **F**3 13 15 29 34 35 38 39 40 44 49 50 54 57 58 59 64 68 70 73 75 76 77 79 81 85 86 87 89 93 97 100 102 107 108 110 111 115 119 120 121 123 124 129 130 131 132 141 146 147 148 149 154 **S** Intermountain Healthcare, Inc., Salt Lake City, UT
Primary Contact: Todd Neubert, Chief Executive Officer
CFO: Royce Stephens, Chief Financial Officer
CMO: David Haselton, Chief Medical Officer
CIO: Susan Hanks, Chief Information Officer
Web address: www.intermountainhealthcare.org/
Control: Other not–for–profit (including NFP Corporation) **Service**: General medical and surgical

Staffed Beds: 87 **Admissions**: 7586 **Census**: 46 **Outpatient Visits**: 61140 **Births**: 2291 **Total Expense ($000)**: 132940 **Payroll Expense ($000)**: 34755 **Personnel**: 577

ROOSEVELT—Duchesne County

★ **UINTAH BASIN MEDICAL CENTER (460019)**, 250 West 300 North, 75–2, Zip 84066–2336; tel. 435/722–6163, (Total facility includes 75 beds in nursing home–type unit) **A**10 20 **F**6 7 11 13 15 17 35 40 43 45 50 52 53 54 57 59 60 62 63 70 73 76 77 79 81 82 84 85 87 89 93 107 108 110 111 115 119 127 128 129 130 131 132 135 146 147 148 154 155 156
Primary Contact: James I. Marshall, President and Chief Executive Officer
CFO: Brent Hales, Chief Financial Officer
CMO: Gary B White, M.D., Chief Medical Staff
CHR: Randall Bennett, Assistant Administrator
Web address: www.ubmc.org
Control: Other not–for–profit (including NFP Corporation) **Service**: General medical and surgical

Staffed Beds: 124 **Admissions**: 1677 **Census**: 60 **Outpatient Visits**: 68311 **Births**: 562 **Total Expense ($000)**: 82900 **Payroll Expense ($000)**: 27468 **Personnel**: 562

SAINT GEORGE—Washington County

⊞ △ **DIXIE REGIONAL MEDICAL CENTER (460021)**, 1380 East Medical Center Drive, Zip 84790–2123; tel. 435/251–1000, (Includes DIXIE REGIONAL MEDICAL CENTER, 544 South 400 East, St George, Utah, Zip 84770; tel. 940/764–7000) **A**1 7 10 **F**3 11 12 13 15 17 18 20 22 24 26 28 29 30 31 34 37 38 39 40 43 44 45 47 48 49 50 51 52 53 54 55 56 57 59 60 64 68 70 71 72 74 75 76 77 78 79 80 81 82 84 85 86 87 89 90 91 92 93 94 96 97 98 100 102 104 107 108 110 111 112 114 115 116 117 118 119 120 121 123 124 129 130 131 132 141 144 146 147 148 149 154 155 156 157 **S** Intermountain Healthcare, Inc., Salt Lake City, UT
Primary Contact: Mitchell Cloward, Administrator
CFO: Steven Vance, Chief Financial Officer
CMO: Steven Van Norman, M.D., Medical Director
CIO: Lance Bedingfield, Director Information Services
CHR: Vicki Wilson, Human Resources Director
CNO: Gary Cunningham, Chief Nursing Officer
Web address: www.intermountainhealthcare.org
Control: Other not–for–profit (including NFP Corporation) **Service**: General medical and surgical

Staffed Beds: 263 **Admissions**: 18848 **Census**: 177 **Outpatient Visits**: 211703 **Births**: 2381 **Total Expense ($000)**: 529228 **Payroll Expense ($000)**: 141842 **Personnel**: 2331

SALT LAKE CITY—Salt Lake County

⊞ **LDS HOSPITAL (460006)**, Eighth Avenue and 'C' Street, Zip 84143–0001; tel. 801/408–1100, **A**1 2 3 5 10 **F**3 4 12 15 29 31 34 35 37 38 39 40 44 45 46 48 49 50 51 53 54 55 56 57 58 59 60 64 66 68 70 73 74 75 76 77 78 79 81 82 84 85 86 87 96 97 98 100 102 107 108 110 111 115 118 119 123 124 126 129 130 131 132 135 136 141 146 147 148 149 154 157 **S** Intermountain Healthcare, Inc., Salt Lake City, UT
Primary Contact: Jim Sheets, Chief Executive Officer and Administrator
CFO: Dan Brady, Chief Financial Officer
CMO: Kerry Fisher, M.D., Medical Director
CIO: David Baird, Chief Information Officer
CHR: Mollee Lamb, Manager Human Resources
CNO: Brandon Vonk, Nurse Administrator
Web address: www.intermountainhealthcare.org
Control: Other not–for–profit (including NFP Corporation) **Service**: General medical and surgical

Staffed Beds: 250 **Admissions**: 12494 **Census**: 126 **Outpatient Visits**: 61343 **Births**: 2115 **Total Expense ($000)**: 273316 **Payroll Expense ($000)**: 73241 **Personnel**: 1176

⊞ **MARIAN CENTER (464012)**, 451 East Bishop Federal Lane, Zip 84115–2357; tel. 801/487–7557, **A**1 10 **F**29 34 98 100 101 103 130
Primary Contact: Lee Kilpack, Chief Executive Officer
Web address: www.stjosephvilla.com
Control: Corporation, Investor–owned (for–profit) **Service**: Psychiatric

Staffed Beds: 14 **Admissions**: 306 **Census**: 9 **Outpatient Visits**: 0 **Births**: 0 **Total Expense ($000)**: 2275 **Personnel**: 27

UT

Hospital, Medicare Provider Number, Address, Telephone, Approval, Facility, and Physician Codes, Health Care System

★ American Hospital Association (AHA) membership   ○ Healthcare Facilities Accreditation Program   ⇑ Center for Improvement in Healthcare Quality Accreditation
☐ The Joint Commission accreditation   ◇ DNV Healthcare Inc. accreditation   △ Commission on Accreditation of Rehabilitation Facilities (CARF) accreditation

© 2019 AHA Guide   *Many Facility Codes have changed. Please refer to the AHA Guide Code Chart.*   Hospitals **A651**

☐ △ **PRIMARY CHILDREN'S HOSPITAL (463301)**, 100 North Mario Capecchi Drive, Zip 84113–1100; tel. 801/662–1000, **A**1 3 5 7 10 **F**3 8 17 19 21 23 25 27 28 29 30 31 32 34 35 36 37 38 39 40 41 43 44 45 46 47 48 49 50 51 53 54 55 57 58 59 60 64 68 71 72 74 75 77 78 79 80 81 82 84 85 86 87 88 89 91 92 93 94 96 97 98 99 100 102 106 107 108 111 115 116 117 118 119 126 129 130 132 134 135 136 137 138 139 141 146 148 149 153 154 156 157 **S** Intermountain Healthcare, Inc., Salt Lake City, UT
Primary Contact: Katy Welkie MBA, R.N., Chief Executive Officer
CMO: Ed Clark, M.D., Chief Medical Officer
CIO: Joe Hales, Chief Information Officer
CHR: Albert Bennett Buckworth, Human Resources Administrative Director
Web address: www.intermountainhealthcare.org
Control: Other not–for–profit (including NFP Corporation) **Service**: Children's general medical and surgical

Staffed Beds: 289 **Admissions**: 13232 **Census**: 192 **Outpatient Visits**: 100664 **Births**: 0 **Total Expense ($000)**: 558036 **Payroll Expense ($000)**: 181321 **Personnel**: 2784

☐ **PROMISE HOSPITAL OF SALT LAKE (462004)**, 8 Avenue, C Street, Zip 84143; tel. 801/408–7110, (Nonreporting) **A**1 10 **S** Promise Healthcare, Boca Raton, FL
Primary Contact: Wayne Kinsey, Chief Executive Officer
CMO: Geoff Harding, Chief Clinical Officer
Web address: www.promise-saltlake.com
Control: Corporation, Investor–owned (for–profit) **Service**: Acute long–term care hospital

Staffed Beds: 41

☐ **SALT LAKE BEHAVIORAL HEALTH (464013)**, 3802 South 700 East, Zip 84106–1182; tel. 801/264–6000, **A**1 10 **F**4 5 29 38 75 98 104 130 135 **S** Universal Health Services, Inc., King of Prussia, PA
Primary Contact: Kreg Gillman, Chief Executive Officer
COO: Jim Hess, Chief Operations Officer
CFO: Daren Woolstenhulme, Chief Financial Officer
CMO: Monica Polk, M.D., Chief Medical Officer
CHR: Robyn Holsten, Human Resources Director
CNO: Suzanne Nelson, R.N., Director of Nursing
Web address: www.saltlakebehavioralhealth.com
Control: Corporation, Investor–owned (for–profit) **Service**: Psychiatric

Staffed Beds: 118 **Admissions**: 2279 **Census**: 60 **Outpatient Visits**: 5372 **Total Expense ($000)**: 25040 **Payroll Expense ($000)**: 9905 **Personnel**: 179

★ ⚕ **SALT LAKE REGIONAL MEDICAL CENTER (460003)**, 1050 East South Temple, Zip 84102–1507; tel. 801/350–4111, (Nonreporting) **A**3 5 10 21 **S** Steward Health Care System, LLC, Dallas, TX
Primary Contact: Dale Johns, FACHE, Chief Executive Officer
COO: Scot Stevens, Assistant Administrator
CFO: Brian Ebright, Chief Financial Officer
CMO: Blake Johnson, M.D., Chief of Staff
CIO: Mark Runyan, Director Information Services
CHR: Carolyn Livingston, Director Human Resources
CNO: Terron Arbon, R.N., Chief Nursing Officer
Web address: www.saltlakeregional.com
Control: Corporation, Investor–owned (for–profit) **Service**: General medical and surgical

Staffed Beds: 132

☐ **SHRINERS HOSPITALS FOR CHILDREN-SALT LAKE CITY (463302)**, 1275 East Fairfax Road, Zip 84103–4399; tel. 801/536–3500, **A**1 3 5 10 **F**3 8 29 32 50 57 58 59 64 67 74 75 77 79 81 85 89 90 93 94 119 128 130 131 143 146 **S** Shriners Hospitals for Children, Tampa, FL
Primary Contact: Kevin Martin, M.P.H., R.N., FACHE, Administrator
CFO: Heath Braby, Director Fiscal Services
CMO: Kristen Carroll, M.D., Chief of Staff
CIO: Mike Allen, Director Information Technology
CHR: Kris Goldman, Director Human Resources
CNO: Gail McGuill, R.N., MSN, Chief Nursing Officer and Administrative Director of Patient Care Services
Web address: www.shrinershospitalsforchildren.org/Hospitals/Locations/SaltLakeCity.aspx
Control: Other not–for–profit (including NFP Corporation) **Service**: Children's orthopedic

Staffed Beds: 45 **Admissions**: 211 **Census**: 3 **Births**: 0

⊞ **ST. MARK'S HOSPITAL (460047)**, 1200 East 3900 South, Zip 84124–1390; tel. 801/268–7111, (Nonreporting) **A**1 3 10 **S** HCA Healthcare, Nashville, TN
Primary Contact: Mark Robinson, FACHE, Chief Executive Officer
CFO: Bryan McKinley, Chief Financial Officer
CMO: J Eric Vanderhooft, M.D., President Medical Staff
CIO: Jesse Trujillo, Chief Information Officer
CHR: Robyn Opheikens, Assistant Administrator Human Resources
Web address: www.stmarkshospital.com
Control: Corporation, Investor–owned (for–profit) **Service**: General medical and surgical

Staffed Beds: 277

★ △ ⚕ **UNIVERSITY OF UTAH HEALTH (460009)**, 50 North Medical Drive, Zip 84132–0002; tel. 801/581–2121, **A**3 5 7 8 10 21 **F**3 5 6 7 8 9 11 12 13 15 16 17 18 20 22 24 26 28 29 30 31 34 35 36 37 38 39 40 42 43 44 45 46 47 48 49 50 51 52 53 54 55 56 57 58 59 60 61 62 64 65 66 68 70 71 72 73 74 75 76 77 78 79 80 81 82 83 84 85 86 87 90 91 92 93 94 95 96 97 98 100 101 102 103 107 108 109 110 111 112 113 114 115 116 117 118 119 120 121 123 124 126 129 130 131 132 134 135 136 137 138 139 140 141 142 143 144 145 146 147 148 149 150 152 154 155 156 157
Primary Contact: Gordon Crabtree, Interim Chief Executive Officer
CFO: Gordon Crabtree, Chief Financial Officer
CMO: Thomas Miller, M.D., Medical Director
CIO: James Turnbull, Chief Information Officer
CHR: Dale A Spartz, Chief Human Resources Officer
CNO: Margaret Pearce, R.N., Ph.D., Chief Nursing Officer
Web address: www.uuhsc.utah.edu
Control: State, Government, nonfederal **Service**: General medical and surgical

Staffed Beds: 593 **Admissions**: 28320 **Census**: 446 **Outpatient Visits**: 2317796 **Births**: 4134 **Total Expense ($000)**: 1631280 **Payroll Expense ($000)**: 587596 **Personnel**: 10589

⚕ **UNIVERSITY OF UTAH NEUROPSYCHIATRIC INSTITUTE (464009)**, 501 South Chipeta Way, Zip 84108–1222; tel. 801/583–2500, **A**3 5 10 21 **F**4 5 34 35 38 58 98 99 100 101 102 103 104 105 106 130 149 153 154
Primary Contact: Ross Van Vranken, Executive Director
CFO: Becky Schaefer, Chief Financial Officer
CMO: James Ashworth, M.D., Medical Director
Web address: www.med.utah.edu/uni
Control: State, Government, nonfederal **Service**: Psychiatric

Staffed Beds: 157 **Admissions**: 4938 **Census**: 127 **Outpatient Visits**: 55121 **Births**: 0 **Total Expense ($000)**: 101602 **Payroll Expense ($000)**: 38863 **Personnel**: 740

⊞ △ **VETERANS AFFAIRS SALT LAKE CITY HEALTH CARE SYSTEM**, 500 Foothill Drive, Zip 84148–0002; tel. 801/582–1565, **A**1 3 5 7 **F**3 4 5 8 12 18 20 22 24 26 28 29 30 31 33 34 35 36 38 39 40 44 45 46 47 48 49 50 53 54 55 56 57 58 59 60 61 62 63 64 65 70 71 74 75 77 78 79 81 82 83 84 85 86 87 90 92 93 94 96 97 98 100 101 102 104 105 106 107 108 109 111 114 115 116 117 118 119 126 127 129 130 132 133 135 143 144 146 147 148 149 151 152 153 154 156 158 **S** Department of Veterans Affairs, Washington, DC
Primary Contact: Shella D. Stovall, R.N., Interim Director
CFO: Val Martin, Director Financial Management Services Center
CMO: Ronald J Gebhart, M.D., Chief of Staff
CIO: Lisa Leonelis, Chief Information Officer
CHR: Lisa Porter, Director Human Resources, Leadership and Education
Web address: www.saltlakecity.va.gov/
Control: Veterans Affairs, Government, federal **Service**: General medical and surgical

Staffed Beds: 123 **Admissions**: 6473 **Census**: 74 **Outpatient Visits**: 708553 **Births**: 0 **Total Expense ($000)**: 582742 **Payroll Expense ($000)**: 212120 **Personnel**: 2617

SANDY—Salt Lake County

⊞ **ALTA VIEW HOSPITAL (460044)**, 9660 South 1300 East, Zip 84094–3793; tel. 801/501–2600, **A**1 2 10 **F**3 12 13 15 29 34 35 38 39 40 43 44 45 46 47 48 49 50 54 56 57 59 64 68 70 75 76 77 78 79 81 85 86 87 92 93 97 102 107 108 110 111 115 118 119 129 130 132 141 146 147 149 154 **S** Intermountain Healthcare, Inc., Salt Lake City, UT
Primary Contact: Lisa A. Paletta, R.N., FACHE, Chief Executive Officer
CFO: Chris Hargis, Manager Finance
CHR: Leslie Bates, Manager Human Resources
Web address: www.intermountainhealthcare.org
Control: Other not–for–profit (including NFP Corporation) **Service**: General medical and surgical

Staffed Beds: 58 **Admissions**: 3720 **Census**: 24 **Outpatient Visits**: 53977 **Births**: 943 **Total Expense ($000)**: 104256 **Payroll Expense ($000)**: 27627 **Personnel**: 464

UT

✠ **HEALTHSOUTH REHABILITATION HOSPITAL OF UTAH (463025)**, 8074 South 1300 East, Zip 84094–0743; tel. 801/561–3400, (Nonreporting) **A**1 10 **S** Encompass Health Corporation, Birmingham, AL
Primary Contact: Jeff Frandsen, Chief Executive Officer
CMO: Joseph VickRoy, M.D., Medical Director
CHR: Troy Jensen, Director Human Resources
Web address: www.healthsouthutah.com
Control: Corporation, Investor–owned (for–profit) **Service**: Rehabilitation

Staffed Beds: 105

SOUTH OGDEN—Weber County

☐ **NORTHERN UTAH REHABILITATION HOSPITAL (463027)**, 5825 Harrison Boulevard, Zip 84403–4316; tel. 801/475–5254, (Nonreporting) **A**1 **S** Ernest Health, Inc., Albuquerque, NM
Primary Contact: Ryan Keele, Chief Executive Officer
COO: Reuben Jessop, Chief Operating Officer
CFO: Daniel J Foster, Chief Financial Officer
CNO: Terina Chapman, Director of Nursing
Web address: www.ernesthealth.com/gallery-item/northern-utah-rehabilitation-hospital/
Control: Other not–for–profit (including NFP Corporation) **Service**: Rehabilitation

Staffed Beds: 20

TOOELE—Tooele County

✠ **MOUNTAIN WEST MEDICAL CENTER (460014)**, 2055 North Main Street, Zip 84074–9819; tel. 435/843–3600, **A**1 10 **F**3 7 13 15 18 29 30 34 40 49 50 51 57 59 64 67 68 70 74 75 76 77 79 81 85 87 89 93 97 102 107 110 111 115 118 119 126 130 132 135 144 146 147 148 156 **S** Quorum Health, Brentwood, TN
Primary Contact: Philip Eaton, Interim Chief Executive Officer
CMO: James Antinori, M.D., Chief of Staff
CIO: Marc Taylor, IS Director
CHR: Matthew Flygare, Director Human Resources
CNO: Yvonne Nielson, Chief Nursing Officer, Director Quality Management and Regulatory Compliance
Web address: www.mountainwestmc.com
Control: Corporation, Investor–owned (for–profit) **Service**: General medical and surgical

Staffed Beds: 44 **Admissions**: 1623 **Census**: 10 **Outpatient Visits**: 88159 **Births**: 465 **Total Expense ($000)**: 37097 **Payroll Expense ($000)**: 14767 **Personnel**: 260

TREMONTON—Box Elder County

★ **BEAR RIVER VALLEY HOSPITAL (460039)**, 905 North 1000 West, Zip 84337–2497; tel. 435/207–4500, **A**10 **F**3 13 15 29 34 35 38 40 44 50 68 75 76 77 81 82 85 87 97 100 102 107 108 110 111 115 118 119 127 141 146 149 154 **S** Intermountain Healthcare, Inc., Salt Lake City, UT
Primary Contact: Brandon Vonk, Administrator
CHR: Joy Sadler, Director Human Resources
CNO: Penny Marshall, Chief Nursing Officer
Web address: www.https://intermountainhealthcare.org/locations/bear-river-valley-hospital/
Control: Other not–for–profit (including NFP Corporation) **Service**: General medical and surgical

Staffed Beds: 13 **Admissions**: 543 **Census**: 3 **Outpatient Visits**: 12821 **Births**: 128 **Total Expense ($000)**: 25275 **Payroll Expense ($000)**: 8602 **Personnel**: 124

VERNAL—Uintah County

✠ **ASHLEY REGIONAL MEDICAL CENTER (460030)**, 150 West 100 North, Zip 84078–2036; tel. 435/789–3342, (Nonreporting) **A**1 10 20 **S** LifePoint Health, Brentwood, TN
Primary Contact: Ben Cluff, Chief Executive Officer
CFO: Chad Labrum, Chief Financial Officer
CMO: Dennis Lewis, M.D., Chief of Staff
CIO: Cameron Winn, Director Information Services
CHR: Deena Mansfield, Director Human Resources
CNO: Greg Gardiner, Chief Clinical Officer
Web address: www.ashleyregional.com
Control: Corporation, Investor–owned (for–profit) **Service**: General medical and surgical

Staffed Beds: 39

WEST JORDAN—Salt Lake County

★ ⇧ **JORDAN VALLEY MEDICAL CENTER (460051)**, 3580 West 9000 South, Zip 84088–8812; tel. 801/561–8888, (Includes MOUNTAIN POINT MEDICAL CENTER, 3000 North Triumph Boulevard, Lehii, Utah, Zip 84043, Lehi, tel. 385/345–3000), (Non-reporting) **A**10 21 **S** Steward Health Care System, LLC, Dallas, TX
Primary Contact: Jon Butterfield, Administrator and Chief Executive Officer
CFO: Kurt Shipley, Chief Financial Officer
CMO: B Dee Allred, M.D., President Medical Staff
Web address: www.jordanvalleymc.com
Control: Partnership, Investor–owned (for–profit) **Service**: General medical and surgical

Staffed Beds: 183

WEST VALLEY CITY—Salt Lake County

★ **JORDAN VALLEY MEDICAL CENTER WEST VALLEY CAMPUS**, 3460 South Pioneer Parkway, Zip 84120–2049; tel. 801/561–8888, (Nonreporting) **S** Steward Health Care System, LLC, Dallas, TX
Primary Contact: Jon R. Butterfield, Administrator and Chief Executive Officer
COO: Jon Butterfield, Administrator and Chief Operating Officer
CFO: Steven Payne, Chief Financial Officer
CMO: Justin Parkinson, M.D., President Medical Staff
CIO: Mark Runyan, Director Information Systems
CHR: Rob Burnett, Director Human Resources
Web address: www.https://www.jordanwestvalley.org
Control: Corporation, Investor–owned (for–profit) **Service**: General medical and surgical

Staffed Beds: 101

UT

Hospital, Medicare Provider Number, Address, Telephone, Approval, Facility, and Physician Codes, Health Care System

★ American Hospital Association (AHA) membership
☐ The Joint Commission accreditation
○ Healthcare Facilities Accreditation Program
◇ DNV Healthcare Inc. accreditation
⇧ Center for Improvement in Healthcare Quality Accreditation
△ Commission on Accreditation of Rehabilitation Facilities (CARF) accreditation

VERMONT

BENNINGTON—Bennington County

☒ **SOUTHWESTERN VERMONT MEDICAL CENTER (470012)**, 100 Hospital Drive, Zip 05201–5004; tel. 802/442–6361, (Nonreporting) **A**1 2 10
Primary Contact: Thomas A. Dee, President and Chief Executive Officer
CFO: Stephen D Majetich, CPA, Chief Financial Officer
CMO: Trey Dobson, M.D., Chief Medical Officer
CIO: Richard Ogilvie, Chief Information Officer
CHR: Rudolph D Weaver, Vice President Human Resources
Web address: www.svhealthcare.org
Control: Other not–for–profit (including NFP Corporation) **Service**: General medical and surgical

Staffed Beds: 77

BERLIN—Washington County

☒ **THE UNIVERSITY OF VERMONT HEALTH NETWORK CENTRAL VERMONT MEDICAL CENTER (470001)**, 130 Fisher Road, Zip 05602–9516, Mailing Address: P.O. Box 547, Barre, Zip 05641–0547; tel. 802/371–4100, (Total facility includes 153 beds in nursing home–type unit) **A**1 2 3 5 10 **F**3 5 11 13 15 18 28 29 30 31 34 35 36 40 44 45 48 49 50 51 53 54 59 63 64 65 68 70 74 75 76 77 78 79 81 82 84 85 86 87 92 93 94 96 97 98 99 100 102 103 104 107 108 110 111 114 118 119 120 121 123 128 130 131 132 135 141 143 144 146 147 148 149
Primary Contact: Anna T. Noonan, President and Chief Operating Officer
CFO: Stephen F. Kenney, Chief Financial Officer
CMO: Philip Brown, D.O., Vice President Medical Affairs
CHR: Robert Patterson, Vice President Human Resources and Rehabilitation Services
CNO: Matthew Choate, Chief Nursing Officer
Web address: www.cvmc.org/
Control: Other not–for–profit (including NFP Corporation) **Service**: General medical and surgical

Staffed Beds: 245 **Admissions**: 4239 **Census**: 168 **Outpatient Visits**: 434124 **Births**: 285 **Total Expense ($000)**: 171559 **Payroll Expense ($000)**: 72590 **Personnel**: 1429

☐ **VERMONT PSYCHIATRIC CARE HOSPITAL (474004)**, 350 Fisher Road, Zip 05602; tel. 802/828–3300, **A**1 10 **F**98 130 135 143 146 149 154
Primary Contact: Melissa Bailey, Commissioner, Department of Mental Health
Web address: www.mentalhealth.vermont.gov/Vermont-psychiatric-care-hospital
Control: State, Government, nonfederal **Service**: Psychiatric

Staffed Beds: 25 **Admissions**: 72 **Census**: 24 **Outpatient Visits**: 0 **Births**: 0 **Total Expense ($000)**: 22289 **Payroll Expense ($000)**: 10160 **Personnel**: 179

BRATTLEBORO—Windham County

★ **BRATTLEBORO MEMORIAL HOSPITAL (470011)**, 17 Belmont Avenue, Zip 05301–3498; tel. 802/257–0341, **A**5 10 **F**3 11 13 15 18 28 29 30 31 34 35 37 40 45 49 50 51 53 55 59 61 64 68 70 74 75 76 78 79 81 85 87 93 97 107 108 110 111 115 118 119 131 132 135 146 147 148 149 154 156
Primary Contact: Steven R. Gordon, President and Chief Executive Officer
CFO: Michael Rogers, Vice President Fiscal Services
CMO: Kathleen McGraw, M.D., Chief Medical Officer
CIO: Jonathan Farina, Chief Information Officer
CHR: William Norwood, Vice President, Human Resources
CNO: Mary Urquhart, R.N., Vice President Patient Care
Web address: www.bmhvt.org
Control: Other not–for–profit (including NFP Corporation) **Service**: General medical and surgical

Staffed Beds: 42 **Admissions**: 1691 **Census**: 17 **Outpatient Visits**: 164221 **Births**: 288 **Total Expense ($000)**: 83706 **Payroll Expense ($000)**: 36173 **Personnel**: 408

☒ **BRATTLEBORO RETREAT (474001)**, Anna Marsh Lane, Zip 05301, Mailing Address: P.O. Box 803, Zip 05302–0803; tel. 802/257–7785, **A**1 5 10 **F**5 29 34 35 44 50 68 75 82 87 98 99 100 101 102 103 104 105 135 149 152 153 154
Primary Contact: Louis Josephson, Ph.D., President and Chief Executive Officer
COO: Gerri Cote, Chief Operating Officer
CFO: Steven Monette, Chief Financial Officer
CMO: Frederick Engstrom, M.D., Chief Medical Officer
CHR: Jeffrey T. Corrigan, Vice President Human Resources
CNO: Linda J. Nagy, MSN, R.N., Chief Nursing Officer
Web address: www.brattlebororetreat.org
Control: Other not–for–profit (including NFP Corporation) **Service**: Psychiatric

Staffed Beds: 119 **Admissions**: 3971 **Census**: 105 **Outpatient Visits**: 29588 **Births**: 0 **Total Expense ($000)**: 73968 **Payroll Expense ($000)**: 45393 **Personnel**: 684

BURLINGTON—Chittenden County

☒ **UNIVERSITY OF VERMONT MEDICAL CENTER (470003)**, 111 Colchester Avenue, Zip 05401–1473; tel. 802/847–0000, (Includes FANNY ALLEN CAMPUS, 101 College Parkway, Colchester, Vermont, Zip 05446–3035; tel. 802/655–1234; MEDICAL CENTER HOSPITAL CAMPUS, 111 Colchester Avenue, Burlington, Vermont, Zip 05401; tel. 802/847–2345; VERMONT CHILDREN'S HOSPITAL, 111 Colchester Avenue, Burlington, Vermont, Zip 05401–1473; tel. 802/847–0000)
A1 2 3 5 8 10 **F**3 4 5 6 7 9 11 12 13 15 17 18 19 20 21 22 23 24 25 26 28 29 30 31 32 34 35 36 37 39 40 43 44 45 46 47 48 49 50 51 52 54 55 56 57 58 59 60 61 63 64 65 66 68 70 72 73 74 75 76 77 78 79 81 82 84 85 86 87 88 89 90 91 92 93 94 96 97 98 99 100 101 102 103 104 105 107 108 110 111 114 115 116 117 118 119 120 121 123 124 126 129 130 131 132 135 136 138 141 142 143 144 145 146 147 148 151 152 153 154 155
Primary Contact: Eileen Whalen, R.N., President and Chief Operating Officer
CFO: Todd Keating, Chief Financial Officer
CMO: Isabelle Desjardins, M.D., Chief Medical Officer
CHR: Jerald Novak, Chief People Officer
Web address: www.uvmhealth.org/medcenter/Pages/default.aspx
Control: Other not–for–profit (including NFP Corporation) **Service**: General medical and surgical

Staffed Beds: 500 **Admissions**: 20379 **Census**: 335 **Outpatient Visits**: 1110664 **Births**: 2186 **Total Expense ($000)**: 1317389 **Payroll Expense ($000)**: 607914 **Personnel**: 7371

COLCHESTER—Chittenden County

FANNY ALLEN CAMPUS See University of Vermont Medical Center, Burlington

MIDDLEBURY—Addison County

★ **PORTER MEDICAL CENTER (471307)**, 115 Porter Drive, Zip 05753–8423; tel. 802/388–4701, (Nonreporting) **A**10 18
Primary Contact: Seleem Choudhury, R.N., MSN, President and Chief Operating Officer
CFO: Steve Ciampa, Vice President Finance
CMO: Fred Kniffin, M.D., Chief Medical Officer
CIO: Rebecca Woods, Chief Information Officer
CHR: David Fuller, Vice President of Human Resources
CNO: Lorraina Smith-Zuba, R.N., MSN, Chief Nursing Officer
Web address: www.portermedical.org
Control: Other not–for–profit (including NFP Corporation) **Service**: General medical and surgical

Staffed Beds: 25

MORRISVILLE—Lamoille County

★ **COPLEY HOSPITAL (471305)**, 528 Washington Highway, Zip 05661–8973; tel. 802/888–8888, (Nonreporting) **A**10 18
Primary Contact: Jeffrey G. White, Interim Chief Executive Officer
COO: Vera A. Jones, Chief Operating Officer
CFO: Debbie Dorain, Chief Financial Officer
CMO: Joel Silverstein, M.D., Chief Medical Officer
CIO: Randy Chesley, Director Information Technology
CHR: Amy Fitzgerald, Human Resources Manager
CNO: Lori Profota, Chief Nursing Officer
Web address: www.copleyvt.org
Control: Other not–for–profit (including NFP Corporation) **Service**: General medical and surgical

Staffed Beds: 25

NEWPORT—Orleans County

★ ⇧ **NORTH COUNTRY HOSPITAL AND HEALTH CENTER (471304)**, 189 Prouty Drive, Zip 05855–9326; tel. 802/334–7331, **A**10 18 21 **F**11 13 15 28 29 30 34 35 40 43 45 50 53 70 74 75 76 77 79 81 82 84 85 89 91 93 107 108 110 111 114 118 119 127 129 130 131 133 135 146 148 149
Primary Contact: Brian Nall, Chief Executive Officer
COO: Thomas Frank, Chief Operating Officer
CFO: Andre Bissonnette, Chief Financial Officer
CHR: William Perket, Vice President Human Resources
CNO: Avril Cochran, R.N., Vice President Patient Care Services
Web address: www.nchsi.com
Control: Other not–for–profit (including NFP Corporation) **Service**: General medical and surgical

Staffed Beds: 25 **Admissions**: 1461 **Census**: 16 **Outpatient Visits**: 67989 **Births**: 200 **Total Expense ($000)**: 83739 **Payroll Expense ($000)**: 39152 **Personnel**: 459

VT

Many Facility Codes have changed. Please refer to the AHA Guide Code Chart. © 2019 AHA Guide

RANDOLPH—Orange County

★ **GIFFORD MEDICAL CENTER (471301)**, 44 South Main Street,
Zip 05060–1381, Mailing Address: P.O. Box 2000, Zip 05060–2000;
tel. 802/728–7000, (Nonreporting) **A**2 5 10 18
Primary Contact: Dan Bennett, President and Chief Executive Officer
CFO: Jeff Hebert, Interim Vice President Finance
CMO: Joshua Plavin, M.D., Medical Director Medicine Division
CIO: Sean Patrick, Director Information Systems
CHR: Janice Davis, Interim Director Human Resources
CNO: Linda Minsinger, Vice President Hospital Division
Web address: www.giffordmed.org
Control: Other not–for–profit (including NFP Corporation) **Service:** General
medical and surgical

Staffed Beds: 52

RUTLAND—Rutland County

✠ **RUTLAND REGIONAL MEDICAL CENTER (470005)**, 160 Allen Street,
Zip 05701–4595; tel. 802/775–7111, **A**1 2 10 **F**3 5 13 15 18 28 29 31 34 37
40 44 45 50 55 57 59 64 65 70 74 76 78 79 81 82 83 84 85 87 92 93 98 100
101 102 104 107 108 109 110 111 115 117 118 119 120 121 123 124 129
130 133 135 146 147 148 149 154 157
Primary Contact: Claudio D. Fort, President and Chief Executive Officer
CFO: Ed Ogorzalek, Chief Financial Officer
CMO: Baxter C Holland, M.D., Chief Medical Officer
CNO: Carol Egan, R.N., MSN, Chief Nursing Officer
Web address: www.rrmc.org
Control: Other not–for–profit (including NFP Corporation) **Service:** General
medical and surgical

Staffed Beds: 126 Admissions: 6471 Census: 83 Outpatient
Visits: 233744 Births: 354 Total Expense ($000): 269365 Payroll Expense ($000): 134144 Personnel: 1421

SAINT ALBANS—Franklin County

✠ **NORTHWESTERN MEDICAL CENTER (470024)**, 133 Fairfield Street,
Zip 05478–1726; tel. 802/524 5911, (Nonreporting) **A**1 2 10 20 **S** QHR, Brentwood, TN
Primary Contact: Jill Berry. Bowen, Chief Executive Officer
COO: Jane Catton, R.N., Chief Operating Officer and Chief Nursing Officer
CFO: Christopher Hickey, Chief Financial Officer
CMO: Lowery Sullivan, M.D., Chief Medical Officer
CIO: Joel Benware, Vice President Information Technology and Compliance
CHR: Thomas C Conley, Vice President, Human Resources and Organizational
Development
CNO: Jane Catton, R.N., Chief Operating Officer and Chief Nursing Officer
Web address: www.northwesternmedicalcenter.org
Control: Other not–for–profit (including NFP Corporation) **Service:** General
medical and surgical

Staffed Beds: 55

SAINT JOHNSBURY—Caledonia County

★ **NORTHEASTERN VERMONT REGIONAL HOSPITAL (471303)**, 1315 Hospital
Drive, Zip 05819–9210, Mailing Address: P.O. Box 905, Zip 05819–0905;
tel. 802/748–8141, (Nonreporting) **A**10 18
Primary Contact: Shawn Tester, Chief Executive Officer
CFO: Robert Hersey, Chief Financial Officer
CMO: Michael Rousse, M.D., Chief Medical Officer
CIO: Shawn Burroughs, Director of Information Services
CHR: Elizabeth Gwatkin, Vice President Human Resources
Web address: www.nvrh.org
Control: Other not–for–profit (including NFP Corporation) **Service:** General
medical and surgical

Staffed Beds: 25

SPRINGFIELD—Windsor County

★ **SPRINGFIELD HOSPITAL (471306)**, 25 Ridgewood Road, Zip 05156–3050,
Mailing Address: 25 Ridgewood Rd, Zip 05156–3050; tel. 802/885–2151,
(Nonreporting) **A**5 10 18
Primary Contact: Joshua Dufresne, Chief of Practice Operations
CFO: Scott Whittemore, Chief Financial Officer and Chief of Ancillary Services
CMO: Richard Marasa, M.D., President Medical Staff
CIO: Kyle Peoples, Director Technology Management Services
CHR: Janet Lyle, Chief Human Resources and Allied Health Services
CNO: Janet Sherer, Chief of Patient Care Services
Web address: www.springfieldmed.org
Control: Other not–for–profit (including NFP Corporation) **Service:** General
medical and surgical

Staffed Beds: 35

TOWNSHEND—Windham County

★ **GRACE COTTAGE HOSPITAL (471300)**, 185 Grafton Road, Zip 05353–0216,
Mailing Address: P.O. Box 216, Zip 05353–0216; tel. 802/365–7357, **A**5 10 18
F3 29 30 34 35 40 50 57 59 64 65 66 68 77 85 93 96 97 104 107 115 119
127 130 132 133 135 146 147 149
Primary Contact: Douglas F. DiVello, President and Chief Executive Officer
COO: Jeanne M Fortier, R.N., Chief Nursing Officer and Interim Chief Operating Officer
CFO: Stephen A Brown, Chief Financial Officer
CMO: Timothy Shafer, M.D., Medical Director
CIO: Tony Marques, Director Information Systems
CHR: Christopher J Lackney, Director Human Resources
CNO: Jeanne M Fortier, R.N., Chief Nursing Officer and Interim Chief Operating Officer
Web address: www.gracecottage.org
Control: Other not–for–profit (including NFP Corporation) **Service:** General
medical and surgical

Staffed Beds: 38 Admissions: 370 Census: 11 Outpatient Visits: 19611
Births: 0 Total Expense ($000): 20248 Payroll Expense ($000): 11791 Personnel: 151

WHITE RIVER JUNCTION—Windsor County

✠ **WHITE RIVER JUNCTION VETERANS AFFAIRS MEDICAL CENTER**, 215 North
Main Street, Zip 05009–0001; tel. 802/295–9363, **A**1 3 5 8 **F**3 4 5 12 18 29 30
31 33 35 36 38 40 45 46 47 48 49 50 53 56 58 59 60 61 63 64 65 70 74 75
77 78 79 81 82 84 85 86 87 92 93 97 98 100 101 102 103 104 107 108 111
114 115 118 119 127 130 132 135 141 143 146 147 148 149 154 156 157
158 **S** Department of Veterans Affairs, Washington, DC
Primary Contact: Brett Rusch, M.D., Acting Director
CFO: Joan Wilmot, Chief Finance Officer
CMO: M. Ganga Hematillake, M.D., Chief of Staff
CIO: Matthew Rafus, Chief Information Officer
CHR: Barbara Nadeau, Chief Human Resources Management Service
Web address: www.whiteriver.va.gov/
Control: Veterans Affairs, Government, federal **Service:** General medical and surgical

Staffed Beds: 76 Admissions: 2926 Census: 33 Outpatient Visits: 284707
Births: 0 Total Expense ($000): 251621 Payroll Expense ($000): 103076 Personnel: 1153

WINDSOR—Windsor County

★ △ **MT. ASCUTNEY HOSPITAL AND HEALTH CENTER (471302)**, 289 County
Road, Zip 05089–9000; tel. 802/674–6711, (Nonreporting) **A**5 7 10 18
Primary Contact: Joseph L. Perras, President and Chief Executive Officer
COO: Paul Calandrella, Chief Operating Officer
CFO: David Sanville, Chief Financial Officer
CHR: Jean Martaniuk, Director Human Resources
CNO: Deanna Orfanidis, Chief Nursing Officer
Web address: www.mtascutneyhospital.org
Control: Other not–for–profit (including NFP Corporation) **Service:** General
medical and surgical

Staffed Beds: 35

VT

VIRGINIA

ABINGDON—Washington County

✠ **JOHNSTON MEMORIAL HOSPITAL (490053)**, 16000 Johnston Memorial Drive, Zip 24211–7659; tel. 276/258–1000, **A**1 2 3 5 10 13 **F**3 8 11 13 15 18 20 22 24 26 28 29 30 31 34 35 36 39 40 44 45 46 47 48 49 51 54 55 57 58 59 60 62 63 64 68 70 74 75 76 77 78 79 81 82 84 85 87 92 93 97 100 107 110 111 114 115 118 119 120 121 122 123 124 129 130 132 135 136 141 144 145 146 147 148 149 154 156 157 **S** Ballad Health, Johnson City, TN
Primary Contact: John Jeter, Chief Executive Officer
COO: Bryan Mullins, Chief Operating Officer
CMO: Brian Condit, M.D., Chief Medical Officer
CIO: Jackson Dale, Director Management Information Services
CHR: Jackie G Phipps, Director Human Resources
CNO: Linda M. Shepherd, Chief Nursing Officer
Web address: www.jmh.org
Control: Other not–for–profit (including NFP Corporation) **Service**: General medical and surgical

Staffed Beds: 116 Admissions: 7692 Census: 79 Outpatient Visits: 226201 Births: 598 Total Expense ($000): 137608 Payroll Expense ($000): 41691 Personnel: 1853

ALDIE—Loudoun County

✠ **ENCOMPASS HEALTH REHABILITATION HOSPITAL OF NORTHERN VIRGINIA (493033)**, 24430 Millstream Drive, Zip 20105–3098; tel. 703/957–2000, **A**1 10 **F**29 75 90 95 135 **S** Encompass Health Corporation, Birmingham, AL
Primary Contact: Alfred Santos, Chief Executive Officer
Web address: www.healthsouthnorthernvirginia.com
Control: Corporation, Investor–owned (for–profit) **Service**: Rehabilitation

Staffed Beds: 60 Admissions: 1701 Census: 54 Outpatient Visits: 0 Births: 0 Total Expense ($000): 25075 Payroll Expense ($000): 12898 Personnel: 197

ALEXANDRIA—Alexandria City County

✠ **INOVA ALEXANDRIA HOSPITAL (490040)**, 4320 Seminary Road, Zip 22304–1535; tel. 703/504–3167, **A**1 2 5 10 **F**3 11 13 14 15 18 20 22 26 28 29 30 31 34 35 38 39 40 41 42 44 45 46 47 48 49 50 51 54 55 56 57 58 59 60 61 63 64 65 68 70 72 74 75 76 77 78 79 81 82 84 85 86 87 91 92 93 100 101 102 107 110 111 114 115 118 119 120 121 123 124 126 129 130 131 132 135 145 146 147 148 149 154 156 157 **S** Inova Health System, Falls Church, VA
Primary Contact: Rina Bansal, Acting President and Chief Nursing Officer
CFO: Todd Lockcuff, Chief Financial Officer
CMO: William L Jackson, Chief Medical Officer
CHR: Hugo Aguas, Vice President Human Resources
Web address: www.inova.org
Control: Other not–for–profit (including NFP Corporation) **Service**: General medical and surgical

Staffed Beds: 318 Admissions: 14891 Census: 169 Outpatient Visits: 176383 Births: 3245 Total Expense ($000): 312638 Payroll Expense ($000): 111588 Personnel: 1437

ALEXANDRIA—Fairfax County

✠ **INOVA MOUNT VERNON HOSPITAL (490122)**, 2501 Parker's Lane, Zip 22306–3209; tel. 703/664–7000, **A**1 2 3 5 10 **F**3 11 14 15 18 28 29 30 31 34 35 38 39 40 44 45 48 49 50 51 54 55 57 58 59 60 61 63 64 65 68 70 74 75 77 78 79 81 82 84 85 86 87 90 91 92 93 94 95 96 98 100 101 102 104 105 107 110 111 114 115 118 119 130 131 132 135 145 146 147 148 149 154 156 157 **S** Inova Health System, Falls Church, VA
Primary Contact: Joseph Pina, M.D., Chief Executive Officer
CFO: Tammy Razmic, Associate Administrator Finance and Chief Financial Officer
CHR: Bev Sugar, Associate Administrator and Director Human Resources
Web address: www.inova.org
Control: Other not–for–profit (including NFP Corporation) **Service**: General medical and surgical

Staffed Beds: 237 Admissions: 8532 Census: 139 Outpatient Visits: 101433 Births: 0 Total Expense ($000): 200662 Payroll Expense ($000): 76240 Personnel: 936

ARLINGTON—Arlington County

✠ **CAPITAL HOSPICE (490129)**, 4715 15th Street North, Zip 22205–2640; tel. 703/538–2065, (Nonreporting) **A**3 10
Primary Contact: Malene S. Davis, R.N., President and Chief Executive Officer
CFO: David Schwind, Chief Financial Officer
CIO: Diane Rigsby, Chief Information Officer
Web address: www.capitalhospice.org
Control: Other not–for–profit (including NFP Corporation) **Service**: Other specialty treatment

Staffed Beds: 15

✠ △ **VIRGINIA HOSPITAL CENTER (490050)**, 1701 North George Mason Drive, Zip 22205–3698; tel. 703/558–5000, (Nonreporting) **A**1 2 3 5 7 10
Primary Contact: James B. Cole, President and Chief Executive Officer
COO: Carl Bahnlein, Executive Vice President and Chief Operating Officer
CFO: Robin Norman, Senior Vice President and Chief Financial Officer
CMO: Jeffrey P DiLisi, Vice President and Chief Medical Officer
CIO: Russ McWey, M.D., Vice President and Chief Information Officer
CHR: Michael Malone, Vice President and Chief Human Resources Officer
CNO: Darlene Vrotsos, R.N., Senior Vice President and Chief Nursing Officer
Web address: www.virginiahospitalcenter.com
Control: Other not–for–profit (including NFP Corporation) **Service**: General medical and surgical

Staffed Beds: 357

BEDFORD—Bedford City County

✠ **CENTRA BEDFORD MEMORIAL HOSPITAL (490088)**, 1613 Oakwood Street, Zip 24523–1213; tel. 540/586–2441, (Total facility includes 111 beds in nursing home–type unit) **A**1 5 10 **F**2 3 11 15 28 29 30 34 35 40 46 53 57 59 63 67 70 81 84 85 86 87 97 107 110 115 119 128 130 143 146 148 **S** Centra Health, Inc., Lynchburg, VA
Primary Contact: Patti Jurkus, Vice President and Chief Executive Officer
CFO: Donald E Lorton, Executive Vice President
CMO: E Allen Joslyn, M.D., Chief Medical Officer
Web address: www.bmhva.com
Control: Other not–for–profit (including NFP Corporation) **Service**: General medical and surgical

Staffed Beds: 145 Admissions: 2087 Census: 112 Outpatient Visits: 42124 Births: 0 Total Expense ($000): 44111 Payroll Expense ($000): 18823 Personnel: 335

BIG STONE GAP—Wise County

✠ **LONESOME PINE HOSPITAL (490114)**, 1990 Holton Avenue East, Zip 24219–3350; tel. 276/523–3111, **A**1 3 5 10 13 **F**3 11 15 29 30 31 34 40 45 50 57 59 63 70 77 78 79 81 82 85 87 93 107 108 110 111 114 118 119 120 121 129 130 135 146 148 **S** Ballad Health, Johnson City, TN
Primary Contact: Mark T. Leonard, Interim Chief Executive Officer
CFO: Regina Day, Executive Vice President of Finance
CMO: Michael Ketcham, President, Medical Staff
CHR: Bobby Collins, Director Human Resources
Web address: www.wellmont.org
Control: Other not–for–profit (including NFP Corporation) **Service**: General medical and surgical

Staffed Beds: 32 Admissions: 1307 Census: 7 Outpatient Visits: 86023 Births: 211 Total Expense ($000): 61331 Payroll Expense ($000): 9594 Personnel: 184

BLACKSBURG—Montgomery County

✠ **LEWISGALE HOSPITAL MONTGOMERY (490110)**, 3700 South Main Street, Zip 24060–7081, Mailing Address: P.O. Box 90004, Zip 24062–9004; tel. 540/951–1111, (Nonreporting) **A**1 3 5 10 12 13 **S** HCA Healthcare, Nashville, TN
Primary Contact: Alan J. Fabian, Chief Executive Officer
COO: Matt Mathias, Chief Operating Officer
CFO: Timothy W Haasken, Chief Financial Officer
CIO: Diron Lane, Director Information Systems
CNO: Ellen Y Linkenhoker, Chief Nursing Officer
Web address: www.lewisgale.com
Control: Corporation, Investor–owned (for–profit) **Service**: General medical and surgical

Staffed Beds: 89

Many Facility Codes have changed. Please refer to the AHA Guide Code Chart.

VA

BOONES MILL—Salem City County

☒ **LEWIS-GALE MEDICAL CENTER (490048)**, 8633 Grassy Hill Rd,
Zip 24065, Mailing Address: 1900 Electric Road, Salem, Zip 24153–7494;
tel. 540/776–4000, (Includes LEWIS-GALE PAVILION, 1902 Braeburn Drive, Salem,
Virginia, Zip 24153–7391; tel. 703/772–2800), (Non-reporting) **A**1 2 3 5 10 **S**
HCA Healthcare, Nashville, TN
Primary Contact: Lance Jones, Chief Executive Officer
COO: Michael Abbott, Chief Operating Officer
CFO: Angela D Reynolds, Chief Financial Officer
CMO: Joseph Nelson, M.D., President Medical Staff
CIO: Beth Cole, Director Information Services
CHR: Dale Beaudoin, Vice President Human Resources
Web address: www.lewis-gale.com
Control: Corporation, Investor–owned (for–profit) **Service:** General medical and surgical

> **Staffed Beds:** 521

BRISTOL—Bristol City County

☒ **REHABILITATION HOSPITAL OF SOUTHWEST VIRGINIA (493034)**, 103 North
Street, Zip 24201–3201; tel. 276/642–7900, (Nonreporting) **A**1 10 **S** Encompass
Health Corporation, Birmingham, AL
Primary Contact: Georgeanne Cole, Chief Executive Officer
Web address: www.rehabilitationhospitalswvirginia.com
Control: Corporation, Investor–owned (for–profit) **Service:** Rehabilitation

> **Staffed Beds:** 25

BURKEVILLE—Nottoway County

☐ **PIEDMONT GERIATRIC HOSPITAL (490134)**, 5001 East Patrick Henry Hwy,
Zip 23922–3460, Mailing Address: P.O. Box 427, Zip 23922–0427; tel. 434/767–4401,
(Nonreporting) **A**1 **S** Virginia Department of Mental Health, Richmond, VA
Primary Contact: Hilton McDaniel, President
CFO: James G Ayers, Chief Financial Officer
CMO: Hugo Falcon, M.D., Director Medical Services
CHR: Michael Wimsatt, Director Human Resources
Web address: www.pgh.dmhmrsas.virginia.gov
Control: State, Government, nonfederal **Service:** Other specialty treatment

> **Staffed Beds:** 135

CATAWBA—Roanoke County

☐ **CATAWBA HOSPITAL (490135)**, 5525 Catawba Hospital Drive,
Zip 24070–2115, Mailing Address: P.O. Box 200, Zip 24070–0200;
tel. 540/375–4200, **A**1 3 10 **F**29 30 35 39 44 50 68 75 77 98 103 130 146
149 **S** Virginia Department of Mental Health, Richmond, VA
Primary Contact: Walton F. Mitchell III, Director
COO: Charles Law, Ph.D., Chief Operating Officer
CFO: Cecil Hardin, CPA, Chief Financial Officer
CMO: Yad Jabbarpour, M.D., Chief of Staff
CIO: Charles Law, Ph.D., Chief Operating Officer
CHR: Patricia Ebbett, Chief Human Resources Officer
CNO: Vicky Fisher, Ph.D., R.N., Chief Nurse Executive
Web address: www.catawba.dbhds.virginia.gov
Control: State, Government, nonfederal **Service:** Psychiatric

> **Staffed Beds:** 110 **Admissions:** 620 **Census:** 103 **Outpatient Visits:** 0
> **Births:** 0 **Total Expense ($000):** 25500 **Payroll Expense ($000):** 13663
> **Personnel:** 263

CHARLOTTESVILLE—Charlottesville City County

★ ⇑ **SENTARA MARTHA JEFFERSON HOSPITAL (490077)**, 500 Martha Jefferson
Drive, Zip 22911–4668; tel. 434/654–7000, **A**2 10 21 **F**3 8 11 12 13 15 18 20
22 26 28 29 30 31 34 35 36 40 41 42 44 45 46 47 48 49 50 53 54 55 56 57
58 59 64 65 67 68 70 74 75 76 77 78 79 81 82 84 85 86 87 89 92 93 94 97
107 108 110 111 114 115 116 117 118 119 120 121 123 124 129 130 131
132 134 135 141 145 146 147 149 154 156 **S** Sentara Healthcare, Norfolk, VA
Primary Contact: Jonathan S. Davis, FACHE, President
COO: Amy Black, R.N., MSN, Chief Operating Officer
CFO: Stewart R Nelson, Vice President and Chief Financial Officer
CMO: F Michael Ashby, M.D., Vice President and Medical Director
CIO: Marijo Lecker, Vice President
CHR: Debbie Desmond, Director Human Resources
Web address: www.marthajefferson.org
Control: Other not–for–profit (including NFP Corporation) **Service:** General
medical and surgical

> **Staffed Beds:** 144 **Admissions:** 9789 **Census:** 96 **Outpatient
> Visits:** 706167 **Births:** 1469 **Total Expense ($000):** 236495 **Payroll
> Expense ($000):** 96500 **Personnel:** 1456

☒ **UNIVERSITY OF VIRGINIA MEDICAL CENTER (490009)**, 1215 Lee Street,
Zip 22908–0001, Mailing Address: P.O. Box 800809, Zip 22908–0809;
tel. 434/924–0211, (Includes UNIVERSITY OF VIRGINIA CHILDREN'S HOSPITAL,
1215 Lee Street, Charlottesville, Virginia, Zip 22908, Mailing Address: P.O. Box
800566, Zip 22908, tel. 434/243–5500) **A**1 2 3 5 8 10 **F**3 4 5 6 7 8 9 11 12
13 15 16 17 18 19 20 21 22 23 24 25 26 27 28 29 30 31 32 34 35 36 37 38
39 40 41 43 44 45 46 47 48 49 50 51 52 54 55 56 57 58 59 60 61 62 63 64
65 66 68 70 71 72 73 74 75 76 77 78 79 80 81 82 83 84 85 86 87 88 89 90
91 92 93 94 97 98 100 101 102 103 104 107 108 110 111 112 114 115 116
117 118 119 120 121 123 124 126 129 130 131 132 134 135 136 137 138
139 140 141 142 143 145 146 147 148 149 153 154 155 156 **S** UVA Health
System, Charlottesville, VA
Primary Contact: Pamela Sutton-Wallace, Chief Executive Officer
COO: William T. Fulkerson, Chief Operating Officer
CFO: Nick Mendyka, Chief Financial Officer
CMO: Chris A. Ghaemmaghami, M.D., Chief Medical Officer
CIO: Richard Skinner, Chief Information Technology Officer
CHR: John Boswell, Chief Human Resources Officer
CNO: Mary E. Dixon, MSN, R.N., Interim Chief Nursing Officer
Web address: www.healthsystem.virginia.edu
Control: State, Government, nonfederal **Service:** General medical and surgical

> **Staffed Beds:** 612 **Admissions:** 28894 **Census:** 494 **Outpatient
> Visits:** 2028845 **Births:** 1868 **Total Expense ($000):** 1611323 **Payroll
> Expense ($000):** 551627 **Personnel:** 8087

CHARLOTTESVILLE—Albemarle County

☒ **UVA TRANSITIONAL CARE HOSPITAL (492011)**, 2965 Ivy Rd (250 West),
Zip 22903–9330; tel. 434/924–8245, **A**1 10 **F**1 3 29 30 60 77 85 94 114 129
130 146 148 149 154 **S** UVA Health System, Charlottesville, VA
Primary Contact: Tracy Turman, Administrator
Web address: www.uvahealth.com/services/transitional-care-hospital
Control: State, Government, nonfederal **Service:** Acute long–term care hospital

> **Staffed Beds:** 30 **Admissions:** 356 **Census:** 28 **Outpatient Visits:** 0
> **Births:** 0 **Total Expense ($000):** 20557 **Payroll Expense ($000):** 7844
> **Personnel:** 128

☒ **UVA-HEALTHSOUTH REHABILITATION HOSPITAL (493029)**, 515 Ray C Hunt
Drive, Zip 22903–2981; tel. 434/244–2000, **A**1 3 5 10 **F**3 28 29 34 35 57 59
74 75 77 90 91 132 148 154 **S** Encompass Health Corporation, Birmingham, AL
Primary Contact: Barbara Adcock Mohr, Chief Executive Officer
CFO: Dianna Gomez, Controller
CMO: Alan Alfano, M.D., Medical Director
CIO: Michael Vanhoy, Director of Quality
CHR: Tonya Loving, Director of Human Resources
CNO: Cherry Herring, Chief Nursing Officer
Web address: www.uvahealthsouth.com
Control: Corporation, Investor–owned (for–profit) **Service:** Rehabilitation

> **Staffed Beds:** 50 **Admissions:** 1178 **Census:** 42 **Outpatient Visits:** 32777
> **Births:** 0 **Total Expense ($000):** 20434 **Payroll Expense ($000):** 12299
> **Personnel:** 225

CHESAPEAKE—Chesapeake City County

★ ○ **CHESAPEAKE REGIONAL MEDICAL CENTER (490120)**, 736
Battlefield Boulevard North, Zip 23320–4941, Mailing Address: P.O. Box 2028,
Zip 23327–2028; tel. 757/312–8121, **A**2 3 10 11 **F**3 8 11 12 13 15 18 20 22
26 28 29 30 31 34 35 37 38 40 44 45 46 49 50 53 54 56 57 58 59 62 63 64
65 66 68 69 70 71 73 74 75 76 77 78 79 81 83 84 85 86 87 89 91 93 100
101 102 107 108 110 111 114 115 118 119 120 121 123 126 129 130 132
135 143 146 147 148 149 154 157
Primary Contact: Reese Jackson, President and Chief Executive Officer
COO: Amber Egyud, R.N., Chief Nursing Officer and Chief Operating Officer
CFO: Stephen C McDonnell, Chief Financial Officer
CMO: Raymond McCue, M.D., Vice President, Medical Affairs and Chief Medical
Officer
CIO: Maurice Bastarache, Chief Information Officer
CHR: Deborah L Rosenburg, Vice President Human Resources
CNO: Amber Egyud, R.N., Chief Nursing Officer and Chief Operating Officer
Web address: www.chesapeakeregional.com
Control: Hospital district or authority, Government, nonfederal **Service:** General
medical and surgical

> **Staffed Beds:** 310 **Admissions:** 15614 **Census:** 180 **Outpatient
> Visits:** 107506 **Births:** 2671 **Total Expense ($000):** 292569 **Payroll
> Expense ($000):** 104373 **Personnel:** 1979

VA

Hospital, Medicare Provider Number, Address, Telephone, Approval, Facility, and Physician Codes, Health Care System

★ American Hospital Association (AHA) membership ○ Healthcare Facilities Accreditation Program ⇑ Center for Improvement in Healthcare Quality Accreditation
☐ The Joint Commission accreditation ◇ DNV Healthcare Inc. accreditation △ Commission on Accreditation of Rehabilitation Facilities (CARF) accreditation

CHRISTIANSBURG—Montgomery County

☒ **CARILION NEW RIVER VALLEY MEDICAL CENTER (490042)**, 2900 Lamb Circle, Zip 24073–6344, Mailing Address: P.O. Box 5, Radford, Zip 24143–0005; tel. 540/731–2000, (Includes CARILION CLINIC SAINT ALBANS HOSPITAL, 2900 Lamb Circle, Christiansburg, Virginia, Zip 24073–6344; tel. 540/731–2000) **A**1 3 5 10 19 **F**3 5 8 12 13 15 18 20 22 24 26 28 29 30 31 34 35 36 40 43 45 47 48 49 50 51 53 57 59 60 62 63 64 65 68 70 74 75 76 77 79 81 82 84 85 86 87 89 91 92 93 96 98 99 102 103 104 105 107 108 110 111 114 115 118 119 126 129 130 131 135 146 147 148 149 154 156 **S** Carilion Clinic, Roanoke, VA
Primary Contact: William Flattery, Vice President and Administrator Western Division
CFO: Rob Vaughan, Chief Financial Officer
CMO: Dennis Means, M.D., Vice President Medical Affairs
CIO: Daniel Borchi, Chief Information Officer
CHR: Patti Jurkus, Director Human Resources
Web address: www.carilionclinic.org/Carilion/cnrv
Control: Other not–for–profit (including NFP Corporation) **Service:** General medical and surgical

Staffed Beds: 99 **Admissions:** 8728 **Census:** 98 **Outpatient Visits:** 102613 **Births:** 1029 **Total Expense ($000):** 177275 **Payroll Expense ($000):** 65139 **Personnel:** 976

CLINTWOOD—Dickenson County

○ **DICKENSON COMMUNITY HOSPITAL (491303)**, 312 Hospital Drive, Zip 24228, Mailing Address: P.O. Box 1440, Zip 24228–1440; tel. 276/926–0300, **A**10 11 18 **F**3 29 40 44 64 77 93 97 98 103 104 107 119 130 148 153 154 156 **S** Ballad Health, Johnson City, TN
Primary Contact: Mark T. Leonard, Chief Executive Officer
CFO: Kevin Morrison, Chief Financial Officer
CMO: Erin Mullins, D.O., Chief Medical Staff
CHR: Valeri J Colyer, Director Human Resources
CNO: Terri Roop, Director Patient Care Services
Web address: www.msha.com/dch
Control: Other not–for–profit (including NFP Corporation) **Service:** General medical and surgical

Staffed Beds: 11 **Admissions:** 255 **Census:** 7 **Outpatient Visits:** 23434 **Births:** 0 **Total Expense ($000):** 9024 **Payroll Expense ($000):** 3561 **Personnel:** 139

CULPEPER—Culpeper County

☒ **NOVANT HEALTH UVA HEALTH SYSTEM CULPEPER MEDICAL CENTER (490019)**, 501 Sunset Lane, Zip 22701–3917, Mailing Address: P.O. Box 592, Zip 22701–0500; tel. 540/829–4100, **A**1 3 5 10 **F**3 7 11 13 15 18 19 28 29 30 31 34 35 36 37 38 39 40 44 45 50 57 59 64 68 70 74 75 76 77 78 79 81 82 85 86 87 89 91 93 94 97 102 107 108 110 111 114 115 119 120 121 123 124 130 132 135 143 145 146 148 154 156 **S** Novant Health, Winston Salem, NC
Primary Contact: Jeff Hetmanski, President and Chief Operating Officer
CFO: David J Plaviak, Interim Chief Financial Officer
CMO: Morton Chiles, M.D., Chief Medical Officer
CIO: Steven Speelman, Director Information Systems
CHR: Susan Edwards, Vice President Human Resources
Web address: www.culpeperhealth.org
Control: Other not–for–profit (including NFP Corporation) **Service:** General medical and surgical

Staffed Beds: 68 **Admissions:** 3280 **Census:** 31 **Outpatient Visits:** 128949 **Births:** 449 **Total Expense ($000):** 99739 **Payroll Expense ($000):** 39026 **Personnel:** 630

DANVILLE—Danville City County

☐ **SOUTHERN VIRGINIA MENTAL HEALTH INSTITUTE (494017)**, 382 Taylor Drive, Zip 24541–4023; tel. 434/799–6220, (Nonreporting) **A**1 10 **S** Virginia Department of Mental Health, Richmond, VA
Primary Contact: William Cook, Director
CFO: Wayne Peters, Administrator
CMO: Pravin Patel, M.D., Acting President and Chief Executive Officer
CIO: Larry Hays, Director Information Technology
CHR: Stephanie Haywood, Director Human Resources
CNO: Kathy M Dodd, Director of Nursing
Web address: www.svmhi.dbhds.virginia.gov
Control: State, Government, nonfederal **Service:** Psychiatric

Staffed Beds: 72

SOVAH HEALTH–DANVILLE (490075)

☒ **SOVAH HEALTH–DANVILLE (490075)**, 142 South Main Street, Zip 24541–2922; tel. 434/799–2100, (Nonreporting) **A**1 2 3 5 10 13 **S** LifePoint Health, Brentwood, TN
Primary Contact: Alan Larson, Chief Executive Officer
CFO: Mark T Anderson, Chief Financial Officer
CMO: James F Starling, M.D., Chief Medical Officer
CIO: David Cartwright, Director Management Information Systems
CNO: Aundrea Mills, Chief Nursing Officer
Web address: www.danvilleregional.com/
Control: Other not–for–profit (including NFP Corporation) **Service:** General medical and surgical

Staffed Beds: 250

DULLES—Loudoun County

★ **STONESPRINGS HOSPITAL CENTER (490145)**, 24440 Stone Spring Boulevard, Zip 20166–2247; tel. 571/349–4000, (Nonreporting) **A**10 **S** HCA Healthcare, Nashville, TN
Primary Contact: Matt Mathias, Chief Executive Officer
COO: Benjamin Brown, Chief Operating Officer
CFO: Candi Christopher, CPA, Chief Financial Officer
CMO: Walter R Zolkiwsky, M.D., Chief Medical Officer
CHR: Tiffani Smith, Chief Human Resources Officer
CNO: Michelle L. Epps, MSN, R.N., Chief Nursing Officer
Web address: www.stonespringshospital.com
Control: Corporation, Investor–owned (for–profit) **Service:** General medical and surgical

Staffed Beds: 124

EMPORIA—Emporia City County

☒ **SOUTHERN VIRGINIA REGIONAL MEDICAL CENTER (490097)**, 727 North Main Street, Zip 23847–1274; tel. 434/348–4400, **A**1 10 **F**3 11 15 28 29 30 40 45 49 50 57 59 64 70 77 78 79 81 85 87 93 98 103 107 115 119 124 129 130 131 133 146 148 154 **S** Community Health Systems, Inc., Franklin, TN
Primary Contact: Wilson A. Thomas, Chief Executive Officer
CFO: Jim Porter, Chief Financial Officer
CMO: Fitzgerald Marcelin, M.D., Chief of Staff
CIO: Larry Gold, Vice President, Information Services
CHR: Becky Parrish, Director Human Resources
CNO: Linda Burnette, R.N., Chief Nursing Officer
Web address: www.svrmc.com
Control: Corporation, Investor–owned (for–profit) **Service:** General medical and surgical

Staffed Beds: 80 **Admissions:** 1525 **Census:** 16 **Births:** 0 **Total Expense ($000):** 32382 **Payroll Expense ($000):** 9987

FAIRFAX—Fairfax County

☒ **INOVA FAIR OAKS HOSPITAL (490101)**, 3600 Joseph Siewick Drive, Zip 22033–1798; tel. 703/391–3600, **A**1 2 3 5 10 **F**3 11 12 13 14 15 18 28 29 30 31 34 35 37 38 39 40 41 44 45 47 48 49 50 51 54 55 57 58 59 60 61 64 65 68 70 72 74 75 76 77 78 79 80 81 82 84 85 86 87 89 91 92 93 100 101 102 107 108 110 111 114 115 118 119 120 121 123 124 126 129 130 131 132 135 146 147 148 149 154 156 157 **S** Inova Health System, Falls Church, VA
Primary Contact: Donald Brideau, M.D., Chief Executive Officer
CFO: Jerry Seager, Assistant Vice President and Chief Financial Officer
CMO: G Michael Lynch, M.D., Chief Medical Officer
CIO: Marshall Ruffin, Chief Information Officer
CHR: Jeanne Robinson, Director Human Resources
Web address: www.inova.org
Control: Other not–for–profit (including NFP Corporation) **Service:** General medical and surgical

Staffed Beds: 201 **Admissions:** 11052 **Census:** 105 **Outpatient Visits:** 95146 **Births:** 3145 **Total Expense ($000):** 256340 **Payroll Expense ($000):** 77633 **Personnel:** 1042

FALLS CHURCH—Fairfax County

☒ **DOMINION HOSPITAL (494023)**, 2960 Sleepy Hollow Road, Zip 22044–2030; tel. 703/536–2000, (Nonreporting) **A**1 3 10 **S** HCA Healthcare, Nashville, TN
Primary Contact: Lee Higginbotham, Chief Executive Officer
CFO: Edward R Stojakovich, Chief Financial Officer
CMO: Gary Litovitz, M.D., Medical Director
CIO: Leslie Gilliam, Director Health Information Management
CHR: Lesley Channell, Vice President Human Resources
Web address: www.dominionhospital.com
Control: Corporation, Investor–owned (for–profit) **Service:** Psychiatric

Staffed Beds: 100

VA

Many Facility Codes have changed. Please refer to the AHA Guide Code Chart. © 2019 AHA Guide

⊞ **INOVA FAIRFAX HOSPITAL (490063)**, 3300 Gallows Road, Zip 22042–3300; tel. 703/776–4001, (Includes INOVA FAIRFAX HOSPITAL FOR CHILDREN, 3300 Gallows Road, Falls Church, Virginia, Zip 22042–3307; tel. 703/776–4002) **A**1 2 3 5 8 10 **F**3 4 5 8 9 11 13 14 15 17 18 19 20 21 22 23 24 25 26 27 28 29 30 31 32 34 35 36 37 38 39 40 41 42 43 44 45 46 47 48 49 50 51 53 54 55 56 57 58 59 60 61 63 64 65 68 70 72 74 75 76 77 78 79 80 81 82 83 84 85 86 87 88 89 91 92 93 98 99 100 101 102 103 104 105 107 108 109 110 111 114 115 118 119 120 121 123 124 126 129 130 131 132 135 137 138 140 141 142 145 146 147 148 149 152 154 156 157 **S** Inova Health System, Falls Church, VA
Primary Contact: Susan T. Carroll, FACHE, Acting President
CFO: Ronald Ewald, Chief Financial Officer
CMO: Joseph Hallal, M.D., Chief Medical Officer
CIO: Geoffrey Brown, Vice President Information Systems
CHR: Ken Hull, Director Human Resources
Web address: www.inova.org
Control: Other not–for–profit (including NFP Corporation) **Service**: General medical and surgical

Staffed Beds: 1031 **Admissions**: 49681 **Census**: 706 **Outpatient Visits**: 424468 **Births**: 10417 **Total Expense ($000)**: 1425227 **Payroll Expense ($000)**: 459986 **Personnel**: 6037

☐ **NORTHERN VIRGINIA MENTAL HEALTH INSTITUTE (494010)**, 3302 Gallows Road, Zip 22042–3398; tel. 703/207–7100, (Nonreporting) **A**1 3 5 10 **S** Virginia Department of Mental Health, Richmond, VA
Primary Contact: Tammy Peacock, Ph.D., Facility Director
CFO: John Poffenbarger, Director Fiscal Services
CMO: R Maxilimien del Rio, M.D., Medical Director
CHR: Cynthia Lott, Director Human Resources
Web address: www.nvmhi.dbhds.virginia.gov
Control: State, Government, nonfederal **Service**: Psychiatric

Staffed Beds: 134

FARMVILLE—Prince Edward County

⊞ **CENTRA SOUTHSIDE COMMUNITY HOSPITAL (490090)**, 800 Oak Street, Zip 23901–1199; tel. 434/392–8811, **A**1 5 10 20 **F**3 11 13 15 18 20 22 26 28 29 30 31 34 35 40 44 45 49 50 57 59 62 63 64 70 74 75 76 77 78 79 81 82 84 85 86 87 89 107 108 110 111 115 118 119 129 130 132 133 146 147 148 154 **S** Centra Health, Inc., Lynchburg, VA
Primary Contact: Thomas Angelo, Chief Executive Officer
Web address: www.sch.centrahealth.com/
Control: Other not–for–profit (including NFP Corporation) **Service**: General medical and surgical

Staffed Beds: 86 **Admissions**: 4023 **Census**: 39 **Outpatient Visits**: 103005 **Births**: 342 **Total Expense ($000)**: 78840 **Payroll Expense ($000)**: 27427 **Personnel**: 421

SOUTHSIDE COMMUNITY HOSPITAL See Centra Southside Community Hospital

FISHERSVILLE—Augusta County

⊞ **AUGUSTA HEALTH (490018)**, 78 Medical Center Drive, Zip 22939–2332, Mailing Address: P.O. Box 1000, Zip 22939–1000; tel. 540/932–4000, **A**1 2 3 10 **F**3 5 7 11 13 15 18 20 22 26 28 29 30 31 32 34 35 38 40 41 44 45 46 47 48 49 50 51 53 54 55 57 58 59 62 63 64 66 68 70 74 75 76 77 78 79 81 82 83 84 85 86 87 89 90 93 96 97 98 100 102 103 104 107 109 110 111 114 115 116 117 118 119 120 121 124 126 128 129 130 131 132 143 144 146 147 148 149 153 154 156 157
Primary Contact: Mary N. Mannix, FACHE, President and Chief Executive Officer
CMO: Richard Embrey, M.D., Chief Medical Officer
CIO: Michael Canfield, Chief Information Officer
CHR: Sue Krzastek, Vice President Human Resources
Web address: www.augustahealth.com
Control: Other not–for–profit (including NFP Corporation) **Service**: General medical and surgical

Staffed Beds: 209 **Admissions**: 10927 **Census**: 117 **Outpatient Visits**: 753799 **Births**: 1105 **Total Expense ($000)**: 318052 **Payroll Expense ($000)**: 138306 **Personnel**: 1947

FORT BELVOIR—Fairfax County

⊞ **FORT BELVOIR COMMUNITY HOSPITAL**, 9300 Dewitt Loop, Zip 22060–5285; tel. 571/231–3224, (Nonreporting) **A**1 3 5 **S** Department of the Army, Office of the Surgeon General, Falls Church, VA
Primary Contact: Colonel Jason S. Wieman, Director
CMO: Lieutenant Colonel Mark D Harris, Deputy Commander Clinical Services
CIO: Terrance Branch, Chief Information Management
Web address: www.fbch.capmed.mil/SitePages/Home.aspx
Control: Department of Defense, Government, federal **Service**: General medical and surgical

Staffed Beds: 46

FRANKLIN—Franklin City County

⊞ **SOUTHAMPTON MEMORIAL HOSPITAL (490092)**, 100 Fairview Drive, Zip 23851–1238, Mailing Address: P.O. Box 817, Zip 23851–0817; tel. 757/569–6100, (Nonreporting) **A**1 10 20 **S** Community Health Systems, Inc., Franklin, TN
Primary Contact: Kimberly W. Marks, Chief Executive Officer
CFO: Steve Ramey, Chief Financial Officer
CMO: Donald Bowling, M.D., Chief Medical Staff
CIO: Kristie Howell, System Information Technology Director
CHR: Loretha Ricks, Human Resources Supervisor
CNO: Laurie Ross, Chief Nursing Officer
Web address: www.smhfranklin.com
Control: Corporation, Investor–owned (for–profit) **Service**: General medical and surgical

Staffed Beds: 72

FREDERICKSBURG—Fredericksburg City County

⊞ **ENCOMPASS HEALTH REHABILITATION HOSPITAL OF FREDERICKSBURG (493032)**, 300 Park Hill Drive, Zip 22401–3387; tel. 540/368–7300, (Nonreporting) **A**1 10 **S** Encompass Health Corporation, Birmingham, AL
Primary Contact: David Cashwell, Chief Executive Officer
Web address: www.fredericksburgrehabhospital.com
Control: Corporation, Investor–owned (for–profit) **Service**: Rehabilitation

Staffed Beds: 40

⊞ **MARY WASHINGTON HOSPITAL (490022)**, 1001 Sam Perry Boulevard, Zip 22401–3354; tel. 540/741–1100, (Includes SNOWDEN AT FREDERICKSBURG, 1200 Sam Perry Boulevard, Fredericksburg, Virginia, Zip 22401–4456; tel. 540/741–3900; Charles Scercy, Corporate Director) **A**1 2 3 5 10 **F**3 5 13 18 22 24 26 28 29 30 31 34 35 36 40 42 43 44 45 46 47 48 49 50 54 55 57 58 59 62 64 70 72 74 75 76 77 78 79 81 83 84 85 86 87 89 92 93 96 98 99 100 101 102 104 105 107 108 111 114 115 118 119 120 121 124 126 129 130 131 132 135 146 147 148 149 152 153 154 **S** Mary Washington Healthcare, Fredericksburg, VA
Primary Contact: Michael P. McDermott, M.D., President and Chief Executive Officer
COO: Thomas Gettinger, Executive Vice President and Chief Operating Officer
CFO: Sean Barden, Executive Vice President and Chief Financial Officer
CMO: Rebecca Bigoney, Executive Vice President and Chief Medical Officer
CIO: Justin K. Box, Senior Vice President & Chief Information Officer
CHR: Kathryn S Wall, Executive Vice President, Human Resources and Organizational Development
CNO: Eileen L Dohmann, R.N., Senior Vice President and Chief Nursing Officer
Web address: www.marywashingtonhealthcare.com
Control: Other not–for–profit (including NFP Corporation) **Service**: General medical and surgical

Staffed Beds: 451 **Admissions**: 24038 **Census**: 294 **Outpatient Visits**: 353792 **Births**: 2356 **Total Expense ($000)**: 414130 **Payroll Expense ($000)**: 121458 **Personnel**: 1793

FREDERICKSBURG—Spotsylvania County

⊞ **SPOTSYLVANIA REGIONAL MEDICAL CENTER (490141)**, 4600 Spotsylvania Parkway, Zip 22408–7762; tel. 540/498–4000, (Nonreporting) **A**1 5 10 **S** HCA Healthcare, Nashville, TN
Primary Contact: David McKnight, CPA, Chief Executive Officer
COO: Roberta Tinch, Chief Operations Officer
Web address: www.spotsrmc.com
Control: Corporation, Investor–owned (for–profit) **Service**: General medical and surgical

Staffed Beds: 100

VA

Hospital, Medicare Provider Number, Address, Telephone, Approval, Facility, and Physician Codes, Health Care System

★ American Hospital Association (AHA) membership
☐ The Joint Commission accreditation
○ Healthcare Facilities Accreditation Program
◇ DNV Healthcare Inc. accreditation
⇑ Center for Improvement in Healthcare Quality Accreditation
△ Commission on Accreditation of Rehabilitation Facilities (CARF) accreditation

© 2019 AHA Guide   *Many Facility Codes have changed. Please refer to the AHA Guide Code Chart.*   Hospitals **A659**

FRONT ROYAL—Warren County

☒ **WARREN MEMORIAL HOSPITAL (490033)**, 1000 North Shenandoah Avenue, Zip 22630–3598; tel. 540/636–0300, (Total facility includes 120 beds in nursing home–type unit) **A**1 3 5 10 **F**3 11 13 15 18 20 22 28 29 30 34 35 36 40 50 53 54 56 57 59 64 65 67 70 75 76 77 79 81 82 85 86 87 93 96 107 108 111 114 118 119 128 130 132 135 144 146 147 148 154 156 **S** Valley Health System, Winchester, VA
Primary Contact: Floyd Heater, President
CFO: Phillip Graybeal, CPA, Chief Financial Officer
CMO: Robert Meltvedt, M.D., Jr Vice President Medical Affairs
CNO: Terri Wright, Vice President and Chief Nursing Officer
Web address: www.valleyhealthlink.com/WMH
Control: Other not–for–profit (including NFP Corporation) **Service**: General medical and surgical

Staffed Beds: 166 **Admissions**: 2355 **Census**: 132 **Outpatient Visits**: 66918 **Births**: 127 **Total Expense ($000)**: 75805 **Payroll Expense ($000)**: 26483 **Personnel**: 460

GALAX—Galax City County

☒ **TWIN COUNTY REGIONAL HEALTHCARE (490115)**, 200 Hospital Drive, Zip 24333–2227; tel. 276/236–8181, **A**1 5 10 20 **F**3 13 14 15 28 29 30 31 32 34 35 38 40 45 50 51 53 57 64 65 68 70 75 76 77 78 79 81 82 85 87 89 93 98 100 101 102 104 107 108 110 111 116 117 119 132 146 147 **S** Duke LifePoint Healthcare, Brentwood, TN
Primary Contact: Dale Alward, Chief Executive Officer
CFO: Marita Caldwell, Chief Financial Officer
CHR: Kristal Herrington, Senior Director, Human Resources
CNO: Agnes A Smith, MSN, R.N., Chief Nursing Officer
Web address: www.tcrh.org
Control: Partnership, Investor–owned (for–profit) **Service**: General medical and surgical

Staffed Beds: 86 **Admissions**: 3130 **Census**: 30

GLOUCESTER—Gloucester County

⇑ **RIVERSIDE WALTER REED HOSPITAL (490130)**, 7519 Hospital Drive, Zip 23061–4178, Mailing Address: P.O. Box 1130; Zip 23061–1130; tel. 804/693–8800, **A**2 10 21 **F**3 15 28 29 34 35 40 44 45 50 51 57 59 60 64 70 71 75 77 78 79 81 85 86 87 92 93 96 107 108 110 111 114 115 116 118 119 120 121 123 130 132 146 147 148 149 **S** Riverside Health System, Newport News, VA
Primary Contact: Esther Muscari. Desimini, Interim Administrator
CHR: Tabetha Holt, Director of Human Resources
Web address: www.riversideonline.com
Control: Other not–for–profit (including NFP Corporation) **Service**: General medical and surgical

Staffed Beds: 30 **Admissions**: 2701 **Census**: 28 **Outpatient Visits**: 89640 **Births**: 0 **Total Expense ($000)**: 62026 **Payroll Expense ($000)**: 21062 **Personnel**: 286

GRUNDY—Buchanan County

☒ **BUCHANAN GENERAL HOSPITAL (490127)**, 1535 Slate Creek Road, Zip 24614–6974; tel. 276/935–1000, **A**1 10 20 **F**3 15 18 28 29 30 34 35 40 41 45 57 59 62 64 70 81 85 87 89 93 107 108 110 115 119 130 132 135 146 148
Primary Contact: Robert D. Ruchti, Chief Executive Officer
COO: Scott M Pittman, Chief Operating Officer
CFO: Kim Boyd, Chief Financial Officer
CIO: Rita Ramey, Director Information Systems
CHR: Wanda B. Stiltner, Director Human Resources
CNO: Patty Dorton, Director of Nursing
Web address: www.bgh.org
Control: Other not–for–profit (including NFP Corporation) **Service**: General medical and surgical

Staffed Beds: 49 **Admissions**: 1067 **Census**: 15 **Outpatient Visits**: 43923 **Births**: 0 **Total Expense ($000)**: 22786 **Payroll Expense ($000)**: 8708 **Personnel**: 202

HAMPTON—Hampton City County

☒ **HAMPTON VETERANS AFFAIRS MEDICAL CENTER**, 100 Emancipation Drive, Zip 23667–0001; tel. 757/722–9961, (Nonreporting) **A**1 3 5 **S** Department of Veterans Affairs, Washington, DC
Primary Contact: Taquisa Simmons, Interim Director
COO: Lorraine B Price, Associate Director
CFO: Terry Grew, Chief Business Office
CMO: Val Gibberman, M.D., Acting Chief of Staff
CIO: Cary Parks, Chief Information Resource Management
Web address: www.hampton.va.gov/
Control: Veterans Affairs, Government, federal **Service**: General medical and surgical

Staffed Beds: 451

★ **SENTARA CAREPLEX HOSPITAL (490093)**, 3000 Coliseum Drive, Zip 23666–5963; tel. 757/736–1000, **A**2 3 5 10 **F**3 8 11 12 13 15 18 20 22 26 28 29 30 31 33 34 35 36 37 38 39 40 41 42 44 45 46 47 48 49 51 54 56 57 58 59 60 61 63 64 68 70 71 74 75 76 77 78 79 80 81 82 83 84 85 86 87 91 92 93 95 96 100 101 107 110 111 113 117 118 119 120 126 129 130 131 134 135 141 146 147 148 149 154 156 **S** Sentara Healthcare, Norfolk, VA
Primary Contact: Kirkpatrick Conley, President
COO: Rita A. Bunch, M.P.H., FACHE, Vice President of Operations
CFO: Cheryl Larner, Chief Financial Officer
CMO: Arthur Greene, M.D., Vice President Medical Affairs
CIO: Thomas Ewing, Director Information Technology
CHR: David Kidd, Manager Human Resources
Web address: www.sentara.com
Control: Other not–for–profit (including NFP Corporation) **Service**: General medical and surgical

Staffed Beds: 169 **Admissions**: 8798 **Census**: 112 **Outpatient Visits**: 422516 **Births**: 347 **Total Expense ($000)**: 212988 **Payroll Expense ($000)**: 83180 **Personnel**: 1432

☒ **U. S. AIR FORCE HOSPITAL**, 77 Nealy Avenue, Zip 23665–2040; tel. 757/764–6969, (Nonreporting) **A**1 3 **S** Department of the Air Force, Washington, DC
Primary Contact: Colonel Susan Pietrykowski, Commander
COO: Colonel Michael Dietz, Administrator
CFO: Major Steven Dadd, Flight Commander Resource Management
CMO: Colonel Paul Gourley, M.D., Chief Hospital Services
CIO: Major Merlinda Vergonio, Chief Information Management and Technology
CHR: Major Steven Dadd, Flight Commander Resource Management
CNO: Colonel Marlene Kerchenski, Chief Nurse
Web address: www.jble.af.mil
Control: Department of Defense, Government, federal **Service**: General medical and surgical

Staffed Beds: 65

HARRISONBURG—Harrisonburg City County

★ ⇑ **SENTARA RMH MEDICAL CENTER (490004)**, 2010 Health Campus Drive, Zip 22801–3293; tel. 540/689–1000, **A**2 5 10 21 **F**3 5 8 11 12 13 15 17 18 20 22 24 26 28 29 30 31 32 34 35 36 41 44 45 46 47 48 49 50 53 54 55 56 57 59 60 61 63 64 65 66 67 68 70 71 73 74 75 76 77 78 79 81 82 84 85 86 87 89 91 92 93 97 98 100 102 104 105 107 108 110 111 115 116 117 118 119 120 121 129 130 131 132 135 141 145 146 147 148 149 152 153 156 157 **S** Sentara Healthcare, Norfolk, VA
Primary Contact: Douglas J. Moyer, President
COO: Richard L Haushalter, Senior Vice President Operations and Chief Operating Officer
CFO: Stewart R Nelson, Vice President and Chief Financial Officer
CMO: Susan McDonald, Vice President, Medical Affairs
CNO: Donna S Hahn, R.N., Vice President Acute Care and Chief Nurse Executive
Web address: www.rmhonline.com
Control: Other not–for–profit (including NFP Corporation) **Service**: General medical and surgical

Staffed Beds: 244 **Admissions**: 13763 **Census**: 145 **Outpatient Visits**: 719253 **Births**: 1865 **Total Expense ($000)**: 332431 **Payroll Expense ($000)**: 134218 **Personnel**: 2152

VA

Many Facility Codes have changed. Please refer to the AHA Guide Code Chart.   © 2019 AHA Guide

HAYMARKET—Prince William County

☒ **NOVANT HEALTH UVA HEALTH SYSTEM HAYMARKET MEDICAL CENTER (490144)**, 15225 Heathcote Boulevard, Zip 20155–4023, Mailing Address: 14535 John Marshall Hwy, Gainesville, Zip 20155–4023; tel. 571/284–1000, (Nonreporting) **A**1 10 **S** Novant Health, Winston Salem, NC
Primary Contact: Stephen Smith, President and Chief Operating Officer
CFO: Charles Coder, Vice President
CMO: Doug Wall, M.D., Vice President of Medical Affairs
CIO: David B Garrett, Senior Vice President and Chief Information Officer
CHR: Tracy Bowers, Vice President Human Resources and Administrative Services
CNO: Maggie C Conklin, M.P.H., Interim Chief Nursing Officer
Web address: www.novanthealth.org
Control: Other not–for–profit (including NFP Corporation) **Service:** General medical and surgical

Staffed Beds: 18

HOPEWELL—Hopewell City County

☒ **JOHN RANDOLPH MEDICAL CENTER (490020)**, 411 West Randolph Road, Zip 23860–2938; tel. 804/541–1600, (Nonreporting) **A**1 2 10 **S** HCA Healthcare, Nashville, TN
Primary Contact: Joseph Mazzo, Chief Executive Officer
CFO: Jennifer Honaker, Chief Financial Officer
CHR: MaDena DuChemin, Assistant Administrator Human Resources
Web address: www.johnrandolphmed.com
Control: Corporation, Investor–owned (for–profit) **Service:** General medical and surgical

Staffed Beds: 112

HOT SPRINGS—Bath County

☒ **BATH COMMUNITY HOSPITAL (491300)**, 106 Park Drive, Zip 24445–2921, Mailing Address: P.O. Box Z, Zip 24445–0750; tel. 540/839–7000, (Nonreporting) **A**1 10 18
Primary Contact: Kathy Landreth, Chief Executive Officer
COO: Mitzi Grey, Chief Operating Officer
CMO: James Redington, M.D., Chief of Staff
CIO: Tracy Bartley, Manager Information Technology
CHR: Patricia Foutz, Director Human Resources
CNO: Kyna Moore, R.N., Director of Nursing
Web address: www.https://bathhospital.org
Control: Other not–for–profit (including NFP Corporation) **Service:** General medical and surgical

Staffed Beds: 25

KILMARNOCK—Lancaster County

☐ **RAPPAHANNOCK GENERAL HOSPITAL (491308)**, 101 Harris Drive, Zip 22482–3880, Mailing Address: P.O. Box 1449, Zip 22482–1449; tel. 804/435–8000, (Nonreporting) **A**1 10 18 **S** Bon Secours Mercy Health, Marriottsville, MD
Primary Contact: Chris Accashian, Chief Executive Officer
Web address: www.https://bonsecours.com/richmond/find-a-facility/rappahannock-general-hospital
Control: Church operated **Service:** General medical and surgical

Staffed Beds: 35

LEBANON—Russell County

☐ **RUSSELL COUNTY MEDICAL CENTER (490002)**, 58 Carroll Street, Zip 24266, Mailing Address: P.O. Box 3600, Zip 24266–0200; tel. 276/883–8000, **A**1 5 10 **F**3 11 15 28 29 30 31 34 35 40 44 45 54 56 57 59 63 64 65 68 70 75 77 78 79 81 85 93 97 98 100 101 102 104 107 108 110 111 114 118 119 127 129 130 133 135 146 147 148 154 **S** Ballad Health, Johnson City, TN
Primary Contact: Stephen K. Givens, Assistant Vice President and Administrator
CMO: Brian Condit, M.D., Vice President Chief Medical Officer, Virginia Operations Medical Staff Services
CHR: Beth Hill, Director Human Resources
CNO: Greta M. Morrison, Assistant Chief Nursing Officer
Web address: www.mountainstateshealth.com/rcmc
Control: Other not–for–profit (including NFP Corporation) **Service:** General medical and surgical

Staffed Beds: 78 **Admissions:** 1543 **Census:** 20 **Outpatient Visits:** 34436 **Births:** 0 **Total Expense ($000):** 25171 **Payroll Expense ($000):** 8342 **Personnel:** 467

LEESBURG—Loudoun County

☒ **INOVA LOUDOUN HOSPITAL (490043)**, 44045 Riverside Parkway, Zip 20176–5101, Mailing Address: P.O. Box 6000, Zip 20177–0600; tel. 703/858–6000, (Total facility includes 100 beds in nursing home–type unit) **A**1 2 5 10 **F**3 5 11 13 14 15 18 20 22 26 28 29 30 31 34 35 37 38 39 40 41 42 43 44 45 48 49 50 54 55 56 57 58 59 60 61 63 64 65 66 67 68 70 71 72 74 75 76 77 78 79 80 81 82 84 85 86 87 89 91 92 93 94 96 98 100 101 102 103 104 105 107 108 110 111 114 115 118 119 120 121 123 126 128 130 131 132 135 145 146 147 148 149 154 156 157 **S** Inova Health System, Falls Church, VA
Primary Contact: Deborah Addo, Chief Executive Officer
CFO: William Bane, Chief Financial Officer
CMO: Christopher Chiantella, M.D., Chief Medical Officer
CHR: Sarah Pavik, Director Human Resources and Guest Services
CNO: Elizabeth Dugan, Ph.D., R.N., MSN, Chief Nursing Officer
Web address: www.inova.org
Control: Other not–for–profit (including NFP Corporation) **Service:** General medical and surgical

Staffed Beds: 279 **Admissions:** 12784 **Census:** 224 **Outpatient Visits:** 149793 **Births:** 2257 **Total Expense ($000):** 294887 **Payroll Expense ($000):** 101165 **Personnel:** 1612

LEXINGTON—Lexington City County

☒ **CARILION STONEWALL JACKSON HOSPITAL (491304)**, 1 Health Circle, Zip 24450–2492; tel. 540/458–3300, **A**1 3 10 18 **F**3 8 11 15 18 28 29 34 35 40 45 50 53 56 57 59 65 68 70 75 77 79 81 85 87 91 93 97 107 108 110 111 115 119 127 129 130 131 132 133 135 146 148 149 **S** Carilion Clinic, Roanoke, VA
Primary Contact: Greg T. Madsen, Chief Executive Officer
CMO: Lyle McClung, M.D., Chief of Staff
Web address: www.carilionclinic.org
Control: Other not–for–profit (including NFP Corporation) **Service:** General medical and surgical

Staffed Beds: 15 **Admissions:** 1210 **Census:** 13 **Outpatient Visits:** 29561 **Births:** 1 **Total Expense ($000):** 35078 **Payroll Expense ($000):** 13116 **Personnel:** 205

LOW MOOR—Alleghany County

☒ **LEWISGALE HOSPITAL ALLEGHANY (490126)**, One ARH Lane, Zip 24457, Mailing Address: P.O. Box 7, Zip 24457–0007; tel. 540/862–6011, (Nonreporting) **A**1 5 10 20 **S** HCA Healthcare, Nashville, TN
Primary Contact: William Windham, Chief Executive Officer
CMO: Michele Ballou, M.D., Chief Medical Staff
CIO: Jeffrey Steelman, Director Information Systems
CHR: Bernard M Campbell, Administrator Human Resources
CNO: Robin Broughman, R.N., Ph.D., Chief Nursing Officer
Web address: www.alleghanyregional.com
Control: Corporation, Investor–owned (for–profit) **Service:** General medical and surgical

Staffed Beds: 146

LURAY—Page County

☒ **PAGE MEMORIAL HOSPITAL (491307)**, 200 Memorial Drive, Zip 22835–1005; tel. 540/743–4561, **A**1 10 18 **F**3 7 8 11 15 28 29 30 34 35 40 53 56 57 59 60 64 66 68 69 74 75 77 79 81 85 93 107 108 110 111 114 119 127 129 130 133 135 143 146 148 154 155 156 **S** Valley Health System, Winchester, VA
Primary Contact: N Travis. Clark, President
CFO: Phillip Graybeal, CPA, Chief Financial Officer
Web address: www.valleyhealthlink.com/page
Control: Other not–for–profit (including NFP Corporation) **Service:** General medical and surgical

Staffed Beds: 25 **Admissions:** 465 **Census:** 10 **Outpatient Visits:** 86186 **Births:** 0 **Total Expense ($000):** 33768 **Payroll Expense ($000):** 14586 **Personnel:** 194

LYNCHBURG—Lynchburg City County

CENTRA HEALTH See Centra Lynchburg General Hospital

VA

Hospital, Medicare Provider Number, Address, Telephone, Approval, Facility, and Physician Codes, Health Care System

★ American Hospital Association (AHA) membership
☐ The Joint Commission accreditation
○ Healthcare Facilities Accreditation Program
◇ DNV Healthcare Inc. accreditation
⇧ Center for Improvement in Healthcare Quality Accreditation
△ Commission on Accreditation of Rehabilitation Facilities (CARF) accreditation

✠ **CENTRA LYNCHBURG GENERAL HOSPITAL (490021)**, 1901 Tate Springs Road, Zip 24501–1109; tel. 434/200–4700, (Includes CENTRA VIRGINIA BAPTIST HOSPITAL, 3300 Rivermont Avenue, Lynchburg, Virginia, Zip 24503–2053; tel. 434/200–4000; LYNCHBURG GENERAL HOSPITAL, 1901 Tate Springs Road, Lynchburg, Virginia, Zip 24501–1167; tel. 434/200–3000) (Total facility includes 413 beds in nursing home–type unit) **A**1 2 3 5 10 **F**2 3 4 5 7 10 11 12 13 15 17 18 19 20 22 24 26 28 29 30 31 34 35 37 38 40 42 43 44 45 46 47 48 49 50 53 54 55 56 57 59 60 61 62 63 64 67 68 70 71 72 73 74 75 76 77 78 79 80 81 82 84 85 86 87 89 90 91 92 93 94 96 98 99 100 101 102 103 104 105 106 107 108 110 111 114 115 119 120 121 123 124 125 126 127 128 129 130 131 132 133 135 143 144 146 147 148 149 152 155 **S** Centra Health, Inc., Lynchburg, VA
Primary Contact: Michael Elliott, Acting Chief Executive Officer
CFO: Lewis C Addison, Senior Vice President and Chief Financial Officer
CMO: Chalmers Nunn, M.D., Chief Medical Officer and Senior Vice President
CIO: Ben Clark, Vice President and Chief Information Officer
CHR: Jan Walker, Director Human Resources
Web address: www.centrahealth.com
Control: Other not–for–profit (including NFP Corporation) **Service**: General medical and surgical

Staffed Beds: 1029 **Admissions**: 30854 **Census**: 754 **Outpatient Visits**: 208495 **Births**: 2663 **Total Expense ($000)**: 789538 **Payroll Expense ($000)**: 296317 **Personnel**: 4858

CENTRA SPECIALTY HOSPITAL (492010), 3300 Rivermont Avenue, Zip 24503–2030; tel. 434/200–1799, (Nonreporting) **A**10
Primary Contact: Kay Bowling, Chief Executive Officer
Control: Partnership, Investor–owned (for–profit) **Service**: Acute long–term care hospital

Staffed Beds: 36

MADISON HEIGHTS—Amherst County

CENTRAL VIRGINIA TRAINING CENTER (490108), 210 East Colony Road, Zip 24572–2005, Mailing Address: P.O. Box 1098, Lynchburg, Zip 24505–1098; tel. 434/947–6326, (Nonreporting) **S** Virginia Department of Mental Health, Richmond, VA
Primary Contact: David Cole, Assistant Director of Administration, Chief Financial Officer, Department of Behavioral Health and D
CFO: Charles Felmlee, Assistant Director Fiscal Services
CMO: Balraj Bawa, M.D., Assistant Director Medical Services
CHR: Burchkhard Blob, Manager Human Resources
Web address: www.cvtc.dmhmrsas.virginia.gov/
Control: State, Government, nonfederal **Service**: Intellectual disabilities

Staffed Beds: 1112

MANASSAS—Manassas City County

✠ **NOVANT HEALTH UVA HEALTH SYSTEM PRINCE WILLIAM MEDICAL CENTER (490045)**, 8700 Sudley Road, Zip 20110–4418, Mailing Address: P.O. Box 2610, Zip 20108–0867; tel. 703/369–8000, (Nonreporting) **A**1 2 10 **S** Novant Health, Winston Salem, NC
Primary Contact: Stephen Smith, President and Chief Operating Officer
CFO: Charles Coder, Vice President
CMO: Doug Wall, M.D., Vice President Medical Affairs
CIO: David B Garrett, Senior Vice President and Chief Information Officer
CHR: Tracy Bowers, Vice President Human Resources and Administrative Services
CNO: Maggie C Conklin, M.P.H., Interim Chief Nurse Officer
Web address: www.pwhs.org
Control: Other not–for–profit (including NFP Corporation) **Service**: General medical and surgical

Staffed Beds: 87

MARION—Smyth County

☐ **SMYTH COUNTY COMMUNITY HOSPITAL (490038)**, 245 Medical Park Drive, Zip 24354, Mailing Address: P.O. Box 880, Zip 24354–0880; tel. 276/378–1000, (Total facility includes 109 beds in nursing home–type unit) **A**1 5 10 **F**3 11 15 18 28 29 30 31 34 35 40 45 50 51 54 57 59 62 64 67 68 70 75 77 78 79 81 85 87 90 93 97 107 110 111 115 118 119 127 128 129 131 132 133 135 144 146 147 148 149 **S** Ballad Health, Johnson City, TN
Primary Contact: James E. Tyler, Chief Executive Officer
CHR: Sue Henderson, Human Resource Manager
CNO: Ethan Collins, R.N., Chief Nursing Officer
Web address: www.msha.com/scch
Control: Other not–for–profit (including NFP Corporation) **Service**: General medical and surgical

Staffed Beds: 153 **Admissions**: 1422 **Census**: 26 **Outpatient Visits**: 58738 **Births**: 0 **Total Expense ($000)**: 36837 **Payroll Expense ($000)**: 12327 **Personnel**: 774

☐ **SOUTHWESTERN VIRGINIA MENTAL HEALTH INSTITUTE (490105)**, 340 Bagley Circle, Zip 24354–3390; tel. 276/783–1200, (Nonreporting) **A**1 10 **S** Virginia Department of Mental Health, Richmond, VA
Primary Contact: Cynthia McClaskey, Ph.D., Director
CIO: Kim Ratliff, Director Health Information Management
Web address: www.swvmhi.dmhmrsas.virginia.gov/
Control: State, Government, nonfederal **Service**: Psychiatric

Staffed Beds: 166

MARTINSVILLE—Martinsville City County

★ **SOVAH HEALTH-MARTINSVILLE (490079)**, 320 Hospital Drive, Zip 24112–1981, Mailing Address: P.O. Box 4788, Zip 24115–4788; tel. 276/666–7200, (Nonreporting) **A**2 5 19 **S** LifePoint Health, Brentwood, TN
Primary Contact: Alan Larson, Market President
CFO: Brandy Hanners, Chief Financial Officer
CIO: Jeff Butker, Chief Information Officer
CHR: Sherry Schofield, Director Human Resources
CNO: Michael Pittman, Chief Nursing Officer
Web address: www.martinsvillehospital.com
Control: Corporation, Investor–owned (for–profit) **Service**: General medical and surgical

Staffed Beds: 150

MECHANICSVILLE—Hanover County

☐ **BON SECOURS MEMORIAL REGIONAL MEDICAL CENTER (490069)**, 8260 Atlee Road, Zip 23116–1844; tel. 804/764–6000, **A**1 2 3 5 10 **F**3 8 11 13 15 17 18 20 22 24 26 28 29 30 31 34 35 37 38 40 44 45 48 49 50 57 58 59 61 62 63 64 70 72 74 76 77 78 79 81 84 85 86 87 92 93 96 102 104 107 108 110 111 114 115 117 118 119 124 126 129 130 146 147 148 149 154 **S** Bon Secours Mercy Health, Marriottsville, MD
Primary Contact: Mark M. Gordon, Chief Executive Officer
COO: Gary A. Welch, Assistant to the Chief Executive Officer and Administrative Director Support Systems
CFO: Stephan F Quiriconi, Vice President Finance
CMO: Sunil K. Sinha, M.D., FACHE, Chief Medical Officer
CIO: Gwen Harding, Site Manager Information Systems
CHR: Rebecca Kamguia, Administrative Director Human Resources
CNO: Jill M Kennedy, R.N., Vice President, Ambulatory Patient Care Services
Web address: www.bonsecours.com
Control: Church operated, Nongovernment, not–for–profit **Service**: General medical and surgical

Staffed Beds: 251 **Admissions**: 13296 **Census**: 177 **Outpatient Visits**: 134717 **Births**: 1188 **Total Expense ($000)**: 368894 **Payroll Expense ($000)**: 109452 **Personnel**: 1588

☐ **SHELTERING ARMS REHABILITATION HOSPITAL (493025)**, 8254 Atlee Road, Zip 23116–1844; tel. 804/764–1000, **A**1 3 10 **F**3 29 30 34 35 50 53 54 57 58 59 64 74 75 77 79 82 86 87 90 91 92 93 94 95 96 104 130 131 132 146 147 148
Primary Contact: Mary A. Zweifel, MS, President and Chief Executive Officer
COO: Amy J Showalter, R.N., Chief Operating Officer
CFO: James Litsinger, CPA, Vice President and Chief Financial Officer
CMO: Hillary Hawkins, M.D., Medical Director
CIO: Chris Sorenson, Chief Information Officer
CHR: Ellen B Vance, Chief Human Resource Officer
CNO: Sandra Eyler, MS, Chief Nursing Officer
Web address: www.shelteringarms.com
Control: Other not–for–profit (including NFP Corporation) **Service**: Rehabilitation

Staffed Beds: 40 **Admissions**: 920 **Census**: 38 **Outpatient Visits**: 84121 **Births**: 0 **Total Expense ($000)**: 19287 **Payroll Expense ($000)**: 12662 **Personnel**: 123

MIDLOTHIAN—Chesterfield County

☐ **BON SECOURS ST. FRANCIS MEDICAL CENTER (490136)**, 13710 St Francis Boulevard, Zip 23114–3267; tel. 804/594–7300, (Nonreporting) **A**1 2 3 5 10 **S** Bon Secours Mercy Health, Marriottsville, MD
Primary Contact: Chris Accashian, Chief Executive Officer
COO: Toni R Ardabell, Chief Executive Officer, Bon Secours Virginia
CFO: Stephan F Quiriconi, Vice President, Finance
CMO: Michael Menen, M.D., Chief Medical Officer
CIO: Terri Spence, Vice President and Regional Chief Information Officer
CNO: Barbara L. Gesme, MSN, Vice President Patient Care Services & Chief Nurse Executive
Web address: www.bonsecours.com/sfmc/default.asp
Control: Church operated **Service**: General medical and surgical

Staffed Beds: 135

Many Facility Codes have changed. Please refer to the AHA Guide Code Chart.   © 2019 AHA Guide

VA

☐ **SHELTERING ARMS HOSPITAL SOUTH (493030)**, 13700 St. Francis Boulevard, Suite 400, Zip 23114–3222; tel. 804/764–1000, **A**1 5 10 **F**3 29 30 34 35 50 54 56 57 58 59 64 74 75 77 79 82 84 86 87 90 91 92 93 94 95 96 100 104 130 131 132 146 148
Primary Contact: Mary A. Zweifel, MS, President and Chief Executive Officer
COO: Amy J Showalter, R.N., Chief Operating Officer
CFO: James Litsinger, CPA, Chief Operating Officer
CMO: Timothy Silver, M.D., Medical Director, SAH-S
CIO: Chris Sorenson, Chief Health Information Officer
CHR: Ellen B Vance, Chief Human Resources Officer
CNO: Sandra Eyler, MS, Chief Nursing Officer
Web address: www.shelteringarms.com
Control: Other not–for–profit (including NFP Corporation) **Service:** Rehabilitation

Staffed Beds: 28 **Admissions:** 594 **Census:** 22 **Outpatient Visits:** 6244
Births: 0 **Total Expense ($000):** 8644 **Payroll Expense ($000):** 4043
Personnel: 76

NEW KENT—New Kent County

☐ **CUMBERLAND HOSPITAL FOR CHILDREN AND ADOLESCENTS (493300)**, 9407 Cumberland Road, Zip 23124–2029; tel. 804/966–2242, **A**1 10 **F**12 28 29 32 35 38 44 50 53 57 59 68 74 75 77 86 87 89 91 96 98 99 100 101 106 130 132 143 148 154 **S** Universal Health Services, Inc., King of Prussia, PA
Primary Contact: Patrice Gay. Brooks, Chief Executive Officer
CFO: Joanne Rial, Chief Financial Officer
CMO: Daniel N Davidow, M.D., Medical Director
CIO: Leslie Bowery, Director of Standards and Compliance
CHR: Kim Ivey, Director of Human Resources
CNO: Paula Roberts, Chief Nursing Officer
Web address: www.cumberlandhospital.com
Control: Corporation, Investor–owned (for–profit) **Service:** Children's general medical and surgical

Staffed Beds: 118 **Admissions:** 243 **Census:** 86 **Outpatient Visits:** 0
Births: 0

NEWPORT NEWS—Newport News City County

☐ **BON SECOURS MARY IMMACULATE HOSPITAL (490041)**, 2 Bernardine Drive, Zip 23602–4499; tel. 757/886–6000, (Nonreporting) **A**1 10 **S** Bon Secours Mercy Health, Marriottsville, MD
Primary Contact: Darlene Stephenson, Chief Executive Officer
COO: Darlene Stephenson, Vice President Operations
CIO: Terri Spence, Vice President Information Services
CHR: Vickie Witcher Humphries, Vice President Human Resources
Web address: www.bonsecourshampton roads.com
Control: Church operated **Service:** General medical and surgical

Staffed Beds: 238

★ **COASTAL VIRGINIA REHABILITATION (493027)**, 245 Chesapeake Avenue, Zip 23607–6038; tel. 757/928–8000, **A**10 **F**34 57 87 90 91 94 96 148 **S** Select Medical Corporation, Mechanicsburg, PA
Primary Contact: Daniel Ballin, Administrator
COO: William B Downey, President and Chief Executive Officer
CFO: Bill Austin, Senior Vice President of Finance
CMO: C Renee Moss, M.D., Chief Medical Officer
CIO: Dennis Loftis, Senior Vice President of Information Systems
CHR: Rob Cuthrell, Director of Human Resources
CNO: Debbie Outlaw, R.N., Director Patient Care Services
Web address: www.riversideonline.com/rri/index.cfm
Control: Partnership, Investor–owned (for–profit) **Service:** Rehabilitation

Staffed Beds: 50 **Admissions:** 830 **Census:** 30 **Outpatient Visits:** 0
Births: 0

NEWPORT NEWS BEHAVIORAL HEALTH CENTER, 17579 Warwick Boulevard, Zip 23603–1343; tel. 757/888–0400, **F**98 99 100 106
Primary Contact: Paul Kirkham, Chief Executive Officer
COO: Paul Kirkham, Chief Executive Officer
CFO: Joe Brooks, Chief Financial Officer
CMO: Avtar Dhillon, M.D., Medical Director
CIO: Terry Rethamel, Director of Support Services
CHR: Shawn Marston, Director Human Resources
CNO: Karen Bruce, Director of Nursing
Web address: www.newportnewsbhc.com/
Control: Corporation, Investor–owned (for–profit) **Service:** Children's hospital psychiatric

Staffed Beds: 132 **Admissions:** 909 **Census:** 105 **Outpatient Visits:** 0
Births: 0 **Total Expense ($000):** 19823 **Payroll Expense ($000):** 8928
Personnel: 205

⇑ **RIVERSIDE REGIONAL MEDICAL CENTER (490052)**, 500 J Clyde Morris Boulevard, Zip 23601–1929; tel. 757/594–2000, (Includes RIVERSIDE BEHAVIORAL HEALTH CENTER, 2244 Executive Drive, Hampton, Virginia, Zip 23666–2430; tel. 757/827–1001; Debra Campbell, R.N., Administrator) **A**2 3 5 10 21 **F**3 4 8 13 15 18 20 22 24 26 28 30 31 36 38 40 43 44 45 49 50 51 54 56 58 60 64 70 72 74 75 76 77 78 79 81 82 84 85 86 87 91 93 94 96 98 99 100 102 103 107 108 110 111 114 115 116 117 118 119 120 121 123 124 126 129 130 131 132 141 143 146 148 149 154 **S** Riverside Health System, Newport News, VA
Primary Contact: Michael J. Doucette, Senior Vice President and Administrator
COO: William B Downey, Chief Operating Officer
CFO: Wade Broughman, Executive Vice President and Chief Financial Officer
CMO: Barry L Gross, M.D., Executive Vice President and Chief Medical Officer
CIO: Dennis Loftis, Senior Vice President and Chief Information Officer
CHR: Sally Hartman, Senior Vice President
CNO: Candice R. Carroll, Nurse Executive
Web address: www.https://www.riversideonline.com/rrmc/index.cfm
Control: Other not–for–profit (including NFP Corporation) **Service:** General medical and surgical

Staffed Beds: 307 **Admissions:** 17875 **Census:** 252 **Outpatient Visits:** 118803 **Births:** 2289 **Total Expense ($000):** 487749 **Payroll Expense ($000):** 141819 **Personnel:** 2111

★ ⇑ **SELECT SPECIALTY HOSPITAL HAMPTON ROADS (492008)**, 245 Chesapeake Avenue, Zip 23607–6038; tel. 757/534–5000, (Nonreporting) **A**10 21 **S** Select Medical Corporation, Mechanicsburg, PA
Primary Contact: Phillip L. Wright, Chief Executive Officer
Web address: www.hamptonroadsspecialtyhospital.com
Control: Other not–for–profit (including NFP Corporation) **Service:** Acute long–term care hospital

Staffed Beds: 25

NORFOLK—Norfolk City County

☐ **BON SECOURS-DEPAUL MEDICAL CENTER (490011)**, 150 Kingsley Lane, Zip 23505–4650; tel. 757/889–5000, (Nonreporting) **A**1 2 3 5 10 **S** Bon Secours Mercy Health, Marriottsville, MD
Primary Contact: Paul Gaden, Chief Executive Officer
CFO: Charmaine Rochester, Vice President Finance
CIO: Lynne Zultanky, Director Corporate Communications and Media Relations
CHR: Vickie Witcher Humphries, Vice President Human Resources
CNO: Michael J. Bratton, R.N., Chief Nurse Executive and Vice President Patient Care Services
Web address: www.bonsecourshamptonroads.com
Control: Church operated **Service:** General medical and surgical

Staffed Beds: 204

☐ ⇑ **CHILDREN'S HOSPITAL OF THE KING'S DAUGHTERS (493301)**, 601 Children's Lane, Zip 23507–1910; tel. 757/668–7000, **A**1 3 5 10 21 **F**3 7 8 9 12 16 17 19 21 23 25 27 29 30 31 32 34 35 39 40 41 44 45 48 49 50 55 57 58 59 60 61 64 65 66 68 72 73 74 75 77 78 79 80 81 82 84 85 86 87 88 89 90 91 92 93 97 99 100 102 107 108 111 115 118 119 129 130 131 132 134 138 144 145 146 148 149 153 154 156
Primary Contact: James D. Dahling, President and Chief Executive Officer
COO: John P Harding, Chief Operating Officer
CFO: Dennis Ryan, Senior Vice President and Chief Financial Officer
CMO: Chris Foley, Chief of Medicine
CIO: Deborah Barnes, Vice President and Chief Information Officer
CHR: Paul J Morlock, FACHE, Vice President Human Resources and Occupational Health
CNO: Karen Mitchell, Vice President Patient Care Services
Web address: www.chkd.org
Control: Other not–for–profit (including NFP Corporation) **Service:** Children's general medical and surgical

Staffed Beds: 185 **Admissions:** 5144 **Census:** 124 **Outpatient Visits:** 313857 **Births:** 0 **Total Expense ($000):** 363341 **Payroll Expense ($000):** 146358 **Personnel:** 2492

HOSPITAL FOR EXTENDED RECOVERY (492007), 600 Gresham Drive, Suite 700, Zip 23507–1904; tel. 757/388–1700, (Nonreporting) **A**10
Primary Contact: Aimee Vergara, Chief Executive Officer
Control: Other not–for–profit (including NFP Corporation) **Service:** Acute long–term care hospital

Staffed Beds: 25

VA

Hospital, Medicare Provider Number, Address, Telephone, Approval, Facility, and Physician Codes, Health Care System

★ American Hospital Association (AHA) membership
☐ The Joint Commission accreditation
○ Healthcare Facilities Accreditation Program
◇ DNV Healthcare Inc. accreditation
⇑ Center for Improvement in Healthcare Quality Accreditation
△ Commission on Accreditation of Rehabilitation Facilities (CARF) accreditation

☐ **KEMPSVILLE CENTER FOR BEHAVIORAL HEALTH**, 860 Kempsville Road,
Zip 23502–3980; tel. 757/461–4565, (Nonreporting) **A**1
Primary Contact: Jaime Fernandez, Chief Executive Officer
Control: Corporation, Investor–owned (for–profit) **Service**: Psychiatric

> **Staffed Beds**: 77

LAKE TAYLOR TRANSITIONAL CARE HOSPITAL (492001), 1309 Kempsville
Road, Zip 23502–2286; tel. 757/461–5001, (Nonreporting) **A**3 5 10
Primary Contact: Thomas J. Orsini, President and Chief Executive Officer
CFO: Robert W Fogg, Director Finance
CMO: Kevin Murray, M.D., Director Medical Services
CIO: Mark Davis, Director Information Systems
CHR: LeeAnn Lowman, Director Human Resources
Web address: www.laketaylor.org
Control: Hospital district or authority, Government, nonfederal **Service**: Acute
long–term care hospital

> **Staffed Beds**: 284

★ ⇑ **SENTARA LEIGH HOSPITAL (490046)**, 830 Kempsville Road,
Zip 23502–3920; tel. 757/261–6000, **A**2 3 5 10 21 **F**3 8 9 11 12 13 15 18 20
22 26 28 29 30 31 33 34 35 36 37 38 39 41 44 45 46 47 48 49 50 53 56 57
58 59 60 61 63 64 65 68 70 71 74 75 76 77 78 79 80 81 82 84 85 86 87 91
92 93 94 96 97 100 102 107 108 110 111 114 119 126 130 131 132 135
141 146 147 148 149 154 156 **S** Sentara Healthcare, Norfolk, VA
Primary Contact: Joanne Inman, President
COO: Howard P. Kern, President and Chief Operating Officer
CFO: Robert Broermann, Senior Vice President and Chief Financial Officer
CMO: Terry Gilliland, M.D., Chief Medical Officer
CIO: Bert Reese, Chief Information Officer
CHR: Michael V Taylor, Senior Vice President Human Resources
CNO: Genemarie McGee, R.N., MS, Chief Nursing Officer
Web address: www.sentara.com
Control: Other not–for–profit (including NFP Corporation) **Service**: General
medical and surgical

> **Staffed Beds**: 250 **Admissions**: 17404 **Census**: 207 **Outpatient
> Visits**: 478936 **Births**: 2158 **Total Expense ($000)**: 300569 **Payroll
> Expense ($000)**: 115494 **Personnel**: 1901

★ ⇑ **SENTARA NORFOLK GENERAL HOSPITAL (490007)**, 600 Gresham Drive,
Zip 23507–1904; tel. 757/388–3000, **A**2 3 5 8 10 21 **F**3 11 12 13 15 16 17
18 20 22 24 26 28 29 30 31 34 35 36 37 38 39 40 41 43 44 45 46 47 49 50
51 52 53 54 55 56 57 58 59 60 61 63 64 65 66 68 70 71 72 74 75 76 77 78
79 80 81 82 84 85 86 87 90 91 92 93 94 96 97 98 100 101 102 103 107 108
110 111 112 114 115 116 117 118 119 120 121 123 124 126 129 130 131
132 135 136 137 138 141 142 145 146 147 148 149 150 152 154 155 156
157 **S** Sentara Healthcare, Norfolk, VA
Primary Contact: Carolyn Carpenter, FACHE, President
CFO: Robert Broermann, Senior Vice President and Chief Financial Officer
CIO: Bert Reese, Chief Information Officer
Web address: www.sentara.com
Control: Other not–for–profit (including NFP Corporation) **Service**: General
medical and surgical

> **Staffed Beds**: 483 **Admissions**: 25505 **Census**: 421 **Outpatient
> Visits**: 1230357 **Births**: 3008 **Total Expense ($000)**: 910740 **Payroll
> Expense ($000)**: 258854 **Personnel**: 3893

NORTON—Norton City County

★ **MOUNTAIN VIEW REGIONAL MEDICAL CENTER (490027)**, 310 Third Street
NE, Zip 24273–1137; tel. 276/679–9100, (Total facility includes 44 beds in
nursing home–type unit) **F**3 11 15 28 29 40 45 50 59 70 75 77 81 85 87 93
107 108 110 111 115 119 128 130 135 **S** Ballad Health, Johnson City, TN
Primary Contact: Mark T. Leonard, Interim Chief Executive Officer
CFO: Regina Day, Executive Director Finance
CMO: Michael Ketcham, Chief Medical Officer
CHR: Bobby Collins, Director Human Resources
Web address: www.wellmont.org
Control: Other not–for–profit (including NFP Corporation) **Service**: General
medical and surgical

> **Staffed Beds**: 70 **Admissions**: 1282 **Census**: 40 **Outpatient Visits**: 44452
> **Births**: 0 **Total Expense ($000)**: 23233 **Payroll Expense ($000)**: 6781
> **Personnel**: 120

☐ **NORTON COMMUNITY HOSPITAL (490001)**, 100 15th Street NW,
Zip 24273–1616; tel. 276/679–9600, **A**1 3 5 10 13 **F**3 11 13 15 18 28 29 30
31 32 34 35 40 45 46 51 53 55 56 57 59 62 64 65 66 68 70 75 76 77 78 79
81 87 90 93 107 108 110 111 115 116 117 118 119 129 130 131 133 135
146 147 148 154 **S** Ballad Health, Johnson City, TN
Primary Contact: Mark T. Leonard, Chief Executive Officer
CFO: Stephen Sawyer, Chief Financial Officer
CMO: Allen Mullens, M.D., Chief Medical Staff
CIO: Judy Lawson, Director Information Services
CHR: Valeri J Colyer, Director Human Resources
Web address: www.msha.com/nch
Control: Other not–for–profit (including NFP Corporation) **Service**: General
medical and surgical

> **Staffed Beds**: 70 **Admissions**: 2845 **Census**: 29 **Outpatient Visits**: 73468
> **Births**: 176 **Total Expense ($000)**: 51701 **Personnel**: 1060

ONANCOCK—Accomack County

★ ⇑ **RIVERSIDE SHORE MEMORIAL HOSPITAL (490037)**, 20480 Market Street,
Zip 23417–4309, Mailing Address: P.O. Box 430, Zip 23417; tel. 757/302–2100,
A2 3 10 20 21 **F**3 13 15 18 28 29 30 31 34 40 45 50 57 59 70 74 75 76 77
78 79 81 85 87 92 93 107 110 111 114 115 118 119 121 129 130 146 149
157 **S** Riverside Health System, Newport News, VA
Primary Contact: John Peterman, Vice President and Administrator
CFO: W William Austin Jr Senior Vice President Finance
CMO: David Jones, Service Chief
CHR: Nicole Miller, Director Human Resources
Web address: www.riversideonline.com
Control: Other not–for–profit (including NFP Corporation) **Service**: General
medical and surgical

> **Staffed Beds**: 22 **Admissions**: 2619 **Census**: 22 **Births**: 338 **Total Expense
> ($000)**: 67625 **Payroll Expense ($000)**: 21122 **Personnel**: 292

⇑ **SHORE MEMORIAL HOSPITAL** See Riverside Shore Memorial Hospital

PEARISBURG—Giles County

⊠ **CARILION GILES COMMUNITY HOSPITAL (491302)**, 159 Hartley Way,
Zip 24134–2471; tel. 540/921–6000, **A**1 5 10 18 **F**3 11 15 18 28 29 30 34 35
36 40 45 50 53 54 57 59 64 65 68 75 77 79 81 85 86 87 91 93 96 107 108
110 111 115 118 119 127 130 133 135 146 147 148 149 154 156 **S** Carilion
Clinic, Roanoke, VA
Primary Contact: William Flattery, Vice President and Administrator Western
Division
CMO: John Tamminen, M.D., President Medical Staff
CHR: Carrie Boggess, Human Resource Generalist
CNO: Veronica Stump, Director of Nursing
Web address: www.https://www.carilionclinic.org
Control: Other not–for–profit (including NFP Corporation) **Service**: General
medical and surgical

> **Staffed Beds**: 10 **Admissions**: 992 **Census**: 13 **Outpatient Visits**: 26178
> **Births**: 3 **Total Expense ($000)**: 30357 **Payroll Expense ($000)**: 11550
> **Personnel**: 196

PETERSBURG—Petersburg City County

☐ **CENTRAL STATE HOSPITAL**, 26317 West Washington Street, Zip 23803–2727,
Mailing Address: P.O. Box 4030, Zip 23803–0030; tel. 804/524–7000, **A**1 3
F29 30 35 38 75 77 87 98 101 102 106 130 132 143 149 157 **S** Virginia
Department of Mental Health, Richmond, VA
Primary Contact: Rebecca Vauter, PsyD, Facility Director
COO: Ann Bailey, Assistant Director Administration
CFO: Robert Kaufman, Director Financial Services
CMO: Ronald O Forbes, M.D., Medical Director
CIO: Jonathan Baber, Director Information Technology
CHR: Tracy Salisbury, Regional Manager Human Resources
CNO: Eva Parham, R.N., Chief Nurse Executive
Web address: www.csh.dbhds.virginia.gov
Control: State, Government, nonfederal **Service**: Psychiatric

> **Staffed Beds**: 277 **Admissions**: 1041 **Census**: 236 **Outpatient Visits**: 0
> **Births**: 0 **Total Expense ($000)**: 68819 **Payroll Expense ($000)**: 38637
> **Personnel**: 858

VA

Many Facility Codes have changed. Please refer to the AHA Guide Code Chart. © 2019 AHA Guide

⊞ **ENCOMPASS HEALTH REHABILITATION HOSPITAL OF PETERSBURG (493031)**, 95 Medical Park Boulevard, Zip 23805–9233; tel. 804/504–8100, (Nonreporting) **A**1 10 **S** Encompass Health Corporation, Birmingham, AL
Primary Contact: Louis Collier, Chief Executive Officer
Web address: www.https://www.encompasshealth.com
Control: Corporation, Investor–owned (for–profit) **Service**: Rehabilitation

Staffed Beds: 53

☐ **HIRAM W. DAVIS MEDICAL CENTER (490104)**, 26317 West Washington Street, Zip 23803–2727, Mailing Address: P.O. Box 4030, Zip 23803–0030; tel. 804/524–7420, (Nonreporting) **A**1 10 **S** Virginia Department of Mental Health, Richmond, VA
Primary Contact: Nichelle Williams, Director
CFO: Robert Kaufman, Fiscal Officer
CHR: Tracy Salisbury, Director Human Resources
Control: State, Government, nonfederal **Service**: Other specialty treatment

Staffed Beds: 10

⊞ **POPLAR SPRINGS HOSPITAL (494022)**, 350 Poplar Drive, Zip 23805–9367; tel. 804/733–6874, (Nonreporting) **A**1 10 **S** Universal Health Services, Inc., King of Prussia, PA
Primary Contact: Nelson Smith, Chief Executive Officer
COO: Rachel Beal, Chief Operating Officer
CFO: Michael Felice, Chief Financial Officer
CMO: Thresa Simon, M.D., Medical Director
CHR: Morris Mitchell, Director Human Resources
Web address: www.poplarsprings.com
Control: Corporation, Investor–owned (for–profit) **Service**: Psychiatric

Staffed Beds: 180

⊞ **SOUTHSIDE REGIONAL MEDICAL CENTER (490067)**, 200 Medical Park Boulevard, Zip 23805–9274; tel. 804/765–5000, **A**1 2 3 5 10 **F**3 12 13 15 17 18 20 22 24 26 28 29 30 31 34 35 40 42 43 45 47 49 50 54 55 56 57 59 60 64 65 70 72 74 75 76 77 78 79 81 82 85 86 87 91 92 93 96 97 98 102 107 108 110 111 114 115 119 120 121 122 123 124 126 130 131 132 135 146 147 148 149 154 156 **S** Community Health Systems, Inc., Franklin, TN
Primary Contact: Trent Nobles, Chief Executive Officer
COO: Jerad Hanlon, Chief Operating Officer
CMO: Boyd Wickizer, M.D., Jr Chief Medical Officer
CIO: Eric Synnestvedt, Director Information Technology
CHR: Irene Duskey, Director Human Resources
CNO: Beverly Bzdek Smith, Chief Nursing Officer
Web address: www.srmconline.com
Control: Corporation, Investor–owned (for–profit) **Service**: General medical and surgical

Staffed Beds: 294 Admissions: 13024 Census: 170

PORTSMOUTH—Portsmouth City County

☐ **BON SECOURS MARYVIEW MEDICAL CENTER (490017)**, 3636 High Street, Zip 23707–3270; tel. 757/398–2200, (Nonreporting) **A**1 2 3 5 10 **S** Bon Secours Mercy Health, Marriottsville, MD
Primary Contact: Paul Gaden, Chief Executive Officer
CFO: Ernest C Padden, Chief Financial Officer
CMO: Warren Austin, M.D., Vice President Medical Affairs
CIO: Terri Spence, Chief Information Officer
CHR: Vickie Witcher Humphries, Director Human Resources
CNO: Leana Fox, Interim Chief Nurse Executive
Web address: www.bonsecourshamptonroads.com
Control: Church operated **Service**: General medical and surgical

Staffed Beds: 466

⊞ **NAVAL MEDICAL CENTER**, 620 John Paul Jones Circle, Zip 23708–2197; tel. 757/953–1980, (Nonreporting) **A**1 2 3 5 **S** Bureau of Medicine and Surgery, Department of the Navy, Falls Church, VA
Primary Contact: Captain Matthew Case, MSC, USN, Executive Officer
CMO: Captain Cynthia J Gantt, Chief of Staff
CIO: Lieutenant Colonel Karen Albany, Chief Information Officer
Web address: www.nmcphc.med.navy.mil/
Control: Department of Defense, Government, federal **Service**: General medical and surgical

Staffed Beds: 274

PULASKI—Pulaski County

⊞ **LEWISGALE HOSPITAL PULASKI (490116)**, 2400 Lee Highway, Zip 24301–2326, Mailing Address: P.O. Box 759, Zip 24301–0759; tel. 540/994–8100, (Nonreporting) **A**1 2 10 **S** HCA Healthcare, Nashville, TN
Primary Contact: Sean Pressman, Chief Executive Officer
CFO: Jeff Kurcab, Chief Financial Officer
CMO: Karanita Ojomo, M.D., Chief of Staff
CIO: Diron Lane, Director Information Systems
CHR: Jana Beckner, Director Human Resources
Web address: www.lewisgale.com/
Control: Corporation, Investor–owned (for–profit) **Service**: General medical and surgical

Staffed Beds: 54

RESTON—Fairfax County

⊞ **RESTON HOSPITAL CENTER (490107)**, 1850 Town Center Parkway, Zip 20190–3219; tel. 703/689–9000, **A**1 2 10 **F**3 11 12 13 15 20 22 26 29 30 31 34 37 40 41 43 45 46 47 48 49 57 59 60 63 64 68 70 72 74 75 76 77 78 79 81 85 86 87 89 93 94 96 102 107 108 110 111 114 115 118 119 120 121 123 124 126 130 132 144 147 148 149 154 **S** HCA Healthcare, Nashville, TN
Primary Contact: John A. Deardorff, President and Chief Executive, Northern Virginia Market
COO: Jane Raymond, Vice President and Chief Operating Officer
CFO: Edward R Stojakovich, Chief Financial Officer
CMO: Walter R Zolkiwsky, M.D., Chief Medical Officer
CIO: Paresh Shah, Director Information Systems
CHR: Lesley Channell, Vice President Human Resources
CNO: Cynthia Glover, R.N., Vice President and Chief Nursing Officer
Web address: www.restonhospital.com
Control: Corporation, Investor–owned (for–profit) **Service**: General medical and surgical

Staffed Beds: 222 Admissions: 13538 Census: 139 Outpatient Visits: 96654 Births: 3388 Total Expense ($000): 221024 Payroll Expense ($000): 84614 Personnel: 793

RICHLANDS—Tazewell County

⊞ **CLINCH VALLEY MEDICAL CENTER (490060)**, 6801 Governor G C Peery Highway, Zip 24641–2194; tel. 276/596–6000, (Total facility includes 24 beds in nursing home–type unit) **A**1 5 10 **F**3 12 13 14 15 17 18 20 22 28 29 30 31 34 35 39 40 41 45 50 55 56 57 59 64 70 75 76 77 78 79 81 85 86 87 89 93 94 97 107 108 110 111 114 115 118 119 120 121 128 129 130 132 134 135 143 144 147 148 149 150 154 **S** LifePoint Health, Brentwood, TN
Primary Contact: Peter Mulkey, Chief Executive Officer
CFO: Jason Schmiedt, Chief Financial Officer
CMO: George Farrell, M.D., Chief Medical Officer
CIO: Chris Perkins, Director Information Services
CHR: John Knowles, Director Human Resources
CNO: Clint Kendall, R.N., Chief Nursing Officer
Web address: www.clinchvalleymedicalcenter.com
Control: Corporation, Investor–owned (for–profit) **Service**: General medical and surgical

Staffed Beds: 95 Admissions: 3555 Census: 40 Outpatient Visits: 96984 Births: 283 Personnel: 508

RICHMOND—Henrico County

☐ **BON SECOURS ST. MARY'S HOSPITAL (490059)**, 5801 Bremo Road, Zip 23226–1907; tel. 804/285–2011, (Includes BON SECOURS ST. MARY'S CHILDREN'S SERVICES, 5801 Bremo Road, Richmond, Virginia, Zip 23226–1907; tel. 804/285–2011) **A**1 2 3 5 10 **F**3 8 11 12 13 15 17 18 19 20 21 22 23 24 25 26 27 28 29 30 31 34 35 37 38 39 40 41 42 44 45 46 47 49 56 57 58 59 61 62 63 64 70 72 74 76 77 78 79 81 84 85 86 87 88 89 91 92 93 97 98 100 101 102 103 107 108 109 110 111 114 115 116 117 118 119 120 121 123 126 129 130 143 145 146 147 148 149 154 156 **S** Bon Secours Mercy Health, Marriottsville, MD
Primary Contact: Francine Barr, R.N., MS, Chief Executive Officer
COO: Francine Barr, R.N., MS, Vice President and Chief Operating Officer
CFO: Stephan F Quiriconi, Chief Financial Officer
CMO: Khiet Trinh, M.D., Chief Medical Officer
CIO: Terri Spence, Chief Information Officer
CHR: Kishah White, Director Human Resources
CNO: Jody A. Bishop, Vice President of Patient Care Services and Chief Nursing Executive
Web address: www.bonsecours.com
Control: Church operated, Nongovernment, not–for–profit **Service**: General medical and surgical

Staffed Beds: 391 Admissions: 20329 Census: 289 Outpatient Visits: 160148 Births: 2071 Total Expense ($000): 540477 Payroll Expense ($000): 171648 Personnel: 2578

VA

Hospital, Medicare Provider Number, Address, Telephone, Approval, Facility, and Physician Codes, Health Care System

★ American Hospital Association (AHA) membership   ○ Healthcare Facilities Accreditation Program   ⇑ Center for Improvement in Healthcare Quality Accreditation
☐ The Joint Commission accreditation   ◇ DNV Healthcare Inc. accreditation   △ Commission on Accreditation of Rehabilitation Facilities (CARF) accreditation

⊠ **ENCOMPASS HEALTH REHABILITATION HOSPITAL OF VIRGINIA (493028),** 5700 Fitzhugh Avenue, Zip 23226–1800; tel. 804/288–5700, (Nonreporting) **A**1 10 **S** Encompass Health Corporation, Birmingham, AL
Primary Contact: Dan Gaskell, Chief Executive Officer
CMO: Roger Giordano, M.D., Medical Director
CIO: Faye Encke, Director Information Management
CHR: Tonya Ferguson, Director Human Resources
CNO: Michelle Anthony, Chief Nursing Officer
Web address: www.https://www.encompasshealth.com
Control: Corporation, Investor–owned (for–profit) **Service:** Rehabilitation

Staffed Beds: 40

⊠ **HENRICO DOCTORS' HOSPITAL (490118),** 1602 Skipwith Road, Zip 23229–5205; tel. 804/289–4500, (Includes HENRICO DOCTORS' HOSPITAL - FOREST, 1602 Skipwith Road, Richmond, Virginia, Zip 23229–5298; tel. 804/289–4500; HENRICO DOCTORS' HOSPITAL - PARHAM, 7700 East Parham Road, Richmond, Virginia, Zip 23294–4301; tel. 804/747–5600; David Donaldson, Chief Executive Officer; HENRICO DOCTORS' HOSPITAL - RETREAT CAMPUS, 2621 Grove Avenue, Richmond, Virginia, Zip 23220–4308; tel. 804/254–5100; William Wagnon, Chief Executive Officer), (Non-reporting) **A**1 2 10 **S** HCA Healthcare, Nashville, TN
Primary Contact: William Wagnon, Chief Executive Officer
COO: Zachary Reed, Chief Operating Officer
CFO: Christopher Denton, Chief Financial Officer
CIO: Daniel Patton, Director Information Systems
CHR: Steven Burgess, Administrator Human Resources
Web address: www.henricodoctorshospital.com
Control: Corporation, Investor–owned (for–profit) **Service:** General medical and surgical

Staffed Beds: 560

KINDRED HOSPITAL RICHMOND See Vibra Hospital of Richmond

⊠ **VIBRA HOSPITAL OF RICHMOND (492009),** 2220 Edward Holland Drive, Zip 23230–2519; tel. 804/678–7000, (Nonreporting) **A**1 10 **S** Vibra Healthcare, Mechanicsburg, PA
Primary Contact: Linda Tiemens, Chief Executive Officer
CMO: Gerard Weeden, Chief Medical Officer
CHR: Jonnitra Peeples, Chief Human Resource Officer
CNO: Crystal Richardson, Chief Nursing Officer
Web address: www.vhrichmond.com
Control: Corporation, Investor–owned (for–profit) **Service:** Acute long–term care hospital

Staffed Beds: 60

RICHMOND—Chesterfield County

JOHNSTON-WILLIS HOSPITAL See Chippenham Hospital, Richmond

RICHMOND—Goochland County

HALLMARK YOUTHCARE - RICHMOND, 12800 West Creek Parkway, Zip 23238–1116; tel. 804/784–2200, (Nonreporting)
Primary Contact: Di Hayes, Chief Executive Officer
Web address: www.hallmarkyouthcare.org
Control: State, Government, nonfederal **Service:** Children's hospital psychiatric

Staffed Beds: 78

RICHMOND—Richmond City County

☐ **BON SECOURS-RICHMOND COMMUNITY HOSPITAL (490094),** 1500 North 28th Street, Zip 23223–5396, Mailing Address: P.O. Box 27184, Zip 23261–7184; tel. 804/225–1700, **A**1 3 10 **F**3 11 15 29 30 31 34 35 38 40 44 45 47 48 50 57 59 63 66 74 77 78 81 84 85 86 87 90 93 98 100 104 107 108 110 111 115 118 119 130 132 146 149 154 156 **S** Bon Secours Mercy Health, Marriottsville, MD
Primary Contact: Mark M. Gordon, Chief Executive Officer
CIO: Jeff Burke, Chief Information Officer
CHR: Shelia White, Director Human Resources
Web address: www.bonsecours.com
Control: Church operated, Nongovernment, not–for–profit **Service:** General medical and surgical

Staffed Beds: 96 **Admissions:** 1703 **Census:** 29 **Outpatient Visits:** 65304 **Births:** 0 **Total Expense ($000):** 107601 **Payroll Expense ($000):** 28154 **Personnel:** 434

★ **CHILDREN'S HOSPITAL OF RICHMOND AT VCU-BROOK ROAD CAMPUS (493302),** 2924 Brook Road, Zip 23220–1298; tel. 804/321–7474, (Nonreporting) **A**3 5 10 **S** VCU Health System, Richmond, VA
Primary Contact: Elias Neujahr, Chief Executive Officer
CFO: James A Deyarmin, Controller
CMO: Eugene A Monasterio, M.D., Medical Director
CIO: Tim Gibbs, Director of Information Technology, Information Security Officer
CNO: Sharon Darby, R.N., FACHE, Vice President, Clinical Operations
Web address: www.chrichmond.org
Control: Other not–for–profit (including NFP Corporation) **Service:** Children's rehabilitation

Staffed Beds: 36

⊠ ⇑ **CHIPPENHAM HOSPITAL (490112),** 7101 Jahnke Road, Zip 23225–4044; tel. 804/320–3911, (Includes CHIPPENHAM MEDICAL CENTER, 7101 Jahnke Road, Richmond, Virginia, Zip 23225; tel. 804/320–3911; JOHNSTON-WILLIS HOSPITAL, 1401 Johnston-Willis Drive, Richmond, Virginia, Zip 23235; tel. 804/330–2000; Zachary McCluskey, Chief Executive Officer), (Non-reporting) **A**1 2 3 5 10 21 **S** HCA Healthcare, Nashville, TN
Primary Contact: Zachary McCluskey, Interim Chief Executive Officer
CFO: Lynn Strader, Chief Financial Officer
CMO: Georgean DeBlois, M.D., Chairman Medical Staff
CIO: Tracy Hechler, Healthcare Director Information Services
CHR: Kris Lukish, Human Resources Officer
Web address: www.cjwmedical.com
Control: Corporation, Investor–owned (for–profit) **Service:** General medical and surgical

Staffed Beds: 765

⊠ △ **HUNTER HOLMES MCGUIRE VETERANS AFFAIRS MEDICAL CENTER-RICHMOND,** 1201 Broad Rock Boulevard, Zip 23249–0002; tel. 804/675–5000, (Nonreporting) **A**1 3 5 7 8 **S** Department of Veterans Affairs, Washington, DC
Primary Contact: J. Ronald. Johnson, Director
COO: Alan Lombardo, Associate Director
CFO: Tanza Westry, Chief Financial Officer
CMO: Julie Beales, M.D., Chief of Staff
CIO: David Dahlstrand, Chief, OI&T
CHR: Adriana H Hamilton, Chief Human Resources Officer
CNO: Marjorie Lyne, Associate Director for Patient Care Services
Web address: www.richmond.va.gov/
Control: Veterans Affairs, Government, federal **Service:** General medical and surgical

Staffed Beds: 381

⊠ **VCU MEDICAL CENTER (490032),** 1250 East Marshall Street, Zip 23298–5051, Mailing Address: P.O. Box 980510, Zip 23298–0510; tel. 804/828–9000, (Includes CHILDREN'S HOSPITAL OF RICHMOND AT VCU, 1000 East Broad Street, Richmond, Virginia, Zip 23219–1918, Mailing Address: P.O. Box 980646, Zip 23298–0646, tel. 804/828–2467; Elias Neujahr, Chief Executive Officer) **A**1 5 8 10 **F**2 3 5 6 8 9 11 12 13 15 16 17 18 19 20 21 22 23 24 25 26 27 28 29 30 31 32 34 35 36 37 38 39 40 41 43 44 45 46 47 48 49 50 51 52 54 55 56 57 58 59 60 61 62 64 65 66 68 70 72 73 74 75 76 78 79 80 81 82 83 84 85 86 87 88 89 90 91 92 93 95 96 97 98 99 100 101 102 103 104 107 108 109 110 111 114 115 116 117 118 119 120 121 123 124 126 129 130 131 132 134 135 136 137 138 139 141 142 143 145 146 147 148 149 150 153 154 156 **S** VCU Health System, Richmond, VA
Primary Contact: Deborah W. Davis, Chief Executive Officer and Vice President Clinical Services
COO: Paul J Wesolowski, Chief Operating Officer
CFO: Melinda Hancock, Chief Financial Officer
CMO: Ron Clark, M.D., Vice President Clinical Activities and Chief Medical Officer
CIO: Susan Steagall, Vice President Information Services
CHR: Maria Curran, Vice President Human Resources
CNO: Deb Zimmermann, R.N., Chief Nursing Officer and Vice President Patient Care Services
Web address: www.vcuhealth.org
Control: Hospital district or authority, Government, nonfederal **Service:** General medical and surgical

Staffed Beds: 812 **Admissions:** 36887 **Census:** 655 **Outpatient Visits:** 888439 **Births:** 2546 **Total Expense ($000):** 1512325 **Payroll Expense ($000):** 498800 **Personnel:** 9115

VA

ROANOKE—Roanoke City County

☒ **CARILION ROANOKE MEMORIAL HOSPITAL (490024)**, 1906 Belleview Avenue Southeast, Zip 24014–1838, Mailing Address: P.O. Box 13367, Zip 24033–3367; tel. 540/981–7000, (Includes CARILION CLINIC CHILDREN'S HOSPITAL, 1906 Belleview Avenue, SE, Roanoke, Virginia, Zip 24014–1838; tel. 540/981–7000; CARILION ROANOKE COMMUNITY HOSPITAL, 101 Elm Avenue SE, Roanoke, Virginia, Zip 24013–2230, Mailing Address: P O Box 12946, Zip 24029–2946, tel. 540/985–8000; ROANOKE MEMORIAL REHABILITATION CENTER, South Jefferson and McClanahan Streets, Roanoke, Virginia, Zip 24014, Mailing Address: P O Box 13367, Zip 24033, tel. 703/342–4541) **A**1 2 3 5 8 10 13 **F**3 4 5 7 8 9 11 12 13 14 15 17 18 19 20 22 24 26 28 29 30 31 32 33 34 35 36 37 38 39 40 41 43 44 45 46 47 48 49 50 51 52 53 54 55 56 57 58 59 60 61 62 63 64 65 66 68 70 71 72 73 74 75 76 77 78 79 81 82 83 84 85 86 87 88 89 90 91 92 93 95 96 97 98 99 100 101 102 103 104 106 107 108 110 111 113 114 115 116 117 118 119 120 121 123 124 126 129 130 131 132 134 135 143 144 146 147 148 149 150 151 154 155 156 157 **S** Carilion Clinic, Roanoke, VA
Primary Contact: Steven C. Arner, President
COO: Steven C. Arner, President
CFO: Donald B Halliwill, Executive Vice President and Chief Financial Officer
CHR: Heather S Shepardson, Vice President Human Resources
CNO: Margaret M. Scheaffel, Chief Nursing Officer
Web address: www.carilionclinic.org
Control: Other not–for–profit (including NFP Corporation) **Service:** General medical and surgical

Staffed Beds: 643 **Admissions:** 40128 **Census:** 566 **Outpatient Visits:** 270634 **Births:** 3157 **Total Expense ($000):** 1214455 **Payroll Expense ($000):** 547190 **Personnel:** 6772

ROCKY MOUNT—Franklin County

☒ **CARILION FRANKLIN MEMORIAL HOSPITAL (490089)**, 180 Floyd Avenue, Zip 24151–1389; tel. 540/483–5277, **A**1 3 10 **F**3 11 15 18 28 29 30 34 35 40 45 50 53 57 59 62 63 65 68 70 75 81 84 85 91 93 96 107 110 115 119 130 132 135 146 149 **S** Carilion Clinic, Roanoke, VA
Primary Contact: Carl T. Cline, Chief Executive Officer
COO: Steven C. Arner, Executive Vice President of Administration
CFO: Donald B Halliwill, Chief Financial Officer
CMO: Patrice M Weiss, Executive Vice President, Administration
CIO: Robert Keith Perry, Senior Vice President, Chief Information Officer
CHR: Paul C. Hudgins, Senior Vice President
CNO: Margaret M. Scheaffel, Chief Nursing Officer
Web address: www.carilionclinic.org/CFMH
Control: Other not–for–profit (including NFP Corporation) **Service:** General medical and surgical

Staffed Beds: 18 **Admissions:** 1472 **Census:** 14 **Outpatient Visits:** 41821 **Births:** 0 **Total Expense ($000):** 39902 **Payroll Expense ($000):** 16038 **Personnel:** 265

SALEM—Salem City County

☒ **SALEM VETERANS AFFAIRS MEDICAL CENTER**, 1970 Roanoke Boulevard, Zip 24153–6478; tel. 540/982–2463, (Total facility includes 60 beds in nursing home–type unit) **A**1 3 5 8 **F**3 4 5 11 18 20 22 24 26 29 30 31 35 36 38 39 40 44 45 46 53 55 56 57 58 59 60 61 63 64 67 70 74 75 77 78 79 80 81 82 83 84 85 86 87 90 92 93 94 96 97 98 100 101 102 104 107 108 111 114 115 116 117 118 119 128 129 130 132 135 146 147 148 149 154 156 157 158 **S** Department of Veterans Affairs, Washington, DC
Primary Contact: Rebecca J. Stackhouse, Medical Center Director
CFO: Codie Walker, Chief Financial Officer
CMO: Anne Hutchins, M.D., Chief of Staff
CIO: Sharon Collins, Chief Information Officer
CHR: Brian Zeman, Chief Human Resources
CNO: Teresa England, R.N., Ph.D., Nurse Executive
Web address: www.salem.va.gov
Control: Veterans Affairs, Government, federal **Service:** General medical and surgical

Staffed Beds: 191 **Admissions:** 4034 **Census:** 96 **Outpatient Visits:** 455714 **Births:** 0 **Total Expense ($000):** 388070 **Payroll Expense ($000):** 136546 **Personnel:** 1816

SOUTH BOSTON—Halifax County

★ ⇑ **SENTARA HALIFAX REGIONAL HOSPITAL (490013)**, 2204 Wilborn Avenue, Zip 24592–1638, (Total facility includes 384 beds in nursing home–type unit) **A**5 10 21 **F**3 5 11 13 14 15 18 20 22 28 29 30 31 34 35 38 39 45 46 47 48 50 56 57 59 61 62 63 64 65 68 70 74 75 76 77 78 79 81 82 84 85 86 87 91 92 93 96 97 101 104 105 107 108 110 111 114 115 118 119 127 128 129 130 131 132 135 141 145 146 147 148 149 152 153 154 **S** Sentara Healthcare, Norfolk, VA
Primary Contact: Jason A. Studley, FACHE, President
CFO: Stewart R Nelson, Vice President and Chief Financial Officer
CMO: Said Iskandar, M.D., Chief Medical Officer
CIO: William Zirkle, Manager Information Systems
CHR: Catherine Howard, Director Human Resources
CNO: Patricia F Thomas, Chief Nursing Officer
Web address: www.hrhs.org
Control: Other not–for–profit (including NFP Corporation) **Service:** General medical and surgical

Staffed Beds: 441 **Admissions:** 4277 **Census:** 383 **Outpatient Visits:** 120874 **Births:** 363 **Total Expense ($000):** 136304 **Payroll Expense ($000):** 54175 **Personnel:** 933

SOUTH HILL—Mecklenburg County

☒ **VCU HEALTH COMMUNITY MEMORIAL HOSPITAL (490098)**, 125 Buena Vista Circle, Zip 23970–1431, Mailing Address: P.O. Box 90, Zip 23970–0090; tel. 434/447–3151, (Total facility includes 136 beds in nursing home–type unit) **A**1 2 10 20 **F**3 11 12 13 15 18 28 29 30 31 34 35 39 40 45 46 49 50 53 54 56 59 62 63 64 65 70 74 75 77 78 79 81 82 84 85 86 87 93 96 97 107 108 110 111 115 119 121 123 127 128 130 131 132 133 135 143 146 147 148 154 **S** VCU Health System, Richmond, VA
Primary Contact: W Scott. Burnette, Chief Executive Officer
CFO: Kenneth Libby, Vice President Finance
CMO: Manhal Saleeby, M.D., Chief of Staff
CIO: Brian Rock, Director of Information Systems
CHR: Maria Stephens, Director Human Resources, Education and Occupational Health and Wellness
CNO: Ursula N Butts, FACHE, Vice President of Patient Care Services
Web address: www.cmh-sh.org
Control: Other not–for–profit (including NFP Corporation) **Service:** General medical and surgical

Staffed Beds: 206 **Admissions:** 3124 **Census:** 123 **Outpatient Visits:** 136736 **Births:** 102 **Total Expense ($000):** 103241 **Payroll Expense ($000):** 48838 **Personnel:** 726

STAFFORD—Stafford County

☒ **STAFFORD HOSPITAL (490140)**, 101 Hospital Center Boulevard, Zip 22554–6200; tel. 540/741–9000, **A**1 5 10 **F**3 13 15 18 20 22 26 29 30 31 34 35 36 39 40 44 45 46 47 48 49 50 54 57 58 59 64 70 73 74 75 76 77 78 79 81 84 85 86 87 92 93 96 102 107 108 110 111 115 118 119 120 122 129 130 131 132 135 146 147 148 149 **S** Mary Washington Healthcare, Fredericksburg, VA
Primary Contact: Michael P. McDermott, M.D., President and Chief Executive Officer
COO: Thomas Gettinger, Executive Vice President and Chief Operating Officer
CFO: Sean Barden, Executive Vice President and Chief Financial Officer
CMO: Rebecca Bigoney, Executive Vice President and Chief Medical Officer
CIO: Justin K. Box, Senior Vice President and Chief Information Officer
CHR: Kathryn S Wall, Executive Vice President Human Resources and Organizational Development
CNO: Eileen L Dohmann, R.N., Senior Vice President and Chief Nursing Officer
Web address: www.mwhc.com
Control: Other not–for–profit (including NFP Corporation) **Service:** General medical and surgical

Staffed Beds: 78 **Admissions:** 5768 **Census:** 45 **Outpatient Visits:** 67685 **Births:** 1250 **Total Expense ($000):** 90124 **Payroll Expense ($000):** 26645 **Personnel:** 375

STAUNTON—Staunton City County

COMMONWEALTH CENTER FOR CHILDREN AND ADOLESCENTS, 1355 Richmond Road, Zip 24401–9146, Mailing Address: Box 4000, Zip 24402–4000; tel. 540/332–2100, (Nonreporting) **A**3 5 **S** Virginia Department of Mental Health, Richmond, VA
Primary Contact: Mary Clare. Smith, Interim Facility Director
Web address: www.ccca.dbhds.virginia.gov
Control: State, Government, nonfederal **Service:** Children's hospital psychiatric

Staffed Beds: 60

VA

Hospital, Medicare Provider Number, Address, Telephone, Approval, Facility, and Physician Codes, Health Care System

★ American Hospital Association (AHA) membership
☐ The Joint Commission accreditation
○ Healthcare Facilities Accreditation Program
◇ DNV Healthcare Inc. accreditation
⇑ Center for Improvement in Healthcare Quality Accreditation
△ Commission on Accreditation of Rehabilitation Facilities (CARF) accreditation

☐ **WESTERN STATE HOSPITAL (494021)**, 103 Valley Center Drive, Zip 24401–9146, Mailing Address: P.O. Box 2500, Zip 24402–2500; tel. 540/332–8000, **A1** 3 5 10 **F3** 29 30 34 39 44 50 53 59 65 68 75 77 86 87 97 98 100 101 130 132 135 146 149 154 **S** Virginia Department of Mental Health, Richmond, VA
Primary Contact: Mary Clare. Smith, Director
CFO: Jon Chapman, Fiscal Officer
CMO: Jonathan Anderson, Medical Director
CIO: Sharon Johnson, Director Health Information Management
CHR: Kimberly Harman, Regional Manager Human Resources
CNO: Diane Pavalonis, Chief Nurse Executive
Web address: www.dbhds.virginia.gov
Control: State, Government, nonfederal **Service:** Psychiatric

Staffed Beds: 246 **Admissions:** 1198 **Census:** 228 **Outpatient Visits:** 171 **Births:** 0 **Total Expense ($000):** 66359 **Payroll Expense ($000):** 34852 **Personnel:** 664

SUFFOLK—Suffolk City County

★ ⍋ **SENTARA OBICI HOSPITAL (490044)**, 2800 Godwin Boulevard, Zip 23434–8038; tel. 757/934–4000, **A2** 3 5 10 21 **F3** 8 11 13 15 18 20 22 26 28 29 30 31 34 35 36 37 38 39 40 41 42 44 45 46 47 48 49 50 54 56 57 58 59 60 61 63 64 65 68 70 74 75 76 77 78 79 81 82 84 85 86 87 91 92 93 94 96 97 98 100 102 107 108 110 111 114 115 118 119 120 121 123 124 126 129 130 131 132 135 141 142 145 146 147 148 149 154 **S** Sentara Healthcare, Norfolk, VA
Primary Contact: Steve Julian, M.D., President
CFO: Mike Mounie, Director Finance
CMO: Steve Julian, M.D., Vice President Medical Affairs
CIO: Alice Oxton, Director Information Technology
CHR: Deborah Ferguson, Human Resources Consultant
Web address: www.sentara.com
Control: Other not–for–profit (including NFP Corporation) **Service:** General medical and surgical

Staffed Beds: 175 **Admissions:** 10449 **Census:** 119 **Outpatient Visits:** 404233 **Births:** 1314 **Total Expense ($000):** 193440 **Payroll Expense ($000):** 78449 **Personnel:** 1257

TAPPAHANNOCK—Essex County

⍋ **RIVERSIDE TAPPAHANNOCK HOSPITAL (490084)**, 618 Hospital Road, Zip 22560–5000; tel. 804/443–3311, **A10** 20 21 **F3** 15 18 26 29 30 31 34 35 36 37 38 40 44 45 49 50 55 56 57 58 59 62 63 64 70 74 75 77 78 79 81 82 84 85 86 87 91 92 93 100 102 107 108 110 111 115 116 117 118 119 130 131 132 135 146 148 149 154 **S** Riverside Health System, Newport News, VA
Primary Contact: Esther Muscari. Desimini, Administrator
CFO: Jeri Sibley, Director Revenue Cycle
CMO: Richard Dunn, M.D., Chief Medical Officer
CHR: Lindsey Custer, Director Human Resources
CNO: Judith Matthews, Nurse Executive
Web address: www.https://www.riversideonline.com
Control: Other not–for–profit (including NFP Corporation) **Service:** General medical and surgical

Staffed Beds: 16 **Admissions:** 1514 **Census:** 15 **Outpatient Visits:** 43488 **Births:** 0 **Total Expense ($000):** 51451 **Payroll Expense ($000):** 16509 **Personnel:** 206

TAZEWELL—Tazewell County

⌘ **CARILION TAZEWELL COMMUNITY HOSPITAL (490117)**, 141 Ben Bolt Avenue, Zip 24651–9700, Mailing Address: 388 Ben Bolt Avenue, Zip 24651; tel. 276/988–8700, **A1** 5 10 **F3** 11 15 29 30 34 40 44 50 57 59 62 64 65 68 75 77 85 87 91 93 107 111 114 119 133 135 146 149 **S** Carilion Clinic, Roanoke, VA
Primary Contact: Kathren Dowdy, MSN, Regional Hospital Senior Director
CMO: Kevin Combs, Chief of Staff
CHR: Carrie Boggess, Human Resources Generalist
CNO: Kathren Dowdy, MSN, Senior Director, Chief Executive Officer and Chief Nursing Officer
Web address: www.carilionclinic.org
Control: Other not–for–profit (including NFP Corporation) **Service:** General medical and surgical

Staffed Beds: 4 **Admissions:** 524 **Census:** 5 **Outpatient Visits:** 14907 **Births:** 0 **Total Expense ($000):** 15612 **Payroll Expense ($000):** 5837 **Personnel:** 97

VA

VIRGINIA BEACH—Virginia Beach City County

★ ⍋ **SENTARA PRINCESS ANNE HOSPITAL (490119)**, 2025 Glenn Mitchell Drive, Zip 23456–0178; tel. 757/507–1000, **A2** 3 5 10 21 **F3** 8 11 13 15 18 20 22 26 28 29 30 31 34 35 36 37 38 39 40 41 44 45 46 47 49 50 53 55 56 57 58 59 60 61 63 64 65 68 70 71 74 75 76 77 78 79 81 82 84 85 86 87 91 92 93 94 96 97 100 101 102 107 108 110 111 114 115 118 119 126 129 130 131 132 135 141 146 147 148 149 154 **S** Sentara Healthcare, Norfolk, VA
Primary Contact: Thomas B. Thames, M.D., President
COO: Howard P. Kern, Chief Operating Officer
CFO: Robert Broermann, Senior Vice President and Chief Financial Officer
CMO: Terry Gilliland, M.D., Senior Vice President and Chief Medical Officer
CIO: Bert Reese, Chief Information Officer
CHR: Michael V Taylor, Vice President Human Resources
CNO: Grace Myers, MSN, Vice President, Nurse Executive
Web address: www.sentara.com
Control: Other not–for–profit (including NFP Corporation) **Service:** General medical and surgical

Staffed Beds: 160 **Admissions:** 11788 **Census:** 139 **Outpatient Visits:** 416313 **Births:** 2238 **Total Expense ($000):** 236026 **Payroll Expense ($000):** 76471 **Personnel:** 1474

★ ⍋ **SENTARA VIRGINIA BEACH GENERAL HOSPITAL (490057)**, 1060 First Colonial Road, Zip 23454–3002; tel. 757/395–8000, **A2** 3 5 10 21 **F3** 5 11 15 17 18 20 22 24 26 28 29 30 31 33 34 35 36 37 38 39 40 41 42 43 44 45 46 47 48 49 50 51 52 53 54 55 56 57 58 59 62 63 64 65 68 70 71 74 75 77 78 79 80 81 82 84 85 86 87 90 91 92 93 94 96 97 98 100 101 102 104 105 107 108 110 111 114 115 118 119 120 121 123 126 129 130 131 132 135 141 142 145 146 147 148 149 152 153 154 155 156 **S** Sentara Healthcare, Norfolk, VA
Primary Contact: Elwood Bernard. Boone III, FACHE, President
CFO: Marley Nacey, Director Finance
CHR: Michelle Meekins, Manager Human Resources
CNO: Peggy Braun, R.N., Vice President Patient Care Services and Chief Nurse Executive
Web address: www.sentara.com
Control: Other not–for–profit (including NFP Corporation) **Service:** General medical and surgical

Staffed Beds: 271 **Admissions:** 14071 **Census:** 205 **Outpatient Visits:** 439442 **Births:** 0 **Total Expense ($000):** 269924 **Payroll Expense ($000):** 110745 **Personnel:** 1734

☐ **VIRGINIA BEACH PSYCHIATRIC CENTER (494025)**, 1100 First Colonial Road, Zip 23454–2403; tel. 757/496–6000, (Nonreporting) **A1** 10 **S** Universal Health Services, Inc., King of Prussia, PA
Primary Contact: Brian Tapman, Interim Chief Executive Officer
Web address: www.vbpcweb.com
Control: Corporation, Investor–owned (for–profit) **Service:** Psychiatric

Staffed Beds: 100

WARRENTON—Fauquier County

⌘ **FAUQUIER HOSPITAL (490023)**, 500 Hospital Drive, Zip 20186–3099; tel. 540/316–5000, (Total facility includes 90 beds in nursing home–type unit) **A1** 2 10 **F3** 10 11 13 15 18 20 28 29 30 31 34 35 39 40 44 45 46 48 49 50 51 53 59 60 68 70 73 76 77 78 79 81 82 93 96 97 107 108 110 111 115 118 119 128 129 130 132 134 146 147 148 149 156 157 **S** LifePoint Health, Brentwood, TN
Primary Contact: Chad Melton, Chief Executive Officer
CFO: Lionel J Phillips, Vice President Financial Services
CIO: Donna Staton, Chief Information Officer
CHR: Katy Reeves, Vice President Human Resources
CNO: Linda Sharkey, R.N., MSN, Vice President Patient Care Services and Chief Nurse Executive
Web address: www.fauquierhealth.org/
Control: Corporation, Investor–owned (for–profit) **Service:** General medical and surgical

Staffed Beds: 160 **Admissions:** 5222 **Census:** 134 **Outpatient Visits:** 62667 **Births:** 769 **Total Expense ($000):** 97835 **Payroll Expense ($000):** 43350

WILLIAMSBURG—James City County

☐ **EASTERN STATE HOSPITAL (490109)**, 4601 Ironbound Road, Zip 23188–2652; tel. 757/253–5161, (Nonreporting) **A1** 10 **S** Virginia Department of Mental Health, Richmond, VA
Primary Contact: John M. Favret, Director
CFO: E Clifford Love, Director Fiscal Services
CMO: Guillermo Schrader, M.D., Acting Medical Director
CIO: Barbara Lambert, Director Healthcare Compliance
CHR: Edie Rogan, Manager Human Resources
Web address: www.esh.dmhmrsas.virginia.gov/
Control: State, Government, nonfederal **Service:** Psychiatric

Staffed Beds: 300

Many Facility Codes have changed. Please refer to the AHA Guide Code Chart.

⇑ **RIVERSIDE DOCTORS' HOSPITAL WILLIAMSBURG (490143)**, 1500 Commonwealth Avenue, Zip 23185–5229; tel. 757/585–2200, **A**3 10 21 **F**3 28 29 34 35 40 44 45 50 57 59 60 64 74 75 77 79 81 82 85 86 87 92 93 107 108 111 114 115 119 120 121 130 132 146 147 148 149 154 **S** Riverside Health System, Newport News, VA
Primary Contact: Steve C. McCary, Administrator
CNO: Arlene Messina, R.N., MSN, Director of Nursing
Web address: www.riversideonline.com/rdhw
Control: Other not–for–profit (including NFP Corporation) **Service:** General medical and surgical

Staffed Beds: 16 **Admissions:** 1583 **Census:** 13 **Outpatient Visits:** 23321 **Births:** 0 **Total Expense ($000):** 38872 **Payroll Expense ($000):** 12516 **Personnel:** 241

WILLIAMSBURG—York County

★ ⇑ **SENTARA WILLIAMSBURG REGIONAL MEDICAL CENTER (490066)**, 100 Sentara Circle, Zip 23188–5713; tel. 757/984–6000, **A**2 10 21 **F**3 8 11 13 15 18 20 22 28 29 30 31 34 35 36 37 38 39 40 41 43 44 45 46 47 48 49 50 51 54 55 56 57 58 59 60 61 63 64 65 68 70 74 75 76 77 78 79 81 82 84 85 86 87 89 90 91 92 93 94 96 97 100 107 108 110 111 114 115 118 119 126 129 130 131 132 135 141 142 146 147 148 149 154 156 **S** Sentara Healthcare, Norfolk, VA
Primary Contact: David J. Masterson, President
CFO: Andreas Roehrle, Director Finance
CMO: Joe Robbins, M.D., Vice President Medical Affairs
CIO: Mike Freeman, Director Information Technology
CHR: Lois B Demerich, Director Human Resources
CNO: Donna Wilmoth, Vice President Patient Care Services and Chief Nursing Officer
Web address: www.sentara.com
Control: Other not–for–profit (including NFP Corporation) **Service:** General medical and surgical

Staffed Beds: 145 **Admissions:** 7737 **Census:** 91 **Outpatient Visits:** 294070 **Births:** 873 **Total Expense ($000):** 165395 **Payroll Expense ($000):** 62731 **Personnel:** 946

☐ **THE PAVILION AT WILLIAMSBURG PLACE (494032)**, 5483 Mooretown Road, Zip 23188–2108; tel. 757/565–0106, (Nonreporting) **A**1 10
Primary Contact: Shirley Repta, Chief Executive Officer
CMO: Avtar Dhilion, Medical Director
CNO: Shedale Tindall, Chief Nursing Officer
Web address: www.pavilionwp.com
Control: Corporation, Investor–owned (for–profit) **Service:** Psychiatric

Staffed Beds: 57

WINCHESTER—Winchester City County

Ⓐ **WINCHESTER MEDICAL CENTER (490005)**, 1040 Amherst Street, Zip 22601–2808, Mailing Address: P.O. Box 3340, Zip 22604–2540; tel. 540/536–8000, **A**1 2 3 5 10 20 **F**3 5 8 11 12 13 15 17 18 20 22 24 26 28 29 30 31 32 34 35 36 38 39 40 41 43 44 45 46 47 49 50 51 54 55 56 57 58 59 61 62 64 65 66 68 70 71 72 74 75 76 77 78 79 80 81 82 84 85 86 87 89 90 91 92 93 97 98 100 101 102 103 104 107 108 110 111 114 115 116 117 118 119 120 121 123 124 129 130 131 132 135 136 146 147 148 149 153 154 155 156 **S** Valley Health System, Winchester, VA
Primary Contact: Grady W. Philips III, President
CFO: Robert Amos, Vice President and Chief Financial Officer
CMO: Nicolas Restrepo, M.D., Vice President Medical Affairs
CIO: Joan Roscoe, Chief Information Officer
CHR: Elizabeth Savage, Senior Vice President and Chief Human Resource Officer and Vice President Community Health and Wellness
CNO: Anne Whiteside, Vice President Nursing
Web address: www.valleyhealthlink.com/WMC
Control: Other not–for–profit (including NFP Corporation) **Service:** General medical and surgical

Staffed Beds: 485 **Admissions:** 20397 **Census:** 332 **Outpatient Visits:** 348987 **Births:** 2210 **Total Expense ($000):** 589294 **Payroll Expense ($000):** 177312 **Personnel:** 2643

WOODBRIDGE—Prince William County

★ ⇑ **SENTARA NORTHERN VIRGINIA MEDICAL CENTER (490113)**, 2300 Opitz Boulevard, Zip 22191–3399; tel. 703/523–1000, **A**2 10 21 **F**3 8 11 12 13 15 18 20 22 26 28 29 30 31 34 35 36 38 40 41 42 44 45 48 49 50 53 54 55 56 57 58 59 60 61 62 63 64 65 66 68 70 71 72 74 75 76 77 78 79 81 82 84 85 86 87 91 92 93 94 96 102 107 108 110 111 114 115 118 119 121 126 130 131 132 135 141 143 145 146 147 148 149 154 156 **S** Sentara Healthcare, Norfolk, VA
Primary Contact: Katherine Johnson, Ph.D., President
CMO: David M Schwartz, D.O., Vice President, Medical Affairs
CIO: Thomas Ewing, Director Information Technology
CHR: Brett Willsie, Vice President Human Resources
CNO: Valerie E Keane, FACHE, Chief Nursing Executive
Web address: www.sentara.com/northernvirginia
Control: Other not–for–profit (including NFP Corporation) **Service:** General medical and surgical

Staffed Beds: 183 **Admissions:** 10021 **Census:** 113 **Outpatient Visits:** 378644 **Births:** 1459 **Total Expense ($000):** 235527 **Payroll Expense ($000):** 84863 **Personnel:** 1085

WOODSTOCK—Shenandoah County

⊞ **VALLEY HEALTH SHENANDOAH MEMORIAL HOSPITAL (491305)**, 759 South Main Street, Zip 22664–1127; tel. 540/459–1100, **A**1 10 18 **F**3 11 15 18 28 29 30 35 40 45 50 53 57 59 64 65 68 69 70 75 77 79 81 82 87 92 93 97 104 107 108 110 111 114 118 119 127 129 130 132 133 135 146 147 148 153 154 155 156 **S** Valley Health System, Winchester, VA
Primary Contact: N Travis. Clark, President
CFO: Phillip Graybeal, CPA, Vice President, Finance
CMO: Greg Byrd, Vice President Medical Affairs
CIO: James Burton, Vice President and Chief Information Officer, Valley Health
CHR: Abbey Rembold, Manager, Human Resource Business Partnerships
CNO: Lisa Heishman, R.N., Vice President
Web address: www.valleyhealthlink.com/shenandoah
Control: Other not–for–profit (including NFP Corporation) **Service:** General medical and surgical

Staffed Beds: 25 **Admissions:** 1503 **Census:** 14 **Outpatient Visits:** 148073 **Births:** 0 **Total Expense ($000):** 62208 **Payroll Expense ($000):** 25675 **Personnel:** 357

WYTHEVILLE—Wythe County

⊞ **WYTHE COUNTY COMMUNITY HOSPITAL (490111)**, 600 West Ridge Road, Zip 24382–1099; tel. 276/228–0200, **A**1 5 10 20 **F**3 12 13 15 18 26 27 28 29 32 34 35 37 40 50 51 57 59 65 68 70 75 76 77 79 81 82 86 87 91 92 93 97 107 110 111 114 119 128 129 130 131 132 133 135 144 146 147 148 154 156 **S** LifePoint Health, Brentwood, TN
Primary Contact: Joseph Wilkins, Chief Executive Officer
COO: Adam Martin, Chief Operating Officer
CFO: John D White, Chief Financial Officer
CMO: George Farrell, M.D., Chief of Staff
CIO: Andrea Harless, Director Information Services
CHR: Kristie E Walker, M.P.H., Director of Human Resources
CNO: Theresa Dix, R.N., Chief Nursing Officer
Web address: www.wcchcares.com
Control: Corporation, Investor–owned (for–profit) **Service:** General medical and surgical

Staffed Beds: 70 **Admissions:** 2077 **Census:** 20 **Outpatient Visits:** 59535 **Births:** 369 **Total Expense ($000):** 38481 **Payroll Expense ($000):** 14719 **Personnel:** 273

VA

WASHINGTON

ABERDEEN—Grays Harbor County

☐ **GRAYS HARBOR COMMUNITY HOSPITAL (500031)**, 915 Anderson Drive, Zip 98520–1006; tel. 360/532–8330, (Nonreporting) **A**1 5 10 20
Primary Contact: Tom Jensen, Chief Executive Officer
CMO: Anne Marie Wong, M.D., Chief Medical Officer
CIO: Brad Wallace, Director Information Services
CHR: Julie Feller, Executive Director Human Resources
CNO: Melanie Brandt Esq Chief Nursing Officer
Web address: www.ghcares.org
Control: Other not–for–profit (including NFP Corporation) **Service**: General medical and surgical

Staffed Beds: 105

ANACORTES—Skagit County

★ ⚕ **ISLAND HOSPITAL (500007)**, 1211 24th Street, Zip 98221–2562; tel. 360/299–1300, **A**2 5 10 21 **F**3 8 11 13 15 28 29 30 31 34 35 40 43 45 50 53 57 59 64 70 75 76 77 78 79 81 82 84 85 86 89 93 96 97 99 100 104 107 108 110 111 114 115 116 119 127 129 130 132 134 135 144 146 147 148 149 157
Primary Contact: Vincent Oliver, FACHE, Administrator
CFO: Elise Cutter, Chief Financial Officer
CIO: Tom Bluhm, Director Information Systems
CNO: Lois Pate, R.N., Chief Nursing Officer
Web address: www.islandhospital.org
Control: Hospital district or authority, Government, nonfederal **Service**: General medical and surgical

Staffed Beds: 43 **Admissions**: 2610 **Census**: 22 **Outpatient Visits**: 109254 **Births**: 441 **Total Expense ($000)**: 98648 **Payroll Expense ($000)**: 41292 **Personnel**: 576

ARLINGTON—Snohomish County

⚕ **CASCADE VALLEY HOSPITAL (500060)**, 330 South Stillaguamish Avenue, Zip 98223–1642; tel. 360/435–2133, (Nonreporting) **A**10 21 **S** Skagit Regional Health, Mount Vernon, WA
Primary Contact: Brian K. Ivie, President and Chief Executive Officer
COO: Jim Geist, Executive Vice President and Chief Operating Officer
CFO: Thomas Litaker, Regional Vice President and Chief Financial Officer
CMO: Rosana Go, M.D., Medical Staff President
CHR: Deborah Martin, Regional Vice President Human Resources
CNO: Michelle Sand, R.N., MSN, Vice President and Chief Nursing Officer
Web address: www.cascadevalley.org
Control: Hospital district or authority, Government, nonfederal **Service**: General medical and surgical

Staffed Beds: 48

AUBURN—King County

☐ **MULTICARE AUBURN MEDICAL CENTER (500015)**, 202 North Division, Plaza One, Zip 98001–4908; tel. 253/833–7711, **A**1 10 **F**3 13 18 20 22 28 29 30 34 35 40 43 45 49 50 51 56 57 64 65 68 70 73 74 75 76 77 79 81 84 85 87 93 96 98 102 103 107 108 111 114 115 119 126 129 130 132 135 146 147 148 149 **S** MultiCare Health System, Tacoma, WA
Primary Contact: Mark T. Smith, JD, CPA, President and Chief Operating Officer
CMO: Chad Krilich, M.D., Chief Med Officer-AMC/CMC
CHR: Kevin B Dull, Senior Vice President Human Potential
CNO: Roseanna Bell, Chief Nurse Executive
Web address: www.https://www.multicare.org/auburn-medical-center/
Control: Other not–for–profit (including NFP Corporation) **Service**: General medical and surgical

Staffed Beds: 153 **Admissions**: 6853 **Census**: 120 **Outpatient Visits**: 72323 **Births**: 1163 **Total Expense ($000)**: 194135 **Payroll Expense ($000)**: 75913 **Personnel**: 760

BELLEVUE—King County

⊞ **OVERLAKE MEDICAL CENTER (500051)**, 1035 116th Avenue NE, Zip 98004–4604; tel. 425/688–5000, **A**1 2 3 5 10 **F**3 8 11 12 13 15 17 18 20 22 24 26 29 30 31 34 35 36 37 38 40 41 43 45 46 47 48 49 54 55 56 57 58 59 61 64 65 68 70 72 73 74 75 76 77 78 79 81 82 84 85 86 87 92 93 97 98 100 101 102 103 104 105 107 108 110 111 114 115 118 119 120 121 123 124 126 130 131 132 135 145 146 147 148 149 153 154 156
Primary Contact: J. Michael Marsh, President and Chief Executive Officer
COO: Thomas DeBord, Chief Operating Officer
CFO: Andrew Tokar, Chief Financial Officer
CMO: David Knoepfler, M.D., Chief Medical Officer
CHR: Lisa M Brock, Chief Human Resource Officer
Web address: www.overlakehospital.org
Control: Other not–for–profit (including NFP Corporation) **Service**: General medical and surgical

Staffed Beds: 292 **Admissions**: 18295 **Census**: 185 **Outpatient Visits**: 240689 **Births**: 3608 **Total Expense ($000)**: 528623 **Payroll Expense ($000)**: 231374 **Personnel**: 2283

BELLINGHAM—Whatcom County

★ △ ⚕ **PEACEHEALTH ST. JOSEPH MEDICAL CENTER (500030)**, 2901 Squalicum Parkway, Zip 98225–1851; tel. 360/734–5400, **A**2 5 7 10 20 21 **F**11 13 18 20 22 24 26 28 29 30 31 34 35 36 39 40 43 45 47 48 49 50 51 57 58 59 63 64 68 70 73 75 76 77 80 81 83 85 87 89 90 93 96 98 100 102 107 108 111 115 119 120 121 123 124 126 130 132 146 148 149 154 **S** PeaceHealth, Vancouver, WA
Primary Contact: Dale Zender, President Hospital Services NW
COO: Stephen R Omta, Chief Operating Officer
CFO: Eric Brettner, NWN Chief Financial Officer
CMO: Chris Sprowl, M.D., Vice President
CIO: Kelly Lundy, Chief Information Officer
CHR: Cindy C Klein, Vice President Human Resources
Web address: www.peacehealth.org
Control: Other not–for–profit (including NFP Corporation) **Service**: General medical and surgical

Staffed Beds: 255 **Admissions**: 15613 **Census**: 191 **Outpatient Visits**: 101806 **Births**: 2031 **Total Expense ($000)**: 423453 **Payroll Expense ($000)**: 148534 **Personnel**: 1669

⚕ **ST. JOSEPH HOSPITAL** See Peacehealth St. Joseph Medical Center

BREMERTON—Kitsap County

⊞ **HARRISON MEDICAL CENTER (500039)**, 2520 Cherry Avenue, Zip 98310–4229; tel. 360/744–3911, **A**1 2 3 5 10 19 **F**3 11 12 13 15 18 20 22 24 26 28 29 30 31 34 35 38 40 43 44 45 46 49 50 54 57 59 60 64 70 73 74 75 76 77 78 79 80 81 82 84 85 86 87 93 94 96 107 108 110 111 114 115 117 119 120 121 124 126 129 130 132 135 144 146 147 148 149 154 **S** CommonSpirit Health, Chicago, IL
Primary Contact: David W. Schultz, FACHE, President, Peninsula Region
COO: Matthew Wheelus, Vice President, Chief Operating Officer
CFO: Mike Fitzgerald, Chief Financial Officer
CMO: David Weiss, M.D., Vice President, Medical Operations, Peninsula Region
CIO: Rand Strobel, Regional Chief Information Officer, Information Technology Services
CHR: Vickie Lackman, Human Resource Director, Peninsula Region
CNO: Jeanell Rasmussen, R.N., Vice President Patient Care Services and Chief Nursing Officer
Web address: www.chifranciscan.org/harrison
Control: Church operated, Nongovernment, not–for–profit **Service**: General medical and surgical

Staffed Beds: 232 **Admissions**: 13266 **Census**: 163 **Outpatient Visits**: 322832 **Births**: 1995 **Total Expense ($000)**: 427226 **Payroll Expense ($000)**: 129272 **Personnel**: 1943

Many Facility Codes have changed. Please refer to the AHA Guide Code Chart.   © 2019 AHA Guide

✠ **NAVAL HOSPITAL BREMERTON**, One Boone Road, Zip 98312–1898;
tel. 360/475–4000, **A**1 3 5 **F**3 5 8 12 13 15 18 29 30 32 33 34 35 38 39 45
50 54 57 59 64 65 67 74 75 76 77 79 81 82 85 86 87 92 93 97 98 99 100
101 104 107 108 111 114 115 119 130 131 132 134 135 144 146 147 149
151 153 154 156 157 **S** Bureau of Medicine and Surgery, Department of the
Navy, Falls Church, VA
Primary Contact: Captain Jeffrey Bitterman, Commanding Officer
CFO: Judith Hogan, Comptroller and Director Resources and Logistics
CIO: Patrick Flaherty, Director Management Information
Web address: www.med.navy.mil/sites/nhbrem/Pages/default.aspx
Control: Department of Defense, Government, federal **Service**: General medical
and surgical

Staffed Beds: 23 **Admissions**: 851 **Census**: 5 **Outpatient Visits**: 274689
Births: 476 **Personnel**: 1200

BREWSTER—Okanogan County

THREE RIVERS HOSPITAL (501324), 507 Hospital Way, Zip 98812–0577,
Mailing Address: P.O. Box 577, Zip 98812–0577; tel. 509/689–2517,
(Nonreporting) **A**10 18
Primary Contact: Scott Graham, Chief Executive Officer
CFO: Jennifer Munson, Chief Financial Officer
CMO: Gordon Tagge, M.D., President Medical Staff
CIO: Edgar Alejandro Arellano, Chief Information Technologist
CHR: Anita Fisk, Director Human Resources
CNO: Gretchen Aguilar, Director Patient Care and Chief Nursing Officer
Web address: www.threerivershospital.net
Control: Hospital district or authority, Government, nonfederal **Service**: General
medical and surgical

Staffed Beds: 20

BURIEN—King County

✠ △ **HIGHLINE MEDICAL CENTER (500011)**, 16251 Sylvester Road SW,
Zip 98166–3052; tel. 206/244–9970, **A**1 2 7 10 **F**3 11 13 15 18 28 29 30 31
34 35 38 40 43 44 45 49 50 51 57 59 60 64 70 72 74 75 76 77 78 79 80 81
85 86 87 92 93 102 107 108 110 111 114 115 117 119 126 129 130 131
132 135 146 147 148 149 **S** CommonSpirit Health, Chicago, IL
Primary Contact: Anthony McLean, President
COO: Russell Woolley, Chief Operating Officer
CMO: Dennis De Leon, M.D., Associate Chief Medical Officer and Vice President
Medical Affairs
CHR: Sharon Royne, Senior Vice President: Human Resources
CNO: Kim Baisch, R.N., Associate Vice President Patient Care Services
Web address: www.https://www.chifranciscan.org/highline-medical-center.html
Control: Church operated, Nongovernment, not-for-profit **Service**: General
medical and surgical

Staffed Beds: 115 **Admissions**: 6923 **Census**: 86 **Outpatient
Visits**: 117782 **Births**: 968 **Total Expense ($000)**: 190981 **Payroll Expense
($000)**: 62240 **Personnel**: 843

✠ **REGIONAL HOSPITAL FOR RESPIRATORY AND COMPLEX CARE (502001)**,
16251 Sylvester Road SW, Zip 98166–3017; tel. 206/248–4548, **A**1 10 **F**1
29 30 44 50 60 75 85 87 130 132 135 148 149 154 **S** CommonSpirit Health,
Chicago, IL
Primary Contact: Anne McBride, Chief Executive Officer
CMO: Embra Roper, Chief Medical Officer
CHR: Valerie Albano, Director, Human Resources
CNO: Christi Sifri, Chief Nursing Executive
Web address: www.regionalhospital.org
Control: Church operated, Nongovernment, not-for-profit **Service**: Acute long-
term care hospital

Staffed Beds: 26 **Admissions**: 182 **Census**: 17 **Outpatient Visits**: 0
Births: 0 **Total Expense ($000)**: 16737 **Payroll Expense ($000)**: 6696
Personnel: 72

CENTRALIA—Lewis County

✠ **PROVIDENCE CENTRALIA HOSPITAL (500019)**, 914 S Scheuber RD,
Zip 98531–9027, Mailing Address: 914 South Scheuber Road, Zip 98531–9027;
tel. 360/736–2803, **A**1 3 5 10 20 **F**3 8 11 13 15 29 30 31 34 35 40 43 50 51
57 58 59 64 68 70 75 76 77 78 79 80 81 82 84 85 86 87 93 107 108 110
111 114 115 116 117 118 119 120 121 123 124 130 132 146 148 149 150
154 **S** Providence St. Joseph Health, Renton, WA
Primary Contact: Medrice Coluccio, R.N., Southwest Region Chief Executive
CFO: Denise Marroni, Chief Financial Officer
CMO: Kevin Caserta, M.D., Chief Medical Officer
CIO: Kerry Miles, Site Director
CHR: Susan Meenk, Vice President Service Area
CNO: Michelle James, Regional Chief Nursing Officer
Web address: www.providence.org
Control: Church operated, Nongovernment, not-for-profit **Service**: General
medical and surgical

Staffed Beds: 91 **Admissions**: 4564 **Census**: 50 **Outpatient Visits**: 296737
Births: 662 **Total Expense ($000)**: 108192 **Payroll Expense ($000)**: 52877
Personnel: 655

CHELAN—Chelan County

★ **LAKE CHELAN COMMUNITY HOSPITAL AND CLINICS (501334)**, 503
East Highland Avenue, Zip 98816–8631, Mailing Address: P.O. Box 908,
Zip 98816–0908; tel. 509/682–3300, (Nonreporting) **A**3 10 18
Primary Contact: Steven D. Patonai, Interim Chief Executive Officer
COO: Brad Hankins, Chief Operating Quality Officer
CFO: Vickie Bodle, Chief Financial Officer
CMO: Ty Witt, M.D., Chief Medical Officer
CIO: Ross Hurd, Chief Information Officer
CHR: DeLynn K Barnett, Director Human Resources
Web address: www.lakechelancommunityhospital.com
Control: Hospital district or authority, Government, nonfederal **Service**: General
medical and surgical

Staffed Beds: 25

CHEWELAH—Stevens County

✠ **PROVIDENCE ST. JOSEPH'S HOSPITAL (501309)**, 500 East Webster Street,
Zip 99109–9523; tel. 509/935–8211, (Total facility includes 40 beds in nursing
home-type unit) **A**1 10 18 **F**3 10 11 15 29 30 34 35 40 43 44 45 57 64 68 75
81 82 84 85 86 87 93 107 114 119 128 130 133 146 148 154 **S** Providence
St. Joseph Health, Renton, WA
Primary Contact: Ronald G. Rehn, Chief Executive Officer
CFO: Helen Andrus, Chief Financial Officer
CMO: Jeff Collins, Chief Medical Officer
CNO: Deborah Watson, R.N., Chief Nursing Officer
Web address: www.washington.providence.org/hospitals/st-josephs-hospital/
Control: Church operated, Nongovernment, not-for-profit **Service**: General
medical and surgical

Staffed Beds: 55 **Admissions**: 482 **Census**: 42 **Outpatient Visits**: 27238
Births: 0 **Total Expense ($000)**: 23614 **Payroll Expense ($000)**: 10129
Personnel: 104

CLARKSTON—Asotin County

★ ⇑ **TRI-STATE MEMORIAL HOSPITAL (501332)**, 1221 Highland Avenue,
Zip 99403–2829, Mailing Address: P.O. Box 189, Zip 99403–0189;
tel. 509/758–5511, (Nonreporting) **A**10 18 21
Primary Contact: Donald Wee, Chief Executive Officer
CFO: Alex Town, Vice President Finance
CMO: Don Greggain, M.D., Physician Network Director
CIO: Joleen Carper, Vice President Quality and Risk
CHR: Regana Davis, Vice President Human Resources
CNO: Rhonda Mason, Vice President of Patient Care Services
Web address: www.tsmh.org
Control: Other not-for-profit (including NFP Corporation) **Service**: General
medical and surgical

Staffed Beds: 25

WA

COLFAX—Whitman County

★ **WHITMAN HOSPITAL AND MEDICAL CENTER (501327)**, 1200 West Fairview Street, Zip 99111–9579; tel. 509/397–3435, **A**10 18 **F**13 15 29 34 35 36 40 43 45 50 53 64 68 75 76 79 81 82 84 85 87 93 107 110 111 119 130 131 133 154 156 **S** Providence St. Joseph Health, Renton, WA
Primary Contact: Hank Hanigan, FACHE, Chief Executive Officer
CFO: Hank Hanigan, FACHE, Interim Chief Financial Officer
CMO: Bryan N Johnson, M.D., Chief Medical Officer
CHR: Michelle Ellis, Director Human Resources
CNO: Pam Akin, R.N., MSN, Chief Nursing Officer
Web address: www.whitmanhospital.org
Control: Hospital district or authority, Government, nonfederal **Service**: General medical and surgical

Staffed Beds: 25 **Admissions**: 847 **Census**: 9 **Outpatient Visits**: 20953
Births: 43 **Total Expense ($000)**: 30819 **Payroll Expense ($000)**: 12238
Personnel: 177

COLVILLE—Stevens County

✉ **PROVIDENCE MOUNT CARMEL HOSPITAL (501326)**, 982 East Columbia Avenue, Zip 99114–3352; tel. 509/685–5100, **A**1 3 10 18 **F**3 11 13 15 29 30 34 35 40 43 44 45 57 64 68 70 75 76 77 79 81 82 84 85 86 87 93 107 108 115 118 119 123 129 131 132 133 146 148 154 **S** Providence St. Joseph Health, Renton, WA
Primary Contact: Ronald G. Rehn, Chief Executive Officer
CFO: Helen Andrus, Chief Financial Officer
CNO: Deborah Watson, R.N., Chief Nursing Officer
Web address: www.mtcarmelhospital.org
Control: Church operated, Nongovernment, not–for–profit **Service**: General medical and surgical

Staffed Beds: 25 **Admissions**: 1008 **Census**: 14 **Outpatient Visits**: 79615
Births: 208 **Total Expense ($000)**: 52142 **Payroll Expense ($000)**: 17086
Personnel: 202

COUPEVILLE—Island County

★ **WHIDBEYHEALTH (501339)**, 101 North Main Street, Zip 98239–3413; tel. 360/678–5151, (Nonreporting) **A**2 10 18
Primary Contact: Ron Telles, Interim Chief Executive Officer
CFO: Ron Telles, Chief Financial Officer
CMO: Gabe Barrio, M.D., Chief of Staff
CNO: Linda Stephens Gipson, MSN, Ph.D., Chief Nursing Officer
Web address: www.https://whidbeyhealth.org/
Control: Hospital district or authority, Government, nonfederal **Service**: General medical and surgical

Staffed Beds: 25

DAVENPORT—Lincoln County

★ **LINCOLN HOSPITAL (501305)**, 10 Nicholls Street, Zip 99122–9729; tel. 509/725–7101, (Nonreporting) **A**10 18
Primary Contact: Tyson Lacy, Chief Executive Officer and Superintendent
CFO: Tim O'Connell, Chief Financial Officer
CMO: Fred Reed, M.D., Chief of Staff
CIO: Elliott Donson, Chief Information Specialist
CHR: Becky Bailey, Director Human Resources
CNO: Jennifer Larmer, R.N., Chief Clinical Officer
Web address: www.lincolnhospital.org
Control: Hospital district or authority, Government, nonfederal **Service**: General medical and surgical

Staffed Beds: 60

DAYTON—Columbia County

COLUMBIA COUNTY HEALTH SYSTEM (501302), 1012 South Third Street, Zip 99328–1696; tel. 509/382–2531, (Nonreporting) **A**10 18
Primary Contact: Shane McGuire, Chief Executive Officer
CHR: Steven J Stahl, Director Human Resources
CNO: Stephanie Carpenter, Director of Nursing Services
Web address: www.cchd-wa.org
Control: County, Government, nonfederal **Service**: General medical and surgical

Staffed Beds: 44

EDMONDS—Snohomish County

⇑ **STEVENS HEALTHCARE** See Swedish/Edmonds

★ ⇑ **SWEDISH/EDMONDS (500026)**, 21601 76th Avenue West, Zip 98026–7506; tel. 425/640–4000, **A**2 10 21 **F**2 3 11 13 15 18 20 22 26 28 29 30 31 34 35 38 40 41 43 45 49 56 59 60 61 64 65 68 70 73 74 75 76 77 78 79 81 82 84 85 87 91 92 93 96 98 100 101 102 104 107 108 111 114 115 116 119 124 126 129 130 131 132 135 141 146 147 148 149 154 **S** Swedish Health Services, Seattle, WA
Primary Contact: Sarah Zabel, Vice President, Operations
CMO: Sandeep Sachdeva, M.D., Vice President Medical Affairs
CNO: Jean Doerge, R.N., MSN, Nurse Executive
Web address: www.swedish.org
Control: Other not–for–profit (including NFP Corporation) **Service**: General medical and surgical

Staffed Beds: 185 **Admissions**: 10859 **Census**: 134 **Outpatient Visits**: 128329 **Births**: 1342 **Total Expense ($000)**: 269626 **Payroll Expense ($000)**: 93452 **Personnel**: 785

ELLENSBURG—Kittitas County

★ **KITTITAS VALLEY HEALTHCARE (501333)**, 603 South Chestnut Street, Zip 98926–3875; tel. 509/962–7302, **A**3 10 18 **F**3 11 13 15 29 30 34 35 37 40 41 43 44 45 46 50 56 57 59 62 63 64 65 68 70 73 75 76 77 79 81 84 85 87 89 93 96 102 104 107 110 111 115 119 127 130 131 132 144 146 147 148 149 154 156
Primary Contact: Julie Petersen, CPA, Chief Executive Officer
CFO: Libby Allgood, Chief Financial Officer
CMO: Don Solberg, M.D., Chief Medical Officer
CIO: Jack Schwartz, Director Information Technology
CHR: Carrie Youngblood, Director of Human Resources
CNO: Vicky Machorro, R.N., Chief Nursing Officer
Web address: www.kvhealthcare.org
Control: Hospital district or authority, Government, nonfederal **Service**: General medical and surgical

Staffed Beds: 25 **Admissions**: 956 **Census**: 7 **Outpatient Visits**: 86737
Births: 320 **Total Expense ($000)**: 78280 **Payroll Expense ($000)**: 40233
Personnel: 511

ELMA—Grays Harbor County

SUMMIT PACIFIC MEDICAL CENTER (501304), 600 East Main Street, Zip 98541–9560; tel. 360/346–2222, (Nonreporting) **A**10 18
Primary Contact: Josh Martin, Chief Executive Officer
COO: Josh Martin, Chief Operating Officer
CFO: James Hansen, Chief Financial Officer
CMO: William Hurley, M.D., Chief Medical Officer
CIO: Jeff Painter, Manager Information Technology
CHR: Mindy Portchy, Manager Human Resources
Web address: www.markreed.org
Control: Corporation, Investor–owned (for–profit) **Service**: General medical and surgical

Staffed Beds: 6

ENUMCLAW—King County

★ **ST. ELIZABETH HOSPITAL (501335)**, 1455 Battersby Avenue, Zip 98022–3634, Mailing Address: P.O. Box 218, Zip 98022–0218; tel. 360/802–8800, **A**10 18 **F**3 13 15 18 29 30 35 38 40 44 45 50 59 64 70 74 75 76 79 81 85 87 93 107 108 110 111 115 119 130 132 133 135 146 147 149 154 **S** CommonSpirit Health, Chicago, IL
Primary Contact: Syd Bersante, R.N., Market President
COO: Joseph Wilczek, Chief Executive Officer
CFO: Philip Hjembo, Chief Financial Officer
CHR: Jerilyn Ray, Manager Human Resources
Web address: www.fhshealth.org
Control: Church operated, Nongovernment, not–for–profit **Service**: General medical and surgical

Staffed Beds: 25 **Admissions**: 1622 **Census**: 15 **Outpatient Visits**: 37461
Births: 352 **Total Expense ($000)**: 48439 **Payroll Expense ($000)**: 17237
Personnel: 267

WA

EPHRATA—Grant County

★ **COLUMBIA BASIN HOSPITAL (501317)**, 200 Nat Washington Way, Zip 98823–1982; tel. 509/754–4631, (Total facility includes 12 beds in nursing home–type unit) **A**10 18 **F**3 10 11 15 29 30 31 34 35 40 50 56 59 65 75 77 84 91 93 97 107 108 111 114 119 127 130 132 133 146
Primary Contact: Rosalinda Kibby, Superintendent and Administrator
CFO: Rhonda Handley, Chief Financial Officer
CMO: Lowell C Allred, M.D., Chief of Staff
CHR: Suzanne Little, Human Resources Specialist
Web address: www.columbiabasinhospital.org
Control: Hospital district or authority, Government, nonfederal **Service:** General medical and surgical

Staffed Beds: 69 **Admissions:** 330 **Census:** 15 **Outpatient Visits:** 19329
Births: 0 **Total Expense ($000):** 19460 **Payroll Expense ($000):** 7845
Personnel: 134

EVERETT—Snohomish County

⊞ △ **PROVIDENCE REGIONAL MEDICAL CENTER EVERETT (500014)**, 1321 Colby Avenue, Zip 98201–1665, Mailing Address: P.O. Box 1147, Zip 98206–1147; tel. 425/261–2000, (Includes PROVIDENCE EVERETT MEDICAL CENTER - COLBY CAMPUS, 1321 Colby Avenue, Everett, Washington, Zip 98206, Mailing Address: P O Box 1147, Zip 98206, tel. 425/261–2000; PROVIDENCE EVERETT MEDICAL CENTER - PACIFIC CAMPUS, Pacific and Nassau Streets, Everett, Washington, Zip 98201, Mailing Address: P O Box 1067, Zip 98206–1067, tel. 206/258–7123) **A**1 2 3 5 7 10 **F**3 4 5 11 12 13 15 18 20 22 24 26 28 29 30 31 32 34 35 36 37 38 40 43 44 45 46 47 48 49 50 54 55 56 57 58 59 61 64 68 70 72 73 74 75 76 77 78 79 80 81 84 85 86 87 89 90 93 94 96 100 107 108 109 110 111 114 115 116 118 119 120 121 123 124 126 129 130 132 135 146 147 148 149 150 154 157 **S** Providence St. Joseph Health, Renton, WA
Primary Contact: Kim Williams, R.N., MS, Chief Executive Officer
CFO: Sheri Feeney, Chief Financial Officer
CMO: Frank Andersen, Interim Chief Medical Officer
CIO: Matt Wonser, Director, Information Services
CHR: Lori A Vocca, Vice President Human Resources
CNO: Barbara M Hyland-Hill, R.N., Chief Nursing Officer
Web address: www.providence.org
Control: Church operated, Nongovernment, not–for–profit **Service:** General medical and surgical

Staffed Beds: 530 **Admissions:** 29876 **Census:** 421 **Outpatient Visits:** 480736 **Births:** 4466 **Total Expense ($000):** 589084 **Payroll Expense ($000):** 259503 **Personnel:** 3098

FEDERAL WAY—King County

⊞ **ST. FRANCIS HOSPITAL (500141)**, 34515 Ninth Avenue South, Zip 98003–6799; tel. 253/944–8100, **A**1 2 3 10 **F**3 8 11 12 13 15 18 20 22 26 28 29 30 31 34 35 38 40 43 44 45 49 50 51 57 59 60 64 70 72 74 75 76 77 78 79 80 81 85 86 87 92 93 107 108 110 111 114 115 117 119 126 129 130 131 132 135 146 147 149 154 **S** CommonSpirit Health, Chicago, IL
Primary Contact: Anthony McLean, Market President
COO: Dino Johnson, R.N., Chief Operating Officer and Chief Nursing Officer
CFO: Mike Fitzgerald, Chief Financial Officer
CMO: Dennis deLeon, M.D., Chief Medical Officer, King Region
CIO: Rand Strobel, Regional Chief Information Officer
CHR: Les Soltis, Director - Human Resources
CNO: Dino Johnson, R.N., Chief Operating Officer and Chief Nursing Officer
Web address: www.fhshealth.org
Control: Church operated, Nongovernment, not–for–profit **Service:** General medical and surgical

Staffed Beds: 124 **Admissions:** 8316 **Census:** 93 **Outpatient Visits:** 168379 **Births:** 1298 **Total Expense ($000):** 205073 **Payroll Expense ($000):** 68150 **Personnel:** 965

FORKS—Clallam County

⇑ **FORKS COMMUNITY HOSPITAL (501325)**, 530 Bogachiel Way, Zip 98331–9120; tel. 360/374–6271, (Nonreporting) **A**10 18 21
Primary Contact: Tim Cournyer, Administrator
CFO: Joe Bradick, Chief Financial Officer
CIO: Andrea Perkins-Peppers, Chief Information Officer
CHR: Cindy Paget, Chief Human Resources Officer
CNO: Laura Kripinski, Chief Nursing Officer
Web address: www.forkshospital.org
Control: Hospital district or authority, Government, nonfederal **Service:** General medical and surgical

Staffed Beds: 45

FRIDAY HARBOR—San Juan County

★ ⇑ **PEACEHEALTH PEACE ISLAND MEDICAL CENTER (501340)**, 1117 Spring Street, Zip 98250–9782; tel. 360/378–2141, **A**5 10 18 21 **F**29 30 31 34 40 45 59 64 65 68 75 78 79 81 97 100 102 104 107 115 119 130 132 135 146 149 154 **S** PeaceHealth, Vancouver, WA
Primary Contact: Merry Ann Keane, Chief Administrative Officer
CFO: Carolyn Foster, Chief Financial Officer
CMO: Michael Sullivan, M.D., Medical Director Emergency Services
CHR: Lorraine Allison, Human Resource Partner
CNO: Sheryl Murphy, Chief Nursing Officer and Director of Clinical Services
Web address: www.peacehealth.org
Control: Church operated, Nongovernment, not–for–profit **Service:** General medical and surgical

Staffed Beds: 10 **Admissions:** 85 **Census:** 1 **Outpatient Visits:** 14081
Births: 0 **Total Expense ($000):** 15149 **Payroll Expense ($000):** 5819
Personnel: 59

GIG HARBOR—Pierce County

⊞ **ST. ANTHONY HOSPITAL (500151)**, 11567 Canterwood Boulevard NW, Zip 98332–5812; tel. 253/530–2000, **A**1 3 10 **F**3 11 15 18 20 29 30 31 34 38 40 44 45 49 50 51 59 60 64 70 74 75 77 78 79 81 85 86 87 92 93 107 108 110 111 114 115 119 126 129 130 131 132 135 146 147 154 **S** CommonSpirit Health, Chicago, IL
Primary Contact: David W. Schultz, FACHE, President, Peninsula Region
Web address: www.chifranciscan.org/
Control: Church operated, Nongovernment, not–for–profit **Service:** General medical and surgical

Staffed Beds: 112 **Admissions:** 5513 **Census:** 72 **Outpatient Visits:** 77245
Births: 0 **Total Expense ($000):** 136507 **Payroll Expense ($000):** 41173
Personnel: 634

GOLDENDALE—Klickitat County

KLICKITAT VALLEY HEALTH (501316), 310 South Roosevelt Avenue, Zip 98620–9201; tel. 509/773–4022, (Nonreporting) **A**10 18
Primary Contact: Leslie Hiebert, Chief Executive Officer
CFO: Jamie Eldred, Controller
CMO: Rod Krehbiel, M.D., Chief of Staff
CIO: Jonathan Hatfield, Supervisor Information Technology
CHR: Herbert Hill, Director Human Resources
CNO: Gwen Cox, Director Nursing Services
Web address: www.kvhealth.net
Control: Hospital district or authority, Government, nonfederal **Service:** General medical and surgical

Staffed Beds: 17

GRAND COULEE—Grant County

COULEE COMMUNITY HOSPITAL See Coulee Medical Center

COULEE MEDICAL CENTER (501308), 411 Fortuyn Road, Zip 99133–8718; tel. 509/633–1753, **A**10 18 **F**8 15 29 32 40 41 43 45 47 48 50 56 57 59 64 65 75 76 79 81 82 83 84 85 86 87 93 97 107 110 114 119 127 128 130 133 144 147 148 149 154 156
Primary Contact: Ramona Hicks, Interim Chief Executive Officer
CFO: Paul Babcock, Chief Financial Officer
CMO: Andrew Castrodale, M.D., Chief Medical Officer
CHR: Heather McCleary, Director Human Resources
Web address: www.cmccares.org
Control: Hospital district or authority, Government, nonfederal **Service:** General medical and surgical

Staffed Beds: 25 **Admissions:** 509 **Census:** 16 **Outpatient Visits:** 27100
Births: 77 **Total Expense ($000):** 31465 **Payroll Expense ($000):** 14354
Personnel: 210

WA

ILWACO—Pacific County

★ **OCEAN BEACH HOSPITAL (501314)**, 174 First Avenue North, Zip 98624–9137, Mailing Address: P.O. Box H, Zip 98624–0258; tel. 360/642–3181, **A**10 18 **F**3 11 15 18 28 29 30 31 34 35 40 43 45 56 57 59 68 75 77 78 79 81 85 86 87 93 97 102 107 111 114 119 127 128 130 132 133 135 149 154 156
Primary Contact: Larry Cohen, Chief Executive Officer
CFO: Kathy Hubbard, Controller
CMO: Patty Malone, M.D., Chief Medical Officer
CIO: Julie P Oakes, R.N., Manager Risk and Quality
CHR: Beth Whitton, Director Human Resources
CNO: Linda Kaino, Chief Nursing Officer
Web address: www.oceanbeachhospital.com
Control: Hospital district or authority, Government, nonfederal **Service**: General medical and surgical

Staffed Beds: 15 **Admissions**: 402 **Census**: 4 **Outpatient Visits**: 40736 **Births**: 0 **Total Expense ($000)**: 27075 **Payroll Expense ($000)**: 11783 **Personnel**: 148

ISSAQUAH—King County

★ ⇑ **SWEDISH/ISSAQUAH (500152)**, 751 NE Blakely Drive, Zip 98029–6201; tel. 425/313–4000, **A**3 10 21 **F**3 12 13 15 18 20 22 29 30 31 34 35 37 38 40 41 45 48 49 50 56 57 58 59 61 64 65 68 70 73 74 75 76 77 78 79 81 82 85 86 87 89 92 93 96 97 102 107 108 110 111 114 115 119 126 129 130 131 132 134 135 141 143 146 147 148 149 154 **S** Swedish Health Services, Seattle, WA
Primary Contact: Guy Hudson, Chief Executive Officer
COO: Jeffery Robert, Chief Operating Officer
Web address: www.swedish.org/issaquah
Control: Other not–for–profit (including NFP Corporation) **Service**: General medical and surgical

Staffed Beds: 153 **Admissions**: 6877 **Census**: 57 **Outpatient Visits**: 126565 **Births**: 1595 **Total Expense ($000)**: 196243 **Payroll Expense ($000)**: 60512 **Personnel**: 504

KENNEWICK—Benton County

⊞ **TRIOS HEALTH (500053)**, 900 South Auburn Street, Zip 99336–5621, Mailing Address: P.O. Box 6128, Zip 99336–0128; tel. 509/586–6111, (Data for 150 days) **A**1 2 3 5 10 13 **F**3 11 12 13 15 18 22 28 29 31 34 35 40 43 45 49 50 56 57 59 64 65 70 73 75 76 77 78 81 82 84 85 87 89 97 107 108 110 111 115 118 119 126 129 130 132 144 146 147 148 156 157 **S** LifePoint Health, Brentwood, TN
Primary Contact: John H. Solheim, Chief Executive Officer
CFO: Jason Hotchkiss, CPA, Chief Financial Officer
CIO: Michael Cloutier, Director Information Services
CHR: Russ Keefer, Chief Human Resources Officer
Web address: www.trioshealth.org
Control: Corporation, Investor–owned (for–profit) **Service**: General medical and surgical

Staffed Beds: 96 **Admissions**: 2259 **Census**: 48 **Outpatient Visits**: 65408 **Births**: 571 **Total Expense ($000)**: 48629 **Payroll Expense ($000)**: 18552 **Personnel**: 647

KIRKLAND—King County

EVERGREEN HEALTHCARE See Evergreenhealth

⊞ **EVERGREENHEALTH (500124)**, 12040 NE 128th Street, Zip 98034–3013; tel. 425/899–1000, **A**1 2 3 5 10 **F**3 8 12 13 15 18 20 22 28 29 30 34 35 37 38 40 42 43 44 45 46 49 50 51 54 55 56 57 58 59 61 62 63 64 65 68 70 71 72 73 74 75 76 78 79 80 81 82 84 85 86 87 89 90 91 92 93 94 95 96 97 100 104 107 108 110 111 114 115 119 120 121 123 124 126 129 130 131 132 134 135 142 144 146 147 148 149 154 156
Primary Contact: Jeffrey Tomlin, M.D., Chief Executive Officer
CFO: Tina Mycroft, Senior Vice President, Chief Financial Officer
CIO: Tom Martin, Senior Vice President, Strategy and Information Technology Officer
CHR: Bob Sampson, Senior Vice President, Human Resources
CNO: Nancee Hofmeister, R.N., Senior Vice President, Chief Nursing Officer
Web address: www.evergreenhealth.com
Control: Hospital district or authority, Government, nonfederal **Service**: General medical and surgical

Staffed Beds: 318 **Admissions**: 15068 **Census**: 168 **Outpatient Visits**: 1166560 **Births**: 4626 **Total Expense ($000)**: 681575 **Payroll Expense ($000)**: 373597 **Personnel**: 3660

FAIRFAX BEHAVIORAL HEALTH (504002), 10200 NE 132nd Street, Zip 98034–2899; tel. 425/821–2000, (Includes FAIRFAX BEHAVIORAL HEALTH EVERETT, 916 Pacific Avenue, Everett, Washington, Zip 98201–4147; tel. 425/821–2000) **A**1 10 **F**29 30 50 64 87 97 98 99 100 101 103 105 130 153 154 **S** Universal Health Services, Inc., King of Prussia, PA
Primary Contact: Beckie Shauinger, Chief Executive Officer
COO: Todd Thama, Chief Operating Officer
CFO: Pam Rhoads, Chief Financial Officer
CMO: Samir Aziz, M.D., Medical Director
CHR: Anne Schreiber, Manager Human Resources
Web address: www.fairfaxhospital.com
Control: Corporation, Investor–owned (for–profit) **Service**: Psychiatric

Staffed Beds: 221 **Admissions**: 5419 **Census**: 186 **Outpatient Visits**: 4623 **Births**: 0 **Total Expense ($000)**: 73850 **Payroll Expense ($000)**: 29186 **Personnel**: 412

LAKEWOOD—Pierce County

⊞ △ **ST. CLARE HOSPITAL (500021)**, 11315 Bridgeport Way SW, Zip 98499–3004; tel. 253/985–1711, **A**1 2 3 7 10 **F**3 8 18 29 30 31 34 35 38 40 44 45 49 50 51 57 59 60 64 70 74 75 77 78 79 80 81 82 85 86 87 92 93 107 108 111 114 119 126 129 130 131 132 135 146 149 154 **S** CommonSpirit Health, Chicago, IL
Primary Contact: Syd Bersante, R.N., President
CFO: Mike Fitzgerald, Chief Financial Officer
CIO: Bruce Elkington, Regional Chief Information Officer
CHR: David C. Lawson, Senior Vice President Human Resources
Web address: www.fhshealth.org
Control: Church operated, Nongovernment, not–for–profit **Service**: General medical and surgical

Staffed Beds: 104 **Admissions**: 5772 **Census**: 83 **Outpatient Visits**: 97756 **Births**: 0 **Total Expense ($000)**: 140886 **Payroll Expense ($000)**: 46888 **Personnel**: 662

LEAVENWORTH—Chelan County

★ **CASCADE MEDICAL CENTER (501313)**, 817 Commercial Street, Zip 98826–1316; tel. 509/548–5815, (Nonreporting) **A**5 10 18
Primary Contact: Diane Blake, Chief Executive Officer
COO: Amy Webb, Chief Operating Officer
CFO: Jim Hopkins, Chief Financial Officer
CMO: Karl Kranz, M.D., Chief of Staff
CIO: Charles Amstutz, Director of Information Technology
CHR: Reyne Boik, Director Human Resources
Web address: www.cascademedical.org
Control: Hospital district or authority, Government, nonfederal **Service**: General medical and surgical

Staffed Beds: 9

LONGVIEW—Cowlitz County

⊞ ⇑ **PEACEHEALTH ST. JOHN MEDICAL CENTER (500041)**, 1615 Delaware Street, Zip 98632–2367, Mailing Address: P.O. Box 3002, Zip 98632–0302; tel. 360/414–2000, **A**1 2 10 21 **F**40 70 76 81 98 **S** PeaceHealth, Vancouver, WA
Primary Contact: Cherelle Montanye-Ireland, Chief Administrative Officer
CFO: Ronald K Benfield, Chief Financial Officer
CMO: Sheila Lynam, M.D., Chief Medical Officer
CHR: Kelley Frengle, Director, Human Resources
Web address: www.peacehealth.org
Control: Church operated, Nongovernment, not–for–profit **Service**: General medical and surgical

Staffed Beds: 180 **Admissions**: 7319 **Census**: 78 **Outpatient Visits**: 112798 **Births**: 786 **Total Expense ($000)**: 191378 **Payroll Expense ($000)**: 76880 **Personnel**: 1004

MARYSVILLE—Snohomish County

☐ **SMOKEY POINT BEHAVIORAL HOSPITAL (504012)**, 3955 156th Street Northeast, Zip 98271; tel. 844/202–5555, (Nonreporting) **A**1 10
Primary Contact: Sally Ann. Schneider, Chief Executive Officer
Web address: www.smokeypointbehavioralhospital.com
Control: Other not–for–profit (including NFP Corporation) **Service**: Psychiatric

Staffed Beds: 115

Many Facility Codes have changed. Please refer to the AHA Guide Code Chart. © 2019 AHA Guide

MEDICAL LAKE—Spokane County

☐ **EASTERN STATE HOSPITAL (504004)**, Maple Street, Zip 99022–0045, Mailing Address: P.O. Box 800, Zip 99022–0800; tel. 509/565–4705, **A**1 3 10 **F**29 30 39 59 65 68 75 77 86 98 100 101 103 130 132 135 143 146 149
Primary Contact: Mark Kettner, Interim Chief Executive Officer
COO: Ronda Kenney, Chief Operating Officer
CMO: Kamal Floura, M.D., Medical Director
CNO: Chet Roshetko, Chief Nursing Officer
Web address: www.dshs.wa.gov/bha/division-state-hospitals/eastern-state-hospital-overview
Control: State, Government, nonfederal **Service**: Psychiatric

Staffed Beds: 317 **Admissions**: 509 **Census**: 268 **Outpatient Visits**: 0 **Births**: 0

MONROE—Snohomish County

★ ⇑ **EVERGREENHEALTH MONROE (500084)**, 14701 179th SE, Zip 98272–1108, Mailing Address: P.O. Box 646, Zip 98272–0646; tel. 360/794–7497, (Nonreporting) **A**10 21
Primary Contact: Lisa LaPlante, Interim Chief Executive Officer
CFO: Scott Olander, Chief Financial Officer
CMO: Jack Handley, M.D., Chief Medical Officer
CIO: John Gepford, Director Information Systems
CHR: Kathryn Rothberg, Director Human Resources
CNO: Brenda West, R.N., MSN, Chief Nursing Officer
Web address: www.evergreenhealthmonroe.com
Control: Hospital district or authority, Government, nonfederal **Service**: General medical and surgical

Staffed Beds: 68

MORTON—Lewis County

★ **ARBOR HEALTH, MORTON HOSPITAL (501319)**, 521 Adams Avenue, Zip 98356–9323, Mailing Address: P.O. Box 1138, Zip 98356–0019; tel. 360/496–5112, **A**10 18 **F**29 34 40 45 50 64 68 81 93 97 107 110 111 114 119 127 129 130 133 135 147 148 154
Primary Contact: Leianne Everett, Chief Executive Officer
CFO: Geoff Hamilton, Interim Chief Financial Officer
CIO: Randy Nielsen, Director Information Technology
CHR: Shannon Kelly, Director Human Resources
CNO: Heidi Anderson, Chief Nursing Officer
Web address: www.https://www.myarborhealth.org/
Control: Hospital district or authority, Government, nonfederal **Service**: General medical and surgical

Staffed Beds: 25 **Admissions**: 234 **Census**: 4 **Outpatient Visits**: 31623 **Total Expense ($000)**: 20700 **Payroll Expense ($000)**: 13027 **Personnel**: 183

MOSES LAKE—Grant County

★ ⇑ **SAMARITAN HEALTHCARE (500033)**, 801 East Wheeler Road, Zip 98837–1899; tel. 509/765–5606, (Nonreporting) **A**5 10 20 21
Primary Contact: Theresa Sullivan, Chief Executive Officer
COO: Kris Neff, Chief Operating Officer
CFO: Alex Town, Chief Financial Officer
CMO: Andrea Carter, M.D., Chief Medical Officer
CNO: Becky DeMers, R.N., Chief Nursing Officer
Web address: www.samaritanhealthcare.com
Control: Hospital district or authority, Government, nonfederal **Service**: General medical and surgical

Staffed Beds: 50

MOUNT VERNON—Skagit County

★ ⇑ **SKAGIT REGIONAL HEALTH (500003)**, 1415 East Kincaid, Zip 98274–4126, Mailing Address: P.O. Box 1376, Zip 98273–1376; tel. 360/424–4111, **A**2 3 5 10 13 19 21 **F**3 11 13 18 20 22 26 28 29 30 31 34 35 36 40 41 43 44 45 46 47 48 49 50 51 53 54 57 59 60 64 68 70 73 75 76 77 78 79 81 82 84 85 86 87 89 93 96 97 98 100 107 108 111 114 115 116 117 118 119 120 121 123 124 126 127 130 131 132 146 147 148 149 154 156 **S** Skagit Regional Health, Mount Vernon, WA
Primary Contact: Brian K. Ivie, President and Chief Executive Officer
COO: Jim Geist, Executive Vice President and Chief Operating Officer
CFO: Paul Ishizuka, Chief Financial Officer
CMO: Jeffrey S. Gibbs, M.D., Regional Vice President Medical Affairs
CIO: John Dwight, Regional Vice President and Chief Information Officer
CHR: Deborah Martin, Regional Vice President Human Resources
CNO: Roxanne Olason, R.N., FACHE, Vice President and Chief Nursing Officer
Web address: www.skagitregionalhealth.org
Control: Hospital district or authority, Government, nonfederal **Service**: General medical and surgical

Staffed Beds: 202 **Admissions**: 8902 **Census**: 111 **Outpatient Visits**: 563499 **Births**: 1060 **Total Expense ($000)**: 395199 **Payroll Expense ($000)**: 176382 **Personnel**: 1940

NEWPORT—Pend Oreille County

NEWPORT HOSPITAL AND HEALTH SERVICES (501310), 714 West Pine Street, Zip 99156–9046; tel. 509/447–2441, (Total facility includes 50 beds in nursing home–type unit) **A**10 18 **F**8 11 13 15 32 34 40 41 42 50 57 59 64 75 76 77 79 81 82 87 89 93 97 107 111 114 119 127 128 130 133 146 147 148
Primary Contact: Thomas W. Wilbur, Chief Executive Officer and Superintendent
COO: Shelley Froehlich, R.N., Director Nursing Services
CMO: Clay Kersting, M.D., Chief Medical Staff
CIO: Walter Price, Director Information Technology
CHR: Joseph Clouse, Chief Administrative Officer
Web address: www.newporthospitalandhealth.org
Control: Hospital district or authority, Government, nonfederal **Service**: General medical and surgical

Staffed Beds: 74 **Admissions**: 487 **Census**: 5

OAK HARBOR—Island County

⊞ **NAVAL HOSPITAL OAK HARBOR**, 3475 North Saratoga Street, Zip 98278–8800; tel. 360/257–9500, (Nonreporting) **A**1 **S** Bureau of Medicine and Surgery, Department of the Navy, Falls Church, VA
Primary Contact: Commander Frederick Joseph. McDonald, Commanding Officer
COO: Lieutenant Michael Bowers, Interim Director for Administration
CFO: Lieutenant Matthew Martin, Director Resource Management
CMO: Lieutenant Commander Catherine Borja, M.D., Chairman Executive Committee Medical Staff
CIO: Gregory Carruth, Head Information Management
CHR: Lieutenant Michael Bowers, Head Human Resources
CNO: Captain Karen Pruett-Baer, Senior Nurse Executive
Web address: www.med.navy.mil/sites/nhoh/Pages/default.aspx
Control: Department of Defense, Government, federal **Service**: General medical and surgical

Staffed Beds: 29

ODESSA—Lincoln County

★ **ODESSA MEMORIAL HEALTHCARE CENTER (501307)**, 502 East Amende Drive, Zip 99159–7003, Mailing Address: P.O. Box 368, Zip 99159–0368; tel. 509/982–2611, (Nonreporting) **A**10 18
Primary Contact: Mo P. Sheldon, FACHE, Chief Executive Officer and Administrator
CFO: Annette Edwards, Chief Financial Officer
CMO: Linda J Powel, M.D., Medical Director
CHR: Jodi J Bailey, Human Resources Director
CNO: Megan Shepard, Director Clinical Services
Web address: www.omhc.org
Control: Hospital district or authority, Government, nonfederal **Service**: General medical and surgical

Staffed Beds: 13

WA

OLYMPIA—Thurston County

✉ **CAPITAL MEDICAL CENTER (500139)**, 3900 Capital Mall Drive SW, Zip 98502–5026; tel. 360/754–5858, (Nonreporting) **A**1 10 **S** LifePoint Health, Brentwood, TN
Primary Contact: Mark S. Turner, Chief Executive Officer
CFO: Brian Anderson, Chief Financial Officer
CMO: Rojesh Sharangpani, M.D., Chief of Staff
CIO: Renee Crotty, Coordinator Marketing and Public Relations
CHR: Dana Vandewege, Director Human Resources
Web address: www.capitalmedical.com
Control: Partnership, Investor–owned (for–profit) **Service**: General medical and surgical

Staffed Beds: 52

✉ △ **PROVIDENCE ST. PETER HOSPITAL (500024)**, 413 Lilly Road NE, Zip 98506–5166; tel. 360/491–9480, **A**1 3 5 7 10 **F**3 5 8 11 13 15 17 18 20 22 24 26 28 29 30 31 34 35 38 40 43 44 46 49 51 53 56 57 58 59 64 68 70 73 74 75 76 77 78 79 80 81 82 84 85 86 87 89 90 91 92 93 95 96 98 99 100 101 102 104 107 108 111 114 115 118 119 126 129 130 132 135 145 146 148 149 150 152 154 **S** Providence St. Joseph Health, Renton, WA
Primary Contact: Medrice Coluccio, R.N., Chief Executive Officer
CFO: Denise Marroni, Chief Financial Officer
CMO: Kevin Caserta, M.D., Chief Medical Officer
CIO: Kerry Miles, Chief Information Officer
CHR: Susan Meenk, Vice President Human Resources
CNO: Michelle James, Chief Nursing Officer
Web address: www.providence.org/swsa/facilities/st_peter_hospital
Control: Church operated, Nongovernment, not–for–profit **Service**: General medical and surgical

Staffed Beds: 349 **Admissions**: 19846 **Census**: 276 **Outpatient Visits**: 392637 **Births**: 2297 **Total Expense ($000)**: 366542 **Payroll Expense ($000)**: 184319 **Personnel**: 2287

OMAK—Okanogan County

MID-VALLEY HOSPITAL (501328), 810 Jasmine, Zip 98841–9578, Mailing Address: P.O. Box 793, Zip 98841–0793; tel. 509/826–1760, **A**5 10 18 **F**3 8 13 15 18 19 26 27 29 34 35 38 40 43 45 48 50 56 57 59 61 64 65 68 75 76 77 79 81 85 87 93 97 102 105 107 108 110 111 115 119 127 130 131 133 147 148 149 152 154 156
Primary Contact: Alan Fisher, Chief Executive Officer
CFO: Scott Attridge, Chief Financial Officer
CMO: Jennifer Thill, Chief of Staff
CIO: Ethan Harris, Manager Information Systems
CHR: Randy Coffell, Manager Human Resources
CNO: Rebecca Christoph, Director Nursing and Patient Care Services
Web address: www.mvhealth.org
Control: Hospital district or authority, Government, nonfederal **Service**: General medical and surgical

Staffed Beds: 28 **Admissions**: 696 **Census**: 5 **Outpatient Visits**: 30368 **Births**: 216 **Total Expense ($000)**: 32960 **Payroll Expense ($000)**: 14865 **Personnel**: 197

OTHELLO—Adams County

★ **OTHELLO COMMUNITY HOSPITAL (501318)**, 315 North 14th Avenue, Zip 99344–1297; tel. 509/488–2636, (Nonreporting) **A**10 18
Primary Contact: Connie Agenbroad, Chief Executive Officer
CFO: Mark Bunch, Director Finance
CHR: Mindy Gonzales, Chief Human Resources Officer
CNO: Tina Bernsen, Chief Nursing Officer
Web address: www.othellocommunityhospital.org
Control: Hospital district or authority, Government, nonfederal **Service**: General medical and surgical

Staffed Beds: 25

PASCO—Franklin County

✉ △ **LOURDES MEDICAL CENTER (501337)**, 520 North Fourth Avenue, Zip 99301–5257; tel. 509/547–7704, (Nonreporting) **A**1 5 7 10 18 **S** LifePoint Health, Brentwood, TN
Primary Contact: John Serle, FACHE, President and Chief Executive Officer
CFO: Frank Becker, Chief Financial Officer
CMO: Venkataraman Sambasivan, M.D., Chief Medical Officer
CIO: Deb Carpenter, Director Information Technology
CHR: Barbara Blood, Executive Director Human Resources
CNO: Denise Clapp, Chief Nursing Officer
Web address: www.lourdeshealth.net
Control: Corporation, Investor–owned (for–profit) **Service**: General medical and surgical

Staffed Beds: 53

POMEROY—Garfield County

★ **GARFIELD COUNTY PUBLIC HOSPITAL DISTRICT (501301)**, 66 North 6th Street, Zip 99347–9705; tel. 509/843–1591, (Nonreporting) **A**10 18
Primary Contact: Julie Leonard, Chief Executive Officer
CFO: Julie Leonard, Chief Financial Officer
CMO: Glenn Jefferson, Chief Medical Officer
CHR: Alicia Scharnhorst, Human Resources and Administrative Assistant
CNO: Barbara DeHerrera, Chief Nursing Officer
Web address: www.pomeroymd.com
Control: Hospital district or authority, Government, nonfederal **Service**: General medical and surgical

Staffed Beds: 45

PORT ANGELES—Clallam County

★ ⇑ **OLYMPIC MEDICAL CENTER (500072)**, 939 Caroline Street, Zip 98362–3997; tel. 360/417–7000, **A**2 3 10 21 **F**3 13 15 18 28 29 30 31 34 40 43 44 45 54 57 58 62 64 70 74 75 76 77 78 79 81 82 85 87 91 93 97 107 108 110 111 114 119 121 123 127 129 131 132 144 146 147 148
Primary Contact: Eric Lewis, Chief Executive Officer
COO: Lorraine Wall, Chief Operating Officer
CFO: Darryl Wolfe, Chief Financial Officer
CMO: R. Scott Kennedy, M.D., Chief Medical Officer and Safety Officer
CHR: Richard Newman, Chief Human Resources Officer
CNO: Ralph Parker, Chief Nursing Officer
Web address: www.olympicmedical.org
Control: Hospital district or authority, Government, nonfederal **Service**: General medical and surgical

Staffed Beds: 67 **Admissions**: 4217 **Census**: 40 **Outpatient Visits**: 478811 **Births**: 481 **Total Expense ($000)**: 201446 **Payroll Expense ($000)**: 96537 **Personnel**: 1466

PORT TOWNSEND—Jefferson County

★ ⇑ **JEFFERSON HEALTHCARE (501323)**, 834 Sheridan Street, Zip 98368–2443; tel. 360/385–2200, (Nonreporting) **A**10 18 21
Primary Contact: Mike Glenn, Chief Executive Officer
COO: Paula Dowdle, Chief Operating Officer
CFO: Hilary Whittington, Chief Financial Officer
CMO: Joe Mattern, M.D., Chief Medical Officer
CHR: Heather Bailey, Chief Human Resources Officer
CNO: Tina Toner, Chief Nursing Officer
Web address: www.jeffersonhealthcare.org
Control: Hospital district or authority, Government, nonfederal **Service**: General medical and surgical

Staffed Beds: 25

PROSSER—Benton County

★ **PROSSER MEMORIAL HEALTH (501312)**, 723 Memorial Street, Zip 99350–1524; tel. 509/786–2222, **A**3 10 18 **F**3 7 11 12 13 15 29 30 34 35 37 40 43 44 50 54 57 59 65 68 75 76 77 79 81 82 85 87 89 91 93 97 107 108 109 110 111 114 115 119 127 128 130 131 132 133 135 143 146 147 148 149 154
Primary Contact: Craig J. Marks, FACHE, Chief Executive Officer
CFO: Tim Cooper, Chief Financial Officer
CIO: Jim Zoesch, Information Technology Director
CNO: Marla Davis, Interim Chief Nursing Officer
Web address: www.pmhmedicalcenter.com/
Control: Hospital district or authority, Government, nonfederal **Service**: General medical and surgical

Staffed Beds: 25 **Admissions**: 1026 **Census**: 8 **Outpatient Visits**: 31148 **Births**: 388 **Total Expense ($000)**: 53012 **Payroll Expense ($000)**: 23287 **Personnel**: 291

PULLMAN—Whitman County

⇑ **PULLMAN REGIONAL HOSPITAL (501331)**, 835 SE Bishop Boulevard, Zip 99163–5512; tel. 509/332–2541, (Nonreporting) **A**10 18 21
Primary Contact: Scott K. Adams, FACHE, Chief Executive Officer
CFO: Steven Febus, Chief Financial Officer
CMO: Gerald L Early, M.D., Chief Medical Officer
CHR: Bernadette Berney, Director Human Resources
Web address: www.pullmanhospital.org
Control: Hospital district or authority, Government, nonfederal **Service**: General medical and surgical

Staffed Beds: 25

WA

PUYALLUP—Pierce County

GOOD SAMARITAN COMMUNITY HEALTHCARE See Multicare Good Samaritan Hospital

☐ △ **MULTICARE GOOD SAMARITAN HOSPITAL (500079)**, 401 15th Avenue SE, Zip 98372–3770, Mailing Address: P.O. Box 1247, Zip 98371–0192; tel. 253/697–4000, **A**1 2 3 5 7 10 **F**3 11 13 17 18 20 22 24 28 29 30 31 34 35 38 40 41 43 45 47 48 50 51 55 56 57 58 59 61 64 65 66 68 70 73 74 75 76 78 79 80 81 82 83 84 85 87 89 90 91 93 96 97 102 106 107 108 111 114 115 116 117 118 119 126 129 130 132 146 147 148 149 154 **S** MultiCare Health System, Tacoma, WA
Primary Contact: Christopher Bredeson, President and Chief Operating Officer
COO: Christopher Bredeson, President and Chief Operating Officer
CMO: Walter Fink, Chief Medical Officer
CHR: Kevin B Dull, Senior Vice President Human Potential
CNO: Lucy Norris, Administrator Interim Chief Nursing Officer
Web address: www.multicare.org/good-samaritan-hospital/
Control: Other not–for–profit (including NFP Corporation) **Service:** General medical and surgical

Staffed Beds: 362 **Admissions:** 18432 **Census:** 257 **Outpatient Visits:** 143392 **Births:** 2141 **Total Expense ($000):** 441068 **Payroll Expense ($000):** 174834 **Personnel:** 1712

QUINCY—Grant County

QUINCY VALLEY MEDICAL CENTER (501320), 908 10th Avenue SW, Zip 98848–1376; tel. 509/787–3531, (Nonreporting) **A**10 18
Primary Contact: Glenda Bishop, Interim Chief Executive Officer
CFO: Dean Taplett, Controller
CMO: Mark Vance, M.D., Chief Medical Officer
CIO: Ruth Vance, Director Information Systems
CHR: Alene Walker, Director Human Resources
Web address: www.quincyhospital.org
Control: County, Government, nonfederal **Service:** General medical and surgical

Staffed Beds: 25

RENTON—King County

⊠ **UW MEDICINE/VALLEY MEDICAL CENTER (500088)**, 400 South 43rd Street, Zip 98055–5714, Mailing Address: P.O. Box 50010, Zip 98058 5010; tel. 425/228–3450, **A**1 2 3 10 **F**3 8 11 13 15 18 19 20 22 26 28 29 30 31 32 34 35 36 37 38 40 43 44 45 48 49 50 51 53 54 55 56 57 58 59 60 64 65 66 68 70 72 74 75 76 77 78 79 81 82 83 84 85 86 87 89 90 91 92 93 94 96 97 100 101 102 104 107 110 111 114 115 118 119 120 121 123 124 126 129 130 131 132 135 144 146 147 148 149 153 156 **S** UW Medicine, Seattle, WA
Primary Contact: Richard D. Roodman, Chief Executive Officer
CFO: Larry Smith, Senior Vice President and Chief Financial Officer
CMO: Kathryn Beattie, M.D., Senior Vice President and Chief Medical Officer
CHR: Barbara Mitchell, Senior Vice President Marketing and Human Resources
CNO: Scott Alleman, Senior Vice President Patient Care Services and Chief Nursing Officer
Web address: www.valleymed.org
Control: Hospital district or authority, Government, nonfederal **Service:** General medical and surgical

Staffed Beds: 311 **Admissions:** 18409 **Census:** 200 **Outpatient Visits:** 718616 **Births:** 3536 **Total Expense ($000):** 649579 **Payroll Expense ($000):** 315906 **Personnel:** 3225

REPUBLIC—Ferry County

★ **FERRY COUNTY MEMORIAL HOSPITAL (501322)**, 36 Klondike Road, Zip 99166–9701; tel. 509/775–3333, (Nonreporting) **A**10 18
Primary Contact: Aaron Edwards, Chief Executive Officer
CFO: Kelly Leslie, Chief Financial Officer
CMO: Farhad H Alrashedy, M.D., Chief Medical Officer
CIO: James Davidson, Director of Information Services
CHR: Michelle Loftis, Human Resources Officer
CNO: Thomas Durham, Chief Nursing Officer
Web address: www.fcphd.org
Control: Hospital district or authority, Government, nonfederal **Service:** General medical and surgical

Staffed Beds: 25

RICHLAND—Benton County

⊠ △ **KADLEC REGIONAL MEDICAL CENTER (500058)**, 888 Swift Boulevard, Zip 99352–3514; tel. 509/946–4611, (Nonreporting) **A**1 2 3 5 7 10 **S** Providence St. Joseph Health, Renton, WA
Primary Contact: Reza Kaleel, Chief Executive Officer
CFO: Spencer Harris, Senior Director Finance
CMO: Dale Hoekema, M.D., Vice President Medical Affairs and Chief Medical Officer
CIO: David Roach, Vice President Information Systems
CHR: Jeffrey A Clark, Vice President Human Resources
CNO: Kirk Harper, R.N., Vice President, Nursing
Web address: www.https://www.kadlec.org
Control: Other not–for–profit (including NFP Corporation) **Service:** General medical and surgical

Staffed Beds: 260

★ **LOURDES COUNSELING CENTER (504008)**, 1175 Carondelet Drive, Zip 99354–3300; tel. 509/943–9104, (Nonreporting) **A**10 **S** LifePoint Health, Brentwood, TN
Primary Contact: Mark Gregson, Interim Chief Executive Officer
CFO: Frank Becker, Chief Financial Officer
CIO: Jared Fleming, Director, Information Services
CHR: Barbara Blood, Director Human Resources
CNO: Denise Clapp, Chief Nursing Officer
Web address: www.lourdeshealth.net
Control: Corporation, Investor–owned (for–profit) **Service:** Psychiatric

Staffed Beds: 20

RITZVILLE—Adams County

★ **EAST ADAMS RURAL HEALTHCARE (501311)**, 903 South Adams Street, Zip 99169–2298; tel. 509/659–1200, (Nonreporting) **A**10 18
Primary Contact: Corey J. Fedie, Chief Executive Officer
COO: Dina McBride, Chief Operating Officer and Director Human Resources
CFO: Gary Bostrom, Chief Executive Officer and Chief Financial Officer
CMO: Charles Sackmann, M.D., Chief of Staff
CIO: Kellie Ottmar, Manager Information Services
CHR: Dina McBride, Chief Operating Officer and Director Human Resources
CNO: Brenda Herr, Chief Nursing Officer
Web address: www.earh.com
Control: Hospital district or authority, Government, nonfederal **Service:** General medical and surgical

Staffed Beds: 20

SEATTLE—King County

⇑ **KAISER PERMANENTE CAPITOL HILL CAMPUS (500052)**, 201 16th Avenue East, Zip 98112–5226; tel. 206/326–3000, (Nonreporting) **A**10 21
Primary Contact: Carol M. Taylor, R.N., Regional Director Clinical Operations
Web address: www.https://www.ghc.org/html/public/locations/capitol-hill
Control: Corporation, Investor–owned (for–profit) **Service:** General medical and surgical

Staffed Beds: 306

⊠ **KINDRED HOSPITAL SEATTLE-NORTHGATE (502002)**, 10631 8th Avenue NE, Zip 98125–7213; tel. 206/364–2050, (Includes KINDRED HOSPITAL SEATTLE-FIRST HILL, 1334 Terry Avenue, Seattle, Washington, Zip 98101–2747; tel. 206/682–2661; Doug McCoy, Chief Executive Officer), (Non-reporting) **A**1 10 **S** Kindred Healthcare, Louisville, KY
Primary Contact: Lerenda Johnson, Interim Chief Executive Officer
CFO: Bruce MacNeill, Chief Financial Officer
Web address: www.kindredhospitalseattle.com/
Control: Corporation, Investor–owned (for–profit) **Service:** Acute long–term care hospital

Staffed Beds: 80

☐ **NAVOS (504009)**, 2600 SW Holden Street, Zip 98126–3505; tel. 206/933–7299, (Nonreporting) **A**1 10
Primary Contact: David Johnson, Chief Executive Officer
COO: Cassie Undlin, Chief Operating Officer
CIO: Mary Sellers, Chief Information Officer
CHR: Karen White, Interim Vice President of Human Resources
CNO: Terry McInerney, Director of Nursing, Inpatient
Web address: www.navos.org
Control: Other not–for–profit (including NFP Corporation) **Service:** Psychiatric

Staffed Beds: 40

WA

Hospital, Medicare Provider Number, Address, Telephone, Approval, Facility, and Physician Codes, Health Care System

★ American Hospital Association (AHA) membership
☐ The Joint Commission accreditation
○ Healthcare Facilities Accreditation Program
◇ DNV Healthcare Inc. accreditation
⇑ Center for Improvement in Healthcare Quality Accreditation
△ Commission on Accreditation of Rehabilitation Facilities (CARF) accreditation

★ △ **SCHICK SHADEL HOSPITAL**, 12101 Ambaum Boulevard SW,
Zip 98146–2651, Mailing Address: P.O. Box 48149, Zip 98148–0149;
tel. 206/244–8100, **A**7 **F**4 130 132
Primary Contact: Philip Herink, Administrator
CFO: Troy Cherry, Chief Financial Officer
CMO: Kayyan Danbdala, M.D., Medical Director
CIO: Peter Vermulen, Director Information Technology
CHR: Elaine Oksendahl, Director Human Resources and Risk Management
Web address: www.schickshadel.com
Control: Corporation, Investor–owned (for–profit) **Service**: Alcoholism and other chemical dependency

Staffed Beds: 55 **Admissions:** 991 **Census:** 27 **Outpatient Visits:** 0
Births: 0 **Total Expense ($000):** 10908 **Payroll Expense ($000):** 5553
Personnel: 74

⊞ **SEATTLE CANCER CARE ALLIANCE (500138)**, 825 Eastlake Avenue
East, Zip 98109–4405, Mailing Address: P.O. Box 19023, Zip 98109–1023;
tel. 206/288–1400, **A**1 2 3 10 **F**3 14 15 29 30 31 34 35 36 38 39 44 45 50 52
55 57 58 59 64 65 68 71 75 77 78 80 81 82 84 86 87 100 104 107 108 110
111 115 117 118 119 120 121 123 130 132 135 136 143 146 147 148 149 154
Primary Contact: Norm Hubbard, Executive Vice President
CFO: Jonathan Tingstad, Vice President and Chief Financial Officer
CMO: Marc Stewart, M.D., Vice President and Medical Director
CIO: David Ackerson, Chief Information Officer
CHR: Han Nachtrieb, Vice President Human Resources
Web address: www.seattlecca.org
Control: Other not–for–profit (including NFP Corporation) **Service**: Cancer

Staffed Beds: 20 **Admissions:** 565 **Census:** 18 **Outpatient Visits:** 82534
Births: 0 **Total Expense ($000):** 607727 **Payroll Expense ($000):** 118519
Personnel: 1288

△ ⇑ **SEATTLE CHILDREN'S HOSPITAL (503300)**, 4800 Sand Point Way
NE, Zip 98105–3901, Mailing Address: P.O. Box 5371, Zip 98145–5005;
tel. 206/987–2000, (Nonreporting) **A**2 3 5 7 10 21
Primary Contact: Jeff Sperring, M.D., Chief Executive Officer
COO: Cindy Gazecki, Senior Vice President, Hospital Operations
CFO: Suzanne Beitel, Senior Vice President and Chief Financial Officer
CMO: David Fisher, M.D., Senior Vice President and Chief Medical Officer
CIO: Zafar Chaudry, M.D., Senior Vice President and Chief Information Officer
CHR: Steven Hurwitz, Senior Vice President Shared Services
CNO: Susan Heath, R.N., Senior Vice President and Chief Nursing Officer
Web address: www.seattlechildrens.org
Control: Other not–for–profit (including NFP Corporation) **Service**: Children's general medical and surgical

Staffed Beds: 316

★ △ ⇑ **SWEDISH MEDICAL CENTER-CHERRY HILL CAMPUS (500025)**, 500
17th Avenue, Zip 98122–5711; tel. 206/320–2000, **A**2 3 5 7 10 21 **F**3 8 11 17
18 20 21 22 23 24 26 27 28 29 30 31 34 35 37 38 40 45 46 53 57 58 59 61
64 65 68 74 75 77 78 79 80 81 82 83 84 85 87 90 91 92 93 97 100 101 102
107 108 109 111 118 119 124 126 129 130 131 132 135 141 143 146 148
149 154 **S** Swedish Health Services, Seattle, WA
Primary Contact: June Altaras, R.N., Chief Executive Officer
CFO: Jeffrey Veilleux, Senior Vice President and Chief Financial Officer
CIO: Janice Newell, Chief Information Officer
Web address: www.swedish.org
Control: Other not–for–profit (including NFP Corporation) **Service**: General medical and surgical

Staffed Beds: 208 **Admissions:** 9691 **Census:** 153 **Outpatient Visits:** 157825 **Births:** 0 **Total Expense ($000):** 505138 **Payroll Expense ($000):** 129114 **Personnel:** 1065

★ ⇑ **SWEDISH MEDICAL CENTER-FIRST HILL (500027)**, 747 Broadway,
Zip 98122–4307; tel. 206/386–6000, (Includes SWEDISH MEDICAL CENTER-
BALLARD, 5300 Tallman Avenue NW, Seattle, Washington, Zip 98107–3932;
tel. 206/782–2700; Jennifer Graves, R.N., MS, Chief Executive) **A**2 3 5 10 21 **F**3
4 5 7 8 11 12 13 15 18 19 20 21 22 23 25 26 29 30 31 32 34 35 36 37 38 39
40 41 42 45 46 47 48 49 52 54 55 56 57 58 59 61 64 65 66 68 70 71 72
73 74 75 76 77 78 79 80 81 82 83 84 85 86 87 88 89 91 92 93 96 97 98 100
101 102 104 107 108 109 110 111 114 115 116 117 118 119 120 121 123
126 127 130 131 132 134 135 136 138 139 141 142 144 146 147 148 149
154 156 **S** Swedish Health Services, Seattle, WA
Primary Contact: June Altaras, R.N., Chief Executive Officer
COO: Gary G Fybel, FACHE, Interim Chief Operating Officer
CFO: Jeffrey Veilleux, Executive Vice President and Chief Financial Officer
CIO: Janice Newell, Chief Information Officer
Web address: www.swedish.org
Control: Other not–for–profit (including NFP Corporation) **Service**: General medical and surgical

Staffed Beds: 689 **Admissions:** 37376 **Census:** 478 **Outpatient Visits:** 564712 **Births:** 8479 **Total Expense ($000):** 1568713 **Payroll Expense ($000):** 422837 **Personnel:** 3159

⊞ △ **UNIVERSITY OF WASHINGTON MEDICAL CENTER (500008)**, 1959 NE
Pacific Street, Zip 98195–6151; tel. 206/598–3300, **A**1 2 3 5 7 8 10 **F**3 9 11
12 13 15 17 18 20 22 24 26 28 29 30 31 32 34 35 36 40 44 45 46 47 48 49
50 52 54 55 56 57 58 59 60 65 68 70 72 74 75 76 77 78 79 81 82 84
85 86 87 90 91 92 93 94 95 96 97 98 100 101 102 104 105 107 108 110
111 114 115 116 117 118 119 120 121 123 124 126 130 131 132 135 136
137 138 139 140 141 142 144 145 146 147 148 149 154 156 **S** UW Medicine,
Seattle, WA
Primary Contact: Geoff Austin, Executive Director
CFO: Jacque Cabe, Chief Financial Officer
CMO: Tom Staiger, Medical Director
CIO: Joy Grosser, Chief Information Officer
CHR: Jennifer J Petritz, Director Human Resources
CNO: Cindy Sayre, Ph.D., R.N., Chief Nursing Officer
Web address: www.uwmedicine.org/uw-medical-center
Control: State, Government, nonfederal **Service**: General medical and surgical

Staffed Beds: 492 **Admissions:** 19350 **Census:** 374 **Outpatient Visits:** 391657 **Births:** 1930 **Total Expense ($000):** 1295283 **Payroll Expense ($000):** 376656 **Personnel:** 4269

★ △ **UW MEDICINE/HARBORVIEW MEDICAL CENTER (500064)**, 325 Ninth
Avenue, Zip 98104–2499, Mailing Address: P.O. Box 359717, Zip 98195–9717;
tel. 206/744–3000, **A**3 5 7 8 10 **F**3 5 6 16 17 20 22 26 29 30 31 32 34 35 36
37 38 40 43 44 45 46 47 48 49 50 56 58 59 60 61 64 65 66 68 70 74 75 77
78 79 80 81 82 84 85 86 87 90 91 92 93 94 96 97 98 100 101 102 104 107
108 111 114 115 118 119 124 129 130 131 132 135 146 147 148 149 150
154 156 **S** UW Medicine, Seattle, WA
Primary Contact: Paul Hayes, R.N., Executive Director
CFO: Kera Dennis, Assistant Administrator, Finance
CMO: J. Richard Goss, M.D., Medical Director
CIO: James Fine, M.D., Chief Information Officer
CHR: Nicki McCraw, Assistant Vice President Human Resources
CNO: Darcy Jaffe, R.N., Chief Nursing Officer
Web address: www.uwmedicine.org/Patient-Care/Locations/HMC/Pages/default.aspx
Control: County, Government, nonfederal **Service**: General medical and surgical

Staffed Beds: 413 **Admissions:** 16716 **Census:** 403 **Outpatient Visits:** 379619 **Births:** 0 **Total Expense ($000):** 1041243 **Payroll Expense ($000):** 380376 **Personnel:** 4282

⊞ **UW MEDICINE/NORTHWEST HOSPITAL & MEDICAL CENTER (500001)**,
1550 North 115th Street, Zip 98133–8401; tel. 206/364–0500, **A**1 2 3 5 10 **F**3
9 13 15 18 20 22 24 26 28 29 30 31 34 35 40 41 43 44 45 46 47 49 50 51
53 54 56 57 58 59 61 64 68 70 73 74 75 76 77 78 79 81 84 85 86 87 92 93
96 97 98 100 102 103 104 105 107 108 110 111 114 115 119 126 130 131
132 146 148 155 **S** UW Medicine, Seattle, WA
Primary Contact: Cynthia Hecker, R.N., Executive Director
CFO: Ketty Hsieh, Senior Director Finance
CMO: Greg Schroedl, M.D., Vice President, Medical and Chief Medical Officer
CIO: Eric Neil, Interim Chief Information Officer
CHR: Linda Olmstead, Director, Human Resources
CNO: Susan Manfredi, R.N., Vice President and Chief Nursing Officer
Web address: www.uwmedicine.org/Patient-Care/Locations/nwh/Pages/default.aspx
Control: Other not–for–profit (including NFP Corporation) **Service**: General medical and surgical

Staffed Beds: 203 **Admissions:** 9749 **Census:** 139 **Outpatient Visits:** 255610 **Births:** 1042 **Total Expense ($000):** 411854 **Payroll Expense ($000):** 171463 **Personnel:** 1914

⊞ △ **VETERANS AFFAIRS PUGET SOUND HEALTH CARE SYSTEM**, 1660
South Columbian Way, Zip 98108–1597; tel. 206/762–1010, (Includes VETERANS
AFFAIRS PUGET SOUND HEALTH CARE SYSTEM-AMERICAN LAKE DIVISION, 9600
Veterans Drive, Tacoma, Washington, Zip 98493–0003; tel. 253/582–8440),
(Non-reporting) **A**1 2 3 5 7 8 **S** Department of Veterans Affairs, Washington, DC
Primary Contact: Michael C. Tadych, FACHE, Director
CFO: Kenneth J Hudson, Chief Financial Officer
CMO: Gordon Starkebaum, M.D., Chief of Staff
CIO: Glenn Zwinger, Manager Information Systems Services
Web address: www.pugetsound.va.gov/
Control: Veterans Affairs, Government, federal **Service**: General medical and surgical

Staffed Beds: 416

WA

✉ △ **VIRGINIA MASON MEDICAL CENTER (500005)**, 1100 Ninth Avenue, Zip 98101–2756, Mailing Address: P.O. Box 900, Zip 98111–0900; tel. 206/223–6600, (Total facility includes 35 beds in nursing home–type unit) **A**1 2 3 5 7 10 **F**2 3 8 11 12 15 17 18 20 22 24 26 28 29 30 31 34 36 40 44 45 46 47 48 49 50 51 55 56 57 58 59 60 61 63 64 65 68 70 74 75 77 78 79 80 81 82 83 84 85 86 87 91 92 93 94 96 97 98 100 101 102 104 107 108 110 111 114 115 117 118 119 120 121 123 126 128 129 130 131 132 135 138 141 142 144 145 146 148 154 156 157 **S** Virginia Mason Health System, Seattle, WA
Primary Contact: Gary Kaplan, M.D., FACHE, Chairman and Chief Executive Officer
CFO: Craig Goodrich, Chief Financial Officer
CMO: Michael Glenn, M.D., Chief Medical Officer
CIO: Bill Poppy, Chief Information Officer
CHR: Kathy J. Shingleton, Ed.D., Vice President, Human Resources
CNO: Charleen Tachibana, R.N., Senior Vice President and Chief Nursing Officer
Web address: www.VirginiaMason.org
Control: Other not–for–profit (including NFP Corporation) **Service:** General medical and surgical

Staffed Beds: 245 **Admissions:** 12538 **Census:** 217 **Outpatient Visits:** 933809 **Births:** 0 **Total Expense ($000):** 1105375 **Payroll Expense ($000):** 534259 **Personnel:** 5165

SEDRO—WOOLLEY–Skagit County

★ ⇑ **PEACEHEALTH UNITED GENERAL MEDICAL CENTER (501329)**, 2000 Hospital Drive, Zip 98284–4327; tel. 360/856–6021, **A**2 10 18 21 **F**3 11 15 29 30 31 34 35 40 43 45 50 57 59 64 68 70 75 77 78 79 81 85 89 92 93 107 108 110 115 118 119 120 121 123 128 129 130 132 133 143 146 148 149 **S** PeaceHealth, Vancouver, WA
Primary Contact: Christopher Johnston, Chief Administrative Officer
CFO: Carolyn Haupt, Chief Financial Officer
CHR: Tracie Skrinde, Senior Human Resources Partner
Web address: www.peacehealth.org/united-general
Control: Church operated, Nongovernment, not–for–profit **Service:** General medical and surgical

Staffed Beds: 25 **Admissions:** 730 **Census:** 10 **Outpatient Visits:** 30252 **Births:** 0 **Total Expense ($000):** 42904 **Payroll Expense ($000):** 15895 **Personnel:** 207

SHELTON—Mason County

★ ⇑ **MASON GENERAL HOSPITAL AND FAMILY OF CLINICS (501336)**, 901 Mountain View Drive, Zip 98584–4401, Mailing Address: P.O. Box 1668, Zip 98584–1611, **A**5 10 18 21 **F**3 11 13 15 29 30 34 35 40 43 45 50 55 57 59 68 70 75 76 79 81 83 85 93 94 97 104 107 110 111 115 119 127 130 132 146 147 148 149 154 156 157
Primary Contact: Eric Moll, Chief Executive Officer
COO: Eileen Branscome, Chief Operating Officer
CFO: Rick Smith, Chief Financial Officer
CMO: Dean Gushee, M.D., Medical Director
CIO: Tom Hornburg, Director Information Systems
CHR: Eileen Branscome, Director Human Resources
CNO: Melissa D Strong, Chief Nursing Officer
Web address: www.masongeneral.com
Control: Hospital district or authority, Government, nonfederal **Service:** General medical and surgical

Staffed Beds: 25 **Admissions:** 1423 **Census:** 11 **Outpatient Visits:** 100899 **Births:** 254 **Total Expense ($000):** 100030 **Payroll Expense ($000):** 48798 **Personnel:** 564

SNOQUALMIE—King County

SNOQUALMIE VALLEY HOSPITAL DISTRICT (501338), 9801 Frontier Avenue SE, Zip 98065–9577; tel. 425/831–2300, **A**10 18 **F**3 18 34 35 40 43 45 56 57 59 64 65 77 85 87 93 97 100 104 107 111 114 119 127 130 131 133 134 143 146 148 149 154
Primary Contact: Kimberly Witkop, M.D., Interim Chief Executive Officer
CMO: Kimberly Witkop, M.D., Chief Medical Officer
CHR: Kimberly D Washburn, Director Human Resources
Web address: www.snoqualmiehospital.org/
Control: Hospital district or authority, Government, nonfederal **Service:** General medical and surgical

Staffed Beds: 25 **Admissions:** 302 **Census:** 23 **Outpatient Visits:** 37500 **Births:** 0 **Total Expense ($000):** 38073 **Payroll Expense ($000):** 17143 **Personnel:** 233

SOUTH BEND—Pacific County

WILLAPA HARBOR HOSPITAL (501303), 800 Alder Street, Zip 98586–4900, Mailing Address: P.O. Box 438, Zip 98586–0438; tel. 360/875–5526, **A**5 10 18 **F**3 11 15 28 29 34 35 40 41 43 45 47 48 50 54 56 59 64 68 77 81 87 97 102 107 119 127 148 149 154 156 157
Primary Contact: Carole Halsan, R.N., Chief Executive Officer
CFO: Terry Stone, Chief Financial Officer and Chief Information Officer
CIO: Terry Stone, Chief Financial Officer and Chief Information Officer
CHR: Krisy L Funkhouser, Manager Human Resources
Web address: www.willapaharborhospital.com
Control: Hospital district or authority, Government, nonfederal **Service:** General medical and surgical

Staffed Beds: 10 **Admissions:** 255 **Census:** 2 **Outpatient Visits:** 25639 **Births:** 0 **Total Expense ($000):** 22370 **Payroll Expense ($000):** 11224 **Personnel:** 116

SPOKANE—Spokane County

✉ **MANN-GRANDSTAFF VETERANS AFFAIRS MEDICAL CENTER**, 4815 North Assembly Street, Zip 99205–6197; tel. 509/434–7000, (Nonreporting) **A**1 3 5 **S** Department of Veterans Affairs, Washington, DC
Primary Contact: Tracye B. Davis, Interim Medical Center Director
COO: Perry Klein, Chief Engineering
CFO: Michael Stuhlmiller, Chief Financial Officer
CIO: Rob Fortenberry, Chief Information Officer
CHR: Jacqueline Ross, Chief Human Resources Officer
CNO: Nancy Benton, Assistant Director Patient Care Services
Web address: www.spokane.va.gov/
Control: Veterans Affairs, Government, federal **Service:** General medical and surgical

Staffed Beds: 68

☐ **MULTICARE DEACONESS HOSPITAL (500044)**, 800 West Fifth Avenue, Zip 99204–2803, Mailing Address: P.O. Box 248, Zip 99210–0248; tel. 509/458–5800, **A**1 3 10 **F**3 8 12 13 15 17 18 20 22 24 26 28 29 30 31 35 40 42 43 45 46 47 48 49 50 51 53 60 64 65 68 70 72 73 74 76 77 78 79 81 82 85 86 87 91 92 94 100 102 104 107 108 109 110 111 114 115 119 124 126 129 130 131 132 146 147 148 149 **S** MultiCare Health System, Tacoma, WA
Primary Contact: Laureen Driscoll, President
CFO: Rodney Higgins, Chief Financial Officer
CMO: David Chen, M.D., Chief Medical Officer
CIO: Richard DeRoche, Manager Information Technology
CHR: Melinda Moore, Director Human Resources
CNO: Jennifer Petrik, Interim Chief Nursing Officer
Web address: www.https://www.multicare.org/deaconess-hospital/
Control: Other not–for–profit (including NFP Corporation) **Service:** General medical and surgical

Staffed Beds: 352 **Admissions:** 9708 **Census:** 150 **Outpatient Visits:** 79990 **Births:** 1329 **Total Expense ($000):** 304875 **Payroll Expense ($000):** 103639 **Personnel:** 1515

✉ △ **PROVIDENCE HOLY FAMILY HOSPITAL (500077)**, 5633 North Lidgerwood Street, Zip 99208–1224; tel. 509/482–0111, **A**1 2 5 7 10 **F**3 8 11 12 13 15 16 18 34 35 37 38 39 40 41 43 45 46 47 48 49 50 53 56 57 58 59 60 61 64 68 70 73 74 75 76 77 78 79 80 81 82 84 85 86 87 92 100 107 108 126 129 130 131 132 143 145 146 147 148 149 154 156 **S** Providence St. Joseph Health, Renton, WA
Primary Contact: Peggy M. Currie, R.N., Chief Operating Officer
COO: Cathy J Simchuk, Chief Operating Officer
CFO: Shelby Stokoe, Chief Financial Officer
CMO: Dean Martz, Chief Medical Officer
CIO: Mark Vogelsang, Director Information Services
CHR: Mark Smith, Director Human Resources
CNO: Sharon Hershman, R.N., Chief Nursing Officer
Web address: www.providence.org
Control: Church operated, Nongovernment, not–for–profit **Service:** General medical and surgical

Staffed Beds: 191 **Admissions:** 7974 **Census:** 97 **Outpatient Visits:** 189542 **Births:** 1179 **Total Expense ($000):** 215341 **Payroll Expense ($000):** 59116 **Personnel:** 795

WA

✠ **PROVIDENCE SACRED HEART MEDICAL CENTER & CHILDREN'S HOSPITAL (500054)**, 101 West Eighth Avenue, Zip 99204–2364, Mailing Address: P.O. Box 2555, Zip 99220–2555; tel. 509/474–3131, (Includes SACRED HEART CHILDREN'S HOSPITAL, 101 West Eight Avenue, Spokane, Washington, Zip 99204–2307, Mailing Address: P.O. Box 2555, Zip 99220–2555, tel. 509/474–4841; Keith Georgeson, M.D., Chief Executive) **A**1 2 3 5 10 **F**8 13 17 18 19 20 21 22 23 24 25 26 27 29 30 31 35 36 37 40 41 43 45 46 47 48 49 56 58 60 70 72 73 74 75 76 78 79 80 81 82 83 84 85 86 87 88 89 92 98 100 101 102 104 107 108 109 111 114 115 118 119 120 121 123 124 126 130 131 132 136 137 138 142 145 146 147 148 149 150 154 156 **S** Providence St. Joseph Health, Renton, WA
Primary Contact: Peggy M. Currie, R.N., Chief Operating Officer
CFO: Shelby Stokoe, Senior Director Finance
CMO: Dean Martz, Chief Medical Officer
CHR: Mark Smith, Director Human Resources
CNO: Susan Stacey, Chief Nursing Officer
Web address: www.shmc.org
Control: Church operated, Nongovernment, not–for–profit **Service**: General medical and surgical

> **Staffed Beds**: 656 **Admissions**: 28087 **Census**: 470 **Outpatient Visits**: 531896 **Total Expense ($000)**: 992883 **Payroll Expense ($000)**: 309298 **Personnel**: 3096

☐ **SHRINERS HOSPITALS FOR CHILDREN-SPOKANE (503302)**, 911 West Fifth Avenue, Zip 99204–2901, Mailing Address: P.O. Box 2472, Zip 99210–2472; tel. 509/455–7844, (Nonreporting) **A**1 3 10 **S** Shriners Hospitals for Children, Tampa, FL
Primary Contact: Peter G. Brewer, Administrator
CFO: Monica Hickman, Director Fiscal Services
CMO: Glen Baird, M.D., Chief of Staff
CIO: Mike Allen, Director Information Services
CHR: Karen Mattern, Director of Human Resources
CNO: Lynda Vilanova, Director Patient Care Services
Web address: www.shrinershospitalsforchildren.org/Hospitals/Locations/Spokane.aspx
Control: Other not–for–profit (including NFP Corporation) **Service**: Children's orthopedic

> **Staffed Beds**: 30

✠ △ **ST. LUKE'S REHABILITATION INSTITUTE (503025)**, 711 South Cowley Street, Zip 99202–1388; tel. 509/473–6000, **A**1 7 10 **F**28 29 30 34 35 36 38 43 50 53 57 58 64 68 74 75 77 79 82 86 87 90 91 92 93 95 130 131 132 135 146 148 149 154 156 157 **S** Providence St. Joseph Health, Renton, WA
Primary Contact: Nancy Webster, Administrator and Chief Operating Officer
CFO: Helen Andrus, Chief Financial Officer
CMO: Gregory Carter, M.D., Chief Medical Officer
CIO: Fred Galusha, Chief Information Officer
CHR: Staci Franz, Director Human Resources
CNO: Kimberly J Ward, Chief Nurse Officer
Web address: www.st-lukes.org
Control: Other not–for–profit (including NFP Corporation) **Service**: Rehabilitation

> **Staffed Beds**: 72 **Admissions**: 1304 **Census**: 56 **Outpatient Visits**: 107355 **Births**: 0 **Total Expense ($000)**: 51702 **Payroll Expense ($000)**: 31968 **Personnel**: 579

VETERANS AFFAIRS MEDICAL CENTER See Mann-Grandstaff Veterans Affairs Medical Center

SPOKANE VALLEY—Spokane County

✠ **MULTICARE VALLEY HOSPITAL (500119)**, 12606 East Mission Avenue, Zip 99216–1090; tel. 509/924–6650, **A**1 3 5 10 **F**3 13 20 29 30 40 45 46 48 49 50 60 68 70 74 76 79 81 85 87 107 108 111 114 115 118 119 131 146 **S** MultiCare Health System, Tacoma, WA
Primary Contact: Gregory George. Repetti III, FACHE, Chief Executive Officer
COO: David Martin, Assistant Administrator
CFO: Justin Voelker, Chief Financial Officer
CMO: David Chen, M.D., Chief Medical Officer
CIO: Brain Jones, Director of Information Technology
CHR: Jamie Caine, Director of Human Resources
CNO: Shannon S Holland, R.N., MSN, Chief Nursing Officer
Web address: www.valleyhospital.org
Control: Other not–for–profit (including NFP Corporation) **Service**: General medical and surgical

> **Staffed Beds**: 123 **Admissions**: 5635 **Census**: 60 **Outpatient Visits**: 53558 **Births**: 651 **Total Expense ($000)**: 119003 **Payroll Expense ($000)**: 48079 **Personnel**: 576

SUNNYSIDE—Yakima County

★ **ASTRIA SUNNYSIDE HOSPITAL (501330)**, 1016 Tacoma Avenue, Zip 98944–2263, Mailing Address: P.O. Box 719, Zip 98944–0719; tel. 509/837–1500, **A**3 10 18 **F**3 8 11 13 15 18 20 22 26 29 30 31 32 34 35 40 41 43 45 46 50 51 54 59 60 62 64 65 68 70 74 76 77 78 79 81 82 87 89 93 100 104 107 108 110 111 115 116 117 119 127 129 130 131 132 133 144 148 153 154 156 **S** Astria Health, Sunnyside, WA
Primary Contact: Brian P. Gibbons Jr, Chief Executive Officer
CFO: Cary Rowan, Chief Financial Officer
CIO: John Andersen, Manager Information Systems
CHR: Elaina Wagner, Director Human Resources
CNO: Mary Beth Tubbs, Chief Nursing Officer
Web address: www.astria.health/
Control: Other not–for–profit (including NFP Corporation) **Service**: General medical and surgical

> **Staffed Beds**: 25 **Admissions**: 1914 **Census**: 16 **Outpatient Visits**: 51190 **Births**: 487

TACOMA—Pierce County

ALLENMORE HOSPITAL See Multicare Tacoma General Hospital, Tacoma

✠ **MADIGAN ARMY MEDICAL CENTER**, Fitzsimmons Drive, Building 9040, Zip 98431–1100; tel. 253/968–1110, (Nonreporting) **A**1 2 3 5 **S** Department of the Army, Office of the Surgeon General, Falls Church, VA
Primary Contact: Colonel Thomas S. Bundt, Commanding Officer
COO: Colonel R Neal David, Administrator and Chief of Staff
CFO: Lieutenant Colonel Bryan Longmuir, Chief Resource Management
CIO: Lieutenant Colonel Andrew Smith, Chief Information Management
CHR: David Aiken, Chief Human Resources Officer
Web address: www.mamc.health.mil/
Control: Department of Defense, Government, federal **Service**: General medical and surgical

> **Staffed Beds**: 200

☐ **MULTICARE MARY BRIDGE CHILDREN'S HOSPITAL AND HEALTH CENTER (503301)**, 317 Martin Luther King Jr Way, Zip 98405–4234, Mailing Address: P.O. Box 5299, Zip 98415–0299; tel. 253/403–1400, **A**1 3 5 10 **F**3 8 19 21 23 25 27 29 30 31 32 34 35 38 39 40 41 43 45 46 48 49 53 54 55 57 58 59 60 61 62 64 65 66 68 71 74 75 78 79 81 82 84 85 86 87 88 89 91 92 93 94 96 97 100 104 107 108 111 114 115 116 117 119 120 121 123 124 126 129 130 131 132 143 144 146 148 149 150 153 154 156 158 **S** MultiCare Health System, Tacoma, WA
Primary Contact: Jeffrey S. Poltawsky, President and Market Leader
COO: Jennifer Hamilton, COO - Mary Bridge
CMO: Iain Asplin, Chief Medical Officer
CHR: Kevin B Dull, Senior Vice President Human Potential
CNO: Diana Brovold, Chief Nurse Executive
Web address: www.multicare.org/marybridge
Control: Other not–for–profit (including NFP Corporation) **Service**: Children's general medical and surgical

> **Staffed Beds**: 75 **Admissions**: 3896 **Census**: 40 **Outpatient Visits**: 154171 **Births**: 0 **Total Expense ($000)**: 247163 **Payroll Expense ($000)**: 95018 **Personnel**: 661

✠ **MULTICARE TACOMA GENERAL HOSPITAL (500129)**, 315 Martin Luther King Jr Way, Zip 98405–4234, Mailing Address: P.O. Box 5299, Zip 98415–0299; tel. 253/403–1000, (Includes ALLENMORE HOSPITAL, 1901 South Union Avenue, Tacoma, Washington, Zip 98405, Mailing Address: P O Box 11414, Zip 98411–0414, tel. 253/459–6633; Sharon Oxendale, President and Chief Operating Officer) **A**1 2 3 10 **F**3 8 12 13 15 17 18 20 22 24 26 28 29 30 31 34 35 36 40 43 45 46 47 48 49 50 51 53 54 55 57 58 59 64 70 72 73 74 75 76 78 79 80 81 82 84 85 87 98 99 100 102 107 108 109 111 114 115 116 117 119 120 121 123 124 126 129 130 131 132 135 146 147 148 149 154 157 **S** MultiCare Health System, Tacoma, WA
Primary Contact: Sharon Oxendale, President and Chief Operating Officer
COO: Julia Truman, Chief Operating Officer
CHR: Kevin B Dull, Senior Vice President Human Potential
CNO: Anita Wolfe, Chief Nurse Executive
Web address: www.multicare.org
Control: Other not–for–profit (including NFP Corporation) **Service**: General medical and surgical

> **Staffed Beds**: 444 **Admissions**: 21437 **Census**: 307 **Outpatient Visits**: 217044 **Births**: 3223 **Total Expense ($000)**: 768383 **Payroll Expense ($000)**: 299785 **Personnel**: 2543

WA

Many Facility Codes have changed. Please refer to the AHA Guide Code Chart.   © 2019 AHA Guide

△ **ST. JOSEPH MEDICAL CENTER (500108)**, 1717 South 'J' Street, Zip 98405–3004, Mailing Address: P.O. Box 2197, Zip 98401–2197; tel. 253/426–4101, **A**1 2 3 7 10 **F**3 11 12 13 18 20 22 24 26 28 29 30 31 34 35 38 40 43 44 45 46 47 48 49 50 51 55 57 58 59 60 63 64 65 70 72 73 74 75 76 77 78 79 80 81 82 84 85 86 87 90 92 93 98 102 107 108 111 114 115 119 124 126 130 131 132 135 145 146 148 149 154 **S** CommonSpirit Health, Chicago, IL
Primary Contact: Syd Bersante, R.N., President
COO: Tim O'Haver, Chief Operating Officer
CFO: Mike Fitzgerald, Chief Financial Officer
CIO: Rand Strobel, Vice President Information Technology and Compliance
CNO: Ruth Flint, Chief Nursing Officer
Web address: www.chifranciscan.org
Control: Church operated, Nongovernment, not–for–profit **Service**: General medical and surgical

Staffed Beds: 366 **Admissions**: 19956 **Census**: 303 **Outpatient Visits**: 208651 **Births**: 4415 **Total Expense ($000)**: 639239 **Payroll Expense ($000)**: 202320 **Personnel**: 3158

VETERANS AFFAIRS PUGET SOUND HEALTH CARE SYSTEM–AMERICAN LAKE DIVISION See Veterans Affairs Puget Sound Health Care System, Seattle

WESTERN STATE HOSPITAL (504003), 9601 Steilacom Boulevard SW, Zip 98498–7213; tel. 253/582–8900, (Nonreporting)
Primary Contact: David Holt, Chief Executive Officer
CFO: Sue Breen, Chief Financial Officer
CMO: James A Polo, M.D., Chief Medical Officer
CHR: Lori Manning, Administrator Human Resources
CNO: Rae Simpson, R.N., Chief Nursing Officer
Web address: www.dshs.wa.gov/bhsia/division-state-hospitals/western-state-hospital
Control: State, Government, nonfederal **Service**: Psychiatric

Staffed Beds: 867

TONASKET—Okanogan County

★ **NORTH VALLEY HOSPITAL (501321)**, 203 South Western Avenue, Zip 98855–8803; tel. 509/486–2151, (Total facility includes 42 beds in nursing home–type unit) **A**10 18 **F**13 15 29 40 43 45 50 59 64 68 75 76 77 79 81 85 86 93 107 110 114 119 128 130 132 133 148
Primary Contact: Scott Graham, Chief Executive Officer
COO: John McReynolds, Chief Operating Officer
CMO: Paul Lacey, M.D., Chief Medical Staff
CIO: Kelly Cariker, Chief Information Officer
CHR: Jan Gonzales, Director Human Resources
Web address: www.nvhospital.org
Control: Hospital district or authority, Government, nonfederal **Service**: General medical and surgical

Staffed Beds: 67 **Admissions**: 360 **Census**: 43 **Outpatient Visits**: 11535 **Births**: 68 **Total Expense ($000)**: 23059 **Payroll Expense ($000)**: 10463 **Personnel**: 190

TOPPENISH—Yakima County

△ **ASTRIA TOPPENISH HOSPITAL (500037)**, 502 West Fourth Avenue, Zip 98948–1616, Mailing Address: P.O. Box 672, Zip 98948–0672; tel. 509/865–3105, (Nonreporting) **A**1 3 10 **S** Astria Health, Sunnyside, WA
Primary Contact: Eric P. Jensen, Chief Executive Officer
CFO: Curtis Herrin, Chief Financial Officer
CHR: Rosa Solorzano, Interim Director Human Resources
Web address: www.astria.health/
Control: Corporation, Investor–owned (for–profit) **Service**: General medical and surgical

Staffed Beds: 48

TUKWILA—King County

☐ **CASCADE BEHAVIORAL HOSPITAL (504011)**, 12844 Military Road South, Zip 98168–3045; tel. 206/244–0180, (Nonreporting) **A**1 10 **S** Acadia Healthcare Company, Inc., Franklin, TN
Primary Contact: Michael Uradnik, Chief Executive Officer
CFO: Gregg Terreson, Chief Financial Officer
CHR: Sherry Cochran, Manager Human Resources
Web address: www.cascadebh.com
Control: Corporation, Investor–owned (for–profit) **Service**: Psychiatric

Staffed Beds: 63

VANCOUVER—Clark County

LEGACY SALMON CREEK HOSPITAL See Legacy Salmon Creek Medical Center

△ **LEGACY SALMON CREEK MEDICAL CENTER (500150)**, 2211 NE 139th Street, Zip 98686–2742; tel. 360/487–1000, **A**1 2 5 10 **F**3 11 13 15 18 20 26 28 29 30 31 32 34 35 37 38 39 40 41 44 45 46 47 49 50 51 55 57 59 60 65 68 70 72 74 75 76 77 78 79 80 81 82 84 85 87 93 94 96 97 107 108 110 111 114 115 116 117 118 119 120 121 126 129 130 132 146 147 148 149 150 **S** Legacy Health, Portland, OR
Primary Contact: Bryce R. Helgerson, Chief Administrative Officer
COO: Michael Newcomb, D.O., Senior Vice President and Chief Operating Officer
CMO: Lewis Low, M.D., Senior Vice President and Chief Medical Officer
CHR: Sonja Steves, Senior Vice President Human Resources
CNO: Carol Bradley, MSN, R.N., Senior Vice President and Chief Nursing Officer
Web address: www.legacyhealth.org
Control: Other not–for–profit (including NFP Corporation) **Service**: General medical and surgical

Staffed Beds: 211 **Admissions**: 15287 **Census**: 156 **Outpatient Visits**: 356537 **Births**: 3450 **Total Expense ($000)**: 329736 **Payroll Expense ($000)**: 164852 **Personnel**: 1789

★ △ ⇑ **PEACEHEALTH SOUTHWEST MEDICAL CENTER (500050)**, 400 NE Mother Joseph Place, Zip 98664–3200, Mailing Address: P.O. Box 1600, Zip 98668–1600; tel. 360/256–2000, (Includes VANCOUVER MEMORIAL CAMPUS, 3400 Main Street, Vancouver, Washington, Zip 98663; tel. 360/514–2000; Sean Gregory, Chief Executive, Columbia Network) **A**2 3 5 7 10 21 **F**3 11 12 13 15 17 18 20 22 24 26 28 29 30 31 34 35 40 42 43 44 45 46 49 50 51 54 57 58 59 60 61 62 63 64 65 68 70 72 73 74 75 76 77 78 79 81 82 84 85 86 87 88 90 92 93 96 97 98 100 101 102 103 104 105 107 108 109 110 111 114 115 116 117 119 120 121 122 124 126 129 130 131 132 135 144 145 146 147 148 153 154 156 **S** PeaceHealth, Vancouver, WA
Primary Contact: Sean Gregory, Chief Executive
COO: Cary Foster, R.N., Chief Operating Officer
CFO: Ronald K Benfield, Chief Financial Officer
CMO: Lawrence Neville, Chief Medical Officer
CIO: Donn McMillan, Senior Director, IST Client Liaison
CHR: Kelley Frengle, Senior Director, Human Resources
CNO: Helen Vos, R.N., Interim Chief Nursing Officer
Web address: www.peacehealth.org
Control: Church operated, Nongovernment, not–for–profit **Service**: General medical and surgical

Staffed Beds: 436 **Admissions**: 19535 **Census**: 204 **Outpatient Visits**: 211211 **Births**: 1885 **Total Expense ($000)**: 519385 **Payroll Expense ($000)**: 190762 **Personnel**: 2631

⇑ **SOUTHWEST WASHINGTON MEDICAL CENTER** See Peacehealth Southwest Medical Center

WALLA WALLA—Walla Walla County

△ **PROVIDENCE ST. MARY MEDICAL CENTER (500002)**, 401 W Poplar Street, Zip 99362–2846, Mailing Address: P.O. Box 1477, Zip 99362–0312; tel. 509/897–3320, **A**1 2 7 10 19 **F**3 13 15 18 20 22 28 29 30 31 34 35 40 43 45 46 49 59 60 62 64 70 74 75 76 77 78 79 80 81 84 85 89 90 92 93 96 97 100 107 108 110 111 114 115 119 120 121 123 124 129 130 132 135 144 146 147 148 149 154 **S** Providence St. Joseph Health, Renton, WA
Primary Contact: Susan Blackburn, Chief Administrative Officer
COO: Susan Blackburn, Chief Operating Officer
CMO: Tim Davidson, M.D., Chief Executive Physician Services
CIO: Martin Manny, Director, I.S.
CNO: Yvonne M Strader, Chief Nursing Officer
Web address: www.washington.providence.org/hospitals/st-mary/
Control: Church operated, Nongovernment, not–for–profit **Service**: General medical and surgical

Staffed Beds: 92 **Admissions**: 5940 **Census**: 63

STATE PENITENTIARY HOSPITAL, 1313 North 13th Street, Zip 99362–8817; tel. 509/525–3610, (Nonreporting)
Primary Contact: Karen Forest, Health Care Manager
Control: State, Government, nonfederal **Service**: Hospital unit of an institution (prison hospital, college infirmary, etc.)

Staffed Beds: 36

WA

Hospital, Medicare Provider Number, Address, Telephone, Approval, Facility, and Physician Codes, Health Care System

★ American Hospital Association (AHA) membership ○ Healthcare Facilities Accreditation Program ⇑ Center for Improvement in Healthcare Quality Accreditation
☐ The Joint Commission accreditation ◇ DNV Healthcare Inc. accreditation △ Commission on Accreditation of Rehabilitation Facilities (CARF) accreditation

WENATCHEE—Chelan County

★ ⚕ **CONFLUENCE HEALTH/CENTRAL WASHINGTON HOSPITAL (500016)**, 1201 South Miller Street, Zip 98801–3201, Mailing Address: P.O. Box 1887, Zip 98807–1887; tel. 509/662–1511, (Total facility includes 22 beds in nursing home–type unit) **A**2 3 10 21 **F**3 12 13 17 18 20 22 24 26 28 29 30 31 34 35 40 43 45 46 47 49 50 53 62 63 64 68 69 70 73 74 75 76 78 79 81 84 85 86 89 91 93 94 95 100 102 107 108 111 114 115 119 126 128 130 146 147 148 149 154 156
Primary Contact: Peter Rutherford, M.D., Chief Executive Officer
COO: Vikki Noyes, Executive Vice President and Chief Operating Officer
CFO: John Doyle, Chief Financial Officer
CMO: Stuart Freed, M.D., Chief Medical Officer
CIO: Robert Pageler, Chief Information Officer
CHR: Jim Wood, Chief Administrative Officer
CNO: Tracey A Kasnic, Senior Vice President Inpatient and Chief Nursing Officer
Web address: www.cwhs.com
Control: Other not–for–profit (including NFP Corporation) **Service**: General medical and surgical

Staffed Beds: 198 **Admissions**: 11577 **Census**: 136 **Outpatient Visits**: 103775 **Births**: 1282 **Total Expense ($000)**: 365989 **Payroll Expense ($000)**: 103257 **Personnel**: 1544

△ **CONFLUENCE HEALTH/WENATCHEE VALLEY HOSPITAL (500148)**, 820 North Chelan Avenue, Zip 98801–2028; tel. 509/663–8711, (Nonreporting) **A**2 5 7 10
Primary Contact: Peter Rutherford, M.D., Chief Executive Officer
COO: Kevin Gilbert, R.N., Vice President
CFO: John Doyle, Chief Financial Officer
CMO: Stuart Freed, M.D., Medical Director
CIO: Robert Pageler, Chief Information Officer
CHR: Jim Wood, Chief Human Resources Officer
CNO: Tracey A Kasnic, Chief Nursing Officer
Web address: www.confluencehealth.org
Control: Partnership, Investor–owned (for–profit) **Service**: General medical and surgical

Staffed Beds: 20

WHITE SALMON—Klickitat County

SKYLINE HOSPITAL (501315), 211 Skyline Drive, Zip 98672–1918, Mailing Address: P.O. Box 99, Zip 98672–0099; tel. 509/493–1101, **A**10 18 **F**3 11 15 29 30 34 35 40 43 45 57 59 64 65 77 81 87 93 97 107 115 119 127 131 133 146 149
Primary Contact: Robert P. Kimmes, Chief Executive Officer
CFO: Brenda Schneider, Chief Financial Officer
CMO: Christopher Samuels, Chief of Staff
CIO: Steve Opbroek, Manager Information Technology
CHR: Jessie Ramos, Manager Human Resources
CNO: Stefanie Boen, Chief Nursing Officer
Web address: www.skylinehospital.org
Control: Hospital district or authority, Government, nonfederal **Service**: General medical and surgical

Staffed Beds: 14 **Admissions**: 211 **Census**: 2 **Outpatient Visits**: 9442 **Births**: 0 **Total Expense ($000)**: 19518 **Payroll Expense ($000)**: 9398 **Personnel**: 126

YAKIMA—Yakima County

⊠ △ **ASTRIA REGIONAL MEDICAL CENTER (500012)**, 110 South Ninth Avenue, Zip 98902–3315; tel. 509/575–5000, (Nonreporting) **A**1 5 7 10 **S** Astria Health, Sunnyside, WA
Primary Contact: Jeff Egbert, Interim Chief Executive Officer
COO: Darrin Cook, Chief Operating Officer
CMO: John Zambito, M.D., Chief of Staff
CNO: Beth Gregory, Interim Chief Nursing Officer
Web address: www.astria.health/
Control: Corporation, Investor–owned (for–profit) **Service**: General medical and surgical

Staffed Beds: 167

⊠ **VIRGINIA MASON MEMORIAL (500036)**, 2811 Tieton Drive, Zip 98902–3761; tel. 509/575–8000, **A**1 2 3 5 10 **F**3 8 9 11 13 15 17 18 20 22 26 28 29 30 31 32 34 35 36 40 41 43 44 45 46 47 48 49 50 51 54 55 57 58 59 62 63 64 68 70 72 73 74 75 76 77 78 79 81 82 84 85 86 87 89 91 92 93 96 97 98 100 102 103 104 107 108 110 111 114 115 116 117 118 119 120 121 123 124 129 130 131 132 135 146 147 148 149 154 156 **S** Virginia Mason Health System, Seattle, WA
Primary Contact: Russ Myers, Chief Executive Officer
COO: Diane Patterson, Senior Vice President, Chief Operating Officer and Chief Nursing Officer
CFO: Tim Reed, Vice President and Chief Financial Officer
CMO: Marty Brueggemann, Chief Medical Officer
CIO: Jeff Yamada, Vice President
CHR: Jolene R. Seda, Vice President People and Culture
CNO: Diane Patterson, Senior Vice President, Chief Operating Officer and Chief Nursing Officer
Web address: www.yakimamemorial.org
Control: Other not–for–profit (including NFP Corporation) **Service**: General medical and surgical

Staffed Beds: 246 **Admissions**: 12343 **Census**: 129 **Outpatient Visits**: 441264 **Births**: 2551 **Total Expense ($000)**: 480027 **Payroll Expense ($000)**: 198176 **Personnel**: 2648

WA

Many Facility Codes have changed. Please refer to the AHA Guide Code Chart. © 2019 AHA Guide

WEST VIRGINIA

BECKLEY—Raleigh County

⇑ **BECKLEY ARH HOSPITAL (510062)**, 306 Stanaford Road, Zip 25801–3142; tel. 304/255–3000, **A**10 21 **F**3 6 11 15 17 18 20 28 29 30 31 34 35 40 43 44 45 46 47 48 49 50 51 54 55 57 59 60 61 62 64 65 70 74 75 77 78 79 81 82 84 85 86 87 89 90 92 93 97 98 99 100 101 102 103 107 108 109 110 111 114 115 116 118 119 129 130 132 146 148 154 156 **S** Appalachian Regional Healthcare, Inc., Lexington, KY
Primary Contact: Rocco K. Massey, Community Chief Executive Officer
CMO: Ahmad Khiami, Chief of Staff
CHR: Sue Thomas, Manager Human Resources
CNO: Angela Rivera, Chief Nursing Officer
Web address: www.arh.org
Control: Other not–for–profit (including NFP Corporation) **Service:** General medical and surgical

Staffed Beds: 160 **Admissions:** 6316 **Census:** 95 **Outpatient Visits:** 82988 **Births:** 0 **Total Expense ($000):** 93651 **Payroll Expense ($000):** 24574 **Personnel:** 536

⊞ **BECKLEY VETERANS AFFAIRS MEDICAL CENTER**, 200 Veterans Avenue, Zip 25801–6499; tel. 304/255–2121, (Nonreporting) **A**1 3 5 **S** Department of Veterans Affairs, Washington, DC
Primary Contact: Stacy J. Vasquez, Director
CFO: Terry Massey, Chief Fiscal Services
CMO: John David Berryman, M.D., Chief of Staff
CIO: Sherry Gregg, Chief Information Technology Officer
CNO: Debra Lynn Legg, Associate Director Patient Care Services and Nurse Executive
Web address: www.beckley.va.gov/
Control: Veterans Affairs, Government, federal **Service:** General medical and surgical

Staffed Beds: 173

⊞ **RALEIGH GENERAL HOSPITAL (510070)**, 1710 Harper Road, Zip 25801–3397; tel. 304/256–4100, **A**1 3 10 19 **F**3 13 15 17 18 20 22 29 30 31 34 35 40 43 45 49 50 57 59 60 64 70 74 75 76 78 79 81 85 87 89 107 108 110 111 114 115 116 117 119 120 126 130 132 146 147 148 149 156 **S** LifePoint Health, Brentwood, TN
Primary Contact: Matthew S. Roberts, Chief Executive Officer
CFO: Randy Harrison, Chief Financial Officer
CMO: Syed Siddiqi, M.D., President Medical Staff
CIO: Kevin Sexton, Director Information Systems
CHR: Chris T Beebe, Director Human Resources
CNO: Alene Lewis, R.N., Chief Nursing Officer
Web address: www.raleighgeneral.com
Control: Corporation, Investor–owned (for–profit) **Service:** General medical and surgical

Staffed Beds: 229 **Admissions:** 10614 **Census:** 132 **Outpatient Visits:** 53359 **Births:** 989 **Total Expense ($000):** 151337 **Payroll Expense ($000):** 52125 **Personnel:** 836

BERKELEY SPRINGS—Morgan County

⊞ **WAR MEMORIAL HOSPITAL (511309)**, One Healthy Way, Zip 25411–7463; tel. 304/258–1234, (Total facility includes 16 beds in nursing home–type unit) **A**1 10 18 **F**3 11 15 18 28 29 30 34 35 40 45 50 53 54 57 59 64 65 77 79 81 85 86 87 93 97 107 110 114 119 129 130 132 133 135 147 155 156 **S** Valley Health System, Winchester, VA
Primary Contact: Thomas S. Kluge, President
CFO: Kathryn Morales, Director of Finance
CMO: Gerald Bechamps, M.D., Vice President Medical Affairs
CHR: Abbey Rembold, Human Resources Senior Generalist
CNO: Heather Sigel, Director of Clinical Services
Web address: www.valleyhealthlink.com/war
Control: Other not–for–profit (including NFP Corporation) **Service:** General medical and surgical

Staffed Beds: 41 **Admissions:** 498 **Census:** 24 **Outpatient Visits:** 40765 **Births:** 0 **Total Expense ($000):** 25197 **Payroll Expense ($000):** 10417 **Personnel:** 150

BLUEFIELD—Mercer County

⊞ **BLUEFIELD REGIONAL MEDICAL CENTER (510071)**, 500 Cherry Street, Zip 24701–3390; tel. 304/327–1100, **A**1 10 13 19 **F**3 8 13 15 18 20 22 28 29 34 40 43 45 46 47 49 50 56 57 59 60 64 68 70 74 75 76 78 79 81 86 89 93 96 107 108 110 111 115 116 118 119 121 124 126 127 129 130 132 144 146 147 156 **S** Community Health Systems, Inc., Franklin, TN
Primary Contact: Timothy A. Bess, Chief Executive Officer
CMO: Joel Shor, M.D., Chief of Staff
CIO: Rose Lasker, Director Information Services
CHR: Sandee Cheynet, Vice President Administrative Services
Web address: www.https://www.bluefieldregional.net
Control: Corporation, Investor–owned (for–profit) **Service:** General medical and surgical

Staffed Beds: 92 **Admissions:** 3063 **Census:** 29 **Outpatient Visits:** 64022 **Births:** 532 **Total Expense ($000):** 80908 **Payroll Expense ($000):** 20672 **Personnel:** 372

BRIDGEPORT—Harrison County

⊞ **UNITED HOSPITAL CENTER (510006)**, 327 Medical Park Drive, Zip 26330–9006; tel. 681/342–1000, **A**1 2 3 5 10 12 13 **F**3 11 13 15 17 18 20 22 26 28 29 30 31 34 35 40 43 44 45 46 47 48 49 50 51 54 55 57 58 59 60 62 63 64 68 70 74 75 76 77 78 79 81 82 84 85 86 87 89 92 93 96 97 98 100 101 107 108 110 111 114 115 117 119 120 121 126 128 129 130 131 132 135 145 146 147 148 149 **S** West Virginia University Health System, Morgantown, WV
Primary Contact: Michael C. Tillman, President and Chief Executive Officer
COO: John Fernandez, Chief Operating Officer
CFO: Jim Rutkowski, Chief Financial Officer
CMO: Eric Radcliffe, M.D., Medical Director
CIO: Brian Cottrill, Chief Information Officer
CHR: Timothy M Allen, Vice President Human Resources
CNO: Stephanie Smart, Chief Nursing Officer
Web address: www.thenewuhc.com
Control: Other not–for–profit (including NFP Corporation) **Service:** General medical and surgical

Staffed Beds: 264 **Admissions:** 12785 **Census:** 174 **Outpatient Visits:** 561036 **Births:** 1018 **Total Expense ($000):** 339734 **Payroll Expense ($000):** 127620 **Personnel:** 2246

BUCKEYE—Pocahontas County

★ **POCAHONTAS MEMORIAL HOSPITAL (511314)**, 150 Duncan Road, Zip 24924; tel. 304/799–7400, **A**10 18 **F**3 7 11 29 30 34 35 40 43 50 56 57 59 64 65 68 75 77 86 89 90 93 97 107 119 127 128 130 132 133 135 149 156
Primary Contact: Mary Beth. Barr, R.N., Chief Executive Officer
COO: Terry Wagner, R.N., Chief Operating Officer
CFO: Jon Boyette, Chief Financial Officer
CMO: Jeffrey Pilney, Chief Medical Officer
CIO: Samuel Walker, Director of IT
CHR: Katie Brown, Coordinator Human Resources
CNO: Kyna Moore, R.N., Chief Nursing Officer
Web address: www.pmhwv.org/
Control: County, Government, nonfederal **Service:** General medical and surgical

Staffed Beds: 24 **Admissions:** 236 **Census:** 3 **Outpatient Visits:** 23865 **Births:** 1 **Total Expense ($000):** 15333 **Payroll Expense ($000):** 7512 **Personnel:** 138

WV

BUCKHANNON—Upshur County

☒ **ST. JOSEPH'S HOSPITAL OF BUCKHANNON (511321)**, 1 Amalia Drive, Zip 26201–2276; tel. 304/473–2000, (Total facility includes 26 beds in nursing home–type unit) **A**1 10 18 **F**3 11 13 15 18 28 29 30 31 34 35 40 43 44 45 50 57 59 64 65 70 75 76 81 83 84 85 87 89 107 110 115 119 128 129 130 132 133 135 144 146 147 156 **S** West Virginia University Health System, Morgantown, WV
Primary Contact: Skip Gjolberg, FACHE, Administrator
CFO: Russell J. Plywaczynski, CPA, Director of Finance
CMO: Bartley Brown, D.O., Chief of Staff
CIO: Brian Williams, Web Services and Information Technology Manager
CHR: Anissa J Hite Davis, Vice President Human Resources
CNO: Annamarie Chidester, R.N., Vice President, Patient Care Services
Web address: www.stj.net
Control: Other not–for–profit (including NFP Corporation) **Service**: General medical and surgical

Staffed Beds: 51 **Admissions**: 850 **Census**: 28 **Outpatient Visits**: 73090
Births: 313 **Total Expense ($000)**: 50274 **Payroll Expense ($000)**: 20727
Personnel: 380

CHARLESTON—Kanawha County

CAMC MEMORIAL HOSPITAL See Charleston Area Medical Center, Charleston

CAMC WOMEN AND CHILDREN'S HOSPITAL See Charleston Area Medical Center, Charleston

★ △ ⇑ **CHARLESTON AREA MEDICAL CENTER (510022)**, 501 Morris Street, Zip 25301–1300, Mailing Address: P.O. Box 1547, Zip 25326–1547; tel. 304/388–5432, (Includes CAMC MEMORIAL HOSPITAL, P.O. Box 2069, Charleston, West Virginia, Zip 25327, Mailing Address: 3200 MacCorkle Avenue SE, Zip 25304, tel. 304/388–5973; Jeffrey L. Oskin, Vice President and Administrator; CAMC TEAYS VALLEY HOSPITAL, 1400 Hospital Drive, Hurricane, West Virginia, Zip 25526–9202; tel. 304/757–1700; Randall H Hodges, FACHE, Vice President and Administrator; CAMC WOMEN AND CHILDREN'S HOSPITAL, 800 Pennsylvania Avenue, Charleston, West Virginia, Zip 25302, Mailing Address: P O Box 6669, Zip 25362, tel. 304/388–5432; Andrew Weber, Vice President and Administrator; GENERAL HOSPITAL, 501 Morris Street, Charleston, West Virginia, Zip 25301, Mailing Address: Box 1393, Zip 25325, tel. 304/388–5432; Michael D Williams, Vice President and Administrator) **A**2 3 5 7 8 10 21 **F**3 7 8 11 12 13 15 17 18 19 20 22 24 26 28 29 30 31 32 34 35 38 39 40 41 43 44 45 46 47 48 49 50 51 52 54 55 56 57 59 60 61 64 65 68 70 72 73 74 75 76 77 78 79 81 82 84 85 86 87 88 89 90 91 92 93 94 95 96 97 98 100 101 102 104 107 108 110 111 114 115 116 117 118 119 120 121 123 124 126 129 130 131 132 134 135 138 143 144 145 146 147 148 149 150 154 156 157
Primary Contact: David L. Ramsey, President and Chief Executive Officer
COO: Glenn Crotty, M.D., Jr Executive Vice President and Chief Operating Officer
CFO: Larry C Hudson, Executive Vice President and Chief Financial Officer
CMO: T Pinckney McIlwain, M.D., Vice President and Chief Medical Officer
CIO: Eileen Clark, Vice President Information Services
CHR: Kristi Snyder, Vice President Human Resources
CNO: Ronald E Moore, R.N., MSN, Vice President Professional Practice and Chief Nursing Officer
Web address: www.camc.org
Control: Other not–for–profit (including NFP Corporation) **Service**: General medical and surgical

Staffed Beds: 846 **Admissions**: 39507 **Census**: 582 **Outpatient Visits**: 743130 **Births**: 2730 **Total Expense ($000)**: 1107166 **Payroll Expense ($000)**: 447898 **Personnel**: 6749

☐ **CHARLESTON SURGICAL HOSPITAL (510091)**, 1306 Kanawha Boulevard East, Zip 25301–3001, Mailing Address: P.O. Box 2271, Zip 25328–2271; tel. 304/343–4371, (Nonreporting) **A**1 10
Primary Contact: Christina Arvon, Administrator and Chief Executive Officer
CMO: James W Candill, M.D., President Medical Staff
Web address: www.eyeandearclinicwv.org
Control: Corporation, Investor–owned (for–profit) **Service**: General medical and surgical

Staffed Beds: 6

GENERAL HOSPITAL See Charleston Area Medical Center, Charleston

☒ **HIGHLAND HOSPITAL (514001)**, 300 56th Street SE, Zip 25304–2361, Mailing Address: P.O. Box 4107, Zip 25364–4107; tel. 304/926–1600, **A**1 10 **F**3 34 35 38 98 99 101 106 130 132 135
Primary Contact: Cynthia A. Persily, Ph.D., R.N., Chief Executive Officer
COO: Rick Rucker, Chief Operating Officer
CFO: Chris K. Miller, Chief Financial Officer
CMO: Kiran S. Devaraj, Chief Medical Officer and Chief Clinical Officer
CIO: Damon Carradine, Director Information Technology
CNO: Leigh Dalton, Director of Nursing and Patient Care Services
Web address: www.highlandhosp.com
Control: Individual, Investor–owned (for–profit) **Service**: Psychiatric

Staffed Beds: 104 **Admissions**: 2083 **Census**: 79 **Outpatient Visits**: 0
Births: 0 **Total Expense ($000)**: 24761 **Payroll Expense ($000)**: 12637
Personnel: 261

☒ **SAINT FRANCIS HOSPITAL (510031)**, 333 Laidley Street, Zip 25301–1628, Mailing Address: P.O. Box 471, Zip 25322–0471; tel. 304/347–6500, (Total facility includes 25 beds in nursing home–type unit) **A**1 10 **F**3 4 11 15 18 20 22 29 30 33 34 35 45 46 47 48 49 51 57 58 59 64 75 77 81 82 97 100 106 107 108 110 111 115 118 119 128 130 144 146 147 148 **S** Thomas Health System, Inc., South Charleston, WV
Primary Contact: Daniel Lauffer, FACHE, President and Chief Executive Officer
COO: Brian Ulery, Senior Vice President and Chief Operating Officer
CFO: Renee Cross, Senior Vice President and Chief Financial Officer
CMO: Matthew Upton, Chief Medical Officer and Chief Medical Information Officer
CIO: Jeremy Taylor, Director Information Services
CHR: Patrick Rawlings, Chief Human Resource Officer
CNO: Rebecca Brannon, R.N., Senior Vice President and Chief Nursing Officer
Web address: www.stfrancishospital.com
Control: Other not–for–profit (including NFP Corporation) **Service**: General medical and surgical

Staffed Beds: 65 **Admissions**: 673 **Census**: 18 **Outpatient Visits**: 70800
Births: 0 **Total Expense ($000)**: 68047 **Payroll Expense ($000)**: 19962
Personnel: 329

☒ **SELECT SPECIALTY HOSPITAL-CHARLESTON (512002)**, 333 Laidley Street, 3rd Floor East, Zip 25301–1614; tel. 304/720–7234, **A**1 10 **F**1 29 74 75 85 130 148 149 **S** Select Medical Corporation, Mechanicsburg, PA
Primary Contact: Frank Weber, Chief Executive Officer
CHR: Sabrina White, Coordinator Human Resources
Web address: www.selectspecialtyhospitals.com/company/locations/charleston.aspx
Control: Corporation, Investor–owned (for–profit) **Service**: Acute long–term care hospital

Staffed Beds: 32 **Admissions**: 376 **Census**: 29 **Outpatient Visits**: 0
Births: 0 **Total Expense ($000)**: 17538 **Payroll Expense ($000)**: 6929
Personnel: 112

CLARKSBURG—Harrison County

☐ **HIGHLAND-CLARKSBURG HOSPITAL (514011)**, 3 Hospital Plaza, Zip 26301–9316; tel. 304/969–3100, **A**1 10 **F**98 99 103
Primary Contact: Vickie Jones, Interim Chief Executive Officer
CFO: Shelly Giaguinto, Chief Financial Officer
CMO: Christi Cooper-Lehki, Chief Clinical Officer
CIO: Kimberly Samuelson, Director of Information Management
CHR: Robert L Boyles, Director of Human Resources
CNO: Melissa Hitt, Director of Nursing
Web address: www.highlandhosp.com
Control: Other not–for–profit (including NFP Corporation) **Service**: Psychiatric

Staffed Beds: 115 **Admissions**: 630 **Census**: 79 **Outpatient Visits**: 0
Births: 0 **Total Expense ($000)**: 25055 **Payroll Expense ($000)**: 13245
Personnel: 305

☒ **LOUIS A. JOHNSON VETERANS AFFAIRS MEDICAL CENTER**, 1 Medical Center Drive, Zip 26301–4199; tel. 304/623–3461, (Nonreporting) **A**1 2 3 5 **S** Department of Veterans Affairs, Washington, DC
Primary Contact: Glenn R. Snider, M.D., Interim Director
CMO: Glenn R Snider, M.D., Chief of Staff
CIO: Michael Matthey, Facility Chief Information Officer
CHR: Ian Jacobs, Chief, Human Resource Management Service
Web address: www.clarksburg.va.gov
Control: Veterans Affairs, Government, federal **Service**: General medical and surgical

Staffed Beds: 71

WV

Many Facility Codes have changed. Please refer to the AHA Guide Code Chart. © 2019 AHA Guide

ELKINS—Randolph County

DAVIS MEDICAL CENTER (510030), Gorman Avenue and Reed Street, Zip 26241, Mailing Address: P.O. Box 1484, Zip 26241–1484; tel. 304/636–3300, **A**1 2 10 20 **F**11 13 15 28 29 30 31 32 34 35 40 49 50 51 54 56 57 59 64 68 69 70 71 75 76 78 79 81 82 84 85 86 87 89 92 94 97 98 103 107 108 109 110 111 115 116 117 118 119 121 123 129 130 132 135 146 147 148 154 **S** Davis Health System, Elkins, WV
Primary Contact: Vance Jackson, FACHE, Chief Executive Officer
COO: Greg Johnson, Vice President of Operations
CFO: Rebecca J Hammer, Chief Financial Officer
CMO: Anne Banfield, Chief, Medical Staff
CIO: Steve Crowl, Director of Information Services
CHR: Jon Steen, Director Human Resources
CNO: Pamela Smithson, R.N., Vice President Nursing
Web address: www.davishealthsystem.com
Control: Other not–for–profit (including NFP Corporation) **Service:** General medical and surgical

Staffed Beds: 80 **Admissions:** 2952 **Census:** 28 **Outpatient Visits:** 137264 **Births:** 372 **Total Expense ($000):** 93545 **Payroll Expense ($000):** 38671 **Personnel:** 711

FAIRMONT—Marion County

FAIRMONT REGIONAL MEDICAL CENTER (510047), 1325 Locust Avenue, Zip 26554–1435; tel. 304/367–7100, (Nonreporting) **A**1 2 10 **S** Alecto Healthcare, Irvine, CA
Primary Contact: Robert S. Adcock, Chief Executive Officer
CFO: Daniel Quance, Chief Financial Officer
CMO: Wes Steele, M.D., Chief of Staff
CIO: Mike Wooddell, Director Information Services
CHR: Jim Harris, Vice President Human Resources
CNO: Michelle L Luffey, MSN, R.N., Chief Nursing Officer
Web address: www.frmcwv.com
Control: Other not–for–profit (including NFP Corporation) **Service:** General medical and surgical

Staffed Beds: 144

GASSAWAY—Braxton County

BRAXTON COUNTY MEMORIAL HOSPITAL (511308), 100 Hoylman DR, Zip 26624–9318, Mailing Address: 100 Hoylman Drive, Zip 26624–9318; tel. 304/364–5156, **A**10 18 **F**3 8 11 15 29 30 32 34 35 40 43 45 57 59 62 64 75 81 97 107 108 114 127 130 133 146 147 149 156
Primary Contact: Karen L. Dowling, MSN, R.N., Interim Chief Executive Officer
CFO: Kimber Knight, Chief Financial Officer
CMO: Russell L Stewart, D.O., Medical Director
CNO: Julia Rose, R.N., Director of Nursing
Web address: www.braxtonmemorial.org
Control: Other not–for–profit (including NFP Corporation) **Service:** General medical and surgical

Staffed Beds: 25 **Admissions:** 196 **Census:** 2 **Outpatient Visits:** 46216 **Births:** 0 **Total Expense ($000):** 17279 **Payroll Expense ($000):** 7656 **Personnel:** 142

GLEN DALE—Marshall County

REYNOLDS MEMORIAL HOSPITAL (510013), 800 Wheeling Avenue, Zip 26038–1697; tel. 304/845–3211, **A**1 10 **F**3 11 13 15 18 20 28 29 30 31 34 35 40 41 44 45 50 53 57 59 62 64 68 70 74 75 76 77 78 79 80 81 85 86 87 107 110 111 114 119 128 130 132 135 146 147 154 **S** West Virginia University Health System, Morgantown, WV
Primary Contact: David F. Hess, M.D., Chief Executive Officer
COO: Kevin Britt, Chief Operating Officer
CFO: William Robert Hunt, Chief Financial Officer
CMO: David F. Hess, M.D., President Medical Staff
CIO: Warren Kelley, Chief Information Officer
CHR: R. Craig Madden, Director Employee Relations
CNO: Carol R Miller, R.N., Chief Nursing Officer
Web address: www.reynoldsmemorial.com
Control: Other not–for–profit (including NFP Corporation) **Service:** General medical and surgical

Staffed Beds: 50 **Admissions:** 1745 **Census:** 18 **Outpatient Visits:** 82461 **Births:** 0 **Total Expense ($000):** 52502 **Payroll Expense ($000):** 25553

GRAFTON—Taylor County

GRAFTON CITY HOSPITAL (511307), 1 Hospital Plaza, Zip 26354–1283; tel. 304/265–0400, **A**10 18 **F**11 15 29 30 32 34 35 38 39 40 45 50 53 54 57 59 61 64 65 75 81 83 84 85 86 87 91 92 93 94 97 100 101 102 104 107 108 110 114 119 127 129 130 131 132 133 135 146 147 149 150 154 156
Primary Contact: Patrick D. Shaw, Chief Executive Officer
CFO: Regina Pickens, Chief Financial Officer
CMO: David B Bender, M.D., Chief Medical Staff
CIO: Jim Harris, Director Information Technology
CHR: Missey Kimbrew, Director Human Resources
CNO: Violet Shaw, R.N., Director of Nursing
Web address: www.graftonhospital.com
Control: City, Government, nonfederal **Service:** General medical and surgical

Staffed Beds: 25 **Admissions:** 362 **Census:** 22 **Outpatient Visits:** 43491 **Births:** 0 **Total Expense ($000):** 18904 **Payroll Expense ($000):** 9903 **Personnel:** 177

GRANTSVILLE—Calhoun County

★ **MINNIE HAMILTON HEALTHCARE CENTER (511303)**, 186 Hospital Drive, Zip 26147–7100; tel. 304/354–9244, (Total facility includes 24 beds in nursing home–type unit) **A**10 18 **F**3 11 15 29 30 32 34 35 36 39 40 41 43 44 50 53 56 57 59 61 64 65 66 68 75 82 84 86 87 93 97 100 107 108 119 127 130 132 133 134 135 143 144 146 147 148 156
Primary Contact: Steve Whited, Chief Executive Officer
CMO: Suresh Balasubramony, M.D., Chief Medical Officer
CIO: Brent Barr, Chief Information Officer
CHR: Sheila Gherke, Director Human Resources
CNO: Kim Houchin, Chief Nursing Officer
Web address: www.mhhcc.com
Control: Other not–for–profit (including NFP Corporation) **Service:** General medical and surgical

Staffed Beds: 42 **Admissions:** 476 **Census:** 28 **Outpatient Visits:** 25981 **Births:** 0 **Total Expense ($000):** 19440 **Payroll Expense ($000):** 12377 **Personnel:** 279

HINTON—Summers County

SUMMERS COUNTY ARH HOSPITAL (511310), Terrace Street, Zip 25951–2407, Mailing Address: Drawer 940, Zip 25951–0940; tel. 304/466–1000, **A**10 18 **F**11 15 29 30 32 34 35 40 43 44 50 54 57 59 62 64 65 71 77 81 82 85 86 87 93 97 107 110 114 119 127 130 133 146 147 148 154 155 **S** Appalachian Regional Healthcare, Inc., Lexington, KY
Primary Contact: Wesley Dangerfield, Community Chief Executive Officer
CMO: Waheed Khan, M.D., President Medical Staff
CIO: Brent Styer, Chief Information Officer
CHR: Beth Elswick, Administrative Assistant
CNO: Sharon Milburn, Chief Nursing Officer
Web address: www.arh.org
Control: Other not–for–profit (including NFP Corporation) **Service:** General medical and surgical

Staffed Beds: 25 **Admissions:** 371 **Census:** 7 **Outpatient Visits:** 25862 **Births:** 0 **Total Expense ($000):** 13472 **Payroll Expense ($000):** 4832 **Personnel:** 105

HUNTINGTON—Cabell County

CABELL HUNTINGTON HOSPITAL (510055), 1340 Hal Greer Boulevard, Zip 25701–0195; tel. 304/526–2000, (Includes HOOPS FAMILY CHILDREN'S HOSPITAL, 1340 Hal Greer Boulevard, Huntington, West Virginia, Zip 25701–3800; tel. 304/526–2000) **A**1 2 3 5 8 10 **F**2 3 5 7 8 9 11 12 13 15 16 18 19 20 22 26 28 29 30 31 32 34 35 37 38 40 41 43 44 45 46 47 48 49 50 51 52 54 55 56 57 58 59 61 62 64 65 70 72 73 74 75 76 77 78 79 81 82 83 84 85 86 87 88 89 91 92 93 94 96 97 104 107 108 110 111 114 115 116 117 118 119 120 121 123 124 126 129 130 131 132 134 135 144 145 146 147 148 149 150 154 156 157 **S** Mountain Health Network, Huntington, WV
Primary Contact: Kevin N. Fowler, President and Chief Executive Officer
CFO: David M Ward, Chief Financial Officer and Chief Acquisition Officer
CMO: Hoyt J Burdick, M.D., Vice President Medical Affairs
CIO: Dennis Lee, Vice President and Chief Information Officer
CHR: Barry Tourigny, Vice President Human Resources and Organizational Development
CNO: Joy S Pelfrey, R.N., MSN, Vice President and Chief Nursing Officer
Web address: www.cabellhuntington.org
Control: Other not–for–profit (including NFP Corporation) **Service:** General medical and surgical

Staffed Beds: 303 **Admissions:** 28337 **Census:** 276 **Outpatient Visits:** 742357 **Births:** 2631 **Total Expense ($000):** 536386 **Payroll Expense ($000):** 176226 **Personnel:** 2679

WV

☐ **CORNERSTONE HOSPITAL OF HUNTINGTON (512003)**, 2900 First Avenue, Two East, Zip 25702–1241; tel. 304/399–2600, **A**1 10 **F**1 29 148 **S** Cornerstone Healthcare Group, Dallas, TX
Primary Contact: Cynthia Isaacs, Chief Executive Officer
CFO: Carla Jeffs, Chief Financial Officer
CMO: William Beam, M.D., Chief of Staff
Web address: www.chghospitals.com
Control: Corporation, Investor–owned (for–profit) **Service**: Acute long–term care hospital

Staffed Beds: 28 **Admissions**: 401 **Census**: 27 **Outpatient Visits**: 0 **Births**: 0 **Total Expense ($000)**: 11392 **Payroll Expense ($000)**: 5072 **Personnel**: 71

✉ **ENCOMPASS HEALTH REHABILITATION HOSPITAL OF HUNTINGTON (513028)**, 6900 West Country Club Drive, Zip 25705–2000; tel. 304/733–1060, **A**1 10 **F**29 34 90 96 148 149 **S** Encompass Health Corporation, Birmingham, AL
Primary Contact: Michael E. Zuliani, Chief Executive Officer
CHR: Jenny Overcash, Director Human Resources
CNO: Ann Evans, Chief Nursing Officer
Web address: www.healthsouthhuntington.com
Control: Corporation, Investor–owned (for–profit) **Service**: Rehabilitation

Staffed Beds: 62 **Admissions**: 1483 **Census**: 51 **Outpatient Visits**: 0 **Births**: 0 **Total Expense ($000)**: 16743 **Payroll Expense ($000)**: 8772 **Personnel**: 170

HUNTINGTON—Wayne County

✉ **HUNTINGTON VETERANS AFFAIRS MEDICAL CENTER**, 1540 Spring Valley Drive, Zip 25704–9300; tel. 304/429–6741, (Nonreporting) **A**1 3 5 **S** Department of Veterans Affairs, Washington, DC
Primary Contact: Brian Nimmo, Director
CIO: Gary Henderson, Chief Information Resources Management Services
Web address: www.huntington.va.gov/
Control: Veterans Affairs, Government, federal **Service**: General medical and surgical

Staffed Beds: 80

HUNTINGTON—Cabell County

☐ **MILDRED MITCHELL-BATEMAN HOSPITAL (514009)**, 1530 Norway Avenue, Zip 25705–1358, Mailing Address: P.O. Box 448, Zip 25709–0448; tel. 304/525–7801, **A**1 3 10 **F**3 4 11 30 68 86 87 97 98 103 130 132 135 143 146 148 149 150 154
Primary Contact: Craig A. Richards, Chief Executive Officer
CFO: Lucille Gedies, Chief Financial Officer
CMO: Shahid Masood, M.D., Clinical Director
CIO: Elias Majdalani, Director Management Information Systems
CHR: Kieth Anne Worden, Director Human Resources
CNO: Patricia Hamilton, R.N., Director of Nursing
Web address: www.batemanhospital.org
Control: State, Government, nonfederal **Service**: Psychiatric

Staffed Beds: 110 **Admissions**: 510 **Census**: 97 **Outpatient Visits**: 0 **Births**: 0 **Total Expense ($000)**: 45717 **Payroll Expense ($000)**: 14404 **Personnel**: 318

☐ **RIVER PARK HOSPITAL (514008)**, 1230 Sixth Avenue, Zip 25701–2312, Mailing Address: P.O. Box 1875, Zip 25719–1875; tel. 304/526–9111, (Nonreporting) **A**1 3 5 10 **S** Universal Health Services, Inc., King of Prussia, PA
Primary Contact: Terry A. Stephens, Chief Executive Officer
CFO: Steve Kuhn, Chief Financial Officer
CMO: Mark A. Hughes, M.D., Medical Director
CIO: James Martin, Chief Information Officer
CHR: Mary Stratton, Director Human Resources
CNO: Michelle Gilliland, Director of Nursing
Web address: www.riverparkhospital.net
Control: Corporation, Investor–owned (for–profit) **Service**: Psychiatric

Staffed Beds: 175

WV

✉ **ST. MARY'S MEDICAL CENTER (510007)**, 2900 First Avenue, Zip 25702–1272; tel. 304/526–1234, (Total facility includes 19 beds in nursing home–type unit) **A**1 2 3 10 **F**3 11 12 13 15 17 18 20 22 24 26 28 29 30 31 32 34 35 36 39 40 42 43 44 45 46 47 48 49 50 53 54 55 57 58 59 60 61 62 64 65 66 67 68 70 74 75 76 77 78 79 81 82 84 85 87 89 90 93 98 100 102 103 107 108 110 111 114 115 118 119 120 121 123 124 126 128 129 130 132 135 144 146 147 154 156 157 **S** Mountain Health Network, Huntington, WV
Primary Contact: Todd Campbell, Chief Executive Officer
CFO: Angela Swearingen, Vice President Finance
CMO: Ernest Lee Taylor, M.D., Vice President Medical Affairs
CIO: David Wendell, Manager, Information Systems
CHR: Susan Beth Robinson, Vice President Human Resources
CNO: Elizabeth Bosley, R.N., FACHE, Vice President Patient Services and Chief Nursing Officer
Web address: www.st-marys.org
Control: Church operated, Nongovernment, not–for–profit **Service**: General medical and surgical

Staffed Beds: 393 **Admissions**: 16072 **Census**: 259 **Outpatient Visits**: 246802 **Births**: 373 **Total Expense ($000)**: 394166 **Payroll Expense ($000)**: 134895 **Personnel**: 2758

KEYSER—Mineral County

✉ **POTOMAC VALLEY HOSPITAL (511315)**, 100 Pin Oak Lane, Zip 26726–5908; tel. 304/597–3500, **A**1 10 18 **F**3 15 18 28 29 34 35 40 44 45 50 54 57 59 63 64 65 66 68 70 71 74 75 77 79 81 82 85 86 87 92 93 97 107 108 110 111 114 119 127 130 131 132 133 135 143 146 148 149 154 156 **S** West Virginia University Health System, Morgantown, WV
Primary Contact: Mark G. Boucot, FACHE, President and Chief Executive Officer
CFO: Marian Cardwell, Chief Financial Officer
CMO: Charles Bess, M.D., Medical Director
CIO: Micah Reel, Director of Bio-Med
CHR: Dianne Smith, Director Personnel and Human Resources
CNO: Mary Ann Billings, Director of Nursing
Web address: www.potomacvalleyhospital.com
Control: Other not–for–profit (including NFP Corporation) **Service**: General medical and surgical

Staffed Beds: 25 **Admissions**: 1009 **Census**: 7 **Outpatient Visits**: 28610 **Births**: 1 **Total Expense ($000)**: 25173 **Payroll Expense ($000)**: 9537 **Personnel**: 245

KINGWOOD—Preston County

★ **PRESTON MEMORIAL HOSPITAL (511312)**, 150 Memorial Drive, Zip 26537–1495; tel. 304/329–1400, **A**10 18 **F**3 12 15 18 28 29 30 34 35 40 43 45 47 48 50 53 55 57 59 64 65 70 74 75 77 79 81 92 93 97 107 108 110 111 114 119 129 132 133 135 144 146 147 148 154 **S** Mon Health System, Morgantown, WV
Primary Contact: Melissa Lockwood, Chief Executive Officer
CFO: Kevin Gessler, Chief Financial Officer
CIO: Beth Horne, System Administrator Information Technology
CHR: Michele Batiste, Director Human Resources
Web address: www.prestonmemorial.org
Control: Other not–for–profit (including NFP Corporation) **Service**: General medical and surgical

Staffed Beds: 25 **Admissions**: 629 **Census**: 8 **Outpatient Visits**: 73683 **Births**: 1 **Total Expense ($000)**: 39700 **Payroll Expense ($000)**: 18811 **Personnel**: 369

LOGAN—Logan County

✉ **LOGAN REGIONAL MEDICAL CENTER (510048)**, 20 Hospital Drive, Zip 25601–3452; tel. 304/831–1101, **A**1 10 20 **F**3 11 13 15 18 20 28 29 31 34 35 40 43 45 49 51 54 57 59 64 65 70 74 75 76 77 78 79 81 82 86 87 89 90 92 93 97 107 108 110 111 114 115 117 118 119 129 130 133 135 146 147 148 **S** LifePoint Health, Brentwood, TN
Primary Contact: Simon Ratliff, Interim Chief Executive Officer
COO: Simon Ratliff, Chief Operating Officer
CFO: Tim Matney, Chief Financial Officer
CMO: Kathy Harvey, D.O., Chief Medical Officer
CIO: Barry Hensley, Director Information Systems
CHR: Jessica Martin, Director Human Resources
CNO: Karen Barnes, Interim Chief Nursing Officer
Web address: www.loganregionalmedicalcenter.com
Control: Corporation, Investor–owned (for–profit) **Service**: General medical and surgical

Staffed Beds: 129 **Admissions**: 4827 **Census**: 64 **Outpatient Visits**: 101084 **Births**: 199 **Total Expense ($000)**: 83880 **Payroll Expense ($000)**: 27144 **Personnel**: 644

Many Facility Codes have changed. Please refer to the AHA Guide Code Chart. © 2019 AHA Guide

MADISON—Boone County

☒ **BOONE MEMORIAL HOSPITAL (511313)**, 701 Madison Avenue,
Zip 25130–1699; tel. 304/369–1230, **A**1 10 18 **F**3 11 15 18 28 29 30 34 35
40 45 47 48 50 53 57 59 65 81 107 108 110 111 114 118 119 127 129 131
133 135 144 156
Primary Contact: Virgil Underwood, Chief Executive Officer
CFO: Randy Foxx, Chief Financial Officer
CMO: Ziad Chanaa, M.D., Chief of Staff
CIO: Susan Shreve, Executive Director Information Technology
CHR: Sheliah Cook, Director Human Resources
CNO: Teresa Meade, R.N., Chief Nursing Officer
Web address: www.bmh.org
Control: Other not–for–profit (including NFP Corporation) **Service**: General
medical and surgical

Staffed Beds: 25 **Admissions**: 802 **Census**: 11 **Births**: 0 **Total Expense**
($000): 35639 **Payroll Expense ($000)**: 12609 **Personnel**: 265

MARTINSBURG—Berkeley County

☒ **BERKELEY MEDICAL CENTER (510008)**, 2500 Hospital Drive,
Zip 25401–3402; tel. 304/264–1000, **A**1 2 3 10 **F**3 8 11 12 13 15 17 18 20 22
28 29 30 31 34 35 38 40 43 44 45 47 49 51 53 54 57 59 62 64 70 72 74 75
76 77 78 79 81 82 84 85 86 87 89 92 93 98 102 103 104 105 107 108 110
111 114 115 118 119 124 126 129 130 131 132 135 143 144 145 146 147
148 154 157 **S** West Virginia University Health System, Morgantown, WV
Primary Contact: Anthony Zelenka, President and Chief Operating Officer
CFO: Anna Buchanan, Vice President Finance and Chief Financial Officer
CIO: Mark Combs, Interim Director System Information Technology
CHR: Justin Ruble, Director, Human Resources
CNO: Donna Clews, Ph.D., R.N., Vice President Patient Care Services
Web address: www.cityhospital.org
Control: Other not–for–profit (including NFP Corporation) **Service**: General
medical and surgical

Staffed Beds: 195 **Admissions**: 8721 **Census**: 105 **Outpatient**
Visits: 279800 **Births**: 1082 **Total Expense ($000)**: 212728 **Payroll**
Expense ($000): 66096 **Personnel**: 1164

☒ **MARTINSBURG VETERANS AFFAIRS MEDICAL CENTER**, 510 Butler Avenue,
Zip 25405–9990; tel. 304/263–0811, (Total facility includes 133 beds in nursing
home–type unit) **A**1 3 5 **F**3 4 5 7 10 15 18 22 24 26 27 28 29 30 31 33 34 35
36 38 39 40 45 46 47 48 49 50 53 55 56 58 59 61 62 63 64 65 66 68 70 74
75 77 78 79 81 82 83 84 85 87 91 92 93 94 97 98 100 101 102 103 104 106
107 108 111 114 115 118 119 127 128 129 130 132 133 135 141 142 143
146 147 148 149 150 151 154 155 156 157 158 **S** Department of Veterans
Affairs, Washington, DC
Primary Contact: Timothy J. Cooke, Medical Center Director and Chief Executive
Officer
COO: Timothy J Cooke, Medical Center Director and Chief Executive Officer
CMO: Jonathan Fierer, M.D., Chief of Staff
CIO: Mary Ann Creel, Chief Information Resource Management
CHR: Brenda Byrd Pelaez, Chief Human Resources Management Office
CNO: Susan George, R.N., M.P.H., Associate Director Patient Care Services
Web address: www.martinsburg.va.gov/
Control: Veterans Affairs, Government, federal **Service**: General medical and
surgical

Staffed Beds: 557 **Admissions**: 4409 **Census**: 175 **Outpatient**
Visits: 516250 **Births**: 0 **Total Expense ($000)**: 334313 **Payroll Expense**
($000): 159620 **Personnel**: 2194

MONTGOMERY—Fayette County

☒ **MONTGOMERY GENERAL HOSPITAL (511318)**, 401 Sixth Avenue,
Zip 25136–2116, Mailing Address: P.O. Box 270, Zip 25136–0270;
tel. 304/442–5151, (Total facility includes 44 beds in nursing home–type unit) **A**1
10 18 **F**3 11 15 29 30 34 35 40 45 49 50 53 57 59 64 67 68 77 81 87 93 97
107 110 111 114 119 128 129 130 131 133 135 146 147 149
Primary Contact: Vickie Gay, Chief Executive Officer
CFO: Sherri Murray, Chief Financial Officer
CMO: Traci Acklin, M.D., Chief of Staff
CIO: Denzil Blevins, Director Information Systems
CHR: Kelly D Frye, Director Human Resources
Web address: www.mghwv.com
Control: Other not–for–profit (including NFP Corporation) **Service**: General
medical and surgical

Staffed Beds: 69 **Admissions**: 404 **Census**: 43 **Outpatient Visits**: 54539
Births: 0 **Total Expense ($000)**: 21972 **Payroll Expense ($000)**: 10698
Personnel: 217

MORGANTOWN—Monongalia County

CHESTNUT RIDGE HOSPITAL See West Virginia University Hospitals, Morgantown

☒ **ENCOMPASS HEALTH REHABILITATION HOSPITAL OF MORGANTOWN**
(513030), 1160 Van Voorhis Road, Zip 26505–3437; tel. 304/598–1100,
(Nonreporting) **A**1 5 10 **S** Encompass Health Corporation, Birmingham, AL
Primary Contact: Tracy Vinciguerra, Chief Executive Officer
CFO: Jason Gizzi, Controller
CMO: Govind Patel, M.D., Medical Director
CIO: Robin Wherry, Risk Manager and Director Quality Assurance and Health
Information Management
CHR: Shannon Hyde, Director Human Resources
CNO: Stacy Jones, Chief Nursing Officer
Web address: www.healthsouthmountainview.com
Control: Corporation, Investor–owned (for–profit) **Service**: Rehabilitation

Staffed Beds: 96

☒ **MON HEALTH MEDICAL CENTER (510024)**, 1200 J D Anderson Drive,
Zip 26505–3486; tel. 304/598–1200, **A**1 2 3 10 **F**3 13 15 17 18 20 22 24
26 28 29 30 31 32 34 35 40 43 45 46 49 50 51 54 55 57 59 60 64 65 68 70
74 75 76 77 78 79 81 82 84 85 86 87 89 97 100 104 107 108 110 111 114
115 116 118 119 120 121 123 126 127 129 130 132 135 145 146 147 148
149 154 156 **S** Mon Health System, Morgantown, WV
Primary Contact: David Goldberg, President and Chief Executive Officer
CMO: Matthew P Darmelio, Chief of Staff
CIO: Steve Carter, Chief Information Officer
CHR: Melissa Shreves Shahnam, Director Human Resources
Web address: www.mongeneral.com
Control: Other not–for–profit (including NFP Corporation) **Service**: General
medical and surgical

Staffed Beds: 185 **Admissions**: 7379 **Census**: 86 **Outpatient**
Visits: 411622 **Births**: 1136 **Total Expense ($000)**: 280572 **Payroll**
Expense ($000): 106360 **Personnel**: 1532

☒ **WEST VIRGINIA UNIVERSITY HOSPITALS (510001)**, 1 Medical Center Drive,
Zip 26506–4749; tel. 304/598–4000, (Includes CHESTNUT RIDGE HOSPITAL,
930 Chestnut Ridge Road, Morgantown, West Virginia, Zip 26505–2854;
tel. 304/293–4000; WEST VIRGINIA UNIVERSITY CHILDREN'S HOSPITAL, 1 Medical
Center Drive, Morgantown, West Virginia, Zip 26506–1200; tel. 800/982–6277)
A1 3 5 8 10 19 **F**3 4 5 7 8 9 11 12 13 15 17 18 19 20 21 22 23 24 25 26 27
28 29 30 31 32 33 34 35 36 37 38 39 40 41 43 44 45 46 47 48 49 50 51 52
53 54 55 56 57 58 59 60 61 64 65 68 70 71 72 74 75 76 77 78 79 80 81 82
83 84 85 86 87 88 89 91 92 93 97 98 99 100 101 102 103 104 105 106 107
108 109 110 111 114 115 116 117 118 119 120 121 123 124 126 127 129
130 131 132 133 135 136 141 143 144 145 146 147 148 149 152 153 154
155 157 **S** West Virginia University Health System, Morgantown, WV
Primary Contact: Albert L. Wright Jr, PharmD, President and Chief Executive Officer
COO: Ron Pellegrino, Chief Operating Officer
CFO: Melissa McCoy, Vice President and Chief Financial Officer
CMO: Judie Charlton, M.D., Chief Medical Officer
CIO: James Venturella, Vice President Information Technology
CHR: Leeann Cerimele, Vice President Human Resources
CNO: Douglas W Mitchell, Vice President and Chief Nursing Officer
Web address: www.health.wvu.edu
Control: Other not–for–profit (including NFP Corporation) **Service**: General
medical and surgical

Staffed Beds: 652 **Admissions**: 29832 **Census**: 562 **Outpatient**
Visits: 883468 **Births**: 1488 **Total Expense ($000)**: 1181487 **Payroll**
Expense ($000): 343044 **Personnel**: 6391

NEW MARTINSVILLE—Wetzel County

☒ **WETZEL COUNTY HOSPITAL (510072)**, 3 East Benjamin Drive,
Zip 26155–2758; tel. 304/455–8000, (Nonreporting) **A**1 10 20
Primary Contact: David F. Hess, M.D., Chief Executive Officer
CFO: Edwin Szewczyk, Chief Financial Officer
CMO: Donald A. Blum, M.D., Chief of Staff
CIO: Amy Frazier, Supervisor Management Information Systems
CHR: Sarah Boley, Director Human Resources
Web address: www.wetzelcountyhospital.com
Control: County, Government, nonfederal **Service**: General medical and surgical

Staffed Beds: 44

WV

Hospital, Medicare Provider Number, Address, Telephone, Approval, Facility, and Physician Codes, Health Care System

★ American Hospital Association (AHA) membership   ○ Healthcare Facilities Accreditation Program   ⇑ Center for Improvement in Healthcare Quality Accreditation
□ The Joint Commission accreditation   ◇ DNV Healthcare Inc. accreditation   △ Commission on Accreditation of Rehabilitation Facilities (CARF) accreditation

OAK HILL—Fayette County

☒ **PLATEAU MEDICAL CENTER (511317)**, 430 Main Street, Zip 25901–3455; tel. 304/469–8600, **A**1 10 18 **F**3 11 15 18 29 34 40 45 46 50 53 57 68 70 75 76 77 79 81 87 93 107 108 110 111 115 119 126 129 133 146 **S** Community Health Systems, Inc., Franklin, TN
Primary Contact: Christopher L. Howe, R.N., Chief Executive Officer
CFO: Heather Hylton, Chief Financial Officer
CMO: Jacob McNeel, D.O., Chief of Staff
CIO: Nick Stover, Director Information Systems
CHR: Tammie Chinn, Director Marketing and Public Relations
CNO: Randell Thompson, Chief Nursing Officer
Web address: www.plateaumedicalcenter.com
Control: Corporation, Investor–owned (for–profit) **Service**: General medical and surgical

Staffed Beds: 25 **Admissions:** 1070 **Census:** 11 **Outpatient Visits:** 32928 **Births:** 0 **Total Expense ($000):** 25501 **Payroll Expense ($000):** 9920 **Personnel:** 182

PARKERSBURG—Wood County

☒ **CAMDEN CLARK MEDICAL CENTER (510058)**, 800 Garfield Avenue, Zip 26101–5378, Mailing Address: P.O. Box 718, Zip 26102–0718; tel. 304/424–2111, **A**1 3 10 19 **F**3 7 8 11 12 13 15 17 18 20 22 24 28 29 30 31 34 35 40 43 45 48 49 50 53 54 57 58 59 60 64 65 66 67 68 70 74 75 76 77 78 79 80 81 82 84 85 86 87 89 92 97 98 107 108 110 111 115 117 119 120 121 123 124 129 130 131 132 135 144 146 147 154 156 157 **S** West Virginia University Health System, Morgantown, WV
Primary Contact: Steve Altmiller, President and Chief Executive Officer
CFO: Carolyn Allen, Vice President and Chief Financial Officer
CMO: David Gnegy, M.D., Vice President of Medical Affairs
CIO: Josh Woods, Director Information Systems
CHR: Tom Heller, Vice President Operations and Human Resources
CNO: Christine S. Daniels, R.N., Chief Nursing Officer
Web address: www.camdenclark.org
Control: Other not–for–profit (including NFP Corporation) **Service**: General medical and surgical

Staffed Beds: 239 **Admissions:** 12635 **Census:** 149 **Outpatient Visits:** 198196 **Births:** 1281 **Total Expense ($000):** 238821 **Payroll Expense ($000):** 69937 **Personnel:** 1839

☒ **ENCOMPASS HEALTH REHABILITATION HOSPITAL OF PARKERSBURG (513027)**, 3 Western Hills Drive, Zip 26105–8122; tel. 304/420–1300, **A**1 10 **F**29 90 96 130 148 149 **S** Encompass Health Corporation, Birmingham, AL
Primary Contact: Alvin R. Lawson, FACHE, JD, Chief Executive Officer
CFO: Jessica Gum, Controller
CMO: Kalapala Rao, M.D., Medical Director
CHR: Julie Swanson, Coordinator Human Resources
CNO: Tonda Hockenberry, Chief Nursing Officer
Web address: www.healthsouthwesternhills.com
Control: Corporation, Investor–owned (for–profit) **Service**: Rehabilitation

Staffed Beds: 40 **Admissions:** 1129 **Census:** 36 **Outpatient Visits:** 0 **Births:** 0 **Total Expense ($000):** 14509 **Payroll Expense ($000):** 6629 **Personnel:** 127

PETERSBURG—Grant County

★ **GRANT MEMORIAL HOSPITAL (511316)**, 117 Hospital Drive, Zip 26847–9566, Mailing Address: P.O. Box 1019, Zip 26847–1019; tel. 304/257–1026, (Total facility includes 20 beds in nursing home–type unit) **A**10 18 **F**3 11 13 15 18 28 29 34 35 40 45 50 57 59 64 65 67 70 75 76 77 79 81 87 93 97 107 108 110 111 114 118 119 128 130 131 132 133 135 146 147 148 149 156 157
Primary Contact: Robert W. Milvet Jr, Chief Executive Officer
CMO: Bruce W Leslie, M.D., Chief of Staff
CIO: Derek Nesselrodt, Director Information Systems
CHR: Ronnie Arbaugh, Director Human Resources
CNO: Kimberly Linville, Chief Nursing Officer
Web address: www.grantmemorial.com
Control: County, Government, nonfederal **Service**: General medical and surgical

Staffed Beds: 45 **Admissions:** 1423 **Census:** 30 **Outpatient Visits:** 44979 **Births:** 245 **Total Expense ($000):** 36638 **Payroll Expense ($000):** 14224 **Personnel:** 310

PHILIPPI—Barbour County

★ **BROADDUS HOSPITAL (511300)**, 1 Healthcare Drive, Zip 26416–9405, Mailing Address: P.O. Box 930, Zip 26416–0930; tel. 304/457–1760, (Total facility includes 60 beds in nursing home–type unit) **A**10 18 **F**3 15 29 30 34 35 40 57 59 64 75 85 87 107 110 115 119 128 130 132 133 135 143 146 **S** Davis Health System, Elkins, WV
Primary Contact: Dana L. Gould, Chief Executive Officer
CFO: Cathy Kalar, Chief Financial Officer
CHR: Penny D Brown, Director of Human Resources
Web address: www.davishealthsystem.org/
Control: Other not–for–profit (including NFP Corporation) **Service**: General medical and surgical

Staffed Beds: 72 **Admissions:** 214 **Census:** 57 **Outpatient Visits:** 21620 **Births:** 0 **Total Expense ($000):** 17790 **Payroll Expense ($000):** 7536 **Personnel:** 140

POINT PLEASANT—Mason County

☒ **PLEASANT VALLEY HOSPITAL (510012)**, 2520 Valley Drive, Zip 25550–2031; tel. 304/675–4340, (Total facility includes 100 beds in nursing home–type unit) **A**1 10 **F**3 11 13 15 17 18 24 26 28 29 30 31 34 35 40 43 45 46 47 48 50 53 56 57 59 64 65 70 74 75 76 77 78 79 81 85 86 87 89 93 107 108 110 111 114 115 118 119 128 129 130 131 132 135 143 144 146 147 148 156 **S** Mountain Health Network, Huntington, WV
Primary Contact: Glen A. Washington, Chief Executive Officer
COO: William A Barker Jr Vice President Administration
CFO: Richard Hogan, Chief Financial Officer
CMO: Agnes Enrico-Simon, M.D., President Medical Staff
CIO: Paula Brooker, Director Information Services
CHR: David A Brown, Director Human Resources and Corporate Compliance
CNO: Amber Findley, Senior Director Nursing Services and NRC Administrator
Web address: www.pvalley.org
Control: Other not–for–profit (including NFP Corporation) **Service**: General medical and surgical

Staffed Beds: 168 **Admissions:** 1936 **Census:** 111 **Outpatient Visits:** 162929 **Births:** 125 **Total Expense ($000):** 64918 **Payroll Expense ($000):** 23332 **Personnel:** 521

PRINCETON—Mercer County

☒ **ENCOMPASS HEALTH REHABILITATION HOSPITAL OF PRINCETON (513026)**, 120 Twelfth Street, Zip 24740–2352; tel. 304/487–8000, (Nonreporting) **A**1 10 **S** Encompass Health Corporation, Birmingham, AL
Primary Contact: Robert Williams, Chief Executive Officer
CFO: Amy Flowers, Controller
CMO: Robert Walker, M.D., Medical Director
CIO: Brian Bales, Director Plant Operations
CHR: Jan Thibodeau, Director Human Resources
CNO: Lisa Lester, Chief Nursing Officer
Web address: www.healthsouthsouthernhills.com
Control: Corporation, Investor–owned (for–profit) **Service**: Rehabilitation

Staffed Beds: 45

☒ **PRINCETON COMMUNITY HOSPITAL (510046)**, 122 12th Street, Zip 24740–2352, Mailing Address: P.O. Box 1369, Zip 24740–1369; tel. 304/487–7000, **A**1 2 10 19 **F**3 11 12 13 15 17 29 30 31 32 34 35 39 40 44 45 46 48 49 50 51 53 57 59 64 65 70 74 75 76 77 78 79 81 85 86 87 89 93 98 100 101 102 103 104 107 108 110 111 114 115 118 119 127 129 130 131 132 135 141 142 144 146 147 149 153
Primary Contact: Jeffrey Lilley, CPA, Chief Executive Officer
CFO: Frank J Sinicrope Jr Vice President Financial Services
CMO: Wesley Asbury, M.D., President Medical Staff
CIO: Stephen A Curry, Director Information Services
CHR: Heather Poff, Director Human Resources
CNO: Rose Morgan, MS, R.N., Vice President Patient Care Services
Web address: www.pchonline.org
Control: City, Government, nonfederal **Service**: General medical and surgical

Staffed Beds: 210 **Admissions:** 7521 **Census:** 106 **Outpatient Visits:** 264799 **Births:** 522 **Total Expense ($000):** 143824 **Payroll Expense ($000):** 53893 **Personnel:** 1072

WV

Many Facility Codes have changed. Please refer to the AHA Guide Code Chart. © 2019 AHA Guide

RANSON—Jefferson County

✉ **JEFFERSON MEDICAL CENTER (511319)**, 300 South Preston Street,
Zip 25438–1631; tel. 304/728–1600, **A**1 3 5 10 18 **F**3 13 30 35 38 40 43 45
64 70 79 81 82 86 87 93 97 107 119 130 131 133 146 147 154 157 **S** West
Virginia University Health System, Morgantown, WV
Primary Contact: Anthony Zelenka, President and Chief Executive Officer
CFO: Anna Buchanan, Vice President Finance and Chief Financial Officer
CMO: David A. Baltierra, M.D., President Medical Staff
CIO: Mark Combs, Chief Information Security Officer
CHR: Justin Ruble, Director Human Resources
CNO: Linda Blanc, R.N., Administrative Director of Nursing
Web address: www.wvuniversityhealthcare.com/locations/Jefferson-Medical-Center.
aspx
Control: Other not–for–profit (including NFP Corporation) **Service:** General
medical and surgical

Staffed Beds: 25 **Admissions:** 1391 **Census:** 11 **Outpatient Visits:** 69500
Births: 182 **Total Expense ($000):** 49144 **Payroll Expense ($000):** 15952
Personnel: 297

RIPLEY—Jackson County

JACKSON GENERAL HOSPITAL (511320), 122 Pinnell Street,
Zip 25271–9101, Mailing Address: P.O. Box 720, Zip 25271–0720;
tel. 304/372–2731, **A**10 18 **F**3 11 15 29 30 34 35 40 43 45 50 51 57 59 64
68 75 79 81 82 85 87 93 107 108 110 114 119 127 132 133
Primary Contact: Stephanie McCoy, President and Chief Executive Officer
CFO: Angela Frame, Chief Financial Officer
CMO: James G Gaal, M.D., Chief of Medical Staff
CIO: John Manley, Director Information Systems
CHR: Jeffrey Tabor, Director Human Resources
Web address: www.jacksongeneral.com
Control: Other not–for–profit (including NFP Corporation) **Service:** General
medical and surgical

Staffed Beds: 25 **Admissions:** 538 **Census:** 8 **Outpatient Visits:** 42895
Births: 0 **Total Expense ($000):** 30248 **Payroll Expense ($000):** 12668
Personnel: 250

ROMNEY—Hampshire County

✉ **HAMPSHIRE MEMORIAL HOSPITAL (511311)**, 363 Sunrise Boulevard,
Zip 26757–4607; tel. 304/822–4561, (Total facility includes 30 beds in nursing
home type unit) **A**1 10 18 **F**3 15 18 29 30 40 45 50 54 59 64 65 71 77 79 81
85 86 93 97 107 110 114 119 127 128 129 130 133 148 154 155 156 157 **S**
Valley Health System, Winchester, VA
Primary Contact: Thomas G. Kluge, President
CFO: Kathryn Moralee, Director of Finance
CMO: Gerald Bechamps, M.D., Vice President of Medical Affairs
CHR: Abbey Rembold, Human Resources Senior Generalist
CNO: Mary Sas, Director of Clinical Services
Web address: www.valleyhealthlink.com/hampshire
Control: Other not–for–profit (including NFP Corporation) **Service:** General
medical and surgical

Staffed Beds: 44 **Admissions:** 448 **Census:** 36 **Outpatient Visits:** 55826
Births: 0 **Total Expense ($000):** 27864 **Payroll Expense ($000):** 11133
Personnel: 170

RONCEVERTE—Greenbrier County

★ ○ **GREENBRIER VALLEY MEDICAL CENTER (510002)**, 202 Maplewood
Avenue, Zip 24970–1334, Mailing Address: P.O. Box 497, Zip 24970–0497;
tel. 304/647–4411, (Nonreporting) **A**3 5 10 11 12 13 **S** Community Health
Systems, Inc., Franklin, TN
Primary Contact: Jim Hobson, Chief Executive Officer
CFO: Paige Adkins, Chief Financial Officer
CMO: John Johnson, M.D., Chief of Staff
CIO: Matt Turley, Interim Director Information Systems
CHR: Melissa Wickline, Director Marketing
CNO: Charlene Warren, R.N., Chief Nursing Officer
Web address: www.gvmc.com
Control: Corporation, Investor–owned (for–profit) **Service:** General medical and
surgical

Staffed Beds: 113

SISTERSVILLE—Tyler County

★ **SISTERSVILLE GENERAL HOSPITAL (511304)**, 314 South Wells Street,
Zip 26175–1098; tel. 304/652–2611, (Nonreporting) **A**10 18
Primary Contact: Brandon Chadock, Interim Chief Executive Officer
COO: Brandon Chadock, Director of Operations
CMO: Amanda Nichols, M.D., Chief of Staff
CIO: Casey Tuttle, Director Information Technology
CNO: Stephen Todd Strickler, Director of Nursing
Web address: www.sistersvillehospital.com
Control: City, Government, nonfederal **Service:** General medical and surgical

Staffed Beds: 12

SOUTH CHARLESTON—Kanawha County

✉ **THOMAS MEMORIAL HOSPITAL (510029)**, 4605 MacCorkle Avenue SW,
Zip 25309–1398; tel. 304/766–3600, **A**1 5 10 **F**3 5 11 13 15 17 18 19 20
22 26 28 29 30 31 32 34 35 40 43 45 49 57 59 64 70 72 76 78 79 81 85
86 89 92 93 97 98 100 102 103 105 107 108 110 111 114 115 118 119
120 121 123 126 129 130 146 147 153 **S** Thomas Health System, Inc., South
Charleston, WV
Primary Contact: Daniel Lauffer, FACHE, President and Chief Executive Officer
COO: Brian Ulery, Chief Operating Officer
CFO: Timothy Skeldon, Chief Financial Officer
CMO: Matthew Upton, Chief Medical Information Officer
CHR: Patrick Rawlings, Human Resources Director
CNO: Rebecca Brannon, R.N., Chief Nursing Officer
Web address: www.thomashealth.org
Control: Other not–for–profit (including NFP Corporation) **Service:** General
medical and surgical

Staffed Beds: 211 **Admissions:** 8116 **Census:** 106 **Outpatient
Visits:** 244508 **Births:** 868 **Total Expense ($000):** 176489 **Payroll Expense
($000):** 60902 **Personnel:** 1366

SPENCER—Roane County

✉ **ROANE GENERAL HOSPITAL (511306)**, 200 Hospital Drive, Zip 25276–1050;
tel. 304/927–4444, (Total facility includes 35 beds in nursing home–type unit) **A**1
10 18 **F**1 3 11 15 18 28 29 34 35 40 43 45 53 57 59 64 65 67 68 81 82 85
89 90 93 97 107 108 110 114 119 127 128 130 132 133 135 148 156
Primary Contact: Douglas E. Bentz, Chief Executive Officer
CFO: Kyle A. Pierson, Chief Financial Officer
CMO: Hong-Kin Ng, M.D., Chief Medical Officer
CIO: Tony Keaton, Director Information Systems
CHR: Jeffery B Hunt, Vice President, Business Development and Support Services
CNO: Julie R. Carr, Chief Nursing Officer
Web address: www.roanegeneralhospital.com
Control: Other not–for–profit (including NFP Corporation) **Service:** General
medical and surgical

Staffed Beds: 60 **Admissions:** 209 **Census:** 35 **Outpatient Visits:** 43945
Births: 0 **Total Expense ($000):** 36275 **Payroll Expense ($000):** 16842
Personnel: 277

SUMMERSVILLE—Nicholas County

★ **SUMMERSVILLE REGIONAL MEDICAL CENTER (510082)**, 400 Fairview
Heights Road, Zip 26651–9308; tel. 304/872–2891, (Nonreporting) **A**10 20
Primary Contact: Karen L. Bowling, MSN, R.N., Interim Chief Executive Officer
CFO: Brian Kelbaugh, Chief Financial Officer
CMO: Bandy Mullins, M.D., Chief of Staff
CIO: Mike Ellison, Information Systems Lead
CHR: David M Henderson, Director Human Resources
CNO: Jennifer McCue, Director Patient Care
Web address: www.https://www.summersvilleregional.org/
Control: City, Government, nonfederal **Service:** General medical and surgical

Staffed Beds: 153

WV

Hospital, Medicare Provider Number, Address, Telephone, Approval, Facility, and Physician Codes, Health Care System

★ American Hospital Association (AHA) membership ○ Healthcare Facilities Accreditation Program ⇑ Center for Improvement in Healthcare Quality Accreditation
☐ The Joint Commission accreditation ◇ DNV Healthcare Inc. accreditation △ Commission on Accreditation of Rehabilitation Facilities (CARF) accreditation

© 2019 AHA Guide   *Many Facility Codes have changed. Please refer to the AHA Guide Code Chart.*   Hospitals **A689**

WEBSTER SPRINGS—Webster County

★ **WEBSTER COUNTY MEMORIAL HOSPITAL (511301)**, 324 Miller Mountain Drive, Zip 26288–1087, Mailing Address: P.O. Box 312, Zip 26288–0312; tel. 304/847–5682, **A**10 18 **F**7 28 30 34 35 40 57 59 64 75 82 87 93 97 107 111 114 119 127 130 133 143 146 147 148 154
Primary Contact: Jim Parker, FACHE, Chief Executive Officer
CIO: Jeannie Fisher, Coordinator Information Technology
CHR: Michelle Holcomb, Human Resources
Web address: www.wcmhwv.org
Control: Other not–for–profit (including NFP Corporation) **Service:** General medical and surgical

Staffed Beds: 15 **Admissions:** 151 **Census:** 1 **Outpatient Visits:** 43916 **Births:** 2 **Total Expense ($000):** 15323 **Payroll Expense ($000):** 8750 **Personnel:** 142

WEIRTON—Brooke County

✠ **WEIRTON MEDICAL CENTER (510023)**, 601 Colliers Way, Zip 26062–5091; tel. 304/797–6000, (Total facility includes 33 beds in nursing home–type unit) **A**1 10 **F**3 9 11 13 15 17 18 20 22 28 29 30 32 34 35 37 40 41 43 45 46 47 48 49 50 51 54 56 57 59 60 61 62 64 68 70 74 75 76 77 78 79 81 82 85 86 87 89 90 92 93 96 97 100 102 107 108 110 111 114 115 116 118 119 124 126 128 129 130 131 132 135 143 145 146 147 148 149 154
Primary Contact: John C. Frankovitch, President and Chief Executive Officer
COO: David S Artman, Chief Operating Officer
CFO: Gene Trout, Chief Financial Officer
CMO: Atul Shetty, Chief of Staff
CIO: Cristen Nopwaskey, Chief Information Officer
CHR: Gabe D'Ortenzio, Director of Human Resources
CNO: Denise P Westwood, Chief Nursing Officer
Web address: www.weirtonmedical.com
Control: Other not–for–profit (including NFP Corporation) **Service:** General medical and surgical

Staffed Beds: 167 **Admissions:** 6713 **Census:** 90 **Outpatient Visits:** 505592 **Births:** 485 **Total Expense ($000):** 185799 **Payroll Expense ($000):** 84005 **Personnel:** 1209

WELCH—Mcdowell County

WELCH COMMUNITY HOSPITAL (510086), 454 McDowell Street, Zip 24801–2097; tel. 304/436–8461, (Total facility includes 59 beds in nursing home–type unit) **A**10 20 **F**3 15 29 35 40 45 50 57 59 64 65 66 67 68 70 75 81 86 87 89 97 107 110 114 119 127 130 135 146 147 148 156
Primary Contact: Mark Simpson, Chief Executive Officer
COO: Heather Smith, Chief Operating Officer
CFO: Johnny Brant, Chief Financial Officer
CMO: Chandra Sharma, M.D., Chief of Staff
CHR: Diana Blankenship, Director Human Resources
Control: State, Government, nonfederal **Service:** General medical and surgical

Staffed Beds: 108 **Admissions:** 589 **Census:** 41 **Outpatient Visits:** 27521 **Births:** 0 **Total Expense ($000):** 29845 **Payroll Expense ($000):** 7403 **Personnel:** 177

WESTON—Lewis County

✠ **STONEWALL JACKSON MEMORIAL HOSPITAL (510038)**, 230 Hospital Plaza, Zip 26452–8558; tel. 304/269–8000, (Data for 273 days) **A**1 10 **F**3 11 13 15 28 29 30 31 35 40 43 45 48 50 56 57 59 62 64 68 70 75 76 78 79 81 85 86 87 93 94 97 107 108 111 114 118 119 129 130 131 132 135 145 146 147 148 157 **S** Mon Health System, Morgantown, WV
Primary Contact: Avah Stalnaker, Chief Executive Officer
COO: Kevin P Stalnaker, CPA, Assistant Chief Executive Officer
CFO: Daris Rosencrance, Chief Financial Officer
CMO: Joseph Snead, Chief of Medical Staff
CIO: Kay Butcher, Director Health Information Management
CHR: Rhonda K Mitchell, Director Human Resources
CNO: Carole Norton, Chief Nursing Officer
Web address: www.stonewallhospital.com
Control: Other not–for–profit (including NFP Corporation) **Service:** General medical and surgical

Staffed Beds: 70 **Admissions:** 1231 **Census:** 16 **Outpatient Visits:** 65580 **Births:** 115 **Total Expense ($000):** 36699 **Payroll Expense ($000):** 15340 **Personnel:** 393

□ **WILLIAM R. SHARPE, JR. HOSPITAL (514010)**, 936 Sharpe Hospital Road, Zip 26452–8550; tel. 304/269–1210, **A**1 3 5 **F**3 11 30 50 53 56 68 75 86 87 98 100 101 103 130 132 143 146 157
Primary Contact: Parker Haddix, Chief Executive Officer
COO: Terry L. Small, Assistant Chief Executive Officer
CFO: Robert J. Kimble, Chief Financial Officer
CIO: Pam Lewis, Chief Compliance Officer
CNO: Cheryl France, M.D., Chief Medical Officer
Web address: www.wvdhhr.org/sharpe
Control: State, Government, nonfederal **Service:** Psychiatric

Staffed Beds: 150 **Admissions:** 197 **Census:** 107 **Outpatient Visits:** 0 **Births:** 0 **Total Expense ($000):** 71906 **Payroll Expense ($000):** 12663 **Personnel:** 420

WHEELING—Ohio County

□ ○ **OHIO VALLEY MEDICAL CENTER (510039)**, 2000 Eoff Street, Zip 26003–3870; tel. 304/234–0123, (Nonreporting) **A**1 2 3 5 10 11 12 13 **S** Alecto Healthcare, Irvine, CA
Primary Contact: Daniel C. Dunmyer, Chief Executive Officer
COO: Kelly Bettem, Vice President, Ambulatory Services
CIO: Michael Martz, Chief Information Officer
CHR: Robert Wright, Senior Human Resource Advisor
CNO: Patsy George, R.N., Vice President and Chief Nursing Officer
Web address: www.ovmc-eorh.com
Control: Corporation, Investor–owned (for–profit) **Service:** General medical and surgical

Staffed Beds: 169

★ **PETERSON HEALTHCARE AND REHABILITATION HOSPITAL (513025)**, 20 Homestead Avenue, Zip 26003–6638; tel. 304/234–0500, (Nonreporting) **A**10
Primary Contact: Diane Miller, Administrator
CFO: Tammy Bortz, Director of Finance
CMO: William Mercer, M.D., Director
CIO: Hope Miller, Director of Medical Records
CHR: Spencer McIlvain, Director of Human Resources
CNO: Charlene Jones, Chief Nursing Officer
Web address: www.petersonrehabilitationhospital.com
Control: Corporation, Investor–owned (for–profit) **Service:** Rehabilitation

Staffed Beds: 172

□ **WHEELING HOSPITAL (510050)**, 1 Medical Park, Zip 26003–6379; tel. 304/243–3000, (Nonreporting) **A**1 2 3 5 10
Primary Contact: Ronald L. Violi, Chief Executive Officer
CMO: Angelo Georges, M.D., President Medical and Dental Staff
CIO: David Rapp, Chief Information Officer
CHR: Kareen Simon, Vice President of Operations
CNO: Kathy Stahl, Chief Nursing Officer
Web address: www.wheelinghospital.org
Control: Church operated **Service:** General medical and surgical

Staffed Beds: 223

WILLIAMSON—Mingo County

✠ **WILLIAMSON MEMORIAL HOSPITAL (510077)**, 859 Alderson Street, Zip 25661–3215, Mailing Address: P.O. Box 1980, Zip 25661–1980; tel. 304/235–2500, **A**1 10 **F**3 8 14 15 18 28 29 30 34 35 36 40 41 45 46 47 48 49 50 51 53 56 57 59 64 65 68 70 75 77 79 81 85 86 87 89 90 93 97 107 108 110 111 114 118 119 129 132 134 135 143 146 149 150 156 157
Primary Contact: Charles Hatfield, Interim Chief Executive Officer
CFO: Robert Haralson, Chief Financial Officer
CMO: C. Donovan Beckett, Chief Medical Officer
CHR: Tammie Chinn, Chief Human Resource Officer
CNO: Stacey Markus, Chief Nursing Officer
Web address: www.williamsonmemorial.net
Control: Hospital district or authority, Government, nonfederal **Service:** General medical and surgical

Staffed Beds: 25 **Admissions:** 420 **Census:** 4 **Outpatient Visits:** 35419 **Births:** 0

WV

Many Facility Codes have changed. Please refer to the AHA Guide Code Chart. © 2019 AHA Guide

WISCONSIN

ALTOONA—Eau Claire County

☐ **OAKLEAF SURGICAL HOSPITAL (520196)**, 1000 OakLeaf Way, Zip 54701–3016; tel. 715/831–8130, **A**1 10 **F**3 37 45 47 48 51 64 68 75 79 80 81 82 85 107 111 114 119 130 149 **S** National Surgical Healthcare, Chicago, IL
Primary Contact: Anne Hargrave-Thomas, Chief Executive Officer
COO: Erma Radke, Director of Operations
CFO: Denise Freid-Scheppke, Chief Accounting Officer
CHR: Nikki Yankton, Director Human Resources
CNO: Jacquelyn Maki, Chief Nursing Officer
Web address: www.oakleafmedical.com
Control: Corporation, Investor–owned (for-profit) **Service**: General medical and surgical

Staffed Beds: 13 **Admissions**: 640 **Census**: 3 **Outpatient Visits**: 11820 **Births**: 0 **Total Expense ($000)**: 55151 **Payroll Expense ($000)**: 14683 **Personnel**: 214

AMERY—Polk County

⊠ **AMERY HOSPITAL AND CLINIC (521308)**, 265 Griffin Street East, Zip 54001–1439; tel. 715/268–8000, **A**1 3 10 18 **F**3 6 11 13 15 28 29 31 32 34 35 36 38 40 45 50 53 54 56 59 64 65 74 75 76 77 78 80 81 82 86 87 89 93 98 99 100 103 104 107 108 110 111 115 119 127 130 131 132 133 143 144 145 146 148 149 152 153 156 **S** HealthPartners, Bloomington, MN
Primary Contact: Debra Rudquist, President and Chief Executive Officer
CMO: James Quenan, M.D., Chief Medical Officer
CIO: Patrice P Wolff, Director Management Information Systems
CHR: Joanne Jackson, Administrator Human Resources, Community Relations and Quality Improvement
Web address: www.amerymedicalcenter.org
Control: Other not–for–profit (including NFP Corporation) **Service**: General medical and surgical

Staffed Beds: 16 **Admissions**: 1195 **Census**: 14 **Outpatient Visits**: 111529 **Births**: 119 **Total Expense ($000)**: 57832 **Payroll Expense ($000)**: 33072 **Personnel**: 282

ANTIGO—Langlade County

⊠ **ASPIRUS LANGLADE HOSPITAL (521350)**, 112 East Fifth Avenue, Zip 54409–2796; tel. 715/623–2331, **A**1 5 10 18 **F**2 3 6 10 11 12 13 15 28 29 30 31 34 35 36 40 43 50 53 54 56 57 59 60 63 64 65 66 68 69 70 75 76 77 78 79 81 82 84 85 86 87 89 92 93 96 97 99 100 101 103 104 107 108 110 111 115 118 119 127 129 130 131 132 133 135 143 144 146 147 148 154 156 **S** Aspirus, Inc., Wausau, WI
Primary Contact: Andrew J. Barth, Executive Director
CFO: Pat Tincher, Director Finance
CHR: Janelle K. Markgraf, SHRM-SCP, SPHR, Director Human Resources and Off Campus Services
CNO: Sherry Bunten, Director Patient Care Services
Web address: www.aspirus.org
Control: Church operated, Nongovernment, not–for–profit **Service**: General medical and surgical

Staffed Beds: 24 **Admissions**: 1309 **Census**: 12 **Outpatient Visits**: 114474 **Births**: 242 **Total Expense ($000)**: 93928 **Payroll Expense ($000)**: 35044 **Personnel**: 371

APPLETON—Outagamie County

⊠ △ **ASCENSION NORTHEAST WISCONSIN ST. ELIZABETH HOSPITAL (520009)**, 1506 South Oneida Street, Zip 54915–1305; tel. 920/738–2000, **A**1 2 3 5 7 10 **F**3 4 5 6 9 11 13 15 17 18 20 22 24 26 28 29 30 31 36 40 43 45 46 47 48 49 56 58 68 69 70 72 74 75 76 77 78 79 80 81 84 85 86 87 88 89 93 94 96 98 99 100 102 103 104 105 107 108 110 111 114 115 116 118 119 120 121 124 126 129 130 131 132 144 145 146 147 148 149 152 **S** Ascension Healthcare, Saint Louis, MO
Primary Contact: Monica Hilt, President and Regional Vice President
CFO: Jeff Badger, Chief Financial Officer
CMO: Lawrence Donatelle, M.D., Vice President Medical Affairs
CIO: Will Weider, Chief Information Officer
CHR: Vince Gallucci, Senior Vice President Human Resources
Web address: www.affinityhealth.org
Control: Church operated, Nongovernment, not–for–profit **Service**: General medical and surgical

Staffed Beds: 190 **Admissions**: 8475 **Census**: 96 **Outpatient Visits**: 227112 **Births**: 1154 **Total Expense ($000)**: 210300 **Payroll Expense ($000)**: 51593 **Personnel**: 822

☐ **THEDACARE REGIONAL MEDICAL CENTER-APPLETON (520160)**, 1818 North Meade Street, Zip 54911–3496; tel. 920/731–4101, **A**1 2 3 5 10 **F**4 9 13 15 17 24 28 29 34 40 51 54 64 70 75 76 78 80 81 82 86 88 89 101 107 108 111 118 119 130 **S** ThedaCare, Inc., Appleton, WI
Primary Contact: Thomas J. Arquilla, Chief Strategy Officer
CFO: Tim Olson, Senior Vice President Finance
CMO: Gregory L Long, M.D., Chief Medical Officer
CIO: Keith Livingston, Senior Vice President and Chief Information Officer
Web address: www.thedacare.org
Control: Other not–for–profit (including NFP Corporation) **Service**: General medical and surgical

Staffed Beds: 147 **Admissions**: 8318 **Census**: 86 **Outpatient Visits**: 197231 **Births**: 1031 **Total Expense ($000)**: 220232 **Payroll Expense ($000)**: 72685 **Personnel**: 1037

ASHLAND—Ashland County

⊠ **MEMORIAL MEDICAL CENTER OF ASHLAND (521359)**, 1615 Maple Lane, Zip 54806–3689; tel. 715/685–5500, (Nonreporting) **A**1 10 18
Primary Contact: Jason T. Douglas, Chief Executive Officer
COO: Karen Hansen, Vice President and Chief Operating Officer
CFO: Kent Dumonseau, Vice President Finance and Information Services
CIO: Todd Reynolds, Chief Information Officer
CHR: Diane Lulich, Director Human Resources
CNO: Kathryn Tuttle, R.N., Director of Nursing
Web address: www.ashlandmmc.com
Control: Other not–for–profit (including NFP Corporation) **Service**: General medical and surgical

Staffed Beds: 35

BALDWIN—St. Croix County

★ **WESTERN WISCONSIN HEALTH (521347)**, 1100 Bergslien Street, Zip 54002–2600; tel. 715/684–3311, **A**10 18 **F**3 6 8 11 13 15 28 29 31 32 34 35 36 38 40 41 43 53 55 56 57 59 64 65 68 71 75 76 77 78 79 80 81 85 86 87 89 90 91 93 96 97 99 100 101 102 103 104 107 108 110 111 114 115 117 118 119 126 127 130 131 132 133 146 147 148 149 150 154 156
Primary Contact: Alison Page, Chief Executive Officer
CMO: Clint Semrau, Chief of Staff
CIO: Kendra Shaw, Chief Information Officer
CHR: Chris Riba, Director Human Resources
Web address: www.https://www.wwhealth.org
Control: Other not–for–profit (including NFP Corporation) **Service**: General medical and surgical

Staffed Beds: 15 **Admissions**: 499 **Census**: 4 **Outpatient Visits**: 57875 **Births**: 187 **Total Expense ($000)**: 41682 **Payroll Expense ($000)**: 19626 **Personnel**: 233

WI

Hospital, Medicare Provider Number, Address, Telephone, Approval, Facility, and Physician Codes, Health Care System

★ American Hospital Association (AHA) membership
☐ The Joint Commission accreditation
○ Healthcare Facilities Accreditation Program
◇ DNV Healthcare Inc. accreditation
⇧ Center for Improvement in Healthcare Quality Accreditation
△ Commission on Accreditation of Rehabilitation Facilities (CARF) accreditation

BARABOO—Sauk County

☒ **SSM HEALTH ST. CLARE HOSPITAL-BARABOO (520057)**, 707 14th Street, Zip 53913–1597; tel. 608/356–1400, **A**1 3 10 **F**11 13 15 28 29 34 36 40 56 64 69 70 75 76 77 78 80 81 82 86 89 93 107 108 116 118 119 130 131 144 154 **S** SSM Health, Saint Louis, MO
Primary Contact: Laura Walczak, President
CFO: Troy Walker, Director Finance
CMO: Maureen Murphy, M.D., Director of Medical Affairs
CIO: Heather Stephens, Director of Information Health Technology
CHR: Jason Stelzer, Director Human Resources
CNO: Ginger Selle, Vice President Patient Care Services
Web address: www.stclare.com
Control: Church operated, Nongovernment, not–for–profit **Service:** General medical and surgical

Staffed Beds: 54 **Admissions:** 1946 **Census:** 17 **Outpatient Visits:** 102108
Births: 187 **Total Expense ($000):** 53450 **Payroll Expense ($000):** 20657
Personnel: 291

BARRON—Barron County

☐ **MAYO CLINIC HEALTH SYSTEM - NORTHLAND IN BARRON (521315)**, 1222 East Woodland Avenue, Zip 54812–1798; tel. 715/537–3186, **A**1 10 18 **F**3 13 15 18 28 29 30 31 32 34 35 38 40 43 44 45 53 54 55 56 57 59 64 65 74 76 77 78 79 80 81 82 84 85 86 87 89 90 93 96 97 100 104 107 110 111 115 129 130 131 132 133 144 145 146 147 148 149 154 156 **S** Mayo Clinic, Rochester, MN
Primary Contact: Michele Eberle, Vice Chair
COO: Karolyn Bartlett, Assistant Administrator
CFO: Paul Bammel, Vice President
CMO: Richard Nagler, M.D., Chief of Staff
CIO: Todd Muden, Section Head Information Management
CHR: Blythe Rinaldi, Vice President
CNO: Patricia Keller, MSN, R.N., Nurse Administrator
Web address: www.luthermidelfortnorthland.org
Control: Other not–for–profit (including NFP Corporation) **Service:** General medical and surgical

Staffed Beds: 23 **Admissions:** 939 **Census:** 13 **Outpatient Visits:** 68179
Births: 96 **Total Expense ($000):** 60029 **Payroll Expense ($000):** 26021
Personnel: 290

BEAVER DAM—Dodge County

☒ **BEAVER DAM COMMUNITY HOSPITALS (520076)**, 707 South University Avenue, Zip 53916–3089; tel. 920/887–7181, (Total facility includes 115 beds in nursing home–type unit) **A**1 10 19 **F**3 6 8 10 11 13 15 17 28 29 30 31 33 34 36 37 40 41 43 44 45 47 53 56 57 59 62 63 64 65 69 70 74 75 76 77 78 79 80 81 82 85 86 87 89 93 96 97 107 110 111 114 115 119 126 128 129 130 131 132 135 143 144 146 147 148 149 150 154 156 157 158 **S** Marshfield Clinic Health System, Marshfield, WI
Primary Contact: Joseph Gilene, Interim Chief Administrative Officer
CMO: Jason Smith, Chief Medical Officer
CHR: Melanie Bruins, Chief Talent Officer
CNO: Carolyn Catton, Interim Chief Patient Care Officer
Web address: www.bdch.com
Control: Other not–for–profit (including NFP Corporation) **Service:** General medical and surgical

Staffed Beds: 163 **Admissions:** 1940 **Census:** 109 **Outpatient Visits:** 90745 **Births:** 273 **Total Expense ($000):** 90784 **Payroll Expense ($000):** 32191 **Personnel:** 510

BELOIT—Rock County

☐ **BELOIT HEALTH SYSTEM (520100)**, 1969 West Hart Road, Zip 53511–2299; tel. 608/364–5011, **A**1 3 10 **F**5 6 9 10 11 12 13 15 17 20 22 24 28 29 34 36 40 43 51 53 54 56 60 62 63 75 76 77 78 80 81 82 86 87 89 93 99 100 101 102 107 108 111 116 118 119 130 131 144 147 154
Primary Contact: Timothy M. McKevett, President and Chief Executive Officer
CFO: William E Groeper, Vice President Finance
CMO: Kenneth Klein, M.D., Vice President Medical Affairs
CHR: Thomas J McCawley, Vice President
CNO: Doris Mulder, Vice President Nursing
Web address: www.beloithealthsystem.org
Control: Other not–for–profit (including NFP Corporation) **Service:** General medical and surgical

Staffed Beds: 103 **Admissions:** 4361 **Census:** 45 **Outpatient Visits:** 336666 **Births:** 379 **Total Expense ($000):** 226750 **Payroll Expense ($000):** 97177 **Personnel:** 1120

BERLIN—Green Lake County

☐ **THEDACARE MEDICAL CENTER-BERLIN (521355)**, 225 Memorial Drive, Zip 54923–1295; tel. 920/361–1313, **A**1 10 18 **F**11 13 15 17 24 28 29 34 40 43 51 53 56 70 75 76 78 80 81 82 86 87 88 89 90 93 107 108 111 116 118 119 130 131 144 147 **S** ThedaCare, Inc., Appleton, WI
Primary Contact: Tammy Bending, Vice President, Critical Access Hospital
CFO: Thomas P Krystowiak, Chief Financial Officer
Web address: www.chnwi.org
Control: Other not–for–profit (including NFP Corporation) **Service:** General medical and surgical

Staffed Beds: 25 **Admissions:** 1169 **Census:** 10 **Outpatient Visits:** 55836
Births: 111 **Total Expense ($000):** 36477 **Payroll Expense ($000):** 15477
Personnel: 215

BLACK RIVER FALLS—Jackson County

☐ **BLACK RIVER MEMORIAL HOSPITAL (521333)**, 711 West Adams Street, Zip 54615–9113; tel. 715/284–5361, **A**1 5 10 18 **F**3 8 11 13 29 30 34 35 40 41 53 56 57 59 62 63 65 69 75 76 77 79 81 84 85 86 89 93 107 111 114 115 116 118 119 129 130 131 132 133 135 144 146 148 149 152 156
Primary Contact: Mary Beth White-Jacobs, FACHE, R.N., Chief Executive Officer
COO: Holly Winn, FACHE, Chief Operating Officer
CFO: Robert Daley, CPA, Chief Financial Officer
CMO: Esteban Miller, Chief Medical Officer
CIO: Robert Daley, CPA, Vice President Fiscal and Information Technology Services
CNO: Melissa Bergerson, R.N., Chief Nursing Officer
Web address: www.brmh.net
Control: Other not–for–profit (including NFP Corporation) **Service:** General medical and surgical

Staffed Beds: 17 **Admissions:** 917 **Census:** 7 **Outpatient Visits:** 13905
Births: 133 **Total Expense ($000):** 53602 **Payroll Expense ($000):** 24347
Personnel: 305

BLOOMER—Chippewa County

☐ **MAYO CLINIC HEALTH SYSTEM - CHIPPEWA VALLEY IN BLOOMER (521314)**, 1501 Thompson Street, Zip 54724–1299; tel. 715/568–2000, **A**1 10 18 **F**3 15 18 28 29 30 32 34 35 38 40 43 44 45 53 54 56 57 59 64 65 77 78 79 80 81 84 85 86 87 89 90 93 96 97 104 107 110 115 129 130 132 133 144 145 146 147 148 149 154 156 **S** Mayo Clinic, Rochester, MN
Primary Contact: Michele Eberle, Vice Chair
Web address: www.bloomermedicalcenter.org
Control: Other not–for–profit (including NFP Corporation) **Service:** General medical and surgical

Staffed Beds: 21 **Admissions:** 450 **Census:** 13 **Outpatient Visits:** 44722
Births: 0 **Total Expense ($000):** 33293 **Payroll Expense ($000):** 15504
Personnel: 177

BOSCOBEL—Grant County

GUNDERSEN BOSCOBEL AREA HOSPITAL AND CLINICS (521344), 205 Parker Street, Zip 53805–1698; tel. 608/375–4112, **A**10 18 **F**11 15 28 29 34 36 38 40 43 53 56 64 75 77 78 81 82 86 87 93 99 100 101 107 108 111 118 119 130 131 144 147 154
Primary Contact: David Hartberg, Chief Executive Officer
CFO: Melissa Uselman, Chief Financial Officer
CMO: Marilu Bintz, M.D., Chief of Staff
CIO: Tonia Midtlien, Information Systems Support Specialist
CHR: Jennifer Dax, Director Human Resources
CNO: Theresa Lynn Braudt, Chief Nursing Officer
Web address: www.gundersenhealth.org/boscobel
Control: Other not–for–profit (including NFP Corporation) **Service:** General medical and surgical

Staffed Beds: 8 **Admissions:** 166 **Census:** 2 **Outpatient Visits:** 34210
Births: 0 **Total Expense ($000):** 17565 **Payroll Expense ($000):** 6096
Personnel: 118

WI

Many Facility Codes have changed. Please refer to the AHA Guide Code Chart. © 2019 AHA Guide

BROOKFIELD—Waukesha County

★ **ASCENSION SOUTHEAST WISCONSIN HOSPITAL - ELMBROOK CAMPUS (520170)**, 19333 West North Avenue, Zip 53045–4198; tel. 262/785–2000, **F3** 4 11 12 13 15 17 18 20 22 24 26 28 29 30 31 34 35 36 40 44 45 46 47 48 49 50 51 56 58 59 64 65 68 70 74 76 77 78 79 80 81 82 84 85 86 87 89 90 92 93 94 100 107 108 110 111 114 115 116 118 119 120 121 123 124 126 130 131 132 135 143 145 146 148 149 153 154 156 **S** Ascension Healthcare, Saint Louis, MO
Primary Contact: Timothy Richman, President and Chief Executive Officer
CFO: Michael Petitt, Director of Finance
CMO: Rita Hanson, M.D., Vice President Medical Affairs
CIO: Andrew Donovan, Director Information Technology
CHR: Christopher Morris, Director Human Resources
Web address: www.https://www.mywheaton.org
Control: Church operated, Nongovernment, not–for–profit **Service:** General medical and surgical

Staffed Beds: 122 **Admissions:** 4490 **Census:** 53 **Outpatient Visits:** 71760 **Births:** 459 **Total Expense ($000):** 122412 **Payroll Expense ($000):** 33593 **Personnel:** 444

BURLINGTON—Racine County

⊠ **AURORA MEDICAL CENTER BURLINGTON (520059)**, 252 McHenry Street, Zip 53105–1828; tel. 262/767–6000, **A1** 2 10 **F3** 8 11 15 17 18 20 26 28 29 30 34 35 36 40 43 44 45 47 48 49 50 51 53 56 57 59 60 68 70 74 75 79 80 81 82 85 86 87 89 93 94 96 100 107 108 109 110 111 115 116 118 119 130 131 132 134 135 146 148 149 **S** Advocate Aurora Health, Downers Grove, IL
Primary Contact: Bob Miller, President
CFO: Stuart Arnett, Vice President Finance and Chief Financial Officer
CIO: Jean Chase, Regional Manager Information Services
CHR: Gene Krauklis, Regional Vice President Human Resources
Web address: www.aurorahealthcare.org
Control: Other not–for–profit (including NFP Corporation) **Service:** General medical and surgical

Staffed Beds: 55 **Admissions:** 2147 **Census:** 22 **Outpatient Visits:** 94807 **Births:** 0 **Total Expense ($000):** 76093 **Payroll Expense ($000):** 24772 **Personnel:** 508

CHILTON—Calumet County

⊠ **ASCENSION CALUMET HOSPITAL (521317)**, 614 Memorial Drive, Zip 53014–1597; tel. 920/849–2386, **A1** 10 18 **F3** 7 11 15 18 28 29 30 31 34 35 40 43 45 54 56 59 64 68 74 75 78 79 80 81 82 85 86 87 89 93 97 107 110 115 119 129 130 131 133 144 146 148 149 156 **S** Ascension Healthcare, Saint Louis, MO
Primary Contact: Jenny Derks, Chief Administrative Officer
CFO: Jeff Badger, Chief Financial Officer
CMO: Mark W Kohrberg, M.D., Chief Medical Officer
CIO: Will Weider, Chief Information Officer
CHR: Beth O'laire, Manager Human Resources
Web address: www.affinityhealth.org
Control: Other not–for–profit (including NFP Corporation) **Service:** General medical and surgical

Staffed Beds: 15 **Admissions:** 329 **Census:** 3 **Outpatient Visits:** 58042 **Births:** 0 **Total Expense ($000):** 25814 **Payroll Expense ($000):** 6567 **Personnel:** 90

CHIPPEWA FALLS—Chippewa County

⊠ **HSHS ST. JOSEPH'S HOSPITAL (520017)**, 2661 County Highway I, Zip 54729–5407; tel. 715/723–1811, **A1** 10 **F3** 4 5 11 13 15 17 28 29 30 34 38 40 41 43 53 54 56 59 62 63 64 69 70 75 76 79 80 81 82 84 87 88 89 93 100 101 102 104 107 110 111 115 119 129 130 132 145 146 147 148 149 154 **S** HSHS Hospital Sisters Health System, Springfield, IL
Primary Contact: Andrew Bagnall, Interim Chief Executive Officer
CFO: David Nelson, FACHE, Divisional Chief Financial Officer
CIO: Kevin Groskreutz, Division Chief Information Officer, Ancillary Systems
CHR: Rick Tolson, Divisional Chief People Officer
CNO: Stella Clark, MSN, R.N., Chief Nursing Officer
Web address: www.stjoeschipfalls.com
Control: Church operated, Nongovernment, not–for–profit **Service:** General medical and surgical

Staffed Beds: 124 **Admissions:** 3090 **Census:** 38 **Outpatient Visits:** 58761 **Births:** 345 **Total Expense ($000):** 59289 **Payroll Expense ($000):** 25778 **Personnel:** 282

COLUMBUS—Columbia County

⊠ **COLUMBUS COMMUNITY HOSPITAL, INC. (521338)**, 1515 Park Avenue, Zip 53925–2402; tel. 920/623–2200, **A1** 10 18 **F3** 8 13 15 16 17 18 28 29 34 35 40 45 47 50 51 54 56 57 59 64 70 75 76 77 78 79 80 81 85 86 88 93 97 115 118 119 130 131 132 133 135 144 146 147 149 156
Primary Contact: John D. Russell, President and Chief Executive Officer
CFO: Phillip G Roberts, Vice President Finance and Chief Financial Officer
CMO: Gary Galvin, M.D., Chief of the Medical Staff
CIO: Phillip G Roberts, Vice President Finance and Chief Financial Officer
CHR: Ann Roundy, Vice President Employee Services
CNO: Jamie Hendrix, Vice President Patient Care Services
Web address: www.cch-inc.com
Control: Other not–for–profit (including NFP Corporation) **Service:** General medical and surgical

Staffed Beds: 25 **Admissions:** 916 **Census:** 7 **Outpatient Visits:** 47929 **Births:** 81 **Total Expense ($000):** 42215 **Payroll Expense ($000):** 17794 **Personnel:** 212

CUBA CITY—Grant County

SOUTHWEST HEALTH CENTER NURSING HOME See Southwest Health, Platteville

CUDAHY—Milwaukee County

AURORA ST. LUKE'S SOUTH SHORE See Aurora St. Luke's Medical Center, Milwaukee

CUMBERLAND—Barron County

☐ **CUMBERLAND HEALTHCARE (521353)**, 1110 Seventh Avenue, Zip 54829–9138; tel. 715/822–2741, **A1** 10 18 **F3** 11 13 15 28 29 30 34 40 43 44 45 46 50 53 55 56 57 59 64 65 75 76 77 78 81 82 86 87 89 92 93 96 97 99 100 103 104 107 114 127 129 130 131 132 133 135 144 146 148 154 156
Primary Contact: Michael Gutsch, Chief Executive Officer and Administrator
COO: Bob Lindberg, Chief Operating Officer
CFO: Angela Martens, Chief Financial Officer
CMO: Tom Lingen, M.D., Chief of Staff
CIO: Jason Morse, Director Information Technology
CHR: Hilary Butzler, Director Human Resources
Web address: www.cumberlandhealthcare.com
Control: Other not–for–profit (including NFP Corporation) **Service:** General medical and surgical

Staffed Beds: 9 **Admissions:** 584 **Census:** 9 **Outpatient Visits:** 12614 **Births:** 55 **Total Expense ($000):** 23747 **Payroll Expense ($000):** 10557 **Personnel:** 154

DARLINGTON—Lafayette County

★ **MEMORIAL HOSPITAL OF LAFAYETTE COUNTY (521312)**, 800 Clay Street, Zip 53530–1228, Mailing Address: P.O. Box 70, Zip 53530–0070; tel. 608/776–4466, **A**10 18 **F**1 3 11 15 18 26 28 29 32 35 40 45 46 47 48 54 56 57 64 68 74 75 79 80 81 82 86 89 90 93 102 107 110 111 114 116 117 119 130 131 133 144 156 **S** UnityPoint Health, West Des Moines, IA
Primary Contact: Kathleen Kuepers, Chief Executive Officer
CFO: Marie Wamsley, Chief Financial Officer
Web address: www.memorialhospitaloflafayettecounty.org
Control: County, Government, nonfederal **Service:** General medical and surgical

Staffed Beds: 25 **Admissions:** 340 **Census:** 3 **Outpatient Visits:** 23392 **Births:** 0 **Total Expense ($000):** 19369 **Payroll Expense ($000):** 6524 **Personnel:** 108

DODGEVILLE—Iowa County

⊠ **UPLAND HILLS HEALTH (521352)**, 800 Compassion Way, Zip 53533–1956, Mailing Address: P.O. Box 800, Zip 53533–0800; tel. 608/930–8000, (Total facility includes 44 beds in nursing home–type unit) **A1** 10 18 **F3** 8 11 13 15 17 28 29 34 36 40 41 43 44 45 50 53 54 56 57 59 63 64 67 68 70 75 76 77 78 79 80 81 82 83 84 85 86 87 88 89 90 93 96 97 107 110 111 114 115 119 127 128 129 130 131 132 133 144 146 147 148 149 156 157
Primary Contact: Lisa W. Schnedler, FACHE, President and Chief Executive Officer
CFO: Karl Pustina, Vice President Finance
CIO: Karen Thuli, Information Systems Coordinator
CHR: Troy Marx, Human Resources Director
CNO: Lynn Hebgen, MSN, R.N., Vice President of Nursing
Web address: www.uplandhillshealth.org
Control: Other not–for–profit (including NFP Corporation) **Service:** General medical and surgical

Staffed Beds: 69 **Admissions:** 1088 **Census:** 48 **Outpatient Visits:** 58836 **Births:** 215 **Total Expense ($000):** 46062 **Payroll Expense ($000):** 20781 **Personnel:** 306

WI

Hospital, Medicare Provider Number, Address, Telephone, Approval, Facility, and Physician Codes, Health Care System

★ American Hospital Association (AHA) membership
☐ The Joint Commission accreditation
○ Healthcare Facilities Accreditation Program
◇ DNV Healthcare Inc. accreditation
⇧ Center for Improvement in Healthcare Quality Accreditation
△ Commission on Accreditation of Rehabilitation Facilities (CARF) accreditation

DURAND—Pepin County

★ **ADVENTHEALTH DURAND (521307)**, 1220 Third Avenue West, Zip 54736–1600, Mailing Address: P.O. Box 224, Zip 54736–0224; tel. 715/672–4211, **A**10 18 **F**3 15 18 19 28 29 30 34 35 40 44 56 57 59 65 68 75 79 81 86 87 89 97 107 109 110 114 117 129 130 132 152 156 **S** AdventHealth, Altamonte Springs, FL
Primary Contact: Douglas R. Peterson, President and Chief Executive Officer
Web address: www.chippewavalleyhospital.com/
Control: Church operated, Nongovernment, not–for–profit **Service**: General medical and surgical

Staffed Beds: 25 **Admissions**: 248 **Census**: 4 **Outpatient Visits**: 26947 **Births**: 0 **Total Expense ($000)**: 14075 **Payroll Expense ($000)**: 5434 **Personnel**: 79

EAGLE RIVER—Vilas County

★ **ASCENSION EAGLE RIVER HOSPITAL (521300)**, 201 Hospital Road, Zip 54521–8835; tel. 715/479–7411, **A**10 18 **F**3 11 15 28 29 30 34 35 40 64 68 75 79 81 82 85 86 87 89 93 107 110 111 115 119 130 133 146 149 152 154 **S** Ascension Healthcare, Saint Louis, MO
Primary Contact: Sandra L. Anderson, President
COO: Laurie Oungst, Vice President, Operations
CFO: Jamon Lamers, Director Finance
CMO: Roderick Brodhead, Chief Medical Officer
CIO: Howard Dobizl, Director Information Technology Services
CHR: Michelle Cornelius, Director Human Resources for Northern Region
CNO: Jacqualyn Monge, Director of Nursing
Web address: www.ministryhealth.org
Control: Church operated, Nongovernment, not–for–profit **Service**: General medical and surgical

Staffed Beds: 14 **Admissions**: 404 **Census**: 4 **Outpatient Visits**: 21659 **Births**: 0 **Total Expense ($000)**: 14758 **Payroll Expense ($000)**: 5244 **Personnel**: 60

EAU CLAIRE—Eau Claire County

▣ △ **HSHS SACRED HEART HOSPITAL (520013)**, 900 West Clairemont Avenue, Zip 54701–6122; tel. 715/717–4121, **A**1 2 3 5 7 10 **F**3 6 11 12 13 15 17 18 20 22 24 28 29 30 31 34 35 38 40 41 43 47 48 49 51 53 54 56 57 59 60 64 69 70 72 74 75 76 78 79 80 81 82 83 84 85 86 87 88 89 90 92 93 96 98 99 100 101 102 103 107 108 110 111 112 115 116 117 118 119 120 121 123 124 126 129 130 132 141 144 145 146 147 149 154 **S** HSHS Hospital Sisters Health System, Springfield, IL
Primary Contact: Andrew Bagnall, President and Chief Executive Officer
CFO: David Nelson, FACHE, Chief Financial Officer
CMO: Humayun Khan, M.D., Chief Medical Officer
CIO: Kevin Groskreutz, Chief Information Officer
CHR: Craig Brenholt, Division Director People Services
CNO: Amy L. Dwyer, R.N., MSN, Chief Nursing Officer
Web address: www.sacredhearteauclaire.org
Control: Church operated, Nongovernment, not–for–profit **Service**: General medical and surgical

Staffed Beds: 205 **Admissions**: 9084 **Census**: 118 **Outpatient Visits**: 82150 **Births**: 840 **Total Expense ($000)**: 183446 **Payroll Expense ($000)**: 61715 **Personnel**: 878

★ **MARSHFIELD MEDICAL CENTER - EAU CLAIRE HOSPITAL**, 2310 Craig Road, Zip 54701–6128; tel. 715/858–8100, (Nonreporting) **S** Marshfield Clinic Health System, Marshfield, WI
Primary Contact: Scott Polenz, CPA, Chief Administrative Officer
Web address: www.https://www.marshfieldclinic.org/locations/centers/Eau%20 Claire%20-%20Marshfield%20Medical%20Center
Control: Other not–for–profit (including NFP Corporation) **Service**: General medical and surgical

Staffed Beds: 44

▢ **MAYO CLINIC HEALTH SYSTEM IN EAU CLAIRE (520070)**, 1221 Whipple Street, Zip 54703–5270, Mailing Address: P.O. Box 4105, Zip 54702; tel. 715/838–3311, **A**1 2 3 5 10 19 **F**3 4 5 6 12 13 15 17 18 20 22 24 26 28 29 30 31 32 34 35 37 38 40 43 44 45 46 49 53 55 56 57 58 59 60 61 64 65 70 72 74 76 77 78 79 80 81 82 84 85 86 87 89 90 92 93 94 96 97 98 99 100 101 102 103 104 105 107 108 110 111 115 116 117 118 119 120 121 124 126 129 130 131 132 134 144 145 146 147 148 149 154 156 157 **S** Mayo Clinic, Rochester, MN
Primary Contact: Richard Helmers, M.D., Regional Vice President
COO: John M Dickey, Chief Administrative Officer
CFO: Denise Mattison, Director Finance and Accounting Services
CMO: Robert C Peck, M.D., Chief Medical Officer
CHR: Kenneth Lee, Division Chair, Human Resource Advisory
CNO: Pamela K. White, R.N., MSN, Chief Nursing Officer
Web address: www.mhs.mayo.edu
Control: Other not–for–profit (including NFP Corporation) **Service**: General medical and surgical

Staffed Beds: 185 **Admissions**: 10656 **Census**: 126 **Outpatient Visits**: 410662 **Births**: 1068 **Total Expense ($000)**: 534579 **Payroll Expense ($000)**: 255223 **Personnel**: 2537

EDGERTON—Rock County

▣ **EDGERTON HOSPITAL AND HEALTH SERVICES (521319)**, 11101 North Sherman Road, Zip 53534–9002; tel. 608/884–3441, **A**1 10 18 **F**3 11 15 18 28 31 40 43 59 64 75 77 81 86 90 93 97 107 108 109 111 119 129 130 133 144 146 148
Primary Contact: Jim Schultz, Chief Executive Officer
CFO: Charles Roader, Vice President Finance
CMO: Brian Stubitsch, M.D., Chief Medical Officer
CIO: JT Johrendt, Information Technology Network Specialist
CHR: Mark Kindschi, Director Human Resources
CNO: Sue Alwin-Popp, Chief Clinical Officer
Web address: www.edgertonhospital.com
Control: Other not–for–profit (including NFP Corporation) **Service**: General medical and surgical

Staffed Beds: 18 **Admissions**: 333 **Census**: 8 **Outpatient Visits**: 16354 **Births**: 0 **Total Expense ($000)**: 20835 **Payroll Expense ($000)**: 9910 **Personnel**: 108

ELK MOUND—Dunn County

VERNON MEMORIAL HEALTHCARE (521348), E8270 660th Ave, Zip 54739–4401, Mailing Address: 507 South Main Street, Viroqua, Zip 54665–2096; tel. 608/637–2101, **A**10 18 **F**5 13 15 28 29 34 36 40 43 56 62 63 64 75 76 77 80 81 82 86 87 89 93 99 100 103 104 107 119 130 131 144
Primary Contact: Kyle Bakkum, Chief Executive Officer and Administrator
COO: Kristy Wiltrout, R.N., Chief Operating Officer
CFO: Mary Koenig, Chief Financial Officer
CIO: Scott Adkins, Manager Information Technology
CHR: Kay Starr, Manager Human Resources
Web address: www.vmh.org
Control: Other not–for–profit (including NFP Corporation) **Service**: General medical and surgical

Staffed Beds: 25 **Admissions**: 1321 **Census**: 9 **Outpatient Visits**: 138807 **Births**: 151 **Total Expense ($000)**: 77374 **Payroll Expense ($000)**: 33611 **Personnel**: 388

ELKHORN—Walworth County

▣ △ **AURORA LAKELAND MEDICAL CENTER (520102)**, W3985 County Road NN, Zip 53121–4389; tel. 262/741–2000, **A**1 2 3 7 10 **F**3 11 13 17 18 29 30 34 35 36 40 43 44 45 46 47 48 50 51 56 57 59 60 68 70 74 75 76 79 80 81 82 84 85 86 89 90 93 94 96 100 107 108 111 115 118 119 127 129 130 131 132 135 146 148 149 **S** Advocate Aurora Health, Downers Grove, IL
Primary Contact: Bob Miller, President
CFO: Stuart Arnett, Regional Vice President Finance
CMO: Greg Gerber, M.D., Chief Medical Officer
CIO: Jean Chase, Regional Manager Information Services
CHR: Gene Krauklis, Regional Vice President Human Resources
Web address: www.aurorahealthcare.org
Control: Other not–for–profit (including NFP Corporation) **Service**: General medical and surgical

Staffed Beds: 67 **Admissions**: 2773 **Census**: 26 **Outpatient Visits**: 70079 **Births**: 710 **Total Expense ($000)**: 53313 **Payroll Expense ($000)**: 19926 **Personnel**: 408

WI

Many Facility Codes have changed. Please refer to the AHA Guide Code Chart. © 2019 AHA Guide

FOND DU LAC—Fond Du Lac County

FOND DU LAC COUNTY MENTAL HEALTH CENTER (524025), 459 East First Street, Zip 54935–4599; tel. 920/929–3502, **A**10 **F**4 38 98 99 102 103 130 152
Primary Contact: J.R. Musunuru, M.D., Executive Director
Web address: www.fdlco.wi.gov
Control: County, Government, nonfederal **Service:** Psychiatric

Staffed Beds: 25 **Admissions:** 862 **Census:** 13 **Outpatient Visits:** 1698 **Births:** 0 **Total Expense ($000):** 3854 **Payroll Expense ($000):** 2624 **Personnel:** 59

☒ △ **ST. AGNES HOSPITAL (520088)**, 430 East Division Street, Zip 54935–4560, Mailing Address: P.O. Box 385, Zip 54936–0385; tel. 920/929–2300, **A**1 2 7 10 20 **F**2 3 5 6 8 11 13 15 18 20 22 24 26 28 29 30 31 33 34 35 36 38 40 43 44 45 46 47 48 49 50 51 53 54 55 56 57 59 60 62 63 64 66 68 69 74 75 76 77 78 79 80 81 82 84 85 86 87 90 92 93 96 97 98 99 100 101 102 103 104 105 107 108 109 110 111 115 118 119 120 121 123 124 126 129 130 131 132 134 135 143 144 146 147 148 149 150 152 153 154 156 **S** SSM Health, Saint Louis, MO
Primary Contact: Katherine Vergos, FACHE, President
CFO: Bonnie Schmitz, Vice President and Chief Financial Officer
CMO: Derek Colmenares, M.D., Chief Medical Officer
CIO: Nancy Birschbach, Vice President and Chief Information Officer
CHR: Sue Edminster, Vice President Human Resources
CNO: Tami Schattschneider, Chief Nursing Officer
Web address: www.agnesian.com
Control: Church operated, Nongovernment, not–for–profit **Service:** General medical and surgical

Staffed Beds: 139 **Admissions:** 6574 **Census:** 73 **Outpatient Visits:** 742924 **Births:** 750 **Total Expense ($000):** 366551 **Payroll Expense ($000):** 136547 **Personnel:** 1466

FORT ATKINSON—Jefferson County

☒ **FORT HEALTHCARE (520071)**, 611 East Sherman Avenue, Zip 53538–1998; tel. 920/568–5000, **A**1 10 **F**3 11 12 13 15 28 29 34 35 40 47 48 50 53 55 56 57 59 68 75 76 77 79 80 81 85 86 87 89 90 93 94 96 107 108 110 111 114 118 119 130 132 135 144 146 147 149 150
Primary Contact: Michael S. Wallace, President and Chief Executive Officer
CFO: James J Nelson, Senior Vice President Finance and Strategic Planning
CMO: Thomas Nordland, Chief Medical Officer
CIO: Christopher Manakas, Chief Information Officer
CHR: Nancy Alstad, Director Human Resources
CNO: Marie Wiesmann, Vice President of Nursing and Chief Nursing Officer
Web address: www.forthealthcare.com
Control: Other not–for–profit (including NFP Corporation) **Service:** General medical and surgical

Staffed Beds: 49 **Admissions:** 1722 **Census:** 13 **Outpatient Visits:** 264992 **Births:** 342 **Total Expense ($000):** 118318 **Payroll Expense ($000):** 38569 **Personnel:** 451

FRANKLIN—Milwaukee County

★ **ASCENSION SOUTHEAST WISCONSIN HOSPITAL - FRANKLIN CAMPUS (520204)**, 10101 South 27th Street, Zip 53132–7209; tel. 414/325–4700, **F**3 15 17 18 20 22 26 29 30 40 43 45 48 49 50 57 64 68 70 74 77 79 81 82 84 85 86 87 91 92 93 96 107 108 110 111 115 119 126 130 131 135 145 146 148 149 **S** Ascension Healthcare, Saint Louis, MO
Primary Contact: Seth R. Teigen, President
CFO: Aaron Bridgeland, Director Finance
CMO: Michelle Graham, M.D., Vice President Medical Affairs
CIO: Gregory Smith, Senior Vice President and Chief Information Officer
CNO: Sheila Gansemer, R.N., Vice President Patient Care Services and Chief Nursing Officer
Web address: www.mywheaton.org/
Control: Church operated, Nongovernment, not–for–profit **Service:** General medical and surgical

Staffed Beds: 44 **Admissions:** 2962 **Census:** 35 **Outpatient Visits:** 93320 **Births:** 0 **Total Expense ($000):** 80117 **Payroll Expense ($000):** 23552 **Personnel:** 313

☒ **MIDWEST ORTHOPEDIC SPECIALTY HOSPITAL (520205)**, 10101 South 27th Street, 2nd Floor, Zip 53132–7209; tel. 414/817–5800, **A**1 3 5 10 **F**3 29 30 34 50 57 68 79 80 81 82 85 86 91 92 94 96 130 131 149 **S** Ascension Healthcare, Saint Louis, MO
Primary Contact: Bernie Sherry, Senior Vice President, Ascension Healthcare, Ministry
CFO: Aaron Bridgeland, Director Finance
CMO: Daniel Guehlstorf, M.D., Chief of Staff
CIO: Gregory Smith, Senior Vice President and Chief Information Officer
Web address: www.mymosh.com/
Control: Partnership, Investor–owned (for–profit) **Service:** General medical and surgical

Staffed Beds: 16 **Admissions:** 1578 **Census:** 9 **Outpatient Visits:** 6493 **Births:** 0 **Total Expense ($000):** 38691 **Payroll Expense ($000):** 6520 **Personnel:** 141

FRIENDSHIP—Adams County

GUNDERSEN MOUNDVIEW HOSPITAL & CLINICS (521309), 402 West Lake Street, Zip 53934–9699, Mailing Address: P.O. Box 40, Zip 53934–0040; tel. 608/339–3331, **A**10 18 **F**6 11 15 28 29 34 36 40 53 56 64 77 81 82 86 87 93 107 108 111 119 130 131 154
Primary Contact: Francisco Perez-Guerra, Chief Executive Officer
Web address: www.moundview.org
Control: Other not–for–profit (including NFP Corporation) **Service:** General medical and surgical

Staffed Beds: 25 **Admissions:** 212 **Census:** 2 **Outpatient Visits:** 41584 **Births:** 0 **Total Expense ($000):** 17570 **Payroll Expense ($000):** 7717 **Personnel:** 115

GLENDALE—Milwaukee County

ORTHOPAEDIC HOSPITAL OF WISCONSIN (520194), 475 West River Woods Parkway, Zip 53212–1081; tel. 414/961–6800, **A**10 **F**29 34 38 53 64 80 81 82 86 93 107 111 119 130 131
Primary Contact: Brian J. Cramer, Chief Executive Officer
CFO: Tom Swiderski, Chief Financial Officer
CMO: Rory Wright, M.D., President Medical Staff
CIO: Todd Heikkinen, Manager Sports Medicine and Rehabilitation Services
CNO: Nanette Johnson, Chief Nursing Officer
Web address: www.ohow.org
Control: Partnership, Investor–owned (for–profit) **Service:** General medical and surgical

Staffed Beds: 30 **Admissions:** 1485 **Census:** 9 **Outpatient Visits:** 39586 **Births:** 0 **Total Expense ($000):** 41987 **Payroll Expense ($000):** 14217 **Personnel:** 199

GRAFTON—Ozaukee County

☒ **AURORA MEDICAL CENTER GRAFTON (520207)**, 975 Port Washington Road, Zip 53024–9201; tel. 262/329–1000, **A**1 2 3 5 10 **F**3 8 12 13 15 17 18 20 22 24 26 28 29 30 31 34 35 36 37 40 41 43 44 45 46 47 48 49 50 51 53 54 59 60 61 66 68 70 72 74 76 76 79 80 81 82 85 86 87 89 92 93 94 96 107 108 110 111 114 115 116 117 118 119 120 121 124 126 130 131 135 146 147 148 149 154 **S** Advocate Aurora Health, Downers Grove, IL
Primary Contact: David Graebner, President
CMO: Doug McManus, Chief Medical Officer
Web address: www.aurorahealthcare.org
Control: Other not–for–profit (including NFP Corporation) **Service:** General medical and surgical

Staffed Beds: 127 **Admissions:** 7844 **Census:** 80 **Outpatient Visits:** 148859 **Births:** 1099 **Total Expense ($000):** 191606 **Payroll Expense ($000):** 58263 **Personnel:** 1187

GRANTSBURG—Burnett County

★ **BURNETT MEDICAL CENTER (521331)**, 257 West St George Avenue, Zip 54840–7827; tel. 715/463–5353, (Total facility includes 50 beds in nursing home–type unit) **A**10 18 **F**2 3 15 28 29 34 35 40 43 44 50 56 57 59 64 75 77 78 80 81 86 87 89 90 93 97 107 110 115 127 128 130 131 132 133 135 144 146 149 152 156 157
Primary Contact: Gordon Lewis, Chief Executive Officer
CFO: Charles J Faught, Chief Financial Officer
CMO: Hans Rechsteiner, M.D., Chief of Staff
CIO: Andy Douglas, Manager Information Technology
CHR: Sandy Hinrichs, Director Human Resources
Web address: www.burnettmedicalcenter.com
Control: Other not–for–profit (including NFP Corporation) **Service:** General medical and surgical

Staffed Beds: 67 **Admissions:** 343 **Census:** 40 **Outpatient Visits:** 29518 **Births:** 1 **Total Expense ($000):** 15477 **Payroll Expense ($000):** 7437 **Personnel:** 139

WI

GREEN BAY—Brown County

⊞ **AURORA BAYCARE MEDICAL CENTER (520193)**, 2845 Greenbrier Road, Zip 54311–6519, Mailing Address: P.O. Box 8900, Zip 54308–8900; tel. 920/288–8000, **A**1 2 10 19 **F**3 12 13 15 17 18 20 22 24 26 28 29 30 31 32 33 34 35 36 37 40 43 44 45 46 47 48 49 50 53 54 57 58 59 64 65 68 70 72 74 75 76 78 79 80 81 82 84 85 86 87 90 91 92 93 94 97 107 108 109 110 111 114 115 116 117 118 119 123 124 126 129 130 131 132 134 135 144 146 147 148 149 154 156 157 **S** Advocate Aurora Health, Downers Grove, IL
Primary Contact: Daniel T. Meyer, President
COO: Daniel T Meyer, President
CFO: Gwen Christensen, Vice President, Finance
CMO: Brian Johnson, M.D., Chief Medical Officer
CIO: Chuck Geurts, Manager Information Technology Client Services
CHR: Elizabeth A Kirby, Senior Director Human Resources
CNO: Heather Schroeder, R.N., Vice President Nursing
Web address: www.aurorabaycare.com
Control: Partnership, Investor–owned (for–profit) **Service**: General medical and surgical

Staffed Beds: 167 **Admissions**: 9730 **Census**: 117 **Outpatient Visits**: 411231 **Births**: 1673 **Total Expense ($000)**: 380157 **Payroll Expense ($000)**: 119130 **Personnel**: 1794

★ ⇑ **BELLIN HOSPITAL (520049)**, 744 South Webster Avenue, Zip 54301–3581, Mailing Address: P.O. Box 23400, Zip 54305–3400; tel. 920/433–3500, **A**2 10 21 **F**3 12 13 15 17 18 20 22 24 26 28 29 30 31 32 35 36 37 40 41 43 45 46 47 48 49 51 53 54 59 62 64 71 74 75 76 77 78 79 80 81 82 83 84 85 86 87 89 90 91 92 96 97 107 108 110 111 115 116 117 118 119 123 124 126 127 129 130 131 132 144 145 146 148 149 154 156
Primary Contact: Chris Woleske, President and Chief Executive Officer
CFO: Jim Dietsche, Chief Financial Officer
CMO: Cynthia Lasecki, M.D., Chief Medical Officer
CIO: John Rocheleau, Vice President Business Support and Information Technology
CHR: Troy L Koebke, Director Human Resources Management
CNO: Laura Hieb, R.N., Chief Nursing Officer
Web address: www.bellin.org
Control: Other not–for–profit (including NFP Corporation) **Service**: General medical and surgical

Staffed Beds: 167 **Admissions**: 8191 **Census**: 80 **Outpatient Visits**: 1092573 **Births**: 1405 **Total Expense ($000)**: 486767 **Payroll Expense ($000)**: 229163 **Personnel**: 2744

⇑ **BELLIN PSYCHIATRIC CENTER (524038)**, 301 East St Joseph Street, Zip 54301, Mailing Address: P.O. Box 23725, Zip 54305–3725; tel. 920/433–3630, **A**3 5 10 21 **F**4 5 6 29 34 36 38 53 54 56 64 75 86 87 98 99 100 101 102 103 104 130 154
Primary Contact: Sharla Baenen, MSN, R.N., President Mental Well Being, Vice President Emergency Medicine, Hospitalists & Medical Subspecialist
CFO: Kevin McGurk, Controller
CIO: Troy Schiesl, Director Information Services
CHR: Troy L Koebke, Director Human Resources
CNO: Crystal Malakar, Team Leader Inpatient Nursing
Web address: www.bellin.org
Control: Church operated, Nongovernment, not–for–profit **Service**: Psychiatric

Staffed Beds: 53 **Admissions**: 1541 **Census**: 21 **Outpatient Visits**: 84487 **Births**: 0 **Total Expense ($000)**: 23325 **Payroll Expense ($000)**: 15590 **Personnel**: 168

BROWN COUNTY COMMUNITY TREATMENT CENTER (524014), 3150 Gershwin Drive, Zip 54311–5899; tel. 920/391–4700, **A**10 **F**98 102 130
Primary Contact: Roberta Morschauser, Administrator
CFO: Margaret Hoff, Account Manager
CMO: Yogesh Pareek, M.D., Clinical Director
CIO: Dawn LaPlant, Manager Health Information Management
CHR: Brent R Miller, Manager Human Resources
Web address: www.co.brown.wi.us/
Control: County, Government, nonfederal **Service**: Psychiatric

Staffed Beds: 16 **Admissions**: 770 **Census**: 11 **Outpatient Visits**: 0 **Births**: 0 **Total Expense ($000)**: 3342 **Payroll Expense ($000)**: 2518 **Personnel**: 61

BROWN COUNTY HUMAN SERVICES MENTAL HEALTH CENTER See Brown County Community Treatment Center

⊞ **HSHS ST. MARY'S HOSPITAL MEDICAL CENTER (520097)**, 1726 Shawano Avenue, Zip 54303–3282; tel. 920/498–4200, **A**1 2 10 **F**3 13 15 17 18 20 22 26 28 29 30 31 34 35 40 43 44 45 46 47 48 49 50 51 53 55 57 59 64 65 68 69 70 74 75 76 77 78 79 80 81 82 84 85 86 87 92 94 96 102 107 108 110 111 114 115 116 117 118 119 130 132 143 145 146 147 148 149 150 154 **S** HSHS Hospital Sisters Health System, Springfield, IL
Primary Contact: Therese B. Pandl, President and Chief Executive Officer
COO: Lawrence J Connors, Chief Operating Officer
CFO: Greg Simia, Chief Financial Officer
CMO: Ken Johnson, Chief Physician Executive
CIO: Shane Miller, Chief Information Officer
CHR: Christine Jensema, Chief People Officer
CNO: Paula Hafeman, Chief Nursing Officer
Web address: www.stmgb.org
Control: Church operated, Nongovernment, not–for–profit **Service**: General medical and surgical

Staffed Beds: 83 **Admissions**: 3725 **Census**: 34 **Outpatient Visits**: 101277 **Births**: 421 **Total Expense ($000)**: 115170 **Payroll Expense ($000)**: 34038 **Personnel**: 433

⊞ **HSHS ST. VINCENT HOSPITAL (520075)**, 835 South Van Buren Street, Zip 54301–3526, Mailing Address: P.O. Box 13508, Zip 54307–3508; tel. 920/433–0111, **A**1 2 10 **F**3 4 5 9 11 12 13 15 17 18 19 20 22 24 26 29 30 31 32 34 35 36 40 43 44 45 49 50 51 56 57 58 59 60 62 64 65 68 70 72 74 75 76 77 78 79 80 81 84 85 86 87 88 89 90 91 92 94 96 107 108 110 111 114 115 116 117 118 119 120 121 123 124 126 129 130 132 135 143 144 146 147 148 149 150 151 **S** HSHS Hospital Sisters Health System, Springfield, IL
Primary Contact: Therese B. Pandl, President and Chief Executive Officer
COO: Brian Charlier, Chief Operating Officer, HSHS St. Vincent Hospital/Prevea Health
CFO: Greg Simia, Chief Financial Officer
CMO: Ken Johnson, Chief Physician Executive
CIO: Shane Miller, Chief Information Officer
CHR: Christine Jensema, Chief Human Resources Officer
CNO: Kenneth E Nelson, R.N., III Chief Nursing Officer
Web address: www.stvincenthospital.org
Control: Church operated, Nongovernment, not–for–profit **Service**: General medical and surgical

Staffed Beds: 255 **Admissions**: 10438 **Census**: 134 **Outpatient Visits**: 145744 **Births**: 1116 **Total Expense ($000)**: 308692 **Payroll Expense ($000)**: 88260 **Personnel**: 1527

WILLOW CREEK BEHAVIORAL HEALTH (524041), 1351 Ontario Road, Zip 54311–8302; tel. 920/328–1220, (Nonreporting) **A**10 **S** Strategic Behavioral Health, LLC, Memphis, TN
Primary Contact: Teena Ahuja, Interim Chief Executive Officer and Regional Vice President of Operations
Web address: www.willowcreekbh.com
Control: Corporation, Investor–owned (for–profit) **Service**: Psychiatric

Staffed Beds: 72

GREENFIELD—Milwaukee County

KINDRED HOSPITAL-MILWAUKEE See Post Acute Medical Specialty Hospital of Milwaukee

⊞ **POST ACUTE MEDICAL SPECIALTY HOSPITAL OF MILWAUKEE (522004)**, 5017 South 110Th Street, Zip 53228–3131; tel. 414/427–8282, **A**1 10 **F**1 29 100 130 **S** Post Acute Medical, LLC, Enola, PA
Primary Contact: Paul E. Qualls, Chief Executive Officer
CMO: Alok Goyal, M.D., Medical Director
CNO: Nancy Cholka, R.N., Chief Nursing Officer
Web address: www.postacutemedical.com/
Control: Individual, Investor–owned (for–profit) **Service**: Children's acute long–term Care

Staffed Beds: 56 **Admissions**: 483 **Census**: 30 **Outpatient Visits**: 0 **Births**: 0 **Total Expense ($000)**: 16037 **Payroll Expense ($000)**: 7371 **Personnel**: 71

WI

Many Facility Codes have changed. Please refer to the AHA Guide Code Chart. © 2019 AHA Guide

HARTFORD—Washington County

✠ **AURORA MEDICAL CENTER IN WASHINGTON COUNTY (520038)**, 1032 East Sumner Street, Zip 53027–1698; tel. 262/673–2300, **A**1 2 10 **F**3 8 11 15 29 30 34 35 36 37 40 41 43 44 45 46 47 48 49 50 53 54 56 57 59 60 64 65 68 74 75 77 79 80 81 82 84 85 86 87 89 90 91 92 93 94 95 96 107 111 114 118 119 129 130 132 135 146 148 149 150 157 **S** Advocate Aurora Health, Downers Grove, IL
Primary Contact: David Graebner, President
CIO: John Sipek, Supervisor Client Services
CNO: Terry Kabitzke-Groth, R.N., Chief Nursing Officer
Web address: www.aurorahealthcare.org
Control: Other not–for–profit (including NFP Corporation) **Service:** General medical and surgical

Staffed Beds: 34 **Admissions:** 1662 **Census:** 14 **Outpatient Visits:** 87022 **Births:** 0 **Total Expense ($000):** 50402 **Payroll Expense ($000):** 19109 **Personnel:** 336

HAYWARD—Sawyer County

★ **HAYWARD AREA MEMORIAL HOSPITAL AND WATER'S EDGE (521336)**, 11040 North State Road 77, Zip 54843–6391; tel. 715/934–4321, (Total facility includes 70 beds in nursing home–type unit) **A**10 18 **F**10 11 13 15 29 34 40 43 51 64 75 76 78 81 82 86 93 107 111 119 128 130
Primary Contact: Luke Beirl, PharmD, Chief Executive Officer
COO: Brad Zeller, Vice President Operations
CFO: Kent Dumonseau, Vice President Finance and Information Services
CHR: Rose Gates, Director Human Resources
Web address: www.https://haywardmemorialhospital.com
Control: Other not–for–profit (including NFP Corporation) **Service:** General medical and surgical

Staffed Beds: 75 **Admissions:** 892 **Census:** 73 **Outpatient Visits:** 14348 **Births:** 155 **Total Expense ($000):** 39059 **Payroll Expense ($000):** 15971 **Personnel:** 219

HILLSBORO—Vernon County

★ **GUNDERSEN ST. JOSEPH'S HOSPITAL AND CLINICS (521304)**, 400 Water Avenue, Zip 54634–9054, Mailing Address: P.O. Box 527, Zip 54634–0527; tel. 608/489–8000, **A**10 18 **F**15 29 34 40 43 53 56 64 69 75 77 80 81 82 86 87 89 90 93 99 100 101 103 104 107 108 130 131 144 147
Primary Contact: Danielle Gearhart, Chief Executive Officer
CFO: Robin Nelson, Chief Financial Officer
CMO: William Cooke, M.D., Chief of Staff
CIO: Danial Phetteplace, Director Information Technology
CHR: Kristle McCole, Clinic Operations Officer and Director Human Resources
Web address: www.gundersenhealth.org/st-josephs
Control: Other not–for–profit (including NFP Corporation) **Service:** General medical and surgical

Staffed Beds: 13 **Admissions:** 298 **Census:** 3 **Outpatient Visits:** 38462 **Births:** 0 **Total Expense ($000):** 20835 **Payroll Expense ($000):** 8606 **Personnel:** 149

HUDSON—St. Croix County

☐ **HUDSON HOSPITAL AND CLINIC (521335)**, 405 Stageline Road, Zip 54016–7848; tel. 715/531–6000, **A**1 3 10 18 **F**5 13 15 28 29 34 38 40 43 53 55 56 64 75 76 78 80 81 86 87 89 93 107 111 119 130 **S** HealthPartners, Bloomington, MN
Primary Contact: Thomas Borowski, FACHE, President
CFO: Douglas E Johnson, Interim Vice President Operations and Chief Financial Officer
CMO: Paul Scott, M.D., Chief of Staff
CHR: Scott J Allen, Director Human Resources
Web address: www.hudsonhospital.org
Control: Other not–for–profit (including NFP Corporation) **Service:** General medical and surgical

Staffed Beds: 24 **Admissions:** 1415 **Census:** 10 **Outpatient Visits:** 47751 **Births:** 588 **Total Expense ($000):** 54293 **Payroll Expense ($000):** 20339 **Personnel:** 223

JANESVILLE—Rock County

✠ **MERCYHEALTH HOSPITAL AND TRAUMA CENTER - JANESVILLE (520066)**, 1000 Mineral Point Avenue, Zip 53548–2982, Mailing Address: P.O. Box 5003, Zip 53547–5003; tel. 608/756–6000, (Nonreporting) **A**1 2 3 10 **S** Mercy Health System, Janesville, WI
Primary Contact: Javon R. Bea, President and Chief Executive Officer
CFO: John Cook, Vice President and Chief Financial Officer
CMO: Mark L. Goelzer, M.D., Director Medical Affairs
CHR: Kathy Harris, Vice President
CNO: Debra Potempa, Vice President
Web address: www.mercyhealthsystem.org
Control: Other not–for–profit (including NFP Corporation) **Service:** General medical and surgical

Staffed Beds: 135

KENOSHA—Kenosha County

✠ **AURORA MEDICAL CENTER KENOSHA (520189)**, 10400 75th Street, Zip 53142–7884; tel. 262/948–5600, **A**1 2 10 **F**3 8 11 13 15 17 18 19 20 22 26 28 29 30 31 34 35 36 40 43 44 45 46 47 48 49 50 51 54 57 59 60 64 68 70 72 74 75 76 79 80 81 82 84 85 86 87 89 93 94 96 100 107 108 110 111 114 115 116 117 118 119 120 121 123 126 129 130 131 132 135 146 147 148 149 154 **S** Advocate Aurora Health, Downers Grove, IL
Primary Contact: Lisa Just, President
COO: Linda A. Gump, Chief Clinical Services Officer
CFO: Laurie B. Yake, Vice President Finance
CMO: James Santarelli, M.D., President Medical Staff
CIO: Debora R. Chapdelaine, Manager Information Technology
CHR: Kellie Nelson, Director Human Resources
CNO: Donna F. Jamieson, Ph.D., R.N., Chief Nursing Officer
Web address: www.aurorahealthcare.org
Control: Other not–for–profit (including NFP Corporation) **Service:** General medical and surgical

Staffed Beds: 79 **Admissions:** 5707 **Census:** 52 **Outpatient Visits:** 198962 **Births:** 862 **Total Expense ($000):** 153839 **Payroll Expense ($000):** 48051 **Personnel:** 1156

☐ **FROEDTERT SOUTH - KENOSHA MEDICAL CENTER (520021)**, 6308 Eighth Avenue, Zip 53143–5082; tel. 262/656–2011, (Includes FROEDTERT SOUTH - ST. CATHERINE'S MEDICAL CENTER, 9555 76th Street, Pleasant Prairie, Wisconsin, Zip 53158–1984, Mailing Address: 6308 Eighth Avenue, Kenosha, Zip 53143–5082, tel. 262/577–8000; Richard O Schmidt Jr, President and Chief Executive Officer) **A**1 2 10 **F**1 11 12 13 15 17 20 22 24 28 29 34 38 40 43 51 53 60 64 70 72 75 76 78 80 81 86 87 90 93 100 102 107 108 111 118 119 130 131 144 147
Primary Contact: Richard O. Schmidt Jr, President and Chief Executive Officer
CFO: Thomas J. Kelley, Executive Vice President and Chief Financial Officer
Web address: www.froedtertsouth.com
Control: Other not–for–profit (including NFP Corporation) **Service:** General medical and surgical

Staffed Beds: 194 **Admissions:** 7828 **Census:** 99 **Outpatient Visits:** 343762 **Births:** 1006 **Total Expense ($000):** 291478 **Payroll Expense ($000):** 134560 **Personnel:** 1732

LA CROSSE—La Crosse County

✠ △ **GUNDERSEN LUTHERAN MEDICAL CENTER (520087)**, 1900 South Avenue, Zip 54601–5467; tel. 608/782–7300, **A**1 2 3 5 7 8 10 **F**3 4 5 6 9 12 13 15 18 19 20 22 24 26 28 29 30 31 32 33 34 35 36 38 40 43 44 45 46 47 48 49 50 51 52 54 55 56 57 59 60 61 63 64 65 68 71 72 74 75 76 77 78 79 80 81 82 84 85 86 87 88 89 90 91 92 93 94 96 97 98 99 100 101 102 103 104 105 107 109 110 111 113 115 116 117 118 119 120 121 123 124 126 129 130 131 132 134 135 143 144 145 146 147 148 149 150 152 153 154 156
Primary Contact: Scott W. Rathgaber, M.D., Chief Executive Officer
COO: Kathy Klock, R.N., Senior Vice President Clinical Operations and Human Resources
CFO: Dara Bartels, Chief Financial Officer
CMO: Greg Thompson, Chief Medical Officer
CIO: Deb Rislow, Chief Information Officer
CHR: Kathy Klock, R.N., Senior Vice President Clinical Operations and Human Resources
Web address: www.gundluth.org
Control: Other not–for–profit (including NFP Corporation) **Service:** General medical and surgical

Staffed Beds: 282 **Admissions:** 14415 **Census:** 190 **Outpatient Visits:** 650645 **Births:** 1678 **Total Expense ($000):** 948216 **Payroll Expense ($000):** 418237 **Personnel:** 3065

WI

⊞ **MAYO CLINIC HEALTH SYSTEM - FRANCISCAN HEALTHCARE IN LA CROSSE (520004)**, 700 West Avenue South, Zip 54601–4783; tel. 608/785–0940, **A**1 2 3 5 10 19 **F**3 6 8 11 13 14 15 18 19 20 22 26 28 30 31 34 35 36 40 41 43 44 45 46 48 49 51 54 56 57 58 59 60 64 65 66 68 69 70 72 74 75 76 77 78 79 80 82 84 85 87 89 90 97 102 107 108 110 111 115 116 117 118 119 120 121 123 126 129 130 135 144 145 146 148 149 154 156 157 158 **S** Mayo Clinic, Rochester, MN
Primary Contact: Paul S. Mueller, Regional Vice President
COO: Joseph J Kruse, Executive Vice President
CFO: Tom Tiggelaar, Vice President Finance
CMO: David Rushlow, Vice President Medical Affairs
CIO: Neal Sanger, Vice President Information Services
Web address: www.franciscanskemp.org
Control: Other not–for–profit (including NFP Corporation) **Service**: General medical and surgical

Staffed Beds: 132 **Admissions**: 4839 **Census**: 59 **Outpatient Visits**: 335392 **Births**: 696 **Total Expense ($000)**: 335600 **Payroll Expense ($000)**: 167156 **Personnel**: 2247

LADYSMITH—Rusk County

★ **MARSHFIELD MEDICAL CENTER - LADYSMITH (521328)**, 900 College Avenue West, Zip 54848–2116; tel. 715/532–5561, **A**10 18 **F**3 11 15 28 29 30 34 35 36 40 43 44 45 50 51 53 56 57 59 64 68 70 77 81 85 86 87 89 93 107 110 111 115 116 117 118 119 127 132 133 144 146 147 148 **S** Marshfield Clinic Health System, Marshfield, WI
Primary Contact: Jeff Euclide, R.N., Chief Executive Officer
CFO: David Kuehn, Chief Financial Officer
CMO: Ganesh Pawar, M.D., Chief of Staff
CHR: Rita Telitz, Chief Administrative Officer
Web address: www.ruskhospital.org
Control: County, Government, nonfederal **Service**: General medical and surgical

Staffed Beds: 25 **Admissions**: 383 **Census**: 4 **Outpatient Visits**: 30347 **Births**: 0 **Total Expense ($000)**: 26495 **Payroll Expense ($000)**: 9981 **Personnel**: 148

LAKE GENEVA—Walworth County

MERCYHEALTH HOSPITAL AND MEDICAL CENTER - WALWORTH (521357), N2950 State Road 67, Zip 53147–2655; tel. 262/245–0535, **A**10 18 **F**9 11 13 15 29 38 40 70 75 76 77 78 81 82 87 89 93 100 101 103 104 107 108 111 118 119 130 131 144 147 **S** Mercy Health System, Janesville, WI
Primary Contact: Javon R. Bea, President and Chief Executive Officer
COO: Jennifer Hallatt, Vice President
CNO: Caryn Lynn Oleston, FACHE, MSN, R.N., Chief Nursing Officer
Web address: www.mercyhealthsystem.org
Control: Other not–for–profit (including NFP Corporation) **Service**: General medical and surgical

Staffed Beds: 17 **Admissions**: 1355 **Census**: 10 **Outpatient Visits**: 165831 **Births**: 149 **Total Expense ($000)**: 82381 **Payroll Expense ($000)**: 19339 **Personnel**: 385

LANCASTER—Grant County

⊞ **GRANT REGIONAL HEALTH CENTER (521322)**, 507 South Monroe Street, Zip 53813–2054; tel. 608/723–2143, **A**1 10 18 **F**3 8 11 13 15 28 29 34 35 36 40 43 52 53 55 56 57 59 64 65 68 69 75 76 77 79 80 81 82 85 86 87 89 90 93 97 107 110 111 115 119 127 130 131 132 133 135 144 146 148 149 154 157 **S** HealthTech Management Services, Brentwood, TN
Primary Contact: David Smith, President and Chief Executive Officer
CFO: Dawn Bandy, Chief Financial Officer
CMO: Jessica Varnam, Chief of Staff
CIO: Ken Kaiser, Coordinator Information Systems
CHR: Stacy L Martin, Director Human Resources
CNO: Jennifer Rutkowski, R.N., MSN, Vice President Professional Services
Web address: www.grantregional.com
Control: Other not–for–profit (including NFP Corporation) **Service**: General medical and surgical

Staffed Beds: 6 **Admissions**: 499 **Census**: 5 **Outpatient Visits**: 26141 **Births**: 156 **Total Expense ($000)**: 31337 **Payroll Expense ($000)**: 14137 **Personnel**: 182

MADISON—Dane County

☐ **MENDOTA MENTAL HEALTH INSTITUTE (524008)**, 301 Troy Drive, Zip 53704–1599; tel. 608/301–1000, **A**1 3 5 10 **F**6 29 34 38 56 75 82 86 87 98 100 101 103 104 130 154
Primary Contact: Greg Van Rybroek, Chief Executive Officer
CFO: Stacie Schiereck, Director Management Services
CMO: Molli Martha Rolli, M.D., Medical Director
CNO: Jane Walters, Director of Nursing
Web address: www.dhfs.state.wi.us
Control: State, Government, nonfederal **Service**: Psychiatric

Staffed Beds: 293 **Admissions**: 571 **Census**: 282 **Outpatient Visits**: 0 **Births**: 0 **Total Expense ($000)**: 90658 **Payroll Expense ($000)**: 47378 **Personnel**: 753

⊞ **SELECT SPECIALTY HOSPITAL-MADISON (522008)**, 801 Braxton Place, Zip 53715–1415; tel. 608/260–2700, **A**1 10 **F**1 29 34 60 75 86 119 130 **S** Select Medical Corporation, Mechanicsburg, PA
Primary Contact: Catherine Heimbecher, Chief Executive Officer
CHR: Mallary Stramowski, Chief Human Resources Officer
CNO: Dana McKinney, Chief Nursing Officer
Web address: www.madison.selectspecialtyhospitals.com
Control: Corporation, Investor–owned (for–profit) **Service**: Acute long–term care hospital

Staffed Beds: 58 **Admissions**: 395 **Census**: 37 **Outpatient Visits**: 0 **Births**: 0 **Total Expense ($000)**: 25153 **Payroll Expense ($000)**: 9779 **Personnel**: 168

⊞ **SSM HEALTH ST. MARY'S HOSPITAL (520083)**, 700 South Park Street, Zip 53715–1830; tel. 608/251–6100, **A**1 3 10 **F**2 9 11 13 15 17 20 22 24 28 29 34 40 43 53 56 64 70 72 77 78 80 81 82 86 89 90 98 100 101 102 103 107 108 118 119 130 141 154 **S** SSM Health, Saint Louis, MO
Primary Contact: Jon Rozenfeld, President
CFO: Steve Caldwell, Vice President Finance and Chief Financial Officer
CHR: Linda Taplin Statz, System Director, Employee Experience
CNO: Ginger Malone MSN, RN-B Chief Nursing Officer
Web address: www.stmarysmadison.com
Control: Church operated, Nongovernment, not–for–profit **Service**: General medical and surgical

Staffed Beds: 362 **Admissions**: 19229 **Census**: 252 **Outpatient Visits**: 98004 **Births**: 2175 **Total Expense ($000)**: 383416 **Payroll Expense ($000)**: 128423 **Personnel**: 1522

⊞ **UNITYPOINT HEALTH MERITER (520089)**, 202 South Park Street, Zip 53715–1507; tel. 608/417–6000, **A**1 3 5 10 **F**3 4 5 9 11 12 13 15 17 18 20 22 26 28 29 30 31 32 34 35 36 37 40 41 43 45 46 48 49 50 53 56 57 58 59 64 65 66 68 70 71 72 74 75 76 78 79 80 81 84 85 86 87 90 92 93 96 97 98 99 100 101 102 103 104 107 108 110 111 115 118 119 126 130 132 135 145 146 147 148 149 154 156 **S** UnityPoint Health, West Des Moines, IA
Primary Contact: Sue Erickson, President and Chief Executive Officer
CFO: Beth Erdman, Chief Financial Officer
CMO: Geoff Priest, M.D., Chief Medical Officer
CIO: Denise Gomez, Assistant Vice President Information Systems
CHR: James Arnett, Vice President Human Resources
CNO: Pat Grunwald, MSN, Chief Nursing Officer
Web address: www.meriter.com
Control: Other not–for–profit (including NFP Corporation) **Service**: General medical and surgical

Staffed Beds: 217 **Admissions**: 16058 **Census**: 188 **Outpatient Visits**: 397227 **Births**: 4844 **Total Expense ($000)**: 436520 **Payroll Expense ($000)**: 180544 **Personnel**: 2082

⊞ **UNIVERSITY HOSPITAL (520098)**, 600 Highland Avenue, Zip 53792–0002; tel. 608/263–6400, (Includes AMERICAN FAMILY CHILDREN'S HOSPITAL, 1675 Highland Avenue, Madison, Wisconsin, Zip 53705; tel. 608/890–5437; Jeffrey S Poltawsky, Senior Vice President) **A**1 2 3 8 10 **F**3 5 8 9 12 15 16 17 18 19 20 21 22 23 24 25 26 27 28 29 30 31 32 34 35 36 37 40 41 43 45 46 47 48 49 50 51 53 54 56 57 58 59 60 61 62 64 68 70 72 74 77 78 79 80 81 82 83 84 85 86 87 88 89 92 93 94 96 97 98 100 102 103 107 108 110 111 112 114 115 116 117 118 119 120 121 123 124 126 129 130 131 132 134 135 136 137 138 139 140 141 142 145 146 147 148 149 153 154 157 **S** UW Health System, Madison, WI
Primary Contact: Alan Kaplan, M.D., Chief Executive Officer
COO: Ron Sliwinski, Chief of Hospital Division
CFO: Robert Flannery, Chief Financial Officer
CMO: Peter Newcomer, M.D., Chief Medical Officer
CIO: Jocelyn DeWitt, Ph.D., Vice President and Chief Information Officer
CNO: Beth Houlahan, R.N., Senior Vice President and Chief Nursing Officer
Web address: www.uwhealth.org
Control: Other not–for–profit (including NFP Corporation) **Service**: General medical and surgical

Staffed Beds: 638 **Admissions**: 33497 **Census**: 472 **Outpatient Visits**: 1016343 **Births**: 3 **Total Expense ($000)**: 1779371 **Payroll Expense ($000)**: 591778 **Personnel**: 8764

WI

Many Facility Codes have changed. Please refer to the AHA Guide Code Chart. © 2019 AHA Guide

□ **UW HEALTH REHABILITATION HOSPITAL (523028)**, 5115 North Biltmore Lane, Zip 53718–2161; tel. 608/592–8100, **A**1 10 **F**29 34 75 86 90 **S** UW Health System, Madison, WI
Primary Contact: Mary Kay. Diderrich, R.N., Chief Executive Officer
CFO: Karen Bindl, CPA, Controller
Web address: www.uwhealth.org
Control: Partnership, Investor–owned (for–profit) **Service**: Rehabilitation

Staffed Beds: 40 **Admissions**: 1060 **Census**: 35 **Outpatient Visits**: 0 **Births**: 0 **Total Expense ($000)**: 18699 **Payroll Expense ($000)**: 8070 **Personnel**: 130

☒ **WILLIAM S. MIDDLETON MEMORIAL VETERANS HOSPITAL**, 2500 Overlook Terrace, Zip 53705–2286; tel. 608/256–1901, (Nonreporting) **A**1 3 5 **S** Department of Veterans Affairs, Washington, DC
Primary Contact: John J. Rohrer, Director
CFO: Evarista Mikell, Assistant Finance Officer
CMO: Alan J Bridges, M.D., Chief of Staff
CIO: Randall Margenau, Chief Information Officer
CHR: Stuart Souders, Chief, Human Resources
CNO: Rebecca Kordahl, R.N., Associate Director, Patient Care Services
Web address: www.madison.va.gov
Control: Veterans Affairs, Government, federal **Service**: General medical and surgical

Staffed Beds: 87

MANITOWOC—Manitowoc County

☒ **HOLY FAMILY MEMORIAL (520107)**, 2300 Western Avenue, Zip 54220–3712, Mailing Address: P.O. Box 1450, Zip 54221–1450; tel. 920/320–2011, **A**1 2 10 **F**3 5 11 13 15 18 20 22 28 29 30 31 32 33 34 35 36 40 43 45 46 47 48 49 50 51 53 54 56 57 58 59 62 63 64 65 70 75 76 77 78 79 80 81 82 85 86 89 91 92 93 96 97 104 107 108 109 110 111 114 115 118 119 120 121 122 123 130 132 135 143 146 148 157 **S** Franciscan Sisters of Christian Charity Sponsored Ministries, Inc., Manitowoc, WI
Primary Contact: Brett Norell, Interim Chief Executive Officer
COO: Jane Curran-Meuli, Chief Operating Officer
CFO: Patricia Huettl, Vice President Finance and Chief Financial Officer
CMO: Steve Driggers, M.D., Chief Medical Officer
CIO: Theron Pappas, Director Management Information Systems
CHR: Laura M Fielding, Administrative Director Organizational Development
CNO: Bonny Range, MSN, Chief Nursing Officer
Web address: www.hfmhealth.org
Control: Church operated, Nongovernment, not–for–profit **Service**: General medical and surgical

Staffed Beds: 67 **Admissions**: 2456 **Census**: 23 **Outpatient Visits**: 223116 **Births**: 173 **Total Expense ($000)**: 137848 **Payroll Expense ($000)**: 64181 **Personnel**: 735

MARINETTE—Marinette County

☒ **AURORA MEDICAL CENTER - BAY AREA (520113)**, 3003 University Drive, Zip 54143–4110; tel. 715/735–6621, **A**1 10 20 **F**3 7 11 13 15 17 18 28 29 30 31 34 40 43 44 45 50 51 54 57 59 70 74 75 76 77 78 79 80 81 82 85 86 87 89 93 96 107 108 109 110 111 114 115 119 120 121 123 124 130 131 143 146 147 148 154 **S** Advocate Aurora Health, Downers Grove, IL
Primary Contact: Edward A. Harding, FACHE, President and Chief Executive Officer
COO: Bernie VanCourt, Chief Operating Officer
CFO: Roger Sneath, Chief Financial Officer
CMO: Richard Stein, M.D., Chief Medical Officer
CIO: Pete Eisenzoph, Director Information Technology
CHR: Ken Joyner, Vice President of Employee Services
CNO: Bernie VanCourt, Interim Chief Nursing Officer
Web address: www.bamc.org
Control: Other not–for–profit (including NFP Corporation) **Service**: General medical and surgical

Staffed Beds: 59 **Admissions**: 2961 **Census**: 26 **Outpatient Visits**: 353189 **Births**: 211 **Total Expense ($000)**: 124207 **Payroll Expense ($000)**: 44238 **Personnel**: 487

MARSHFIELD—Wood County

☒ △ **MARSHFIELD MEDICAL CENTER (520037)**, 611 St Joseph Avenue, Zip 54449–1898; tel. 715/387–1713, (Includes MARSHFIELD CHILDEN'S HOSPITAL, 611 Saint Joseph Avenue, Marshfield, Wisconsin, Zip 54449–1832; tel. 715/387–1713) **A**1 2 5 7 10 20 **F**4 6 9 11 12 13 15 16 17 20 22 24 28 29 34 40 43 51 55 56 64 69 70 72 75 76 78 80 81 82 86 87 88 89 90 93 98 102 107 108 111 116 118 119 130 131 144 147 154 **S** Marshfield Clinic Health System, Marshfield, WI
Primary Contact: Ned H. Wolf, Chief Administrative Officer
CFO: William J Hinner, Vice President Financial Analysis and Planning Ministry Health Care
CMO: Peter Stamas, M.D., Vice President Medical Affairs
CIO: Will Weider, Chief Information Officer
CHR: Cheryl F Zima, Vice President Human Resources Ministry Health Care
CNO: Robin Kretschman, MSN, R.N., Vice President Patient Care Services
Web address: www.stjosephs-marshfield.org
Control: Other not–for–profit (including NFP Corporation) **Service**: General medical and surgical

Staffed Beds: 200 **Admissions**: 13077 **Census**: 195 **Outpatient Visits**: 51014 **Births**: 967 **Total Expense ($000)**: 271530 **Payroll Expense ($000)**: 75265 **Personnel**: 1585

NORWOOD HEALTH CENTER (524019), 1600 North Chestnut Avenue, Zip 54449–1499; tel. 715/384–2188, (Total facility includes 28 beds in nursing home–type unit) **A**10 **F**3 4 30 69 75 98 99 100 101 102 103 104 106 128 130 143 146 148 154
Primary Contact: Jordan Bruce, Administrator
CFO: Jo Timmerman, Manager Accounting
CHR: Larry Shear, Administrative Assistant
Web address: www.co.wood.wi.us/norwood/index.htm
Control: County, Government, nonfederal **Service**: Psychiatric

Staffed Beds: 44 **Admissions**: 460 **Census**: 31 **Outpatient Visits**: 0 **Births**: 0 **Total Expense ($000)**: 4023 **Payroll Expense ($000)**: 1950 **Personnel**: 37

MAUSTON—Juneau County

□ **MILE BLUFF MEDICAL CENTER (520109)**, 1050 Division Street, Zip 53948–1997; tel. 608/847–6161, (Total facility includes 97 beds in nursing home–type unit) **A**1 5 10 20 **F**10 11 13 15 28 29 34 36 40 43 54 56 60 64 69 75 76 77 78 80 81 82 86 87 89 93 107 108 111 118 119 125 128 130 131 144
Primary Contact: James M. O'Keefe, President and Chief Executive Officer
CFO: Francis James Fish, Vice President and Chief Financial Officer
CMO: Tim Bjelland Esq Physician
CHR: Sue Wafle, Director, Human Resources
CNO: Jean Surguy, Vice President, Chief Nursing Officer
Web address: www.milebluff.com
Control: Other not–for–profit (including NFP Corporation) **Service**: General medical and surgical

Staffed Beds: 111 **Admissions**: 1053 **Census**: 110 **Outpatient Visits**: 177290 **Births**: 140 **Total Expense ($000)**: 84883 **Payroll Expense ($000)**: 41472 **Personnel**: 444

MEDFORD—Taylor County

☒ **ASPIRUS MEDFORD HOSPITAL & CLINICS, INC. (521324)**, 135 South Gibson Street, Zip 54451; tel. 715/748–8100, (Total facility includes 78 beds in nursing home–type unit) **A**1 10 18 **F**3 8 10 11 13 15 28 29 31 34 35 36 40 41 43 45 50 53 55 56 57 58 59 60 64 65 68 71 75 76 77 78 81 82 85 86 87 89 90 93 97 107 110 111 115 116 117 118 119 125 127 128 129 130 131 132 133 135 144 146 147 148 149 156 **S** Aspirus, Inc., Wausau, WI
Primary Contact: Dale Hustedt, Chief Executive Officer
CFO: Greg Shaw, Vice President, Finance
CMO: Erik Branstetter, M.D., Chief Medical Officer
CIO: Todd Richardson, Chief Information Officer
CHR: Angela C. Hupf, Vice President Human Resources and Community Relations
CNO: Barb Lato, Chief Nursing Officer
Web address: www.aspirus.org
Control: Other not–for–profit (including NFP Corporation) **Service**: General medical and surgical

Staffed Beds: 93 **Admissions**: 838 **Census**: 64 **Outpatient Visits**: 84595 **Births**: 262 **Total Expense ($000)**: 66441 **Payroll Expense ($000)**: 26153 **Personnel**: 334

WI

Hospital, Medicare Provider Number, Address, Telephone, Approval, Facility, and Physician Codes, Health Care System

★ American Hospital Association (AHA) membership
□ The Joint Commission accreditation
○ Healthcare Facilities Accreditation Program
◇ DNV Healthcare Inc. accreditation
⇑ Center for Improvement in Healthcare Quality Accreditation
△ Commission on Accreditation of Rehabilitation Facilities (CARF) accreditation

MENOMONIE—Dunn County

☐ **MAYO CLINIC HEALTH SYSTEM - RED CEDAR IN MENOMONIE (521340)**, 2321 Stout Road, Zip 54751–2397; tel. 715/235–5531, **A**1 5 10 18 **F**3 13 15 17 18 28 29 30 31 32 34 35 38 40 43 44 45 53 54 55 56 57 59 64 65 70 74 76 77 78 79 80 81 82 84 85 86 87 89 90 93 94 96 97 99 100 101 102 103 104 107 108 110 111 115 119 129 130 131 132 133 144 145 146 147 148 149 154 156 **S** Mayo Clinic, Rochester, MN
Primary Contact: Steven Lindberg, Chief Administrative Officer
CFO: Jeanie Lubinsky, Chief Financial Officer
CMO: Mark Deyo Svendsen, M.D., Medical Director
CIO: Frank Wrogg, Director Information Technology
CHR: Leann Wurtzel, Director Human Resources
Web address: www.rcmc-mhs.org
Control: Other not–for–profit (including NFP Corporation) **Service**: General medical and surgical

Staffed Beds: 25 **Admissions:** 1059 **Census:** 10 **Outpatient Visits:** 107357 **Births:** 260 **Total Expense ($000):** 82942 **Payroll Expense ($000):** 38037 **Personnel:** 370

RED CEDAR MEDICAL CENTER-MAYO HEALTH SYSTEM See Mayo Clinic Health System - Red Cedar In Menomonie

MENOMONEE FALLS—Waukesha County

☒ △ **COMMUNITY MEMORIAL HOSPITAL (520103)**, W180 N8085 Town Hall Road, Zip 53051–3518, Mailing Address: P.O. Box 408, Zip 53052–0408; tel. 262/251–1000, **A**1 2 3 5 7 10 **F**3 4 5 9 11 13 15 17 20 22 24 26 28 29 30 31 34 35 37 38 40 43 44 45 46 47 49 50 51 54 56 57 59 60 62 64 65 66 68 70 72 74 75 76 77 78 79 80 81 83 84 85 86 89 90 93 97 98 100 101 102 103 104 107 108 110 111 114 115 116 117 118 119 120 121 123 126 129 130 131 132 135 143 145 146 147 148 149 150 156 **S** Froedtert Health, Milwaukee, WI
Primary Contact: Teresa M. Lux, President and Chief Operating Officer
COO: Allen Ericson, Chief Operating Officer, Community Hospital Division and President, St. Joseph's Hospital
CFO: Scott Hawig, Senior Vice President of Finance, Chief Financial Officer and Treasurer
CMO: David Goldberg, M.D., Vice President Medical Affairs and Chief Medical Officer
CHR: Keith Allen, Senior Vice President and Chief Human Resources Officer
Web address: www.communitymemorial.com
Control: Other not–for–profit (including NFP Corporation) **Service**: General medical and surgical

Staffed Beds: 202 **Admissions:** 8932 **Census:** 99 **Outpatient Visits:** 108469 **Births:** 774 **Total Expense ($000):** 259327 **Payroll Expense ($000):** 83917 **Personnel:** 1200

MEQUON—Ozaukee County

☒ **ASCENSION COLUMBIA ST. MARY'S HOSPITAL OZAUKEE (520027)**, 13111 North Port Washington Road, Zip 53097–2416; tel. 262/243–7300, **A**1 2 10 **F**3 4 5 9 15 17 18 20 22 24 26 28 29 30 31 34 35 36 38 40 43 45 46 48 49 50 51 53 54 56 57 58 59 64 66 68 70 74 77 78 79 80 81 84 85 86 89 91 93 94 96 97 98 100 102 103 105 107 108 110 111 114 116 118 119 120 121 123 126 130 132 135 144 145 146 147 148 149 153 156 **S** Ascension Healthcare, Saint Louis, MO
Primary Contact: Kelly Elkins, President and Chief Executive Officer
CFO: Rhonda Anderson, Executive Vice President Finance and Chief Financial Officer
CMO: David Shapiro, M.D., Vice President Medical Affairs and Chief Medical Officer
CIO: Mary Paul, Chief Information Officer
CHR: Cheryl Hill, Vice President Human Resources
Web address: www.columbia-stmarys.org
Control: Church operated, Nongovernment, not–for–profit **Service**: General medical and surgical

Staffed Beds: 112 **Admissions:** 4647 **Census:** 61 **Outpatient Visits:** 259580 **Births:** 0 **Total Expense ($000):** 189184 **Payroll Expense ($000):** 53817 **Personnel:** 667

MERRILL—Lincoln County

☒ **ASCENSION GOOD SAMARITAN HOSPITAL (521339)**, 601 South Center Avenue, Zip 54452–3404; tel. 715/536–5511, **A**1 10 18 **F**3 11 15 28 29 30 31 34 35 40 43 45 50 57 64 65 75 80 81 82 86 87 89 93 97 107 108 110 111 115 119 130 133 144 146 147 149 154 **S** Ascension Healthcare, Saint Louis, MO
Primary Contact: Jeremy Normington-Slay, FACHE, Chief Executive Officer
CFO: David Jirovec, Director Finance
CHR: Nancy Kwiesielewicz, Human Resources Manager
CNO: Kristine McGarigle, R.N., Vice President Patient Care
Web address: www.ministryhealth.org
Control: Church operated, Nongovernment, not–for–profit **Service**: General medical and surgical

Staffed Beds: 10 **Admissions:** 481 **Census:** 3 **Outpatient Visits:** 19510 **Births:** 0 **Total Expense ($000):** 18136 **Payroll Expense ($000):** 6565 **Personnel:** 70

GOOD SAMARITAN HEALTH CENTER OF MERRILL See Ascension Good Samaritan Hospital

MILWAUKEE—Milwaukee County

☒ **ASCENSION COLUMBIA ST. MARY'S HOSPITAL MILWAUKEE (520051)**, 2301 North Lake Drive, Zip 53211–4508; tel. 414/291–1000, (Includes COLUMBIA ST. MARY'S COLUMBIA HOSPITAL, 2025 East Newport Avenue, Milwaukee, Wisconsin, Zip 53211–2990; tel. 414/961–3300; COLUMBIA ST. MARY'S MILWAUKEE HOSPITAL, 2323 North Lake Drive, Milwaukee, Wisconsin, Zip 53211–9682, Mailing Address: P O Box 503, Zip 53201–0503, tel. 414/291–1000) **A**1 2 3 5 10 19 **F**3 4 9 12 13 15 16 17 18 20 22 24 26 28 29 30 31 33 34 35 36 38 40 43 45 46 47 48 49 50 51 53 54 56 57 58 59 64 66 68 70 72 74 76 77 78 79 80 81 84 85 86 87 89 91 92 93 94 96 97 98 100 102 103 104 105 107 108 110 111 114 115 116 117 118 119 120 121 123 126 130 132 135 144 145 146 147 148 149 152 153 156 **S** Ascension Healthcare, Saint Louis, MO
Primary Contact: Travis Andersen, Chief Executive Officer
CFO: Rhonda Anderson, Executive Vice President Finance and Chief Financial Officer
CMO: David Shapiro, M.D., Vice President Medical Affairs and Chief Medical Officer
CIO: Mary Paul, Chief Information Officer
CHR: Cheryl Hill, Vice President Human Resources
Web address: www.columbia-stmarys.org
Control: Church operated, Nongovernment, not–for–profit **Service**: General medical and surgical

Staffed Beds: 288 **Admissions:** 11922 **Census:** 175 **Outpatient Visits:** 627368 **Births:** 2750 **Total Expense ($000):** 483854 **Payroll Expense ($000):** 198584 **Personnel:** 1999

☒ **ASCENSION COLUMBIA ST. MARY'S MILWAUKEE HOSPITAL (523025)**, 2323 North Lake Drive, Zip 53211–4508, Mailing Address: 2301 North Lake Drive, Zip 53211–4508; tel. 414/585–1000, **A**1 10 **F**9 29 30 56 64 77 86 90 93 100 102 103 130 131 132 **S** Ascension Healthcare, Saint Louis, MO
Primary Contact: Kelly Elkins, President and Chief Executive Officer
CFO: Rhonda Anderson, Executive Vice President Finance and Chief Financial Officer
CMO: David Shapiro, M.D., Vice President Medical Affairs and Chief Medical Officer
CIO: Mary Paul, Vice President and Chief Information Officer
CHR: Cheryl Hill, Vice President Human Resources
Web address: www.columbia-stmarys.org/SHRI
Control: Church operated, Nongovernment, not–for–profit **Service**: Rehabilitation

Staffed Beds: 31 **Admissions:** 277 **Census:** 13 **Outpatient Visits:** 9576 **Births:** 0 **Total Expense ($000):** 13424 **Payroll Expense ($000):** 5078 **Personnel:** 53

☒ **ASCENSION SOUTHEAST WISCONSIN HOSPITAL - ST. FRANCIS CAMPUS (520078)**, 3237 South 16th Street, Zip 53215; tel. 414/647–5000, **A**1 2 10 **F**3 4 5 11 13 15 17 18 20 22 24 26 28 30 31 34 35 38 40 44 45 46 47 49 50 54 56 57 64 68 70 74 76 77 78 79 80 81 82 84 85 86 87 92 93 98 100 101 102 103 104 105 107 108 110 111 114 115 120 121 129 130 131 135 145 146 147 148 149 152 153 **S** Ascension Healthcare, Saint Louis, MO
Primary Contact: Seth R. Teigen, President
CFO: Aaron Bridgeland, Director Finance
CMO: Michelle Graham, M.D., Vice President Medical Affairs
CIO: Gregory Smith, Senior Vice President and Chief Information Officer
Web address: www.mywheaton.org/stfrancis
Control: Church operated, Nongovernment, not–for–profit **Service**: General medical and surgical

Staffed Beds: 152 **Admissions:** 6145 **Census:** 88 **Outpatient Visits:** 162133 **Births:** 599 **Total Expense ($000):** 170182 **Payroll Expense ($000):** 50926 **Personnel:** 705

☒ **ASCENSION SOUTHEAST WISCONSIN HOSPITAL - ST. JOSEPH'S CAMPUS (520136)**, 5000 West Chambers Street, Zip 53210–1650; tel. 414/447–2000, **A**1 3 5 10 **F**3 4 6 11 13 15 17 18 20 22 28 29 30 31 34 35 40 43 44 45 46 49 50 53 54 56 57 59 64 65 68 70 72 74 76 77 78 79 80 81 82 84 85 86 87 89 91 92 93 94 96 97 100 104 107 108 110 111 114 115 117 118 119 128 129 130 131 132 135 144 146 147 148 149 150 153 154 156 **S** Ascension Healthcare, Saint Louis, MO
Primary Contact: Kevin Kluesner, Chief Administrative Officer
CFO: Michael Petitt, Director of Finance
CMO: Rita Hanson, M.D., Vice President Medical Affairs
CIO: Andrew Donovan, Regional Director Information Services
CHR: Christopher Morris, Senior Director, Human Resources
Web address: www.mywheaton.org/stjoseph
Control: Church operated, Nongovernment, not–for–profit **Service**: General medical and surgical

Staffed Beds: 370 **Admissions:** 6734 **Census:** 92 **Outpatient Visits:** 268126 **Births:** 2071 **Total Expense ($000):** 206623 **Payroll Expense ($000):** 63823 **Personnel:** 795

WI

Many Facility Codes have changed. Please refer to the AHA Guide Code Chart. © 2019 AHA Guide

★ △ **AURORA SINAI MEDICAL CENTER (520064)**, 945 North 12th Street, Zip 53233–1337, Mailing Address: P.O. Box 342, Zip 53201–0342; tel. 414/219–2000, **A**2 3 5 7 8 **F**3 6 11 12 13 15 18 26 29 30 31 32 34 35 36 37 38 40 43 44 45 46 49 50 51 54 56 57 59 60 65 68 72 74 75 76 77 78 79 80 81 84 85 86 87 90 91 92 93 94 96 102 107 108 110 111 114 119 120 121 123 126 129 130 131 132 135 146 147 148 149 150 154 **S** Advocate Aurora Health, Downers Grove, IL
Primary Contact: Jessica Bauer, President
CHR: Heidi Grow, Director Human Resources
CNO: Ania Horner, R.N., MSN, Vice President and Chief Nurse Executive
Web address: www.aurorahealthcare.org
Control: Other not–for–profit (including NFP Corporation) **Service:** General medical and surgical

Staffed Beds: 202 **Admissions:** 8148 **Census:** 110 **Outpatient Visits:** 239823 **Births:** 2505 **Total Expense ($000):** 194918 **Payroll Expense ($000):** 70068 **Personnel:** 1703

⊠ △ **AURORA ST. LUKE'S MEDICAL CENTER (520138)**, 2900 West Oklahoma Avenue, Zip 53215–4330, Mailing Address: P.O. Box 2901, Zip 53201–2901; tel. 414/649–6000, (Includes AURORA ST. LUKE'S SOUTH SHORE, 5900 South Lake Drive, Cudahy, Wisconsin, Zip 53110–8903; tel. 414/769–9000) **A**1 2 3 5 7 8 10 19 **F**1 3 4 5 11 12 15 17 18 19 20 22 24 26 28 29 30 31 34 35 36 37 38 40 41 43 44 45 46 47 48 49 50 51 54 56 57 58 59 60 64 65 66 68 70 74 75 78 79 80 81 82 84 85 86 87 89 90 91 92 93 94 95 96 98 100 101 102 103 104 105 107 108 109 110 111 112 115 116 117 118 119 120 121 123 124 126 129 130 132 134 135 136 137 138 139 140 142 145 146 148 149 153 154 **S** Advocate Aurora Health, Downers Grove, IL
Primary Contact: Marie Golanowski, R.N., MS, President
CFO: Nan Nelson, Senior Vice President Finance
CMO: Jeffrey A. Smith, M.D., Senior Vice President and Chief Medical Officer
CIO: Philip Loftus, Ph.D., Vice President and Chief Information Officer
CHR: Thomas C Ter Horst, Vice President Human Resources
CNO: Faye Zwieg, R.N., Vice President and Chief Nursing Officer
Web address: www.aurorahealthcare.org
Control: Other not–for–profit (including NFP Corporation) **Service:** General medical and surgical

Staffed Beds: 711 **Admissions:** 32598 **Census:** 547 **Outpatient Visits:** 617494 **Births:** 0 **Total Expense ($000):** 1155134 **Payroll Expense ($000):** 338634 **Personnel:** 6723

⊠ **CHILDREN'S HOSPITAL OF WISCONSIN (523300)**, 9000 West Wisconsin Avenue, Zip 53226–4810, Mailing Address: P.O. Box 1997, Zip 53201–1997; tel. 414/266–2000, **A**1 3 5 10 **F**12 20 22 24 28 29 34 36 38 40 43 51 54 60 61 64 72 75 77 78 81 82 86 87 88 89 93 99 100 104 107 108 111 116 118 119 130 131 136 137 138 140 141 **S** Children's Hospital and Health System, Milwaukee, WI
Primary Contact: Peggy N. Troy, President and Chief Executive Officer
CFO: Marc Cadieux, Corporate Vice President and Chief Financial Officer
CMO: Michael Gutzeit, M.D., Chief Medical Officer
CIO: Michael B Nauman, Chief Information Officer
CHR: Thomas Shanahan, Vice President, Human Resources
CNO: Nancy K Korom, Chief Nursing Officer and Vice President
Web address: www.chw.org
Control: Other not–for–profit (including NFP Corporation) **Service:** Children's general medical and surgical

Staffed Beds: 184 **Admissions:** 8943 **Census:** 184 **Outpatient Visits:** 404287 **Births:** 0 **Total Expense ($000):** 613476 **Payroll Expense ($000):** 188488 **Personnel:** 2616

⊠ △ **CLEMENT J. ZABLOCKI VETERANS AFFAIRS MEDICAL CENTER**, 5000 West National Avenue, Zip 53295–0001; tel. 414/384–2000, (Nonreporting) **A**1 2 3 5 7 **S** Department of Veterans Affairs, Washington, DC
Primary Contact: Daniel Zomchek, Ph.D., Chief Executive Officer and Medical Center Director
COO: James McClain, Deputy Director
CFO: John Lasota, Assistant Finance Officer
CMO: Michael Erdmann, M.D., Chief of Staff
CIO: Bryan Vail, Chief Information Officer
CHR: Kay Schwieger, Chief Human Resources Officer
CNO: Mary E. Brunn, R.N., Acting Associate Director Nursing
Web address: www.milwaukee.va.gov/
Control: Veterans Affairs, Government, federal **Service:** General medical and surgical

Staffed Beds: 637

⊠ △ **FROEDTERT AND THE MEDICAL COLLEGE OF WISCONSIN FROEDTERT HOSPITAL (520177)**, 9200 West Wisconsin Avenue, Zip 53226–3596, Mailing Address: P.O. Box 26099, Zip 53226–0099; tel. 414/805–3000, **A**1 2 3 5 7 8 10 19 **F**3 6 8 9 12 13 15 17 18 20 22 24 26 29 30 31 34 35 37 38 40 43 44 45 46 47 48 49 50 51 52 54 55 56 57 58 59 60 61 64 65 66 68 70 74 75 76 77 78 79 80 81 84 85 86 87 90 91 92 93 94 95 96 97 100 107 108 110 111 112 113 114 115 116 117 118 119 120 121 123 124 126 129 130 131 132 135 136 137 138 139 140 141 142 143 145 146 147 148 149 150 154 **S** Froedtert Health, Milwaukee, WI
Primary Contact: Catherine Buck, MSN, R.N., President
CFO: Scott Hawig, Senior Vice President Finance, Chief Financial Officer and Treasurer
CMO: Lee Biblo, M.D., Chief Medical Officer
CHR: Keith Allen, Senior Vice President and Chief Human Resources Officer
CNO: Kathleen Bechtel, MSN, R.N., Vice President Patient Care Services and Chief Nursing Officer
Web address: www.froedtert.com
Control: Other not–for–profit (including NFP Corporation) **Service:** General medical and surgical

Staffed Beds: 604 **Admissions:** 29357 **Census:** 481 **Outpatient Visits:** 855881 **Births:** 3023 **Total Expense ($000):** 1503228 **Payroll Expense ($000):** 368394 **Personnel:** 5720

★ **MILWAUKEE COUNTY BEHAVIORAL HEALTH DIVISION (524001)**, 9455 Watertown Plank Road, Zip 53226–3559; tel. 414/257–6995, **A**3 5 10 **F**35 44 98 99 100 101 102 104 106 134 146 149 153 157
Primary Contact: Michael Lappen, Chief Executive Officer
COO: Jennifer Bergersen, Interim Chief Operating Officer
CFO: Randy Oleszak, Director Fiscal Services
CMO: John Schneider, M.D., Medical Director
CIO: Chris Lindberg, Chief Information Officer
CHR: Ara Garcia, Manager Human Resources
CNO: Nancy Ann Marigomen, R.N., Director of Nursing
Web address: www.milwaukeecounty.org
Control: County, Government, nonfederal **Service:** Psychiatric

Staffed Beds: 50 **Admissions:** 1414 **Census:** 49 **Outpatient Visits:** 7751 **Births:** 0 **Total Expense ($000):** 205117 **Payroll Expense ($000):** 31345 **Personnel:** 462

⊠ **SELECT SPECIALTY HOSPITAL-MILWAUKEE (522006)**, 8901 West Lincoln Avenue, 2nd Floor, Zip 53227–2409, Mailing Address: West Allis, tel. 414/328–7700, **A**1 10 **F**1 29 60 78 100 130 **S** Select Medical Corporation, Mechanicsburg, PA
Primary Contact: Dennis Mattes, Chief Executive Officer
CMO: Matt Mathai, M.D., Medical Director
CHR: Chris Froh, Senior Coordinator Human Resources
CNO: Jane Cerra, Market Nurse Executive and Chief Nursing Officer
Web address: www.selectspecialtyhospitals.com/company/locations/milwaukee.aspx
Control: Corporation, Investor–owned (for–profit) **Service:** Acute long–term care hospital

Staffed Beds: 63 **Admissions:** 502 **Census:** 46 **Outpatient Visits:** 0 **Births:** 0 **Total Expense ($000):** 27980 **Payroll Expense ($000):** 10315 **Personnel:** 151

MONROE—Green County

⊠ **MONROE CLINIC (520028)**, 515 22nd Avenue, Zip 53566–1598; tel. 608/324–2000, **A**1 3 10 13 **F**6 9 13 15 17 28 29 34 38 40 43 55 56 62 63 70 75 76 77 80 81 82 86 89 90 93 99 100 101 102 103 104 107 108 111 119 130 131 144 147 154 **S** SSM Health, Saint Louis, MO
Primary Contact: Michael B. Sanders, President and Chief Executive Officer
CFO: Jim Nemeth, Chief Financial Officer
CIO: Carrie Blum, Chief Information Officer
CHR: Jane Monahan, Vice President Ministry, Spiritual Care and Human Resources
CNO: Paula Elmer, R.N., MSN, Vice President and Chief Nursing Officer
Web address: www.monroeclinic.org
Control: Other not–for–profit (including NFP Corporation) **Service:** General medical and surgical

Staffed Beds: 58 **Admissions:** 2688 **Census:** 24 **Outpatient Visits:** 274583 **Births:** 517 **Total Expense ($000):** 173102 **Payroll Expense ($000):** 85670 **Personnel:** 1049

WI

Hospital, Medicare Provider Number, Address, Telephone, Approval, Facility, and Physician Codes, Health Care System

★ American Hospital Association (AHA) membership
□ The Joint Commission accreditation
○ Healthcare Facilities Accreditation Program
◇ DNV Healthcare Inc. accreditation
⇈ Center for Improvement in Healthcare Quality Accreditation
△ Commission on Accreditation of Rehabilitation Facilities (CARF) accreditation

MONROE—Rock County

✠ **SSM HEALTH ST. MARY'S HOSPITAL JANESVILLE (520208)**, 515 22nd Ave, Zip 53566, Mailing Address: 3400 East Racine Steeet, Janesville, Zip 53546–2344; tel. 608/373–8000, **A**1 10 **F**13 28 29 34 38 40 43 64 70 75 76 80 81 86 87 89 90 107 108 111 119 130 154 **S** SSM Health, Saint Louis, MO
Primary Contact: Benjamin Layman, President
Web address: www.stmarysjanesville.com
Control: Church operated, Nongovernment, not–for–profit **Service**: General medical and surgical

Staffed Beds: 50 **Admissions**: 2768 **Census**: 24 **Outpatient Visits**: 33179 **Births**: 494 **Total Expense ($000)**: 58618 **Payroll Expense ($000)**: 19297 **Personnel**: 298

NEENAH—Winnebago County

☐ **CHILDREN'S HOSPITAL OF WISCONSIN-FOX VALLEY (523302)**, 130 Second Street, Zip 54956–2883; tel. 920/969–7900, **A**1 10 **F**34 64 72 75 86 89 93 130 154 **S** Children's Hospital and Health System, Milwaukee, WI
Primary Contact: Peggy N. Troy, President and Chief Executive Officer
COO: Debra Franckowiak, Executive Director
CFO: Marc Cadieux, Corporate Vice President and Chief Financial Officer
CMO: Paul Myers, M.D., Neonatologist and Chief Medical Officer
CIO: Michael B Nauman, Chief Information Officer and Corporate Vice President
CHR: Thomas Shanahan, Vice President, Human Resources
CNO: Nancy K Korom, Chief Nursing Officer and Vice President
Web address: www.chw.org
Control: Other not–for–profit (including NFP Corporation) **Service**: Children's general medical and surgical

Staffed Beds: 19 **Admissions**: 619 **Census**: 19 **Outpatient Visits**: 15418 **Births**: 0 **Total Expense ($000)**: 31752 **Payroll Expense ($000)**: 12629 **Personnel**: 140

☐ **THEDACARE REGIONAL MEDICAL CENTER-NEENAH (520045)**, 130 Second Street, Zip 54956–2883, Mailing Address: P.O. Box 2021, Zip 54957–2021; tel. 920/729–3100, **A**1 2 3 10 **F**4 5 9 12 13 15 17 28 29 34 40 43 51 64 70 75 76 78 80 81 82 86 88 90 98 101 107 108 111 118 119 130 **S** ThedaCare, Inc., Appleton, WI
Primary Contact: Mark Thompson, System Chief Financial Officer
CFO: Tim Olson, Senior Vice President Finance
CMO: Gregory L Long, M.D., Chief Medical Officer
CIO: Keith Livingston, Senior Vice President and Chief Information Officer
Web address: www.thedacare.org
Control: Other not–for–profit (including NFP Corporation) **Service**: General medical and surgical

Staffed Beds: 164 **Admissions**: 8179 **Census**: 90 **Outpatient Visits**: 121424 **Births**: 1453 **Total Expense ($000)**: 173283 **Payroll Expense ($000)**: 65730 **Personnel**: 842

NEILLSVILLE—Clark County

★ **MARSHFIELD MEDICAL CENTER - NEILLSVILLE (521323)**, 216 Sunset Place, Zip 54456–1799; tel. 715/743–3101, **A**10 18 **F**3 10 11 15 28 29 30 40 41 43 45 56 64 75 77 79 80 81 82 85 86 89 93 97 107 111 115 119 127 130 131 132 133 144 146 147 148 154 **S** Marshfield Clinic Health System, Marshfield, WI
Primary Contact: Ryan T. Neville, FACHE, President and Chief Executive Officer
CMO: Timothy Meyer, M.D., Chief of Staff
CIO: Derrick Longdo, Director Information Systems
CHR: Tamie Zarak, Director Human Resources
Web address: www.memorialmedcenter.org
Control: Other not–for–profit (including NFP Corporation) **Service**: General medical and surgical

Staffed Beds: 16 **Admissions**: 325 **Census**: 14 **Outpatient Visits**: 20632 **Births**: 0 **Total Expense ($000)**: 25332 **Payroll Expense ($000)**: 11959 **Personnel**: 167

NEW LONDON—Outagamie County

☐ **THEDACARE MEDICAL CENTER-NEW LONDON (521326)**, 1405 Mill Street, Zip 54961–0307, Mailing Address: P.O. Box 307, Zip 54961–0307; tel. 920/531–2000, **A**1 10 18 **F**7 11 13 15 28 29 34 40 43 56 64 75 76 80 81 82 86 87 89 90 93 107 108 111 119 131 141 **S** ThedaCare, Inc., Appleton, WI
Primary Contact: William Schmidt, President and Chief Executive Officer
CFO: Betty Gehring, Finance Director, Operations
CMO: Paul Hoell, M.D., President Medical Staff
CNO: Peggy School, Director of Nursing
Web address: www.thedacare.org
Control: Other not–for–profit (including NFP Corporation) **Service**: General medical and surgical

Staffed Beds: 25 **Admissions**: 736 **Census**: 8 **Outpatient Visits**: 41785 **Births**: 92 **Total Expense ($000)**: 23838 **Payroll Expense ($000)**: 10283 **Personnel**: 116

NEW RICHMOND—St. Croix County

✠ **WESTFIELDS HOSPITAL AND CLINIC (521345)**, 535 Hospital Road, Zip 54017–1449; tel. 715/243–2600, **A**1 3 10 18 **F**1 3 13 15 18 28 29 30 31 32 34 35 37 38 40 43 44 45 47 50 56 57 59 64 65 68 70 75 76 77 78 80 81 82 86 87 89 90 93 94 97 104 105 107 110 111 115 119 129 130 131 132 133 144 145 146 148 149 152 153 154 156 157 **S** HealthPartners, Bloomington, MN
Primary Contact: Steven Massey, President and Chief Executive Officer
CFO: Jason J. Luhrs, Vice President Fiscal Services
CMO: David O DeGear, M.D., Vice President Medical Affairs
CIO: Patrice P Wolff, Director Information Services
CHR: Chad P Engstrom, Director Human Resources
Web address: www.westfieldshospital.com
Control: Other not–for–profit (including NFP Corporation) **Service**: General medical and surgical

Staffed Beds: 25 **Admissions**: 919 **Census**: 7 **Outpatient Visits**: 92705 **Births**: 109 **Total Expense ($000)**: 61469 **Payroll Expense ($000)**: 20204 **Personnel**: 324

OCONOMOWOC—Waukesha County

✠ **OCONOMOWOC MEMORIAL HOSPITAL (520062)**, 791 Summit Avenue, Zip 53066–3896; tel. 262/569–9400, **A**1 2 10 **F**3 11 13 15 18 20 22 26 28 29 30 31 32 34 37 40 41 43 44 45 46 47 48 49 50 56 57 59 64 65 68 74 75 76 78 79 81 83 84 85 87 89 93 97 100 101 102 107 108 109 110 111 112 114 115 117 118 120 121 126 130 133 135 146 147 148 149 153 154 156 157 **S** ProHealth Care, Inc., Waukesha, WI
Primary Contact: Susan A. Edwards, President and Chief Executive Officer
COO: Mary Jo O'Malley, R.N., MS, Vice President Diagnostics and Support Services
CMO: Brian Lipman, M.D., Medical Director and Medical Staff Services
CIO: Christine Bessler, Vice President Information Services
CHR: Edward Malindzak, Chief Human Resources Officer
CNO: Catherine Rapp, R.N., MS, Vice President Nursing
Web address: www.prohealthcare.org/locations/locations-v2-detail/?id=1123
Control: Other not–for–profit (including NFP Corporation) **Service**: General medical and surgical

Staffed Beds: 58 **Admissions**: 2949 **Census**: 24 **Outpatient Visits**: 78486 **Births**: 280 **Total Expense ($000)**: 96293 **Payroll Expense ($000)**: 23523 **Personnel**: 305

✠ **ROGERS MEMORIAL HOSPITAL, INC. (524018)**, 34700 Valley Road, Zip 53066–4599; tel. 262/646–4411, (Includes ROGERS MEMORIAL HOSPITAL-BROWN DEER, 4600 West Schroeder Drive, Brown Deer, Wisconsin, Zip 53223; tel. 414/865–2500; Jim Kubicek, Vice President, Operations; ROGERS MEMORIAL HOSPITAL-WEST ALLIS, 11101 West Lincoln Avenue, West Allis, Wisconsin, Zip 53227; tel. 414/327–3000; T Orvin Fillman, Dr.PH, Vice President, Operations) **A**1 3 10 **F**4 5 29 34 38 53 54 75 86 87 98 99 100 101 102 103 104 130 154
Primary Contact: Paul A. Mueller, Chief Executive Officer, Hospital Division
CFO: Gerald A Noll, Chief Financial Officer
CMO: Peter M Lake, M.D., Chief Medical Officer
CIO: Wayne Mattson, Management Information Systems Specialist
CHR: Renee A. Patterson, Vice President Employment and Training Services
CNO: Teresa L Schultz, R.N., Vice President of Patient Care
Web address: www.rogershospital.org
Control: Other not–for–profit (including NFP Corporation) **Service**: Psychiatric

Staffed Beds: 202 **Admissions**: 9245 **Census**: 165 **Outpatient Visits**: 78474 **Births**: 0 **Total Expense ($000)**: 143020 **Payroll Expense ($000)**: 89061 **Personnel**: 1058

OCONTO—Oconto County

⇑ **BELLIN HEALTH OCONTO HOSPITAL (521356)**, 820 Arbutus Avenue, Zip 54153–2004, Mailing Address: P.O. Box 357, Zip 54153–0357; tel. 920/835–1100, **A**10 18 21 **F**15 29 40 43 51 62 64 78 80 81 82 90 99 100 101 107 111 119 130 144 154
Primary Contact: Laura Hieb, R.N., Chief Executive Officer
CHR: Troy L Koebke, Human Resource Director
Web address: www.bellin.org/facilities_amenities/oconto_hospital_medical_center/
Control: Other not–for–profit (including NFP Corporation) **Service**: General medical and surgical

Staffed Beds: 6 **Admissions**: 155 **Census**: 1 **Outpatient Visits**: 17952 **Births**: 1 **Total Expense ($000)**: 50523 **Payroll Expense ($000)**: 20424 **Personnel**: 176

WI

Many Facility Codes have changed. Please refer to the AHA Guide Code Chart. © 2019 AHA Guide

OCONTO FALLS—Oconto County

★ **HSHS ST. CLARE MEMORIAL HOSPITAL (521310)**, 855 South Main Street, Zip 54154–1296; tel. 920/846–3444, **A**10 18 **F**3 11 15 28 29 30 34 35 40 43 44 50 56 57 59 64 65 68 75 77 79 80 81 85 86 87 89 90 94 96 107 108 110 111 114 119 127 129 130 132 133 144 146 147 148 154 **S** HSHS Hospital Sisters Health System, Springfield, IL
Primary Contact: Christopher Brabant, President and Chief Executive Officer
CFO: Greg Simia, Chief Financial Officer
CMO: Ken Johnson, Chief Physician Executive
CIO: Shane Miller, Chief Information Officer
CHR: Christine Jensema, Chief Human Resources Officer
CNO: Paula Hafeman, Chief Nursing Officer
Web address: www.stclarememorial.org
Control: Church operated, Nongovernment, not–for–profit **Service:** General medical and surgical

Staffed Beds: 20 **Admissions:** 328 **Census:** 3 **Outpatient Visits:** 18261 **Births:** 0 **Total Expense ($000):** 29650 **Payroll Expense ($000):** 7746 **Personnel:** 110

OSCEOLA—Polk County

★ **OSCEOLA MEDICAL CENTER (521318)**, 2600 65th Avenue, Zip 54020–4370, Mailing Address: P.O. Box 218, Zip 54020–0218; tel. 715/294–2111, **A**10 18 **F**3 8 11 13 15 28 29 31 32 34 35 40 41 43 45 50 53 56 57 59 65 66 70 75 76 77 78 81 85 86 87 89 93 96 97 107 110 111 115 119 129 132 133 135 144 146 148 149 150 154
Primary Contact: Jeffrey K. Meyer, Interim Chief Executive Officer
CMO: Rene Milner, Chief Medical Officer
CIO: Shawn Kammerud, Manager Information Services
CHR: Margie Evenson, Manager Human Resources
Web address: www.osceolamedicalcenter.com
Control: Other not–for–profit (including NFP Corporation) **Service:** General medical and surgical

Staffed Beds: 18 **Admissions:** 454 **Census:** 4 **Outpatient Visits:** 17525 **Births:** 104 **Total Expense ($000):** 36108 **Payroll Expense ($000):** 12834 **Personnel:** 218

OSHKOSH—Winnebago County

★ △ **ASCENSION NORTHEAST WISCONSIN MERCY HOSPITAL (520048)**, 500 South Oakwood Road, Zip 54904–7944; tel. 920/223–2000, **A**2 7 10 **F**3 4 5 11 13 15 16 17 18 20 22 26 28 29 30 31 34 35 38 40 43 45 46 47 48 49 50 51 53 56 64 68 70 74 75 76 78 79 80 81 82 84 85 86 87 88 90 92 93 96 98 103 104 107 108 110 111 114 115 119 120 121 122 123 126 129 130 131 132 144 146 147 148 149 **S** Ascension Healthcare, Saint Louis, MO
Primary Contact: Denise Parrish, Interim Chief Administrative Officer
CFO: Jeff Badger, Chief Financial Officer
CMO: Mark W Kehrberg, M.D., Senior Vice President and Chief Medical Officer
CIO: Will Weider, Chief Information Officer
CHR: Vince Gallucci, Senior Vice President Human Resources
Web address: www.affinityhealth.org
Control: Church operated, Nongovernment, not–for–profit **Service:** General medical and surgical

Staffed Beds: 120 **Admissions:** 3942 **Census:** 39 **Outpatient Visits:** 125093 **Births:** 495 **Total Expense ($000):** 92509 **Payroll Expense ($000):** 24132 **Personnel:** 392

⊠ ○ **AURORA MEDICAL CENTER OF OSHKOSH (520198)**, 855 North Westhaven Drive, Zip 54904–7668; tel. 920/456–6000, **A**1 2 10 11 **F**3 8 11 12 13 15 17 18 20 22 26 29 30 34 37 40 43 47 49 53 54 56 60 64 68 70 71 74 75 76 78 79 80 81 82 85 86 87 92 93 94 107 108 109 110 111 114 115 117 118 119 120 121 123 129 130 131 145 146 147 148 149 154 **S** Advocate Aurora Health, Downers Grove, IL
Primary Contact: John B. Newman, President
CFO: Sandra Ewald, Vice President Finance
CMO: Bruce L Van Cleave, M.D., Senior Vice President and Chief Medical Officer
CIO: Philip Loftus, Ph.D., Vice President and Chief Information Officer
CHR: Linda Mingus, Director Human Resources
CNO: Mary Beth Kingston, Ph.D., R.N., MSN, Executive Vice President and Chief Nursing Officer
Web address: www.aurorahealthcare.com
Control: Other not–for–profit (including NFP Corporation) **Service:** General medical and surgical

Staffed Beds: 72 **Admissions:** 3317 **Census:** 29 **Outpatient Visits:** 153785 **Births:** 661 **Total Expense ($000):** 127641 **Payroll Expense ($000):** 36751 **Personnel:** 1005

OSSEO—Trempealeau County

☐ **MAYO CLINIC HEALTH SYSTEM - OAKRIDGE IN OSSEO (521302)**, 13025 Eighth Street, Zip 54758–7634, Mailing Address: P.O. Box 70, Zip 54758–0070; tel. 715/597–3121, **A**1 10 18 **F**3 15 18 28 29 30 32 34 35 38 40 43 44 45 53 54 56 57 59 64 65 77 79 80 84 85 86 87 90 93 96 97 107 110 115 129 130 132 133 144 146 148 149 154 156 **S** Mayo Clinic, Rochester, MN
Primary Contact: Dean Eide, Vice President
Web address: www.mayoclinichealthsystem.org/locations/osseo
Control: Other not–for–profit (including NFP Corporation) **Service:** General medical and surgical

Staffed Beds: 16 **Admissions:** 368 **Census:** 11 **Outpatient Visits:** 29123 **Births:** 0 **Total Expense ($000):** 22403 **Payroll Expense ($000):** 11235 **Personnel:** 133

PARK FALLS—Price County

★ **FLAMBEAU HOSPITAL (521325)**, 98 Sherry Avenue, Zip 54552–1467, Mailing Address: P.O. Box 310, Zip 54552–0310; tel. 715/762–2484, **A**10 18 **F**11 15 28 29 34 40 53 56 62 63 64 69 75 77 80 81 82 86 89 90 93 107 108 119 130 131 144 154 **S** Marshfield Clinic Health System, Marshfield, WI
Primary Contact: James R. Braun, Chief Administrative Officer and Chief Financial Officer
CMO: Yusuf Kasirye, M.D., Chief of Staff
CHR: Elizabeth Harrop, Director, Human Resources
CNO: Elizabeth Schreiber, R.N., Director Patient Care Services
Web address: www.flambeauhospital.org
Control: Other not–for–profit (including NFP Corporation) **Service:** General medical and surgical

Staffed Beds: 25 **Admissions:** 500 **Census:** 4 **Outpatient Visits:** 26522 **Births:** 0 **Total Expense ($000):** 22825 **Payroll Expense ($000):** 9304 **Personnel:** 172

PEWAUKEE—Waukesha County

⊠ **LIFECARE HOSPITALS OF WISCONSIN (522007)**, 2400 Golf Road, Zip 53072–5590; tel. 262/524–2600, **A**1 10 **F**1 29 34 77 86 93 107 130 **S** LifeCare Management Services, Plano, TX
Primary Contact: David Chaudier, Chief Executive Officer
CMO: John Daniels, M.D., Medical Director
CHR: Stephanie Matter, Manager Human Resources
CNO: Angela Osowski, Chief Nursing Officer
Web address: www.lifecare-hospitals.com
Control: Corporation, Investor–owned (for–profit) **Service:** Acute long–term care hospital

Staffed Beds: 30 **Admissions:** 405 **Census:** 29 **Outpatient Visits:** 0 **Births:** 0 **Total Expense ($000):** 16687 **Payroll Expense ($000):** 8656 **Personnel:** 128

PLATTEVILLE—Grant County

⊠ **SOUTHWEST HEALTH (521354)**, 1400 Eastside Road, Zip 53818–9800; tel. 608/348–2331, (Includes SOUTHWEST HEALTH CENTER NURSING HOME, 808 South Washington Street, Cuba City, Wisconsin, Zip 53807; tel. 608/744–2161) (Total facility includes 78 beds in nursing home–type unit) **A**1 10 18 **F**2 3 6 7 13 15 28 29 34 35 36 40 43 45 46 47 48 49 50 56 57 59 64 65 75 76 77 79 80 81 82 83 84 85 86 87 93 94 96 97 98 100 101 102 103 104 107 110 111 112 115 119 127 128 129 130 131 132 133 135 143 144 146 147 148 149 153 156
Primary Contact: Dan D. Rohrbach, President
CFO: Matthew Streeter, Chief Financial Officer
CMO: Andrew Klann, D.O., Chief of Staff
CIO: Todd Lull, Director Information Technology
CHR: Holly Beehn, Director Human Resources
CNO: Suzi Okey, Director of Nursing
Web address: www.southwesthealth.org
Control: Other not–for–profit (including NFP Corporation) **Service:** General medical and surgical

Staffed Beds: 113 **Admissions:** 1055 **Census:** 86 **Outpatient Visits:** 75317 **Births:** 185 **Total Expense ($000):** 55749 **Payroll Expense ($000):** 27467 **Personnel:** 481

WI

PORTAGE—Columbia County

☐ **DIVINE SAVIOR HEALTHCARE (520041)**, 2817 New Pinery Road, Zip 53901–9240, Mailing Address: P.O. Box 387, Zip 53901–0387; tel. 608/742–4131, (Total facility includes 123 beds in nursing home–type unit) **A**1 3 10 **F**4 7 11 12 13 15 28 34 36 40 43 54 55 60 62 64 69 70 75 76 77 78 80 81 82 86 87 90 93 107 108 111 118 119 128 130 131 144 147 154
Primary Contact: Michael Decker, President and Chief Executive Officer
CFO: Marlin Pete Nelson, Vice President Fiscal Services
CMO: Elizabeth Strabel, M.D., Chief Medical Staff
CHR: Carol J Bank, Vice President Human Resources
Web address: www.dshealthcare.com
Control: Church operated, Nongovernment, not–for–profit **Service**: General medical and surgical

Staffed Beds: 132 **Admissions**: 1934 **Census**: 109 **Outpatient Visits**: 156014 **Births**: 192 **Total Expense ($000)**: 81414 **Payroll Expense ($000)**: 44142 **Personnel**: 651

PRAIRIE DU CHIEN—Crawford County

★ **CROSSING RIVERS HEALTH MEDICAL CENTER (521330)**, 37868 US Highway 18, Zip 53821–8416; tel. 608/357–2000, **A**10 18 **F**11 13 15 28 29 31 34 35 36 40 41 50 53 56 57 59 63 64 65 68 75 76 77 79 81 82 83 84 86 87 93 97 107 110 111 115 117 119 126 129 130 131 132 133 135 144 146 147 148 154
Primary Contact: William P. Sexton, Chief Executive Officer
CFO: Dave Breitbach, Chief Financial Officer
CMO: Steven Bush, Chief Medical Officer
CIO: John Daane, Information Systems Officer
CHR: Samantha Donahue, Director Human Resources
Web address: www.crossingrivers.org
Control: Other not–for–profit (including NFP Corporation) **Service**: General medical and surgical

Staffed Beds: 25 **Admissions**: 893 **Census**: 10 **Outpatient Visits**: 8910 **Births**: 155 **Total Expense ($000)**: 52456 **Payroll Expense ($000)**: 20717 **Personnel**: 284

PRAIRIE DU SAC—Sauk County

○ **SAUK PRAIRIE HEALTHCARE (520095)**, 260 26th Street, Zip 53578–1599; tel. 608/643–3311, **A**3 10 11 **F**3 8 11 13 15 16 28 29 32 34 35 36 38 40 41 43 45 48 53 54 55 56 57 59 65 69 75 77 79 80 81 82 85 86 89 90 93 97 102 107 108 110 111 115 118 119 127 129 130 131 132 133 135 144 146 147 149 156
Primary Contact: Shawn Lerch, Chief Executive Officer
CFO: James Dregney, Vice President Finance and Operations, Chief Financial Officer
CMO: John McAuliffe, M.D., Medical Director
CIO: Richard C Bonjour, Chief Information Officer
CHR: Robbi E Bos, Vice President Human Resources
CNO: Denise Marie Cole-Ouzounian, MSN, R.N., Vice President Patient Services
Web address: www.saukprairiehealthcare.org/
Control: Other not–for–profit (including NFP Corporation) **Service**: General medical and surgical

Staffed Beds: 36 **Admissions**: 1909 **Census**: 11 **Outpatient Visits**: 118351 **Births**: 353 **Total Expense ($000)**: 89360 **Payroll Expense ($000)**: 42411 **Personnel**: 491

RACINE—Racine County

⊞ △ **ASCENSION ALL SAINTS (520096)**, 3801 Spring Street, Zip 53405–1690; tel. 262/687–4011, **A**1 2 7 10 19 **F**3 4 5 6 13 15 17 18 20 22 24 26 28 29 30 31 34 35 38 40 43 44 45 46 47 48 49 50 51 53 56 57 58 59 64 65 66 68 70 72 74 76 77 78 79 80 81 82 84 85 86 87 89 90 91 92 93 94 96 97 98 99 100 101 102 103 104 105 107 108 110 111 114 115 118 119 120 121 123 124 126 129 130 131 132 134 135 143 146 147 148 149 150 152 153 156 **S** Ascension Healthcare, Saint Louis, MO
Primary Contact: Kristin McManmon, President
CFO: Jeanne Gramza, Director Finance
CMO: Jerry Hardacre, M.D., Chief of Staff
CIO: Joanne Bisterfeldt, Chief Information Officer
CHR: Mary Jo Wodicka, Vice President Human Resources
Web address: www.allsaintshealth.com
Control: Church operated, Nongovernment, not–for–profit **Service**: General medical and surgical

Staffed Beds: 278 **Admissions**: 12271 **Census**: 158 **Outpatient Visits**: 571963 **Births**: 1561 **Total Expense ($000)**: 342393 **Payroll Expense ($000)**: 96351 **Personnel**: 1549

REEDSBURG—Sauk County

⊞ **REEDSBURG AREA MEDICAL CENTER (521351)**, 2000 North Dewey Street, Zip 53959–1097; tel. 608/524–6487, **A**1 5 10 18 **F**3 8 11 13 15 17 28 29 30 31 32 34 35 40 41 43 45 48 49 50 51 53 54 57 59 64 65 66 70 75 76 77 78 79 80 81 82 85 86 87 88 89 93 96 97 107 110 114 127 129 130 131 132 133 135 144 146 147 148 156
Primary Contact: Robert Van Meeteren, President and Chief Executive Officer
COO: Dale Turner, Chief Operating Officer
CFO: Barry Borchert, Vice President Finance
Web address: www.ramchealth.com
Control: Other not–for–profit (including NFP Corporation) **Service**: General medical and surgical

Staffed Beds: 25 **Admissions**: 904 **Census**: 7 **Outpatient Visits**: 95411 **Births**: 225 **Total Expense ($000)**: 71577 **Payroll Expense ($000)**: 31527 **Personnel**: 522

RHINELANDER—Oneida County

⊞ **ASCENSION ST. MARY'S HOSPITAL (520019)**, 2251 North Shore Drive, Zip 54501–6710; tel. 715/361–2000, (Includes ST. MARY'S HOSPITAL, 1044 Kabel Avenue, Rhinelander, Wisconsin, Zip 54501; tel. 715/369–6600) **A**1 3 5 10 20 **F**3 4 5 13 15 28 29 30 31 34 35 40 54 59 64 74 75 76 78 79 80 81 82 84 85 86 87 89 93 97 98 99 100 101 103 104 107 108 110 111 115 116 119 120 121 123 126 127 130 131 132 135 144 146 148 149 154 156 **S** Ascension Healthcare, Saint Louis, MO
Primary Contact: Sandra L. Anderson, President
COO: Laurie Oungst, Vice President and Chief Operating Officer
CFO: Jamon Lamers, Director Finance
CMO: Mark Banas, M.D., Chief Medical Officer
CIO: Howard Dobizl, Director Information Services for the Northern Region
CHR: Michelle Cornelius, Director Human Resources for the Northern Region
CNO: Christine Krebs, Director or Nursing
Web address: www.ministryhealth.org
Control: Church operated, Nongovernment, not–for–profit **Service**: General medical and surgical

Staffed Beds: 64 **Admissions**: 2712 **Census**: 29 **Outpatient Visits**: 107788 **Births**: 249 **Total Expense ($000)**: 135360 **Payroll Expense ($000)**: 43435 **Personnel**: 335

RICE LAKE—Barron County

⊞ **MARSHFIELD MEDICAL CENTER - RICE LAKE (520011)**, 1700 West Stout Street, Zip 54868–5000; tel. 715/234–1515, **A**1 10 20 **F**3 7 8 11 13 15 18 26 28 29 31 32 34 35 40 43 45 51 53 56 57 59 60 62 63 64 65 70 75 76 77 78 79 80 81 84 85 86 89 93 97 107 109 111 112 119 124 129 130 132 135 146 147 156 **S** Marshfield Clinic Health System, Marshfield, WI
Primary Contact: Bradley D. Groseth, Chief Administrative Officer
COO: Cindy Arts-Strenke, R.N., Chief Operating Officer and Chief Nursing Officer
CFO: Jacqueline Klein, Chief Financial Officer
CMO: John L. Olson, M.D., Medical Director
CIO: Brad Gerrits, Director Information Systems
CHR: Kathy Mitchell, Director Human Resources
Web address: www.lakeviewmedical.com
Control: Other not–for–profit (including NFP Corporation) **Service**: General medical and surgical

Staffed Beds: 40 **Admissions**: 2108 **Census**: 16 **Outpatient Visits**: 101230 **Births**: 458 **Total Expense ($000)**: 66293 **Payroll Expense ($000)**: 22820

RICHLAND CENTER—Richland County

⊞ **RICHLAND HOSPITAL (521341)**, 333 East Second Street, Zip 53581–1914; tel. 608/647–6321, **A**1 5 10 18 **F**3 12 13 15 28 31 34 35 37 40 43 49 50 56 57 59 64 65 68 70 75 76 78 79 80 81 85 86 89 92 93 97 107 110 115 119 127 129 130 131 132 133 135 143 146 148 149 154
Primary Contact: Bruce E. Roesler, FACHE, Chief Executive Officer
CFO: Karen Traynor, Chief Financial Officer
CMO: David May, Chief of Staff
CIO: Jerry Cooper, Manager Data Processing
CHR: Rhonda Sutton, Director Human Resources
CNO: Cindy Hanold, Chief Nursing Officer
Web address: www.richlandhospital.com
Control: Other not–for–profit (including NFP Corporation) **Service**: General medical and surgical

Staffed Beds: 25 **Admissions**: 1088 **Census**: 11 **Outpatient Visits**: 53761 **Births**: 141 **Total Expense ($000)**: 40291 **Payroll Expense ($000)**: 17545 **Personnel**: 253

WI

RIPON—Fond Du Lac County

✠ **RIPON MEDICAL CENTER (521321)**, 845 Parkside Street, Zip 54971–8505, Mailing Address: P.O. Box 390, Zip 54971–0390; tel. 920/748–3101, **A**1 5 10 18 **F**3 11 15 17 18 28 29 30 31 32 34 35 40 43 44 45 50 51 53 57 59 66 68 69 70 75 77 79 80 81 82 85 86 87 88 89 93 96 97 107 108 109 110 111 114 118 119 130 131 132 133 134 135 143 144 146 147 148 149 150 154 156 **S** SSM Health, Saint Louis, MO
Primary Contact: DeAnn Thurmer, President and Chief Nursing Officer
CFO: Bonnie Schmitz, Chief Financial Officer
CMO: Derek Colmenares, M.D., Chief Medical Officer
CIO: Nancy Birschbach, Vice President and Chief Information Officer
CHR: Sue Edminster, Vice President Human Resources
CNO: DeAnn Thurmer, President and Chief Nursing Officer
Web address: www.agnesian.com
Control: Church operated, Nongovernment, not–for–profit **Service:** General medical and surgical

Staffed Beds: 16 **Admissions:** 556 **Census:** 5 **Outpatient Visits:** 31115 **Births:** 0 **Total Expense ($000):** 27659 **Payroll Expense ($000):** 11171 **Personnel:** 124

RIVER FALLS—St. Croix County

✠ **RIVER FALLS AREA HOSPITAL (521349)**, 1629 East Division Street, Zip 54022–1571; tel. 715/425–6155, **A**1 2 10 18 **F**3 11 13 15 28 29 30 31 34 35 40 43 44 50 51 53 64 75 76 78 79 80 81 82 84 86 87 89 90 93 97 107 111 117 119 129 130 131 133 135 146 147 148 149 154 **S** Allina Health, Minneapolis, MN
Primary Contact: Helen J. Strike, R.N., President
COO: William Frommelt, Director Operations and Finance
CFO: William Frommelt, Director Operations and Finance
CHR: Kristen Novak, Manager Human Resources
Web address: www.allina.com
Control: Other not–for–profit (including NFP Corporation) **Service:** General medical and surgical

Staffed Beds: 18 **Admissions:** 749 **Census:** 5 **Outpatient Visits:** 18607 **Births:** 90 **Total Expense ($000):** 38909 **Payroll Expense ($000):** 14593 **Personnel:** 141

SHAWANO—Shawano County

☐ **THEDACARE MEDICAL CENTER-SHAWANO (521346)**, 100 County Road B, Zip 54166–2127; tel. 715/526–2111, **A**1 5 10 18 **F**11 13 15 28 29 34 40 53 64 75 76 77 78 80 81 82 86 87 90 102 107 108 111 118 119 130 131 154 **S** ThedaCare, Inc., Appleton, WI
Primary Contact: William Schmidt, Chief Executive Officer
CFO: Kerry Lee Blanke, Chief Financial Officer
CMO: Mindy Frimodig, D.O., President Medical Staff ThedaCare Physicians Shawano
CIO: Jennifer Quinn, Quality and Safety Coordinator
CNO: Patricia A Angelucci, MS, R.N., Director Patient Care Services
Web address: www.shawanomed.org
Control: Other not–for–profit (including NFP Corporation) **Service:** General medical and surgical

Staffed Beds: 22 **Admissions:** 1463 **Census:** 12 **Outpatient Visits:** 80831 **Births:** 242 **Total Expense ($000):** 37422 **Payroll Expense ($000):** 18117 **Personnel:** 193

SHEBOYGAN—Sheboygan County

✠ **AURORA SHEBOYGAN MEMORIAL MEDICAL CENTER (520035)**, 2629 North Seventh Street, Zip 53083–4998; tel. 920/451–5000, **A**1 2 10 19 **F**3 4 5 13 17 18 20 22 26 28 29 30 31 32 34 35 36 40 41 43 44 45 49 50 53 56 57 58 59 60 64 65 68 70 72 74 75 76 78 79 80 81 82 84 85 86 87 89 92 93 94 98 99 100 102 103 104 105 107 108 111 112 114 115 117 118 119 120 121 123 126 129 130 131 132 135 143 146 147 148 149 150 152 153 154 **S** Advocate Aurora Health, Downers Grove, IL
Primary Contact: David Graebner, President
CFO: Pamela Ott, Vice President Finance
CMO: Andrea Gavin, M.D., Chief Medical officer
CIO: Steve Serketich, Manager Information Services
CHR: Stacie A Schneider, Director Human Resources
CNO: Lori Knitt, Chief Nursing Officer
Web address: www.aurorahealthcare.org
Control: Other not–for–profit (including NFP Corporation) **Service:** General medical and surgical

Staffed Beds: 127 **Admissions:** 5447 **Census:** 49 **Outpatient Visits:** 101461 **Births:** 915 **Total Expense ($000):** 129243 **Payroll Expense ($000):** 39486 **Personnel:** 733

☒ **HSHS ST. NICHOLAS HOSPITAL (520044)**, 3100 Superior Avenue, Zip 53081–1948; tel. 920/459–8300, **A**1 2 10 **F**3 8 11 13 15 17 18 20 22 28 29 30 31 34 35 36 38 40 43 44 45 47 50 53 54 57 59 60 62 63 64 65 70 71 74 75 76 77 79 80 81 84 85 86 87 89 90 93 107 108 110 111 114 115 116 117 118 119 120 126 129 130 132 146 148 149 154 **S** HSHS Hospital Sisters Health System, Springfield, IL
Primary Contact: Justin Selle, Chief Executive Officer
CFO: Greg Simia, Chief Financial Officer
CMO: Ken Johnson, Chief Physician Executive
CIO: Shane Miller, Chief Information Officer
CHR: Christine Jensema, Chief People Officer
CNO: Mary Martin, MSN, R.N., Chief Nursing Officer
Web address: www.stnicholashospital.org
Control: Church operated, Nongovernment, not–for–profit **Service:** General medical and surgical

Staffed Beds: 46 **Admissions:** 2124 **Census:** 19 **Outpatient Visits:** 78837 **Births:** 259 **Total Expense ($000):** 72908 **Payroll Expense ($000):** 21966 **Personnel:** 281

SHELL LAKE—Washburn County

☐ **INDIANHEAD MEDICAL CENTER (521342)**, 113 Fourth Avenue, Zip 54871–4457, Mailing Address: P.O. Box 300, Zip 54871–0300; tel. 715/468–7833, **A**1 10 18 **F**15 28 34 40 43 56 62 64 80 81 86 89 93 107 119 130 144
Primary Contact: Shannon Jack, Administrator
CFO: Michael Elliott, Controller
CMO: Allan Haesemeyer, M.D., Chief of Staff
CHR: Gwen Nielsen, Manager Human Resources
Web address: www.indianheadmedicalcenter.com
Control: Corporation, Investor–owned (for–profit) **Service:** General medical and surgical

Staffed Beds: 16 **Admissions:** 303 **Census:** 4 **Outpatient Visits:** 17989 **Births:** 0 **Total Expense ($000):** 8844 **Payroll Expense ($000):** 3485 **Personnel:** 87

SPARTA—Monroe County

MAYO CLINIC HEALTH SYSTEM - FRANCISCAN HEALTHCARE IN SPARTA (521305), 310 West Main Street, Zip 54656–2171; tel. 608/269–2132, **A**10 18 **F**1 3 8 11 15 28 29 30 34 35 40 41 43 45 56 57 59 65 66 68 77 79 80 81 84 85 89 90 93 97 107 110 115 119 127 130 131 133 146 148 149 154 156 **S** Mayo Clinic, Rochester, MN
Primary Contact: Kimberly Hawthorne, Administrator
COO: Joseph J Kruse, Chief Administrative Officer
CFO: Tom Tiggelaar, Vice President Finance ad Chief Financial Officer
CMO: Tracy Warsing, M.D., Site Leader Chief of Staff
CHR: Mike J Hesch, Regional Administrator Human Resources
Web address: www.mayoclinichealthsystem.org
Control: Church operated, Nongovernment, not–for–profit **Service:** General medical and surgical

Staffed Beds: 15 **Admissions:** 299 **Census:** 10 **Outpatient Visits:** 38057 **Births:** 0 **Total Expense ($000):** 29566 **Payroll Expense ($000):** 12928 **Personnel:** 136

SPOONER—Washburn County

★ **SPOONER HEALTH (521332)**, 1280 Chandler Drive, Zip 54801–1299; tel. 715/635–2111, **A**10 18 **F**3 11 15 29 30 31 34 35 40 43 45 50 56 57 59 62 64 65 68 78 79 80 81 85 86 87 89 90 93 97 103 107 111 119 129 130 132 133 135 146 148 **S** HealthTech Management Services, Brentwood, TN
Primary Contact: Michael Schafer, Chief Executive Officer and Administrator
CFO: Rebecca Busch, Chief Financial Officer
CMO: Mark Van Etten, M.D., Chief of Staff
CHR: Cindy Rouzer, Director Human Resources
CNO: Clint Miller, Chief Nursing Officer
Web address: www.spoonerhealth.com
Control: Other not–for–profit (including NFP Corporation) **Service:** General medical and surgical

Staffed Beds: 18 **Admissions:** 427 **Census:** 6 **Outpatient Visits:** 23180 **Births:** 0 **Total Expense ($000):** 22662 **Payroll Expense ($000):** 7791 **Personnel:** 116

WI

Hospital, Medicare Provider Number, Address, Telephone, Approval, Facility, and Physician Codes, Health Care System

★ American Hospital Association (AHA) membership
☐ The Joint Commission accreditation
○ Healthcare Facilities Accreditation Program
◇ DNV Healthcare Inc. accreditation
⇧ Center for Improvement in Healthcare Quality Accreditation
△ Commission on Accreditation of Rehabilitation Facilities (CARF) accreditation

ST CROIX FALLS—Polk County

★ **ST. CROIX REGIONAL MEDICAL CENTER (521337)**, 235 State Street, Zip 54024–4117; tel. 715/483–3261, **A**10 18 **F**6 9 11 13 15 28 29 34 36 40 43 51 55 56 64 70 75 76 77 78 81 82 86 87 93 99 100 101 104 107 108 111 116 118 119 130 131 144 147 154
Primary Contact: David Dobosenski, Chief Executive Officer
CFO: Sally Bajak, Chief Financial Officer
CMO: Jeffrey Hall, DPM, Chief Medical Officer
CIO: Brent McCurdy, Director Management Information
CHR: Betsy Nordby, Director of Human Resources
CNO: Laura J. Jensen, Vice President Patient Care Services
Web address: www.scrmc.org
Control: Other not–for–profit (including NFP Corporation) **Service**: General medical and surgical

Staffed Beds: 25 **Admissions**: 1471 **Census**: 13 **Outpatient Visits**: 190950
Births: 278 **Total Expense ($000)**: 91618 **Payroll Expense ($000)**: 42866
Personnel: 440

STANLEY—Chippewa County

★ **ASCENSION OUR LADY OF VICTORY HOSPITAL (521311)**, 1120 Pine Street, Zip 54768–1297; tel. 715/644–5571, **A**10 18 **F**3 15 28 29 30 34 35 40 43 45 50 59 64 65 75 80 81 85 86 87 89 93 94 96 97 107 110 114 127 130 131 133 144 146 147 148 149 154 **S** Ascension Healthcare, Saint Louis, MO
Primary Contact: Jeremy Normington-Slay, FACHE, President
CFO: Terri Lewandowski, Director Financial Services
Web address: www.ministryhealth.org
Control: Church operated, Nongovernment, not–for–profit **Service**: General medical and surgical

Staffed Beds: 6 **Admissions**: 219 **Census**: 3 **Outpatient Visits**: 22323
Births: 0 **Total Expense ($000)**: 15975 **Payroll Expense ($000)**: 5693
Personnel: 65

STEVENS POINT—Portage County

✠ **ASCENSION ST. MICHAEL'S HOSPITAL (520002)**, 900 Illinois Avenue, Zip 54481–3196; tel. 715/346–5000, **A**1 3 10 19 **F**3 5 13 15 17 29 30 31 34 40 43 44 45 48 50 51 56 57 59 64 65 68 70 72 74 76 77 78 79 80 81 84 85 86 87 89 90 93 97 98 99 100 101 102 103 104 106 107 108 111 114 115 118 119 120 121 123 124 129 130 131 132 135 144 146 147 148 149 150 **S** Ascension Healthcare, Saint Louis, MO
Primary Contact: Jeremy Normington-Slay, FACHE, President, North Central Region
CFO: William J Hinner, Vice President Financial Analysis and Planning
CIO: Will Weider, Chief Information Officer
CHR: Celia Shaunessy, Vice President Human Resources
CNO: Tom Veeser, Chief Nursing Officer
Web address: www.ministryhealth.org/SMH/home.nws
Control: Church operated, Nongovernment, not–for–profit **Service**: General medical and surgical

Staffed Beds: 35 **Admissions**: 4088 **Census**: 34 **Outpatient Visits**: 256689
Births: 442 **Total Expense ($000)**: 180239 **Payroll Expense ($000)**: 67447

SAINT MICHAEL'S HOSPITAL See Ascension St. Michael's Hospital

STOUGHTON—Dane County

☐ **STOUGHTON HOSPITAL ASSOCIATION (521343)**, 900 Ridge Street, Zip 53589–1864; tel. 608/873–6611, **A**1 5 10 18 **F**3 4 6 8 15 28 29 34 35 36 40 41 43 50 53 54 56 57 59 62 64 65 68 70 71 74 75 77 79 80 81 85 86 87 89 90 91 93 98 100 103 107 114 129 130 131 132 133 135 144 146 147 148 149 152
Primary Contact: Daniel DeGroot, President and Chief Executive Officer
CFO: Karen Myers, Vice President Financial Services
CMO: Guirish Agni, M.D., Chief of Staff
CIO: Karen Myers, Vice President Financial Services
CHR: Christopher Schmitz, Associate Vice President, Director Human Resources
CNO: Teresa Lindfors, Chief Nursing Officer and Vice President, Patient Services
Web address: www.stoughtonhospital.com
Control: Other not–for–profit (including NFP Corporation) **Service**: General medical and surgical

Staffed Beds: 32 **Admissions**: 936 **Census**: 15 **Outpatient Visits**: 55103
Births: 1 **Total Expense ($000)**: 44871 **Payroll Expense ($000)**: 19547
Personnel: 284

STURGEON BAY—Door County

★ **DOOR COUNTY MEDICAL CENTER (521358)**, 323 South 18th Avenue, Zip 54235–1495; tel. 920/743–5566, (Total facility includes 30 beds in nursing home–type unit) **A**10 18 **F**3 8 11 13 15 17 28 29 30 31 32 34 35 36 40 43 44 45 47 50 56 57 59 61 64 65 66 70 75 76 77 78 79 80 81 82 84 85 86 87 89 90 93 97 107 108 111 115 118 119 126 127 128 129 130 132 133 135 144 145 146 147 148 149 156
Primary Contact: Brian Stephens, President and Chief Executive Officer
CFO: Adam Gingery, Chief Financial Officer
CMO: James Heise, Chief Medical Officer
CIO: Mary Lopas, Chief Information Officer
CHR: Kelli Bowling, Chief Culture Officer
CNO: Jody Boes, Vice President Patient Care Services
Web address: www.dcmedical.org
Control: Church operated, Nongovernment, not–for–profit **Service**: General medical and surgical

Staffed Beds: 55 **Admissions**: 1391 **Census**: 39 **Outpatient Visits**: 134224
Births: 136 **Total Expense ($000)**: 80774 **Payroll Expense ($000)**: 42159
Personnel: 497

DOOR COUNTY MEMORIAL HOSPITAL See Door County Medical Center

SUMMIT—Waukesha County

✠ ○ **AURORA MEDICAL CENTER SUMMIT (520206)**, 36500 Aurora Drive, Zip 53066–4899; tel. 262/434–1000, **A**1 2 10 11 **F**3 8 11 12 13 15 17 18 20 22 26 28 29 30 31 32 34 35 36 40 41 43 44 45 47 48 49 50 53 54 57 58 59 60 64 68 70 72 74 75 76 79 80 81 82 85 86 87 89 90 93 94 96 102 107 108 110 111 114 115 116 117 118 119 120 121 123 126 129 130 131 132 134 135 146 147 148 149 154 157 **S** Advocate Aurora Health, Downers Grove, IL
Primary Contact: Michael Bergmann, President
Web address: www.aurorahealthcare.org
Control: Other not–for–profit (including NFP Corporation) **Service**: General medical and surgical

Staffed Beds: 91 **Admissions**: 4218 **Census**: 44 **Outpatient Visits**: 105162
Births: 473 **Total Expense ($000)**: 115836 **Payroll Expense ($000)**: 37627
Personnel: 925

SUPERIOR—Douglas County

✠ **ESSENTIA HEALTH ST. MARY'S HOSPITAL OF SUPERIOR (521329)**, 3500 Tower Avenue, Zip 54880–5395; tel. 715/817–7000, **A**1 10 18 **F**11 15 28 29 34 40 56 75 77 78 80 81 82 86 87 90 93 99 104 107 119 130 **S** Essentia Health, Duluth, MN
Primary Contact: Terry Jacobson, Administrator and Chief Executive Officer
Web address: www.essentiahealth.org/
EssentiaHealthStMarysHospitalofSuperiorFoundation/overview.aspx
Control: Other not–for–profit (including NFP Corporation) **Service**: General medical and surgical

Staffed Beds: 25 **Admissions**: 546 **Census**: 8 **Outpatient Visits**: 54902 **Births**: 0
Total Expense ($000): 55689 **Payroll Expense ($000)**: 28523 **Personnel**: 210

TOMAH—Monroe County

✠ **TOMAH MEMORIAL HOSPITAL (521320)**, 321 Butts Avenue, Zip 54660–1412; tel. 608/372–2181, **A**1 10 18 **F**11 12 13 28 34 40 43 54 63 64 76 77 80 81 82 86 87 89 90 93 107 108 111 119 130 144 154 **S** HealthTech Management Services, Brentwood, TN
Primary Contact: Philip J. Stuart, Administrator and Chief Executive Officer
CFO: Joseph Zeps, Vice President Finance
CIO: LaVonne Smith, Director Health Information Technology
CHR: Brenda Reinert, Director Human Resources
CNO: Tracy Myhre, R.N., MSN, Chief Nursing Officer
Web address: www.tomahhospital.org
Control: Other not–for–profit (including NFP Corporation) **Service**: General medical and surgical

Staffed Beds: 25 **Admissions**: 966 **Census**: 9 **Outpatient Visits**: 43060
Births: 268 **Total Expense ($000)**: 51360 **Payroll Expense ($000)**: 21896
Personnel: 295

✠ **VA MEDICAL CENTER**, 500 East Veterans Street, Zip 54660–3105; tel. 608/372–3971, (Nonreporting) **A**1 3 5 **S** Department of Veterans Affairs, Washington, DC
Primary Contact: Victoria Brahm, R.N., MSN, Medical Center Director
CFO: Jane Mashak-Ekern, Fiscal Officer
CMO: David Houlihan, M.D., Chief of Staff
CIO: Edward Hensel, Chief Information Officer
CHR: David Dechant, Chief Human Resources Officer
Web address: www.tomah.va.gov
Control: Veterans Affairs, Government, federal **Service**: General medical and surgical

Staffed Beds: 71

WI

Many Facility Codes have changed. Please refer to the AHA Guide Code Chart. © 2019 AHA Guide

TOMAHAWK—Lincoln County

★ **ASCENSION SACRED HEART HOSPITAL (521313)**, 401 West Mohawk Drive, Zip 54487–2274; tel. 715/453–7700, **A**10 18 **F**3 5 15 28 29 30 34 40 57 59 75 77 80 81 85 86 87 89 93 97 99 100 101 104 107 119 130 131 133 146 148 149 154 **S** Ascension Healthcare, Saint Louis, MO
Primary Contact: Sandra L. Anderson, President and Chief Executive Officer
COO: Laurie Oungst, Vice President, Operations
CFO: Jamon Lamers, Director Finance
CMO: Russ Sudbury, M.D., President Medical Staff
CIO: Howard Dobizl, Director Information Technology Services
CHR: Michelle Cornelius, Director Human Resources
CNO: Christine Krebs, Director of Nursing
Web address: www.ministryhealth.org
Control: Church operated, Nongovernment, not–for–profit **Service**: General medical and surgical

Staffed Beds: 8 **Admissions**: 245 **Census**: 2 **Outpatient Visits**: 22380
Births: 0 **Total Expense ($000)**: 14057 **Payroll Expense ($000)**: 6429
Personnel: 53

TWO RIVERS—Manitowoc County

⊞ **AURORA MEDICAL CENTER - MANITOWOC COUNTY (520034)**, 5000 Memorial Drive, Zip 54241–3900, Mailing Address: 2845 Greenbrier Road, Green Bay, Zip 54311–8900; tel. 920/794–5000, **A**1 2 10 **F**3 8 11 13 28 29 30 33 34 35 36 40 41 43 46 48 49 56 57 58 59 64 65 75 76 78 79 80 81 82 86 87 89 91 93 94 96 97 107 108 109 110 111 112 115 117 119 120 121 123 124 129 130 131 132 135 146 147 148 149 154 156 **S** Advocate Aurora Health, Downers Grove, IL
Primary Contact: Cathie A. Kocourek, President
COO: Carrie L Penovich, Chief Clinical Services Officer
CFO: Sandra Ewald, President (Green Bay/Manitowoc Market)
CMO: Paul Mihalakakos, M.D., Chief of Staff
CIO: Preston Simons, Chief Information Officer
CHR: Elizabeth A Kirby, Senior Director Human Resources
CNO: Jolene Elizabeth Ramirez, R.N., Chief Nursing Officer, Vice President Nursing Services
Web address: www.aurorahealthcare.org
Control: Other not–for–profit (including NFP Corporation) **Service**: General medical and surgical

Staffed Beds: 62 **Admissions**: 2113 **Census**: 16 **Outpatient Visits**: 89584
Births: 404 **Total Expense ($000)**: 60995 **Payroll Expense ($000)**: 19033
Personnel: 356

WATERFORD—Racine County

☐ **LAKEVIEW SPECIALTY HOSPITAL AND REHAB (522005)**, 1701 Sharp Road, Zip 53185–5214; tel. 262/534–7297, **A**1 10 **F**1 29 34 38 53 60 64 75 86 87 90 93 130
Primary Contact: Jerry Amato, President and Chief Operating Officer
Web address: www.lakeviewsystem.com
Control: Corporation, Investor–owned (for–profit) **Service**: Acute long–term care hospital

Staffed Beds: 39 **Admissions**: 239 **Census**: 28 **Outpatient Visits**: 4550
Births: 0 **Total Expense ($000)**: 16852 **Payroll Expense ($000)**: 7390
Personnel: 129

WATERTOWN—Dodge County

⊞ **WATERTOWN REGIONAL MEDICAL CENTER (520116)**, 125 Hospital Drive, Zip 53098–3303; tel. 920/261–4210, **A**1 10 **F**10 11 13 15 20 22 28 29 34 36 40 53 54 56 64 69 75 76 77 78 80 82 86 87 89 90 93 98 104 107 108 111 118 119 125 130 131 144 147 154 **S** LifePoint Health, Brentwood, TN
Primary Contact: Richard Keddington, Chief Executive Officer
COO: John P Kosanovich, President
CFO: John Graf, Senior Vice President
CIO: Jennifer Laughlin, Chief Information Officer
CHR: Duane Floyd, Vice President Human Resources and Professional Services
Web address: www.watertownregional.com/Main/Home.aspx
Control: Corporation, Investor–owned (for–profit) **Service**: General medical and surgical

Staffed Beds: 64 **Admissions**: 1986 **Census**: 18 **Outpatient Visits**: 80030
Births: 222 **Total Expense ($000)**: 88292 **Payroll Expense ($000)**: 40265
Personnel: 590

WAUKESHA—Waukesha County

☐ **REHABILITATION HOSPITAL OF WISCONSIN (523027)**, 1625 Coldwater Creek Drive, Zip 53188–8028; tel. 262/521–8800, **A**1 10 **F**28 29 34 64 75 86 90 93 100 130 **S** Kindred Healthcare, Louisville, KY
Primary Contact: John R. Robertstad, FACHE, Chief Executive Officer
COO: Brad Anderson, Chief Operating Officer
CMO: Tim McAvoy, M.D., Medical Director
CHR: Jenny Franke, Director Human Resources
CNO: Sharon Behrens, R.N., MSN, Chief Clinical Officer
Web address: www.rehabhospitalwi.com
Control: Partnership, Investor–owned (for–profit) **Service**: Rehabilitation

Staffed Beds: 40 **Admissions**: 900 **Census**: 33 **Outpatient Visits**: 7375
Births: 0 **Total Expense ($000)**: 14830 **Payroll Expense ($000)**: 8025
Personnel: 145

WAUKESHA COUNTY MENTAL HEALTH CENTER (524026), 2501 Airport Road, Zip 53188; tel. 262/548–7950, **A**10 **F**4 29 50 87 98 103 130
Primary Contact: Jeff Lewis, Administrator
CFO: Randy R Setzer, Financial Services Manager
Web address: www.waukeshacounty.gov/
Control: County, Government, nonfederal **Service**: Psychiatric

Staffed Beds: 28 **Admissions**: 641 **Census**: 21 **Outpatient Visits**: 0 **Births**: 0
Total Expense ($000): 7595 **Payroll Expense ($000)**: 4133 **Personnel**: 62

⊞ **WAUKESHA MEMORIAL HOSPITAL (520008)**, 725 American Avenue, Zip 53188–5099; tel. 262/928–1000, **A**1 2 3 5 10 **F**3 4 5 11 12 13 18 20 22 24 26 28 29 30 31 32 33 34 37 40 41 43 44 45 46 47 48 49 50 56 57 58 59 64 65 66 68 72 74 75 76 78 79 80 81 82 83 84 85 87 89 93 97 98 100 101 102 104 105 107 108 109 110 111 112 114 115 116 117 118 119 120 121 126 129 130 132 133 135 146 147 148 149 151 152 153 154 156 157 **S** ProHealth Care, Inc., Waukesha, WI
Primary Contact: Susan A. Edwards, Chief Executive Officer
CMO: James D Gardner, M.D., Vice President and Chief Medical Officer
CIO: Rodney Dykehouse, Senior Vice President Information Services
CHR: Nadine T Guirl, Senior Vice President Human Resources
Web address: www.prohealthcare.org/locations/locations-v2-detail/?id=1119
Control: Other not–for–profit (including NFP Corporation) **Service**: General medical and surgical

Staffed Beds: 262 **Admissions**: 12850 **Census**: 139 **Outpatient Visits**: 446426 **Births**: 1792 **Total Expense ($000)**: 441219 **Payroll Expense ($000)**: 117452 **Personnel**: 1725

WAUPACA—Waupaca County

☐ **THEDACARE MEDICAL CENTER-WAUPACA (521334)**, 800 Riverside Drive, Zip 54981–1999; tel. 715/258–1000, **A**1 5 10 18 **F**11 13 17 28 29 34 40 64 70 75 76 78 80 81 82 86 87 88 89 90 107 111 119 130 144 147 **S** ThedaCare, Inc., Appleton, WI
Primary Contact: David Geroe, Vice President Critical Access Hospitals
CFO: Kerry Lee Blanke, Director Financial Services
CMO: James Williams, M.D., Chief of Staff
CHR: Kevin Gossens, Director Human Resources
Web address: www.riversidemedical.org
Control: Other not–for–profit (including NFP Corporation) **Service**: General medical and surgical

Staffed Beds: 25 **Admissions**: 985 **Census**: 9 **Outpatient Visits**: 62191 **Births**: 113
Total Expense ($000): 30583 **Payroll Expense ($000)**: 13169 **Personnel**: 143

WAUPUN—Dodge County

⊞ **WAUPUN MEMORIAL HOSPITAL (521327)**, 620 West Brown Street, Zip 53963–1799; tel. 920/324–5581, **A**1 10 18 **F**3 11 13 15 18 28 29 30 31 34 35 40 43 44 45 50 51 57 59 60 66 68 69 70 75 76 77 79 81 82 85 86 87 93 96 97 107 108 109 110 114 118 119 124 130 131 132 133 134 135 143 144 146 147 148 149 150 156 **S** SSM Health, Saint Louis, MO
Primary Contact: DeAnn Thurmer, President and Chief Nursing Officer
CFO: Bonnie Schmitz, Chief Financial Officer
CMO: Derek Colmenares, M.D., Chief Medical Officer
CIO: Nancy Birschbach, Vice President and Chief Information Officer
CHR: Sue Edminster, Vice President Human Resources
CNO: DeAnn Thurmer, President and Chief Nursing Officer
Web address: www.agnesian.com
Control: Church operated, Nongovernment, not–for–profit **Service**: General medical and surgical

Staffed Beds: 25 **Admissions**: 878 **Census**: 7 **Outpatient Visits**: 59621
Births: 167 **Total Expense ($000)**: 36378 **Payroll Expense ($000)**: 15415
Personnel: 178

WI

Hospital, Medicare Provider Number, Address, Telephone, Approval, Facility, and Physician Codes, Health Care System

★ American Hospital Association (AHA) membership   ○ Healthcare Facilities Accreditation Program   ⇧ Center for Improvement in Healthcare Quality Accreditation
☐ The Joint Commission accreditation   ◇ DNV Healthcare Inc. accreditation   △ Commission on Accreditation of Rehabilitation Facilities (CARF) accreditation

---

© 2019 AHA Guide   *Many Facility Codes have changed. Please refer to the AHA Guide Code Chart.*   Hospitals **A707**

WAUSAU—Marathon County

⊞ △ **ASPIRUS WAUSAU HOSPITAL, INC. (520030)**, 333 Pine Ridge Boulevard, Zip 54401–4187; tel. 715/847–2121, **A**1 2 3 5 7 10 **F**3 6 7 8 10 11 12 13 15 17 18 20 22 24 26 28 29 30 31 34 35 36 37 40 43 44 45 46 47 49 50 51 54 55 56 57 58 59 60 64 65 68 69 70 71 72 74 75 76 78 79 80 81 82 83 84 85 86 87 89 90 92 93 96 97 100 102 103 107 108 110 111 114 115 116 117 118 119 120 121 123 124 126 129 130 132 134 135 144 145 146 147 148 154 156 **S** Aspirus, Inc., Wausau, WI
Primary Contact: Darrell Lentz, President
CFO: Sidney C Sczygelski, Senior Vice President Finance and Chief Financial Officer
CMO: Ryan Andrews, M.D., Chief Medical Officer
CNO: Jeannine Burnat Nosko, Vice President Patient Care
Web address: www.aspirus.org
Control: Other not–for–profit (including NFP Corporation) **Service**: General medical and surgical

> **Staffed Beds:** 247 **Admissions:** 12146 **Census:** 158 **Outpatient Visits:** 133721 **Births:** 1361 **Total Expense ($000):** 444525 **Payroll Expense ($000):** 148726 **Personnel:** 2083

⊞ **NORTH CENTRAL HEALTH CARE (524017)**, 1100 Lake View Drive, Zip 54403–6785; tel. 715/848–4600, (Total facility includes 174 beds in nursing home–type unit) **A**1 3 10 **F**4 5 29 38 75 80 87 98 99 102 103 104 128 130 154
Primary Contact: Michael Loy, Interim Chief Executive Officer
CFO: Brenda Glodowski, Chief Financial Officer
CHR: Sue Matis, Director Human Resources
Web address: www.norcen.org
Control: County, Government, nonfederal **Service**: Psychiatric

> **Staffed Beds:** 216 **Admissions:** 1208 **Census:** 193 **Outpatient Visits:** 186209 **Births:** 0 **Total Expense ($000):** 45468 **Payroll Expense ($000):** 18225 **Personnel:** 360

NORTH CENTRAL HEALTH CARE FACILITIES See North Central Health Care

WAUWATOSA—Milwaukee County

⊞ **AURORA PSYCHIATRIC HOSPITAL (524000)**, 1220 Dewey Avenue, Zip 53213–2598; tel. 414/454–6600, **A**1 3 5 10 **F**4 5 29 30 32 34 35 38 44 50 54 59 64 68 75 86 87 98 99 100 101 103 104 105 106 130 132 134 135 149 152 153 **S** Advocate Aurora Health, Downers Grove, IL
Primary Contact: Peter Carlson, President, Behavioral Health Services
CFO: Susan Dwyer, Vice President Finance
CMO: Anthony Meyer, M.D., Medical Director
CIO: Philip Loftus, Ph.D., Vice President and Chief Information Officer
CHR: Pamela Gamb, Manager Human Resources
CNO: Jamie Lewiston, R.N., MSN, Chief Nursing Officer
Web address: www.aurorahealthcare.org
Control: Other not–for–profit (including NFP Corporation) **Service**: Psychiatric

> **Staffed Beds:** 91 **Admissions:** 5538 **Census:** 64 **Outpatient Visits:** 78918 **Births:** 0 **Total Expense ($000):** 39872 **Payroll Expense ($000):** 20269 **Personnel:** 472

WEST ALLIS—Milwaukee County

⊞ **AURORA WEST ALLIS MEDICAL CENTER (520139)**, 8901 West Lincoln Avenue, Zip 53227–2409, Mailing Address: P.O. Box 27901, Zip 53227–0901; tel. 414/328–6000, **A**1 2 3 10 **F**3 11 12 13 15 29 30 31 32 34 35 37 38 40 43 44 45 46 49 50 52 54 55 56 57 59 64 65 68 70 72 74 75 76 78 79 80 81 82 84 85 86 87 91 93 94 95 96 97 107 108 110 111 114 115 116 117 118 119 120 121 123 126 130 132 134 135 146 147 148 149 154 **S** Advocate Aurora Health, Downers Grove, IL
Primary Contact: Richard A. Kellar, President
COO: Gerard Colman, Chief Operating Officer
CFO: Chris Hemmer, Director Finance
CMO: Andrew McDonagh, M.D., Chief Medical Officer
CIO: Philip Loftus, Ph.D., Chief Information Officer
CHR: Shannon Christenson, Director Human Resources
CNO: Kathy Becker, Ph.D., R.N., Vice President and Chief Nursing Officer
Web address: www.aurorahealthcare.org
Control: Other not–for–profit (including NFP Corporation) **Service**: General medical and surgical

> **Staffed Beds:** 218 **Admissions:** 11512 **Census:** 122 **Outpatient Visits:** 163097 **Births:** 3505 **Total Expense ($000):** 201497 **Payroll Expense ($000):** 70546 **Personnel:** 1960

WEST BEND—Washington County

⊞ **ST. JOSEPH'S HOSPITAL (520063)**, 3200 Pleasant Valley Road, Zip 53095–9274; tel. 262/836–5533, **A**1 2 3 5 10 **F**3 9 13 15 26 28 29 30 31 34 35 38 40 43 44 45 46 47 49 50 51 54 56 57 58 59 60 64 65 66 68 74 75 76 77 78 79 80 81 84 85 86 89 101 107 108 110 111 114 115 116 117 118 119 120 121 123 129 130 132 135 143 145 146 147 148 149 150 156 **S** Froedtert Health, Milwaukee, WI
Primary Contact: Allen Ericson, President
COO: Allen Ericson, Chief Operating Officer, Community Hospital Division and President, St. Joseph's Hospital
CFO: Scott Hawig, Senior Vice President of Finance, Chief Financial Officer and Treasurer
CMO: Patrick Gardner, M.D., Associate Vice President, Medical Affairs, St. Joseph's Hospital
CHR: Eric Humphrey, Senior Vice President, Chief Human Resources Officer
CNO: Shelly Waala, Vice President Patient Care Services and Chief Nursing Officer
Web address: www.froedtert.com
Control: Other not–for–profit (including NFP Corporation) **Service**: General medical and surgical

> **Staffed Beds:** 70 **Admissions:** 3876 **Census:** 39 **Outpatient Visits:** 88957 **Births:** 663 **Total Expense ($000):** 133816 **Payroll Expense ($000):** 36687 **Personnel:** 508

WESTON—Marathon County

⊞ **ASCENSION SAINT CLARE'S HOSPITAL (520202)**, 3400 Ministry Parkway, Zip 54476–5220; tel. 715/393–3000, **A**1 10 **F**3 11 13 17 18 20 22 24 26 29 30 31 34 35 40 43 44 45 46 47 48 49 50 51 57 59 64 65 68 70 72 74 76 78 79 80 81 82 84 85 86 87 89 97 126 130 132 135 146 147 148 149 150 154 **S** Ascension Healthcare, Saint Louis, MO
Primary Contact: Jeremy Normington-Slay, FACHE, President, North Central Region
CFO: Charlotte Esselman, Director Finance
CIO: Tammy Hawkey, Manager Information Technology Client Services
CHR: Nancy Kwiesielewicz, Human Resources Manager
CNO: Sally E. Zillman, Interim Vice President, Patient Care Services
Web address: www.ministryhealth.org
Control: Church operated, Nongovernment, not–for–profit **Service**: General medical and surgical

> **Staffed Beds:** 60 **Admissions:** 5203 **Census:** 54 **Outpatient Visits:** 23913 **Births:** 522 **Total Expense ($000):** 141502 **Payroll Expense ($000):** 29238 **Personnel:** 362

WHITEHALL—Trempealeau County

★ **GUNDERSEN TRI-COUNTY HOSPITAL AND CLINICS (521316)**, 18601 Lincoln Street, Zip 54773–8605; tel. 715/538–4361, (Total facility includes 47 beds in nursing home–type unit) **A**10 18 **F**5 6 7 10 11 15 28 34 40 43 53 54 56 64 75 78 81 82 86 87 93 99 100 104 107 108 128 130 144 154
Primary Contact: Joni Olson, Chief Executive Officer
CFO: Roxane K Schliech, Chief Financial Officer
CMO: Kim B Breidenbach, Medical Director
CIO: John Waldera, Director Information Technology
CHR: Jill Wesener Dieck, Human Resources Operations Manager
CNO: Kelsey N Underwood, Director of Nursing
Web address: www.gundersenhealth.org/tri-county
Control: Other not–for–profit (including NFP Corporation) **Service**: General medical and surgical

> **Staffed Beds:** 50 **Admissions:** 362 **Census:** 45 **Outpatient Visits:** 33689 **Births:** 0 **Total Expense ($000):** 18203 **Payroll Expense ($000):** 7711 **Personnel:** 144

WILD ROSE—Waushara County

THEDA CARE MEDICAL CENTER - WILD ROSE (521303), 601 Grove Avenue, Zip 54984–6903, Mailing Address: P.O. Box 243, Zip 54984–0243; tel. 920/622–3257, **A**10 18 **F**11 15 28 29 34 40 43 56 64 75 77 80 81 86 87 89 90 93 99 100 101 102 103 104 107 111 119 131 144 147 **S** ThedaCare, Inc., Appleton, WI
Primary Contact: Tammy Bending, Vice President
CFO: Thomas P Krystowiak, Vice President Finance
CMO: Michael Staudinger, M.D., Chief of Staff
Web address: www.wildrosehospital.org
Control: Other not–for–profit (including NFP Corporation) **Service**: General medical and surgical

> **Staffed Beds:** 25 **Admissions:** 278 **Census:** 5 **Outpatient Visits:** 18055 **Births:** 0 **Total Expense ($000):** 7848 **Payroll Expense ($000):** 5215 **Personnel:** 67

WI

Many Facility Codes have changed. Please refer to the AHA Guide Code Chart. © 2019 AHA Guide

WINNEBAGO—Winnebago County

☐ **WINNEBAGO MENTAL HEALTH INSTITUTE (524002)**, 1300 South Drive,
Zip 54985, Mailing Address: Box 9, Zip 54985–0009; tel. 920/235–4910, **A**1 3 5
10 **F**3 4 29 30 57 59 75 82 86 87 98 99 103 130 132 135 146 149
Primary Contact: Byran Bartow, Director
COO: Chris Craggs, Deputy Director
CFO: Lisa Spanbauer, Financial Program Supervisor
CMO: Randy Kerswill, M.D., Medical Director
CIO: Terrance J. Sweet, Director Information Technology
CHR: Mary Howard, Director Human Resources
CNO: Lori Monroe, Director of Nursing
Web address: www.dhfs.state.wi.us/mh_winnebago
Control: State, Government, nonfederal **Service**: Psychiatric

Staffed Beds: 184 Admissions: 3388 Census: 171 Outpatient Visits: 0
Births: 0 Total Expense ($000): 73579 Payroll Expense ($000): 36414
Personnel: 606

WISCONSIN RAPIDS—Wood County

⊞ **ASPIRUS RIVERVIEW HOSPITAL AND CLINICS, INC. (520033)**, 410 Dewey
Street, Zip 54494–4715, Mailing Address: P.O. Box 8080, Zip 54495–8080;
tel. 715/423–6060, **A**1 2 10 **F**3 4 13 15 17 28 30 31 32 34 35 40 43 45 50 56
57 59 64 65 68 69 70 74 75 76 77 78 79 80 81 84 85 86 88 89 90 93 97 98
107 108 110 111 115 117 118 119 120 121 124 127 129 130 131 132 135
143 146 148 154 156 157 **S** Aspirus, Inc., Wausau, WI
Primary Contact: Todd Burch, Chief Executive Officer
CFO: Nancy Roth-Mallek, Vice President of Finance
CMO: Thomas Voelker, M.D., Chief Medical Officer
CIO: Marjorie Tell, Vice President Information Technology
CHR: Jessica Fox, Director of Human Resources
CNO: Peggy Ose, FACHE, MSN, R.N., Chief Nursing Officer
Web address: www.aspirus.org
Control: Other not–for–profit (including NFP Corporation) **Service**: General
medical and surgical

Staffed Beds: 75 Admissions: 2975 Census: 24 Outpatient Visits: 51005
Births: 500 Total Expense ($000): 116802 Payroll Expense ($000): 44652
Personnel: 435

WOODRUFF—Oneida County

⊞ **HOWARD YOUNG MEDICAL CENTER (520091)**, 240 Maple Street,
Zip 54568–9190, Mailing Address: P.O. Box 470, Zip 54568–0470;
tel. 715/356–8000, **A**1 10 20 **F**3 11 13 15 28 29 30 34 35 40 43 44 45 46
50 59 64 66 68 75 76 77 79 80 81 82 84 85 86 87 88 89 93 95 96 97 107
110 111 115 119 126 129 130 135 146 148 149 152 153 154 **S** Ascension
Healthcare, Saint Louis, MO
Primary Contact: Sandra L. Anderson, President and Chief Executive Officer
COO: Laurie Oungst, Vice President, Operations
CFO: Jamon Lamers, Director Finance
CMO: John Crump, M.D., Medical Staff President
CIO: Howard Dobizl, Director Information Technology Services
CHR: Michelle Cornelius, Director Human Resources
CNO: Jacqualyn Monge, Director of Nursing
Web address: www.ministryhealth.org
Control: Church operated, Nongovernment, not–for–profit **Service**: General
medical and surgical

Staffed Beds: 50 Admissions: 2315 Census: 23 Outpatient Visits: 38402
Births: 268 Total Expense ($000): 48592 Payroll Expense ($000): 16698
Personnel: 225

WI

WYOMING

AFTON—Lincoln County

★ **STAR VALLEY MEDICAL CENTER (531313)**, 901 Adams Street,
Zip 83110–9621, Mailing Address: P.O. Box 579, Zip 83110–0579;
tel. 307/885–5800, (Total facility includes 24 beds in nursing home–type unit) **A**5
10 18 **F**3 7 11 12 13 15 28 29 31 34 35 36 40 41 43 45 46 47 48 49 50 51
56 57 59 64 65 70 75 77 78 79 81 82 84 85 87 92 93 97 107 108 109 110
111 112 115 119 128 129 130 131 132 133 141 144 145 146 148 152 154
156 157
Primary Contact: Bren Lowe, Chief Executive Officer
COO: Mike Hunsaker, Chief Operating Officer
CFO: Chad Turner, Chief Financial Officer
CMO: Donald Kirk, M.D., Chief of Staff
CIO: Amy R Johnson, R.N., Quality Improvement Safety Officer
CHR: Trevor Merritt, Director Human Resources
CNO: Derek Greenwald, Chief Nursing Officer
Web address: www.svmcwy.org
Control: Hospital district or authority, Government, nonfederal **Service**: General
medical and surgical

Staffed Beds: 46 **Admissions**: 772 **Census**: 27 **Outpatient Visits**: 39132
Births: 94 **Total Expense ($000)**: 48257 **Payroll Expense ($000)**: 20469
Personnel: 356

BASIN—Big Horn County

SOUTH BIG HORN COUNTY HOSPITAL (531301), 388 South U S Highway 20,
Zip 82410–8902; tel. 307/568–3311, (Nonreporting) **A**10 18
Primary Contact: Vincent DiFranco, Interim Chief Executive Officer
Web address: www.midwayclinic.com
Control: Hospital district or authority, Government, nonfederal **Service**: General
medical and surgical

Staffed Beds: 43

BUFFALO—Johnson County

★ **JOHNSON COUNTY HEALTHCARE CENTER (531308)**, 497 West Lott Street,
Zip 82834–1691; tel. 307/684–5521, (Total facility includes 44 beds in nursing
home–type unit) **A**10 18 **F**3 11 13 15 28 31 34 40 45 53 57 59 62 63 67 70 76
78 79 81 89 93 97 107 119 130 131 132 133 146
Primary Contact: Sean McCallister, Chief Executive Officer
CMO: Blaine Ruby, M.D., Chief of Staff
CIO: Laurie Hansen, Director of Administration
CHR: Karen Ferguson, Director Human Resources
CNO: Mary Whaley, Director of Acute Care
Web address: www.jchealthcare.com
Control: Hospital district or authority, Government, nonfederal **Service**: General
medical and surgical

Staffed Beds: 59 **Admissions**: 495 **Census**: 50 **Outpatient Visits**: 18609
Births: 42 **Total Expense ($000)**: 21976 **Payroll Expense ($000)**: 11721
Personnel: 204

CASPER—Natrona County

☐ **ELKHORN VALLEY REHABILITATION HOSPITAL (533027)**, 5715 East 2nd
Street, Zip 82609–4322; tel. 307/265–0005, **A**1 10 **F**29 34 35 50 75 77 82 86
87 91 93 96 132 143 148 149 154 **S** Ernest Health, Inc., Albuquerque, NM
Primary Contact: Connie Longwell, Chief Executive Officer
Web address: www.evrh.ernesthealth.com/
Control: Corporation, Investor–owned (for–profit) **Service**: Rehabilitation

Staffed Beds: 41 **Admissions**: 700 **Census**: 29 **Outpatient Visits**: 3074
Births: 0 **Total Expense ($000)**: 14608 **Payroll Expense ($000)**: 6396

MOUNTAIN VIEW REGIONAL HOSPITAL (530033), 6550 East Second
Street, Zip 82609–4321, Mailing Address: P.O. Box 51888, Zip 82605–1888;
tel. 307/995–8100, (Nonreporting) **A**10 **S** National Surgical Healthcare,
Chicago, IL
Primary Contact: Thomas Kopitnik, Acting Chief Executive Officer
Web address: www.mountainviewregionalhospital.com
Control: Partnership, Investor–owned (for–profit) **Service**: Surgical

Staffed Beds: 23

⇑ **SUMMIT MEDICAL CENTER (530034)**, 6350 East 2nd Street,
Zip 82609–4264; tel. 307/232–6600, **A**21 **F**3 15 29 45 49 79 81 89 107 110
111 119 129
Primary Contact: Jan Winter Clark, R.N., Chief Executive Officer
COO: Mindi L. Pile, Chief Operations Officer
CFO: Calvin Carey, Chief Financial Officer
CMO: Joseph Vigneri, M.D., Chief Medical Officer
CNO: Vanessa Sorensen, Chief Nursing Officer
Web address: www.summitmedicalcasper.com/
Control: Corporation, Investor–owned (for–profit) **Service**: General medical and
surgical

Staffed Beds: 16 **Admissions**: 236 **Census**: 1 **Outpatient Visits**: 4429
Births: 0 **Total Expense ($000)**: 17417 **Payroll Expense ($000)**: 3107
Personnel: 53

☐ **WYOMING BEHAVIORAL INSTITUTE (534004)**, 2521 East 15th Street,
Zip 82609–4126; tel. 307/237–7444, (Nonreporting) **A**1 10 **S** Universal Health
Services, Inc., King of Prussia, PA
Primary Contact: Mike Phillips, Chief Executive Officer
CFO: Carmel Bickford, Chief Financial Officer
CMO: Steven Brown, M.D., Medical Director
CHR: Jon Barra, Director Human Resources
Web address: www.wbihelp.com
Control: Corporation, Investor–owned (for–profit) **Service**: Psychiatric

Staffed Beds: 129

⊞ **WYOMING MEDICAL CENTER (530012)**, 1233 East Second Street,
Zip 82601–2988; tel. 307/577–7201, **A**1 3 5 10 20 **F**3 7 11 12 13 18 20 22
24 28 29 30 31 34 35 40 41 43 45 46 48 49 50 51 53 57 59 60 61 68 70 74
76 79 81 82 85 86 87 89 97 102 107 108 115 118 119 120 121 123 124 126
129 130 132 135 144 146 147 148
Primary Contact: Michele Chulick, President and Chief Executive Officer
CFO: Yvonne Wigington, Vice President, Chief Financial Officer
CMO: Carol M Solie, M.D., Chief Medical Officer
CIO: Rob Pettigrew, Director Information Technology
CNO: David Gardner, MSN, Chief Nursing Officer
Web address: www.https://wyomingmedicalcenter.org/
Control: Other not–for–profit (including NFP Corporation) **Service**: General
medical and surgical

Staffed Beds: 235 **Admissions**: 8742 **Census**: 94 **Outpatient Visits**: 88253
Births: 986 **Total Expense ($000)**: 215286 **Payroll Expense ($000)**: 78843
Personnel: 1122

CHEYENNE—Laramie County

⊞ △ **CHEYENNE REGIONAL MEDICAL CENTER (530014)**, 214 East 23rd
Street, Zip 82001–3790; tel. 307/634–2273, **A**1 2 3 5 7 10 20 **F**3 5 8 12 13 15
18 20 22 24 26 28 29 30 31 32 34 35 37 38 40 43 44 45 46 47 48 49 50 51
55 56 57 59 60 61 62 63 64 65 68 70 73 74 76 77 78 79 81 82 83 84 85 86
87 89 90 91 92 93 96 97 98 100 101 102 104 107 108 111 115 116 117 118
119 120 121 122 123 124 126 128 130 131 135 143 146 147 148 149 153
154 157
Primary Contact: Patrick Madigan, Interim Chief Executive Officer
COO: Robin Roling, FACHE, MS, R.N., Chief Operating Officer
CFO: Neil W Bertrand, Interim Chief Financial Officer
CMO: Jeffrey Chapman, M.D., Chief Medical Officer
CNO: Tracy Garcia, MS, Chief Nursing Officer
Web address: www.cheyenneregional.org/
Control: County, Government, nonfederal **Service**: General medical and surgical

Staffed Beds: 238 **Admissions**: 9955 **Census**: 128 **Outpatient
Visits**: 185812 **Births**: 1203 **Total Expense ($000)**: 290014 **Payroll
Expense ($000)**: 118427 **Personnel**: 1927

WY

Many Facility Codes have changed. Please refer to the AHA Guide Code Chart. © 2019 AHA Guide

CHEYENNE VETERANS AFFAIRS MEDICAL CENTER, 2360 East Pershing Boulevard, Zip 82001–5392; tel. 307/778–7550, (Nonreporting) **A**1 3 **S** Department of Veterans Affairs, Washington, DC
Primary Contact: Paul L. Roberts, Director
CFO: Melvin Cranford, Chief Fiscal Services
CMO: Roger Johnson, M.D., Chief of Staff
CIO: Liz McCulloch, Chief Information Resource Management Systems
CHR: Ron Lester, Chief Human Resources
Web address: www.cheyenne.va.gov/
Control: Veterans Affairs, Government, federal **Service:** General medical and surgical

Staffed Beds: 61

CODY—Park County

★ **WEST PARK HOSPITAL (531312)**, 707 Sheridan Avenue, Zip 82414–3409; tel. 307/527–7501, (Total facility includes 87 beds in nursing home–type unit) **A**5 10 18 **F**3 4 5 6 7 11 13 15 18 20 22 28 29 30 31 34 35 37 38 40 43 45 46 50 54 55 56 57 59 62 63 64 65 68 70 74 75 76 77 78 79 81 84 85 86 87 93 97 99 100 102 103 104 107 108 110 111 114 115 119 120 124 126 127 128 130 131 132 133 135 145 146 147 148 149 151 154 156 **S** QHR, Brentwood, TN
Primary Contact: Douglas A. McMillan, Administrator and Chief Executive Officer
CFO: Patrick G McConnell, Chief Financial Officer
CMO: Gary Hart, M.D., Chief Medical Officer
CHR: Dick Smith, Director Human Resources
Web address: www.westparkhospital.org
Control: Hospital district or authority, Government, nonfederal **Service:** General medical and surgical

Staffed Beds: 112 **Admissions:** 1743 **Census:** 90 **Outpatient Visits:** 108137 **Births:** 234 **Total Expense ($000):** 97123 **Payroll Expense ($000):** 40185 **Personnel:** 545

DOUGLAS—Converse County

★ **MEMORIAL HOSPITAL OF CONVERSE COUNTY (531302)**, 111 South Fifth Street, Zip 82633–2434, Mailing Address: P.O. Box 1450, Zip 82633–1450; tel. 307/358–2122, **A**10 18 **F**3 7 8 11 13 15 28 29 30 32 34 43 45 46 57 59 64 65 69 70 74 75 76 79 81 82 85 86 87 89 94 97 107 109 110 111 115 116 117 118 119 126 127 128 129 130 131 133 135 143 144 146 147 148 149 150 154 156
Primary Contact: Ryan K. Smith, Chief Executive Officer
COO: Karl Edward Hertz, Assistant Administrator
CFO: Curtis R. Dugger, Chief Financial Officer
CMO: James Morgan, M.D., Chief Medical Officer
CIO: Dave Patterson, Chief Information Officer
CHR: Linda York, Director Human Resource
CNO: Cristy Dicklich-Cobb, Chief Nursing Officer
Web address: www.conversehospital.com
Control: County, Government, nonfederal **Service:** General medical and surgical

Staffed Beds: 25 **Admissions:** 746 **Census:** 7 **Outpatient Visits:** 20160 **Births:** 126 **Total Expense ($000):** 53372 **Payroll Expense ($000):** 27704 **Personnel:** 325

EVANSTON—Uinta County

✉ **EVANSTON REGIONAL HOSPITAL (530032)**, 190 Arrowhead Drive, Zip 82930–9266; tel. 307/789–3636, **A**1 10 20 **F**3 11 13 15 29 34 35 40 43 45 48 60 64 65 70 74 75 76 77 79 81 82 85 86 87 89 93 97 107 108 111 115 119 126 127 128 129 131 133 146 147 148 149 **S** Quorum Health, Brentwood, TN
Primary Contact: Cheri Willard, MSN, R.N., Interim Chief Executive Officer
CHR: Joshua Jones, Director Human Resources
CNO: Cheri Willard, MSN, R.N., Chief Nursing Officer
Web address: www.evanstonregionalhospital.com
Control: Corporation, Investor–owned (for–profit) **Service:** General medical and surgical

Staffed Beds: 42 **Admissions:** 675 **Census:** 4 **Outpatient Visits:** 21692 **Births:** 187 **Personnel:** 161

WYOMING STATE HOSPITAL (534001), 830 Highway 150 South, Zip 82931–5341, Mailing Address: P.O. Box 177, Zip 82931–0177; tel. 307/789–3464, **A**10 **F**29 30 39 53 57 61 74 98 154
Primary Contact: Rich Dunkley, Administrator
CFO: Paul Mullenax, Business Manager
CIO: Steve Baldwin, Manager Information Technology
Web address: www.health.wyo.gov/statehospital/index.html
Control: State, Government, nonfederal **Service:** Psychiatric

Staffed Beds: 103 **Admissions:** 169 **Census:** 71 **Births:** 0

GILLETTE—Campbell County

★ ⇑ **CAMPBELL COUNTY HEALTH (530002)**, 501 South Burma Avenue, Zip 82716–3426, Mailing Address: P.O. Box 3011, Zip 82717–3011; tel. 307/682–8811, (Total facility includes 160 beds in nursing home–type unit) **A**10 20 21 **F**3 5 7 11 13 15 18 20 22 26 28 29 30 31 34 35 38 40 41 43 45 46 47 48 49 50 53 54 56 59 60 62 63 64 65 68 70 71 73 74 75 76 77 78 79 81 82 85 86 87 91 92 93 94 96 97 98 99 100 101 102 103 104 107 108 109 110 111 115 118 119 120 121 123 125 129 130 131 132 134 135 143 144 146 147 148 149 152 153 154 157
Primary Contact: Andy Fitzgerald, Chief Executive Officer
COO: Colleen Heeter, Chief Operating Officer
CFO: Dalton Huber, Chief Financial Officer
CIO: Chris Harrison, Manager Information Systems
CHR: John A Fitch, Vice President Human Resources
CNO: Deb L Tonn, Vice President Patient Care
Web address: www.ccmh.net
Control: Hospital district or authority, Government, nonfederal **Service:** General medical and surgical

Staffed Beds: 215 **Admissions:** 2566 **Census:** 168 **Outpatient Visits:** 171369 **Births:** 675 **Total Expense ($000):** 182399 **Payroll Expense ($000):** 85030

JACKSON—Teton County

✉ ⇑ **ST. JOHN'S MEDICAL CENTER AND LIVING CENTER (530015)**, 625 East Broadway Street, Zip 83001–8642, Mailing Address: P.O. Box 428, Zip 83001–0428; tel. 307/733–3636, (Total facility includes 60 beds in nursing home–type unit) **A**1 5 10 20 21 **F**3 10 11 13 15 18 26 28 29 30 31 32 34 35 37 38 39 40 43 45 46 47 48 49 50 51 53 54 56 57 59 62 63 65 66 68 70 74 75 76 77 78 79 81 82 84 85 86 93 94 97 99 101 107 108 110 111 114 115 119 120 126 127 128 129 130 131 132 133 135 143 144 145 146 147 148 149 150 154 156 157
Primary Contact: Paul Beaupre', M.D., Chief Executive Officer
COO: Gary Tauner, Chief Operating Officer
CFO: John Kren, Chief Financial Officer
CIO: Lance Spranger, Chief Information Officer
CNO: Lynn Kirman, R.N., Chief Nursing Officer
Web address: www.tetonhospital.org
Control: Hospital district or authority, Government, nonfederal **Service:** General medical and surgical

Staffed Beds: 105 **Admissions:** 2009 **Census:** 60 **Outpatient Visits:** 86372 **Births:** 420 **Total Expense ($000):** 116349 **Payroll Expense ($000):** 49259 **Personnel:** 747

KEMMERER—Lincoln County

★ **SOUTH LINCOLN MEDICAL CENTER (531315)**, 711 Onyx Street, Zip 83101–3214; tel. 307/877–4401, (Total facility includes 24 beds in nursing home–type unit) **A**10 18 **F**7 29 34 35 40 45 47 57 59 64 65 70 76 79 81 82 87 89 93 97 107 110 119 128 133 143 144 146 148
Primary Contact: Karl Sundberg, Chief Executive Officer
CFO: Curtis Nielson, Chief Financial Officer
CMO: G Christopher Krell, M.D., Chief of Staff
CIO: Kristin Housley, Chief Information Officer
CNO: Kathi Parks, Director of Nursing
Web address: www.southlincolnmedical.com
Control: Hospital district or authority, Government, nonfederal **Service:** General medical and surgical

Staffed Beds: 28 **Admissions:** 152 **Census:** 23 **Outpatient Visits:** 10717 **Births:** 28 **Total Expense ($000):** 9050 **Payroll Expense ($000):** 7388

LARAMIE—Albany County

✉ **IVINSON MEMORIAL HOSPITAL (530025)**, 255 North 30th Street, Zip 82072–5140; tel. 307/742–2141, (Nonreporting) **A**1 3 10 20
Primary Contact: Doug Faus, FACHE, Chief Executive Officer
COO: Holly Zajic, Chief Operating Officer
CFO: James G Bands IV Chief Financial Officer
CMO: John Ullrich, M.D., Chief of Staff
CIO: Brandon Lewis, Director of Information Technology
CHR: Kayla Parry, Manager Human Resources
CNO: Nicole Roonery, Chief Nursing Officer
Web address: www.ivinsonhospital.org
Control: Hospital district or authority, Government, nonfederal **Service:** General medical and surgical

Staffed Beds: 99

Hospital, Medicare Provider Number, Address, Telephone, Approval, Facility, and Physician Codes, Health Care System

★ American Hospital Association (AHA) membership
□ The Joint Commission accreditation
○ Healthcare Facilities Accreditation Program
◇ DNV Healthcare Inc. accreditation
⇑ Center for Improvement in Healthcare Quality Accreditation
△ Commission on Accreditation of Rehabilitation Facilities (CARF) accreditation

WY

© 2019 AHA Guide   *Many Facility Codes have changed. Please refer to the AHA Guide Code Chart.*   Hospitals **A711**

LOVELL—Big Horn County

★ **NORTH BIG HORN HOSPITAL DISTRICT (531309)**, 1115 Lane 12, Zip 82431–9537; tel. 307/548–5200, (Total facility includes 72 beds in nursing home–type unit) **A**10 18 **F**1 7 10 15 18 29 30 31 32 34 35 38 40 45 50 57 59 62 63 65 68 71 75 77 78 79 81 85 87 90 93 97 107 108 110 114 119 127 128 129 130 131 132 133 135 146 148 154 155 156
Primary Contact: Rick Schroeder, Chief Executive Officer
CFO: Lori Smith, Chief Financial Officer
CMO: Richard Jay, D.O., Chief of Staff
CIO: Lisa Strom, Director Information Systems
CHR: Barbara Shumway, Director Human Resources
Web address: www.nbhh.com
Control: Hospital district or authority, Government, nonfederal **Service:** General medical and surgical

Staffed Beds: 81 **Admissions:** 364 **Census:** 74 **Outpatient Visits:** 15506 **Births:** 0 **Total Expense ($000):** 21746 **Payroll Expense ($000):** 8904

LUSK—Niobrara County

★ **NIOBRARA HEALTH AND LIFE CENTER (531314)**, 921 Ballencee Avenue, Zip 82225, Mailing Address: P.O. Box 780, Zip 82225–0780; tel. 307/334–4000, (Nonreporting) **A**10 18
Primary Contact: Nathan Hough, Chief Executive Officer
Web address: www.niobrarahospital.com
Control: Hospital district or authority, Government, nonfederal **Service:** General medical and surgical

Staffed Beds: 24

NEWCASTLE—Weston County

★ **WESTON COUNTY HEALTH SERVICES (531303)**, 1124 Washington Boulevard, Zip 82701–2972; tel. 307/746–4491, (Total facility includes 58 beds in nursing home–type unit) **A**10 18 **F**3 28 29 35 40 41 43 50 57 59 62 64 77 93 107 114 119 129 130 135 148 **S** Regional Health, Rapid City, SD
Primary Contact: Maureen K. Cadwell, Chief Executive Officer
CFO: Lynn Moller, Chief Financial Officer
CMO: Chuck Franklin, M.D., Chief Medical Staff
CIO: Terri Frye, Information Technology Officer
CHR: Julie A Sindlinger, Director of Human Resources
Web address: www.wchs-wy.org
Control: Hospital district or authority, Government, nonfederal **Service:** General medical and surgical

Staffed Beds: 70 **Admissions:** 110 **Census:** 60 **Outpatient Visits:** 26778 **Births:** 0 **Total Expense ($000):** 18343 **Payroll Expense ($000):** 8025 **Personnel:** 159

POWELL—Park County

★ **POWELL VALLEY HEALTHCARE (531310)**, 777 Avenue 'H', Zip 82435–2296; tel. 307/754–2267, (Total facility includes 100 beds in nursing home–type unit) **A**10 18 **F**7 10 11 13 14 15 18 28 29 34 35 40 45 56 57 59 65 67 70 75 76 79 81 82 85 87 89 97 107 110 111 115 128 130 131 133 135 144 146 147 149 156
Primary Contact: Terry Odom, Chief Executive Officer
CFO: Mike Long, Chief Financial Officer
CMO: Valerie Lengfelder, M.D., Chief of Staff
CIO: Joshua Baxter, Director, Information Systems
CHR: Cassie Tinsley, Director, Human Resources
CNO: Arleen Campeau, R.N., Vice President of Patient Care Services, Chief Nursing Officer
Web address: www.pvhc.org
Control: Hospital district or authority, Government, nonfederal **Service:** General medical and surgical

Staffed Beds: 125 **Admissions:** 555 **Census:** 87 **Outpatient Visits:** 29718 **Births:** 156 **Total Expense ($000):** 47844 **Payroll Expense ($000):** 22434 **Personnel:** 398

RAWLINS—Carbon County

★ **MEMORIAL HOSPITAL OF CARBON COUNTY (531316)**, 2221 West Elm Street, Zip 82301–5108, Mailing Address: P.O. Box 460, Zip 82301–0460; tel. 307/324–2221, (Nonreporting) **A**10 18 **S** QHR, Brentwood, TN
Primary Contact: Robert Quist, Interim Chief Executive Officer
CFO: David Pike, Interim Chief Financial Officer
CMO: David Cesko, M.D., Chief of Staff
CIO: Toby Schaef, Director Information Technology
Web address: www.imhcc.com
Control: County, Government, nonfederal **Service:** General medical and surgical

Staffed Beds: 25

RIVERTON—Fremont County

⊠ **SAGEWEST HEALTH CARE AT RIVERTON (530008)**, 2100 West Sunset Drive, Zip 82501–2274; tel. 307/856–4161, (Includes SAGEWEST HEALTH CARE AT LANDER, 1320 Bishop Randall Drive, Lander, Wyoming, Zip 82520–3996; tel. 307/332–4420; Stephen M Erixon, Chief Executive Officer) **A**1 10 20 **F**3 11 13 15 18 20 22 28 29 34 35 39 40 43 45 50 57 59 68 70 74 75 76 77 79 81 85 87 93 97 107 108 110 111 114 115 119 129 130 146 147 148 149 **S** LifePoint Health, Brentwood, TN
Primary Contact: Robert Alan. Daugherty, Chief Executive Officer
COO: Derrick Brumfield, Chief Operating Officer
CFO: Jennifer Hamilton, Chief Financial Officer
CMO: Cielette Karn, M.D., Chief of Staff
CIO: Linda Tice, Director Information Systems
CHR: Dawn Nelson, Director Human Resources
CNO: Vickie Bessey, MSN, R.N., Chief Nursing Officer
Web address: www.sagewesthealthcare.com
Control: Corporation, Investor–owned (for–profit) **Service:** General medical and surgical

Staffed Beds: 93 **Admissions:** 2520 **Census:** 23 **Outpatient Visits:** 43322 **Births:** 407 **Total Expense ($000):** 47965 **Payroll Expense ($000):** 20119 **Personnel:** 251

ROCK SPRINGS—Sweetwater County

⇑ **ASPEN MOUNTAIN MEDICAL CENTER (530035)**, 4401 College Drive, Zip 82901–3507; tel. 307/352–8900, **A**21 **F**89 107 111 112 126 129 145 149
Primary Contact: Cody Barnhart, Chief Executive Officer
Web address: www.aspenmountainmc.com
Control: Partnership, Investor–owned (for–profit) **Service:** General medical and surgical

Staffed Beds: 16 **Admissions:** 175 **Census:** 1 **Outpatient Visits:** 4459 **Births:** 0

⊠ **MEMORIAL HOSPITAL OF SWEETWATER COUNTY (530011)**, 1200 College Drive, Zip 82901–5868, Mailing Address: P.O. Box 1359, Zip 82902–1359; tel. 307/362–3711, **A**1 10 20 **F**3 11 13 15 28 29 30 31 34 35 40 43 48 57 59 60 64 68 70 75 76 77 78 79 81 82 87 93 96 97 107 110 111 114 115 118 119 120 121 122 123 129 130 131 132 135 146 147 148 154
Primary Contact: Irene Richardson, Chief Executive Officer
COO: Mandeep Gill, Chief Operating Officer
CFO: Tami Love, Chief Financial Officer
CMO: Sigsbee Duck, M.D., President, Medical Staff
CHR: Amber Fisk, Director Human Resources
CNO: Kallie Mikkelsen, Vice President Nursing
Web address: www.sweetwatermemorial.com/default.aspx
Control: County, Government, nonfederal **Service:** General medical and surgical

Staffed Beds: 58 **Admissions:** 1606 **Census:** 12 **Outpatient Visits:** 148476 **Births:** 479 **Total Expense ($000):** 88699 **Payroll Expense ($000):** 37360 **Personnel:** 469

SHERIDAN—Sheridan County

⊠ **SHERIDAN MEMORIAL HOSPITAL (530006)**, 1401 West Fifth Street, Zip 82801–2799; tel. 307/672–1000, (Nonreporting) **A**1 10 20
Primary Contact: Michael McCafferty, Chief Executive Officer
CMO: John Addlesperger, D.O., Chief Medical Officer
CIO: Nyle Morgan, Chief Information Officer
CHR: Len Gross, Chief Human Resources Officer
Web address: www.sheridanhospital.org
Control: County, Government, nonfederal **Service:** General medical and surgical

Staffed Beds: 88

⊠ **SHERIDAN VETERANS AFFAIRS MEDICAL CENTER**, 1898 Fort Road, Zip 82801–8320; tel. 307/672–3473, (Nonreporting) **A**1 **S** Department of Veterans Affairs, Washington, DC
Primary Contact: Pamela Crowell, Director
COO: Chandra Lake, Associate Director
CFO: Donna Fuerstenberg, Fiscal Chief
CMO: Wendell Robison, M.D., Chief of Staff
CIO: Anthony Giljum, Chief Information Officer
CHR: James Hardin, Human Resources Officer
Web address: www.sheridan.va.gov/
Control: Veterans Affairs, Government, federal **Service:** Psychiatric

Staffed Beds: 145

WY

SUNDANCE—Crook County

★ **CROOK COUNTY MEDICAL SERVICES DISTRICT (531311)**, 713 Oak Street, Zip 82729, Mailing Address: P.O. Box 517, Zip 82729–0517; tel. 307/283–3501, **A**10 18 **F**7 40 41 44 57 59 64 65 68 75 89 107 111 114 119 127 128 130 133 143 146 148 149 150 **S** Regional Health, Rapid City, SD
Primary Contact: Nathan Hough, Chief Executive Officer
CFO: Betty Meyers, Chief Financial Officer
CMO: Jeremi Villano, M.D., Chief of Staff
CHR: Patricia Feist, Manager Human Resources
Web address: www.ccmsd.org/
Control: Hospital district or authority, Government, nonfederal **Service**: Acute long–term care hospital

Staffed Beds: 16 **Admissions**: 65 **Census**: 1 **Births**: 0

THERMOPOLIS—Hot Springs County

★ **HOT SPRINGS COUNTY MEMORIAL HOSPITAL (531304)**, 150 East Arapahoe Street, Zip 82443–2498; tel. 307/864–3121, **A**10 18 **F**3 11 13 15 28 29 31 34 35 40 43 45 50 57 59 64 68 75 76 81 82 85 89 97 107 108 110 111 115 119 127 130 133 135 145 146 **S** HealthTech Management Services, Brentwood, TN
Primary Contact: Margie Molitor, FACHE, R.N., Chief Executive Officer
CFO: Shelly Larson, Chief Financial Officer
CHR: Patti Jeunehomme, Director Human Resources
CNO: Sarah Aliff, Ph.D., Chief Nursing Officer
Web address: www.hscmh.org
Control: Hospital district or authority, Government, nonfederal **Service**: General medical and surgical

Staffed Beds: 25 **Admissions**: 365 **Census**: 4 **Outpatient Visits**: 14374 **Births**: 71 **Total Expense ($000)**: 19714 **Payroll Expense ($000)**: 7438 **Personnel**: 127

TORRINGTON—Goshen County

☒ **COMMUNITY HOSPITAL (531307)**, 2000 Campbell Drive, Zip 82240–1597; tel. 307/532–4181, **A**1 10 18 **F**15 18 40 43 70 76 89 **S** Banner Health, Phoenix, AZ
Primary Contact: Shelby Olind, Interim Chief Executive Officer
CMO: Bonnie Randolph, M.D., Chief of Staff
CIO: Rod Miller, Chief Information Technology
Web address: www.bannerhealth.com/Locations/Wyoming/Community+Hospital/
Control: Other not–for–profit (including NFP Corporation) **Service**: General medical and surgical

Staffed Beds: 20 **Admissions**: 512 **Census**: 5 **Births**: 62 **Total Expense ($000)**: 29413 **Payroll Expense ($000)**: 12700 **Personnel**: 143

WHEATLAND—Platte County

☒ **PLATTE COUNTY MEMORIAL HOSPITAL (531305)**, 201 14th Street, Zip 82201–3201, Mailing Address: P.O. Box 848, Zip 82201–0848; tel. 307/322–3636, **A**1 10 18 **F**3 7 76 **S** Banner Health, Phoenix, AZ
Primary Contact: Hoyt Skabelund, Chief Executive Officer
CFO: James Cussins, Chief Financial Officer
CMO: Willard Woods, M.D., Chief Medical Officer
CIO: Robin May, Director Information Systems
CHR: Sandy Dugger, Chief Human Resources Officer
Web address: www.https://www.bannerhealth.com/locations/wheatland/platte-county-memorial-hospital
Control: Other not–for–profit (including NFP Corporation) **Service**: General medical and surgical

Staffed Beds: 25 **Admissions**: 428 **Census**: 4 **Outpatient Visits**: 22273 **Births**: 37 **Total Expense ($000)**: 23592 **Payroll Expense ($000)**: 10217 **Personnel**: 172

WORLAND—Washakie County

★ **WASHAKIE MEDICAL CENTER (531306)**, 400 South 15th Street, Zip 82401–3531, Mailing Address: P.O. Box 700, Zip 82401–0700; tel. 307/347–3221, **A**10 18 **F**3 8 11 13 15 29 31 37 39 40 43 46 53 56 57 59 64 65 68 70 75 76 78 81 85 93 107 109 110 111 115 119 133 146 148 149 154 **S** Banner Health, Phoenix, AZ
Primary Contact: Jay Stallings, Chief Executive Officer
CFO: Jennifer Montgomery, Chief Financial Officer
CMO: Ryan Clifford, M.D., Chief of Staff
CHR: Jerry Clipp, Manager Human Resources
Web address: www.washakiemedicalcenter.com
Control: Other not–for–profit (including NFP Corporation) **Service**: General medical and surgical

Staffed Beds: 18 **Admissions**: 489 **Census**: 5 **Births**: 32 **Total Expense ($000)**: 27030 **Payroll Expense ($000)**: 9051 **Personnel**: 107

Hospital, Medicare Provider Number, Address, Telephone, Approval, Facility, and Physician Codes, Health Care System

★ American Hospital Association (AHA) membership
☐ The Joint Commission accreditation
○ Healthcare Facilities Accreditation Program
◇ DNV Healthcare Inc. accreditation
⇑ Center for Improvement in Healthcare Quality Accreditation
△ Commission on Accreditation of Rehabilitation Facilities (CARF) accreditation

WY

AMERICAN SAMOA

LYNDON B. JOHNSON TROPICAL MEDICAL CENTER (640001), Faga'alu Village, Zip 96799, Mailing Address: P.O. Box LBJ, Zip 96799; tel. 684/633–1222, (Nonreporting) **A**10
Primary Contact: Taufete's John. Faumuina, Chief Executive Officer
Web address: www.asmca.org
Control: State, Government, nonfederal **Service**: General medical and surgical

Staffed Beds: 125

GUAM

AGANA—Guam County

☒ **U. S. NAVAL HOSPITAL GUAM**, Building #50 Farenholt Avenue, Zip 96910, Mailing Address: PSC 490, Box 208, FPO, Zip 96540; tel. 671/344–9340, (Nonreporting) **A**1 **S** Bureau of Medicine and Surgery, Department of the Navy, Falls Church, VA
Primary Contact: Captain Daniel Cornwell, Command Officer
Web address: www.med.navy.mil/sites/usnhguam/Pages/default.aspx
Control: Department of Defense, Government, federal **Service**: General medical and surgical

Staffed Beds: 55

DEDEDO—Guam County

★ **GUAM REGIONAL MEDICAL CITY (650003)**, 133 Route 3, Zip 96932, Mailing Address: P.O. Box 3830, Hagatna, Zip 96932; tel. 671/645–5500, (Nonreporting) **A**10
Primary Contact: Gloria Long, Chief Operating Officer
Web address: www.grmc.gu/
Control: Corporation, Investor–owned (for–profit) **Service**: General medical and surgical

Staffed Beds: 130

TAMUNING—Guam County

☐ **GUAM MEMORIAL HOSPITAL AUTHORITY (650001)**, 850 Governor Carlos G Camacho Road, Zip 96913; tel. 671/647–2108, (Nonreporting) **A**1 10
Primary Contact: Joseph P. Verga, FACHE, Chief Executive Officer
CFO: Alan Ulrich, Chief Financial Officer
CMO: James J Stadler, M.D., Associate Administrator Medical Services
CIO: Vince Quichocho, Manager Information Systems
CHR: Elizabeth Claros, Administrator Personnel Services
Web address: www.gmha.org
Control: Hospital district or authority, Government, nonfederal **Service**: General medical and surgical

Staffed Beds: 104

MARSHALL ISLANDS

KWAJALEIN ISLAND—Guam County

KWAJALEIN HOSPITAL, U S Army Kwajalein Atoll, Zip 96960, Mailing Address: Box 1702, APO, UNIT, Zip 96555–5000; tel. 805/355–2225, (Nonreporting) **S** Department of the Army, Office of the Surgeon General, Falls Church, VA
Primary Contact: Elaine McMahon, Administrator
Control: Department of Defense, Government, federal **Service**: General medical and surgical

Staffed Beds: 14

NORTHERN MARIANA ISLANDS

SAIPAN—Guam County

★ **COMMONWEALTH HEALTH CENTER (660001)**, Navy Hill Road, Zip 96950, Mailing Address: P.O. Box 500409, Zip 96950; tel. 670/234–8950, (Nonreporting) **A**10
Primary Contact: Esther L. Muna, FACHE, Chief Executive Officer
CFO: Priscilla Maratita Iakopo, Chief Financial Officer
CMO: John M Tudela, M.D., Director of Medical Affairs
CIO: Anthony Reyes, Information Technology Director
CHR: Clarinda Ngiraisui, Director, Human Resources
CNO: Leslie Camacho, R.N., Director of Nursing
Web address: www.chcc.gov.mp
Control: Corporation, Investor–owned (for–profit) **Service**: General medical and surgical

Staffed Beds: 86

PUERTO RICO

AGUADILLA—Aguadilla County

☒ **HOSPITAL BUEN SAMARITANO (400079)**, Carr #2 Km 141–1 Ave Severiano Cuevas, Zip 00603, Mailing Address: P.O. Box 4055, Zip 00605–4055; tel. 787/658–0000, **A**1 10 **F**3 13 14 15 29 30 34 40 41 45 57 59 65 70 74 75 76 77 78 79 81 87 89 107 111 114 119 130 146 148 149 157
Primary Contact: Marilyn Morales, Chief Executive Officer
CFO: Edwin Orama Acevedo, Financial Supervisor
CMO: Arturo Cedeno Llorens, M.D., Medical Director
CHR: Jose Garcia Rivera, Director Human Resources
CNO: Eneida Alicea Perez, Interim Nursing Director
Web address: www.hbspr.org
Control: Other not–for–profit (including NFP Corporation) **Service**: General medical and surgical

Staffed Beds: 145 **Admissions**: 5053 **Census**: 80 **Outpatient Visits**: 31127 **Births**: 18 **Total Expense ($000)**: 36068 **Payroll Expense ($000)**: 10246 **Personnel**: 407

AIBONITO—Aibonito County

☒ **CENTRO DE SALUD CONDUCTUAL MENONITA-CIMA (404009)**, Carretera Estatal 14 Interior, Zip 00705, Mailing Address: P.O. Box 871, Zip 00705; tel. 787/714–2462, (Nonreporting) **A**1 10
Primary Contact: Pedro Melendez, Chief Executive Officer
Web address: www.menonitacima.org
Control: Other not–for–profit (including NFP Corporation) **Service**: Psychiatric

Staffed Beds: 20

⊞ **MENNONITE GENERAL HOSPITAL (400018)**, Calle Jose C Vasquez, Zip 00705, Mailing Address: P.O. Box 372800, Cayey, Zip 00737–2800; tel. 787/535–1001, (Nonreporting) **A**1 10
Primary Contact: Pedro Melendez, Chief Executive Officer
COO: Marta R Mercado Suro, Chief Operating Officer
CFO: Jose E Solivan, Chief Financial Officer
CMO: Victor Hernandez Miranda, M.D., Chief of Staff
CIO: Daniza Morales, Manager Information System
CHR: Evelyn Padilla Ortiz, Director Human Resources
CNO: Gloria Mercado, Director of Nursing
Web address: www.hospitalmenonita.com
Control: Other not–for–profit (including NFP Corporation) **Service:** General medical and surgical

Staffed Beds: 143

ARECIBO—Arecibo County

⊞ **HOSPITAL METROPOLITANO DR. SUSONI (400117)**, Calle Palma #55, Zip 00612, Mailing Address: P.O. Box 145200, Zip 00614; tel. 787/650–1030, (Nonreporting) **A**1 10
Primary Contact: Yelitza Lucena, Executive Director
CFO: Francisco Silva, Financial Director
CMO: Ada S Miranda, M.D., Medical Director
CIO: Mayra Montano, Director Information Systems
CHR: Janira Hernandez, Coordinator Human Resources
CNO: Damaris Rios, Executive Nursing Director
Web address: www.metropavia.com/DrSusoni.cfm
Control: Corporation, Investor–owned (for–profit) **Service:** General medical and surgical

Staffed Beds: 130

⊞ **HOSPITAL PAVIA ARECIBO (400087)**, 129 San Luis Avenue, Zip 00612, Mailing Address: P.O. Box 659, Zip 00613; tel. 787/650–7272, (Nonreporting) **A**1 10
Primary Contact: Jose Luis Rodriguez Collazo, Executive Director
COO: Jamie Rivera, Chief Financial Officer
CFO: Agustin Gonzalez, Director Finance
CMO: Antoine Pavia, M.D., Medical Director
CIO: David Valle, Chief Information Officer
CHR: Yesenia Natal, Coordinator Human Resources
CNO: Iris Toledo, Chief Nursing Officer
Web address: www.cayetano@xsn.net
Control: Corporation, Investor–owned (for–profit) **Service:** General medical and surgical

Staffed Beds: 184

BAYAMON—Bayamon County

★ **DOCTOR'S CENTER OF BAYAMON (400102)**, Extension Hermanas Davila, Zip 00960, Mailing Address: P.O. Box 2957, Zip 00960; tel. 787/622–5420, (Nonreporting) **A**10
Primary Contact: Maria Marte, Administrator
Web address: www.https://www.tuhospitalfamiliar.com
Control: Corporation, Investor–owned (for–profit) **Service:** General medical and surgical

Staffed Beds: 91

⊞ **HOSPITAL HERMANOS MELENDEZ (400032)**, Route 2, KM 11–7, Zip 00960, Mailing Address: P.O. Box 306, Zip 00960; tel. 787/620–8181, (Includes PUERTO RICO CHILDREN'S HOSPITAL, P O Box 1999, Bayamon, Puerto Rico, Zip 00960; tel. 787/474–1378; Tania Conde, Administrator), (Non-reporting) **A**1 3 10
Primary Contact: Richard Machado, M.D., President and Chief Executive Officer
CFO: Luz D Medina, Controller
CMO: Norma Ortiz, M.D., Medical Director
CIO: Leticia Santana, Administrator Medical Records
Web address: www.hospitalhermanosmelendez.net
Control: Corporation, Investor–owned (for–profit) **Service:** General medical and surgical

Staffed Beds: 211

⊞ **HOSPITAL SAN PABLO (400109)**, Calle Santa Cruz 70, Zip 00961–7020, Mailing Address: P.O. Box 236, Zip 00960–0236; tel. 787/740–4747, (Nonreporting) **A**1 3 5 10
Primary Contact: Claudia V. Guzman, Chief Executive Officer and Managing Director
Web address: www.sanpablo.com
Control: Corporation, Investor–owned (for–profit) **Service:** General medical and surgical

Staffed Beds: 400

⊞ **HOSPITAL UNIVERSITARIO DR. RAMON RUIZ ARNAU (400105)**, Avenue Laurel #100, Santa Juanita, Zip 00956; tel. 787/787–5151, (Nonreporting) **A**1 3 5 10 **S** Puerto Rico Department of Health, San Juan, PR
Primary Contact: Prudencio A. Laureano, Chief Executive Officer
CFO: Elsie Morales, Chief Financial Officer
CMO: Hector Cintron Principe, M.D., Director
CIO: Irma Duprey, Administrator Medical Records
CHR: Aurea De Leon, Chief Human Resources Officer
Web address: www.salud.gov.pr/Dept-de-Salud/Pages/Nuestros-Hospitales.aspx
Control: State, Government, nonfederal **Service:** General medical and surgical

Staffed Beds: 101

CABO ROJO—Cabo Rojo County

⊞ **HOSPITAL PSIQUIATRICO METROPOLITANO (404007)**, 108 Munoz Rivera Street, Zip 00623–4060, Mailing Address: P.O. Box 910, Zip 00623–0910; tel. 787/851–2025, (Nonreporting) **A**1 10
Primary Contact: Marco Reyes, Executive Director
Web address: www.metropavia.com/CaboRojo.cfm
Control: Other not–for–profit (including NFP Corporation) **Service:** Psychiatric

Staffed Beds: 43

CAGUAS—Caguas County

⊞ **HIMA SAN PABLO CAGUAS (400120)**, Avenida Munoz Marin, Zip 00726, Mailing Address: P.O. Box 4980; Zip 00726; tel. 787/653–3434, (Nonreporting) **A**1 2 3 5 10
Primary Contact: Maria E. Jacobo Moreno, Administrator
CFO: Luis A Arroyo, Chief Financial Officer
CMO: Ivan E Del Toro, M.D., Medical Director
CIO: Giovanni Piereschi, Vice President Enterprise Information and Chief Information Officer
CHR: Elena Robinson, Chief Human Resources Officer
CNO: Elenia Berrios, Chief Nursing Officer
Web address: www.himasanpablo.com
Control: Partnership, Investor–owned (for–profit) **Service:** General medical and surgical

Staffed Beds: 415

⊞ **HOSPITAL MENONITA DE CAGUAS (400104)**, P.O. Box 6660, Zip 00726–6660; tel. 787/653–0550, (Nonreporting) **A**1 5 10
Primary Contact: Pedro Melendez, Executive Director
Web address: www.sistemamenonita.com
Control: Other not–for–profit (including NFP Corporation) **Service:** General medical and surgical

Staffed Beds: 25

CAROLINA—Carolina County

⊞ **HOSPITAL DE LA UNIVERSIDAD DE PUERTO RICO/DR. FEDERICO TRILLA (400112)**, 65th Infanteria, KM 8 3, Zip 00984, Mailing Address: P.O. Box 6021, Zip 00984; tel. 787/757–1800, (Nonreporting) **A**1 3 5 10
Primary Contact: Diraida Maldonado, Chief Executive Officer
COO: Diraida Maldonado, Chief Executive Officer
CFO: Yolanda Quinonez, Chief Financial Officer
CMO: Marina Roman, M.D., Medical Director
CIO: Francisco Perez, Manager Management Information Systems
CHR: Betzaida Jimenez, Director Human Resources
Web address: www.hospitalupr.org
Control: Corporation, Investor–owned (for–profit) **Service:** General medical and surgical

Staffed Beds: 250

CASTANER—Lares County

★ **CASTANER GENERAL HOSPITAL (400010)**, KM 64–2, Route 135, Zip 00631, Mailing Address: P.O. Box 1003, Zip 00631; tel. 787/829–5010, (Nonreporting) **A**5 10
Primary Contact: Domingo Monroig, Executive Director
COO: Agustin Ponce, Supervisor Maintenance
CFO: Guillermo Jimenez, Director Finance
CMO: Jose O Rodriguez, M.D., Medical Director
CIO: Domingo Monroig, Executive Director
CHR: Nydimar Salcedo, Chief Human Resources Officer
CNO: Margarita Rentas, R.N., Nursing Director
Web address: www.hospitalcastaner.com
Control: Other not–for–profit (including NFP Corporation) **Service:** General medical and surgical

Staffed Beds: 24

Hospital, Medicare Provider Number, Address, Telephone, Approval, Facility, and Physician Codes, Health Care System

★ American Hospital Association (AHA) membership
◻ The Joint Commission accreditation
◯ Healthcare Facilities Accreditation Program
◇ DNV Healthcare Inc. accreditation
⇑ Center for Improvement in Healthcare Quality Accreditation
△ Commission on Accreditation of Rehabilitation Facilities (CARF) accreditation

CAYEY—Cayey County

⊠ **HOSPITAL MENONITA DE CAYEY (400013)**, 4 H Mendoza Street,
Zip 00736–3801, Mailing Address: P.O. Box 373130, Zip 00737–3130;
tel. 787/263–1001, (Nonreporting) **A**1 5 10
Primary Contact: Pedro Melendez, Chief Executive Director
COO: Leda Marta R Mercado, Chief Operating Officer
CFO: Jose E Solivan, Chief Financial Officer
CMO: Luis J Rodriquez Saenz, M.D., Medical Director
CIO: Daniza Morales, Chief Information Officer
CHR: Evelyn Padilla Ortiz, Director Human Resources
Web address: www.hospitalmenonita.com
Control: Other not–for–profit (including NFP Corporation) **Service:** General
medical and surgical

Staffed Beds: 242

CIDRA—Cidra County

⊠ **FIRST HOSPITAL PANAMERICANO (404004)**, State Road 787 KM 1 5,
Zip 00739, Mailing Address: P.O. Box 1400, Zip 00739; tel. 787/739–5555,
(Nonreporting) **A**1 3 5 10 **S** Universal Health Services, Inc., King of Prussia, PA
Primary Contact: Astro Munoz, Executive Director
COO: Tim McCarthy, President Puerto Rico Division
CFO: Arthur Fernandez, Chief Financial Officer
CMO: Arlene Martinez–Nieto, M.D., Chief Medical Officer
CIO: Tomas Rodriguez, Chief Information Technology Officer
CHR: Shirley Ayala, Director Human Resources
Web address: www.hospitalpanamericano.com
Control: Corporation, Investor–owned (for–profit) **Service:** Psychiatric

Staffed Beds: 153

COTO LAUREL—Ponce County

★ **HOSPITAL SAN CRISTOBAL (400113)**, 506 Carr Road, Zip 00780;
tel. 787/848–2100, (Nonreporting) **A**3 5 10
Primary Contact: Pedro L. Benetti-Loyola, Administrator
COO: Pedro L Benetti-Loyola, Senior Executive and Vice President
CFO: Marian Collazo, Director Finance
CMO: Ramon Rodriguez Rivas, M.D., Medical Director
CIO: Ramon Acevedo, Supervisor Information Systems
CHR: Candie Rodriguez, Director Human Resources
Web address: www.hospitalsancristobal.com
Control: Corporation, Investor–owned (for–profit) **Service:** Other specialty treatment

Staffed Beds: 103

FAJARDO—Fajardo County

★ **CARIBBEAN MEDICAL CENTER (400131)**, 151 Avenue Osvaldo Molina,
Zip 00738–4013, Mailing Address: Call Box 70006, Zip 00738–7006;
tel. 787/801–0081, (Nonreporting) **A**10
Primary Contact: Ana Oliveras Laguna, Administrator
CMO: Miguel Rodriguez, Medical Director
Web address: www.caribbeanmedicalcenter.com
Control: Other not–for–profit (including NFP Corporation) **Service:** General
medical and surgical

Staffed Beds: 39

⊠ **HOSPITAL SAN PABLO DEL ESTE (400125)**, Avenida General Valero, 404,
Zip 00738, Mailing Address: P.O. Box 1028, Zip 00738–1028; tel. 787/863–0505,
(Nonreporting) **A**1 10
Primary Contact: Venus V. Ramirez, Executive Director
CFO: Luis A Arroyo, Chief Financial Officer
CMO: Manuel Navas, M.D., Medical Director
CHR: Vilma Rodriguez, Director Human Resources
Web address: www.sanpablo.com
Control: Corporation, Investor–owned (for–profit) **Service:** General medical and
surgical

Staffed Beds: 221

GUAYAMA—Guayama County

⊠ **HOSPITAL EPISCOPAL SAN LUCAS GUAYAMA (400048)**, Avenue Pedro
Albizu Campos, Zip 00784, Mailing Address: P.O. Box 10011, Zip 00785–1006;
tel. 787/864–4300, (Nonreporting) **A**1 3 5 10
Primary Contact: Elyonel Ponton, Executive Director
COO: Arnaldo Rodriguez Sanchez, M.D., Chief Operating Officer
CFO: Rosemary De La Cruz, Chief Financial Officer
CMO: Gerson Jimenez, M.D., Medical Director
CHR: Ivette Lacot, Director Human Resources
Web address: www.ssepr.com
Control: Church operated, Nongovernment, not–for–profit **Service:** General
medical and surgical

Staffed Beds: 115

GUAYNABO—Guaynabo County

PROFESSIONAL HOSPITAL GUAYNABO (400122), Carretera 199
Km 1.2 Avenue, Zip 00969, Mailing Address: P.O. Box 1609, Zip 00970;
tel. 787/708–6560, (Nonreporting) **A**5 10
Primary Contact: Leonardo Valentin, Chief Executive Officer
Web address: www.professionalhospital.com
Control: Other not–for–profit (including NFP Corporation) **Service:** Psychiatric

Staffed Beds: 54

HATO REY—San Juan County

⊠ **I. GONZALEZ MARTINEZ ONCOLOGIC HOSPITAL (400012)**, Puerto Rico
Medical Center, Zip 00935, Mailing Address: P.O. Box 191811, Zip 00919–1811;
tel. 787/765–2382, (Nonreporting) **A**1 2 3 5 10
Primary Contact: Jorge De Jesus, Executive Director
COO: Felix Ortiz Baez, Administrator
CFO: Yolanda Quinones, Director Finance
CMO: Carlos Chevere, M.D., Medical Director
CHR: Luz Maria Hernandez, Director Human Resources
Control: Other not–for–profit (including NFP Corporation) **Service:** Cancer

Staffed Beds: 57

HUMACAO—Humacao County

HOSPITAL DR. DOMINGUEZ See Hospital Oriente

⊠ **HOSPITAL HIMA DE HUMACAO (400005)**, 3 Font Martelo Street,
Zip 00791–3342, Mailing Address: P.O. Box 639, Zip 00792–0639;
tel. 787/656–2424, (Nonreporting) **A**1 10
Primary Contact: Aixa Irizarry, Executive Director
COO: Carlos M Pineiro, President
CFO: Luis A Arroyo, Chief Financial Officer
CMO: Francisco R. Carballo, M.D., Medical Director
CIO: Giovanni Piereschi, Vice President Management Information Systems
CHR: Iris Abreu, Supervisor Human Resources
Web address: www.himasanpablo.com
Control: Corporation, Investor–owned (for–profit) **Service:** General medical and
surgical

Staffed Beds: 64

★ **HOSPITAL ORIENTE (400011)**, 300 Font Martelo Street, Zip 00791–3230,
Mailing Address: P.O. Box 699, Zip 00792–0699; tel. 787/852–0505,
(Nonreporting) **A**10
Primary Contact: Efrain Pinero, Administrator
CFO: Ivonne Rivera, Director Finance
CMO: Carmelo Herrero, M.D., Medical Director
CHR: Ivonne Lopez, Director Human Resources
Control: Corporation, Investor–owned (for–profit) **Service:** General medical and
surgical

Staffed Beds: 60

★ **RYDER MEMORIAL HOSPITAL (400007)**, 355 Font Martelo Street,
Zip 00791–3249, Mailing Address: P O Box 859, Zip 00792–0859;
tel. 787/852–0768, (Nonreporting) **A**5 10
Primary Contact: Jose R. Feliciano, Chief Executive Officer
CFO: Jose O Ortiz, Chief Financial Officer
CMO: Raul Ramos Pereira, M.D., Medical Director
CIO: Joseph V Cruz, Chief Information Officer
CHR: Maria Figueroa, Director Human Resources
CNO: Aurelis Burgus, Nursing Director
Web address: www.hryder@prtc.net
Control: Other not–for–profit (including NFP Corporation) **Service:** General
medical and surgical

Staffed Beds: 227

MANATI—Manati County

⊠ **DOCTORS CENTER (400118)**, KM 47–7, Zip 00674, Mailing Address: P.O. Box
30532, Zip 00674; tel. 787/854–3322, (Nonreporting) **A**1 10
Primary Contact: Belinda L. Toro Palacios, Executive Director
Web address: www.https://www.tuhospitalfamiliar.com
Control: Corporation, Investor–owned (for–profit) **Service:** General medical and
surgical

Staffed Beds: 250

★ **ENCOMPASS HEALTH REHABILITATION HOSPITAL OF MANATI (403026)**, Carretera 2, Kilometro 47 7, Zip 00674; tel. 787/621–3800, (Nonreporting) **A**10 **S** Encompass Health Corporation, Birmingham, AL
Primary Contact: Enid Y. Gonzalez, Chief Executive Officer
CFO: Jesus M Corazon, Controller
CMO: Jamie L Marrero, M.D., Medical Director
CHR: Erika Landrau, Director Human Resources
CNO: Evelyn Diaz, R.N., Chief Nursing Officer
Web address: www.healthsouth.com
Control: Corporation, Investor–owned (for–profit) **Service:** Rehabilitation

Staffed Beds: 40

⊞ **HOSPITAL MANATI MEDICAL CENTER (400114)**, Calle Hernandez, Carrion 668, Zip 00674, Mailing Address: P.O. Box 1142, Zip 00674–1142; tel. 787/621–3700, (Nonreporting) **A**1 3 5 10
Primary Contact: Jose S. Rosado, Executive Director
CFO: Noriselle Rivera-Pol, Vice President Finance
CMO: Luis R Rosa-Toledo, M.D., Medical Director
CIO: Alberto Medina, Information Technology Senior Consultant
CHR: Nilda Paravisini, Director Human Resources
Web address: www.manatimedical.com
Control: Corporation, Investor–owned (for–profit) **Service:** General medical and surgical

Staffed Beds: 235

MAYAGUEZ—Mayaguez County

⊞ **BELLA VISTA HOSPITAL (400014)**, State Road 349, Zip 00680, Mailing Address: P.O. Box 1750, Zip 00681; tel. 787/834–6000, (Nonreporting) **A**1 3 5 10
Primary Contact: Luis Rivera Maldonado, Executive Director
CFO: Enrique Rivera, Chief Financial Officer
CMO: Miguel Cruz, M.D., Medical Director
CHR: Benjamin Astacio, Director Human Resources
Web address: www.bvhpr.org
Control: Church operated, Nongovernment, not–for–profit **Service:** General medical and surgical

Staffed Beds: 157

⊞ **DR. RAMON E. BETANCES HOSPITAL-MAYAGUEZ MEDICAL CENTER BRANCH (400103)**, 410 Hostos Avenue, Zip 00680–1501, Mailing Address: P.O. Box 600, Zip 00681–0600; tel. 787/652–9200, (Nonreporting) **A**1 3 5 10
Primary Contact: Idelfonso Vargas, Executive Director
CMO: Milton D Carrero, M.D., Medical Director
CHR: Betsmari Medina, Director Human Resources
Web address: www.mayaguezmedical.com
Control: State, Government, nonfederal **Service:** General medical and surgical

Staffed Beds: 189

★ **HOSPITAL PEREA (400123)**, 15 Basora Street, Zip 00681, Mailing Address: P.O. Box 170, Zip 00681; tel. 787/834–0101, (Nonreporting) **A**3 10 **S** United Medical Corporation, Windermere, FL
Primary Contact: Jorge I. Martinez, Executive Director
CFO: Joannie Garcia, CPA, Director Finance
CMO: Humberto Olivencia, M.D., Medical Director
Web address: www.paviahealth.com/perea_hospital.htm
Control: Corporation, Investor–owned (for–profit) **Service:** General medical and surgical

Staffed Beds: 103

★ **HOSPITAL SAN ANTONIO (018487)**, Calle Dr Ramon Emeterio Betances N #18, Zip 00680, Mailing Address: P.O. Box 546, Zip 00681–0546; tel. 787/834–0050, (Nonreporting) **A**3 5
Primary Contact: Francisco Martinez, Executive Director
Web address: www.hsaipr.com/
Control: Other not–for–profit (including NFP Corporation) **Service:** General medical and surgical

Staffed Beds: 25

MOCA—Moca County

★ **HOSPITAL SAN CARLOS BORROMEO (400111)**, 550 Concepcion Vera Ayala, Zip 00676, Mailing Address: P.O. Box 68, Zip 00676; tel. 787/877–8000, **A**10 **F**8 15 29 30 40 45 68 74 75 76 79 81 87 89 107 110 111 114 119 130 148
Primary Contact: Rosaida M. Crespo, Executive Director
COO: Rosaida M Crespo, Executive Director
CFO: Irma Cabrera, Finance Director
CMO: Erick Nieves, M.D., Medical Director
CIO: Juan Carlos Soto, Director Information Systems
CHR: Migdalia Ortiz, Director Human Resources
CNO: Luz M Velez, Director-Administration of Nursing Services
Web address: www.hscbpr.org
Control: Other not–for–profit (including NFP Corporation) **Service:** General medical and surgical

Staffed Beds: 108 **Admissions:** 3791 **Census:** 52 **Outpatient Visits:** 32208 **Births:** 435 **Total Expense ($000):** 24363 **Payroll Expense ($000):** 7512 **Personnel:** 288

PONCE—Ponce County

⊞ **DR. PILA'S HOSPITAL (400003)**, Avenida Las Americas, Zip 00731, Mailing Address: P.O. Box 1910, Zip 00733–1910; tel. 787/848–5600, (Nonreporting) **A**1 5 10
Primary Contact: Rafael Alvarado, Chief Executive Officer
Web address: www.drpila.com
Control: Other not–for–profit (including NFP Corporation) **Service:** General medical and surgical

Staffed Beds: 143

⊞ **HOSPITAL DE DAMAS (400022)**, 2213 Ponce Bypass, Zip 00717; tel. 787/840–8686, (Nonreporting) **A**1 3 5 10
Primary Contact: Maria Mercedes Torres. Bernal, Administrator
CFO: Julio Colon, Financial Director
CMO: Pedro Benitez, M.D., Medical Director
CIO: Bienvenido Ortiz, Coordinator Information Systems
CHR: Gilberto Cuevas, Director Human Resources
CNO: Sandra Dominicci, Nursing Director
Web address: www.hospitaldamas.com/
Control: Other not–for–profit (including NFP Corporation) **Service:** General medical and surgical

Staffed Beds: 201

HOSPITAL DE PSIQUIATRIA FORENSE, Road 14, Zip 00731; tel. 787/844–0210, (Nonreporting)
Primary Contact: Nemuel O. Artlles, FACHE, Administrator
Web address: www.bestmentalhealthfacilities.com/hospital-psiquiatria-forenseponce-in-ponce-pr-731/
Control: State, Government, nonfederal **Service:** Psychiatric

Staffed Beds: 25

★ **INSPIRA PONCE (404008)**, Calle Guadalupe, #184, Piso2, Zip 00730; tel. 787/709–4130, (Nonreporting) **A**10
Primary Contact: Alberto M. Varela, M.D., President
Web address: www.inspirapr.com
Control: Corporation, Investor–owned (for–profit) **Service:** Psychiatric

Staffed Beds: 30

⊞ **ST. LUKE'S EPISCOPAL HOSPITAL (400044)**, 917 Tito Castro Avenue, Zip 00731–4717, Mailing Address: P.O. Box 336810, Zip 00733–6810; tel. 787/844–2080, (Nonreporting) **A**1 3 5 10
Primary Contact: Jose M. Torres, Executive Director
CFO: Carlos Valentin, Chief Financial Officer
CMO: Jesus Cruz Correa, Chief Medical Officer
CIO: Jose Abrams, Chief Information Officer
CHR: Hector Troche Garcin, Human Resources Director
CNO: Zoraida Vega, MSN, R.N., Chief Nursing Officer
Web address: www.sanlucaspr.com
Control: Church operated, Nongovernment, not–for–profit **Service:** General medical and surgical

Staffed Beds: 334

Hospital, Medicare Provider Number, Address, Telephone, Approval, Facility, and Physician Codes, Health Care System

★ American Hospital Association (AHA) membership ○ Healthcare Facilities Accreditation Program ⇑ Center for Improvement in Healthcare Quality Accreditation
□ The Joint Commission accreditation ◇ DNV Healthcare Inc. accreditation △ Commission on Accreditation of Rehabilitation Facilities (CARF) accreditation

RIO PIEDRAS—San Juan County

✠ **UNIVERSITY PEDIATRIC HOSPITAL (403301)**, Barrio Monacenno, Carretera 22, Zip 00935, Mailing Address: P.O. Box 191079, San Juan, Zip 00910–1070; tel. 787/777–3535, (Nonreporting) **A**1 3 5 10 **S** Puerto Rico Department of Health, San Juan, PR
Primary Contact: Gloria Hernandez, Executive Director
CMO: Myrna Quinones Feliciano, M.D., Medical Director
Web address: www.md.rcm.upr.edu/pediatrics/university_pediatric_hospital.php
Control: State, Government, nonfederal **Service**: Children's general medical and surgical

Staffed Beds: 145

SAN GERMAN—San German County

✠ **HOSPITAL DE LA CONCEPCION (400021)**, Carr 2, Km 173, Bo Cain Alto, Zip 00683–3920, Mailing Address: P.O. Box 285, Zip 00683–0285; tel. 787/892–1860, (Nonreporting) **A**1 3 5 10
Primary Contact: Felicita Bonilla, Administrator
COO: Gustavo Almodovar, Executive Director
CFO: Lizmari Calderon, Director Finance
CMO: Ivan Acosta, M.D., Medical Director
CIO: Daniel Ferreira, Director Management Information Systems
CHR: Ada Bermudez, Director Human Resources
CNO: Amanda Caraballo, Nursing Director
Web address: www.hospitalconcepcion.org
Control: Church operated, Nongovernment, not-for-profit **Service**: General medical and surgical

Staffed Beds: 187

★ **HOSPITAL METROPOLITANO SAN GERMAN (400126)**, Calle Javilla Al Costado Parque de Bombas, Zip 00683, Mailing Address: P.O. Box 63, Zip 00683; tel. 787/892–5300, (Nonreporting) **A**10
Primary Contact: Luis A. Berdiel, Executive Director
Control: Corporation, Investor–owned (for–profit) **Service**: Other specialty treatment

Staffed Beds: 76

SAN JUAN—San Juan County

✠ **ASHFORD PRESBYTERIAN COMMUNITY HOSPITAL (400001)**, 1451 Avenue Ashford, Zip 00907–1511, Mailing Address: P.O. Box 9020032, Zip 00902–0032; tel. 787/721–2160, **A**1 3 5 10 **F**3 8 11 13 15 18 28 30 40 41 45 46 49 51 53 57 59 65 70 72 75 79 81 82 87 91 93 107 110 111 114 116 118 119 130 131 135 145 146 147 148
Primary Contact: Pedro J. Gonzalez, FACHE, Chief Executive Officer
COO: Obdulia Medina, Associate Director for Administrative Support, Clinical Management and Ambulatory Care
CFO: Mayra Torres, CPA, Chief Financial Officer
CMO: Francisco de Torres, M.D., Medical Director
CIO: Sigfredo Irizarry, Information Technology Director
CHR: Irma Carrillo, Director Human Resources
CNO: Itza Soto, MSN, Nursing Executive
Web address: www.presbypr.com
Control: Other not–for–profit (including NFP Corporation) **Service**: General medical and surgical

Staffed Beds: 174 Admissions: 7632 Census: 108 Outpatient Visits: 39918 Births: 2010 Total Expense ($000): 62912 Payroll Expense ($000): 18534 Personnel: 622

✠ **AUXILIO MUTUO HOSPITAL (400016)**, Ponce De Leon Avenue, Zip 00918–1000, Mailing Address: P.O. Box 191227, Zip 00919–1227; tel. 787/758–2000, **A**1 3 5 10 **F**3 8 13 15 17 18 20 22 24 26 29 30 31 40 41 45 46 49 53 54 58 64 65 70 72 74 75 76 78 79 81 88 89 90 93 97 107 108 110 111 114 115 116 117 118 119 120 121 123 124 129 130 131 136 138 139 142 146 148 156
Primary Contact: Jorge L Matta. Serrano, Administrator
COO: Carmen Martin, Associate Administrator
CFO: Maria L Marti, Director Fiscal Services
CMO: Jose Isado, M.D., Medical Director
CIO: Edgardo Rodriguez, Director Management Information Systems
CHR: Maria Vega, Director Human Resources
Web address: www.auxiliomutuo.com
Control: Other not–for–profit (including NFP Corporation) **Service**: General medical and surgical

Staffed Beds: 472 Admissions: 17043 Census: 313 Outpatient Visits: 1372668 Births: 712 Total Expense ($000): 227329 Payroll Expense ($000): 76943 Personnel: 2030

✠ **CARDIOVASCULAR CENTER OF PUERTO RICO AND THE CARIBBEAN (400124)**, Americo Miranda Centro Medico, Zip 00936, Mailing Address: P.O. Box 366528, Zip 00936–6528; tel. 787/754–8500, (Nonreporting) **A**1 3 5 10 **S** Puerto Rico Department of Health, San Juan, PR
Primary Contact: Carlos Cabrera, Executive Director
COO: Wilfredo Rabelo Millan, Chief Operating Officer
CFO: Arthur J Fernandez del Valle, Chief Financial Officer
CMO: Jose E Novoa Loyola, M.D., Medical Director
CIO: Eugenio Torres Ayala, Director Information Systems
CHR: Myriam T Rodriguez Schmidt, Director Human Resources
CNO: Pedro Laureano Cantre, Chief Nursing Officer
Web address: www.cardiovascular.gobierno.pr
Control: State, Government, nonfederal **Service**: General medical and surgical

Staffed Beds: 139

★ **DOCTORS' CENTER HOSPITAL SAN JUAN (400006)**, 1395 San Rafael Street, Zip 00909–2518, Mailing Address: Box 11338, Santurce Station, Zip 00910–3428; tel. 787/999–7620, (Nonreporting) **A**10
Primary Contact: Norma Marrero, Executive Administrator
COO: Norma Marrero, Executive Administrator
CFO: Alejandro Santiago, Director Finance
CMO: Ubaldo Santiago, M.D., Chairman
CIO: Luis Alicea, Chief Information Officer
CHR: Carmen Perez, Director Human Resources
CNO: Lesbia Lopez, Chief Nursing Officer
Web address: www.tuhospitalfamiliar.com
Control: Corporation, Investor–owned (for–profit) **Service**: General medical and surgical

Staffed Beds: 133

★ **ENCOMPASS HEALTH REHABILITATION HOSPITAL OF SAN JUAN (403025)**, University Hospital, 3rd Floor, Zip 00923, Mailing Address: P.O. Box 70344, Zip 00923; tel. 787/274–5100, (Nonreporting) **A**3 5 10 **S** Encompass Health Corporation, Birmingham, AL
Primary Contact: Daniel Del Castillo, Chief Executive Officer
CFO: Jesus M Corazon, Controller
CMO: Eduardo Ramos, M.D., Medical Director
CHR: Frances Fuentes, Coordinator Human Resources
CNO: Zamarys Rivera, R.N., Chief Nursing Officer
Web address: www.healthsouthsanjuan.com
Control: Corporation, Investor–owned (for–profit) **Service**: Rehabilitation

Staffed Beds: 32

HOSPITAL CUIDADO AGUDO ESPECIALIZADO EN PACIENTES POLITRAUMATIZADOS (400127), Carr. Num. 22 BO. Monacillos, Centro Medico, Zip 00922–2129, Mailing Address: P.O. Box 2129, Zip 00922–2129; tel. 787/777–3535, (Nonreporting)
Primary Contact: Victor L. Medina Cruz, M.D., Administrator
Web address: www.asempr.org
Control: Other not–for–profit (including NFP Corporation) **Service**: General medical and surgical

Staffed Beds: 25

★ **HOSPITAL DE PSIQUIATRIA (404006)**, Dr. Ramon Fernandez Marina, P O Box 2100, Zip 00936; tel. 787/766–4646, (Nonreporting) **A**5
Primary Contact: Elizabeth De Santiago, Executive Director
CMO: Brunilda Vazquez, Medical Director
CHR: Idalia Garcia, Chief Human Resources Officer
Control: State, Government, nonfederal **Service**: Psychiatric

Staffed Beds: 141

✠ **HOSPITAL DEL MAESTRO (400004)**, 550 Sergio Cuevas, Zip 00918–3741, Mailing Address: P.O. Box 364708, Zip 00936–4708; tel. 787/758–8383, (Nonreporting) **A**1 10
Primary Contact: Jorge Torres. Otero, Executive Director
CFO: Marisol Vargas, Director Finance
CMO: Jose Montalvo, M.D., Medical Director
CIO: Laura Rodriguez, Director Medical Records
CHR: Orlando Santiago, Human Resources Officer
Web address: www.hospitaldelmaestro.org
Control: Corporation, Investor–owned (for–profit) **Service**: General medical and surgical

Staffed Beds: 250

Many Facility Codes have changed. Please refer to the AHA Guide Code Chart.

HOSPITAL METROPOLITAN (400106), 1785 Carr 21, Zip 00921–3399, Mailing Address: P.O. Box 11981, Zip 00922; tel. 787/782–9999, (Nonreporting) **A**1 10
Primary Contact: Domingo Nevarez, Chief Executive Officer
CFO: Maritza Rodriguez, Chief Financial Officer
CMO: Maria de los Angeles Correa, M.D., Medical Director
CIO: Manuel Santiago, Chief Information Officer
Control: Corporation, Investor–owned (for–profit) **Service**: General medical and surgical

Staffed Beds: 127

HOSPITAL PAVIA-HATO REY (400128), 435 Ponce De Leon Avenue, Zip 00917–3428, Mailing Address: P.O. Box 190828, Zip 00917–3428; tel. 787/641–2323, (Nonreporting) **A**1 3 5 10 **S** United Medical Corporation, Windermere, FL
Primary Contact: Guillermo Pastrana, Executive Director
Web address: www.paviahealth.com
Control: Corporation, Investor–owned (for–profit) **Service**: General medical and surgical

Staffed Beds: 180

HOSPITAL PAVIA-SANTURCE (400019), 1462 Asia Street, Zip 00909–2143, Mailing Address: Box 11137, Santurce Station, Zip 00910–1137; tel. 787/727–6060, (Nonreporting) **A**1 10 **S** United Medical Corporation, Windermere, FL
Primary Contact: Jose Luis. Rodriguez, Chief Executive Officer
CFO: Francisco Espina, Director Finance
Web address: www.paviahealth.com
Control: Corporation, Investor–owned (for–profit) **Service**: General medical and surgical

Staffed Beds: 197

★ **HOSPITAL PSIQUIATRICO CORRECCIONAL**, PMB 302 P O Box 70344, Zip 00936; tel. 939/225–2400, (Nonreporting)
Primary Contact: Felicita E. Alvarado, Administrator
Web address: www.www2.pr.gov/Directorios/Pages/InfoAgencia.aspx?PRIFA=220
Control: State, Government, nonfederal **Service**: General medical and surgical

Staffed Beds: 25

HOSPITAL SAN FRANCISCO (400098), 371 Avenida De Diego, Zip 00923–1711, Mailing Address: P.O. Box 29025, Zip 00929–0025; tel. 787/767–5100, (Nonreporting) **A**1 10 **S** United Medical Corporation, Windermere, FL
Primary Contact: Marcos Aguila, Chief Executive Officer
CFO: Lizzette Rodriguez, Director Finance
CMO: Hector L Cotto, M.D., Medical Director
CIO: Deborah Nieves, Director Management Information Systems
CHR: Sugehi Santiago, Director
Web address: www.metropavia.com/SanFrancisco.ctm
Control: Corporation, Investor–owned (for–profit) **Service**: General medical and surgical

Staffed Beds: 133

★ **HOSPITAL SAN GERARDO (400121)**, 138 Avenue Winston Churchill, Zip 00926–6013; tel. 787/761–8383, (Nonreporting)
Primary Contact: Henry Ruberte, Administrator
Web address: www.https://hospitales.cybo.com/PR-biz/hospital-san-gerardo_2P
Control: Other not–for–profit (including NFP Corporation) **Service**: Chronic disease

Staffed Beds: 60

★ **INDUSTRIAL HOSPITAL**, Puerto Rico Medical Center, Zip 00936, Mailing Address: P.O. Box 365028, Zip 00936; tel. 787/754–2525, (Nonreporting)
Primary Contact: Jane Vega, Executive Director
CFO: Robert Bernier Casanova, Chief Financial Officer
CMO: Carmen Carrasquillo, M.D., Medical Director
CHR: Sonia M Lebron, Human Resources Specialist
Control: State, Government, nonfederal **Service**: General medical and surgical

Staffed Beds: 108

SAN JUAN CAPESTRANO HOSPITAL (404005), Rural Route 2, Box 11, Zip 00926; tel. 787/625–2900, (Nonreporting) **A**1 5 10 **S** Acadia Healthcare Company, Inc., Franklin, TN
Primary Contact: Marta Rivera. Plaza, Chief Executive Officer and Managing Director
CFO: Julia Cruz, Chief Financial Officer
CMO: Jose' Alonso, M.D., Medical Director
CIO: Ana Morandeira, Director Marketing
CHR: Luis Rivera, Director Human Resources
Web address: www.sjcapestrano.com
Control: Corporation, Investor–owned (for–profit) **Service**: Psychiatric

Staffed Beds: 158

SAN JUAN CITY HOSPITAL (400015), Puerto Rico Medical Center, Zip 00928, Mailing Address: PMB 79, P O Box 70344, Zip 00936–8344; tel. 787/766–2222, (Nonreporting) **A**1 3 5 10
Primary Contact: James F. Nieves, Executive Director
COO: Norma Marcano, Chief Operating Officer
CFO: Jaime Rodriguez, Chief Financial Officer
CMO: Raul Reyes, M.D., Medical Director
CIO: Gustavo Mesa, Chief Information Officer
CHR: Jose Garcia, Chief Human Resources Officer
Web address: www.massalud.com
Control: City, Government, nonfederal **Service**: General medical and surgical

Staffed Beds: 267

UNIVERSITY HOSPITAL (400061), Nineyas 869 Rio Piedras, Zip 00922, Mailing Address: P.O. Box 2116, Zip 00922; tel. 787/754–0101, (Nonreporting) **A**1 3 5 10 **S** Puerto Rico Department of Health, San Juan, PR
Primary Contact: Jorge Matta. Gonzalez, Executive Director
CFO: Janet Baez, Director
CMO: Ricardo Moscoso, M.D., Medical Director
CIO: Josue Martinez, Coordinator Information Systems
CHR: Ramomita Navarro, Director Human Resources
Control: State, Government, nonfederal **Service**: General medical and surgical

Staffed Beds: 220

△ **VETERANS AFFAIRS CARIBBEAN HEALTHCARE SYSTEM**, 10 Casia Street, Zip 00921–3201; tel. 787/641–7582, (Nonreporting) **A**1 2 3 5 7 8 **S** Department of Veterans Affairs, Washington, DC
Primary Contact: Carlos R. Escobar, FACHE, Director
CFO: Oscar Rodriguez, Chief Fiscal Officer
CIO: Manuel Negron, Chief Information Technology Service
CHR: Omar Ahmed, Acting Manager Human Resources
CNO: Kathleen Ruiz, M.D., Associate Director Patient Care Services
Web address: www.caribbean.va.gov/
Control: Veterans Affairs, Government, federal **Service**: General medical and surgical

Staffed Beds: 422

SANTURCE—San Juan County

SAN JORGE CHILDREN'S HOSPITAL, 258 San Jorge Street, Santurce, Zip 00912–3310, Mailing Address: P.O. Box 6308, San Juan, Zip 00912–3310; tel. 787/727–1000, (Nonreporting) **A**1 3 5 **S** United Medical Corporation, Windermere, FL
Primary Contact: Domingo Cruz, Senior Vice President Operations
CFO: Jose Marrero, Director Finance
CMO: Luis Clavell, M.D., Medical Director
CIO: Rogelio Caballero, Chief Information Systems
CHR: Odette Burgos, Supervisor Human Resources
CNO: Leticia Fuentes, Nursing Director
Web address: www.sanjorgechildrenshospital.com
Control: Corporation, Investor–owned (for–profit) **Service**: Children's general medical and surgical

Staffed Beds: 167

Hospital, Medicare Provider Number, Address, Telephone, Approval, Facility, and Physician Codes, Health Care System

★ American Hospital Association (AHA) membership
□ The Joint Commission accreditation
○ Healthcare Facilities Accreditation Program
◇ DNV Healthcare Inc. accreditation
⇧ Center for Improvement in Healthcare Quality Accreditation
△ Commission on Accreditation of Rehabilitation Facilities (CARF) accreditation

UTUADO—San Juan County

★ **METROPOLITANO DE LA MONTANA (400130)**, Calle Issac Gonzalez Martinez, Zip 00641, Mailing Address: P.O. Box 2600, Zip 00641; tel. 787/933–1100, (Nonreporting) **A**3 10
Primary Contact: Yelitza Sanchez. Rodriguez, Executive Director
Web address: www.metropavia.com/DeLaMontana.cfm
Control: Corporation, Investor–owned (for–profit) **Service:** General medical and surgical

Staffed Beds: 25

VEGA BAJA—Vega Alta County

★ **WILMA N. VAZQUEZ MEDICAL CENTER (400115)**, KM 39 1/2 Road 2, Call Box 7001, Zip 00694; tel. 787/858–1580, (Nonreporting) **A**10
Primary Contact: Ramon J. Vilar, Administrator
COO: Jose O Pabon, Director Operations
CFO: Youdie Reynolds-Gossette, Controller
CMO: Jorge Feria, M.D., President Medical Staff
CIO: Miguel Aponte, Supervisor Management Information Systems
CHR: Aymette Garcia, Manager Human Resources
Control: Corporation, Investor–owned (for–profit) **Service:** General medical and surgical

Staffed Beds: 150

YAUCO—Yauco County

☒ **HOSPITAL PAVIA YAUCO (400110)**, Carretera 128 KM 1.0, Zip 00698, Mailing Address: P.O. Box 5643, Zip 00698; tel. 787/856–1000, (Nonreporting) **A**1 5 10
Primary Contact: Dinorah Hernandez Esq, Executive Director
CFO: Elizabeth Gonzalez, CPA, Financial Director
CMO: Juan Pillot, M.D., Esq Medical Director
CIO: Edson Ortiz, Chief Information Officer
Web address: www.metropavia.com/facilities/hospitals/pavia-yauco/?lang=en/
Control: Corporation, Investor–owned (for–profit) **Service:** General medical and surgical

Staffed Beds: 115

VIRGIN ISLANDS

CHRISTIANSTED—St. Croix County

☐ **GOVERNOR JUAN F. LUIS HOSPITAL (480002)**, 4007 Estate Diamond Ruby, Zip 00820–4421; tel. 340/778–6311, (Nonreporting) **A**1 10
Primary Contact: Darice S. Plaskett, R.N., FACHE, Interim Chief Executive Officer
CFO: Rosalie Javois, Chief Financial Officer
CMO: Robert Centeno, M.D., Chief Medical Officer
CIO: Reuben D Molloy, Chief Information Officer
CHR: Joan Jean-Baptiste, Vice President Human Resources
Web address: www.jflusvi.org
Control: State, Government, nonfederal **Service:** General medical and surgical

Staffed Beds: 165

SAINT THOMAS—St. Thomas County

☐ **SCHNEIDER REGIONAL MEDICAL CENTER (480001)**, 9048 Sugar Estate, Charlotte Amalie, Zip 00802; tel. 340/776–8311, (Nonreporting) **A**1 10
Primary Contact: Bernard Wheatley, FACHE, Chief Executive Officer
CMO: Thelma Ruth Watson, M.D., Medical Director
CIO: J C Creque, Director Management Information Systems
CHR: Marlene J Adams, Director Human Resources
Web address: www.rlshospital.org
Control: State, Government, nonfederal **Service:** General medical and surgical

Staffed Beds: 86

U.S. Government Hospitals
Outside the United States, by Area

GERMANY

Heidelberg: ★ Heidelberg Army Community Hospital, APO, CMR 242, AE 09042

Landstuhl: ★ Landstuhl Army Regional Medical Center, APO, CMR 402, AE 09180

Wuerzburg: ★ Wuerzburg Army Community Hospital, APO, USAMEDDAC Wuerzburg, Ut 26610, AE 09244

ITALY

Naples: ★ U. S. Naval Hospital, FPO, none, AE 09619

JAPAN

Yokosuka: ★ U. S. Naval Hospital, Box 1487, UNIT 96350

SOUTH KOREA

Seoul: ★ Brian Allgood Army Community Hospital, 121st General Hospital, UNIT 96205

SPAIN

Rota: ★ U. S. Naval Hospital, Rota, FPO, PSC 819, Box 18, AE 09645–2500

TAIWAN

Taipei: ★ U. S. Naval Hospital Taipei, No 300 Shin–Pai Road, Sec 2

Index of Hospitals

This section is an index of all hospitals in alphabetical order by hospital name, followed by the city, state, and page reference to the hospital's listing in Section A.

A

ABBEVILLE AREA MEDICAL CENTER, ABBEVILLE, SC, p. A549

ABBEVILLE GENERAL HOSPITAL, ABBEVILLE, LA, p. A262

ABBOTT NORTHWESTERN HOSPITAL, MINNEAPOLIS, MN, p. A335

ABILENE REGIONAL MEDICAL CENTER, ABILENE, TX, p. A581

ABINGTON HOSPITAL, ABINGTON, PA, p. A519

ABINGTON–LANSDALE HOSPITAL JEFFERSON HEALTH, LANSDALE, PA, p. A529

ABRAHAM LINCOLN MEMORIAL HOSPITAL, LINCOLN, IL, p. A188

ABRAZO ARROWHEAD CAMPUS, GLENDALE, AZ, p. A30

ABRAZO CENTRAL CAMPUS, PHOENIX, AZ, p. A32

ABRAZO SCOTTSDALE CAMPUS, PHOENIX, AZ, p. A32

ABRAZO WEST CAMPUS, GOODYEAR, AZ, p. A30

ABROM KAPLAN MEMORIAL HOSPITAL, KAPLAN, LA, p. A270

ACADIA GENERAL HOSPITAL, CROWLEY, LA, p. A266

ACADIA–ST. LANDRY HOSPITAL, CHURCH POINT, LA, p. A265

ACCEL REHABILITATION HOSPITAL OF PLANO, PLANO, TX, p. A629

ACCESS HOSPITAL DAYTON, DAYTON, OH, p. A481

ACCORD REHABILIATION HOSPITAL, PLAQUEMINE, LA, p. A277

ACMH HOSPITAL, KITTANNING, PA, p. A528

ACOMA–CANONCITO–LAGUNA HOSPITAL, ACOMA, NM, p. A416

ACUITY SPECIALTY HOSPITAL OF NEW JERSEY, ATLANTIC CITY, NJ, p. A403

ACUITY SPECIALTY HOSPITAL OF SOUTHERN NEW JERSEY, WILLINGBORO, NJ, p. A415

ACUITY SPECIALTY HOSPITALS OHIO VALLEY, STEUBENVILLE, OH, p. A491

AD HOSPITAL EAST, HOUSTON, TX, p. A610

ADAIR COUNTY HEALTH SYSTEM, GREENFIELD, IA, p. A223

ADAMS COUNTY REGIONAL MEDICAL CENTER, SEAMAN, OH, p. A490

ADAMS MEMORIAL HOSPITAL, DECATUR, IN, p. A202

ADCARE HOSPITAL OF WORCESTER, WORCESTER, MA, p. A305

ADDISON GILBERT HOSPITAL, GLOUCESTER, MASSACHUSETTS (see BEVERLY HOSPITAL), p. A299

ADENA GREENFIELD MEDICAL CENTER, GREENFIELD, OH, p. A484

ADENA MEDICAL CENTER, CHILLICOTHE, OH, p. A475

ADENA PIKE MEDICAL CENTER, WAVERLY, OH, p. A493

ADIRONDACK HEALTH, SARANAC LAKE, NY, p. A443

ADVANCED CARE HOSPITAL OF MONTANA, BILLINGS, MT, p. A374

ADVANCED CARE HOSPITAL OF SOUTHERN NEW MEXICO, LAS CRUCES, NM, p. A418

ADVANCED CARE HOSPITAL OF WHITE COUNTY, SEARCY, AR, p. A48

ADVANCED DIAGNOSTICS HOSPITAL, HOUSTON, TX, p. A610

ADVANCED SPECIALTY HOSPITAL OF TOLEDO, TOLEDO, OH, p. A492

ADVANCED SURGICAL HOSPITAL, WASHINGTON, PA, p. A543

ADVENTHEALTH ALTAMONTE SPRINGS, ALTAMONTE SPRINGS, FL, p. A116

ADVENTHEALTH APOPKA, APOPKA, FL, p. A117

ADVENTHEALTH CARROLLWOOD, TAMPA, FL, p. A141

ADVENTHEALTH CELEBRATION, CELEBRATION, FL, p. A119

ADVENTHEALTH CENTRAL TEXAS, KILLEEN, TX, p. A618

ADVENTHEALTH CONNERTON, LAND O'LAKES, FL, p. A127

ADVENTHEALTH DADE CITY, DADE CITY, FL, p. A121

ADVENTHEALTH DAYTONA BEACH, DAYTONA BEACH, FL, p. A121

ADVENTHEALTH DELAND, DELAND, FL, p. A121

ADVENTHEALTH DURAND, DURAND, WI, p. A694

ADVENTHEALTH FISH MEMORIAL, ORANGE CITY, FL, p. A134

ADVENTHEALTH GORDON, CALHOUN, GA, p. A149

ADVENTHEALTH HEART OF FLORIDA, DAVENPORT, FL, p. A121

ADVENTHEALTH HENDERSONVILLE, HENDERSONVILLE, NC, p. A456

ADVENTHEALTH KISSIMMEE, KISSIMMEE, FL, p. A126

ADVENTHEALTH LAKE WALES, LAKE WALES, FL, p. A127

ADVENTHEALTH MANCHESTER, MANCHESTER, KY, p. A257

ADVENTHEALTH MURRAY, CHATSWORTH, GA, p. A150

ADVENTHEALTH NEW SMYRNA BEACH, NEW SMYRNA BEACH, FL, p. A133

ADVENTHEALTH NORTH PINELLAS, TARPON SPRINGS, FL, p. A142

ADVENTHEALTH OCALA, OCALA, FL, p. A133

ADVENTHEALTH ORLANDO, ORLANDO, FL, p. A134

ADVENTHEALTH PALM COAST, PALM COAST, FL, p. A135

ADVENTHEALTH ROLLINS BROOK, LAMPASAS, TX, p. A619

ADVENTHEALTH SEBRING, SEBRING, FL, p. A139

ADVENTHEALTH SHAWNEE MISSION, SHAWNEE MISSION, KS, p. A245

ADVENTHEALTH TAMPA, TAMPA, FL, p. A141

ADVENTHEALTH WATERMAN, TAVARES, FL, p. A142

ADVENTHEALTH WAUCHULA, WAUCHULA, FL, p. A143

ADVENTHEALTH WESLEY CHAPEL, WESLEY CHAPEL, FL, p. A143

ADVENTHEALTH WINTER PARK, WINTER PARK, FL, p. A144

ADVENTHEALTH ZEPHYRHILLS, ZEPHYRHILLS, FL, p. A144

ADVENTIST HEALTH – TULARE, TULARE, CA, p. A92

ADVENTIST HEALTH AND RIDEOUT, MARYSVILLE, CA, p. A71

ADVENTIST HEALTH BAKERSFIELD, BAKERSFIELD, CA, p. A52

ADVENTIST HEALTH CASTLE, KAILUA, HI, p. A165

ADVENTIST HEALTH CLEAR LAKE, CLEARLAKE, CA, p. A54

ADVENTIST HEALTH GLENDALE, LOS ANGELES, CA, p. A65

ADVENTIST HEALTH HOWARD MEMORIAL, WILLITS, CA, p. A95

ADVENTIST HEALTH LODI MEMORIAL, LODI, CA, p. A64

ADVENTIST HEALTH MEDICAL CENTER – TEHACHAPI VALLEY, TEHACHAPI, CA, p. A91

ADVENTIST HEALTH PORTLAND, PORTLAND, OR, p. A516

ADVENTIST HEALTH SONORA, SONORA, CA, p. A90

ADVENTIST HEALTH ST. HELENA, SAINT HELENA, CA, p. A82

ADVENTIST HEALTH ST. HELENA, VALLEJO, CA, p. A93

ADVENTIST HEALTH WHITE MEMORIAL, LOS ANGELES, CA, p. A66

ADVENTIST HEALTHCARE PHYSICAL HEALTH AND REHABILITATION, ROCKVILLE, MD, p. A293

ADVENTIST HEALTHCARE SHADY GROVE MEDICAL CENTER, ROCKVILLE, MD, p. A293

ADVENTIST HEALTHCARE WASHINGTON ADVENTIST HOSPITAL, TAKOMA PARK, MD, p. A293

ADVENTIST HEALTHTILLAMOOK, TILLAMOOK, OR, p. A518

ADVENTIST MEDICAL CENTER – HANFORD, HANFORD, CA, p. A61

ADVENTIST MEDICAL CENTER – HINSDALE, HINSDALE, IL, p. A186

ADVENTIST MEDICAL CENTER BOLINGBROOK, BOLINGBROOK, IL, p. A174

ADVENTIST MEDICAL CENTER GLENOAKS, GLENDALE HEIGHTS, IL, p. A184

ADVENTIST MEDICAL CENTER LAGRANGE, LA GRANGE, IL, p. A187

ADVENTIST MEDICAL CENTER–REEDLEY, REEDLEY, CA, p. A80

ADVOCATE BETHANY HOSPITAL, CHICAGO, ILLINOIS (see RML SPECIALTY HOSPITAL), p. A176

ADVOCATE BROMENN MEDICAL CENTER, NORMAL, IL, p. A191

ADVOCATE BROMENN REGIONAL MEDICAL CENTER, NORMAL, ILLINOIS (see ADVOCATE BROMENN MEDICAL CENTER), p. A191

ADVOCATE CHRIST MEDICAL CENTER, OAK LAWN, IL, p. A191

ADVOCATE CONDELL MEDICAL CENTER, LIBERTYVILLE, IL, p. A188

ADVOCATE EUREKA HOSPITAL, EUREKA, IL, p. A182

ADVOCATE GOOD SAMARITAN HOSPITAL, DOWNERS GROVE, IL, p. A181

ADVOCATE GOOD SHEPHERD HOSPITAL, BARRINGTON, IL, p. A174

ADVOCATE ILLINOIS MASONIC MEDICAL CENTER, CHICAGO, IL, p. A176

ADVOCATE LUTHERAN GENERAL HOSPITAL, PARK RIDGE, IL, p. A192

ADVOCATE SHERMAN HOSPITAL, ELGIN, IL, p. A182

ADVOCATE SOUTH SUBURBAN HOSPITAL, HAZEL CREST, IL, p. A185

ADVOCATE TRINITY HOSPITAL, CHICAGO, IL, p. A176

AHMC ANAHEIM REGIONAL MEDICAL CENTER, ANAHEIM, CA, p. A50

AIKEN REGIONAL MEDICAL CENTERS, AIKEN, SC, p. A549

AKRON CHILDREN'S HOSPITAL, AKRON, OH, p. A471

ALAMANCE REGIONAL MEDICAL CENTER, BURLINGTON, NC, p. A450

ALAMEDA HOSPITAL, ALAMEDA, CA, p. A50

ALASKA NATIVE MEDICAL CENTER, ANCHORAGE, AK, p. A25

ALASKA PSYCHIATRIC INSTITUTE, ANCHORAGE, AK, p. A25

ALASKA REGIONAL HOSPITAL, ANCHORAGE, AK, p. A25

ALBANY MEDICAL CENTER, ALBANY, NY, p. A422

ALBANY MEMORIAL HOSPITAL, ALBANY, NY, p. A422

ALBANY STRATTON VETERANS AFFAIRS MEDICAL CENTER, ALBANY, NY, p. A422

ALBERT EINSTEIN MEDICAL CENTER, PHILADELPHIA, PENNSYLVANIA (see EINSTEIN MEDICAL CENTER PHILADELPHIA), p. A534

ALBERT J. SOLNIT PSYCHIATRIC CENTER – SOUTH CAMPUS, MIDDLETOWN, CT, p. A109

ALEDA E. LUTZ VETERANS AFFAIRS MEDICAL CENTER, SAGINAW, MI, p. A321

ALEXANDRIA VETERANS AFFAIRS HEALTH CARE SYSTEM, PINEVILLE, LA, p. A277

ALEXIAN BROTHERS BEHAVIORAL HEALTH HOSPITAL, HOFFMAN ESTATES, IL, p. A186

ALFRED I. DUPONT HOSPITAL FOR CHILDREN, WILMINGTON, DE, p. A114

ALHAMBRA HOSPITAL MEDICAL CENTER, ALHAMBRA, CA, p. A50

ALICE PECK DAY MEMORIAL HOSPITAL, LEBANON, NH, p. A400

ALLEGAN GENERAL HOSPITAL, ALLEGAN, MI, p. A306

ALLEGHANY MEMORIAL HOSPITAL, SPARTA, NC, p. A462

ALLEGHENY GENERAL HOSPITAL, PITTSBURGH, PA, p. A537

ALLEGHENY VALLEY HOSPITAL, NATRONA HEIGHTS, PA, p. A533

ALLEGIANCE BEHAVIORAL HEALTH CENTER OF PLAINVIEW, PLAINVIEW, TX, p. A629

ALLEGIANCE BEHAVIORAL HEALTH CENTERS OF MONROE, WEST MONROE, LA, p. A280

ALLEGIANCE SPECIALTY HOSPITAL OF GREENVILLE, GREENVILLE, MS, p. A347

ALLEGIANCE SPECIALTY HOSPITAL OF KILGORE, KILGORE, TX, p. A618

ALLEGIANCE SPECIALTY HOSPITAL OF LITTLE ROCK, LITTLE ROCK, ARKANSAS (see CORNERSTONE HOSPITAL OF LITTLE ROCK), p. A44

ALLEN COUNTY REGIONAL HOSPITAL, IOLA, KS, p. A237

ALLEN MEMORIAL HOSPITAL, WATERLOO, IOWA (see UNITYPOINT HEALTH – ALLEN HOSPITAL), p. A231

ALLEN PARISH COMMUNITY HEALTHCARE, KINDER, LA, p. A270

ALLENDALE COUNTY HOSPITAL, FAIRFAX, SC, p. A552

ALLENMORE HOSPITAL, TACOMA, WASHINGTON (see MULTICARE TACOMA GENERAL HOSPITAL), p. A680

ALLIANCE COMMUNITY HOSPITAL, ALLIANCE, OH, p. A471

ALLIANCE HEALTH CENTER, MERIDIAN, MS, p. A351

ALLIANCE HEALTHCARE SYSTEM, HOLLY SPRINGS, MS, p. A348

ALLIANCEHEALTH CLINTON, CLINTON, OK, p. A498

ALLIANCEHEALTH DURANT, DURANT, OK, p. A499

ALLIANCEHEALTH MADILL, MADILL, OK, p. A501

ALLIANCEHEALTH MIDWEST, MIDWEST CITY, OK, p. A502

ALLIANCEHEALTH PONCA CITY, PONCA CITY, OK, p. A506

ALLIANCEHEALTH SEMINOLE, SEMINOLE, OK, p. A507

ALLIANCEHEALTH WOODWARD, WOODWARD, OK, p. A510

ALLIED SERVICES REHABILITATION HOSPITAL, SCRANTON, PA, p. A540

ALOMERE HEALTH, ALEXANDRIA, MN, p. A327

ALTA BATES SUMMIT MEDICAL CENTER – SUMMIT CAMPUS, OAKLAND, CA, p. A75

ALTA BATES SUMMIT MEDICAL CENTER, BERKELEY, CA, p. A52

ALTA VIEW HOSPITAL, SANDY, UT, p. A652

ALTA VISTA REGIONAL HOSPITAL, LAS VEGAS, NM, p. A419

ALTON MEMORIAL HOSPITAL, ALTON, IL, p. A173

ALTON MENTAL HEALTH CENTER, ALTON, IL, p. A173

ALTOONA REGIONAL HEALTH SYSTEM, ALTOONA, PENNSYLVANIA (see UPMC ALTOONA), p. A519

ALTRU HEALTH SYSTEM, GRAND FORKS, ND, p. A467

ALTUS BAYTOWN HOSPITAL, BAYTOWN, TX, p. A587

ALTUS HOUSTON HOSPITAL, HOUSTON, TX, p. A610

ALVARADO HOSPITAL MEDICAL CENTER, SAN DIEGO, CA, p. A83

ALVARADO PARKWAY INSTITUTE BEHAVIORAL HEALTH SYSTEM, LA MESA, CA, p. A63

ALVIN C. YORK CAMPUS, MURFREESBORO, TENNESSEE (see TENNESSEE VALLEY HEALTHCARE SYSTEM), p. A576

ALVIN DIAGNOSTIC AND URGENT CARE CENTER, ALVIN, TEXAS (see HCA HOUSTON HEALTHCARE CLEAR LAKE), p. A582

AMARILLO VETERANS AFFAIRS HEALTH CARE SYSTEM, AMARILLO, TX, p. A582

AMERICAN FORK HOSPITAL, AMERICAN FORK, UT, p. A647

AMERY HOSPITAL AND CLINIC, AMERY, WI, p. A691

AMG MERCY, OKLAHOMA CITY, OK, p. A503

AMG PHYSICAL REHABILITATION HOSPITAL, COVINGTON, LA, p. A266

AMG SPECIALTY HOSPITAL – LAS VEGAS, LAS VEGAS, NV, p. A394

AMG SPECIALTY HOSPITAL, SAN ANTONIO, TX, p. A633

AMG SPECIALTY HOSPITAL–ALBUQUERQUE, ALBUQUERQUE, NM, p. A416

AMG SPECIALTY HOSPITAL–HOUMA, HOUMA, LA, p. A268

AMG SPECIALTY HOSPITAL–LAFAYETTE, LAFAYETTE, LA, p. A270

AMG SPECIALTY HOSPITAL–WICHITA, WICHITA, KS, p. A247

AMG SPECIALTY HOSPITAL–ZACHARY, ZACHARY, LA, p. A280

AMITA HEALTH ELK GROVE VILLAGE, ELK GROVE VILLAGE, IL, p. A182

AMITA HEALTH HOFFMAN ESTATES, HOFFMAN ESTATES, IL, p. A186

AMITA HEALTH HOLY FAMILY MEDICAL CENTER, DES PLAINES, IL, p. A181

AMITA HEALTH MERCY MEDICAL CENTER, AURORA, IL, p. A173

AMITA HEALTH RESURRECTION MEDICAL CENTER, CHICAGO, IL, p. A176

AMITA HEALTH SAINT FRANCIS HOSPITAL EVANSTON, EVANSTON, IL, p. A182

AMITA HEALTH SAINT JOSEPH HOSPITAL, CHICAGO, IL, p. A176

AMITA HEALTH SAINT JOSEPH HOSPITAL, ELGIN, IL, p. A182

AMITA HEALTH SAINT JOSEPH MEDICAL CENTER, JOLIET, IL, p. A187

AMITA HEALTH SAINTS MARY & ELIZABETH MEDICAL CENTER, CHICAGO, IL, p. A176

AMITA HEALTH ST. MARY'S HOSPITAL, KANKAKEE, IL, p. A187

ANAHEIM GLOBAL MEDICAL CENTER, ANAHEIM, CA, p. A50

ANAHEIM MEDICAL CENTER, ANAHEIM, CA, p. A50

ANCHOR HOSPITAL, ATLANTA, GA, p. A145

ANCORA PSYCHIATRIC HOSPITAL, HAMMONTON, NJ, p. A406

ANDALUSIA HEALTH, ANDALUSIA, AL, p. A13

ANDERSON COUNTY HOSPITAL, GARNETT, KS, p. A235

ANDERSON HOSPITAL, MARYVILLE, IL, p. A188

ANDERSON REGIONAL HEALTH SYSTEM, MERIDIAN, MS, p. A351

ANDERSON REGIONAL HEALTH SYSTEM SOUTH, MERIDIAN, MS, p. A351

ANDREW MCFARLAND MENTAL HEALTH CENTER, SPRINGFIELD, IL, p. A196

ANDROSCOGGIN VALLEY HOSPITAL, BERLIN, NH, p. A399

ANDRUS PAVILION, YONKERS, NEW YORK (see ST. JOHN'S RIVERSIDE HOSPITAL), p. A448

ANGEL MEDICAL CENTER, FRANKLIN, NC, p. A454

ANIMAS SURGICAL HOSPITAL, DURANGO, CO, p. A99

ANMED HEALTH CANNON, PICKENS, SC, p. A556

ANMED HEALTH MEDICAL CENTER, ANDERSON, SC, p. A549

ANMED HEALTH REHABILITATION HOSPITAL, ANDERSON, SC, p. A549

ANN & ROBERT H. LURIE CHILDREN'S HOSPITAL OF CHICAGO, CHICAGO, IL, p. A176

ANNA JAQUES HOSPITAL, NEWBURYPORT, MA, p. A301

ANNE ARUNDEL MEDICAL CENTER, ANNAPOLIS, MD, p. A286

ANNIE JEFFREY MEMORIAL COUNTY HEALTH CENTER, OSCEOLA, NE, p. A390

ANNIE PENN HOSPITAL, REIDSVILLE, NORTH CAROLINA (see MOSES H. CONE MEMORIAL HOSPITAL), p. A461

ANOKA–METROPOLITAN REGIONAL TREATMENT CENTER, ANOKA, MN, p. A327

ANSON GENERAL HOSPITAL, ANSON, TX, p. A583

ANTELOPE MEMORIAL HOSPITAL, NELIGH, NE, p. A388

ANTELOPE VALLEY HOSPITAL, LANCASTER, CA, p. A64

APOLLO BEHAVIORAL HEALTH HOSPITAL, BATON ROUGE, LA, p. A263

APPALACHIAN BEHAVIORAL HEALTHCARE, ATHENS, OH, p. A472

APPLETON AREA HEALTH SERVICES, APPLETON, MN, p. A327

APPLING HEALTHCARE SYSTEM, BAXLEY, GA, p. A148

ARBOR HEALTH, MORTON HOSPITAL, MORTON, WA, p. A675

ARBOUR H. R. I. HOSPITAL, BROOKLINE, MA, p. A297

ARBOUR HOSPITAL, BOSTON, MA, p. A294

ARBOUR–FULLER HOSPITAL, ATTLEBORO, MA, p. A294

ARBUCKLE MEMORIAL HOSPITAL, SULPHUR, OK, p. A508

ARCHBOLD HOSPITAL, ARCHBOLD, OHIO (see COMMUNITY HOSPITALS AND WELLNESS CENTERS), p. A472

ARH OUR LADY OF THE WAY, MARTIN, KY, p. A257

ARISE AUSTIN MEDICAL CENTER, AUSTIN, TX, p. A584

ARIZONA ORTHOPEDIC SURGICAL HOSPITAL, CHANDLER, AZ, p. A28

ARIZONA SPINE AND JOINT HOSPITAL, MESA, AZ, p. A31

ARIZONA STATE HOSPITAL, PHOENIX, AZ, p. A33

ARKANSAS CHILDREN'S HOSPITAL, LITTLE ROCK, AR, p. A44

ARKANSAS CHILDREN'S NORTHWEST, SPRINGDALE, AR, p. A48

ARKANSAS CONTINUED CARE HOSPITAL, JONESBORO, AR, p. A43

ARKANSAS HEART HOSPITAL, LITTLE ROCK, AR, p. A44

ARKANSAS METHODIST MEDICAL CENTER, PARAGOULD, AR, p. A47

ARKANSAS STATE HOSPITAL, LITTLE ROCK, AR, p. A44

ARKANSAS SURGICAL HOSPITAL, NORTH LITTLE ROCK, AR, p. A46

ARKANSAS VALLEY REGIONAL MEDICAL CENTER, LA JUNTA, CO, p. A102

ARMS ACRES, CARMEL, NY, p. A425

ARNOLD PALMER HOSPITAL FOR CHILDREN, ORLANDO, FL, p. A134

ARNOT OGDEN MEDICAL CENTER, ELMIRA, NY, p. A427

AROOSTOOK HEALTH CENTER, MARS HILL, MAINE (see THE AROOSTOOK MEDICAL CENTER), p. A284

ARROWHEAD BEHAVIORAL HEALTH HOSPITAL, MAUMEE, OH, p. A487

ARROWHEAD REGIONAL MEDICAL CENTER, COLTON, CA, p. A55

ARROYO GRANDE COMMUNITY HOSPITAL, ARROYO GRANDE, CA, p. A51

ARTESIA GENERAL HOSPITAL, ARTESIA, NM, p. A417

ASANTE ASHLAND COMMUNITY HOSPITAL, ASHLAND, OR, p. A511

ASANTE ROGUE REGIONAL MEDICAL CENTER, MEDFORD, OR, p. A515

ASANTE THREE RIVERS MEDICAL CENTER, GRANTS PASS, OR, p. A513

ASCENSION ALL SAINTS, RACINE, WI, p. A704

ASCENSION BORGESS HOSPITAL, KALAMAZOO, MI, p. A315

ASCENSION BORGESS–LEE HOSPITAL, DOWAGIAC, MI, p. A310

ASCENSION BRIGHTON CENTER FOR RECOVERY, BRIGHTON, MI, p. A307

ASCENSION CALUMET HOSPITAL, CHILTON, WI, p. A693

ASCENSION COLUMBIA ST. MARY'S HOSPITAL MILWAUKEE, MILWAUKEE, WI, p. A700

ASCENSION COLUMBIA ST. MARY'S HOSPITAL OZAUKEE, MEQUON, WI, p. A700

ASCENSION COLUMBIA ST. MARY'S MILWAUKEE HOSPITAL, MILWAUKEE, WI, p. A700

ASCENSION CRITTENTON HOSPITAL MEDICAL CENTER, ROCHESTER, MI, p. A320

ASCENSION EAGLE RIVER HOSPITAL, EAGLE RIVER, WI, p. A694

ASCENSION GENESYS HOSPITAL, GRAND BLANC, MI, p. A312

ASCENSION GOOD SAMARITAN HOSPITAL, MERRILL, WI, p. A700

ASCENSION MACOMB–OAKLAND HOSPITAL, WARREN, MI, p. A324

ASCENSION NORTHEAST WISCONSIN MERCY HOSPITAL, OSHKOSH, WI, p. A703

ASCENSION NORTHEAST WISCONSIN ST. ELIZABETH HOSPITAL, APPLETON, WI, p. A691

ASCENSION OF PROVIDENCE HOSPITAL, SOUTHFIELD CAMPUS, SOUTHFIELD, MI, p. A322

ASCENSION OUR LADY OF VICTORY HOSPITAL, STANLEY, WI, p. A706

ASCENSION RIVER DISTRICT HOSPITAL, EAST CHINA, MI, p. A311

ASCENSION SACRED HEART HOSPITAL, TOMAHAWK, WI, p. A707

ASCENSION SAINT CLARE'S HOSPITAL, WESTON, WI, p. A708

ASCENSION SETON EDGAR B. DAVIS HOSPITAL, LULING, TX, p. A622

ASCENSION SETON HAYS, KYLE, TX, p. A618

ASCENSION SETON HIGHLAND LAKES, BURNET, TX, p. A590

ASCENSION SETON MEDICAL CENTER AUSTIN, AUSTIN, TX, p. A584

ASCENSION SETON NORTHWEST, AUSTIN, TX, p. A584

ASCENSION SETON SHOAL CREEK, AUSTIN, TX, p. A585

ASCENSION SETON SMITHVILLE, SMITHVILLE, TX, p. A637

ASCENSION SETON SOUTHWEST, AUSTIN, TX, p. A585

ASCENSION SETON WILLIAMSON, ROUND ROCK, TX, p. A632

ASCENSION SOUTHEAST WISCONSIN HOSPITAL – ELMBROOK CAMPUS, BROOKFIELD, WI, p. A693

ASCENSION SOUTHEAST WISCONSIN HOSPITAL – FRANKLIN CAMPUS, FRANKLIN, WI, p. A695

ASCENSION SOUTHEAST WISCONSIN HOSPITAL – ST. FRANCIS CAMPUS, MILWAUKEE, WI, p. A700

ASCENSION SOUTHEAST WISCONSIN HOSPITAL – ST. JOSEPH'S CAMPUS, MILWAUKEE, WI, p. A700

ASCENSION ST. JOHN HOSPITAL, DETROIT, MI, p. A309

ASCENSION ST. JOSEPH HOSPITAL, TAWAS CITY, MI, p. A323

ASCENSION ST. MARY'S HOSPITAL, RHINELANDER, WI, p. A704

ASCENSION ST. MARY'S OF MICHIGAN, SAGINAW, MI, p. A321

ASCENSION ST. MICHAEL'S HOSPITAL, STEVENS POINT, WI, p. A706

ASCENSION STANDISH HOSPITAL, STANDISH, MI, p. A323

ASCENSION VIA CHRISTI HOSPITAL, PITTSBURG, KS, p. A244

ASCENSION VIA CHRISTI HOSPITAL ON ST. TERESA, WICHITA, KS, p. A247

ASCENSION VIA CHRISTI HOSPITAL, MANHATTAN, MANHATTAN, KS, p. A240

ASCENSION VIA CHRISTI REHABILITATION HOSPITAL, WICHITA, KS, p. A247

ASCENSION VIA CHRISTI ST. FRANCIS, MULVANE, KS, p. A241

ASHE MEMORIAL HOSPITAL, JEFFERSON, NC, p. A457

ASHEVILLE SPECIALTY HOSPITAL, ASHEVILLE, NC, p. A449

ASHFORD PRESBYTERIAN COMMUNITY HOSPITAL, SAN JUAN, PR, p. A718

ASHLAND HEALTH CENTER, ASHLAND, KS, p. A232

ASHLEY COUNTY MEDICAL CENTER, CROSSETT, AR, p. A40

ASHLEY MEDICAL CENTER, ASHLEY, ND, p. A465

ASHLEY REGIONAL MEDICAL CENTER, VERNAL, UT, p. A653

ASHTABULA COUNTY MEDICAL CENTER, ASHTABULA, OH, p. A472

ASPEN MOUNTAIN MEDICAL CENTER, ROCK SPRINGS, WY, p. A712

ASPEN VALLEY HOSPITAL, ASPEN, CO, p. A96

ASPIRE HEALTH PARTNERS, ORLANDO, FL, p. A134

ASPIRE HOSPITAL, CONROE, TX, p. A593

ASPIRUS IRON RIVER HOSPITALS & CLINICS, INC., IRON RIVER, MI, p. A315

ASPIRUS IRONWOOD HOSPITALS & CLINICS, INC., IRONWOOD, MI, p. A315

ASPIRUS KEWEENAW HOSPITAL, INC., LAURIUM, MI, p. A316

ASPIRUS LANGLADE HOSPITAL, ANTIGO, WI, p. A691

ASPIRUS MEDFORD HOSPITAL & CLINICS, INC., MEDFORD, WI, p. A699

ASPIRUS ONTONAGON HOSPITAL, INC., ONTONAGON, MI, p. A319

ASPIRUS RIVERVIEW HOSPITAL AND CLINICS, INC., WISCONSIN RAPIDS, WI, p. A709

ASPIRUS WAUSAU HOSPITAL, INC., WAUSAU, WI, p. A708

ASSUMPTION COMMUNITY HOSPITAL, NAPOLEONVILLE, LA, p. A274

ASTRIA REGIONAL MEDICAL CENTER, YAKIMA, WA, p. A682

ASTRIA SUNNYSIDE HOSPITAL, SUNNYSIDE, WA, p. A680

ASTRIA TOPPENISH HOSPITAL, TOPPENISH, WA, p. A681

ATASCADERO STATE HOSPITAL, ATASCADERO, CA, p. A51

ATCHISON HOSPITAL, ATCHISON, KS, p. A232

ATHENS–LIMESTONE HOSPITAL, ATHENS, AL, p. A13

ATHOL HOSPITAL, ATHOL, MA, p. A294

ATLANTA VETERANS AFFAIRS MEDICAL CENTER, DECATUR, GA, p. A151

ATLANTIC GENERAL HOSPITAL, BERLIN, MD, p. A288

ATLANTICARE REGIONAL MEDICAL CENTER, ATLANTIC CITY, NJ, p. A403

ATLANTICARE REGIONAL MEDICAL CENTER–MAINLAND DIVISION, POMONA, NEW JERSEY (see ATLANTICARE REGIONAL MEDICAL CENTER), p. A411

ATMORE COMMUNITY HOSPITAL, ATMORE, AL, p. A14

ATOKA COUNTY MEDICAL CENTER, ATOKA, OK, p. A496

ATRIUM HEALTH ANSON, WADESBORO, NC, p. A463

ATRIUM HEALTH CABARRUS, CONCORD, NC, p. A452

ATRIUM HEALTH CLEVELAND, SHELBY, NC, p. A462

ATRIUM HEALTH KINGS MOUNTAIN, KINGS MOUNTAIN, NC, p. A457

ATRIUM HEALTH LINCOLN, LINCOLNTON, NC, p. A458
ATRIUM HEALTH PINEVILLE, CHARLOTTE, NC, p. A451
ATRIUM HEALTH STANLY, ALBEMARLE, NC, p. A449
ATRIUM HEALTH UNION, MONROE, NC, p. A458
ATRIUM HEALTH UNIVERSITY CITY, CHARLOTTE, NC, p. A451
ATRIUM HEALTH'S CAROLINAS MEDICAL CENTER, CHARLOTTE, NC, p. A451
ATRIUM HEALTH'S CAROLINAS REHABILITATION, CHARLOTTE, NC, p. A451
ATRIUM MEDICAL CENTER, MIDDLETOWN, OH, p. A487
ATRIUM MEDICAL CENTER, STAFFORD, TX, p. A638
ATRIUM MEDICAL CENTER OF CORINTH, CORINTH, TX, p. A594
AUBURN COMMUNITY HOSPITAL, AUBURN, NY, p. A423
AUDUBON COUNTY MEMORIAL HOSPITAL AND CLINICS, AUDUBON, IA, p. A217
AUGUSTA HEALTH, FISHERSVILLE, VA, p. A659
AUGUSTA UNIVERSITY MEDICAL CENTER, AUGUSTA, GA, p. A147
AULTMAN HOSPITAL, CANTON, OH, p. A474
AULTMAN ORRVILLE HOSPITAL, ORRVILLE, OH, p. A489
AULTMAN SPECIALTY HOSPITAL, CANTON, OH, p. A474
AURELIA OSBORN FOX MEMORIAL HOSPITAL, ONEONTA, NY, p. A440
AURORA BAYCARE MEDICAL CENTER, GREEN BAY, WI, p. A696
AURORA BEHAVIORAL HEALTH SYSTEM EAST, TEMPE, AZ, p. A36
AURORA BEHAVIORAL HEALTH SYSTEM WEST, GLENDALE, AZ, p. A30
AURORA BEHAVIORAL HEALTHCARE SAN DIEGO, SAN DIEGO, CA, p. A83
AURORA CHARTER OAK HOSPITAL, COVINA, CA, p. A55
AURORA LAKELAND MEDICAL CENTER, ELKHORN, WI, p. A694
AURORA MEDICAL CENTER – BAY AREA, MARINETTE, WI, p. A699
AURORA MEDICAL CENTER – MANITOWOC COUNTY, TWO RIVERS, WI, p. A707
AURORA MEDICAL CENTER BURLINGTON, BURLINGTON, WI, p. A693
AURORA MEDICAL CENTER GRAFTON, GRAFTON, WI, p. A695
AURORA MEDICAL CENTER IN WASHINGTON COUNTY, HARTFORD, WI, p. A697
AURORA MEDICAL CENTER KENOSHA, KENOSHA, WI, p. A697
AURORA MEDICAL CENTER OF OSHKOSH, OSHKOSH, WI, p. A703
AURORA MEDICAL CENTER SUMMIT, SUMMIT, WI, p. A706
AURORA PSYCHIATRIC HOSPITAL, WAUWATOSA, WI, p. A708
AURORA SANTA ROSA HOSPITAL, SANTA ROSA, CA, p. A89
AURORA SHEBOYGAN MEMORIAL MEDICAL CENTER, SHEBOYGAN, WI, p. A705
AURORA SINAI MEDICAL CENTER, MILWAUKEE, WI, p. A701
AURORA ST. LUKE'S MEDICAL CENTER, MILWAUKEE, WI, p. A701
AURORA ST. LUKE'S SOUTH SHORE, CUDAHY, WISCONSIN (see AURORA ST. LUKE'S MEDICAL CENTER), p. A693
AURORA WEST ALLIS MEDICAL CENTER, WEST ALLIS, WI, p. A708
AUSTEN RIGGS CENTER, STOCKBRIDGE, MA, p. A304
AUSTIN LAKES HOSPITAL, AUSTIN, TX, p. A585
AUSTIN OAKS HOSPITAL, AUSTIN, TX, p. A585
AUSTIN STATE HOSPITAL, AUSTIN, TX, p. A585
AUXILIO MUTUO HOSPITAL, SAN JUAN, PR, p. A718
AVAIL HEALTH LAKE CHARLES HOSPITAL, LAKE CHARLES, LA, p. A271
AVALA, COVINGTON, LA, p. A266
AVENTURA HOSPITAL AND MEDICAL CENTER, AVENTURA, FL, p. A117
AVERA CREIGHTON HOSPITAL, CREIGHTON, NE, p. A384
AVERA DE SMET MEMORIAL HOSPITAL, DE SMET, SD, p. A560
AVERA DELLS AREA HEALTH CENTER, DELL RAPIDS, SOUTH DAKOTA (see AVERA DELLS AREA HOSPITAL), p. A560
AVERA DELLS AREA HOSPITAL, DELL RAPIDS, SD, p. A560
AVERA FLANDREAU HOSPITAL, FLANDREAU, SD, p. A561
AVERA FLANDREAU MEDICAL CENTER, FLANDREAU, SOUTH DAKOTA (see AVERA FLANDREAU HOSPITAL), p. A561
AVERA GETTYSBURG HOSPITAL, GETTYSBURG, SD, p. A561
AVERA GREGORY HOSPITAL, GREGORY, SD, p. A561
AVERA HAND COUNTY MEMORIAL HOSPITAL, MILLER, SD, p. A562
AVERA HEART HOSPITAL OF SOUTH DAKOTA, SIOUX FALLS, SD, p. A563
AVERA HOLY FAMILY HOSPITAL, ESTHERVILLE, IA, p. A222
AVERA MARSHALL REGIONAL MEDICAL CENTER, MARSHALL, MN, p. A335

AVERA MCKENNAN HOSPITAL AND UNIVERSITY HEALTH CENTER, SIOUX FALLS, SD, p. A563
AVERA MERRILL PIONEER HOSPITAL, ROCK RAPIDS, IA, p. A229
AVERA QUEEN OF PEACE HOSPITAL, MITCHELL, SD, p. A562
AVERA SACRED HEART HOSPITAL, YANKTON, SD, p. A565
AVERA ST. ANTHONY'S HOSPITAL, O'NEILL, NE, p. A390
AVERA ST. BENEDICT HEALTH CENTER, PARKSTON, SD, p. A562
AVERA ST. LUKE'S HOSPITAL, ABERDEEN, SD, p. A559
AVERA ST. MARY'S HOSPITAL, PIERRE, SD, p. A562
AVERA TYLER HOSPITAL, TYLER, MN, p. A341
AVERA WESKOTA MEMORIAL HOSPITAL, WESSINGTON SPRINGS, SD, p. A565
AVISTA ADVENTIST HOSPITAL, LOUISVILLE, CO, p. A104
AVITA ONTARIO HOSPITAL, ONTARIO, OH, p. A489
AVOYELLES HOSPITAL, MARKSVILLE, LA, p. A273

B

BACHARACH INSTITUTE FOR REHABILITATION, POMONA, NJ, p. A411
BACON COUNTY HOSPITAL AND HEALTH SYSTEM, ALMA, GA, p. A145
BAILEY MEDICAL CENTER, OWASSO, OK, p. A506
BAKERSFIELD HEART HOSPITAL, BAKERSFIELD, CA, p. A52
BAKERSFIELD MEMORIAL HOSPITAL, BAKERSFIELD, CA, p. A52
BALDPATE HOSPITAL, GEORGETOWN, MA, p. A299
BALDWIN PARK MEDICAL CENTER, BALDWIN PARK, CA, p. A51
BALL MEMORIAL HOSPITAL, MUNCIE, INDIANA (see INDIANA UNIVERSITY HEALTH BALL MEMORIAL HOSPITAL), p. A211
BALLARD REHABILITATION HOSPITAL, SAN BERNARDINO, CA, p. A83
BALLINGER MEMORIAL HOSPITAL, BALLINGER, TX, p. A586
BANNER – UNIVERSITY MEDICAL CENTER PHOENIX, PHOENIX, AZ, p. A33
BANNER – UNIVERSITY MEDICAL CENTER SOUTH, TUCSON, AZ, p. A37
BANNER – UNIVERSITY MEDICAL CENTER TUCSON, TUCSON, AZ, p. A37
BANNER BAYWOOD MEDICAL CENTER, MESA, AZ, p. A31
BANNER BEHAVIORAL HEALTH HOSPITAL – SCOTTSDALE, SCOTTSDALE, AZ, p. A35
BANNER BOSWELL MEDICAL CENTER, SUN CITY, AZ, p. A36
BANNER CASA GRANDE MEDICAL CENTER, CASA GRANDE, AZ, p. A28
BANNER CHILDREN'S HOSPITAL, MESA, ARIZONA (see CARDON CHILDREN'S MEDICAL CENTER), p. A31
BANNER CHURCHILL COMMUNITY HOSPITAL, FALLON, NV, p. A393
BANNER DEL E. WEBB MEDICAL CENTER, SUN CITY WEST, AZ, p. A36
BANNER DESERT MEDICAL CENTER, MESA, AZ, p. A31
BANNER ESTRELLA MEDICAL CENTER, PHOENIX, AZ, p. A33
BANNER FORT COLLINS MEDICAL CENTER, FORT COLLINS, CO, p. A100
BANNER GATEWAY MEDICAL CENTER, GILBERT, AZ, p. A29
BANNER GOLDFIELD MEDICAL CENTER, APACHE JUNCTION, AZ, p. A28
BANNER HEART HOSPITAL, MESA, AZ, p. A31
BANNER IRONWOOD MEDICAL CENTER, SAN TAN VALLEY, AZ, p. A35
BANNER LASSEN MEDICAL CENTER, SUSANVILLE, CA, p. A91
BANNER PAYSON MEDICAL CENTER, PAYSON, AZ, p. A32
BANNER THUNDERBIRD MEDICAL CENTER, GLENDALE, AZ, p. A30
BAPTIST EMERGENCY HOSPITAL, SAN ANTONIO, TX, p. A633
BAPTIST HEALTH – FORT SMITH, FORT SMITH, AR, p. A42
BAPTIST HEALTH – VAN BUREN, VAN BUREN, AR, p. A49
BAPTIST HEALTH CORBIN, CORBIN, KY, p. A250
BAPTIST HEALTH EXTENDED CARE HOSPITAL, LITTLE ROCK, AR, p. A44
BAPTIST HEALTH FLOYD, NEW ALBANY, IN, p. A212
BAPTIST HEALTH LA GRANGE, LA GRANGE, KY, p. A254
BAPTIST HEALTH LEXINGTON, LEXINGTON, KY, p. A254
BAPTIST HEALTH LOUISVILLE, LOUISVILLE, KY, p. A256
BAPTIST HEALTH MADISONVILLE, MADISONVILLE, KY, p. A257
BAPTIST HEALTH MEDICAL CENTER – CONWAY, CONWAY, AR, p. A40

BAPTIST HEALTH MEDICAL CENTER – NORTH LITTLE ROCK, NORTH LITTLE ROCK, AR, p. A46
BAPTIST HEALTH MEDICAL CENTER–ARKADELPHIA, ARKADELPHIA, AR, p. A39
BAPTIST HEALTH MEDICAL CENTER–HEBER SPRINGS, HEBER SPRINGS, AR, p. A43
BAPTIST HEALTH MEDICAL CENTER–HOT SPRING COUNTY, MALVERN, AR, p. A45
BAPTIST HEALTH MEDICAL CENTER–LITTLE ROCK, LITTLE ROCK, AR, p. A44
BAPTIST HEALTH MEDICAL CENTER–STUTTGART, STUTTGART, AR, p. A49
BAPTIST HEALTH PADUCAH, PADUCAH, KY, p. A259
BAPTIST HEALTH REHABILITATION INSTITUTE, LITTLE ROCK, AR, p. A45
BAPTIST HEALTH RICHMOND, RICHMOND, KY, p. A260
BAPTIST HEALTH SOUTH FLORIDA, BAPTIST HOSPITAL OF MIAMI, MIAMI, FL, p. A130
BAPTIST HEALTH SOUTH FLORIDA, DOCTORS HOSPITAL, CORAL GABLES, FL, p. A120
BAPTIST HEALTH SOUTH FLORIDA, HOMESTEAD HOSPITAL, HOMESTEAD, FL, p. A125
BAPTIST HEALTH SOUTH FLORIDA, MARINERS HOSPITAL, TAVERNIER, FL, p. A142
BAPTIST HEALTH SOUTH FLORIDA, SOUTH MIAMI HOSPITAL, MIAMI, FL, p. A130
BAPTIST HEALTH SOUTH FLORIDA, WEST KENDALL BAPTIST HOSPITAL, MIAMI, FL, p. A130
BAPTIST HOSPITAL, PENSACOLA, FL, p. A136
BAPTIST HOSPITAL OF COCKE COUNTY, NEWPORT, TENNESSEE (see TENNOVA NEWPORT MEDICAL CENTER), p. A578
BAPTIST HOSPITALS OF SOUTHEAST TEXAS, BEAUMONT, TX, p. A587
BAPTIST MEDICAL CENTER, SAN ANTONIO, TX, p. A633
BAPTIST MEDICAL CENTER ATTALA, KOSCIUSKO, MS, p. A350
BAPTIST MEDICAL CENTER BEACHES, JACKSONVILLE BEACH, FL, p. A126
BAPTIST MEDICAL CENTER EAST, MONTGOMERY, AL, p. A21
BAPTIST MEDICAL CENTER JACKSONVILLE, JACKSONVILLE, FL, p. A125
BAPTIST MEDICAL CENTER LEAKE, CARTHAGE, MS, p. A345
BAPTIST MEDICAL CENTER NASSAU, FERNANDINA BEACH, FL, p. A122
BAPTIST MEDICAL CENTER SOUTH, MONTGOMERY, AL, p. A21
BAPTIST MEDICAL CENTER YAZOO, YAZOO CITY, MS, p. A355
BAPTIST MEMORIAL HOSPITAL – CALHOUN, CALHOUN CITY, MS, p. A345
BAPTIST MEMORIAL HOSPITAL – MEMPHIS, MEMPHIS, TN, p. A574
BAPTIST MEMORIAL HOSPITAL FOR WOMEN, MEMPHIS, TN, p. A574
BAPTIST MEMORIAL HOSPITAL–BOONEVILLE, BOONEVILLE, MS, p. A345
BAPTIST MEMORIAL HOSPITAL–CARROLL COUNTY, HUNTINGDON, TN, p. A571
BAPTIST MEMORIAL HOSPITAL–COLLIERVILLE, COLLIERVILLE, TN, p. A568
BAPTIST MEMORIAL HOSPITAL–DESOTO, SOUTHAVEN, MS, p. A354
BAPTIST MEMORIAL HOSPITAL–GOLDEN TRIANGLE, COLUMBUS, MS, p. A346
BAPTIST MEMORIAL HOSPITAL–NORTH MISSISSIPPI, OXFORD, MS, p. A352
BAPTIST MEMORIAL HOSPITAL–TIPTON, COVINGTON, TN, p. A568
BAPTIST MEMORIAL HOSPITAL–UNION CITY, UNION CITY, TN, p. A580
BAPTIST MEMORIAL HOSPITAL–UNION COUNTY, NEW ALBANY, MS, p. A352
BAPTIST MEMORIAL REHABILITATION HOSPITAL, GERMANTOWN, TN, p. A570
BAPTIST MEMORIAL RESTORATIVE CARE HOSPITAL, MEMPHIS, TN, p. A574
BARAGA COUNTY MEMORIAL HOSPITAL, L'ANSE, MI, p. A316
BARBOURVILLE ARH HOSPITAL, BARBOURVILLE, KY, p. A249
BARIX CLINICS OF PENNSYLVANIA, LANGHORNE, PA, p. A529
BARLOW RESPIRATORY HOSPITAL, LOS ANGELES, CA, p. A66
BARNES–JEWISH HOSPITAL, SAINT LOUIS, MO, p. A369
BARNES–JEWISH ST. PETERS HOSPITAL, SAINT PETERS, MO, p. A371
BARNES–JEWISH WEST COUNTY HOSPITAL, SAINT LOUIS, MO, p. A369
BARNES–KASSON COUNTY HOSPITAL, SUSQUEHANNA, PA, p. A542
BARNESVILLE HOSPITAL, BARNESVILLE, OH, p. A472

BARRETT HOSPITAL & HEALTHCARE, DILLON, MT, p. A376
BARSTOW COMMUNITY HOSPITAL, BARSTOW, CA, p. A52
BARTLETT REGIONAL HOSPITAL, JUNEAU, AK, p. A26
BARTON MEMORIAL HOSPITAL, SOUTH LAKE TAHOE, CA, p. A90
BARTOW REGIONAL MEDICAL CENTER, BARTOW, FL, p. A117
BASSETT ARMY COMMUNITY HOSPITAL, FORT WAINWRIGHT, AK, p. A26
BASSETT MEDICAL CENTER, COOPERSTOWN, NY, p. A426
BASTROP REHABILITATION HOSPITAL, MONROE, LA, p. A274
BATES COUNTY MEMORIAL HOSPITAL, BUTLER, MO, p. A357
BATH COMMUNITY HOSPITAL, HOT SPRINGS, VA, p. A661
BATH VETERANS AFFAIRS MEDICAL CENTER, BATH, NY, p. A423
BATON ROUGE BEHAVIORAL HOSPITAL, BATON ROUGE, LA, p. A263
BATON ROUGE GENERAL MEDICAL CENTER, BATON ROUGE, LA, p. A263
BATON ROUGE REHABILITATION HOSPITAL, BATON ROUGE, LA, p. A263
BATTLE CREEK VETERANS AFFAIRS MEDICAL CENTER, BATTLE CREEK, MI, p. A307
BATTLE MOUNTAIN GENERAL HOSPITAL, BATTLE MOUNTAIN, NV, p. A393
BAXTER REGIONAL MEDICAL CENTER, MOUNTAIN HOME, AR, p. A46
BAY AREA HOSPITAL, COOS BAY, OR, p. A512
BAY MEDICAL SACRED HEART, PANAMA CITY, FL, p. A135
BAY PINES VETERANS AFFAIRS HEALTHCARE SYSTEM, BAY PINES, FL, p. A117
BAYCARE ALLIANT HOSPITAL, DUNEDIN, FL, p. A122
BAYFRONT HEALTH BROOKSVILLE, BROOKSVILLE, FL, p. A119
BAYFRONT HEALTH PORT CHARLOTTE, PORT CHARLOTTE, FL, p. A137
BAYFRONT HEALTH PUNTA GORDA, PUNTA GORDA, FL, p. A137
BAYFRONT HEALTH ST. PETERSBURG, SAINT PETERSBURG, FL, p. A138
BAYHEALTH MEDICAL CENTER, DOVER, DE, p. A113
BAYHEALTH MEDICAL CENTER, MILFORD MEMORIAL HOSPITAL, MILFORD, DE, p. A113
BAYLOR ORTHOPEDIC AND SPINE HOSPITAL AT ARLINGTON, ARLINGTON, TX, p. A583
BAYLOR SCOTT & WHITE ALL SAINTS MEDICAL CENTER – FORT WORTH, FORT WORTH, TX, p. A604
BAYLOR SCOTT & WHITE CONTINUING CARE HOSPITAL– TEMPLE, TEMPLE, TX, p. A639
BAYLOR SCOTT & WHITE EMERGENCY HOSPITAL – BURLESON, BURLESON, TX, p. A590
BAYLOR SCOTT & WHITE EMERGENCY HOSPITAL – ROCKWALL, ROCKWALL, TX, p. A631
BAYLOR SCOTT & WHITE EMERGENCY HOSPITAL–AUBREY, AUBREY, TX, p. A584
BAYLOR SCOTT & WHITE EMERGENCY MEDICAL CENTER– CEDAR PARK, CEDAR PARK, TX, p. A592
BAYLOR SCOTT & WHITE HEART & VASCULAR HOSPITAL– DALLAS, DALLAS, TX, p. A595
BAYLOR SCOTT & WHITE HOSPITAL MEDICAL CENTER – BRENHAM, BRENHAM, TX, p. A589
BAYLOR SCOTT & WHITE HOSPITAL MEDICAL CENTER – COLLEGE STATION, COLLEGE STATION, TX, p. A592
BAYLOR SCOTT & WHITE INSTITUTE FOR REHABILITATION – DALLAS, DALLAS, TX, p. A595
BAYLOR SCOTT & WHITE INSTITUTE FOR REHABILITATION – LAKEWAY, LAKEWAY, TX, p. A619
BAYLOR SCOTT & WHITE INSTITUTE FOR REHABILITATION– FORT WORTH, FORT WORTH, TX, p. A604
BAYLOR SCOTT & WHITE INSTITUTE FOR REHABILITATION– FRISCO, FRISCO, TX, p. A606
BAYLOR SCOTT & WHITE MEDICAL CENTER – CARROLLTON, CARROLLTON, TX, p. A591
BAYLOR SCOTT & WHITE MEDICAL CENTER – CENTENNIAL, FRISCO, TX, p. A606
BAYLOR SCOTT & WHITE MEDICAL CENTER – GRAPEVINE, GRAPEVINE, TX, p. A608
BAYLOR SCOTT & WHITE MEDICAL CENTER – HILLCREST, WACO, TX, p. A644
BAYLOR SCOTT & WHITE MEDICAL CENTER – LAKE POINTE, ROWLETT, TX, p. A632
BAYLOR SCOTT & WHITE MEDICAL CENTER – LLANO, LLANO, TX, p. A621
BAYLOR SCOTT & WHITE MEDICAL CENTER – MARBLE FALLS, MARBLE FALLS, TX, p. A623
BAYLOR SCOTT & WHITE MEDICAL CENTER – PLANO, PLANO, TX, p. A629
BAYLOR SCOTT & WHITE MEDICAL CENTER – ROUND ROCK, ROUND ROCK, TX, p. A632
BAYLOR SCOTT & WHITE MEDICAL CENTER – SUNNYVALE, SUNNYVALE, TX, p. A639

BAYLOR SCOTT & WHITE MEDICAL CENTER – TAYLOR, TAYLOR, TX, p. A639
BAYLOR SCOTT & WHITE MEDICAL CENTER – TEMPLE, TEMPLE, TX, p. A639
BAYLOR SCOTT & WHITE MEDICAL CENTER – TROPHY CLUB, TROPHY CLUB, TX, p. A641
BAYLOR SCOTT & WHITE MEDICAL CENTER AT – MCKINNEY, MCKINNEY, TX, p. A624
BAYLOR SCOTT & WHITE MEDICAL CENTER–FRISCO, FRISCO, TX, p. A606
BAYLOR SCOTT & WHITE MEDICAL CENTER–IRVING, IRVING, TX, p. A616
BAYLOR SCOTT & WHITE MEDICAL CENTER–UPTOWN, DALLAS, TX, p. A595
BAYLOR SCOTT & WHITE MEDICAL CENTER–WAXAHACHIE, WAXAHACHIE, TX, p. A644
BAYLOR SCOTT & WHITE SURGICAL HOSPITAL FORT WORTH, FORT WORTH, TX, p. A604
BAYLOR SCOTT & WHITE SURGICAL HOSPITAL–SHERMAN, SHERMAN, TX, p. A636
BAYLOR SCOTT & WHITE TEXAS SPINE & JOINT HOSPITAL– TYLER, TYLER, TX, p. A642
BAYLOR SCOTT & WHITE THE HEART HOSPITAL PLANO, PLANO, TX, p. A629
BAYLOR SCOTT & WHITE THE HEART HOSPITAL–DENTON, DENTON, TX, p. A599
BAYLOR ST. LUKE'S MEDICAL CENTER, HOUSTON, TX, p. A610
BAYLOR ST. LUKE'S MEDICAL CENTER MCNAIR CAMPUS, HOUSTON, TX, p. A610
BAYLOR SURGICAL HOSPITAL AT LAS COLINAS, IRVING, TX, p. A616
BAYLOR UNIVERSITY MEDICAL CENTER, DALLAS, TX, p. A596
BAYNE–JONES ARMY COMMUNITY HOSPITAL, FORT POLK, LA, p. A267
BAYPOINTE BEHAVIORAL HEALTH, MOBILE, AL, p. A20
BAYSHORE MEDICAL CENTER, PASADENA, TX, p. A628
BAYSIDE COMMUNITY HOSPITAL, ANAHUAC, TX, p. A583
BAYSTATE FRANKLIN MEDICAL CENTER, GREENFIELD, MA, p. A299
BAYSTATE MEDICAL CENTER, SPRINGFIELD, MA, p. A303
BAYSTATE NOBLE HOSPITAL, WESTFIELD, MA, p. A304
BAYSTATE WING HOSPITAL, PALMER, MA, p. A302
BCA STONECREST HOSPITAL, DETROIT, MICHIGAN (see STONECREST CENTER), p. A309
BEACHAM MEMORIAL HOSPITAL, MAGNOLIA, MS, p. A350
BEACON BEHAVIORAL HOSPITAL – NEW ORLEANS, NEW ORLEANS, LA, p. A275
BEACON BEHAVIORAL HOSPITAL, BUNKIE, LA, p. A265
BEACON BEHAVIORAL HOSPITAL, LUTCHER, LA, p. A272
BEACON BEHAVIORAL HOSPITAL NORTHSHORE, LACOMBE, LA, p. A270
BEACON CHILDREN'S HOSPITAL, LUVERNE, AL, p. A20
BEAR LAKE MEMORIAL HOSPITAL, MONTPELIER, ID, p. A170
BEAR RIVER VALLEY HOSPITAL, TREMONTON, UT, p. A653
BEAR VALLEY COMMUNITY HOSPITAL, BIG BEAR LAKE, CA, p. A53
BEARTOOTH BILLINGS CLINIC, RED LODGE, MT, p. A379
BEATRICE COMMUNITY HOSPITAL AND HEALTH CENTER, BEATRICE, NE, p. A383
BEAUFORT COUNTY HOSPITAL, WASHINGTON, NORTH CAROLINA (see VIDANT BEAUFORT HOSPITAL), p. A463
BEAUFORT MEMORIAL HOSPITAL, BEAUFORT, SC, p. A549
BEAUMONT HOSPITAL – DEARBORN, DEARBORN, MI, p. A309
BEAUMONT HOSPITAL – FARMINGTON HILLS, FARMINGTON HILLS, MI, p. A311
BEAUMONT HOSPITAL – GROSSE POINTE, GROSSE POINTE, MI, p. A313
BEAUMONT HOSPITAL – ROYAL OAK, ROYAL OAK, MI, p. A321
BEAUMONT HOSPITAL – TAYLOR, TAYLOR, MI, p. A323
BEAUMONT HOSPITAL – TRENTON, TRENTON, MI, p. A324
BEAUMONT HOSPITAL – TROY, TROY, MI, p. A324
BEAUMONT HOSPITAL, WAYNE, WAYNE, MI, p. A324
BEAUREGARD HEALTH SYSTEM, DE RIDDER, LA, p. A266
BEAVER COUNTY MEMORIAL HOSPITAL, BEAVER, OK, p. A497
BEAVER DAM COMMUNITY HOSPITALS, BEAVER DAM, WI, p. A692
BEAVER VALLEY HOSPITAL, BEAVER, UT, p. A647
BECKETT SPRINGS, WEST CHESTER, OH, p. A494
BECKLEY ARH HOSPITAL, BECKLEY, WV, p. A683
BECKLEY VETERANS AFFAIRS MEDICAL CENTER, BECKLEY, WV, p. A683
BEDFORD REGIONAL MEDICAL CENTER, BEDFORD, INDIANA (see INDIANA UNIVERSITY HEALTH BEDFORD HOSPITAL), p. A199

BEDFORD VETERANS AFFAIRS MEDICAL CENTER, EDITH NOURSE ROGERS MEMORIAL VETERANS HOSPITAL, BEDFORD, MA, p. A294
BEEBE HEALTHCARE, LEWES, DE, p. A113
BEHAVIORAL CENTER OF MICHIGAN, WARREN, MI, p. A324
BEHAVIORAL HOSPITAL OF BELLAIRE, HOUSTON, TX, p. A610
BELLA VISTA HOSPITAL, MAYAGUEZ, PR, p. A717
BELLEVUE HOSPITAL, BELLEVUE, OH, p. A473
BELLIN HEALTH OCONTO HOSPITAL, OCONTO, WI, p. A702
BELLIN HOSPITAL, GREEN BAY, WI, p. A696
BELLIN PSYCHIATRIC CENTER, GREEN BAY, WI, p. A696
BELLVILLE GENERAL HOSPITAL, BELLVILLE, TEXAS (see CHI ST. JOSEPH HEALTH BELLVILLE HOSPITAL), p. A588
BELMONT BEHAVIORAL HOSPITAL, PHILADELPHIA, PA, p. A534
BELMONT PINES HOSPITAL, YOUNGSTOWN, OH, p. A495
BELOIT HEALTH SYSTEM, BELOIT, WI, p. A692
BELTON REGIONAL MEDICAL CENTER, BELTON, MO, p. A356
BENEDICTINE HOSPITAL, KINGSTON, NEW YORK (see HEALTH ALLIANCE HOSPITAL – MARY'S AVENUE CAMPUS), p. A430
BENEFIS HEALTH SYSTEM, GREAT FALLS, MT, p. A377
BENEFIS TETON MEDICAL CENTER, CHOTEAU, MT, p. A375
BENEWAH COMMUNITY HOSPITAL, SAINT MARIES, ID, p. A171
BENNETT COUNTY HOSPITAL AND NURSING HOME, MARTIN, SD, p. A561
BENSON HOSPITAL, BENSON, AZ, p. A28
BERGER HEALTH SYSTEM, CIRCLEVILLE, OH, p. A477
BERKELEY MEDICAL CENTER, MARTINSBURG, WV, p. A687
BERKSHIRE MEDICAL CENTER, PITTSFIELD, MA, p. A302
BERNARD MITCHELL HOSPITAL, CHICAGO, ILLINOIS (see UNIVERSITY OF CHICAGO MEDICAL CENTER), p. A177
BERTRAND CHAFFEE HOSPITAL, SPRINGVILLE, NY, p. A444
BERWICK HOSPITAL CENTER, BERWICK, PA, p. A520
BETH ISRAEL DEACONESS HOSPITAL PLYMOUTH, PLYMOUTH, MA, p. A302
BETH ISRAEL DEACONESS HOSPITAL–MILTON, MILTON, MA, p. A301
BETH ISRAEL DEACONESS HOSPITAL–NEEDHAM CAMPUS, NEEDHAM, MA, p. A301
BETH ISRAEL DEACONESS MEDICAL CENTER, BOSTON, MA, p. A294
BETHESDA HOSPITAL, SAINT PAUL, MN, p. A339
BETHESDA HOSPITAL EAST, BOYNTON BEACH, FL, p. A118
BETHESDA NORTH HOSPITAL, CINCINNATI, OH, p. A475
BETHESDA REHABILITATION HOSPITAL, BATON ROUGE, LA, p. A263
BEVERLY HOSPITAL, BEVERLY, MA, p. A294
BEVERLY HOSPITAL, MONTEBELLO, CA, p. A72
BHC ALHAMBRA HOSPITAL, ROSEMEAD, CA, p. A81
BIBB MEDICAL CENTER, CENTREVILLE, AL, p. A16
BIENVILLE MEDICAL CENTER, ARCADIA, LA, p. A263
BIG BEND REGIONAL MEDICAL CENTER, ALPINE, TX, p. A582
BIG HORN COUNTY MEMORIAL HOSPITAL, HARDIN, MT, p. A377
BIG SANDY MEDICAL CENTER, BIG SANDY, MT, p. A374
BIG SKY MEDICAL CENTER, BIG SKY, MT, p. A374
BIG SOUTH FORK MEDICAL CENTER, ONEIDA, TN, p. A578
BIG SPRING STATE HOSPITAL, BIG SPRING, TX, p. A588
BIGFORK VALLEY HOSPITAL, BIGFORK, MN, p. A328
BILLINGS CLINIC, BILLINGS, MT, p. A374
BINGHAM MEMORIAL HOSPITAL, BLACKFOOT, ID, p. A167
BINGHAMTON GENERAL HOSPITAL, BINGHAMTON, NEW YORK (see UNITED HEALTH SERVICES HOSPITALS– BINGHAMTON), p. A423
BIRMINGHAM VETERANS AFFAIRS MEDICAL CENTER, BIRMINGHAM, AL, p. A14
BLACK HILLS SURGICAL HOSPITAL, RAPID CITY, SD, p. A563
BLACK RIVER MEMORIAL HOSPITAL, BLACK RIVER FALLS, WI, p. A692
BLACKFEET COMMUNITY HOSPITAL, SAINT MARY, MT, p. A380
BLACKFORD COMMUNITY HOSPITAL, HARTFORD CITY, INDIANA (see INDIANA UNIVERSITY HEALTH BLACKFORD HOSPITAL), p. A206
BLACKWELL REGIONAL HOSPITAL, BLACKWELL, OK, p. A497
BLADEN COUNTY HOSPITAL, ELIZABETHTOWN, NORTH CAROLINA (see CAPE FEAR VALLEY – BLADEN COUNTY HOSPITAL), p. A454
BLAKE MEDICAL CENTER, BRADENTON, FL, p. A118
BLANCHARD VALLEY HOSPITAL, FINDLAY, OH, p. A483
BLECKLEY MEMORIAL HOSPITAL, COCHRAN, GA, p. A150
BLESSING HOSPITAL, QUINCY, IL, p. A194
BLOOMINGTON HOSPITAL, BLOOMINGTON, INDIANA (see INDIANA UNIVERSITY HEALTH BLOOMINGTON HOSPITAL), p. A200

BLOOMINGTON HOSPITAL OF ORANGE COUNTY, PAOLI, INDIANA (see INDIANA UNIVERSITY HEALTH PAOLI HOSPITAL), p. A213
BLOOMINGTON MEADOWS HOSPITAL, BLOOMINGTON, IN, p. A200
BLOUNT MEMORIAL HOSPITAL, MARYVILLE, TN, p. A574
BLUE MOUNTAIN HOSPITAL, BLANDING, UT, p. A647
BLUE MOUNTAIN HOSPITAL DISTRICT, JOHN DAY, OR, p. A514
BLUE RIDGE REGIONAL HOSPITAL, SPRUCE PINE, NC, p. A462
BLUEFIELD REGIONAL MEDICAL CENTER, BLUEFIELD, WV, p. A683
BLUEGRASS COMMUNITY HOSPITAL, VERSAILLES, KY, p. A261
BLUFFTON HOSPITAL, BLUFFTON, OH, p. A473
BLUFFTON REGIONAL MEDICAL CENTER, BLUFFTON, IN, p. A200
BLYTHEDALE CHILDREN'S HOSPITAL, VALHALLA, NY, p. A446
BOB WILSON MEMORIAL GRANT COUNTY HOSPITAL, ULYSSES, KS, p. A247
BOCA RATON COMMUNITY HOSPITAL, BOCA RATON, FL, p. A118
BOCA RATON REGIONAL HOSPITAL, BOCA RATON, FL, p. A118
BOISE BEHAVIORAL HEALTH HOSPITAL, BOISE, IDAHO (see SAFE HAVEN HOSPITAL OF TREASURE VALLEY), p. A167
BOISE VETERANS AFFAIRS MEDICAL CENTER, BOISE, ID, p. A167
BOLIVAR GENERAL HOSPITAL, BOLIVAR, TN, p. A566
BOLIVAR MEDICAL CENTER, CLEVELAND, MS, p. A346
BON SECOURS BALTIMORE HEALTH SYSTEM, BALTIMORE, MD, p. A286
BON SECOURS COMMUNITY HOSPITAL, PORT JERVIS, NY, p. A442
BON SECOURS MARY IMMACULATE HOSPITAL, NEWPORT NEWS, VA, p. A663
BON SECOURS MARYVIEW MEDICAL CENTER, PORTSMOUTH, VA, p. A665
BON SECOURS MEMORIAL REGIONAL MEDICAL CENTER, MECHANICSVILLE, VA, p. A662
BON SECOURS ST. FRANCIS HEALTH SYSTEM, GREENVILLE, SC, p. A553
BON SECOURS ST. FRANCIS HOSPITAL, CHARLESTON, SC, p. A549
BON SECOURS ST. FRANCIS MEDICAL CENTER, MIDLOTHIAN, VA, p. A662
BON SECOURS ST. MARY'S HOSPITAL, RICHMOND, VA, p. A665
BON SECOURS–DEPAUL MEDICAL CENTER, NORFOLK, VA, p. A663
BON SECOURS–RICHMOND COMMUNITY HOSPITAL, RICHMOND, VA, p. A666
BONNER GENERAL HOSPITAL, SANDPOINT, ID, p. A172
BOONE COUNTY HEALTH CENTER, ALBION, NE, p. A382
BOONE COUNTY HOSPITAL, BOONE, IA, p. A218
BOONE HOSPITAL CENTER, COLUMBIA, MO, p. A359
BOONE MEMORIAL HOSPITAL, MADISON, WV, p. A687
BOSTON CHILDREN'S HOSPITAL, BOSTON, MA, p. A295
BOSTON MEDICAL CENTER, BOSTON, MA, p. A295
BOTHWELL REGIONAL HEALTH CENTER, SEDALIA, MO, p. A371
BOULDER CITY HOSPITAL, BOULDER CITY, NV, p. A393
BOULDER COMMUNITY HEALTH, BOULDER, CO, p. A96
BOUNDARY COMMUNITY HOSPITAL, BONNERS FERRY, ID, p. A168
BOURBON COMMUNITY HOSPITAL, PARIS, KY, p. A259
BOURNEWOOD HEALTH SYSTEMS, BROOKLINE, MA, p. A297
BOWDLE HOSPITAL, BOWDLE, SD, p. A559
BOX BUTTE GENERAL HOSPITAL, ALLIANCE, NE, p. A382
BOYS TOWN NATIONAL RESEARCH HOSPITAL, OMAHA, NE, p. A388
BOZEMAN HEALTH, BOZEMAN, MT, p. A375
BRADFORD HEALTH SERVICES AT HUNTSVILLE, MADISON, AL, p. A20
BRADFORD HEALTH SERVICES AT WARRIOR LODGE, WARRIOR, AL, p. A24
BRADFORD REGIONAL MEDICAL CENTER, BRADFORD, PA, p. A521
BRADLEY CENTER OF ST. FRANCIS, COLUMBUS, GA, p. A150
BRADLEY COUNTY MEDICAL CENTER, WARREN, AR, p. A49
BRADLEY MEMORIAL, SOUTHINGTON, CT, p. A111
BRANDON REGIONAL HOSPITAL, BRANDON, FL, p. A119
BRANDYWINE HOSPITAL, COATESVILLE, PA, p. A523
BRATTLEBORO MEMORIAL HOSPITAL, BRATTLEBORO, VT, p. A654
BRATTLEBORO RETREAT, BRATTLEBORO, VT, p. A654
BRAXTON COUNTY MEMORIAL HOSPITAL, GASSAWAY, WV, p. A685

BRECKINRIDGE MEMORIAL HOSPITAL, HARDINSBURG, KY, p. A253
BRENNER CHILDREN'S HOSPITAL & HEALTH SERVICES, WINSTON, NORTH CAROLINA (see WAKE FOREST BAPTIST MEDICAL CENTER), p. A464
BRENTWOOD BEHAVIORAL HEALTHCARE OF MISSISSIPPI, JACKSON, MS, p. A348
BRENTWOOD HOSPITAL, SHREVEPORT, LA, p. A278
BRENTWOOD SPRINGS, NEWBURGH, IN, p. A212
BRIDGEPOINT CONTINUING CARE HOSPITAL, MARRERO, LA, p. A273
BRIDGEPOINT HOSPITAL CAPITOL HILL, WASHINGTON, DC, p. A115
BRIDGEPOINT HOSPITAL NATIONAL HARBOR, WASHINGTON, DC, p. A115
BRIDGEPORT HOSPITAL, BRIDGEPORT, CT, p. A107
BRIDGES MEDICAL CENTER, ADA, MINNESOTA (see ESSENTIA HEALTH ADA), p. A326
BRIDGETON HEALTH CENTER, BRIDGETON, NEW JERSEY (see INSPIRA MEDICAL CENTER–VINELAND), p. A404
BRIDGEWATER STATE HOSPITAL, BRIDGEWATER, MA, p. A296
BRIDGTON HOSPITAL, BRIDGTON, ME, p. A282
BRIGHAM AND WOMEN'S FAULKNER HOSPITAL, BOSTON, MA, p. A295
BRIGHAM AND WOMEN'S HOSPITAL, BOSTON, MA, p. A295
BRIGHAM CITY COMMUNITY HOSPITAL, BRIGHAM CITY, UT, p. A647
BRISTOL BAY AREA HEALTH CORPORATION, DILLINGHAM, AK, p. A26
BRISTOL HOSPITAL, BRISTOL, CT, p. A107
BRISTOL REGIONAL MEDICAL CENTER, BRISTOL, TN, p. A566
BRISTOW MEDICAL CENTER, BRISTOW, OK, p. A497
BROADDUS HOSPITAL, PHILIPPI, WV, p. A688
BROADLAWNS MEDICAL CENTER, DES MOINES, IA, p. A221
BROADWATER HEALTH CENTER, TOWNSEND, MT, p. A380
BRODSTONE MEMORIAL HOSPITAL, SUPERIOR, NE, p. A392
BRONSON BATTLE CREEK HOSPITAL, BATTLE CREEK, MI, p. A307
BRONSON LAKEVIEW HOSPITAL, PAW PAW, MI, p. A319
BRONSON METHODIST HOSPITAL, KALAMAZOO, MI, p. A315
BRONSON SOUTH HAVEN HOSPITAL, SOUTH HAVEN, MI, p. A322
BRONSON VICKSBURG HOSPITAL, VICKSBURG, MICHIGAN (see BRONSON METHODIST HOSPITAL), p. A324
BROOK LANE HEALTH SERVICES, HAGERSTOWN, MD, p. A291
BROOKDALE HOSPITAL MEDICAL CENTER, NEW YORK, NEW YORK (see MOUNT SINAI BETH ISRAEL), p. A432
BROOKE ARMY MEDICAL CENTER, FORT SAM HOUSTON, TEXAS (see BROOKE ARMY MEDICAL CENTER), p. A604
BROOKE ARMY MEDICAL CENTER, FORT SAM HOUSTON, TX, p. A604
BROOKE GLEN BEHAVIORAL HOSPITAL, FORT WASHINGTON, PA, p. A526
BROOKHAVEN HOSPITAL, TULSA, OK, p. A508
BROOKINGS HEALTH SYSTEM, BROOKINGS, SD, p. A559
BROOKS COUNTY HOSPITAL, QUITMAN, GA, p. A158
BROOKS MEMORIAL HOSPITAL, DUNKIRK, NY, p. A427
BROOKS REHABILITATION HOSPITAL, JACKSONVILLE, FL, p. A125
BROOKWOOD BAPTIST MEDICAL CENTER, BIRMINGHAM, AL, p. A14
BROUGHTON HOSPITAL, MORGANTON, NC, p. A458
BROWARD HEALTH CORAL SPRINGS, CORAL SPRINGS, FL, p. A120
BROWARD HEALTH IMPERIAL POINT, FORT LAUDERDALE, FL, p. A122
BROWARD HEALTH MEDICAL CENTER, FORT LAUDERDALE, FL, p. A122
BROWARD HEALTH NORTH, DEERFIELD BEACH, FL, p. A121
BROWN COUNTY COMMUNITY TREATMENT CENTER, GREEN BAY, WI, p. A696
BROWN COUNTY HOSPITAL, AINSWORTH, NE, p. A382
BROWN COUNTY HUMAN SERVICES MENTAL HEALTH CENTER, GREEN BAY, WISCONSIN (see BROWN COUNTY COMMUNITY TREATMENT CENTER), p. A696
BROWNFIELD REGIONAL MEDICAL CENTER, BROWNFIELD, TX, p. A589
BROWNWOOD REGIONAL MEDICAL CENTER, BROWNWOOD, TX, p. A590
BRUNSWICK PSYCH CENTER, AMITYVILLE, NY, p. A422
BRYAN MEDICAL CENTER, LINCOLN, NE, p. A386
BRYAN W. WHITFIELD MEMORIAL HOSPITAL, DEMOPOLIS, AL, p. A17
BRYCE HOSPITAL, TUSCALOOSA, AL, p. A24
BRYLIN HOSPITALS, BUFFALO, NY, p. A424
BRYN MAWR HOSPITAL, BRYN MAWR, PA, p. A521

BRYN MAWR REHABILITATION HOSPITAL, MALVERN, PA, p. A530
BRYNN MARR HOSPITAL, JACKSONVILLE, NC, p. A456
BSA HOSPITAL, LLC, AMARILLO, TX, p. A582
BUCHANAN COUNTY HEALTH CENTER, INDEPENDENCE, IA, p. A224
BUCHANAN GENERAL HOSPITAL, GRUNDY, VA, p. A660
BUCKS COUNTY CAMPUS, LANGHORNE, PENNSYLVANIA (see JEFFERSON HEALTH NORTHEAST), p. A529
BUCKTAIL MEDICAL CENTER, RENOVO, PA, p. A540
BUCYRUS HOSPITAL, BUCYRUS, OH, p. A474
BUENA VISTA REGIONAL MEDICAL CENTER, STORM LAKE, IA, p. A230
BUFFALO HOSPITAL, BUFFALO, MN, p. A329
BUFFALO PSYCHIATRIC CENTER, BUFFALO, NY, p. A424
BULLOCK COUNTY HOSPITAL, UNION SPRINGS, AL, p. A24
BUNKIE GENERAL HOSPITAL, BUNKIE, LA, p. A265
BURDETT BIRTH CENTER, TROY, NY, p. A445
BURGESS HEALTH CENTER, ONAWA, IA, p. A227
BURKE MEDICAL CENTER, WAYNESBORO, GA, p. A163
BURKE REHABILITATION HOSPITAL, WHITE PLAINS, NY, p. A447
BURNETT MEDICAL CENTER, GRANTSBURG, WI, p. A695
BUTLER COUNTY HEALTH CARE CENTER, DAVID CITY, NE, p. A384
BUTLER HEALTH SYSTEM, BUTLER, PA, p. A521
BUTLER HOSPITAL, PROVIDENCE, RI, p. A547
BYRD REGIONAL HOSPITAL, LEESVILLE, LA, p. A272

C

CABELL HUNTINGTON HOSPITAL, HUNTINGTON, WV, p. A685
CABINET PEAKS MEDICAL CENTER, LIBBY, MT, p. A378
CACHE VALLEY HOSPITAL, NORTH LOGAN, UT, p. A649
CALAIS REGIONAL HOSPITAL, CALAIS, ME, p. A282
CALDWELL MEDICAL CENTER, PRINCETON, KY, p. A260
CALDWELL MEMORIAL HOSPITAL, COLUMBIA, LA, p. A265
CALDWELL UNC HEALTH CARE, LENOIR, NC, p. A457
CALHOUN–LIBERTY HOSPITAL, BLOUNTSTOWN, FL, p. A118
CALIFORNIA HOSPITAL MEDICAL CENTER, LOS ANGELES, CA, p. A66
CALIFORNIA MEDICAL FACILITY, VACAVILLE, CA, p. A93
CALIFORNIA MENS COLONY CORRECTIONAL TREATMENT CENTER, SAN LUIS OBISPO, CA, p. A87
CALIFORNIA PACIFIC MEDICAL CENTER, SAN FRANCISCO, CA, p. A85
CALIFORNIA PACIFIC MEDICAL CENTER–DAVIES CAMPUS, SAN FRANCISCO, CA, p. A85
CALIFORNIA PACIFIC MEDICAL CENTER–ST. LUKE'S CAMPUS, SAN FRANCISCO, CA, p. A85
CALIFORNIA REHABILITATION INSTITUTE, LOS ANGELES, CA, p. A66
CALLAWAY DISTRICT HOSPITAL, CALLAWAY, NE, p. A383
CALVERTHEALTH MEDICAL CENTER, PRINCE FREDERICK, MD, p. A293
CAMBRIDGE BEHAVIORAL HOSPITAL, CAMBRIDGE, OH, p. A474
CAMBRIDGE HEALTH ALLIANCE, CAMBRIDGE, MA, p. A297
CAMBRIDGE MEDICAL CENTER, CAMBRIDGE, MN, p. A329
CAMC MEMORIAL HOSPITAL, CHARLESTON, WEST VIRGINIA (see CHARLESTON AREA MEDICAL CENTER), p. A684
CAMC WOMEN AND CHILDREN'S HOSPITAL, CHARLESTON, WEST VIRGINIA (see CHARLESTON AREA MEDICAL CENTER), p. A684
CAMDEN CLARK MEDICAL CENTER, PARKERSBURG, WV, p. A688
CAMDEN GENERAL HOSPITAL, CAMDEN, TN, p. A566
CAMERON HOSPITAL, CAMERON, TX, p. A591
CAMERON MEMORIAL COMMUNITY HOSPITAL, ANGOLA, IN, p. A199
CAMERON REGIONAL MEDICAL CENTER, CAMERON, MO, p. A357
CAMPBELL COUNTY HEALTH, GILLETTE, WY, p. A711
CANANDAIGUA VETERANS AFFAIRS MEDICAL CENTER, CANANDAIGUA, NY, p. A425
CANCER TREATMENT CENTERS OF AMERICA–EASTERN REGIONAL MEDICAL CENTER, PHILADELPHIA, PA, p. A534
CANDLER COUNTY HOSPITAL, METTER, GA, p. A157
CANDLER HOSPITAL, SAVANNAH, GA, p. A160
CANONSBURG HOSPITAL, CANONSBURG, PA, p. A522
CANTON–POTSDAM HOSPITAL, POTSDAM, NY, p. A442
CANYON RIDGE HOSPITAL, CHINO, CA, p. A54
CANYON VISTA MEDICAL CENTER, SIERRA VISTA, AZ, p. A36
CAPE COD HOSPITAL, HYANNIS, MA, p. A299

CAPE CORAL HOSPITAL, CAPE CORAL, FL, p. A119
CAPE FEAR VALLEY – BLADEN COUNTY HOSPITAL, ELIZABETHTOWN, NC, p. A454
CAPE FEAR VALLEY MEDICAL CENTER, FAYETTEVILLE, NC, p. A454
CAPE REGIONAL HEALTH SYSTEM, CAPE MAY COURT HOUSE, NJ, p. A404
CAPITAL DISTRICT PSYCHIATRIC CENTER, ALBANY, NY, p. A422
CAPITAL HEALTH MEDICAL CENTER–HOPEWELL, PENNINGTON, NJ, p. A410
CAPITAL HEALTH REGIONAL MEDICAL CENTER, TRENTON, NJ, p. A413
CAPITAL HOSPICE, ARLINGTON, VA, p. A656
CAPITAL MEDICAL CENTER, OLYMPIA, WA, p. A676
CAPITAL REGION MEDICAL CENTER, JEFFERSON CITY, MO, p. A361
CAPITAL REGIONAL MEDICAL CENTER, TALLAHASSEE, FL, p. A140
CAPROCK HOSPITAL, BRYAN, TX, p. A590
CAPTAIN JAMES A. LOVELL FEDERAL HEALTH CARE CENTER, NORTH CHICAGO, IL, p. A191
CARDINAL HILL REHABILITATION HOSPITAL, LEXINGTON, KY, p. A254
CARDINAL HILL SPECIALTY HOSPITAL, FORT THOMAS, KENTUCKY (see SELECT SPECIALTY HOSPITAL–NORTHERN KENTUCKY), p. A252
CARDIOVASCULAR CENTER OF PUERTO RICO AND THE CARIBBEAN, SAN JUAN, PR, p. A718
CARDON CHILDREN'S MEDICAL CENTER, MESA, ARIZONA (see BANNER DESERT MEDICAL CENTER), p. A31
CAREONE AT HACKENSACK UNIVERSITY MEDICAL CENTER AT PASCACK VALLEY, WESTWOOD, NJ, p. A415
CAREONE AT RARITAN BAY MEDICAL CENTER, PERTH AMBOY, NJ, p. A410
CAREONE AT TRINITAS REGIONAL MEDICAL CENTER, ELIZABETH, NJ, p. A405
CAREPARTNERS HEALTH SERVICES, ASHEVILLE, NC, p. A449
CAREPOINT HEALTH BAYONNE MEDICAL CENTER, BAYONNE, NJ, p. A403
CAREPOINT HEALTH CHRIST HOSPITAL, JERSEY CITY, NJ, p. A407
CAREPOINT HEALTH HOBOKEN UNIVERSITY MEDICAL CENTER, HOBOKEN, NJ, p. A406
CARIBBEAN MEDICAL CENTER, FAJARDO, PR, p. A716
CARIBOU MEMORIAL HOSPITAL AND LIVING CENTER, SODA SPRINGS, ID, p. A172
CARILION FRANKLIN MEMORIAL HOSPITAL, ROCKY MOUNT, VA, p. A667
CARILION GILES COMMUNITY HOSPITAL, PEARISBURG, VA, p. A664
CARILION NEW RIVER VALLEY MEDICAL CENTER, CHRISTIANSBURG, VA, p. A658
CARILION ROANOKE MEMORIAL HOSPITAL, ROANOKE, VA, p. A667
CARILION STONEWALL JACKSON HOSPITAL, LEXINGTON, VA, p. A661
CARILION TAZEWELL COMMUNITY HOSPITAL, TAZEWELL, VA, p. A668
CARITAS GOOD SAMARITAN MEDICAL CENTER, BROCKTON, MASSACHUSETTS (see GOOD SAMARITAN MEDICAL CENTER), p. A296
CARITAS ST. ELIZABETH'S MEDICAL CENTER, BRIGHTON, MASSACHUSETTS (see ST. ELIZABETH'S MEDICAL CENTER), p. A296
CARL ALBERT COMMUNITY MENTAL HEALTH CENTER, MCALESTER, OK, p. A502
CARL R. DARNALL ARMY MEDICAL CENTER, FORT HOOD, TX, p. A604
CARL VINSON VETERANS AFFAIRS MEDICAL CENTER, DUBLIN, GA, p. A152
CARLE FOUNDATION HOSPITAL, URBANA, IL, p. A197
CARLE HOOPESTON REGIONAL HEALTH CENTER, HOOPESTON, IL, p. A186
CARLE RICHLAND MEMORIAL HOSPITAL, OLNEY, IL, p. A192
CARLINVILLE AREA HOSPITAL, CARLINVILLE, IL, p. A175
CARLSBAD MEDICAL CENTER, CARLSBAD, NM, p. A417
CARNEGIE TRI–COUNTY MUNICIPAL HOSPITAL, CARNEGIE, OK, p. A497
CARNEY HOSPITAL, BOSTON, MA, p. A295
CARO CENTER, CARO, MI, p. A308
CAROLINA CENTER FOR BEHAVIORAL HEALTH, GREER, SC, p. A554
CAROLINA PINES REGIONAL MEDICAL CENTER, HARTSVILLE, SC, p. A554
CAROLINAEAST HEALTH SYSTEM, NEW BERN, NC, p. A459
CAROLINAS CONTINUECARE HOSPITAL AT PINEVILLE, CHARLOTTE, NC, p. A451
CAROLINAS CONTINUECARE HOSPITAL AT UNIVERSITY, CHARLOTTE, NC, p. A451

CAROLINAS HEALTHCARE SYSTEM BLUE RIDGE, MORGANTON, NC, p. A459
CAROMONT REGIONAL MEDICAL CENTER, GASTONIA, NC, p. A454
CARONDELET HOLY CROSS HOSPITAL, NOGALES, AZ, p. A32
CARONDELET ST. JOSEPH'S HOSPITAL, TUCSON, AZ, p. A37
CARONDELET ST. MARY'S HOSPITAL, TUCSON, AZ, p. A37
CARRIS HEALTH – REDWOOD, REDWOOD FALLS, MN, p. A338
CARROLL COUNTY MEMORIAL HOSPITAL, CARROLLTON, KY, p. A250
CARROLL COUNTY MEMORIAL HOSPITAL, CARROLLTON, MO, p. A358
CARROLL HOSPITAL CENTER, WESTMINSTER, MD, p. A293
CARROLLTON SPRINGS, CARROLLTON, TX, p. A591
CARRUS REHABILITATION HOSPITAL, SHERMAN, TX, p. A637
CARRUS SPECIALTY HOSPITAL, SHERMAN, TX, p. A637
CARSON TAHOE CONTINUING CARE HOSPITAL, CARSON CITY, NV, p. A393
CARSON TAHOE HEALTH, CARSON CITY, NV, p. A393
CARSON VALLEY MEDICAL CENTER, GARDNERVILLE, NV, p. A394
CARTERET HEALTH CARE, MOREHEAD CITY, NC, p. A458
CARTERSVILLE MEDICAL CENTER, CARTERSVILLE, GA, p. A149
CARTHAGE AREA HOSPITAL, CARTHAGE, NY, p. A425
CARY MEDICAL CENTER, CARIBOU, ME, p. A282
CASA COLINA HOSPITAL AND HEALTH SYSTEMS, POMONA, CA, p. A78
CASCADE BEHAVIORAL HOSPITAL, TUKWILA, WA, p. A681
CASCADE MEDICAL CENTER, CASCADE, ID, p. A168
CASCADE MEDICAL CENTER, LEAVENWORTH, WA, p. A674
CASCADE VALLEY HOSPITAL, ARLINGTON, WA, p. A670
CASEY COUNTY HOSPITAL, LIBERTY, KY, p. A255
CASS COUNTY MEMORIAL HOSPITAL, ATLANTIC, IA, p. A217
CASS REGIONAL MEDICAL CENTER, HARRISONVILLE, MO, p. A361
CASSIA REGIONAL HOSPITAL, BURLEY, ID, p. A168
CASTANER GENERAL HOSPITAL, CASTANER, PR, p. A715
CASTLE ROCK ADVENTIST HOSPITAL, CASTLE ROCK, CO, p. A97
CASTLEVIEW HOSPITAL, PRICE, UT, p. A650
CATALINA ISLAND MEDICAL CENTER, AVALON, CA, p. A51
CATAWBA HOSPITAL, CATAWBA, VA, p. A657
CATAWBA VALLEY MEDICAL CENTER, HICKORY, NC, p. A456
CATHOLIC MEDICAL CENTER, MANCHESTER, NH, p. A401
CATSKILL REGIONAL MEDICAL CENTER, HARRIS, NY, p. A429
CAVALIER COUNTY MEMORIAL HOSPITAL AND CLINICS, LANGDON, ND, p. A468
CAYUGA MEDICAL CENTER AT ITHACA, ITHACA, NY, p. A429
CCC AT PINEVIEW HOSPITAL, LAKESIDE, AZ, p. A31
CCM HEALTH, MONTEVIDEO, MN, p. A336
CEDAR CITY HOSPITAL, CEDAR CITY, UT, p. A647
CEDAR COUNTY MEMORIAL HOSPITAL, EL DORADO SPRINGS, MO, p. A359
CEDAR CREST HOSPITAL AND RESIDENTIAL TREATMENT CENTER, BELTON, TX, p. A588
CEDAR HILLS HOSPITAL, PORTLAND, OR, p. A516
CEDAR PARK REGIONAL MEDICAL CENTER, CEDAR PARK, TX, p. A592
CEDAR RIDGE HOSPITAL, OKLAHOMA CITY, OK, p. A503
CEDAR SPRINGS HOSPITAL, COLORADO SPRINGS, CO, p. A97
CEDARS–SINAI MEDICAL CENTER, LOS ANGELES, CA, p. A66
CENTENNIAL HILLS HOSPITAL MEDICAL CENTER, LAS VEGAS, NV, p. A394
CENTENNIAL MEDICAL CENTER, NASHVILLE, TENNESSEE (see TRISTAR CENTENNIAL MEDICAL CENTER), p. A576
CENTENNIAL PEAKS HOSPITAL, LOUISVILLE, CO, p. A104
CENTER FOR BEHAVIORAL MEDICINE, KANSAS CITY, MO, p. A362
CENTER FOR FORENSIC PSYCHIATRY, SALINE, MI, p. A322
CENTERPOINT MEDICAL CENTER, INDEPENDENCE, MO, p. A361
CENTERPOINTE HOSPITAL, SAINT CHARLES, MO, p. A368
CENTERPOINTE HOSPITAL OF COLUMBIA, COLUMBIA, MO, p. A359
CENTERSTONE HOSPITAL, BRADENTON, FL, p. A118
CENTINELA HOSPITAL MEDICAL CENTER, INGLEWOOD, CA, p. A62
CENTRA BEDFORD MEMORIAL HOSPITAL, BEDFORD, VA, p. A656
CENTRA HEALTH, LYNCHBURG, VIRGINIA (see CENTRA LYNCHBURG GENERAL HOSPITAL), p. A661
CENTRA LYNCHBURG GENERAL HOSPITAL, LYNCHBURG, VA, p. A662
CENTRA SOUTHSIDE COMMUNITY HOSPITAL, FARMVILLE, VA, p. A659
CENTRA SPECIALTY HOSPITAL, LYNCHBURG, VA, p. A662

CENTRACARE HEALTH–LONG PRAIRIE, LONG PRAIRIE, MN, p. A334
CENTRACARE HEALTH–MELROSE, MELROSE, MN, p. A335
CENTRACARE HEALTH–MONTICELLO, MONTICELLO, MN, p. A336
CENTRACARE HEALTH–PAYNESVILLE, PAYNESVILLE, MN, p. A337
CENTRACARE HEALTH–SAUK CENTRE, SAUK CENTRE, MN, p. A340
CENTRAL ALABAMA VETERANS HEALTH CARE SYSTEM, MONTGOMERY, AL, p. A21
CENTRAL ARKANSAS VETERANS HEALTHCARE SYSTEM, LITTLE ROCK, AR, p. A45
CENTRAL CAROLINA HOSPITAL, SANFORD, NC, p. A462
CENTRAL FLORIDA BEHAVIORAL HOSPITAL, ORLANDO, FL, p. A134
CENTRAL FLORIDA REGIONAL HOSPITAL, SANFORD, FL, p. A139
CENTRAL HOSPITAL OF BOWIE, BOWIE, TX, p. A589
CENTRAL INDIANA AMG SPECIALTY HOSPITAL, MUNCIE, IN, p. A212
CENTRAL LOUISIANA STATE HOSPITAL, PINEVILLE, LA, p. A277
CENTRAL LOUISIANA SURGICAL HOSPITAL, ALEXANDRIA, LA, p. A262
CENTRAL MAINE MEDICAL CENTER, LEWISTON, ME, p. A283
CENTRAL MONTANA MEDICAL CENTER, LEWISTOWN, MT, p. A378
CENTRAL NEW YORK PSYCHIATRIC CENTER, MARCY, NEW YORK (see MOUNT SINAI WEST HOSPITAL), p. A431
CENTRAL PENINSULA HOSPITAL, SOLDOTNA, AK, p. A27
CENTRAL PRISON HOSPITAL, RALEIGH, NC, p. A460
CENTRAL REGIONAL HOSPITAL, BUTNER, NC, p. A450
CENTRAL STATE HOSPITAL, LOUISVILLE, KY, p. A256
CENTRAL STATE HOSPITAL, MILLEDGEVILLE, GA, p. A157
CENTRAL STATE HOSPITAL, PETERSBURG, VA, p. A664
CENTRAL TEXAS MEDICAL CENTER, SAN MARCOS, TX, p. A636
CENTRAL TEXAS REHABILITATION HOSPITAL, AUSTIN, TX, p. A585
CENTRAL TEXAS VETERANS AFFAIRS HEALTH CARE SYSTEM, OLIN E. TEAGUE VETERANS MEDICAL CENTER, TEMPLE, TEXAS (see CENTRAL TEXAS VETERANS HEALTH CARE SYSTEM), p. A639
CENTRAL TEXAS VETERANS HEALTH CARE SYSTEM, TEMPLE, TX, p. A640
CENTRAL TEXAS VETERANS HEALTH CARE SYSTEM, DORIS MILLER VETERANS MEDICAL CENTER, WACO, TEXAS (see CENTRAL TEXAS VETERANS HEALTH CARE SYSTEM), p. A644
CENTRAL VALLEY GENERAL HOSPITAL, HANFORD, CA, p. A61
CENTRAL VALLEY MEDICAL CENTER, NEPHI, UT, p. A649
CENTRAL VALLEY SPECIALTY HOSPITAL, MODESTO, CA, p. A72
CENTRAL VIRGINIA TRAINING CENTER, MADISON HEIGHTS, VA, p. A662
CENTRASTATE HEALTHCARE SYSTEM, FREEHOLD, NJ, p. A406
CENTRO DE SALUD CONDUCTUAL MENONITA–CIMA, AIBONITO, PR, p. A714
CGH MEDICAL CENTER, STERLING, IL, p. A197
CHADRON COMMUNITY HOSPITAL AND HEALTH SERVICES, CHADRON, NE, p. A384
CHAMBERS MEMORIAL HOSPITAL, DANVILLE, AR, p. A41
CHAMBERSBURG HOSPITAL, CHAMBERSBURG, PA, p. A522
CHAN SOON–SHIONG MEDICAL CENTER, WINDBER, PA, p. A545
CHANDLER REGIONAL MEDICAL CENTER, CHANDLER, AZ, p. A28
CHAPMAN GLOBAL MEDICAL CENTER, ORANGE, CA, p. A76
CHARLES A. CANNON MEMORIAL HOSPITAL, NEWLAND, NC, p. A459
CHARLES GEORGE VETERANS AFFAIRS MEDICAL CENTER, ASHEVILLE, NC, p. A449
CHARLESTON AREA MEDICAL CENTER, CHARLESTON, WV, p. A684
CHARLESTON SURGICAL HOSPITAL, CHARLESTON, WV, p. A684
CHARLIE NORWOOD VETERANS AFFAIRS MEDICAL CENTER, AUGUSTA, GA, p. A147
CHARLOTTE HUNGERFORD HOSPITAL, TORRINGTON, CT, p. A111
CHARLTON MEMORIAL HOSPITAL, FALL RIVER, MASSACHUSETTS (see SOUTHCOAST HOSPITALS GROUP), p. A298
CHASE COUNTY COMMUNITY HOSPITAL, IMPERIAL, NE, p. A386
CHATHAM HOSPITAL, SILER CITY, NC, p. A462

CHATUGE REGIONAL HOSPITAL AND NURSING HOME, HIAWASSEE, GA, p. A154

CHEROKEE INDIAN HOSPITAL, CHEROKEE, NC, p. A452

CHEROKEE MEDICAL CENTER, GAFFNEY, SC, p. A553

CHEROKEE NATION W.W. HASTINGS INDIAN HOSPITAL, TAHLEQUAH, OK, p. A508

CHEROKEE REGIONAL MEDICAL CENTER, CHEROKEE, IA, p. A219

CHERRY COUNTY HOSPITAL, VALENTINE, NE, p. A392

CHERRY HOSPITAL, GOLDSBORO, NC, p. A455

CHESAPEAKE REGIONAL MEDICAL CENTER, CHESAPEAKE, VA, p. A657

CHESHIRE MEDICAL CENTER, KEENE, NH, p. A400

CHESTER MENTAL HEALTH CENTER, CHESTER, IL, p. A176

CHESTER RIVER HOSPITAL CENTER, CHESTERTOWN, MARYLAND (see UNIVERSITY OF MARYLAND SHORE MEDICAL CENTER AT CHESTERTOWN), p. A289

CHESTNUT HILL HOSPITAL, PHILADELPHIA, PA, p. A534

CHESTNUT RIDGE HOSPITAL, MORGANTOWN, WEST VIRGINIA (see WEST VIRGINIA UNIVERSITY HOSPITALS), p. A687

CHEYENNE COUNTY HOSPITAL, SAINT FRANCIS, KS, p. A244

CHEYENNE REGIONAL MEDICAL CENTER, CHEYENNE, WY, p. A710

CHEYENNE VETERANS AFFAIRS MEDICAL CENTER, CHEYENNE, WY, p. A711

CHG CORNERSTONE HOSPITAL CONROE, CONROE, TX, p. A593

CHG HOSPITAL TUCSON, LLC, TUCSON, AZ, p. A37

CHI FLAGET MEMORIAL HOSPITAL, BARDSTOWN, KY, p. A249

CHI HEALTH CREIGHTON UNIVERSITY MEDICAL CENTER – BERGAN MERCY, OMAHA, NE, p. A388

CHI HEALTH GOOD SAMARITAN, KEARNEY, NE, p. A386

CHI HEALTH IMMANUEL, OMAHA, NE, p. A389

CHI HEALTH LAKESIDE, OMAHA, NE, p. A389

CHI HEALTH MERCY CORNING, CORNING, IA, p. A219

CHI HEALTH MERCY COUNCIL BLUFFS, COUNCIL BLUFFS, IA, p. A220

CHI HEALTH MIDLANDS, PAPILLION, NE, p. A390

CHI HEALTH MISSOURI VALLEY, MISSOURI VALLEY, IA, p. A226

CHI HEALTH NEBRASKA HEART, LINCOLN, NE, p. A386

CHI HEALTH PLAINVIEW, PLAINVIEW, NE, p. A391

CHI HEALTH SAINT FRANCIS, GRAND ISLAND, NE, p. A385

CHI HEALTH SCHUYLER, SCHUYLER, NE, p. A391

CHI HEALTH ST ELIZABETH, LINCOLN, NE, p. A387

CHI HEALTH ST. MARY'S, NEBRASKA CITY, NE, p. A388

CHI LAKEWOOD HEALTH, BAUDETTE, MN, p. A328

CHI LISBON HEALTH, LISBON, ND, p. A468

CHI MEMORIAL, CHATTANOOGA, TN, p. A567

CHI MEMORIAL HOSPITAL – GEORGIA, FORT OGLETHORPE, GA, p. A153

CHI MERCY HEALTH, VALLEY CITY, ND, p. A469

CHI OAKES HOSPITAL, OAKES, ND, p. A469

CHI OUR LADY OF PEACE, LOUISVILLE, KY, p. A256

CHI SAINT JOSEPH BEREA, BEREA, KY, p. A249

CHI SAINT JOSEPH EAST, LEXINGTON, KY, p. A254

CHI SAINT JOSEPH HEALTH, LEXINGTON, KY, p. A255

CHI SAINT JOSEPH LONDON, LONDON, KY, p. A255

CHI ST ALEXIUS HEALTH CARRINGTON MEDICAL CENTER, CARRINGTON, ND, p. A465

CHI ST. ALEXIUS HEALTH – DICKINSON MEDICAL CENTER, DICKINSON, ND, p. A466

CHI ST. ALEXIUS HEALTH – WILLISTON MEDICAL CENTER, WILLISTON, ND, p. A470

CHI ST. ALEXIUS HEALTH, BISMARCK, ND, p. A465

CHI ST. ALEXIUS HEALTH DEVILS LAKE HOSPITAL, DEVILS LAKE, ND, p. A466

CHI ST. ALEXIUS HEALTH GARRISON, GARRISON, ND, p. A467

CHI ST. ANTHONY HOSPITAL, PENDLETON, OR, p. A515

CHI ST. FRANCIS HEALTH, BRECKENRIDGE, MN, p. A329

CHI ST. GABRIEL'S HEALTH, LITTLE FALLS, MN, p. A334

CHI ST. JOSEPH HEALTH BELLVILLE, BELLVILLE, TX, p. A588

CHI ST. JOSEPH HEALTH BURLESON HOSPITAL, CALDWELL, TX, p. A591

CHI ST. JOSEPH HEALTH GRIMES HOSPITAL, NAVASOTA, TX, p. A626

CHI ST. JOSEPH HEALTH MADISON HOSPITAL, MADISONVILLE, TX, p. A623

CHI ST. JOSEPH HEALTH REHABILITATION HOSPITAL, AN AFFILIATE OF ENCOMPASS HEALTH, BRYAN, TX, p. A590

CHI ST. JOSEPH REGIONAL HEALTH CENTER, BRYAN, TX, p. A590

CHI ST. JOSEPH'S HEALTH, PARK RAPIDS, MN, p. A337

CHI ST. LUKE'S HEALTH – PATIENTS MEDICAL CENTER, PASADENA, TX, p. A628

CHI ST. LUKE'S HEALTH BRAZOSPORT, LAKE JACKSON, TX, p. A619

CHI ST. LUKE'S HEALTH MEMORIAL LIVINGSTON, LIVINGSTON, TX, p. A621

CHI ST. LUKE'S HEALTH MEMORIAL LUFKIN, LUFKIN, TX, p. A622

CHI ST. LUKE'S HEALTH MEMORIAL SAN AUGUSTINE, SAN AUGUSTINE, TX, p. A636

CHI ST. LUKE'S HEALTH–LAKESIDE HOSPITAL, THE WOODLANDS, TX, p. A640

CHI ST. LUKE'S HEALTH–THE WOODLANDS HOSPITAL, THE WOODLANDS, TX, p. A640

CHI ST. LUKE'S HOSPITAL – THE VINTAGE HOSPITAL, HOUSTON, TX, p. A611

CHI ST. VINCENT HOT SPRINGS, HOT SPRINGS, AR, p. A43

CHI ST. VINCENT HOT SPRINGS REHABILITATION HOSPITAL, HOT SPRINGS, AR, p. A43

CHI ST. VINCENT INFIRMARY MEDICAL CENTER, LITTLE ROCK, AR, p. A45

CHI ST. VINCENT MEDICAL CENTER–NORTH, SHERWOOD, AR, p. A48

CHI ST. VINCENT MORRILTON, MORRILTON, AR, p. A46

CHI ST. VINCENT SHERWOOD REHABILITATION HOSPITAL, SHERWOOD, AR, p. A48

CHICAGO LAKESHORE HOSPITAL, CHICAGO, IL, p. A177

CHICAGO LYING–IN (CLI), CHICAGO, ILLINOIS (see UNIVERSITY OF CHICAGO MEDICAL CENTER), p. A177

CHICAGO–READ MENTAL HEALTH CENTER, CHICAGO, IL, p. A177

CHICKASAW NATION MEDICAL CENTER, ADA, OK, p. A496

CHICOT MEMORIAL MEDICAL CENTER, LAKE VILLAGE, AR, p. A44

CHILD AND ADOLESCENT BEHAVIORAL HEALTH SERVICES, WILLMAR, MN, p. A342

CHILDREN'S HEALTHCARE OF ATLANTA, ATLANTA, GA, p. A146

CHILDREN'S HOSPITAL, NEW ORLEANS, LA, p. A275

CHILDREN'S HOSPITAL AND MEDICAL CENTER, OMAHA, NE, p. A389

CHILDREN'S HOSPITAL COLORADO, AURORA, CO, p. A96

CHILDREN'S HOSPITAL LOS ANGELES, LOS ANGELES, CA, p. A66

CHILDREN'S HOSPITAL OF OKLAHOMA, OKLAHOMA CITY, OKLAHOMA (see OU MEDICAL CENTER), p. A503

CHILDREN'S HOSPITAL OF ORANGE COUNTY, ORANGE, CA, p. A76

CHILDREN'S HOSPITAL OF PHILADELPHIA, PHILADELPHIA, PA, p. A534

CHILDREN'S HOSPITAL OF RICHMOND AT VCU–BROOK ROAD CAMPUS, RICHMOND, VA, p. A666

CHILDREN'S HOSPITAL OF SAN ANTONIO, SAN ANTONIO, TX, p. A633

CHILDREN'S HOSPITAL OF THE KING'S DAUGHTERS, NORFOLK, VA, p. A663

CHILDREN'S HOSPITAL OF WISCONSIN, MILWAUKEE, WI, p. A701

CHILDREN'S HOSPITAL OF WISCONSIN–FOX VALLEY, NEENAH, WI, p. A702

CHILDREN'S HOSPITALS AND CLINICS OF MINNESOTA, MINNEAPOLIS, MN, p. A335

CHILDREN'S MEDICAL CENTER DALLAS, DALLAS, TX, p. A596

CHILDREN'S MEDICAL CENTER PLANO, PLANO, TX, p. A629

CHILDREN'S MEMORIAL HOSPITAL, CHICAGO, ILLINOIS (see ANN & ROBERT H. LURIE CHILDREN'S HOSPITAL OF CHICAGO), p. A177

CHILDREN'S MERCY HOSPITAL KANSAS, OVERLAND PARK, KS, p. A243

CHILDREN'S MERCY HOSPITAL KANSAS CITY, KANSAS CITY, MO, p. A362

CHILDREN'S NATIONAL HEALTH SYSTEM, WASHINGTON, DC, p. A115

CHILDREN'S OF ALABAMA, BIRMINGHAM, AL, p. A14

CHILDREN'S SPECIALIZED HOSPITAL, NEW BRUNSWICK, NJ, p. A409

CHILDRESS REGIONAL MEDICAL CENTER, CHILDRESS, TX, p. A592

CHILLICOTHE VETERANS AFFAIRS MEDICAL CENTER, CHILLICOTHE, OH, p. A475

CHILTON MEDICAL CENTER, POMPTON PLAINS, NJ, p. A411

CHINESE HOSPITAL, SAN FRANCISCO, CA, p. A85

CHINLE COMPREHENSIVE HEALTH CARE FACILITY, CHINLE, AZ, p. A29

CHINO VALLEY MEDICAL CENTER, CHINO, CA, p. A54

CHIPPENHAM HOSPITAL, RICHMOND, VA, p. A666

CHOATE MENTAL HEALTH CENTER, ANNA, IL, p. A173

CHOC CHILDREN'S AT MISSION HOSPITAL, MISSION VIEJO, CA, p. A72

CHOCTAW GENERAL HOSPITAL, BUTLER, AL, p. A15

CHOCTAW HEALTH CENTER, PHILADELPHIA, MS, p. A352

CHOCTAW MEMORIAL HOSPITAL, HUGO, OK, p. A501

CHOCTAW NATION HEALTH CARE CENTER, TALIHINA, OK, p. A508

CHOCTAW REGIONAL MEDICAL CENTER, ACKERMAN, MS, p. A344

CHRIST HOSPITAL, CINCINNATI, OH, p. A475

CHRISTIAN HEALTH CARE CENTER, WYCKOFF, NJ, p. A415

CHRISTIAN HOSPITAL, SAINT LOUIS, MO, p. A369

CHRISTIANA CARE HEALTH SYSTEM, NEWARK, DE, p. A113

CHRISTUS COUSHATTA HEALTH CARE CENTER, COUSHATTA, LA, p. A266

CHRISTUS DUBUIS HOSPITAL OF ALEXANDRIA, ALEXANDRIA, LA, p. A262

CHRISTUS DUBUIS HOSPITAL OF BEAUMONT, BEAUMONT, TX, p. A587

CHRISTUS DUBUIS HOSPITAL OF FORT SMITH, FORT SMITH, AR, p. A42

CHRISTUS DUBUIS HOSPITAL OF HOT SPRINGS, HOT SPRINGS NATIONAL PARK, AR, p. A43

CHRISTUS DUBUIS HOSPITAL OF PARIS, PARIS, TX, p. A627

CHRISTUS GOOD SHEPHERD MEDICAL CENTER–MARSHALL, MARSHALL, TX, p. A623

CHRISTUS HEALTH SHREVEPORT–BOSSIER, SHREVEPORT, LA, p. A278

CHRISTUS MOTHER FRANCES HOSPITAL – JACKSONVILLE, JACKSONVILLE, TX, p. A616

CHRISTUS MOTHER FRANCES HOSPITAL – SULPHUR SPRINGS, SULPHUR SPRINGS, TX, p. A638

CHRISTUS MOTHER FRANCES HOSPITAL – TYLER, TYLER, TX, p. A642

CHRISTUS MOTHER FRANCES HOSPITAL – WINNSBORO, WINNSBORO, TX, p. A646

CHRISTUS OCHSNER LAKE AREA HOSPITAL, LAKE CHARLES, LA, p. A272

CHRISTUS OCHSNER ST. PATRICK HOSPITAL SOUTHWEST LOUISIANA, LAKE CHARLES, LA, p. A272

CHRISTUS SANTA ROSA HEALTH SYSTEM, SAN ANTONIO, TX, p. A633

CHRISTUS SOUTHEAST TEXAS HOSPITAL – ST. ELIZABETH, BEAUMONT, TX, p. A587

CHRISTUS SOUTHEAST TEXAS JASPER MEMORIAL, JASPER, TX, p. A616

CHRISTUS SOUTHEAST TEXAS ORTHOPEDIC SPECIALTY CENTER, BEAUMONT, TX, p. A587

CHRISTUS SPOHN HOSPITAL ALICE, ALICE, TX, p. A581

CHRISTUS SPOHN HOSPITAL BEEVILLE, BEEVILLE, TX, p. A588

CHRISTUS SPOHN HOSPITAL CORPUS CHRISTI MEMORIAL, CORPUS CHRISTI, TX, p. A594

CHRISTUS SPOHN HOSPITAL KLEBERG, KINGSVILLE, TX, p. A618

CHRISTUS ST. CATHERINE HOSPITAL, KATY, TEXAS (see HOUSTON METHODIST CONTINUING CARE HOSPITAL), p. A617

CHRISTUS ST. FRANCES CABRINI HOSPITAL, ALEXANDRIA, LA, p. A262

CHRISTUS ST. MICHAEL HEALTH SYSTEM, TEXARKANA, TX, p. A640

CHRISTUS ST. MICHAEL REHABILITATION HOSPITAL, TEXARKANA, TX, p. A640

CHRISTUS ST. VINCENT REGIONAL MEDICAL CENTER, SANTA FE, NM, p. A420

CHRISTUS TRINITY MOTHER FRANCES REHABILITATION HOSPITAL, A PARTNER OF ENCOMPASS HEALTH, TYLER, TX, p. A642

CIBOLA GENERAL HOSPITAL, GRANTS, NM, p. A418

CIMARRON MEMORIAL HOSPITAL, BOISE CITY, OK, p. A497

CINCINNATI CHILDREN'S HOSPITAL MEDICAL CENTER, CINCINNATI, OH, p. A475

CINCINNATI VETERANS AFFAIRS MEDICAL CENTER, CINCINNATI, OH, p. A476

CIRCLES OF CARE, MELBOURNE, FL, p. A129

CITIZENS BAPTIST MEDICAL CENTER, TALLADEGA, AL, p. A23

CITIZENS MEDICAL CENTER, COLBY, KS, p. A233

CITIZENS MEDICAL CENTER, COLUMBIA, LA, p. A266

CITIZENS MEDICAL CENTER, VICTORIA, TX, p. A643

CITIZENS MEMORIAL HOSPITAL, BOLIVAR, MO, p. A356

CITRUS MEMORIAL HEALTH SYSTEM, INVERNESS, FL, p. A125

CITRUS VALLEY MEDICAL CENTER–INTER COMMUNITY CAMPUS, COVINA, CA, p. A56

CITY HOSPITAL AT WHITE ROCK, DALLAS, TX, p. A596

CITY OF HOPE'S HELFORD CLINICAL RESEARCH HOSPITAL, DUARTE, CA, p. A57

CLAIBORNE COUNTY MEDICAL CENTER, PORT GIBSON, MS, p. A353

CLAIBORNE MEDICAL CENTER, TAZEWELL, TN, p. A580

CLAIBORNE MEMORIAL MEDICAL CENTER, HOMER, LA, p. A268

CLARA BARTON HOSPITAL, HOISINGTON, KS, p. A236
CLARA MAASS MEDICAL CENTER, BELLEVILLE, NJ, p. A403
CLAREMORE INDIAN HOSPITAL, CLAREMORE, OK, p. A498
CLARIAN ARNETT HOSPITAL, LAFAYETTE, INDIANA (see INDIANA UNIVERSITY HEALTH ARNETT HOSPITAL), p. A209
CLARIAN HEALTH PARTNERS, INDIANAPOLIS, INDIANA (see INDIANA UNIVERSITY HEALTH UNIVERSITY HOSPITAL), p. A206
CLARIAN NORTH MEDICAL CENTER, CARMEL, INDIANA (see INDIANA UNIVERSITY HEALTH NORTH HOSPITAL), p. A201
CLARIAN WEST MEDICAL CENTER, AVON, INDIANA (see INDIANA UNIVERSITY HEALTH WEST HOSPITAL), p. A199
CLARINDA REGIONAL HEALTH CENTER, CLARINDA, IA, p. A219
CLARION HOSPITAL, CLARION, PA, p. A522
CLARION PSYCHIATRIC CENTER, CLARION, PA, p. A522
CLARITY CHILD GUIDANCE CENTER, SAN ANTONIO, TX, p. A633
CLARK FORK VALLEY HOSPITAL, PLAINS, MT, p. A379
CLARK MEMORIAL HEALTH, JEFFERSONVILLE, IN, p. A208
CLARK REGIONAL MEDICAL CENTER, WINCHESTER, KY, p. A261
CLARKE COUNTY HOSPITAL, OSCEOLA, IA, p. A228
CLARKS SUMMIT STATE HOSPITAL, CLARKS SUMMIT, PA, p. A522
CLAXTON–HEPBURN MEDICAL CENTER, OGDENSBURG, NY, p. A440
CLAY COUNTY HOSPITAL, ASHLAND, AL, p. A13
CLAY COUNTY HOSPITAL, FLORA, IL, p. A183
CLAY COUNTY MEDICAL CENTER, CLAY CENTER, KS, p. A233
CLAY COUNTY MEMORIAL HOSPITAL, HENRIETTA, TX, p. A610
CLEAR LAKE REHABILITATION HOSPITAL, WEBSTER, TEXAS (see KINDRED REHABILITATION HOSPITAL CLEAR LAKE), p. A644
CLEARVISTA HEALTH AND WELLNESS, LORAIN, OH, p. A486
CLEARWATER VALLEY HOSPITAL AND CLINICS, OROFINO, ID, p. A170
CLEMENT J. ZABLOCKI VETERANS AFFAIRS MEDICAL CENTER, MILWAUKEE, WI, p. A701
CLEVELAND AREA HOSPITAL, CLEVELAND, OK, p. A498
CLEVELAND CLINIC, CLEVELAND, OH, p. A477
CLEVELAND CLINIC AKRON GENERAL, AKRON, OH, p. A471
CLEVELAND CLINIC AKRON GENERAL LODI HOSPITAL, LODI, OH, p. A485
CLEVELAND CLINIC AVON HOSPITAL, AVON, OH, p. A472
CLEVELAND CLINIC CHILDREN'S HOSPITAL FOR REHABILITATION, CLEVELAND, OH, p. A477
CLEVELAND CLINIC FAIRVIEW HOSPITAL, CLEVELAND, OH, p. A477
CLEVELAND CLINIC FLORIDA, WESTON, FL, p. A144
CLEVELAND CLINIC INDIAN RIVER HOSPITAL, VERO BEACH, FL, p. A143
CLEVELAND CLINIC MARTIN NORTH HOSPITAL, STUART, FL, p. A140
CLEVELAND CLINIC REHABILITATION HOSPITAL, AVON, OH, p. A472
CLEVELAND CLINIC UNION HOSPITAL, DOVER, OH, p. A482
CLEVELAND CLINIC, MEDINA HOSPITAL, MEDINA, OH, p. A487
CLEVELAND EMERGENCY HOSPITAL, CLEVELAND, TX, p. A592
CLIFTON SPRINGS HOSPITAL AND CLINIC, CLIFTON SPRINGS, NY, p. A426
CLIFTON T. PERKINS HOSPITAL CENTER, JESSUP, MD, p. A291
CLIFTON–FINE HOSPITAL, STAR LAKE, NY, p. A444
CLINCH MEMORIAL HOSPITAL, HOMERVILLE, GA, p. A155
CLINCH VALLEY MEDICAL CENTER, RICHLANDS, VA, p. A665
CLOUD COUNTY HEALTH CENTER, CONCORDIA, KS, p. A234
CLOVIS COMMUNITY MEDICAL CENTER, CLOVIS, CA, p. A55
CMH REGIONAL HEALTH SYSTEM, WILMINGTON, OH, p. A494
COAL COUNTY GENERAL HOSPITAL, COALGATE, OK, p. A498
COAST PLAZA DOCTORS HOSPITAL, NORWALK, CA, p. A74
COAST PLAZA HOSPITAL, NORWALK, CA, p. A74
COASTAL CAROLINA HOSPITAL, HARDEEVILLE, SC, p. A554
COASTAL HARBOR TREATMENT CENTER, SAVANNAH, GA, p. A160
COASTAL VIRGINIA REHABILITATION, NEWPORT NEWS, VA, p. A663
COATESVILLE VETERANS AFFAIRS MEDICAL CENTER, COATESVILLE, PA, p. A523
COBALT REHABILITATION HOSPITAL, SURPRISE, AZ, p. A36
COBALT REHABILITATION HOSPITAL OF NEW ORLEANS, NEW ORLEANS, LA, p. A275
COBLESKILL REGIONAL HOSPITAL, COBLESKILL, NY, p. A426
COBRE VALLEY COMMUNITY HOSPITAL, GLOBE, ARIZONA (see COBRE VALLEY REGIONAL MEDICAL CENTER), p. A30

COBRE VALLEY REGIONAL MEDICAL CENTER, GLOBE, AZ, p. A30
COCHRAN MEMORIAL HOSPITAL, MORTON, TX, p. A625
COFFEE REGIONAL MEDICAL CENTER, DOUGLAS, GA, p. A152
COFFEY COUNTY HOSPITAL, BURLINGTON, KS, p. A233
COFFEYVILLE REGIONAL MEDICAL CENTER, COFFEYVILLE, KS, p. A233
COGDELL MEMORIAL HOSPITAL, SNYDER, TX, p. A637
COLEMAN COUNTY MEDICAL CENTER, COLEMAN, TX, p. A592
COLISEUM MEDICAL CENTERS, MACON, GA, p. A156
COLISEUM NORTHSIDE HOSPITAL, MACON, GA, p. A156
COLLEGE HOSPITAL CERRITOS, CERRITOS, CA, p. A54
COLLEGE HOSPITAL COSTA MESA, COSTA MESA, CA, p. A55
COLLEGE MEDICAL CENTER, LONG BEACH, CA, p. A65
COLLEGE STATION MEDICAL CENTER, COLLEGE STATION, TX, p. A592
COLLETON MEDICAL CENTER, WALTERBORO, SC, p. A558
COLLINGSWORTH GENERAL HOSPITAL, WELLINGTON, TX, p. A645
COLONEL FLORENCE A. BLANCHFIELD ARMY COMMUNITY HOSPITAL, FORT CAMPBELL, KY, p. A252
COLORADO ACUTE LONG TERM HOSPITAL, DENVER, CO, p. A98
COLORADO CANYONS HOSPITAL AND MEDICAL CENTER, FRUITA, CO, p. A101
COLORADO MENTAL HEALTH INSTITUTE AT FORT LOGAN, DENVER, CO, p. A98
COLORADO MENTAL HEALTH INSTITUTE AT PUEBLO, PUEBLO, CO, p. A104
COLORADO PLAINS MEDICAL CENTER, FORT MORGAN, CO, p. A100
COLORADO RIVER MEDICAL CENTER, NEEDLES, CA, p. A74
COLQUITT REGIONAL MEDICAL CENTER, MOULTRIE, GA, p. A158
COLUMBIA BASIN HOSPITAL, EPHRATA, WA, p. A673
COLUMBIA COUNTY HEALTH SYSTEM, DAYTON, WA, p. A672
COLUMBIA MEMORIAL HOSPITAL, ASTORIA, OR, p. A511
COLUMBIA MEMORIAL HOSPITAL, HUDSON, NY, p. A429
COLUMBUS COMMUNITY HOSPITAL, COLUMBUS, NE, p. A384
COLUMBUS COMMUNITY HOSPITAL, COLUMBUS, TX, p. A593
COLUMBUS COMMUNITY HOSPITAL, INC., COLUMBUS, WI, p. A693
COLUMBUS DUBLIN SPRINGS, DUBLIN, OH, p. A482
COLUMBUS HOSPITAL LTACH, NEWARK, NJ, p. A409
COLUMBUS REGIONAL HEALTHCARE SYSTEM, WHITEVILLE, NC, p. A463
COLUMBUS REGIONAL HOSPITAL, COLUMBUS, IN, p. A201
COLUMBUS SPECIALTY HOSPITAL, COLUMBUS, GA, p. A150
COMANCHE COUNTY HOSPITAL, COLDWATER, KS, p. A233
COMANCHE COUNTY MEDICAL CENTER, COMANCHE, TX, p. A593
COMANCHE COUNTY MEMORIAL HOSPITAL, LAWTON, OK, p. A501
COMER CHILDREN'S HOSPITAL, CHICAGO, ILLINOIS (see UNIVERSITY OF CHICAGO MEDICAL CENTER), p. A177
COMMONWEALTH CENTER FOR CHILDREN AND ADOLESCENTS, STAUNTON, VA, p. A667
COMMONWEALTH HEALTH CENTER, SAIPAN, MP, p. A714
COMMONWEALTH REGIONAL SPECIALTY HOSPITAL, BOWLING GREEN, KY, p. A249
COMMUNITY AND MISSION HOSPITALS OF HUNTINGTON PARK, HUNTINGTON PARK, CA, p. A62
COMMUNITY BEHAVIORAL HEALTH CENTER, FRESNO, CA, p. A59
COMMUNITY BEHAVIORAL HEALTH HOSPITAL – ALEXANDRIA, ALEXANDRIA, MN, p. A327
COMMUNITY BEHAVIORAL HEALTH HOSPITAL – ANNANDALE, ANNANDALE, MN, p. A327
COMMUNITY BEHAVIORAL HEALTH HOSPITAL – BAXTER, BAXTER, MN, p. A328
COMMUNITY BEHAVIORAL HEALTH HOSPITAL – BEMIDJI, BEMIDJI, MN, p. A328
COMMUNITY BEHAVIORAL HEALTH HOSPITAL – FERGUS FALLS, FERGUS FALLS, MN, p. A332
COMMUNITY BEHAVIORAL HEALTH HOSPITAL – ROCHESTER, ROCHESTER, MN, p. A338
COMMUNITY CARE HOSPITAL, NEW ORLEANS, LA, p. A275
COMMUNITY FIRST MEDICAL CENTER, CHICAGO, IL, p. A177
COMMUNITY GENERAL HEALTH CENTER, FORT FAIRFIELD, MAINE (see THE AROOSTOOK MEDICAL CENTER), p. A283
COMMUNITY HEALTHCARE SYSTEM, ONAGA, KS, p. A242
COMMUNITY HOSPITAL, GRAND JUNCTION, CO, p. A101
COMMUNITY HOSPITAL, MCCOOK, NE, p. A387
COMMUNITY HOSPITAL, MUNSTER, IN, p. A212
COMMUNITY HOSPITAL, OKLAHOMA CITY, OK, p. A505
COMMUNITY HOSPITAL, TALLASSEE, AL, p. A23

COMMUNITY HOSPITAL, TORRINGTON, WY, p. A713
COMMUNITY HOSPITAL, TRINITY, FL, p. A143
COMMUNITY HOSPITAL, WATERVLIET, MICHIGAN (see LAKELAND HOSPITAL), p. A324
COMMUNITY HOSPITAL ASSOCIATION, FAIRFAX, MISSOURI (see COMMUNITY HOSPITAL–FAIRFAX), p. A360
COMMUNITY HOSPITAL EAST, INDIANAPOLIS, IN, p. A206
COMMUNITY HOSPITAL NORTH, INDIANAPOLIS, IN, p. A206
COMMUNITY HOSPITAL OF ANACONDA, ANACONDA, MT, p. A374
COMMUNITY HOSPITAL OF ANDERSON & MADISON COUNTY, ANDERSON, IN, p. A199
COMMUNITY HOSPITAL OF BREMEN, BREMEN, IN, p. A200
COMMUNITY HOSPITAL OF HUNTINGTON PARK, HUNTINGTON PARK, CA, p. A62
COMMUNITY HOSPITAL OF SAN BERNARDINO, SAN BERNARDINO, CA, p. A83
COMMUNITY HOSPITAL OF STAUNTON, STAUNTON, IL, p. A197
COMMUNITY HOSPITAL OF THE MONTEREY PENINSULA, MONTEREY, CA, p. A73
COMMUNITY HOSPITAL SOUTH, INDIANAPOLIS, IN, p. A206
COMMUNITY HOSPITAL–FAIRFAX, FAIRFAX, MO, p. A360
COMMUNITY HOSPITALS AND WELLNESS CENTERS, BRYAN, OH, p. A474
COMMUNITY HOSPITALS AND WELLNESS CENTERS– MONTPELIER, MONTPELIER, OH, p. A488
COMMUNITY HOWARD REGIONAL HEALTH, KOKOMO, IN, p. A209
COMMUNITY HOWARD SPECIALTY HOSPITAL, KOKOMO, IN, p. A209
COMMUNITY MEDICAL CENTER, MISSOULA, MT, p. A378
COMMUNITY MEDICAL CENTER, TOMS RIVER, NJ, p. A413
COMMUNITY MEDICAL CENTER HEALTHCARE SYSTEM, SCRANTON, PENNSYLVANIA (see GEISINGER–COMMUNITY MEDICAL CENTER), p. A540
COMMUNITY MEDICAL CENTER, INC., FALLS CITY, NE, p. A384
COMMUNITY MEMORIAL HEALTHCARE, MARYSVILLE, KS, p. A240
COMMUNITY MEMORIAL HOSPITAL, BURKE, SD, p. A559
COMMUNITY MEMORIAL HOSPITAL, CLOQUET, MN, p. A330
COMMUNITY MEMORIAL HOSPITAL, HAMILTON, NY, p. A429
COMMUNITY MEMORIAL HOSPITAL, HICKSVILLE, OH, p. A484
COMMUNITY MEMORIAL HOSPITAL, MENOMONEE FALLS, WI, p. A700
COMMUNITY MEMORIAL HOSPITAL, REDFIELD, SD, p. A563
COMMUNITY MEMORIAL HOSPITAL, SUMNER, IA, p. A230
COMMUNITY MEMORIAL HOSPITAL, TURTLE LAKE, ND, p. A469
COMMUNITY MEMORIAL HOSPITAL, VENTURA, CA, p. A93
COMMUNITY MENTAL HEALTH CENTER, LAWRENCEBURG, IN, p. A210
COMMUNITY REGIONAL MEDICAL CENTER, FRESNO, CA, p. A59
COMMUNITY–GENERAL HOSPITAL OF GREATER SYRACUSE, SYRACUSE, NEW YORK (see UPSTATE UNIVERSITY HOSPITAL AT COMMUNITY GENERAL), p. A445
COMPASS BEHAVIORAL CENTER OF ALEXANDRIA, ALEXANDRIA, LA, p. A262
COMPASS BEHAVIORAL CENTER OF HOUMA, HOUMA, LA, p. A268
COMPASS BEHAVIORAL CENTER OF LAFAYETTE, LAFAYETTE, LA, p. A270
COMPASS MEMORIAL HEALTHCARE, MARENGO, IA, p. A226
COMPLEX CARE HOSPITAL AT RIDGELAKE, SARASOTA, FL, p. A139
COMPLEX CARE HOSPITAL AT TENAYA, LAS VEGAS, NV, p. A394
CONCHO COUNTY HOSPITAL, EDEN, TX, p. A601
CONCORD HOSPITAL, CONCORD, NH, p. A399
CONEMAUGH MEMORIAL MEDICAL CENTER, JOHNSTOWN, PA, p. A528
CONEMAUGH MEYERSDALE MEDICAL CENTER, MEYERSDALE, PA, p. A532
CONEMAUGH MINERS MEDICAL CENTER, HASTINGS, PA, p. A527
CONEMAUGH NASON MEDICAL CENTER, ROARING SPRING, PA, p. A540
CONFLUENCE HEALTH/CENTRAL WASHINGTON HOSPITAL, WENATCHEE, WA, p. A682
CONFLUENCE HEALTH/WENATCHEE VALLEY HOSPITAL, WENATCHEE, WA, p. A682
CONIFER PARK, GLENVILLE, NY, p. A428
CONNALLY MEMORIAL MEDICAL CENTER, FLORESVILLE, TX, p. A604
CONNECTICUT CHILDREN'S MEDICAL CENTER, HARTFORD, CT, p. A108
CONNECTICUT DEPARTMENT OF CORRECTION'S HOSPITAL, SOMERS, CT, p. A110

CONNECTICUT MENTAL HEALTH CENTER, NEW HAVEN, CT, p. A109

CONNECTICUT VALLEY HOSPITAL, MIDDLETOWN, CT, p. A109

CONNECTICUT VETERANS HOME AND HOSPITAL, ROCKY HILL, CT, p. A110

CONTINUECARE HOSPITAL AT BAPTIST HEALTH CORBIN, CORBIN, KY, p. A250

CONTINUECARE HOSPITAL AT BAPTIST HEALTH PADUCAH, PADUCAH, KY, p. A259

CONTINUECARE HOSPITAL AT HENDRICK MEDICAL CENTER, ABILENE, TX, p. A581

CONTINUECARE HOSPITAL AT MADISONVILLE, MADISONVILLE, KY, p. A257

CONTINUECARE HOSPITAL AT MEDICAL CENTER (ODESSA), ODESSA, TX, p. A626

CONTINUECARE HOSPITAL AT PALMETTO HEALTH BAPTIST, COLUMBIA, SC, p. A551

CONTINUING CARE HOSPITAL, LEXINGTON, KY, p. A255

CONTRA COSTA REGIONAL MEDICAL CENTER, MARTINEZ, CA, p. A71

CONWAY BEHAVIORAL HEALTH HOSPITAL, CONWAY, AR, p. A40

CONWAY MEDICAL CENTER, CONWAY, SC, p. A552

CONWAY REGIONAL MEDICAL CENTER, CONWAY, AR, p. A40

CONWAY REGIONAL REHABILITATION HOSPITAL, CONWAY, AR, p. A40

COOK CHILDREN'S MEDICAL CENTER, FORT WORTH, TX, p. A604

COOK HOSPITAL & CARE CENTER, COOK, MN, p. A330

COOK MEDICAL CENTER–A CAMPUS OF TIFT REGIONAL MEDICAL CENTER, ADEL, GA, p. A145

COOKEVILLE REGIONAL MEDICAL CENTER, COOKEVILLE, TN, p. A568

COOLEY DICKINSON HOSPITAL, NORTHAMPTON, MA, p. A301

COON MEMORIAL HOSPITAL, DALHART, TX, p. A595

COOPER UNIVERSITY HEALTH CARE, CAMDEN, NJ, p. A404

COOPERSTOWN MEDICAL CENTER, COOPERSTOWN, ND, p. A466

COORDINATED HEALTH–BETHLEHEM, BETHLEHEM, PA, p. A520

COOSA VALLEY MEDICAL CENTER, SYLACAUGA, AL, p. A23

COPIAH COUNTY MEDICAL CENTER, HAZLEHURST, MS, p. A348

COPLEY HOSPITAL, MORRISVILLE, VT, p. A654

COPPER QUEEN COMMUNITY HOSPITAL, BISBEE, AZ, p. A28

COPPER SPRINGS HOSPITAL, AVONDALE, AZ, p. A28

COQUILLE VALLEY HOSPITAL, COQUILLE, OR, p. A512

CORAL GABLES HOSPITAL, CORAL GABLES, FL, p. A120

CORDELL MEMORIAL HOSPITAL, CORDELL, OK, p. A498

CORDOVA COMMUNITY MEDICAL CENTER, CORDOVA, AK, p. A25

CORNERSTONE BEHAVIORAL HEALTH HOSPITAL OF UNION COUNTY, BERKELEY HEIGHTS, NJ, p. A403

CORNERSTONE HOSPITAL OF AUSTIN, AUSTIN, TX, p. A585

CORNERSTONE HOSPITAL OF BOSSIER CITY, BOSSIER CITY, LA, p. A265

CORNERSTONE HOSPITAL OF HOUSTON AT CLEARLAKE, WEBSTER, TX, p. A644

CORNERSTONE HOSPITAL OF HUNTINGTON, HUNTINGTON, WV, p. A686

CORNERSTONE HOSPITAL OF LITTLE ROCK, LITTLE ROCK, AR, p. A45

CORNERSTONE HOSPITAL OF OKLAHOMA–MUSKOGEE, MUSKOGEE, OK, p. A502

CORNERSTONE HOSPITAL OF OKLAHOMA–SHAWNEE, SHAWNEE, OK, p. A507

CORNERSTONE HOSPITAL OF SOUTHWEST LOUISIANA, LAKE CHARLES, LA, p. A272

CORNERSTONE HOSPITAL–MEDICAL CENTER OF HOUSTON, HOUSTON, TX, p. A611

CORNERSTONE HOSPITAL–WEST MONROE, WEST MONROE, LA, p. A280

CORNERSTONE OF MEDICAL ARTS CENTER HOSPITAL, FRESH MEADOWS, NY, p. A428

CORNERSTONE REGIONAL HOSPITAL, EDINBURG, TX, p. A601

CORONA REGIONAL MEDICAL CENTER, CORONA, CA, p. A55

CORPUS CHRISTI MEDICAL CENTER, CORPUS CHRISTI, TX, p. A594

CORTLAND REGIONAL MEDICAL CENTER, CORTLAND, NY, p. A426

CORYELL HEALTH, GATESVILLE, TX, p. A607

COSHOCTON REGIONAL MEDICAL CENTER, COSHOCTON, OH, p. A480

COTEAU DES PRAIRIES HOSPITAL, SISSETON, SD, p. A564

COTTAGE HOSPITAL, WOODSVILLE, NH, p. A402

COTTAGE REHABILITATION HOSPITAL, SANTA BARBARA, CA, p. A88

COTTONWOOD SPRINGS HOSPITAL, OLATHE, KS, p. A242

COULEE COMMUNITY HOSPITAL, GRAND COULEE, WASHINGTON (see COULEE MEDICAL CENTER), p. A673

COULEE MEDICAL CENTER, GRAND COULEE, WA, p. A673

COVENANT CHILDREN'S HOSPITAL, LUBBOCK, TX, p. A621

COVENANT HEALTHCARE, SAGINAW, MI, p. A321

COVENANT HOSPITAL PLAINVIEW, PLAINVIEW, TX, p. A629

COVENANT HOSPITAL–LEVELLAND, LEVELLAND, TX, p. A620

COVENANT MEDICAL CENTER, LUBBOCK, TX, p. A621

COVENANT SPECIALTY HOSPITAL, LUBBOCK, TX, p. A621

COVINGTON BEHAVIORIAL HEALTH, COVINGTON, LA, p. A266

COVINGTON COUNTY HOSPITAL, COLLINS, MS, p. A346

COX BARTON COUNTY MEMORIAL HOSPITAL, LAMAR, MO, p. A364

COX MEDICAL CENTER BRANSON, BRANSON, MO, p. A357

COX MEDICAL CENTERS, SPRINGFIELD, MO, p. A371

COX MONETT HOSPITAL, MONETT, MO, p. A366

COZAD COMMUNITY HEALTH SYSTEM, COZAD, NE, p. A384

CRAIG HOSPITAL, ENGLEWOOD, CO, p. A100

CRANE MEMORIAL HOSPITAL, CRANE, TX, p. A595

CRAWFORD COUNTY MEMORIAL HOSPITAL, DENISON, IA, p. A221

CRAWFORD MEMORIAL HOSPITAL, ROBINSON, IL, p. A194

CREEK NATION COMMUNITY HOSPITAL, OKEMAH, OK, p. A503

CRENSHAW COMMUNITY HOSPITAL, LUVERNE, AL, p. A20

CRESCENT MEDICAL CENTER LANCASTER, LANCASTER, TX, p. A619

CRESTWOOD MEDICAL CENTER, HUNTSVILLE, AL, p. A19

CRESTWYN BEHAVIORAL HEALTH, MEMPHIS, TN, p. A574

CRETE AREA MEDICAL CENTER, CRETE, NE, p. A384

CRISP REGIONAL HOSPITAL, CORDELE, GA, p. A151

CRITTENDEN COUNTY HOSPITAL, MARION, KY, p. A257

CROCKETT MEDICAL CENTER, CROCKETT, TX, p. A595

CROOK COUNTY MEDICAL SERVICES DISTRICT, SUNDANCE, WY, p. A713

CROSBYTON CLINIC HOSPITAL, CROSBYTON, TX, p. A595

CROSS CREEK HOSPITAL, AUSTIN, TX, p. A585

CROSSING RIVERS HEALTH MEDICAL CENTER, PRAIRIE DU CHIEN, WI, p. A704

CROSSRIDGE COMMUNITY HOSPITAL, WYNNE, AR, p. A49

CROSSROADS COMMUNITY HOSPITAL, MOUNT VERNON, IL, p. A190

CROUSE HEALTH, SYRACUSE, NY, p. A445

CROW/NORTHERN CHEYENNE HOSPITAL, CROW AGENCY, MT, p. A375

CROZER–CHESTER MEDICAL CENTER, UPLAND, PA, p. A543

CUBA MEMORIAL HOSPITAL, CUBA, NY, p. A426

CUERO COMMUNITY HOSPITAL, CUERO, TX, p. A595

CULBERSON HOSPITAL, VAN HORN, TX, p. A643

CULLMAN REGIONAL MEDICAL CENTER, CULLMAN, AL, p. A16

CUMBERLAND COUNTY HOSPITAL, BURKESVILLE, KY, p. A250

CUMBERLAND HALL HOSPITAL, HOPKINSVILLE, KY, p. A253

CUMBERLAND HEALTHCARE, CUMBERLAND, WI, p. A693

CUMBERLAND HOSPITAL FOR CHILDREN AND ADOLESCENTS, NEW KENT, VA, p. A663

CUMBERLAND MEDICAL CENTER, CROSSVILLE, TN, p. A568

CURAHEALTH HERITAGE VALLEY, BEAVER, PA, p. A520

CURAHEALTH HOSPITAL OKLAHOMA CITY, OKLAHOMA CITY, OK, p. A503

CURAHEALTH HOSPITAL STOUGHTON, STOUGHTON, MA, p. A304

CURAHEALTH NASHVILLE, NASHVILLE, TN, p. A576

CURAHEALTH NEW ORLEANS, NEW ORLEANS, LA, p. A275

CURAHEALTH PHOENIX, PEORIA, ARIZONA (see CURAHEALTH PHOENIX), p. A32

CURAHEALTH PHOENIX, PHOENIX, AZ, p. A33

CURAHEALTH PITTSBURGH, OAKDALE, PA, p. A533

CURAHEALTH TUCSON, TUCSON, AZ, p. A37

CURRY GENERAL HOSPITAL, GOLD BEACH, OR, p. A513

CUSTER REGIONAL HOSPITAL, CUSTER, SD, p. A560

CUYAHOGA FALLS GENERAL HOSPITAL, CUYAHOGA FALLS, OHIO (see WESTERN RESERVE HOSPITAL), p. A480

CUYUNA REGIONAL MEDICAL CENTER, CROSBY, MN, p. A330

CYPRESS CREEK HOSPITAL, HOUSTON, TX, p. A611

CYPRESS GROVE BEHAVIORAL HEALTH, BASTROP, LA, p. A263

CYPRESS POINTE SURGICAL HOSPITAL, HAMMOND, LA, p. A268

D

D. W. MCMILLAN MEMORIAL HOSPITAL, BREWTON, AL, p. A15

DAHL MEMORIAL HEALTHCARE ASSOCIATION, EKALAKA, MT, p. A376

DAKOTA PLAINS SURGICAL CENTER, ABERDEEN, SD, p. A559

DALE MEDICAL CENTER, OZARK, AL, p. A22

DALLAS BEHAVIORAL HEALTHCARE HOSPITAL, DESOTO, TX, p. A600

DALLAS COUNTY HOSPITAL, PERRY, IA, p. A228

DALLAS COUNTY MEDICAL CENTER, FORDYCE, AR, p. A42

DALLAS MEDICAL CENTER, DALLAS, TX, p. A596

DALLAS REGIONAL MEDICAL CENTER, MESQUITE, TX, p. A624

DAMERON HOSPITAL, STOCKTON, CA, p. A90

DANA–FARBER CANCER INSTITUTE, BOSTON, MA, p. A295

DANBURY HOSPITAL, DANBURY, CT, p. A107

DANIEL DRAKE CENTER FOR POST ACUTE CARE, CINCINNATI, OH, p. A476

DANIELS MEMORIAL HEALTHCARE CENTER, SCOBEY, MT, p. A380

DANVILLE STATE HOSPITAL, DANVILLE, PA, p. A523

DARTMOUTH–HITCHCOCK MEDICAL CENTER, LEBANON, NH, p. A400

DAVID GRANT USAF MEDICAL CENTER, TRAVIS AFB, CA, p. A92

DAVIESS COMMUNITY HOSPITAL, WASHINGTON, IN, p. A216

DAVIS COUNTY HOSPITAL, BLOOMFIELD, IA, p. A218

DAVIS HOSPITAL AND MEDICAL CENTER, LAYTON, UT, p. A648

DAVIS MEDICAL CENTER, ELKINS, WV, p. A685

DAVIS REGIONAL MEDICAL CENTER, STATESVILLE, NC, p. A462

DAY KIMBALL HOSPITAL, PUTNAM, CT, p. A110

DAYTON CHILDREN'S HOSPITAL, DAYTON, OH, p. A481

DAYTON VETERANS AFFAIRS MEDICAL CENTER, DAYTON, OH, p. A481

DCH REGIONAL MEDICAL CENTER, TUSCALOOSA, AL, p. A24

DE GRAFF MEMORIAL HOSPITAL, NORTH TONAWANDA, NEW YORK (see KALEIDA HEALTH), p. A439

DE SOTO REGIONAL HEALTH SYSTEM, MANSFIELD, LA, p. A273

DEACONESS GATEWAY HOSPITAL, NEWBURGH, IN, p. A213

DEACONESS MIDTOWN HOSPITAL, EVANSVILLE, IN, p. A203

DEBORAH HEART AND LUNG CENTER, BROWNS MILLS, NJ, p. A404

DECATUR COUNTY GENERAL HOSPITAL, PARSONS, TN, p. A578

DECATUR COUNTY HOSPITAL, LEON, IA, p. A225

DECATUR COUNTY MEMORIAL HOSPITAL, GREENSBURG, IN, p. A205

DECATUR HEALTH SYSTEMS, OBERLIN, KS, p. A242

DECATUR MEMORIAL HOSPITAL, DECATUR, IL, p. A180

DECATUR MORGAN HOSPITAL, DECATUR, AL, p. A16

DECKERVILLE COMMUNITY HOSPITAL, DECKERVILLE, MI, p. A309

DEER LODGE MEDICAL CENTER, DEER LODGE, MT, p. A376

DEER'S HEAD HOSPITAL CENTER, SALISBURY, MD, p. A293

DEKALB HEALTH, AUBURN, IN, p. A199

DEKALB REGIONAL MEDICAL CENTER, FORT PAYNE, AL, p. A18

DEL AMO HOSPITAL, TORRANCE, CA, p. A91

DELANO REGIONAL MEDICAL CENTER, DELANO, CA, p. A56

DELAWARE COUNTY MEMORIAL HOSPITAL, DREXEL HILL, PA, p. A524

DELAWARE PSYCHIATRIC CENTER, NEW CASTLE, DE, p. A113

DELL CHILDREN'S MEDICAL CENTER OF CENTRAL TEXAS, AUSTIN, TX, p. A585

DELL SETON MEDICAL CENTER AT THE UNIVERSITY OF TEXAS, AUSTIN, TX, p. A585

DELRAY MEDICAL CENTER, DELRAY BEACH, FL, p. A121

DELTA COMMUNITY MEDICAL CENTER, DELTA, UT, p. A647

DELTA COUNTY MEMORIAL HOSPITAL, DELTA, CO, p. A98

DELTA MEDICAL CENTER, MEMPHIS, TN, p. A574

DELTA MEMORIAL HOSPITAL, DUMAS, AR, p. A41

DELTA REGIONAL MEDICAL CENTER, GREENVILLE, MS, p. A347

DENVER HEALTH, DENVER, CO, p. A98

DENVER SPRINGS, ENGLEWOOD, CO, p. A100

DEQUINCY MEMORIAL HOSPITAL, DEQUINCY, LA, p. A267

DES MOINES DIVISION, DES MOINES, IOWA (see VETERANS AFFAIRS CENTRAL IOWA HEALTH CARE SYSTEM), p. A221

DESERT PARKWAY BEHAVIORAL HEALTHCARE HOSPITAL, LAS VEGAS, NV, p. A395
DESERT REGIONAL MEDICAL CENTER, PALM SPRINGS, CA, p. A76
DESERT SPRINGS HOSPITAL MEDICAL CENTER, LAS VEGAS, NV, p. A395
DESERT VALLEY HOSPITAL, VICTORVILLE, CA, p. A94
DESERT VIEW HOSPITAL, PAHRUMP, NV, p. A397
DESERT VIEW REGIONAL MEDICAL CENTER, PAHRUMP, NEVADA (see DESERT VIEW HOSPITAL), p. A397
DESERT WILLOW TREATMENT CENTER, LAS VEGAS, NV, p. A395
DESOTO MEMORIAL HOSPITAL, ARCADIA, FL, p. A117
DETAR HEALTHCARE SYSTEM, VICTORIA, TX, p. A643
DEVEREUX ADVANCED BEHAVIORAL HEALTH GEORGIA, KENNESAW, GA, p. A155
DEVEREUX CHILDREN'S BEHAVIORAL HEALTH CENTER, MALVERN, PA, p. A530
DEVEREUX HOSPITAL AND CHILDREN'S CENTER OF FLORIDA, MELBOURNE, FL, p. A129
DEVEREUX TEXAS TREATMENT NETWORK, LEAGUE CITY, TX, p. A620
DEWITT HOSPITAL, DEWITT, AR, p. A41
DICKENSON COMMUNITY HOSPITAL, CLINTWOOD, VA, p. A658
DICKINSON COUNTY HEALTHCARE SYSTEM, IRON MOUNTAIN, MI, p. A314
DIGNITY HEALTH ARIZONA GENERAL HOSPITAL, LAVEEN, AZ, p. A31
DIGNITY HEALTH EAST VALLEY REHABILITATION HOSPITAL, CHANDLER, AZ, p. A28
DILEY RIDGE MEDICAL CENTER, CANAL WINCHESTER, OH, p. A474
DIMMIT REGIONAL HOSPITAL, CARRIZO SPRINGS, TX, p. A591
DISTRICT ONE HOSPITAL, FARIBAULT, MN, p. A332
DIVINE SAVIOR HEALTHCARE, PORTAGE, WI, p. A704
DIXIE REGIONAL MEDICAL CENTER, SAINT GEORGE, UT, p. A651
DMC – CHILDREN'S HOSPITAL OF MICHIGAN, DETROIT, MI, p. A309
DMC – DETROIT RECEIVING HOSPITAL, DETROIT, MI, p. A310
DMC – REHABILITATION INSTITUTE OF MICHIGAN, DETROIT, MI, p. A310
DMC – SINAI-GRACE HOSPITAL, DETROIT, MI, p. A310
DMC HARPER UNIVERSITY HOSPITAL, DETROIT, MI, p. A310
DMC HURON VALLEY-SINAI HOSPITAL, COMMERCE TOWNSHIP, MI, p. A309
DOCTORS CENTER, MANATI, PR, p. A716
DOCTORS COMMUNITY HOSPITAL, LANHAM, MD, p. A291
DOCTORS HOSPITAL, AUGUSTA, GA, p. A147
DOCTORS HOSPITAL OF LAREDO, LAREDO, TX, p. A619
DOCTORS HOSPITAL OF MANTECA, MANTECA, CA, p. A70
DOCTORS HOSPITAL OF SARASOTA, SARASOTA, FL, p. A139
DOCTORS MEDICAL CENTER OF MODESTO, MODESTO, CA, p. A72
DOCTORS MEMORIAL HOSPITAL, BONIFAY, FL, p. A118
DOCTORS NEUROPSYCHIATRIC HOSPITAL AND RESEARCH INSTITUTE, BREMEN, IN, p. A200
DOCTORS' CENTER HOSPITAL SAN JUAN, SAN JUAN, PR, p. A718
DOCTOR'S CENTER OF BAYAMON, BAYAMON, PR, p. A715
DOCTOR'S HOSPITAL, LEAWOOD, KS, p. A239
DOCTOR'S HOSPITAL AT RENAISSANCE, EDINBURG, TX, p. A601
DOCTOR'S MEMORIAL HOSPITAL, PERRY, FL, p. A136
DODGE COUNTY HOSPITAL, EASTMAN, GA, p. A153
DOMINICAN HOSPITAL, SANTA CRUZ, CA, p. A88
DOMINION HOSPITAL, FALLS CHURCH, VA, p. A658
DONALSONVILLE HOSPITAL, DONALSONVILLE, GA, p. A152
DOOR COUNTY MEDICAL CENTER, STURGEON BAY, WI, p. A706
DOOR COUNTY MEMORIAL HOSPITAL, STURGEON BAY, WISCONSIN (see DOOR COUNTY MEDICAL CENTER), p. A706
DORMINY MEDICAL CENTER, FITZGERALD, GA, p. A153
DOROTHEA DIX PSYCHIATRIC CENTER, BANGOR, ME, p. A281
DOUGLAS COUNTY COMMUNITY MENTAL HEALTH CENTER, OMAHA, NE, p. A389
DOUGLAS COUNTY MEMORIAL HOSPITAL, ARMOUR, SD, p. A559
DOVER BEHAVIORAL HEALTH SYSTEM, DOVER, DE, p. A113
DOWN EAST COMMUNITY HOSPITAL, MACHIAS, ME, p. A284
DOYLESTOWN HOSPITAL, DOYLESTOWN, PA, p. A524
DR. DAN C. TRIGG MEMORIAL HOSPITAL, TUCUMCARI, NM, p. A421
DR. J. CORRIGAN MENTAL HEALTH CENTER, FALL RIVER, MA, p. A298
DR. PILA'S HOSPITAL, PONCE, PR, p. A717

DR. RAMON E. BETANCES HOSPITAL-MAYAGUEZ MEDICAL CENTER BRANCH, MAYAGUEZ, PR, p. A717
DR. SOLOMON CARTER FULLER MENTAL HEALTH CENTER, BOSTON, MA, p. A295
DREW MEMORIAL HEALTH SYSTEM, MONTICELLO, AR, p. A46
DRISCOLL CHILDREN'S HOSPITAL, CORPUS CHRISTI, TX, p. A594
DRUMRIGHT REGIONAL HOSPITAL, DRUMRIGHT, OK, p. A498
DUANE L. WATERS HOSPITAL, JACKSON, MI, p. A315
DUBUIS HOSPITAL OF HOUSTON, HOUSTON, TEXAS (see CORNERSTONE HOSPITAL-MEDICAL CENTER OF HOUSTON), p. A611
DUBUIS HOSPITAL OF PORT ARTHUR, PORT ARTHUR, TEXAS (see CHRISTUS DUBUIS HOSPITAL OF PORT ARTHUR), p. A630
DUKE RALEIGH HOSPITAL, RALEIGH, NC, p. A460
DUKE REGIONAL HOSPITAL, DURHAM, NC, p. A452
DUKE UNIVERSITY HOSPITAL, DURHAM, NC, p. A453
DUKES MEMORIAL HOSPITAL, PERU, IN, p. A213
DUNCAN REGIONAL HOSPITAL, DUNCAN, OK, p. A498
DUNDY COUNTY HOSPITAL, BENKELMAN, NE, p. A383
DUNES SURGICAL HOSPITAL, DAKOTA DUNES, SD, p. A560
DUNN MEMORIAL HOSPITAL, BEDFORD, INDIANA (see ST. VINCENT DUNN HOSPITAL), p. A199
DUPONT HOSPITAL, FORT WAYNE, IN, p. A203
DURHAM REGIONAL HOSPITAL, DURHAM, NORTH CAROLINA (see DUKE REGIONAL HOSPITAL), p. A453
DURHAM VETERANS AFFAIRS MEDICAL CENTER, DURHAM, NC, p. A453
DWIGHT DAVID EISENHOWER ARMY MEDICAL CENTER, FORT GORDON, GA, p. A153

E

E. A. CONWAY MEDICAL CENTER, MONROE, LOUISIANA (see OCHSNER LSU HEALTH SHREVEPORT – MONROE MEDICAL CENTER), p. A274
EAGLEVILLE HOSPITAL, EAGLEVILLE, PA, p. A524
EARLE E. MORRIS ALCOHOL AND DRUG TREATMENT CENTER, COLUMBIA, SC, p. A551
EAST ADAMS RURAL HEALTHCARE, RITZVILLE, WA, p. A677
EAST ALABAMA MEDICAL CENTER, OPELIKA, AL, p. A22
EAST CARROLL PARISH HOSPITAL, LAKE PROVIDENCE, LA, p. A272
EAST CENTRAL REGIONAL HOSPITAL, AUGUSTA, GA, p. A147
EAST CENTRAL REGIONAL HOSPITAL, GRACEWOOD, GA, p. A154
EAST COOPER MEDICAL CENTER, MOUNT PLEASANT, SC, p. A555
EAST COOPER REGIONAL MEDICAL CENTER, MOUNT PLEASANT, SOUTH CAROLINA (see EAST COOPER MEDICAL CENTER), p. A555
EAST EL PASO PHYSICIANS MEDICAL CENTER, EL PASO, TEXAS (see FOUNDATION SURGICAL HOSPITAL OF EL PASO), p. A601
EAST GEORGIA REGIONAL MEDICAL CENTER, STATESBORO, GA, p. A161
EAST JEFFERSON GENERAL HOSPITAL, METAIRIE, LA, p. A273
EAST LIVERPOOL CITY HOSPITAL, EAST LIVERPOOL, OH, p. A482
EAST LOS ANGELES DOCTORS HOSPITAL, LOS ANGELES, CA, p. A66
EAST MISSISSIPPI STATE HOSPITAL, MERIDIAN, MS, p. A351
EAST MORGAN COUNTY HOSPITAL, BRUSH, CO, p. A97
EAST OHIO REGIONAL HOSPITAL, MARTINS FERRY, OH, p. A486
EAST ORANGE GENERAL HOSPITAL, EAST ORANGE, NJ, p. A405
EAST RIDGE HOSPITAL, EAST RIDGE, TENNESSEE (see PARKRIDGE MEDICAL CENTER), p. A569
EAST TENNESSEE CHILDREN'S HOSPITAL, KNOXVILLE, TN, p. A572
EASTAR HEALTH SYSTEM, EAST CAMPUS, MUSKOGEE, OKLAHOMA (see SAINT FRANCIS HOSPITAL MUSKOGEE), p. A502
EASTERN IDAHO REGIONAL MEDICAL CENTER, IDAHO FALLS, ID, p. A169
EASTERN LONG ISLAND HOSPITAL, GREENPORT, NY, p. A428
EASTERN LOUISIANA MENTAL HEALTH SYSTEM, JACKSON, LA, p. A269

EASTERN NEW MEXICO MEDICAL CENTER, ROSWELL, NM, p. A420
EASTERN NIAGARA HOSPITAL, LOCKPORT, NY, p. A430
EASTERN OKLAHOMA MEDICAL CENTER, POTEAU, OK, p. A506
EASTERN PLUMAS HEALTH CARE, PORTOLA, CA, p. A79
EASTERN SHORE HOSPITAL CENTER, CAMBRIDGE, MD, p. A289
EASTERN STATE HOSPITAL, LEXINGTON, KY, p. A255
EASTERN STATE HOSPITAL, MEDICAL LAKE, WA, p. A675
EASTERN STATE HOSPITAL, WILLIAMSBURG, VA, p. A668
EASTLAND MEMORIAL HOSPITAL, EASTLAND, TX, p. A600
EASTON HOSPITAL, EASTON, PA, p. A524
EASTPOINTE HOSPITAL, DAPHNE, AL, p. A16
EASTSIDE MEDICAL CENTER, SNELLVILLE, GA, p. A160
EASTSIDE PSYCHIATRIC HOSPITAL, TALLAHASSEE, FL, p. A140
EATON RAPIDS MEDICAL CENTER, EATON RAPIDS, MI, p. A311
ED FRASER MEMORIAL HOSPITAL AND BAKER COMMUNITY HEALTH CENTER, MACCLENNY, FL, p. A128
EDEN MEDICAL CENTER, CASTRO VALLEY, CA, p. A54
EDEN SPRINGS HEALTH CARE CENTER, GREEN SPRINGS, OH, p. A484
EDGEFIELD COUNTY HEALTHCARE, EDGEFIELD, SC, p. A552
EDGERTON HOSPITAL AND HEALTH SERVICES, EDGERTON, WI, p. A694
EDGEWOOD SURGICAL HOSPITAL, TRANSFER, PA, p. A542
EDMOND MEDICAL CENTER, EDMOND, OKLAHOMA (see OU MEDICAL CENTER EDMOND), p. A499
EDWARD HINES, JR. VETERANS AFFAIRS HOSPITAL, HINES, IL, p. A185
EDWARD HOSPITAL, NAPERVILLE, IL, p. A190
EDWARDS COUNTY MEDICAL CENTER, KINSLEY, KS, p. A238
EDWIN SHAW REHAB, CUYAHOGA FALLS, OH, p. A480
EFFINGHAM HOSPITAL, SPRINGFIELD, GA, p. A160
EINSTEIN MEDICAL CENTER MONTGOMERY, EAST NORRITON, PA, p. A524
EINSTEIN MEDICAL CENTER PHILADELPHIA, PHILADELPHIA, PA, p. A534
EISENHOWER MEDICAL CENTER, RANCHO MIRAGE, CA, p. A79
EL CAMINO HOSPITAL, MOUNTAIN VIEW, CA, p. A73
EL CAMPO MEMORIAL HOSPITAL, EL CAMPO, TX, p. A601
EL CENTRO REGIONAL MEDICAL CENTER, EL CENTRO, CA, p. A57
EL PASO BEHAVIORAL HEALTH SYSTEM, EL PASO, TX, p. A601
EL PASO CHILDREN'S HOSPITAL, EL PASO, TX, p. A601
EL PASO LTAC HOSPITAL, EL PASO, TX, p. A602
EL PASO PSYCHIATRIC CENTER, EL PASO, TX, p. A602
ELBERT MEMORIAL HOSPITAL, ELBERTON, GA, p. A153
ELEAH MEDICAL CENTER, ELBOW LAKE, MINNESOTA (see PRAIRIE RIDGE HOSPITAL AND HEALTH SERVICES), p. A331
ELEANOR SLATER HOSPITAL, CRANSTON, RI, p. A547
ELECTRA MEMORIAL HOSPITAL, ELECTRA, TX, p. A603
ELGIN MENTAL HEALTH CENTER, ELGIN, IL, p. A182
ELKHART GENERAL HOSPITAL, ELKHART, IN, p. A202
ELKHORN VALLEY REHABILITATION HOSPITAL, CASPER, WY, p. A710
ELKVIEW GENERAL HOSPITAL, HOBART, OK, p. A500
ELLENVILLE REGIONAL HOSPITAL, ELLENVILLE, NY, p. A427
ELLETT MEMORIAL HOSPITAL, APPLETON CITY, MO, p. A356
ELLINWOOD DISTRICT HOSPITAL, ELLINWOOD, KS, p. A234
ELLIOT HOSPITAL, MANCHESTER, NH, p. A401
ELLIS FISCHEL CANCER CENTER, COLUMBIA, MISSOURI (see UNIVERSITY OF MISSOURI HEALTH CARE), p. A359
ELLIS HOSPITAL, SCHENECTADY, NY, p. A444
ELLIS HOSPITAL HEALTH CENTER, SCHENECTADY, NEW YORK (see ELLIS HOSPITAL), p. A444
ELLIS HOSPITAL MCCLELLAN CAMPUS, SCHENECTADY, NEW YORK (see ELLIS HOSPITAL HEALTH CENTER), p. A444
ELLSWORTH COUNTY MEDICAL CENTER, ELLSWORTH, KS, p. A234
ELLWOOD CITY MEDICAL CENTER, LLC, ELLWOOD CITY, PA, p. A525
ELMHURST HOSPITAL, ELMHURST, IL, p. A182
ELMIRA PSYCHIATRIC CENTER, ELMIRA, NY, p. A427
ELMORE COMMUNITY HOSPITAL, WETUMPKA, AL, p. A24
ELY-BLOOMENSON COMMUNITY HOSPITAL, ELY, MN, p. A331
EMANUEL MEDICAL CENTER, SWAINSBORO, GA, p. A161
EMANUEL MEDICAL CENTER, TURLOCK, CA, p. A92
EMERALD COAST BEHAVIORAL HOSPITAL, PANAMA CITY, FL, p. A135
EMERSON HOSPITAL, CONCORD, MA, p. A298
EMINENT MEDICAL CENTER, RICHARDSON, TX, p. A630
EMMA PENDLETON BRADLEY HOSPITAL, EAST PROVIDENCE, RI, p. A547

EMORY DECATUR HOSPITAL, DECATUR, GA, p. A152
EMORY HILLANDALE HOSPITAL, LITHONIA, GA, p. A156
EMORY JOHNS CREEK HOSPITAL, JOHNS CREEK, GA, p. A155
EMORY LONG–TERM ACUTE CARE, DECATUR, GA, p. A152
EMORY REHABILITATION HOSPITAL, ATLANTA, GA, p. A146
EMORY SAINT JOSEPH'S HOSPITAL OF ATLANTA, ATLANTA, GA, p. A146
EMORY UNIVERSITY HOSPITAL, ATLANTA, GA, p. A146
EMORY UNIVERSITY HOSPITAL MIDTOWN, ATLANTA, GA, p. A146
ENCINO HOSPITAL MEDICAL CENTER, LOS ANGELES, CA, p. A66
ENCOMPASS HEALTH HARMARVILLE REHABILITATION HOSPITAL, PITTSBURGH, PA, p. A537
ENCOMPASS HEALTH LAKESHORE REHABILITATION HOSPITAL, BIRMINGHAM, AL, p. A14
ENCOMPASS HEALTH NITTANY VALLEY REHABILITATION HOSPITAL, PLEASANT GAP, PA, p. A539
ENCOMPASS HEALTH READING REHABILITATION HOSPITAL, READING, PA, p. A539
ENCOMPASS HEALTH REHABILITATION HOSPITAL MIDLAND ODESSA, MIDLAND, TX, p. A624
ENCOMPASS HEALTH REHABILITATION HOSPITAL OF ABILENE, ABILENE, TX, p. A581
ENCOMPASS HEALTH REHABILITATION HOSPITAL OF ALEXANDRIA, ALEXANDRIA, LA, p. A262
ENCOMPASS HEALTH REHABILITATION HOSPITAL OF ALTAMONTE SPRINGS, ALTAMONTE SPRINGS, FL, p. A117
ENCOMPASS HEALTH REHABILITATION HOSPITAL OF ALTOONA, ALTOONA, PA, p. A519
ENCOMPASS HEALTH REHABILITATION HOSPITAL OF ARLINGTON, ARLINGTON, TX, p. A583
ENCOMPASS HEALTH REHABILITATION HOSPITAL OF AUSTIN, AUSTIN, TX, p. A585
ENCOMPASS HEALTH REHABILITATION HOSPITAL OF BAKERSFIELD, BAKERSFIELD, CA, p. A52
ENCOMPASS HEALTH REHABILITATION HOSPITAL OF BRAINTREE, BRAINTREE, MA, p. A296
ENCOMPASS HEALTH REHABILITATION HOSPITAL OF CHARLESTON, CHARLESTON, SC, p. A550
ENCOMPASS HEALTH REHABILITATION HOSPITAL OF CHATTANOOGA, CHATTANOOGA, TN, p. A567
ENCOMPASS HEALTH REHABILITATION HOSPITAL OF CITY VIEW, FORT WORTH, TX, p. A605
ENCOMPASS HEALTH REHABILITATION HOSPITAL OF COLUMBIA, COLUMBIA, SC, p. A551
ENCOMPASS HEALTH REHABILITATION HOSPITAL OF CONCORD, CONCORD, NH, p. A399
ENCOMPASS HEALTH REHABILITATION HOSPITAL OF CYPRESS, HOUSTON, TX, p. A611
ENCOMPASS HEALTH REHABILITATION HOSPITAL OF DALLAS, DALLAS, TX, p. A596
ENCOMPASS HEALTH REHABILITATION HOSPITAL OF DESERT CANYON, LAS VEGAS, NV, p. A395
ENCOMPASS HEALTH REHABILITATION HOSPITAL OF DOTHAN, DOTHAN, AL, p. A17
ENCOMPASS HEALTH REHABILITATION HOSPITAL OF EAST VALLEY, MESA, AZ, p. A31
ENCOMPASS HEALTH REHABILITATION HOSPITAL OF ERIE, ERIE, PA, p. A525
ENCOMPASS HEALTH REHABILITATION HOSPITAL OF FLORENCE, FLORENCE, SC, p. A552
ENCOMPASS HEALTH REHABILITATION HOSPITAL OF FORT WORTH, FORT WORTH, TX, p. A605
ENCOMPASS HEALTH REHABILITATION HOSPITAL OF FRANKLIN, FRANKLIN, TN, p. A569
ENCOMPASS HEALTH REHABILITATION HOSPITAL OF FREDERICKSBURG, FREDERICKSBURG, VA, p. A659
ENCOMPASS HEALTH REHABILITATION HOSPITAL OF GADSDEN, GADSDEN, AL, p. A18
ENCOMPASS HEALTH REHABILITATION HOSPITAL OF GULFPORT, GULFPORT, MS, p. A347
ENCOMPASS HEALTH REHABILITATION HOSPITAL OF HENDERSON, HENDERSON, NV, p. A394
ENCOMPASS HEALTH REHABILITATION HOSPITAL OF HUMBLE, HUMBLE, TX, p. A615
ENCOMPASS HEALTH REHABILITATION HOSPITAL OF HUNTINGTON, HUNTINGTON, WV, p. A686
ENCOMPASS HEALTH REHABILITATION HOSPITAL OF JONESBORO, JONESBORO, AR, p. A44
ENCOMPASS HEALTH REHABILITATION HOSPITAL OF KINGSPORT, KINGSPORT, TN, p. A572
ENCOMPASS HEALTH REHABILITATION HOSPITAL OF LARGO, LARGO, FL, p. A128
ENCOMPASS HEALTH REHABILITATION HOSPITAL OF LAS VEGAS, LAS VEGAS, NV, p. A395
ENCOMPASS HEALTH REHABILITATION HOSPITAL OF MANATI, MANATI, PR, p. A717

ENCOMPASS HEALTH REHABILITATION HOSPITAL OF MECHANICSBURG, MECHANICSBURG, PA, p. A531
ENCOMPASS HEALTH REHABILITATION HOSPITAL OF MEMPHIS, MEMPHIS, TN, p. A574
ENCOMPASS HEALTH REHABILITATION HOSPITAL OF MIAMI, CUTLER BAY, FL, p. A120
ENCOMPASS HEALTH REHABILITATION HOSPITAL OF MODESTO, MODESTO, CA, p. A72
ENCOMPASS HEALTH REHABILITATION HOSPITAL OF MONTGOMERY, MONTGOMERY, AL, p. A21
ENCOMPASS HEALTH REHABILITATION HOSPITAL OF MORGANTOWN, MORGANTOWN, WV, p. A687
ENCOMPASS HEALTH REHABILITATION HOSPITAL OF NEW ENGLAND, WOBURN, MA, p. A305
ENCOMPASS HEALTH REHABILITATION HOSPITAL OF NORTH MEMPHIS, MEMPHIS, TN, p. A574
ENCOMPASS HEALTH REHABILITATION HOSPITAL OF NORTHERN VIRGINIA, ALDIE, VA, p. A656
ENCOMPASS HEALTH REHABILITATION HOSPITAL OF NORTHWEST TUCSON, TUCSON, AZ, p. A37
ENCOMPASS HEALTH REHABILITATION HOSPITAL OF OCALA, OCALA, FL, p. A133
ENCOMPASS HEALTH REHABILITATION HOSPITAL OF PANAMA CITY, PANAMA CITY, FL, p. A135
ENCOMPASS HEALTH REHABILITATION HOSPITAL OF PARKERSBURG, PARKERSBURG, WV, p. A688
ENCOMPASS HEALTH REHABILITATION HOSPITAL OF PEARLAND, PEARLAND, TX, p. A628
ENCOMPASS HEALTH REHABILITATION HOSPITAL OF PETERSBURG, PETERSBURG, VA, p. A665
ENCOMPASS HEALTH REHABILITATION HOSPITAL OF PLANO, PLANO, TX, p. A629
ENCOMPASS HEALTH REHABILITATION HOSPITAL OF PRINCETON, PRINCETON, WV, p. A688
ENCOMPASS HEALTH REHABILITATION HOSPITAL OF RICHARDSON, RICHARDSON, TX, p. A631
ENCOMPASS HEALTH REHABILITATION HOSPITAL OF ROCK HILL, ROCK HILL, SC, p. A556
ENCOMPASS HEALTH REHABILITATION HOSPITAL OF ROUND ROCK, ROUND ROCK, TX, p. A632
ENCOMPASS HEALTH REHABILITATION HOSPITAL OF SAN ANTONIO, SAN ANTONIO, TX, p. A634
ENCOMPASS HEALTH REHABILITATION HOSPITAL OF SAN JUAN, SAN JUAN, PR, p. A718
ENCOMPASS HEALTH REHABILITATION HOSPITAL OF SARASOTA, SARASOTA, FL, p. A139
ENCOMPASS HEALTH REHABILITATION HOSPITAL OF SCOTTSDALE, SCOTTSDALE, AZ, p. A35
ENCOMPASS HEALTH REHABILITATION HOSPITAL OF SEWICKLEY, SEWICKLEY, PA, p. A541
ENCOMPASS HEALTH REHABILITATION HOSPITAL OF SHELBY COUNTY, PELHAM, AL, p. A22
ENCOMPASS HEALTH REHABILITATION HOSPITAL OF SPRING HILL, BROOKSVILLE, FL, p. A119
ENCOMPASS HEALTH REHABILITATION HOSPITAL OF SUGAR LAND, SUGAR LAND, TX, p. A638
ENCOMPASS HEALTH REHABILITATION HOSPITAL OF SUNRISE, SUNRISE, FL, p. A140
ENCOMPASS HEALTH REHABILITATION HOSPITAL OF TALLAHASSEE, TALLAHASSEE, FL, p. A140
ENCOMPASS HEALTH REHABILITATION HOSPITAL OF TEXARKANA, TEXARKANA, TX, p. A640
ENCOMPASS HEALTH REHABILITATION HOSPITAL OF THE MID–CITIES, BEDFORD, TX, p. A588
ENCOMPASS HEALTH REHABILITATION HOSPITAL OF TINTON FALLS, TINTON FALLS, NJ, p. A413
ENCOMPASS HEALTH REHABILITATION HOSPITAL OF TREASURE COAST, VERO BEACH, FL, p. A143
ENCOMPASS HEALTH REHABILITATION HOSPITAL OF TUSTIN, TUSTIN, CA, p. A92
ENCOMPASS HEALTH REHABILITATION HOSPITAL OF VIRGINIA, RICHMOND, VA, p. A666
ENCOMPASS HEALTH REHABILITATION HOSPITAL OF WESTERN MASSACHUSETTS, LUDLOW, MA, p. A300
ENCOMPASS HEALTH REHABILITATION HOSPITAL OF WICHITA FALLS, WICHITA FALLS, TX, p. A645
ENCOMPASS HEALTH REHABILITATION HOSPITAL OF YORK, YORK, PA, p. A546
ENCOMPASS HEALTH REHABILITATION HOSPITAL THE VINTAGE, HOUSTON, TX, p. A611
ENCOMPASS HEALTH REHABILITATION HOSPITAL THE WOODLANDS, CONROE, TX, p. A593
ENCOMPASS HEALTH REHABILITATION HOSPITAL VISION PARK, SHENANDOAH, TX, p. A636
ENCOMPASS HEALTH REHABILITATION HOSPITAL, A PARTNER OF WASHINGTON REGIONAL, FAYETTEVILLE, AR, p. A41
ENCOMPASS HEALTH REHABILITATION INSTITUTE OF TUCSON, TUCSON, AZ, p. A37

ENCOMPASS HEALTH VALLEY OF THE SUN REHABILITATION HOSPITAL, GLENDALE, AZ, p. A30
ENCOMPASS REHABILITATION HOSPITAL OF LAKEVIEW, ELIZABETHTOWN, KY, p. A251
ENCOMPASS REHABILITATION HOSPITAL OF NORTH ALABAMA, HUNTSVILLE, AL, p. A19
ENCOMPASSS HEALTH REHABILITATION HOSPITAL OF FORT SMITH, FORT SMITH, AR, p. A42
ENDLESS MOUNTAIN HEALTH SYSTEMS, MONTROSE, PA, p. A532
ENGLEWOOD COMMUNITY HOSPITAL, ENGLEWOOD, FL, p. A122
ENGLEWOOD HOSPITAL AND MEDICAL CENTER, ENGLEWOOD, NJ, p. A405
ENLOE MEDICAL CENTER, CHICO, CA, p. A54
ENNIS REGIONAL MEDICAL CENTER, ENNIS, TX, p. A603
EPHRAIM MCDOWELL FORT LOGAN HOSPITAL, STANFORD, KY, p. A261
EPHRAIM MCDOWELL JAMES B. HAGGIN MEMORIAL HOSPITAL, HARRODSBURG, KY, p. A253
EPHRAIM MCDOWELL REGIONAL MEDICAL CENTER, DANVILLE, KY, p. A251
ERIE COUNTY MEDICAL CENTER, BUFFALO, NY, p. A424
ERIE VETERANS AFFAIRS MEDICAL CENTER, ERIE, PA, p. A525
ERLANGER BLEDSOE HOSPITAL, PIKEVILLE, TN, p. A578
ERLANGER MEDICAL CENTER, CHATTANOOGA, TN, p. A567
ERLANGER WESTERN CAROLINA HOSPITAL, MURPHY, NC, p. A459
ERLANGER WOMEN'S EAST HOSPITAL, CHATTANOOGA, TENNESSEE (see ERLANGER EAST HOSPITAL), p. A567
ESKENAZI HEALTH, INDIANAPOLIS, IN, p. A206
ESSENTIA HEALTH ADA, ADA, MN, p. A327
ESSENTIA HEALTH DULUTH, DULUTH, MN, p. A331
ESSENTIA HEALTH FARGO, FARGO, ND, p. A466
ESSENTIA HEALTH FOSSTON, FOSSTON, MN, p. A332
ESSENTIA HEALTH NORTHERN PINES MEDICAL CENTER, AURORA, MN, p. A328
ESSENTIA HEALTH SANDSTONE, SANDSTONE, MN, p. A340
ESSENTIA HEALTH ST. JOSEPH'S MEDICAL CENTER, BRAINERD, MN, p. A329
ESSENTIA HEALTH ST. MARY'S – DETROIT LAKES, DETROIT LAKES, MN, p. A330
ESSENTIA HEALTH ST. MARY'S HOSPITAL OF SUPERIOR, SUPERIOR, WI, p. A706
ESSENTIA HEALTH ST. MARY'S MEDICAL CENTER, DULUTH, MN, p. A331
ESSENTIA HEALTH–DEER RIVER, DEER RIVER, MN, p. A330
ESSENTIA HEALTH–GRACEVILLE, GRACEVILLE, MN, p. A332
ESSENTIA HEALTH–VIRGINIA, VIRGINIA, MN, p. A341
ESSEX COUNTY HOSPITAL CENTER, CEDAR GROVE, NJ, p. A404
ESTES PARK MEDICAL CENTER, ESTES PARK, CO, p. A100
EUCLID HOSPITAL, EUCLID, OH, p. A482
EUREKA COMMUNITY HEALTH SERVICES AVERA, EUREKA, SD, p. A560
EUREKA COMMUNITY HOSPITAL, EUREKA, ILLINOIS (see ADVOCATE EUREKA HOSPITAL), p. A182
EUREKA SPRINGS HOSPITAL, EUREKA SPRINGS, AR, p. A41
EVANGELICAL COMMUNITY HOSPITAL, LEWISBURG, PA, p. A530
EVANS MEMORIAL HOSPITAL, CLAXTON, GA, p. A150
EVANS U. S. ARMY COMMUNITY HOSPITAL, FORT CARSON, CO, p. A100
EVANSTON REGIONAL HOSPITAL, EVANSTON, WY, p. A711
EVANSVILLE PSYCHIATRIC CHILDREN CENTER, EVANSVILLE, IN, p. A203
EVANSVILLE STATE HOSPITAL, EVANSVILLE, IN, p. A203
EVERETT TOWER, OKLAHOMA CITY, OKLAHOMA (see OU MEDICAL CENTER), p. A503
EVERGREEN HEALTHCARE, KIRKLAND, WASHINGTON (see EVERGREENHEALTH), p. A674
EVERGREEN MEDICAL CENTER, EVERGREEN, AL, p. A17
EVERGREENHEALTH, KIRKLAND, WA, p. A674
EVERGREENHEALTH MONROE, MONROE, WA, p. A675
EXCELA FRICK HOSPITAL, MOUNT PLEASANT, PA, p. A532
EXCELA HEALTH WESTMORELAND HOSPITAL, GREENSBURG, PA, p. A526
EXCELA LATROBE AREA HOSPITAL, LATROBE, PA, p. A529
EXCELSIOR SPRINGS HOSPITAL, EXCELSIOR SPRINGS, MO, p. A359
EXETER HOSPITAL, EXETER, NH, p. A400
EXTENDED CARE HOSPITAL, NEW ORLEANS, LA, p. A275
EYE AND EAR HOSPITAL OF PITTSBURGH, PITTSBURGH, PENNSYLVANIA (see UPMC PRESBYTERIAN), p. A537

F

F. F. THOMPSON HOSPITAL, CANANDAIGUA, NY, p. A425
F. W. HUSTON MEDICAL CENTER, WINCHESTER, KS, p. A247
FAIRBANKS, INDIANAPOLIS, IN, p. A206
FAIRBANKS MEMORIAL HOSPITAL, FAIRBANKS, AK, p. A26
FAIRCHILD MEDICAL CENTER, YREKA, CA, p. A95
FAIRFAX BEHAVIORAL HEALTH, KIRKLAND, WA, p. A674
FAIRFAX COMMUNITY HOSPITAL, FAIRFAX, OK, p. A499
FAIRFAX MEMORIAL HOSPITAL, FAIRFAX, OKLAHOMA (see FAIRFAX COMMUNITY HOSPITAL), p. A499
FAIRFIELD MEDICAL CENTER, LANCASTER, OH, p. A485
FAIRFIELD MEMORIAL HOSPITAL, FAIRFIELD, IL, p. A183
FAIRLAWN REHABILITATION HOSPITAL, WORCESTER, MA, p. A305
FAIRMONT HOSPITAL, SAN LEANDRO, CA, p. A87
FAIRMONT REGIONAL MEDICAL CENTER, FAIRMONT, WV, p. A685
FAIRMOUNT BEHAVIORAL HEALTH SYSTEM, PHILADELPHIA, PA, p. A534
FAIRVIEW DEVELOPMENTAL CENTER, COSTA MESA, CA, p. A55
FAIRVIEW HOSPITAL, GREAT BARRINGTON, MA, p. A299
FAIRVIEW LAKES HEALTH SERVICES, WYOMING, MN, p. A343
FAIRVIEW NORTHLAND MEDICAL CENTER, PRINCETON, MN, p. A338
FAIRVIEW PARK HOSPITAL, DUBLIN, GA, p. A152
FAIRVIEW REGIONAL MEDICAL CENTER, FAIRVIEW, OK, p. A500
FAIRVIEW RIDGES HOSPITAL, BURNSVILLE, MN, p. A329
FAIRVIEW RIVERSIDE HOSPITAL, MINNEAPOLIS, MINNESOTA (see UNIVERSITY OF MINNESOTA MEDICAL CENTER, FAIRVIEW), p. A335
FAIRVIEW SOUTHDALE HOSPITAL, EDINA, MN, p. A331
FAITH COMMUNITY HOSPITAL, JACKSBORO, TX, p. A616
FAITH REGIONAL HEALTH SERVICES, NORFOLK, NE, p. A388
FALL RIVER HOSPITAL, HOT SPRINGS, SD, p. A561
FALLON MEDICAL COMPLEX, BAKER, MT, p. A374
FALLS COMMUNITY HOSPITAL AND CLINIC, MARLIN, TX, p. A623
FALMOUTH HOSPITAL, FALMOUTH, MA, p. A298
FANNIN REGIONAL HOSPITAL, BLUE RIDGE, GA, p. A148
FANNY ALLEN CAMPUS, COLCHESTER, VERMONT (see UNIVERSITY OF VERMONT MEDICAL CENTER), p. A654
FARGO VETERANS AFFAIRS HEALTH CARE SYSTEM, FARGO, ND, p. A466
FAULKTON AREA MEDICAL CENTER, FAULKTON, SD, p. A560
FAUQUIER HOSPITAL, WARRENTON, VA, p. A668
FAWCETT MEMORIAL HOSPITAL, PORT CHARLOTTE, FL, p. A137
FAXTON ST. LUKE'S HEALTHCARE, UTICA, NY, p. A446
FAYETTE COUNTY HOSPITAL, VANDALIA, IL, p. A197
FAYETTE COUNTY MEMORIAL HOSPITAL, WASHINGTON COURT HOUSE, OH, p. A493
FAYETTE MEDICAL CENTER, FAYETTE, AL, p. A18
FAYETTE REGIONAL HEALTH SYSTEM, CONNERSVILLE, IN, p. A201
FAYETTEVILLE VETERANS AFFAIRS MEDICAL CENTER, FAYETTEVILLE, NC, p. A454
FEDERAL CORRECTIONAL INSTITUTE HOSPITAL, LITTLETON, CO, p. A103
FEDERAL MEDICAL CENTER, LEXINGTON, KY, p. A255
FERRELL HOSPITAL, ELDORADO, IL, p. A181
FERRY COUNTY MEMORIAL HOSPITAL, REPUBLIC, WA, p. A677
FHN MEMORIAL HOSPITAL, FREEPORT, IL, p. A183
FIELD MEMORIAL COMMUNITY HOSPITAL, CENTREVILLE, MS, p. A345
FILLMORE COMMUNITY HOSPITAL, FILLMORE, UT, p. A648
FILLMORE COUNTY HOSPITAL, GENEVA, NE, p. A385
FINGER LAKES HOSPITAL, GENEVA, NY, p. A428
FINLEY HOSPITAL, DUBUQUE, IOWA (see UNITYPOINT HEALTH – FINLEY HOSPITAL), p. A222
FIRELANDS REGIONAL HEALTH SYSTEM, SANDUSKY, OH, p. A490
FIRST BAPTIST MEDICAL CENTER, DALLAS, TX, p. A596
FIRST CARE HEALTH CENTER, PARK RIVER, ND, p. A469
FIRST CARE MEDICAL SERVICES, FOSSTON, MINNESOTA (see ESSENTIA HEALTH FOSSTON), p. A332
FIRST HOSPITAL PANAMERICANO, CIDRA, PR, p. A716
FIRST HOSPITAL WYOMING VALLEY, KINGSTON, PA, p. A528
FIRST SURGICAL HOSPITAL, BELLAIRE, TX, p. A588
FIRST TEXAS HOSPITAL, HOUSTON, TX, p. A611
FIRSTHEALTH MONTGOMERY MEMORIAL HOSPITAL, TROY, NC, p. A463

FIRSTHEALTH MOORE REGIONAL HOSPITAL, PINEHURST, NC, p. A460
FIRSTLIGHT HEALTH SYSTEM, MORA, MN, p. A336
FISHER COUNTY HOSPITAL DISTRICT, ROTAN, TX, p. A632
FISHER-TITUS MEDICAL CENTER, NORWALK, OH, p. A488
FISHERMEN'S HOSPITAL, MARATHON, FL, p. A129
FITZGIBBON HOSPITAL, MARSHALL, MO, p. A365
FLAGLER HOSPITAL, SAINT AUGUSTINE, FL, p. A138
FLAGSTAFF MEDICAL CENTER, FLAGSTAFF, AZ, p. A29
FLAMBEAU HOSPITAL, PARK FALLS, WI, p. A703
FLEMING COUNTY HOSPITAL, FLEMINGSBURG, KY, p. A251
FLINT RIVER COMMUNITY HOSPITAL, MONTEZUMA, GA, p. A157
FLORIDA MEDICAL CENTER, FORT LAUDERDALE, FL, p. A122
FLORIDA STATE HOSPITAL, CHATTAHOOCHEE, FL, p. A119
FLOWERS HOSPITAL, DOTHAN, AL, p. A17
FLOYD CHEROKEE MEDICAL CENTER, CENTRE, AL, p. A16
FLOYD COUNTY MEDICAL CENTER, CHARLES CITY, IA, p. A219
FLOYD MEDICAL CENTER, ROME, GA, p. A159
FLOYD VALLEY HEALTHCARE, LE MARS, IA, p. A225
FOND DU LAC COUNTY MENTAL HEALTH CENTER, FOND DU LAC, WI, p. A695
FOOTHILL PRESBYTERIAN HOSPITAL, GLENDORA, CA, p. A60
FOOTHILL REGIONAL MEDICAL CENTER, TUSTIN, CA, p. A92
FORBES HOSPITAL, MONROEVILLE, PA, p. A532
FOREST HEALTH MEDICAL CENTER, YPSILANTI, MI, p. A325
FOREST VIEW PSYCHIATRIC HOSPITAL, GRAND RAPIDS, MI, p. A312
FORKS COMMUNITY HOSPITAL, FORKS, WA, p. A673
FORREST CITY MEDICAL CENTER, FORREST CITY, AR, p. A42
FORREST GENERAL HOSPITAL, HATTIESBURG, MS, p. A348
FORT BELKNAP SERVICE UNIT, HARLEM, MT, p. A377
FORT BELVOIR COMMUNITY HOSPITAL, FORT BELVOIR, VA, p. A659
FORT DUNCAN REGIONAL MEDICAL CENTER, EAGLE PASS, TX, p. A600
FORT HAMILTON HOSPITAL, HAMILTON, OH, p. A484
FORT HEALTHCARE, FORT ATKINSON, WI, p. A695
FORT LAUDERDALE HOSPITAL, FORT LAUDERDALE, FL, p. A122
FORT LOUDOUN MEDICAL CENTER, LENOIR CITY, TN, p. A573
FORT MADISON COMMUNITY HOSPITAL, FORT MADISON, IA, p. A223
FORT SANDERS REGIONAL MEDICAL CENTER, KNOXVILLE, TN, p. A572
FORT WALTON BEACH MEDICAL CENTER, FORT WALTON BEACH, FL, p. A123
FORT WASHINGTON MEDICAL CENTER, OXEN HILL, MD, p. A292
FOUNDATION SURGICAL HOSPITAL OF EL PASO, EL PASO, TX, p. A602
FOUNDATION SURGICAL HOSPITAL OF SAN ANTONIO, SAN ANTONIO, TX, p. A634
FOUNDATIONS BEHAVIORAL HEALTH, DOYLESTOWN, PA, p. A524
FOUNTAIN VALLEY REGIONAL HOSPITAL AND MEDICAL CENTER, FOUNTAIN VALLEY, CA, p. A58
FOUR COUNTY COUNSELING CENTER, LOGANSPORT, IN, p. A210
FOUR WINDS HOSPITAL, KATONAH, NY, p. A429
FOUR WINDS HOSPITAL, SARATOGA SPRINGS, NY, p. A443
FOX CHASE CANCER CENTER–AMERICAN ONCOLOGIC HOSPITAL, PHILADELPHIA, PA, p. A534
FRANCES MAHON DEACONESS HOSPITAL, GLASGOW, MT, p. A376
FRANCISCAN CHILDREN'S, BRIGHTON, MA, p. A296
FRANCISCAN HEALTH CARMEL, CARMEL, IN, p. A201
FRANCISCAN HEALTH CRAWFORDSVILLE, CRAWFORDSVILLE, IN, p. A202
FRANCISCAN HEALTH CROWN POINT, CROWN POINT, IN, p. A202
FRANCISCAN HEALTH DYER, DYER, IN, p. A202
FRANCISCAN HEALTH HAMMOND, HAMMOND, IN, p. A205
FRANCISCAN HEALTH INDIANAPOLIS, INDIANAPOLIS, IN, p. A207
FRANCISCAN HEALTH LAFAYETTE EAST, LAFAYETTE, IN, p. A209
FRANCISCAN HEALTH MICHIGAN CITY, MICHIGAN CITY, IN, p. A211
FRANCISCAN HEALTH MOORESVILLE, MOORESVILLE, IN, p. A211
FRANCISCAN HEALTH OLYMPIA FIELDS, OLYMPIA FIELDS, IL, p. A192
FRANCISCAN HEALTH RENSSELAER, RENSSELAER, IN, p. A214
FRANCISCAN HEALTHCARE MUNSTER, MUNSTER, IN, p. A212

FRANKFORT REGIONAL MEDICAL CENTER, FRANKFORT, KY, p. A252
FRANKLIN COUNTY MEDICAL CENTER, PRESTON, ID, p. A171
FRANKLIN COUNTY MEMORIAL HOSPITAL, FRANKLIN, NE, p. A384
FRANKLIN COUNTY MEMORIAL HOSPITAL, MEADVILLE, MS, p. A351
FRANKLIN FOUNDATION HOSPITAL, FRANKLIN, LA, p. A267
FRANKLIN GENERAL HOSPITAL, HAMPTON, IA, p. A223
FRANKLIN HOSPITAL DISTRICT, BENTON, IL, p. A174
FRANKLIN MEDICAL CENTER, WINNSBORO, LA, p. A280
FRANKLIN MEMORIAL HOSPITAL, FARMINGTON, ME, p. A283
FRANKLIN REGIONAL HOSPITAL, FRANKLIN, NH, p. A400
FRANKLIN SQUARE HOSPITAL CENTER, BALTIMORE, MARYLAND (see MEDSTAR FRANKLIN SQUARE MEDICAL CENTER), p. A288
FRANKLIN WOODS COMMUNITY HOSPITAL, JOHNSON CITY, TN, p. A571
FREDERICK REGIONAL HEALTH SYSTEM, FREDERICK, MD, p. A290
FREDONIA REGIONAL HOSPITAL, FREDONIA, KS, p. A235
FREEMAN HEALTH SYSTEM, JOPLIN, MO, p. A362
FREEMAN NEOSHO HOSPITAL, NEOSHO, MO, p. A366
FREEMAN REGIONAL HEALTH SERVICES, FREEMAN, SD, p. A561
FREESTONE MEDICAL CENTER, FAIRFIELD, TX, p. A603
FREMONT HOSPITAL, FREMONT, CA, p. A58
FREMONT MEDICAL CENTER, YUBA CITY, CA, p. A95
FRENCH HOSPITAL MEDICAL CENTER, SAN LUIS OBISPO, CA, p. A87
FRESNO HEART AND SURGICAL HOSPITAL, FRESNO, CA, p. A59
FRESNO MEDICAL CENTER, FRESNO, CA, p. A59
FRESNO SURGICAL HOSPITAL, FRESNO, CA, p. A59
FRIEND COMMUNITY HEALTHCARE SYSTEM, FRIEND, NE, p. A385
FRIENDS HOSPITAL, PHILADELPHIA, PA, p. A534
FRIO REGIONAL HOSPITAL, PEARSALL, TX, p. A628
FRISBIE MEMORIAL HOSPITAL, ROCHESTER, NH, p. A402
FROEDTERT AND THE MEDICAL COLLEGE OF WISCONSIN FROEDTERT HOSPITAL, MILWAUKEE, WI, p. A701
FROEDTERT SOUTH – KENOSHA MEDICAL CENTER, KENOSHA, WI, p. A697
FRYE REGIONAL MEDICAL CENTER, HICKORY, NC, p. A456
FULTON COUNTY HEALTH CENTER, WAUSEON, OH, p. A493
FULTON COUNTY HOSPITAL, SALEM, AR, p. A48
FULTON COUNTY MEDICAL CENTER, MC CONNELLSBURG, PA, p. A531
FULTON MEDICAL CENTER, FULTON, MO, p. A360
FULTON STATE HOSPITAL, FULTON, MO, p. A360

G

G. WERBER BRYAN PSYCHIATRIC HOSPITAL, COLUMBIA, SC, p. A551
G.V. (SONNY) MONTGOMERY VETERANS AFFAIRS MEDICAL CENTER, JACKSON, MS, p. A348
GADSDEN REGIONAL MEDICAL CENTER, GADSDEN, AL, p. A18
GALESBURG COTTAGE HOSPITAL, GALESBURG, IL, p. A183
GALION HOSPITAL, GALION, OH, p. A483
GALLUP INDIAN MEDICAL CENTER, GALLUP, NM, p. A418
GARDEN CITY HOSPITAL, GARDEN CITY, MI, p. A312
GARDEN GROVE HOSPITAL AND MEDICAL CENTER, GARDEN GROVE, CA, p. A60
GARDEN PARK MEDICAL CENTER, GULFPORT, MS, p. A347
GARFIELD COUNTY HEALTH CENTER, JORDAN, MT, p. A378
GARFIELD COUNTY PUBLIC HOSPITAL DISTRICT, POMEROY, WA, p. A676
GARFIELD MEDICAL CENTER, MONTEREY PARK, CA, p. A73
GARFIELD MEMORIAL HOSPITAL, PANGUITCH, UT, p. A650
GARFIELD PARK HOSPITAL, CHICAGO, IL, p. A177
GARLAND BEHAVIORAL HOSPITAL, GARLAND, TX, p. A607
GARRETT REGIONAL MEDICAL CENTER, OAKLAND, MD, p. A292
GASTON MEMORIAL HOSPITAL, GASTONIA, NORTH CAROLINA (see CAROMONT REGIONAL MEDICAL CENTER), p. A454
GATEWAY REGIONAL MEDICAL CENTER, GRANITE CITY, IL, p. A184
GATEWAY REHABILITATION HOSPITAL, FLORENCE, KY, p. A251
GATEWAYS HOSPITAL AND MENTAL HEALTH CENTER, LOS ANGELES, CA, p. A66

GAYLORD HOSPITAL, WALLINGFORD, CT, p. A111
GEARY COMMUNITY HOSPITAL, JUNCTION CITY, KS, p. A237
GEISINGER ENCOMPASS HEALTH REHABILITATION HOSPITAL, DANVILLE, PA, p. A523
GEISINGER HOLY SPIRIT, CAMP HILL, PA, p. A521
GEISINGER JERSEY SHORE HOSPITAL, JERSEY SHORE, PA, p. A528
GEISINGER MEDICAL CENTER, DANVILLE, PA, p. A523
GEISINGER WYOMING VALLEY MEDICAL CENTER, WILKES BARRE, PA, p. A544
GEISINGER–BLOOMSBURG HOSPITAL, BLOOMSBURG, PA, p. A521
GEISINGER–COMMUNITY MEDICAL CENTER, SCRANTON, PA, p. A540
GEISINGER–LEWISTOWN HOSPITAL, LEWISTOWN, PA, p. A530
GENERAL HOSPITAL, CHARLESTON, WEST VIRGINIA (see CHARLESTON AREA MEDICAL CENTER), p. A684
GENERAL LEONARD WOOD ARMY COMMUNITY HOSPITAL, FORT LEONARD WOOD, MO, p. A360
GENESIS BEHAVIORAL HOSPITAL, BREAUX BRIDGE, LA, p. A265
GENESIS HEALTHCARE SYSTEM, ZANESVILLE, OH, p. A495
GENESIS MEDICAL CENTER, DAVENPORT, DAVENPORT, IA, p. A220
GENESIS MEDICAL CENTER, DEWITT, DE WITT, IA, p. A220
GENESIS MEDICAL CENTER, SILVIS, SILVIS, IL, p. A196
GENESIS MEDICAL CENTER–ALEDO, ALEDO, IL, p. A173
GENOA MEDICAL FACILITIES, GENOA, NE, p. A385
GEORGE AND MARIE BACKUS CHILDREN'S HOSPITAL, SAVANNAH, GA, p. A160
GEORGE C GRAPE COMMUNITY HOSPITAL, HAMBURG, IA, p. A223
GEORGE E. WEEMS MEMORIAL HOSPITAL, APALACHICOLA, FL, p. A117
GEORGE REGIONAL HOSPITAL, LUCEDALE, MS, p. A350
GEORGE WASHINGTON UNIVERSITY HOSPITAL, WASHINGTON, DC, p. A115
GEORGETOWN BEHAVIORAL HEALTH INSTITUTE, GEORGETOWN, TX, p. A607
GEORGETOWN COMMUNITY HOSPITAL, GEORGETOWN, KY, p. A252
GEORGETOWN UNIVERSITY HOSPITAL, WASHINGTON, DC, p. A115
GEORGIA REGIONAL HOSPITAL AT ATLANTA, DECATUR, GA, p. A152
GEORGIA REGIONAL HOSPITAL AT SAVANNAH, SAVANNAH, GA, p. A160
GERALD CHAMPION REGIONAL MEDICAL CENTER, ALAMOGORDO, NM, p. A416
GIBSON AREA HOSPITAL AND HEALTH SERVICES, GIBSON CITY, IL, p. A184
GIBSON GENERAL HOSPITAL, PRINCETON, IN, p. A214
GIFFORD MEDICAL CENTER, RANDOLPH, VT, p. A655
GILA REGIONAL MEDICAL CENTER, SILVER CITY, NM, p. A420
GILLETTE CHILDREN'S SPECIALTY HEALTHCARE, SAINT PAUL, MN, p. A339
GIRARD MEDICAL CENTER, GIRARD, KS, p. A235
GLACIAL RIDGE HEALTH SYSTEM, GLENWOOD, MN, p. A332
GLADES GENERAL HOSPITAL, BELLE GLADE, FL, p. A117
GLEN COVE HOSPITAL, GLEN COVE, NY, p. A428
GLEN OAKS HOSPITAL, GREENVILLE, TX, p. A608
GLEN ROSE MEDICAL CENTER, GLEN ROSE, TX, p. A607
GLENBEIGH HOSPITAL AND OUTPATIENT CENTERS, ROCK CREEK, OH, p. A490
GLENCOE REGIONAL HEALTH, GLENCOE, MN, p. A332
GLENDALE MEMORIAL HOSPITAL AND HEALTH CENTER, GLENDALE, CA, p. A60
GLENDIVE MEDICAL CENTER, GLENDIVE, MT, p. A376
GLENDORA COMMUNITY HOSPITAL, GLENDORA, CA, p. A61
GLENN MEDICAL CENTER, WILLOWS, CA, p. A95
GLENS FALLS HOSPITAL, GLENS FALLS, NY, p. A428
GLENWOOD REGIONAL MEDICAL CENTER, WEST MONROE, LA, p. A280
GOLDEN PLAINS COMMUNITY HOSPITAL, BORGER, TX, p. A589
GOLDEN VALLEY MEMORIAL HEALTHCARE, CLINTON, MO, p. A358
GOLETA VALLEY COTTAGE HOSPITAL, SANTA BARBARA, CA, p. A88
GOLISANO CHILDREN'S HOSPITAL OF SOUTHWEST FLORIDA, FORT MYERS, FL, p. A123
GONZALES HEALTHCARE SYSTEMS, GONZALES, TX, p. A608
GOOD SAMARITAN COMMUNITY HEALTHCARE, PUYALLUP, WASHINGTON (see MULTICARE GOOD SAMARITAN HOSPITAL), p. A677
GOOD SAMARITAN HEALTH CENTER OF MERRILL, MERRILL, WISCONSIN (see ASCENSION GOOD SAMARITAN HOSPITAL), p. A700

GOOD SAMARITAN HEALTH SYSTEMS, KEARNEY, NEBRASKA (see CHI HEALTH GOOD SAMARITAN), p. A386
GOOD SAMARITAN HOSPITAL, BAKERSFIELD, CA, p. A52
GOOD SAMARITAN HOSPITAL, CINCINNATI, OH, p. A476
GOOD SAMARITAN HOSPITAL, LOS ANGELES, CA, p. A66
GOOD SAMARITAN HOSPITAL, SAN JOSE, CA, p. A86
GOOD SAMARITAN HOSPITAL, VINCENNES, IN, p. A216
GOOD SAMARITAN HOSPITAL AND MEDICAL CENTER, PORTLAND, OREGON (see LEGACY GOOD SAMARITAN MEDICAL CENTER), p. A516
GOOD SAMARITAN HOSPITAL MEDICAL CENTER, WEST ISLIP, NY, p. A447
GOOD SAMARITAN HOSPITAL OF MARYLAND, BALTIMORE, MARYLAND (see MEDSTAR GOOD SAMARITAN HOSPITAL), p. A286
GOOD SAMARITAN MEDICAL CENTER, BROCKTON, MA, p. A296
GOOD SAMARITAN MEDICAL CENTER, LAFAYETTE, CO, p. A102
GOOD SAMARITAN MEDICAL CENTER, WEST PALM BEACH, FL, p. A144
GOOD SAMARITAN REGIONAL HEALTH CENTER, MOUNT VERNON, IL, p. A190
GOOD SAMARITAN REGIONAL MEDICAL CENTER, CORVALLIS, OR, p. A512
GOOD SAMARITAN REGIONAL MEDICAL CENTER, SUFFERN, NY, p. A445
GOOD SHEPHERD HEALTH CARE SYSTEM, HERMISTON, OR, p. A513
GOOD SHEPHERD PENN PARTNERS SPECIALTY HOSPITAL AT RITTENHOUSE, PHILADELPHIA, PA, p. A534
GOOD SHEPHERD REHABILITATION HOSPITAL, ALLENTOWN, PA, p. A519
GOOD SHEPHERD SPECIALTY HOSPITAL, BETHLEHEM, PA, p. A520
GOODALL–WITCHER HOSPITAL AUTHORITY, CLIFTON, TX, p. A592
GOODLAND REGIONAL MEDICAL CENTER, GOODLAND, KS, p. A235
GORDON MEMORIAL HEALTH SERVICES, GORDON, NE, p. A385
GOSHEN GENERAL HOSPITAL, GOSHEN, INDIANA (see GOSHEN HEALTH), p. A205
GOSHEN HEALTH, GOSHEN, IN, p. A205
GOTHENBURG HEALTH, GOTHENBURG, NE, p. A385
GOTTLIEB MEMORIAL HOSPITAL, MELROSE PARK, IL, p. A189
GOUVERNEUR HOSPITAL, GOUVERNEUR, NY, p. A428
GOVE COUNTY MEDICAL CENTER, QUINTER, KS, p. A244
GOVERNOR JUAN F. LUIS HOSPITAL, CHRISTIANSTED, VI, p. A720
GRACE COTTAGE HOSPITAL, TOWNSHEND, VT, p. A655
GRACE HOSPITAL, CLEVELAND, OH, p. A477
GRACE MEDICAL CENTER, LUBBOCK, TX, p. A622
GRACEVILLE HEALTH CENTER, GRACEVILLE, MINNESOTA (see ESSENTIA HEALTH–GRACEVILLE), p. A332
GRADY GENERAL HOSPITAL, CAIRO, GA, p. A149
GRADY MEMORIAL HOSPITAL, ATLANTA, GA, p. A146
GRADY MEMORIAL HOSPITAL, CHICKASHA, OK, p. A498
GRAFTON CITY HOSPITAL, GRAFTON, WV, p. A685
GRAHAM COUNTY HOSPITAL, HILL CITY, KS, p. A236
GRAHAM HOSPITAL ASSOCIATION, CANTON, IL, p. A175
GRAHAM REGIONAL MEDICAL CENTER, GRAHAM, TX, p. A608
GRAND ITASCA CLINIC AND HOSPITAL, GRAND RAPIDS, MN, p. A333
GRAND JUNCTION VETERANS HEALTH CARE SYSTEM, GRAND JUNCTION, CO, p. A101
GRAND RIVER HOSPITAL DISTRICT, RIFLE, CO, p. A105
GRAND STRAND REGIONAL MEDICAL CENTER, MYRTLE BEACH, SC, p. A556
GRAND VIEW HEALTH, SELLERSVILLE, PA, p. A541
GRANDE RONDE HOSPITAL, LA GRANDE, OR, p. A514
GRANDVIEW MEDICAL CENTER, BIRMINGHAM, AL, p. A14
GRANDVIEW MEDICAL CENTER, DAYTON, OH, p. A481
GRANITE COUNTY MEDICAL CENTER, PHILIPSBURG, MT, p. A379
GRANITE FALLS HEALTH, GRANITE FALLS, MN, p. A333
GRANT MEMORIAL HOSPITAL, PETERSBURG, WV, p. A688
GRANT REGIONAL HEALTH CENTER, LANCASTER, WI, p. A698
GRANT–BLACKFORD MENTAL HEALTH CENTER, MARION, IN, p. A211
GRANVILLE HEALTH SYSTEM, OXFORD, NC, p. A460
GRATIOT MEDICAL CENTER, ALMA, MICHIGAN (see MIDMICHIGAN MEDICAL CENTER–GRATIOT), p. A306
GRAYS HARBOR COMMUNITY HOSPITAL, ABERDEEN, WA, p. A670
GREAT FALLS CLINIC HOSPITAL, GREAT FALLS, MT, p. A377
GREAT PLAINS HEALTH, NORTH PLATTE, NE, p. A388

GREAT PLAINS REGIONAL MEDICAL CENTER, ELK CITY, OK, p. A499
GREAT RIVER HEALTH SYSTEM, WEST BURLINGTON, IA, p. A231
GREAT RIVER MEDICAL CENTER, BLYTHEVILLE, AR, p. A39
GREATER BALTIMORE MEDICAL CENTER, BALTIMORE, MD, p. A288
GREATER BINGHAMTON HEALTH CENTER, BINGHAMTON, NY, p. A423
GREATER EL MONTE COMMUNITY HOSPITAL, SOUTH EL MONTE, CA, p. A90
GREATER PEORIA SPECIALTY HOSPITAL, PEORIA, ILLINOIS (see KINDRED HOSPITAL PEORIA), p. A193
GREATER REGIONAL MEDICAL CENTER, CRESTON, IA, p. A220
GREELEY COUNTY HEALTH SERVICES, TRIBUNE, KS, p. A246
GREENBRIER VALLEY MEDICAL CENTER, RONCEVERTE, WV, p. A689
GREENE COUNTY GENERAL HOSPITAL, LINTON, IN, p. A210
GREENE COUNTY HEALTH SYSTEM, EUTAW, AL, p. A17
GREENE COUNTY HOSPITAL, LEAKESVILLE, MS, p. A350
GREENE COUNTY MEDICAL CENTER, JEFFERSON, IA, p. A225
GREENE MEMORIAL HOSPITAL, XENIA, OH, p. A494
GREENEVILLE COMMUNITY HOSPITAL EAST, GREENEVILLE, TN, p. A570
GREENEVILLE COMMUNITY HOSPITAL WEST, GREENEVILLE, TN, p. A570
GREENLEAF BEHAVIORAL HEALTH HOSPITAL, VALDOSTA, GA, p. A162
GREENWICH HOSPITAL, GREENWICH, CT, p. A108
GREENWOOD COUNTY HOSPITAL, EUREKA, KS, p. A235
GREENWOOD LEFLORE HOSPITAL, GREENWOOD, MS, p. A347
GREENWOOD REGIONAL REHABILITATION HOSPITAL, GREENWOOD, SC, p. A554
GREYSTONE PARK PSYCHIATRIC HOSPITAL, MORRIS PLAINS, NJ, p. A408
GRIFFIN HOSPITAL, DERBY, CT, p. A107
GRIFFIN MEMORIAL HOSPITAL, NORMAN, OK, p. A503
GRISELL MEMORIAL HOSPITAL DISTRICT ONE, RANSOM, KS, p. A244
GRITMAN MEDICAL CENTER, MOSCOW, ID, p. A170
GROVE CITY MEDICAL CENTER, GROVE CITY, PA, p. A526
GROVE HILL MEMORIAL HOSPITAL, GROVE HILL, AL, p. A19
GROVER C. DILS MEDICAL CENTER, CALIENTE, NV, p. A393
GROVER M. HERMANN HOSPITAL, CALLICOON, NY, p. A425
GRUNDY COUNTY MEMORIAL HOSPITAL, GRUNDY CENTER, IA, p. A223
GUADALUPE COUNTY HOSPITAL, SANTA ROSA, NM, p. A420
GUADALUPE REGIONAL MEDICAL CENTER, SEGUIN, TX, p. A636
GUAM MEMORIAL HOSPITAL AUTHORITY, TAMUNING, GU, p. A714
GUAM REGIONAL MEDICAL CITY, DEDEDO, GU, p. A714
GUIDANCE CENTER, FLAGSTAFF, AZ, p. A29
GULF BREEZE HOSPITAL, GULF BREEZE, FL, p. A124
GULF COAST MEDICAL CENTER, FORT MYERS, FL, p. A123
GULF COAST REGIONAL MEDICAL CENTER, PANAMA CITY, FL, p. A135
GULF STATES LONG TERM ACUTE CARE OF NEW BRAUNFELS, NEW BRAUNFELS, TEXAS (see POST ACUTE/WARM SPRINGS SPECIALTY HOSPITAL OF NEW BRAUNFELS), p. A626
GULFPORT BEHAVIORAL HEALTH SYSTEM, GULFPORT, MS, p. A347
GUNDERSEN BOSCOBEL AREA HOSPITAL AND CLINICS, BOSCOBEL, WI, p. A692
GUNDERSEN LUTHERAN MEDICAL CENTER, LA CROSSE, WI, p. A697
GUNDERSEN MOUNDVIEW HOSPITAL & CLINICS, FRIENDSHIP, WI, p. A695
GUNDERSEN PALMER LUTHERAN HOSPITAL AND CLINICS, WEST UNION, IA, p. A231
GUNDERSEN ST. JOSEPH'S HOSPITAL AND CLINICS, HILLSBORO, WI, p. A697
GUNDERSEN TRI–COUNTY HOSPITAL AND CLINICS, WHITEHALL, WI, p. A708
GUNNISON VALLEY HOSPITAL, GUNNISON, CO, p. A101
GUNNISON VALLEY HOSPITAL, GUNNISON, UT, p. A648
GUTHRIE CORNING HOSPITAL, CORNING, NY, p. A426
GUTHRIE COUNTY HOSPITAL, GUTHRIE CENTER, IA, p. A223
GUTHRIE ROBERT PACKER HOSPITAL, SAYRE, PA, p. A540
GUTHRIE TOWANDA MEMORIAL HOSPITAL, TOWANDA, PA, p. A542
GUTHRIE TROY COMMUNITY HOSPITAL, TROY, PA, p. A542
GUTTENBERG MUNICIPAL HOSPITAL, GUTTENBERG, IA, p. A223
GWINNETT HOSPITAL SYSTEM, LAWRENCEVILLE, GA, p. A156
GWINNETT MEDICAL CENTER–DULUTH, DULUTH, GA, p. A152

H

H. C. WATKINS MEMORIAL HOSPITAL, QUITMAN, MS, p. A353
H. LEE MOFFITT CANCER CENTER AND RESEARCH INSTITUTE, TAMPA, FL, p. A141
HABERSHAM MEDICAL CENTER, DEMOREST, GA, p. A152
HACIENDA CHILDREN'S HOSPITAL, MESA, AZ, p. A31
HACKENSACK MERIDIAN HEALTH BAYSHORE COMMUNITY HOSPITAL, HOLMDEL, NJ, p. A406
HACKENSACK MERIDIAN HEALTH CARRIER CLINIC, BELLE MEAD, NJ, p. A403
HACKENSACK MERIDIAN HEALTH HACKENSACK UNIVERSITY MEDICAL CENTER, HACKENSACK, NJ, p. A406
HACKENSACK MERIDIAN HEALTH JERSEY SHORE UNIVERSITY MEDICAL CENTER, NEPTUNE, NJ, p. A408
HACKENSACK MERIDIAN HEALTH JFK JOHNSON REHABILITATION INSTITUTE, EDISON, NJ, p. A405
HACKENSACK MERIDIAN HEALTH JFK MEDICAL CENTER, EDISON, NJ, p. A405
HACKENSACK MERIDIAN HEALTH MOUNTAINSIDE MEDICAL CENTER, MONTCLAIR, NJ, p. A408
HACKENSACK MERIDIAN HEALTH OCEAN MEDICAL CENTER, BRICK TOWNSHIP, NJ, p. A404
HACKENSACK MERIDIAN HEALTH PALISADES MEDICAL CENTER, NORTH BERGEN, NJ, p. A410
HACKENSACK MERIDIAN HEALTH PASCACK VALLEY MEDICAL CENTER; WESTWOOD, NJ, p. A415
HACKENSACK MERIDIAN HEALTH RARITAN BAY MEDICAL CENTER, PERTH AMBOY, NJ, p. A411
HACKENSACK MERIDIAN HEALTH RIVERVIEW MEDICAL CENTER, RED BANK, NJ, p. A412
HACKENSACK MERIDIAN HEALTH SHORE REHABILITATION INSTITUTE, BRICK, NJ, p. A403
HACKENSACK MERIDIAN HEALTH SOUTHERN OCEAN MEDICAL CENTER, MANAHAWKIN, NJ, p. A408
HACKETTSTOWN MEDICAL CENTER, HACKETTSTOWN, NJ, p. A406
HAHNEMANN UNIVERSITY HOSPITAL, PHILADELPHIA, PA, p. A534
HALE COUNTY HOSPITAL, GREENSBORO, AL, p. A19
HALE HO'OLA HAMAKUA, HONOKAA, HI, p. A164
HALIFAX HEALTH MEDICAL CENTER OF DAYTONA BEACH, DAYTONA BEACH, FL, p. A121
HALIFAX REGIONAL MEDICAL CENTER, ROANOKE RAPIDS, NC, p. A461
HALLMARK YOUTHCARE – RICHMOND, RICHMOND, VA, p. A666
HAMILTON CENTER, TERRE HAUTE, IN, p. A215
HAMILTON COUNTY HOSPITAL, SYRACUSE, KS, p. A246
HAMILTON GENERAL HOSPITAL, HAMILTON, TX, p. A609
HAMILTON HOSPITAL, OLNEY, TX, p. A627
HAMILTON HOSPITAL, WEBSTER CITY, IOWA (see VAN DIEST MEDICAL CENTER), p. A231
HAMILTON MEDICAL CENTER, DALTON, GA, p. A151
HAMILTON MEMORIAL HOSPITAL DISTRICT, MCLEANSBORO, IL, p. A188
HAMMOND–HENRY HOSPITAL, GENESEO, IL, p. A184
HAMOT MEDICAL CENTER, ERIE, PENNSYLVANIA (see UPMC HAMOT), p. A525
HAMPSHIRE MEMORIAL HOSPITAL, ROMNEY, WV, p. A689
HAMPSTEAD HOSPITAL, HAMPSTEAD, NH, p. A400
HAMPTON BEHAVIORAL HEALTH CENTER, WESTAMPTON, NJ, p. A415
HAMPTON REGIONAL MEDICAL CENTER, VARNVILLE, SC, p. A558
HAMPTON VETERANS AFFAIRS MEDICAL CENTER, HAMPTON, VA, p. A660
HANCOCK COUNTY HEALTH SYSTEM, BRITT, IA, p. A218
HANCOCK COUNTY HOSPITAL, SNEEDVILLE, TN, p. A579
HANCOCK MEDICAL CENTER, BAY SAINT LOUIS, MS, p. A344
HANCOCK REGIONAL HOSPITAL, GREENFIELD, IN, p. A205
HANNIBAL REGIONAL HOSPITAL, HANNIBAL, MO, p. A361
HANOVER HOSPITAL, HANOVER, KS, p. A236
HANS P. PETERSON MEMORIAL HOSPITAL, PHILIP, SOUTH DAKOTA (see PHILIP HEALTH SERVICES), p. A562
HANSEN FAMILY HOSPITAL, IOWA FALLS, IA, p. A225
HANSFORD HOSPITAL, SPEARMAN, TX, p. A637
HARBOR BEACH COMMUNITY HOSPITAL, HARBOR BEACH, MI, p. A314
HARBOR HOSPITAL, BALTIMORE, MARYLAND (see MEDSTAR HARBOR HOSPITAL), p. A286
HARBOR OAKS HOSPITAL, NEW BALTIMORE, MI, p. A318
HARBOR–UCLA MEDICAL CENTER, TORRANCE, CA, p. A91
HARDEMAN COUNTY MEMORIAL HOSPITAL, QUANAH, TX, p. A630

HARDIN COUNTY GENERAL HOSPITAL, ROSICLARE, IL, p. A195
HARDIN MEDICAL CENTER, SAVANNAH, TN, p. A579
HARDIN MEMORIAL HEALTH, ELIZABETHTOWN, KY, p. A251
HARDTNER MEDICAL CENTER, OLLA, LA, p. A276
HARLAN ARH HOSPITAL, HARLAN, KY, p. A253
HARLAN COUNTY HEALTH SYSTEM, ALMA, NE, p. A382
HARLINGEN MEDICAL CENTER, HARLINGEN, TX, p. A609
HARMON MEDICAL AND REHABILITATION HOSPITAL, LAS VEGAS, NV, p. A395
HARMON MEMORIAL HOSPITAL, HOLLIS, OK, p. A500
HARNETT HEALTH SYSTEM, DUNN, NC, p. A452
HARNEY DISTRICT HOSPITAL, BURNS, OR, p. A511
HARPER COUNTY COMMUNITY HOSPITAL, BUFFALO, OK, p. A497
HARPER UNIVERSITY HOSPITAL, DETROIT, MICHIGAN (see DMC HARPER UNIVERSITY HOSPITAL), p. A310
HARRINGTON HOSPITAL, SOUTHBRIDGE, MA, p. A303
HARRIS HEALTH SYSTEM, HOUSTON, TX, p. A611
HARRIS REGIONAL HOSPITAL, SYLVA, NC, p. A463
HARRISBURG MEDICAL CENTER, HARRISBURG, IL, p. A184
HARRISON COMMUNITY HOSPITAL, CADIZ, OH, p. A474
HARRISON COUNTY COMMUNITY HOSPITAL, BETHANY, MO, p. A356
HARRISON COUNTY HOSPITAL, CORYDON, IN, p. A201
HARRISON MEDICAL CENTER, BREMERTON, WA, p. A670
HARRISON MEMORIAL HOSPITAL, CYNTHIANA, KY, p. A251
HARRY S. TRUMAN MEMORIAL VETERANS HOSPITAL, COLUMBIA, MO, p. A359
HARSHA BEHAVIORAL CENTER, TERRE HAUTE, IN, p. A215
HARTFORD HOSPITAL, HARTFORD, CT, p. A108
HARTGROVE HOSPITAL, CHICAGO, IL, p. A177
HASKELL COUNTY COMMUNITY HOSPITAL, STIGLER, OK, p. A507
HASKELL COUNTY HEALTHCARE SYSTEM, STIGLER, OKLAHOMA (see HASKELL COUNTY COMMUNITY HOSPITAL), p. A507
HASKELL MEMORIAL HOSPITAL, HASKELL, TX, p. A609
HAVASU REGIONAL MEDICAL CENTER, LAKE HAVASU CITY, AZ, p. A31
HAVEN BEHAVIORAL HOSPITAL OF EASTERN PENNSYLVANIA, READING, PA, p. A539
HAVEN BEHAVIORAL HOSPITAL OF FRISCO, FRISCO, TX, p. A606
HAVEN BEHAVIORAL HOSPITAL OF PHILADELPHIA, PHILADELPHIA, PA, p. A534
HAVEN BEHAVIORAL SENIOR CARE OF ALBUQUERQUE, ALBUQUERQUE, NM, p. A416
HAVEN BEHAVIORAL SENIOR CARE OF DAYTON, DAYTON, OH, p. A481
HAVEN SENIOR HORIZONS, PHOENIX, AZ, p. A33
HAVENWYCK HOSPITAL, AUBURN HILLS, MI, p. A306
HAWARDEN REGIONAL HEALTHCARE, HAWARDEN, IA, p. A224
HAWKINS COUNTY MEMORIAL HOSPITAL, ROGERSVILLE, TN, p. A579
HAWTHORN CENTER, NORTHVILLE, MI, p. A319
HAWTHORN CHILDREN PSYCHIATRIC HOSPITAL, SAINT LOUIS, MO, p. A369
HAXTUN HOSPITAL DISTRICT, HAXTUN, CO, p. A102
HAYES GREEN BEACH MEMORIAL HOSPITAL, CHARLOTTE, MI, p. A308
HAYS MEDICAL CENTER, HAYS, KS, p. A236
HAYWARD AREA MEMORIAL HOSPITAL AND WATER'S EDGE, HAYWARD, WI, p. A697
HAYWOOD REGIONAL MEDICAL CENTER, CLYDE, NC, p. A452
HAZARD ARH REGIONAL MEDICAL CENTER, HAZARD, KY, p. A253
HAZEL HAWKINS MEMORIAL HOSPITAL, HOLLISTER, CA, p. A61
HCA HOUSTON HEALTHCARE CLEAR LAKE, LEAGUE CITY, TX, p. A620
HCA HOUSTON HEALTHCARE CONROE, CONROE, TX, p. A593
HCA HOUSTON HEALTHCARE NORTHWEST, HOUSTON, TX, p. A611
HCA HOUSTON HEALTHCARE TOMBALL, TOMBALL, TX, p. A641
HEALDSBURG DISTRICT HOSPITAL, HEALDSBURG, CA, p. A61
HEALTH ALLIANCE HOSPITAL – BROADWAY CAMPUS, KINGSTON, NY, p. A430
HEALTH ALLIANCE HOSPITAL – MARY'S AVENUE CAMPUS, KINGSTON, NY, p. A430
HEALTH CENTRAL HOSPITAL, OCOEE, FL, p. A133
HEALTH FIRST CAPE CANAVERAL HOSPITAL, COCOA BEACH, FL, p. A120

HEALTH FIRST HOLMES REGIONAL MEDICAL CENTER, MELBOURNE, FL, p. A129
HEALTH FIRST PALM BAY HOSPITAL, PALM BAY, FL, p. A135
HEALTH FIRST VIERA HOSPITAL, MELBOURNE, FL, p. A129
HEALTHBRIDGE CHILDREN'S HOSPITAL, ORANGE, CA, p. A76
HEALTHBRIDGE CHILDREN'S HOSPITAL OF HOUSTON, HOUSTON, TX, p. A611
HEALTHCENTER NORTHWEST, KALISPELL, MONTANA (see THE HEALTHCENTER), p. A378
HEALTHMARK REGIONAL MEDICAL CENTER, DEFUNIAK SPRINGS, FL, p. A121
HEALTHSOURCE SAGINAW, INC., SAGINAW, MI, p. A321
HEALTHSOUTH CHESAPEAKE REHABILITATION HOSPITAL, SALISBURY, MD, p. A293
HEALTHSOUTH DEACONESS REHABILITATION HOSPITAL, EVANSVILLE, IN, p. A203
HEALTHSOUTH NORTHERN KENTUCKY REHABILITATION HOSPITAL, EDGEWOOD, KY, p. A251
HEALTHSOUTH REHABILITATION HOSPITAL, CUTLER BAY, FL, p. A120
HEALTHSOUTH REHABILITATION HOSPITAL AT DRAKE, CINCINNATI, OH, p. A476
HEALTHSOUTH REHABILITATION HOSPITAL AT MARTIN HEALTH, STUART, FL, p. A140
HEALTHSOUTH REHABILITATION HOSPITAL OF BATON ROUGE, BATON ROUGE, LOUISIANA (see BATON ROUGE REHABILITATION HOSPITAL), p. A263
HEALTHSOUTH REHABILITATION HOSPITAL OF COLORADO SPRINGS, COLORADO SPRINGS, CO, p. A97
HEALTHSOUTH REHABILITATION HOSPITAL OF DAYTON, DAYTON, OH, p. A481
HEALTHSOUTH REHABILITATION HOSPITAL OF LITTLETON, LITTLETON, CO, p. A103
HEALTHSOUTH REHABILITATION HOSPITAL OF MIDDLETOWN, MIDDLETOWN, DE, p. A113
HEALTHSOUTH REHABILITATION HOSPITAL OF NEW MEXICO, ALBUQUERQUE, NM, p. A416
HEALTHSOUTH REHABILITATION HOSPITAL OF TOMS RIVER, TOMS RIVER, NJ, p. A413
HEALTHSOUTH REHABILITATION HOSPITAL OF UTAH, SANDY, UT, p. A653
HEALTHSOUTH REHABILITATION HOSPITAL OF VINELAND, VINELAND, NJ, p. A413
HEALTHSOUTH RIDGELAKE HOSPITAL, SARASOTA, FL, p. A139
HEART HOSPITAL OF LAFAYETTE, LAFAYETTE, LA, p. A270
HEART OF AMERICA MEDICAL CENTER, RUGBY, ND, p. A469
HEART OF TEXAS MEMORIAL HOSPITAL, BRADY, TX, p. A589
HEART OF THE ROCKIES REGIONAL MEDICAL CENTER, SALIDA, CO, p. A105
HEARTLAND BEHAVIORAL HEALTH SERVICES, NEVADA, MO, p. A366
HEARTLAND BEHAVIORAL HEALTHCARE, MASSILLON, OH, p. A487
HEARTLAND REGIONAL MEDICAL CENTER, MARION, IL, p. A188
HEARTLAND SPINE & SPECIALTY HOSPITAL, OVERLAND PARK, KANSAS (see THE UNIVERSITY OF KANSAS HOSPITAL – INDIAN CREEK CAMPUS), p. A243
HEATHERHILL CARE COMMUNITIES, CHARDON, OH, p. A475
HEBER VALLEY HOSPITAL, HEBER CITY, UT, p. A648
HEBREW REHABILITATION CENTER, ROSLINDALE, MA, p. A302
HEBREW SENIOR CARE, WEST HARTFORD, CT, p. A112
HEDRICK MEDICAL CENTER, CHILLICOTHE, MO, p. A358
HEGG HEALTH CENTER AVERA, ROCK VALLEY, IA, p. A229
HELEN HAYES HOSPITAL, WEST HAVERSTRAW, NY, p. A447
HELEN KELLER HOSPITAL, SHEFFIELD, AL, p. A23
HELEN M. SIMPSON REHABILITATION HOSPITAL, HARRISBURG, PA, p. A526
HELEN NEWBERRY JOY HOSPITAL, NEWBERRY, MI, p. A319
HELENA REGIONAL MEDICAL CENTER, HELENA, AR, p. A43
HEMET VALLEY MEDICAL CENTER, HEMET, CA, p. A61
HEMPHILL COUNTY HOSPITAL, CANADIAN, TX, p. A591
HENDERSON COUNTY COMMUNITY HOSPITAL, LEXINGTON, TN, p. A573
HENDERSON HEALTH CARE SERVICES, HENDERSON, NE, p. A386
HENDERSON HOSPITAL, HENDERSON, NV, p. A394
HENDRICK HEALTH SYSTEM, ABILENE, TX, p. A581
HENDRICKS COMMUNITY HOSPITAL ASSOCIATION, HENDRICKS, MN, p. A333
HENDRICKS REGIONAL HEALTH, DANVILLE, IN, p. A202
HENDRY REGIONAL MEDICAL CENTER, CLEWISTON, FL, p. A120
HENNEPIN HEALTHCARE, MINNEAPOLIS, MN, p. A335
HENRICO DOCTORS' HOSPITAL, RICHMOND, VA, p. A666
HENRY COMMUNITY HEALTH, NEW CASTLE, IN, p. A212
HENRY COUNTY HEALTH CENTER, MOUNT PLEASANT, IA, p. A227

HENRY COUNTY HOSPITAL, NAPOLEON, OH, p. A488
HENRY COUNTY MEDICAL CENTER, PARIS, TN, p. A578
HENRY FORD ALLEGIANCE HEALTH, JACKSON, MI, p. A315
HENRY FORD ALLEGIANCE SPECIALTY HOSPITAL, JACKSON, MI, p. A315
HENRY FORD HOSPITAL, DETROIT, MI, p. A310
HENRY FORD KINGSWOOD HOSPITAL, FERNDALE, MI, p. A311
HENRY FORD MACOMB HOSPITALS, CLINTON TOWNSHIP, MI, p. A309
HENRY FORD WEST BLOOMFIELD HOSPITAL, WEST BLOOMFIELD, MI, p. A324
HENRY FORD WYANDOTTE HOSPITAL, WYANDOTTE, MI, p. A325
HENRY MAYO NEWHALL HOSPITAL, VALENCIA, CA, p. A93
HEREFORD REGIONAL MEDICAL CENTER, HEREFORD, TX, p. A610
HERINGTON MUNICIPAL HOSPITAL, HERINGTON, KS, p. A236
HERITAGE OAKS HOSPITAL, SACRAMENTO, CA, p. A81
HERITAGE VALLEY HEALTH SYSTEM, BEAVER, PA, p. A520
HERMANN AREA DISTRICT HOSPITAL, HERMANN, MO, p. A361
HERMANN DRIVE SURGICAL HOSPITAL, HOUSTON, TX, p. A611
HERRIN HOSPITAL, HERRIN, IL, p. A185
HEYWOOD HOSPITAL, GARDNER, MA, p. A299
HI–DESERT MEDICAL CENTER, JOSHUA TREE, CA, p. A62
HIALEAH HOSPITAL, HIALEAH, FL, p. A124
HIAWATHA COMMUNITY HOSPITAL, HIAWATHA, KS, p. A236
HICKORY TRAIL HOSPITAL, DESOTO, TX, p. A600
HIGGINS GENERAL HOSPITAL, BREMEN, GA, p. A148
HIGH POINT MEDICAL CENTER, HIGH POINT, NC, p. A456
HIGHLAND COMMUNITY HOSPITAL, PICAYUNE, MS, p. A353
HIGHLAND DISTRICT HOSPITAL, HILLSBORO, OH, p. A484
HIGHLAND HOSPITAL, CHARLESTON, WV, p. A684
HIGHLAND HOSPITAL, OAKLAND, CA, p. A75
HIGHLAND HOSPITAL, ROCHESTER, NY, p. A442
HIGHLAND RIDGE HOSPITAL, MIDVALE, UT, p. A648
HIGHLAND SPRINGS HOSPITAL, HIGHLAND HILLS, OH, p. A484
HIGHLAND–CLARKSBURG HOSPITAL, CLARKSBURG, WV, p. A684
HIGHLANDS ARH REGIONAL MEDICAL CENTER, PRESTONSBURG, KY, p. A259
HIGHLANDS BEHAVIORAL HEALTH SYSTEM, LITTLETON, CO, p. A103
HIGHLANDS HOSPITAL, CONNELLSVILLE, PA, p. A523
HIGHLANDS MEDICAL CENTER, SCOTTSBORO, AL, p. A23
HIGHLANDS REGIONAL MEDICAL CENTER, SEBRING, FL, p. A139
HIGHLANDS REHABILITATION HOSPITAL, EL PASO, TX, p. A602
HIGHLANDS–CASHIERS HOSPITAL, HIGHLANDS, NC, p. A456
HIGHLINE MEDICAL CENTER, BURIEN, WA, p. A671
HIGHPOINT HEALTH, LAWRENCEBURG, IN, p. A210
HIGHSMITH–RAINEY SPECIALTY HOSPITAL, FAYETTEVILLE, NC, p. A454
HILL COUNTRY MEMORIAL HOSPITAL, FREDERICKSBURG, TX, p. A606
HILL CREST BEHAVIORAL HEALTH SERVICES, BIRMINGHAM, AL, p. A14
HILL HOSPITAL OF SUMTER COUNTY, YORK, AL, p. A24
HILL REGIONAL HOSPITAL, HILLSBORO, TX, p. A610
HILLCREST HOSPITAL – SOUTH, TULSA, OK, p. A508
HILLCREST HOSPITAL, CLEVELAND, OH, p. A477
HILLCREST HOSPITAL CLAREMORE, CLAREMORE, OK, p. A498
HILLCREST HOSPITAL CUSHING, CUSHING, OK, p. A498
HILLCREST HOSPITAL HENRYETTA, HENRYETTA, OK, p. A500
HILLCREST HOSPITAL PRYOR, PRYOR, OK, p. A506
HILLCREST MEDICAL CENTER, TULSA, OK, p. A508
HILLS & DALES GENERAL HOSPITAL, CASS CITY, MI, p. A308
HILLSBORO AREA HOSPITAL, HILLSBORO, IL, p. A185
HILLSBORO COMMUNITY HOSPITAL, HILLSBORO, KS, p. A236
HILLSDALE HOSPITAL, HILLSDALE, MI, p. A314
HILLSIDE REHABILITATION HOSPITAL, WARREN, OH, p. A493
HILO MEDICAL CENTER, HILO, HI, p. A164
HILTON HEAD HOSPITAL, HILTON HEAD ISLAND, SC, p. A554
HIMA SAN PABLO CAGUAS, CAGUAS, PR, p. A715
HIRAM W. DAVIS MEDICAL CENTER, PETERSBURG, VA, p. A665
HOAG MEMORIAL HOSPITAL PRESBYTERIAN, NEWPORT BEACH, CA, p. A74
HOAG ORTHOPEDIC INSTITUTE, IRVINE, CA, p. A62
HOCKING VALLEY COMMUNITY HOSPITAL, LOGAN, OH, p. A485
HODGEMAN COUNTY HEALTH CENTER, JETMORE, KS, p. A237
HOKE HOSPITAL, RAEFORD, NC, p. A460

HOLDENVILLE GENERAL HOSPITAL, HOLDENVILLE, OK, p. A500
HOLLAND HOSPITAL, HOLLAND, MI, p. A314
HOLLY HILL HOSPITAL, RALEIGH, NC, p. A460
HOLLYWOOD PRESBYTERIAN MEDICAL CENTER, LOS ANGELES, CA, p. A67
HOLSTON VALLEY MEDICAL CENTER, KINGSPORT, TN, p. A572
HOLTON COMMUNITY HOSPITAL, HOLTON, KS, p. A237
HOLY CROSS GERMANTOWN HOSPITAL, GERMANTOWN, MD, p. A290
HOLY CROSS HOSPITAL, CHICAGO, IL, p. A177
HOLY CROSS HOSPITAL, FORT LAUDERDALE, FL, p. A122
HOLY CROSS HOSPITAL, SILVER SPRING, MD, p. A293
HOLY CROSS HOSPITAL, TAOS, NM, p. A421
HOLY FAMILY HOSPITAL, METHUEN, MA, p. A300
HOLY FAMILY MEDICAL CENTER, DES PLAINES, ILLINOIS (see AMITA HEALTH HOLY FAMILY MEDICAL CENTER), p. A181
HOLY FAMILY MEMORIAL, MANITOWOC, WI, p. A699
HOLY NAME HOSPITAL, TEANECK, NEW JERSEY (see HOLY NAME MEDICAL CENTER), p. A413
HOLY NAME MEDICAL CENTER, TEANECK, NJ, p. A413
HOLY REDEEMER HOSPITAL, MEADOWBROOK, PA, p. A531
HOLY ROSARY HEALTHCARE, MILES CITY, MT, p. A378
HOLY ROSARY MEDICAL CENTER, ONTARIO, OREGON (see SAINT ALPHONSUS MEDICAL CENTER – ONTARIO), p. A515
HOLYOKE MEDICAL CENTER, HOLYOKE, MA, p. A299
HOLZER MEDICAL CENTER – JACKSON, JACKSON, OH, p. A484
HOLZER MEDICAL CENTER, GALLIPOLIS, OH, p. A483
HONORHEALTH DEER VALLEY MEDICAL CENTER, PHOENIX, AZ, p. A33
HONORHEALTH JOHN C. LINCOLN MEDICAL CENTER, PHOENIX, AZ, p. A33
HONORHEALTH REHABILITATION HOSPITAL, SCOTTSDALE, AZ, p. A35
HONORHEALTH SCOTTSDALE OSBORN MEDICAL CENTER, SCOTTSDALE, AZ, p. A35
HONORHEALTH SCOTTSDALE SHEA MEDICAL CENTER, SCOTTSDALE, AZ, p. A35
HONORHEALTH SCOTTSDALE THOMPSON PEAK MEDICAL CENTER, SCOTTSDALE, AZ, p. A36
HOOD MEMORIAL HOSPITAL, AMITE, LA, p. A262
HOPEDALE MEDICAL COMPLEX, HOPEDALE, IL, p. A186
HOPI HEALTH CARE CENTER, KEAMS CANYON, AZ, p. A30
HORIZON SPECIALTY HOSPITAL, LAS VEGAS, NV, p. A395
HORN MEMORIAL HOSPITAL, IDA GROVE, IA, p. A224
HORSHAM CLINIC, AMBLER, PA, p. A520
HOSPITAL BUEN SAMARITANO, AGUADILLA, PR, p. A714
HOSPITAL CUIDADO AGUDO ESPECIALIZADO EN PACIENTES POLITRAUMATIZADOS, SAN JUAN, PR, p. A718
HOSPITAL DE DAMAS, PONCE, PR, p. A717
HOSPITAL DE LA CONCEPCION, SAN GERMAN, PR, p. A718
HOSPITAL DE LA UNIVERSIDAD DE PUERTO RICO/DR. FEDERICO TRILLA, CAROLINA, PR, p. A715
HOSPITAL DE PSIQUIATRIA, SAN JUAN, PR, p. A718
HOSPITAL DE PSIQUIATRIA FORENSE, PONCE, PR, p. A717
HOSPITAL DEL MAESTRO, SAN JUAN, PR, p. A718
HOSPITAL DISTRICT 6 – HARPER CAMPUS, HARPER, KS, p. A236
HOSPITAL DISTRICT NO 1 OF RICE COUNTY, LYONS, KS, p. A240
HOSPITAL DR. DOMINGUEZ, HUMACAO, PUERTO RICO (see HOSPITAL ORIENTE), p. A716
HOSPITAL EPISCOPAL SAN LUCAS GUAYAMA, GUAYAMA, PR, p. A716
HOSPITAL FOR EXTENDED RECOVERY, NORFOLK, VA, p. A663
HOSPITAL FOR SPECIAL CARE, NEW BRITAIN, CT, p. A109
HOSPITAL HERMANOS MELENDEZ, BAYAMON, PR, p. A715
HOSPITAL HIMA DE HUMACAO, HUMACAO, PR, p. A716
HOSPITAL MANATI MEDICAL CENTER, MANATI, PR, p. A717
HOSPITAL MENONITA DE CAGUAS, CAGUAS, PR, p. A715
HOSPITAL MENONITA DE CAYEY, CAYEY, PR, p. A716
HOSPITAL METROPOLITAN, SAN JUAN, PR, p. A719
HOSPITAL METROPOLITANO DR. SUSONI, ARECIBO, PR, p. A715
HOSPITAL METROPOLITANO SAN GERMAN, SAN GERMAN, PR, p. A718
HOSPITAL OF SAINT RAPHAEL, NEW HAVEN, CT, p. A109
HOSPITAL OF THE UNIVERSITY OF PENNSYLVANIA, PHILADELPHIA, PA, p. A535
HOSPITAL ORIENTE, HUMACAO, PR, p. A716
HOSPITAL PAVIA ARECIBO, ARECIBO, PR, p. A715
HOSPITAL PAVIA YAUCO, YAUCO, PR, p. A720
HOSPITAL PAVIA–HATO REY, SAN JUAN, PR, p. A719
HOSPITAL PAVIA–SANTURCE, SAN JUAN, PR, p. A719
HOSPITAL PEREA, MAYAGUEZ, PR, p. A717

HOSPITAL PSIQUIATRICO CORRECCIONAL, SAN JUAN, PR, p. A719
HOSPITAL PSIQUIATRICO METROPOLITANO, CABO ROJO, PR, p. A715
HOSPITAL SAN ANTONIO, MAYAGUEZ, PR, p. A717
HOSPITAL SAN CARLOS BORROMEO, MOCA, PR, p. A717
HOSPITAL SAN CRISTOBAL, COTO LAUREL, PR, p. A716
HOSPITAL SAN FRANCISCO, SAN JUAN, PR, p. A719
HOSPITAL SAN GERARDO, SAN JUAN, PR, p. A719
HOSPITAL SAN PABLO, BAYAMON, PR, p. A715
HOSPITAL SAN PABLO DEL ESTE, FAJARDO, PR, p. A716
HOSPITAL UNIVERSITARIO DR. RAMON RUIZ ARNAU, BAYAMON, PR, p. A715
HOT SPRINGS COUNTY MEMORIAL HOSPITAL, THERMOPOLIS, WY, p. A713
HOULTON REGIONAL HOSPITAL, HOULTON, ME, p. A283
HOUSTON BEHAVIORAL HEALTHCARE HOSPITAL, HOUSTON, TX, p. A611
HOUSTON COUNTY COMMUNITY HOSPITAL, ERIN, TN, p. A569
HOUSTON MEDICAL CENTER, WARNER ROBINS, GA, p. A163
HOUSTON METHODIST BAYTOWN HOSPITAL, BAYTOWN, TX, p. A587
HOUSTON METHODIST CLEAR LAKE HOSPITAL, NASSAU BAY, TX, p. A626
HOUSTON METHODIST CONTINUING CARE HOSPITAL, KATY, TX, p. A617
HOUSTON METHODIST HOSPITAL, HOUSTON, TX, p. A612
HOUSTON METHODIST SUGAR LAND HOSPITAL, SUGAR LAND, TX, p. A638
HOUSTON METHODIST THE WOODLANDS HOSPITAL, THE WOODLANDS, TX, p. A641
HOUSTON METHODIST WEST HOSPITAL, HOUSTON, TX, p. A612
HOUSTON METHODIST WILLOWBROOK HOSPITAL, HOUSTON, TX, p. A612
HOUSTON PHYSICIANS HOSPITAL, WEBSTER, TX, p. A644
HOWARD COUNTY COMMUNITY HOSPITAL, SAINT PAUL, NEBRASKA (see HOWARD COUNTY MEDICAL CENTER), p. A391
HOWARD COUNTY GENERAL HOSPITAL, COLUMBIA, MD, p. A290
HOWARD COUNTY MEDICAL CENTER, SAINT PAUL, NE, p. A391
HOWARD MEMORIAL HOSPITAL, NASHVILLE, AR, p. A46
HOWARD REGIONAL HEALTH SYSTEM, KOKOMO, INDIANA (see COMMUNITY HOWARD REGIONAL HEALTH), p. A209
HOWARD REGIONAL HEALTH SYSTEM WEST CAMPUS SPECIALTY HOSPITAL, KOKOMO, INDIANA (see COMMUNITY HOWARD SPECIALTY HOSPITAL), p. A209
HOWARD UNIVERSITY HOSPITAL, WASHINGTON, DC, p. A115
HOWARD YOUNG MEDICAL CENTER, WOODRUFF, WI, p. A709
HSHS GOOD SHEPHERD HOSPITAL, SHELBYVILLE, IL, p. A195
HSHS HOLY FAMILY HOSPITAL IN GREENVILLE, GREENVILLE, IL, p. A184
HSHS SACRED HEART HOSPITAL, EAU CLAIRE, WI, p. A694
HSHS ST. ANTHONY'S MEMORIAL HOSPITAL, EFFINGHAM, IL, p. A181
HSHS ST. CLARE MEMORIAL HOSPITAL, OCONTO FALLS, WI, p. A703
HSHS ST. ELIZABETH'S HOSPITAL, O'FALLON, IL, p. A192
HSHS ST. FRANCIS HOSPITAL, LITCHFIELD, IL, p. A188
HSHS ST. JOHN'S HOSPITAL, SPRINGFIELD, IL, p. A196
HSHS ST. JOSEPH'S HOSPITAL, BREESE, IL, p. A174
HSHS ST. JOSEPH'S HOSPITAL, CHIPPEWA FALLS, WI, p. A693
HSHS ST. JOSEPH'S HOSPITAL, HIGHLAND, IL, p. A185
HSHS ST. MARY'S HOSPITAL, DECATUR, IL, p. A181
HSHS ST. MARY'S HOSPITAL MEDICAL CENTER, GREEN BAY, WI, p. A696
HSHS ST. NICHOLAS HOSPITAL, SHEBOYGAN, WI, p. A705
HSHS ST. VINCENT HOSPITAL, GREEN BAY, WI, p. A696
HUDSON COUNTY MEADOWVIEW PSYCHIATRIC HOSPITAL, SECAUCUS, NJ, p. A412
HUDSON HOSPITAL AND CLINIC, HUDSON, WI, p. A697
HUDSON REGIONAL HOSPITAL, SECAUCUS, NJ, p. A412
HUGGINS HOSPITAL, WOLFEBORO, NH, p. A402
HUGH CHATHAM MEMORIAL HOSPITAL, ELKIN, NC, p. A454
HUGHSTON HOSPITAL, COLUMBUS, GA, p. A150
HUHUKAM MEMORIAL HOSPITAL, SACATON, AZ, p. A35
HUMBOLDT COUNTY MEMORIAL HOSPITAL, HUMBOLDT, IA, p. A224
HUMBOLDT COUNTY MENTAL HEALTH, EUREKA, CA, p. A57
HUMBOLDT GENERAL HOSPITAL, WINNEMUCCA, NV, p. A398
HUNT REGIONAL MEDICAL CENTER, GREENVILLE, TX, p. A608
HUNTER HOLMES MCGUIRE VETERANS AFFAIRS MEDICAL CENTER–RICHMOND, RICHMOND, VA, p. A666

HUNTERDON HEALTHCARE, FLEMINGTON, NJ, p. A406
HUNTINGTON BEACH HOSPITAL, HUNTINGTON BEACH, CA, p. A62
HUNTINGTON CREEK RECOVERY CENTER, SHICKSHINNY, PA, p. A541
HUNTINGTON HOSPITAL, HUNTINGTON, NY, p. A429
HUNTINGTON MEMORIAL HOSPITAL, PASADENA, CA, p. A77
HUNTINGTON VETERANS AFFAIRS MEDICAL CENTER, HUNTINGTON, WV, p. A686
HUNTSVILLE HOSPITAL, HUNTSVILLE, AL, p. A19
HUNTSVILLE MEMORIAL HOSPITAL, HUNTSVILLE, TX, p. A615
HURLEY MEDICAL CENTER, FLINT, MI, p. A311
HURON REGIONAL MEDICAL CENTER, HURON, SD, p. A561
HUTCHINSON HEALTH, HUTCHINSON, MN, p. A333
HUTCHINSON REGIONAL MEDICAL CENTER, HUTCHINSON, KS, p. A237

I

I. GONZALEZ MARTINEZ ONCOLOGIC HOSPITAL, HATO REY, PR, p. A716
IBERIA MEDICAL CENTER, NEW IBERIA, LA, p. A274
IBERIA REHABILITATION HOSPITAL, NEW IBERIA, LA, p. A275
ICARE REHABILITATION HOSPITAL, FLOWER MOUND, TX, p. A604
IDAHO ELKS REHABILITATION HOSPITAL, BOISE, IDAHO (see ST. LUKE'S REHABILITATION HOSPITAL), p. A167
ILLINI COMMUNITY HOSPITAL, PITTSFIELD, IL, p. A193
ILLINOIS VALLEY COMMUNITY HOSPITAL, PERU, IL, p. A193
IMPERIAL POINT MEDICAL CENTER, FORT LAUDERDALE, FL, p. A122
INCLINE VILLAGE COMMUNITY HOSPITAL, INCLINE VILLAGE, NV, p. A394
INDIAN HEALTH SERVICE – QUENTIN N. BURDICK MEMORIAL HEALTH CARE FACILITY, BELCOURT, ND, p. A465
INDIAN HEALTH SERVICE HOSPITAL, RAPID CITY, SD, p. A563
INDIAN PATH MEDICAL CENTER, KINGSPORT, TN, p. A572
INDIANA REGIONAL MEDICAL CENTER, INDIANA, PA, p. A528
INDIANA UNIVERSITY HEALTH ARNETT HOSPITAL, LAFAYETTE, IN, p. A209
INDIANA UNIVERSITY HEALTH BALL MEMORIAL HOSPITAL, MUNCIE, IN, p. A212
INDIANA UNIVERSITY HEALTH BEDFORD HOSPITAL, BEDFORD, IN, p. A199
INDIANA UNIVERSITY HEALTH BLACKFORD HOSPITAL, HARTFORD CITY, IN, p. A206
INDIANA UNIVERSITY HEALTH BLOOMINGTON HOSPITAL, BLOOMINGTON, IN, p. A200
INDIANA UNIVERSITY HEALTH FRANKFORT, FRANKFORT, IN, p. A204
INDIANA UNIVERSITY HEALTH JAY HOSPITAL, PORTLAND, IN, p. A213
INDIANA UNIVERSITY HEALTH METHODIST HOSPITAL, FRANKFORT, INDIANA (see INDIANA UNIVERSITY HEALTH UNIVERSITY HOSPITAL), p. A204
INDIANA UNIVERSITY HEALTH NORTH HOSPITAL, CARMEL, IN, p. A201
INDIANA UNIVERSITY HEALTH PAOLI HOSPITAL, PAOLI, IN, p. A213
INDIANA UNIVERSITY HEALTH TIPTON HOSPITAL, TIPTON, IN, p. A215
INDIANA UNIVERSITY HEALTH UNIVERSITY HOSPITAL, INDIANAPOLIS, IN, p. A207
INDIANA UNIVERSITY HEALTH WEST HOSPITAL, AVON, IN, p. A199
INDIANA UNIVERSITY HEALTH WHITE MEMORIAL HOSPITAL, MONTICELLO, IN, p. A211
INDIANA UNIVERSITY HOSPITAL, INDIANAPOLIS, INDIANA (see INDIANA UNIVERSITY HEALTH UNIVERSITY HOSPITAL), p. A207
INDIANHEAD MEDICAL CENTER, SHELL LAKE, WI, p. A705
INDUSTRIAL HOSPITAL, SAN JUAN, PR, p. A719
INFIRMARY LONG TERM ACUTE CARE HOSPITAL, MOBILE, AL, p. A20
INGALLS MEMORIAL HOSPITAL, HARVEY, IL, p. A185
INNOVIS HEALTH, FARGO, NORTH DAKOTA (see ESSENTIA HEALTH FARGO), p. A466
INOVA ALEXANDRIA HOSPITAL, ALEXANDRIA, VA, p. A656
INOVA FAIR OAKS HOSPITAL, FAIRFAX, VA, p. A658
INOVA FAIRFAX HOSPITAL, FALLS CHURCH, VA, p. A659
INOVA LOUDOUN HOSPITAL, LEESBURG, VA, p. A661
INOVA MOUNT VERNON HOSPITAL, ALEXANDRIA, VA, p. A656
INSPIRA MEDICAL CENTER–ELMER, ELMER, NJ, p. A405

INSPIRA MEDICAL CENTER–VINELAND, VINELAND, NJ, p. A413
INSPIRA MEDICAL CENTER–WOODBURY, WOODBURY, NJ, p. A415
INSPIRE PONCE, PONCE, PR, p. A717
INSPIRE SPECIALTY HOSPITAL, MIDWEST CITY, OK, p. A502
INSTITUTE FOR ORTHOPAEDIC SURGERY, LIMA, OH, p. A485
INTEGRIS BAPTIST MEDICAL CENTER, OKLAHOMA CITY, OK, p. A504
INTEGRIS BASS BAPTIST HEALTH CENTER, ENID, OK, p. A499
INTEGRIS BASS BEHAVIORAL HEALTH SYSTEM, ENID, OKLAHOMA (see INTEGRIS BASS MEADOWLAKE), p. A499
INTEGRIS BASS PAVILION, ENID, OK, p. A499
INTEGRIS CANADIAN VALLEY HOSPITAL, YUKON, OK, p. A510
INTEGRIS DEACONESS, OKLAHOMA CITY, OK, p. A504
INTEGRIS GROVE HOSPITAL, GROVE, OK, p. A500
INTEGRIS HEALTH EDMOND, EDMOND, OK, p. A499
INTEGRIS MENTAL HEALTH SYSTEM–SPENCER, SPENCER, OKLAHOMA (see INTEGRIS BAPTIST MEDICAL CENTER), p. A507
INTEGRIS MIAMI HOSPITAL, MIAMI, OK, p. A502
INTEGRIS SOUTHWEST MEDICAL CENTER, OKLAHOMA CITY, OK, p. A504
INTERMOUNTAIN HOSPITAL, BOISE, ID, p. A167
INTERMOUNTAIN MEDICAL CENTER, MURRAY, UT, p. A649
INTRACARE NORTH HOSPITAL, HOUSTON, TX, p. A612
IOWA CITY VETERANS AFFAIRS HEALTH CARE SYSTEM, IOWA CITY, IA, p. A224
IOWA LUTHERAN HOSPITAL, DES MOINES, IOWA (see UNITYPOINT HEALTH–IOWA LUTHERAN HOSPITAL), p. A221
IOWA MEDICAL AND CLASSIFICATION CENTER, CORALVILLE, IA, p. A219
IOWA SPECIALTY HOSPITAL–BELMOND, BELMOND, IA, p. A217
IOWA SPECIALTY HOSPITAL–CLARION, CLARION, IA, p. A219
IRA DAVENPORT MEMORIAL HOSPITAL, BATH, NY, p. A423
IRAAN GENERAL HOSPITAL, IRAAN, TX, p. A615
IREDELL HEALTH SYSTEM, STATESVILLE, NC, p. A463
IRON COUNTY MEDICAL CENTER, PILOT KNOB, MO, p. A367
IROQUOIS MEMORIAL HOSPITAL AND RESIDENT HOME, WATSEKA, IL, p. A197
IRWIN ARMY COMMUNITY HOSPITAL, JUNCTION CITY, KS, p. A237
IRWIN COUNTY HOSPITAL, OCILLA, GA, p. A158
ISLAND HOSPITAL, ANACORTES, WA, p. A670
IVINSON MEMORIAL HOSPITAL, LARAMIE, WY, p. A711
IZARD COUNTY MEDICAL CENTER, CALICO ROCK, AR, p. A40

J

J. ARTHUR DOSHER MEMORIAL HOSPITAL, SOUTHPORT, NC, p. A462
J. C. BLAIR MEMORIAL HOSPITAL, HUNTINGDON, PA, p. A527
J. D. MCCARTY CENTER FOR CHILDREN WITH DEVELOPMENTAL DISABILITIES, NORMAN, OK, p. A503
JACK C. MONTGOMERY VETERANS AFFAIRS MEDICAL CENTER, MUSKOGEE, OK, p. A502
JACK HUGHSTON MEMORIAL HOSPITAL, PHENIX CITY, AL, p. A22
JACKSON BEHAVIORAL HEALTH HOSPITAL, MIAMI, FL, p. A130
JACKSON COUNTY HOSPITAL DISTRICT, EDNA, TX, p. A601
JACKSON COUNTY MEMORIAL HOSPITAL, ALTUS, OK, p. A496
JACKSON COUNTY REGIONAL HEALTH CENTER, MAQUOKETA, IA, p. A226
JACKSON GENERAL HOSPITAL, RIPLEY, WV, p. A689
JACKSON HEALTH SYSTEM, MIAMI, FL, p. A130
JACKSON HOSPITAL, MARIANNA, FL, p. A129
JACKSON HOSPITAL AND CLINIC, MONTGOMERY, AL, p. A21
JACKSON MEDICAL CENTER, JACKSON, AL, p. A20
JACKSON NORTH MEDICAL CENTER, NORTH MIAMI BEACH, FL, p. A133
JACKSON PARISH HOSPITAL, JONESBORO, LA, p. A269
JACKSON PARK HOSPITAL AND MEDICAL CENTER, CHICAGO, IL, p. A177
JACKSON PURCHASE MEDICAL CENTER, MAYFIELD, KY, p. A257
JACKSON SOUTH COMMUNITY HOSPITAL, MIAMI, FL, p. A130
JACKSON–MADISON COUNTY GENERAL HOSPITAL, JACKSON, TN, p. A571

JACOBSON MEMORIAL HOSPITAL CARE CENTER, ELGIN, ND, p. A466
JAMES A. HALEY VETERANS' HOSPITAL–TAMPA, TAMPA, FL, p. A141
JAMES CANCER HOSPITAL AND SOLOVE RESEARCH INSTITUTE, COLUMBUS, OH, p. A479
JAMES E. VAN ZANDT VETERANS AFFAIRS MEDICAL CENTER, ALTOONA, PA, p. A519
JAMES H. QUILLEN VETERANS AFFAIRS MEDICAL CENTER, MOUNTAIN HOME, TN, p. A576
JAMESTOWN REGIONAL MEDICAL CENTER, JAMESTOWN, ND, p. A468
JANE PHILLIPS MEDICAL CENTER, BARTLESVILLE, OK, p. A497
JANE PHILLIPS NOWATA HEALTH CENTER, NOWATA, OK, p. A503
JANE TODD CRAWFORD HOSPITAL, GREENSBURG, KY, p. A252
JASPER GENERAL HOSPITAL, BAY SPRINGS, MS, p. A344
JASPER MEMORIAL HOSPITAL, MONTICELLO, GA, p. A158
JAVON BEA HOSPITAL–ROCKTON, ROCKFORD, IL, p. A194
JAY HOSPITAL, JAY, FL, p. A126
JEANES HOSPITAL, PHILADELPHIA, PA, p. A535
JEFF DAVIS HOSPITAL, HAZLEHURST, GA, p. A154
JEFFERSON COMMUNITY HEALTH AND LIFE, FAIRBURY, NE, p. A384
JEFFERSON COUNTY HEALTH CENTER, FAIRFIELD, IA, p. A222
JEFFERSON COUNTY HOSPITAL, FAYETTE, MS, p. A346
JEFFERSON COUNTY HOSPITAL, WAURIKA, OK, p. A510
JEFFERSON COUNTY MEMORIAL HOSPITAL, WINCHESTER, KANSAS (see F. W. HUSTON MEDICAL CENTER), p. A247
JEFFERSON DAVIS COMMUNITY HOSPITAL, PRENTISS, MS, p. A353
JEFFERSON HEALTH NORTHEAST, PHILADELPHIA, PA, p. A535
JEFFERSON HEALTHCARE, PORT TOWNSEND, WA, p. A676
JEFFERSON HOSPITAL, JEFFERSON HILLS, PA, p. A528
JEFFERSON HOSPITAL, LOUISVILLE, GA, p. A156
JEFFERSON MEDICAL CENTER, RANSON, WV, p. A689
JEFFERSON METHODIST HOSPITAL, PHILADELPHIA, PENNSYLVANIA (see THOMAS JEFFERSON UNIVERSITY HOSPITALS), p. A535
JEFFERSON REGIONAL MEDICAL CENTER, PINE BLUFF, AR, p. A47
JEFFERSON STRATFORD HOSPITAL, STRATFORD, NEW JERSEY (see JEFFERSON STRATFORD HOSPITAL), p. A412
JEFFERSON STRATFORD HOSPITAL, STRATFORD, NJ, p. A413
JEFFERSON WASHINGTON TOWNSHIP HOSPITAL, TURNERSVILLE, NEW JERSEY (see JEFFERSON STRATFORD HOSPITAL), p. A413
JELLICO COMMUNITY HOSPITAL, JELLICO, TN, p. A571
JENKINS COUNTY MEDICAL CENTER, MILLEN, GA, p. A157
JENNERSVILLE HOSPITAL, WEST GROVE, PA, p. A544
JENNIE EDMUNDSON HOSPITAL, COUNCIL BLUFFS, IOWA (see METHODIST JENNIE EDMUNDSON HOSPITAL), p. A220
JENNIE M. MELHAM MEMORIAL MEDICAL CENTER, BROKEN BOW, NE, p. A383
JENNIE STUART MEDICAL CENTER, HOPKINSVILLE, KY, p. A253
JENNINGS AMERICAN LEGION HOSPITAL, JENNINGS, LA, p. A269
JENNINGS SENIOR CARE HOSPITAL, JENNINGS, LA, p. A269
JEROLD PHELPS COMMUNITY HOSPITAL, GARBERVILLE, CA, p. A60
JEROME GOLDEN CENTER FOR BEHAVIORAL HEALTH, INC., WEST PALM BEACH, FL, p. A144
JERSEY CITY MEDICAL CENTER, JERSEY CITY, NJ, p. A407
JERSEY COMMUNITY HOSPITAL, JERSEYVILLE, IL, p. A186
JESSE BROWN VETERANS AFFAIRS MEDICAL CENTER, CHICAGO, IL, p. A177
JEWELL COUNTY HOSPITAL, MANKATO, KS, p. A240
JEWISH HOME OF SAN FRANCISCO, SAN FRANCISCO, CA, p. A85
JEWISH HOSPITAL, LOUISVILLE, KY, p. A256
JEWISH HOSPITAL–SHELBYVILLE, SHELBYVILLE, KY, p. A260
JFK MEDICAL CENTER, ATLANTIS, FL, p. A117
JFK MEDICAL CENTER NORTH CAMPUS, WEST PALM BEACH, FL, p. A144
JIM TALIAFERRO COMMUNITY MENTAL HEALTH, LAWTON, OK, p. A501
JOHN C. FREMONT HEALTHCARE DISTRICT, MARIPOSA, CA, p. A71
JOHN C. STENNIS MEMORIAL HOSPITAL, DE KALB, MS, p. A346
JOHN D. ARCHBOLD MEMORIAL HOSPITAL, THOMASVILLE, GA, p. A161

JOHN D. DINGELL VETERANS AFFAIRS MEDICAL CENTER, DETROIT, MI, p. A310
JOHN F. KENNEDY MEMORIAL HOSPITAL, INDIO, CA, p. A62
JOHN H. STROGER JR. HOSPITAL OF COOK COUNTY, CHICAGO, IL, p. A177
JOHN HEINZ INSTITUTE OF REHABILITATION MEDICINE, WILKES, PA, p. A545
JOHN J. MADDEN MENTAL HEALTH CENTER, HINES, IL, p. A185
JOHN J. PERSHING VETERANS AFFAIRS MEDICAL CENTER, POPLAR BLUFF, MO, p. A367
JOHN MUIR BEHAVIORAL HEALTH CENTER, CONCORD, CA, p. A55
JOHN MUIR MEDICAL CENTER, CONCORD, CONCORD, CA, p. A55
JOHN MUIR MEDICAL CENTER, WALNUT CREEK, WALNUT CREEK, CA, p. A94
JOHN PETER SMITH HOSPITAL, FORT WORTH, TEXAS (see JPS HEALTH NETWORK), p. A605
JOHN RANDOLPH MEDICAL CENTER, HOPEWELL, VA, p. A661
JOHN T. MATHER MEMORIAL HOSPITAL, PORT JEFFERSON, NY, p. A441
JOHNS COMMUNITY HOSPITAL, TAYLOR, TEXAS (see BAYLOR SCOTT & WHITE MEDICAL CENTER – TAYLOR), p. A639
JOHNS HOPKINS ALL CHILDREN'S HOSPITAL, SAINT PETERSBURG, FL, p. A138
JOHNS HOPKINS BAYVIEW MEDICAL CENTER, BALTIMORE, MD, p. A286
JOHNS HOPKINS HOSPITAL, BALTIMORE, MD, p. A286
JOHNSON CITY MEDICAL CENTER, JOHNSON CITY, TN, p. A571
JOHNSON COUNTY COMMUNITY HOSPITAL, MOUNTAIN CITY, TN, p. A576
JOHNSON COUNTY HEALTHCARE CENTER, BUFFALO, WY, p. A710
JOHNSON COUNTY HOSPITAL, TECUMSEH, NE, p. A392
JOHNSON MEMORIAL HEALTH SERVICES, DAWSON, MN, p. A330
JOHNSON MEMORIAL HOSPITAL, FRANKLIN, IN, p. A204
JOHNSON MEMORIAL MEDICAL CENTER, STAFFORD SPRINGS, CT, p. A111
JOHNSON REGIONAL MEDICAL CENTER, CLARKSVILLE, AR, p. A40
JOHNSTON HEALTH, SMITHFIELD, NC, p. A462
JOHNSTON MEMORIAL HOSPITAL, ABINGDON, VA, p. A656
JOHNSTON MEMORIAL HOSPITAL, TISHOMINGO, OKLAHOMA (see MERCY HOSPITAL TISHOMINGO), p. A508
JOHNSTON R. BOWMAN HEALTH CENTER, CHICAGO, ILLINOIS (see RUSH UNIVERSITY MEDICAL CENTER), p. A178
JOHNSTON–WILLIS HOSPITAL, RICHMOND, VIRGINIA (see CHIPPENHAM HOSPITAL), p. A666
JOINT TOWNSHIP DISTRICT MEMORIAL HOSPITAL, SAINT MARYS, OH, p. A490
JONES MEMORIAL HOSPITAL, WELLSVILLE, NY, p. A447
JORDAN VALLEY MEDICAL CENTER, WEST JORDAN, UT, p. A653
JORDAN VALLEY MEDICAL CENTER WEST VALLEY CAMPUS, WEST VALLEY CITY, UT, p. A653
JOYCE EISENBERG–KEEFER MEDICAL CENTER, RESEDA, CA, p. A80
JPS HEALTH NETWORK, FORT WORTH, TX, p. A605
JULIAN F. KEITH ALCOHOL AND DRUG ABUSE TREATMENT CENTER, BLACK MOUNTAIN, NC, p. A450
JUPITER MEDICAL CENTER, JUPITER, FL, p. A126

K

KADLEC REGIONAL MEDICAL CENTER, RICHLAND, WA, p. A677
KAHUKU MEDICAL CENTER, KAHUKU, HI, p. A165
KAISER FOUNDATION HOSPITAL, MARTINEZ, CA, p. A71
KAISER FOUNDATION MENTAL HEALTH CENTER, LOS ANGELES, CA, p. A67
KAISER PERMANENTE ANTIOCH MEDICAL CENTER, ANTIOCH, CA, p. A50
KAISER PERMANENTE BALDWIN PARK MEDICAL CENTER, BALDWIN PARK, CA, p. A51
KAISER PERMANENTE CAPITOL HILL CAMPUS, SEATTLE, WA, p. A677
KAISER PERMANENTE DOWNEY MEDICAL CENTER, DOWNEY, CA, p. A56
KAISER PERMANENTE FONTANA MEDICAL CENTER, FONTANA, CA, p. A58

KAISER PERMANENTE FREMONT MEDICAL CENTER, FREMONT, CA, p. A59
KAISER PERMANENTE FRESNO MEDICAL CENTER, FRESNO, CA, p. A59
KAISER PERMANENTE LOS ANGELES MEDICAL CENTER, LOS ANGELES, CA, p. A67
KAISER PERMANENTE MANTECA MEDICAL CENTER, MANTECA, CA, p. A71
KAISER PERMANENTE MEDICAL CENTER, HONOLULU, HI, p. A164
KAISER PERMANENTE MORENO VALLEY MEDICAL CENTER, MORENO VALLEY, CA, p. A73
KAISER PERMANENTE OAKLAND MEDICAL CENTER, OAKLAND, CA, p. A75
KAISER PERMANENTE ORANGE COUNTY ANAHEIM MEDICAL CENTER, ANAHEIM, CA, p. A50
KAISER PERMANENTE PANORAMA CITY MEDICAL CENTER, LOS ANGELES, CA, p. A67
KAISER PERMANENTE REDWOOD CITY MEDICAL CENTER, REDWOOD CITY, CA, p. A80
KAISER PERMANENTE RICHMOND MEDICAL CENTER, RICHMOND, CA, p. A80
KAISER PERMANENTE RIVERSIDE MEDICAL CENTER, RIVERSIDE, CA, p. A81
KAISER PERMANENTE ROSEVILLE MEDICAL CENTER, ROSEVILLE, CA, p. A81
KAISER PERMANENTE SACRAMENTO MEDICAL CENTER, SACRAMENTO, CA, p. A81
KAISER PERMANENTE SAN DIEGO MEDICAL CENTER, SAN DIEGO, CA, p. A83
KAISER PERMANENTE SAN FRANCISCO MEDICAL CENTER, SAN FRANCISCO, CA, p. A85
KAISER PERMANENTE SAN JOSE MEDICAL CENTER, SAN JOSE, CA, p. A86
KAISER PERMANENTE SAN LEANDRO MEDICAL CENTER, SAN LEANDRO, CA, p. A87
KAISER PERMANENTE SAN RAFAEL MEDICAL CENTER, SAN RAFAEL, CA, p. A87
KAISER PERMANENTE SANTA CLARA MEDICAL CENTER, SANTA CLARA, CA, p. A88
KAISER PERMANENTE SANTA ROSA MEDICAL CENTER, SANTA ROSA, CA, p. A89
KAISER PERMANENTE SOUTH BAY MEDICAL CENTER, LOS ANGELES, CA, p. A67
KAISER PERMANENTE SOUTH SACRAMENTO MEDICAL CENTER, SACRAMENTO, CA, p. A82
KAISER PERMANENTE SOUTH SAN FRANCISCO, SOUTH SAN FRANCISCO, CA, p. A90
KAISER PERMANENTE VACAVILLE MEDICAL CENTER, VACAVILLE, CA, p. A93
KAISER PERMANENTE VALLEJO MEDICAL CENTER, VALLEJO, CA, p. A93
KAISER PERMANENTE WALNUT CREEK MEDICAL CENTER, WALNUT CREEK, CA, p. A94
KAISER PERMANENTE WEST LOS ANGELES MEDICAL CENTER, LOS ANGELES, CA, p. A67
KAISER PERMANENTE WOODLAND HILLS MEDICAL CENTER, LOS ANGELES, CA, p. A67
KAISER SUNNYSIDE MEDICAL CENTER, CLACKAMAS, OR, p. A512
KAISER WESTSIDE MEDICAL CENTER, HILLSBORO, OR, p. A513
KALAMAZOO PSYCHIATRIC HOSPITAL, KALAMAZOO, MI, p. A316
KALEIDA HEALTH, BUFFALO, NY, p. A424
KALISPELL REGIONAL HEALTHCARE, KALISPELL, MT, p. A378
KALKASKA MEMORIAL HEALTH CENTER, KALKASKA, MI, p. A316
KANE COUNTY HOSPITAL, KANAB, UT, p. A648
KANSAS CITY ORTHOPAEDIC INSTITUTE, LEAWOOD, KS, p. A239
KANSAS CITY VETERANS AFFAIRS MEDICAL CENTER, KANSAS CITY, MO, p. A362
KANSAS HEART HOSPITAL, WICHITA, KS, p. A247
KANSAS MEDICAL CENTER, ANDOVER, KS, p. A232
KANSAS NEUROLOGICAL INSTITUTE, TOPEKA, KS, p. A246
KANSAS REHABILITATION HOSPITAL, TOPEKA, KS, p. A246
KANSAS SPINE AND SPECIALTY HOSPITAL, WICHITA, KS, p. A248
KANSAS SURGERY AND RECOVERY CENTER, WICHITA, KS, p. A248
KAPIOLANI MEDICAL CENTER FOR WOMEN & CHILDREN, HONOLULU, HI, p. A164
KARMANOS CANCER CENTER, DETROIT, MI, p. A310
KATE DISHMAN REHABILITATION HOSPITAL, BEAUMONT, TX, p. A587
KATHERINE SHAW BETHEA HOSPITAL, DIXON, IL, p. A181
KAUAI VETERANS MEMORIAL HOSPITAL, WAIMEA, HI, p. A166

KAWEAH DELTA MEDICAL CENTER, VISALIA, CA, p. A94
KA'U HOSPITAL, PAHALA, HI, p. A166
KEARNEY COUNTY HEALTH SERVICES, MINDEN, NE, p. A387
KEARNEY REGIONAL MEDICAL CENTER, KEARNEY, NE, p. A386
KEARNY COUNTY HOSPITAL, LAKIN, KS, p. A238
KECK HOSPITAL OF USC, LOS ANGELES, CA, p. A67
KEDREN COMMUNITY MENTAL HEALTH CENTER, LOS ANGELES, CA, p. A67
KEEFE MEMORIAL HOSPITAL, CHEYENNE WELLS, CO, p. A97
KELL WEST REGIONAL HOSPITAL, WICHITA FALLS, TX, p. A645
KELLER ARMY COMMUNITY HOSPITAL, WEST POINT, NY, p. A447
KEMPSVILLE CENTER FOR BEHAVIORAL HEALTH, NORFOLK, VA, p. A664
KENDALL REGIONAL MEDICAL CENTER, MIAMI, FL, p. A130
KENMARE COMMUNITY HOSPITAL, KENMARE, ND, p. A468
KENMORE MERCY HOSPITAL, KENMORE, NY, p. A430
KENNEDY KRIEGER INSTITUTE, BALTIMORE, MD, p. A286
KENNEDY MEMORIAL HOSPITALS–UNIVERSITY MEDICAL CENTER, STRATFORD, NEW JERSEY (see JEFFERSON STRATFORD HOSPITAL), p. A413
KENSINGTON HOSPITAL, PHILADELPHIA, PA, p. A535
KENT COUNTY MEMORIAL HOSPITAL, WARWICK, RI, p. A548
KENTFIELD REHABILITATION AND SPECIALTY HOSPITAL, KENTFIELD, CA, p. A62
KENTUCKY RIVER MEDICAL CENTER, JACKSON, KY, p. A254
KEOKUK COUNTY HEALTH CENTER, SIGOURNEY, IA, p. A229
KERN MEDICAL CENTER, BAKERSFIELD, CA, p. A52
KERN VALLEY HEALTHCARE DISTRICT, LAKE ISABELLA, CA, p. A63
KERRVILLE DIVISION, KERRVILLE, TEXAS (see SOUTH TEXAS VETERANS HEALTH CARE SYSTEM), p. A617
KERRVILLE STATE HOSPITAL, KERRVILLE, TX, p. A617
KERSHAWHEALTH, CAMDEN, SC, p. A549
KESSLER INSTITUTE FOR REHABILITATION, CHESTER, NEW JERSEY (see KESSLER INSTITUTE FOR REHABILITATION), p. A404
KESSLER INSTITUTE FOR REHABILITATION, SADDLE BROOK, NEW JERSEY (see KESSLER INSTITUTE FOR REHABILITATION), p. A412
KESSLER INSTITUTE FOR REHABILITATION, WEST ORANGE, NEW JERSEY (see KESSLER INSTITUTE FOR REHABILITATION), p. A414
KESSLER INSTITUTE FOR REHABILITATION, WEST ORANGE, NJ, p. A414
KESSLER MARLTON REHABILITATION, MARLTON, NJ, p. A408
KETTERING MEDICAL CENTER, KETTERING, OH, p. A485
KIDSPEACE CHILDREN'S HOSPITAL, OREFIELD, PA, p. A533
KIMBALL HEALTH SERVICES, KIMBALL, NE, p. A386
KIMBLE HOSPITAL, JUNCTION, TX, p. A617
KINDRED CHICAGO LAKESHORE, CHICAGO, ILLINOIS (see KINDRED CHICAGO–CENTRAL HOSPITAL), p. A178
KINDRED CHICAGO–CENTRAL HOSPITAL, CHICAGO, IL, p. A178
KINDRED HOSPITAL BAY AREA–TAMPA, TAMPA, FL, p. A141
KINDRED HOSPITAL CENTRAL TAMPA, TAMPA, FL, p. A141
KINDRED HOSPITAL CHICAGO NORTH, CHICAGO, ILLINOIS (see KINDRED CHICAGO–CENTRAL HOSPITAL), p. A178
KINDRED HOSPITAL CHICAGO–NORTHLAKE, NORTHLAKE, IL, p. A191
KINDRED HOSPITAL CLEAR LAKE, WEBSTER, TX, p. A644
KINDRED HOSPITAL DALLAS CENTRAL, DALLAS, TX, p. A596
KINDRED HOSPITAL DENVER SOUTH, DENVER, CO, p. A99
KINDRED HOSPITAL EL PASO, EL PASO, TX, p. A602
KINDRED HOSPITAL FARGO, FARGO, NORTH DAKOTA (see VIBRA HOSPITAL OF FARGO), p. A466
KINDRED HOSPITAL HOUSTON MEDICAL CENTER, HOUSTON, TX, p. A612
KINDRED HOSPITAL INDIANAPOLIS NORTH, INDIANAPOLIS, IN, p. A207
KINDRED HOSPITAL LAS VEGAS–SAHARA, HENDERSON, NV, p. A394
KINDRED HOSPITAL LIMA, LIMA, OH, p. A485
KINDRED HOSPITAL LOUISVILLE AT JEWISH HOSPITAL, LOUISVILLE, KENTUCKY (see KINDRED HOSPITAL–LOUISVILLE), p. A256
KINDRED HOSPITAL MELBOURNE, MELBOURNE, FL, p. A129
KINDRED HOSPITAL NEW JERSEY – RAHWAY, RAHWAY, NEW JERSEY (see KINDRED HOSPITAL–NEW JERSEY MORRIS COUNTY), p. A411
KINDRED HOSPITAL NEW JERSEY – WAYNE, WAYNE, NEW JERSEY (see KINDRED HOSPITAL–NEW JERSEY MORRIS COUNTY), p. A414
KINDRED HOSPITAL NORTH FLORIDA, GREEN COVE SPRINGS, FL, p. A124
KINDRED HOSPITAL NORTHLAND, KANSAS CITY, MO, p. A362

KINDRED HOSPITAL NORTHWEST INDIANA, HAMMOND, IN, p. A205
KINDRED HOSPITAL OCALA, OCALA, FL, p. A133
KINDRED HOSPITAL PARK VIEW, SPRINGFIELD, MASSACHUSETTS (see VIBRA HOSPITAL OF WESTERN MASSACHUSETTS), p. A303
KINDRED HOSPITAL PEORIA, PEORIA, IL, p. A193
KINDRED HOSPITAL RANCHO, RANCHO CUCAMONGA, CA, p. A79
KINDRED HOSPITAL RICHMOND, RICHMOND, VIRGINIA (see VIBRA HOSPITAL OF RICHMOND), p. A666
KINDRED HOSPITAL RIVERSIDE, PERRIS, CA, p. A78
KINDRED HOSPITAL ROME, ROME, GA, p. A159
KINDRED HOSPITAL SAN ANTONIO CENTRAL, SAN ANTONIO, TX, p. A634
KINDRED HOSPITAL SEATTLE–NORTHGATE, SEATTLE, WA, p. A677
KINDRED HOSPITAL SOUTH BAY, GARDENA, CA, p. A60
KINDRED HOSPITAL SOUTH FLORIDA–FORT LAUDERDALE, FORT LAUDERDALE, FL, p. A123
KINDRED HOSPITAL SOUTH PHILADELPHIA, PHILADELPHIA, PA, p. A535
KINDRED HOSPITAL SUGAR LAND, SUGAR LAND, TX, p. A638
KINDRED HOSPITAL TARRANT COUNTY–ARLINGTON, ARLINGTON, TX, p. A583
KINDRED HOSPITAL THE PALM BEACHES, RIVIERA BEACH, FL, p. A137
KINDRED HOSPITAL TOMBALL, TOMBALL, TX, p. A641
KINDRED HOSPITAL–ALBUQUERQUE, ALBUQUERQUE, NM, p. A416
KINDRED HOSPITAL–AMARILLO, AMARILLO, TEXAS (see VIBRA HOSPITAL OF AMARILLO), p. A582
KINDRED HOSPITAL–AURORA, AURORA, CO, p. A96
KINDRED HOSPITAL–BALDWIN PARK, BALDWIN PARK, CA, p. A51
KINDRED HOSPITAL–BREA, BREA, CA, p. A53
KINDRED HOSPITAL–CHARLESTON, MT. PLEASANT, SOUTH CAROLINA (see VIBRA HOSPITAL OF CHARLESTON), p. A555
KINDRED HOSPITAL–CHATTANOOGA, CHATTANOOGA, TN, p. A567
KINDRED HOSPITAL–CORPUS CHRISTI, CORPUS CHRISTI, TEXAS (see PAM SPECIALTY HOSPITAL OF CORPUS CHRISTI SOUTH), p. A594
KINDRED HOSPITAL–DALLAS, DALLAS, TX, p. A596
KINDRED HOSPITAL–DAYTON, DAYTON, OH, p. A481
KINDRED HOSPITAL–DENVER, DENVER, CO, p. A99
KINDRED HOSPITAL–FORT WORTH, FORT WORTH, TX, p. A605
KINDRED HOSPITAL–GREENSBORO, GREENSBORO, NC, p. A455
KINDRED HOSPITAL–HOUSTON NORTHWEST, HOUSTON, TX, p. A612
KINDRED HOSPITAL–INDIANAPOLIS, INDIANAPOLIS, IN, p. A207
KINDRED HOSPITAL–LA MIRADA, LA MIRADA, CA, p. A63
KINDRED HOSPITAL–LOS ANGELES, LOS ANGELES, CA, p. A67
KINDRED HOSPITAL–LOUISVILLE, LOUISVILLE, KY, p. A256
KINDRED HOSPITAL–MANSFIELD, MANSFIELD, TX, p. A623
KINDRED HOSPITAL–MILWAUKEE, GREENFIELD, WISCONSIN (see POST ACUTE MEDICAL SPECIALTY HOSPITAL OF MILWAUKEE), p. A696
KINDRED HOSPITAL–NEW JERSEY MORRIS COUNTY, DOVER, NJ, p. A404
KINDRED HOSPITAL–ONTARIO, ONTARIO, CA, p. A76
KINDRED HOSPITAL–PHILADELPHIA, PHILADELPHIA, PA, p. A535
KINDRED HOSPITAL–SAN ANTONIO, SAN ANTONIO, TX, p. A634
KINDRED HOSPITAL–SAN DIEGO, SAN DIEGO, CA, p. A83
KINDRED HOSPITAL–SAN FRANCISCO BAY AREA, SAN LEANDRO, CA, p. A87
KINDRED HOSPITAL–ST. LOUIS, SAINT LOUIS, MO, p. A369
KINDRED HOSPITAL–SYCAMORE, SYCAMORE, IL, p. A197
KINDRED HOSPITAL–WESTMINSTER, WESTMINSTER, CA, p. A94
KINDRED REHABILITATION HOSPITAL AMARILLO, AMARILLO, TEXAS (see VIBRA REHABILITATION HOSPITAL OF AMARILLO), p. A582
KINDRED REHABILITATION HOSPITAL CLEAR LAKE, WEBSTER, TX, p. A645
KINDRED REHABILITATION HOSPITAL NORTHEAST HOUSTON, HUMBLE, TX, p. A615
KINGMAN COMMUNITY HOSPITAL, KINGMAN, KS, p. A238
KINGMAN REGIONAL MEDICAL CENTER, KINGMAN, AZ, p. A30
KINGSTON HOSPITAL, KINGSTON, NEW YORK (see HEALTH ALLIANCE HOSPITAL – BROADWAY CAMPUS), p. A430
KINGWOOD EMERGENCY HOSPITAL, KINGWOOD, TX, p. A618

KINGWOOD MEDICAL CENTER, KINGWOOD, TX, p. A618
KINGWOOD PINES HOSPITAL, KINGWOOD, TX, p. A618
KINGWOOD SPECIALTY HOSPITAL, KINGWOOD, TEXAS (see MEMORIAL HERMANN SURGICAL HOSPITAL KINGWOOD), p. A618
KING'S DAUGHTERS MEDICAL CENTER, ASHLAND, KY, p. A249
KING'S DAUGHTERS MEDICAL CENTER, BROOKHAVEN, MS, p. A345
KING'S DAUGHTERS MEDICAL CENTER OHIO, PORTSMOUTH, OH, p. A490
KING'S DAUGHTERS' HEALTH, MADISON, IN, p. A210
KIOWA COUNTY MEMORIAL HOSPITAL, GREENSBURG, KS, p. A236
KIOWA DISTRICT HEALTHCARE, KIOWA, KS, p. A238
KIRBY MEDICAL CENTER, MONTICELLO, IL, p. A190
KIRKBRIDE CENTER, PHILADELPHIA, PA, p. A535
KIT CARSON COUNTY HEALTH SERVICE DISTRICT, BURLINGTON, CO, p. A97
KITTITAS VALLEY HEALTHCARE, ELLENSBURG, WA, p. A672
KITTSON MEMORIAL HEALTHCARE CENTER, HALLOCK, MN, p. A333
KLICKITAT VALLEY HEALTH, GOLDENDALE, WA, p. A673
KNAPP MEDICAL CENTER, WESLACO, TX, p. A645
KNOX COMMUNITY HOSPITAL, MOUNT VERNON, OH, p. A488
KNOX COUNTY HOSPITAL, KNOX CITY, TX, p. A618
KNOXVILLE DIVISION, KNOXVILLE, IOWA (see VETERANS AFFAIRS CENTRAL IOWA HEALTH CARE SYSTEM), p. A225
KNOXVILLE HOSPITAL & CLINICS, KNOXVILLE, IA, p. A225
KOHALA HOSPITAL, KOHALA, HI, p. A166
KONA COMMUNITY HOSPITAL, KEALAKEKUA, HI, p. A166
KOOTENAI HEALTH, COEUR D'ALENE, ID, p. A169
KOSCIUSKO COMMUNITY HOSPITAL, WARSAW, IN, p. A216
KOSSUTH REGIONAL HEALTH CENTER, ALGONA, IA, p. A217
KUAKINI MEDICAL CENTER, HONOLULU, HI, p. A164
KULA HOSPITAL, KULA, HI, p. A166
KVC PRAIRIE RIDGE PSYCHIATRIC HOSPITAL, KANSAS CITY, KS, p. A238
KWAJALEIN HOSPITAL, KWAJALEIN ISLAND, MH, p. A714

L

LA PALMA INTERCOMMUNITY HOSPITAL, LA PALMA, CA, p. A63
LA PAZ REGIONAL HOSPITAL, PARKER, AZ, p. A32
LA PORTE HOSPITAL, LA PORTE, IN, p. A209
LA PORTE REGIONAL HEALTH SYSTEM, LA PORTE, INDIANA (see LA PORTE HOSPITAL), p. A209
LA RABIDA CHILDREN'S HOSPITAL, CHICAGO, IL, p. A178
LABETTE HEALTH, PARSONS, KS, p. A243
LAC+USC MEDICAL CENTER, LOS ANGELES, CA, p. A68
LAC–OLIVE VIEW–UCLA MEDICAL CENTER, LOS ANGELES, CA, p. A68
LACKEY MEMORIAL HOSPITAL, FOREST, MS, p. A347
LADY OF THE SEA GENERAL HOSPITAL, CUT OFF, LA, p. A266
LAFAYETTE GENERAL MEDICAL CENTER, LAFAYETTE, LA, p. A271
LAFAYETTE GENERAL SURGICAL HOSPITAL, LAFAYETTE, LA, p. A271
LAFAYETTE PHYSICAL REHABILITATION HOSPITAL, LAFAYETTE, LA, p. A271
LAFAYETTE REGIONAL HEALTH CENTER, LEXINGTON, MO, p. A364
LAFAYETTE REGIONAL REHABILITATION HOSPITAL, LAFAYETTE, IN, p. A209
LAFAYETTE SURGICAL SPECIALTY HOSPITAL, LAFAYETTE, LA, p. A271
LAGUNA HONDA HOSPITAL AND REHABILITATION CENTER, SAN FRANCISCO, CA, p. A85
LAHEY HOSPITAL & MEDICAL CENTER, BURLINGTON, BURLINGTON, MA, p. A297
LAIRD HOSPITAL, UNION, MS, p. A354
LAKE BUTLER HOSPITAL HAND SURGERY CENTER, LAKE BUTLER, FL, p. A127
LAKE CHARLES MEMORIAL HOSPITAL, LAKE CHARLES, LA, p. A272
LAKE CHELAN COMMUNITY HOSPITAL AND CLINICS, CHELAN, WA, p. A671
LAKE CITY COMMUNITY HOSPITAL, LAKE CITY, SC, p. A555
LAKE CITY MEDICAL CENTER, LAKE CITY, FL, p. A127
LAKE CUMBERLAND REGIONAL HOSPITAL, SOMERSET, KY, p. A260
LAKE DISTRICT HOSPITAL, LAKEVIEW, OR, p. A514

LAKE FOREST HOSPITAL, LAKE FOREST, ILLINOIS (see NORTHWESTERN MEDICINE LAKE FOREST HOSPITAL), p. A187
LAKE GRANBURY MEDICAL CENTER, GRANBURY, TX, p. A608
LAKE HEALTH, CONCORD TOWNSHIP, OH, p. A480
LAKE HURON MEDICAL CENTER, PORT HURON, MI, p. A320
LAKE MARTIN COMMUNITY HOSPITAL, DADEVILLE, AL, p. A16
LAKE NORMAN REGIONAL MEDICAL CENTER, MOORESVILLE, NC, p. A458
LAKE PINES HOSPITAL, KENNER, LA, p. A270
LAKE REGION HEALTHCARE, FERGUS FALLS, MN, p. A332
LAKE REGIONAL HEALTH SYSTEM, OSAGE BEACH, MO, p. A366
LAKE TAYLOR TRANSITIONAL CARE HOSPITAL, NORFOLK, VA, p. A664
LAKE VIEW HOSPITAL, TWO HARBORS, MN, p. A341
LAKELAND BEHAVIORAL HEALTH SYSTEM, SPRINGFIELD, MO, p. A371
LAKELAND COMMUNITY HOSPITAL, HALEYVILLE, AL, p. A19
LAKELAND HOSPITAL, WATERVLIET, WATERVLIET, MI, p. A324
LAKELAND REGIONAL HEALTH MEDICAL CENTER, LAKELAND, FL, p. A127
LAKES REGION GENERAL HOSPITAL, LACONIA, NH, p. A400
LAKES REGIONAL HEALTHCARE, SPIRIT LAKE, IA, p. A230
LAKESIDE BEHAVIORAL HEALTH SYSTEM, MEMPHIS, TN, p. A575
LAKESIDE MEDICAL CENTER, BELLE GLADE, FL, p. A117
LAKESIDE WOMEN'S HOSPITAL, OKLAHOMA CITY, OK, p. A504
LAKEVIEW BEHAVIORAL HEALTH, NORCROSS, GA, p. A158
LAKEVIEW HOSPITAL, BOUNTIFUL, UT, p. A647
LAKEVIEW HOSPITAL, STILLWATER, MN, p. A341
LAKEVIEW SPECIALTY HOSPITAL AND REHAB, WATERFORD, WI, p. A707
LAKEWOOD HEALTH SYSTEM, STAPLES, MN, p. A341
LAKEWOOD RANCH MEDICAL CENTER, BRADENTON, FL, p. A118
LAKEWOOD REGIONAL MEDICAL CENTER, LAKEWOOD, CA, p. A64
LALLIE KEMP MEDICAL CENTER, INDEPENDENCE, LA, p. A269
LAMB HEALTHCARE CENTER, LITTLEFIELD, TX, p. A620
LANAI COMMUNITY HOSPITAL, LANAI CITY, HI, p. A166
LANCASTER REHABILITATION HOSPITAL, LANCASTER, PA, p. A528
LANDMANN–JUNGMAN MEMORIAL HOSPITAL AVERA, SCOTLAND, SD, p. A563
LANDMARK HOSPITAL OF ATHENS, ATHENS, GA, p. A146
LANDMARK HOSPITAL OF CAPE GIRARDEAU, CAPE GIRARDEAU, MO, p. A357
LANDMARK HOSPITAL OF COLUMBIA, COLUMBIA, MO, p. A359
LANDMARK HOSPITAL OF JOPLIN, JOPLIN, MO, p. A362
LANDMARK HOSPITAL OF SALT LAKE CITY, MURRAY, UT, p. A649
LANDMARK HOSPITAL OF SAVANNAH, SAVANNAH, GA, p. A160
LANDMARK HOSPITAL OF SOUTHWEST FLORIDA, NAPLES, FL, p. A132
LANDMARK MEDICAL CENTER, WOONSOCKET, RI, p. A548
LANDMARK MEDICAL CENTER–FOGARTY UNIT, NORTH SMITHFIELD, RHODE ISLAND (see LANDMARK MEDICAL CENTER), p. A547
LANE COUNTY HOSPITAL, DIGHTON, KS, p. A234
LANE REGIONAL MEDICAL CENTER, ZACHARY, LA, p. A280
LANKENAU HOSPITAL, WYNNEWOOD, PENNSYLVANIA (see LANKENAU MEDICAL CENTER), p. A546
LANKENAU MEDICAL CENTER, WYNNEWOOD, PA, p. A546
LAREDO MEDICAL CENTER, LAREDO, TX, p. A620
LAREDO REHABILITATION HOSPITAL, LAREDO, TX, p. A620
LAREDO SPECIALTY HOSPITAL, LAREDO, TX, p. A620
LARGO MEDICAL CENTER, LARGO, FL, p. A128
LARKIN COMMUNITY HOSPITAL BEHAVIORAL HEALTH SERVICES, HOLLYWOOD, FL, p. A124
LARKIN COMMUNITY HOSPITAL–PALM SPRINGS CAMPUS, HIALEAH, FL, p. A124
LARKIN COMMUNITY HOSPITAL–SOUTH MIAMI CAMPUS, SOUTH MIAMI, FL, p. A140
LARNED STATE HOSPITAL, LARNED, KS, p. A238
LARRY B. ZIEVERINK, SR. ALCOHOLISM TREATMENT CENTER, RALEIGH, NC, p. A460
LARUE D. CARTER MEMORIAL HOSPITAL, INDIANAPOLIS, IN, p. A207
LAS ENCINAS HOSPITAL, PASADENA, CA, p. A77
LAS PALMAS MEDICAL CENTER, EL PASO, TX, p. A602
LASALLE GENERAL HOSPITAL, JENA, LA, p. A269
LAUREATE PSYCHIATRIC CLINIC AND HOSPITAL, TULSA, OK, p. A508

LAUREL OAKS BEHAVIORAL HEALTH CENTER, DOTHAN, AL, p. A17

LAUREL RIDGE TREATMENT CENTER, SAN ANTONIO, TX, p. A634

LAVACA MEDICAL CENTER, HALLETTSVILLE, TX, p. A608

LAWNWOOD REGIONAL MEDICAL CENTER & HEART INSTITUTE, FORT PIERCE, FL, p. A123

LAWRENCE + MEMORIAL HOSPITAL, NEW LONDON, CT, p. A110

LAWRENCE COUNTY HOSPITAL, MONTICELLO, MS, p. A351

LAWRENCE COUNTY MEMORIAL HOSPITAL, LAWRENCEVILLE, IL, p. A187

LAWRENCE GENERAL HOSPITAL, LAWRENCE, MA, p. A299

LAWRENCE MEDICAL CENTER, MOULTON, AL, p. A21

LAWRENCE MEMORIAL HOSPITAL, WALNUT RIDGE, AR, p. A49

LAWRENCE MEMORIAL HOSPITAL OF MEDFORD, MEDFORD, MASSACHUSETTS (see MELROSEWAKEFIELD HEALTHCARE), p. A300

LAWTON INDIAN HOSPITAL, LAWTON, OK, p. A501

LAYTON HOSPITAL, LAYTON, UT, p. A648

LDS HOSPITAL, SALT LAKE CITY, UT, p. A651

LE BONHEUR CHILDREN'S HOSPITAL, MEMPHIS, TENNESSEE (see METHODIST HEALTHCARE MEMPHIS HOSPITALS), p. A575

LEA REGIONAL MEDICAL CENTER, HOBBS, NM, p. A418

LEAD–DEADWOOD REGIONAL HOSPITAL, DEADWOOD, SD, p. A560

LEAHI HOSPITAL, HONOLULU, HI, p. A164

LEBANON VETERANS AFFAIRS MEDICAL CENTER, LEBANON, PA, p. A529

LECOM CORRY MEMORIAL HOSPITAL, CORRY, PA, p. A523

LECOM HEALTH MILLCREEK COMMUNITY HOSPITAL, ERIE, PA, p. A525

LECONTE MEDICAL CENTER, SEVIERVILLE, TN, p. A579

LEE MEMORIAL HOSPITAL, FORT MYERS, FL, p. A123

LEESBURG REGIONAL MEDICAL CENTER, LEESBURG, FL, p. A128

LEESVILLE REHABILITATION HOSPITAL, LEESVILLE, LA, p. A272

LEE'S SUMMIT MEDICAL CENTER, LEE'S SUMMIT, MO, p. A364

LEGACY EMANUEL MEDICAL CENTER, PORTLAND, OR, p. A516

LEGACY GOOD SAMARITAN MEDICAL CENTER, PORTLAND, OR, p. A516

LEGACY MERIDIAN PARK MEDICAL CENTER, TUALATIN, OR, p. A518

LEGACY MOUNT HOOD MEDICAL CENTER, GRESHAM, OR, p. A513

LEGACY SALMON CREEK HOSPITAL, VANCOUVER, WASHINGTON (see LEGACY SALMON CREEK MEDICAL CENTER), p. A681

LEGACY SALMON CREEK MEDICAL CENTER, VANCOUVER, WA, p. A681

LEGACY SILVERTON MEDICAL CENTER, SILVERTON, OR, p. A518

LEGENT ORTHOPEDIC + SPINE, SAN ANTONIO, TX, p. A633

LEHIGH REGIONAL MEDICAL CENTER, LEHIGH ACRES, FL, p. A128

LEHIGH VALLEY HOSPITAL – HAZLETON, HAZLETON, PA, p. A527

LEHIGH VALLEY HOSPITAL – POCONO, EAST STROUDSBURG, PA, p. A524

LEHIGH VALLEY HOSPITAL – SCHUYLKILL, POTTSVILLE, PA, p. A539

LEHIGH VALLEY HOSPITAL, ALLENTOWN, PA, p. A519

LEMUEL SHATTUCK HOSPITAL, JAMAICA PLAIN, MA, p. A299

LEONARD J. CHABERT MEDICAL CENTER, HOUMA, LA, p. A268

LEONARD MORSE HOSPITAL, NATICK, MASSACHUSETTS (see METROWEST MEDICAL CENTER), p. A301

LEVI HOSPITAL, HOT SPRINGS NATIONAL PARK, AR, p. A43

LEVINDALE HEBREW HOSPITAL AND NURSING, BALTIMORE, MD, p. A286

LEWIS AND CLARK SPECIALTY HOSPITAL, YANKTON, SD, p. A565

LEWIS COUNTY GENERAL HOSPITAL, LOWVILLE, NEW YORK (see LONG ISLAND JEWISH MEDICAL CENTER), p. A430

LEWIS–GALE MEDICAL CENTER, BOONES MILL, VA, p. A657

LEWISGALE HOSPITAL ALLEGHANY, LOW MOOR, VA, p. A661

LEWISGALE HOSPITAL MONTGOMERY, BLACKSBURG, VA, p. A656

LEWISGALE HOSPITAL PULASKI, PULASKI, VA, p. A665

LEXINGTON MEDICAL CENTER, WEST COLUMBIA, SC, p. A558

LEXINGTON MEMORIAL HOSPITAL, LEXINGTON, NORTH CAROLINA (see WAKE FOREST BAPTIST HEALTH–LEXINGTON MEDICAL CENTER), p. A458

LEXINGTON REGIONAL HEALTH CENTER, LEXINGTON, NE, p. A386

LEXINGTON VETERANS AFFAIRS MEDICAL CENTER, LEXINGTON, KY, p. A255

LIBERTY DAYTON REGIONAL MEDICAL CENTER, LIBERTY, TX, p. A620

LIBERTY HEALTHCARE SYSTEMS, RUSTON, LOUISIANA (see SERENITY SPRINGS SPECIALTY HOSPITAL), p. A277

LIBERTY HOSPITAL, LIBERTY, MO, p. A364

LIBERTY MEDICAL CENTER, CHESTER, MT, p. A375

LIBERTY REGIONAL MEDICAL CENTER, HINESVILLE, GA, p. A154

LIBERTYHEALTH–MEADOWLANDS HOSPITAL MEDICAL CENTER, SECAUCUS, NEW JERSEY (see HUDSON REGIONAL HOSPITAL), p. A412

LICKING MEMORIAL HOSPITAL, NEWARK, OH, p. A488

LIFE LINE HOSPITAL, STEUBENVILLE, OH, p. A491

LIFEBRITE COMMUNITY HOSPITAL OF EARLY, BLAKELY, GA, p. A148

LIFEBRITE COMMUNITY HOSPITAL OF STOKES, DANBURY, NC, p. A452

LIFECARE HOSPITAL OF DAYTON, MIAMISBURG, OH, p. A487

LIFECARE HOSPITALS OF CHESTER COUNTY, WEST CHESTER, PA, p. A544

LIFECARE HOSPITALS OF DALLAS, DALLAS, TX, p. A596

LIFECARE HOSPITALS OF NORTH CAROLINA, ROCKY MOUNT, NC, p. A461

LIFECARE HOSPITALS OF NORTH TEXAS, DALLAS, TEXAS (see LIFECARE HOSPITALS OF DALLAS), p. A596

LIFECARE HOSPITALS OF PITTSBURGH, PITTSBURGH, PA, p. A537

LIFECARE HOSPITALS OF SAN ANTONIO, SAN ANTONIO, TX, p. A634

LIFECARE HOSPITALS OF SHREVEPORT–WILLIS KNIGHTON, SHREVEPORT, LA, p. A278

LIFECARE HOSPITALS OF WISCONSIN, PEWAUKEE, WI, p. A703

LIFECARE MEDICAL CENTER, ROSEAU, MN, p. A339

LIFESCAPE, SIOUX FALLS, SD, p. A563

LIFESTREAM BEHAVIORAL CENTER, LEESBURG, FL, p. A128

LIGHTHOUSE BEHAVIORAL HEALTH HOSPITAL, CONWAY, SC, p. A552

LILLIAN M. HUDSPETH MEMORIAL HOSPITAL, SONORA, TX, p. A637

LIMA MEMORIAL HEALTH SYSTEM, LIMA, OH, p. A485

LIMESTONE MEDICAL CENTER, GROESBECK, TX, p. A608

LINCOLN COMMUNITY HOSPITAL AND NURSING HOME, HUGO, CO, p. A102

LINCOLN COUNTY HEALTH SYSTEM, FAYETTEVILLE, TN, p. A569

LINCOLN COUNTY HOSPITAL, LINCOLN, KS, p. A240

LINCOLN COUNTY MEDICAL CENTER, RUIDOSO, NM, p. A420

LINCOLN DIVISION, LINCOLN, NEBRASKA (see VETERANS AFFAIRS NEBRASKA–WESTERN IOWA HEALTH CARE SYSTEM – LINCOLN), p. A387

LINCOLN HOSPITAL, DAVENPORT, WA, p. A672

LINCOLN PRAIRIE BEHAVIORAL HEALTH CENTER, SPRINGFIELD, IL, p. A196

LINCOLN REGIONAL CENTER, LINCOLN, NE, p. A387

LINCOLN SURGICAL HOSPITAL, LINCOLN, NE, p. A387

LINCOLN TRAIL BEHAVIORAL HEALTH SYSTEM, RADCLIFF, KY, p. A260

LINCOLNHEALTH, DAMARISCOTTA, ME, p. A282

LINDEN OAKS HOSPITAL, NAPERVILLE, IL, p. A190

LINDNER CENTER OF HOPE, MASON, OH, p. A487

LINDSAY MUNICIPAL HOSPITAL, LINDSAY, OK, p. A501

LINDSBORG COMMUNITY HOSPITAL, LINDSBORG, KS, p. A240

LINTON HOSPITAL, LINTON, ND, p. A468

LITTLE COLORADO MEDICAL CENTER, WINSLOW, AZ, p. A38

LITTLE COMPANY OF MARY HOSPITAL AND HEALTH CARE CENTERS, EVERGREEN PARK, IL, p. A183

LITTLE FALLS HOSPITAL, LITTLE FALLS, NY, p. A430

LITTLE RIVER MEMORIAL HOSPITAL, ASHDOWN, AR, p. A39

LITTLETON ADVENTIST HOSPITAL, LITTLETON, CO, p. A103

LITTLETON REGIONAL HEALTHCARE, LITTLETON, NH, p. A401

LIVENGRIN FOUNDATION, BENSALEM, PA, p. A520

LIVINGSTON HEALTHCARE, LIVINGSTON, MT, p. A378

LIVINGSTON HOSPITAL AND HEALTHCARE SERVICES, SALEM, KY, p. A260

LIVINGSTON REGIONAL HOSPITAL, LIVINGSTON, TN, p. A573

LMH HEALTH, LAWRENCE, KS, p. A239

LOGAN COUNTY HOSPITAL, OAKLEY, KS, p. A242

LOGAN MEMORIAL HOSPITAL, RUSSELLVILLE, KY, p. A260

LOGAN REGIONAL HOSPITAL, LOGAN, UT, p. A648

LOGAN REGIONAL MEDICAL CENTER, LOGAN, WV, p. A686

LOGANSPORT MEMORIAL HOSPITAL, LOGANSPORT, IN, p. A210

LOGANSPORT STATE HOSPITAL, LOGANSPORT, IN, p. A210

LOMA LINDA UNIVERSITY BEHAVIORAL MEDICINE CENTER, REDLANDS, CA, p. A80

LOMA LINDA UNIVERSITY CHILDREN'S HOSPITAL, LOMA LINDA, CA, p. A64

LOMA LINDA UNIVERSITY HEART & SURGICAL HOSPITAL, LOMA LINDA, CA, p. A64

LOMA LINDA UNIVERSITY MEDICAL CENTER, LOMA LINDA, CA, p. A64

LOMA LINDA UNIVERSITY MEDICAL CENTER–MURRIETA, MURRIETA, CA, p. A73

LOMPOC VALLEY MEDICAL CENTER, LOMPOC, CA, p. A64

LONE PEAK HOSPITAL, DRAPER, UT, p. A647

LONE STAR BEHAVIORAL HEALTH, CYPRESS, TX, p. A595

LONESOME PINE HOSPITAL, BIG STONE GAP, VA, p. A656

LONG ISLAND COMMUNITY HOSPITAL, PATCHOGUE, NY, p. A441

LONG PRAIRIE MEMORIAL HOSPITAL AND HOME, LONG PRAIRIE, MINNESOTA (see CENTRACARE HEALTH–LONG PRAIRIE), p. A334

LONG TERM ACUTE CARE OF ACADIANA, LAFAYETTE, LOUISIANA (see AMG SPECIALTY HOSPITAL–LAFAYETTE), p. A271

LONG TERM CARE HOSPITAL, MONTGOMERY, ALABAMA (see NOLAND HOSPITAL MONTGOMERY), p. A21

LONG–TERM ACUTE CARE HOSPITAL, MOSAIC LIFE CARE AT ST. JOSEPH, SAINT JOSEPH, MO, p. A368

LONGLEAF HOSPITAL, ALEXANDRIA, LA, p. A262

LONGMONT UNITED HOSPITAL, LONGMONT, CO, p. A103

LONGVIEW REGIONAL MEDICAL CENTER, LONGVIEW, TX, p. A621

LORETTO HOSPITAL, CHICAGO, IL, p. A178

LORING HOSPITAL, SAC CITY, IA, p. A229

LOS ALAMITOS MEDICAL CENTER, LOS ALAMITOS, CA, p. A65

LOS ALAMOS MEDICAL CENTER, LOS ALAMOS, NM, p. A419

LOS ANGELES COMMUNITY HOSPITAL AT LOS ANGELES, LOS ANGELES, CA, p. A68

LOS ANGELES COMMUNITY HOSPITAL OF NORWALK, NORWALK, CA, p. A74

LOS ANGELES COUNTY CENTRAL JAIL HOSPITAL, LOS ANGELES, CA, p. A68

LOS ANGELES MEDICAL CENTER, LOS ANGELES, CA, p. A68

LOS NINOS HOSPITAL, PHOENIX, AZ, p. A33

LOS ROBLES HOSPITAL AND MEDICAL CENTER, THOUSAND OAKS, CA, p. A91

LOST RIVERS MEDICAL CENTER, ARCO, ID, p. A167

LOUIS A. JOHNSON VETERANS AFFAIRS MEDICAL CENTER, CLARKSBURG, WV, p. A684

LOUIS A. WEISS MEMORIAL HOSPITAL, CHICAGO, IL, p. A178

LOUIS STOKES CLEVELAND VETERANS AFFAIRS MEDICAL CENTER, CLEVELAND, OH, p. A478

LOUISIANA EXTENDED CARE HOSPITAL OF KENNER, NEW ORLEANS, LOUISIANA (see EXTENDED CARE HOSPITAL), p. A275

LOUISIANA EXTENDED CARE HOSPITAL OF LAFAYETTE, LAFAYETTE, LA, p. A271

LOUISIANA EXTENDED CARE HOSPITAL OF NATCHITOCHES, NATCHITOCHES, LA, p. A274

LOUISIANA EXTENDED CARE HOSPITAL WEST MONROE, WEST MONROE, LA, p. A280

LOURDES COUNSELING CENTER, RICHLAND, WA, p. A677

LOURDES HOSPITAL, PADUCAH, KY, p. A259

LOURDES MEDICAL CENTER, PASCO, WA, p. A676

LOURDES MEDICAL CENTER OF BURLINGTON COUNTY, WILLINGBORO, NJ, p. A415

LOVELACE MEDICAL CENTER, ALBUQUERQUE, NM, p. A416

LOVELACE REGIONAL HOSPITAL – ROSWELL, ROSWELL, NM, p. A420

LOVELACE UNM REHABILITATION HOSPITAL, ALBUQUERQUE, NM, p. A416

LOVELACE WESTSIDE HOSPITAL, ALBUQUERQUE, NM, p. A416

LOVELACE WOMEN'S HOSPITAL, ALBUQUERQUE, NM, p. A416

LOWELL GENERAL HOSPITAL, LOWELL, MA, p. A300

LOWER BUCKS HOSPITAL, BRISTOL, PA, p. A521

LOWER KEYS MEDICAL CENTER, KEY WEST, FL, p. A126

LOWER UMPQUA HOSPITAL DISTRICT, REEDSPORT, OR, p. A517

LOYOLA UNIVERSITY MEDICAL CENTER, MAYWOOD, IL, p. A189

LUBBOCK HEART & SURGICAL HOSPITAL, LUBBOCK, TX, p. A622

LUCAS COUNTY HEALTH CENTER, CHARITON, IA, p. A219

LUCILE SALTER PACKARD CHILDREN'S HOSPITAL STANFORD, PALO ALTO, CA, p. A77

LUTHERAN HOSPITAL, CLEVELAND, OH, p. A478

LUTHERAN HOSPITAL OF INDIANA, FORT WAYNE, IN, p. A204

LUTHERAN MEDICAL CENTER, WHEAT RIDGE, CO, p. A106

LYNDON B JOHNSON GENERAL HOSPITAL, HOUSTON, TEXAS (see HARRIS HEALTH SYSTEM), p. A612
LYNDON B. JOHNSON TROPICAL MEDICAL CENTER, PAGO PAGO, AS, p. A714
LYNN COUNTY HOSPITAL DISTRICT, TAHOKA, TX, p. A639
LYONS DIVISION, LYONS, NEW JERSEY (see VETERANS AFFAIRS NEW JERSEY HEALTH CARE SYSTEM), p. A407

M

MACKINAC STRAITS HEALTH SYSTEM, INC., SAINT IGNACE, MI, p. A321
MACNEAL HOSPITAL, BERWYN, IL, p. A174
MACON COMMUNITY HOSPITAL, LAFAYETTE, TN, p. A572
MAD RIVER COMMUNITY HOSPITAL, ARCATA, CA, p. A51
MADELIA COMMUNITY HOSPITAL, MADELIA, MN, p. A334
MADERA COMMUNITY HOSPITAL, MADERA, CA, p. A70
MADIGAN ARMY MEDICAL CENTER, TACOMA, WA, p. A680
MADISON COUNTY HEALTH CARE SYSTEM, WINTERSET, IA, p. A231
MADISON COUNTY MEMORIAL HOSPITAL, MADISON, FL, p. A128
MADISON HEALTH, LONDON, OH, p. A486
MADISON HEALTHCARE SERVICES, MADISON, MN, p. A334
MADISON MEDICAL CENTER, FREDERICKTOWN, MO, p. A360
MADISON MEMORIAL HOSPITAL, REXBURG, ID, p. A171
MADISON PARISH HOSPITAL, TALLULAH, LA, p. A279
MADISON REGIONAL HEALTH SYSTEM, MADISON, SD, p. A561
MADISON STATE HOSPITAL, MADISON, IN, p. A211
MADISON VALLEY MEDICAL CENTER, ENNIS, MT, p. A376
MADONNA REHABILITATION HOSPITAL, LINCOLN, NE, p. A387
MADONNA REHABILITATION HOSPITAL, OMAHA, NE, p. A389
MADONNA REHABILITATION SPECIALTY HOSPITAL, OMAHA, NE, p. A389
MAGEE GENERAL HOSPITAL, MAGEE, MS, p. A350
MAGEE REHABILITATION HOSPITAL, PHILADELPHIA, PA, p. A535
MAGNOLIA BEHAVIORAL HOSPITAL OF EAST TEXAS, LONGVIEW, TX, p. A621
MAGNOLIA REGIONAL HEALTH CENTER, CORINTH, MS, p. A346
MAGNOLIA REGIONAL MEDICAL CENTER, MAGNOLIA, AR, p. A45
MAGRUDER MEMORIAL HOSPITAL, PORT CLINTON, OH, p. A490
MAHASKA HEALTH PARTNERSHIP, OSKALOOSA, IA, p. A228
MAHNOMEN HEALTH CENTER, MAHNOMEN, MN, p. A334
MAHONING VALLEY HOSPITAL, BOARDMAN, OHIO (see VIBRA HOSPITAL OF MAHONING VALLEY), p. A473
MAINE MEDICAL CENTER, PORTLAND, ME, p. A284
MAINE VETERANS AFFAIRS MEDICAL CENTER, AUGUSTA, ME, p. A281
MAINEGENERAL MEDICAL CENTER, AUGUSTA, ME, p. A281
MAINEGENERAL MEDICAL CENTER–AUGUSTA CAMPUS, AUGUSTA, MAINE (see MAINEGENERAL MEDICAL CENTER), p. A281
MAJOR HOSPITAL, SHELBYVILLE, IN, p. A214
MALVERN INSTITUTE, MALVERN, PA, p. A531
MAMMOTH HOSPITAL, MAMMOTH LAKES, CA, p. A70
MANATEE MEMORIAL HOSPITAL, BRADENTON, FL, p. A118
MANCHESTER MEMORIAL HOSPITAL, MANCHESTER, CT, p. A108
MANCHESTER VETERANS AFFAIRS MEDICAL CENTER, MANCHESTER, NH, p. A401
MANGUM REGIONAL MEDICAL CENTER, MANGUM, OK, p. A501
MANHATTAN SURGICAL, MANHATTAN, KS, p. A240
MANIILAQ HEALTH CENTER, KOTZEBUE, AK, p. A26
MANN–GRANDSTAFF VETERANS AFFAIRS MEDICAL CENTER, SPOKANE, WA, p. A679
MANNING REGIONAL HEALTHCARE CENTER, MANNING, IA, p. A226
MAPLE GROVE HOSPITAL, MAPLE GROVE, MN, p. A335
MARCUS DALY MEMORIAL HOSPITAL, HAMILTON, MT, p. A377
MARGARET MARY HEALTH, BATESVILLE, IN, p. A199
MARGARET R. PARDEE MEMORIAL HOSPITAL, HENDERSONVILLE, NC, p. A456
MARGARETVILLE HOSPITAL, MARGARETVILLE, NEW YORK (see NEW YORK CITY CHILDREN'S CENTER), p. A431
MARIA PARHAM MEDICAL CENTER, HENDERSON, NC, p. A455
MARIAN CENTER, SALT LAKE CITY, UT, p. A651

MARIAN REGIONAL MEDICAL CENTER, SANTA MARIA, CA, p. A89
MARIAS MEDICAL CENTER, SHELBY, MT, p. A380
MARICOPA INTEGRATED HEALTH SYSTEM, PHOENIX, AZ, p. A33
MARIETTA MEMORIAL HOSPITAL, MARIETTA, OH, p. A486
MARINA DEL REY HOSPITAL, MARINA DEL REY, CA, p. A71
MARINHEALTH MEDICAL CENTER, GREENBRAE, CA, p. A61
MARION COUNTY MEDICAL CENTER, MULLINS, SOUTH CAROLINA (see MUSC HEALTH MARION MEDICAL CENTER), p. A556
MARION GENERAL HOSPITAL, COLUMBIA, MS, p. A346
MARION GENERAL HOSPITAL, MARION, IN, p. A211
MARION VETERANS AFFAIRS MEDICAL CENTER, MARION, IL, p. A188
MARK TWAIN MEDICAL CENTER, SAN ANDREAS, CA, p. A83
MARLETTE REGIONAL HOSPITAL, MARLETTE, MI, p. A317
MARSHALL BROWNING HOSPITAL, DU QUOIN, IL, p. A181
MARSHALL COUNTY HEALTHCARE CENTER AVERA, BRITTON, SD, p. A559
MARSHALL COUNTY HOSPITAL, BENTON, KY, p. A249
MARSHALL MEDICAL CENTER, LEWISBURG, TN, p. A573
MARSHALL MEDICAL CENTER, PLACERVILLE, CA, p. A78
MARSHALL MEDICAL CENTER NORTH, GUNTERSVILLE, AL, p. A19
MARSHALL MEDICAL CENTER SOUTH, BOAZ, AL, p. A15
MARSHFIELD MEDICAL CENTER – EAU CLAIRE HOSPITAL, EAU CLAIRE, WI, p. A694
MARSHFIELD MEDICAL CENTER – LADYSMITH, LADYSMITH, WI, p. A698
MARSHFIELD MEDICAL CENTER – NEILLSVILLE, NEILLSVILLE, WI, p. A702
MARSHFIELD MEDICAL CENTER – RICE LAKE, RICE LAKE, WI, p. A704
MARSHFIELD MEDICAL CENTER, MARSHFIELD, WI, p. A699
MARTHA'S VINEYARD HOSPITAL, OAK BLUFFS, MA, p. A302
MARTIN ARMY COMMUNITY HOSPITAL, FORT BENNING, GA, p. A153
MARTIN COUNTY HOSPITAL DISTRICT, STANTON, TX, p. A638
MARTIN GENERAL HOSPITAL, WILLIAMSTON, NC, p. A463
MARTIN LUTHER KING, JR. COMMUNITY HOSPITAL, LOS ANGELES, CA, p. A68
MARTINSBURG VETERANS AFFAIRS MEDICAL CENTER, MARTINSBURG, WV, p. A687
MARY BRECKINRIDGE ARH HOSPITAL, HYDEN, KY, p. A254
MARY FREE BED REHABILITATION HOSPITAL, GRAND RAPIDS, MI, p. A312
MARY GREELEY MEDICAL CENTER, AMES, IA, p. A217
MARY LANNING HEALTHCARE, HASTINGS, NE, p. A385
MARY RUTAN HOSPITAL, BELLEFONTAINE, OH, p. A473
MARY S HARPER GERIATRIC PSYCHIATRY CENTER, TUSCALOOSA, AL, p. A24
MARY SHIELS HOSPITAL, DALLAS, TEXAS (see BAYLOR SCOTT & WHITE MEDICAL CENTER-UPTOWN), p. A596
MARY WASHINGTON HOSPITAL, FREDERICKSBURG, VA, p. A659
MARYMOUNT HOSPITAL, GARFIELD HEIGHTS, OH, p. A483
MASON DISTRICT HOSPITAL, HAVANA, IL, p. A185
MASON GENERAL HOSPITAL AND FAMILY OF CLINICS, SHELTON, WA, p. A679
MASONICARE HEALTH CENTER, WALLINGFORD, CT, p. A111
MASSAC MEMORIAL HOSPITAL, METROPOLIS, IL, p. A189
MASSACHUSETTS EYE AND EAR, BOSTON, MA, p. A295
MASSACHUSETTS GENERAL HOSPITAL, BOSTON, MA, p. A295
MASSENA MEMORIAL HOSPITAL, MASSENA, NEW YORK (see NEW YORK–PRESBYTERIAN HOSPITAL), p. A431
MAT–SU REGIONAL MEDICAL CENTER, PALMER, AK, p. A27
MATAGORDA REGIONAL MEDICAL CENTER, BAY CITY, TX, p. A587
MATHENY MEDICAL AND EDUCATIONAL CENTER, PEAPACK, NJ, p. A410
MAUI MEMORIAL MEDICAL CENTER, WAILUKU, HI, p. A166
MAURY REGIONAL HOSPITAL, COLUMBIA, TN, p. A568
MAYERS MEMORIAL HOSPITAL DISTRICT, FALL RIVER MILLS, CA, p. A58
MAYHILL HOSPITAL, DENTON, TX, p. A599
MAYO CLINIC HEALTH SYSTEM – ALBERT LEA AND AUSTIN, ALBERT LEA, MN, p. A327
MAYO CLINIC HEALTH SYSTEM – CHIPPEWA VALLEY IN BLOOMER, BLOOMER, WI, p. A692
MAYO CLINIC HEALTH SYSTEM – FRANCISCAN HEALTHCARE IN LA CROSSE, LA CROSSE, WI, p. A698
MAYO CLINIC HEALTH SYSTEM – FRANCISCAN HEALTHCARE IN SPARTA, SPARTA, WI, p. A705
MAYO CLINIC HEALTH SYSTEM – NORTHLAND IN BARRON, BARRON, WI, p. A692
MAYO CLINIC HEALTH SYSTEM – OAKRIDGE IN OSSEO, OSSEO, WI, p. A703

MAYO CLINIC HEALTH SYSTEM – RED CEDAR IN MENOMONIE, MENOMONIE, WI, p. A700
MAYO CLINIC HEALTH SYSTEM IN CANNON FALLS, CANNON FALLS, MN, p. A329
MAYO CLINIC HEALTH SYSTEM IN EAU CLAIRE, EAU CLAIRE, WI, p. A694
MAYO CLINIC HEALTH SYSTEM IN FAIRMONT, FAIRMONT, MN, p. A331
MAYO CLINIC HEALTH SYSTEM IN LAKE CITY, LAKE CITY, MN, p. A334
MAYO CLINIC HEALTH SYSTEM IN MANKATO, MANKATO, MN, p. A334
MAYO CLINIC HEALTH SYSTEM IN NEW PRAGUE, NEW PRAGUE, MN, p. A336
MAYO CLINIC HEALTH SYSTEM IN RED WING, RED WING, MN, p. A338
MAYO CLINIC HEALTH SYSTEM IN SAINT JAMES, SAINT JAMES, MN, p. A339
MAYO CLINIC HEALTH SYSTEM IN SPRINGFIELD, SPRINGFIELD, MN, p. A341
MAYO CLINIC HEALTH SYSTEM IN WASECA, WASECA, MN, p. A342
MAYO CLINIC HOSPITAL – ROCHESTER, ROCHESTER, MN, p. A338
MAYO CLINIC HOSPITAL, PHOENIX, AZ, p. A33
MAYO CLINIC HOSPITAL IN FLORIDA, JACKSONVILLE, FL, p. A125
MAYO REGIONAL HOSPITAL, DOVER, ME, p. A283
MCALESTER REGIONAL HEALTH CENTER, MCALESTER, OK, p. A502
MCBRIDE ORTHOPEDIC HOSPITAL, OKLAHOMA CITY, OK, p. A504
MCCAMEY COUNTY HOSPITAL DISTRICT, MCCAMEY, TX, p. A624
MCCONE COUNTY HEALTH CENTER, CIRCLE, MT, p. A375
MCCREADY HEALTH, CRISFIELD, MD, p. A290
MCCULLOUGH-HYDE MEMORIAL HOSPITAL/TRIHEALTH, OXFORD, OH, p. A489
MCCURTAIN MEMORIAL HOSPITAL, IDABEL, OK, p. A501
MCDONOUGH DISTRICT HOSPITAL, MACOMB, IL, p. A188
MCDOWELL ARH HOSPITAL, MCDOWELL, KY, p. A258
MCDOWELL HOSPITAL, MARION, NC, p. A458
MCGEHEE HOSPITAL, MCGEHEE, AR, p. A45
MCKAY–DEE HOSPITAL, OGDEN, UT, p. A649
MCKEE MEDICAL CENTER, LOVELAND, CO, p. A104
MCKENZIE COUNTY HEALTHCARE SYSTEM, WATFORD CITY, ND, p. A470
MCKENZIE HEALTH SYSTEM, SANDUSKY, MI, p. A322
MCKENZIE–WILLAMETTE MEDICAL CENTER, SPRINGFIELD, OR, p. A518
MCLANE CHILDREN'S HOSPITAL SCOTT & WHITE, TEMPLE, TEXAS (see BAYLOR SCOTT & WHITE MEDICAL CENTER – TEMPLE), p. A640
MCLAREN BAY REGION, BAY CITY, MI, p. A307
MCLAREN BAY SPECIAL CARE, BAY CITY, MI, p. A307
MCLAREN CARO REGION, CARO, MI, p. A308
MCLAREN CENTRAL MICHIGAN, MOUNT PLEASANT, MI, p. A318
MCLAREN FLINT, FLINT, MI, p. A311
MCLAREN GREATER LANSING, LANSING, MI, p. A316
MCLAREN LAPEER REGION, LAPEER, MI, p. A316
MCLAREN MACOMB, MOUNT CLEMENS, MI, p. A318
MCLAREN NORTHERN MICHIGAN, PETOSKEY, MI, p. A319
MCLAREN OAKLAND, PONTIAC, MI, p. A320
MCLAREN PORT HURON, PORT HURON, MI, p. A320
MCLAREN THUMB REGION, BAD AXE, MI, p. A307
MCLEAN HOSPITAL, BELMONT, MA, p. A294
MCLEOD HEALTH CHERAW, CHERAW, SC, p. A550
MCLEOD HEALTH CLARENDON, MANNING, SC, p. A555
MCLEOD LORIS SEACOAST HOSPITAL, LORIS, SC, p. A555
MCLEOD MEDICAL CENTER DARLINGTON, DARLINGTON, SC, p. A552
MCLEOD MEDICAL CENTER DILLON, DILLON, SC, p. A552
MCLEOD REGIONAL MEDICAL CENTER, FLORENCE, SC, p. A552
MCPHERSON HOSPITAL, MCPHERSON, KS, p. A240
MEADE DISTRICT HOSPITAL, MEADE, KS, p. A240
MEADOW WOOD BEHAVIORAL HEALTH SYSTEM, NEW CASTLE, DE, p. A113
MEADOWBROOK REHABILITATION HOSPITAL, GARDNER, KS, p. A235
MEADOWBROOK SPECIALTY HOSPITAL OF TULSA, TULSA, OKLAHOMA (see POST ACUTE MEDICAL SPECIALTY HOSPITAL OF TULSA), p. A509
MEADOWS PSYCHIATRIC CENTER, CENTRE HALL, PA, p. A522
MEADOWS REGIONAL MEDICAL CENTER, VIDALIA, GA, p. A162
MEADOWVIEW REGIONAL MEDICAL CENTER, MAYSVILLE, KY, p. A257

MEADVILLE MEDICAL CENTER, MEADVILLE, PA, p. A531

MEASE COUNTRYSIDE HOSPITAL, SAFETY HARBOR, FL, p. A138

MEASE DUNEDIN HOSPITAL, DUNEDIN, FL, p. A122

MEDCENTRAL – MANSFIELD HOSPITAL, MANSFIELD, OHIO (see OHIOHEALTH MEDCENTRAL MANSFIELD HOSPITAL), p. A486

MEDICAL ARTS HOSPITAL, LAMESA, TX, p. A619

MEDICAL BEHAVIORAL HOSPITAL OF MISHAWAKA, KNOX, IN, p. A209

MEDICAL CENTER AT BOWLING GREEN, BOWLING GREEN, KY, p. A250

MEDICAL CENTER AT FRANKLIN, FRANKLIN, KY, p. A252

MEDICAL CENTER AT SCOTTSVILLE, SCOTTSVILLE, KY, p. A260

MEDICAL CENTER BARBOUR, EUFAULA, AL, p. A17

MEDICAL CENTER ENTERPRISE, ENTERPRISE, AL, p. A17

MEDICAL CENTER HEALTH SYSTEM, ODESSA, TX, p. A627

MEDICAL CENTER HOSPITAL, ODESSA, TEXAS (see MEDICAL CENTER HEALTH SYSTEM), p. A627

MEDICAL CENTER OF AURORA, AURORA, CO, p. A96

MEDICAL CENTER OF LOUISIANA AT NEW ORLEANS, NEW ORLEANS, LOUISIANA (see UNIVERSITY MEDICAL CENTER), p. A275

MEDICAL CENTER OF PEACH COUNTY, NAVICENT HEALTH, BRYON, GA, p. A149

MEDICAL CENTER OF SOUTH ARKANSAS, EL DORADO, AR, p. A41

MEDICAL CENTER OF SOUTHEAST TEXAS, BEAUMONT, TX, p. A587

MEDICAL CENTER OF TRINITY, TRINITY, FL, p. A143

MEDICAL CENTER, NAVICENT HEALTH, MACON, GA, p. A156

MEDICAL CITY ALLIANCE, FORT WORTH, TX, p. A605

MEDICAL CITY ARLINGTON, ARLINGTON, TX, p. A583

MEDICAL CITY DALLAS, DALLAS, TX, p. A597

MEDICAL CITY DENTON, DENTON, TX, p. A599

MEDICAL CITY FORT WORTH, FORT WORTH, TX, p. A605

MEDICAL CITY GREEN OAKS HOSPITAL, DALLAS, TX, p. A597

MEDICAL CITY LAS COLINAS, IRVING, TX, p. A616

MEDICAL CITY LEWISVILLE, LEWISVILLE, TX, p. A620

MEDICAL CITY MCKINNEY, MCKINNEY, TX, p. A624

MEDICAL CITY NORTH HILLS, NORTH RICHLAND HILLS, TX, p. A626

MEDICAL CITY PLANO, PLANO, TX, p. A629

MEDICAL CITY WEATHERFORD, WEATHERFORD, TX, p. A644

MEDICAL COLLEGE OF GEORGIA HEALTH, AUGUSTA, GA, p. A147

MEDICAL PARK HOSPITAL, WINSTON, NORTH CAROLINA (see NOVANT HEALTH MEDICAL PARK HOSPITAL), p. A464

MEDICAL WEST, BESSEMER, AL, p. A14

MEDICINE LODGE MEMORIAL HOSPITAL, MEDICINE LODGE, KS, p. A241

MEDINA COMMUNITY HOSPITAL, HONDO, TEXAS (see MEDINA REGIONAL HOSPITAL), p. A610

MEDINA MEMORIAL HOSPITAL, MEDINA, NEW YORK (see NYU LANGONE ORTHOPEDIC HOSPITAL), p. A431

MEDINA REGIONAL HOSPITAL, HONDO, TX, p. A610

MEDSTAR FRANKLIN SQUARE MEDICAL CENTER, BALTIMORE, MD, p. A288

MEDSTAR GEORGETOWN UNIVERSITY HOSPITAL, WASHINGTON, DC, p. A115

MEDSTAR GOOD SAMARITAN HOSPITAL, BALTIMORE, MD, p. A286

MEDSTAR HARBOR HOSPITAL, BALTIMORE, MD, p. A287

MEDSTAR MONTGOMERY MEDICAL CENTER, OLNEY, MD, p. A292

MEDSTAR NATIONAL REHABILITATION HOSPITAL, WASHINGTON, DC, p. A115

MEDSTAR SOUTHERN MARYLAND HOSPITAL CENTER, CLINTON, MD, p. A289

MEDSTAR ST. MARY'S HOSPITAL, LEONARDTOWN, MD, p. A292

MEDSTAR UNION MEMORIAL HOSPITAL, BALTIMORE, MD, p. A287

MEDSTAR WASHINGTON HOSPITAL CENTER, WASHINGTON, DC, p. A116

MEE MEMORIAL HOSPITAL, KING CITY, CA, p. A62

MEEKER MEMORIAL HOSPITAL, LITCHFIELD, MN, p. A334

MELBOURNE REGIONAL MEDICAL CENTER, MELBOURNE, FL, p. A129

MELISSA MEMORIAL HOSPITAL, HOLYOKE, CO, p. A102

MELROSEWAKEFIELD HEALTHCARE, MELROSE, MA, p. A300

MEMORIAL COMMUNITY HEALTH, AURORA, NE, p. A382

MEMORIAL COMMUNITY HOSPITAL AND HEALTH SYSTEM, BLAIR, NE, p. A383

MEMORIAL HEALTH, MARYSVILLE, OH, p. A486

MEMORIAL HEALTH, SAVANNAH, GA, p. A160

MEMORIAL HEALTH CARE SYSTEMS, SEWARD, NE, p. A391

MEMORIAL HEALTH SYSTEM, ABILENE, KS, p. A232

MEMORIAL HEALTHCARE, OWOSSO, MI, p. A319

MEMORIAL HERMANN – TEXAS MEDICAL CENTER, HOUSTON, TX, p. A612

MEMORIAL HERMANN BAPTIST FANNIN BEHAVIORAL HEALTH CENTER, BEAUMONT, TEXAS (see BAPTIST HOSPITALS OF SOUTHEAST TEXAS FANNIN BEHAVIORAL HEALTH CENTER), p. A587

MEMORIAL HERMANN FIRST COLONY HOSPITAL, SUGAR LAND, TX, p. A638

MEMORIAL HERMANN GREATER HEIGHTS HOSPITAL, HOUSTON, TX, p. A612

MEMORIAL HERMANN KATY HOSPITAL, KATY, TX, p. A617

MEMORIAL HERMANN MEMORIAL CITY MEDICAL CENTER, HOUSTON, TX, p. A613

MEMORIAL HERMANN NORTHEAST, HUMBLE, TX, p. A615

MEMORIAL HERMANN REHABILITATION HOSPITAL – KATY, KATY, TX, p. A617

MEMORIAL HERMANN SOUTHEAST HOSPITAL, HOUSTON, TEXAS (see MEMORIAL HERMANN GREATER HEIGHTS HOSPITAL), p. A613

MEMORIAL HERMANN SOUTHWEST HOSPITAL, HOUSTON, TEXAS (see MEMORIAL HERMANN GREATER HEIGHTS HOSPITAL), p. A613

MEMORIAL HERMANN SUGAR LAND HOSPITAL, SUGAR LAND, TX, p. A638

MEMORIAL HERMANN SURGICAL HOSPITAL KINGWOOD, KINGWOOD, TX, p. A618

MEMORIAL HERMANN THE WOODLANDS HOSPITAL, THE WOODLANDS, TEXAS (see MEMORIAL HERMANN GREATER HEIGHTS HOSPITAL), p. A641

MEMORIAL HERMANN TOMBALL HOSPITAL, TOMBALL, TX, p. A641

MEMORIAL HOSPITAL, AURORA, NEBRASKA (see MEMORIAL COMMUNITY HEALTH), p. A382

MEMORIAL HOSPITAL, BELLEVILLE, IL, p. A174

MEMORIAL HOSPITAL, CARTHAGE, IL, p. A175

MEMORIAL HOSPITAL, CHESTER, IL, p. A176

MEMORIAL HOSPITAL, MCPHERSON, KANSAS (see MCPHERSON HOSPITAL), p. A240

MEMORIAL HOSPITAL, NORTH CONWAY, NH, p. A402

MEMORIAL HOSPITAL, SEMINOLE, TX, p. A636

MEMORIAL HOSPITAL AND HEALTH CARE CENTER, JASPER, IN, p. A208

MEMORIAL HOSPITAL AND MANOR, BAINBRIDGE, GA, p. A148

MEMORIAL HOSPITAL AT GULFPORT, GULFPORT, MS, p. A347

MEMORIAL HOSPITAL EAST, SHILOH, IL, p. A196

MEMORIAL HOSPITAL JACKSONVILLE, JACKSONVILLE, FL, p. A125

MEMORIAL HOSPITAL LOS BANOS, LOS BANOS, CA, p. A70

MEMORIAL HOSPITAL MIRAMAR, MIRAMAR, FL, p. A132

MEMORIAL HOSPITAL OF CARBON COUNTY, RAWLINS, WY, p. A712

MEMORIAL HOSPITAL OF CARBONDALE, CARBONDALE, IL, p. A175

MEMORIAL HOSPITAL OF CONVERSE COUNTY, DOUGLAS, WY, p. A711

MEMORIAL HOSPITAL OF GARDENA, GARDENA, CA, p. A60

MEMORIAL HOSPITAL OF LAFAYETTE COUNTY, DARLINGTON, WI, p. A693

MEMORIAL HOSPITAL OF SOUTH BEND, SOUTH BEND, IN, p. A215

MEMORIAL HOSPITAL OF STILWELL, STILWELL, OK, p. A508

MEMORIAL HOSPITAL OF SWEETWATER COUNTY, ROCK SPRINGS, WY, p. A712

MEMORIAL HOSPITAL OF TAMPA, TAMPA, FL, p. A141

MEMORIAL HOSPITAL OF TEXAS COUNTY, GUYMON, OK, p. A500

MEMORIAL HOSPITAL PEMBROKE, PEMBROKE PINES, FL, p. A136

MEMORIAL HOSPITAL WEST, PEMBROKE PINES, FL, p. A136

MEMORIAL MEDICAL CENTER – LEE CAMPUS, JOHNSTOWN, PENNSYLVANIA (see CONEMAUGH MEMORIAL MEDICAL CENTER), p. A528

MEMORIAL MEDICAL CENTER, LAS CRUCES, NM, p. A418

MEMORIAL MEDICAL CENTER, MODESTO, CA, p. A72

MEMORIAL MEDICAL CENTER, PORT LAVACA, TX, p. A630

MEMORIAL MEDICAL CENTER, SPRINGFIELD, IL, p. A196

MEMORIAL MEDICAL CENTER OF ASHLAND, ASHLAND, WI, p. A691

MEMORIAL REGIONAL HEALTH, CRAIG, CO, p. A98

MEMORIAL REGIONAL HOSPITAL, HOLLYWOOD, FL, p. A124

MEMORIAL SATILLA HEALTH, WAYCROSS, GA, p. A163

MEMORIAL SPECIALTY HOSPITAL, LAKE CHARLES, LA, p. A272

MEMORIALCARE, LONG BEACH MEMORIAL MEDICAL CENTER, LONG BEACH, CA, p. A65

MEMORIALCARE, MILLER CHILDREN'S & WOMEN'S HOSPITAL LONG BEACH, LONG BEACH, CA, p. A65

MEMORIALCARE, ORANGE COAST MEMORIAL MEDICAL CENTER, FOUNTAIN VALLEY, CA, p. A58

MEMORIALCARE, SADDLEBACK MEMORIAL MEDICAL CENTER, LAGUNA HILLS, CA, p. A63

MEMPHIS MENTAL HEALTH INSTITUTE, MEMPHIS, TN, p. A575

MEMPHIS VETERANS AFFAIRS MEDICAL CENTER, MEMPHIS, TN, p. A575

MENA REGIONAL HEALTH SYSTEM, MENA, AR, p. A46

MENDOCINO COAST DISTRICT HOSPITAL, FORT BRAGG, CA, p. A58

MENDOTA MENTAL HEALTH INSTITUTE, MADISON, WI, p. A698

MENIFEE VALLEY MEDICAL CENTER, SUN CITY, CA, p. A91

MENLO PARK SURGICAL HOSPITAL, MENLO PARK, CA, p. A71

MENNINGER CLINIC, HOUSTON, TX, p. A613

MENNONITE GENERAL HOSPITAL, AIBONITO, PR, p. A715

MENORAH MEDICAL CENTER, OVERLAND PARK, KS, p. A243

MENTAL HEALTH INSTITUTE, CHEROKEE, IA, p. A219

MENTAL HEALTH INSTITUTE, INDEPENDENCE, IA, p. A224

MENTAL HEALTH SERVICES FOR CLARK AND MADISON COUNTIES, SPRINGFIELD, OH, p. A491

MERCER HEALTH, COLDWATER, OH, p. A478

MERCY ALLEN HOSPITAL, OBERLIN, OH, p. A489

MERCY FITZGERALD HOSPITAL, DARBY, PA, p. A524

MERCY GENERAL HOSPITAL, SACRAMENTO, CA, p. A82

MERCY GILBERT MEDICAL CENTER, GILBERT, AZ, p. A29

MERCY HEALTH – ANDERSON HOSPITAL, CINCINNATI, OH, p. A476

MERCY HEALTH – CLERMONT HOSPITAL, BATAVIA, OH, p. A472

MERCY HEALTH – FAIRFIELD HOSPITAL, FAIRFIELD, OH, p. A483

MERCY HEALTH – MARCUM AND WALLACE, IRVINE, KY, p. A254

MERCY HEALTH – ST. CHARLES HOSPITAL, OREGON, OH, p. A489

MERCY HEALTH – ST. ELIZABETH BOARDMAN HOSPITAL, BOARDMAN, OH, p. A473

MERCY HEALTH – ST. ELIZABETH YOUNGSTOWN HOSPITAL, YOUNGSTOWN, OH, p. A495

MERCY HEALTH – ST. JOSEPH WARREN HOSPITAL, WARREN, OH, p. A493

MERCY HEALTH – ST. RITA'S MEDICAL CENTER, LIMA, OH, p. A485

MERCY HEALTH – WEST HOSPITAL, CINCINNATI, OH, p. A476

MERCY HEALTH – WILLARD HOSPITAL, WILLARD, OH, p. A494

MERCY HEALTH HACKLEY CAMPUS, MUSKEGON, MI, p. A318

MERCY HEALTH LOVE COUNTY, MARIETTA, OK, p. A502

MERCY HEALTH SAINT MARY'S, GRAND RAPIDS, MI, p. A313

MERCY HEALTH, LAKESHORE CAMPUS, SHELBY, MI, p. A322

MERCY HOSPITAL, BUFFALO, NY, p. A424

MERCY HOSPITAL, COON RAPIDS, MN, p. A330

MERCY HOSPITAL, MOOSE LAKE, MN, p. A336

MERCY HOSPITAL, MOUNDRIDGE, KS, p. A241

MERCY HOSPITAL ADA, ADA, OK, p. A496

MERCY HOSPITAL AND MEDICAL CENTER, CHICAGO, IL, p. A178

MERCY HOSPITAL ARDMORE, ARDMORE, OK, p. A496

MERCY HOSPITAL AURORA, AURORA, MO, p. A356

MERCY HOSPITAL BERRYVILLE, BERRYVILLE, AR, p. A39

MERCY HOSPITAL BOONEVILLE, BOONEVILLE, AR, p. A40

MERCY HOSPITAL CARTHAGE, CARTHAGE, MO, p. A358

MERCY HOSPITAL CASSVILLE, CASSVILLE, MO, p. A358

MERCY HOSPITAL COLUMBUS, COLUMBUS, KS, p. A233

MERCY HOSPITAL FORT SMITH, FORT SMITH, AR, p. A42

MERCY HOSPITAL HEALDTON, HEALDTON, OK, p. A500

MERCY HOSPITAL JEFFERSON, FESTUS, MO, p. A360

MERCY HOSPITAL JOPLIN, JOPLIN, MO, p. A362

MERCY HOSPITAL KINGFISHER, KINGFISHER, OK, p. A501

MERCY HOSPITAL LEBANON, LEBANON, MO, p. A364

MERCY HOSPITAL LINCOLN, TROY, MO, p. A372

MERCY HOSPITAL LOGAN COUNTY, GUTHRIE, OK, p. A500

MERCY HOSPITAL OF DEFIANCE, DEFIANCE, OH, p. A481

MERCY HOSPITAL OF FOLSOM, FOLSOM, CA, p. A58

MERCY HOSPITAL OF SCRANTON, SCRANTON, PENNSYLVANIA (see REGIONAL HOSPITAL OF SCRANTON), p. A540

MERCY HOSPITAL OKLAHOMA CITY, OKLAHOMA CITY, OK, p. A504

MERCY HOSPITAL OZARK, OZARK, AR, p. A47

MERCY HOSPITAL PARIS, PARIS, AR, p. A47

MERCY HOSPITAL ROGERS, ROGERS, AR, p. A48

MERCY HOSPITAL SOUTH, SAINT LOUIS, MO, p. A369

MERCY HOSPITAL SPRINGFIELD, SPRINGFIELD, MO, p. A371

MERCY HOSPITAL ST. LOUIS, SAINT LOUIS, MO, p. A368

MERCY HOSPITAL TISHOMINGO, TISHOMINGO, OK, p. A508

MERCY HOSPITAL WALDRON, WALDRON, AR, p. A49

MERCY HOSPITAL WASHINGTON, WASHINGTON, MO, p. A373

MERCY HOSPITAL WATONGA, WATONGA, OK, p. A510

MERCY HOSPITALS OF BAKERSFIELD, BAKERSFIELD, CA, p. A52

MERCY MEDICAL CENTER – CEDAR RAPIDS, CEDAR RAPIDS, IA, p. A218

MERCY MEDICAL CENTER, BALTIMORE, MD, p. A288

MERCY MEDICAL CENTER, CANTON, OH, p. A474

MERCY MEDICAL CENTER, NAMPA, IDAHO (see SAINT ALPHONSUS MEDICAL CENTER – NAMPA), p. A170

MERCY MEDICAL CENTER, ROCKVILLE CENTRE, NY, p. A443

MERCY MEDICAL CENTER, ROSEBURG, OR, p. A517

MERCY MEDICAL CENTER, SPRINGFIELD, MA, p. A303

MERCY MEDICAL CENTER MERCED, MERCED, CA, p. A71

MERCY MEDICAL CENTER MOUNT SHASTA, MOUNT SHASTA, CA, p. A73

MERCY MEDICAL CENTER NORTH, POWELL, TENNESSEE (see TENNOVA NORTH KNOXVILLE MEDICAL CENTER), p. A578

MERCY MEDICAL CENTER REDDING, REDDING, CA, p. A79

MERCY MEDICAL CENTER WEST, KNOXVILLE, TENNESSEE (see TENNOVA TURKEY CREEK MEDICAL CENTER), p. A572

MERCY MEDICAL CENTER–DUBUQUE, DUBUQUE, IA, p. A222

MERCY MEDICAL CENTER–DYERSVILLE, DYERSVILLE, IA, p. A222

MERCY MEMORIAL HOSPITAL, URBANA, OH, p. A492

MERCY PHILADELPHIA HOSPITAL, PHILADELPHIA, PENNSYLVANIA (see MERCY FITZGERALD HOSPITAL), p. A535

MERCY REGIONAL MEDICAL CENTER, DURANGO, CO, p. A99

MERCY REGIONAL MEDICAL CENTER, LORAIN, OH, p. A486

MERCY REGIONAL MEDICAL CENTER, VILLE PLATTE, LA, p. A280

MERCY REHABILITATION HOSPITAL OKLAHOMA CITY, OKLAHOMA CITY, OK, p. A504

MERCY REHABILITATION HOSPITAL ST. LOUIS, CHESTERFIELD, MO, p. A358

MERCY REHABILITION HOSPITAL SPRINGFIELD, SPRINGFIELD, MO, p. A372

MERCY SAN JUAN MEDICAL CENTER, CARMICHAEL, CA, p. A54

MERCY ST. ANNE HOSPITAL, TOLEDO, OH, p. A492

MERCY ST. FRANCIS HOSPITAL, MOUNTAIN VIEW, MO, p. A366

MERCY ST. VINCENT MEDICAL CENTER, TOLEDO, OH, p. A492

MERCY TIFFIN HOSPITAL, TIFFIN, OH, p. A491

MERCY HEALTH HOSPITAL AND MEDICAL CENTER – HARVARD, HARVARD, IL, p. A184

MERCYHEALTH HOSPITAL AND MEDICAL CENTER – WALWORTH, LAKE GENEVA, WI, p. A698

MERCY HEALTH HOSPITAL AND TRAUMA CENTER – JANESVILLE, JANESVILLE, WI, p. A697

MERCYONE CEDAR FALLS MEDICAL CENTER, CEDAR FALLS, IA, p. A218

MERCYONE CENTERVILLE MEDICAL CENTER, CENTERVILLE, IA, p. A218

MERCYONE CLINTON MEDICAL CENTER, CLINTON, IA, p. A219

MERCYONE CLIVE REHABILITATION HOSPITAL, CLIVE, IA, p. A219

MERCYONE DES MOINES MEDICAL CENTER, DES MOINES, IA, p. A221

MERCYONE ELKADER MEDICAL CENTER, ELKADER, IA, p. A222

MERCYONE IOWA CITY MEDICAL CENTER, IOWA CITY, IA, p. A224

MERCYONE NEW HAMPTON MEDICAL CENTER, NEW HAMPTON, IA, p. A227

MERCYONE NEWTON MEDICAL CENTER, NEWTON, IA, p. A227

MERCYONE NORTH IOWA MEDICAL CENTER, MASON CITY, IA, p. A226

MERCYONE OAKLAND MEDICAL CENTER, OAKLAND, NE, p. A388

MERCYONE OELWEIN MEDICAL CENTER, OELWEIN, IA, p. A227

MERCYONE PRIMGHAR MEDICAL CENTER, PRIMGHAR, IA, p. A228

MERCYONE SIOUXLAND MEDICAL CENTER, SIOUX CITY, IA, p. A230

MERCYONE WATERLOO MEDICAL CENTER, WATERLOO, IA, p. A231

MERIDIAN HEALTH SERVICES, MUNCIE, IN, p. A212

MERIT HEALTH BILOXI, BILOXI, MS, p. A344

MERIT HEALTH CENTRAL, JACKSON, MS, p. A349

MERIT HEALTH MADISON, CANTON, MS, p. A345

MERIT HEALTH NATCHEZ, NATCHEZ, MS, p. A352

MERIT HEALTH RANKIN, BRANDON, MS, p. A345

MERIT HEALTH RIVER OAKS, FLOWOOD, MS, p. A346

MERIT HEALTH RIVER REGION, VICKSBURG, MS, p. A355

MERIT HEALTH WESLEY, HATTIESBURG, MS, p. A348

MERIT HEALTH WOMAN'S HOSPITAL, FLOWOOD, MS, p. A347

MERITCARE MAYVILLE UNION HOSPITAL, MAYVILLE, NORTH DAKOTA (see SANFORD MAYVILLE MEDICAL CENTER), p. A468

MERITCARE MEDICAL CENTER, FARGO, NORTH DAKOTA (see SANFORD MEDICAL CENTER FARGO), p. A466

MERITCARE THIEF RIVER FALLS NORTHWEST MEDICAL CENTER, THIEF RIVER FALLS, MINNESOTA (see SANFORD MEDICAL CENTER THIEF RIVER FALLS), p. A341

MERITUS MEDICAL CENTER, HAGERSTOWN, MD, p. A291

MERRICK MEDICAL CENTER, CENTRAL CITY, NE, p. A383

MESA HILLS SPECIALTY HOSPITAL, EL PASO, TX, p. A602

MESA SPRINGS, FORT WORTH, TX, p. A605

MESA VIEW REGIONAL HOSPITAL, MESQUITE, NV, p. A396

MESCALERO PUBLIC HEALTH SERVICE INDIAN HOSPITAL, MESCALERO, NM, p. A419

MESILLA VALLEY HOSPITAL, LAS CRUCES, NM, p. A418

MESQUITE REHABILITATION INSTITUTE, MESQUITE, TX, p. A624

MESQUITE SPECIALTY HOSPITAL, MESQUITE, TX, p. A624

METHODIST AMBULATORY SURGERY HOSPITAL – NORTHWEST, SAN ANTONIO, TX, p. A634

METHODIST BEHAVIORAL HOSPITAL OF ARKANSAS, MAUMELLE, AR, p. A45

METHODIST CHARLTON MEDICAL CENTER, DALLAS, TX, p. A597

METHODIST DALLAS MEDICAL CENTER, DALLAS, TX, p. A597

METHODIST FREMONT HEALTH, FREMONT, NE, p. A385

METHODIST HEALTHCARE MEMPHIS HOSPITALS, MEMPHIS, TN, p. A575

METHODIST HEALTHCARE OLIVE BRANCH HOSPITAL, OLIVE BRANCH, MS, p. A352

METHODIST HOSPITAL, FRANKFORT, INDIANA (see INDIANA UNIVERSITY HEALTH METHODIST HOSPITAL), p. A204

METHODIST HOSPITAL, HENDERSON, KY, p. A253

METHODIST HOSPITAL, SAN ANTONIO, TX, p. A634

METHODIST HOSPITAL FOR SURGERY, ADDISON, TX, p. A581

METHODIST HOSPITAL OF CHICAGO, CHICAGO, IL, p. A178

METHODIST HOSPITAL OF SACRAMENTO, SACRAMENTO, CA, p. A82

METHODIST HOSPITAL OF SOUTHERN CALIFORNIA, ARCADIA, CA, p. A51

METHODIST HOSPITAL SOUTH, JOURDANTON, TX, p. A616

METHODIST HOSPITAL UNION COUNTY, MORGANFIELD, KY, p. A260

METHODIST HOSPITALS, GARY, IN, p. A205

METHODIST JENNIE EDMUNDSON HOSPITAL, COUNCIL BLUFFS, IA, p. A220

METHODIST LE BONHEUR GERMANTOWN HOSPITAL, GERMANTOWN, TENNESSEE (see METHODIST HEALTHCARE MEMPHIS HOSPITALS), p. A570

METHODIST MANSFIELD MEDICAL CENTER, MANSFIELD, TX, p. A623

METHODIST MCKINNEY HOSPITAL, MCKINNEY, TX, p. A624

METHODIST MEDICAL CENTER OF ILLINOIS, PEORIA, ILLINOIS (see UNITYPOINT HEALTH – PEORIA), p. A193

METHODIST MEDICAL CENTER OF OAK RIDGE, OAK RIDGE, TN, p. A578

METHODIST REHABILITATION CENTER, JACKSON, MS, p. A349

METHODIST REHABILITATION HOSPITAL, DALLAS, TX, p. A597

METHODIST RICHARDSON MEDICAL CENTER, RICHARDSON, TX, p. A631

METHODIST SOUTHLAKE HOSPITAL, SOUTHLAKE, TX, p. A637

METHODIST STONE OAK HOSPITAL, SAN ANTONIO, TX, p. A634

METHODIST SUGAR LAND HOSPITAL, SUGAR LAND, TEXAS (see HOUSTON METHODIST SUGAR LAND HOSPITAL), p. A638

METHODIST WEST HOUSTON HOSPITAL, HOUSTON, TEXAS (see HOUSTON METHODIST WEST HOSPITAL), p. A613

METHODIST WILLOWBROOK HOSPITAL, HOUSTON, TEXAS (see HOUSTON METHODIST WILLOWBROOK HOSPITAL), p. A613

METHODIST WOMEN'S HOSPITAL, ELKHORN, NEBRASKA (see NEBRASKA METHODIST HOSPITAL), p. A384

METRO HEALTH – UNIVERSITY OF MICHIGAN HEALTH, WYOMING, MI, p. A325

METROHEALTH MEDICAL CENTER, CLEVELAND, OH, p. A478

METROPOLITAN ST. LOUIS PSYCHIATRIC CENTER, SAINT LOUIS, MO, p. A369

METROPOLITAN STATE HOSPITAL, NORWALK, CA, p. A75

METROPOLITANO DE LA MONTANA, UTUADO, PR, p. A720

METROSOUTH MEDICAL CENTER, BLUE ISLAND, IL, p. A174

METROWEST MEDICAL CENTER, FRAMINGHAM, MA, p. A298

MIAMI COUNTY MEDICAL CENTER, PAOLA, KS, p. A243

MIAMI HEART CAMPUS AT MOUNT SINAI MEDICAL CENTER, MIAMI BEACH, FL, p. A131

MIAMI JEWISH HOME AND HOSPITAL FOR AGED, MIAMI, FL, p. A130

MIAMI VALLEY HOSPITAL, DAYTON, OH, p. A481

MIAMI VETERANS AFFAIRS HEALTHCARE SYSTEM, MIAMI, FL, p. A130

MICHAEL E. DEBAKEY VETERANS AFFAIRS MEDICAL CENTER, HOUSTON, TX, p. A613

MICHIANA BEHAVIORAL HEALTH CENTER, PLYMOUTH, IN, p. A213

MICHIGAN MEDICINE, ANN ARBOR, MI, p. A306

MID COAST HOSPITAL, BRUNSWICK, ME, p. A282

MID–AMERICA REHABILITATION HOSPITAL, SHAWNEE MISSION, KS, p. A245

MID–COLUMBIA MEDICAL CENTER, THE DALLES, OR, p. A518

MID–HUDSON FORENSIC PSYCHIATRIC CENTER, NEW HAMPTON, NEW YORK (see NYC HEALTH + HOSPITALS / HENRY J CARTER SPECIALTY HOSPITAL AND MEDICAL CENTER), p. A432

MID–JEFFERSON EXTENDED CARE HOSPITAL, NEDERLAND, TX, p. A626

MID–VALLEY HOSPITAL, OMAK, WA, p. A676

MIDDLE PARK MEDICAL CENTER–KREMMLING, KREMMLING, CO, p. A102

MIDDLE TENNESSEE MENTAL HEALTH INSTITUTE, NASHVILLE, TN, p. A576

MIDDLESBORO ARH HOSPITAL, MIDDLESBORO, KY, p. A258

MIDDLESEX HOSPITAL, MIDDLETOWN, CT, p. A109

MIDLAND MEMORIAL HOSPITAL, MIDLAND, TX, p. A624

MIDMICHIGAN MEDICAL CENTER – ALPENA, ALPENA, MI, p. A306

MIDMICHIGAN MEDICAL CENTER – WEST BRANCH, WEST BRANCH, MI, p. A325

MIDMICHIGAN MEDICAL CENTER–CLARE, CLARE, MI, p. A309

MIDMICHIGAN MEDICAL CENTER–GLADWIN, GLADWIN, MI, p. A312

MIDMICHIGAN MEDICAL CENTER–GRATIOT, ALMA, MI, p. A306

MIDMICHIGAN MEDICAL CENTER–MIDLAND, MIDLAND, MI, p. A318

MIDSTATE MEDICAL CENTER, MERIDEN, CT, p. A108

MIDWEST MEDICAL CENTER, GALENA, IL, p. A183

MIDWEST ORTHOPEDIC SPECIALTY HOSPITAL, FRANKLIN, WI, p. A695

MIDWEST SURGICAL HOSPITAL, OMAHA, NE, p. A389

MIDWESTERN REGIONAL MEDICAL CENTER, ZION, IL, p. A198

MIKE O'CALLAGHAN FEDERAL HOSPITAL, NELLIS AFB, NV, p. A396

MILAN GENERAL HOSPITAL, MILAN, TN, p. A576

MILBANK AREA HOSPITAL AVERA, MILBANK, SD, p. A562

MILDRED MITCHELL–BATEMAN HOSPITAL, HUNTINGTON, WV, p. A686

MILE BLUFF MEDICAL CENTER, MAUSTON, WI, p. A699

MILFORD HOSPITAL, MILFORD, CT, p. A109

MILFORD REGIONAL MEDICAL CENTER, MILFORD, MA, p. A301

MILFORD VALLEY MEMORIAL HOSPITAL, MILFORD, UT, p. A648

MILLARD FILLMORE SUBURBAN HOSPITAL, WILLIAMSVILLE, NEW YORK (see KALEIDA HEALTH), p. A448

MILLE LACS HEALTH SYSTEM, ONAMIA, MN, p. A337

MILLER COUNTY HOSPITAL, COLQUITT, GA, p. A150

MILLINOCKET REGIONAL HOSPITAL, MILLINOCKET, ME, p. A284

MILLS HEALTH CENTER, SAN MATEO, CA, p. A87

MILLS–PENINSULA HEALTH SERVICES, BURLINGAME, CA, p. A53

MILLWOOD HOSPITAL, ARLINGTON, TX, p. A583

MILWAUKEE COUNTY BEHAVIORAL HEALTH DIVISION, MILWAUKEE, WI, p. A701

MIMBRES MEMORIAL HOSPITAL, DEMING, NM, p. A418

MINDEN MEDICAL CENTER, MINDEN, LA, p. A274

MINERAL COMMUNITY HOSPITAL, SUPERIOR, MT, p. A380

MINERS' COLFAX MEDICAL CENTER, RATON, NM, p. A419

MINIDOKA MEMORIAL HOSPITAL, RUPERT, ID, p. A171

MINIDOKA MEMORIAL HOSPITAL AND EXTENDED CARE FACILITY, RUPERT, IDAHO (see MINIDOKA MEMORIAL HOSPITAL), p. A171

MINIMALLY INVASIVE SURGERY HOSPITAL, LENEXA, KS, p. A239

MINNEAPOLIS VETERANS AFFAIRS HEALTH CARE SYSTEM, MINNEAPOLIS, MN, p. A336

MINNEOLA DISTRICT HOSPITAL, MINNEOLA, KS, p. A241

MINNIE HAMILTON HEALTHCARE CENTER, GRANTSVILLE, WV, p. A685
MIRACLE MILE MEDICAL CENTER, LOS ANGELES, CA, p. A68
MIRIAM HOSPITAL, PROVIDENCE, RI, p. A547
MISSION COMMUNITY HOSPITAL, LOS ANGELES, CA, p. A68
MISSION HOSPITAL, ASHEVILLE, NC, p. A449
MISSION HOSPITAL, MISSION VIEJO, CA, p. A72
MISSION REGIONAL MEDICAL CENTER, MISSION, TX, p. A625
MISSISSIPPI BAPTIST MEDICAL CENTER, JACKSON, MS, p. A349
MISSISSIPPI STATE HOSPITAL, WHITFIELD, MS, p. A355
MISSOURI BAPTIST MEDICAL CENTER, SAINT LOUIS, MO, p. A369
MISSOURI BAPTIST SULLIVAN HOSPITAL, SULLIVAN, MO, p. A372
MISSOURI DELTA MEDICAL CENTER, SIKESTON, MO, p. A371
MISSOURI RIVER MEDICAL CENTER, FORT BENTON, MT, p. A376
MITCHELL COUNTY HOSPITAL, CAMILLA, GA, p. A149
MITCHELL COUNTY HOSPITAL, COLORADO CITY, TX, p. A593
MITCHELL COUNTY HOSPITAL HEALTH SYSTEMS, BELOIT, KS, p. A232
MITCHELL COUNTY REGIONAL HEALTH CENTER, OSAGE, IA, p. A228
MIZELL MEMORIAL HOSPITAL, OPP, AL, p. A22
MOAB REGIONAL HOSPITAL, MOAB, UT, p. A648
MOBERLY REGIONAL MEDICAL CENTER, MOBERLY, MO, p. A365
MOBILE INFIRMARY MEDICAL CENTER, MOBILE, AL, p. A20
MOBRIDGE REGIONAL HOSPITAL, MOBRIDGE, SD, p. A562
MOCCASIN BEND MENTAL HEALTH INSTITUTE, CHATTANOOGA, TN, p. A567
MODESTO MEDICAL CENTER, MODESTO, CA, p. A72
MODOC MEDICAL CENTER, ALTURAS, CA, p. A50
MOHAWK VALLEY PSYCHIATRIC CENTER, UTICA, NY, p. A446
MOLOKAI GENERAL HOSPITAL, KAUNAKAKAI, HI, p. A166
MON HEALTH MEDICAL CENTER, MORGANTOWN, WV, p. A687
MONADNOCK COMMUNITY HOSPITAL, PETERBOROUGH, NH, p. A402
MONCRIEF ARMY COMMUNITY HOSPITAL, FORT JACKSON, SC, p. A553
MONMOUTH MEDICAL CENTER, LONG BRANCH CAMPUS, LONG BRANCH, NJ, p. A407
MONMOUTH MEDICAL CENTER, SOUTHERN CAMPUS, LAKEWOOD, NJ, p. A407
MONONGAHELA VALLEY HOSPITAL, MONONGAHELA, PA, p. A532
MONROE CARELL JR. CHILDREN'S HOSPITAL AT VANDERBILT, NASHVILLE, TENNESSEE (see VANDERBILT UNIVERSITY MEDICAL CENTER), p. A576
MONROE CLINIC, MONROE, WI, p. A701
MONROE COUNTY HOSPITAL, FORSYTH, GA, p. A153
MONROE COUNTY HOSPITAL, MONROEVILLE, AL, p. A21
MONROE COUNTY HOSPITAL AND CLINICS, ALBIA, IA, p. A217
MONROE COUNTY MEDICAL CENTER, TOMPKINSVILLE, KY, p. A261
MONROE HOSPITAL, BLOOMINGTON, IN, p. A200
MONROE REGIONAL HOSPITAL, ABERDEEN, MS, p. A344
MONROE SURGICAL HOSPITAL, MONROE, LA, p. A274
MONROVIA MEMORIAL HOSPITAL, MONROVIA, CA, p. A72
MONTANA STATE HOSPITAL, WARM SPRINGS, MT, p. A380
MONTCLAIR HOSPITAL MEDICAL CENTER, MONTCLAIR, CA, p. A72
MONTEFIORE MOUNT VERNON, MOUNT VERNON, NEW YORK (see BRONXCARE HEALTH SYSTEM), p. A432
MONTEFIORE NEW ROCHELLE, NEW ROCHELLE, NEW YORK (see MOUNT SINAI BETH ISRAEL BROOKLYN), p. A432
MONTEFIORE ST. LUKE'S CORNWALL, NEWBURGH, NY, p. A439
MONTEREY PARK HOSPITAL, MONTEREY PARK, CA, p. A73
MONTEVISTA HOSPITAL, LAS VEGAS, NV, p. A395
MONTGOMERY COUNTY EMERGENCY SERVICE, NORRISTOWN, PA, p. A533
MONTGOMERY COUNTY MEMORIAL HOSPITAL, RED OAK, IA, p. A228
MONTGOMERY DIVISION, MONTGOMERY, ALABAMA (see CENTRAL ALABAMA VETERANS HEALTH CARE SYSTEM), p. A21
MONTGOMERY GENERAL HOSPITAL, MONTGOMERY, WV, p. A687
MONTPELIER HOSPITAL, MONTPELIER, OHIO (see COMMUNITY HOSPITALS AND WELLNESS CENTERS), p. A488
MONTROSE MEMORIAL HOSPITAL, MONTROSE, CO, p. A104
MOORE COUNTY HOSPITAL DISTRICT, DUMAS, TX, p. A600
MOREHOUSE GENERAL HOSPITAL, BASTROP, LA, p. A263

MORGAN COUNTY ARH HOSPITAL, WEST LIBERTY, KY, p. A261
MORGAN MEMORIAL HOSPITAL, MADISON, GA, p. A157
MORRILL COUNTY COMMUNITY HOSPITAL, BRIDGEPORT, NE, p. A383
MORRIS COUNTY HOSPITAL, COUNCIL GROVE, KS, p. A234
MORRIS HOSPITAL & HEALTHCARE CENTERS, MORRIS, IL, p. A190
MORRISON COMMUNITY HOSPITAL, MORRISON, IL, p. A190
MORRISTOWN MEDICAL CENTER, MORRISTOWN, NJ, p. A408
MORRISTOWN–HAMBLEN HEALTHCARE SYSTEM, MORRISTOWN, TN, p. A576
MORROW COUNTY HOSPITAL, MOUNT GILEAD, OH, p. A488
MORTON COUNTY HEALTH SYSTEM, ELKHART, KS, p. A234
MORTON HOSPITAL AND MEDICAL CENTER, TAUNTON, MA, p. A304
MORTON PLANT HOSPITAL, CLEARWATER, FL, p. A119
MORTON PLANT NORTH BAY HOSPITAL, NEW PORT RICHEY, FL, p. A132
MOSAIC LIFE CARE AT ST. JOSEPH – MEDICAL CENTER, SAINT JOSEPH, MO, p. A368
MOSAIC MEDICAL CENTER – ALBANY, ALBANY, MO, p. A356
MOSAIC MEDICAL CENTER – MARYVILLE, MARYVILLE, MO, p. A365
MOSES H. CONE MEMORIAL HOSPITAL, GREENSBORO, NC, p. A455
MOSES TAYLOR HOSPITAL, SCRANTON, PA, p. A540
MOTION PICTURE AND TELEVISION FUND HOSPITAL AND RESIDENTIAL SERVICES, LOS ANGELES, CA, p. A68
MOUNT AUBURN HOSPITAL, CAMBRIDGE, MA, p. A297
MOUNT CARMEL, COLUMBUS, OH, p. A479
MOUNT CARMEL NEW ALBANY SURGICAL HOSPITAL, NEW ALBANY, OH, p. A488
MOUNT CARMEL ST. ANN'S, WESTERVILLE, OH, p. A494
MOUNT DESERT ISLAND HOSPITAL, BAR HARBOR, ME, p. A281
MOUNT GRANT GENERAL HOSPITAL, HAWTHORNE, NV, p. A394
MOUNT NITTANY MEDICAL CENTER, STATE COLLEGE, PA, p. A541
MOUNT SINAI HOSPITAL, CHICAGO, IL, p. A178
MOUNT SINAI MEDICAL CENTER, MIAMI BEACH, FL, p. A131
MOUNT SINAI REHABILITATION HOSPITAL, HARTFORD, CT, p. A108
MOUNT ST. MARY'S HOSPITAL AND HEALTH CENTER, LEWISTON, NY, p. A430
MOUNTAIN LAKES MEDICAL CENTER, CLAYTON, GA, p. A150
MOUNTAIN RIVER BIRTHING AND SURGERY CENTER, BLACKFOOT, ID, p. A167
MOUNTAIN VALLEY REGIONAL REHABILITATION HOSPITAL, PRESCOTT VALLEY, AZ, p. A35
MOUNTAIN VIEW HOSPITAL, GADSDEN, AL, p. A18
MOUNTAIN VIEW HOSPITAL, IDAHO FALLS, ID, p. A169
MOUNTAIN VIEW HOSPITAL, PAYSON, UT, p. A650
MOUNTAIN VIEW REGIONAL HOSPITAL, CASPER, WY, p. A710
MOUNTAIN VIEW REGIONAL MEDICAL CENTER, NORTON, VA, p. A664
MOUNTAIN VISTA MEDICAL CENTER, MESA, AZ, p. A31
MOUNTAIN WEST MEDICAL CENTER, TOOELE, UT, p. A653
MOUNTAINVIEW HOSPITAL, LAS VEGAS, NV, p. A395
MOUNTAINVIEW MEDICAL CENTER, WHITE SULPHUR SPRINGS, MT, p. A381
MOUNTAINVIEW REGIONAL MEDICAL CENTER, LAS CRUCES, NM, p. A419
MOUNTAIN'S EDGE HOSPITAL, LAS VEGAS, NV, p. A395
MOUNTRAIL COUNTY MEDICAL CENTER, STANLEY, ND, p. A469
MT. ASCUTNEY HOSPITAL AND HEALTH CENTER, WINDSOR, VT, p. A655
MT. GRAHAM REGIONAL MEDICAL CENTER, SAFFORD, AZ, p. A35
MT. SAN RAFAEL HOSPITAL, TRINIDAD, CO, p. A106
MT. WASHINGTON PEDIATRIC HOSPITAL, BALTIMORE, MD, p. A287
MUENSTER MEMORIAL HOSPITAL, MUENSTER, TX, p. A625
MULESHOE AREA MEDICAL CENTER, MULESHOE, TX, p. A625
MULTICARE AUBURN MEDICAL CENTER, AUBURN, WA, p. A670
MULTICARE DEACONESS HOSPITAL, SPOKANE, WA, p. A679
MULTICARE GOOD SAMARITAN HOSPITAL, PUYALLUP, WA, p. A677
MULTICARE MARY BRIDGE CHILDREN'S HOSPITAL AND HEALTH CENTER, TACOMA, WA, p. A680
MULTICARE TACOMA GENERAL HOSPITAL, TACOMA, WA, p. A680
MULTICARE VALLEY HOSPITAL, SPOKANE VALLEY, WA, p. A680
MUNISING MEMORIAL HOSPITAL, MUNISING, MI, p. A318

MUNSON HEALTHCARE CADILLAC HOSPITAL, CADILLAC, MI, p. A308
MUNSON HEALTHCARE CHARLEVOIX HOSPITAL, CHARLEVOIX, MI, p. A308
MUNSON HEALTHCARE GRAYLING HOSPITAL, GRAYLING, MI, p. A313
MUNSON HEALTHCARE MANISTEE HOSPITAL, MANISTEE, MI, p. A317
MUNSON HEALTHCARE OTSEGO MEMORIAL HOSPITAL, GAYLORD, MI, p. A312
MUNSON MEDICAL CENTER, TRAVERSE CITY, MI, p. A323
MURRAY COUNTY MEDICAL CENTER, SLAYTON, MN, p. A340
MURRAY–CALLOWAY COUNTY HOSPITAL, MURRAY, KY, p. A258
MUSC HEALTH CHESTER MEDICAL CENTER, CHESTER, SC, p. A550
MUSC HEALTH FLORENCE MEDICAL CENTER, FLORENCE, SC, p. A553
MUSC HEALTH LANCASTER MEDICAL CENTER, LANCASTER, SC, p. A555
MUSC HEALTH MARION MEDICAL CENTER, MULLINS, SC, p. A556
MUSC HEALTH OF MEDICAL UNIVERSITY OF SOUTH CAROLINA, CHARLESTON, SC, p. A550
MUSCOGEE CREEK NATION MEDICAL CENTER, OKMULGEE, OK, p. A506
MUSCOGEE CREEK NATION PHYSICAL REHABILITATION CENTER, OKMULGEE, OK, p. A506
MUSKOGEE REGIONAL MEDICAL CENTER, MUSKOGEE, OKLAHOMA (see SAINT FRANCIS HOSPITAL MUSKOGEE), p. A502
MYRTUE MEDICAL CENTER, HARLAN, IA, p. A224

N

NACOGDOCHES MEDICAL CENTER, NACOGDOCHES, TX, p. A625
NACOGDOCHES MEMORIAL HOSPITAL, NACOGDOCHES, TX, p. A626
NANTICOKE MEMORIAL HOSPITAL, SEAFORD, DE, p. A114
NANTUCKET COTTAGE HOSPITAL, NANTUCKET, MA, p. A301
NAPA STATE HOSPITAL, NAPA, CA, p. A74
NASH UNC HEALTH CARE, ROCKY MOUNT, NC, p. A461
NASHOBA VALLEY MEDICAL CENTER, AYER, MA, p. A294
NASHVILLE GENERAL HOSPITAL, NASHVILLE, TN, p. A576
NASSAU UNIVERSITY MEDICAL CENTER, EAST MEADOW, NY, p. A427
NATCHAUG HOSPITAL, MANSFIELD CENTER, CT, p. A108
NATCHITOCHES REGIONAL MEDICAL CENTER, NATCHITOCHES, LA, p. A274
NATHAN LITTAUER HOSPITAL AND NURSING HOME, GLOVERSVILLE, NY, p. A428
NATIONAL INSTITUTES OF HEALTH CLINICAL CENTER, BETHESDA, MD, p. A289
NATIONAL JEWISH HEALTH, DENVER, CO, p. A99
NATIONAL NAVAL MEDICAL CENTER, BETHESDA, MARYLAND (see WALTER REED NATIONAL MILITARY MEDICAL CENTER), p. A289
NATIONAL PARK MEDICAL CENTER, HOT SPRINGS, AR, p. A43
NATIONAL REHABILITATION HOSPITAL, WASHINGTON, DC, p. A116
NATIONWIDE CHILDREN'S HOSPITAL, COLUMBUS, OH, p. A479
NATIVIDAD MEDICAL CENTER, SALINAS, CA, p. A82
NATURE COAST REGIONAL HOSPITAL, WILLISTON, FL, p. A144
NAVAL HOSPITAL BEAUFORT, BEAUFORT, SC, p. A549
NAVAL HOSPITAL BREMERTON, BREMERTON, WA, p. A671
NAVAL HOSPITAL CAMP LEJEUNE, CAMP LEJEUNE, NC, p. A450
NAVAL HOSPITAL CAMP PENDLETON, CAMP PENDLETON, CA, p. A54
NAVAL HOSPITAL JACKSONVILLE, JACKSONVILLE, FL, p. A125
NAVAL HOSPITAL LEMOORE, LEMOORE, CA, p. A64
NAVAL HOSPITAL OAK HARBOR, OAK HARBOR, WA, p. A675
NAVAL HOSPITAL PENSACOLA, PENSACOLA, FL, p. A136
NAVAL MEDICAL CENTER, PORTSMOUTH, VA, p. A665
NAVAL MEDICAL CENTER SAN DIEGO, SAN DIEGO, CA, p. A83
NAVARRO REGIONAL HOSPITAL, CORSICANA, TX, p. A594
NAVICENT HEALTH BALDWIN, MILLEDGEVILLE, GA, p. A157
NAVOS, SEATTLE, WA, p. A677
NAZARETH HOSPITAL, PHILADELPHIA, PA, p. A535

NCH BAKER HOSPITAL, NAPLES, FL, p. A132
NEA BAPTIST MEMORIAL HOSPITAL, JONESBORO, AR, p. A44
NEBRASKA MEDICINE – BELLEVUE, BELLEVUE, NE, p. A383
NEBRASKA MEDICINE – NEBRASKA MEDICAL CENTER, OMAHA, NE, p. A389
NEBRASKA METHODIST HOSPITAL, OMAHA, NE, p. A389
NEBRASKA PENAL AND CORRECTIONAL HOSPITAL, LINCOLN, NE, p. A387
NEBRASKA SPINE HOSPITAL, OMAHA, NE, p. A389
NELL J. REDFIELD MEMORIAL HOSPITAL, MALAD CITY, ID, p. A170
NELSON COUNTY HEALTH SYSTEM, MCVILLE, ND, p. A468
NEMAHA COUNTY HOSPITAL, AUBURN, NE, p. A382
NEMAHA VALLEY COMMUNITY HOSPITAL, SENECA, KS, p. A245
NEMOURS CHILDREN'S HOSPITAL, ORLANDO, FL, p. A134
NEOSHO MEMORIAL REGIONAL MEDICAL CENTER, CHANUTE, KS, p. A233
NESHOBA COUNTY GENERAL HOSPITAL, PHILADELPHIA, MS, p. A353
NESS COUNTY HOSPITAL DISTRICT NO 2, NESS CITY, KS, p. A241
NEURODIAGNOSTIC INSTITUTE AND ADVANCED TREATMENT CENTER, INDIANAPOLIS, IN, p. A207
NEUROPSYCHIATRIC HOSPITAL OF INDIANAPOLIS, INDIANAPOLIS, IN, p. A207
NEVADA REGIONAL MEDICAL CENTER, NEVADA, MO, p. A366
NEW BRAUNFELS REGIONAL REHABILITATION HOSPITAL, NEW BRAUNFELS, TX, p. A626
NEW BRIDGE MEDICAL CENTER, PARAMUS, NJ, p. A410
NEW ENGLAND BAPTIST HOSPITAL, BOSTON, MA, p. A296
NEW ENGLAND REHABILITATION HOSPITAL OF PORTLAND, PORTLAND, ME, p. A284
NEW ENGLAND SINAI HOSPITAL AND REHABILITATION CENTER, STOUGHTON, MA, p. A304
NEW HAMPSHIRE HOSPITAL, CONCORD, NH, p. A399
NEW HANOVER REGIONAL MEDICAL CENTER, WILMINGTON, NC, p. A464
NEW LONDON HOSPITAL, NEW LONDON, NH, p. A401
NEW MEXICO BEHAVIORAL HEALTH INSTITUTE AT LAS VEGAS, LAS VEGAS, NM, p. A419
NEW MEXICO REHABILITATION CENTER, ROSWELL, NM, p. A420
NEW MEXICO VETERANS AFFAIRS HEALTH CARE SYSTEM – RAYMOND G. MURPHY MEDICAL CENTER, ALBUQUERQUE, NM, p. A417
NEW ORLEANS EAST HOSPITAL, NEW ORLEANS, LA, p. A275
NEW ULM MEDICAL CENTER, NEW ULM, MN, p. A337
NEW YORK–PRESBYTERIAN HOSPITAL, WESTCHESTER DIVISION, WHITE PLAINS, NEW YORK (see NEW YORK–PRESBYTERIAN HOSPITAL), p. A447
NEW YORK–PRESBYTERIAN/HUDSON VALLEY HOSPITAL, CORTLANDT MANOR, NY, p. A426
NEWARK BETH ISRAEL MEDICAL CENTER, NEWARK, NJ, p. A409
NEWARK–WAYNE COMMUNITY HOSPITAL, NEWARK, NY, p. A439
NEWBERRY COUNTY MEMORIAL HOSPITAL, NEWBERRY, SC, p. A556
NEWMAN MEMORIAL HOSPITAL, SHATTUCK, OK, p. A507
NEWMAN REGIONAL HEALTH, EMPORIA, KS, p. A234
NEWPORT BAY HOSPITAL, NEWPORT BEACH, CA, p. A74
NEWPORT HOSPITAL, NEWPORT, RI, p. A547
NEWPORT HOSPITAL AND HEALTH SERVICES, NEWPORT, WA, p. A675
NEWPORT NEWS BEHAVIORAL HEALTH CENTER, NEWPORT NEWS, VA, p. A663
NEWTON MEDICAL CENTER, NEWTON, KS, p. A241
NEWTON MEDICAL CENTER, NEWTON, NJ, p. A410
NEWTON–WELLESLEY HOSPITAL, NEWTON LOWER FALLS, MA, p. A301
NEXUS SPECIALTY HOSPITAL, SHENANDOAH, TX, p. A636
NEXUS SPECIALTY HOSPITAL THE WOODLANDS, THE WOODLANDS, TX, p. A641
NIAGARA FALLS MEMORIAL MEDICAL CENTER, NIAGARA FALLS, NY, p. A439
NICHOLAS H. NOYES MEMORIAL HOSPITAL, DANSVILLE, NY, p. A426
NICKLAUS CHILDREN'S HOSPITAL, MIAMI, FL, p. A131
NIOBRARA HEALTH AND LIFE CENTER, LUSK, WY, p. A712
NIOBRARA VALLEY HOSPITAL, LYNCH, NE, p. A387
NIX HEALTH CARE SYSTEM, SAN ANTONIO, TX, p. A634
NOCONA GENERAL HOSPITAL, NOCONA, TX, p. A626
NOLAND HOSPITAL ANNISTON, ANNISTON, AL, p. A13
NOLAND HOSPITAL BIRMINGHAM, BIRMINGHAM, AL, p. A15
NOLAND HOSPITAL DOTHAN, DOTHAN, AL, p. A17
NOLAND HOSPITAL MONTGOMERY, MONTGOMERY, AL, p. A21
NOLAND HOSPITAL SHELBY, ALABASTER, AL, p. A13
NOLAND HOSPITAL TUSCALOOSA, TUSCALOOSA, AL, p. A24

NOR–LEA HOSPITAL DISTRICT, LOVINGTON, NM, p. A419
NORMAN REGIONAL HEALTH SYSTEM, NORMAN, OK, p. A503
NORMAN REGIONAL MOORE, MOORE, OKLAHOMA (see NORMAN REGIONAL HEALTH SYSTEM), p. A502
NORRISTOWN STATE HOSPITAL, NORRISTOWN, PA, p. A533
NORTH ALABAMA MEDICAL CENTER, FLORENCE, AL, p. A18
NORTH ALABAMA SPECIALTY HOSPITAL, ATHENS, AL, p. A14
NORTH ARKANSAS REGIONAL MEDICAL CENTER, HARRISON, AR, p. A42
NORTH BALDWIN INFIRMARY, BAY MINETTE, AL, p. A14
NORTH BIG HORN HOSPITAL DISTRICT, LOVELL, WY, p. A712
NORTH CADDO MEDICAL CENTER, VIVIAN, LA, p. A280
NORTH CANYON MEDICAL CENTER, GOODING, ID, p. A169
NORTH CAROLINA SPECIALTY HOSPITAL, DURHAM, NC, p. A453
NORTH CENTRAL HEALTH CARE, WAUSAU, WI, p. A708
NORTH CENTRAL HEALTH CARE FACILITIES, WAUSAU, WISCONSIN (see NORTH CENTRAL HEALTH CARE), p. A708
NORTH CENTRAL SURGICAL CENTER, DALLAS, TX, p. A597
NORTH COLORADO MEDICAL CENTER, GREELEY, CO, p. A101
NORTH COUNTRY HOSPITAL AND HEALTH CENTER, NEWPORT, VT, p. A654
NORTH COUNTRY REGIONAL HOSPITAL, BEMIDJI, MINNESOTA (see SANFORD BEMIDJI MEDICAL CENTER), p. A328
NORTH DAKOTA STATE HOSPITAL, JAMESTOWN, ND, p. A468
NORTH FLORIDA REGIONAL MEDICAL CENTER, GAINESVILLE, FL, p. A123
NORTH FLORIDA/SOUTH GEORGIA VETERAN'S HEALTH SYSTEM, GAINESVILLE, FL, p. A123
NORTH HAWAII COMMUNITY HOSPITAL, KAMUELA, HI, p. A165
NORTH KANSAS CITY HOSPITAL, NORTH KANSAS CITY, MO, p. A366
NORTH LITTLE ROCK DIVISION, NORTH LITTLE ROCK, ARKANSAS (see CENTRAL ARKANSAS VETERANS HEALTHCARE SYSTEM), p. A47
NORTH MEMORIAL HEALTH HOSPITAL, ROBBINSDALE, MN, p. A338
NORTH METRO MEDICAL CENTER, JACKSONVILLE, AR, p. A43
NORTH MISSISSIPPI MEDICAL CENTER – TUPELO, TUPELO, MS, p. A354
NORTH MISSISSIPPI MEDICAL CENTER GILMORE–AMORY, AMORY, MS, p. A344
NORTH MISSISSIPPI MEDICAL CENTER–EUPORA, EUPORA, MS, p. A346
NORTH MISSISSIPPI MEDICAL CENTER–HAMILTON, HAMILTON, AL, p. A19
NORTH MISSISSIPPI MEDICAL CENTER–IUKA, IUKA, MS, p. A348
NORTH MISSISSIPPI MEDICAL CENTER–PONTOTOC, PONTOTOC, MS, p. A353
NORTH MISSISSIPPI MEDICAL CENTER–WEST POINT, WEST POINT, MS, p. A355
NORTH MISSISSIPPI STATE HOSPITAL, TUPELO, MS, p. A354
NORTH OAK REGIONAL MEDICAL CENTER, SENATOBIA, MS, p. A354
NORTH OAKS MEDICAL CENTER, HAMMOND, LA, p. A268
NORTH OAKS REHABILITATION HOSPITAL, HAMMOND, LA, p. A268
NORTH OKALOOSA MEDICAL CENTER, CRESTVIEW, FL, p. A120
NORTH OTTAWA COMMUNITY HOSPITAL, GRAND HAVEN, MI, p. A312
NORTH PHILADELPHIA HEALTH SYSTEM, PHILADELPHIA, PA, p. A536
NORTH RUNNELS HOSPITAL, WINTERS, TX, p. A646
NORTH SHORE CHILDREN'S HOSPITAL, SALEM, MASSACHUSETTS (see MASSGENERAL FOR CHILDREN AT NORTH SHORE MEDICAL CENTER), p. A303
NORTH SHORE HEALTH, GRAND MARAIS, MN, p. A332
NORTH SHORE MEDICAL CENTER, MIAMI, FL, p. A131
NORTH SHORE MEDICAL CENTER, SALEM, MA, p. A303
NORTH SHORE UNIVERSITY HOSPITAL, MANHASSET, NEW YORK (see NEW YORK–PRESBYTERIAN HOSPITAL), p. A430
NORTH SIDE HOSPITAL, JOHNSON CITY, TENNESSEE (see FRANKLIN WOODS COMMUNITY HOSPITAL), p. A571
NORTH STAR BEHAVIORAL HEALTH SYSTEM, ANCHORAGE, AK, p. A25
NORTH SUBURBAN MEDICAL CENTER, THORNTON, CO, p. A105
NORTH SUNFLOWER MEDICAL CENTER, RULEVILLE, MS, p. A354
NORTH TAMPA BEHAVIORAL HEALTH, WESLEY CHAPEL, FL, p. A143

NORTH TEXAS MEDICAL CENTER, GAINESVILLE, TX, p. A607
NORTH TEXAS STATE HOSPITAL, VERNON, TX, p. A643
NORTH TEXAS STATE HOSPITAL, WICHITA FALLS CAMPUS, WICHITA FALLS, TX, p. A645
NORTH VALLEY HEALTH CENTER, WARREN, MN, p. A342
NORTH VALLEY HOSPITAL, TONASKET, WA, p. A681
NORTH VALLEY HOSPITAL, WHITEFISH, MT, p. A381
NORTH VISTA HOSPITAL, NORTH LAS VEGAS, NV, p. A396
NORTHBAY MEDICAL CENTER, FAIRFIELD, CA, p. A57
NORTHBAY VACAVALLEY HOSPITAL, VACAVILLE, CA, p. A93
NORTHBROOK BEHAVIORAL HEALTH HOSPITAL, BLACKWOOD, NJ, p. A403
NORTHCOAST BEHAVIORAL HEALTHCARE, NORTHFIELD, OH, p. A488
NORTHCREST MEDICAL CENTER, SPRINGFIELD, TN, p. A579
NORTHEAST GEORGIA MEDICAL CENTER, GAINESVILLE, GA, p. A154
NORTHEAST GEORGIA MEDICAL CENTER BARROW, WINDER, GA, p. A163
NORTHEAST GEORGIA MEDICAL CENTER BRASELTON, BRASELTON, GA, p. A148
NORTHEAST REGIONAL MEDICAL CENTER, KIRKSVILLE, MO, p. A363
NORTHEAST REHABILITATION HOSPITAL, SALEM, NH, p. A402
NORTHEASTERN CENTER, AUBURN, IN, p. A199
NORTHEASTERN HEALTH SYSTEM, TAHLEQUAH, OK, p. A508
NORTHEASTERN HEALTH SYSTEM SEQUOYAH, SALLISAW, OK, p. A507
NORTHEASTERN NEVADA REGIONAL HOSPITAL, ELKO, NV, p. A393
NORTHEASTERN VERMONT REGIONAL HOSPITAL, SAINT JOHNSBURY, VT, p. A655
NORTHERN ARIZONA VETERANS AFFAIRS HEALTH CARE SYSTEM, PRESCOTT, AZ, p. A34
NORTHERN CALIFORNIA REHABILITATION HOSPITAL, REDDING, CA, p. A79
NORTHERN COCHISE COMMUNITY HOSPITAL, WILLCOX, AZ, p. A38
NORTHERN COLORADO LONG TERM ACUTE HOSPITAL, JOHNSTOWN, CO, p. A102
NORTHERN COLORADO REHABILITATION HOSPITAL, JOHNSTOWN, CO, p. A102
NORTHERN DUTCHESS HOSPITAL, RHINEBECK, NY, p. A442
NORTHERN HOSPITAL OF SURRY COUNTY, MOUNT AIRY, NC, p. A459
NORTHERN IDAHO ADVANCED CARE HOSPITAL, POST FALLS, ID, p. A171
NORTHERN INYO HOSPITAL, BISHOP, CA, p. A53
NORTHERN LIGHT BLUE HILL HOSPITAL, BLUE HILL, ME, p. A282
NORTHERN LIGHT CA DEAN HOSPITAL, GREENVILLE, ME, p. A283
NORTHERN LIGHT EASTERN MAINE MEDICAL CENTER, BANGOR, ME, p. A281
NORTHERN LIGHT INLAND HOSPITAL, WATERVILLE, ME, p. A285
NORTHERN LIGHT MAINE COAST HOSPITAL, ELLSWORTH, ME, p. A283
NORTHERN LIGHT MERCY HOSPITAL, PORTLAND, ME, p. A284
NORTHERN LOUISIANA MEDICAL CENTER, RUSTON, LA, p. A277
NORTHERN MAINE MEDICAL CENTER, FORT KENT, ME, p. A283
NORTHERN MONTANA HEALTH CARE, HAVRE, MT, p. A377
NORTHERN NAVAJO MEDICAL CENTER, SHIPROCK, NM, p. A420
NORTHERN NEVADA ADULT MENTAL HEALTH SERVICES, SPARKS, NV, p. A398
NORTHERN NEVADA MEDICAL CENTER, SPARKS, NV, p. A398
NORTHERN ROCKIES MEDICAL CENTER, CUT BANK, MT, p. A375
NORTHERN UTAH REHABILITATION HOSPITAL, SOUTH OGDEN, UT, p. A653
NORTHERN VIRGINIA MENTAL HEALTH INSTITUTE, FALLS CHURCH, VA, p. A659
NORTHERN WESTCHESTER HOSPITAL, MOUNT KISCO, NEW YORK (see BRONXCARE HEALTH SYSTEM), p. A432
NORTHFIELD HOSPITAL AND CLINICS, NORTHFIELD, MN, p. A337
NORTHLAKE BEHAVIORAL HEALTH SYSTEM, MANDEVILLE, LA, p. A273
NORTHLAND LTAC HOSPITAL, KANSAS CITY, MISSOURI (see KINDRED HOSPITAL NORTHLAND), p. A362
NORTHLIGHT SEBASTICOOK VALLEY HOSPITAL, PITTSFIELD, ME, p. A284
NORTHPORT VETERANS AFFAIRS MEDICAL CENTER, NORTHPORT, NY, p. A439

NORTHRIDGE HOSPITAL MEDICAL CENTER, LOS ANGELES, CA, p. A68
NORTHRIDGE MEDICAL CENTER, COMMERCE, GA, p. A151
NORTHSHORE GLENBROOK HOSPITAL, GLENVIEW, ILLINOIS (see NORTHSHORE UNIVERSITY HEALTH SYSTEM), p. A184
NORTHSHORE HIGHLAND PARK HOSPITAL, HIGHLAND PARK, ILLINOIS (see NORTHSHORE UNIVERSITY HEALTH SYSTEM), p. A185
NORTHSHORE REGIONAL MEDICAL CENTER, SLIDELL, LOUISIANA (see OCHSNER MEDICAL CENTER – NORTH SHORE), p. A278
NORTHSHORE SPECIALTY HOSPITAL, COVINGTON, LOUISIANA (see PAM SPECIALTY HOSPITAL OF COVINGTON), p. A266
NORTHSHORE UNIVERSITY HEALTH SYSTEM, EVANSTON, IL, p. A182
NORTHSIDE HOSPITAL, ATLANTA, GA, p. A146
NORTHSIDE HOSPITAL, SAINT PETERSBURG, FL, p. A138
NORTHSIDE HOSPITAL–CHEROKEE, CANTON, GA, p. A149
NORTHSIDE HOSPITAL–FORSYTH, CUMMING, GA, p. A151
NORTHWEST CENTER FOR BEHAVIORAL HEALTH, FORT SUPPLY, OK, p. A500
NORTHWEST COMMUNITY HOSPITAL, ARLINGTON HEIGHTS, IL, p. A173
NORTHWEST FLORIDA COMMUNITY HOSPITAL, CHIPLEY, FL, p. A119
NORTHWEST HEALTH PHYSICIANS' SPECIALTY HOSPITAL, FAYETTEVILLE, AR, p. A41
NORTHWEST HILLS SURGICAL HOSPITAL, AUSTIN, TX, p. A586
NORTHWEST HOSPITAL, RANDALLSTOWN, MD, p. A293
NORTHWEST MEDICAL CENTER – SPRINGDALE, SPRINGDALE, AR, p. A48
NORTHWEST MEDICAL CENTER, MARGATE, FL, p. A129
NORTHWEST MEDICAL CENTER, TUCSON, AZ, p. A37
NORTHWEST MEDICAL CENTER, WINFIELD, AL, p. A24
NORTHWEST MISSISSIPPI MEDICAL CENTER, CLARKSDALE, MS, p. A345
NORTHWEST MISSOURI PSYCHIATRIC REHABILITATION CENTER, SAINT JOSEPH, MO, p. A368
NORTHWEST OHIO PSYCHIATRIC HOSPITAL, TOLEDO, OH, p. A492
NORTHWEST SPECIALTY HOSPITAL, POST FALLS, ID, p. A171
NORTHWEST SURGICAL HOSPITAL, OKLAHOMA CITY, OK, p. A504
NORTHWEST TEXAS HEALTHCARE SYSTEM, AMARILLO, TX, p. A582
NORTHWESTERN MEDICAL CENTER, SAINT ALBANS, VT, p. A655
NORTHWESTERN MEDICINE CENTRAL DUPAGE HOSPITAL, WINFIELD, IL, p. A198
NORTHWESTERN MEDICINE DELNOR HOSPITAL, GENEVA, IL, p. A184
NORTHWESTERN MEDICINE KISHWAUKEE HOSPITAL, DEKALB, IL, p. A181
NORTHWESTERN MEDICINE LAKE FOREST HOSPITAL, LAKE FOREST, IL, p. A187
NORTHWESTERN MEDICINE MARIANJOY REHABILITATION HOSPITAL, WHEATON, IL, p. A198
NORTHWESTERN MEDICINE MCHENRY, MCHENRY, IL, p. A189
NORTHWESTERN MEDICINE VALLEY WEST HOSPITAL, SANDWICH, IL, p. A195
NORTHWESTERN MEMORIAL HOSPITAL, CHICAGO, IL, p. A178
NORTHWOOD DEACONESS HEALTH CENTER, NORTHWOOD, ND, p. A469
NORTON CHILDREN'S HOSPITAL, LOUISVILLE, KY, p. A256
NORTON COMMUNITY HOSPITAL, NORTON, VA, p. A664
NORTON COUNTY HOSPITAL, NORTON, KS, p. A242
NORTON HEALTHCARE PAVILION, LOUISVILLE, KENTUCKY (see NORTON HOSPITAL), p. A256
NORTON HOSPITAL, LOUISVILLE, KY, p. A256
NORTON SOUND REGIONAL HOSPITAL, NOME, AK, p. A26
NORWALK HOSPITAL, NORWALK, CT, p. A110
NORWEGIAN AMERICAN HOSPITAL, CHICAGO, IL, p. A179
NORWOOD HEALTH CENTER, MARSHFIELD, WI, p. A699
NORWOOD HOSPITAL, NORWOOD, MA, p. A302
NOVANT HEALTH BRUNSWICK MEDICAL CENTER, BOLIVIA, NC, p. A450
NOVANT HEALTH CHARLOTTE ORTHOPAEDIC HOSPITAL, CHARLOTTE, NC, p. A451
NOVANT HEALTH FORSYTH MEDICAL CENTER, WINSTON, NC, p. A464
NOVANT HEALTH HUNTERSVILLE MEDICAL CENTER, HUNTERSVILLE, NC, p. A456
NOVANT HEALTH MATTHEWS MEDICAL CENTER, MATTHEWS, NC, p. A458

NOVANT HEALTH MEDICAL PARK HOSPITAL, WINSTON, NC, p. A464
NOVANT HEALTH PRESBYTERIAN MEDICAL CENTER, CHARLOTTE, NC, p. A451
NOVANT HEALTH ROWAN MEDICAL CENTER, SALISBURY, NC, p. A461
NOVANT HEALTH THOMASVILLE MEDICAL CENTER, THOMASVILLE, NC, p. A463
NOVANT HEALTH UVA HEALTH SYSTEM CULPEPER MEDICAL CENTER, CULPEPER, VA, p. A658
NOVANT HEALTH UVA HEALTH SYSTEM HAYMARKET MEDICAL CENTER, HAYMARKET, VA, p. A661
NOVANT HEALTH UVA HEALTH SYSTEM PRINCE WILLIAM MEDICAL CENTER, MANASSAS, VA, p. A662
NOVATO COMMUNITY HOSPITAL, NOVATO, CA, p. A75
NOXUBEE GENERAL HOSPITAL, MACON, MS, p. A350
NYACK HOSPITAL, NYACK, NY, p. A440
NYU WINTHROP HOSPITAL, MINEOLA, NEW YORK (see NEW YORK–PRESBYTERIAN HOSPITAL), p. A431

O

OAK HILL HOSPITAL, BROOKSVILLE, FL, p. A119
OAK VALLEY HOSPITAL DISTRICT, OAKDALE, CA, p. A75
OAKBEND MEDICAL CENTER, RICHMOND, TX, p. A631
OAKDALE COMMUNITY HOSPITAL, OAKDALE, LA, p. A276
OAKLAND MEDICAL CENTER, OAKLAND, CA, p. A75
OAKLAWN HOSPITAL, MARSHALL, MI, p. A317
OAKLAWN PSYCHIATRIC CENTER, GOSHEN, IN, p. A205
OAKLEAF SURGICAL HOSPITAL, ALTOONA, WI, p. A691
OAKWOOD SPRINGS, OKLAHOMA CITY, OK, p. A504
OASIS BEHAVIORAL HEALTH – CHANDLER, CHANDLER, AZ, p. A28
OASIS HOSPITAL, PHOENIX, AZ, p. A33
O'BLENESS MEMORIAL HOSPITAL, ATHENS, OH, p. A472
OCALA REGIONAL MEDICAL CENTER, OCALA, FL, p. A133
OCEAN BEACH HOSPITAL, ILWACO, WA, p. A674
OCEAN SPRINGS HOSPITAL, OCEAN SPRINGS, MISSISSIPPI (see SINGING RIVER HEALTH SYSTEM), p. A352
OCEANS BEHAVIORAL HEALTH CENTER PERMIAN BASIN, MIDLAND, TX, p. A624
OCEANS BEHAVIORAL HOSPITAL ABILENE, ABILENE, TX, p. A581
OCEANS BEHAVIORAL HOSPITAL KATY, KATY, TX, p. A617
OCEANS BEHAVIORAL HOSPITAL LONGVIEW, LONGVIEW, TX, p. A621
OCEANS BEHAVIORAL HOSPITAL LUFKIN, LUFKIN, TX, p. A622
OCEANS BEHAVIORAL HOSPITAL OF ALEXANDRIA, ALEXANDRIA, LA, p. A262
OCEANS BEHAVIORAL HOSPITAL OF BATON ROUGE, BATON ROUGE, LA, p. A263
OCEANS BEHAVIORAL HOSPITAL OF BROUSSARD, BROUSSARD, LA, p. A265
OCEANS BEHAVIORAL HOSPITAL OF CROWLEY, RAYNE, LA, p. A277
OCEANS BEHAVIORAL HOSPITAL OF DE RIDDER, DERIDDER, LA, p. A267
OCEANS BEHAVIORAL HOSPITAL OF GREATER NEW ORLEANS, KENNER, LA, p. A270
OCEANS BEHAVIORAL HOSPITAL OF KENTWOOD, KENTWOOD, LA, p. A270
OCEANS BEHAVIORAL HOSPITAL OF LAKE CHARLES, LAKE CHARLES, LA, p. A272
OCEANS BEHAVIORAL HOSPITAL OF OPELOUSAS, OPELOUSAS, LA, p. A276
OCH REGIONAL MEDICAL CENTER, STARKVILLE, MS, p. A354
OCHILTREE GENERAL HOSPITAL, PERRYTON, TX, p. A628
OCHSNER LSU HEALTH SHREVEPORT – MONROE MEDICAL CENTER, MONROE, LA, p. A274
OCHSNER LSU HEALTH SHREVPORT – ACADEMIC MEDICAL CENTER, SHREVEPORT, LA, p. A278
OCHSNER MEDICAL CENTER – BATON ROUGE, BATON ROUGE, LA, p. A263
OCHSNER MEDICAL CENTER – KENNER, KENNER, LA, p. A270
OCHSNER MEDICAL CENTER – NORTH SHORE, SLIDELL, LA, p. A279
OCHSNER MEDICAL CENTER, NEW ORLEANS, LA, p. A275
OCHSNER REHABILITATON HOSPITAL WEST CAMPUS, JEFFERSON, LA, p. A269
OCHSNER ST. ANNE GENERAL HOSPITAL, RACELAND, LA, p. A277
O'CONNOR HOSPITAL, DELHI, NY, p. A426

O'CONNOR HOSPITAL, SAN JOSE, CA, p. A86
OCONOMOWOC MEMORIAL HOSPITAL, OCONOMOWOC, WI, p. A702
ODESSA MEMORIAL HEALTHCARE CENTER, ODESSA, WA, p. A675
ODESSA REGIONAL MEDICAL CENTER, ODESSA, TX, p. A627
ODESSA REGIONAL MEDICAL CENTER SOUTH CAMPUS, ODESSA, TX, p. A627
OGALLALA COMMUNITY HOSPITAL, OGALLALA, NE, p. A388
OGDEN REGIONAL MEDICAL CENTER, OGDEN, UT, p. A650
OHIO COUNTY HOSPITAL, HARTFORD, KY, p. A253
OHIO HOSPITAL FOR PSYCHIATRY, COLUMBUS, OH, p. A479
OHIO STATE UNIVERSITY WEXNER MEDICAL CENTER, COLUMBUS, OH, p. A479
OHIO VALLEY HOSPITAL, MCKEES ROCKS, PA, p. A531
OHIO VALLEY MEDICAL CENTER, WHEELING, WV, p. A690
OHIO VALLEY SURGICAL HOSPITAL, SPRINGFIELD, OH, p. A491
OHIOHEALTH DOCTORS HOSPITAL, COLUMBUS, OH, p. A479
OHIOHEALTH DUBLIN METHODIST HOSPITAL, DUBLIN, OH, p. A482
OHIOHEALTH GRADY MEMORIAL HOSPITAL, DELAWARE, OH, p. A482
OHIOHEALTH GRANT MEDICAL CENTER, COLUMBUS, OH, p. A479
OHIOHEALTH HARDIN MEMORIAL HOSPITAL, KENTON, OH, p. A485
OHIOHEALTH MARION GENERAL HOSPITAL, MARION, OH, p. A486
OHIOHEALTH MEDCENTRAL MANSFIELD HOSPITAL, MANSFIELD, OH, p. A486
OHIOHEALTH MEDCENTRAL SHELBY HOSPITAL, SHELBY, OH, p. A491
OHIOHEALTH REHABILITATION HOSPITAL, COLUMBUS, OH, p. A479
OHIOHEALTH RIVERSIDE METHODIST HOSPITAL, COLUMBUS, OH, p. A480
OHSU HOSPITAL, PORTLAND, OR, p. A516
OJAI VALLEY COMMUNITY HOSPITAL, OJAI, CA, p. A75
OKEENE MUNICIPAL HOSPITAL, OKEENE, OK, p. A503
OKLAHOMA CENTER FOR ORTHOPEDIC AND MULTI-SPECIALTY SURGERY, OKLAHOMA CITY, OK, p. A504
OKLAHOMA CITY VETERANS AFFAIRS MEDICAL CENTER, OKLAHOMA CITY, OK, p. A504
OKLAHOMA FORENSIC CENTER, VINITA, OK, p. A510
OKLAHOMA HEART HOSPITAL, OKLAHOMA CITY, OK, p. A505
OKLAHOMA HEART HOSPITAL SOUTH CAMPUS, OKLAHOMA CITY, OK, p. A505
OKLAHOMA SPINE HOSPITAL, OKLAHOMA CITY, OK, p. A505
OKLAHOMA STATE UNIVERSITY MEDICAL CENTER, TULSA, OK, p. A509
OKLAHOMA SURGICAL HOSPITAL, TULSA, OK, p. A509
OLATHE MEDICAL CENTER, OLATHE, KS, p. A242
OLD VINEYARD BEHAVIORAL HEALTH SERVICES, WINSTON, NC, p. A464
OLEAN GENERAL HOSPITAL, OLEAN, NY, p. A440
OLMSTED MEDICAL CENTER, ROCHESTER, MN, p. A338
OLYMPIA MEDICAL CENTER, LOS ANGELES, CA, p. A68
OLYMPIC MEDICAL CENTER, PORT ANGELES, WA, p. A676
OMEGA HOSPITAL, METAIRIE, LA, p. A273
ONECORE HEALTH, OKLAHOMA CITY, OK, p. A505
ONEIDA HEALTHCARE, ONEIDA, NY, p. A440
ONSLOW MEMORIAL HOSPITAL, JACKSONVILLE, NC, p. A457
OPELOUSAS GENERAL HEALTH SYSTEM, OPELOUSAS, LA, p. A276
OPTIM MEDICAL CENTER – SCREVEN, SYLVANIA, GA, p. A161
OPTIM MEDICAL CENTER – TATTNALL, REIDSVILLE, GA, p. A158
OPTIMA SPECIALTY HOSPITAL, LAFAYETTE, LOUISIANA (see VERMILION BEHAVIORAL HEALTH SYSTEMS – SOUTH CAMPUS), p. A271
OPTIONS BEHAVIORAL HEALTH SYSTEM, INDIANAPOLIS, IN, p. A207
ORANGE CITY AREA HEALTH SYSTEM, ORANGE CITY, IA, p. A227
ORANGE COUNTY GLOBAL MEDICAL CENTER, INC., SANTA ANA, CA, p. A88
ORANGE COUNTY IRVINE MEDICAL CENTER, IRVINE, CA, p. A62
ORANGE PARK MEDICAL CENTER, ORANGE PARK, FL, p. A134
ORANGE REGIONAL MEDICAL CENTER, MIDDLETOWN, NEW YORK (see MOUNT SINAI WEST), p. A431
ORCHARD HOSPITAL, GRIDLEY, CA, p. A61
OREGON STATE HOSPITAL, SALEM, OR, p. A517
OREM COMMUNITY HOSPITAL, OREM, UT, p. A650
ORLANDO REGIONAL MEDICAL CENTER, ORLANDO, FL, p. A134
ORLANDO VA MEDICAL CENTER, ORLANDO, FL, p. A134

ORO VALLEY HOSPITAL, ORO VALLEY, AZ, p. A32
OROVILLE HOSPITAL, OROVILLE, CA, p. A76
ORTHOCOLORADO HOSPITAL, LAKEWOOD, CO, p. A102
ORTHOINDY HOSPITAL, INDIANAPOLIS, IN, p. A207
ORTHONEBRASKA HOSPITAL, OMAHA, NE, p. A390
ORTHOPAEDIC HOSPITAL OF LUTHERAN HEALTH NETWORK, FORT WAYNE, IN, p. A204
ORTHOPAEDIC HOSPITAL OF WISCONSIN, GLENDALE, WI, p. A695
ORTONVILLE AREA HEALTH SERVICES, ORTONVILLE, MN, p. A337
OSAGE BEACH CENTER FOR COGNITIVE DISORDERS, OSAGE BEACH, MO, p. A366
OSAWATOMIE STATE HOSPITAL AT ADAIR ACUTE CARE, OSAWATOMIE, KS, p. A242
OSBORNE COUNTY MEMORIAL HOSPITAL, OSBORNE, KS, p. A242
OSCAR G. JOHNSON VETERANS AFFAIRS MEDICAL CENTER, IRON MOUNTAIN, MI, p. A315
OSCEOLA COMMUNITY HOSPITAL, SIBLEY, IA, p. A229
OSCEOLA MEDICAL CENTER, OSCEOLA, WI, p. A703
OSCEOLA REGIONAL MEDICAL CENTER, KISSIMMEE, FL, p. A126
OSF HEALTHCARE SAINT ANTHONY'S HEALTH CENTER, ALTON, IL, p. A173
OSF HEART OF MARY MEDICAL CENTER, URBANA, IL, p. A197
OSF HOLY FAMILY MEDICAL CENTER, MONMOUTH, IL, p. A189
OSF SACRED HEART MEDICAL CENTER, DANVILLE, IL, p. A180
OSF SAINT ANTHONY MEDICAL CENTER, ROCKFORD, IL, p. A195
OSF SAINT ELIZABETH MEDICAL CENTER, OTTAWA, IL, p. A192
OSF SAINT FRANCIS MEDICAL CENTER, PEORIA, IL, p. A193
OSF SAINT JAMES – JOHN W. ALBRECHT MEDICAL CENTER, PONTIAC, IL, p. A194
OSF SAINT LUKE MEDICAL CENTER, KEWANEE, IL, p. A187
OSF SAINT PAUL MEDICAL CENTER, MENDOTA, IL, p. A189
OSF ST. FRANCIS HOSPITAL AND MEDICAL GROUP, ESCANABA, MI, p. A311
OSF ST. JOSEPH MEDICAL CENTER, BLOOMINGTON, IL, p. A174
OSF ST. MARY MEDICAL CENTER, GALESBURG, IL, p. A183
OSMOND GENERAL HOSPITAL, OSMOND, NE, p. A390
OSS ORTHOPAEDIC HOSPITAL, YORK, PA, p. A546
OSSINING CORRECTIONAL FACILITIES HOSPITAL, OSSINING, NY, p. A441
OSWEGO HOSPITAL, OSWEGO, NY, p. A441
OTHELLO COMMUNITY HOSPITAL, OTHELLO, WA, p. A676
OTIS R. BOWEN CENTER FOR HUMAN SERVICES, WARSAW, IN, p. A216
OTTAWA COUNTY HEALTH CENTER, MINNEAPOLIS, KS, p. A241
OTTO KAISER MEMORIAL HOSPITAL, KENEDY, TX, p. A617
OTTUMWA REGIONAL HEALTH CENTER, OTTUMWA, IA, p. A228
OU MEDICAL CENTER, OKLAHOMA CITY, OK, p. A505
OU MEDICAL CENTER EDMOND, EDMOND, OKLAHOMA (see OU MEDICAL CENTER), p. A499
OUACHITA COUNTY MEDICAL CENTER, CAMDEN, AR, p. A40
OUACHITA MEDICAL CENTER, CAMDEN, ARKANSAS (see OUACHITA COUNTY MEDICAL CENTER), p. A40
OUR CHILDREN'S HOUSE, DALLAS, TX, p. A597
OUR LADY OF BELLEFONTE HOSPITAL, ASHLAND, KY, p. A249
OUR LADY OF LOURDES MEDICAL CENTER, CAMDEN, NJ, p. A404
OUR LADY OF LOURDES MEMORIAL HOSPITAL, INC., BINGHAMTON, NY, p. A424
OUR LADY OF LOURDES REGIONAL MEDICAL CENTER, LAFAYETTE, LA, p. A271
OUR LADY OF THE ANGELS HOSPITAL, BOGALUSA, LA, p. A264
OUR LADY OF THE LAKE REGIONAL MEDICAL CENTER, BATON ROUGE, LA, p. A264
OUR LADY OF THE RESURRECTION MEDICAL CENTER, CHICAGO, ILLINOIS (see COMMUNITY FIRST MEDICAL CENTER), p. A179
OVERLAKE MEDICAL CENTER, BELLEVUE, WA, p. A670
OVERLAND PARK REGIONAL MEDICAL CENTER, OVERLAND PARK, KS, p. A243
OVERLOOK MEDICAL CENTER, SUMMIT, NJ, p. A413
OVERTON BROOKS VETERANS AFFAIRS MEDICAL CENTER, SHREVEPORT, LA, p. A278
OVIEDO MEDICAL CENTER, OVIEDO, FL, p. A135
OWATONNA HOSPITAL, OWATONNA, MN, p. A337
OWENSBORO HEALTH MUHLENBERG COMMUNITY HOSPITAL, GREENVILLE, KY, p. A252

OWENSBORO HEALTH REGIONAL HOSPITAL, OWENSBORO, KY, p. A258
OZARK HEALTH MEDICAL CENTER, CLINTON, AR, p. A40
OZARKS COMMUNITY HOSPITAL, GRAVETTE, AR, p. A42
OZARKS MEDICAL CENTER, WEST PLAINS, MO, p. A373

P

PACIFIC GROVE HOSPITAL, RIVERSIDE, CA, p. A81
PACIFICA HOSPITAL OF THE VALLEY, LOS ANGELES, CA, p. A68
PAGE HOSPITAL, PAGE, AZ, p. A32
PAGE MEMORIAL HOSPITAL, LURAY, VA, p. A661
PAGOSA SPRINGS MEDICAL CENTER, PAGOSA SPRINGS, CO, p. A104
PALACIOS COMMUNITY MEDICAL CENTER, PALACIOS, TX, p. A627
PALESTINE REGIONAL MEDICAL CENTER–EAST, PALESTINE, TX, p. A627
PALI MOMI MEDICAL CENTER, AIEA, HI, p. A164
PALM BEACH GARDENS MEDICAL CENTER, PALM BEACH GARDENS, FL, p. A135
PALMDALE REGIONAL MEDICAL CENTER, PALMDALE, CA, p. A77
PALMETTO GENERAL HOSPITAL, HIALEAH, FL, p. A124
PALMETTO LOWCOUNTRY BEHAVIORAL HEALTH, CHARLESTON, SC, p. A550
PALMS OF PASADENA HOSPITAL, SAINT PETERSBURG, FL, p. A138
PALMS WEST HOSPITAL, LOXAHATCHEE, FL, p. A128
PALO ALTO COUNTY HEALTH SYSTEM, EMMETSBURG, IA, p. A222
PALO PINTO GENERAL HOSPITAL, MINERAL WELLS, TX, p. A625
PALO VERDE BEHAVIORAL HEALTH, TUCSON, AZ, p. A38
PALO VERDE HOSPITAL, BLYTHE, CA, p. A53
PALOMAR MEDICAL CENTER, ESCONDIDO, CA, p. A57
PALOMAR MEDICAL CENTER POWAY, POWAY, CA, p. A79
PALOS HEALTH, PALOS HEIGHTS, IL, p. A192
PAM REHABILITATION HOSPITAL OF BEAUMONT, BEAUMONT, TX, p. A587
PAM REHABILITATION HOSPITAL OF CENTENNIAL HILLS, LAS VEGAS, NV, p. A395
PAM REHABILITATION HOSPITAL OF TULSA, TULSA, OK, p. A509
PAM REHABILITATION HOSPITAL OF VICTORIA, VICTORIA, TX, p. A643
PAM SPECIALTY HOSPITAL OF CORPUS CHRISTI SOUTH, CORPUS CHRISTI, TX, p. A594
PAM SPECIALTY HOSPITAL OF COVINGTON, COVINGTON, LA, p. A266
PAM SPECIALTY HOSPITAL OF HAMMOND, HAMMOND, LA, p. A268
PAM SPECIALTY HOSPITAL OF LUFKIN, LUFKIN, TX, p. A622
PAM SPECIALTY HOSPITAL OF VICTORIA NORTH, VICTORIA, TX, p. A643
PAM SPECIALTY HOSPITAL OF VICTORIA SOUTH, VICTORIA, TX, p. A644
PAM SPECIALTY HOSPITAL OF WILKES–BARRE, WILKES BARRE, PA, p. A544
PAMPA REGIONAL MEDICAL CENTER, PAMPA, TX, p. A627
PANA COMMUNITY HOSPITAL, PANA, IL, p. A192
PANOLA MEDICAL CENTER, BATESVILLE, MS, p. A344
PANORAMA CITY MEDICAL CENTER, LOS ANGELES, CALIFORNIA (see KAISER PERMANENTE PANORAMA CITY MEDICAL CENTER), p. A68
PAOLI HOSPITAL, PAOLI, PA, p. A533
PAPPAS REHABILITATION HOSPITAL FOR CHILDREN, CANTON, MA, p. A297
PARADISE VALLEY HOSPITAL, NATIONAL CITY, CA, p. A74
PARIS COMMUNITY HOSPITAL, PARIS, IL, p. A192
PARIS REGIONAL MEDICAL CENTER, PARIS, TX, p. A628
PARK CITY HOSPITAL, PARK CITY, UT, p. A650
PARK NICOLLET METHODIST HOSPITAL, SAINT LOUIS PARK, MN, p. A339
PARK PLACE SURGICAL HOSPITAL, LAFAYETTE, LA, p. A271
PARK PLAZA HOSPITAL, HOUSTON, TX, p. A613
PARK ROYAL HOSPITAL, FORT MYERS, FL, p. A123
PARKER ADVENTIST HOSPITAL, PARKER, CO, p. A104
PARKLAND HEALTH & HOSPITAL SYSTEM, DALLAS, TX, p. A597
PARKLAND HEALTH CENTER – FARMINGTON COMMUNITY, FARMINGTON, MO, p. A360
PARKLAND HEALTH CENTER–BONNE TERRE, BONNE TERRE, MO, p. A356

PARKLAND MEDICAL CENTER, DERRY, NH, p. A399
PARKRIDGE MEDICAL CENTER, CHATTANOOGA, TN, p. A567
PARKSIDE PSYCHIATRIC HOSPITAL AND CLINIC, TULSA, OK, p. A509
PARKVIEW COMMUNITY HOSPITAL MEDICAL CENTER, RIVERSIDE, CA, p. A81
PARKVIEW HOSPITAL, WHEELER, TX, p. A645
PARKVIEW HUNTINGTON HOSPITAL, HUNTINGTON, IN, p. A206
PARKVIEW LAGRANGE HOSPITAL, LAGRANGE, IN, p. A210
PARKVIEW MEDICAL CENTER, PUEBLO, CO, p. A104
PARKVIEW NOBLE HOSPITAL, KENDALLVILLE, IN, p. A208
PARKVIEW ORTHO HOSPITAL, FORT WAYNE, IN, p. A204
PARKVIEW REGIONAL HOSPITAL, MEXIA, TX, p. A624
PARKVIEW REGIONAL MEDICAL CENTER, FORT WAYNE, IN, p. A204
PARKVIEW WABASH HOSPITAL, WABASH, IN, p. A216
PARKVIEW WHITLEY HOSPITAL, COLUMBIA CITY, IN, p. A201
PARKWAY MEDICAL CENTER, DECATUR, ALABAMA (see DECATUR MORGAN HOSPITAL PARKWAY CAMPUS), p. A16
PARKWEST MEDICAL CENTER, KNOXVILLE, TN, p. A572
PARKWOOD BEHAVIORAL HEALTH SYSTEM, OLIVE BRANCH, MS, p. A352
PARMER COUNTY COMMUNITY HOSPITAL, FRIONA, TEXAS (see PARMER MEDICAL CENTER), p. A606
PARMER MEDICAL CENTER, FRIONA, TX, p. A606
PARRISH MEDICAL CENTER, TITUSVILLE, FL, p. A143
PARSONS STATE HOSPITAL AND TRAINING CENTER, PARSONS, KS, p. A243
PASSAVANT AREA HOSPITAL, JACKSONVILLE, IL, p. A186
PATHWAY REHABILITATION HOSPITAL, BOSSIER CITY, LA, p. A265
PATHWAYS OF TENNESSEE, JACKSON, TN, p. A571
PATIENTS CHOICE MEDICAL CENTER OF SMITH COUNTY, RALEIGH, MS, p. A353
PATIENTS MEDICAL CENTER, PASADENA, TEXAS (see CHI ST. LUKE'S HEALTH – PATIENTS MEDICAL CENTER), p. A628
PATIENTS' HOSPITAL OF REDDING, REDDING, CA, p. A79
PATRICK B. HARRIS PSYCHIATRIC HOSPITAL, ANDERSON, SC, p. A549
PATTON STATE HOSPITAL, PATTON, CA, p. A77
PAUL B. HALL REGIONAL MEDICAL CENTER, PAINTSVILLE, KY, p. A259
PAUL OLIVER MEMORIAL HOSPITAL, FRANKFORT, MI, p. A312
PAULDING COUNTY HOSPITAL, PAULDING, OH, p. A489
PAWHUSKA HOSPITAL, PAWHUSKA, OK, p. A506
PAWNEE COUNTY MEMORIAL HOSPITAL AND RURAL HEALTH CLINIC, PAWNEE CITY, NE, p. A390
PEACEHEALTH COTTAGE GROVE COMMUNITY MEDICAL CENTER, COTTAGE GROVE, OR, p. A512
PEACEHEALTH KETCHIKAN MEDICAL CENTER, KETCHIKAN, AK, p. A26
PEACEHEALTH PEACE HARBOR MEDICAL CENTER, FLORENCE, OR, p. A512
PEACEHEALTH PEACE ISLAND MEDICAL CENTER, FRIDAY HARBOR, WA, p. A673
PEACEHEALTH SACRED HEART MEDICAL CENTER AT RIVERBEND, SPRINGFIELD, OR, p. A518
PEACEHEALTH SACRED HEART MEDICAL CENTER UNIVERSITY DISTRICT, EUGENE, OR, p. A512
PEACEHEALTH SOUTHWEST MEDICAL CENTER, VANCOUVER, WA, p. A681
PEACEHEALTH ST. JOHN MEDICAL CENTER, LONGVIEW, WA, p. A674
PEACEHEALTH ST. JOSEPH MEDICAL CENTER, BELLINGHAM, WA, p. A670
PEACEHEALTH UNITED GENERAL MEDICAL CENTER, SEDRO, WA, p. A679
PEACHFORD BEHAVIORAL HEALTH SYSTEM, ATLANTA, GA, p. A146
PEAK BEHAVIORAL HEALTH SERVICES, SANTA TERESA, NM, p. A420
PEAK VIEW BEHAVIORAL HEALTH, COLORADO SPRINGS, CO, p. A97
PEARL RIVER COUNTY HOSPITAL, POPLARVILLE, MS, p. A353
PEARLAND MEDICAL CENTER, PEARLAND, TX, p. A628
PECONIC BAY MEDICAL CENTER, RIVERHEAD, NY, p. A442
PECOS COUNTY MEMORIAL HOSPITAL, FORT STOCKTON, TX, p. A604
PELHAM MEDICAL CENTER, GREER, SC, p. A554
PELLA REGIONAL HEALTH CENTER, PELLA, IA, p. A228
PEMBINA COUNTY MEMORIAL HOSPITAL AND WEDGEWOOD MANOR, CAVALIER, ND, p. A466
PEMBROKE HOSPITAL, PEMBROKE, MA, p. A302
PEMISCOT MEMORIAL HEALTH SYSTEM, HAYTI, MO, p. A361
PEN BAY MEDICAL CENTER, ROCKPORT, ME, p. A285
PENDER COMMUNITY HOSPITAL, PENDER, NE, p. A391
PENDER MEMORIAL HOSPITAL, BURGAW, NC, p. A450

PENINSULA REGIONAL MEDICAL CENTER, SALISBURY, MD, p. A293

PENN HIGHLANDS BROOKVILLE, BROOKVILLE, PA, p. A521

PENN HIGHLANDS CLEARFIELD, CLEARFIELD, PA, p. A522

PENN HIGHLANDS DUBOIS, DUBOIS, PA, p. A524

PENN HIGHLANDS ELK, SAINT MARYS, PA, p. A540

PENN MEDICINE CHESTER COUNTY HOSPITAL, WEST CHESTER, PA, p. A544

PENN MEDICINE LANCASTER GENERAL HOSPITAL, LANCASTER, PA, p. A529

PENN MEDICINE PRINCETON MEDICAL CENTER, PLAINSBORO, NJ, p. A411

PENN PRESBYTERIAN MEDICAL CENTER, PHILADELPHIA, PA, p. A536

PENN STATE HEALTH ST. JOSEPH, READING, PA, p. A539

PENN STATE HERSHEY REHABILITATION HOSPITAL, HUMMELSTOWN, PA, p. A527

PENN STATE MILTON S. HERSHEY MEDICAL CENTER, HERSHEY, PA, p. A527

PENNSYLVANIA HOSPITAL, PHILADELPHIA, PA, p. A536

PENNSYLVANIA PSYCHIATRIC INSTITUTE, HARRISBURG, PA, p. A526

PENOBSCOT BAY MEDICAL CENTER, ROCKPORT, MAINE (see PEN BAY MEDICAL CENTER), p. A285

PENOBSCOT VALLEY HOSPITAL, LINCOLN, ME, p. A283

PENROSE–ST. FRANCIS HEALTH SERVICES, COLORADO SPRINGS, CO, p. A98

PERHAM HEALTH, PERHAM, MN, p. A337

PERIMETER BEHAVIORAL HOSPITAL OF SPRINGFIELD, SPRINGFIELD, MO, p. A372

PERIMETER BEHAVIORAL HOSPITAL OF WEST MEMPHIS, WEST MEMPHIS, AR, p. A49

PERKINS COUNTY HEALTH SERVICES, GRANT, NE, p. A385

PERMIAN REGIONAL MEDICAL CENTER, ANDREWS, TX, p. A583

PERRY COMMUNITY HOSPITAL, LINDEN, TN, p. A573

PERRY COUNTY GENERAL HOSPITAL, RICHTON, MS, p. A353

PERRY COUNTY MEMORIAL HOSPITAL, PERRYVILLE, MO, p. A367

PERRY COUNTY MEMORIAL HOSPITAL, TELL CITY, IN, p. A215

PERRY HOSPITAL, PERRY, GA, p. A158

PERRY MEMORIAL HOSPITAL, PRINCETON, IL, p. A194

PERSHING GENERAL HOSPITAL, LOVELOCK, NV, p. A396

PERSHING MEMORIAL HOSPITAL, BROOKFIELD, MO, p. A357

PERSON MEMORIAL HOSPITAL, ROXBORO, NC, p. A461

PETALUMA VALLEY HOSPITAL, PETALUMA, CA, p. A78

PETERSBURG MEDICAL CENTER, PETERSBURG, AK, p. A27

PETERSON HEALTHCARE AND REHABILITATION HOSPITAL, WHEELING, WV, p. A690

PETERSON REGIONAL MEDICAL CENTER, KERRVILLE, TX, p. A618

PHELPS HEALTH, ROLLA, MO, p. A368

PHELPS MEMORIAL HEALTH CENTER, HOLDREGE, NE, p. A386

PHELPS MEMORIAL HOSPITAL CENTER, SLEEPY HOLLOW, NY, p. A444

PHILADELPHIA VETERANS AFFAIRS MEDICAL CENTER, PHILADELPHIA, PA, p. A536

PHILIP HEALTH SERVICES, PHILIP, SD, p. A562

PHILLIPS COUNTY HEALTH SYSTEMS, PHILLIPSBURG, KS, p. A243

PHILLIPS COUNTY HOSPITAL, MALTA, MT, p. A378

PHILLIPS EYE INSTITUTE, MINNEAPOLIS, MN, p. A336

PHOEBE PUTNEY MEMORIAL HOSPITAL, ALBANY, GA, p. A145

PHOEBE SUMTER MEDICAL CENTER, AMERICUS, GA, p. A145

PHOEBE WORTH MEDICAL CENTER, SYLVESTER, GA, p. A161

PHOENIX CHILDREN'S HOSPITAL, PHOENIX, AZ, p. A34

PHOENIX VETERANS AFFAIRS HEALTH CARE SYSTEM, PHOENIX, AZ, p. A34

PHOENIXVILLE HOSPITAL, PHOENIXVILLE, PA, p. A537

PHS SANTA FE INDIAN HOSPITAL, SANTA FE, NM, p. A420

PHYSICIANS ALLIANCE HOSPITAL OF HOUMA, HOUMA, LOUISIANA (see AMG SPECIALTY HOSPITAL–HOUMA), p. A268

PHYSICIANS BEHAVIORAL HOSPITAL, SHREVEPORT, LA, p. A278

PHYSICIANS CARE SURGICAL HOSPITAL, ROYERSFORD, PA, p. A540

PHYSICIANS MEDICAL CENTER, HOUMA, LA, p. A268

PHYSICIANS REGIONAL – PINE RIDGE, NAPLES, FL, p. A132

PHYSICIANS SURGICAL HOSPITAL – QUAIL CREEK, AMARILLO, TX, p. A582

PHYSICIANS' HOSPITAL IN ANADARKO, ANADARKO, OK, p. A496

PHYSICIANS' MEDICAL CENTER, NEW ALBANY, IN, p. A212

PICKENS COUNTY MEDICAL CENTER, CARROLLTON, AL, p. A16

PIEDMONT ATHENS REGIONAL MEDICAL CENTER, ATHENS, GA, p. A145

PIEDMONT COLUMBUS REGIONAL MIDTOWN, COLUMBUS, GA, p. A150

PIEDMONT COLUMBUS REGIONAL NORTHSIDE, COLUMBUS, GA, p. A150

PIEDMONT FAYETTE HOSPITAL, FAYETTEVILLE, GA, p. A153

PIEDMONT GERIATRIC HOSPITAL, BURKEVILLE, VA, p. A657

PIEDMONT HENRY HOSPITAL, STOCKBRIDGE, GA, p. A161

PIEDMONT HOSPITAL, ATLANTA, GA, p. A146

PIEDMONT MEDICAL CENTER, ROCK HILL, SC, p. A556

PIEDMONT MOUNTAINSIDE HOSPITAL, JASPER, GA, p. A155

PIEDMONT NEWNAN HOSPITAL, NEWNAN, GA, p. A158

PIEDMONT NEWTON HOSPITAL, COVINGTON, GA, p. A151

PIEDMONT ROCKDALE HOSPITAL, CONYERS, GA, p. A151

PIEDMONT WALTON HOSPITAL, MONROE, GA, p. A157

PIGGOTT COMMUNITY HOSPITAL, PIGGOTT, AR, p. A47

PIH HEALTH HOSPITAL – DOWNEY, DOWNEY, CA, p. A56

PIH HEALTH HOSPITAL – WHITTIER, WHITTIER, CA, p. A95

PIKE COUNTY MEMORIAL HOSPITAL, LOUISIANA, MO, p. A364

PIKES PEAK REGIONAL HOSPITAL, WOODLAND PARK, CO, p. A106

PIKEVILLE MEDICAL CENTER, PIKEVILLE, KY, p. A259

PILGRIM PSYCHIATRIC CENTER, BRENTWOOD, NY, p. A424

PINCKNEYVILLE COMMUNITY HOSPITAL, PINCKNEYVILLE, IL, p. A193

PINE CREEK MEDICAL CENTER, DALLAS, TX, p. A597

PINE REST CHRISTIAN MENTAL HEALTH SERVICES, GRAND RAPIDS, MI, p. A313

PINNACLE HOSPITAL, CROWN POINT, IN, p. A202

PINNACLE POINTE HOSPITAL, LITTLE ROCK, AR, p. A45

PINNACLE REGIONAL HOSPITAL, BOONVILLE, MO, p. A357

PINNACLEHEALTH AT COMMUNITY GENERAL OSTEOPATHIC HOSPITAL, HARRISBURG, PENNSYLVANIA (see UPMC PINNACLE HARRISBURG), p. A527

PIONEER MEDICAL CENTER, BIG TIMBER, MT, p. A374

PIONEER MEMORIAL HOSPITAL, HEPPNER, OR, p. A513

PIONEER MEMORIAL HOSPITAL AND HEALTH SERVICES, VIBORG, SD, p. A565

PIONEER SPECIALTY HOSPITAL, PONTIAC, MI, p. A320

PIONEERS MEDICAL CENTER, MEEKER, CO, p. A104

PIONEERS MEMORIAL HEALTHCARE DISTRICT, BRAWLEY, CA, p. A53

PIPESTONE COUNTY MEDICAL CENTER AVERA, PIPESTONE, MN, p. A338

PITT COUNTY MEMORIAL HOSPITAL, GREENVILLE, NORTH CAROLINA (see VIDANT MEDICAL CENTER), p. A455

PLACENTIA–LINDA HOSPITAL, PLACENTIA, CA, p. A78

PLAINS MEMORIAL HOSPITAL, DIMMITT, TX, p. A600

PLAINS REGIONAL MEDICAL CENTER, CLOVIS, NM, p. A417

PLAINVIEW HOSPITAL, PLAINVIEW, NY, p. A441

PLANO SURGICAL HOSPITAL, PLANO, TX, p. A629

PLANTATION GENERAL HOSPITAL, PLANTATION, FL, p. A137

PLATEAU MEDICAL CENTER, OAK HILL, WV, p. A688

PLATTE COUNTY MEMORIAL HOSPITAL, WHEATLAND, WY, p. A713

PLATTE HEALTH CENTER AVERA, PLATTE, SD, p. A562

PLATTE VALLEY MEDICAL CENTER, BRIGHTON, CO, p. A97

PLAZA SPECIALTY HOSPITAL, HOUSTON, TX, p. A613

PLEASANT VALLEY HOSPITAL, POINT PLEASANT, WV, p. A688

PLUMAS DISTRICT HOSPITAL, QUINCY, CA, p. A79

PLYMOUTH MEDICAL CENTER, PLYMOUTH, IN, p. A213

POCAHONTAS COMMUNITY HOSPITAL, POCAHONTAS, IA, p. A228

POCAHONTAS MEMORIAL HOSPITAL, BUCKEYE, WV, p. A683

POCASSET MENTAL HEALTH CENTER, POCASSET, MA, p. A302

POINCIANA MEDICAL CENTER, KISSIMMEE, FL, p. A127

POINTE COUPEE GENERAL HOSPITAL, NEW ROADS, LA, p. A276

POLK MEDICAL CENTER, CEDARTOWN, GA, p. A149

POMERENE HOSPITAL, MILLERSBURG, OH, p. A488

POMONA VALLEY HOSPITAL MEDICAL CENTER, POMONA, CA, p. A78

PONDERA MEDICAL CENTER, CONRAD, MT, p. A375

PONTIAC GENERAL HOSPITAL, PONTIAC, MI, p. A320

POPLAR BLUFF REGIONAL MEDICAL CENTER, POPLAR BLUFF, MO, p. A367

POPLAR COMMUNITY HOSPITAL, POPLAR, MT, p. A379

POPLAR SPRINGS HOSPITAL, PETERSBURG, VA, p. A665

PORT ST. LUCIE HOSPITAL, PORT ST LUCIE, FL, p. A137

PORTER ADVENTIST HOSPITAL, DENVER, CO, p. A99

PORTER MEDICAL CENTER, MIDDLEBURY, VT, p. A654

PORTER REGIONAL HOSPITAL, VALPARAISO, IN, p. A215

PORTER–STARKE SERVICES, VALPARAISO, IN, p. A216

PORTERVILLE DEVELOPMENTAL CENTER, PORTERVILLE, CA, p. A78

PORTNEUF MEDICAL CENTER, POCATELLO, ID, p. A171

PORTSMOUTH REGIONAL HOSPITAL, PORTSMOUTH, NH, p. A402

POST ACUTE MEDICAL SPECIALTY HOSPITAL OF CORPUS CHRISTI – NORTH, CORPUS CHRISTI, TX, p. A594

POST ACUTE MEDICAL SPECIALTY HOSPITAL OF MILWAUKEE, GREENFIELD, WI, p. A696

POST ACUTE MEDICAL SPECIALTY HOSPITAL OF TEXARKANA – NORTH, TEXARKANA, TX, p. A640

POST ACUTE MEDICAL SPECIALTY HOSPITAL OF TULSA, TULSA, OK, p. A509

POST ACUTE REHABILITATION HOSPITAL OF ALLEN, ALLEN, TX, p. A581

POST ACUTE/WARM SPRINGS SPECIALTY HOSPITAL OF LULING, LULING, TX, p. A623

POST ACUTE/WARM SPRINGS SPECIALTY HOSPITAL OF NEW BRAUNFELS, NEW BRAUNFELS, TX, p. A626

POST ACUTE/WARM SPRINGS SPECIALTY HOSPITAL OF SAN ANTONIO, SAN ANTONIO, TX, p. A635

POTOMAC RIDGE BEHAVIORAL HEALTH, ROCKVILLE, MARYLAND (see ADVENTIST BEHAVIORAL HEALTH AND WELLNESS SERVICES), p. A293

POTOMAC VALLEY HOSPITAL, KEYSER, WV, p. A686

POTTSTOWN HOSPITAL, POTTSTOWN, PA, p. A539

POWELL VALLEY HEALTHCARE, POWELL, WY, p. A712

POWER COUNTY HOSPITAL DISTRICT, AMERICAN FALLS, ID, p. A167

PRAGUE COMMUNITY HOSPITAL, PRAGUE, OK, p. A506

PRAIRIE COMMUNITY HEALTH CENTER, TERRY, MONTANA (see PRAIRIE COMMUNITY HOSPITAL), p. A380

PRAIRIE COMMUNITY HOSPITAL, TERRY, MT, p. A380

PRAIRIE LAKES HEALTHCARE SYSTEM, WATERTOWN, SD, p. A565

PRAIRIE RIDGE HOSPITAL AND HEALTH SERVICES, ELBOW LAKE, MN, p. A331

PRAIRIE ST. JOHN'S, FARGO, ND, p. A466

PRAIRIE VIEW, NEWTON, KS, p. A242

PRAIRIECARE – BROOKLYN PARK, BROOKLYN PARK, MN, p. A329

PRATT REGIONAL MEDICAL CENTER, PRATT, KS, p. A244

PRATTVILLE BAPTIST HOSPITAL, PRATTVILLE, AL, p. A23

PREMIER SURGICAL INSTITUTE, GALENA, KS, p. A235

PRENTICE WOMEN'S HOSPITAL, CHICAGO, ILLINOIS (see NORTHWESTERN MEMORIAL HOSPITAL), p. A179

PRESBYTERIAN ESPANOLA HOSPITAL, ESPANOLA, NM, p. A418

PRESBYTERIAN HOSPITAL, ALBUQUERQUE, NM, p. A417

PRESBYTERIAN HOSPITAL, CHARLOTTE, NORTH CAROLINA (see NOVANT HEALTH PRESBYTERIAN MEDICAL CENTER), p. A451

PRESBYTERIAN SANTA FE MEDICAL CENTER, SANTA FE, NM, p. A420

PRESBYTERIAN TOWER, OKLAHOMA CITY, OKLAHOMA (see OU MEDICAL CENTER), p. A505

PRESBYTERIAN–ORTHOPAEDIC HOSPITAL, CHARLOTTE, NORTH CAROLINA (see NOVANT HEALTH CHARLOTTE ORTHOPAEDIC HOSPITAL), p. A451

PRESBYTERIAN–ST. LUKE'S MEDICAL CENTER, DENVER, CO, p. A99

PRESENTATION MEDICAL CENTER, ROLLA, ND, p. A469

PRESTON MEMORIAL HOSPITAL, KINGWOOD, WV, p. A686

PREVOST MEMORIAL HOSPITAL, DONALDSONVILLE, LA, p. A267

PRIMARY CHILDREN'S HOSPITAL, SALT LAKE CITY, UT, p. A652

PRINCETON BAPTIST MEDICAL CENTER, BIRMINGHAM, AL, p. A15

PRINCETON COMMUNITY HOSPITAL, PRINCETON, WV, p. A688

PRISMA HEALTH BAPTIST EASLEY HOSPITAL, EASLEY, SC, p. A552

PRISMA HEALTH BAPTIST HOSPITAL, COLUMBIA, SC, p. A551

PRISMA HEALTH BAPTIST PARKRIDGE HOSPITAL, COLUMBIA, SC, p. A551

PRISMA HEALTH GREENVILLE MEMORIAL HOSPITAL, GREENVILLE, SC, p. A553

PRISMA HEALTH GREER MEMORIAL HOSPITAL, GREER, SC, p. A554

PRISMA HEALTH HILLCREST HOSPITAL, SIMPSONVILLE, SC, p. A557

PRISMA HEALTH LAURENS COUNTY HOSPITAL, CLINTON, SC, p. A550

PRISMA HEALTH NORTH GREENVILLE LTACH, TRAVELERS REST, SC, p. A557

PRISMA HEALTH OCONEE MEMORIAL HOSPITAL, SENECA, SC, p. A557

PRISMA HEALTH PATEWOOD HOSPITAL, GREENVILLE, SC, p. A553
PRISMA HEALTH RICHLAND HOSPITAL, COLUMBIA, SC, p. A551
PRISMA HEALTH TUOMEY HOSPITAL, SUMTER, SC, p. A557
PROFESSIONAL HOSPITAL GUAYNABO, GUAYNABO, PR, p. A716
PROGRESS WEST HOSPITAL, O'FALLON, MO, p. A366
PROMEDICA BAY PARK HOSPITAL, OREGON, OH, p. A489
PROMEDICA BIXBY HOSPITAL, ADRIAN, MI, p. A306
PROMEDICA COLDWATER REGIONAL HOSPITAL, COLDWATER, MI, p. A309
PROMEDICA DEFIANCE REGIONAL HOSPITAL, DEFIANCE, OH, p. A482
PROMEDICA FLOWER HOSPITAL, SYLVANIA, OH, p. A491
PROMEDICA FOSTORIA COMMUNITY HOSPITAL, FOSTORIA, OH, p. A483
PROMEDICA HERRICK HOSPITAL, TECUMSEH, MI, p. A323
PROMEDICA MEMORIAL HOSPITAL, FREMONT, OH, p. A483
PROMEDICA MONROE REGIONAL HOSPITAL, MONROE, MI, p. A318
PROMEDICA TOLEDO HOSPITAL, TOLEDO, OH, p. A492
PROMISE HOSPITAL BATON ROUGE – MAIN CAMPUS, BATON ROUGE, LA, p. A264
PROMISE HOSPITAL OF DALLAS, DALLAS, TX, p. A598
PROMISE HOSPITAL OF EAST LOS ANGELES, LOS ANGELES, CA, p. A68
PROMISE HOSPITAL OF FLORIDA AT THE VILLAGES, OXFORD, FL, p. A135
PROMISE HOSPITAL OF FORT MYERS, FORT MYERS, FL, p. A123
PROMISE HOSPITAL OF LOUISIANA – SHREVEPORT CAMPUS, SHREVEPORT, LA, p. A278
PROMISE HOSPITAL OF MIAMI, MIAMI LAKES, FL, p. A131
PROMISE HOSPITAL OF MISS LOU, VIDALIA, LA, p. A279
PROMISE HOSPITAL OF OVERLAND PARK, OVERLAND PARK, KS, p. A243
PROMISE HOSPITAL OF PHOENIX, MESA, AZ, p. A32
PROMISE HOSPITAL OF SALT LAKE, SALT LAKE CITY, UT, p. A652
PROMISE HOSPITAL OF VICKSBURG, VICKSBURG, MS, p. A355
PROMISE HOSPITAL OF WICHITA FALLS, WICHITA FALLS, TX, p. A645
PROMISE SPECIALTY HOSPITAL OF SHREVEPORT, SHREVEPORT, LOUISIANA (see PROMISE HOSPITAL OF LOUISIANA – SHREVEPORT CAMPUS), p. A278
PROSSER MEMORIAL HEALTH, PROSSER, WA, p. A676
PROVENA MERCY MEDICAL CENTER, AURORA, ILLINOIS (see AMITA HEALTH MERCY MEDICAL CENTER), p. A174
PROVENA SAINT JOSEPH HOSPITAL, ELGIN, ILLINOIS (see AMITA HEALTH SAINT JOSEPH HOSPITAL), p. A182
PROVENA SAINT JOSEPH MEDICAL CENTER, JOLIET, ILLINOIS (see AMITA HEALTH SAINT JOSEPH MEDICAL CENTER), p. A187
PROVENA ST. MARY'S HOSPITAL, KANKAKEE, ILLINOIS (see AMITA HEALTH ST. MARY'S HOSPITAL), p. A187
PROVIDENCE – PROVIDENCE PARK HOSPITAL, NOVI CAMPUS, NOVI, MICHIGAN (see ASCENSION OF PROVIDENCE HOSPITAL, SOUTHFIELD CAMPUS), p. A319
PROVIDENCE ALASKA MEDICAL CENTER, ANCHORAGE, AK, p. A25
PROVIDENCE CENTRALIA HOSPITAL, CENTRALIA, WA, p. A671
PROVIDENCE HEALTHCARE NETWORK, WACO, TX, p. A644
PROVIDENCE HOLY CROSS MEDICAL CENTER, MISSION HILLS, CA, p. A71
PROVIDENCE HOLY FAMILY HOSPITAL, SPOKANE, WA, p. A679
PROVIDENCE HOOD RIVER MEMORIAL HOSPITAL, HOOD RIVER, OR, p. A513
PROVIDENCE HOSPITAL, COLUMBIA, SC, p. A551
PROVIDENCE HOSPITAL, MOBILE, AL, p. A20
PROVIDENCE HOSPITAL NORTHEAST, COLUMBIA, SOUTH CAROLINA (see PROVIDENCE HOSPITAL), p. A551
PROVIDENCE HOSPITAL OF NORTH HOUSTON, HOUSTON, TX, p. A613
PROVIDENCE KODIAK ISLAND MEDICAL CENTER, KODIAK, AK, p. A26
PROVIDENCE LITTLE COMPANY OF MARY MEDICAL CENTER – TORRANCE, TORRANCE, CA, p. A92
PROVIDENCE LITTLE COMPANY OF MARY MEDICAL CENTER SAN PEDRO, LOS ANGELES, CA, p. A69
PROVIDENCE MEDFORD MEDICAL CENTER, MEDFORD, OR, p. A515
PROVIDENCE MEDICAL CENTER, KANSAS CITY, KS, p. A238
PROVIDENCE MEDICAL CENTER, WAYNE, NE, p. A392
PROVIDENCE MILWAUKIE HOSPITAL, MILWAUKIE, OR, p. A515

PROVIDENCE MOUNT CARMEL HOSPITAL, COLVILLE, WA, p. A672
PROVIDENCE NEWBERG MEDICAL CENTER, NEWBERG, OR, p. A515
PROVIDENCE PORTLAND MEDICAL CENTER, PORTLAND, OR, p. A516
PROVIDENCE REGIONAL MEDICAL CENTER EVERETT, EVERETT, WA, p. A673
PROVIDENCE SACRED HEART MEDICAL CENTER & CHILDREN'S HOSPITAL, SPOKANE, WA, p. A680
PROVIDENCE SAINT JOHN'S HEALTH CENTER, SANTA MONICA, CA, p. A89
PROVIDENCE SAINT JOSEPH MEDICAL CENTER, BURBANK, CA, p. A53
PROVIDENCE SEASIDE HOSPITAL, SEASIDE, OR, p. A518
PROVIDENCE SEWARD MEDICAL CENTER, SEWARD, AK, p. A27
PROVIDENCE ST. JOSEPH MEDICAL CENTER, POLSON, MT, p. A379
PROVIDENCE ST. JOSEPH'S HOSPITAL, CHEWELAH, WA, p. A671
PROVIDENCE ST. MARY MEDICAL CENTER, WALLA WALLA, WA, p. A681
PROVIDENCE ST. PATRICK HOSPITAL, MISSOULA, MT, p. A379
PROVIDENCE ST. PETER HOSPITAL, OLYMPIA, WA, p. A676
PROVIDENCE ST. VINCENT MEDICAL CENTER, PORTLAND, OR, p. A517
PROVIDENCE TARZANA MEDICAL CENTER, LOS ANGELES, CA, p. A69
PROVIDENCE VALDEZ MEDICAL CENTER, VALDEZ, AK, p. A27
PROVIDENCE VETERANS AFFAIRS MEDICAL CENTER, PROVIDENCE, RI, p. A547
PROVIDENCE WILLAMETTE FALLS MEDICAL CENTER, OREGON CITY, OR, p. A515
PROVIDENT HOSPITAL OF COOK COUNTY, CHICAGO, IL, p. A179
PROVO CANYON BEHAVIORAL HOSPITAL, OREM, UT, p. A650
PROWERS MEDICAL CENTER, LAMAR, CO, p. A103
PSYCHIATRIC INSTITUTE OF WASHINGTON, WASHINGTON, DC, p. A116
PSYCHIATRIC PAVILION NEW ORLEANS, NEW ORLEANS, LOUISIANA (see BEACON BEHAVIORAL HOSPITAL – NEW ORLEANS), p. A275
PULASKI MEMORIAL HOSPITAL, WINAMAC, IN, p. A216
PULLMAN REGIONAL HOSPITAL, PULLMAN, WA, p. A676
PUNXSUTAWNEY AREA HOSPITAL, PUNXSUTAWNEY, PA, p. A539
PURCELL MUNICIPAL HOSPITAL, PURCELL, OK, p. A506
PUSHMATAHA HOSPITAL, ANTLERS, OK, p. A498
PUTNAM COMMUNITY MEDICAL CENTER, PALATKA, FL, p. A135
PUTNAM COUNTY HOSPITAL, GREENCASTLE, IN, p. A205
PUTNAM COUNTY MEMORIAL HOSPITAL, UNIONVILLE, MO, p. A372
PUTNAM GENERAL HOSPITAL, EATONTON, GA, p. A153
PUTNAM HOSPITAL CENTER, CARMEL, NY, p. A425

Q

QUAIL RUN BEHAVIORAL HEALTH, PHOENIX, AZ, p. A34
QUEEN OF THE VALLEY MEDICAL CENTER, NAPA, CA, p. A74
QUILLEN REHABILITATION HOSPITAL, JOHNSON CITY, TN, p. A571
QUINCY VALLEY MEDICAL CENTER, QUINCY, WA, p. A677

R

RADY CHILDREN'S HOSPITAL – SAN DIEGO, SAN DIEGO, CA, p. A84
RADY CHILDREN'S HOSPITAL AND HEALTH CENTER, SAN DIEGO, CA, p. A84
RAINY LAKE MEDICAL CENTER, INTERNATIONAL FALLS, MN, p. A333
RALEIGH GENERAL HOSPITAL, BECKLEY, WV, p. A683
RALPH H. JOHNSON VETERANS AFFAIRS MEDICAL CENTER, CHARLESTON, SC, p. A550
RANCHO LOS AMIGOS NATIONAL REHABILITATION CENTER, DOWNEY, CA, p. A56

RANDOLPH HOSPITAL, ASHEBORO, NC, p. A449
RANGE REGIONAL HEALTH SERVICES, HIBBING, MN, p. A333
RANGELY DISTRICT HOSPITAL, RANGELY, CO, p. A105
RANKEN JORDAN PEDIATRIC BRIDGE HOSPITAL, MARYLAND HEIGHTS, MO, p. A365
RANKIN COUNTY HOSPITAL DISTRICT, RANKIN, TX, p. A630
RANSOM MEMORIAL HOSPITAL, OTTAWA, KS, p. A242
RAPID CITY REGIONAL HOSPITAL, RAPID CITY, SD, p. A563
RAPIDES REGIONAL MEDICAL CENTER, ALEXANDRIA, LA, p. A262
RAPPAHANNOCK GENERAL HOSPITAL, KILMARNOCK, VA, p. A661
RAULERSON HOSPITAL, OKEECHOBEE, FL, p. A133
RAWLINS COUNTY HEALTH CENTER, ATWOOD, KS, p. A232
RAY COUNTY MEMORIAL HOSPITAL, RICHMOND, MO, p. A367
RC HOSPITAL AND CLINICS, OLIVIA, MN, p. A337
READING HOSPITAL, WEST READING, PA, p. A544
READING HOSPITAL REHABILITATION AT WYOMISSING, WYOMISSING, PA, p. A545
REAGAN MEMORIAL HOSPITAL, BIG LAKE, TX, p. A588
REBOUND BEHAVIORAL HEALTH, LANCASTER, SC, p. A555
RECEPTION AND MEDICAL CENTER, LAKE BUTLER, FL, p. A127
RED BAY HOSPITAL, RED BAY, AL, p. A23
RED BUD REGIONAL HOSPITAL, RED BUD, IL, p. A194
RED CEDAR MEDICAL CENTER–MAYO HEALTH SYSTEM, MENOMONIE, WISCONSIN (see MAYO CLINIC HEALTH SYSTEM – RED CEDAR IN MENOMONIE), p. A700
RED LAKE INDIAN HEALTH SERVICE HOSPITAL, RED LAKE, MN, p. A338
RED RIVER BEHAVIORAL CENTER, BOSSIER CITY, LA, p. A265
RED RIVER BEHAVIORAL HEALTH SYSTEM, GRAND FORKS, ND, p. A467
RED RIVER HOSPITAL, LLC, WICHITA FALLS, TX, p. A646
REDINGTON–FAIRVIEW GENERAL HOSPITAL, SKOWHEGAN, ME, p. A285
REDLANDS COMMUNITY HOSPITAL, REDLANDS, CA, p. A80
REDMOND REGIONAL MEDICAL CENTER, ROME, GA, p. A159
REDWOOD MEMORIAL HOSPITAL, FORTUNA, CA, p. A58
REEDSBURG AREA MEDICAL CENTER, REEDSBURG, WI, p. A704
REEVES COUNTY HOSPITAL, PECOS, TX, p. A628
REEVES MEMORIAL MEDICAL CENTER, BERNICE, LA, p. A264
REFUGIO COUNTY MEMORIAL HOSPITAL, REFUGIO, TX, p. A630
REGENCY HOSPITAL CLEVELAND EAST, WARRENSVILLE HEIGHTS, OH, p. A493
REGENCY HOSPITAL OF CENTRAL GEORGIA, MACON, GA, p. A156
REGENCY HOSPITAL OF COLUMBUS, COLUMBUS, OH, p. A480
REGENCY HOSPITAL OF FLORENCE, FLORENCE, SC, p. A553
REGENCY HOSPITAL OF GREENVILLE, GREENVILLE, SC, p. A553
REGENCY HOSPITAL OF MERIDIAN, MERIDIAN, MS, p. A351
REGENCY HOSPITAL OF MINNEAPOLIS, GOLDEN VALLEY, MN, p. A332
REGENCY HOSPITAL OF NORTHWEST ARKANSAS – SPRINGDALE, SPRINGDALE, AR, p. A49
REGENCY HOSPITAL OF NORTHWEST INDIANA, EAST CHICAGO, IN, p. A202
REGENCY HOSPITAL OF SOUTH ATLANTA, EAST POINT, GA, p. A153
REGENCY HOSPITAL OF TOLEDO, SYLVANIA, OH, p. A491
REGINA HOSPITAL, HASTINGS, MN, p. A333
REGIONAL GENERAL HOSPITAL, WILLISTON, FL, p. A144
REGIONAL HEALTH SERVICES OF HOWARD COUNTY, CRESCO, IA, p. A220
REGIONAL HOSPITAL FOR RESPIRATORY AND COMPLEX CARE, BURIEN, WA, p. A671
REGIONAL HOSPITAL OF SCRANTON, READING, PA, p. A540
REGIONAL MEDICAL CENTER, MANCHESTER, IA, p. A226
REGIONAL MEDICAL CENTER, ORANGEBURG, SC, p. A556
REGIONAL MEDICAL CENTER BAYONET POINT, HUDSON, FL, p. A125
REGIONAL MEDICAL CENTER OF CENTRAL ALABAMA, GREENVILLE, AL, p. A19
REGIONAL MEDICAL CENTER OF SAN JOSE, SAN JOSE, CA, p. A86
REGIONAL MENTAL HEALTH CENTER, MERRILLVILLE, IN, p. A211
REGIONAL ONE HEALTH, MEMPHIS, TN, p. A575
REGIONAL ONE HEALTH EXTENDED CARE HOSPITAL, MEMPHIS, TN, p. A575
REGIONAL REHABILITATION HOSPITAL, PHENIX CITY, AL, p. A22
REGIONAL WEST GARDEN COUNTY, OSHKOSH, NE, p. A390

REGIONAL WEST MEDICAL CENTER, SCOTTSBLUFF, NE, p. A391

REGIONS HOSPITAL, SAINT PAUL, MN, p. A340

REHABILITATION HOSPITAL OF FORT WAYNE, FORT WAYNE, IN, p. A204

REHABILITATION HOSPITAL OF INDIANA, INDIANAPOLIS, IN, p. A207

REHABILITATION HOSPITAL OF JENNINGS, JENNINGS, LA, p. A269

REHABILITATION HOSPITAL OF NORTHERN ARIZONA, FLAGSTAFF, AZ, p. A29

REHABILITATION HOSPITAL OF NORTHWEST OHIO, TOLEDO, OH, p. A492

REHABILITATION HOSPITAL OF OVERLAND PARK, OVERLAND PARK, KS, p. A243

REHABILITATION HOSPITAL OF RHODE ISLAND, NORTH SMITHFIELD, RI, p. A547

REHABILITATION HOSPITAL OF SAVANNAH, SAVANNAH, GA, p. A160

REHABILITATION HOSPITAL OF SOUTHERN NEW MEXICO, LAS CRUCES, NM, p. A419

REHABILITATION HOSPITAL OF SOUTHWEST VIRGINIA, BRISTOL, VA, p. A657

REHABILITATION HOSPITAL OF THE NORTHWEST, POST FALLS, ID, p. A171

REHABILITATION HOSPITAL OF THE PACIFIC, HONOLULU, HI, p. A165

REHABILITATION HOSPITAL OF WISCONSIN, WAUKESHA, WI, p. A707

REHABILITATION HOSPITAL, NAVICENT HEALTH, MACON, GA, p. A157

REHABILITATION INSTITUTE OF OREGON, PORTLAND, OREGON (see LEGACY GOOD SAMARITAN MEDICAL CENTER), p. A516

REHOBOTH MCKINLEY CHRISTIAN HEALTH CARE SERVICES, GALLUP, NM, p. A418

REID HEALTH, RICHMOND, IN, p. A214

RENAISSANCE SPECIALTY HOSPITAL OF CENTRAL INDIANA, MUNCIE, INDIANA (see CENTRAL INDIANA AMG SPECIALTY HOSPITAL), p. A212

RENO BEHAVIORAL HEALTHCARE HOSPITAL, RENO, NV, p. A397

RENOWN REGIONAL MEDICAL CENTER, RENO, NV, p. A397

RENOWN REHABILITATION HOSPITAL, RENO, NV, p. A397

RENOWN SOUTH MEADOWS MEDICAL CENTER, RENO, NV, p. A397

REPUBLIC COUNTY HOSPITAL, BELLEVILLE, KS, p. A232

RESEARCH BELTON HOSPITAL, BELTON, MISSOURI (see BELTON REGIONAL MEDICAL CENTER), p. A356

RESEARCH MEDICAL CENTER, KANSAS CITY, MO, p. A362

RESOLUTE HEALTH, NEW BRAUNFELS, TX, p. A626

RESTON HOSPITAL CENTER, RESTON, VA, p. A665

RESURRECTION MEDICAL CENTER, CHICAGO, ILLINOIS (see AMITA HEALTH RESURRECTION MEDICAL CENTER), p. A179

REYNOLDS MEMORIAL HOSPITAL, GLEN DALE, WV, p. A685

RHEA MEDICAL CENTER, DAYTON, TN, p. A569

RHODE ISLAND HOSPITAL, PROVIDENCE, RI, p. A548

RICE MEDICAL CENTER, EAGLE LAKE, TX, p. A600

RICE MEMORIAL HOSPITAL, WILLMAR, MN, p. A342

RICELAND MEDICAL CENTER, WINNIE, TX, p. A646

RICHARD H. HUTCHINGS PSYCHIATRIC CENTER, SYRACUSE, NY, p. A445

RICHARD L. ROUDEBUSH VETERANS AFFAIRS MEDICAL CENTER, INDIANAPOLIS, IN, p. A207

RICHARDSON MEDICAL CENTER, RAYVILLE, LA, p. A277

RICHLAND HOSPITAL, RICHLAND CENTER, WI, p. A704

RICHLAND PARISH HOSPITAL, DELHI, LA, p. A267

RICHMOND STATE HOSPITAL, RICHMOND, IN, p. A214

RIDDLE HOSPITAL, MEDIA, PA, p. A531

RIDDLE MEMORIAL HOSPITAL, MEDIA, PENNSYLVANIA (see RIDDLE HOSPITAL), p. A531

RIDGE BEHAVIORAL HEALTH SYSTEM, LEXINGTON, KY, p. A255

RIDGECREST REGIONAL HOSPITAL, RIDGECREST, CA, p. A80

RIDGEVIEW BEHAVIORAL HOSPITAL, MIDDLE POINT, OH, p. A487

RIDGEVIEW INSTITUTE, SMYRNA, GA, p. A160

RIDGEVIEW LE SUEUR MEDICAL CENTER, LE SUEUR, MN, p. A334

RIDGEVIEW MEDICAL CENTER, WACONIA, MN, p. A342

RIDGEVIEW PSYCHIATRIC HOSPITAL AND CENTER, OAK RIDGE, TN, p. A578

RIDGEVIEW SIBLEY MEDICAL CENTER, ARLINGTON, MN, p. A327

RILEY HOSPITAL, MERIDIAN, MISSISSIPPI (see ANDERSON REGIONAL HEALTH SYSTEM SOUTH), p. A351

RILEY HOSPITAL FOR CHILDREN, INDIANAPOLIS, INDIANA (see RILEY HOSPITAL FOR CHILDREN AT INDIANA UNIVERSITY HEALTH), p. A208

RILEY HOSPITAL FOR CHILDREN AT INDIANA UNIVERSITY HEALTH, INDIANAPOLIS, INDIANA (see INDIANA UNIVERSITY HEALTH UNIVERSITY HOSPITAL), p. A208

RINGGOLD COUNTY HOSPITAL, MOUNT AYR, IA, p. A226

RIO GRANDE HOSPITAL, DEL NORTE, CO, p. A98

RIO GRANDE REGIONAL HOSPITAL, MCALLEN, TX, p. A623

RIO GRANDE STATE CENTER/SOUTH TEXAS HEALTH CARE SYSTEM, HARLINGEN, TX, p. A609

RIPON MEDICAL CENTER, RIPON, WI, p. A705

RIVENDELL BEHAVIORAL HEALTH, BOWLING GREEN, KY, p. A250

RIVENDELL BEHAVIORAL HEALTH SERVICES OF ARKANSAS, BENTON, AR, p. A39

RIVER BEND HOSPITAL, WEST LAFAYETTE, IN, p. A216

RIVER CREST HOSPITAL, SAN ANGELO, TX, p. A632

RIVER FALLS AREA HOSPITAL, RIVER FALLS, WI, p. A705

RIVER HOSPITAL, ALEXANDRIA BAY, NY, p. A422

RIVER OAKS HOSPITAL, NEW ORLEANS, LA, p. A275

RIVER PARK HOSPITAL, HUNTINGTON, WV, p. A686

RIVER PLACE BEHAVIORAL HEALTH, LA PLACE, LA, p. A270

RIVER POINT BEHAVIORAL HEALTH, JACKSONVILLE, FL, p. A125

RIVER VALLEY MEDICAL CENTER, DARDANELLE, AR, p. A41

RIVEREDGE HOSPITAL, FOREST PARK, IL, p. A183

RIVERLAND MEDICAL CENTER, FERRIDAY, LA, p. A267

RIVERSIDE CENTER FOR BEHAVIORAL MEDICINE, RIVERSIDE, CA, p. A81

RIVERSIDE COMMUNITY HOSPITAL, RIVERSIDE, CA, p. A81

RIVERSIDE DOCTORS' HOSPITAL WILLIAMSBURG, WILLIAMSBURG, VA, p. A669

RIVERSIDE HOSPITAL OF LOUISIANA, ALEXANDRIA, LA, p. A262

RIVERSIDE MEDICAL CENTER, FRANKLINTON, LA, p. A267

RIVERSIDE MEDICAL CENTER, KANKAKEE, IL, p. A187

RIVERSIDE MEDICAL CENTER, RIVERSIDE, CA, p. A81

RIVERSIDE REGIONAL MEDICAL CENTER, NEWPORT NEWS, VA, p. A663

RIVERSIDE SHORE MEMORIAL HOSPITAL, ONANCOCK, VA, p. A664

RIVERSIDE TAPPAHANNOCK HOSPITAL, TAPPAHANNOCK, VA, p. A668

RIVERSIDE UNIVERSITY HEALTH SYSTEM–MEDICAL CENTER, MORENO VALLEY, CA, p. A73

RIVERSIDE WALTER REED HOSPITAL, GLOUCESTER, VA, p. A660

RIVERTON HOSPITAL, RIVERTON, UT, p. A651

RIVERVALLEY BEHAVIORAL HEALTH HOSPITAL, OWENSBORO, KY, p. A259

RIVERVIEW BEHAVIORAL HEALTH, TEXARKANA, AR, p. A49

RIVERVIEW HEALTH, CROOKSTON, MN, p. A330

RIVERVIEW HEALTH, NOBLESVILLE, IN, p. A213

RIVERVIEW PSYCHIATRIC CENTER, AUGUSTA, ME, p. A281

RIVERVIEW REGIONAL MEDICAL CENTER, CARTHAGE, TN, p. A566

RIVERVIEW REGIONAL MEDICAL CENTER, GADSDEN, AL, p. A18

RIVERWOOD HEALTHCARE CENTER, AITKIN, MN, p. A327

RIVERWOODS BEHAVIORAL HEALTH SYSTEM, RIVERDALE, GA, p. A159

RIVER'S EDGE HOSPITAL AND CLINIC, SAINT PETER, MN, p. A340

RMC ANNISTON, ANNISTON, AL, p. A13

RMC–STRINGFELLOW MEMORIAL HOSPITAL, ANNISTON, AL, p. A13

RML SPECIALTY HOSPITAL, HINSDALE, IL, p. A186

ROANE GENERAL HOSPITAL, SPENCER, WV, p. A689

ROANE MEDICAL CENTER, HARRIMAN, TN, p. A570

ROBERT E. BUSH NAVAL HOSPITAL, TWENTYNINE PALMS, CA, p. A92

ROBERT J. DOLE VETERANS AFFAIRS MEDICAL CENTER, WICHITA, KS, p. A248

ROBERT WOOD JOHNSON UNIVERSITY HOSPITAL, NEW BRUNSWICK, NJ, p. A409

ROBERT WOOD JOHNSON UNIVERSITY HOSPITAL AT HAMILTON, HAMILTON, NJ, p. A406

ROBERT WOOD JOHNSON UNIVERSITY HOSPITAL RAHWAY, RAHWAY, NJ, p. A411

ROBERT WOOD JOHNSON UNIVERSITY HOSPITAL SOMERSET, SOMERVILLE, NJ, p. A412

ROBLEY REX VETERANS AFFAIRS MEDICAL CENTER, LOUISVILLE, KY, p. A256

ROCHELLE COMMUNITY HOSPITAL, ROCHELLE, IL, p. A194

ROCHESTER GENERAL HOSPITAL, ROCHESTER, NY, p. A442

ROCHESTER PSYCHIATRIC CENTER, ROCHESTER, NY, p. A442

ROCK COUNTY HOSPITAL, BASSETT, NE, p. A382

ROCK PRAIRIE BEHAVIORAL HEALTH, COLLEGE STATION, TX, p. A593

ROCK REGIONAL HOSPITAL, DERBY, KS, p. A234

ROCK SPRINGS, GEORGETOWN, TX, p. A607

ROCKCASTLE REGIONAL HOSPITAL AND RESPIRATORY CARE CENTER, MOUNT VERNON, KY, p. A258

ROCKFORD CENTER, NEWARK, DE, p. A113

ROCKLAND CHILDREN'S PSYCHIATRIC CENTER, ORANGEBURG, NY, p. A440

ROCKLAND PSYCHIATRIC CENTER, ORANGEBURG, NY, p. A441

ROCKLEDGE REGIONAL MEDICAL CENTER, ROCKLEDGE, FL, p. A138

ROCKVILLE GENERAL HOSPITAL, VERNON, CT, p. A111

ROGER MILLS MEMORIAL HOSPITAL, CHEYENNE, OK, p. A497

ROGER WILLIAMS MEDICAL CENTER, PROVIDENCE, RI, p. A548

ROGERS MEMORIAL HOSPITAL, INC., OCONOMOWOC, WI, p. A702

ROLLING HILLS HOSPITAL, ADA, OK, p. A496

ROLLING HILLS HOSPITAL, FRANKLIN, TN, p. A569

ROLLING PLAINS MEMORIAL HOSPITAL, SWEETWATER, TX, p. A639

ROME MEMORIAL HOSPITAL, ROME, NY, p. A443

RONALD REAGAN UCLA MEDICAL CENTER, LOS ANGELES, CA, p. A69

ROOKS COUNTY HEALTH CENTER, PLAINVILLE, KS, p. A244

ROOSEVELT GENERAL HOSPITAL, PORTALES, NM, p. A419

ROOSEVELT MEDICAL CENTER, CULBERTSON, MT, p. A375

ROOSEVELT WARM SPRINGS REHABILITATION AND SPECIALTY HOSPITALS – LTAC, WARM SPRINGS, GA, p. A162

ROOSEVELT WARM SPRINGS REHABILITATION HOSPITAL – REHAB, WARM SPRINGS, GA, p. A162

ROPER HOSPITAL, CHARLESTON, SC, p. A550

ROPER ST. FRANCIS MOUNT PLEASANT HOSPITAL, MOUNT PLEASANT, SC, p. A555

ROSE MEDICAL CENTER, DENVER, CO, p. A99

ROSEBUD HEALTH CARE CENTER, FORSYTH, MT, p. A376

ROSELAND COMMUNITY HOSPITAL, CHICAGO, IL, p. A179

ROSWELL PARK COMPREHENSIVE CANCER CENTER, BUFFALO, NY, p. A424

ROTARY REHABILITATION HOSPITAL, MOBILE, ALABAMA (see MOBILE INFIRMARY MEDICAL CENTER), p. A20

ROTHMAN SPECIALTY HOSPITAL, BENSALEM, PA, p. A520

ROUNDUP MEMORIAL HEALTHCARE, ROUNDUP, MT, p. A380

ROXBOROUGH MEMORIAL HOSPITAL, PHILADELPHIA, PA, p. A536

ROXBURY TREATMENT CENTER, SHIPPENSBURG, PA, p. A541

ROYAL OAKS HOSPITAL, WINDSOR, MO, p. A373

RUBY VALLEY MEDICAL CENTER, SHERIDAN, MT, p. A380

RUMFORD HOSPITAL, RUMFORD, ME, p. A285

RUSH COUNTY MEMORIAL HOSPITAL, LA CROSSE, KS, p. A238

RUSH FOUNDATION HOSPITAL, MERIDIAN, MS, p. A351

RUSH MEMORIAL HOSPITAL, RUSHVILLE, IN, p. A214

RUSH OAK PARK HOSPITAL, OAK PARK, IL, p. A191

RUSH UNIVERSITY MEDICAL CENTER, CHICAGO, IL, p. A179

RUSH–COPLEY MEDICAL CENTER, AURORA, IL, p. A174

RUSK REHABILITATION HOSPITAL, COLUMBIA, MO, p. A359

RUSK STATE HOSPITAL, RUSK, TX, p. A632

RUSSELL COUNTY HOSPITAL, RUSSELL SPRINGS, KY, p. A260

RUSSELL COUNTY MEDICAL CENTER, LEBANON, VA, p. A661

RUSSELL MEDICAL, ALEXANDER CITY, AL, p. A13

RUSSELL REGIONAL HOSPITAL, RUSSELL, KS, p. A244

RUSSELLVILLE HOSPITAL, RUSSELLVILLE, AL, p. A23

RUSTON REGIONAL SPECIALTY HOSPITAL, RUSTON, LA, p. A277

RUTGERS UNIVERSITY BEHAVIORAL HEALTHCARE, PISCATAWAY, NJ, p. A411

RUTHERFORD REGIONAL HEALTH SYSTEM, RUTHERFORDTON, NC, p. A461

RUTLAND REGIONAL MEDICAL CENTER, RUTLAND, VT, p. A655

RWJBARNABAS HEALTH BEHAVIORAL HEALTH CENTER AND NETWORK, TOMS RIVER, NJ, p. A413

RYDER MEMORIAL HOSPITAL, HUMACAO, PR, p. A716

S

SABETHA COMMUNITY HOSPITAL, SABETHA, KS, p. A244

SABINE COUNTY HOSPITAL, HEMPHILL, TX, p. A609

SABINE MEDICAL CENTER, MANY, LA, p. A273

SACRED HEART HOSPITAL ON THE EMERALD COAST, MIRAMAR BEACH, FL, p. A132

SACRED HEART HOSPITAL ON THE GULF, PORT ST JOE, FL, p. A137
SACRED HEART HOSPITAL PENSACOLA, PENSACOLA, FL, p. A136
SACRED OAK MEDICAL CENTER, HOUSTON, TX, p. A613
SAFE HAVEN HOSPITAL OF POCATELLO, POCATELLO, ID, p. A171
SAFE HAVEN HOSPITAL OF TREASURE VALLEY, BOISE, ID, p. A167
SAGAMORE CHILDREN'S PSYCHIATRIC CENTER, DIX HILLS, NY, p. A427
SAGE MEMORIAL HOSPITAL, GANADO, AZ, p. A29
SAGE REHABILITATION HOSPITAL, BATON ROUGE, LA, p. A264
SAGE SPECIALTY HOSPITAL (LTAC), DENHAM SPRINGS, LA, p. A267
SAGECREST HOSPITAL OF GRAPEVINE, GRAPEVINE, TX, p. A608
SAGEWEST HEALTH CARE AT RIVERTON, RIVERTON, WY, p. A712
SAINT AGNES HEALTHCARE, BALTIMORE, MD, p. A287
SAINT AGNES MEDICAL CENTER, FRESNO, CA, p. A59
SAINT ALPHONSUS MEDICAL CENTER – BAKER CITY, BAKER CITY, OR, p. A511
SAINT ALPHONSUS MEDICAL CENTER – NAMPA, NAMPA, ID, p. A170
SAINT ALPHONSUS MEDICAL CENTER – ONTARIO, ONTARIO, OR, p. A515
SAINT ALPHONSUS REGIONAL MEDICAL CENTER, BOISE, ID, p. A168
SAINT ANNE'S HOSPITAL, FALL RIVER, MA, p. A298
SAINT ANTHONY HOSPITAL, CHICAGO, IL, p. A179
SAINT ANTHONY MEMORIAL, MICHIGAN CITY, INDIANA (see FRANCISCAN HEALTH MICHIGAN CITY), p. A211
SAINT BARNABAS BEHAVIORAL HEALTH CENTER, TOMS RIVER, NEW JERSEY (see RWJBARNABAS HEALTH BEHAVIORAL HEALTH CENTER AND NETWORK), p. A413
SAINT BARNABAS MEDICAL CENTER, LIVINGSTON, NJ, p. A407
SAINT CAMILLUS MEDICAL CENTER, HURST, TX, p. A615
SAINT CLARE'S DENVILLE HOSPITAL, DENVILLE, NJ, p. A404
SAINT CLARE'S HEALTH CENTER AT SUSSEX, SUSSEX, NEW JERSEY (see SAINT CLARE'S DENVILLE HOSPITAL), p. A413
SAINT CLARE'S HOSPITAL/BOONTON TOWNSHIP, BOONTON TOWNSHIP, NEW JERSEY (see SAINT CLARE'S DENVILLE HOSPITAL), p. A403
SAINT CLARE'S HOSPITAL/DENVILLE, DENVILLE, NEW JERSEY (see SAINT CLARE'S DENVILLE HOSPITAL), p. A404
SAINT ELIZABETHS HOSPITAL, WASHINGTON, DC, p. A116
SAINT ELIZABETH'S MEDICAL CENTER, WABASHA, MN, p. A342
SAINT FRANCIS HEART HOSPITAL, TULSA, OKLAHOMA (see SAINT FRANCIS HOSPITAL), p. A509
SAINT FRANCIS HOSPITAL, CHARLESTON, WV, p. A684
SAINT FRANCIS HOSPITAL, EVANSTON, ILLINOIS (see AMITA HEALTH SAINT FRANCIS HOSPITAL EVANSTON), p. A182
SAINT FRANCIS HOSPITAL, MEMPHIS, TN, p. A575
SAINT FRANCIS HOSPITAL, TULSA, OK, p. A509
SAINT FRANCIS HOSPITAL AND MEDICAL CENTER, HARTFORD, CT, p. A108
SAINT FRANCIS HOSPITAL MUSKOGEE, MUSKOGEE, OK, p. A502
SAINT FRANCIS HOSPITAL SOUTH, TULSA, OK, p. A509
SAINT FRANCIS HOSPITAL VINITA, VINITA, OK, p. A510
SAINT FRANCIS HOSPITAL–BARTLETT, BARTLETT, TN, p. A566
SAINT FRANCIS MEDICAL CENTER, CAPE GIRARDEAU, MO, p. A357
SAINT FRANCIS MEMORIAL HOSPITAL, SAN FRANCISCO, CA, p. A85
SAINT JOHN HOSPITAL, LEAVENWORTH, KS, p. A239
SAINT JOSEPH HEALTH SYSTEM, MISHAWAKA, IN, p. A211
SAINT JOSEPH HOSPITAL, CHICAGO, ILLINOIS (see AMITA HEALTH SAINT JOSEPH HOSPITAL), p. A179
SAINT JOSEPH HOSPITAL, DENVER, CO, p. A99
SAINT JOSEPH MOUNT STERLING, MOUNT STERLING, KY, p. A258
SAINT JOSEPH'S HOSPITAL OF ATLANTA, ATLANTA, GA, p. A146
SAINT JOSEPH'S MEDICAL CENTER, YONKERS, NY, p. A448
SAINT LOUISE REGIONAL HOSPITAL, GILROY, CA, p. A60
SAINT LUKE INSTITUTE, SILVER SPRING, MD, p. A293
SAINT LUKE'S COMMUNITY HOSPITAL AT LEAWOOD, LEAWOOD, KS, p. A239
SAINT LUKE'S CUSHING HOSPITAL, LEAVENWORTH, KS, p. A239
SAINT LUKE'S EAST HOSPITAL, LEE'S SUMMIT, MO, p. A364

SAINT LUKE'S HOSPITAL OF KANSAS CITY, KANSAS CITY, MO, p. A363
SAINT LUKE'S NORTH HOSPITAL – BARRY ROAD, KANSAS CITY, MO, p. A363
SAINT LUKE'S SOUTH HOSPITAL, OVERLAND PARK, KS, p. A243
SAINT MARGARET MERCY HEALTHCARE CENTERS, HAMMOND, INDIANA (see FRANCISCAN HEALTH HAMMOND), p. A206
SAINT MARGARET MERCY HEALTHCARE CENTERS–SOUTH CAMPUS, DYER, INDIANA (see FRANCISCAN HEALTH DYER), p. A202
SAINT MARY'S HOSPITAL, WATERBURY, CT, p. A111
SAINT MARY'S REGIONAL MEDICAL CENTER, RENO, NV, p. A397
SAINT MARY'S REGIONAL MEDICAL CENTER, RUSSELLVILLE, AR, p. A48
SAINT MICHAEL'S HOSPITAL, STEVENS POINT, WISCONSIN (see ASCENSION ST. MICHAEL'S HOSPITAL), p. A706
SAINT MICHAEL'S MEDICAL CENTER, NEWARK, NJ, p. A409
SAINT PETER'S UNIVERSITY HOSPITAL, NEW BRUNSWICK, NJ, p. A409
SAINT SIMONS BY–THE–SEA HOSPITAL, SAINT SIMONS ISLAND, GA, p. A159
SAINT THOMAS DEKALB HOSPITAL, SMITHVILLE, TN, p. A579
SAINT THOMAS HICKMAN HOSPITAL, CENTERVILLE, TN, p. A567
SAINT THOMAS HIGHLANDS HOSPITAL, SPARTA, TN, p. A579
SAINT THOMAS HOSPITAL FOR SPINAL SURGERY, NASHVILLE, TN, p. A576
SAINT THOMAS MIDTOWN HOSPITAL, NASHVILLE, TN, p. A577
SAINT THOMAS RIVER PARK HOSPITAL, MC MINNVILLE, TN, p. A574
SAINT THOMAS RUTHERFORD HOSPITAL, MURFREESBORO, TN, p. A576
SAINT THOMAS STONES RIVER HOSPITAL, WOODBURY, TN, p. A580
SAINT THOMAS WEST HOSPITAL, NASHVILLE, TN, p. A577
SAINT VINCENT HOSPITAL, ERIE, PA, p. A525
SAINT VINCENT HOSPITAL, WORCESTER, MA, p. A305
SAINTS MARY & ELIZABETH MEDICAL CENTER, CHICAGO, ILLINOIS (see AMITA HEALTH SAINTS MARY & ELIZABETH MEDICAL CENTER), p. A179
SAINTS MEDICAL CENTER, LOWELL, MASSACHUSETTS (see LOWELL GENERAL HOSPITAL), p. A300
SAKAKAWEA MEDICAL CENTER, HAZEN, ND, p. A467
SALEM HEALTH WEST VALLEY, DALLAS, OR, p. A512
SALEM HOSPITAL, SALEM, MASSACHUSETTS (see SALEM CAMPUS), p. A303
SALEM HOSPITAL, SALEM, OR, p. A517
SALEM MEDICAL CENTER, SALEM, NJ, p. A412
SALEM MEMORIAL DISTRICT HOSPITAL, SALEM, MO, p. A371
SALEM REGIONAL MEDICAL CENTER, SALEM, OH, p. A490
SALEM TOWNSHIP HOSPITAL, SALEM, IL, p. A195
SALEM VETERANS AFFAIRS MEDICAL CENTER, SALEM, VA, p. A667
SALINA REGIONAL HEALTH CENTER, SALINA, KS, p. A245
SALINA SURGICAL HOSPITAL, SALINA, KS, p. A245
SALINAS VALLEY MEMORIAL HEALTHCARE SYSTEM, SALINAS, CA, p. A83
SALINE MEMORIAL HOSPITAL, BENTON, AR, p. A39
SALT LAKE BEHAVIORAL HEALTH, SALT LAKE CITY, UT, p. A652
SALT LAKE REGIONAL MEDICAL CENTER, SALT LAKE CITY, UT, p. A652
SAM RAYBURN MEMORIAL VETERANS CENTER, BONHAM, TEXAS (see VETERANS AFFAIRS NORTH TEXAS HEALTH CARE SYSTEM), p. A589
SAMARITAN ALBANY GENERAL HOSPITAL, ALBANY, OR, p. A511
SAMARITAN BEHAVIORAL HEALTH CENTER–DESERT SAMARITAN MEDICAL CENTER, MESA, ARIZONA (see BANNER DESERT MEDICAL CENTER), p. A32
SAMARITAN HEALTHCARE, MOSES LAKE, WA, p. A675
SAMARITAN HOSPITAL – MAIN CAMPUS, TROY, NY, p. A445
SAMARITAN HOSPITAL, MACON, MO, p. A365
SAMARITAN LEBANON COMMUNITY HOSPITAL, LEBANON, OR, p. A514
SAMARITAN MEDICAL CENTER, WATERTOWN, NY, p. A447
SAMARITAN NORTH LINCOLN HOSPITAL, LINCOLN CITY, OR, p. A514
SAMARITAN PACIFIC COMMUNITIES HOSPITAL, NEWPORT, OR, p. A515
SAME DAY SURGERY CENTER, RAPID CITY, SD, p. A563
SAMPSON REGIONAL MEDICAL CENTER, CLINTON, NC, p. A452
SAMUEL MAHELONA MEMORIAL HOSPITAL, KAPAA, HI, p. A166

SAMUEL SIMMONDS MEMORIAL HOSPITAL, BARROW, AK, p. A25
SAN ANGELO COMMUNITY MEDICAL CENTER, SAN ANGELO, TX, p. A632
SAN ANTONIO BEHAVIORAL HEALTHCARE HOSPITAL, SAN ANTONIO, TX, p. A635
SAN ANTONIO REGIONAL HOSPITAL, UPLAND, CA, p. A93
SAN ANTONIO STATE HOSPITAL, SAN ANTONIO, TX, p. A635
SAN BERNARDINO MOUNTAINS COMMUNITY HOSPITAL DISTRICT, LAKE ARROWHEAD, CA, p. A63
SAN CARLOS APACHE HEALTHCARE CORPORATION, PERIDOT, AZ, p. A32
SAN DIEGO COUNTY PSYCHIATRIC HOSPITAL, SAN DIEGO, CA, p. A84
SAN DIEGO MEDICAL CENTER, SAN DIEGO, CA, p. A84
SAN DIMAS COMMUNITY HOSPITAL, SAN DIMAS, CA, p. A85
SAN FRANCISCO MEDICAL CENTER, SAN FRANCISCO, CA, p. A85
SAN FRANCISCO VA MEDICAL CENTER, SAN FRANCISCO, CA, p. A85
SAN GABRIEL VALLEY MEDICAL CENTER, SAN GABRIEL, CA, p. A86
SAN GORGONIO MEMORIAL HOSPITAL, BANNING, CA, p. A52
SAN JOAQUIN GENERAL HOSPITAL, FRENCH CAMP, CA, p. A59
SAN JOAQUIN VALLEY REHABILITATION HOSPITAL, FRESNO, CA, p. A59
SAN JORGE CHILDREN'S HOSPITAL, SANTURCE, PR, p. A719
SAN JOSE BEHAVIORAL HEALTH, SAN JOSE, CA, p. A86
SAN JOSE MEDICAL CENTER, SAN JOSE, CA, p. A86
SAN JUAN CAPESTRANO HOSPITAL, SAN JUAN, PR, p. A719
SAN JUAN CITY HOSPITAL, SAN JUAN, PR, p. A719
SAN JUAN HEALTH SERVICE DISTRICT, MONTICELLO, UT, p. A649
SAN JUAN REGIONAL MEDICAL CENTER, FARMINGTON, NM, p. A418
SAN LEANDRO HOSPITAL, SAN LEANDRO, CA, p. A87
SAN LUIS VALLEY HEALTH, ALAMOSA, CO, p. A96
SAN LUIS VALLEY HEALTH CONEJOS COUNTY HOSPITAL, LA JARA, CO, p. A102
SAN MATEO MEDICAL CENTER, SAN MATEO, CA, p. A87
SAN RAMON REGIONAL MEDICAL CENTER, SAN RAMON, CA, p. A88
SANFORD ABERDEEN MEDICAL CENTER, ABERDEEN, SD, p. A559
SANFORD BAGLEY MEDICAL CENTER, BAGLEY, MN, p. A328
SANFORD BEMIDJI MEDICAL CENTER, BEMIDJI, MN, p. A328
SANFORD BISMARCK, BISMARCK, ND, p. A465
SANFORD CANBY MEDICAL CENTER, CANBY, MN, p. A329
SANFORD CANTON INWOOD MEDICAL CENTER, CANTON, SD, p. A559
SANFORD CHAMBERLAIN MEDICAL CENTER, CHAMBERLAIN, SD, p. A560
SANFORD CLEAR LAKE MEDICAL CENTER, CLEAR LAKE, SD, p. A560
SANFORD HEALTH, BISMARCK, NORTH DAKOTA (see SANFORD BISMARCK), p. A465
SANFORD HILLSBORO MEDICAL CENTER, HILLSBORO, ND, p. A468
SANFORD JACKSON MEDICAL CENTER, JACKSON, MN, p. A333
SANFORD LUVERNE MEDICAL CENTER, LUVERNE, MN, p. A334
SANFORD MAYVILLE MEDICAL CENTER, MAYVILLE, ND, p. A468
SANFORD MEDICAL CENTER FARGO, FARGO, ND, p. A467
SANFORD MEDICAL CENTER THIEF RIVER FALLS, THIEF RIVER FALLS, MN, p. A341
SANFORD MID DAKOTA MEDICAL CENTER, CHAMBERLAIN, SOUTH DAKOTA (see SANFORD CHAMBERLAIN MEDICAL CENTER), p. A560
SANFORD REGIONAL HOSPITAL WORTHINGTON, WORTHINGTON, MINNESOTA (see SANFORD WORTHINGTON MEDICAL CENTER), p. A343
SANFORD SHELDON MEDICAL CENTER, SHELDON, IA, p. A229
SANFORD THIEF RIVER FALLS BEHAVIORAL HEALTH CENTER, THIEF RIVER FALLS, MN, p. A341
SANFORD TRACY MEDICAL CENTER, TRACY, MN, p. A341
SANFORD USD MEDICAL CENTER, SIOUX FALLS, SD, p. A564
SANFORD VERMILLION MEDICAL CENTER, VERMILLION, SD, p. A564
SANFORD WEBSTER MEDICAL CENTER, WEBSTER, SOUTH DAKOTA (see SANFORD WEBSTER MEDICAL CENTER), p. A565
SANFORD WEBSTER MEDICAL CENTER, WEBSTER, SD, p. A565
SANFORD WESTBROOK MEDICAL CENTER, WESTBROOK, MN, p. A342

SANFORD WHEATON MEDICAL CENTER, WHEATON, MN, p. A342
SANFORD WORTHINGTON MEDICAL CENTER, WORTHINGTON, MN, p. A343
SANPETE VALLEY HOSPITAL, MOUNT PLEASANT, UT, p. A649
SANTA BARBARA COTTAGE HOSPITAL, SANTA BARBARA, CA, p. A88
SANTA BARBARA COUNTY PSYCHIATRIC HEALTH FACILITY, SANTA BARBARA, CA, p. A88
SANTA CLARA VALLEY MEDICAL CENTER, SAN JOSE, CA, p. A87
SANTA CRUZ VALLEY REGIONAL HOSPITAL, GREEN VALLEY, AZ, p. A30
SANTA ROSA MEDICAL CENTER, MILTON, FL, p. A132
SANTA ROSA MEMORIAL HOSPITAL, SANTA ROSA, CA, p. A89
SANTA YNEZ VALLEY COTTAGE HOSPITAL, SOLVANG, CA, p. A90
SANTIAM HOSPITAL, STAYTON, OR, p. A518
SARAH BUSH LINCOLN HEALTH CENTER, MATTOON, IL, p. A188
SARAH D. CULBERTSON MEMORIAL HOSPITAL, RUSHVILLE, IL, p. A195
SARASOTA MEMORIAL HEALTH CARE SYSTEM, SARASOTA, FL, p. A139
SARATOGA HOSPITAL, SARATOGA SPRINGS, NY, p. A444
SATANTA DISTRICT HOSPITAL AND LONG TERM CARE, SATANTA, KS, p. A245
SAUK PRAIRIE HEALTHCARE, PRAIRIE DU SAC, WI, p. A704
SAUNDERS MEDICAL CENTER, WAHOO, NE, p. A392
SAVOY MEDICAL CENTER, MAMOU, LA, p. A273
SCA HOUSTON HOSPITAL FOR SPECIALIZED SURGERY, HOUSTON, TX, p. A613
SCENIC MOUNTAIN MEDICAL CENTER, BIG SPRING, TX, p. A588
SCHEURER HOSPITAL, PIGEON, MI, p. A319
SCHICK SHADEL HOSPITAL, SEATTLE, WA, p. A678
SCHLEICHER COUNTY MEDICAL CENTER, ELDORADO, TX, p. A603
SCHNECK MEDICAL CENTER, SEYMOUR, IN, p. A214
SCHNEIDER REGIONAL MEDICAL CENTER, SAINT THOMAS, VI, p. A720
SCHOOLCRAFT MEMORIAL HOSPITAL, MANISTIQUE, MI, p. A317
SCHUYLER HOSPITAL, MONTOUR FALLS, NEW YORK (see MONTEFIORE MEDICAL CENTER), p. A431
SCHWAB REHABILITATION HOSPITAL, CHICAGO, IL, p. A179
SCOTLAND COUNTY HOSPITAL, MEMPHIS, MO, p. A365
SCOTLAND COUNTY MEMORIAL HOSPITAL, MEMPHIS, MISSOURI (see SCOTLAND COUNTY HOSPITAL), p. A365
SCOTLAND HEALTH CARE SYSTEM, LAURINBURG, NC, p. A457
SCOTT COUNTY HOSPITAL, SCOTT CITY, KS, p. A245
SCOTT MEMORIAL HEALTH, SCOTTSBURG, IN, p. A214
SCOTT REGIONAL HOSPITAL, MORTON, MS, p. A352
SCOTTSDALE LIBERTY HOSPITAL, SCOTTSDALE, AZ, p. A36
SCRIPPS GREEN HOSPITAL, LA JOLLA, CA, p. A62
SCRIPPS MEMORIAL HOSPITAL–ENCINITAS, ENCINITAS, CA, p. A57
SCRIPPS MEMORIAL HOSPITAL–LA JOLLA, LA JOLLA, CA, p. A63
SCRIPPS MERCY HOSPITAL, SAN DIEGO, CA, p. A84
SCRIPPS MERCY HOSPITAL CHULA VISTA, CHULA VISTA, CA, p. A54
SE TEXAS ER & HOSPITAL, HUMBLE, TX, p. A615
SEA PINES REHABILITATION HOSPITAL, MELBOURNE, FL, p. A129
SEARHC MT. EDGECUMBE HOSPITAL, SITKA, AK, p. A27
SEASIDE BEHAVIORAL CENTER, NEW ORLEANS, LA, p. A276
SEASIDE HEALTH SYSTEM, BATON ROUGE, LA, p. A264
SEATTLE CANCER CARE ALLIANCE, SEATTLE, WA, p. A678
SEATTLE CHILDREN'S HOSPITAL, SEATTLE, WA, p. A678
SEBASTIAN RIVER MEDICAL CENTER, SEBASTIAN, FL, p. A139
SEDAN CITY HOSPITAL, SEDAN, KS, p. A245
SEDGWICK COUNTY HEALTH CENTER, JULESBURG, CO, p. A102
SEILING REGIONAL MEDICAL CENTER, SEILING, OK, p. A507
SELBY GENERAL HOSPITAL, MARIETTA, OH, p. A486
SELECT REHABILITATION HOSPITAL OF DENTON, DENTON, TX, p. A599
SELECT REHABILITATION HOSPITAL OF SAN ANTONIO, SAN ANTONIO, TX, p. A635
SELECT SPECIALTY HOSPITAL – BELHAVEN, JACKSON, MS, p. A349
SELECT SPECIALTY HOSPITAL – BOARDMAN, BOARDMAN, OH, p. A473
SELECT SPECIALTY HOSPITAL – CINCINNATI NORTH, CINCINNATI, OH, p. A476

SELECT SPECIALTY HOSPITAL – CLEVELAND FAIRHILL, CLEVELAND, OHIO (see SELECT SPECIALTY HOSPITAL – CLEVELAND GATEWAY), p. A478
SELECT SPECIALTY HOSPITAL – CLEVELAND GATEWAY, CLEVELAND, OH, p. A478
SELECT SPECIALTY HOSPITAL – DALLAS DOWNTOWN, DALLAS, TX, p. A598
SELECT SPECIALTY HOSPITAL – LINCOLN, LINCOLN, NE, p. A387
SELECT SPECIALTY HOSPITAL – SAN DIEGO, SAN DIEGO, CA, p. A84
SELECT SPECIALTY HOSPITAL – SPECTRUM HEALTH, GRAND RAPIDS, MI, p. A313
SELECT SPECIALTY HOSPITAL DAYTONA BEACH, DAYTONA BEACH, FL, p. A121
SELECT SPECIALTY HOSPITAL HAMPTON ROADS, NEWPORT NEWS, VA, p. A663
SELECT SPECIALTY HOSPITAL MIDTOWN ATLANTA, ATLANTA, GA, p. A147
SELECT SPECIALTY HOSPITAL OF SOUTHEAST OHIO, NEWARK, OH, p. A488
SELECT SPECIALTY HOSPITAL–AKRON, AKRON, OH, p. A471
SELECT SPECIALTY HOSPITAL–ANN ARBOR, YPSILANTI, MI, p. A325
SELECT SPECIALTY HOSPITAL–AUGUSTA, AUGUSTA, GA, p. A147
SELECT SPECIALTY HOSPITAL–BATTLE CREEK, BATTLE CREEK, MI, p. A307
SELECT SPECIALTY HOSPITAL–BIRMINGHAM, BIRMINGHAM, AL, p. A15
SELECT SPECIALTY HOSPITAL–CAMP HILL, CAMP HILL, PA, p. A521
SELECT SPECIALTY HOSPITAL–CANTON, CANTON, OH, p. A474
SELECT SPECIALTY HOSPITAL–CHARLESTON, CHARLESTON, WV, p. A684
SELECT SPECIALTY HOSPITAL–CINCINNATI, CINCINNATI, OH, p. A476
SELECT SPECIALTY HOSPITAL–COLUMBUS, COLUMBUS, OH, p. A480
SELECT SPECIALTY HOSPITAL–DALLAS, CARROLLTON, TX, p. A591
SELECT SPECIALTY HOSPITAL–DANVILLE, DANVILLE, PA, p. A523
SELECT SPECIALTY HOSPITAL–DES MOINES, DES MOINES, IA, p. A221
SELECT SPECIALTY HOSPITAL–DOWNRIVER, WYANDOTTE, MI, p. A325
SELECT SPECIALTY HOSPITAL–DURHAM, DURHAM, NC, p. A453
SELECT SPECIALTY HOSPITAL–ERIE, ERIE, PA, p. A525
SELECT SPECIALTY HOSPITAL–EVANSVILLE, EVANSVILLE, IN, p. A203
SELECT SPECIALTY HOSPITAL–FLINT, FLINT, MI, p. A311
SELECT SPECIALTY HOSPITAL–FORT SMITH, FORT SMITH, AR, p. A42
SELECT SPECIALTY HOSPITAL–GAINESVILLE, GAINESVILLE, FL, p. A123
SELECT SPECIALTY HOSPITAL–GREENSBORO, GREENSBORO, NC, p. A455
SELECT SPECIALTY HOSPITAL–GROSSE POINTE, GROSSE POINTE, MI, p. A313
SELECT SPECIALTY HOSPITAL–GULFPORT, GULFPORT, MS, p. A348
SELECT SPECIALTY HOSPITAL–HARRISBURG, HARRISBURG, PENNSYLVANIA (see SELECT SPECIALTY HOSPITAL–CAMP HILL), p. A527
SELECT SPECIALTY HOSPITAL–JACKSON, JACKSON, MS, p. A349
SELECT SPECIALTY HOSPITAL–JOHNSTOWN, JOHNSTOWN, PA, p. A528
SELECT SPECIALTY HOSPITAL–KANSAS CITY, KANSAS CITY, KS, p. A238
SELECT SPECIALTY HOSPITAL–LAUREL HIGHLANDS, LATROBE, PA, p. A529
SELECT SPECIALTY HOSPITAL–LEXINGTON, LEXINGTON, KY, p. A255
SELECT SPECIALTY HOSPITAL–LONGVIEW, LONGVIEW, TX, p. A621
SELECT SPECIALTY HOSPITAL–MACOMB COUNTY, MOUNT CLEMENS, MI, p. A318
SELECT SPECIALTY HOSPITAL–MADISON, MADISON, WI, p. A698
SELECT SPECIALTY HOSPITAL–MCKEESPORT, MCKEESPORT, PA, p. A531
SELECT SPECIALTY HOSPITAL–MEMPHIS, MEMPHIS, TN, p. A575
SELECT SPECIALTY HOSPITAL–MIAMI, MIAMI, FL, p. A131
SELECT SPECIALTY HOSPITAL–MILWAUKEE, MILWAUKEE, WI, p. A701

SELECT SPECIALTY HOSPITAL–MUSKEGON, MUSKEGON, MI, p. A318
SELECT SPECIALTY HOSPITAL–NASHVILLE, NASHVILLE, TN, p. A577
SELECT SPECIALTY HOSPITAL–NORTH KNOXVILLE, POWELL, TN, p. A578
SELECT SPECIALTY HOSPITAL–NORTHEAST NEW JERSEY, ROCHELLE PARK, NJ, p. A412
SELECT SPECIALTY HOSPITAL–NORTHERN KENTUCKY, FORT THOMAS, KY, p. A252
SELECT SPECIALTY HOSPITAL–OKLAHOMA CITY, OKLAHOMA CITY, OK, p. A505
SELECT SPECIALTY HOSPITAL–OMAHA, OMAHA, NE, p. A390
SELECT SPECIALTY HOSPITAL–ORLANDO, ORLANDO, FL, p. A134
SELECT SPECIALTY HOSPITAL–PALM BEACH, LAKE WORTH, FL, p. A127
SELECT SPECIALTY HOSPITAL–PANAMA CITY, PANAMA CITY, FL, p. A136
SELECT SPECIALTY HOSPITAL–PENSACOLA, PENSACOLA, FL, p. A136
SELECT SPECIALTY HOSPITAL–PHOENIX, PHOENIX, AZ, p. A34
SELECT SPECIALTY HOSPITAL–PHOENIX DOWNTOWN, PHOENIX, AZ, p. A34
SELECT SPECIALTY HOSPITAL–PITTSBURGH/UPMC, PITTSBURGH, PA, p. A537
SELECT SPECIALTY HOSPITAL–PONTIAC, PONTIAC, MI, p. A320
SELECT SPECIALTY HOSPITAL–QUAD CITIES, DAVENPORT, IA, p. A220
SELECT SPECIALTY HOSPITAL–SAGINAW, SAGINAW, MI, p. A321
SELECT SPECIALTY HOSPITAL–SAVANNAH, SAVANNAH, GA, p. A160
SELECT SPECIALTY HOSPITAL–SIOUX FALLS, SIOUX FALLS, SD, p. A564
SELECT SPECIALTY HOSPITAL–SPRINGFIELD, SPRINGFIELD, MO, p. A372
SELECT SPECIALTY HOSPITAL–ST. LOUIS, SAINT CHARLES, MO, p. A368
SELECT SPECIALTY HOSPITAL–TALLAHASSEE, TALLAHASSEE, FL, p. A140
SELECT SPECIALTY HOSPITAL–TRI CITIES, BRISTOL, TN, p. A566
SELECT SPECIALTY HOSPITAL–TULSA MIDTOWN, TULSA, OK, p. A509
SELECT SPECIALTY HOSPITAL–WESTERN MICHIGAN, MUSKEGON, MICHIGAN (see SELECT SPECIALTY HOSPITAL–MUSKEGON), p. A318
SELECT SPECIALTY HOSPITAL–WICHITA, WICHITA, KS, p. A248
SELECT SPECIALTY HOSPITAL–WILMINGTON, WILMINGTON, DE, p. A114
SELECT SPECIALTY HOSPITAL–YORK, YORK, PENNSYLVANIA (see SELECT SPECIALTY HOSPITAL–CAMP HILL), p. A546
SELECT SPECIALTY HOSPITAL–YOUNGSTOWN, YOUNGSTOWN, OH, p. A495
SELF REGIONAL HEALTHCARE, GREENWOOD, SC, p. A554
SENECA HEALTHCARE DISTRICT, CHESTER, CA, p. A54
SENTARA ALBEMARLE MEDICAL CENTER, ELIZABETH CITY, NC, p. A453
SENTARA CAREPLEX HOSPITAL, HAMPTON, VA, p. A660
SENTARA HALIFAX REGIONAL HOSPITAL, SOUTH BOSTON, VA, p. A667
SENTARA LEIGH HOSPITAL, NORFOLK, VA, p. A664
SENTARA MARTHA JEFFERSON HOSPITAL, CHARLOTTESVILLE, VA, p. A657
SENTARA NORFOLK GENERAL HOSPITAL, NORFOLK, VA, p. A664
SENTARA NORTHERN VIRGINIA MEDICAL CENTER, WOODBRIDGE, VA, p. A669
SENTARA OBICI HOSPITAL, SUFFOLK, VA, p. A668
SENTARA PRINCESS ANNE HOSPITAL, VIRGINIA BEACH, VA, p. A668
SENTARA RMH MEDICAL CENTER, HARRISONBURG, VA, p. A660
SENTARA VIRGINIA BEACH GENERAL HOSPITAL, VIRGINIA BEACH, VA, p. A668
SENTARA WILLIAMSBURG REGIONAL MEDICAL CENTER, WILLIAMSBURG, VA, p. A669
SEQUEL POMEGRANATE HEALTH SYSTEMS, COLUMBUS, OH, p. A480
SEQUOIA HOSPITAL, REDWOOD CITY, CA, p. A80
SERENITY SPRINGS SPECIALTY HOSPITAL, RUSTON, LA, p. A277
SETON MEDICAL CENTER, DALY CITY, CA, p. A56
SETON MEDICAL CENTER HARKER HEIGHTS, HARKER HEIGHTS, TX, p. A609
SEVEN HILLS HOSPITAL, HENDERSON, NV, p. A394

© 2019 AHA Guide

SEVEN RIVERS REGIONAL MEDICAL CENTER, CRYSTAL RIVER, FL, p. A120

SEVIER VALLEY HOSPITAL, RICHFIELD, UT, p. A651

SEWICKLEY VALLEY HOSPITAL, (A DIVISION OF VALLEY MEDICAL FACILITIES), SEWICKLEY, PA, p. A541

SEYMOUR HOSPITAL, SEYMOUR, TX, p. A636

SHAMROCK GENERAL HOSPITAL, SHAMROCK, TX, p. A636

SHANDS LAKE SHORE REGIONAL MEDICAL CENTER, LAKE CITY, FL, p. A127

SHANDS LIVE OAK REGIONAL MEDICAL CENTER, LIVE OAK, FL, p. A128

SHANDS STARKE, STARKE, FL, p. A140

SHANDS STARKE REGIONAL MEDICAL CENTER, STARKE, FL, p. A140

SHANNON MEDICAL CENTER, SAN ANGELO, TX, p. A633

SHARE MEDICAL CENTER, ALVA, OK, p. A496

SHARKEY–ISSAQUENA COMMUNITY HOSPITAL, ROLLING FORK, MS, p. A354

SHARON HOSPITAL, SHARON, CT, p. A110

SHARON REGIONAL MEDICAL CENTER, SHARON, PA, p. A541

SHARP CHULA VISTA MEDICAL CENTER, CHULA VISTA, CA, p. A54

SHARP CORONADO HOSPITAL AND HEALTHCARE CENTER, CORONADO, CA, p. A55

SHARP GROSSMONT HOSPITAL, LA MESA, CA, p. A63

SHARP MEMORIAL HOSPITAL, SAN DIEGO, CA, p. A84

SHARP MESA VISTA HOSPITAL, SAN DIEGO, CA, p. A84

SHASTA REGIONAL MEDICAL CENTER, REDDING, CA, p. A80

SHELBY BAPTIST MEDICAL CENTER, ALABASTER, AL, p. A13

SHELTERING ARMS HOSPITAL SOUTH, MIDLOTHIAN, VA, p. A663

SHELTERING ARMS REHABILITATION HOSPITAL, MECHANICSVILLE, VA, p. A662

SHENANDOAH MEDICAL CENTER, SHENANDOAH, IA, p. A229

SHENANGO VALLEY CAMPUS, FARRELL, PENNSYLVANIA (see UPMC HORIZON), p. A526

SHEPHERD CENTER, ATLANTA, GA, p. A147

SHEPPARD PRATT HEALTH SYSTEM, BALTIMORE, MD, p. A288

SHERIDAN COMMUNITY HOSPITAL, SHERIDAN, MI, p. A322

SHERIDAN COUNTY HEALTH COMPLEX, HOXIE, KS, p. A237

SHERIDAN MEMORIAL HOSPITAL, PLENTYWOOD, MT, p. A379

SHERIDAN MEMORIAL HOSPITAL, SHERIDAN, WY, p. A712

SHERIDAN VETERANS AFFAIRS MEDICAL CENTER, SHERIDAN, WY, p. A712

SHERMAN HOSPITAL, ELGIN, ILLINOIS (see ADVOCATE SHERMAN HOSPITAL), p. A182

SHERMAN OAKS HOSPITAL, LOS ANGELES, CA, p. A69

SHIRLEY RYAN ABILITYLAB, CHICAGO, IL, p. A179

SHOALS HOSPITAL, MUSCLE SHOALS, AL, p. A22

SHODAIR CHILDREN'S HOSPITAL, HELENA, MT, p. A377

SHORE MEDICAL CENTER, SOMERS POINT, NJ, p. A412

SHORE MEMORIAL HOSPITAL, ONANCOCK, VIRGINIA (see RIVERSIDE SHORE MEMORIAL HOSPITAL), p. A664

SHOSHONE MEDICAL CENTER, KELLOGG, ID, p. A169

SHRINERS HOSPITALS FOR CHILDREN – CINCINNATI, CINCINNATI, OH, p. A476

SHRINERS HOSPITALS FOR CHILDREN–BOSTON, BOSTON, MA, p. A296

SHRINERS HOSPITALS FOR CHILDREN–CHICAGO, CHICAGO, IL, p. A179

SHRINERS HOSPITALS FOR CHILDREN–GALVESTON, GALVESTON, TX, p. A607

SHRINERS HOSPITALS FOR CHILDREN–GREENVILLE, GREENVILLE, SC, p. A554

SHRINERS HOSPITALS FOR CHILDREN–HONOLULU, HONOLULU, HI, p. A165

SHRINERS HOSPITALS FOR CHILDREN–HOUSTON, HOUSTON, TX, p. A613

SHRINERS HOSPITALS FOR CHILDREN–NORTHERN CALIFORNIA, SACRAMENTO, CA, p. A82

SHRINERS HOSPITALS FOR CHILDREN–PHILADELPHIA, PHILADELPHIA, PA, p. A536

SHRINERS HOSPITALS FOR CHILDREN–PORTLAND, PORTLAND, OR, p. A516

SHRINERS HOSPITALS FOR CHILDREN–SALT LAKE CITY, SALT LAKE CITY, UT, p. A652

SHRINERS HOSPITALS FOR CHILDREN–SHREVEPORT, SHREVEPORT, LA, p. A278

SHRINERS HOSPITALS FOR CHILDREN–SPOKANE, SPOKANE, WA, p. A680

SHRINERS HOSPITALS FOR CHILDREN–SPRINGFIELD, SPRINGFIELD, MA, p. A303

SHRINERS HOSPITALS FOR CHILDREN–ST. LOUIS, SAINT LOUIS, MO, p. A370

SHRINERS HOSPITALS FOR CHILDREN–TAMPA, TAMPA, FL, p. A142

SIBLEY MEMORIAL HOSPITAL, WASHINGTON, DC, p. A116

SIDNEY HEALTH CENTER, SIDNEY, MT, p. A380

SIDNEY REGIONAL MEDICAL CENTER, SIDNEY, NE, p. A391

SIERRA NEVADA MEMORIAL HOSPITAL, GRASS VALLEY, CA, p. A61

SIERRA TUCSON, TUCSON, AZ, p. A38

SIERRA VIEW MEDICAL CENTER, PORTERVILLE, CA, p. A79

SIERRA VISTA HOSPITAL, SACRAMENTO, CA, p. A82

SIERRA VISTA HOSPITAL, TRUTH OR CONSEQUENCES, NM, p. A421

SIERRA VISTA REGIONAL MEDICAL CENTER, SAN LUIS OBISPO, CA, p. A87

SIGNATURE HEALTHCARE BROCKTON HOSPITAL, BROCKTON, MA, p. A296

SIGNATURE PSYCHIATRIC HOSPITAL, KANSAS CITY, MO, p. A363

SILOAM SPRINGS REGIONAL HOSPITAL, SILOAM SPRINGS, AR, p. A48

SILVER CROSS HOSPITAL, NEW LENOX, IL, p. A191

SILVER HILL HOSPITAL, NEW CANAAN, CT, p. A109

SILVER LAKE MEDICAL CENTER, LOS ANGELES, CA, p. A69

SILVER OAKS BEHAVIORAL HOSPITAL, NEW LENOX, IL, p. A191

SIMI VALLEY HOSPITAL, SIMI VALLEY, CA, p. A89

SIMPSON GENERAL HOSPITAL, MENDENHALL, MS, p. A351

SINAI HOSPITAL OF BALTIMORE, BALTIMORE, MD, p. A287

SINGING RIVER HEALTH SYSTEM, PASCAGOULA, MS, p. A352

SIOUX CENTER HEALTH, SIOUX CENTER, IA, p. A229

SIOUX FALLS SPECIALTY HOSPITAL, SIOUX FALLS, SD, p. A564

SIOUX FALLS VETERANS AFFAIRS HEALTH CARE SYSTEM, SIOUX FALLS, SD, p. A564

SISKIN HOSPITAL FOR PHYSICAL REHABILITATION, CHATTANOOGA, TN, p. A567

SISTER KENNY REHABILITATION INSTITUTE, MINNEAPOLIS, MINNESOTA (see ABBOTT NORTHWESTERN HOSPITAL), p. A336

SISTERS OF CHARITY HOSPITAL OF BUFFALO, BUFFALO, NY, p. A425

SISTERSVILLE GENERAL HOSPITAL, SISTERSVILLE, WV, p. A689

SITKA COMMUNITY HOSPITAL, SITKA, AK, p. A27

SKAGIT REGIONAL HEALTH, MOUNT VERNON, WA, p. A675

SKY LAKES MEDICAL CENTER, KLAMATH FALLS, OR, p. A514

SKY RIDGE MEDICAL CENTER, LONE TREE, CO, p. A103

SKYLINE HOSPITAL, WHITE SALMON, WA, p. A682

SLEEPY EYE MEDICAL CENTER, SLEEPY EYE, MN, p. A340

SLIDELL MEMORIAL HOSPITAL, SLIDELL, LA, p. A279

SMDC MEDICAL CENTER, DULUTH, MINNESOTA (see ESSENTIA HEALTH DULUTH), p. A331

SMITH COUNTY MEMORIAL HOSPITAL, SMITH CENTER, KS, p. A246

SMOKEY POINT BEHAVIORAL HOSPITAL, MARYSVILLE, WA, p. A674

SMYTH COUNTY COMMUNITY HOSPITAL, MARION, VA, p. A662

SNOQUALMIE VALLEY HOSPITAL DISTRICT, SNOQUALMIE, WA, p. A679

SOCORRO GENERAL HOSPITAL, SOCORRO, NM, p. A421

SOIN MEDICAL CENTER, BEAVERCREEK, OH, p. A473

SOLARA HOSPITAL HARLINGEN, HARLINGEN, TX, p. A609

SOLARA HOSPITAL MCALLEN, MCALLEN, TX, p. A623

SOLDIERS AND SAILORS MEMORIAL HOSPITAL OF YATES COUNTY, PENN YAN, NY, p. A441

SOMERVILLE HOSPITAL, SOMERVILLE, MASSACHUSETTS (see CAMBRIDGE HEALTH ALLIANCE), p. A303

SONOMA DEVELOPMENTAL CENTER, ELDRIDGE, CA, p. A57

SONOMA VALLEY HOSPITAL, SONOMA, CA, p. A90

SONOMA WEST MEDICAL CENTER, SEBASTOPOL, CA, p. A89

SONORA BEHAVIORAL HEALTH HOSPITAL, TUCSON, AZ, p. A38

SOUTH BALDWIN REGIONAL MEDICAL CENTER, FOLEY, AL, p. A18

SOUTH BATON ROUGE REHABILITATION HOSPITAL, GONZALES, LOUISIANA (see UNITED MEDICAL REHABILITATION HOSPITAL – GONZALES), p. A267

SOUTH BAY HOSPITAL, SUN CITY CENTER, FL, p. A140

SOUTH BIG HORN COUNTY HOSPITAL, BASIN, WY, p. A710

SOUTH CAMERON MEMORIAL HOSPITAL, CAMERON, LA, p. A265

SOUTH CAROLINA DEPARTMENT OF CORRECTIONS HOSPITAL, COLUMBIA, SC, p. A551

SOUTH CENTRAL KANSAS MEDICAL CENTER, ARKANSAS CITY, KS, p. A232

SOUTH CENTRAL REGIONAL MEDICAL CENTER, LAUREL, MS, p. A350

SOUTH COAST GLOBAL MEDICAL CENTER, SANTA ANA, CA, p. A88

SOUTH COUNTY HOSPITAL, WAKEFIELD, RI, p. A548

SOUTH DAVIS COMMUNITY HOSPITAL, BOUNTIFUL, UT, p. A647

SOUTH FLORIDA BAPTIST HOSPITAL, PLANT CITY, FL, p. A137

SOUTH FLORIDA STATE HOSPITAL, HOLLYWOOD, FL, p. A124

SOUTH GEORGIA MEDICAL CENTER, VALDOSTA, GA, p. A162

SOUTH GEORGIA MEDICAL CENTER BERRIEN CAMPUS, NASHVILLE, GA, p. A158

SOUTH GEORGIA MEDICAL CENTER LANIER CAMPUS, LAKELAND, GA, p. A155

SOUTH HAVEN COMMUNITY HOSPITAL, SOUTH HAVEN, MICHIGAN (see BRONSON SOUTH HAVEN HOSPITAL), p. A322

SOUTH LAKE HOSPITAL, CLERMONT, FL, p. A120

SOUTH LINCOLN MEDICAL CENTER, KEMMERER, WY, p. A711

SOUTH LYON MEDICAL CENTER, YERINGTON, NV, p. A398

SOUTH MISSISSIPPI COUNTY REGIONAL MEDICAL CENTER, OSCEOLA, AR, p. A47

SOUTH MISSISSIPPI STATE HOSPITAL, PURVIS, MS, p. A353

SOUTH NASSAU COMMUNITIES HOSPITAL, OCEANSIDE, NY, p. A440

SOUTH OAKS HOSPITAL, AMITYVILLE, NY, p. A422

SOUTH PENINSULA HOSPITAL, HOMER, AK, p. A26

SOUTH POINTE HOSPITAL, WARRENSVILLE HEIGHTS, OH, p. A493

SOUTH SACRAMENTO MEDICAL CENTER, SACRAMENTO, CA, p. A82

SOUTH SHORE HOSPITAL, CHICAGO, IL, p. A179

SOUTH SHORE HOSPITAL, SOUTH WEYMOUTH, MA, p. A303

SOUTH SUNFLOWER COUNTY HOSPITAL, INDIANOLA, MS, p. A348

SOUTH TEXAS HEALTH SYSTEM, EDINBURG, TX, p. A601

SOUTH TEXAS REHABILITATION HOSPITAL, BROWNSVILLE, TX, p. A589

SOUTH TEXAS SPINE AND SURGICAL HOSPITAL, SAN ANTONIO, TX, p. A635

SOUTH TEXAS SURGICAL HOSPITAL, CORPUS CHRISTI, TX, p. A594

SOUTH TEXAS VETERANS HEALTH CARE SYSTEM, SAN ANTONIO, TX, p. A635

SOUTHAMPTON MEMORIAL HOSPITAL, FRANKLIN, VA, p. A659

SOUTHCOAST BEHAVIORAL HEALTH, DARTMOUTH, MA, p. A298

SOUTHCOAST HOSPITALS GROUP, FALL RIVER, MA, p. A298

SOUTHEAST ALABAMA MEDICAL CENTER, DOTHAN, AL, p. A17

SOUTHEAST COLORADO HOSPITAL DISTRICT, SPRINGFIELD, CO, p. A105

SOUTHEAST GEORGIA HEALTH SYSTEM BRUNSWICK CAMPUS, BRUNSWICK, GA, p. A148

SOUTHEAST GEORGIA HEALTH SYSTEM CAMDEN CAMPUS, SAINT MARYS, GA, p. A159

SOUTHEAST HEALTH CENTER OF STODDARD COUNTY, DEXTER, MO, p. A359

SOUTHEAST HOSPITAL, CAPE GIRARDEAU, MO, p. A358

SOUTHEAST MICHIGAN SURGICAL HOSPITAL, WARREN, MI, p. A324

SOUTHEAST MISSOURI MENTAL HEALTH CENTER, FARMINGTON, MO, p. A360

SOUTHEAST REGIONAL MEDICAL CENTER, KENTWOOD, LA, p. A270

SOUTHEAST REHABILITATION HOSPITAL, LAKE VILLAGE, AR, p. A44

SOUTHEASTERN HEALTH, LUMBERTON, NC, p. A458

SOUTHEASTERN KENTUCKY MEDICAL CENTER, PINEVILLE, KY, p. A259

SOUTHEASTERN OHIO REGIONAL MEDICAL CENTER, CAMBRIDGE, OH, p. A474

SOUTHEASTERN REGIONAL MEDICAL CENTER, NEWNAN, GA, p. A158

SOUTHERN ARIZONA VETERANS AFFAIRS HEALTH CARE SYSTEM, TUCSON, AZ, p. A38

SOUTHERN CALIFORNIA HOSPITAL AT CULVER CITY, CULVER CITY, CA, p. A56

SOUTHERN CALIFORNIA HOSPITAL AT HOLLYWOOD, LOS ANGELES, CA, p. A69

SOUTHERN CALIFORNIA HOSPITAL AT VAN NUYS, LOS ANGELES, CALIFORNIA (see SOUTHERN CALIFORNIA HOSPITAL AT HOLLYWOOD), p. A69

SOUTHERN COOS HOSPITAL AND HEALTH CENTER, BANDON, OR, p. A511

SOUTHERN HILLS HOSPITAL AND MEDICAL CENTER, LAS VEGAS, NV, p. A395

SOUTHERN INDIANA REHABILITATION HOSPITAL, NEW ALBANY, IN, p. A212

SOUTHERN INYO HEALTHCARE DISTRICT, LONE PINE, CA, p. A65

SOUTHERN KENTUCKY REHABILITATION HOSPITAL, BOWLING GREEN, KY, p. A250
SOUTHERN MAINE HEALTH CARE – BIDDEFORD MEDICAL CENTER, BIDDEFORD, ME, p. A282
SOUTHERN MARYLAND HOSPITAL CENTER, CLINTON, MARYLAND (see MEDSTAR SOUTHERN MARYLAND HOSPITAL CENTER), p. A290
SOUTHERN NEVADA ADULT MENTAL HEALTH SERVICES, LAS VEGAS, NV, p. A395
SOUTHERN NEW HAMPSHIRE MEDICAL CENTER, NASHUA, NH, p. A401
SOUTHERN OHIO MEDICAL CENTER, PORTSMOUTH, OH, p. A490
SOUTHERN REGIONAL MEDICAL CENTER, RIVERDALE, GA, p. A159
SOUTHERN SURGICAL HOSPITAL, SLIDELL, LA, p. A279
SOUTHERN TENNESSEE REGIONAL HEALTH SYSTEM–LAWRENCEBURG, LAWRENCEBURG, TN, p. A573
SOUTHERN TENNESSEE REGIONAL HEALTH SYSTEM–PULASKI, PULASKI, TN, p. A578
SOUTHERN TENNESSEE REGIONAL HEALTH SYSTEM–SEWANEE, SEWANEE, TENNESSEE (see SOUTHERN TENNESSEE REGIONAL HEALTH SYSTEM–WINCHESTER), p. A579
SOUTHERN TENNESSEE REGIONAL HEALTH SYSTEM–WINCHESTER, WINCHESTER, TN, p. A580
SOUTHERN VIRGINIA MENTAL HEALTH INSTITUTE, DANVILLE, VA, p. A658
SOUTHERN VIRGINIA REGIONAL MEDICAL CENTER, EMPORIA, VA, p. A658
SOUTHERN WINDS HOSPITAL, HIALEAH, FL, p. A124
SOUTHLAKE CAMPUS, MERRILLVILLE, INDIANA (see METHODIST HOSPITALS), p. A211
SOUTHSIDE COMMUNITY HOSPITAL, FARMVILLE, VIRGINIA (see CENTRA SOUTHSIDE COMMUNITY HOSPITAL), p. A659
SOUTHSIDE HOSPITAL, BAY SHORE, NY, p. A423
SOUTHSIDE REGIONAL MEDICAL CENTER, PETERSBURG, VA, p. A665
SOUTHWEST CONNECTICUT MENTAL HEALTH SYSTEM, BRIDGEPORT, CT, p. A107
SOUTHWEST GENERAL HEALTH CENTER, MIDDLEBURG HEIGHTS, OH, p. A487
SOUTHWEST GENERAL HOSPITAL, SAN ANTONIO, TX, p. A635
SOUTHWEST GEORGIA REGIONAL MEDICAL CENTER, CUTHBERT, GA, p. A151
SOUTHWEST HEALTH, PLATTEVILLE, WI, p. A703
SOUTHWEST HEALTH CENTER NURSING HOME, CUBA CITY, WISCONSIN (see SOUTHWEST HEALTH), p. A693
SOUTHWEST HEALTH SYSTEM, CORTEZ, CO, p. A98
SOUTHWEST HEALTHCARE SERVICES, BOWMAN, ND, p. A465
SOUTHWEST HEALTHCARE SYSTEM, MURRIETA, CA, p. A74
SOUTHWEST MEDICAL CENTER, LIBERAL, KS, p. A239
SOUTHWEST MISSISSIPPI REGIONAL MEDICAL CENTER, MCCOMB, MS, p. A350
SOUTHWEST WASHINGTON MEDICAL CENTER, VANCOUVER, WASHINGTON (see PEACEHEALTH SOUTHWEST MEDICAL CENTER), p. A681
SOUTHWESTERN MEDICAL CENTER, LAWTON, OK, p. A501
SOUTHWESTERN REGIONAL MEDICAL CENTER, TULSA, OK, p. A509
SOUTHWESTERN VERMONT MEDICAL CENTER, BENNINGTON, VT, p. A654
SOUTHWESTERN VIRGINIA MENTAL HEALTH INSTITUTE, MARION, VA, p. A662
SOUTHWOOD PSYCHIATRIC HOSPITAL, PITTSBURGH, PA, p. A537
SOVAH HEALTH–DANVILLE, DANVILLE, VA, p. A658
SOVAH HEALTH–MARTINSVILLE, MARTINSVILLE, VA, p. A662
SPALDING REHABILITATION HOSPITAL, AURORA, CO, p. A96
SPANISH PEAKS REGIONAL HEALTH CENTER, WALSENBURG, CO, p. A106
SPARROW CARSON HOSPITAL, CARSON CITY, MI, p. A308
SPARROW CLINTON HOSPITAL, SAINT JOHNS, MI, p. A322
SPARROW HOSPITAL, LANSING, MI, p. A316
SPARROW IONIA HOSPITAL, IONIA, MI, p. A314
SPARROW SPECIALTY HOSPITAL, LANSING, MI, p. A316
SPARTA COMMUNITY HOSPITAL, SPARTA, IL, p. A196
SPARTANBURG HOSPITAL FOR RESTORATIVE CARE, SPARTANBURG, SC, p. A557
SPARTANBURG MEDICAL CENTER – CHURCH STREET CAMPUS, SPARTANBURG, SC, p. A557
SPARTANBURG MEDICAL CENTER – MARY BLACK, SPARTANBURG, SC, p. A557
SPAULDING HOSPITAL CAMBRIDGE, CAMBRIDGE, MASSACHUSETTS (see SPAULDING HOSPITAL FOR CONTINUING MEDICAL CARE CAMBRIDGE), p. A297

SPAULDING HOSPITAL FOR CONTINUING MEDICAL CARE CAMBRIDGE, CAMBRIDGE, MA, p. A297
SPAULDING REHABILITATION HOSPITAL, CHARLESTOWN, MA, p. A298
SPAULDING REHABILITATION HOSPITAL CAPE COD, EAST SANDWICH, MA, p. A298
SPEARE MEMORIAL HOSPITAL, PLYMOUTH, NH, p. A402
SPEARFISH REGIONAL HOSPITAL, SPEARFISH, SD, p. A564
SPECIALISTS HOSPITAL – SHREVEPORT, SHREVEPORT, LA, p. A278
SPECIALTY HOSPITAL, MONROE, LA, p. A274
SPECIALTY HOSPITAL, ROME, GA, p. A159
SPECIALTY HOSPITAL JACKSONVILLE, JACKSONVILLE, FL, p. A126
SPECIALTY HOSPITAL OF CENTRAL JERSEY, LAKEWOOD, NJ, p. A407
SPECIALTY HOSPITAL OF LORAIN, AMHERST, OH, p. A471
SPECIALTY HOSPITAL OF MERIDIAN, MERIDIAN, MS, p. A351
SPECIALTY REHABILITATION HOSPITAL OF COUSHATTA, COUSHATTA, LA, p. A266
SPECTRUM HEALTH – BUTTERWORTH HOSPITAL, GRAND RAPIDS, MI, p. A313
SPECTRUM HEALTH BIG RAPIDS HOSPITAL, BIG RAPIDS, MI, p. A307
SPECTRUM HEALTH GERBER MEMORIAL, FREMONT, MI, p. A312
SPECTRUM HEALTH KELSEY HOSPITAL, LAKEVIEW, MICHIGAN (see SPECTRUM HEALTH UNITED HOSPITAL), p. A316
SPECTRUM HEALTH LAKELAND, SAINT JOSEPH, MI, p. A322
SPECTRUM HEALTH LUDINGTON HOSPITAL, LUDINGTON, MI, p. A317
SPECTRUM HEALTH PENNOCK, HASTINGS, MI, p. A314
SPECTRUM HEALTH REED CITY HOSPITAL, REED CITY, MI, p. A320
SPECTRUM HEALTH UNITED HOSPITAL, GREENVILLE, MI, p. A313
SPECTRUM HEALTH ZEELAND COMMUNITY HOSPITAL, ZEELAND, MI, p. A326
SPENCER HOSPITAL, SPENCER, IA, p. A230
SPINE HOSPITAL OF LOUISIANA (FORMALLY THE NEUROMEDICAL CENTER SURGICAL HOSPITAL), BATON ROUGE, LA, p. A264
SPIRE CANE CREEK REHABILITATION HOSPITAL, MARTIN, TN, p. A573
SPOONER HEALTH, SPOONER, WI, p. A705
SPOTSYLVANIA REGIONAL MEDICAL CENTER, FREDERICKSBURG, VA, p. A659
SPRING GROVE HOSPITAL CENTER, BALTIMORE, MD, p. A288
SPRING HARBOR HOSPITAL, WESTBROOK, ME, p. A285
SPRING MOUNTAIN SAHARA, LAS VEGAS, NV, p. A395
SPRING MOUNTAIN TREATMENT CENTER, LAS VEGAS, NV, p. A396
SPRING VALLEY HOSPITAL MEDICAL CENTER, LAS VEGAS, NV, p. A396
SPRING VIEW HOSPITAL, LEBANON, KY, p. A254
SPRINGBROOK BEHAVIORAL HEALTH SYSTEM, TRAVELERS REST, SC, p. A557
SPRINGBROOK HOSPITAL, BROOKSVILLE, FL, p. A119
SPRINGFIELD HOSPITAL, SPRINGFIELD, PENNSYLVANIA (see CROZER–CHESTER MEDICAL CENTER), p. A541
SPRINGFIELD HOSPITAL, SPRINGFIELD, VT, p. A655
SPRINGFIELD HOSPITAL CENTER, SYKESVILLE, MD, p. A293
SPRINGFIELD REGIONAL MEDICAL CENTER, SPRINGFIELD, OH, p. A491
SPRINGHILL MEDICAL CENTER, SPRINGHILL, LA, p. A279
SPRINGHILL MEMORIAL HOSPITAL, MOBILE, AL, p. A20
SPRINGWOODS BEHAVIORAL HEALTH HOSPITAL, FAYETTEVILLE, AR, p. A41
SSM CARDINAL GLENNON CHILDREN'S HOSPITAL, SAINT LOUIS, MO, p. A370
SSM HEALTH DEPAUL HOSPITAL – ST. LOUIS, BRIDGETON, MO, p. A357
SSM HEALTH SAINT LOUIS UNIVERSITY HOSPITAL, SAINT LOUIS, MO, p. A370
SSM HEALTH ST. ANTHONY HOSPITAL – OKLAHOMA CITY, OKLAHOMA CITY, OK, p. A505
SSM HEALTH ST. ANTHONY HOSPITAL – SHAWNEE, SHAWNEE, OK, p. A507
SSM HEALTH ST. CLARE HOSPITAL – FENTON, FENTON, MO, p. A360
SSM HEALTH ST. CLARE HOSPITAL–BARABOO, BARABOO, WI, p. A692
SSM HEALTH ST. JOSEPH – ST. CHARLES, SAINT CHARLES, MO, p. A368
SSM HEALTH ST. JOSEPH – WENTZVILLE, WENTZVILLE, MISSOURI (see SSM HEALTH ST. JOSEPH – ST. CHARLES), p. A373

SSM HEALTH ST. JOSEPH HOSPITAL – LAKE SAINT LOUIS, LAKE SAINT LOUIS, MO, p. A364
SSM HEALTH ST. MARY'S HOSPITAL – AUDRAIN, MEXICO, MO, p. A365
SSM HEALTH ST. MARY'S HOSPITAL – JEFFERSON CITY, JEFFERSON CITY, MO, p. A361
SSM HEALTH ST. MARY'S HOSPITAL – ST. LOUIS, SAINT LOUIS, MO, p. A370
SSM HEALTH ST. MARY'S HOSPITAL, MADISON, WI, p. A698
SSM HEALTH ST. MARY'S HOSPITAL CENTRALIA, CENTRALIA, IL, p. A175
SSM HEALTH ST. MARY'S HOSPITAL JANESVILLE, MONROE, WI, p. A702
SSM SELECT REHABILITATION HOSPITAL, RICHMOND HEIGHTS, MO, p. A367
ST LUKE'S HOSPITAL – ALLENTOWN CAMPUS, ALLENTOWN, PENNSYLVANIA (see ST. LUKE'S UNIVERSITY HOSPITAL – BETHLEHEM CAMPUS), p. A519
ST. AGNES HOSPITAL, FOND DU LAC, WI, p. A695
ST. ALEXIUS HOSPITAL – BROADWAY CAMPUS, SAINT LOUIS, MO, p. A370
ST. ALOISIUS MEDICAL CENTER, HARVEY, ND, p. A467
ST. ANDREW'S HEALTH CENTER, BOTTINEAU, ND, p. A465
ST. ANTHONY COMMUNITY HOSPITAL, WARWICK, NY, p. A446
ST. ANTHONY HOSPITAL, GIG HARBOR, WA, p. A673
ST. ANTHONY HOSPITAL, LAKEWOOD, CO, p. A103
ST. ANTHONY MEDICAL CENTER, CROWN POINT, INDIANA (see FRANCISCAN HEALTH CROWN POINT), p. A202
ST. ANTHONY NORTH HEALTH CAMPUS, WESTMINSTER, CO, p. A106
ST. ANTHONY REGIONAL HOSPITAL, CARROLL, IA, p. A218
ST. ANTHONY SUMMIT MEDICAL CENTER, FRISCO, CO, p. A100
ST. ANTHONY'S HOSPITAL, SAINT PETERSBURG, FL, p. A138
ST. ANTHONY'S MEDICAL CENTER, MORRILTON, ARKANSAS (see CHI ST. VINCENT MORRILTON), p. A46
ST. ANTHONY'S REHABILITATION HOSPITAL, LAUDERDALE LAKES, FL, p. A128
ST. BERNARD HOSPITAL AND HEALTH CARE CENTER, CHICAGO, IL, p. A180
ST. BERNARD PARISH HOSPITAL, CHALMETTE, LA, p. A265
ST. BERNARDINE MEDICAL CENTER, SAN BERNARDINO, CA, p. A83
ST. BERNARDS FIVE RIVERS, POCAHONTAS, AR, p. A47
ST. BERNARDS MEDICAL CENTER, JONESBORO, AR, p. A44
ST. CATHERINE HOSPITAL, EAST CHICAGO, IN, p. A202
ST. CATHERINE HOSPITAL, GARDEN CITY, KS, p. A235
ST. CATHERINE MEMORIAL HOSPITAL, NEW ORLEANS, LA, p. A276
ST. CATHERINE OF SIENA MEDICAL CENTER, SMITHTOWN, NY, p. A444
ST. CATHERINE'S REHABILITATION HOSPITAL, NORTH MIAMI, FL, p. A133
ST. CHARLES BEND, BEND, OR, p. A511
ST. CHARLES HOSPITAL, PORT JEFFERSON, NY, p. A441
ST. CHARLES MADRAS, MADRAS, OR, p. A514
ST. CHARLES MERCY HOSPITAL, OREGON, OHIO (see MERCY HEALTH – ST. CHARLES HOSPITAL), p. A489
ST. CHARLES PARISH HOSPITAL, LULING, LA, p. A272
ST. CHARLES PRINEVILLE, PRINEVILLE, OR, p. A517
ST. CHARLES REDMOND, REDMOND, OR, p. A517
ST. CHARLES SURGICAL HOSPITAL, NEW ORLEANS, LA, p. A276
ST. CHRISTOPHER'S HOSPITAL FOR CHILDREN, PHILADELPHIA, PA, p. A536
ST. CLAIR HOSPITAL, PITTSBURGH, PA, p. A537
ST. CLAIRE HEALTHCARE, MOREHEAD, KY, p. A258
ST. CLARE HOSPITAL, LAKEWOOD, WA, p. A674
ST. CLARE MEDICAL CENTER, CRAWFORDSVILLE, INDIANA (see FRANCISCAN HEALTH CRAWFORDSVILLE), p. A202
ST. CLOUD HOSPITAL, SAINT CLOUD, MN, p. A339
ST. CLOUD REGIONAL MEDICAL CENTER, SAINT CLOUD, FL, p. A138
ST. CLOUD VETERANS AFFAIRS HEALTH CARE SYSTEM, SAINT CLOUD, MN, p. A339
ST. CROIX REGIONAL MEDICAL CENTER, ST CROIX FALLS, WI, p. A706
ST. DAVID'S MEDICAL CENTER, AUSTIN, TX, p. A586
ST. DAVID'S NORTH AUSTIN MEDICAL CENTER, AUSTIN, TX, p. A586
ST. DAVID'S ROUND ROCK MEDICAL CENTER, ROUND ROCK, TX, p. A632
ST. DAVID'S SOUTH AUSTIN MEDICAL CENTER, AUSTIN, TX, p. A586
ST. DOMINIC–JACKSON MEMORIAL HOSPITAL, JACKSON, MS, p. A349
ST. ELIAS SPECIALTY HOSPITAL, ANCHORAGE, AK, p. A25
ST. ELIZABETH CENTRAL, LAFAYETTE, INDIANA (see FRANCISCAN HEALTH LAFAYETTE CENTRAL), p. A209

ST. ELIZABETH COMMUNITY HOSPITAL, RED BLUFF, CA, p. A79

ST. ELIZABETH EDGEWOOD, EDGEWOOD, KY, p. A251

ST. ELIZABETH FLORENCE, FLORENCE, KY, p. A252

ST. ELIZABETH FORT THOMAS, FORT THOMAS, KY, p. A252

ST. ELIZABETH GRANT, WILLIAMSTOWN, KY, p. A261

ST. ELIZABETH HEALTH SERVICES, BAKER CITY, OREGON (see SAINT ALPHONSUS MEDICAL CENTER – BAKER CITY), p. A511

ST. ELIZABETH HEALTHCARE FLORENCE, FLORENCE, KENTUCKY (see ST. ELIZABETH FLORENCE), p. A252

ST. ELIZABETH HEALTHCARE FORT THOMAS, FORT THOMAS, KENTUCKY (see ST. ELIZABETH FORT THOMAS), p. A252

ST. ELIZABETH HEALTHCARE–EDGEWOOD, EDGEWOOD, KENTUCKY (see ST. ELIZABETH EDGEWOOD), p. A251

ST. ELIZABETH HOSPITAL, ENUMCLAW, WA, p. A672

ST. ELIZABETH MEDICAL CENTER, UTICA, NY, p. A446

ST. ELIZABETH MEDICAL CENTER–GRANT COUNTY, WILLIAMSTOWN, KENTUCKY (see ST. ELIZABETH GRANT), p. A261

ST. ELIZABETH MEDICAL CENTER–NORTH, COVINGTON, KENTUCKY (see ST. ELIZABETH COVINGTON), p. A251

ST. ELIZABETH'S MEDICAL CENTER, BROCKTON, MA, p. A296

ST. FRANCIS HOSPITAL, COLUMBUS, GA, p. A150

ST. FRANCIS HOSPITAL, FEDERAL WAY, WA, p. A673

ST. FRANCIS HOSPITAL, WILMINGTON, DE, p. A114

ST. FRANCIS HOSPITAL AND HEALTH CENTERS – SOUTH CAMPUS, INDIANAPOLIS, INDIANA (see FRANCISCAN HEALTH INDIANAPOLIS), p. A208

ST. FRANCIS HOSPITAL, THE HEART CENTER, ROSLYN, NY, p. A443

ST. FRANCIS HOSPITAL–MOORESVILLE, MOORESVILLE, INDIANA (see FRANCISCAN HEALTH MOORESVILLE), p. A211

ST. FRANCIS MEDICAL CENTER, LYNWOOD, CA, p. A70

ST. FRANCIS MEDICAL CENTER, MONROE, LA, p. A274

ST. FRANCIS MEDICAL CENTER, TRENTON, NJ, p. A413

ST. FRANCIS MEMORIAL HOSPITAL, WEST POINT, NE, p. A392

ST. FRANCIS REGIONAL MEDICAL CENTER, SHAKOPEE, MN, p. A340

ST. FRANCIS SPECIALTY HOSPITAL, MONROE, LOUISIANA (see SPECIALTY HOSPITAL), p. A274

ST. HELENA PARISH HOSPITAL, GREENSBURG, LA, p. A268

ST. JAMES BEHAVIORAL HEALTH HOSPITAL, GONZALES, LA, p. A267

ST. JAMES HEALTHCARE, BUTTE, MT, p. A375

ST. JAMES HOSPITAL AND HEALTH CENTERS, OLYMPIA FIELDS, ILLINOIS (see FRANCISCAN HEALTH OLYMPIA FIELDS), p. A192

ST. JAMES MERCY HOSPITAL, HORNELL, NY, p. A429

ST. JAMES PARISH HOSPITAL, LUTCHER, LA, p. A273

ST. JOHN BROKEN ARROW, BROKEN ARROW, OK, p. A497

ST. JOHN MEDICAL CENTER, TULSA, OK, p. A510

ST. JOHN MEDICAL CENTER, WESTLAKE, OH, p. A494

ST. JOHN OWASSO, OWASSO, OK, p. A506

ST. JOHN REHABILITATION HOSPITAL, BROKEN ARROW, OK, p. A497

ST. JOHN SAPULPA, SAPULPA, OK, p. A507

ST. JOHN VIANNEY HOSPITAL, DOWNINGTOWN, PA, p. A524

ST. JOHN WEST SHORE HOSPITAL, WESTLAKE, OHIO (see ST. JOHN MEDICAL CENTER), p. A494

ST. JOHN'S HOSPITAL, MAPLEWOOD, MN, p. A335

ST. JOHN'S MEDICAL CENTER AND LIVING CENTER, JACKSON, WY, p. A711

ST. JOHN'S MERCY CHILDREN'S HOSPITAL, SAINT LOUIS, MISSOURI (see MERCY CHILDREN'S HOSPITAL ST. LOUIS), p. A370

ST. JOHN'S MERCY MEDICAL CENTER, SAINT LOUIS, MISSOURI (see MERCY HOSPITAL ST. LOUIS), p. A368

ST. JOHN'S PLEASANT VALLEY HOSPITAL, CAMARILLO, CA, p. A53

ST. JOHN'S REGIONAL MEDICAL CENTER, OXNARD, CA, p. A76

ST. JOHN'S RIVERSIDE HOSPITAL, YONKERS, NY, p. A448

ST. JOSEPH HEALTH SERVICES OF RHODE ISLAND, NORTH PROVIDENCE, RI, p. A547

ST. JOSEPH HOSPITAL, BANGOR, ME, p. A281

ST. JOSEPH HOSPITAL, BELLINGHAM, WASHINGTON (see PEACEHEALTH ST. JOSEPH MEDICAL CENTER), p. A670

ST. JOSEPH HOSPITAL, BETHPAGE, NY, p. A423

ST. JOSEPH HOSPITAL, EUREKA, CA, p. A57

ST. JOSEPH HOSPITAL, FORT WAYNE, IN, p. A204

ST. JOSEPH HOSPITAL, NASHUA, NH, p. A401

ST. JOSEPH HOSPITAL, ORANGE, CA, p. A76

ST. JOSEPH HOSPITAL FOR SPECIALTY CARE, PROVIDENCE, RHODE ISLAND (see ST. JOSEPH HEALTH SERVICES OF RHODE ISLAND), p. A548

ST. JOSEPH MEDICAL CENTER, HOUSTON, TX, p. A613

ST. JOSEPH MEDICAL CENTER, KANSAS CITY, MO, p. A363

ST. JOSEPH MEDICAL CENTER, TACOMA, WA, p. A681

ST. JOSEPH MEMORIAL HOSPITAL, MURPHYSBORO, IL, p. A190

ST. JOSEPH MERCY ANN ARBOR, YPSILANTI, MI, p. A325

ST. JOSEPH MERCY CHELSEA, CHELSEA, MI, p. A308

ST. JOSEPH MERCY LIVINGSTON HOSPITAL, HOWELL, MI, p. A314

ST. JOSEPH MERCY OAKLAND, PONTIAC, MI, p. A320

ST. JOSEPH REGIONAL MEDICAL CENTER, LEWISTON, ID, p. A170

ST. JOSEPH'S BEHAVIORAL HEALTH CENTER, STOCKTON, CA, p. A90

ST. JOSEPH'S CANDLER HOSPITAL, SAVANNAH, GA, p. A160

ST. JOSEPH'S HOSPITAL, ELMIRA, NY, p. A427

ST. JOSEPH'S HOSPITAL, SAINT PAUL, MN, p. A340

ST. JOSEPH'S HOSPITAL, SAVANNAH, GA, p. A160

ST. JOSEPH'S HOSPITAL, TAMPA, FL, p. A142

ST. JOSEPH'S HOSPITAL, WEST BEND, WI, p. A708

ST. JOSEPH'S HOSPITAL AND MEDICAL CENTER, PHOENIX, AZ, p. A34

ST. JOSEPH'S HOSPITAL HEALTH CENTER, SYRACUSE, NY, p. A445

ST. JOSEPH'S HOSPITAL OF BUCKHANNON, BUCKHANNON, WV, p. A684

ST. JOSEPH'S MEDICAL CENTER, BRAINERD, MINNESOTA (see ESSENTIA HEALTH ST. JOSEPH'S MEDICAL CENTER), p. A329

ST. JOSEPH'S MEDICAL CENTER, STOCKTON, CA, p. A91

ST. JOSEPH'S MERCY–NORTH, ROMEO, MICHIGAN (see HENRY FORD MACOMB HOSPITALS), p. A321

ST. JOSEPH'S UNIVERSITY MEDICAL CENTER, PATERSON, NJ, p. A410

ST. JUDE CHILDREN'S RESEARCH HOSPITAL, MEMPHIS, TN, p. A575

ST. JUDE MEDICAL CENTER, FULLERTON, CA, p. A60

ST. LANDRY EXTENDED CARE HOSPITAL, OPELOUSAS, LA, p. A276

ST. LAWRENCE PSYCHIATRIC CENTER, OGDENSBURG, NY, p. A440

ST. LAWRENCE REHABILITATION CENTER, LAWRENCEVILLE, NJ, p. A407

ST. LOUIS CHILDREN'S HOSPITAL, SAINT LOUIS, MO, p. A370

ST. LOUIS PSYCHIATRIC REHABILITATION CENTER, SAINT LOUIS, MO, p. A370

ST. LUCIE MEDICAL CENTER, PORT ST. LUCIE, FL, p. A137

ST. LUKE COMMUNITY HEALTHCARE, RONAN, MT, p. A379

ST. LUKE HOSPITAL AND LIVING CENTER, MARION, KS, p. A240

ST. LUKE'S – GNADEN HUETTEN CAMPUS, LEHIGHTON, PA, p. A530

ST. LUKE'S BAPTIST HOSPITAL, SAN ANTONIO, TEXAS (see BAPTIST MEDICAL CENTER), p. A625

ST. LUKE'S BEHAVIORAL HEALTH CENTER, PHOENIX, AZ, p. A34

ST. LUKE'S CAMPUS, UTICA, NEW YORK (see FAXTON ST. LUKE'S HEALTHCARE), p. A446

ST. LUKE'S CORNWALL HOSPITAL – CORNWALL CAMPUS, CORNWALL, NEW YORK (see MONTEFIORE ST. LUKE'S CORNWALL), p. A426

ST. LUKE'S DES PERES HOSPITAL, SAINT LOUIS, MO, p. A370

ST. LUKE'S ELMORE, MOUNTAIN HOME, ID, p. A170

ST. LUKE'S EPISCOPAL HOSPITAL, PONCE, PR, p. A717

ST. LUKE'S HOSPITAL – ANDERSON CAMPUS, EASTON, PA, p. A525

ST. LUKE'S HOSPITAL – MINERS CAMPUS, COALDALE, PA, p. A522

ST. LUKE'S HOSPITAL – QUAKERTOWN CAMPUS, QUAKERTOWN, PA, p. A539

ST. LUKE'S HOSPITAL – WARREN CAMPUS, PHILLIPSBURG, NJ, p. A411

ST. LUKE'S HOSPITAL, CEDAR RAPIDS, IOWA (see UNITYPOINT HEALTH – ST. LUKE'S HOSPITAL), p. A218

ST. LUKE'S HOSPITAL, CHESTERFIELD, MO, p. A358

ST. LUKE'S HOSPITAL, COLUMBUS, NC, p. A452

ST. LUKE'S HOSPITAL, DULUTH, MN, p. A331

ST. LUKE'S HOSPITAL, MAUMEE, OH, p. A487

ST. LUKE'S HOSPITAL, NEW BEDFORD, MASSACHUSETTS (see SOUTHCOAST HOSPITALS GROUP), p. A301

ST. LUKE'S JEROME, JEROME, ID, p. A169

ST. LUKE'S MAGIC VALLEY MEDICAL CENTER, TWIN FALLS, ID, p. A172

ST. LUKE'S MCCALL, MCCALL, ID, p. A170

ST. LUKE'S MEDICAL CENTER, CROSBY, ND, p. A466

ST. LUKE'S MEDICAL CENTER, PHOENIX, AZ, p. A34

ST. LUKE'S MERIDIAN MEDICAL CENTER, MERIDIAN, IDAHO (see ST. LUKE'S REGIONAL MEDICAL CENTER), p. A170

ST. LUKE'S MONROE, STROUDSBURG, PA, p. A542

ST. LUKE'S NAMPA, NAMPA, ID, p. A170

ST. LUKE'S REGIONAL MEDICAL CENTER, BOISE, ID, p. A168

ST. LUKE'S REHABILITATION HOSPITAL, BOISE, ID, p. A168

ST. LUKE'S REHABILITATION HOSPITAL, CHESTERFIELD, MO, p. A358

ST. LUKE'S REHABILITATION INSTITUTE, SPOKANE, WA, p. A680

ST. LUKE'S SACRED HEART CAMPUS, ALLENTOWN, PA, p. A519

ST. LUKE'S SUGAR LAND HOSPITAL, SUGAR LAND, TX, p. A638

ST. LUKE'S UNIVERSITY HOSPITAL – BETHLEHEM CAMPUS, BETHLEHEM, PA, p. A520

ST. LUKE'S WOOD RIVER MEDICAL CENTER, KETCHUM, ID, p. A170

ST. MARGARET'S HOSPITAL, SPRING VALLEY, IL, p. A196

ST. MARK'S HOSPITAL, SALT LAKE CITY, UT, p. A652

ST. MARK'S MEDICAL CENTER, LA GRANGE, TX, p. A619

ST. MARTIN HOSPITAL, BREAUX BRIDGE, LA, p. A265

ST. MARY MEDICAL CENTER, APPLE VALLEY, CA, p. A51

ST. MARY MEDICAL CENTER, HOBART, IN, p. A206

ST. MARY MEDICAL CENTER, LANGHORNE, PA, p. A529

ST. MARY MEDICAL CENTER, LONG BEACH, CA, p. A65

ST. MARY MERCY HOSPITAL, LIVONIA, MI, p. A317

ST. MARY REHABILITATION HOSPITAL, LANGHORNE, PA, p. A529

ST. MARY–CORWIN MEDICAL CENTER, PUEBLO, CO, p. A105

ST. MARY'S GENERAL HOSPITAL, PASSAIC, NJ, p. A410

ST. MARY'S GOOD SAMARITAN HOSPITAL, GREENSBORO, GA, p. A154

ST. MARY'S HEALTH CARE SYSTEM, ATHENS, GA, p. A145

ST. MARY'S HEALTHCARE, AMSTERDAM, NEW YORK (see ST. MARY'S HEALTHCARE), p. A422

ST. MARY'S HEALTHCARE, AMSTERDAM, NY, p. A422

ST. MARY'S HOSPITAL, COTTONWOOD, ID, p. A169

ST. MARY'S HOSPITAL AND MEDICAL CENTER, GRAND JUNCTION, CO, p. A101

ST. MARY'S HOSPITAL AND REHABILITATION CENTER, MINNEAPOLIS, MINNESOTA (see UNIVERSITY OF MINNESOTA MEDICAL CENTER, FAIRVIEW), p. A336

ST. MARY'S INNOVIS HEALTH, DETROIT LAKES, MINNESOTA (see ESSENTIA HEALTH ST. MARY'S – DETROIT LAKES), p. A330

ST. MARY'S JEFFERSON MEMORIAL HOSPITAL, JEFFERSON CITY, TENNESSEE (see TENNOVA HEALTHCARE–JEFFERSON MEMORIAL HOSPITAL), p. A571

ST. MARY'S MEDICAL CENTER, BLUE SPRINGS, MO, p. A356

ST. MARY'S MEDICAL CENTER, DULUTH, MINNESOTA (see ESSENTIA HEALTH ST. MARY'S MEDICAL CENTER), p. A331

ST. MARY'S MEDICAL CENTER, HUNTINGTON, WV, p. A686

ST. MARY'S MEDICAL CENTER, SAN FRANCISCO, CA, p. A86

ST. MARY'S MEDICAL CENTER, WEST PALM BEACH, FL, p. A144

ST. MARY'S REGIONAL MEDICAL CENTER, ENID, OK, p. A499

ST. MARY'S REGIONAL MEDICAL CENTER, LEWISTON, ME, p. A283

ST. MARY'S SACRED HEART HOSPITAL, LAVONIA, GA, p. A156

ST. MICHAEL'S HOSPITAL AVERA, TYNDALL, SD, p. A564

ST. PETERSBURG GENERAL HOSPITAL, SAINT PETERSBURG, FL, p. A139

ST. PETER'S HOSPITAL, ALBANY, NY, p. A422

ST. PETER'S HOSPITAL, HELENA, MT, p. A377

ST. ROSE DOMINICAN HOSPITALS – ROSE DE LIMA CAMPUS, HENDERSON, NV, p. A394

ST. ROSE DOMINICAN HOSPITALS – SAN MARTIN CAMPUS, LAS VEGAS, NV, p. A396

ST. ROSE DOMINICAN HOSPITALS – SIENA CAMPUS, HENDERSON, NV, p. A394

ST. ROSE HOSPITAL, HAYWARD, CA, p. A61

ST. TAMMANY PARISH HOSPITAL, COVINGTON, LA, p. A266

ST. THERESA SPECIALTY HOSPITAL, KENNER, LA, p. A270

ST. THOMAS MORE HOSPITAL, CANON CITY, CO, p. A97

ST. VINCENT ANDERSON, ANDERSON, IN, p. A199

ST. VINCENT CARMEL HOSPITAL, CARMEL, IN, p. A201

ST. VINCENT CHARITY MEDICAL CENTER, CLEVELAND, OH, p. A478

ST. VINCENT CLAY HOSPITAL, BRAZIL, IN, p. A200

ST. VINCENT DUNN HOSPITAL, BEDFORD, IN, p. A200

ST. VINCENT EVANSVILLE, EVANSVILLE, IN, p. A203

ST. VINCENT FISHERS HOSPITAL, FISHERS, IN, p. A203

ST. VINCENT GENERAL HOSPITAL DISTRICT, LEADVILLE, CO, p. A103

ST. VINCENT HEALTHCARE, BILLINGS, MT, p. A374

ST. VINCENT HEART CENTER, INDIANAPOLIS, IN, p. A206

ST. VINCENT INDIANAPOLIS HOSPITAL, INDIANAPOLIS, IN, p. A208

ST. VINCENT JENNINGS HOSPITAL, NORTH VERNON, IN, p. A213

ST. VINCENT KOKOMO, KOKOMO, IN, p. A209
ST. VINCENT MEDICAL CENTER, LOS ANGELES, CA, p. A69
ST. VINCENT MERCY HOSPITAL, ELWOOD, IN, p. A203
ST. VINCENT RANDOLPH HOSPITAL, WINCHESTER, IN, p. A216
ST. VINCENT SALEM HOSPITAL, SALEM, IN, p. A214
ST. VINCENT SETON SPECIALTY HOSPITAL, INDIANAPOLIS, IN, p. A208
ST. VINCENT WARRICK, BOONVILLE, IN, p. A200
ST. VINCENT WILLIAMSPORT HOSPITAL, WILLIAMSPORT, IN, p. A216
ST. VINCENT'S BEHAVIORAL HEALTH, WESTPORT, CT, p. A112
ST. VINCENT'S BIRMINGHAM, BIRMINGHAM, AL, p. A15
ST. VINCENT'S BLOUNT, ONEONTA, AL, p. A22
ST. VINCENT'S CHILTON HOSPITAL, CLANTON, AL, p. A16
ST. VINCENT'S EAST, BIRMINGHAM, AL, p. A15
ST. VINCENT'S MEDICAL CENTER, BRIDGEPORT, CT, p. A107
ST. VINCENT'S MEDICAL CENTER CLAY COUNTY, MIDDLEBURG, FL, p. A132
ST. VINCENT'S MEDICAL CENTER RIVERSIDE, JACKSONVILLE, FL, p. A126
ST. VINCENT'S MEDICAL CENTER SOUTHSIDE, JACKSONVILLE, FL, p. A126
ST. VINCENT'S ST. CLAIR, PELL CITY, AL, p. A22
STAFFORD COUNTY HOSPITAL, STAFFORD, KS, p. A246
STAFFORD HOSPITAL, STAFFORD, VA, p. A667
STAMFORD HOSPITAL, STAMFORD, CT, p. A111
STANDING ROCK SERVICE UNIT, FORT YATES HOSPITAL, INDIAN HEALTH SERVICE, DHHS, FORT YATES, ND, p. A467
STANFORD HEALTH CARE – VALLEYCARE, PLEASANTON, CA, p. A78
STANFORD HEALTH CARE, PALO ALTO, CA, p. A77
STANISLAUS SURGICAL HOSPITAL, MODESTO, CA, p. A72
STANTON COUNTY HOSPITAL, JOHNSON, KS, p. A237
STAR MEDICAL CENTER, PLANO, TX, p. A629
STAR VALLEY MEDICAL CENTER, AFTON, WY, p. A710
STARKE HOSPITAL, KNOX, IN, p. A208
STARKE MEMORIAL HOSPITAL, KNOX, INDIANA (see STARKE HOSPITAL), p. A208
STARR COUNTY MEMORIAL HOSPITAL, RIO GRANDE CITY, TX, p. A631
STARR REGIONAL MEDICAL CENTER, ATHENS, TN, p. A566
STATE CORRECTIONAL INSTITUTION AT CAMP HILL, CAMP HILL, PA, p. A521
STATE HOSPITAL NORTH, OROFINO, ID, p. A171
STATE HOSPITAL SOUTH, BLACKFOOT, ID, p. A167
STATE PENITENTIARY HOSPITAL, WALLA WALLA, WA, p. A681
STE. GENEVIEVE COUNTY MEMORIAL HOSPITAL, STE GENEVIEVE, MO, p. A372
STEELE MEMORIAL MEDICAL CENTER, SALMON, ID, p. A172
STEPHENS COUNTY HOSPITAL, TOCCOA, GA, p. A162
STEPHENS MEMORIAL HOSPITAL, BRECKENRIDGE, TX, p. A589
STEPHENS MEMORIAL HOSPITAL, NORWAY, ME, p. A284
STERLING REGIONAL MEDCENTER, STERLING, CO, p. A105
STERLING SURGICAL HOSPITAL, SLIDELL, LA, p. A279
STERLINGTON REHABILITATION HOSPITAL, BASTROP, LA, p. A263
STEVEN AND ALEXANDRA COHEN CHILDREN'S MEDICAL CENTER OF NEW YORK, NEW HYDE PARK, NEW YORK (see LONG ISLAND JEWISH MEDICAL CENTER), p. A432
STEVENS COMMUNITY MEDICAL CENTER, MORRIS, MN, p. A336
STEVENS COUNTY HOSPITAL, HUGOTON, KS, p. A237
STEVENS HEALTHCARE, EDMONDS, WASHINGTON (see SWEDISH/EDMONDS), p. A672
STEWART & LYNDA RESNICK NEUROPSYCHIATRIC HOSPITAL AT UCLA, LOS ANGELES, CA, p. A69
STEWART MEMORIAL COMMUNITY HOSPITAL, LAKE CITY, IA, p. A225
STILLWATER BILLINGS CLINIC, COLUMBUS, MT, p. A375
STILLWATER MEDICAL CENTER, STILLWATER, OK, p. A507
STILLWATER MEDICAL PERRY, PERRY, OK, p. A506
STONE COUNTY HOSPITAL, WIGGINS, MS, p. A355
STONE COUNTY MEDICAL CENTER, MOUNTAIN VIEW, AR, p. A46
STONECREST CENTER, DETROIT, MI, p. A310
STONESPRINGS CENTER, DULLES, VA, p. A658
STONEWALL JACKSON MEMORIAL HOSPITAL, WESTON, WV, p. A690
STONEWALL MEMORIAL HOSPITAL, ASPERMONT, TX, p. A584
STONY BROOK UNIVERSITY HOSPITAL, STONY BROOK, NY, p. A444
STORMONT VAIL HEALTH, TOPEKA, KS, p. A246
STORY COUNTY MEDICAL CENTER, NEVADA, IA, p. A227

STOUGHTON HOSPITAL ASSOCIATION, STOUGHTON, WI, p. A706
STRAITH HOSPITAL FOR SPECIAL SURGERY, SOUTHFIELD, MI, p. A323
STRATEGIC BEHAVIORAL HEALTH – CHARLOTTE, CHARLOTTE, NC, p. A452
STRATEGIC BEHAVIORAL HEALTH – RALEIGH, GARNER, NC, p. A454
STRATEGIC BEHAVIORAL HEALTH – WILMINGTON, LELAND, NC, p. A457
STRAUB MEDICAL CENTER, HONOLULU, HI, p. A165
STREAMWOOD BEHAVIORAL HEALTH CENTER, STREAMWOOD, IL, p. A197
STRONG MEMORIAL HOSPITAL OF THE UNIVERSITY OF ROCHESTER, ROCHESTER, NY, p. A443
STROUD REGIONAL MEDICAL CENTER, STROUD, OK, p. A508
STS. MARY & ELIZABETH HOSPITAL, LOUISVILLE, KY, p. A256
STURDY MEMORIAL HOSPITAL, ATTLEBORO, MA, p. A294
STURGIS HOSPITAL, STURGIS, MI, p. A323
STURGIS REGIONAL HOSPITAL, STURGIS, SD, p. A564
SUBURBAN COMMUNITY HOSPITAL, NORRISTOWN, PA, p. A533
SUBURBAN HOSPITAL, BETHESDA, MD, p. A289
SUGAR LAND REHABILITATION HOSPITAL, SUGAR LAND, TEXAS (see ENCOMPASS HEALTH REHABILITATION HOSPITAL OF SUGAR LAND), p. A638
SULLIVAN COUNTY COMMUNITY HOSPITAL, SULLIVAN, IN, p. A215
SULLIVAN COUNTY MEMORIAL HOSPITAL, MILAN, MO, p. A365
SUMMA AKRON CITY HOSPITAL, AKRON, OHIO (see SUMMA HEALTH SYSTEM), p. A471
SUMMA HEALTH SYSTEM, AKRON, OHIO (see SUMMA HEALTH SYSTEM), p. A471
SUMMA HEALTH SYSTEM, AKRON, OH, p. A471
SUMMA REHAB HOSPITAL, AKRON, OH, p. A471
SUMMA SAINT THOMAS HOSPITAL, AKRON, OHIO (see SUMMA HEALTH SYSTEM), p. A471
SUMMERLIN HOSPITAL MEDICAL CENTER, LAS VEGAS, NV, p. A396
SUMMERS COUNTY ARH HOSPITAL, HINTON, WV, p. A685
SUMMERSVILLE REGIONAL MEDICAL CENTER, SUMMERSVILLE, WV, p. A689
SUMMIT BEHAVIORAL HEALTHCARE, CINCINNATI, OH, p. A476
SUMMIT HEALTHCARE REGIONAL MEDICAL CENTER, SHOW LOW, AZ, p. A36
SUMMIT MEDICAL CENTER, CASPER, WY, p. A710
SUMMIT MEDICAL CENTER, EDMOND, OK, p. A499
SUMMIT OAKS HOSPITAL, SUMMIT, NJ, p. A413
SUMMIT PACIFIC MEDICAL CENTER, ELMA, WA, p. A672
SUMMIT SURGICAL, HUTCHINSON, KS, p. A237
SUMMITRIDGE HOSPITAL, LAWRENCEVILLE, GA, p. A156
SUMNER COUNTY HOSPITAL DISTRICT 1, CALDWELL, KS, p. A233
SUMNER REGIONAL MEDICAL CENTER, GALLATIN, TN, p. A570
SUMNER REGIONAL MEDICAL CENTER, WELLINGTON, KS, p. A247
SUN BEHAVIORAL COLUMBUS, COLUMBUS, OH, p. A480
SUN BEHAVIORAL HOUSTON, HOUSTON, TX, p. A614
SUN BEHAVIORAL KENTUCKY, ERLANGER, KY, p. A251
SUNCOAST BEHAVIORAL HEALTH CENTER, BRADENTON, FL, p. A119
SUNDANCE HOSPITAL ARLINGTON, ARLINGTON, TX, p. A583
SUNNYVIEW REHABILITATION HOSPITAL, SCHENECTADY, NY, p. A444
SUNRISE CANYON HOSPITAL, LUBBOCK, TX, p. A622
SUNRISE HOSPITAL AND MEDICAL CENTER, LAS VEGAS, NV, p. A396
SURGEONS CHOICE MEDICAL CENTER, SOUTHFIELD, MI, p. A323
SURGERY SPECIALTY HOSPITALS OF AMERICA, PASADENA, TX, p. A628
SURGICAL HOSPITAL AT SOUTHWOODS, YOUNGSTOWN, OH, p. A495
SURGICAL HOSPITAL OF OKLAHOMA, OKLAHOMA CITY, OK, p. A505
SURGICAL INSTITUTE OF READING, WYOMISSING, PA, p. A545
SURGICAL SPECIALTY CENTER AT COORDINATED HEALTH, ALLENTOWN, PA, p. A519
SURGICAL SPECIALTY CENTER OF BATON ROUGE, BATON ROUGE, LA, p. A264
SURPRISE VALLEY HEALTH CARE DISTRICT, CEDARVILLE, CA, p. A54
SUSAN B. ALLEN MEMORIAL HOSPITAL, EL DORADO, KS, p. A234

SUTTER AMADOR HOSPITAL, JACKSON, CA, p. A62
SUTTER AUBURN FAITH HOSPITAL, AUBURN, CA, p. A51
SUTTER CENTER FOR PSYCHIATRY, SACRAMENTO, CA, p. A82
SUTTER COAST HOSPITAL, CRESCENT CITY, CA, p. A56
SUTTER DAVIS HOSPITAL, DAVIS, CA, p. A56
SUTTER DELTA MEDICAL CENTER, ANTIOCH, CA, p. A50
SUTTER HEALTH KAHI MOHALA, EWA BEACH, HI, p. A164
SUTTER LAKESIDE HOSPITAL, LAKEPORT, CA, p. A64
SUTTER MATERNITY AND SURGERY CENTER OF SANTA CRUZ, SANTA CRUZ, CA, p. A89
SUTTER MEDICAL CENTER, SACRAMENTO, SACRAMENTO, CA, p. A82
SUTTER ROSEVILLE MEDICAL CENTER, ROSEVILLE, CA, p. A81
SUTTER SANTA ROSA REGIONAL HOSPITAL, SANTA ROSA, CA, p. A89
SUTTER SOLANO MEDICAL CENTER, VALLEJO, CA, p. A93
SUTTER SURGICAL HOSPITAL – NORTH VALLEY, YUBA CITY, CA, p. A95
SUTTER TRACY COMMUNITY HOSPITAL, TRACY, CA, p. A92
SWAIN COMMUNITY HOSPITAL, BRYSON CITY, NC, p. A450
SWEDISH COVENANT HOSPITAL, CHICAGO, IL, p. A180
SWEDISH MEDICAL CENTER, ENGLEWOOD, CO, p. A100
SWEDISH MEDICAL CENTER–CHERRY HILL CAMPUS, SEATTLE, WA, p. A678
SWEDISH MEDICAL CENTER–FIRST HILL, SEATTLE, WA, p. A678
SWEDISH/EDMONDS, EDMONDS, WA, p. A672
SWEDISH/ISSAQUAH, ISSAQUAH, WA, p. A674
SWEDISHAMERICAN – A DIVISION OF UW HEALTH, ROCKFORD, IL, p. A195
SWEENY COMMUNITY HOSPITAL, SWEENY, TX, p. A639
SWEETWATER HOSPITAL, SWEETWATER, TN, p. A580
SWIFT COUNTY – BENSON HEALTH SERVICES, BENSON, MN, p. A328
SWISHER MEMORIAL HEALTHCARE SYSTEM, TULIA, TX, p. A642
SYCAMORE MEDICAL CENTER, MIAMISBURG, OH, p. A487
SYCAMORE SHOALS HOSPITAL, ELIZABETHTON, TN, p. A569
SYCAMORE SPRINGS HOSPITAL, LAFAYETTE, IN, p. A210
SYRACUSE AREA HEALTH, SYRACUSE, NE, p. A392
SYRACUSE VETERANS AFFAIRS MEDICAL CENTER, SYRACUSE, NY, p. A445
SYRINGA HOSPITAL AND CLINICS, GRANGEVILLE, ID, p. A169

T

T. C. THOMPSON CHILDREN'S HOSPITAL, CHATTANOOGA, TENNESSEE (see ERLANGER MEDICAL CENTER), p. A567
T. J. SAMSON COMMUNITY HOSPITAL, GLASGOW, KY, p. A252
T.J. HEALTH COLUMBIA, COLUMBIA, KY, p. A250
TAHOE FOREST HOSPITAL DISTRICT, TRUCKEE, CA, p. A92
TAHOE PACIFIC HOSPITALS, SPARKS, NV, p. A398
TALLAHASSEE MEMORIAL HEALTHCARE, TALLAHASSEE, FL, p. A141
TALLAHATCHIE GENERAL HOSPITAL, CHARLESTON, MS, p. A345
TAMPA GENERAL HOSPITAL, TAMPA, FL, p. A142
TANNER MEDICAL CENTER–CARROLLTON, CARROLLTON, GA, p. A149
TANNER MEDICAL CENTER–VILLA RICA, VILLA RICA, GA, p. A162
TANNER MEDICAL CENTER/EAST ALABAMA, WEDOWEE, AL, p. A24
TAUNTON STATE HOSPITAL, TAUNTON, MA, p. A304
TAYLOR HARDIN SECURE MEDICAL FACILITY, TUSCALOOSA, AL, p. A24
TAYLOR HOSPITAL, RIDLEY PARK, PENNSYLVANIA (see CROZER–CHESTER MEDICAL CENTER), p. A540
TAYLOR REGIONAL HOSPITAL, CAMPBELLSVILLE, KY, p. A250
TAYLOR REGIONAL HOSPITAL, HAWKINSVILLE, GA, p. A154
TAYLORVILLE MEMORIAL HOSPITAL, TAYLORVILLE, IL, p. A197
TECHE REGIONAL MEDICAL CENTER, MORGAN CITY, LA, p. A274
TELECARE HERITAGE PSYCHIATRIC HEALTH CENTER, OAKLAND, CA, p. A75
TEMECULA VALLEY HOSPITAL, TEMECULA, CA, p. A91
TEMPLE UNIVERSITY HOSPITAL, PHILADELPHIA, PA, p. A536
TEN BROECK DUPONT, LOUISVILLE, KENTUCKY (see THE BROOK AT DUPONT), p. A256

TEN BROECK TENNESSEE TREATMENT FACILITY, COOKEVILLE, TN, p. A568
TEN LAKES CENTER, DENNISON, OH, p. A482
TENNESSEE VALLEY HEALTHCARE SYSTEM, NASHVILLE, TN, p. A577
TENNOVA HEALTHCARE – CLEVELAND, CLEVELAND, TN, p. A568
TENNOVA HEALTHCARE–CLARKSVILLE, CLARKSVILLE, TN, p. A568
TENNOVA HEALTHCARE–HARTON, TULLAHOMA, TN, p. A580
TENNOVA HEALTHCARE–JEFFERSON MEMORIAL HOSPITAL, JEFFERSON CITY, TN, p. A571
TENNOVA HEALTHCARE–LAFOLLETTE MEDICAL CENTER, LA FOLLETTE, TN, p. A572
TENNOVA HEALTHCARE–SHELBYVILLE, SHELBYVILLE, TN, p. A579
TENNOVA NEWPORT MEDICAL CENTER, NEWPORT, TN, p. A578
TENNOVA NORTH KNOXVILLE MEDICAL CENTER, POWELL, TN, p. A578
TERRE HAUTE REGIONAL HOSPITAL, TERRE HAUTE, IN, p. A215
TERREBONNE GENERAL MEDICAL CENTER, HOUMA, LA, p. A269
TERRELL STATE HOSPITAL, TERRELL, TX, p. A640
TETON VALLEY HEALTH CARE, DRIGGS, ID, p. A169
TEWKSBURY HOSPITAL, TEWKSBURY, MA, p. A304
TEXAS CENTER FOR INFECTIOUS DISEASE, SAN ANTONIO, TX, p. A635
TEXAS CHILDREN'S HOSPITAL, HOUSTON, TX, p. A614
TEXAS COUNTY MEMORIAL HOSPITAL, HOUSTON, MO, p. A361
TEXAS GENERAL HOSPITAL, GRAND PRAIRIE, TX, p. A608
TEXAS HEALTH ARLINGTON MEMORIAL HOSPITAL, ARLINGTON, TX, p. A583
TEXAS HEALTH CENTER FOR DIAGNOSTIC & SURGERY, PLANO, TX, p. A630
TEXAS HEALTH HARRIS METHODIST HOSPITAL ALLIANCE, FORT WORTH, TX, p. A605
TEXAS HEALTH HARRIS METHODIST HOSPITAL AZLE, AZLE, TX, p. A586
TEXAS HEALTH HARRIS METHODIST HOSPITAL CLEBURNE, CLEBURNE, TX, p. A592
TEXAS HEALTH HARRIS METHODIST HOSPITAL FORT WORTH, FORT WORTH, TX, p. A605
TEXAS HEALTH HARRIS METHODIST HOSPITAL HURST–EULESS–BEDFORD, BEDFORD, TX, p. A588
TEXAS HEALTH HARRIS METHODIST HOSPITAL SOUTHLAKE, SOUTHLAKE, TX, p. A637
TEXAS HEALTH HARRIS METHODIST HOSPITAL SOUTHWEST FORT WORTH, FORT WORTH, TX, p. A606
TEXAS HEALTH HARRIS METHODIST HOSPITAL STEPHENVILLE, STEPHENVILLE, TX, p. A638
TEXAS HEALTH HEART & VASCULAR HOSPITAL ARLINGTON, ARLINGTON, TX, p. A584
TEXAS HEALTH HOSPITAL, CARROLLTON, TX, p. A591
TEXAS HEALTH HUGULEY HOSPITAL FORT WORTH SOUTH, BURLESON, TX, p. A590
TEXAS HEALTH PRESBYTERIAN HOSPITAL ALLEN, ALLEN, TX, p. A582
TEXAS HEALTH PRESBYTERIAN HOSPITAL DALLAS, DALLAS, TX, p. A598
TEXAS HEALTH PRESBYTERIAN HOSPITAL DENTON, DENTON, TX, p. A599
TEXAS HEALTH PRESBYTERIAN HOSPITAL FLOWER MOUND, FLOWER MOUND, TX, p. A604
TEXAS HEALTH PRESBYTERIAN HOSPITAL KAUFMAN, KAUFMAN, TX, p. A617
TEXAS HEALTH PRESBYTERIAN HOSPITAL OF ROCKWALL, ROCKWALL, TX, p. A631
TEXAS HEALTH PRESBYTERIAN HOSPITAL PLANO, PLANO, TX, p. A630
TEXAS HEALTH PRESBYTERIAN HOSPITAL WINNSBORO, WINNSBORO, TEXAS (see CHRISTUS MOTHER FRANCES HOSPITAL – WINNSBORO), p. A646
TEXAS HEALTH SPECIALTY HOSPITAL, FORT WORTH, TX, p. A606
TEXAS HOSPITAL FOR ADVANCED MEDICINE, DALLAS, TEXAS (see DALLAS MEDICAL CENTER), p. A598
TEXAS INSTITUTE FOR SURGERY AT TEXAS HEALTH PRESBYTERIAN DALLAS, DALLAS, TX, p. A598
TEXAS NEUROREHAB CENTER, AUSTIN, TX, p. A586
TEXAS ORTHOPEDIC HOSPITAL, HOUSTON, TX, p. A614
TEXAS REHABILITATION HOSPITAL OF ARLINGTON, ARLINGTON, TX, p. A584
TEXAS REHABILITATION HOSPITAL OF FORT WORTH, FORT WORTH, TX, p. A606
TEXAS SCOTTISH RITE HOSPITAL FOR CHILDREN, DALLAS, TX, p. A598
TEXAS STAR RECOVERY, AUSTIN, TX, p. A586

TEXOMA MEDICAL CENTER, DENISON, TX, p. A599
THAYER COUNTY HEALTH SERVICES, HEBRON, NE, p. A386
THE ACADIA HOSPITAL, BANGOR, ME, p. A281
THE AROOSTOOK MEDICAL CENTER, PRESQUE ISLE, ME, p. A284
THE BRIDGEWAY, NORTH LITTLE ROCK, AR, p. A47
THE BROOK AT DUPONT, LOUISVILLE, KY, p. A256
THE BROOK HOSPITAL – KMI, LOUISVILLE, KY, p. A257
THE CENTERS, OCALA, FL, p. A133
THE CHILDREN'S CENTER REHABILITATION HOSPITAL, BETHANY, OK, p. A497
THE CHILDREN'S HOME OF PITTSBURGH, PITTSBURGH, PA, p. A537
THE CHILDREN'S INSTITUTE OF PITTSBURGH, PITTSBURGH, PA, p. A537
THE COLONY ER HOSPITAL, THE COLONY, TX, p. A640
THE CONNECTICUT HOSPICE, BRANFORD, CT, p. A107
THE CORE INSTITUTE SPECIALTY HOSPITAL, PHOENIX, AZ, p. A34
THE HEALTHCENTER, KALISPELL, MT, p. A378
THE HOSPITAL AT WESTLAKE MEDICAL CENTER, AUSTIN, TX, p. A586
THE HOSPITAL OF CENTRAL CONNECTICUT, NEW BRITAIN, CT, p. A109
THE HOSPITALS OF PROVIDENCE EAST CAMPUS, EL PASO, TX, p. A602
THE HOSPITALS OF PROVIDENCE MEMORIAL CAMPUS, EL PASO, TX, p. A602
THE HOSPITALS OF PROVIDENCE SIERRA CAMPUS, EL PASO, TX, p. A603
THE HOSPITALS OF PROVIDENCE TRANSMOUNTAIN CAMPUS, EL PASO, TX, p. A603
THE HSC PEDIATRIC CENTER, WASHINGTON, DC, p. A116
THE JEWISH HOSPITAL – MERCY HEALTH, CINCINNATI, OH, p. A476
THE MEDICAL CENTER ALBANY, ALBANY, KY, p. A249
THE MEDICAL CENTER AT CAVERNA, HORSE CAVE, KY, p. A253
THE MEDICAL CENTER OF SOUTHEAST TEXAS, PORT ARTHUR, TX, p. A630
THE METHODIST HOSPITAL, HOUSTON, TEXAS (see HOUSTON METHODIST HOSPITAL), p. A614
THE NEUROMEDICAL CENTER REHABILITATION HOSPITAL, BATON ROUGE, LA, p. A264
THE ORTHOPEDIC SPECIALTY HOSPITAL, MURRAY, UT, p. A649
THE OUTER BANKS HOSPITAL, NAGS HEAD, NC, p. A450
THE PAVILION, CHAMPAIGN, IL, p. A175
THE PAVILION AT WILLIAMSBURG PLACE, WILLIAMSBURG, VA, p. A669
THE PHYSICIANS CENTRE HOSPITAL, BRYAN, TX, p. A590
THE QUEEN'S MEDICAL CENTER, HONOLULU, HI, p. A165
THE REHABILITATION INSTITUTE OF ST. LOUIS, SAINT LOUIS, MO, p. A371
THE UNIVERSITY OF KANSAS HOSPITAL, KANSAS CITY, KS, p. A238
THE UNIVERSITY OF TOLEDO MEDICAL CENTER, TOLEDO, OH, p. A492
THE UNIVERSITY OF VERMONT HEALTH NETWORK – ALICE HYDE MEDICAL CENTER, MALONE, NEW YORK (see JAMES J. PETERS VETERANS AFFAIRS MEDICAL CENTER), p. A430
THE UNIVERSITY OF VERMONT HEALTH NETWORK CENTRAL VERMONT MEDICAL CENTER, BERLIN, VT, p. A654
THE UNIVERSITY OF VERMONT HEALTH NETWORK ELIZABETHTOWN COMMUNITY HOSPITAL, ELIZABETHTOWN, NY, p. A427
THE UNIVERSITY OF VERMONT HEALTH NETWORK–CHAMPLAIN VALLEY PHYSICIANS HOSPITAL, PLATTSBURGH, NY, p. A441
THE VILLAGES REGIONAL HOSPITAL, THE VILLAGES, FL, p. A142
THE VINES, OCALA, FL, p. A133
THE WILLIAM W. BACKUS HOSPITAL, NORWICH, CT, p. A110
THE WILLOUGH AT NAPLES, NAPLES, FL, p. A132
THE WOMEN'S HOSPITAL, NEWBURGH, IN, p. A213
THE WOODS AT PARKSIDE, GAHANNA, OH, p. A483
THEDA CARE MEDICAL CENTER – WILD ROSE, WILD ROSE, WI, p. A708
THEDACARE MEDICAL CENTER–BERLIN, BERLIN, WI, p. A692
THEDACARE MEDICAL CENTER–NEW LONDON, NEW LONDON, WI, p. A702
THEDACARE MEDICAL CENTER–SHAWANO, SHAWANO, WI, p. A705
THEDACARE MEDICAL CENTER–WAUPACA, WAUPACA, WI, p. A707
THEDACARE REGIONAL MEDICAL CENTER–APPLETON, APPLETON, WI, p. A691
THEDACARE REGIONAL MEDICAL CENTER–NEENAH, NEENAH, WI, p. A702

THIBODAUX REGIONAL MEDICAL CENTER, THIBODAUX, LA, p. A279
THOMAS B. FINAN CENTER, CUMBERLAND, MD, p. A290
THOMAS H. BOYD MEMORIAL HOSPITAL, CARROLLTON, IL, p. A175
THOMAS HOSPITAL, FAIRHOPE, AL, p. A18
THOMAS JEFFERSON UNIVERSITY HOSPITALS, PHILADELPHIA, PA, p. A536
THOMAS MEMORIAL HOSPITAL, SOUTH CHARLESTON, WV, p. A689
THOMPSON HEALTH, CANANDAIGUA, NEW YORK (see F. F. THOMPSON HOSPITAL), p. A425
THOREK MEMORIAL HOSPITAL, CHICAGO, IL, p. A180
THREE GABLES SURGERY CENTER, PROCTORVILLE, OH, p. A490
THREE RIVERS BEHAVIORAL HEALTH, WEST COLUMBIA, SC, p. A558
THREE RIVERS HEALTH, THREE RIVERS, MI, p. A323
THREE RIVERS HOSPITAL, BREWSTER, WA, p. A671
THREE RIVERS HOSPITAL, WAVERLY, TN, p. A580
THREE RIVERS MEDICAL CENTER, LOUISA, KY, p. A255
THROCKMORTON COUNTY MEMORIAL HOSPITAL, THROCKMORTON, TX, p. A641
TIDELANDS GEORGETOWN MEMORIAL HOSPITAL, GEORGETOWN, SC, p. A553
TIDELANDS WACCAMAW COMMUNITY HOSPITAL, MURRELLS INLET, SC, p. A556
TIFT REGIONAL MEDICAL CENTER, TIFTON, GA, p. A162
TIMPANOGOS REGIONAL HOSPITAL, OREM, UT, p. A650
TIOGA MEDICAL CENTER, TIOGA, ND, p. A469
TIPPAH COUNTY HOSPITAL, RIPLEY, MS, p. A354
TIPTON HOSPITAL, TIPTON, INDIANA (see INDIANA UNIVERSITY HEALTH TIPTON HOSPITAL), p. A215
TIRR MEMORIAL HERMANN, HOUSTON, TX, p. A614
TITUS REGIONAL MEDICAL CENTER, MOUNT PLEASANT, TX, p. A625
TITUSVILLE AREA HOSPITAL, TITUSVILLE, PA, p. A542
TMC BONHAM HOSPITAL, BONHAM, TX, p. A589
TMC FOR CHILDREN, TUCSON, ARIZONA (see TMC HEALTHCARE), p. A38
TMC HEALTHCARE, TUCSON, AZ, p. A38
TOBEY HOSPITAL, WAREHAM, MASSACHUSETTS (see SOUTHCOAST HOSPITALS GROUP), p. A304
TOMAH MEMORIAL HOSPITAL, TOMAH, WI, p. A706
TOPS SURGICAL SPECIALTY HOSPITAL, HOUSTON, TX, p. A614
TORRANCE MEMORIAL MEDICAL CENTER, TORRANCE, CA, p. A92
TORRANCE STATE HOSPITAL, TORRANCE, PA, p. A542
TOUCHETTE REGIONAL HOSPITAL, CENTREVILLE, IL, p. A175
TOURO INFIRMARY, NEW ORLEANS, LA, p. A276
TOWNER COUNTY MEDICAL CENTER, CANDO, ND, p. A465
TRACE REGIONAL HOSPITAL, HOUSTON, MS, p. A348
TRANSYLVANIA REGIONAL HOSPITAL, BREVARD, NC, p. A450
TREASURE VALLEY HOSPITAL, BOISE, ID, p. A168
TREGO COUNTY–LEMKE MEMORIAL HOSPITAL, WAKEENEY, KS, p. A247
TRENTON PSYCHIATRIC HOSPITAL, TRENTON, NJ, p. A413
TRI PARISH REHABILITATION HOSPITAL, LEESVILLE, LA, p. A272
TRI VALLEY HEALTH SYSTEM, CAMBRIDGE, NE, p. A383
TRI-CITY MEDICAL CENTER, OCEANSIDE, CA, p. A75
TRI-COUNTY HOSPITAL, WADENA, MN, p. A342
TRI-STATE MEMORIAL HOSPITAL, CLARKSTON, WA, p. A671
TRI-WARD GENERAL HOSPITAL, BERNICE, LOUISIANA (see REEVES MEMORIAL MEDICAL CENTER), p. A264
TRIANGLE EAST NURSING CARE CENTER, WILSON, NORTH CAROLINA (see WILMED NURSING CARE CENTER), p. A464
TRIANGLE SPRINGS HOSPITAL, RALEIGH, NC, p. A460
TRIDENT MEDICAL CENTER, CHARLESTON, SC, p. A550
TRIGG COUNTY HOSPITAL, CADIZ, KY, p. A250
TRIHEALTH EVENDALE HOSPITAL, CINCINNATI, OH, p. A476
TRIHEALTH REHABILITATION HOSPITAL, CINCINNATI, OH, p. A477
TRINITAS REGIONAL MEDICAL CENTER, ELIZABETH, NJ, p. A405
TRINITY HEALTH, MINOT, ND, p. A469
TRINITY HEALTH SYSTEM, STEUBENVILLE, OH, p. A491
TRINITY HOSPITAL, WEAVERVILLE, CA, p. A94
TRINITY HOSPITAL, WOLF POINT, MT, p. A381
TRINITY HOSPITAL TWIN CITY, DENNISON, OH, p. A482
TRIOS HEALTH, KENNEWICK, WA, p. A674
TRIPLER ARMY MEDICAL CENTER, HONOLULU, HI, p. A165
TRISTAR ASHLAND CITY MEDICAL CENTER, ASHLAND CITY, TN, p. A566
TRISTAR CENTENNIAL MEDICAL CENTER, NASHVILLE, TN, p. A577
TRISTAR GREENVIEW REGIONAL HOSPITAL, BOWLING GREEN, KY, p. A250

TRISTAR HENDERSONVILLE MEDICAL CENTER, HENDERSONVILLE, TN, p. A570
TRISTAR HORIZON MEDICAL CENTER, DICKSON, TN, p. A569
TRISTAR SKYLINE MEDICAL CENTER, NASHVILLE, TN, p. A577
TRISTAR SOUTHERN HILLS MEDICAL CENTER, NASHVILLE, TN, p. A577
TRISTAR STONECREST MEDICAL CENTER, SMYRNA, TN, p. A579
TRISTAR SUMMIT MEDICAL CENTER, HERMITAGE, TN, p. A570
TRIUMPH HOSPITAL – CENTRAL DAKOTAS, MANDAN, NORTH DAKOTA (see VIBRA HOSPITAL OF CENTRAL DAKOTAS), p. A468
TRIUMPH HOSPITAL EL PASO, EL PASO, TEXAS (see KINDRED HOSPITAL EL PASO), p. A603
TRIUMPH HOSPITAL LIMA, LIMA, OHIO (see KINDRED HOSPITAL LIMA), p. A485
TRIUMPH HOSPITAL NORTHWEST, HOUSTON, TEXAS (see KINDRED HOSPITAL SPRING), p. A614
TRIUMPH HOSPITAL NORTHWEST INDIANA, HAMMOND, INDIANA (see KINDRED HOSPITAL NORTHWEST INDIANA), p. A206
TRIUMPH HOSPITAL PHILADELPHIA, PHILADELPHIA, PENNSYLVANIA (see KINDRED HOSPITAL SOUTH PHILADELPHIA), p. A536
TRIUMPH HOSPITAL SOUTHWEST, SUGAR LAND, TEXAS (see KINDRED HOSPITAL SUGAR LAND), p. A638
TROUSDALE MEDICAL CENTER, HARTSVILLE, TN, p. A570
TROY REGIONAL MEDICAL CENTER, TROY, AL, p. A23
TRUMAN MEDICAL CENTER–HOSPITAL HILL, KANSAS CITY, MO, p. A363
TRUMAN MEDICAL CENTER–LAKEWOOD, KANSAS CITY, MO, p. A363
TRUMBULL MEMORIAL HOSPITAL, WARREN, OH, p. A493
TRUSTPOINT HOSPITAL, MURFREESBORO, TN, p. A576
TRUSTPOINT REHABILITATION HOSPITAL OF LUBBOCK, LUBBOCK, TX, p. A622
TSEHOOTSOOI MEDICAL CENTER, FORT DEFIANCE, AZ, p. A29
TUALITY FOREST GROVE HOSPITAL, FOREST GROVE, OREGON (see TUALITY HEALTHCARE), p. A513
TUALITY HEALTHCARE, HILLSBORO, OR, p. A513
TUBA CITY REGIONAL HEALTH CARE CORPORATION, TUBA CITY, AZ, p. A37
TUFTS MEDICAL CENTER, BOSTON, MA, p. A296
TUG VALLEY ARH REGIONAL MEDICAL CENTER, SOUTH WILLIAMSON, KY, p. A260
TULANE HEALTH SYSTEM, NEW ORLEANS, LA, p. A276
TULSA SPINE AND SPECIALTY HOSPITAL, TULSA, OK, p. A510
TURNING POINT HOSPITAL, MOULTRIE, GA, p. A158
TURQUOISE LODGE HOSPITAL, ALBUQUERQUE, NM, p. A417
TUSCALOOSA VETERANS AFFAIRS MEDICAL CENTER, TUSCALOOSA, AL, p. A24
TUSKEGEE DIVISION, TUSKEGEE, ALABAMA (see CENTRAL ALABAMA VETERANS HEALTH CARE SYSTEM), p. A24
TWELVE CLANS UNITY HOSPITAL, WINNEBAGO, NE, p. A392
TWIN CITIES COMMUNITY HOSPITAL, TEMPLETON, CA, p. A91
TWIN CITIES HOSPITAL, NICEVILLE, FL, p. A133
TWIN COUNTY REGIONAL HEALTHCARE, GALAX, VA, p. A660
TWIN LAKES REGIONAL MEDICAL CENTER, LEITCHFIELD, KY, p. A254
TWIN VALLEY BEHAVIORAL HEALTHCARE, COLUMBUS, OH, p. A480
TWO RIVERS BEHAVIORAL HEALTH SYSTEM, KANSAS CITY, MO, p. A363
TYLER CONTINUECARE HOSPITAL, TYLER, TX, p. A642
TYLER COUNTY HOSPITAL, WOODVILLE, TX, p. A646
TYLER HOLMES MEMORIAL HOSPITAL, WINONA, MS, p. A355
TYLER MEMORIAL HOSPITAL, TUNKHANNOCK, PA, p. A542
TYRONE HOSPITAL, TYRONE, PA, p. A542

U

U. S. AIR FORCE HOSPITAL, HAMPTON, VA, p. A660
U. S. AIR FORCE MEDICAL CENTER KEESLER, KEESLER AFB, MS, p. A349
U. S. AIR FORCE REGIONAL HOSPITAL, EGLIN AFB, FL, p. A122
U. S. AIR FORCE REGIONAL HOSPITAL, ELMENDORF AFB, AK, p. A26
U. S. NAVAL HOSPITAL GUAM, AGANA, GU, p. A714
U. S. PENITENTIARY INFIRMARY, LEWISBURG, PA, p. A530

U. S. PUBLIC HEALTH SERVICE INDIAN HOSPITAL, CASS LAKE, MN, p. A330
U. S. PUBLIC HEALTH SERVICE INDIAN HOSPITAL, CROWNPOINT, NM, p. A417
U. S. PUBLIC HEALTH SERVICE INDIAN HOSPITAL, EAGLE BUTTE, SD, p. A560
U. S. PUBLIC HEALTH SERVICE INDIAN HOSPITAL, PARKER, AZ, p. A32
U. S. PUBLIC HEALTH SERVICE INDIAN HOSPITAL, PINE RIDGE, SD, p. A562
U. S. PUBLIC HEALTH SERVICE INDIAN HOSPITAL, ROSEBUD, SD, p. A563
U. S. PUBLIC HEALTH SERVICE INDIAN HOSPITAL, ZUNI, NM, p. A421
U. S. PUBLIC HEALTH SERVICE INDIAN HOSPITAL–SELLS, SELLS, AZ, p. A36
U. S. PUBLIC HEALTH SERVICE INDIAN HOSPITAL–WHITERIVER, WHITERIVER, AZ, p. A38
U. S. PUBLIC HEALTH SERVICE PHOENIX INDIAN MEDICAL CENTER, PHOENIX, AZ, p. A34
UAB HIGHLANDS, BIRMINGHAM, ALABAMA (see UNIVERSITY OF ALABAMA HOSPITAL), p. A15
UAMS MEDICAL CENTER, LITTLE ROCK, AR, p. A45
UC IRVINE MEDICAL CENTER, ORANGE, CA, p. A76
UC SAN DIEGO HEALTH, SAN DIEGO, CA, p. A84
UCHEALTH BROOMFIELD HOSPITAL, BROOMFIELD, CO, p. A97
UCHEALTH GRANDVIEW HOSPITAL, COLORADO SPRINGS, CO, p. A98
UCHEALTH LONGS PEAK HOSPITAL, LONGMONT, CO, p. A103
UCHEALTH MEDICAL CENTER OF THE ROCKIES, LOVELAND, CO, p. A104
UCHEALTH MEMORIAL HOSPITAL, COLORADO SPRINGS, CO, p. A98
UCHEALTH POUDRE VALLEY HOSPITAL, FORT COLLINS, CO, p. A100
UCHEALTH YAMPA VALLEY MEDICAL CENTER, STEAMBOAT SPRINGS, CO, p. A105
UCLA MEDICAL CENTER–SANTA MONICA, SANTA MONICA, CA, p. A89
UCONN, JOHN DEMPSEY HOSPITAL, FARMINGTON, CT, p. A108
UCSF BENIOFF CHILDREN'S HOSPITAL OAKLAND, OAKLAND, CA, p. A75
UCSF MEDICAL CENTER, SAN FRANCISCO, CA, p. A86
UF HEALTH JACKSONVILLE, JACKSONVILLE, FL, p. A126
UF HEALTH REHAB HOSPITAL, GAINESVILLE, FL, p. A124
UF HEALTH SHANDS HOSPITAL, GAINESVILLE, FL, p. A124
UH AVON REHABILITATION HOSPITAL, AVON, OH, p. A472
UH PORTAGE MEDICAL CENTER, RAVENNA, OH, p. A490
UH REGIONAL HOSPITALS, CLEVELAND, OH, p. A478
UH REHABILITATION HOSPITAL, BEACHWOOD, OH, p. A473
UHS CHENANGO MEMORIAL HOSPITAL, NORWICH, NY, p. A440
UHS DELAWARE VALLEY HOSPITAL, WALTON, NY, p. A446
UINTAH BASIN MEDICAL CENTER, ROOSEVELT, UT, p. A651
UKIAH VALLEY MEDICAL CENTER, UKIAH, CA, p. A93
UMASS MEMORIAL HEALTHALLIANCE–CLINTON HOSPITAL, LEOMINSTER, MA, p. A300
UMASS MEMORIAL MEDICAL CENTER, WORCESTER, MA, p. A305
UMASS MEMORIAL–MARLBOROUGH HOSPITAL, MARLBOROUGH, MA, p. A300
UNC LENOIR HEALTHCARE, KINSTON, NC, p. A457
UNC REX HEALTH CARE, RALEIGH, NC, p. A460
UNC ROCKINGHAM HEALTH CARE, EDEN, NC, p. A453
UNICOI COUNTY MEMORIAL HOSPITAL, ERWIN, TN, p. A569
UNION CAMPUS, LYNN, MASSACHUSETTS (see NORTH SHORE MEDICAL CENTER), p. A300
UNION COUNTY GENERAL HOSPITAL, CLAYTON, NM, p. A417
UNION COUNTY HOSPITAL, ANNA, IL, p. A173
UNION GENERAL HOSPITAL, BLAIRSVILLE, GA, p. A148
UNION GENERAL HOSPITAL, FARMERVILLE, LA, p. A267
UNION HOSPITAL, ELKTON, MD, p. A290
UNION HOSPITAL, LYNN, MASSACHUSETTS (see UNION CAMPUS), p. A300
UNION HOSPITAL, TERRE HAUTE, IN, p. A215
UNION HOSPITAL CLINTON, CLINTON, IN, p. A201
UNION MEDICAL CENTER, UNION, SC, p. A558
UNION MEMORIAL HOSPITAL, BALTIMORE, MARYLAND (see MEDSTAR UNION MEMORIAL HOSPITAL), p. A287
UNIONTOWN HOSPITAL, UNIONTOWN, PA, p. A543
UNITED HEALTH SERVICES HOSPITALS–BINGHAMTON, BINGHAMTON, NY, p. A424
UNITED HOSPITAL, SAINT PAUL, MN, p. A340
UNITED HOSPITAL CENTER, BRIDGEPORT, WV, p. A683
UNITED HOSPITAL DISTRICT, BLUE EARTH, MN, p. A328
UNITED MEDICAL CENTER, WASHINGTON, DC, p. A116

UNITED MEDICAL REHABILITATION HOSPITAL, GRETNA, LA, p. A268
UNITED MEDICAL REHABILITATION HOSPITAL, HAMMOND, LA, p. A268
UNITED MEMORIAL MEDICAL CARE, HOUSTON, TX, p. A614
UNITED MEMORIAL MEDICAL CENTER, BATAVIA, NY, p. A423
UNITED REGIONAL HEALTH CARE SYSTEM, WICHITA FALLS, TX, p. A646
UNITY HEALTH CENTER, SHAWNEE, OKLAHOMA (see SSM HEALTH ST. ANTHONY HOSPITAL – SHAWNEE), p. A507
UNITY HEALTH WHITE COUNTY MEDICAL CENTER, SEARCY, AR, p. A48
UNITY HOSPITAL, ROCHESTER, NY, p. A443
UNITY MEDICAL & SURGICAL HOSPITAL, MISHAWAKA, IN, p. A211
UNITY MEDICAL CENTER, GRAFTON, ND, p. A467
UNITY MEDICAL CENTER, MANCHESTER, TN, p. A573
UNITY PSYCHIATRIC CARE–CLARKSVILLE, CLARKSVILLE, TN, p. A568
UNITY PSYCHIATRIC CARE–COLUMBIA, COLUMBIA, TN, p. A568
UNITY PSYCHIATRIC CARE–HUNTSVILLE, HUNTSVILLE, AL, p. A19
UNITY PSYCHIATRIC CARE–MARTIN, MARTIN, TN, p. A573
UNITYPOINT HEALTH – ALLEN HOSPITAL, WATERLOO, IA, p. A231
UNITYPOINT HEALTH – FINLEY HOSPITAL, DUBUQUE, IA, p. A222
UNITYPOINT HEALTH – GRINNELL REGIONAL MEDICAL CENTER, GRINNELL, IA, p. A223
UNITYPOINT HEALTH – IOWA METHODIST MEDICAL CENTER, DES MOINES, IA, p. A221
UNITYPOINT HEALTH – JONES REGIONAL MEDICAL CENTER, ANAMOSA, IA, p. A217
UNITYPOINT HEALTH – MARSHALLTOWN, MARSHALLTOWN, IA, p. A226
UNITYPOINT HEALTH – PEORIA, PEORIA, IL, p. A193
UNITYPOINT HEALTH – PROCTOR, PEORIA, IL, p. A193
UNITYPOINT HEALTH – ST. LUKES'S SIOUX CITY, SIOUX CITY, IA, p. A230
UNITYPOINT HEALTH – ST. LUKE'S HOSPITAL, CEDAR RAPIDS, IA, p. A218
UNITYPOINT HEALTH – TRINITY BETTENDORF, BETTENDORF, IA, p. A217
UNITYPOINT HEALTH – TRINITY MOLINE, MOLINE, ILLINOIS (see UNITYPOINT HEALTH – TRINITY ROCK ISLAND), p. A189
UNITYPOINT HEALTH – TRINITY MUSCATINE, MUSCATINE, IA, p. A227
UNITYPOINT HEALTH – TRINITY REGIONAL MEDICAL CENTER, FORT DODGE, IA, p. A222
UNITYPOINT HEALTH – TRINITY ROCK ISLAND, ROCK ISLAND, IL, p. A194
UNITYPOINT HEALTH MERITER, MADISON, WI, p. A698
UNITYPOINT HEALTH–IOWA LUTHERAN HOSPITAL, DES MOINES, IA, p. A221
UNITYPOINT HEALTH–KEOKUK, KEOKUK, IA, p. A225
UNITYPOINT HEALTH–PEKIN HOSPITAL, PEKIN, IL, p. A193
UNIVERSITY BEHAVIORAL HEALTH OF DENTON, DENTON, TX, p. A599
UNIVERSITY HEALTH SYSTEM, SAN ANTONIO, TX, p. A635
UNIVERSITY HOSPITAL, AUGUSTA, GA, p. A147
UNIVERSITY HOSPITAL, MADISON, WI, p. A698
UNIVERSITY HOSPITAL, NEWARK, NJ, p. A409
UNIVERSITY HOSPITAL, SAN JUAN, PR, p. A719
UNIVERSITY HOSPITAL AND CLINICS, LAFAYETTE, LA, p. A271
UNIVERSITY HOSPITAL AND MEDICAL CENTER, TAMARAC, FL, p. A141
UNIVERSITY HOSPITAL MCDUFFIE, THOMSON, GA, p. A161
UNIVERSITY HOSPITAL SCHOOL, IOWA CITY, IOWA (see CENTER FOR DISABILITIES AND DEVELOPMENT), p. A224
UNIVERSITY HOSPITAL SUMMERVILLE, AUGUSTA, GA, p. A147
UNIVERSITY HOSPITALS AHUJA MEDICAL CENTER, BEACHWOOD, OH, p. A473
UNIVERSITY HOSPITALS CLEVELAND MEDICAL CENTER, CLEVELAND, OH, p. A478
UNIVERSITY HOSPITALS CONNEAUT MEDICAL CENTER, CONNEAUT, OH, p. A480
UNIVERSITY HOSPITALS ELYRIA MEDICAL CENTER, ELYRIA, OH, p. A482
UNIVERSITY HOSPITALS GEAUGA MEDICAL CENTER, CHARDON, OH, p. A475
UNIVERSITY HOSPITALS GENEVA MEDICAL CENTER, GENEVA, OH, p. A484
UNIVERSITY HOSPITALS PARMA MEDICAL CENTER, PARMA, OH, p. A489
UNIVERSITY HOSPITALS SAMARITAN MEDICAL CENTER, ASHLAND, OH, p. A472

UNIVERSITY MEDICAL CENTER, LAS VEGAS, NV, p. A396
UNIVERSITY MEDICAL CENTER, LUBBOCK, TX, p. A622
UNIVERSITY MEDICAL CENTER, NEW ORLEANS, LA, p. A275
UNIVERSITY MEDICAL CENTER AT PRINCETON, PLAINSBORO, NEW JERSEY (see PENN MEDICINE PRINCETON MEDICAL CENTER), p. A411
UNIVERSITY MEDICAL CENTER OF EL PASO, EL PASO, TX, p. A603
UNIVERSITY OF ALABAMA HOSPITAL, BIRMINGHAM, AL, p. A15
UNIVERSITY OF CALIFORNIA SAN DIEGO MEDICAL CENTER, SAN DIEGO, CA, p. A84
UNIVERSITY OF CALIFORNIA, DAVIS MEDICAL CENTER, SACRAMENTO, CA, p. A82
UNIVERSITY OF CHICAGO MEDICAL CENTER, CHICAGO, IL, p. A180
UNIVERSITY OF CINCINNATI MEDICAL CENTER, CINCINNATI, OH, p. A477
UNIVERSITY OF COLORADO HOSPITAL, AURORA, CO, p. A96
UNIVERSITY OF ILLINOIS HOSPITAL & HEALTH SCIENCES SYSTEM, CHICAGO, IL, p. A180
UNIVERSITY OF IOWA HOSPITALS AND CLINICS, IOWA CITY, IA, p. A224
UNIVERSITY OF KANSAS HEALTH SYSTEM GREAT BEND CAMPUS, GREAT BEND, KS, p. A235
UNIVERSITY OF KANSAS HEALTH SYSTEM PAWNEE VALLEY CAMPUS, LARNED, KS, p. A239
UNIVERSITY OF KANSAS HEALTH SYSTEM ST. FRANCIS CAMPUS, TOPEKA, KS, p. A246
UNIVERSITY OF KENTUCKY ALBERT B. CHANDLER HOSPITAL, LEXINGTON, KY, p. A255
UNIVERSITY OF KENTUCKY HOSPITAL, LEXINGTON, KENTUCKY (see UNIVERSITY OF KENTUCKY ALBERT B. CHANDLER HOSPITAL), p. A255
UNIVERSITY OF LOUISVILLE HOSPITAL, LOUISVILLE, KY, p. A257
UNIVERSITY OF MARYLAND BALTIMORE WASHINGTON MEDICAL CENTER, GLEN BURNIE, MD, p. A291
UNIVERSITY OF MARYLAND CAPITAL REGION HEALTH PRINCE GEORGE'S HOSPITAL CENTER, CHEVERLY, MD, p. A289
UNIVERSITY OF MARYLAND CHARLES REGIONAL MEDICAL CENTER, LA PLATA, MD, p. A291
UNIVERSITY OF MARYLAND HARFORD MEMORIAL HOSPITAL, HAVRE DE GRACE, MD, p. A291
UNIVERSITY OF MARYLAND MEDICAL CENTER, BALTIMORE, MD, p. A287
UNIVERSITY OF MARYLAND MEDICAL CENTER MIDTOWN CAMPUS, BALTIMORE, MD, p. A287
UNIVERSITY OF MARYLAND REHABILITATION & ORTHOPAEDIC INSTITUTE, BALTIMORE, MD, p. A288
UNIVERSITY OF MARYLAND SHORE MEDICAL CENTER AT CHESTERTOWN, CHESTERTOWN, MD, p. A289
UNIVERSITY OF MARYLAND SHORE MEDICAL CENTER AT DORCHESTER, CAMBRIDGE, MD, p. A289
UNIVERSITY OF MARYLAND SHORE MEDICAL CENTER AT EASTON, EASTON, MD, p. A290
UNIVERSITY OF MARYLAND ST. JOSEPH MEDICAL CENTER, TOWSON, MD, p. A293
UNIVERSITY OF MARYLAND UPPER CHESAPEAKE MEDICAL CENTER, BEL AIR, MD, p. A288
UNIVERSITY OF MIAMI HOSPITAL AND CLINICS, MIAMI, FL, p. A131
UNIVERSITY OF MINNESOTA HOSPITAL AND CLINIC, MINNEAPOLIS, MINNESOTA (see UNIVERSITY OF MINNESOTA MEDICAL CENTER, FAIRVIEW), p. A336
UNIVERSITY OF MINNESOTA MEDICAL CENTER, FAIRVIEW, MINNEAPOLIS, MN, p. A336
UNIVERSITY OF MISSISSIPPI MEDICAL CENTER, JACKSON, MS, p. A349
UNIVERSITY OF MISSISSIPPI MEDICAL CENTER GRENADA, GRENADA, MS, p. A347
UNIVERSITY OF MISSISSIPPI MEDICAL CENTER HOLMES COUNTY, LEXINGTON, MS, p. A350
UNIVERSITY OF MISSOURI HEALTH CARE, COLUMBIA, MO, p. A359
UNIVERSITY OF NEW MEXICO HOSPITALS, ALBUQUERQUE, NM, p. A417
UNIVERSITY OF NORTH CAROLINA HOSPITALS, CHAPEL HILL, NC, p. A451
UNIVERSITY OF TENNESSEE MEDICAL CENTER, KNOXVILLE, TN, p. A572
UNIVERSITY OF TEXAS HARRIS COUNTY PSYCHIATRIC CENTER, HOUSTON, TX, p. A614
UNIVERSITY OF TEXAS M.D. ANDERSON CANCER CENTER, HOUSTON, TX, p. A614
UNIVERSITY OF TEXAS MEDICAL BRANCH, GALVESTON, TX, p. A607
UNIVERSITY OF TEXAS SOUTHWESTERN MEDICAL CENTER, DALLAS, TX, p. A598
UNIVERSITY OF UTAH HEALTH, SALT LAKE CITY, UT, p. A652

UNIVERSITY OF UTAH NEUROPSYCHIATRIC INSTITUTE, SALT LAKE CITY, UT, p. A652
UNIVERSITY OF VERMONT MEDICAL CENTER, BURLINGTON, VT, p. A654
UNIVERSITY OF VIRGINIA MEDICAL CENTER, CHARLOTTESVILLE, VA, p. A657
UNIVERSITY OF WASHINGTON MEDICAL CENTER, SEATTLE, WA, p. A678
UNIVERSITY PEDIATRIC HOSPITAL, RIO PIEDRAS, PR, p. A718
UNM SANDOVAL REGIONAL MEDICAL CENTER, INC., RIO RANCHO, NM, p. A419
UP HEALTH SYSTEM–BELL, ISHPEMING, MI, p. A315
UP HEALTH SYSTEM–MARQUETTE, MARQUETTE, MI, p. A317
UP HEALTH SYSTEM–PORTAGE, HANCOCK, MI, p. A314
UPLAND HILLS HEALTH, DODGEVILLE, WI, p. A693
UPMC ALTOONA, ALTOONA, PA, p. A520
UPMC BEDFORD MEMORIAL, EVERETT, PA, p. A526
UPMC CARLISLE, CARLISLE, PA, p. A522
UPMC CHAUTAUQUA WCA, JAMESTOWN, NY, p. A429
UPMC CHILDREN'S HOSPITAL OF PITTSBURGH, PITTSBURGH, PA, p. A538
UPMC COLE, COUDERSPORT, PA, p. A523
UPMC EAST, MONROEVILLE, PA, p. A532
UPMC HAMOT, ERIE, PA, p. A525
UPMC HANOVER, HANOVER, PA, p. A526
UPMC HORIZON, FARRELL, PA, p. A526
UPMC JAMESON, NEW CASTLE, PA, p. A533
UPMC KANE, KANE, PA, p. A528
UPMC LITITZ, LITITZ, PA, p. A530
UPMC MAGEE–WOMENS HOSPITAL, PITTSBURGH, PA, p. A538
UPMC MCKEESPORT, MCKEESPORT, PA, p. A531
UPMC MEMORIAL, YORK, PA, p. A546
UPMC MERCY, PITTSBURGH, PA, p. A538
UPMC MONTEFIORE, PITTSBURGH, PENNSYLVANIA (see UPMC PRESBYTERIAN), p. A538
UPMC NORTHWEST, SENECA, PA, p. A541
UPMC PASSAVANT, PITTSBURGH, PA, p. A538
UPMC PASSAVANT CRANBERRY, CRANBERRY, PENNSYLVANIA (see UPMC PASSAVANT), p. A523
UPMC PINNACLE HARRISBURG, HARRISBURG, PA, p. A527
UPMC PRESBYTERIAN, PITTSBURGH, PA, p. A538
UPMC SOMERSET HOSPITAL, SOMERSET, PA, p. A541
UPMC ST. MARGARET, PITTSBURGH, PA, p. A538
UPMC SUSQUEHANNA DIVINE PROVIDENCE CAMPUS, WILLIAMSPORT, PA, p. A545
UPMC SUSQUEHANNA LOCK HAVEN, LOCK HAVEN, PA, p. A530
UPMC SUSQUEHANNA MUNCY, MUNCY, PA, p. A532
UPMC SUSQUEHANNA SOLDIERS + SAILORS, WELLSBORO, PA, p. A544
UPMC SUSQUEHANNA SUNBURY, SUNBURY, PA, p. A542
UPMC SUSQUEHANNA WILLIAMSPORT, WILLIAMSPORT, PA, p. A545
UPPER CONNECTICUT VALLEY HOSPITAL, COLEBROOK, NH, p. A399
UPPER VALLEY MEDICAL CENTER, TROY, OH, p. A492
UPSON REGIONAL MEDICAL CENTER, THOMASTON, GA, p. A161
UPSTATE UNIVERSITY HOSPITAL, SYRACUSE, NY, p. A445
USA CHILDREN'S AND WOMEN'S HOSPITAL, MOBILE, AL, p. A20
USA HEALTH UNIVERSITY HOSPITAL, MOBILE, AL, p. A21
USC NORRIS COMPREHENSIVE CANCER CENTER, LOS ANGELES, CA, p. A69
USC UNIVERSITY HOSPITAL, LOS ANGELES, CA, p. A70
USC VERDUGO HILLS HOSPITAL, GLENDALE, CA, p. A60
USMD HOSPITAL AT ARLINGTON, ARLINGTON, TX, p. A584
USMD HOSPITAL AT FORT WORTH, FORT WORTH, TX, p. A606
UT HEALTH ATHENS, ATHENS, TX, p. A584
UT HEALTH CARTHAGE, CARTHAGE, TX, p. A591
UT HEALTH HENDERSON, HENDERSON, TX, p. A610
UT HEALTH JACKSONVILLE, JACKSONVILLE, TX, p. A616
UT HEALTH NORTH CAMPUS TYLER, TYLER, TX, p. A642
UT HEALTH PITTSBURG, PITTSBURG, TX, p. A628
UT HEALTH QUITMAN, QUITMAN, TX, p. A630
UT HEALTH REHABILITATION HOSPITAL, TYLER, TX, p. A642
UT HEALTH SPECIALTY HOSPITAL, TYLER, TX, p. A642
UT HEALTH TYLER, TYLER, TX, p. A642
UTAH STATE HOSPITAL, PROVO, UT, p. A650
UTAH VALLEY HOSPITAL, PROVO, UT, p. A651
UTAH VALLEY SPECIALTY HOSPITAL, PROVO, UT, p. A651
UVA TRANSITIONAL CARE HOSPITAL, CHARLOTTESVILLE, VA, p. A657
UVA–HEALTHSOUTH REHABILITATION HOSPITAL, CHARLOTTESVILLE, VA, p. A657
UVALDE MEMORIAL HOSPITAL, UVALDE, TX, p. A643
UW HEALTH REHABILITATION HOSPITAL, MADISON, WI, p. A699

UW MEDICINE/HARBORVIEW MEDICAL CENTER, SEATTLE, WA, p. A678
UW MEDICINE/NORTHWEST HOSPITAL & MEDICAL CENTER, SEATTLE, WA, p. A678
UW MEDICINE/VALLEY MEDICAL CENTER, RENTON, WA, p. A677

V

VA GREATER LOS ANGELES HEALTHCARE SYSTEM, LOS ANGELES, CA, p. A70
VA LONG BEACH HEALTHCARE SYSTEM, LONG BEACH, CA, p. A65
VA MEDICAL CENTER, TOMAH, WI, p. A706
VA PALO ALTO HEALTH CARE SYSTEM, PALO ALTO, CA, p. A77
VA PORTLAND HEALTHCARE SYSTEM, PORTLAND, OR, p. A516
VA SAN DIEGO HEALTHCARE SYSTEM, SAN DIEGO, CA, p. A84
VAIL HEALTH, VAIL, CO, p. A106
VAL VERDE REGIONAL MEDICAL CENTER, DEL RIO, TX, p. A599
VALIR REHABILITATION HOSPITAL, OKLAHOMA CITY, OK, p. A505
VALLE VISTA HEALTH SYSTEM, GREENWOOD, IN, p. A205
VALLEY BAPTIST MEDICAL CENTER–BROWNSVILLE, RIO HONDO, TX, p. A631
VALLEY BAPTIST MEDICAL CENTER–HARLINGEN, HARLINGEN, TX, p. A609
VALLEY BEHAVIORAL HEALTH SYSTEM, BARLING, AR, p. A39
VALLEY CHILDREN'S HEALTHCARE, MADERA, CA, p. A70
VALLEY COUNTY HEALTH SYSTEM, ORD, NE, p. A390
VALLEY FORGE MEDICAL CENTER AND HOSPITAL, NORRISTOWN, PA, p. A533
VALLEY HEALTH SHENANDOAH MEMORIAL HOSPITAL, WOODSTOCK, VA, p. A669
VALLEY HOSPITAL, RIDGEWOOD, NJ, p. A412
VALLEY HOSPITAL MEDICAL CENTER, LAS VEGAS, NV, p. A396
VALLEY HOSPITAL PHOENIX, PHOENIX, AZ, p. A34
VALLEY MEMORIAL, LIVERMORE, CA, p. A64
VALLEY PRESBYTERIAN HOSPITAL, LOS ANGELES, CA, p. A70
VALLEY REGIONAL HOSPITAL, CLAREMONT, NH, p. A399
VALLEY REGIONAL MEDICAL CENTER, BROWNSVILLE, TX, p. A590
VALLEY VIEW HOSPITAL, GLENWOOD SPRINGS, CO, p. A101
VALLEY VIEW MEDICAL CENTER, FORT MOHAVE, AZ, p. A29
VALOR HEALTH, EMMETT, ID, p. A169
VAN BUREN COUNTY HOSPITAL, KEOSAUQUA, IA, p. A225
VAN DIEST MEDICAL CENTER, WEBSTER CITY, IA, p. A231
VAN MATRE ENCOMPASS HEALTH, ROCKFORD, IL, p. A195
VAN WERT COUNTY HOSPITAL, VAN WERT, OH, p. A493
VANDERBILT PSYCHIATRIC HOSPITAL, NASHVILLE, TENNESSEE (see VANDERBILT UNIVERSITY MEDICAL CENTER), p. A577
VANDERBILT STALLWORTH REHABILITATION HOSPITAL, NASHVILLE, TN, p. A577
VANDERBILT UNIVERSITY MEDICAL CENTER, NASHVILLE, TN, p. A577
VANDERBILT WILSON COUNTY HOSPITAL, LEBANON, TN, p. A573
VANTAGE POINT OF NORTHWEST ARKANSAS, FAYETTEVILLE, AR, p. A41
VASSAR BROTHERS MEDICAL CENTER, POUGHKEEPSIE, NY, p. A442
VAUGHAN REGIONAL MEDICAL CENTER, SELMA, AL, p. A23
VCU HEALTH COMMUNITY MEMORIAL HOSPITAL, SOUTH HILL, VA, p. A667
VCU MEDICAL CENTER, RICHMOND, VA, p. A666
VENICE REGIONAL BAYFRONT HEALTH, VENICE, FL, p. A143
VENTURA COUNTY MEDICAL CENTER, VENTURA, CA, p. A93
VERDE VALLEY MEDICAL CENTER, COTTONWOOD, AZ, p. A29
VERITAS COLLABORATIVE, ATLANTA, GA, p. A147
VERITAS COLLABORATIVE, DURHAM, NC, p. A453
VERMILION BEHAVIORAL HEALTH SYSTEMS – NORTH CAMPUS, LAFAYETTE, LA, p. A271
VERMONT PSYCHIATRIC CARE HOSPITAL, BERLIN, VT, p. A654
VERNON MEMORIAL HEALTHCARE, ELK MOUND, WI, p. A694
VETERAN AFFAIRS HUDSON VALLEY HEALTH CARE SYSTEM–CASTLE POINT CAMPUS, WAPPINGERS, NEW YORK (see VETERANS AFFAIRS HUDSON VALLEY HEALTH CARE SYSTEM), p. A446

VETERANS AFFAIRS ANN ARBOR HEALTHCARE SYSTEM, ANN ARBOR, MI, p. A306

VETERANS AFFAIRS BLACK HILLS HEALTH CARE SYSTEM, FORT MEADE, SD, p. A561

VETERANS AFFAIRS BOSTON HEALTHCARE SYSTEM, WEST ROXBURY, MA, p. A304

VETERANS AFFAIRS BOSTON HEALTHCARE SYSTEM BROCKTON DIVISION, BROCKTON, MA, p. A297

VETERANS AFFAIRS CARIBBEAN HEALTHCARE SYSTEM, SAN JUAN, PR, p. A719

VETERANS AFFAIRS CENTRAL CALIFORNIA HEALTH CARE SYSTEM, FRESNO, CA, p. A60

VETERANS AFFAIRS CENTRAL IOWA HEALTH CARE SYSTEM, DES MOINES, IA, p. A221

VETERANS AFFAIRS CENTRAL WESTERN MASSACHUSETTS HEALTHCARE SYSTEM, LEEDS, MA, p. A300

VETERANS AFFAIRS CONNECTICUT HEALTHCARE SYSTEM, WEST HAVEN, CT, p. A112

VETERANS AFFAIRS EASTERN COLORADO HEALTH CARE SYSTEM, DENVER, CO, p. A99

VETERANS AFFAIRS EASTERN KANSAS HEALTH CARE SYSTEM, TOPEKA, KS, p. A246

VETERANS AFFAIRS EASTERN KANSAS HEALTH CARE SYSTEM–COLMERY-O'NEIL VETERANS AFFAIRS MEDICAL CENTER, TOPEKA, KANSAS (see VETERANS AFFAIRS EASTERN KANSAS HEALTH CARE SYSTEM), p. A246

VETERANS AFFAIRS EASTERN KANSAS HEALTH CARE SYSTEM–DWIGHT D. EISENHOWER VETERANS AFFAIRS MEDICAL CENTER, LEAVENWORTH, KANSAS (see VETERANS AFFAIRS EASTERN KANSAS HEALTH CARE SYSTEM), p. A239

VETERANS AFFAIRS EDWARD HINES, JR. HOSPITAL, HINES, ILLINOIS (see EDWARD HINES, JR. VETERANS AFFAIRS HOSPITAL), p. A185

VETERANS AFFAIRS GULF COAST VETERANS HEALTH CARE SYSTEM, BILOXI, MS, p. A344

VETERANS AFFAIRS HEALTH CARE SYSTEM, FARGO, NORTH DAKOTA (see FARGO VETERANS AFFAIRS HEALTH CARE SYSTEM), p. A467

VETERANS AFFAIRS HUDSON VALLEY HEALTH CARE SYSTEM, MONTROSE, NEW YORK (see NYC HEALTH + HOSPITALS / HENRY J CARTER SPECIALTY HOSPITAL AND MEDICAL CENTER), p. A431

VETERANS AFFAIRS ILLIANA HEALTH CARE SYSTEM, DANVILLE, IL, p. A180

VETERANS AFFAIRS LOMA LINDA HEALTHCARE SYSTEM, LOMA LINDA, CA, p. A64

VETERANS AFFAIRS MARYLAND HEALTH CARE SYSTEM–BALTIMORE DIVISION, BALTIMORE, MD, p. A288

VETERANS AFFAIRS MARYLAND HEALTH CARE SYSTEM–PERRY POINT DIVISION, PERRY POINT, MARYLAND (see VETERANS AFFAIRS MARYLAND HEALTH CARE SYSTEM–BALTIMORE DIVISION), p. A293

VETERANS AFFAIRS MEDICAL CENTER – ALEXANDRIA, PINEVILLE, LOUISIANA (see ALEXANDRIA VETERANS AFFAIRS HEALTH CARE SYSTEM), p. A277

VETERANS AFFAIRS MEDICAL CENTER, AUGUSTA, GA, p. A148

VETERANS AFFAIRS MEDICAL CENTER, AUGUSTA, MAINE (see MAINE VETERANS AFFAIRS MEDICAL CENTER), p. A281

VETERANS AFFAIRS MEDICAL CENTER, BATTLE CREEK, MICHIGAN (see BATTLE CREEK VETERANS AFFAIRS MEDICAL CENTER), p. A307

VETERANS AFFAIRS MEDICAL CENTER, BIRMINGHAM, ALABAMA (see BIRMINGHAM VETERANS AFFAIRS MEDICAL CENTER), p. A15

VETERANS AFFAIRS MEDICAL CENTER, BOISE, IDAHO (see BOISE VETERANS AFFAIRS MEDICAL CENTER), p. A168

VETERANS AFFAIRS MEDICAL CENTER, CHILLICOTHE, OHIO (see CHILLICOTHE VETERANS AFFAIRS MEDICAL CENTER), p. A475

VETERANS AFFAIRS MEDICAL CENTER, CINCINNATI, OHIO (see CINCINNATI VETERANS AFFAIRS MEDICAL CENTER), p. A477

VETERANS AFFAIRS MEDICAL CENTER, CLEVELAND, OHIO (see LOUIS STOKES CLEVELAND VETERANS AFFAIRS MEDICAL CENTER), p. A478

VETERANS AFFAIRS MEDICAL CENTER, COATESVILLE, PENNSYLVANIA (see COATESVILLE VETERANS AFFAIRS MEDICAL CENTER), p. A523

VETERANS AFFAIRS MEDICAL CENTER, DAYTON, OHIO (see DAYTON VETERANS AFFAIRS MEDICAL CENTER), p. A481

VETERANS AFFAIRS MEDICAL CENTER, DECATUR, GA, p. A152

VETERANS AFFAIRS MEDICAL CENTER, ERIE, PENNSYLVANIA (see ERIE VETERANS AFFAIRS MEDICAL CENTER), p. A525

VETERANS AFFAIRS MEDICAL CENTER, FAYETTEVILLE, NORTH CAROLINA (see FAYETTEVILLE VETERANS AFFAIRS MEDICAL CENTER), p. A454

VETERANS AFFAIRS MEDICAL CENTER, GRAND JUNCTION, CO, p. A101

VETERANS AFFAIRS MEDICAL CENTER, IRON MOUNTAIN, MICHIGAN (see OSCAR G. JOHNSON VETERANS AFFAIRS MEDICAL CENTER), p. A315

VETERANS AFFAIRS MEDICAL CENTER, KANSAS CITY, MISSOURI (see KANSAS CITY VETERANS AFFAIRS MEDICAL CENTER), p. A363

VETERANS AFFAIRS MEDICAL CENTER, LAKE CITY, FL, p. A127

VETERANS AFFAIRS MEDICAL CENTER, LEBANON, PENNSYLVANIA (see LEBANON VETERANS AFFAIRS MEDICAL CENTER), p. A529

VETERANS AFFAIRS MEDICAL CENTER, MANCHESTER, NEW HAMPSHIRE (see MANCHESTER VETERANS AFFAIRS MEDICAL CENTER), p. A401

VETERANS AFFAIRS MEDICAL CENTER, MEMPHIS, TENNESSEE (see MEMPHIS VETERANS AFFAIRS MEDICAL CENTER), p. A575

VETERANS AFFAIRS MEDICAL CENTER, MIAMI, FL, p. A131

VETERANS AFFAIRS MEDICAL CENTER, MINNEAPOLIS, MINNESOTA (see MINNEAPOLIS VETERANS AFFAIRS HEALTH CARE SYSTEM), p. A336

VETERANS AFFAIRS MEDICAL CENTER, OKLAHOMA CITY, OKLAHOMA (see OKLAHOMA CITY VETERANS AFFAIRS MEDICAL CENTER), p. A505

VETERANS AFFAIRS MEDICAL CENTER, PHILADELPHIA, PENNSYLVANIA (see PHILADELPHIA VETERANS AFFAIRS MEDICAL CENTER), p. A537

VETERANS AFFAIRS MEDICAL CENTER, PORTLAND, OREGON (see VA PORTLAND HEALTHCARE SYSTEM), p. A516

VETERANS AFFAIRS MEDICAL CENTER, PROVIDENCE, RHODE ISLAND (see PROVIDENCE VETERANS AFFAIRS MEDICAL CENTER), p. A548

VETERANS AFFAIRS MEDICAL CENTER, SAINT CLOUD, MINNESOTA (see ST. CLOUD VETERANS AFFAIRS HEALTH CARE SYSTEM), p. A339

VETERANS AFFAIRS MEDICAL CENTER, SALISBURY, NORTH CAROLINA (see W. G. (BILL) HEFFNER VETERANS AFFAIRS MEDICAL CENTER), p. A461

VETERANS AFFAIRS MEDICAL CENTER, SAN FRANCISCO, CA, p. A86

VETERANS AFFAIRS MEDICAL CENTER, SPOKANE, WASHINGTON (see MANN–GRANDSTAFF VETERANS AFFAIRS MEDICAL CENTER), p. A680

VETERANS AFFAIRS MEDICAL CENTER, SYRACUSE, NEW YORK (see SYRACUSE VETERANS AFFAIRS MEDICAL CENTER), p. A445

VETERANS AFFAIRS MEDICAL CENTER, WASHINGTON, DC, p. A116

VETERANS AFFAIRS MEDICAL CENTER, WEST PALM BEACH, FL, p. A144

VETERANS AFFAIRS MEDICAL CENTER, WILKES, PENNSYLVANIA (see WILKES–BARRE VETERANS AFFAIRS MEDICAL CENTER), p. A545

VETERANS AFFAIRS MEDICAL CENTER HOT SPRINGS CAMPUS, HOT SPRINGS, SOUTH DAKOTA (see VETERANS AFFAIRS BLACK HILLS HEALTH CARE SYSTEM), p. A561

VETERANS AFFAIRS MEDICAL CENTER WEST ROXBURY DIVISION, WEST ROXBURY, MASSACHUSETTS (see VETERANS AFFAIRS BOSTON HEALTHCARE SYSTEM BROCKTON DIVISION), p. A304

VETERANS AFFAIRS MEDICAL CENTER–LOUISVILLE, LOUISVILLE, KENTUCKY (see ROBLEY REX VETERANS AFFAIRS MEDICAL CENTER), p. A257

VETERANS AFFAIRS MONTANA HEALTH CARE SYSTEM, FORT HARRISON, MT, p. A376

VETERANS AFFAIRS NEBRASKA–WESTERN IOWA HEALTH CARE SYSTEM – LINCOLN, LINCOLN, NE, p. A387

VETERANS AFFAIRS NEBRASKA–WESTERN IOWA HEALTH CARE SYSTEM, OMAHA, NE, p. A390

VETERANS AFFAIRS NEW JERSEY HEALTH CARE SYSTEM, EAST ORANGE, NJ, p. A405

VETERANS AFFAIRS NORTH TEXAS HEALTH CARE SYSTEM, DALLAS, TX, p. A598

VETERANS AFFAIRS NORTHERN INDIANA HEALTH CARE SYSTEM, FORT WAYNE, IN, p. A204

VETERANS AFFAIRS NORTHERN INDIANA HEALTH CARE SYSTEM–MARION CAMPUS, MARION, INDIANA (see VETERANS AFFAIRS NORTHERN INDIANA HEALTH CARE SYSTEM), p. A211

VETERANS AFFAIRS PACIFIC ISLANDS HEALTH CARE SYSTEM, HONOLULU, HI, p. A165

VETERANS AFFAIRS PALO ALTO HEALTH CARE SYSTEM, LIVERMORE DIVISION, LIVERMORE, CA, p. A64

VETERANS AFFAIRS PITTSBURGH HEALTHCARE SYSTEM, PITTSBURGH, PA, p. A538

VETERANS AFFAIRS PUGET SOUND HEALTH CARE SYSTEM, SEATTLE, WA, p. A678

VETERANS AFFAIRS PUGET SOUND HEALTH CARE SYSTEM–AMERICAN LAKE DIVISION, TACOMA, WASHINGTON (see VETERANS AFFAIRS PUGET SOUND HEALTH CARE SYSTEM), p. A681

VETERANS AFFAIRS ROSEBURG HEALTHCARE SYSTEM, ROSEBURG, OR, p. A517

VETERANS AFFAIRS SALT LAKE CITY HEALTH CARE SYSTEM, SALT LAKE CITY, UT, p. A652

VETERANS AFFAIRS SIERRA NEVADA HEALTH CARE SYSTEM, RENO, NV, p. A397

VETERANS AFFAIRS SOUTHERN NEVADA HEALTHCARE SYSTEM, NORTH LAS VEGAS, NV, p. A396

VETERANS AFFAIRS ST. LOUIS HEALTH CARE SYSTEM, SAINT LOUIS, MO, p. A371

VETERANS AFFAIRS TENNESSEE VALLEY HEALTHCARE SYSTEM, NASHVILLE, TENNESSEE (see TENNESSEE VALLEY HEALTHCARE SYSTEM), p. A577

VETERANS AFFAIRS WESTERN NEW YORK HEALTHCARE SYSTEM–BATAVIA DIVISION, BATAVIA, NY, p. A423

VETERANS AFFAIRS WESTERN NEW YORK HEALTHCARE SYSTEM–BUFFALO DIVISION, BUFFALO, NY, p. A425

VETERANS HEALTH CARE SYSTEM OF THE OZARKS, FAYETTEVILLE, AR, p. A41

VETERANS MEMORIAL HOSPITAL, WAUKON, IA, p. A231

VIA CHRISTI REGIONAL MEDICAL CENTER, MULVANE, KANSAS (see ASCENSION VIA CHRISTI ST. FRANCIS), p. A241

VIBRA HOSPITAL OF AMARILLO, AMARILLO, TX, p. A582

VIBRA HOSPITAL OF BOISE, BOISE, ID, p. A168

VIBRA HOSPITAL OF CENTRAL DAKOTAS, MANDAN, ND, p. A468

VIBRA HOSPITAL OF CHARLESTON, MT. PLEASANT, SC, p. A555

VIBRA HOSPITAL OF DENVER, THORNTON, CO, p. A106

VIBRA HOSPITAL OF FARGO, FARGO, ND, p. A467

VIBRA HOSPITAL OF MAHONING VALLEY, BOARDMAN, OH, p. A473

VIBRA HOSPITAL OF NORTHERN CALIFORNIA, REDDING, CA, p. A80

VIBRA HOSPITAL OF NORTHWESTERN INDIANA, CROWN POINT, IN, p. A202

VIBRA HOSPITAL OF RICHMOND, RICHMOND, VA, p. A666

VIBRA HOSPITAL OF SACRAMENTO, FOLSOM, CA, p. A58

VIBRA HOSPITAL OF SOUTHEASTERN MASSACHUSETTS, NEW BEDFORD, MA, p. A301

VIBRA HOSPITAL OF SOUTHEASTERN MICHIGAN, LLC, LINCOLN PARK, MI, p. A317

VIBRA HOSPITAL OF WESTERN MASSACHUSETTS, SPRINGFIELD, MA, p. A304

VIBRA HOSPITAL OF WESTERN MASSACHUSETTS–CENTRAL CAMPUS, ROCHDALE, MASSACHUSETTS (see VIBRA HOSPITAL OF WESTERN MASSACHUSETTS), p. A302

VIBRA REHABILITATION HOSPITAL OF AMARILLO, AMARILLO, TX, p. A582

VIBRA REHABILITATION HOSPITAL OF DENVER, THORNTON, CO, p. A106

VIBRA SPECIALTY HOSPITAL AT DESOTO, DESOTO, TX, p. A600

VIBRA SPECIALTY HOSPITAL OF PORTLAND, PORTLAND, OR, p. A516

VICTOR VALLEY GLOBAL MEDICAL CENTER, VICTORVILLE, CA, p. A94

VIDANT BEAUFORT HOSPITAL, WASHINGTON, NC, p. A463

VIDANT BERTIE HOSPITAL, WINDSOR, NC, p. A464

VIDANT CHOWAN HOSPITAL, EDENTON, NC, p. A453

VIDANT DUPLIN HOSPITAL, KENANSVILLE, NC, p. A457

VIDANT EDGECOMBE HOSPITAL, TARBORO, NC, p. A463

VIDANT MEDICAL CENTER, GREENVILLE, NC, p. A455

VIDANT ROANOKE–CHOWAN HOSPITAL, AHOSKIE, NC, p. A449

VILLA FELICIANA MEDICAL COMPLEX, JACKSON, LA, p. A269

VIRGINIA BEACH PSYCHIATRIC CENTER, VIRGINIA BEACH, VA, p. A668

VIRGINIA GAY HOSPITAL, VINTON, IA, p. A230

VIRGINIA HOSPITAL CENTER, ARLINGTON, VA, p. A656

VIRGINIA MASON MEDICAL CENTER, SEATTLE, WA, p. A679

VIRGINIA MASON MEMORIAL, YAKIMA, WA, p. A682

VIRTUA MARLTON, MARLTON, NJ, p. A408

VIRTUA MEMORIAL, MOUNT HOLLY, NJ, p. A408

VIRTUA MEMORIAL HOSPITAL BURLINGTON COUNTY, MOUNT HOLLY, NEW JERSEY (see VIRTUA MEMORIAL), p. A408

VIRTUA VOORHEES, VOORHEES, NJ, p. A414

VISTA DEL MAR HOSPITAL, VENTURA, CA, p. A94

VISTA HEALTH, WAUKEGAN, IL, p. A198

VISTA HOSPITAL OF SOUTH BAY, GILROY, CA, p. A60

VISTA SPECIALTY HOSPITAL OF SAN GABRIEL VALLEY, BALDWIN PARK, CA, p. A51

W

W. G. (BILL) HEFFNER VETERANS AFFAIRS MEDICAL CENTER, SALISBURY, NC, p. A461
W. J. MANGOLD MEMORIAL HOSPITAL, LOCKNEY, TX, p. A621
WABASH GENERAL HOSPITAL, MOUNT CARMEL, IL, p. A190
WABASH VALLEY HOSPITAL, WEST LAFAYETTE, INDIANA (see RIVER BEND HOSPITAL), p. A216
WADLEY REGIONAL MEDICAL CENTER, TEXARKANA, TX, p. A640
WADLEY REGIONAL MEDICAL CENTER AT HOPE, HOPE, AR, p. A43
WAGNER COMMUNITY MEMORIAL HOSPITAL AVERA, WAGNER, SD, p. A565
WAGONER COMMUNITY HOSPITAL, WAGONER, OK, p. A510
WAHIAWA GENERAL HOSPITAL, WAHIAWA, HI, p. A166
WAKE FOREST BAPTIST HEALTH – WILKES MEDICAL CENTER, NORTH WILKESBORO, NC, p. A459
WAKE FOREST BAPTIST HEALTH–DAVIE MEDICAL CENTER, BERMUDA RUN, NC, p. A449
WAKE FOREST BAPTIST HEALTH–LEXINGTON MEDICAL CENTER, LEXINGTON, NC, p. A458
WAKE FOREST BAPTIST MEDICAL CENTER, WINSTON, NC, p. A464
WAKEMED CARY HOSPITAL, CARY, NC, p. A450
WAKEMED RALEIGH CAMPUS, RALEIGH, NC, p. A461
WALDEN BEHAVIORAL CARE, WALTHAM, MA, p. A304
WALDO COUNTY GENERAL HOSPITAL MAINE HEALTH, BELFAST, ME, p. A282
WALKER BAPTIST MEDICAL CENTER, JASPER, AL, p. A20
WALLOWA MEMORIAL HOSPITAL, ENTERPRISE, OR, p. A512
WALTER B. JONES ALCOHOL AND DRUG ABUSE TREATMENT CENTER, GREENVILLE, NC, p. A455
WALTER P. REUTHER PSYCHIATRIC HOSPITAL, WESTLAND, MI, p. A325
WALTER REED NATIONAL MILITARY MEDICAL CENTER, BETHESDA, MD, p. A289
WALTHALL COUNTY GENERAL HOSPITAL, TYLERTOWN, MS, p. A354
WALTON REHABILITATION HOSPITAL, AUGUSTA, GA, p. A148
WAMEGO HEALTH CENTER, WAMEGO, KS, p. A247
WAR MEMORIAL HOSPITAL, BERKELEY SPRINGS, WV, p. A683
WAR MEMORIAL HOSPITAL, SAULT SAINTE MARIE, MI, p. A322
WARD MEMORIAL HOSPITAL, MONAHANS, TX, p. A625
WARM SPRINGS MEDICAL CENTER, WARM SPRINGS, GA, p. A162
WARM SPRINGS REHABILITATION HOSPITAL OF KYLE, KYLE, TX, p. A619
WARM SPRINGS REHABILITATION HOSPITAL OF SAN ANTONIO, SAN ANTONIO, TX, p. A635
WARM SPRINGS SPECIALTY HOSPITAL OF LULING, LULING, TEXAS (see POST ACUTE/WARM SPRINGS SPECIALTY HOSPITAL OF LULING), p. A623
WARNER HOSPITAL AND HEALTH SERVICES, CLINTON, IL, p. A180
WARREN GENERAL HOSPITAL, WARREN, PA, p. A543
WARREN MEMORIAL HOSPITAL, FRONT ROYAL, VA, p. A660
WARREN STATE HOSPITAL, WARREN, PA, p. A543
WASHAKIE MEDICAL CENTER, WORLAND, WY, p. A713
WASHINGTON COUNTY HEALTH SYSTEM, HAGERSTOWN, MARYLAND (see MERITUS MEDICAL CENTER), p. A291
WASHINGTON COUNTY HOSPITAL, CHATOM, AL, p. A16
WASHINGTON COUNTY HOSPITAL, NASHVILLE, IL, p. A191
WASHINGTON COUNTY HOSPITAL, PLYMOUTH, NC, p. A460
WASHINGTON COUNTY HOSPITAL, WASHINGTON, KS, p. A247
WASHINGTON COUNTY HOSPITAL AND CLINICS, WASHINGTON, IA, p. A230
WASHINGTON COUNTY MEMORIAL HOSPITAL, POTOSI, MO, p. A367
WASHINGTON COUNTY REGIONAL MEDICAL CENTER, SANDERSVILLE, GA, p. A159
WASHINGTON DC VETERANS AFFAIRS MEDICAL CENTER, WASHINGTON, DC, p. A116
WASHINGTON HEALTH SYSTEM GREENE, WAYNESBURG, PA, p. A543
WASHINGTON HOSPITAL, WASHINGTON, PA, p. A543
WASHINGTON HOSPITAL CENTER, WASHINGTON, DC, p. A116
WASHINGTON HOSPITAL HEALTHCARE SYSTEM, FREMONT, CA, p. A59
WASHINGTON REGIONAL MEDICAL CENTER, FAYETTEVILLE, AR, p. A42

WATAUGA MEDICAL CENTER, BOONE, NC, p. A450
WATERBURY HOSPITAL, WATERBURY, CT, p. A112
WATERTOWN REGIONAL MEDICAL CENTER, WATERTOWN, WI, p. A707
WATSONVILLE COMMUNITY HOSPITAL, WATSONVILLE, CA, p. A94
WAUKESHA COUNTY MENTAL HEALTH CENTER, WAUKESHA, WI, p. A707
WAUKESHA MEMORIAL HOSPITAL, WAUKESHA, WI, p. A707
WAUPUN MEMORIAL HOSPITAL, WAUPUN, WI, p. A707
WAVERLY HEALTH CENTER, WAVERLY, IA, p. A231
WAYNE COUNTY HOSPITAL, CORYDON, IA, p. A220
WAYNE COUNTY HOSPITAL, MONTICELLO, KY, p. A258
WAYNE GENERAL HOSPITAL, WAYNESBORO, MS, p. A355
WAYNE HEALTHCARE, GREENVILLE, OH, p. A484
WAYNE MEDICAL CENTER, WAYNESBORO, TN, p. A580
WAYNE MEMORIAL HOSPITAL, HONESDALE, PA, p. A527
WAYNE MEMORIAL HOSPITAL, JESUP, GA, p. A155
WAYNE UNC HEALTH CARE, GOLDSBORO, NC, p. A455
WAYNESBORO HOSPITAL, WAYNESBORO, PA, p. A543
WEATHERFORD REGIONAL HOSPITAL, WEATHERFORD, OK, p. A510
WEATHERFORD REHABILITATION HOSPITAL, WEATHERFORD, TX, p. A644
WEBSTER COUNTY COMMUNITY HOSPITAL, RED CLOUD, NE, p. A391
WEBSTER COUNTY MEMORIAL HOSPITAL, WEBSTER SPRINGS, WV, p. A690
WEED ARMY COMMUNITY HOSPITAL, FORT IRWIN, CA, p. A58
WEEKS MEDICAL CENTER, LANCASTER, NH, p. A400
WEIRTON MEDICAL CENTER, WEIRTON, WV, p. A690
WEISBROD MEMORIAL COUNTY HOSPITAL, EADS, CO, p. A100
WEISER MEMORIAL HOSPITAL, WEISER, ID, p. A172
WEISMAN CHILDREN'S REHABILITATION HOSPITAL, MARLTON, NJ, p. A408
WEKIVA SPRINGS, JACKSONVILLE, FL, p. A126
WELCH COMMUNITY HOSPITAL, WELCH, WV, p. A690
WELLBRIDGE HEALTHCARE GREATER DALLAS, PLANO, TX, p. A630
WELLBRIDGE HEALTHCARE OF FORT WORTH, FORT WORTH, TX, p. A606
WELLBRIDGE HEATLHCARE OF SAN MARCOS, SAN MARCOS, TX, p. A636
WELLINGTON REGIONAL MEDICAL CENTER, WELLINGTON, FL, p. A143
WELLSPAN EPHRATA COMMUNITY HOSPITAL, EPHRATA, PA, p. A525
WELLSPAN GETTYSBURG HOSPITAL, GETTYSBURG, PA, p. A526
WELLSPAN GOOD SAMARITAN HOSPITAL, LEBANON, PA, p. A530
WELLSPAN PHILHAVEN, MOUNT GRETNA, PA, p. A532
WELLSPAN SURGERY AND REHABILITATION HOSPITAL, YORK, PA, p. A546
WELLSPAN YORK HOSPITAL, YORK, PA, p. A546
WELLSTAR ATLANTA MEDICAL CENTER, ATLANTA, GA, p. A147
WELLSTAR COBB HOSPITAL, AUSTELL, GA, p. A148
WELLSTAR DOUGLAS HOSPITAL, DOUGLASVILLE, GA, p. A152
WELLSTAR KENNESTONE HOSPITAL, MARIETTA, GA, p. A157
WELLSTAR NORTH FULTON HOSPITAL, ROSWELL, GA, p. A159
WELLSTAR PAULDING HOSPITAL, HIRAM, GA, p. A154
WELLSTAR SPALDING REGIONAL HOSPITAL, GRIFFIN, GA, p. A154
WELLSTAR SYLVAN GROVE HOSPITAL, JACKSON, GA, p. A155
WELLSTAR WEST GEORGIA MEDICAL CENTER, LAGRANGE, GA, p. A155
WELLSTAR WINDY HILL HOSPITAL, MARIETTA, GA, p. A157
WELLSTONE REGIONAL HOSPITAL, JEFFERSONVILLE, IN, p. A208
WENTWORTH–DOUGLASS HOSPITAL, DOVER, NH, p. A399
WERNERSVILLE STATE HOSPITAL, WERNERSVILLE, PA, p. A544
WESLACO REGIONAL REHABILITATION HOSPITAL, WESLACO, TX, p. A645
WESLEY HEALTHCARE CENTER, WICHITA, KS, p. A248
WESLEY REHABILITATION HOSPITAL, WICHITA, KS, p. A248
WESLEY WOODS GERIATRIC HOSPITAL OF EMORY UNIVERSITY, ATLANTA, GA, p. A147
WEST ANAHEIM MEDICAL CENTER, ANAHEIM, CA, p. A50
WEST BOCA MEDICAL CENTER, BOCA RATON, FL, p. A118
WEST CALCASIEU CAMERON HOSPITAL, SULPHUR, LA, p. A279
WEST CARROLL MEMORIAL HOSPITAL, OAK GROVE, LA, p. A276

WEST CENTRAL GEORGIA REGIONAL HOSPITAL, COLUMBUS, GA, p. A151
WEST CHESTER HOSPITAL, WEST CHESTER, OH, p. A494
WEST COVINA MEDICAL CENTER, WEST COVINA, CA, p. A94
WEST FELICIANA PARISH HOSPITAL, SAINT FRANCISVILLE, LA, p. A277
WEST FLORIDA COMMUNITY CARE CENTER, MILTON, FL, p. A132
WEST FLORIDA HOSPITAL, PENSACOLA, FL, p. A136
WEST FLORIDA REHABILITATION INSTITUTE, PENSACOLA, FL, p. A136
WEST GABLES REHABILITATION HOSPITAL, MIAMI, FL, p. A131
WEST HILLS HOSPITAL, RENO, NV, p. A397
WEST HILLS HOSPITAL AND MEDICAL CENTER, LOS ANGELES, CA, p. A70
WEST HOLT MEDICAL SERVICES, ATKINSON, NE, p. A382
WEST HOUSTON MEDICAL CENTER, HOUSTON, TX, p. A614
WEST JEFFERSON MEDICAL CENTER, MARRERO, LA, p. A273
WEST LOS ANGELES MEDICAL CENTER, LOS ANGELES, CA, p. A70
WEST OAKS HOSPITAL, HOUSTON, TX, p. A615
WEST PALM BEACH VETERANS AFFAIRS MEDICAL CENTER, WEST PALM BEACH, FL, p. A144
WEST PARK HOSPITAL, CODY, WY, p. A711
WEST PENN HOSPITAL, PITTSBURGH, PA, p. A538
WEST RIVER REGIONAL MEDICAL CENTER, HETTINGER, ND, p. A468
WEST SPRINGS HOSPITAL, GRAND JUNCTION, CO, p. A101
WEST SUBURBAN MEDICAL CENTER, OAK PARK, IL, p. A192
WEST TENNESSEE HEALTHCARE DYERSBURG HOSPITAL, DYERSBURG, TN, p. A569
WEST TENNESSEE HEALTHCARE VOLUNTEER HOSPITAL, MARTIN, TN, p. A574
WEST TEXAS VETERANS AFFAIRS HEALTH CARE SYSTEM, BIG SPRING, TX, p. A588
WEST VALLEY MEDICAL CENTER, CALDWELL, ID, p. A168
WEST VIRGINIA UNIVERSITY HOSPITALS, MORGANTOWN, WV, p. A687
WESTCHESTER GENERAL HOSPITAL, MIAMI, FL, p. A131
WESTCHESTER MEDICAL CENTER, VALHALLA, NY, p. A446
WESTERLY HOSPITAL, WESTERLY, RI, p. A548
WESTERN ARIZONA REGIONAL MEDICAL CENTER, BULLHEAD CITY, AZ, p. A28
WESTERN MARYLAND HOSPITAL CENTER, HAGERSTOWN, MD, p. A291
WESTERN MARYLAND REGIONAL MEDICAL CENTER, CUMBERLAND, MD, p. A290
WESTERN MASSACHUSETTS HOSPITAL, WESTFIELD, MA, p. A305
WESTERN MENTAL HEALTH INSTITUTE, BOLIVAR, TN, p. A566
WESTERN MISSOURI MEDICAL CENTER, WARRENSBURG, MO, p. A372
WESTERN NEW YORK CHILDREN'S PSYCHIATRIC CENTER, WEST SENECA, NY, p. A447
WESTERN PENNSYLVANIA HOSPITAL – FORBES REGIONAL CAMPUS, MONROEVILLE, PENNSYLVANIA (see FORBES HOSPITAL), p. A532
WESTERN PLAINS MEDICAL COMPLEX, DODGE CITY, KS, p. A234
WESTERN PSYCHIATRIC INSTITUTE AND CLINIC, PITTSBURGH, PENNSYLVANIA (see UPMC PRESBYTERIAN), p. A538
WESTERN REGIONAL MEDICAL CENTER, GOODYEAR, AZ, p. A30
WESTERN RESERVE HOSPITAL, CUYAHOGA FALLS, OH, p. A481
WESTERN STATE HOSPITAL, HOPKINSVILLE, KY, p. A253
WESTERN STATE HOSPITAL, STAUNTON, VA, p. A668
WESTERN STATE HOSPITAL, TACOMA, WA, p. A681
WESTERN WISCONSIN HEALTH, BALDWIN, WI, p. A691
WESTFIELD MEMORIAL HOSPITAL, WESTFIELD, NY, p. A447
WESTFIELDS HOSPITAL AND CLINIC, NEW RICHMOND, WI, p. A702
WESTLAKE HOSPITAL, MELROSE PARK, IL, p. A189
WESTON COUNTY HEALTH SERVICES, NEWCASTLE, WY, p. A712
WESTPARK SPRINGS, RICHMOND, TX, p. A631
WESTSIDE REGIONAL MEDICAL CENTER, PLANTATION, FL, p. A137
WESTSIDE SURGICAL HOSPITAL, HOUSTON, TX, p. A615
WETZEL COUNTY HOSPITAL, NEW MARTINSVILLE, WV, p. A687
WHEATLAND MEMORIAL HEALTHCARE, HARLOWTON, MT, p. A377
WHEELING HOSPITAL, WHEELING, WV, p. A690
WHIDBEYHEALTH, COUPEVILLE, WA, p. A672

WHIDDEN MEMORIAL HOSPITAL, EVERETT, MASSACHUSETTS (see CAMBRIDGE HEALTH ALLIANCE), p. A298

WHITE COMMUNITY HOSPITAL, AURORA, MINNESOTA (see ESSENTIA HEALTH NORTHERN PINES MEDICAL CENTER), p. A328

WHITE MOUNTAIN REGIONAL MEDICAL CENTER, SPRINGERVILLE, AZ, p. A36

WHITE PLAINS HOSPITAL CENTER, WHITE PLAINS, NY, p. A448

WHITE RIVER JUNCTION VETERANS AFFAIRS MEDICAL CENTER, WHITE RIVER JUNCTION, VT, p. A655

WHITE RIVER MEDICAL CENTER, BATESVILLE, AR, p. A39

WHITESBURG ARH HOSPITAL, WHITESBURG, KY, p. A261

WHITING FORENSIC HOSPITAL, MIDDLETOWN, CT, p. A109

WHITINSVILLE MEDICAL CENTER, WHITINSVILLE, MASSACHUSETTS (see MILFORD REGIONAL MEDICAL CENTER), p. A305

WHITMAN HOSPITAL AND MEDICAL CENTER, COLFAX, WA, p. A672

WHITTIER HOSPITAL MEDICAL CENTER, WHITTIER, CA, p. A95

WHITTIER PAVILION, HAVERHILL, MA, p. A299

WHITTIER REHABILITATION HOSPITAL, BRADFORD, MA, p. A296

WHITTIER REHABILITATION HOSPITAL, WESTBOROUGH, MA, p. A304

WICHITA COUNTY HEALTH CENTER, LEOTI, KS, p. A239

WICHITA SPECIALTY HOSPITAL, WICHITA, KANSAS (see AMG SPECIALTY HOSPITAL–WICHITA), p. A248

WICKENBURG COMMUNITY HOSPITAL, WICKENBURG, AZ, p. A38

WILBARGER GENERAL HOSPITAL, VERNON, TX, p. A643

WILCOX MEDICAL CENTER, LIHUE, HI, p. A166

WILKES–BARRE GENERAL HOSPITAL, WILKES, PA, p. A545

WILKES–BARRE VETERANS AFFAIRS MEDICAL CENTER, WILKES, PA, p. A545

WILLAMETTE VALLEY MEDICAL CENTER, MCMINNVILLE, OR, p. A514

WILLAPA HARBOR HOSPITAL, SOUTH BEND, WA, p. A679

WILLIAM BEAUMONT ARMY MEDICAL CENTER, EL PASO, TX, p. A603

WILLIAM BEE RIRIE HOSPITAL, ELY, NV, p. A393

WILLIAM J. MCCORD ADOLESCENT TREATMENT FACILITY, ORANGEBURG, SC, p. A556

WILLIAM NEWTON HOSPITAL, WINFIELD, KS, p. A248

WILLIAM P. CLEMENTS, JR. UNIVERSITY HOSPITAL, DALLAS, TX, p. A598

WILLIAM R. SHARPE, JR. HOSPITAL, WESTON, WV, p. A690

WILLIAM S. HALL PSYCHIATRIC INSTITUTE, COLUMBIA, SC, p. A551

WILLIAM S. MIDDLETON MEMORIAL VETERANS HOSPITAL, MADISON, WI, p. A699

WILLIAMSBURG REGIONAL HOSPITAL, KINGSTREE, SC, p. A554

WILLIAMSON MEDICAL CENTER, FRANKLIN, TN, p. A570

WILLIAMSON MEMORIAL HOSPITAL, WILLIAMSON, WV, p. A690

WILLIAMSPORT HOSPITAL AND MEDICAL CENTER, WILLIAMSPORT, PENNSYLVANIA (see UPMC SUSQUEHANNA WILLIAMSPORT), p. A545

WILLINGWAY HOSPITAL, STATESBORO, GA, p. A161

WILLIS–KNIGHTON BOSSIER HEALTH CENTER, BOSSIER CITY, LOUISIANA (see WK BOSSIER HEALTH CENTER), p. A265

WILLIS–KNIGHTON MEDICAL CENTER, SHREVEPORT, LA, p. A278

WILLOW CREEK BEHAVIORAL HEALTH, GREEN BAY, WI, p. A696

WILLOW CREST HOSPITAL, MIAMI, OK, p. A502

WILLOW ROCK CENTER, SAN LEANDRO, CA, p. A87

WILLOW SPRINGS CENTER, RENO, NV, p. A397

WILLS MEMORIAL HOSPITAL, WASHINGTON, GA, p. A163

WILMA N. VAZQUEZ MEDICAL CENTER, VEGA BAJA, PR, p. A720

WILMINGTON TREATMENT CENTER, WILMINGTON, NC, p. A464

WILMINGTON VETERANS AFFAIRS MEDICAL CENTER, WILMINGTON, DE, p. A114

WILSON MEDICAL CENTER, NEODESHA, KS, p. A241

WILSON MEDICAL CENTER, WILSON, NC, p. A464

WILSON MEMORIAL HOSPITAL, SIDNEY, OH, p. A491

WILSON MEMORIAL REGIONAL MEDICAL CENTER, JOHNSON CITY, NEW YORK (see UNITED HEALTH SERVICES HOSPITALS–BINGHAMTON), p. A429

WILSON N. JONES MEDICAL CENTER, SHERMAN, TEXAS (see WILSON N. JONES REGIONAL MEDICAL CENTER), p. A637

WILSON N. JONES REGIONAL MEDICAL CENTER, SHERMAN, TX, p. A637

WINCHESTER HOSPITAL, WINCHESTER, MA, p. A305

WINCHESTER MEDICAL CENTER, WINCHESTER, VA, p. A669

WINDHAM COMMUNITY MEMORIAL HOSPITAL, WILLIMANTIC, CT, p. A112

WINDHAM HOSPITAL, WILLIMANTIC, CT, p. A112

WINDHAVEN PSYCHIATRIC HOSPITAL, PRESCOTT VALLEY, AZ, p. A35

WINDMOOR HEALTHCARE OF CLEARWATER, CLEARWATER, FL, p. A120

WINDOM AREA HOSPITAL, WINDOM, MN, p. A343

WINDSOR–LAURELWOOD CENTER FOR BEHAVIORAL MEDICINE, WILLOUGHBY, OH, p. A494

WINKLER COUNTY MEMORIAL HOSPITAL, KERMIT, TX, p. A617

WINN ARMY COMMUNITY HOSPITAL, HINESVILLE, GA, p. A154

WINN PARISH MEDICAL CENTER, WINNFIELD, LA, p. A280

WINNEBAGO MENTAL HEALTH INSTITUTE, WINNEBAGO, WI, p. A709

WINNER REGIONAL HEALTHCARE CENTER, WINNER, SD, p. A565

WINNESHIEK MEDICAL CENTER, DECORAH, IA, p. A221

WINNIE PALMER HOSPITAL FOR WOMEN AND BABIES, ORLANDO, FL, p. A134

WINONA HEALTH, WINONA, MN, p. A343

WINSTON MEDICAL CENTER, LOUISVILLE, MS, p. A350

WINTER HAVEN HOSPITAL, WINTER HAVEN, FL, p. A144

WIREGRASS MEDICAL CENTER, GENEVA, AL, p. A18

WISE HEALTH SYSTEM, DECATUR, TX, p. A598

WISHEK COMMUNITY HOSPITAL AND CLINICS, WISHEK, ND, p. A470

WITHAM HEALTH SERVICES, LEBANON, IN, p. A210

WM. JENNINGS BRYAN DORN VETERANS AFFAIRS MEDICAL CENTER, COLUMBIA, SC, p. A552

WOMACK ARMY MEDICAL CENTER, FORT BRAGG, NC, p. A454

WOMAN'S HOSPITAL, BATON ROUGE, LA, p. A264

WOMAN'S HOSPITAL OF TEXAS, HOUSTON, TX, p. A615

WOMEN & INFANTS HOSPITAL OF RHODE ISLAND, PROVIDENCE, RI, p. A548

WOMEN AND CHILDREN'S HOSPITAL, BUFFALO, NEW YORK (see KALEIDA HEALTH), p. A425

WOOD COUNTY HOSPITAL, BOWLING GREEN, OH, p. A473

WOODLAND HEALTHCARE, WOODLAND, CA, p. A95

WOODLAND HEIGHTS MEDICAL CENTER, LUFKIN, TX, p. A622

WOODLAND SPRINGS HOSPITAL, CONROE, TX, p. A593

WOODLANDS SPECIALTY HOSPITAL; THE WOODLANDS, TX, p. A641

WOODLAWN HOSPITAL, ROCHESTER, IN, p. A214

WOODWINDS HEALTH CAMPUS, WOODBURY, MN, p. A343

WOOSTER COMMUNITY HOSPITAL, WOOSTER, OH, p. A494

WORCESTER RECOVERY CENTER AND HOSPITAL, WORCESTER, MA, p. A305

WRANGELL MEDICAL CENTER, WRANGELL, AK, p. A27

WRAY COMMUNITY DISTRICT HOSPITAL, WRAY, CO, p. A106

WRIGHT MEMORIAL HOSPITAL, TRENTON, MO, p. A372

WRIGHT PATTERSON MEDICAL CENTER, WRIGHT, OH, p. A494

WYANDOT MEMORIAL HOSPITAL, UPPER SANDUSKY, OH, p. A492

WYOMING BEHAVIORAL INSTITUTE, CASPER, WY, p. A710

WYOMING COUNTY COMMUNITY HOSPITAL, WARSAW, NY, p. A446

WYOMING MEDICAL CENTER, CASPER, WY, p. A710

WYOMING STATE HOSPITAL, EVANSTON, WY, p. A711

WYOMING VALLEY HEALTH CARE SYSTEM, WILKES, PENNSYLVANIA (see WILKES–BARRE GENERAL HOSPITAL), p. A545

WYTHE COUNTY COMMUNITY HOSPITAL, WYTHEVILLE, VA, p. A669

Y

YALE–NEW HAVEN HOSPITAL, NEW HAVEN, CT, p. A110

YALOBUSHA GENERAL HOSPITAL, WATER VALLEY, MS, p. A355

YAVAPAI REGIONAL MEDICAL CENTER, PRESCOTT, AZ, p. A35

YOAKUM COMMUNITY HOSPITAL, YOAKUM, TX, p. A646

YOAKUM COUNTY HOSPITAL, DENVER CITY, TX, p. A600

YORK GENERAL, YORK, NE, p. A392

YORK HOSPITAL, YORK, ME, p. A285

YOUTH VILLAGES INNER HARBOUR CAMPUS, DOUGLASVILLE, GA, p. A152

YUKON–KUSKOKWIM DELTA REGIONAL HOSPITAL, BETHEL, AK, p. A25

YUMA DISTRICT HOSPITAL, YUMA, CO, p. A106

YUMA REGIONAL MEDICAL CENTER, YUMA, AZ, p. A38

YUMA REHABILITATION HOSPITAL, A PARTNERSHIP OF ENCOMPASS HEALTH AND YRMC, YUMA, AZ, p. A38

Z

ZEELAND COMMUNITY HOSPITAL, ZEELAND, MICHIGAN (see SPECTRUM HEALTH ZEELAND COMMUNITY HOSPITAL), p. A326

ZUCKERBERG SAN FRANCISCO GENERAL HOSPITAL AND TRAUMA CENTER, SAN FRANCISCO, CA, p. A86

Index of Health Care Professionals

This section is an index of the key health care professionals for the hospitals and/or health care systems listed in this publication. The index is in alphabetical order, by individual, followed by the title, institutional affiliation, city, state and page reference to the hospital and/or health care system listing in section A and/or B.

A

AAGARD, Kim, Chief Financial Officer, Tri–County Hospital, Wadena, MN, p. A342

AALBORG, Chase, Vice President and Chief Financial Officer, Adventist Medical Center Glenoaks, Glendale Heights, IL, p. A184

AASVED, Craig E., Chief Executive Officer, Shodair Children'S Hospital, Helena, MT, p. A377

ABAIR, Cynthia, Associate Director, Va San Diego Healthcare System, San Diego, CA, p. A84

ABANG, Toni, M.D., Medical Director, Encompass Rehabilitation Hospital Of Lakeview, Elizabethtown, KY, p. A251

ABBATE, Anthony, Director of Information Services, San Ramon Regional Medical Center, San Ramon, CA, p. A88

ABBATIELLO, Michael, Chief Financial Officer, Spring Harbor Hospital, Westbrook, ME, p. A285

ABBEY, Kurt, Chief Nursing Officer, Ozarks Medical Center, West Plains, MO, p. A373

ABBOTT, Dana, Market Human Resources Director, Shands Live Oak Regional Medical Center, Live Oak, FL, p. A128

ABBOTT, Jody, Senior Vice President and Chief Operating Officer, North Kansas City Hospital, North Kansas City, MO, p. A366

ABBOTT, Justin, M.D., Medical Director, Sevier Valley Hospital, Richfield, UT, p. A651

ABBOTT, Michael, Chief Operating Officer, Lewis–Gale Medical Center, Boones Mill, VA, p. A657

ABBOTT, Peggy L., President and Chief Executive Officer, Ouachita County Medical Center, Camden, AR, p. A40

ABBOUD, Josie, President and Chief Executive Officer, Nebraska Methodist Hospital, Omaha, NE, p. A389

ABDA, William, Chief Human Resources Officer, Clarks Summit State Hospital, Clarks Summit, PA, p. A522

ABDELKARIM, Riad Z., M.D., Vice President and Chief Medical Officer, St. Mary Medical Center, Apple Valley, CA, p. A51

ABDELNASER, Mohammad, Chief Nursing Officer, Centinela Hospital Medical Center, Inglewood, CA, p. A62

ABE, Ann
Administrator and Chief Operating Officer, Orange County Global Medical Center, Inc., Santa Ana, CA, p. A88
Interim Chief Executive Officer, Orange County Global Medical Center, Inc., Santa Ana, CA, p. A88

ABEL, Danielle, Vice President of Patient Care Services, Chi Lakewood Health, Baudette, MN, p. A328

ABEL, Doug, Chief Information Officer, North Kansas City Hospital, North Kansas City, MO, p. A366

ABEL, Jeffrey, M.D., Chief Medical Officer, Ogden Regional Medical Center, Ogden, UT, p. A650

ABEL, Kevin, Chief Executive Officer, North Valley Hospital, Whitefish, MT, p. A381

ABEL, Stacy L, Vice President People and Culture, Craig Hospital, Englewood, CO, p. A100

ABELLERA, Roland, Vice President and Chief Operating Officer, St. Bernard Hospital And Health Care Center, Chicago, IL, p. A180

ABELY, Susan Cerrone
Chief Information Officer, St. Joseph Health Services Of Rhode Island, North Providence, RI, p. A547
Vice President and Chief Information Officer, Roger Williams Medical Center, Providence, RI, p. A548

ABERCROMBIE, David
Controller, Baptist Health South Florida, Homestead Hospital, Homestead, FL, p. A125
Controller, Baptist Health South Florida, Mariners Hospital, Tavernier, FL, p. A142

ABERCROMBIE, David E., Chief Executive Officer, Montgomery County Memorial Hospital, Red Oak, IA, p. A228

ABERCROMBIE, Zach, Chief Financial Officer, Citizens Baptist Medical Center, Talladega, AL, p. A23

ABERNATHY, Clint, President and Chief Operating Officer, Texas Health Harris Methodist Hospital Alliance, Fort Worth, TX, p. A605

ABERNETHY, Robert, Interim Chief Financial Officer, Medical Center Health System, Odessa, TX, p. A627

ABLA, Mike, Director of Nursing, Griffin Memorial Hospital, Norman, OK, p. A503

ABNEY, Stuart, Controller, Jasper Memorial Hospital, Monticello, GA, p. A158

ABOUD, Al, CPA, Chief Financial Officer, Hackensack Meridian Health Mountainside Medical Center, Montclair, NJ, p. A408

ABRAHAM, Akram, M.D., Chief of Staff, Harmon Memorial Hospital, Hollis, OK, p. A500

ABRAHAM, Brian, Chief Executive Officer, Mesquite Rehabilitation Institute, Mesquite, TX, p. A624

ABRAHAM, JiJi
Area Chief Financial Officer, Kaiser Permanente Moreno Valley Medical Center, Moreno Valley, CA, p. A73
Chief Financial Officer, Kaiser Permanente Riverside Medical Center, Riverside, CA, p. A81

ABRAHAMSON–BATY, Sherri, Director Patient Care Services, Cambridge Medical Center, Cambridge, MN, p. A329

ABRAHAMY, Ran, M.D., Chief of Staff, University Hospital And Medical Center, Tamarac, FL, p. A141

ABRAMS, Jose, Chief Information Officer, St. Luke'S Episcopal Hospital, Ponce, PR, p. A717

ABREU, Iris, Supervisor Human Resources, Hospital Hima De Humacao, Humacao, PR, p. A716

ABREU, John, Vice President and Chief Financial Officer, Portneuf Medical Center, Pocatello, ID, p. A171

ABRINA, Sofia
Administrator, Montclair Hospital Medical Center, Montclair, CA, p. A72
Chief Executive Officer, Glendora Community Hospital, Glendora, CA, p. A61

ABRUTZ, Joseph F., Jr, Administrator, Cameron Regional Medical Center, Cameron, MO, p. A357

ABSALON, Jeffrey, M.D.
Chief Physician Officer, St. Charles Bend, Bend, OR, p. A511
Chief Physician Officer, St. Charles Redmond, Redmond, OR, p. A517

ABSHIER, Trey
Chief Executive Officer, Central Florida Regional Hospital, Sanford, FL, p. A139
Chief Executive Officer, North Shore Medical Center, Miami, FL, p. A131

ABUNDO, Manuel, M.D., Chief of Staff, Wahiawa General Hospital, Wahiawa, HI, p. A166

ABY, Sherry, Director Information Management, Upmc Carlisle, Carlisle, PA, p. A522

ACCASHIAN, Chris
Chief Executive Officer, Bon Secours St. Francis Medical Center, Midlothian, VA, p. A662
Chief Executive Officer, Rappahannock General Hospital, Kilmarnock, VA, p. A661

ACETO, Anthony, Vice President Human Resources, Norwalk Hospital, Norwalk, CT, p. A110

ACEVEDO, Edwin Orama, Financial Supervisor, Hospital Buen Samaritano, Aguadilla, PR, p. A714

ACEVEDO, Elizabeth, Director Human Resources, Houston Methodist Willowbrook Hospital, Houston, TX, p. A612

ACEVEDO, Ramon, Supervisor Information Systems, Hospital San Cristobal, Coto Laurel, PR, p. A716

ACEVEDO, Vanessa, Interim Chief Executive Officer, Chg Hospital Tucson, Llc, Tucson, AZ, p. A37

ACHARYA, Ganesh, Chief Executive Officer, Good Samaritan Hospital, Bakersfield, CA, p. A52

ACHEBE, James Bob, M.D., President Medical Staff, South Shore Hospital, Chicago, IL, p. A179

ACHTER, Dick, Chief Financial Officer, Barrett Hospital & Healthcare, Dillon, MT, p. A376

ACHURY, Dario, Director of Information Management, St. Anthony'S Rehabilitation Hospital, Lauderdale Lakes, FL, p. A128

ACKER, David B., President and Chief Executive Officer, Canton–Potsdam Hospital, Potsdam, NY, p. A442

ACKER, Peter W., President and Chief Executive Officer, Atrium Health Lincoln, Lincolnton, NC, p. A458

ACKERMAN, Kenneth F.
Chair, Hospital Operation, Mayo Clinic Hospital – Rochester, Rochester, MN, p. A338
Hospital Administrator, Mayo Clinic Hospital – Rochester, Rochester, MN, p. A338

ACKERSON, David, Chief Information Officer, Seattle Cancer Care Alliance, Seattle, WA, p. A678

ACKERT, Sara, Associate Director, Sioux Falls Veterans Affairs Health Care System, Sioux Falls, SD, p. A564

ACKLAND, Jeanne, Director of Finance, Fillmore County Hospital, Geneva, NE, p. A385

ACKLEY, Michael
Chief Financial Officer, Kentucky River Medical Center, Jackson, KY, p. A254
Chief Financial Officer, Three Rivers Medical Center, Louisa, KY, p. A255

ACKLIN, Traci, M.D., Chief of Staff, Montgomery General Hospital, Montgomery, WV, p. A687

ACKMAN, Jeffrey D., M.D., Chief of Staff, Shriners Hospitals For Children–Chicago, Chicago, IL, p. A179

ACKMAN, Laura, Chief Operating Officer and Administrator, Essentia Health Northern Pines Medical Center, Aurora, MN, p. A328

ACOSTA, Ivan, M.D., Medical Director, Hospital De La Concepcion, San German, PR, p. A718

ACOSTA, Louis, M.D., Chief of Staff, Silver Lake Medical Center, Los Angeles, CA, p. A69

ACOSTA, Todd, R.N., Chief Nursing Officer, Hood Memorial Hospital, Amite, LA, p. A262

ACOSTA–CARLSON, Francisca, M.D., Chief of Staff, Lexington Regional Health Center, Lexington, NE, p. A386

ACOSTA–CRUZ, Maridel, Chief Executive Officer, First Texas Hospital, Houston, TX, p. A611

ACREE, Charis L, Vice President and Chief Operating Officer, Wellstar West Georgia Medical Center, Lagrange, GA, p. A155

ADAIR, Dale K, M.D., Chief Medical Officer, Wernersville State Hospital, Wernersville, PA, p. A544

ADAIR, Julie, Interim Corporate Chief Human Resources Officer, Fresno Heart And Surgical Hospital, Fresno, CA, p. A59

ADAIR–TRIPLETT, Alonna, Chief Nurse Executive, Claremore Indian Hospital, Claremore, OK, p. A498

ADAM, Sheryl, Chief Financial Officer, Hanover Hospital, Hanover, KS, p. A236

ADAM, Suzanne, D.O., Medical Director, Encompass Health Reading Rehabilitation Hospital, Reading, PA, p. A539

ADAMO, James D., M.D., Medical Director, Harbor Oaks Hospital, New Baltimore, MI, p. A318

ADAMO, Peter J., President and Chief Executive Officer, Waterbury Hospital, Waterbury, CT, p. A112

ADAMOLEKUN, Michelle
Chief Human Resource Officer, St. Vincent'S Medical Center Riverside, Jacksonville, FL, p. A126
Vice President Human Resource Market Lead Florida/ Alabama Ministry Market, Sacred Heart Hospital Pensacola, Pensacola, FL, p. A136

ADAMS, Aaron
President, St. Charles Bend, Bend, OR, p. A511
President, St. Charles Redmond, Redmond, OR, p. A517

ADAMS, Alan L., Administrator, Memorial Hospital Of Stilwell, Stilwell, OK, p. A508

ADAMS, Bob, Director Information Services, Bay Area Hospital, Coos Bay, OR, p. A512

ADAMS, Brian
Chief Executive Officer, Adventhealth Heart Of Florida, Davenport, FL, p. A121
Chief Executive Officer, Adventhealth Lake Wales, Lake Wales, FL, p. A127
President and Chief Executive Officer, Adventhealth Connerton, Land O'Lakes, FL, p. A127

ADAMS, Bryan D., Chief Executive Officer, Greenleaf Behavioral Health Hospital, Valdosta, GA, p. A162

ADAMS, Carla, Chief Nursing Officer, Northern Nevada Medical Center, Sparks, NV, p. A398

ADAMS, Cathleen, Chief Nursing Officer, Carepartners Health Services, Asheville, NC, p. A449

ADAMS, Charlotte, Director of Human Resources, Carolina Pines Regional Medical Center, Hartsville, SC, p. A554

ADAMS, Chris, Vice President Patient Care Services, Good Samaritan Regional Health Center, Mount Vernon, IL, p. A190

ADAMS, Cynthia, Vice President Human Resources, Tristar Stonecrest Medical Center, Smyrna, TN, p. A579

ADAMS, Denise, Human Resources Generalist, Hancock County Hospital, Sneedville, TN, p. A579

ADAMS, Elizabeth, R.N., Chief Nursing Officer, Oak Hill Hospital, Brooksville, FL, p. A119

ADAMS, Emmy
Chief Financial Officer, Mayhill Hospital, Denton, TX, p. A599
Chief Financial Officer, Provo Canyon Behavioral Hospital, Orem, UT, p. A650

ADAMS, Essie, Director of Nursing, Kedren Community Mental Health Center, Los Angeles, CA, p. A67

ADAMS, Felicia M, MS, Chief Nursing Officer, Mid–Columbia Medical Center, The Dalles, OR, p. A518

ADAMS, Gini, Director Employee and Public Relations, Yuma District Hospital, Yuma, CO, p. A106

ADAMS, Heather, Chief Nursing Officer, John F. Kennedy Memorial Hospital, Indio, CA, p. A62

ADAMS, Jason, M.D., Medical Staff President, Forest Health Medical Center, Ypsilanti, MI, p. A325

ADAMS, Jennifer B, Chief Operating Officer and Chief Financial Officer, Lake City Medical Center, Lake City, FL, p. A127

ADAMS, Jo, Director Human Resources, Donalsonville Hospital, Donalsonville, GA, p. A152

ADAMS, J'Dee, Chief Operating Officer, North Canyon Medical Center, Gooding, ID, p. A169

ADAMS, Karen, Vice President Human Resources, Baxter Regional Medical Center, Mountain Home, AR, p. A46

ADAMS, Kelly, Chief Executive Officer, Santa Cruz Valley Regional Hospital, Green Valley, AZ, p. A30

ADAMS, Kimberly, Manager Human Resources, Carroll County Memorial Hospital, Carrollton, KY, p. A250

ADAMS, Lana, Chief Financial Officer, Lafayette General Medical Center, Lafayette, LA, p. A271

ADAMS, Leslie, Chief Nursing Executive, Chi Saint Joseph Berea, Berea, KY, p. A249

ADAMS, Mark A., President and Chief Executive Officer, Methodist Rehabilitation Center, Jackson, MS, p. A349

ADAMS, Mark B., Chief Executive Officer, Ogden Regional Medical Center, Ogden, UT, p. A650

ADAMS, Mark C., M.D., Chief Medical Officer, El Camino Hospital, Mountain View, CA, p. A73

ADAMS, Marlene J, Director Human Resources, Schneider Regional Medical Center, Saint Thomas, VI, p. A720

ADAMS, Marsha, Interim Director Human Resources, Texas Health Harris Methodist Hospital Cleburne, Cleburne, TX, p. A592

ADAMS, Martin D., CPA, Vice President Finance and Chief Financial Officer, Paris Community Hospital, Paris, IL, p. A192

ADAMS, Mary Jane, R.N., MSN, Senior Vice President and Chief Nursing Officer, University Of Louisville Hospital, Louisville, KY, p. A257

ADAMS, Matthew, Administrator, Oklahoma State University Medical Center, Tulsa, OK, p. A509

ADAMS, Michael, Chief Operating Officer, Scottsdale Liberty Hospital, Scottsdale, AZ, p. A36

ADAMS, Mike, M.D., Chief Medical Officer, Gateway Regional Medical Center, Granite City, IL, p. A184

ADAMS, Nancy D., R.N., Senior Vice President and Chief Operating Officer, Western Maryland Regional Medical Center, Cumberland, MD, p. A290

ADAMS, Norma, Director Human Resources, Southern Regional Medical Center, Riverdale, GA, p. A159

ADAMS, Patsy, Vice President Human Resources, Redmond Regional Medical Center, Rome, GA, p. A159

ADAMS, Renee, Director Information Technology, Chan Soon–Shiong Medical Center, Windber, PA, p. A545

ADAMS, Robert H, Vice President Operations, Hackensack Meridian Health Jersey Shore University Medical Center, Neptune, NJ, p. A408

ADAMS, Robin, Director Human Resources, Reeves Memorial Medical Center, Bernice, LA, p. A264

ADAMS, Russell, M.D., Chief Medical Officer, Unitypoint Health – Marshalltown, Marshalltown, IA, p. A226

ADAMS, Scott K., Chief Executive Officer, Pullman Regional Hospital, Pullman, WA, p. A676

ADAMS, Shannon, Chief Financial Officer, Avera Holy Family Hospital, Estherville, IA, p. A222

ADAMS, Sharon
Chief Nursing Officer, Danbury Hospital, Danbury, CT, p. A107
Chief Operating Officer, Danbury Hospital, Danbury, CT, p. A107

ADAMS, Shaun, Chief Financial Officer, Tennova Healthcare–Harton, Tullahoma, TN, p. A580

ADAMS, Shawn, Chief Financial Officer, Christus Southeast Texas Hospital – St. Elizabeth, Beaumont, TX, p. A587

ADAMS, Susan, Chief Nursing Officer and Chief Operating Officer, Specialty Hospital Of Lorain, Amherst, OH, p. A471

ADAMS, T Gard, M.D., Chief of Staff, Mclaren Caro Region, Caro, MI, p. A308

ADAMS, Tony, President, Barix Clinics Of Pennsylvania, Langhorne, PA, p. A529

ADAMSKI, Joseph, Chief Nursing Officer, Encompass Health Rehabilitation Hospital Of Concord, Concord, NH, p. A399

ADAMSON, James, Chief Executive Officer, Mountain View Hospital, Idaho Falls, ID, p. A169

ADAMSON, Nancy, Chief Nursing Officer, Banner Del E. Webb Medical Center, Sun City West, AZ, p. A36

ADCOCK, Robert S., Chief Executive Officer, Fairmont Regional Medical Center, Fairmont, WV, p. A685

ADCOCK, Tanya M., President, St. Mary'S Good Samaritan Hospital, Greensboro, GA, p. A154

ADCOCK, William, Chief Financial Officer, Union General Hospital, Farmerville, LA, p. A267

ADCOCK MOHR, Barbara, Chief Executive Officer, Uva–Healthsouth Rehabilitation Hospital, Charlottesville, VA, p. A657

ADDINGTON, Tom, Chief Information Officer, Saint Michael'S Medical Center, Newark, NJ, p. A409

ADDISON, Holland M, M.D., Medical Director, Select Specialty Hospital – Belhaven, Jackson, MS, p. A349

ADDISON, John Bruce, D.O., Chief Medical Officer, Mccamey County Hospital District, Mccamey, TX, p. A624

ADDISON, Lenora, Vice President Patient Care and Nursing, Medstar Harbor Hospital, Baltimore, MD, p. A287

ADDISON, Lewis C, Senior Vice President and Chief Financial Officer, Centra Lynchburg General Hospital, Lynchburg, VA, p. A662

ADDLESPERGER, John, D.O., Chief Medical Officer, Sheridan Memorial Hospital, Sheridan, WY, p. A712

ADDO, Deborah, Chief Executive Officer, Inova Loudoun Hospital, Leesburg, VA, p. A661

ADEEL, Mohammed, Medical Director, Healthsouth Deaconess Rehabilitation Hospital, Evansville, IN, p. A203

ADEMA, Carolyn, Vice President, Human Resources, St. Tammany Parish Hospital, Covington, LA, p. A266

ADEN, Susie, Director of IP Services, Pocahontas Community Hospital, Pocahontas, IA, p. A228

ADER, Michael H, M.D., Vice President Medical Affairs, Upmc Hanover, Hanover, PA, p. A526

ADERS, Deb, MS, R.N., Vice President Patient Care Services, Chief Nursing Officer, Yuma Regional Medical Center, Yuma, AZ, p. A38

ADESSO, Patrick
Director Information Technology and Systems, Memorial Hospital Jacksonville, Jacksonville, FL, p. A125
Director Information Technology and Systems, Specialty Hospital Jacksonville, Jacksonville, FL, p. A126

ADKINS, Garry, Chief Information Officer, Usa Children'S And Women'S Hospital, Mobile, AL, p. A20

ADKINS, Gary W, Chief Executive Officer, Parkview Noble Hospital, Kendallville, IN, p. A208

ADKINS, Gary W., President, Parkview Noble Hospital, Kendallville, IN, p. A208

ADKINS, Kedrick D., Chief Financial Officer, Mayo Clinic Hospital – Rochester, Rochester, MN, p. A338

ADKINS, Kevin, Director Human Resources, Medical City Green Oaks Hospital, Dallas, TX, p. A597

ADKINS, Melisa, Chief Executive Officer, Heartland Regional Medical Center, Marion, IL, p. A188

ADKINS, Michael, Chief Operating Officer, Hca Houston Healthcare Northwest, Houston, TX, p. A611

ADKINS, Paige, Chief Financial Officer, Greenbrier Valley Medical Center, Ronceverte, WV, p. A689

ADKINS, Raymond, Chief Information Officer, Peninsula Regional Medical Center, Salisbury, MD, p. A293

ADKINS, Scott, Manager Information Technology, Vernon Memorial Healthcare, Elk Mound, WI, p. A694

ADKINS, Tyler, Chief Financial Officer, Vaughan Regional Medical Center, Selma, AL, p. A23

ADLER, Josh, M.D., Chief Medical Officer, Ucsf Medical Center, San Francisco, CA, p. A86

ADLER, Kenneth, M.D., Medical Director, Arrowhead Behavioral Health Hospital, Maumee, OH, p. A487

ADLER, Maurita, Director Information Services, Gottlieb Memorial Hospital, Melrose Park, IL, p. A189

ADMA, Vishal, M.D., Medical Director, Kvc Prairie Ridge Psychiatric Hospital, Kansas City, KS, p. A238

ADORNATO, Sara F., Executive Director, Barnes–Kasson County Hospital, Susquehanna, PA, p. A542

ADORNETTO–GARCIA, Debra, MSN, R.N., Chief Nursing Officer, Banner Gateway Medical Center, Gilbert, AZ, p. A29

ADREAN, Christina
Chief Executive Officer, Pam Specialty Hospital Of Victoria North, Victoria, TX, p. A643
Chief Executive Officer, Pam Specialty Hospital Of Victoria South, Victoria, TX, p. A644

ADRIAANSE, Steven W, Vice President and Chief Human Resources Officer, Tallahassee Memorial Healthcare, Tallahassee, FL, p. A141

ADVEY, Linda, Manager Information Systems, Glenbeigh Hospital And Outpatient Centers, Rock Creek, OH, p. A490

AEMMER, Anthony, Director of Nursing, Wellstone Regional Hospital, Jeffersonville, IN, p. A208

AFENYA, Kenneth, M.D., Chief of Staff, Baptist Memorial Hospital–Tipton, Covington, TN, p. A568

AFIFI, Alaa Y, M.D., Chief of Staff, Corona Regional Medical Center, Corona, CA, p. A55

AFLAK, Ziba, Chief Financial Officer, Kindred Hospital–San Francisco Bay Area, San Leandro, CA, p. A87

AFZAL, Muhammed, M.D., Chief of Staff, Sutter Medical Center, Sacramento, Sacramento, CA, p. A82

AGANA, Ben, M.D., Medical Director, Encompass Health Rehabilitation Hospital The Woodlands, Conroe, TX, p. A593

AGEE, Joan, Vice President Patient Care Services, St. Joseph Regional Medical Center, Lewiston, ID, p. A170

AGENBROAD, Connie, Chief Executive Officer, Othello Community Hospital, Othello, WA, p. A676

AGLOINGA, Roy, Chief Administrative Officer, Norton Sound Regional Hospital, Nome, AK, p. A26

AGNEW, Mary Christine, R.N., Senior Vice President and Chief Nursing Officer, Reading Hospital, West Reading, PA, p. A544

AGNI, Guirish, M.D., Chief of Staff, Stoughton Hospital Association, Stoughton, WI, p. A706

AGOSTINI, Irene, M.D., Chief Medical Officer, University Of New Mexico Hospitals, Albuquerque, NM, p. A417

AGOSTO, Paula M, R.N., MSN, Senior Vice President and Chief Nursing Officer, Children'S Hospital Of Philadelphia, Philadelphia, PA, p. A534

AGRELA, Ramona, Associate Chancellor & Chief Human Resources Executive, Uc Irvine Medical Center, Orange, CA, p. A76

AGRESTI, Katie, R.N., Director Patient Care Services, Lecom Health Millcreek Community Hospital, Erie, PA, p. A525

AGUAS, Hugo, Vice President Human Resources, Inova Alexandria Hospital, Alexandria, VA, p. A656

AGUERO, Samuel, Chief Operating Officer, Adventhealth Deland, Deland, FL, p. A121

AGUILA, Marcos, Chief Executive Officer, Hospital San Francisco, San Juan, PR, p. A719

AGUILAR, Gretchen, Director Patient Care and Chief Nursing Officer, Three Rivers Hospital, Brewster, WA, p. A671

AGUILAR, Marisa
Chief Operating Officer, Valley Baptist Medical Center–Brownsville, Rio Hondo, TX, p. A631
Interim Chief Nursing Officer, Valley Baptist Medical Center–Brownsville, Rio Hondo, TX, p. A631

AGUILERA, Louie, Director Information Technology, Foundation Surgical Hospital Of El Paso, El Paso, TX, p. A602

AGUINAGA, Miguel, M.D., FACS, Medical Director, Advanced Care Hospital Of White County, Searcy, AR, p. A48

AGUIRRE, Jose, M.D., Medical Director, Carson Tahoe Continuing Care Hospital, Carson City, NV, p. A393

AGUIRRE, Kim, Director Finance, Northern Cochise Community Hospital, Willcox, AZ, p. A38

AGWUNOBI, Andrew, Chief Executive Officer, Uconn, John Dempsey Hospital, Farmington, CT, p. A108

AHAINE, Israel, Chief Nursing Officer, West Oaks Hospital, Houston, TX, p. A615

AHEARN, Patrick
Chief Executive Officer, Community Medical Center, Toms River, NJ, p. A413
Chief Operating Officer and Senior Vice President, Saint Barnabas Medical Center, Livingston, NJ, p. A407
Chief Operating Officer, Community Medical Center, Toms River, NJ, p. A413

AHL, Dennis, Director Information Technology, Jefferson Community Health And Life, Fairbury, NE, p. A384

AHLERS, Tim, Chief Executive Officer, Guttenberg Municipal Hospital, Guttenberg, IA, p. A223

AHMAD, Shariq, M.D., Chief of Staff, Baptist Hospitals Of Southeast Texas, Beaumont, TX, p. A587

AHMED, Ashraf, M.D., Senior Vice President Physician and Hospital Services, Alliance Community Hospital, Alliance, OH, p. A471

AHMED, Bilal, M.D., Medical Director, Wyoming County Community Hospital, Warsaw, NY, p. A446

AHMED, Imtiaz, Chief of Staff, Mercy Hospital Ada, Ada, OK, p. A496

AHMED, Mohammed Shafeeq, M.D., Vice President of Medical Affairs and Chief Medical Officer, Howard County General Hospital, Columbia, MD, p. A290

AHMED, Omar, Acting Manager Human Resources, Veterans Affairs Caribbean Healthcare System, San Juan, PR, p. A719

AHMED, Sajid, Chief Information and Innovation Officer, Martin Luther King, Jr. Community Hospital, Los Angeles, CA, p. A68
AHMED, Shabeer A, M.D., Clinical Director, Community Behavioral Health Hospital – Annandale, Annandale, MN, p. A327
AHNER, Dawn, Chief Financial Officer, Renown Rehabilitation Hospital, Reno, NV, p. A397
AHRENS, C Todd., President and Chief Executive Officer, Hannibal Regional Hospital, Hannibal, MO, p. A361
AHUJA, Teena, Interim Chief Executive Officer and Regional Vice President of Operations, Willow Creek Behavioral Health, Green Bay, WI, p. A696
AIELLO, Louis
Chief Financial Officer, St. Elizabeth Medical Center, Utica, NY, p. A446
Senior Vice President and Chief Financial Officer, Faxton St. Luke'S Healthcare, Utica, NY, p. A446
AIKEN, David, Chief Human Resources Officer, Madigan Army Medical Center, Tacoma, WA, p. A680
AIKEN, Patsy, Coordinator Human Resource, Spearfish Regional Hospital, Spearfish, SD, p. A564
AIKEN, Richard, M.D., Medical Director, Lakeland Behavioral Health System, Springfield, MO, p. A371
AILOR, Lorie, Chief Executive Officer, Orthopaedic Hospital Of Lutheran Health Network, Fort Wayne, IN, p. A204
AINTABLIAN, Susan, Chief Information Officer, Lac–Olive View–Ucla Medical Center, Los Angeles, CA, p. A68
AIONA, Michael, M.D., Chief of Staff, Shriners Hospitals For Children–Portland, Portland, OR, p. A516
AIRHART, Steven
Chief Executive Officer, Garfield Park Hospital, Chicago, IL, p. A177
Chief Executive Officer, Hartgrove Hospital, Chicago, IL, p. A177
AIROSUS, Diane, Chief Financial Officer, Pembroke Hospital, Pembroke, MA, p. A302
AISEN, Mindy, M.D., Chief Medical Officer, Rancho Los Amigos National Rehabilitation Center, Downey, CA, p. A56
AISENBREY, Lisa, Administrator Human Resources and Support Services, Sidney Health Center, Sidney, MT, p. A380
AIYELAWO, Pius, Chief Operating Officer, National Institutes Of Health Clinical Center, Bethesda, MD, p. A289
AJANAH, Muhammed, M.D., Clinical Director, Clifton T. Perkins Hospital Center, Jessup, MD, p. A291
AJMAL, Farooq, Vice President and Chief Information Officer, Nassau University Medical Center, East Meadow, NY, p. A427
AKENS, Rick, Director Human Resources and Labor Relations, Methodist Medical Center Of Oak Ridge, Oak Ridge, TN, p. A578
AKERS, Earl, Supervisor Information Technology, Salina Surgical Hospital, Salina, KS, p. A245
AKERSON, Jeffrey D., M.D., Chief Medical Officer, Nebraska Medicine – Bellevue, Bellevue, NE, p. A383
AKHRAS, Omar, M.D., Chief of Staff, Putnam General Hospital, Eatonton, GA, p. A153
AKHTAR, M. Osman, Chief Operating Officer, St. John'S Hospital, Maplewood, MN, p. A335
AKIF, Joe, Chief Clinical Officer and Chief Nursing Officer, Warren General Hospital, Warren, PA, p. A543
AKIN, Pam, R.N., MSN, Chief Nursing Officer, Whitman Hospital And Medical Center, Colfax, WA, p. A672
AKIN, Terry, Chief Executive Officer, Moses H. Cone Memorial Hospital, Greensboro, NC, p. A455
AKINS, Tina, Director Human Resources, Lost Rivers Medical Center, Arco, ID, p. A167
AKIYOSHI, Derek, Chief Executive Officer, Leahi Hospital, Honolulu, HI, p. A164
AKOPYAN, George, Director Human Resources, Centinela Hospital Medical Center, Inglewood, CA, p. A62
AL–HASHMI, Samer, M.D., Chief Medical Staff, Stevens County Hospital, Hugoton, KS, p. A237
ALAGAR, Ravi, M.D., Medical Director, Curahealth Pittsburgh, Oakdale, PA, p. A533
ALAM, Md, Chief Information Officer, Brookdale Hospital Medical Center, New York, NY, p. A432
ALAM, Muhammad M, M.D., Medical Director, Turning Point Hospital, Moultrie, GA, p. A158
ALAMEDDINE, Hala, Chief Nursing Executive, Kindred Hospital Sugar Land, Sugar Land, TX, p. A638
ALASZEWSKI, Lydia, Chief Nursing Officer, Select Specialty Hospital–Macomb County, Mount Clemens, MI, p. A318
ALBANO, Valerie, Director, Human Resources, Regional Hospital For Respiratory And Complex Care, Burien, WA, p. A671
ALBANY, Karen, Chief Information Officer, Naval Medical Center, Portsmouth, VA, p. A665
ALBAUM, Michael, M.D., Senior Vice President and Chief Medical Officer, Southern Maine Health Care – Biddeford Medical Center, Biddeford, ME, p. A282
ALBERS, Craig, President and Chief Operating Officer, Mercy Health – St. Charles Hospital, Oregon, OH, p. A489
ALBERT, Debra, MSN, R.N., Senior Vice President Patient Care and Chief Nursing Officer, University Of Chicago Medical Center, Chicago, IL, p. A180
ALBERT, Todd, M.D., Surgeon–in–Chief and Medical Director, Brookdale Hospital Medical Center, New York, NY, p. A432
ALBERTS, Patrick J, Senior Vice President and Chief Operating Officer, Monongahela Valley Hospital, Monongahela, PA, p. A532
ALBERTSON, Chris
Chief Executive Officer, Presentation Medical Center, Rolla, ND, p. A469
Director Human Resources, Presentation Medical Center, Rolla, ND, p. A469
ALBERTSON, Robert, M.D., Chief Medical Officer, Henry Ford Allegiance Specialty Hospital, Jackson, MI, p. A315
ALBIN, James
Chief Information Officer, Baylor St. Luke'S Medical Center, Houston, TX, p. A610
Chief Information Officer, Regional Medical Center, Orangeburg, SC, p. A556
ALBIN, Lonnie, Interim Chief Executive Officer, Highlands Medical Center, Scottsboro, AL, p. A23
ALBOSTA, Kevin, Vice President, Chief Financial Officer, Covenant Healthcare, Saginaw, MI, p. A321
ALBRECHT, David L.
President, District One Hospital, Faribault, MN, p. A332
President, Owatonna Hospital, Owatonna, MN, p. A337
ALBRECHT, John, Chief of Staff, Union Hospital Clinton, Clinton, IN, p. A201
ALBRECHT, Sandra, Interim Chief Financial Officer, Singing River Health System, Pascagoula, MS, p. A352
ALBRIGHT, Bill, Director Human Resources, Stewart Memorial Community Hospital, Lake City, IA, p. A225
ALBRIGHT, Leslie, Vice President Information Systems, Bethesda Hospital East, Boynton Beach, FL, p. A118
ALBRIGHT, Sara Z, Vice President Human Resources, Bassett Medical Center, Cooperstown, NY, p. A426
ALBRIGHT, Tammy
Chief Executive Officer, Greeneville Community Hospital East, Greeneville, TN, p. A570
President, Greeneville Community Hospital West, Greeneville, TN, p. A570
ALBRIGHT, Tina, Director Human Resources, National Park Medical Center, Hot Springs, AR, p. A43
ALCOCER, Deborah, Chief Information Officer, South Texas Rehabilitation Hospital, Brownsville, TX, p. A589
ALDANA, Eladio, Manager Information Systems, College Hospital Costa Mesa, Costa Mesa, CA, p. A55
ALDER, Cal, Director Information Technology, Rock County Hospital, Bassett, NE, p. A382
ALDERFER, Jennifer, President, Good Samaritan Medical Center, Lafayette, CO, p. A102
ALDERMAN, Una, Chief Executive Officer, Northern Idaho Advanced Care Hospital, Post Falls, ID, p. A171
ALDRED, Linda W, Senior Vice President, Texas Children'S Hospital, Houston, TX, p. A614
ALDREDGE, Sarah, M.D., Chief Medical Officer, Essentia Health Sandstone, Sandstone, MN, p. A340
ALDRICH, Alan, Chief Financial Officer, Central Montana Medical Center, Lewistown, MT, p. A378
ALDRICH, Jim, Chief Executive Officer, Select Specialty Hospital – Spectrum Health, Grand Rapids, MI, p. A313
ALDRIDGE, Cassandra Haynes, Chief Human Resources Officer, Phoebe Sumter Medical Center, Americus, GA, p. A145
ALDRIDGE, Kenneth, M.D., Vice President Medical Affairs, Dch Regional Medical Center, Tuscaloosa, AL, p. A24
ALEEM, Asaf, M.D., Medical Director, Peachford Behavioral Health System, Atlanta, GA, p. A146
ALEMAN, Ralph A., President and Chief Executive Officer, Citrus Memorial Health System, Inverness, FL, p. A125
ALEXAITIS, Irene, R.N., Vice President of Nursing and Patient Services and Chief Nursing Officer, Uf Health Shands Hospital, Gainesville, FL, p. A124
ALEXANDA, Lisa, M.D., Vice President Medical Affairs, Parrish Medical Center, Titusville, FL, p. A143
ALEXANDER, Alan B., Vice President and Administrator, The Medical Center At Caverna, Horse Cave, KY, p. A253
ALEXANDER, Amy, Chief Executive Officer, Highlands Behavioral Health System, Littleton, CO, p. A103
ALEXANDER, Angie, Chief Executive Officer, Allegiance Behavioral Health Center Of Plainview, Plainview, TX, p. A629
ALEXANDER, April, Director Human Resources, Brookdale Hospital Medical Center, New York, NY, p. A432
ALEXANDER, Bobby, R.N., Chief Nursing Officer, Pinnacle Pointe Hospital, Little Rock, AR, p. A45
ALEXANDER, Brenda, System Vice President, Human Resources, Ssm Health St. Mary'S Hospital Centralia, Centralia, IL, p. A175
ALEXANDER, Brian, Chief Executive Officer, Sutter Roseville Medical Center, Roseville, CA, p. A81
ALEXANDER, Craig, Chief Operating Officer, Thomas B. Finan Center, Cumberland, MD, p. A290
ALEXANDER, David, Senior Vice President and Chief Financial Officer, St. Joseph'S University Medical Center, Paterson, NJ, p. A410
ALEXANDER, Dean, President and Chief Executive Officer, Christus Santa Rosa Health System, San Antonio, TX, p. A633
ALEXANDER, Debra, Chief Information Officer, Safe Haven Hospital Of Treasure Valley, Boise, ID, p. A167
ALEXANDER, Drew, Chief Nursing Officer, Cedar County Memorial Hospital, El Dorado Springs, MO, p. A359
ALEXANDER, Fred, M.D., Medical Director, Kaiser Permanente West Los Angeles Medical Center, Los Angeles, CA, p. A67
ALEXANDER, Jack, M.D., Chief Medical Officer, Mayo Clinic Health System In Red Wing, Red Wing, MN, p. A338
ALEXANDER, Jane, Director Facility Administrative Services, Sagamore Children'S Psychiatric Center, Dix Hills, NY, p. A427
ALEXANDER, Jeffrey, Chief Executive Officer, Encompass Health Rehabilitation Hospital Of Spring Hill, Brooksville, FL, p. A119
ALEXANDER, Jeremy, Chief Executive Officer, Fort Madison Community Hospital, Fort Madison, IA, p. A223
ALEXANDER, Josette, Director, Human Resources, Ohiohealth Rehabilitation Hospital, Columbus, OH, p. A479
ALEXANDER, Lisa, Vice President Patient Services and Chief Nursing Officer, University Of Kansas Health System St. Francis Campus, Topeka, KS, p. A246
ALEXANDER, Thomas, Chief Executive Officer, Vibra Specialty Hospital At Desoto, Desoto, TX, p. A600
ALEXANDER–HINES, Joyce, R.N., MSN, Associate Director, Patient Care Services, Fayetteville Veterans Affairs Medical Center, Fayetteville, NC, p. A454
ALFANO, Alan, M.D., Medical Director, Uva–Healthsouth Rehabilitation Hospital, Charlottesville, VA, p. A657
ALFANO, Anthony, Vice President Executive Director, Montefiore New Rochelle, New Rochelle, NY, p. A432
ALFORD, Charles, Vice President Financial Services, Vidant Edgecombe Hospital, Tarboro, NC, p. A463
ALFORD, Jon, Chief Financial Officer, Medical City Plano, Plano, TX, p. A629
ALFORD, Karla, Chief Information Officer, Greater Regional Medical Center, Creston, IA, p. A220
ALFORD, Michelle, R.N., MSN, Director of Nursing, Washington County Hospital, Chatom, AL, p. A16
ALFRED, Lorrie, Director Human Resources, Southern Surgical Hospital, Slidell, LA, p. A279
ALGER, Steve, Senior Vice President and Chief Financial Officer, Lakes Regional Healthcare, Spirit Lake, IA, p. A230
ALHADEFF, Joseph, President, Oss Orthopaedic Hospital, York, PA, p. A546
ALI, Irfan, Director Information Services, Saint Agnes Medical Center, Fresno, CA, p. A59
ALI, Mirza Z, M.D., Chief of Staff, Wilkes–Barre Veterans Affairs Medical Center, Wilkes, PA, p. A545
ALI, Muhammad, M.D., Chief Medical Officer, Sanford Tracy Medical Center, Tracy, MN, p. A341
ALI, Syed Asif, M.D., Chief of Staff, Syracuse Veterans Affairs Medical Center, Syracuse, NY, p. A445
ALI–KHAN, Mir, M.D., Medical Director, Canyon Ridge Hospital, Chino, CA, p. A54
ALI–KHAN, Mujtaba, D.O., Chief Medical Officer, Hca Houston Healthcare Conroe, Conroe, TX, p. A593
ALICE, Patricia K., Chief Executive Officer, Arizona Orthopedic Surgical Hospital, Chandler, AZ, p. A28
ALICEA, Luis, Chief Information Officer, Doctors' Center Hospital San Juan, San Juan, PR, p. A718
ALICEA PEREZ, Eneida, Interim Nursing Director, Hospital Buen Samaritano, Aguadilla, PR, p. A714
ALIFF, Sarah, Ph.D., Chief Nursing Officer, Hot Springs County Memorial Hospital, Thermopolis, WY, p. A713
ALKHOULI, Hassan, M.D.
Chief Medical Officer, Garden Grove Hospital And Medical Center, Garden Grove, CA, p. A60
Chief Medical Officer, West Anaheim Medical Center, Anaheim, CA, p. A50
Medical Director, Huntington Beach Hospital, Huntington Beach, CA, p. A62
ALLA, Vamseedhar, M.D., Director Medical Staff, Connecticut Veterans Home And Hospital, Rocky Hill, CT, p. A110
ALLARD, Joan, Director Human Resources, Adventhealth Heart Of Florida, Davenport, FL, p. A121
ALLARD, Marie, Finance Manager, Ascension Brighton Center For Recovery, Brighton, MI, p. A307
ALLATT, Richard, M.D., Medical Director, Encompass Health Nittany Valley Rehabilitation Hospital, Pleasant Gap, PA, p. A539

ALLDREDGE, Kim, Director Human Resources, Lawrence County Memorial Hospital, Lawrenceville, IL, p. A187

ALLEMAN, Scott, Senior Vice President Patient Care Services and Chief Nursing Officer, Uw Medicine/Valley Medical Center, Renton, WA, p. A677

ALLEN, Audrey, Coordinator Benefits, Dallas County Medical Center, Fordyce, AR, p. A42

ALLEN, Brian, M.D., President Medical Staff, Georgetown Community Hospital, Georgetown, KY, p. A252

ALLEN, Candice, Director of Nursing, Rio Grande Hospital, Del Norte, CO, p. A98

ALLEN, Carolyn
Chief Financial Officer, Saint Michael'S Medical Center, Newark, NJ, p. A409
Vice President and Chief Financial Officer, Camden Clark Medical Center, Parkersburg, WV, p. A688

ALLEN, Dawn, R.N., Chief Clinical Officer, Carris Health – Redwood, Redwood Falls, MN, p. A338

ALLEN, Devon, M.D., Chief of Medical Staff, Samuel Simmonds Memorial Hospital, Barrow, AK, p. A25

ALLEN, Donald, Chief Operating Officer, Unity Medical & Surgical Hospital, Mishawaka, IN, p. A211

ALLEN, Jason
Chief Operating Officer, Brook Lane Health Services, Hagerstown, MD, p. A291
Director Patient Care Services, Brook Lane Health Services, Hagerstown, MD, p. A291

ALLEN, Jean, Human Resources Director, Bleckley Memorial Hospital, Cochran, GA, p. A150

ALLEN, Jennifer, Vice President Human Resources, Plantation General Hospital, Plantation, FL, p. A137

ALLEN, John, Chief Information Officer, Holzer Medical Center, Gallipolis, OH, p. A483

ALLEN, John P., President, St. Mary'S Medical Center, San Francisco, CA, p. A86

ALLEN, Judy, Human Resource Specialist, Carl Albert Community Mental Health Center, Mcalester, OK, p. A502

ALLEN, Kandice K., Chief Executive Officer, Share Medical Center, Alva, OK, p. A496

ALLEN, Karen A, R.N., Chief Nursing Officer, Butler Health System, Butler, PA, p. A521

ALLEN, Keith
Senior Vice President and Chief Human Resources Officer, Community Memorial Hospital, Menomonee Falls, WI, p. A700
Senior Vice President and Chief Human Resources Officer, Froedtert And The Medical College Of Wisconsin Froedtert Hospital, Milwaukee, WI, p. A701

ALLEN, Kent, Director Human Resources, Midmichigan Medical Center – West Branch, West Branch, MI, p. A325

ALLEN, Linda M, Vice President Human Resources, The Children'S Institute Of Pittsburgh, Pittsburgh, PA, p. A537

ALLEN, Lucretia, Director Human Resources, Sweetwater Hospital, Sweetwater, TN, p. A580

ALLEN, Mark, Chief Operating Officer, Marian Regional Medical Center, Santa Maria, CA, p. A89

ALLEN, Mary Beth, Vice President Human Resources, Emory University Hospital, Atlanta, GA, p. A146

ALLEN, Mike
Director Information Services, Adventhealth Shawnee Mission, Shawnee Mission, KS, p. A245
Director Information Services, Shriners Hospitals For Children–Spokane, Spokane, WA, p. A680
Director Information Technology, Shriners Hospitals For Children–Salt Lake City, Salt Lake City, UT, p. A652

ALLEN, Myrna, R.N., MS, Chief Operating and Nursing Officer, Martin Luther King, Jr. Community Hospital, Los Angeles, CA, p. A68

ALLEN, Nancy, R.N., MS, Director, Patient Services and Chief Nursing Executive, Advocate Eureka Hospital, Eureka, IL, p. A182

ALLEN, Nikki, Patient Care Executive, Sutter Amador Hospital, Jackson, CA, p. A62

ALLEN, Patty, St. John's Vice President Finance, Hshs St. John'S Hospital, Springfield, IL, p. A196

ALLEN, R Keith, Senior Vice President Human Resources, University Of Maryland Medical Center, Baltimore, MD, p. A287

ALLEN, Richard
Chief Executive Officer, Palmdale Regional Medical Center, Palmdale, CA, p. A77
Chief Executive Officer, Warren General Hospital, Warren, PA, p. A543

ALLEN, Rob, Chief Executive Officer, Sitka Community Hospital, Sitka, AK, p. A27

ALLEN, Robert, President and Chief Executive Officer, Hollywood Presbyterian Medical Center, Los Angeles, CA, p. A67

ALLEN, Robert, M.D., Chief Medical Officer, Mercy Hospital Of Folsom, Folsom, CA, p. A58

ALLEN, Scott J, Director Human Resources, Hudson Hospital And Clinic, Hudson, WI, p. A697

ALLEN, Timothy J.
Chief Executive Officer, Leonard J. Chabert Medical Center, Houma, LA, p. A268
Chief Executive Officer, Ochsner St. Anne General Hospital, Raceland, LA, p. A277

ALLEN, Timothy M, Vice President Human Resources, United Hospital Center, Bridgeport, WV, p. A683

ALLEN, Vicki, Chief Financial Officer, Chicot Memorial Medical Center, Lake Village, AR, p. A44

ALLEN, Vicki, R.N., MS, Vice President Patient Care Services and Chief Nursing Officer, Harnett Health System, Dunn, NC, p. A452

ALLEN, Wain, M.D., Medical Director, Park City Hospital, Park City, UT, p. A650

ALLEN, Wayne, Interim Chief Executive Officer, Mendocino Coast District Hospital, Fort Bragg, CA, p. A58

ALLEN, Zac, CPA, Chief Financial Officer, Floyd Cherokee Medical Center, Centre, AL, p. A16

ALLEN–DAVIS, Jandel, President and Chief Executive Officer, Craig Hospital, Englewood, CO, p. A100

ALLENSWORTH, Ed, M.D., Medical Director, Saint Francis Hospital Vinita, Vinita, OK, p. A510

ALLEY, David, Chief Financial Officer, Starr Regional Medical Center, Athens, TN, p. A566

ALLEY, John L., Chief Executive Officer, Woodlawn Hospital, Rochester, IN, p. A214

ALLEY, Jon, D.O., President Medical Staff, Cameron Memorial Community Hospital, Angola, IN, p. A199

ALLEY, Steve B, M.D., Chief of Staff, Crosbyton Clinic Hospital, Crosbyton, TX, p. A595

ALLGEIER, Patricia, R.N., Chief Nursing Officer, Boys Town National Research Hospital, Omaha, NE, p. A388

ALLGOOD, Libby, Chief Financial Officer, Kittitas Valley Healthcare, Ellensburg, WA, p. A672

ALLICON, Keary T, Vice President Finance and Chief Financial Officer, Baystate Wing Hospital, Palmer, MA, p. A302

ALLIES, Karla, Director Human Resources, Rosebud Health Care Center, Forsyth, MT, p. A376

ALLINSON, Randy, R.N., Chief Nursing Officer, Central Valley Medical Center, Nephi, UT, p. A649

ALLISON, Lorraine, Human Resource Partner, Peacehealth Peace Island Medical Center, Friday Harbor, WA, p. A673

ALLISON, Steve, Director Human Resources, Logan County Hospital, Oakley, KS, p. A242

ALLISON, William E., Senior Vice President and Chief Operating Officer, Administration, South Nassau Communities Hospital, Oceanside, NY, p. A440

ALLMAN, Rex, M.D., President Medical Staff, Pulaski Memorial Hospital, Winamac, IN, p. A216

ALLORE, Gary, President, Mercy Health Hackley Campus, Muskegon, MI, p. A318

ALLPHIN, Allan, M.D., Chief of Staff, Mercy Hospital Springfield, Springfield, MO, p. A371

ALLPORT, Jeff, Vice President, Chief Information Officer, Valley Presbyterian Hospital, Los Angeles, CA, p. A70

ALLRED, Al W, Chief Financial Officer, Adventhealth New Smyrna Beach, New Smyrna Beach, FL, p. A133

ALLRED, B Dee, M.D., President Medical Staff, Jordan Valley Medical Center, West Jordan, UT, p. A653

ALLRED, Lowell C, M.D., Chief of Staff, Columbia Basin Hospital, Ephrata, WA, p. A673

ALLRED, William, M.D., Vice President Medical Affairs, St. John Medical Center, Tulsa, OK, p. A510

ALLSOP, Brian, Director Human Resources, Central Valley Medical Center, Nephi, UT, p. A649

ALLSTOTT, Patti, Administrative Coordinator Human Resources and Grant Writer, Pioneer Memorial Hospital, Heppner, OR, p. A513

ALLUSON, Valerie, M.D., Chief Medical Officer, Hackensack Meridian Health Mountainside Medical Center, Montclair, NJ, p. A408

ALMAUHY, Deborah, R.N., Chief Nursing Officer, Emory Rehabilitation Hospital, Atlanta, GA, p. A146

ALMEIDA, Sergio, Director Information Systems, West Houston Medical Center, Houston, TX, p. A614

ALMEIDA–SUAREZ, Mario, M.D., Chief of Staff, Larkin Community Hospital–South Miami Campus, South Miami, FL, p. A140

ALMENDINGER, J Todd., President and Chief Executive Officer, Magruder Memorial Hospital, Port Clinton, OH, p. A490

ALMETER, Connie, Director of Nursing (Acute), Wyoming County Community Hospital, Warsaw, NY, p. A446

ALMETER, Marilyn, Chief Nursing Officer, United Memorial Medical Center, Batavia, NY, p. A423

ALMODOVAR, Gustavo, Executive Director, Hospital De La Concepcion, San German, PR, p. A718

ALMOHAMMED, Salah, Chief of Staff, Ut Health Carthage, Carthage, TX, p. A591

ALO, Kathleen, Chief Nursing Officer, Mammoth Hospital, Mammoth Lakes, CA, p. A70

ALONSO, Gwen, Chief Nursing Officer, Adventhealth Zephyrhills, Zephyrhills, FL, p. A144

ALONSO, Jose', M.D., Medical Director, San Juan Capestrano Hospital, San Juan, PR, p. A719

ALONZO, Patti, Manager Human Resources, Pacifica Hospital Of The Valley, Los Angeles, CA, p. A68

ALPERT, Jeffrey, M.D., Medical Director, Wichita County Health Center, Leoti, KS, p. A239

ALPERT, Len, Director Human Resources, Larkin Community Hospital Behavioral Health Services, Hollywood, FL, p. A124

ALRASHEDY, Farhad H, M.D., Chief Medical Officer, Ferry County Memorial Hospital, Republic, WA, p. A677

ALSADON, Danielle, Clinic/Hospital Manager, Kenmare Community Hospital, Kenmare, ND, p. A468

ALSIP, Bryan, M.D., Executive Vice President, Chief Medical Officer, University Health System, San Antonio, TX, p. A635

ALSTAD, Nancy, Director Human Resources, Fort Healthcare, Fort Atkinson, WI, p. A695

ALT, Melinda, Chief Financial Officer, Audubon County Memorial Hospital And Clinics, Audubon, IA, p. A217

ALTARAS, June
Chief Executive Officer, Swedish Medical Center–Cherry Hill Campus, Seattle, WA, p. A678
Chief Executive Officer, Swedish Medical Center–First Hill, Seattle, WA, p. A678

ALTENBURGER, Andy, Chief Information Officer, Marietta Memorial Hospital, Marietta, OH, p. A486

ALTENDORF, Amanda, Chief Human Resources and Quality Management, Red River Behavioral Health System, Grand Forks, ND, p. A467

ALTHOEN, David, Director Financial Planning and Analysis, Forest Health Medical Center, Ypsilanti, MI, p. A325

ALTHOUSE, Douglas, Chief Medical Staff, Kearney County Health Services, Minden, NE, p. A387

ALTMAN, Alexander B, Chief Financial Officer, Union County General Hospital, Clayton, NM, p. A417

ALTMAN, Angie, Director Human Resources, Shands Lake Shore Regional Medical Center, Lake City, FL, p. A127

ALTMAN, Brett, Chief Executive Officer, Cass County Memorial Hospital, Atlantic, IA, p. A217

ALTMAN, Deana, Interim Chief Nursing Officer, Harney District Hospital, Burns, OR, p. A511

ALTMAN, Harold, M.D., Chief Medical Officer, Acmh Hospital, Kittanning, PA, p. A528

ALTMILLER, Steve, President and Chief Executive Officer, Camden Clark Medical Center, Parkersburg, WV, p. A688

ALTOM, Andy, President and Chief Executive Officer, Methodist Behavioral Hospital Of Arkansas, Maumelle, AR, p. A45

ALTOSE, Murray, M.D., Chief of Staff, Louis Stokes Cleveland Veterans Affairs Medical Center, Cleveland, OH, p. A478

ALTSHULER, Keith, President and Chief Administrative Officer, Fort Sanders Regional Medical Center, Knoxville, TN, p. A572

ALUISE, Tony, Chief Executive Officer, Three Gables Surgery Center, Proctorville, OH, p. A490

ALURI, Bapu, M.D., Chief Medical Officer, Yuma Rehabilitation Hospital, A Partnership Of Encompass Health And Yrmc, Yuma, AZ, p. A38

ALVARADO, Felicita E., Administrator, Hospital Psiquiatrico Correccional, San Juan, PR, p. A719

ALVARADO, Rafael, Chief Executive Officer, Dr. Pila'S Hospital, Ponce, PR, p. A717

ALVARADO, Ramona, Interim Manager Human Resources, Adventist Medical Center–Reedley, Reedley, CA, p. A80

ALVAREZ, Dena C, R.N., COO & Chief Compliance Officer, Brodstone Memorial Hospital, Superior, NE, p. A392

ALVAREZ, Janie, Accounting Director, Cornerstone Regional Hospital, Edinburg, TX, p. A601

ALVAREZ, Jose, M.D., Chief Medical Staff, Circles Of Care, Melbourne, FL, p. A129

ALVAREZ, Maria Charlotte, M.D., Chief of Staff, Sheridan Community Hospital, Sheridan, MI, p. A322

ALVAREZ, Valerie, Executive Assistant, Adventist Medical Center–Reedley, Reedley, CA, p. A80

ALVEY, Raymond, Chief Financial Officer, Ssm Health Saint Louis University Hospital, Saint Louis, MO, p. A370

ALWARD, Dale, Chief Executive Officer, Twin County Regional Healthcare, Galax, VA, p. A660

ALWIN–POPP, Sue, Chief Clinical Officer, Edgerton Hospital And Health Services, Edgerton, WI, p. A694

ALWINE, Steven, Chief Executive Officer, Encompass Health Rehabilitation Hospital Of York, York, PA, p. A546

ALZEIN, Bashar, M.D., President Medical Staff, Illini Community Hospital, Pittsfield, IL, p. A193

AMADO, Mitchell, Senior Vice President Finance and Chief Financial Officer, Glens Falls Hospital, Glens Falls, NY, p. A428

AMANTEA, Paul, Director Finance, University Hospitals Geauga Medical Center, Chardon, OH, p. A475

AMAR, Eugene, Jr, Administrator, Kohala Hospital, Kohala, HI, p. A166

AMARANTOS, Stacie, Chief Operating Officer, Catalina Island Medical Center, Avalon, CA, p. A51

AMATO, Jerry, President and Chief Operating Officer, Lakeview Specialty Hospital And Rehab, Waterford, WI, p. A707

AMBERSON, Rosemarie, Vice President Human Resources, Aventura Hospital And Medical Center, Aventura, FL, p. A117

AMBROSE, Sherie, Chief Nurse Executive, Sequoia Hospital, Redwood City, CA, p. A80

AMBROSIANI, Michael, Chief Financial Officer, Knox Community Hospital, Mount Vernon, OH, p. A488

AMBROSINI, Joseph, Director Human Resources, Olympia Medical Center, Los Angeles, CA, p. A68

AMEEN, David J., Interim President and Chief Executive Officer, St. Francis Memorial Hospital, West Point, NE, p. A392

AMENT, Arlinda K, R.N., Interim Chief Nursing Officer, Beatrice Community Hospital And Health Center, Beatrice, NE, p. A383

AMENT, Rick, Chief Executive Officer, Robert J. Dole Veterans Affairs Medical Center, Wichita, KS, p. A248

AMERSON, Jeff, Director Information System, West Florida Hospital, Pensacola, FL, p. A136

AMES, Becky, Chief Executive Officer, Medical Center Of Southeast Texas, Beaumont, TX, p. A587

AMES, Lance, Interim Chief Executive Officer, South Texas Health System, Edinburg, TX, p. A601

AMIN, Saad, Medical Director Hospital, Kindred Hospital–Greensboro, Greensboro, NC, p. A455

AMMAZZALORSO, Michael, M.D., Chief Medical Officer, Nyu Winthrop Hospital, Mineola, NY, p. A431

AMMONS, Angela, Administrator, Clinch Memorial Hospital, Homerville, GA, p. A155

AMMONS, Eric, President, Mercy Hospital Jefferson, Festus, MO, p. A360

AMODO, Mitch, Vice President and Chief Financial Officer, Orange Regional Medical Center, Middletown, NY, p. A431

AMOH, Eric, Chief Executive Officer, Behavioral Hospital Of Bellaire, Houston, TX, p. A610

AMOROSE, Carl, Vice President Finance, Norton Hospital, Louisville, KY, p. A256

AMOROSO, Mitzo, Chief Information Officer, Brookdale Hospital Medical Center, New York, NY, p. A432

AMOS, John R.
Chief Executive Officer, Yavapai Regional Medical Center, Prescott, AZ, p. A35
President and Chief Executive Officer, Yavapai Regional Medical Center, Prescott, AZ, p. A35

AMOS, Robert, Vice President and Chief Financial Officer, Winchester Medical Center, Winchester, VA, p. A669

AMOX, Mark J., Chief Operating Officer, Sunrise Hospital And Medical Center, Las Vegas, NV, p. A396

AMSBERRY, Shelly, Director of Nursing, Jennie M. Melham Memorial Medical Center, Broken Bow, NE, p. A383

AMSTUTZ, Charles, Director of Information Technology, Cascade Medical Center, Leavenworth, WA, p. A674

AMYX, Maleigha, Chief Information Officer, Rockcastle Regional Hospital And Respiratory Care Center, Mount Vernon, KY, p. A258

ANASTASI, Frank, Chief Financial Officer, Pennsylvania Hospital, Philadelphia, PA, p. A536

ANAYA, Sandra J., Chief Executive Officer, Palo Verde Hospital, Blythe, CA, p. A53

ANCHONDO, Laura, Administrator Human Resources, Kindred Hospital El Paso, El Paso, TX, p. A602

ANCZAK, Deb, Interim Chief Executive Officer, Livingston Healthcare, Livingston, MT, p. A378

ANDERER, Tammy, Acting President, Geisinger Jersey Shore Hospital, Jersey Shore, PA, p. A528

ANDERS, Anna, R.N., MSN, Vice President and Chief Nursing Officer, Carson Tahoe Health, Carson City, NV, p. A393

ANDERS, James M, Administrator and Chief Operating Officer, Kennedy Krieger Institute, Baltimore, MD, p. A286

ANDERS, Mark, Administrator, Villa Feliciana Medical Complex, Jackson, LA, p. A269

ANDERS, Robert, Chief Financial Officer, Ouachita County Medical Center, Camden, AR, p. A40

ANDERSEN, Connie, R.N., MS, Chief Nursing Officer, Sarasota Memorial Health Care System, Sarasota, FL, p. A139

ANDERSEN, Donia L, Director of Nursing, Centennial Peaks Hospital, Louisville, CO, p. A104

ANDERSEN, Frank, Interim Chief Medical Officer, Providence Regional Medical Center Everett, Everett, WA, p. A673

ANDERSEN, Janet
Chief Financial Officer, Ut Health Pittsburg, Pittsburg, TX, p. A628
Chief Financial Officer, Ut Health Quitman, Quitman, TX, p. A630

ANDERSEN, John, Manager Information Systems, Astria Sunnyside Hospital, Sunnyside, WA, p. A680

ANDERSEN, Sue
Chief Financial Officer, French Hospital Medical Center, San Luis Obispo, CA, p. A87
Vice President and Service Area and Chief Financial Officer, Marian Regional Medical Center, Santa Maria, CA, p. A89

ANDERSEN, Tracy, Chief Information Officer, St. Mary'S Regional Medical Center, Enid, OK, p. A499

ANDERSEN, Travis, Chief Executive Officer, Ascension Columbia St. Mary'S Hospital Milwaukee, Milwaukee, WI, p. A700

ANDERSEN, Wendy, Director Human Resources, Eastern Idaho Regional Medical Center, Idaho Falls, ID, p. A169

ANDERSON, Alison, Chief Nursing Officer, Select Specialty Hospital–Sioux Falls, Sioux Falls, SD, p. A564

ANDERSON, Allen, Administrator, Avera Tyler Hospital, Tyler, MN, p. A341

ANDERSON, Allyson, President, Legacy Meridian Park Medical Center, Tualatin, OR, p. A518

ANDERSON, Angie, Director Information Technology, Crawford County Memorial Hospital, Denison, IA, p. A221

ANDERSON, Benjamin, Chief Executive Officer and Administrator, Kearny County Hospital, Lakin, KS, p. A238

ANDERSON, Bill, Chief Executive Officer, Lakeview Behavioral Health, Norcross, GA, p. A158

ANDERSON, Brad
Chief Financial Officer, Community Memorial Hospital, Cloquet, MN, p. A330
Chief Operating Officer, Rehabilitation Hospital Of Wisconsin, Waukesha, WI, p. A707

ANDERSON, Braden, Chief Executive Officer, Caprock Hospital, Bryan, TX, p. A590

ANDERSON, Brian
Chief Financial Officer, Capital Medical Center, Olympia, WA, p. A676
Chief Financial Officer, Simi Valley Hospital, Simi Valley, CA, p. A89

ANDERSON, Brian A., D.O., Chief of Staff, Myrtue Medical Center, Harlan, IA, p. A224

ANDERSON, Calandra, Vice President Patient Care and Chief Nursing Officer, Mclaren Oakland, Pontiac, MI, p. A320

ANDERSON, Charles, M.D., Chief Medical Officer, Desert Regional Medical Center, Palm Springs, CA, p. A76

ANDERSON, Cherri, Chief Nursing Officer, Banner Behavioral Health Hospital – Scottsdale, Scottsdale, AZ, p. A35

ANDERSON, Christine, Chief Nursing Officer and Vice President of Patient Care Services, Lincolnhealth, Damariscotta, ME, p. A282

ANDERSON, Conde Nevin, M.D., Chief of Staff, Detar Healthcare System, Victoria, TX, p. A643

ANDERSON, Craig, Director Management Information Systems, River Bend Hospital, West Lafayette, IN, p. A216

ANDERSON, Dale, Chief Executive Officer, North Metro Medical Center, Jacksonville, AR, p. A43

ANDERSON, Dana, Administrator, Long–Term Acute Care Hospital, Mosaic Life Care At St. Joseph, Saint Joseph, MO, p. A368

ANDERSON, Darla, Chief Financial Officer, Ridgeview Sibley Medical Center, Arlington, MN, p. A327

ANDERSON, Dave, Vice President and Administrator, Atrium Health Anson, Wadesboro, NC, p. A463

ANDERSON, Dave, FACHE, Vice President Administration, Atrium Health Union, Monroe, NC, p. A458

ANDERSON, David, Chief Executive Officer, Jackson Purchase Medical Center, Mayfield, KY, p. A257

ANDERSON, Dianne J., President and Chief Executive Officer, Lawrence General Hospital, Lawrence, MA, p. A299

ANDERSON, Donna K, R.N., Chief Nursing Officer, Anmed Health Cannon, Pickens, SC, p. A556

ANDERSON, Duke, President and Chief Executive Officer, Hillsdale Hospital, Hillsdale, MI, p. A314

ANDERSON, Edwin, M.D., Chief of Staff and Chief Medical Officer, Bigfork Valley Hospital, Bigfork, MN, p. A328

ANDERSON, Gaynell, M.D., Medical Director, Ssm Health St. Anthony Hospital – Shawnee, Shawnee, OK, p. A507

ANDERSON, Gina, Human Resources Officer, Riverview Regional Medical Center, Carthage, TN, p. A566

ANDERSON, Heidi, Chief Nursing Officer, Arbor Health, Morton Hospital, Morton, WA, p. A675

ANDERSON, Jason, Chief Financial Officer, Mackinac Straits Health System, Inc., Saint Ignace, MI, p. A321

ANDERSON, Jay
President, Northwestern Medicine Kishwaukee Hospital, Dekalb, IL, p. A181
President, Northwestern Medicine Valley West Hospital, Sandwich, IL, p. A195

ANDERSON, Joann, President and Chief Executive Officer, Southeastern Health, Lumberton, NC, p. A458

ANDERSON, Jodie, Director Human Resources, Mitchell County Regional Health Center, Osage, IA, p. A228

ANDERSON, John D., Administrator, Marshall Medical Center South, Boaz, AL, p. A15

ANDERSON, John G.
President and Chief Executive Officer, Anderson Regional Health System South, Meridian, MS, p. A351
President and Chief Executive Officer, Anderson Regional Health System, Meridian, MS, p. A351

ANDERSON, Jonathan, Medical Director, Western State Hospital, Staunton, VA, p. A668

ANDERSON, Kathleen, Director, Acute Clinical Systems, Prisma Health Laurens County Hospital, Clinton, SC, p. A550

ANDERSON, Kenneth, M.D., Vice President and Chief Medical Officer, Baptist Health Louisville, Louisville, KY, p. A256

ANDERSON, Kimball S., Chief Executive Officer, Timpanogos Regional Hospital, Orem, UT, p. A650

ANDERSON, Kristin, Director, Human Resources, California Hospital Medical Center, Los Angeles, CA, p. A66

ANDERSON, Libby, Chief Financial Officer, Satanta District Hospital And Long Term Care, Satanta, KS, p. A245

ANDERSON, Louis, Chief Financial Officer, Mcleod Health Cheraw, Cheraw, SC, p. A550

ANDERSON, Lucia E, Senior Vice President Operations and Chief Nurse Executive, Lake Region Healthcare, Fergus Falls, MN, p. A332

ANDERSON, Mark
Chief Financial Officer, North Oaks Medical Center, Hammond, LA, p. A268
Chief Financial Officer, North Oaks Rehabilitation Hospital, Hammond, LA, p. A268

ANDERSON, Mark T, Chief Financial Officer, Sovah Health–Danville, Danville, VA, p. A658

ANDERSON, Michael, President, Ucsf Medical Center, San Francisco, CA, p. A86

ANDERSON, Michael Bruce, Ph.D., Chief Operating Officer, Metropolitan St. Louis Psychiatric Center, Saint Louis, MO, p. A369

ANDERSON, Mickey, M.D., Vice President Medical Affairs, Chi Flaget Memorial Hospital, Bardstown, KY, p. A249

ANDERSON, Patricia, Chief Nursing Officer, Riverview Regional Medical Center, Carthage, TN, p. A566

ANDERSON, Patrick
Chief Information Officer and Senior Vice President, Hoag Memorial Hospital Presbyterian, Newport Beach, CA, p. A74
Chief Information Officer, Memorial Medical Center, Modesto, CA, p. A72

ANDERSON, Paula, Administrative Director Human Resources, Endless Mountain Health Systems, Montrose, PA, p. A532

ANDERSON, Randy, Interim Chief Executive Officer, Roundup Memorial Healthcare, Roundup, MT, p. A380

ANDERSON, Rhena
Chief Nursing Officer, Nexus Specialty Hospital The Woodlands, The Woodlands, TX, p. A641
Chief Nursing Officer, Nexus Specialty Hospital, Shenandoah, TX, p. A636

ANDERSON, Rhonda
Executive Vice President Finance and Chief Financial Officer, Ascension Columbia St. Mary'S Hospital Milwaukee, Milwaukee, WI, p. A700
Executive Vice President Finance and Chief Financial Officer, Ascension Columbia St. Mary'S Hospital Ozaukee, Mequon, WI, p. A700
Executive Vice President Finance and Chief Financial Officer, Ascension Columbia St. Mary'S Milwaukee Hospital, Milwaukee, WI, p. A700

ANDERSON, Rick, M.D., Senior Vice President and Chief Medical Officer, Tmc Healthcare, Tucson, AZ, p. A38

ANDERSON, Rob, Chief Executive Officer, The Hospitals Of Providence Sierra Campus, El Paso, TX, p. A603

ANDERSON, Robert C, Interim Chief Financial Officer, Alameda Hospital, Alameda, CA, p. A50

ANDERSON, Robert G., Jr, President, Osf Saint Francis Medical Center, Peoria, IL, p. A193

ANDERSON, Rohan, Chief Information Officer, Doctors Memorial Hospital, Bonifay, FL, p. A118

ANDERSON, Rosemary, Administrator, Ccc At Pineview Hospital, Lakeside, AZ, p. A31

ANDERSON, Sandra L.
President and Chief Executive Officer, Ascension Sacred Heart Hospital, Tomahawk, WI, p. A707

President and Chief Executive Officer, Howard Young Medical Center, Woodruff, WI, p. A709

President, Ascension Eagle River Hospital, Eagle River, WI, p. A694

President, Ascension St. Mary'S Hospital, Rhinelander, WI, p. A704

ANDERSON, Scott, Chief Medical Officer, Banner Del E. Webb Medical Center, Sun City West, AZ, p. A36

ANDERSON, Sharla, Chief Executive Officer, Christus Trinity Mother Frances Rehabilitation Hospital, A Partner Of Encompass Health, Tyler, TX, p. A642

ANDERSON, Shawn, Chief Operating Officer, Cary Medical Center, Caribou, ME, p. A282

ANDERSON, Sims, Manager Facility Automation, Terrell State Hospital, Terrell, TX, p. A640

ANDERSON, Stephanie
Executive Vice President and Chief Operating Officer, Woman'S Hospital, Baton Rouge, LA, p. A264
Interim Chief Executive Officer, Woman'S Hospital, Baton Rouge, LA, p. A264

ANDERSON, Stephen, M.D., Chief Medical Officer, Plymouth Medical Center, Plymouth, IN, p. A213

ANDERSON, Steven, Chief Executive Officer, University Of Kansas Health System St. Francis Campus, Topeka, KS, p. A246

ANDERSON, Susan, Director Information Systems, Texas Health Presbyterian Hospital Plano, Plano, TX, p. A630

ANDERSON, Suzanne P., Nurse Administrator, Intermountain Medical Center, Murray, UT, p. A649

ANDERSON, Terry, R.N., Director of Nursing Services, Ccm Health, Montevideo, MN, p. A336

ANDERSON, Thomas, Vice President Medical Affairs, Lakeview Hospital, Stillwater, MN, p. A341

ANDERSON, Thomas, M.D.
Vice President Medical Affairs, Chambersburg Hospital, Chambersburg, PA, p. A522
Vice President Medical Affairs, Waynesboro Hospital, Waynesboro, PA, p. A543

ANDERSON, Tim, Controller, Van Matre Encompass Health, Rockford, IL, p. A195

ANDERSON, Timothy Craig, Chief Nursing Officer, Bristol Regional Medical Center, Bristol, TN, p. A566

ANDERSON, Traci, Chief Financial Officer, Memorial Hospital, Seminole, TX, p. A636

ANDERSON, Valerie, Chief Nursing Officer, Select Specialty Hospital–Tri Cities, Bristol, TN, p. A566

ANDERSON, William, Medical Director, Rosebud Health Care Center, Forsyth, MT, p. A376

ANDERT, Nancy, Director Human Resources, Murray County Medical Center, Slayton, MN, p. A340

ANDERT, Vicki, Chief Executive Officer, River Valley Medical Center, Dardanelle, AR, p. A41

ANDERTON, Scott, Chief Financial Officer, Coliseum Medical Centers, Macon, GA, p. A156

ANDRADA, Sally, Chief Information Officer, Los Alamitos Medical Center, Los Alamitos, CA, p. A65

ANDRADE, Marise, Controller, Southern Inyo Healthcare District, Lone Pine, CA, p. A65

ANDRAE, Andrea, Chief Financial Officer, St. Luke'S – Gnaden Huetten Campus, Lehighton, PA, p. A530

ANDRE, Katelyn, Human Resource Coordinator, Select Specialty Hospital–Macomb County, Mount Clemens, MI, p. A318

ANDREAS, Ginger, Coordinator Personnel and Credentialing, El Campo Memorial Hospital, El Campo, TX, p. A601

ANDREAS, Lori, Chief Executive Officer and Administrator, Appleton Area Health Services, Appleton, MN, p. A327

ANDREASEN, Raymond, M.D., Chief Medical Officer–Inpatient, California Medical Facility, Vacaville, CA, p. A93

ANDRES, Chad, Chief Information Officer, Desert View Hospital, Pahrump, NV, p. A397

ANDRES, Elizabeth, Director Human Resources, Atascadero State Hospital, Atascadero, CA, p. A51

ANDRES, Leonidas, M.D., Chief of Staff, Riceland Medical Center, Winnie, TX, p. A646

ANDRESEN, Daniel, Chief information Officer, Mercy Medical Center Merced, Merced, CA, p. A71

ANDREW, Sigrid, Director, James E. Van Zandt Veterans Affairs Medical Center, Altoona, PA, p. A519

ANDREWS, Callie, President, Wellstar Cobb Hospital, Austell, GA, p. A148

ANDREWS, Carolle, Vice President, Interim Human Resources Officer, Uconn, John Dempsey Hospital, Farmington, CT, p. A108

ANDREWS, Charles, Director Information Technology, West Springs Hospital, Grand Junction, CO, p. A101

ANDREWS, David, Manager Information Systems, Chicot Memorial Medical Center, Lake Village, AR, p. A44

ANDREWS, Jim, Chief Financial Officer, North Okaloosa Medical Center, Crestview, FL, p. A120

ANDREWS, John, M.D., Chief of Staff, Ut Health Tyler, Tyler, TX, p. A642

ANDREWS, Kathy, Chief Financial Officer, Kindred Hospital–Philadelphia, Philadelphia, PA, p. A535

ANDREWS, Lisa, Director Human Resources, Lancaster Rehabilitation Hospital, Lancaster, PA, p. A528

ANDREWS, Michael, Coordinator Information Systems, Harlan County Health System, Alma, NE, p. A382

ANDREWS, Mike, Associate Administrator and Chief Operating Officer, Och Regional Medical Center, Starkville, MS, p. A354

ANDREWS, Paul
Chief Executive Officer, The Brook At Dupont, Louisville, KY, p. A256
Chief Executive Officer, The Brook Hospital – Kmi, Louisville, KY, p. A257

ANDREWS, Rebecca, Chief Financial Officer, Vibra Hospital Of Northern California, Redding, CA, p. A80

ANDREWS, Ryan, M.D., Chief Medical Officer, Aspirus Wausau Hospital, Inc., Wausau, WI, p. A708

ANDREWS, Steve, Chief Financial Officer, Three Rivers Health, Three Rivers, MI, p. A323

ANDREWS, Sue E., Chief Financial Officer, O'Connor Hospital, Delhi, NY, p. A426

ANDREWS, Susan E., Chief Executive Officer, Touro Infirmary, New Orleans, LA, p. A276

ANDREWS, Terri, Director Information Technology, Alamance Regional Medical Center, Burlington, NC, p. A450

ANDRO, Ronald J., President and Chief Executive Officer, West Penn Hospital, Pittsburgh, PA, p. A538

ANDRUS, Helen
Chief Financial Officer, Providence Mount Carmel Hospital, Colville, WA, p. A672
Chief Financial Officer, Providence St. Joseph'S Hospital, Chewelah, WA, p. A671
Chief Financial Officer, St. Luke'S Rehabilitation Institute, Spokane, WA, p. A680

ANDRUS, Jonathon, Chief Executive Officer, Fairchild Medical Center, Yreka, CA, p. A95

ANDURSKY, John S., President and Chief Executive Officer, Highlands Hospital, Connellsville, PA, p. A523

ANFINSON, Julie, Director Human Resources, Mercyone Siouxland Medical Center, Sioux City, IA, p. A230

ANGELI, Maribeth, Chief Nursing Officer, Berwick Hospital Center, Berwick, PA, p. A520

ANGELL, Deborah, Chief Financial Officer, Syracuse Veterans Affairs Medical Center, Syracuse, NY, p. A445

ANGELL, Nancy, Associate Administrator Personnel, Sagamore Children'S Psychiatric Center, Dix Hills, NY, p. A427

ANGELO, Gregory, Chief Fiscal Program, Brookdale Hospital Medical Center, New York, NY, p. A432

ANGELO, Thomas, Chief Executive Officer, Centra Southside Community Hospital, Farmville, VA, p. A659

ANGELUCCI, Patricia A, MS, R.N., Director Patient Care Services, Thedacare Medical Center–Shawano, Shawano, WI, p. A705

ANGERAMI, Deborah
Chief Operating Officer, Health First Community Hospitals, Health First Cape Canaveral Hospital, Cocoa Beach, FL, p. A120
Chief Operating Officer, Health First Community Hospitals, Health First Palm Bay Hospital, Palm Bay, FL, p. A135
Chief Operating Officer, Health First Viera Hospital, Melbourne, FL, p. A129

ANGERMEIER, Elizabeth, Director of Nursing, Evansville Psychiatric Children Center, Evansville, IN, p. A203

ANGLE, Mary Ann, R.N., FACHE, Chief Nursing Officer, Tristar Summit Medical Center, Hermitage, TN, p. A570

ANGLIM, John, Human Resources Client Manager, Providence Seaside Hospital, Seaside, OR, p. A518

ANGLIN, Jason, Chief Executive Officer, Memorial Medical Center, Port Lavaca, TX, p. A630

ANGLIN, Kristine, Human Resources Manager, Willow Springs Center, Reno, NV, p. A397

ANGUS, Jolyn M, R.N., Chief Nursing Officer, Miami Valley Hospital, Dayton, OH, p. A481

ANISKO RYAN, Karen, Director Business Development and Communications, Uc San Diego Health, San Diego, CA, p. A84

ANMUTH, Craig, M.D., Medical Director, Bacharach Institute For Rehabilitation, Pomona, NJ, p. A411

ANNARINO, Phillip, Vice President Human Resources, Fisher–Titus Medical Center, Norwalk, OH, p. A488

ANNARUMO, Beverly, President, Ellwood City Medical Center, Llc, Ellwood City, PA, p. A525

ANNECHARICO, Mary Alice
System Vice President and Chief Information Officer, Henry Ford Hospital, Detroit, MI, p. A310
System Vice President and Chief Information Officer, Henry Ford West Bloomfield Hospital, West Bloomfield, MI, p. A324
System Vice President and Chief Information Officer, Henry Ford Wyandotte Hospital, Wyandotte, MI, p. A325

ANNESSER, Sue, Director Information Systems, Freeman Neosho Hospital, Neosho, MO, p. A366

ANOATUBBY, Chris, Deputy Secretary of Health, Chickasaw Nation Medical Center, Ada, OK, p. A496

ANOLIK, Adam, Chief Financial Officer, Highland Hospital, Rochester, NY, p. A442

ANSALDO, Luanne, Chief Operating Officer, Aventura Hospital And Medical Center, Aventura, FL, p. A117

ANSHUTZ, Margie, Chief Development Officer, Hamilton Center, Terre Haute, IN, p. A215

ANSI, Azena, Manager Health Information Management, Horizon Specialty Hospital, Las Vegas, NV, p. A395

ANSLEY, Pamela, Director Finance, Sutter Center For Psychiatry, Sacramento, CA, p. A82

ANSON, Ashley, Chief Executive Officer, Texas Health Hospital, Carrollton, TX, p. A591

ANTCZAK, Brett, Chief Executive Officer, Palo Alto County Health System, Emmetsburg, IA, p. A222

ANTCZAK, Kenneth, Vice President Human Resources, St. Mary Mercy Hospital, Livonia, MI, p. A317

ANTES, John, President, Missouri Baptist Medical Center, Saint Louis, MO, p. A369

ANTHONY, Ashley, Chief Executive Officer, Delta Memorial Hospital, Dumas, AR, p. A41

ANTHONY, Harry C., M.D., Chief Medical Officer, Nanticoke Memorial Hospital, Seaford, DE, p. A114

ANTHONY, Jean, President and Chief Executive Officer, Hills & Dales General Hospital, Cass City, MI, p. A308

ANTHONY, Kim, Director Human Resources, Burke Medical Center, Waynesboro, GA, p. A163

ANTHONY, Mark, Executive Vice President and Chief Operating Officer, Ascension Borgess Hospital, Kalamazoo, MI, p. A315

ANTHONY, Michelle, Chief Nursing Officer, Encompass Health Rehabilitation Hospital Of Virginia, Richmond, VA, p. A666

ANTHONY, Paula
Vice President Information Services, Ut Health Pittsburg, Pittsburg, TX, p. A628
Vice President Information Services, Ut Health Rehabilitation Hospital, Tyler, TX, p. A642
Vice President Information Services, Ut Health Specialty Hospital, Tyler, TX, p. A642
Vice President Information Services, Ut Health Tyler, Tyler, TX, p. A642

ANTHONY, Robert, Chief Financial Officer, Kirkbride Center, Philadelphia, PA, p. A535

ANTINELLI, Mark, Manager Human Resources, Syracuse Veterans Affairs Medical Center, Syracuse, NY, p. A445

ANTINORI, James, M.D., Chief of Staff, Mountain West Medical Center, Tooele, UT, p. A653

ANTLE, Sue, Director of Nursing, Casey County Hospital, Liberty, KY, p. A255

ANTOINE, Greg, M.D., Chief of Staff, Fayetteville Veterans Affairs Medical Center, Fayetteville, NC, p. A454

ANTON, Lourdes, Director Human Resources, Larkin Community Hospital–Palm Springs Campus, Hialeah, FL, p. A124

ANTONACCI, Amy, MSN, R.N., Vice President Nursing Services, Alliance Community Hospital, Alliance, OH, p. A471

ANTONECCHIA, Paul, M.D., Vice President Medical Affairs and Chief Medical Officer, St. John'S Riverside Hospital, Yonkers, NY, p. A448

ANTONSON, Pete, Chief Executive Officer, Northwood Deaconess Health Center, Northwood, ND, p. A469

ANTONUCCI, Lawrence
President and Chief Executive Officer, Cape Coral Hospital, Cape Coral, FL, p. A119
President and Chief Executive Officer, Gulf Coast Medical Center, Fort Myers, FL, p. A123
President and Chief Executive Officer, Lee Memorial Hospital, Fort Myers, FL, p. A123

ANTRUM, Sheila, R.N., President, Ucsf Medical Center, San Francisco, CA, p. A86

ANUSZKIEWICZ, Dawn, Chief Operating Officer, Reading Hospital, West Reading, PA, p. A544

ANWAR, Muhammad, M.D., Chief Medical Officer, Encino Hospital Medical Center, Los Angeles, CA, p. A66

ANYEBE, Abiola
Interim Chief Executive Officer, Kindred Hospital San Antonio Central, San Antonio, TX, p. A634
Interim Chief Executive Officer, Kindred Hospital–San Antonio, San Antonio, TX, p. A634

ANZALDUA, Brandon, Chief Financial Officer, Riverside Medical Center, Franklinton, LA, p. A267

ANZURES, Rosey, Acting Chief Financial Officer, Central Texas Veterans Health Care System, Temple, TX, p. A640
APIKI, Zessica L, Accountant, Molokai General Hospital, Kaunakakai, HI, p. A166
APKON, Michael, Chief Executive Officer, Tufts Medical Center, Boston, MA, p. A296
APLAND, Wendy, Interim Chief Financial Officer, Peacehealth Sacred Heart Medical Center University District, Eugene, OR, p. A512
APOLINAR, Adam, Chief Nursing Officer, Uvalde Memorial Hospital, Uvalde, TX, p. A643
APOLIONA, Nicole, M.D., Medical Director, Kula Hospital, Kula, HI, p. A166
APONTE, Miguel, Supervisor Management Information Systems, Wilma N. Vazquez Medical Center, Vega Baja, PR, p. A720
APPLEBAUM, Jon D., President and Chief Operating Officer, Novant Health Thomasville Medical Center, Thomasville, NC, p. A463
APPLEGEET, Carol, MSN, R.N., Vice President and Chief Nursing Officer, Fort Hamilton Hospital, Hamilton, OH, p. A484
APPLETON, Joe, M.D., Chief of Surgery, Milan General Hospital, Milan, TN, p. A576
APRILE, Patricia, Chief Operating Officer, Southern Maine Health Care – Biddeford Medical Center, Biddeford, ME, p. A282
AQUILINA, Anthony, D.O., Chief Medical Officer, Geisinger–Community Medical Center, Scranton, PA, p. A540
AQUILINA, Joanne, Vice President Finance and Chief Financial Officer, Bethesda Hospital East, Boynton Beach, FL, p. A118
AQUINO, Jonathon F., Chief Executive Officer, San Gabriel Valley Medical Center, San Gabriel, CA, p. A86
ARA, Farideh, Interim Chief Nursing Officer, Hollywood Presbyterian Medical Center, Los Angeles, CA, p. A67
ARABIT, Aleen D., Chief Executive Officer, San Antonio Behavioral Healthcare Hospital, San Antonio, TX, p. A635
ARAD, Lana
Chief Financial Officer, Good Samaritan Hospital, San Jose, CA, p. A86
Chief Financial Officer, Mountainview Hospital, Las Vegas, NV, p. A395
ARAGON, Juliette, Finance Director, Turquoise Lodge Hospital, Albuquerque, NM, p. A417
ARAKELIAN, Armen
Chief Information Officer, Fulton County Medical Center, Mc Connellsburg, PA, p. A531
Chief Information Officer, J. C. Blair Memorial Hospital, Huntingdon, PA, p. A527
ARANDA, Heather R, R.N., MSN, Chief Nursing Officer, F. W. Huston Medical Center, Winchester, KS, p. A247
ARANIO, Lani, Regional Director Human Resources, Samuel Mahelona Memorial Hospital, Kapaa, HI, p. A166
ARATOW, Michael, M.D., Chief Information Officer, San Mateo Medical Center, San Mateo, CA, p. A87
ARAUJO, Marianne D, R.N., Ph.D., FACHE, Vice President Nursing and Chief Nurse Executive, Advocate Good Shepherd Hospital, Barrington, IL, p. A174
ARAUJO, Markeeta, Chief Nursing Officer, Desert View Hospital, Pahrump, NV, p. A397
ARBAUGH, Ronnie, Director Human Resources, Grant Memorial Hospital, Petersburg, WV, p. A688
ARBON, Terron, R.N., Chief Nursing Officer, Salt Lake Regional Medical Center, Salt Lake City, UT, p. A652
ARBUTHNOT, Rena, Director Human Resources, Shriners Hospitals For Children–Shreveport, Shreveport, LA, p. A278
ARCANGELI, Barbara J., Vice President Human Resources, Newport Hospital, Newport, RI, p. A547
ARCE, Daisy, President Medical Staff, Weslaco Regional Rehabilitation Hospital, Weslaco, TX, p. A645
ARCENEAUX, Larrie, Chief Clinical Officer, Promise Hospital Baton Rouge – Main Campus, Baton Rouge, LA, p. A264
ARCENEAUX, Trina, Assistant Chief Financial Officer, Promise Hospital Baton Rouge – Main Campus, Baton Rouge, LA, p. A264
ARCH, Chrissy, Chief Financial Officer, Cherokee Indian Hospital, Cherokee, NC, p. A452
ARCH, John K., Director, Boys Town National Research Hospital, Omaha, NE, p. A388
ARCHAMBEAULT, Shirley, Chief Information Officer, Medical City Lewisville, Lewisville, TX, p. A620
ARCHER, David, Director Information Systems, Tristar Ashland City Medical Center, Ashland City, TN, p. A566
ARCHER, Doug, Administrator, Memorial Hospital Los Banos, Los Banos, CA, p. A70
ARCHER, Joe, Chief Information Officer, Victor Valley Global Medical Center, Victorville, CA, p. A94
ARCHER, Matt
Chief Executive Officer, Complex Care Hospital At Tenaya, Las Vegas, NV, p. A394
Chief Executive Officer, Tahoe Pacific Hospitals, Sparks, NV, p. A398
ARCHER, Stuart
Chief Executive Officer, Oceans Healthcare, Oceans Behavioral Hospital Of De Ridder, Deridder, LA, p. A267
Chief Executive Officer, Oceans Behavioral Hospital Katy, Katy, TX, p. A617
ARCHER–DUSTE, Helen, Chief Operating Officer, Kaiser Permanente San Francisco Medical Center, San Francisco, CA, p. A85
ARCHEY, Eugene, Chief Information Technology, Va Greater Los Angeles Healthcare System, Los Angeles, CA, p. A70
ARCHIBOLD, Robert, Director, Human Resources, St. Anthony North Health Campus, Westminster, CO, p. A106
ARCHIBONG, Henry, Vice President, Information Services and Technology, University Of Maryland Capital Region Health Prince George'S Hospital Center, Cheverly, MD, p. A289
ARCHULETA, Michael, Chief Information Technology Officer, Mt. San Rafael Hospital, Trinidad, CO, p. A106
ARCIDI, Alfred J.
Senior Vice President, Whittier Rehabilitation Hospital, Bradford, MA, p. A296
Senior Vice President, Whittier Rehabilitation Hospital, Westborough, MA, p. A304
ARCIDI, Alfred L., Chief Executive Officer, Whittier Pavilion, Haverhill, MA, p. A299
ARCILLA, Jelden, R.N., Vice President and Chief Nursing Officer, Honorhealth John C. Lincoln Medical Center, Phoenix, AZ, p. A33
ARD, Sheila, Chief Nursing Officer, Huntsville Memorial Hospital, Huntsville, TX, p. A615
ARDABELL, Toni R, Chief Executive Officer, Bon Secours Virginia, Bon Secours St. Francis Medical Center, Midlothian, VA, p. A662
ARDEMAGNI, Jeff, Chief Financial Officer, Medical City Arlington, Arlington, TX, p. A583
ARDESHNA, Harish, Pulmonologist & Chief Medical Officer, Bluffton Regional Medical Center, Bluffton, IN, p. A200
ARDION, Doug, M.D., Chief Medical Officer, Nch Baker Hospital, Naples, FL, p. A132
ARDOIN, Cody, Director Human Resources, Mercy Regional Medical Center, Ville Platte, LA, p. A280
ARDOLIC, Brahim, Chief Executive Officer, Brookdale Hospital Medical Center, New York, NY, p. A432
ARDEAUX, Rene, Vice President and Chief Operating Officer, Springhill Memorial Hospital, Mobile, AL, p. A20
ARELLANO, Edgar Alejandro, Chief Information Technologist, Three Rivers Hospital, Brewster, WA, p. A671
ARENDS, Candace, R.N., Chief Nursing Officer, United Hospital District, Blue Earth, MN, p. A320
ARETINO, Sandi, Chief Executive Officer, Tsehootsooi Medical Center, Fort Defiance, AZ, p. A29
ARGUELLO–VASQUEZ, Mabel, R.N., Executive Nurse Administrator, New Mexico Behavioral Health Institute At Las Vegas, Las Vegas, NM, p. A419
ARGYROS, Gregory J., Senior Vice President and President, Medstar Washington Hospital Center, Washington, DC, p. A116
ARIAS, Taffy J., Chief Executive Officer, Gila Regional Medical Center, Silver City, NM, p. A420
ARISPE, Joe, Director Information Systems, Wise Health System, Decatur, TX, p. A598
ARIZMENDEZ, Maria Elena, M.D., Medical Director, Baylor Scott & White Institute For Rehabilitation – Lakeway, Lakeway, TX, p. A619
ARIZPE, Robert C., Superintendent, San Antonio State Hospital, San Antonio, TX, p. A635
ARKEMA, Ashley, Director of Human Resources, Pella Regional Health Center, Pella, IA, p. A228
ARKIN, Melissa, Chief Executive Officer, Parkridge Medical Center, Chattanooga, TN, p. A567
ARLEDGE, Denton, Vice President and Chief Information Officer, Wakemed Cary Hospital, Cary, NC, p. A450
ARLEDGE, William, Administrator and Chief Financial Officer, Genesis Behavioral Hospital, Breaux Bridge, LA, p. A265
ARLIEN, Dana, M.D., Chief Medical Officer, Willow Springs Center, Reno, NV, p. A397
ARMAND, Sandra, Director, Lafayette General Medical Center, Lafayette, LA, p. A271
ARMBRUSTER, Kent A W, M.D., Vice President Medical Affairs, Little Company Of Mary Hospital And Health Care Centers, Evergreen Park, IL, p. A183
ARMBRUSTER, Rebecca, M.D., Chief Medical Officer, Jeanes Hospital, Philadelphia, PA, p. A535
ARMENTOR, Lance, Chief Executive Officer, Avail Health Lake Charles Hospital, Lake Charles, LA, p. A271
ARMFIELD, Ben
Associate Administrator, Fresno Heart And Surgical Hospital, Fresno, CA, p. A59
Chief Financial Officer, Fresno Heart And Surgical Hospital, Fresno, CA, p. A59
ARMOUR, Dale, Chief Financial Officer, Melbourne Regional Medical Center, Melbourne, FL, p. A129
ARMOUR, John, Chief Financial Officer, Bayshore Medical Center, Pasadena, TX, p. A628
ARMSTRONG, Alan, M.D., Chief Medical Officer, Pine Rest Christian Mental Health Services, Grand Rapids, MI, p. A313
ARMSTRONG, Deborah, Chief Executive Officer, Piedmont Henry Hospital, Stockbridge, GA, p. A161
ARMSTRONG, Eleze, Chief Operating Officer, Sierra Vista Regional Medical Center, San Luis Obispo, CA, p. A87
ARMSTRONG, Gary, Executive Vice President, Methodist Rehabilitation Center, Jackson, MS, p. A349
ARMSTRONG, Jeffery, CPA, Chief Financial Officer, Granville Health System, Oxford, NC, p. A460
ARMSTRONG, Jeremy, Chief Executive Officer, Mitchell County Hospital Health Systems, Beloit, KS, p. A232
ARMSTRONG, Kim, Chief Financial Officer, Windom Area Hospital, Windom, MN, p. A343
ARMSTRONG, Kyle, President, Baylor Scott & White Medical Center At – Mckinney, Mckinney, TX, p. A624
ARMSTRONG, Lori, R.N., MSN, Chief Nursing Officer, Kaiser Permanente Santa Clara Medical Center, Santa Clara, CA, p. A88
ARMSTRONG, Mark, M.D., Medical Director, Baylor Scott & White Medical Center–Uptown, Dallas, TX, p. A595
ARMSTRONG, Neil G, FACHE, Vice President and Chief Operating Officer, Upmc Susquehanna Divine Providence Campus, Williamsport, PA, p. A545
ARMSTRONG, Paula, Chief Financial Officer, Kaiser Permanente Fresno Medical Center, Fresno, CA, p. A59
ARMSTRONG, Robert E., Senior Vice President and Chief Operating Officer, Lima Memorial Health System, Lima, OH, p. A485
ARMSTRONG, Roger
Interim Chief Financial Officer, Pioneers Memorial Healthcare District, Brawley, CA, p. A53
Vice President Finance and Chief Financial Officer, Unitypoint Health – Proctor, Peoria, IL, p. A193
ARMSTRONG, William C
Senior Vice President and Chief Financial Officer, Mercy Medical Center, Rockville Centre, NY, p. A443
Vice President and Chief Financial Officer, St. Francis Hospital, The Heart Center, Roslyn, NY, p. A443
ARMSTRONG–HUFF, Glenda, Assistant Superintendent, Texas Center For Infectious Disease, San Antonio, TX, p. A635
ARNDELL, Scott, Chief Financial Officer, Twin Lakes Regional Medical Center, Leitchfield, KY, p. A254
ARNER, Steven C.
Executive Vice President of Administration, Carilion Franklin Memorial Hospital, Rocky Mount, VA, p. A667
President, Carilion Roanoke Memorial Hospital, Roanoke, VA, p. A667
ARNESON, Brenda, Administrative Assistant, St. Andrew'S Health Center, Bottineau, ND, p. A465
ARNESON, Garrett, Chief Executive Officer, Acuity Specialty Hospital Of Southern New Jersey, Willingboro, NJ, p. A415
ARNETT, Jacob, Chief Information Technology Officer, Lakeside Behavioral Health System, Memphis, TN, p. A575
ARNETT, James, Vice President Human Resources, Unitypoint Health Meriter, Madison, WI, p. A698
ARNETT, Randal M., President and Chief Executive Officer, Southern Ohio Medical Center, Portsmouth, OH, p. A490
ARNETT, Sallie, Vice President Information Systems, Licking Memorial Hospital, Newark, OH, p. A488
ARNETT, Stuart
Regional Vice President Finance, Aurora Lakeland Medical Center, Elkhorn, WI, p. A694
Vice President Finance and Chief Financial Officer, Aurora Medical Center Burlington, Burlington, WI, p. A693
ARNHART, Carol, Vice President Finance and Chief Financial Officer, Siskin Hospital For Physical Rehabilitation, Chattanooga, TN, p. A567
ARNOLD, Ann, M.D., Medical Director, Medical City Plano, Plano, TX, p. A629
ARNOLD, Dustin, D.O., Chief Medical Officer, Unitypoint Health – St. Luke'S Hospital, Cedar Rapids, IA, p. A218
ARNOLD, Jeffrey, M.D., Chief Medical Officer, Santa Clara Valley Medical Center, San Jose, CA, p. A87
ARNOLD, Kimberly N, R.N., Chief Nursing Officer and Interim Chief Quality Officer, Alliancehealth Woodward, Woodward, OK, p. A510
ARNOLD, Leslie, Chief Executive Officer and Administrator, Chi St. Vincent Morrilton, Morrilton, AR, p. A46
ARNOLD, Scott, Senior Vice President Information Systems, Tampa General Hospital, Tampa, FL, p. A142

ARNTZ, Mary, Manager Business Office and Executive Assistant, Physicians' Medical Center, New Albany, IN, p. A212

AROCHA, Joe, Chief of Staff, Alleghany Memorial Hospital, Sparta, NC, p. A462

AROCHO, Jacqueline, Administrator, Baycare Alliant Hospital, Dunedin, FL, p. A122

ARORA, Pamela
Senior Vice President and Chief Information Officer, Children'S Medical Center Plano, Plano, TX, p. A629
Senior Vice President Information Systems, Children'S Medical Center Dallas, Dallas, TX, p. A596

ARORA, Sat, M.D., President Medical and Dental Staff, Crozer–Chester Medical Center, Upland, PA, p. A543

ARQUILLA, Thomas J., Chief Strategy Officer, Thedacare Regional Medical Center–Appleton, Appleton, WI, p. A691

ARRANTS, Diane, Chief Information Officer, Kershawhealth, Camden, SC, p. A549

ARROGANTE, Revelyn, M.D., Medical Director, Northern Colorado Rehabilitation Hospital, Johnstown, CO, p. A102

ARROWOOD, Melina, Interim President and Chief Nursing Officer, Transylvania Regional Hospital, Brevard, NC, p. A450

ARROYO, Luis A
Chief Financial Officer, Hima San Pablo Caguas, Caguas, PR, p. A715
Chief Financial Officer, Hospital Hima De Humacao, Humacao, PR, p. A716
Chief Financial Officer, Hospital San Pablo Del Este, Fajardo, PR, p. A716

ARSENAULT, Lisa, Vice President Human Resources and Compliance, Millinocket Regional Hospital, Millinocket, ME, p. A284

ARSLANPAY, Robin F., Director Human Resources, Lifecare Hospitals Of Pittsburgh, Pittsburgh, PA, p. A537

ARSURA, Edward, M.D., Chief Medical Officer, Brookdale Hospital Medical Center, New York, NY, p. A432

ARTENSTEIN, Andrew, M.D., Chief Physician Executive, Chief Academic Officer and President, Baystate Medical Practices, Baystate Medical Center, Springfield, MA, p. A303

ARTERBURN, Catherine T, R.N., Vice President Human Resources, Sidney Regional Medical Center, Sidney, NE, p. A391

ARTHUR, John
Chief Financial Officer, St. Vincent Mercy Hospital, Elwood, IN, p. A203
Chief Financial Officer, St. Vincent Randolph Hospital, Winchester, IN, p. A216

ARTHUR, Rita K, Director Human Resources, Littleton Adventist Hospital, Littleton, CO, p. A103

ARTILES, Nemuel O., Administrator, Hospital De Psiquiatria Forense, Ponce, PR, p. A717

ARTMAN, David S, Chief Operating Officer, Weirton Medical Center, Weirton, WV, p. A690

ARTS–STRENKE, Cindy, R.N., Chief Operating Officer and Chief Nursing Officer, Marshfield Medical Center – Rice Lake, Rice Lake, WI, p. A704

ARUNAMATA, Peti, Interim Area Director Information Technology, Kaiser Permanente San Francisco Medical Center, San Francisco, CA, p. A85

ARVIDSON, Betty, Chief Financial Officer, Riverview Health, Crookston, MN, p. A330

ARVIN, Douglas, Vice President Finance and Chief Financial Officer, Wellstar Kennestone Hospital, Marietta, GA, p. A157

ARVIN, Jon A, M.D., Chief Medical Officer, Rockcastle Regional Hospital And Respiratory Care Center, Mount Vernon, KY, p. A258

ARVON, Christina, Administrator and Chief Executive Officer, Charleston Surgical Hospital, Charleston, WV, p. A684

ARZOUMANIAN, Aimee, Chief Operating Officer, Baptist Health – Fort Smith, Fort Smith, AR, p. A42

ASADA, Bonnie, Chief Nursing Officer, Alvarado Parkway Institute Behavioral Health System, La Mesa, CA, p. A63

ASAFTEI, Laura, Administrative Director, Adventhealth Zephyrhills, Zephyrhills, FL, p. A144

ASAOKA, Danny
Executive Director Information Systems, Memorialcare, Long Beach Memorial Medical Center, Long Beach, CA, p. A65
Executive Director Information Systems, Memorialcare, Miller Children'S & Women'S Hospital Long Beach, Long Beach, CA, p. A65

ASBURY, Wesley, M.D., President Medical Staff, Princeton Community Hospital, Princeton, WV, p. A688

ASCHOFF, Jodi, Chief Financial Officer, Osmond General Hospital, Osmond, NE, p. A390

ASH, Michael A, Chief Transformation Officer, Nebraska Medicine – Nebraska Medical Center, Omaha, NE, p. A389

ASH, Richard M., Chief Executive Officer, United Hospital District, Blue Earth, MN, p. A328

ASHBY, F Michael, M.D., Vice President and Medical Director, Sentara Martha Jefferson Hospital, Charlottesville, VA, p. A657

ASHBY, Fred, Director Information Technology, Fort Washington Medical Center, Oxen Hill, MD, p. A292

ASHBY, Kim, Vice President of Finance, Baptist Health Madisonville, Madisonville, KY, p. A257

ASHBY, Pamela, Vice President Human Resources, Medstar National Rehabilitation Hospital, Washington, DC, p. A115

ASHBY, Rae A., Director Human Resources, Sullivan County Memorial Hospital, Milan, MO, p. A365

ASHCOM, Thomas L., Chief Executive Officer, Kansas Heart Hospital, Wichita, KS, p. A247

ASHENFELTER, Kathy, Chief Financial Officer, Swedish Medical Center, Englewood, CO, p. A100

ASHKENASE, Donald L, Executive Vice President and Chief Operating Officer, Nassau University Medical Center, East Meadow, NY, p. A427

ASHLEY, Ada, HIM Director, Lifebrite Community Hospital Of Stokes, Danbury, NC, p. A452

ASHLEY, Dennis H
Vice President Human Resources, Montefiore Mount Vernon, Mount Vernon, NY, p. A432
Vice President Human Resources, Montefiore New Rochelle, New Rochelle, NY, p. A432

ASHLEY, Kent, Chief Financial Officer, Mesa Springs, Fort Worth, TX, p. A605

ASHLEY, Sharon, MSN, Chief Nursing Officer, Adams County Regional Medical Center, Seaman, OH, p. A490

ASHLEY, Stanley, M.D., Senior Vice President Medical Affairs and Chief Medical Officer, Brigham And Women'S Hospital, Boston, MA, p. A295

ASHMENT, Kerry, Chief Executive Officer, Kindred Hospital– San Diego, San Diego, CA, p. A83

ASHRAF, Mirza, M.D., Medical Director, Carthage Area Hospital, Carthage, NY, p. A425

ASHTON, Michael, Administrator, Bayhealth Medical Center, Dover, DE, p. A113

ASHWORTH, Fred, Chief Financial Officer, Regional Medical Center Of San Jose, San Jose, CA, p. A86

ASHWORTH, James, M.D., Medical Director, University Of Utah Neuropsychiatric Institute, Salt Lake City, UT, p. A652

ASHWORTH, Jerry
Senior Vice President and Chief Executive Officer, Memorial Hermann Rehabilitation Hospital – Katy, Katy, TX, p. A617
Senior Vice President and Chief Executive Officer, Tirr Memorial Hermann, Houston, TX, p. A614

ASIC, Jason, Chief Operating Officer, Mercy Health – West Hospital, Cincinnati, OH, p. A476

ASKEW, Pam, R.N., Vice President Patient Care Services, Unitypoint Health – Trinity Muscatine, Muscatine, IA, p. A227

ASKINS, Stephen, M.D., Chief of Staff, Lake City Community Hospital, Lake City, SC, p. A555

ASLIN, Judy, MSN, R.N., Vice President and Chief Nursing Officer, Southeast Hospital, Cape Girardeau, MO, p. A358

ASPEL, Tracy, Chief Nursing Officer, Northern Inyo Hospital, Bishop, CA, p. A53

ASPLIN, Iain, Chief Medical Officer, Multicare Mary Bridge Children'S Hospital And Health Center, Tacoma, WA, p. A680

ASPLUND, David, Chief Operating Officer, Motion Picture And Television Fund Hospital And Residential Services, Los Angeles, CA, p. A68

ASSAAD, Haney, Vice President Medical Affairs, North Ottawa Community Hospital, Grand Haven, MI, p. A312

ASSAVAPISITKUL, Colleen, R.N., Patient Care Executive, Adventist Health Clear Lake, Clearlake, CA, p. A54

ASTACIO, Benjamin, Director Human Resources, Bella Vista Hospital, Mayaguez, PR, p. A717

ASTLEFORD, Daniel, Vice President Operations, Lafayette Regional Health Center, Lexington, MO, p. A364

ATADERO, Robyn, R.N., Chief Nursing Officer, Pioneers Memorial Healthcare District, Brawley, CA, p. A53

ATCHISON, Garfield, Chief Executive Officer, Frye Regional Medical Center, Hickory, NC, p. A456

ATCHISON, Marcie
Vice President Human Resources, Memorialcare, Long Beach Memorial Medical Center, Long Beach, CA, p. A65
Vice President Human Resources, Memorialcare, Miller Children'S & Women'S Hospital Long Beach, Long Beach, CA, p. A65

ATCHLEY, Mark, Vice President and Chief Financial Officer, Medical City Dallas, Dallas, TX, p. A597

ATHERTON, Dorie, Manager Human Resources, University Behavioral Health Of Denton, Denton, TX, p. A599

ATHEY, Alycia, Director of Nursing, Prairie Ridge Hospital And Health Services, Elbow Lake, MN, p. A331

ATKIN, Suzanne, M.D., Chief Medical Officer, University Hospital, Newark, NJ, p. A409

ATKINS, Christa, Administrator, Commonwealth Regional Specialty Hospital, Bowling Green, KY, p. A249

ATKINS, James, PharmD, Chief Operating Officer, Piedmont Henry Hospital, Stockbridge, GA, p. A161

ATKINS, Jim, Director Employee Services, St. Luke'S Rehabilitation Hospital, Boise, ID, p. A168

ATKINS, Melissa, Chief Executive Officer, Graham County Hospital, Hill City, KS, p. A236

ATKINS, Tracy, Chief Operating and Nursing Officer, Orchard Hospital, Gridley, CA, p. A61

ATKINSON, Andrew, Chief Operating Officer, Fulton State Hospital, Fulton, MO, p. A360

ATKINSON, James, M.D., Medical Director, Ucla Medical Center–Santa Monica, Santa Monica, CA, p. A89

ATKINSON, Johnie M, Chief Human Resources Officer, Saint Vincent Hospital, Erie, PA, p. A525

ATTEBURY, Mary, Chief Operating Officer, Northwest Missouri Psychiatric Rehabilitation Center, Saint Joseph, MO, p. A368

ATTENBURY, Kristen, Commanding Officer, Naval Hospital Lemoore, Lemoore, CA, p. A64

ATTERBERG, Linda, Chief Information Officer, Unitypoint Health–Keokuk, Keokuk, IA, p. A225

ATTLESEY–PRIES, Jacqueline M, MS, R.N., Chief Nursing Officer, Vice President, Boulder Community Health, Boulder, CO, p. A96

ATTRIDGE, Scott
Chief Financial Officer, Chi St. Anthony Hospital, Pendleton, OR, p. A515
Chief Financial Officer, Mid–Valley Hospital, Omak, WA, p. A676

ATTY, James, Chief Executive Officer, Waverly Health Center, Waverly, IA, p. A231

ATWAL, Money, Chief Information Officer, Hilo Medical Center, Hilo, HI, p. A164

ATWOOD, Julie, Director Human Resources, San Bernardino Mountains Community Hospital District, Lake Arrowhead, CA, p. A63

ATWOOD, Linda, Chief Nursing Officer, Merit Health Woman'S Hospital, Flowood, MS, p. A347

AUBEL, Eugenia, President, St. Elizabeth Boardman Hospital, Mercy Health – St. Elizabeth Boardman Hospital, Boardman, OH, p. A473

AUBIN, Michael D, President, Baptist Medical Center Jacksonville, Jacksonville, FL, p. A125

AUBRY, Michael, Director Information Systems, Adventist Medical Center – Hanford, Hanford, CA, p. A61

AUBUCHON, Christy, Director Personnel, Washington County Memorial Hospital, Potosi, MO, p. A367

AUCKER, Kendra A.
President and Chief Executive Officer, Evangelical Community Hospital, Lewisburg, PA, p. A530
Vice President Operations, Evangelical Community Hospital, Lewisburg, PA, p. A530

AUCKERMAN, Graydon Todd, Chief Nursing Officer, Ohiohealth Rehabilitation Hospital, Columbus, OH, p. A479

AUD, Pam, Chief Clinical Officer, Andalusia Health, Andalusia, AL, p. A13

AUDETT, John R, M.D., Medical Director Clinical Affairs, Overlook Medical Center, Summit, NJ, p. A413

AUERBACH, Lorraine P., President and Chief Executive Officer, Dameron Hospital, Stockton, CA, p. A90

AUERSWALD, Chris, Interim Chief Executive Officer and Chief Financial Officer, Chicot Memorial Medical Center, Lake Village, AR, p. A44

AUGSBURGER, Marc, President and Chief Executive Officer, Mclaren Caro Region, Caro, MI, p. A308

AUGSBURGER, Tod, President and Chief Executive Officer, Lexington Medical Center, West Columbia, SC, p. A558

AUGSBURGER, Tod, FACHE, Senior Vice President and Chief Operating Officer, Lexington Medical Center, West Columbia, SC, p. A558

AUGUST, Brad, Director Information Systems, Fairfield Memorial Hospital, Fairfield, IL, p. A183

AUGUST, Prudence, Chief Information Officer, Palomar Medical Center, Escondido, CA, p. A57

AUGUSTIN, Robert, Director Human Resources, Southern Tennessee Regional Health System–Lawrenceburg, Lawrenceburg, TN, p. A573

AUGUSTIN, W Walter, CPA, Vice President Financial Services and Chief Financial Officer, University Of Maryland Rehabilitation & Orthopaedic Institute, Baltimore, MD, p. A288

AUGUSTINE, David, Chief Executive Officer, Trego County– Lemke Memorial Hospital, Wakeeney, KS, p. A247

AUGUSTUS, Richard, M.D., Chief Medical Officer, West Valley Medical Center, Caldwell, ID, p. A168

AUGUSTYNIAK, Becky, Director Human Resources, Piedmont Columbus Regional Northside, Columbus, GA, p. A150

AUKES, Amy
  Human Resources Analyst, Avera Flandreau Hospital, Flandreau, SD, p. A561
  Regional Manager of Human Resources, Avera Dells Area Hospital, Dell Rapids, SD, p. A560
AURAND, Brendan, Director, Human Resources, Fairmount Behavioral Health System, Philadelphia, PA, p. A534
AURILIO, Lisa, R.N., MSN, Chief Operating Officer, Akron Children'S Hospital, Akron, OH, p. A471
AUSMAN, Dan F., President and Chief Executive Officer, Methodist Hospital Of Southern California, Arcadia, CA, p. A51
AUSTIN, Aaron
  Market Vice President Human Resources, Chi St. Vincent Hot Springs, Hot Springs, AR, p. A43
  Market Vice President Human Resources, Chi St. Vincent Infirmary Medical Center, Little Rock, AR, p. A45
  Market Vice President Human Resources, Chi St. Vincent Morrilton, Morrilton, AR, p. A46
AUSTIN, Bill, Senior Vice President of Finance, Coastal Virginia Rehabilitation, Newport News, VA, p. A663
AUSTIN, Dan
  Director Information Technology, Arkansas Methodist Medical Center, Paragould, AR, p. A47
  Manager Data Processing, Ashley County Medical Center, Crossett, AR, p. A40
AUSTIN, Donnica, Vice President, Operations, Holy Cross Hospital, Chicago, IL, p. A177
AUSTIN, Geoff, Executive Director, University Of Washington Medical Center, Seattle, WA, p. A678
AUSTIN, Joe, Executive Vice President and Chief Operating Officer, Phoebe Putney Memorial Hospital, Albany, GA, p. A145
AUSTIN, Sherri, MSN, R.N., Chief Nursing Officer, Wrangell Medical Center, Wrangell, AK, p. A27
AUSTIN, Tommye, Ph.D., R.N., MSN, Chief Nursing Executive, University Health System, San Antonio, TX, p. A635
AUSTIN, W William, Senior Vice President Finance, Riverside Shore Memorial Hospital, Onancock, VA, p. A664
AUSTIN, Warren, M.D., Vice President Medical Affairs, Bon Secours Maryview Medical Center, Portsmouth, VA, p. A665
AUSTIN-MOORE, Gale, Director Area Technology, Kaiser Permanente Vallejo Medical Center, Vallejo, CA, p. A93
AUSTRIA, Ramon, R.N., Chief Nursing Officer, Baylor Scott & White Institute For Rehabilitation – Lakeway, Lakeway, TX, p. A619
AUTELLI, Oscar, Chief Information Officer, Lac+Usc Medical Center, Los Angeles, CA, p. A68
AUTREY, Pamela Spencer, R.N., Ph.D., MSN, Chief Nursing Officer, Medical West, Bessemer, AL, p. A14
AUTRY, Paula R., President and Chief Executive Officer, Henry Ford Allegiance Health, Jackson, MI, p. A315
AVANT, Andre, Facility Automation Manager, Texas Center For Infectious Disease, San Antonio, TX, p. A635
AVATO, Rich, Director, St. Mary'S Medical Center, West Palm Beach, FL, p. A144
AVELINO, Joseph, Chief Executive Officer, College Medical Center, Long Beach, CA, p. A65
AVERETT, Elaine, Chief Financial Officer, Grove Hill Memorial Hospital, Grove Hill, AL, p. A19
AVERILL, Clark, Director Information Technology, St. Luke'S Hospital, Duluth, MN, p. A331
AVERNA, Russell
  Vice President Human Resources, Spaulding Rehabilitation Hospital, Charlestown, MA, p. A298
  Vice President of Human Resources, Spaulding Rehabilitation Hospital Cape Cod, East Sandwich, MA, p. A298
AVERY, Danny, Chief Financial Officer and Chief Operating Officer, Mangum Regional Medical Center, Mangum, OK, p. A501
AVERY, Donald R., President and Chief Executive Officer, Fairview Park Hospital, Dublin, GA, p. A152
AVERY, John B., III, Administrator, Perry Community Hospital, Linden, TN, p. A573
AVERY, Jonathan, Chief Administrative Officer, Legacy Good Samaritan Medical Center, Portland, OR, p. A516
AVERY, Scott B., Chief Operating Officer, Paris Regional Medical Center, Paris, TX, p. A628
AVIADO, Gail, Chief Nursing Officer, Montclair Hospital Medical Center, Montclair, CA, p. A72
AVIGDOR, Lauren, Director Human Resources, Advanced Specialty Hospital Of Toledo, Toledo, OH, p. A492
AVILA, Brandi, Chief Nursing Officer, Martin County Hospital District, Stanton, TX, p. A638
AVILA, Patrick, Chief Operating Officer, Belton Regional Medical Center, Belton, MO, p. A356
AVVISATO, Michael, Senior Vice President and Chief Financial Officer, Allied Services Rehabilitation Hospital, Scranton, PA, p. A540

AVVISATO, Mike, Vice President and Chief Financial Officer, John Heinz Institute Of Rehabilitation Medicine, Wilkes, PA, p. A545
AWALD, Tamara, Chief Nursing Officer and Chief Operating Officer, Plymouth Medical Center, Plymouth, IN, p. A213
AWALT, Scott, Chief Financial Officer, Sanford Hillsboro Medical Center, Hillsboro, ND, p. A468
AWAN, Naveed, Chief Executive Officer, St. Helena Parish Hospital, Greensburg, LA, p. A268
AWOLOWO, Yinusa, Business Officer, Brookdale Hospital Medical Center, New York, NY, p. A432
AWWAD, Emad, Director Care Delivery Sites Information Systems and Technology, Lakeview Hospital, Stillwater, MN, p. A341
AXTELL, Vicki, Director Human Resources, Livingston Healthcare, Livingston, MT, p. A378
AYALA, Jose L, M.D., Chief Medical Officer, Valley Baptist Medical Center–Brownsville, Rio Hondo, TX, p. A631
AYALA, Lisa, R.N., Director Human Resources, Specialty Hospital Jacksonville, Jacksonville, FL, p. A126
AYALA, Shirley, Director Human Resources, First Hospital Panamericano, Cidra, PR, p. A716
AYCOCK, Mark, Chief Operating Officer, Spartanburg Medical Center – Church Street Campus, Spartanburg, SC, p. A557
AYERS, James G, Chief Financial Officer, Piedmont Geriatric Hospital, Burkeville, VA, p. A657
AYERS, Jessi, Chief Financial Officer, Person Memorial Hospital, Roxboro, NC, p. A461
AYERS, Matthew, Chief Administrative Officer, Norton Hospital, Louisville, KY, p. A256
AYERS, Pam, Chief Nursing Officer, North Oak Regional Medical Center, Senatobia, MS, p. A354
AYOUB, John J., Chief Executive Officer, Mobridge Regional Hospital, Mobridge, SD, p. A562
AYRES, Robert, Director Information Systems, Firelands Regional Health System, Sandusky, OH, p. A490
AYRES, Shane, Chief Financial Officer, Sanford Wheaton Medical Center, Wheaton, MN, p. A342
AZAR, Richard, Chief Operating Officer, Ucla Medical Center–Santa Monica, Santa Monica, CA, p. A89
AZAR, Robert, Chief Operating Officer, Ucla Medical Center–Santa Monica, Santa Monica, CA, p. A89
AZCONA, Alain
  Chief Executive Officer, Aurora Behavioral Healthcare San Diego, San Diego, CA, p. A83
  Director Business Development, Aurora Behavioral Healthcare San Diego, San Diego, CA, p. A83
AZCUY, Karla, Acting Chief Human Resources Officer, Va Portland Healthcare System, Portland, OR, p. A516
AZEVEDO, Michael, M.D., Medical Director, San Joaquin Valley Rehabilitation Hospital, Fresno, CA, p. A59
AZIZ, Samir, M.D., Medical Director, Fairfax Behavioral Health, Kirkland, WA, p. A674
AZURE, Vernon, Clinical Director, Indian Health Service – Quentin N. Burdick Memorial Health Care Facility, Belcourt, ND, p. A465

B

BAAS, Dina, Director Financial Services, Orange City Area Health System, Orange City, IA, p. A227
BABAKANIAN, Ed, Chief Information Officer, Uc San Diego Health, San Diego, CA, p. A84
BABB, A. Mitch, Vice President, Operations, Duke Regional Hospital, Durham, NC, p. A452
BABB, Cindy, Executive Director Human Resources and Organizational Effectiveness, St. Vincent Kokomo, Kokomo, IN, p. A209
BABB, Dan, Chief Financial Officer, Dmc – Rehabilitation Institute Of Michigan, Detroit, MI, p. A310
BABB, Donald J., Chief Executive Officer, Citizens Memorial Hospital, Bolivar, MO, p. A356
BABB, Kathy, Manager Human Resources, Clifton Springs Hospital And Clinic, Clifton Springs, NY, p. A426
BABCOCK, Daniel, Chief Executive Officer, Marlette Regional Hospital, Marlette, MI, p. A317
BABCOCK, Jordon, Chief Executive Officer, Springwoods Behavioral Health Hospital, Fayetteville, AR, p. A41
BABCOCK, Kimberly, Administrative Director of Operations, Kalkaska Memorial Health Center, Kalkaska, MI, p. A316
BABCOCK, Paul, Chief Financial Officer, Coulee Medical Center, Grand Coulee, WA, p. A673
BABCOCK, Robert, M.D., Interim Chief of Staff, Bath Veterans Affairs Medical Center, Bath, NY, p. A423

BABE, Heather, M.D., Chief of Staff, Shenandoah Medical Center, Shenandoah, IA, p. A229
BABER, Jonathan, Director Information Technology, Central State Hospital, Petersburg, VA, p. A664
BABICH, Eli, Chief Nursing Officer, Select Specialty Hospital–Pittsburgh/Upmc, Pittsburgh, PA, p. A537
BABUSCIO, Cathy, Director Human Resources, Mat–Su Regional Medical Center, Palmer, AK, p. A27
BACA, Modesto, Chief Information Officer, Amarillo Veterans Affairs Health Care System, Amarillo, TX, p. A582
BACH, Dawn M, MS, Chief Clinical Officer, Buena Vista Regional Medical Center, Storm Lake, IA, p. A230
BACHA, Fadi, M.D., Chief Medical Officer, Select Specialty Hospital–Lexington, Lexington, KY, p. A255
BACHELDOR, H Lee, D.O., Chief Medical Officer, Ascension River District Hospital, East China, MI, p. A311
BACHELIER, Erin, Human Resource Administrator, Ranken Jordan Pediatric Bridge Hospital, Maryland Heights, MO, p. A365
BACHER, Beth, Chief Executive Officer, Encompass Health Valley Of The Sun Rehabilitation Hospital, Glendale, AZ, p. A30
BACHMAN, John Page, Corporate Vice President, St. John Medical Center, Tulsa, OK, p. A510
BACHMAN, Judith Lynn
  Chief Operating Officer, Fox Chase Cancer Center–American Oncologic Hospital, Philadelphia, PA, p. A534
  Chief Operating Officer, Jeanes Hospital, Philadelphia, PA, p. A535
BACHMAN, Roberta, Director Human Resources, Riverview Behavioral Health, Texarkana, AR, p. A49
BACHMEIER, Susan T., MSN, R.N., Chief Nursing Officer, Wake Forest Baptist Health–Davie Medical Center, Bermuda Run, NC, p. A449
BACK, Barbara, Manager Human Resources, Encino Hospital Medical Center, Los Angeles, CA, p. A66
BACON, Jeff, D.O., Chief Medical Officer, Sterling Regional Medcenter, Sterling, CO, p. A105
BADEN, Robert M, Chief Financial Officer, Lompoc Valley Medical Center, Lompoc, CA, p. A64
BADEN, Thomas, Chief Information Officer, Community Behavioral Health Hospital – Rochester, Rochester, MN, p. A338
BADGER, Jeff
  Chief Financial Officer, Ascension Calumet Hospital, Chilton, WI, p. A693
  Chief Financial Officer, Ascension Northeast Wisconsin Mercy Hospital, Oshkosh, WI, p. A703
  Chief Financial Officer, Ascension Northeast Wisconsin St. Elizabeth Hospital, Appleton, WI, p. A691
BADINGER, Sandy, Chief Financial Officer, Slidell Memorial Hospital, Slidell, LA, p. A279
BAENEN, Sharla, President Mental Well Being, Vice President Emergency Medicine, Hospitalists & Medical Subspecialist, Bellin Psychiatric Center, Green Bay, WI, p. A696
BAER, Douglas M., Chief Executive Officer, Brooks Rehabilitation Hospital, Jacksonville, FL, p. A125
BAEZ, Janet, Director, University Hospital, San Juan, PR, p. A719
BAEZ, Juan, M.D., President Medical Staff, Robert Wood Johnson University Hospital Rahway, Rahway, NJ, p. A411
BAFFONE, Karen, R.N., Chief Nursing Officer, Tahoe Forest Hospital District, Truckee, CA, p. A92
BAGGERLY, Karen, Chief Nursing Officer and Vice President, Covenant Medical Center, Lubbock, TX, p. A621
BAGGETT, Al, M.D., Interim Chief of Staff, Taylor Regional Hospital, Hawkinsville, GA, p. A154
BAGGETT, Margarita, MSN, R.N.
  Chief Nursing Officer, Uc San Diego Health, San Diego, CA, p. A84
  Interim Chief Operating Officer, Uc San Diego Health, San Diego, CA, p. A84
BAGLEY, Brenda, Director Human Resources, Tmc Bonham Hospital, Bonham, TX, p. A589
BAGNALL, Andrew
  Interim Chief Executive Officer, Hshs St. Joseph'S Hospital, Chippewa Falls, WI, p. A693
  President and Chief Executive Officer, Hshs Sacred Heart Hospital, Eau Claire, WI, p. A694
BAGNELL, Kelly, M.D., Chief of Staff, Providence St. Joseph Medical Center, Polson, MT, p. A379
BAHL, Barry I, Director, St. Cloud Veterans Affairs Health Care System, Saint Cloud, MN, p. A339
BAHLS, Fredrick, M.D., Chief of Staff, Veterans Affairs Central Iowa Health Care System, Des Moines, IA, p. A221
BAHNLEIN, Carl, Executive Vice President and Chief Operating Officer, Virginia Hospital Center, Arlington, VA, p. A656
BAIG, Mirza, Medical Director, Uh Rehabilitation Hospital, Beachwood, OH, p. A473

BAILEY, Ann, Assistant Director Administration, Central State Hospital, Petersburg, VA, p. A664

BAILEY, Becky, Director Human Resources, Lincoln Hospital, Davenport, WA, p. A672

BAILEY, Becky, R.N., Director Nursing, Kansas Surgery And Recovery Center, Wichita, KS, p. A248

BAILEY, Brenda, Assistant Administrator, Windsor–Laurelwood Center For Behavioral Medicine, Willoughby, OH, p. A494

BAILEY, Bruce P.
Chief Executive Officer, Tidelands Georgetown Memorial Hospital, Georgetown, SC, p. A553
Chief Executive Officer, Tidelands Waccamaw Community Hospital, Murrells Inlet, SC, p. A556

BAILEY, Cheryl, R.N., Chief Nursing Officer Vice President Patient Care Services, Cullman Regional Medical Center, Cullman, AL, p. A16

BAILEY, Cori, Accountant, Tyler Holmes Memorial Hospital, Winona, MS, p. A355

BAILEY, Craig, Chief Executive Officer and Administrator, Colorado Acute Long Term Hospital, Denver, CO, p. A98

BAILEY, Dan, Director Information Systems, Norton Sound Regional Hospital, Nome, AK, p. A26

BAILEY, David, Chief Executive Officer, Community Hospital Of Bremen, Bremen, IN, p. A200

BAILEY, Dawn A, R.N., Vice President Nursing and Chief Nursing Officer, Euclid Hospital, Euclid, OH, p. A482

BAILEY, Dianne, Chief Information Officer, Pana Community Hospital, Pana, IL, p. A192

BAILEY, Heather, Chief Human Resources Officer, Jefferson Healthcare, Port Townsend, WA, p. A676

BAILEY, Jodi J, Human Resources Director, Odessa Memorial Healthcare Center, Odessa, WA, p. A675

BAILEY, John E., Chief Financial Officer, Moore County Hospital District, Dumas, TX, p. A600

BAILEY, Jonathan D., Chief Executive Officer and Administrator, Hansford Hospital, Spearman, TX, p. A637

BAILEY, Jonathan T, Chief Operating Officer, Stamford Hospital, Stamford, CT, p. A111

BAILEY, Joy, Director Information Technology, Sutter Amador Hospital, Jackson, CA, p. A62

BAILEY, Joyce, Vice President Patient Care, Chi St. Anthony Hospital, Pendleton, OR, p. A515

BAILEY, Kathy C., President and Chief Executive Officer, Carolinas Healthcare System Blue Ridge, Morganton, NC, p. A459

BAILEY, Larry, President, Indiana University Health Paoli Hospital, Paoli, IN, p. A213

BAILEY, Leisa, M.D., Chief of Staff, Doctors Memorial Hospital, Bonifay, FL, p. A118

BAILEY, Lori, R.N., Vice President and Chief Nursing Officer, Ottumwa Regional Health Center, Ottumwa, IA, p. A228

BAILEY, Marquita, Chief Nursing Officer, Dekalb Regional Medical Center, Fort Payne, AL, p. A18

BAILEY, Melissa, Commissioner, Department of Mental Health, Vermont Psychiatric Care Hospital, Berlin, VT, p. A654

BAILEY, Mikeana, Director Human Resources, Brownwood Regional Medical Center, Brownwood, TX, p. A590

BAILEY, Robert W, Chief Information Officer, Hawthorn Center, Northville, MI, p. A319

BAILEY, Ron, Chief Financial Officer, Franklin Foundation Hospital, Franklin, LA, p. A267

BAILEY, Scott
Chief Financial Officer, Saint Francis Hospital Muskogee, Muskogee, OK, p. A502
Chief Operating Officer, Saint Mary'S Regional Medical Center, Russellville, AR, p. A48

BAILEY, Thomas, Chief Operating Officer, Bothwell Regional Health Center, Sedalia, MO, p. A371

BAILEY, Travis A, Vice President Administration, St. Claire Healthcare, Morehead, KY, p. A258

BAILEY–NEWELL, Susan, Vice President Human Resources, Baylor St. Luke'S Medical Center, Houston, TX, p. A610

BAILEY–OETKER, Jessica, Director Quality and Medical Staff, Providence Willamette Falls Medical Center, Oregon City, OR, p. A515

BAIN, Joel, Director Information Services, Tristar Summit Medical Center, Hermitage, TN, p. A570

BAIN, Mark, Chief Human Resources, Veterans Affairs Connecticut Healthcare System, West Haven, CT, p. A112

BAIN, Pat, Chief Nursing Officer, Lower Bucks Hospital, Bristol, PA, p. A521

BAIO, Katie, Human Resource Director, Adventist Medical Center Bolingbrook, Bolingbrook, IL, p. A174

BAIR, Ada, Chief Executive Officer, Memorial Hospital, Carthage, IL, p. A175

BAIR, Andrew P., Chief Executive Officer, Ellsworth County Medical Center, Ellsworth, KS, p. A234

BAIR, Connie, Human Resources Assistant, Pike County Memorial Hospital, Louisiana, MO, p. A364

BAIRD, David
Chief Information Officer, Lds Hospital, Salt Lake City, UT, p. A651
Chief Information Officer, The Orthopedic Specialty Hospital, Murray, UT, p. A649
Director of Information Systems, Intermountain Medical Center, Murray, UT, p. A649

BAIRD, Donna, Vice President Corporate Services, Bay Medical Sacred Heart, Panama City, FL, p. A135

BAIRD, Glen, M.D., Chief of Staff, Shriners Hospitals For Children–Spokane, Spokane, WA, p. A680

BAIRD, John D., Chief Executive Officer, Metrosouth Medical Center, Blue Island, IL, p. A174

BAISCH, Kim, R.N., Associate Vice President Patient Care Services, Highline Medical Center, Burien, WA, p. A671

BAISDEN, Monica, Director Human Resources, Memorial Hermann Northeast, Humble, TX, p. A615

BAISE, Patricia
Chief Executive Officer, Franklin Woods Community Hospital, Johnson City, TN, p. A571
Chief Executive Officer, Johnson City Medical Center, Johnson City, TN, p. A571

BAJAK, Sally, Chief Financial Officer, St. Croix Regional Medical Center, St Croix Falls, WI, p. A706

BAJARI, Pamela R, R.N., Nurse Executive MHSATS, Community Behavioral Health Hospital – Rochester, Rochester, MN, p. A338

BAKAR, Anne L.
President and Chief Executive Officer, Telecare Heritage Psychiatric Health Center, Oakland, CA, p. A75
President and Chief Executive Officer, Willow Rock Center, San Leandro, CA, p. A87

BAKER, Alison, M.D., Chief of Staff, Missouri Baptist Sullivan Hospital, Sullivan, MO, p. A372

BAKER, Annessa, Site Executive and Chief Nursing Officer, Jewish Hospital–Shelbyville, Shelbyville, KY, p. A260

BAKER, Bonnie, Vice President Finance and Chief Financial Officer, Butler Hospital, Providence, RI, p. A547

BAKER, Bonnie, M.D., Chief Medical Services, Veterans Health Care System Of The Ozarks, Fayetteville, AR, p. A41

BAKER, Brenda, Chief Financial Officer, Riverview Health, Noblesville, IN, p. A213

BAKER, Cindi, Chief Operating Officer, Riverwood Healthcare Center, Aitkin, MN, p. A327

BAKER, Damon, D.O., Chief Medical Officer, Oklahoma State University Medical Center, Tulsa, OK, p. A509

BAKER, Deborah
Chief Nursing Officer, Helen Newberry Joy Hospital, Newberry, MI, p. A319
Vice President, Nursing, Johns Hopkins Hospital, Baltimore, MD, p. A286
Vice President, Patient Care Services, Mount Auburn Hospital, Cambridge, MA, p. A297

BAKER, Denis, Chief Information Officer, Sarasota Memorial Health Care System, Sarasota, FL, p. A139

BAKER, Erin, Chief Nursing Officer, Eminent Medical Center, Richardson, TX, p. A630

BAKER, Frank, Chief Information Officer, Mary Breckinridge Arh Hospital, Hyden, KY, p. A254

BAKER, Gary E., Senior Vice President and Chief Executive Officer, Honorhealth Scottsdale Shea Medical Center, Scottsdale, AZ, p. A35

BAKER, Harlan T, Department Leader Information Systems, Mcdonough District Hospital, Macomb, IL, p. A188

BAKER, J Matthew, M.D., President Medical Staff, Bertrand Chaffee Hospital, Springville, NY, p. A444

BAKER, Jason, Administrator, Christus Dubuis Hospital Of Beaumont, Beaumont, TX, p. A587

BAKER, Joann, Administrator, Doctors Memorial Hospital, Bonifay, FL, p. A118

BAKER, Joel, D.O., Chief Medical Officer, Wayne County Hospital, Corydon, IA, p. A220

BAKER, Judy, Chief Financial Officer, Kindred Hospital–Mansfield, Mansfield, TX, p. A623

BAKER, Maia, MSN, Chief Nurse Executive, Rio Grande State Center/South Texas Health Care System, Harlingen, TX, p. A609

BAKER, Mark A., Chief Executive Officer, Jack Hughston Memorial Hospital, Phenix City, AL, p. A22

BAKER, Melissa
Director, Human Resources, Providence Little Company Of Mary Medical Center – Torrance, Torrance, CA, p. A92
Director, Human Resources, Providence Little Company Of Mary Medical Center San Pedro, Los Angeles, CA, p. A69

BAKER, Michelle, Director Information Systems, Indiana University Health White Memorial Hospital, Monticello, IN, p. A211

BAKER, Nichelle A, Chair Human Resources, Mayo Clinic Hospital, Phoenix, AZ, p. A33

BAKER, Paige, MSN, R.N., Chief Nursing Officer, Lee'S Summit Medical Center, Lee'S Summit, MO, p. A364

BAKER, Paula F, President and Chief Executive Officer, Freeman Health System, Joplin, MO, p. A362

BAKER, Paula F., President and Chief Executive Officer, Freeman Health System, Joplin, MO, p. A362

BAKER, Peter, Senior Vice President and Administrator, Loma Linda University Medical Center–Murrieta, Murrieta, CA, p. A73

BAKER, R Hal, M.D., Vice President and Chief Information Officer, Wellspan York Hospital, York, PA, p. A546

BAKER, Reese, Director Information Systems, Crittenden County Hospital, Marion, KY, p. A257

BAKER, Ron, Chief Executive Officer, Saint Luke'S East Hospital, Lee'S Summit, MO, p. A364

BAKER, Roni, Director of Nursing, Herington Municipal Hospital, Herington, KS, p. A236

BAKER, Sharon, Director Support Services, Fairbanks, Indianapolis, IN, p. A206

BAKER, Steve, Vice President and Chief Technology and Information Officer, Columbus Regional Hospital, Columbus, IN, p. A201

BAKER, Vanya, Director, Wake Forest Baptist Health – Wilkes Medical Center, North Wilkesboro, NC, p. A459

BAKER, W Douglas., Director, Julian F. Keith Alcohol And Drug Abuse Treatment Center, Black Mountain, NC, p. A450

BAKER–WITT, Francine, Chief Executive Officer, Effingham Hospital, Springfield, GA, p. A160

BAKEWELL, Nancy
Administrator, Monroe Hospital, Bloomington, IN, p. A200
Chief Nursing Officer, Monroe Hospital, Bloomington, IN, p. A200

BAKHTIER, Hasan, M.D., Medical Director, Community Mental Health Center, Lawrenceburg, IN, p. A210

BAKICH, Sandy, Director Information Management, Delano Regional Medical Center, Delano, CA, p. A56

BAKKEN, Mary, Executive Vice President and Chief Operating Officer, Silver Cross Hospital, New Lenox, IL, p. A191

BAKKUM, Kyle, Chief Executive Officer and Administrator, Vernon Memorial Healthcare, Elk Mound, WI, p. A694

BAKOS, Marty, Chief Financial Officer, Mountain Vista Medical Center, Mesa, AZ, p. A31

BALASIA, Tim, Chief Financial Officer, Johnson Memorial Hospital, Franklin, IN, p. A204

BALASUBRAMONY, Suresh, M.D., Chief Medical Officer, Minnie Hamilton Healthcare Center, Grantsville, WV, p. A685

BALASUNDARAM, Anusuya, M.D., Medical Director, Hampton Behavioral Health Center, Westampton, NJ, p. A415

BALAZY, Thomas E, M.D., Medical Director, Craig Hospital, Englewood, CO, p. A100

BALCAVAGE, Thomas, Vice President Chief Patient Safety and Quality Officer, Jefferson Stratford Hospital, Stratford, NJ, p. A413

BALCEZAK, Thomas, M.D., Senior Vice President Medical Affairs and Chief Medical Officer, Yale–New Haven Hospital, New Haven, CT, p. A110

BALDAUF, Robb, Coordinator Information Systems, Cleveland Clinic Akron General Lodi Hospital, Lodi, OH, p. A485

BALDERRAMA, Jose, Vice President Human Resources, Valley Hospital, Ridgewood, NJ, p. A412

BALDOSARO, Thomas
Chief Financial Officer, Inspira Medical Center–Elmer, Elmer, NJ, p. A405
Chief Financial Officer, Inspira Medical Center–Vineland, Vineland, NJ, p. A413

BALDRIDGE, Dava, R.N., Chief Nursing Officer, Hillcrest Hospital – South, Tulsa, OK, p. A508

BALDWIN, Barbara, Chief Information Officer, Anne Arundel Medical Center, Annapolis, MD, p. A286

BALDWIN, Bruce A., Chief Executive Officer, Newberry County Memorial Hospital, Newberry, SC, p. A556

BALDWIN, Chad, Interim Chief Executive Officer, Westside Surgical Hospital, Houston, TX, p. A615

BALDWIN, Ellen, R.N., Chief Nursing Officer, Texas Health Center For Diagnostic & Surgery, Plano, TX, p. A630

BALDWIN, Erin, M.P.H., Chief Operating Officer, Mahaska Health Partnership, Oskaloosa, IA, p. A228

BALDWIN, Linda, Chief Nursing Officer, Ogallala Community Hospital, Ogallala, NE, p. A388

BALDWIN, Nathan, M.D., President Medical Staff, Baptist Memorial Hospital–Booneville, Booneville, MS, p. A345

BALDWIN, Stephen, Chief Operating Officer, Touro Infirmary, New Orleans, LA, p. A276

BALDWIN, Steve
Manager Information Technology, Wyoming State Hospital, Evanston, WY, p. A711
Vice President Finance, The Willough At Naples, Naples, FL, p. A132

BALDWIN, William, Chief Information Officer, Ashe Memorial Hospital, Jefferson, NC, p. A457

BALES, Brian, Director Plant Operations, Encompass Health Rehabilitation Hospital Of Princeton, Princeton, WV, p. A688
BALES, Correen, Executive Director Human Resources, Unm Sandoval Regional Medical Center, Inc., Rio Rancho, NM, p. A419
BALES, Glenn, Chief Financial Officer, Providence Saint Joseph Medical Center, Burbank, CA, p. A53
BALES–CHUBB, Denyse, Chief Executive Officer, Adventhealth Tampa, Tampa, FL, p. A141
BALKO, Tom, Manager Information Systems, Carris Health – Redwood, Redwood Falls, MN, p. A338
BALL, Cassie, Chief Financial Officer, Colleton Medical Center, Walterboro, SC, p. A558
BALL, Charlie, Chief Operating Officer, Specialty Rehabilitation Hospital Of Coushatta, Coushatta, LA, p. A266
BALL, Connie, Chief Financial Officer, Specialty Rehabilitation Hospital Of Coushatta, Coushatta, LA, p. A266
BALL, Craig, Chief Executive Officer, Specialty Rehabilitation Hospital Of Coushatta, Coushatta, LA, p. A266
BALL, James, Chief Operating Officer, Executive, St. Anthony'S Rehabilitation Hospital, Lauderdale Lakes, FL, p. A128
BALL, Jim, Chief Operating Officer, St. Catherine'S Rehabilitation Hospital, North Miami, FL, p. A133
BALL, Johnny Percy, Assistant Administrator Human Resources, South Georgia Medical Center, Valdosta, GA, p. A162
BALL, Rodney, Vice President Finance, Atrium Health Cabarrus, Concord, NC, p. A452
BALLANCE, William, Chief of Medical Staff, Vidant Bertie Hospital, Windsor, NC, p. A464
BALLARD, Christine
President, Upmc Susquehanna Muncy, Muncy, PA, p. A532
Vice President Human Resources, Upmc Susquehanna Soldiers + Sailors, Wellsboro, PA, p. A544
BALLARD, Jerry, Director Information Systems, Central Florida Regional Hospital, Sanford, FL, p. A139
BALLARD, John, Chief Executive Officer, Kentucky River Medical Center, Jackson, KY, p. A254
BALLARD, Lorraine L, Director Human Resources, St. Helena Parish Hospital, Greensburg, LA, p. A268
BALLARD, Marsha, Human Resources, Christus Mother Frances Hospital – Jacksonville, Jacksonville, TX, p. A616
BALLARD, Terri, Chief Nursing Officer, Healthsouth Northern Kentucky Rehabilitation Hospital, Edgewood, KY, p. A251
BALLESTERO, Susan, Vice President and Chief Human Resources Officer, Saint Peter'S University Hospital, New Brunswick, NJ, p. A409
BALLEW, Cheryl, Human Resources Director, Encompass Health Rehabilitation Hospital Of Las Vegas, Las Vegas, NV, p. A395
BALLIETT, Matt, Chief Information Officer, Coal County General Hospital, Coalgate, OK, p. A498
BALLIN, Daniel, Administrator, Coastal Virginia Rehabilitation, Newport News, VA, p. A663
BALLINGHOFF, James R, MSN, R.N., Chief Nursing Officer and Associate Executive Director, Penn Presbyterian Medical Center, Philadelphia, PA, p. A536
BALLMAN, Patricia, Director, Westfield Memorial Hospital, Westfield, NY, p. A447
BALLOU, Michele, M.D., Chief Medical Staff, Lewisgale Hospital Alleghany, Low Moor, VA, p. A661
BALOGA–ALTIERI, Bonnie, Ph.D., R.N., Vice President Patient Care Services and Chief Nursing Officer, Children'S Specialized Hospital, New Brunswick, NJ, p. A409
BALSANO, Tony, Vice President Finance, Saint Francis Medical Center, Cape Girardeau, MO, p. A357
BALSAR, Jeffrey R., President and Chief Executive Officer Vanderbilt Medical Center and Dean, Vanderbilt University Scho, Vanderbilt University Medical Center, Nashville, TN, p. A577
BALT, David, D.O., Chief Medical Officer, Avera Queen Of Peace Hospital, Mitchell, SD, p. A562
BALTIERRA, David A., M.D., President Medical Staff, Jefferson Medical Center, Ranson, WV, p. A689
BALTZ, Phyllis, Chief Executive Officer, Methodist Hospital Of Sacramento, Sacramento, CA, p. A82
BALUKOFF, Sam, Interim Administrator, Geisinger Medical Center, Danville, PA, p. A523
BALULGA, Josefina, M.D., Clinical Director, Florida State Hospital, Chattahoochee, FL, p. A119
BALUNTANSKI, Brian, Chief Financial Officer, Mclaren Macomb, Mount Clemens, MI, p. A318
BALZ, Pat, Vice President Operations Human Resources, Baylor Scott & White Medical Center – Temple, Temple, TX, p. A639
BALZANO, Janice, President and Chief Executive Officer, St. Petersburg General Hospital, Saint Petersburg, FL, p. A139
BAMAN, Raj, D.O., President Medical Staff, Samaritan North Lincoln Hospital, Lincoln City, OR, p. A514
BAMBURG, Jeanna, Chief Executive Officer, Bayshore Medical Center, Pasadena, TX, p. A628
BAME, Jeremiah, R.N., Chief Nursing Officer, Piedmont Newton Hospital, Covington, GA, p. A151
BAMMEL, Paul, Vice President, Mayo Clinic Health System – Northland In Barron, Barron, WI, p. A692
BANAS, Mark, M.D., Chief Medical Officer, Ascension St. Mary'S Hospital, Rhinelander, WI, p. A704
BANBURY, Brian, Director Site Information Systems, Advocate Christ Medical Center, Oak Lawn, IL, p. A191
BANCHY, Pamela, Chief Information Officer, Western Reserve Hospital, Cuyahoga Falls, OH, p. A481
BANCO, Leonard, M.D., Senior Vice President and Chief Medical Officer, Bristol Hospital, Bristol, CT, p. A107
BANDFIELD–KEOUGH, Kathryn, Vice President Patient Care Services, Munson Healthcare Cadillac Hospital, Cadillac, MI, p. A308
BANDLA, H., M.D., Chief Clinical Affairs, Walter P. Reuther Psychiatric Hospital, Westland, MI, p. A325
BANDS, James G, Chief Financial Officer, Ivinson Memorial Hospital, Laramie, WY, p. A711
BANDY, Dawn, Chief Financial Officer, Grant Regional Health Center, Lancaster, WI, p. A698
BANDY, Don, Director Information Technology, Integris Deaconess, Oklahoma City, OK, p. A504
BANDY, Jennifer, Human Resource Business Partner, Wake Forest Baptist Health–Davie Medical Center, Bermuda Run, NC, p. A449
BANDY, P Ross, M.D., Chief Medical Officer and Chief of Staff, Levi Hospital, Hot Springs National Park, AR, p. A43
BANE, Brian R, Vice President Human Resources, Rush Memorial Hospital, Rushville, IN, p. A214
BANE, Harrison, President, Good Samaritan Medical Center, Brockton, MA, p. A296
BANE, William, Chief Financial Officer, Inova Loudoun Hospital, Leesburg, VA, p. A661
BANFIELD, Anne, Chief, Medical Staff, Davis Medical Center, Elkins, WV, p. A685
BANG, W J, M.D., Chief of Staff, Reeves County Hospital, Pecos, TX, p. A628
BANGA, Alok, M.D., Medical Director, Sierra Vista Hospital, Sacramento, CA, p. A82
BANIEWICZ, John, M.D., Chief Medical Officer, Lake Health, Concord Township, OH, p. A480
BANK, Carol J, Vice President Human Resources, Divine Savior Healthcare, Portage, WI, p. A704
BANKER, Julie G, R.N., MSN, Chief Nursing Officer, Lehigh Regional Medical Center, Lehigh Acres, FL, p. A128
BANKERS, Diane, Chief Nursing Officer, Firstlight Health System, Mora, MN, p. A336
BANKS, Chester, Director Human Resources, East Orange General Hospital, East Orange, NJ, p. A405
BANKS, Elizabeth, Chief Executive Officer, Summit Behavioral Healthcare, Cincinnati, OH, p. A476
BANKS, Matthew, Chief Executive Officer, Davis Regional Medical Center, Statesville, NC, p. A462
BANKS, Maureen
President, Spaulding Hospital For Continuing Medical Care Cambridge, Cambridge, MA, p. A297
President, Spaulding Rehabilitation Hospital Cape Cod, East Sandwich, MA, p. A298
BANKS, Maureen, FACHE, MS, R.N., Chief Operating Officer, Spaulding Rehabilitation Hospital, Charlestown, MA, p. A298
BANKS, Robbi, Vice President, Human Resources, Medical Center Health System, Odessa, TX, p. A627
BANKS, Walter, Director Human Resources, Baptist Memorial Hospital–Desoto, Southaven, MS, p. A354
BANKSTON, Doug, Director Technical Services, North Oaks Medical Center, Hammond, LA, p. A268
BANKTSON, Julie, Manager Human Resources, Paul Oliver Memorial Hospital, Frankfort, MI, p. A312
BANNER, Fred, Chief Information Officer, Shore Medical Center, Somers Point, NJ, p. A412
BANSAL, Rina, Acting President and Chief Nursing Officer, Inova Alexandria Hospital, Alexandria, VA, p. A656
BANTZ, Steve, Manager Information Technology, Grundy County Memorial Hospital, Grundy Center, IA, p. A223
BANUEDOS, Jorge, Director Human Resources, Metropolitan State Hospital, Norwalk, CA, p. A75
BAQUET, Shawn, Chief of Staff, Iberia Medical Center, New Iberia, LA, p. A274
BARACSKAY, Donald J., II, Chief Executive Officer, The Centers, Ocala, FL, p. A133
BARANSKI, Kenneth, Chief Financial Officer, Hills & Dales General Hospital, Cass City, MI, p. A308
BARANSKI, Monica
President, Mclaren Bay Region, Bay City, MI, p. A307
President, Mclaren Bay Special Care, Bay City, MI, p. A307
BARBA, James J., President and Chief Executive Officer, Albany Medical Center, Albany, NY, p. A422
BARBADIAN, John, Vice President Human Resources, Adventist Health – Tulare, Tulare, CA, p. A92
BARBAREE, Jerry, Director Human Resources, Baptist Memorial Hospital – Memphis, Memphis, TN, p. A574
BARBARIN, LaSharndra, Chief Executive Officer, Medical City Lewisville, Lewisville, TX, p. A620
BARBAROTTA, Ann Marie., Executive Director, Brookdale Hospital Medical Center, New York, NY, p. A432
BARBEE, Daniel, Chief Executive Officer, The University Of Toledo Medical Center, Toledo, OH, p. A492
BARBEE, Ovell, Senior Vice President, Human Resources, Spectrum Health – Butterworth Hospital, Grand Rapids, MI, p. A313
BARBER, Chris B., President and Chief Executive Officer, St. Bernards Medical Center, Jonesboro, AR, p. A44
BARBER, Eric A., President and Chief Executive Officer, Mary Lanning Healthcare, Hastings, NE, p. A385
BARBER, Karen, Chief Executive Officer, Yoakum Community Hospital, Yoakum, TX, p. A646
BARBER, Keith, Chief Executive Officer, Houston Methodist Willowbrook Hospital, Houston, TX, p. A612
BARBER, Michael, Chief Operating Officer, Penn Medicine Chester County Hospital, West Chester, PA, p. A544
BARBER, Richard, M.D., Chief Medical Officer, Wake Forest Baptist Health – Wilkes Medical Center, North Wilkesboro, NC, p. A459
BARBER, Roxann E, Regional Ambulatory Care and Ancillary Services Officer, Amita Health Mercy Medical Center, Aurora, IL, p. A173
BARBER, Scott, Vice President, Camden General Hospital, Camden, TN, p. A566
BARBER, Wendi, Vice President Finance and Chief Financial Officer, Adventhealth Hendersonville, Hendersonville, NC, p. A456
BARBINI, Gerald J., President and Chief Executive Officer, Allegan General Hospital, Allegan, MI, p. A306
BARBO, Steve, Chief Executive Officer, Citizens Medical Center, Columbia, LA, p. A266
BARBOUR, Alexis, Director Finance, Columbus Dublin Springs, Dublin, OH, p. A482
BARBOUR, Michael B, Chief Nursing Officer, Emerald Coast Behavioral Hospital, Panama City, FL, p. A135
BARBUAT, James P, Chief Financial Officer, Gunnison Valley Hospital, Gunnison, CO, p. A101
BARCELLONA, Nicholas J., Chief Financial Officer, Upmc Children'S Hospital Of Pittsburgh, Pittsburgh, PA, p. A538
BARCHI, Daniel, Senior Vice President, Technical Services and Chief Information Officer, Bridgeport Hospital, Bridgeport, CT, p. A107
BARCLAY, Bonnie, Chief Nursing Officer, Lifecare Hospitals Of Chester County, West Chester, PA, p. A544
BARCLAY, Duane, D.O., Chief Medical Officer, Emory Hillandale Hospital, Lithonia, GA, p. A156
BARCLAY, Emily, Vice President Human Resources, Dana–Farber Cancer Institute, Boston, MA, p. A295
BARCLAY, Jeremy, Chief Executive Officer, St. David'S Round Rock Medical Center, Round Rock, TX, p. A632
BARCLAY, Rick, Vice President Support Services, Mercy Hospital Rogers, Rogers, AR, p. A48
BARCUS, Krista, Human Resources Leader, Mosaic Medical Center – Maryville, Maryville, MO, p. A365
BARDEN, Sean
Executive Vice President and Chief Financial Officer, Mary Washington Hospital, Fredericksburg, VA, p. A659
Executive Vice President and Chief Financial Officer, Stafford Hospital, Stafford, VA, p. A667
BARDIER, Catherine, Vice President, Human Resources, Elliot Hospital, Manchester, NH, p. A401
BARDWELL, Carol A, R.N., MSN, Chief Nurse Executive, Martha'S Vineyard Hospital, Oak Bluffs, MA, p. A302
BARDWELL, Sheila, Director Information Systems, Baptist Memorial Hospital–Golden Triangle, Columbus, MS, p. A346
BARE, Christina, Director of Business Operations, Carle Richland Memorial Hospital, Olney, IL, p. A192
BAREFOOT, Denise, Director of Information Technology, Carolina Pines Regional Medical Center, Hartsville, SC, p. A554
BAREIS, Charles, M.D., Medical Director, Macneal Hospital, Berwyn, IL, p. A174
BARELA, Barbara, Director Human Resources, Gila Regional Medical Center, Silver City, NM, p. A420
BARFIELD, Donna, Chief Nursing Officer, West Tennessee Healthcare Volunteer Hospital, Martin, TN, p. A574
BARHAM, Ed, M.D., Chief of Staff, Merit Health Woman'S Hospital, Flowood, MS, p. A347

BARIAS, Emmanuel, Interim Chief Executive Officer, Memorial Hospital Of Texas County, Guymon, OK, p. A500

BARIOLA, Christopher L., Chief Executive Officer, Baptist Memorial Rehabilitation Hospital, Germantown, TN, p. A570

BARKER, Alanna, Director Human Resources, Metrosouth Medical Center, Blue Island, IL, p. A174

BARKER, James, Chief Executive Officer, Munson Healthcare Manistee Hospital, Manistee, MI, p. A317

BARKER, Karen, Vice President and Chief Information Officer, Sinai Hospital Of Baltimore, Baltimore, MD, p. A287

BARKER, Kathryn L, Chief Human Resources Management, Veterans Health Care System Of The Ozarks, Fayetteville, AR, p. A41

BARKER, Kendra, Administrator, University Of Kansas Health System Pawnee Valley Campus, Larned, KS, p. A239

BARKER, Louise, Chief Executive Officer, Central Louisiana Surgical Hospital, Alexandria, LA, p. A262

BARKER, Richard, Administrator and Chief Executive Officer, Mercy Health Love County, Marietta, OK, p. A502

BARKER, Russell
  Community Chief Executive Officer, Mcdowell Arh Hospital, Mcdowell, KY, p. A258
  Information Officer, U. S. Public Health Service Indian Hospital–Whiteriver, Whiteriver, AZ, p. A38

BARKER, William A, Vice President Administration, Pleasant Valley Hospital, Point Pleasant, WV, p. A688

BARKHYMER, Mary C, R.N., MSN, Vice President Patient Care Services and Chief Nursing Officer, Upmc St. Margaret, Pittsburgh, PA, p. A538

BARKMAN, Joseph, Vice President Financial Services, Oaklawn Psychiatric Center, Goshen, IN, p. A205

BARKSDALE, Mary, Director Human Resources, Person Memorial Hospital, Roxboro, NC, p. A461

BARLAGE, Seth, Associate Medical Center Director, John J. Pershing Veterans Affairs Medical Center, Poplar Bluff, MO, p. A367

BARLEY, Leonard, M.D., Chief Medical Officer, Windsor–Laurelwood Center For Behavioral Medicine, Willoughby, OH, p. A494

BARLEY, Tammy, Director, Human Resources, Encompass Health Rehabilitation Hospital Of Jonesboro, Jonesboro, AR, p. A44

BARLIS, Ellen, Chief Financial Officer, Brookdale Hospital Medical Center, New York, NY, p. A432

BARLOW, Mark, M.D., Chief Medical Officer and President Medical Staff, Cornerstone Hospital Of Houston At Clearlake, Webster, TX, p. A644

BARLOW, Roddex, Chief Operating Officer, The Hospitals Of Providence Memorial Campus, El Paso, TX, p. A602

BARMECHA, Jitendra, M.D., M.P.H., Senior Vice President and Chief Information Officer, Brookdale Hospital Medical Center, New York, NY, p. A432

BARNARD, Kerri, Director Human Resources, Larned State Hospital, Larned, KS, p. A238

BARNARD, Lawrence, President and Chief Executive Officer, St. Rose Dominican Hospitals – San Martin Campus, Las Vegas, NV, p. A396

BARNCORD, Sharon, Human Resource Business Partner, Kaiser Permanente South San Francisco, South San Francisco, CA, p. A90

BARNELL, Phil, Chief Medical Officer, Hshs St. Mary'S Hospital, Decatur, IL, p. A181

BARNES, Alan, Chief Financial Officer, North Star Behavioral Health System, Anchorage, AK, p. A25

BARNES, Becky, Chief Operating Officer, St. David'S North Austin Medical Center, Austin, TX, p. A586

BARNES, Bridget, Vice President and Chief Information Officer, Ohsu Hospital, Portland, OR, p. A516

BARNES, Deborah, Vice President and Chief Information Officer, Children'S Hospital Of The King'S Daughters, Norfolk, VA, p. A663

BARNES, Donald K, Chief Human Resources Officer, Duke Raleigh Hospital, Raleigh, NC, p. A460

BARNES, Douglas A, M.D., Chief of Staff, Shriners Hospitals For Children–Houston, Houston, TX, p. A613

BARNES, Elbert, M.D., Chief Medical Officer, Medical Center Of Trinity, Trinity, FL, p. A143

BARNES, Gary, Senior Vice President, Chief Information Officer, Medical Center Health System, Odessa, TX, p. A627

BARNES, Gloria V., MSN, Assistant Vice President Patient Care Services, Southeastern Regional Medical Center, Newnan, GA, p. A158

BARNES, Jacqueline, Manager Health Information, Select Specialty Hospital–Jackson, Jackson, MS, p. A349

BARNES, Jeff, Director Information Technology, Girard Medical Center, Girard, KS, p. A235

BARNES, John, Administrative Director Human Resources, Beverly Hospital, Montebello, CA, p. A72

BARNES, Karen, Interim Chief Nursing Officer, Logan Regional Medical Center, Logan, WV, p. A686

BARNES, Larry, Vice President Information Technology, Salina Regional Health Center, Salina, KS, p. A245

BARNES, Leslie
  Chief Executive Officer, Parkview Medical Center, Pueblo, CO, p. A104
  Chief Financial Officer, Parkview Medical Center, Pueblo, CO, p. A104

BARNES, Marla, Director of Nursing, Pushmataha Hospital, Antlers, OK, p. A496

BARNES, Michael, Chief Information Officer, North Valley Hospital, Whitefish, MT, p. A381

BARNES, P. Marie, Director, Human Resources, North Mississippi Medical Center–Pontotoc, Pontotoc, MS, p. A353

BARNES, Sherry, Director Health Information and Quality Management, Rolling Hills Hospital, Ada, OK, p. A496

BARNETT, DeLynn K, Director Human Resources, Lake Chelan Community Hospital And Clinics, Chelan, WA, p. A671

BARNETT, Frederick, M.D., Chief of Staff, Adventhealth Central Texas, Killeen, TX, p. A618

BARNETT, Julia, Chief Nursing Officer, Union General Hospital, Blairsville, GA, p. A148

BARNETT, Kelly, Human Resource Officer, Brownfield Regional Medical Center, Brownfield, TX, p. A589

BARNETT, Laura, Executive Director, Human Resources, Brigham And Women'S Faulkner Hospital, Boston, MA, p. A295

BARNETT, Lori, President and Chief Operating Officer, Guthrie Troy Community Hospital, Troy, PA, p. A542

BARNETT, Pam, R.N., Director of Nursing, Highland District Hospital, Hillsboro, OH, p. A484

BARNETT, Shawn
  Senior Vice President and Chief Financial Officer, Chi St. Vincent Hot Springs, Hot Springs, AR, p. A43
  Senior Vice President and Chief Financial Officer, Chi St. Vincent Infirmary Medical Center, Little Rock, AR, p. A45
  Senior Vice President and Chief Financial Officer, Chi St. Vincent Medical Center–North, Sherwood, AR, p. A48
  Senior Vice President and Chief Financial Officer, Chi St. Vincent Morrilton, Morrilton, AR, p. A46

BARNETT, Steve, President and Chief Executive Officer, Mckenzie Health System, Sandusky, MI, p. A322

BARNETT, Tom, Chief Information Officer, Highland Hospital, Rochester, NY, p. A442

BARNETTE, Brian, Chief Information Officer, Shepherd Center, Atlanta, GA, p. A147

BARNHARDT, Bonnie, Executive Director Human Resources, Ridgeview Le Sueur Medical Center, Le Sueur, MN, p. A334

BARNHART, Cody, Chief Executive Officer, Aspen Mountain Medical Center, Rock Springs, WY, p. A712

BARNHART, David, Director Information Systems, Rockledge Regional Medical Center, Rockledge, FL, p. A138

BARNHART, J. T.
  Chief Executive Officer, Dallas Medical Center, Dallas, TX, p. A596
  Chief Executive Officer, Tennova Healthcare – Cleveland, Cleveland, TN, p. A568

BARNHART, Jeff, Chief Executive Officer, Hereford Regional Medical Center, Hereford, TX, p. A610

BARNO, Jill, M.D., Chief Medical Officer, Berger Health System, Circleville, OH, p. A477

BARONE, Richard, M.D., Medical Director, Montefiore New Rochelle, New Rochelle, NY, p. A432

BARR, Ann
  Chief Information Officer – Bay Area, California Pacific Medical Center–St. Luke'S Campus, San Francisco, CA, p. A85
  Chief Information Officer – Bay Area, California Pacific Medical Center, San Francisco, CA, p. A85
  Chief Information Officer, Sutter Health Bay Area, Sutter Maternity And Surgery Center Of Santa Cruz, Santa Cruz, CA, p. A89
  Interim Chief Financial Officer, Adventhealth Dade City, Dade City, FL, p. A121

BARR, Brent, Chief Information Officer, Minnie Hamilton Healthcare Center, Grantsville, WV, p. A685

BARR, Bret A., President and Chief Executive Officer, Conway Medical Center, Conway, SC, p. A552

BARR, Francine, Chief Executive Officer, Bon Secours St. Mary'S Hospital, Richmond, VA, p. A665

BARR, Francine, R.N., MS, Vice President and Chief Operating Officer, Bon Secours St. Mary'S Hospital, Richmond, VA, p. A665

BARR, Kristine, Vice President Communication Services, O'Bleness Memorial Hospital, Athens, OH, p. A472

BARR, Kyle, Senior Vice President, Chief Team Resources Officer, Mease Countryside Hospital, Safety Harbor, FL, p. A138

BARR, Kyle J
  Senior Vice President, Chief Team Resources Officer, Mease Dunedin Hospital, Dunedin, FL, p. A122
  Senior Vice President, Chief Team Resources Officer, Morton Plant North Bay Hospital, New Port Richey, FL, p. A132

BARR, Mary Beth., Chief Executive Officer, Pocahontas Memorial Hospital, Buckeye, WV, p. A683

BARRA, Jon, Director Human Resources, Wyoming Behavioral Institute, Casper, WY, p. A710

BARRACLOUGH, Grant, R.N., Chief Nursing Officer, Castleview Hospital, Price, UT, p. A650

BARRALL, Audrey
  Director Human Resources, Adventist Health Clear Lake, Clearlake, CA, p. A54
  Director Human Resources, Adventist Health St. Helena, Saint Helena, CA, p. A82

BARRERA, Edward, Director Communications, Encino Hospital Medical Center, Los Angeles, CA, p. A66

BARRERA, Liflor, Manager Human Resources, Wahiawa General Hospital, Wahiawa, HI, p. A166

BARRERA–RICHARDS, Ursula, Human Resource Director, Northwest Ohio Psychiatric Hospital, Toledo, OH, p. A492

BARRERE, Davie Ann, Coordinator Information Technology, Dahl Memorial Healthcare Association, Ekalaka, MT, p. A376

BARRETT, Anne J, Associate Executive Director Human Resources, Southside Hospital, Bay Shore, NY, p. A423

BARRETT, Bill, Manager Human Resources, Wilson N. Jones Regional Medical Center, Sherman, TX, p. A637

BARRETT, Cindy, Administrative Assistant, Patton State Hospital, Patton, CA, p. A77

BARRETT, Hannah, Director of Nursing, North Sunflower Medical Center, Ruleville, MS, p. A354

BARRETT, James W., Jr, Chief Executive Officer, Richardson Medical Center, Rayville, LA, p. A277

BARRETT, Jason P., Chief Executive Officer, Flagler Hospital, Saint Augustine, FL, p. A138

BARRETT, John, Regional Director Human Resources, Franciscan Health Michigan City, Michigan City, IN, p. A211

BARRETT, Kerry Flynn, Vice President Human Resources, Northern Westchester Hospital, Mount Kisco, NY, p. A432

BARRETT, Kristen, Chief Executive Officer, Promise Hospital Of Overland Park, Overland Park, KS, p. A243

BARRETT, Lynn, Chief Nursing Officer, Centerpoint Medical Center, Independence, MO, p. A361

BARRETT, Nichole, Interim Administrator, Mercy Hospital Healdton, Healdton, OK, p. A500

BARRETT, Pam, Human Resources Director, Colorado River Medical Center, Needles, CA, p. A74

BARRETT, Pamella, Director of Nursing, Pam Specialty Hospital Of Victoria South, Victoria, TX, p. A644

BARRICK, Lisa, Controller, Encompass Health Rehabilitation Hospital Of Scottsdale, Scottsdale, AZ, p. A35

BARRILLEAUX, Scott G., Chief Executive Officer, Drew Memorial Health System, Monticello, AR, p. A46

BARRIO, Gabe, M.D., Chief of Staff, Whidbeyhealth, Coupeville, WA, p. A672

BARRIOS, Luis, Chief Information Officer, Brookdale Hospital Medical Center, New York, NY, p. A432

BARROCAS, Albert, M.D., Chief Medical Officer, Wellstar Atlanta Medical Center, Atlanta, GA, p. A147

BARRON, Kathleen, Executive Director, Temple University Hospital, Philadelphia, PA, p. A536

BARRON, Steven R., Interim Chief Executive Officer, San Gorgonio Memorial Hospital, Banning, CA, p. A52

BARROW, Robert, Chief Executive Officer, Pontiac General Hospital, Pontiac, MI, p. A320

BARROW, William F., II, Chief Executive Officer, Beauregard Health System, De Ridder, LA, p. A266

BARROWS, Cheryl, Vice President Human Resources, Sturdy Memorial Hospital, Attleboro, MA, p. A294

BARRY, Rick, Director Information Systems, Baylor Scott & White Medical Center–Frisco, Frisco, TX, p. A606

BARRY, Thomas, Chief Executive Officer, Pulaski Memorial Hospital, Winamac, IN, p. A216

BARSOM, Michael, Executive Director, Metropolitan State Hospital, Norwalk, CA, p. A75

BARSOUM, Wael, President, Cleveland Clinic Florida, Weston, FL, p. A144

BARSTAD, Stacy
  Chief Executive Officer, Sanford Tracy Medical Center, Tracy, MN, p. A341
  Chief Executive Officer, Sanford Westbrook Medical Center, Westbrook, MN, p. A342

BARTA, Brian, Assistant Administrator and Chief Financial Officer, William Newton Hospital, Winfield, KS, p. A248

BARTAL, Ely, Chief Executive Officer, Kansas Surgery And Recovery Center, Wichita, KS, p. A248

BARTAL, Ely, M.D., Chief Executive Officer and Medical Director, Kansas Surgery And Recovery Center, Wichita, KS, p. A248

BARTELL, Michael, Chief Executive Officer, Encompass Health Lakeshore Rehabilitation Hospital, Birmingham, AL, p. A14

BARTELS, Bruce J., Interim Chief Executive Officer, Lafayette Physical Rehabilitation Hospital, Lafayette, LA, p. A271

BARTELS, Dara, Chief Financial Officer, Gundersen Lutheran Medical Center, La Crosse, WI, p. A697

BARTELS, Jennifer, Director Human Resources, Pawnee County Memorial Hospital And Rural Health Clinic, Pawnee City, NE, p. A390

BARTH, Andrew J., Executive Director, Aspirus Langlade Hospital, Antigo, WI, p. A691

BARTH, Marci, Chief Nursing Officer, Fayette County Hospital, Vandalia, IL, p. A197

BARTH, Tara, Chief Nursing Officer, Western Arizona Regional Medical Center, Bullhead City, AZ, p. A28

BARTHEL, Gayle, Coordinator Human Resources, Select Specialty Hospital–Flint, Flint, MI, p. A311

BARTHOLOMEW, Brenda, Chief Nursing Officer, Gunnison Valley Hospital, Gunnison, UT, p. A648

BARTHOLOMEW, K A, M.D., Medical Director, Faulkton Area Medical Center, Faulkton, SD, p. A560

BARTHOLOMEW, Shelley, Director Human Resources, Decatur County General Hospital, Parsons, TN, p. A578

BARTILSON, Jim, Manager Information Systems, South Peninsula Hospital, Homer, AK, p. A26

BARTLETT, Beth, MSN, R.N., Vice President Nursing, Chi Health Saint Francis, Grand Island, NE, p. A385

BARTLETT, Freda, Director of Nursing, Crosbyton Clinic Hospital, Crosbyton, TX, p. A595

BARTLETT, Karolyn, Assistant Administrator, Mayo Clinic Health System – Northland In Barron, Barron, WI, p. A692

BARTLETT, Regina, Chief Executive Officer, Tristar Hendersonville Medical Center, Hendersonville, TN, p. A570

BARTLETT, Richard, M.D., Chief Medical Officer, Odessa Regional Medical Center South Campus, Odessa, TX, p. A627

BARTLETT, Ronald E, Chief Financial Officer, Boston Medical Center, Boston, MA, p. A295

BARTLETT, Thomas G., III, Administrator, Laird Hospital, Union, MS, p. A354

BARTLETT, Wayne, Director Information Systems, Alvarado Hospital Medical Center, San Diego, CA, p. A83

BARTLEY, Tracy, Manager Information Technology, Bath Community Hospital, Hot Springs, VA, p. A661

BARTOLETTI, Freddy, M.D., Chief of Staff, Community Hospital Of Anaconda, Anaconda, MT, p. A374

BARTOLOTTA, Carmen J., R.N., Vice President, Patient Care Services and Chief Nursing Officer, Missouri Baptist Sullivan Hospital, Sullivan, MO, p. A372

BARTON, Douglas, M.D., Chief Medical Officer, Ssm Health St. Joseph – St. Charles, Saint Charles, MO, p. A368

BARTON, Josiah, Director Information Technology, Mobridge Regional Hospital, Mobridge, SD, p. A562

BARTON, Michelle, Chief Operating Officer, Milford Valley Memorial Hospital, Milford, UT, p. A648

BARTON, Thomas, M.D., Medical Director, Tops Surgical Specialty Hospital, Houston, TX, p. A614

BARTON, Vikki, R.N., Chief Nursing Officer, Collingsworth General Hospital, Wellington, TX, p. A645

BARTOW, Byran, Director, Winnebago Mental Health Institute, Winnebago, WI, p. A709

BARWIS, Kurt A., President and Chief Executive Officer, Bristol Hospital, Bristol, CT, p. A107

BARYLSKE, Ben, Chief Financial Officer, St. Bernards Medical Center, Jonesboro, AR, p. A44

BASA, Rhea, Director Human Resources, Morrill County Community Hospital, Bridgeport, NE, p. A383

BASA-REYES, Fiona, Chief Executive Officer, Kindred Hospital–Baldwin Park, Baldwin Park, CA, p. A51

BASEY, Marjorie, Chief Financial Officer, Rehabilitation Hospital Of Indiana, Indianapolis, IN, p. A207

BASH, Camille, Chief Financial Officer, Doctors Community Hospital, Lanham, MD, p. A291

BASILE, Michele S.
Chief Executive Officer, Kindred Hospital South Philadelphia, Philadelphia, PA, p. A535
Interim Chief Executive Officer, Kindred Hospital–Philadelphia, Philadelphia, PA, p. A535

BASQUE, Tonya, Chief Nursing Officer, Freestone Medical Center, Fairfield, TX, p. A603

BASQUILL, Debra, Director Human Resources, Jennersville Hospital, West Grove, PA, p. A544

BASRIA, Deborah, Human Resources Payroll Administrator, Kindred Hospital Bay Area–Tampa, Tampa, FL, p. A141

BASS, Andrew C., M.D., Medical Director, Shands Live Oak Regional Medical Center, Live Oak, FL, p. A128

BASS, Darren, President, Cox Monett Hospital, Monett, MO, p. A366

BASS, Louis A., Chief Executive Officer, Rmc Anniston, Anniston, AL, p. A13

BASS, Sonya, MS, Chief Nursing Officer, Colorado Plains Medical Center, Fort Morgan, CO, p. A100

BASSETT, Eugene, President and Chief Executive Officer, St. Rose Dominican Hospitals – Siena Campus, Henderson, NV, p. A394

BASSETT, Keri, Human Resources Business Partner, Florida State Hospital, Chattahoochee, FL, p. A119

BASSETT, Kimberly S.
Chief Executive Officer, St. Joseph Medical Center, Houston, TX, p. A613
President, St. Joseph Medical Center, Houston, TX, p. A613

BASSO, Amanda J., Chief Executive Officer, Crossroads Community Hospital, Mount Vernon, IL, p. A190

BASSO, Marty
Chief Financial Officer, Sibley Memorial Hospital, Washington, DC, p. A116
Senior Vice President Finance, Suburban Hospital, Bethesda, MD, p. A289

BASTARACHE, Maurice, Chief Information Officer, Chesapeake Regional Medical Center, Chesapeake, VA, p. A657

BASTIANELLO, Carol, Director Human Resources, Aspirus Iron River Hospitals & Clinics, Inc., Iron River, MI, p. A315

BASTIEN, Samuel A., IV, Chief Executive Officer, Four Winds Hospital, Saratoga Springs, NY, p. A443

BASTING, Gregory, M.D.
Vice President Medical Affairs, Allied Services Rehabilitation Hospital, Scranton, PA, p. A540
Vice President Medical Affairs, John Heinz Institute Of Rehabilitation Medicine, Wilkes, PA, p. A545

BATA, Katie
Vice President Human Resources, Advocate Illinois Masonic Medical Center, Chicago, IL, p. A176
Vice President Human Resources, Advocate Lutheran General Hospital, Park Ridge, IL, p. A192

BATAL, Lucille M., Administrator, Baldpate Hospital, Georgetown, MA, p. A299

BATCHELOR, Dale, M.D., Chief Medical Officer, Saint Thomas West Hospital, Nashville, TN, p. A577

BATCHELOR, Daniela, Director Human Resources, Springhill Memorial Hospital, Mobile, AL, p. A20

BATCHLOR, Elaine, Chief Executive Officer, Martin Luther King, Jr. Community Hospital, Los Angeles, CA, p. A68

BATDORF, Karyn, Director of Human Resources, Monroe Hospital, Bloomington, IN, p. A200

BATEMAN, Bryan, Chief Executive Officer, Poplar Bluff Regional Medical Center, Poplar Bluff, MO, p. A367

BATEMAN, Gary, Chief Information Technology, Adair County Health System, Greenfield, IA, p. A223

BATEMAN, Jana, R.N., Chief Nursing Officer, Ut Health Jacksonville, Jacksonville, TX, p. A616

BATEMAN, Kenneth, President and Chief Executive Officer, Southeast Hospital, Cape Girardeau, MO, p. A358

BATEMAN, Mark T, Interim Chief Operating Officer, Saint Agnes Medical Center, Fresno, CA, p. A59

BATES, Christine, Chief Nursing Officer, Shodair Children'S Hospital, Helena, MT, p. A377

BATES, Don, Chief Executive Officer, Golden Plains Community Hospital, Borger, TX, p. A589

BATES, Earl, Director Information Technology, Western Mental Health Institute, Bolivar, TN, p. A566

BATES, Joe, M.D., Clinical Director, Rusk State Hospital, Rusk, TX, p. A632

BATES, Leslie, Manager Human Resources, Alta View Hospital, Sandy, UT, p. A652

BATES, Margaret, Chief of Staff, Good Samaritan Hospital, Los Angeles, CA, p. A66

BATES, Ondrea, Senior Vice President, Operations and Continuum of Care, Henry Ford Allegiance Health, Jackson, MI, p. A315

BATES, Richard, Vice President of Medical Affairs, Midmichigan Medical Center – Alpena, Alpena, MI, p. A306

BATES, Robert A., Chief Financial Officer, St. Vincent Carmel Hospital, Carmel, IN, p. A201

BATES, Victoria A., Director Human Resources, Salem Medical Center, Salem, NJ, p. A412

BATH, Harneet, M.D., Vice President, Chief Medicine Officer, Osf Saint Anthony Medical Center, Rockford, IL, p. A195

BATISTE, Michele, Director Human Resources, Preston Memorial Hospital, Kingwood, WV, p. A686

BATORY, Robert J, Vice President Human Resources, Wellspan York Hospital, York, PA, p. A546

BATRASH, Ahmad, Chief of Staff, Kansas City Veterans Affairs Medical Center, Kansas City, MO, p. A362

BATSHAW, Mark L, M.D., Physician–in–Chief, Executive Vice President and Chief Academic Officer, Children'S National Health System, Washington, DC, p. A115

BATTEY, Patrick M., Chief Executive Officer, Piedmont Hospital, Atlanta, GA, p. A146

BATTISTA, Edward
Vice President Human Resources, California Pacific Medical Center–St. Luke'S Campus, San Francisco, CA, p. A85
Vice President Human Resources, California Pacific Medical Center, San Francisco, CA, p. A85
Vice President Human Resources, Good Samaritan Hospital, San Jose, CA, p. A86

BATTLE, Joe, Director, James A. Haley Veterans' Hospital–Tampa, Tampa, FL, p. A141

BATTLES, Lindsay, Director Human Resources, Encompass Health Rehabilitation Hospital Of Dallas, Dallas, TX, p. A596

BATTS, Kayla, Manager Human Resources, Baptist Health La Grange, La Grange, KY, p. A254

BATTY, Jill I, Chief Financial Officer, Cambridge Health Alliance, Cambridge, MA, p. A297

BATTY, Mark, Chief Executive Officer, Rochelle Community Hospital, Rochelle, IL, p. A194

BATULIS, Scott, President and Chief Executive Officer, Orange Regional Medical Center, Middletown, NY, p. A431

BATY, Krista, R.N., Chief Nursing Officer, Cedar Park Regional Medical Center, Cedar Park, TX, p. A592

BATZEL, Linnane, M.D., Senior Vice President Quality and Medical Affairs and Chief Medical Officer, Upmc Altoona, Altoona, PA, p. A520

BAUER, Jeremy
Director of Finance, West Holt Medical Services, Atkinson, NE, p. A382
Interim Chief Executive Officer, West Holt Medical Services, Atkinson, NE, p. A382

BAUER, Jessica, President, Aurora Sinai Medical Center, Milwaukee, WI, p. A701

BAUER, John, Chief Operating Officer, Pam Specialty Hospital Of Covington, Covington, LA, p. A266

BAUER, Jonathan, Director Information Systems, Upmc Somerset Hospital, Somerset, PA, p. A541

BAUER, Kyle, Chief Executive Officer, Cuyuna Regional Medical Center, Crosby, MN, p. A330

BAUER, Lafe, Vice President, Post Acute Care Services and Chief Administrative Officer, Daniel Drake Center For Post Acute Care, Cincinnati, OH, p. A476

BAUER, Roberta, M.D., Acting Chair Medical Staff, Cleveland Clinic Children'S Hospital For Rehabilitation, Cleveland, OH, p. A477

BAUER, Sandra A., Director Human Resources, Jefferson Community Health And Life, Fairbury, NE, p. A384

BAUER, Shar, Executive Secretary, Wishek Community Hospital And Clinics, Wishek, ND, p. A470

BAUER, Tracy, Chief Executive Officer, Midwest Medical Center, Galena, IL, p. A183

BAUER, William, Vice President Finance and Chief Financial Officer, Lehigh Valley Hospital – Hazleton, Hazleton, PA, p. A527

BAUER, William, M.D., Medical Director, Montevista Hospital, Las Vegas, NV, p. A395

BAUGHMAN, Nathan, Chief Nursing Officer, Putnam County Memorial Hospital, Unionville, MO, p. A372

BAUM, David, M.D., Senior Vice President Medical Services, F. F. Thompson Hospital, Canandaigua, NY, p. A425

BAUM, Judy
Chief Executive Officer, Mountain Valley Regional Rehabilitation Hospital, Rehabilitation Hospital Of Northern Arizona, Flagstaff, AZ, p. A29
Chief Executive Officer, Mountain Valley Regional Rehabilitation Hospital, Prescott Valley, AZ, p. A35

BAUMAN, Chris, Director of Nursing, Ballard Rehabilitation Hospital, San Bernardino, CA, p. A83

BAUMAN, Jonathan, M.D., Chief Medical Officer, Four Winds Hospital, Katonah, NY, p. A429

BAUMAN, Stephen R., Medical Center Director, Veterans Affairs Central California Health Care System, Fresno, CA, p. A60

BAUMERT, Steven P., President and Chief Executive Officer, Methodist Jennie Edmundson Hospital, Council Bluffs, IA, p. A220

BAUMGARDNER, David, Director Information Management, Cleveland Clinic Union Hospital, Dover, OH, p. A482

BAUMGARTNER, David, Interim President, Mercy Health Saint Mary'S, Grand Rapids, MI, p. A313

BAUMGARTNER, Jennifer, Chief Information Officer, Perkins County Health Services, Grant, NE, p. A385

BAUMGARTNER, Michael A., President, Ssm Health St. Mary'S Hospital – Jefferson City, Jefferson City, MO, p. A361

BAUNCHALK, James M, Deputy Chief Clinical Services, Dwight David Eisenhower Army Medical Center, Fort Gordon, GA, p. A153

BAUSCHKA, Martha F., R.N., Vice President and Chief Nursing Officer, Southwest General Health Center, Middleburg Heights, OH, p. A487

BAUTE, Corey
  Vice President Human Resources, Franciscan Health Indianapolis, Indianapolis, IN, p. A207
  Vice President of Human Resource, Franciscan Health Carmel, Carmel, IN, p. A201
BAVA, Michele, Director Human Resources, Doctors Medical Center Of Modesto, Modesto, CA, p. A72
BAVERSO, Lou, Vice President Operations, Upmc Magee–Womens Hospital, Pittsburgh, PA, p. A538
BAW, Joseph, Chief Operating Officer, Riveredge Hospital, Forest Park, IL, p. A183
BAWA, Balraj, M.D., Assistant Director Medical Services, Central Virginia Training Center, Madison Heights, VA, p. A662
BAXA, Erin, M.D., Chief Medical Officer, Osborne County Memorial Hospital, Osborne, KS, p. A242
BAXLEY, Edmond Russell., III, President and Chief Executive Officer, Beaufort Memorial Hospital, Beaufort, SC, p. A549
BAXTER, Greg, M.D., Senior Vice President Medical Affairs and Chief Medical Officer, Elliot Hospital, Manchester, NH, p. A401
BAXTER, Joshua, Director, Information Systems, Powell Valley Healthcare, Powell, WY, p. A712
BAXTER, Kyle, Chief Operating Officer, Musc Health Florence Medical Center, Florence, SC, p. A553
BAYARDO, Fernando, M.D., Chief Medical Officer, Presbyterian Espanola Hospital, Espanola, NM, p. A418
BAYER, Brian, Information Technology Site Leader, Kalamazoo Psychiatric Hospital, Kalamazoo, MI, p. A316
BAYLESS, Victoria, President and Chief Executive Officer, Anne Arundel Medical Center, Annapolis, MD, p. A286
BAYOUMY, Sam, Chief Executive Officer, Cleveland Clinic Rehabilitation Hospital, Avon, OH, p. A472
BAYTOS, David G., President, Methodist Healthcare Olive Branch Hospital, Olive Branch, MS, p. A352
BAYUS, Robin, Chief Financial Officer, Rancho Los Amigos National Rehabilitation Center, Downey, CA, p. A56
BAZELEY, Stephen, M.D., Vice President Medical Affairs, St. Luke'S Hospital, Maumee, OH, p. A487
BAZEMORE, Webster Carl., Interim Medical Director, Fayetteville Veterans Affairs Medical Center, Fayetteville, NC, p. A454
BEA, Javon R.
  Chief Executive Officer, Mercyhealth Hospital And Medical Center – Harvard, Harvard, IL, p. A184
  President and Chief Executive Officer, Javon Bea Hospital–Rockton, Rockford, IL, p. A194
  President and Chief Executive Officer, Mercyhealth Hospital And Medical Center – Walworth, Lake Geneva, WI, p. A698
  President and Chief Executive Officer, Mercyhealth Hospital And Trauma Center – Janesville, Janesville, WI, p. A697
BEACH, Karrie, Vice President Finance, Syracuse Area Health, Syracuse, NE, p. A392
BEACH, Sarah, Director of Nursing, Jerold Phelps Community Hospital, Garberville, CA, p. A60
BEADMAN, Cindi, Director Medical Records, Hospital District 6 – Harper Campus, Harper, KS, p. A236
BEAL, Christopher, M.D., Chief of Staff, Sparrow Clinton Hospital, Saint Johns, MI, p. A322
BEAL, Dwight, Chief Fiscal Services, Jack C. Montgomery Veterans Affairs Medical Center, Muskogee, OK, p. A502
BEAL, Rachel, Chief Operating Officer, Poplar Springs Hospital, Petersburg, VA, p. A665
BEAL, Walter Edwin., Chief Executive Officer, Central Regional Hospital, Butner, NC, p. A450
BEALES, Julie, M.D., Chief of Staff, Hunter Holmes Mcguire Veterans Affairs Medical Center–Richmond, Richmond, VA, p. A666
BEAM, William, M.D., Chief of Staff, Cornerstone Hospital Of Huntington, Huntington, WV, p. A686
BEAMAN, Frank, Chief Executive Officer, Faith Community Hospital, Jacksboro, TX, p. A616
BEAMES, Bo
  Chief Executive Officer, Miners' Colfax Medical Center, Raton, NM, p. A419
  Interim Chief Executive Officer, Miners' Colfax Medical Center, Raton, NM, p. A419
BEAN, Howard, M.D., Chief Medical Officer, Spartanburg Medical Center – Mary Black, Spartanburg, SC, p. A557
BEAN, Roberta, R.N., Associate Chief Nursing Officer, Banner Fort Collins Medical Center, Fort Collins, CO, p. A100
BEAN, Todd, Chief Medical Officer, Cass County Memorial Hospital, Atlantic, IA, p. A217
BEAR, John, Hospital Administrator Officer and Supervisor Human Resources, Lawton Indian Hospital, Lawton, OK, p. A501
BEARD, Amy, Chief Nursing Officer, Brookwood Baptist Medical Center, Birmingham, AL, p. A14
BEARD, Angie, R.N.
  Chief Nursing Officer, Houston County Community Hospital, Erin, TN, p. A569

Chief Nursing Officer, Northcrest Medical Center, Springfield, TN, p. A579
BEARD, Bert, Chief Executive Officer, Maria Parham Medical Center, Henderson, NC, p. A455
BEARD, Chris, Chief Nursing Officer, Brownfield Regional Medical Center, Brownfield, TX, p. A589
BEARD, Edward L., President and Chief Executive Officer, Catawba Valley Medical Center, Hickory, NC, p. A456
BEARD, Gerald C, Chief Operating Officer, Healthmark Regional Medical Center, Defuniak Springs, FL, p. A121
BEARD, Joan, Chief Nursing Officer, Northwest Florida Community Hospital, Chipley, FL, p. A119
BEARD, Rhonda, Director Human Resources, Palestine Regional Medical Center–East, Palestine, TX, p. A627
BEARD, Robert, Chief Clinical Officer, Vibra Hospital Of Northwestern Indiana, Crown Point, IN, p. A202
BEARD, Tim
  Chief Executive Officer, Cimarron Memorial Hospital, Boise City, OK, p. A497
  Director, Information Technology, Cimarron Memorial Hospital, Boise City, OK, p. A497
BEARDEN, Amy, R.N., MSN, Vice President Patient Care Services and Chief Nursing Officer, St. Luke'S Magic Valley Medical Center, Twin Falls, ID, p. A172
BEARDEN, Cindy, Chief Nursing Officer, Two Rivers Behavioral Health System, Kansas City, MO, p. A363
BEARDEN, Stephen, Chief Financial Officer, Tristar Hendersonville Medical Center, Hendersonville, TN, p. A570
BEASLEY, Carla, Director of Nursing, Mitchell County Hospital, Camilla, GA, p. A149
BEASLEY, Jared, R.N., Vice President Patient Care, Parkview Lagrange Hospital, Lagrange, IN, p. A210
BEASLEY, Ruth, Director Human Resources, Vanderbilt Stallworth Rehabilitation Hospital, Nashville, TN, p. A577
BEASLEY, Tareka, Director Human Resources, Riverwoods Behavioral Health System, Riverdale, GA, p. A159
BEATTIE, Kathryn, M.D., Senior Vice President and Chief Medical Officer, Uw Medicine/Valley Medical Center, Renton, WA, p. A677
BEATTIE, Mac, Computer Network Specialist, Deer'S Head Hospital Center, Salisbury, MD, p. A293
BEATTY, Alan L, Vice President Human Resources, Shore Medical Center, Somers Point, NJ, p. A412
BEATTY, Ann, Director Human Resources, Cleveland Clinic Fairview Hospital, Cleveland, OH, p. A477
BEATTY, Jim, Chief Operating Officer, Overland Park Regional Medical Center, Overland Park, KS, p. A243
BEATTY, Robert, Chief Operating Officer, Highland Ridge Hospital, Midvale, UT, p. A648
BEATTY, Talia, Director Human Resources, Upmc Susquehanna Sunbury, Sunbury, PA, p. A542
BEATY, Holly, Chief Financial Officer, South Central Kansas Medical Center, Arkansas City, KS, p. A232
BEATY, Susan R, Administrator, Firsthealth Moore Regional Hospital, Pinehurst, NC, p. A460
BEAUBIEN, Troy, Director Information Services, Manatee Memorial Hospital, Bradenton, FL, p. A118
BEAUCHAMP, Bill, Chief Financial Officer, St. Luke'S Sugar Land Hospital, Sugar Land, TX, p. A638
BEAUCHANE, Nichole, Director Information Technology, Riverview Health, Crookston, MN, p. A330
BEAUDOIN, Dale, Vice President Human Resources, Lewis–Gale Medical Center, Boones Mill, VA, p. A657
BEAUDOIN, Paul, Chief Financial Officer, Day Kimball Hospital, Putnam, CT, p. A110
BEAUDRY, Carl Bo.
  Chief Executive Officer, Cedar Park Regional Medical Center, Cedar Park, TX, p. A592
  President, The Medical Center Of Southeast Texas, Port Arthur, TX, p. A630
BEAULAC, Gary, Chief Operating Officer, Henry Ford Macomb Hospitals, Clinton Township, MI, p. A309
BEAULIEU, Jennifer, Director of Nursing, Intermountain Hospital, Boise, ID, p. A167
BEAULIEU, Lynn, Chief Nursing Officer, Walton Rehabilitation Hospital, Augusta, GA, p. A148
BEAULIEU, Michael Gregory, M.D., Chief Medical Officer, Helen Newberry Joy Hospital, Newberry, MI, p. A319
BEAUPRE', Paul, Chief Executive Officer, St. John'S Medical Center And Living Center, Jackson, WY, p. A711
BEAVEN, Stacey, R.N., Chief Nursing Officer, Saint Thomas Rutherford Hospital, Murfreesboro, TN, p. A576
BEAVER, Michael D, Chief Executive Officer, Methodist Hospital, San Antonio, TX, p. A634
BEAVER, Patrick, MSN, R.N., Chief Nursing Officer, East Cooper Medical Center, Mount Pleasant, SC, p. A555
BEAVER, Rhonda, Chief Operating Officer, Creek Nation Community Hospital, Okemah, OK, p. A503

BECHAMPS, Gerald, M.D.
  Vice President Medical Affairs, War Memorial Hospital, Berkeley Springs, WV, p. A683
  Vice President of Medical Affairs, Hampshire Memorial Hospital, Romney, WV, p. A689
BECHTEL, Kathleen, MSN, R.N., Vice President Patient Care Services and Chief Nursing Officer, Froedtert And The Medical College Of Wisconsin Froedtert Hospital, Milwaukee, WI, p. A701
BECHTLE, Mavis, Chief Executive Officer, Select Specialty Hospital–Northern Kentucky, Fort Thomas, KY, p. A252
BECK, Allan, Chief Executive Officer, Baylor Orthopedic And Spine Hospital At Arlington, Arlington, TX, p. A583
BECK, Ann
  Vice President and Chief Financial Officer, Carson Tahoe Continuing Care Hospital, Carson City, NV, p. A393
  Vice President Finance, Carson Tahoe Health, Carson City, NV, p. A393
BECK, Brynn, Chief Executive Officer, Utah Valley Specialty Hospital, Provo, UT, p. A651
BECK, David, Chief Operating Officer, Lane Regional Medical Center, Zachary, LA, p. A280
BECK, Debbie, Manager Human Resource and Payroll, Ochiltree General Hospital, Perryton, TX, p. A628
BECK, Gary E., Administrator, Sevier Valley Hospital, Richfield, UT, p. A651
BECK, Howard, M.D., Chief of Staff, Grace Medical Center, Lubbock, TX, p. A622
BECK, J Christopher, D.O., President Medical Staff, Aspen Valley Hospital, Aspen, CO, p. A96
BECK, Rebecca, President, Hancock County Hospital, Sneedville, TN, p. A579
BECK, Steve, MS, Chief Human Resource Officer, Kearney Regional Medical Center, Kearney, NE, p. A386
BECK STELLA, Caitlin, Chief Executive Officer, Memorial Regional Hospital, Hollywood, FL, p. A124
BECK,PHR,MHROD, Brian, Vice President Human Resources, Oak Valley Hospital District, Oakdale, CA, p. A75
BECKER, Brian, Vice President Medical Affairs and Chief Medical Officer, Providence Healthcare Network, Waco, TX, p. A644
BECKER, Cindy, Vice President and Chief Operating Officer, Highland Hospital, Rochester, NY, p. A442
BECKER, Colleen, Chief Nursing Officer, Osf Healthcare Saint Anthony'S Health Center, Alton, IL, p. A173
BECKER, Eric
  Chief Executive Officer, Texas Orthopedic Hospital, Houston, TX, p. A614
  Chief Operating Officer, Research Medical Center, Kansas City, MO, p. A362
BECKER, Frank
  Chief Financial Officer, Lourdes Counseling Center, Richland, WA, p. A677
  Chief Financial Officer, Lourdes Medical Center, Pasco, WA, p. A676
BECKER, Kathleen R., Chief Executive Officer, University Of New Mexico Hospitals, Albuquerque, NM, p. A417
BECKER, Kathy, Ph.D., R.N., Vice President and Chief Nursing Officer, Aurora West Allis Medical Center, West Allis, WI, p. A708
BECKER, Kelly, Administrative Coordinator Human Resources, Kindred Hospital Indianapolis North, Indianapolis, IN, p. A207
BECKER, Ralph W, Vice President, Chief Financial Officer, Saint Mary'S Hospital, Waterbury, CT, p. A111
BECKER, Sherri, Chief Executive Officer, Select Specialty Hospital–Canton, Canton, OH, p. A474
BECKES, Hap, Director Information Systems, Sullivan County Community Hospital, Sullivan, IN, p. A215
BECKETT, C. Donovan, Chief Medical Officer, Williamson Memorial Hospital, Williamson, WV, p. A690
BECKHAM, Steve, Director Human Resources, Magee General Hospital, Magee, MS, p. A350
BECKMANN, Gregory, Regional President, Chi Health Plainview, Plainview, NE, p. A391
BECKMANN, Lauren, Vice President Patient Services and Chief Nursing Officer, Barnes–Jewish St. Peters Hospital, Saint Peters, MO, p. A371
BECKNER, Jana, Director Human Resources, Lewisgale Hospital Pulaski, Pulaski, VA, p. A665
BECKSVOORT, Jennifer F, Senior Human Resource Business Partner, Spectrum Health Zeeland Community Hospital, Zeeland, MI, p. A326
BECKWITH, Jami, Director Human Resources, Choctaw Nation Health Care Center, Talihina, OK, p. A508
BEDDOE, Chris, Chief Executive Officer, Sabine Medical Center, Many, LA, p. A273
BEDELL, Mikael, M.D., Medical Director, Cascade Medical Center, Cascade, ID, p. A168

BEDFORD, Tim, Chief Executive Officer, Emerald Coast Behavioral Hospital, Panama City, FL, p. A135
BEDGER, Kathy, Chief Nursing Officer, Penn Highlands Clearfield, Clearfield, PA, p. A522
BEDI, Andrew, Chief Operating Officer, Tristar Greenview Regional Hospital, Bowling Green, KY, p. A250
BEDICK, Jennifer L., Deputy Commander Nursing, Tripler Army Medical Center, Honolulu, HI, p. A165
BEDINGFIELD, Lance, Director Information Services, Dixie Regional Medical Center, Saint George, UT, p. A651
BEDSOLE, Jessica, Director, Human Resources, Wellstar Paulding Hospital, Hiram, GA, p. A154
BEDZYK, J. Paul, Deputy Director Administration, Elmira Psychiatric Center, Elmira, NY, p. A427
BEEBE, Chris T, Director Human Resources, Raleigh General Hospital, Beckley, WV, p. A683
BEEBY, Lori, Director Information Systems, Community Hospital, Mccook, NE, p. A387
BEECHLER, Jane, Director Healthcare Information Systems, Wyoming County Community Hospital, Warsaw, NY, p. A446
BEECHY, Andrew, Manager Information Technology Systems, Lee'S Summit Medical Center, Lee'S Summit, MO, p. A364
BEED, Donna E, Chief Information Management Division, Tripler Army Medical Center, Honolulu, HI, p. A165
BEEDLE, Chester
Chief Financial Officer, Kern Valley Healthcare District, Lake Isabella, CA, p. A63
Interim Chief Financial Officer, Adventist Health Medical Center – Tehachapi Valley, Tehachapi, CA, p. A91
BEEDY, Scott, Chief Financial Officer, Hansford Hospital, Spearman, TX, p. A637
BEEG, Gregg M., Interim President and Chief Executive Officer, Oaklawn Hospital, Marshall, MI, p. A317
BEEHN, Holly, Director Human Resources, Southwest Health, Platteville, WI, p. A703
BEELER, Janelle E, Human Resource Manager, Baraga County Memorial Hospital, L'Anse, MI, p. A316
BEER, Ronald R.
Chief Administrative Officer, Geisinger Wyoming Valley Medical Center, Wilkes Barre, PA, p. A544
Chief Administrative Officer, Geisinger–Community Medical Center, Scranton, PA, p. A540
BEESON, John C, M.D., Chief Medical Officer, Christus St. Vincent Regional Medical Center, Santa Fe, NM, p. A420
BEGALSKE, Kathy, Chief Nursing Officer, Gundersen Palmer Lutheran Hospital And Clinics, West Union, IA, p. A231
BEGAN, Victoria D., President and Chief Executive Officer, San Carlos Apache Healthcare Corporation, Peridot, AZ, p. A32
BEGAY, Trudy, Human Resources Specialist, Hopi Health Care Center, Keams Canyon, AZ, p. A30
BEGAYE, Lorraine, Supervisory Human Resource Specialist, Chinle Comprehensive Health Care Facility, Chinle, AZ, p. A29
BEGGANE, Thomas, Manager Human Resources, Lac–Olive View–Ucla Medical Center, Los Angeles, CA, p. A68
BEGLEY, Robyn, R.N., Chief Nursing Officer, Atlanticare Regional Medical Center, Atlantic City, NJ, p. A403
BEGNAUD, Laura, Administrator, United Medical Rehabilitation Hospital, Hammond, LA, p. A268
BEHAN, Lawrence, Vice President Administration and Finance, Chief Financial Officer, Walden Behavioral Care, Waltham, MA, p. A304
BEHM, Anthony, D.O., Chief of Staff, Erie Veterans Affairs Medical Center, Erie, PA, p. A525
BEHNE, Carl P., Chief Executive Officer, Greene County Medical Center, Jefferson, IA, p. A225
BEHNER, Bruce M, Chief Operating Officer, Knox Community Hospital, Mount Vernon, OH, p. A488
BEHNKEN, Nick, IT Director, Red Bud Regional Hospital, Red Bud, IL, p. A194
BEHRENDT, Darcy, R.N., Vice President, Patient Care Services, Chi Health Missouri Valley, Missouri Valley, IA, p. A226
BEHRENDTSEN, Ole, Interim Director, Santa Barbara County Psychiatric Health Facility, Santa Barbara, CA, p. A88
BEHRENDTSEN, Ole, M.D., Medical Director, Santa Barbara County Psychiatric Health Facility, Santa Barbara, CA, p. A88
BEHRENS, Colleen, Director Information Technology, Community Memorial Healthcare, Marysville, KS, p. A240
BEHRENS, Karen, Director Technology Services, Perry Memorial Hospital, Princeton, IL, p. A194
BEHRENS, Sharon, R.N., MSN, Chief Clinical Officer, Rehabilitation Hospital Of Wisconsin, Waukesha, WI, p. A707
BEIDELSCHIES, Sandra, MSN, R.N., Vice President Patient Services, Wood County Hospital, Bowling Green, OH, p. A473
BEIERMAN, Jennifer, Director Human Resources, Boone County Health Center, Albion, NE, p. A382
BEIGHLE, John, Flight Chief Medical Information Systems, Wright Patterson Medical Center, Wright, OH, p. A494
BEIGI, Richard, President, Upmc Magee–Womens Hospital, Pittsburgh, PA, p. A538
BEIKMAN, Sara, Director of Nursing, Clay County Medical Center, Clay Center, KS, p. A233
BEILER, Jeffrey, Chief Operating Officer, Horsham Clinic, Ambler, PA, p. A520
BEINDIT, Dawn, Labor Relations Partner, Ascension River District Hospital, East China, MI, p. A311
BEIRL, Luke, Chief Executive Officer, Hayward Area Memorial Hospital And Water'S Edge, Hayward, WI, p. A697
BEISSEL, Rachel, Chief Nursing Officer, Southern Coos Hospital And Health Center, Bandon, OR, p. A511
BEISWENGER, Joel, Chief Executive Officer, Tri–County Hospital, Wadena, MN, p. A342
BEITCHER, Bob, Chief Executive Officer, Motion Picture And Television Fund Hospital And Residential Services, Los Angeles, CA, p. A68
BEITEL, Suzanne, Senior Vice President and Chief Financial Officer, Seattle Children'S Hospital, Seattle, WA, p. A678
BEITING, Mark, Vice President Human Resources, Alta Bates Summit Medical Center – Summit Campus, Oakland, CA, p. A75
BEITZEL, Mark, Director Information Systems, Advocate Lutheran General Hospital, Park Ridge, IL, p. A192
BEJNAR, Darla, M.D., Chief Medical Officer, Socorro General Hospital, Socorro, NM, p. A421
BELAIR, Norman, Senior Vice President and Chief Financial Officer, Southern Maine Health Care – Biddeford Medical Center, Biddeford, ME, p. A282
BELANGER, Robert, Administrator Director, Sanford Bagley Medical Center, Bagley, MN, p. A328
BELCASTRO, Marc, D.O., Chief Medical Officer, Miami Valley Hospital, Dayton, OH, p. A481
BELCHER, Debbie, Director Human Resource, Baylor Scott & White Institute For Rehabilitation – Lakeway, Lakeway, TX, p. A619
BELCHER, Laura, Administrator, The Medical Center Albany, Albany, KY, p. A249
BELDECOS, Athena, M.D., Medical Director, Vibra Hospital Of Charleston, Mt. Pleasant, SC, p. A555
BELGARDE, Donna, Human Resources Specialist, Indian Health Service – Quentin N. Burdick Memorial Health Care Facility, Belcourt, ND, p. A466
BELHASEN, F K, M.D., Medical Director, Paul B. Hall Regional Medical Center, Paintsville, KY, p. A259
BELJIN, Dawn, R.N., Chief Nursing Officer, Venice Regional Bayfront Health, Venice, FL, p. A143
BELKOSKI, Dave, Chief Financial Officer, University Hospital Mcduffie, Thomson, GA, p. A161
BELKOSKI, David, Senior Vice President and Chief Financial Officer, University Hospital, Augusta, GA, p. A147
BELL, Billie, Chief Nursing Officer, Medina Regional Hospital, Hondo, TX, p. A610
BELL, Brian, Associate Administrator and Chief Operating Officer, National Park Medical Center, Hot Springs, AR, p. A43
BELL, Cindy, Director Finance, Willow Crest Hospital, Miami, OK, p. A502
BELL, Gary C., Chief Executive Officer, Lehigh Regional Medical Center, Lehigh Acres, FL, p. A128
BELL, Gordon, M.D., Chief of Staff, Frances Mahon Deaconess Hospital, Glasgow, MT, p. A376
BELL, Heath, Vice President, Information Services, Northwestern Medicine Valley West Hospital, Sandwich, IL, p. A195
BELL, Hollis, M.D., Medical Director, Mercy Rehabilition Hospital Springfield, Springfield, MO, p. A372
BELL, Kae, Chief Financial Officer, Brentwood Hospital, Shreveport, LA, p. A278
BELL, Kenneth, Chief Executive Officer, Encompass Health Rehabilitation Hospital Of Scottsdale, Scottsdale, AZ, p. A35
BELL, Madeline, President and Chief Executive Officer, Children'S Hospital Of Philadelphia, Philadelphia, PA, p. A534
BELL, Michael J., Chief Executive Officer, Hialeah Hospital, Hialeah, FL, p. A124
BELL, Pam, Vice President Patient Care Services and Chief Nursing Officer, Amita Health Resurrection Medical Center, Chicago, IL, p. A176
BELL, Randall C, M.D., Medical Director, Lifecare Hospitals Of San Antonio, San Antonio, TX, p. A634
BELL, Roderick, Chief Financial Officer, College Hospital Cerritos, Cerritos, CA, p. A54
BELL, Roseanna, Chief Nurse Executive, Multicare Auburn Medical Center, Auburn, WA, p. A670
BELL, Sammie, Chief Financial Officer, Tallahatchie General Hospital, Charleston, MS, p. A345
BELL, Scot, Chief Medical Officer, Anderson Regional Health System, Meridian, MS, p. A351
BELL, Sonja, Coordinator Human Resources, Sedgwick County Health Center, Julesburg, CO, p. A102
BELL, Stuart, M.D., Vice President, Medical Affairs, Medstar Union Memorial Hospital, Baltimore, MD, p. A287
BELL, Talana, Chief Financial Officer, Flowers Hospital, Dothan, AL, p. A17
BELL, Tammie, Director Human Resources, West Tennessee Healthcare Volunteer Hospital, Martin, TN, p. A574
BELL, W Scot, M.D., Chief Medical Officer, Rush Foundation Hospital, Meridian, MS, p. A351
BELLAMY, David, Chief Financial Officer, Mclaren Northern Michigan, Petoskey, MI, p. A319
BELLATTY, Christine, Acting Director of Nursing, Dorothea Dix Psychiatric Center, Bangor, ME, p. A281
BELLEAU, Christopher, M.D., Medical Director, Sage Rehabilitation Hospital, Baton Rouge, LA, p. A264
BELLEAU, Donella, Director Human Resources, Graham County Hospital, Hill City, KS, p. A236
BELLO, Stephen, Executive Director, Brookdale Hospital Medical Center, New York, NY, p. A432
BELLUCCI, Alessandro, Executive Director, North Shore University Hospital, Manhasset, NY, p. A430
BELLUCY, Regina, Vice President Human Resources, Bethesda Hospital East, Boynton Beach, FL, p. A118
BELMONT, Chris, Chief Information Officer and Vice President, University Of Texas M.D. Anderson Cancer Center, Houston, TX, p. A614
BELMONT, James
Associate Director, Northern Arizona Veterans Affairs Health Care System, Prescott, AZ, p. A34
Interim Director, Lexington Veterans Affairs Medical Center, Lexington, KY, p. A255
BELONGEA, M. Anselma, Chief Operating Officer, Osf Healthcare Saint Anthony'S Health Center, Alton, IL, p. A173
BELT, Katrina, Chief Financial Officer, Baptist Medical Center East, Montgomery, AL, p. A21
BELTRAN, Grace, Director Human Resources, Foundation Surgical Hospital Of El Paso, El Paso, TX, p. A602
BELTZ, John, Chief Financial Officer, Hendry Regional Medical Center, Clewiston, FL, p. A120
BELZER, Leslie, Director Human Resources, Howard County Medical Center, Saint Paul, NE, p. A391
BEMENT, Douglas J, Chief Financial Officer, Kosciusko Community Hospital, Warsaw, IN, p. A216
BEN, Sabrina, Director Human Resources, North Star Behavioral Health System, Anchorage, AK, p. A25
BENAQUISTA, Kathleen, Executive Vice President and Chief Financial Officer, Maricopa Integrated Health System, Phoenix, AZ, p. A33
BENAVIDES, Christina, Director Employee Services, Otto Kaiser Memorial Hospital, Kenedy, TX, p. A617
BENCITO ACAAC, Norie Lee Reyes, R.N., MS, Executive Director, Loma Linda University Behavioral Medicine Center, Redlands, CA, p. A80
BENDER, Bob, Vice–President Hospital Finance and Operations, Bristol Regional Medical Center, Bristol, TN, p. A566
BENDER, Brad, M.D., Chief of Staff, North Florida/South Georgia Veteran'S Health System, Gainesville, FL, p. A123
BENDER, Daniel, Chief Executive Officer, South Bay Hospital, Sun City Center, FL, p. A140
BENDER, David, Chief Executive Officer, Gouverneur Hospital, Gouverneur, NY, p. A428
BENDER, David B, M.D., Chief Medical Staff, Grafton City Hospital, Grafton, WV, p. A685
BENDINELLI, Emily, Director of Nurses, Ashley County Medical Center, Crossett, AR, p. A40
BENDING, Tammy
Vice President, Critical Access Hospital, Thedacare Medical Center–Berlin, Berlin, WI, p. A692
Vice President, Theda Care Medical Center – Wild Rose, Wild Rose, WI, p. A708
BENDYNA, Peter J., Director Human Resources and Civil Service Administrator, Wyoming County Community Hospital, Warsaw, NY, p. A446
BENEDICT, Brian, Director of Information Technology, Murray–Calloway County Hospital, Murray, KY, p. A258
BENEDICT, Eva, President and Chief Executive Officer, Jones Memorial Hospital, Wellsville, NY, p. A447
BENEDICT, Joy M, Director Human Resources, Baptist Health Richmond, Richmond, KY, p. A260
BENEFIELD, Marlene, Director Human Resources, Floyd Cherokee Medical Center, Centre, AL, p. A16
BENEPAL, Jaspreet, Chief Nursing Officer, Contra Costa Regional Medical Center, Martinez, CA, p. A71

BENET, Miguel, M.D., Chief Medical Officer, Medical City Las Colinas, Irving, TX, p. A616

BENETTI–LOYOLA, Pedro L, Senior Executive and Vice President, Hospital San Cristobal, Coto Laurel, PR, p. A716

BENETTI–LOYOLA, Pedro L., Administrator, Hospital San Cristobal, Coto Laurel, PR, p. A716

BENFIELD, Angie, Human Resources Generalist, Union Medical Center, Union, SC, p. A558

BENFIELD, Justin, Southern Region Chief Operating Officer, Prisma Health Laurens County Hospital, Clinton, SC, p. A550

BENFIELD, Ronald K
  Chief Financial Officer, Peacehealth Southwest Medical Center, Vancouver, WA, p. A681
  Chief Financial Officer, Peacehealth St. John Medical Center, Longview, WA, p. A674

BENGSTON, Jennifer, M.D., Chief Medical Officer, Valley County Health System, Ord, NE, p. A390

BENGYAK, Daniel, Vice President, Administrative Services, Montefiore St. Luke'S Cornwall, Newburgh, NY, p. A439

BENHAM, D'Linda, Director of Nursing, Fisher County Hospital District, Rotan, TX, p. A632

BENINK, Eric, M.D., Chief Medical Officer, Medical City Arlington, Arlington, TX, p. A583

BENITEZ, Pedro, M.D., Medical Director, Hospital De Damas, Ponce, PR, p. A717

BENJAMIN, Christian, Commander, Mike O'Callaghan Federal Hospital, Nellis Afb, NV, p. A396

BENJAMIN, Lucia, Chief Nursing Officer, West Gables Rehabilitation Hospital, Miami, FL, p. A131

BENNER, Brenda, Director Human Resources, Encompass Health Rehabilitation Hospital Of Sarasota, Sarasota, FL, p. A139

BENNETT, Anthony, M.D., Chief Clinical Affairs, Baptist Health Medical Center–Little Rock, Little Rock, AR, p. A44

BENNETT, Bart
  Chief Financial Officer, Springbrook Behavioral Health System, Travelers Rest, SC, p. A557
  Chief Information Technology Officer, Springbrook Behavioral Health System, Travelers Rest, SC, p. A557

BENNETT, Courtney, Human Resource Manager, Alleghany Memorial Hospital, Sparta, NC, p. A462

BENNETT, Dan, President and Chief Executive Officer, Gifford Medical Center, Randolph, VT, p. A655

BENNETT, Darnell, Director Finance, Horizon Specialty Hospital, Las Vegas, NV, p. A395

BENNETT, E Kyle., President and Chief Executive Officer, Memorial Hospital And Health Care Center, Jasper, IN, p. A208

BENNETT, Edwin, Controller, Turning Point Hospital, Moultrie, GA, p. A158

BENNETT, Elizabeth, Interim Chief Executive Officer, Tri Parish Rehabilitation Hospital, Leesville, LA, p. A272

BENNETT, Fay, Vice President Employee Services, Guadalupe Regional Medical Center, Seguin, TX, p. A636

BENNETT, Gary, M.D., Chief of Medical Staff, Chapman Global Medical Center, Orange, CA, p. A76

BENNETT, James, Chief Executive Officer, Surgical Institute Of Reading, Wyomissing, PA, p. A545

BENNETT, Kay R
  System Director Human Resources, Baptist Medical Center South, Montgomery, AL, p. A21
  Vice President Human Resources, Baptist Medical Center East, Montgomery, AL, p. A21

BENNETT, Kimberly, R.N., Director of Nursing, Christus Dubuis Hospital Of Alexandria, Alexandria, LA, p. A262

BENNETT, Laura, Interim Chief Executive Officer, Central Montana Medical Center, Lewistown, MT, p. A378

BENNETT, Laurie, Director Human Resources, Sarasota Memorial Health Care System, Sarasota, FL, p. A139

BENNETT, Lee W
  Chief Financial Officer, Sitka Community Hospital, Sitka, AK, p. A27
  Interim Chief Financial Officer, Cordova Community Medical Center, Cordova, AK, p. A25

BENNETT, Leo, M.D., Deputy Commander Clinical Services, Bassett Army Community Hospital, Fort Wainwright, AK, p. A26

BENNETT, Lisa, Chief Financial Officer, Waverly Health Center, Waverly, IA, p. A231

BENNETT, Mary Ann, Chief Nursing Officer, Glendora Community Hospital, Glendora, CA, p. A61

BENNETT, Mary Ann, R.N., Chief Operating Officer and Chief Nursing Officer, Springbrook Behavioral Health System, Travelers Rest, SC, p. A557

BENNETT, Melissa, Chief Nursing Officer, Trumbull Memorial Hospital, Warren, OH, p. A493

BENNETT, Randall, Assistant Administrator, Uintah Basin Medical Center, Roosevelt, UT, p. A651

BENNETT, Richard G., President, Johns Hopkins Bayview Medical Center, Baltimore, MD, p. A286

BENNETT, Richard I, Senior Vice President and Chief Financial Officer, Delaware County Memorial Hospital, Drexel Hill, PA, p. A524

BENNETT, Robert, M.D., Medical Director, Millwood Hospital, Arlington, TX, p. A583

BENNETT, Ron, Chief Financial Officer, Abilene Regional Medical Center, Abilene, TX, p. A581

BENNETT, Sharon, Manager Information Systems, Cobre Valley Regional Medical Center, Globe, AZ, p. A30

BENNETT, Sheila, R.N., Vice President & Chief Nursing Officer, Floyd Medical Center, Rome, GA, p. A159

BENNETT, Tony N., Chief Executive Officer, Encompass Health Rehabilitation Hospital Of Panama City, Panama City, FL, p. A135

BENNETT, Wayne, Chief Financial Officer, Franklin Memorial Hospital, Farmington, ME, p. A283

BENOIT, Linda, Human Resource Officer, Cavalier County Memorial Hospital And Clinics, Langdon, ND, p. A468

BENOIT, Paul, Associate Administrator, Central Louisiana State Hospital, Pineville, LA, p. A277

BENOIT, Rebecca, R.N., Chief Nursing Officer, Lafayette General Medical Center, Lafayette, LA, p. A271

BENSEMA, David, Chief Information Officer, Baptist Health La Grange, La Grange, KY, p. A254

BENSEN, Carol, MSN, R.N., Chief Nursing Officer, Providence St. Patrick Hospital, Missoula, MT, p. A379

BENSON, Cheryl, Chief Operating Officer, Wernersville State Hospital, Wernersville, PA, p. A544

BENSON, Chris, Chief Financial Officer, Dekalb Regional Medical Center, Fort Payne, AL, p. A18

BENSON, Eric, Vice President Human Resources & Wellness, Sarah Bush Lincoln Health Center, Mattoon, IL, p. A188

BENSON, Kathryn, Human Resources Partner, Avera St. Anthony'S Hospital, O'Neill, NE, p. A390

BENSON, Kevin, Chief Financial Officer, Ortonville Area Health Services, Ortonville, MN, p. A337

BENTLEY, Scott, Chief Financial Officer, Woman'S Hospital Of Texas, Houston, TX, p. A615

BENTON, Edred, Chief Executive Officer and Chief Operating Officer, Cleveland Area Hospital, Cleveland, OK, p. A498

BENTON, Nancy, Assistant Director Patient Care Services, Mann–Grandstaff Veterans Affairs Medical Center, Spokane, WA, p. A679

BENTOUNSI, Karima, Chief Executive Officer, Dmc Huron Valley–Sinai Hospital, Commerce Township, MI, p. A309

BENTZ, Douglas E., Chief Executive Officer, Roane General Hospital, Spencer, WV, p. A689

BENVENUTTI, Cathy, Human Resource Director, Hancock Medical Center, Bay Saint Louis, MS, p. A344

BENWARE, Joel, Vice President Information Technology and Compliance, Northwestern Medical Center, Saint Albans, VT, p. A655

BENZ, Mark A.
  President and Chief Executive Officer, Carondelet St. Joseph'S Hospital, Tucson, AZ, p. A37
  President and Chief Executive Officer, Carondelet St. Mary'S Hospital, Tucson, AZ, p. A37

BENZ, Robert, M.D., Chief Medical Officer, Lankenau Medical Center, Wynnewood, PA, p. A546

BENZEL, Cindy, Manager Human Resources, Sanford Vermillion Medical Center, Vermillion, SD, p. A564

BEPLER, Gerold, President and Chief Executive Officer, Karmanos Cancer Center, Detroit, MI, p. A310

BERARDI, Paula, Manager Human Resources, Bournewood Health Systems, Brookline, MA, p. A297

BERCHER, Richard, M.D., Chief Medical Officer, Paris Regional Medical Center, Paris, TX, p. A628

BERCI, Haya, Executive Director of Nursing, Joyce Eisenberg–Keefer Medical Center, Reseda, CA, p. A80

BERDIEL, Luis A., Executive Director, Hospital Metropolitano San German, San German, PR, p. A718

BERENS, Jeff, MS, Chief Nursing Officer, Sanford Vermillion Medical Center, Vermillion, SD, p. A564

BERENTES, Amy, Executive Vice President and Chief Operating Officer, Mercyone Clinton Medical Center, Clinton, IA, p. A219

BERENTES, Amy, R.N., MSN, Vice President Patient Care Services, Mercyone Clinton Medical Center, Clinton, IA, p. A219

BERETTA, Dante, M.D., Chief of Staff, Centracare Health–Melrose, Melrose, MN, p. A335

BERG, Gary L, D.O., Chief Medical Officer, Ascension Macomb–Oakland Hospital, Warren, MI, p. A324

BERG, James, President, Texas Health Presbyterian Hospital Dallas, Dallas, TX, p. A598

BERG, Jon, M.D., Chief of Staff, Northwood Deaconess Health Center, Northwood, ND, p. A469

BERG, Katie, Chief Financial Officer, Cuyuna Regional Medical Center, Crosby, MN, p. A330

BERG, Tony L., M.D., Chief of Staff, Winner Regional Healthcare Center, Winner, SD, p. A565

BERG, William, Chief Information Officer, Naval Hospital Pensacola, Pensacola, FL, p. A136

BERGE, Ron, Executive Vice President and Chief Operating Officer, National Jewish Health, Denver, CO, p. A99

BERGEAUX, Scott, M.D., Chief Medical Staff, Abrom Kaplan Memorial Hospital, Kaplan, LA, p. A270

BERGEMANN, John, Director Human Resources, Crouse Health, Syracuse, NY, p. A445

BERGEN, Jan L., President and Chief Executive Officer, Penn Medicine Lancaster General Hospital, Lancaster, PA, p. A529

BERGER, George, Controller, Encompass Health Rehabilitation Hospital Of Altoona, Altoona, PA, p. A519

BERGERON, Johnny, Manager Information Technology, Avoyelles Hospital, Marksville, LA, p. A273

BERGERON, Pierre, Information Services Director, Wellington Regional Medical Center, Wellington, FL, p. A143

BERGERSEN, Jennifer, Interim Chief Operating Officer, Milwaukee County Behavioral Health Division, Milwaukee, WI, p. A701

BERGERSON, Melissa, R.N., Chief Nursing Officer, Black River Memorial Hospital, Black River Falls, WI, p. A692

BERGES, Iris, Chief Executive Officer, Larkin Community Hospital Behavioral Health Services, Hollywood, FL, p. A124

BERGFORT, Joe, Chief Information Officer, Ucsf Medical Center, San Francisco, CA, p. A86

BERGHOLM, Brenda, MSN, R.N., Chief Nursing Officer, Caribou Memorial Hospital And Living Center, Soda Springs, ID, p. A172

BERGMAN, Angela, Director of Quality, Risk and Health Information Management, Van Matre Encompass Health, Rockford, IL, p. A195

BERGMAN, Chris, Chief Financial Officer, Dayton Children'S Hospital, Dayton, OH, p. A481

BERGMAN, Jim, Director Human Resources, Northeast Regional Medical Center, Kirksville, MO, p. A363

BERGMAN–EVANS, Brenda, Chief Nursing Officer, Chi Health Midlands, Papillion, NE, p. A390

BERGMANN, Michael, President, Aurora Medical Center Summit, Summit, WI, p. A706

BERGMANN, Peter U., President, University Hospitals Parma Medical Center, Parma, OH, p. A489

BERGMEIER, Cindy, Chief Operating Officer, Rapides Regional Medical Center, Alexandria, LA, p. A262

BERGQUIST, Susan, Human Resources Generalist, Kindred Hospital–La Mirada, La Mirada, CA, p. A63

BERGSTEDT, Sharon, Director of Nursing, Alaska Psychiatric Institute, Anchorage, AK, p. A25

BERGSTROM, Jenny, Project Manager Information Technology, Cloud County Health Center, Concordia, KS, p. A234

BERKOWITZ, David J, Vice President and Chief Operating Officer, Hackensack Meridian Health Palisades Medical Center, North Bergen, NJ, p. A410

BERKRAM, Treasure, Chief Financial Officer, Northern Rockies Medical Center, Cut Bank, MT, p. A375

BERLINGHOFF, Kathleen, Director Human Resources, Sharon Hospital, Sharon, CT, p. A110

BERLOT, Alvin, M.D., Medical Director, Bucktail Medical Center, Renovo, PA, p. A540

BERLOWITZ, Dan, M.D., M.P.H., Acting Chief of Staff, Bedford Veterans Affairs Medical Center, Edith Nourse Rogers Memorial Veterans Hospital, Bedford, MA, p. A294

BERLUCCHI, Scott A., President and Chief Executive Officer, Auburn Community Hospital, Auburn, NY, p. A423

BERLYN, Maria, Assistant Vice President Nursing Services, John Heinz Institute Of Rehabilitation Medicine, Wilkes, PA, p. A545

BERMAN, Alan S., M.D., Medical Director, Mountain Valley Regional Rehabilitation Hospital, Prescott Valley, AZ, p. A35

BERMAN, Manuel S, President and Chief Executive Officer, Tuality Healthcare, Hillsboro, OR, p. A513

BERMUDEZ, Ada, Director Human Resources, Hospital De La Concepcion, San German, PR, p. A718

BERMUDEZ, Armand, M.D., Medical Director, Select Specialty Hospital Of Southeast Ohio, Newark, OH, p. A488

BERMUDEZ, Yuri, M.D., Chief of Staff, South Texas Health System, Edinburg, TX, p. A601

BERNAL, Hector
  Chief Executive Officer, Pam Specialty Hospital Of Corpus Christi South, Corpus Christi, TX, p. A594
  Chief Executive Officer, Post Acute Medical Specialty Hospital Of Corpus Christi – North, Corpus Christi, TX, p. A594

BERNAL, Maria Mercedes Torres., Administrator, Hospital De Damas, Ponce, PR, p. A717

BERNARD, David P., Chief Executive Officer, Houston Methodist Baytown Hospital, Baytown, TX, p. A587

BERNARD, Donald P
Chief Financial Officer, St. John'S Pleasant Valley Hospital, Camarillo, CA, p. A53
Chief Financial Officer, St. John'S Regional Medical Center, Oxnard, CA, p. A76
BERNARD, Doug, M.D., Chief Medical Officer, White River Medical Center, Batesville, AR, p. A39
BERNARD, Mark L., Chief Executive Officer, Resolute Health, New Braunfels, TX, p. A626
BERNARD, Robert, M.D., Chief of Staff, Alexandria Veterans Affairs Health Care System, Pineville, LA, p. A277
BERNARD, Traci, President, Chief Executive Officer and Chief Operating Officer, Texas Health Harris Methodist Hospital Southlake, Southlake, TX, p. A637
BERNARDO, Maria, M.D., Chief of Staff, Bullock County Hospital, Union Springs, AL, p. A24
BERNASEK, Robert, M.D.
Chief Medical Officer, Southeast Georgia Health System Camden Campus, Saint Marys, GA, p. A159
Vice President and Chief Medical Officer, Southeast Georgia Health System Brunswick Campus, Brunswick, GA, p. A148
BERNATIS, Terry D., Director Human Resources, Community Healthcare System, Onaga, KS, p. A242
BERND, Jason, President and Chief Operating Officer, Novant Health Charlotte Orthopaedic Hospital, Charlotte, NC, p. A451
BERNERT–YAP, Kellie, Director Human Resources, Vibra Specialty Hospital Of Portland, Portland, OR, p. A516
BERNEY, Bernadette, Director Human Resources, Pullman Regional Hospital, Pullman, WA, p. A676
BERNHARDT–KADLEC, Peggy, Chief Human Resources Officer, Searhc Mt. Edgecumbe Hospital, Sitka, AK, p. A27
BERNICK, Michael, Executive Vice President and Chief Financial Officer, Clarity Child Guidance Center, San Antonio, TX, p. A633
BERNIER, Justin, R.N., Director of Nursing, Seaside Behavioral Center, New Orleans, LA, p. A276
BERNS, Erin, Director Human Resources, Veterans Memorial Hospital, Waukon, IA, p. A231
BERNSEN, Tina, Chief Nursing Officer, Othello Community Hospital, Othello, WA, p. A676
BERNSTEIN, Lee
Regional Executive Vice President and Chief Operating Officer, Ssm Health St. Clare Hospital – Fenton, Fenton, MO, p. A360
Regional Executive Vice President and Chief Operating Officer, Ssm Health St. Joseph – St. Charles, Saint Charles, MO, p. A368
Regional Executive Vice President of Hospital and Chief Operating Officer, Ssm Health St. Joseph Hospital – Lake Saint Louis, Lake Saint Louis, MO, p. A364
BERNSTEIN, Les, Chief Information Officer, Cookeville Regional Medical Center, Cookeville, TN, p. A568
BERNSTEIN, Michael, Chief Financial Officer, Adventist Health – Tulare, Tulare, CA, p. A92
BERNSTEIN, Paul E, M.D., Area Medical Director, Kaiser Permanente San Diego Medical Center, San Diego, CA, p. A83
BERRIOS, Elenia, Chief Nursing Officer, Hima San Pablo Caguas, Caguas, PR, p. A715
BERRY, Carlos E., M.D., Acting Chief of Staff, Tuscaloosa Veterans Affairs Medical Center, Tuscaloosa, AL, p. A24
BERRY, David T., President, Children's Health Clinical Operations, Our Children'S House, Dallas, TX, p. A597
BERRY, Deborah, Director of Operations, Greene County Hospital, Leakesville, MS, p. A350
BERRY, Greg, Chief Financial Officer, Doctors Medical Center Of Modesto, Modesto, CA, p. A72
BERRY, James T., Executive Vice President and Administrator, Northeastern Health System, Tahlequah, OK, p. A508
BERRY, Julie, Chief Information Officer, Saint Anne'S Hospital, Fall River, MA, p. A298
BERRY, Linda, Vice President Human Resources, Guthrie Towanda Memorial Hospital, Towanda, PA, p. A542
BERRY, Rebecca
Senior Director Human Resources, St. Charles Prineville, Prineville, OR, p. A517
Vice President Human Resources, St. Charles Bend, Bend, OR, p. A511
Vice President Human Resources, St. Charles Redmond, Redmond, OR, p. A517
BERRY–BARBOSA, Lisa, Vice President Human Resources, Beth Israel Deaconess Hospital Plymouth, Plymouth, MA, p. A302
BERRYMAN, John David, M.D., Chief of Staff, Beckley Veterans Affairs Medical Center, Beckley, WV, p. A683
BERRYMAN, William R, M.D., Chief of Staff, Grand Junction Veterans Health Care System, Grand Junction, CO, p. A101
BERSANTE, Syd
Market President, St. Elizabeth Hospital, Enumclaw, WA, p. A672
President, St. Clare Hospital, Lakewood, WA, p. A674
President, St. Joseph Medical Center, Tacoma, WA, p. A681
BERSHAD, Joshua M, M.D., Senior Vice President Medical Affairs and Chief Medical Officer, Robert Wood Johnson University Hospital, New Brunswick, NJ, p. A409
BERSINGER, David, M.D., Chief of Staff, Mcleod Health Cheraw, Cheraw, SC, p. A550
BERT, Alisa, Chief Financial Officer, Aventura Hospital And Medical Center, Aventura, FL, p. A117
BERTHIL, Emmanuel, Chief Clinical Officer, Vibra Hospital Of Southeastern Massachusetts, New Bedford, MA, p. A301
BERTKE, Bradley J., President and Chief Operating Officer, Mercy St. Anne Hospital, Toledo, OH, p. A492
BERTRAND, Joan L., Vice President Human Resources, Adcare Hospital Of Worcester, Worcester, MA, p. A305
BERTRAND, Neil W, Interim Chief Financial Officer, Cheyenne Regional Medical Center, Cheyenne, WY, p. A710
BERTSCH, Darrold, Chief Executive Officer, Sakakawea Medical Center, Hazen, ND, p. A467
BERTSCH, John, M.D., Chief of Staff, Euclid Hospital, Euclid, OH, p. A482
BERWALD, Margaret, R.N., MSN, Senior Vice President Patient Services, Torrance Memorial Medical Center, Torrance, CA, p. A92
BERZ, Derek, Chief Operating Officer, Kaiser Permanente Los Angeles Medical Center, Los Angeles, CA, p. A67
BESCOE, Bradley, Chief Financial Officer, Straith Hospital For Special Surgery, Southfield, MI, p. A323
BESHEL, Michael, R.N., Vice President Patient Care and Chief Nursing Officer, Nazareth Hospital, Philadelphia, PA, p. A535
BESIO, Adam, Chief Information Officer, Memorial Medical Center, Port Lavaca, TX, p. A630
BESPALEC, Jason, M.D., Chief of Staff, Fillmore County Hospital, Geneva, NE, p. A385
BESS, Amy, Chief Financial Officer, Mizell Memorial Hospital, Opp, AL, p. A22
BESS, Charles, M.D., Medical Director, Potomac Valley Hospital, Keyser, WV, p. A686
BESS, Timothy A., Chief Executive Officer, Bluefield Regional Medical Center, Bluefield, WV, p. A683
BESSE, Kim
Executive Vice President and Chief Human Resource Officer, Children'S Medical Center Dallas, Dallas, TX, p. A596
Executive Vice President and Chief Human Resource Officer, Children'S Medical Center Plano, Plano, TX, p. A629
BESSEY, Kerry, Senior Vice President and Chief Human Resources Officer, Brookdale Hospital Medical Center, New York, NY, p. A432
BESSEY, Vickie, MSN, R.N., Chief Nursing Officer, Sagewest Health Care At Riverton, Riverton, WY, p. A712
BESSLER, Christine, Vice President Information Services, Oconomowoc Memorial Hospital, Oconomowoc, WI, p. A702
BESSLER, September, Director, Human Resources, Brookings Health System, Brookings, SD, p. A559
BESSON, Kathleen, Executive Vice President and Chief Operating Officer, Caromont Regional Medical Center, Gastonia, NC, p. A454
BESST, Kara, President and Chief Executive Officer, Gritman Medical Center, Moscow, ID, p. A170
BESTEN, Robert, Chief Financial Officer, Mary Breckinridge Arh Hospital, Hyden, KY, p. A254
BESTGEN, Pat, Manager Human Resources, Cameron Regional Medical Center, Cameron, MO, p. A357
BESWICK, Elizabeth, Vice President Human Resources and Public Relations, Carteret Health Care, Morehead City, NC, p. A458
BETANCOURT, Erika, Coordinator Human Resources, Cornerstone Regional Hospital, Edinburg, TX, p. A601
BETTCHER, Sue, R.N., Vice President of Nursing Services, Community Hospital Of Bremen, Bremen, IN, p. A200
BETTEM, Kelly, Vice President, Ambulatory Services, Ohio Valley Medical Center, Wheeling, WV, p. A690
BETTINELLI, Stephanie M, Vice President of Human Resources, Winchester Hospital, Winchester, MA, p. A305
BETTS, Brooks, Director Information Systems and Chief Information Officer, Pen Bay Medical Center, Rockport, ME, p. A285
BETTS, Crystal
Chief Financial Officer, Incline Village Community Hospital, Incline Village, NV, p. A394
Chief Financial Officer, Tahoe Forest Hospital District, Truckee, CA, p. A92
BETTS, Kristen A, Director Team Resources, St. Anthony'S Hospital, Saint Petersburg, FL, p. A138
BETTS, Tracy, Chief Financial Officer, Hardeman County Memorial Hospital, Quanah, TX, p. A630
BETZ, Paul, Administrator, Dch Regional Medical Center, Tuscaloosa, AL, p. A24
BEUCLER, MSN, RN, BS–NE, FACHE, Lori A, R.N., Vice President and Chief Nursing Officer, Upmc Susquehanna Williamsport, Williamsport, PA, p. A545
BEUERLEIN, Jennifer, Chief Executive Officer, Post Acute Rehabilitation Hospital Of Allen, Allen, TX, p. A581
BEUS, Lance, Chief Executive Officer, Cmh Regional Health System, Wilmington, OH, p. A494
BEUTKE, Kenneth, President, Osf Saint Elizabeth Medical Center, Ottawa, IL, p. A192
BEVARD, Julie, Vice President Human Resources, Perkins County Health Services, Grant, NE, p. A385
BEVEL, John, Manager Information Systems, Shriners Hospitals For Children–Northern California, Sacramento, CA, p. A82
BEVERLY, Douglas H., Chief Executive Officer, Encompass Rehabilitation Hospital Of North Alabama, Huntsville, AL, p. A19
BEVERLY, Esther, Vice President Human Resources, Tri–City Medical Center, Oceanside, CA, p. A75
BEVERS, Donald, Chief Financial Officer, Salem Medical Center, Salem, NJ, p. A412
BEYER, Jim, Administrative Director Human Resources, Norman Regional Health System, Norman, OK, p. A503
BEYER, Laurie, Senior Vice President and Chief Financial Officer, Union Hospital, Elkton, MD, p. A290
BEYER, Teri, Chief Information Officer, Quality, Rice Memorial Hospital, Willmar, MN, p. A342
BEZARD, Herve, M.D., Chief of Staff, Boulder City Hospital, Boulder City, NV, p. A393
BHAGAT, Sarah, Chief Operating Officer and Vice President of Organizational Effectiveness, Lakeland Regional Health Medical Center, Lakeland, FL, p. A127
BHAMBI, Brijesh, M.D., Chief Medical Officer, Bakersfield Heart Hospital, Bakersfield, CA, p. A52
BHAMBRA, Jody, Chief Nursing Officer, Hartgrove Hospital, Chicago, IL, p. A177
BHANDARI, Raj, M.D., Physician–In–Chief, Kaiser Permanente San Jose Medical Center, San Jose, CA, p. A86
BHARUCHA, Bomi, Chief Financial Officer, Reeves County Hospital, Pecos, TX, p. A628
BHATEJA, Renu, M.D., President Medical Staff, Ridgeview Psychiatric Hospital And Center, Oak Ridge, TN, p. A578
BHATIA, Sanjay, Chief Medical Officer, Lower Bucks Hospital, Bristol, PA, p. A521
BHAYANI, Sam B, M.D., Chief Medical Officer, Barnes–Jewish West County Hospital, Saint Louis, MO, p. A369
BHOORASINGH, Merlene, Administrator, Kindred Hospital Ocala, Ocala, FL, p. A133
BHUCHAR, Subodh, M.D., Chief of Staff, Kindred Hospital Sugar Land, Sugar Land, TX, p. A638
BIAGIONI, Donna K, R.N., MSN, Director of Nursing, Maniilaq Health Center, Kotzebue, AK, p. A26
BIALORUCKI, Tom, Chief Information Officer, Adena Pike Medical Center, Waverly, OH, p. A493
BIANCHI, Patty, Chief Executive Officer, Pershing General Hospital, Lovelock, NV, p. A396
BIAS, Richard R, Chief Operating Officer, Lahey Hospital & Medical Center, Burlington, Burlington, MA, p. A297
BIBAL, Antoinette, Director Human Resources, Kindred Hospital–Baldwin Park, Baldwin Park, CA, p. A51
BIBB, Jeff, Chief Operating Officer, Oklahoma Center For Orthopedic And Multi–Specialty Surgery, Oklahoma City, OK, p. A504
BIBB, Lisa, Director Human Resources, San Angelo Community Medical Center, San Angelo, TX, p. A632
BIBBY, John, Regional Vice President, Human Resources, Santa Rosa Memorial Hospital, Santa Rosa, CA, p. A89
BIBEAU, Roland R., President and Chief Operating Officer, Novant Health Matthews Medical Center, Matthews, NC, p. A458
BIBER, Carl, Chief Financial Officer, Columbus Regional Healthcare System, Whiteville, NC, p. A463
BIBLO, Lee, M.D., Chief Medical Officer, Froedtert And The Medical College Of Wisconsin Froedtert Hospital, Milwaukee, WI, p. A701
BIBY, Thomas, Chief Executive Officer, Pam Rehabilitation Hospital Of Tulsa, Tulsa, OK, p. A509
BICKEL, George, Director, Information Systems, Merit Health Biloxi, Biloxi, MS, p. A344
BICKEL, Jim, President and Chief Executive Officer, Columbus Regional Hospital, Columbus, IN, p. A201
BICKERSTAFF, Detra, Vice President, Human Resources, Wellstar Atlanta Medical Center, Atlanta, GA, p. A147
BICKFORD, Carmel, Chief Financial Officer, Wyoming Behavioral Institute, Casper, WY, p. A710

BICKFORD, David, Chief Information Officer, Melissa Memorial Hospital, Holyoke, CO, p. A102

BIDDLE, Kenneth, Controller, Kensington Hospital, Philadelphia, PA, p. A535

BIDES, Adrienne, Assistant Chief Financial Officer and Budget Analyst, Big Spring State Hospital, Big Spring, TX, p. A588

BIDLEMAN, Angie, Chief Nursing Officer, Jane Phillips Medical Center, Bartlesville, OK, p. A497

BIE, Gary E, CPA, Chief Financial Officer, Stony Brook University Hospital, Stony Brook, NY, p. A444

BIEBER, Courtney, Director Information Systems, Mercy Regional Medical Center, Ville Platte, LA, p. A280

BIEBER, Judi, Senior Vice President Human Resources, Beth Israel Deaconess Medical Center, Boston, MA, p. A294

BIEDIGER, Daniel F, Vice President Human Resources, Firsthealth Moore Regional Hospital, Pinehurst, NC, p. A460

BIEDRON, Janet, Chief Executive Officer, Lifecare Hospitals Of Chester County, West Chester, PA, p. A544

BIEGERT, Dara, Vice President Human Resources, Medical City Lewisville, Lewisville, TX, p. A620

BIEGLER, Elizabeth Anne, R.N.
Chief Nursing Officer, Ohiohealth Dublin Methodist Hospital, Dublin, OH, p. A482
Chief Nursing Officer, Ohiohealth Grady Memorial Hospital, Delaware, OH, p. A482

BIEHL, Albert, M.D., Vice President Medical Affairs, Bethesda Hospital East, Boynton Beach, FL, p. A118

BIEHL, Benjamin, M.D., Chief Medical Officer, Johnson County Hospital, Tecumseh, NE, p. A392

BIEKER, Jeff, Director Human Resource, Trego County–Lemke Memorial Hospital, Wakeeney, KS, p. A247

BIEL, Christopher, Chief Information Officer, Goodland Regional Medical Center, Goodland, KS, p. A235

BIELECKI, Thomas A, Chief Financial Officer, Geisinger Wyoming Valley Medical Center, Wilkes Barre, PA, p. A544

BIEN, John, Vice President Finance, United Hospital, Saint Paul, MN, p. A340

BIENIEK, Sherrie, M.D., Medical Director, Fort Lauderdale Hospital, Fort Lauderdale, FL, p. A122

BIER, Alan, M.D., Executive Vice President and Chief Medical Officer, Gwinnett Hospital System, Lawrenceville, GA, p. A156

BIERI, Bryan, Manager Finance, Kansas City Veterans Affairs Medical Center, Kansas City, MO, p. A362

BIERLE, Dennis, Chief Operating Officer, Nebraska Medicine – Nebraska Medical Center, Omaha, NE, p. A389

BIERMAN, Debra, Associate Executive Director Human Resources, North Shore University Hospital, Manhasset, NY, p. A430

BIERMAN, Joan, Vice President Finance, Cherokee Regional Medical Center, Cherokee, IA, p. A219

BIERMAN, Marcia, M.D., Chief of Staff, North Shore Medical Center, Miami, FL, p. A131

BIERMAN, Ronald L., Chief Executive Officer, Trumbull Memorial Hospital, Warren, OH, p. A493

BIERSCHENK, Cindy
Director of Financial Services, Jenkins County Medical Center, Millen, GA, p. A157
Finance Director, Optim Medical Center – Screven, Sylvania, GA, p. A161

BIERSCHENK, Kevin, Chief Executive Officer, Union General Hospital, Blairsville, GA, p. A148

BIERUT, Barbara, Chief Financial Officer, Encompass Health Rehabilitation Hospital Of Sarasota, Sarasota, FL, p. A139

BIEVER, Kimberlie, Hospital Commander, General Leonard Wood Army Community Hospital, Fort Leonard Wood, MO, p. A360

BIGANDO, Kelli, Chief Nursing Officer, Mercy Hospital Joplin, Joplin, MO, p. A362

BIGELOW, Timothy, Director Human Resources, Butler Hospital, Providence, RI, p. A547

BIGGAR, Carrie, Chief Financial Officer, Osceola Regional Medical Center, Kissimmee, FL, p. A126

BIGGERSTAFF, David, Chief Operating Officer, Children'S Hospital Colorado, Aurora, CO, p. A96

BIGGS, Daniel, Director Human Resources, Valley View Hospital, Glenwood Springs, CO, p. A101

BIGGS, Jeremy, President and Chief Administrative Officer, Methodist Medical Center Of Oak Ridge, Oak Ridge, TN, p. A578

BIGGS, Kelly, M.D., Chief Medical Officer, Tyrone Hospital, Tyrone, PA, p. A542

BIGGS, Lee, M.D., Chief Medical Officer, Trident Medical Center, Charleston, SC, p. A550

BIGGS, R. Lee, M.D., Chief Medical Officer, Eastern Idaho Regional Medical Center, Idaho Falls, ID, p. A169

BIGLER, Pamela, R.N., Senior Vice President, Chief Nursing Officer, Carle Foundation Hospital, Urbana, IL, p. A197

BIGLEY, John, M.D., Medical Director, Kaiser Permanente Baldwin Park Medical Center, Baldwin Park, CA, p. A51

BIGNAULT, Jon, M.D., Chief of Staff, Athens–Limestone Hospital, Athens, AL, p. A13

BIGONEY, Rebecca
Executive Vice President and Chief Medical Officer, Mary Washington Hospital, Fredericksburg, VA, p. A659
Executive Vice President and Chief Medical Officer, Stafford Hospital, Stafford, VA, p. A667

BIHUNIAK, Peter, Vice President Finance, Robert Wood Johnson University Hospital Rahway, Rahway, NJ, p. A411

BILELLO, Rene, Manager Information System, Teche Regional Medical Center, Morgan City, LA, p. A274

BILES, Lauren, Administrator, Access Hospital Dayton, Dayton, OH, p. A481

BILEY, Monica, Chief Nursing Officer, Sierra Nevada Memorial Hospital, Grass Valley, CA, p. A61

BILL, Charles E., Chief Executive Officer, Bartlett Regional Hospital, Juneau, AK, p. A26

BILLECI, Theresa, Executive Director, Porterville Developmental Center, Porterville, CA, p. A78

BILLIG, Samantha, Chief Executive Officer, Encompass Health Rehabilitation Hospital Of Henderson, Henderson, NV, p. A394

BILLINGS, Cathy, Interim Executive Director, Northwest Center For Behavioral Health, Fort Supply, OK, p. A500

BILLINGS, Mark, Chief Operating Officer, Halifax Health Medical Center Of Daytona Beach, Daytona Beach, FL, p. A121

BILLINGS, Mary Ann, Director of Nursing, Potomac Valley Hospital, Keyser, WV, p. A686

BILLINGSLEA, Anidra, Health Insurance Management, Encompass Health Rehabilitation Hospital Of Montgomery, Montgomery, AL, p. A21

BILLINGTON, Carole, R.N., MSN, Vice President Operations, Chief Nursing Officer, Saint Anne'S Hospital, Fall River, MA, p. A298

BILLMEYER, Joe, Director, Information Services, Mercy Medical Center–Dubuque, Dubuque, IA, p. A222

BILLS, James, Chief Executive Officer, Logan Memorial Hospital, Russellville, KY, p. A260

BILLY, Frank, Chief Financial Officer, Kindred Hospital Bay Area–Tampa, Tampa, FL, p. A141

BILUNKA, Dianne C, Director Human Resources, Clarion Psychiatric Center, Clarion, PA, p. A522

BINDER, Dore, M.D., Chief Medical Officer, Woman'S Hospital, Baton Rouge, LA, p. A264

BINDERMAN, Judi, Chief Information Technology Officer and Chief Medical Informatics Officer, St. Francis Medical Center, Lynwood, CA, p. A70

BINDERMAN, Warren S., Chief Financial Officer, Lifebrite Community Hospital Of Stokes, Danbury, NC, p. A452

BINDL, Karen, CPA, Controller, Uw Health Rehabilitation Hospital, Madison, WI, p. A699

BINGHAM, Julie, IT Supervisor, San Juan Health Service District, Monticello, UT, p. A649

BINGHAM, Leslie, Senior Vice President and Chief Executive Officer, Valley Baptist Medical Center–Brownsville, Rio Hondo, TX, p. A631

BINGHAM, Paulette, Director Nursing Services, Ohio Valley Hospital, Mckees Rocks, PA, p. A531

BINGMAN, Ryan, Director Operations, Grundy County Memorial Hospital, Grundy Center, IA, p. A223

BINKLEY, Leonard, Interim Chief Financial Officer, Teche Regional Medical Center, Morgan City, LA, p. A274

BINKLEY, Sharon, Director Human Resources, Fairfax Community Hospital, Fairfax, OK, p. A499

BINTZ, Marilu, M.D., Chief of Staff, Gundersen Boscobel Area Hospital And Clinics, Boscobel, WI, p. A692

BIRCH, Misty, Director Human Resources, Castleview Hospital, Price, UT, p. A650

BIRCHMEIER, Kevin, Director Human Resources, Covenant Healthcare, Saginaw, MI, p. A321

BIRD, Alan, Chief Executive Officer, Adams County Regional Medical Center, Seaman, OH, p. A490

BIRD, Jace, M.D., Chief Medical Officer, Missouri River Medical Center, Fort Benton, MT, p. A376

BIRD, Jeffrey C., President, Indiana University Health Ball Memorial Hospital, Muncie, IN, p. A212

BIRD, Lindsay, Director Finance, South Pointe Hospital, Warrensville Heights, OH, p. A493

BIRD, Michele
Chief Human Resources Officer, Hemet Valley Medical Center, Hemet, CA, p. A61
Chief Human Resources Officer, Menifee Valley Medical Center, Sun City, CA, p. A91

BIRDSONG, Brady, Chief Information Officer, Saint Elizabeths Hospital, Washington, DC, p. A116

BIREN, David, Chief Financial Officer, Mayo Clinic Health System In Lake City, Lake City, MN, p. A334

BIRENBERG, Allan, Vice President Medical Affairs, Medstar Harbor Hospital, Baltimore, MD, p. A287

BIRI, Abel, Chief Executive Officer, Adventhealth Waterman, Tavares, FL, p. A142

BIRKEL, Sue M, R.N., Director of Nursing, Butler County Health Care Center, David City, NE, p. A384

BIRKHOFER, Colleen, Chief Nursing Officer, Trenton Psychiatric Hospital, Trenton, NJ, p. A413

BIRMINGHAM, Karen, Director Human Resources, West Springs Hospital, Grand Junction, CO, p. A101

BIRSCHBACH, Nancy
Vice President and Chief Information Officer, Ripon Medical Center, Ripon, WI, p. A705
Vice President and Chief Information Officer, St. Agnes Hospital, Fond Du Lac, WI, p. A695
Vice President and Chief Information Officer, Waupun Memorial Hospital, Waupun, WI, p. A707

BISDORF, Jonathan, Director Information Technology, Ohio Valley Surgical Hospital, Springfield, OH, p. A491

BISH, Carol, Human Resources Coordinator, Prisma Health North Greenville Ltach, Travelers Rest, SC, p. A557

BISHARA, Reemon, M.D., Medical Director, Coastal Harbor Treatment Center, Savannah, GA, p. A160

BISHOP, Amy Leigh, Director Human Resources, Red Bay Hospital, Red Bay, AL, p. A23

BISHOP, Bill, Chief Information Officer, Colquitt Regional Medical Center, Moultrie, GA, p. A158

BISHOP, Bryan, Chief Financial Officer, Heartland Behavioral Health Services, Nevada, MO, p. A366

BISHOP, Elizabeth, Business Office Manager, Salina Surgical Hospital, Salina, KS, p. A245

BISHOP, Glenda, Interim Chief Executive Officer, Quincy Valley Medical Center, Quincy, WA, p. A677

BISHOP, Janice E, R.N., Chief Nursing Officer, Tewksbury Hospital, Tewksbury, MA, p. A304

BISHOP, Jim, Chief Financial Officer, Sullivan County Community Hospital, Sullivan, IN, p. A215

BISHOP, Jody A., Vice President of Patient Care Services and Chief Nursing Executive, Bon Secours St. Mary'S Hospital, Richmond, VA, p. A665

BISHOP, John
Chief Executive Officer, Marcus Daly Memorial Hospital, Hamilton, MT, p. A377
Chief Executive Officer, Memorialcare, Long Beach Memorial Medical Center, Long Beach, CA, p. A65
Chief Executive Officer, Memorialcare, Miller Children'S & Women'S Hospital Long Beach, Long Beach, CA, p. A65

BISHOP, Regina L., Administrator, Providence Kodiak Island Medical Center, Kodiak, AK, p. A26

BISHOP, Steve, Chief Financial Officer, Up Health System–Portage, Hancock, MI, p. A314

BISIGNANI, Thomas, Chief Financial Officer, Moses Taylor Hospital, Scranton, PA, p. A540

BISSENDEN, Chris, Director Human Resources, Ogden Regional Medical Center, Ogden, UT, p. A650

BISSET, George, M.D., Chief Medical Officer, Children'S Hospital, New Orleans, LA, p. A275

BISSONETTE, Christine, R.N., Service Line Director for Acute Services, Kalkaska Memorial Health Center, Kalkaska, MI, p. A316

BISSONNETTE, Andre, Chief Financial Officer, North Country Hospital And Health Center, Newport, VT, p. A654

BISTERFELDT, Joanne, Chief Information Officer, Ascension All Saints, Racine, WI, p. A704

BITAR, Adib, M.D., Medical Director, Aurora Charter Oak Hospital, Covina, CA, p. A55

BITAR, Ali, M.D., Vice President Medical Affairs, Dmc – Rehabilitation Institute Of Michigan, Detroit, MI, p. A310

BITHER, Dean, Chief Financial Officer, Northern Light Inland Hospital, Waterville, ME, p. A285

BITNER, Janet, Chief Operating Officer, Texas Neurorehab Center, Austin, TX, p. A586

BITSILLY, Christina, Human Resource Specialist, U. S. Public Health Service Indian Hospital, Crownpoint, NM, p. A417

BITTERMAN, Jeffrey, Commanding Officer, Naval Hospital Bremerton, Bremerton, WA, p. A671

BITTNER, Augustine, Chief Information Officer, Robley Rex Veterans Affairs Medical Center, Louisville, KY, p. A256

BITTNER, David, Chief Financial Officer, Mount Sinai Rehabilitation Hospital, Hartford, CT, p. A108

BITZ, Joan, Chief Nursing Officer, Meeker Memorial Hospital, Litchfield, MN, p. A334

BIUSO, Joseph, M.D., Vice President and Chief of Medical Affairs, Floyd Medical Center, Rome, GA, p. A159

BIXLER, David, Chief Executive Officer, Rhea Medical Center, Dayton, TN, p. A569

BJARNASON, Dana, Ph.D., R.N., Vice President and Chief Nursing Officer, Ohsu Hospital, Portland, OR, p. A516

BJELLAND, Tim, Physician, Mile Bluff Medical Center, Mauston, WI, p. A699

BJERKE, Carolyn, Director Human Resources, Mercy Hospital Kingfisher, Kingfisher, OK, p. A501

BJERKE, Erik, Chief Executive Officer, Madison Healthcare Services, Madison, MN, p. A334
BJERKNES, Dan
Director Human Resources, Chi St. Alexius Health – Williston Medical Center, Williston, ND, p. A470
Market Leader, Chi St. Alexius Health – Williston Medical Center, Williston, ND, p. A470
BJORDAHL, Kevin, M.D., Chief Medical Officer, Milbank Area Hospital Avera, Milbank, SD, p. A562
BJORNSTAD, Brad, M.D., Vice President and Chief Medical Officer, Adventhealth Tampa, Tampa, FL, p. A141
BLABER, Reginald, President, Our Lady Of Lourdes Medical Center, Camden, NJ, p. A404
BLACK, Amy, Risk Manager/PI Director, Brynn Marr Hospital, Jacksonville, NC, p. A456
BLACK, Amy, R.N., MSN, Chief Operating Officer, Sentara Martha Jefferson Hospital, Charlottesville, VA, p. A657
BLACK, Charles, Chief Financial Officer, Rockcastle Regional Hospital And Respiratory Care Center, Mount Vernon, KY, p. A258
BLACK, Douglas, Vice President of Operations, Christian Hospital, Saint Louis, MO, p. A369
BLACK, Gary E., President and Chief Executive Officer, Unc Lenoir Healthcare, Kinston, NC, p. A457
BLACK, Jason, Vice President and Chief Nursing Officer, Glendale Memorial Hospital And Health Center, Glendale, CA, p. A60
BLACK, Jessica, Chief Executive Officer, Copper Springs Hospital, Avondale, AZ, p. A28
BLACK, Marcey, Chief Financial Officer, Northwest Florida Community Hospital, Chipley, FL, p. A119
BLACK, Maria, Interim Administrator, Utah Valley Hospital, Provo, UT, p. A651
BLACK, Marilynn
Chief Information Officer, Northern Arizona Healthcare, Flagstaff Medical Center, Flagstaff, AZ, p. A29
Chief Information Officer, Northern Arizona Healthcare, Verde Valley Medical Center, Cottonwood, AZ, p. A29
BLACK, Michael, Director Human Resources, East Georgia Regional Medical Center, Statesboro, GA, p. A161
BLACK, Paul S
Chief Financial Officer, Scott Regional Hospital, Morton, MS, p. A352
Controller, H. C. Watkins Memorial Hospital, Quitman, MS, p. A353
BLACK, Paul S., Chief Executive Officer, Winston Medical Center, Louisville, MS, p. A350
BLACK, Robert O., Chief Executive Officer, Linton Hospital, Linton, ND, p. A468
BLACK, Ronald, M.D., Chief Medical Officer, Clark Fork Valley Hospital, Plains, MT, p. A379
BLACK, Stacy, MSN, R.N.
Associate Chief Nursing Officer, Medical Center Of Aurora, Aurora, CO, p. A96
Chief Nursing Officer, Spalding Rehabilitation Hospital, Aurora, CO, p. A96
BLACK, Stephen, Health Care System Director, St. Cloud Veterans Affairs Health Care System, Saint Cloud, MN, p. A339
BLACK, Terri, Network Manager, Lucas County Health Center, Chariton, IA, p. A219
BLACK, Tim, Director Human Resources, Timpanogos Regional Hospital, Orem, UT, p. A650
BLACKADAR, Sam, M.D., Medical Director, Cordova Community Medical Center, Cordova, AK, p. A25
BLACKBEAR, Annabelle, Human Resources Specialist, U. S. Public Health Service Indian Hospital, Pine Ridge, SD, p. A562
BLACKBURN, Christy, R.N., Chief Nursing Officer, Candler County Hospital, Metter, GA, p. A157
BLACKBURN, Donovan, Chief Executive Officer, Pikeville Medical Center, Pikeville, KY, p. A259
BLACKBURN, Lisa R, Director Human Resources, St. Margaret'S Hospital, Spring Valley, IL, p. A196
BLACKBURN, Mary, Vice President Operations and Chief Practice Officer, Hugh Chatham Memorial Hospital, Elkin, NC, p. A454
BLACKBURN, Susan
Chief Administrative Officer, Providence St. Mary Medical Center, Walla Walla, WA, p. A681
Chief Operating Officer, Providence St. Mary Medical Center, Walla Walla, WA, p. A681
BLACKFORD, Nate, President, Mosaic Medical Center – Maryville, Maryville, MO, p. A365
BLACKHAM, Cami, R.N., Nurse Administrator, Sevier Valley Hospital, Richfield, UT, p. A651
BLACKHURST, Kristi, Interim Vice President Operations, Asante Rogue Regional Medical Center, Medford, OR, p. A515
BLACKMON, Jenean
Assistant Vice President and Chief Information Officer, Mcleod Medical Center Dillon, Dillon, SC, p. A552
Associate Vice President and Chief Information Officer, Mcleod Regional Medical Center, Florence, SC, p. A552
BLACKWELL, David, Vice President Operations, Baylor Scott & White Medical Center – Hillcrest, Waco, TX, p. A644
BLACKWELL, Jack, Chief Financial Officer, Highlands Arh Regional Medical Center, Prestonsburg, KY, p. A259
BLACKWELL, James, President and Chief Executive Officer, Clara Barton Hospital, Hoisington, KS, p. A236
BLACKWELL, Kelsie, Chief Financial Officer, Placentia–Linda Hospital, Placentia, CA, p. A78
BLACKWELL, Lenore, Director Human Resources, Tennova Healthcare–Harton, Tullahoma, TN, p. A580
BLACKWELL, Timothy, Manager Human Resources, Rolling Hills Hospital, Ada, OK, p. A496
BLACKWOOD, Jim, Chief Executive Officer, Tallahatchie General Hospital, Charleston, MS, p. A345
BLACKWOOD, Mark, M.D., Chief of Staff, Bolivar Medical Center, Cleveland, MS, p. A346
BLAD, Nathan
Chief Executive Officer, Rc Hospital And Clinics, Olivia, MN, p. A337
Chief Financial Officer, Rc Hospital And Clinics, Olivia, MN, p. A337
BLADEN, Anthony M., Vice President Human Resources, Calverthealth Medical Center, Prince Frederick, MD, p. A293
BLAHA, Bill, Manager Information Technology, Tri–County Hospital, Wadena, MN, p. A342
BLAHNIK, David, Chief Operating Officer, Twin Valley Behavioral Healthcare, Columbus, OH, p. A480
BLAIN, Brenda, MSN, Senior Vice President and Chief Nursing Executive, Bayhealth Medical Center, Dover, DE, p. A113
BLAIR, Diane, Human Resources and Admissions, Chi Health Plainview, Plainview, NE, p. A391
BLAIR, Heidi L, Vice President Administration, Centerstone Hospital, Bradenton, FL, p. A118
BLAIR, Jan, Director Human Resources, Cmh Regional Health System, Wilmington, OH, p. A494
BLAIR, Judy, Senior Vice President Clinical Services and Chief Nursing Officer, Adventist Health Glendale, Los Angeles, CA, p. A65
BLAIR, Mark, M.D., Medical Director, Columbus Dublin Springs, Dublin, OH, p. A482
BLAIR, Melinda Lee, Vice President and Chief Nursing Officer, Baptist Health Richmond, Richmond, KY, p. A260
BLAIR, Raymond W, M.D., Chief of Staff, Ennis Regional Medical Center, Ennis, TX, p. A603
BLAIR, Robert D., Chief Executive Officer, Spine Hospital Of Louisiana (Formally The Neuromedical Center Surgical Hospital), Baton Rouge, LA, p. A264
BLAKE, Alan, M.D., President Medical Staff, Samaritan Lebanon Community Hospital, Lebanon, OR, p. A514
BLAKE, Daphne, R.N., MSN, Chief Nursing Officer, Guadalupe Regional Medical Center, Seguin, TX, p. A636
BLAKE, Diane, Chief Executive Officer, Cascade Medical Center, Leavenworth, WA, p. A674
BLAKE, Jean, Chief Nursing Officer, University Hospitals Cleveland Medical Center, Cleveland, OH, p. A478
BLAKE, Kelly, Chief Executive Officer, Select Specialty Hospital–Johnstown, Johnstown, PA, p. A528
BLAKE, Robert, Chief Human Resources Officer Southwest Market, Memorial Hermann Sugar Land Hospital, Sugar Land, TX, p. A638
BLAKE, Skylier, Chief Executive Officer, El Paso Ltac Hospital, El Paso, TX, p. A602
BLAKE, Steven, Corporate Chief Financial Officer, East Los Angeles Doctors Hospital, Los Angeles, CA, p. A66
BLAKELEY, Scott, Chief Executive Officer, Sundance Hospital Arlington, Arlington, TX, p. A583
BLAKELY, Michelle, FACHE, Ph.D.
Associate Director, Jesse Brown Veterans Affairs Medical Center, Chicago, IL, p. A177
Chief Operating Officer, Norwegian American Hospital, Chicago, IL, p. A179
BLAKENEY, Dell, Vice President and Chief Information Officer, South Central Regional Medical Center, Laurel, MS, p. A350
BLAKEY GORMAN, Mary, Director Human Resources, Northwest Missouri Psychiatric Rehabilitation Center, Saint Joseph, MO, p. A368
BLALOCK, Anthony P., M.D., Chief Medical Officer, Our Lady Of Lourdes Regional Medical Center, Lafayette, LA, p. A271
BLALOCK, Tracey, MSN, R.N., Chief Nurse Executive, Medical Center, Navicent Health, Macon, GA, p. A156
BLANC, Linda, R.N., Administrative Director of Nursing, Jefferson Medical Center, Ranson, WV, p. A689
BLANCHARD, Charmaine, Chief Nursing Officer, Healthsouth Rehabilitation Hospital At Martin Health, Stuart, FL, p. A140
BLANCHARD, Timothy D, Chief Financial Officer, Kingman Regional Medical Center, Kingman, AZ, p. A30
BLANCHARD, Todd, Administrator, Willis–Knighton Medical Center, Shreveport, LA, p. A278
BLANCHAT, Tim, Chief Information Officer, Catawba Valley Medical Center, Hickory, NC, p. A456
BLANCHETTE, Edward A., Director, Connecticut Department Of Correction'S Hospital, Somers, CT, p. A110
BLANCO, Andres, Director Management Information Systems, Westside Regional Medical Center, Plantation, FL, p. A137
BLAND, Andrew C., M.D., Vice President and Chief Medical Officer, Hamilton Medical Center, Dalton, GA, p. A151
BLAND, Casey, Director of Nursing, Rush Foundation Hospital, Meridian, MS, p. A351
BLAND, David, Chief Executive Officer, South Davis Community Hospital, Bountiful, UT, p. A647
BLAND, Douglas, Manager Information Services, Spring View Hospital, Lebanon, KY, p. A254
BLANEY, Gerard
Vice President Finance and Interim Chief Financial Officer, Einstein Medical Center Philadelphia, Philadelphia, PA, p. A534
Vice President, Finance, Einstein Medical Center Montgomery, East Norriton, PA, p. A524
BLANK, Arthur J., President and Chief Executive Officer, Mount Desert Island Hospital, Bar Harbor, ME, p. A281
BLANK, Kim
Director Human Resources, Lake Region Healthcare, Fergus Falls, MN, p. A332
Director Human Resources, Prairie Ridge Hospital And Health Services, Elbow Lake, MN, p. A331
BLANKE, Kerry Lee
Chief Financial Officer, Thedacare Medical Center–Shawano, Shawano, WI, p. A705
Director Financial Services, Thedacare Medical Center–Waupaca, Waupaca, WI, p. A707
BLANKENSHIP, Diana, Director Human Resources, Welch Community Hospital, Welch, WV, p. A690
BLANKENSHIP, Jeff, CPA
Chief Financial Officer, Pathways Of Tennessee, Jackson, TN, p. A571
Vice President and Chief Financial Officer, Jackson–Madison County General Hospital, Jackson, TN, p. A571
BLANSKY, Richard, M.D., Chief Medical Officer, Our Lady Of Lourdes Memorial Hospital, Inc., Binghamton, NY, p. A424
BLANTON, Forest
Administrator Process Engineering, Memorial Regional Hospital, Hollywood, FL, p. A124
Chief Information Officer, Memorial Hospital Pembroke, Pembroke Pines, FL, p. A136
Chief Information Officer, Memorial Hospital West, Pembroke Pines, FL, p. A136
Senior VP and Chief Information Officer, Memorial Hospital Miramar, Miramar, FL, p. A132
BLANTON, James
Chief Financial Officer, Ut Health Rehabilitation Hospital, Tyler, TX, p. A642
Chief Financial Officer, Ut Health Specialty Hospital, Tyler, TX, p. A642
BLANTON, Kevin, D.O., Chief of Staff, Goodall–Witcher Hospital Authority, Clifton, TX, p. A592
BLANTON, Ron, Chief Fiscal Services, Boise Veterans Affairs Medical Center, Boise, ID, p. A167
BLASER, Joseph, Chief Medical Officer, Fayette County Hospital, Vandalia, IL, p. A197
BLASER, Karla, Director Human Resources, Unitypoint Health – Trinity Muscatine, Muscatine, IA, p. A227
BLASING, Amy, Chief Executive Officer, Lovelace Westside Hospital, Albuquerque, NM, p. A416
BLASINGAME, Billy, Chief Executive Officer, Continuecare Hospital At Hendrick Medical Center, Abilene, TX, p. A581
BLASIUS, Rita
Assistant Administrator and Chief Financial Officer, Avera St. Benedict Health Center, Parkston, SD, p. A562
President and Chief Executive Officer, Avera St. Benedict Health Center, Parkston, SD, p. A562
BLASKO, Edward, Chief of Staff, Atrium Health Anson, Wadesboro, NC, p. A463
BLASY, Christopher, D.O., Chief of Staff, Carl Vinson Veterans Affairs Medical Center, Dublin, GA, p. A152
BLAUSTEIN, Ron, Chief Financial Officer, Ann & Robert H. Lurie Children'S Hospital Of Chicago, Chicago, IL, p. A176
BLAUWET, Judy, M.P.H., R.N.
Senior Vice President of Hospital Operations and Chief Nursing Officer, Avera Mckennan Hospital And University Health Center, Sioux Falls, SD, p. A563
Senior Vice President Operations and Chief Nursing Officer, Avera Mckennan Hospital And University Health Center, Sioux Falls, SD, p. A563

BLAYLOCK, Darrell, Chief Executive Officer, West Tennessee Healthcare Volunteer Hospital, Martin, TN, p. A574

BLAYLOCK, Kevin, Chief Executive Officer, Oklahoma Spine Hospital, Oklahoma City, OK, p. A505

BLAYLOCK, L Dwayne., Chief Executive Officer, Merit Health River Oaks, Flowood, MS, p. A346

BLAZAKIS, Shelly, Director Human Resources Services, Scripps Memorial Hospital–La Jolla, La Jolla, CA, p. A63

BLAZEK, Dennis, Chief Information Officer, Clarke County Hospital, Osceola, IA, p. A228

BLAZEK, Robert, System Director, Human Resources Business Partners, Elmhurst Hospital, Elmhurst, IL, p. A182

BLAZIER, Patty, Chief Nursing Officer, Hamilton Memorial Hospital District, Mcleansboro, IL, p. A189

BLEAK, Jason, Chief Executive Officer, Battle Mountain General Hospital, Battle Mountain, NV, p. A393

BLECHA, Timothy, M.D., Medical Director, Brodstone Memorial Hospital, Superior, NE, p. A392

BLEDSOE, Dana, President, Nemours Children'S Hospital, Orlando, FL, p. A134

BLEDSOE, Richard, Director Information Systems, Cherokee Medical Center, Gaffney, SC, p. A553

BLENDERMAN, Robert, Senior Vice President and Chief Operating Officer, Brookdale Hospital Medical Center, New York, NY, p. A432

BLESI, Michael, Director Information Technology, Rainy Lake Medical Center, International Falls, MN, p. A333

BLESSING, Brian, Chief Financial Officer, Texas Health Harris Methodist Hospital Azle, Azle, TX, p. A586

BLEVINS, Bonnie, R.N., Chief Financial Officer, Faith Community Hospital, Jacksboro, TX, p. A616

BLEVINS, Denzil, Director Information Systems, Montgomery General Hospital, Montgomery, WV, p. A687

BLEVINS, Matthew H, Chief Operating Officer, Flowers Hospital, Dothan, AL, p. A17

BLEVINS, Matthew H., Chief Executive Officer, Barstow Community Hospital, Barstow, CA, p. A52

BLEVINS, Pam, R.N.
Director Information Technology Member Hospitals Mission, Mcdowell Hospital, Marion, NC, p. A458
Director, Clinical Informatics, Blue Ridge Regional Hospital, Spruce Pine, NC, p. A462

BLIGHTON, Gordon, Director Resource Management, Naval Hospital Camp Pendleton, Camp Pendleton, CA, p. A54

BLINCO, Lynne, Chief Executive Officer, Healthsouth Rehabilitation Hospital Of Dayton, Dayton, OH, p. A481

BLISS, Howard, Director of Information Systems, Helen Newberry Joy Hospital, Newberry, MI, p. A319

BLIVEN, Donna, Vice President Patient Care Services and Chief Nursing Officer, Jones Memorial Hospital, Wellsville, NY, p. A447

BLOB, Burchkhard, Manager Human Resources, Central Virginia Training Center, Madison Heights, VA, p. A662

BLOCHLINGER, Pamela, Acting Vice President Finance, Cloud County Health Center, Concordia, KS, p. A234

BLOCK, Annie, Director Human Resources, Poplar Community Hospital, Poplar, MT, p. A379

BLOCK, Deborah, Vice President Nursing and Chief Nursing Officer, Navicent Health Baldwin, Milledgeville, GA, p. A157

BLOCK, Linn, R.N., Chief Nursing Officer, Manning Regional Healthcare Center, Manning, IA, p. A226

BLODGETT, Debbie, Director Fiscal Services, Ochiltree General Hospital, Perryton, TX, p. A628

BLOEMER, Brad, Vice President Finance and Chief Financial Officer, Arkansas Methodist Medical Center, Paragould, AR, p. A47

BLOMBERG, Emily, Chief Operating Officer, Hennepin Healthcare, Minneapolis, MN, p. A335

BLOMQUIST, David, Director Information Technology, Mckenzie–Willamette Medical Center, Springfield, OR, p. A518

BLOMSTEDT, Jason, Chief of Staff, Community Hospital, Mccook, NE, p. A387

BLOOD, Barbara
Director Human Resources, Lourdes Counseling Center, Richland, WA, p. A677
Executive Director Human Resources, Lourdes Medical Center, Pasco, WA, p. A676

BLOOM, Laura, Director Human Resources, Coffee Regional Medical Center, Douglas, GA, p. A152

BLOOM, Rob, Chief Financial Officer, Carthage Area Hospital, Carthage, NY, p. A425

BLOOMQUIST, Aaron
Chief Financial Officer, Maple Grove Hospital, Maple Grove, MN, p. A335
Chief Financial Officer, North Memorial Health Hospital, Robbinsdale, MN, p. A338

BLOUGH, Daniel D., Jr, Chief Executive Officer, Punxsutawney Area Hospital, Punxsutawney, PA, p. A539

BLOW, Osbert, President and Chief Medical Officer, Christus Spohn Hospital Corpus Christi Memorial, Corpus Christi, TX, p. A594

BLUE, Jan L, Vice President Human Resources, Hoag Memorial Hospital Presbyterian, Newport Beach, CA, p. A74

BLUE, Lee Ann, MSN, R.N., Chief Nursing Officer and Executive Vice President Patient Care Services, Eskenazi Health, Indianapolis, IN, p. A206

BLUHM, Tom, Director Information Systems, Island Hospital, Anacortes, WA, p. A670

BLUM, Carrie, Chief Information Officer, Monroe Clinic, Monroe, WI, p. A701

BLUM, Daniel, President, Phelps Memorial Hospital Center, Sleepy Hollow, NY, p. A444

BLUM, Donald A., M.D., Chief of Staff, Wetzel County Hospital, New Martinsville, WV, p. A687

BLUM, Walter B, M.D., Chief of Staff, Mcleod Medical Center Dillon, Dillon, SC, p. A552

BLUNK, Jim, D.O., Chief Medical Officer, Sumner County Hospital District 1, Caldwell, KS, p. A233

BLURTON, SPHR,SHRM–SCP, Cheri
Director Human Resources, HIPAA Privacy Officer, Great River Medical Center, Blytheville, AR, p. A39
Director Human Resources, South Mississippi County Regional Medical Center, Osceola, AR, p. A47

BLYE, Colleen M, Executive Vice President and Chief Financial Officer, Brookdale Hospital Medical Center, New York, NY, p. A432

BLYTHE, Thomas W, System Vice President Human Resources, Good Samaritan Regional Health Center, Mount Vernon, IL, p. A190

BOAL, Jeremy, President, Brookdale Hospital Medical Center, New York, NY, p. A432

BOARD, Patricia, Vice President Human Resources, Community Hospital Of Bremen, Bremen, IN, p. A200

BOAS, Erik, Chief Financial Officer, University Of Maryland Charles Regional Medical Center, La Plata, MD, p. A291

BOATMAN, Robert, Director Information Technology, Richmond State Hospital, Richmond, IN, p. A214

BOATRIGHT, Donna, Chief Executive Officer, Rolling Plains Memorial Hospital, Sweetwater, TX, p. A639

BOBBITT, James, Vice President Human Resources, Group Ministry Market, Saint Agnes Healthcare, Baltimore, MD, p. A287

BOBEK, Bruce, President Professional Staff, Columbia Memorial Hospital, Astoria, OR, p. A511

BOBO, Matt, Chief Information Officer, Meade District Hospital, Meade, KS, p. A240

BOCCELLATO, Judy, R.N., MSN, Chief Nursing Officer, Specialty Hospital Of Central Jersey, Lakewood, NJ, p. A407

BOCHATON, Philippe, President, Baylor Scott & White Medical Center – Round Rock, Round Rock, TX, p. A632

BOCKENEK, William, M.D., Chief Medical Officer, Atrium Health'S Carolinas Rehabilitation, Charlotte, NC, p. A451

BODE, Edwin J, Chief Financial Officer, Mid–Columbia Medical Center, The Dalles, OR, p. A518

BODENHAM, Steve, Senior Manager Clinical Engineering, Indiana University Health North Hospital, Carmel, IN, p. A201

BODENNER, Nancy, Director Human Resources, Ascension St. Joseph Hospital, Tawas City, MI, p. A323

BODENSTEINER, Kim, Chief Financial Officer, Essentia Health Fosston, Fosston, MN, p. A332

BODIN, Donna L, Vice President, Woman'S Hospital, Baton Rouge, LA, p. A264

BODINE, Maureen, Chief Clinical Officer, Kindred Hospital–San Diego, San Diego, CA, p. A83

BODLE, Vickie, Chief Financial Officer, Lake Chelan Community Hospital And Clinics, Chelan, WA, p. A671

BODLOVIC, Kirk
Vice President and Chief Financial Officer, Providence St. Joseph Medical Center, Polson, MT, p. A379
WMSA Chief Financial Officer, Providence St. Patrick Hospital, Missoula, MT, p. A379

BODNAR, Darrell, Director Information, Weeks Medical Center, Lancaster, NH, p. A400

BODWELL, Amy, Vice President Finance, Methodist Richardson Medical Center, Richardson, TX, p. A631

BOECKMANN, Patricia, R.N., Chief Operating Officer and Chief Nursing Officer, Straub Medical Center, Honolulu, HI, p. A165

BOEHM, Scott D, Executive Vice President Human Resources and Facilities, Sanford Bismarck, Bismarck, ND, p. A465

BOEHMER, Bernard, M.D., Medical Director, Cassia Regional Hospital, Burley, ID, p. A168

BOEMER, Sally Mason
Chief Financial Officer, North Shore Medical Center, Salem, MA, p. A303

Senior Vice President Finance, Massachusetts General Hospital, Boston, MA, p. A295

BOEMMEL, Michael, Vice President and Chief Financial Officer, Medstar National Rehabilitation Hospital, Washington, DC, p. A115

BOEN, Stefanie, Chief Nursing Officer, Skyline Hospital, White Salmon, WA, p. A682

BOER, Jeff, Director Information Technology, Pulaski Memorial Hospital, Winamac, IN, p. A216

BOERGER, Judy, MSN, Chief Nursing Executive, Parkview Regional Medical Center, Fort Wayne, IN, p. A204

BOERGER, Kathy, Director Human Resources, Upper Valley Medical Center, Troy, OH, p. A492

BOERSCHEL, Viva, Director of Nursing, Floyd County Medical Center, Charles City, IA, p. A219

BOERSEMA, Arend, Director Human Resources, Kirkbride Center, Philadelphia, PA, p. A535

BOERSMA, Wendy, Vice President, Nursing and Chief Nursing Officer, Henry Ford Allegiance Health, Jackson, MI, p. A315

BOES, Jody, Vice President Patient Care Services, Door County Medical Center, Sturgeon Bay, WI, p. A706

BOESE, Chris, Vice President and Chief Nursing Officer, Regions Hospital, Saint Paul, MN, p. A340

BOGARD, Tim, Manager Information Technology, Highland District Hospital, Hillsboro, OH, p. A484

BOGARDUS, Tim, Chief Executive Officer, Oasis Hospital, Phoenix, AZ, p. A33

BOGEN, Mark A., CPA, Senior Vice President, Finance, South Nassau Communities Hospital, Oceanside, NY, p. A440

BOGERS, Christina, Chief Clinical Officer, North Valley Hospital, Whitefish, MT, p. A381

BOGGESS, Carrie
Human Resource Generalist, Carilion Giles Community Hospital, Pearisburg, VA, p. A664
Human Resources Generalist, Carilion Tazewell Community Hospital, Tazewell, VA, p. A668

BOGGS, Lynn Ingram., Chief Executive Officer, Habersham Medical Center, Demorest, GA, p. A152

BOGGUS, Bradley, Chief Financial Officer, Cmh Regional Health System, Wilmington, OH, p. A494

BOGLE, Bryan, Chief Executive Officer, Winn Parish Medical Center, Winnfield, LA, p. A280

BOGLE, William J, Director Information Systems, North Arkansas Regional Medical Center, Harrison, AR, p. A42

BOGOLIN, Lore, MSN, R.N., Chief Nursing Officer and Vice President Care Services, Vassar Brothers Medical Center, Poughkeepsie, NY, p. A442

BOHACH, Christopher, DPM, Chief of Staff, Mercy Health – Willard Hospital, Willard, OH, p. A494

BOHALL, Karen, Director Human Resources, Upmc Chautauqua Wca, Jamestown, NY, p. A429

BOHATY, Richard, Director Information Technology, Chi Health St Elizabeth, Lincoln, NE, p. A387

BOHLIN, Sarah, Human Resources Director, North Carolina Specialty Hospital, Durham, NC, p. A453

BOHN, Terry, Director, Human Resources, Orange County Global Medical Center, Inc., Santa Ana, CA, p. A88

BOHNEN, Christa N, Director Human Resources, Ellsworth County Medical Center, Ellsworth, KS, p. A234

BOHNENKAMP, Russ, Chief Financial Officer, Chadron Community Hospital And Health Services, Chadron, NE, p. A384

BOIK, Reyne, Director Human Resources, Cascade Medical Center, Leavenworth, WA, p. A674

BOIKE, Darlene, Chief Financial Officer, Ccm Health, Montevideo, MN, p. A336

BOILEAU, Michel, M.D., Chief Clinical Officer, St. Charles Prineville, Prineville, OR, p. A517

BOILY, Cindy, MSN, R.N.
Senior Vice President and Chief Nursing Officer, Wakemed Cary Hospital, Cary, NC, p. A450
Senior Vice President and Chief Nursing Officer, Wakemed Raleigh Campus, Raleigh, NC, p. A461

BOIS, Alain, R.N., Director of Nursing, Northern Maine Medical Center, Fort Kent, ME, p. A283

BOISVERT, Gerald J, Vice President and Chief Financial Officer, Connecticut Children'S Medical Center, Hartford, CT, p. A108

BOJO, Rolland, Administrator, Grover M. Hermann Hospital, Callicoon, NY, p. A425

BOJO, Rolland, R.N., Chief Nursing Officer, Administrator Patient Care and Services, Catskill Regional Medical Center, Harris, NY, p. A429

BOKON, Mark, Chief Information Officer, Northwest Medical Center – Springdale, Springdale, AR, p. A48

BOKOVITZ, Beverly A, R.N., Chief Nursing Officer, University Of Cincinnati Medical Center, Cincinnati, OH, p. A477

BOLAND, Albert, Vice President Operations, Upmc Jameson, New Castle, PA, p. A533

BOLAND, E. Kay, R.N., MS, Vice President and Chief Nursing Officer, United Health Services Hospitals–Binghamton, Binghamton, NY, p. A424
BOLANDER, Patrick C
Chief Financial Officer, East Cooper Medical Center, Mount Pleasant, SC, p. A555
Chief Financial Officer, Georgetown Community Hospital, Georgetown, KY, p. A252
BOLCAVAGE, Ted, Vice President Division Controller, Inpatient, Ohiohealth Rehabilitation Hospital, Columbus, OH, p. A479
BOLDA, Craig, Chief Operating Officer, St. Catherine Hospital, East Chicago, IN, p. A202
BOLDT, Stephanie, Chief Operating Officer, Thayer County Health Services, Hebron, NE, p. A386
BOLDUC, Tiana, Chief Information Officer, Mercy Hospital Ozark, Ozark, AR, p. A47
BOLEN, David, Vice President and Chief Financial Officer, Passavant Area Hospital, Jacksonville, IL, p. A186
BOLEN, Shannon, Director Human Resources, Baptist Memorial Hospital–Booneville, Booneville, MS, p. A345
BOLES, Glen
Vice President and Chief Financial Officer, Christus St. Michael Health System, Texarkana, TX, p. A640
Vice President and Chief Financial Officer, Christus St. Michael Rehabilitation Hospital, Texarkana, TX, p. A640
BOLES, Lee, Assistant Administrator and Chief Financial Officer, Hunt Regional Medical Center, Greenville, TX, p. A608
BOLEWARE, Mike, Administrator, Franklin County Memorial Hospital, Meadville, MS, p. A351
BOLEY, Jason, M.D., Medical Director, Rock Prairie Behavioral Health, College Station, TX, p. A593
BOLEY, Sarah, Director Human Resources, Wetzel County Hospital, New Martinsville, WV, p. A687
BOLIN, Cris, Chief Financial Officer, Grand River Hospital District, Rifle, CO, p. A105
BOLIN, Kari, Chief Nursing Officer, Putnam Community Medical Center, Palatka, FL, p. A135
BOLIN, Paul, Vice President and Chief Human Resources Officer, The Acadia Hospital, Bangor, ME, p. A281
BOLINGER, John, M.D., Vice President Medical Affairs, Union Hospital, Terre Haute, IN, p. A215
BOLLARD, Robert, Chief Financial Officer, Encompass Health Rehabilitation Hospital Of Henderson, Henderson, NV, p. A394
BOLLICH, Mary, Director of Nurses, Amg Specialty Hospital–Lafayette, Lafayette, LA, p. A270
BOLLIER, Sheila A., Chief Executive Officer, Encompass Health Rehabilitation Hospital Of Cypress, Houston, TX, p. A611
BOLLINGER, Bill, Chief Information Officer, Carroll County Memorial Hospital, Carrollton, MO, p. A358
BOLLINGER, Bruce, M.D., Medical Director, Baylor Scott & White Surgical Hospital Fort Worth, Fort Worth, TX, p. A604
BOLLMANN, Brett, Administrator, Memorial Hospital, Chester, IL, p. A176
BOLLU, Prabhu, Director Information Technology, Wilson N. Jones Regional Medical Center, Sherman, TX, p. A637
BOLOGNA, Monica, R.N., Chief Nursing Officer, West Jefferson Medical Center, Marrero, LA, p. A273
BOLOGNANI, Laurie, Human Resources Officer, Speare Memorial Hospital, Plymouth, NH, p. A402
BOLOR, Erlinda, R.N., Chief Nursing Officer, San Joaquin General Hospital, French Camp, CA, p. A59
BOLTER, Cindy, Chief Nursing and Operations Officer, John Muir Behavioral Health Center, Concord, CA, p. A55
BOLTON, Jeffrey W., Chief Administrative Officer, Mayo Clinic Hospital – Rochester, Rochester, MN, p. A338
BOMAR, Jacob, Director Information Technology, Hardin Medical Center, Savannah, TN, p. A579
BOMBA, Douglas, Chief Financial Officer, Cameron Memorial Community Hospital, Angola, IN, p. A199
BOMGAARS, Scott, M.D., Vice President Medical Affairs, Methodist Jennie Edmundson Hospital, Council Bluffs, IA, p. A220
BOMSTAD, Heather, MSN, R.N., Vice President Patient Care Services and Chief Nursing Officer, Osf Saint Paul Medical Center, Mendota, IL, p. A189
BONACORSO, Donna, Interim Chief Nursing Officer, Community Medical Center, Toms River, NJ, p. A413
BONACQUISTI, Gary, M.D., Chief Medical Officer, Texas Health Presbyterian Hospital Of Rockwall, Rockwall, TX, p. A631
BONAR, Carrie, Chief Information Officer, Southern California Hospital At Culver City, Culver City, CA, p. A56
BONAR, Lynette, Chief Executive Officer, Tuba City Regional Health Care Corporation, Tuba City, AZ, p. A37
BONAR, Robert, Jr, Chief Executive Officer, Children'S Hospitals And Clinics Of Minnesota, Minneapolis, MN, p. A335
BONASORO, Cheryl L, MSN, R.N., Vice President of Nursing and Chief Operating Officer, Nashoba Valley Medical Center, Ayer, MA, p. A294
BONAZZOLA, Michael, M.D., Interim Chief Medical Officer, Ohsu Hospital, Portland, OR, p. A516
BONCZEK, Mary Ellen, R.N., Chief Nursing Executive, New Hanover Regional Medical Center, Wilmington, NC, p. A464
BOND, Lee, Chief Executive Officer, Singing River Health System, Pascagoula, MS, p. A352
BOND, Rodney, Director of Information Technology, Northern Hospital Of Surry County, Mount Airy, NC, p. A459
BOND, Sharon, Director Human Resources, College Station Medical Center, College Station, TX, p. A592
BONDEROFF, Scott, President, O'Connor Hospital, Delhi, NY, p. A426
BONDI, Blaise, Chief Financial Officer, Baylor Scott & White Medical Center – Centennial, Frisco, TX, p. A606
BONDURANT, Barry, Administrator and Chief Executive Officer, Baptist Memorial Hospital–Union City, Union City, TN, p. A580
BONDURANT, Charles, Chief Information Officer, Meadows Regional Medical Center, Vidalia, GA, p. A162
BONE, Janice, Human Resources, Marshall County Hospital, Benton, KY, p. A249
BONEY, Rebecca, R.N., Chief Nursing Officer, Healthsouth Rehabilitation Hospital Of Middletown, Middletown, DE, p. A113
BONFILIO, Nicholas, M.D., Chief of Staff, Great Falls Clinic Hospital, Great Falls, MT, p. A377
BONI, Shirley M, Administrative Officer, San Carlos Apache Healthcare Corporation, Peridot, AZ, p. A32
BONILLA, Felicita, Administrator, Hospital De La Concepcion, San German, PR, p. A718
BONJOUR, Richard C, Chief Information Officer, Sauk Prairie Healthcare, Prairie Du Sac, WI, p. A704
BONNECARRERE, Anthony, Controller, St. Bernard Parish Hospital, Chalmette, LA, p. A265
BONNER, Brad L., Executive Director, Human Resources and General Counsel, Crawford County Memorial Hospital, Denison, IA, p. A221
BONNER, Gwen, Chief Operating Officer, Saint Francis Hospital–Bartlett, Bartlett, TN, p. A566
BONNER, Kimber, R.N., Vice President Patient Care Services, Chi Health Good Samaritan, Kearney, NE, p. A386
BONNER, Lenne
President, Clearwater Valley Hospital And Clinics, Orofino, ID, p. A170
President, St. Mary'S Hospital, Cottonwood, ID, p. A169
BONNER, Robert
Chief Financial Officer, Glendora Community Hospital, Glendora, CA, p. A61
Chief Financial Officer, Montclair Hospital Medical Center, Montclair, CA, p. A72
BONO, Anthony, Chief Nursing Officer, Grove City Medical Center, Grove City, PA, p. A526
BONOMO, Carrie, M.D., Chief of Staff, Riverland Medical Center, Ferriday, LA, p. A267
BONTHRON, Rikki S, Chief Financial Officer, Franklin Hospital District, Benton, IL, p. A174
BONTRAGER, Mandy, Director Nursing, Holton Community Hospital, Holton, KS, p. A237
BONZO, Kelly, Director, Baptist Health Richmond, Richmond, KY, p. A260
BOO, Thomas, M.D., Chief of Staff, Northern Inyo Hospital, Bishop, CA, p. A53
BOOHER, Terresa O., Vice President of Patient Care Services, Highlands Arh Regional Medical Center, Prestonsburg, KY, p. A259
BOOKER, Angela, Director of Nursing Services, Teton Valley Health Care, Driggs, ID, p. A169
BOONE, Donna, MS, R.N., Chief Nursing Officer, Medical City Weatherford, Weatherford, TX, p. A644
BOONE, Elwood Bernard., III, President, Sentara Virginia Beach General Hospital, Virginia Beach, VA, p. A668
BOONE, Richard, Chief Financial Officer, Johnson City Medical Center, Johnson City, TN, p. A571
BOORAS, Laura, Vice President Human Resources, Coliseum Medical Centers, Macon, GA, p. A156
BOORNAZIAN, John, M.D., Chief Medical Officer, Huggins Hospital, Wolfeboro, NH, p. A402
BOOTH, Christy, Chief Human Resources Officer, Doctors Memorial Hospital, Bonifay, FL, p. A118
BOOTH, Daniel
Vice President Operations and Chief Human Resources Officer, Northern Light Inland Hospital, Waterville, ME, p. A285
Vice President Operations, Northern Light Inland Hospital, Waterville, ME, p. A285
BORCHERS, Jonathan, M.D., Chief Medical Officer, Washington County Memorial Hospital, Potosi, MO, p. A367
BORCHERT, Barry, Vice President Finance, Reedsburg Area Medical Center, Reedsburg, WI, p. A704
BORCHI, Daniel, Chief Information Officer, Carilion New River Valley Medical Center, Christiansburg, VA, p. A658
BORDEN, Eric, Chief Operating Officer and Chief Financial Officer, Jewell County Hospital, Mankato, KS, p. A240
BORDEN, Sandy, Chief Financial Officer, Brodstone Memorial Hospital, Superior, NE, p. A392
BORDENKIRCHER, Kimberly Hupp., Chief Executive Officer, Henry County Hospital, Napoleon, OH, p. A488
BORDERS, James, M.D., Chief Medical Officer, Baptist Health Lexington, Lexington, KY, p. A254
BORDO, David, M.D.
Chief Medical Officer, Amita Health Holy Family Medical Center, Des Plaines, IL, p. A181
Chief Medical Officer, Amita Health Resurrection Medical Center, Chicago, IL, p. A176
Vice President and Chief Medical Officer, Community First Medical Center, Chicago, IL, p. A177
BOREL, Patricia, Chief Financial Officer, Mercyone Elkader Medical Center, Elkader, IA, p. A222
BOREN, Kevin
Chief Financial Officer, Essentia Health Duluth, Duluth, MN, p. A331
Chief Financial Officer, Essentia Health Northern Pines Medical Center, Aurora, MN, p. A328
BORENS, Dwan, Chief Nursing Officer, St. John Broken Arrow, Broken Arrow, OK, p. A497
BORER, Tom, Vice President Operations, Promedica Fostoria Community Hospital, Fostoria, OH, p. A483
BORG, David E., Chief of Medical Staff, Community Medical Center, Inc., Falls City, NE, p. A384
BORGERSON, Carol, Chief Financial Officer, Madison Healthcare Services, Madison, MN, p. A334
BORGSTROM, Christopher, Associate Administrator, Coastal Carolina Hospital, Hardeeville, SC, p. A554
BORGSTROM, Marna P., Chief Executive Officer, Yale–New Haven Hospital, New Haven, CT, p. A110
BORING, Ron, Senior Vice President and Chief Operating Officer, Mcleod Regional Medical Center, Florence, SC, p. A552
BORIS, Diane, Chief Financial Officer, Lehigh Valley Hospital – Schuylkill, Pottsville, PA, p. A539
BORIS, Jamie, M.D., President Medical Staff, Washington Health System Greene, Waynesburg, PA, p. A543
BORJA, Catherine, M.D., Chairman Executive Committee Medical Staff, Naval Hospital Oak Harbor, Oak Harbor, WA, p. A675
BORMANN, Jim, Director Human Resources, Passavant Area Hospital, Jacksonville, IL, p. A186
BORN, Michael J., President and Chief Executive Officer, Swedishamerican – A Division Of Uw Health, Rockford, IL, p. A195
BORNICK, Brian, Chief Information Officer, Minneapolis Veterans Affairs Health Care System, Minneapolis, MN, p. A336
BORNMANN, Debra, Chief Executive Officer, Warm Springs Rehabilitation Hospital Of San Antonio, San Antonio, TX, p. A635
BOROWSKI, Thomas, President, Hudson Hospital And Clinic, Hudson, WI, p. A697
BORRENPOHL, James, Market Site Director, Community Hospital Of San Bernardino, San Bernardino, CA, p. A83
BORSOS, Dean B., Medical Center Director, James H. Quillen Veterans Affairs Medical Center, Mountain Home, TN, p. A576
BORTEL, Karol, Vice President Financial Services, Wood County Hospital, Bowling Green, OH, p. A473
BORTKE, Todd, Director Information Systems, Chi St. Alexius Health, Bismarck, ND, p. A465
BORTZ, Tammy, Director of Finance, Peterson Healthcare And Rehabilitation Hospital, Wheeling, WV, p. A690
BORUS, Zachary A., M.D., Medical Chief of Staff, Lakes Regional Healthcare, Spirit Lake, IA, p. A230
BORYSZAK, Martin, President and Chief Executive Officer, Sisters Of Charity Hospital Of Buffalo, Buffalo, NY, p. A425
BORZON, Eve, R.N., Chief Operating Officer, Brookdale Hospital Medical Center, New York, NY, p. A432
BOS, Robbi E, Vice President Human Resources, Sauk Prairie Healthcare, Prairie Du Sac, WI, p. A704
BOSCIA, Michael, Chief Financial Officer, Bartow Regional Medical Center, Bartow, FL, p. A117
BOSCO, John, Senior Vice President and Chief Information Officer, Brookdale Hospital Medical Center, New York, NY, p. A432
BOSCO, Maureen, Executive Director, Central New York Psychiatric Center, Marcy, NY, p. A431
BOSER, Andrew, Chief Executive Officer, Cuba Memorial Hospital, Cuba, NY, p. A426

BOSHUT, Sami, Chief Information Officer, Brookdale Hospital Medical Center, New York, NY, p. A432

BOSLEY, Elizabeth, R.N., FACHE, Vice President Patient Services and Chief Nursing Officer, St. Mary'S Medical Center, Huntington, WV, p. A686

BOSO, William, Executive Director, Administrator, Southern Indiana Rehabilitation Hospital, New Albany, IN, p. A212

BOST, Cecelia, Chief Operating Officer, Alliance Healthcare System, Holly Springs, MS, p. A348

BOST, Marcus, Director Information Services and Chief Information Officer, Adena Greenfield Medical Center, Greenfield, OH, p. A484

BOSTER, Brian, M.D., Medical Director, Select Specialty Hospital–Cincinnati, Cincinnati, OH, p. A476

BOSTIC, Deborah, R.N., Chief Nursing Officer, Texas Health Presbyterian Hospital Denton, Denton, TX, p. A599

BOSTIC, William, Administrative Assistant Human Resources, Surprise Valley Health Care District, Cedarville, CA, p. A54

BOSTON, Barbara, Interim Chief Operating Officer, Hahnemann University Hospital, Philadelphia, PA, p. A534

BOSTON, Scott, M.D., Chief Medical Officer, Passavant Area Hospital, Jacksonville, IL, p. A186

BOSTON–LEARY, Katie, Vice President and Chief Nursing Officer, UMPGHC, University Of Maryland Capital Region Health Prince George'S Hospital Center, Cheverly, MD, p. A289

BOSTROM, Brenda, Director of Nursing, Coteau Des Prairies Hospital, Sisseton, SD, p. A564

BOSTROM, Gary, Chief Executive Officer and Chief Financial Officer, East Adams Rural Healthcare, Ritzville, WA, p. A677

BOSTROM, Stuart, M.D., Director Medical Affairs, Sutter Roseville Medical Center, Roseville, CA, p. A81

BOSTWICK, John, Interim Chief Financial Officer, Henderson County Community Hospital, Lexington, TN, p. A573

BOSTWICK, Monte J., Market Chief Executive Officer, Chi St. Luke'S Health Memorial Lufkin, Lufkin, TX, p. A622

BOSTWICK, Shari, Director Human Resources, New London Hospital, New London, NH, p. A401

BOSWELL, Debbie, Chief Operating Officer and Chief Nursing Officer, Mercy Medical Center, Roseburg, OR, p. A517

BOSWELL, Diane, Director Human Resources and Marketing, Salem Township Hospital, Salem, IL, p. A195

BOSWELL, John, Chief Human Resources Officer, University Of Virginia Medical Center, Charlottesville, VA, p. A657

BOSWELL, William D., M.D., Chief Medical Officer, City Of Hope'S Helford Clinical Research Hospital, Duarte, CA, p. A57

BOSWINKEL, Jan, M.D., Vice President Medical Operations and Chief Safety Officer, Children'S Hospital Of Philadelphia, Philadelphia, PA, p. A534

BOSWORTH, Dawn, Director Human Resources, Arrowhead Behavioral Health Hospital, Maumee, OH, p. A487

BOTAK, Geoff, Chief Executive Officer, Malvern Institute, Malvern, PA, p. A531

BOTHNER, Joan, M.D., Chief Medical Officer, Children'S Hospital Colorado, Aurora, CO, p. A96

BOTHUN, Crystal, Chief Financial Officer, Johnson Memorial Health Services, Dawson, MN, p. A330

BOTINE, Gary, Vice President, Chief Financial Officer, Mary Greeley Medical Center, Ames, IA, p. A217

BOTLER, Joel, M.D., Chief Medical Officer, Maine Medical Center, Portland, ME, p. A284

BOTNEY, Mitchell, M.D., Vice President Medical Affairs and Chief Medical Officer, Missouri Baptist Medical Center, Saint Louis, MO, p. A369

BOTTENFIELD, Dana, Vice President Human Resources, St. Jude Children'S Research Hospital, Memphis, TN, p. A575

BOTTGER, Barry, Chief Financial Officer, Republic County Hospital, Belleville, KS, p. A232

BOTTOM, Paige, Director Operations, Wilmington Treatment Center, Wilmington, NC, p. A464

BOUCHER, Travis, Chief Financial Officer, Speare Memorial Hospital, Plymouth, NH, p. A402

BOUCK, Nancy, Senior Director of Human Resources, Mclaren Thumb Region, Bad Axe, MI, p. A307

BOUCOT, Mark G.
President and Chief Executive Officer, Garrett Regional Medical Center, Oakland, MD, p. A292
President and Chief Executive Officer, Potomac Valley Hospital, Keyser, WV, p. A686

BOUDREAUX, Angela, Director Information Technology, St. Charles Parish Hospital, Luling, LA, p. A272

BOUDREAUX, Scott, Chief Executive Officer, Avala, Covington, LA, p. A266

BOUFFARD, Rodney, Superintendent, Riverview Psychiatric Center, Augusta, ME, p. A281

BOUGHAL, Ginni, Director Health Information and Information Technology, Peacehealth Peace Harbor Medical Center, Florence, OR, p. A512

BOUHAROUN, Khalil, Chief Information Officer, The Hsc Pediatric Center, Washington, DC, p. A116

BOULA, Rodney, Chief Executive Officer, Calais Regional Hospital, Calais, ME, p. A282

BOULENGER, Albert Leon, Chief Executive Officer, Baptist Health South Florida, Baptist Hospital Of Miami, Miami, FL, p. A130

BOUQUET, Sheena
Vice President, Lafayette General Medical Center, Lafayette, LA, p. A271
Vice President, Lafayette General Surgical Hospital, Lafayette, LA, p. A271

BOUQUIO, George, Director Human Resources, Brookdale Hospital Medical Center, New York, NY, p. A432

BOUR, Eric, Chief Executive Officer, Piedmont Newton Hospital, Covington, GA, p. A151

BOURGEOIS, Jeff A., President and Chief Executive Officer, San Juan Regional Medical Center, Farmington, NM, p. A418

BOURLAND, Don, Vice President Human Resources, Peacehealth Peace Harbor Medical Center, Florence, OR, p. A512

BOURLAND, Renee, Human Resources Specialist, San Antonio State Hospital, San Antonio, TX, p. A635

BOURN, Jennifer, Director, Health Information Services and Medical Staff Services, Centerpointe Hospital, Saint Charles, MO, p. A368

BOURNE, Kara, R.N., MSN, Chief Nursing Officer and Chief Operating Officer, Foothill Regional Medical Center, Tustin, CA, p. A92

BOURNE, Kimberly L., Chief Executive Officer, Taylorville Memorial Hospital, Taylorville, IL, p. A197

BOURQUE, Teresa, Sr. Administrator for Nursing/Chief Nurse, Hurley Medical Center, Flint, MI, p. A311

BOUTROS, Akram, President and Chief Executive Officer, Metrohealth Medical Center, Cleveland, OH, p. A478

BOUTROS, Nashaat, M.D., Clinical Director, Center For Behavioral Medicine, Kansas City, MO, p. A362

BOUTWELL, Wayne B., Chief Executive Officer, Regency Hospital Of Central Georgia, Macon, GA, p. A156

BOUYEA, Lawanda Janine, Director Human Resources, Natividad Medical Center, Salinas, CA, p. A82

BOVA, Sheila, Chief Financial Officer, Kindred Hospital– Albuquerque, Albuquerque, NM, p. A416

BOVIO, Ernest L., Chief Operating Officer, Unc Rex Health Care, Raleigh, NC, p. A460

BOWE, Christopher, Interim Chief Executive Officer, Atrium Health'S Carolinas Medical Center, Charlotte, NC, p. A451

BOWE, Christopher, M.D., Chief Medical Officer, Medical Affairs, St. Mary'S Regional Medical Center, Lewiston, ME, p. A283

BOWEN, Aaron, Chief Executive Officer, Arizona State Hospital, Phoenix, AZ, p. A33

BOWEN, Christine, R.N., Chief Nursing Officer, Dmc Harper University Hospital, Detroit, MI, p. A310

BOWEN, Jill Berry., Chief Executive Officer, Northwestern Medical Center, Saint Albans, VT, p. A655

BOWEN, Rodger W, M.P.H., Chief Financial Officer, Scenic Mountain Medical Center, Big Spring, TX, p. A588

BOWEN, Stephen, Administrator, Lavaca Medical Center, Hallettsville, TX, p. A608

BOWEN, Tim, Vice President and Administrator, Baptist Health Medical Center – Conway, Conway, AR, p. A40

BOWER, David, M.D., Chief of Staff, Atlanta Veterans Affairs Medical Center, Decatur, GA, p. A151

BOWER, James, M.D., Chief Medical Officer, Research Medical Center, Kansas City, MO, p. A362

BOWER, Kay, Associate Director for Patient Care Services, Battle Creek Veterans Affairs Medical Center, Battle Creek, MI, p. A307

BOWERMAN, Joeann, Director of Nursing, Chambers Memorial Hospital, Danville, AR, p. A41

BOWERMAN, Stephen, Senior Vice President, Chief Financial Officer, Midland Memorial Hospital, Midland, TX, p. A624

BOWERS, Daniel, Chief Operating Officer, Riverside Community Hospital, Riverside, CA, p. A81

BOWERS, David N, M.D., Medical Director, Siskin Hospital For Physical Rehabilitation, Chattanooga, TN, p. A567

BOWERS, Melodee, Director Human Resources, Carle Hoopeston Regional Health Center, Hoopeston, IL, p. A186

BOWERS, Michael
Head Human Resources, Naval Hospital Oak Harbor, Oak Harbor, WA, p. A675
Interim Director for Administration, Naval Hospital Oak Harbor, Oak Harbor, WA, p. A675

BOWERS, Sharon, R.N., Manager of Community, Public and Employee Relations, Sheridan Community Hospital, Sheridan, MI, p. A322

BOWERS, Tracy
Vice President Human Resources and Administrative Services, Novant Health Uva Health System Haymarket Medical Center, Haymarket, VA, p. A661
Vice President Human Resources and Administrative Services, Novant Health Uva Health System Prince William Medical Center, Manassas, VA, p. A662

BOWERY, Leslie, Director of Standards and Compliance, Cumberland Hospital For Children And Adolescents, New Kent, VA, p. A663

BOWES, Arthur, Senior Vice President Human Resources, North Shore Medical Center, Salem, MA, p. A303

BOWES, William, Chief Financial Officer, Uams Medical Center, Little Rock, AR, p. A45

BOWLEG, Teresa, R.N., Chief Nursing Officer, Erlanger Western Carolina Hospital, Murphy, NC, p. A459

BOWLES, Patrica, R.N., Chief Nursing Officer, Franklin County Medical Center, Preston, ID, p. A171

BOWLES, Tara, Employee Relations Director, Rawlins County Health Center, Atwood, KS, p. A232

BOWLING, Donald, M.D., Chief Medical Staff, Southampton Memorial Hospital, Franklin, VA, p. A659

BOWLING, Karen, Chief Information Officer, St. Mary'S Regional Medical Center, Lewiston, ME, p. A283

BOWLING, Karen L.
Interim Chief Executive Officer, Braxton County Memorial Hospital, Gassaway, WV, p. A685
Interim Chief Executive Officer, Summersville Regional Medical Center, Summersville, WV, p. A689

BOWLING, Kay, Chief Executive Officer, Centra Specialty Hospital, Lynchburg, VA, p. A662

BOWLING, Kelli, Chief Culture Officer, Door County Medical Center, Sturgeon Bay, WI, p. A706

BOWLING, Nancy, Director Human Resources, Shoals Hospital, Muscle Shoals, AL, p. A22

BOWMAN, Dyan, Director Human Resources, Newberry County Memorial Hospital, Newberry, SC, p. A556

BOWMAN, Jeff, Interim Chief Executive Officer, South Central Kansas Medical Center, Arkansas City, KS, p. A232

BOWMAN, Joe, Chief Financial Officer, Tristar Ashland City Medical Center, Ashland City, TN, p. A566

BOWMAN, Joseph E, Chief Financial Officer, Tristar Stonecrest Medical Center, Smyrna, TN, p. A579

BOWMAN, Julie, Senior Vice President, Patient Care and Chief Nursing Officer, Phoenix Children'S Hospital, Phoenix, AZ, p. A34

BOWMAN, Mark, M.D., President Medical Staff, Adventist Healthtillamook, Tillamook, OR, p. A518

BOWMAN, Maureen, Vice President and Chief Nursing Officer, Beaumont Hospital – Royal Oak, Royal Oak, MI, p. A321

BOWMAN, Scott, Administrator, Sweetwater Hospital, Sweetwater, TN, p. A580

BOWMAN, William, M.D., Vice President Medical Affairs, Moses H. Cone Memorial Hospital, Greensboro, NC, p. A455

BOWMER, Carolyn, Human Resources Director, Lmh Health, Lawrence, KS, p. A239

BOWSER, John, Vice President, Chief Financial Officer, Osf Saint Luke Medical Center, Kewanee, IL, p. A187

BOX, Darrel, Chief Executive Officer, Lafayette Regional Health Center, Lexington, MO, p. A364

BOX, Justin K.
Senior Vice President & Chief Information Officer, Mary Washington Hospital, Fredericksburg, VA, p. A659
Senior Vice President and Chief Information Officer, Stafford Hospital, Stafford, VA, p. A667

BOXELL, Shelley, R.N.
Chief Nursing Officer, Rehabilitation Hospital Of Fort Wayne, Fort Wayne, IN, p. A204
Interim Chief Operating Officer, Rehabilitation Hospital Of Fort Wayne, Fort Wayne, IN, p. A204

BOYCE, Charlotte, Chief Nursing Officer, Encompass Health Rehabilitation Hospital Of North Memphis, Memphis, TN, p. A574

BOYD, Aaron, M.D., Chief Medical Officer, Norman Regional Health System, Norman, OK, p. A503

BOYD, Andre, Sr Executive Vice President, Hospital Division, New Hanover Regional Medical Center, Wilmington, NC, p. A464

BOYD, Cathy, Chief Nursing Officer, Select Specialty Hospital–Pontiac, Pontiac, MI, p. A320

BOYD, Christopher L., Senior Vice President and Area Manager, Kaiser Permanente Santa Clara Medical Center, Santa Clara, CA, p. A88

BOYD, Diana, Vice President Nursing, Cleveland Clinic Union Hospital, Dover, OH, p. A482

BOYD, Donald, Executive Vice President and Chief Operating Officer, Kaleida Health, Buffalo, NY, p. A424

BOYD, Ellen, Director Human Resources, Emanuel Medical Center, Swainsboro, GA, p. A161

BOYD, Jason E, Chief Operating Officer, Tristar Skyline Medical Center, Nashville, TN, p. A577
BOYD, John, III
Chief Executive Officer and Chief Medical Officer, Baylor Scott & White Medical Center – Temple, Temple, TX, p. A639
Chief Executive Officer, Baylor Scott & White Medical Center – Temple, Temple, TX, p. A639
BOYD, John W., Chief Executive Officer, Sutter Center For Psychiatry, Sacramento, CA, p. A82
BOYD, Kenneth, Chief Operating Officer, Maury Regional Hospital, Columbia, TN, p. A568
BOYD, Kim, Chief Financial Officer, Buchanan General Hospital, Grundy, VA, p. A660
BOYD, Lance, Chief Executive Officer, Merit Health Natchez, Natchez, MS, p. A352
BOYD, Roy, Chief Financial Officer, Wilkes–Barre General Hospital, Wilkes, PA, p. A545
BOYD, Steven, R.N., Nurse Executive, Levi Hospital, Hot Springs National Park, AR, p. A43
BOYD, Travis, Manager, Information Technology, Mercy Hospital Lincoln, Troy, MO, p. A372
BOYER, Aurelia, Senior Vice President and Chief Information Officer, Brookdale Hospital Medical Center, New York, NY, p. A432
BOYER, Charlene, Chief Nursing Officer, Kaiser Permanente Oakland Medical Center, Oakland, CA, p. A75
BOYER, Cheryl T.
Vice President Human Resources, Levindale Hebrew Hospital And Nursing, Baltimore, MD, p. A286
Vice President Human Resources, Sinai Hospital Of Baltimore, Baltimore, MD, p. A287
BOYER, Craig, Vice President Finance, Sanford Bemidji Medical Center, Bemidji, MN, p. A328
BOYER, Jim, Vice President Information Technology and Chief Information Officer, Rush Memorial Hospital, Rushville, IN, p. A214
BOYER, Roderick, M.D., Medical Director, Select Specialty Hospital–Downriver, Wyandotte, MI, p. A325
BOYER, Steve, M.D., Chief Medical Officer, Regional West Garden County, Oshkosh, NE, p. A390
BOYER, William, Chief Financial Officer, Community Memorial Hospital, Redfield, SD, p. A563
BOYETTE, Jon, Chief Financial Officer, Pocahontas Memorial Hospital, Buckeye, WV, p. A683
BOYKIN, Arthur, M.D., Chief of Staff, Gadsden Regional Medical Center, Gadsden, AL, p. A18
BOYKIN, Doyle, Administrator, Presbyterian Hospital, Albuquerque, NM, p. A417
BOYKIN, George G., Chief Executive Officer, Strategic Behavioral Health – Charlotte, Charlotte, NC, p. A452
BOYLE, Donna, Director, Jfk Medical Center North Campus, West Palm Beach, FL, p. A144
BOYLE, James W, M.D., Chief Medical Officer, Upmc Passavant, Pittsburgh, PA, p. A538
BOYLE, Kathy, R.N., Ph.D., Chief Nursing Officer, Denver Health, Denver, CO, p. A98
BOYLE, Linda Lake, Director, Central Alabama Veterans Health Care System, Montgomery, AL, p. A21
BOYLE, Lisa, M.D., Vice President Medical Affairs and Medical Director, Medstar Georgetown University Hospital, Washington, DC, p. A115
BOYLE, Patrick R
Vice President Human Resources, Finger Lakes Hospital, Geneva, NY, p. A428
Vice President Human Resources, Soldiers And Sailors Memorial Hospital Of Yates County, Penn Yan, NY, p. A441
BOYLE, Thomas W, Chief Financial Officer, St. Lawrence Rehabilitation Center, Lawrenceville, NJ, p. A407
BOYLES, Clay
Director Human Resources, Peachford Behavioral Health System, Atlanta, GA, p. A146
Executive Director, Human Resources, Piedmont Newnan Hospital, Newnan, GA, p. A158
BOYLES, George, Senior Vice President of Finance and Chief Financial Officer, Mercer Health, Coldwater, OH, p. A478
BOYLES, Lee
Chief Executive Officer, St. Anthony Summit Medical Center, Frisco, CO, p. A100
President, Chi St. Gabriel'S Health, Little Falls, MN, p. A334
BOYLES, Mary Gen, Chief Nursing Officer, Encompass Health Rehabilitation Hospital Of Altoona, Altoona, PA, p. A519
BOYLES, Robert L, Director of Human Resources, Highland–Clarksburg Hospital, Clarksburg, WV, p. A684
BOYNTON, James P, Chief Financial Officer, Carolina Center For Behavioral Health, Greer, SC, p. A554
BOYNTON, Kimberly, President and Chief Executive Officer, Crouse Health, Syracuse, NY, p. A445
BOYNTON, Stephanie, Administrator, Erlanger Bledsoe Hospital, Pikeville, TN, p. A578
BOYO, Tosan O., Chief Operating Officer, Zuckerberg San Francisco General Hospital And Trauma Center, San Francisco, CA, p. A86
BOYSEN, Doug, Chief Legal Counsel and Vice President Human Resources, Good Samaritan Regional Medical Center, Corvallis, OR, p. A512
BOYSEN, James, M.D., Executive Medical Director, Texas Neurorehab Center, Austin, TX, p. A586
BOZZUTO, Elizabeth, R.N., Chief Nursing Officer and Vice President, Saint Mary'S Hospital, Waterbury, CT, p. A111
BRAASCH, David A., President, Alton Memorial Hospital, Alton, IL, p. A173
BRABANT, Christopher, President and Chief Executive Officer, Hshs St. Clare Memorial Hospital, Oconto Falls, WI, p. A703
BRABY, Heath, Director Fiscal Services, Shriners Hospitals For Children–Salt Lake City, Salt Lake City, UT, p. A652
BRACEY, Donny, Director Information Services, Marion General Hospital, Columbia, MS, p. A346
BRACK, Nancy R, Vice President Human Resources, Syracuse Area Health, Syracuse, NE, p. A392
BRACKEEN, Steven W, R.N., Chief Nursing Officer, Northwest Mississippi Medical Center, Clarksdale, MS, p. A345
BRACKEN, Thomas H, M.D., Vice President Medical Affairs, Mille Lacs Health System, Onamia, MN, p. A337
BRACKETT, Lori, Director Human Resources, Encompass Health Rehabilitation Hospital Of Bakersfield, Bakersfield, CA, p. A52
BRACKLEY, Donna, R.N., MSN, Senior Vice President Patient Care Services, John Muir Medical Center, Concord, Concord, CA, p. A55
BRACKS, Adam, Chief Executive Officer, Siloam Springs Regional Hospital, Siloam Springs, AR, p. A48
BRACY, Dale, Chief Financial Officer, College Hospital Costa Mesa, Costa Mesa, CA, p. A55
BRADBURY, Monica, Chief Executive Officer, Clarks Summit State Hospital, Clarks Summit, PA, p. A522
BRADDOCK, Mary B, Director Human Resources, Palo Pinto General Hospital, Mineral Wells, TX, p. A625
BRADEN, Pamela, Administrator, Cambridge Behavioral Hospital, Cambridge, OH, p. A474
BRADFORD, Beth, Director Human Resources, Floyd Medical Center, Rome, GA, p. A159
BRADFORD, John, Chief Financial Officer, Murray Calloway County Hospital, Murray, KY, p. A258
BRADFORD, Randy L., Chief Executive Officer, Eastern Shore Hospital Center, Cambridge, MD, p. A289
BRADFORD, Scot, Chief Information Officer, Baylor Scott & White Medical Center – Trophy Club, Trophy Club, TX, p. A641
BRADFORD, Susan, Director Nursing, Kansas Heart Hospital, Wichita, KS, p. A247
BRADICK, Joe, Chief Financial Officer, Forks Community Hospital, Forks, WA, p. A673
BRADLEY, Betsy, Coordinator Performance Improvement, Central State Hospital, Milledgeville, GA, p. A157
BRADLEY, Carol, MSN, R.N.
Senior Vice President and Chief Nursing Officer, Legacy Meridian Park Medical Center, Tualatin, OR, p. A518
Senior Vice President and Chief Nursing Officer, Legacy Salmon Creek Medical Center, Vancouver, WA, p. A681
BRADLEY, Connie, R.N., MSN, FACHE
Chief Nursing Officer, Health First Cape Canaveral Hospital, Cocoa Beach, FL, p. A120
Chief Nursing Officer, Health First Palm Bay Hospital, Palm Bay, FL, p. A135
Senior Vice President and Chief Nursing Officer, Health First Viera Hospital, Melbourne, FL, p. A129
BRADLEY, Deidre, Vice President Human Resources, Clark Regional Medical Center, Winchester, KY, p. A261
BRADLEY, Douglas, M.D., Chief Medical Officer, Belton Regional Medical Center, Belton, MO, p. A356
BRADLEY, Eric, Director Computer Information Services, Summit Behavioral Healthcare, Cincinnati, OH, p. A476
BRADLEY, Linda, Chief Executive Officer, Centinela Hospital Medical Center, Inglewood, CA, p. A62
BRADLEY, Lisa, CPA, Chief Financial Officer, Glenwood Regional Medical Center, West Monroe, LA, p. A280
BRADLEY, Louis, Chief Executive Officer, Mesquite Specialty Hospital, Mesquite, TX, p. A624
BRADLEY, Louis P., Jr
Chief Executive Officer, Promise Hospital Of Dallas, Dallas, TX, p. A598
Chief Executive Officer, Promise Hospital Of Wichita Falls, Wichita Falls, TX, p. A645
BRADLEY, Melody, Chief Nursing Officer, Miracle Mile Medical Center, Los Angeles, CA, p. A68
BRADLEY, Michelle, Director Health Information Management, Amg Specialty Hospital–Wichita, Wichita, KS, p. A247
BRADLEY, Sara, Chief Financial Officer, Oklahoma State University Medical Center, Tulsa, OK, p. A509
BRADLEY, Stacye, R.N., Chief Nursing Officer, Union County General Hospital, Clayton, NM, p. A417
BRADSHAW, Benjamin, M.D., President Medical Staff, Texas Health Presbyterian Hospital Kaufman, Kaufman, TX, p. A617
BRADSHAW, David
Chief Information Officer, Memorial Hermann – Texas Medical Center, Houston, TX, p. A612
Chief Information Officer, Memorial Hermann Greater Heights Hospital, Houston, TX, p. A612
Chief Information, Planning and Marketing Officer, Memorial Hermann Memorial City Medical Center, Houston, TX, p. A613
BRADSHAW, Jeremy, Chief Executive Officer, Mountainview Hospital, Las Vegas, NV, p. A395
BRADSHAW, Justin, Chief Executive Officer, Banner Desert Medical Center, Mesa, AZ, p. A31
BRADSHAW, Pamela, Vice President, Chief Operating Officer and Chief Nursing Officer, Shannon Medical Center, San Angelo, TX, p. A633
BRADSHAW, Rita, Director Human Resources, Chatuge Regional Hospital And Nursing Home, Hiawassee, GA, p. A154
BRADSHAW, Thomas A, Vice President Operations, Wayne Unc Health Care, Goldsboro, NC, p. A455
BRADTMILLER DNP, RN, Theresa, MSN, R.N., Chief Nursing Officer, Adams Memorial Hospital, Decatur, IN, p. A202
BRADY, Dan, Chief Financial Officer, Lds Hospital, Salt Lake City, UT, p. A651
BRADY, James, Area Information Officer, Kaiser Permanente Orange County Anaheim Medical Center, Anaheim, CA, p. A50
BRADY, Jeff
Chief Information Officer, Tug Valley Arh Regional Medical Center, South Williamson, KY, p. A260
Director Information Systems, Hazard Arh Regional Medical Center, Hazard, KY, p. A253
Director Information Systems, Mcdowell Arh Hospital, Mcdowell, KY, p. A258
Director Information Systems, Morgan County Arh Hospital, West Liberty, KY, p. A261
BRADY, John, Vice President Physician Services and Organizational Planning, Northwestern Medicine Marianjoy Rehabilitation Hospital, Wheaton, IL, p. A198
BRADY, Karen, R.N., MSN, Vice President, Chief Nursing Officer, Legacy Silverton Medical Center, Silverton, OR, p. A518
BRADY, Kit, Vice President Human Resources, Education and Guest Experience, Gillette Children'S Specialty Healthcare, Saint Paul, MN, p. A339
BRADY, Lisa, Senior Vice President and Chief Operating Officer, St. Joseph'S University Medical Center, Paterson, NJ, p. A410
BRADY, Mike, Director Information Technology, Up Health System–Bell, Ishpeming, MI, p. A315
BRADY, Tim, Director Information Systems, Mt. Washington Pediatric Hospital, Baltimore, MD, p. A287
BRAGDON, Carol, Director Human Resources, Saint Thomas Rutherford Hospital, Murfreesboro, TN, p. A576
BRAGG, Craig, Chief Executive Officer, Trustpoint Rehabilitation Hospital Of Lubbock, Lubbock, TX, p. A622
BRAGG, Deborah L, Senior Vice President, Finance, Decatur Memorial Hospital, Decatur, IL, p. A180
BRAGG, Krista A., MSN, Chief Operating Officer, Forbes Hospital, Monroeville, PA, p. A532
BRAGG, Lisa, Vice President Human Resources, Knox Community Hospital, Mount Vernon, OH, p. A488
BRAHM, Victoria, Medical Center Director, Va Medical Center, Tomah, WI, p. A706
BRAIN, David, Interim Vice President Finance, St. James Healthcare, Butte, MT, p. A375
BRAITHWAITE, Robert, President and Chief Executive Officer, Hoag Memorial Hospital Presbyterian, Newport Beach, CA, p. A74
BRAKENHOFF, Jason, Director Information Services, Presbyterian–St. Luke'S Medical Center, Denver, CO, p. A99
BRALY, Cindy Ridge, MAAL, R.N., Chief Nursing Officer, Surgical Hospital Of Oklahoma, Oklahoma City, OK, p. A505
BRANCH, Terrance, Chief Information Management, Fort Belvoir Community Hospital, Fort Belvoir, VA, p. A659
BRANCHICK, James, Senior Vice President and Area Manager, Kaiser Permanente Downey Medical Center, Downey, CA, p. A56
BRANCO, Patrick J., Chief Executive Officer, Heart Of America Medical Center, Rugby, ND, p. A469

BRANDENBURG, Ronald, Vice President and Chief Financial Officer, Holy Cross Hospital, Fort Lauderdale, FL, p. A122

BRANDENBURG, Valerie, Director Human Resources, Northwest Hospital, Randallstown, MD, p. A293

BRANDIS, Destin, Chief Information Officer, William Bee Ririe Hospital, Ely, NV, p. A393

BRANDNER, Nicholas R., Chief Executive Officer, Freeman Regional Health Services, Freeman, SD, p. A561

BRANDON, Deborah, Director Total Quality Management, Eastern Louisiana Mental Health System, Jackson, LA, p. A269

BRANDON, Heather, Vice President of Finance, Grant, Ohiohealth Grant Medical Center, Columbus, OH, p. A479

BRANDOS, Orla, Vice President of Patient Care Services and Chief Nursing Officer, Newport Hospital, Newport, RI, p. A547

BRANDSTATER, Ronda, Vice President Patient Care, Grandview Medical Center, Dayton, OH, p. A481

BRANDT, Debbie, Director Human Resources, Community Hospital, Munster, IN, p. A212

BRANDT, Lauren, Chief Clinical Officer, Central Texas Rehabilitation Hospital, Austin, TX, p. A585

BRANDT, Matthew, Chief Financial Officer, St. Alexius Hospital – Broadway Campus, Saint Louis, MO, p. A370

BRANDT, Melanie, Chief Nursing Officer, Grays Harbor Community Hospital, Aberdeen, WA, p. A670

BRANDT, Rob, Chief Executive Officer, Mountainview Medical Center, White Sulphur Springs, MT, p. A381

BRANDT, Steve, M.D., Chief of Staff, Dale Medical Center, Ozark, AL, p. A22

BRANN, Terry, Chief Financial Officer, Mainegeneral Medical Center, Augusta, ME, p. A281

BRANNAN, Debbie
Chief Financial Officer, George Regional Hospital, Lucedale, MS, p. A350
Chief Financial Officer, Greene County Hospital, Leakesville, MS, p. A350

BRANNEN, Charles C, Senior Vice President and Chief Operating Officer, Southeast Alabama Medical Center, Dothan, AL, p. A17

BRANNIGAN, Timothy, Director Information Services, Platte Valley Medical Center, Brighton, CO, p. A97

BRANNON, Jeffrey M., Chief Executive Officer, Wiregrass Medical Center, Geneva, AL, p. A18

BRANNON, Jim, Vice President Human Resources, Atlantic General Hospital, Berlin, MD, p. A288

BRANNON, Linda, Vice President Human Resources, Circles Of Care, Melbourne, FL, p. A129

BRANNON, Rebecca, R.N.
Chief Nursing Officer, Thomas Memorial Hospital, South Charleston, WV, p. A689
Senior Vice President and Chief Nursing Officer, Saint Francis Hospital, Charleston, WV, p. A684

BRANSCOME, Eileen
Chief Operating Officer, Mason General Hospital And Family Of Clinics, Shelton, WA, p. A679
Director Human Resources, Mason General Hospital And Family Of Clinics, Shelton, WA, p. A679

BRANSCUM, Suzette, Director of Nursing, Vantage Point Of Northwest Arkansas, Fayetteville, AR, p. A41

BRANSON, Brett, M.D., Chief Medical Officer, Tristar Hendersonville Medical Center, Hendersonville, TN, p. A570

BRANSTETTER, Erik, M.D., Chief Medical Officer, Aspirus Medford Hospital & Clinics, Inc., Medford, WI, p. A699

BRANSTETTER, Steve, Chief Executive Officer, Nevada Regional Medical Center, Nevada, MO, p. A366

BRANT, Johnny, Chief Financial Officer, Welch Community Hospital, Welch, WV, p. A690

BRANT, Mick, Chief Executive Officer, Gothenburg Health, Gothenburg, NE, p. A385

BRANT-LUCICH, Kim, Director, Information Systems, Providence Little Company Of Mary Medical Center San Pedro, Los Angeles, CA, p. A69

BRANTZ, Jerry, Chief Executive Officer and Chief Financial Officer, Shoshone Medical Center, Kellogg, ID, p. A169

BRASEL, James, Chief Financial Officer, Jane Phillips Medical Center, Bartlesville, OK, p. A497

BRASSINGER, Cindy, Chief Operating Officer, Vibra Hospital Of Southeastern Michigan, Llc, Lincoln Park, MI, p. A317

BRATCHER, Tammy
Director Information Technology, South Mississippi County Regional Medical Center, Osceola, AR, p. A47
Director System Information Technology, Great River Medical Center, Blytheville, AR, p. A39

BRATKO, Eddie, Chief Operating Officer, Mercy Hospital, Buffalo, NY, p. A424

BRATTON, Michael J., R.N., Chief Nurse Executive and Vice President Patient Care Services, Bon Secours–Depaul Medical Center, Norfolk, VA, p. A663

BRATTVET, William W., Chief Executive Officer, Haven Behavioral Hospital Of Frisco, Frisco, TX, p. A606

BRAUDT, Theresa Lynn, Chief Nursing Officer, Gundersen Boscobel Area Hospital And Clinics, Boscobel, WI, p. A692

BRAUGHTON, David, Chief Operating Officer, Lifestream Behavioral Center, Leesburg, FL, p. A128

BRAUN, James R., Chief Administrative Officer and Chief Financial Officer, Flambeau Hospital, Park Falls, WI, p. A703

BRAUN, Matthew, Chief Information Officer, Unm Sandoval Regional Medical Center, Inc., Rio Rancho, NM, p. A419

BRAUN, Peggy, R.N., Vice President Patient Care Services and Chief Nurse Executive, Sentara Virginia Beach General Hospital, Virginia Beach, VA, p. A668

BRAUN, Richard G, CPA
Senior Vice President and Chief Financial Officer, Bradford Regional Medical Center, Bradford, PA, p. A521
Senior Vice President and Chief Financial Officer, Olean General Hospital, Olean, NY, p. A440

BRAUN, Tim, Chief Operation Officer, Carroll County Memorial Hospital, Carrollton, MO, p. A358

BRAVERMAN, Kelly, President, Indiana University Health Frankfort, Frankfort, IN, p. A204

BRAVERMAN, Steven E., Director, Edward Hines, Jr. Veterans Affairs Hospital, Hines, IL, p. A185

BRAVO, Sonia A., Chief Nurse Executive, Kaiser Permanente Moreno Valley Medical Center, Moreno Valley, CA, p. A73

BRAVO, Stacey, Vice President Human Resources, Medical City Denton, Denton, TX, p. A599

BRAWLEY, Carrie, Administrator, Unity Psychiatric Care–Martin, Martin, TN, p. A573

BRAXL-COLE, Kim, Chief Financial Officer, Broward Health North, Deerfield Beach, FL, p. A121

BRAXTON, Edwin R, Director Human Resources, Lompoc Valley Medical Center, Lompoc, CA, p. A64

BRAY, Jason, Chief Information Officer, Mcalester Regional Health Center, Mcalester, OK, p. A502

BRAY, John, M.D., Medical Director, Select Specialty Hospital–Pensacola, Pensacola, FL, p. A136

BRAY, Karen A, R.N., MSN, Vice President Patient Care Services, Washington Hospital, Washington, PA, p. A543

BRAY, Pam, Director of Nursing and Director Inpatient Services, Upmc Kane, Kane, PA, p. A528

BRAYFORD, Amy, Chief Human Resources Officer, Geisinger Medical Center, Danville, PA, p. A523

BRAYTON, Jackie, Vice President Human Resources, Portsmouth Regional Hospital, Portsmouth, NH, p. A402

BRAYTON, Ranee C.
Chief Executive Officer, Moberly Regional Medical Center, Moberly, MO, p. A365
Chief Executive Officer, Northeast Regional Medical Center, Kirksville, MO, p. A363

BRAZ, Marcus, Chief Executive Officer, Encompass Health Rehabilitation Hospital Of Sarasota, Sarasota, FL, p. A139

BRAZEL, Gary, M.D., Chief Medical Officer, St. Vincent Mercy Hospital, Elwood, IN, p. A203

BRAZIL, Wendy, Chief Operating Officer, Neosho Memorial Regional Medical Center, Chanute, KS, p. A233

BREA, Christie, Manager Human Resources, Promise Hospital Of Phoenix, Mesa, AZ, p. A32

BREADY, Sharon
Chief Executive Officer, Careone At Hacksensack University Medical Center At Pascack Valley, Westwood, NJ, p. A415
Chief Executive Officer, Careone At Raritan Bay Medical Center, Perth Amboy, NJ, p. A410
Chief Executive Officer, Careone At Trinitas Regional Medical Center, Elizabeth, NJ, p. A405

BREAKWELL, Michael, R.N., Nurse Executive, Twin Valley Behavioral Healthcare, Columbus, OH, p. A480

BREAZEALE, Scott, Chief Nursing Officer, Neshoba County General Hospital, Philadelphia, MS, p. A353

BREDESON, Christopher, President and Chief Operating Officer, Multicare Good Samaritan Hospital, Puyallup, WA, p. A677

BREDTHAUER, Vicki, R.N., Director of Nursing, Valley County Health System, Ord, NE, p. A390

BREEDEN, Patricia, M.D., Chief of Staff, Lexington Veterans Affairs Medical Center, Lexington, KY, p. A255

BREEDEN, Susan M., Administrator and Chief Executive Officer, Baptist Memorial Hospital–Carroll County, Huntingdon, TN, p. A571

BREEDLOVE, Jean Ann, Chief Information Officer, Children'S Mercy Hospital Kansas, Overland Park, KS, p. A243

BREEDLOVE, Stacey, Chief Nursing Officer, Christus St. Michael Rehabilitation Hospital, Texarkana, TX, p. A640

BREEDVELD, Stacey, R.N., MSN, Associate Director for Patient Care, Veterans Affairs Ann Arbor Healthcare System, Ann Arbor, MI, p. A306

BREEN, Charles J, M.D., Medical Director, Sanford Hillsboro Medical Center, Hillsboro, ND, p. A468

BREEN, Donna, M.D., Chief of Staff, Avoyelles Hospital, Marksville, LA, p. A273

BREEN, Sue, Chief Financial Officer, Western State Hospital, Tacoma, WA, p. A681

BREEN, Thomas, Vice President and Chief Financial Officer, South County Hospital, Wakefield, RI, p. A548

BREHMER, Jennifer, Director of Patient Care, New Ulm Medical Center, New Ulm, MN, p. A337

BREIDENBACH, Kim B, Medical Director, Gundersen Tri–County Hospital And Clinics, Whitehall, WI, p. A708

BREIDSTER, Cara, Chief Financial Officer, Indiana University Health Arnett Hospital, Lafayette, IN, p. A209

BREITBACH, Dave, Chief Financial Officer, Crossing Rivers Health Medical Center, Prairie Du Chien, WI, p. A704

BREITENBACH, Ray, M.D., Chief of Staff, Pontiac General Hospital, Pontiac, MI, p. A320

BREITFELDER, Michelle, Chief Nursing Officer, Piedmont Mountainside Hospital, Jasper, GA, p. A155

BREITLING, Bryan, Administrator, Avera Hand County Memorial Hospital, Miller, SD, p. A562

BREKKE, Erin, Director Human Resources, Burgess Health Center, Onawa, IA, p. A227

BRELAND, Kelly R, CPA, Director Support Services, Mississippi State Hospital, Whitfield, MS, p. A355

BREMER, David, D.O., Chief of Staff, Midmichigan Medical Center–Clare, Clare, MI, p. A309

BRENAN, Kevin, Chief Financial Officer, Emory Saint Joseph'S Hospital Of Atlanta, Atlanta, GA, p. A146

BRENDEN, Stephanie D, Vice President Finance, Columbia Memorial Hospital, Astoria, OR, p. A511

BRENDLE, Judi, Vice President Clinical Support and Chief Nursing Officer, Bassett Medical Center, Cooperstown, NY, p. A426

BRENDLER, Stephen, Director Information Systems, Hilton Head Hospital, Hilton Head Island, SC, p. A554

BRENHOLT, Craig, Division Director People Services, Hshs Sacred Heart Hospital, Eau Claire, WI, p. A694

BRENKLE, George, Chief Information Officer, Umass Memorial Medical Center, Worcester, MA, p. A305

BRENN, Andrea, R.N., Chief Nursing Officer, Texoma Medical Center, Denison, TX, p. A599

BRENNAN, Angela, M.D., Chief of Staff, Howard County Medical Center, Saint Paul, NE, p. A391

BRENNAN, Kevin F, CPA, Executive Vice President and Chief Financial Officer, Geisinger Medical Center, Danville, PA, p. A523

BRENNAN, Lina, Site Administrator, Soldiers And Sailors Memorial Hospital Of Yates County, Penn Yan, NY, p. A441

BRENNAN, Noreen, Chief Nursing Officer, Brookdale Hospital Medical Center, New York, NY, p. A432

BRENNAN, Patrick, Director Information System Technology, Ssm Health Saint Louis University Hospital, Saint Louis, MO, p. A370

BRENNAN, Patrick J, M.D., Senior Vice President and Chief Medical Officer, Hospital Of The University Of Pennsylvania, Philadelphia, PA, p. A535

BRENNAN, Theresa, M.D., Chief Medical Officer, University Of Iowa Hospitals And Clinics, Iowa City, IA, p. A224

BRENNER, Pattie, R.N., Chief Nursing Officer, Encompass Health Rehabilitation Hospital Of Largo, Largo, FL, p. A128

BRENNER, William, Chief Financial Officer, Kindred Hospital–Indianapolis, Indianapolis, IN, p. A207

BRES, Thomas, Senior Vice President and Chief Administrative Officer, Sparrow Hospital, Lansing, MI, p. A316

BRESCIA, Michael J, M.D., Executive Medical Director, Brookdale Hospital Medical Center, New York, NY, p. A432

BRESLIN, Susan, R.N., MSN, Vice President Patient Care Services and Chief Nursing Officer, Emory Decatur Hospital, Decatur, GA, p. A152

BRESNAHAN, Patti, Director Human Resources, Mercy Medical Center, Canton, OH, p. A474

BRESSLER, Kathy, Division Senior Vice President and Chief Operating Officer, Chi Health Lakeside, Omaha, NE, p. A389

BRETT, Mark, Chief Executive Officer, Sparrow Hospital, Lansing, MI, p. A316

BRETTNER, Eric, NWN Chief Financial Officer, Peacehealth St. Joseph Medical Center, Bellingham, WA, p. A670

BREUDER, Andrew, M.D., Chief of Staff, Manchester Veterans Affairs Medical Center, Manchester, NH, p. A401

BREUER, Rick, Chief Executive Officer and Administrator, Community Memorial Hospital, Cloquet, MN, p. A330

BREUM, Linda G, R.N., MSN, Chief Nursing Officer, Adventhealth New Smyrna Beach, New Smyrna Beach, FL, p. A133

BREVING, Robert, M.D., Chief of Staff, National Park Medical Center, Hot Springs, AR, p. A43

BREWER, Aimee, President, NorthBay Healthcare Group, Northbay Medical Center, Fairfield, CA, p. A57

BREWER, Becca, Chief Operations Officer, Falls Community Hospital And Clinic, Marlin, TX, p. A623

BREWER, David, Associate Vice President Finance and Operations, Promedica Memorial Hospital, Fremont, OH, p. A483

BREWER, Douglas L., Chief Executive Officer, Bryan W. Whitfield Memorial Hospital, Demopolis, AL, p. A17

BREWER, Jennifer
Chief Executive Officer, Encompass Health Rehabilitation Hospital The Woodlands, Conroe, TX, p. A593
Chief Executive Officer, Encompass Health Rehabilitation Hospital Vision Park, Shenandoah, TX, p. A636

BREWER, Jim, M.P.H., Chief Financial Officer, Healthmark Regional Medical Center, Defuniak Springs, FL, p. A121

BREWER, Kaye, Chief Human Resources Officer, Maury Regional Hospital, Columbia, TN, p. A568

BREWER, Kelley, President, Lakeside Women'S Hospital, Oklahoma City, OK, p. A504

BREWER, Luke, Acting Chief Executive Officer, Swisher Memorial Healthcare System, Tulia, TX, p. A642

BREWER, Peter G., Administrator, Shriners Hospitals For Children–Spokane, Spokane, WA, p. A680

BREWER, Rebecca, FACHE, Chief Operating Officer, Adventhealth Lake Wales, Lake Wales, FL, p. A127

BREWER, Ruby, Senior Vice President, Chief Nursing and Quality Officer, East Jefferson General Hospital, Metairie, LA, p. A273

BREWER, Traci, R.N., Chief Clinical Officer, Kindred Hospital Dallas Central, Dallas, TX, p. A596

BREXLER, James L., President and Chief Executive Officer, Doylestown Hospital, Doylestown, PA, p. A524

BREYFOGLE, Cynthia, Director, Charles George Veterans Affairs Medical Center, Asheville, NC, p. A449

BREZA, Lisa, R.N., Vice President and Chief Nursing Officer, Robert Wood Johnson University Hospital At Hamilton, Hamilton, NJ, p. A406

BREZNY, Angie, Director Human Resources, Prague Community Hospital, Prague, OK, p. A506

BRIA, Susan, Chief Nursing Officer, Shelby Baptist Medical Center, Alabaster, AL, p. A13

BRIAN, David, Chief Information Officer, Shriners Hospitals For Children – Cincinnati, Cincinnati, OH, p. A476

BRICE ROSHELL, Jade, M.D., Chief Medical Officer, Shelby Baptist Medical Center, Alabaster, AL, p. A13

BRICHER, Joan
Senior Vice President Finance and Chief Financial Officer, Goleta Valley Cottage Hospital, Santa Barbara, CA, p. A88
Senior Vice President Finance and Chief Financial Officer, Santa Barbara Cottage Hospital, Santa Barbara, CA, p. A88

BRICKHOUSE, Jerimiah
Chief Information Officer, St. Charles Bend, Bend, OR, p. A511
Chief Information Officer, St. Charles Redmond, Redmond, OR, p. A517

BRICKNER, Derek, President Medical Staff, Jamestown Regional Medical Center, Jamestown, ND, p. A468

BRIDEAU, Donald, Chief Executive Officer, Inova Fair Oaks Hospital, Fairfax, VA, p. A658

BRIDEAU, Leo P., Interim President and Chief Executive Officer, St. James Mercy Hospital, Hornell, NY, p. A429

BRIDEN, David, Chief Information Officer, Exeter Hospital, Exeter, NH, p. A400

BRIDGE, Lauren M, R.N., Chief Nursing Officer, Kaiser Sunnyside Medical Center, Clackamas, OR, p. A512

BRIDGELAND, Aaron
Director Finance, Ascension Southeast Wisconsin Hospital – Franklin Campus, Franklin, WI, p. A695
Director Finance, Ascension Southeast Wisconsin Hospital – St. Francis Campus, Milwaukee, WI, p. A700
Director Finance, Midwest Orthopedic Specialty Hospital, Franklin, WI, p. A695

BRIDGES, Alan J, M.D., Chief of Staff, William S. Middleton Memorial Veterans Hospital, Madison, WI, p. A699

BRIDGES, Carol, M.D., Medical Director, Broadwater Health Center, Townsend, MT, p. A380

BRIDGES, James M, Executive Vice President and Chief Operating Officer, Prisma Health Baptist Hospital, Columbia, SC, p. A551

BRIDGES, Jane Ann, Chief Financial Officer, Nacogdoches Memorial Hospital, Nacogdoches, TX, p. A626

BRIDGES, Mary, Director Human Resources, Ouachita County Medical Center, Camden, AR, p. A40

BRIDGES, Richard, M.D., Chief of Staff, Hood Memorial Hospital, Amite, LA, p. A262

BRIDGES, Stephanie, Chief Executive Officer, Encompass Health Rehabilitation Hospital Of Memphis, Memphis, TN, p. A574

BRIDGEWATER, Melinda, Director, Information Services, Montana State Hospital, Warm Springs, MT, p. A380

BRIESEMEISTER, Eric, Chief Executive Officer, Unitypoint Health – Jones Regional Medical Center, Anamosa, IA, p. A217

BRIETE, Mark, M.D., Vice President Medical Affairs, Mercy Hospital Jefferson, Festus, MO, p. A360

BRIGGS, Deborah, Vice President Human Resources, Marketing, Volunteer Services and Community Relations, Ellenville Regional Hospital, Ellenville, NY, p. A427

BRIGGS, Gary, Vice President Human Resources, Tristar Southern Hills Medical Center, Nashville, TN, p. A577

BRIGGS, Michael, M.D., Chief Medical Officer, Essentia Health Fargo, Fargo, ND, p. A466

BRIGGS, Paul, Executive Vice President and Chief Operating Officer, Presbyterian Hospital, Albuquerque, NM, p. A417

BRIGGS, Sharlet, Market Chief Executive Officer and President, Adventist Health Bakersfield, Bakersfield, CA, p. A52

BRIGGS, Sharlet, Ph.D., Chief Operating Officer, Adventist Health Bakersfield, Bakersfield, CA, p. A52

BRIGGS, Thomas, Chief Financial Officer, Alliancehealth Madill, Madill, OK, p. A501

BRIGGS, Vicki R., Chief Executive Officer, Ut Health Tyler, Tyler, TX, p. A642

BRIGHAM, Randy, Chief Human Resource Officer, Estes Park Medical Center, Estes Park, CO, p. A100

BRIGHT, Cheryl, Executive Director, Fairview Developmental Center, Costa Mesa, CA, p. A55

BRIGHT, Janet L, Vice President, Chief Nursing Officer, Novant Health Forsyth Medical Center, Winston, NC, p. A464

BRIGHT, Kim, M.D., Clinical Director, Springfield Hospital Center, Sykesville, MD, p. A293

BRILEY, Jay, President, Vidant Duplin Hospital, Kenansville, NC, p. A457

BRILL, Beth K., Senior Director Human Resources, Barnesville Hospital, Barnesville, OH, p. A472

BRILL, Elizabeth, M.D., Chief Operating Officer, Ohiohealth Riverside Methodist Hospital, Columbus, OH, p. A480

BRILL, Karen, R.N., Chief Nursing Officer, Vice President Care, Gillette Children'S Specialty Healthcare, Saint Paul, MN, p. A339

BRILLI, Richard, M.D., Chief Medical Officer, Nationwide Children'S Hospital, Columbus, OH, p. A479

BRILLIANT, Lawrence, Vice President and Chief Medical Officer, St. Mary Medical Center, Langhorne, PA, p. A529

BRILLIANT, Lawrence, M.D., Vice President and Chief Medical Officer, St. Mary Medical Center, Langhorne, PA, p. A529

BRILLIANT, Steven, M.D., Chief of Staff, Veterans Affairs Sierra Nevada Health Care System, Reno, NV, p. A397

BRIM, Celena, Chief Financial Officer, Palestine Regional Medical Center–East, Palestine, TX, p. A627

BRINDLE, Charles B, M.D., Chief Medical Staff, Iowa Specialty Hospital–Belmond, Belmond, IA, p. A217

BRINER, Junior, Chief Operating Officer, Lawrence Memorial Hospital, Walnut Ridge, AR, p. A49

BRINER, Scott, Chief Executive Officer, Sweeny Community Hospital, Sweeny, TX, p. A639

BRINKERHOFF, Douglas, M.D., Clinical Director, San Carlos Apache Healthcare Corporation, Peridot, AZ, p. A32

BRINKHAUS, Theresa, Chief Financial Officer, St. Helena Parish Hospital, Greensburg, LA, p. A268

BRINKLEY, Charles, Chief Financial Officer, Merit Health Biloxi, Biloxi, MS, p. A344

BRINKMAN, Dan, Chief Executive Officer, Hilo Medical Center, Hilo, HI, p. A164

BRINKMAN, Dan, R.N., Chief Operating Officer, Hilo Medical Center, Hilo, HI, p. A164

BRINKMAN, Janet, Director Human Resources, Colorado Plains Medical Center, Fort Morgan, CO, p. A100

BRINSON, David, Director Information Technology, Parkview Wabash Hospital, Wabash, IN, p. A216

BRINSON, Pam, Nurse Executive, South Mississippi State Hospital, Purvis, MS, p. A353

BRIONES, Melba, M.D., Medical Director, Evansville State Hospital, Evansville, IN, p. A203

BRIONES, Randy, Chief Executive Officer, Kindred Hospital Tomball, Tomball, TX, p. A641

BRISBOE, Mark
VP and Chief Financial Officer, Sparrow Clinton Hospital, Saint Johns, MI, p. A322
VP and Chief Financial Officer, Sparrow Ionia Hospital, Ionia, MI, p. A314

BRISCOE, Betsy, Chief Executive Officer, Pecos County Memorial Hospital, Fort Stockton, TX, p. A604

BRISCOE, Charles G, FACHE
Chief Operating Officer, Houston Medical Center, Warner Robins, GA, p. A163
Chief Operating Officer, Perry Hospital, Perry, GA, p. A158

BRISCOE, Janell
Chief Executive Officer, Encompass Health Rehabilitation Hospital Of City View, Fort Worth, TX, p. A605
Chief Executive Officer, Encompass Health Rehabilitation Hospital Of Fort Worth, Fort Worth, TX, p. A605

BRISENDINE, Chad
Chief Information Officer, St. Luke'S Hospital – Quakertown Campus, Quakertown, PA, p. A539
Chief Information Officer, St. Luke'S University Hospital – Bethlehem Campus, Bethlehem, PA, p. A520
Vice President and Chief Information Officer, St. Luke'S Hospital – Miners Campus, Coaldale, PA, p. A522

BRISSE, Thomas M., President and Chief Executive Officer, Mclaren Macomb, Mount Clemens, MI, p. A318

BRISTER, Kim, Director Human Resources, Wellspan Gettysburg Hospital, Gettysburg, PA, p. A526

BRISTER, Marilyn, M.D., Chief of Staff, Texas Health Harris Methodist Hospital Stephenville, Stephenville, TX, p. A638

BRISTOW, Clyde A., R.N., Senior Director Nursing and Clinical Services, Chief Nursing Officer, Wake Forest Baptist Health–Lexington Medical Center, Lexington, NC, p. A458

BRITO, Manuela, Chief Financial Officer Post Acute Care, Brookdale Hospital Medical Center, New York, NY, p. A432

BRITT, Kevin, Chief Operating Officer, Reynolds Memorial Hospital, Glen Dale, WV, p. A685

BRITT, Key, Associate Director, Greenwood Leflore Hospital, Greenwood, MS, p. A347

BRITT, Linda, Director Information Systems, Baptist Memorial Hospital–North Mississippi, Oxford, MS, p. A352

BRITT, Suzanne, Director Human Resources, Samaritan Hospital, Macon, MO, p. A365

BRITT, Tommy, Vice President of Human Resources, Wellstar West Georgia Medical Center, Lagrange, GA, p. A155

BRITTAIN, Libby, Director Human Resources, Steele Memorial Medical Center, Salmon, ID, p. A172

BRITTON, David, Interim Chief Financial Officer, Medina Memorial Hospital, Medina, NY, p. A431

BRITTON, John, Vice President Information Services, Fisher–Titus Medical Center, Norwalk, OH, p. A488

BRITTON, Natalie, Manager Employee Relations, Legacy Silverton Medical Center, Silverton, OR, p. A518

BRITTON, William N, Associate Administrator Finance, Alfred I. Dupont Hospital For Children, Wilmington, DE, p. A114

BRIX, Hsiu–chin, R.N., Director of Nursing, St. Lawrence Rehabilitation Center, Lawrenceville, NJ, p. A407

BROADWATER, Gary W, Chief Financial Officer, Mccready Health, Crisfield, MD, p. A290

BROADWAY, Chris, Manager Information Technology, Mayers Memorial Hospital District, Fall River Mills, CA, p. A58

BROBERG, John, Chief Executive Officer, Hiawatha Community Hospital, Hiawatha, KS, p. A236

BROBST, Mary, R.N., MSN, Senior Vice President Patient Care Services and Chief Nursing Officer, Mercy Medical Center – Cedar Rapids, Cedar Rapids, IA, p. A218

BROCATO, Ray, Chief Financial Officer, Rolling Hills Hospital, Franklin, TN, p. A569

BROCCARD, Alain, M.D., Chief Medical Officer, St. Vincent Seton Specialty Hospital, Indianapolis, IN, p. A208

BROCK, B. J., Nursing Director, Higgins General Hospital, Bremen, GA, p. A148

BROCK, Jamie, Vice President Human Resources, Chan Soon–Shiong Medical Center, Windber, PA, p. A545

BROCK, Kyle, Vice President Human Resources, Glens Falls Hospital, Glens Falls, NY, p. A428

BROCK, Lisa M, Chief Human Resource Officer, Overlake Medical Center, Bellevue, WA, p. A670

BROCK, Melinda, Director Human Resources, Alliancehealth Woodward, Woodward, OK, p. A510

BROCK, Nancy, Chief Financial Officer, Houston Methodist Continuing Care Hospital, Katy, TX, p. A617

BROCK, Paul, Administrator, East Central Regional Hospital, Augusta, GA, p. A147

BROCK, Robert
Chief Financial Officer and Vice President, Adventhealth Rollins Brook, Lampasas, TX, p. A619
Vice President Finance, Arh Our Lady Of The Way, Martin, KY, p. A257

BROCK, Shea C., Chief Financial Officer, Navarro Regional Hospital, Corsicana, TX, p. A594

BROCK, Steve, Chief Financial Officer, Lynn County Hospital District, Tahoka, TX, p. A639

BROCK, Tammy, MSN, R.N., Chief Nursing Officer, Rockcastle Regional Hospital And Respiratory Care Center, Mount Vernon, KY, p. A258

BROCK, Theresa, Vice President Nursing, Good Shepherd Health Care System, Hermiston, OR, p. A513

BROCK, William, Chief Information Officer, Atlanta Veterans Affairs Medical Center, Decatur, GA, p. A151

BROCKERT, Nicholas, President, Saint Luke'S Cushing Hospital, Leavenworth, KS, p. A239

BROCKETTE, Darby, Chief Executive Officer, Rehabilitation Hospital Of The Northwest, Post Falls, ID, p. A171

BROCKHAUS, Jennifer, Chief Information Officer, Sidney Regional Medical Center, Sidney, NE, p. A391

BROCKHOUSE, Dena M, Director Human Resources, Mercyone Iowa City Medical Center, Iowa City, IA, p. A224

BROCKMAN, Vicki, R.N., Chief Nursing Officer, Texas Health Harris Methodist Hospital Cleburne, Cleburne, TX, p. A592

BROCKMEYER, Heather, Human Resource Administrative Officer, Nevada Regional Medical Center, Nevada, MO, p. A366

BROCKMEYER, JoEllyn, Director Human Resources, Indiana University Health White Memorial Hospital, Monticello, IN, p. A211

BROCKUS, Harry
Chief Executive Officer, Carle Hoopeston Regional Health Center, Hoopeston, IL, p. A186
Chief Executive Officer, Carle Richland Memorial Hospital, Olney, IL, p. A192

BROCKWELL, Linda, Director of Nursing, Administrative, Wickenburg Community Hospital, Wickenburg, AZ, p. A38

BRODBECK, Kathleen, Chief Nursing Officer, St. James Mercy Hospital, Hornell, NY, p. A429

BRODBECK, Lisa, Chief Financial Officer, Medical City Lewisville, Lewisville, TX, p. A620

BRODERSEN, Benjamin, Chief Operating Officer, Venice Regional Bayfront Health, Venice, FL, p. A143

BRODHEAD, Roderick, Chief Medical Officer, Ascension Eagle River Hospital, Eagle River, WI, p. A694

BRODHEAD, Ross
Manager Human Resources, St. Vincent Mercy Hospital, Elwood, IN, p. A203
Senior Director, Human Resource, St. Vincent Anderson, Anderson, IN, p. A199
Senior Director, Human Resources, St. Vincent Carmel Hospital, Carmel, IN, p. A201

BRODIAN, Craig R, Vice President Human Resources, Johns Hopkins Bayview Medical Center, Baltimore, MD, p. A286

BRODY, Anne Marie, Director Information Systems Customer Service, Providence Saint Joseph Medical Center, Burbank, CA, p. A53

BROEKHUIS, Arlyn
Chief Information Officer, Sanford Medical Center Fargo, Fargo, ND, p. A467
Vice President and Chief Information Officer, Sanford Usd Medical Center, Sioux Falls, SD, p. A564

BROERMANN, Robert
Senior Vice President and Chief Financial Officer, Sentara Leigh Hospital, Norfolk, VA, p. A664
Senior Vice President and Chief Financial Officer, Sentara Norfolk General Hospital, Norfolk, VA, p. A664
Senior Vice President and Chief Financial Officer, Sentara Princess Anne Hospital, Virginia Beach, VA, p. A668

BROGGER, Portlyn, Divisional President, Rehabilitation Hospital Of Overland Park, Overland Park, KS, p. A243

BROHAWN, Bill, Chief of Staff, Trace Regional Hospital, Houston, MS, p. A348

BROKAW, Sara, Vice President Patient Care Services, Bellevue Hospital, Bellevue, OH, p. A473

BROKENSHIRE, Shelia Kay, Vice President of Nursing, Van Wert County Hospital, Van Wert, OH, p. A493

BROMAN, Craig J., President, St. Cloud Hospital, Saint Cloud, MN, p. A339

BROMLEY, Trudy, Vice President Human Resources, Jfk Medical Center, Atlantis, FL, p. A117

BRONHARD, John, CPA, Corporate Vice President, Chief Financial Officer and Treasurer, Umass Memorial Healthalliance–Clinton Hospital, Leominster, MA, p. A300

BROOCKS, Kelli C, Director Human Resources, Public Relations and Physician Recruitment, Beauregard Health System, De Ridder, LA, p. A266

BROOKE, William R, M.D., President Medical Staff, Pickens County Medical Center, Carrollton, AL, p. A16

BROOKER, Doug A., Chief Financial Officer, Bryan W. Whitfield Memorial Hospital, Demopolis, AL, p. A17

BROOKER, Paula, Director Information Services, Pleasant Valley Hospital, Point Pleasant, WV, p. A688

BROOKER, Susan E, R.N., Chief Clinical Officer, Vibra Specialty Hospital Of Portland, Portland, OR, p. A516

BROOKES, Jeffrey, M.D.
Chief Medical Officer, Parkview Lagrange Hospital, Lagrange, IN, p. A210
Medical Director, Parkview Whitley Hospital, Columbia City, IN, p. A201

BROOKMAN, Mark
Chief Information Officer, Medical Center At Bowling Green, Bowling Green, KY, p. A250
Chief Information Officer, Medical Center At Scottsville, Scottsville, KY, p. A260

Chief Information Officer, The Medical Center Albany, Albany, KY, p. A249
Vice President and Chief Information Officer, Medical Center At Franklin, Franklin, KY, p. A252
Vice President, Chief Information Officer, The Medical Center At Caverna, Horse Cave, KY, p. A253

BROOKS, Albert, M.D., Chief Medical Staff Services, Washington Hospital Healthcare System, Fremont, CA, p. A59

BROOKS, Anthony, Chief Information Officer, Miami Veterans Affairs Healthcare System, Miami, FL, p. A130

BROOKS, April, Chief Nursing Officer, Encompass Health Rehabilitation Hospital Of Columbia, Columbia, SC, p. A551

BROOKS, Barbara, Interim Chief Financial Officer, St. Mark'S Medical Center, La Grange, TX, p. A619

BROOKS, Brian, Information Manager, Dewitt Hospital, Dewitt, AR, p. A41

BROOKS, Colin B., Chief Financial Officer, Southwest General Hospital, San Antonio, TX, p. A635

BROOKS, David, M.D., Chief Medical Officer, Valley View Hospital, Glenwood Springs, CO, p. A101

BROOKS, Gary, Chief Operating Officer, Tahoe Pacific Hospitals, Sparks, NV, p. A398

BROOKS, Helen M., Chief Executive Officer, Presbyterian Santa Fe Medical Center, Santa Fe, NM, p. A420

BROOKS, J Michael, M.D., Chief Medical Officer, Calverthealth Medical Center, Prince Frederick, MD, p. A293

BROOKS, Jeffrey, M.D., Chief Medical Officer, Parkview Huntington Hospital, Huntington, IN, p. A206

BROOKS, Jerome M., Chief Executive Officer, Select Specialty Hospital–Dallas, Carrollton, TX, p. A591

BROOKS, Joe, Chief Financial Officer, Newport News Behavioral Health Center, Newport News, VA, p. A663

BROOKS, Les, System Director Information Technology, Santa Rosa Memorial Hospital, Santa Rosa, CA, p. A89

BROOKS, Lisa, Chief Financial Officer, Comanche County Hospital, Coldwater, KS, p. A233

BROOKS, Lori, Director Human Resources, Red Bud Regional Hospital, Red Bud, IL, p. A194

BROOKS, Nick, Director of Information Systems, Citrus Memorial Health System, Inverness, FL, p. A125

BROOKS, Patrice Gay., Chief Executive Officer, Cumberland Hospital For Children And Adolescents, New Kent, VA, p. A663

BROOKS, Steven Michael, Vice President Human Resources, Southeastern Ohio Regional Medical Center, Cambridge, OH, p. A474

BROOKS, Troy, Chief Financial Officer, Conway Regional Medical Center, Conway, AR, p. A40

BROOKSHIRE, Tim, Chief Operating Officer, Prisma Health Patewood Hospital, Greenville, SC, p. A553

BROOKSHIRE–HEAVIN, Keri S., Senior Vice President and Chief Nursing Officer, Phelps Health, Rolla, MO, p. A368

BROOME, J. Scott, Chief Executive Officer, Vibra Hospital Of Charleston, Mt. Pleasant, SC, p. A555

BROPHY, Beth, Interim VP for Human Resources, Hurley Medical Center, Flint, MI, p. A311

BROSE, Tamara, Director Human Resources, Thayer County Health Services, Hebron, NE, p. A386

BROSIUS, William, Chief Financial Officer, University Of Maryland Capital Region Health Prince George'S Hospital Center, Cheverly, MD, p. A289

BROSNAHAN, Jan, Chief Financial Officer, Winona Health, Winona, MN, p. A343

BROSNAN, Kimberly, Director Human Resources, Norwood Hospital, Norwood, MA, p. A302

BROST, Wade, Executive Director, Anoka–Metropolitan Regional Treatment Center, Anoka, MN, p. A327

BROTEN, Kurt
Chief Financial Officer, Palmdale Regional Medical Center, Palmdale, CA, p. A77
Chief Financial Officer, Vista Del Mar Hospital, Ventura, CA, p. A94

BROTHMAN, Joe, Assistant Vice President, Information Systems, Medstar Washington Hospital Center, Washington, DC, p. A116

BROUGHMAN, Robin, R.N., Ph.D., Chief Nursing Officer, Lewisgale Hospital Alleghany, Low Moor, VA, p. A661

BROUGHMAN, Wade
Chief Financial Officer, Southcoast Hospitals Group, Fall River, MA, p. A298
Executive Vice President and Chief Financial Officer, Riverside Regional Medical Center, Newport News, VA, p. A663

BROUSSARD, Heidi, Chief Nursing Officer, Abbeville General Hospital, Abbeville, LA, p. A262

BROUSSARD, Kari, Chief Nursing Officer, Oakdale Community Hospital, Oakdale, LA, p. A276

BROUWER, Heath, Administrator, Douglas County Memorial Hospital, Armour, SD, p. A559

BROVOLD, Diana, Chief Nurse Executive, Multicare Mary Bridge Children'S Hospital And Health Center, Tacoma, WA, p. A680

BROWDER, Renate, R.N., Director of Nursing, Lake City Community Hospital, Lake City, SC, p. A555

BROWER, Laura E, R.N., MSN, Chief Nursing Officer, Augusta University Medical Center, Augusta, GA, p. A147

BROWN, Alisa, Administrative Assistant, Dewitt Hospital, Dewitt, AR, p. A41

BROWN, Angel, Director Human Resources, Morton Plant Hospital, Clearwater, FL, p. A119

BROWN, Ann R.
Director, Atlanta Veterans Affairs Medical Center, Decatur, GA, p. A151
Director, Va Greater Los Angeles Healthcare System, Los Angeles, CA, p. A70

BROWN, Austin, Chief Operating Officer, Bayfront Health St. Petersburg, Saint Petersburg, FL, p. A138

BROWN, B Blaine, Vice President and General Counsel, Prattville Baptist Hospital, Prattville, AL, p. A23

BROWN, Barbra, MS, R.N., Interim Chief Nursing Officer and Vice President of Nursing, Alice Peck Day Memorial Hospital, Lebanon, NH, p. A400

BROWN, Bartley, D.O., Chief of Staff, St. Joseph'S Hospital Of Buckhannon, Buckhannon, WV, p. A684

BROWN, Benjamin, Chief Operating Officer, Stonesprings Hospital Center, Dulles, VA, p. A658

BROWN, Bryan, Executive Director, Mercy Hospital Fort Smith, Fort Smith, AR, p. A42

BROWN, Chad J., President, Wake Forest Baptist Health–Davie Medical Center, Bermuda Run, NC, p. A449

BROWN, Cheryl, Chief Executive Officer, Henderson Health Care Services, Henderson, NE, p. A386

BROWN, Chistiane, Assistant Vice President, Medstar Montgomery Medical Center, Olney, MD, p. A292

BROWN, Christi, Director Human Resources, Our Lady Of The Angels Hospital, Bogalusa, LA, p. A264

BROWN, Chuck, Administrator, Bethesda North Hospital, Cincinnati, OH, p. A475

BROWN, Crystal, M.D., Medical Director, Medical Center Of Peach County, Navicent Health, Bryon, GA, p. A149

BROWN, Cynthia, Director of Nursing, Hill Hospital Of Sumter County, York, AL, p. A24

BROWN, Damon, Interim Chief Executive Officer, Alliancehealth Seminole, Seminole, OK, p. A507

BROWN, Darin, Vice President Finance, Henry Community Health, New Castle, IN, p. A212

BROWN, David A, Director Human Resources and Corporate Compliance, Pleasant Valley Hospital, Point Pleasant, WV, p. A688

BROWN, Deana, Director Administrative Services, Franciscan Health Rensselear, Rensselaer, IN, p. A214

BROWN, Deborah, Chief Nursing Officer, Logan Memorial Hospital, Russellville, KY, p. A260

BROWN, Debra L, Area Financial Officer, Kaiser Permanente Manteca Medical Center, Manteca, CA, p. A71

BROWN, Debra M., Vice President, Chief Nursing Officer and Chief Operating Officer, Dell Children'S Medical Center Of Central Texas, Austin, TX, p. A585

BROWN, Denise, Vice President Human Resources, Amita Health Saint Joseph Hospital, Chicago, IL, p. A176

BROWN, Derek, Chief Information Officer, Jellico Community Hospital, Jellico, TN, p. A571

BROWN, Doris, Chief Executive Officer, Gordon Memorial Health Services, Gordon, NE, p. A385

BROWN, Ed
Chief Financial Officer, Cibola General Hospital, Grants, NM, p. A418
Chief Information Officer, Medical Center, Navicent Health, Macon, GA, p. A156

BROWN, Eric, M.D., Physician Executive, Prisma Health Richland Hospital, Columbia, SC, p. A551

BROWN, Geoffrey
Chief Information Officer, Piedmont Fayette Hospital, Fayetteville, GA, p. A153
Chief Information Officer, Piedmont Mountainside Hospital, Jasper, GA, p. A155
Vice President Information Systems, Inova Fairfax Hospital, Falls Church, VA, p. A659

BROWN, Howard, Chief Financial Officer, North Shore Medical Center, Miami, FL, p. A131

BROWN, Hugh, Chief Executive Officer, St. David'S Medical Center, Austin, TX, p. A586

BROWN, James H, Chief Financial Officer, Centerpoint Medical Center, Independence, MO, p. A361

BROWN, Janice, Chief Financial Officer, Coosa Valley Medical Center, Sylacauga, AL, p. A23

BROWN, Jason
Director Information Systems, Sanford Sheldon Medical Center, Sheldon, IA, p. A229
Director, Sycamore Medical Center, Miamisburg, OH, p. A487

BROWN, Jason, M.D., Chief Medical Officer, Banner Goldfield Medical Center, Apache Junction, AZ, p. A28

BROWN, Jay
Senior Vice President, Chief Information Officer, West Chester Hospital, West Chester, OH, p. A494
Vice President and Chief Information Officer, University Of Cincinnati Medical Center, Cincinnati, OH, p. A477

BROWN, Jayma, R.N., Director of Nursing, Mercyone Oakland Medical Center, Oakland, NE, p. A388

BROWN, Jeffrey P, M.D., Chief Medical Officer, Indiana University Health Arnett Hospital, Lafayette, IN, p. A209

BROWN, Jenny, Director of Human Resources, Vidant Beaufort Hospital, Washington, NC, p. A463

BROWN, Jill, Chief Financial Officer, Miller County Hospital, Colquitt, GA, p. A150

BROWN, Jim
Chief Executive Officer, Kingwood Medical Center, Kingwood, TX, p. A618
Director Information Technology, Lynn County Hospital District, Tahoka, TX, p. A639

BROWN, Jon, Chief Information Officer, Mission Hospital, Asheville, NC, p. A449

BROWN, Joni, Director Human Resources, Rehabilitation Hospital Of Indiana, Indianapolis, IN, p. A207

BROWN, Joseph C.
Vice President Operations, Baylor Scott & White Medical Center – Plano, Plano, TX, p. A629
Vice President Operations, Baylor Scott & White Medical Center – Round Rock, Round Rock, TX, p. A632

BROWN, Karen
Manager Information Technology, Guthrie Towanda Memorial Hospital, Towanda, PA, p. A542
Senior Director of Human Resources, Bridgepoint Hospital Capitol Hill, Washington, DC, p. A115

BROWN, Karen C, Vice President Chief Operating Officer, Osf Saint Anthony Medical Center, Rockford, IL, p. A195

BROWN, Katie, Coordinator Human Resources, Pocahontas Memorial Hospital, Buckeye, WV, p. A683

BROWN, Kendra, Job Requisition Coordinator, Rusk State Hospital, Rusk, TX, p. A632

BROWN, Kendra, MSN, R.N., Director of Nursing, Kearney County Health Services, Minden, NE, p. A387

BROWN, Kenneth A, Vice President and Chief Human Resource Officer, Pratt Regional Medical Center, Pratt, KS, p. A244

BROWN, Kevin, Chief Executive Officer, La Paz Regional Hospital, Parker, AZ, p. A32

BROWN, Kris, Associate Director, Bay Pines Veterans Affairs Healthcare System, Bay Pines, FL, p. A117

BROWN, LaRay, President and Chief Executive Officer, Brookdale Hospital Medical Center, New York, NY, p. A432

BROWN, Laura, Chief Executive Officer, Sun Behavioral Houston, Houston, TX, p. A614

BROWN, Lewis, Director Information Technology, Bsa Hospital, Llc, Amarillo, TX, p. A582

BROWN, Lisa, Director of Nursing, Pearl River County Hospital, Poplarville, MS, p. A353

BROWN, Liz, Manager Human Resources, Gunnison Valley Hospital, Gunnison, UT, p. A648

BROWN, Lorenzo, Chief Executive Officer, Adventhealth Deland, Deland, FL, p. A121

BROWN, Lori, Chief Nursing Officer, Baptist Memorial Hospital–Union City, Union City, TN, p. A580

BROWN, Lori J., R.N., FACHE, Chief Nursing Officer, Hennepin Healthcare, Minneapolis, MN, p. A335

BROWN, Margaret, Director Medical Records, Vantage Point Of Northwest Arkansas, Fayetteville, AR, p. A41

BROWN, Mark R, Chief Nursing Officer, Seton Medical Center, Daly City, CA, p. A56

BROWN, Markham, M.D., Chief Medical Staff, Mike O'Callaghan Federal Hospital, Nellis Afb, NV, p. A396

BROWN, Marlon, Human Resources, Essex County Hospital Center, Cedar Grove, NJ, p. A404

BROWN, Martin, Vice President Information Services and Chief Information Officer, Nathan Littauer Hospital And Nursing Home, Gloversville, NY, p. A428

BROWN, Mary Beth, Director Human Resources, Bertrand Chaffee Hospital, Springville, NY, p. A444

BROWN, Mary W, Senior Vice President Operations, St. Joseph'S Hospital Health Center, Syracuse, NY, p. A445

BROWN, Michael, D.O., Chief of Staff, Tmc Bonham Hospital, Bonham, TX, p. A589

BROWN, Michael L.
Regional President and Chief Executive Officer, Amita Health Mercy Medical Center, Aurora, IL, p. A173
Regional President and Chief Executive Officer, Amita Health Saint Joseph Hospital, Elgin, IL, p. A182

BROWN, Mike, Chief Financial Officer, Carlinville Area Hospital, Carlinville, IL, p. A175

BROWN, Molly B., Chief Operating Officer, University Of Mississippi Medical Center Grenada, Grenada, MS, p. A347

BROWN, Natalie, Chief Human Resources Management Services, Memphis Veterans Affairs Medical Center, Memphis, TN, p. A575

BROWN, Pam, Human Resources Manager, Unity Psychiatric Care–Columbia, Columbia, TN, p. A568

BROWN, Pat, R.N., Chief Nursing Officer, San Gorgonio Memorial Hospital, Banning, CA, p. A52

BROWN, Patsy, Site Coordinator Human Resources, Erlanger Bledsoe Hospital, Pikeville, TN, p. A578

BROWN, Penny D, Director of Human Resources, Broaddus Hospital, Philippi, WV, p. A688

BROWN, Philip, D.O., Vice President Medical Affairs, The University Of Vermont Health Network Central Vermont Medical Center, Berlin, VT, p. A654

BROWN, Phyllis, Chief Executive Officer, Marshall Medical Center, Lewisburg, TN, p. A573

BROWN, Randal, M.D., Chief of Medical Staff, Guadalupe County Hospital, Santa Rosa, NM, p. A420

BROWN, Regenia, Vice President Human Resources, Magnolia Regional Health Center, Corinth, MS, p. A346

BROWN, Rex H., President and Chief Executive Officer, Hillsboro Area Hospital, Hillsboro, IL, p. A185

BROWN, Rickie F, Chief Financial Officer, Monroe County Medical Center, Tompkinsville, KY, p. A261

BROWN, Rita, Director Human Resources, Richardson Medical Center, Rayville, LA, p. A277

BROWN, Robert, Chief Operating Officer, Parkview Community Hospital Medical Center, Riverside, CA, p. A81

BROWN, Roberta, Chief Nursing Officer, Community Hospital Of Staunton, Staunton, IL, p. A197

BROWN, Robin, Chief Information Officer and Compliance Officer, St. Joseph Medical Center, Houston, TX, p. A613

BROWN, Scott, Chief Financial Officer, Valir Rehabilitation Hospital, Oklahoma City, OK, p. A505

BROWN, Sharon
Deputy Commander Nursing, Winn Army Community Hospital, Hinesville, GA, p. A154
Vice President Human Resources, Sierra View Medical Center, Porterville, CA, p. A79
Vice President Patient Care and Chief Nursing Officer, St. Mary Medical Center, Langhorne, PA, p. A529

BROWN, Sherry, Director Human Resources, Cleveland Area Hospital, Cleveland, OK, p. A498

BROWN, Stephen A, Chief Financial Officer, Grace Cottage Hospital, Townshend, VT, p. A655

BROWN, Steve
Chief Information Officer, Wellstar Sylvan Grove Hospital, Jackson, GA, p. A156
Director Information Systems, Wellstar Spalding Regional Hospital, Griffin, GA, p. A154
Health Services Director, U. S. Penitentiary Infirmary, Lewisburg, PA, p. A530

BROWN, Steve, M.D., Chief Quality Officer, Saint Alphonsus Regional Medical Center, Boise, ID, p. A168

BROWN, Steven
Vice President Finance, Anderson Regional Health System South, Meridian, MS, p. A351
Vice President Finance, Anderson Regional Health System, Meridian, MS, p. A351
Vice President Fiscal Affairs, Mary Rutan Hospital, Bellefontaine, OH, p. A473

BROWN, Steven, M.D., Medical Director, Wyoming Behavioral Institute, Casper, WY, p. A710

BROWN, Susan
Chief Human Resources Officer, Wellstar North Fulton Hospital, Roswell, GA, p. A159
Chief Nursing Officer, El Paso Behavioral Health System, El Paso, TX, p. A601

BROWN, Terry L, Chief Financial Officer, Raulerson Hospital, Okeechobee, FL, p. A133

BROWN, Theodore
Chief Operating Officer, Community Howard Regional Health, Kokomo, IN, p. A209
Vice President Financial Services, Community Howard Regional Health, Kokomo, IN, p. A209

BROWN, Todd A, M.D., Medical Director, Logan Regional Hospital, Logan, UT, p. A648

BROWN, Tom, M.D., President Medical Staff, Wayne Healthcare, Greenville, OH, p. A484

BROWN, Traci, Human Resources Generalist, Medical Arts Hospital, Lamesa, TX, p. A619

BROWN, Wendy W, M.D., M.P.H., Chief of Staff, Jesse Brown Veterans Affairs Medical Center, Chicago, IL, p. A177

BROWN, William A., Chief Executive Officer, Brookdale Hospital Medical Center, New York, NY, p. A432

BROWN, Willie, Director Administration, Naval Hospital Beaufort, Beaufort, SC, p. A549

BROWN, Winfield S.
President and Chief Executive Officer, Athol Hospital, Athol, MA, p. A294
President and Chief Executive Officer, Heywood Hospital, Gardner, MA, p. A299

BROWN–ROBERTS, Bonita, Director Information Systems, Advocate Trinity Hospital, Chicago, IL, p. A176

BROWN–SMITH, Clarissa, Director Fiscal Services, Shriners Hospitals For Children–Shreveport, Shreveport, LA, p. A278

BROWN–TEZERA, Belina, MSN, Associate Director Patient Care Services, John D. Dingell Veterans Affairs Medical Center, Detroit, MI, p. A310

BROWNE, John
Assistant Administrator Finance, Kindred Hospital–Brea, Brea, CA, p. A53
Senior Chief Financial Officer, Kindred Hospital Riverside, Perris, CA, p. A78

BROWNE, Mark, M.D.
Chief Medical Officer, Roane Medical Center, Harriman, TN, p. A570
Covenant Health, Senior Vice President and Chief Medical Officer, Methodist Medical Center Of Oak Ridge, Oak Ridge, TN, p. A578

BROWNER, Warren S.
Chief Executive Officer, California Pacific Medical Center–St. Luke'S Campus, San Francisco, CA, p. A85
Chief Executive Officer, California Pacific Medical Center, San Francisco, CA, p. A85

BROWNEWELL, Victoria, Chief Nursing Officer, Houston Methodist West Hospital, Houston, TX, p. A612

BROWNFIELD, Mona, M.D., Chief Medical Staff, Pinnacle Regional Hospital, Boonville, MO, p. A357

BROWNING, Douglas, Chief Financial Officer, Texas Health Center For Diagnostic & Surgery, Plano, TX, p. A630

BROWNING, Michael
Chief Financial Officer, Madison Health, London, OH, p. A486
Chief Financial Officer, Promedica Flower Hospital, Sylvania, OH, p. A491

BROWNING, Susan, Executive Director, Brookdale Hospital Medical Center, New York, NY, p. A432

BROWNLEE, Tamarah, Vice President, Human Resources, Indiana University Health West Hospital, Avon, IN, p. A199

BROWNSTEIN, Richard, M.D., Chief of Staff, Northwest Mississippi Medical Center, Clarksdale, MS, p. A345

BROWNSWORTH, Ray, Chief Executive Officer, Van Buren County Hospital, Keosauqua, IA, p. A225

BROYLES, Susan, Director Human Resources and Safety, Unicoi County Memorial Hospital, Erwin, TN, p. A569

BRUBAKER, Kathy M., R.N., MSN, Vice President and Chief Nursing Officer, St. Joseph Mercy Chelsea, Chelsea, MI, p. A308

BRUBAKER, Margaret M, Senior Vice President Human Resources, Brookdale Hospital Medical Center, New York, NY, p. A432

BRUCE, Bill, Chief Executive Officer, Crawford County Memorial Hospital, Denison, IA, p. A221

BRUCE, Caleigh, Vice President Human Resources, Ferrell Hospital, Eldorado, IL, p. A181

BRUCE, Jordan, Administrator, Norwood Health Center, Marshfield, WI, p. A699

BRUCE, Karen, Director of Nursing, Newport News Behavioral Health Center, Newport News, VA, p. A663

BRUCE, Michael D., Chief Executive Officer, Lake Martin Community Hospital, Dadeville, AL, p. A16

BRUCE, Mike, Chief Financial Officer, Elmore Community Hospital, Wetumpka, AL, p. A24

BRUCE, Scott, Vice President Operations, St. Mary'S Healthcare, Amsterdam, NY, p. A422

BRUCKNER, Alison, Chief Operating Officer, Cass County Memorial Hospital, Atlantic, IA, p. A217

BRUDNICKI, Gary F, Senior Executive Vice President, Chief Operating Officer and Chief Financial Officer, Westchester Medical Center, Valhalla, NY, p. A446

BRUEGGEMANN, Marty, Chief Medical Officer, Virginia Mason Memorial, Yakima, WA, p. A682

BRUENING, Teri Tipton, MSN, Chief Nursing Officer and Vice President Patient Care Services, Nebraska Methodist Hospital, Omaha, NE, p. A389

BRUENS, Dennis, Vice President Operations, St. Thomas More Hospital, Canon City, CO, p. A97

BRUFF, Edward, President and Chief Executive Officer, Covenant Healthcare, Saginaw, MI, p. A321

BRUGGEMAN, Chris, Chief Operating Officer, Riverview Health, Crookston, MN, p. A330

BRUHL, Lisa G, Chief Operating Officer, Lallie Kemp Medical Center, Independence, LA, p. A269

BRUHL, Steven, Chief Medical Officer, Mercy Tiffin Hospital, Tiffin, OH, p. A491

BRUHN, Julie, R.N., MS, Associate Director Patient Care and Nurse Executive, Fargo Veterans Affairs Health Care System, Fargo, ND, p. A466

BRUI, Thomas M, Director Resource Management, Naval Hospital Lemoore, Lemoore, CA, p. A64

BRUINS, Melanie, Chief Talent Officer, Beaver Dam Community Hospitals, Beaver Dam, WI, p. A692

BRUMFIELD, Derrick, Chief Operating Officer, Sagewest Health Care At Riverton, Riverton, WY, p. A712

BRUMFIELD, Rita, R.N., MSN, Chief Nursing Officer, Ste. Genevieve County Memorial Hospital, Ste Genevieve, MO, p. A372

BRUMMER, Amy, R.N., MSN, Chief Nursing Officer, Saint Luke'S North Hospital – Barry Road, Kansas City, MO, p. A363

BRUMMETT, Vince, Chief Executive Officer, Parkwood Behavioral Health System, Olive Branch, MS, p. A352

BRUNDAGE, Kelsey B., Director Human Resources, Arkansas Valley Regional Medical Center, La Junta, CO, p. A102

BRUNDISE, Cynthia, Vice President Human Resources, Ssm Health St. Anthony Hospital – Oklahoma City, Oklahoma City, OK, p. A505

BRUNELLE, Diane, MSN, R.N., Director Patient Care Services and Chief Nursing Officer, Shriners Hospitals For Children– Springfield, Springfield, MA, p. A303

BRUNER, Deborah, Chief Executive Officer and Administrator, Minneola District Hospital, Minneola, KS, p. A241

BRUNING, Troy, Director Information Technology, Meeker Memorial Hospital, Litchfield, MN, p. A334

BRUNKE, Renea, Vice President Human Resources, Chandler Regional Medical Center, Chandler, AZ, p. A28

BRUNN, Mary E., R.N., Acting Associate Director Nursing, Clement J. Zablocki Veterans Affairs Medical Center, Milwaukee, WI, p. A701

BRUNO, Catherine, FACHE, Chief Information Officer, Northern Light Eastern Maine Medical Center, Bangor, ME, p. A281

BRUNO, John P, Senior Vice President Human Resources, St. Joseph'S University Medical Center, Paterson, NJ, p. A410

BRUNO, Judy, President, Vidant Roanoke–Chowan Hospital, Ahoskie, NC, p. A449

BRUNS, Susan, Chief Nursing Officer, Phoebe Sumter Medical Center, Americus, GA, p. A145

BRUNSCHEON, Keagan, Manager, Human Resources, Grundy County Memorial Hospital, Grundy Center, IA, p. A223

BRUNSING, Alisa A., Chief Financial Officer, St. Francis Memorial Hospital, West Point, NE, p. A392

BRUNSON, Pamela J, Director Human Resources, South Baldwin Regional Medical Center, Foley, AL, p. A18

BRUNT, C Hal, M.D., Medical Director, Lakeside Behavioral Health System, Memphis, TN, p. A575

BRUNTON, Hope, Chief Manpower Branch, Irwin Army Community Hospital, Junction City, KS, p. A237

BRUNTZ, Troy, President and Chief Executive Officer, Community Hospital, Mccook, NE, p. A387

BRUSCO, Louis, M.D., Chief Medical Officer, Morristown Medical Center, Morristown, NJ, p. A408

BRUSVEN, Jessica, Chief Executive Officer, Marias Medical Center, Shelby, MT, p. A380

BRUTON, Jeff, Director Human Resources, Fairview Park Hospital, Dublin, GA, p. A152

BRUUN, Edward, President and Chief Executive Officer, Sparrow Clinton Hospital, Saint Johns, MI, p. A322

BRVENIK, Richard A., President, Carteret Health Care, Morehead City, NC, p. A458

BRYAN, Darlene, R.N., Chief Nursing Officer, Humboldt General Hospital, Winnemucca, NV, p. A398

BRYAN, Douglas, President, Medical Staff, Mercyhealth Hospital And Medical Center – Harvard, Harvard, IL, p. A184

BRYAN, Jason, Director Human Resources, Middle Park Medical Center–Kremmling, Kremmling, CO, p. A102

BRYAN, Kenneth E, FACHE, President and Chief Executive Officer, Harnett Health System, Dunn, NC, p. A452

BRYAN, Linda, Vice President Human Resources, Fawcett Memorial Hospital, Port Charlotte, FL, p. A137

BRYAN, Lynda, Vice President Human Resources, Northwest Medical Center, Margate, FL, p. A129

BRYAN, Margaret, Administrator, Shriners Hospitals For Children–Northern California, Sacramento, CA, p. A82

BRYAN, Sarah, Manager Human Resources, Deaconess Gateway Hospital, Newburgh, IN, p. A213

BRYAN–SMITH, Lissa, Chief Administrative Officer, Geisinger–Bloomsburg Hospital, Bloomsburg, PA, p. A521

BRYANT, Amy, Chief Financial Officer, Cornerstone Hospital Of Southwest Louisiana, Lake Charles, LA, p. A272

BRYANT, Dawn, Vice President Human Resources, North Kansas City Hospital, North Kansas City, MO, p. A366

BRYANT, Gary
   Chief Financial Officer, Carepoint Health Bayonne Medical Center, Bayonne, NJ, p. A403
   Executive Vice President and Chief Financial Officer, Carepoint Health Christ Hospital, Jersey City, NJ, p. A407

BRYANT, Gerald W, R.N., Chief Nursing Officer, Baylor Scott & White Medical Center – Temple, Temple, TX, p. A639

BRYANT, Justin O., Chief Operating Officer, Grandview Medical Center, Birmingham, AL, p. A14

BRYANT, Karen, Chief Support Services Officer, Prowers Medical Center, Lamar, CO, p. A103

BRYANT, Kay, Executive Director Human Resources, Saint Clare'S Denville Hospital, Denville, NJ, p. A404

BRYANT, Lidia, Director Human Resources, Ottumwa Regional Health Center, Ottumwa, IA, p. A228

BRYANT, Lisa G, Director Human Resources, Anmed Health Cannon, Pickens, SC, p. A556

BRYANT, Marcia, R.N., Vice President, Clinical Operations, The Outer Banks Hospital, Nags Head, NC, p. A459

BRYANT, Maureen A., President, Northwestern Medicine Delnor Hospital, Geneva, IL, p. A184

BRYANT, Pam, Director Human Resources, Helen Keller Hospital, Sheffield, AL, p. A23

BRYANT, Ronald
   President, Baystate Franklin Medical Center, Greenfield, MA, p. A299
   President, Baystate Noble Hospital, Westfield, MA, p. A304

BRYANT, Rusty, Director Information Technology, Drew Memorial Health System, Monticello, AR, p. A46

BRYANT, Samantha, Chief Nursing Officer, Rhea Medical Center, Dayton, TN, p. A569

BRYANT, William, Chief Executive Officer, Lifecare Hospital Of Dayton, Miamisburg, OH, p. A487

BRYANT–MOBLEY, Phyllis, M.D., Director Medical Services, William S. Hall Psychiatric Institute, Columbia, SC, p. A551

BRYCE, Keith, Vice President Finance and Chief Financial Officer, Mt. Graham Regional Medical Center, Safford, AZ, p. A35

BRYER, Alex, Director Information Management, Los Robles Hospital And Medical Center, Thousand Oaks, CA, p. A91

BRYNER, Jennifer, Director Nursing, Petersburg Medical Center, Petersburg, AK, p. A27

BRYSON, Kellie, Director Human Resources, The Hospital At Westlake Medical Center, Austin, TX, p. A586

BRZEZINSKI, Christina, Chief Nursing Officer, Coastal Carolina Hospital, Hardeeville, SC, p. A554

BUCCELLATO, Vito, Chief Executive Officer, Hackensack Meridian Health Jersey Shore University Medical Center, Neptune, NJ, p. A408

BUCCI, Annette, Vice President Human Resources, Burke Rehabilitation Hospital, White Plains, NY, p. A447

BUCCIARELLI, Brant, Chief Information Officer, Riverview Health, Noblesville, IN, p. A213

BUCCOLO, Martin A., Chief Executive Officer, Four Winds Hospital, Katonah, NY, p. A429

BUCH, Naishadh, Chief Operating Officer, Lompoc Valley Medical Center, Lompoc, CA, p. A64

BUCHANAN, Anna
   Vice President Finance and Chief Financial Officer, Berkeley Medical Center, Martinsburg, WV, p. A687
   Vice President Finance and Chief Financial Officer, Jefferson Medical Center, Ranson, WV, p. A689

BUCHANAN, Donna, Director Nursing, Stroud Regional Medical Center, Stroud, OK, p. A508

BUCHANAN, Jean, Director Human Resources, Broughton Hospital, Morganton, NC, p. A458

BUCHANAN, Kyle, President, Helen Keller Hospital, Sheffield, AL, p. A23

BUCHANAN, Robert, Chief Information Officer, Anna Jaques Hospital, Newburyport, MA, p. A301

BUCHANAN, Toni, Chief Financial Officer, Unicoi County Memorial Hospital, Erwin, TN, p. A569

BUCHANAN, Tracy, Chief Executive Officer and President, Carepartners Health Services, Asheville, NC, p. A449

BUCHART, Phyllis, Chief Operating Officer, Marina Del Rey Hospital, Marina Del Rey, CA, p. A71

BUCHE, Karen, Chief Human Resource Officer, Douglas County Community Mental Health Center, Omaha, NE, p. A389

BUCHELE, Paula, Chief Human Resources, Bay Pines Veterans Affairs Healthcare System, Bay Pines, FL, p. A117

BUCHER, Ben
   Chief Executive Officer, Towner County Medical Center, Cando, ND, p. A465
   Interim Chief Executive Officer, Mountrail County Medical Center, Stanley, ND, p. A469

BUCHHEIT, Anne, Coordinator Mental Health Local Information Systems, Buffalo Psychiatric Center, Buffalo, NY, p. A424

BUCHHEIT, Joe, Chief Financial Officer, Our Lady Of Bellefonte Hospital, Ashland, KY, p. A249

BUCHHOLZ, Kari, Director Health Information Management, Wishek Community Hospital And Clinics, Wishek, ND, p. A470

BUCHNESS, Michael P., M.D., Director Medical, Deer'S Head Hospital Center, Salisbury, MD, p. A293

BUCK, Catherine, President, Froedtert And The Medical College Of Wisconsin Froedtert Hospital, Milwaukee, WI, p. A701

BUCK, Linda K, Vice President Human Resources, Unitypoint Health – Proctor, Peoria, IL, p. A193

BUCK, Nathan, R.N., Nursing Manager, Mountain River Birthing And Surgery Center, Blackfoot, ID, p. A167

BUCK, Phylis, Controller, Encompass Health Rehabilitation Hospital Of Texarkana, Texarkana, TX, p. A640

BUCK, Shelly, Chief Nursing Executive and Chief Operating Officer, Bon Secours Baltimore Health System, Baltimore, MD, p. A286

BUCK, Tavia, Chief Nursing Officer, Roper St. Francis Mount Pleasant Hospital, Mount Pleasant, SC, p. A555

BUCKHOY, Sandra, Chief Clinical Officer, Kindred Hospital Chicago–Northlake, Northlake, IL, p. A191

BUCKLEY, David, Acting Chief Information Management Services, Oklahoma City Veterans Affairs Medical Center, Oklahoma City, OK, p. A504

BUCKLEY, John, M.D., President Medical Staff, Vibra Hospital Of Denver, Thornton, CO, p. A106

BUCKLEY, Kalvin, Director Information Systems, Woodland Heights Medical Center, Lufkin, TX, p. A622

BUCKLEY, Karen L, R.N., Chief Nursing Officer, Community Behavioral Health Center, Fresno, CA, p. A59

BUCKLEY, Martha, Chief Medical Informatics Officer, Fairfield Medical Center, Lancaster, OH, p. A485

BUCKMINSTER, Joe, Manager Information Technology, Community Medical Center, Inc., Falls City, NE, p. A384

BUCKNER, Marlys, Chief Nursing Officer, Cox Barton County Memorial Hospital, Lamar, MO, p. A364

BUCKNER, Twila, R.N., Chief Nursing Officer, Cass Regional Medical Center, Harrisonville, MO, p. A361

BUCKWORTH, Albert Bennett, Human Resources Administrative Director, Primary Children'S Hospital, Salt Lake City, UT, p. A652

BUDA, Jeff, Chief Information Officer, Floyd Medical Center, Rome, GA, p. A159

BUDD, Edward, President and Chief Executive Officer, Thorek Memorial Hospital, Chicago, IL, p. A180

BUDZINSKY, Chris
   Vice President Nursing and Chief Nursing Officer Alexian Brothers Acute Care Ministries, Amita Health Hoffman Estates, Hoffman Estates, IL, p. A186
   Vice President, Nursing and Chief Nursing Officer, Amita Health Elk Grove Village, Elk Grove Village, IL, p. A182

BUE, Cheryl, Health Information Transcriptionist, Faulkton Area Medical Center, Faulkton, SD, p. A560

BUEHLER, Bonnie, Chief Information Officer, St. Mary Medical Center, Langhorne, PA, p. A529

BUEHRLE, Jeff, Chief Financial Officer, Banner – University Medical Center South, Tucson, AZ, p. A37

BUELL, Jack, Director Information Services, Sutter Lakeside Hospital, Lakeport, CA, p. A64

BUER, Shane, Vice President, Human Resources, Mercyone Clinton Medical Center, Clinton, IA, p. A219

BUFFENBARGER, Andrew, Chief Compliance Officer, Kirby Medical Center, Monticello, IL, p. A190

BUFFINGTON, John, Chief Operating Officer, San Juan Regional Medical Center, Farmington, NM, p. A418

BUFFINGTON, Mike, Manager Information Technology, Kansas Medical Center, Andover, KS, p. A232

BUFKIN, Ben, Human Resource Director, Bolivar Medical Center, Cleveland, MS, p. A346

BUGALLO–MUROS, Mariana, Vice President Chief Human Resources Officer, H. Lee Moffitt Cancer Center And Research Institute, Tampa, FL, p. A141

BUGAYONG, Carol, Human Resources Director, Encompass Health Rehabilitation Hospital Of Tallahassee, Tallahassee, FL, p. A140

BUGNA, Eric, M.D., Chief of Staff, Eastern Plumas Health Care, Portola, CA, p. A79

BUHLKE, Brian, M.D., Medical Director, Genoa Medical Facilities, Genoa, NE, p. A385

BUI, Steven, M.D., Chief of Staff, Orange County Global Medical Center, Inc., Santa Ana, CA, p. A88

BUIT, Timothy, Executive Vice President and Chief Financial Officer, Bellevue Hospital, Bellevue, OH, p. A473

BULAU, Chris, Manager Information Technology, Ridgeview Sibley Medical Center, Arlington, MN, p. A327

BULEN, Susan R., M.D., Medical Director, Encompass Health Rehabilitation Hospital Of Northwest Tucson, Tucson, AZ, p. A37

BULFIN, Joey, R.N., Interim Chief Executive Officer, St. Mary'S Medical Center, West Palm Beach, FL, p. A144
BULLARD, Brandon
Chief Financial Officer, Bailey Medical Center, Owasso, OK, p. A506
Chief Financial Officer, Baptist Health – Fort Smith, Fort Smith, AR, p. A42
Chief Financial Officer, Hillcrest Hospital Claremore, Claremore, OK, p. A498
Interim Chief Executive Officer, Baptist Health – Fort Smith, Fort Smith, AR, p. A42
Interim Chief Executive Officer, Baptist Health – Van Buren, Van Buren, AR, p. A49
BULLARD, John, Director Information Technology, St. Mary'S Hospital And Medical Center, Grand Junction, CO, p. A101
BULLARD, Patrick, Chief Financial Officer, Fayetteville Veterans Affairs Medical Center, Fayetteville, NC, p. A454
BULLINGTON, Benjamin P, M.D., Chief of Staff, Pioneer Medical Center, Big Timber, MT, p. A374
BULLINGTON, Gina, Chief Nursing Officer, Tristar Horizon Medical Center, Dickson, TN, p. A569
BULLOCK, David, Director Information Services, Northwest Medical Center, Tucson, AZ, p. A37
BULLOCK, Deann, M.D., Chief Medical Officer, Nashville General Hospital, Nashville, TN, p. A576
BULLOCK, Lance, M.D., Medical Director, St. James Behavioral Health Hospital, Gonzales, LA, p. A267
BULLOCK, Scott, Director Information Systems, Barstow Community Hospital, Barstow, CA, p. A52
BULMAN, Laurie, Director Human Resources, Winneshiek Medical Center, Decorah, IA, p. A221
BULMASH, Jack, M.D., Chief of Staff, Edward Hines, Jr. Veterans Affairs Hospital, Hines, IL, p. A185
BUMAN, Karen, MSN, Chief Nursing Executive, Myrtue Medical Center, Harlan, IA, p. A224
BUMANN, Tim, D.O., Chief of Staff, Abilene Regional Medical Center, Abilene, TX, p. A581
BUMBAUGH, Christopher, Executive Director Human Resource and Organizational Development, Western Maryland Regional Medical Center, Cumberland, MD, p. A290
BUMGARDNER, Charles
Chief Information Officer, Southeast Georgia Health System Brunswick Campus, Brunswick, GA, p. A148
Director, Southeast Georgia Health System Camden Campus, Saint Marys, GA, p. A159
BUMGARNER, William J., President, Spencer Hospital, Spencer, IA, p. A230
BUMP, Cathy, Interim Chief Executive Officer, Methodist Ambulatory Surgery Hospital – Northwest, San Antonio, TX, p. A634
BUMP, Cathy, R.N., Chief Nursing Officer, Methodist Ambulatory Surgery Hospital – Northwest, San Antonio, TX, p. A634
BUNCH, David V., President and Chief Administrative Officer, Cumberland Medical Center, Crossville, TN, p. A568
BUNCH, Elicia, Chief Executive Officer, Centennial Peaks Hospital, Louisville, CO, p. A104
BUNCH, Jimm, President and Chief Executive Officer, Adventhealth Hendersonville, Hendersonville, NC, p. A456
BUNCH, Kim, Director Information Technology, Marshall Medical Center North, Guntersville, AL, p. A19
BUNCH, Mark, Director Finance, Othello Community Hospital, Othello, WA, p. A676
BUNCH, Mike, Executive Vice President, Chief Operating Officer and Chief Financial Officer, Kershawhealth, Camden, SC, p. A549
BUNCH, Rita A., M.P.H., FACHE, Vice President of Operations, Sentara Careplex Hospital, Hampton, VA, p. A660
BUNCH, Terri, MSN, R.N., MSN, Chief Nursing Officer, White River Medical Center, Batesville, AR, p. A39
BUND, Linda, Chief Information Officer and Director Education, Brookdale Hospital Medical Center, New York, NY, p. A432
BUNDT, Thomas S., Commanding Officer, Madigan Army Medical Center, Tacoma, WA, p. A680
BUNDY, Michael N.
Chief Operating Officer, Prisma Health Baptist Hospital, Columbia, SC, p. A551
Chief Operating Officer, Prisma Health Baptist Parkridge Hospital, Columbia, SC, p. A551
BUNKER, Marla, Vice President Nursing and Chief Operating Officer, War Memorial Hospital, Sault Sainte Marie, MI, p. A322
BUNN, Barry, M.D., Chief of Staff, Vidant Edgecombe Hospital, Tarboro, NC, p. A463
BUNNELL, Emily Ann, Chief Nurse Executive, Senior Director of Acute Care, Upmc Cole, Coudersport, PA, p. A523
BUNNER, Blake, Chief Executive Officer, Healthsouth Deaconess Rehabilitation Hospital, Evansville, IN, p. A203
BUNSELMEYER, Becky, Director Information Services, Memorial Hospital, Chester, IL, p. A176
BUNTEN, Sherry, Director Patient Care Services, Aspirus Langlade Hospital, Antigo, WI, p. A691
BUNTING, Katherine, Esq, Chief Executive Officer, Fairfield Memorial Hospital, Fairfield, IL, p. A183
BUNTYN, Diane, MSN, R.N., Vice President Patient Care Services, Southeast Alabama Medical Center, Dothan, AL, p. A17
BUNYARD, Steve
President, Ohiohealth Dublin Methodist Hospital, Dublin, OH, p. A482
President, Ohiohealth Grady Memorial Hospital, Delaware, OH, p. A482
BUONGIORNO, Michael J
Executive Vice President Finance and Chief Financial Officer, Bryn Mawr Hospital, Bryn Mawr, PA, p. A521
Vice President Finance, Lankenau Medical Center, Wynnewood, PA, p. A546
BUPP, Steven, M.D., Medical Director, Sonora Behavioral Health Hospital, Tucson, AZ, p. A38
BURBANK, Jimmy, Chief Information Officer, U. S. Public Health Service Indian Hospital, Crownpoint, NM, p. A417
BURCH, Debra, Chief Nursing Officer, Burke Medical Center, Waynesboro, GA, p. A163
BURCH, Lee, Director Management Information Systems, Bayfront Health Brooksville, Brooksville, FL, p. A119
BURCH, Todd, Chief Executive Officer, Aspirus Riverview Hospital And Clinics, Inc., Wisconsin Rapids, WI, p. A709
BURCHELL, Pam, Director Human Resources, Lawnwood Regional Medical Center & Heart Institute, Fort Pierce, FL, p. A123
BURCHETT, Claudia L, R.N., Vice President of Patient Services, Southern Ohio Medical Center, Portsmouth, OH, p. A490
BURCHETT, Travis, Troop Commander Human Resources, Colonel Florence A. Blanchfield Army Community Hospital, Fort Campbell, KY, p. A252
BURCZEUSKI, Jason
Controller, Arms Acres, Carmel, NY, p. A425
Controller, Conifer Park, Glenville, NY, p. A428
BURD, David, Chief Executive Officer, Thayer County Health Services, Hebron, NE, p. A386
BURDEN, Jennifer, Human Resources Director, Tristar Centennial Medical Center, Nashville, TN, p. A577
BURDEN, Matthew J., President and Chief Executive Officer, Porter–Starke Services, Valparaiso, IN, p. A216
BURDETTE, Mario, Chief Nursing Officer, East Georgia Regional Medical Center, Statesboro, GA, p. A161
BURDICK, Ginny
Senior Vice President and Chief Human Resources Officer, Clovis Community Medical Center, Clovis, CA, p. A55
Vice President Human Resources, Community Behavioral Health Center, Fresno, CA, p. A59
Vice President Human Resources, Community Regional Medical Center, Fresno, CA, p. A59
BURDICK, Hoyt J, M.D., Vice President Medical Affairs, Cabell Huntington Hospital, Huntington, WV, p. A685
BURGE, Eugene H., Jr, Chief Executive Officer, Savoy Medical Center, Mamou, LA, p. A273
BURGER, Janice, Chief Executive, Providence St. Vincent Medical Center, Portland, OR, p. A517
BURGESS, Angela, Chief Information Officer, Randolph Hospital, Asheboro, NC, p. A449
BURGESS, Daniel, Chief Information Officer, Mainegeneral Medical Center, Augusta, ME, p. A281
BURGESS, Deborah, R.N., Chief Nursing Officer, Pam Specialty Hospital Of Lufkin, Lufkin, TX, p. A622
BURGESS, John, Director Information Services, Hocking Valley Community Hospital, Logan, OH, p. A485
BURGESS, Steven, Administrator Human Resources, Henrico Doctors' Hospital, Richmond, VA, p. A666
BURGHART, Steven, President, Ssm Cardinal Glennon Children'S Hospital, Saint Louis, MO, p. A370
BURGOS, Odette, Supervisor Human Resources, San Jorge Children'S Hospital, Santurce, PR, p. A719
BURGUILLOS, Richard, Chief Financial Officer, Careone At Raritan Bay Medical Center, Perth Amboy, NJ, p. A410
BURGUS, Aurelis, Nursing Director, Ryder Memorial Hospital, Humacao, PR, p. A716
BURICK, Adam, M.D.
Chief Medical Officer, Pam Specialty Hospital Of Covington, Covington, LA, p. A266
Chief Medical Officer, Pam Specialty Hospital Of Victoria North, Victoria, TX, p. A643
Chief Medical Officer, Pam Specialty Hospital Of Victoria South, Victoria, TX, p. A644
BURICK, Marsha, Chief Financial Officer, Central Florida Behavioral Hospital, Orlando, FL, p. A134
BURINGRUD, Duane, M.D., Chief Medical and Quality Officer, Palomar Medical Center, Escondido, CA, p. A57
BURISH, Brent, Chief Executive Officer, St. Cloud Regional Medical Center, Saint Cloud, FL, p. A138
BURK, Kaye, Administrator, Noland Hospital Dothan, Dothan, AL, p. A17
BURK, Thomas J, Chief Operating Officer, Danville State Hospital, Danville, PA, p. A523
BURKE, Brian, M.D., President Medical Staff, Fairview Hospital, Great Barrington, MA, p. A299
BURKE, Brigid, Chief Financial Officer, Pondera Medical Center, Conrad, MT, p. A375
BURKE, Christopher D., Chief Executive Officer, Cedar Springs Hospital, Colorado Springs, CO, p. A97
BURKE, David J, Director Finance and Chief Financial Officer, Nantucket Cottage Hospital, Nantucket, MA, p. A301
BURKE, Dennis E., President and Chief Executive Officer, Good Shepherd Health Care System, Hermiston, OR, p. A513
BURKE, Dorothy, Chief Financial Officer, Southeast Colorado Hospital District, Springfield, CO, p. A105
BURKE, Greg, M.D., Medical Director, Geisinger Encompass Health Rehabilitation Hospital, Danville, PA, p. A523
BURKE, Jack J, MS, R.N., Chief Operating Officer and Chief Nursing Officer, Antelope Valley Hospital, Lancaster, CA, p. A64
BURKE, James, M.D.
Senior Vice President and Chief Medical Officer, Honorhealth Scottsdale Osborn Medical Center, Scottsdale, AZ, p. A35
Senior Vice President and Chief Medical Officer, Honorhealth Scottsdale Shea Medical Center, Scottsdale, AZ, p. A35
BURKE, James M., Vice President Finance, Chief Nursing Executive Medical Surgical Hospitals, Kent County Memorial Hospital, Warwick, RI, p. A548
BURKE, Jeff, Chief Information Officer, Bon Secours–Richmond Community Hospital, Richmond, VA, p. A666
BURKE, John, Chief Financial Officer, Nyack Hospital, Nyack, NY, p. A440
BURKE, Julie, Director Human Resources, New England Sinai Hospital And Rehabilitation Center, Stoughton, MA, p. A304
BURKE, Marsha, Senior Vice President and Chief Financial Officer, Wellstar Windy Hill Hospital, Marietta, GA, p. A157
BURKE, Michael, Senior Vice President and Corporate Chief Financial Officer, Brookdale Hospital Medical Center, New York, NY, p. A432
BURKE, Paul, Administrator, Schleicher County Medical Center, Eldorado, TX, p. A603
BURKE, Rebecca, R.N., MS, Senior Vice President and Chief Nursing Officer, Kent County Memorial Hospital, Warwick, RI, p. A548
BURKE, Richard Aron, M.D., Chief Medical Officer, Community Hospital–Fairfax, Fairfax, MO, p. A360
BURKE, Rose, Associate Director Patient Care Services, Marion Veterans Affairs Medical Center, Marion, IL, p. A188
BURKE, Ryan, Vice President, Human Resources, Citrus Valley Medical Center–Inter Community Campus, Covina, CA, p. A56
BURKE, Timothy, M.D., Medical Director, The Brook Hospital – Kmi, Louisville, KY, p. A257
BURKEL, Greg, Chief Financial Officer, Regional Health Services Of Howard County, Cresco, IA, p. A220
BURKEL, Gregory, Chief Financial Officer, Mitchell County Regional Health Center, Osage, IA, p. A228
BURKET, Mark, Chief Executive Officer, Platte Health Center Avera, Platte, SD, p. A562
BURKETT, Doug, Manager Information Technology, Regional Medical Center Of Central Alabama, Greenville, AL, p. A19
BURKETT, Eric, M.D., Vice President Medical Affairs, Monmouth Medical Center, Long Branch Campus, Long Branch, NJ, p. A407
BURKETT, Evan, Chief Human Resource Officer, Sanford Usd Medical Center, Sioux Falls, SD, p. A564
BURKEY, Brent, President and Chief Executive Officer, Fisher–Titus Medical Center, Norwalk, OH, p. A488
BURKEY, Kathleen, R.N., MSN, Vice President, Patient Care Service and Chief Nursing Officer, Grand View Health, Sellersville, PA, p. A541
BURKHARDT, Raye M., Chief Nurse Executive, Kaiser Permanente Fontana Medical Center, Fontana, CA, p. A58
BURKHART, Brad, Assistant Administrator, Harlan Arh Hospital, Harlan, KY, p. A253
BURKHART, Steven, M.D., Chief Medical Officer, Crittenden County Hospital, Marion, KY, p. A257
BURKHART, Tracy, Vice President Information Services, St. Luke'S Sacred Heart Campus, Allentown, PA, p. A519
BURKHOLDER, Adrienne, Director Human Resources, Amg Specialty Hospital–Wichita, Wichita, KS, p. A247
BURKS, Felicia, Chief Financial Officer, U. S. Air Force Regional Hospital, Elmendorf Afb, AK, p. A26
BURKS, Matt, Director Information Technology, Unity Medical Center, Manchester, TN, p. A573

BURKS, Melvin, Chief Executive Officer, Hamilton Center, Terre Haute, IN, p. A215

BURKS, Tami
Chief Fiscal Services, Iraan General Hospital, Iraan, TX, p. A615
Comptroller, Rankin County Hospital District, Rankin, TX, p. A630

BURLESON, Linda, Administrative Secretary, Clay County Memorial Hospital, Henrietta, TX, p. A610

BURLESON, Stan, M.D., Chief Medical Staff, Dewitt Hospital, Dewitt, AR, p. A41

BURLING, Chris, M.D., Chief of Staff, Titus Regional Medical Center, Mount Pleasant, TX, p. A625

BURLINGAME DEAL, Penney, Chief Executive Officer, Onslow Memorial Hospital, Jacksonville, NC, p. A457

BURMAN, Don
Director, Veterans Affairs Nebraska–Western Iowa Health Care System – Lincoln, Lincoln, NE, p. A387
Director, Veterans Affairs Nebraska–Western Iowa Health Care System, Omaha, NE, p. A390

BURMESTER, Mark A, Vice President Strategy and Communications, Kaiser Sunnyside Medical Center, Clackamas, OR, p. A512

BURNAM, Gregg, Chief Information Officer and Manager Business Office, Mangum Regional Medical Center, Mangum, OK, p. A501

BURNELL, Lori, R.N., Ph.D., Senior Vice President and Chief Nursing Officer, Valley Presbyterian Hospital, Los Angeles, CA, p. A70

BURNES BOLTON, Linda, Dr.PH, R.N., Chief Health Equity Officer, Cedars–Sinai Medical Center, Los Angeles, CA, p. A66

BURNETT, Anthony, M.D., Medical Director, Julian F. Keith Alcohol And Drug Abuse Treatment Center, Black Mountain, NC, p.A450

BURNETT, Brad, Chief Financial Officer, Heart Of Texas Memorial Hospital, Brady, TX, p. A589

BURNETT, Brenda, R.N., Vice President Patient Care Services and Chief Nursing Officer, Titusville Area Hospital, Titusville, PA, p. A542

BURNETT, Cindi, Chief Human Resources Officer, Madison County Memorial Hospital, Madison, FL, p. A128

BURNETT, Mark, President and Chief Executive Officer, Scott County Hospital, Scott City, KS, p. A245

BURNETT, Michael, Chief Executive Officer, Piedmont Athens Regional Medical Center, Athens, GA, p. A145

BURNETT, Rob, Director Human Resources, Jordan Valley Medical Center West Valley Campus, West Valley City, UT, p. A653

BURNETT, Tasha, Director of Nursing, Falls Community Hospital And Clinic, Marlin, TX, p. A623

BURNETTE, Linda, R.N., Chief Nursing Officer, Southern Virginia Regional Medical Center, Emporia, VA, p. A658

BURNETTE, Peg, Chief Financial Officer, Denver Health, Denver, CO, p. A98

BURNETTE, Sheri, Chief Executive Officer and Administrator, Cornerstone Hospital Of Bossier City, Bossier City, LA, p. A265

BURNETTE, W Scott., Chief Executive Officer, Vcu Health Community Memorial Hospital, South Hill, VA, p. A667

BURNEY, Sibte, M.D., Senior Vice President Medical Affairs and Chief Medical Officer, Brookdale Hospital Medical Center, New York, NY, p. A432

BURNHAM, Sharon, Director of Nursing, Simpson General Hospital, Mendenhall, MS, p. A351

BURNS, Barry, Vice President, Methodist Ambulatory Surgery Hospital – Northwest, San Antonio, TX, p. A634

BURNS, Becky L, Manager Health Information Management, Ellinwood District Hospital, Ellinwood, KS, p. A234

BURNS, Bruce R., Chief Financial Officer, Concord Hospital, Concord, NH, p. A399

BURNS, Helen K, Ph.D., R.N.
Senior Vice President and Chief Nursing Officer, Excela Frick Hospital, Mount Pleasant, PA, p. A532
Senior Vice President and Chief Nursing Officer, Excela Health Westmoreland Hospital, Greensburg, PA, p. A526
Senior Vice President and Chief Nursing Officer, Excela Latrobe Area Hospital, Latrobe, PA, p. A529

BURNS, Helene M, MSN, R.N., Chief Nursing Executive, Jefferson Stratford Hospital, Stratford, NJ, p. A413

BURNS, Jeff, Manager of Information Technology, Mary Free Bed Rehabilitation Hospital, Grand Rapids, MI, p. A312

BURNS, Jon P
Chief Information Officer, University Of Maryland Medical Center, Baltimore, MD, p. A287
Senior Vice President and Chief Information Officer, University Of Maryland Baltimore Washington Medical Center, Glen Burnie, MD, p. A291
Senior Vice President and Chief Information Officer, University Of Maryland Medical Center Midtown Campus, Baltimore, MD, p. A287

BURNS, Katherine, Vice President Human Resources, High Point Medical Center, High Point, NC, p. A456

BURNS, Kathryn I., R.N., Director of Nursing, Medicine Lodge Memorial Hospital, Medicine Lodge, KS, p. A241

BURNS, Larry P, Chief Operating Officer, Yavapai Regional Medical Center, Prescott, AZ, p. A35

BURNS, Lori, Administrator, Victor Valley Global Medical Center, Victorville, CA, p. A94

BURNS, Patricia, Chief Executive Officer, Jfk Medical Center North Campus, West Palm Beach, FL, p. A144

BURNS, Patrick, Vice President Finance, Acmh Hospital, Kittanning, PA, p. A528

BURNS, Rhonda, Director Human Resources, Caldwell Medical Center, Princeton, KY, p. A260

BURNS, Steve, Chief Operating Officer, Cumberland County Hospital, Burkesville, KY, p. A250

BURNS, Steven, Director Fiscal Services, Summit Behavioral Healthcare, Cincinnati, OH, p. A476

BURNS, Terry M., President, Kettering Medical Center, Kettering, OH, p. A485

BURNS, Tom, M.D., Chief of Staff, The Hospital At Westlake Medical Center, Austin, TX, p. A586

BURNS–CHISTENSON, Katherine, Human Resource Director, Grand Itasca Clinic And Hospital, Grand Rapids, MN, p. A333

BURNS–TISDALE, Susan, Senior Vice President Clinical Operations, Interim CNO, Exeter Hospital, Exeter, NH, p. A400

BURRELL, Carol H.
Chief Executive Officer, Northeast Georgia Medical Center Braselton, Braselton, GA, p. A148
Chief Executive Officer, Northeast Georgia Medical Center, Gainesville, GA, p. A154

BURRESS, Lori, Vice President Patient Services and Chief Nursing Officer, Mt. Graham Regional Medical Center, Safford, AZ, p. A35

BURRIS, Bradley D., Chief Executive Officer, Pipestone County Medical Center Avera, Pipestone, MN, p. A338

BURRIS, Don, Chief Executive Officer, Foundation Surgical Hospital Of El Paso, El Paso, TX, p. A602

BURRIS, Lisa, Director Human Resources, Southern Indiana Rehabilitation Hospital, New Albany, IN, p. A212

BURRIS, Olga, Human Resource/Executive Assistant, North Oak Regional Medical Center, Senatobia, MS, p. A354

BURRISS, Jessica, Chief Financial Officer, Encompass Health Rehabilitation Hospital Of Columbia, Columbia, SC, p. A551

BURRISS, Stephen W., President, Unc Rex Health Care, Raleigh, NC, p. A460

BURROUGHS, Shawn, Director of Information Services, Northeastern Vermont Regional Hospital, Saint Johnsbury, VT, p. A655

BURROUGHS, Steven, Chief Financial Officer, Palms West Hospital, Loxahatchee, FL, p. A128

BURROUGHS, Susan R, FACHE, Chief Operating Officer, Kershawhealth, Camden, SC, p. A549

BURROUGHS, Valentine, M.D., Chief Medical Officer, East Orange General Hospital, East Orange, NJ, p. A405

BURROWS, Susan M, Vice President Human Resources, Martin Luther King, Jr. Community Hospital, Los Angeles, CA, p. A68

BURRUS, Gary, Director Information Technology, Winner Regional Healthcare Center, Winner, SD, p. A565

BURT, Alan, Director Information Services, Sunrise Hospital And Medical Center, Las Vegas, NV, p. A396

BURT, Linda K, Corporate Vice President Finance, Nebraska Methodist Hospital, Omaha, NE, p. A389

BURT, Noel F, Ph.D., Chief Human Resources Officer, Moses H. Cone Memorial Hospital, Greensboro, NC, p. A455

BURT, Suzanne M., Director Human Resources, Mercyone Waterloo Medical Center, Waterloo, IA, p. A231

BURTCH, Gloria, Director Human Resources, Cornerstone Of Medical Arts Center Hospital, Fresh Meadows, NY, p. A428

BURTCHELL, Scott, Director Information Systems, Northern Light Maine Coast Hospital, Ellsworth, ME, p. A283

BURTON, Angela, Privacy Officer, Wayne County Hospital, Monticello, KY, p. A258

BURTON, Charles, Chief Human Resources, Carl R. Darnall Army Medical Center, Fort Hood, TX, p. A604

BURTON, James, Vice President and Chief Information Officer, Valley Health, Valley Health Shenandoah Memorial Hospital, Woodstock, VA, p. A669

BURTON, Luanne, Director Human Resources, Encompass Health Rehabilitation Hospital Of Columbia, Columbia, SC, p. A551

BURTON, Robert, Manager Finance, Utah State Hospital, Provo, UT, p. A650

BURTON, Stacey R., Director Human Resources, Muscogee Creek Nation Medical Center, Okmulgee, OK, p. A506

BURY, Peter, Vice President Finance, Ohiohealth Riverside Methodist Hospital, Columbus, OH, p. A480

BUSBY, Jay, M.D., President Medical Staff, Franklin Medical Center, Winnsboro, LA, p. A280

BUSCH, Michael D
Executive Vice President and Chief Operating Officer, Excela Frick Hospital, Mount Pleasant, PA, p. A532
Executive Vice President and Chief Operating Officer, Excela Health Westmoreland Hospital, Greensburg, PA, p. A526
Executive Vice President and Chief Operating Officer, Excela Latrobe Area Hospital, Latrobe, PA, p. A529

BUSCH, Michael D.
Executive Vice President and Chief Operating Officer, Excela Frick Hospital, Mount Pleasant, PA, p. A532
Executive Vice President and Chief Operating Officer, Excela Latrobe Area Hospital, Latrobe, PA, p. A529

BUSCH, Rebecca, Chief Financial Officer, Spooner Health, Spooner, WI, p. A705

BUSCH, Steve, Chief Operating Officer, Midwest Medical Center, Galena, IL, p. A183

BUSH, Amy, Vice President Operations, Upmc Mckeesport, Mckeesport, PA, p. A531

BUSH, Bruce A, M.D., Senior Vice President Medical Affairs, Indiana Regional Medical Center, Indiana, PA, p. A528

BUSH, Doug, President, Promedica Defiance Regional Hospital, Defiance, OH, p. A482

BUSH, Michael, M.D., Chief Medical Officer, Holy Rosary Healthcare, Miles City, MT, p. A378

BUSH, Stephen, Chief Financial Officer, Tmc Healthcare, Tucson, AZ, p. A38

BUSH, Steven, Chief Medical Officer, Crossing Rivers Health Medical Center, Prairie Du Chien, WI, p. A704

BUSH, Wayne, M.D., Chief of Staff, Tristar Greenview Regional Hospital, Bowling Green, KY, p. A250

BUSHART, Phyllis, R.N., Chief Operating Officer, Providence Tarzana Medical Center, Los Angeles, CA, p. A69

BUSHART, Stephanie, Chief Financial Officer, Ochsner Medical Center – Baton Rouge, Baton Rouge, LA, p. A263

BUSHELL, Michael, President, Saint Anne'S Hospital, Fall River, MA, p. A298

BUSHEY, Dale, Chief Financial Officer, Oss Orthopaedic Hospital, York, PA, p. A546

BUSHMAN, Jerry, Chief Nursing Officer, Brigham City Community Hospital, Brigham City, UT, p. A647

BUSHNELL, Andrew, M.D., Interim Chief Medical Officer, Rome Memorial Hospital, Rome, NY, p. A443

BUSHNELL, Kim, MSN, R.N., Vice President, Patient Care Services, Mercy Medical Center, Baltimore, MD, p. A288

BUSINELLE, Denise, Chief Financial Officer, Avala, Covington, LA, p. A266

BUSKEY, Irene, Director Human Resources, Southside Regional Medical Center, Petersburg, VA, p. A665

BUSS, Theresa L, Regional Vice President Human Resources, Windham Hospital, Willimantic, CT, p. A112

BUSSELL, Walter
Chief Financial Officer, Memorial Hospital West, Pembroke Pines, FL, p. A136
Chief Financial Officer, Memorial Regional Hospital, Hollywood, FL, p. A124

BUSSIERE, Mark, Administrator Human Resources, New Hampshire Hospital, Concord, NH, p. A399

BUSSLER, David, Chief Information Officer, Sheridan Community Hospital, Sheridan, MI, p. A322

BUSTLE, John P., Chief Executive Officer, Bates County Memorial Hospital, Butler, MO, p. A357

BUTCHER, Gina, Chief Financial Officer, Garden City Hospital, Garden City, MI, p. A312

BUTCHER, Kay, Director Health Information Management, Stonewall Jackson Memorial Hospital, Weston, WV, p. A690

BUTE, Phil, Manager Information Technology, Clay County Hospital, Flora, IL, p. A183

BUTERBAUGH, Roger W, Chief Human Resources Officer, Charlie Norwood Veterans Affairs Medical Center, Augusta, GA, p. A147

BUTKER, Jeff, Chief Information Officer, Sovah Health–Martinsville, Martinsville, VA, p. A662

BUTLER, Anita M., Chief Executive Officer, Spartanburg Hospital For Restorative Care, Spartanburg, SC, p. A557

BUTLER, Brad, Network Administrator, Cox Barton County Memorial Hospital, Lamar, MO, p. A364

BUTLER, Carol A, R.N., MSN, VP Patient Care Services & Operations, St. Anthony North Health Campus, Westminster, CO, p. A106

BUTLER, Catherine, M.D., Chief Medical Staff, Hancock County Health System, Britt, IA, p. A218

BUTLER, Chris, Chief Information Officer, Monmouth Medical Center, Long Branch Campus, Long Branch, NJ, p. A407

BUTLER, Dana, M.D., Medical Director, Sunrise Canyon Hospital, Lubbock, TX, p. A622

BUTLER, David, President and Chief Executive Officer, Adventist Healthtillamook, Tillamook, OR, p. A518

BUTLER, Debby
Director Human Resources, Wadley Regional Medical Center At Hope, Hope, AR, p. A43
Director Human Resources, Wadley Regional Medical Center, Texarkana, TX, p. A640
BUTLER, Keith L., Chief Executive Officer, Iraan General Hospital, Iraan, TX, p. A615
BUTLER, LaDonna, Chief Nursing Officer, Encompass Health Rehabilitation Hospital Of Tustin, Tustin, CA, p. A92
BUTLER, Linda H., M.D., Chief Medical Officer, Unc Rex Health Care, Raleigh, NC, p. A460
BUTLER, Margaret, Vice President Human Resources, Abbott Northwestern Hospital, Minneapolis, MN, p. A335
BUTLER, Margaret E, Vice President Chief Operating Officer, Seton Northwest Hospital, Ascension Seton Northwest, Austin, TX, p. A584
BUTLER, Monique, Chief Medical Officer, Swedish Medical Center, Englewood, CO, p. A100
BUTLER, Randy, Chief Financial Officer, West Florida Hospital, Pensacola, FL, p. A136
BUTLER, Rosemary M, R.N., MSN, Chief Nurse Executive, Kaiser Permanente Riverside Medical Center, Riverside, CA, p. A81
BUTLER, Scott A., Chief Executive Officer, Select Specialty Hospital–Evansville, Evansville, IN, p. A203
BUTLER, Stuart, Director Information Technology, Sweeny Community Hospital, Sweeny, TX, p. A639
BUTT, Zaahra, Chief Executive Officer, Select Specialty Hospital–Grosse Pointe, Grosse Pointe, MI, p. A313
BUTTELL, Phil, Chief Executive Officer, Menorah Medical Center, Overland Park, KS, p. A243
BUTTER, Hazel, Manager Human Resources, Hammond–Henry Hospital, Geneseo, IL, p. A184
BUTTERFIELD, Cindy, Director, Fiscal and Administrative Services, Connecticut Valley Hospital, Middletown, CT, p. A109
BUTTERFIELD, Jon
Administrator and Chief Executive Officer, Jordan Valley Medical Center, West Jordan, UT, p. A653
Administrator and Chief Operating Officer, Jordan Valley Medical Center West Valley Campus, West Valley City, UT, p. A653
BUTTERFIELD, Jon R., Administrator and Chief Executive Officer, Jordan Valley Medical Center West Valley Campus, West Valley City, UT, p. A653
BUTTERMORE, Bruce
Director Human Resources, Parkview Lagrange Hospital, Lagrange, IN, p. A210
Manager Human Resources, Parkview Noble Hospital, Kendallville, IN, p. A208
BUTTON, Charlie A., Chief Executive Officer, Regional Medical Center, Manchester, IA, p. A226
BUTTS, Cody, President, Cherokee Medical Center, Gaffney, SC, p. A553
BUTTS, Paula Yvonne, Chief Nursing Officer, Piedmont Henry Hospital, Stockbridge, GA, p. A161
BUTTS, Ursula N, FACHE, Vice President of Patient Care Services, Vcu Health Community Memorial Hospital, South Hill, VA, p. A667
BUTZINE, Bart, Director Information Technology, Community Hospital, Grand Junction, CO, p. A101
BUTZLER, Hilary, Director Human Resources, Cumberland Healthcare, Cumberland, WI, p. A693
BUUCK, Brian, Chief Executive Officer, Ridgeview Psychiatric Hospital And Center, Oak Ridge, TN, p. A578
BUZACHERO, Victor, Corporate Senior Vice President for Innovation, Human Resources and Performance Management, Scripps Green Hospital, La Jolla, CA, p. A62
BYARS, Stephanie, Chief Nursing Officer, Unity Medical Center, Manchester, TN, p. A573
BYDA, Jeff, Vice President Information Technology, Mercy Fitzgerald Hospital, Darby, PA, p. A524
BYERS, John, M.D., Medical Director, Select Specialty Hospital–Tri Cities, Bristol, TN, p. A566
BYERS, Suzann, Director of Nursing, Southern Indiana Rehabilitation Hospital, New Albany, IN, p. A212
BYERS, William J., Chief Information Officer, Western Maryland Regional Medical Center, Cumberland, MD, p. A290
BYLER, Karen, Information Technology Generalist, Warren State Hospital, Warren, PA, p. A543
BYNUM, Justin, Chief Financial Officer, Saint Anthony Hospital, Chicago, IL, p. A179
BYORICK, Joseph, Senior Vice President and Chief Financial Officer, Penn Medicine Lancaster General Hospital, Lancaster, PA, p. A529
BYRD, Catherine, Vice President Patient Services, Parkview Noble Hospital, Kendallville, IN, p. A208
BYRD, David, Chief Financial Officer, The Hospitals Of Providence Transmountain Campus, El Paso, TX, p. A603

BYRD, Greg, Vice President Medical Affairs, Valley Health Shenandoah Memorial Hospital, Woodstock, VA, p. A669
BYRD, Lu, R.N., MSN, Vice President Hospital Operations and Chief Nursing Officer, Billings Clinic, Billings, MT, p. A374
BYRD, O Wayne, M.D., Chief of Staff, H. C. Watkins Memorial Hospital, Quitman, MS, p. A353
BYRD, Rebecca, President Medical Staff, Grandview Medical Center, Birmingham, AL, p. A14
BYRD–PELAEZ, Brenda, Chief Human Resources Management Office, Martinsburg Veterans Affairs Medical Center, Martinsburg, WV, p. A687
BYRNE, Frank J, Vice President Finance, Newport Hospital, Newport, RI, p. A547
BYRNE, John, M.D., Vice President and Chief Medical Officer, Baylor St. Luke'S Medical Center, Houston, TX, p. A610
BYRNES, Jeremy M., Chief Executive Officer, Kingwood Emergency Hospital, Kingwood, TX, p. A618
BYRNES, Matthew C, M.D., Chief Medical Officer, St. Catherine Hospital, Garden City, KS, p. A235
BYROM, David, Chief Executive Officer, Coryell Health, Gatesville, TX, p. A607

C

CAAMANO, Tero, Director Information Technology, Saint Clare'S Denville Hospital, Denville, NJ, p. A404
CABALLERO, Rogelio, Chief Information Systems, San Jorge Children'S Hospital, Santurce, PR, p. A719
CABE, Jacque, Chief Financial Officer, University Of Washington Medical Center, Seattle, WA, p. A678
CABIGAO, Edwin, Chief Nursing Officer, Jewish Home Of San Francisco, San Francisco, CA, p. A85
CABIRO, Michael, Chief Executive Officer, Encompass Health Rehabilitation Hospital Of Pearland, Pearland, TX, p. A628
CABRERA, Carlos, Executive Director, Cardiovascular Center Of Puerto Rico And The Caribbean, San Juan, PR, p. A718
CABRERA, Irma, Finance Director, Hospital San Carlos Borromeo, Moca, PR, p. A717
CABRERA, Sheelah, Chief Information Officer, La Rabida Children'S Hospital, Chicago, IL, p. A178
CABUNOC, Brenda, Chief Human Resources, Va Greater Los Angeles Healthcare System, Los Angeles, CA, p. A70
CACCAMISE, Chad, Director Information Services, United Memorial Medical Center, Batavia, NY, p. A423
CACCAMO, Michael, M.D.
Chief Medical Officer, Greene Memorial Hospital, Xenia, OH, p. A494
Chief Medical Officer, Soin Medical Center, Beavercreek, OH, p. A473
CACCIAMANI, John D., Chief Executive Officer, Chestnut Hill Hospital, Philadelphia, PA, p. A534
CADE, Paul, Administrator and Chief Executive Officer, Baptist Memorial Hospital–Golden Triangle, Columbus, MS, p. A346
CADIEUX, Marc
Corporate Vice President and Chief Financial Officer, Children'S Hospital Of Wisconsin–Fox Valley, Neenah, WI, p. A702
Corporate Vice President and Chief Financial Officer, Children'S Hospital Of Wisconsin, Milwaukee, WI, p. A701
CADIGAN, Elizabeth, R.N., MSN, Senior Vice President Patient Care Services and Chief Nursing Officer, Cambridge Health Alliance, Cambridge, MA, p. A297
CADOGAN, David, Chief Medical Officer, Alaska Regional Hospital, Anchorage, AK, p. A25
CADORETTE, Brenda E, Chief Nursing Officer, Berkshire Medical Center, Pittsfield, MA, p. A302
CADWELL, Carrie, Chief Executive Officer, Four County Counseling Center, Logansport, IN, p. A210
CADWELL, Jason, Chief Financial Officer, Four County Counseling Center, Logansport, IN, p. A210
CADWELL, Maureen K., Chief Executive Officer, Weston County Health Services, Newcastle, WY, p. A712
CADY, Kathy, Coordinator Human Resources, Accounts Payable and Payroll, Safe Haven Hospital Of Treasure Valley, Boise, ID, p. A167
CADY, Thomas, Vice President Human Resources, Heywood Hospital, Gardner, MA, p. A299
CADY, Tina, Controller, The Women'S Hospital, Newburgh, IN, p. A213
CAFASSO, Michael
Chief Executive Officer, St. Mary–Corwin Medical Center, Pueblo, CO, p. A105
Chief Operating Officer, St. Mary–Corwin Medical Center, Pueblo, CO, p. A105

CAGLE, Jennifer, Director of Nursing, North Mississippi Medical Center–Hamilton, Hamilton, AL, p. A19
CAGLE, Karen, Chief Nursing Officer, Select Specialty Hospital–Nashville, Nashville, TN, p. A577
CAGLE, LaDonna, HIM Appeals Coordinator III, Monroe Hospital, Bloomington, IN, p. A200
CAGNA, Ralph A
Director Information Technology Operations, Cleveland Clinic Health System South Market, Marymount Hospital, Garfield Heights, OH, p. A483
Director Information Technology, South Pointe Hospital, Warrensville Heights, OH, p. A493
CAHALAN, Jay P., Chief Executive Officer, Columbia Memorial Hospital, Hudson, NY, p. A429
CAHILL, Joseph, Executive Vice President and Chief Operating Officer, South Shore Hospital, South Weymouth, MA, p. A303
CAHILL, Marty, Chief Executive Officer, Samaritan Lebanon Community Hospital, Lebanon, OR, p. A514
CAHILL, Patricia, Vice President, Patient Care Services and Chief Nursing Officer, Brookdale Hospital Medical Center, New York, NY, p. A432
CAHO–MOONEY, Linda, Chief Financial Officer, Claiborne County Medical Center, Port Gibson, MS, p. A353
CAHOE, Mary, Chief Nursing Officer, Iroquois Memorial Hospital And Resident Home, Watseka, IL, p. A197
CAHOJ, Lindsey, Chief Nursing Officer, Select Specialty Hospital–Wichita, Wichita, KS, p. A248
CAICEDO, Christian H., President, Upmc Carlisle, Carlisle, PA, p. A522
CAIN, Amy, District Director Human Resources, Kindred Hospital South Philadelphia, Philadelphia, PA, p. A535
CAIN, Mark, Chief Executive Officer, Tennova Healthcare–Lafollette Medical Center, La Follette, TN, p. A572
CAIN, Roxie, Chief Financial Officer, Big Horn County Memorial Hospital, Hardin, MT, p. A377
CAIN, William, Controller, Penn Highlands Clearfield, Clearfield, PA, p. A522
CAINE, Jamie, Director of Human Resources, Multicare Valley Hospital, Spokane Valley, WA, p. A680
CAIRNS, Craig, M.D., Vice President Medical Affairs, Licking Memorial Hospital, Newark, OH, p. A488
CALAIS, C Matthew, Senior Vice President and Chief Information Officer, Legacy Good Samaritan Medical Center, Portland, OR, p. A516
CALAIS, Daniel, Jr, Superintendent, Bridgewater State Hospital, Bridgewater, MA, p. A296
CALAMARI, Frank A., President and Chief Executive Officer, Brookdale Hospital Medical Center, New York, NY, p. A432
CALAMARI, Jacquelyn MSN, MS, Chief Nursing Officer and Vice President, Patient Care Services, Middlesex Hospital, Middletown, CT, p. A109
CALANDRELLA, Paul, Chief Operating Officer, Mt. Ascutney Hospital And Health Center, Windsor, VT, p. A655
CALANDRIELLO, John, Vice President and Chief Financial Officer, Hackensack Meridian Health Palisades Medical Center, North Bergen, NJ, p. A410
CALARCO, Marge, Chief Nursing Executive, Michigan Medicine, Ann Arbor, MI, p. A306
CALAWAY, Shearmaine, Director Human Resources, East Mississippi State Hospital, Meridian, MS, p. A351
CALBONE, Angelo G., President and Chief Executive Officer, Saratoga Hospital, Saratoga Springs, NY, p. A444
CALBY, Elizabeth, Vice President Human Resources, Advocate Good Samaritan Hospital, Downers Grove, IL, p. A181
CALDARI, Patricia, Vice President, Brookdale Hospital Medical Center, New York, NY, p. A432
CALDAS, Robert, D.O., Chief Medical Officer, Southcoast Hospitals Group, Fall River, MA, p. A298
CALDEIRA, Amy, Director Information Technology and Systems, Fort Walton Beach Medical Center, Fort Walton Beach, FL, p. A123
CALDERA, Ken, Director Human Resources, Kessler Institute For Rehabilitation, West Orange, NJ, p. A414
CALDERON, Lizmari, Director Finance, Hospital De La Concepcion, San German, PR, p. A718
CALDWELL, Carolyn P., President and Chief Executive Officer, St. Mary Medical Center, Long Beach, CA, p. A65
CALDWELL, Charles, M.D., Chief of Staff, Byrd Regional Hospital, Leesville, LA, p. A272
CALDWELL, Dan, Chief Executive Officer, South Texas Health System, Edinburg, TX, p. A601
CALDWELL, Dari, President and Chief Operating Officer, Novant Health Rowan Medical Center, Salisbury, NC, p. A461
CALDWELL, Eric, Director Finance, Northside Hospital–Forsyth, Cumming, GA, p. A151
CALDWELL, Marita, Chief Financial Officer, Twin County Regional Healthcare, Galax, VA, p. A660

CALDWELL, Matthew T.
President and Chief Executive Officer, Mercy Memorial Hospital, Urbana, OH, p. A492
President, Bon Secours St. Francis Health System, Greenville, SC, p. A553

CALDWELL, Nesa, Chief Nursing Officer, Solara Hospital Harlingen, Harlingen, TX, p. A609

CALDWELL, Noah, Vice President and Chief Information Officer, South Nassau Communities Hospital, Oceanside, NY, p. A440

CALDWELL, Paul, Facility Coordinator Information Technology Customer Relations, Page Hospital, Page, AZ, p. A32

CALDWELL, Steve, Vice President Finance and Chief Financial Officer, Ssm Health St. Mary'S Hospital, Madison, WI, p. A698

CALDWELL, William E., Jr
Chief Executive Officer, Conemaugh Memorial Medical Center, Johnstown, PA, p. A528
Chief Executive Officer, Wilson Medical Center, Wilson, NC, p. A464

CALEY, Carl
Chief Financial Officer, Spring Valley Hospital Medical Center, Las Vegas, NV, p. A396
Chief Financial Officer, St. Cloud Regional Medical Center, Saint Cloud, FL, p. A138

CALEYO, Kristy, Chief Executive Officer, Curahealth New Orleans, New Orleans, LA, p. A275

CALHOUN, Cathy, Director Human Resources, River Point Behavioral Health, Jacksonville, FL, p. A125

CALHOUN, Joshua, M.D., Medical Director, Hawthorn Children Psychiatric Hospital, Saint Louis, MO, p. A369

CALHOUN, Kirk A., President, Ut Health North Campus Tyler, Tyler, TX, p. A642

CALHOUN, Robert, Chief Executive Officer, Merit Health Biloxi, Biloxi, MS, p. A344

CALHOUN, Timothy
Vice President Finance and Chief Financial Officer, Spectrum Health Lakeland, Saint Joseph, MI, p. A322
Vice President Finance, Chief Financial Officer, Lakeland Hospital, Watervliet, Watervliet, MI, p. A324

CALHOUN, William, Chief Executive Officer, Kearney Regional Medical Center, Kearney, NE, p. A386

CALIA, Christopher, Vice President Human Resources, Chi St. Luke'S Health Brazosport, Lake Jackson, TX, p. A619

CALIFORNIA, Randy, Chief Operating Officer, Warren General Hospital, Warren, PA, p. A543

CALIME, Erica, Director Human Resources, Baylor Scott & White Medical Center – Carrollton, Carrollton, TX, p. A591

CALIVA, Todd, Chief Executive Officer, Hca Houston Healthcare Clear Lake, League City, TX, p. A620

CALKIN, Steven, D.O., Vice President Medical Affairs, Mclaren Oakland, Pontiac, MI, p. A320

CALKINS, Paul, M.D., Chief Medical Officer, Indiana University Health North Hospital, Carmel, IN, p. A201

CALL, Carie, Computer Support, Cassia Regional Hospital, Burley, ID, p. A168

CALL, Stacie, Chief Nursing Officer, Mercy Health – St. Elizabeth Boardman Hospital, Boardman, OH, p. A473

CALL, Stacie, R.N., Vice President Patient Care and Chief Nursing Officer, East Liverpool City Hospital, East Liverpool, OH, p. A482

CALLAGHAN, James, III, President and Chief Executive Officer, Franciscan Health Indianapolis, Indianapolis, IN, p. A207

CALLAGHAN, Peter, President and Chief Executive Officer, Columbus Hospital Ltach, Newark, NJ, p. A409

CALLAHAN, Ame, Acting Manager Resource Management Service, Northern Arizona Veterans Affairs Health Care System, Prescott, AZ, p. A34

CALLAHAN, Charles D, Ph.D., Executive Vice President and Chief Operating Officer, Memorial Medical Center, Springfield, IL, p. A196

CALLAHAN, Christopher M, Vice President Human Resources, Exeter Hospital, Exeter, NH, p. A400

CALLAHAN, Kelly, Public Information Officer, Elgin Mental Health Center, Elgin, IL, p. A182

CALLAHAN, Kevin J., President and Chief Executive Officer, Exeter Hospital, Exeter, NH, p. A400

CALLAHAN, Larry A., Senior Vice President Human Resources, Grady Memorial Hospital, Atlanta, GA, p. A146

CALLAHAN, Mark, Chief Operating Officer, Mary Lanning Healthcare, Hastings, NE, p. A385

CALLAHAN, Mary Beth, Chief Financial Officer, Mclaren Lapeer Region, Lapeer, MI, p. A316

CALLAHAN, Neil, Chief Executive Officer, Brooke Glen Behavioral Hospital, Fort Washington, PA, p. A526

CALLAHAN, Robert W., Jr, Interim Director, Wilmington Veterans Affairs Medical Center, Wilmington, DE, p. A114

CALLAHAN, Shannon, Director Human Resources, Sitka Community Hospital, Sitka, AK, p. A27

CALLAHAN, William, Chief Information Management Division, Bayne–Jones Army Community Hospital, Fort Polk, LA, p. A267

CALLAN, Michael, Executive Vice President and Chief Financial Officer, Kidspeace Children'S Hospital, Orefield, PA, p. A533

CALLAS, Robin B, R.N., Vice President Human Resources, Rutherford Regional Health System, Rutherfordton, NC, p. A461

CALLAWAY, Blair, Chief Financial Officer, Texas Orthopedic Hospital, Houston, TX, p. A614

CALLENS, Don, M.D., Chief Medical Officer, Liberty Dayton Regional Medical Center, Liberty, TX, p. A620

CALLENS, Paul A., Director, North Mississippi State Hospital, Tupelo, MS, p. A354

CALLISTE, Gregory, Chief Executive Officer, Brookdale Hospital Medical Center, New York, NY, p. A432

CALLISTER, T Brian, M.D., Chief Medical Officer, Tahoe Pacific Hospitals, Sparks, NV, p. A398

CALLMAN, Mark, M.D., Chief Medical Officer, Fawcett Memorial Hospital, Port Charlotte, FL, p. A137

CALLOWAY, Maria, R.N., MSN, Chief Nursing Officer, Central Florida Regional Hospital, Sanford, FL, p. A139

CALUBAQUIB, Evelyn, Chief Nursing Officer, Greater El Monte Community Hospital, South El Monte, CA, p. A90

CALVARUSO, Gaspare, President, Capital Region Medical Center, Jefferson City, MO, p. A361

CALVERT, Mandy, Director Information Systems, Southern Coos Hospital And Health Center, Bandon, OR, p. A511

CALVERT, Sarah, Chief Nursing Officer, Mcgehee Hospital, Mcgehee, AR, p. A45

CALVIN, Harley, D.O., Chief Medical Officer, Rush County Memorial Hospital, La Crosse, KS, p. A238

CALVIN, Irene, Vice President Human Resources, South Oaks Hospital, Amityville, NY, p. A422

CALVIN, Jeff, Chief Financial Officer, Michiana Behavioral Health Center, Plymouth, IN, p. A213

CAMACHO, Leslie, R.N., Director of Nursing, Commonwealth Health Center, Saipan, MP, p. A714

CAMARDELLO, Heidi, Vice President Patient Care Services and Chief Nursing Officer, Little Falls Hospital, Little Falls, NY, p. A430

CAMERON, Carl, Director Information Systems, Holyoke Medical Center, Holyoke, MA, p. A299

CAMERON, Don, Chief Operating Officer, Allegiance Behavioral Health Center Of Plainview, Plainview, TX, p. A629

CAMERON, Kim, Manager Health Information Services, Patients' Hospital Of Redding, Redding, CA, p. A79

CAMMACK, Geri, R.N., Director of Nursing, Lost Rivers Medical Center, Arco, ID, p. A167

CAMMENGA, Randall, M.D., Vice President Medical Affairs, Goshen Health, Goshen, IN, p. A205

CAMP, David, Director Human Resources, St. Mary'S Regional Medical Center, Enid, OK, p. A499

CAMP, Kendra, Chief Executive Officer, Amg Specialty Hospital–Albuquerque, Albuquerque, NM, p. A416

CAMPA, Melissa, Controller, Kindred Hospital El Paso, El Paso, TX, p. A602

CAMPANA, Thomas, M.D., Chief of Staff, Spectrum Health Reed City Hospital, Reed City, MI, p. A320

CAMPANELLA, Alfred, Chief Information Officer, Virtua Voorhees, Voorhees, NJ, p. A414

CAMPAS, Janice, Chief Financial Officer, Wichita County Health Center, Leoti, KS, p. A239

CAMPBELL, Al, Senior Vice President and Chief Operating Officer, Fort Washington Medical Center, Oxen Hill, MD, p. A292

CAMPBELL, Amy, Chief Financial Officer, Community Hospital North, Indianapolis, IN, p. A206

CAMPBELL, Andrew, Associate Executive Director, Brookdale Hospital Medical Center, New York, NY, p. A432

CAMPBELL, April, Director Human Resources, Broadwater Health Center, Townsend, MT, p. A380

CAMPBELL, Bernard M, Administrator Human Resources, Lewisgale Hospital Alleghany, Low Moor, VA, p. A661

CAMPBELL, Brian, Director Professional Services, U. S. Public Health Service Indian Hospital–Whiteriver, Whiteriver, AZ, p. A38

CAMPBELL, C Scott, Market Chief Executive Officer, Physicians Regional – Pine Ridge, Naples, FL, p. A132

CAMPBELL, Christine, Controller, Vanderbilt Stallworth Rehabilitation Hospital, Nashville, TN, p. A577

CAMPBELL, Cinthia, Chief Nursing Officer, Encompass Health Rehabilitation Hospital Of Chattanooga, Chattanooga, TN, p. A567

CAMPBELL, David, Administrator, Perry Hospital, Perry, GA, p. A158

CAMPBELL, Dean, Vice President Information Services and Chief Information Officer, Good Samaritan Hospital, Los Angeles, CA, p. A66

CAMPBELL, Deborah, Administrator, Thomas H. Boyd Memorial Hospital, Carrollton, IL, p. A175

CAMPBELL, Debra, Administrator, Riverside Regional Medical Center, Newport News, VA, p. A663

CAMPBELL, Emily, Vice President Human Resources, The University Of Vermont Health Network – Alice Hyde Medical Center, Malone, NY, p. A430

CAMPBELL, Eric, Chief Financial Officer, Oswego Hospital, Oswego, NY, p. A441

CAMPBELL, Gary, Chief Executive Officer, St. Vincent General Hospital District, Leadville, CO, p. A103

CAMPBELL, Ivy, Director of Nursing, Community Medical Center, Inc., Falls City, NE, p. A384

CAMPBELL, Jennie, Chief Financial Officer, Baylor Scott & White Medical Center – Llano, Llano, TX, p. A621

CAMPBELL, John
Chief Information Officer, Spaulding Hospital For Continuing Medical Care Cambridge, Cambridge, MA, p. A297
Chief Information Officer, Spaulding Rehabilitation Hospital Cape Cod, East Sandwich, MA, p. A298
Chief Information Officer, Spaulding Rehabilitation Hospital, Charlestown, MA, p. A298

CAMPBELL, Kathy, Interim Chief Nursing Officer, Holston Valley Medical Center, Kingsport, TN, p. A572

CAMPBELL, Kevin, Chief Executive Officer, Saint Thomas Hickman Hospital, Centerville, TN, p. A567

CAMPBELL, Matthew J., Esq, Chief Executive Officer, Select Specialty Hospital–Saginaw, Saginaw, MI, p. A321

CAMPBELL, Melissa, Chief Financial Officer and Controller, Mercy Rehabilitation Hospital Springfield, Springfield, MO, p. A372

CAMPBELL, Melvin, M.D., Medical Staff Chairman, Brown County Hospital, Ainsworth, NE, p. A382

CAMPBELL, Pamela, M.D., Medical Director, Lincoln Prairie Behavioral Health Center, Springfield, IL, p. A196

CAMPBELL, Philip, Vice President Information Services, Calverthealth Medical Center, Prince Frederick, MD, p. A293

CAMPBELL, Sandra M., R.N., Chief Nursing Officer, Dodge County Hospital, Eastman, GA, p. A153

CAMPBELL, Scott, Interim Chief Executive Officer, Ut Health Athens, Athens, TX, p. A584

CAMPBELL, Shari, Chief Operating Officer, Kearny County Hospital, Lakin, KS, p. A238

CAMPBELL, Sharon J, Director, Human Resources, Adventhealth Hendersonville, Hendersonville, NC, p. A456

CAMPBELL, Sherry May, Director of Human Resources, Medical Records, Seaside Behavioral Center, New Orleans, LA, p. A276

CAMPBELL, Stephen J, Chief Operating Officer, Pioneers Memorial Healthcare District, Brawley, CA, p. A53

CAMPBELL, Susie, Chief Executive Officer, Community Hospital Of Staunton, Staunton, IL, p. A197

CAMPBELL, Suzannah
President, St. Vincent'S Blount, Oneonta, AL, p. A22
President, St. Vincent'S East, Birmingham, AL, p. A15
President, St. Vincent'S St. Clair, Pell City, AL, p. A22

CAMPBELL, Suzanne, R.N., Director Patient Services, Spearfish Regional Hospital, Spearfish, SD, p. A564

CAMPBELL, Teresa, R.N., Chief Nursing Executive, Sutter Lakeside Hospital, Lakeport, CA, p. A64

CAMPBELL, Todd, Chief Executive Officer, St. Mary'S Medical Center, Huntington, WV, p. A686

CAMPBELL, Vicky, Vice President Mental Health and Support Services, Providence Healthcare Network, Waco, TX, p. A644

CAMPEAU, Arleen, R.N., Vice President of Patient Care Services, Chief Nursing Officer, Powell Valley Healthcare, Powell, WY, p. A712

CAMPO, Mary Beth, MS, R.N., Director of Nursing, Eastern Niagara Hospital, Lockport, NY, p. A430

CAMPOS, Christina, Administrator, Guadalupe County Hospital, Santa Rosa, NM, p. A420

CAMPOS, Emilio, Department Head Information Technology, Guadalupe County Hospital, Santa Rosa, NM, p. A420

CAMPOVERDE, Jacqueline, Business Manager, Essex County Hospital Center, Cedar Grove, NJ, p. A404

CAMPS, Lourdes, Chief Operating Officer, Hialeah Hospital, Hialeah, FL, p. A124

CANADY, Carolyn, Chief Financial Officer, Sierra Nevada Memorial Hospital, Grass Valley, CA, p. A61

CANADY, Michael R.
Chief Executive Officer, Holzer Medical Center – Jackson, Jackson, OH, p. A484
Interim Chief Executive Officer, Holzer Medical Center, Gallipolis, OH, p. A483

CANALE, Joseph
Acting Chief Executive Officer, Ancora Psychiatric Hospital, Hammonton, NJ, p. A406
Business Manager, Trenton Psychiatric Hospital, Trenton, NJ, p. A413

CANALES, Joe
Director Human Resources, Ascension Seton Edgar B. Davis Hospital, Luling, TX, p. A622
Director Human Resources, Ascension Seton Shoal Creek, Austin, TX, p. A585
Vice President Human Resources, Ministry Market Texas, Dell Seton Medical Center At The University Of Texas, Austin, TX, p. A585
Vice President Human Resources, Ascension Seton Medical Center Austin, Austin, TX, p. A584
Vice President, Ascension and Human Resources Officer, Texas Market, Ascension Seton Northwest, Austin, TX, p. A584
CANARD, Robert Shannon., Chief Executive Officer, Select Specialty Hospital – Belhaven, Jackson, MS, p. A349
CANCEL, Diana, Director Human Resources, Glendora Community Hospital, Glendora, CA, p. A61
CANDELA, Chris, President and Chief Executive Officer, Mclaren Lapeer Region, Lapeer, MI, p. A316
CANDILL, James W, M.D., President Medical Staff, Charleston Surgical Hospital, Charleston, WV, p. A684
CANDIO, Christine M., President and Chief Executive Officer, St. Luke'S Hospital, Chesterfield, MO, p. A358
CANDULLO, Carl, Chief Information Officer, Adventhealth Ocala, Ocala, FL, p. A133
CANEDO, Jim, Chief Financial Officer, College Medical Center, Long Beach, CA, p. A65
CANFIELD, Brian, Chief Operating Officer, Firsthealth Moore Regional Hospital, Pinehurst, NC, p. A460
CANFIELD, Michael, Chief Information Officer, Augusta Health, Fishersville, VA, p. A659
CANIZARO, Tom, Vice President and Chief Financial Officer, South Central Regional Medical Center, Laurel, MS, p. A350
CANLAS, Emma, Chief Financial Officer, Valley View Medical Center, Fort Mohave, AZ, p. A29
CANNARA, Christopher, Chief Executive Officer, Kindred Hospital–New Jersey Morris County, Dover, NJ, p. A404
CANNIFF, Christopher, Executive Director, Human Resources, Harrington Hospital, Southbridge, MA, p. A303
CANNING, John, Chief Financial Officer, Blythedale Children'S Hospital, Valhalla, NY, p. A446
CANNINGTON, H D, Interim Chief Financial Officer, Fishermen'S Hospital, Marathon, FL, p. A129
CANNON, Brenda, R.N., Director of Nursing, Greeneville Community Hospital East, Greeneville, TN, p. A570
CANNON, Gayle, Director Human Resources, Childress Regional Medical Center, Childress, TX, p. A592
CANNON, Heather, M.D., Medical Director, Neshoba County General Hospital, Philadelphia, MS, p. A353
CANNON, Linda, Chief Medical Records Services, San Diego County Psychiatric Hospital, San Diego, CA, p. A84
CANNON, Robert W., President, Barnes–Jewish Hospital, Saint Louis, MO, p. A369
CANO, Daniel, M.D., Chief Medical Officer, Citizens Medical Center, Victoria, TX, p. A643
CANSLER, Vicki A, Chief Human Resource Officer, Piedmont Hospital, Atlanta, GA, p. A146
CANTLEY, J Scott., President and Chief Executive Officer, Marietta Memorial Hospital, Marietta, OH, p. A486
CANTRE, Pedro Laureano, Chief Nursing Officer, Cardiovascular Center Of Puerto Rico And The Caribbean, San Juan, PR, p. A718
CANTRELL, David, CPA, Vice President and Chief Financial Officer, West Hills Hospital And Medical Center, Los Angeles, CA, p. A70
CANTRELL, Dedra
Chief Information Officer, Emory Saint Joseph'S Hospital Of Atlanta, Atlanta, GA, p. A146
Chief Information Officer, Emory University Hospital Midtown, Atlanta, GA, p. A146
CANTRELL, Eric
Chief Executive Officer, Nexus Specialty Hospital The Woodlands, The Woodlands, TX, p. A641
Chief Executive Officer, Nexus Specialty Hospital, Shenandoah, TX, p. A636
CANTU, Andrew, Chief Financial Officer, Kern Medical Center, Bakersfield, CA, p. A52
CANTU, Janie, Director Human Resources, Crosbyton Clinic Hospital, Crosbyton, TX, p. A595
CAPECE, Vincent G., Jr, President and Chief Executive Officer, Middlesex Hospital, Middletown, CT, p. A109
CAPERS, Travis, President, Ssm Health St. Mary'S Hospital – St. Louis, Saint Louis, MO, p. A370
CAPILI, Anthony, M.D., Chief of Staff, Bayside Community Hospital, Anahuac, TX, p. A583
CAPIOLA, Richard, M.D., Chief Medical Officer, Baton Rouge Behavioral Hospital, Baton Rouge, LA, p. A263
CAPITELLI, Robert, M.D., Senior Vice President and Chief Medical Officer, St. Tammany Parish Hospital, Covington, LA, p. A266
CAPITULO, Kathleen, Ph.D., R.N., Chief Nurse Executive, Brookdale Hospital Medical Center, New York, NY, p. A432
CAPIZZI, Thomas, Vice President Human Resources, Choc Children'S At Mission Hospital, Mission Viejo, CA, p. A72
CAPLAN, Margaret B., Director, Veterans Affairs Hudson Valley Health Care System, Montrose, NY, p. A431
CAPLE, Jocelyn, Interim President and Chief Executive Officer, Frisbie Memorial Hospital, Rochester, NH, p. A402
CAPLE, Jocelyn, M.D., Chief Medical Officer, Frisbie Memorial Hospital, Rochester, NH, p. A402
CAPLES, Greg, Chief Executive Officer, Coliseum Northside Hospital, Macon, GA, p. A156
CAPO, Ann Marie, R.N., Chief Nursing Officer, Vice President, Quality and Patient Services, Uconn, John Dempsey Hospital, Farmington, CT, p. A108
CAPOROSO, Robyn, Chief Executive Officer, Trenton Psychiatric Hospital, Trenton, NJ, p. A413
CAPOTE, Henry, Interim Chief Financial Officer, Coral Gables Hospital, Coral Gables, FL, p. A120
CAPPEL, Blaine, Director Information Systems, Memorial Health System, Abilene, KS, p. A232
CAPPLEMAN, Troy, M.D., Chief of Staff, Tippah County Hospital, Ripley, MS, p. A354
CAPPS, Anita, R.N., Chief Nursing Executive, Community Hospital South, Indianapolis, IN, p. A206
CAPPS, Kim, Chief Financial Officer, Hayes Green Beach Memorial Hospital, Charlotte, MI, p. A308
CAPPS, Melissa, Site Leader Information Technology, St. Luke'S Magic Valley Medical Center, Twin Falls, ID, p. A172
CAPPS, Rick, Chief Financial Officer, Cumberland County Hospital, Burkesville, KY, p. A250
CAPRICO, Rick, Chief Financial Officer, Catskill Regional Medical Center, Harris, NY, p. A429
CAPSHAW, Marcia, Chief Operating Officer, West Central Georgia Regional Hospital, Columbus, GA, p. A151
CAPUANO, Terry Ann, R.N., MSN, FACHE, Executive Vice President and Chief Operating Officer, Lehigh Valley Hospital, Allentown, PA, p. A519
CAPUANO, Tony, Chief Operating Officer, Saint Francis Hospital Muskogee, Muskogee, OK, p. A502
CAPUTO, Louis, Chief Executive Officer, Tristar Stonecrest Medical Center, Smyrna, TN, p. A579
CAPUTO, Michael, Chief Information Officer, Musc Health Of Medical University Of South Carolina, Charleston, SC, p. A550
CARABALLO, Amanda, Nursing Director, Hospital De La Concepcion, San German, PR, p. A718
CARACCIOLO, Kevin, Chief Human Resources Officer, Palm Beach Gardens Medical Center, Palm Beach Gardens, FL, p. A135
CARACCIOLO, Mary Jo, Human Resource Director, Wellington Regional Medical Center, Wellington, FL, p. A143
CARALIS, George P, Interim Chief Executive Officer, Brookdale Hospital Medical Center, New York, NY, p. A432
CARBALLO, Francisco R., M.D., Medical Director, Hospital Hima De Humacao, Humacao, PR, p. A716
CARBONE, Davide M., Chief Executive Officer, Osceola Regional Medical Center, Kissimmee, FL, p. A126
CARBONE, Dominick, M.D., Chief of Staff, Hugh Chatham Memorial Hospital, Elkin, NC, p. A454
CARD, Dean
Chief Financial Officer, Kindred Hospital South Florida–Fort Lauderdale, Fort Lauderdale, FL, p. A123
Chief Financial Officer, Kindred Hospital The Palm Beaches, Riviera Beach, FL, p. A137
CARD, Edwin, President Medical Staff, Mcdonough District Hospital, Macomb, IL, p. A188
CARD, Mike, Chief Information Officer, Audubon County Memorial Hospital And Clinics, Audubon, IA, p. A217
CARDA, Greg, Vice President Finance, Missouri Delta Medical Center, Sikeston, MO, p. A371
CARDELL, Melinda H.
Interim Chief Information Officer, Roper St. Francis Mount Pleasant Hospital, Mount Pleasant, SC, p. A555
Interim Vice President and Chief Information Officer, Roper Hospital, Charleston, SC, p. A550
CARDENAS, Lydia, Director Human Resources, River Crest Hospital, San Angelo, TX, p. A632
CARDENAS, Mark, Director Plant Operations, Vibra Hospital Of Northern California, Redding, CA, p. A80
CARDENAS, Mitzi
Chief Administrative Officer, Truman Medical Center–Hospital Hill, Kansas City, MO, p. A363
Chief Administrative Officer, Truman Medical Center–Lakewood, Kansas City, MO, p. A363
CARDIFF, Michael, Systems Supervisor, Abrom Kaplan Memorial Hospital, Kaplan, LA, p. A270
CARDLE, Lori, Senior Vice President, Chief Operating Officer, Valley Presbyterian Hospital, Los Angeles, CA, p. A70
CARDOZA, Phuong, Interim Chief Executive Officer, Cypress Creek Hospital, Houston, TX, p. A611
CARDWELL, Marian, Chief Financial Officer, Potomac Valley Hospital, Keyser, WV, p. A686
CAREY, Ann
Chief Information Officer, St. Vincent'S Medical Center Southside, Jacksonville, FL, p. A126
Vice President and Chief Information Officer, St. Vincent'S Medical Center Riverside, Jacksonville, FL, p. A126
CAREY, Calvin, Chief Financial Officer, Summit Medical Center, Casper, WY, p. A710
CAREY, Eric R, Vice President Information Systems and Chief Information Officer, Valley Hospital, Ridgewood, NJ, p. A412
CAREY, Jeannie, R.N., Director Patient Care, Stillwater Medical Perry, Perry, OK, p. A506
CAREY, Robin, Director of Nursing, Jasper Memorial Hospital, Monticello, GA, p. A158
CARIGSON, John, Chief Financial Officer, Covenant Specialty Hospital, Lubbock, TX, p. A621
CARIKER, Kelly, Chief Information Officer, North Valley Hospital, Tonasket, WA, p. A681
CARLE, Chris, Senior Vice President and Chief Operating Officer, St. Elizabeth Florence, Florence, KY, p. A252
CARLETON, David
Chief Information Officer, Heritage Valley Health System, Beaver, PA, p. A520
Chief Information Officer, Sewickley Valley Hospital, (A Division Of Valley Medical Facilities), Sewickley, PA, p. A541
CARLIN, Diane, Chief Executive Officer, Antelope Memorial Hospital, Neligh, NE, p. A388
CARLINO, Tracy, R.N., Chief Nursing Officer, Virtua Marlton, Marlton, NJ, p. A408
CARLISLE, Charles, Director, East Mississippi State Hospital, Meridian, MS, p. A351
CARLISLE, Sandy, Manager Human Resources, Holzer Medical Center – Jackson, Jackson, OH, p. A484
CARLOCK, Carey, Chief Executive Officer, Riveredge Hospital, Forest Park, IL, p. A183
CARLOS, Ilona, M.D., President Medical Staff, Thorek Memorial Hospital, Chicago, IL, p. A180
CARLSON, Bev, Chief Financial Officer, Delta County Memorial Hospital, Delta, CO, p. A98
CARLSON, Brian J.
Chief Executive Officer, Sanford Thief River Falls Behavioral Health Center, Thief River Falls, MN, p. A341
Executive Director, Sanford Medical Center Thief River Falls, Thief River Falls, MN, p. A341
CARLSON, Daniel, M.D., Chief Medical Officer, Holston Valley Medical Center, Kingsport, TN, p. A572
CARLSON, Jeffrey, Interim Chief Executive Officer, Allegheny Valley Hospital, Natrona Heights, PA, p. A533
CARLSON, Kellie, Director Human Resources, Coastal Harbor Treatment Center, Savannah, GA, p. A160
CARLSON, Kim, Director Human Resources, Essentia Health Northern Pines Medical Center, Aurora, MN, p. A328
CARLSON, Kurt, Chief Executive Officer, Otis R. Bowen Center For Human Services, Warsaw, IN, p. A216
CARLSON, Lisa, Chief Financial Officer, Adena Pike Medical Center, Waverly, OH, p. A493
CARLSON, Peter, President, Behavioral Health Services, Aurora Psychiatric Hospital, Wauwatosa, WI, p. A708
CARLSON, Richard, Chief Financial Officer, Crawford Memorial Hospital, Robinson, IL, p. A194
CARLSON, Sandee, Director of Nursing, Essentia Health Duluth, Duluth, MN, p. A331
CARLSON, Sarah, Director Human Resources, Essentia Health St. Joseph'S Medical Center, Brainerd, MN, p. A329
CARLSON, Scott, Director, Mary Greeley Medical Center, Ames, IA, p. A217
CARLSON, Wendie, Chief Human Resources Officer, Jackson–Madison County General Hospital, Jackson, TN, p. A571
CARLSON, Wendy, Director Human Resources, Pathways Of Tennessee, Jackson, TN, p. A571
CARLTON, Andrew, Administrator, Atrium Medical Center Of Corinth, Corinth, TX, p. A594
CARLTON, Roy, Chief Financial Officer, Walter B. Jones Alcohol And Drug Abuse Treatment Center, Greenville, NC, p. A455
CARLTON, Terrie, R.N., Vice President & Chief Nursing Officer, Prisma Health Tuomey Hospital, Sumter, SC, p. A557
CARLYLE, Dave, Director Human Resources, Wayne County Hospital, Corydon, IA, p. A220
CARMAN, Susan, Chief Information Officer, United Health Services Hospitals–Binghamton, Binghamton, NY, p. A424
CARMAN, Thomas H., President and Chief Executive Officer, Samaritan Medical Center, Watertown, NY, p. A447
CARMELLINI, Tracy, M.D., Chief of Staff, Jennersville Hospital, West Grove, PA, p. A544
CARMEN, Lee, Associate Vice President Health Care Information Systems, University Of Iowa Hospitals And Clinics, Iowa City, IA, p. A224

CARMICHAEL, Craig, Vice President, Operations, University Of Maryland St. Joseph Medical Center, Towson, MD, p. A293
CARMICHAEL, Gavin H, FACHE, Chief Operating Officer, Alaska Psychiatric Institute, Anchorage, AK, p. A25
CARMICHAEL, Gavin H., Acting Chief Executive Officer, Alaska Psychiatric Institute, Anchorage, AK, p. A25
CARMODY, James, Vice President Human Resources, Wilkes–Barre General Hospital, Wilkes, PA, p. A545
CARNAHAN, David, Chief Executive Officer, Quail Run Behavioral Health, Phoenix, AZ, p. A34
CARNAHAN, Robert H., II, Chief Executive Officer, Banner Churchill Community Hospital, Fallon, NV, p. A393
CARNES, Ruth, Manager Human Resources, Jennings American Legion Hospital, Jennings, LA, p. A269
CARNEY, Adrienne, R.N., Director Nursing and Surgical Services, Kearney Regional Medical Center, Kearney, NE, p. A386
CARNEY, Eric, Chief Executive Officer, Monmouth Medical Center, Long Branch Campus, Long Branch, NJ, p. A407
CARNEY, Glenn
Chief Executive Officer, Wilson N. Jones Regional Medical Center, Sherman, TX, p. A637
Chief Operating Officer, Central Florida Regional Hospital, Sanford, FL, p. A139
CARNEY, Judi, M.D., President Medical Staff, Baptist Memorial Hospital For Women, Memphis, TN, p. A574
CARNEY, Kevin, Senior Information Systems Analyst, Pine Creek Medical Center, Dallas, TX, p. A597
CARNEY, Michael J., Chief Executive Officer, Brentwood Behavioral Healthcare Of Mississippi, Jackson, MS, p. A348
CARO, Vique, Chief Information Officer, Cincinnati Veterans Affairs Medical Center, Cincinnati, OH, p. A476
CAROLINA, Dorinda, Chief Human Resources Officer, Jefferson Health Northeast, Philadelphia, PA, p. A535
CARON, Jacqueline, Chief Human Resources, Birmingham Veterans Affairs Medical Center, Birmingham, AL, p. A14
CARON, William J.
Chief Executive Officer, Veterans Affairs Southern Nevada Healthcare System, North Las Vegas, NV, p. A396
Director, Southern Arizona Veterans Affairs Health Care System, Tucson, AZ, p. A38
CAROSELLI, Cynthia A., R.N., Ph.D., Chief Nursing Officer, Brookdale Hospital Medical Center, New York, NY, p. A432
CAROZZA, Sally, Director Human Resources, West Penn Hospital, Pittsburgh, PA, p. A538
CARPEL, Emmett, M.D., Medical Director and Chief of Staff, Phillips Eye Institute, Minneapolis, MN, p. A336
CARPENTER, Carolyn, President, Sentara Norfolk General Hospital, Norfolk, VA, p. A664
CARPENTER, Curt, Manager Information Technology, Coquille Valley Hospital, Coquille, OR, p. A512
CARPENTER, Deb, Director Information Technology, Lourdes Medical Center, Pasco, WA, p. A676
CARPENTER, Jackie, Office Manager, Rock County Hospital, Bassett, NE, p. A382
CARPENTER, Leah A., Administrator and Chief Executive Officer, Memorial Hospital West, Pembroke Pines, FL, p. A136
CARPENTER, Stephanie, Director of Nursing Services, Columbia County Health System, Dayton, WA, p. A672
CARPER, Joleen, Vice President Quality and Risk, Tri–State Memorial Hospital, Clarkston, WA, p. A671
CARR, Ann, R.N., Chief Nursing Officer, Saint Francis Hospital Vinita, Vinita, OK, p. A510
CARR, David, M.D., Physician Medical Director, The Rehabilitation Institute Of St. Louis, Saint Louis, MO, p. A371
CARR, Deborah, Vice President Human Resources, Orange Regional Medical Center, Middletown, NY, p. A431
CARR, Diane, Chief Information Officer, Brookdale Hospital Medical Center, New York, NY, p. A432
CARR, George, Chief Information Officer, Bryan Medical Center, Lincoln, NE, p. A386
CARR, James, Chief Information Officer, Brookdale Hospital Medical Center, New York, NY, p. A432
CARR, Julie R., Chief Nursing Officer, Roane General Hospital, Spencer, WV, p. A689
CARR, Kay
Chief Information Officer, Bryn Mawr Hospital, Bryn Mawr, PA, p. A521
Chief Information Officer, Bryn Mawr Rehabilitation Hospital, Malvern, PA, p. A530
Chief Information Officer, Lankenau Medical Center, Wynnewood, PA, p. A546
Senior Vice President and Chief Information Officer, Paoli Hospital, Paoli, PA, p. A533
CARR, Randall
Director Human Resources, Parkwest Medical Center, Knoxville, TN, p. A572
Director Human Resources, Roane Medical Center, Harriman, TN, p. A570
CARR, Sheila, Chief Executive Officer, Wekiva Springs, Jacksonville, FL, p. A126
CARR, Tim, Chief Financial Officer, Methodist Ambulatory Surgery Hospital – Northwest, San Antonio, TX, p. A634
CARRADINE, Damon, Director Information Technology, Highland Hospital, Charleston, WV, p. A684
CARRANZA, Diana
Associate Director, Veterans Affairs Illiana Health Care System, Danville, IL, p. A180
Interim Director, Veterans Affairs Illiana Health Care System, Danville, IL, p. A180
CARRASCO, Carlos, Chief Operating Officer, Orlando Regional Medical Center, Orlando, FL, p. A134
CARRASCO, Michelle, Director Human Resources, Palo Verde Behavioral Health, Tucson, AZ, p. A38
CARRASCO, Victor, Chief Executive Officer, Kindred Hospital Rancho, Rancho Cucamonga, CA, p. A79
CARRASQUILLO, Carmen, M.D., Medical Director, Industrial Hospital, San Juan, PR, p. A719
CARREJO, Angela, Director Human Resources, Nor–Lea Hospital District, Lovington, NM, p. A419
CARRELLI, Bobbie, Director Human Resources, Summit Behavioral Healthcare, Cincinnati, OH, p. A476
CARREON, Aleana, Executive Director, Sonoma Developmental Center, Eldridge, CA, p. A57
CARRERO, Milton D, M.D., Medical Director, Dr. Ramon E. Betances Hospital–Mayaguez Medical Center Branch, Mayaguez, PR, p. A717
CARRICO, Tom, Vice President of Operations, Hardin Memorial Health, Elizabethtown, KY, p. A251
CARRIER, Jeffrey, R.N., Chief Clinical Officer, Freeman Health System, Joplin, MO, p. A362
CARRIERE, Archie, Information Technology Technician, Northlake Behavioral Health System, Mandeville, LA, p. A273
CARRIGG, John M.
Executive Vice President and Chief Operating Officer, United Health Services Hospitals–Binghamton, Binghamton, NY, p. A424
President and Chief Executive Officer, United Health Services Hospitals–Binghamton, Binghamton, NY, p. A424
CARRILLO, Irma, Director Human Resources, Ashford Presbyterian Community Hospital, San Juan, PR, p. A718
CARRILLO, Todd, Chief Information Officer, Yoakum County Hospital, Denver City, TX, p. A600
CARRILLO, Zulema, Superintendent, El Paso Psychiatric Center, El Paso, TX, p. A602
CARRINGER, Rick, Vice President and Chief Financial Officer, Methodist Medical Center Of Oak Ridge, Oak Ridge, TN, p. A578
CARRINGTON, Ebone', Chief Executive Officer and Chief Operating Officer, Brookdale Hospital Medical Center, New York, NY, p. A432
CARROCINO, Joanne, President and Chief Executive Officer, Cape Regional Health System, Cape May Court House, NJ, p. A404
CARROLL, Candice R., Nurse Executive, Riverside Regional Medical Center, Newport News, VA, p. A663
CARROLL, Eric, Chief Executive Officer, Unicoi County Memorial Hospital, Erwin, TN, p. A569
CARROLL, Jack, Director Human Resources, Spaulding Hospital For Continuing Medical Care Cambridge, Cambridge, MA, p. A297
CARROLL, Jack A., President and Chief Executive Officer, Magee Rehabilitation Hospital, Philadelphia, PA, p. A535
CARROLL, Jacqueline, Director Human Resources, Los Alamos Medical Center, Los Alamos, NM, p. A419
CARROLL, Jaime, Department Head, Walter Reed National Military Medical Center, Bethesda, MD, p. A289
CARROLL, Jaime, R.N., Vice President Nursing, Sentara Albemarle Medical Center, Elizabeth City, NC, p. A453
CARROLL, James H, Chief Information Officer, St. John Medical Center, Westlake, OH, p. A494
CARROLL, Jan, MSN, M.P.H., R.N., Chief Nursing Officer, Canton–Potsdam Hospital, Potsdam, NY, p. A442
CARROLL, John, M.D., Chief Medical Officer, St. James Mercy Hospital, Hornell, NY, p. A429
CARROLL, Jonathan, Chief Information Officer, Uconn, John Dempsey Hospital, Farmington, CT, p. A108
CARROLL, Karen Manuel, R.N., Vice President Patient Care Services, Beaufort Memorial Hospital, Beaufort, SC, p. A549
CARROLL, Kristen, M.D., Chief of Staff, Shriners Hospitals For Children–Salt Lake City, Salt Lake City, UT, p. A652
CARROLL, Leonard, M.D., Chief of Staff, Hendry Regional Medical Center, Clewiston, FL, p. A120
CARROLL, Michael W., Administrator, Richland Parish Hospital, Delhi, LA, p. A267
CARROLL, Peggy, Chief Information Officer, Palos Health, Palos Heights, IL, p. A192
CARROLL, Richard, M.D.
Chief Medical officer, Adventist Medical Center Bolingbrook, Bolingbrook, IL, p. A174
Vice President and Chief Medical Officer, Adventist Medical Center Glenoaks, Glendale Heights, IL, p. A184
CARROLL, Susan T., Acting President, Inova Fairfax Hospital, Falls Church, VA, p. A659
CARROLL, Terri L, Vice President Financial Services, Hillsboro Area Hospital, Hillsboro, IL, p. A185
CARROLL, William, M.D., Chief Medical Executive, Sutter Santa Rosa Regional Hospital, Santa Rosa, CA, p. A89
CARRON, Patrick E., President and Chief Executive Officer, Perry County Memorial Hospital, Perryville, MO, p. A367
CARRUTH, Gregory, Head Information Management, Naval Hospital Oak Harbor, Oak Harbor, WA, p. A675
CARSON, Carole, Director of Nursing Operations, Rehabilitation Hospital Of Southern New Mexico, Las Cruces, NM, p. A419
CARSON, Debbie, Director Human Resources, Promise Hospital Of Vicksburg, Vicksburg, MS, p. A355
CARSON, Kara Jo, Chief Financial Officer, Pinckneyville Community Hospital, Pinckneyville, IL, p. A193
CARSTENS, Cynthia L., Chief Executive Officer, Stewart Memorial Community Hospital, Lake City, IA, p. A225
CARSTENSEN, Karla, Director Patient Care, Avera Dells Area Hospital, Dell Rapids, SD, p. A560
CARTAGENA, Maria, M.D., Chief Medical Officer, Brylin Hospitals, Buffalo, NY, p. A424
CARTER, Andrea, M.D., Chief Medical Officer, Samaritan Healthcare, Moses Lake, WA, p. A675
CARTER, Barbara, Chief Nursing Officer, Cimarron Memorial Hospital, Boise City, OK, p. A497
CARTER, Billie, Chief Executive Officer, Stonewall Memorial Hospital, Aspermont, TX, p. A584
CARTER, Bob, Interim Chief Executive Officer, Eastern Oklahoma Medical Center, Poteau, OK, p. A506
CARTER, Carolyn Lizann, Chief Nursing Officer, Broward Health Coral Springs, Coral Springs, FL, p. A120
CARTER, Charla, Human Resource Officer, Uvalde Memorial Hospital, Uvalde, TX, p. A643
CARTER, Christen, Director Public Relations, Roosevelt Warm Springs Rehabilitation Hospital – Rehab, Warm Springs, GA, p. A162
CARTER, D. Montez., Chief Executive Officer, St. Mary'S Health Care System, Athens, GA, p. A145
CARTER, Dennis, M.D., Chief of Staff, Eastern Oklahoma Medical Center, Poteau, OK, p. A506
CARTER, Donna, Chief Information Officer and Security Officer, Russell Medical, Alexander City, AL, p. A13
CARTER, Donna, MSN, R.N., Chief Nursing Officer, Minden Medical Center, Minden, LA, p. A274
CARTER, Douglas S, M.D., Vice President and Chief Medical Officer, Major Hospital, Shelbyville, IN, p. A214
CARTER, Gary L, M.D., Vice President and Chief Medical Officer, North Kansas City Hospital, North Kansas City, MO, p. A366
CARTER, Gregory, M.D., Chief Medical Officer, St. Luke'S Rehabilitation Institute, Spokane, WA, p. A680
CARTER, Jessica Y, Chief Financial Officer, Crisp Regional Hospital, Cordele, GA, p. A151
CARTER, Jim, Chief Operating Officer, Grady General Hospital, Cairo, GA, p. A149
CARTER, Josh, Chief Executive Officer, Memphis Mental Health Institute, Memphis, TN, p. A575
CARTER, Leonard, Campus Administrator, South Georgia Medical Center, Valdosta, GA, p. A162
CARTER, Leonard M, Chief Human Resources Officer, Fhn Memorial Hospital, Freeport, IL, p. A183
CARTER, Leslia, Administrator, North Mississippi Medical Center–Pontotoc, Pontotoc, MS, p. A353
CARTER, Lisa, Chief Executive Officer, Johnson City Medical Center, Johnson City, TN, p. A571
CARTER, Malinda Yvonne, Vice President Human Resources, Saint Anthony Hospital, Chicago, IL, p. A179
CARTER, Marcia, Director Human Resources, Bluegrass Community Hospital, Versailles, KY, p. A261
CARTER, Michael, Administrator Information Technology, Northwest Ohio Psychiatric Hospital, Toledo, OH, p. A492
CARTER, Michael, M.D., Chief Medical Officer, Houston County Community Hospital, Erin, TN, p. A569
CARTER, Misty, Vice President Human Resources and Ancillary Services, Great Plains Regional Medical Center, Elk City, OK, p. A499
CARTER, Priscilla, Chief Financial Officer, Mesa Hills Specialty Hospital, El Paso, TX, p. A602
CARTER, Rebecca W., President and Chief Nursing Officer, Blue Ridge Regional Hospital, Spruce Pine, NC, p. A462

CARTER, Rebecca W., MSN, R.N., FACHE, President and Chief Nursing Officer, Blue Ridge Regional Hospital, Spruce Pine, NC, p. A462

CARTER, Richard, District Chief Executive Officer, Hunt Regional Medical Center, Greenville, TX, p. A608

CARTER, Richard, M.D.
Chief Medical Director, Hamilton County Hospital, Syracuse, KS, p. A246
Chief of Staff, Tennova Healthcare–Jefferson Memorial Hospital, Jefferson City, TN, p. A571

CARTER, Shanti, Chief Executive Officer, Kingwood Pines Hospital, Kingwood, TX, p. A618

CARTER, Steve, Chief Information Officer, Mon Health Medical Center, Morgantown, WV, p. A687

CARTER, Teresa, Vice President Patient Care Services, Onecore Health, Oklahoma City, OK, p. A505

CARTER, Tomika, Chief Executive Officer, Greystone Park Psychiatric Hospital, Morris Plains, NJ, p. A408

CARTER, Vickie, Information Systems Director, Sumner Regional Medical Center, Gallatin, TN, p. A570

CARTWRIGHT, Bryan, Chief Information Technology Officer, Missouri River Medical Center, Fort Benton, MT, p. A376

CARTWRIGHT, David, Director Management Information Systems, Sovah Health–Danville, Danville, VA, p. A658

CARTWRIGHT, David A, Vice President Finance and Support Services, Advocate Condell Medical Center, Libertyville, IL, p. A188

CARTWRIGHT, Debra, Chief Financial Officer, St. Joseph Medical Center, Kansas City, MO, p. A363

CARTWRIGHT, Michelle, Chief Financial Officer, St. Mary'S Medical Center, West Palm Beach, FL, p. A144

CARUCCI, Dean, Chief Executive Officer, Portsmouth Regional Hospital, Portsmouth, NH, p. A402

CARUGATI, Diane, Chief Operating Officer, Friends Hospital, Philadelphia, PA, p. A534

CARUSO, Diane M, MSN, Chief Nursing Officer, Encompass Health Rehabilitation Hospital Of Scottsdale, Scottsdale, AZ, p. A35

CARUSO, Don, Chief Executive Officer and President, Cheshire Medical Center, Keene, NH, p. A400

CARUSO, Don, M.D., Chief Medical Officer, Cheshire Medical Center, Keene, NH, p. A400

CARVER, Carol, MSN, R.N., Vice President Patient Services, Clarity Child Guidance Center, San Antonio, TX, p. A633

CARVER, Deborah, Chief Nursing Officer, Providence Tarzana Medical Center, Los Angeles, CA, p. A69

CARVER, Gary J., M.D., Chief Medical Officer, Coshocton Regional Medical Center, Coshocton, OH, p. A480

CARVETH, Barbara, Chief Financial Officer, University Of Colorado Hospital, Aurora, CO, p. A96

CARYER, Steve, Chief Financial Officer, Community Memorial Hospital, Hicksville, OH, p. A484

CARYNSKI, Paula A., President, Osf Saint Anthony Medical Center, Rockford, IL, p. A195

CASABONA, Nicholas, Chief Information Officer, Nyu Winthrop Hospital, Mineola, NY, p. A431

CASANO, Jayleen, Ph.D., FACHE, Chief Operations and Nursing Officer, Abrazo Central Campus, Phoenix, AZ, p. A32

CASANOVA, Robert Bernier, Chief Financial Officer, Industrial Hospital, San Juan, PR, p. A719

CASAREZ, Margaret, Chief Financial Officer, San Joaquin Valley Rehabilitation Hospital, Fresno, CA, p. A59

CASAREZ, Teresa, Director Human Resources, New Mexico Rehabilitation Center, Roswell, NM, p. A420

CASE, Cliff, Chief Financial Officer, Mineral Community Hospital, Superior, MT, p. A380

CASE, Ed, Executive Vice President and Chief Financial Officer, Shirley Ryan Abilitylab, Chicago, IL, p. A179

CASE, Harvey, President, Vidant Beaufort Hospital, Washington, NC, p. A463

CASE, Helen M, Chief Nursing Officer, Nemours Children'S Hospital, Orlando, FL, p. A134

CASE, Jeannia, Chief Nursing Officer, Central Hospital Of Bowie, Bowie, TX, p. A589

CASE, Matthew, Executive Officer, Naval Medical Center, Portsmouth, VA, p. A665

CASE, Nancy, Chief Nursing Officer, Daviess Community Hospital, Washington, IN, p. A216

CASERTA, Kevin, M.D.
Chief Medical Officer, Providence Centralia Hospital, Centralia, WA, p. A671
Chief Medical Officer, Providence St. Peter Hospital, Olympia, WA, p. A676

CASEY, Dina, Human Resources Officer, Lane County Hospital, Dighton, KS, p. A234

CASEY, Joseph, Interim President and Chief Executive Officer, Sturdy Memorial Hospital, Attleboro, MA, p. A294

CASEY, Kevin, M.D., Chief Clinical Officer, Mercy Health – St. Rita'S Medical Center, Lima, OH, p. A485

CASEY, Kevin John., President, Rochester General Hospital, Rochester, NY, p. A442

CASH, Jeff, Senior Vice President and Chief Information Officer, Mercy Medical Center – Cedar Rapids, Cedar Rapids, IA, p. A218

CASH, Jordan, President, Integris Southwest Medical Center, Oklahoma City, OK, p. A504

CASHEN CHACON, Chanda, Executive Vice President and Chief Operating Officer, Arkansas Children'S Hospital, Little Rock, AR, p. A44

CASHMAN, Tim, Chief Financial Officer, Estes Park Medical Center, Estes Park, CO, p. A100

CASHWELL, David, Chief Executive Officer, Encompass Health Rehabilitation Hospital Of Fredericksburg, Fredericksburg, VA, p. A659

CASIANO, Manuel, M.D., Senior Vice President Medical Affairs, Frederick Regional Health System, Frederick, MD, p. A290

CASILLAS, Rosalind C, Chief Nursing Officer, Lawrence Memorial Hospital, Walnut Ridge, AR, p. A49

CASNER, Trina, President and Chief Executive Officer, Pana Community Hospital, Pana, IL, p. A192

CASOLA, Frances, Senior Vice President Operations, Saint Joseph'S Medical Center, Yonkers, NY, p. A448

CASON, Amy, MSN, Chief Nursing Officer, Tristar Stonecrest Medical Center, Smyrna, TN, p. A579

CASON, Cathy, Chief Financial Officer, Jeff Davis Hospital, Hazlehurst, GA, p. A154

CASON, Diane, Chief Information Officer, Controller and Director Human Resources, Lake Butler Hospital Hand Surgery Center, Lake Butler, FL, p. A127

CASON, Randall R., Senior Administrator, Ascension Via Christi Hospital, Pittsburg, KS, p. A244

CASON, Will, Vice President Human Resources, Mercy Health – St. Rita'S Medical Center, Lima, OH, p. A485

CASPERSON, William, Vice President Medical Affairs, Memorial Hospital East, Shiloh, IL, p. A196

CASPERSON, William, M.D., Vice President Medical Affairs, Memorial Hospital, Belleville, IL, p. A174

CASS, Julene J, R.N., Director of Nursing, Community Memorial Hospital, Redfield, SD, p. A563

CASS, Paul, D.O., Chief Medical & Clinical Integration Officer, Wentworth–Douglass Hospital, Dover, NH, p. A399

CASSADY, Perry, M.D., Medical Director, Physicians' Medical Center, New Albany, IN, p. A212

CASSEDY, Ryan, Chief Administrative Officer, Rehabilitation Hospital Of Fort Wayne, Fort Wayne, IN, p. A204

CASSEL, Asenath, Chief Nursing Officer, Wellington Regional Medical Center, Wellington, FL, p. A143

CASSEL, Kari
Senior Vice President and Chief Information Officer, Uf Health Jacksonville, Jacksonville, FL, p. A126
Senior Vice President and Chief Information Officer, Uf Health Shands Hospital, Gainesville, FL, p. A124

CASSELL, Sally D, Manager Human Resources, Ozark Health Medical Center, Clinton, AR, p. A40

CASSIDY, Donna
Administrator, Ascension Borgess Hospital, Kalamazoo, MI, p. A315
Chief Nursing Executive, Bronson South Haven Hospital, South Haven, MI, p. A322

CASSIDY, Joseph J, Vice President, Holy Redeemer Hospital, Meadowbrook, PA, p. A531

CASSINGHAM, Brandi, Chief Nursing Officer, Memorialcare, Saddleback Memorial Medical Center, Laguna Hills, CA, p. A63

CASSLE, Susie, R.N., MSN, Vice President Nursing Services, Hendrick Health System, Abilene, TX, p. A581

CASTALDO, Jennifer, R.N., Vice President, Patient Care and Chief Nursing Officer, Henry Mayo Newhall Hospital, Valencia, CA, p. A93

CASTANEDA, Edmundo, President, Mercy General Hospital, Sacramento, CA, p. A82

CASTANEDA, Marissa, Chief Operating Officer and Director Marketing, Doctor'S Hospital At Renaissance, Edinburg, TX, p. A601

CASTANEDA, Trevor, Chief Executive Officer, Baylor Scott & White Medical Center–Frisco, Frisco, TX, p. A606

CASTEEL, Brian, Information Technology Technician, Hardin County General Hospital, Rosiclare, IL, p. A195

CASTEEL, Karen, Director Human Resources, Palms Of Pasadena Hospital, Saint Petersburg, FL, p. A138

CASTEEL, Lisa, Chief Executive Officer, Henry County Medical Center, Paris, TN, p. A578

CASTEEL, Rick
Vice President Management Information Systems and Chief Information Officer, University Of Maryland Harford Memorial Hospital, Havre De Grace, MD, p. A291
Vice President Management Information Systems and Chief Information Officer, University Of Maryland Upper Chesapeake Medical Center, Bel Air, MD, p. A288

CASTILLO, Carol, Medical Director, Sonoma Developmental Center, Eldridge, CA, p. A57

CASTILLO, Dan A., Chief Executive Officer, Lac+Usc Medical Center, Los Angeles, CA, p. A68

CASTILLO, Edgar, Chief Financial Officer, Larkin Community Hospital–South Miami Campus, South Miami, FL, p. A140

CASTILLO, Paul, Chief Financial Officer, Michigan Medicine, Ann Arbor, MI, p. A306

CASTILLO, Ralph A., Chief Executive Officer, Morgan Memorial Hospital, Madison, GA, p. A157

CASTILLO, Randall, Chief Executive Officer, St. Mary Medical Center, Apple Valley, CA, p. A51

CASTILLO, Renee, Chief Nursing Officer, Plains Memorial Hospital, Dimmitt, TX, p. A600

CASTILLO, Rita S, R.N., Vice President, Quality, Risk and Safety, Methodist Hospital South, Jourdanton, TX, p. A616

CASTLE, Dorothy, Director Human Resources, North Mississippi Medical Center–Eupora, Eupora, MS, p. A346

CASTLE, Eric, Director Information Services, Lawnwood Regional Medical Center & Heart Institute, Fort Pierce, FL, p. A123

CASTLE, Samantha, Chief Executive Officer, Carrollton Springs, Carrollton, TX, p. A591

CASTLEBERRY, Ginger, Corporate Risk Manager, Quality and Patient Safety, Valir Rehabilitation Hospital, Oklahoma City, OK, p. A505

CASTLEDINE, Ed, Chief Executive Officer, St. Luke'S Nampa, Nampa, ID, p. A170

CASTLEMAN, Pam, MSN, Chief Nursing Officer, Regional One Health, Memphis, TN, p. A575

CASTOR, Susan, Chief Nursing Officer, Healthsouth Rehabilitation Hospital Of Toms River, Toms River, NJ, p. A413

CASTRO, Ana, Director Information Technology, Gerald Champion Regional Medical Center, Alamogordo, NM, p. A416

CASTRO, Craig
Chief Executive Officer, Clovis Community Medical Center, Clovis, CA, p. A55
Chief Information Officer, Community Regional Medical Center, Fresno, CA, p. A59

CASTRO, Darcy, Director Human Resources, Garfield Medical Center, Monterey Park, CA, p. A73

CASTRO, Jill, M.D., Medical Director, Healthsouth Rehabilitation Hospital Of Littleton, Littleton, CO, p. A103

CASTRO, Pete, D.O., Chief of Staff, Heart Of Texas Memorial Hospital, Brady, TX, p. A589

CASTRO, Richard
Chief Executive Officer, Ahmc Anaheim Regional Medical Center, Anaheim, CA, p. A50
Chief Executive Officer, Whittier Hospital Medical Center, Whittier, CA, p. A95

CASTRODALE, Andrew, M.D., Chief Medical Officer, Coulee Medical Center, Grand Coulee, WA, p. A673

CASTRONUEVO, Joseph, Director Information Management, St. Lawrence Rehabilitation Center, Lawrenceville, NJ, p. A407

CASWELL, Lori, Director Information Technology, Good Samaritan Medical Center, Brockton, MA, p. A296

CASWELL, Penny, Director of Nursing, Bloomington Meadows Hospital, Bloomington, IN, p. A200

CATALA, Lucy, Vice President Finance, Baylor Scott & White All Saints Medical Center – Fort Worth, Fort Worth, TX, p. A604

CATALDO, Linda, Human Resources Secretary, Prevost Memorial Hospital, Donaldsonville, LA, p. A267

CATALDO, Vincent A., Administrator, Prevost Memorial Hospital, Donaldsonville, LA, p. A267

CATALIOTTI, Palmira, Senior Vice President, Chief Financial Officer and Treasurer, Nyu Winthrop Hospital, Mineola, NY, p. A431

CATANIA, Joseph M., Chief Executive Officer, St. Anthony'S Rehabilitation Hospital, Lauderdale Lakes, FL, p. A128

CATAUDELLA, Mary, Corporate Director Human Resources, Jersey City Medical Center, Jersey City, NJ, p. A407

CATENA, Cornelio R., President and Chief Executive Officer, Wilkes–Barre General Hospital, Wilkes, PA, p. A545

CATES, Brett, Director Information Services, Medical City Weatherford, Weatherford, TX, p. A644

CATES, Jessica, Fiscal Manager, Western State Hospital, Hopkinsville, KY, p. A253

CATHEY, Michele, Interim Chief Financial officer, Martin County Hospital District, Stanton, TX, p. A638

CATHEY, Walt, Chief Executive Officer, Covenant Medical Center, Lubbock, TX, p. A621

CATINO, Anne, MS, R.N., Vice President and Chief Nursing Officer, Holy Redeemer Hospital, Meadowbrook, PA, p. A531

CATTALANI, Mark, M.D., Clinical Director, Richard H. Hutchings Psychiatric Center, Syracuse, NY, p. A445

CATTELL, JoAnne, Chief Nursing Officer, St. Petersburg General Hospital, Saint Petersburg, FL, p. A139

CATTELL, Nancy E, Vice President Human Resources, Liberty Hospital, Liberty, MO, p. A364

CATTON, Carolyn, Interim Chief Patient Care Officer, Beaver Dam Community Hospitals, Beaver Dam, WI, p. A692

CATTON, Jane, R.N., Chief Operating Officer and Chief Nursing Officer, Northwestern Medical Center, Saint Albans, VT, p. A655

CAUBLE, David, Executive Vice President and Chief Financial Officer, Children'S Mercy Hospital Kansas City, Kansas City, MO, p. A362

CAUDILL, Allan, M.D., Chief of Staff, Bronson South Haven Hospital, South Haven, MI, p. A322

CAUDILL, David, Administrator, Grisell Memorial Hospital District One, Ransom, KS, p. A244

CAUGHELL, David, M.D., Chief of Staff, Jane Phillips Nowata Health Center, Nowata, OK, p. A503

CAUGHEY, Michelle, M.D., Physician In Chief, Kaiser Permanente South San Francisco, South San Francisco, CA, p. A90

CAUGHMAN, Katie
Chief Financial Officer, St. John Broken Arrow, Broken Arrow, OK, p. A497
Chief Financial Officer, St. John Owasso, Owasso, OK, p. A506

CAUSEY, Cynthia, Associate Administrator Human and Mission Services, Mcleod Medical Center Dillon, Dillon, SC, p. A552

CAUSEY, Jack M., Chief Executive Officer, Leesville Rehabilitation Hospital, Leesville, LA, p. A272

CAUSEY, Jennifer, Chief Executive Officer, Select Specialty Hospital–Nashville, Nashville, TN, p. A577

CAUWENBERG, Jude, M.D., Chief of Staff, Ashtabula County Medical Center, Ashtabula, OH, p. A472

CAVA, Anthony V., President, Robert Wood Johnson University Hospital Somerset, Somerville, NJ, p. A412

CAVAGNARO, Charles E, M.D., Interim Chief Medical officer, Umass Memorial Medical Center, Worcester, MA, p. A305

CAVANAUGH, Cheryl, Senior Director Human Resources, Valley Regional Hospital, Claremont, NH, p. A399

CAVANAUGH, Paul, Director Human Resources, Friends Hospital, Philadelphia, PA, p. A534

CAVAZOS, David–Paul, Chief Executive Officer, Republic County Hospital, Belleville, KS, p. A232

CAVE, Chuck, CPA, Chief Financial Officer, Wilson N. Jones Regional Medical Center, Sherman, TX, p. A637

CAVELL, Richard, M.D., Medical Director, Ochsner Lsu Health Shreveport – Monroe Medical Center, Monroe, LA, p. A274

CAVEN, Tom, M.D., Vice President, Medical Director, Dell Seton Medical Center At The University Of Texas, Austin, TX, p. A585

CAVENEY, Timothy, President, South Shore Hospital, Chicago, IL, p. A179

CAVERNO, John
Chief Human Resources Officer, Excela Frick Hospital, Mount Pleasant, PA, p. A532
Chief Human Resources Officer, Excela Health Westmoreland Hospital, Greensburg, PA, p. A526

CAWLEY, Karen
Chief Executive Officer, Curahealth Phoenix, Phoenix, AZ, p. A33
Chief Executive Officer, Select Specialty Hospital–Phoenix, Phoenix, AZ, p. A34

CAWLEY, Kevin J, Interim Chief Financial Officer, Mclaren Thumb Region, Bad Axe, MI, p. A307

CAWLEY, Patrick J, Chief Executive Officer, MUSC Health and Vice President for Health Affairs, University, Musc Health Of Medical University Of South Carolina, Charleston, SC, p. A550

CAWLEY, Patrick J., Chief Executive Officer, MUSC Health and Vice President for Health Affairs, University, Musc Health Of Medical University Of South Carolina, Charleston, SC, p. A550

CAWOOD, Marina, Administrative Assistant, Middlesboro Arh Hospital, Middlesboro, KY, p. A258

CAYER, Gerald, Chief Executive Officer, Lewis County General Hospital, Lowville, NY, p. A430

CAYTON, Mical, Area Information Officer, Kaiser Permanente Antioch Medical Center, Antioch, CA, p. A50

CAZARES, Erik, Chief Operating Officer, The Hospitals Of Providence Sierra Campus, El Paso, TX, p. A603

CAZAYOUX, John, Chief Financial Officer, Pointe Coupee General Hospital, New Roads, LA, p. A276

CAZES, Anna Leah
Interim Chief Nursing Officer, Senior Vice President and Chief Operating Officer, Lake Charles Memorial Hospital, Lake Charles, LA, p. A272
Interim Chief Nursing Officer, Senior Vice President, Chief Operating Officer, Lake Charles Memorial Hospital, Lake Charles, LA, p. A272

CECAVA, Eric
Chief Operating Officer, Adena Medical Center, Chillicothe, OH, p. A475
Chief Operating Officer, Adena Pike Medical Center, Waverly, OH, p. A493

CECCHINI, Marina T., Administrator, Uf Health Rehab Hospital, Gainesville, FL, p. A124

CECH, Bob, Regional Finance Officer, Amita Health Saints Mary & Elizabeth Medical Center, Chicago, IL, p. A176

CECIL, Bruce, Chief Financial Officer, Fresno Surgical Hospital, Fresno, CA, p. A59

CECIL, Janell, R.N., MSN, Senior Vice President and Chief Nursing Officer, University Of Tennessee Medical Center, Knoxville, TN, p. A572

CECIL, Jason, Vice President, Information, Capital Region Medical Center, Jefferson City, MO, p. A361

CECIL, Jon C
Chief Human Resource Officer, Cape Coral Hospital, Cape Coral, FL, p. A119
Chief Human Resource Officer, Gulf Coast Medical Center, Fort Myers, FL, p. A123
Chief Human Resource Officer, Lee Memorial Hospital, Fort Myers, FL, p. A123

CEDENO LLORENS, Arturo, M.D., Medical Director, Hospital Buen Samaritano, Aguadilla, PR, p. A714

CEDILLO, Alaina, Interim Administrator, Marion General Hospital, Columbia, MS, p. A346

CEDOTAL, Kiley P., Chief Executive Officer, Promise Hospital Baton Rouge – Main Campus, Baton Rouge, LA, p. A264

CELLA, Ann S, R.N., Senior Vice President, Patient Care Services, St. Francis Hospital, The Heart Center, Roslyn, NY, p. A443

CELLA, Robert, M.D.
Chief Medical Officer, Albany Memorial Hospital, Albany, NY, p. A422
Chief Medical Officer, St. Peter'S Hospital, Albany, NY, p. A422

CELSOR, Reba, Chief Executive Officer, West Tennessee Healthcare Dyersburg Hospital, Dyersburg, TN, p. A569

CELUCH, Paul
Chief Human Resource Officer, East Los Angeles Doctors Hospital, Los Angeles, CA, p. A66
Corporate Human Resources Director, Community Hospital Of Huntington Park, Huntington Park, CA, p. A62

CEMATE, David D, FACHE, Senior Vice President and Chief Operating Officer, Mercy Medical Center, Canton, OH, p. A474

CEMENO, Michael J, Chief Information Officer, Waterbury Hospital, Waterbury, CT, p. A112

CENTENO, Robert, M.D., Chief Medical Officer, Governor Juan F. Luis Hospital, Christiansted, VI, p. A720

CEPEDA, Aaron, Director Nursing Operations, South Texas Rehabilitation Hospital, Brownsville, TX, p. A589

CERALDI, Christopher, M.D., Chief of Staff, Abbeville Area Medical Center, Abbeville, SC, p. A549

CERCEO, Richard, Executive Vice President and Chief Operating Officer, Mercy Hospital And Medical Center, Chicago, IL, p. A178

CERIMELE, Joseph, D.O., Medical Director, Hillside Rehabilitation Hospital, Warren, OH, p. A493

CERIMELE, Leeann, Vice President Human Resources, West Virginia University Hospitals, Morgantown, WV, p. A687

CERISE, Fred, Chief Executive Officer, Parkland Health & Hospital System, Dallas, TX, p. A597

CERNAVA, Joanne, Director Human Resources, Kessler Marlton Rehabilitation, Marlton, NJ, p. A408

CERNOCH, Desiree, Director of Nurses, El Campo Memorial Hospital, El Campo, TX, p. A601

CERRA, Jane, Market Nurse Executive and Chief Nursing Officer, Select Specialty Hospital–Milwaukee, Milwaukee, WI, p. A701

CERULLO, Timothy J., Chief Executive Officer, Bayfront Health Port Charlotte, Port Charlotte, FL, p. A137

CERVANTES, Jason
Chief Information Officer, East Los Angeles Doctors Hospital, Los Angeles, CA, p. A66
Corporate Chief Information Officer, Community Hospital Of Huntington Park, Huntington Park, CA, p. A62

CERVINO, Noel A., President and Chief Executive Officer, University Of Maryland Charles Regional Medical Center, La Plata, MD, p. A291

CESAREZ, Margaret, Chief Financial Officer, Gateway Rehabilitation Hospital, Florence, KY, p. A251

CESCA, Ken, Vice President Human Resources, Midstate Medical Center, Meriden, CT, p. A108

CESKO, David, M.D., Chief of Staff, Memorial Hospital Of Carbon County, Rawlins, WY, p. A712

CHA, Wontae, Chief Operating Officer, Hollywood Presbyterian Medical Center, Los Angeles, CA, p. A67

CHA BRIDIER, Vicky, Chief Operating Officer, College Station Medical Center, College Station, TX, p. A592

CHABALOWSKI, Edward, Chief Financial Officer, Phoenixville Hospital, Phoenixville, PA, p. A537

CHABOT, Judy, Chief Nursing Officer, Los Alamitos Medical Center, Los Alamitos, CA, p. A65

CHACKO, Benson
Chief Operating Officer, The Hospitals Of Providence Sierra Campus, El Paso, TX, p. A603
Vice President, Operations, Baylor Scott & White Medical Center – Lake Pointe, Rowlett, TX, p. A632

CHACON, Barbara, Chief Financial Officer, The Core Institute Specialty Hospital, Phoenix, AZ, p. A34

CHADEK, Richard, M.D., Clinical Director, Lawton Indian Hospital, Lawton, OK, p. A501

CHADHA, Beenu, Chief Financial Officer, San Ramon Regional Medical Center, San Ramon, CA, p. A88

CHADOCK, Brandon
Director of Operations, Sistersville General Hospital, Sistersville, WV, p. A689
Interim Chief Executive Officer, Sistersville General Hospital, Sistersville, WV, p. A689

CHADWICK, Robyn, President, Ascension Via Christi Hospital On St. Teresa, Wichita, KS, p. A247

CHADWICK, Sharon M, Director Human Resources, Abrazo Arrowhead Campus, Glendale, AZ, p. A30

CHAFFIN, Linda, Director Medical Review, Baptist Memorial Hospital–Booneville, Booneville, MS, p. A345

CHAHANOVICH, Jen, President and Chief Executive Officer, Wilcox Medical Center, Lihue, HI, p. A166

CHALFANT, Cathie, Director Human Resources, Harrison County Community Hospital, Bethany, MO, p. A356

CHALIAN, Christopher, M.D., Medical Director, Casa Colina Hospital And Health Systems, Pomona, CA, p. A78

CHALK, Jackie, Director Human Resources, Encompass Health Rehabilitation Hospital Of Largo, Largo, FL, p. A128

CHALKE, Dennis, Senior Vice President, Chief Financial Officer and Treasurer, Baystate Medical Center, Springfield, MA, p. A303

CHALONER, Robert S, Chief Administrative Officer, Stony Brook University Hospital, Stony Brook, NY, p. A444

CHALPHANT, Steve, Director Information Management Service Line, Wm. Jennings Bryan Dorn Veterans Affairs Medical Center, Columbia, SC, p. A552

CHALTRY, Richard, M.D., Director Medical Staff, Aspirus Ontonagon Hospital, Inc., Ontonagon, MI, p. A319

CHALTRY, William, Chief Nursing Officer, New Mexico Rehabilitation Center, Roswell, NM, p. A420

CHALUPA, Rebecca, MSN, R.N., Chief Nursing Officer, Houston Methodist Baytown Hospital, Baytown, TX, p. A587

CHAMBERLIN, Kim, Vice President Patient Services and Chief Nursing Officer, Mercyone North Iowa Medical Center, Mason City, IA, p. A226

CHAMBERS, Bradley
President and Senior Vice President, MedStar Health, Medstar Good Samaritan Hospital, Baltimore, MD, p. A286
President, Medstar Union Memorial Hospital, Baltimore, MD, p. A287

CHAMBERS, Gwen, Executive Director Human Resources, Methodist Hospital Of Southern California, Arcadia, CA, p. A51

CHAMBERS, Matthew
Chief Information Officer, Baylor Scott & White Medical Center – Round Rock, Round Rock, TX, p. A632
Chief Information Officer, Baylor Scott & White Medical Center – Temple, Temple, TX, p. A639

CHAMBERS, Regina, Vice President Human Resource, Rome Memorial Hospital, Rome, NY, p. A443

CHAMBLEE, Jane, Manager Human Resources, North Mississippi Medical Center–Iuka, Iuka, MS, p. A348

CHAMBLESS, Lesley
Assistant Vice President Human Resources, Atrium Health Lincoln, Lincolnton, NC, p. A458
Assistant Vice President Workforce Relations, Atrium Health Cabarrus, Concord, NC, p. A452

CHAMBLISS, James W, Chief of Staff, Magnolia Regional Medical Center, Magnolia, AR, p. A45

CHAMPAGNE, Charles D., Chief Financial Officer, Northeast Rehabilitation Hospital, Salem, NH, p. A402

CHAMPAGNE, Laurie, Controller, Curahealth New Orleans, New Orleans, LA, p. A275

CHAMPAVANNARATH, Vilakon, Director Information Systems, Bartow Regional Medical Center, Bartow, FL, p. A117

CHAMPION, Joshua I, Director, Adventhealth Palm Coast, Palm Coast, FL, p. A135

CHAN, Eric, Chief Executive Officer, Surgery Specialty Hospitals Of America, Pasadena, TX, p. A628

CHAN, Fred, Chief Financial Officer, Intracare North Hospital, Houston, TX, p. A612

CHAN, Joyce, Chief Human Resources Officer, Centracare Health–Melrose, Melrose, MN, p. A335

CHAN, Thomas T., Chief Financial Officer, Meritus Medical Center, Hagerstown, MD, p. A291
CHANAA, Ziad, M.D., Chief of Staff, Boone Memorial Hospital, Madison, WV, p. A687
CHANAGA, Luis, Chief Financial Officer, Grandview Medical Center, Dayton, OH, p. A481
CHANCE, Andre, Chief Financial Officer, Brookdale Hospital Medical Center, New York, NY, p. A432
CHANDIO, Adam, Administrator, The Orthopedic Specialty Hospital, Murray, UT, p. A649
CHANDLER, Carla, Vice President and Chief Financial Officer, Emory University Hospital, Atlanta, GA, p. A146
CHANDLER, Christopher, Chief Executive Officer, Monroe Regional Hospital, Aberdeen, MS, p. A344
CHANDLER, Laurie
Chairman, Prairie Community Hospital, Terry, MT, p. A380
Financial Officer, Prairie Community Hospital, Terry, MT, p. A380
CHANDLER, Loren, President, Mount Sinai Hospital, Chicago, IL, p. A178
CHANDLER, Mike, Administrator, Willis–Knighton Medical Center, Shreveport, LA, p. A278
CHANDLER, Ryan
Chief Executive Officer, Northwest Texas Healthcare System, Amarillo, TX, p. A582
Chief Executive Officer, Piedmont Columbus Regional Midtown, Columbus, GA, p. A150
CHANDLER, Vincent, Director Information Services, Porterville Developmental Center, Porterville, CA, p. A78
CHANDLER, Wendy
Assistant Administrator Human Resources, Christus Ochsner St. Patrick Hospital Southwest Louisiana, Lake Charles, LA, p. A272
Regional Vice President Human Resources, Christus St. Frances Cabrini Hospital, Alexandria, LA, p. A262
Vice President Human Resources, Christus Health Shreveport–Bossier, Shreveport, LA, p. A278
CHANDRAN, Kutty, M.D., Regional Medical Officer, Broward Health Coral Springs, Coral Springs, FL, p. A120
CHANDRASENA, Anita, M.D., Vice President Medical Affairs, Sequoia Hospital, Redwood City, CA, p. A80
CHANDY, Joseph, Administrator, Methodist Hospital Of Chicago, Chicago, IL, p. A178
CHANG, Alex, Chief Operating Officer, Englewood Community Hospital, Englewood, FL, p. A122
CHANG, Jason
Chief Medical Officer and Vice President of Medical Affairs, Rehabilitation Hospital Of The Pacific, Honolulu, HI, p. A165
Executive Vice President and Chief Operating Officer, The Queen'S Medical Center, Honolulu, HI, p. A165
CHANG, Sang–ick, M.D., M.P.H., Chief Medical Officer, Highland Hospital, Oakland, CA, p. A75
CHANNELL, Lesley
Vice President Human Resources, Reston Hospital Center, Reston, VA, p. A665
Vice President Human Resources, Dominion Hospital, Falls Church, VA, p. A658
CHAPDELAINE, Debora R., Manager Information Technology, Aurora Medical Center Kenosha, Kenosha, WI, p. A697
CHAPITAL, Alyssa B, M.D., Medical Director, Mayo Clinic Hospital, Mayo Clinic Hospital, Phoenix, AZ, p. A33
CHAPLIN, Steven, M.D., Medical Director, Sutter Health Kahi Mohala, Ewa Beach, HI, p. A164
CHAPMAN, Bradley, President, Penn Highlands Elk, Saint Marys, PA, p. A540
CHAPMAN, Cully, Chief Financial Officer, Lutheran Hospital Of Indiana, Fort Wayne, IN, p. A204
CHAPMAN, Emily, Chief Medical Officer, Children'S Hospitals And Clinics Of Minnesota, Minneapolis, MN, p. A335
CHAPMAN, Jeffrey, M.D., Chief Medical Officer, Cheyenne Regional Medical Center, Cheyenne, WY, p. A710
CHAPMAN, Jon, Fiscal Officer, Western State Hospital, Staunton, VA, p. A668
CHAPMAN, Judy, Interim Director Information Systems, Upmc Susquehanna Lock Haven, Lock Haven, PA, p. A530
CHAPMAN, Karen
Director Human Resources, Musc Health Chester Medical Center, Chester, SC, p. A550
Human Resources Director, Musc Health Lancaster Medical Center, Lancaster, SC, p. A555
CHAPMAN, Kathleen, Deputy Director, Patient Care Services, Va Portland Healthcare System, Portland, OR, p. A516
CHAPMAN, Kathy, R.N., Chief Clinical Officer and Vice President of Patient Services, Allegan General Hospital, Allegan, MI, p. A306
CHAPMAN, Patrick
Assistant Vice President Operations, Jfk Medical Center North Campus, West Palm Beach, FL, p. A144
Chief Executive Officer, Tippah County Hospital, Ripley, MS, p. A354
CHAPMAN, Rachel, Nurse Manager, Noland Hospital Birmingham, Birmingham, AL, p. A15
CHAPMAN, Rick, Chief Information Officer, Kindred Hospital North Florida, Green Cove Springs, FL, p. A124
CHAPMAN, Roland, Chief Information Officer, Northern Navajo Medical Center, Shiprock, NM, p. A420
CHAPMAN, Teresa, Vice President Human Resources, Northwestern Medicine Marianjoy Rehabilitation Hospital, Wheaton, IL, p. A198
CHAPMAN, Terina, Director of Nursing, Northern Utah Rehabilitation Hospital, South Ogden, UT, p. A653
CHAPPELL, Brandee, Director of Nursing, Lifecare Hospitals Of North Carolina, Rocky Mount, NC, p. A461
CHAPPELL, Pamela, R.N.
Assistant Administrator, Louisiana Extended Care Hospital West Monroe, West Monroe, LA, p. A280
Assistant Administrator, Specialty Hospital, Monroe, LA, p. A274
CHAPPELL, Robert, M.D., Chief Medical Officer and Chief Quality Officer, Huntsville Hospital, Huntsville, AL, p. A19
CHAPPELL, Teresa, Chief Information Officer, Johnston Health, Smithfield, NC, p. A462
CHAPPLE, Albert J., R.N., Chief Clinical Officer, Kindred Rehabilitation Hospital Northeast Houston, Humble, TX, p. A615
CHAPPLE, Scott, Chief Operating Officer, Oroville Hospital, Oroville, CA, p. A76
CHARARA, Kassem, Chief Medical Officer, Beaumont Hospital – Taylor, Taylor, MI, p. A323
CHARBENEAU, Ryan, M.D., Chief Medical Officer, St. David'S North Austin Medical Center, Austin, TX, p. A586
CHARDAVOYNE, Alan, Chief Financial Officer, The University Of Vermont Health Network Elizabethtown Community Hospital, Elizabethtown, NY, p. A427
CHARLAT, Richard A, Chief of Staff, Iowa City Veterans Affairs Health Care System, Iowa City, IA, p. A224
CHARLES, Charlotte, Director Acute Patient Services, Madison Regional Health System, Madison, SD, p. A561
CHARLES, John, M.D., Chief Medical Officer, Mcleod Loris Seacoast Hospital, Loris, SC, p. A555
CHARLES, Sally, Coordinator Human Resources, Grace Medical Center, Lubbock, TX, p. A622
CHARLES, Timothy L., President and Chief Executive Officer, Mercy Medical Center – Cedar Rapids, Cedar Rapids, IA, p. A218
CHARLIER, Brian, Chief Operating Officer, HSHS St. Vincent Hospital/Prevea Health, Hshs St. Vincent Hospital, Green Bay, WI, p. A696
CHARLTON, Beth, Vice President Patient Services and Chief Nursing Officer, Covenant Healthcare, Saginaw, MI, p. A321
CHARLTON, Francis, M.D., Chief Medical Staff, St. Mary'S Medical Center, San Francisco, CA, p. A86
CHARLTON, Judie, M.D., Chief Medical Officer, West Virginia University Hospitals, Morgantown, WV, p. A687
CHARMEL, Patrick, President and Chief Executive Officer, Griffin Hospital, Derby, CT, p. A107
CHARTIER, Bridgett, Director of Nursing, Beartooth Billings Clinic, Red Lodge, MT, p. A379
CHARTIER, Terry
Director, Information Systems, Mercyone New Hampton Medical Center, New Hampton, IA, p. A227
Director, Information Systems, Mercyone North Iowa Medical Center, Mason City, IA, p. A226
CHARVAT, Peter, M.D., Chief Medical Officer, St. Joseph'S Hospital, Tampa, FL, p. A142
CHASE, Jean
Regional Manager Information Services, Aurora Lakeland Medical Center, Elkhorn, WI, p. A694
Regional Manager Information Services, Aurora Medical Center Burlington, Burlington, WI, p. A693
CHASE, Kyle, Chief Financial Officer, Glacial Ridge Health System, Glenwood, MN, p. A332
CHASE, Layla, Interim Chief Financial Officer, Bunkie General Hospital, Bunkie, LA, p. A265
CHASE, Linda K., Ph.D., R.N., Division Senior Vice President and Chief Nursing Officer, Chi Health Lakeside, Omaha, NE, p. A389
CHASE, Pansy, Director Human Resources, Vidant Duplin Hospital, Kenansville, NC, p. A457
CHASE, Robert, M.D.
Chief Medical Officer, Westlake Hospital, Melrose Park, IL, p. A189
Physician Advisor, West Suburban Medical Center, Oak Park, IL, p. A192
CHASE, Susan, Vice President, Atrium Health'S Carolinas Rehabilitation, Charlotte, NC, p. A451
CHASIN, Marc, M.D., Chief Information Officer, St. Luke'S Regional Medical Center, Boise, ID, p. A168
CHASSE, Floyd, Vice President Human Resources, Erlanger Medical Center, Chattanooga, TN, p. A567
CHASTAIN, James G., Director, Mississippi State Hospital, Whitfield, MS, p. A355
CHASTAIN, Stephen L, M.D., Chief Medical Officer, Healthsouth Rehabilitation Hospital At Martin Health, Stuart, FL, p. A140
CHASTANG, Mark J., Chief Executive Officer, Saint Elizabeths Hospital, Washington, DC, p. A116
CHASTANT, Lee, Chief Executive Officer, West Feliciana Parish Hospital, Saint Francisville, LA, p. A277
CHATANI, Kumar
Chief Information Officer, Mount Sinai Health System, Brookdale Hospital Medical Center, New York, NY, p. A432
Senior Vice President and Chief Information Officer Mount Sinai Health System, Brookdale Hospital Medical Center, New York, NY, p. A432
CHATELAIN, Alicia, Director Human Resource, Hood Memorial Hospital, Amite, LA, p. A262
CHATELAIN, Vincent, Director Business Development, River Oaks Hospital, New Orleans, LA, p. A275
CHATLEY, Alice M, R.N., MSN, Vice President Acute Care Services, Ssm Health St. Mary'S Hospital – Jefferson City, Jefferson City, MO, p. A361
CHATMAN, Hubert, Chief Civilian Personnel, Wright Patterson Medical Center, Wright, OH, p. A494
CHATMAN, Jim, Chief Financial Officer, Maria Parham Medical Center, Henderson, NC, p. A455
CHATMAN, Mary
Chief Executive Officer, Wellstar Kennestone Hospital, Marietta, GA, p. A157
Chief Executive Officer, Wellstar Windy Hill Hospital, Marietta, GA, p. A157
CHATTERJEE, Kanan, M.D., Chief of Staff, Lebanon Veterans Affairs Medical Center, Lebanon, PA, p. A529
CHATTERTON, Bryan, Chief Executive Officer, Kindred Hospital–Indianapolis, Indianapolis, IN, p. A207
CHAUDHARY, Shahid, M.D., Chief Medical Officer, Avera St. Luke'S Hospital, Aberdeen, SD, p. A559
CHAUDHRY, Riaz, M.D., Chief Medical Officer, Mercy Health – St. Charles Hospital, Oregon, OH, p. A489
CHAUDHURI, Sumanta, M.D.
Chief Medical Officer, Hemet Valley Medical Center, Hemet, CA, p. A61
Chief Medical Officer, Menifee Valley Medical Center, Sun City, CA, p. A91
CHAUDIER, David, Chief Executive Officer, Lifecare Hospitals Of Wisconsin, Pewaukee, WI, p. A703
CHAUDRY, Zafar, M.D., Senior Vice President and Chief Information Officer, Seattle Children'S Hospital, Seattle, WA, p. A678
CHAUHAN, Varun, Chief Executive Officer, Kentfield Rehabilitation And Specialty Hospital, Kentfield, CA, p. A62
CHAUSSARD, David, Chief Executive Officer, Hillcrest Hospital Claremore, Claremore, OK, p. A498
CHAVEZ, Irene, Senior Vice President and Area Manager, Kaiser Permanente San Jose Medical Center, San Jose, CA, p. A86
CHAVEZ, Shari, Chief Nursing Officer, Swedish Medical Center, Englewood, CO, p. A100
CHAVEZ, Steven, Vice President Finance and Operations, Kettering Medical Center, Kettering, OH, p. A485
CHAVEZ, Virgil, Director Information Technology, Tsehootsooi Medical Center, Fort Defiance, AZ, p. A29
CHAVIS, Anthony D, M.D., Vice President Enterprise Medical Officer, Community Hospital Foundation, Community Hospital Of The Monterey Peninsula, Monterey, CA, p. A73
CHAWLA, Nikki, M.D., Medical Director, Alliancehealth Seminole, Seminole, OK, p. A507
CHAYER, Olivia, Director, Human Resources, York Hospital, York, ME, p. A285
CHAYKIN, Lee B., Chief Executive Officer, Aventura Hospital And Medical Center, Aventura, FL, p. A117
CHECK, Arthur, M.D., Chief Medical Officer, Story County Medical Center, Nevada, IA, p. A227
CHECKETTS, Lannie
Chief Financial Officer, Saint Alphonsus Medical Center – Nampa, Nampa, ID, p. A170
Chief Financial Officer, Saint Alphonsus Medical Center – Ontario, Ontario, OR, p. A515
CHEE, Darlene, Acting Chief Executive Officer, Chinle Comprehensive Health Care Facility, Chinle, AZ, p. A29
CHEEK, Collin, Administrator, Baptist Memorial Hospital – Calhoun, Calhoun City, MS, p. A345
CHEEK, Holly, Vice President and Chief Nursing Officer, Columbus Regional Hospital, Columbus, IN, p. A201
CHEEK, Michael, Chief Financial Officer, Christus Good Shepherd Medical Center–Marshall, Marshall, TX, p. A623
CHEEK, Ramona, MS, R.N., Chief Nursing Officer, Mercy Health – Fairfield Hospital, Fairfield, OH, p. A483

CHEEMA, Linde, Vice President Human Resources, Sequoia Hospital, Redwood City, CA, p. A80

CHEESEMAN, Karen, Chief Executive Officer, Mackinac Straits Health System, Inc., Saint Ignace, MI, p. A321

CHEEVER, Liz, Administrator, Miracle Mile Medical Center, Los Angeles, CA, p. A68

CHEKURU, Naidu, M.D., Chief Medical Officer, Covenant Specialty Hospital, Lubbock, TX, p. A621

CHELLAPPA, Sheila, M.D., Chief of Staff, Coatesville Veterans Affairs Medical Center, Coatesville, PA, p. A523

CHEN, Bonny, M.D., Vice President and Chief Medical Officer, Adventist Medical Center – Hinsdale, Hinsdale, IL, p. A186

CHEN, David, M.D.
    Chief Medical Officer, Multicare Deaconess Hospital, Spokane, WA, p. A679
    Chief Medical Officer, Multicare Valley Hospital, Spokane Valley, WA, p. A680

CHEN, Helen, M.D., Chief Medical Officer, Hebrew Rehabilitation Center, Roslindale, MA, p. A302

CHEN, Stephen, M.D., Chief Medicare, Alhambra Hospital Medical Center, Alhambra, CA, p. A50

CHEN, Van, M.D., Medical Director, Ballard Rehabilitation Hospital, San Bernardino, CA, p. A83

CHENEY, David, Chief Executive Officer, Sutter Medical Center, Sacramento, Sacramento, CA, p. A82

CHENG, Alice, President and Chief Executive Officer, Beverly Hospital, Montebello, CA, p. A72

CHENG, Rebecca
    Chief Financial Officer, California Hospital Medical Center, Los Angeles, CA, p. A66
    Chief Financial Officer, Glendale Memorial Hospital And Health Center, Glendale, CA, p. A60

CHENG, Ringo, Director Information Technology, Surgery Specialty Hospitals Of America, Pasadena, TX, p. A628

CHENNAULT, Paula, Administrator, Unity Psychiatric Care–Columbia, Columbia, TN, p. A568

CHENOWETH, Judy, Chief Nursing Officer, Russell County Hospital, Russell Springs, KY, p. A260

CHERAMIE, Bennett, Vice President Information Technology, Baton Rouge General Medical Center, Baton Rouge, LA, p. A263

CHERAY, James, M.D., Chief Medical Officer, Menorah Medical Center, Overland Park, KS, p. A243

CHERMSIDE, Paula L., Chief Executive Officer, Aspirus Ironwood Hospitals & Clinics, Inc., Ironwood, MI, p. A315

CHERONE, Nancy, Executive Director and Administrator, Nazareth Hospital, Philadelphia, PA, p. A535

CHERRY, Deano, Chief Information Officer, Upmc Kane, Kane, PA, p. A528

CHERRY, Jean, Executive Vice President, Commonwealth Regional Specialty Hospital, Bowling Green, KY, p. A249

CHERRY, Jonathan M., President and Chief Executive Officer, Lifestream Behavioral Center, Leesburg, FL, p. A128

CHERRY, Kris, Ph.D., R.N., Chief Nursing Officer, Saint Francis Hospital–Bartlett, Bartlett, TN, p. A566

CHERRY, Michael, Chief Financial Officer, Tennova Healthcare–Lafollette Medical Center, La Follette, TN, p. A572

CHERRY, Robert, M.D., Chief Medical and Quality Officer, Ronald Reagan Ucla Medical Center, Los Angeles, CA, p. A69

CHERRY, Troy, Chief Financial Officer, Schick Shadel Hospital, Seattle, WA, p. A678

CHESLEK, Ingrid, R.N., Chief Nursing Officer, Mary Free Bed Rehabilitation Hospital, Grand Rapids, MI, p. A312

CHESLEY, Jeanine, Chief Executive Officer, New England Rehabilitation Hospital Of Portland, Portland, ME, p. A284

CHESLEY, Judy S, M.D., Chief of Staff, Sanford Luverne Medical Center, Luverne, MN, p. A334

CHESLEY, Randy, Director Information Technology, Copley Hospital, Morrisville, VT, p. A654

CHESLEY, Walter, Senior Vice President Human Resources, Hennepin Healthcare, Minneapolis, MN, p. A335

CHESNOS, Richard C, Senior Vice President Finance and Chief Financial Officer, St. Clair Hospital, Pittsburgh, PA, p. A537

CHESSARE, John B., President and Chief Executive Officer, Greater Baltimore Medical Center, Baltimore, MD, p. A288

CHESSON, Andrew, Chief Medical Officer, Catawba Valley Medical Center, Hickory, NC, p. A456

CHESSUM, George
    Senior Vice President and Chief Information Officer, Community First Medical Center, Chicago, IL, p. A177
    Senior Vice President Information Systems and Chief Information Officer, Amita Health Saint Joseph Hospital, Chicago, IL, p. A176
    Vice President Information Systems, Amita Health Saint Francis Hospital Evanston, Evanston, IL, p. A182

CHESTER, Julie, Vice President Human Resources, University Hospitals Cleveland Medical Center, Cleveland, OH, p. A478

CHESTER, Linnes L, USAF, MSC, Administrator, Mike O'Callaghan Federal Hospital, Nellis Afb, NV, p. A396

CHESTER, William, Manager Human Resources, Grand Junction Veterans Health Care System, Grand Junction, CO, p. A101

CHESTNUT–RAULS, Monica, Vice President Human Resources, Peconic Bay Medical Center, Riverhead, NY, p. A442

CHEUNG, Alan, M.D., Vice President Medical Affairs, Adventist Health Castle, Kailua, HI, p. A165

CHEUNG, Marilou, Assistant Administrator Finance, Kaiser Permanente Woodland Hills Medical Center, Los Angeles, CA, p. A67

CHEUNG, Raymond, M.D., Chief of Staff, San Ramon Regional Medical Center, San Ramon, CA, p. A88

CHEVERE, Carlos, M.D., Medical Director, I. Gonzalez Martinez Oncologic Hospital, Hato Rey, PR, p. A716

CHEYNET, Sandee, Vice President Administrative Services, Bluefield Regional Medical Center, Bluefield, WV, p. A683

CHHABRA, Ankit, Director Finance, Cleveland Clinic Fairview Hospital, Cleveland, OH, p. A477

CHHIKARA, Subir, President and Founder, Crockett Medical Center, Crockett, TX, p. A595

CHIACCHIARO, Peter, Vice President Human Resources, St. Joseph Hospital, Bethpage, NY, p. A423

CHIANESE, Charles, Vice President, Chief Operating Officer, Children'S Specialized Hospital, New Brunswick, NJ, p. A409

CHIANTELLA, Christopher, M.D., Chief Medical Officer, Inova Loudoun Hospital, Leesburg, VA, p. A661

CHIAVETTA, Robert, Vice President Finance, United Memorial Medical Center, Batavia, NY, p. A423

CHIBAYA, Daniel, Chief Information Officer, Adventist Health And Rideout, Marysville, CA, p. A71

CHICK, Melanie, Chief Executive Officer, Baylor Scott & White Medical Center – Trophy Club, Trophy Club, TX, p. A641

CHICKEN, Kurt, Director Support Services, Gundersen Palmer Lutheran Hospital And Clinics, West Union, IA, p. A231

CHIDESTER, Annamarie, R.N., Vice President, Patient Care Services, St. Joseph'S Hospital Of Buckhannon, Buckhannon, WV, p. A684

CHIEFFO, Ron, Chief Information Officer, Colorado River Medical Center, Needles, CA, p. A74

CHILCOTT, Stephen, Associate Director Human Resources, University Of California, Davis Medical Center, Sacramento, CA, p. A82

CHILD, Clint L, R.N., Chief Nursing Officer, Saint Alphonsus Medical Center – Nampa, Nampa, ID, p. A170

CHILDERS, Bethany, Director Human Resources, Methodist Fremont Health, Fremont, NE, p. A385

CHILDERS, James R, Vice President & Chief Financial Officer, Gibson General Hospital, Princeton, IN, p. A214

CHILDERS, Linda, Director Human Resources, Wallowa Memorial Hospital, Enterprise, OR, p. A512

CHILDERS, Scott W., Administrator, Mercy Hospital Lebanon, Lebanon, MO, p. A364

CHILDS, Joe, M.D., Vice President Medical Services, East Tennessee Children'S Hospital, Knoxville, TN, p. A572

CHILDS, Michelle, Chief Human Resources Officer, Salinas Valley Memorial Healthcare System, Salinas, CA, p. A83

CHILES, Kevin, Vice President Human Resources, Hutchinson Regional Medical Center, Hutchinson, KS, p. A237

CHILES, Morton, M.D., Chief Medical Officer, Novant Health Uva Health System Culpeper Medical Center, Culpeper, VA, p. A658

CHILESE, Melody, Chief Nurse Executive, Hawthorn Children Psychiatric Hospital, Saint Louis, MO, p. A369

CHILESKI, Andy, Chief Information Officer and Vice President Facilities, Berger Health System, Circleville, OH, p. A477

CHILL, Martha O'Regan
    Chief Information Officer, Bristol Regional Medical Center, Bristol, TN, p. A566
    Interim Chief Information Officer, Hancock County Hospital, Sneedville, TN, p. A579

CHILSON, Terrance, Chief of Staff, Tyler Memorial Hospital, Tunkhannock, PA, p. A542

CHILTON, Bryan, Director Information Systems, Navarro Regional Hospital, Corsicana, TX, p. A594

CHILTON, Hal, Senior Vice President and Chief Operating Officer, Adventist Health St. Helena, Saint Helena, CA, p. A82

CHIN, Ellyn, Vice President Finance, Gottlieb Memorial Hospital, Melrose Park, IL, p. A189

CHINBURG, Paul, M.D., Medical Director, Lane County Hospital, Dighton, KS, p. A234

CHING, Angelica
    Director Information Systems, Garfield Medical Center, Monterey Park, CA, p. A73
    Director Information Systems, Monterey Park Hospital, Monterey Park, CA, p. A73

CHINN, Tammie
    Chief Human Resource Officer, Williamson Memorial Hospital, Williamson, WV, p. A690
    Director Marketing and Public Relations, Plateau Medical Center, Oak Hill, WV, p. A688

CHINN, Terri, Vice President Finance, St. Mary'S Hospital And Medical Center, Grand Junction, CO, p. A101

CHINNOCK, Richard, Chief Medical Officer, LLUCH, Loma Linda University Children'S Hospital, Loma Linda, CA, p. A64

CHIOLO, Denise, Chief Human Resources Officer, Phoenixville Hospital, Phoenixville, PA, p. A537

CHIPMAN, Glen, Chief Financial Officer, Healthsource Saginaw, Inc., Saginaw, MI, p. A321

CHIRICHELLA, Joseph, President and Chief Executive Officer, Deborah Heart And Lung Center, Browns Mills, NJ, p. A404

CHISHOLM, Sharon, Entity Human Resource Officer, Texas Health Presbyterian Hospital Allen, Allen, TX, p. A582

CHISSELL, Herbert G, M.D., Chief Medical Officer, Torrance State Hospital, Torrance, PA, p. A542

CHITCHYAN, Ara, M.D., Medical Director, Roosevelt Warm Springs Rehabilitation Hospital – Rehab, Warm Springs, GA, p. A162

CHIUSANO, Jennifer, R.N., Chief Nursing Officer, Saint Francis Hospital, Memphis, TN, p. A575

CHIVERS, John
    Chief Financial Officer, Ridgecrest Regional Hospital, Ridgecrest, CA, p. A80
    Senior Vice President Finance, Sierra View Medical Center, Porterville, CA, p. A79

CHMURA, David, Chief Information Officer, Copper Queen Community Hospital, Bisbee, AZ, p. A28

CHOATE, Charlotte, Director Information Systems, University Hospital Summerville, Augusta, GA, p. A147

CHOATE, Matthew, Chief Nursing Officer, The University Of Vermont Health Network Central Vermont Medical Center, Berlin, VT, p. A654

CHOCKLETT, Wyatt, Chief Operating Officer, Largo Medical Center, Largo, FL, p. A128

CHOINIERE, Leon, Vice President, Chief Financial Officer, St. Mary Medical Center, Long Beach, CA, p. A65

CHOINKA, Keith A, Vice President Information Systems and Chief Information Officer, St. Joseph Hospital, Nashua, NH, p. A401

CHOKSHI, Sushil, M.D., Chief Medical Officer, Faith Community Hospital, Jacksboro, TX, p. A616

CHOLGER, Dave, Chief Financial Officer, Woodlawn Hospital, Rochester, IN, p. A214

CHOLKA, Nancy, R.N., Chief Nursing Officer, Post Acute Medical Specialty Hospital Of Milwaukee, Greenfield, WI, p. A696

CHONG, Johnnette, Chief Financial Officer, Los Angeles Community Hospital At Los Angeles, Los Angeles, CA, p. A68

CHORD, Ginger, Coordinator Human Resources, Sturgis Regional Hospital, Sturgis, SD, p. A564

CHOREY, Raymond M., President and Chief Executive Officer, Southeastern Ohio Regional Medical Center, Cambridge, OH, p. A474

CHOU, David, Vice President, Chief Information and Digital Officer, Children'S Mercy Hospital Kansas City, Kansas City, MO, p. A362

CHOU, Rebecca, Director Information Systems, Palestine Regional Medical Center–East, Palestine, TX, p. A627

CHOUDHURY, Golam, Chief of Staff, Desert Springs Hospital Medical Center, Las Vegas, NV, p. A395

CHOUDHURY, Seleem, President and Chief Operating Officer, Porter Medical Center, Middlebury, VT, p. A654

CHOY, Ann N., Manager Human Resources and Payroll, Kuakini Medical Center, Honolulu, HI, p. A164

CHOZINSKI, Joseph P, M.D., Deputy Commander Clinical Services, Brooke Army Medical Center, Fort Sam Houston, TX, p. A604

CHRICEOL, Earlene, Chief Nursing Officer, Richardson Medical Center, Rayville, LA, p. A277

CHRISTENSEN, Carl
    Senior Vice President and Chief Information Officer, Northwestern Memorial HealthCare, Northwestern Memorial Hospital, Chicago, IL, p. A178
    Senior Vice President, Chief Information Officer, Northwestern Medicine Kishwaukee Hospital, Dekalb, IL, p. A181

CHRISTENSEN, Claudia, Director, Human Resources, Mills–Peninsula Health Services, Burlingame, CA, p. A53

CHRISTENSEN, Connie, Chief Financial Officer, Morrill County Community Hospital, Bridgeport, NE, p. A383

CHRISTENSEN, David, M.D., Senior Vice President and Chief Medical Officer, Valley Children'S Healthcare, Madera, CA, p. A70

CHRISTENSEN, Elizabeth B, Director Human Resources, Northern Light Mercy Hospital, Portland, ME, p. A284

CHRISTENSEN, G N, M.D., Chief Medical Officer, William Bee Ririe Hospital, Ely, NV, p. A393
CHRISTENSEN, Gwen, Vice President, Finance, Aurora Baycare Medical Center, Green Bay, WI, p. A696
CHRISTENSEN, Jeffrey, Chief Executive Officer, Encompass Health Rehabilitation Institute Of Tucson, Tucson, AZ, p. A37
CHRISTENSEN, Kim, Interim Chief Nursing Executive, Sheridan Community Hospital, Sheridan, MI, p. A322
CHRISTENSEN, Mark
Chief Financial Officer, Weiser Memorial Hospital, Weiser, ID, p. A172
Director, Finance, Cassia Regional Hospital, Burley, ID, p. A168
CHRISTENSEN, Marti, Director of Psychiatric Nursing, Douglas County Community Mental Health Center, Omaha, NE, p. A389
CHRISTENSEN, Micheal, Interim Chief Executive Officer, Drumright Regional Hospital, Drumright, OK, p. A498
CHRISTENSEN, Scott, Chief Executive Officer, Delta Regional Medical Center, Greenville, MS, p. A347
CHRISTENSEN, Todd, Vice President, Finance, Grand Itasca Clinic And Hospital, Grand Rapids, MN, p. A333
CHRISTENSEN, Troy, Chief Financial Officer, Madison Memorial Hospital, Rexburg, ID, p. A171
CHRISTENSEN, W R, M.D., Chief of Staff, Ut Health Pittsburg, Pittsburg, TX, p. A628
CHRISTENSEN–MORES, Donna, JD, Director Human Resources, Myrtue Medical Center, Harlan, IA, p. A224
CHRISTENSON, Ron, Chief Financial Officer, Morris County Hospital, Council Grove, KS, p. A234
CHRISTENSON, Shannon, Director Human Resources, Aurora West Allis Medical Center, West Allis, WI, p. A708
CHRISTIAN, Bruce C.
Chief Executive Officer, Adventist Medical Center Bolingbrook, Bolingbrook, IL, p. A174
President and Chief Executive Officer, Adventist Medical Center Glenoaks, Glendale Heights, IL, p. A184
CHRISTIAN, Glenn, Administrator, Mayo Clinic Health System In Cannon Falls, Cannon Falls, MN, p. A329
CHRISTIAN, Greg
Senior Vice President, Area Manager – San Bernardino County Area, Kaiser Permanente Fontana Medical Center, Fontana, CA, p. A58
Sr Vice President, Area Manager – San Bernardino County Area, Kaiser Permanente Fontana Medical Center, Fontana, CA, p. A58
CHRISTIAN, Karolyne, Director Human Resources, Byrd Regional Hospital, Leesville, LA, p. A272
CHRISTIAN, Lynn, R.N., MSN, Division Director, Acute Care Nursing, Centracare Health–Monticello, Monticello, MN, p. A336
CHRISTIAN, Michael, Chief Operating Officer, St. John Sapulpa, Sapulpa, OK, p. A507
CHRISTIANO, Barbara, Vice President, Patient Care Services and Chief Nursing Officer, Penn Medicine Princeton Medical Center, Plainsboro, NJ, p. A411
CHRISTIANSEN, Anne, Chief Financial Officer, Pioneer Memorial Hospital And Health Services, Viborg, SD, p. A565
CHRISTIANSEN, Hilary, Chief Financial Officer, George C Grape Community Hospital, Hamburg, IA, p. A223
CHRISTIANSEN, Keith, Chief Nursing Officer, Select Specialty Hospital–Erie, Erie, PA, p. A525
CHRISTIANSEN, Lia
Chief Operating Officer, Acute Care Hospitals, Fairview Lakes Health Services, Wyoming, MN, p. A343
Chief Operating Officer, Acute Care Hospitals, Fairview Northland Medical Center, Princeton, MN, p. A338
Chief Operating Officer, Acute Care Hospitals, St. John'S Hospital, Maplewood, MN, p. A335
Chief Operating Officer, Acute Care Hospitals, St. Joseph'S Hospital, Saint Paul, MN, p. A340
Chief Operating Officer, Acute Care Hospitals, Woodwinds Health Campus, Woodbury, MN, p. A343
CHRISTIANSEN, Sara, Interim Director Human Resources, Ridgeview Sibley Medical Center, Arlington, MN, p. A327
CHRISTIANSON, Chad, Chief Executive Officer, Ocala Regional Medical Center, Ocala, FL, p. A133
CHRISTIANSON, Delano, Administrator, Centracare Health–Sauk Centre, Sauk Centre, MN, p. A340
CHRISTIE, Janet L., Senior Vice President Human Resources, Uf Health Shands Hospital, Gainesville, FL, p. A124
CHRISTINE, Gerald, Chief Financial Officer, Lakewood Ranch Medical Center, Bradenton, FL, p. A118
CHRISTION, Lydia, Director Human Resources, Encompass Health Rehabilitation Hospital Of Dothan, Dothan, AL, p. A17
CHRISTISON, George, M.D., Medical Director, Patton State Hospital, Patton, CA, p. A77
CHRISTMAN, Lawrence, Chief Financial Officer and Chief Operating Officer, Riverview Health, Noblesville, IN, p. A213
CHRISTMAN, Thomas C, Director Plant Operations, Kindred Hospital–St. Louis, Saint Louis, MO, p. A369
CHRISTNER, Jane, Chief Nursing Officer, Mclaren Thumb Region, Bad Axe, MI, p. A307
CHRISTOPH, Rebecca, Director Nursing and Patient Care Services, Mid–Valley Hospital, Omak, WA, p. A676
CHRISTOPHEL, Randal, President and Chief Executive Officer, Goshen Health, Goshen, IN, p. A205
CHRISTOPHER, Candi, CPA, Chief Financial Officer, Stonesprings Hospital Center, Dulles, VA, p. A658
CHRISTOPHER, Sue, Vice President, Human Resources, Baptist Health Floyd, New Albany, IN, p. A212
CHRISTOPHERSEN, Kristin, Chief Nursing Officer, Fountain Valley Regional Hospital And Medical Center, Fountain Valley, CA, p. A58
CHRISTY, Rose, Executive Director of Medical Services, Hamilton Center, Terre Haute, IN, p. A215
CHU, Betty, M.D., Chief Medical Officer and Vice President of Medical Affairs, Henry Ford West Bloomfield Hospital, West Bloomfield, MI, p. A324
CHU, Edward, Chief Financial Officer, Leahi Hospital, Honolulu, HI, p. A164
CHUA, Jesus, M.D., Chief of Staff, Franklin Foundation Hospital, Franklin, LA, p. A267
CHUE, Bevins, M.D., Medical Director, Encompass Health Rehabilitation Hospital Of Desert Canyon, Las Vegas, NV, p. A395
CHUGDEN, Robert, M.D., Chief Medical Officer, West Jefferson Medical Center, Marrero, LA, p. A273
CHUKWUMA, Lilian, Chief Financial Officer, United Medical Center, Washington, DC, p. A116
CHULICK, Michele, President and Chief Executive Officer, Wyoming Medical Center, Casper, WY, p. A710
CHUN, Ryan, Information Resources Management, San Francisco Va Medical Center, San Francisco, CA, p. A85
CHUNG, Esther, Chief Operating Officer, St. David'S Medical Center, Austin, TX, p. A586
CHUNG, Maria, CPA, Director Fiscal Services, Shriners Hospitals For Children–Boston, Boston, MA, p. A296
CHUNG, Michael, Chief Financial Officer, Greater El Monte Community Hospital, South El Monte, CA, p. A90
CHUNG, William, M.D., Chief of Staff, Chinese Hospital, San Francisco, CA, p. A85
CHUNN, Ashley, Director of Nursing, Atmore Community Hospital, Atmore, AL, p. A14
CHURCH, Brian, Senior Vice President and Chief Financial Officer, Phoebe Putney Memorial Hospital, Albany, GA, p. A145
CHURCH, Kim
Manager Human Resources, G. Werber Bryan Psychiatric Hospital, Columbia, SC, p. A551
Manager Human Resources, William S. Hall Psychiatric Institute, Columbia, SC, p. A551
CHURCH, Rhonda, Director Human Resources, Bastrop Rehabilitation Hospital, Monroe, LA, p. A274
CHURCHILL, Brigitte, Director of Human Resources, Memorial Satilla Health, Waycross, GA, p. A163
CHURCHILL, Larry, Director Information Services, Alliancehealth Woodward, Woodward, OK, p. A510
CHURCHILL, Sandi, Vice President Business Development and Operations, Professional Services, Advocate Good Samaritan Hospital, Downers Grove, IL, p. A181
CHURCHILL, Timothy A.
Interim Chief Executive Officer, Franklin Memorial Hospital, Farmington, ME, p. A283
President, Stephens Memorial Hospital, Norway, ME, p. A284
CHURCHWELL, Kevin B, M.D., President and Chief Operating Officer, Boston Children'S Hospital, Boston, MA, p. A295
CIAMPA, Amy, Chief Financial Officer, Park Royal Hospital, Fort Myers, FL, p. A123
CIAMPA, Steve, Vice President Finance, Porter Medical Center, Middlebury, VT, p. A654
CIANCIOTTO CROYLE, Allison, Vice President of Human Resources, Mercy Medical Center, Rockville Centre, NY, p. A443
CIANFLONE, Laura, Director Human Resources, Kenmore Mercy Hospital, Kenmore, NY, p. A430
CIAREFELLA, Donna, Director Human Resources, Vibra Hospital Of Western Massachusetts, Springfield, MA, p. A304
CICCARELLI, John, Director Information Technology, Parkview Community Hospital Medical Center, Riverside, CA, p. A81
CICCARELLI, Thomas, Chief Information Officer, East Orange General Hospital, East Orange, NJ, p. A405
CICCONE, Josie, Director, Human Resources, Garden City Hospital, Garden City, MI, p. A312
CICERI, David P, M.D., Chief Medical Officer, Baylor Scott & White Continuing Care Hospital–Temple, Temple, TX, p. A639
CICIRETTI, Mary Louise, Director Human Resources, Riddle Hospital, Media, PA, p. A531
CIENCEWICKI, Michael, M.D., Vice President Medical Affairs, Hackensack Meridian Health Raritan Bay Medical Center, Perth Amboy, NJ, p. A411
CIHA, Clayton, President and Chief Executive Officer, Alexian Brothers Behavioral Health Hospital, Hoffman Estates, IL, p. A186
CIHAK, Scott A., President and Chief Executive Officer, Tristar Centennial Medical Center, Nashville, TN, p. A577
CIMA, Robert R., M.D., Medical Director, Hospital Operations, Mayo Clinic Hospital – Rochester, Rochester, MN, p. A338
CIMINO, Michael A., Chief Financial Officer, Banner Behavioral Health Hospital – Scottsdale, Scottsdale, AZ, p. A35
CIMMINO, Denise, MSN, R.N., Assistant Vice President, Nursing and Patient Care Services, Carepoint Health Christ Hospital, Jersey City, NJ, p. A407
CINTRON, Jacob, President and Chief Executive Officer, University Medical Center Of El Paso, El Paso, TX, p. A603
CIOFFI, Cheryl, R.N., Senior Vice President Patient Care Services and Chief Nursing Officer, Frederick Regional Health System, Frederick, MD, p. A290
CIOTA, Mark, Chief Executive Officer, Mayo Clinic Health System – Albert Lea And Austin, Albert Lea, MN, p. A327
CIRALDO, Lou, Information Services Representative, University Hospitals Geauga Medical Center, Chardon, OH, p. A475
CIRBA, Michael, Chief Information Officer, Good Shepherd Specialty Hospital, Bethlehem, PA, p. A520
CIRO, Maria, Director Human Resources, Acuity Specialty Hospital Of New Jersey, Atlantic City, NJ, p. A403
CIROCCO, Anthony, Chief Financial Officer, Dignity Health Arizona General Hospital, Laveen, AZ, p. A31
CIRONE, Laura, Manager Human Resources, Rochelle Community Hospital, Rochelle, IL, p. A194
CITA, Bob, Chief Information Officer, Searhc Mt. Edgecumbe Hospital, Sitka, AK, p. A27
CITAK, Michael, M.D., Chief Medical Officer, Lake Cumberland Regional Hospital, Somerset, KY, p. A260
CITRO, Tina, R.N., Chief Nursing Officer, Vice President, Patient Services, Wellspan Ephrata Community Hospital, Ephrata, PA, p. A525
CIUFO, Donna, R.N., Vice President and Chief Nurse Executive, Hackensack Meridian Health Southern Ocean Medical Center, Manahawkin, NJ, p. A408
CIVIC, Dave, M.D., Associate Director Clinical Services, U. S. Public Health Service Phoenix Indian Medical Center, Phoenix, AZ, p. A34
CIVITELLO, Dean
Vice President Human Resources, Saint Joseph'S Medical Center, Yonkers, NY, p. A448
Vice President, Human Resources, Public Relations and Development, The University Of Vermont Health Network–Champlain Valley Physicians Hospital, Plattsburgh, NY, p. A441
CLAASSENS, Nicolise, Nurse Executive, West Central Georgia Regional Hospital, Columbus, GA, p. A151
CLABAUGH, John, Director Human Resources, Saint Luke'S East Hospital, Lee'S Summit, MO, p. A364
CLABUESCH, Paul, President and Chief Executive Officer, Harbor Beach Community Hospital, Harbor Beach, MI, p. A314
CLACK, Deborah, Chief Nursing Officer, Hunt Regional Medical Center, Greenville, TX, p. A608
CLAEYS, David, Chief Executive Officer, Beaumont Hospital Dearborn, Dearborn, MI, p. A309
CLAIR OLIVER, Delores, Chief Clinical Officer and Chief Operating Officer, Bridgepoint Hospital Capitol Hill, Washington, DC, p. A115
CLANCY, Mikki, Chief Operating Officer, Miami Valley Hospital, Dayton, OH, p. A481
CLANCY, Patricia, M.D., Director Medical Services, Maniilaq Health Center, Kotzebue, AK, p. A26
CLAPP, Ann R, Director Human Resources, Encompass Health Rehabilitation Hospital Of Texarkana, Texarkana, TX, p. A640
CLAPP, Denise
Chief Nursing Officer, Lourdes Counseling Center, Richland, WA, p. A677
Chief Nursing Officer, Lourdes Medical Center, Pasco, WA, p. A676
CLAPP, William, M.D., Chief of Medical Staff, Methodist Hospital Union County, Morganfield, KY, p. A258
CLARK, Allan W, M.D., Medical Director, Southwood Psychiatric Hospital, Pittsburgh, PA, p. A537
CLARK, Ashley, Coordinator Human Resources, Noland Hospital Birmingham, Birmingham, AL, p. A15

CLARK, Ben, Vice President and Chief Information Officer, Centra Lynchburg General Hospital, Lynchburg, VA, p. A662

CLARK, Christopher, President and Chief Executive Officer, Saint Vincent Hospital, Erie, PA, p. A525

CLARK, Dale, Chief Operating Officer, Holston Valley Medical Center, Kingsport, TN, p. A572

CLARK, Dave, Interim Chief Executive Officer, Hardeman County Memorial Hospital, Quanah, TX, p. A630

CLARK, Debra, Chief Nursing Officer, Bayfront Health Port Charlotte, Port Charlotte, FL, p. A137

CLARK, Denise, Chief Nursing Officer, Holy Cross Hospital, Taos, NM, p. A421

CLARK, Ed, M.D., Chief Medical Officer, Primary Children'S Hospital, Salt Lake City, UT, p. A652

CLARK, Eileen, Vice President Information Services, Charleston Area Medical Center, Charleston, WV, p. A684

CLARK, Janice, Manager Human Resources, Garfield Park Hospital, Chicago, IL, p. A177

CLARK, Jason, Director Quality Improvement, Risk Management and Information System, Greenwood County Hospital, Eureka, KS, p. A235

CLARK, Jeff, Director Information Systems, Graham Regional Medical Center, Graham, TX, p. A608

CLARK, Jeffrey
Administrator, Memorial Specialty Hospital, Lake Charles, LA, p. A272
Chief Nursing Officer, Cornerstone Hospital Of Southwest Louisiana, Lake Charles, LA, p. A272

CLARK, Jeffrey A, Vice President Human Resources, Kadlec Regional Medical Center, Richland, WA, p. A677

CLARK, Jeremy L., Market Chief Executive Officer, Hilton Head Hospital, Hilton Head Island, SC, p. A554

CLARK, Judith, Chief Financial Officer, Greeneville Community Hospital West, Greeneville, TN, p. A570

CLARK, Karen
Director Administrative Services, Sonoma Developmental Center, Eldridge, CA, p. A57
Vice President Patient Care Services, St. Mary'S Regional Medical Center, Lewiston, ME, p. A283

CLARK, Karen, MS, R.N., Vice President Operations, Advocate South Suburban Hospital, Hazel Crest, IL, p. A185

CLARK, Kent, M.D., Chief Medical Affairs and Quality, Waldo County General Hospital Maine Health, Belfast, ME, p. A282

CLARK, Lisa, Director Human Resources, Willamette Valley Medical Center, Mcminnville, OR, p. A514

CLARK, Mark
Chief Information Officer, Uchealth Yampa Valley Medical Center, Steamboat Springs, CO, p. A105
Human Resources Liaison, U. S. Air Force Regional Hospital, Elmendorf Afb, AK, p. A26

CLARK, Mark A
Vice President Operations, Good Samaritan Regional Health Center, Mount Vernon, IL, p. A190
Vice President Operations, Ssm Health St. Mary'S Hospital Centralia, Centralia, IL, p. A175

CLARK, Michael
Executive Vice President and Chief Financial Officer, Fhn Memorial Hospital, Freeport, IL, p. A183
Fiscal Administrative Manager, Connecticut Veterans Home And Hospital, Rocky Hill, CT, p. A110

CLARK, Michael A, Chief Operating Officer, Mckay–Dee Hospital, Ogden, UT, p. A649

CLARK, Michael A., Administrator, Mckay–Dee Hospital, Ogden, UT, p. A649

CLARK, N Travis.
President, Page Memorial Hospital, Luray, VA, p. A661
President, Valley Health Shenandoah Memorial Hospital, Woodstock, VA, p. A669

CLARK, Nancy, Vice President Human Resources, Regional Medical Center Of San Jose, San Jose, CA, p. A86

CLARK, Patrick, Manager Information Technology, Sunnyview Rehabilitation Hospital, Schenectady, NY, p. A444

CLARK, Paul A., President and Chief Executive Officer, Merrick Medical Center, Central City, NE, p. A383

CLARK, Paulette, Chief Human Resource Officer, Roseland Community Hospital, Chicago, IL, p. A179

CLARK, Randal, Vice President Finance, Northlight Sebasticook Valley Hospital, Pittsfield, ME, p. A284

CLARK, Renee, Senior Vice President and Chief Operating Officer, Southcoast Hospitals Group, Fall River, MA, p. A298

CLARK, Rhonda, Interim Chief Nursing Officer, Alta Vista Regional Hospital, Las Vegas, NM, p. A419

CLARK, Robert J., President and Chief Executive Officer, Bristol Bay Area Health Corporation, Dillingham, AK, p. A26

CLARK, Robin, Chief Nursing Officer, Select Specialty Hospital–Greensboro, Greensboro, NC, p. A455

CLARK, Rodney, Chief Operating Officer, North Sunflower Medical Center, Ruleville, MS, p. A354

CLARK, Ron, M.D., Vice President Clinical Activities and Chief Medical Officer, Vcu Medical Center, Richmond, VA, p. A666

CLARK, Sharon, Director Human Resources, Hillsboro Area Hospital, Hillsboro, IL, p. A185

CLARK, Shawn, Director Information Systems, The Physicians Centre Hospital, Bryan, TX, p. A590

CLARK, Stella, MSN, R.N., Chief Nursing Officer, Hshs St. Joseph'S Hospital, Chippewa Falls, WI, p. A693

CLARK, Teresa, Chief Executive Officer and Administrator, Wichita County Health Center, Leoti, KS, p. A239

CLARK, Teresa J, R.N., MS, Chief Nursing Officer, Cook Children'S Medical Center, Fort Worth, TX, p. A604

CLARK, Theo, Director Financial Services, Promise Hospital Of Phoenix, Mesa, AZ, p. A32

CLARK, Thomas A., Regional President and Chief Executive Officer, Avera Queen Of Peace Hospital, Mitchell, SD, p. A562

CLARK, Troy
Chief Executive Officer, Encompass Health Rehabilitation Hospital Of Kingsport, Kingsport, TN, p. A572
Interim Administrator, Dr. Dan C. Trigg Memorial Hospital, Tucumcari, NM, p. A421

CLARK, William, M.D., Chief Clinical Affairs, Caro Center, Caro, MI, p. A308

CLARK, William H, Chief Financial Officer, Caldwell Memorial Hospital, Columbia, LA, p. A265

CLARKE, Clifton, Vice President Medical Management, Advocate Illinois Masonic Medical Center, Chicago, IL, p. A176

CLARKE, James, M.D., Vice President Medical Affairs and Clinical Effectiveness, Hackensack Meridian Health Ocean Medical Center, Brick Township, NJ, p. A404

CLAROS, Elizabeth, Administrator Personnel Services, Guam Memorial Hospital Authority, Tamuning, GU, p. A714

CLARY, Brandon, President and Chief Executive Officer, Anmed Health Cannon, Pickens, SC, p. A556

CLARY, Elizabeth P, Vice President Behavioral Health, Parkwest Medical Center, Knoxville, TN, p. A572

CLATANOFF, Kris, Director Human Resources, St. Joseph Medical Center, Houston, TX, p. A613

CLAUDY, Frank, M.D., Vice President Medical Staff Affairs, Genesis Medical Center, Davenport, Davenport, IA, p. A220

CLAUNCH, Jeremy, Chief Financial Officer, Power County Hospital District, American Falls, ID, p. A167

CLAUSEN, Patricia J, R.N., Chief Nurse Executive, Kaiser Permanente Downey Medical Center, Downey, CA, p. A56

CLAUSSEN, Denise, R.N., MSN, Chief Nursing Officer, Texas Health Presbyterian Hospital Kaufman, Kaufman, TX, p. A617

CLAUSSEN, Tammy, Chief Human Resource Officer, Tri Valley Health System, Cambridge, NE, p. A383

CLAVELL, Luis, M.D., Medical Director, San Jorge Children'S Hospital, Santurce, PR, p. A719

CLAWSON, Tonya, Manager Human Resources, Mercyone Centerville Medical Center, Centerville, IA, p. A218

CLAXTON, Tracey
Chief Financial Officer, Jennersville Hospital, West Grove, PA, p. A544
Chief Financial Officer, Musc Health Chester Medical Center, Chester, SC, p. A550

CLAY, David, Chief Executive Officer, Lower Keys Medical Center, Key West, FL, p. A126

CLAY, Elysia, Chief Nursing Officer, Encompass Health Rehabilitation Hospital Of Dallas, Dallas, TX, p. A596

CLAYMORE, Krystal, Chief Financial Officer, Great Plains Health, North Platte, NE, p. A388

CLAYPOOL, Blain, Chief Executive Officer, St. Joseph Regional Medical Center, Lewiston, ID, p. A170

CLAYTON, Edward, Chief Executive Officer, Phelps Health, Rolla, MO, p. A368

CLAYTON, Kent G.
Chief Executive Officer, Los Alamitos Medical Center, Los Alamitos, CA, p. A65
Interim Chief Executive Officer, Placentia–Linda Hospital, Placentia, CA, p. A78

CLAYTON, Melissa S., CPA, Chief Financial Officer, Northlake Behavioral Health System, Mandeville, LA, p. A273

CLEARY, Gerard M., M.D., Senior Vice President, Chief of Staff and Chief Medical Officer, Abington Hospital, Abington, PA, p. A519

CLEARY, Mary Elizabeth., President, Macneal Hospital, Berwyn, IL, p. A174

CLEARY, Steven R, Chief Financial Officer, Overland Park Regional Medical Center, Overland Park, KS, p. A243

CLEAVER, Chuck, Vice President and Chief Financial Officer, Cleveland Clinic Martin North Hospital, Stuart, FL, p. A140

CLECKLER, Jason, Chief Executive Officer, Delta County Memorial Hospital, Delta, CO, p. A98

CLEGG, Travis, Vice President, Operations, Adventist Health Castle, Kailua, HI, p. A165

CLELAND, Dub, Chief Financial Officer, Oklahoma Surgical Hospital, Tulsa, OK, p. A509

CLELAND, William H, M.D., Chief Medical Officer, University Of Mississippi Medical Center, Jackson, MS, p. A349

CLEMEN, Linda, Vice President and Chief Nursing Officer, Katherine Shaw Bethea Hospital, Dixon, IL, p. A181

CLEMENT, Bernie, Chief Information Officer, Thibodaux Regional Medical Center, Thibodaux, LA, p. A279

CLEMENT, Bruce, Chief Operating Officer, Slidell Memorial Hospital, Slidell, LA, p. A279

CLEMENT, Charles, Chief Executive Officer, Searhc Mt. Edgecumbe Hospital, Sitka, AK, p. A27

CLEMENT, Mark C., President, Bethesda North Hospital, Cincinnati, OH, p. A475

CLEMENT, Michelle, Executive Assistant/Human Resources Director, Roundup Memorial Healthcare, Roundup, MT, p. A380

CLEMENTS, James, Chief Executive Officer, Cullman Regional Medical Center, Cullman, AL, p. A16

CLEMENTS, John R, Chief Financial Officer, Mccullough–Hyde Memorial Hospital/Trihealth, Oxford, OH, p. A489

CLEMENTS, Morgan, Director of Human Resources, Anmed Health Rehabilitation Hospital, Anderson, SC, p. A549

CLEMMENSEN, Scott
Vice President Human Resources and Leadership Enhancement, Capital Health Medical Center–Hopewell, Pennington, NJ, p. A410
Vice President Human Resources and Leadership Enhancement, Capital Health Regional Medical Center, Trenton, NJ, p. A413

CLEMMER, Deb, Vice President Human Resources, Bothwell Regional Health Center, Sedalia, MO, p. A371

CLEMONS, Deneace, Chief Operating Officer, Twin Lakes Regional Medical Center, Leitchfield, KY, p. A254

CLER, Leslie, M.D., Chief Medical Officer, Methodist Dallas Medical Center, Dallas, TX, p. A597

CLERE, Trevor, Director Information Technology, Mercy Medical Center, Canton, OH, p. A474

CLEVELAND, Austin B., Chief Executive Officer, Cornerstone Hospital Of Southwest Louisiana, Lake Charles, LA, p. A272

CLEVELAND, Cynthia, Ph.D., R.N., Associate Director for Patient Care Services and Nurse Executive, Birmingham Veterans Affairs Medical Center, Birmingham, AL, p. A14

CLEVENGER, Erin R, Chief Nursing Officer and Director of Quality, Memorial Medical Center, Port Lavaca, TX, p. A630

CLEVINGER, Betty, Chief Nursing Officer, Community Memorial Hospital, Hicksville, OH, p. A484

CLEWS, Donna, Ph.D., R.N., Vice President Patient Care Services, Berkeley Medical Center, Martinsburg, WV, p. A687

CLIFFORD, Joan, Medical Center Director and Chief Executive Officer, Bedford Veterans Affairs Medical Center, Edith Nourse Rogers Memorial Veterans Hospital, Bedford, MA, p. A294

CLIFFORD, Michael J, Director Finance, Wayne Memorial Hospital, Honesdale, PA, p. A527

CLIFFORD, Ryan, M.D., Chief of Staff, Washakie Medical Center, Worland, WY, p. A713

CLINE, Carl T., Chief Executive Officer, Carilion Franklin Memorial Hospital, Rocky Mount, VA, p. A667

CLINE, Vickie, Director Human Resources, Mosaic Medical Center – Albany, Albany, MO, p. A356

CLINGENPEEL, Jeremy, Administrator, Satanta District Hospital And Long Term Care, Satanta, KS, p. A245

CLINGER, Dallas, Administrator, Power County Hospital District, American Falls, ID, p. A167

CLINITE, Ed, D.O., Chief of Staff, Adventist Health Sonora, Sonora, CA, p. A90

CLINTON, Lee, Chief Executive Officer, Titusville Area Hospital, Titusville, PA, p. A542

CLINTON, Lori, Chief Nursing Officer, Sparta Community Hospital, Sparta, IL, p. A196

CLIPP, Jerry, Manager Human Resources, Washakie Medical Center, Worland, WY, p. A713

CLISTER, Martha L, Director Human Resources, Canonsburg Hospital, Canonsburg, PA, p. A522

CLOHSEY, Maria, Director of Nursing, Hackensack Meridian Health Shore Rehabilitation Institute, Brick, NJ, p. A403

CLONCH, Les, Chief Information Officer, Texas Scottish Rite Hospital For Children, Dallas, TX, p. A598

CLONTS, Jolene, Director Human Resources, Logan Regional Hospital, Logan, UT, p. A648

CLOONAN, Shawn, Executive Vice President and Chief Operating Officer, Memorial Hermann – Texas Medical Center, Houston, TX, p. A612

CLOSE, Debra, Chief Executive Officer, Dukes Memorial Hospital, Peru, IN, p. A213

CLOUD, Avery, Vice President and Chief Information Officer, New Hanover Regional Medical Center, Wilmington, NC, p. A464
CLOUD, Sylvia, Director Human Resources, Silver Lake Medical Center, Los Angeles, CA, p. A69
CLOUGH, Jeanette G., President and Chief Executive Officer, Mount Auburn Hospital, Cambridge, MA, p. A297
CLOUGH, Sheila, Chief Executive Officer, Asante Ashland Community Hospital, Ashland, OR, p. A511
CLOUGH–BERRY, Cherie, Vice President, Finance, Hampstead Hospital, Hampstead, NH, p. A400
CLOUSE, Joseph, Chief Administrative Officer, Newport Hospital And Health Services, Newport, WA, p. A675
CLOUSE DAY, Sherry, Vice President Finance, Mercy Hospital Berryville, Berryville, AR, p. A39
CLOUTIER, Jonathan, Manager, Information Services, Buffalo Hospital, Buffalo, MN, p. A329
CLOUTIER, Michael, Director Information Services, Trios Health, Kennewick, WA, p. A674
CLOVER, Robert
Interim Superintendent, Larue D. Carter Memorial Hospital, Indianapolis, IN, p. A207
Superintendent and Chief Executive Officer, Logansport State Hospital, Logansport, IN, p. A210
Superintendent, Neurodiagnostic Institute And Advanced Treatment Center, Indianapolis, IN, p. A207
CLOWARD, Mitchell, Administrator, Dixie Regional Medical Center, Saint George, UT, p. A651
CLOWES, Jennifer, Chief Financial Officer, Broadwater Health Center, Townsend, MT, p. A380
CLUCK, Robert N, M.D., Vice President and Medical Director, Texas Health Arlington Memorial Hospital, Arlington, TX, p. A583
CLUFF, Ben, Chief Executive Officer, Ashley Regional Medical Center, Vernal, UT, p. A653
CLUNN, Amy, M.D., Medical Director, Encompass Health Rehabilitation Hospital Of Ocala, Ocala, FL, p. A133
CLUTE, Gerald B., Chief Executive Officer, East Los Angeles Doctors Hospital, Los Angeles, CA, p. A66
CLUTTS, Kathaleen, Chief Human Resources Officer, St. Luke'S Des Peres Hospital, Saint Louis, MO, p. A370
CLYNE, Mary Ellen, President and Chief Executive Officer, Clara Maass Medical Center, Belleville, NJ, p. A403
CMIEL, Peggy, R.N., Chief Nursing Officer, Chinese Hospital, San Francisco, CA, p. A85
COAKLEY, Jeff, Executive Vice President and Chief Operating Officer, Oswego Hospital, Oswego, NY, p. A441
COATES, Jennifer, Coordinator Information Technology, Purcell Municipal Hospital, Purcell, OK, p. A506
COATES, Robert, M.D., Vice President, Medical Affairs, Hunterdon Healthcare, Flemington, NJ, p. A406
COATS, Daniel J., Chief Executive Officer, Oklahoma Center For Orthopedic And Multi–Specialty Surgery, Oklahoma City, OK, p. A504
COATS, John, M.D., Chief Medical Staff, Morehouse General Hospital, Bastrop, LA, p. A263
COATS, Kevin
Chief Financial Officer, Baylor Scott & White Medical Center–Frisco, Frisco, TX, p. A606
Chief Operating Officer and Chief Financial Officer, Baylor Scott & White Medical Center–Frisco, Frisco, TX, p. A606
COBARRUBIAS, Samuel, M.D., Chief of Staff, Clinch Memorial Hospital, Homerville, GA, p. A155
COBB, April, Chief Nursing Officer, Encompass Health Lakeshore Rehabilitation Hospital, Birmingham, AL, p. A14
COBB, Heidi, R.N., Chief Nursing Officer, Medical Arts Hospital, Lamesa, TX, p. A619
COBB, Janice M, R.N., Chief Nursing Officer, Tennessee Valley Healthcare System, Nashville, TN, p. A577
COBB, Jason E., Chief Executive Officer, Rapides Regional Medical Center, Alexandria, LA, p. A262
COBB, Jeff, Information Technologist, Guthrie County Hospital, Guthrie Center, IA, p. A223
COBB, Lindsay, Director Human Resources, Cypress Grove Behavioral Health, Bastrop, LA, p. A263
COBB, Mark, Chief Executive Officer, Cape Fear Valley – Bladen County Hospital, Elizabethtown, NC, p. A454
COBB, Stephen, M.D., Chief Medical Officer, Presbyterian–St. Luke'S Medical Center, Denver, CO, p. A99
COBB, Tammy, Chief Financial Officer, Tennova Healthcare–Shelbyville, Shelbyville, TN, p. A579
COBBLE, Emlyn, Vice President and Chief Support Officer, Parkwest Medical Center, Knoxville, TN, p. A572
COBURN, Brad, Vice President, Human Resources, Orange Park Medical Center, Orange Park, FL, p. A134
COBURN, Meridith
Vice President Information Services, Saint Francis Hospital, Tulsa, OK, p. A509
Vice President, Information Systems, Saint Francis Hospital South, Tulsa, OK, p. A509
COBURN, Paul, Chief Financial Officer, Cypress Grove Behavioral Health, Bastrop, LA, p. A263
COBURN, Thomas C., M.D., Chief Medical Officer, Middle Park Medical Center–Kremmling, Kremmling, CO, p. A102
COCCA, Lisa, Chief Executive Officer, Belmont Pines Hospital, Youngstown, OH, p. A495
COCCHI, Dean, Chief Financial Officer, Kindred Hospital Ocala, Ocala, FL, p. A133
COCH, William, M.D., Medical Director, Jones Memorial Hospital, Wellsville, NY, p. A447
COCHRAN, Avril, R.N., Vice President Patient Care Services, North Country Hospital And Health Center, Newport, VT, p. A654
COCHRAN, Dan, Chief Operating Officer, Mountain River Birthing And Surgery Center, Blackfoot, ID, p. A167
COCHRAN, Daniel, Vice President and Chief Financial Officer, Adventist Healthcare Shady Grove Medical Center, Rockville, MD, p. A293
COCHRAN, Janice, R.N., Director Patient Care, Christus Dubuis Hospital Of Paris, Paris, TX, p. A627
COCHRAN, Kenneth, President and Chief Executive Officer, Opelousas General Health System, Opelousas, LA, p. A276
COCHRAN, Lena, Director of Finance, Highlands–Cashiers Hospital, Highlands, NC, p. A456
COCHRAN, Lynn, R.N., System Vice President Operations, Chief Nursing Officer, Edward Hospital, Naperville, IL, p. A190
COCHRAN, Sherry, Manager Human Resources, Cascade Behavioral Hospital, Tukwila, WA, p. A681
COCHRAN, Willie, M.D., Chief of Staff, Southern Regional Medical Center, Riverdale, GA, p. A159
COCHRANE, Andrew S., Chief Executive Officer, Maple Grove Hospital, Maple Grove, MN, p. A335
COCHRANE, Donna R., Chief Nursing Officer, Liberty Regional Medical Center, Hinesville, GA, p. A154
COCHRANE, Robert K., Vice President Finance and Chief Financial Officer, Frisbie Memorial Hospital, Rochester, NH, p. A402
COCKAYNE, Heather, Chief Financial Officer, Clifton–Fine Hospital, Star Lake, NY, p. A444
COCKFIELD, Costa, Chief Nursing Officer, Musc Health Florence Medical Center, Florence, SC, p. A553
COCKING, Kathy, R.N., Director of Clinical Services, Carson Valley Medical Center, Gardnerville, NV, p. A394
COCKRELL, Christopher, Executive Director Human Resources, Providence Hospital, Mobile, AL, p. A20
COCKRELL, Dennis, Director Human Resources, Gritman Medical Center, Moscow, ID, p. A170
COCKRELL, Tim, Chief Executive Officer, Patients Choice Medical Center Of Smith County, Raleigh, MS, p. A353
COCO, Jeffrey, M.D., Chief Medical Officer, Touro Infirmary, New Orleans, LA, p. A276
CODEN, Charles
Vice President, Novant Health Uva Health System Haymarket Medical Center, Haymarket, VA, p. A661
Vice President, Novant Health Uva Health System Prince William Medical Center, Manassas, VA, p. A662
CODER, Denise, Chief Human Resource Officer, Cass County Memorial Hospital, Atlantic, IA, p. A217
COF, Jason, M.D., Medical Director, Covington Behavioral Health, Covington, LA, p. A266
COE, Susan
Regional Vice President Human Resources, University Of Maryland Shore Medical Center At Dorchester, Cambridge, MD, p. A289
Regional Vice President Human Resources, University Of Maryland Shore Medical Center At Easton, Easton, MD, p. A290
Vice President Human Resources, University Of Maryland Shore Medical Center At Chestertown, Chestertown, MD, p. A289
COELLO, Jennifer, Chief Operating Officer, East Ohio Regional Hospital, Martins Ferry, OH, p. A486
COEN, Vickie, Chief Clinical Officer and Nurse Executive, Pana Community Hospital, Pana, IL, p. A192
COFFEE, Paula, Director Human Resources, Ascension St. Mary'S Of Michigan, Saginaw, MI, p. A321
COFFEE, Robert, Chief Information Officer, Creek Nation Community Hospital, Okemah, OK, p. A503
COFFELL, Randy, Manager Human Resources, Mid–Valley Hospital, Omak, WA, p. A676
COFFEY, Douglas W, R.N., MSN, Chief Nursing Officer, St. Mary'S Regional Medical Center, Enid, OK, p. A499
COFFEY, Joseph, Director Facility Administration, Rochester Psychiatric Center, Rochester, NY, p. A442
COFFEY, Judy
Senior Vice President and Area Manager, Kaiser Permanente San Rafael Medical Center, San Rafael, CA, p. A87
Senior Vice President and Area Manager, Kaiser Permanente Santa Rosa Medical Center, Santa Rosa, CA, p. A89
COFFEY, Kevin, Chief Executive Officer, Winner Regional Healthcare Center, Winner, SD, p. A565
COFFEY, M. Justin, Vice President and Chief Information Officer, Medical Director Center for Brain Stimulation, Menninger Clinic, Houston, TX, p. A613
COFFEY, Nancy, Interim Administrator and Director Emergency Department, Lake Charles Memorial Hospital, Lake Charles, LA, p. A272
COFFING, Sylvia K, R.N., MSN, Chief Nursing and Compliance Officer, Unity Medical & Surgical Hospital, Mishawaka, IN, p. A211
COFFMAN, Brian, Director Information System, National Park Medical Center, Hot Springs, AR, p. A43
COFFMAN, Courtney, Vice President, Finance and Chief Financial Officer, Penn State Health St. Joseph, Reading, PA, p. A539
COFFMAN, Joan, President and Chief Executive Officer, St. Tammany Parish Hospital, Covington, LA, p. A266
COFFMAN BARNES, Julie, M.D., Chief Medical Officer, Redmond Regional Medical Center, Rome, GA, p. A159
COGGINS, David, Chief Executive Officer, Encompass Health Rehabilitation Hospital Of New England, Woburn, MA, p. A305
COGGINS, Lisa, Chief Nursing Officer, Morton Hospital And Medical Center, Taunton, MA, p. A304
COGGINS, Parkes, Vice President Hospital Integration, Spartanburg Medical Center – Mary Black, Spartanburg, SC, p. A557
COHEN, Jason, M.D., Chief Medical Officer, North Valley Hospital, Whitefish, MT, p. A381
COHEN, Jeffrey, President, Allegheny General Hospital, Pittsburgh, PA, p. A537
COHEN, Kathleena, MSN, R.N., Director of Nursing, Hampton Behavioral Health Center, Westampton, NJ, p. A415
COHEN, Larry, Chief Executive Officer, Ocean Beach Hospital, Ilwaco, WA, p. A674
COHEN, Lisa, Chief Financial Officer, New London Hospital, New London, NH, p. A401
COHEN, Mark, M.D., Chief Medical Officer, Piedmont Hospital, Atlanta, GA, p. A146
COHEN, Philip A., Chief Executive Officer, Monterey Park Hospital, Monterey Park, CA, p. A73
COHICK, Jim, Chief Executive Officer, Kindred Hospital–Sycamore, Sycamore, IL, p. A197
COKER, Cindy, Vice President, Patient Care Services, Vidant Chowan Hospital, Edenton, NC, p. A453
COKER, Tina, MSN, Chief Nursing Officer, Henderson Hospital, Henderson, NV, p. A394
COLADONATO, Angela R., R.N., MSN, Chief Nursing Officer, Penn Medicine Chester County Hospital, West Chester, PA, p. A544
COLAMARIA, James, Director of Nursing, Four Winds Hospital, Saratoga Springs, NY, p. A443
COLAS, Chuck, M.D., Medical Director, Surprise Valley Health Care District, Cedarville, CA, p. A54
COLBURN, Douglas, Chief Information Officer, Piedmont Columbus Regional Northside, Columbus, GA, p. A150
COLBURN, Tim A., President and Chief Executive Officer, Berger Health System, Circleville, OH, p. A477
COLBY, Dennis, M.D., Chief of Staff, Iowa Specialty Hospital–Clarion, Clarion, IA, p. A219
COLBY, Karen M, MS, Chief Nursing Officer, Shirley Ryan Abilitylab, Chicago, IL, p. A179
COLBY, Ruth A., President and Chief Executive Officer, Silver Cross Hospital, New Lenox, IL, p. A191
COLBY, Scott, President, Upper Connecticut Valley Hospital, Colebrook, NH, p. A399
COLCHER, Marian W., President and Chief Executive Officer, Valley Forge Medical Center And Hospital, Norristown, PA, p. A533
COLCHER, Robert E, M.D., Medical Director, Valley Forge Medical Center And Hospital, Norristown, PA, p. A533
COLE, Annette E., R.N., MSN, Vice President and Chief Nursing Officer, Sky Lakes Medical Center, Klamath Falls, OR, p. A514
COLE, Bernadette Green, R.N., Chief Nursing Officer, Munson Healthcare Charlevoix Hospital, Charlevoix, MI, p. A308
COLE, Beth, Director Information Services, Lewis–Gale Medical Center, Boones Mill, VA, p. A657
COLE, Cal, Director Information Systems, Winter Haven Hospital, Winter Haven, FL, p. A144
COLE, Carlene, Manager Human Resources, Kittson Memorial Healthcare Center, Hallock, MN, p. A333
COLE, Dale, Director, Human Resources, Corona Regional Medical Center, Corona, CA, p. A55
COLE, David, Assistant Director of Administration, Chief Financial Officer, Department of Behavioral Health and D, Central Virginia Training Center, Madison Heights, VA, p. A662

COLE, Donas, President, Baylor Scott & White Medical Center – Lake Pointe, Rowlett, TX, p. A632

COLE, Dylan, Chief Medical Officer, Moab Regional Hospital, Moab, UT, p. A648

COLE, F Sessions, M.D., Chief Medical Officer, St. Louis Children'S Hospital, Saint Louis, MO, p. A370

COLE, Georgeanne, Chief Executive Officer, Rehabilitation Hospital Of Southwest Virginia, Bristol, VA, p. A657

COLE, James B., President and Chief Executive Officer, Virginia Hospital Center, Arlington, VA, p. A656

COLE, Jason
Regional Chief Financial Officer, Baylor Scott & White Medical Center – Round Rock, Round Rock, TX, p. A632
Senior Director, Management Information Systems, Suburban Hospital, Bethesda, MD, p. A289

COLE, Lori, Director Information Technology, Wayne Unc Health Care, Goldsboro, NC, p. A455

COLE, Missy, Director Human Resources, Encompass Health Rehabilitation Hospital, A Partner Of Washington Regional, Fayetteville, AR, p. A41

COLE, Nancye, MS, R.N., FACHE, Chief Nursing Officer, Lovelace Medical Center, Albuquerque, NM, p. A416

COLE, Robert, Chief Operating Officer, Connecticut Mental Health Center, New Haven, CT, p. A109

COLE, Sherman W., Interim Chief Executive Officer, Osawatomie State Hospital At Adair Acute Care, Osawatomie, KS, p. A242

COLE, William Clifford, M.D., Chief of Staff, Leconte Medical Center, Sevierville, TN, p. A579

COLE-OUZOUNIAN, Denise Marie, MSN, R.N., Vice President Patient Services, Sauk Prairie Healthcare, Prairie Du Sac, WI, p. A704

COLEMAN, Alisa, Chief Executive Officer, Ferrell Hospital, Eldorado, IL, p. A181

COLEMAN, Anne, Administrator, St. Vincent Indianapolis Hospital, Indianapolis, IN, p. A208

COLEMAN, Curt
Administrator, Jackson County Regional Health Center, Maquoketa, IA, p. A226
Chief Executive Officer, Genesis Medical Center, Dewitt, De Witt, IA, p. A220

COLEMAN, D. Scott, M.D., Medical Director, Livingston Healthcare, Livingston, MT, p. A378

COLEMAN, Donna, Coordinator Human Resources, Jackson County Hospital District, Edna, TX, p. A601

COLEMAN, Jim L, Chief Operating Officer, Parkridge Medical Center, Chattanooga, TN, p. A567

COLEMAN, Karen, Director of Nursing, Grove Hill Memorial Hospital, Grove Hill, AL, p. A19

COLEMAN, Kevin, M.D., Chief Medical Officer, Grand River Hospital District, Rifle, CO, p. A105

COLEMAN, Melissa, Director Human Resources, Encompass Health Rehabilitation Hospital Of Sewickley, Sewickley, PA, p. A541

COLEMAN, Robert
Chief Executive Officer, Baptist Medical Center Attala, Kosciusko, MS, p. A350
Chief Executive Officer, Baptist Medical Center Yazoo, Yazoo City, MS, p. A355

COLEMAN, Shane, Chief Information Officer, Palo Pinto General Hospital, Mineral Wells, TX, p. A625

COLEMAN, Stanley, Director Human Resources, Texas Rehabilitation Hospital Of Arlington, Arlington, TX, p. A584

COLERICK, Steven, Chief Executive Officer, Buena Vista Regional Medical Center, Storm Lake, IA, p. A230

COLETTA, Antonio
Vice President Human Resources, Advocate Bromenn Medical Center, Normal, IL, p. A191
Vice President Human Resources, Advocate Eureka Hospital, Eureka, IL, p. A182

COLETTA, Diane, Vice President Human Resources, Royal Oaks Hospital, Windsor, MO, p. A373

COLETTI, Edmund, Chief Executive Officer, Helen Hayes Hospital, West Haverstraw, NY, p. A447

COLEY, Aaron, Chief Financial Officer, Orange County, Memorialcare, Saddleback Memorial Medical Center, Laguna Hills, CA, p. A63

COLEY, Brenda
Executive Director, Adventhealth Central Texas, Killeen, TX, p. A618
Executive Director, Adventhealth Rollins Brook, Lampasas, TX, p. A619

COLGAN, Teresa, Vice President Nursing, Great River Health System, West Burlington, IA, p. A231

COLGLAZIER, Garrett, Director Health Information Management, Sabetha Community Hospital, Sabetha, KS, p. A244

COLINERI, Lori, R.N., Senior Vice President Nursing and Chief Nursing Officer, Robert Wood Johnson University Hospital, New Brunswick, NJ, p. A409

COLL, Shawni, D.O., Chief Medical Officer, Tahoe Forest Hospital District, Truckee, CA, p. A92

COLL, Tammy L., Chief Executive Officer, Mountain Lakes Medical Center, Clayton, GA, p. A150

COLLADO, Raquel, Vice President Human Resources, Brookdale Hospital Medical Center, New York, NY, p. A432

COLLAZO, Marian, Director Finance, Hospital San Cristobal, Coto Laurel, PR, p. A716

COLLETT, John, Vice President and Chief Financial Officer, Cayuga Medical Center At Ithaca, Ithaca, NY, p. A429

COLLETT, Josh, Director Human Resources, Southeastern Kentucky Medical Center, Pineville, KY, p. A259

COLLETTI, Teresa, Director Patient Services, South Florida Baptist Hospital, Plant City, FL, p. A137

COLLEY, Sarah, Senior Vice President Human Resources, Regional One Health, Memphis, TN, p. A575

COLLIER, Betty, Chief Human Resources Officer, Johnson Regional Medical Center, Clarksville, AR, p. A40

COLLIER, Brad, Director, Piedmont Newton Hospital, Covington, GA, p. A151

COLLIER, Jack, M.D., Chief of Staff, Mountainview Hospital, Las Vegas, NV, p. A395

COLLIER, Louis, Chief Executive Officer, Encompass Health Rehabilitation Hospital Of Petersburg, Petersburg, VA, p. A665

COLLIER, Margaret P., Chief Executive Officer, Ridgeview Institute, Smyrna, GA, p. A160

COLLIER, Shari, Chief Financial Officer, Presbyterian–St. Luke'S Medical Center, Denver, CO, p. A99

COLLINI, M. Patrick, M.D., President Medical Staff, Usmd Hospital At Arlington, Arlington, TX, p. A584

COLLINS, Alesha Danielle, MSN, R.N., Chief Nursing Officer, Howard Memorial Hospital, Nashville, AR, p. A46

COLLINS, Annasue, Chief Nursing Officer, Ten Broeck Tennessee Treatment Facility, Cookeville, TN, p. A568

COLLINS, Ava Jo, FACHE, Chief Operating Officer, Saint Vincent Hospital, Worcester, MA, p. A305

COLLINS, Bobby
Director Human Resources, Lonesome Pine Hospital, Big Stone Gap, VA, p. A656
Director Human Resources, Mountain View Regional Medical Center, Norton, VA, p. A664

COLLINS, Chauncey, Chief Operating Officer and Chief Financial Officer, Austen Riggs Center, Stockbridge, MA, p. A304

COLLINS, Daniel, M.D., Clinical Director, New Mexico Behavioral Health Institute At Las Vegas, Las Vegas, NM, p. A419

COLLINS, Dennis, Chief Financial Officer, The Brook Hospital – Kmi, Louisville, KY, p. A257

COLLINS, Edmund, Chief Information Officer, Cleveland Clinic Martin North Hospital, Stuart, FL, p. A140

COLLINS, Ethan, R.N., Chief Nursing Officer, Smyth County Community Hospital, Marion, VA, p. A662

COLLINS, Frances, Director of Nursing, Andrew Mcfarland Mental Health Center, Springfield, IL, p. A196

COLLINS, Harold E, JD, Chief Financial Officer, Franciscan Healthcare Munster, Munster, IN, p. A212

COLLINS, James M., President and Chief Executive Officer, St. Clair Hospital, Pittsburgh, PA, p. A537

COLLINS, Jeff, Chief Medical Officer, Providence St. Joseph'S Hospital, Chewelah, WA, p. A671

COLLINS, Jeffrey A, Chief Executive Officer, Kaiser Permanente Oakland Medical Center, Oakland, CA, p. A75

COLLINS, Jeffrey A., Senior Vice President and Area Manager, Kaiser Permanente Oakland Medical Center, Oakland, CA, p. A75

COLLINS, John
Corporate Chief Financial Officer, Chapman Global Medical Center, Orange, CA, p. A76
Chief Financial Officer, Anaheim Global Medical Center, Anaheim, CA, p. A50
Chief Financial Officer, Orange County Global Medical Center, Inc., Santa Ana, CA, p. A88
Chief Financial Officer, South Coast Global Medical Center, Santa Ana, CA, p. A88

COLLINS, John F., President and Chief Executive Officer, Nyu Winthrop Hospital, Mineola, NY, p. A431

COLLINS, John P., Medical Center Director, Veterans Affairs Central Western Massachusetts Healthcare System, Leeds, MA, p. A300

COLLINS, John R, Chief Financial Officer, Hemet Valley Medical Center, Hemet, CA, p. A61

COLLINS, Karen S., Chief Executive Officer, Lady Of The Sea General Hospital, Cut Off, LA, p. A266

COLLINS, Kevin J., M.D., Medical Director, Chi St. Vincent Sherwood Rehabilitation Hospital, Sherwood, AR, p. A48

COLLINS, Kimberly, M.D., Chief of Staff, Saint Thomas Dekalb Hospital, Smithville, TN, p. A579

COLLINS, Lainie, Human Resources Partner, St. Vincent Clay Hospital, Brazil, IN, p. A200

COLLINS, Leonora, Chief Nursing Officer, Nashville General Hospital, Nashville, TN, p. A576

COLLINS, Michael F.
Chief Executive Officer, Manchester Memorial Hospital, Manchester, CT, p. A108
Chief Executive Officer, Rockville General Hospital, Vernon, CT, p. A111

COLLINS, Pam, Director Human Resources, Avala, Covington, LA, p. A266

COLLINS, Pamela, Vice President Chief Patient Services Officer, Mccullough–Hyde Memorial Hospital/Trihealth, Oxford, OH, p. A489

COLLINS, Richard F, M.D., Executive Vice President and Chief Medical Officer, Jefferson Hospital, Jefferson Hills, PA, p. A528

COLLINS, Ricky M, M.D., Chief of Staff, Whitesburg Arh Hospital, Whitesburg, KY, p. A261

COLLINS, Ronald, Chief Financial Officer, Pampa Regional Medical Center, Pampa, TX, p. A627

COLLINS, Sharon
Chief Executive Officer, Russell Regional Hospital, Russell, KS, p. A244
Chief Information Officer, Salem Veterans Affairs Medical Center, Salem, VA, p. A667

COLLINS, Teresa, Chief Executive Officer and Chief Nursing Officer, Saint Luke'S Community Hospital At Leawood, Leawood, KS, p. A239

COLLINS, Thomas M., President, Chairman and Chief Executive Officer, Medical City Green Oaks Hospital, Dallas, TX, p. A597

COLLIPP, Dan, M.D., Chief of Staff, Wayne Memorial Hospital, Jesup, GA, p. A155

COLLISON, June, President, Community Hospital Of San Bernardino, San Bernardino, CA, p. A83

COLLOM, Bobbie, Nursing Director, North Runnels Hospital, Winters, TX, p. A646

COLMAN, Gerard, Chief Operating Officer, Aurora West Allis Medical Center, West Allis, WI, p. A708

COLMENARES, Derek, M.D.
Chief Medical Officer, Ripon Medical Center, Ripon, WI, p. A705
Chief Medical Officer, St. Agnes Hospital, Fond Du Lac, WI, p. A695
Chief Medical Officer, Waupun Memorial Hospital, Waupun, WI, p. A707

COLOMBO, Armando, Chief Operating Officer, Sheppard Pratt Health System, Baltimore, MD, p. A288

COLON, Julio, Financial Director, Hospital De Damas, Ponce, PR, p. A717

COLON, Omar, M.D., Medical Director, Encompass Health Rehabilitation Hospital Of Plano, Plano, TX, p. A629

COLONES, Robert L., President and Chief Executive Officer, Mcleod Regional Medical Center, Florence, SC, p. A552

COLONNELLI, Kim, Chief Nursing Officer, Corona Regional Medical Center, Corona, CA, p. A55

COLORADO, Judy, R.N., Chief Nursing Officer, Monmouth Medical Center, Southern Campus, Lakewood, NJ, p. A407

COLPITTS, Robert, Chief Human Resource Service, Bedford Veterans Affairs Medical Center, Edith Nourse Rogers Memorial Veterans Hospital, Bedford, MA, p. A294

COLSDEN, Kristen, Director of Nursing, Osmond General Hospital, Osmond, NE, p. A390

COLSON, Wayne, Chief Financial Officer, Southwestern Medical Center, Lawton, OK, p. A501

COLTHARP, Missy, Director, Baptist Memorial Hospital–Union County, New Albany, MS, p. A352

COLTON, Jan, M.D., Acting Clinical Director, U. S. Public Health Service Indian Hospital, Pine Ridge, SD, p. A562

COLUCCI, Eugene, Vice President Finance, Greenwich Hospital, Greenwich, CT, p. A108

COLUCCIO, Medrice
Chief Executive Officer, Providence St. Peter Hospital, Olympia, WA, p. A676
Southwest Region Chief Executive, Providence Centralia Hospital, Centralia, WA, p. A671

COLVARD, Dusty, Manager Information Technology, Adventist Health Medical Center – Tehachapi Valley, Tehachapi, CA, p. A91

COLVERT, Richard, Chief Information Officer, Royal Oaks Hospital, Windsor, MO, p. A373

COLVIN, Garren
Chief Executive Officer, St. Elizabeth Edgewood, Edgewood, KY, p. A251
Chief Executive Officer, St. Elizabeth Florence, Florence, KY, p. A252
Chief Executive Officer, St. Elizabeth Fort Thomas, Fort Thomas, KY, p. A252
Chief Executive Officer, St. Elizabeth Grant, Williamstown, KY, p. A261

COLVIN, William, Human Resources Officer, Claiborne Memorial Medical Center, Homer, LA, p. A268

COLWELL, Dean, D.O., Vice President Medical Affairs, Ohiohealth Doctors Hospital, Columbus, OH, p. A479

COLWELL, Melodie, Chief Financial Officer, Drew Memorial Health System, Monticello, AR, p. A46

COLYER, Valeri J
Director Human Resources, Dickenson Community Hospital, Clintwood, VA, p. A658
Director Human Resources, Norton Community Hospital, Norton, VA, p. A664

COMAIANNI, Sheri, Vice President Human Resources, Bakersfield Memorial Hospital, Bakersfield, CA, p. A52

COMBEST, Felton, M.D., Vice President Medical Affairs, Magnolia Regional Health Center, Corinth, MS, p. A346

COMBETTA, Jeffery, M.D., Medical Director, Bastrop Rehabilitation Hospital, Monroe, LA, p. A274

COMBS, Kevin, Chief of Staff, Carilion Tazewell Community Hospital, Tazewell, VA, p. A668

COMBS, Mark
Chief Information Security Officer, Jefferson Medical Center, Ranson, WV, p. A689
Interim Director System Information Technology, Berkeley Medical Center, Martinsburg, WV, p. A687

COMBS, Meri, R.N., Vice President and Chief Nursing Officer, Madera Community Hospital, Madera, CA, p. A70

COMBS, Mike, Manager Information Technology, Holdenville General Hospital, Holdenville, OK, p. A500

COMBS, Will, Director Information Technology, Harrison Community Hospital, Cadiz, OH, p. A474

COMER, Fannessa, Chief Executive Officer, Northern Navajo Medical Center, Shiprock, NM, p. A420

COMER, Jennifer, M.D., Medical Director, Valle Vista Health System, Greenwood, IN, p. A205

COMER, Randy
Chief Financial Officer, Athens–Limestone Hospital, Athens, AL, p. A13
Chief Operating Officer, Athens–Limestone Hospital, Athens, AL, p. A13

COMER, Scott M, Vice President Human Resources, Marshall Medical Center, Placerville, CA, p. A78

COMER, William J., Chief Executive Officer, Paradise Valley Hospital, National City, CA, p. A74

COMERFORD, Jennifer, Manager Information Services, Midstate Medical Center, Meriden, CT, p. A108

COMITO, Arthur, Chief Financial Officer, Easton Hospital, Easton, PA, p. A524

COMITTO, Judy, Vice President Information Services and Chief Information Officer, Trinitas Regional Medical Center, Elizabeth, NJ, p. A405

COMP, Susan, Senior Vice President and Chief Nursing Officer, Upmc Pinnacle Harrisburg, Harrisburg, PA, p. A527

COMPTON, Brenda, Manager Information Technology, Plumas District Hospital, Quincy, CA, p. A79

COMPTON, Carri, Administrative Officer, Heartland Behavioral Health Services, Nevada, MO, p. A366

COMPTON, Mark, Chief Financial Officer, Greeneville Community Hospital East, Greeneville, TN, p. A570

COMPTON, Randy, Information Technology and System Director, Logan Memorial Hospital, Russellville, KY, p. A260

CONANT, Cathy, Chief Human Resources and Personnel, Eastern Plumas Health Care, Portola, CA, p. A79

CONANT, Merrill, M.D., Chief of Staff, Western Plains Medical Complex, Dodge City, KS, p. A234

CONANT, Sonya, Senior Director Human Resources, Alaska Native Medical Center, Anchorage, AK, p. A25

CONAWAY, E Edwin, M.D., Vice President Medical Affairs and Chief Medical Officer, Southeastern Ohio Regional Medical Center, Cambridge, OH, p. A474

CONCANNON, Laura, M.D., Regional Chief Medical Officer, Amita Health Saints Mary & Elizabeth Medical Center, Chicago, IL, p. A176

CONCEPCION, Walter, Chief Executive Officer, West Gables Rehabilitation Hospital, Miami, FL, p. A131

CONDE, Tania, Administrator, Hospital Hermanos Melendez, Bayamon, PR, p. A715

CONDIT, Brian, M.D.
Chief Medical Officer, Johnston Memorial Hospital, Abingdon, VA, p. A656
Vice President Chief Medical Officer, Virginia Operations Medical Staff Services, Russell County Medical Center, Lebanon, VA, p. A661

CONDIT, Edward, President and Chief Executive Officer, St. Mary'S General Hospital, Passaic, NJ, p. A410

CONDOLUCI, David, M.D., Senior Vice President and Chief Medical Officer, Jefferson Stratford Hospital, Stratford, NJ, p. A413

CONDON, Joseph
Director Human Resources, Texas Health Specialty Hospital, Fort Worth, TX, p. A606

Entity Human Resources Officer, Texas Health Harris Methodist Hospital Fort Worth, Fort Worth, TX, p. A605

CONDRY, Donna, Director Human Resources, Unitypoint Health – Jones Regional Medical Center, Anamosa, IA, p. A217

CONE, Maryann, Chief Operating Officer, Sharp Grossmont Hospital, La Mesa, CA, p. A63

CONEJO, David, Chief Executive Officer, Rehoboth Mckinley Christian Health Care Services, Gallup, NM, p. A418

CONFALONE, Daniel, Chief Financial Officer and Vice President Finance, St. Mary Medical Center, Langhorne, PA, p. A529

CONFER, James, Manager Information Systems, Clarion Hospital, Clarion, PA, p. A522

CONGDON, James B, M.D., Medical Director, Horsham Clinic, Ambler, PA, p. A520

CONGER, Sue, Chief Operating Officer, Eastside Psychiatric Hospital, Tallahassee, FL, p. A140

CONKLIN, Maggie C, M.P.H.
Interim Chief Nurse Officer, Novant Health Uva Health System Prince William Medical Center, Manassas, VA, p. A662
Interim Chief Nursing Officer, Novant Health Uva Health System Haymarket Medical Center, Haymarket, VA, p. A661

CONKLIN, Michael E, Chief Financial Officer, St. Joseph Health Services Of Rhode Island, North Providence, RI, p. A547

CONKLIN, Robin, R.N., Chief Nursing Officer, Carondelet St. Joseph'S Hospital, Tucson, AZ, p. A37

CONKLIN, Stacey A, Chief Nursing Officer, South Nassau Communities Hospital, Oceanside, NY, p. A440

CONKLING, Victoria, Vice President, Patient Services and Chief Nursing Officer, Uhs Delaware Valley Hospital, Walton, NY, p. A446

CONLEY, Christopher, M.D., President of the Medical Staff, Tristar Skyline Medical Center, Nashville, TN, p. A577

CONLEY, Joanna J., Chief Executive Officer, Tristar Southern Hills Medical Center, Nashville, TN, p. A577

CONLEY, Kenneth, Chief Financial Officer, Baptist Memorial Hospital – Calhoun, Calhoun City, MS, p. A345

CONLEY, Kirkpatrick, President, Sentara Careplex Hospital, Hampton, VA, p. A660

CONLEY, Melissa, Director Human Resources, Midwest Medical Center, Galena, IL, p. A183

CONLEY, Michelle E, R.N., Chief Nursing Officer, Jefferson Health Northeast, Philadelphia, PA, p. A535

CONLEY, Teressa
President and Chief Executive Officer, St. Rose Dominican Hospitals – Rose De Lima Campus, Henderson, NV, p. A394
Vice President and Chief Operating Officer, St. Rose Dominican Hospitals – Rose De Lima Campus, Henderson, NV, p. A394

CONLEY, Theresa, Manager Human Resources, Cherokee Regional Medical Center, Cherokee, IA, p. A219

CONLEY, Thomas C, Vice President, Human Resources and Organizational Development, Northwestern Medical Center, Saint Albans, VT, p. A655

CONLON, John, M.D., Chief Medical Officer, Saint Anne'S Hospital, Fall River, MA, p. A298

CONN, Chris, Chief Financial Officer, Poinciana Medical Center, Kissimmee, FL, p. A127

CONN, Stephanie, Administrator and Chief Nursing Officer, Coshocton Regional Medical Center, Coshocton, OH, p. A480

CONNAWAY, Jessica, Director Human Resources, Crossroads Community Hospital, Mount Vernon, IL, p. A190

CONNEL, Lorene, Chief Human Resources Management Service, Veterans Affairs Eastern Colorado Health Care System, Denver, CO, p. A99

CONNELL, Eric, Chief Executive Officer, Daniels Memorial Healthcare Center, Scobey, MT, p. A380

CONNELL, Faith, Director of Nursing, Turning Point Hospital, Moultrie, GA, p. A158

CONNELL, Pam, Manager Human Resources, Windsor–Laurelwood Center For Behavioral Medicine, Willoughby, OH, p. A494

CONNELLEY, Bertha Mary, Director Human Resources, Austen Riggs Center, Stockbridge, MA, p. A304

CONNELLY, Jac, Chief Financial Officer, Rose Medical Center, Denver, CO, p. A99

CONNELLY, Kathryn, Manager Information Technology, Connecticut Valley Hospital, Middletown, CT, p. A109

CONNELLY, Michael P., CPA, FACHE, Executive Vice President and Chief Financial Officer, Melrosewakefield Healthcare, Melrose, MA, p. A300

CONNELLY, Steven, M.D., President and Chief Medical Officer, Park Nicollet Methodist Hospital, Saint Louis Park, MN, p. A339

CONNER, Chad, Administrator, Northern Louisiana Medical Center, Ruston, LA, p. A277

CONNER, Jeff, M.D., Chief Medical Staff, Loma Linda University Medical Center–Murrieta, Murrieta, CA, p. A73

CONNER, June, Chief Operating Officer, Emory University Hospital, Atlanta, GA, p. A146

CONNER, Laurie A., President, Mercyone Newton Medical Center, Newton, IA, p. A227

CONNER, Stacey, Director Personnel, Ed Fraser Memorial Hospital And Baker Community Health Center, Macclenny, FL, p. A128

CONNERS, Stephanie, Senior Executive Vice President Chief Operating Officer and Chief Nursing Officer, Cooper University Health Care, Camden, NJ, p. A404

CONNERTON, Kathryn, President and Chief Executive Officer, Our Lady Of Lourdes Memorial Hospital, Inc., Binghamton, NY, p. A424

CONNOLLY, Christine, M.D., Chief of Staff, Keefe Memorial Hospital, Cheyenne Wells, CO, p. A97

CONNOLLY, Seam, Commissioner, Connecticut Veterans Home And Hospital, Rocky Hill, CT, p. A110

CONNOLLY, Teresa, R.N., Chief Nursing Officer, Mayo Clinic Hospital, Phoenix, AZ, p. A33

CONNOR, Brian, President, Christus Spohn Hospital Corpus Christi Memorial, Corpus Christi, TX, p. A594

CONNOR, Paul J., III, President and Chief Executive Officer, Eastern Long Island Hospital, Greenport, NY, p. A428

CONNOR, William, Assistant Administrator and Director Human Resources, River Hospital, Alexandria Bay, NY, p. A422

CONNORS, Alfred, M.D., Executive Vice President and Chief Quality Officer and Interim Chief Medical Officer, Metrohealth Medical Center, Cleveland, OH, p. A478

CONNORS, Lawrence J, Chief Operating Officer, Hshs St. Mary'S Hospital Medical Center, Green Bay, WI, p. A696

CONNORS, Michael
Senior Vice President and Chief Financial Officer, Cape Cod Hospital, Hyannis, MA, p. A299
Senior Vice President and Chief Financial Officer, Falmouth Hospital, Falmouth, MA, p. A298

CONNORS, Robert, President, Helen DeVos Children's Hospital, Spectrum Health – Butterworth Hospital, Grand Rapids, MI, p. A313

CONNOVICH, Ron D
Chief Financial Officer and Chief Operating Officer, Soin Medical Center, Beavercreek, OH, p. A473
Chief Financial Officer, Greene Memorial Hospital, Xenia, OH, p. A494

CONNY, Sophia, Deputy Administrative Officer, U. S. Public Health Service Indian Hospital, Pine Ridge, SD, p. A562

CONRAD, Daniel S., President, Phillips Eye Institute, Minneapolis, MN, p. A336

CONRAD, Elizabeth P., Senior Vice President and Chief Human Resource Officer, Lahey Hospital & Medical Center, Burlington, Burlington, MA, p. A297

CONRAD, Heidi, Vice President and Chief Financial Officer, Regions Hospital, Saint Paul, MN, p. A340

CONRATH, Mark, Chief Financial Officer, Drumright Regional Hospital, Drumright, OK, p. A498

CONROW–VERVERIS, Stacy, Director Human Resources, Mineral Community Hospital, Superior, MT, p. A380

CONROY, Joanne M., President and Chief Executive Officer, Dartmouth–Hitchcock Medical Center, Lebanon, NH, p. A400

CONROY, Michael, Chief Financial Officer, Pine Creek Medical Center, Dallas, TX, p. A597

CONROY, Mike, Chief Financial Officer, Methodist Mckinney Hospital, Mckinney, TX, p. A624

CONROY, Tracy, Chief Executive Officer, Daviess Community Hospital, Washington, IN, p. A216

CONSBRUCK, Todd
Chief Executive Officer, Avera Creighton Hospital, Creighton, NE, p. A384
President and Chief Executive Officer, Avera St. Anthony'S Hospital, O'Neill, NE, p. A390

CONSIDINE, William H., President, Akron Children'S Hospital, Akron, OH, p. A471

CONSIGLIO, Gayle, Chief Information Officer, Mclaren Lapeer Region, Lapeer, MI, p. A316

CONSIGNEY, Ginger, Vice President Human Resources, Lake Charles Memorial Hospital, Lake Charles, LA, p. A272

CONSOLVER, Roberta, Chief Information Officer, Healthbridge Children'S Hospital, Orange, CA, p. A76

CONSTANT, Jean–Charles, Administrator, Dover Behavioral Health System, Dover, DE, p. A113

CONSTANTINE–CASTILLO, Candida, MSN, R.N., Chief Nursing Officer, South Texas Health System, Edinburg, TX, p. A601

CONTE, John, Director Facility Services and Real Estate, Wayne Memorial Hospital, Honesdale, PA, p. A527

CONTI, John, Director Finance, Shriners Hospitals For Children–Greenville, Greenville, SC, p. A554

CONTRERAS, Amy, Chief Nursing Officer, Milford Valley Memorial Hospital, Milford, UT, p. A648

CONTRERAS, Marta, Chief Nursing Officer and Chief Operating Officer, Foundation Surgical Hospital Of El Paso, El Paso, TX, p. A602

CONTRERAS, Theresa, Chief Executive Officer, Arrowhead Behavioral Health Hospital, Maumee, OH, p. A487

CONVERY, Luanne, Vice President Patient Care Services, Putnam Hospital Center, Carmel, NY, p. A425

CONWAY, Jimmy, M.D., President Medical Staff, Northwest Surgical Hospital, Oklahoma City, OK, p. A504

CONWAY, Kevin, Chief Information Officer, Upmc Mercy, Pittsburgh, PA, p. A538

CONWILL, Michael, Director Human Resources, Corpus Christi Medical Center, Corpus Christi, TX, p. A594

CONYERS, Robin, Administrator, Chi Health Creighton University Medical Center – Bergan Mercy, Omaha, NE, p. A388

COOGAN, Ben, Chief Operating Officer, Medical City Arlington, Arlington, TX, p. A583

COOK, Aaron, Director Information Services, Christus Ochsner Lake Area Hospital, Lake Charles, LA, p. A272

COOK, Alan, Chief Medical Officer, Central Regional Hospital, Butner, NC, p. A450

COOK, Anthony, M.D., Chief of Staff, Avera Holy Family Hospital, Estherville, IA, p. A222

COOK, Brooke, Director of Nursing, Strategic Behavioral Health – Wilmington, Leland, NC, p. A457

COOK, Carla, Director of Nursing, Scotland County Hospital, Memphis, MO, p. A365

COOK, Darrin
  Chief Executive Officer and Administrator, Horizon Specialty Hospital, Las Vegas, NV, p. A395
  Chief Operating Officer, Astria Regional Medical Center, Yakima, WA, p. A682

COOK, David, Manager Information Systems, Christus Dubuis Hospital Of Hot Springs, Hot Springs National Park, AR, p. A43

COOK, David A, Vice President and Chief Financial Officer, University Hospitals Elyria Medical Center, Elyria, OH, p. A482

COOK, Elizabeth, Chief Information Officer, Mizell Memorial Hospital, Opp, AL, p. A22

COOK, G. Anthony, M.D., Medical Director, Hemphill County Hospital, Canadian, TX, p. A591

COOK, Greg, Chief Executive Officer, Castleview Hospital, Price, UT, p. A650

COOK, Heidi, Chief Nursing Officer, Warner Hospital And Health Services, Clinton, IL, p. A180

COOK, Jana, Vice President and Chief Financial Officer, Phelps Health, Rolla, MO, p. A368

COOK, Janie, Director Information Systems, Passavant Area Hospital, Jacksonville, IL, p. A186

COOK, John
  Interim Chief Information Officer, University Of California, Davis Medical Center, Sacramento, CA, p. A82
  Senior Vice President & Chief Financial Officer, Javon Bea Hospital–Rockton, Rockford, IL, p. A194
  Vice President and Chief Financial Officer, Mercyhealth Hospital And Trauma Center – Janesville, Janesville, WI, p. A697

COOK, Katheryn, R.N., Nurse Executive, Cincinnati Veterans Affairs Medical Center, Cincinnati, OH, p. A476

COOK, Kathy, President, Mercy Health – St. Joseph Warren Hospital, Warren, OH, p. A493

COOK, Kevin S., Chief Executive Officer, University Of Mississippi Medical Center, Jackson, MS, p. A349

COOK, Kim, Interim Clinical Applications Services Manager, Tri–City Medical Center, Oceanside, CA, p. A75

COOK, LaMont, Administrator, F. W. Huston Medical Center, Winchester, KS, p. A247

COOK, Linda, Vice President Human Resources, St. Joseph Hospital, Eureka, CA, p. A57

COOK, Lottie, Superintendent, Evansville Psychiatric Children Center, Evansville, IN, p. A203

COOK, Marcia, Director Information Technology, Bates County Memorial Hospital, Butler, MO, p. A357

COOK, Mary Ann, R.N., Director of Nursing, Red Lake Indian Health Service Hospital, Red Lake, MN, p. A338

COOK, Natalie
  Administrative Director of Human Resources, Manchester Memorial Hospital, Manchester, CT, p. A108
  Administrative Director, Human Resources, Rockville General Hospital, Vernon, CT, p. A111

COOK, Pamela W, Chief Financial Officer, Trace Regional Hospital, Houston, MS, p. A348

COOK, Patrick, Vice President Support Services, Morgan Memorial Hospital, Madison, GA, p. A157

COOK, Paul, M.D., Chief Medical Officer, Baylor Scott & White Medical Center – Llano, Llano, TX, p. A621

COOK, Robert, Chief Nursing Officer, Twin Cities Community Hospital, Templeton, CA, p. A91

COOK, Scott
  Chief Financial Officer, Garland Behavioral Hospital, Garland, TX, p. A607
  Chief Information Officer, Johnson Regional Medical Center, Clarksville, AR, p. A40

COOK, Sheliah, Director Human Resources, Boone Memorial Hospital, Madison, WV, p. A687

COOK, Sherry P, R.N., MSN, Chief Nursing Executive, Merit Health River Oaks, Flowood, MS, p. A346

COOK, Stacey M, MS, Vice President, Human Resources, University Of Maryland Charles Regional Medical Center, La Plata, MD, p. A291

COOK, Thomas M, Chief Financial Officer, Good Samaritan Hospital, Vincennes, IN, p. A216

COOK, Wendy J., Chief Financial Officer, Piedmont Athens Regional Medical Center, Athens, GA, p. A145

COOK, William
  Associate Warden Business Service, California Mens Colony Correctional Treatment Center, San Luis Obispo, CA, p. A87
  Director, Southern Virginia Mental Health Institute, Danville, VA, p. A658
  President and Chief Executive Officer, Vail Health, Vail, CO, p. A106

COOKE, Barbara, Director Health Information Systems, Montefiore Mount Vernon, Mount Vernon, NY, p. A432

COOKE, David, R.N.
  Chief Nursing Officer, Sutter Surgical Hospital – North Valley, Yuba City, CA, p. A95
  Chief Operating Officer, Hi–Desert Medical Center, Joshua Tree, CA, p. A62

COOKE, Nancy, Chief Financial Officer, Medical City Weatherford, Weatherford, TX, p. A644

COOKE, Rebecca L, Director Human Resources, Kearney County Health Services, Minden, NE, p. A387

COOKE, Timothy J, Medical Center Director and Chief Executive Officer, Martinsburg Veterans Affairs Medical Center, Martinsburg, WV, p. A687

COOKE, Timothy J., Medical Center Director and Chief Executive Officer, Martinsburg Veterans Affairs Medical Center, Martinsburg, WV, p. A687

COOKE, William, M.D., Chief of Staff, Gundersen St. Joseph'S Hospital And Clinics, Hillsboro, WI, p. A697

COOL, Megan, Interim Chief Executive Officer and Chief Operating Officer, Methodist Hospital, San Antonio, TX, p. A634

COOLEY, Andrew, M.D., Chief Medical Officer, Eastern State Hospital, Lexington, KY, p. A255

COOLEY–JOHNSON, Sonja, Chief Nursing Officer, Fairlawn Rehabilitation Hospital, Worcester, MA, p. A305

COOMBS, James, Chief Executive Officer, Grand River Hospital District, Rifle, CO, p. A105

COOMBS, Teri, R.N., Director Nursing Services, Cascade Medical Center, Cascade, ID, p. A168

COOMES, Larry, Chief Executive Officer, Queen Of The Valley Medical Center, Napa, CA, p. A74

COOMLER, Mimi, R.N., Vice President and Chief Nursing Officer, Tmc Healthcare, Tucson, AZ, p. A38

COONER, Suzanne, Chief Executive Officer, Audubon County Memorial Hospital And Clinics, Audubon, IA, p. A217

COONEY, Darlene, Director Nursing, Sumner Regional Medical Center, Wellington, KS, p. A247

COONEY, Lauri Ann, Director Nursing, Wheatland Memorial Healthcare, Harlowton, MT, p. A377

COONEY, Marina, Medical Director, Montgomery County Emergency Service, Norristown, PA, p. A533

COOPER, Alisa, Manager Financial Resources, Michael E. Debakey Veterans Affairs Medical Center, Houston, TX, p. A613

COOPER, Alison, Chief Financial Officer, Ward Memorial Hospital, Monahans, TX, p. A625

COOPER, Allison, Administrator, Physicians Behavioral Hospital, Shreveport, LA, p. A278

COOPER, Ben, Administrator, Oceans Behavioral Hospital Of Alexandria, Alexandria, LA, p. A262

COOPER, Brenda, Director Quality and Human Resources, Lecom Corry Memorial Hospital, Corry, PA, p. A523

COOPER, Casey, Chief Executive Officer, Cherokee Indian Hospital, Cherokee, NC, p. A452

COOPER, Curtis, Manager Information Systems, Pioneers Medical Center, Meeker, CO, p. A104

COOPER, Donald, Director Information Systems, Tennova Healthcare–Harton, Tullahoma, TN, p. A580

COOPER, Douglas, M.D., Chief Medical Officer, Grundy County Memorial Hospital, Grundy Center, IA, p. A223

COOPER, Ian, Chief Executive Officer, Post Acute Medical Specialty Hospital Of Tulsa, Tulsa, OK, p. A509

COOPER, Jerry, Manager Data Processing, Richland Hospital, Richland Center, WI, p. A704

COOPER, Jon, Chief Administrative Officer, Norton Hospital, Louisville, KY, p. A256

COOPER, Pamela, Director Finance, Providence Seaside Hospital, Seaside, OR, p. A518

COOPER, Shawnee, Director Human Resources, Magnolia Regional Medical Center, Magnolia, AR, p. A45

COOPER, Tim, Chief Financial Officer, Prosser Memorial Health, Prosser, WA, p. A676

COOPER–LEHKI, Christi, Chief Clinical Officer, Highland–Clarksburg Hospital, Clarksburg, WV, p. A684

COOPER–LOHR, Willie, Chief Financial Officer, Barnesville Hospital, Barnesville, OH, p. A472

COOPERMAN, Todd, M.D., Medical Director, Encompass Health Rehabilitation Hospital Of Tinton Falls, Tinton Falls, NJ, p. A413

COOPWOOD, Reginald W., President and Chief Executive Officer, Regional One Health, Memphis, TN, p. A575

COOTS, Aaron, Information Technology Director, Mason District Hospital, Havana, IL, p. A185

COPE, Brent A., Chief Executive Officer, Silver Lake Medical Center, Los Angeles, CA, p. A69

COPE, Dave, Director Information Systems, Marshall County Hospital, Benton, KY, p. A249

COPE, Mary, R.N., Chief Clinical Officer, Spanish Peaks Regional Health Center, Walsenburg, CO, p. A106

COPE, Yvette Renee, Chief Nurse Executive, Lompoc Valley Medical Center, Lompoc, CA, p. A64

COPELAND, Carolyn, Business Administrator, Madison State Hospital, Madison, IN, p. A211

COPELAND, Darlinda, Chief Operating Officer, Adventhealth Daytona Beach, Daytona Beach, FL, p. A121

COPELAND, Gail, Director Management Information Systems, Crossridge Community Hospital, Wynne, AR, p. A49

COPELAND, Gearline, R.N., Chief Nursing Officer, Saint Thomas Highlands Hospital, Sparta, TN, p. A579

COPELAND, Kristie M., Interim Chief Nursing Officer, Claiborne Memorial Medical Center, Homer, LA, p. A268

COPELAND, Robert, Interim Chief Executive Officer, Covenant Hospital Plainview, Plainview, TX, p. A629

COPELAND, Stephen, Chief Financial Officer, Cypress Creek Hospital, Houston, TX, p. A611

COPELAND, Willie Mae, Chief Financial Officer, Harmon Memorial Hospital, Hollis, OK, p. A500

COPELAND, Yolanda, R.N., Senior Vice President Patient Care Services and Chief Nursing Officer, Saint Agnes Healthcare, Baltimore, MD, p. A287

COPEN, Greg, Chief Information Officer, Haywood Regional Medical Center, Clyde, NC, p. A452

COPENHAVER, Kathy, Director Human Resources, Haven Behavioral Hospital Of Eastern Pennsylvania, Reading, PA, p. A539

COPES, Tammy, Director Information Systems, Ascension Standish Hospital, Standish, MI, p. A323

COPPEDGE, Mitch, M.D., Chief Medical Officer, Grady Memorial Hospital, Chickasha, OK, p. A498

COPPLE, Brad
  Vice President Operations, Northwestern Medicine Valley West Hospital, Sandwich, IL, p. A195
  Vice President, Operations, Northwestern Medicine Kishwaukee Hospital, Dekalb, IL, p. A181

COPPLE, Robert C., Senior Administrator, Ascension Via Christi Hospital, Manhattan, Manhattan, KS, p. A240

CORA, Michelle, Director Human Resources, Beaumont Hospital – Trenton, Trenton, MI, p. A324

CORAZON, Jesus M
  Controller, Encompass Health Rehabilitation Hospital Of Manati, Manati, PR, p. A717
  Controller, Encompass Health Rehabilitation Hospital Of San Juan, San Juan, PR, p. A718

CORBEIL, John, Chief Executive Officer, Kingwood Medical Center, Kingwood, TX, p. A618

CORBET, Mark, Interim Chief Financial Officer, Lac+Usc Medical Center, Los Angeles, CA, p. A68

CORBETT, David, M.D., Chief of Staff, Northwest Medical Center, Winfield, AL, p. A24

CORBI, Kelly, Chief Operating Officer, Northwest Hospital, Randallstown, MD, p. A293

CORBIN, Michelle, M.D., Chief of Staff, Deer Lodge Medical Center, Deer Lodge, MT, p. A376

CORCIMIGLIA, Michael, Chief Operating Officer, Wyoming County Community Hospital, Warsaw, NY, p. A446

CORCORAN, John Russell, Vice President Medical Affairs, South County Hospital, Wakefield, RI, p. A548

CORCORAN, Joseph C., D.O.
  Chief Medical Officer, Brandon Regional Hospital, Brandon, FL, p. A119
  Chief Medical Officer, South Bay Hospital, Sun City Center, FL, p. A140

CORCORAN, Kevin, Chief Financial Officer, Westside Regional Medical Center, Plantation, FL, p. A137
CORCORAN, Nancy R, Senior Vice President Human Resources and Quality Service, Hackensack Meridian Health Hackensack University Medical Center, Hackensack, NJ, p. A406
CORCORAN, Rose, R.N., Chief Nursing Executive, Sutter Coast Hospital, Crescent City, CA, p. A56
CORD, Jennifer, R.N., Chief Nursing Officer, Mission Hospital, Mission Viejo, CA, p. A72
CORDDRY, David, Chief Financial Officer, Ten Broeck Tennessee Treatment Facility, Cookeville, TN, p. A568
CORDEAU, Peter, President, Norwalk Hospital, Norwalk, CT, p. A110
CORDER, Earline, Chief Fiscal, Charlie Norwood Veterans Affairs Medical Center, Augusta, GA, p. A147
CORDER, Scott, Controller, Healthsouth Rehabilitation Hospital At Drake, Cincinnati, OH, p. A476
CORDERO, Edwin, Chief Financial Officer, Valley Baptist Medical Center–Brownsville, Rio Hondo, TX, p. A631
CORDES, Debra, Chief Nursing Officer, Rehabilitation Hospital Of Indiana, Indianapolis, IN, p. A207
CORDIA, Jennifer, Vice President and Chief Nursing Executive, Christian Hospital, Saint Louis, MO, p. A369
CORDOVA, Mandelyn, R.N., Director of Nurses, Guadalupe County Hospital, Santa Rosa, NM, p. A420
CORDOVA, Martin, Director Information Services, Centinela Hospital Medical Center, Inglewood, CA, p. A62
CORDOVA, Sheila
Chief Operating Officer and Chief Nursing Officer, Aurora Charter Oak Hospital, Covina, CA, p. A55
Director Clinical Services and Chief Operating Officer, Aurora Charter Oak Hospital, Covina, CA, p. A55
CORDOVES, America, Controller, Jerome Golden Center For Behavioral Health, Inc., West Palm Beach, FL, p. A144
CORDUM, Shelly L., R.N., MSN, Vice President Nursing and Chief Nursing Officer, Ssm Health Depaul Hospital – St. Louis, Bridgeton, MO, p. A357
CORDY, Roy, M.D., President Medical Staff, Presentation Medical Center, Rolla, ND, p. A469
COREA, Rohan, Director Healthcare Information Technology, College Medical Center, Long Beach, CA, p. A65
COREY, Mark, Chief Financial Officer, Behavioral Center Of Michigan, Warren, MI, p. A324
CORKERY, Thomas B, D.O., Chief Medical Officer, Canonsburg Hospital, Canonsburg, PA, p. A522
CORLEY, Becky, Director Human Resources, Tyler Holmes Memorial Hospital, Winona, MS, p. A355
CORLEY, Janet, Accountant, Malvern Institute, Malvern, PA, p. A531
CORLEY, Juli, Chief Information Officer, Edgefield County Healthcare, Edgefield, SC, p. A552
CORMIER, Philip M., Chief Executive Officer, Beverly Hospital, Beverly, MA, p. A294
CORN, Rick, Chief Information Officer, Huntsville Hospital, Huntsville, AL, p. A19
CORNEJO, C Susan
Chief Financial Officer, Sacred Heart Hospital Pensacola, Pensacola, FL, p. A136
Chief Operating Officer, Providence Hospital, Mobile, AL, p. A20
CORNEJO, Juan, M.D., Chief of Staff, Perry County Memorial Hospital, Tell City, IN, p. A215
CORNELIUS, David, Director Information Systems, Parkridge Medical Center, Chattanooga, TN, p. A567
CORNELIUS, Margaret E, Vice President Human Resources, Brookdale Hospital Medical Center, New York, NY, p. A432
CORNELIUS, Michelle
Director Human Resources for Northern Region, Ascension Eagle River Hospital, Eagle River, WI, p. A694
Director Human Resources for the Northern Region, Ascension St. Mary'S Hospital, Rhinelander, WI, p. A704
Director Human Resources, Ascension Sacred Heart Hospital, Tomahawk, WI, p. A707
Director Human Resources, Howard Young Medical Center, Woodruff, WI, p. A709
CORNELIUS, Senta, Director Human Resources, West Valley Medical Center, Caldwell, ID, p. A168
CORNELIUS, Teresa, R.N., Interim Chief Nursing Officer, Hshs St. Joseph'S Hospital, Highland, IL, p. A185
CORNET, Trina, JD, Vice President Human Resources, Brookdale Hospital Medical Center, New York, NY, p. A432
CORNETT, Sheila, Manager Human Resources, Hazard Arh Regional Medical Center, Hazard, KY, p. A253
CORNETT, Suzanne, Director Human Resources, Southern Kentucky Rehabilitation Hospital, Bowling Green, KY, p. A250
CORNICELLI, Kari
Chief Financial Officer, Sharp Grossmont Hospital, La Mesa, CA, p. A63
Chief Financial Officer, Sharp Memorial Hospital, San Diego, CA, p. A84
Chief Financial Officer, Sharp Mesa Vista Hospital, San Diego, CA, p. A84
CORNWALL, Thomas, M.D., Medical Director, Holly Hill Hospital, Raleigh, NC, p. A460
CORNWELL, Cheryl, Chief Financial Officer, Great Falls Clinic Hospital, Great Falls, MT, p. A377
CORNWELL, Cheryl J, Chief Financial Officer, Lake District Hospital, Lakeview, OR, p. A514
CORNWELL, Daniel, Command Officer, U. S. Naval Hospital Guam, Agana, GU, p. A714
CORNWELL, Richard, Chief Executive Officer, Surprise Valley Health Care District, Cedarville, CA, p. A54
CORONA JR., Robert J, Chief Executive Officer, Upstate University Hospital, Syracuse, NY, p. A445
CORONEL, Jorge, Chief Information Officer, Regional Hospital Of Scranton, Reading, PA, p. A540
CORPORA, Don, Executive Vice President and Chief Human Resources Officer, Cleveland Clinic Akron General, Akron, OH, p. A471
CORRADO, Bob, Chief Information Officer, Canandaigua Veterans Affairs Medical Center, Canandaigua, NY, p. A425
CORRADO, Theresa, Director Finance, St. Luke'S Hospital – Quakertown Campus, Quakertown, PA, p. A539
CORREA, Elizabeth, Director Information Management, Big Spring State Hospital, Big Spring, TX, p. A588
CORREA, Leo, Chief Executive Officer and Administrator, St. Catherine Hospital, East Chicago, IN, p. A202
CORREA, Maria de los Angeles, M.D., Medical Director, Hospital Metropolitan, San Juan, PR, p. A719
CORREA, Omar, Chief Financial Officer, Texas Neurorehab Center, Austin, TX, p. A586
CORREA, Sharon, Vice President and Chief Information Officer, Adventist Health Glendale, Los Angeles, CA, p. A65
CORRELL, Anne, Chief Clinical Officer, Kindred Hospital–Greensboro, Greensboro, NC, p. A455
CORRIGAN, Heidi, Manager Human Resources, Trinity Hospital, Weaverville, CA, p. A94
CORRIGAN, Jeffrey T.
Vice President Human Resources, Brattleboro Retreat, Brattleboro, VT, p. A654
Vice President Human Resources, Day Kimball Hospital, Putnam, CT, p. A110
CORRIGAN, Paula, Vice President and Chief Financial Officer, Osf Saint James – John W. Albrecht Medical Center, Pontiac, IL, p. A194
CORS, William K., M.D., Senior Medical Director, Lehigh Valley Hospital – Pocono, East Stroudsburg, PA, p. A524
CORSO, David, Vice President Critical Access Hospitals, Thedacare Medical Center–Waupaca, Waupaca, WI, p. A707
CORTI, Ronald J., President and Chief Executive Officer, St. John'S Riverside Hospital, Yonkers, NY, p. A448
CORUM, Sharon, Chief Financial Officer, Kingwood Pines Hospital, Kingwood, TX, p. A618
CORWIN, Nancy
Chief Nursing Officer, Summit Surgical, Hutchinson, KS, p. A237
Chief Operating Officer, Summit Surgical, Hutchinson, KS, p. A237
CORWIN, Steven J., President and Chief Executive Officer, Brookdale Hospital Medical Center, New York, NY, p. A432
CORZINE, Judy, Administrative Director and Chief Information Officer, Stormont Vail Health, Topeka, KS, p. A246
COSBY, Christopher, Chief Executive Officer, Poinciana Medical Center, Kissimmee, FL, p. A127
COSBY, Dwan, Manager Human Resources, Mclaren Oakland, Pontiac, MI, p. A320
COSBY, Ernestine Y., Vice President Clinical Services and Chief Nursing Officer, Sheppard Pratt Health System, Baltimore, MD, p. A288
COSENTINO, Andrew B., President, Saint Alphonsus Regional Medical Center, Boise, ID, p. A168
COSLETT, John, R.N., Chief Nursing Officer, Kansas Spine And Specialty Hospital, Wichita, KS, p. A248
COSTA, Christopher P., M.D., Chief of Staff, Gordon Memorial Health Services, Gordon, NE, p. A385
COSTA, Joe
Acting Chief Fiscal Officer, Veterans Affairs Boston Healthcare System Brockton Division, Brockton, MA, p. A297
Chief Financial Officer, Veterans Affairs Boston Healthcare System, West Roxbury, MA, p. A304
COSTA, Mark E, Executive Director, Kaiser Permanente Orange County Anaheim Medical Center, Anaheim, CA, p. A50
COSTA, Mark E., Executive Director, Kaiser Permanente Orange County Anaheim Medical Center, Anaheim, CA, p. A50
COSTA, Michael G, Vice President Human Resources, Chi St. Joseph Regional Health Center, Bryan, TX, p. A590
COSTAKIS, Angie, Chief Information Officer, Claiborne Memorial Medical Center, Homer, LA, p. A268
COSTANTINO, Vincent, Vice President Operations and Human Resources, Hackensack Meridian Health Raritan Bay Medical Center, Perth Amboy, NJ, p. A411
COSTANZO, Kristin L., Direct–In–Market Lead Human Relations Partner, St. Vincent'S Blount, Oneonta, AL, p. A22
COSTELLA, Jeane L, Vice President, New York–Presbyterian/ Hudson Valley Hospital, Cortlandt Manor, NY, p. A426
COSTELLO, Jeff
Chief Financial Officer, Beacon Health System, Memorial Hospital Of South Bend, South Bend, IN, p. A215
Chief Financial Officer, Elkhart General Hospital, Elkhart, IN, p. A202
COSTELLO, Jodi
Chief Executive Officer, Select Specialty Hospital – Boardman, Boardman, OH, p. A473
Chief Executive Officer, Select Specialty Hospital–Youngstown, Youngstown, OH, p. A495
COSTIC, Andrew
Regional Chief Financial Officer, Abraham Lincoln Memorial Hospital, Lincoln, IL, p. A188
Regional Chief Financial Officer, Taylorville Memorial Hospital, Taylorville, IL, p. A197
COSTNER, Marc, Chief Financial Officer, Chestnut Hill Hospital, Philadelphia, PA, p. A534
COTA, Scott, M.D., Director Medical Services, Naval Hospital Lemoore, Lemoore, CA, p. A64
COTE, Gerri, Chief Operating Officer, Brattleboro Retreat, Brattleboro, VT, p. A654
COTE, Mary, Director Human Resources, New England Rehabilitation Hospital Of Portland, Portland, ME, p. A284
COTT, Gary, M.D., Executive Vice President Medical and Clinical Services, National Jewish Health, Denver, CO, p. A99
COTTEN, Brandon, Chief Financial Officer, Dewitt Hospital, Dewitt, AR, p. A41
COTTER, Bonny, Chief Nursing Officer, Baraga County Memorial Hospital, L'Anse, MI, p. A316
COTTER, Brian, Chief Operating Officer, Southern Inyo Healthcare District, Lone Pine, CA, p. A65
COTTER, Carole
Senior Vice President and Chief Information Officer, Emma Pendleton Bradley Hospital, East Providence, RI, p. A547
Senior Vice President and Chief Information Officer, Rhode Island Hospital, Providence, RI, p. A548
Vice President and Chief Information Officer, Miriam Hospital, Providence, RI, p. A547
COTTERILL, Allison, Chief Nursing Officer, Mercy General Hospital, Sacramento, CA, p. A82
COTTERMAN, Rob, Chief Executive Officer, Middle Tennessee Mental Health Institute, Nashville, TN, p. A576
COTTINGHAM, Jerod, Director Information Systems, Carlinville Area Hospital, Carlinville, IL, p. A175
COTTLE, Jeremy, Chief Executive Officer, Provo Canyon Behavioral Hospital, Orem, UT, p. A650
COTTLE, Mike, Chief Information Officer, Newton Medical Center, Newton, KS, p. A241
COTTO, Hector L, M.D., Medical Director, Hospital San Francisco, San Juan, PR, p. A719
COTTON, C Gerald, Interim Chief Operating Officer, Baptist Medical Center Leake, Carthage, MS, p. A345
COTTON, Michael, Chief Financial Officer, Gadsden Regional Medical Center, Gadsden, AL, p. A18
COTTON, Toni, R.N., Chief Nursing Officer, Harris Health System, Houston, TX, p. A611
COTTRILL, Brian, Chief Information Officer, United Hospital Center, Bridgeport, WV, p. A683
COUCH, Beulah, Director Human Resources, Mary Breckinridge Arh Hospital, Hyden, KY, p. A254
COUCH, Bill, Chief Financial Officer, Ashley County Medical Center, Crossett, AR, p. A40
COUCH, Chad, Chief Medical Officer, Bristol Regional Medical Center, Bristol, TN, p. A566
COUCHMAN, Diane, Vice President Patient Care Services and Chief Nursing Executive, Calverthealth Medical Center, Prince Frederick, MD, p. A293
COUGHENOUR, James, Administrator, Community Behavioral Health Hospital – Baxter, Baxter, MN, p. A328
COUGHLIN, Ann, Director Human Resources, Boundary Community Hospital, Bonners Ferry, ID, p. A168
COUGHLIN, Cynthia, MS, R.N., Chief Nursing Officer, Cheshire Medical Center, Keene, NH, p. A400
COUGHLIN, Kevin B., President and Chief Executive Officer, Beth Israel Deaconess Hospital Plymouth, Plymouth, MA, p. A302

COULTER, Barbara
  Director Information Systems, Franciscan Health Indianapolis, Indianapolis, IN, p. A207
  Director Information Systems, Franciscan Health Mooresville, Mooresville, IN, p. A211
COUNTS, Virginia, Manager Human Resources, Baylor Scott & White Hospital Medical Center – Brenham, Brenham, TX, p. A589
COUNTY–TEEMER, Vickie, Coordinator Human Resources, Mitchell County Hospital, Camilla, GA, p. A149
COURIS, John D., Chief Executive Officer, Tampa General Hospital, Tampa, FL, p. A142
COURNYER, Tim, Administrator, Forks Community Hospital, Forks, WA, p. A673
COURREGE, Gary, Chief Information Officer, Jennings American Legion Hospital, Jennings, LA, p. A269
COURTOIS, Harold, Chief Executive Officer, Memorial Health System, Abilene, KS, p. A232
COURTOIS, Robert, Vice President Finance, Munson Healthcare Otsego Memorial Hospital, Gaylord, MI, p. A312
COURY, Justin, Chief Operating Officer, Tristar Centennial Medical Center, Nashville, TN, p. A577
COURY, Tiffany, Chief Operating Officer, Northern Nevada Medical Center, Sparks, NV, p. A398
COUSAR, Myra, Director Human Resources, Baptist Memorial Hospital–Tipton, Covington, TN, p. A568
COUSINEAU, Cathy, Director Human Resources, Kaiser Permanente Woodland Hills Medical Center, Los Angeles, CA, p. A67
COUTURE, Maureen, Chief Nursing Officer and Vice President Nursing, Cardinal Hill Rehabilitation Hospital, Lexington, KY, p. A254
COUVILLON, Larry, M.D., Chief Medical Officer, Memorial Hospital At Gulfport, Gulfport, MS, p. A347
COVAULT, Julie, Vice President Finance, Wilson Memorial Hospital, Sidney, OH, p. A491
COVAULT, Myra, Associate Vice President of Human Resources, Hardin Memorial Health, Elizabethtown, KY, p. A251
COVELL, Nancy, Director Human Resources, Cameron Memorial Community Hospital, Angola, IN, p. A199
COVELLI, Margaret, R.N., Chief Nursing Officer, Spring Valley Hospital Medical Center, Las Vegas, NV, p. A396
COVERT, David G., Chief Executive Officer, South Texas Surgical Hospital, Corpus Christi, TX, p. A594
COVERT, Kathy, MSN, Vice President Workforce Development and Organizational Development, Schneck Medical Center, Seymour, IN, p. A214
COVERT, Terri, Vice President Human Resources, Mission Hospital, Mission Viejo, CA, p. A72
COVINGTON, Casey, M.D., President Elect, Medical Staff, Jennie Stuart Medical Center, Hopkinsville, KY, p. A253
COVINGTON, Celia, MSN, R.N., Director of Nursing, St. Mary'S Good Samaritan Hospital, Greensboro, GA, p. A154
COVINGTON, Jerome, M.D., Chief Medical Officer, Lower Keys Medical Center, Key West, FL, p. A126
COVONE, Ann Marie, Senior Vice President and Chief Financial Officer, Brookdale Hospital Medical Center, New York, NY, p. A432
COWAN, Christopher, Senior Vice President and Chief Human Resources Officer, Christiana Care Health System, Newark, DE, p. A113
COWAN, J W., Administrator, Choctaw General Hospital, Butler, AL, p. A15
COWAN, Leslie, R.N., Chief Nursing Officer, Henry Community Health, New Castle, IN, p. A212
COWAN, Ronald M, Vice President Information Systems, Geisinger–Lewistown Hospital, Lewistown, PA, p. A530
COWART, Mark, Facility Chief Information Officer, Carl Vinson Veterans Affairs Medical Center, Dublin, GA, p. A152
COWART, Timothy, Administrator, Springbrook Hospital, Brooksville, FL, p. A119
COWLES, John, Chief Financial Officer, Silver Lake Medical Center, Los Angeles, CA, p. A69
COWLING, Phyllis A., President and Chief Executive Officer, United Regional Health Care System, Wichita Falls, TX, p. A646
COX, Amber, Director Human Resources, Ut Health Carthage, Carthage, TX, p. A591
COX, Brian, Director Information Systems, Baptist Health Floyd, New Albany, IN, p. A212
COX, Carla C., Chief Nursing Officer, Indiana University Health Ball Memorial Hospital, Muncie, IN, p. A212
COX, Chandler, Director Human Resources, Mena Regional Health System, Mena, AR, p. A46
COX, Christopher, Chief Nursing Officer, Baptist Health Extended Care Hospital, Little Rock, AR, p. A44
COX, David W, Chief Financial Officer, Marinhealth Medical Center, Greenbrae, CA, p. A61

COX, Debbie D, Administrative Director Human Resources, Central Texas Medical Center, San Marcos, TX, p. A636
COX, Denida A., Chief Nursing Officer, South Georgia Medical Center, Valdosta, GA, p. A162
COX, Dianne E, Vice President of Human Resources, Kaweah Delta Medical Center, Visalia, CA, p. A94
COX, Dina, Director Human Resources, Kansas Rehabilitation Hospital, Topeka, KS, p. A246
COX, Dorothy, Manager Information Systems, Hackettstown Medical Center, Hackettstown, NJ, p. A406
COX, Gwen, Director Nursing Services, Klickitat Valley Health, Goldendale, WA, p. A673
COX, Jeffrey
  Chief Information Officer, Glendora Community Hospital, Glendora, CA, p. A61
  Director Information Technology, San Dimas Community Hospital, San Dimas, CA, p. A85
COX, Keith, Chief Executive Officer and Administrator, Lifecare Hospitals Of Shreveport–Willis Knighton, Shreveport, LA, p. A278
COX, Kenneth, Interim Chief Financial Officer, Mckenzie County Healthcare System, Watford City, ND, p. A470
COX, Leigh, Chief Information Officer, Wellstar Windy Hill Hospital, Marietta, GA, p. A157
COX, Lynna B, Director Health Information Services, Anson General Hospital, Anson, TX, p. A583
COX, Randy, Chief Information Officer, St. Vincent Indianapolis Hospital, Indianapolis, IN, p. A208
COX, Sandra, Controller, Permian Regional Medical Center, Andrews, TX, p. A583
COX, Sheila, Director Human Resources, Cibola General Hospital, Grants, NM, p. A418
COX, Steven, M.D., Chief Medical Officer, Ut Health North Campus Tyler, Tyler, TX, p. A642
COY, Nelson, Director Human Resources, Tahoe Pacific Hospitals, Sparks, NV, p. A398
COYE, Ed
  Director Information Technology Mission Health System Hospitals, Angel Medical Center, Franklin, NC, p. A454
  Director Information Technology, Transylvania Regional Hospital, Brevard, NC, p. A450
COYLE, Michael F., Chief Executive Officer, Ely–Bloomenson Community Hospital, Ely, MN, p. A331
COYNE, Rose, Interim CFO, Haywood Regional Medical Center, Clyde, NC, p. A452
COZART, Adrienne, Senior Vice President Human Resources, University Medical Center, Lubbock, TX, p. A622
CRABB, David W, M.D., Chief Medical Officer, Eskenazi Health, Indianapolis, IN, p. A206
CRABB, Ian, M.D., Chief Medical Officer, Orthonebraska Hospital, Omaha, NE, p. A390
CRABBE, Amy J.
  Senior Vice President Human Resources, Watauga Medical Center, Boone, NC, p. A450
  Vice President People Services, Charles A. Cannon Memorial Hospital, Newland, NC, p. A459
CRABDREE, Nathan, Chief Financial Officer, Rapides Regional Medical Center, Alexandria, LA, p. A262
CRABTREE, Gordon
  Chief Financial Officer, University Of Utah Health, Salt Lake City, UT, p. A652
  Interim Chief Executive Officer, University Of Utah Health, Salt Lake City, UT, p. A652
CRABTREE, John D, M.D., Chief of Staff, Tennova Healthcare–Harton, Tullahoma, TN, p. A580
CRABTREE, Robert, M.D., Chief of Staff and Medical Director, Physicians Surgical Hospital – Quail Creek, Amarillo, TX, p. A582
CRABTREE, Susan, Director Human Resources, Simi Valley Hospital, Simi Valley, CA, p. A89
CRACOLICI, Frank J., President and Chief Executive Officer, St. Vincent Medical Center, Los Angeles, CA, p. A69
CRACROFT, Davis, M.D., Senior Director Medical Affairs, Scripps Mercy Hospital, San Diego, CA, p. A84
CRAFT, Brian, Group Finance Officer, Texas Health Presbyterian Hospital Dallas, Dallas, TX, p. A598
CRAFT, Christina, Director Information Systems, Washington County Hospital, Plymouth, NC, p. A460
CRAFT, Kirby, Chief Information Officer, Magee General Hospital, Magee, MS, p. A350
CRAFTS, Nicholas, Chief Executive Officer, Houston Physicians Hospital, Webster, TX, p. A644
CRAGGS, Chris, Deputy Director, Winnebago Mental Health Institute, Winnebago, WI, p. A709
CRAIG, Alan, M.D., Chief Medical Officer, Princeton Baptist Medical Center, Birmingham, AL, p. A15
CRAIG, Celine H, Director Human Resources, King'S Daughters Medical Center, Brookhaven, MS, p. A345
CRAIG, Donnette, Director Human Resources, Christus Coushatta Health Care Center, Coushatta, LA, p. A266

CRAIG, Elizabeth J, MSN, Chief Nursing Officer and Vice President Patient Services, Temple University Hospital, Philadelphia, PA, p. A536
CRAIG, Emmett
  Chief Human Resources Officer, Knapp Medical Center, Weslaco, TX, p. A645
  Director Human Resources, Harlingen Medical Center, Harlingen, TX, p. A609
CRAIG, Jeff, Chief Human Resource Management, Veterans Affairs Maryland Health Care System–Baltimore Division, Baltimore, MD, p. A288
CRAIG, Mike
  Chief Financial Officer, Indiana University Health Bloomington Hospital, Bloomington, IN, p. A200
  Vice President, Chief Financial Officer, Indiana University Health Bedford Hospital, Bedford, IN, p. A199
CRAIG, Pamela, R.N., Chief Nursing Officer, Seton Medical Center Harker Heights, Harker Heights, TX, p. A609
CRAIG, Patrice, Manager Human Resources, Southern Arizona Veterans Affairs Health Care System, Tucson, AZ, p. A38
CRAIG, Rebecca W, Vice President and Chief Financial Officer, Wayne Unc Health Care, Goldsboro, NC, p. A455
CRAIG, Scott, M.D., Medical Director, Encompass Health Rehabilitation Hospital Of Franklin, Franklin, TN, p. A569
CRAIG, Sherry, Director Human Resources, Trace Regional Hospital, Houston, MS, p. A348
CRAIG, Steven, Chief Operating Officer and Acting Chief Executive Officer, Surgeons Choice Medical Center, Southfield, MI, p. A323
CRAIG, Steven, Ph.D., Chief Operating Officer and Acting Chief Executive Officer, Surgeons Choice Medical Center, Southfield, MI, p. A323
CRAIG, William J, CPA, Chief Financial Officer, Howard Memorial Hospital, Nashville, AR, p. A46
CRAIGER, Lisa, Chief Nursing Officer, Indiana University Health Jay Hospital, Portland, IN, p. A213
CRAIGIN, Jane, Chief Executive Officer, St. Vincent Williamsport Hospital, Williamsport, IN, p. A216
CRAIN, Greg, Senior Vice President and Administrator, Baptist Health Medical Center–Little Rock, Little Rock, AR, p. A44
CRAIN, Michelle B., Administrator and Chief Operating Officer, Heart Hospital Of Lafayette, Lafayette, LA, p. A270
CRAMBES, Terry, Manager Finance, Warren State Hospital, Warren, PA, p. A543
CRAMER, Brian J., Chief Executive Officer, Orthopaedic Hospital Of Wisconsin, Glendale, WI, p. A695
CRAMER, James R
  Vice President and Chief Information Officer, Honorhealth Scottsdale Osborn Medical Center, Scottsdale, AZ, p. A35
  Vice President and Chief Information Officer, Honorhealth Scottsdale Shea Medical Center, Scottsdale, AZ, p. A35
CRAMER, Lonnie
  Chief Operating Officer, Penrose–St. Francis Health Services, Colorado Springs, CO, p. A98
  President, Uchealth Broomfield Hospital, Broomfield, CO, p. A97
  President, Uchealth Longs Peak Hospital, Longmont, CO, p. A103
CRANDELL, Kristy, M.D., Medical Staff President, Red Bay Hospital, Red Bay, AL, p. A23
CRANE, Leslie, Interim Chief Executive Officer, Bear Lake Memorial Hospital, Montpelier, ID, p. A170
CRANFORD, Melvin, Chief Fiscal Services, Cheyenne Veterans Affairs Medical Center, Cheyenne, WY, p. A711
CRATON, Deborah W, M.D., Chief Medical Officer, St. Vincent Dunn Hospital, Bedford, IN, p. A200
CRATTY, Michael, M.D.
  Chief Medical Officer, Heritage Valley Health System, Beaver, PA, p. A520
  Chief Medical Officer, Sewickley Valley Hospital, (A Division Of Valley Medical Facilities), Sewickley, PA, p. A541
CRAVEN, Darcy, President, Kaleida Health, Buffalo, NY, p. A424
CRAVEY, Lavonda, Chief Financial Officer, Coffee Regional Medical Center, Douglas, GA, p. A152
CRAW, David, Coordinator Information Technology, Dundy County Hospital, Benkelman, NE, p. A383
CRAWFORD, Allen, Chief Nursing Officer, Jeff Davis Hospital, Hazlehurst, GA, p. A154
CRAWFORD, Arnita, Director Human Resources, Woman'S Hospital Of Texas, Houston, TX, p. A615
CRAWFORD, Jim, Chief Financial Officer, Lawrence Medical Center, Moulton, AL, p. A21
CRAWFORD, John W
  Chief Financial Officer, Muscogee Creek Nation Medical Center, Okmulgee, OK, p. A506
  Chief Financial Officer, St. John Sapulpa, Sapulpa, OK, p. A507
CRAWFORD, Linda, R.N., MSN, Chief Nursing Officer, Cookeville Regional Medical Center, Cookeville, TN, p. A568

CRAWFORD, Lucinda
Vice President Financial Services, Vidant Duplin Hospital, Kenansville, NC, p. A457
Vice President of Patient Care Services, Vidant Beaufort Hospital, Washington, NC, p. A463

CRAWFORD, Pam, R.N., Ph.D., Vice President of Nursing and Chief Nursing Officer, Ohiohealth Medcentral Mansfield Hospital, Mansfield, OH, p. A486

CRAWFORD, Randy, Chief Executive Officer, Appling Healthcare System, Baxley, GA, p. A148

CRAWFORD, Ryan, Director Talent, Southwestern Regional Medical Center, Tulsa, OK, p. A509

CRAWFORD, Susan, Manager Human Resources, Fayette County Hospital, Vandalia, IL, p. A197

CRAWFORD, Thomas, Chicago Market Chief Information Officer, Louis A. Weiss Memorial Hospital, Chicago, IL, p. A178

CRAWFORD, Tom
Vice President Human Resources, Emory Hillandale Hospital, Lithonia, GA, p. A156
Vice President Human Resources, Emory Long–Term Acute Care, Decatur, GA, p. A152

CRAWFORD, Traci, Commander, Moncrief Army Community Hospital, Fort Jackson, SC, p. A553

CRAWFORD, Wendy, Chief Human Resource Officer, Honorhealth Scottsdale Thompson Peak Medical Center, Scottsdale, AZ, p. A36

CRAYTON, Cory
Director Information Systems, Northeast Georgia Medical Center Barrow, Winder, GA, p. A163
Director of Information Systems, Piedmont Walton Hospital, Monroe, GA, p. A157

CREAL, Sharon, Vice President Financial Operations, Scripps Memorial Hospital–Encinitas, Encinitas, CA, p. A57

CREAMER, Julie L., President, Northwestern Memorial Hospital and Senior Vice President Northwestern Memorial HealthCare, Northwestern Memorial Hospital, Chicago, IL, p. A178

CREAMER, Ken, Chief Human Resource, Amarillo Veterans Affairs Health Care System, Amarillo, TX, p. A582

CREASMAN, Ginny L, Associate Director, Richard L. Roudebush Veterans Affairs Medical Center, Indianapolis, IN, p. A207

CREASY, Mike, Chief Executive Officer, Decatur County General Hospital, Parsons, TN, p. A578

CREEL, Keith, Vice President Operations, Christus Good Shepherd Medical Center–Marshall, Marshall, TX, p. A623

CREEL, Mary Ann, Chief Information Resource Management, Martinsburg Veterans Affairs Medical Center, Martinsburg, WV, p. A687

CREIGHTON, Peggy F, R.N., Director of Nursing, Methodist Hospital Union County, Morganfield, KY, p. A258

CRENSHAW, Neville, D.O., Chief of Staff, Unitypoint Health–Keokuk, Keokuk, IA, p. A225

CRENSHAW, Rachel H., Chief Operating Officer, Jack Hughston Memorial Hospital, Phenix City, AL, p. A22

CRENSHAW, William, M.D., Chief of Staff, Lady Of The Sea General Hospital, Cut Off, LA, p. A266

CREPEAU, Diana, Director Human Resources, Healthsouth Rehabilitation Hospital Of Colorado Springs, Colorado Springs, CO, p. A97

CREPS, Barbara, Director Human Resources and Accounting, Okeene Municipal Hospital, Okeene, OK, p. A503

CREQUE, J C, Director Management Information Systems, Schneider Regional Medical Center, Saint Thomas, VI, p. A720

CRESPO, Rosaida M, Executive Director, Hospital San Carlos Borromeo, Moca, PR, p. A717

CRESPO, Rosaida M., Executive Director, Hospital San Carlos Borromeo, Moca, PR, p. A717

CREVLING, Charles, Chief Financial Officer, Valley View Hospital, Glenwood Springs, CO, p. A101

CREWS, Carol
Chief Financial Officer, Higgins General Hospital, Bremen, GA, p. A148
Chief Financial Officer, Tanner Medical Center–Carrollton, Carrollton, GA, p. A149
Senior Vice President and Chief Financial Officer, Tanner Medical Center–Villa Rica, Villa Rica, GA, p. A162

CREWS, Kimberly, Vice President and Chief Financial Officer, Catawba Valley Medical Center, Hickory, NC, p. A456

CREWS, Paul, Director, Durham Veterans Affairs Medical Center, Durham, NC, p. A453

CRIBBS, Sammie, Vice President Clinical Services and Chief Nursing Officer, North Arkansas Regional Medical Center, Harrison, AR, p. A42

CRIBBS, Susan, D.O., Chief of Staff, Adventist Health Medical Center – Tehachapi Valley, Tehachapi, CA, p. A91

CRIDER, Terry, Information Technology Site Manager, Nea Baptist Memorial Hospital, Jonesboro, AR, p. A44

CRIGER, Sara J., President, Mercy Hospital, Coon Rapids, MN, p. A330

CRILLY, Tom
Executive Vice President and Chief Financial Officer, Unity Hospital, Rochester, NY, p. A443
Executive Vice President, Chief Financial Officer, Rochester Regional Health, Newark–Wayne Community Hospital, Newark, NY, p. A439

CRIM, Marcia, Chief Executive Officer, Usmd Hospital At Arlington, Arlington, TX, p. A584

CRIM, Marcia, R.N., MSN, Chief Nursing Officer and Chief Executive Officer, Usmd Hospital At Arlington, Arlington, TX, p. A584

CRINER, Mark, Director Information Technology, Memorial Health Care Systems, Seward, NE, p. A391

CRINER, Tonya, Human Resource Lead, Blackwell Regional Hospital, Blackwell, OK, p. A497

CRIPE, Kimberly C.
President and Chief Executive Officer, Children'S Hospital Of Orange County, Orange, CA, p. A76
President and Chief Executive Officer, Choc Children'S At Mission Hospital, Mission Viejo, CA, p. A72

CRIPPS, Eric, Chief Financial Officer, De Soto Regional Health System, Mansfield, LA, p. A273

CRISTY, Kirk, Chief Financial Officer, Sanford Bismarck, Bismarck, ND, p. A465

CRISWELL, Jodie, Vice President of Fiscal Services, Hammond–Henry Hospital, Geneseo, IL, p. A184

CRITCHLEY, Dan, Chief Information Officer, Banner – University Medical Center Tucson, Tucson, AZ, p. A37

CRITTENDEN, Shana, Chief Operating Officer, North Shore Medical Center, Miami, FL, p. A131

CROCE, Martin, M.D., Senior Vice President and Chief Medical Officer, Regional One Health, Memphis, TN, p. A575

CROCKER, Daniel, M.D., Chief Medical Officer, Lifecare Hospitals Of North Carolina, Rocky Mount, NC, p. A461

CROCKETT, James Scott, M.D., Chief of Staff, Falls Community Hospital And Clinic, Marlin, TX, p. A623

CROCKETT, John, Chief Information Officer, Guidance Center, Flagstaff, AZ, p. A29

CROCKETT, Mandy Lee
Director Human Resources, San Luis Valley Health Conejos County Hospital, La Jara, CO, p. A102
Director Human Resources, San Luis Valley Health, Alamosa, CO, p. A96

CROCKETT, Richard, Director, Overton Brooks Veterans Affairs Medical Center, Shreveport, LA, p. A278

CROCKETT, Timothy D, Chief Financial Officer, Breckinridge Memorial Hospital, Hardinsburg, KY, p. A253

CROFFUT, Tom, Chief Financial Officer, Centerpointe Hospital, Saint Charles, MO, p. A368

CROFT, Kim, R.N., Executive Director Human Resources, Pomerene Hospital, Millersburg, OH, p. A488

CROFTON, Michael
Chief Financial Officer, Good Samaritan Hospital, Cincinnati, OH, p. A476
Chief Financial Officer, Trihealth Evendale Hospital, Cincinnati, OH, p. A476
Senior Vice President and Chief Financial Officer, Bethesda North Hospital, Cincinnati, OH, p. A475

CROKER, James, Director Information Systems, St. Bernardine Medical Center, San Bernardino, CA, p. A83

CROLEY, John S., Chief Executive Officer and Chief Financial Officer, Texas Institute For Surgery At Texas Health Presbyterian Dallas, Dallas, TX, p. A598

CRONER, Robert, Senior Vice President and Chief Human Resources Officer, Children'S Hospital Of Philadelphia, Philadelphia, PA, p. A534

CRONIN, Annamarie, Director Human Resources, Encompass Health Rehabilitation Hospital Of New England, Woburn, MA, p. A305

CRONIN, David J, Regional Vice President Human Resources, Good Samaritan Medical Center, Brockton, MA, p. A296

CRONIN–WAELDE, Deborah L, MSN, R.N., Senior Vice President Clinical Operations and Chief Nursing Officer, Melrosewakefield Healthcare, Melrose, MA, p. A300

CROOKS, John, Chair Information Services, Mayo Clinic Hospital In Florida, Jacksonville, FL, p. A125

CROOM, Jon–Paul, President, Wellstar North Fulton Hospital, Roswell, GA, p. A159

CROPPER, Ronnie, Chief Operating Officer, Warren State Hospital, Warren, PA, p. A543

CROSBY, Evalie M, CPA, Vice President Finance and Chief Financial Officer, Alice Peck Day Memorial Hospital, Lebanon, NH, p. A400

CROSBY, Robert
Chief Financial Officer, Athol Hospital, Athol, MA, p. A294
Senior Vice President and Chief Financial Officer, Heywood Hospital, Gardner, MA, p. A299

CROSHAW, Diane S, Vice President Human Resources, Bacharach Institute For Rehabilitation, Pomona, NJ, p. A411

CROSLAND, Telita, Commander, Colonel Florence A. Blanchfield Army Community Hospital, Fort Campbell, KY, p. A252

CROSS, Carol, CPA, Chief Financial Officer, Northeast Regional Medical Center, Kirksville, MO, p. A363

CROSS, John D., Chief Executive Officer, Kindred Hospital Sugar Land, Sugar Land, TX, p. A638

CROSS, Lynda, R.N., Director of Nurses, Nemaha Valley Community Hospital, Seneca, KS, p. A245

CROSS, Patricia, Chief Executive Officer, Life Line Hospital, Steubenville, OH, p. A491

CROSS, Renee, Senior Vice President and Chief Financial Officer, Saint Francis Hospital, Charleston, WV, p. A684

CROSSAN, Eric, Chief Executive Officer, Walton Rehabilitation Hospital, Augusta, GA, p. A148

CROSSLAND, Jeanne, Director of Nursing, Shamrock General Hospital, Shamrock, TX, p. A636

CROSSLEY, Kent, M.D., Chief of Staff, Minneapolis Veterans Affairs Health Care System, Minneapolis, MN, p. A336

CROSSMAN, Margaret, M.D., Chief Medical Officer, Halifax Health Medical Center Of Daytona Beach, Daytona Beach, FL, p. A121

CROTEAU, Gary, Assistant Vice President and Chief Information Officer, South County Hospital, Wakefield, RI, p. A548

CROTTY, Glenn, M.D., Executive Vice President and Chief Operating Officer, Charleston Area Medical Center, Charleston, WV, p. A684

CROTTY, Renee, Coordinator Marketing and Public Relations, Capital Medical Center, Olympia, WA, p. A676

CROUCH, Amy, Chief Financial Officer, Promedica Coldwater Regional Hospital, Coldwater, MI, p. A309

CROUCH, James, Vice President Technical Services, Mosaic Medical Center – Albany, Albany, MO, p. A356

CROUCH, Matthew, Chief Executive Officer and Managing Director, Peachford Behavioral Health System, Atlanta, GA, p. A146

CROUSE, Autumn, Chief Financial Officer, Behavioral Hospital Of Bellaire, Houston, TX, p. A610

CROUT, Tom, MS, Director Human Resources, Central Louisiana State Hospital, Pineville, LA, p. A277

CROW, Angie, Director Finance, Saint Thomas Hospital For Spinal Surgery, Nashville, TN, p. A576

CROW, Regina W, Chief Nursing Officer, Bothwell Regional Health Center, Sedalia, MO, p. A371

CROW, Ronda, Chief Nursing Officer, Moore County Hospital District, Dumas, TX, p. A600

CROWDER, Andy, Chief Information Officer and Corporate Senior Vice President, Scripps Green Hospital, La Jolla, CA, p. A62

CROWDER, Lonna, Director of Nursing, Phillips County Hospital, Malta, MT, p. A378

CROWE, Arthur, Director Information Systems, Peconic Bay Medical Center, Riverhead, NY, p. A442

CROWE, Darren, Chief Executive Officer, Crow/Northern Cheyenne Hospital, Crow Agency, MT, p. A375

CROWELL, Lynn, Chief Executive Officer, Arkansas Valley Regional Medical Center, La Junta, CO, p. A102

CROWELL, Pamela, Director, Sheridan Veterans Affairs Medical Center, Sheridan, WY, p. A712

CROWELL, Robin, Chief Nursing Officer and Chief Operating Officer, Saint Thomas Hickman Hospital, Centerville, TN, p. A567

CROWL, Steve, Director of Information Services, Davis Medical Center, Elkins, WV, p. A685

CROWLEY, Thomas, President and Chief Executive Officer, Saint Elizabeth'S Medical Center, Wabasha, MN, p. A342

CRUDDAS, Brian, Chief Operating Officer, Bayfront Health Port Charlotte, Port Charlotte, FL, p. A137

CRUIKSHANK, Jennifer, Chief Executive Officer, Riverside University Health System–Medical Center, Moreno Valley, CA, p. A73

CRUM, Aaron, M.D., Senior Vice President, Assistant Chief Executive Officer and Chief Medical Officer, Pikeville Medical Center, Pikeville, KY, p. A259

CRUM, Dennis L, Senior Vice President and Chief Financial Officer, Tift Regional Medical Center, Tifton, GA, p. A162

CRUM, Jarett, Hospital Director, Baypointe Behavioral Health, Mobile, AL, p. A20

CRUMB, Robert, Chief Executive Officer, Schoolcraft Memorial Hospital, Manistique, MI, p. A317

CRUMLEY, Vickie L, Chief Human Resources Officer, Mary Rutan Hospital, Bellefontaine, OH, p. A473

CRUMP, John, M.D., Medical Staff President, Howard Young Medical Center, Woodruff, WI, p. A709

CRUMP, Rick, Chief Financial Officer, Lakeland Behavioral Health System, Springfield, MO, p. A371

CRUMPTON, Patsy Sue, R.N., Chief Nursing Officer, National Park Medical Center, Hot Springs, AR, p. A43
CRUSE, Ray, Chief Executive Officer, Lakeland Hospital, Watervliet, Watervliet, MI, p. A324
CRUSON, Jim, Chief Information Officer, Riverview Behavioral Health, Texarkana, AR, p. A49
CRUTCHFIELD, David, Vice President, Information Services & Chief Information Officer, Conway Medical Center, Conway, SC, p. A552
CRUTHIRDS, Richard, Director Information Systems, Peterson Regional Medical Center, Kerrville, TX, p. A618
CRUZ, Arlene, Director, Rush Oak Park Hospital, Oak Park, IL, p. A191
CRUZ, Domingo, Senior Vice President Operations, San Jorge Children'S Hospital, Santurce, PR, p. A719
CRUZ, Joseph V, Chief Information Officer, Ryder Memorial Hospital, Humacao, PR, p. A716
CRUZ, Julia, Chief Financial Officer, San Juan Capestrano Hospital, San Juan, PR, p. A719
CRUZ, Michael, Senior Vice President Operations, Bsa Hospital, Llc, Amarillo, TX, p. A582
CRUZ, Miguel, Medical Staff Credentialing Coordinator, Encompass Health Rehabilitation Hospital Of Miami, Cutler Bay, FL, p. A120
CRUZ, Miguel, M.D., Medical Director, Bella Vista Hospital, Mayaguez, PR, p. A717
CRUZ, Obed, Vice President and Chief Nursing Officer, Adventist Medical Center Bolingbrook, Bolingbrook, IL, p. A174
CRUZ CORREA, Jesus, Chief Medical Officer, St. Luke'S Episcopal Hospital, Ponce, PR, p. A717
CRYER, Betty, R.N., Administrator/Chief Nursing Officer, Anderson Regional Health System South, Meridian, MS, p. A351
CRYER, Selena, Director Human Resources, Ennis Regional Medical Center, Ennis, TX, p. A603
CRYNES, Kristin, Executive Director of Nursing, Greene County General Hospital, Linton, IN, p. A210
CSEPKE, Cheryl, Controller, Kindred Rehabilitation Hospital Northeast Houston, Humble, TX, p. A615
CUBELLIS, Guido J., Chief Executive Officer, Cornerstone Hospital–Medical Center Of Houston, Houston, TX, p. A611
CUELLAR, Eddie, Vice President Information Systems, Methodist Hospital, San Antonio, TX, p. A634
CUELLAR, Jacob, Chief Executive Officer, Laurel Ridge Treatment Center, San Antonio, TX, p. A634
CUENCA, Derrick, Chief Executive Officer, Mountainview Regional Medical Center, Las Cruces, NM, p. A419
CUEVAS, Gilberto, Director Human Resources, Hospital De Damas, Ponce, PR, p. A717
CUEVAS, Jacki, Director Health Information Services, Regional Rehabilitation Hospital, Phenix City, AL, p. A22
CUFF, Randy, Chief Operating Officer, Central Valley Medical Center, Nephi, UT, p. A649
CULBERSON, David K., Chief Executive Officer, San Joaquin General Hospital, French Camp, CA, p. A59
CULBERT, Devon, Controller, The Hospital At Westlake Medical Center, Austin, TX, p. A586
CULLEN, Barry, Chief Executive Officer, Southeast Michigan Surgical Hospital, Warren, MI, p. A324
CULLEN, John, Chief Executive Officer, Thomas B. Finan Center, Cumberland, MD, p. A290
CULLEN, John, M.D., Chief of Staff and Medical Director Long Term Care, Providence Valdez Medical Center, Valdez, AK, p. A27
CULLEN, Kelly, R.N., Executive Vice President and Chief Operating Officer, Tampa General Hospital, Tampa, FL, p. A142
CULLEN, Michael, Senior Vice President and Chief Financial Officer, South Shore Hospital, South Weymouth, MA, p. A303
CULLEN, Neil, Director Human Resources, Encompass Health Rehabilitation Hospital Of Northwest Tucson, Tucson, AZ, p. A37
CULLEN, Paul T, M.D., Vice President Medical Affairs, Washington Hospital, Washington, PA, p. A543
CULLISON, Rebecca, President, Methodist Healthcare Memphis Hospitals, Memphis, TN, p. A575
CULLITON, Gerald F., Medical Center Director, Veterans Affairs Connecticut Healthcare System, West Haven, CT, p. A112
CULP, Judy, Chief Financial Officer, Hill Regional Hospital, Hillsboro, TX, p. A610
CULPEPPER, Michelle, Director Human Resources, Chicago Lakeshore Hospital, Chicago, IL, p. A177
CULVER, Douglas, Chief Financial Officer, Mercy Hospital Carthage, Carthage, MO, p. A358
CULVER, Shawna, Director Information Systems, Western Plains Medical Complex, Dodge City, KS, p. A234
CUMBEE, Lib, Director Information Systems, Providence Hospital, Columbia, SC, p. A551
CUMBIE, Dan L, Chief Nursing Officer, Flowers Hospital, Dothan, AL, p. A17
CUMBO, Adam, Chief Financial Officer, Dukes Memorial Hospital, Peru, IN, p. A213
CUMING, Richard, R.N., MSN, Ed.D., Chief Nurse Executive, Christiana Care Health System, Newark, DE, p. A113
CUMMING, John, Interim Chief Executive Officer, Hennepin Healthcare, Minneapolis, MN, p. A335
CUMMINGS, Allana, Chief Information Officer, Children'S Healthcare Of Atlanta, Atlanta, GA, p. A146
CUMMINGS, Brooke, Chief Financial Officer, Our Lady Of The Angels Hospital, Bogalusa, LA, p. A264
CUMMINGS, Gabrielle, President, Northshore University Health System, Evanston, IL, p. A182
CUMMINGS, Greg, Chief Financial Officer, Baylor Scott & White Texas Spine & Joint Hospital–Tyler, Tyler, TX, p. A642
CUMMINGS, Jerry, Chief Operating Officer, Putnam County Memorial Hospital, Unionville, MO, p. A372
CUMMINGS, Kelly, Chief Nursing Officer, Abington–Lansdale Hospital Jefferson Health, Lansdale, PA, p. A529
CUMMINGS, Steve, M.D., Chief of Medical Staff, Stillwater Medical Center, Stillwater, OK, p. A507
CUMMINGS, Steven, Chief Operating Officer and Chief Information Officer, Baystate Noble Hospital, Westfield, MA, p. A304
CUMMINS, Frank L, Vice President Human Resources, Honorhealth Deer Valley Medical Center, Phoenix, AZ, p. A33
CUMMINS, Thomas H., M.D., Chief Medical Officer, Bon Secours St. Francis Health System, Greenville, SC, p. A553
CUNNIGHAM, James, D.O., Chief of Staff, Audubon County Memorial Hospital And Clinics, Audubon, IA, p. A217
CUNNINGHAM, Becky, Controller, Salem Memorial District Hospital, Salem, MO, p. A371
CUNNINGHAM, Brian, Chief Executive Officer, Wahiawa General Hospital, Wahiawa, HI, p. A166
CUNNINGHAM, Carol, Administrative Assistant, Highland Ridge Hospital, Midvale, UT, p. A648
CUNNINGHAM, Connie, Chief Information Officer, Ellwood City Medical Center, Llc, Ellwood City, PA, p. A525
CUNNINGHAM, Debbie
President, Moses H. Cone Memorial Hospital, Greensboro, NC, p. A455
Senior Vice President, Cone Health and President, Maternal, Child and Behavioral Health Services, Moses H. Cone Memorial Hospital, Greensboro, NC, p. A455
CUNNINGHAM, Dennis J., M.D., Chief Medical Officer, Mclaren Macomb, Mount Clemens, MI, p. A318
CUNNINGHAM, Gail, Interim Chief Medical Officer, University Of Maryland St. Joseph Medical Center, Towson, MD, p. A293
CUNNINGHAM, Gary, Chief Nursing Officer, Dixie Regional Medical Center, Saint George, UT, p. A651
CUNNINGHAM, James C, M.D., Chief Medical Officer, Cook Children'S Medical Center, Fort Worth, TX, p. A604
CUNNINGHAM, Julie, Associate Administrator and Chief Human Resources Officer, Pioneers Memorial Healthcare District, Brawley, CA, p. A53
CUNNINGHAM, Keith W, M.D., Medical Director, Encompass Health Rehabilitation Hospital Of Scottsdale, Scottsdale, AZ, p. A35
CUNNINGHAM, M Edward., Chief Executive Officer, Gateway Regional Medical Center, Granite City, IL, p. A184
CUNNINGHAM, Peggy, Chief Executive Officer, Peak Behavioral Health Services, Santa Teresa, NM, p. A420
CUNNINGHAM, Regina, Chief Executive Officer, Hospital Of The University Of Pennsylvania, Philadelphia, PA, p. A535
CUPPS, Cheryl, Director Finance, Griffin Memorial Hospital, Norman, OK, p. A503
CURD, R Blake., Chief Executive Officer, Sioux Falls Specialty Hospital, Sioux Falls, SD, p. A564
CURLING, Susan, M.D., Chief Medical Officer, Memorial Hermann Northeast, Humble, TX, p. A615
CURNEL, Robin, MSN, Chief Operating Officer and Chief Nursing Officer, Crittenden County Hospital, Marion, KY, p. A257
CURRAN, Dezerae, Director Human Resources, Osawatomie State Hospital At Adair Acute Care, Osawatomie, KS, p. A242
CURRAN, Maria, Vice President Human Resources, Vcu Medical Center, Richmond, VA, p. A666
CURRAN, Michael, President, Crozer–Chester Medical Center, Upland, PA, p. A543
CURRAN, Todd A., M.D., President Medical Staff, Oss Orthopaedic Hospital, York, PA, p. A546
CURRAN–MEULI, Jane, Chief Operating Officer, Holy Family Memorial, Manitowoc, WI, p. A699
CURRANS, Sheila, Chief Executive Officer, Harrison Memorial Hospital, Cynthiana, KY, p. A251
CURREN, Robert
Director Information Technology, Center For Behavioral Medicine, Kansas City, MO, p. A362
Western Region Chief Information Technology Officer, Northwest Missouri Psychiatric Rehabilitation Center, Saint Joseph, MO, p. A368
CURRIE, Michelle, Chief Financial Officer, Red River Behavioral Health System, Grand Forks, ND, p. A467
CURRIE, Peggy M.
Chief Operating Officer, Providence Holy Family Hospital, Spokane, WA, p. A679
Chief Operating Officer, Providence Sacred Heart Medical Center & Children'S Hospital, Spokane, WA, p. A680
CURRIE, Scott D, Vice President and Chief Financial Officer, Midmichigan Medical Center–Midland, Midland, MI, p. A318
CURRIN, Randy, Chief Executive Officer, Blake Medical Center, Bradenton, FL, p. A118
CURRY, Cheryl, Chief Financial Officer, Littleton Adventist Hospital, Littleton, CO, p. A103
CURRY, Christopher, Chief Executive Officer, Kindred Hospital Peoria, Peoria, IL, p. A193
CURRY, Jeffrey T
Executive Vice President and Chief Financial Officer, Excela Frick Hospital, Mount Pleasant, PA, p. A532
Executive Vice President and Chief Financial Officer, Excela Health Westmoreland Hospital, Greensburg, PA, p. A526
CURRY, Robert H, President and Chief Executive Officer, Citrus Valley Medical Center–Inter Community Campus, Covina, CA, p. A56
CURRY, Robert H.
President and Chief Executive Officer, Citrus Valley Medical Center–Inter Community Campus, Covina, CA, p. A56
President and Chief Executive Officer, Foothill Presbyterian Hospital, Glendora, CA, p. A60
CURRY, Stephen A, Director Information Services, Princeton Community Hospital, Princeton, WV, p. A688
CURRY, Steve, Regional Director Human Resources, Four County Counseling Center, Logansport, IN, p. A210
CURRY, Timothey, Chief Executive Officer, Avoyelles Hospital, Marksville, LA, p. A273
CURRY–PELYAK, Mary Jane, R.N., Vice President and Chief Clinical Officer, The Villages Regional Hospital, The Villages, FL, p. A142
CURTI, Tate, Senior Vice President and Chief Operating Officer, Southern New Hampshire Medical Center, Nashua, NH, p. A401
CURTIN, Sean, Chief Financial Officer, The University Of Vermont Health Network – Alice Hyde Medical Center, Malone, NY, p. A430
CURTIS, Bryan, Chief Information Officer, Memorial Regional Health, Craig, CO, p. A98
CURTIS, Edgar J., President and Chief Executive Officer, Memorial Medical Center, Springfield, IL, p. A196
CURTIS, George, Chief Information Officer, Houston Medical Center, Warner Robins, GA, p. A163
CURTIS, Janis, Interim Director Information Technology, Duke Raleigh Hospital, Raleigh, NC, p. A460
CURTIS, Joy U, Senior Vice President Human Resources, Cambridge Health Alliance, Cambridge, MA, p. A297
CURTIS, Lorna, Chief Financial Officer, John F. Kennedy Memorial Hospital, Indio, CA, p. A62
CURTIS, Michael, Chief Administrative Officer, Mckenzie County Healthcare System, Watford City, ND, p. A470
CURTIS, Tracie, Business Partner Human Resources, Cleveland Clinic, Medina Hospital, Medina, OH, p. A487
CURTRIGHT, Jonathan W., Chief Executive Officer, University Of Missouri Health Care, Columbia, MO, p. A359
CURVIN, Thomas J, M.D., Chief of Staff, Rankin County Hospital District, Rankin, TX, p. A630
CUSA, Philip L., Hospital Director, Eastpointe Hospital, Daphne, AL, p. A16
CUSACK, Michele, Senior Vice President and Chief Financial Officer, Southside Hospital, Bay Shore, NY, p. A423
CUSACK, Susan, Executive Director, Mercy Fitzgerald Hospital, Darby, PA, p. A524
CUSACK–MCGUIRK, Joan, President and Chief Executive Officer, Montefiore St. Luke'S Cornwall, Newburgh, NY, p. A439
CUSANO, Susan, Director Human Resources, Four Winds Hospital, Katonah, NY, p. A429
CUSENZ, Bruce J, M.D., Medical Director, Eastern Niagara Hospital, Lockport, NY, p. A430
CUSHING, Ginger, Chief Executive Officer, Lifebrite Community Hospital Of Early, Blakely, GA, p. A148
CUSHING, Heidi, Chief Financial Officer, Harlan County Health System, Alma, NE, p. A382
CUSHING, Herbert, M.D., Chief Medical Officer, Temple University Hospital, Philadelphia, PA, p. A536
CUSHMAN, Bonnie, Chief Financial Officer, Northern Colorado Rehabilitation Hospital, Johnstown, CO, p. A102

CUSSINS, James, Chief Financial Officer, Platte County Memorial Hospital, Wheatland, WY, p. A713

CUSTER, Joshua, Director Finance, St. Luke'S Magic Valley Medical Center, Twin Falls, ID, p. A172

CUSTER, Lindsey, Director Human Resources, Riverside Tappahannock Hospital, Tappahannock, VA, p. A668

CUSTER–MITCHELL, Marilyn J., President, Parkview Wabash Hospital, Wabash, IN, p. A216

CUSTIN, Melinda, Chief Information Officer, Jps Health Network, Fort Worth, TX, p. A605

CUSTODIO, David, President Summa Health System Akron, Summa Health System, Akron, OH, p. A471

CUSUMANO, Margaret M, R.N., MSN, Vice President Patient Care Services and Chief Nursing Officer, Saint Joseph'S Medical Center, Yonkers, NY, p. A448

CUTHRELL, Rob, Director of Human Resources, Coastal Virginia Rehabilitation, Newport News, VA, p. A663

CUTLIFF, Bryan, Chief Executive Officer, Select Specialty Hospital–Ann Arbor, Ypsilanti, MI, p. A325

CUTOLO, Edward, M.D., Chief of Staff, James A. Haley Veterans' Hospital–Tampa, Tampa, FL, p. A141

CUTRELL, Carrie, Chief Nursing Officer, Arkansas Valley Regional Medical Center, La Junta, CO, p. A102

CUTRIGHT, Bruce E, MS, Vice President Human Resources, Mary Lanning Healthcare, Hastings, NE, p. A385

CUTSFORTH, Shawn, Information Systems Officer, Pioneer Memorial Hospital, Heppner, OR, p. A513

CUTTER, Elise, Chief Financial Officer, Island Hospital, Anacortes, WA, p. A670

CUZZOLA, Anthony, Vice President and Administrator, Hackensack Meridian Health Jfk Johnson Rehabilitation Institute, Edison, NJ, p. A405

CYBORON, Abigail, Chief Financial Officer, Chase County Community Hospital, Imperial, NE, p. A386

CYE, Mark, Chief Executive Officer, Medina Memorial Hospital, Medina, NY, p. A431

CYR, Kristin, R.N., MSN, Senior Nursing Executive and Vice President of Patient Care Services, Northern Light Maine Coast Hospital, Ellsworth, ME, p. A283

CYTLAK, David
Chief Financial Officer, Blanchard Valley Hospital, Findlay, OH, p. A483
Vice President Finance, Bluffton Hospital, Bluffton, OH, p. A473

CZAHOR, John, IT Site Executive, University Of Maryland Charles Regional Medical Center, La Plata, MD, p. A291

CZAJKOWSKI, Cheryl, Associate Director Patient and Nursing Services, Syracuse Veterans Affairs Medical Center, Syracuse, NY, p. A445

CZEREW, Jane, Vice President Clinical Services and Quality, Spectrum Health Zeeland Community Hospital, Zeeland, MI, p. A326

CZYMBOR, Mary, Chief Medical Officer, Milford Regional Medical Center, Milford, MA, p. A301

CZYZ, AnneMarie, R.N., Ed.D., Chief Operating Officer and Chief Nursing Officer, St. Joseph'S Hospital Health Center, Syracuse, NY, p. A445

D

DAANE, John, Information Systems Officer, Crossing Rivers Health Medical Center, Prairie Du Chien, WI, p. A704

DABNEY, Ann, Manager Human Resources, Spring View Hospital, Lebanon, KY, p. A254

DACE, Linda, Vice President Finance, Mcdonough District Hospital, Macomb, IL, p. A188

D'ACCURZIO, Albert, M.D., Medical Director, St. Elizabeth Medical Center, Utica, NY, p. A446

DADD, Steven, Flight Commander Resource Management, U. S. Air Force Hospital, Hampton, VA, p. A660

DADO, Joe
Chief Information Officer, Conemaugh Memorial Medical Center, Johnstown, PA, p. A528
Chief Information Officer, Conemaugh Miners Medical Center, Hastings, PA, p. A527

DAEGER, Brian, Chief Financial Officer and Vice President Financial Services, Margaret Mary Health, Batesville, IN, p. A199

DAFFRON, Eric Allen, Division Director, Information Systems, Southeast Alabama Medical Center, Dothan, AL, p. A17

DAGENBACH, Pete, Chief Financial Officer, Adams County Regional Medical Center, Seaman, OH, p. A490

DAGGETT, Jake, Chief Executive Officer, Texas Rehabilitation Hospital Of Fort Worth, Fort Worth, TX, p. A606

DAHDUL, Adnan, M.D., Medical Director, Encompass Health Rehabilitation Hospital Of Western Massachusetts, Ludlow, MA, p. A300

DAHL, Robert, President and Chief Executive Officer, Amita Health Resurrection Medical Center, Chicago, IL, p. A176

DAHLBERG, Connie, Director Business and Employee, Sleepy Eye Medical Center, Sleepy Eye, MN, p. A340

DAHLHAUSEN, Daniel J, M.D., President of Medical Staff/ Chief Medical Officer, Anmed Health Cannon, Pickens, SC, p. A556

DAHLING, James D., President and Chief Executive Officer, Children'S Hospital Of The King'S Daughters, Norfolk, VA, p. A663

DAHLQUIST, Clay, M.D., Chief Medical Officer, Waverly Health Center, Waverly, IA, p. A231

DAHLSTRAND, David, Chief, OI&T, Hunter Holmes Mcguire Veterans Affairs Medical Center–Richmond, Richmond, VA, p. A666

DAHLSTROM, Sheri, R.N., Chief Nursing Officer, Banner Estrella Medical Center, Phoenix, AZ, p. A33

DAIGLE, Cindy, Chief Financial Officer, Northern Maine Medical Center, Fort Kent, ME, p. A283

DAIGLE, Jennifer, R.N., Director of Nursing and Utilization Review, Carolina Center For Behavioral Health, Greer, SC, p. A554

DAIGLE, Richard
Chief Information Officer, Manchester Memorial Hospital, Manchester, CT, p. A108
Chief Information Officer, Rockville General Hospital, Vernon, CT, p. A111

DAIKER, David, Chief Information Resource Management, Veterans Affairs Nebraska–Western Iowa Health Care System – Lincoln, Lincoln, NE, p. A387

DAILEY, Gina, Chief Financial Officer, Pinnacle Pointe Hospital, Little Rock, AR, p. A45

DAILEY, Jacqueline, Chief Information Officer, West Penn Hospital, Pittsburgh, PA, p. A538

DAILEY, Richard R, D.O., President Medical Staff, Ellett Memorial Hospital, Appleton City, MO, p. A356

DAISLEY, Samuel, D.O., Vice President Medical Affairs, Upmc Horizon, Farrell, PA, p. A526

DAJCZAK, Stanislaw, M.D., Chief of Staff, Promedica Defiance Regional Hospital, Defiance, OH, p. A482

DALBY, William, Director Fiscal Services, Shriners Hospitals For Children–Northern California, Sacramento, CA, p. A82

DALE, Jackson
Director Management Information Services, Johnston Memorial Hospital, Abingdon, VA, p. A656
Site Manager Information Systems, Indian Path Medical Center, Kingsport, TN, p. A572

DALE, Jae, Chief Executive Officer, Kosciusko Community Hospital, Warsaw, IN, p. A216

DALEBOUT, Kenneth, Site Administrator, Arroyo Grande Community Hospital, Arroyo Grande, CA, p. A61

DALEY, Robert, CPA
Chief Financial Officer, Black River Memorial Hospital, Black River Falls, WI, p. A692
Vice President Fiscal and Information Technology Services, Black River Memorial Hospital, Black River Falls, WI, p. A692

DALGAI, Netrisha, Director of Operations, Sage Memorial Hospital, Ganado, AZ, p. A29

DALL, Jamie, Chief Financial Officer, New Hampshire Hospital, Concord, NH, p. A399

DALLER, Sue, R.N., Assistant Administrator Nursing, Hermann Area District Hospital, Hermann, MO, p. A361

DALLEY, Mark F., Administrator, Gunnison Valley Hospital, Gunnison, UT, p. A648

DALLIS, Donna, R.N., Vice President Patient Care, Northeastern Health System, Tahlequah, OK, p. A508

DALPOAS, Dolan, President and Chief Executive Officer, Abraham Lincoln Memorial Hospital, Lincoln, IL, p. A188

DALTON, Deana, Human Resources, San Juan Health Service District, Monticello, UT, p. A649

DALTON, Eric
Administrator, Tanner Medical Center–Villa Rica, Villa Rica, GA, p. A162
Chief Financial Officer, Memorial Medical Center, Modesto, CA, p. A72
Chief Financial Officer, Sutter Tracy Community Hospital, Tracy, CA, p. A92

DALTON, John, President, Northern Light Inland Hospital, Waterville, ME, p. A285

DALTON, Leigh, Director of Nursing and Patient Care Services, Highland Hospital, Charleston, WV, p. A684

DALTON, Nissi, Manager Human Resources, Baylor Scott & White Institute For Rehabilitation–Fort Worth, Fort Worth, TX, p. A604

DALTON, Valerie, Administrator, Oceans Behavioral Hospital Of Baton Rouge, Baton Rouge, LA, p. A263

DALTON, Wayne, Chief Financial Officer, Lakeview Hospital, Bountiful, UT, p. A647

DALY, Cindy, R.N., Director of Nursing, Syringa Hospital And Clinics, Grangeville, ID, p. A169

DALY, Derek, Chief Executive Officer, Blue Mountain Hospital District, John Day, OR, p. A514

DALY, Linda, Vice President Human Resources, Auburn Community Hospital, Auburn, NY, p. A423

DALY, Thomas M, CPA, Chief Financial Officer, University Hospital, Newark, NJ, p. A409

DAMA, Sunil, M.D., Medical Director, Select Specialty Hospital – Cincinnati North, Cincinnati, OH, p. A476

DAMBOISE, Robin, Director Human Resources, Northern Maine Medical Center, Fort Kent, ME, p. A283

D'AMBROSIO, Matthew, MSN, R.N., Chief Nursing Officer, Encompass Health Rehabilitation Hospital Of San Antonio, San Antonio, TX, p. A634

DAMIANO, Louis, President, Holy Cross Hospital, Silver Spring, MD, p. A293

D'AMICO, David, Chief Financial Officer, St. Anthony'S Rehabilitation Hospital, Lauderdale Lakes, FL, p. A128

D'AMICO, Kenneth, Chief Executive Officer, Amg Specialty Hospital – Las Vegas, Las Vegas, NV, p. A394

D'AMICO, Paul, M.D., Chief of Staff, Atrium Health Stanly, Albemarle, NC, p. A449

DAMM, Julie, Chief Financial Officer, Hancock County Health System, Britt, IA, p. A218

DAMMEYER, Matt, Ph.D., Chief Operating Officer, Central Peninsula Hospital, Soldotna, AK, p. A27

DAMODARAN, A N, M.D., President Medical Staff, Starke Hospital, Knox, IN, p. A208

DAMON, Chad, Contractor, St. Vincent Dunn Hospital, Bedford, IN, p. A200

DAMON, Kerry, Director Human Resources, Baystate Franklin Medical Center, Greenfield, MA, p. A299

D'AMORE, Seanna, Director Human Resources, Penn Highlands Elk, Saint Marys, PA, p. A540

DAMRON, Greg, Vice President Finance and Chief Financial Officer, Augusta University Medical Center, Augusta, GA, p. A147

DAMRON, Paul, Chief Financial Officer, Highlands Regional Medical Center, Sebring, FL, p. A139

DAMRON, Tony, Senior Vice President and Chief Information Officer, Pikeville Medical Center, Pikeville, KY, p. A259

DAMSCHRODER, Robin, Chief Operating Officer, St. Joseph Mercy Livingston Hospital, Howell, MI, p. A314

DANBDALA, Kayyan, M.D., Medical Director, Schick Shadel Hospital, Seattle, WA, p. A678

DANCY, Peter C, Jr, Director, Alexandria Veterans Affairs Health Care System, Pineville, LA, p. A277

DANDORPH, Michael J, President and Chief Operating Officer, Rush University Medical Center, Chicago, IL, p. A179

DANE, Brenda, Director, Human Resources, Highlands Regional Medical Center, Sebring, FL, p. A139

DANE, Jeff, Executive Vice President and Chief Financial Officer, University Medical Center, Lubbock, TX, p. A622

DANEFF, Jeffrey, Chief Financial Officer, Porter Regional Hospital, Valparaiso, IN, p. A215

DANELLO, Sherry, MSN, R.N.
Vice President and Chief Nursing Officer, Candler Hospital, Savannah, GA, p. A160
Vice President and Chief Nursing Officer, St. Joseph'S Hospital, Savannah, GA, p. A160

DANESHMAND, Alex, D.O., Chief Patient Safety Officer, Lee Memorial Hospital, Fort Myers, FL, p. A123

DANG, Cynthia, Vice President Human Resources, Medical City North Hills, North Richland Hills, TX, p. A626

D'ANGELO, Jennifer, Vice President Information Services, Christian Health Care Center, Wyckoff, NJ, p. A415

DANGERFIELD, Wesley, Community Chief Executive Officer, Summers County Arh Hospital, Hinton, WV, p. A685

D'ANGINA, Joseph, Area Finance Officer, Kaiser Permanente Vallejo Medical Center, Vallejo, CA, p. A93

DANIEL, Christopher W., Administrator, Sterling Surgical Hospital, Slidell, LA, p. A279

DANIEL, Dena, Director Information Systems, Jackson County Memorial Hospital, Altus, OK, p. A496

DANIEL, Joyce, Chief Nursing Officer, Blackwell Regional Hospital, Blackwell, OK, p. A497

DANIEL, Karen
Chief Executive Officer, Warm Springs Medical Center, Warm Springs, GA, p. A162
Director Human Resources, Bibb Medical Center, Centreville, AL, p. A16

DANIEL, Ron, Manager Information Systems, Matheny Medical And Educational Center, Peapack, NJ, p. A410

DANIEL, S., M.D., Chief Medical Officer, Spring Valley Hospital Medical Center, Las Vegas, NV, p. A396

DANIELS, Alex, Chief Nurse Executive, U. S. Public Health Service Indian Hospital, Crownpoint, NM, p. A417

DANIELS, Andrew J., Chief Executive Officer, Memorial Regional Health, Craig, CO, p. A98
DANIELS, Andy, Chief Operating Officer, Bucyrus Hospital, Bucyrus, OH, p. A474
DANIELS, Anita, Director, Brookdale Hospital Medical Center, New York, NY, p. A432
DANIELS, Betty, M.D., Chief of Staff, St. Bernardine Medical Center, San Bernardino, CA, p. A83
DANIELS, Christine S., R.N., Chief Nursing Officer, Camden Clark Medical Center, Parkersburg, WV, p. A688
DANIELS, Craig M, Chief Financial Officer, Moab Regional Hospital, Moab, UT, p. A648
DANIELS, D. Jeffery., Chief Executive Officer, Mountain River Birthing And Surgery Center, Blackfoot, ID, p. A167
DANIELS, Don, Executive Vice President and Chief Operating Officer, Swedishamerican – A Division Of Uw Health, Rockford, IL, p. A195
DANIELS, Don, M.D., Chief Medical Officer, Adventhealth Rollins Brook, Lampasas, TX, p. A619
DANIELS, Janette, Chief Executive Officer, Chi St. Vincent Hot Springs Rehabilitation Hospital, Hot Springs, AR, p. A43
DANIELS, John, M.D., Medical Director, Lifecare Hospitals Of Wisconsin, Pewaukee, WI, p. A703
DANIELS, Judy, Vice President Human Resources, Our Lady Of Bellefonte Hospital, Ashland, KY, p. A249
DANIELS, Karen, MSN, R.N., Chief Nursing Officer, Halifax Regional Medical Center, Roanoke Rapids, NC, p. A461
DANIELS, Kristin, Manager Human Resources, Sutter Center For Psychiatry, Sacramento, CA, p. A82
DANIELS, Mark, M.D., Vice President Physician Enterprise, Northwestern Medicine Delnor Hospital, Geneva, IL, p. A184
DANIELS, S Janette, Director Human Resources, Encompasss Health Rehabilitation Hospital Of Fort Smith, Fort Smith, AR, p. A42
DANIELS, Sarah, Vice President, Information Technology, Mayo Clinic Health System In Mankato, Mankato, MN, p. A334
DANIELS, Todd, M.D., Medical Director, Encompass Health Rehabilitation Hospital Of Arlington, Arlington, TX, p. A583
DANIELS, Troy P, Chief Human Resources Officer, Forrest General Hospital, Hattiesburg, MS, p. A348
DANIELS, W. Peter, Executive Vice President and Chief Operating Officer, Carepoint Health Bayonne Medical Center, Bayonne, NJ, p. A403
DANIELSON, Carol, R.N., Senior Vice President and Chief Nursing Officer, Gwinnett Hospital System, Lawrenceville, GA, p. A156
DANIELYAN, Arman, M.D., Chief of Staff, John Muir Behavioral Health Center, Concord, CA, p. A55
DANN, Doreen, R.N., Chief Operating Officer, Victor Valley Global Medical Center, Victorville, CA, p. A94
DANNA, Denise, Chief Nursing Officer, University Medical Center, New Orleans, LA, p. A275
DANNENBERG, Walt, Director, Va Long Beach Healthcare System, Long Beach, CA, p. A65
DANNER, Cynthia, Chief Nursing Officer, Northeast Georgia Medical Center Braselton, Braselton, GA, p. A148
DANOWSKI, Dale G, R.N., Senior Vice President, Chief Nursing Officer, St. Vincent'S Medical Center, Bridgeport, CT, p. A107
DANSBY, Tommy, Chief Medical Officer, Cypress Grove Behavioral Health, Bastrop, LA, p. A263
DANUSER, James, Chief Information Officer, Veterans Affairs Central Iowa Health Care System, Des Moines, IA, p. A221
DAOUD, Joudat, M.D., Chief of Staff, Promedica Coldwater Regional Hospital, Coldwater, MI, p. A309
D'APOLLO, Julie, R.N., Director of Nursing, Hampstead Hospital, Hampstead, NH, p. A400
D'AQUILA, Richard, President, Yale–New Haven Hospital, New Haven, CT, p. A110
DARBONNE, Tina, Chief Financial Officer, Central Louisiana State Hospital, Pineville, LA, p. A277
DARBY, Kristin, Chief Information Officer, Cancer Treatment Centers Of America–Eastern Regional Medical Center, Philadelphia, PA, p. A534
DARBY, Sharon, R.N., FACHE, Vice President, Clinical Operations, Children'S Hospital Of Richmond At Vcu–Brook Road Campus, Richmond, VA, p. A666
DARCY, Deborah, Human Resources, Chg Hospital Tucson, Llc, Tucson, AZ, p. A37
DARDANO, Anthony, M.D., Chief Medical Officer, Delray Medical Center, Delray Beach, FL, p. A121
DARDEAU, Sean T., Chief Executive Officer, Porter Regional Hospital, Valparaiso, IN, p. A215
DAREY, Roland, M.D., Medical Director, Wamego Health Center, Wamego, KS, p. A247
DARLING, Cory, Chief Operating Officer, Memorial Hospital Jacksonville, Jacksonville, FL, p. A125
DARMELIO, Matthew P, Chief of Staff, Mon Health Medical Center, Morgantown, WV, p. A687
DARNAUER, Kristina, M.D., Chief of Staff, Hospital District No 1 Of Rice County, Lyons, KS, p. A240
DARNELL, Chris, Administrator, Big Sky Medical Center, Big Sky, MT, p. A374
DARNELL, Linda, Director Management Information Systems, King'S Daughters' Health, Madison, IN, p. A210
DARRINGTON, Gilbert, Director Human Resources, Jackson Hospital And Clinic, Montgomery, AL, p. A21
DARVIN, Ken, M.D., Chief of Staff, Stroud Regional Medical Center, Stroud, OK, p. A508
DASARO, Lynda, Director Human Resources, Sutter Roseville Medical Center, Roseville, CA, p. A81
DASCENZO, Douglas R, MSN, R.N., Chief Nursing Officer, St. Joseph Mercy Oakland, Pontiac, MI, p. A320
DASCOULIAS, Kristine, Interim Chief Nursing Officer, Memorial Hospital, North Conway, NH, p. A402
DASHIELD, Luanne G, Personnel Administrator, Deer'S Head Hospital Center, Salisbury, MD, p. A293
DASKALAKIS, Tom G, Chief Administrative Officer, West Chester Hospital, West Chester, OH, p. A494
DASKALAKIS, Tom G., Chief Administrative Officer, West Chester Hospital, West Chester, OH, p. A494
DASKEVICH, Cris, Chief Executive Officer, Children'S Hospital Of San Antonio, San Antonio, TX, p. A633
DASS, Karla, Director Human Resources, Regional General Hospital, Williston, FL, p. A144
DASSENKO, Dennis, Chief Information Officer, Essentia Health Duluth, Duluth, MN, p. A331
DAUBERT, Stephanie
Chief Financial Officer, Nebraska Medicine – Bellevue, Bellevue, NE, p. A383
Chief Financial Officer, Nebraska Medicine – Nebraska Medical Center, Omaha, NE, p. A389
DAUBY, Randall W., Chief Executive Officer, Pinckneyville Community Hospital, Pinckneyville, IL, p. A193
DAUGHDRILL, Diane, Director Human Resources, Jefferson Davis Community Hospital, Prentiss, MS, p. A353
DAUGHERTY, Beth Ann, R.N., M.P.H., Vice President Care Services and Chief Nursing Executive, Sparrow Clinton Hospital, Saint Johns, MI, p. A322
DAUGHERTY, Don, Director Information Systems, Fleming County Hospital, Flemingsburg, KY, p. A251
DAUGHERTY, Marney, Worklife Services Consultant, Ascension Brighton Center For Recovery, Brighton, MI, p. A307
DAUGHERTY, Robert Alan., Chief Executive Officer, Sagewest Health Care At Riverton, Riverton, WY, p. A712
DAUGHERTY, Stephen J.
Chief Executive Officer, Coliseum Medical Centers, Macon, GA, p. A156
Interim Chief Executive Officer, Coliseum Medical Centers, Macon, GA, p. A156
DAUGHTRY, Chris, Chief Executive Officer, Encompass Health Rehabilitation Hospital Of Columbia, Columbia, SC, p. A551
DAUM, Karen, R.N., MS, Vice President and Chief Nursing Officer, Passavant Area Hospital, Jacksonville, IL, p. A186
D'AURIA, Joseph, Director Finance, Morristown Medical Center, Morristown, NJ, p. A408
DAUTERIVE, F Ralph, M.D., Vice President Medical Affairs, Ochsner Medical Center – Baton Rouge, Baton Rouge, LA, p. A263
DAVACHI, Khosrow, Chief Medical Officer, Bridgepoint Hospital National Harbor, Washington, DC, p. A115
DAVE, Bhasker J, M.D., Superintendent, Mental Health Institute, Independence, IA, p. A224
DAVE, Bhasker J., Superintendent, Mental Health Institute, Independence, IA, p. A224
DAVENPORT, David, Director Human Resources, Washington County Hospital, Nashville, IL, p. A191
DAVENPORT, Douglas, Interim Chief Financial Officer, Mercyone Iowa City Medical Center, Iowa City, IA, p. A224
DAVENPORT, Ginger, Director Human Resources, Promise Hospital Of Dallas, Dallas, TX, p. A598
DAVENPORT, Paula, Chief Nursing Officer, Princeton Baptist Medical Center, Birmingham, AL, p. A15
DAVES, Ronnie, Chief Executive Officer, North Okaloosa Medical Center, Crestview, FL, p. A120
DAVE', Rajesh J, M.D., Executive Vice President and Chief Medical Officer, United Health Services Hospitals–Binghamton, Binghamton, NY, p. A424
DAVID, Biff, Administrator, St. Landry Extended Care Hospital, Opelousas, LA, p. A276
DAVID, Daphne G., President and Chief Executive Officer, North Suburban Medical Center, Thornton, CO, p. A105
DAVID, Michelle, Chief Executive Officer, Valley Hospital Phoenix, Phoenix, AZ, p. A34
DAVID, R Neal, Administrator and Chief of Staff, Madigan Army Medical Center, Tacoma, WA, p. A680
DAVID, Robert G., President, St. John Medical Center, Westlake, OH, p. A494
DAVIDOFF, Ravin, M.D., Chief Medical Officer, Boston Medical Center, Boston, MA, p. A295
DAVIDOW, Daniel N M.D., Medical Director, Cumberland Hospital For Children And Adolescents, New Kent, VA, p. A663
DAVIDSON, Brian, President and Chief Medical Officer, St. Mary'S Hospital And Medical Center, Grand Junction, CO, p. A101
DAVIDSON, Camille, Director Human Resources, Stanton County Hospital, Johnson, KS, p. A237
DAVIDSON, Diane, Senior Vice President Human Resources, Essentia Health Duluth, Duluth, MN, p. A331
DAVIDSON, Dianne, Chief Operating Officer, Union General Hospital, Farmerville, LA, p. A267
DAVIDSON, Elizabeth, R.N., MSN, Vice President, Patient Care Services, Osf Saint James – John W. Albrecht Medical Center, Pontiac, IL, p. A194
DAVIDSON, Gary, Senior Vice President and Chief Information Officer, Penn Medicine Lancaster General Hospital, Lancaster, PA, p. A529
DAVIDSON, Gary, M.D., Medical Director, Select Specialty Hospital–Johnstown, Johnstown, PA, p. A528
DAVIDSON, James
Chief Executive Officer, Saint Mary'S Regional Medical Center, Russellville, AR, p. A48
Director of Information Services, Ferry County Memorial Hospital, Republic, WA, p. A677
DAVIDSON, James N., Troop Commander, Tripler Army Medical Center, Honolulu, HI, p. A165
DAVIDSON, Judy, R.N., Chief Nursing Officer, Porter Regional Hospital, Valparaiso, IN, p. A215
DAVIDSON, Nancy, Senior Vice President and Chief Financial Officer, Jackson County Memorial Hospital, Altus, OK, p. A496
DAVIDSON, Rocky, Chief Financial Officer, Larkin Community Hospital Behavioral Health Services, Hollywood, FL, p. A124
DAVIDSON, Stephen, Director Human Resources, Lafayette Regional Health Center, Lexington, MO, p. A364
DAVIDSON, Stuart, President Medical Staff, Mount Desert Island Hospital, Bar Harbor, ME, p. A281
DAVIDSON, Tim, M.D., Chief Executive Physician Services, Providence St. Mary Medical Center, Walla Walla, WA, p. A681
DAVIDSON, Tori, R.N., Chief Nursing Officer, Tsehootsooi Medical Center, Fort Defiance, AZ, p. A29
DAVILA, Susan, Chief Executive Officer, Desert View Hospital, Pahrump, NV, p. A397
DAVIN, Joni, Director Information and Business Management Service Line, Veterans Affairs Eastern Kansas Health Care System, Topeka, KS, p. A246
DAVINI, John, Vice President, St. Rose Hospital, Hayward, CA, p. A61
DAVIS, Adam
Chief Information Officer, Cornerstone Hospital–West Monroe, West Monroe, LA, p. A280
Director Information Technology, Chg Hospital Tucson, Llc, Tucson, AZ, p. A37
DAVIS, Amelia, Director of Nursing, Crossridge Community Hospital, Wynne, AR, p. A49
DAVIS, Andrew L, Chief Operating Officer, Erie County Medical Center, Buffalo, NY, p. A424
DAVIS, Andy, Chief Operating Officer, St. Vincent'S Birmingham, Birmingham, AL, p. A15
DAVIS, Anne, Director Human Resources, Mason District Hospital, Havana, IL, p. A185
DAVIS, Astrid, R.N., Chief Nursing Officer, Wellspan York Hospital, York, PA, p. A546
DAVIS, Autherine, Director Human Resources, D. W. Mcmillan Memorial Hospital, Brewton, AL, p. A15
DAVIS, Barry L., President and Chief Executive Officer, Arkansas Methodist Medical Center, Paragould, AR, p. A47
DAVIS, Ben, Chief Executive Officer, Osceola Community Hospital, Sibley, IA, p. A229
DAVIS, Betty, Director Administrative Services, Porterville Developmental Center, Porterville, CA, p. A78
DAVIS, Brenda, Vice President Patient Services, Indiana University Health Bedford Hospital, Bedford, IN, p. A199
DAVIS, Brent, Chief Financial Officer, Central Valley Medical Center, Nephi, UT, p. A649
DAVIS, Charissa, Chief Nursing Officer and Director of Nursing, Oasis Behavioral Health – Chandler, Chandler, AZ, p. A28
DAVIS, Charlotte C, Director Human Resources, Lincoln Trail Behavioral Health System, Radcliff, KY, p. A260
DAVIS, Cheryl, M.D., Chief Medical Officer, Scotland Health Care System, Laurinburg, NC, p. A457

DAVIS, Dan, Managing Director and Chief Financial Officer, Integris Southwest Medical Center, Oklahoma City, OK, p. A504

DAVIS, Daniel E, Chief Financial Officer, Kingwood Medical Center, Kingwood, TX, p. A618

DAVIS, Darcy, Chief Financial Officer, Lakeside Medical Center, Belle Glade, FL, p. A117

DAVIS, David, Chief Operating Officer, Western Maryland Hospital Center, Hagerstown, MD, p. A291

DAVIS, Deborah W., Chief Executive Officer and Vice President Clinical Services, Vcu Medical Center, Richmond, VA, p. A666

DAVIS, Debra K., Director of Operations, Winner Regional Healthcare Center, Winner, SD, p. A565

DAVIS, Deland, Chief Financial Officer, Indian Health Service – Quentin N. Burdick Memorial Health Care Facility, Belcourt, ND, p. A465

DAVIS, Dell, Director Information Systems, United Memorial Medical Care, Houston, TX, p. A614

DAVIS, Dustin, Chief Executive Officer, Woodland Springs Hospital, Conroe, TX, p. A593

DAVIS, Elaine, Chief Nursing Officer and Vice President Patient Services, Rmc Anniston, Anniston, AL, p. A13

DAVIS, Evan, Director Technology and Environmental Services, Barbourville Arh Hospital, Barbourville, KY, p. A249

DAVIS, Gannon, Director Human Resources, Medical West, Bessemer, AL, p. A14

DAVIS, Gary, Vice President Information Systems, Baptist Medical Center, San Antonio, TX, p. A633

DAVIS, Heather, Administrator, Scott Regional Hospital, Morton, MS, p. A352

DAVIS, Heather, M.D., Chief of Staff, Pender Memorial Hospital, Burgaw, NC, p. A450

DAVIS, Howard Z, M.D., Chief Medical Officer, Providence Tarzana Medical Center, Los Angeles, CA, p. A69

DAVIS, Jack, Vice President Human Resources, Faxton St. Luke'S Healthcare, Utica, NY, p. A446

DAVIS, James R.
Chief Executive Officer, University Hospital Summerville, Augusta, GA, p. A147
Chief Executive Officer, University Hospital, Augusta, GA, p. A147

DAVIS, Janet, R.N., MS, Senior Vice President and Chief Nursing Officer, Tampa General Hospital, Tampa, FL, p. A142

DAVIS, Janice, Interim Director Human Resources, Gifford Medical Center, Randolph, VT, p. A655

DAVIS, Jeff, Chief Financial Officer, Harrison County Hospital, Corydon, IN, p. A201

DAVIS, Jeffrey, D.O., Chief Medical Officer, St. Mary'S Medical Center, West Palm Beach, FL, p. A144

DAVIS, Jeremy P., President and Chief Executive Officer, Grande Ronde Hospital, La Grande, OR, p. A514

DAVIS, John, Chief Human Resources Officer, Bristol Bay Area Health Corporation, Dillingham, AK, p. A26

DAVIS, Johnnie, Director Human Resources, Medicine Lodge Memorial Hospital, Medicine Lodge, KS, p. A241

DAVIS, Jon, Chief Financial Officer, Community Hospital– Fairfax, Fairfax, MO, p. A360

DAVIS, Jonathan S., President, Sentara Martha Jefferson Hospital, Charlottesville, VA, p. A657

DAVIS, Karen, Chief Nursing Officer and Vice President, Nursing, Howard County General Hospital, Columbia, MD, p. A290

DAVIS, Kassi, Director Patient Care Services, Willow Crest Hospital, Miami, OK, p. A502

DAVIS, Kelly, Chief Nursing Officer, Anmed Health Rehabilitation Hospital, Anderson, SC, p. A549

DAVIS, Kenneth, Assistant Vice President Information Systems, Kennedy Krieger Institute, Baltimore, MD, p. A286

DAVIS, Kenneth, M.D., Chief Medical Officer, Christus Santa Rosa Health System, San Antonio, TX, p. A633

DAVIS, LaKeitha, Director Human Resources, Medical Center Of South Arkansas, El Dorado, AR, p. A41

DAVIS, Lance, PharmD, Associate Director, Miami Veterans Affairs Healthcare System, Miami, FL, p. A130

DAVIS, Lora, Chief Executive Officer, Regional Rehabilitation Hospital, Phenix City, AL, p. A22

DAVIS, Lorraine, Vice President Human Resources, Horn Memorial Hospital, Ida Grove, IA, p. A224

DAVIS, Lyle E., Administrator, Cozad Community Health System, Cozad, NE, p. A384

DAVIS, Malene S., President and Chief Executive Officer, Capital Hospice, Arlington, VA, p. A656

DAVIS, Marcey, Chief Executive Officer, Ut Health Tyler, Tyler, TX, p. A642

DAVIS, Margaret, Chief Operating Officer, Pecos County Memorial Hospital, Fort Stockton, TX, p. A604

DAVIS, Mark, Director Information Systems, Lake Taylor Transitional Care Hospital, Norfolk, VA, p. A664

DAVIS, Mark, M.D., Chief of Staff, Newberry County Memorial Hospital, Newberry, SC, p. A556

DAVIS, Marla, Interim Chief Nursing Officer, Prosser Memorial Health, Prosser, WA, p. A676

DAVIS, Matt, Chief Executive Officer, Hca Houston Healthcare Conroe, Conroe, TX, p. A593

DAVIS, Myra, Senior Vice President and Chief Information Officer, Texas Children'S Hospital, Houston, TX, p. A614

DAVIS, Myrna, Manager Human Resources, Palo Verde Hospital, Blythe, CA, p. A53

DAVIS, Natalie, R.N., Interim Chief Nursing Officer, Mcleod Health Clarendon, Manning, SC, p. A555

DAVIS, Pam, Chief Nursing Officer, Galesburg Cottage Hospital, Galesburg, IL, p. A183

DAVIS, Patricia, Chief Nursing Officer, South Central Kansas Medical Center, Arkansas City, KS, p. A232

DAVIS, Paula M, Chief Human Resources Officer, Sonoma Valley Hospital, Sonoma, CA, p. A90

DAVIS, Rachel, Director, Sharp Coronado Hospital And Healthcare Center, Coronado, CA, p. A55

DAVIS, Randy
Chief Executive Officer, Northcrest Medical Center, Springfield, TN, p. A579
Vice President and Chief Information Officer, Cgh Medical Center, Sterling, IL, p. A197

DAVIS, Ray
Administrative Director Information Systems, The Hospitals Of Providence Sierra Campus, El Paso, TX, p. A603
Administrative Director, The Hospitals Of Providence Memorial Campus, El Paso, TX, p. A602
Chief Information Officer, The Hospitals Of Providence Transmountain Campus, El Paso, TX, p. A603

DAVIS, Regana, Vice President Human Resources, Tri–State Memorial Hospital, Clarkston, WA, p. A671

DAVIS, Richard
Chief Executive Officer, Central Peninsula Hospital, Soldotna, AK, p. A27
Chief Financial Officer, George Washington University Hospital, Washington, DC, p. A115
Chief Financial Officer, Saint Barnabas Medical Center, Livingston, NJ, p. A407

DAVIS, Richard O., President, Sibley Memorial Hospital, Washington, DC, p. A116

DAVIS, Rick, Chief Operating Officer and Support Services, Coshocton Regional Medical Center, Coshocton, OH, p. A480

DAVIS, Robert, Chief Nursing Officer, Adventhealth Palm Coast, Palm Coast, FL, p. A135

DAVIS, Roger K, Director Human Resources, Bourbon Community Hospital, Paris, KY, p. A259

DAVIS, Ronald Anthony, Chief Financial Officer UCLA Hospital System, Stewart & Lynda Resnick Neuropsychiatric Hospital At Ucla, Los Angeles, CA, p. A69

DAVIS, Roy, M.D., Chief Medical Officer, Providence Alaska Medical Center, Anchorage, AK, p. A25

DAVIS, Scott
Chief Executive Officer, Hca Houston Healthcare Northwest, Houston, TX, p. A611
Manager Information Technology, Arkansas Surgical Hospital, North Little Rock, AR, p. A46

DAVIS, Shawn, Chief Information Officer, Tuba City Regional Health Care Corporation, Tuba City, AZ, p. A37

DAVIS, Sondra, Vice President Human Resources & System Development, Harnett Health System, Dunn, NC, p. A452

DAVIS, Stephanie, Controller, Healthsouth Rehabilitation Hospital Of Colorado Springs, Colorado Springs, CO, p. A97

DAVIS, Steve, Chief Financial Officer, Shands Lake Shore Regional Medical Center, Lake City, FL, p. A127

DAVIS, Steven T., Chief Executive Officer, Clarion Hospital, Clarion, PA, p. A522

DAVIS, Takeisha C., President and Chief Executive Officer, New Orleans East Hospital, New Orleans, LA, p. A275

DAVIS, Tamara, R.N., Chief Nurse Executive Officer, Sutter Davis Hospital, Davis, CA, p. A56

DAVIS, Tammy, Director Human Resources, Union County Hospital, Anna, IL, p. A173

DAVIS, Terry, Manager Information Systems, Atchison Hospital, Atchison, KS, p. A232

DAVIS, Teshia, Chief Clinical Officer, Carolinas Continuecare Hospital At Pineville, Charlotte, NC, p. A451

DAVIS, Toby, Chief Nursing Officer, Good Samaritan Hospital, Bakersfield, CA, p. A52

DAVIS, Todd, Executive Director of Information Systems, Hendricks Regional Health, Danville, IN, p. A202

DAVIS, Todd, M.D., Vice President Medical Affairs, Patient Safety Officer, Caromont Regional Medical Center, Gastonia, NC, p. A454

DAVIS, Tommy, M.D., Chief of Staff, Oakdale Community Hospital, Oakdale, LA, p. A276

DAVIS, Tracy, Chief Executive Officer, Neuropsychiatric Hospital Of Indianapolis, Indianapolis, IN, p. A207

DAVIS, Tracye B., Interim Medical Center Director, Mann–Grandstaff Veterans Affairs Medical Center, Spokane, WA, p. A679

DAVIS, Trish, Chief Nursing Officer, Santa Rosa Medical Center, Milton, FL, p. A132

DAVIS, Verlene, Director Human Resources, Blue Mountain Hospital District, John Day, OR, p. A514

DAVIS, Wayne, Manager Human Resources, Jesse Brown Veterans Affairs Medical Center, Chicago, IL, p. A177

DAVIS, Wendy, Associate Vice President and Chief Human Resource Officer, The University Of Toledo Medical Center, Toledo, OH, p. A492

DAVIS, MSN, Dan, R.N., Nurse Administrator, Park City Hospital, Park City, UT, p. A650

DAVIS–HAGENS, Patricia, Central Market Leader and President, The Jewish Hospital – Mercy Health, Cincinnati, OH, p. A476

DAVISON, Katie, Executive Director, Human Resources, Nash Unc Health Care, Rocky Mount, NC, p. A461

DAVISON, Trish, R.N., Chief Nursing Officer, Regional West Garden County, Oshkosh, NE, p. A390

DAVISSON, Deborah, MSN, Chief Nursing Officer and Vice President, Patient Care Services, Holy Cross Hospital, Chicago, IL, p. A177

DAVY, Larry, Chief Executive Officer, Wallowa Memorial Hospital, Enterprise, OR, p. A512

DAWE, Jacqueline, R.N., Chief Nursing Officer, Lakes Region General Hospital, Laconia, NH, p. A400

DAWES, John M., Chief Executive Officer, Rusk Rehabilitation Hospital, Columbia, MO, p. A359

DAWKINS, David, Director Human Resources, Doctor'S Memorial Hospital, Perry, FL, p. A136

DAWSON, Cindy, MSN, R.N., Chief Nursing Executive, University Of Iowa Hospitals And Clinics, Iowa City, IA, p. A224

DAWSON, Kane A., Chief Executive Officer, Mission Regional Medical Center, Mission, TX, p. A625

DAWSON, Theresa, MSN, R.N., Chief Nursing Officer, Oaklawn Hospital, Marshall, MI, p. A317

DAWSON, Trang, Chief Information Officer, Baylor Scott & White Emergency Hospital–Aubrey, Aubrey, TX, p. A584

DAWSON, Troy, M.D., President Medical Staff, Antelope Memorial Hospital, Neligh, NE, p. A388

DAX, Jennifer, Director Human Resources, Gundersen Boscobel Area Hospital And Clinics, Boscobel, WI, p. A692

DAY, Gordy, M.D., Medical Director, Schleicher County Medical Center, Eldorado, TX, p. A603

DAY, John M., Chief Executive Officer, Unity Medical & Surgical Hospital, Mishawaka, IN, p. A211

DAY, Mark, Chief Financial Officer, Twin Cities Hospital, Niceville, FL, p. A133

DAY, Regina
Chief Executive Officer, Hawkins County Memorial Hospital, Rogersville, TN, p. A579
Director of Finance, Hancock County Hospital, Sneedville, TN, p. A579
Executive Director Finance, Mountain View Regional Medical Center, Norton, VA, p. A664
Executive Vice President of Finance, Lonesome Pine Hospital, Big Stone Gap, VA, p. A656

DAY, Scott, Vice President Human Resources, Lutheran Medical Center, Wheat Ridge, CO, p. A106

DAY, Sherry Clouse, CPA
Chief Financial Officer, Mercy Hospital Cassville, Cassville, MO, p. A358
Chief Financial Officer, Mercy St. Francis Hospital, Mountain View, MO, p. A366
Vice President Finance and Regional Chief Financial Officer, Mercy Hospital Aurora, Aurora, MO, p. A356

DAY, Therese, Chief Financial Officer, Umass Memorial Medical Center, Worcester, MA, p. A305

DAY, Victoria, Chief Financial Officer and Vice President of Ancillary Services, Sharp Coronado Hospital And Healthcare Center, Coronado, CA, p. A55

DAYAO, Jerome, Chief Nursing Officer, Arrowhead Regional Medical Center, Colton, CA, p. A55

DE BOND, Virginia, Chief Financial Officer, Woodlands Specialty Hospital, The Woodlands, TX, p. A641

DE BRUYCKER, Allison, Chief Executive Officer, Riverview Behavioral Health, Texarkana, AR, p. A49

DE FARIA, Ludmila, M.D., Chief Medical Officer, Eastside Psychiatric Hospital, Tallahassee, FL, p. A140

DE JESUS, Alexander, M.D., Medical Director, Encompass Health Rehabilitation Hospital Of Sarasota, Sarasota, FL, p. A139

DE JESUS, Jorge, Executive Director, I. Gonzalez Martinez Oncologic Hospital, Hato Rey, PR, p. A716

DE LA CRUZ, Rosemary, Chief Financial Officer, Hospital Episcopal San Lucas Guayama, Guayama, PR, p. A716

DE LA GARZA, Josiah, Chief Operating Officer, Baylor Scott & White Medical Center – Sunnyvale, Sunnyvale, TX, p. A639

DE LA PAZ, Christine, Director Human Resources, Aurora Charter Oak Hospital, Covina, CA, p. A55

DE LEON, Aurea, Chief Human Resources Officer, Hospital Universitario Dr. Ramon Ruiz Arnau, Bayamon, PR, p. A715

DE LEON, Darcy, Executive Director, Human Resources, Adventist Health Howard Memorial, Willits, CA, p. A95

DE LEON, Dennis, M.D., Associate Chief Medical Officer and Vice President Medical Affairs, Highline Medical Center, Burien, WA, p. A671

DE LOS REYES, Jay, Chief Executive Officer, Lake Huron Medical Center, Port Huron, MI, p. A320

DE LOS SANTOS, Conrad, President Medical Staff, Medical West, Bessemer, AL, p. A14

DE LOS SANTOS, Ruben, M.D., Chief Medical Officer, Fort Duncan Regional Medical Center, Eagle Pass, TX, p. A600

DE NESHEREA, Alexander, M.D., Chief Medical Officer, Dartmouth–Hitchcock Medical Center, Lebanon, NH, p. A400

DE ONIS, Luis, Interim Chief Human Resources Officer, Stony Brook University Hospital, Stony Brook, NY, p. A444

DE PIANO, Linda, Chief Executive Officer, Jerome Golden Center For Behavioral Health, Inc., West Palm Beach, FL, p. A144

DE SANTIAGO, Elizabeth, Executive Director, Hospital De Psiquiatria, San Juan, PR, p. A718

DE SHAZO, Sheri, Senior Vice President and Hospital Administrator, Wakemed Raleigh Campus, Raleigh, NC, p. A461

DE TORRES, Francisco, M.D., Medical Director, Ashford Presbyterian Community Hospital, San Juan, PR, p. A718

DEAK, Terry, Chief Financial Officer, Adventist Health Lodi Memorial, Lodi, CA, p. A64

DEAKYNE, John R, Chief Financial Officer, Saint Mary'S Regional Medical Center, Reno, NV, p. A397

DEAL, Lisa, Budget Analyst, U. S. Public Health Service Indian Hospital, Eagle Butte, SD, p. A560

DEAL, Roy, Chief Medical Officer, Emerald Coast Behavioral Hospital, Panama City, FL, p. A135

DEAN, Douglas B, Chief Human Resources Officer, Children'S Of Alabama, Birmingham, AL, p. A14

DEAN, Douglas F., Jr, Chief Executive Officer, Elliot Hospital, Manchester, NH, p. A401

DEAN, Joel, Director Information Services, Piedmont Medical Center, Rock Hill, SC, p. A556

DEAN, Laura L, Director Human Resources, Wilson Medical Center, Neodesha, KS, p. A241

DEAN, Les, President and Chief Executive Officer, Sumner Regional Medical Center, Wellington, KS, p. A247

DEAN, Marty, Administrator, Oceans Behavioral Hospital Of Kentwood, Kentwood, LA, p. A270

DEAN, Ronald, Chief Executive Officer, Troy Regional Medical Center, Troy, AL, p. A23

DEAN, Sam, Administrator, Usa Health University Hospital, Mobile, AL, p. A21

DEAN, Thomas, M.D., Chief of Staff, Avera Weskota Memorial Hospital, Wessington Springs, SD, p. A565

DEANGELIS, Lisa, M.D., Acting Physician–in–Chief, Brookdale Hospital Medical Center, New York, NY, p. A432

DEARDORFF, John A., President and Chief Executive, Northern Virginia Market, Reston Hospital Center, Reston, VA, p. A665

DEARY, Shirley, Director Human Resources, Glenbeigh Hospital And Outpatient Centers, Rock Creek, OH, p. A490

DEASON, Lori, Director, Lakeside Behavioral Health System, Memphis, TN, p. A575

DEATER, Gary A, Vice President Administration, Human Resources and Risk Management, Witham Health Services, Lebanon, IN, p. A210

DEATON, David, Chief Executive Officer, Ozark Health Medical Center, Clinton, AR, p. A40

DEATON, Eric, Executive Vice President, Chief Operating Officer and Corporate Operating, Hancock County Hospital, Sneedville, TN, p. A579

DEATON, Mike, Chief Financial Officer, Ozark Health Medical Center, Clinton, AR, p. A40

DEATON, Susan Renodin, Human Resources Director, Logan Memorial Hospital, Russellville, KY, p. A260

DEATON, Timothy C., Chief Executive Officer, Curahealth Nashville, Nashville, TN, p. A576

DEBBAS, Elias, M.D., President Medical Staff, Fort Washington Medical Center, Oxen Hill, MD, p. A292

DEBEVEC, Teresa, Chief Executive Officer and Administrator, Cook Hospital & Care Center, Cook, MN, p. A330

DEBLANC, Hunt, M.D., Chief of Staff, Opelousas General Health System, Opelousas, LA, p. A276

DEBLASIS, John, Vice President, Harrison Community Hospital, Cadiz, OH, p. A474

DEBLIEUX, Dawna, Vice President Patient Care Services and Chief Nurse Executive, Natchitoches Regional Medical Center, Natchitoches, LA, p. A274

DEBLOIS, Georgean, M.D., Chairman Medical Staff, Chippenham Hospital, Richmond, VA, p. A666

DEBLOUW, Christina, Chief Executive Officer, Select Specialty Hospital-Flint, Flint, MI, p. A311

DEBOER, Cynthia D, Chief Financial Officer, Cedar Springs Hospital, Colorado Springs, CO, p. A97

DEBOER, K. C., President and Chief Executive Officer, Prairie Lakes Healthcare System, Watertown, SD, p. A565

DEBOLT, Larry W, Chief Financial Officer, Bluffton Regional Medical Center, Bluffton, IN, p. A200

DEBONA, Paul, Chief Executive Officer, Baylor Scott & White Surgical Hospital Fort Worth, Fort Worth, TX, p. A604

DEBONO, Julie, Director, Human Resources, Umass Memorial Healthalliance–Clinton Hospital, Leominster, MA, p. A300

DEBORD, Thomas, Chief Operating Officer, Overlake Medical Center, Bellevue, WA, p. A670

DEBRUYCKER, Allison, Administrator, Magnolia Behavioral Hospital Of East Texas, Longview, TX, p. A621

DECASPERIS, Ilyssa, Director of Human Resources, Parkview Community Hospital Medical Center, Riverside, CA, p. A81

DECELIS, Lori, Director Human Resources, Hampton Behavioral Health Center, Westampton, NJ, p. A415

DECELL, Daniela, Chief Executive Officer, Medical City Las Colinas, Irving, TX, p. A616

DECHABERT, Rebecca, Acting Director Personnel, Brookdale Hospital Medical Center, New York, NY, p. A432

DECHANT, David, Chief Human Resources Officer, Va Medical Center, Tomah, WI, p. A706

DECKARD, Rick, Chief Fiscal Service, Chillicothe Veterans Affairs Medical Center, Chillicothe, OH, p. A475

DECKARD, Steven D, Vice President Human Resources, Indiana University Health Bloomington Hospital, Bloomington, IN, p. A200

DECKER, Diann, Chief Human Resource Officer, Provo Canyon Behavioral Hospital, Orem, UT, p. A650

DECKER, Janet, Assistant Vice President, Information Systems, Medstar Union Memorial Hospital, Baltimore, MD, p. A287

DECKER, Jeanine, Manager Human Resources, Arizona State Hospital, Phoenix, AZ, p. A33

DECKER, Kevin, Chief Executive Officer, Forrest City Medical Center, Forrest City, AR, p. A42

DECKER, Michael, President and Chief Executive Officer, Divine Savior Healthcare, Portage, WI, p. A704

DECORTE, Raymond P, M.D., Chief Medical Officer, East Jefferson General Hospital, Metairie, LA, p. A273

DECREMER, Dean, Information Systems Manager, Dickinson County Healthcare System, Iron Mountain, MI, p. A314

DEE, Thomas A., President and Chief Executive Officer, Southwestern Vermont Medical Center, Bennington, VT, p. A654

DEEN, Cecelia, Chief Nursing Officer, Southeast Colorado Hospital District, Springfield, CO, p. A105

DEERING, Linda, President, Advocate Sherman Hospital, Elgin, IL, p. A182

DEERING, Lisa
  Administrator, Heatherhill Care Communities, Chardon, OH, p. A475
  Chief Executive Officer, Regency Hospital Cleveland East, Warrensville Heights, OH, p. A493

DEETER, Joe, MS, Director Information Systems, Clifton–Fine Hospital, Star Lake, NY, p. A444

DEFIGUIEREDO, Kathy, Director, Information Technology, Chi St. Luke'S Health Memorial Livingston, Livingston, TX, p. A621

DEFOE, Mike, Chief Financial Officer, Perry Memorial Hospital, Princeton, IL, p. A194

DEFORD, Drexel, Chief Information Officer, Scripps Mercy Hospital, San Diego, CA, p. A84

DEFRANCESCO, Anthony, Associate Director, Va Long Beach Healthcare System, Long Beach, CA, p. A65

DEFREECE, Daniel, Interim President, Chi Health St. Mary'S, Nebraska City, NE, p. A388

DEFURIO, Anthony C, Executive Vice President Chief Financial Officer, Atrium Health'S Carolinas Medical Center, Charlotte, NC, p. A451

DEFURIO, Ken, President and Chief Executive Officer, Butler Health System, Butler, PA, p. A521

DEGEAR, David O, M.D., Vice President Medical Affairs, Westfields Hospital And Clinic, New Richmond, WI, p. A702

DEGENNARO, Vincent, M.D., Chief of Staff, Miami Veterans Affairs Healthcare System, Miami, FL, p. A130

DEGNAN, William, Vice President Finance, Jefferson Health Northeast, Philadelphia, PA, p. A535

DEGRAVELLE, Eric, Director Human Resources, Thibodaux Regional Medical Center, Thibodaux, LA, p. A279

DEGROOD, Robert, M.D., Chief Medical Staff, Musc Health Marion Medical Center, Mullins, SC, p. A556

DEGROOT, Daniel, President and Chief Executive Officer, Stoughton Hospital Association, Stoughton, WI, p. A706

DEGROOT, Randy, President and Chief Executive Officer, Promedica Coldwater Regional Hospital, Coldwater, MI, p. A309

DEHAAI, Sarah, R.N., Director of Nursing, Avera Hand County Memorial Hospital, Miller, SD, p. A562

DEHART, Kristen, Chief Executive Officer, Excelsior Springs Hospital, Excelsior Springs, MO, p. A359

DEHAVEN, Bryce, Chief Financial Officer, Medical Center Of Aurora, Aurora, CO, p. A96

DEHERRERA, Barbara, Chief Nursing Officer, Garfield County Public Hospital District, Pomeroy, WA, p. A676

DEHNING, Cielo, M.D., Medical Director, Mid–America Rehabilitation Hospital, Shawnee Mission, KS, p. A245

DEIBEL, Justin, Senior Vice President and Chief Financial Officer, Mercy Medical Center, Baltimore, MD, p. A288

DEININGER, Robert, Chief Executive Officer, Adventhealth Fish Memorial, Orange City, FL, p. A134

DEIS, Terrence G.
  President, Chi Saint Joseph Berea, Berea, KY, p. A249
  President, Chi Saint Joseph London, London, KY, p. A255
  President, Saint Joseph Mount Sterling, Mount Sterling, KY, p. A258

DEITRICK, Diana, Director Information Services, Devereux Hospital And Children'S Center Of Florida, Melbourne, FL, p. A129

DEITSCHMANN, Michael, Chief Financial Officer, Butler Health System, Butler, PA, p. A521

DEJACO, Lynn S, Chief Financial Officer, Firsthealth Moore Regional Hospital, Pinehurst, NC, p. A460

DEJESUS, David, Senior Vice President Human Resources, Southcoast Hospitals Group, Fall River, MA, p. A298

DEJONG, Tyler
  Vice President, Operational Finance, Chi Health Midlands, Papillion, NE, p. A390
  Vice President, Operational Finance, Chi Health St Elizabeth, Lincoln, NE, p. A387

DEKEYZER, Ron, Regional Director Information Systems, Christus St. Vincent Regional Medical Center, Santa Fe, NM, p. A420

DEKOK, Joni, Chief Nursing Officer, Sanford Sheldon Medical Center, Sheldon, IA, p. A229

DEKONING, Bernard L., M.D., Chief of Staff, Wm. Jennings Bryan Dorn Veterans Affairs Medical Center, Columbia, SC, p. A552

DEKREY, Dale, MS, Associate Director Operations and Resources, Fargo Veterans Affairs Health Care System, Fargo, ND, p. A466

DEKREY, Daniel, M.D., Chief of Staff, Sanford Bemidji Medical Center, Bemidji, MN, p. A328

DEKRUSE, Jet L., Administrator, Humboldt County Mental Health, Eureka, CA, p. A57

DEL CASTILLO, Daniel, Chief Executive Officer, Encompass Health Rehabilitation Hospital Of San Juan, San Juan, PR, p. A718

DEL GAUDIO, Frank J., Director and Chief Executive Officer, Essex County Hospital Center, Cedar Grove, NJ, p. A404

DEL RIO, R Maxilimien, M.D., Medical Director, Northern Virginia Mental Health Institute, Falls Church, VA, p. A659

DEL TORO, Gustavo, M.D., Chief Medical Officer, Brookdale Hospital Medical Center, New York, NY, p. A432

DEL TORO, Ivan E, M.D., Medical Director, Hima San Pablo Caguas, Caguas, PR, p. A715

DELA TORRE, Victor, Command Legal Officer, Naval Hospital Lemoore, Lemoore, CA, p. A64

DELAGARDELLE, Pamela K., President and Chief Executive Officer, Unitypoint Health – Allen Hospital, Waterloo, IA, p. A231

DELAHANTY, Paula
  Regional Chief Nursing Officer, Pen Bay Medical Center, Rockport, ME, p. A285
  Regional Chief Nursing Officer, Waldo County General Hospital Maine Health, Belfast, ME, p. A282

DELANCEY, Darlene, Interim Director, Albany Stratton Veterans Affairs Medical Center, Albany, NY, p. A422

DELANEY, Bryan, Director Information Technology, Crossroads Community Hospital, Mount Vernon, IL, p. A190

DELANEY, Kristi, Director, Human Resources, Siskin Hospital For Physical Rehabilitation, Chattanooga, TN, p. A567

DELANEY, Patrick, Administrative Director, Operations, Robert Wood Johnson University Hospital Somerset, Somerville, NJ, p. A412

DELATTE, Sandra, Director Human Resources, Villa Feliciana Medical Complex, Jackson, LA, p. A269
DELAVAN, Karen, Interim Director Human Resources, Comanche County Medical Center, Comanche, TX, p. A593
DELEON, Arsenio V, M.D., Chief Medical Officer, Select Specialty Hospital–Macomb County, Mount Clemens, MI, p. A318
DELEON, Dennis, M.D., Chief Medical Officer, King Region, St. Francis Hospital, Federal Way, WA, p. A673
DELEON, John, Chief Executive Officer, Select Rehabilitation Hospital Of San Antonio, San Antonio, TX, p. A635
DELEON, Joseph, President, Texas Health Harris Methodist Hospital Fort Worth, Fort Worth, TX, p. A605
DELEON, Sherilene, Chief Financial Officer, Spring Mountain Treatment Center, Las Vegas, NV, p. A396
DELFS, Michael, President and Chief Executive Officer, Jamestown Regional Medical Center, Jamestown, ND, p. A468
DELGADO, Eric, Chief Financial Officer, Lakewood Regional Medical Center, Lakewood, CA, p. A64
DELGADO, Lupe, Coordinator Human Resources, Kindred Hospital Sugar Land, Sugar Land, TX, p. A638
DELGADO, Pete, President and Chief Executive Officer, Salinas Valley Memorial Healthcare System, Salinas, CA, p. A83
DELGRECO, Trish, Director of Nursing, Ohiohealth Medcentral Shelby Hospital, Shelby, OH, p. A491
D'ELIA, Peter, Chief Financial Officer, Saint Vincent Hospital, Worcester, MA, p. A305
DELIEN, Rudie, Director of Human Resources, Devereux Advanced Behavioral Health Georgia, Kennesaw, GA, p. A155
DELLA FLORA, Thomas, Vice President and Chief Information Officer, Catholic Medical Center, Manchester, NH, p. A401
DELLEA, Eugene A., President, Fairview Hospital, Great Barrington, MA, p. A299
DELLICKER, Sandra, Director of Human Resources, Saint Anne'S Hospital, Fall River, MA, p. A298
DELLOCONO, John, Senior Vice President and Chief Financial Officer, Centrastate Healthcare System, Freehold, NJ, p. A406
DELLSPERGER, Kevin, M.D., Chief Medical Officer, Augusta University Medical Center, Augusta, GA, p. A147
DELONG, Patricia, Chief Nursing Officer, Essentia Health St. Joseph'S Medical Center, Brainerd, MN, p. A329
DELORENZO, David, Senior Director Human Resources, Sisters Of Charity Hospital Of Buffalo, Buffalo, NY, p. A426
DELORME, Robert, Vice President Medical Affairs, Community Memorial Hospital, Hamilton, NY, p. A429
DELVEAUX, Joe, Manager Information Services, St. Francis Regional Medical Center, Shakopee, MN, p. A340
DEMAIO, Joan, Vice President Nursing, Milford Hospital, Milford, CT, p. A109
DEMARCO, Victor, Chief Financial Officer, Brookdale Hospital Medical Center, New York, NY, p. A432
DEMAREST, Pamela, MSN, R.N., Chief Nursing Officer, Unm Sandoval Regional Medical Center, Inc., Rio Rancho, NM, p. A419
DEMASIE, Dennis, Vice President Information Systems and Chief Information Officer, Rush–Copley Medical Center, Aurora, IL, p. A174
DEMATTEO, Kathleen, Chief Information Officer, Danbury Hospital, Danbury, CT, p. A107
DEMBLA, Preeti, Chief Medical Officer and Medical Director, Rehabilitation Hospital Of Fort Wayne, Fort Wayne, IN, p. A204
DEMERICH, Lois B, Director Human Resources, Sentara Williamsburg Regional Medical Center, Williamsburg, VA, p. A669
DEMERS, Becky, R.N., Chief Nursing Officer, Samaritan Healthcare, Moses Lake, WA, p. A675
DEMERS, Stephen
Chief Executive Officer, University Of Miami Hospital And Clinics, Miami, FL, p. A131
Chief Operating Officer, University Of Miami Hospital And Clinics, Miami, FL, p. A131
DEMETRIADES, James, Vice President, Operations, Penn Medicine Princeton Medical Center, Plainsboro, NJ, p. A411
DEMING, Mark, Administrator, Finance and Support, Beaumont Hospital – Taylor, Taylor, MI, p. A323
DEMING, Peggy, Executive Vice President and Chief Financial Officer, University Health System, San Antonio, TX, p. A635
DEMING, Terra, Director Human Resources, Munson Healthcare Otsego Memorial Hospital, Gaylord, MI, p. A312
DEMLAKIAN, Vahan, Director of Human Resources, Gateways Hospital And Mental Health Center, Los Angeles, CA, p. A66
DEMMEL, Ruth, M.D., Chief Medical Officer, Perkins County Health Services, Grant, NE, p. A385
DEMOE, Sara, Chief Financial Officer, North Canyon Medical Center, Gooding, ID, p. A169
DEMORLIS, John, M.D., Chief Medical Staff, Salem Memorial District Hospital, Salem, MO, p. A371
DEMORROW, Dawn P, Chief Human Resources Service, Wilkes–Barre Veterans Affairs Medical Center, Wilkes, PA, p. A545
DEMOSS, Jill, Finance Manager, Guttenberg Municipal Hospital, Guttenberg, IA, p. A223
DEMPSEY, Jeffrey, President, Mercy St. Vincent Medical Center, Toledo, OH, p. A492
DEMPSEY, John J., Chief Executive Officer, Little Colorado Medical Center, Winslow, AZ, p. A38
DEMURO, Rob, M.D., Chief Medical Officer, The University Of Vermont Health Network Elizabethtown Community Hospital, Elizabethtown, NY, p. A427
DENCKLAU, Larry, D.O., Chief of Staff, Baylor Scott & White Medical Center – Lake Pointe, Rowlett, TX, p. A632
DENEFF, Randall, Vice President Finance, Mary Free Bed Rehabilitation Hospital, Grand Rapids, MI, p. A312
DENEGRI, David, Chief Financial Officer, Parkwood Behavioral Health System, Olive Branch, MS, p. A352
DENG, Mei, Chief Financial Officer, T. J. Samson Community Hospital, Glasgow, KY, p. A252
DENHAM, Stephanie, Chief Financial Officer and Human Resources Officer, Phillips County Hospital, Malta, MT, p. A378
DENIGRIS, Deborah, Chief Nursing Officer, Brookdale Hospital Medical Center, New York, NY, p. A432
DENIKE, Michael, D.O., Vice President, Medical Affairs, Blanchard Valley Hospital, Findlay, OH, p. A483
DENIO, Arthur E, Vice President and Chief Financial Officer, Northbay Medical Center, Fairfield, CA, p. A57
DENIRO, Lori, Regional Chief Nursing Officer, Mercy Health – St. Elizabeth Youngstown Hospital, Youngstown, OH, p. A495
DENISIENKO, Mary, Vice President Human Resources, Palos Health, Palos Heights, IL, p. A192
DENISON, Rita, Director of Information Systems, Sturgis Hospital, Sturgis, MI, p. A323
DENKER, Jill, Executive Director Human Resources, Lexington Regional Health Center, Lexington, NE, p. A386
DENMARK, Donald, M.D.
Chief Medical Officer, Carondelet St. Joseph'S Hospital, Tucson, AZ, p. A37
Chief Medical Officer, Carondelet St. Mary'S Hospital, Tucson, AZ, p. A37
DENNETT, Bryan, M.D., Chief of Staff, William Newton Hospital, Winfield, KS, p. A248
DENNIS, Kera, Assistant Administrator, Finance, Uw Medicine/Harborview Medical Center, Seattle, WA, p. A678
DENNIS, Michael, Director, William J. Mccord Adolescent Treatment Facility, Orangeburg, SC, p. A556
DENNISON, Cynthia, Chief Financial Officer, Mercy Allen Hospital, Oberlin, OH, p. A489
DENNY, Donald, M.D., Senior Vice President, Medical Affairs, Penn Medicine Princeton Medical Center, Plainsboro, NJ, p. A411
DENO, Mark S, Chief Operating Officer, Medical Center Of Aurora, Aurora, CO, p. A96
DENSLEY, Tina, Chief Executive Officer, Weatherford Rehabilitation Hospital, Weatherford, TX, p. A644
DENSON, Anna, Human Resources Specialist, Choctaw Health Center, Philadelphia, MS, p. A352
DENSON, Paula Lajean, M.D., President, Tyler County Hospital, Woodville, TX, p. A646
DENT, Bruce, Human Resources Director, Heber Valley Hospital, Heber City, UT, p. A648
DENTEN, Jane, MSN, R.N., Chief Nurse Executive, Advocate Lutheran General Hospital, Park Ridge, IL, p. A192
DENTON, Brian, Administrator, Mercy Hospital Kingfisher, Kingfisher, OK, p. A501
DENTON, Christopher, Chief Financial Officer, Henrico Doctors' Hospital, Richmond, VA, p. A666
DENTON, Genise, Manager Human Resources, John J. Pershing Veterans Affairs Medical Center, Poplar Bluff, MO, p. A367
DENTON, Joe, Executive Vice President and Chief Financial Officer, Mobile Infirmary Medical Center, Mobile, AL, p. A20
DENTON, Renee, Chief Operating Officer, Freeman Neosho Hospital, Neosho, MO, p. A366
DENTON, Roy, M.D., Chief Medical Officer, Conway Regional Rehabilitation Hospital, Conway, AR, p. A40
DENTON, Tony, JD, Senior Vice President and Chief Operating Officer, University of Michigan Health System, Michigan Medicine, Ann Arbor, MI, p. A306
DENTONI, Terry, Chief Nursing Officer, Zuckerberg San Francisco General Hospital And Trauma Center, San Francisco, CA, p. A86
DENTRY, Timothy, Interim President, Northern Light Eastern Maine Medical Center, Bangor, ME, p. A281
DENUCCI, Alex, Chief Financial Officer, Franciscan Children'S, Brighton, MA, p. A296
DEPASQUALE, Joseph, M.D., Interim Chief Medical Officer, Saint Michael'S Medical Center, Newark, NJ, p. A409
DEPAULIS, Hugh, Interim Vice President and Chief Financial Officer, Mercyone Siouxland Medical Center, Sioux City, IA, p. A230
DEPKO, Mike, Director Information Technology, Brown County Hospital, Ainsworth, NE, p. A382
DEPLONTY, Sandy, Senior Director Clinical Services, War Memorial Hospital, Sault Sainte Marie, MI, p. A322
DEPOMPEI, Patricia, President, University Hospitals Cleveland Medical Center, Cleveland, OH, p. A478
DEPOOTER, Stephen, Chief Information Officer, Norwegian American Hospital, Chicago, IL, p. A179
DEPPERMAN, Kristi, Chief Financial Officer, Memphis Veterans Affairs Medical Center, Memphis, TN, p. A575
DEPPERT, Eric, M.D., Chief Medical Officer, Manatee Memorial Hospital, Bradenton, FL, p. A118
DEPRATO, Jeremy, Director Information Technology, Spine Hospital Of Louisiana (Formally The Neuromedical Center Surgical Hospital), Baton Rouge, LA, p. A264
D'ERAMO, John, Chief Operating Officer, Connecticut Valley Hospital, Middletown, CT, p. A109
DERAMUS, Brenda, Manager Human Resources, Sutter Lakeside Hospital, Lakeport, CA, p. A64
DERFLINGER, Terri, Site Administrator, Mercyone Oelwein Medical Center, Oelwein, IA, p. A227
DERK, Tammy, Chief Executive Officer, Lancaster Rehabilitation Hospital, Lancaster, PA, p. A528
DERKS, Jenny, Chief Administrative Officer, Ascension Calumet Hospital, Chilton, WI, p. A693
DERMAN, Nancy, Director Human Resources, Southwest Connecticut Mental Health System, Bridgeport, CT, p. A107
DEROCHE, Richard, Manager Information Technology, Multicare Deaconess Hospital, Spokane, WA, p. A679
DERONCEREY, Josiane, Director Human Resources, Carepoint Health Christ Hospital, Jersey City, NJ, p. A407
DERONDE, Kevin, Chief Executive Officer, Mahaska Health Partnership, Oskaloosa, IA, p. A228
DEROSSITT, James, M.D., Chief of Staff, Forrest City Medical Center, Forrest City, AR, p. A42
DEROUEN, George Patrick., Chief Executive Officer, Oakdale Community Hospital, Oakdale, LA, p. A276
DEROUEN, Jason, Director Management Information Systems, Grace Medical Center, Lubbock, TX, p. A622
DERRICO, Patricia, FACHE, R.N., Chief Nursing Officer, Coliseum Northside Hospital, Macon, GA, p. A156
DERSCH, Stephen, M.D., President Medical Staff, Regency Hospital Of Florence, Florence, SC, p. A553
DERUS, Charles, M.D., Vice President Medical Management, Advocate Good Samaritan Hospital, Downers Grove, IL, p. A181
DERUYTER, David N., M.D., President Medical Staff, Select Specialty Hospital Midtown Atlanta, Atlanta, GA, p. A147
DERYNCK, Dodie, Chief Nursing Officer, Avera Marshall Regional Medical Center, Marshall, MN, p. A335
DESAI, Colleen, Chief Nursing Officer, Holyoke Medical Center, Holyoke, MA, p. A299
DESAI, Nimesh, M.D., Medical Director, Massena Memorial Hospital, Massena, NY, p. A431
DESAI, Shailesh, M.D., Chief of Staff, Mercyone Primghar Medical Center, Primghar, IA, p. A228
DESALVO, Susan, Manager Human Resources, Bath Veterans Affairs Medical Center, Bath, NY, p. A423
DESANTIS, Vincent, Vice President Finance, Phelps Memorial Hospital Center, Sleepy Hollow, NY, p. A444
DESART, Amy, Vice President, Chief Financial Officer, Missouri Baptist Medical Center, Saint Louis, MO, p. A369
DESCENT, Karen T., Chief Nursing Officer, Parkview Community Hospital Medical Center, Riverside, CA, p. A81
DESCHAMBEAU, Wayne G., President and Chief Executive Officer, Wayne Healthcare, Greenville, OH, p. A484
DESCHENE, Normand E., Chief Executive Officer, Lowell General Hospital, Lowell, MA, p. A300
DESCHRYVER, Joseph, Chief Executive Officer, Good Samaritan Hospital, San Jose, CA, p. A86
DESEI, Nitin, M.D., Medical Director, Regional Rehabilitation Hospital, Phenix City, AL, p. A22
DESIMINI, Esther Muscari.
Administrator, Riverside Tappahannock Hospital, Tappahannock, VA, p. A668
Interim Administrator, Riverside Walter Reed Hospital, Gloucester, VA, p. A660
DESIMONE, Maureen, Chief Operating Officer, Blythedale Children'S Hospital, Valhalla, NY, p. A446

DESIMONE, Shane, M.D., Chief of Staff, Jane Todd Crawford Hospital, Greensburg, KY, p. A252
DESJARDINS, Isabelle, M.D., Chief Medical Officer, University Of Vermont Medical Center, Burlington, VT, p. A654
DESJEUNES, Carol, Vice President and Chief Operating Officer, Psychiatric Institute Of Washington, Washington, DC, p. A116
DESMARTEAU, Lisa Jo, Chief Financial Officer, Miami Jewish Home And Hospital For Aged, Miami, FL, p. A130
DESMOND, Debbie, Director Human Resources, Sentara Martha Jefferson Hospital, Charlottesville, VA, p. A657
DESMOND, Heather, Chief Financial Officer, Bibb Medical Center, Centreville, AL, p. A16
DESMOND, Jeffrey, M.D., Chief Medical Officer, Michigan Medicine, Ann Arbor, MI, p. A306
DESMOND, P Craig., Chief Executive Officer, Southwest General Hospital, San Antonio, TX, p. A635
DESOTELLE, Robert C., President and Chief Executive Officer, Continuing Care Hospital, Lexington, KY, p. A255
DESOTO, James, M.D.
  Vice President Medical Affairs, Mercy Medical Center Redding, Redding, CA, p. A79
  Vice President Medical Affairs, St. Elizabeth Community Hospital, Red Bluff, CA, p. A79
DESOUZA–VAN BLARICUM, Jacqueline, President and Chief Executive Officer, Riverside Community Hospital, Riverside, CA, p. A81
DESPRES, Paul J., Chief Executive Officer, Eleanor Slater Hospital, Cranston, RI, p. A547
DESROCHES, Jeff, Director Information Systems, Ahmc Anaheim Regional Medical Center, Anaheim, CA, p. A50
DESROSIERS, Chelsea Lee, Chief Financial Officer, Cary Medical Center, Caribou, ME, p. A282
DESTEFANO, Geraldine, R.N., MS, Chief Nursing Officer, Jfk Medical Center North Campus, West Palm Beach, FL, p. A144
DESTEFANO, Stephen, Chief Financial Officer, Magee Rehabilitation Hospital, Philadelphia, PA, p. A535
DETILLIO, Joshua, Chief Executive Officer, Palms West Hospital, Loxahatchee, FL, p. A128
DETTERMAN, B Lynn.
  President and Chief Executive Officer, Mercy Health – Willard Hospital, Willard, OH, p. A494
  President and Chief Executive Officer, Mercy Hospital Of Defiance, Defiance, OH, p. A481
  President and Chief Executive Officer, Mercy Tiffin Hospital, Tiffin, OH, p. A491
DETTMER, Brantley, Administrator and Chief Operating Officer, Kaiser Westside Medical Center, Hillsboro, OR, p. A513
DETWILER, Eric, Director Information Technology, Barnes–Kasson County Hospital, Susquehanna, PA, p. A542
DEURMIER, Carol, Chief Executive Officer, St. Michael'S Hospital Avera, Tyndall, SD, p. A564
DEUTSCH, Stephen, Vice President Operations and Support, Spencer Hospital, Spencer, IA, p. A230
DEVANATHAN, Raja, M.D., Chief Medical Officer, Vibra Hospital Of Northwestern Indiana, Crown Point, IN, p. A202
DEVARAJ, Kiran S., Chief Medical Officer and Chief Clinical Officer, Highland Hospital, Charleston, WV, p. A684
DEVARAJAN, Vadakkipalayam N., Chief Medical Staff, St. Charles Parish Hospital, Luling, LA, p. A272
DEVAULT, Jennifer, Vice President Associate Services, F. F. Thompson Hospital, Canandaigua, NY, p. A425
DEVAULT, Rosanne, Chief Financial Officer, Mckenzie–Willamette Medical Center, Springfield, OR, p. A518
DEVAULT, Roseann M, Chief Financial Officer, Tennova Healthcare–Jefferson Memorial Hospital, Jefferson City, TN, p. A571
DEVAUX, Sheri, Information Technology Manager, Connecticut Veterans Home And Hospital, Rocky Hill, CT, p. A110
DEVERA, Rozelle, Director of Information Systems, Gateways Hospital And Mental Health Center, Los Angeles, CA, p. A66
DEVEREUX, Chris, Human Resources Director, Business Partner, Edward Hospital, Naperville, IL, p. A190
DEVILLE, Linda F., Chief Executive Officer, Bunkie General Hospital, Bunkie, LA, p. A265
DEVIN, Brian V., Chief Executive Officer, Pappas Rehabilitation Hospital For Children, Canton, MA, p. A297
DEVIN, Joseph, Chief Financial Officer, Boone County Hospital, Boone, IA, p. A218
DEVINE, Kathryn, Vice President Human Resources, Upmc Presbyterian, Pittsburgh, PA, p. A538
DEVITA, James, M.D., Chief Medical Officer, Tewksbury Hospital, Tewksbury, MA, p. A304
DEVITO, Joseph M, Vice President Finance and Chief Operating Officer, Geisinger–Bloomsburg Hospital, Bloomsburg, PA, p. A521
DEVLIN, James, Director Information Systems, St. Cloud Regional Medical Center, Saint Cloud, FL, p. A138
DEVORE, Druery, Chief of Medical Staff, Northern Hospital Of Surry County, Mount Airy, NC, p. A459
DEVORSETZ, Marc, Chief Executive Officer, Baylor Scott & White Surgical Hospital–Sherman, Sherman, TX, p. A636
DEW, Douglas, M.D., President Medical Staff, Flagler Hospital, Saint Augustine, FL, p. A138
DEWAN, Vijay, M.D., Clinical Director, Lincoln Regional Center, Lincoln, NE, p. A387
DEWANE, Patti, Vice President Finance and Treasurer, Swedishamerican – A Division Of Uw Health, Rockford, IL, p. A195
DEWAR, William, M.D., Chief of Staff, Wayne Memorial Hospital, Honesdale, PA, p. A527
DEWBERRY, Robbie, Chief Executive Officer, Mitchell County Hospital, Colorado City, TX, p. A593
DEWERFF, Michael, Chief Financial Officer, Unitypoint Health – Iowa Methodist Medical Center, Des Moines, IA, p. A221
DEWISPELARE, Cheryl M, Chief Human Resources Officer, Veterans Affairs Nebraska–Western Iowa Health Care System, Omaha, NE, p. A390
DEWITT, Alan Neil, Chief Medical Officer, Summit Healthcare Regional Medical Center, Show Low, AZ, p. A36
DEWITT, Jocelyn, Ph.D., Vice President and Chief Information Officer, University Hospital, Madison, WI, p. A698
DEWORTH, Gerald M, Associate Director, Carl Vinson Veterans Affairs Medical Center, Dublin, GA, p. A152
DEXTER, Heather, Chief Executive Officer, Emory Saint Joseph'S Hospital Of Atlanta, Atlanta, GA, p. A146
DEXTER, Nadine, Chief Executive Officer, West Hills Hospital, Reno, NV, p. A397
DEXTER, Sue, Administrative Department Leader Human Resources, Mcdonough District Hospital, Macomb, IL, p. A188
DEYARMIN, James A, Controller, Children'S Hospital Of Richmond At Vcu–Brook Road Campus, Richmond, VA, p. A666
DEYNOODT, Mary, Interim Chief Executive Officer and Chief Operating Officer, Ochsner Medical Center, New Orleans, LA, p. A275
DEYO–ALLERS, Margaret, Vice President, Chief Nursing Officer, Montefiore St. Luke'S Cornwall, Newburgh, NY, p. A439
DEYOUNG, Keith, M.D., Chief Medical Staff, Wallowa Memorial Hospital, Enterprise, OR, p. A512
DHAWAN, Ajay, M.D., Chief of Staff, Veterans Affairs Northern Indiana Health Care System, Fort Wayne, IN, p. A204
DHAWAN, Rahul, M.D., Chief Medical Officer, St. Francis Medical Center, Lynwood, CA, p. A70
DHILION, Avtar, Medical Director, The Pavilion At Williamsburg Place, Williamsburg, VA, p. A669
DHILLON, Avtar, M.D., Medical Director, Newport News Behavioral Health Center, Newport News, VA, p. A663
DHULIPALA, Vasudeva, M.D., Medical Director, Encompass Health Rehabilitation Hospital Of Alexandria, Alexandria, LA, p. A262
DHUPER, Aman, President and Chief Executive Officer, St. Rose Hospital, Hayward, CA, p. A61
DI BERNARDO, Deborah, Chief Information Officer, Saint Joseph'S Medical Center, Yonkers, NY, p. A448
DIAL, Jody S, Chief Financial Officer, Timpanogos Regional Hospital, Orem, UT, p. A650
DIAL, Ray D., Director of Nursing, Nebraska Medicine – Bellevue, Bellevue, NE, p. A383
DIALTO, Margaret, Regional Chief Human Resource Officer, Brookdale Hospital Medical Center, New York, NY, p. A432
DIAMOND, Anne, President and Chief Executive Officer, Day Kimball Hospital, Putnam, CT, p. A110
DIAMOND, Kevin M., M.D., Chief Medical Officer, Lawrence Memorial Hospital, Walnut Ridge, AR, p. A49
DIAMOND, Lester K., President, St. Dominic–Jackson Memorial Hospital, Jackson, MS, p. A349
DIAMOND, Timothy, Chief Information Officer, Methodist Hospitals, Gary, IN, p. A205
DIANDA–MARTIN, Barb, Chief Nursing Officer, Mercy St. Anne Hospital, Toledo, OH, p. A492
DIANGELO, John A.
  President and Chief Executive Officer, Inspira Medical Center–Elmer, Elmer, NJ, p. A405
  President and Chief Executive Officer, Inspira Medical Center–Vineland, Vineland, NJ, p. A413
  President and Chief Executive Officer, Inspira Medical Center–Woodbury, Woodbury, NJ, p. A415
DIASIO, Anthony J, Chief Financial Officer, Fox Chase Cancer Center–American Oncologic Hospital, Philadelphia, PA, p. A534
DIATI, Raquel, Chief Executive Officer, Sacred Oak Medical Center, Houston, TX, p. A613
DIAZ, Al, Chief Executive Officer, Kindred Hospital Rome, Rome, GA, p. A159
DIAZ, Evelyn, R.N., Chief Nursing Officer, Encompass Health Rehabilitation Hospital Of Manati, Manati, PR, p. A717
DIAZ, Georgina
  Chief Executive Officer, Jackson Health System, Miami, FL, p. A130
  Chief Operating Officer, Palmetto General Hospital, Hialeah, FL, p. A124
DIAZ, Janine, Human Resources Manager, Emory Rehabilitation Hospital, Atlanta, GA, p. A146
DIAZ, Jesse, Chief Information Officer, Phoebe Putney Memorial Hospital, Albany, GA, p. A145
DIAZ, Jimmy, Director Information Technology, Odessa Regional Medical Center, Odessa, TX, p. A627
DIAZ, Jose, Director Information Systems, St. Vincent Evansville, Evansville, IN, p. A203
DIAZ, Ron, Manager Operations, Albany Stratton Veterans Affairs Medical Center, Albany, NY, p. A422
DIAZ, Sandra, Administrator, Baptist Emergency Hospital, San Antonio, TX, p. A633
DIAZ, Steve, M.D., Chief Medical Officer, Mainegeneral Medical Center, Augusta, ME, p. A281
DIBBLE, Lynn, Vice President Patient Care Services, Guthrie Towanda Memorial Hospital, Towanda, PA, p. A542
DIBNER, David A, Senior Vice President Hospital Operations and Musculoskeletal Strategic Areas, Brookdale Hospital Medical Center, New York, NY, p. A432
DICESARE, Jan, Vice President Financial Operations, St. Vincent'S East, Birmingham, AL, p. A15
DICICCO, Marilyn, Director Human Resources, Chestnut Hill Hospital, Philadelphia, PA, p. A534
DICK, Andy, Director Information Services, Saline Memorial Hospital, Benton, AR, p. A39
DICK, David, Chief Executive Officer, Huron Regional Medical Center, Huron, SD, p. A561
DICK, Deanna, Chief Executive Officer, U. S. Public Health Service Phoenix Indian Medical Center, Phoenix, AZ, p. A34
DICK, Lynette, Director of Support Services, Ellsworth County Medical Center, Ellsworth, KS, p. A234
DICK, Mollie, Coordinator Human Resources, Wayne County Hospital, Monticello, KY, p. A258
DICK, Myra, Manager Business Office, Amg Specialty Hospital–Wichita, Wichita, KS, p. A247
DICKE, Timothy, Chief Executive Officer, Orthoindy Hospital, Indianapolis, IN, p. A207
DICKENS, Betty, Director Human Resources, Sierra Tucson, Tucson, AZ, p. A38
DICKENS, Shelby, Director, Patient Care Services, Fort Madison Community Hospital, Fort Madison, IA, p. A223
DICKERSON, Gene, M.D., Vice President Medical Affairs, Prisma Health Tuomey Hospital, Sumter, SC, p. A557
DICKERSON, Kathy, Chief Financial Officer, Encompass Health Rehabilitation Hospital Of Arlington, Arlington, TX, p. A583
DICKERSON, Michelle, Chief Nursing Officer, Frye Regional Medical Center, Hickory, NC, p. A456
DICKERSON, Sandra, Chief Executive Officer, Greenwood County Hospital, Eureka, KS, p. A235
DICKERSON, Taylor, Chief Information Officer, Lake City Medical Center, Lake City, FL, p. A127
DICKERSON, Toby, Chief Information Resources Management Services, Durham Veterans Affairs Medical Center, Durham, NC, p. A453
DICKEY, Ashley, Director Human Resources, Benson Hospital, Benson, AZ, p. A28
DICKEY, John M, Chief Administrative Officer, Mayo Clinic Health System In Eau Claire, Eau Claire, WI, p. A694
DICKEY, Mark, Director Business Development, Valir Rehabilitation Hospital, Oklahoma City, OK, p. A505
DICKEY, Sarah J., Human Resource Director, Marshall Browning Hospital, Du Quoin, IL, p. A181
DICKEY, Sarah S., Executive Director, Human Resource People and Culture, Mahaska Health Partnership, Oskaloosa, IA, p. A228
DICKINSON, Ashley, Chief Executive Officer, La Porte Hospital, La Porte, IN, p. A209
DICKINSON, Cathy C, Vice President Human Resources, Baptist Health Medical Center – North Little Rock, North Little Rock, AR, p. A46
DICKINSON, Lani, Chief Executive Officer, Emanuel Medical Center, Turlock, CA, p. A92
DICKLICH–COBB, Cristy, Chief Nursing Officer, Memorial Hospital Of Converse County, Douglas, WY, p. A711
DICKMAN, Kathy, Director of Information Systems, Highpoint Health, Lawrenceburg, IN, p. A210
DICKREITER, Adrian, Vice President Technology, Nix Health Care System, San Antonio, TX, p. A634
DICKS, Mandy, Director of Nursing, Lake Butler Hospital Hand Surgery Center, Lake Butler, FL, p. A127
DICKSON, Anita, Director Human Resources, St. Bernards Five Rivers, Pocahontas, AR, p. A47
DICKSON, Scott, Director Information Technology, Reeves Memorial Medical Center, Bernice, LA, p. A264

DICKSON, Thomas C., Chief Executive Officer, Sutter Amador Hospital, Jackson, CA, p. A62
DICKSON, William, Executive Director, Capital District Psychiatric Center, Albany, NY, p. A422
DIDDLE, Derrick, Chief Information Officer, Colorado Canyons Hospital And Medical Center, Fruita, CO, p. A101
DIDENKO, Dima, Chief Financial Officer, Adventhealth Tampa, Tampa, FL, p. A141
DIDERRICH, Mary Kay., Chief Executive Officer, Uw Health Rehabilitation Hospital, Madison, WI, p. A699
DIDRIKSON, Lynne, M.D., Chief Medical Officer, Cavalier County Memorial Hospital And Clinics, Langdon, ND, p. A468
DIEBLING, Tara, Chief Executive Officer, Cardinal Hill Rehabilitation Hospital, Lexington, KY, p. A254
DIEDERICH, John A, Senior Vice President Operations and Chief Operating Officer, Rush–Copley Medical Center, Aurora, IL, p. A174
DIEDRICH, Michele, R.N., Chief Nursing Officer, Vice President Patient Care, Baptist Health Medical Center–Little Rock, Little Rock, AR, p. A44
DIEHL, Robert, President, Mark Twain Medical Center, San Andreas, CA, p. A83
DIENER, D Michael., Chief Executive Officer, Fayette County Memorial Hospital, Washington Court House, OH, p. A493
DIERKENS, Janelle, Chief Administration Officer, Brookdale Hospital Medical Center, New York, NY, p. A432
DIERKER, Anne, Vice President Hospital Services, Unitypoint Health–Pekin Hospital, Pekin, IL, p. A193
DIERS, Suzanne, R.N., Director Patient Care Services, Shriners Hospitals For Children–Portland, Portland, OR, p. A516
DIESTEL, Peter, Senior Vice President and Chief Operating Officer, Valley Hospital, Ridgewood, NJ, p. A412
DIETER, Brian, President and Chief Executive Officer, Mary Greeley Medical Center, Ames, IA, p. A217
DIETERICH, Kevin, Director Information Services, Northern Light Inland Hospital, Waterville, ME, p. A285
DIETLIN, Steve, Chief Executive Officer, Tri–City Medical Center, Oceanside, CA, p. A75
DIETRICH, Brenda, Chief Human Resources Officer, Banner Boswell Medical Center, Sun City, AZ, p. A36
DIETRICH, Jill, Medical Center Director, Dayton Veterans Affairs Medical Center, Dayton, OH, p. A481
DIETRICK, Brian, Director Information Systems, Wilson Medical Center, Wilson, NC, p. A464
DIETSCH, Barry, Chief Financial Officer, Virginia Gay Hospital, Vinton, IA, p. A230
DIETSCHE, Jim, Chief Financial Officer, Bellin Hospital, Green Bay, WI, p. A696
DIETZ, Brian, Interim Chief Executive Officer, Mcdonough District Hospital, Macomb, IL, p. A188
DIETZ, Michael, Administrator, U. S. Air Force Hospital, Hampton, VA, p. A660
DIETZE, Zachary K., Chief Executive Officer, Seton Medical Center Harker Heights, Harker Heights, TX, p. A609
DIFRANCO, Vincent, Interim Chief Executive Officer, South Big Horn County Hospital, Basin, WY, p. A710
DIGUILIO, Jason, Controller, Uh Avon Rehabilitation Hospital, Avon, OH, p. A472
DIIESO, Nicholas T, R.N., Chief Operating Officer, Mount Auburn Hospital, Cambridge, MA, p. A297
DIIORIO, Emil, Chief Executive Officer, Surgical Specialty Center At Coordinated Health, Allentown, PA, p. A519
DIKE, Charles, M.D., Chief of Staff, Sanford Worthington Medical Center, Worthington, MN, p. A343
DIKOS, Julie A., President and Chief Executive Officer, Asheville Specialty Hospital, Asheville, NC, p. A449
DILALLO, Kevin, Chief Executive Officer, Manatee Memorial Hospital, Bradenton, FL, p. A118
DILISI, Jeffrey P, Vice President and Chief Medical Officer, Virginia Hospital Center, Arlington, VA, p. A656
DILLARD, Sharon, Chief Nursing Officer, Poinciana Medical Center, Kissimmee, FL, p. A127
DILLEHUNT, David B
Chief Information Officer, Firsthealth Montgomery Memorial Hospital, Troy, NC, p. A463
Chief Information Officer, Firsthealth Moore Regional Hospital, Pinehurst, NC, p. A460
DILLIE, Codie, Chief Executive Officer, Select Specialty Hospital–Quad Cities, Davenport, IA, p. A220
DILLION, Tim, Vice President of Human Resources, Devereux Hospital And Children'S Center Of Florida, Melbourne, FL, p. A129
DILLON, Jim, Chief Financial Officer, Rangely District Hospital, Rangely, CO, p. A105
DILLON, Lorie, Chief Executive Officer, Geisinger Encompass Health Rehabilitation Hospital, Danville, PA, p. A523
DILLON, Mary E, MS, R.N., Vice President Patient Care Services, Sisters Of Charity Hospital Of Buffalo, Buffalo, NY, p. A425
DILORETO, David, M.D., Executive Vice President and Chief Medical Officer, Amita Health Saint Francis Hospital Evanston, Evanston, IL, p. A182
DIMAMBRO, Christina, Chief Financial Officer, Havasu Regional Medical Center, Lake Havasu City, AZ, p. A31
DIMARCO, Lisa, R.N., FACHE, Vice President Patient Care Service and Chief Nursing Officer, Little Company Of Mary Hospital And Health Care Centers, Evergreen Park, IL, p. A183
DIMARE, John, M.D., Medical Director, Foothill Presbyterian Hospital, Glendora, CA, p. A60
DIMEK, Carolyn, Acting Superintendent, Dorothea Dix Psychiatric Center, Bangor, ME, p. A281
DIMICHELE, Maria, Administrative Assistant, Kensington Hospital, Philadelphia, PA, p. A535
DIMITROVA, Gergana, M.D., Medical Director, Carolina Center For Behavioral Health, Greer, SC, p. A554
DIMM, Adam, Chief Executive Officer, J. C. Blair Memorial Hospital, Huntingdon, PA, p. A527
DIMMICK, Scott, Senior Vice President and Chief Human Resources Officer, Lakeland Regional Health Medical Center, Lakeland, FL, p. A127
DIMOND, Margaret, President and Chief Executive Officer, Mclaren Oakland, Pontiac, MI, p. A320
DIMURIA, Asja, Chief Financial Officer, Abrazo West Campus, Goodyear, AZ, p. A30
DINARDO, Mark, Chief Nursing Officer, Encompass Health Rehabilitation Hospital Of Modesto, Modesto, CA, p. A72
DINGER, Bradley
Chief Financial Officer, Upmc Hamot, Erie, PA, p. A525
Financial Representative, Upmc Northwest, Seneca, PA, p. A541
DINGILIAN, John, M.D., Chief Medical Officer, Simi Valley Hospital, Simi Valley, CA, p. A89
DINGLE, Steve, M.D., Chief Medical Officer, Arizona State Hospital, Phoenix, AZ, p. A33
DINGLEDINE, Jon, Senior Director Human Resources and Support Services, Mercer Health, Coldwater, OH, p. A478
DINGLER, Chance, M.D., Chief Medical Officer, Nocona General Hospital, Nocona, TX, p. A626
DINHAM, Vilma L, R.N., Chief Nursing Officer, Encino Hospital Medical Center, Los Angeles, CA, p. A66
DINKHA, Duncan, M.D., Chief of Staff, Morrison Community Hospital, Morrison, IL, p. A190
DINKINS, Vicki, Director Human Resources, South Georgia Medical Center Lanier Campus, Lakeland, GA, p. A155
DINON, Nancy, Vice President Human Resources, Health Central Hospital, Ocoee, FL, p. A133
DION, Jeffrey P., Vice President and Chief Financial Officer, Holy Family Hospital, Methuen, MA, p. A300
DIPALMA, Maureen, Chief Financial Officer, Tewksbury Hospital, Tewksbury, MA, p. A304
DIPAOLO, Joseph
President, Hackettstown Medical Center, Hackettstown, NJ, p. A406
President, Newton Medical Center, Newton, NJ, p. A410
DIPIETRO, Sandra P, Chief Financial Officer, St. Tammany Parish Hospital, Covington, LA, p. A266
DISANTE, Ginger, Chief Nursing Executive, Christus Health Shreveport–Bossier, Shreveport, LA, p. A278
DISLER, Jordi K., President, Parkview Lagrange Hospital, Lagrange, IN, p. A210
DISPOTO, Martha, R.N., Chief Nurse Executive, Anaheim Medical Center, Kaiser Permanente Orange County Anaheim Medical Center, Anaheim, CA, p. A50
DISWOOD, Lavenia, R.N., Chief Nurse Executive, Northern Navajo Medical Center, Shiprock, NM, p. A420
DITMANSON, Paul, M.D., Clinical Director, Red Lake Indian Health Service Hospital, Red Lake, MN, p. A338
DITMAR, Angela, President, Spectrum Health Pennock, Hastings, MI, p. A314
DITORO, Michael, Chief Operating Officer, Westlake Hospital, Melrose Park, IL, p. A189
DITTBENNER, Beth, Regional Director, Human Resources, Mayo Clinic Health System In Mankato, Mankato, MN, p. A334
DITTBERNER, Deborah S., M.D., Chief Medical Officer, Alomere Health, Alexandria, MN, p. A327
DITTO, Debbie, CPA, Controller, Lincoln Trail Behavioral Health System, Radcliff, KY, p. A260
DITURO, Beth, Divisional Chief Information Officer, Brookdale Hospital Medical Center, New York, NY, p. A432
DITZLER, Andru, Chief Information Officer, Lebanon Veterans Affairs Medical Center, Lebanon, PA, p. A529
DIVELLO, Douglas F., President and Chief Executive Officer, Grace Cottage Hospital, Townshend, VT, p. A655
DIX, Roger J, Vice President Finance, Hannibal Regional Hospital, Hannibal, MO, p. A361
DIX, Theresa, R.N., Chief Nursing Officer, Wythe County Community Hospital, Wytheville, VA, p. A669
DIXON, Christy, Chief Human Resources Officer, Encompass Health Rehabilitation Hospital Of Humble, Humble, TX, p. A615
DIXON, Debbie, Director Human Resources, Pampa Regional Medical Center, Pampa, TX, p. A627
DIXON, Del, Chief Information Officer, South Shore Hospital, South Weymouth, MA, p. A303
DIXON, Florine, Chief Operating Officer, Memorial Hospital, Carthage, IL, p. A175
DIXON, Gregg
Chief Financial Officer, Asheville Specialty Hospital, Asheville, NC, p. A449
Chief Financial Officer, Carepartners Health Services, Asheville, NC, p. A449
DIXON, John, Chief Medical Officer, Mobile Infirmary Medical Center, Mobile, AL, p. A20
DIXON, Lisa, Business Partner and Human Resource Director, Linden Oaks Hospital, Naperville, IL, p. A190
DIXON, Mary E., MSN, R.N., Interim Chief Nursing Officer, University Of Virginia Medical Center, Charlottesville, VA, p. A657
DIXON, Michael, Director Human Resources, Self Regional Healthcare, Greenwood, SC, p. A554
DIXON, Michael L, Vice President, Human Resources, Beaumont Hospital – Royal Oak, Royal Oak, MI, p. A321
DIXON, Shannon, Manager Business Office, Weisbrod Memorial County Hospital, Eads, CO, p. A100
DIXON, Todd, Chief Executive Officer, Navicent Health Baldwin, Milledgeville, GA, p. A157
DOAK, Scott
System Vice President, Human Resources, University Of North Carolina Hospitals, Chapel Hill, NC, p. A451
Vice President, Human Resources, Unc Rex Health Care, Raleigh, NC, p. A460
DOAN, Angela, Chief Financial Officer, Scott Memorial Health, Scottsburg, IN, p. A214
DOANE, Peter, M.D.
Chief Medical Officer, Franklin Regional Hospital, Franklin, NH, p. A400
Chief Medical Officer, Lakes Region General Hospital, Laconia, NH, p. A400
DOBBINS, Jim, Vice President Human Resources, Unc Lenoir Healthcare, Kinston, NC, p. A457
DOBBS, Jacee, Chief Information Officer, Citizens Medical Center, Colby, KS, p. A233
DOBBS, Stephanie, Chief Nursing Officer, Sanford Clear Lake Medical Center, Clear Lake, SD, p. A560
DOBIE, Linda, R.N., JD, Vice President, Legal Affairs, Torrance Memorial Medical Center, Torrance, CA, p. A92
DOBIN, Jennifer, Executive Vice President Human Resources, Carepoint Health Bayonne Medical Center, Bayonne, NJ, p. A403
DOBIZL, Howard
Director Information Services for the Northern Region, Ascension St. Mary'S Hospital, Rhinelander, WI, p. A704
Director Information Technology Services, Ascension Eagle River Hospital, Eagle River, WI, p. A694
Director Information Technology Services, Ascension Sacred Heart Hospital, Tomahawk, WI, p. A707
Director Information Technology Services, Howard Young Medical Center, Woodruff, WI, p. A709
DOBKIN, Eric D, M.D., Vice President Medical Affairs, Suburban Hospital, Bethesda, MD, p. A289
DOBOSENSKI, David, Chief Executive Officer, St. Croix Regional Medical Center, St Croix Falls, WI, p. A706
DOBOSH, Joseph J, Vice President and Chief Financial Officer, Children'S Specialized Hospital, New Brunswick, NJ, p. A409
DOBRAWA, Stanley
Area Information Officer, Kaiser Permanente San Rafael Medical Center, San Rafael, CA, p. A87
Area Information Officer, Kaiser Permanente Santa Rosa Medical Center, Santa Rosa, CA, p. A89
DOBRINSKI, Sandra, Director of Nursing, Comanche County Hospital, Coldwater, KS, p. A233
DOBROVICH, Michael, M.D., Chief Medical Officer, St. John Medical Center, Westlake, OH, p. A494
DOBSON, Glenda, Chief Executive Officer, Cypress Pointe Surgical Hospital, Hammond, LA, p. A268
DOBSON, Glenn E
Regional Chief Financial Officer, Aspirus Keweenaw Hospital, Inc., Laurium, MI, p. A316
Vice President, Finance and Chief Financial Officer, Aspirus Iron River Hospitals & Clinics, Inc., Iron River, MI, p. A315
DOBSON, Trey, M.D., Chief Medical Officer, Southwestern Vermont Medical Center, Bennington, VT, p. A654
DODD, John, Vice President Human Resources, Central Peninsula Hospital, Soldotna, AK, p. A27
DODD, Kathy M, Director of Nursing, Southern Virginia Mental Health Institute, Danville, VA, p. A658

DODD, Pam, Chief Operating Officer, Harper County Community Hospital, Buffalo, OK, p. A497

DODD, Randy, President, Adventist Health – Tulare, Tulare, CA, p. A92

DODDS, George, M.D., Medical Director, Gouverneur Hospital, Gouverneur, NY, p. A428

DODDS, Rick A.
President, Greene Memorial Hospital, Xenia, OH, p. A494
President, Soin Medical Center, Beavercreek, OH, p. A473

DODDS, Sheryl, Chief Clinical Officer, Adventhealth Orlando, Orlando, FL, p. A134

DODERER, Marcella
President and Chief Executive Officer, Arkansas Children'S Hospital, Little Rock, AR, p. A44
President and Chief Executive Officer, Arkansas Children'S Northwest, Springdale, AR, p. A48

DODGE, Terry, M.D., Chief of Staff, Musc Health Chester Medical Center, Chester, SC, p. A550

DODSON, Louise, R.N.
Chief Nursing Officer, Wagoner Community Hospital, Wagoner, OK, p. A510
Chief Operating Officer and Chief Nursing Officer, Wagoner Community Hospital, Wagoner, OK, p. A510

DODSON, Paige, M.D., M.P.H., Chief Medical Officer, Susan B. Allen Memorial Hospital, El Dorado, KS, p. A234

DOEHRING, Christopher, M.D.
Vice President Medical Affairs, Franciscan Health Indianapolis, Indianapolis, IN, p. A207
Vice President of Medical Affairs, Franciscan Health Carmel, Carmel, IN, p. A201

DOELING, Mariann, President, Chi St Alexius Health Carrington Medical Center, Carrington, ND, p. A465

DOELLING, James, Executive Director, Battle Creek Veterans Affairs Medical Center, Battle Creek, MI, p. A307

DOERFLER, Mary P., Chief Human Resources Officer, Central Texas Veterans Health Care System, Temple, TX, p. A640

DOERGE, Jean, R.N., MSN, Nurse Executive, Swedish/Edmonds, Edmonds, WA, p. A672

DOERGE, Jean B, MS, R.N., Chief Nursing Executive, Unitypoint Health – Trinity Bettendorf, Bettendorf, IA, p. A217

DOERING, Dean, Chief Executive Officer, Central Prison Hospital, Raleigh, NC, p. A460

DOERR, Brian, Chief Information Officer, Continuecare Hospital At Baptist Health Corbin, Corbin, KY, p. A250

DOGGETT, Geri, Director Business, East Mississippi State Hospital, Meridian, MS, p. A351

DOGGETT, Sherri L, Vice President Patient Services, Mercyone Centerville Medical Center, Centerville, IA, p. A218

DOHERTY, Allison, Chief Financial Officer, Spine Hospital Of Louisiana (Formally The Neuromedical Center Surgical Hospital), Baton Rouge, LA, p. A264

DOHERTY, Bryan, Management Information Technology Services I, Sagamore Children'S Psychiatric Center, Dix Hills, NY, p. A427

DOHERTY, Dan, Vice President, Operations, Advocate Trinity Hospital, Chicago, IL, p. A176

DOHERTY, Donna, R.N., Vice President of Nursing and Chief Nursing Officer, Beth Israel Deaconess Hospital Plymouth, Plymouth, MA, p. A302

DOHERTY, John
Co–President, M Health, University Of Minnesota Medical Center, Fairview, Minneapolis, MN, p. A336
Vice President Finance, University Of Minnesota Medical Center, Fairview, Minneapolis, MN, p. A336

DOHERTY, Randy, Chief Executive Officer, Encompass Health Rehabilitation Hospital Of Braintree, Braintree, MA, p. A296

DOHERTY, Ray, Director Information Technology, Cmh Regional Health System, Wilmington, OH, p. A494

DOHMANN, Eileen L, R.N.
Senior Vice President and Chief Nursing Officer, Mary Washington Hospital, Fredericksburg, VA, p. A659
Senior Vice President and Chief Nursing Officer, Stafford Hospital, Stafford, VA, p. A667

DOIDGE, John C, Vice President Finance, Glencoe Regional Health, Glencoe, MN, p. A332

DOKKEN, Susan, Chief Human Resources, St. Joseph Regional Medical Center, Lewiston, ID, p. A170

DOKSUM, Kathryn, Director Finance, Samaritan North Lincoln Hospital, Lincoln City, OR, p. A514

DOLAN, Lisa, Interim Chief Executive Officer, St. Joseph Hospital, Fort Wayne, IN, p. A204

DOLAN, Mary, Regional Director Information Services and HIPAA Security Official, Shriners Hospitals For Children–Boston, Boston, MA, p. A296

DOLAN, Steve, Chief Information Officer, Eastpointe Hospital, Daphne, AL, p. A16

DOLBEE, Hilary, Chief Financial Officer, Monroe Hospital, Bloomington, IN, p. A200

DOLBIN, Kathy, Director of Human Resources, Mercy Allen Hospital, Oberlin, OH, p. A489

DOLEN, Cassie, Vice President Finance and Chief Financial Officer, Hutchinson Regional Medical Center, Hutchinson, KS, p. A237

DOLLINS, Gary, Director Management Information Systems, Poplar Bluff Regional Medical Center, Poplar Bluff, MO, p. A367

DOLORESCO, Laureen, R.N., Associate Director for Patient Care and Nursing Services, James A. Haley Veterans' Hospital–Tampa, Tampa, FL, p. A141

DOMALESKI, Vareen O'Keefe, MS, R.N., Vice Patient Care Services and Chief Nursing Officer, Emma Pendleton Bradley Hospital, East Providence, RI, p. A547

DOMANICO, Lee, Chief Executive Officer, Marinhealth Medical Center, Greenbrae, CA, p. A61

DOMANN, Debbie, Director of Operations, Fillmore County Hospital, Geneva, NE, p. A385

DOMANSKY, John, Vice President Operations, Rutherford Regional Health System, Rutherfordton, NC, p. A461

DOMAYER, Cory, Chief Financial Officer, Adventhealth Palm Coast, Palm Coast, FL, p. A135

DOMBROUSKI, Joyce, Chief Executive Officer, Providence St. Patrick Hospital, Missoula, MT, p. A379

DOMEIER, Sandy, Director Patient Care Services, Ridgeview Sibley Medical Center, Arlington, MN, p. A327

DOMINGO, Connie, M.D., Medical Director, Weisman Children'S Rehabilitation Hospital, Marlton, NJ, p. A408

DOMINGUE, Buffy, Chief Executive Officer, Lafayette Surgical Specialty Hospital, Lafayette, LA, p. A271

DOMINGUEZ, Brenda, Director Human Resources, Cypress Creek Hospital, Houston, TX, p. A611

DOMINGUEZ, Ed, President Medical Staff, Vibra Specialty Hospital At Desoto, Desoto, TX, p. A600

DOMINGUEZ, Marie, Commander, Martin Army Community Hospital, Fort Benning, GA, p. A153

DOMINICCI, Sandra, Nursing Director, Hospital De Damas, Ponce, PR, p. A717

DOMINIQUE, Ravon, Chief Nursing Officer, Brentwood Hospital, Shreveport, LA, p. A278

DOMINSKI, Paul, Vice President Human Resources, Park Nicollet Methodist Hospital, Saint Louis Park, MN, p. A339

DOMMER, Matthew, M.D., Chief Medical Officer, Bronson Lakeview Hospital, Paw Paw, MI, p. A319

DOMON, Steven, M.D., Medical Director, Arkansas State Hospital, Little Rock, AR, p. A44

DONAHEY, Kenneth C., Chief Executive Officer, Oviedo Medical Center, Oviedo, FL, p. A135

DONAHUE, Edward, M.D., Chief Medical Officer, St. Joseph'S Hospital And Medical Center, Phoenix, AZ, p. A34

DONAHUE, Kristine Marie, Administrator, Clinical Operations, Beaumont Hospital – Taylor, Taylor, MI, p. A323

DONAHUE, Michael, M.D., Medical Director, Select Specialty Hospital–Pittsburgh/Upmc, Pittsburgh, PA, p. A537

DONAHUE, Ruth, R.N., Chief Nursing Officer, Harrison County Hospital, Corydon, IN, p. A201

DONAHUE, Samantha, Director Human Resources, Crossing Rivers Health Medical Center, Prairie Du Chien, WI, p. A704

DONALD, Steve, M.D., Chief of Staff, Washington County Hospital, Chatom, AL, p. A16

DONALDSON, Brooke G, Assistant Administrator Human Resources, Jackson Hospital, Marianna, FL, p. A129

DONALDSON, David, Chief Executive Officer, Henrico Doctors' Hospital, Richmond, VA, p. A666

DONALDSON, Jill, Vice President Operations, Medstar Harbor Hospital, Baltimore, MD, p. A287

DONALDSON, Les, M.D., Chief of Staff, Roosevelt General Hospital, Portales, NM, p. A419

DONALDSON, Lori, Chief Financial Officer, Uc San Diego Health, San Diego, CA, p. A84

DONALDSON, Nesha, Chief Operating Officer, Cullman Regional Medical Center, Cullman, AL, p. A16

DONALDSON, Shirley, Chief Financial Officer, New Mexico Rehabilitation Center, Roswell, NM, p. A420

DONATELLE, Lawrence, M.D., Vice President Medical Affairs, Ascension Northeast Wisconsin St. Elizabeth Hospital, Appleton, WI, p. A691

DONATO, Cyndy, Vice President, Human Resources, Missouri Baptist Medical Center, Saint Louis, MO, p. A369

DONAWAY, Duane, Director Information Technology, Hendrick Health System, Abilene, TX, p. A581

DONELAN, Matthias B, M.D., Chief of Staff, Shriners Hospitals For Children–Boston, Boston, MA, p. A296

DONENWIRTH, Karl, Vice President Information Services, Northcoast Behavioral Healthcare, Northfield, OH, p. A488

DONGILLI, Paul, Jr
President and Chief Executive Officer, Madonna Rehabilitation Hospital, Lincoln, NE, p. A387
President and Chief Executive Officer, Madonna Rehabilitation Hospital, Omaha, NE, p. A389

President and Chief Executive Officer, Madonna Rehabilitation Specialty Hospital, Omaha, NE, p. A389

DONHAM, Guyle, M.D., Chief of Staff, Comanche County Medical Center, Comanche, TX, p. A593

DONICA, Joanna, Director Human Resource, Pam Rehabilitation Hospital Of Beaumont, Beaumont, TX, p. A587

DONLEY, Linda, Vice President Operations, Ira Davenport Memorial Hospital, Bath, NY, p. A423

DONLIN, Bruce, Director Information Services, Mount Desert Island Hospital, Bar Harbor, ME, p. A281

DONLIN, John
Director Human Resources, Shriners Hospitals For Children–Springfield, Springfield, MA, p. A303
Regional Director Human Resources – Boston, Erie, and Springfield, Shriners Hospitals For Children–Boston, Boston, MA, p. A296

DONNELLY, James E, Chief Nursing Officer and Vice President Patient Care Services, Upmc Hamot, Erie, PA, p. A525

DONNELLY, Sheryl, Human Resources Specialist, State Hospital South, Blackfoot, ID, p. A167

DONNELY, Lisa, Controller II, Central Texas Rehabilitation Hospital, Austin, TX, p. A585

DONOFRIO, Kathryn, Chief Nursing Officer, Swedish Covenant Hospital, Chicago, IL, p. A180

DONOGHUE, Alicia, Director Human Resources, Eastpointe Hospital, Daphne, AL, p. A16

DONOHUE, Mary Ann T, Ph.D., R.N., Chief Patient Care Services Officer, Stony Brook University Hospital, Stony Brook, NY, p. A444

DONOHUE–RYAN, MaryAnn, Ph.D., Vice President Patient Care Services, Englewood Hospital And Medical Center, Englewood, NJ, p. A405

DONOVAN, Andrew
Director Information Technology, Ascension Southeast Wisconsin Hospital – Elmbrook Campus, Brookfield, WI, p. A693
Regional Director Information Services, Ascension Southeast Wisconsin Hospital – St. Joseph'S Campus, Milwaukee, WI, p. A700

DONOVAN, James W, President and Chief Executive Officer, Lincolnhealth, Damariscotta, ME, p. A282

DONOVAN, James W., President and Chief Executive Officer, Lincolnhealth, Damariscotta, ME, p. A282

DONOVAN, Jenny, Director Human Resources, Wright Memorial Hospital, Trenton, MO, p. A372

DONOVAN, Kevin
President and Chief Executive Officer, Franklin Regional Hospital, Franklin, NH, p. A400
President and Chief Executive Officer, Lakes Region General Hospital, Laconia, NH, p. A400

DONOVAN, Mary, Controller, Encompass Health Rehabilitation Institute Of Tucson, Tucson, AZ, p. A37

DONOVAN, Mike, Chief Financial Officer, Lemuel Shattuck Hospital, Jamaica Plain, MA, p. A299

DONOVAN, Patrick, M.D., Director Medical Staff, Encompass Health Rehabilitation Hospital Of Fort Worth, Fort Worth, TX, p. A605

DONSON, Elliott, Chief Information Specialist, Lincoln Hospital, Davenport, WA, p. A672

DONZE, Richard D, D.O., Senior Vice President Medical Affairs, Penn Medicine Chester County Hospital, West Chester, PA, p. A544

DOODY, Kris A., Chief Executive Officer, Cary Medical Center, Caribou, ME, p. A282

DOOKEERAM, David, Chief Operating Officer, Porter Adventist Hospital, Denver, CO, p. A99

DOOLEY, Kimberly H., Administrator, Lafayette General Surgical Hospital, Lafayette, LA, p. A271

DOOLEY, Lisa, Health Information Officer, Middlesboro Arh Hospital, Middlesboro, KY, p. A258

DOOLEY, Mark J., Chief Executive Officer, Putnam Community Medical Center, Palatka, FL, p. A135

DOOLING, Edward, Vice President, Human Resources, Masonicare Health Center, Wallingford, CT, p. A111

DOOLITTLE, Jon D., Regional President, Mosaic Medical Center – Albany, Albany, MO, p. A356

DOORENBOS, Pamela, M.D., Vice President, Medical Affairs, Maple Grove Hospital, Maple Grove, MN, p. A335

DOORN, Douglas, Chief Executive Officer, Lewis And Clark Specialty Hospital, Yankton, SD, p. A565

DORAIN, Debbie, Chief Financial Officer, Copley Hospital, Morrisville, VT, p. A654

DORAN, Judy, Vice President of Hospital Services and Chief Nurse Executive, Atrium Health Stanly, Albemarle, NC, p. A449

DORAN, Ken, Interim Chief Executive Officer, Carson Tahoe Health, Carson City, NV, p. A393

DORAN, T, M.D., Chief of Staff, Perry Memorial Hospital, Princeton, IL, p. A194

DORIA, Thomas
Vice President and Patient Services – West, Morton Plant North Bay Hospital, New Port Richey, FL, p. A132
Vice President and Patient Services West, St. Anthony'S Hospital, Saint Petersburg, FL, p. A138
Vice President Patient Services – West, Morton Plant Hospital, Clearwater, FL, p. A119
Vice President, Patient Services and Chief Nursing Officer, Mease Countryside Hospital, Safety Harbor, FL, p. A138
Vice President, Patient Services and Chief Nursing Officer, Mease Dunedin Hospital, Dunedin, FL, p. A122
DORION, Heath, Physician Administrator, Mercy Health – St. Elizabeth Boardman Hospital, Boardman, OH, p. A473
DORITY, Paula, Director Human Resources, Martin County Hospital District, Stanton, TX, p. A638
DORMAN, Christopher, President and Chief Executive Officer, Tift Regional Medical Center, Tifton, GA, p. A162
DORMAN, Doug, Vice President Human Resources, Prisma Health Greenville Memorial Hospital, Greenville, SC, p. A553
DORMAN, Julie, Human Resources Director, Parkwood Behavioral Health System, Olive Branch, MS, p. A352
DORMAN, Stephen, M.D., Chief Medical Officer, New Mexico Rehabilitation Center, Roswell, NM, p. A420
DORNOFF, Edward G., Associate Director, Battle Creek Veterans Affairs Medical Center, Battle Creek, MI, p. A307
DOROGY, Sharon, Chief Information Officer, The Children'S Institute Of Pittsburgh, Pittsburgh, PA, p. A537
DOROTHY, Jonnie, Senior Director Human Resources, Massena Memorial Hospital, Massena, NY, p. A431
DORR, Amy
Vice President Human Resources, Mclaren Greater Lansing, Lansing, MI, p. A316
Vice President Human Resources, Mclaren Lapeer Region, Lapeer, MI, p. A316
DORRIS, Steve, Chief Financial Officer, Poplar Bluff Regional Medical Center, Poplar Bluff, MO, p. A367
DORSCH, Anthony, Chief Financial Officer, Providence Alaska Medical Center, Anchorage, AK, p. A25
DORSEY, Bob, Human Resources Coordinator, Select Specialty Hospital – Lincoln, Lincoln, NE, p. A387
DORSEY, John I, M.D., Vice President Physician Services and Chief Medical Officer, Javon Bea Hospital–Rockton, Rockford, IL, p. A194
DORSEY, Michael A., Chief Executive Officer, Johnson Regional Medical Center, Clarksville, AR, p. A40
DORSEY, William, Board Chairman and Chief Executive Officer, Jackson Park Hospital And Medical Center, Chicago, IL, p. A177
DORST, Jake, Chief Information Officer, Tahoe Forest Hospital District, Truckee, CA, p. A92
D'ORTENZIO, Gabe, Director of Human Resources, Weirton Medical Center, Weirton, WV, p. A690
DORTON, Patty, Director of Nursing, Buchanan General Hospital, Grundy, VA, p. A660
D'ORTONA, Cary, President, Orlando Regional Medical Center, Orlando, FL, p. A134
DOSHI, Nikunj, D.O., Chief Medical Officer, Banner Gateway Medical Center, Gilbert, AZ, p. A29
DOSI, Abhishek, Chief Executive Officer, Sutter Solano Medical Center, Vallejo, CA, p. A93
DOSS, Delilah, Director, Human Resources, Mountainview Regional Medical Center, Las Cruces, NM, p. A419
DOSS, Mounir F, Executive Vice President and Chief Financial Officer, Brookdale Hospital Medical Center, New York, NY, p. A432
DOSSETT, Jeffrey, Chief Operating Officer, Abrazo West Campus, Goodyear, AZ, p. A30
DOSSETT, Phyllis, Director of Clinical Services, Hancock County Hospital, Sneedville, TN, p. A579
DOSTAL, Drew H., Chief Executive Officer, Ogallala Community Hospital, Ogallala, NE, p. A388
DOTEN, Charles, Chief Executive Officer, Promise Hospital Of Miami, Miami Lakes, FL, p. A131
DOTTS–MCCOOL, Michelle, Chief Nursing Officer, St. Vincent Dunn Hospital, Bedford, IN, p. A200
DOTY, Jennifer, Chief Executive Officer, Sidney Health Center, Sidney, MT, p. A380
DOTY, Lisa, Manager Human Resources, Desert View Hospital, Pahrump, NV, p. A397
DOUBLE, Ron
Chief Information Officer, Parkview Huntington Hospital, Huntington, IN, p. A206
Chief Information Officer, Parkview Noble Hospital, Kendallville, IN, p. A208
Chief Information Technology Officer, Parkview Lagrange Hospital, Lagrange, IN, p. A210
DOUCETTE, Diane, President, Mount Carmel New Albany Surgical Hospital, New Albany, OH, p. A488

DOUCETTE, Elmer H, Chief Financial Officer, Redington–Fairview General Hospital, Skowhegan, ME, p. A285
DOUCETTE, Michael J., Senior Vice President and Administrator, Riverside Regional Medical Center, Newport News, VA, p. A663
DOUD, Tony
Controller, Ascension St. Joseph Hospital, Tawas City, MI, p. A323
Controller, Ascension Standish Hospital, Standish, MI, p. A323
DOUGHERTY, Chuck, Chief Information Officer, Shenandoah Medical Center, Shenandoah, IA, p. A229
DOUGHERTY, David, Chief Information Management Officer, Irwin Army Community Hospital, Junction City, KS, p. A237
DOUGHERTY, James, Commander, U. S. Air Force Medical Center Keesler, Keesler Afb, MS, p. A349
DOUGHERTY, Terry, Director Human Resources, Bryn Mawr Hospital, Bryn Mawr, PA, p. A521
DOUGHTY, Cathy, Vice President Human Resources, Sheppard Pratt Health System, Baltimore, MD, p. A288
DOUGHTY, Linda, Chief Nursing Officer, Alaska Regional Hospital, Anchorage, AK, p. A25
DOUGHTY, Stephanie
Chief Financial Officer, Uchealth Medical Center Of The Rockies, Loveland, CO, p. A104
Chief Financial Officer, Uchealth Poudre Valley Hospital, Fort Collins, CO, p. A100
DOUGLAS, Andy, Manager Information Technology, Burnett Medical Center, Grantsburg, WI, p. A695
DOUGLAS, Debbie, Director Human Resources, Putnam County Memorial Hospital, Unionville, MO, p. A372
DOUGLAS, Doug, Interim Vice President Human Resources, Beaufort Memorial Hospital, Beaufort, SC, p. A549
DOUGLAS, Errol A., MS, Vice President, Human Resources, Roswell Park Comprehensive Cancer Center, Buffalo, NY, p. A424
DOUGLAS, Jason T., Chief Executive Officer, Memorial Medical Center Of Ashland, Ashland, WI, p. A691
DOUGLAS, Johnna, Human Resources Manager, Massac Memorial Hospital, Metropolis, IL, p. A189
DOUGLAS, Kay, Human Resources Director, Musc Health Florence Medical Center, Florence, SC, p. A553
DOUGLAS, Pam, Chief Nursing Officer, Putnam General Hospital, Eatonton, GA, p. A153
DOUGLAS, Paul, Vice President Human Resources, Baton Rouge General Medical Center, Baton Rouge, LA, p. A263
DOUGLAS, Phillip B, Chairman and Chief Executive Officer, Lifecare Hospitals Of Dallas, Dallas, TX, p. A596
DOUGLAS–WALSH, Marlene, Chief Executive Officer, Kirkbride Center, Philadelphia, PA, p. A535
DOUVILLE, Arthur, M.D.
Chief Medical Officer, O'Connor Hospital, San Jose, CA, p. A86
Chief Medical Officer, Saint Louise Regional Hospital, Gilroy, CA, p. A60
DOVEL, Melissa, Manager Human Resources, Atrium Medical Center Of Corinth, Corinth, TX, p. A594
DOVER, Jerry, Chief Executive Officer, Sullivan County Memorial Hospital, Milan, MO, p. A365
DOVNARSKY, James, M.D., Director Pulmonary Medical, Kindred Hospital South Philadelphia, Philadelphia, PA, p. A535
DOW, Alan, Chief Financial Officer, Southern Coos Hospital And Health Center, Bandon, OR, p. A511
DOW, Janet, R.N., Chief Nursing Officer, Santiam Hospital, Stayton, OR, p. A518
DOW, Korry, President, Nashoba Valley Medical Center, Ayer, MA, p. A294
DOW, Laura, Chief Financial Officer, Memorial Health, Savannah, GA, p. A160
DOWDLE, Paula, Chief Operating Officer, Jefferson Healthcare, Port Townsend, WA, p. A676
DOWDY, Kathren, Regional Hospital Senior Director, Carilion Tazewell Community Hospital, Tazewell, VA, p. A668
DOWDY, Kathren, MSN, Senior Director, Chief Executive Officer and Chief Nursing Officer, Carilion Tazewell Community Hospital, Tazewell, VA, p. A668
DOWELL, James, Administrator and Chief Executive Officer, Little River Memorial Hospital, Ashdown, AR, p. A39
DOWERS, Christopher, Chief Executive Officer, Bloomington Meadows Hospital, Bloomington, IN, p. A200
DOWERS, Cindy, Chief Nursing Officer, Harsha Behavioral Center, Terre Haute, IN, p. A215
DOWGUN, Richard, Chief Information Officer, St. Francis Medical Center, Trenton, NJ, p. A413
DOWLING, Deanna, R.N., Chief Nursing Officer, Promise Hospital Of Wichita Falls, Wichita Falls, TX, p. A645
DOWLING, Lisa, Manager Finance, Mercy Hospital Tishomingo, Tishomingo, OK, p. A508

DOWN, Melanie Falls, Site Manager, Crow/Northern Cheyenne Hospital, Crow Agency, MT, p. A375
DOWN, Philip B., Chief Executive Officer, Doctors Community Hospital, Lanham, MD, p. A291
DOWNARD, Diane, Chief Financial Officer, Coal County General Hospital, Coalgate, OK, p. A498
DOWNES, Patrick, Chief Executive Officer, East Cooper Medical Center, Mount Pleasant, SC, p. A555
DOWNES, Thomas, Interim Chief Executive Officer, Uchealth Yampa Valley Medical Center, Steamboat Springs, CO, p. A105
DOWNEY, William B
Chief Operating Officer, Riverside Regional Medical Center, Newport News, VA, p. A663
President and Chief Executive Officer, Coastal Virginia Rehabilitation, Newport News, VA, p. A663
DOWNIE, Beth, Chief Information Officer, Newton–Wellesley Hospital, Newton Lower Falls, MA, p. A301
DOWNING, James R., Chief Executive Officer, St. Jude Children'S Research Hospital, Memphis, TN, p. A575
DOWNING, Jeff, R.N., MS, Chief Nursing Officer, National Jewish Health, Denver, CO, p. A99
DOWNS, Bryan, Director Information Systems, Central Peninsula Hospital, Soldotna, AK, p. A27
DOWNS, Kenny, Chief Executive Officer, Cordell Memorial Hospital, Cordell, OK, p. A498
DOWNS, Lisa M, R.N., Chief Nursing Officer, Sarah D. Culbertson Memorial Hospital, Rushville, IL, p. A195
DOWNS, Patricia, Director Human Resources, Northern Nevada Medical Center, Sparks, NV, p. A398
DOWNS, Ray, Senior Staff Accountant, Healthmark Regional Medical Center, Defuniak Springs, FL, p. A121
DOWNS, Steven, Chief Financial Officer, St. Luke'S Des Peres Hospital, Saint Louis, MO, p. A370
DOWNS, Stuart D., Vice President and Chief Operating Officer, Wellstar Atlanta Medical Center, Atlanta, GA, p. A147
DOYLE, Christopher, Chief Executive Officer, Physicians Care Surgical Hospital, Royersford, PA, p. A540
DOYLE, Craig, Director and Chief Information Officer, St. Tammany Parish Hospital, Covington, LA, p. A266
DOYLE, Jay, President and Chief Executive Officer, St. James Healthcare, Butte, MT, p. A375
DOYLE, John
Chief Financial Officer, Confluence Health/Central Washington Hospital, Wenatchee, WA, p. A682
Chief Financial Officer, Confluence Health/Wenatchee Valley Hospital, Wenatchee, WA, p. A682
Vice President Finance, Paoli Hospital, Paoli, PA, p. A533
DOYLE, Kelly, Chief Executive Officer, Rothman Specialty Hospital, Bensalem, PA, p. A520
DOYLE, Mark, Administrator and Chief Executive Officer, Memorial Hospital Pembroke, Pembroke Pines, FL, p. A136
DOYLE, Matt, Chief Executive Officer, Strategic Behavioral Health – Raleigh, Garner, NC, p. A454
DOYLE, Matthew, Chief Financial Officer, Methodist Hospitals, Gary, IN, p. A205
DOYLE, Michael, M.D., Vice President Medical Affairs, Vassar Brothers Medical Center, Poughkeepsie, NY, p. A442
DOZIER, Carol
Chief Financial Officer, Lifestream Behavioral Center, Leesburg, FL, p. A128
President and Chief Executive Officer, King'S Daughters' Health, Madison, IN, p. A210
DOZIER, Michael, Vice President, Chief Information Officer, Lafayette General Medical Center, Lafayette, LA, p. A271
DOZIER, Mike, Chief Information Officer, Southeast Hospital, Cape Girardeau, MO, p. A358
DRABANT, Leah, Director of Finance, Complex Care Hospital At Ridgelake, Sarasota, FL, p. A139
DRAEGER, Anne, Chief Nursing Officer, Owatonna Hospital, Owatonna, MN, p. A337
DRAEGER, Trish, Chief Nursing Officer, Healthsouth Deaconess Rehabilitation Hospital, Evansville, IN, p. A203
DRAIME, D. Eric
Vice President and Chief Financial Officer, Avita Ontario Hospital, Ontario, OH, p. A489
Vice President and Chief Financial Officer, Galion Hospital, Galion, OH, p. A483
DRAKE, Carolyn, Director of Nursing, Milan General Hospital, Milan, TN, p. A576
DRAKE, Derek Scott, Chief Nursing Officer, St. Francis Medical Center, Lynwood, CA, p. A70
DRAKE, Marian, Chief Financial Officer, Greenwood County Hospital, Eureka, KS, p. A235
DRAKE, Megan, Chief Operating Officer, Shelby Baptist Medical Center, Alabaster, AL, p. A13
DRANSFIELD, Darin, Chief Executive Officer, Franklin County Medical Center, Preston, ID, p. A171

DRAPER, Jason, Chief Financial Officer, West Tennessee Healthcare Volunteer Hospital, Martin, TN, p. A574

DRAPER, Terri, Director of Operations, Hillsdale Hospital, Hillsdale, MI, p. A314

DRAPER, Vivian, Chief Financial Officer, U. S. Public Health Service Indian Hospital–Sells, Sells, AZ, p. A36

DREGNEY, James, Vice President Finance and Operations, Chief Financial Officer, Sauk Prairie Healthcare, Prairie Du Sac, WI, p. A704

DREHER, Craig, Chief Information Officer, Northern Light Mercy Hospital, Portland, ME, p. A284

DREHER, Ronald, Finance Officer, Robert J. Dole Veterans Affairs Medical Center, Wichita, KS, p. A248

DREHR, Sammie, Chief Nursing Officer, Detar Healthcare System, Victoria, TX, p. A643

DRENTH, Nancy E, R.N., Director Ancillary Services, Sanford Luverne Medical Center, Luverne, MN, p. A334

DRESSLER, Kaeli, R.N., MSN, Chief Nursing Officer, Peterson Regional Medical Center, Kerrville, TX, p. A618

DREW, Jeff, Fiscal Officer, Aleda E. Lutz Veterans Affairs Medical Center, Saginaw, MI, p. A321

DREW, Jim, Chief Information Officer, Saint Thomas Midtown Hospital, Nashville, TN, p. A577

DREW, Laura, Chief Operating Officer, Piedmont Columbus Regional Northside, Columbus, GA, p. A150

DREWS, Manty, Chief Information Officer, Adventist Health Sonora, Sonora, CA, p. A90

DREXLER, Diane, R.N., Chief Nursing Officer, Yavapai Regional Medical Center, Prescott, AZ, p. A35

DRIESSNACK, Hans, Chief Executive Officer, Northwest Medical Center – Springdale, Springdale, AR, p. A48

DRIGGERS, Steve, M.D., Chief Medical Officer, Holy Family Memorial, Manitowoc, WI, p. A699

DRIGGS, Christi, Chief Financial Officer, Phillips County Health Systems, Phillipsburg, KS, p. A243

DRINKWATER, Jinia, R.N., Director Patient Care Services, Encompass Health Rehabilitation Hospital Of Braintree, Braintree, MA, p. A296

DRINKWATER, Linda, Chief Financial Officer, Waldo County General Hospital Maine Health, Belfast, ME, p. A282

DRINKWITZ, Jeremy, President and Chief Executive Officer, Mercy Hospital Joplin, Joplin, MO, p. A362

DRISCOLL, Kelly, President and Chief Executive Officer, Faith Regional Health Services, Norfolk, NE, p. A388

DRISCOLL, Laureen, President, Multicare Deaconess Hospital, Spokane, WA, p. A679

DRISCOLL, Nancy, Chief Nursing Officer, Longmont United Hospital, Longmont, CO, p. A103

DRISCOLL, Philip J, Jr, Chief Executive Officer, Kessler Institute For Rehabilitation, West Orange, NJ, p. A414

DROEGE, Marie T, Chief Executive Officer, Select Specialty Hospital–St. Louis, Saint Charles, MO, p. A368

DRONE, Marilyn, R.N., MSN, Vice President, CNO, St. Mary Medical Center, Apple Valley, CA, p. A51

DROZD, Carol, Chief Operating Officer, St. Mark'S Medical Center, La Grange, TX, p. A619

DRUMMOND, Gregory, Chief Executive Officer, Wellbridge Heatlhcare Of San Marcos, San Marcos, TX, p. A636

DRURY, Dennis, Director Information Technology, Northern Cochise Community Hospital, Willcox, AZ, p. A38

DRVARIC, David M, M.D., Chief of Staff, Shriners Hospitals For Children–Springfield, Springfield, MA, p. A303

DRY, Laurence
Chief Operating Officer, Acute Care Hospitals Northern Region, Amita Health Elk Grove Village, Elk Grove Village, IL, p. A182
Chief Operating Officer, Acute Care Hospitals Northern Region, Amita Health Hoffman Estates, Hoffman Estates, IL, p. A186

DRYMON, Lisa, Manager, Fairfax Community Hospital, Fairfax, OK, p. A499

DRZEWIECKI–BURGER, Mary Jo, Administrative Manager, Caro Center, Caro, MI, p. A308

D'SOUZA, Carol, Chief Human Resources Officer, Banner Casa Grande Medical Center, Casa Grande, AZ, p. A28

D'SOUZA, Gladys, Chief Nursing Officer, Barlow Respiratory Hospital, Los Angeles, CA, p. A66

DU PONT, Karen, Chief Human Resource Officer, Casa Colina Hospital And Health Systems, Pomona, CA, p. A78

DUANE, Paul K
Chief Financial Officer and Office of Health Reform, Prisma Health Baptist Hospital, Columbia, SC, p. A551
Chief Financial Officer and Office of Health Reform, Prisma Health Richland Hospital, Columbia, SC, p. A551

DUARTE, Ray, Director, Information Technology and Services, Monmouth Medical Center, Southern Campus, Lakewood, NJ, p. A407

DUBICKI, Robert, Executive Vice President and Chief Operating Officer, Brookdale Hospital Medical Center, New York, NY, p. A432

DUBROCA, Darryl S., Chief Executive Officer and Managing Director, Spring Mountain Sahara, Las Vegas, NV, p. A395

DUBROW, Melissa
Chief Operating Officer, Waynesboro Hospital, Waynesboro, PA, p. A543
Vice President and Chief Operating Officer, Waynesboro Hospital, Waynesboro, PA, p. A543

DUBRUYNE, Sharon, Director Human Resources, College Hospital Costa Mesa, Costa Mesa, CA, p. A55

DUCEY, Ann, Chief Information Officer, Boys Town National Research Hospital, Omaha, NE, p. A388

DUCHARME, Adele, Chief Executive Officer, Saint Luke'S North Hospital – Barry Road, Kansas City, MO, p. A363

DUCHARME, Maria, R.N., Senior Vice President Patient Care Services and Chief Nursing Officer, Miriam Hospital, Providence, RI, p. A547

DUCHEMIN, MaDena, Assistant Administrator Human Resources, John Randolph Medical Center, Hopewell, VA, p. A661

DUCHENE, Pam, R.N., Vice President Patient Care Services, St. Joseph Hospital, Nashua, NH, p. A401

DUCHESNEAU, Angy, Senior Director Human Resources, Lakeview Hospital, Stillwater, MN, p. A341

DUCK, Sandra, Administrator, Central Louisiana State Hospital, Pineville, LA, p. A277

DUCK, Sigsbee, M.D., President, Medical Staff, Memorial Hospital Of Sweetwater County, Rock Springs, WY, p. A712

DUCKER, Thomas, M.D., Chief of Staff, Peterson Regional Medical Center, Kerrville, TX, p. A618

DUCKERT, Jon, Chief Executive Officer, Baylor Scott & White Medical Center – Sunnyvale, Sunnyvale, TX, p. A639

DUCKWORTH, Bob, Director Information Systems, Medical West, Bessemer, AL, p. A14

DUDLEY, Edward L, Executive Vice President and Chief Financial Officer, Catholic Medical Center, Manchester, NH, p. A401

DUDLEY, Heather, Director Administrative Services, Brookhaven Hospital, Tulsa, OK, p. A508

DUDLEY, W. Steve, CPA, Chief Financial Officer, Ed Fraser Memorial Hospital And Baker Community Health Center, Macclenny, FL, p. A128

DUET, Kendrick, Chief Operating Officer, Leonard J. Chabert Medical Center, Houma, LA, p. A268

DUFF, James, M.D., Chief Medical Officer, Cox Medical Center Branson, Branson, MO, p. A357

DUFF, Jim, Chief Financial Officer, Colorado Mental Health Institute At Pueblo, Pueblo, CO, p. A104

DUFF, Mary Claire, CPA, Chief Financial Officer, Ridgeview Psychiatric Hospital And Center, Oak Ridge, TN, p. A578

DUFFEE, Patrick, Director Medical Information Systems, Delta Medical Center, Memphis, TN, p. A574

DUFFEY, DNP, RN, NEA–BC, Pamela, Chief Executive Officer, Texas Health Specialty Hospital, Fort Worth, TX, p. A606

DUFFEY, DNP, RN, NEA–BC, Pamela, MSN, R.N., Chief Nursing Officer, Texas Health Specialty Hospital, Fort Worth, TX, p. A606

DUFFIN, Kelly L, Operations Officer, Intermountain Medical Center, Murray, UT, p. A649

DUFFORD, Shawn, M.D., Vice President Medical Affairs and Chief Medical Officer, Saint Joseph Hospital, Denver, CO, p. A99

DUFFY, Beth, Chief Operating Officer, Einstein Medical Center Montgomery, East Norriton, PA, p. A524

DUFFY, Daniel, D.O., Chief Medical Director, Healthsource Saginaw, Inc., Saginaw, MI, p. A321

DUFFY, Kenneth, M.D., Medical Director, Seiling Regional Medical Center, Seiling, OK, p. A507

DUFFY, Marie Theresa
Chief Hospital Executive, Carepoint Health Christ Hospital, Jersey City, NJ, p. A407
Chief Operating Officer, Carepoint Health Christ Hospital, Jersey City, NJ, p. A407

DUFFY, Pamela, MSN, R.N.
Vice President Operations and Chief Nursing Executive, Northwestern Medicine Valley West Hospital, Sandwich, IL, p. A195
Vice President Operations and Chief Nursing Officer, Northwestern Medicine Kishwaukee Hospital, Dekalb, IL, p. A181

DUFFY, Timothy W, General Director, Albany Medical Center, Albany, NY, p. A422

DUFFY, William, Interim Chief Nursing Officer, Norwegian American Hospital, Chicago, IL, p. A179

DUFRESNE, Joshua, Chief of Practice Operations, Springfield Hospital, Springfield, VT, p. A655

DUFT, Ryan, R.N., Chief Nursing Officer, Fredonia Regional Hospital, Fredonia, KS, p. A235

DUGAN, Elizabeth, Ph.D., R.N., MSN, Chief Nursing Officer, Inova Loudoun Hospital, Leesburg, VA, p. A661

DUGAN, Gary, M.D., Vice President Medical Affairs, Penn Highlands Dubois, Dubois, PA, p. A524

DUGAS, Gina, Chief Financial Officer, Woman'S Hospital, Baton Rouge, LA, p. A264

DUGAS, Sheri, Director Health Information Management, Oakdale Community Hospital, Oakdale, LA, p. A276

DUGGAL, Harpreet, M.D., Medical Director, Department of Health and Human Services, Humboldt County Mental Health, Eureka, CA, p. A57

DUGGAN, James E, Director Human Resources, Western Massachusetts Hospital, Westfield, MA, p. A305

DUGGAN, Margaret M., M.D., Chief Medical Officer, Brigham And Women'S Faulkner Hospital, Boston, MA, p. A295

DUGGAN, Tonya, Director Human Resources, Northern Louisiana Medical Center, Ruston, LA, p. A277

DUGGAR, Susan, MSN, Vice President Nursing, Spartanburg Medical Center – Church Street Campus, Spartanburg, SC, p. A557

DUGGER, Curtis R., Chief Financial Officer, Memorial Hospital Of Converse County, Douglas, WY, p. A711

DUGGER, Sandy, Chief Human Resources Officer, Platte County Memorial Hospital, Wheatland, WY, p. A713

DUHAIME, Robert A, R.N., Senior Vice President Clinical Operations and Chief Nursing Officer, Catholic Medical Center, Manchester, NH, p. A401

DUHANEY–WEST, Aphreikah, Chief Executive Officer, Clark Regional Medical Center, Winchester, KY, p. A261

DUHE, Louis, Senior Director Information Technology, George Washington University Hospital, Washington, DC, p. A115

DUHE, Louis H., Executor Director, Information Services, Piedmont Athens Regional Medical Center, Athens, GA, p. A145

DUHON, Thomas, Director Human Resources, Heart Hospital Of Lafayette, Lafayette, LA, p. A270

DUKE, Ezekiel, M.D., Chief of Staff, Knox County Hospital, Knox City, TX, p. A618

DUKE, Kelly, Chief Operating Officer, Kit Carson County Health Service District, Burlington, CO, p. A97

DUKE, Lee M, M.D., Senior Vice President and Chief Physician Executive, Penn Medicine Lancaster General Hospital, Lancaster, PA, p. A529

DUKES, Brenda, Director Human Resources, Sonoma Developmental Center, Eldridge, CA, p. A57

DUKOFF, Ruth, M.D., Medical Director, North Star Behavioral Health System, Anchorage, AK, p. A25

DULANEY, Paul, M.D., Chief of Staff, Troy Regional Medical Center, Troy, AL, p. A23

DULIN, Misty, CAH, Director, Mercyone Primghar Medical Center, Primghar, IA, p. A228

DULING, Ruth, Chief Executive Officer, Girard Medical Center, Girard, KS, p. A235

DULL, David, M.D., Chief Medical Officer, Penrose–St. Francis Health Services, Colorado Springs, CO, p. A98

DULL, Kevin B
Senior Vice President Human Potential, Multicare Auburn Medical Center, Auburn, WA, p. A670
Senior Vice President Human Potential, Multicare Good Samaritan Hospital, Puyallup, WA, p. A677
Senior Vice President Human Potential, Multicare Mary Bridge Children'S Hospital And Health Center, Tacoma, WA, p. A680
Senior Vice President Human Potential, Multicare Tacoma General Hospital, Tacoma, WA, p. A680

DULNY, David
Chief Financial Officer, Providence Medical Center, Kansas City, KS, p. A238
Chief Financial Officer, Saint John Hospital, Leavenworth, KS, p. A239

DUMAIS, Mark, M.D., Chief Medical Officer, Northridge Hospital Medical Center, Los Angeles, CA, p. A68

DUMAL, Jennifer, R.N., Chief Operating Officer of Clinical and Chief Nursing Officer, Memorial Hospital At Gulfport, Gulfport, MS, p. A347

DUMKE, Steve, FACHE, Executive Vice President and Chief Operating Officer, Christian Health Care Center, Wyckoff, NJ, p. A415

DUMONSEAU, Kent
Vice President Finance and Information Services, Hayward Area Memorial Hospital And Water'S Edge, Hayward, WI, p. A697
Vice President Finance and Information Services, Memorial Medical Center Of Ashland, Ashland, WI, p. A691

DUMONT, Amy, MSN, R.N., FACHE, Chief Nursing Officer, Concord Hospital, Concord, NH, p. A399

DUMONT, Frank, Assistant Vice President Human Resources and Corporate Compliance, Eastern Long Island Hospital, Greenport, NY, p. A428

DUNAVAN, Chad, R.N., Vice President, Chief Nursing Officer, Medical Center Health System, Odessa, TX, p. A627

DUNBAR, Trey, President, Our Lady Of The Lake Regional Medical Center, Baton Rouge, LA, p. A264
DUNCAN, Allison, Chief Financial Officer, Arrowhead Behavioral Health Hospital, Maumee, OH, p. A487
DUNCAN, Barbara, Chief Financial Officer, Habersham Medical Center, Demorest, GA, p. A152
DUNCAN, Charles, M.D., Medical Director, Kindred Hospital–San Antonio, San Antonio, TX, p. A634
DUNCAN, Cindy
Director Human Resources, Roosevelt General Hospital, Portales, NM, p. A419
Manager Human Resources, Plains Regional Medical Center, Clovis, NM, p. A417
DUNCAN, Cynthia, Chief Executive Officer, Roger Mills Memorial Hospital, Cheyenne, OK, p. A497
DUNCAN, Erika, Vice President Human Resources, St. Joseph'S Hospital Health Center, Syracuse, NY, p. A445
DUNCAN, Jeremy, Director Information Systems, Lawrence Medical Center, Moulton, AL, p. A21
DUNCAN, Jimmy, Senior Vice President and Chief People Officer, Arkansas Children'S Hospital, Little Rock, AR, p. A44
DUNCAN, Joani, Chief Human Resource Officer, Ann & Robert H. Lurie Children'S Hospital Of Chicago, Chicago, IL, p. A176
DUNCAN, Leeann, Director Patient Care Services, Harbor Oaks Hospital, New Baltimore, MI, p. A318
DUNCAN, Linda, Director Human Resources, Lee'S Summit Medical Center, Lee'S Summit, MO, p. A364
DUNCAN, Lyman, Chief Financial Officer, San Juan Health Service District, Monticello, UT, p. A649
DUNCAN, Michael J., President and Chief Executive Officer, Penn Medicine Chester County Hospital, West Chester, PA, p. A544
DUNCAN, Nathan, Chief Executive Officer, Lakeland Behavioral Health System, Springfield, MO, p. A371
DUNCAN, Thomas M, Executive Vice President and Chief Financial Officer, Miami Valley Hospital, Dayton, OH, p. A481
DUNCAN, Traci A, Vice President, Chief Nursing Officer, Northbay Medical Center, Fairfield, CA, p. A57
DUNFORD, Bill, Manager, Northside Hospital–Cherokee, Canton, GA, p. A149
DUNHAM, Cathy, Vice President Human Resources, Mcpherson Hospital, Mcpherson, KS, p. A240
DUNHAM, Shelly, Chief Executive Officer, Okeene Municipal Hospital, Okeene, OK, p. A503
DUNIO, Gina, Chief Human Resources, James E. Van Zandt Veterans Affairs Medical Center, Altoona, PA, p. A519
DUNKEL, Jason, President and Chief Executive Officer, Adventhealth North Pinellas, Tarpon Springs, FL, p. A142
DUNKER, Karla, Chief Executive Officer, Sedgwick County Health Center, Julesburg, CO, p. A102
DUNKIEL, Barbara, Director Human Resources, Encompass Health Rehabilitation Hospital Of Sunrise, Sunrise, FL, p. A140
DUNKIN, Jackie J., Director Human Resources, Platte Valley Medical Center, Brighton, CO, p. A97
DUNKIN, John, Executive Director, Amita Health Elk Grove Village, Elk Grove Village, IL, p. A182
DUNKLE, David, Vice President Medical Affairs, Johnson Memorial Hospital, Franklin, IN, p. A204
DUNKLEY, Rich, Administrator, Wyoming State Hospital, Evanston, WY, p. A711
DUNLAP, Cyndy, R.N., FACHE, Chief Nursing Officer, Providence Healthcare Network, Waco, TX, p. A644
DUNLAY, Sherry, R.N., MSN
Vice President Chief Nursing Officer, Integris Bass Pavilion, Enid, OK, p. A499
Vice President Patient Care Services and Chief Nursing Officer, Ssm Health St. Mary'S Hospital Centralia, Centralia, IL, p. A175
DUNLEAVY, Christopher, Senior Vice President Finance and Chief Financial Officer, Brigham And Women'S Hospital, Boston, MA, p. A295
DUNLEY, Pamela L., Chief Executive Officer, Elmhurst Hospital, Elmhurst, IL, p. A182
DUNLOP, James H, CPA
Chief Financial Officer, Sisters Of Charity Hospital Of Buffalo, Buffalo, NY, p. A425
Executive Vice President and Chief Financial Officer, Kenmore Mercy Hospital, Kenmore, NY, p. A430
Senior Vice President Finance and Chief Financial Officer, Mercy Hospital, Buffalo, NY, p. A424
DUNMYER, Daniel C., Chief Executive Officer, Ohio Valley Medical Center, Wheeling, WV, p. A690
DUNN, Daniel N, Vice President Operations, Wentworth-Douglass Hospital, Dover, NH, p. A399
DUNN, Denise, R.N., Chief Nursing Officer, Baptist Health Madisonville, Madisonville, KY, p. A257
DUNN, E D, Vice President Human Resources, Virtua Memorial, Mount Holly, NJ, p. A408
DUNN, Hope, Chief Nursing Officer, Encompass Health Rehabilitation Hospital Of East Valley, Mesa, AZ, p. A31
DUNN, Jack, M.D., Chief of Staff, La Paz Regional Hospital, Parker, AZ, p. A32
DUNN, Janice
Chief Financial Officer, Plymouth Medical Center, Plymouth, IN, p. A213
Chief Financial Officer, Southeast Georgia Health System Camden Campus, Saint Marys, GA, p. A159
Vice President and Chief Financial Officer, Southeast Georgia Health System Brunswick Campus, Brunswick, GA, p. A148
DUNN, Jim, Ph.D., Chief Human Resource Officer, Atrium Health'S Carolinas Medical Center, Charlotte, NC, p. A451
DUNN, Leonard, M.D., Chief Medical Officer, Baycare Alliant Hospital, Dunedin, FL, p. A122
DUNN, Marcy
Vice President Information Services and Chief Information Officer, Good Samaritan Hospital Medical Center, West Islip, NY, p. A447
Vice President Information Services and Chief Information Officer, Mercy Medical Center, Rockville Centre, NY, p. A443
Vice President Information Services and Chief Information Officer, St. Francis Hospital, The Heart Center, Roslyn, NY, p. A443
DUNN, Margie, Director Human Resources, Middle Tennessee Mental Health Institute, Nashville, TN, p. A576
DUNN, Nicholas, Director Information Systems, Mena Regional Health System, Mena, AR, p. A46
DUNN, Patrick A, R.N., Chief Nursing Officer, Lea Regional Medical Center, Hobbs, NM, p. A418
DUNN, Richard, M.D., Chief Medical Officer, Riverside Tappahannock Hospital, Tappahannock, VA, p. A668
DUNN, Rosemary, R.N., Chief Nursing Officer, Cape Regional Health System, Cape May Court House, NJ, p. A404
DUNN, Sheila, Assistant Administrator Human Resources, Dale Medical Center, Ozark, AL, p. A22
DUNN, Tandra, Director of Nursing, San Luis Valley Health Conejos County Hospital, La Jara, CO, p. A102
DUNN, Terry, Director Information Technology, Battle Mountain General Hospital, Battle Mountain, NV, p. A393
DUNNAM, Lorie, Chief Executive Officer, Oceans Behavioral Health Center Permian Basin, Midland, TX, p. A624
DUNNING, David K., Medical Center Director and Chief Executive Officer, Memphis Veterans Affairs Medical Center, Memphis, TN, p. A575
DUNPHY ALEXANDER, Shannon, Director, Mercyhealth Hospital And Medical Center – Harvard, Harvard, IL, p. A184
DUNWOODY, Robert, Chief Financial Officer, Lawnwood Regional Medical Center & Heart Institute, Fort Pierce, FL, p. A123
DUPPER, Harold, Chief Financial Officer, Platte Valley Medical Center, Brighton, CO, p. A97
DUPRE, Charlotte W., Chief Executive Officer, Southern Regional Medical Center, Riverdale, GA, p. A159
DUPREE, Lucy G, Director Human Resources, Columbia Memorial Hospital, Astoria, OR, p. A511
DUPREY, Irma, Administrator Medical Records, Hospital Universitario Dr. Ramon Ruiz Arnau, Bayamon, PR, p. A715
DUPUIS, Pamela M, R.N., Senior Vice President Patient Care Services, Montefiore New Rochelle, New Rochelle, NY, p. A432
DUQUETTE, Connie, Director Human Resources, Sharp Memorial Hospital, San Diego, CA, p. A84
DUQUETTE, William M., Chief Executive Officer, Baptist Health South Florida, South Miami Hospital, Miami, FL, p. A130
DURAN, Jody, Manager Information Systems, Livingston Healthcare, Livingston, MT, p. A378
DURAND, Crista F., President, Newport Hospital, Newport, RI, p. A547
DURAND, Mark, Assistant Administrator Operations, Christus Southeast Texas Jasper Memorial, Jasper, TX, p. A616
DURANT, Charles E., Jr, Chief Executive Officer, Calhoun-Liberty Hospital, Blountstown, FL, p. A118
DURBAK, Ivan, Chief Information Officer, Brookdale Hospital Medical Center, New York, NY, p. A432
DURBIN, Melissa Ann, R.N., MSN, Chief Nursing Officer, Boca Raton Regional Hospital, Boca Raton, FL, p. A118
DURDEN, Rhonda, Chief Financial Officer, Emanuel Medical Center, Swainsboro, GA, p. A161
DURFLINGER, Kathy
Vice President and Chief Nursing Officer, Avita Ontario Hospital, Ontario, OH, p. A489
Vice President and Chief Nursing Officer, Galion Hospital, Galion, OH, p. A483
DURGIN, Manal, Network Medical Director, Devereux Hospital And Children'S Center Of Florida, Melbourne, FL, p. A129
DURHAM, Karla, Director of Information Systems, Baptist Health Madisonville, Madisonville, KY, p. A257
DURHAM, Linda, Director Human Resources, Henderson County Community Hospital, Lexington, TN, p. A573
DURHAM, Thomas, Chief Nursing Officer, Ferry County Memorial Hospital, Republic, WA, p. A677
DURIS, Deb, Director of Nursing, Northwest Ohio Psychiatric Hospital, Toledo, OH, p. A492
DURNEY, Gerry, Chief Operating Officer, Good Samaritan Regional Medical Center, Suffern, NY, p. A445
DURNIAT–SUSHRSTEDT, Karen, Nurse Executive, Appalachian Behavioral Healthcare, Athens, OH, p. A472
DURNIOK, Brian
Interim President and Chief Executive Officer, Upmc Chautauqua Wca, Jamestown, NY, p. A429
President, Upmc Northwest, Seneca, PA, p. A541
Vice President Operations, Upmc Northwest, Seneca, PA, p. A541
DURON, Kety, Vice President Human Resources, Stanford Health Care, Palo Alto, CA, p. A77
DUROVICH, Christopher J., President and Chief Executive Officer, Children'S Medical Center Dallas, Dallas, TX, p. A596
DURR, Durinda, Vice President and Chief Nursing Officer, Rome Memorial Hospital, Rome, NY, p. A443
DURRENCE, Liz, Chief Operating Officer, Brandon Regional Hospital, Brandon, FL, p. A119
DURRETT, Johnathan, Chief Executive Officer, Fredonia Regional Hospital, Fredonia, KS, p. A235
DURST, Geoff, Vice President Finance, Avera St. Luke'S Hospital, Aberdeen, SD, p. A559
DURST, Sue, R.N., MS, Vice President Plant Operations, Mclaren Macomb, Mount Clemens, MI, p. A318
DURSTELER, Courtney, Chief Human Resources Officer, Franklin County Medical Center, Preston, ID, p. A171
DURYEE, Edward E, Director Information Systems, Saint Francis Medical Center, Cape Girardeau, MO, p. A357
DUSANG, Nina, Vice President Finance and Chief Financial Officer, Dch Regional Medical Center, Tuscaloosa, AL, p. A24
DUSENBERY, Jack, President and Chief Executive Officer, Mercyone Waterloo Medical Center, Waterloo, IA, p. A231
DUTCHER, Phillip C, Chief Operating Officer, Nch Baker Hospital, Naples, FL, p. A132
DUTHE, Robert J, Director Information Systems and Chief Information Officer, Cortland Regional Medical Center, Cortland, NY, p. A426
DUTIA, Nimal, M.D., Chief Medical Staff, Holzer Medical Center – Jackson, Jackson, OH, p. A484
DUTMERS, David, Manager, Information Services, Spectrum Health United Hospital, Greenville, MI, p. A313
DUTTON, Angela, Chief Human Resources Management Service, Robley Rex Veterans Affairs Medical Center, Louisville, KY, p. A256
DUTTON, Rebecca, Director Human Resources, Larue D. Carter Memorial Hospital, Indianapolis, IN, p. A207
DUTTON, Teresa, R.N., Chief Nursing Officer, Baylor Scott & White Surgical Hospital–Sherman, Sherman, TX, p. A636
DUVAL, Rob, Chief Human Resources Officer, Emma Pendleton Bradley Hospital, East Providence, RI, p. A547
DUVALL, Richard, Chief Executive Officer, Carthage Area Hospital, Carthage, NY, p. A425
DUVVURI, Vikas, M.D., Medical Director, Fremont Hospital, Fremont, CA, p. A58
DWIGHT, John, Regional Vice President and Chief Information Officer, Skagit Regional Health, Mount Vernon, WA, p. A675
DWORAK, Paige, Chief Executive Officer, East Orange General Hospital, East Orange, NJ, p. A405
DWORKIN, Darren, Senior Vice President Enterprise Information Systems and Chief Information Officer, Cedars–Sinai Medical Center, Los Angeles, CA, p. A66
DWORKIN, Jack H, M.D., Vice President Medical Affairs and Chief Medical Officer, Centrastate Healthcare System, Freehold, NJ, p. A406
DWORKIN, Paul, M.D., Physician–in–Chief, Connecticut Children'S Medical Center, Hartford, CT, p. A108
DWYER, Amy L., R.N., MSN, Chief Nursing Officer, Hshs Sacred Heart Hospital, Eau Claire, WI, p. A694
DWYER, Cathy, Senior Administrator Information Systems, Burke Rehabilitation Hospital, White Plains, NY, p. A447
DWYER, James P, D.O.
Executive Vice President and Chief Medical Officer, Virtua Memorial, Mount Holly, NJ, p. A408
Executive Vice President and Chief Medical Officer, Virtua Voorhees, Voorhees, NJ, p. A414
DWYER, Mark, Chief Executive Officer, The Rehabilitation Institute Of St. Louis, Saint Louis, MO, p. A371

DWYER, Susan, Vice President Finance, Aurora Psychiatric Hospital, Wauwatosa, WI, p. A708

DWYER, William, Vice President and Chief Human Resources Officer, Children'S Specialized Hospital, New Brunswick, NJ, p. A409

DYBDAL, Landon, Chief Executive Officer, Garfield County Health Center, Jordan, MT, p. A378

DYCHE, Ginny, Director Community Relations, Aspen Valley Hospital, Aspen, CO, p. A96

DYCUS, Steve, Director Marketing and Public Relations, Williamson Medical Center, Franklin, TN, p. A570

DYE, Chris, Director Information Systems, Arh Our Lady Of The Way, Martin, KY, p. A257

DYE, Dana, Vice President, Administrator and Chief Executive Officer, Baptist Memorial Hospital – Memphis, Memphis, TN, p. A574

DYE, David Bryan, M.D., Chief Medical Officer, Purcell Municipal Hospital, Purcell, OK, p. A506

DYE, Emily, Vice President Human Resources, Tristar Summit Medical Center, Hermitage, TN, p. A570

DYE, Leslie, Chief Executive Officer, Phs Santa Fe Indian Hospital, Santa Fe, NM, p. A420

DYER, Ed, Chief Executive Officer, Stroud Regional Medical Center, Stroud, OK, p. A508

DYER, Edward L, Chief Executive Officer, Cornerstone Hospital Of Austin, Austin, TX, p. A585

DYER, Shelly, Interim Chief Executive Officer, Prague Community Hospital, Prague, OK, p. A506

DYKEHOUSE, Rod, Chief Information Officer, Penn State Milton S. Hershey Medical Center, Hershey, PA, p. A527

DYKEHOUSE, Rodney, Senior Vice President Information Services, Waukesha Memorial Hospital, Waukesha, WI, p. A707

DYKES, Bradford W., President and Chief Executive Officer, Indiana University Health Bedford Hospital, Bedford, IN, p. A199

DYKSTERHOUSE, Trevor J., President, Forest Health Medical Center, Ypsilanti, MI, p. A325

DYKSTRA, Lisa, Senior Vice President and Chief Information Officer, Ann & Robert H. Lurie Children'S Hospital Of Chicago, Chicago, IL, p. A176

DYLE, Amanda
    Chief Financial Officer, Princeton Baptist Medical Center, Birmingham, AL, p. A15
    Chief Financial Officer, Walker Baptist Medical Center, Jasper, AL, p. A20

DYRKACZ, Anna, Chief Financial Officer, Vibra Hospital Of Western Massachusetts, Springfield, MA, p. A304

DYSART–CREDEUR, Amy, Administrator, Oceans Behavioral Hospital Of Broussard, Broussard, LA, p. A265

DZIEDZICKI, Ron, R.N., Chief Operating Officer, University Hospitals Cleveland Medical Center, Cleveland, OH, p. A478

DZIESINSKI, Ray R, Vice President and Chief Financial Officer, Sheppard Pratt Health System, Baltimore, MD, p. A288

E

EADS, Barry, Chief Nursing Officer, Encompass Health Rehabilitation Hospital Of Gadsden, Gadsden, AL, p. A18

EADS, Ted, Interim Chief Nursing Officer, St. Vincent Carmel Hospital, Carmel, IN, p. A201

EAGAR, Troy, Director Human Resources, Mountain Valley Regional Rehabilitation Hospital, Prescott Valley, AZ, p. A35

EAGEN, Mary K, R.N., MS, Executive Vice President, Chief Nursing Officer, Parkland Health & Hospital System, Dallas, TX, p. A597

EAKER, Blake, Interim Director Information Services, Uvalde Memorial Hospital, Uvalde, TX, p. A643

EAKS, C. Alan., Chief Executive Officer and Managing Director, Spring Mountain Treatment Center, Las Vegas, NV, p. A396

EAMRANOND, Pracha, M.D., Senior Vice President Population Health and Medical Affairs, Lawrence General Hospital, Lawrence, MA, p. A299

EARDLEY, Robert K, Senior Vice President and Chief Information Officer, Houston Methodist Hospital, Houston, TX, p. A612

EARL, Mindy, Health Information Manager, Power County Hospital District, American Falls, ID, p. A167

EARLE, Audra, Chief Executive Officer, Watsonville Community Hospital, Watsonville, CA, p. A94

EARLEY, Robert, President and Chief Executive Officer, Jps Health Network, Fort Worth, TX, p. A605

EARLEY, Tom, Chief Financial Officer, Alliancehealth Woodward, Woodward, OK, p. A510

EARLY, Elfie, Manager Data Services, Georgia Regional Hospital At Atlanta, Decatur, GA, p. A152

EARLY, Gerald L, M.D., Chief Medical Officer, Pullman Regional Hospital, Pullman, WA, p. A676

EARLY, Kathy, Chief Executive Officer and Chief Nursing Officer, Usmd Hospital At Fort Worth, Fort Worth, TX, p. A606

EARNSHAW, Dallas, Superintendent, Utah State Hospital, Provo, UT, p. A650

EASLEY, Evan, M.D., Chief Medical Officer, Carson Valley Medical Center, Gardnerville, NV, p. A394

EASLEY, Mike, Vice President and Chief Operating Officer, Sabine County Hospital, Hemphill, TX, p. A609

EASSON, Jacob, Chief Financial Officer, Blackwell Regional Hospital, Blackwell, OK, p. A497

EAST, Becky, CPA, Senior Vice President, Chief Financial Officer, Bronson Lakeview Hospital, Paw Paw, MI, p. A319

EASTBURG, Mark C., President and Chief Executive Officer, Pine Rest Christian Mental Health Services, Grand Rapids, MI, p. A313

EASTER, Susan, Chief Nursing Officer, Palacios Community Medical Center, Palacios, TX, p. A627

EASTERLING, Jamie, Executive Director, Operations, Good Samaritan Hospital, Cincinnati, OH, p. A476

EASTERWOOD, Diane J, Human Resources Business Partner, Kaiser Permanente San Francisco Medical Center, San Francisco, CA, p. A85

EASTHOPE, Kerry, Area Finance Officer, Kaiser Permanente Antioch Medical Center, Antioch, CA, p. A50

EASTMAN, David, Interim Chief Executive Officer, Adventist Health Medical Center – Tehachapi Valley, Tehachapi, CA, p. A91

EASTON, Laura J, President and Chief Executive Officer, Caldwell Unc Health Care, Lenoir, NC, p. A457

EASTON, Laura J., President and Chief Executive Officer, Caldwell Unc Health Care, Lenoir, NC, p. A457

EATHERLY, Theresa, Chief Financial Officer, United Memorial Medical Care, Houston, TX, p. A614

EATON, Philip, Interim Chief Executive Officer, Mountain West Medical Center, Tooele, UT, p. A653

EAVENSON, Steve, Vice President Finance, Mercy Health Saint Mary'S, Grand Rapids, MI, p. A313

EAVES, Dan, Chief Executive Officer, Marshall Browning Hospital, Du Quoin, IL, p. A181

EBANGIT, Ruth, M.D., Chief of Staff and Medical Officer, Throckmorton County Memorial Hospital, Throckmorton, TX, p. A641

EBBETT, Patricia, Chief Human Resources Officer, Catawba Hospital, Catawba, VA, p. A657

EBELING, April, Chief Executive Officer, Amg Specialty Hospital–Zachary, Zachary, LA, p. A280

EBERHARDT, Lisa, Chief Nursing Officer, Clark Fork Valley Hospital, Plains, MT, p. A379

EBERLE, Michele
    Vice Chair, Mayo Clinic Health System – Chippewa Valley In Bloomer, Bloomer, WI, p. A692
    Vice Chair, Mayo Clinic Health System – Northland In Barron, Barron, WI, p. A692

EBERSOLE, Nathan, Controller, Calhoun–Liberty Hospital, Blountstown, FL, p. A118

EBERT, Larry W., Jr, Chief Executive Officer, Piedmont Walton Hospital, Monroe, GA, p. A157

EBERT, Michael, M.D., Chief of Staff, Veterans Affairs Connecticut Healthcare System, West Haven, CT, p. A112

EBERT–LOOMIS, Cynthia, R.N., Chief Nursing Officer, Summit Healthcare Regional Medical Center, Show Low, AZ, p. A36

EBERTH, Denise A, Chief Human Resources Officer, Allegan General Hospital, Allegan, MI, p. A306

EBNER, Joseph, M.D., Chief Medical Officer, Speare Memorial Hospital, Plymouth, NH, p. A402

EBRIGHT, Brian, Chief Financial Officer, Salt Lake Regional Medical Center, Salt Lake City, UT, p. A652

ECKELS, Dan, Chief Financial Officer, Washington Regional Medical Center, Fayetteville, AR, p. A42

ECKENFELS, Susan, Chief Financial Officer, Ste. Genevieve County Memorial Hospital, Ste Genevieve, MO, p. A372

ECKERT, Mark, Vice President Finance, Ochsner Medical Center – Kenner, Kenner, LA, p. A270

ECKERT, Mary L., President and Chief Executive Officer, Lecom Health Millcreek Community Hospital, Erie, PA, p. A525

ECKERT, Susan E., R.N., MSN, Senior Vice President and Chief Nursing Officer, Medstar Washington Hospital Center, Washington, DC, p. A116

ECKFORD, Marjorie, Chief Nursing Officer, Menlo Park Surgical Hospital, Menlo Park, CA, p. A71

ECKLAND, Christopher, M.D., Chief Medical Officer, Miami County Medical Center, Paola, KS, p. A243

ECKSTEIN, Becca, Executive Director, Veritas Collaborative, Durham, NC, p. A453

ECKSTEIN, Melissa, Chief Executive Officer, Palo Verde Behavioral Health, Tucson, AZ, p. A38

ECKSTEIN, William, Chief Executive Officer and Chief Financial Officer, Columbus Specialty Hospital, Columbus, GA, p. A150

EDALATI, David, M.D., Medical Director, Meadowbrook Rehabilitation Hospital, Gardner, KS, p. A235

EDDEY, Gary E, M.D., Medical Director, Matheny Medical And Educational Center, Peapack, NJ, p. A410

EDDINGTON, Tonya, Coordinator Human Resources, Select Specialty Hospital–Springfield, Springfield, MO, p. A372

EDDLEMAN, Patricia, Fiscal Officer, Heartland Behavioral Healthcare, Massillon, OH, p. A487

EDDY, Lee Anne, Senior Vice President and Chief Nursing Officer, Arkansas Children'S Hospital, Little Rock, AR, p. A44

EDELMAN, Marc D, Vice President Operations, Bristol Hospital, Bristol, CT, p. A107

EDEN, Tina M, Director of Nursing, Virginia Gay Hospital, Vinton, IA, p. A230

EDENFIELD, Janet, Director Financial Services, Georgia Regional Hospital At Savannah, Savannah, GA, p. A160

EDGAR, Joseph H, Senior Vice President Operations, Wellspan Gettysburg Hospital, Gettysburg, PA, p. A526

EDGAR, Nancy, Vice President Human Resources, Methodist Hospital, San Antonio, TX, p. A634

EDGAR, Steven, President and Chief Executive Officer, Medical City Denton, Denton, TX, p. A599

EDIN, Scott D, Vice President, Finance and Chief Financial Officer, Northfield Hospital And Clinics, Northfield, MN, p. A337

EDINGTON, Brent, Director Information Services, Pomerene Hospital, Millersburg, OH, p. A488

EDLER, Susie, R.N., Chief Nursing Officer, Dallas Behavioral Healthcare Hospital, Desoto, TX, p. A600

EDMINSTER, Sue
    Vice President Human Resources, Ripon Medical Center, Ripon, WI, p. A705
    Vice President Human Resources, St. Agnes Hospital, Fond Du Lac, WI, p. A695
    Vice President Human Resources, Waupun Memorial Hospital, Waupun, WI, p. A707

EDMISTEN, Cathy, Chief Operating Officer, Memorial Hospital Of Tampa, Tampa, FL, p. A141

EDMONDS, Kelly, Chief Financial Officer, Western Maryland Hospital Center, Hagerstown, MD, p. A291

EDMONDSON, Bobby, Controller, Regional Rehabilitation Hospital, Phenix City, AL, p. A22

EDMONDSON, Cory, President and Chief Executive Officer, Peterson Regional Medical Center, Kerrville, TX, p. A618

EDMONDSON, James H., Chief Executive Officer, Southern Tennessee Regional Health System–Pulaski, Pulaski, TN, p. A578

EDMUNDS, Liza, Director Human Resources, Tennova Healthcare–Clarksville, Clarksville, TN, p. A568

EDNEY, Daniel, M.D., Chief of Staff, Promise Hospital Of Vicksburg, Vicksburg, MS, p. A355

EDWARD, Adolphe, Chief Executive Officer, El Centro Regional Medical Center, El Centro, CA, p. A57

EDWARDS, Aaron, Chief Executive Officer, Ferry County Memorial Hospital, Republic, WA, p. A677

EDWARDS, Angela Imelda, R.N., Chief Nurse Executive, Brookdale Hospital Medical Center, New York, NY, p. A432

EDWARDS, Annette, Chief Financial Officer, Odessa Memorial Healthcare Center, Odessa, WA, p. A675

EDWARDS, Becky, Manager Human Resources, Irwin County Hospital, Ocilla, GA, p. A158

EDWARDS, Bruce
    Vice President Human Resources, Heritage Valley Health System, Beaver, PA, p. A520
    Vice President Human Resources, Sewickley Valley Hospital, (A Division Of Valley Medical Facilities), Sewickley, PA, p. A541

EDWARDS, Chris, M.D.
    Chief Medical Officer, Piedmont Columbus Regional Midtown, Columbus, GA, p. A150
    Chief Medical Officer, Piedmont Columbus Regional Northside, Columbus, GA, p. A150

EDWARDS, Dana, Chief Financial Officer, Sea Pines Rehabilitation Hospital, Melbourne, FL, p. A129

EDWARDS, Dennis, M.D., Vice President Medical Affairs, Chi Health Good Samaritan, Kearney, NE, p. A386

EDWARDS, Gregg
    Chief People Officer, Asante Rogue Regional Medical Center, Medford, OR, p. A515
    Chief People Officer, Asante Three Rivers Medical Center, Grants Pass, OR, p. A513
    Vice President Human Resources, Asante Ashland Community Hospital, Ashland, OR, p. A511

EDWARDS, Jeff, Manager Information Services, Mendocino Coast District Hospital, Fort Bragg, CA, p. A58

EDWARDS, Jonita, Director Human Resources, Dmc – Children'S Hospital Of Michigan, Detroit, MI, p. A309

EDWARDS, Kathleen, Manager Information Systems Operation, Encompass Health Rehabilitation Hospital Of Altoona, Altoona, PA, p. A519

EDWARDS, Marti, MSN, R.N., Chief Nursing Officer, Rml Specialty Hospital, Hinsdale, IL, p. A186

EDWARDS, Matt, Vice President Nursing Services and Chief Nursing Officer, Anderson Regional Health System, Meridian, MS, p. A351

EDWARDS, Michelle, Executive Vice President Information Technology, Prisma Health Baptist Hospital, Columbia, SC, p. A551

EDWARDS, Nicki E, Ph.D., R.N., Interim Chief Nursing Officer, Sierra Vista Regional Medical Center, San Luis Obispo, CA, p. A87

EDWARDS, Rebecca
Chief Human Resources Officer, Penn Highlands Brookville, Brookville, PA, p. A521
Director Human Resources, Martin General Hospital, Williamston, NC, p. A463

EDWARDS, Rick, Vice President and Chief Financial Officer, Hancock Regional Hospital, Greenfield, IN, p. A205

EDWARDS, Samuel, M.D., Chief of Staff, Adventhealth Deland, Deland, FL, p. A121

EDWARDS, Steven D., President and Chief Executive Officer, Cox Medical Centers, Springfield, MO, p. A371

EDWARDS, Susan, Vice President Human Resources, Novant Health Uva Health System Culpeper Medical Center, Culpeper, VA, p. A658

EDWARDS, Susan A.
Chief Executive Officer, Waukesha Memorial Hospital, Waukesha, WI, p. A707
President and Chief Executive Officer, Oconomowoc Memorial Hospital, Oconomowoc, WI, p. A702

EDWARDS, Terry, Controller, Atrium Health Kings Mountain, Kings Mountain, NC, p. A457

EDWARDS, Todd, Director Information Management Systems, Chi St. Luke'S Health Brazosport, Lake Jackson, TX, p. A619

EDWARDS, William, Information Technology Generalist, Wernersville State Hospital, Wernersville, PA, p. A544

EESLEY, Michael S, Chief Executive Officer, Northwestern Medicine Mchenry, Mchenry, IL, p. A189

EESLEY, Michael S., Chief Executive Officer, Northwestern Medicine Mchenry, Mchenry, IL, p. A189

EGAN, Carol, R.N., MSN, Chief Nursing Officer, Rutland Regional Medical Center, Rutland, VT, p. A655

EGAN, Kim, Executive Director Human Resources, Regions Hospital, Saint Paul, MN, p. A340

EGAN, Timothy, President and Chief Executive Officer, Roseland Community Hospital, Chicago, IL, p. A179

EGBERT, James, Chief of Staff, Vidant Beaufort Hospital, Washington, NC, p. A463

EGBERT, Jeff, Interim Chief Executive Officer, Astria Regional Medical Center, Yakima, WA, p. A682

EGERTON, W Eugene, M.D., Chief Medical Officer, University Of Maryland Medical Center Midtown Campus, Baltimore, MD, p. A287

EGGEN, Caity, Chief Human Resource Officer, Cuyuna Regional Medical Center, Crosby, MN, p. A330

EGGERS, Judy, Manager Human Resources, Alliance Healthcare System, Holly Springs, MS, p. A348

EGGLESTON, Brett, Chief Executive Officer, Callaway District Hospital, Callaway, NE, p. A383

EGGLESTON, Kirk W., Commanding Officer, Winn Army Community Hospital, Hinesville, GA, p. A154

EGGLESTON, Lara
Finance Manager, University Hospitals Conneaut Medical Center, Conneaut, OH, p. A480
Finance Manager, University Hospitals Geneva Medical Center, Geneva, OH, p. A484

EGGLESTON, Ryan, Chief Financial Officer, Desert View Hospital, Pahrump, NV, p. A397

EGYUD, Amber, R.N., Chief Nursing Officer and Chief Operating Officer, Chesapeake Regional Medical Center, Chesapeake, VA, p. A657

EHASZ, James, Chief Financial Officer, Copper Queen Community Hospital, Bisbee, AZ, p. A28

EHLER, Phyllis, Director Human Resources, Avera St. Benedict Health Center, Parkston, SD, p. A562

EHLERS, Jeffrey, Chief Financial Officer, Memorial Health, Marysville, OH, p. A486

EHLINGER, Forrest, System Chief Financial Officer, Benefis Health System, Great Falls, MT, p. A377

EHLKE, Ranae, Administrative Secretary and Coordinator Risk Management and Human Resources, Kenmare Community Hospital, Kenmare, ND, p. A468

EHLY, Ronda S, R.N., Chief Nursing Officer, Mary Lanning Healthcare, Hastings, NE, p. A385

EHN, Jerry, Chief Operating Officer, Northfield Hospital And Clinics, Northfield, MN, p. A337

EHN, Nicole, M.D., Chief of Staff, Van Diest Medical Center, Webster City, IA, p. A231

EHRAT, Michael, Chief Executive Officer, Englewood Community Hospital, Englewood, FL, p. A122

EHRENBERGER, David, M.D., Chief Medical Officer, Avista Adventist Hospital, Louisville, CO, p. A104

EHRICH, Laurie, Chief Communications Officer, Wayne County Hospital, Corydon, IA, p. A220

EHRLICH, Frank, M.D.
Chief Medical Officer, Health Alliance Hospital – Broadway Campus, Kingston, NY, p. A430
Chief Medical Officer, Health Alliance Hospital – Mary'S Avenue Campus, Kingston, NY, p. A430

EHRLICH, Susan P., Chief Executive Officer, Zuckerberg San Francisco General Hospital And Trauma Center, San Francisco, CA, p. A86

EHTISHAM, Saad, R.N., FACHE, Senior Vice President and Chief Operating Officer, Leesburg Regional Medical Center, Leesburg, FL, p. A128

EICHENAUER, Donald T., Chief Executive Officer, Wyoming County Community Hospital, Warsaw, NY, p. A446

EICHENBERGER, Daniel J., President and Chief Executive Officer, Baptist Health Floyd, New Albany, IN, p. A212

EICHER, Natasha, President and Chief Executive Officer, Dekalb Health, Auburn, IN, p. A199

EIDAM, JoEllen, Chief Executive Officer, Adams Memorial Hospital, Decatur, IN, p. A202

EIDE, Dean, Vice President, Mayo Clinic Health System – Oakridge In Osseo, Osseo, WI, p. A703

EIDE, Tom, Chief Financial Officer, Prairie St. John'S, Fargo, ND, p. A466

EIG, Blair, M.D., Senior Vice President Medical Affairs, Holy Cross Hospital, Silver Spring, MD, p. A293

EIKE, Gail, Chief Financial Officer, Sanford Jackson Medical Center, Jackson, MN, p. A333

EILBRACHT, Hans, Chief Information Officer, Hamilton Center, Terre Haute, IN, p. A215

EILER, John M, Administrative Director, Barnes–Jewish Hospital, Saint Louis, MO, p. A369

EIMERS, Katy, Human Resources Officer, Syringa Hospital And Clinics, Grangeville, ID, p. A169

EIPE, Joseph, M.D., Chief Medical Officer, Pacifica Hospital Of The Valley, Los Angeles, CA, p. A68

EISCHENS, Shelby, Chief Medical Officer, Brookings Health System, Brookings, SD, p. A559

EISELE, Karla, M.D., Clinical Director, State Hospital North, Orofino, ID, p. A171

EISEMANN, Bradley, Administrator, Beacon Children'S Hospital, Luverne, AL, p. A20

EISEN, Robert A, Vice President Human Resources, Northern California Region, Queen Of The Valley Medical Center, Napa, CA, p. A74

EISENMAN, Edward, Chief Executive Officer, Sunnyview Rehabilitation Hospital, Schenectady, NY, p. A444

EISENMANN, Claudia, Chief Executive Officer, Gibson General Hospital, Princeton, IN, p. A214

EISENTRAGER, Steve, President, Ohio Valley Surgical Hospital, Springfield, OH, p. A491

EISENZOPH, Pete, Director Information Technology, Aurora Medical Center – Bay Area, Marinette, WI, p. A699

EISMAN, Michael, M.D., Medical Director, Schuyler Hospital, Montour Falls, NY, p. A431

EISNER, Nina W., Chief Executive Officer and Managing Director, Ridge Behavioral Health System, Lexington, KY, p. A255

EITUTUS, Jason, Chief Executive Officer, Rock Regional Hospital, Derby, KS, p. A234

EITZEN, Tamara, Chief Nursing Officer, Fairview Regional Medical Center, Fairview, OK, p. A500

EIXENBERGER, Timothy D., Chief Nursing Officer, Southcoast Hospitals Group, Fall River, MA, p. A298

EKENGREN, Francie H, M.D., Chief Medical Officer, Wesley Healthcare Center, Wichita, KS, p. A248

EKEREN, Douglas R., Regional President and Chief Executive Officer, Avera Sacred Heart Hospital, Yankton, SD, p. A565

EKPO, Felix, Manager, Information Systems, Arrowhead Regional Medical Center, Colton, CA, p. A55

EL KHALILI, Nizar, M.D., Medical Director, Sycamore Springs Hospital, Lafayette, IN, p. A210

EL–DALATI, Sam, M.D., Chief Medical Officer, Mercy Regional Medical Center, Lorain, OH, p. A486

EL–MELIGI, Christi J., Chief Executive Officer, Sage Memorial Hospital, Ganado, AZ, p. A29

EL–SOLH, Ali, M.D., Interim Chief of Staff, Veterans Affairs Western New York Healthcare System–Buffalo Division, Buffalo, NY, p. A425

ELAM, Lora, R.N., Chief Nursing Officer, Wayne County Hospital, Monticello, KY, p. A258

ELAM, Moses D, M.D., Physician–in–Chief, Kaiser Permanente Manteca Medical Center, Manteca, CA, p. A71

ELARBEE, Vernon, Director of Human Resources, Adventhealth North Pinellas, Tarpon Springs, FL, p. A142

ELBERT, Darlene M, R.N., MS, Assistant Administrator and Chief Nursing Officer, Kossuth Regional Health Center, Algona, IA, p. A217

ELBERT, Darlene M., Chief Executive Officer and Chief Nursing Officer, Kossuth Regional Health Center, Algona, IA, p. A217

ELDER, Deborah, Director Human Resources, Scenic Mountain Medical Center, Big Spring, TX, p. A588

ELDIDY, Rene, M.D., Chief of Staff, Centracare Health–Long Prairie, Long Prairie, MN, p. A334

ELDRED, Jamie, Controller, Klickitat Valley Health, Goldendale, WA, p. A673

ELDRIDGE, Janet, Director Human Resources and Personnel, Brooks County Hospital, Quitman, GA, p. A158

ELDRIDGE, Jim, Area Financial Officer, Kaiser Permanente Sacramento Medical Center, Sacramento, CA, p. A81

ELDRIDGE, Laurie, Chief Financial Officer, Marshall Medical Center, Placerville, CA, p. A78

ELDRIDGE, Lisa, Human Resources Officer, Thomas H. Boyd Memorial Hospital, Carrollton, IL, p. A175

ELEGANT, Bruce M., President and Chief Executive Officer, Rush Oak Park Hospital, Oak Park, IL, p. A191

ELFERT, Mike, Director Information Services, Lourdes Medical Center Of Burlington County, Willingboro, NJ, p. A415

ELGARICO, David, Chief Executive Officer, Mckenzie–Willamette Medical Center, Springfield, OR, p. A518

ELI, Bev, Chief Nursing Officer, Cox Monett Hospital, Monett, MO, p. A366

ELIAS, Jose, Director Information Technology, Fort Duncan Regional Medical Center, Eagle Pass, TX, p. A600

ELICH, Elizabeth, Chief Human Resources Officer, Piedmont Medical Center, Rock Hill, SC, p. A556

ELIOT, Jason L, Vice President Human Resources, Integris Baptist Medical Center, Oklahoma City, OK, p. A504

ELKINGTON, Bruce, Regional Chief Information Officer, St. Clare Hospital, Lakewood, WA, p. A674

ELKINGTON, Mark, M.D., Chief Medical Officer, Willow Crest Hospital, Miami, OK, p. A502

ELKINS, Carl, Director Information Technology, Adventhealth Rollins Brook, Lampasas, TX, p. A619

ELKINS, James N., Director, Texas Center For Infectious Disease, San Antonio, TX, p. A635

ELKINS, Kelly
President and Chief Executive Officer, Ascension Columbia St. Mary'S Hospital Ozaukee, Mequon, WI, p. A700
President and Chief Executive Officer, Ascension Columbia St. Mary'S Milwaukee Hospital, Milwaukee, WI, p. A700

ELKINS, Wendy, Director Operations, Dundy County Hospital, Benkelman, NE, p. A383

ELLARD, Sam, Chief Executive Officer, Riverland Medical Center, Ferriday, LA, p. A267

ELLEDGE, David, Controller, Select Specialty Hospital–North Knoxville, Powell, TN, p. A578

ELLEN, Jonathan D, M.D., Medical Director, Encompass Health Rehabilitation Hospital Of Memphis, Memphis, TN, p. A574

ELLENBURG, Cynthia, Director Health Information Services, Prisma Health Baptist Easley Hospital, Easley, SC, p. A552

ELLER, Bill, Director Information Technology, El Campo Memorial Hospital, El Campo, TX, p. A601

ELLER, Steven M
Chief Human Resources Officer, Memorial Hospital Of South Bend, South Bend, IN, p. A215
Vice President Human Resources, Elkhart General Hospital, Elkhart, IN, p. A202

ELLER, Troy, Chief Financial Officer, Guthrie County Hospital, Guthrie Center, IA, p. A223

ELLERSON, Thomas, Chief Information Officer, Our Lady Of Lourdes Memorial Hospital, Inc., Binghamton, NY, p. A424

ELLEY, Michael, Chief Information Officer, Owensboro Health Regional Hospital, Owensboro, KY, p. A258

ELLINGTON, Christopher, Executive Vice President and Chief Financial Officer, University Of North Carolina Hospitals, Chapel Hill, NC, p. A451

ELLIOTT, Amy, M.D., Director Medical Affairs, District One Hospital, Faribault, MN, p. A332

ELLIOTT, Barb
Chief Financial Officer, Fairbanks, Indianapolis, IN, p. A206
Interim President and Chief Executive Officer, Fairbanks, Indianapolis, IN, p. A206

ELLIOTT, Charles W., Jr, Chief Executive Officer, Johnston Health, Smithfield, NC, p. A462

ELLIOTT, Jim
Director Human Resources, Bryce Hospital, Tuscaloosa, AL, p. A24
Director Human Resources, Mary S Harper Geriatric Psychiatry Center, Tuscaloosa, AL, p. A24
ELLIOTT, Laura, Director Human Resources, Northeastern Nevada Regional Hospital, Elko, NV, p. A393
ELLIOTT, Lee Ann, R.N., Director of Nursing, Select Rehabilitation Hospital Of Denton, Denton, TX, p. A599
ELLIOTT, Michael
Acting Chief Executive Officer, Centra Lynchburg General Hospital, Lynchburg, VA, p. A662
Controller, Indianhead Medical Center, Shell Lake, WI, p. A705
ELLIOTT, Michael, M.D., Chief Medical Officer and Senior Vice President of Medical Affairs, Avera Mckennan Hospital And University Health Center, Sioux Falls, SD, p. A563
ELLIOTT, Peyton
Chief Executive Officer, Park Plaza Hospital, Houston, TX, p. A613
Chief Executive Officer, Plaza Specialty Hospital, Houston, TX, p. A613
ELLIOTT, R James, Vice President Human Resources, Charlotte Hungerford Hospital, Torrington, CT, p. A111
ELLIOTT, Randi, MSN, Chief Nursing Officer, Baylor Scott & White Medical Center–Frisco, Frisco, TX, p. A606
ELLIOTT, Rhonda M., Director Information Technology and Meaningful Use, Person Memorial Hospital, Roxboro, NC, p. A461
ELLIOTT, Robin, Personnel Officer, Community Memorial Hospital, Sumner, IA, p. A230
ELLIOTT, Shane, Associate Director Administration, Veterans Affairs Loma Linda Healthcare System, Loma Linda, CA, p. A64
ELLIOTT, Thomas, President, Mercy Rehabilitation Hospital Oklahoma City, Oklahoma City, OK, p. A504
ELLIS, Amanda, Chief Financial Officer, Barbourville Arh Hospital, Barbourville, KY, p. A249
ELLIS, Angela, R.N., Chief Nursing Officer, Terre Haute Regional Hospital, Terre Haute, IN, p. A215
ELLIS, Ashley, Chief Executive Officer, Haven Senior Horizons, Phoenix, AZ, p. A33
ELLIS, Bob, Director of Nursing, D. W. Mcmillan Memorial Hospital, Brewton, AL, p. A15
ELLIS, Cynthia, Chief Nursing Officer, Merit Health Rankin, Brandon, MS, p. A345
ELLIS, Deb, Director Human Resources, Stillwater Medical Perry, Perry, OK, p. A506
ELLIS, Kristin, Controller, Munson Healthcare Cadillac Hospital, Cadillac, MI, p. A308
ELLIS, Lisa, Chief Operating Officer, Alliancehealth Midwest, Midwest City, OK, p. A502
ELLIS, Mark, Director Information Technology, Lakeview Hospital, Bountiful, UT, p. A647
ELLIS, Michael, M.D., Chief Medical Officer, The University Of Toledo Medical Center, Toledo, OH, p. A492
ELLIS, Michael J., Chief Executive Officer, Hill Regional Hospital, Hillsboro, TX, p. A610
ELLIS, Michelle, Director Human Resources, Whitman Hospital And Medical Center, Colfax, WA, p. A672
ELLIS, Mike, Chief Financial Officer, Mendocino Coast District Hospital, Fort Bragg, CA, p. A58
ELLIS, Nichole, Chief Medical Officer, Hillsdale Hospital, Hillsdale, MI, p. A314
ELLIS, Paula, Administrator, Saint John Hospital, Leavenworth, KS, p. A239
ELLIS, Richard, Chief Executive Officer, Tennova Healthcare–Harton, Tullahoma, TN, p. A580
ELLIS, Scott, D.O., Chief Medical Officer, Memorial Regional Health, Craig, CO, p. A98
ELLIS, Susan Renee', R.N., MSN, Vice President of Patient Care Service, Highlands Arh Regional Medical Center, Prestonsburg, KY, p. A259
ELLIS, Tammy, FACHE, R.N., Vice President Patient Services, Texas Health Huguley Hospital Fort Worth South, Burleson, TX, p. A590
ELLIS, Thomas J, Vice President Human Resources, Mt. Washington Pediatric Hospital, Baltimore, MD, p. A287
ELLIS, Wendel, D.O., Chief Medical Staff, Greeley County Health Services, Tribune, KS, p. A246
ELLISON, Darcy, R.N., MSN, Senior Vice President, Chief Nursing Officer and Inpatient Flow, St. Vincent Evansville, Evansville, IN, p. A203
ELLISON, Keith, Chief Nursing Officer, Big Bend Regional Medical Center, Alpine, TX, p. A582
ELLISON, Laura, Chief Financial Officer, Bon Secours Baltimore Health System, Baltimore, MD, p. A286
ELLISON, Mike, Information Systems Lead, Summersville Regional Medical Center, Summersville, WV, p. A689
ELLISON, Patricia, Chief Financial Officer, Galesburg Cottage Hospital, Galesburg, IL, p. A183
ELLSWORTH, Anthon, Director Information Technology, Mt. Graham Regional Medical Center, Safford, AZ, p. A35
ELMER, Paula, R.N., MSN, Vice President and Chief Nursing Officer, Monroe Clinic, Monroe, WI, p. A701
ELMORE, Kevin, Chief Information Officer, Covenant Hospital–Levelland, Levelland, TX, p. A620
ELMORE, Nadine, Chief Executive Officer, Dahl Memorial Healthcare Association, Ekalaka, MT, p. A376
ELROD, Emily, R.N.
Chief Nursing Officer, Saint Thomas Dekalb Hospital, Smithville, TN, p. A579
Director of Nursing, Saint Thomas Stones River Hospital, Woodbury, TN, p. A580
ELROD, James K., Chief Executive Officer, Willis–Knighton Medical Center, Shreveport, LA, p. A278
ELROD, Keri, Administrator, Willis–Knighton Medical Center, Shreveport, LA, p. A278
ELS, Veronica, Chief Nursing Officer, Lafayette General Surgical Hospital, Lafayette, LA, p. A271
ELSBERRY, Kevin, Senior Vice President Human Resources, Mercyone Des Moines Medical Center, Des Moines, IA, p. A221
ELSBREE, Heidi, Vice President People and Culture, Javon Bea Hospital–Rockton, Rockford, IL, p. A194
ELSE, Ryan, M.D., Vice President Medical Affairs, Mercy Hospital, Coon Rapids, MN, p. A330
ELSESSER, William, Chief Executive Officer, Kindred Hospital Tomball, Tomball, TX, p. A641
ELSWICK, Beth, Administrative Assistant, Summers County Arh Hospital, Hinton, WV, p. A685
ELWELL, Richard, Senior Vice President and Chief Financial Officer, Elliot Hospital, Manchester, NH, p. A401
ELWELL, Russell, M.D., Medical Director, Westfield Memorial Hospital, Westfield, NY, p. A447
ELY, Thomas L, D.O., Chief Medical Officer, Tennova Healthcare–Clarksville, Clarksville, TN, p. A568
EMAMGHORAISHI, Anna, Human Resources, Inspire Specialty Hospital, Midwest City, OK, p. A502
EMANUEL, Kate, Director Human Resources, Clarke County Hospital, Osceola, IA, p. A228
EMBREE, Steve, Chief Financial Officer, Up Health System–Marquette, Marquette, MI, p. A317
EMBREY, Jeffrey, M.D., Chief Medical Officer, Baylor Scott & White Medical Center–Irving, Irving, TX, p. A616
EMBREY, Richard, M.D., Chief Medical Officer, Augusta Health, Fishersville, VA, p. A659
EMBURY, Stuart, M.D., Chief Medical Officer, Phelps Memorial Health Center, Holdrege, NE, p. A386
EMDUR, Larry, D.O., Chief Medical Officer, Alvarado Hospital Medical Center, San Diego, CA, p. A83
EMEOTT, Sandra, R.N., Chief Nursing Officer, Northwest Medical Center, Margate, FL, p. A129
EMERSON, Leah, Director of Nursing, St. Luke Community Healthcare, Ronan, MT, p. A379
EMERSON, Sherri Leigh, Chief Operating Officer, Texas Health Heart & Vascular Hospital Arlington, Arlington, TX, p. A584
EMERY, Andrew, Chief Executive Officer, Bayfront Health Punta Gorda, Punta Gorda, FL, p. A137
EMERY, John, Chief Executive Officer, Shands Starke Regional Medical Center, Starke, FL, p. A140
EMGE, Joann, Chief Executive Officer, Sparta Community Hospital, Sparta, IL, p. A196
EMIG, Laura, Director Marketing Operations, Encompass Health Rehabilitation Hospital Of York, York, PA, p. A546
EMMINGER, Dianne, Vice President Information Services, Acmh Hospital, Kittanning, PA, p. A528
EMMONS, Jennifer, Chief Operating Officer & Director of Physician Services, Carle Richland Memorial Hospital, Olney, IL, p. A192
EMON, Dee, R.N., Chief Information Officer, Wake Forest Baptist Health–Lexington Medical Center, Lexington, NC, p. A458
EMPEDRAD, Globert, Chief Clinical Officer, Curahealth Tucson, Tucson, AZ, p. A37
EMPEY, Dennis
Chief Financial Officer, Kenmare Community Hospital, Kenmare, ND, p. A468
Chief Financial Officer, Trinity Health, Minot, ND, p. A469
ENCAPERA, Kimberly, M.D., Medical Director, Rehabilitation Hospital Of Southern New Mexico, Las Cruces, NM, p. A419
ENCE, Michael, Computer Specialist, Sanpete Valley Hospital, Mount Pleasant, UT, p. A649
ENCKE, Faye, Director Information Management, Encompass Health Rehabilitation Hospital Of Virginia, Richmond, VA, p. A666
ENDEN, Jay, M.D., Medical Director, Southside Hospital, Bay Shore, NY, p. A423
ENDERS, Robert A., Jr, President, Chatham Hospital, Siler City, NC, p. A462
ENDOM, Beth W, R.N., MSN, Vice President and Chief Nursing Officer, South Central Regional Medical Center, Laurel, MS, p. A350
ENG, Bland, Chief Executive Officer, Brandon Regional Hospital, Brandon, FL, p. A119
ENG, Jeffrey, M.D., Medical Director, Encompass Health Rehabilitation Hospital Of Montgomery, Montgomery, AL, p. A21
ENGBERS, Jon, M.D., President, Hegg Health Center Avera, Rock Valley, IA, p. A229
ENGBRECHT, Chad, Chief Financial Officer, Alvarado Parkway Institute Behavioral Health System, La Mesa, CA, p. A63
ENGEL, David, Chief Executive Officer and Administrator, Southeast Colorado Hospital District, Springfield, CO, p. A105
ENGEL, Dawn M, Chief Nursing Officer, Geary Community Hospital, Junction City, KS, p. A237
ENGELKE, Brian, Chief Financial Officer, Community Hospital Of Staunton, Staunton, IL, p. A197
ENGESSER, Edward, Chief Financial Officer and Chief Information Officer, Barlow Respiratory Hospital, Los Angeles, CA, p. A66
ENGFEHR, Tricia A, Chief Human Resources, Selby General Hospital, Marietta, OH, p. A486
ENGLAND, Dave, Director Human Resources, Lakeland Behavioral Health System, Springfield, MO, p. A371
ENGLAND, Leslie, Chief of Staff, Merit Health Natchez, Natchez, MS, p. A352
ENGLAND, Mary Ann, Chief Nurse Executive, Wilcox Medical Center, Lihue, HI, p. A166
ENGLAND, Richard N, Chief Financial Officer, Palo Verde Behavioral Health, Tucson, AZ, p. A38
ENGLAND, Stacy, Community Chief Nursing Officer, Middlesboro Arh Hospital, Middlesboro, KY, p. A258
ENGLAND, Teresa, R.N., Ph.D., Nurse Executive, Salem Veterans Affairs Medical Center, Salem, VA, p. A667
ENGLE, Dana E., Chief Executive Officer, Madison Health, London, OH, p. A486
ENGLE, Lisa, Director Information Technology, Texoma Medical Center, Denison, TX, p. A599
ENGLE, Sharon, Director Clinical Services, Noland Hospital Birmingham, Birmingham, AL, p. A15
ENGLE–RAMIREZ, Jeanette, Chief Executive Officer, Menlo Park Surgical Hospital, Menlo Park, CA, p. A71
ENGLEHART, Jay, M.D., Medical Director, Southeast Missouri Mental Health Center, Farmington, MO, p. A360
ENGLERTH, LaDonna, Administrator, East Carroll Parish Hospital, Lake Providence, LA, p. A272
ENGLISH, Anne L, Director Human Resources, Uhs Chenango Memorial Hospital, Norwich, NY, p. A440
ENGLISH, Brett, Chief Financial Officer, Spartanburg Medical Center – Mary Black, Spartanburg, SC, p. A557
ENGLISH, Dennis, M.D., Vice President Medical Affairs, Upmc Magee–Womens Hospital, Pittsburgh, PA, p. A538
ENGLISH, Jeff
President, St. Mary'S Sacred Heart Hospital, Lavonia, GA, p. A156
Vice President Human Resources, St. Mary'S Health Care System, Athens, GA, p. A145
ENGLISH, Julene, Director Human Resources, Kentfield Rehabilitation And Specialty Hospital, Kentfield, CA, p. A62
ENGLISH, Kathy L, R.N., MSN, Executive Vice President and Chief Operating Officer, Children'S Hospital And Medical Center, Omaha, NE, p. A389
ENGLISH, Laurie, Senior Vice President and Chief Human Resource Officer, Excela Latrobe Area Hospital, Latrobe, PA, p. A529
ENGSTROM, Chad P, Director Human Resources, Westfields Hospital And Clinic, New Richmond, WI, p. A702
ENGSTROM, Frederick, M.D., Chief Medical Officer, Brattleboro Retreat, Brattleboro, VT, p. A654
ENICKS, Charles, Chief Information Officer, Augusta University Medical Center, Augusta, GA, p. A147
ENJADY, Rainey, Administrative Officer, Mescalero Public Health Service Indian Hospital, Mescalero, NM, p. A419
ENNEN, Mark S, Director of Finance, Hshs Holy Family Hospital In Greenville, Greenville, IL, p. A184
ENNEN, Philip L.
President and Chief Executive Officer, Community Hospitals And Wellness Centers–Montpelier, Montpelier, OH, p. A488
Vice President and Chief Executive Officer, Community Hospitals And Wellness Centers, Bryan, OH, p. A474
ENNIS, Debra, Vice President and Chief Nursing Officer, Texas Health Harris Methodist Hospital Southlake, Southlake, TX, p. A637
ENNIS, Virgil, Chief Information Officer, Helen Hayes Hospital, West Haverstraw, NY, p. A447
ENOCHS, Darren, Director Human Resources, Promise Hospital Of Overland Park, Overland Park, KS, p. A243

ENOKA, Christina, Director Human Resources and Risk Management, Sutter Health Kahi Mohala, Ewa Beach, HI, p. A164
ENRICO–SIMON, Agnes, M.D., President Medical Staff, Pleasant Valley Hospital, Point Pleasant, WV, p. A688
ENSEY, Jeremy, Chief Executive Officer, St. Luke Hospital And Living Center, Marion, KS, p. A240
ENSLEY, Terrasina, Director Human Resources, Fannin Regional Hospital, Blue Ridge, GA, p. A148
ENSMINGER, Jennifer, Chief Operating Officer, College Medical Center, Long Beach, CA, p. A65
ENSRUDE, Layne, Chief Financial Officer, First Care Health Center, Park River, ND, p. A469
ENTIN, Ari, Chief Information Officer, Natividad Medical Center, Salinas, CA, p. A82
ENTLER, Paul, D.O., Medical Director, Sparrow Specialty Hospital, Lansing, MI, p. A316
ENTWISTLE, David, President and Chief Executive Officer, Stanford Health Care, Palo Alto, CA, p. A77
ENTZMINGER, Julie, Manager Human Resources, Chi Oakes Hospital, Oakes, ND, p. A469
EOLOFF, Eric J., President, Mercy Hospital Washington, Washington, MO, p. A373
EPPERSON, Elysia, Director Human Resources, Ut Health Jacksonville, Jacksonville, TX, p. A616
EPPERSON, James, Interim Chief Nursing Officer, Grandview Medical Center, Birmingham, AL, p. A14
EPPERSON, Jeff, Chief Financial Officer, Millwood Hospital, Arlington, TX, p. A583
EPPLER, Todd, Chief Executive Officer, De Soto Regional Health System, Mansfield, LA, p. A273
EPPS, Donna
Vice President and Chief Human Resources Officer, Lawrence + Memorial Hospital, New London, CT, p. A110
Vice President, Chief Human Resource Officer, Westerly Hospital, Westerly, RI, p. A548
EPPS, Jerry, M.D., Senior Vice President and Chief Medical Officer, University Of Tennessee Medical Center, Knoxville, TN, p. A572
EPPS, Michelle L., MSN, R.N., Chief Nursing Officer, Stonesprings Hospital Center, Dulles, VA, p. A658
EPSTEIN, Michael, M.D., Senior Vice President Medical Affairs, Johns Hopkins All Children'S Hospital, Saint Petersburg, FL, p. A138
ERDMAN, Beth, Chief Financial Officer, Unitypoint Health Meriter, Madison, WI, p. A690
ERDMAN, Donja, Chief Financial Officer, Marcus Daly Memorial Hospital, Hamilton, MT, p. A377
ERDMAN, John, M.D., Chief of Staff, Chi Memorial Hospital Georgia, Fort Oglethorpe, GA, p. A153
ERDMANN, Michael, M.D., Chief of Staff, Clement J. Zablocki Veterans Affairs Medical Center, Milwaukee, WI, p. A701
ERDOS, Joseph, M.D., Chief Information Officer, Veterans Affairs Connecticut Healthcare System, West Haven, CT, p. A112
ERDRICH, Louis P., Acting Chief Executive Officer, U. S. Public Health Service Indian Hospital, Cass Lake, MN, p. A330
EREMAN, Melissa, R.N., Chief Nursing Officer, Coleman County Medical Center, Coleman, TX, p. A592
ERGLE, Jeanine, Chief Financial Officer, Bay Pines Veterans Affairs Healthcare System, Bay Pines, FL, p. A117
ERICKSON, Ashley M., Chief Executive Officer, Sanford Aberdeen Medical Center, Aberdeen, SD, p. A559
ERICKSON, Brent J, Administrator, Wright Patterson Medical Center, Wright, OH, p. A494
ERICKSON, Doug, Chief Financial Officer, Prague Community Hospital, Prague, OK, p. A506
ERICKSON, Jake, Chief Executive Officer, Bingham Memorial Hospital, Blackfoot, ID, p. A167
ERICKSON, Jeannette Ives., Interim President and Chief Executive Officer, Nantucket Cottage Hospital, Nantucket, MA, p. A301
ERICKSON, Karyn, Director Human Resources, Delta Medical Center, Memphis, TN, p. A574
ERICKSON, Kerrie, Vice President Finance, Stevens Community Medical Center, Morris, MN, p. A336
ERICKSON, Laura, R.N., Chief Nursing Officer, Pondera Medical Center, Conrad, MT, p. A375
ERICKSON, Nancy
Administrator Information Systems, Kossuth Regional Health Center, Algona, IA, p. A217
Human Resource Director, Southern Inyo Healthcare District, Lone Pine, CA, p. A65
ERICKSON, Robert J., President, Amita Health Saint Joseph Medical Center, Joliet, IL, p. A187
ERICKSON, Sue, President and Chief Executive Officer, Unitypoint Health Meriter, Madison, WI, p. A698
ERICKSON, Vonnie, Human Resource Manager, Ccm Health, Montevideo, MN, p. A336
ERICSON, Allen
Chief Operating Officer, Community Hospital Division and President, St. Joseph's Hospital, Community Memorial Hospital, Menomonee Falls, WI, p. A700
Chief Operating Officer, Community Hospital Division and President, St. Joseph's Hospital, St. Joseph'S Hospital, West Bend, WI, p. A708
President, St. Joseph'S Hospital, West Bend, WI, p. A708
ERICSON, Bob, Chief Financial Officer, Hemphill County Hospital, Canadian, TX, p. A591
ERICSON, Kim
Vice President Finance, Fairview Lakes Health Services, Wyoming, MN, p. A343
Vice President Finance, Fairview Northland Medical Center, Princeton, MN, p. A338
ERIXON, Stephen M, Chief Executive Officer, Sagewest Health Care At Riverton, Riverton, WY, p. A712
ERKEN, Carole L, Human Resources Leader, Kaiser Permanente Panorama City Medical Center, Los Angeles, CA, p. A67
ERLING, Brian
Group Chief Medical Officer, St. Anthony Hospital, Lakewood, CO, p. A103
Interim Chief Executive Officer, Penrose–St. Francis Health Services, Colorado Springs, CO, p. A98
ERMANN, William, President and Chief Executive Officer, Southwest Medical Center, Liberal, KS, p. A239
ERTEL, Matthew, Chief Financial Officer, Gibson Area Hospital And Health Services, Gibson City, IL, p. A184
ERUKHIMOU, Jeffrey, M.D., Medical Director, Curahealth Heritage Valley, Beaver, PA, p. A520
ERVIN, Fulton
Chief Financial Officer, Mcleod Regional Medical Center, Florence, SC, p. A552
Senior Vice President and Chief Financial Officer, Mcleod Medical Center Dillon, Dillon, SC, p. A552
ERVIN, Joan, Administrator, Mcleod Medical Center Dillon, Dillon, SC, p. A552
ERVIN, Paul D, Chief Financial Officer, Valley Behavioral Health System, Barling, AR, p. A39
ERVIN, Richard, Chief Financial Officer, Hca Houston Healthcare Tomball, Tomball, TX, p. A641
ERVING–MENGEL, Tammi, R.N., MSN, Vice President, Chief Nursing Officer, High Point Medical Center, High Point, NC, p. A456
ERWAY, Robert, Director for Administration, Brookdale Hospital Medical Center, New York, NY, p. A432
ERWIN, Connie, Manager, Samaritan Lebanon Community Hospital, Lebanon, OR, p. A514
ESCHENBRENNER, Wade, Chief Financial Officer, Lexington Regional Health Center, Lexington, NE, p. A386
ESCOBAR, Carlos R., Director, Veterans Affairs Caribbean Healthcare System, San Juan, PR, p. A719
ESHLEMAN, James, D.O., President Medical Staff, Stephens Memorial Hospital, Norway, ME, p. A291
ESKER, Jerry, President and Chief Executive Officer, Sarah Bush Lincoln Health Center, Mattoon, IL, p. A188
ESLAVA, Lee, Chief Medical Officer, South Baldwin Regional Medical Center, Foley, AL, p. A18
ESPARZA, Becky, Human Resources, Crane Memorial Hospital, Crane, TX, p. A595
ESPARZA, Caroline, R.N.
Senior Vice President, Chief Operating Officer and Chief Nurse Officer, Simi Valley Hospital, Simi Valley, CA, p. A89
Sr. VP, COO & CNO, Simi Valley Hospital, Simi Valley, CA, p. A89
ESPELAND, Darryl, D.O.
Chief Medical Staff, Fallon Medical Complex, Baker, MT, p. A374
Medical Director, Dahl Memorial Healthcare Association, Ekalaka, MT, p. A376
ESPELAND, David, Chief Executive Officer, Fallon Medical Complex, Baker, MT, p. A374
ESPINA, Francisco, Director Finance, Hospital Pavia–Santurce, San Juan, PR, p. A719
ESPINOZA, John, Chief Human Resources Officer, University Medical Center, Las Vegas, NV, p. A396
ESPINOZA, Judy, Chief Human Resources Officer, Ascension Via Christi St. Francis, Mulvane, KS, p. A241
ESPINOZA, Richard, Chief Administrative Officer, Highland Hospital, Oakland, CA, p. A75
ESPOSITO, Mary H, Assistant Executive Director, Devereux Advanced Behavioral Health Georgia, Kennesaw, GA, p. A155
ESPOSITO, Pamela, Director Administration, Buffalo Psychiatric Center, Buffalo, NY, p. A424
ESPY, Christine, Division Director, Mid–Columbia Medical Center, The Dalles, OR, p. A518
ESROCK, Brett A.
Chief Executive Officer, Health First Holmes Regional Medical Center, Melbourne, FL, p. A129
President, Health First Cape Canaveral Hospital, Cocoa Beach, FL, p. A120
President, Health First Palm Bay Hospital, Palm Bay, FL, p. A135
President, Health First Viera Hospital, Melbourne, FL, p. A129
ESSELMAN, Charlotte, Director Finance, Ascension Saint Clare'S Hospital, Weston, WI, p. A708
ESSMYER, Dale, M.D., Chief of Staff, Sullivan County Memorial Hospital, Milan, MO, p. A365
ESTAY, Mike, Chief Financial Officer, Hood Memorial Hospital, Amite, LA, p. A262
ESTES, Benton D, Materials Management, Baptist Medical Center Yazoo, Yazoo City, MS, p. A355
ESTES, Mary, Director Information Systems, St. Luke'S Des Peres Hospital, Saint Louis, MO, p. A370
ESTES, Stephen A., Chief Executive Officer, Rockcastle Regional Hospital And Respiratory Care Center, Mount Vernon, KY, p. A258
ESTEVEZ, Aurora, M.D., Chief Medical Officer, Texas Health Presbyterian Hospital Dallas, Dallas, TX, p. A598
ESTEVEZ, Mercy, Administrator, Port St. Lucie Hospital, Port St Lucie, FL, p. A137
ESTRADA, Luis, Director Multifacility Information Systems, North Shore Medical Center, Miami, FL, p. A131
ESTRADA, Marina, Director Human Resources, El Paso Children'S Hospital, El Paso, TX, p. A601
ESTRELLA, Mario B, Chief Nursing Officer, Nacogdoches Medical Center, Nacogdoches, TX, p. A625
ETCHASON, Barbara, HR Manager, West Gables Rehabilitation Hospital, Miami, FL, p. A131
ETCITTY, Ronnye, Director Human Resources, Rehoboth Mckinley Christian Health Care Services, Gallup, NM, p. A418
ETHERIDGE, Darold, Vice President and Chief Financial Officer, Wellstar Cobb Hospital, Austell, GA, p. A148
ETHERINGTON, Betty, Chief Financial Officer, Humboldt County Memorial Hospital, Humboldt, IA, p. A224
ETHERINGTON, Rosalie, Superintendent and Chief Executive Officer, North Dakota State Hospital, Jamestown, ND, p. A468
ETHRIDGE, Sandy, Interim Chief Operating Officer, Baptist Medical Center, San Antonio, TX, p. A633
ETTER, Carl J.
Chief Executive and Senior Vice President, Scripps Memorial Hospital–Encinitas, Encinitas, CA, p. A57
Chief Executive Officer, Scripps Green Hospital, La Jolla, CA, p. A62
Chief Executive Officer, Scripps Memorial Hospital–La Jolla, La Jolla, CA, p. A63
ETTESTAD, Donita, R.N., MS, Chief Nursing Officer, Rainy Lake Medical Center, International Falls, MN, p. A333
ETZEL, Glen T., M.D., Chief of Staff, Castleview Hospital, Price, UT, p. A650
ETZLER, Randal M., Chief Human Resources Officer, Yuma Regional Medical Center, Yuma, AZ, p. A38
EUBANKS, Bill, Senior Vice President and Chief Information Officer, University Medical Center, Lubbock, TX, p. A622
EUBANKS, Susan, Chief Executive Officer, Page Hospital, Page, AZ, p. A32
EUCLIDE, Jeff, Chief Executive Officer, Marshfield Medical Center – Ladysmith, Ladysmith, WI, p. A698
EULIARTE, Mary Ann, R.N.
Chief Nursing Officer, Memorial Hermann Rehabilitation Hospital – Katy, Katy, TX, p. A617
Chief Operating Officer, Memorial Hermann Rehabilitation Hospital – Katy, Katy, TX, p. A617
EURE, Thomas, Vice President Administration, Carolinas Healthcare System Blue Ridge, Morganton, NC, p. A459
EUSEBIO, Barbara, R.N., JD, Vice President, Chief Nurse Executive, St. Mary'S Medical Center, San Francisco, CA, p. A86
EUSTACE, Scott, Director Health Information Technology, Trenton Psychiatric Hospital, Trenton, NJ, p. A413
EVANCHO, Timothy R., Chief Financial Officer, Southeastern Ohio Regional Medical Center, Cambridge, OH, p. A474
EVANDER, Justin N.
Administrator and Chief Operating Officer, Kaiser Sunnyside Medical Center, Clackamas, OR, p. A512
Chief Financial Officer, Kaiser Sunnyside Medical Center, Clackamas, OR, p. A512
EVANOFF, John, M.D., Vice President Medical Affairs, Promedica Flower Hospital, Sylvania, OH, p. A491
EVANS, Ann, Chief Nursing Officer, Encompass Health Rehabilitation Hospital Of Huntington, Huntington, WV, p. A686
EVANS, Bonnie A., Chief Executive Officer, Kessler Institute For Rehabilitation, West Orange, NJ, p. A414
EVANS, Brian, Chief Information Officer, Milford Hospital, Milford, CT, p. A109

EVANS, Brian, Esq, President and Chief Executive Officer, Sierra Nevada Memorial Hospital, Grass Valley, CA, p. A61

EVANS, Brian G., Chief Executive Officer, Clarke County Hospital, Osceola, IA, p. A228

EVANS, Cindy, R.N., MS, Chief Nursing Officer, Legacy Good Samaritan Medical Center, Portland, OR, p. A516

EVANS, Dave, Chief Financial Officer, Community Hospital Of San Bernardino, San Bernardino, CA, p. A83

EVANS, Dawn, Manager Information Technology, Ssm Health St. Mary'S Hospital – Audrain, Mexico, MO, p. A365

EVANS, Dwight, M.D., Chief of Staff, Veterans Affairs Loma Linda Healthcare System, Loma Linda, CA, p. A64

EVANS, Eric, Chief Executive Officer, Hca Houston Healthcare Tomball, Tomball, TX, p. A641

EVANS, George, Vice President and Chief Information Officer, Candler Hospital, Savannah, GA, p. A160

EVANS, Heath, President, Bay Medical Sacred Heart, Panama City, FL, p. A135

EVANS, Janice, Chief Financial Officer, John J. Madden Mental Health Center, Hines, IL, p. A185

EVANS, Jeff W., Vice President Information and Technology, Hannibal Regional Hospital, Hannibal, MO, p. A361

EVANS, Jeremy, Vice President Operations, Kootenai Health, Coeur D'Alene, ID, p. A169

EVANS, Kelley, Chief Administrative Officer, Beartooth Billings Clinic, Red Lodge, MT, p. A379

EVANS, Lola, Director of Nursing, Surgeons Choice Medical Center, Southfield, MI, p. A323

EVANS, Lorrie, Director Human Resources, Laurel Oaks Behavioral Health Center, Dothan, AL, p. A17

EVANS, Melinda S
Vice President Finance, Chi Saint Joseph East, Lexington, KY, p. A254
Vice President Finance, Chi Saint Joseph Health, Lexington, KY, p. A255

EVANS, Michael C., Chief Executive Officer and Deputy Director of Finance and Administration, Santa Barbara County Psychiatric Health Facility, Santa Barbara, CA, p. A88

EVANS, Rod, Chief Information Officer, Community Healthcare System, Onaga, KS, p. A242

EVANS, Ronald A., M.D., Chief Medical Officer, Citizens Memorial Hospital, Bolivar, MO, p. A356

EVANS, Sam, Chief Human Resources Management, G.V. (Sonny) Montgomery Veterans Affairs Medical Center, Jackson, MS, p. A348

EVANS, Scott, Senior Vice President and Chief Executive Officer, Sharp Grossmont Hospital, La Mesa, CA, p. A63

EVANS, Sharon Lagina, R.N.
Assistant Chief Nursing Officer, Jenkins County Medical Center, Millen, GA, p. A157
Assistant Chief Nursing Officer, Optim Medical Center – Screven, Sylvania, GA, p. A161

EVANS, Susan, Chief Nursing Officer, Old Vineyard Behavioral Health Services, Winston, NC, p. A464

EVANS, Tim, Assistant Financial Director, Devereux Children'S Behavioral Health Center, Malvern, PA, p. A530

EVANS, Timothy, Vice President and Chief Financial Officer, Self Regional Healthcare, Greenwood, SC, p. A554

EVANS–HARRISON, Martina, R.N., MSN, Chief Nurse Executive, Methodist Hospital Of Sacramento, Sacramento, CA, p. A82

EVE, John, Vice President Human Resources and Education, Wilson Memorial Hospital, Sidney, OH, p. A491

EVELIUS, Karen, Director Human Resources, Medstar Harbor Hospital, Baltimore, MD, p. A287

EVELYN, David M, M.D., Vice President Medical Affairs, Cayuga Medical Center At Ithaca, Ithaca, NY, p. A429

EVENS, James, Executive Director, Human Resources and General Services, Upmc Cole, Coudersport, PA, p. A523

EVENSON, Laura, Chief Nursing Officer, Mayo Clinic Health System In Mankato, Mankato, MN, p. A334

EVENSON, Margie, Manager Human Resources, Osceola Medical Center, Osceola, WI, p. A703

EVERDING, Dawn, President and Chief Financial Officer, Community Memorial Hospital, Sumner, IA, p. A230

EVERETT, Curren, Chief Executive Officer, Fulton County Hospital, Salem, AR, p. A48

EVERETT, John, Chief Financial Officer, Cogdell Memorial Hospital, Snyder, TX, p. A637

EVERETT, Leianne, Chief Executive Officer, Arbor Health, Morton Hospital, Morton, WA, p. A675

EVERETT, Neil, Vice President Human Resources, Uh Portage Medical Center, Ravenna, OH, p. A490

EVERHART, Martin S, Senior Vice President Human Resources, Robert Wood Johnson University Hospital, New Brunswick, NJ, p. A409

EVERLY, Nanette, Manager Human Resources and Administrative Assistant, Jefferson County Health Center, Fairfield, IA, p. A222

EVERS, Andrea, Director Information Technology, Haxtun Hospital District, Haxtun, CO, p. A102

EVERS, Anthony, Chief Financial Officer, Katherine Shaw Bethea Hospital, Dixon, IL, p. A181

EVERS–MANLY, Shirley, Chief Nursing Officer, Howard University Hospital, Washington, DC, p. A115

EVERSOLE, Matt, Regional Vice President Information Services, Mercy Health – Anderson Hospital, Cincinnati, OH, p. A476

EVERT, Barbara, M.D.
Vice President Medical Affairs, Ohiohealth Dublin Methodist Hospital, Dublin, OH, p. A482
Vice President Medical Affairs, Ohiohealth Grady Memorial Hospital, Delaware, OH, p. A482

EVINS, Starling C, M.D., Chief of Staff, Williamson Medical Center, Franklin, TN, p. A570

EVISCHI, Deland
Chief Financial Officer, Ssm Health St. Mary'S Hospital Centralia, Centralia, IL, p. A175
Regional Chief Financial Officer, Southern Illinois, Good Samaritan Regional Health Center, Mount Vernon, IL, p. A190

EVOLGA, Nancy K, Director Human Resources, Adventhealth New Smyrna Beach, New Smyrna Beach, FL, p. A133

EWALD, Luanne T., Chief Executive Officer, Dmc – Children'S Hospital Of Michigan, Detroit, MI, p. A309

EWALD, Ronald, Chief Financial Officer, Inova Fairfax Hospital, Falls Church, VA, p. A659

EWALD, Sandra
President (Green Bay/Manitowoc Market), Aurora Medical Center – Manitowoc County, Two Rivers, WI, p. A707
Vice President Finance, Aurora Medical Center Of Oshkosh, Oshkosh, WI, p. A703

EWELL, Dorene L, Director Human Resources and Education, Harrisburg Medical Center, Harrisburg, IL, p. A184

EWELL, Sandy, Chief Nursing Officer, Timpanogos Regional Hospital, Orem, UT, p. A650

EWING, Catherine, M.D., Chief Nursing Officer, Baylor Scott & White Institute For Rehabilitation–Fort Worth, Fort Worth, TX, p. A604

EWING, Chandler, Chief Executive Officer, Select Specialty Hospital–Jackson, Jackson, MS, p. A349

EWING, Corey, Chief Executive Officer, Gadsden Regional Medical Center, Gadsden, AL, p. A18

EWING, Hella, Vice President Patient Care Services and Chief Nursing Officer, East Tennessee Children'S Hospital, Knoxville, TN, p. A572

EWING, Steven, Chief Financial Officer, San Angelo Community Medical Center, San Angelo, TX, p. A632

EWING, Thomas
Director Information Technology, Sentara Careplex Hospital, Hampton, VA, p. A660
Director Information Technology, Sentara Northern Virginia Medical Center, Woodbridge, VA, p. A669

EXLINE, Michael
Chief Financial Officer, Carrus Rehabilitation Hospital, Sherman, TX, p. A637
Chief Financial Officer, Carrus Specialty Hospital, Sherman, TX, p. A637

EYE, Jeffrey L, R.N., Vice President Patient Care Services, Murray–Calloway County Hospital, Murray, KY, p. A258

EYLER, Sandra, MS
Chief Nursing Officer, Sheltering Arms Hospital South, Midlothian, VA, p. A663
Chief Nursing Officer, Sheltering Arms Rehabilitation Hospital, Mechanicsville, VA, p. A662

EZZIE, Michael, Director of Medical Education and Interim Vice President of Medical Affairs, Ohiohealth Grant Medical Center, Columbus, OH, p. A479

F

FABER, Chris, Human Resources Analyst, Stanford Health Care – Valleycare, Pleasanton, CA, p. A78

FABER, Tammy, Director Human Resources, Hegg Health Center Avera, Rock Valley, IA, p. A229

FABIAN, Alan J., Chief Executive Officer, Lewisgale Hospital Montgomery, Blacksburg, VA, p. A656

FABIAN, Roxanne, Director of Nursing–Acute Care, Lifecare Medical Center, Roseau, MN, p. A339

FABIANO, Tom, Director Human Resources, Mount Auburn Hospital, Cambridge, MA, p. A297

FABIN, Peggy, Director Human Resources, Phillips County Health Systems, Phillipsburg, KS, p. A243

FABRICK, Peter, Vice President Clinical Operations, Mountain View Hospital, Idaho Falls, ID, p. A169

FABRY, Joseph, D.O., Chief of Staff, Sutter Maternity And Surgery Center Of Santa Cruz, Santa Cruz, CA, p. A89

FACKRELL, Sherlyn, Finance Controller, Grover C. Dils Medical Center, Caliente, NV, p. A393

FACTEAU, Patrick M., Chief Financial Officer, Massena Memorial Hospital, Massena, NY, p. A431

FADALE, Sean, President and Chief Executive Officer, Community Memorial Hospital, Hamilton, NY, p. A429

FADLER, Jeannie, R.N., Vice President Patient Care Services, Saint Francis Medical Center, Cape Girardeau, MO, p. A357

FAGAN, Erin, Manager Human Resources, George Washington University Hospital, Washington, DC, p. A115

FAGAN, Mary, MSN, R.N., Chief Nursing Officer, Rady Children'S Hospital – San Diego, San Diego, CA, p. A84

FAGAN, Michael, Senior Vice President Finance, Brookdale Hospital Medical Center, New York, NY, p. A432

FAGBONGBE, Eniola, M.D., Chief Medical Staff, Grove Hill Memorial Hospital, Grove Hill, AL, p. A19

FAGERBERG, Lesley, Vice President Fiscal Services, Heart Of The Rockies Regional Medical Center, Salida, CO, p. A105

FAGERHAUG, Larry, Director Human Resources, Carson Tahoe Continuing Care Hospital, Carson City, NV, p. A393

FAGERSTROM, Joel, Executive Vice President and Chief Operating Officer, St. Luke'S Hospital – Miners Campus, Coaldale, PA, p. A522

FAGG, Cindy, Fiscal Officer, Battle Mountain General Hospital, Battle Mountain, NV, p. A393

FAHERTY, Jay, Chief Executive Officer, Select Specialty Hospital–Tallahassee, Tallahassee, FL, p. A140

FAHEY, Dana, Manager Management Information Systems, Santa Barbara County Psychiatric Health Facility, Santa Barbara, CA, p. A88

FAHEY, Linda L, R.N., Chief Information Officer and Senior Vice President Quality Systems, Decatur Memorial Hospital, Decatur, IL, p. A180

FAHEY, Patrick, M.D., Chief Medical Officer, Rml Specialty Hospital, Hinsdale, IL, p. A186

FAHEY, Stephen P, Executive Director, Sierra Tucson, Tucson, AZ, p. A38

FAHEY, Stephen P., Executive Director, Sierra Tucson, Tucson, AZ, p. A38

FAHEY, Walter, Chief Information Officer, Brookdale Hospital Medical Center, New York, NY, p. A432

FAILE, J Gene., Chief Executive Officer and President, Wake Forest Baptist Health – Wilkes Medical Center, North Wilkesboro, NC, p. A459

FAILLA, Richard, Chief Executive Officer, Montevista Hospital, Las Vegas, NV, p. A395

FAIN, Marilyn, R.N., MSN, Chief Operating Officer, Banner Fort Collins Medical Center, Fort Collins, CO, p. A100

FAIN, Nona, Ph.D., R.N., Director of Nursing, Belmont Behavioral Hospital, Philadelphia, PA, p. A534

FAIRBANKS, Bruce, Vice President and Chief Financial Officer, Southeast Hospital, Cape Girardeau, MO, p. A358

FAIRBANKS, Trish, R.N., Associate Vice President and Chief Nursing Officer, Linden Oaks Hospital, Naperville, IL, p. A190

FAIRCHILD, David, M.D., Chief Medical Officer, Tufts Medical Center, Boston, MA, p. A296

FAIRCLOTH, Karen, Chief Financial Officer, Memorial Hospital And Manor, Bainbridge, GA, p. A148

FAIRFAX, Tom, Director Information Systems, Bothwell Regional Health Center, Sedalia, MO, p. A371

FAIRFAX, Walter, M.D., Chief Medical Officer, Kootenai Health, Coeur D'Alene, ID, p. A169

FAIRLEY, Dawn Ann, M.D., Chief of Staff, Putnam County Memorial Hospital, Unionville, MO, p. A372

FAIRLEY, Susan, Chief Nursing Officer, Barton Memorial Hospital, South Lake Tahoe, CA, p. A90

FAISAL, Mohammad, President Medical Staff, Shands Lake Shore Regional Medical Center, Lake City, FL, p. A127

FALCON, Hugo, M.D., Director Medical Services, Piedmont Geriatric Hospital, Burkeville, VA, p. A657

FALCONE, Lynn, Chief Executive Officer, Cuero Community Hospital, Cuero, TX, p. A595

FALGOUT, Charlene, Chief Nursing Officer, St. Francis Hospital, Columbus, GA, p. A150

FALIVENA, Richard, D.O., M.P.H., Vice President and Chief Medical Officer, Saratoga Hospital, Saratoga Springs, NY, p. A444

FALK, Chelsie, Chief Nursing Officer, Sanford Wheaton Medical Center, Wheaton, MN, p. A342

FALKENBERRY, Jody, Director Information Systems, Monroe County Hospital, Monroeville, AL, p. A21

FALL, J Mark., Chief Executive Officer, Henry Ford Allegiance Specialty Hospital, Jackson, MI, p. A315

FALLIS, Susan, Chief Nursing Officer, Buffalo Psychiatric Center, Buffalo, NY, p. A424

FALLON, Jeanne M.
Chief Information Officer, Falmouth Hospital, Falmouth, MA, p. A298

Senior Vice President and Chief Information Officer, Cape Cod Hospital, Hyannis, MA, p. A299
FALLON, L J, JD, Executive Vice President, Chief Legal and Human Resources Officer, Carle Foundation Hospital, Urbana, IL, p. A197
FALO, Carol, Chief Executive Officer, Curahealth Pittsburgh, Oakdale, PA, p. A533
FALTERMAN, James B, M.D., Medical Director, University Hospital And Clinics, Lafayette, LA, p. A271
FANALE, Linda, Chief Financial Officer, Conemaugh Miners Medical Center, Hastings, PA, p. A527
FANKHAUSER, John, Chief Executive Officer, Ventura County Medical Center, Ventura, CA, p. A93
FANNIN, Allyson, Human Resources Officer, Lasalle General Hospital, Jena, LA, p. A269
FANNIN, Pam, Coordinator Human Resources, Lifecare Hospital Of Dayton, Miamisburg, OH, p. A487
FANNON, Susan, Chief Nursing Officer, Indian Path Medical Center, Kingsport, TN, p. A572
FANSLER, Janet, R.N., Executive Vice President and Chief Nurse Executive, Lakeland Regional Health Medical Center, Lakeland, FL, p. A127
FANTANO, Gene, Chief Financial Officer, Aurora Behavioral Healthcare San Diego, San Diego, CA, p. A83
FARAH, Tony, M.D., President Medical Staff, Allegheny General Hospital, Pittsburgh, PA, p. A537
FARBER, Bobbi, M.D., Chief Medical Officer, St. Francis Hospital, Columbus, GA, p. A150
FARBER, Nancy D., Chief Executive Officer, Washington Hospital Healthcare System, Fremont, CA, p. A59
FARBER, Niceta, Chief Executive Officer, Sheridan County Health Complex, Hoxie, KS, p. A237
FARBER, Stephen D., Chief Financial Officer, Kindred Hospital–New Jersey Morris County, Dover, NJ, p. A404
FARELL, Clay, Chief Operation Officer, Los Alamitos Medical Center, Los Alamitos, CA, p. A65
FARGASON, Crayton A, M.D., Medical Director, Children'S Of Alabama, Birmingham, AL, p. A14
FARGUSON, Jack, Director Information Technology, Tmc Bonham Hospital, Bonham, TX, p. A589
FARINA, Albert M, Chief Financial Officer, Montefiore Mount Vernon, Mount Vernon, NY, p. A432
FARINA, Jonathan, Chief Information Officer, Brattleboro Memorial Hospital, Brattleboro, VT, p. A654
FARISH, Audra, Vice President Human Resources, Emory Saint Joseph'S Hospital Of Atlanta, Atlanta, GA, p. A146
FARKAS, Laura, Director Human Resources, Fairview Hospital, Great Barrington, MA, p. A299
FARLEY, Chris, Chief Financial Officer, Willow Springs Center, Reno, NV, p. A397
FARMER, Kathleen, Assistant Administrator Finance and Chief Financial Officer, El Centro Regional Medical Center, El Centro, CA, p. A57
FARMER, Pat, Coordinator Human Resources and Safety Officer, Institute For Orthopaedic Surgery, Lima, OH, p. A485
FARMER, William, M.D., Chief of Staff, Evergreen Medical Center, Evergreen, AL, p. A17
FARNHAM, Diane, Acting Director Human Resources, Lallie Kemp Medical Center, Independence, LA, p. A269
FARNHAM, Krista, Chief Executive, Providence Portland Medical Center, Portland, OR, p. A516
FARO, Joan, M.D., Chief Medical Officer, John T. Mather Memorial Hospital, Port Jefferson, NY, p. A441
FARR, Lorraine, Manager Human Resources, Georgia Regional Hospital At Atlanta, Decatur, GA, p. A152
FARR, Ronald, Chief Financial Officer, Jewish Hospital, Louisville, KY, p. A256
FARR, William L, M.D., Chief Medical Officer, University Hospital, Augusta, GA, p. A147
FARRAGE, Jim, M.D., Medical Director, Southern Kentucky Rehabilitation Hospital, Bowling Green, KY, p. A250
FARRAND, Cynthia B, President, Moses H. Cone Memorial Hospital, Greensboro, NC, p. A455
FARRAR, William, Interim Chief Executive Officer, James Cancer Hospital And Solove Research Institute, Columbus, OH, p. A479
FARRAUTO, Joseph, Director Human Resources, Eastern Niagara Hospital, Lockport, NY, p. A430
FARRELL, America S., Chief Executive Officer, College Station Medical Center, College Station, TX, p. A592
FARRELL, Brenda, Vice President Finance, Long Island Community Hospital, Patchogue, NY, p. A441
FARRELL, Coleen M, Vice President Human Resources, Mid Coast Hospital, Brunswick, ME, p. A282
FARRELL, George, M.D.
Chief Medical Officer, Clinch Valley Medical Center, Richlands, VA, p. A665
Chief of Staff, Wythe County Community Hospital, Wytheville, VA, p. A669
FARRELL, Kathleen, Chief Administrative Officer, Abington–Lansdale Hospital Jefferson Health, Lansdale, PA, p. A529
FARRELL, Roy, M.D., Chief Medical Officer, Carondelet Holy Cross Hospital, Nogales, AZ, p. A32
FARRELL, Scott, M.D., Vice President Medical Affairs, Promedica Memorial Hospital, Fremont, OH, p. A483
FARRELL, Steven E, M.D., Chief Medical Officer, Forrest General Hospital, Hattiesburg, MS, p. A348
FARRELL, Terence, President, Mercy Hospital Ada, Ada, OK, p. A496
FARRELL, Teresa, Chief Human Resources Officer, Nacogdoches Medical Center, Nacogdoches, TX, p. A625
FARRELL, Timothy, Executive Director, St. Lawrence Psychiatric Center, Ogdensburg, NY, p. A440
FARRELLY, Irene, Vice President and Chief Information Officer, Brookdale Hospital Medical Center, New York, NY, p. A432
FARRER, Brandy H, R.N., Chief Nursing Officer, Medical City Denton, Denton, TX, p. A599
FARRINGTON, Robyn, Chief Nursing Officer, Broward Health Medical Center, Fort Lauderdale, FL, p. A122
FARRIS, James R., Chief Executive Officer, Union County Hospital, Anna, IL, p. A173
FARRIS, Jason, Chief Nursing Officer, Inspire Specialty Hospital, Midwest City, OK, p. A502
FARRISH, John, Health Information Director, University Of Mississippi Medical Center Grenada, Grenada, MS, p. A347
FARROW, Diane, Manager Information Technology and Systems, Willamette Valley Medical Center, Mcminnville, OR, p. A514
FARROW, Rachel, Interim Chief Executive Officer, Seiling Regional Medical Center, Seiling, OK, p. A507
FARSHAO, Nosratian, M.D., Chief Medical Staff, Memorial Hospital Of Gardena, Gardena, CA, p. A60
FARUGIA, Celeste, R.N., MSN, Chief Nurse Executive, Kaiser Permanente Panorama City Medical Center, Los Angeles, CA, p. A67
FARWELL, Brenda
Director Human Resources, Providence Medical Center, Kansas City, KS, p. A238
Director Human Resources, Saint John Hospital, Leavenworth, KS, p. A239
FASANO, Philip, Chief Information Officer, Kaiser Permanente Sacramento Medical Center, Sacramento, CA, p. A81
FASHINA, Olawale, M.D., Chief of Staff, Central Texas Veterans Health Care System, Temple, TX, p. A640
FAST, Gary, M.D., Medical Director, Prairie View, Newton, KS, p. A242
FASTHORSE, Lena, Supervisor Human Resource, U. S. Public Health Service Indian Hospital–Whiteriver, Whiteriver, AZ, p. A38
FATCH, Casey, Chief Executive Officer, Shasta Regional Medical Center, Redding, CA, p. A80
FATTIG, Marty, Chief Executive Officer, Nemaha County Hospital, Auburn, NE, p. A382
FATULA, Suzette
Chief Financial Officer, Oakdale Community Hospital, Oakdale, LA, p. A276
Chief Financial Officer, Winn Parish Medical Center, Winnfield, LA, p. A280
FAUBION, Matthew, M.D., Clinical Director, Kerrville State Hospital, Kerrville, TX, p. A617
FAUCETT, Michael, Chief Operating Officer, Lake City Community Hospital, Lake City, SC, p. A555
FAUCHER, Kimberly, M.D., Chief Medical Officer, Adventist Health Howard Memorial, Willits, CA, p. A95
FAUCHEUX, Lisa, Director Human Resources, St. James Parish Hospital, Lutcher, LA, p. A273
FAUGHT, Charles J, Chief Financial Officer, Burnett Medical Center, Grantsburg, WI, p. A695
FAUL, Jennifer, Chief Operating Officer, Prairie St. John'S, Fargo, ND, p. A466
FAULIS, Karen, Chief Executive Officer, Hi–Desert Medical Center, Joshua Tree, CA, p. A62
FAULKNER, Cheryl, Director of Nursing, Mckenzie County Healthcare System, Watford City, ND, p. A470
FAULKNER, Cynthia, R.N., Chief Nursing Executive, Pender Memorial Hospital, Burgaw, NC, p. A450
FAULKNER, David, Interim Chief Executive Officer, Sierra Vista Hospital, Truth Or Consequences, NM, p. A421
FAULKNER, Kristi, Vice President Organizational Growth, United Regional Health Care System, Wichita Falls, TX, p. A646
FAULKNER, Laura, Chief Human Resource Management Service, Lexington Veterans Affairs Medical Center, Lexington, KY, p. A255
FAULKNER, Sharon
Administrator, Sage Specialty Hospital (Ltac), Denham Springs, LA, p. A267
Chief Nursing Officer, Sage Specialty Hospital (Ltac), Denham Springs, LA, p. A267
FAUMUINA, Taufete's John., Chief Executive Officer, Lyndon B. Johnson Tropical Medical Center, Pago Pago, AS, p. A714
FAUS, Doug, Chief Executive Officer, Ivinson Memorial Hospital, Laramie, WY, p. A711
FAUST, Cheryl, Chief Nursing Officer, Edgefield County Healthcare, Edgefield, SC, p. A552
FAUST, Christina, Chief Financial Officer, Avoyelles Hospital, Marksville, LA, p. A273
FAUTHEREE, Greg, M.D., Medical Director, Spine Hospital Of Louisiana (Formally The Neuromedical Center Surgical Hospital), Baton Rouge, LA, p. A264
FAVATA, Valerie, R.N., MS, Chief Nursing Officer, Oswego Hospital, Oswego, NY, p. A441
FAVRET, John M., Director, Eastern State Hospital, Williamsburg, VA, p. A668
FAY, Brian, Director Information Systems, Sidney Health Center, Sidney, MT, p. A380
FAYEN, Edward J, Associate Administrator Operations and Support, Washington Hospital Healthcare System, Fremont, CA, p. A59
FAYRE, Gail, M.D., Medical Director, Anna Jaques Hospital, Newburyport, MA, p. A301
FAZIO, Charles, Chief Health Officer and Medical Director Health Plan, Regions Hospital, Saint Paul, MN, p. A340
FEAGIN, Bridgett
Chief Financial Officer, Dmc – Detroit Receiving Hospital, Detroit, MI, p. A310
Chief Financial Officer, Dmc Harper University Hospital, Detroit, MI, p. A310
FEASEL, Jeff, Chief Executive Officer, Halifax Health Medical Center Of Daytona Beach, Daytona Beach, FL, p. A121
FEATHER, Leroy P, Vice President Finance, Community Hospitals And Wellness Centers, Bryan, OH, p. A474
FEAZELL, Kayla, Chief Executive Officer, Encompass Health Rehabilitation Hospital Of Gadsden, Gadsden, AL, p. A18
FEBRY, Ricardo, M.D., Medical Director, St. Theresa Specialty Hospital, Kenner, LA, p. A270
FEBUS, Steven, Chief Financial Officer, Pullman Regional Hospital, Pullman, WA, p. A676
FEDER, Diane, R.N., FACHE, Senior Vice President and Chief Operating Officer, Witham Health Services, Lebanon, IN, p. A210
FEDERICO, Skip, Director Information Systems, Ayala, Covington, LA, p. A266
FEDERINKO, David, Chief Information Officer, Allegan General Hospital, Allegan, MI, p. A306
FEDIE, Corey J., Chief Executive Officer, East Adams Rural Healthcare, Ritzville, WA, p. A677
FEDORA, Deborah, Director Human Resources, Paoli Hospital, Paoli, PA, p. A533
FEELEY, Daniel, Interim Chief Financial Officer, Medstar Southern Maryland Hospital Center, Clinton, MD, p. A289
FEEMAN, Kimberly
Interim Chief Executive Officer, Pennsylvania Psychiatric Institute, Harrisburg, PA, p. A526
Senior Vice President and Chief Operating Officer, Wellspan Good Samaritan Hospital, Lebanon, PA, p. A530
FEEN, Jim, Senior Vice President and Chief Information Officer, Southcoast Hospitals Group, Fall River, MA, p. A298
FEENEY, Daniel, M.D., Medical Director, Brentwood Hospital, Shreveport, LA, p. A278
FEENEY, Sheri, Chief Financial Officer, Providence Regional Medical Center Everett, Everett, WA, p. A673
FEESS, David, President and Chief Executive Officer, Liberty Hospital, Liberty, MO, p. A364
FEGAN, Claudia, M.D., Chief Medical Officer, John H. Stroger Jr. Hospital Of Cook County, Chicago, IL, p. A177
FEGHALI, Georges, M.D.
Senior Vice President Quality and Chief Medical Officer, Bethesda North Hospital, Cincinnati, OH, p. A475
Senior Vice President Quality and Chief Medical Officer, Good Samaritan Hospital, Cincinnati, OH, p. A476
FEH, Godwin
Interim Administrator, Pawhuska Hospital, Pawhuska, OK, p. A506
Interim Chief Executive Officer, Mangum Regional Medical Center, Mangum, OK, p. A501
FEHRING, Marcia, Chief Financial Officer, Horn Memorial Hospital, Ida Grove, IA, p. A224
FEICKERT, Brent, Chief Financial Officer, Unitypoint Health – Trinity Regional Medical Center, Fort Dodge, IA, p. A222
FEIDT, Leslie, Chief Information Officer, Erie County Medical Center, Buffalo, NY, p. A424
FEIGENBAUM, Avi, Chief Executive Officer, Northbrook Behavioral Health Hospital, Blackwood, NJ, p. A403
FEIKE, Jeffrey, President and Chief Administrative Officer, Fort Loudoun Medical Center, Lenoir City, TN, p. A573

FEILMEIER, Patricia A., R.N., Chief Nursing Officer, Piedmont Medical Center, Rock Hill, SC, p. A556
FEILNER, Margaret, Director Information Services, Ssm Health St. Joseph – St. Charles, Saint Charles, MO, p. A368
FEINBERG, Daniel, M.D., Chief Medical Officer, Pennsylvania Hospital, Philadelphia, PA, p. A536
FEINBERG, Jason, M.D.
  Vice President Medical Affairs and Chief Medical Officer, Finger Lakes Hospital, Geneva, NY, p. A428
  Vice President Medical Affairs and Chief Medical Officer, Soldiers And Sailors Memorial Hospital Of Yates County, Penn Yan, NY, p. A441
FEISAL, J Philip., President and Chief Executive Officer, Spartanburg Medical Center – Church Street Campus, Spartanburg, SC, p. A557
FEIST, Patricia, Manager Human Resources, Crook County Medical Services District, Sundance, WY, p. A713
FEISTRITZER, Nancye R., Chief Nursing Officer, Emory University Hospital, Atlanta, GA, p. A146
FELDMAN, David L, Executive Vice President and Treasurer, Circles Of Care, Melbourne, FL, p. A129
FELDMAN, David L., President and Chief Executive Officer, Circles Of Care, Melbourne, FL, p. A129
FELDMAN, Deborah A., President and Chief Executive Officer, Dayton Children'S Hospital, Dayton, OH, p. A481
FELDMAN, Joel
  Regional President, St. Vincent Indianapolis Hospital, Indianapolis, IN, p. A208
  Regional President, St. Vincent Seton Specialty Hospital, Indianapolis, IN, p. A208
FELDMAN, Mitchell S., Chief Executive Officer, West Boca Medical Center, Boca Raton, FL, p. A118
FELDMANN, Scott, Director Information Technology, Ssm Health Depaul Hospital – St. Louis, Bridgeton, MO, p. A357
FELDSTEIN, Charles S, M.D., Vice President Medical Affairs, St. Rose Hospital, Hayward, CA, p. A61
FELEGE, Lester, Controller, Encompass Health Rehabilitation Hospital Of New England, Woburn, MA, p. A305
FELICE, Michael, Chief Financial Officer, Poplar Springs Hospital, Petersburg, VA, p. A665
FELICETTI, Jacqueline, Chief Human Resource Officer, Penn Medicine Chester County Hospital, West Chester, PA, p. A544
FELICIANO, Jose R., Chief Executive Officer, Ryder Memorial Hospital, Humacao, PR, p. A716
FELICIANO, Myrna Quinones, M.D., Medical Director, University Pediatric Hospital, Rio Piedras, PR, p. A718
FELICIANO, Pablo, Manager Human Resources, Veterans Affairs Central Western Massachusetts Healthcare System, Leeds, MA, p. A300
FELIZ, Miriam, M.D., Medical Director, St. Catherine'S Rehabilitation Hospital, North Miami, FL, p. A133
FELKNER, Joseph G
  Chief Financial Officer, Health First Viera Hospital, Melbourne, FL, p. A129
  Executive Vice President and Chief Financial Officer, Health First Palm Bay Hospital, Palm Bay, FL, p. A135
  Executive Vice President/Chief Financial Officer, Health First Holmes Regional Medical Center, Melbourne, FL, p. A129
  Senior Vice President Finance and Chief Financial Officer, Health First Cape Canaveral Hospital, Cocoa Beach, FL, p. A120
FELL, David, M.D., Chief Medical Officer, Tulsa Spine And Specialty Hospital, Tulsa, OK, p. A510
FELLER, Alicia, Chief Executive Officer, Southwest Connecticut Mental Health System, Bridgeport, CT, p. A107
FELLER, Julie, Executive Director Human Resources, Grays Harbor Community Hospital, Aberdeen, WA, p. A670
FELLOWS, Rhonda, R.N., Chief Nursing Officer, Van Buren County Hospital, Keosauqua, IA, p. A225
FELLOWS, Steven A
  Executive Vice President and Chief Operating Officer, Goleta Valley Cottage Hospital, Santa Barbara, CA, p. A88
  Executive Vice President and Chief Operating Officer, Santa Barbara Cottage Hospital, Santa Barbara, CA, p. A88
  Executive Vice President and Chief Operating Officer, Santa Ynez Valley Cottage Hospital, Solvang, CA, p. A90
FELMLEE, Charles, Assistant Director Fiscal Services, Central Virginia Training Center, Madison Heights, VA, p. A662
FELTMAN, Steven, CPA, Chief Financial Officer, Essentia Health–Virginia, Virginia, MN, p. A341
FELTON, David
  Manager Information Systems, Waldo County General Hospital Maine Health, Belfast, ME, p. A282
  Regional Chief Information Officer, Lincolnhealth, Damariscotta, ME, p. A282

FELTS, Dave, Chief Information Systems, Logan Regional Hospital, Logan, UT, p. A648
FELTZ, Stacy, Manager Human Resource, Hillsdale Hospital, Hillsdale, MI, p. A314
FENDER, Tamra, Chief Nursing Officer, Marias Medical Center, Shelby, MT, p. A380
FENDT, Phil, Chief Financial Officer, Memorial Community Health, Aurora, NE, p. A382
FENELLO, Michael A., Administrator and West Region Chief Executive Officer, St. Luke'S Magic Valley Medical Center, Twin Falls, ID, p. A172
FENER, Michael
  Executive Director, North Shore University Hospital, Manhasset, NY, p. A430
  Executive Director, Plainview Hospital, Plainview, NY, p. A441
FENN, Mark, Director Human Resources, Pulaski Memorial Hospital, Winamac, IN, p. A216
FENNELL, Charles, Vice President Information Management, St. Joseph'S Hospital Health Center, Syracuse, NY, p. A445
FENNELL, Colin, M.D., Chief Medical Officer, Riverview Health, Crookston, MN, p. A330
FENNELL, David, M.D., Acting Medical Director, Atascadero State Hospital, Atascadero, CA, p. A51
FENOUGHTY, Michelle, M.D., Chief Medical Officer, Vice President of Medical Affairs, Hendricks Regional Health, Danville, IN, p. A202
FENSKE, Bill, Chief Financial Officer, Rice Memorial Hospital, Willmar, MN, p. A342
FENSTERLE, Chris, Chief Operating Officer, Frye Regional Medical Center, Hickory, NC, p. A456
FENWICK, Sandra L., Chief Executive Officer, Boston Children'S Hospital, Boston, MA, p. A295
FEOLA, Ferd, Chief Information Officer, Lehigh Valley Hospital – Pocono, East Stroudsburg, PA, p. A524
FERCH, Wayne
  President and Chief Executive Officer, Adventist Medical Center – Hanford, Hanford, CA, p. A61
  President and Chief Executive Officer, Adventist Medical Center–Reedley, Reedley, CA, p. A80
  President and Chief Executive Officer, Central Valley General Hospital, Hanford, CA, p. A61
FERDOUS, Riza, Health Services Director, Ossining Correctional Facilities Hospital, Ossining, NY, p. A441
FERGUS, Janie
  Director and Chief Information Officer, Chi Saint Joseph East, Lexington, KY, p. A254
  Director and Chief Information Officer, Chi Saint Joseph Health, Lexington, KY, p. A255
FERGUS, Linda, Manager Information Technology, Allegheny Valley Hospital, Natrona Heights, PA, p. A533
FERGUSON, Allison, Director Human Resources, Avoyelles Hospital, Marksville, LA, p. A273
FERGUSON, Cathy, R.N., MSN, Vice President and Chief Nursing Officer, Hamilton Medical Center, Dalton, GA, p. A151
FERGUSON, Cheryl L, Associate Administrator, Sanford Canby Medical Center, Canby, MN, p. A329
FERGUSON, Clifford, Director Information Technology and Systems, Bayshore Medical Center, Pasadena, TX, p. A628
FERGUSON, Daniel, Chief of Staff, Grove City Medical Center, Grove City, PA, p. A526
FERGUSON, Deborah
  Director, Human Resources, Sentara Albemarle Medical Center, Elizabeth City, NC, p. A453
  Human Resources Consultant, Sentara Obici Hospital, Suffolk, VA, p. A668
FERGUSON, Denise, Chief Nursing Officer, Baptist Memorial Hospital–Collierville, Collierville, TN, p. A568
FERGUSON, G Thomas, Senior Vice President and Chief Human Resources Officer, Brookdale Hospital Medical Center, New York, NY, p. A432
FERGUSON, Gordon B., President and Chief Executive Officer, Saint Thomas Rutherford Hospital, Murfreesboro, TN, p. A576
FERGUSON, Karen, Director Human Resources, Johnson County Healthcare Center, Buffalo, WY, p. A710
FERGUSON, Marla J., Commanding Officer, Bayne–Jones Army Community Hospital, Fort Polk, LA, p. A267
FERGUSON, Michael, Chief Financial Officer, Harbor Oaks Hospital, New Baltimore, MI, p. A318
FERGUSON, Nina L, Director Human Resources, Little Colorado Medical Center, Winslow, AZ, p. A38
FERGUSON, Randy, Information Systems Manager, Fairchild Medical Center, Yreka, CA, p. A95
FERGUSON, Rick, Chief Executive Officer, Oklahoma Surgical Hospital, Tulsa, OK, p. A509
FERGUSON, Tonya, Director Human Resources, Encompass Health Rehabilitation Hospital Of Virginia, Richmond, VA, p. A666

FERGUSON, Zeta, Chief Human Resources, Atlanta Veterans Affairs Medical Center, Decatur, GA, p. A151
FERIA, Jorge, M.D., President Medical Staff, Wilma N. Vazquez Medical Center, Vega Baja, PR, p. A720
FERNANDES, Roxanne, R.N., Chief Nursing Officer, Children'S Hospitals And Clinics Of Minnesota, Minneapolis, MN, p. A335
FERNANDEZ, Alexander, Chief Financial Officer, Broward Health Medical Center, Fort Lauderdale, FL, p. A122
FERNANDEZ, Arthur, Chief Financial Officer, First Hospital Panamericano, Cidra, PR, p. A716
FERNANDEZ, Benigno J, M.D., Executive Medical Director, Laurel Ridge Treatment Center, San Antonio, TX, p. A634
FERNANDEZ, Darlene, Chief Financial Officer, Unm Sandoval Regional Medical Center, Inc., Rio Rancho, NM, p. A419
FERNANDEZ, Jaime, Chief Executive Officer, Kempsville Center For Behavioral Health, Norfolk, VA, p. A664
FERNANDEZ, Jean, Chief Information Officer, Beth Israel Deaconess Hospital–Milton, Milton, MA, p. A301
FERNANDEZ, John, Chief Operating Officer, United Hospital Center, Bridgeport, WV, p. A683
FERNANDEZ, John R., President and Chief Executive Officer, Massachusetts Eye And Ear, Boston, MA, p. A295
FERNANDEZ, Marco, R.N., MSN, Chief Nursing Officer, Saint Thomas Midtown Hospital, Nashville, TN, p. A577
FERNANDEZ, Mark, M.D., Chief of Staff and President Medical Staff, Illinois Valley Community Hospital, Peru, IL, p. A193
FERNANDEZ, Richard W., President and Chief Executive Officer, Beth Israel Deaconess Hospital–Milton, Milton, MA, p. A301
FERNANDEZ, Ruben D, R.N., Vice President and Chief Nursing Officer, Hackensack Meridian Health Palisades Medical Center, North Bergen, NJ, p. A410
FERNANDEZ, Tracey, Chief Financial Officer, St. Mary Medical Center, Apple Valley, CA, p. A51
FERNANDEZ DEL VALLE, Arthur J, Chief Financial Officer, Cardiovascular Center Of Puerto Rico And The Caribbean, San Juan, PR, p. A718
FERNANDEZ–BRAVO, Grisel, Administrator and Chief Executive Officer, Memorial Hospital Miramar, Miramar, FL, p. A132
FERNYAK, Susan, M.D., Interim Chief Medical Officer & Chief Quality Officer, San Mateo Medical Center, San Mateo, CA, p. A87
FERRACANE, Tony, Vice President Human Resources, St. Mary Medical Center, Hobart, IN, p. A206
FERRANTI, Jeffrey, M.D., Chief Information Officer, Duke University Hospital, Durham, NC, p. A453
FERRARO, Lisa, Senior Vice President and Chief Operating Officer, Virtua Marlton, Marlton, NJ, p. A408
FERRAROTTI, Gianna, Director Human Resources North Region, Ohiohealth Marion General Hospital, Marion, OH, p. A486
FERREIRA, Daniel, Director Management Information Systems, Hospital De La Concepcion, San German, PR, p. A718
FERRELL, Angie
  Director Human Resources, Mercy Health – Anderson Hospital, Cincinnati, OH, p. A476
  Director Human Resources, Mercy Health – Clermont Hospital, Batavia, OH, p. A472
FERRELL, Eileen Brennan, MS, R.N., Vice President and Chief Nursing Officer, Medstar Georgetown University Hospital, Washington, DC, p. A115
FERRELL, Jennifer, Chief Nursing Officer, Encompass Health Rehabilitation Hospital Of Memphis, Memphis, TN, p. A574
FERRELL, Leslie, Chief Nursing Officer, Harrisburg Medical Center, Harrisburg, IL, p. A184
FERRELL, Ronald, Chief Information Officer, New Mexico Veterans Affairs Health Care System – Raymond G. Murphy Medical Center, Albuquerque, NM, p. A417
FERREN, Alison, Vice President Information Technology and Chief Information Officer, Abington–Lansdale Hospital Jefferson Health, Lansdale, PA, p. A529
FERRIS, David, Chief Nursing Officer and Vice President Patient Care Services, Claxton–Hepburn Medical Center, Ogdensburg, NY, p. A440
FERRIS, Joseph, Chief Financial Officer, Veterans Affairs Black Hills Health Care System, Fort Meade, SD, p. A561
FERRIS, Michael, M.D., Chief Medical Officer, Chi Health St Elizabeth, Lincoln, NE, p. A387
FERRIS, Norma, R.N., MS, Chief Nursing Officer, Spring Mountain Treatment Center, Las Vegas, NV, p. A396
FERRONI, Karen, M.D., Medical Director, Holyoke Medical Center, Holyoke, MA, p. A299
FERRY, Jane, M.D., Vice President Medical Affairs, Grand View Health, Sellersville, PA, p. A541
FERTIG, Ashley
  Chief Nursing Officer, University Hospitals Conneaut Medical Center, Conneaut, OH, p. A480

Chief Nursing Officer, University Hospitals Geneva Medical Center, Geneva, OH, p. A484

FESSER, James, Chief Nursing Officer, Palo Pinto General Hospital, Mineral Wells, TX, p. A625

FESSLER, Paula, MSN, R.N., Chief Nursing Executive, Westchester Medical Center, Valhalla, NY, p. A446

FETTEROLF, Kim, R.N., Chief Clinical Officer, Acuity Specialty Hospital Of Southern New Jersey, Willingboro, NJ, p. A415

FETTO, Julie, R.N., Chief Nursing Officer, Cleveland Clinic, Medina Hospital, Medina, OH, p. A487

FEUCHT, Jason, Chief Financial Officer, Kossuth Regional Health Center, Algona, IA, p. A217

FEUER, Tammy, Chief Executive Officer, Healthsouth Rehabilitation Hospital Of Vineland, Vineland, NJ, p. A413

FEUNNING, Charles, M.D., Chief Medical Officer, Western Reserve Hospital, Cuyahoga Falls, OH, p. A481

FIBIYI, Abayomi, Chief Human Resources Officer, North Vista Hospital, North Las Vegas, NV, p. A396

FICCHI, Adrienne, Vice President Information Management, Philadelphia Veterans Affairs Medical Center, Philadelphia, PA, p. A536

FICICCHY, Teri, R.N., MSN, Chief Nursing Officer, Bon Secours St. Francis Health System, Greenville, SC, p. A553

FICK, Beverly
Chief Nursing Officer, Desert Regional Medical Center, Palm Springs, CA, p. A76
Chief Nursing Officer, Doctors Hospital Of Manteca, Manteca, CA, p. A70

FIDLER, Soniya, MS, Chief Human Resources and Compliance Officer, Uchealth Yampa Valley Medical Center, Steamboat Springs, CO, p. A105

FIELD, Clifford, M.D., Medical Director, Ka'U Hospital, Pahala, HI, p. A166

FIELD, Edward, Administrator, Loma Linda University Behavioral Medicine Center, Redlands, CA, p. A80

FIELD, Kori, Director of Nursing, Brodstone Memorial Hospital, Superior, NE, p. A392

FIELD, Laurie, Director Human Resources, Eaton Rapids Medical Center, Eaton Rapids, MI, p. A311

FIELDER, Barb, Vice President Finance, St. Joseph Mercy Chelsea, Chelsea, MI, p. A308

FIELDING, Colene, Manager Business Office, Baylor Scott & White Medical Center–Uptown, Dallas, TX, p. A595

FIELDING, Laura M, Administrative Director Organizational Development, Holy Family Memorial, Manitowoc, WI, p. A699

FIELDS, Donald R., Community Chief Executive Officer, Harlan Arh Hospital, Harlan, KY, p. A253

FIELDS, Greg, Director Information Technology, Elbert Memorial Hospital, Elberton, GA, p. A153

FIERER, Jonathan, M.D., Chief of Staff, Martinsburg Veterans Affairs Medical Center, Martinsburg, WV, p. A687

FIERRO, Barbara, Director, Human Resources, St. Francis Hospital, The Heart Center, Roslyn, NY, p. A442

FIETEK, Denise, Information Technology, Rio Grande Hospital, Del Norte, CO, p. A98

FIFE, Stephen, Chief Financial Officer, Cape Fear Valley – Bladen County Hospital, Elizabethtown, NC, p. A454

FIFIELD, Michael, Vice President Human Resources, Oneida Healthcare, Oneida, NY, p. A440

FIGGINS, Tara, Director Human Resources, Davis Hospital And Medical Center, Layton, UT, p. A648

FIGUEROA, Maria, Director Human Resources, Ryder Memorial Hospital, Humacao, PR, p. A716

FIGUEROA, Roseann, Director Human Resources, Doctors Hospital Of Laredo, Laredo, TX, p. A619

FIGUERORA PERALTA, Wanda, President and Chief Executive Officer, Rivervalley Behavioral Health Hospital, Owensboro, KY, p. A259

FIKE, Ruthita J, Chief Executive Officer, Loma Linda University Behavioral Medicine Center, Redlands, CA, p. A80

FILADORA, Victor A, M.D., MS, Chief Clinical Services, Roswell Park Comprehensive Cancer Center, Buffalo, NY, p. A424

FILER, Christine, Director Human Resources, Encompass Health Rehabilitation Hospital Of Altoona, Altoona, PA, p. A519

FILES, Ashley S, Director Human Resources and Public Relations and Marketing, Winn Parish Medical Center, Winnfield, LA, p. A280

FILES, Carol, Chief Financial Officer, Advanced Diagnostics Hospital, Houston, TX, p. A610

FILIPINI, Alfred, Manager Human Resources, Ancora Psychiatric Hospital, Hammonton, NJ, p. A406

FILIPOWICZ, Thomas, M.D., Medical Director, St. Luke'S Hospital – Quakertown Campus, Quakertown, PA, p. A539

FILLER, Richard, Chief Financial Officer, Berger Health System, Circleville, OH, p. A477

FILLER, Scott, Chief Executive Officer, Encompass Health Rehabilitation Hospital Of Altoona, Altoona, PA, p. A519

FILLINGIM, Jed, Acting Chief Operating Officer and Associate Director, G.V. (Sonny) Montgomery Veterans Affairs Medical Center, Jackson, MS, p. A348

FILLIPO, Brian, M.D., Chief Medical Officer, Guthrie Robert Packer Hospital, Sayre, PA, p. A540

FILLMAN, Donald, M.D., Chief Medical Officer, Guthrie County Hospital, Guthrie Center, IA, p. A223

FILLMAN, Orvin, Chief Executive Officer, Rock Prairie Behavioral Health, College Station, TX, p. A593

FILLMAN, T Orvin, Vice President, Operations, Rogers Memorial Hospital, Inc., Oconomowoc, WI, p. A702

FILOSA, Frank, Fiscal Manager, Washington Dc Veterans Affairs Medical Center, Washington, DC, p. A116

FILOSA, Shannon M., Executive Director Women's and Children, Saint Francis Hospital, Tulsa, OK, p. A509

FILSON, Debbie, Chief Financial Officer, Ashland Health Center, Ashland, KS, p. A232

FINAN, Timothy J.
President and Chief Executive Officer, Bradford Regional Medical Center, Bradford, PA, p. A521
President and Chief Executive Officer, Olean General Hospital, Olean, NY, p. A440

FINCH, John
Chief Information and Community Officer, Health Alliance Hospital – Mary'S Avenue Campus, Kingston, NY, p. A430
Vice President Information Services, Health Alliance Hospital – Broadway Campus, Kingston, NY, p. A430

FINCH, Kenneth A., President and Chief Executive Officer, Texas Health Huguley Hospital Fort Worth South, Burleson, TX, p. A590

FINCH, Kim, Chief Nursing Officer, Kosciusko Community Hospital, Warsaw, IN, p. A216

FINCH, Robert D., Director, Human Resources, Piedmont Athens Regional Medical Center, Athens, GA, p. A145

FINCH, Roy
Chief Executive Officer, Palestine Regional Medical Center–East, Palestine, TX, p. A627
Chief Operating Officer, Longview Regional Medical Center, Longview, TX, p. A621

FINCH, Steve, Chief Financial Officer, Guidance Center, Flagstaff, AZ, p. A29

FINCH, Teresa, Chief Financial Officer, Trident Medical Center, Charleston, SC, p. A550

FINCHER, Jodi, Administrator, St. Joseph Medical Center, Kansas City, MO, p. A363

FINCHER, Jodi, R.N., Vice President Patient Care Services, Saint John Hospital, Leavenworth, KS, p. A239

FINDLAY, Andrew L., Deputy Commander Clinical Services, Tripler Army Medical Center, Honolulu, HI, p. A165

FINDLAY, Kelly, Director of Nurses, Pawnee County Memorial Hospital And Rural Health Clinic, Pawnee City, NE, p. A390

FINDLEY, Amber, Senior Director Nursing Services and NRC Administrator, Pleasant Valley Hospital, Point Pleasant, WV, p. A688

FINDLEY, John T, M.D., Chief Medical Officer, Beatrice Community Hospital And Health Center, Beatrice, NE, p. A383

FINE, Amy, Chief Executive Officer, Southern Coos Hospital And Health Center, Bandon, OR, p. A511

FINE, James, M.D., Chief Information Officer, Uw Medicine/Harborview Medical Center, Seattle, WA, p. A678

FINE, Mathew N., M.D., Chief Medical Officer, Oroville Hospital, Oroville, CA, p. A76

FINELLI, Frederick, M.D., Vice President Medical Affairs, Medstar Montgomery Medical Center, Olney, MD, p. A292

FINELLI, Peter, Chief Financial Officer, Banner Payson Medical Center, Payson, AZ, p. A32

FINESTEIN, Brian, Chief Executive Officer, Saint Clare'S Denville Hospital, Denville, NJ, p. A404

FINETTI, Yoany, R.N., Vice President Patient Care Services Chief Nurse Officer, Barnes–Jewish West County Hospital, Saint Louis, MO, p. A369

FINK, Renee, CPA, Chief Financial Officer, Dundy County Hospital, Benkelman, NE, p. A383

FINK, Tom, Vice President Regional Finance Officer, Range Regional Health Services, Hibbing, MN, p. A333

FINK, Walter, Chief Medical Officer, Multicare Good Samaritan Hospital, Puyallup, WA, p. A677

FINKEL, Naomi, Nurse Executive, Montgomery County Emergency Service, Norristown, PA, p. A533

FINKENBINER, Joy, Vice President, Operations, Ascension Genesys Hospital, Grand Blanc, MI, p. A312

FINLAYSON, Susan D, MSN, R.N., Senior Vice President of MMC Operations, Mercy Medical Center, Baltimore, MD, p. A288

FINLEY, Alan, Chief Operating Officer, Conway Regional Medical Center, Conway, AR, p. A40

FINLEY, Delvecchio
Chief Executive Officer, Alameda Hospital, Alameda, CA, p. A50

Chief Executive Officer, Highland Hospital, Oakland, CA, p. A75

FINLEY, Jane
Senior Vice President & Area Manager, Kaiser Permanente San Diego Medical Center, San Diego, CA, p. A83
Senior Vice President and Area Manager, Kaiser Permanente San Diego Medical Center, San Diego, CA, p. A83

FINLEY, Kelly, Customer Site Executive, Mclaren Oakland, Pontiac, MI, p. A320

FINLEY, Kevan, Chief Executive Officer, Oklahoma Forensic Center, Vinita, OK, p. A510

FINLEY, Mike, M.D., Chief Medical Officer, Christus St. Michael Health System, Texarkana, TX, p. A640

FINLEY, Tommy, Chief Information Officer, Rutherford Regional Health System, Rutherfordton, NC, p. A461

FINLEY, Waynea
Corporate Director Human Resources, Pam Specialty Hospital Of Victoria North, Victoria, TX, p. A643
Manager Human Resources, Pam Specialty Hospital Of Victoria South, Victoria, TX, p. A644
Senior Vice President Human Resources, Pam Specialty Hospital Of Covington, Covington, LA, p. A266
System Director Human Resources, Warm Springs Rehabilitation Hospital Of San Antonio, San Antonio, TX, p. A635

FINLEY–HAZLE, Gabrielle, Chief Executive Officer, St. Mary'S Medical Center, West Palm Beach, FL, p. A144

FINN, Barry C., President and Chief Executive Officer, Rush–Copley Medical Center, Aurora, IL, p. A174

FINN, Patricia, Chief Executive Officer, Fulton County Health Center, Wauseon, OH, p. A493

FINNEGAN, Jay, Chief Executive Officer, St. Lucie Medical Center, Port St Lucie, FL, p. A137

FINNEGAN, Mary Jane, Chief Nursing Officer, St. Catherine Of Siena Medical Center, Smithtown, NY, p. A444

FINNEGAN, Patti, Chief Operating Officer, Ssm Select Rehabilitation Hospital, Richmond Heights, MO, p. A367

FINNERTY, Kimberley, MSN, R.N., Chief Nursing Officer, Jefferson Hospital, Jefferson Hills, PA, p. A528

FINNEY, David, R.N., Vice President Nursing, Uhs Chenango Memorial Hospital, Norwich, NY, p. A440

FINNEY, Michele, Chief Executive Officer, Desert Regional Medical Center, Palm Springs, CA, p. A76

FINSTAD, Gary A, M.D., Chief of Staff, Kern Valley Healthcare District, Lake Isabella, CA, p. A63

FIORE–LOPEZ, Nicolette, R.N., Chief Nursing Officer, St. Charloc Hospital, Port Jefferson, NY, p. A441

FIORET, Phil, M.D., Vice President Medical Affairs, King'S Daughters Medical Center, Ashland, KY, p. A249

FIORICA, James, M.D., Chief Medical Officer, Sarasota Memorial Health Care System, Sarasota, FL, p. A139

FIRES, Wiley M, Administrator, Shamrock General Hospital, Shamrock, TX, p. A636

FIRES, Wiley M, Administrator, Shamrock General Hospital, Shamrock, TX, p. A636

FIRMAN, Russell, M.D., Chief Medical Officer, Cortland Regional Medical Center, Cortland, NY, p. A426

FIRMIN, Kelli, Interim Chief Nursing Officer, Pre–Op and PACU Manager, Surgical Specialty Center Of Baton Rouge, Baton Rouge, LA, p. A264

FIRMINGER, Barbara, Chief Administrative Officer, Verde Valley Medical Center, Cottonwood, AZ, p. A29

FIRTCH, William, M.D., Physician In Chief, Kaiser Permanente Redwood City Medical Center, Redwood City, CA, p. A80

FISCHBACH, John T., Vice President of Finance, Chief Financial Officer, Lima Memorial Health System, Lima, OH, p. A485

FISCHELS, Diane, Senior Vice President and Chief Operating Officer, Mercyone North Iowa Medical Center, Mason City, IA, p. A226

FISCHER, Jason
Chief Information Officer, Pih Health Hospital – Downey, Downey, CA, p. A56
Chief Information Officer, Pih Health Hospital – Whittier, Whittier, CA, p. A95

FISCHER, JC, Director Human Resources, Mercy Regional Medical Center, Lorain, OH, p. A486

FISCHER, Lisa, Director Human Resources, Brown County Hospital, Ainsworth, NE, p. A382

FISCHER, Patricia, President and Chief Executive Officer, Hshs St. Elizabeth'S Hospital, O'Fallon, IL, p. A192

FISCHER, Rebecca J, Chief Financial Officer, Brookdale Hospital Medical Center, New York, NY, p. A432

FISCHER, Robert, M.D., Medical Director, Methodist Hospital For Surgery, Addison, TX, p. A581

FISCHER, Sandra, Director Human Resources, W. G. (Bill) Heffner Veterans Affairs Medical Center, Salisbury, NC, p. A461

FISCHER, Steven P, Chief Financial Officer, Beth Israel Deaconess Medical Center, Boston, MA, p. A294

FISCHER, Tamara, Chief Nursing Officer, Okeene Municipal Hospital, Okeene, OK, p. A503

FISER, David, Vice President and Chief Information Officer, Cleveland Clinic Akron General, Akron, OH, p. A471

FISH, Carolyn, Director Human Resources, Mission Community Hospital, Los Angeles, CA, p. A68

FISH, Elizabeth
 Chief Information Officer, University Of Maryland Shore Medical Center At Dorchester, Cambridge, MD, p. A289
 Chief Information Officer, University Of Maryland Shore Medical Center At Easton, Easton, MD, p. A290
 Senior Director Site Executive and Information Technology, University Of Maryland Shore Medical Center At Chestertown, Chestertown, MD, p. A289

FISH, Eric, M.D., Vice President of Medical Affairs and Chief Medical Officers, Schneck Medical Center, Seymour, IN, p. A214

FISH, Francis James, Vice President and Chief Financial Officer, Mile Bluff Medical Center, Mauston, WI, p. A699

FISHBAUGHER, David, Chief Medical Information, Mercyone Iowa City Medical Center, Iowa City, IA, p. A224

FISHEL, Stephanie, Vice President Patient Care Services and Chief Nursing Officer, Nathan Littauer Hospital And Nursing Home, Gloversville, NY, p. A428

FISHER, Alan, Chief Executive Officer, Mid–Valley Hospital, Omak, WA, p. A676

FISHER, Charles, Chief Executive Officer, U. S. Public Health Service Indian Hospital, Eagle Butte, SD, p. A560

FISHER, David
 Director Information Systems, Upmc Lititz, Lititz, PA, p. A530
 Vice President Human Resources, Signature Healthcare Brockton Hospital, Brockton, MA, p. A296

FISHER, David, M.D., Senior Vice President and Chief Medical Officer, Seattle Children'S Hospital, Seattle, WA, p. A678

FISHER, Diane, R.N., VP, Patient Care Services, Munson Healthcare Otsego Memorial Hospital, Gaylord, MI, p. A312

FISHER, Irvin, Director, Information Services, Hahnemann University Hospital, Philadelphia, PA, p. A534

FISHER, J. Matthew, Chief Financial Officer, Russell Medical, Alexander City, AL, p. A13

FISHER, Jacob, Chief Executive Officer, Palms Of Pasadena Hospital, Saint Petersburg, FL, p. A138

FISHER, Jan E, Executive Vice President, Chief Operating Officer and Chief Administrative Officer, Upmc Susquehanna Williamsport, Williamsport, PA, p. A545

FISHER, Jan E.
 President, Upmc Altoona, Altoona, PA, p. A520
 President, Upmc Bedford Memorial, Everett, PA, p. A526

FISHER, Jeannie, Coordinator Information Technology, Webster County Memorial Hospital, Webster Springs, WV, p. A690

FISHER, Jennifer A, Manager Human Resources, Henry County Hospital, Napoleon, OH, p. A488

FISHER, Jessica Marie., Chief Executive Officer, Tri Valley Health System, Cambridge, NE, p. A383

FISHER, John, M.D., Chief Medical Officer, Martin Luther King, Jr. Community Hospital, Los Angeles, CA, p. A68

FISHER, Kerry, M.D., Medical Director, Lds Hospital, Salt Lake City, UT, p. A651

FISHER, Lynn, M.D., Chief of Staff, Rooks County Health Center, Plainville, KS, p. A244

FISHER, Mahana, M.D., Medical Director, Blue Mountain Hospital, Blanding, UT, p. A647

FISHER, Mark, Chief Human Resources Officer, Los Alamitos Medical Center, Los Alamitos, CA, p. A65

FISHER, Mathew, M.D., Medical Director, Springbrook Behavioral Health System, Travelers Rest, SC, p. A557

FISHER, Michael, President and Chief Executive Officer, Cincinnati Children'S Hospital Medical Center, Cincinnati, OH, p. A475

FISHER, Michael W., Director, Va Portland Healthcare System, Portland, OR, p. A516

FISHER, Richard, President and Chief Executive Officer, Fox Chase Cancer Center–American Oncologic Hospital, Philadelphia, PA, p. A534

FISHER, Robert E, Chief Financial Officer, Coquille Valley Hospital, Coquille, OR, p. A512

FISHER, Ryan
 Director Human Resources, Bluffton Hospital, Bluffton, OH, p. A473
 Director of Human Resources, Blanchard Valley Hospital, Findlay, OH, p. A483

FISHER, Sharon, M.D., Chief of Staff, Bartlett Regional Hospital, Juneau, AK, p. A26

FISHER, Sharon, R.N., Chief Nursing Officer, Tyrone Hospital, Tyrone, PA, p. A542

FISHER, Teresa, Chief Nursing Officer, Lakewood Health System, Staples, MN, p. A341

FISHER, Teresa, R.N., Chief Nursing Officer, Fort Loudoun Medical Center, Lenoir City, TN, p. A573

FISHER, Thomas, Senior Vice President and Chief Financial Officer, University Of Tennessee Medical Center, Knoxville, TN, p. A572

FISHER, Vicky, Ph.D., R.N., Chief Nurse Executive, Catawba Hospital, Catawba, VA, p. A657

FISHER–FORD, Karen, Director of Health Information Management, West Central Georgia Regional Hospital, Columbus, GA, p. A151

FISHKIN, Edward, M.D., Medical Director, Brookdale Hospital Medical Center, New York, NY, p. A432

FISK, Amber, Director Human Resources, Memorial Hospital Of Sweetwater County, Rock Springs, WY, p. A712

FISK, Anita, Director Human Resources, Three Rivers Hospital, Brewster, WA, p. A671

FISK, Kathryn M, Chief Human Resources Officer, El Camino Hospital, Mountain View, CA, p. A73

FISK, Kellee J., Chief People and Strategy Officer, Altru Health System, Grand Forks, ND, p. A467

FISLER, Eileen, Chief Financial Officer, Pacifica Hospital Of The Valley, Los Angeles, CA, p. A68

FITCH, Andrew, Chief Financial Officer, St. Elias Specialty Hospital, Anchorage, AK, p. A25

FITCH, James A, Director Human Resources, Houston Methodist Continuing Care Hospital, Katy, TX, p. A617

FITCH, John A, Vice President Human Resources, Campbell County Health, Gillette, WY, p. A711

FITE, David, Director Information Technology, Towner County Medical Center, Cando, ND, p. A465

FITE, Theresa, R.N., Chief Financial Officer, Fleming County Hospital, Flemingsburg, KY, p. A251

FITTERMAN, Nick, Executive Director, Huntington Hospital, Huntington, NY, p. A429

FITTS, Barry
 Chief Information Officer, Hillside Rehabilitation Hospital, Warren, OH, p. A493
 Chief Information Officer, Trumbull Memorial Hospital, Warren, OH, p. A493

FITZGERALD, Amy, Human Resources Manager, Copley Hospital, Morrisville, VT, p. A654

FITZGERALD, Andy, Chief Executive Officer, Campbell County Health, Gillette, WY, p. A711

FITZGERALD, Kerri, Executive Director, Hackensack Meridian Health Shore Rehabilitation Institute, Brick, NJ, p. A403

FITZGERALD, Mike
 Chief Financial Officer, Harrison Medical Center, Bremerton, WA, p. A670
 Chief Financial Officer, St. Clare Hospital, Lakewood, WA, p. A674
 Chief Financial Officer, St. Francis Hospital, Federal Way, WA, p. A673
 Chief Financial Officer, St. Joseph Medical Center, Tacoma, WA, p. A681

FITZGERALD, Patty, Staff Services, Munson Healthcare Charlevoix Hospital, Charlevoix, MI, p. A308

FITZGERALD, Philip, Chief Operating Officer, John F. Kennedy Memorial Hospital, Indio, CA, p. A62

FITZGERALD, Thomas J., III, Director, Va Palo Alto Health Care System, Palo Alto, CA, p. A77

FITZMAURICE, Dennis, Vice President, Professional Services, Community First Medical Center, Chicago, IL, p. A177

FITZPATRICK, Anna, Director Human Resources, St. Anthony Regional Hospital, Carroll, IA, p. A218

FITZPATRICK, Daniel, Director Human Resources, Whitesburg Arh Hospital, Whitesburg, KY, p. A261

FITZPATRICK, James, M.D., Vice President Medical Affairs, Kenmore Mercy Hospital, Kenmore, NY, p. A430

FITZPATRICK, Leigh Ann, Superintendent, Kerrville State Hospital, Kerrville, TX, p. A617

FITZSIMMONS, Shaun, Director Information Technology Services, Community Medical Center, Toms River, NJ, p. A413

FITZSIMONS, Patricia Sue, R.N., Ph.D., Senior Vice President Patient Services, Yale–New Haven Hospital, New Haven, CT, p. A110

FLACH, Shannan, Chief Executive Officer, Kingman Community Hospital, Kingman, KS, p. A238

FLACK, Charles, Interim Chief Information Officer, Orange County Global Medical Center, Inc., Santa Ana, CA, p. A88

FLAHERTY, John
 Chief Financial Officer, Encompass Health Rehabilitation Hospital Of Western Massachusetts, Ludlow, MA, p. A300
 Controller, Fairlawn Rehabilitation Hospital, Worcester, MA, p. A305

FLAHERTY, Linda, R.N., Senior Vice President, Patient Care Services, Mclean Hospital, Belmont, MA, p. A294

FLAHERTY, Patrick, Director Management Information, Naval Hospital Bremerton, Bremerton, WA, p. A671

FLAHERTY, Steve, Chief Executive Officer, Warm Springs Rehabilitation Hospital Of San Antonio, San Antonio, TX, p. A635

FLAHERTY, Tom, Assistant Administrator, Los Angeles County Central Jail Hospital, Los Angeles, CA, p. A68

FLAKE, Robert
 Chief Executive Officer, Middle Park Medical Center–Kremmling, Kremmling, CO, p. A102
 Chief Financial Officer, Middle Park Medical Center–Kremmling, Kremmling, CO, p. A102

FLAMING, Patrick, R.N., Director Inpatient Operations, Prairie View, Newton, KS, p. A242

FLAMM, Cindy, Manager Quality, Choate Mental Health Center, Anna, IL, p. A173

FLANAGAN, Carl J., Chief Financial Officer, La Paz Regional Hospital, Parker, AZ, p. A32

FLANAGAN, Craig, Chief Financial Officer, Unitypoint Health – Allen Hospital, Waterloo, IA, p. A231

FLANAGAN, Michael J, Senior Vice President and Chief Operating Officer, St. Clair Hospital, Pittsburgh, PA, p. A537

FLANAGAN, Thomas, M.D., Medical Director, Aurora Behavioral Healthcare San Diego, San Diego, CA, p. A83

FLANAGAN, Tom, Chief Executive Officer, Osage Beach Center For Cognitive Disorders, Osage Beach, MO, p. A366

FLANARY, Tresha, R.N., Chief Clinical Services Officer, Wamego Health Center, Wamego, KS, p. A247

FLANDERS, David, Chief Operating Officer, Candler County Hospital, Metter, GA, p. A157

FLANIGAN, Erin, Vice President Human Resources, Wentworth–Douglass Hospital, Dover, NH, p. A399

FLANIGAN, Kevin, Chief Executive Officer, Northern Inyo Hospital, Bishop, CA, p. A53

FLANNERY, Lindsay, R.N., Vice President Patient Care Services, Avera Sacred Heart Hospital, Yankton, SD, p. A565

FLANNERY, Maureen, Vice President Clinic Operations, Straub Medical Center, Honolulu, HI, p. A165

FLANNERY, Patrick, Administrator, Christus St. Michael Rehabilitation Hospital, Texarkana, TX, p. A640

FLANNERY, Robert, Chief Financial Officer, University Hospital, Madison, WI, p. A698

FLANZ, Bruce J., President and Chief Executive Officer, Brookdale Hospital Medical Center, New York, NY, p. A432

FLASCHENRIEM, Julie, Chief Information Officer, Park Nicollet Methodist Hospital, Saint Louis Park, MN, p. A339

FLASHER, Sara, Chief Nurse Executive, Warren State Hospital, Warren, PA, p. A543

FLATOW, Evan, President, Brookdale Hospital Medical Center, New York, NY, p. A432

FLATT, G Wayne, D.O., Chief Medical Director, Pushmataha Hospital, Antlers, OK, p. A496

FLATTERY, William
 Vice President and Administrator Western Division, Carilion Giles Community Hospital, Pearisburg, VA, p. A664
 Vice President and Administrator Western Division, Carilion New River Valley Medical Center, Christiansburg, VA, p. A658

FLAVIO, Chuck, Chief Executive Officer, Saint Simons By–The–Sea Hospital, Saint Simons Island, GA, p. A159

FLECHSIG, Randolph K., Administrator, Sheridan Community Hospital, Sheridan, MI, p. A322

FLECK, Julie, Chief Operating Officer, Parkview Ortho Hospital, Fort Wayne, IN, p. A204

FLECKENSTEIN, Casey, Nurse Manager, Monroe County Hospital, Forsyth, GA, p. A153

FLEEGEL, Monica, Director Human Resources, Mayo Clinic Health System – Albert Lea And Austin, Albert Lea, MN, p. A327

FLEENOR, Dennis, Administrator, Muleshoe Area Medical Center, Muleshoe, TX, p. A625

FLEET, Aaron, R.N., Chief Nursing Officer, Baylor Scott & White Texas Spine & Joint Hospital–Tyler, Tyler, TX, p. A642

FLEISCHMANN, Craig, Vice President Finance, University Of Maryland Medical Center Midtown Campus, Baltimore, MD, p. A287

FLEISCHMANN, Tim, Chief Financial Officer, Tuality Healthcare, Hillsboro, OR, p. A513

FLEISHMAN, Samuel A, M.D., Chief Medical Officer, Cape Fear Valley Medical Center, Fayetteville, NC, p. A454

FLEITES, Fernando, Senior Vice President Human Resources, Bon Secours St. Francis Health System, Greenville, SC, p. A553

FLEMER, Andrew, Chief Operating Officer, South Georgia Medical Center, Valdosta, GA, p. A162

FLEMING, Jared, Director, Information Services, Lourdes Counseling Center, Richland, WA, p. A677

FLEMING, Joshua, Vice President Chief Clinical Officer, Leesburg Regional Medical Center, Leesburg, FL, p. A128

FLEMING, Michael, Chief People Officer, Banner – University Medical Center Phoenix, Phoenix, AZ, p. A33

FLEMING, Shane
 Chief Financial Officer, Capital Health Medical Center–Hopewell, Pennington, NJ, p. A410

Chief Financial Officer, Capital Health Regional Medical Center, Trenton, NJ, p. A413
FLEMING, William P, Chief Operating Officer, Norwood Hospital, Norwood, MA, p. A302
FLEMMING, Libby, Controller and Chief Information Officer, South Georgia Medical Center Lanier Campus, Lakeland, GA, p. A155
FLEMMING, Michael, Administrator, Cornerstone Behavioral Health Hospital Of Union County, Berkeley Heights, NJ, p. A403
FLESNER, Lynn, Director of Nursing, Glacial Ridge Health System, Glenwood, MN, p. A332
FLETCHALL, Terry L., President and Chief Executive Officer, Santiam Hospital, Stayton, OR, p. A518
FLETCHER, Audrey, Chief Operating Officer, Madison Memorial Hospital, Rexburg, ID, p. A171
FLETCHER, Bill, Director Information Technology, Pinnacle Regional Hospital, Boonville, MO, p. A357
FLETCHER, Chris, Director of Human Resources, Fishermen'S Hospital, Marathon, FL, p. A129
FLETCHER, Jennifer, Chief of Staff, Decatur County Memorial Hospital, Greensburg, IN, p. A205
FLETCHER, John, Chief Executive Officer, Patrick B. Harris Psychiatric Hospital, Anderson, SC, p. A549
FLETCHER, John R., President, Lehigh Valley Hospital – Hazleton, Hazleton, PA, p. A527
FLETCHER, Kathy, R.N., MSN, Interim Chief Nursing Officer, Val Verde Regional Medical Center, Del Rio, TX, p. A599
FLETCHER, Kevin, Director Information Systems, Medical City Mckinney, Mckinney, TX, p. A624
FLETCHER, Michael, M.D., Vice President and Chief Medical Officer, Hancock Regional Hospital, Greenfield, IN, p. A205
FLETCHER, Stephanie L, CPA, Chief Financial Officer, Union General Hospital, Blairsville, GA, p. A148
FLETCHER–JANZEN, David, Chief Executive Officer, Chicago Lakeshore Hospital, Chicago, IL, p. A177
FLETT, Will, Vice President Finance and Chief Financial Officer, Avera Queen Of Peace Hospital, Mitchell, SD, p. A562
FLICEK, David, President and Chief Executive Officer, Avera Mckennan Hospital And University Health Center, Sioux Falls, SD, p. A563
FLICKEMA, James, Vice President Market Development, Munson Healthcare Otsego Memorial Hospital, Gaylord, MI, p. A312
FLICKINGER, Kenneth E, Chief Financial Officer, Penn Medicine Chester County Hospital, West Chester, PA, p. A544
FLINCHBAUGH, Robert, D.O., Chief Medical Officer, Winneshiek Medical Center, Decorah, IA, p. A221
FLINN, Charles, Vice President, Chief Operating Officer, Saint Mary'S Hospital, Waterbury, CT, p. A111
FLINN, James, Chief Executive Officer, St. Luke'S Medical Center, Phoenix, AZ, p. A34
FLINT, Jennifer, Chief Financial Officer, Laird Hospital, Union, MS, p. A354
FLINT, Ruth, Chief Nursing Officer, St. Joseph Medical Center, Tacoma, WA, p. A681
FLIPPO, Mary Elizabeth, R.N., MSN, Vice President and Chief Nursing Officer, Cleveland Clinic Martin North Hospital, Stuart, FL, p. A140
FLIS, James D, Chief Financial Officer, Livengrin Foundation, Bensalem, PA, p. A520
FLOOD, James, Director Information Systems, Claxton–Hepburn Medical Center, Ogdensburg, NY, p. A440
FLOREN, Joshua, President, Texas Health Presbyterian Hospital Plano, Plano, TX, p. A630
FLORENTINE, Erich
Chief People Officer, Inspira Medical Center–Elmer, Elmer, NJ, p. A405
Chief People Officer, Inspira Medical Center–Vineland, Vineland, NJ, p. A413
FLORES, Andrea, Director, Information Systems, Providence Little Company Of Mary Medical Center – Torrance, Torrance, CA, p. A92
FLORES, Debbie
Chief Executive Officer, Banner Del E. Webb Medical Center, Sun City West, AZ, p. A36
Interim Chief Executive Officer, Banner Boswell Medical Center, Sun City, AZ, p. A36
FLORES, Debra A, R.N., MS, President and Chief Operating Officer, Valley Children'S Healthcare, Madera, CA, p. A70
FLORES, Jacob, Chief Information Officer, Frio Regional Hospital, Pearsall, TX, p. A628
FLORES, Jerome
Chief Financial Officer and Chief Operating Officer, Kahuku Medical Center, Kahuku, HI, p. A165
Chief Financial Officer, Sunrise Canyon Hospital, Lubbock, TX, p. A622
FLORES, Linda, R.N., MSN, Vice President Nursing Services, Parkview Medical Center, Pueblo, CO, p. A104
FLORES, Rick, Interim Chief Executive Officer, Big Bend Regional Medical Center, Alpine, TX, p. A582
FLORKOWSKI, Douglas, Chief Executive Officer, Crawford Memorial Hospital, Robinson, IL, p. A194
FLOURA, Kamal, M.D., Medical Director, Eastern State Hospital, Medical Lake, WA, p. A675
FLOWE, Kenneth, M.D., Chief Medical Officer, Rice Memorial Hospital, Willmar, MN, p. A342
FLOWERS, Amy, Controller, Encompass Health Rehabilitation Hospital Of Princeton, Princeton, WV, p. A688
FLOWERS, Deborah, Director Human Resources, Monroe County Hospital, Forsyth, GA, p. A153
FLOWERS, Frank M., M.D.
Area Medical Director, Kaiser Permanente Moreno Valley Medical Center, Moreno Valley, CA, p. A73
Area Medical Director, Kaiser Permanente Riverside Medical Center, Riverside, CA, p. A81
FLOWERS, Michael, Director Information Management, Calhoun–Liberty Hospital, Blountstown, FL, p. A118
FLOWERS, Scott, Vice President Professional Services, Thibodaux Regional Medical Center, Thibodaux, LA, p. A279
FLOWERS, Susan S, MSN, R.N., Chief Nursing Officer, Cumberland County Hospital, Burkesville, KY, p. A250
FLOWERS, Taylor, Senior Vice President Human Resources, Onslow Memorial Hospital, Jacksonville, NC, p. A457
FLOYD, Dorothy, Superintendent, Terrell State Hospital, Terrell, TX, p. A640
FLOYD, Duane, Vice President Human Resources and Professional Services, Watertown Regional Medical Center, Watertown, WI, p. A707
FLOYD, Greg, Chief Executive Officer, Lafayette Regional Rehabilitation Hospital, Lafayette, IN, p. A209
FLOYD, Kiley, Chief Executive Officer, Nemaha Valley Community Hospital, Seneca, KS, p. A245
FLOYD, Miranda, R.N., Chief Nursing Officer, Mosaic Medical Center – Albany, Albany, MO, p. A356
FLOYD, Robert, D.O., Chief Medical Staff, Davis County Hospital, Bloomfield, IA, p. A218
FLOYD, Terri, Chief Financial Officer, Bates County Memorial Hospital, Butler, MO, p. A357
FLOYD, William Brian., President, Vidant Medical Center, Greenville, NC, p. A455
FLUGUM, Aaron, Chief Executive Officer, Mercyone New Hampton Medical Center, New Hampton, IA, p. A227
FLUKE, Cinda, R.N., Chief Nursing Officer, Saint Joseph Mount Sterling, Mount Sterling, KY, p. A258
FLUTY, Lisa, Director Information Services, Baptist Health Lexington, Lexington, KY, p. A254
FLYGARE, Matthew, Director Human Resources, Mountain West Medical Center, Tooele, UT, p. A653
FLYNN, Brian, Chief Human Resources Officer, Veterans Affairs Northern Indiana Health Care System, Fort Wayne, IN, p. A204
FLYNN, Chanda, R.N., MSN, Chief Nursing Officer, Spartanburg Medical Center – Mary Black, Spartanburg, SC, p. A557
FLYNN, Cheryl, Senior Vice President Chief Human Resources Officer, Methodist Charlton Medical Center, Dallas, TX, p. A597
FLYNN, James, Chief Executive Officer, Galesburg Cottage Hospital, Galesburg, IL, p. A183
FLYNN, Julianne, M.D., Chief of Staff, South Texas Veterans Health Care System, San Antonio, TX, p. A635
FLYNN, Kristin, Chief Human Resources Officer, Sierra Vista Regional Medical Center, San Luis Obispo, CA, p. A87
FLYNN, Matthew J, Chief Financial Officer West Region, Northwestern Medicine Valley West Hospital, Sandwich, IL, p. A195
FLYNN, Patrick, Chief Financial Officer, Warm Springs Medical Center, Warm Springs, GA, p. A162
FOARD, Mesa, Director Information technology, William S. Hall Psychiatric Institute, Columbia, SC, p. A551
FOGARTY, John M., President and Chief Executive Officer, Beth Israel Deaconess Hospital–Needham Campus, Needham, MA, p. A301
FOGARTY, Kathleen R., Director, Kansas City Veterans Affairs Medical Center, Kansas City, MO, p. A362
FOGELSON, Julia, R.N., Chief Operating Officer and Chief Nursing Executive, French Hospital Medical Center, San Luis Obispo, CA, p. A87
FOGG, Jay Trevor, Chief Nursing Officer, Western Plains Medical Complex, Dodge City, KS, p. A234
FOGG, Robert W, Director Finance, Lake Taylor Transitional Care Hospital, Norfolk, VA, p. A664
FOLDS, Jesse, Director of Information Technologies, Merit Health Wesley, Hattiesburg, MS, p. A348
FOLEY, Chris, Chief of Medicine, Children'S Hospital Of The King'S Daughters, Norfolk, VA, p. A663
FOLEY, James T, CPA, Vice President and Chief Financial Officer, Shore Medical Center, Somers Point, NJ, p. A412
FOLEY, Jay, President and Chief Executive Officer, Southwestern Regional Medical Center, Tulsa, OK, p. A509
FOLEY, John, Chief Information Officer, Allegheny General Hospital, Pittsburgh, PA, p. A537
FOLEY, Michael, M.D., Chief Medical Officer, North Okaloosa Medical Center, Crestview, FL, p. A120
FOLEY, Regina, Chief Operating Officer, Hackensack Meridian Health Southern Ocean Medical Center, Manahawkin, NJ, p. A408
FOLEY, Regina, R.N., FACHE, Vice President Nursing and Operations, Hackensack Meridian Health Ocean Medical Center, Brick Township, NJ, p. A404
FOLK, Jeffrey R M.D., Vice President Medical Affairs and Chief Medical Officer, Piedmont Newnan Hospital, Newnan, GA, p. A158
FOLKENBERG, Todd, Chief Executive Officer, Porter Adventist Hospital, Denver, CO, p. A99
FOLL, Gary R, Chief Financial Officer, Atchison Hospital, Atchison, KS, p. A232
FOLLETT, Traci, Director Clinical Informatics, Sierra View Medical Center, Porterville, CA, p. A79
FOLSKE, Lance, Chief Executive Officer, Sun Behavioral Columbus, Columbus, OH, p. A480
FOLSOM, Lori S, Assistant Vice President Human Resources, Tift Regional Medical Center, Tifton, GA, p. A162
FOLTZ, JoAnn M., Chief Executive Officer, Sanford Wheaton Medical Center, Wheaton, MN, p. A342
FONDESSY, Terrence, M.D., Vice President Medical Affairs, Promedica Fostoria Community Hospital, Fostoria, OH, p. A483
FONDREN, Shay, Administrator, Hale County Hospital, Greensboro, AL, p. A19
FONKEN, Paul, M.D., Chief of Staff, Estes Park Medical Center, Estes Park, CO, p. A100
FONTAINE–WESTHART, Mark, Associate Director, Bedford Veterans Affairs Medical Center, Edith Nourse Rogers Memorial Veterans Hospital, Bedford, MA, p. A294
FONTENAULT, Richard, Director Information Systems, Medical City Green Oaks Hospital, Dallas, TX, p. A597
FONTENELLE, Mary, Executive Nurse Director, Eastern Louisiana Mental Health System, Jackson, LA, p. A269
FONTENOT, Jude, Administrator, Lafayette General Medical Center, Lafayette, LA, p. A271
FONZIE, Juril, Director Human Resources, Helena Regional Medical Center, Helena, AR, p. A43
FOOTE, Donald E, Fiscal Officer, Wilkes–Barre Veterans Affairs Medical Center, Wilkes, PA, p. A545
FOOTE, John, Chief Information Officer, Manchester Veterans Affairs Medical Center, Manchester, NH, p. A401
FOOTE, Mark, Chief Financial Officer, Madera Community Hospital, Madera, CA, p. A70
FORAND, Angela, Director, William S. Hall Psychiatric Institute, Columbia, SC, p. A551
FORBES, Bill, Chief Executive Officer, South Georgia Medical Center, Valdosta, GA, p. A162
FORBES, Brenda, Controller, Encompasss Health Rehabilitation Hospital Of Fort Smith, Fort Smith, AR, p. A42
FORBES, Dan, Vice President Human Resources, Ohsu Hospital, Portland, OR, p. A516
FORBES, Jonathan, Director Human Resources, Ashtabula County Medical Center, Ashtabula, OH, p. A472
FORBES, Ronald O, M.D., Medical Director, Central State Hospital, Petersburg, VA, p. A664
FORBORT, Gordy, Chief Financial Officer, Firstlight Health System, Mora, MN, p. A336
FORD, Alisa, Vice President Human Resources, The University Of Kansas Hospital, Kansas City, KS, p. A238
FORD, Angelique, Administrator Human Resources, Spring Valley Hospital Medical Center, Las Vegas, NV, p. A396
FORD, Cora, Vice President Human Resources, Our Lady Of The Lake Regional Medical Center, Baton Rouge, LA, p. A264
FORD, Frank, President, St. Luke'S Sacred Heart Campus, Allentown, PA, p. A519
FORD, James, Director Human Resources, Baptist Health – Van Buren, Van Buren, AR, p. A49
FORD, Karen, Chief Nursing Officer, Sabine Medical Center, Many, LA, p. A273
FORD, LeeAnn, Director Human Resources and Imaging, The Physicians Centre Hospital, Bryan, TX, p. A590
FORD, Marcia F, Chief Operating Officer, Hawthorn Children Psychiatric Hospital, Saint Louis, MO, p. A369
FORD, Mary Carroll, Chief Information Officer, Einstein Medical Center Montgomery, East Norriton, PA, p. A524
FORD, Michael, Vice President Patient Services, Wood County Hospital, Bowling Green, OH, p. A473
FORD, Veronica, Vice President Human Resources, University Of Maryland Capital Region Health Prince George'S Hospital Center, Cheverly, MD, p. A289

FORDE, Steve, Chief Executive Officer, Nelson County Health System, Mcville, ND, p. A468

FORDHAM, Karen, Chief Executive Officer, Venice Regional Bayfront Health, Venice, FL, p. A143

FORDYCE, Brian, Director Information Technology, Roosevelt Medical Center, Culbertson, MT, p. A375

FOREMAN, Christopher, Director Human Resources, Santa Rosa Medical Center, Milton, FL, p. A132

FOREMAN, Kim, M.D., Chief of Staff, Baylor Scott & White Texas Spine & Joint Hospital–Tyler, Tyler, TX, p. A642

FOREMAN, Lee Ann
Vice President Human Resources, Mississippi Baptist Medical Center, Jackson, MS, p. A349
Vice President Human Resources, Select Specialty Hospital – Belhaven, Jackson, MS, p. A349

FOREMAN, Nena, Chief Nursing Officer, Palo Verde Hospital, Blythe, CA, p. A53

FORESE, Laura, M.D., M.P.H., Executive Vice President and Chief Medical Officer, Brookdale Hospital Medical Center, New York, NY, p. A432

FOREST, Karen, Health Care Manager, State Penitentiary Hospital, Walla Walla, WA, p. A681

FORET, Chris, M.D., Chief of Staff, Riverside Medical Center, Franklinton, LA, p. A267

FORET, Robert, Chief Financial Officer, Yoakum Community Hospital, Yoakum, TX, p. A646

FORGE, Brenda J, Vice President, Human Resources, Regional West Medical Center, Scottsbluff, NE, p. A391

FORGEY, Warren, President and Chief Executive Officer, Schneck Medical Center, Seymour, IN, p. A214

FORKEL, Todd
Interim Chief Executive Officer, Avera St. Mary'S Hospital, Pierre, SD, p. A562
President and Chief Executive Officer, Avera St. Luke'S Hospital, Aberdeen, SD, p. A559

FORKNER, Christine, Executive Vice President and Chief Financial Officer, National Jewish Health, Denver, CO, p. A99

FORNIER–JOHNSON, Michelle, Group Vice President Human Resources, St. Anthony Hospital, Lakewood, CO, p. A103

FORREST, Brian, Vice President Human Resources, Cayuga Medical Center At Ithaca, Ithaca, NY, p. A429

FORREST, Mary Helen, R.N., Chief Nursing Officer, Uams Medical Center, Little Rock, AR, p. A45

FORREST, Molly, President and Chief Executive Officer, Joyce Eisenberg–Keefer Medical Center, Reseda, CA, p. A80

FORRESTER, John M, Director Information Services, Hamilton Medical Center, Dalton, GA, p. A151

FORSCH, Randall T, M.D., M.P.H., Chief Medical Officer, St. Joseph Mercy Chelsea, Chelsea, MI, p. A308

FORSTER, Tracy B, R.N., Senior Director of Nursing, Novant Health Matthews Medical Center, Matthews, NC, p. A458

FORSTNER, Jim
Chief Executive Officer, Emory Decatur Hospital, Decatur, GA, p. A152
Chief Executive Officer, Emory Hillandale Hospital, Lithonia, GA, p. A156
Chief Executive Officer, Emory Long–Term Acute Care, Decatur, GA, p. A152

FORSYTH, Beth, Chief Operating Officer, Good Samaritan Medical Center, Lafayette, CO, p. A102

FORSYTH, Larry, Director Information Services, Ou Medical Center, Oklahoma City, OK, p. A505

FORT, Claudio D., President and Chief Executive Officer, Rutland Regional Medical Center, Rutland, VT, p. A655

FORT, Glenn, Chief Medical Officer, Landmark Medical Center, Woonsocket, RI, p. A548

FORTENBERRY, Denise, Chief Nursing Officer and Chief Compliance Officer, Cypress Pointe Surgical Hospital, Hammond, LA, p. A268

FORTENBERRY, Doris, Coordinator Human Resources, Delta Memorial Hospital, Dumas, AR, p. A41

FORTENBERRY, Rob, Chief Information Officer, Mann–Grandstaff Veterans Affairs Medical Center, Spokane, WA, p. A679

FORTIER, Jeanne M, R.N., Chief Nursing Officer and Interim Chief Operating Officer, Grace Cottage Hospital, Townshend, VT, p. A655

FORTIN, Amanda, Manager Finance, Decatur Health Systems, Oberlin, KS, p. A242

FORTIN, Laura, R.N., Chief Operating Officer, St. Joseph Medical Center, Houston, TX, p. A613

FORTNEY, John
Chief Medical Officer, Adena Pike Medical Center, Waverly, OH, p. A493
Senior System Medical Advisor, Adena Medical Center, Chillicothe, OH, p. A475

FORTNEY, Robert, MS, R.N., Chief Nursing Officer and Vice President of Patient Care, Illinois Valley Community Hospital, Peru, IL, p. A193

FORTUNE, Michelle, Chief Executive Officer, St. Luke'S Hospital, Columbus, NC, p. A452

FOSBERG, Renee, Chief Information Officer, Emerson Hospital, Concord, MA, p. A298

FOSINA, Michael, President, Brookdale Hospital Medical Center, New York, NY, p. A432

FOSNESS, Nick, Chief Executive Officer, Marshall County Healthcare Center Avera, Britton, SD, p. A559

FOSNOCHT, Kevin, M.D., Chief Medical Officer and Associate Executive Director, Penn Presbyterian Medical Center, Philadelphia, PA, p. A536

FOSS, Coleman, Chief Executive Officer, Wellstar West Georgia Medical Center, Lagrange, GA, p. A155

FOSS, David, Chief Information Officer, New London Hospital, New London, NH, p. A401

FOSS, John T., Vice President, Operations, Mercy Health, Lakeshore Campus, Shelby, MI, p. A322

FOSS, R Coleman, Chief Executive Officer, Tennova Healthcare – Cleveland, Cleveland, TN, p. A568

FOSTER, Barbara A, Regional Human Resources Director, Select Specialty Hospital–Wilmington, Wilmington, DE, p. A114

FOSTER, Becky
Employee Relations Specialist, Sanford Tracy Medical Center, Tracy, MN, p. A341
Employee Relations Specialist, Sanford Westbrook Medical Center, Westbrook, MN, p. A342

FOSTER, Bob, Chief Information Officer, South Georgia Medical Center, Valdosta, GA, p. A162

FOSTER, Brian, Chief Information Officer, Vail Health, Vail, CO, p. A106

FOSTER, Carolyn, Chief Financial Officer, Peacehealth Peace Island Medical Center, Friday Harbor, WA, p. A673

FOSTER, Charles, Regional Director Human Resources, Christus Southeast Texas Hospital – St. Elizabeth, Beaumont, TX, p. A587

FOSTER, Chris, Director Health Information Management, Deer Lodge Medical Center, Deer Lodge, MT, p. A376

FOSTER, Daniel J, Chief Financial Officer, Northern Utah Rehabilitation Hospital, South Ogden, UT, p. A653

FOSTER, Don, Chief Executive Officer, St. Luke'S Rehabilitation Hospital, Chesterfield, MO, p. A358

FOSTER, Gary, Vice President and Chief Financial Officer, Saratoga Hospital, Saratoga Springs, NY, p. A444

FOSTER, Gary, R.N.
Associate Administrator, Banner Estrella Medical Center, Phoenix, AZ, p. A33
Chief Operating Officer, Peacehealth Southwest Medical Center, Vancouver, WA, p. A681

FOSTER, Kennetha, Chief Nursing Officer, Mission Regional Medical Center, Mission, TX, p. A625

FOSTER, Larry, Chief Executive Officer, Kindred Chicago–Central Hospital, Chicago, IL, p. A178

FOSTER, Michael, Director Information Systems, East Cooper Medical Center, Mount Pleasant, SC, p. A555

FOSTER, Mike, Manager Information Systems, Moab Regional Hospital, Moab, UT, p. A648

FOSTER, Mitzi, Director Information Services, Southern Tennessee Regional Health System–Pulaski, Pulaski, TN, p. A578

FOSTER, Nancy, Vice President, Human Resources, Hendricks Regional Health, Danville, IN, p. A202

FOSTER, Rebecca, MSN, R.N., Chief Nursing Officer, Cumberland Medical Center, Crossville, TN, p. A568

FOSTER, Robert, Director Human Resources, Regional Medical Center Of Central Alabama, Greenville, AL, p. A19

FOSTER, Stephanie, MSN, R.N., Chief Nursing Officer, Longview Regional Medical Center, Longview, TX, p. A621

FOSTER, Steven, Chief Executive Officer, Chi St. Luke'S Health – Patients Medical Center, Pasadena, TX, p. A628

FOSTER, Terri, Hospital Finance Officer, Baylor Scott & White Medical Center – Grapevine, Grapevine, TX, p. A608

FOSTER, Timothy, Acting Chief Medical Officer, Newton–Wellesley Hospital, Newton Lower Falls, MA, p. A301

FOSTER, Wanda, R.N., MS, FACHE, MSN, Vice President Nursing, Mcdonough District Hospital, Macomb, IL, p. A188

FOTIADIS, George, M.D., Chief of Staff, Clarke County Hospital, Osceola, IA, p. A228

FOTTER, Robert, Chief Financial Officer, Pennsylvania Psychiatric Institute, Harrisburg, PA, p. A526

FOTTER, Robert L, Chief Financial Officer, Littleton Regional Healthcare, Littleton, NH, p. A401

FOUCH, Loren, Chief Executive Officer, Mayhill Hospital, Denton, TX, p. A599

FOUGHT, Scott, Vice President Finance, Promedica Bay Park Hospital, Oregon, OH, p. A489

FOULKE, Elvia, Executive Vice President and Chief Operating Officer, Foothill Presbyterian Hospital, Glendora, CA, p. A60

FOUNTAIN, Aaron, Chief Information Officer, Brandon Regional Hospital, Brandon, FL, p. A119

FOUNTAIN, Wesley D, Chief Financial Officer, St. David'S South Austin Medical Center, Austin, TX, p. A586

FOUREZ, Yvonne, Chief Financial Officer, Washington County Memorial Hospital, Potosi, MO, p. A367

FOURNIER, Warren, Chief Executive Officer and Medical Director, Richmond State Hospital, Richmond, IN, p. A214

FOURRE, Mark
Chief Executive Officer, Waldo County General Hospital Maine Health, Belfast, ME, p. A282
President and Chief Executive Officer, Pen Bay Medical Center, Rockport, ME, p. A285

FOUSE, Carla
Administrator and Chief Nursing Officer, St. Vincent Randolph Hospital, Winchester, IN, p. A216
Chief Nursing Officer, St. Vincent Randolph Hospital, Winchester, IN, p. A216

FOUSE, Sarah, Associate Director of Patient Services, Captain James A. Lovell Federal Health Care Center, North Chicago, IL, p. A191

FOUST, Lisa
Senior Vice President Human Resources, John Muir Behavioral Health Center, Concord, CA, p. A55
Senior Vice President Human Resources, John Muir Medical Center, Concord, Concord, CA, p. A55
Senior Vice President, Human Resources, John Muir Medical Center, Walnut Creek, Walnut Creek, CA, p. A94

FOUST–COFIELD, Misti, R.N., Vice President and Chief Nursing Officer, Reid Health, Richmond, IN, p. A214

FOUTS, Kyle, Interim Administrator, Montana State Hospital, Warm Springs, MT, p. A380

FOUTS, Phillip, Chief Financial Officer, Fannin Regional Hospital, Blue Ridge, GA, p. A148

FOUTZ, Patricia, Director Human Resources, Bath Community Hospital, Hot Springs, VA, p. A661

FOWLER, Andrew, Vice President Information Services, Atlantic General Hospital, Berlin, MD, p. A288

FOWLER, Barry, Director Human and System Resources, Clark Fork Valley Hospital, Plains, MT, p. A379

FOWLER, Brian, Information Technology Director, Jeff Davis Hospital, Hazlehurst, GA, p. A154

FOWLER, Jennifer, Chief Nurse Officer, Central State Hospital, Louisville, KY, p. A256

FOWLER, Kate, Chief Financial Officer, West Valley Medical Center, Caldwell, ID, p. A168

FOWLER, Kevin, Director Finance, Putnam County Hospital, Greencastle, IN, p. A205

FOWLER, Kevin N., President and Chief Executive Officer, Cabell Huntington Hospital, Huntington, WV, p. A685

FOWLER, Marcia, Chief Executive Officer, Bournewood Health Systems, Brookline, MA, p. A297

FOWLER, Maureen, Director Human Resources, Conifer Park, Glenville, NY, p. A428

FOWLER, Ruth, Senior Vice President and Chief Financial Officer, Children'S Healthcare Of Atlanta, Atlanta, GA, p. A146

FOWLER, Ryan, Chief Administrative Officer, Lower Umpqua Hospital District, Reedsport, OR, p. A517

FOWLER, Sean, Chief Executive Officer, Southern California Hospital At Culver City, Culver City, CA, p. A56

FOWLER, Steven, M.D., President Medical Staff, Genesis Medical Center, Dewitt, De Witt, IA, p. A220

FOX, Alan, Chief Financial Officer, Saint Francis Memorial Hospital, San Francisco, CA, p. A85

FOX, Carol J., M.D., Senior Vice President and Chief Medical Officer, Excela Latrobe Area Hospital, Latrobe, PA, p. A529

FOX, David R., Vice President and Chief Operating Officer, Baxter Regional Medical Center, Mountain Home, AR, p. A46

FOX, Debra, Chief Nursing Officer, University Medical Center, Las Vegas, NV, p. A396

FOX, Devin, M.D., Vice President Medical Operations, Chi Health Creighton University Medical Center – Bergan Mercy, Omaha, NE, p. A388

FOX, Jay
Chief Executive Officer, Baylor Scott & White Medical Center – Taylor, Taylor, TX, p. A639
President, Baylor Scott & White Medical Center – Round Rock, Round Rock, TX, p. A632

FOX, Jerry, Chief Information Officer, Alton Memorial Hospital, Alton, IL, p. A173

FOX, Jessica, Director of Human Resources, Aspirus Riverview Hospital And Clinics, Inc., Wisconsin Rapids, WI, p. A709

FOX, John, M.D., Medical Director, Select Specialty Hospital – San Diego, San Diego, CA, p. A84

FOX, John A., M.D., Chief of Staff, Shriners Hospitals For Children–Shreveport, Shreveport, LA, p. A278

FOX, Leana, Interim Chief Nurse Executive, Bon Secours Maryview Medical Center, Portsmouth, VA, p. A665

FOX, Randy, Director Performance Improvement and Risk Management, Lakeland Behavioral Health System, Springfield, MO, p. A371

FOX, Starla, Director of Nursing, Bristol Bay Area Health Corporation, Dillingham, AK, p. A26

FOX, Susan, President and Chief Executive Officer, White Plains Hospital Center, White Plains, NY, p. A448

FOXX, Randy, Chief Financial Officer, Boone Memorial Hospital, Madison, WV, p. A687

FOY, Gregory S., Human Resources System Leader, Scheurer Hospital, Pigeon, MI, p. A319

FRABLE, Arthur H., Chief Executive Officer, Humboldt General Hospital, Winnemucca, NV, p. A398

FRACHISEUR, Kenny, Chief Information Officer, Ouachita County Medical Center, Camden, AR, p. A40

FRACICA, Phil, M.D., Vice President and Chief Medical Officer, Mercy Gilbert Medical Center, Gilbert, AZ, p. A29

FRACK, Darla, R.N., Vice President, Patient Services, St. Luke'S Hospital – Anderson Campus, Easton, PA, p. A525

FRACK, Gina, Chief Executive Officer, Norton County Hospital, Norton, KS, p. A242

FRAGEN, Andrew, M.D., Chief Medical Officer, Community Hospital Of San Bernardino, San Bernardino, CA, p. A83

FRAHER, Francis D, Vice President, Finance, Northwestern Memorial Hospital, Northwestern Memorial Hospital, Chicago, IL, p. A178

FRAIOLA, Anthony, Associate Administrator Administrative and Support Services, Hawaii State Hospital, Kaneohe, HI, p. A166

FRAKER, Steve, Chief Financial Officer, Banner Churchill Community Hospital, Fallon, NV, p. A393

FRALICKER, Tammy, MS, R.N., Chief Nursing Officer, Crawford Memorial Hospital, Robinson, IL, p. A194

FRAME, Angela, Chief Financial Officer, Jackson General Hospital, Ripley, WV, p. A689

FRAME, Ken, Chief Nursing Officer, Ashtabula County Medical Center, Ashtabula, OH, p. A472

FRANCE, Cheryl, M.D., Chief Medical Officer, William R. Sharpe, Jr. Hospital, Weston, WV, p. A690

FRANCE, James, M.D., Chief of Staff, Conway Regional Medical Center, Conway, AR, p. A40

FRANCE, Larry O., Commander, Weed Army Community Hospital, Fort Irwin, CA, p. A58

FRANCETICH, Kane, Chief Information Officer, Gritman Medical Center, Moscow, ID, p. A170

FRANCIOLI, Carl H, Vice President Finance, Johns Hopkins Bayview Medical Center, Baltimore, MD, p. A286

FRANCIS, Carolyn, R.N., MSN, Director of Nursing, Lasalle General Hospital, Jena, LA, p. A269

FRANCIS, Christy, Chief Executive Officer, Hemphill County Hospital, Canadian, TX, p. A591

FRANCIS, Duane, Interim Chief Executive Officer, Wilson Memorial Hospital, Sidney, OH, p. A491

FRANCIS, Jeffrey, Vice President Finance and Chief Financial Officer, Methodist Jennie Edmundson Hospital, Council Bluffs, IA, p. A220

FRANCIS, Lana B., Chief Executive Officer, Lasalle General Hospital, Jena, LA, p. A269

FRANCIS, Mark J, President and Chief Executive Officer, Colorado Canyons Hospital And Medical Center, Fruita, CO, p. A101

FRANCIS, Mark J., President and Chief Executive Officer, Colorado Canyons Hospital And Medical Center, Fruita, CO, p. A101

FRANCIS, Perry, Supervisory Information Technology Specialist, Chinle Comprehensive Health Care Facility, Chinle, AZ, p. A29

FRANCIS, Rebekah, JD
Chief Financial Officer, Aurora Behavioral Health System East, Tempe, AZ, p. A36
Chief Financial Officer, Aurora Behavioral Health System West, Glendale, AZ, p. A30

FRANCISCO, Gerard E., M.D., Chief Medical Officer, Tirr Memorial Hermann, Houston, TX, p. A614

FRANCKOWIAK, Debra, Executive Director, Children'S Hospital Of Wisconsin–Fox Valley, Neenah, WI, p. A702

FRANCO, Glenda, Director, Human Resources, Vibra Hospital Of Sacramento, Folsom, CA, p. A58

FRANCO, Luis, M.D., Medical Director, United Medical Rehabilitation Hospital, Hammond, LA, p. A268

FRANCO, Richard, Chief Financial Officer, Community First Medical Center, Chicago, IL, p. A177

FRANCO, Richard A., Vice President and Chief Financial Officer, Northwestern Medicine Lake Forest Hospital, Lake Forest, IL, p. A187

FRANCO, Roger, Director Human Resources, Brookdale Hospital Medical Center, New York, NY, p. A432

FRANCO, Rosemary, Chief Nursing Officer, Cochran Memorial Hospital, Morton, TX, p. A625

FRANCOIS, Fritz, M.D., Chief Medical Officer, Brookdale Hospital Medical Center, New York, NY, p. A432

FRANDSEN, Jeff, Chief Executive Officer, Healthsouth Rehabilitation Hospital Of Utah, Sandy, UT, p. A653

FRANK, Barbara, Human Resource Specialist, Caro Center, Caro, MI, p. A308

FRANK, Cathrine, Chairperson, Henry Ford Kingswood Hospital, Ferndale, MI, p. A311

FRANK, Daniel
Chief Financial Officer, Craig Hospital, Englewood, CO, p. A100
Chief Financial Officer, Longmont United Hospital, Longmont, CO, p. A103

FRANK, Debra, Chief Financial Officer, Ness County Hospital District No 2, Ness City, KS, p. A241

FRANK, James, Chief Executive Officer, Providence Medical Center, Wayne, NE, p. A392

FRANK, Kevin, Chief Executive Officer, Mercy Regional Medical Center, Ville Platte, LA, p. A280

FRANK, Kim, Chief Human Resources Officer, Virginia Gay Hospital, Vinton, IA, p. A230

FRANK, Patricia, Chief Nursing Officer, Henry County Hospital, Napoleon, OH, p. A488

FRANK, Robert A
Senior Vice President of Operations, University Of Maryland Shore Medical Center At Chestertown, Chestertown, MD, p. A289
Senior Vice President of Operations, University Of Maryland Shore Medical Center At Easton, Easton, MD, p. A290
Senior Vice President Operations, University Of Maryland Shore Medical Center At Dorchester, Cambridge, MD, p. A289

FRANK, Thomas, Chief Operating Officer, North Country Hospital And Health Center, Newport, VT, p. A654

FRANK–LIGHTFOOT, Loraine, Vice President, Patient Care Services and Chief Nursing Officer, Munson Medical Center, Traverse City, MI, p. A323

FRANKE, Craig, Medical Director, Texas Star Recovery, Austin, TX, p. A586

FRANKE, Jenny, Director Human Resources, Rehabilitation Hospital Of Wisconsin, Waukesha, WI, p. A707

FRANKE, John, Chief Financial Officer, Baptist Health Lexington, Lexington, KY, p. A254

FRANKE, Paul, M.D., Chief Medical Officer, Alaska Native Medical Center, Anchorage, AK, p. A26

FRANKEL, Harris, M.D., Interim Chief Medical Officer, Nebraska Medicine – Nebraska Medical Center, Omaha, NE, p. A389

FRANKEL, Michele, Associate Executive Director Finance, Glen Cove Hospital, Glen Cove, NY, p. A428

FRANKEN, Stephanie, Vice President Operational Finance, Chi St. Alexius Health – Dickinson Medical Center, Dickinson, ND, p. A466

FRANKL, Angie, Director Human Resources, Adair County Health System, Greenfield, IA, p. A223

FRANKLIN, Chuck, M.D., Chief Medical Staff, Weston County Health Services, Newcastle, WY, p. A712

FRANKLIN, Clay, Chief Executive Officer, Alliancehealth Midwest, Midwest City, OK, p. A502

FRANKLIN, Ed, Chief Human Resources Officer, Page Hospital, Page, AZ, p. A32

FRANKLIN, Jennifer, R.N., Chief Clinical Officer, Yoakum Community Hospital, Yoakum, TX, p. A646

FRANKLIN, Matthew, Director Human Resources, Warren General Hospital, Warren, PA, p. A543

FRANKLIN, Michael A., President and Chief Executive Officer, Atlantic General Hospital, Berlin, MD, p. A288

FRANKLIN, Michelle, Chief Executive Officer, Sullivan County Community Hospital, Sullivan, IN, p. A215

FRANKLIN, Tammy, Manager Personnel and Marketing, Covenant Hospital–Levelland, Levelland, TX, p. A620

FRANKO, Stephen
Senior Vice President and Chief Financial Officer, St. Vincent'S Medical Center, Bridgeport, CT, p. A107
Vice President Finance and Chief Financial Officer, Mount St. Mary'S Hospital And Health Center, Lewiston, NY, p. A430
Vice President Finance and Chief Financial Officer, Regional Hospital Of Scranton, Reading, PA, p. A540

FRANKOVITCH, John C., President and Chief Executive Officer, Weirton Medical Center, Weirton, WV, p. A690

FRANKS, Cathy, Chief Operating Officer, Izard County Medical Center, Calico Rock, AR, p. A40

FRANKS, Charles, Chief Human Resources, Louis Stokes Cleveland Veterans Affairs Medical Center, Cleveland, OH, p. A478

FRANKS, Dennis
Chief Executive Officer, Neosho Memorial Regional Medical Center, Chanute, KS, p. A233

Interim Chief Financial Officer, Pontiac General Hospital, Pontiac, MI, p. A320
Vice President Operations, Pontiac General Hospital, Pontiac, MI, p. A320

FRANSEN, Mitchell, Chief Financial Officer, Mesa View Regional Hospital, Mesquite, NV, p. A396

FRANSON, John K, M.D., Chief Medical Staff, Caribou Memorial Hospital And Living Center, Soda Springs, ID, p. A172

FRANTZ, Steven, Chief Financial Officer, Saint Francis Hospital, Memphis, TN, p. A575

FRANTZ, Vincent, M.D., Chief of Staff, Plumas District Hospital, Quincy, CA, p. A79

FRANZ, Eric, Vice President, Finance and Chief Financial Officer, Graham Hospital Association, Canton, IL, p. A175

FRANZ, Staci, Director Human Resources, St. Luke'S Rehabilitation Institute, Spokane, WA, p. A680

FRANZELLA, Susan, Human Resource Business Partner, Kaiser Permanente San Jose Medical Center, San Jose, CA, p. A86

FRARDO, Virgil, M.D., Medical Director, Encompass Health Rehabilitation Hospital Of Wichita Falls, Wichita Falls, TX, p. A645

FRASCA, Edith, Controller and Chief Financial Officer, The Pavilion, Champaign, IL, p. A175

FRASCH, Sara, Chief Human Resource Officer, University Of New Mexico Hospitals, Albuquerque, NM, p. A417

FRASER, Cathryn H., Chief Human Resources Officer, Mayo Clinic Hospital – Rochester, Rochester, MN, p. A338

FRASER, James, Administrator Finance, Ascension Via Christi Hospital, Manhattan, Manhattan, KS, p. A240

FRASIER, Nora, R.N., FACHE, Chief Nursing Officer, Methodist Mansfield Medical Center, Mansfield, TX, p. A623

FRASURE, Jane, Human Resources, Baylor Scott & White Medical Center – Llano, Llano, TX, p. A621

FRATZKE, Mark, President and Chief Executive Officer, Seton Medical Center, Daly City, CA, p. A56

FRAUENHOFER, Chris, Chief Financial Officer, Northern Light Maine Coast Hospital, Ellsworth, ME, p. A283

FRAZIER, Amy, Supervisor Management Information Systems, Wetzel County Hospital, New Martinsville, WV, p. A687

FRAZIER, Brandon, Chief Financial Officer, River Oaks Hospital, New Orleans, LA, p. A275

FRAZIER, Derrick A., Chief Executive Officer, Morehouse General Hospital, Bastrop, LA, p. A263

FRAZIER, Joel L, M.D., Medical Director, Onecore Health, Oklahoma City, OK, p. A505

FRAZIER, Kimberly, R.N., Chief Nursing Officer, East Los Angeles Doctors Hospital, Los Angeles, CA, p. A66

FRAZIER, Shane, Chief Executive Officer, Pinnacle Pointe Hospital, Little Rock, AR, p. A45

FREAS, Mary Ann, Senior Vice President and Chief Financial Officer, Southwest General Health Center, Middleburg Heights, OH, p. A487

FRED, Mark, R.N., Chief Operating Officer, Kirby Medical Center, Monticello, IL, p. A190

FREDEBOELLING, Elizabeth E., Chief Nursing Officer, Dell Children'S Medical Center Of Central Texas, Austin, TX, p. A585

FREDERICK, Brenda, Director Human Resources, Laurel Ridge Treatment Center, San Antonio, TX, p. A634

FREDERICK, Dessa, Manager Human Resources, St. James Behavioral Health Hospital, Gonzales, LA, p. A267

FREDERICK, Gretchen A, R.N., Director Patient Care Services, Buffalo Hospital, Buffalo, MN, p. A329

FREDERICK, John, Chief Financial Officer, West Central Georgia Regional Hospital, Columbus, GA, p. A151

FREDERICK, Ryannon, Chief Nursing Officer, Mayo Clinic Hospital In Florida, Jacksonville, FL, p. A125

FREDERICKS, Raymond F., Central Regional President, Hackensack Meridian Health Jfk Medical Center, Edison, NJ, p. A405

FREDERICKSON, Kathy, Information Systems Site Lead, Sutter Delta Medical Center, Antioch, CA, p. A50

FREDETTE, Beth, Chief Information Officer, Dayton Children'S Hospital, Dayton, OH, p. A481

FREDRICH, Nancy, R.N., Chief Clinical Officer, Pinnacle Regional Hospital, Boonville, MO, p. A357

FREDRICK, Joyce, Associate Director, Veterans Affairs Central Western Massachusetts Healthcare System, Leeds, MA, p. A300

FREDRICK, Rick, Director Information Technology, Cottage Hospital, Woodsville, NH, p. A402

FREDRICKSON, Kelley, Director Information Services, Medical City Fort Worth, Fort Worth, TX, p. A605

FREDRICKSON, Mark A, M.D., Medical Director, Encompass Health Rehabilitation Hospital Midland Odessa, Midland, TX, p. A624

FREEBERN, Joseph, Executive Director, Mid–Hudson Forensic Psychiatric Center, New Hampton, NY, p. A432

FREEBORN, Fawn, Human Resources Generalist, Schoolcraft Memorial Hospital, Manistique, MI, p. A317

FREEBURG, Rick
Chief Executive Officer, Baptist Health South Florida, Mariners Hospital, Tavernier, FL, p. A142
Chief Executive Officer, Fishermen'S Hospital, Marathon, FL, p. A129

FREEBURN, Mark, Chief Executive Officer, Helen M. Simpson Rehabilitation Hospital, Harrisburg, PA, p. A526

FREED, Nancy, Chief Financial Officer, Seiling Regional Medical Center, Seiling, OK, p. A507

FREED, Stuart, M.D.
Chief Medical Officer, Confluence Health/Central Washington Hospital, Wenatchee, WA, p. A682
Medical Director, Confluence Health/Wenatchee Valley Hospital, Wenatchee, WA, p. A682

FREED–SIGURDSSON, Anna, M.D., Medical Director, Encompass Health Rehabilitation Hospital Of Dallas, Dallas, TX, p. A596

FREEDMAN, Barry R, President and Chief Executive Officer, Einstein Medical Center Philadelphia, Philadelphia, PA, p. A534

FREEDMAN, Barry R., President and Chief Executive Officer, Einstein Medical Center Philadelphia, Philadelphia, PA, p. A534

FREEDMAN, Kenneth, M.D., Chief Medical Officer, Lemuel Shattuck Hospital, Jamaica Plain, MA, p. A299

FREEDMAN, Rick, Commanding Officer, Naval Hospital Camp Lejeune, Camp Lejeune, NC, p. A450

FREEHILL, Sarah, Chief Nursing Officer, Arbuckle Memorial Hospital, Sulphur, OK, p. A508

FREEHOF, Leonard, Chief Executive Officer and Managing Director, Spring Valley Hospital Medical Center, Las Vegas, NV, p. A396

FREELAND, R Alan, M.D., Chief Clinical Officer, Twin Valley Behavioral Healthcare, Columbus, OH, p. A480

FREEMAN, Brian, President, Atrium Health Stanly, Albemarle, NC, p. A449

FREEMAN, Diane, R.N., Assistant Vice President and Chief Nursing Officer, Chi St. Luke'S Health–Lakeside Hospital, The Woodlands, TX, p. A640

FREEMAN, Gail, Chief Nursing Officer, San Gabriel Valley Medical Center, San Gabriel, CA, p. A86

FREEMAN, Jerry, Chief, Human Resources Management Services, Durham Veterans Affairs Medical Center, Durham, NC, p. A453

FREEMAN, Kimberlee, Vice President Patient Care Services and Chief Nursing Officer, Wayne Healthcare, Greenville, OH, p. A484

FREEMAN, Marianne, Vice President Human Resources, Piedmont Rockdale Hospital, Conyers, GA, p. A151

FREEMAN, Michael
Director Human Resources, Alta Vista Regional Hospital, Las Vegas, NM, p. A419
Director Human Resources, Huhukam Memorial Hospital, Sacaton, AZ, p. A35

FREEMAN, Mike, Director Information Technology, Sentara Williamsburg Regional Medical Center, Williamsburg, VA, p. A669

FREEMAN, Peggy, Chief Physicians Services Officer, Dickinson County Healthcare System, Iron Mountain, MI, p. A314

FREEMAN, Richard
Chief Medical Officer, St. Vincent Indianapolis Hospital, Indianapolis, IN, p. A208
President and Chief Executive Officer, Robert Wood Johnson University Hospital At Hamilton, Hamilton, NJ, p. A406

FREEMAN, Robert, Director Human Resources, Baptist Health – Fort Smith, Fort Smith, AR, p. A42

FREESE DECKER, Christina, President and Chief Executive Officer, Spectrum Health – Butterworth Hospital, Grand Rapids, MI, p. A313

FREGOLI, Fabian, M.D., Chief Medical Officer, St. Joseph Mercy Oakland, Pontiac, MI, p. A320

FREID–SCHEPPKE, Denise, Chief Accounting Officer, Oakleaf Surgical Hospital, Altoona, WI, p. A691

FREIER, Toby, President, New Ulm Medical Center, New Ulm, MN, p. A337

FREIJ, Walid, M.D., Chief of Staff, Vaughan Regional Medical Center, Selma, AL, p. A23

FREILICH, Josh, Vice President and Chief Nurse Executive, Mercy Hospital Of Folsom, Folsom, CA, p. A58

FREIMARK, Jeffrey P., Chief Executive Officer, Miami Jewish Home And Hospital For Aged, Miami, FL, p. A130

FREISCHLAG, Julie Ann, Chief Executive Officer, Wake Forest Baptist Medical Center, Winston, NC, p. A464

FREITAG, Donald, M.D., Chief Medical Officer, Lynn County Hospital District, Tahoka, TX, p. A639

FRELING, Eric, M.D., Director Medical Staff Affairs, Memorial Hospital West, Pembroke Pines, FL, p. A136

FRENCH, Chad, Chief Executive Officer, Regional Medical Center Of Central Alabama, Greenville, AL, p. A19

FRENCH, Dean, Chief Executive Officer, Community Medical Center, Missoula, MT, p. A378

FRENCH, Dean O, M.D., Chief of Staff, Faith Regional Health Services, Norfolk, NE, p. A388

FRENCH, Holly, Chief Financial Officer, Newman Regional Health, Emporia, KS, p. A234

FRENCH, Lori, Manager Human Resources, Fulton State Hospital, Fulton, MO, p. A360

FRENCH, Toni, Manager Human Resources, Callaway District Hospital, Callaway, NE, p. A383

FRENCH, Tracy
Chief Financial Officer, Banner Goldfield Medical Center, Apache Junction, AZ, p. A28
Chief Financial Officer, Banner Ironwood Medical Center, San Tan Valley, AZ, p. A35

FRENGLE, Kelley
Director, Human Resources, Peacehealth St. John Medical Center, Longview, WA, p. A674
Senior Director, Human Resources, Peacehealth Southwest Medical Center, Vancouver, WA, p. A681

FRENIER, Karen, President, Orlando Regional Medical Center, Orlando, FL, p. A134

FRERER, Mary
Chief Human Resources Officer, Freeman Health System, Joplin, MO, p. A362
Chief Human Resources Officer, Freeman Neosho Hospital, Neosho, MO, p. A366

FRERICHS, Craig, Chief Information Technology Service, Grand Junction Veterans Health Care System, Grand Junction, CO, p. A101

FRESQUEZ, Juan, President, Methodist Mansfield Medical Center, Mansfield, TX, p. A623

FREUDENBERG, Liz, Chief Financial Officer, Healthsouth Rehabilitation Hospital Of Littleton, Littleton, CO, p. A103

FREUDENBERGER, Joe, Chief Executive Officer, Oakbend Medical Center, Richmond, TX, p. A631

FREY, Jack, Acting Business Manager, Greystone Park Psychiatric Hospital, Morris Plains, NJ, p. A408

FREY, James, Acting Manager Human Resources, Greystone Park Psychiatric Hospital, Morris Plains, NJ, p. A408

FREY, Jeff, Business Administrator, Andrew Mcfarland Mental Health Center, Springfield, IL, p. A196

FREY, Paul, Director Information Technology Applications, Orthoindy Hospital, Indianapolis, IN, p. A207

FREY, Rachel, Director Human Resources, Athens–Limestone Hospital, Athens, AL, p. A13

FREYER, Mary, Chief Operating Officer, Little Company Of Mary Hospital And Health Care Centers, Evergreen Park, IL, p. A183

FREYER, Sharon, R.N., Chief Nursing Officer, Baptist Health Paducah, Paducah, KY, p. A259

FREYMULLER, Robert S., Chief Executive Officer, Summerlin Hospital Medical Center, Las Vegas, NV, p. A396

FREYSINGER, Edward E., Chief Administrative Officer, Peacehealth Ketchikan Medical Center, Ketchikan, AK, p. A26

FREYTAG, Peter, Senior Vice President Finance and Chief Financial Officer, Bristol Hospital, Bristol, CT, p. A107

FRIARTE, Pedro, Director of Physician Services, Coral Gables Hospital, Coral Gables, FL, p. A120

FRIAS, Patricio A., President and Chief Executive Officer, Rady Children'S Hospital – San Diego, San Diego, CA, p. A84

FRICK, Mark P, Senior Vice President Human Resources, Upmc Somerset Hospital, Somerset, PA, p. A541

FRICK, Mary Jo, Director Finance, St. Catherine'S Rehabilitation Hospital, North Miami, FL, p. A133

FRICKE, Rhett D., Chief Executive Officer, Ballinger Memorial Hospital, Ballinger, TX, p. A586

FRIDAY, Jason, M.D., Medical Director, Aurora Behavioral Health System East, Tempe, AZ, p. A36

FRIDAY, Lisa, Director Human Resources, Christus Ochsner Lake Area Hospital, Lake Charles, LA, p. A272

FRIDKIN, Marjorie, M.D., Chief Medical Officer, Garrett Regional Medical Center, Oakland, MD, p. A292

FRIED, Guy, M.D., Chief Medical Officer, Magee Rehabilitation Hospital, Philadelphia, PA, p. A535

FRIED, Tera, Manager Human Resources, West River Regional Medical Center, Hettinger, ND, p. A468

FRIEDEN, Robert
Vice President Information Systems, Genesis Medical Center, Davenport, Davenport, IA, p. A220
Vice President Information Systems, Genesis Medical Center, Silvis, Silvis, IL, p. A196
Vice President, Information Services and Chief Information Officer, Genesis Medical Center–Aledo, Aledo, IL, p. A173

FRIEDENBACH, Daryl, Director Fiscal Services, Floyd Valley Healthcare, Le Mars, IA, p. A225

FRIEDLY, Jennifer
Chief Operating Officer and Vice President, Unitypoint Health – Allen Hospital, Waterloo, IA, p. A231
President, Unitypoint Health – Marshalltown, Marshalltown, IA, p. A226

FRIEDMAN, Jonathan, Public Affairs Officer, Captain James A. Lovell Federal Health Care Center, North Chicago, IL, p. A191

FRIEDMAN, Lloyd, Interim President and Chief Operating Officer, Milford Hospital, Milford, CT, p. A109

FRIEDMAN, Lloyd, M.D., Vice President Medical Affairs and Chief Operating Officer, Milford Hospital, Milford, CT, p. A109

FRIEDMAN, Ross, Chief Executive Officer, Summit Oaks Hospital, Summit, NJ, p. A413

FRIEL, Donald F., Executive Vice President, Holy Redeemer Hospital, Meadowbrook, PA, p. A531

FRIEL, John P., Chief Executive Officer, Bear Valley Community Hospital, Big Bear Lake, CA, p. A53

FRIELING, Jeff
Chief Information Officer, Pathways Of Tennessee, Jackson, TN, p. A571
Vice President and Chief Information Officer, Jackson–Madison County General Hospital, Jackson, TN, p. A571
Vice President Information Systems, Camden General Hospital, Camden, TN, p. A566

FRIEND, Chad, Director, T. J. Samson Community Hospital, Glasgow, KY, p. A252

FRIEND, Lori, Human Resources Director, Alliancehealth Seminole, Seminole, OK, p. A507

FRIERSON, Cathy, Chief Human Resource Officer, Danbury Hospital, Danbury, CT, p. A107

FRIES, Richard W, Vice President Finance, Allegheny General Hospital, Pittsburgh, PA, p. A537

FRIESEL, Dawn, Director of Finance, Pawnee County Memorial Hospital And Rural Health Clinic, Pawnee City, NE, p. A390

FRIESEN, Dale L, Chief Financial Officer, Henry Ford Allegiance Specialty Hospital, Jackson, MI, p. A315

FRIESEN, Lynette, Manager Human Resources, Henderson Health Care Services, Henderson, NE, p. A386

FRIGO, Dave
Vice President Financial Planning and Treasury, Cleveland Clinic Akron General, Akron, OH, p. A471
Chief Financial Officer, Edwin Shaw Rehab, Cuyahoga Falls, OH, p. A480
Director Finance and Controller, Cleveland Clinic Akron General Lodi Hospital, Lodi, OH, p. A485

FRIGON, Shelby, Chief Financial Officer, Saint Luke'S South Hospital, Overland Park, KS, p. A243

FRIGY, Alan, M.D., President Medical Staff, Pana Community Hospital, Pana, IL, p. A192

FRIMODIG, Mindy, D.O., President Medical Staff ThedaCare Physicians Shawano, Thedacare Medical Center–Shawano, Shawano, WI, p. A705

FRISBEE, Kent, Director Human Resources, Saint Thomas Highlands Hospital, Sparta, TN, p. A579

FRISINA, Marcy, Chief Nursing Officer, South Bay Hospital, Sun City Center, FL, p. A140

FRITSCH, William, M.D., Medical Director, Landmark Hospital Of Cape Girardeau, Cape Girardeau, MO, p. A357

FRITTON, Amy, Controller, Sierra Tucson, Tucson, AZ, p. A38

FRITTS, Doris, Executive Director, Same Day Surgery Center, Rapid City, SD, p. A563

FRITTS, Robert G, Chief Financial Officer and Senior Vice President, Carolinas Healthcare System Blue Ridge, Morganton, NC, p. A459

FRITZ, Howard P, M.D., Vice President, Medical Affairs and Chief Medical Officer, Glens Falls Hospital, Glens Falls, NY, p. A428

FRITZ, Robert, Chief Information Officer, Brook Lane Health Services, Hagerstown, MD, p. A291

FROCHTZWAJG, Stanley, M.D., Chief Medical Officer, Community Memorial Hospital, Ventura, CA, p. A93

FROEHLICH, Shelley, R.N., Director Nursing Services, Newport Hospital And Health Services, Newport, WA, p. A675

FROEMKE, Janet, Human Resources Officer, Chi Lisbon Health, Lisbon, ND, p. A468

FROESE, Kristi, Vice President Clinical Operations, Chi St. Luke'S Health Memorial Livingston, Livingston, TX, p. A621

FROESE, Kristi, R.N., Chief Nursing Officer, Chi St. Luke'S Health Memorial Livingston, Livingston, TX, p. A621

FROH, Chris, Senior Coordinator Human Resources, Select Specialty Hospital–Milwaukee, Milwaukee, WI, p. A701

FROHNHOFER, Erin J
Director Human Resources, Southwood Psychiatric Hospital, Pittsburgh, PA, p. A537
Vice President Human Resources, Ohio Valley Hospital, Mckees Rocks, PA, p. A531

FROISLAND, Jeffrey R, Chief Financial Officer, Mayo Clinic Hospital, Phoenix, AZ, p. A33

FROMHOLD, John A., President and Chief Executive Officer, Hackensack Meridian Health Mountainside Medical Center, Montclair, NJ, p. A408

FROMM, Daniel
Chief Financial Officer, Bethesda Hospital, Saint Paul, MN, p. A339
Chief Financial Officer, St. John'S Hospital, Maplewood, MN, p. A335
Chief Financial Officer, St. Joseph'S Hospital, Saint Paul, MN, p. A340
Chief Financial Officer, Woodwinds Health Campus, Woodbury, MN, p. A343

FROMME, Richard, Chief Financial Officer, Cavalier County Memorial Hospital And Clinics, Langdon, ND, p. A468

FROMMELT, William, Director Operations and Finance, River Falls Area Hospital, River Falls, WI, p. A705

FRONZA, Sarah, President, Legacy Silverton Medical Center, Silverton, OR, p. A518

FROSCH, Kevin, Chief Financial Officer, Medina Regional Hospital, Hondo, TX, p. A610

FROST, Eric, Associate Vice President Human Resources, Upstate University Hospital, Syracuse, NY, p. A445

FROST, Joan, R.N., Chief Operating Officer, Mercy Hospital Washington, Washington, MO, p. A373

FROST, Mark I, M.D.
Senior Vice President Medical Affairs, Saint Francis Health System, Saint Francis Hospital, Tulsa, OK, p. A509
Senior Vice President Medical Affairs, Laureate Psychiatric Clinic And Hospital, Tulsa, OK, p. A508
Senior Vice President Medical Affairs, Saint Francis Hospital South, Tulsa, OK, p. A509

FROWNFELTER, Penny, Chief Nursing Officer, Encompass Health Nittany Valley Rehabilitation Hospital, Pleasant Gap, PA, p. A539

FRUGE, Janie, Chief Executive Officer, West Calcasieu Cameron Hospital, Sulphur, LA, p. A279

FRUM, Judy, R.N., Chief Nursing Officer, Memorial Hospital Pembroke, Pembroke Pines, FL, p. A136

FRY, Kenneth, Chief Financial Officer, Saint Alphonsus Regional Medical Center, Boise, ID, p. A168

FRY, Robin, CPA, Markct Controller, Kindred Hospital Dallas Central, Dallas, TX, p. A596

FRY, Terry, R.N., Chief Nursing Officer, Upper Valley Medical Center, Troy, OH, p. A492

FRYE, Kelly D, Director Human Resources, Montgomery General Hospital, Montgomery, WV, p. A687

FRYE, Terri, Information Technology Officer, Weston County Health Services, Newcastle, WY, p. A712

FRYFOGLE, Anthoney, Chief Information Officer, George Regional Hospital, Lucedale, MS, p. A350

FUCHS, Mary Ann, R.N., Vice President Patient Care and System Chief Nurse Executive, Duke University Hospital, Durham, NC, p. A453

FUEHRER, Susan, Director, Louis Stokes Cleveland Veterans Affairs Medical Center, Cleveland, OH, p. A478

FUENTES, Frances, Coordinator Human Resources, Encompass Health Rehabilitation Hospital Of San Juan, San Juan, PR, p. A718

FUENTES, Leticia, Nursing Director, San Jorge Children'S Hospital, Santurce, PR, p. A719

FUENTES, Michelle, President, Adventist Health Sonora, Sonora, CA, p. A90

FUENTES, Miguel A, Jr, President and Chief Executive Officer, Brookdale Hospital Medical Center, New York, NY, p. A432

FUENTES, Miguel A, Jr, President and Chief Executive Officer, Brookdale Hospital Medical Center, New York, NY, p. A432

FUERSTENBERG, Donna, Fiscal Chief, Sheridan Veterans Affairs Medical Center, Sheridan, WY, p. A712

FUGATTE, Cheryl, MSN, Vice President and Chief Nursing Officer, Jewish Hospital, Louisville, KY, p. A256

FUGITT, Jacki L., Director Employee Relations, Osf Saint Francis Medical Center, Peoria, IL, p. A193

FUGLER, Shawna, R.N., Chief Nursing Officer, Memorial Hermann Surgical Hospital Kingwood, Kingwood, TX, p. A618

FUHRMAN, Bradley, M.D., Physician in Chief, El Paso Children'S Hospital, El Paso, TX, p. A601

FUHRMAN, Dennis, Vice President Finance, Essentia Health Fargo, Fargo, ND, p. A466

FUHRO, Mary, Chief Nursing Officer, Newark Beth Israel Medical Center, Newark, NJ, p. A409

FUHS, Veronica
Chief Executive Officer, Davis County Hospital, Bloomfield, IA, p. A218
Chief Executive Officer, Monroe County Hospital And Clinics, Albia, IA, p. A217

FUJINAKA, Jason, Manager Information System, Wahiawa General Hospital, Wahiawa, HI, p. A166

FULCHER, Cathe, Superintendent, Evansville State Hospital, Evansville, IN, p. A203

FULCHER, Kimberly, Chief Human Resources Officer, Halifax Health Medical Center Of Daytona Beach, Daytona Beach, FL, p. A121

FULCHER, Martha, Chief Nursing Officer, Och Regional Medical Center, Starkville, MS, p. A354

FULCO, Mark M., President, Mercy Medical Center, Springfield, MA, p. A303

FULKERSON, Judy, Director Human Resources, Tristar Greenview Regional Hospital, Bowling Green, KY, p. A250

FULKERSON, Kimberly, Chief Nursing Officer, Dupont Hospital, Fort Wayne, IN, p. A203

FULKERSON, Richard, Director Fiscal Services, Shriners Hospitals For Children–Springfield, Springfield, MA, p. A303

FULKERSON, William T., Chief Operating Officer, University Of Virginia Medical Center, Charlottesville, VA, p. A657

FULKS, Chris, Vice President Finance, Lake Huron Medical Center, Port Huron, MI, p. A320

FULLBRIGHT, Gary D., Comptroller, Citizens Memorial Hospital, Bolivar, MO, p. A356

FULLER, Cara
Vice President Human Resources, Unitypoint Health – Trinity Bettendorf, Bettendorf, IA, p. A217
Vice President Human Resources, Unitypoint Health – Trinity Rock Island, Rock Island, IL, p. A194

FULLER, Cheryl, Director Information Resources, Kansas Neurological Institute, Topeka, KS, p. A246

FULLER, Dale, Vice President and Chief Information Officer, Upmc Altoona, Altoona, PA, p. A520

FULLER, David, Vice President of Human Resources, Porter Medical Center, Middlebury, VT, p. A654

FULLER, Debbie, Director Health Information Systems and Chief Information Officer, Doctors Medical Center Of Modesto, Modesto, CA, p. A72

FULLER, Harrington, Information Technology Director, Hendry Regional Medical Center, Clewiston, FL, p. A120

FULLER, Jane, Vice President Human Resources, North Florida Regional Medical Center, Gainesville, FL, p. A123

FULLER, Jeremy, Director Information Systems, Hca Houston Healthcare Conroe, Conroe, TX, p. A593

FULLER, Marion, Chief of Staff, Munson Healthcare Manistee Hospital, Manistee, MI, p. A317

FULLER, Scott O.
President and Chief Executive Officer, Ascension Seton Edgar B. Davis Hospital, Luling, TX, p. A622
President and Chief Executive Officer, Ascension Seton Highland Lakes, Burnet, TX, p. A590
President and Chief Executive Officer, Ascension Seton Smithville, Smithville, TX, p. A637

FULLER–WILLIAMS, Vonetta, Director Human Resources Strategic and Business Services, Baylor Scott & White Medical Center–Irving, Irving, TX, p. A616

FULLMER, John, Chief Financial Officer, Bingham Memorial Hospital, Blackfoot, ID, p. A167

FULLUM, Jane, Vice President Patient Care Services, East Alabama Medical Center, Opelika, AL, p. A22

FULTON, Lorna, Director Human Resources, Vibra Hospital Of Denver, Thornton, CO, p. A106

FULTON, Lynn, President, Osf St. Joseph Medical Center, Bloomington, IL, p. A174

FUNDERBURG, Michelle, Director Human Resources, Stephens Memorial Hospital, Breckenridge, TX, p. A589

FUNDERBURK, Mark, President and Chief Executive Officer, University Medical Center, Lubbock, TX, p. A622

FUNG, Adrian, Director Information Systems, Vanderbilt Wilson County Hospital, Lebanon, TN, p. A573

FUNK, Luann A, Administrative Assistant and Manager Human Resources, Pana Community Hospital, Pana, IL, p. A192

FUNKHOUSER, Krisy L, Manager Human Resources, Willapa Harbor Hospital, South Bend, WA, p. A679

FUQUA, David, Director Human Resources Management, Ochsner Lsu Health Shreveport – Academic Medical Center, Shreveport, LA, p. A278

FUQUA, David G., Chief Executive Officer, Marshall County Hospital, Benton, KY, p. A249

FUQUA, Leon, Chief Operating Officer, Wise Health System, Decatur, TX, p. A598

FURER, Darnell F, MS, R.N., Vice President Patient Care Services and Chief Nursing Officer, Lehigh Valley Hospital – Schuylkill, Pottsville, PA, p. A539

FURGURSON, Carol, Chief Operating Officer, Saint Louise Regional Hospital, Gilroy, CA, p. A60

FURLOW, Pete, Director Information Technology Services, Rmc Anniston, Anniston, AL, p. A13

FURNAS, David, Chief Information Officer, Gila Regional Medical Center, Silver City, NM, p. A420

FURNEY, June, R.N., Director of Nursing, Brooks County Hospital, Quitman, GA, p. A158

FURNISS, Scott, Vice President and Chief Financial Officer, Saint Agnes Healthcare, Baltimore, MD, p. A287

FURR, Robert, Director Information Services, Anmed Health Cannon, Pickens, SC, p. A556

FUSCHILLO, Ronald
Chief Information Officer, Renown Rehabilitation Hospital, Reno, NV, p. A397
Chief Information Officer, Renown South Meadows Medical Center, Reno, NV, p. A397

FUSCO, Gina, Chief Executive Officer, Foundations Behavioral Health, Doylestown, PA, p. A524

FUSELIER, Gerald, Chief Operating Officer, Savoy Medical Center, Mamou, LA, p. A273

FUSELIER, Michael, FACHE, CPA, R.N., Chief Financial Officer, Central Louisiana Surgical Hospital, Alexandria, LA, p. A262

FUSILERO, Jane, Vice President Chief Nursing Officer, H. Lee Moffitt Cancer Center And Research Institute, Tampa, FL, p. A141

FUSTON, Kathie, Director Human Resources, Moore County Hospital District, Dumas, TX, p. A600

FUTCH, Margaret A., Chief Executive Officer, Encompass Health Rehabilitation Hospital Of Dothan, Dothan, AL, p. A17

FUTRAL, Cindy, Director Human Resources, Elmore Community Hospital, Wetumpka, AL, p. A24

FUTRELL, Cynthia, MSN, R.N., Chief Nursing Officer, Marion General Hospital, Marion, IN, p. A211

FYBEL, Gary G, FACHE, Interim Chief Operating Officer, Swedish Medical Center–First Hill, Seattle, WA, p. A678

G

GAAL, James G, M.D., Chief of Medical Staff, Jackson General Hospital, Ripley, WV, p. A689

GAASCH, Andrew
Chief Financial Officer, Parker Adventist Hospital, Parker, CO, p. A104
Chief Financial Officer, Porter Adventist Hospital, Denver, CO, p. A99

GABALDON, Karen, Chief Management Information Systems, West Palm Beach Veterans Affairs Medical Center, West Palm Beach, FL, p. A144

GABEL, Christopher, Chief Operating Officer, Larkin Community Hospital Behavioral Health Services, Hollywood, FL, p. A124

GABEL, Kelly, Chief of Staff, Citizens Medical Center, Colby, KS, p. A233

GABEL, Marcia, Chief Financial Officer, Lane County Hospital, Dighton, KS, p. A234

GABLE, Beth, Administrative Assistant, Jasper General Hospital, Bay Springs, MS, p. A344

GABLENZ, Gordon, Vice President Finance, Ridgeview Medical Center, Waconia, MN, p. A342

GABORIAULT, Randall, Chief Information Officer, Christiana Care Health System, Newark, DE, p. A113

GABRIEL, Scott F, President, Parkview Whitley Hospital, Columbia City, IN, p. A201

GABRIEL, Scott F., President, Parkview Whitley Hospital, Columbia City, IN, p. A201

GABRIEL, Shirley, Vice President and Chief Information Officer, University Hospital, Augusta, GA, p. A147

GABRIEL, Stacey, President and Chief Executive Officer, Hocking Valley Community Hospital, Logan, OH, p. A485

GABRIELE, Joan, Deputy Executive Director, Brookdale Hospital Medical Center, New York, NY, p. A432

GABRYEL, Timothy, M.D., Vice President Medical Affairs and Medical Director, Mercy Hospital, Buffalo, NY, p. A424

GABUAT, Jesse, Chief Nursing Officer, Plantation General Hospital, Plantation, FL, p. A137

GAC, Deborah, Vice President Human Resources, Valley Presbyterian Hospital, Los Angeles, CA, p. A70

GADALLAH, Yousri, M.D., Chief Medical Officer, Pershing General Hospital, Lovelock, NV, p. A396

GADDAM, Sumalatha, Senior Vice President and Chief Information Officer, Kent County Memorial Hospital, Warwick, RI, p. A548

GADDAM, Summa, Chief Information Officer, Butler Hospital, Providence, RI, p. A547

GADDIS, Cathryn H, Director Human Resources, Rivervalley Behavioral Health Hospital, Owensboro, KY, p. A259

GADDY, Pam, Director, Patient Care Services and Chief Nursing Officer, Firsthealth Montgomery Memorial Hospital, Troy, NC, p. A463

GADE, Swami P, M.D., Medical Director, Tioga Medical Center, Tioga, ND, p. A469
GADEN, Paul
Chief Executive Officer, Bon Secours Maryview Medical Center, Portsmouth, VA, p. A665
Chief Executive Officer, Bon Secours–Depaul Medical Center, Norfolk, VA, p. A663
GAEDE, John, Director Information Systems, El Centro Regional Medical Center, El Centro, CA, p. A57
GAFFOLI, Jill, Director Human Resources, Physicians Regional – Pine Ridge, Naples, FL, p. A132
GAFFORD, Deborah, Chief Financial Officer, Menorah Medical Center, Overland Park, KS, p. A243
GAFFORD, Grady Paul, Chief Financial Officer, Brownfield Regional Medical Center, Brownfield, TX, p. A589
GAGE, Bobby, Director Information Technology, Wabash General Hospital, Mount Carmel, IL, p. A190
GAGE, Eileen, R.N.
Vice President Nursing, Finger Lakes Hospital, Geneva, NY, p. A428
Vice President Nursing, Soldiers And Sailors Memorial Hospital Of Yates County, Penn Yan, NY, p. A441
GAGE, Kevin, Chief Financial Officer, Stamford Hospital, Stamford, CT, p. A111
GAGE, Mark, D.O., Medical Director, Brookhaven Hospital, Tulsa, OK, p. A508
GAGE, Susan, Financial Manager, Veterans Affairs Western New York Healthcare System–Buffalo Division, Buffalo, NY, p. A425
GAGE, Weldon, Chief Financial Officer, University Of Texas M.D. Anderson Cancer Center, Houston, TX, p. A614
GAGLIARDI, Teresa, Vice President of Hospital Operations and Site Administrator, Trinity Hospital Twin City, Dennison, OH, p. A482
GAGLIARDI, Teresa, R.N., Chief Nursing Officer, Trinity Hospital Twin City, Dennison, OH, p. A482
GAGLIO, Anthony, Interim President and Chief Executive Officer, Menninger Clinic, Houston, TX, p. A613
GAGLIO, Anthony, CPA, Senior Vice President and Chief Financial Officer, Menninger Clinic, Houston, TX, p. A613
GAGNE, Cheryl, Vice President Patient Care Services and Chief Nursing Officer, Southern New Hampshire Medical Center, Nashua, NH, p. A401
GAGNON, Andy, Manager Information Technology, Ascension Via Christi Hospital, Manhattan, Manhattan, KS, p. A240
GAINER, Rolf B., Chief Executive Officer, Brookhaven Hospital, Tulsa, OK, p. A508
GAINES, Jeffrey, M.D., Vice President and Chief Medical Officer, Newport Hospital, Newport, RI, p. A547
GAINEY, Rachel, Administrator, Mcleod Health Clarendon, Manning, SC, p. A555
GAINEY, Shari W
Chief Human Resource Officer, Tanner Medical Center–Villa Rica, Villa Rica, GA, p. A162
Human Resource Director, Higgins General Hospital, Bremen, GA, p. A148
GAJ, Steve, Facility Chief Information Officer, Louis Stokes Cleveland Veterans Affairs Medical Center, Cleveland, OH, p. A478
GAJEWSKI, Christie, Director Human Resources, Pinckneyville Community Hospital, Pinckneyville, IL, p. A193
GALANG, Michael, M.D.
Chief Information Officer, Mercy Hospital, Buffalo, NY, p. A424
Chief Information Officer, Sisters Of Charity Hospital Of Buffalo, Buffalo, NY, p. A425
GALARNEAU, Ciprian, Director Information Systems, Tri Valley Health System, Cambridge, NE, p. A383
GALARNEAU, Gerard, M.D., Regional Chief Medical Officer, Catskill Regional Medical Center, Harris, NY, p. A429
GALATI, John P, Chief Executive Officer, Brooks Memorial Hospital, Dunkirk, NY, p. A427
GALAVIZ, Veronica, Chief Financial Officer, Lovelace Regional Hospital – Roswell, Roswell, NM, p. A420
GALBRAITH, Kathleen B., President, Duke Regional Hospital, Durham, NC, p. A452
GALDIERI, Lou, President, Morton Plant Hospital, Clearwater, FL, p. A119
GALE, Gabrielle, Chief Financial Officer, Lighthouse Behavioral Health Hospital, Conway, SC, p. A552
GALE, Melissa, Chief Executive Officer, Landmann–Jungman Memorial Hospital Avera, Scotland, SD, p. A563
GALE, Michael, Chief Financial Officer, Bournewood Health Systems, Brookline, MA, p. A297
GALEY, John P, M.D., Chief Medical Officer, Schoolcraft Memorial Hospital, Manistique, MI, p. A317
GALFANO, Victor J., Chief Executive Officer, Central Indiana Amg Specialty Hospital, Muncie, IN, p. A212
GALIPEAU, Michelle, Director Human Resources, St. Vincent'S Birmingham, Birmingham, AL, p. A15
GALKOWSKI, James, Associate Director for Operations, Fayetteville Veterans Affairs Medical Center, Fayetteville, NC, p. A454
GALLAGHER, Chris, M.D., Chief Medical Officer, Christus Mother Frances Hospital – Sulphur Springs, Sulphur Springs, TX, p. A638
GALLAGHER, Deborah, Manager Human Resources, Ojai Valley Community Hospital, Ojai, CA, p. A75
GALLAGHER, Doug, Director Human Resources, Carolinas Continuecare Hospital At Pineville, Charlotte, NC, p. A451
GALLAGHER, J. P., President and Chief Executive Officer, Northshore University Health System, Evanston, IL, p. A182
GALLAGHER, James, Chief Executive Officer, Oasis Behavioral Health – Chandler, Chandler, AZ, p. A28
GALLAGHER, Jeannie
Chief Human Resource Officer, North Colorado Medical Center, Greeley, CO, p. A101
jeanie.gallagher@bannerhealth.com, Mckee Medical Center, Loveland, CO, p. A104
GALLAGHER, Karen, Vice President Human Resources and Learning, Brooks Rehabilitation Hospital, Jacksonville, FL, p. A125
GALLAGHER, Karen M, MSN, Chief Nursing Office, Vice President Operations, Amita Health St. Mary'S Hospital, Kankakee, IL, p. A187
GALLAGHER, Pamela, Chief Financial Officer, Providence Hospital, Columbia, SC, p. A551
GALLAGHER, Regen, D.O., Chief Medical Officer, Cary Medical Center, Caribou, ME, p. A282
GALLAGHER, Sherry, Director Nursing, Department of Health and Human Services, Humboldt County Mental Health, Eureka, CA, p. A57
GALLAHOM, Gerty, Director Human Resources, Maniilaq Health Center, Kotzebue, AK, p. A26
GALLARDO, Kathleen, Chief Nursing Officer, Select Specialty Hospital–Flint, Flint, MI, p. A311
GALLARDO, Laura, Chief Operating Officer, Kaiser Permanente Panorama City Medical Center, Los Angeles, CA, p. A67
GALLARDO, Ysidro, Associate Administrator Human Resources, Hazel Hawkins Memorial Hospital, Hollister, CA, p. A61
GALLATI, Todd, President and Chief Executive Officer, Trident Medical Center, Charleston, SC, p. A550
GALLAY, Emily, Vice President and Chief Information Officer, Spectrum Health Lakeland, Saint Joseph, MI, p. A322
GALLEGO, Janeen, Chief Nursing Officer, West Hills Hospital And Medical Center, Los Angeles, CA, p. A70
GALLEGOS, Colleen, Director Human Resources, Guadalupe County Hospital, Santa Rosa, NM, p. A420
GALLEGOS, Enrique, Chief Executive Officer, Laredo Medical Center, Laredo, TX, p. A620
GALLEGOS, Kelly, Administrator, San Luis Valley Health Conejos County Hospital, La Jara, CO, p. A102
GALLEGOS, Ken, Director Support Services and Information Technology, Medina Regional Hospital, Hondo, TX, p. A610
GALLI, Jodi B., R.N., Chief Nursing Officer, Kaiser Permanente Redwood City Medical Center, Redwood City, CA, p. A80
GALLIART, Mark, Chief Executive Officer, Mcbride Orthopedic Hospital, Oklahoma City, OK, p. A504
GALLIK, Becky, Information Systems Manager, Firstlight Health System, Mora, MN, p. A336
GALLO, Carrie, Chief Nursing Officer, Western Reserve Hospital, Cuyahoga Falls, OH, p. A481
GALLO, Ronald, Director Human Resources, Blythedale Children'S Hospital, Valhalla, NY, p. A446
GALLOGLY–SIMON, Catherine A, R.N., MS, Chief Nursing Officer, Brookdale Hospital Medical Center, New York, NY, p. A432
GALLUCCI, Vince
Senior Vice President Human Resources, Ascension Northeast Wisconsin Mercy Hospital, Oshkosh, WI, p. A703
Senior Vice President Human Resources, Ascension Northeast Wisconsin St. Elizabeth Hospital, Appleton, WI, p. A691
GALT, Nick
Chief Financial Officer, Medical City Las Colinas, Irving, TX, p. A616
Chief Financial Officer, Medical City North Hills, North Richland Hills, TX, p. A626
GALUSHA, Fred, Chief Information Officer, St. Luke'S Rehabilitation Institute, Spokane, WA, p. A680
GALVIN, Gary, M.D., Chief of the Medical Staff, Columbus Community Hospital, Inc., Columbus, WI, p. A693
GALYON, Darlene, Director Human Resources, Choctaw Memorial Hospital, Hugo, OK, p. A501
GAMACHE, Cynde, R.N., Vice President and Chief Nursing Officer, Baptist Hospital, Pensacola, FL, p. A136
GAMB, Pamela, Manager Human Resources, Aurora Psychiatric Hospital, Wauwatosa, WI, p. A708
GAMBLA, Kurt, D.O., Chief Medical Officer, Beaufort Memorial Hospital, Beaufort, SC, p. A549
GAMBLE, Allen J., Interim Chief Executive Officer, Chadron Community Hospital And Health Services, Chadron, NE, p. A384
GAMBLE, Brian, Chief Financial Officer, Karmanos Cancer Center, Detroit, MI, p. A310
GAMBLE, Kathleen, Fiscal Officer, Patton State Hospital, Patton, CA, p. A77
GAMBLE, Robert, M.D., Chief of Staff, Terrebonne General Medical Center, Houma, LA, p. A269
GAMBLE, Troy B, M.D., Chief Medical Staff, Williamsburg Regional Hospital, Kingstree, SC, p. A554
GAMBOA, Eileen, Director Human Resources, Oakbend Medical Center, Richmond, TX, p. A631
GAMBRELL, Titus E., Vice President and Chief Nursing Officer, St. Mary'S Health Care System, Athens, GA, p. A145
GAMET, Nicki
Administrator, Mercy Hospital Aurora, Aurora, MO, p. A356
Administrator, Mercy Hospital Cassville, Cassville, MO, p. A358
GAMEZ, Kriss, Director Human Resources, Baylor Scott & White Medical Center – Plano, Plano, TX, p. A629
GAMINO, Randall, Director Perot Site, St. Joseph'S Medical Center, Stockton, CA, p. A91
GAMMIERE, Thomas A, Chief Executive Officer, Scripps Mercy Hospital, San Diego, CA, p. A84
GAMMIERE, Thomas A., Chief Executive, Senior Vice President, Scripps Mercy Hospital, San Diego, CA, p. A84
GANDHI, Tejas, Ph.D., Chief Operating Officer, Baystate Medical Center, Springfield, MA, p. A303
GANDY, Galina, Vice President Information Technology, Columbia Memorial Hospital, Astoria, OR, p. A511
GANDY, Patrick W., Jr, Executive Vice President and Chief Executive Officer, Lafayette General Medical Center, Lafayette, LA, p. A271
GANGULY, Devabrata, M.D., Medical Director, Christus Dubuis Hospital Of Paris, Paris, TX, p. A627
GANGULY, Indranil, Vice President and Chief Information Officer, Hackensack Meridian Health Jfk Medical Center, Edison, NJ, p. A405
GANGULY, Neal, Chief Information Officer, Hackensack Meridian Health Jfk Johnson Rehabilitation Institute, Edison, NJ, p. A405
GANLEY, Evan, Manager Human Resources, Lifecare Hospitals Of Chester County, West Chester, PA, p. A544
GANN, Lisa, R.N., Chief Nursing Officer, Tristar Hendersonville Medical Center, Hendersonville, TN, p. A570
GANN, Michele, Vice President Patient Services, Mercy Hospital Berryville, Berryville, AR, p. A39
GANNON, Ronnie, Director Information Services, Tristar Southern Hills Medical Center, Nashville, TN, p. A577
GANNOTTA, Richard, Chief Executive Officer, Uc Irvine Medical Center, Orange, CA, p. A76
GANS, Bruce M, M.D., Executive Vice President and Chief Medical Officer, Kessler Institute For Rehabilitation, West Orange, NJ, p. A414
GANSEMER, Sheila, R.N., Vice President Patient Care Services and Chief Nursing Officer, Ascension Southeast Wisconsin Hospital – Franklin Campus, Franklin, WI, p. A695
GANSKE, Jary, Chief Financial Officer, Methodist Mansfield Medical Center, Mansfield, TX, p. A623
GANTNER, John J., President and Chief Executive Officer, Robert Wood Johnson University Hospital, New Brunswick, NJ, p. A409
GANTT, Cynthia J, Chief of Staff, Naval Medical Center, Portsmouth, VA, p. A665
GANTZER, Ann M, Ph.D., R.N., Vice President Patient Services and Chief Nursing Officer, Swedishamerican – A Division Of Uw Health, Rockford, IL, p. A195
GARAY, Kenneth, M.D., Chief Medical Officer, Jersey City Medical Center, Jersey City, NJ, p. A407
GARBANZOS, Del, Director Human Resources, Delano Regional Medical Center, Delano, CA, p. A56
GARBARINO, James, Chief Financial Officer, Clay County Medical Center, Clay Center, KS, p. A233
GARBER, Mary, Vice President Finance, Mercy Hospital Ada, Ada, OK, p. A496
GARCIA, Andrew T., Interim Director, Central Texas Veterans Health Care System, Temple, TX, p. A640
GARCIA, Antonio M.
Chief Nursing Officer, Memorialcare, Long Beach Memorial Medical Center, Long Beach, CA, p. A65
Chief Nursing Officer, Memorialcare, Miller Children'S & Women'S Hospital Long Beach, Long Beach, CA, p. A65
GARCIA, Ara, Manager Human Resources, Milwaukee County Behavioral Health Division, Milwaukee, WI, p. A701

GARCIA, Aymette, Manager Human Resources, Wilma N. Vazquez Medical Center, Vega Baja, PR, p. A720

GARCIA, Danette, Director Human Resources, Encompass Health Valley Of The Sun Rehabilitation Hospital, Glendale, AZ, p. A30

GARCIA, Estevan, M.D., Chief Medical Officer, Cooley Dickinson Hospital, Northampton, MA, p. A301

GARCIA, Evangeline, M.D., Clinical Director, Eastern Shore Hospital Center, Cambridge, MD, p. A289

GARCIA, Georgina R., Executive Director, Kaiser Permanente West Los Angeles Medical Center, Los Angeles, CA, p. A67

GARCIA, Gerard, Chief Human Resource Officer, University Hospital, Newark, NJ, p. A409

GARCIA, Idalia, Chief Human Resources Officer, Hospital De Psiquiatria, San Juan, PR, p. A718

GARCIA, Iris, Director, Information Services, Jerome Golden Center For Behavioral Health, Inc., West Palm Beach, FL, p. A144

GARCIA, Irma, Job Coordinator, Rio Grande State Center/ South Texas Health Care System, Harlingen, TX, p. A609

GARCIA, Jacob, Chief Information Officer, Little Colorado Medical Center, Winslow, AZ, p. A38

GARCIA, Jannina, Director of Human Resources, Adventhealth Fish Memorial, Orange City, FL, p. A134

GARCIA, Joanne, Chief Operating Officer, Kindred Chicago–Central Hospital, Chicago, IL, p. A178

GARCIA, Joannie, CPA, Director Finance, Hospital Perea, Mayaguez, PR, p. A717

GARCIA, Jose, Chief Human Resources Officer, San Juan City Hospital, San Juan, PR, p. A719

GARCIA, Jose, M.D., Chief Medical Staff, Dundy County Hospital, Benkelman, NE, p. A383

GARCIA, Kathleen, Controller, Brookdale Hospital Medical Center, New York, NY, p. A432

GARCIA, Luis Mario, Director Human Resources, Houston Methodist Sugar Land Hospital, Sugar Land, TX, p. A638

GARCIA, Margaret, Manager Human Resources, Baylor Scott & White Medical Center–Frisco, Frisco, TX, p. A606

GARCIA, Michael A, Vice President and Chief Information Officer, Jackson Health System, Miami, FL, p. A130

GARCIA, Orlando, M.D., Chief Medical Officer, Hialeah Hospital, Hialeah, FL, p. A124

GARCIA, Robert W, M.D., Chief Medical Officer, Iraan General Hospital, Iraan, TX, p. A615

GARCIA, Roland
Senior Vice President and Chief Information Officer, Baptist Medical Center Beaches, Jacksonville Beach, FL, p. A126
Senior Vice President and Chief Information Officer, Baptist Medical Center Jacksonville, Jacksonville, FL, p. A125

GARCIA, Rudy, Chief Executive Officer, Westchester General Hospital, Miami, FL, p. A131

GARCIA, Sharon, Human Resources Representative, Medina Regional Hospital, Hondo, TX, p. A610

GARCIA, Shawn, Manager Human Resources, Memorial Hospital Los Banos, Los Banos, CA, p. A70

GARCIA, Sylvia, Chief Accounting Officer, South Texas Spine And Surgical Hospital, San Antonio, TX, p. A635

GARCIA, Tracy, MS, Chief Nursing Officer, Cheyenne Regional Medical Center, Cheyenne, WY, p. A710

GARCIN, Hector Troche, Human Resources Director, St. Luke'S Episcopal Hospital, Ponce, PR, p. A717

GARD, Emily, Chief Clinical Officer, Kindred Hospital–San Francisco Bay Area, San Leandro, CA, p. A87

GARDEPE, Cynthia, Director, Human Resources, Uhs Delaware Valley Hospital, Walton, NY, p. A446

GARDINER, Greg, Chief Clinical Officer, Ashley Regional Medical Center, Vernal, UT, p. A653

GARDINER, Karen, Human Resources Director, Bayfront Health Port Charlotte, Port Charlotte, FL, p. A137

GARDNER, Carla, Director of Nursing, Munson Healthcare Grayling Hospital, Grayling, MI, p. A313

GARDNER, David, MSN, Chief Nursing Officer, Wyoming Medical Center, Casper, WY, p. A710

GARDNER, Debra C., Administrator, Ten Lakes Center, Dennison, OH, p. A482

GARDNER, Greg, Senior Vice President and Chief Financial Officer, Cleveland Clinic Indian River Hospital, Vero Beach, FL, p. A143

GARDNER, Jacque, Administrative Assistant, Clinic Manager, Co–Chief Financial Officer and Chief Human Resources, Mccone County Health Center, Circle, MT, p. A375

GARDNER, James D, M.D., Vice President and Chief Medical Officer, Waukesha Memorial Hospital, Waukesha, WI, p. A707

GARDNER, Joel, D.O., Chief Medical Officer, Brigham City Community Hospital, Brigham City, UT, p. A647

GARDNER, Kristin Day, Chief Nursing Officer, Berger Health System, Circleville, OH, p. A477

GARDNER, Michelle, M.D., Clinical Director, Dorothea Dix Psychiatric Center, Bangor, ME, p. A281

GARDNER, Patrick, M.D., Associate Vice President, Medical Affairs, St. Joseph's Hospital, St. Joseph'S Hospital, West Bend, WI, p. A708

GARDNER, Robb, Chief Executive Officer, Henry County Health Center, Mount Pleasant, IA, p. A227

GARDNER, Sharon, Manager Information Systems, Ssm Health St. Joseph Hospital – Lake Saint Louis, Lake Saint Louis, MO, p. A364

GARDNER, William, Chief Clinical Officer, Bartlett Regional Hospital, Juneau, AK, p. A26

GARDNER, Zoe, Manager Human Resources, Sharp Chula Vista Medical Center, Chula Vista, CA, p. A54

GARES, Donna, Chief Executive Officer, Select Specialty Hospital–Wilmington, Wilmington, DE, p. A114

GARISON, Jerri, President, Baylor Scott & White Medical Center – Plano, Plano, TX, p. A629

GARISON, Jerri, R.N., Interim Chief Executive Officer and Chief Operating Officer, Baylor Scott & White Medical Center – Carrollton, Carrollton, TX, p. A591

GARKO, Michael, Chief Financial Officer, St. Vincent Medical Center, Los Angeles, CA, p. A69

GARLETS, Mary, Director Human Resources, Mayo Clinic Health System In Cannon Falls, Cannon Falls, MN, p. A329

GARMAN, Denise M, Director Human Resources, Wellspan Good Samaritan Hospital, Lebanon, PA, p. A530

GARMAN, Michael, Chief Financial Officer, Avera St. Anthony'S Hospital, O'Neill, NE, p. A390

GARMAN, Patrick M., Commander, Evans U. S. Army Community Hospital, Fort Carson, CO, p. A100

GARNAS, David, Administrator, Cloud County Health Center, Concordia, KS, p. A234

GARNER, Douglas, Vice President, Thomas Hospital, Fairhope, AL, p. A18

GARNER, Mario J., Chief Executive Officer, Chi St. Luke'S Hospital – The Vintage Hospital, Houston, TX, p. A611

GARNER, Stephen, Chief Operating Officer, Delray Medical Center, Delray Beach, FL, p. A121

GARNETT, Mark, M.D., Chief of Staff, Hansford Hospital, Spearman, TX, p. A637

GARONE, Marlene, M.D., Vice President Medical Affairs and Medical Director, Upmc Chautauqua Wca, Jamestown, NY, p. A429

GARRARD, Michael Eric., Chief Executive Officer, Emory Rehabilitation Hospital, Atlanta, GA, p. A146

GARRED, John, M.D., Chief Medical Officer, Burgess Health Center, Onawa, IA, p. A227

GARREN OSTER, Cynthia, Human Resource Manager, South Coast Global Medical Center, Santa Ana, CA, p. A88

GARRETT, Alan H., Chief Executive Officer, Carson Tahoe Health, Carson City, NV, p. A393

GARRETT, Courtney, CPA, Senior Vice President, Chief Financial Officer, Children'S Hospital, New Orleans, LA, p. A275

GARRETT, Dana M., R.N., Nursing Services Administrator, Taylor Regional Hospital, Campbellsville, KY, p. A250

GARRETT, David B
Senior Vice President and Chief Information Officer, Novant Health Brunswick Medical Center, Bolivia, NC, p. A450
Senior Vice President and Chief Information Officer, Novant Health Charlotte Orthopaedic Hospital, Charlotte, NC, p. A451
Senior Vice President and Chief Information Officer, Novant Health Forsyth Medical Center, Winston, NC, p. A464
Senior Vice President and Chief Information Officer, Novant Health Huntersville Medical Center, Huntersville, NC, p. A456
Senior Vice President and Chief Information Officer, Novant Health Matthews Medical Center, Matthews, NC, p. A458
Senior Vice President and Chief Information Officer, Novant Health Medical Park Hospital, Winston, NC, p. A464
Senior Vice President and Chief Information Officer, Novant Health Rowan Medical Center, Salisbury, NC, p. A461
Senior Vice President and Chief Information Officer, Novant Health Thomasville Medical Center, Thomasville, NC, p. A463
Senior Vice President and Chief Information Officer, Novant Health Uva Health System Haymarket Medical Center, Haymarket, VA, p. A661
Senior Vice President and Chief Information Officer, Novant Health Uva Health System Prince William Medical Center, Manassas, VA, p. A662
Senior Vice President Information Technology, Novant Health Presbyterian Medical Center, Charlotte, NC, p. A451

GARRETT, Josh, Chief of Staff, Habersham Medical Center, Demorest, GA, p. A152

GARRETT, Kevin C., M.D.
Medical Executive East Region, St. Joseph'S Hospital, Saint Paul, MN, p. A340
Medical Executive, East Region, Woodwinds Health Campus, Woodbury, MN, p. A343

GARRETT, Matthew, Director Information Systems, Flowers Hospital, Dothan, AL, p. A17

GARRETT, Nancy, Chief Analytics and Information Technology Officer, Hennepin Healthcare, Minneapolis, MN, p. A335

GARRETT, Scott, Director of IS, Ottumwa Regional Health Center, Ottumwa, IA, p. A228

GARRICK, Renee, M.D., Executive Medical Director, Westchester Medical Center, Valhalla, NY, p. A446

GARRIOTT, Edie, Director Human Resources, Community Hospital South, Indianapolis, IN, p. A206

GARRISON, Christopher, M.D., Medical Director, Central Texas Rehabilitation Hospital, Austin, TX, p. A585

GARRISON, Eric L, Chief Information Officer, Greeneville Community Hospital East, Greeneville, TN, p. A570

GARRISON, Tina, President, Ssm Health St. Clare Hospital – Fenton, Fenton, MO, p. A360

GARRISON, Wes, Chief Nursing Officer, St. Luke'S Sugar Land Hospital, Sugar Land, TX, p. A638

GARRITY, Elizabeth, Director Human Resources, Hudson Regional Hospital, Secaucus, NJ, p. A412

GARRITY, Nerissa, Chief Financial Officer, Kula Hospital, Kula, HI, p. A166

GARROW, Dina, Chief Nursing Officer and Chief Operating Officer, Kindred Hospital–Baldwin Park, Baldwin Park, CA, p. A51

GARTLAND, Bryce D., Chief Executive Officer, Emory University Hospital, Atlanta, GA, p. A146

GARTMAN, Kathy Degenstein, Chief Nursing Officer, Medical Center Of South Arkansas, El Dorado, AR, p. A41

GARTNER, Katie, Director Health Information Management, Chi Health Good Samaritan, Kearney, NE, p. A386

GARTON, Debra, R.N., Chief Nursing Officer, Oss Orthopaedic Hospital, York, PA, p. A546

GARVEY, James
Hospital Operations, Essentia Health Duluth, Duluth, MN, p. A331
Senior Vice President Hospital Practice, Essentia Health East, Essentia Health St. Mary'S Medical Center, Duluth, MN, p. A331

GARVEY, Rita, Chief Nursing Officer, Lawrence County Memorial Hospital, Lawrenceville, IL, p. A187

GARVEY, Thomas J, Senior Vice President Operations and Chief Financial Officer, Swedish Covenant Hospital, Chicago, IL, p. A180

GARVIN, Jan, Vice President Human Resources, Bryan Medical Center, Lincoln, NE, p. A386

GARY, Al, COO, Simpson General Hospital, Mendenhall, MS, p. A351

GARZA, Art, Chief Executive Officer, Valley Regional Medical Center, Brownsville, TX, p. A590

GARZA, Ismelda, Director Information Systems, Comanche County Medical Center, Comanche, TX, p. A593

GARZA, Leo, Chief Executive Officer, South Texas Rehabilitation Hospital, Brownsville, TX, p. A589

GARZA, Oscar, M.D., Chief Medical Staff, Frio Regional Hospital, Pearsall, TX, p. A628

GARZA, Teri, Director Health Information Services, Knapp Medical Center, Weslaco, TX, p. A645

GARZA, Tom, Director Fiscal and Support, Rio Grande State Center/South Texas Health Care System, Harlingen, TX, p. A609

GASBARRE, Christopher, D.O., Community Medical Director, Spearfish Regional Hospital, Spearfish, SD, p. A564

GASH, Deborah
Chief Information Officer, Saint Luke'S Hospital Of Kansas City, Kansas City, MO, p. A363
Chief Information Officer, Saint Luke'S South Hospital, Overland Park, KS, p. A243

GASKELL, Dan, Chief Executive Officer, Encompass Health Rehabilitation Hospital Of Virginia, Richmond, VA, p. A666

GASKILL, Harold, III, Chief Executive Officer, First Baptist Medical Center, Dallas, TX, p. A596

GASKILL, Paulette Sue, Executive Director of Nursing, St. Vincent Clay Hospital, Brazil, IN, p. A200

GASKILL–HAMES, Michelle, Senior Vice President & Area Manager, Kaiser Permanente Redwood City Medical Center, Redwood City, CA, p. A80

GASKINS, Michael, Director Information Technology, Lincoln Community Hospital And Nursing Home, Hugo, CO, p. A102

GASKINS, Michael W., President, Upmc Hanover, Hanover, PA, p. A526

GASPAR, Gabrielle, M.D., Chief Medical Officer, Doctors Medical Center Of Modesto, Modesto, CA, p. A72

GASQUE, James, M.D., Chief Hospital Services, U. S. Air Force Medical Center Keesler, Keesler Afb, MS, p. A349

GASTINEAU, Trent, Chief Executive Officer, Tulsa Spine And Specialty Hospital, Tulsa, OK, p. A510

GASTON, Jan, Administrator, Jasper Memorial Hospital, Monticello, GA, p. A158

GASTON, Kathy, Chief Nursing Officer, Baptist Medical Center East, Montgomery, AL, p. A21

GASTON, Tammy, Chief Information Officer, Smith County Memorial Hospital, Smith Center, KS, p. A246

GATES, Misty, Chief Financial Officer, Forrest City Medical Center, Forrest City, AR, p. A42

GATES, Rose, Director Human Resources, Hayward Area Memorial Hospital And Water'S Edge, Hayward, WI, p. A697

GATES, Tracy, Vice President Operations and Chief Operating Officer, Cortland Regional Medical Center, Cortland, NY, p. A426

GATHERS, Mary
   Director Information Systems, Mckay–Dee Hospital, Ogden, UT, p. A649
   Director Information Systems, Utah Valley Hospital, Provo, UT, p. A651
   Manager Information Systems, American Fork Hospital, American Fork, UT, p. A647

GATLIFF, Peggy, Chief Financial Officer, Northside Hospital, Saint Petersburg, FL, p. A138

GATLIFF, Rob, Chief of Medical Staff, Washington County Regional Medical Center, Sandersville, GA, p. A159

GATO, Carlos A, Director of Human Resources, Fort Lauderdale Hospital, Fort Lauderdale, FL, p. A122

GATRELL, Kristi, Chief Executive Officer, Big Horn County Memorial Hospital, Hardin, MT, p. A377

GATTO, Tony, Director Management Information Systems, Brookdale Hospital Medical Center, New York, NY, p. A432

GAUBERT, Steve C, Chief Financial Officer, Thibodaux Regional Medical Center, Thibodaux, LA, p. A279

GAUER, Natalie, Administrator, Milbank Area Hospital Avera, Milbank, SD, p. A562

GAUG, Mathew P., Executive Director of Information Technology, Lima Memorial Health System, Lima, OH, p. A485

GAUGHAN, Thomas, M.D., Chief Medical Officer, Kingman Regional Medical Center, Kingman, AZ, p. A30

GAUL, Mike, Director Information Technology, Golden Valley Memorial Healthcare, Clinton, MO, p. A358

GAULKE, Becky, Chief Nursing Officer, Ely–Bloomenson Community Hospital, Ely, MN, p. A331

GAULT, Cindy L., Chief Financial Officer, Union Medical Center, Union, SC, p. A558

GAURON, Patricia, Director Human Resources, Holy Family Hospital, Methuen, MA, p. A300

GAUSE, Levi Nathan, M.D., Chief Information Officer and Vice President Health System Informatics, Great River Health System, West Burlington, IA, p. A231

GAUTHIER, Paul, Chief Information Resources Management, Veterans Affairs Montana Health Care System, Fort Harrison, MT, p. A376

GAUTNEY, Steven, Chief Executive Officer, Crisp Regional Hospital, Cordele, GA, p. A151

GAVALCHIK, Stephen M., Community Chief Executive Officer, Morgan County Arh Hospital, West Liberty, KY, p. A261

GAVIN, Andrea, M.D., Chief Medical officer, Aurora Sheboygan Memorial Medical Center, Sheboygan, WI, p. A705

GAVIN, Donald, Chief Financial Officer, Southern Tennessee Regional Health System–Pulaski, Pulaski, TN, p. A578

GAVIN, Patrick J., President and Chief Executive Officer, Hunterdon Healthcare, Flemington, NJ, p. A406

GAVIN, Todd, Chief Medical Officer, Madelia Community Hospital, Madelia, MN, p. A334

GAVORA, George, Director Program Evaluation, Brookdale Hospital Medical Center, New York, NY, p. A432

GAVULIC, Melany
   President & Chief Executive Officer, Hurley Medical Center, Flint, MI, p. A311
   Senior Vice President Operations & COO, Hurley Medical Center, Flint, MI, p. A311

GAW, Kris, Executive Vice President and Chief Operating Officer, Maricopa Integrated Health System, Phoenix, AZ, p. A33

GAWALUCK, David
   Vice President and Chief Information Officer, Excela Frick Hospital, Mount Pleasant, PA, p. A532
   Vice President and Chief Information Officer, Excela Health Westmoreland Hospital, Greensburg, PA, p. A526
   Vice President and Chief Information Officer, Excela Latrobe Area Hospital, Latrobe, PA, p. A529

GAWITH, Marlene, Director of Nursing, Ottawa County Health Center, Minneapolis, KS, p. A241

GAWLER, William, Chief Information Officer, Chillicothe Veterans Affairs Medical Center, Chillicothe, OH, p. A475

GAWNE, Bernard B, M.D., Vice President and Chief Medical Officer, Christ Hospital, Cincinnati, OH, p. A475

GAY, Christophe, M.D., Chief of Staff, Chi St Joseph Health Bellville Hospital, Bellville, TX, p. A588

GAY, Don, Director Human Resources, West Hills Hospital, Reno, NV, p. A397

GAY, Kent E., M.D., Chief of Medical Staff, Arkansas Valley Regional Medical Center, La Junta, CO, p. A102

GAY, Kristi
   Chief Financial Officer, Chi St. Luke'S Health Memorial Lufkin, Lufkin, TX, p. A622
   Chief Financial Officer, Chi St. Luke'S Health Memorial San Augustine, San Augustine, TX, p. A636

GAY, Michael, Chief Operating Officer, Habersham Medical Center, Demorest, GA, p. A152

GAY, Perry, President and Chief Executive Officer, Logansport Memorial Hospital, Logansport, IN, p. A210

GAY, Vickie, Chief Executive Officer, Montgomery General Hospital, Montgomery, WV, p. A687

GAYNE, William, Chief Financial Officer, Medstar Washington Hospital Center, Washington, DC, p. A116

GAYNOR, Sheila, Director Human Resources, Perry County Memorial Hospital, Tell City, IN, p. A215

GAYTKO, Caren, Chief Nursing Officer, Regency Hospital Of Minneapolis, Golden Valley, MN, p. A332

GAZAWAY, William, Information Technology Security Officer, Alliancehealth Ponca City, Ponca City, OK, p. A506

GAZECKI, Cindy, Senior Vice President, Hospital Operations, Seattle Children'S Hospital, Seattle, WA, p. A678

GEARHART, Danielle, Chief Executive Officer, Gundersen St. Joseph'S Hospital And Clinics, Hillsboro, WI, p. A697

GEARHART, Heidi, Director Information Systems, Arkansas Valley Regional Medical Center, La Junta, CO, p. A102

GEARY, David S, Chief Financial Officer, Cache Valley Hospital, North Logan, UT, p. A649

GEARY, Herb J
   Chief Nursing Officer, Santa Ynez Valley Cottage Hospital, Solvang, CA, p. A90
   Vice President Patient Care Services and Chief Nursing Officer, Santa Barbara Cottage Hospital, Santa Barbara, CA, p. A88

GEBAUER, Laurie, Director Patient Care, Orange City Area Health System, Orange City, IA, p. A227

GEBHARD, Scott
   Chief Operating Officer, Hackensack Meridian Health Jfk Johnson Rehabilitation Institute, Edison, NJ, p. A405
   Executive VP and Chief Operating Officer, Hackensack Meridian Health Jfk Medical Center, Edison, NJ, p. A405

GEBHART, Cheryl
   Chief Human Resources Officer, Tuality Healthcare, Hillsboro, OR, p. A513
   Director Human Resources Providence Health Plan and Providence Medical Group, Providence Newberg Medical Center, Newberg, OR, p. A515

GEBHART, Jim, Jr, President, Mercy Hospital Oklahoma City, Oklahoma City, OK, p. A504

GEBHART, Ronald J, M.D., Chief of Staff, Veterans Affairs Salt Lake City Health Care System, Salt Lake City, UT, p. A652

GECKLE, Rachel, Chief Human Resource Officer, Fulton County Health Center, Wauseon, OH, p. A493

GEDDINGS, Toni, Director Human Resources, Cullman Regional Medical Center, Cullman, AL, p. A16

GEDIES, Lucille, Chief Financial Officer, Mildred Mitchell–Bateman Hospital, Huntington, WV, p. A686

GEE, Kyle
   Chief Financial Officer, Beartooth Billings Clinic, Red Lodge, MT, p. A379
   Chief Financial Officer, Pioneer Medical Center, Big Timber, MT, p. A374
   Regional Vice President Financial Operations, Roundup Memorial Healthcare, Roundup, MT, p. A380

GEER, Nicholas, Chief Financial Officer, Dallas Medical Center, Dallas, TX, p. A596

GEERTS, Jodi, Chief Nursing Officer, Henry County Health Center, Mount Pleasant, IA, p. A227

GEESEY, Wanda, Director Human Resources, Pennsylvania Psychiatric Institute, Harrisburg, PA, p. A526

GEHA, Andrew, D.O., President Medical Staff, Floyd Valley Healthcare, Le Mars, IA, p. A225

GEHLAUF, Dee Ann, Senior Vice President Business and Organization Development, Marietta Memorial Hospital, Marietta, OH, p. A486

GEHLHAUSEN, Sherri, Assistant Chief Financial Officer, Logansport Memorial Hospital, Logansport, IN, p. A210

GEHRIG, Ryan, President, Mercy Hospital Fort Smith, Fort Smith, AR, p. A42

GEHRING, Betty, Finance Director, Operations, Thedacare Medical Center–New London, New London, WI, p. A702

GEHRING, Jay, Director Information Systems, Kingman Community Hospital, Kingman, KS, p. A238

GEHRING, Mikaela, Chief Operating Officer, Compass Memorial Healthcare, Marengo, IA, p. A226

GEHRING, Samuel, M.D., Chief of Staff, Fleming County Hospital, Flemingsburg, KY, p. A251

GEHRING, Terri
   President and Chief Executive Officer, Mcpherson Hospital, Mcpherson, KS, p. A240
   Vice President Operations, Mcpherson Hospital, Mcpherson, KS, p. A240

GEHRKE, Ryan, Chief Executive Officer, Eminent Medical Center, Richardson, TX, p. A630

GEIER, Joyce, Director Nursing, Girard Medical Center, Girard, KS, p. A235

GEIER, Kathy, Director of Nursing, Chase County Community Hospital, Imperial, NE, p. A386

GEIGER, Deb, Executive Director of Acute Care, Harbor Beach Community Hospital, Harbor Beach, MI, p. A314

GEIGER, Ralph, M.D., Chief of Staff, Sebastian River Medical Center, Sebastian, FL, p. A139

GEIGLE, Joseph, Director Human Resources, Fort Hamilton Hospital, Hamilton, OH, p. A484

GEIL, Kristie A, Vice President, Chief Nursing Officer, Cgh Medical Center, Sterling, IL, p. A197

GEISLER, Linda W, R.N., FACHE, Vice President Patient Services, Centrastate Healthcare System, Freehold, NJ, p. A406

GEISSLER, Bonnie, R.N., Chief Nursing Officer, Vice President Patient Care Services, Clara Maass Medical Center, Belleville, NJ, p. A403

GEIST, Jim
   Executive Vice President and Chief Operating Officer, Cascade Valley Hospital, Arlington, WA, p. A670
   Executive Vice President and Chief Operating Officer, Skagit Regional Health, Mount Vernon, WA, p. A675

GEISTER, Bennett, Chief Executive Officer, Hillcrest Hospital – South, Tulsa, OK, p. A508

GEITZ, Cheri, Director Human Resources, Hansen Family Hospital, Iowa Falls, IA, p. A225

GEITZ, James, M.D., Chief of Staff, Newman Regional Health, Emporia, KS, p. A234

GEIVER, Betsy, Chief Human Resources Officer, Sioux Falls Veterans Affairs Health Care System, Sioux Falls, SD, p. A564

GELDHOF, Jay
   Director Information Systems, Greater El Monte Community Hospital, South El Monte, CA, p. A90
   Director Information Systems, Whittier Hospital Medical Center, Whittier, CA, p. A95

GELFAND, Andrew, M.D., Medical Director, Our Children'S House, Dallas, TX, p. A597

GELL, Michael, Director Human Resources, Boys Town National Research Hospital, Omaha, NE, p. A388

GELLASCH, Tara L, Chief Medical Officer, United Memorial Medical Center, Batavia, NY, p. A423

GELLER, Harold S., Chief Executive Officer, Chi St Anthony Hospital, Pendleton, OR, p. A515

GELLER, Mark, President and Chief Executive Officer, Nyack Hospital, Nyack, NY, p. A440

GELLER, Warren, President and Chief Executive Officer, Englewood Hospital And Medical Center, Englewood, NJ, p. A405

GEMBOL, Leslie, MSN, R.N., Chief Nursing Officer, Baylor Scott & White Medical Center – Round Rock, Round Rock, TX, p. A632

GENESIO, Sabina, Finance Officer for Institutes, Colorado Mental Health Institute At Fort Logan, Denver, CO, p. A98

GENEVRO, Thomas A, Vice President Human Resources, Butler Health System, Butler, PA, p. A521

GENGLE, Tim F, Director Human Resources, North Ottawa Community Hospital, Grand Haven, MI, p. A312

GENGLER, Laraine, Chief Financial Officer, Lindsborg Community Hospital, Lindsborg, KS, p. A240

GENNA, Nick, Administrator, Treasure Valley Hospital, Boise, ID, p. A168

GENNARO, John, Director, Erie Veterans Affairs Medical Center, Erie, PA, p. A525

GENOVESE, Vincent P, M.D., President Medical Staff, Owensboro Health Muhlenberg Community Hospital, Greenville, KY, p. A252

GENSERT, Kurt G, FACHE, R.N., Vice President Operations, Platte Valley Medical Center, Brighton, CO, p. A97

GENTILE, John, M.D.
   Vice President Medical Affairs, Alta Bates Summit Medical Center – Summit Campus, Oakland, CA, p. A75
   Vice President Medical Affairs, Alta Bates Summit Medical Center, Berkeley, CA, p. A52

GENTNER, Kim, Chief Financial Officer, Deckerville Community Hospital, Deckerville, MI, p. A309

GENTNER, Rocky, Chief Financial Officer, Newport Bay Hospital, Newport Beach, CA, p. A74

GENTRY, Jeanine, Chief Executive Officer, Steele Memorial Medical Center, Salmon, ID, p. A172

GENTRY, Jennifer, R.N., Chief Nursing Officer, Christus Spohn Hospital Corpus Christi Memorial, Corpus Christi, TX, p. A594

GENTRY, Laura, Administrator, Medical Center Of Peach County, Navicent Health, Bryon, GA, p. A149

GENTRY, Lee, Vice President and Administrator, Baptist Health Extended Care Hospital, Little Rock, AR, p. A44

GENTRY, Margie, Controller, T. J. Samson Community Hospital, Glasgow, KY, p. A252

GEOGHEGAN, Jeffrey, Chief Financial Officer, Uconn, John Dempsey Hospital, Farmington, CT, p. A108

GEORGE, Alan E, Chief Operating Officer, St. Francis Hospital, Columbus, GA, p. A150

GEORGE, Brad, Director Information Systems, Parkland Medical Center, Derry, NH, p. A399

GEORGE, Dana, Chief Human Resources Officer, Abrazo Central Campus, Phoenix, AZ, p. A32

GEORGE, Daniel M, Executive Vice President, Operations, Covenant Healthcare, Saginaw, MI, p. A321

GEORGE, Denise
Interim Chief Executive Officer, Sharon Hospital, Sharon, CT, p. A110
President, Northern Dutchess Hospital, Rhinebeck, NY, p. A442

GEORGE, Gary, Senior Vice President Human Resources, Mercy St. Vincent Medical Center, Toledo, OH, p. A492

GEORGE, P A, M.D., Chief of Staff, Madison Medical Center, Fredericktown, MO, p. A360

GEORGE, Patsy, R.N., Vice President and Chief Nursing Officer, Ohio Valley Medical Center, Wheeling, WV, p. A690

GEORGE, Saju, Chief Executive Officer, Garden City Hospital, Garden City, MI, p. A312

GEORGE, Shayne, Chief Executive Officer, Memorial Health, Savannah, GA, p. A160

GEORGE, Susan, R.N., M.P.H., Associate Director Patient Care Services, Martinsburg Veterans Affairs Medical Center, Martinsburg, WV, p. A687

GEORGE, Tracy L, Chief Financial Officer, St. James Parish Hospital, Lutcher, LA, p. A273

GEORGE, William, M.D., Chief of Staff, Beartooth Billings Clinic, Red Lodge, MT, p. A379

GEORGES, Angelo, M.D., President Medical and Dental Staff, Wheeling Hospital, Wheeling, WV, p. A690

GEORGESON, Keith, Chief Executive, Providence Sacred Heart Medical Center & Children'S Hospital, Spokane, WA, p. A680

GEORGOFF, Julie, Vice President of Finance and Chief Financial Officer, Magruder Memorial Hospital, Port Clinton, OH, p. A490

GEPFORD, John, Director Information Systems, Evergreenhealth Monroe, Monroe, WA, p. A675

GERARD, Greg Donavan., President, Baptist Health Richmond, Richmond, KY, p. A260

GERBER, Allen, M.D., Chief of Staff, Baptist Health Medical Center–Hot Spring County, Malvern, AR, p. A45

GERBER, Andrew J., President and Chief Executive Officer, Silver Hill Hospital, New Canaan, CT, p. A109

GERBER, Andrew J., M.D., Ph.D., President and Medical Director, Silver Hill Hospital, New Canaan, CT, p. A109

GERBER, Greg, M.D., Chief Medical Officer, Aurora Lakeland Medical Center, Elkhorn, WI, p. A694

GERDES, Isaac, Chief Executive Officer, Sanford Webster Medical Center, Webster, SD, p. A565

GERDTS, Elizabeth, Chief Nursing Officer, Brookdale Hospital Medical Center, New York, NY, p. A432

GERE, Zsaber, Chief Human Resource Officer, Banner Behavioral Health Hospital – Scottsdale, Scottsdale, AZ, p. A35

GERETY, Meghan, M.D., Chief of Staff, New Mexico Veterans Affairs Health Care System – Raymond G. Murphy Medical Center, Albuquerque, NM, p. A417

GERHART, Paul, Chief Financial Officer, Sanford Canton–Inwood Medical Center, Canton, SD, p. A559

GERIG, Stacey L.
Chief Executive Officer, Odessa Regional Medical Center South Campus, Odessa, TX, p. A627
Chief Executive Officer, Odessa Regional Medical Center, Odessa, TX, p. A627

GERING, Paul, M.D., Vice President Medical Affairs, Saint Alphonsus Medical Center – Ontario, Ontario, OR, p. A515

GERKE, Daniel, Chief Nursing Officer, Wright Patterson Medical Center, Wright, OH, p. A494

GERKE, Sarah, Manager Human Resources, Warner Hospital And Health Services, Clinton, IL, p. A180

GERLACH, Carl, Chief Financial Officer, Curry General Hospital, Gold Beach, OR, p. A513

GERLACH, Judith LeAnn, Chief Nursing Officer, Helena Regional Medical Center, Helena, AR, p. A43

GERLACH, Matthew S
Chief Operating Officer, Children'S Hospital Of Orange County, Orange, CA, p. A76
Chief Operating Officer, Choc Children'S At Mission Hospital, Mission Viejo, CA, p. A72

GERMANY, Alan, Chief Operating Officer, Adventist Health – Tulare, Tulare, CA, p. A92

GERNDT, Angie, Human Resources Manager, Mercyone Elkader Medical Center, Elkader, IA, p. A222

GERNHART, Diana, Senior Vice President and Hospital Chief Financial Officer, Ohsu Hospital, Portland, OR, p. A516

GERRIOR, Marilyn, R.N., MSN, Chief Nursing Executive, Saint Louise Regional Hospital, Gilroy, CA, p. A60

GERRITS, Brad, Director Information Systems, Marshfield Medical Center – Rice Lake, Rice Lake, WI, p. A704

GERSON, Elaine, Chief Clinical Officer and General Counsel, Aspen Valley Hospital, Aspen, CO, p. A96

GERSTENBERGER, Linda
Vice President Human Resources, St. Rose Dominican Hospitals – San Martin Campus, Las Vegas, NV, p. A396
Vice President Human Resources, St. Rose Dominican Hospitals – Siena Campus, Henderson, NV, p. A394

GERSTNER, Nancy, Manager Human Resources, Robert J. Dole Veterans Affairs Medical Center, Wichita, KS, p. A248

GERTH, P. Kevin, Chief of Staff, Spectrum Health Gerber Memorial, Fremont, MI, p. A312

GERVELER, Patrick M, Vice President Finance and Chief Financial Officer, Blessing Hospital, Quincy, IL, p. A194

GESME, Barbara L., MSN, Vice President Patient Care Services & Chief Nurse Executive, Bon Secours St. Francis Medical Center, Midlothian, VA, p. A662

GESSLER, Kevin, Chief Financial Officer, Preston Memorial Hospital, Kingwood, WV, p. A686

GESSLING, Heather, M.D., Chief Medical Officer, Moberly Regional Medical Center, Moberly, MO, p. A365

GESSNER, Christopher A., President and Chief Executive Officer, University Of Colorado Hospital, Aurora, CO, p. A96

GETCHIUS, Joseph, Director Information Technology, Benewah Community Hospital, Saint Maries, ID, p. A171

GETMAN, Sylvia, President and Chief Executive Officer, Adirondack Health, Saranac Lake, NY, p. A443

GETSAY, Timothy, Chief Information Officer, Vice President of Performance & Information Mgmt, Gillette Children'S Specialty Healthcare, Saint Paul, MN, p. A339

GETTINGER, Thomas
Executive Vice President and Chief Operating Officer, Mary Washington Hospital, Fredericksburg, VA, p. A659
Executive Vice President and Chief Operating Officer, Stafford Hospital, Stafford, VA, p. A667

GETTINGS, Scott, M.D., Senior Vice President and Chief Medical Officer, Health First Viera Hospital, Melbourne, FL, p. A129

GETTYS, Sky, Chief Financial Officer, Fairfield Medical Center, Lancaster, OH, p. A485

GETZ, Liz, Chief Information Officer, Aultman Hospital, Canton, OH, p. A474

GEUDER, Denise, Vice President Patient Care Service and Chief Nursing Officer, Southwestern Regional Medical Center, Tulsa, OK, p. A509

GEURTS, Chuck, Manager Information Technology Client Services, Aurora Baycare Medical Center, Green Bay, WI, p. A696

GEWECKE, Tyler, Information Technology Technician, Fillmore County Hospital, Geneva, NE, p. A385

GFELLER, Michael, Director Information Systems, Medical City Plano, Plano, TX, p. A629

GHAEMMAGHAMI, Chris A., M.D., Chief Medical Officer, University Of Virginia Medical Center, Charlottesville, VA, p. A657

GHAFFARI, Bahram, President, Delano Regional Medical Center, Delano, CA, p. A56

GHALI, Sara, Chief Financial Officer, Santa Cruz Valley Regional Hospital, Green Valley, AZ, p. A30

GHERINGHELLI, Thomas, Senior Vice President, Chief Financial Officer, New England Baptist Hospital, Boston, MA, p. A296

GHERKE, Sheila, Director Human Resources, Minnie Hamilton Healthcare Center, Grantsville, WV, p. A685

GHIDOTTI, Craig J, Vice President Human Resources, Lake Health, Concord Township, OH, p. A480

GHINASSI, Frank A., President and Chief Executive Officer, Rutgers University Behavioral Healthcare, Piscataway, NJ, p. A411

GHION, christopher, Vice President and Chief Information Officer, Adventist Healthcare Shady Grove Medical Center, Rockville, MD, p. A293

GHULUM, Evelyn, Chief Financial Officer, Jellico Community Hospital, Jellico, TN, p. A571

GIAGUINTO, Shelly, Chief Financial Officer, Highland–Clarksburg Hospital, Clarksburg, WV, p. A684

GIAMPA, Patricia L, Chief Nursing Officer, Searhc Mt. Edgecumbe Hospital, Sitka, AK, p. A27

GIANELLI, Arthur A., President, Brookdale Hospital Medical Center, New York, NY, p. A432

GIANG, Vernon, M.D.
Chief Medical Executive, California Pacific Medical Center–St. Luke'S Campus, San Francisco, CA, p. A85
Chief Medical Executive, California Pacific Medical Center, San Francisco, CA, p. A85

GIANGARDELLA, Mike, Vice President Finance and Administration, Salem Regional Medical Center, Salem, OH, p. A490

GIANNONE, John, M.D., Delaware Valley Hospital Medical Director, Uhs Delaware Valley Hospital, Walton, NY, p. A446

GIANNOSA, Amy, Director Human Resources, Havenwyck Hospital, Auburn Hills, MI, p. A306

GIANNUZZI, Donna, R.N., Chief Nursing Officer, Lee Memorial Hospital, Fort Myers, FL, p. A123

GIANSANTE, Joseph, Vice President Human Resources, Ellis Hospital, Schenectady, NY, p. A444

GIARDINA, Deborah, Director Human Resources and Medical Staff Services, Rehabilitation Hospital Of Fort Wayne, Fort Wayne, IN, p. A204

GIBB, Matthew, M.D., Executive Vice President and System Chief Medical Officer, Carle Foundation Hospital, Urbana, IL, p. A197

GIBB, Randall K., Chief Executive Officer, Billings Clinic, Billings, MT, p. A374

GIBB, Randall K., M.D., Chief Executive Officer, Billings Clinic, Billings, MT, p. A374

GIBBENS, Lori, Controller, Encompass Health Rehabilitation Hospital Of Erie, Erie, PA, p. A525

GIBBERMAN, Val, M.D., Acting Chief of Staff, Hampton Veterans Affairs Medical Center, Hampton, VA, p. A660

GIBBES, Gregg
Chief Executive Officer, Covington County Hospital, Collins, MS, p. A346
Chief Executive Officer, Magee General Hospital, Magee, MS, p. A350

GIBBONS, Barbara, Vice President Patient Care Services, St. Joseph Hospital, Bethpage, NY, p. A423

GIBBONS, Brian P., Jr, Chief Executive Officer, Astria Sunnyside Hospital, Sunnyside, WA, p. A680

GIBBONS, David, President, Upmc Hamot, Erie, PA, p. A525

GIBBONS, Jason, Chief Financial Officer, Minidoka Memorial Hospital, Rupert, ID, p. A171

GIBBS, Christopher Michael, Director Information Management Systems, Taylor Regional Hospital, Campbellsville, KY, p. A250

GIBBS, Jeffrey S., M.D., Regional Vice President Medical Affairs, Skagit Regional Health, Mount Vernon, WA, p. A675

GIBBS, Kenneth, President and Chief Executive Officer, Brookdale Hospital Medical Center, New York, NY, p. A432

GIBBS, Michael, President, Avera Heart Hospital Of South Dakota, Sioux Falls, SD, p. A563

GIBBS, Parker, M.D., Chief Medical Officer, Uf Health Shands Hospital, Gainesville, FL, p. A124

GIBBS, Tim, Director of Information Technology, Information Security Officer, Children'S Hospital Of Richmond At Vcu–Brook Road Campus, Richmond, VA, p. A666

GIBBS, Vickie, Director Nursing, Phillips County Health Systems, Phillipsburg, KS, p. A243

GIBBS–MCELVY, Shelana, M.D., Medical Director, Encompass Health Rehabilitation Hospital Of Sewickley, Sewickley, PA, p. A541

GIBNEY, Thomas, Senior Vice President and Chief Financial Officer, Montefiore St. Luke'S Cornwall, Newburgh, NY, p. A439

GIBSON, Armetria, Human Resources Generalist, Select Specialty Hospital Midtown Atlanta, Atlanta, GA, p. A147

GIBSON, Belinda D, R.N., Senior Vice President Patient Services, Bsa Hospital, Llc, Amarillo, TX, p. A582

GIBSON, Connie, R.N., Director Human Resources, Cherokee Medical Center, Gaffney, SC, p. A553

GIBSON, David R., Chief Executive Officer, Carl R. Darnall Army Medical Center, Fort Hood, TX, p. A604

GIBSON, Elizabeth, Director Human Resources, Mid–America Rehabilitation Hospital, Shawnee Mission, KS, p. A245

GIBSON, J. Francis., Administrator and Chief Executive Officer, Orem Community Hospital, Orem, UT, p. A650

GIBSON, Jack, Administrator, Noland Hospital Tuscaloosa, Tuscaloosa, AL, p. A24

GIBSON, Joel, Vice President Human Resources, Henry Ford Macomb Hospitals, Clinton Township, MI, p. A309

GIBSON, Mary Helen, Director Human Resources, Floyd Valley Healthcare, Le Mars, IA, p. A225

GIBSON, Megan, Nurse Manager, River Bend Hospital, West Lafayette, IN, p. A216

GIBSON, Todd, Chief Financial Officer, Medical City Denton, Denton, TX, p. A599

GICCA, Ron, Chief Executive Officer, Melbourne Regional Medical Center, Melbourne, FL, p. A129

GICZI, Mary Beth, Director Human Resources, Encompass Health Rehabilitation Hospital Of Scottsdale, Scottsdale, AZ, p. A35

GIDDINGS, Carleen, Information Technology System Leader, Scheurer Hospital, Pigeon, MI, p. A319
GIDEON, Daniel L., Chief Executive Officer, Pine Creek Medical Center, Dallas, TX, p. A597
GIEGER, Julie
Chief Financial Officer, Lackey Memorial Hospital, Forest, MS, p. A347
Chief Financial Officer, Monroe Regional Hospital, Aberdeen, MS, p. A344
GIER, Jennifer, Director Human Resources, Brynn Marr Hospital, Jacksonville, NC, p. A456
GIERTUGA, Garry, Site Manager Human Resources, Adventist Medical Center Lagrange, La Grange, IL, p. A187
GIESE, Kristine A, Chief Operating Officer, Providence Medical Center, Wayne, NE, p. A392
GIFFORD, Ellen, Director Human Resources, Integris Deaconess, Oklahoma City, OK, p. A504
GIGLIO, Aimee M., Chief Human Resources Officer, Dartmouth–Hitchcock Medical Center, Lebanon, NH, p. A400
GIGLIOTTI, Vicki, Chief Clinical Officer, Moab Regional Hospital, Moab, UT, p. A648
GIJANTO, Charles
Interim Chief Executive Officer, Claxton–Hepburn Medical Center, Ogdensburg, NY, p. A440
Interim Chief Executive Officer, Massena Memorial Hospital, Massena, NY, p. A431
GIL, Julio, Manager Information Services, Hazel Hawkins Memorial Hospital, Hollister, CA, p. A61
GILBERT, Andrea F., President, Bryn Mawr Hospital, Bryn Mawr, PA, p. A521
GILBERT, Carla, Director Finance, Cedar County Memorial Hospital, El Dorado Springs, MO, p. A359
GILBERT, Christy
Interim Chief Executive Officer, Doctors Neuropsychiatric Hospital And Research Institute, Bremen, IN, p. A200
President and Chief Operating Officer, Medical Behavioral Hospital Of Mishawaka, Knox, IN, p. A209
GILBERT, Jack, Vice President Finance and Facilities, Advocate Illinois Masonic Medical Center, Chicago, IL, p. A176
GILBERT, Kevin, R.N., Vice President, Confluence Health/ Wenatchee Valley Hospital, Wenatchee, WA, p. A682
GILBERT, Kim, R.N., Chief Nursing Officer, Electra Memorial Hospital, Electra, TX, p. A603
GILBERT, Thomas, Director Information Technology Services, Lake Cumberland Regional Hospital, Somerset, KY, p. A260
GILBERT, Thomas D.
Chief Executive Officer, Wadley Regional Medical Center At Hope, Hope, AR, p. A43
Chief Executive Officer, Wadley Regional Medical Center, Texarkana, TX, p. A640
GILBERT, William L., Hospital Director, Arrowhead Regional Medical Center, Colton, CA, p. A55
GILBERTSON, Gerry, Administrator, Centracare Health–Melrose, Melrose, MN, p. A335
GILBERTSON, Gerry, FACHE, Administrator, Centracare Health–Melrose, Melrose, MN, p. A335
GILCHRIST, Doug, Chief Operating Officer, Summit Healthcare Regional Medical Center, Show Low, AZ, p. A36
GILDAY, Matt, Vice President of Human Resources, Tristar Hendersonville Medical Center, Hendersonville, TN, p. A570
GILDON, Lisa
Group Financial Officer, Texas Health Presbyterian Hospital Allen, Allen, TX, p. A582
Vice President and Chief Financial Officer, Texas Health Presbyterian Hospital Plano, Plano, TX, p. A630
GILENE, Joseph, Interim Chief Administrative Officer, Beaver Dam Community Hospitals, Beaver Dam, WI, p. A692
GILES, Charles, M.D., President Medical Staff, T.J. Health Columbia, Columbia, KY, p. A250
GILES, Jared, Chief Operating Officer, Southwest Healthcare System, Murrieta, CA, p. A74
GILES, Steve, Chief Information Officer, Hollywood Presbyterian Medical Center, Los Angeles, CA, p. A67
GILG, Ronald, Assistant Vice President Talent, Cancer Treatment Centers Of America–Eastern Regional Medical Center, Philadelphia, PA, p. A534
GILGEN, Steve, Chief Financial Officer, Erlanger Western Carolina Hospital, Murphy, NC, p. A459
GILJUM, Anthony, Chief Information Officer, Sheridan Veterans Affairs Medical Center, Sheridan, WY, p. A712
GILKEY, Edward, M.D., Vice President Medical Affairs, St. Luke'S Hospital – Warren Campus, Phillipsburg, NJ, p. A411
GILL, Brian, Chief Executive Officer, Millwood Hospital, Arlington, TX, p. A583
GILL, Mandeep, Chief Operating Officer, Memorial Hospital Of Sweetwater County, Rock Springs, WY, p. A712
GILL, Margaret, Chief Executive Officer, Delray Medical Center, Delray Beach, FL, p. A121
GILL, Mark, Vice President Finance and Chief Financial Officer, Cape Regional Health System, Cape May Court House, NJ, p. A404
GILLAM, Sally A, R.N., Chief Nursing Officer, St. David'S South Austin Medical Center, Austin, TX, p. A586
GILLARD, Austin M., Chief Executive Officer, Clay County Medical Center, Clay Center, KS, p. A233
GILLEN, Mark T
Director Finance and Operations, Owatonna Hospital, Owatonna, MN, p. A337
Director of Operations, Owatonna Hospital, Owatonna, MN, p. A337
GILLES, Ken
Associate Chief Information Officer, Essentia Health St. Mary'S – Detroit Lakes, Detroit Lakes, MN, p. A330
Chief Information Officer, Essentia Health Fargo, Fargo, ND, p. A466
GILLESPIE, Anne, R.N., Associate Director Patient Care and Nursing Services, Veterans Affairs Loma Linda Healthcare System, Loma Linda, CA, p. A64
GILLESPIE, Bob
Chief Executive Officer, Connally Memorial Medical Center, Floresville, TX, p. A604
Chief Operating Officer, Connally Memorial Medical Center, Floresville, TX, p. A604
GILLESPIE, Christina L., Chief Executive Officer, Harrison County Community Hospital, Bethany, MO, p. A356
GILLESPIE, Curt, Chief Executive Officer, Mental Health Services For Clark And Madison Counties, Springfield, OH, p. A491
GILLESPIE, Karen, Director Human Resources, Anderson County Hospital, Garnett, KS, p. A235
GILLESPIE, Lisa, M.D., Chief Medical Officer, Piedmont Rockdale Hospital, Conyers, GA, p. A151
GILLESPIE, Richard, Chief Executive Officer, Jefferson County Hospital, Waurika, OK, p. A510
GILLESPIE, Tim, Manager Information Systems, Carle Richland Memorial Hospital, Olney, IL, p. A192
GILLETTE, Karen, Associate Director Patient Care Services, Memphis Veterans Affairs Medical Center, Memphis, TN, p. A575
GILLETTE, Nicole, R.N., Chief Nursing Officer, Midmichigan Medical Center – West Branch, West Branch, MI, p. A325
GILLETTE, Robert, Chief Information Officer, St. Elizabeth Medical Center, Utica, NY, p. A446
GILLETTE, Tom, Senior Vice President and Chief Information Officer, Mount Sinai Medical Center, Miami Beach, FL, p. A131
GILLIAM, David, M.D., Medical Director, Bloomington Meadows Hospital, Bloomington, IN, p. A200
GILLIAM, Eric, President, Chi Saint Joseph East, Lexington, KY, p. A254
GILLIAM, Leslie, Director Health Information Management, Dominion Hospital, Falls Church, VA, p. A658
GILLIAN, Tom, Chief Operating Officer, River Bend Hospital, West Lafayette, IN, p. A216
GILLIAND, Michael, M.D., Chief of Staff, Chi St. Luke'S Health Brazosport, Lake Jackson, TX, p. A619
GILLILAND, Michelle, Director of Nursing, River Park Hospital, Huntington, WV, p. A686
GILLILAND, Sharon, Chief of Staff, Baraga County Memorial Hospital, L'Anse, MI, p. A316
GILLILAND, Terry, M.D.
Chief Medical Officer, Sentara Leigh Hospital, Norfolk, VA, p. A664
Senior Vice President and Chief Medical Officer, Sentara Princess Anne Hospital, Virginia Beach, VA, p. A668
GILLIS, Anne, Chief Financial Officer, Holy Cross Hospital, Silver Spring, MD, p. A293
GILLMAN, Kreg, Chief Executive Officer, Salt Lake Behavioral Health, Salt Lake City, UT, p. A652
GILLY, Mike, Chief Information Officer, Our Lady Of The Angels Hospital, Bogalusa, LA, p. A264
GILMAN, Howard, M.D., Medical Executive, Christian Health Care Center, Wyckoff, NJ, p. A415
GILMAN, James K., Chief Executive Officer, National Institutes Of Health Clinical Center, Bethesda, MD, p. A289
GILMAN, Kim
Chief Executive Officer and Chief Nursing Officer, Southwest Georgia Regional Medical Center, Cuthbert, GA, p. A151
Chief Executive Officer, Phoebe Worth Medical Center, Sylvester, GA, p. A161
Chief Nursing Officer, Phoebe Worth Medical Center, Sylvester, GA, p. A161
GILMORE, Hugh V, M.D., Vice President Medical Affairs, Ascension Seton Williamson, Round Rock, TX, p. A632
GILMORE, Joshua, Chief Executive Officer, Iron County Medical Center, Pilot Knob, MO, p. A367
GILMORE, Phillip K., Chief Executive Officer, Ashley County Medical Center, Crossett, AR, p. A40
GILMORE, Stephen, Chief Financial Officer, Piedmont Medical Center, Rock Hill, SC, p. A556
GILPIN, Michael W., Vice President Human Resources, Sampson Regional Medical Center, Clinton, NC, p. A452
GILSON, Sheila, R.N., Chief Operating Officer, Kaiser Permanente Redwood City Medical Center, Redwood City, CA, p. A80
GILTNER, Michelle, Interim Chief Nursing Officer, Uh Regional Hospitals, Cleveland, OH, p. A478
GIN, Nancy, M.D., Area Associate Medical Director, Kaiser Permanente Orange County Anaheim Medical Center, Anaheim, CA, p. A50
GINDER, Phil, Chief Executive Officer, Hodgeman County Health Center, Jetmore, KS, p. A237
GINGERY, Adam, Chief Financial Officer, Door County Medical Center, Sturgeon Bay, WI, p. A706
GINGRAS, Sean, CPA, Chief Financial Officer, Centerstone Hospital, Bradenton, FL, p. A118
GINGRICH, Curtis, Chief Operating Officer, Ohiohealth Marion General Hospital, Marion, OH, p. A486
GINGRICH, Joye, Director Patient Care Services and Chief Nursing Officer, J. C. Blair Memorial Hospital, Huntingdon, PA, p. A527
GINGRICH, Mary, Director Health Care Services, Kansas Neurological Institute, Topeka, KS, p. A246
GINN, Bobby, Chief Operating Officer, Crestwood Medical Center, Huntsville, AL, p. A19
GINN, Doug, Executive Vice President Operations, Peak Behavioral Health Services, Santa Teresa, NM, p. A420
GINNATY, Rayn, Vice President Nursing, Benefis Health System, Great Falls, MT, p. A377
GINSBERG, Jo–Ann M., Director, Marion Veterans Affairs Medical Center, Marion, IL, p. A188
GINSBERG, Ronald L, M.D., Vice President Medical Affairs, Northwest Hospital, Randallstown, MD, p. A293
GINSBURG, J Lawrence, M.D., Vice President Medical Affairs, Evangelical Community Hospital, Lewisburg, PA, p. A530
GINTER, Gary, System Vice President and Chief Information Officer, Miami Valley Hospital, Dayton, OH, p. A481
GINTOLI, Eric M., Administrator, Seaside Health System, Baton Rouge, LA, p. A264
GINTZIG, Donald R.
President and Chief Executive Officer, Wakemed Cary Hospital, Cary, NC, p. A450
President and Chief Executive Officer, Wakemed Raleigh Campus, Raleigh, NC, p. A461
GIOIA, Anthony, Chief Financial Officer, Orthoindy Hospital, Indianapolis, IN, p. A207
GIORDANO, Paul D., Senior Vice President, Human Resources, South Nassau Communities Hospital, Oceanside, NY, p. A440
GIORDANO, Peter, Senior Director Human Resources, Harrison Community Hospital, Cadiz, OH, p. A474
GIORDANO, Roger, M.D., Medical Director, Encompass Health Rehabilitation Hospital Of Virginia, Richmond, VA, p. A666
GIORDANO, Susan, Chief Nursing Officer, Hackensack Meridian Health Pascack Valley Medical Center, Westwood, NJ, p. A415
GIPP, Jana, Chief Executive Officer, Standing Rock Service Unit, Fort Yates Hospital, Indian Health Service, Dhhs, Fort Yates, ND, p. A467
GIPSON, Linda Stephens, MSN, Ph.D., Chief Nursing Officer, Whidbeyhealth, Coupeville, WA, p. A672
GIRALT, Juana
Chief Financial Officer, River Crest Hospital, San Angelo, TX, p. A632
Interim Chief Executive Officer, River Crest Hospital, San Angelo, TX, p. A632
GIRARD, Thomas R
Vice President Human Resources, Lincolnhealth, Damariscotta, ME, p. A282
Vice President Human Resources, Pen Bay Medical Center, Rockport, ME, p. A285
GIRARDEAU, Brian, Director Information System, East Georgia Regional Medical Center, Statesboro, GA, p. A161
GIRARDIER, Cheryl, Director Information Technology, Lecom Health Millcreek Community Hospital, Erie, PA, p. A525
GIRARDY, James, M.D., Vice President, Chief Surgical Officer, Osf Saint Anthony Medical Center, Rockford, IL, p. A195
GIRTY, Tara, Director Human Resources, Kiowa District Healthcare, Kiowa, KS, p. A238
GISH, Kevin, Administrator and Vice President, Essentia Health Fosston, Fosston, MN, p. A332
GISI, Dale, President, Mercy Health – St. Rita'S Medical Center, Lima, OH, p. A485
GISLER, Greg, Chief Financial Officer, Mcbride Orthopedic Hospital, Oklahoma City, OK, p. A504

GISLESON, Joni, Director Finance, Gundersen Palmer Lutheran Hospital And Clinics, West Union, IA, p. A231

GITMAN, Michael, M.D., Medical Director, North Shore University Hospital, Manhasset, NY, p. A430

GITTELMAN, Michael B
Administrator, University Of Miami Hospital And Clinics, Miami, FL, p. A131
Chief Executive Officer, University Of Miami Hospital And Clinics, Miami, FL, p. A131

GITTLER, Michelle, M.D., Medical Director, Schwab Rehabilitation Hospital, Chicago, IL, p. A179

GITZINGER, Matthew, Director of Operations, Vidant Duplin Hospital, Kenansville, NC, p. A457

GIUDICE, William A, Vice President and Chief Financial Officer, Tallahassee Memorial Healthcare, Tallahassee, FL, p. A141

GIULIANELLI, Victor, President and Chief Executive Officer, St. Mary'S Healthcare, Amsterdam, NY, p. A422

GIVENS, Michael K, FACHE, Administrator, St. Bernards Medical Center, Jonesboro, AR, p. A44

GIVENS, Patricia, R.N., Chief Nursing Officer, Children'S Hospital Colorado, Aurora, CO, p. A96

GIVENS, Seth, Chief Human Resource Officer, Drew Memorial Health System, Monticello, AR, p. A46

GIVENS, Stephen K., Assistant Vice President and Administrator, Russell County Medical Center, Lebanon, VA, p. A661

GIZZI, Jason, Controller, Encompass Health Rehabilitation Hospital Of Morgantown, Morgantown, WV, p. A687

GJOLBERG, Skip, Administrator, St. Joseph'S Hospital Of Buckhannon, Buckhannon, WV, p. A684

GLADEN, Tracy, Chief Financial Officer, Twin Valley Behavioral Healthcare, Columbus, OH, p. A480

GLADSTONE, Art
Chief Executive Officer, Pali Momi Medical Center, Aiea, HI, p. A164
Chief Executive Officer, Straub Medical Center, Honolulu, HI, p. A165

GLANVILLE, Tristan, Chief Financial Officer, Adirondack Health, Saranac Lake, NY, p. A443

GLANZER, Elgin, Chief Financial Officer, Memorial Health System, Abilene, KS, p. A232

GLASBERG, Michael, Senior Vice President, Chief Operating Officer, Dameron Hospital, Stockton, CA, p. A90

GLASER, Ruth, President, Pender Memorial Hospital, Burgaw, NC, p. A450

GLASGO, Leah, Chief Executive Officer, Unitypoint Health – Trinity Regional Medical Center, Fort Dodge, IA, p. A222

GLASNAPP, Sherry L., Director, Douglas County Community Mental Health Center, Omaha, NE, p. A389

GLASS, Ian, M.D., Chief Medical Officer, Hca Houston Healthcare Tomball, Tomball, TX, p. A641

GLASS, Ina Louise, Administrator, Ephraim Mcdowell Fort Logan Hospital, Stanford, KY, p. A261

GLASS, Kyle, Chief Financial Officer, Adventhealth Deland, Deland, FL, p. A121

GLASS, Steven, Chief Financial Officer, Cleveland Clinic, Cleveland, OH, p. A477

GLASS, Wendy, Director Human Resources, Colleton Medical Center, Walterboro, SC, p. A558

GLASSBURN, David, Vice President Finance and Chief Financial Officer, Harlingen Medical Center, Harlingen, TX, p. A609

GLASSCOCK, Sheryl, Chief Nursing Officer, Lake Cumberland Regional Hospital, Somerset, KY, p. A260

GLASSMAN, Kimberly S, Ph.D., R.N., Chief Nursing Officer, Brookdale Hospital Medical Center, New York, NY, p. A432

GLAUBKE, Nancy, Chief Executive Officer, Valley County Health System, Ord, NE, p. A390

GLAVIN, Jolene, R.N., MSN, Director Nursing, Salina Surgical Hospital, Salina, KS, p. A245

GLAZIER, Stephen, Chief Operating Officer, University Of Texas Harris County Psychiatric Center, Houston, TX, p. A614

GLEASON, Jeffrey J, M.D., Chief Medical Officer, Cookeville Regional Medical Center, Cookeville, TN, p. A568

GLEASON, Joe, Chief Operating Officer, Tristar Stonecrest Medical Center, Smyrna, TN, p. A579

GLEASON, Vallerie L., President and Chief Executive Officer, Newton Medical Center, Newton, KS, p. A241

GLEN, Diane M, Assistant Administrator, Barnes–Jewish West County Hospital, Saint Louis, MO, p. A369

GLENN, Chris, Chief Financial Officer, Orange Park Medical Center, Orange Park, FL, p. A134

GLENN, Daphne, Chief Executive Officer, Trihealth Rehabilitation Hospital, Cincinnati, OH, p. A477

GLENN, Gary
Director Information Technology, Carrus Rehabilitation Hospital, Sherman, TX, p. A637
Director Information Technology, Carrus Specialty Hospital, Sherman, TX, p. A637

GLENN, Jeannette, Vice President Human Resources, Education and Training, Mcleod Regional Medical Center, Florence, SC, p. A552

GLENN, Michael, M.D., Chief Medical Officer, Virginia Mason Medical Center, Seattle, WA, p. A679

GLENN, Mike, Chief Executive Officer, Jefferson Healthcare, Port Townsend, WA, p. A676

GLENN, Wil A, Director Communications, Larry B. Zieverink, Sr. Alcoholism Treatment Center, Raleigh, NC, p. A460

GLENNING, Robert, Executive Vice President Finance and Chief Financial Officer, Hackensack Meridian Health Hackensack University Medical Center, Hackensack, NJ, p. A406

GLESSNER, Theresa, Chief Nursing Officer, Eastern Region, Newark–Wayne Community Hospital, Newark, NY, p. A439

GLICK, Jennifer, Manager Clinical Informatics, Oaklawn Psychiatric Center, Goshen, IN, p. A205

GLIDDEN, Nancy
Chief Financial Officer and Vice President Finance, Mayo Regional Hospital, Dover, ME, p. A283
Chief Financial Officer, Calais Regional Hospital, Calais, ME, p. A282

GLIDEWELL, Calvin E, Jr, Chief Executive Officer, Broward Health Medical Center, Fort Lauderdale, FL, p. A122

GLIHA, Frank, Vice President of Patient Care, Mary Rutan Hospital, Bellefontaine, OH, p. A473

GLIHA, Jennie, Chief Human Resource Officer, Aurelia Osborn Fox Memorial Hospital, Oneonta, NY, p. A440

GLIMCHER, Laurie H., President and Chief Executive Officer, Dana–Farber Cancer Institute, Boston, MA, p. A295

GLIMP, Richard, M.D.
Chief Medical Officer, Providence Little Company Of Mary Medical Center – Torrance, Torrance, CA, p. A92
Chief Medical Officer, Providence Little Company Of Mary Medical Center San Pedro, Los Angeles, CA, p. A69

GLINES, Grant L, Vice President Operation Finance, Mercy Medical Center, Roseburg, OR, p. A517

GLODOWSKI, Brenda, Chief Financial Officer, North Central Health Care, Wausau, WI, p. A708

GLOFF, Vicki, Chief Financial Officer, Goodall–Witcher Hospital Authority, Clifton, TX, p. A592

GLOGGNER, Peter, Chief Human Resources Officer, Jupiter Medical Center, Jupiter, FL, p. A126

GLONER, James, Senior Vice President, North Philadelphia Health System, Philadelphia, PA, p. A536

GLORIA–BARRAZA, Patricia, Coordinator Human Resources, Mayhill Hospital, Denton, TX, p. A599

GLOTZBACK, Lee, Director Human Resources, Citrus Memorial Health System, Inverness, FL, p. A125

GLOVER, Cynthia, R.N., Vice President and Chief Nursing Officer, Reston Hospital Center, Reston, VA, p. A665

GLOVER, Doug, Controller, William S. Hall Psychiatric Institute, Columbia, SC, p. A551

GLOVER, Leslie, Director Operations, Cherokee Medical Center, Gaffney, SC, p. A553

GLOWA, Meghan, Director Human Resources, Sunnyview Rehabilitation Hospital, Schenectady, NY, p. A444

GLOWCZEWSKI, Jason
Chief Operating Officer, University Hospitals Conneaut Medical Center, Conneaut, OH, p. A480
Chief Operating Officer, University Hospitals Geneva Medical Center, Geneva, OH, p. A484

GLUCHOWSKI, Jeanne, Executive Director, Conifer Park, Glenville, NY, p. A428

GLUECK, Dane, M.D., Chief of Staff, Progress West Hospital, O'Fallon, MO, p. A366

GLYER, David
Vice President Finance, Community Memorial Hospital, Ventura, CA, p. A93
Vice President Finance, Ojai Valley Community Hospital, Ojai, CA, p. A75

GLYNN, Cindy, Director Human Resources, Regional Rehabilitation Hospital, Phenix City, AL, p. A22

GLYNN, John
Chief Information Officer, Rochester General Hospital, Rochester, NY, p. A442
Executive Vice President, Chief Information Officer, Rochester Regional Health, Newark–Wayne Community Hospital, Newark, NY, p. A439
Senior Vice President and Chief Information Officer, Unity Hospital, Rochester, NY, p. A443

GLYNN, Margaret, M.D., Chief Medical Officer, North Mississippi Medical Center–Iuka, Iuka, MS, p. A348

GLYNN, Shari, Vice President Finance and Chief Financial Officer, Eaton Rapids Medical Center, Eaton Rapids, MI, p. A311

GNAGEY, Keith, Chief Executive Officer, Teton Valley Health Care, Driggs, ID, p. A169

GNAM, Gwen, R.N., MSN, Chief Nursing Officer, Henry Ford Hospital, Detroit, MI, p. A310

GNANN, Andrew, Vice President Operations, St. Vincent'S East, Birmingham, AL, p. A15

GNEGY, David, M.D., Vice President of Medical Affairs, Camden Clark Medical Center, Parkersburg, WV, p. A688

GO, Rosana, M.D., Medical Staff President, Cascade Valley Hospital, Arlington, WA, p. A670

GOACHER, Brad, Vice President Administration, Alton Memorial Hospital, Alton, IL, p. A173

GOAD, Pat, Director Human Resources, Hillcrest Hospital Claremore, Claremore, OK, p. A498

GOBEL, Bret, Chief Financial Officer, Sierra Vista Hospital, Truth Or Consequences, NM, p. A421

GOBELL, James, Chief Financial Officer, Unitypoint Health – St. Lukes'S Sioux City, Sioux City, IA, p. A230

GOBER, Dennis, Interim Chief Executive Officer, Rolling Hills Hospital, Ada, OK, p. A496

GOBER, Kirby, Chief Executive Officer, Throckmorton County Memorial Hospital, Throckmorton, TX, p. A641

GOBLE, Jonathan R., Interim President, Ingalls Memorial Hospital, Harvey, IL, p. A185

GOBLE, Mandy C., President and Chief Executive Officer, Mary Rutan Hospital, Bellefontaine, OH, p. A473

GOCHE, Jeanne, Interim Chief Executive Officer, Dickinson County Healthcare System, Iron Mountain, MI, p. A314

GOCHENOUR, Julia, Manager Information Systems, West River Regional Medical Center, Hettinger, ND, p. A468

GOCHNOUR, SPHR, SHRM–SCP, Eric, Manager Human Resources, Minidoka Memorial Hospital, Rupert, ID, p. A171

GODAMUNNE, Karim, M.D., Chief Medical Officer, Wellstar North Fulton Hospital, Roswell, GA, p. A159

GODBEE, Mitchell, Chief of Staff, Capital Region Medical Center, Jefferson City, MO, p. A361

GODBOLD, Steven, Vice President Operations and Chief Operating Officer, East Tennessee Children'S Hospital, Knoxville, TN, p. A572

GODDARD, Mark, M.D., Medical Director, Healthsouth Rehabilitation Hospital At Drake, Cincinnati, OH, p. A476

GODDARD, Nichole, Chief Operating Officer, South Region, Community Hospital South, Indianapolis, IN, p. A206

GODFREY, John, M.D., Vice President and Chief Executive Officer, Hardin Memorial Health, Elizabethtown, KY, p. A251

GODFREY, Katrina, Director Human Resources, Mercy Hospital Ada, Ada, OK, p. A496

GODFREY, Kristine, Director Human Resources, Tennova Healthcare – Cleveland, Cleveland, TN, p. A568

GODINA, Gabriel, M.D., Chief of Staff, Ogallala Community Hospital, Ogallala, NE, p. A388

GODINEZ, Roxanna M., Chief Executive Officer, Cornerstone Regional Hospital, Edinburg, TX, p. A601

GODLEY, James R, Vice President of Human Resources, Mayo Regional Hospital, Dover, ME, p. A283

GODLEY, Patrick, Chief Financial Officer, Contra Costa Regional Medical Center, Martinez, CA, p. A71

GODWIN, Herman A, M.D., Senior Vice President and Medical Director, Watauga Medical Center, Boone, NC, p. A450

GODWIN, Robin M., MSN, Vice President of Nursing, Sacred Heart Hospital On The Gulf, Port St Joe, FL, p. A137

GOEB–BURKETT, Michele, R.N., MSN, Chief Nursing Officer, Adventhealth Daytona Beach, Daytona Beach, FL, p. A121

GOEBEL, Bret, Chief Financial Officer, Guadalupe County Hospital, Santa Rosa, NM, p. A420

GOEBEL, Cecilia B, R.N., Chief Nursing Officer, Susan B. Allen Memorial Hospital, El Dorado, KS, p. A234

GOEBEL, Donna, M.D., Chief Nursing Officer, Mitchell County Hospital, Colorado City, TX, p. A593

GOEBEL, Michael, Chief Executive Officer, Parker Adventist Hospital, Parker, CO, p. A104

GOEHRING, Jennifer, R.N., Assistant Chief Nursing Officer, Ascension Via Christi Hospital, Manhattan, Manhattan, KS, p. A240

GOEL, Amitabh, M.D., Chief Medical Officer, University Hospitals Geneva Medical Center, Geneva, OH, p. A484

GOEL, Ash, Senior Vice President Information Technology & Chief Information Officer, Bronson Lakeview Hospital, Paw Paw, MI, p. A319

GOEL, Vineet, Chief Medical Officer, Atrium Health Lincoln, Lincolnton, NC, p. A458

GOELZ, Gary, R.N., Chief Nursing Officer, Shands Lake Shore Regional Medical Center, Lake City, FL, p. A127

GOELZER, Mark L., M.D., Director Medical Affairs, Mercyhealth Hospital And Trauma Center – Janesville, Janesville, WI, p. A697

GOERINGER, Dawn Marie, Chief Clinical Care Officer, O'Connor Hospital, San Jose, CA, p. A86

GOETTSCH, Barry, Chief Executive Officer, Compass Memorial Healthcare, Marengo, IA, p. A226

GOFF, Gary E., M.D., Medical Director, Promise Hospital Of Dallas, Dallas, TX, p. A598

GOFF, Kerry D., Chief Executive Officer, Reeves Memorial Medical Center, Bernice, LA, p. A264

GOFF, Vivian, Chief Executive Officer, Landmark Hospital Of Athens, Athens, GA, p. A145

GOGGIN, Daniel
Senior Vice President and Chief Financial Officer, Chi St. Joseph Health Burleson Hospital, Caldwell, TX, p. A591
Senior Vice President and Chief Financial Officer, Chi St. Joseph Health Grimes Hospital, Navasota, TX, p. A626

GOGGIN, Kathy, Director of Finance, Devereux Advanced Behavioral Health Georgia, Kennesaw, GA, p. A155

GOING, Rita, Director of Critical Access Hospitals, Mercyone Oakland Medical Center, Oakland, NE, p. A388

GOINS, Rick, Chief Executive Officer, Massac Memorial Hospital, Metropolis, IL, p. A189

GOLAN, Marc
Chief Financial Officer, Franciscan Health Crown Point, Crown Point, IN, p. A202
Chief Financial Officer, Franciscan Health Hammond, Hammond, IN, p. A205
Regional Chief Financial Officer, Franciscan Health Michigan City, Michigan City, IN, p. A211

GOLANOWSKI, Marie, President, Aurora St. Luke'S Medical Center, Milwaukee, WI, p. A701

GOLBIN, Jason, M.D., Chief Medical Officer, St. Catherine Of Siena Medical Center, Smithtown, NY, p. A444

GOLD, Barbara, M.D., Chief Medical Officer, University Of Minnesota Medical Center, Fairview, Minneapolis, MN, p. A336

GOLD, Joseph, M.D., Chief Medical Officer, Mclean Hospital, Belmont, MA, p. A294

GOLD, Larry, Vice President, Information Services, Southern Virginia Regional Medical Center, Emporia, VA, p. A658

GOLDA, David, Administrator and Vice President, St. Charles Madras, Madras, OR, p. A514

GOLDAMMER, Kyle, Chief Financial Officer, Sioux Falls Specialty Hospital, Sioux Falls, SD, p. A564

GOLDBERG, David, President and Chief Executive Officer, Mon Health Medical Center, Morgantown, WV, p. A687

GOLDBERG, David, M.D., Vice President Medical Affairs and Chief Medical Officer, Community Memorial Hospital, Menomonee Falls, WI, p. A700

GOLDBERG, Frederick, M.D., Vice President Medical Affairs and Chief Medical Officer, Nathan Littauer Hospital And Nursing Home, Gloversville, NY, p. A428

GOLDBERG, Gary, M.D., Chief Medical Officer, North Hawaii Community Hospital, Kamuela, HI, p. A165

GOLDBERG, Jonathan, Senior Vice President and Chief Information Officer, Arkansas Children'S Hospital, Little Rock, AR, p. A44

GOLDBERG, Michael, Executive Director, Brookdale Hospital Medical Center, New York, NY, p. A432

GOLDBERG, Paul R, Chief Financial Officer, Jersey City Medical Center, Jersey City, NJ, p. A407

GOLDBERG, Stephanie J, MSN, R.N., Senior Vice President and Chief Nursing Officer, Brookdale Hospital Medical Center, New York, NY, p. A432

GOLDEN, Joy, Chief Executive Officer, Lakeside Behavioral Health System, Memphis, TN, p. A575

GOLDEN, William, M.D., Chief Medical Officer, East Alabama Medical Center, Opelika, AL, p. A22

GOLDENSTEIN, Rachel, R.N., Chief Nursing Officer, Buchanan County Health Center, Independence, IA, p. A224

GOLDFARB, I William, Chief Medical Officer, West Penn Hospital, Pittsburgh, PA, p. A538

GOLDFARB, Timothy, Interim Chief Executive Officer, Ohsu Hospital, Portland, OR, p. A516

GOLDFRACH, Andrew, Chief Executive Officer, Uh Avon Rehabilitation Hospital, Avon, OH, p. A472

GOLDHAGEN, Michele, M.D., Chief Medical Officer, Russell Medical, Alexander City, AL, p. A13

GOLDIS, Glenn, Chief Medical Officer, Kern Medical Center, Bakersfield, CA, p. A52

GOLDMAN, Eric, Chief Executive Officer, Lawnwood Regional Medical Center & Heart Institute, Fort Pierce, FL, p. A123

GOLDMAN, Kris, Director Human Resources, Shriners Hospitals For Children–Salt Lake City, Salt Lake City, UT, p. A652

GOLDSMITH, Cheri L.
Director Financial Services, Parkland Health Center – Farmington Community, Farmington, MO, p. A360
Director Financial Services, Parkland Health Center–Bonne Terre, Bonne Terre, MO, p. A356

GOLDSMITH, Dana L, M.D., Vice President Medical Affairs, Pen Bay Medical Center, Rockport, ME, p. A285

GOLDSTEIN, Allan, M.D., Medical Director and Chief of Staff, Select Specialty Hospital–Birmingham, Birmingham, AL, p. A15

GOLDSTEIN, David, M.D., Chief Medical Officer, Contra Costa Regional Medical Center, Martinez, CA, p. A71

GOLDSTEIN, Gerald, M.D., Senior Vice President and Chief Medical Officer, Western Maryland Regional Medical Center, Cumberland, MD, p. A290

GOLDSTEIN, Lawrence, M.D., Chief Medical Officer, Vibra Hospital Of Mahoning Valley, Boardman, OH, p. A473

GOLDSTEIN, Lisa, Executive Vice President and Chief Operating Officer, Brookdale Hospital Medical Center, New York, NY, p. A432

GOLDSTEIN, Mark L., President and Chief Executive Officer, Anna Jaques Hospital, Newburyport, MA, p. A301

GOLDSTEIN, Steven I.
President and Chief Executive Officer, Highland Hospital, Rochester, NY, p. A442
President and Chief Executive Officer, Strong Memorial Hospital Of The University Of Rochester, Rochester, NY, p. A443

GOLDSZER, Robert, M.D., Senior Vice President and Chief Medical Officer, Mount Sinai Medical Center, Miami Beach, FL, p. A131

GOLICH, Jacob, Chief Executive Officer, Mountain Vista Medical Center, Mesa, AZ, p. A31

GOLIGHTLY, Beverly, Director Information Technology, St. Vincent'S East, Birmingham, AL, p. A15

GOLKE, Rynae, Director Human Resources, Jacobson Memorial Hospital Care Center, Elgin, ND, p. A466

GOLL, Cheri, MSN, R.N., Chief Nursing Executive, Advocate Sherman Hospital, Elgin, IL, p. A182

GOLLAHER, Jeffrey, Chief Executive Officer, Hendricks Community Hospital Association, Hendricks, MN, p. A333

GOLLINGER, Mary A, MS, R.N., Director of Nursing, Schwab Rehabilitation Hospital, Chicago, IL, p. A179

GOLOLOBOV, Alexey, Chief Financial Officer, Columbus Hospital Ltach, Newark, NJ, p. A409

GOLOVAN, Ronald, M.D., Vice President Medical Operations, Lutheran Hospital, Cleveland, OH, p. A478

GOMBAR, Greg A, Chief Financial Officer, Atrium Health University City, Charlotte, NC, p. A451

GOMBERG, Sandra, Chief Operating Officer, Jefferson Health Northeast, Philadelphia, PA, p. A535

GOMBERT, Laurie H., Administrator, Coordinated Health–Bethlehem, Bethlehem, PA, p. A520

GOMES, Bob, President and Chief Executive Officer, Canyon Vista Medical Center, Sierra Vista, AZ, p. A36

GOMES, Carol, FACHE, Chief Operating Officer, Stony Brook University Hospital, Stony Brook, NY, p. A444

GOMEZ, Carmen, Director Human Resources, North Shore Medical Center, Miami, FL, p. A131

GOMEZ, Denise, Assistant Vice President Information Systems, Unitypoint Health Meriter, Madison, WI, p. A698

GOMEZ, Dianna, Controller, Uva–Healthsouth Rehabilitation Hospital, Charlottesville, VA, p. A657

GOMEZ, Dolores S., R.N., Chief Operating Officer, Mills–Peninsula Health Services, Burlingame, CA, p. A53

GOMEZ, Gloria, M.D., Medical Director, East Mississippi State Hospital, Meridian, MS, p. A351

GOMEZ, Jay Michael, Chief Financial Officer, Memorial Hermann Surgical Hospital Kingwood, Kingwood, TX, p. A618

GOMEZ, Jesse, Vice President Human Resources, Ut Health North Campus Tyler, Tyler, TX, p. A642

GOMEZ, Mike, Site Manager Medical Information Systems, Our Lady Of Bellefonte Hospital, Ashland, KY, p. A249

GOMEZ, Omar, M.D., Chief of Staff, Cornerstone Regional Hospital, Edinburg, TX, p. A601

GOMEZ, Richard, Assistant Vice President Information Technology Division, Hillcrest Medical Center, Tulsa, OK, p. A508

GOMEZ, Robin, Administrator, Alvarado Hospital Medical Center, San Diego, CA, p. A83

GOMEZ–LUNA, Sandra, Medical Director, Southwest Connecticut Mental Health System, Bridgeport, CT, p. A107

GOMILA, Michael, Administrator, Baton Rouge Behavioral Hospital, Baton Rouge, LA, p. A263

GOMPF, Shelly, Director Human Resources, Alomere Health, Alexandria, MN, p. A327

GONCZ, Gray, Vice President of Medical Affairs, Trinity Health System, Steubenville, OH, p. A491

GONDER, Christie, R.N., Chief Nursing Officer, Salinas Valley Memorial Healthcare System, Salinas, CA, p. A83

GONGAWARE, Robert, Senior Vice President Finance, Indiana Regional Medical Center, Indiana, PA, p. A528

GONZALES, Amy, Director of Human Resources, Mckenzie County Healthcare System, Watford City, ND, p. A470

GONZALES, Angela, Manager Human Resources, San Mateo Medical Center, San Mateo, CA, p. A87

GONZALES, Ed
Vice President Human Resources, Marian Regional Medical Center, Santa Maria, CA, p. A89
Vice President Human Resources, St. John'S Pleasant Valley Hospital, Camarillo, CA, p. A53
Vice President Human Resources, St. John'S Regional Medical Center, Oxnard, CA, p. A76

GONZALES, Jan, Director Human Resources, North Valley Hospital, Tonasket, WA, p. A681

GONZALES, Mike, Chief Financial Officer, Select Specialty Hospital – San Diego, San Diego, CA, p. A84

GONZALES, Mindy, Chief Human Resources Officer, Othello Community Hospital, Othello, WA, p. A676

GONZALES, Rachel Ann., Chief Executive Officer, Madison Memorial Hospital, Rexburg, ID, p. A171

GONZALEZ, Agustin, Director Finance, Hospital Pavia Arecibo, Arecibo, PR, p. A715

GONZALEZ, Alan, Chief Operating Officer, Fort Duncan Regional Medical Center, Eagle Pass, TX, p. A600

GONZALEZ, Aurelio, Chief Financial Officer, University Hospital And Medical Center, Tamarac, FL, p. A141

GONZALEZ, David, Chief Clinical Officer, Advanced Diagnostics Hospital, Houston, TX, p. A610

GONZALEZ, David, M.D., Medical Director, Brook Lane Health Services, Hagerstown, MD, p. A291

GONZALEZ, Dinah L., Chief Financial Officer, Knapp Medical Center, Weslaco, TX, p. A645

GONZALEZ, Elizabeth, CPA, Financial Director, Hospital Pavia Yauco, Yauco, PR, p. A720

GONZALEZ, Enid Y., Chief Executive Officer, Encompass Health Rehabilitation Hospital Of Manati, Manati, PR, p. A717

GONZALEZ, Jacqueline, Senior Vice President and Chief Nursing Officer, Nicklaus Children'S Hospital, Miami, FL, p. A131

GONZALEZ, Jaime, Administrator, St. Catherine'S Rehabilitation Hospital, North Miami, FL, p. A133

GONZALEZ, Jerry, Interim Chief Nursing Officer, Las Palmas Medical Center, El Paso, TX, p. A602

GONZALEZ, Jorge F, M.D.
Chief Medical Officer, Adventhealth Sebring, Sebring, FL, p. A139
Vice President and Chief Nursing Officer, Adventhealth Wauchula, Wauchula, FL, p. A143

GONZALEZ, Jorge Matta., Executive Director, University Hospital, San Juan, PR, p. A719

GONZALEZ, Laura, Interim Chief Nurse Executive, South Shore Hospital, Chicago, IL, p. A179

GONZALEZ, Pedro J., Chief Executive Officer, Ashford Presbyterian Community Hospital, San Juan, PR, p. A718

GONZALEZ, Roberto, Executive Director Human Resources, Carepoint Health Hoboken University Medical Center, Hoboken, NJ, p. A406

GONZALEZ, Susan, Director of Clinical Services, Stanislaus Surgical Hospital, Modesto, CA, p. A72

GONZALEZ, Victoria, Chief Financial Officer, The Hospitals Of Providence Sierra Campus, El Paso, TX, p. A603

GONZALEZ–FAJARDO, Ana, Human Resources Director, Palmetto General Hospital, Hialeah, FL, p. A124

GOOCH, Mathew
Area Chief Executive Officer, Encompass Health Reading Rehabilitation Hospital, Reading, PA, p. A539
Chief Executive Officer, Healthsouth Rehabilitation Hospital Of Middletown, Middletown, DE, p. A113

GOOD, Jo, Director of Nursing, Palmetto Lowcountry Behavioral Health, Charleston, SC, p. A550

GOOD, Vance A, M.D., Chief Medical Staff, Guthrie Troy Community Hospital, Troy, PA, p. A542

GOODALL, David, M.D., Chief Medical Staff, Essentia Health–Deer River, Deer River, MN, p. A330

GOODBALIAN, Terry
Regional Chief Financial Officer, Henry Ford West Bloomfield Hospital, West Bloomfield, MI, p. A324
Vice President Finance and Chief Financial Officer, Henry Ford Macomb Hospitals, Clinton Township, MI, p. A309
Vice President, Finance and Chief Financial Officer, Henry Ford Wyandotte Hospital, Wyandotte, MI, p. A325

GOODE, Jennifer, Director Human Resources, Russell County Hospital, Russell Springs, KY, p. A260

GOODE, Lori, Director Human Resources, Baptist Memorial Hospital–Union County, New Albany, MS, p. A352

GOODE, Richard P., Executive Vice President and Chief Financial Officer, Children'S Medical Center Dallas, Dallas, TX, p. A596

GOODE, Vicky, Director Human Resources, Lifecare Hospitals Of North Carolina, Rocky Mount, NC, p. A461

GOODIN, Scott, Chief Financial Officer, Chinese Hospital, San Francisco, CA, p. A85

GOODING, Lari, Chief Executive Officer, Allendale County Hospital, Fairfax, SC, p. A552

GOODLETT, Lisa, Administrator Finance and Support Services, Musc Health Of Medical University Of South Carolina, Charleston, SC, p. A550

GOODMAN, Brenda, Chief Nursing Officer, Medical Center Of Peach County, Navicent Health, Bryon, GA, p. A149

GOODMAN, Charlene, Director Human Resources, Rush County Memorial Hospital, La Crosse, KS, p. A238

GOODMAN, Darrell, Chief Information Officer, Hi–Desert Medical Center, Joshua Tree, CA, p. A62

GOODMAN, David M, Ph.D., Chief Information Officer, Veterans Affairs Boston Healthcare System, West Roxbury, MA, p. A304

GOODMAN, Doug, Vice President Human Resources, Brandon Regional Hospital, Brandon, FL, p. A119

GOODMAN, Josie, Hospital Director, Central State Hospital, Louisville, KY, p. A256

GOODMAN, Louis, Senior Vice President Human Resources, Monongahela Valley Hospital, Monongahela, PA, p. A532

GOODMAN, Mary Jo, Chief Operating Officer, Park Plaza Hospital, Houston, TX, p. A613

GOODMAN, Shane, Chief Nursing Officer, De Soto Regional Health System, Mansfield, LA, p. A273

GOODMAN, Steven, Chief Operating Officer, Willow Crest Hospital, Miami, OK, p. A502

GOODMAN, William H., Vice President Medical Affairs, Chief Medical Officer, Catholic Medical Center, Manchester, NH, p. A401

GOODNER, Beth, Chief Executive Officer, Trustpoint Hospital, Murfreesboro, TN, p. A576

GOODNOW, John H., Chief Executive Officer, Benefis Health System, Great Falls, MT, p. A377

GOODPASTER, Amber, Chief Financial Officer, Clark Regional Medical Center, Winchester, KY, p. A261

GOODRICH, C Harlan, Vice President and Chief Information Officer, Midmichigan Medical Center–Midland, Midland, MI, p. A318

GOODRICH, Craig, Chief Financial Officer, Virginia Mason Medical Center, Seattle, WA, p. A679

GOODROW, Darrin
Chief Information Officer, The University Of Vermont Health Network – Alice Hyde Medical Center, Malone, NY, p. A430
Chief Information Officer, The University Of Vermont Health Network Elizabethtown Community Hospital, Elizabethtown, NY, p. A427

GOODSON, David, Chief Executive Officer, Encompass Health Rehabilitation Hospital Of Alexandria, Alexandria, LA, p. A262

GOODSPEED, Darwin, Director, Sioux Falls Veterans Affairs Health Care System, Sioux Falls, SD, p. A564

GOODSTEIN, Ruth, Controller, Encompass Health Rehabilitation Hospital Of Sunrise, Sunrise, FL, p. A140

GOODWIN, Jeremy, M.D., President, Medical Staff, Monroe County Hospital, Forsyth, GA, p. A153

GOODWIN, Jeronica, Senior Director Human Resources, Howard University Hospital, Washington, DC, p. A115

GOODWIN, Keith D., President and Chief Executive Officer, East Tennessee Children'S Hospital, Knoxville, TN, p. A572

GOODWIN, Linda, Chief Operating Officer and Chief Nursing Executive, Mercyone Des Moines Medical Center, Des Moines, IA, p. A221

GOODWIN, W Jarrad, M.D., Director, University Of Miami Hospital And Clinics, Miami, FL, p. A131

GOPALAKRISHNAN, Paari, M.D., Chief Medical Officer, Kent County Memorial Hospital, Warwick, RI, p. A548

GOPALAM, Gopinath, Chief Executive Officer, Apollo Behavioral Health Hospital, Baton Rouge, LA, p. A263

GOPINATH, Anil, FACHE, M.D., Regional Chief Medical Officer, Amita Health Mercy Medical Center, Aurora, IL, p. A173

GORAB, Robert, M.D., Chief Medical Officer, Hoag Orthopedic Institute, Irvine, CA, p. A62

GORANSON, Ken, Chief Financial Officer, Benson Hospital, Benson, AZ, p. A28

GORBY, Cherie, Chief Operations Officer, Uchealth Memorial Hospital, Colorado Springs, CO, p. A98

GORBY, Karen S., Chief Executive Officer and Chief Nursing Officer, Angel Medical Center, Franklin, NC, p. A454

GORCZYCA, Julie A, R.N., Chief Nursing Officer, Ascension Genesys Hospital, Grand Blanc, MI, p. A312

GORDIN, Peggy
Acting President, St. Louis Children'S Hospital, Saint Louis, MO, p. A370
Vice President, Patient Care Services and Chief Nursing Officer, St. Louis Children'S Hospital, Saint Louis, MO, p. A370

GORDON, Cyndy, Chief Operating Officer, Adventist Health And Rideout, Marysville, CA, p. A71

GORDON, Kevin, M.D., Chief of Staff, Alliancehealth Durant, Durant, OK, p. A499

GORDON, Mandy, Human Resource Coordinator, Phoebe Worth Medical Center, Sylvester, GA, p. A161

GORDON, Mark, Chief Nursing Officer, Kern Valley Healthcare District, Lake Isabella, CA, p. A63

GORDON, Mark M.
Chief Executive Officer, Bon Secours Memorial Regional Medical Center, Mechanicsville, VA, p. A662
Chief Executive Officer, Bon Secours–Richmond Community Hospital, Richmond, VA, p. A666

GORDON, Nancy Gail, R.N., MSN, Chief Nursing Officer and Vice President of Nursing, Baptist Health South Florida, Homestead Hospital, Homestead, FL, p. A125

GORDON, Robert, Manager Information Systems, Halifax Regional Medical Center, Roanoke Rapids, NC, p. A461

GORDON, Steve
Chief Operating Officer, Osceola Regional Medical Center, Kissimmee, FL, p. A126
Director Human Resources, Lake City Medical Center, Lake City, FL, p. A127

GORDON, Steven R., President and Chief Executive Officer, Brattleboro Memorial Hospital, Brattleboro, VT, p. A654

GORDON, Susan, R.N., Chief Nursing Officer, Upmc Memorial, York, PA, p. A546

GORDON, Thomas, Chief Information Officer, Virtua Marlton, Marlton, NJ, p. A408

GORDON, Wayne
Chief Financial Officer, Memorial Hermann Rehabilitation Hospital – Katy, Katy, TX, p. A617
Chief Financial Officer, Tirr Memorial Hermann, Houston, TX, p. A614

GORE, Carol, MSN, R.N., Chief Nursing Officer, Saint Mary'S Regional Medical Center, Russellville, AR, p. A48

GORE, Tim, Chief Financial Officer, Rivendell Behavioral Health, Bowling Green, KY, p. A250

GOREAU, Judy, R.N., Director of Nursing, Eastside Psychiatric Hospital, Tallahassee, FL, p. A140

GORELICK, Marc, President and Chief Executive Officer, Children'S Hospitals And Clinics Of Minnesota, Minneapolis, MN, p. A335

GOREY, Peter, Administrative Coordinator, Rockland Children'S Psychiatric Center, Orangeburg, NY, p. A440

GORLEWSKI, Todd, Senior Vice President and Chief Financial Officer, Brookdale Hospital Medical Center, New York, NY, p. A432

GORMAN, Brandon, Chief Financial Officer, Bradley County Medical Center, Warren, AR, p. A49

GORMAN, Jodie, Director Human Resources, Salem Memorial District Hospital, Salem, MO, p. A371

GORMAN, Kathleen, MSN, R.N., Executive Vice President Patient Care Services and Chief Operating Officer, Children'S National Health System, Washington, DC, p. A115

GORMLEY, Ann H, Senior Vice President Human Resources, Upmc Pinnacle Harrisburg, Harrisburg, PA, p. A527

GORMSEN, David, D.O., Vice President and Chief Medical Officer, Mercy Medical Center, Canton, OH, p. A474

GORN, Angela, Vice President, Norton Sound Regional Hospital, Nome, AK, p. A26

GORSUCH, Penelope Franklin, Associate Director Patient Care Services, Dayton Veterans Affairs Medical Center, Dayton, OH, p. A481

GOSCH, Shawn, Chief Financial Officer, Burgess Health Center, Onawa, IA, p. A227

GOSEY, J, M.D., Medical Director, Southern Surgical Hospital, Slidell, LA, p. A279

GOSHE, Nick, Chief Executive Officer, Rangely District Hospital, Rangely, CO, p. A105

GOSHIA, Rob, Chief Financial Officer, Paulding County Hospital, Paulding, OH, p. A489

GOSLEE, Belle, Chief Nursing Officer, Healthsouth Chesapeake Rehabilitation Hospital, Salisbury, MD, p. A293

GOSNEY, Brett, Chief Executive Officer, Animas Surgical Hospital, Durango, CO, p. A99

GOSS, Ella M., Chief Executive Officer, Providence Alaska Medical Center, Anchorage, AK, p. A25

GOSS, J. Richard, M.D., Medical Director, Uw Medicine/ Harborview Medical Center, Seattle, WA, p. A678

GOSS, Norma, R.N., Chief Nursing Officer, Chi Flaget Memorial Hospital, Bardstown, KY, p. A249

GOSS, Roger, Chief Information Officer, North Sunflower Medical Center, Ruleville, MS, p. A354

GOSSELIN, Gail
Director Human Resources, Landmark Medical Center, Woonsocket, RI, p. A548
Director Human Resources, Rehabilitation Hospital Of Rhode Island, North Smithfield, RI, p. A547

GOSSENS, Kevin, Director Human Resources, Thedacare Medical Center–Waupaca, Waupaca, WI, p. A707

GOSSETT, Lisa, MSN, R.N., Chief Nursing Officer, Ohiohealth Riverside Methodist Hospital, Columbus, OH, p. A480

GOTSOULIAS, Kostas, Interim Chief Executive Officer, Aspire Hospital, Conroe, TX, p. A593

GOTTI, Sreekant, Director Information Systems, Desert Valley Hospital, Victorville, CA, p. A94

GOTTLE, L. Gill, Senior Vice President and Chief Financial Officer, Robert Wood Johnson University Hospital At Hamilton, Hamilton, NJ, p. A406

GOTTLIEB, Harold, M.D., Chief Medical Officer, Memorial Hermann Memorial City Medical Center, Houston, TX, p. A613

GOTTLIEB, Jonathan, M.D., Senior Vice President and Chief Medical Officer, University Of Maryland Medical Center, Baltimore, MD, p. A287

GOTTSCHALK, Amy, M.D., Chief Medical Officer, Verde Valley Medical Center; Vice President Quality, Northern Arizona Healthcare, Verde Valley Medical Center, Cottonwood, AZ, p. A29

GOTTSCHALL, Dan, Senior Vice President and Chief Clinical Officer, St. Vincent'S Medical Center, Bridgeport, CT, p. A107

GOUGEON, Michele L, Executive Vice President and Chief Operating Officer, Mclean Hospital, Belmont, MA, p. A294

GOUGH, Galal S, M.D., Chief of Staff, Coast Plaza Hospital, Norwalk, CA, p. A74

GOUGH, Michelle, Chief Nursing Officer, Southwest Mississippi Regional Medical Center, Mccomb, MS, p. A350

GOULD, Christine, Director Human Resources, Martha'S Vineyard Hospital, Oak Bluffs, MA, p. A302

GOULD, Dana L., Chief Executive Officer, Broaddus Hospital, Philippi, WV, p. A688

GOULD, Jacquelyn M, MS, R.N., Vice President Patient Care Services and Chief Nursing Officer, Wellspan Good Samaritan Hospital, Lebanon, PA, p. A530

GOULD, Robert, President and Chief Executive Officer, Western Regional Medical Center, Goodyear, AZ, p. A30

GOULD, Tamara, R.N., Vice President Clinical Services and Chief Nursing Officer, Wabash General Hospital, Mount Carmel, IL, p. A190

GOULD, William R, Vice President Human Resources, Saint Joseph Hospital, Denver, CO, p. A99

GOULET, James P, Vice President Operations, Columbus Community Hospital, Columbus, NE, p. A384

GOULSON, Dan, M.D., Chief Medical Officer, Our Lady Of Bellefonte Hospital, Ashland, KY, p. A249

GOURLEY, Paul, M.D., Chief Hospital Services, U. S. Air Force Hospital, Hampton, VA, p. A660

GOVE, Cynthia A, Chief Operating Officer, Hampstead Hospital, Hampstead, NH, p. A400

GOVERO, Chris, Director of Operations, Hshs St. Joseph'S Hospital, Highland, IL, p. A185

GOVINDAIAH, Rajesh G., M.D., Chief Medical Officer, Memorial Medical Center, Springfield, IL, p. A196

GOVORCHIN, Pete, Senior Vice President Operations, Midwestern Regional Medical Center, Zion, IL, p. A198

GOWEN, Tina, System Controller, Westfield Memorial Hospital, Westfield, NY, p. A447

GOWER, Gary, Chief Information Officer, Appling Healthcare System, Baxley, GA, p. A148

GOYAL, Alok, M.D., Medical Director, Post Acute Medical Specialty Hospital Of Milwaukee, Greenfield, WI, p. A696

GOYAL, Deepak, M.D., Chief of Staff, Jacobson Memorial Hospital Care Center, Elgin, ND, p. A466

GOYKOVICH, Stephen, D.O., Chief Medical Officer, Geisinger Jersey Shore Hospital, Jersey Shore, PA, p. A528

GOYTIA–LEOS, Dina, M.D., Chief of Staff, Nix Health Care System, San Antonio, TX, p. A634

GOZA, Brian, Chief Information Officer, Hemphill County Hospital, Canadian, TX, p. A591

GRABER, Donald, M.D., Medical Director, Richmond State Hospital, Richmond, IN, p. A214

GRABOSO, Rebecca, Vice President and Chief Nurse Executive, Hackensack Meridian Health Riverview Medical Center, Red Bank, NJ, p. A412

GRABOWSKI, David, Chief Executive Officer, Meadows Psychiatric Center, Centre Hall, PA, p. A522

GRACE, Jeffery, M.D., Clinical Director, Buffalo Psychiatric Center, Buffalo, NY, p. A424

GRACE, Michael A., President, Upmc Mercy, Pittsburgh, PA, p. A538

GRACE, Richard, Chief Administrative Officer, Mayo Clinic Health System In Saint James, Saint James, MN, p. A339

GRACE, Robert, Chief Financial Officer, Kendall Regional Medical Center, Miami, FL, p. A130

GRACE, Walter, Chief Executive Officer and Administrator, Baptist Memorial Hospital–Union County, New Albany, MS, p. A352

GRACIE, Michael, Chief Information Officer, Veterans Health Care System Of The Ozarks, Fayetteville, AR, p. A41

GRADDY, Steve W
Chief Financial Officer, Freeman Health System, Joplin, MO, p. A362
Chief Financial Officer, Freeman Neosho Hospital, Neosho, MO, p. A366

GRADNEY, Angel, Chief Executive Officer, Kindred Hospital Clear Lake, Webster, TX, p. A644

GRADY, John M, Associate Director, Veterans Affairs Hudson Valley Health Care System, Montrose, NY, p. A431

GRADY, Kevin, M.D., Chief Medical Officer, Ascension St. John Hospital, Detroit, MI, p. A309

GRADY, Phillip L., Administrator, Shriners Hospitals For
 Children–St. Louis, Saint Louis, MO, p. A370
GRADY, Raymond, President and Chief Executive Officer,
 Methodist Hospitals, Gary, IN, p. A205
GRAEBER, Tod
 Administrator, Chi St. Alexius Health Garrison, Garrison,
  ND, p. A467
 Administrator, Community Memorial Hospital, Turtle Lake,
  ND, p. A469
GRAEBNER, David
 President, Aurora Medical Center Grafton, Grafton, WI,
  p. A695
 President, Aurora Medical Center In Washington County,
  Hartford, WI, p. A697
 President, Aurora Sheboygan Memorial Medical Center,
  Sheboygan, WI, p. A705
GRAEBNER, Nancy Kay., President and Chief Executive
 Officer, St. Joseph Mercy Chelsea, Chelsea, MI, p. A308
GRAF, John, Senior Vice President, Watertown Regional
 Medical Center, Watertown, WI, p. A707
GRAFTON, Jennifer, Chief Financial Officer, Shands Live Oak
 Regional Medical Center, Live Oak, FL, p. A128
GRAGG, Connie, Director Human Resources, Saint Mary'S
 Regional Medical Center, Russellville, AR, p. A48
GRAH, John A., Chief Executive Officer, Lakewood Regional
 Medical Center, Lakewood, CA, p. A64
GRAHAM, Bill, President, Sequoia Hospital, Redwood City,
 CA, p. A80
GRAHAM, Bonnie S., Director, San Francisco Va Medical
 Center, San Francisco, CA, p. A85
GRAHAM, Brenda, Chief Nursing Officer, Barbourville Arh
 Hospital, Barbourville, KY, p. A249
GRAHAM, Brooke, Human Resources Manager, Franklin
 Woods Community Hospital, Johnson City, TN, p. A571
GRAHAM, Christopher W, Chief Financial Officer, Community
 Memorial Hospital, Hamilton, NY, p. A429
GRAHAM, Connie, Public Information Officer, Mercy Health
 Love County, Marietta, OK, p. A502
GRAHAM, David B, M.D., Senior Vice President and Chief
 Information Officer, Memorial Medical Center, Springfield,
 IL, p. A196
GRAHAM, Gail L., Director, Veterans Affairs Central Iowa
 Health Care System, Des Moines, IA, p. A221
GRAHAM, Jeff, President and Chief Executive Officer, Adena
 Medical Center, Chillicothe, OH, p. A475
GRAHAM, John, Chief Financial Officer, Jefferson Hospital,
 Louisville, GA, p. A156
GRAHAM, John, M.D., Vice President Medical Affairs, Day
 Kimball Hospital, Putnam, CT, p. A110
GRAHAM, John W, Chief Administrative Officer, Jefferson
 Stratford Hospital, Stratford, NJ, p. A413
GRAHAM, Jon, Chief Finance Officer, Vidant Roanoke–Chowan
 Hospital, Ahoskie, NC, p. A449
GRAHAM, Kathryn, Director Communications and Community
 Relations, Novato Community Hospital, Novato, CA,
 p. A75
GRAHAM, Larry M., President and Chief Executive Officer,
 Lake Charles Memorial Hospital, Lake Charles, LA,
 p. A272
GRAHAM, Michelle, M.D.
 Vice President Medical Affairs, Ascension Southeast
  Wisconsin Hospital – Franklin Campus, Franklin, WI,
  p. A695
 Vice President Medical Affairs, Ascension Southeast
  Wisconsin Hospital – St. Francis Campus, Milwaukee,
  WI, p. A700
GRAHAM, Scott
 Chief Executive Officer, North Valley Hospital, Tonasket,
  WA, p. A681
 Chief Executive Officer, Three Rivers Hospital, Brewster,
  WA, p. A671
GRAHAM, Shauna, Director of Professional Services Human
 Resources, Marketing Foundation, Merrick Medical Center,
 Central City, NE, p. A383
GRAHAM, Susan, R.N., Nurse Executive, Healthsource
 Saginaw, Inc., Saginaw, MI, p. A321
GRAHAM, Yolanda, M.D., Medical Director, Devereux
 Advanced Behavioral Health Georgia, Kennesaw, GA,
 p. A155
GRAMER, Johanna, Director Human Resources, Mimbres
 Memorial Hospital, Deming, NM, p. A418
GRAMS, Shannon, Chief Executive Officer, Select Specialty
 Hospital–Fort Smith, Fort Smith, AR, p. A42
GRAMZA, Jeanne, Director Finance, Ascension All Saints,
 Racine, WI, p. A704
GRANADO–VILLAR, Deise, M.D., Chief Medical Officer and
 Senior Vice President Medical Affairs, Nicklaus Children'S
 Hospital, Miami, FL, p. A131
GRANATH, Brad, M.D., Chief of Staff, Humboldt General
 Hospital, Winnemucca, NV, p. A398

GRANATO, Jerome, M.D.
 Senior Vice President and Chief Medical Officer, Excela
  Frick Hospital, Mount Pleasant, PA, p. A532
 Senior Vice President and Chief Medical Officer, Excela
  Health Westmoreland Hospital, Greensburg, PA, p. A526
GRAND, Lawrence N, MS, R.N., Chief Operating Officer,
 Hunterdon Healthcare, Flemington, NJ, p. A406
GRANDIOSI, Joe, Director Information Technology, Southern
 Hills Hospital And Medical Center, Las Vegas, NV, p. A395
GRANER, Terry J., R.N., Chief Nursing Officer, Hutchinson
 Health, Hutchinson, MN, p. A333
GRANNELL, James, Chief Medical Officer, Sturgis Hospital,
 Sturgis, MI, p. A323
GRANT, Chad M., President and Chief Executive Officer,
 Mclaren Flint, Flint, MI, p. A311
GRANT, Cheryl, Director Information Systems, Coastal
 Carolina Hospital, Hardeeville, SC, p. A554
GRANT, Gail, Director Human Resources, Chi St. Francis
 Health, Breckenridge, MN, p. A329
GRANT, Mikki, Chief Information Officer, Fort Belknap Service
 Unit, Harlem, MT, p. A377
GRANT, Samuel, Chief Financial Officer, Stephens Memorial
 Hospital, Breckenridge, TX, p. A589
GRANT, Timothy M., M.D., Chief Medical Officer, Parkridge
 Medical Center, Chattanooga, TN, p. A567
GRANT, Tonya, Director Human Resources, T.J. Health
 Columbia, Columbia, KY, p. A250
GRANT, Will, Chief Financial Officer, Anmed Health Cannon,
 Pickens, SC, p. A556
GRANTHAM, Charlie, Manager Information Systems, Musc
 Health Marion Medical Center, Mullins, SC, p. A556
GRANTHAM, James, Administrator and Chief Executive
 Officer, Baptist Memorial Hospital–Booneville, Booneville,
 MS, p. A345
GRANVILLE, Sabrina M, Senior Vice President and Chief
 Human Resources Officer, Lowell General Hospital, Lowell,
 MA, p. A300
GRANZOW, Steven L., Chief Executive Officer, Lincoln County
 Hospital, Lincoln, KS, p. A240
GRASER, David, Vice President and Chief Information Officer,
 Hillcrest Hospital – South, Tulsa, OK, p. A508
GRASS, Linda J., President, Easton Hospital, Easton, PA,
 p. A524
GRASSER, Tierney Lynn, Senior Vice President and Chief
 Financial Officer, Olathe Medical Center, Olathe, KS,
 p. A242
GRATCH, Amie, Director Financial Services, Lifecare Hospitals
 Of Dallas, Dallas, TX, p. A596
GRATE, Anthony, Controller, Kindred Hospital–Greensboro,
 Greensboro, NC, p. A455
GRATRIX, Katie E., Administrative Assistant III, Alaska
 Psychiatric Institute, Anchorage, AK, p. A25
GRATZ, Silvia, D.O., Chief Medical Officer, Fairmount
 Behavioral Health System, Philadelphia, PA, p. A534
GRAU, Leah, Director Human Resources, Tulane Health
 System, New Orleans, LA, p. A276
GRAUMANN, Julie, Director, Alliancehealth Clinton, Clinton,
 OK, p. A498
GRAVES, Amanda, Chief Information Systems, Washington Dc
 Veterans Affairs Medical Center, Washington, DC, p. A116
GRAVES, Bruce, M.D., Chief of Staff, Hale Ho'Ola Hamakua,
 Honokaa, HI, p. A164
GRAVES, Buddy, Chief Information Officer, Southern Surgical
 Hospital, Slidell, LA, p. A279
GRAVES, Deborah, President and Chief Operating Officer,
 Levindale Hebrew Hospital And Nursing, Baltimore, MD,
 p. A286
GRAVES, Elsie, Chief Nursing Officer, Central Texas Medical
 Center, San Marcos, TX, p. A636
GRAVES, Jared, Chief Financial Officer, Byrd Regional
 Hospital, Leesville, LA, p. A272
GRAVES, Jennifer, Chief Executive, Swedish Medical Center–
 First Hill, Seattle, WA, p. A678
GRAVES, Jimmy, Interim Chief Executive Officer, Jefferson
 Davis Community Hospital, Prentiss, MS, p. A353
GRAVES, John A., Chief Executive Officer, Dimmit Regional
 Hospital, Carrizo Springs, TX, p. A591
GRAY, Albert, Chief Executive Officer, The Children'S Center
 Rehabilitation Hospital, Bethany, OK, p. A497
GRAY, Amy, Chief Executive Officer, Chi St. Joseph Health
 Rehabilitation Hospital, An Affiliate Of Encompass Health,
 Bryan, TX, p. A590
GRAY, Anthony, Chief Financial Officer, Lac–Olive View–Ucla
 Medical Center, Los Angeles, CA, p. A68
GRAY, Bob, Chief Financial Officer, Aspire Hospital, Conroe,
 TX, p. A593
GRAY, Brett, Director Human Resource, Sanpete Valley
 Hospital, Mount Pleasant, UT, p. A649
GRAY, Carrie, Director of Nursing, Riverview Behavioral
 Health, Texarkana, AR, p. A49

GRAY, Clarence, Chief Financial Officer, Tristar Horizon
 Medical Center, Dickson, TN, p. A569
GRAY, Cynthia, Interim Chief Financial Officer, Alliancehealth
 Midwest, Midwest City, OK, p. A502
GRAY, Eric, Chief Financial Officer, Encompass Health
 Rehabilitation Hospital Of Memphis, Memphis, TN, p. A574
GRAY, Gary, Chief Executive Officer, Natividad Medical Center,
 Salinas, CA, p. A82
GRAY, Janis
 Chief Information Officer, Dupont Hospital, Fort Wayne,
  IN, p. A203
 Chief Information Officer, Rehabilitation Hospital Of Fort
  Wayne, Fort Wayne, IN, p. A204
GRAY, Jason, M.D., Chief Medical Officer, Mercy Medical
 Center, Roseburg, OR, p. A517
GRAY, Jeremy, Chief Operating Officer, Saint Thomas Midtown
 Hospital, Nashville, TN, p. A577
GRAY, Judy
 Vice President Human Resources, Albany Memorial Hospital,
  Albany, NY, p. A422
 Vice President Human Resources, St. Peter'S Hospital,
  Albany, NY, p. A422
GRAY, Karen D, Director Human Resources, Vibra Hospital Of
 Southeastern Michigan, Llc, Lincoln Park, MI, p. A317
GRAY, Kris David, Chief Medical Officer, Adventhealth Daytona
 Beach, Daytona Beach, FL, p. A121
GRAY, Larry W., President, Baptist Health Louisville, Louisville,
 KY, p. A256
GRAY, Marty, R.N., Director of Nursing, Wyandot Memorial
 Hospital, Upper Sandusky, OH, p. A492
GRAY, Mary, Director Human Resources, Lehigh Regional
 Medical Center, Lehigh Acres, FL, p. A128
GRAY, Michelle, Nurse Executive, Atrium Medical Center Of
 Corinth, Corinth, TX, p. A594
GRAY, Mike, Corporate Vice President Human Resources, Ut
 Health Tyler, Tyler, TX, p. A642
GRAY, Patricia, Director Health Information Management,
 Cumberland Hall Hospital, Hopkinsville, KY, p. A253
GRAY, Rick, Chief Executive Officer, Culberson Hospital, Van
 Horn, TX, p. A643
GRAY, Roshanda, Assistant Administrator, Memorial Medical
 Center, Port Lavaca, TX, p. A630
GRAY, Sarah, Vice President Information Services, East
 Alabama Medical Center, Opelika, AL, p. A22
GRAY, Stephen, Chief Executive Officer, Eden Medical Center,
 Castro Valley, CA, p. A54
GRAY, Tami, Chief Financial Officer, Irwin County Hospital,
 Ocilla, GA, p. A158
GRAY, Teresa, President, Integris Canadian Valley Hospital,
 Yukon, OK, p. A510
GRAY, Terry, Vice President Human Resources, Emanuel
 Medical Center, Turlock, CA, p. A92
GRAY, Thomas, M.D., Medical Director, Montana State
 Hospital, Warm Springs, MT, p. A380
GRAY, Tracy
 Chief Information Officer, Grady General Hospital, Cairo,
  GA, p. A149
 Chief Information Officer, Mitchell County Hospital, Camilla,
  GA, p. A149
 Senior Vice President Information Services, John D.
  Archbold Memorial Hospital, Thomasville, GA, p. A161
GRAYBEAL, Phillip, CPA
 Chief Financial Officer, Page Memorial Hospital, Luray, VA,
  p. A661
 Chief Financial Officer, Warren Memorial Hospital, Front
  Royal, VA, p. A660
 Vice President, Finance, Valley Health Shenandoah
  Memorial Hospital, Woodstock, VA, p. A669
GRAYBILL, Matthew P, Vice President, Human Resources and
 Chief Administrative Officer, Dayton Children'S Hospital,
 Dayton, OH, p. A481
GRAYSON, Barbara, Vice President Human Resources, Mercy
 Hospital Washington, Washington, MO, p. A373
GREAKER, Mark, Chief Information Officer, Brookdale Hospital
 Medical Center, New York, NY, p. A432
GREAR, Esther, Director Hospital Social Work and Assistant
 Hospital Administrator, Windhaven Psychiatric Hospital,
 Prescott Valley, AZ, p. A35
GREASON, Linda, Vice President Human Resources, Milford
 Regional Medical Center, Milford, MA, p. A301
GREBOSKY, Jamie, M.D., Vice President of Medical Affairs,
 Asante Rogue Regional Medical Center, Medford, OR,
 p. A515
GRECCO, Jamie
 Chief Human Resource Executive, Brookdale Hospital
  Medical Center, New York, NY, p. A432
 Director Human Resources Post Acute, Brookdale Hospital
  Medical Center, New York, NY, p. A432
GRECO, Andrew, Chief Financial Officer, Brookdale Hospital
 Medical Center, New York, NY, p. A432

GRECO, Margaret, Chief Human Resources, Keller Army Community Hospital, West Point, NY, p. A447
GREELEY, Donna, Director Human Resources, Spalding Rehabilitation Hospital, Aurora, CO, p. A96
GREELEY, Gerald, Chief Information Officer, Signature Healthcare Brockton Hospital, Brockton, MA, p. A296
GREEN, Amber, Chief Operating Officer and Chief Nursing Officer, St. Luke'S Mccall, Mccall, ID, p. A170
GREEN, Amber, R.N., Chief Operating Officer and Chief Nursing Officer, St. Luke'S Mccall, Mccall, ID, p. A170
GREEN, Angela, Chief Executive Officer, Kindred Hospital–St. Louis, Saint Louis, MO, p. A369
GREEN, Barbara, Director Human Resources, O'Connor Hospital, Delhi, NY, p. A426
GREEN, Brenda, Director of Nursing, Ruby Valley Medical Center, Sheridan, MT, p. A380
GREEN, Calvin, Chief Executive Officer, Mercy Regional Medical Center, Ville Platte, LA, p. A280
GREEN, Christi, R.N., MS, Vice President, Human Resources, Frisbie Memorial Hospital, Rochester, NH, p. A402
GREEN, Dante, Assistant Vice President Operations, New Orleans East Hospital, New Orleans, LA, p. A275
GREEN, Darryl, Director Administration, Naval Hospital Jacksonville, Jacksonville, FL, p. A125
GREEN, David, Chief Human Resources, West Palm Beach Veterans Affairs Medical Center, West Palm Beach, FL, p. A144
GREEN, David F., M.D., Chief Medical Officer, Concord Hospital, Concord, NH, p. A399
GREEN, Debra Jane, R.N., Director of Nursing, Turquoise Lodge Hospital, Albuquerque, NM, p. A417
GREEN, Elizabeth, Chief Human Resources Officer, Cooper University Health Care, Camden, NJ, p. A404
GREEN, Garry Kim., Administrator, Shriners Hospitals For Children–Shreveport, Shreveport, LA, p. A278
GREEN, Gayle, Director of Nursing, Hale Ho'Ola Hamakua, Honokaa, HI, p. A164
GREEN, Gene E., President and Chief Executive Officer, South Shore Hospital, South Weymouth, MA, p. A303
GREEN, John
Chief Operating Officer, Iredell Health System, Statesville, NC, p. A463
Vice President Finance, St. Peter'S Hospital, Helena, MT, p. A377
GREEN, Jon, Chief Executive Officer, Bleckley Memorial Hospital, Cochran, GA, p. A150
GREEN, Jonna, Interim Administrator, Pemiscot Memorial Health System, Hayti, MO, p. A361
GREEN, Julie, Vice President Human Resources, Cheshire Medical Center, Keene, NH, p. A400
GREEN, Karen, Chief Information Officer, Brooks Rehabilitation Hospital, Jacksonville, FL, p. A125
GREEN, Kaye, Chief Executive Officer, Roosevelt General Hospital, Portales, NM, p. A419
GREEN, Ladonna, Director Human Resources, Glen Rose Medical Center, Glen Rose, TX, p. A607
GREEN, Larry D., Jr, Chief Executive Officer, Windhaven Psychiatric Hospital, Prescott Valley, AZ, p. A35
GREEN, Marsha, Administrator and Chief Operating Officer, Essentia Health–Deer River, Deer River, MN, p. A330
GREEN, Meredith, Senior Vice President and Chief Nursing Officer, Washington Regional Medical Center, Fayetteville, AR, p. A42
GREEN, Patrick
President and Chief Executive Officer, Lawrence + Memorial Hospital, New London, CT, p. A110
President and Chief Executive Officer, Westerly Hospital, Westerly, RI, p. A548
GREEN, Paul, Chief Clinical Officer, Kindred Hospital–Aurora, Aurora, CO, p. A96
GREEN, Rhonda G., Administrator, Lallie Kemp Medical Center, Independence, LA, p. A269
GREEN, Rose Marie, Director Human Resources, Humboldt General Hospital, Winnemucca, NV, p. A398
GREEN, Steve, Comptroller, Jasper General Hospital, Bay Springs, MS, p. A344
GREEN, Susan, Senior Vice President Finance, Chief Financial Officer, Lowell General Hospital, Lowell, MA, p. A300
GREEN, Tracy V., Chief Financial Officer, Brookdale Hospital Medical Center, New York, NY, p. A432
GREEN, Trent, President, Legacy Emanuel Medical Center, Portland, OR, p. A516
GREEN, Vince, Chief Operating Officer, St. Joseph Hospital, Fort Wayne, IN, p. A204
GREEN, Vincent, Medical Director, Prisma Health Laurens County Hospital, Clinton, SC, p. A550
GREENBERG, Mark, M.D.
Chief Medical Officer, Cape Coral Hospital, Cape Coral, FL, p. A119
Medical Director, Gulf Coast Medical Center, Fort Myers, FL, p. A123
GREENBLATT, James, M.D., Chief Medical Officer, Vice President Medical Clinical Services, Walden Behavioral Care, Waltham, MA, p. A304
GREENE, Arthur, M.D., Vice President Medical Affairs, Sentara Careplex Hospital, Hampton, VA, p. A660
GREENE, Beth, Chief Operating Officer, Cherokee Indian Hospital, Cherokee, NC, p. A452
GREENE, Bradley, Chief Financial Officer, Wellstar Douglas Hospital, Douglasville, GA, p. A152
GREENE, Casey, Vice President and Chief Operating Officer, Unitypoint Health – St. Luke'S Hospital, Cedar Rapids, IA, p. A218
GREENE, Chelsea, Manager Human Resources, Guttenberg Municipal Hospital, Guttenberg, IA, p. A223
GREENE, Cora, Senior Director, Chief Nursing Officer, Novant Health Rowan Medical Center, Salisbury, NC, p. A461
GREENE, Dustin, Chief Executive Officer, Tristar Horizon Medical Center, Dickson, TN, p. A569
GREENE, Erin, Coordinator Human Resources, Kindred Hospital–San Francisco Bay Area, San Leandro, CA, p. A87
GREENE, Melodi, R.N., MS, Chief Nursing Officer, Community Howard Regional Health, Kokomo, IN, p. A209
GREENE, Palmer, R.N., Chief Nursing Officer, Sierra Vista Hospital, Truth Or Consequences, NM, p. A421
GREENE, Robert, Director Information Technology, Promise Hospital Of Miss Lou, Vidalia, LA, p. A279
GREENE, Scott, Chief Information Officer, Tennova Healthcare–Clarksville, Clarksville, TN, p. A568
GREENE, Todd
Chief Executive Officer, Arizona Spine And Joint Hospital, Mesa, AZ, p. A31
Chief Executive Officer, Physicians Surgical Hospital – Quail Creek, Amarillo, TX, p. A582
GREENE, Tracie, Director Human Resources, Brigham City Community Hospital, Brigham City, UT, p. A647
GREENFIELD, Tadd, Executive Vice President and Chief Operating Officer, Regional West Medical Center, Scottsbluff, NE, p. A391
GREENLEE, Kathryn M, R.N.
Vice President, Clinical Services/CNO, Promedica Bixby Hospital, Adrian, MI, p. A306
Vice President, Clinical Services/CNO, Promedica Herrick Hospital, Tecumseh, MI, p. A323
GREENMAN, Jennifer, Vice President Chief Information Officer, H. Lee Moffitt Cancer Center And Research Institute, Tampa, FL, p. A141
GREENMAN, Sharon, Director Human Resources, Melissa Memorial Hospital, Holyoke, CO, p. A102
GREENWALD, Derek, Chief Nursing Officer, Star Valley Medical Center, Afton, WY, p. A710
GREENWOOD, Annette June, Chief Nursing Officer, Riverside Community Hospital, Riverside, CA, p. A81
GREENWOOD, Les, M.D., President, Medical Staff, Davis Hospital And Medical Center, Layton, UT, p. A648
GREENWOOD, Susan, R.N., Vice President and Chief Nursing Officer, St. Bernards Medical Center, Jonesboro, AR, p. A44
GREER, Troy, Chief Executive Officer, Lovelace Medical Center, Albuquerque, NM, p. A416
GREGG, Richard, M.D., Medical Director, Lifecare Hospital Of Dayton, Miamisburg, OH, p. A487
GREGG, Shawna, Director Human Resources, Porterville Developmental Center, Porterville, CA, p. A78
GREGG, Sherry, Chief Information Technology Officer, Beckley Veterans Affairs Medical Center, Beckley, WV, p. A683
GREGG, Tom, Vice President Human Resources, Chi St. Alexius Health, Bismarck, ND, p. A465
GREGG, Travis, Director of Strategy and Business Development, Kearney Regional Medical Center, Kearney, NE, p. A386
GREGGAIN, Don, M.D., Physician Network Director, Tri–State Memorial Hospital, Clarkston, WA, p. A671
GREGONIS, Michael, Comptroller, Naval Hospital Jacksonville, Jacksonville, FL, p. A125
GREGOR, Brian, Manager Information Technology Operations, Glendale Memorial Hospital And Health Center, Glendale, CA, p. A60
GREGORIAN, Myra, Vice President and Chief Human Resources Officer, Children'S Hospital Los Angeles, Los Angeles, CA, p. A66
GREGORICH, Miki, Director Human Resources, Pioneer Medical Center, Big Timber, MT, p. A374
GREGORY, Adina
Chief Nursing Officer, University Of Kansas Health System Great Bend Campus, Great Bend, KS, p. A235
Chief Operating Officer, University Of Kansas Health System Great Bend Campus, Great Bend, KS, p. A235
GREGORY, Audrey, Chief Executive Officer, Saint Francis Hospital, Memphis, TN, p. A575
GREGORY, Ben, Chief Executive Officer, Walter B. Jones Alcohol And Drug Abuse Treatment Center, Greenville, NC, p. A455
GREGORY, Beth, Interim Chief Nursing Officer, Astria Regional Medical Center, Yakima, WA, p. A682
GREGORY, Jan, Chief of Human Resources, Crittenden County Hospital, Marion, KY, p. A257
GREGORY, Jay, M.D., Chief Medical Officer, Saint Francis Hospital Muskogee, Muskogee, OK, p. A502
GREGORY, Jim, Controller, Methodist Hospital Of Chicago, Chicago, IL, p. A178
GREGORY, Jody S, R.N., Chief Nursing Officer, Encompass Health Rehabilitation Hospital Of Wichita Falls, Wichita Falls, TX, p. A645
GREGORY, Luke, Chief Executive Officer, Vanderbilt University Medical Center, Nashville, TN, p. A577
GREGORY, Paul, Acting Director, Veterans Affairs Montana Health Care System, Fort Harrison, MT, p. A376
GREGORY, Phyllis, Registered Health Information Administrator, Southern Inyo Healthcare District, Lone Pine, CA, p. A65
GREGORY, Sean
Chief Executive, Columbia Network, Peacehealth Southwest Medical Center, Vancouver, WA, p. A681
Chief Executive, Peacehealth Southwest Medical Center, Vancouver, WA, p. A681
GREGORY, Shawn, Chief Financial Officer, St. Petersburg General Hospital, Saint Petersburg, FL, p. A139
GREGORY, Trip, Senior Vice President Human Resources, Prisma Health Baptist Hospital, Columbia, SC, p. A551
GREGOS, Ruth, Director Finance, Shriners Hospitals For Children–Tampa, Tampa, FL, p. A142
GREGSON, Mark, Interim Chief Executive Officer, Lourdes Counseling Center, Richland, WA, p. A677
GREIMAN, Alan W., Chief Executive Officer and President, Royal Oaks Hospital, Windsor, MO, p. A373
GREINER, Walter, Chief Financial Officer, Atlanticare Regional Medical Center, Atlantic City, NJ, p. A403
GREINER, William, M.D., Chief of Staff, F. W. Huston Medical Center, Winchester, KS, p. A247
GRENALDO, Paul, Executive Vice President and Chief Operating Officer, Doctors Community Hospital, Lanham, MD, p. A291
GRENDON, M Todd, M.D., President Medical Staff, Amita Health Saint Joseph Hospital, Chicago, IL, p. A176
GRENIER, Raymond, Chief Financial Officer, Memorial Medical Center, Las Cruces, NM, p. A418
GRENNAN, M. Joseph, M.D., Senior Vice President and Chief Medical Officer, Reading Hospital, West Reading, PA, p. A544
GRESHAM, Paula, Vice President, Hospital Administrator, Tanner Medical Center–Villa Rica, Villa Rica, GA, p. A162
GREW, Kate, MSN, R.N., Vice President/Chief Nurse Executive, Atrium Health Cabarrus, Concord, NC, p. A452
GREW, Terry, Chief Business Office, Hampton Veterans Affairs Medical Center, Hampton, VA, p. A660
GREY, Michael, M.D., Interim Chief Medical Officer, Saint Francis Hospital And Medical Center, Hartford, CT, p. A108
GREY, Mitzi, Chief Operating Officer, Bath Community Hospital, Hot Springs, VA, p. A661
GRIBBIN, John, President and Chief Executive Officer, Centrastate Healthcare System, Freehold, NJ, p. A406
GRICE, William N., Executive Director, Kaiser Permanente Los Angeles Medical Center, Los Angeles, CA, p. A67
GRICUS, Peggy, R.N., Vice President, Patient Care Services and Chief Nursing Officer, Silver Cross Hospital, New Lenox, IL, p. A191
GRIDLEY, Mark, President and Chief Executive Officer, Fhn Memorial Hospital, Freeport, IL, p. A183
GRIEP, John, M.D., Chief Medical Director, St. Catherine Hospital, East Chicago, IN, p. A202
GRIEST, Mary, Vice President Finance and Chief Financial Officer, University Hospitals Samaritan Medical Center, Ashland, OH, p. A472
GRIFFES, Carol, Administrator, Duane L. Waters Hospital, Jackson, MI, p. A315
GRIFFIN, Amy, Vice President Patient Care Services, John D. Archbold Memorial Hospital, Thomasville, GA, p. A161
GRIFFIN, Barbara J, MSN, R.N., Chief Nursing Officer, Rapides Regional Medical Center, Alexandria, LA, p. A262
GRIFFIN, Betty, Interim Chief Nursing Officer, Musc Health Chester Medical Center, Chester, SC, p. A550
GRIFFIN, Brad, Chief Executive Officer, Gulf Coast Regional Medical Center, Panama City, FL, p. A135
GRIFFIN, Brian, Director Information Services, Springhill Medical Center, Springhill, LA, p. A279
GRIFFIN, Charles, Director of Nursing, Clay County Hospital, Ashland, AL, p. A13

GRIFFIN, Cindy
Chief Nursing Officer, Liberty Dayton Regional Medical Center, Liberty, TX, p. A620
Director Human Resources, Medical Center Barbour, Eufaula, AL, p. A17
GRIFFIN, Dean A., Chief Executive Officer, Lawrence Medical Center, Moulton, AL, p. A21
GRIFFIN, Douglas, M.D., Vice President Medical Officer, Sanford Medical Center Fargo, Fargo, ND, p. A467
GRIFFIN, Holly, R.N., Chief Nursing Officer, Lady Of The Sea General Hospital, Cut Off, LA, p. A266
GRIFFIN, James, Manager Information Systems, Martin General Hospital, Williamston, NC, p. A463
GRIFFIN, Jeannine, M.D., Chief of Staff, Memorial Medical Center, Port Lavaca, TX, p. A630
GRIFFIN, Jeff, Assistant Vice President Finance, Atrium Health Anson, Wadesboro, NC, p. A463
GRIFFIN, Joe, Controller, Encompass Health Rehabilitation Hospital Of Round Rock, Round Rock, TX, p. A632
GRIFFIN, Kathryn, Chief Nurse Executive, Terrell State Hospital, Terrell, TX, p. A640
GRIFFIN, Margaret Elizabeth., Chief Executive Officer, Honorhealth John C. Lincoln Medical Center, Phoenix, AZ, p. A33
GRIFFIN, Matthew, M.D., Chief Medical Officer, St. Mary Mercy Hospital, Livonia, MI, p. A317
GRIFFIN, Paulette, Director Human Resources, Dmc – Sinai–Grace Hospital, Detroit, MI, p. A310
GRIFFIN, Philip, Director of Operations, Rochester Psychiatric Center, Rochester, NY, p. A442
GRIFFIN–JONES, Christie, R.N., Chief Nursing Officer, Encompass Health Rehabilitation Hospital Of Humble, Humble, TX, p. A615
GRIFFIN–MAHON, Selena, Assistant Vice President Human Resources, Brookdale Hospital Medical Center, New York, NY, p. A432
GRIFFIS, Daniel, M.D., Chief Medical Officer, Syringa Hospital And Clinics, Grangeville, ID, p. A169
GRIFFITH, Barbara, Vice President Human Resources, St. Anthony'S Rehabilitation Hospital, Lauderdale Lakes, FL, p. A128
GRIFFITH, Barbara, M.D., Chief Medical Officer, Duke Regional Hospital, Durham, NC, p. A452
GRIFFITH, David, M.D., Medical Director, Texas Center For Infectious Disease, San Antonio, TX, p. A635
GRIFFITH, H. Wes, Chief Financial Officer, Tennova Healthcare – Cleveland, Cleveland, TN, p. A568
GRIFFITH, James D, Chief Operating Officer, El Camino Hospital, Mountain View, CA, p. A73
GRIFFITH, Jeanne, Chief Nursing Officer, Coryell Health, Gatesville, TX, p. A607
GRIFFITH, John H., President and Chief Executive Officer, Kedren Community Mental Health Center, Los Angeles, CA, p. A67
GRIFFITH, Joshua, Manager Human Resources, Presbyterian Espanola Hospital, Espanola, NM, p. A418
GRIFFITH, Leah, Chief Executive Officer, Big Sandy Medical Center, Big Sandy, MT, p. A374
GRIFFITH, Maria, Director Human Resources, Signature Psychiatric Hospital, Kansas City, MO, p. A363
GRIFFITH, Patti, R.N., MS, Chief Nursing Officer, Methodist Hospital For Surgery, Addison, TX, p. A581
GRIFFITHS, Mark, Director Management Information Systems, Incline Village Community Hospital, Incline Village, NV, p. A394
GRIGG, Dan, Chief Executive Officer, Harney District Hospital, Burns, OR, p. A511
GRIGG, William E., Senior Vice President and Chief Financial Officer, Methodist Hospital Of Southern California, Arcadia, CA, p. A51
GRIGGS, Shannon, Interim Chief Executive Officer, Research Medical Center, Kansas City, MO, p. A362
GRIGGS, Stacie, MIS Analyst, North Mississippi Medical Center–West Point, West Point, MS, p. A355
GRIGSBY, Jan, Vice President and Chief Financial Officer, Springhill Memorial Hospital, Mobile, AL, p. A20
GRIGSON, John A, Vice President and Chief Financial Officer, Covenant Medical Center, Lubbock, TX, p. A621
GRILL, Laura D., Chief Executive Officer, East Alabama Medical Center, Opelika, AL, p. A22
GRILLO, Jorge C, Chief Information Officer, Canton–Potsdam Hospital, Potsdam, NY, p. A442
GRILLS, Kathy, Director Human Resources, Encompass Health Harmarville Rehabilitation Hospital, Pittsburgh, PA, p. A537
GRIM, Andrew, Chief Financial Officer, San Gabriel Valley Medical Center, San Gabriel, CA, p. A86
GRIMES, Paula, R.N., MSN, Chief Nursing Officer, Nea Baptist Memorial Hospital, Jonesboro, AR, p. A44
GRIMES, Teresa G., Chief Executive Officer, Washington County Hospital, Chatom, AL, p. A16

GRIMES, Walter, Director Information Technology, Christus Good Shepherd Medical Center–Marshall, Marshall, TX, p. A623
GRIMLEY, Karen A, Chief Nursing Executive, Ronald Reagan Ucla Medical Center, Los Angeles, CA, p. A69
GRIMM, Debra, MS, R.N., Vice President and Chief Nursing Officer, Long Island Community Hospital, Patchogue, NY, p. A441
GRIMM, Tamara, R.N., Chief Clinical Officer and Chief Nursing Officer, Cornerstone Hospital Of Bossier City, Bossier City, LA, p. A265
GRIMM, William, Chief Information Officer, Henry County Hospital, Napoleon, OH, p. A488
GRIMMER, Michael, Chief Operating Officer, Athol Hospital, Athol, MA, p. A294
GRIMSHAW, Bruce P., Chief Executive Officer, Southern California Hospital At Hollywood, Los Angeles, CA, p. A69
GRIMSHAW, Matthew, Market Chief Executive Officer, Trinity Health System, Steubenville, OH, p. A491
GRIMSLEY, Denise, Vice President and Administrator, Adventhealth Wauchula, Wauchula, FL, p. A143
GRINER, Alisa R, Director, Human Resources, Memorial Health, Savannah, GA, p. A160
GRINER, Ginny, Director Human Resources, George E. Weems Memorial Hospital, Apalachicola, FL, p. A117
GRIPPI, Michael, M.D., Chief Medical Officer, Good Shepherd Penn Partners Specialty Hospital At Rittenhouse, Philadelphia, PA, p. A534
GRISH, John, Chief Financial Officer, Johnson Memorial Medical Center, Stafford Springs, CT, p. A111
GRISHOW, Cathy, Director Human Resources, Ellett Memorial Hospital, Appleton City, MO, p. A356
GRISIER, Douglas, D.O., Medical Director, Encompass Health Rehabilitation Hospital Of Erie, Erie, PA, p. A525
GRISNAK, Karen, R.N., Chief Operating Officer and Assistant Administrator Quality Services, Kaiser Permanente Vallejo Medical Center, Vallejo, CA, p. A93
GRISPINO, Frank, Vice President Operations, Mosaic Medical Center – Maryville, Maryville, MO, p. A365
GRISSOM, Robyn, Director of Human Resources, Osf Healthcare Saint Anthony'S Health Center, Alton, IL, p. A173
GRISSOM, Tina, Chief Information Technology Officer, Arkansas State Hospital, Little Rock, AR, p. A44
GROCE, Vicky, Chief Nursing Officer, Lincoln County Health System, Fayetteville, TN, p. A569
GROCHALA, Eugene
Vice President Information Systems, Capital Health Medical Center–Hopewell, Pennington, NJ, p. A410
Vice President Information Systems, Capital Health Regional Medical Center, Trenton, NJ, p. A413
GROCHOLSKI, James F., Chief Executive Officer, Wesley Rehabilitation Hospital, Wichita, KS, p. A248
GROENIG, Matt, Vice President Finance, St. Luke'S Mccall, Mccall, ID, p. A170
GROEPER, William E, Vice President Finance, Beloit Health System, Beloit, WI, p. A692
GROEPPER, Ronald
Senior Vice President and Area Manager, Kaiser Permanente San Francisco Medical Center, San Francisco, CA, p. A85
Senior Vice President and Area Manager, Kaiser Permanente South San Francisco, South San Francisco, CA, p. A90
GRONERT, Thomas, Chief Information Officer, University Of Maryland St. Joseph Medical Center, Towson, MD, p. A293
GRONEWOLD, Russell, Chief Financial Officer, Bryan Medical Center, Lincoln, NE, p. A386
GRONOW, Thomas, Chief Operating Officer, University Of Colorado Hospital, Aurora, CO, p. A96
GROOM, Scott C, Senior Vice President and Chief Information Officer, Huntington Hospital, Huntington, NY, p. A429
GROOMS, Kim, Administrator, King'S Daughters Medical Center Ohio, Portsmouth, OH, p. A490
GROOMS, Richard Walter, Chief Human Resources Officer, Anmed Health Medical Center, Anderson, SC, p. A549
GROS, Albert, M.D., Chief Medical Officer, St. David'S South Austin Medical Center, Austin, TX, p. A586
GROS, Mark, Director Human Resources, United Medical Rehabilitation Hospital, Hammond, LA, p. A268
GROSECLOSE, Cathy, Vice President Patient Care Services, Grady Memorial Hospital, Chickasha, OK, p. A498
GROSETH, Bradley D., Chief Administrative Officer, Marshfield Medical Center – Rice Lake, Rice Lake, WI, p. A704
GROSHANS, Adam, President, Springfield Regional Medical Center, Springfield, OH, p. A491
GROSKREUTZ, Kevin
Chief Information Officer, Hshs Sacred Heart Hospital, Eau Claire, WI, p. A694
Division Chief Information Officer, Ancillary Systems, Hshs St. Joseph'S Hospital, Chippewa Falls, WI, p. A693

GROSS, Barry L, M.D., Executive Vice President and Chief Medical Officer, Riverside Regional Medical Center, Newport News, VA, p. A663
GROSS, Cathy, Director Health Information Management Systems, Wrangell Medical Center, Wrangell, AK, p. A27
GROSS, Cindy, Director of Finance, Barnes–Jewish St. Peters Hospital, Saint Peters, MO, p. A371
GROSS, Denton, Director Information Services, Larue D. Carter Memorial Hospital, Indianapolis, IN, p. A207
GROSS, Kristin, Director Information Technology Center, Avera Mckennan Hospital And University Health Center, Sioux Falls, SD, p. A563
GROSS, Len, Chief Human Resources Officer, Sheridan Memorial Hospital, Sheridan, WY, p. A712
GROSS, Mark
Executive Vice President and Chief Financial Officer, Bronson South Haven Hospital, South Haven, MI, p. A322
Senior Business Director Finance, Mercy Health, Lakeshore Campus, Shelby, MI, p. A322
Vice President Finance and Chief Financial Officer, North Ottawa Community Hospital, Grand Haven, MI, p. A312
GROSS, Paul, Human Services and Finance Officer, Larry B. Zieverink, Sr. Alcoholism Treatment Center, Raleigh, NC, p. A460
GROSS, Peter A, M.D., Senior Vice President and Chief Medical Officer, Hackensack Meridian Health Hackensack University Medical Center, Hackensack, NJ, p. A406
GROSS, Randy, Chief Operating Officer, Kendall Regional Medical Center, Miami, FL, p. A130
GROSS, Tina, MSN, R.N., Chief Nursing Officer, Sparrow Specialty Hospital, Lansing, MI, p. A316
GROSSER, Joy, Chief Information Officer, University Of Washington Medical Center, Seattle, WA, p. A678
GROSSMAN, Drew, Chief Executive Officer, St. Mary'S Medical Center, Blue Springs, MO, p. A356
GROSSMAN, Hannah, M.D., Chief Medical Officer, Los Robles Hospital And Medical Center, Thousand Oaks, CA, p. A91
GROSSMAN, Martin, Chief of Staff, Aventura Hospital And Medical Center, Aventura, FL, p. A117
GROSSMAN, Robert I., Chief Executive Officer, Brookdale Hospital Medical Center, New York, NY, p. A432
GROSSO, Michael, M.D., Senior Vice President Medical Affairs, Huntington Hospital, Huntington, NY, p. A429
GROTE, Brad, Chief Operating Officer, Glendale Memorial Hospital And Health Center, Glendale, CA, p. A60
GROTELUSCHEN, Ronald J., Chief Financial Officer, Coastal Carolina Hospital, Hardeeville, SC, p. A554
GROTH, McGarrett, Chief of Staff, Atchison Hospital, Atchison, KS, p. A232
GROVE, Gene, M.D., Chief of Staff, Elkhart General Hospital, Elkhart, IN, p. A202
GROVE, Julia, Chief Nursing Officer, Jackson Purchase Medical Center, Mayfield, KY, p. A257
GROVER, James, Manager Data Processing, Atascadero State Hospital, Atascadero, CA, p. A51
GROVES, Ned, Executive Vice President and Administrator, Brookdale Hospital Medical Center, New York, NY, p. A432
GROVES, Tandy, Coordinator Human Resources, Bailey Medical Center, Owasso, OK, p. A506
GROW, Heidi, Director Human Resources, Aurora Sinai Medical Center, Milwaukee, WI, p. A701
GROW, Julie E, Chief Financial Officer, Hocking Valley Community Hospital, Logan, OH, p. A485
GROWSE, Michael, M.D., Clinical Director, Federal Medical Center, Lexington, KY, p. A255
GRUBB, Michael
Chief Financial Officer, Bridgepoint Hospital Capitol Hill, Washington, DC, p. A115
Chief Financial Officer, Bridgepoint Hospital National Harbor, Washington, DC, p. A115
GRUBB, Nora, Chief Financial Officer, Big Sandy Medical Center, Big Sandy, MT, p. A374
GRUBBS, John, Chief Operating Officer, Ssm Select Rehabilitation Hospital, Richmond Heights, MO, p. A367
GRUBER, Scott, M.D., Chief of Staff, John D. Dingell Veterans Affairs Medical Center, Detroit, MI, p. A310
GRUEN, Jeremy, Director Information Systems, Pike County Memorial Hospital, Louisiana, MO, p. A364
GRUHONJIC, Osman, Chief Financial Officer, Lehigh Regional Medical Center, Lehigh Acres, FL, p. A128
GRUN, Joseph, Chief Information Officer, Brookdale Hospital Medical Center, New York, NY, p. A432
GRUNDIG, Kevin, Chief Human Resource Officer, Brookdale Hospital Medical Center, New York, NY, p. A432
GRUNHOVD, April, Vice President of Patient Care Services and Chief Nursing Officer, Riverview Health, Crookston, MN, p. A330
GRUNWALD, Pat, MSN, Chief Nursing Officer, Unitypoint Health Meriter, Madison, WI, p. A698

GRUVER, Laquita, Fiscal Officer, Grand Junction Veterans Health Care System, Grand Junction, CO, p. A101
GRZYBOWSKI, John, M.D., Medical Director, Mayo Clinic Health System – Albert Lea And Austin, Albert Lea, MN, p. A327
GUACCIO, Anthony, President and Chief Executive Officer, Swedish Covenant Hospital, Chicago, IL, p. A180
GUADAGNOLI, Donald, M.D., Chief Medical Officer, Cape Cod Hospital, Hyannis, MA, p. A299
GUAJARDO, Carlos, Chief Financial Officer, South Texas Health System, Edinburg, TX, p. A601
GUAJARDO, Michael, Director Finance, Christus Spohn Hospital Alice, Alice, TX, p. A581
GUARINO, Celia, R.N., MSN, Vice President and Chief Nursing Officer, Holy Cross Hospital, Silver Spring, MD, p. A293
GUARINO, Rick, M.D., Vice President Medical Affairs, Wilson Medical Center, Wilson, NC, p. A464
GUARNESCHELLI, Philip, Interim Chief Executive Officer, Upmc Pinnacle Harrisburg, Harrisburg, PA, p. A527
GUARNI, Andrew, Chief Financial Officer, Hoag Memorial Hospital Presbyterian, Newport Beach, CA, p. A74
GUARNIERI, Candace
Chief Financial Officer, Phoebe Worth Medical Center, Sylvester, GA, p. A161
Chief Financial Officer, Southwest Georgia Regional Medical Center, Cuthbert, GA, p. A151
GUARRACINO, Joseph, Senior Vice President and Chief Financial Officer, White Plains Hospital Center, White Plains, NY, p. A448
GUARRERA, Frank, Executive Vice President and Chief Financial Officer, Motion Picture And Television Fund Hospital And Residential Services, Los Angeles, CA, p. A68
GUBERMAN, Wayne, Director Finance, Matheny Medical And Educational Center, Peapack, NJ, p. A410
GUDAHL, Shanna, Manager Human Resources, United Hospital District, Blue Earth, MN, p. A328
GUEHLSTORF, Daniel, M.D., Chief of Staff, Midwest Orthopedic Specialty Hospital, Franklin, WI, p. A695
GUELKER, Rhonda, Senior Director Finance, Rolling Plains Memorial Hospital, Sweetwater, TX, p. A639
GUERIN, Stephanie, Chief Nursing Officer, Encompass Health Rehabilitation Hospital Of Round Rock, Round Rock, TX, p. A632
GUERRERO, Bonnie, Director Human Resources, Valley View Medical Center, Fort Mohave, AZ, p. A29
GUERRERO, Kerrie, R.N., MSN, Vice President and Chief Nursing Officer, Houston Methodist The Woodlands Hospital, The Woodlands, TX, p. A641
GUERRERO, Marisa, Director Human Resources, Laredo Specialty Hospital, Laredo, TX, p. A620
GUERRIERO, John A., Chief of Staff, Berwick Hospital Center, Berwick, PA, p. A520
GUERRIERO, Marianne, Nurse Executive, Christian Health Care Center, Wyckoff, NJ, p. A415
GUESMAN, Kim, R.N., Chief Nursing Officer, Beaumont Hospital – Farmington Hills, Farmington Hills, MI, p. A311
GUEST, William, M.D., Senior Vice President and Chief Medical Officer, Tift Regional Medical Center, Tifton, GA, p. A162
GUEVARA, Al, Jr, President, Chi St. Luke'S Health Brazosport, Lake Jackson, TX, p. A619
GUFFEY, Jay, Chief Executive Officer, Mercy Rehabilitation Hospital Springfield, Springfield, MO, p. A372
GUGEL, Paul, Manager Information Technology, Marlette Regional Hospital, Marlette, MI, p. A317
GUGLIELMI, Diane, Vice President, Human Resources, Berger Health System, Circleville, OH, p. A477
GUGLIELMO, Elaine, Vice President Human Resources and Organizational Development, Stamford Hospital, Stamford, CT, p. A111
GUIDO–ALLEN, Debra, Vice President and Chief Nursing Officer, Beaumont Hospital – Troy, Troy, MI, p. A324
GUIDRY, Charles W, Chief Operating Officer, Abbeville General Hospital, Abbeville, LA, p. A262
GUIDRY, Linda, Human Resources Generalist, Abrom Kaplan Memorial Hospital, Kaplan, LA, p. A270
GUIDRY, Lloyd, Chief Operating Officer, Lady Of The Sea General Hospital, Cut Off, LA, p. A266
GUIDRY, Ruth, Chief Nursing Officer, Lafayette Surgical Specialty Hospital, Lafayette, LA, p. A271
GUIDRY, Stephanie A., Chief Executive Officer, Franklin Foundation Hospital, Franklin, LA, p. A267
GUIDRY, Trisha, Administrator, Baton Rouge Rehabilitation Hospital, Baton Rouge, LA, p. A263
GUIGNIER, Liz, Vice President Human Resources, Eisenhower Medical Center, Rancho Mirage, CA, p. A79
GUILFOIL, Thomas, Director Human Resources, Baystate Wing Hospital, Palmer, MA, p. A302
GUILLORY, Larry, Chief Human Resources Officer, Baylor Scott & White Emergency Hospital–Aubrey, Aubrey, TX, p. A584
GUILLORY, Nicholas D., Administrator, Oceans Behavioral Hospital Of Lake Charles, Lake Charles, LA, p. A272
GUILLORY, Pamela
Chief Nursing Officer, Methodist Hospital South, Jourdanton, TX, p. A616
Interim Chief Executive Officer, Methodist Hospital South, Jourdanton, TX, p. A616
GUIMARAES, Antonio, M.D., Clinical Director, U. S. Public Health Service Indian Hospital, Cass Lake, MN, p. A330
GUIMENTO, Robert, President, Brookdale Hospital Medical Center, New York, NY, p. A432
GUINA, Michelle, Manager Human Resources, Sutter Surgical Hospital – North Valley, Yuba City, CA, p. A95
GUINANE, Gerard, Vice President Human Resources, Swedishamerican – A Division Of Uw Health, Rockford, IL, p. A195
GUIRL, Nadine T, Senior Vice President Human Resources, Waukesha Memorial Hospital, Waukesha, WI, p. A707
GUISE, Linda, Senior Human Resource Consultant, Indiana University Health Jay Hospital, Portland, IN, p. A213
GULARTE, Steven, Chief Executive Officer, Bayside Community Hospital, Anahuac, TX, p. A583
GULL, Joann Bernadette, Chief Nursing Officer, Brookdale Hospital Medical Center, New York, NY, p. A432
GULRICH, Erica, Chief Executive Officer, Northwest Medical Center, Margate, FL, p. A129
GUM, Jessica, Controller, Encompass Health Rehabilitation Hospital Of Parkersburg, Parkersburg, WV, p. A688
GUMATO, Sixta, M.D., Chief Medical Officer, Crane Memorial Hospital, Crane, TX, p. A595
GUMBEL, Wendy, Director of Human Resources, Healthsouth Deaconess Rehabilitation Hospital, Evansville, IN, p. A203
GUMBS, Milton A, M.D., Vice President and Medical Director, Brookdale Hospital Medical Center, New York, NY, p. A432
GUMMADI, Subhaker, M.D., Chief Medical Staff, Promise Hospital Baton Rouge – Main Campus, Baton Rouge, LA, p. A264
GUMP, Linda A., Chief Clinical Services Officer, Aurora Medical Center Kenosha, Kenosha, WI, p. A697
GUNABALAN, Ryan, Chief Executive Officer, Behavioral Center Of Michigan, Warren, MI, p. A324
GUNASEKARAN, Suresh, Chief Executive Officer, University Of Iowa Hospitals And Clinics, Iowa City, IA, p. A224
GUNDLAPALLI, Madhu, M.D., Clinical Director, Utah State Hospital, Provo, UT, p. A650
GUNDT, Kristin, Chief Nursing Officer, Community Hospital, Grand Junction, CO, p. A101
GUNKEL, Jeff, Chief Information Officer, Jamestown Regional Medical Center, Jamestown, ND, p. A468
GUNN, Deborah, Chief Information Officer, W. G. (Bill) Heffner Veterans Affairs Medical Center, Salisbury, NC, p. A461
GUNNELL, Nancy
Chief Human Resource Officer, West Suburban Medical Center, Oak Park, IL, p. A192
Chief Human Resource Officer, Westlake Hospital, Melrose Park, IL, p. A189
GUNNERSEN, Nils, Administrator, Bertrand Chaffee Hospital, Springville, NY, p. A444
GUNTLOW, Ann Marie, Chief Nursing Officer, Ellenville Regional Hospital, Ellenville, NY, p. A427
GUNUKULA, Srinivas, M.D., Chief of Staff, Dallas Regional Medical Center, Mesquite, TX, p. A624
GUOYAVATIN, Kora
Chief Financial Officer, Garden Grove Hospital And Medical Center, Garden Grove, CA, p. A60
Chief Financial Officer, West Anaheim Medical Center, Anaheim, CA, p. A50
GUPTA, Anil, M.D., Chief of Staff, Kindred Hospital–Baldwin Park, Baldwin Park, CA, p. A51
GUPTA, Arun, M.D., Vice President Medical Affairs, South Pointe Hospital, Warrensville Heights, OH, p. A493
GUPTA, Ashok K, M.D., Chief of Staff, Eaton Rapids Medical Center, Eaton Rapids, MI, p. A311
GUPTA, John, Executive Vice President and Chief Operating Officer, Brookdale Hospital Medical Center, New York, NY, p. A432
GUPTA, Saurabh, Chief Medical Officer, Rockford Center, Newark, DE, p. A113
GUPTA, Vijay D, M.D., President and Chief Executive Officer, Franciscan Healthcare Munster, Munster, IN, p. A212
GURR, Lory, Chief Human Resources Division, Evans U. S. Army Community Hospital, Fort Carson, CO, p. A100
GURRAD, Trece, Vice President Patient Care Services, Columbia Memorial Hospital, Astoria, OR, p. A511
GURROLA, Jose, Administrator, New Mexico Rehabilitation Center, Roswell, NM, p. A420
GURULE, Eric, Chief Information Officer, Turquoise Lodge Hospital, Albuquerque, NM, p. A417
GURUNG, Anju, M.D., Chief Medical Officer, Mahnomen Health Center, Mahnomen, MN, p. A334
GUSHEE, Dean, M.D., Medical Director, Mason General Hospital And Family Of Clinics, Shelton, WA, p. A679
GUSHO, Michael, Chief Financial Officer, St. Joseph Mercy Oakland, Pontiac, MI, p. A320
GUSMANO, Jane
Interim Vice President Finance, Memorial Hospital East, Shiloh, IL, p. A196
Interim Vice President Finance, Memorial Hospital, Belleville, IL, p. A174
GUSTAFSON, Brian, Chief Financial Officer, Veterans Affairs Montana Health Care System, Fort Harrison, MT, p. A376
GUSTAFSON, Connie, Director of Nursing, Jacobson Memorial Hospital Care Center, Elgin, ND, p. A466
GUSTAFSON, Michael, President, Umass Memorial Medical Center, Worcester, MA, p. A305
GUSTER, Cherie M, R.N., MSN, Senior Vice President and Chief Nursing Officer, Cleveland Clinic Akron General, Akron, OH, p. A471
GUSTILO, Maria, M.D., Medical Director, Osawatomie State Hospital At Adair Acute Care, Osawatomie, KS, p. A242
GUSTIN, Michael, Information Technology, John J. Pershing Veterans Affairs Medical Center, Poplar Bluff, MO, p. A367
GUTHMILLER, Martin W., Chief Executive Officer, Orange City Area Health System, Orange City, IA, p. A227
GUTHRIE, Pamela A, Chief Human Resources Officer, Hillcrest Hospital Pryor, Pryor, OK, p. A506
GUTHRIE, Todd, Chief of Staff, Mercy Medical Center Mount Shasta, Mount Shasta, CA, p. A73
GUTIERREZ, Lori, Chief Financial Officer, Rochelle Community Hospital, Rochelle, IL, p. A194
GUTIERREZ, Michelle
Executive Director Human Resources, Orange County, Memorialcare, Saddleback Memorial Medical Center, Laguna Hills, CA, p. A63
Executive Director Human Resources, Memorialcare, Orange Coast Memorial Medical Center, Fountain Valley, CA, p. A58
GUTIERREZ, Noe, Chief Financial Officer, Lake Granbury Medical Center, Granbury, TX, p. A608
GUTIERREZ, Santiago, M.D., Chief Medical Officer, Doctors Hospital Of Laredo, Laredo, TX, p. A619
GUTIERREZ, Vickie, Director of Patient Care, Dr. Dan C. Trigg Memorial Hospital, Tucumcari, NM, p. A421
GUTIERREZ, Victor A, M.D., Medical Director, Allegiance Behavioral Health Center Of Plainview, Plainview, TX, p. A629
GUTJAHR, Susan, Reimbursement Specialist, Sparta Community Hospital, Sparta, IL, p. A196
GUTMAN, Luisa, Senior Vice President and Chief Operating Officer, Holy Cross Hospital, Fort Lauderdale, FL, p. A122
GUTNICK, Michael, Executive Vice President and Chief Financial Officer, Brookdale Hospital Medical Center, New York, NY, p. A432
GUTOW, Andrew, M.D., Medical Director, Menlo Park Surgical Hospital, Menlo Park, CA, p. A71
GUTOWSKI, Jennifer S., Director, Veterans Affairs Pacific Islands Health Care System, Honolulu, HI, p. A165
GUTSCH, Michael, Chief Executive Officer and Administrator, Cumberland Healthcare, Cumberland, WI, p. A693
GUTSCHENRITTER, John, Chief Financial Officer, Wilson Medical Center, Neodesha, KS, p. A241
GUTTENBERG, Ellen, Chief Operating Officer, Frances Mahon Deaconess Hospital, Glasgow, MT, p. A376
GUTTIN, Enrique, M.D., FACS, Chief of Staff, Wilmington Veterans Affairs Medical Center, Wilmington, DE, p. A114
GUTTMACHER, Laurence, M.D., Clinical Director, Rochester Psychiatric Center, Rochester, NY, p. A442
GUTZEIT, Michael, M.D., Chief Medical Officer, Children'S Hospital Of Wisconsin, Milwaukee, WI, p. A701
GUY, Glenda, Director, Health Information Management, Ten Broeck Tennessee Treatment Facility, Cookeville, TN, p. A568
GUY, Kimberly, President, St. Joseph'S Hospital, Tampa, FL, p. A142
GUYETTE, William, M.D., President Medical Staff, Livingston Hospital And Healthcare Services, Salem, KY, p. A260
GUZ, Andrew, Chief Executive Officer, Lakewood Ranch Medical Center, Bradenton, FL, p. A118
GUZAK, Jason, Chief Financial Officer, Rock Springs, Georgetown, TX, p. A607
GUZMAN, Claudia V., Chief Executive Officer and Managing Director, Hospital San Pablo, Bayamon, PR, p. A715
GUZMAN, David, Chief Financial Officer, Brookdale Hospital Medical Center, New York, NY, p. A432
GUZMAN, Lisa, Human Resource Vice President, Redlands Community Hospital, Redlands, CA, p. A80
GWATKIN, Elizabeth, Vice President Human Resources, Northeastern Vermont Regional Hospital, Saint Johnsbury, VT, p. A655
GWYN, Andrea, Chief Operating Officer, Terre Haute Regional Hospital, Terre Haute, IN, p. A215

GWYN, Brian
President and Chief Executive Officer, Atrium Health Cleveland, Shelby, NC, p. A462
President and Chief Executive Officer, Atrium Health Kings Mountain, Kings Mountain, NC, p. A457
President Chief Operating Officer, Atrium Health Cleveland, Shelby, NC, p. A462

GYIMAH, Ed, Chief Financial Officer, Howard University Hospital, Washington, DC, p. A115

GYNTHER, Tracy, R.N., Vice President and Chief Nursing Officer, Wellstar West Georgia Medical Center, Lagrange, GA, p. A155

H

HAACK, Sally, Vice President and Director of Human Resources, St. Francis Regional Medical Center, Shakopee, MN, p. A340

HAACK, Wanda, MSN, R.N., Chief Nursing Officer, Genesis Medical Center, Dewitt, De Witt, IA, p. A220

HAAG, Adam, Manager Information Technology, Coffey County Hospital, Burlington, KS, p. A233

HAAGENSON, Deb, R.N., Vice President of Patient Care, Chi St. Joseph'S Health, Park Rapids, MN, p. A337

HAAK, Karen S., R.N., MSN, Chief Nursing Officer, Good Samaritan Hospital, Vincennes, IN, p. A216

HAAS, Christine, Chief Information Officer, Geisinger Jersey Shore Hospital, Jersey Shore, PA, p. A528

HAAS, Robert, M.D., Chief Medical Officer, Liberty Hospital, Liberty, MO, p. A364

HAAS, Steven J
Chief Financial Officer, Health Alliance Hospital – Broadway Campus, Kingston, NY, p. A430
Chief Financial Officer, Health Alliance Hospital – Mary'S Avenue Campus, Kingston, NY, p. A430

HAAS, Susan, Director Human Resources, Aurora Behavioral Healthcare San Diego, San Diego, CA, p. A83

HAASE, Patricia, Director Information Technology and Communications, Marian Regional Medical Center, Santa Maria, CA, p. A89

HAASE, Ronald
Chief Human Resources Officer, Northern Arizona Healthcare, Flagstaff Medical Center, Flagstaff, AZ, p. A29
Chief Human Resources Officer, Northern Arizona Healthcare, Verde Valley Medical Center, Cottonwood, AZ, p. A29

HAASKEN, Timothy W, Chief Financial Officer, Lewisgale Hospital Montgomery, Blacksburg, VA, p. A656

HABIB, Noel, M.D., Chief Medical Officer, Huhukam Memorial Hospital, Sacaton, AZ, p. A35

HABIS, Saba, M.D., Chief Medical Officer, Freeman Health System, Joplin, MO, p. A362

HABOWSKI, Michael J., President and Chief Executive Officer, Ashtabula County Medical Center, Ashtabula, OH, p. A472

HACHEY, Michael
Senior Vice President and Chief Financial Officer, Emerson Hospital, Concord, MA, p. A298
Senior Vice President and Chief Financial Officer, Northern Light Mercy Hospital, Portland, ME, p. A284

HACKBARTH, John, CPA, Senior Vice President Finance and Chief Financial Officer, Owensboro Health Regional Hospital, Owensboro, KY, p. A258

HACKER, Daniel, Human Resource Business Partner, Eastern State Hospital, Lexington, KY, p. A255

HACKER, Leanne, Chief Financial Officer, Eastern New Mexico Medical Center, Roswell, NM, p. A420

HACKER, Mary Dee, R.N., Vice President, Patient Care Services and Chief Nursing Officer, Children'S Hospital Los Angeles, Los Angeles, CA, p. A66

HACKER, Phil, Chief Financial Officer, Lane Regional Medical Center, Zachary, LA, p. A280

HACKER, Phillip
Chief Financial Officer, Stone County Medical Center, Mountain View, AR, p. A46
Chief Financial Officer, White River Medical Center, Batesville, AR, p. A39

HACKETT, Leslie, Chief Nursing Officer, Covenant Hospital Plainview, Plainview, TX, p. A629

HACKSTEDDE, Anita, President and Chief Executive Officer, Salem Regional Medical Center, Salem, OH, p. A490

HACKSTEDDE, Anita, M.D., Vice President Medical Affairs, Salem Regional Medical Center, Salem, OH, p. A490

HADAWAY, Krystal, Director Human Resources, Healthsource Saginaw, Inc., Saginaw, MI, p. A321

HADDAD, Housam, M.D., Chief of Staff, Casey County Hospital, Liberty, KY, p. A255

HADDADIN, Maen, M.D., President Medical Staff, Chi Health Mercy Corning, Corning, IA, p. A219

HADDIX, Parker, Chief Executive Officer, William R. Sharpe, Jr. Hospital, Weston, WV, p. A690

HADDOX, Melissa, Controller, Encompass Health Rehabilitation Hospital Of Cypress, Houston, TX, p. A611

HADLEY, Gerard, Vice President Finance for Brigham & Women's Faulkner Hospital and Vice President Finance and Controller, Brigham And Women'S Faulkner Hospital, Boston, MA, p. A295

HADLEY, H Roger, M.D., Vice President, Medical Affairs, Loma Linda University Medical Center, Loma Linda, CA, p. A64

HADLEY, Steven N, Chief Financial Officer, Kansas Medical Center, Andover, KS, p. A232

HADLEY, Susan, MS, Chief Nursing Officer, Dickinson County Healthcare System, Iron Mountain, MI, p. A314

HADZEGA, Angela, Chief Financial Officer, Upmc Kane, Kane, PA, p. A528

HAEFELE, John, M.D., Chief Medical Officer, Community Memorial Healthcare, Marysville, KS, p. A240

HAEHN, Debra, Chief Financial Officer, Clay County Memorial Hospital, Henrietta, TX, p. A610

HAENELT, Michael, Chief Information Management, Weed Army Community Hospital, Fort Irwin, CA, p. A58

HAESEMEYER, Allan, M.D., Chief of Staff, Indianhead Medical Center, Shell Lake, WI, p. A705

HAESEMEYER, Christa, Chief Nursing Officer, Lincoln County Hospital, Lincoln, KS, p. A240

HAFEMAN, Paula
Chief Nursing Officer, Hshs St. Clare Memorial Hospital, Oconto Falls, WI, p. A703
Chief Nursing Officer, Hshs St. Mary'S Hospital Medical Center, Green Bay, WI, p. A696

HAFFEY, Robert
President and Chief Operating Officer, Kent County Memorial Hospital, Warwick, RI, p. A548
President, Delaware County Memorial Hospital, Drexel Hill, PA, p. A524

HAFIZ, Irfan, Vice President Medical Affairs, Northwestern Medicine Mchenry, Mchenry, IL, p. A189

HAGAN, Donald E, Chief Financial Officer, Detar Healthcare System, Victoria, TX, p. A643

HAGAN, Eric, Executive Vice President and Administrator, Medical Center At Scottsville, Scottsville, KY, p. A260

HAGAN, Frank, Senior Vice President Finance, Saint Joseph'S Medical Center, Yonkers, NY, p. A448

HAGEDORN, Tammy, Chief Human Resource Officer, Genesis Medical Center–Aledo, Aledo, IL, p. A173

HAGEL, Bonnie, Chief Financial Officer, Logan County Hospital, Oakley, KS, p. A242

HAGELBERG, Robbi, Vice President Nursing Services and Chief Nursing Officer, Lakeview Hospital, Stillwater, MN, p. A341

HAGELTHORN, Diane, Human Resources Generalist, Modoc Medical Center, Alturas, CA, p. A50

HAGEN, Lynne D, Human Resources Officer, Avera Mckennan Hospital And University Health Center, Sioux Falls, SD, p. A563

HAGEN, Mary, R.N., MSN, VP and Chief Nursing Officer, Unitypoint Health – Allen Hospital, Waterloo, IA, p. A231

HAGEN, Paulette, Human Resources and Administrative Services Director, Centracare Health–Paynesville, Paynesville, MN, p. A337

HAGENS, Paul, Vice President Human Resources, Doctors Community Hospital, Lanham, MD, p. A291

HAGER, Robin, Chief Operating Officer, Complex Care Hospital At Tenaya, Las Vegas, NV, p. A394

HAGERSTROM, Paige A, System Director of Talent Management, St. Joseph Hospital, Bangor, ME, p. A281

HAGERTY, Cindy, Assistant Chief Nurse Officer and Administrator of Operations, Ascension Via Christi Rehabilitation Hospital, Wichita, KS, p. A247

HAGGARD, Tommy, Chief Executive Officer, Bluegrass Community Hospital, Versailles, KY, p. A261

HAGGERTY, Cheryl Kay, Chief Nursing Officer, Assistant Chief Executive Officer, Mercyone New Hampton Medical Center, New Hampton, IA, p. A227

HAGLER, Dan, M.D., Vice President and Chief Medical Officer, Atrium Health Cabarrus, Concord, NC, p. A452

HAGLUND, Nicole, Vice President of Nursing Services, Providence Medical Center, Wayne, NE, p. A392

HAGOOD, Teena, Chief Nursing Officer, Kimble Hospital, Junction, TX, p. A617

HAGWELL, Mick, Chief Financial Officer, Aspirus Ironwood Hospitals & Clinics, Inc., Ironwood, MI, p. A315

HAGY, Kelly, Director Human Resources, Cumberland Hall Hospital, Hopkinsville, KY, p. A253

HAGY, Michelle, Senior Vice President and Chief Financial Officer, Pikeville Medical Center, Pikeville, KY, p. A259

HAHEY, Joanne A
Senior Vice President and Chief Financial Officer, University Of Maryland Shore Medical Center At Dorchester, Cambridge, MD, p. A289
Senior Vice President and Chief Financial Officer, University Of Maryland Shore Medical Center At Easton, Easton, MD, p. A290
Vice President Finance and Chief Financial Officer, University Of Maryland Shore Medical Center At Chestertown, Chestertown, MD, p. A289

HAHN, Donna S, R.N., Vice President Acute Care and Chief Nurse Executive, Sentara Rmh Medical Center, Harrisonburg, VA, p. A660

HAHN, Jen, Finance Manager, Uh Portage Medical Center, Ravenna, OH, p. A490

HAHN, Joseph, M.D., Chief of Staff, Cleveland Clinic, Cleveland, OH, p. A477

HAHN, Kurt, M.D., Acting Clinical Director, Elmira Psychiatric Center, Elmira, NY, p. A427

HAHN, Lisa, R.N., Chief Nursing Officer, Ahmc Anaheim Regional Medical Center, Anaheim, CA, p. A50

HAHN, Lori, Vice President Nursing Services, Chi St. Alexius Health – Williston Medical Center, Williston, ND, p. A470

HAHN, Peter, President and Chief Executive Officer, Metro Health – University Of Michigan Health, Wyoming, MI, p. A325

HAHN, Stephen, Deputy to the President and Chief Operating Officer, University Of Texas M.D. Anderson Cancer Center, Houston, TX, p. A614

HAHS, Seth, Chief of Staff, Salem Township Hospital, Salem, IL, p. A195

HAIGH, Sara, Associate Director, Durham Veterans Affairs Medical Center, Durham, NC, p. A453

HAIGLER, Tonda V., Chief Operating Officer, Merit Health Biloxi, Biloxi, MS, p. A344

HAIL, Brian, Chief Executive Officer, Cherokee Nation W.W. Hastings Indian Hospital, Tahlequah, OK, p. A508

HAIN, Jim, Chief Operating Officer, Lexington Regional Health Center, Lexington, NE, p. A386

HAINES, Christopher, D.O., Vice President and Chief Medical Officer, Children'S Specialized Hospital, New Brunswick, NJ, p. A409

HAIR, Denise J., Vice President of Nursing Services and Chief Nursing Officer, Dameron Hospital, Stockton, CA, p. A90

HAIR, Kelly, Director Information Systems and Data Analytics, Abbeville General Hospital, Abbeville, LA, p. A262

HAIR, Troy, Chief Financial Officer, Abbeville General Hospital, Abbeville, LA, p. A262

HAIRGROVE, Heath, Chief Executive Officer, Dequincy Memorial Hospital, Dequincy, LA, p. A267

HAISLIP, Heidi, M.D., Chief of Staff, Alliancehealth Madill, Madill, OK, p. A501

HAIZLIP, Thomas M, M.D., Chief of Staff, Charles A. Cannon Memorial Hospital, Newland, NC, p. A459

HAJEK, Julie, Director Human Resources, St. David'S Medical Center, Austin, TX, p. A586

HAKENSON, Diana, Director of Patient Care Services, Newport Bay Hospital, Newport Beach, CA, p. A74

HALAMA, George, Vice President Finance, Mcpherson Hospital, Mcpherson, KS, p. A240

HALAMKA, John, M.D., Chief Information Officer, Beth Israel Deaconess Medical Center, Boston, MA, p. A294

HALDEMAN, Larry, M.D., Executive Vice President and Chief Medical Officer, Wellstar Windy Hill Hospital, Marietta, GA, p. A157

HALDER, Ranjay, M.D., Chief Medical Director, Centerstone Hospital, Bradenton, FL, p. A118

HALE, Becky, Director Human Resources, Hill Regional Hospital, Hillsboro, TX, p. A610

HALE, Byron, Chief Financial Officer, Ut Health Tyler, Tyler, TX, p. A642

HALE, Danny, Director Human Resources, Southwestern Medical Center, Lawton, OK, p. A501

HALE, Donna, Director of Nursing, Baptist Memorial Rehabilitation Hospital, Germantown, TN, p. A570

HALE, Ken, Executive Director of Operations, Mercy Allen Hospital, Oberlin, OH, p. A489

HALE, Kirsten
Coordinator Health Information Services, University Hospitals Conneaut Medical Center, Conneaut, OH, p. A480
Coordinator Health Information Systems and Coding, University Hospitals Geneva Medical Center, Geneva, OH, p. A484

HALE, Margie, Chief Executive Officer, Baraga County Memorial Hospital, L'Anse, MI, p. A316

HALE, Renae, Chief Nursing Officer, Lincoln Prairie Behavioral Health Center, Springfield, IL, p. A196

HALE, Ron, Superintendent, Colorado Mental Health Institute At Pueblo, Pueblo, CO, p. A104

HALE, Steven D., Chief Executive Officer, Weiser Memorial Hospital, Weiser, ID, p. A172
HALE, Tonia, Chief Nursing Officer, Tennova Newport Medical Center, Newport, TN, p. A578
HALEN, Catherine, Vice President Human Resources, Beebe Healthcare, Lewes, DE, p. A113
HALES, Brent, Chief Financial Officer, Uintah Basin Medical Center, Roosevelt, UT, p. A651
HALES, Joe, Chief Information Officer, Primary Children'S Hospital, Salt Lake City, UT, p. A652
HALEY, DeLeigh, Chief Executive Officer, Ut Health Jacksonville, Jacksonville, TX, p. A616
HALEY, James, M.D., Senior Vice President and Chief Medical Officer, Unity Hospital, Rochester, NY, p. A443
HALEY, Leon L., Jr, Chief Executive Officer, Uf Health Jacksonville, Jacksonville, FL, p. A126
HALEY, Thomas
Division Assistant Vice President Business Relationship Management, Chi Health Creighton University Medical Center – Bergan Mercy, Omaha, NE, p. A388
Information Technology Services Site Director, Chi Health Mercy Council Bluffs, Council Bluffs, IA, p. A220
Information Technology Systems Site Director, Chi Health Lakeside, Omaha, NE, p. A389
Information Technology Systems Site Director, Chi Health Midlands, Papillion, NE, p. A390
HALFEN, John, M.D., Medical Director, Lakewood Health System, Staples, MN, p. A341
HALFORD, Dianne, Chief Financial Officer, Saint Clare'S Denville Hospital, Denville, NJ, p. A404
HALIMI, Hamid, M.D., Medical Director, Select Specialty Hospital–Ann Arbor, Ypsilanti, MI, p. A325
HALL, Becky, R.N., Director Nursing, Rumford Hospital, Rumford, ME, p. A285
HALL, Catherine, Manager Human Resources, Jefferson Hospital, Louisville, GA, p. A156
HALL, Charles
Interim Chief Executive Officer, Alliancehealth Durant, Durant, OK, p. A499
Interim Chief Executive Officer, Alliancehealth Madill, Madill, OK, p. A501
HALL, Dan, R.N., Chief Operating Officer, St. John Owasso, Owasso, OK, p. A506
HALL, David
Chief Information Officer, Southeastern Kentucky Medical Center, Pineville, KY, p. A259
Senior Vice President and Chief Operating Officer, University Of Tennessee Medical Center, Knoxville, TN, p. A572
HALL, Gary, Vice President of Information Technology, Estes Park Medical Center, Estes Park, CO, p. A100
HALL, Geoffrey, Chief Executive Officer, Edwin Shaw Rehab, Cuyahoga Falls, OH, p. A480
HALL, George, M.D.
Vice President Medical Affairs, St. Elizabeth Florence, Florence, KY, p. A252
Vice President Medical Affairs, St. Elizabeth Fort Thomas, Fort Thomas, KY, p. A252
HALL, James, M.D., Chief Medical Officer, Pampa Regional Medical Center, Pampa, TX, p. A627
HALL, Jeanne, Director Information Systems, Shriners Hospitals For Children–St. Louis, Saint Louis, MO, p. A370
HALL, Jeffrey, DPM, Chief Medical Officer, St. Croix Regional Medical Center, St Croix Falls, WI, p. A706
HALL, Jeremy, Assistant Administrator and Chief Financial Officer, Middlesboro Arh Hospital, Middlesboro, KY, p. A258
HALL, Jim, Acting Chief Information Officer, Central Arkansas Veterans Healthcare System, Little Rock, AR, p. A45
HALL, Kathy J., Administrator, St. Vincent Warrick, Boonville, IN, p. A200
HALL, Kenneth C, R.N., Chief Nursing Officer, Saint Joseph Health System, Mishawaka, IN, p. A211
HALL, Kent, M.D., Vice President and Chief Medical Officer, The University Of Vermont Health Network–Champlain Valley Physicians Hospital, Plattsburgh, NY, p. A441
HALL, Margaret, M.D., Chief Medical Officer, Lakeside Women'S Hospital, Oklahoma City, OK, p. A504
HALL, Mary A, Chief Medical Staff, Mcdowell Arh Hospital, Mcdowell, KY, p. A258
HALL, Melissa
Chief Executive Officer, Munising Memorial Hospital, Munising, MI, p. A318
Chief Nursing Officer, Coffey County Hospital, Burlington, KS, p. A233
HALL, Morrison, Chief Financial Officer, Pender Memorial Hospital, Burgaw, NC, p. A450
HALL, Patricia, Director, John J. Pershing Veterans Affairs Medical Center, Poplar Bluff, MO, p. A367
HALL, Richard, Chief Executive Officer, Samuel Simmonds Memorial Hospital, Barrow, AK, p. A25
HALL, Roger L.
President, Sacred Heart Hospital On The Emerald Coast, Miramar Beach, FL, p. A132
President, Sacred Heart Hospital On The Gulf, Port St Joe, FL, p. A137
HALL, Ryan, Vice President, Providence Hospital, Columbia, SC, p. A551
HALL, Sally, Manager Human Resources, South Texas Spine And Surgical Hospital, San Antonio, TX, p. A635
HALL, Stephanie, M.D.
Chief Medical Officer, Keck Hospital Of Usc, Los Angeles, CA, p. A67
Chief Medical Officer, Usc Verdugo Hills Hospital, Glendale, CA, p. A60
Medical Director, Usc Norris Comprehensive Cancer Center, Los Angeles, CA, p. A69
HALL, Steve, Chief Financial Officer, Unitypoint Health–Pekin Hospital, Pekin, IL, p. A193
HALL, Terry E., Chief of Staff, Harrison County Community Hospital, Bethany, MO, p. A356
HALL, Trena F., Interim Chief Executive Officer, Highlands Arh Regional Medical Center, Prestonsburg, KY, p. A259
HALL, Trudy
Vice President Medical Affairs and Interim Chief Executive Officer, University Of Maryland Capital Region Health Prince George'S Hospital Center, Cheverly, MD, p. A289
Vice President, Medical Affairs, University Of Maryland Capital Region Health Prince George'S Hospital Center, Cheverly, MD, p. A289
HALL, Veronica, Interim President and Chief Executive Officer, Henry Ford Hospital, Detroit, MI, p. A310
HALL, Wyatt, M.D., Chief Medical Officer, Longmont United Hospital, Longmont, CO, p. A103
HALL–OLSEN, Kathy, Administrator, Weisman Children'S Rehabilitation Hospital, Marlton, NJ, p. A408
HALLAL, Joseph, M.D., Chief Medical Officer, Inova Fairfax Hospital, Falls Church, VA, p. A659
HALLATT, Jennifer
Chief Operating Officer, Mercyhealth Hospital And Medical Center – Harvard, Harvard, IL, p. A184
Vice President, Mercyhealth Hospital And Medical Center – Walworth, Lake Geneva, WI, p. A698
HALLEY, Andrea, Vice President of Non–Clinical Operations/ Director Human Resources, Hopedale Medical Complex, Hopedale, IL, p. A186
HALLEY, Lisa B, Vice President Human Resources, Holzer Medical Center, Gallipolis, OH, p. A483
HALLIDAY, Lisa, Director Accounting Services, Taylor Regional Hospital, Hawkinsville, GA, p. A154
HALLIWILL, Donald B
Chief Financial Officer, Carilion Franklin Memorial Hospital, Rocky Mount, VA, p. A667
Executive Vice President and Chief Financial Officer, Carilion Roanoke Memorial Hospital, Roanoke, VA, p. A667
HALLMARK, Todd
Chief Executive Officer, Choctaw Nation Health Care Center, Talihina, OK, p. A508
Chief Operating Officer, Choctaw Nation Health Care Center, Talihina, OK, p. A508
HALLOCK, Mirya, Administrator, Webster County Community Hospital, Red Cloud, NE, p. A391
HALLORAN, Abigail, Chief Executive Officer, Haven Behavioral Hospital Of Philadelphia, Philadelphia, PA, p. A534
HALLORAN, Teresa, Ph.D., R.N.
Vice President Nursing Services, Memorial Hospital East, Shiloh, IL, p. A196
Vice President Nursing Services, Memorial Hospital, Belleville, IL, p. A174
HALPIN, Kim, Director Human Resources, Arms Acres, Carmel, NY, p. A425
HALSAN, Carole, Chief Executive Officer, Willapa Harbor Hospital, South Bend, WA, p. A679
HALSELL, David, Senior Vice President and Chief Financial Officer, Lake Regional Health System, Osage Beach, MO, p. A366
HALSTEAD, Lisa, Chief Nursing Officer, Integris Miami Hospital, Miami, OK, p. A502
HALSTEAD, Rhonda, President, Penn Highlands Clearfield, Clearfield, PA, p. A522
HALTER, Bev, Director Human Resources and Payroll, Liberty Medical Center, Chester, MT, p. A375
HALTER, Kevin, Chief Executive Officer, Our Lady Of Bellefonte Hospital, Ashland, KY, p. A249
HALTOM, Shannon, Vice President, Patient Care Services, Chi St. Luke'S Health Brazosport, Lake Jackson, TX, p. A619
HALVORSEN, Lisa, Chief Nurse Executive, Providence Milwaukie Hospital, Milwaukie, OR, p. A515
HALVORSON, Marla, Director Human Resources, St. Luke'S Hospital, Duluth, MN, p. A331
HAM, Michael, Chief Executive Officer, Park Royal Hospital, Fort Myers, FL, p. A123
HAMAM, Hisham, M.D., Chief of Staff, Northern Cochise Community Hospital, Willcox, AZ, p. A38
HAMAN, Timothy, M.D., Vice President Medical Affairs, Christus Ochsner St. Patrick Hospital Southwest Louisiana, Lake Charles, LA, p. A272
HAMATY, Edward G., D.O., Chief Medical Officer, Acuity Specialty Hospital Of Southern New Jersey, Willingboro, NJ, p. A415
HAMB, Aaron, M.D., Chief Medical Officer, Provident Hospital Of Cook County, Chicago, IL, p. A179
HAMBLIN, Garth, Chief Financial Officer, Bear Valley Community Hospital, Big Bear Lake, CA, p. A53
HAMBLIN, James, Chief Financial Officer, White Mountain Regional Medical Center, Springerville, AZ, p. A36
HAMBLIN, Scott, M.D., President Medical Staff, White Mountain Regional Medical Center, Springerville, AZ, p. A36
HAMBRIDGE, Mark, Director Information Systems, Livingston Regional Hospital, Livingston, TN, p. A573
HAMBY, Kelley, Vice President Patient Care, Baptist Health Medical Center – North Little Rock, North Little Rock, AR, p. A46
HAMEL, Cathleen, Chief Nurse Executive, St. Rose Dominican Hospitals – Siena Campus, Henderson, NV, p. A394
HAMEL, Loren, President and Chief Executive Officer, Spectrum Health Lakeland, Saint Joseph, MI, p. A322
HAMEL, Susan, Chief Nursing Officer, St. Luke'S Hospital, Duluth, MN, p. A331
HAMILL, Dave H., President and Chief Executive Officer, Hampton Regional Medical Center, Varnville, SC, p. A558
HAMILTON, Adriana H, Chief Human Resources Officer, Hunter Holmes Mcguire Veterans Affairs Medical Center–Richmond, Richmond, VA, p. A666
HAMILTON, Aggie, Chief Human Resources, Veterans Affairs Montana Health Care System, Fort Harrison, MT, p. A376
HAMILTON, Brandy, Chief Executive Officer, Suncoast Behavioral Health Center, Bradenton, FL, p. A119
HAMILTON, Catherine, Chief Nursing Officer, Hedrick Medical Center, Chillicothe, MO, p. A358
HAMILTON, Chanda, Chief Information Officer, Clifton T. Perkins Hospital Center, Jessup, MD, p. A291
HAMILTON, Dan, Chief Operating Officer, Nor–Lea Hospital District, Lovington, NM, p. A419
HAMILTON, David, Chief Information Officer, Southwest Mississippi Regional Medical Center, Mccomb, MS, p. A350
HAMILTON, Geoff, Interim Chief Financial Officer, Arbor Health, Morton Hospital, Morton, WA, p. A675
HAMILTON, Jennifer
Chief Financial Officer, Sagewest Health Care At Riverton, Riverton, WY, p. A712
COO – Mary Bridge, Multicare Mary Bridge Children'S Hospital And Health Center, Tacoma, WA, p. A680
HAMILTON, John Shanon., Administrator, St. Vincent'S Chilton Hospital, Clanton, AL, p. A16
HAMILTON, Kevin M., M.D., Chief Medical Officer, Tristar Summit Medical Center, Hermitage, TN, p. A570
HAMILTON, Marci, Chief Nursing Officer, Orthopaedic Hospital Of Lutheran Health Network, Fort Wayne, IN, p. A204
HAMILTON, Marilyn, Director Human Resources, Promise Hospital Baton Rouge – Main Campus, Baton Rouge, LA, p. A264
HAMILTON, Matthew, Chief Executive Officer, United Medical Center, Washington, DC, p. A116
HAMILTON, Michelle, Human Resource Manager, Turning Point Hospital, Moultrie, GA, p. A158
HAMILTON, Nancy, Chief Human and Learning Resources, Veterans Affairs New Jersey Health Care System, East Orange, NJ, p. A405
HAMILTON, Patricia, Chief Executive Officer, Rebound Behavioral Health, Lancaster, SC, p. A555
HAMILTON, Patricia, R.N., Director of Nursing, Mildred Mitchell–Bateman Hospital, Huntington, WV, p. A686
HAMILTON, Peggy, Chief Financial Officer, Bayside Community Hospital, Anahuac, TX, p. A583
HAMILTON, Phil, Chief Executive Officer, Pershing Memorial Hospital, Brookfield, MO, p. A357
HAMILTON, Randal S., Chief Executive Officer, Select Specialty Hospital–Panama City, Panama City, FL, p. A136
HAMILTON, Scott, Vice President and Chief Financial Officer, Parkwest Medical Center, Knoxville, TN, p. A572
HAMILTON, Sharon, Chief Nursing Officer, Encompass Health Rehabilitation Hospital Of Panama City, Panama City, FL, p. A135
HAMILTON, Terry, President, Ascension Macomb–Oakland Hospital, Warren, MI, p. A324
HAMILTON, Tom, M.D., Chief of Staff, Decatur County General Hospital, Parsons, TN, p. A578
HAMILTON–BEYER, Maggie, Chief Financial Officer, Knoxville Hospital & Clinics, Knoxville, IA, p. A225

HAMLIN, Faye, Manager Human Resources, Julian F. Keith Alcohol And Drug Abuse Treatment Center, Black Mountain, NC, p. A450

HAMM, Jay, Chief Operating Officer, Prisma Health Richland Hospital, Columbia, SC, p. A551

HAMM, Sonja, Vice President Human and Foundation Resources, Lakes Regional Healthcare, Spirit Lake, IA, p. A230

HAMMAKER, Barry, M.D., Chief Medical Officer and Chief Clinical Officer, Vail Health, Vail, CO, p. A106

HAMMAN, Baron L., M.D., Chief Medical Officer, Texas Health Heart & Vascular Hospital Arlington, Arlington, TX, p. A584

HAMMEL, Leah, Acting Administrator, Chester Mental Health Center, Chester, IL, p. A176

HAMMER, Kristine, Director of Finance, Centracare Health–Monticello, Monticello, MN, p. A336

HAMMER, Rebecca J, Chief Financial Officer, Davis Medical Center, Elkins, WV, p. A685

HAMMERAN, Kevin R., Chief Executive Officer and Administrator, Baptist Memorial Hospital For Women, Memphis, TN, p. A574

HAMMES, Paul, Chief Executive Officer, Hugh Chatham Memorial Hospital, Elkin, NC, p. A454

HAMMETT, Doran, Chief Financial Officer, Petersburg Medical Center, Petersburg, AK, p. A27

HAMMETT, Richard A., President and Chief Executive Officer, Swedish Medical Center, Englewood, CO, p. A100

HAMMOCK, Preston W., President, Alamance Regional Medical Center, Burlington, NC, p. A450

HAMMOND, Flora, M.D., Chief Medical Affairs, Rehabilitation Hospital Of Indiana, Indianapolis, IN, p. A207

HAMMOND, Michael
  Chief Financial Officer, Lourdes Medical Center Of Burlington County, Willingboro, NJ, p. A415
  Chief Financial Officer, Our Lady Of Lourdes Medical Center, Camden, NJ, p. A404

HAMMOND, Nancy, M.D., Vice President, Chief Medical Officer, Saint Agnes Healthcare, Baltimore, MD, p. A287

HAMMOND, Patti, Chief Operating Officer, Adirondack Health, Saranac Lake, NY, p. A443

HAMMOND, Reed, Chief Operating Officer, Hca Houston Healthcare Conroe, Conroe, TX, p. A593

HAMMONDS, Janie, Human Resources Officer, Columbus Community Hospital, Columbus, TX, p. A593

HAMNER, Candy, Vice President and Chief Nursing Officer, Levindale Hebrew Hospital And Nursing, Baltimore, MD, p. A286

HAMON, Eric
  Executive Vice President and Chief Financial Officer, Driscoll Children'S Hospital, Corpus Christi, TX, p. A594
  Interim President and Chief Executive Officer, Driscoll Children'S Hospital, Corpus Christi, TX, p. A594

HAMPF, Carl, M.D., Chief Medical Officer, Saint Thomas Hospital For Spinal Surgery, Nashville, TN, p. A576

HAMPTON, Angie, Director Human Resources, Porter Regional Hospital, Valparaiso, IN, p. A215

HAMPTON, Connie, R.N., Associate Director for Patient Care Services, Carl Vinson Veterans Affairs Medical Center, Dublin, GA, p. A152

HAMPTON, Jeff, Director Information Systems, Lehigh Regional Medical Center, Lehigh Acres, FL, p. A128

HAMPTON, Mary Ann, MSN, R.N., Chief Nursing Officer, St. Luke'S Des Peres Hospital, Saint Louis, MO, p. A370

HAMRICK, Jan, Chief Financial Officer, Dodge County Hospital, Eastman, GA, p. A153

HAMSTRA, Nancy, Chief Operating Officer, University Hospital, Newark, NJ, p. A409

HAMULA, Michelle, Director of Nursing and Quality, Chan Soon–Shiong Medical Center, Windber, PA, p. A545

HANCOCK, Brian, Director, Richard L. Roudebush Veterans Affairs Medical Center, Indianapolis, IN, p. A207

HANCOCK, J Brian, M.D., Chief of Staff, Fargo Veterans Affairs Health Care System, Fargo, ND, p. A466

HANCOCK, Katherine, R.N., Executive Chief Nursing Officer, Cleveland Clinic, Cleveland, OH, p. A477

HANCOCK, Kerry, Director Human Resources, Bacon County Hospital And Health System, Alma, GA, p. A145

HANCOCK, Lori, Chief Business Officer, West Palm Beach Veterans Affairs Medical Center, West Palm Beach, FL, p. A144

HANCOCK, Melinda, Chief Financial Officer, Vcu Medical Center, Richmond, VA, p. A666

HANCOCK, Myrna, Director Financial Services, Choctaw Health Center, Philadelphia, MS, p. A352

HANCOCK, Sharon, Chief Human Resources Officer, Mccullough–Hyde Memorial Hospital/Trihealth, Oxford, OH, p. A489

HANCOCK, Todd, President and Chief Executive Officer, Christus Good Shepherd Medical Center–Marshall, Marshall, TX, p. A623

HANDEL, Daniel, M.D.
  Chief Medical Officer, Musc Health Of Medical University Of South Carolina, Charleston, SC, p. A550
  Vice President, Chief Medical Officer, Indiana University Health Bloomington Hospital, Bloomington, IN, p. A200

HANDLER, Michael, M.D., Vice President Medical Affairs and Chief Medical Officer, Ssm Health St. Joseph Hospital – Lake Saint Louis, Lake Saint Louis, MO, p. A364

HANDLEY, Charles
  Chief Financial Officer, Plaza Specialty Hospital, Houston, TX, p. A613
  Chief Financial Officer, The Hospitals Of Providence Memorial Campus, El Paso, TX, p. A602

HANDLEY, Donna
  President, The William W. Backus Hospital, Norwich, CT, p. A110
  President, Windham Hospital, Willimantic, CT, p. A112

HANDLEY, Jack, M.D., Chief Medical Officer, Evergreenhealth Monroe, Monroe, WA, p. A675

HANDLEY, Rhonda, Chief Financial Officer, Columbia Basin Hospital, Ephrata, WA, p. A673

HANDOL, Nelson, M.D., Medical Director, Laurel Oaks Behavioral Health Center, Dothan, AL, p. A17

HANDWERK, Ashley, Director, Human Resources, Medstar Union Memorial Hospital, Baltimore, MD, p. A287

HANDY, Steven P., Chief Executive Officer, Uniontown Hospital, Uniontown, PA, p. A543

HANEFELD, Darlene, Chief Human Resources Officer, Banner Churchill Community Hospital, Fallon, NV, p. A393

HANENBURG, Thomas S., Senior Vice President and Area Manager, Kaiser Permanente San Leandro Medical Center, San Leandro, CA, p. A87

HANEY, Kathryn, Controller, Encompass Health Valley Of The Sun Rehabilitation Hospital, Glendale, AZ, p. A30

HANEY, Lisa, Chief Executive Officer, St. Mary Rehabilitation Hospital, Langhorne, PA, p. A529

HANGER, Kelvin, Chief Executive Officer, Trihealth Evendale Hospital, Cincinnati, OH, p. A476

HANIGAN, Hank, Chief Executive Officer, Whitman Hospital And Medical Center, Colfax, WA, p. A672

HANIGAN, Hank, FACHE, Interim Chief Financial Officer, Whitman Hospital And Medical Center, Colfax, WA, p. A672

HANISCH, Denise, M.D., Chief of Staff, Avera St. Mary'S Hospital, Pierre, SD, p. A562

HANKINS, Brad, Chief Operating Quality Officer, Lake Chelan Community Hospital And Clinics, Chelan, WA, p. A671

HANKINS, Steven D., Chief Operating Officer, Evans U. S. Army Community Hospital, Fort Carson, CO, p. A100

HANKS, John, Director Information Systems, East Tennessee Children'S Hospital, Knoxville, TN, p. A572

HANKS, Susan, Chief Information Officer, Riverton Hospital, Riverton, UT, p. A651

HANLEY, Bob, Chief Human Resources Officer, University Of Chicago Medical Center, Chicago, IL, p. A180

HANLEY, Darlene S., President and Chief Executive Officer, St. Lawrence Rehabilitation Center, Lawrenceville, NJ, p. A407

HANLEY, Mathew, Chief Financial Officer, Osf Healthcare Saint Anthony'S Health Center, Alton, IL, p. A173

HANLEY, Patrick, D.O., Interim Vice President Medical Affairs, St. Luke'S – Gnaden Huetten Campus, Lehighton, PA, p. A530

HANLON, Jerad, Chief Operating Officer, Southside Regional Medical Center, Petersburg, VA, p. A665

HANLON, John, President and Chief Executive Officer, Little Company Of Mary Hospital And Health Care Centers, Evergreen Park, IL, p. A183

HANNA, Casey, M.D., Chief of Staff, Wagoner Community Hospital, Wagoner, OK, p. A510

HANNA, Don, Interim Chief Executive Officer, Providence Seward Medical Center, Seward, AK, p. A27

HANNA, Mitchell J.
  Chief Executive Officer, Sutter Auburn Faith Hospital, Auburn, CA, p. A51
  Chief Executive Officer, Sutter Coast Hospital, Crescent City, CA, p. A56

HANNA, Philip S., Chief Executive Officer, North Oak Regional Medical Center, Senatobia, MS, p. A354

HANNA, Robb, Executive Director Information Technology, Lexington Regional Health Center, Lexington, NE, p. A386

HANNAH, Jill, Director Human Resources, James Cancer Hospital And Solove Research Institute, Columbus, OH, p. A479

HANNAPEL, Andrew, Chief Medical Officer, Chatham Hospital, Siler City, NC, p. A462

HANNERS, Brandy, Chief Financial Officer, Sovah Health–Martinsville, Martinsville, VA, p. A662

HANNERS, Rodney B.
  Chief Executive Officer, Keck Hospital Of Usc, Los Angeles, CA, p. A67

  Chief Executive Officer, Usc Norris Comprehensive Cancer Center, Los Angeles, CA, p. A69

HANNON, Edward J., President, Chi Health Saint Francis, Grand Island, NE, p. A385

HANNON, Patricia, Chief Nursing Officer, Vaughan Regional Medical Center, Selma, AL, p. A23

HANOLD, Cindy, Chief Nursing Officer, Richland Hospital, Richland Center, WI, p. A704

HANS, Christopher, Chief Financial Officer, Riverside University Health System–Medical Center, Moreno Valley, CA, p. A73

HANSCOM, Kristine, Chief Financial Officer, Tufts Medical Center, Boston, MA, p. A296

HANSCOME, Joyce, Chief Information Officer, Doctors Community Hospital, Lanham, MD, p. A291

HANSEL, Jimmie W., Chief Executive Officer, Edwards County Medical Center, Kinsley, KS, p. A238

HANSEN, Carolyn, Chief Nursing Officer, Bingham Memorial Hospital, Blackfoot, ID, p. A167

HANSEN, Chris, Senior Vice President and Chief Information Officer, The University Of Kansas Hospital, Kansas City, KS, p. A238

HANSEN, Gayle B, R.N.
  Chief Integration Officer, Mayo Clinic Health System In Saint James, Saint James, MN, p. A339
  Chief Operating Officer, Mayo Clinic Health System In Fairmont, Fairmont, MN, p. A331

HANSEN, James, Chief Financial Officer, Summit Pacific Medical Center, Elma, WA, p. A672

HANSEN, Jay, Director Information Services, Prisma Health Oconee Memorial Hospital, Seneca, SC, p. A557

HANSEN, Karen, Vice President and Chief Operating Officer, Memorial Medical Center Of Ashland, Ashland, WI, p. A691

HANSEN, Kristy, CPA, Chief Financial Officer, Myrtue Medical Center, Harlan, IA, p. A224

HANSEN, Kyle, Corporate Director Information Systems, Riverside Medical Center, Kankakee, IL, p. A187

HANSEN, Kyle A., Chief Executive Officer, Logan Regional Hospital, Logan, UT, p. A648

HANSEN, Laurie
  Director of Administration, Johnson County Healthcare Center, Buffalo, WY, p. A710
  Vice President of Operations, Emory Johns Creek Hospital, Johns Creek, GA, p. A155

HANSEN, Linda, Director Human Resources, Bakersfield Heart Hospital, Bakersfield, CA, p. A52

HANSEN, Michael T., President and Chief Executive Officer, Columbus Community Hospital, Columbus, NE, p. A384

HANSEN, Michelle, Director, Chi Health Good Samaritan, Kearney, NE, p. A386

HANSEN, Misty, Chief Financial Officer, Banner – University Medical Center Tucson, Tucson, AZ, p. A37

HANSEN, Paul, Administrator, Maniilaq Health Center, Kotzebue, AK, p. A26

HANSEN, Steven, Director Information Technology, Healdsburg District Hospital, Healdsburg, CA, p. A61

HANSEN, Tim, Interim Chief Human Resource Officer, Denver Health, Denver, CO, p. A98

HANSERT, Benjamin K., Administrator, North Baldwin Infirmary, Bay Minette, AL, p. A14

HANSON, Brent, Chief Executive Officer, Select Specialty Hospital–Des Moines, Des Moines, IA, p. A221

HANSON, Debbie, Interim Chief Financial Officer, Dickinson County Healthcare System, Iron Mountain, MI, p. A314

HANSON, Denise, Information Technology Specialist, St. Cloud Veterans Affairs Health Care System, Saint Cloud, MN, p. A339

HANSON, Emily, M.D., President, Medical Staff, St. Joseph Memorial Hospital, Murphysboro, IL, p. A190

HANSON, Gregory S., Chief Executive Officer, Clark Fork Valley Hospital, Plains, MT, p. A379

HANSON, Jesica, Vice President and Chief Financial Officer, Bakersfield Memorial Hospital, Bakersfield, CA, p. A52

HANSON, Jim, Director Information Systems, Avera Queen Of Peace Hospital, Mitchell, SD, p. A562

HANSON, Lesley, Director Human Resources, Lake District Hospital, Lakeview, OR, p. A514

HANSON, Mary Ann, Director Personnel, Mental Health Institute, Cherokee, IA, p. A219

HANSON, Paul A., President, Sanford Usd Medical Center, Sioux Falls, SD, p. A564

HANSON, Rhonda, Director Human Resources, Huron Regional Medical Center, Huron, SD, p. A561

HANSON, Rita, M.D.
  Vice President Medical Affairs, Ascension Southeast Wisconsin Hospital – Elmbrook Campus, Brookfield, WI, p. A693
  Vice President Medical Affairs, Ascension Southeast Wisconsin Hospital – St. Joseph'S Campus, Milwaukee, WI, p. A700

HANSON, Samantha, Chief Human Resources Officer, Children'S Hospitals And Clinics Of Minnesota, Minneapolis, MN, p. A335

HANSON, Tamra, Human Resource Manager, Dorothea Dix Psychiatric Center, Bangor, ME, p. A281

HANYAK, Diana, Chief Executive Officer, Encompass Health Rehabilitation Hospital of Tustin, Tustin, CA, p. A92

HANZLIK, Debra Dawn, R.N., Director of Nursing, Niobrara Valley Hospital, Lynch, NE, p. A387

HAPNEY, Sherry, Chief Financial Officer, Encompass Health Rehabilitation Hospital of Fort Worth, Fort Worth, TX, p. A605

HAPPEL, Terry J, M.D., Vice President and Chief Medical Officer, Chandler Regional Medical Center, Chandler, AZ, p. A28

HAQQANI, Rahim, M.D., Medical Director, Dallas Behavioral Healthcare Hospital, Desoto, TX, p. A600

HAQUE, Haroon, M.D., Medical Director, Chg Hospital Tucson, Llc, Tucson, AZ, p. A37

HAQUE, Syed, Vice President and Chief Information Officer, Loretto Hospital, Chicago, IL, p. A178

HARA, Karen, Personnel Management Specialist, Hawaii State Hospital, Kaneohe, HI, p. A166

HARALDSON, Richard, Chief Executive Officer, Beatrice Community Hospital And Health Center, Beatrice, NE, p. A383

HARALSON, Gregory, Senior Vice President and Chief Executive Officer, Memorial Hermann – Texas Medical Center, Houston, TX, p. A612

HARALSON, Robert, Chief Financial Officer, Williamson Memorial Hospital, Williamson, WV, p. A690

HARARI, Jack L, M.D., Chief Medical Officer, West Boca Medical Center, Boca Raton, FL, p. A118

HARBAUGH, Charles, Director Human Resources, Mountain Lakes Medical Center, Clayton, GA, p. A150

HARBAUGH, Ken, Vice President and Chief Financial Officer, Osf Saint Francis Medical Center, Peoria, IL, p. A193

HARBERTS, Jerry, Information Technologist, Madison Healthcare Services, Madison, MN, p. A334

HARBIN, Cathy
  Chief Nursing Officer, Roosevelt Warm Springs Rehabilitation And Specialty Hospitals – Ltac, Warm Springs, GA, p. A162
  Chief Nursing Officer, Roosevelt Warm Springs Rehabilitation Hospital – Rehab, Warm Springs, GA, p. A162

HARBIN, Jason, Director of Nursing, Ward Memorial Hospital, Monahans, TX, p. A625

HARBISON, Damon R., President, Ssm Health St. Mary'S Hospital Centralia, Centralia, IL, p. A175

HARCHENKO, Vern, M.D., Chief of Staff, Chi St. Alexius Health Garrison, Garrison, ND, p. A467

HARCLERODE, Timothy
  Chief Executive Officer, Conemaugh Miners Medical Center, Hastings, PA, p. A527
  Chief Executive Officer, Conemaugh Nason Medical Center, Roaring Spring, PA, p. A540

HARCOMBE, Douglas
  Administrator, Adventhealth Orlando, Orlando, FL, p. A134
  Chief Executive Officer, Adventhealth Orlando, Orlando, FL, p. A134

HARCOURT, Jenifer, Chief Operating Officer, Riverwoods Behavioral Health System, Riverdale, GA, p. A159

HARCOURT, Roxane, Interim Administrator, Uf Health Shands Hospital, Gainesville, FL, p. A124

HARCUP, Craig, M.D., Hospital Medical Director, Complex Care Hospital At Ridgelake, Sarasota, FL, p. A139

HARDACRE, Jerry, M.D., Chief of Staff, Ascension All Saints, Racine, WI, p. A704

HARDAGE, Tony, Assistant Vice President and Administrator, Baptist Health Medical Center–Arkadelphia, Arkadelphia, AR, p. A39

HARDAN, Terry, Director Human Resources, Longview Regional Medical Center, Longview, TX, p. A621

HARDCASTLE, Brad, Chief Financial Officer, South Baldwin Regional Medical Center, Foley, AL, p. A18

HARDCASTLE, Kathy, Director Human Resources, Texas Health Presbyterian Hospital Denton, Denton, TX, p. A599

HARDEE, Gary R, M.D., Medical Director, Plains Memorial Hospital, Dimmitt, TX, p. A600

HARDEMAN, Diane, Director Personnel, Stephens County Hospital, Toccoa, GA, p. A162

HARDEN, Diane P
  Chief Financial Officer, Leesburg Regional Medical Center, Leesburg, FL, p. A128
  Senior Vice President and Chief Financial Officer, The Villages Regional Hospital, The Villages, FL, p. A142

HARDEN, Jeffrey M, Chief Nursing Officer, Meadows Regional Medical Center, Vidalia, GA, p. A162

HARDESTY, Keith, Chief Financial Officer, Springfield Hospital Center, Sykesville, MD, p. A293

HARDICK, Cindy, Human Resources Coordinator, Select Specialty Hospital–Ann Arbor, Ypsilanti, MI, p. A325

HARDIE, Rebecca Kay, Chief Nursing Officer, Baylor Scott & White Medical Center – Hillcrest, Waco, TX, p. A644

HARDIN, Cecil, CPA, Chief Financial Officer, Catawba Hospital, Catawba, VA, p. A657

HARDIN, James, Human Resources Officer, Sheridan Veterans Affairs Medical Center, Sheridan, WY, p. A712

HARDIN, Leslie, Chief Executive Officer and Chief Financial Officer, Seymour Hospital, Seymour, TX, p. A636

HARDIN, Marci, Manager Information Technology, Nevada Regional Medical Center, Nevada, MO, p. A366

HARDIN, Mark, M.D., Medical Director, Ed Fraser Memorial Hospital And Baker Community Health Center, Macclenny, FL, p. A128

HARDIN, Nicholas, Chief Executive Officer, Encompass Health Rehabilitation Hospital Of Sugar Land, Sugar Land, TX, p. A638

HARDING, Andrew D., Chief Executive Officer, Metrowest Medical Center, Framingham, MA, p. A298

HARDING, Barry, Interim Chief Executive Officer and Chief Financial Officer, Sumner Regional Medical Center, Wellington, KS, p. A247

HARDING, Christina, Vice President Finance, Mount Desert Island Hospital, Bar Harbor, ME, p. A281

HARDING, Denise, Director Human Resources, Plumas District Hospital, Quincy, CA, p. A79

HARDING, Edward A., President and Chief Executive Officer, Aurora Medical Center – Bay Area, Marinette, WI, p. A699

HARDING, Geoff, Chief Clinical Officer, Promise Hospital Of Salt Lake, Salt Lake City, UT, p. A652

HARDING, Gwen, Site Manager Information Systems, Bon Secours Memorial Regional Medical Center, Mechanicsville, VA, p. A662

HARDING, Helen, Chief Nursing Officer, Fairfield Medical Center, Lancaster, OH, p. A485

HARDING, John P, Chief Operating Officer, Children'S Hospital Of The King'S Daughters, Norfolk, VA, p. A663

HARDING, Rick, Chief Executive Officer, Perimeter Behavioral Hospital Of Springfield, Springfield, MO, p. A372

HARDISON, Randall, M.D., Chief Medical Officer, Arizona Orthopedic Surgical Hospital, Chandler, AZ, p. A28

HARDMAN, Danny, Chief Executive Officer, University Medical Center, New Orleans, LA, p. A275

HARDMAN, Joe, M.D., Chief Medical Officer, Tuality Healthcare, Hillsboro, OR, p. A513

HARDWICK, Garry, R.N., Chief Operating Officer, Newport Bay Hospital, Newport Beach, CA, p. A74

HARDY, Bob, Chief Operating Officer, Opelousas General Health System, Opelousas, LA, p. A276

HARDY, James, D.O., Chief of Staff, Dayton Veterans Affairs Medical Center, Dayton, OH, p. A481

HARDY, Janice, Chief Human Resource Management Service, Central Alabama Veterans Health Care System, Montgomery, AL, p. A21

HARDY, Kevin, Chief Financial Officer, Encompass Health Rehabilitation Hospital Of Treasure Coast, Vero Beach, FL, p. A143

HARDY, LaBon, Chief Information Officer, Ralph H. Johnson Veterans Affairs Medical Center, Charleston, SC, p. A550

HARDY, Melanie, D.O., Chief of Staff, Marias Medical Center, Shelby, MT, p. A380

HARDY, Raymond, Controller, Encompass Health Rehabilitation Hospital Of Las Vegas, Las Vegas, NV, p. A395

HARDY, Valonia, Chief Healthy Living Officer, Tsehootsooi Medical Center, Fort Defiance, AZ, p. A29

HARGENS, Scott James.
  Administrator and Chief Executive Officer, Avera Dells Area Hospital, Dell Rapids, SD, p. A560
  Administrator and Chief Executive Officer, Avera Flandreau Hospital, Flandreau, SD, p. A561

HARGER, Anita
  Chief Human Resource Officer, Kingman Regional Medical Center, Kingman, AZ, p. A30
  Director Human Resources, Mercy Gilbert Medical Center, Gilbert, AZ, p. A29

HARGETT, Fred M
  Executive Vice President and Chief Financial Officer, Novant Health Brunswick Medical Center, Bolivia, NC, p. A450
  Executive Vice President and Chief Financial Officer, Novant Health Charlotte Orthopaedic Hospital, Charlotte, NC, p. A451
  Executive Vice President and Chief Financial Officer, Novant Health Forsyth Medical Center, Winston, NC, p. A464
  Executive Vice President and Chief Financial Officer, Novant Health Huntersville Medical Center, Huntersville, NC, p. A456
  Executive Vice President and Chief Financial Officer, Novant Health Matthews Medical Center, Matthews, NC, p. A458

Executive Vice President and Chief Financial Officer, Novant Health Medical Park Hospital, Winston, NC, p. A464

Executive Vice President and Chief Financial Officer, Novant Health Presbyterian Medical Center, Charlotte, NC, p. A451

Executive Vice President and Chief Financial Officer, Novant Health Rowan Medical Center, Salisbury, NC, p. A461

Executive Vice President and Chief Financial Officer, Novant Health Thomasville Medical Center, Thomasville, NC, p. A463

HARGETT, Stephen A, Senior Vice President and Chief Financial Officer, Marina Del Rey Hospital, Marina Del Rey, CA, p. A71

HARGIS, Chris, Manager Finance, Alta View Hospital, Sandy, UT, p. A652

HARGRAVE, Dallas, Human Resources Director, Bartlett Regional Hospital, Juneau, AK, p. A26

HARGRAVE, David, Chief Information Officer, Ward Memorial Hospital, Monahans, TX, p. A625

HARGRAVE–THOMAS, Anne, Chief Executive Officer, Oakleaf Surgical Hospital, Altoona, WI, p. A691

HARGRODER, Ty, M.D., Chief of Staff, Acadia–St. Landry Hospital, Church Point, LA, p. A265

HARGROVE, Ben, Human Resources Director, Lifestream Behavioral Center, Leesburg, FL, p. A128

HARGROVE, Jeno, R.N., Director of Nursing, Columbus Community Hospital, Columbus, TX, p. A593

HARGROVE, Tressa B, Director Human Resources, Jackson Purchase Medical Center, Mayfield, KY, p. A257

HARIHARAN, Parma, M.D., Chief of Staff, Mercy Health – Clermont Hospital, Batavia, OH, p. A472

HARKER, Jodie, Director Human Resources, Van Diest Medical Center, Webster City, IA, p. A231

HARKEY, Shirley S., R.N., FACHE, Interim Vice President and Chief Nursing Officer, Unc Lenoir Healthcare, Kinston, NC, p. A457

HARKINS, Shelly, M.D.
  Chief Medical Officer, Hshs St. Elizabeth'S Hospital, O'Fallon, IL, p. A192
  Chief Medical Officer, St. Peter'S Hospital, Helena, MT, p. A377

HARKLEROAD, Rod, Chief Executive Officer, Haywood Regional Medical Center, Clyde, NC, p. A452

HARKNESS, Charles, D.O., Vice President Medical Affairs, Southeast Alabama Medical Center, Dothan, AL, p. A17

HARLAN, Kevin W., President, Joint Township District Memorial Hospital, Saint Marys, OH, p. A490

HARLAN, Thomas P., Chief Executive Officer, Continuecare Hospital At Palmetto Health Baptist, Columbia, SC, p. A551

HARLE, Connie, Chief Nursing Officer, Range Regional Health Services, Hibbing, MN, p. A333

HARLESS, Andrea, Director Information Services, Wythe County Community Hospital, Wytheville, VA, p. A669

HARLESS, Cheryl, Chief Nursing Officer, Doctors Medical Center Of Modesto, Modesto, CA, p. A72

HARLIN, Tim, M.D., Chief Operations Officer, Denver Health, Denver, CO, p. A98

HARLING, Roxanne, Chief Nursing Officer, Abraham Lincoln Memorial Hospital, Lincoln, IL, p. A188

HARLOVIC, Michael, President and Chief Executive Officer, Oswego Hospital, Oswego, NY, p. A441

HARLOW, Donald, Director of Information Services, Mountainview Regional Medical Center, Las Cruces, NM, p. A419

HARLOW, Tammy, Chief Nursing Officer, Elbert Memorial Hospital, Elberton, GA, p. A153

HARLOW, Thomas R., President, Wellspan Good Samaritan Hospital, Lebanon, PA, p. A530

HARLOWE, Michael, President and Chief Executive Officer, Indiana University Health Tipton Hospital, Tipton, IN, p. A215

HARMAN, Kenneth, Chief Executive Officer, Pioneers Medical Center, Meeker, CO, p. A104

HARMAN, Kimberly, Regional Manager Human Resources, Western State Hospital, Staunton, VA, p. A668

HARMATZ, Alan, M.D., Chief Medical Officer, Blake Medical Center, Bradenton, FL, p. A118

HARMON, Amy, Chief Financial Officer, Elkview General Hospital, Hobart, OK, p. A500

HARMON, Connie, Director of Nursing, Lakeland Hospital, Watervliet, Watervliet, MI, p. A324

HARMON, David, D.O., Vice President Medical Services, Rivervalley Behavioral Health Hospital, Owensboro, KY, p. A259

HARMON, James
  Information Technology, Cypress Creek Hospital, Houston, TX, p. A611
  Network Administrator, West Oaks Hospital, Houston, TX, p. A615

HARMON, Jennifer, Director of Human Resources, St. Cloud Regional Medical Center, Saint Cloud, FL, p. A138

HARMON, Thomas, M.D., Vice President Medical Affairs, Ohiohealth Riverside Methodist Hospital, Columbus, OH, p. A480

HARMOND, Joshua, Assistant Chief Financial Officer, Northwest Health Physicians' Specialty Hospital, Fayetteville, AR, p. A41

HARMS, Arlene, Chief Executive Officer, Rio Grande Hospital, Del Norte, CO, p. A98

HARMS, George
Chief Financial Officer, Hays Medical Center, Hays, KS, p. A236
Chief Financial Officer, University Of Kansas Health System Pawnee Valley Campus, Larned, KS, p. A239

HARNED, Barbara, R.N., MSN, Chief Nursing Officer, Monroe County Hospital, Monroeville, AL, p. A21

HARNESS, Phil, Chief Executive Officer, Doctor'S Hospital, Leawood, KS, p. A239

HARNEY, Geraldine, Chief Financial Officer, U. S. Public Health Service Phoenix Indian Medical Center, Phoenix, AZ, p. A34

HARPE, Michael, Vice President Human Resources, Community Hospital Of Anderson & Madison County, Anderson, IN, p. A199

HARPER, Cindy, Manager Patient Data, Westfield Memorial Hospital, Westfield, NY, p. A447

HARPER, Corwin N
Administrator, Kaiser Permanente Manteca Medical Center, Manteca, CA, p. A71
Senior Vice President and Area Manager, Kaiser Permanente Manteca Medical Center, Manteca, CA, p. A71

HARPER, Corwin N.
Senior Vice President and Area Manager, Kaiser Permanente Manteca Medical Center, Manteca, CA, p. A71
Senior Vice President and Area Manager, Kaiser Permanente Vallejo Medical Center, Vallejo, CA, p. A93

HARPER, David
Chief Information Officer, Wills Memorial Hospital, Washington, GA, p. A163
Director, Site Information Systems, Advocate Eureka Hospital, Eureka, IL, p. A182

HARPER, Eric, Chief Information Officer, Southeastern Health, Lumberton, NC, p. A458

HARPER, Heather L., Chief Executive Officer, Lovelace Regional Hospital – Roswell, Roswell, NM, p. A420

HARPER, James F, Senior Vice President and Chief Human Resources Officer, Tidelands Georgetown Memorial Hospital, Georgetown, SC, p. A553

HARPER, Kirk, R.N., Vice President, Nursing, Kadlec Regional Medical Center, Richland, WA, p. A677

HARPER, R Andrew, M.D., Medical Director, University Of Texas Harris County Psychiatric Center, Houston, TX, p. A614

HARPER, Wally G, Vice President Human Resources, Gaylord Hospital, Wallingford, CT, p. A111

HARPER, William F, M.D., Chief of Staff, Birmingham Veterans Affairs Medical Center, Birmingham, AL, p. A14

HARR, Donald, Controller, Ray County Memorial Hospital, Richmond, MO, p. A367

HARREL, Mark, Chief Executive Officer, Phelps Memorial Health Center, Holdrege, NE, p. A386

HARRELL, Aaron, Director, Grove Hill Memorial Hospital, Grove Hill, AL, p. A19

HARRELL, Joy, R.N., Chief Nursing Officer, Mimbres Memorial Hospital, Deming, NM, p. A418

HARRELL, Michael
Chief Executive Officer, Promise Hospital Of Miss Lou, Vidalia, LA, p. A279
Chief Executive Officer, Promise Hospital Of Vicksburg, Vicksburg, MS, p. A355

HARRELL, Paula, Chief Nursing Officer, Regional One Health Extended Care Hospital, Memphis, TN, p. A575

HARRELL, Steven W, FACHE, Chief Operating Officer, Adventhealth New Smyrna Beach, New Smyrna Beach, FL, p. A133

HARRELL, Thomas, Commander, U. S. Air Force Medical Center Keesler, Keesler Afb, MS, p. A349

HARRELSON, Rick, M.D., President Medical Staff, Medical Center Enterprise, Enterprise, AL, p. A17

HARRIER, Margie, MSN, R.N., Medical Center Chief Operations Officer, Kaiser Permanente Orange County Anaheim Medical Center, Anaheim, CA, p. A50

HARRIGER, Richard, Director of Emergency Services, Kimball Health Services, Kimball, NE, p. A386

HARRILSON, Annette, Chief Clinical Officer, Select Specialty Hospital Midtown Atlanta, Atlanta, GA, p. A147

HARRINGTON, Dan, Chief Operating Officer and Director Human Resources, Williamsburg Regional Hospital, Kingstree, SC, p. A554

HARRINGTON, Dawn, Chief Information Officer, University Of New Mexico Hospitals, Albuquerque, NM, p. A417

HARRINGTON, Hal, Vice President Human Resources, Merit Health River Region, Vicksburg, MS, p. A355

HARRINGTON, Jason, President and Chief Executive Officer, Lakes Regional Healthcare, Spirit Lake, IA, p. A230

HARRINGTON, Jeff, Chief Financial Officer, Children'S Hospital Colorado, Aurora, CO, p. A96

HARRINGTON, Joseph P., Chief Executive Officer, Healdsburg District Hospital, Healdsburg, CA, p. A61

HARRINGTON, Kathleen, Vice President Human Resources, Beth Israel Deaconess Hospital–Milton, Milton, MA, p. A301

HARRIS, Alicia, Director Fiscal Services, Mississippi State Hospital, Whitfield, MS, p. A355

HARRIS, Allen, M.D., Clinical Director, South Mississippi State Hospital, Purvis, MS, p. A353

HARRIS, Betty J, Director Human Resources, Southern California Hospital At Culver City, Culver City, CA, p. A56

HARRIS, Burt
Acting Chief Executive Officer, Canyon Ridge Hospital, Chino, CA, p. A54
Chief Financial Officer, Canyon Ridge Hospital, Chino, CA, p. A54

HARRIS, C Martin, M.D.
Chief Information Officer, Cleveland Clinic Children'S Hospital For Rehabilitation, Cleveland, OH, p. A477
Chief Information Officer, Cleveland Clinic Fairview Hospital, Cleveland, OH, p. A477
Chief Information Officer, Lutheran Hospital, Cleveland, OH, p. A478

HARRIS, Denise H., R.N., MSN, Chief Nursing Officer, Baptist Health South Florida, West Kendall Baptist Hospital, Miami, FL, p. A130

HARRIS, Diana, Chief Nursing Officer, Cape Fear Valley – Bladen County Hospital, Elizabethtown, NC, p. A454

HARRIS, Donna, Chief Executive Officer, Encompass Health Rehabilitation Hospital Of Jonesboro, Jonesboro, AR, p. A44

HARRIS, Dory, Director Human Resource, Teton Valley Health Care, Driggs, ID, p. A169

HARRIS, Ethan, Manager Information Systems, Mid–Valley Hospital, Omak, WA, p. A676

HARRIS, Howard, Vice President Human Resources, Regional Medical Center, Orangeburg, SC, p. A556

HARRIS, Jan, R.N., Director of Nursing, Stonewall Memorial Hospital, Aspermont, TX, p. A584

HARRIS, Janice M, Director Human Resources, University Medical Center Of El Paso, El Paso, TX, p. A603

HARRIS, Jen, Director Health Information Management, Chase County Community Hospital, Imperial, NE, p. A386

HARRIS, Jerald, Chief Information Officer, Cornerstone Hospital Of Houston At Clearlake, Webster, TX, p. A644

HARRIS, Jim
Director Information Technology, Grafton City Hospital, Grafton, WV, p. A685
Vice President Human Resources, Fairmont Regional Medical Center, Fairmont, WV, p. A685

HARRIS, Jo ell, R.N., Chief Nursing Officer, Forest View Psychiatric Hospital, Grand Rapids, MI, p. A312

HARRIS, Joanne, Director Human Resources, Mount Desert Island Hospital, Bar Harbor, ME, p. A281

HARRIS, John, Chief Executive Officer, Memorial Medical Center, Las Cruces, NM, p. A418

HARRIS, John B., Vice President Finance and Chief Financial Officer, Community Hospital Of Anderson & Madison County, Anderson, IN, p. A199

HARRIS, Julie
Chief Financial Officer, Riceland Medical Center, Winnie, TX, p. A646
Controller, Anmed Health Rehabilitation Hospital, Anderson, SC, p. A549

HARRIS, Karen, R.N., Chief Nursing and Operations Officer, Henry Ford West Bloomfield Hospital, West Bloomfield, MI, p. A324

HARRIS, Kathy, Vice President, Mercyhealth Hospital And Trauma Center – Janesville, Janesville, WI, p. A697

HARRIS, Kevin, Director Information Systems, Titus Regional Medical Center, Mount Pleasant, TX, p. A625

HARRIS, Kristin, Chief Executive Officer, Garland Behavioral Hospital, Garland, TX, p. A607

HARRIS, Laurie, Chief Accountant, Kerrville State Hospital, Kerrville, TX, p. A617

HARRIS, Lee, Assistant Administrator Support Services, Memorial Hospital And Manor, Bainbridge, GA, p. A148

HARRIS, Leslie, MSN, R.N., Chief Nursing Officer, Forrest City Medical Center, Forrest City, AR, p. A42

HARRIS, Lisa E., Chief Executive Officer, Eskenazi Health, Indianapolis, IN, p. A206

HARRIS, Madeline, R.N., Vice President and Chief Nursing Officer, The Queen'S Medical Center, Honolulu, HI, p. A165

HARRIS, Marianna, Administrator, Osborne County Memorial Hospital, Osborne, KS, p. A242

HARRIS, Mark D, Deputy Commander Clinical Services, Fort Belvoir Community Hospital, Fort Belvoir, VA, p. A659

HARRIS, Merilyn, Administrator, Ka'U Hospital, Pahala, HI, p. A166

HARRIS, Michael, M.D., Chief Medical Officer, Englewood Hospital And Medical Center, Englewood, NJ, p. A405

HARRIS, Miriam, Director Finance, Oklahoma Forensic Center, Vinita, OK, p. A510

HARRIS, R Brian, M.D., Chief of Staff, Reeves Memorial Medical Center, Bernice, LA, p. A264

HARRIS, Robert M, M.D., President Medical and Dental Staff, New Bridge Medical Center, Paramus, NJ, p. A410

HARRIS, Shelly, Chief Executive Officer, Indian Health Service – Quentin N. Burdick Memorial Health Care Facility, Belcourt, ND, p. A465

HARRIS, Shirley, M.D., President Medical Staff, Mosaic Medical Center – Maryville, Maryville, MO, p. A365

HARRIS, Spencer, Senior Director Finance, Kadlec Regional Medical Center, Richland, WA, p. A677

HARRIS, Stuart, M.D., Chief of Staff, Trigg County Hospital, Cadiz, KY, p. A250

HARRIS, Sue, Vice President and Chief Nursing Officer, Methodist Medical Center Of Oak Ridge, Oak Ridge, TN, p. A578

HARRIS, Susan, Director Fiscal Services, Shriners Hospitals For Children – Cincinnati, Cincinnati, OH, p. A476

HARRIS, Susan, R.N., Chief Operating Officer, Medical Center, Navicent Health, Macon, GA, p. A156

HARRIS, Sylvia, Fiscal Director, Moccasin Bend Mental Health Institute, Chattanooga, TN, p. A567

HARRIS, Timothy, M.D., Chief Quality Officer, Texas Health Presbyterian Hospital Denton, Denton, TX, p. A599

HARRIS, Vena, Director Human Resources, Minneola District Hospital, Minneola, KS, p. A241

HARRIS, William R, Chief Information Officer, Lawton Indian Hospital, Lawton, OK, p. A501

HARRISON, Charles, Chief Executive Officer, San Bernardino Mountains Community Hospital District, Lake Arrowhead, CA, p. A63

HARRISON, Chris, Manager Information Systems, Campbell County Health, Gillette, WY, p. A711

HARRISON, Denise, Associate Director, Veterans Affairs Nebraska–Western Iowa Health Care System, Omaha, NE, p. A390

HARRISON, Dyan, Manager Health Information, Ochiltree General Hospital, Perryton, TX, p. A628

HARRISON, George E., M.D., Chief Medical Officer, Fairview Park Hospital, Dublin, GA, p. A152

HARRISON, Jo L, Vice President of Patient Care Services, Southwest Medical Center, Liberal, KS, p. A239

HARRISON, Kathleen, Chief Executive Officer, Mccready Health, Crisfield, MD, p. A290

HARRISON, Marva, R.N., Vice President and Chief Nursing Officer, Integris Southwest Medical Center, Oklahoma City, OK, p. A504

HARRISON, Randy, Chief Financial Officer, Raleigh General Hospital, Beckley, WV, p. A683

HARROD, Tracy, Director of Nursing, Greenwood County Hospital, Eureka, KS, p. A235

HARRON, Rick, Chief Financial Officer, Dominican Hospital, Santa Cruz, CA, p. A88

HARROP, Elizabeth, Director, Human Resources, Flambeau Hospital, Park Falls, WI, p. A703

HARSHAWAT, Paras, M.D., Medical Director, Harsha Behavioral Center, Terre Haute, IN, p. A215

HARSHAWAT, Roopam, President and Chief Executive Officer, Harsha Behavioral Center, Terre Haute, IN, p. A215

HARSHBARGER, Catherine S., Chief Executive Officer, Banner Lassen Medical Center, Susanville, CA, p. A91

HARSY, Brice, Chief Financial Officer, Marshall Browning Hospital, Du Quoin, IL, p. A181

HART, Amy, Chief Operating Officer, Cuyuna Regional Medical Center, Crosby, MN, p. A330

HART, Betsy, Chief Operating Officer, Northridge Hospital Medical Center, Los Angeles, CA, p. A68

HART, Denise, Director Human Resources, Sullivan County Community Hospital, Sullivan, IN, p. A215

HART, Donna, Chief Information Officer, Provident Hospital Of Cook County, Chicago, IL, p. A179

HART, Elizabeth, R.N., MSN, Chief Nursing Officer, Providence Saint Joseph Medical Center, Burbank, CA, p. A53

HART, Gary, M.D., Chief Medical Officer, West Park Hospital, Cody, WY, p. A711

HART, James, M.D., Medical Director, Rolling Hills Hospital, Franklin, TN, p. A569

HART, Joline, Vice President Human Resources, Franklin Memorial Hospital, Farmington, ME, p. A283

HART, Joseph, Director Finance and Support Services, Putnam Hospital Center, Carmel, NY, p. A425

HART, Kenneth, President, Saint Alphonsus Medical Center – Ontario, Ontario, OR, p. A515

HART, Lisa, Chief Executive Officer, Elkview General Hospital, Hobart, OK, p. A500

HART, Monique, Chief Financial Officer, Baptist Memorial Hospital–Tipton, Covington, TN, p. A568

HART, Pat, Director Human Resources, Three Rivers Medical Center, Louisa, KY, p. A255

HART, Richard, Chief Financial Officer, Stanislaus Surgical Hospital, Modesto, CA, p. A72

HART, Scott, Controller, Encompass Rehabilitation Hospital Of Lakeview, Elizabethtown, KY, p. A251

HART–FLYNN, Wilma, Ph.D., R.N., Chief Nursing Officer, Morristown–Hamblen Healthcare System, Morristown, TN, p. A576

HARTBERG, David, Chief Executive Officer, Gundersen Boscobel Area Hospital And Clinics, Boscobel, WI, p. A692

HARTE, Brian J., President, Cleveland Clinic Akron General, Akron, OH, p. A471

HARTGRAVES, Steve L., President and Chief Executive Officer, Jackson County Memorial Hospital, Altus, OK, p. A496

HARTKE, Michael, Executive Vice President, Chief Operating Officer, Northwest Community Hospital, Arlington Heights, IL, p. A173

HARTLEY, Barbara, Chief Medical Officer, Benson Hospital, Benson, AZ, p. A28

HARTLEY, Diane L, Director of Patient Care Services, Beaumont Hospital, Wayne, Wayne, MI, p. A324

HARTLEY, Melinda D., R.N., Vice President Patient Care Services, Perry Hospital, Perry, GA, p. A158

HARTLEY, Michael, MS, Chief Nursing Officer, Holly Hill Hospital, Raleigh, NC, p. A460

HARTLEY, Randall W, Chief Operating Officer, Nemours Children'S Hospital, Orlando, FL, p. A134

HARTLEY, Shauna, Administrator, Turquoise Lodge Hospital, Albuquerque, NM, p. A417

HARTLEY, Shawn
Chief Financial Officer, Caldwell Unc Health Care, Lenoir, NC, p. A457
Chief Financial Officer, Nash Unc Health Care, Rocky Mount, NC, p. A461

HARTLEY, Wannah, Controller, Winkler County Memorial Hospital, Kermit, TX, p. A617

HARTMAN, Daphane, Director Information Systems, College Station Medical Center, College Station, TX, p. A592

HARTMAN, Don, Director Human Resources, Sutter Davis Hospital, Davis, CA, p. A56

HARTMAN, Kathleen, Chief Nursing Officer, Metrosouth Medical Center, Blue Island, IL, p. A174

HARTMAN, Mark, Interim Chief Financial Officer, St. Joseph Medical Center, Houston, TX, p. A613

HARTMAN, Sally, Senior Vice President, Riverside Regional Medical Center, Newport News, VA, p. A663

HARTMAN, Susan, Chief Executive Officer, Encompass Health Nittany Valley Rehabilitation Hospital, Pleasant Gap, PA, p. A539

HARTMANN, Doreen, Chief Financial Officer, St. Joseph'S Behavioral Health Center, Stockton, CA, p. A90

HARTMANN, Peter M, M.D., Vice President Medical Affairs, Wellspan York Hospital, York, PA, p. A546

HARTMANN, Rob, Assistant Director Human Resources Management, Ochsner Lsu Health Shreveport – Monroe Medical Center, Monroe, LA, p. A274

HARTNETT, Tammy, Employee Relations Manager, Unitypoint Health – St. Lukes'S Sioux City, Sioux City, IA, p. A230

HARTSELL, Henry, Executive Director, Griffin Memorial Hospital, Norman, OK, p. A503

HARTSELL, Scott, Chief Operating Officer, Bayfront Health Brooksville, Brooksville, FL, p. A119

HARTTER, Lynn E, Director Human Resources, Nemaha Valley Community Hospital, Seneca, KS, p. A245

HARTUNG, Andy, Director Information Systems, Self Regional Healthcare, Greenwood, SC, p. A554

HARTWELL, Tim, Chief Human Resources, Marion Veterans Affairs Medical Center, Marion, IL, p. A188

HARTWICK, Bryan
Vice President Human Resources, Alton Memorial Hospital, Alton, IL, p. A173
Vice President Human Resources, Christian Hospital, Saint Louis, MO, p. A369

HARTWIG, Michael, M.D., Chief of Staff, Stillwater Medical Perry, Perry, OK, p. A506

HARTZOG, Rick, Chief Information Officer, Merit Health Madison, Canton, MS, p. A345

HARVEY, Alice, Director of Nursing, Heatherhill Care Communities, Chardon, OH, p. A475

HARVEY, Jennifer, Director Human Resources, Golden Plains Community Hospital, Borger, TX, p. A589

HARVEY, John
Chief Executive Officer, Oklahoma Heart Hospital South Campus, Oklahoma City, OK, p. A505
Chief Executive Officer, Oklahoma Heart Hospital, Oklahoma City, OK, p. A505

HARVEY, John, M.D., Chief Executive Officer, Oklahoma Heart Hospital, Oklahoma City, OK, p. A505

HARVEY, Kathy, D.O., Chief Medical Officer, Logan Regional Medical Center, Logan, WV, p. A686

HARVEY, Linda, Chief Financial Officer, West Feliciana Parish Hospital, Saint Francisville, LA, p. A277

HARVEY, Michael, President and Chief Executive Officer, Syracuse Area Health, Syracuse, NE, p. A392

HARVEY, Paul
Chief Executive Officer, Christus Mother Frances Hospital – Winnsboro, Winnsboro, TX, p. A646
President and Chief Executive Officer, Christus Mother Frances Hospital – Sulphur Springs, Sulphur Springs, TX, p. A638

HARVILL, Brian
Vice President Financial Services, Vidant Bertie Hospital, Windsor, NC, p. A464
Vice President Financial Services, Vidant Chowan Hospital, Edenton, NC, p. A453

HARVIN, Schley, Information Technology Technician, Hood Memorial Hospital, Amite, LA, p. A262

HASBROUCK, Matthew Steven, Chief Operating Officer, Memorial Health, Savannah, GA, p. A160

HASELTON, David, Chief Medical Officer, Riverton Hospital, Riverton, UT, p. A651

HASHMI, Faraz, Chief Executive Officer, Central Hospital Of Bowie, Bowie, TX, p. A589

HASHMI, Mubashir, Chief Information Officer, Pacifica Hospital Of The Valley, Los Angeles, CA, p. A68

HASHMI, Suleman, President and Chief Executive Officer, Texas General Hospital, Grand Prairie, TX, p. A608

HASKELL, Jeffrey, M.D., Chief Medical Staff, Lost Rivers Medical Center, Arco, ID, p. A167

HASKINS, Don, Administrative Director Human Resources, Southwest Mississippi Regional Medical Center, Mccomb, MS, p. A350

HASLETT, Tom, Interim Chief Information Officer, Macneal Hospital, Berwyn, IL, p. A174

HASNI, Kamran, M.D., Chief of Medical Staff, Barbourville Arh Hospital, Barbourville, KY, p. A249

HASS, Roxanne, Director of Nursing, Chi St. Joseph Health Madison Hospital, Madisonville, TX, p. A623

HASSAN, Tariq, M.D., Associate Director of Patient Care, Captain James A. Lovell Federal Health Care Center, North Chicago, IL, p. A191

HASSANI, Dahlia, Vice President of Medical Affairs, Baylor Scott & White All Saints Medical Center – Fort Worth, Fort Worth, TX, p. A604

HASSELBRACK, Jeni, Director Human Resources, Adventhealth Gordon, Calhoun, GA, p. A149

HAST, Anne S, R.N., Director of Nursing, Advanced Surgical Hospital, Washington, PA, p. A543

HAST, Anne S., Chief Executive Officer, Advanced Surgical Hospital, Washington, PA, p. A543

HASTIN, Kathy, Administrative Assistant Human Resources, River Valley Medical Center, Dardanelle, AR, p. A41

HASTINGS, Clare, R.N., Ph.D., Chief Nurse Officer, National Institutes Of Health Clinical Center, Bethesda, MD, p. A289

HASTINGS, Sarah M, Executive Director, Ridgeview Medical Center, Waconia, MN, p. A342

HATCH, Brooke, Director Human Resource, Bradley County Medical Center, Warren, AR, p. A49

HATCH, Tammy, Manager, Northlight Sebasticook Valley Hospital, Pittsfield, ME, p. A284

HATCHEL, Kimberly Kay, Chief Nursing Officer, Blake Medical Center, Bradenton, FL, p. A118

HATCHER, Amy, Senior Vice President and Chief Financial Officer, Children'S Hospital And Medical Center, Omaha, NE, p. A389

HATCHER, Julie, Vice President Human Resources, O'Connor Hospital, San Jose, CA, p. A86

HATCHES, Ann
Director, Human Resources, Holy Cross Hospital, Chicago, IL, p. A177
Interim Director Human Resources, Mount Sinai Hospital, Chicago, IL, p. A178

HATFIELD, Chad, Chief Executive Officer, Northeast Georgia Medical Center Barrow, Winder, GA, p. A163

HATFIELD, Charles, Interim Chief Executive Officer, Williamson Memorial Hospital, Williamson, WV, p. A690

HATFIELD, Jonathan, Supervisor Information Technology, Klickitat Valley Health, Goldendale, WA, p. A673

HATFIELD, Timothy A., Community Chief Executive Officer, Tug Valley Arh Regional Medical Center, South Williamson, KY, p. A260

HATHAWAY, William, M.D., Chief Medical Officer, Mission Hospital, Asheville, NC, p. A449

HATHCOCK, Claudette
Administrative Director Human Resources, University Of Mississippi Medical Center Grenada, Grenada, MS, p. A347
Human Resources Director, University Of Mississippi Medical Center Holmes County, Lexington, MS, p. A350

HATIRAS, Spiros, President and Chief Executive Officer, Holyoke Medical Center, Holyoke, MA, p. A299

HATLESTAD, Jill, Vice President Human Resources and Marketing, Glencoe Regional Health, Glencoe, MN, p. A332

HATMAKER, Michael, Vice President Support Services and Admin Nursing Home, Leconte Medical Center, Sevierville, TN, p. A579

HATTEM–SCHIFFMAN, Marita, President, Midmichigan Medical Center–Gratiot, Alma, MI, p. A306

HATTER, Jason, Chief Human Resource Officer, Princeton Baptist Medical Center, Birmingham, AL, p. A15

HATTERER–HOAG, Dawn, Director Human Resources, Psychiatric Institute Of Washington, Washington, DC, p. A116

HATTON, Tad, Vice President Chief Operating Officer, Ascension Seton Medical Center Austin, Austin, TX, p. A584

HAUBL, Eileen, Senior Vice President and Chief Financial Officer, Mission Hospital, Mission Viejo, CA, p. A72

HAUG, Darin L., President and Chief Executive Officer, Fitzgibbon Hospital, Marshall, MO, p. A365

HAUG, Darin L., D.O., President & Chief Executive Officer, Fitzgibbon Hospital, Marshall, MO, p. A365

HAUGE, Meri, R.N., MSN, Associate Director of Patient Care Services and Nurse Executive, St. Cloud Veterans Affairs Health Care System, Saint Cloud, MN, p. A339

HAUGER, Clint, Chief Executive Officer, Palmetto Lowcountry Behavioral Health, Charleston, SC, p. A550

HAUGH, William, Administrator, Georgetown Community Hospital, Georgetown, KY, p. A252

HAUGHEY, Tracie, Chief Executive Officer and Chief Financial Officer, Wills Memorial Hospital, Washington, GA, p. A163

HAULER, Jennifer, D.O., Chief Medical Officer, Upper Valley Medical Center, Troy, OH, p. A492

HAUPERT, John M., President and Chief Executive Officer, Grady Memorial Hospital, Atlanta, GA, p. A146

HAUPT, Carolyn, Chief Financial Officer, Peacehealth United General Medical Center, Sedro, WA, p. A679

HAUPT, William, Administrator, Adventhealth Orlando, Orlando, FL, p. A134

HAUSAUER, Patricia K, Director Finance, Baptist Medical Center Nassau, Fernandina Beach, FL, p. A122

HAUSE, Eileen, Chief Executive Officer, Kensington Hospital, Philadelphia, PA, p. A535

HAUSER, Mark J, M.D., Chief Medical Officer, Baptist Health South Florida, Baptist Hospital Of Miami, Miami, FL, p. A130

HAUSER, Megan, Director Human Resources, Shriners Hospitals For Children–Philadelphia, Philadelphia, PA, p. A536

HAUSHALTER, Brandon, Chief Executive Officer, Kendall Regional Medical Center, Miami, FL, p. A130

HAUSHALTER, Richard L, Senior Vice President Operations and Chief Operating Officer, Sentara Rmh Medical Center, Harrisonburg, VA, p. A660

HAUSMANN, Jena, President and Chief Executive Officer, Children'S Hospital Colorado, Aurora, CO, p. A96

HAVARD, Greg, Chief Executive Officer, George Regional Hospital, Lucedale, MS, p. A350

HAVEN, Adrian C, Site Manager, Gallup Indian Medical Center, Gallup, NM, p. A418

HAVENS, Jennifer, Chief Executive Officer, Unitypoint Health – Grinnell Regional Medical Center, Grinnell, IA, p. A223

HAVERSTOCK, Loren, Manager Human Resources, Harrison County Hospital, Corydon, IN, p. A201

HAVICAN, Gary C.
President, Midstate Medical Center, Meriden, CT, p. A108
President, The Hospital Of Central Connecticut, New Britain, CT, p. A109

HAVRILLA, David A, Chief Financial Officer, Medstar Montgomery Medical Center, Olney, MD, p. A292

HAWIG, Scott
Senior Vice President Finance, Chief Financial Officer and Treasurer, Froedtert And The Medical College Of Wisconsin Froedtert Hospital, Milwaukee, WI, p. A701
Senior Vice President of Finance, Chief Financial Officer and Treasurer, Community Memorial Hospital, Menomonee Falls, WI, p. A700
Senior Vice President of Finance, Chief Financial Officer and Treasurer, St. Joseph'S Hospital, West Bend, WI, p. A708

HAWK, Kevin, Chief Executive Officer, Hillcrest Hospital Cushing, Cushing, OK, p. A498

HAWKEY, Tammy, Manager Information Technology Client Services, Ascension Saint Clare'S Hospital, Weston, WI, p. A708
HAWKINS, Bryan, Controller, Firsthealth Montgomery Memorial Hospital, Troy, NC, p. A463
HAWKINS, Ellis, President, Ssm Health Depaul Hospital – St. Louis, Bridgeton, MO, p. A357
HAWKINS, Hillary, M.D., Medical Director, Sheltering Arms Rehabilitation Hospital, Mechanicsville, VA, p. A662
HAWKINS, Jason F., Chief Administrative Officer, Peacehealth Peace Harbor Medical Center, Florence, OR, p. A512
HAWKINS, Kidada, Chief Executive Officer, Shoals Hospital, Muscle Shoals, AL, p. A22
HAWKINS, Roy L., Jr, Senior Vice President and Chief Executive Officer, Jackson Health System, Miami, FL, p. A130
HAWKINS, Sheri, Chief Nursing Officer, Adventhealth Shawnee Mission, Shawnee Mission, KS, p. A245
HAWKINS, Tami, R.N., MSN, Vice President Patient Care and Chief Nursing Officer, Texas Health Presbyterian Hospital Of Rockwall, Rockwall, TX, p. A631
HAWKINSON, Curtis R., Chief Executive Officer, Community Memorial Healthcare, Marysville, KS, p. A240
HAWLEY, Jason, Director of Information Services and Security, Yuma District Hospital, Yuma, CO, p. A106
HAWLEY, William, President and Chief Executive Officer, Fawcett Memorial Hospital, Port Charlotte, FL, p. A137
HAWS, Bradley, Chief Financial Officer, University Of Iowa Hospitals And Clinics, Iowa City, IA, p. A224
HAWTHORNE, Caryn, Vice President Finance and Chief Finance Officer, East Tennessee Children'S Hospital, Knoxville, TN, p. A572
HAWTHORNE, Kimberly, Administrator, Mayo Clinic Health System – Franciscan Healthcare In Sparta, Sparta, WI, p. A705
HAWTOF, Jeffrey, M.D., Vice President Medical Operations and Informatics, Beebe Healthcare, Lewes, DE, p. A113
HAY, Fraser, President, Texas Health Harris Methodist Hospital Hurst–Euless–Bedford, Bedford, TX, p. A588
HAYDEN, Crystal, MSN, R.N., Senior Vice President and Chief Nursing Officer, Nash Unc Health Care, Rocky Mount, NC, p. A461
HAYDEN, James, M.D., Chief Medical Officer, J. C. Blair Memorial Hospital, Huntingdon, PA, p. A527
HAYDEN, Jamie, Chief Financial Officer, Eastland Memorial Hospital, Eastland, TX, p. A600
HAYDEN, John
Senior Vice President and Chief Human Resources Officer, Bronson Lakeview Hospital, Paw Paw, MI, p. A319
Senior Vice President and Human Resources Officer, Bronson Battle Creek Hospital, Battle Creek, MI, p. A307
Vice President and Chief Human Resources Officer, Bronson Methodist Hospital, Kalamazoo, MI, p. A315
HAYDEN, Karen, Director Health Information Services, Performance Improvement and Risk Management, Valle Vista Health System, Greenwood, IN, p. A205
HAYDEN–PUGH, Beverly P., R.N., Senior Vice President and Chief Nursing Officer, Valley Children'S Healthcare, Madera, CA, p. A70
HAYEK, Anthony, D.O., Medical Director, Edwin Shaw Rehab, Cuyahoga Falls, OH, p. A480
HAYES, David R, Chief Financial Officer, T.J. Health Columbia, Columbia, KY, p. A250
HAYES, Deborah Marie, R.N., MS, MSN, Chief Operating Officer, Christ Hospital, Cincinnati, OH, p. A475
HAYES, Di, Chief Executive Officer, Hallmark Youthcare – Richmond, Richmond, VA, p. A666
HAYES, Donna, Controller, Decatur County General Hospital, Parsons, TN, p. A578
HAYES, Elaine, Controller, Sts. Mary & Elizabeth Hospital, Louisville, KY, p. A256
HAYES, Farrell, Chief Financial Officer, Chi Memorial Hospital – Georgia, Fort Oglethorpe, GA, p. A153
HAYES, James L, Director Human Resources, Western State Hospital, Hopkinsville, KY, p. A253
HAYES, Jeffrey A, Vice President System Operations, Fisher–Titus Medical Center, Norwalk, OH, p. A488
HAYES, Jo, Chief Nursing Officer, Horn Memorial Hospital, Ida Grove, IA, p. A224
HAYES, June, Chief Financial Officer, Harrisburg Medical Center, Harrisburg, IL, p. A184
HAYES, Kathe, Executive Director, Western New York Children'S Psychiatric Center, West Seneca, NY, p. A447
HAYES, Kelly, Chief Financial Officer, Methodist Hospital For Surgery, Addison, TX, p. A581
HAYES, Kevin, M.D., Chief of Staff, Monroe Regional Hospital, Aberdeen, MS, p. A344
HAYES, Lisa G., Chief Clinical Officer, Central Indiana Amg Specialty Hospital, Muncie, IN, p. A212
HAYES, Lynnette, Chief Nursing Officer, Golden Valley Memorial Healthcare, Clinton, MO, p. A358
HAYES, Paul, Executive Director, Uw Medicine/Harborview Medical Center, Seattle, WA, p. A678
HAYES, Sharon, Chief Executive Officer, Bayfront Health St. Petersburg, Saint Petersburg, FL, p. A138
HAYES, Stacy, R.N., Chief Nursing Officer, Arizona Spine And Joint Hospital, Mesa, AZ, p. A31
HAYES, Susan, Director Human Resources, Southeastern Health, Lumberton, NC, p. A458
HAYES, Tammy A., R.N., MS, Chief Nurse Executive and Long Term Care Administrator, Northfield Hospital And Clinics, Northfield, MN, p. A337
HAYES, Thomas P., Chief Executive Officer, Eastern Plumas Health Care, Portola, CA, p. A79
HAYES, Warren, Chief of Staff, Montgomery County Memorial Hospital, Red Oak, IA, p. A228
HAYES, William M., Chief Executive Officer, Northside Hospital–Cherokee, Canton, GA, p. A149
HAYGOOD, Rachel Joy, Director Information Technology, Tyler County Hospital, Woodville, TX, p. A646
HAYHURST, Leslie, Director Information Systems, Washington Health System Greene, Waynesburg, PA, p. A543
HAYMAN, Judy A., Director, Syracuse Veterans Affairs Medical Center, Syracuse, NY, p. A445
HAYN, Jed, Chief Information Officer, Walter B. Jones Alcohol And Drug Abuse Treatment Center, Greenville, NC, p. A455
HAYNES, Deatosha D., Interim Associates Director for Patient, Veterans Affairs Gulf Coast Veterans Health Care System, Biloxi, MS, p. A344
HAYNES, Elaine S, R.N., MSN, Vice President Patient Services and Chief Nursing Executive, Atrium Health Lincoln, Lincolnton, NC, p. A458
HAYNES, Jamil, Regional Director Human Resources, Integris Miami Hospital, Miami, OK, p. A502
HAYNES, Jill, Financial Coach, Bath Veterans Affairs Medical Center, Bath, NY, p. A423
HAYNES, John H, M.D., Chief of Medical Staff, North Caddo Medical Center, Vivian, LA, p. A280
HAYNES, Laurie, Chief Financial Officer, Gulf Coast Regional Medical Center, Panama City, FL, p. A135
HAYNES, Mark, M.D., Chief of Staff, Claiborne Memorial Medical Center, Homer, LA, p. A268
HAYNES, Robert Gerard., Chief Executive Officer, Guadalupe Regional Medical Center, Seguin, TX, p. A636
HAYNES, Tina, Interim Chief Executive Officer, Claiborne Memorial Medical Center, Homer, LA, p. A268
HAYNES, William, Director Information Technology, Central Louisiana State Hospital, Pineville, LA, p. A277
HAYREH, Davinder, M.D., Medical Director, Metropolitan St. Louis Psychiatric Center, Saint Louis, MO, p. A369
HAYS, Cheryl M, FACHE, Administrator and Chief Operating Officer, Marshall Medical Center North, Guntersville, AL, p. A19
HAYS, Cheryl M., Administrator and Chief Operating Officer, Marshall Medical Center North, Guntersville, AL, p. A19
HAYS, Chuck, President and Chief Executive Officer, Mainegeneral Medical Center, Augusta, ME, p. A281
HAYS, Harry, Chief Executive Officer, Carroll County Memorial Hospital, Carrollton, KY, p. A250
HAYS, Kathie, MSN, R.N., Chief Nursing Officer, West Chester Hospital, West Chester, OH, p. A494
HAYS, Larry, Director Information Technology, Southern Virginia Mental Health Institute, Danville, VA, p. A658
HAYS, Richard, M.D., Chief Medical Officer, Wellington Regional Medical Center, Wellington, FL, p. A143
HAYS, Richard O, Chief Fiscal Service, Veterans Affairs Southern Nevada Healthcare System, North Las Vegas, NV, p. A396
HAYS, Timothy A, Vice President Human Resources, Johnston Health, Smithfield, NC, p. A462
HAYTAIAN, Mike, Head Director Information Resources Management, Naval Hospital Jacksonville, Jacksonville, FL, p. A125
HAYWOOD, Nancy
Chief Financial Officer, Ascension Genesys Hospital, Grand Blanc, MI, p. A312
Chief Financial Officer, Ascension St. Mary'S Of Michigan, Saginaw, MI, p. A321
HAYWOOD, Stephanie, Director Human Resources, Southern Virginia Mental Health Institute, Danville, VA, p. A658
HAZELBAKER, Matthew, M.D., President Medical Staff, Memorial Health, Marysville, OH, p. A486
HEAD, David, M.D., Chief Medical Staff, Norton Sound Regional Hospital, Nome, AK, p. A26
HEAD, Susan, Director Nursing Services, Blackfeet Community Hospital, Saint Mary, MT, p. A380
HEADLEE, Melissa, Interim Chief Executive Officer, Harper County Community Hospital, Buffalo, OK, p. A497
HEALY, John, Manager Information Technology, Friends Hospital, Philadelphia, PA, p. A534
HEALY–COLLIER, Kathy, Chief Operating Officer, Brookwood Baptist Medical Center, Birmingham, AL, p. A14
HEARD, Alex, M.D., Chief Medical Officer, Falmouth Hospital, Falmouth, MA, p. A298
HEARD, Charles, M.D., Chief of Staff, Orlando Regional Medical Center, Orlando, FL, p. A134
HEARD, Heather, Director Human Resources, Holdenville General Hospital, Holdenville, OK, p. A500
HEARD, John E., Chief Executive Officer, Mcgehee Hospital, Mcgehee, AR, p. A45
HEARD, M Denise, Director Business Services, North Mississippi Medical Center–Pontotoc, Pontotoc, MS, p. A353
HEARING, Ava, Chief Nursing Officer, Atrium Medical Center, Stafford, TX, p. A638
HEARING, Tim, Associate Information Technology Director, Raulerson Hospital, Okeechobee, FL, p. A133
HEARNE, Diane, Director Human Resources, Arizona Spine And Joint Hospital, Mesa, AZ, p. A31
HEARNSBERGER, John, M.D., Chief of Staff, Howard Memorial Hospital, Nashville, AR, p. A46
HEATER, Floyd, President, Warren Memorial Hospital, Front Royal, VA, p. A660
HEATH, Ed, Chief Executive Officer, Owensboro Health Muhlenberg Community Hospital, Greenville, KY, p. A252
HEATH, Lisa, M.D., President Medical Staff, Saint Luke'S South Hospital, Overland Park, KS, p. A243
HEATH, Megan, Chief Nursing Officer, Gordon Memorial Health Services, Gordon, NE, p. A385
HEATH, Merry, Chief Nursing Officer, Piedmont Fayette Hospital, Fayetteville, GA, p. A153
HEATH, Susan, R.N., Senior Vice President and Chief Nursing Officer, Seattle Children'S Hospital, Seattle, WA, p. A678
HEATH, William, Chief Executive Officer, Regency Hospital Of Meridian, Meridian, MS, p. A351
HEATHERLY, Steve
Chief Executive Officer, Harris Regional Hospital, Sylva, NC, p. A463
Chief Executive Officer, Swain Community Hospital, Bryson City, NC, p. A450
HEATHERLY–LLOYD, Sara, Chief Operating Officer, Tennova Healthcare–Lafollette Medical Center, La Follette, TN, p. A572
HEATLEY, Mark A, Associate Administrator, Turning Point Hospital, Moultrie, GA, p. A158
HEATON, Crystal, Director of Finance, St. Vincent Warrick, Boonville, IN, p. A200
HEBBERD, Hilda, R.N., MSN, Senior Director Clinical Services, Marlette Regional Hospital, Marlette, MI, p. A317
HEBEL, Barbara, Vice President Human Resources, Doylestown Hospital, Doylestown, PA, p. A524
HEBERT, Bryan, Director Information Systems, The Medical Center Of Southeast Texas, Port Arthur, TX, p. A630
HEBERT, Carol, Director Human Resources, The Medical Center Of Southeast Texas, Port Arthur, TX, p. A630
HEBERT, Gerard, Chief Financial Officer, Texoma Medical Center, Denison, TX, p. A599
HEBERT, Jeff, Interim Vice President Finance, Gifford Medical Center, Randolph, VT, p. A655
HEBERT, Katherine D., Chief Executive Officer, University Hospital And Clinics, Lafayette, LA, p. A271
HEBERT, Rachel, Chief Financial Officer, Heart Hospital Of Lafayette, Lafayette, LA, p. A270
HEBERT, Timothy, Director Human Resources, Teche Regional Medical Center, Morgan City, LA, p. A274
HEBGEN, Lynn, MSN, R.N., Vice President of Nursing, Upland Hills Health, Dodgeville, WI, p. A693
HEBL, James, Regional Vice President, Mayo Clinic Health System In Mankato, Mankato, MN, p. A334
HEBRA, Andre, M.D., Chief Medical Officer, Nemours Children'S Hospital, Orlando, FL, p. A134
HECHLER, Tracy, Healthcare Director Information Services, Chippenham Hospital, Richmond, VA, p. A666
HECHT, David, M.D., Chief of Staff, James H. Quillen Veterans Affairs Medical Center, Mountain Home, TN, p. A576
HECKATHORNE, Daniel R, Chief Financial Officer, Memorial Hospital Of Gardena, Gardena, CA, p. A60
HECKER, Cynthia, Executive Director, Uw Medicine/Northwest Hospital & Medical Center, Seattle, WA, p. A678
HECKER, Julie, Vice President, Operations, Upmc Mercy, Pittsburgh, PA, p. A538
HECKER, Lisa, Director Human Resources, Hedrick Medical Center, Chillicothe, MO, p. A358
HECKERMAN, Ray, Chief Executive Officer and Managing Director, Coastal Harbor Treatment Center, Savannah, GA, p. A160
HECKERT, Robert J., Jr, Chief Executive Officer, Gerald Champion Regional Medical Center, Alamogordo, NM, p. A416

HEDBERG, Beth, R.N., Director Nursing, Lindsborg Community Hospital, Lindsborg, KS, p. A240
HEDDE, Charles C, M.D., Chief Medical Officer, Good Samaritan Hospital, Vincennes, IN, p. A216
HEDDEN, Tyler
Chief Operating Officer, Santa Rosa Memorial Hospital, Santa Rosa, CA, p. A89
Interim Chief Executive Officer, Santa Rosa Memorial Hospital, Santa Rosa, CA, p. A89
HEDDERMAN, Michael, Senior Vice President Finance and Chief Financial Officer, Northwestern Medicine Marianjoy Rehabilitation Hospital, Wheaton, IL, p. A198
HEDGES, David, Chief Financial Officer, Southwestern Regional Medical Center, Tulsa, OK, p. A509
HEDLUND, Chris, Director Information Systems, Community Hospital–Fairfax, Fairfax, MO, p. A360
HEDRIX, Michael D., Administrator and President, Essentia Health Sandstone, Sandstone, MN, p. A340
HEEGAARD, William, M.D., Chief Medical Officer, Hennepin Healthcare, Minneapolis, MN, p. A335
HEEMANN, John, Vice President and Chief Information Officer, Aspire Hospital, Conroe, TX, p. A593
HEETER, Colleen, Chief Operating Officer, Campbell County Health, Gillette, WY, p. A711
HEFFERNAN, Paul F, Vice President Human Resources, Women & Infants Hospital Of Rhode Island, Providence, RI, p. A548
HEFFERNAN, Rebecca, Director Human Resources, Metrowest Medical Center, Framingham, MA, p. A298
HEFFERS, Margaret, Assistant Vice President Human Resources, Geisinger Wyoming Valley Medical Center, Wilkes Barre, PA, p. A544
HEFFLINGER, Larry, Chief Information Officer, Fulton County Health Center, Wauseon, OH, p. A493
HEFLIN, Clyde, M.D., Chief Medical Officer, Curahealth Nashville, Nashville, TN, p. A576
HEFLIN, Eric, Chief Executive Officer, Amg Mercy, Oklahoma City, OK, p. A503
HEFNER, Donna J., President and Chief Executive Officer, Sierra View Medical Center, Porterville, CA, p. A79
HEFNER, Katherine, MSN, Chief Nursing Officer, St. Luke'S Hospital, Columbus, NC, p. A452
HEFNER, Kathy, Chief Nursing Officer, Mcdowell Hospital, Marion, NC, p. A458
HEGGEM, Mark, M.D., Chief Medical Officer, Riverwood Healthcare Center, Aitkin, MN, p. A327
HEGGEN, Steve, Administrative Director Human Resources, St. Joseph Hospital, Fort Wayne, IN, p. A204
HEGGER, John, Director Information Systems, Union County Hospital, Anna, IL, p. A173
HEGLAND, Larry T, M.D., Chief Medical Officer, Decatur Memorial Hospital, Decatur, IL, p. A180
HEGSTROM, Michael T, M.D., Chief Medical Officer, Geisinger–Lewistown Hospital, Lewistown, PA, p. A530
HEICHERT, Susan
Chief Information Officer, Mercy Hospital, Coon Rapids, MN, p. A330
Senior Vice President and Chief Information Officer, Abbott Northwestern Hospital, Minneapolis, MN, p. A335
Senior Vice President, United Hospital, Saint Paul, MN, p. A340
HEIDT, Robert, Director Information Systems, Pembina County Memorial Hospital And Wedgewood Manor, Cavalier, ND, p. A466
HEIFNER, Bruce, Chief Financial Officer, Pella Regional Health Center, Pella, IA, p. A228
HEIFNER, Robert A., Chief Executive Officer, St. Luke'S Sugar Land Hospital, Sugar Land, TX, p. A638
HEIKKINEN, Todd, Manager Sports Medicine and Rehabilitation Services, Orthopaedic Hospital Of Wisconsin, Glendale, WI, p. A695
HEILMAN, Brooke, Chief Financial Officer, Bowdle Hospital, Bowdle, SD, p. A559
HEIM, Chad, Management Information System Director, Lifestream Behavioral Center, Leesburg, FL, p. A128
HEIM, Nicole, Chief Information Officer, Milford Regional Medical Center, Milford, MA, p. A301
HEIM, Tonya, R.N., MSN, Vice President Patient Services and Chief Nursing Officer, Memorial Hospital And Health Care Center, Jasper, IN, p. A208
HEIMAN, Thomas, Vice President Information Services and Chief Information Officer, John T. Mather Memorial Hospital, Port Jefferson, NY, p. A441
HEIMBECHER, Catherine, Chief Executive Officer, Select Specialty Hospital–Madison, Madison, WI, p. A698
HEIN, Jodi, Chief Nursing Officer, Providence Holy Cross Medical Center, Mission Hills, CA, p. A71
HEINE, Ann, Chief Executive Officer, Surgical Specialty Center Of Baton Rouge, Baton Rouge, LA, p. A264
HEINEMANN, Don, Administrator and Chief Executive Officer, Blount Memorial Hospital, Maryville, TN, p. A574
HEINEMEIER, Robert, Interim Chief Financial Officer, Sonoma West Medical Center, Sebastopol, CA, p. A89
HEINISCH, Sheri, Compliance Officer, Chi Lisbon Health, Lisbon, ND, p. A468
HEINRICH, Bill, Chief Financial Officer, Adventhealth Zephyrhills, Zephyrhills, FL, p. A144
HEINRICH, Caleb, Chief Financial Officer, Adventhealth North Pinellas, Tarpon Springs, FL, p. A142
HEINRICH, DR. Michelle, Interim Chief Executive Officer, Se Texas Er & Hospital, Humble, TX, p. A615
HEINRICH, Kerry
Chief Executive Officer, Loma Linda University Children'S Hospital, Loma Linda, CA, p. A64
Chief Executive Officer, Loma Linda University Medical Center, Loma Linda, CA, p. A64
HEINRICH, Michael G., Senior Vice President and Chief Financial Officer, Unitypoint Health – St. Luke'S Hospital, Cedar Rapids, IA, p. A218
HEINRICHS, Alice, CPA, Chief Financial Officer, Van Diest Medical Center, Webster City, IA, p. A231
HEINRICHS, Leann, M.D., Chief of Staff, Thayer County Health Services, Hebron, NE, p. A386
HEINS, Patrick, President, Vidant Edgecombe Hospital, Tarboro, NC, p. A463
HEINSOHN, Carmel, M.D., Medical Director, Bournewood Health Systems, Brookline, MA, p. A297
HEINTZ, Shirley, R.N., MS, Vice President Patient Care, Liberty Hospital, Liberty, MO, p. A364
HEINZE, Kyle, Coordinator Information Technology, Riveredge Hospital, Forest Park, IL, p. A183
HEINZMAN, Jerry, Senior Vice President and Chief Financial Officer, Sampson Regional Medical Center, Clinton, NC, p. A452
HEINZMANN, Bill, Director Human Resources, Texoma Medical Center, Denison, TX, p. A599
HEISE, James, Chief Medical Officer, Door County Medical Center, Sturgeon Bay, WI, p. A706
HEISE, Teresa, Coordinator Management Information Systems, Pender Community Hospital, Pender, NE, p. A391
HEISEL, Diane, Acting Director, Center For Forensic Psychiatry, Saline, MI, p. A322
HEISER, Eric, Chief Information Resource Management, Sioux Falls Veterans Affairs Health Care System, Sioux Falls, SD, p. A564
HEISHMAN, Lisa, R.N., Vice President, Valley Health Shenandoah Memorial Hospital, Woodstock, VA, p. A669
HEISMEYER, Joyce, Chief Operating Officer, Kansas Heart Hospital, Wichita, KS, p. A247
HEISSER, Randy, M.D., Medical Director, Kindred Hospital–Chattanooga, Chattanooga, TN, p. A567
HEIT, Ryan, Chief Financial Officer, Northern Nevada Medical Center, Sparks, NV, p. A398
HEITHAUS, Carolyn, Chief Financial Officer, Calverthealth Medical Center, Prince Frederick, MD, p. A293
HEITMEYER, Paulette, Administrator and Chief Operating Officer, Marina Del Rey Hospital, Marina Del Rey, CA, p. A71
HEITZENRATER, James F., Chief Executive Officer, W. J. Mangold Memorial Hospital, Lockney, TX, p. A621
HEITZMAN, Cynthia, R.N., Chief Nursing Officer, Seven Rivers Regional Medical Center, Crystal River, FL, p. A120
HELDT, Katie, Chief Nursing Officer, Greene County Medical Center, Jefferson, IA, p. A225
HELFER, Cassandra, Chief Financial Officer, Ralph H. Johnson Veterans Affairs Medical Center, Charleston, SC, p. A550
HELGERSON, Bryce R., Chief Administrative Officer, Legacy Salmon Creek Medical Center, Vancouver, WA, p. A681
HELGESEN, Roald, Chief Executive Officer, Alaska Native Medical Center, Anchorage, AK, p. A25
HELGESON, Heidi E, M.D., Chief Medical Officer, Rio Grande Hospital, Del Norte, CO, p. A98
HELGET, Peggy, R.N., MSN, Vice President Patient Services and Chief Nursing Officer, Methodist Jennie Edmundson Hospital, Council Bluffs, IA, p. A220
HELLA, Timothy, Chief Information Officer, Munson Healthcare Otsego Memorial Hospital, Gaylord, MI, p. A312
HELLAND, Don, M.D., Chief Medical Officer, Roosevelt Medical Center, Culbertson, MT, p. A375
HELLE, Dan, Human Resources Officer, Iowa City Veterans Affairs Health Care System, Iowa City, IA, p. A224
HELLE, Tara, Human Resources Lead, Palo Alto County Health System, Emmetsburg, IA, p. A222
HELLELAND, Brian, Chief Executive Officer, St. Jude Medical Center, Fullerton, CA, p. A60
HELLER, Michael, Chief Financial Officer, Lecom Corry Memorial Hospital, Corry, PA, p. A523
HELLER, Tom, Vice President Operations and Human Resources, Camden Clark Medical Center, Parkersburg, WV, p. A688
HELM, Carrie, Chief Executive Officer, Arkansas Surgical Hospital, North Little Rock, AR, p. A46
HELM, Pamela E., Executive Director, Devereux Texas Treatment Network, League City, TX, p. A620
HELMERS, Richard, Regional Vice President, Mayo Clinic Health System In Eau Claire, Eau Claire, WI, p. A694
HELMES, Claudia, R.N., Chief Nursing Officer, Banner Lassen Medical Center, Susanville, CA, p. A91
HELMICKI, Soni, Chief Executive Officer, Wellbridge Healthcare Of Fort Worth, Fort Worth, TX, p. A606
HELMS, Candace, Director Information Services, Good Samaritan Medical Center, West Palm Beach, FL, p. A144
HELMS, Ella Raye., Chief Executive Officer, Cogdell Memorial Hospital, Snyder, TX, p. A637
HELMS, James, Vice President Finance, Jones Memorial Hospital, Wellsville, NY, p. A447
HELMS, Joseph, Director Information Systems, Dekalb Regional Medical Center, Fort Payne, AL, p. A18
HELPER, Mark A, Corporate Vice President and Chief Financial Officer, Munson Medical Center, Traverse City, MI, p. A323
HELSEL, David S., Chief Executive Officer, Spring Grove Hospital Center, Baltimore, MD, p. A288
HELSEL, Elizabeth, Chief Executive Officer, U. S. Public Health Service Indian Hospital, Parker, AZ, p. A32
HELSPER, Richard S, Chief Operating Officer, Genesis Healthcare System, Zanesville, OH, p. A495
HELSTROM, James, Chief Medical Officer, Fox Chase Cancer Center–American Oncologic Hospital, Philadelphia, PA, p. A534
HELTON, Fay, Director Medical Records, Red River Hospital, Llc, Wichita Falls, TX, p. A646
HELTON, R.J, D.O., Chief of Staff, Coal County General Hospital, Coalgate, OK, p. A498
HELTON, Stephanie, Chief Financial Officer, Weatherford Regional Hospital, Weatherford, OK, p. A510
HELVEY, John, Chief Information Officer, Orchard Hospital, Gridley, CA, p. A61
HEMATILLAKE, M. Ganga, M.D., Chief of Staff, White River Junction Veterans Affairs Medical Center, White River Junction, VT, p. A655
HEMBREE, Greg, Senior Vice President and Chief Financial Officer, St. Francis Hospital, Columbus, GA, p. A150
HEMKER, Debbie, Senior Vice President and Area Manager, Kaiser Permanente Fresno Medical Center, Fresno, CA, p. A59
HEMMER, Chris, Director Finance, Aurora West Allis Medical Center, West Allis, WI, p. A708
HEMMING, Stuart, Chief Operating Officer, Portsmouth Regional Hospital, Portsmouth, NH, p. A402
HEMPEL, Stephen, M.D., President Medical Staff, Spectrum Health Lakeland, Saint Joseph, MI, p. A322
HEMPHILL, Dana, Manager Human Resources, Shoshone Medical Center, Kellogg, ID, p. A169
HEMPHILL, Robyn, Chief Executive Officer and Chief Nursing Officer, Monroe Surgical Hospital, Monroe, LA, p. A274
HEMPLER, Shannan, Director Human Resources, Norton County Hospital, Norton, KS, p. A242
HEMSATH, Randolph, M.D., Medical Director, Suncoast Behavioral Health Center, Bradenton, FL, p. A119
HEMSTEAD, Peter, Chief Operating Officer, Doctors Hospital Of Sarasota, Sarasota, FL, p. A139
HENDEE, Daniel, Director, Philadelphia Veterans Affairs Medical Center, Philadelphia, PA, p. A536
HENDEL, Dawna, R.N., Chief Nursing Officer and Vice President Patient Care Services, Providence Saint John'S Health Center, Santa Monica, CA, p. A89
HENDERSHOT, Richard
Chief Financial Officer, Casey County Hospital, Liberty, KY, p. A255
Chief Financial Officer, Jane Todd Crawford Hospital, Greensburg, KY, p. A252
HENDERSON, Claudia, Chief Human Resources, St. Elizabeth'S Medical Center, Brockton, MA, p. A296
HENDERSON, David K, M.D., Deputy Director Clinical Care, National Institutes Of Health Clinical Center, Bethesda, MD, p. A289
HENDERSON, David M, Director Human Resources, Summersville Regional Medical Center, Summersville, WV, p. A689
HENDERSON, Deborah, Acting Chief Financial Officer, Harry S. Truman Memorial Veterans Hospital, Columbia, MO, p. A359
HENDERSON, Donald G.
President and Chief Executive Officer, Leesburg Regional Medical Center, Leesburg, FL, p. A128
President and Chief Executive Officer, The Villages Regional Hospital, The Villages, FL, p. A142
HENDERSON, Gary, Chief Information Resources Management Services, Huntington Veterans Affairs Medical Center, Huntington, WV, p. A686

HENDERSON, Jace, Chief Financial Officer, Parkview Hospital, Wheeler, TX, p. A645

HENDERSON, Jessica, Manager Human Resources, Fitzgibbon Hospital, Marshall, MO, p. A365

HENDERSON, John
Chief Human Resources Management, James H. Quillen Veterans Affairs Medical Center, Mountain Home, TN, p. A576
Chief Information Officer, Choc Children'S At Mission Hospital, Mission Viejo, CA, p. A72
Vice President and Chief Information Officer, Children'S Hospital Of Orange County, Orange, CA, p. A76

HENDERSON, John, M.D., Chief Medical Officer, Unity Health White County Medical Center, Searcy, AR, p. A48

HENDERSON, Katherine
President and Chief Executive Officer, Ascension Seton Hays, Kyle, TX, p. A618
President and Chief Executive Officer, Ascension Seton Northwest, Austin, TX, p. A584
President and Chief Executive Officer, Ascension Seton Southwest, Austin, TX, p. A585
President and Chief Executive Officer, Ascension Seton Williamson, Round Rock, TX, p. A632

HENDERSON, Kathy, Director Human Resources, Willow Crest Hospital, Miami, OK, p. A502

HENDERSON, Larry, M.D., Medical Director, Greene County Hospital, Leakesville, MS, p. A350

HENDERSON, Lisa
Chief Operating Officer, Palacios Community Medical Center, Palacios, TX, p. A627
Chief Operations Officer, Palacios Community Medical Center, Palacios, TX, p. A627

HENDERSON, Lori, Chief Nursing Officer, Vice President Clinical, Colorado Canyons Hospital And Medical Center, Fruita, CO, p. A101

HENDERSON, Lorrie, Chief Executive Officer, Huhukam Memorial Hospital, Sacaton, AZ, p. A35

HENDERSON, Melody, Ph.D., R.N., Chief Operating Officer and Chief Nursing Officer, Golden Plains Community Hospital, Borger, TX, p. A589

HENDERSON, Mike, Human Resources Director, Forest View Psychiatric Hospital, Grand Rapids, MI, p. A312

HENDERSON, Pamela S, Vice President Human Resources, Memorial Hospital Of Carbondale, Carbondale, IL, p. A175

HENDERSON, Patricia, R.N., Vice President Nursing and Clinical Services, Glencoe Regional Health, Glencoe, MN, p. A332

HENDERSON, Paula
Chief Human Resources Officer, University Of Mississippi Medical Center, Jackson, MS, p. A349
Vice President Human Resources, University Of Maryland Medical Center Midtown Campus, Baltimore, MD, p. A287
Vice President Human Resources, University Of Maryland Rehabilitation & Orthopaedic Institute, Baltimore, MD, p. A288

HENDERSON, Peggy, Director Health Information, Rmc–Stringfellow Memorial Hospital, Anniston, AL, p. A13

HENDERSON, Rex, M.D., Chief of Staff, Mcdowell Hospital, Marion, NC, p. A458

HENDERSON, Sue, Human Resource Manager, Smyth County Community Hospital, Marion, VA, p. A662

HENDERSON, Travis, M.D., Chief of Staff, Mobridge Regional Hospital, Mobridge, SD, p. A562

HENDERSON, Vickie, M.D., Chief Medical Officer, Saint Mary'S Regional Medical Center, Russellville, AR, p. A48

HENDERSON, Volante, Director Human Resources, Walton Rehabilitation Hospital, Augusta, GA, p. A148

HENDRICK, Kirk, Director Information Systems, Northside Hospital, Saint Petersburg, FL, p. A138

HENDRICKS, Barbara, Interim Human Resources Director, Galesburg Cottage Hospital, Galesburg, IL, p. A183

HENDRICKS, Marcia
Chief Executive Officer, Adair County Health System, Greenfield, IA, p. A223
Chief Executive Officer, Madison County Health Care System, Winterset, IA, p. A231

HENDRICKS, Nicole Smith, Chief Operating Officer, Regional Medical Center, Orangeburg, SC, p. A556

HENDRICKSEN, Sherry, R.N., MSN, Chief Nursing Officer, Continuecare Hospital At Hendrick Medical Center, Abilene, TX, p. A581

HENDRICKSON, Leslie, Director Human Resources, Coteau Des Prairies Hospital, Sisseton, SD, p. A564

HENDRICKSON, Roman, M.D., Medical Director, Ruby Valley Medical Center, Sheridan, MT, p. A380

HENDRIX, Angie, Director of Nursing, Evergreen Medical Center, Evergreen, AL, p. A17

HENDRIX, Billie, R.N., Director of Nursing, W. J. Mangold Memorial Hospital, Lockney, TX, p. A621

HENDRIX, Jamie, Vice President Patient Care Services, Columbus Community Hospital, Inc., Columbus, WI, p. A693

HENDRIX, Michael, Chief Financial Officer, St. Mary'S Regional Medical Center, Lewiston, ME, p. A283

HENDRIX, Michael A., Chief Financial Officer, St. Joseph Hospital, Bangor, ME, p. A281

HENDRY, Christopher, M.D., Chief Medical Officer, Medical Center, Navicent Health, Macon, GA, p. A156

HENDRYX, Joel, M.D., Chief Medical Officer, University Medical Center Of El Paso, El Paso, TX, p. A603

HENES, Jean M., MSN, R.N., Director of Nursing, Avera Creighton Hospital, Creighton, NE, p. A384

HENESSEE, Nolan, Vice President and Chief Information Officer, St. Joseph'S Hospital, Savannah, GA, p. A160

HENINGER, Bev, Director of Nursing, Kenmare Community Hospital, Kenmare, ND, p. A468

HENKE, Georgia, Operational Account Manager, Osf Healthcare Saint Anthony'S Health Center, Alton, IL, p. A173

HENKE, Mark, Chief Financial Officer, Mena Regional Health System, Mena, AR, p. A46

HENKENIUS, Jim, Chief Financial Officer, Stewart Memorial Community Hospital, Lake City, IA, p. A225

HENLEY, Donald, Vice President Human Resources, Grove City Medical Center, Grove City, PA, p. A526

HENNEBOLD, Julie, R.N., Interim Chief Nursing Officer, Winner Regional Healthcare Center, Winner, SD, p. A565

HENNELLY, John, Chief Executive Officer, Saint Louise Regional Hospital, Gilroy, CA, p. A60

HENNENBERG, Shayla, Director Human Resources, Essentia Health Ada, Ada, MN, p. A327

HENNESSEY, Ruth E, President, Good Samaritan Hospital Medical Center, West Islip, NY, p. A447

HENNESSY, John, Chief Financial Officer, Bonner General Hospital, Sandpoint, ID, p. A172

HENNESSY, Mark, Chief Financial Officer, Riveredge Hospital, Forest Park, IL, p. A183

HENNIGAN, Michael, M.D., Medical Director, Encompass Health Rehabilitation Hospital Of Panama City, Panama City, FL, p. A135

HENNIKA, Billi Jo, Vice President Operations, Mckenzie Health System, Sandusky, MI, p. A322

HENNING, Cindy, R.N., Chief Nursing Officer, Hca Houston Healthcare Northwest, Houston, TX, p. A611

HENNING, William C., Administrator and Chief Executive Officer, Baptist Memorial Hospital–North Mississippi, Oxford, MS, p. A352

HENNIS, Michelle, Administrative Director Financial Services, Grace Hospital, Cleveland, OH, p. A477

HENRICI, Michael, Associate Administrator, Roxborough Memorial Hospital, Philadelphia, PA, p. A536

HENRICKS, William, Ph.D., Vice President and Chief Operating Officer, Ascension Seton Shoal Creek, Austin, TX, p. A585

HENRY, Aden, R.N., Vice President, Patient Care, La Rabida Children'S Hospital, Chicago, IL, p. A178

HENRY, Andrea, Director of Nursing, Sweetwater Hospital, Sweetwater, TN, p. A580

HENRY, Anna, Chief Information Officer, Kimble Hospital, Junction, TX, p. A617

HENRY, Chris, Associate Administrator and Chief Financial Officer, Washington Hospital Healthcare System, Fremont, CA, p. A59

HENRY, Dane W., Chief Executive Officer, Lake Regional Health System, Osage Beach, MO, p. A366

HENRY, David, President and Chief Executive Officer, Northern Montana Health Care, Havre, MT, p. A377

HENRY, Debbie, Vice President and Chief Financial Officer, Baxter Regional Medical Center, Mountain Home, AR, p. A46

HENRY, Donna, Vice President of Nursing Services, Four County Counseling Center, Logansport, IN, p. A210

HENRY, Edwina J, Assistant Chief Nursing Officer, Parkview Regional Hospital, Mexia, TX, p. A624

HENRY, Hannah, Interim Vice President of Human Resources, Emory Johns Creek Hospital, Johns Creek, GA, p. A155

HENRY, Heather, Information Technology Manager, Hammond–Henry Hospital, Geneseo, IL, p. A184

HENRY, James L, Director Human Resources, Sea Pines Rehabilitation Hospital, Melbourne, FL, p. A129

HENRY, Joy, R.N., Chief of Nursing, Faith Community Hospital, Jacksboro, TX, p. A616

HENRY, Joyce, Controller, Encompass Health Rehabilitation Hospital Of York, York, PA, p. A546

HENRY, Kelsea, Chief Financial Officer, Memorial Regional Health, Craig, CO, p. A98

HENRY, Peter, M.D., Chief Medical Officer, Essentia Health St. Joseph'S Medical Center, Brainerd, MN, p. A329

HENRY, Roshonda, Chief Nursing Officer, Encompass Health Rehabilitation Hospital Of Cypress, Houston, TX, p. A611

HENRY, Tim, Accountant, Chatuge Regional Hospital And Nursing Home, Hiawassee, GA, p. A154

HENRY, William
Director Human Resources, Ut Health Henderson, Henderson, TX, p. A610
Director Human Resources, Ut Health Quitman, Quitman, TX, p. A630

HENSEL, David, Director Financial Operations, Ohiohealth Grady Memorial Hospital, Delaware, OH, p. A482

HENSEL, Edward, Chief Information Officer, Va Medical Center, Tomah, WI, p. A706

HENSLEIGH, David, Director Medical Staff, Clay County Hospital, Ashland, AL, p. A13

HENSLEY, Angela, Director of Nursing, Pathways Of Tennessee, Jackson, TN, p. A571

HENSLEY, Anna
Chief Operating Officer, Ohiohealth Dublin Methodist Hospital, Dublin, OH, p. A482
Chief Operating Officer, Ohiohealth Grady Memorial Hospital, Delaware, OH, p. A482

HENSLEY, Barry, Director Information Systems, Logan Regional Medical Center, Logan, WV, p. A686

HENSLEY, Kristy, Director Human Resources, Orthoindy Hospital, Indianapolis, IN, p. A207

HENSON, Judith
Vice President Patient Care Services, Southeast Georgia Health System Brunswick Campus, Brunswick, GA, p. A148
Vice President, Patient Care Services, Southeast Georgia Health System Camden Campus, Saint Marys, GA, p. A159

HENSON, Lily, M.D., Chief Medical Officer, Piedmont Henry Hospital, Stockbridge, GA, p. A161

HENSON, Maureen, Vice President Human Resources, Rapid City Regional Hospital, Rapid City, SD, p. A563

HENSON, Pam, Executive Director, Pathways Of Tennessee, Jackson, TN, p. A571

HENSON, Steve, Chief Executive Officer, Bradley County Medical Center, Warren, AR, p. A49

HENTHORN, Cheryl, Chief Executive Officer, Summa Rehab Hospital, Akron, OH, p. A471

HENTON, Thomas, Chief Executive Officer, Carnegie Tri–County Municipal Hospital, Carnegie, OK, p. A497

HENTZEN PAGE, Ann, Chief Executive Officer, Summit Surgical, Hutchinson, KS, p. A237

HENTZEN PAGE, Ann, M.D., Medical Director, Summit Surgical, Hutchinson, KS, p. A237

HENZE, Rick, Chief Financial Officer, St. Mary'S Healthcare, Amsterdam, NY, p. A422

HEPNER, Tim, M.D., Chief Medical Officer, St. John Owasso, Owasso, OK, p. A506

HERALD, Kathleen R, Vice President and Chief Information Officer, Lexington Medical Center, West Columbia, SC, p. A558

HERB, Beth, Administrator, State Correctional Institution At Camp Hill, Camp Hill, PA, p. A521

HERBECK, Marilyn, Coordinator Human Resources, Community Hospital Of Staunton, Staunton, IL, p. A197

HERBEL, Aaron, Administrator, Mercy Hospital, Moundridge, KS, p. A241

HERBER, Steven
President and Chief Executive Officer, Adventist Health St. Helena, Saint Helena, CA, p. A82
President and Chief Executive Officer, Adventist Health St. Helena, Vallejo, CA, p. A93

HERBERGER, Eva, Administrator Human Resources, Usc Verdugo Hills Hospital, Glendale, CA, p. A60

HERBERT, Daniel, M.D., Medical Administrative Officer, Millinocket Regional Hospital, Millinocket, ME, p. A284

HERBERT, Laurie, Vice President Operations, Three Rivers Health, Three Rivers, MI, p. A323

HERBERT, Teresa, M.D., Chief Medical Officer, Adventhealth Hendersonville, Hendersonville, NC, p. A456

HERBOLD, Charlotte, Manager Business Officer, Garfield County Health Center, Jordan, MT, p. A378

HERBST, Gary, Chief Executive Officer, Kaweah Delta Medical Center, Visalia, CA, p. A94

HERCHENHAHN, Gina, Chief Executive Officer, Landmark Hospital Of Salt Lake City, Murray, UT, p. A649

HERD, Jacqueline, Executive Vice President and Chief Nursing Officer, Grady Memorial Hospital, Atlanta, GA, p. A146

HERDER, Debbie, Controller, Promise Hospital Of Wichita Falls, Wichita Falls, TX, p. A645

HERDON, Lori, President and Chief Executive Officer, Atlanticare Regional Medical Center, Atlantic City, NJ, p. A403

HERFORT, Oliver, M.D., Chief Medical Officer, Valley Regional Hospital, Claremont, NH, p. A399

HERGET, Jordan
Chief Operating Officer, Good Samaritan Hospital, San Jose, CA, p. A86
President and Chief Executive Officer, O'Connor Hospital, San Jose, CA, p. A86
Senior Vice President and Manager, Kaiser Permanente Roseville Medical Center, Roseville, CA, p. A81

HERING, John, M.D., Chief Medical Officer, Centracare Health–Monticello, Monticello, MN, p. A336

HERING, Kristine, R.N., Chief Nursing Officer, Speare Memorial Hospital, Plymouth, NH, p. A402

HERINK, Philip, Administrator, Schick Shadel Hospital, Seattle, WA, p. A678

HERKIMER, Eileen, Director Human Resources, United Memorial Medical Center, Batavia, NY, p. A423

HERLONG, John, Medical Staff President, Unc Lenoir Healthcare, Kinston, NC, p. A457

HERMAN, Jeff, Chief Executive Officer, Prairie St. John'S, Fargo, ND, p. A466

HERMAN, John J., Chief Executive Officer, Ochsner Medical Center – North Shore, Slidell, LA, p. A279

HERMAN, Michael
Chief Executive Officer, Riverview Regional Medical Center, Carthage, TN, p. A566
Chief Executive Officer, Trousdale Medical Center, Hartsville, TN, p. A570

HERMANN, Terri, R.N., Chief Nursing Officer, Franklin Hospital District, Benton, IL, p. A174

HERMES, Dina, Chief Financial Officer, Golden Plains Community Hospital, Borger, TX, p. A589

HERMOSA, Mercy, Director of Information System, Coral Gables Hospital, Coral Gables, FL, p. A120

HERNANDEZ, Ashley, Chief Information Technology Officer, Pender Memorial Hospital, Burgaw, NC, p. A450

HERNANDEZ, Debra T.
Vice President, Chief Operating Officer and Chief Nursing Officer, Dell Seton Medical Center At The University Of Texas, Austin, TX, p. A585
Vice President, Chief Operation Officer and Chief Nursing Officer, Dell Seton Medical Center At The University Of Texas, Austin, TX, p. A585

HERNANDEZ, Dennis, Chief Medical Officer, Adventhealth New Smyrna Beach, New Smyrna Beach, FL, p. A133

HERNANDEZ, Diane
Area Finance Officer, Kaiser Permanente San Rafael Medical Center, San Rafael, CA, p. A87
Area Finance Officer, Kaiser Permanente Santa Rosa Medical Center, Santa Rosa, CA, p. A89

HERNANDEZ, Dinorah, Esq, Executive Director, Hospital Pavia Yauco, Yauco, PR, p. A720

HERNANDEZ, George B., Jr, President and Chief Executive Officer, University Health System, San Antonio, TX, p. A635

HERNANDEZ, Gloria, Executive Director, University Pediatric Hospital, Rio Piedras, PR, p. A718

HERNANDEZ, Janira, Coordinator Human Resources, Hospital Metropolitano Dr. Susoni, Arecibo, PR, p. A715

HERNANDEZ, Kim, Chief Human Resources Officer, Sage Specialty Hospital (Ltac), Denham Springs, LA, p. A267

HERNANDEZ, Kristen, Director Human Resources, Healthsouth Rehabilitation Hospital Of New Mexico, Albuquerque, NM, p. A416

HERNANDEZ, Leonard, Chief Executive Officer, Coffey County Hospital, Burlington, KS, p. A233

HERNANDEZ, Lilly, Human Resources Director, Catalina Island Medical Center, Avalon, CA, p. A51

HERNANDEZ, Lisa J., R.N., Vice President, Patient Care Continuum and Chief Nursing Officer, Sarah Bush Lincoln Health Center, Mattoon, IL, p. A188

HERNANDEZ, Luz Maria, Director Human Resources, I. Gonzalez Martinez Oncologic Hospital, Hato Rey, PR, p. A716

HERNANDEZ, Matt, Director of Information Technology and System, Kendall Regional Medical Center, Miami, FL, p. A130

HERNANDEZ, Reyna, Chief Financial Officer, Encompass Health Rehabilitation Hospital Of Miami, Cutler Bay, FL, p. A120

HERNANDEZ, Sandi, Controller, Lafayette General Surgical Hospital, Lafayette, LA, p. A271

HERNANDEZ, Susan, R.N.
Chief Nurse Executive, University Of Texas Southwestern Medical Center, Dallas, TX, p. A598
Chief Nursing Officer, Rice Medical Center, Eagle Lake, TX, p. A600

HERNANDEZ–KEEBLE, Sonia, Superintendent, Rio Grande State Center/South Texas Health Care System, Harlingen, TX, p. A609

HERNANDEZ–LICHTL, Javier, Chief Executive Officer, Baptist Health South Florida, West Kendall Baptist Hospital, Miami, FL, p. A130

HERNDON, Amy, Chief Finance Officer, Morristown–Hamblen Healthcare System, Morristown, TN, p. A576

HERNDON, David N., M.D., Chief of Staff, Shriners Hospitals For Children–Galveston, Galveston, TX, p. A607

HERNDON, Lori S., President and Chief Executive Officer, Atlanticare Regional Medical Center, Atlantic City, NJ, p. A403

HERNDON, Robert Scott
Chief Financial Officer, Ascension Seton Shoal Creek, Austin, TX, p. A585
Vice President Chief Financial Officer, Ascension Seton Medical Center Austin, Austin, TX, p. A584

HERNDON, Sandra, CPA, Chief Financial Officer, Bleckley Memorial Hospital, Cochran, GA, p. A150

HERNDON, Scott, FACHE
Chief Financial Officer, Ministry Market Texas, Dell Seton Medical Center At The University Of Texas, Austin, TX, p. A585
Chief Financial Officer, Texas Market, Ascension Seton Northwest, Austin, TX, p. A584

HERNE, Mose, Chief Executive Officer, Hopi Health Care Center, Keams Canyon, AZ, p. A30

HEROLD, Mary, Director Human Resources, Share Medical Center, Alva, OK, p. A496

HERPFER, Caroline, Chief Nursing Officer, Arizona Orthopedic Surgical Hospital, Chandler, AZ, p. A28

HERR, Brenda, Chief Nursing Officer, East Adams Rural Healthcare, Ritzville, WA, p. A677

HERR, Michael, Chief Operating Officer, Starr Regional Medical Center, Athens, TN, p. A566

HERRARA, Espie, Chief Financial Officer, Peak Behavioral Health Services, Santa Teresa, NM, p. A420

HERRERA, Jocelyn A.
Director Human Resources, Kaiser Permanente Orange County Anaheim Medical Center, Anaheim, CA, p. A50
Human Resources Director, Kaiser Permanente San Diego Medical Center, San Diego, CA, p. A83

HERRERA, Veronica, Director Human Resources, Las Encinas Hospital, Pasadena, CA, p. A77

HERRERA, Yamila, Director Human Resources, Hialeah Hospital, Hialeah, FL, p. A124

HERRERO, Carmelo, M.D., Medical Director, Hospital Oriente, Humacao, PR, p. A716

HERRICK, Brian, M.D., Chief Information Officer, Cambridge Health Alliance, Cambridge, MA, p. A297

HERRIN, Curtis
Chief Financial Officer, Astria Toppenish Hospital, Toppenish, WA, p. A681
Chief Financial Officer, Upmc Memorial, York, PA, p. A546

HERRING, Davey, M.D., Chief Medical Officer, Dorminy Medical Center, Fitzgerald, GA, p. A153

HERRING, Donnette, Chief Information Officer, Vidant Medical Center, Greenville, NC, p. A455

HERRING, Randy, M.D., Chief of Staff, Coon Memorial Hospital, Dalhart, TX, p. A595

HERRING, Sherry, Chief Nursing Officer, Uva–Healthsouth Rehabilitation Hospital, Charlottesville, VA, p. A657

HERRINGTON, Bruce, M.D., Chief Medical Officer, South Georgia Medical Center Lanier Campus, Lakeland, GA, p. A155

HERRINGTON, Kristal, Senior Director, Human Resources, Twin County Regional Healthcare, Galax, VA, p. A660

HERRMAN, Edward, President and Chief Executive Officer, Hays Medical Center, Hays, KS, p. A236

HERRMANN, Lee, Chief Healthcare Technology Officer, Santa Clara Valley Medical Center, San Jose, CA, p. A87

HERRMANN, Tim, Administrator, Peacehealth Cottage Grove Community Medical Center, Cottage Grove, OR, p. A512

HERRON, Katherine, Director Human Resources, Richard H. Hutchings Psychiatric Center, Syracuse, NY, p. A445

HERRON, Mary Beth, Director of Human Resources, Illinois Valley Community Hospital, Peru, IL, p. A193

HERSEY, Robert, Chief Financial Officer, Northeastern Vermont Regional Hospital, Saint Johnsbury, VT, p. A655

HERSHBERGER, Brandy, Chief Nursing Officer, Fawcett Memorial Hospital, Port Charlotte, FL, p. A137

HERSHBERGER, Scott, Acting Chief Information Management Services, Battle Creek Veterans Affairs Medical Center, Battle Creek, MI, p. A307

HERSHMAN, Sharon, R.N., Chief Nursing Officer, Providence Holy Family Hospital, Spokane, WA, p. A679

HERSHMANN, Michael, Medical Center Director, Veterans Affairs Northern Indiana Health Care System, Fort Wayne, IN, p. A204

HERTEL, Holly, Director Nursing, Larned State Hospital, Larned, KS, p. A238

HERTZ, Karl Edward, Assistant Administrator, Memorial Hospital Of Converse County, Douglas, WY, p. A711

HERWIG, Brian J., President and Chief Executive Officer, Perry County Memorial Hospital, Tell City, IN, p. A215

HERZBERG, Deborah L., Administrator, Avera Holy Family Hospital, Estherville, IA, p. A222

HERZL–BETZ, Kenneth, M.D.
Chief Medical Officer and Senior Vice President Medical Affairs, St. Joseph'S Hospital, Elmira, NY, p. A427
Chief Medical Officer, Arnot Ogden Medical Center, Elmira, NY, p. A427

HERZOG, Dean, Chief Financial Officer, Kona Community Hospital, Kealakekua, HI, p. A166

HERZOG, Vearnail, Chief Executive Officer, Allegiance Specialty Hospital Of Greenville, Greenville, MS, p. A347

HESCH, Dennis, Executive Vice President Finance, System Chief Financial Officer, Carle Foundation Hospital, Urbana, IL, p. A197

HESCH, Mike J, Regional Administrator Human Resources, Mayo Clinic Health System – Franciscan Healthcare In Sparta, Sparta, WI, p. A705

HESS, David F.
Chief Executive Officer, Reynolds Memorial Hospital, Glen Dale, WV, p. A685
Chief Executive Officer, Wetzel County Hospital, New Martinsville, WV, p. A687

HESS, David F., M.D., President Medical Staff, Reynolds Memorial Hospital, Glen Dale, WV, p. A685

HESS, Heidi, Chief Nursing Officer, Genesis Medical Center–Aledo, Aledo, IL, p. A173

HESS, Jim, Chief Operations Officer, Salt Lake Behavioral Health, Salt Lake City, UT, p. A652

HESS, Michael, M.D., Chief Medical Officer, Lakeview Hospital, Bountiful, UT, p. A647

HESS, Pamela
Chief Financial Officer, Saint Thomas Midtown Hospital, Nashville, TN, p. A577
Chief Financial Officer, Saint Thomas West Hospital, Nashville, TN, p. A577

HESS, Phil, Chief Executive Officer, Wellspan Philhaven, Mount Gretna, PA, p. A532

HESS, Steve
Vice President & Chief Information Officer, Uchealth Medical Center Of The Rockies, Loveland, CO, p. A104
Vice President Information Services and Chief Information Officer, University Of Colorado Hospital, Aurora, CO, p. A96

HESS, Susan, Director Human Resources, J. C. Blair Memorial Hospital, Huntingdon, PA, p. A527

HESSE, Fred, M.D., Medical Director, Arms Acres, Carmel, NY, p. A425

HESSE, Nancy, President and Chief Executive Officer, Cancer Treatment Centers Of America–Eastern Regional Medical Center, Philadelphia, PA, p. A534

HESSELRODE, Renee, Director Health Information Management, Landmark Hospital Of Cape Girardeau, Cape Girardeau, MO, p. A357

HESSHEIMER, Susan, Director Human Resources, Johnson County Hospital, Tecumseh, NE, p. A392

HESSING, Jeffrey, M.D., Medical Director, Treasure Valley Hospital, Boise, ID, p. A168

HESSMAN, Mary Pat, Chief Fiscal, Northport Veterans Affairs Medical Center, Northport, NY, p. A439

HESTER, Amber, Chief Executive Officer, Encompass Health Rehabilitation Hospital Of Gulfport, Gulfport, MS, p. A347

HESTER, Charles H., CPA, Chief Financial Officer, Northwest Mississippi Medical Center, Clarksdale, MS, p. A345

HESTER, Josh, Chief Operating Officer, Gadsden Regional Medical Center, Gadsden, AL, p. A18

HESTER, Joyce, CPA, Senior Vice President and Chief Financial Officer, Christus Mother Frances Hospital – Tyler, Tyler, TX, p. A642

HESTER, Kathy, Chief Nursing Officer, Orange Park Medical Center, Orange Park, FL, p. A134

HESTER, Michael, Chief Executive Officer, Stephens County Hospital, Toccoa, GA, p. A162

HESTON, Cathy, Chief Nursing Officer, Three Rivers Medical Center, Louisa, KY, p. A255

HETHERINGTON, Ray, Network Administrator, Wheatland Memorial Healthcare, Harlowton, MT, p. A377

HETLETVED, Beth, Director of Nurses, Chi St. Alexius Health Garrison, Garrison, ND, p. A467

HETMANSKI, Jeff, President and Chief Operating Officer, Novant Health Uva Health System Culpeper Medical Center, Culpeper, VA, p. A658

HETT, Samantha, Manager Human Resources, Satanta District Hospital And Long Term Care, Satanta, KS, p. A245

HETTICH, E Paul, Chief Financial Officer, Brylin Hospitals, Buffalo, NY, p. A424

HETTINGER, JoAnn, R.N., Director of Patient Care Services, Avera Weskota Memorial Hospital, Wessington Springs, SD, p. A565

HETTINGER, MaryLou, Director Quality Management, Devereux Children'S Behavioral Health Center, Malvern, PA, p. A530

HETTINGER, Tiffany Erin, Associate Chief Nursing Officer, North Colorado Medical Center, Greeley, CO, p. A101

HETU, Maureen, Chief Information Officer, Our Lady Of Lourdes Medical Center, Camden, NJ, p. A404

HETZ, Mark
Chief Information Officer, Asante Ashland Community Hospital, Ashland, OR, p. A511
Chief Information Officer, Asante Rogue Regional Medical Center, Medford, OR, p. A515
Chief Information Officer, Asante Three Rivers Medical Center, Grants Pass, OR, p. A513

HEURING, Ron, Director Information Systems, Perry County Memorial Hospital, Perryville, MO, p. A367

HEURTIN, John, Chief Financial Officer, Lee'S Summit Medical Center, Lee'S Summit, MO, p. A364

HEUSER, Keith E., Market President, Chi Mercy Health, Valley City, ND, p. A469

HEUSTON, Melanie M, Chief Nursing Office, Meritus Medical Center, Hagerstown, MD, p. A291

HEWSTON, MaryAnn, R.N., Chief Nurse Executive, Meadville Medical Center, Meadville, PA, p. A531

HEYDON, Larry, President and Chief Executive Officer, Johnson Memorial Hospital, Franklin, IN, p. A204

HEYN, Matthew M., Chief Executive Officer, Ransom Memorial Hospital, Ottawa, KS, p. A242

HIATT, Tim, Chief Information Officer, Brodstone Memorial Hospital, Superior, NE, p. A392

HIBBARD, Carrie, Human Resource Business Partner, Adventist Healthcare Physical Health And Rehabilitation, Rockville, MD, p. A293

HIBBS, Cathy, Chief Executive Officer, Carlsbad Medical Center, Carlsbad, NM, p. A417

HIBEN, Daniel, Chief Executive Officer, Crittenden County Hospital, Marion, KY, p. A257

HIBSCHMAN, Kimberly, Chief Financial Officer, Riverview Behavioral Health, Texarkana, AR, p. A49

HICK, Claire, Chief Executive Officer, Longleaf Hospital, Alexandria, LA, p. A262

HICKEY, Beth, Vice President, Finance, Advocate Lutheran General Hospital, Park Ridge, IL, p. A192

HICKEY, Christopher, Chief Financial Officer, Northwestern Medical Center, Saint Albans, VT, p. A655

HICKEY, Conner, Chief Operating Officer, Woodland Heights Medical Center, Lufkin, TX, p. A622

HICKEY, Marcia H, Senior Vice President Operations, Hebrew Senior Care, West Hartford, CT, p. A112

HICKEY–BOYNTON, Meg
Chief Financial Officer, Community Hospital Of Anaconda, Anaconda, MT, p. A374
Director Human Resources and Marketing, Community Hospital Of Anaconda, Anaconda, MT, p. A374

HICKLING, Andrea, Vice President of Finance and Chief Financial Officer, Northern Hospital Of Surry County, Mount Airy, NC, p. A459

HICKLING, Karen, Director Human Resources, Palmdale Regional Medical Center, Palmdale, CA, p. A77

HICKMAN, George, Executive Vice President and Chief Information Officer, Albany Medical Center, Albany, NY, p. A422

HICKMAN, Louise, R.N., Vice President of Patient Care Services, Jefferson Regional Medical Center, Pine Bluff, AR, p. A47

HICKMAN, Monica, Director Fiscal Services, Shriners Hospitals For Children–Spokane, Spokane, WA, p. A680

HICKMAN, Sherie C., Chief Executive Officer, Sutter Delta Medical Center, Antioch, CA, p. A50

HICKMAN, Troy, Director Human Resources, Hospital District 6 – Harper Campus, Harper, KS, p. A236

HICKS, Christia, Vice President Human Resources, Eskenazi Health, Indianapolis, IN, p. A206

HICKS, Crystal, R.N., Chief Nursing Officer, Harrison County Community Hospital, Bethany, MO, p. A356

HICKS, Dana, Director of Nursing, Izard County Medical Center, Calico Rock, AR, p. A40

HICKS, Janelle, R.N., Vice President Patient Services, Hocking Valley Community Hospital, Logan, OH, p. A485

HICKS, Joan, Chief Information Officer, University Of Alabama Hospital, Birmingham, AL, p. A15

HICKS, John R., President and Chief Executive Officer, Platte Valley Medical Center, Brighton, CO, p. A97

HICKS, Michael, President and Chief Executive Officer, Hshs St. Mary'S Hospital, Decatur, IL, p. A181

HICKS, Michael L, Senior Vice President and Chief Operating Officer, Ingalls Memorial Hospital, Harvey, IL, p. A185

HICKS, Ramona, Interim Chief Executive Officer, Coulee Medical Center, Grand Coulee, WA, p. A673

HICKS, Scott, Vice President, Clark Memorial Health, Jeffersonville, IN, p. A208

HICKS, Susan, Chief Executive Officer, Sky Ridge Medical Center, Lone Tree, CO, p. A103

HICKS, Tim
Administrator, Muscogee Creek Nation Medical Center, Okmulgee, OK, p. A506
Administrator, Muscogee Creek Nation Physical Rehabilitation Center, Okmulgee, OK, p. A506

HICKS, William, Chief Executive Officer, Brookdale Hospital Medical Center, New York, NY, p. A432

HICKSON, Stan, Chief Executive Officer, Johnson City Medical Center, Johnson City, TN, p. A571

HIDAY, Holly, Director Human Resources, Kalamazoo Psychiatric Hospital, Kalamazoo, MI, p. A316

HIEB, Dorothy, Director Human Resources, Sanford Chamberlain Medical Center, Chamberlain, SD, p. A560

HIEB, Laura, Chief Executive Officer, Bellin Health Oconto Hospital, Oconto, WI, p. A702

HIEB, Laura, R.N., Chief Nursing Officer, Bellin Hospital, Green Bay, WI, p. A696

HIEBERT, Leslie, Chief Executive Officer, Klickitat Valley Health, Goldendale, WA, p. A673

HIGA, Russel, JD, Regional Director Human Resources, Leahi Hospital, Honolulu, HI, p. A164

HIGDON, Kevin J, Chief Financial Officer, Saint Joseph Health System, Mishawaka, IN, p. A211

HIGGINBOTHAM, G Douglas, President and Chief Executive Officer, South Central Regional Medical Center, Laurel, MS, p. A350

HIGGINBOTHAM, Lee, Chief Executive Officer, Dominion Hospital, Falls Church, VA, p. A658

HIGGINS, Alana
Regional Information Management Executive, Christus St. Michael Health System, Texarkana, TX, p. A640
Regional Information Management Executive, Christus St. Michael Rehabilitation Hospital, Texarkana, TX, p. A640

HIGGINS, John, Vice President and Chief Financial Officer, Good Samaritan Medical Center, Lafayette, CO, p. A102

HIGGINS, Kevin A, Chief Financial Officer, Olmsted Medical Center, Rochester, MN, p. A338

HIGGINS, Larisa, Administrator and Chief Operating Officer, Laredo Rehabilitation Hospital, Laredo, TX, p. A620

HIGGINS, Larry, Vice President Human Resources, King'S Daughters Medical Center, Ashland, KY, p. A249

HIGGINS, Michael, Commander, David Grant Usaf Medical Center, Travis Afb, CA, p. A92

HIGGINS, Rodney, Chief Financial Officer, Multicare Deaconess Hospital, Spokane, WA, p. A679

HIGGINS, Thomas, M.D., Chief Medical Officer, Baystate Franklin Medical Center, Greenfield, MA, p. A299

HIGGINS, William, M.D., Vice President Medical Affairs, New York–Presbyterian/Hudson Valley Hospital, Cortlandt Manor, NY, p. A426

HIGGINS BOWERS, Shirley, Senior Vice President Human Resources, Hackensack Meridian Health Jfk Medical Center, Edison, NJ, p. A405

HIGGINSON, David, Executive Vice President and Chief Administrative Officer, Phoenix Children'S Hospital, Phoenix, AZ, p. A34

HIGH, Kim, Chief Financial Officer, Baptist Memorial Hospital–Union County, New Albany, MS, p. A352

HIGHTOWER, Bernita, Chief Human Resources, Martin Army Community Hospital, Fort Benning, GA, p. A153

HIGHTOWER, Skip
Chief Financial Officer, Brooks County Hospital, Quitman, GA, p. A158
Chief Financial Officer, Grady General Hospital, Cairo, GA, p. A149
Senior Vice President and Chief Financial Officer, John D. Archbold Memorial Hospital, Thomasville, GA, p. A161
Senior Vice President and Chief Financial Officer, Mitchell County Hospital, Camilla, GA, p. A149

HIJECK, Thomas W., R.N., MS, Vice President Nursing Services and Chief Nursing Officer, Harrington Hospital, Southbridge, MA, p. A303

HILAMAN, Brad L, M.D., Chief Medical Officer, J. Arthur Dosher Memorial Hospital, Southport, NC, p. A462

HILDEBRAND, Randall, M.D., Chief Medical Officer, University Of Kansas Health System Great Bend Campus, Great Bend, KS, p. A235

HILDEBRANDT, James, D.O., Vice President Medical Affairs, Sarah Bush Lincoln Health Center, Mattoon, IL, p. A188

HILDRETH, Beth, Vice President Human Resources, Ohiohealth Medcentral Mansfield Hospital, Mansfield, OH, p. A486

HILDRETH, Joe, Director Information Technology, Three Rivers Hospital, Waverly, TN, p. A580

HILDWEIN, Robin, Chief Information Officer, Boca Raton Regional Hospital, Boca Raton, FL, p. A118

HILFIGER, Janie
Chief Administrative Officer, Upmc Susquehanna Soldiers + Sailors, Wellsboro, PA, p. A544
President, Upmc Cole, Coudersport, PA, p. A523

HILL, Beth, Director Human Resources, Russell County Medical Center, Lebanon, VA, p. A661

HILL, Cheryl
Vice President Human Resources, Ascension Columbia St. Mary'S Hospital Milwaukee, Milwaukee, WI, p. A700
Vice President Human Resources, Ascension Columbia St. Mary'S Hospital Ozaukee, Mequon, WI, p. A700
Vice President Human Resources, Ascension Columbia St. Mary'S Milwaukee Hospital, Milwaukee, WI, p. A700

HILL, Chris, Information Technology, Anchor Hospital, Atlanta, GA, p. A145

HILL, Herbert, Director Human Resources, Klickitat Valley Health, Goldendale, WA, p. A673

HILL, Jack
Chief Operating Officer and Administrator, The Jewish Hospital – Mercy Health, Cincinnati, OH, p. A476
Vice President and Chief Operating Officer, Union Hospital Clinton, Clinton, IN, p. A201

HILL, James P, Senior Vice President Administrative Services, Medstar Washington Hospital Center, Washington, DC, p. A116

HILL, Janice, Administrator, Baptist Memorial Restorative Care Hospital, Memphis, TN, p. A574

HILL, Jason, M.D., Chief Medical Officer, Choctaw Nation Health Care Center, Talihina, OK, p. A508

HILL, Jill, Director Information Technology, Utah State Hospital, Provo, UT, p. A650

HILL, Joe B, Vice President Human Resources, Trident Medical Center, Charleston, SC, p. A550

HILL, John, President and Chief Executive Officer, Bozeman Health, Bozeman, MT, p. A375

HILL, Kalisha, M.D., Chief Medical Officer, Amita Health St. Mary'S Hospital, Kankakee, IL, p. A187

HILL, Karen
Departmental Personnel Officer, Zuckerberg San Francisco General Hospital And Trauma Center, San Francisco, CA, p. A86
Director Human Resources, Baylor Scott & White Institute For Rehabilitation – Dallas, Dallas, TX, p. A595

HILL, Karen S, R.N., FACHE, Chief Operating Officer and Chief Nursing Officer, Baptist Health Lexington, Lexington, KY, p. A254

HILL, Kerry, Chief Financial Officer, Vista Health, Waukegan, IL, p. A198

HILL, Leo, Chief Information Officer, Massachusetts Eye And Ear, Boston, MA, p. A295

HILL, M. Scott.
President and Chief Executive Officer, Piedmont Columbus Regional Midtown, Columbus, GA, p. A150
President and Chief Executive Officer, Piedmont Columbus Regional Northside, Columbus, GA, p. A150

HILL, Nancy, R.N., Chief Nursing Officer, Johnson Regional Medical Center, Clarksville, AR, p. A40

HILL, Nancy L, R.N., MSN, Chief Operating Officer, Medical City North Hills, North Richland Hills, TX, p. A626

HILL, Nancy L., Chief Operating Officer, Medical City North Hills, North Richland Hills, TX, p. A626

HILL, Ned, Chief Executive Officer, Mesa View Regional Hospital, Mesquite, NV, p. A396

HILL, Robert, M.D.
Chief Medical Officer, Ascension Borgess–Lee Hospital, Dowagiac, MI, p. A310
Vice President Medical Staff Affairs, Ascension Borgess Hospital, Kalamazoo, MI, p. A315

HILL, Ryan
Interim Administrator, Essentia Health St. Mary'S – Detroit Lakes, Detroit Lakes, MN, p. A330
Senior Financial Advisor, Essentia Health St. Mary'S – Detroit Lakes, Detroit Lakes, MN, p. A330

HILL, Stephen, Vice President and Chief Nursing Officer, Valley Baptist Medical Center–Harlingen, Harlingen, TX, p. A609

HILL, Stuart, Vice President and Treasurer, Unity Health White County Medical Center, Searcy, AR, p. A48

HILL, Timothy, Chief Operating Officer, Uams Medical Center, Little Rock, AR, p. A45

HILL–DAVIS, Nancy L, Vice President Human Resources, Mercy Hospital And Medical Center, Chicago, IL, p. A178

HILLARY, Maureen, Chief Nursing Officer, Hayes Green Beach Memorial Hospital, Charlotte, MI, p. A308

HILLEGASS, Bonnie Essex., Chief Executive Officer, Harmon Medical And Rehabilitation Hospital, Las Vegas, NV, p. A395

HILLESTAD, Tammy, Chief Nursing Officer, Brookings Health System, Brookings, SD, p. A559

HILLIARD, David J, D.O., Chief of Staff, Barnesville Hospital, Barnesville, OH, p. A472
HILLIARD, Jamie, Director of Information Technology, University Of Kansas Health System St. Francis Campus, Topeka, KS, p. A246
HILLIS, David W., Chairman and Chief Executive Officer, Adcare Hospital Of Worcester, Worcester, MA, p. A305
HILLIS, Jeffrey W, Chief Operating Officer, Adcare Hospital Of Worcester, Worcester, MA, p. A305
HILLIS–CLARK, Patricia, Executive Director, Devereux Children'S Behavioral Health Center, Malvern, PA, p. A530
HILLMAN, Brandon, Interim Administrator, Director of Hospital Services, Christus Coushatta Health Care Center, Coushatta, LA, p. A266
HILLS, Cindi, Director Human Resources, Riverwood Healthcare Center, Aitkin, MN, p. A327
HILLYER, Lisa L, Human Resources Manager, Box Butte General Hospital, Alliance, NE, p. A382
HILT, Monica, President and Regional Vice President, Ascension Northeast Wisconsin St. Elizabeth Hospital, Appleton, WI, p. A691
HILTON, Craig, Chief Executive Officer and Managing Director, Hampton Behavioral Health Center, Westampton, NJ, p. A415
HILTON, Daniel, M.D., Chief of Staff, Fountain Valley Regional Hospital And Medical Center, Fountain Valley, CA, p. A58
HILTON, Lois, Director Human Resources, Desoto Memorial Hospital, Arcadia, FL, p. A117
HILTON, Neil A., President and Chief Executive Officer, Perkins County Health Services, Grant, NE, p. A385
HILTON–SIEBERT, Stephanie, President and Chief Executive Officer, Marion General Hospital, Marion, IN, p. A211
HILTUNEN, Theresa, Entity Information Officer, Penn Presbyterian Medical Center, Philadelphia, PA, p. A536
HILTZ, Paul C.
Chief Executive Officer, Nch Baker Hospital, Naples, FL, p. A132
President and Chief Executive Officer, Mercy Medical Center, Canton, OH, p. A474
HIMES, Judy N., MSN, R.N., Chief Nursing Officer, Penn State Milton S. Hershey Medical Center, Hershey, PA, p. A527
HINCHEY, Paul P.
President and Chief Executive Officer, Candler Hospital, Savannah, GA, p. A160
President and Chief Executive Officer, St. Joseph'S Hospital, Savannah, GA, p. A160
HINCKLEY, Fran X., Chief Information Officer, North Shore Medical Center, Salem, MA, p. A303
HINDMAN, Robbie, Vice President Patient Care Services and Chief Nursing Officer, Walker Baptist Medical Center, Jasper, AL, p. A20
HINDS, Bob, Executive Director, Bradford Health Services At Huntsville, Madison, AL, p. A20
HINE, Kristy, Associate Vice President Finance, Geisinger–Lewistown Hospital, Lewistown, PA, p. A530
HINE, Rhonda, R.N., Interim Chief Nursing Executive, Mason District Hospital, Havana, IL, p. A185
HINEMAN, Elizabeth, M.D., Chief Medical Staff, Scott County Hospital, Scott City, KS, p. A245
HINER, Jill, Vice President and Chief Financial Officer, Western Reserve Hospital, Cuyahoga Falls, OH, p. A481
HINER, Peggy, Director Human Resources, Wheatland Memorial Healthcare, Harlowton, MT, p. A377
HINES, Andrew, Administrator, St. James Behavioral Health Hospital, Gonzales, LA, p. A267
HINES, Frederick W., President and Chief Executive Officer, Clarity Child Guidance Center, San Antonio, TX, p. A633
HINES, JeDonne, Chief Financial Officer, Intermountain Hospital, Boise, ID, p. A167
HINES, Linda, Vice President Information Technology and Information Systems, University Of Maryland Rehabilitation & Orthopaedic Institute, Baltimore, MD, p. A288
HINES, Lisa, Director Nursing, Eastern Shore Hospital Center, Cambridge, MD, p. A289
HINES, Mary Beth, D.O., Chief Medical Officer, Up Health System–Portage, Hancock, MI, p. A314
HINESLEY, Jay, Chief Executive Officer, Vanderbilt Wilson County Hospital, Lebanon, TN, p. A573
HINKLE, Stacey, Director Information Technology, Banner Desert Medical Center, Mesa, AZ, p. A31
HINNER, William J
Vice President Financial Analysis and Planning Ministry Health Care, Marshfield Medical Center, Marshfield, WI, p. A699
Vice President Financial Analysis and Planning, Ascension St. Michael'S Hospital, Stevens Point, WI, p. A706
HINOJOSA, Anna, MSN, R.N., Interim Chief Nursing Officer, Knapp Medical Center, Weslaco, TX, p. A645
HINRICHS, Becky Kay, Vice President Human Resources, Riverside Medical Center, Kankakee, IL, p. A187
HINRICHS, Sandy, Director Human Resources, Burnett Medical Center, Grantsburg, WI, p. A695
HINSHAW, Bruce, Director Human Resources, Artesia General Hospital, Artesia, NM, p. A417
HINSON, Lee, Chief Nursing Officer, Merit Health Natchez, Natchez, MS, p. A352
HINTZ, Lori, Coordinator Information Systems, Rochester Psychiatric Center, Rochester, NY, p. A442
HINTZE, Hartland
Chief Nursing Officer, Banner Payson Medical Center, Payson, AZ, p. A32
Chief Nursing Officer, Northern Louisiana Medical Center, Ruston, LA, p. A277
HINTZE, Paul, M.D., Vice President Medical Affairs, Mercy Hospital St. Louis, Saint Louis, MO, p. A368
HIOTT, Jimmy O., III, Chief Executive Officer, Colleton Medical Center, Walterboro, SC, p. A558
HIPKISS, Tom, Vice President Finance, Forbes Hospital, Monroeville, PA, p. A532
HIRKALER, Kim, Director Human Resources, Bon Secours Community Hospital, Port Jervis, NY, p. A442
HIROMOTO, Brenda, Director of Nursing, Rehabilitation Hospital Of The Pacific, Honolulu, HI, p. A165
HIRSCH, Edward, M.D., Vice President Chief Medical and Quality Officer, Kaweah Delta Medical Center, Visalia, CA, p. A94
HIRSCH, Leslie D., Interim Chief Executive Officer and President, Saint Peter'S University Hospital, New Brunswick, NJ, p. A409
HIRSCH, Ted W, Senior Executive Director, Kalispell Regional Healthcare, Kalispell, MT, p. A378
HIRST, Barb, R.N., Vice President Human Resources and Chief Nursing Officer, Salem Regional Medical Center, Salem, OH, p. A490
HISE, Landon E.
Chief Executive Officer, Alliancehealth Clinton, Clinton, OK, p. A498
Interim Chief Executive Officer, Alliancehealth Woodward, Woodward, OK, p. A510
HISEY, Commie, D.O., Chief of Staff, Gonzales Healthcare Systems, Gonzales, TX, p. A608
HITE DAVIS, Anissa J, Vice President Human Resources, St. Joseph'S Hospital Of Buckhannon, Buckhannon, WV, p. A684
HITT, John, M.D., Executive Vice President and Chief Medical Officer, Maricopa Integrated Health System, Phoenix, AZ, p. A33
HITT, Melissa, Director of Nursing, Highland–Clarksburg Hospital, Clarksburg, WV, p. A684
HITT, Patricia A, Associate Director, Grand Junction Veterans Health Care System, Grand Junction, CO, p. A101
HIXENBAUGH, Cynthia, Director Human Resources, Pershing General Hospital, Lovelock, NV, p. A396
HIXSON, Kim, Vice President of Financial Officer and Chief Financial Officer, Providence Medical Center, Wayne, NE, p. A392
HJEMBO, Philip, Chief Financial Officer, St. Elizabeth Hospital, Enumclaw, WA, p. A672
HLAHOL, Jan, Manager Human Resources, Cleveland Clinic Children'S Hospital For Rehabilitation, Cleveland, OH, p. A477
HLUCHY, Nicholas, Business Analyst, Support Services Manager, Baton Rouge Rehabilitation Hospital, Baton Rouge, LA, p. A263
HO, Kingman, M.D., Senior Vice President, Chief Medical and Care Innovation Officer, Henry Mayo Newhall Hospital, Valencia, CA, p. A93
HO–SHING, Viodelda, Deputy Director Administration, Brookdale Hospital Medical Center, New York, NY, p. A432
HOAG, Abby, Director, Human Resources, Uh Avon Rehabilitation Hospital, Avon, OH, p. A472
HOAGBIN, Joseph, M.D.
Chief Medical Officer, Chi Health Immanuel, Omaha, NE, p. A389
Chief Quality Officer, Chi Health Mercy Council Bluffs, Council Bluffs, IA, p. A220
HOAR, Brad, Director Information and Technology, Cedar Park Regional Medical Center, Cedar Park, TX, p. A592
HOARD, Kaylee S., Chief Financial Officer, Cook Hospital & Care Center, Cook, MN, p. A330
HOBACK, Kim, Supervisor Information Systems, Athens–Limestone Hospital, Athens, AL, p. A13
HOBAN, Donna, M.D., Senior Vice President and Chief Medical Officer, Beaumont Hospital – Grosse Pointe, Grosse Pointe, MI, p. A313
HOBAN, Douglas M, Vice President and Chief Financial Officer, Mercy Hospital Lebanon, Lebanon, MO, p. A364
HOBAN, Robert E.
President, Ascension River District Hospital, East China, MI, p. A311
President, Ascension St. John Hospital, Detroit, MI, p. A309
HOBART, Robert, Director Management Information Systems, Heartland Behavioral Healthcare, Massillon, OH, p. A487
HOBBS, Donna, Nurse Executive, U. S. Public Health Service Indian Hospital–Sells, Sells, AZ, p. A36
HOBBS, Ed, Director Information Services, Dekalb Health, Auburn, IN, p. A199
HOBBS, Emilie, Director Human Resources, Woodland Heights Medical Center, Lufkin, TX, p. A622
HOBBS, Keith, Chief Executive Officer, Usc Verdugo Hills Hospital, Glendale, CA, p. A60
HOBBS, Mike, Chief Financial Officer, Clay County Hospital, Flora, IL, p. A183
HOBBS, Steve E.
Chief Financial Officer, North Alabama Medical Center, Florence, AL, p. A18
Chief Financial Officer, Shoals Hospital, Muscle Shoals, AL, p. A22
HOBBS, Tommy, Chief Executive Officer, Illinois Valley Community Hospital, Peru, IL, p. A193
HOBGOOD, Lisa, Chief Information Officer, Deaconess Gateway Hospital, Newburgh, IN, p. A213
HOBGOOD, Marcus, Director Information Services, Ochsner Lsu Health Shrevport – Academic Medical Center, Shreveport, LA, p. A278
HOBSON, Christopher Brian, Chief Operating Officer, Bristol Regional Medical Center, Bristol, TN, p. A566
HOBSON, Jim, Chief Executive Officer, Greenbrier Valley Medical Center, Ronceverte, WV, p. A689
HOCATE, Crispin P, Professional and Support Services Officer, Texas Health Presbyterian Hospital Allen, Allen, TX, p. A582
HOCHENBERG, Paul S, Executive Director, Westchester Medical Center, Valhalla, NY, p. A446
HOCHSTETLER, Amy, Chief Financial Officer, Orthopaedic Hospital Of Lutheran Health Network, Fort Wayne, IN, p. A204
HOCK, Douglas G, Executive Vice President and Chief Operating Officer, Children'S Hospital Of Philadelphia, Philadelphia, PA, p. A534
HOCKADAY, Christina P., Chief Executive Officer, Assumption Community Hospital, Napoleonville, LA, p. A274
HOCKENBERRY, Michael A., Senior Vice President and Chief Operating Officer, Upmc Hanover, Hanover, PA, p. A526
HOCKENBERRY, Tonda, Chief Nursing Officer, Encompass Health Rehabilitation Hospital Of Parkersburg, Parkersburg, WV, p. A688
HOCKERSMITH, Lisa K., Vice President Human Resources, Kern Medical Center, Bakersfield, CA, p. A52
HOCKING, Barbara, Chief Nursing Officer, St. Luke'S Regional Medical Center, Boise, ID, p. A168
HOCKING, Dale E, Chief Financial Officer, Jupiter Medical Center, Jupiter, FL, p. A126
HOCKING, Patrick
Chief Financial Officer, Asante Ashland Community Hospital, Ashland, OR, p. A511
Chief Financial Officer, Asante Rogue Regional Medical Center, Medford, OR, p. A515
Chief Financial Officer, Asante Three Rivers Medical Center, Grants Pass, OR, p. A513
HOCUM, Timothy, Chief Financial Officer, Providence Kodiak Island Medical Center, Kodiak, AK, p. A26
HODGE, Ian, Chief Executive Officer, Yuma Rehabilitation Hospital, A Partnership Of Encompass Health And Yrmc, Yuma, AZ, p. A38
HODGE, Lisa, Director, Human Resources, Rolling Hills Hospital, Franklin, TN, p. A569
HODGE, Montie, Vice President Information Technology and Chief Information Officer, Regional West Medical Center, Scottsbluff, NE, p. A391
HODGE, Pamela, R.N., Chief Nursing Officer and Coordinator Performance Improvement, Jellico Community Hospital, Jellico, TN, p. A571
HODGES, Alan, Chief Executive Officer, Hancock Medical Center, Bay Saint Louis, MS, p. A344
HODGES, Calvin, Director Human Resources, Alliancehealth Ponca City, Ponca City, OK, p. A506
HODGES, Craig, Director Information Services, Hancock Medical Center, Bay Saint Louis, MS, p. A344
HODGES, Dawn, Director Human Resources, Grand River Hospital District, Rifle, CO, p. A105
HODGES, Jay, Chief Financial Officer, Tmc Bonham Hospital, Bonham, TX, p. A589
HODGES, Leisha, Human Resources Officer, Eastland Memorial Hospital, Eastland, TX, p. A600
HODGES, Randall H, Vice President and Administrator, Charleston Area Medical Center, Charleston, WV, p. A684
HODGIN, Robin, R.N., Vice President of Patient Services and Chief Nursing Officer, Northern Hospital Of Surry County, Mount Airy, NC, p. A459

HODGSON, Judith Ann, Chief Nursing Officer, Cheyenne County Hospital, Saint Francis, KS, p. A244
HODNETT, Laura, Interim Chief Nursing Officer, Glen Rose Medical Center, Glen Rose, TX, p. A607
HODSON, Don, M.D., Chief Medical Officer, St. Luke Hospital And Living Center, Marion, KS, p. A240
HOEFER, Bill, Chief Operating Officer, Mercy Hospital South, Saint Louis, MO, p. A369
HOEFLING, Tracy, Chief Financial Officer, Deaconess Gateway Hospital, Newburgh, IN, p. A213
HOEFS, Dennis, Manager Information Technology, New Mexico Rehabilitation Center, Roswell, NM, p. A420
HOEHN, Charles, President, Medical Staff, Van Wert County Hospital, Van Wert, OH, p. A493
HOEHNS, Brent, M.D., Chief of Medical Staff, Knoxville Hospital & Clinics, Knoxville, IA, p. A225
HOEKEMA, Dale, M.D., Vice President Medical Affairs and Chief Medical Officer, Kadlec Regional Medical Center, Richland, WA, p. A677
HOEKSTRA, James, President, High Point Medical Center, High Point, NC, p. A456
HOELL, Paul, M.D., President Medical Staff, Thedacare Medical Center–New London, New London, WI, p. A702
HOELSCHER, Steven C, Chief Operating Officer, Valley Regional Medical Center, Brownsville, TX, p. A590
HOERTZ, Joanne, Vice President of Nursing, Brooks Rehabilitation Hospital, Jacksonville, FL, p. A125
HOESCH, Marty, Director Information Systems, North Suburban Medical Center, Thornton, CO, p. A105
HOEY, Amy J, R.N., MS, Executive Vice President and Chief Operating Officer, Lowell General Hospital, Lowell, MA, p. A300
HOFER, Maggie, Human Resources Representative, Hawarden Regional Healthcare, Hawarden, IA, p. A224
HOFF, David L., Chief Executive Officer, Wayne Memorial Hospital, Honesdale, PA, p. A527
HOFF, Deanna, R.N., Director of Nursing, Bacon County Hospital And Health System, Alma, GA, p. A145
HOFF, Linda, Senior Vice President and Chief Financial Officer, Legacy Mount Hood Medical Center, Gresham, OR, p. A513
HOFF, Margaret, Account Manager, Brown County Community Treatment Center, Green Bay, WI, p. A696
HOFFER, Nolan, Senior Director, St. Luke'S Rehabilitation Hospital, Boise, ID, p. A168
HOFFMAN, Brad, Administrative Director Human Resources, Adventhealth Shawnee Mission, Shawnee Mission, KS, p. A245
HOFFMAN, Brian, M.D., Chief Medical Services, Veterans Affairs Boston Healthcare System, West Roxbury, MA, p. A304
HOFFMAN, Carole, Vice President, Parkridge Medical Center, Chattanooga, TN, p. A567
HOFFMAN, Chris, Chief Operating Officer, Highlands Arh Regional Medical Center, Prestonsburg, KY, p. A259
HOFFMAN, Daniel, M.D., Administrative Medical Director, Good Samaritan Regional Health Center, Mount Vernon, IL, p. A190
HOFFMAN, Debbie, Vice President Patient Services, Mosaic Medical Center – Maryville, Maryville, MO, p. A365
HOFFMAN, Debra, Human Resources Manager, Kern Valley Healthcare District, Lake Isabella, CA, p. A63
HOFFMAN, Howard, M.D., Medical Director, Psychiatric Institute Of Washington, Washington, DC, p. A116
HOFFMAN, Jerry, Chief Financial Officer, Platte Health Center Avera, Platte, SD, p. A562
HOFFMAN, Joseph E, Senior Vice President and Chief Financial Officer, University Of Maryland Medical Center, Baltimore, MD, p. A287
HOFFMAN, Marcus, Area Chief Financial Officer, Kaiser Permanente Orange County Anaheim Medical Center, Anaheim, CA, p. A50
HOFFMAN, Rex, M.D., Chief Medical Officer, Providence Holy Cross Medical Center, Mission Hills, CA, p. A71
HOFFMAN, Robert P, R.N., Chief Nursing Officer, Wilkes–Barre General Hospital, Wilkes, PA, p. A545
HOFFMAN, Tom, Manager Information Systems, Wayne Memorial Hospital, Honesdale, PA, p. A527
HOFFMAN, Val, Chief Financial Officer, Granite Falls Health, Granite Falls, MN, p. A333
HOFFMANN, Wanda, Director Human Resources, River Oaks Hospital, New Orleans, LA, p. A275
HOFIUS, Chuck, Chief Executive Officer, Perham Health, Perham, MN, p. A337
HOFLER, Linda D, Ph.D., R.N., FACHE, Senior Vice President, Nurse Executive, Vidant Medical Center, Greenville, NC, p. A455
HOFMAN, William, Manager Information Technology, Wake Forest Baptist Health – Wilkes Medical Center, North Wilkesboro, NC, p. A459
HOFMEIER, Sara, Executive Director, Veritas Collaborative, Durham, NC, p. A453
HOFMEISTER, Nancee, R.N., Senior Vice President, Chief Nursing Officer, Evergreenhealth, Kirkland, WA, p. A674
HOFSTETTER, Peter A.
Chief Executive Officer, Petersburg Medical Center, Petersburg, AK, p. A27
Chief Executive Officer, Willamette Valley Medical Center, Mcminnville, OR, p. A514
HOGAN, Dan, Chief Financial Officer, Desoto Memorial Hospital, Arcadia, FL, p. A117
HOGAN, Judith, Comptroller and Director Resources and Logistics, Naval Hospital Bremerton, Bremerton, WA, p. A671
HOGAN, Michael, Chief Resource Management, General Leonard Wood Army Community Hospital, Fort Leonard Wood, MO, p. A360
HOGAN, Richard, Chief Financial Officer, Pleasant Valley Hospital, Point Pleasant, WV, p. A688
HOGAN, Richard H, CPA, Chief Financial Officer, Landmark Hospital Of Cape Girardeau, Cape Girardeau, MO, p. A357
HOGAN, Sean, President, Mercy Hospital South, Saint Louis, MO, p. A369
HOGAN, Timothy J.
President, RMC and BMC, Hackensack Meridian Health Bayshore Community Hospital, Holmdel, NJ, p. A406
President, RMC and BMC, Hackensack Meridian Health Riverview Medical Center, Red Bank, NJ, p. A412
HOGDSON, Judy, R.N., Chief Nursing Officer, Hospital District No 1 Of Rice County, Lyons, KS, p. A240
HOGGARD GREEN, Jill
Chief Executive Officer, The Queen'S Medical Center, Honolulu, HI, p. A165
President, Mission Hospital, Asheville, NC, p. A449
HOGUE, Vicky, R.N., Vice President Patient Services and Chief Nursing Officer, Wellstar Paulding Hospital, Hiram, GA, p. A154
HOHENBERGER, Joseph, Chief Financial Officer, Ferrell Hospital, Eldorado, IL, p. A181
HOHENSHELL, Valerie, Director of Clinical Services, Gonzales Healthcare Systems, Gonzales, TX, p. A608
HOHN, Craig, Chief Executive Officer, Avera Merrill Pioneer Hospital, Rock Rapids, IA, p. A229
HOLBERT, Brandon, Director, Information Services, Ocala Regional Medical Center, Ocala, FL, p. A133
HOLBROOK, Chip, M.D., Chief of Staff, Simpson General Hospital, Mendenhall, MS, p. A351
HOLBROOK, Curtis, M.D., Chief Medical Officer, Baylor Scott & White Surgical Hospital–Sherman, Sherman, TX, p. A636
HOLCOMB, Holly, R.N.
Chie Operating Officer, Childress Regional Medical Center, Childress, TX, p. A592
Chief Operating Officer, Childress Regional Medical Center, Childress, TX, p. A592
HOLCOMB, Michelle, Human Resources, Webster County Memorial Hospital, Webster Springs, WV, p. A690
HOLDEMAN, Royce, Chief Financial Officer, Mercy Hospital, Moundridge, KS, p. A241
HOLDEN, Teal A., Chief Executive Officer, Memorial Hermann Surgical Hospital Kingwood, Kingwood, TX, p. A618
HOLDER, Hal
Director Finance, Ssm Health Depaul Hospital – St. Louis, Bridgeton, MO, p. A357
Regional Chief Financial Officer–Hospital Operations, Ssm Health St. Clare Hospital – Fenton, Fenton, MO, p. A360
Regional Chief Financial Officer, Ssm Health St. Joseph Hospital – Lake Saint Louis, Lake Saint Louis, MO, p. A364
HOLDER, Jennifer, Chief Nursing Officer, Trousdale Medical Center, Hartsville, TN, p. A570
HOLDER, Kasey, M.D., Vice President Medical Affairs, St. Bernards Medical Center, Jonesboro, AR, p. A44
HOLDER, Michelle, Nurse Executive, Straith Hospital For Special Surgery, Southfield, MI, p. A323
HOLDER, Spencer, Chief Financial Officer, Riverland Medical Center, Ferriday, LA, p. A267
HOLDER–HOOPER, Donna, Chief Human Resource Officer, Healthsouth Rehabilitation Hospital At Martin Health, Stuart, FL, p. A140
HOLEKAMP, Nicholas, M.D., Chief Medical Officer, Ranken Jordan Pediatric Bridge Hospital, Maryland Heights, MO, p. A365
HOLGUIN, Brenda, Manager Human Resources, El Paso Behavioral Health System, El Paso, TX, p. A601
HOLGUIN, Mindee, Manager Human Resources, Sierra Vista Hospital, Truth Or Consequences, NM, p. A421
HOLIFIELD, Tracy, Director Information Systems, Merit Health Central, Jackson, MS, p. A349
HOLINER, Joel, M.D., Executive Medical Director, Medical City Green Oaks Hospital, Dallas, TX, p. A597
HOLIVER, John J., Chief Executive Officer, St. Joseph Health Services Of Rhode Island, North Providence, RI, p. A547
HOLLAND, Baxter C, M.D., Chief Medical Officer, Rutland Regional Medical Center, Rutland, VT, p. A655
HOLLAND, Brad D., President and Chief Executive Officer, Hendrick Health System, Abilene, TX, p. A581
HOLLAND, Charles, President and Chief Executive Officer, St. Bernard Hospital And Health Care Center, Chicago, IL, p. A180
HOLLAND, David
Chief Information Officer, Herrin Hospital, Herrin, IL, p. A185
Vice President Chief Innovation Officer, Memorial Hospital Of Carbondale, Carbondale, IL, p. A175
Vice President Information Services, St. Joseph Memorial Hospital, Murphysboro, IL, p. A190
HOLLAND, Gabrielle, Chief Financial Officer, Baylor Surgical Hospital At Las Colinas, Irving, TX, p. A616
HOLLAND, Kevin
Chief Executive Officer, CHRISTUS Southwestern Louisiana, Christus Ochsner Lake Area Hospital, Lake Charles, LA, p. A272
Chief Executive Officer, CHRISTUS Southwestern Louisiana, Christus Ochsner St. Patrick Hospital Southwest Louisiana, Lake Charles, LA, p. A272
HOLLAND, Kwi, Vice President Information Services, Knox Community Hospital, Mount Vernon, OH, p. A488
HOLLAND, Megan, Chief Medical Officer and Family Practitioner, Southern Coos Hospital And Health Center, Bandon, OR, p. A511
HOLLAND, Michael, Chief Executive Officer, Rehabilitation Hospital Of Jennings, Jennings, LA, p. A269
HOLLAND, Penny, Associate Director for Patient Care Services, Aleda E. Lutz Veterans Affairs Medical Center, Saginaw, MI, p. A321
HOLLAND, Shannon S, R.N., MSN, Chief Nursing Officer, Multicare Valley Hospital, Spokane Valley, WA, p. A680
HOLLAND, Sharron, Chief Financial Officer, Baptist Memorial Hospital–Carroll County, Huntingdon, TN, p. A571
HOLLAND, Stephen, M.D., Vice President Chief Medical Officer and Medical Director, Gaylord Hospital, Wallingford, CT, p. A111
HOLLEMAN, James, M.D., Chief of Staff, St. Luke'S Hospital, Columbus, NC, p. A452
HOLLEMAN, Stephen B, Chief Financial Officer, Shepherd Center, Atlanta, GA, p. A147
HOLLEY, Brenda, Chief Nursing Officer, Lovelace Westside Hospital, Albuquerque, NM, p. A416
HOLLIDAY, Jonathan, Manager Information Technology, Mercyone Elkader Medical Center, Elkader, IA, p. A222
HOLLIMAN, Emily L., Chief Executive Officer, Hackensack Meridian Health Pascack Valley Medical Center, Westwood, NJ, p. A415
HOLLIN, Sheara, Chief Operating Officer, Hospital Of The University Of Pennsylvania, Philadelphia, PA, p. A535
HOLLINGS, Derrick O., Chief Financial Officer, Hennepin Healthcare, Minneapolis, MN, p. A335
HOLLINGSWORTH, Carl, Chief Financial Officer, Artesia General Hospital, Artesia, NM, p. A417
HOLLINGSWORTH, Christine, Chief Financial Officer, Phoenix Veterans Affairs Health Care System, Phoenix, AZ, p. A34
HOLLINGSWORTH, Nancy, President and Chief Executive Officer, Saint Agnes Medical Center, Fresno, CA, p. A59
HOLLINGSWORTH, Sherri, Chief Human Resources Officer, Pih Health Hospital – Downey, Downey, CA, p. A56
HOLLIS, Carla, Chief Executive Officer, Triangle Springs Hospital, Raleigh, NC, p. A460
HOLLIS, Gary W, Comptroller, Arkansas State Hospital, Little Rock, AR, p. A44
HOLLIS, Roy, Chief Executive Officer, Houston Behavioral Healthcare Hospital, Houston, TX, p. A611
HOLLISTER, Jerry, Chief Executive Officer, Northeastern Center, Auburn, IN, p. A199
HOLLISTER, Richard, President of Medical Staff, Exeter Hospital, Exeter, NH, p. A400
HOLLON, Kim Norton., President and Chief Executive Officer, Signature Healthcare Brockton Hospital, Brockton, MA, p. A296
HOLLOWAY, Kristina, Chief Human Resources Officer, Healdsburg District Hospital, Healdsburg, CA, p. A61
HOLLOWAY, Myra, Director Human Resources Management, Central State Hospital, Milledgeville, GA, p. A157
HOLLOWAY, Walter R, Chief Medical Officer, Ozarks Medical Center, West Plains, MO, p. A373
HOLLOWAY, Whitney, Chief Financial Officer, Berwick Hospital Center, Berwick, PA, p. A520
HOLM, Mary Ann, Office Clerk, Tioga Medical Center, Tioga, ND, p. A469
HOLM, Stan, President and Chief Executive Officer, Olathe Medical Center, Olathe, KS, p. A242

HOLMAN, Resha T, Chief Nurse Executive Officer, Northridge Hospital Medical Center, Los Angeles, CA, p. A68

HOLMAN, Steve M., Chief Executive Officer, Union Hospital, Terre Haute, IN, p. A215

HOLMBERG, Daniel, M.D., Director of Medical Affairs, New Ulm Medical Center, New Ulm, MN, p. A337

HOLMES, Dawne
Chief Financial Officer, Greenwood Leflore Hospital, Greenwood, MS, p. A347
Interim Chief Executive Officer, Greenwood Leflore Hospital, Greenwood, MS, p. A347

HOLMES, Diana, Chief Nursing Officer, Central Regional Hospital, Butner, NC, p. A450

HOLMES, Ginnie, Chief Financial Officer, Electra Memorial Hospital, Electra, TX, p. A603

HOLMES, Heather, Director Health Information Systems, Merit Health Rankin, Brandon, MS, p. A345

HOLMES, Heidi, Chief Information Officer, Oklahoma State University Medical Center, Tulsa, OK, p. A509

HOLMES, James R., President and Chief Executive Officer, Redlands Community Hospital, Redlands, CA, p. A80

HOLMES, John, Business Manager, Ancora Psychiatric Hospital, Hammonton, NJ, p. A406

HOLMES, Phillip Walter, M.D., Chief of Staff, Prairie Ridge Hospital And Health Services, Elbow Lake, MN, p. A331

HOLMES, Terry R, M.D., Clinical Director, Moccasin Bend Mental Health Institute, Chattanooga, TN, p. A567

HOLMES, Troy
Chief Financial Officer, Advanced Specialty Hospital Of Toledo, Toledo, OH, p. A492
Interim Chief Executive Officer and Chief Financial Officer, Advanced Specialty Hospital Of Toledo, Toledo, OH, p. A492

HOLMSTROM, Tallulah, M.D.
Chief Medical Officer, Carolina Pines Regional Medical Center, Hartsville, SC, p. A554
Chief Medical Officer, Kershawhealth, Camden, SC, p. A549

HOLOM, Randall G., Chief Executive Officer, Frances Mahon Deaconess Hospital, Glasgow, MT, p. A376

HOLSAPPLE, Kim, Human Resource Specialist, Chester Mental Health Center, Chester, IL, p. A176

HOLSCHBACH, Dennis, Chief Financial Officer, Ruby Valley Medical Center, Sheridan, MT, p. A380

HOLSON, Debbie C, R.N., MSN, Chief Operating Officer, The Hsc Pediatric Center, Washington, DC, p. A116

HOLSON, Debbie C., Chief Operating Officer, The Hsc Pediatric Center, Washington, DC, p. A116

HOLSTEN, Robyn, Human Resources Director, Salt Lake Behavioral Health, Salt Lake City, UT, p. A652

HOLT, Clayton, Chief Executive Officer, San Juan Health Service District, Monticello, UT, p. A649

HOLT, David, Chief Executive Officer, Western State Hospital, Tacoma, WA, p. A681

HOLT, Kory
Assistant Vice President for Financial Integration, Avera Flandreau Hospital, Flandreau, SD, p. A561
Division Controller Network Operations, Avera Dells Area Hospital, Dell Rapids, SD, p. A560

HOLT, Peter, M.D., Director Medical Affairs, Saint Luke'S Hospital Of Kansas City, Kansas City, MO, p. A363

HOLT, Richard, R.N., Associate Director Patient Care Services, Veterans Affairs St. Louis Health Care System, Saint Louis, MO, p. A371

HOLT, Sherry, Director Human Resources, Unity Medical Center, Manchester, TN, p. A573

HOLT, Stephen R., Director, Veterans Affairs North Texas Health Care System, Dallas, TX, p. A598

HOLT, Tabetha, Director of Human Resources, Riverside Walter Reed Hospital, Gloucester, VA, p. A660

HOLT, Thomas, M.D., Medical Staff President, Good Shepherd Health Care System, Hermiston, OR, p. A513

HOLT, Thomas A, Chief Financial Officer, Hca Houston Healthcare Conroe, Conroe, TX, p. A593

HOLT, Will, Director Information Technology, Harrison County Community Hospital, Bethany, MO, p. A356

HOLTER, Lee H., Chief Financial Officer, Heart Of America Medical Center, Rugby, ND, p. A469

HOLTHAUS, Julie K, Director Human Resources, Sabetha Community Hospital, Sabetha, KS, p. A244

HOLTHAUS, Monica, Chief Financial Officer, Community Healthcare System, Onaga, KS, p. A242

HOLTMAN, Jean, Vice President, Human Resources, St. Mary Medical Center, Apple Valley, CA, p. A51

HOLTZ, George, Director Human Resources, Sharp Grossmont Hospital, La Mesa, CA, p. A63

HOLTZ, Jennifer, Director Finance, Centracare Health–Paynesville, Paynesville, MN, p. A337

HOLTZ, Noel, M.D., Chief Medical Officer, Wellstar Douglas Hospital, Douglasville, GA, p. A152

HOLTZMAN, Michael, M.D., Medical Director, Kindred Hospital–St. Louis, Saint Louis, MO, p. A369

HOLUBEK, William, M.D., Chief Medical Officer, Carepoint Health Christ Hospital, Jersey City, NJ, p. A407

HOLYFIELD, Asia, Manager Business Office, Lifecare Hospitals Of Pittsburgh, Pittsburgh, PA, p. A537

HOLZER, Traci, Chief Human Resources Officer, Doctors Hospital Of Manteca, Manteca, CA, p. A70

HOMA, Jim, Chief Executive Officer, Heatherhill Care Communities, Chardon, OH, p. A475

HOMER, Kenneth, M.D., Chief Medical Officer, Holy Cross Hospital, Fort Lauderdale, FL, p. A122

HOMYK, Linda
Chief Nursing Officer, Heritage Valley Health System, Beaver, PA, p. A520
Chief Nursing Officer, Sewickley Valley Hospital, (A Division Of Valley Medical Facilities), Sewickley, PA, p. A541

HONAKER, Jennifer, Chief Financial Officer, John Randolph Medical Center, Hopewell, VA, p. A661

HONEA, Bert, M.D.
Associate Chief Medical Officer Northern Colorado, Banner Fort Collins Medical Center, Fort Collins, CO, p. A100
Medical Director, Mckee Medical Center, Loveland, CO, p. A104

HONEA, Bruce, Director Information Services, Christus Coushatta Health Care Center, Coushatta, LA, p. A266

HONEA, Michael, Chief Financial Officer, Glen Rose Medical Center, Glen Rose, TX, p. A607

HONEYCUTT, Cynthia, Director Human Resources, Moccasin Bend Mental Health Institute, Chattanooga, TN, p. A567

HONEYCUTT, Robert C.
Chief Executive Officer, Ennis Regional Medical Center, Ennis, TX, p. A603
Chief Executive Officer, Parkview Regional Hospital, Mexia, TX, p. A624

HONSINGER, Melissa, Chief Operating Officer, St. Luke'S Rehabilitation Hospital, Boise, ID, p. A168

HONTS, Gary, Chief Executive Officer, John F. Kennedy Memorial Hospital, Indio, CA, p. A62

HOOD, Brenda, Chief Executive Officer, Curahealth Hospital Oklahoma City, Oklahoma City, OK, p. A503

HOOD, Cliff, Chief Operating Officer, Central Regional Hospital, Butner, NC, p. A450

HOOD, Gary, Chief Information Officer, Fayette County Hospital, Vandalia, IL, p. A197

HOOD, Kathy, Administrative Assistant Human Resources, Union General Hospital, Blairsville, GA, p. A148

HOOD, Ron, M.D., Chief of Staff, Sutter Amador Hospital, Jackson, CA, p. A62

HOOD, Sam, Director Human Resources, Heartland Regional Medical Center, Marion, IL, p. A188

HOOD, Thomas, Chief Operating Officer, King'S Daughters Medical Center, Brookhaven, MS, p. A345

HOOK, Diane, Chief Financial Officer, Wayne County Hospital, Corydon, IA, p. A220

HOOKER, Melvin, Chief Human Resources, New Mexico Veterans Affairs Health Care System – Raymond G. Murphy Medical Center, Albuquerque, NM, p. A417

HOOKER, Rita, Administrative Director Information Services, Bon Secours St. Francis Health System, Greenville, SC, p. A553

HOOLAHAN, Susan E, R.N., MSN, Vice President Patient Care Services and Chief Nursing Officer, Upmc Passavant, Pittsburgh, PA, p. A538

HOOLAHAN, Susan E., President, Upmc Passavant, Pittsburgh, PA, p. A538

HOOP, Heather, Human Resources Generalist, Adams County Regional Medical Center, Seaman, OH, p. A490

HOOPER, Grady A., Chief Executive Officer, Hamilton General Hospital, Hamilton, TX, p. A609

HOOPER, Jason R., President and Chief Executive Officer, Kvc Prairie Ridge Psychiatric Hospital, Kansas City, KS, p. A238

HOOPER, Joseph, President and Chief Executive Officer, Community Howard Regional Health, Kokomo, IN, p. A209

HOOPER, Robert A, Director Human Resources, Tristar Skyline Medical Center, Nashville, TN, p. A577

HOOPINGARNER, Darrick, Chief Operating Officer, Dupont Hospital, Fort Wayne, IN, p. A203

HOOPINGARNER, Traci, R.N., Chief Nursing Officer, Lmh Health, Lawrence, KS, p. A239

HOOVER, Alvin, Chief Executive Officer, King'S Daughters Medical Center, Brookhaven, MS, p. A345

HOOVER, Craig A., Chief Executive Officer, Vibra Rehabilitation Hospital Of Denver, Thornton, CO, p. A106

HOOVER, Garrett W., President, Guthrie Corning Hospital, Corning, NY, p. A426

HOOVER, Jeremy Steven, Chief Information Officer, Kiowa County Memorial Hospital, Greensburg, KS, p. A236

HOOVER, John, Chief Operating Officer, Eastside Medical Center, Snellville, GA, p. A160

HOPE, Lisa R, Director Human Resources, Owensboro Health Muhlenberg Community Hospital, Greenville, KY, p. A252

HOPE, Steve, Vice President Corporate Services, Methodist Rehabilitation Center, Jackson, MS, p. A349

HOPE, William, Chief of Medical Staff, Vidant Chowan Hospital, Edenton, NC, p. A453

HOPKINS, Frances F, Chief Financial Officer, Sabine Medical Center, Many, LA, p. A273

HOPKINS, Jason, Director, Human Resources, Hamilton Medical Center, Dalton, GA, p. A151

HOPKINS, Jim, Chief Financial Officer, Cascade Medical Center, Leavenworth, WA, p. A674

HOPKINS, John, M.D., Chief of Staff, Avera Hand County Memorial Hospital, Miller, SD, p. A562

HOPKINS, Joy, Vice President Patient Care Services, Osf St. Francis Hospital And Medical Group, Escanaba, MI, p. A311

HOPKINS, Kelli, Director Human Resources, Baptist Health Medical Center–Hot Spring County, Malvern, AR, p. A45

HOPKINS, Ken, Vice President Finance and Chief Financial Officer, Norman Regional Health System, Norman, OK, p. A503

HOPKINS, Kevin, Vice President of Operations, Chi Memorial Hospital – Georgia, Fort Oglethorpe, GA, p. A153

HOPKINS, Larry, Chief Medical Officer, Indiana University Health Tipton Hospital, Tipton, IN, p. A215

HOPKINS, Ronald, D.O., Chief of Staff, Nor–Lea Hospital District, Lovington, NM, p. A419

HOPKINS, William, Director Finance, Atrium Health'S Carolinas Rehabilitation, Charlotte, NC, p. A451

HOPP, Eva, Chief Nurse Executive, Pinckneyville Community Hospital, Pinckneyville, IL, p. A193

HOPPER, Tasha
Chief Executive Officer, The Hospitals Of Providence Transmountain Campus, El Paso, TX, p. A603
Chief Operating Officer, The Hospitals Of Providence Transmountain Campus, El Paso, TX, p. A603

HOPPS, Deborah, Chief Executive Officer, Baylor Scott & White Institute For Rehabilitation – Lakeway, Lakeway, TX, p. A619

HOPSON, W Briggs, M.D., Clinical Medical Director, Merit Health River Region, Vicksburg, MS, p. A355

HOPSTAD, Kyle, Chief Executive Officer, Broadwater Health Center, Townsend, MT, p. A380

HOPWOOD, James, Chief Financial Officer, Promise Hospital Of Miss Lou, Vidalia, LA, p. A279

HOPWOOD, Jennifer, Chief Nursing Officer, Vice President Patient Care, Osf Saint Francis Medical Center, Peoria, IL, p. A193

HORAN, Gary S, President and Chief Executive Officer, Trinitas Regional Medical Center, Elizabeth, NJ, p. A405

HORAN, Gary S., President and Chief Executive Officer, Trinitas Regional Medical Center, Elizabeth, NJ, p. A405

HORATH, Kevin, Vice President Human Resources, Decatur Memorial Hospital, Decatur, IL, p. A180

HORCH, David, Chief Executive, California Medical Facility, Vacaville, CA, p. A93

HORECKA, Richard, Chief Medical Officer, Swift County – Benson Health Services, Benson, MN, p. A328

HORINECK, Kim, Chief Human Resource Officer, Goodland Regional Medical Center, Goodland, KS, p. A235

HORINEK, ReChelle, Chief Financial Officer, Trego County–Lemke Memorial Hospital, Wakeeney, KS, p. A247

HORN, Debbie, Controller, Texas Rehabilitation Hospital Of Arlington, Arlington, TX, p. A584

HORN, Jeff, Director of Support Services, Indiana University Health Jay Hospital, Portland, IN, p. A213

HORN, Jon, M.D., Chief of Staff, Northeast Georgia Medical Center Barrow, Winder, GA, p. A163

HORN, LeeAnn, Chief Nurse Executive, Providence Kodiak Island Medical Center, Kodiak, AK, p. A26

HORN, Sarah
Chief Nursing Officer, Salem Health West Valley, Dallas, OR, p. A512
Chief Nursing Officer, Salem Hospital, Salem, OR, p. A517

HORN, Syndi, Director Information Systems, Memorial Hospital, Carthage, IL, p. A175

HORNBURG, Tom, Director Information Systems, Mason General Hospital And Family Of Clinics, Shelton, WA, p. A679

HORNE, Beth, System Administrator Information Technology, Preston Memorial Hospital, Kingwood, WV, p. A686

HORNE, Eilene, Manager Human Resources, Mountain View Hospital, Idaho Falls, ID, p. A169

HORNE, J Mark, Senior Vice President, Ambulatory Services and Chief Operating Officer, Grand View Health, Sellersville, PA, p. A541

HORNE, Perry, Chief Nursing Officer, St. Cloud Regional Medical Center, Saint Cloud, FL, p. A138

HORNER, Ania, R.N., MSN, Vice President and Chief Nurse Executive, Aurora Sinai Medical Center, Milwaukee, WI, p. A701

HORNER, Bryan, President and Chief Executive Officer, Shannon Medical Center, San Angelo, TX, p. A633

HORNER, Cheryl, Supervisor Data Processing, Community Hospital Of Staunton, Staunton, IL, p. A197

HORNER, Eva, Assistant Executive Director Operations, Devereux Hospital And Children'S Center Of Florida, Melbourne, FL, p. A129

HORNER, John M., President and Chief Executive Officer, Major Hospital, Shelbyville, IN, p. A214

HORNICK, Gregory, MSN, Chief Nursing Officer, Martin General Hospital, Williamston, NC, p. A463

HORNSBY, Donny, Director Fiscal Services, Memphis Mental Health Institute, Memphis, TN, p. A575

HORNUNG, Dona, Director Information and Technology Services, Doctors Hospital, Augusta, GA, p. A147

HORNUNG, Kurt, Director, Medical Center Of Trinity, Trinity, FL, p. A143

HORRIGAN, Timothy, M.D., Chief Quality Officer, Unitypoint Health – Allen Hospital, Waterloo, IA, p. A231

HORSLEY, Steve, Vice President and Chief Information Officer, Moses H. Cone Memorial Hospital, Greensboro, NC, p. A455

HORSMAN, Sandra, Director, Veterans Affairs Black Hills Health Care System, Fort Meade, SD, p. A561

HORST, Brad, Director Human Resources, Hca Houston Healthcare Clear Lake, League City, TX, p. A620

HORST, Joanna, MSN, R.N., Chief Nursing Officer, St. Christopher'S Hospital For Children, Philadelphia, PA, p. A536

HORSTMAN, Jennifer M, R.N., Chief Nursing Officer and Chief Information Officer, Fairbanks, Indianapolis, IN, p. A206

HORSTMANN, Steve, Vice President Operations, North Memorial Health Hospital, Robbinsdale, MN, p. A338

HORTILLOSA, Maria, M.D., Chief of Staff, Middlesboro Arh Hospital, Middlesboro, KY, p. A258

HORTON, Alan, Administrator, Putnam General Hospital, Eatonton, GA, p. A153

HORTON, Greg, Director Support Services, State Hospital South, Blackfoot, ID, p. A167

HORTON, Jerrilyn, R.N., Chief Nursing Officer, Dewitt Hospital, Dewitt, AR, p. A41

HORTON, Jim, Chief Executive Officer, Rankin County Hospital District, Rankin, TX, p. A630

HORTON, Kenny, Director Information Systems, Walker Baptist Medical Center, Jasper, AL, p. A20

HORTON, Landon, Director of Nursing, Valley Behavioral Health System, Barling, AR, p. A39

HORTON, Marie, Director Associate Relations, Bartow Regional Medical Center, Bartow, FL, p. A117

HORTON, Sammy, Chief of Staff, Brownwood Regional Medical Center, Brownwood, TX, p. A590

HORTON, Warren, Information Technologist, Baptist Health Medical Center–Stuttgart, Stuttgart, AR, p. A49

HORVAT, Kami, Chief Financial Officer, West Covina Medical Center, West Covina, CA, p. A94

HORVATH, Alex
Vice President and Chief Human Resources Officer, Tmc Healthcare, Tucson, AZ, p. A38
Vice President Human Resources, Methodist Hospitals, Gary, IN, p. A205

HORVATH, Holly, Director of Nursing, Jerome Golden Center For Behavioral Health, Inc., West Palm Beach, FL, p. A144

HOSS, Laurna, Human Resource Coordinator, Select Specialty Hospital–Omaha, Omaha, NE, p. A390

HOSTEENEZ, Vivie, Chief Financial Officer, San Carlos Apache Healthcare Corporation, Peridot, AZ, p. A32

HOSTETTER, Lynne, Vice President Human Resources, The Hsc Pediatric Center, Washington, DC, p. A116

HOTA, Bala, Interim Chief Information Officer, John H. Stroger Jr. Hospital Of Cook County, Chicago, IL, p. A177

HOTALING, Andrew, Chief Executive Officer, Forest View Psychiatric Hospital, Grand Rapids, MI, p. A312

HOTCHKISS, Jason, CPA
Chief Financial Officer, Ottumwa Regional Health Center, Ottumwa, IA, p. A228
Chief Financial Officer, Trios Health, Kennewick, WA, p. A674

HOTCHKISS, Kaleigh, Controller, Encompass Health Rehabilitation Hospital Of Northwest Tucson, Tucson, AZ, p. A37

HOTES, Lawrence S, M.D., Chief Medical Officer, New England Sinai Hospital And Rehabilitation Center, Stoughton, MA, p. A304

HOTOVY, Patrick, M.D., Chief of Staff, York General, York, NE, p. A392

HOUCHIN, Kim, Chief Nursing Officer, Minnie Hamilton Healthcare Center, Grantsville, WV, p. A685

HOUCK, Nanette, R.N., Chief Nursing Executive, Excelsior Springs Hospital, Excelsior Springs, MO, p. A359

HOUGH, Nathan
Chief Executive Officer, Crook County Medical Services District, Sundance, WY, p. A713
Chief Executive Officer, Niobrara Health And Life Center, Lusk, WY, p. A712

HOUGHTON, Roxan, Director Human Resources, Promise Hospital Of Miss Lou, Vidalia, LA, p. A279

HOULAHAN, Beth, R.N., Senior Vice President and Chief Nursing Officer, University Hospital, Madison, WI, p. A698

HOULE, David, Executive Vice President and Chief Financial Officer, Hebrew Senior Care, West Hartford, CT, p. A112

HOULIHAN, David, M.D., Chief of Staff, Va Medical Center, Tomah, WI, p. A706

HOULTON, Andrew, M.D., Chief Medical Officer, North Memorial Health Hospital, Robbinsdale, MN, p. A338

HOUMANN, Lars D, President, Adventhealth Orlando, Orlando, FL, p. A134

HOUNSHELL, Jacqueline, Chief Financial Officer, Leconte Medical Center, Sevierville, TN, p. A579

HOURANY, Joseph, Chief Medical Officer, Montclair Hospital Medical Center, Montclair, CA, p. A72

HOUSAND, Jill, Director Human Resources, Mesa Springs, Fort Worth, TX, p. A605

HOUSE, David
Vice President and Chief Information Officer, Baptist Health Medical Center – North Little Rock, North Little Rock, AR, p. A46
Vice President and Chief Information Officer, Baptist Health Medical Center–Arkadelphia, Arkadelphia, AR, p. A39
Vice President and Chief Information Officer, Baptist Health Medical Center–Little Rock, Little Rock, AR, p. A44
Vice President and Chief Information Officer, Baptist Health Rehabilitation Institute, Little Rock, AR, p. A45
Vice President, Baptist Health Extended Care Hospital, Little Rock, AR, p. A44

HOUSE, John, M.D., Chief of Staff, Eureka Springs Hospital, Eureka Springs, AR, p. A41

HOUSER, David, M.D., Vice President Medical Affairs, Rapid City Regional Hospital, Rapid City, SD, p. A563

HOUSER, Robert, Chief Executive Officer, Pioneer Memorial Hospital, Heppner, OR, p. A513

HOUSER, Sara, Chief Nursing Officer, Ashe Memorial Hospital, Jefferson, NC, p. A457

HOUSER–HANFELDER, Sallie, Director, Veterans Affairs Eastern Colorado Health Care System, Denver, CO, p. A99

HOUSH, Joe, District Director Human Resources, Kindred Hospital–Indianapolis, Indianapolis, IN, p. A207

HOUSLEY, Kristin, Chief Information Officer, South Lincoln Medical Center, Kemmerer, WY, p. A711

HOUSMAN, Bradley W., M.D., Chief Medical Officer, Baptist Health Paducah, Paducah, KY, p. A259

HOUSTON, Anthony, FACHE, Chief Operating Officer, Chi Memorial, Chattanooga, TN, p. A567

HOUSTON, Jerry, Director Information Systems, Jennie Stuart Medical Center, Hopkinsville, KY, p. A253

HOUSTON, Sally, M.D., Executive Vice President and Chief Medical Officer, Tampa General Hospital, Tampa, FL, p. A142

HOVAN, Keith A, President and Chief Executive Officer, Southcoast Hospitals Group, Fall River, MA, p. A298

HOVAN, Keith A., President and Chief Executive Officer, Southcoast Hospitals Group, Fall River, MA, p. A298

HOVDENES, Jodi Lynn, R.N., Vice President Patient Care, Chi St Alexius Health Carrington Medical Center, Carrington, ND, p. A465

HOVENS, Michael R., M.D., Chief Medical Officer, Panola Medical Center, Batesville, MS, p. A344

HOWARD, Andrew, Chief Executive Officer, Select Specialty Hospital–North Knoxville, Powell, TN, p. A578

HOWARD, Catherine, Director Human Resources, Sentara Halifax Regional Hospital, South Boston, VA, p. A667

HOWARD, Cindy, Director Financial Services, Nell J. Redfield Memorial Hospital, Malad City, ID, p. A170

HOWARD, Dan, Director, Information Services, San Gorgonio Memorial Hospital, Banning, CA, p. A52

HOWARD, Daniel, Chief Financial Officer, Maine Veterans Affairs Medical Center, Augusta, ME, p. A281

HOWARD, Darcy, Chief Financial Officer, Citizens Medical Center, Colby, KS, p. A233

HOWARD, Deanna S., Interim President and Chief Executive Officer, Valley Regional Hospital, Claremont, NH, p. A399

HOWARD, Gary L, Senior Vice President and Chief Financial Officer, Hamilton Medical Center, Dalton, GA, p. A151

HOWARD, Greg M
Director Human Resource, Health Alliance Hospital – Broadway Campus, Kingston, NY, p. A430
Vice President Human Resources, Health Alliance Hospital – Mary'S Avenue Campus, Kingston, NY, p. A430

HOWARD, Gwenyth, Vice President Finance, St. Thomas More Hospital, Canon City, CO, p. A97

HOWARD, Lisa M, Associate Director, Veterans Affairs Sierra Nevada Health Care System, Reno, NV, p. A397

HOWARD, Lisa M., Director, Veterans Affairs Sierra Nevada Health Care System, Reno, NV, p. A397

HOWARD, Loy M., Chief Operating Officer, Tanner Medical Center–Carrollton, Carrollton, GA, p. A149

HOWARD, Mark L., Chief Executive Officer, Fairmount Behavioral Health System, Philadelphia, PA, p. A534

HOWARD, Mary, Director Human Resources, Winnebago Mental Health Institute, Winnebago, WI, p. A709

HOWARD, Melissa, Chief Nurse Executive, ICH & FPH, Citrus Valley Medical Center–Inter Community Campus, Covina, CA, p. A56

HOWARD, Michele, Vice President Nursing Services, Perry County Memorial Hospital, Tell City, IN, p. A215

HOWARD, Mike, Chief Operating Officer, North Alabama Medical Center, Florence, AL, p. A18

HOWARD, Opal R, Executive Director Human Resources, Adventhealth Daytona Beach, Daytona Beach, FL, p. A121

HOWARD, Pamela B., Chief Executive Officer, Administrator and Risk Manager, Lake Butler Hospital Hand Surgery Center, Lake Butler, FL, p. A127

HOWARD, Ron, Chief Financial Officer, Holly Hill Hospital, Raleigh, NC, p. A460

HOWARD, Sabra, Manager Human Resources, Harlan Arh Hospital, Harlan, KY, p. A253

HOWARD, Shawn, Interim Chief Executive Officer, Atoka County Medical Center, Atoka, OK, p. A496

HOWARD, Teresa, Manager Human Resources, Yoakum County Hospital, Denver City, TX, p. A600

HOWARD, Tom, Chief Financial Officer, Texas Health Presbyterian Hospital Flower Mound, Flower Mound, TX, p. A604

HOWARD, Win, Chief Executive Officer, Asante Three Rivers Medical Center, Grants Pass, OR, p. A513

HOWARD–CROW, Dallis, Chief Human Resources Officer, Emory University Hospital Midtown, Atlanta, GA, p. A146

HOWAT, Greg, Vice President Human Resources, Northern Light Eastern Maine Medical Center, Bangor, ME, p. A281

HOWDEN, William, Vice President Nursing, Good Samaritan Regional Medical Center, Corvallis, OR, p. A512

HOWE, Christopher L., Chief Executive Officer, Plateau Medical Center, Oak Hill, WV, p. A688

HOWE, Debbie, Chief Executive Officer, Weatherford Regional Hospital, Weatherford, OK, p. A510

HOWE, James L, Director Human Resources, Pinnacle Pointe Hospital, Little Rock, AR, p. A45

HOWE, Judson, Chief Financial Officer, Adventist Health Howard Memorial, Willits, CA, p. A95

HOWE, Vicki, Health Information Management, Ness County Hospital District No 2, Ness City, KS, p. A241

HOWELL, Amy M, Director Human Resources, St. Luke'S Behavioral Health Center, Phoenix, AZ, p. A34

HOWELL, Bradley C., Chief Executive Officer, Pioneer Medical Center, Big Timber, MT, p. A374

HOWELL, Carrie, Chief Financial Officer, Barstow Community Hospital, Barstow, CA, p. A52

HOWELL, Diana, Director Human Resources, Hca Houston Healthcare Conroe, Conroe, TX, p. A593

HOWELL, Jerry, Administrator, Sabine County Hospital, Hemphill, TX, p. A609

HOWELL, Jill, Chief Nursing Officer, St. Luke'S Jerome, Jerome, ID, p. A169

HOWELL, Kathy A, Vice President Human Resources, Lexington Medical Center, West Columbia, SC, p. A558

HOWELL, Kristie, System Information Technology Director, Southampton Memorial Hospital, Franklin, VA, p. A659

HOWELL, Nathan, Chief Executive Officer, Southern Maine Health Care – Biddeford Medical Center, Biddeford, ME, p. A282

HOWELL, Pat, Chief Nursing Officer, Syracuse Area Health, Syracuse, NE, p. A392

HOWELL, Ronene, Director Health Information Management, Bryce Hospital, Tuscaloosa, AL, p. A24

HOWELL, Sheri, Deputy Commander Nursing, Brooke Army Medical Center, Fort Sam Houston, TX, p. A604

HOWELL, Timothy W., R.N., Senior Vice President and Chief Nursing Officer, University Medical Center, Lubbock, TX, p. A622

HOWELLS, Stephen, Chief Financial Officer, Kane County Hospital, Kanab, UT, p. A648

HOWERTER, Mark, M.D., President Medical Staff, Columbus Community Hospital, Columbus, NE, p. A384

HOWERTON, Russell M, M.D., Chief Medical Officer, Wake Forest Baptist Medical Center, Winston, NC, p. A464

HOWERTON, Shawn, Chief Executive Officer and President, Medical Staff, Sampson Regional Medical Center, Clinton, NC, p. A452

HOWERTON, Shawn, M.D., Chief Executive Officer and President, Medical Staff, Sampson Regional Medical Center, Clinton, NC, p. A452

HOY, Jonathan B, Chief Financial Officer, Duke Regional Hospital, Durham, NC, p. A452

HOYER, Sara, Director Administrative Services, Kansas Neurological Institute, Topeka, KS, p. A246

HOYES, Garry W, Chief Executive Officer, Columbus Dublin Springs, Dublin, OH, p. A482

HOYES, Garry W., Chief Executive Officer, Columbus Dublin Springs, Dublin, OH, p. A482

HOYOS, Kent, Chief Information Officer, Pomona Valley Hospital Medical Center, Pomona, CA, p. A78

HOYT, Nancy Gerilyn, R.N., Vice President Operations/Clinical and Chief Nursing Officer, Mercy Regional Medical Center, Durango, CO, p. A99

HRDLICKA, Stephanie, Chief Executive Officer, Vermilion Behavioral Health Systems – North Campus, Lafayette, LA, p. A271

HRIT, Barbara, Controller, Beaumont Hospital – Farmington Hills, Farmington Hills, MI, p. A311

HRITZ, Diane, Chief Financial Officer, Advanced Surgical Hospital, Washington, PA, p. A543

HRUBIAK, Dan, Associate Computer Program Analyst, Western New York Children'S Psychiatric Center, West Seneca, NY, p. A447

HRUBY, Deidre, Director of Patient Care, Madelia Community Hospital, Madelia, MN, p. A334

HSIEH, Ketty, Senior Director Finance, Uw Medicine/ Northwest Hospital & Medical Center, Seattle, WA, p. A678

HSU, Wah Chung, Senior Vice President Finance, San Antonio Regional Hospital, Upland, CA, p. A93

HUANG, Hanna, Chief Executive Officer, Laredo Specialty Hospital, Laredo, TX, p. A620

HUANG, Joseph, M.D., Chief Medical and Quality Officer, Legacy Silverton Medical Center, Silverton, OR, p. A518

HUBBARD, Bill, Vice President, Operations, Atrium Health Cabarrus, Concord, NC, p. A452

HUBBARD, Blake W., Chief Executive Officer, Foundation Surgical Hospital Of San Antonio, San Antonio, TX, p. A634

HUBBARD, Brent, President and Chief Operating Officer, Mercy Hospital Springfield, Springfield, MO, p. A371

HUBBARD, Brent, FACHE
Chief Operating Officer, Mercy Hospital Ozark, Ozark, AR, p. A47
Chief Operating Officer, Mercy Hospital Paris, Paris, AR, p. A47
Chief Operating Officer, Mercy Hospital Springfield, Springfield, MO, p. A371
Chief Operating Officer, Mercy Hospital Waldron, Waldron, AR, p. A49

HUBBARD, Daniel, Chief Financial Officer, Sioux Falls Veterans Affairs Health Care System, Sioux Falls, SD, p. A564

HUBBARD, Gwen, Chief Nursing Officer, Sierra Vista Hospital, Sacramento, CA, p. A82

HUBBARD, Kathy
Controller, Ocean Beach Hospital, Ilwaco, WA, p. A674
Manager Human Resources, Nell J. Redfield Memorial Hospital, Malad City, ID, p. A170

HUBBARD, Lisa, Vice President and Chief Nursing Executive, Mercy Medical Center Mount Shasta, Mount Shasta, CA, p. A73

HUBBARD, Mark, Vice President Risk Management, Loma Linda University Behavioral Medicine Center, Redlands, CA, p. A80

HUBBARD, Norm, Executive Vice President, Seattle Cancer Care Alliance, Seattle, WA, p. A678

HUBBARD, Tyson, Director Human Resources, Stanislaus Surgical Hospital, Modesto, CA, p. A72

HUBBS, Olas A., III, President and Chief Executive Officer, Memorial Health, Marysville, OH, p. A486

HUBEL, Edward T., President, Baptist Medical Center Nassau, Fernandina Beach, FL, p. A122

HUBER, Dalton, Chief Financial Officer, Campbell County Health, Gillette, WY, p. A711

HUBER, Joseph M, Chief Financial Officer, Hospital Of The University Of Pennsylvania, Philadelphia, PA, p. A535

HUBER, Timothy
Vice President and Chief Financial Officer, Mercyone Cedar Falls Medical Center, Cedar Falls, IA, p. A218
Vice President and Chief Financial Officer, Mercyone Oelwein Medical Center, Oelwein, IA, p. A227
Vice President and Chief Financial Officer, Mercyone Waterloo Medical Center, Waterloo, IA, p. A231

HUBER, Vicki Lynn, R.N., MSN, Chief Nursing Officer, Abrazo Scottsdale Campus, Phoenix, AZ, p. A32

HUBLEY, Grover, M.D., President Medical Staff, Chi St. Joseph Health Madison Hospital, Madisonville, TX, p. A623

HUBSCHMAN, Gary
Administrative Director Finance, Sutter Auburn Faith Hospital, Auburn, CA, p. A51
Administrative Director Finance, Sutter Roseville Medical Center, Roseville, CA, p. A81

HUCK, Karma, Chief Operating Officer, Scott County Hospital, Scott City, KS, p. A245

HUCKABEE, Mike, Network Administrator, Coryell Health, Gatesville, TX, p. A607

HUCKABY, Don, Chief Information Management Service, Veterans Affairs Eastern Colorado Health Care System, Denver, CO, p. A99

HUDA, Edith, Director Human Resources, Daniels Memorial Healthcare Center, Scobey, MT, p. A380

HUDAK, Corey, Director Human Resources, Upmc Memorial, York, PA, p. A546

HUDDLESTON, Tina, R.N., Chief Nursing Officer, Baylor Scott & White Medical Center – Trophy Club, Trophy Club, TX, p. A641

HUDGENS, Roselyn, Director Human Resources, Ballinger Memorial Hospital, Ballinger, TX, p. A586

HUDGINS, Laura E, Assistant Administrator, Jasper Memorial Hospital, Monticello, GA, p. A158

HUDGINS, Paul C., Senior Vice President, Carilion Franklin Memorial Hospital, Rocky Mount, VA, p. A667

HUDSON, Beth, Chief Nursing Officer, Baylor Scott & White Institute For Rehabilitation – Dallas, Dallas, TX, p. A595

HUDSON, Delilah, Controller, Covington County Hospital, Collins, MS, p. A346

HUDSON, Gary Mikeal, Administrator, Ut Health Carthage, Carthage, TX, p. A591

HUDSON, Gary Mikeal., Administrator, Ut Health Carthage, Carthage, TX, p. A591

HUDSON, Guy, Chief Executive Officer, Swedish/Issaquah, Issaquah, WA, p. A674

HUDSON, Janell, Director, Nursing and Clinical Services, Sanford Medical Center Thief River Falls, Thief River Falls, MN, p. A341

HUDSON, Jason Dan., Chief Executive Officer, Encompass Health Rehabilitation Hospital Of Tinton Falls, Tinton Falls, NJ, p. A413

HUDSON, Kenneth J, Chief Financial Officer, Veterans Affairs Puget Sound Health Care System, Seattle, WA, p. A678

HUDSON, Kent, Chief Financial Officer, Kingman Community Hospital, Kingman, KS, p. A238

HUDSON, Larry C, Executive Vice President and Chief Financial Officer, Charleston Area Medical Center, Charleston, WV, p. A684

HUDSON, Maggie, Chief Financial and Operations Officer, Santiam Hospital, Stayton, OR, p. A518

HUDSON, Mike, Administrator, Federal Correctional Institute Hospital, Littleton, CO, p. A103

HUDSON, Norma, Chief Financial Officer, Del Amo Hospital, Torrance, CA, p. A91

HUDSON, Pamela, Chief Executive Officer, Crestwood Medical Center, Huntsville, AL, p. A19

HUDSON, Robbi, Chief Executive Officer, Encompass Health Rehabilitation Hospital Of Wichita Falls, Wichita Falls, TX, p. A645

HUDSON–JINKS, Therese M., R.N., MSN, Chief Nursing Officer, Tufts Medical Center, Boston, MA, p. A296

HUELSKAMP, Donald, Interim Chief Financial Officer, Harrison Community Hospital, Cadiz, OH, p. A474

HUENERGARDT, Sam D., Chief Executive Officer, Adventhealth Shawnee Mission, Shawnee Mission, KS, p. A245

HUERTA, Brad, Chief Executive Officer and Administrator, Lost Rivers Medical Center, Arco, ID, p. A167

HUERTA, Guillermo, M.D., Chief Medical Officer, Select Specialty Hospital–Omaha, Omaha, NE, p. A390

HUERTA, Jose, Chief Executive Officer, Mesa Hills Specialty Hospital, El Paso, TX, p. A602

HUERTER, Holly
Vice President Human Resources, Methodist Jennie Edmundson Hospital, Council Bluffs, IA, p. A220
Vice President Human Resources, Nebraska Methodist Hospital, Omaha, NE, p. A389

HUESMAN, Carol, Chief Information Officer, Major Hospital, Shelbyville, IN, p. A214

HUETTL, Patricia, Vice President Finance and Chief Financial Officer, Holy Family Memorial, Manitowoc, WI, p. A699

HUFF, Jeff, Assistant Administrator Finance, Fayette Medical Center, Fayette, AL, p. A18

HUFF, Michael H., Chief Executive Officer, Hamilton Hospital, Olney, TX, p. A627

HUFF, Shelly E, Manager Human Resources, Indiana University Health Tipton Hospital, Tipton, IN, p. A215

HUFFINE, Daniel, Chief Financial Officer, St. David'S Medical Center, Austin, TX, p. A586

HUFFMAN, David, Vice President and Controller, Select Specialty Hospital–Wilmington, Wilmington, DE, p. A114

HUFFMAN, James, Chief Executive Officer and Administrator, Baptist Memorial Hospital–Desoto, Southaven, MS, p. A354

HUFFMAN, Joshua, M.D., Chief Medical Staff, Chi Saint Joseph Berea, Berea, KY, p. A249

HUFFMAN, Sherry, Administrator Human Resources, Beaumont Hospital – Dearborn, Dearborn, MI, p. A309

HUFFMAN, Teresa, Chief Executive Officer, Texas Rehabilitation Hospital Of Arlington, Arlington, TX, p. A584

HUFFMAN, Tim, Western Region Director, Information Systems Business Relationships, Baylor Scott & White Medical Center–Irving, Irving, TX, p. A616

HUFFNER, William, M.D.
Chief Medical Officer, University Of Maryland Shore Medical Center At Chestertown, Chestertown, MD, p. A289
Chief Medical Officer, University Of Maryland Shore Medical Center At Easton, Easton, MD, p. A290
Vice President Medical Affairs, University Of Maryland Shore Medical Center At Dorchester, Cambridge, MD, p. A289

HUFFSTUTLER, Brandon, Chief Information Officer, Electra Memorial Hospital, Electra, TX, p. A603

HUFNAGEL, Keith, Director Human Resources, Stillwater Medical Center, Stillwater, OK, p. A507

HUGAR, Joseph G., President, Sharon Regional Medical Center, Sharon, PA, p. A541

HUGGINS, Lois, Chief Human Resources Officer and Senior Vice President Human Resources, Shirley Ryan Abilitylab, Chicago, IL, p. A179

HUGGINS, Michael C, Administrator Network System, Eastern Oklahoma Medical Center, Poteau, OK, p. A506

HUGHES, April, Chief Financial Officer, Peachford Behavioral Health System, Atlanta, GA, p. A146

HUGHES, Beth, President, Mercyone Siouxland Medical Center, Sioux City, IA, p. A230

HUGHES, Bill, Chief Nursing Officer, Granville Health System, Oxford, NC, p. A460

HUGHES, Brandon, Director Human Resources, Hermann Area District Hospital, Hermann, MO, p. A361

HUGHES, Chad
Chief Information Officer, North Texas State Hospital, Wichita Falls Campus, Wichita Falls, TX, p. A645
Information Officer, North Texas State Hospital, Vernon, TX, p. A643

HUGHES, David L., Administrator, Crenshaw Community Hospital, Luverne, AL, p. A20

HUGHES, David S, Chief Financial Officer, Vidant Medical Center, Greenville, NC, p. A455

HUGHES, Dustan, M.D., Vice President Medical Affairs, Saint Alphonsus Medical Center – Nampa, Nampa, ID, p. A170

HUGHES, Elisabeth, Director Human Resources and Community Relations, Fairview Regional Medical Center, Fairview, OK, p. A500

HUGHES, James, Director Human Resources, Lake Cumberland Regional Hospital, Somerset, KY, p. A260

HUGHES, Jessica, Director Finance, Hawarden Regional Healthcare, Hawarden, IA, p. A224

HUGHES, Lee, R.N., Chief Nursing Officer, Flint River Community Hospital, Montezuma, GA, p. A157

HUGHES, Leigh Ann, Chief Financial Officer, Hardin Medical Center, Savannah, TN, p. A579

HUGHES, Lori, R.N., MSN
Chief Nursing Officer, Vice President Operations & Patient Care Services, Cottage Hospital, Woodsville, NH, p. A402
Chief Nursing Officer, Vice President Operations and Patient Care Services, Cottage Hospital, Woodsville, NH, p. A402

HUGHES, Mark A., M.D., Medical Director, River Park Hospital, Huntington, WV, p. A686

HUGHES, Michael, President, Summa Health System Barberton, Summa Health System, Akron, OH, p. A471

HUGHES, Robert K.
Chief Executive Officer, Brookdale Hospital Medical Center, New York, NY, p. A432
Executive Director, Brookdale Hospital Medical Center, New York, NY, p. A432

HUGHES, Susan, Interim Director Human Resources, Winner Regional Healthcare Center, Winner, SD, p. A565

HUGHES, Terry, Director Information Systems, Nantucket Cottage Hospital, Nantucket, MA, p. A301

HUGHES, Thomas, President, St. Joseph Health Services Of Rhode Island, North Providence, RI, p. A547

HUGHES, Veronica, Chief Nursing Officer, Mesilla Valley Hospital, Las Cruces, NM, p. A418

HUGHES–MICKEL, Leann, Chief Information Officer, Touro Infirmary, New Orleans, LA, p. A276

HUGHS, Mary, Chief Human Resources Officer, Our Lady Of Lourdes Memorial Hospital, Inc., Binghamton, NY, p. A424

HUGHSON, John R., Chief Executive Officer, Frio Regional Hospital, Pearsall, TX, p. A628

HUGO, Chris, M.D., Chief of Staff, Guttenberg Municipal Hospital, Guttenberg, IA, p. A223

HULBERT, Kim, R.N., Chief Clinical Officer, Madison County Health Care System, Winterset, IA, p. A231

HULETT, Rachelle, Vice President Human Resources, Mclaren Flint, Flint, MI, p. A311

HULETT, Wendi, Chief Nursing Officer, Artesia General Hospital, Artesia, NM, p. A417

HULL, Brad, Chief Financial Officer, Dale Medical Center, Ozark, AL, p. A22

HULL, Debbie, Chief Financial Officer, Fisher County Hospital District, Rotan, TX, p. A632

HULL, Kathy, President and Chief Executive Officer, Illini Community Hospital, Pittsfield, IL, p. A193

HULL, Ken, Director Human Resources, Inova Fairfax Hospital, Falls Church, VA, p. A659

HULL, Lauren, Chief Operating Officer, Porter Regional Hospital, Valparaiso, IN, p. A215

HULLANDER, Angie, Administrator and Special Operations, Chi Memorial Hospital – Georgia, Fort Oglethorpe, GA, p. A153

HULLINGER, Scott, Chief Executive Officer, Silver Oaks Behavioral Hospital, New Lenox, IL, p. A191

HULSE, Mark, MSN, Chief Digital Officer, City Of Hope'S Helford Clinical Research Hospital, Duarte, CA, p. A57

HULSEY, Cathy, Manager of Human Resources, Chi Memorial Hospital – Georgia, Fort Oglethorpe, GA, p. A153

HULSEY, Grant, Director Information Technology, Baylor Scott & White Surgical Hospital–Sherman, Sherman, TX, p. A636

HULSEY, Kelly, MSN, R.N., Chief Nursing Officer, Piedmont Hospital, Atlanta, GA, p. A146

HUMBERT, Gilbert Glenn, R.N., Chief Nursing Officer, Our Lady Of Lourdes Regional Medical Center, Lafayette, LA, p. A271

HUMBLE, Kathryn G., Chief Human Resources Officer, Beatrice Community Hospital And Health Center, Beatrice, NE, p. A383

HUMBLE, Linnea, Director of Finance, Sutter Lakeside Hospital, Lakeport, CA, p. A64

HUME, Diana, Manager Human Resources, Methodist Mckinney Hospital, Mckinney, TX, p. A624

HUMES, Karen, Chief Information Officer, Titusville Area Hospital, Titusville, PA, p. A542

HUMES, Ronny, Chief Executive Officer, Magnolia Regional Health Center, Corinth, MS, p. A346

HUMME, Sarah, MSN, R.N.
Chief Nursing Officer, Southwest General Hospital, San Antonio, TX, p. A635
Chief Operating Officer, Southwest General Hospital, San Antonio, TX, p. A635

HUMMEL, Angela, Vice President Human Resources, Evangelical Community Hospital, Lewisburg, PA, p. A530

HUMMELKE, Arlita, Manager Human Resources, Mercy Hospital Tishomingo, Tishomingo, OK, p. A508

HUMMER, Denise, R.N., Vice President Administrative Services, Community Memorial Hospital, Hamilton, NY, p. A429

HUMPHREY, Dale, Chief Executive Officer, Saint Thomas River Park Hospital, Mc Minnville, TN, p. A574

HUMPHREY, Eric, Senior Vice President, Chief Human Resources Officer, St. Joseph'S Hospital, West Bend, WI, p. A708

HUMPHREY, James, Vice President Talent Resources and Human Resources for South Side Operating Group, Penrose–St. Francis Health Services, Colorado Springs, CO, p. A98

HUMPHREY, Randy, Chief Financial Officer, Merit Health Wesley, Hattiesburg, MS, p. A348

HUMPHREY, Richard, Executive Vice President and Chief Financial Officer, Parkland Health & Hospital System, Dallas, TX, p. A597

HUMPHREYS, Corina, Chief Executive Officer, Weslaco Regional Rehabilitation Hospital, Weslaco, TX, p. A645

HUMPHREYS, Lynn, Director Human Resources, Henry County Health Center, Mount Pleasant, IA, p. A227

HUMPHRIES, Vickie Witcher
Director Human Resources, Bon Secours Maryview Medical Center, Portsmouth, VA, p. A665
Vice President Human Resources, Bon Secours Mary Immaculate Hospital, Newport News, VA, p. A663
Vice President Human Resources, Bon Secours–Depaul Medical Center, Norfolk, VA, p. A663

HUNDAL, Ranjit, M.D., Chief Medical Executive, Mills–Peninsula Health Services, Burlingame, CA, p. A53

HUNGER, Bryan, Chief Executive Officer, Jefferson County Health Center, Fairfield, IA, p. A222

HUNGER, Dennis, Chief Operating Officer, Ottumwa Regional Health Center, Ottumwa, IA, p. A228

HUNSAKER, Mike, Chief Operating Officer, Star Valley Medical Center, Afton, WY, p. A710

HUNSBERGER, Tom, Director Human Resources, Olmsted Medical Center, Rochester, MN, p. A338

HUNSICKER, Elizabeth, Chief Executive Officer, West Valley Medical Center, Caldwell, ID, p. A168

HUNT, Amy, Director Human Resources, Menorah Medical Center, Overland Park, KS, p. A243

HUNT, Cheri, R.N., Vice President Patient Care Services and Chief Nursing Officer, Children'S Mercy Hospital Kansas City, Kansas City, MO, p. A362

HUNT, Cheryl, Chief Nursing Officer, St. Peter'S Hospital, Helena, MT, p. A377

HUNT, Chris, President, Clay County Hospital, Flora, IL, p. A183

HUNT, Christopher, Director, Information Technologies, FISO, Helena Regional Medical Center, Helena, AR, p. A43

HUNT, D Deann, Director of Human Resources, Gibson General Hospital, Princeton, IN, p. A214

HUNT, Deloris, Chief Human Resources Officer, Michigan Medicine, Ann Arbor, MI, p. A306

HUNT, Don, M.D., Vice President Patient Centered Care and Chief Nursing Officer, Ut Health North Campus Tyler, Tyler, TX, p. A642

HUNT, Jeffery B, Vice President, Business Development and Support Services, Roane General Hospital, Spencer, WV, p. A689

HUNT, John R., Chief Executive Officer, Encompass Health Rehabilitation Hospital Of Western Massachusetts, Ludlow, MA, p. A300

HUNT, Julie, R.N., MS, Chief Nursing Officer, Oro Valley Hospital, Oro Valley, AZ, p. A32

HUNT, Karen, Executive Director, Harsha Behavioral Center, Terre Haute, IN, p. A215

HUNT, Kathy, Chief Executive Officer, Eden Springs Health Care Center, Green Springs, OH, p. A484

HUNT, Lynelle, Director of Nursing, Indian Health Service – Quentin N. Burdick Memorial Health Care Facility, Belcourt, ND, p. A465

HUNT, Mary Miles., Chief Executive Officer, Ballard Rehabilitation Hospital, San Bernardino, CA, p. A83

HUNT, MaryJane, Chief Clinical Officer, Knoxville Hospital & Clinics, Knoxville, IA, p. A225

HUNT, Nick, Interim Director of Nursing, Mercy Hospital Waldron, Waldron, AR, p. A49

HUNT, Richard, M.D., Chief Operating Officer, Kaiser Sunnyside Medical Center, Clackamas, OR, p. A512

HUNT, Sharon, Interim Chief Financial Officer, Pecos County Memorial Hospital, Fort Stockton, TX, p. A604

HUNT, Vanessa, Director Human Resources, Hca Houston Healthcare Tomball, Tomball, TX, p. A641

HUNT, W. Jeffrey., Chief Executive Officer, Brandywine Hospital, Coatesville, PA, p. A523

HUNT, William Robert, Chief Financial Officer, Reynolds Memorial Hospital, Glen Dale, WV, p. A685

HUNTER, Bridgette, Chief Executive Officer, Select Specialty Hospital–Kansas City, Kansas City, KS, p. A238

HUNTER, Byron, Vice President Human Resources, Cape Regional Health System, Cape May Court House, NJ, p. A404

HUNTER, Diana, Director of Nursing, Fort Belknap Service Unit, Harlem, MT, p. A377

HUNTER, Fred, Chief Executive Officer, Desert Valley Hospital, Victorville, CA, p. A94

HUNTER, George, Interim Chief Human Resources Officer, Tuba City Regional Health Care Corporation, Tuba City, AZ, p. A37

HUNTER, John G., Chief Executive Officer, Ohsu Hospital, Portland, OR, p. A516

HUNTER, Ken, Chief Executive Officer, Kimball Health Services, Kimball, NE, p. A386

HUNTER, Linda, Chief Nursing Officer, Spring View Hospital, Lebanon, KY, p. A254

HUNTER, Mary Ann, Director Nursing Services, Prisma Health Baptist Easley Hospital, Easley, SC, p. A552

HUNTER, Melissa, Chief Nursing Officer, Lake Regional Health System, Osage Beach, MO, p. A366

HUNTER, Stephanie, Chief Human Resources Officer, Veterans Affairs Ann Arbor Healthcare System, Ann Arbor, MI, p. A306

HUNTER, Terri Lynn, R.N., Nurse Administrator, American Fork Hospital, American Fork, UT, p. A647

HUNTER, Tracy, Chief Human Resources Officer, East Cooper Medical Center, Mount Pleasant, SC, p. A555

HUNTLEY, Adrienne
Chief Human Resources Officer, Saint Francis Hospital–Bartlett, Bartlett, TN, p. A566
Director Human Resources, Encompass Health Rehabilitation Hospital Of North Memphis, Memphis, TN, p. A574

HUNTLEY, Devin, Chief Operating Officer, Providence St. Joseph Medical Center, Polson, MT, p. A379

HUNTON, David, M.D., Chief Medical Officer, Mercy Hospital Fort Smith, Fort Smith, AR, p. A42

HUNTSINGER, Kelli, Chief Operating Officer, Northern Inyo Hospital, Bishop, CA, p. A53

HUPF, Angela C., Vice President Human Resources and Community Relations, Aspirus Medford Hospital & Clinics, Inc., Medford, WI, p. A699

HUPP, Diane, R.N., Vice President Support Services and Patient Care Services, Upmc Children'S Hospital Of Pittsburgh, Pittsburgh, PA, p. A538

HURD, Debra J., MS, R.N.
Vice President and Chief Nursing Officer, St. Joseph'S Hospital, Saint Paul, MN, p. A340
Vice President and Chief Nursing Officer, Woodwinds Health Campus, Woodbury, MN, p. A343

HURD, Ross, Chief Information Officer, Lake Chelan Community Hospital And Clinics, Chelan, WA, p. A671

HURFORD, Bill, Chief Medical Officer, University Of Cincinnati Medical Center, Cincinnati, OH, p. A477

HURLBUT, Marty, M.D., Medical Director, Encompass Health Rehabilitation Hospital, A Partner Of Washington Regional, Fayetteville, AR, p. A41

HURLEY, Al, Chief Operating Officer, Essentia Health Fargo, Fargo, ND, p. A466

HURLEY, Jeff, Vice President Human Resources, Flagler Hospital, Saint Augustine, FL, p. A138

HURLEY, Sandra, Chief Nursing Officer, Valley View Hospital, Glenwood Springs, CO, p. A101

HURLEY, William, M.D., Chief Medical Officer, Summit Pacific Medical Center, Elma, WA, p. A672

HUROWITZ, Marc P., President and Chief Executive Officer, Jeanes Hospital, Philadelphia, PA, p. A535

HURSH, John, Vice President Human Resources, Cox Medical Centers, Springfield, MO, p. A371

HURSHE, Joseph R., President, Ascension Of Providence Hospital, Southfield Campus, Southfield, MI, p. A322

HURST, Kyle, Chief Operations Officer, Northwest Ohio Psychiatric Hospital, Toledo, OH, p. A492

HURST, Paul, M.D., Chief Medical Officer, Banner Heart Hospital, Mesa, AZ, p. A31

HURST, Steve, Information Technology Specialist, Haskell County Community Hospital, Stigler, OK, p. A507

HURT, Carol Anne, Chief Nursing Officer, Tippah County Hospital, Ripley, MS, p. A354

HURT, Christie, M.D., Chief of Staff and Medical Director, Mercy Hospital Aurora, Aurora, MO, p. A356

HURT, Kelly, Chief Human Resources Officer Northern Colorado and Western Region, Banner Fort Collins Medical Center, Fort Collins, CO, p. A100

HURT, Todd, Administrator, State Hospital North, Orofino, ID, p. A171

HURWITZ, Steven, Senior Vice President Shared Services, Seattle Children'S Hospital, Seattle, WA, p. A678

HUSAIN, Syed Arshad, M.D., Executive Vice President and Chief Medical Officer, Royal Oaks Hospital, Windsor, MO, p. A373

HUSEBY, Custer, Chief Executive Officer, Vibra Hospital Of Fargo, Fargo, ND, p. A467

HUSHER, Phil, Chief Financial Officer, Winner Regional Healthcare Center, Winner, SD, p. A565

HUSHING–KLINE, Bob, Hospital Administrator, Atascadero State Hospital, Atascadero, CA, p. A51

HUSKEY, Jeff, Chief Executive Officer and Administrator, Clay County Memorial Hospital, Henrietta, TX, p. A610

HUSS, Cathy, Chief Financial Officer, Lifecare Medical Center, Roseau, MN, p. A339

HUSSAIN, Hamid, M.D., Medical Director, Our Lady Of The Angels Hospital, Bogalusa, LA, p. A264

HUSSAIN, Iftikhar, Chief Financial Officer, El Camino Hospital, Mountain View, CA, p. A73

HUSSEY, Jamie, Chief Information Officer, Jackson Hospital, Marianna, FL, p. A129

HUSSEY, Stephen, M.D., Chief of Staff, Lake District Hospital, Lakeview, OR, p. A514

HUSSON, Charles, Regional Chief Medical Officer, Ascension Genesys Hospital, Grand Blanc, MI, p. A312

HUSTEDT, Dale, Chief Executive Officer, Aspirus Medford Hospital & Clinics, Inc., Medford, WI, p. A699

HUSTON, Jennifer, Chief Nursing Officer, Adventhealth Lake Wales, Lake Wales, FL, p. A127

HUSTON, William R, Senior Vice President and Chief Financial Officer, Texas Scottish Rite Hospital For Children, Dallas, TX, p. A598

HUTCHENRIDER, E. Kenneth., Jr, President, Methodist Richardson Medical Center, Richardson, TX, p. A631

HUTCHENS, Zachary, M.D., Chief Medical Officer, Saint Thomas Hickman Hospital, Centerville, TN, p. A567

HUTCHES, Trampas, Chief Executive Officer, Melissa Memorial Hospital, Holyoke, CO, p. A102

HUTCHESON, Lorie, Vice President of Human Resources, Shepherd Center, Atlanta, GA, p. A147
HUTCHESON, Lou Ellen, M.D., Chief of Staff, Bacon County Hospital And Health System, Alma, GA, p. A145
HUTCHINGS, Lisa, Chief Financial Officer, Dmc – Children'S Hospital Of Michigan, Detroit, MI, p. A309
HUTCHINS, Anne, M.D., Chief of Staff, Salem Veterans Affairs Medical Center, Salem, VA, p. A667
HUTCHINS, Michael T., Administrator, Jay Hospital, Jay, FL, p. A126
HUTCHINS–OTERO, Kathy, Chief Clinical Officer, Kindred Rehabilitation Hospital Clear Lake, Webster, TX, p. A645
HUTCHINSON, R. Michael, Chief Executive Officer, Mee Memorial Hospital, King City, CA, p. A62
HUTCHISON, Barbra, Director Medical Records, Richland Parish Hospital, Delhi, LA, p. A267
HUTCHISON, Florence N., M.D., Chief of Staff, Ralph H. Johnson Veterans Affairs Medical Center, Charleston, SC, p. A550
HUTCHISON, Lewis, Vice President Operations and Quality, Ashtabula County Medical Center, Ashtabula, OH, p. A472
HUTCHSIN, Joel, M.D., Chief Medical Staff, Holton Community Hospital, Holton, KS, p. A237
HUTH, Michael, Chief Financial Officer, Sycamore Springs Hospital, Lafayette, IN, p. A210
HUTH, Richard
    Administrator, South Georgia Medical Center Berrien Campus, Nashville, GA, p. A158
    Administrator, South Georgia Medical Center Lanier Campus, Lakeland, GA, p. A155
HUTH, Thomas, M.D., Vice President Medical Affairs, Reid Health, Richmond, IN, p. A214
HUTSELL, Dick, Vice President Information Technology Services, Saint Louise Regional Hospital, Gilroy, CA, p. A60
HUTSELL, Richard, Vice President and Chief Information Officer, Daughters of Charity Health System, O'Connor Hospital, San Jose, CA, p. A86
HUTSON, Donald, President and Chief Executive Officer, Harrisburg Medical Center, Harrisburg, IL, p. A184
HUTSON, Joy M, Director Human Resources, Merit Health Rankin, Brandon, MS, p. A345
HUTSON, Marty, Chief Financial Officer, St. Mary'S Health Care System, Athens, GA, p. A145
HUTSON, Wayne
    Chief Financial Officer, Union Hospital Clinton, Clinton, IN, p. A201
    Executive Vice President and Chief Financial Officer, Union Hospital, Terre Haute, IN, p. A216
HUTT, Si William, Administrator, Heber Valley Hospital, Heber City, UT, p. A648
HUTTER, Elizabeth, Chief Executive Officer, Cedar Hills Hospital, Portland, OR, p. A516
HUVAL, Shauelle, Director Finance, St. Martin Hospital, Breaux Bridge, LA, p. A265
HUYNH, Thai, M.D., Chief of Medical Staff, El Campo Memorial Hospital, El Campo, TX, p. A601
HYATT, Charlotte, MSN, R.N., Chief Operating Officer and Chief Nursing Officer, Henry Ford Allegiance Specialty Hospital, Jackson, MI, p. A315
HYATT, David W.
    President, Indiana University Health Blackford Hospital, Hartford City, IN, p. A206
    President, Indiana University Health Jay Hospital, Portland, IN, p. A213
HYATT, Ronnie, Senior Vice President Finance and Chief Financial Officer, Bon Secours St. Francis Health System, Greenville, SC, p. A553
HYBERGER, Trey, Director Information Technology, Hardin Memorial Health, Elizabethtown, KY, p. A251
HYDE, Devon, Vice President, Chief Administrative Officer, Presbyterian Hospital, Albuquerque, NM, p. A417
HYDE, Jane E., President, Wellspan Gettysburg Hospital, Gettysburg, PA, p. A526
HYDE, Keith, Chief Executive, Providence Milwaukie Hospital, Milwaukie, OR, p. A515
HYDE, Robert, Human Resources Business Partner, Kaiser Permanente Santa Clara Medical Center, Santa Clara, CA, p. A88
HYDE, Shannon, Director Human Resources, Encompass Health Rehabilitation Hospital Of Morgantown, Morgantown, WV, p. A687
HYDE, Stephanie, Chief Executive Officer, Tyler Continuecare Hospital, Tyler, TX, p. A642
HYDE, Steve, Chief Executive Officer, Paris Regional Medical Center, Paris, TX, p. A628
HYDER, LouAnn, Director Information Integrity Management, Cardinal Hill Rehabilitation Hospital, Lexington, KY, p. A254
HYDER, Shiraz, M.D., Director Medical Affairs, Chi St. Alexius Health, Bismarck, ND, p. A465

HYLAND, Donna W., President and Chief Executive Officer, Children'S Healthcare Of Atlanta, Atlanta, GA, p. A146
HYLAND, Jaquelyn, M.D., Chief Medical Officer, University Of Kansas Health System St. Francis Campus, Topeka, KS, p. A246
HYLAND–HILL, Barbara M, R.N., Chief Nursing Officer, Providence Regional Medical Center Everett, Everett, WA, p. A673
HYLTON, Heather, Chief Financial Officer, Plateau Medical Center, Oak Hill, WV, p. A688
HYMAN, Bruce, M.D., Vice President Clinical Performance, Advocate Sherman Hospital, Elgin, IL, p. A182
HYMBAUGH, Mitzi, Chief Personnel, Ringgold County Hospital, Mount Ayr, IA, p. A226
HYMEL, Paul, Chief Financial Officer, Abrazo Central Campus, Phoenix, AZ, p. A32
HYNES, Kristi, Director Human Resources, Georgetown Behavioral Health Institute, Georgetown, TX, p. A607
HYNES, Mary, Manager Information Services, United Hospital District, Blue Earth, MN, p. A328
HYNOSKI, Michael, Chief Information Resource Management, James E. Van Zandt Veterans Affairs Medical Center, Altoona, PA, p. A519
HYTRY, Steven, Chief Executive Officer, Del Amo Hospital, Torrance, CA, p. A91

I

IACUONE, Karen
    Chief Nursing Officer and Chief Operating Officer, Pioneers Medical Center, Meeker, CO, p. A104
    Chief Nursing Officer, Pioneers Medical Center, Meeker, CO, p. A104
IAKOPO, Priscilla Maratita, Chief Financial Officer, Commonwealth Health Center, Saipan, MP, p. A714
IANNACCONE, Robert C., Chief Executive Officer, Saint Michael'S Medical Center, Newark, NJ, p. A409
IBARRA, Daniel, Chief Financial Officer, Crane Memorial Hospital, Crane, TX, p. A595
IBARRA, Kyle, Director Information Systems, Geary Community Hospital, Junction City, KS, p. A237
IBRAHIM, Tajudeen, Interim Business Administrator, Elgin Mental Health Center, Elgin, IL, p. A182
ICKOWSKI, Michael F, Vice President and Chief Financial Officer, Regional West Medical Center, Scottsbluff, NE, p. A391
IDBEIS, Badr, Chief Executive Officer, Kansas Medical Center, Andover, KS, p. A232
IDOINE–FRIES, Julie, Chief Executive Officer, Select Specialty Hospital – Cleveland Gateway, Cleveland, OH, p. A478
IDSTEIN, Mary, Chief Financial Officer, Porter–Starke Services, Valparaiso, IN, p. A216
IERARDI, Joseph P., Chief Executive Officer, Wayne Memorial Hospital, Jesup, GA, p. A155
IERO, Tony, Director Management Information Systems, North Philadelphia Health System, Philadelphia, PA, p. A536
IFTINIUK, Alan, Chief Executive Officer, French Hospital Medical Center, San Luis Obispo, CA, p. A87
IGO, Angela, MSN, R.N., Chief Nursing Officer, Fitzgibbon Hospital, Marshall, MO, p. A365
ILGENFRITZ, Carter, Chief Executive Officer, Physicians Medical Center, Houma, LA, p. A268
IMBIMBO, Richard, Chief Financial Officer, Hahnemann University Hospital, Philadelphia, PA, p. A534
IMHOFF, Sarah, Business Administrator, Chester Mental Health Center, Chester, IL, p. A176
IMLAY, Ralph, M.D., Chief of Staff, Hospital District 6 – Harper Campus, Harper, KS, p. A236
IMLER, Jim
    Director Human Resources, Gothenburg Health, Gothenburg, NE, p. A385
    Director Human Resources, Kimball Health Services, Kimball, NE, p. A386
IMMITI, Vincent F., Director, Veterans Affairs New Jersey Health Care System, East Orange, NJ, p. A405
IMMORDINO, Jonathan R, Chief Financial Officer, Rockledge Regional Medical Center, Rockledge, FL, p. A138
IMSEIS, Mikhail, M.D., Chief of Staff, Ness County Hospital District No 2, Ness City, KS, p. A241
IN, Henry, Director Human Resources, Dallas Behavioral Healthcare Hospital, Desoto, TX, p. A600
INGE, Laura, Chief Executive Officer, Kindred Hospital Northland, Kansas City, MO, p. A362
INGE, Ray, Vice President Human Resources, Pomona Valley Hospital Medical Center, Pomona, CA, p. A78

INGHAM, Raymond V., President and Chief Executive Officer, Witham Health Services, Lebanon, IN, p. A210
INGLIS, Suzanne, MSN, FACHE, Senior Vice President Nursing Services, Fisher–Titus Medical Center, Norwalk, OH, p. A488
INGRAM, Karen, Director Human Resources, Baptist Memorial Hospital For Women, Memphis, TN, p. A574
INGRAM, Nathan Daniel., Chief Executive Officer and Owner, Lone Star Behavioral Health, Cypress, TX, p. A595
INGWERSON, Connie, Chief Financial Officer, Nemaha Valley Community Hospital, Seneca, KS, p. A245
INHOFE, Kyle, Chief Human Resources Officer, Oklahoma City Veterans Affairs Medical Center, Oklahoma City, OK, p. A504
INMAN, Debbie, Chief Nursing Officer, Physicians Surgical Hospital – Quail Creek, Amarillo, TX, p. A582
INMAN, Joanne, President, Sentara Leigh Hospital, Norfolk, VA, p. A664
INMAN, Julie, Regional Executive Officer, Southeast Missouri Mental Health Center, Farmington, MO, p. A360
INNOCENTI, John, Sr, President and Chief Executive Officer, Upmc Presbyterian, Pittsburgh, PA, p. A538
INO, Alan, Chief Financial Officer, Good Samaritan Hospital, Los Angeles, CA, p. A66
INOUYE, Valerie, Chief Financial Officer, Zuckerberg San Francisco General Hospital And Trauma Center, San Francisco, CA, p. A86
INSCHO, Kimberly, Vice President Human Resources and Marketing, Margaret Mary Health, Batesville, IN, p. A199
INSERRA, Toni A., Interim Administrator, South Lyon Medical Center, Yerington, NV, p. A398
INSKEEP, Johnathan, Chief Information Officer, Caribou Memorial Hospital And Living Center, Soda Springs, ID, p. A172
INZANA, Lou, Senior Vice President and Chief Financial Officer, Maine Medical Center, Portland, ME, p. A284
IPSAN, Charlotte, Chief Administrative Officer, Norton Hospital, Louisville, KY, p. A256
IQBAL, Nayyar, M.D., Director Medical Staff, Western State Hospital, Hopkinsville, KY, p. A253
IRELAND, Amy, Chief Financial Officer, Carroll County Memorial Hospital, Carrollton, MO, p. A358
IRELAND, Daniel P., President, United Memorial Medical Center, Batavia, NY, p. A423
IRISH, Kevin
    Chief Information Officer, Franklin Regional Hospital, Franklin, NH, p. A400
    Chief Information Officer, Lakes Region General Hospital, Laconia, NH, p. A400
IRISH–CLARDY, Katherine, M.D., Chief Medical Officer, Baptist Health – Fort Smith, Fort Smith, AR, p. A42
IRIZARRI, David, Director Information Technology, Northwest Medical Center, Margate, FL, p. A129
IRIZARRY, Aixa, Executive Director, Hospital Hima De Humacao, Humacao, PR, p. A716
IRIZARRY, Lourdes, M.D., Chief of Staff, Albany Stratton Veterans Affairs Medical Center, Albany, NY, p. A422
IRIZARRY, Sigfredo, Information Technology Director, Ashford Presbyterian Community Hospital, San Juan, PR, p. A718
IRVIN, Debbie, Director Health Information Management, Bhc Alhambra Hospital, Rosemead, CA, p. A81
IRVIN, Donna, Director Human Resources, Baylor Scott & White Medical Center – Trophy Club, Trophy Club, TX, p. A641
IRVIN, Mary, R.N., MSN, Senior Vice President and Chief Nursing Officer, Bethesda North Hospital, Cincinnati, OH, p. A475
IRVIN, Michael, Chief Executive Officer, Bayfront Health Brooksville, Brooksville, FL, p. A119
IRVIN, Miriam, CNO, Encompass Health Rehabilitation Hospital, A Partner Of Washington Regional, Fayetteville, AR, p. A41
IRVING, Edith E, R.N., MS, FACHE, Chief Nursing Officer, West Valley Medical Center, Caldwell, ID, p. A168
IRVING, Kelly Ann, Associate Director for Patient Care Services, Michael E. Debakey Veterans Affairs Medical Center, Houston, TX, p. A613
IRVING, Mark, Manager Management Information Systems, Osf St. Francis Hospital And Medical Group, Escanaba, MI, p. A311
IRWIN, Robert G, Vice President Information Systems, Robert Wood Johnson University Hospital, New Brunswick, NJ, p. A409
IRWIN, Ruth, Associate Director Clinical Operations, Stewart & Lynda Resnick Neuropsychiatric Hospital At Ucla, Los Angeles, CA, p. A69
IRWIN, Vivian, Chief Financial Officer and Controller, Encompass Health Rehabilitation Hospital Midland Odessa, Midland, TX, p. A624
ISAAC, Lisa, Chief Nursing Officer, Choctaw Nation Health Care Center, Talihina, OK, p. A508

ISAAC, Regina, Director of Nursing, Choctaw Health Center, Philadelphia, MS, p. A352

ISAACKS, David, Director, Harry S. Truman Memorial Veterans Hospital, Columbia, MO, p. A359

ISAACKS, Scott R., Director and Chief Executive Officer, Ralph H. Johnson Veterans Affairs Medical Center, Charleston, SC, p. A550

ISAACS, Cynthia
Chief Executive Officer, Cornerstone Hospital Of Huntington, Huntington, WV, p. A686
Chief Executive Officer, Solara Hospital Harlingen, Harlingen, TX, p. A609

ISAACS, Diane, Director of Nursing, Ouachita County Medical Center, Camden, AR, p. A40

ISAACS, Michael R, Vice President Human Resources, Vista Health, Waukegan, IL, p. A198

ISAACSON, Sara, Chief Nursing Officer, Mad River Community Hospital, Arcata, CA, p. A51

ISADO, Jose, M.D., Medical Director, Auxilio Mutuo Hospital, San Juan, PR, p. A718

ISBELL, Samantha, R.N., Chief Nursing Officer, Hamilton Hospital, Olney, TX, p. A627

ISBELL, Sherri, Chief Information Officer, Virginia Gay Hospital, Vinton, IA, p. A230

ISBELL, Todd, R.N., MSN, Chief Nursing Officer, Memorial Health, Savannah, GA, p. A160

ISEMANN, William R., President and Chief Executive Officer, Kidspeace Children'S Hospital, Orefield, PA, p. A533

ISENMANN, Debra, Human Resources Generalist, Cox Monett Hospital, Monett, MO, p. A366

ISHIZUKA, Paul, Chief Financial Officer, Skagit Regional Health, Mount Vernon, WA, p. A675

ISHKANIAN, Gary, M.D., Vice President Medical Affairs, Montefiore Mount Vernon, Mount Vernon, NY, p. A432

ISKANDAR, Said, M.D., Chief Medical Officer, Sentara Halifax Regional Hospital, South Boston, VA, p. A667

ISLAM, Asad, M.D., Chief Medical Officer, Mayhill Hospital, Denton, TX, p. A599

ISLEY, L Lee., President and Chief Executive Officer, Nash Unc Health Care, Rocky Mount, NC, p. A461

ISMAIL, Asad, M.D., Medical Director, Wellstone Regional Hospital, Jeffersonville, IN, p. A208

ISMAIL, Hummayun, M.D., Medical Director, Select Specialty Hospital–Wilmington, Wilmington, DE, p. A114

ISOM, Julie, Director Human Resources, Lakeview Hospital, Bountiful, UT, p. A647

ISON, Tamara
Chief Financial Officer, Wellstar Sylvan Grove Hospital, Jackson, GA, p. A155
Chief Operating Officer, Wellstar Spalding Regional Hospital, Griffin, GA, p. A154
Senior Vice President and President, Wellstar Spalding Regional Hospital, Griffin, GA, p. A154
Senior Vice President and President, Wellstar Sylvan Grove Hospital, Jackson, GA, p. A155

ISON, William G, Human Resources Manager, Select Specialty Hospital–Tri Cities, Bristol, TN, p. A566

ISQUIERDO, Maria E.
Executive Director, Human Resources, Saint Francis Hospital South, Tulsa, OK, p. A509
Executive Director, Human Resources, Saint Francis Hospital, Tulsa, OK, p. A509

ISRAEL, Corry, Director Human Resources, Western Plains Medical Complex, Dodge City, KS, p. A234

ISRAEL, Michael D., President and Chief Executive Officer, Westchester Medical Center, Valhalla, NY, p. A446

ISSACS, Cynthia, Chief Executive Officer, Solara Hospital Harlingen, Harlingen, TX, p. A609

ISSAI, Alice H., President, Adventist Health Glendale, Los Angeles, CA, p. A65

ITAGAKI, Brian, M.D., Chief of Staff, St. Vincent Medical Center, Los Angeles, CA, p. A69

ITO, Derek, Director Human Resources, Shriners Hospitals For Children–Honolulu, Honolulu, HI, p. A165

IVERSON, Caryn, MSN, Chief Nursing Officer, Memorial Medical Center, Las Cruces, NM, p. A418

IVES, Matthew
Chief Executive Officer and Chief Financial Officer, Keokuk County Health Center, Sigourney, IA, p. A229
Interim Chief Executive Officer and Chief Financial Officer, Keokuk County Health Center, Sigourney, IA, p. A229

IVES ERICKSON, Jeanette R, MS, R.N., Senior Vice President Patient Care and Chief Nurse, Massachusetts General Hospital, Boston, MA, p. A295

IVEY, Kim, Director of Human Resources, Cumberland Hospital For Children And Adolescents, New Kent, VA, p. A663

IVEY, Misty, Human Resources Manager, Washington County Regional Medical Center, Sandersville, GA, p. A159

IVIE, Brian K.
President and Chief Executive Officer, Cascade Valley Hospital, Arlington, WA, p. A670
President and Chief Executive Officer, Skagit Regional Health, Mount Vernon, WA, p. A675

IVORY, Brenda, Chief Executive Officer, South Texas Health System, Edinburg, TX, p. A601

IVY, Michael, Interim Chief Executive Officer, Bridgeport Hospital, Bridgeport, CT, p. A107

IVY, Michael, M.D., Senior Vice President for Medical Affairs and Chief Medical Officer, Bridgeport Hospital, Bridgeport, CT, p. A107

IYER, Raju, Senior Vice President and Chief Financial Officer, Ucsf Medical Center, San Francisco, CA, p. A86

IZAKOVIC, Martin, M.D., Vice President Medical Staff Affairs and Chief Medical Officer, Mercyone Iowa City Medical Center, Iowa City, IA, p. A224

IZZI, Denine, Senior Director Information Technology, Robert Wood Johnson University Hospital Rahway, Rahway, NJ, p. A411

J

JABBARPOUR, Yad, M.D., Chief of Staff, Catawba Hospital, Catawba, VA, p. A657

JABERG, Janie, President and Chief Executive Officer, Wayne Unc Health Care, Goldsboro, NC, p. A455

JABLONSKI, Kevin, Chief Nursing Officer, Christus Mother Frances Hospital – Winnsboro, Winnsboro, TX, p. A646

JABLONSKI, Kevin M, Chief Nursing Officer, Ut Health Athens, Athens, TX, p. A584

JABLONSKI, Mark, Vice President Mission Integration, St. Jude Medical Center, Fullerton, CA, p. A60

JABOUR, Leon John
Regional Chief Information Officer, Wellspan Ephrata Community Hospital, Ephrata, PA, p. A525
Regional Chief Information Officer, Wellspan Good Samaritan Hospital, Lebanon, PA, p. A530

JACK, Claudia L, Director Associate Relations, Bayfront Health Brooksville, Brooksville, FL, p. A119

JACK, Dennis D., Chief Executive Officer, Wilbarger General Hospital, Vernon, TX, p. A643

JACK, Shannon, Administrator, Indianhead Medical Center, Shell Lake, WI, p. A705

JACKES, Frederick D, Assistant Administrator and Director Human Resources, Valley Forge Medical Center And Hospital, Norristown, PA, p. A533

JACKLIN, Bonnie, R.N., MSN, Chief Nursing Officer, Mckay–Dee Hospital, Ogden, UT, p. A649

JACKSON, Alan, M.D., Medical Director, Roseland Community Hospital, Chicago, IL, p. A179

JACKSON, Angelica, Director of Nursing, Anchor Hospital, Atlanta, GA, p. A145

JACKSON, Barbara, Acting Facility Director, Taylor Hardin Secure Medical Facility, Tuscaloosa, AL, p. A24

JACKSON, Bryan G, Vice President and Chief Financial Officer, Jefferson Regional Medical Center, Pine Bluff, AR, p. A47

JACKSON, Carolyn, Chief Executive Officer, Saint Vincent Hospital, Worcester, MA, p. A305

JACKSON, Cindy, Director Human Resources, Phelps Memorial Health Center, Holdrege, NE, p. A386

JACKSON, Collette, R.N., Director of Clinical Services, St. Theresa Specialty Hospital, Kenner, LA, p. A270

JACKSON, Corey D., Executive Vice President and Chief Talent Officer, Parkland Health & Hospital System, Dallas, TX, p. A597

JACKSON, Cynthia, Vice President Human Resources, Raulerson Hospital, Okeechobee, FL, p. A133

JACKSON, Daniel, Vice President, Administrator, Wellstar Atlanta Medical Center, Atlanta, GA, p. A147

JACKSON, Darryl, D.O., Chief of Staff, Prague Community Hospital, Prague, OK, p. A506

JACKSON, David, Chief Financial Officer, Baptist Medical Center Leake, Carthage, MS, p. A345

JACKSON, Erin, Human Resources Specialist, Baptist Medical Center Nassau, Fernandina Beach, FL, p. A122

JACKSON, Evan, Vice President Information Technology, Middlesex Hospital, Middletown, CT, p. A109

JACKSON, Frank D., Facility Chief Information Officer, Veterans Affairs Illiana Health Care System, Danville, IL, p. A180

JACKSON, Gary, D.O., Medical Director, Lincoln County Medical Center, Ruidoso, NM, p. A420

JACKSON, Holly, Chief Operating Officer, Gulf Coast Regional Medical Center, Panama City, FL, p. A135

JACKSON, James, M.D., Chief of Staff, Cornerstone Hospital Of Bossier City, Bossier City, LA, p. A265

JACKSON, James E T., Chief Administrative Officer, San Leandro Hospital, San Leandro, CA, p. A87

JACKSON, James H., Jr, Chief Executive Officer, Och Regional Medical Center, Starkville, MS, p. A354

JACKSON, James V., Budget Director, Saint Elizabeths Hospital, Washington, DC, p. A116

JACKSON, Jeffrey, M.D., Medical Director, Houston Methodist Sugar Land Hospital, Sugar Land, TX, p. A638

JACKSON, Jennifer, Director Human Resources, Madison County Health Care System, Winterset, IA, p. A231

JACKSON, Joanne, Administrator Human Resources, Community Relations and Quality Improvement, Amery Hospital And Clinic, Amery, WI, p. A691

JACKSON, Jodie A., Associate Director, Brookdale Hospital Medical Center, New York, NY, p. A432

JACKSON, John J, President, Firsthealth Moore Regional Hospital, Pinehurst, NC, p. A460

JACKSON, Judy, Director Health Information Management and Privacy Officer, Shodair Children'S Hospital, Helena, MT, p. A377

JACKSON, Kevin
Interim Chief Executive Officer, Harnett Health System, Dunn, NC, p. A452
On Site Administrator, Highsmith–Rainey Specialty Hospital, Fayetteville, NC, p. A454

JACKSON, Kiland, Chief Information Officer, Bunkie General Hospital, Bunkie, LA, p. A265

JACKSON, Lynn, Administrator, Northside Hospital–Forsyth, Cumming, GA, p. A151

JACKSON, Margaret G., R.N., Vice President Patient Care Services and Chief Nursing Officer, Brookdale Hospital Medical Center, New York, NY, p. A432

JACKSON, Meg, Director Information Technology, Beauregard Health System, De Ridder, LA, p. A266

JACKSON, Melinda R, Director Human Resources, Bates County Memorial Hospital, Butler, MO, p. A357

JACKSON, Melonie, Human Resource Business Partner, Spectrum Health Big Rapids Hospital, Big Rapids, MI, p. A307

JACKSON, Michelle, Chief Financial Officer, Bhc Alhambra Hospital, Rosemead, CA, p. A81

JACKSON, Patsy, Director of Nursing, Jay Hospital, Jay, FL, p. A126

JACKSON, Phillip E.
Vice President & CEO, Erlanger Medical Center, Chattanooga, TN, p. A567
Vice President and CEO, Erlanger Medical Center, Chattanooga, TN, p. A567

JACKSON, Reese, President and Chief Executive Officer, Chesapeake Regional Medical Center, Chesapeake, VA, p. A657

JACKSON, Robert
Chief Financial Officer, Alliance Health Center, Meridian, MS, p. A351
Chief Financial Officer, Signature Psychiatric Hospital, Kansas City, MO, p. A363

JACKSON, Robert, Jr, Chief Executive Officer, Grove City Medical Center, Grove City, PA, p. A526

JACKSON, Robin E., Interim Acting Director, Charlie Norwood Veterans Affairs Medical Center, Augusta, GA, p. A147

JACKSON, Stephanie, M.D., Vice President and Chief Medical Officer, Honorhealth Scottsdale Thompson Peak Medical Center, Scottsdale, AZ, p. A36

JACKSON, Tamara, Chief Nursing Officer, Piedmont Athens Regional Medical Center, Athens, GA, p. A145

JACKSON, Thomas W., Chief Executive Officer, St. David'S North Austin Medical Center, Austin, TX, p. A586

JACKSON, Tom, Chief Financial Officer, Tristar Centennial Medical Center, Nashville, TN, p. A577

JACKSON, Vance, Chief Executive Officer, Davis Medical Center, Elkins, WV, p. A685

JACKSON, Victor, Chief Executive Officer, Vibra Specialty Hospital Of Portland, Portland, OR, p. A516

JACKSON, W. Anthony
Chief Executive Officer, Bon Secours St. Francis Hospital, Charleston, SC, p. A549
Chief Executive Officer, Roper Hospital, Charleston, SC, p. A550
Chief Executive Officer, Roper St. Francis Mount Pleasant Hospital, Mount Pleasant, SC, p. A555

JACKSON, William, Director Medical Records, Millwood Hospital, Arlington, TX, p. A583

JACKSON, William L, Chief Medical Officer, Inova Alexandria Hospital, Alexandria, VA, p. A656

JACKSON, William L., M.D., Executive Vice President, Chief Medical Officer, Erlanger Medical Center, Chattanooga, TN, p. A567

JACO, Mary, Administrator, Shriners Hospitals For Children–Galveston, Galveston, TX, p. A607

JACOB, Briana, Chief Executive Officer, Harbor Oaks Hospital, New Baltimore, MI, p. A318

JACOB, Jan, Interim Administrator, Ascension St. Joseph Hospital, Tawas City, MI, p. A323

JACOBI, Diane, Chief of Staff, Ssm Health St. Mary'S Hospital – Audrain, Mexico, MO, p. A365

JACOBI, Elizabeth
Associate Director Human Resources, Rancho Los Amigos National Rehabilitation Center, Downey, CA, p. A56
Human Resources Director, Lac+Usc Medical Center, Los Angeles, CA, p. A68

JACOBO MORENO, Maria E., Administrator, Hima San Pablo Caguas, Caguas, PR, p. A715

JACOBS, Anastasia, Chief Human Resources Officer, Robert Wood Johnson University Hospital Somerset, Somerville, NJ, p. A412

JACOBS, Andrea, Chief Operating Officer, South Pointe Hospital, Warrensville Heights, OH, p. A493

JACOBS, Barbara S, MSN, Vice President, Nursing and Chief Nursing Officer, Anne Arundel Medical Center, Annapolis, MD, p. A286

JACOBS, Brian, M.D., Vice President Chief Information Officer and Chief Medical Information Officer, Children'S National Health System, Washington, DC, p. A115

JACOBS, Donna K., President, Ssm Health St. Mary'S Hospital – Audrain, Mexico, MO, p. A365

JACOBS, Greg, Manager, Mclaren Bay Special Care, Bay City, MI, p. A307

JACOBS, Ian, Chief, Human Resource Management Service, Louis A. Johnson Veterans Affairs Medical Center, Clarksburg, WV, p. A684

JACOBS, Jenny
Director Human Resources, Osf Holy Family Medical Center, Monmouth, IL, p. A189
Director Human Resources, Osf St. Mary Medical Center, Galesburg, IL, p. A183

JACOBS, Julie
Chief Financial Officer, Warren General Hospital, Warren, PA, p. A543
Director Human Resources, Oklahoma Forensic Center, Vinita, OK, p. A510

JACOBS, Lori, Chief Financial Officer, Edgefield County Healthcare, Edgefield, SC, p. A552

JACOBS, Richard, Vice President Finance and Chief Financial Officer, Canton–Potsdam Hospital, Potsdam, NY, p. A442

JACOBS, Robert
Regional Director Information Management, Christus Southeast Texas Hospital – St. Elizabeth, Beaumont, TX, p. A587
Regional Information Management Executive, Christus Southeast Texas Jasper Memorial, Jasper, TX, p. A616

JACOODG, Ronnie, M.D., Chief Medical Officer, Asheville Specialty Hospital, Asheville, NC, p. A449

JACOBS, Trace, Director Information Technology, Santiam Hospital, Stayton, OR, p. A518

JACOBS, Yolanda, Coordinator Human Resources, Cornerstone Hospital Of Houston At Clearlake, Webster, TX, p. A644

JACOBS–KENNER, Jerrie, President, Saint Luke'S Hospital Of Kansas City, Kansas City, MO, p. A363

JACOBSEN, Barry, Chief Executive Officer, Myrtue Medical Center, Harlan, IA, p. A224

JACOBSON, Becky, Vice President Finance, St. Vincent Heart Center, Indianapolis, IN, p. A206

JACOBSON, Carlton, Vice President of Finance, Adventist Health Clear Lake, Clearlake, CA, p. A54

JACOBSON, Carolyn
Chief Human Resource Officer, St. Joseph'S Hospital, Saint Paul, MN, p. A340
Chief Human Resource Officer, Woodwinds Health Campus, Woodbury, MN, p. A343
Chief Human Resources Officer, Bethesda Hospital, Saint Paul, MN, p. A339
Chief Human Resources Officer, St. John'S Hospital, Maplewood, MN, p. A335

JACOBSON, Gary, M.D., Chief Medical Officer, Pembroke Hospital, Pembroke, MA, p. A302

JACOBSON, Janet, Director Human Resources, Lakewood Health System, Staples, MN, p. A341

JACOBSON, Jenny, Manager Human Resources, Sanford Hillsboro Medical Center, Hillsboro, ND, p. A468

JACOBSON, John, Chief Financial Officer, Martin General Hospital, Williamston, NC, p. A463

JACOBSON, Lisa, Director of Nursing, Community Hospital Of Huntington Park, Huntington Park, CA, p. A62

JACOBSON, Mark, D.O., Vice President Medical Affairs, Wellspan Ephrata Community Hospital, Ephrata, PA, p. A525

JACOBSON, Mary Jo, Chief Executive Officer, San Joaquin Valley Rehabilitation Hospital, Fresno, CA, p. A59

JACOBSON, Randolph, Chief Financial Officer, Hackensack Meridian Health Carrier Clinic, Belle Mead, NJ, p. A403

JACOBSON, Renae A., Human Resources Officer, Ralph H. Johnson Veterans Affairs Medical Center, Charleston, SC, p. A550

JACOBSON, Sam, Director Management Information Systems, Community Memorial Hospital, Cloquet, MN, p. A330

JACOBSON, Shirley
Chief Financial Officer, Community Behavioral Health Hospital – Alexandria, Alexandria, MN, p. A327
Chief Financial Officer, Community Behavioral Health Hospital – Rochester, Rochester, MN, p. A338

JACOBSON, Terry, Administrator and Chief Executive Officer, Essentia Health St. Mary'S Hospital Of Superior, Superior, WI, p. A706

JACOBY, Jamie, Chief Financial Officer, Cimarron Memorial Hospital, Boise City, OK, p. A497

JACQUAY, Dena M, Chief Human Resource Officer, Parkview Huntington Hospital, Huntington, IN, p. A206

JACQUES, Alistar
Chief Information Officer, Bethesda Hospital, Saint Paul, MN, p. A339
Chief Information Officer, St. John'S Hospital, Maplewood, MN, p. A335

JACQUES, Teresa, Interim Chief Financial Officer, Adventist Medical Center–Reedley, Reedley, CA, p. A80

JADCZAK, Audrey, R.N., FACHE
Vice President Chief Nursing Officer, Our Lady Of Lourdes Medical Center, Camden, NJ, p. A404
Vice President/Chief Nursing Officer, Lourdes Medical Center Of Burlington County, Willingboro, NJ, p. A415

JADEJA, Neerav, Administrator, Paradise Valley Hospital, National City, CA, p. A74

JADWIN, Anne, R.N., MSN, Chief Nursing Officer, Fox Chase Cancer Center–American Oncologic Hospital, Philadelphia, PA, p. A534

JAEGER, Shiuvaun, M.D., Chief of Staff, Tri Valley Health System, Cambridge, NE, p. A383

JAFF, Michael R., President, Newton–Wellesley Hospital, Newton Lower Falls, MA, p. A301

JAFFE, Darcy, R.N., Chief Nursing Officer, Uw Medicine/Harborview Medical Center, Seattle, WA, p. A678

JAFFE, Richard, M.D., Medical Director, Belmont Behavioral Hospital, Philadelphia, PA, p. A534

JAFFER, Amir, M.D., Senior Vice President Medical Affairs, Brookdale Hospital Medical Center, New York, NY, p. A432

JAGER, Jonathon R, Chief Information Officer, St. Francis Hospital, Columbus, GA, p. A150

JAGER, Linda, Director Finance, Avera Weskota Memorial Hospital, Wessington Springs, SD, p. A565

JAGGI, Michael, D.O., Vice President and Chief Medical Officer, Hurley Medical Center, Flint, MI, p. A311

JAGOE, Patricia, Assistant Vice President Patient Care, Johnson Memorial Medical Center, Stafford Springs, CT, p. A111

JAHAN, Mohammad S, M.D., Clinical Director, Middle Tennessee Mental Health Institute, Nashville, TN, p. A576

JAHN, Barbara A., Chief Operating Officer, Saint Joseph Hospital, Denver, CO, p. A99

JAHN, David B., President and Chief Executive Officer, War Memorial Hospital, Sault Sainte Marie, MI, p. A322

JAHN, Gregory L., Chief Executive Officer, St. Luke'S Behavioral Health Center, Phoenix, AZ, p. A34

JAHN, Kim C, Chief Plant Operations and Chief Information Officer, Manning Regional Healthcare Center, Manning, IA, p. A226

JAHNIG, Jay A, Chief Executive Officer, Faulkton Area Medical Center, Faulkton, SD, p. A560

JAHRE, Jeffrey, M.D., Vice President Medical and Academic Affairs, St. Luke'S University Hospital – Bethlehem Campus, Bethlehem, PA, p. A520

JAIN, Anil, Chief Financial Officer, St. Francis Medical Center, Lynwood, CA, p. A70

JAIN, Ashok, M.D., Senior Vice President and Chief Medical Officer, Beaumont Hospital, Wayne, Wayne, MI, p. A324

JAKOUBECK, Denise, Director Human Resources, Hancock County Health System, Britt, IA, p. A218

JAKUBOWSKI, Michael, M.D., Chief Medical Officer, Mary Free Bed Rehabilitation Hospital, Grand Rapids, MI, p. A312

JALBERT, Susan L, R.N., MS, Vice President Patient Care Services and Chief Nursing Officer, Northwest Hospital, Randallstown, MD, p. A293

JALOMO, Angie, Chief Nursing Officer, Lynn County Hospital District, Tahoka, TX, p. A639

JAMES, Annette, R.N., MSN, Chief Nursing Officer, Creek Nation Community Hospital, Okemah, OK, p. A503

JAMES, Bruce, President and Chief Executive Officer, Cleveland Clinic Union Hospital, Dover, OH, p. A482

JAMES, Craig, President, Alleghany Memorial Hospital, Sparta, NC, p. A462

JAMES, Donald, D.O., Senior Vice President and Chief Medical Officer, Phelps Health, Rolla, MO, p. A368

JAMES, Douglas, Chief Nursing Officer, Caldwell Medical Center, Princeton, KY, p. A260

JAMES, Gregory L, D.O., Chief Medical Officer, St. Vincent'S Birmingham, Birmingham, AL, p. A15

JAMES, Jaime, Entity Finance Officer, Texas Health Harris Methodist Hospital Hurst–Euless–Bedford, Bedford, TX, p. A588

JAMES, Janet, Director Human Resources, Trigg County Hospital, Cadiz, KY, p. A250

JAMES, Jobie, Chief Financial Officer, West Calcasieu Cameron Hospital, Sulphur, LA, p. A279

JAMES, Karen, Regional Director, Human Resources, The William W. Backus Hospital, Norwich, CT, p. A110

JAMES, Ken, President and Chief Executive Officer of East Market, Mercy Health – Anderson Hospital, Cincinnati, OH, p. A476

JAMES, Laura, Director Human Resources, St. Francis Medical Center, Trenton, NJ, p. A413

JAMES, Michael
Chief Operations Officer, Jackson Hospital And Clinic, Montgomery, AL, p. A21
Information Technology Technical Support Specialist 1, Villa Feliciana Medical Complex, Jackson, LA, p. A269

JAMES, Michelle
Chief Nursing Officer, Providence St. Peter Hospital, Olympia, WA, p. A676
Regional Chief Nursing Officer, Providence Centralia Hospital, Centralia, WA, p. A671

JAMES, Robert L, Director Human Resources, Beaumont Hospital, Wayne, Wayne, MI, p. A324

JAMES, Shelia, Director of Nursing, Riverland Medical Center, Ferriday, LA, p. A267

JAMES, Sherrie, Chief Executive Officer, The Bridgeway, North Little Rock, AR, p. A47

JAMES, Taya, Director, Mercy Hospital Berryville, Berryville, AR, p. A39

JAMES, Teri, Chief Financial Officer, Lafayette Regional Health Center, Lexington, MO, p. A364

JAMES, Thomas L, M.D., Chief Medical Officer, Trumbull Memorial Hospital, Warren, OH, p. A493

JAMES, Wesley, Chief Financial Officer, Piedmont Henry Hospital, Stockbridge, GA, p. A161

JAMES, William B., President, Wake Forest Baptist Health–Lexington Medical Center, Lexington, NC, p. A458

JAMES–NIELSEN, Lori, President, Tuality Healthcare, Hillsboro, OR, p. A513

JAMESON, David, M.D., Chief of Staff, Annie Jeffrey Memorial County Health Center, Osceola, NE, p. A390

JAMESON, Eileen, Chief Operating Officer, Abington Hospital, Abington, PA, p. A519

JAMIESON, Donna F., Ph.D., R.N., Chief Nursing Officer, Aurora Medical Center Kenosha, Kenosha, WI, p. A697

JAMIESON, Pamela, Vice President Patient Care Services and Chief Nursing Officer, University Of Maryland St. Joseph Medical Center, Towson, MD, p. A293

JAMIN, David, Chief Financial Officer, St. Mary'S Regional Medical Center, Enid, OK, p. A499

JANDIAL, Rajnish, M.D., Chief Medical Officer, San Dimas Community Hospital, San Dimas, CA, p. A85

JANEK, James D., Chief Executive Officer, Rice Medical Center, Eagle Lake, TX, p. A600

JANERELLA, Wendy, Controller, Bucktail Medical Center, Renovo, PA, p. A540

JANGDHARI, Kalautie, Director, West Texas Veterans Affairs Health Care System, Big Spring, TX, p. A588

JANICAK, Dan, Chief Financial Officer, University Of Mississippi Medical Center, Jackson, MS, p. A349

JANIS, Terry, Assistant Vice President, Park Plaza Hospital, Houston, TX, p. A613

JANKOWSKI, Stan, Vice President and Chief Information Officer, Hospital For Special Care, New Britain, CT, p. A109

JANLOO, Arman, M.D., Chief Medical Staff, Fairfax Community Hospital, Fairfax, OK, p. A499

JANOSO, John R., Chief Executive Officer, Fairfield Medical Center, Lancaster, OH, p. A485

JANSEN, David, Vice President Human Resources, Karmanos Cancer Center, Detroit, MI, p. A310

JANSEN, John, Management Information Specialist, Hawaii State Hospital, Kaneohe, HI, p. A166

JANSEN, Robert, M.D., Chief Medical Officer, Grady Memorial Hospital, Atlanta, GA, p. A146

JANSSEN, Kathy, Director Medical Records, Mountrail County Medical Center, Stanley, ND, p. A469

JANSSEN, Paul, President and Chief Executive Officer, Henry Community Health, New Castle, IN, p. A212

JANTZEN, Daniel, Chief Financial Officer, Dartmouth–Hitchcock Medical Center, Lebanon, NH, p. A400

JANTZEN, Tammi, Chief Operating Officer, Okeene Municipal Hospital, Okeene, OK, p. A503

JANUS, Tammy, Senior Vice President Human Resources, Mercy Medical Center, Baltimore, MD, p. A288

JANZEN, Wes, Chief Information Officer, Wamego Health Center, Wamego, KS, p. A247

JAQUEZ, Jason
  Director Human Resources, Greater El Monte Community Hospital, South El Monte, CA, p. A90
  Human Resource Director, Ahmc Anaheim Regional Medical Center, Anaheim, CA, p. A50

JARAMILLO, Charles, Chief Operating Officer, New Mexico Behavioral Health Institute At Las Vegas, Las Vegas, NM, p. A419

JARBOE, Joe, Director Human Resources, Kosciusko Community Hospital, Warsaw, IN, p. A216

JARBOE, Lori, Chief Executive Officer, Encompass Rehabilitation Hospital Of Lakeview, Elizabethtown, KY, p. A251

JARMER, Ryan, Chief Information Officer, Naval Medical Center San Diego, San Diego, CA, p. A83

JAROPILLO, Erwin, Director Information Systems, Adventhealth Lake Wales, Lake Wales, FL, p. A127

JARREAU, Jeff
  Chief Human Resources Officer, North Oaks Medical Center, Hammond, LA, p. A268
  Senior Vice President, Human Resources, North Oaks Health System, North Oaks Rehabilitation Hospital, Hammond, LA, p. A268

JARREAU, Valerie Sparks, R.N., Chief Nursing Officer, Pointe Coupee General Hospital, New Roads, LA, p. A276

JARRELL, Lindsey, Vice President Information Services, St. Joseph'S Hospital, Tampa, FL, p. A142

JARRETT, Adam D, M.D., Executive Vice President and Chief Medical Officer, Holy Name Medical Center, Teaneck, NJ, p. A413

JARRY, Jacques, Administrator, Bullock County Hospital, Union Springs, AL, p. A24

JARRY, Patricia, Manager Human Resources, Crenshaw Community Hospital, Luverne, AL, p. A20

JARVIS, Dinah, Director of Nursing, Southeastern Kentucky Medical Center, Pineville, KY, p. A259

JARVIS, Keith, Director Information Systems, Longview Regional Medical Center, Longview, TX, p. A621

JARVIS, Susan, Vice President Operations, Sanford Medical Center Fargo, Fargo, ND, p. A467

JARVIS, Tammy, Vice President Clinical Services and Chief Nursing Officer, Texas Institute For Surgery At Texas Health Presbyterian Dallas, Dallas, TX, p. A598

JASPER, Harry, Chief Financial Officer, Jerold Phelps Community Hospital, Garberville, CA, p. A60

JASPER, Jerry, Chief Executive Officer, Brownfield Regional Medical Center, Brownfield, TX, p. A589

JATCZAK, Tracy E, CPA, Chief Financial Officer, Box Butte General Hospital, Alliance, NE, p. A382

JAUERSACK, Dawn, Vice President and Chief Financial Officer, Boca Raton Regional Hospital, Boca Raton, FL, p. A118

JAURON, Jason, Director Human Resources, Orange City Area Health System, Orange City, IA, p. A227

JAVED, Saad, Administrator, Riceland Medical Center, Winnie, TX, p. A646

JAVOIS, Laurent D.
  Chief Executive Officer, St. Louis Psychiatric Rehabilitation Center, Saint Louis, MO, p. A370
  Regional Executive Officer, Hawthorn Children Psychiatric Hospital, Saint Louis, MO, p. A369
  Regional Executive Officer, Metropolitan St. Louis Psychiatric Center, Saint Louis, MO, p. A369

JAVOIS, Rosalie, Chief Financial Officer, Governor Juan F. Luis Hospital, Christiansted, VI, p. A720

JAY, Richard, D.O., Chief of Staff, North Big Horn Hospital District, Lovell, WY, p. A712

JEAKLE, James, Chief Medical Officer, Munson Healthcare Charlevoix Hospital, Charlevoix, MI, p. A308

JEAN–BAPTISTE, Joan, Vice President Human Resources, Governor Juan F. Luis Hospital, Christiansted, VI, p. A720

JEAN–LOUIS, Marie S, R.N., Chief Nursing Officer, Brookdale Hospital Medical Center, New York, NY, p. A432

JEANS, Joe, CPA, Chief Financial Officer, Johnson Regional Medical Center, Clarksville, AR, p. A40

JEANSONNE, Corey, Chief Nursing Officer, Bunkie General Hospital, Bunkie, LA, p. A265

JEDLICKA, Colleen, R.N., JD, Chief Nursing Officer, Comanche County Medical Center, Comanche, TX, p. A593

JEFFERIES, Kanika, Executive Director, Brookdale Hospital Medical Center, New York, NY, p. A432

JEFFERSON, Glenn, Chief Medical Officer, Garfield County Public Hospital District, Pomeroy, WA, p. A676

JEFFERSON, Kelly, Vice President, Operations, Osf St. Francis Hospital And Medical Group, Escanaba, MI, p. A311

JEFFRESS, Chuck, Vice President Fiscal Services, Chi St. Luke'S Health Brazosport, Lake Jackson, TX, p. A619

JEFFREY, Paul A, President, Moses H. Cone Memorial Hospital, Greensboro, NC, p. A455

JEFFRIES, John, Director Finance, Hshs St. Joseph'S Hospital, Breese, IL, p. A174

JEFFS, Carla, Chief Financial Officer, Cornerstone Hospital Of Huntington, Huntington, WV, p. A686

JEHAN, Sayed, M.D., Interim Medical Director, Larned State Hospital, Larned, KS, p. A238

JELALIAN, Christine, M.D., Medical Director, Montefiore St. Luke'S Cornwall, Newburgh, NY, p. A439

JELDEN, Dennis, M.D., Chief of Staff, Melissa Memorial Hospital, Holyoke, CO, p. A102

JELKS, Kim, Fiscal Officer, Villa Feliciana Medical Complex, Jackson, LA, p. A269

JEMJEMIAN, Norair, Senior Vice President and Area Manager, Kaiser Permanente Vacaville Medical Center, Vacaville, CA, p. A93

JENE, Suzanne L., Chief Operating Officer, Tennessee Valley Healthcare System, Nashville, TN, p. A577

JENKINS, Bonnie
  Chief Financial Officer, Mercy General Hospital, Sacramento, CA, p. A82
  Chief Financial Officer, Methodist Hospital Of Sacramento, Sacramento, CA, p. A82

JENKINS, Brian, Director Human Resources, Arbour–Fuller Hospital, Attleboro, MA, p. A294

JENKINS, Constance, Commander, Bassett Army Community Hospital, Fort Wainwright, AK, p. A26

JENKINS, Debbie, Chief Human Resources Management Service, Veterans Affairs Sierra Nevada Health Care System, Reno, NV, p. A397

JENKINS, Denise, Chief Clinical Officer, Kindred Hospital–Brea, Brea, CA, p. A53

JENKINS, Freddie, Administrator, Wright Patterson Medical Center, Wright, OH, p. A494

JENKINS, Jimmy, M.D., Chief Medical Officer, Geary Community Hospital, Junction City, KS, p. A237

JENKINS, Keith, Director, Human Resources, Grandview Medical Center, Dayton, OH, p. A481

JENKINS, Kevin, President and Chief Executive Officer, St. Anthony North Health Campus, Westminster, CO, p. A106

JENKINS, Kris, Administrator, Altus Houston Hospital, Houston, TX, p. A610

JENKINS, Linda, R.N., Vice President Patient Care Services, St. Jude Medical Center, Fullerton, CA, p. A60

JENKINS, Maynard, Regional Vice President Human Resources, Sutter Maternity And Surgery Center Of Santa Cruz, Santa Cruz, CA, p. A89

JENKINS, Michelle, M.D., President Medical Staff, Herrin Hospital, Herrin, IL, p. A185

JENKINS, Rebecca, Director Human Resources Management, Harrison Memorial Hospital, Cynthiana, KY, p. A251

JENKINS, Ruth, Chief Financial Officer, Ridgeview Institute, Smyrna, GA, p. A160

JENKINS, Timothy, M.D., Area Medical Director and Chief of Staff, Kaiser Permanente Fontana Medical Center, Fontana, CA, p. A58

JENNER, Jody J., President and Chief Executive Officer, Broadlawns Medical Center, Des Moines, IA, p. A221

JENNETTE, Brian, Chief Financial Officer, Northside Hospital–Cherokee, Canton, GA, p. A149

JENNINGS, Jason
  President, Baylor Scott & White Hospital Medical Center – Brenham, Brenham, TX, p. A589
  President, Baylor Scott & White Hospital Medical Center – College Station, College Station, TX, p. A592

JENNINGS, Keith, Chief Information Officer, Massachusetts General Hospital, Boston, MA, p. A295

JENNINGS, Lawrence, Chief of Staff, Wabash General Hospital, Mount Carmel, IL, p. A190

JENNINGS, Lee Ann, R.N., Vice President, Nursing Services, Wise Health System, Decatur, TX, p. A598

JENNINGS, Marilyn, Director Human Resources, Arise Austin Medical Center, Austin, TX, p. A584

JENNINGS, Mark, Chief Information Officer, Saint Anthony Hospital, Chicago, IL, p. A179

JENNINGS, Peter, M.D., Chief Medical Officer, Sacred Heart Hospital Pensacola, Pensacola, FL, p. A136

JENNINGS, Shayla, Human Resources Director, Montgomery County Memorial Hospital, Red Oak, IA, p. A228

JENNINGS, William, President and Chief Executive Officer, Reading Hospital, West Reading, PA, p. A544

JENSEMA, Christine
  Chief Human Resources Officer, Hshs St. Clare Memorial Hospital, Oconto Falls, WI, p. A703
  Chief Human Resources Officer, Hshs St. Vincent Hospital, Green Bay, WI, p. A696
  Chief People Officer, Hshs St. Mary'S Hospital Medical Center, Green Bay, WI, p. A696
  Chief People Officer, Hshs St. Nicholas Hospital, Sheboygan, WI, p. A705

JENSEN, Amy, Director Human Resources, Promedica Coldwater Regional Hospital, Coldwater, MI, p. A309

JENSEN, Annelise, Vice President and Chief Nursing Officer, Methodist Healthcare Olive Branch Hospital, Olive Branch, MS, p. A352

JENSEN, Beth, Director Clinic Operations, Mobridge Regional Hospital, Mobridge, SD, p. A562

JENSEN, Christopher, Chief Financial Officer, Three Rivers Behavioral Health, West Columbia, SC, p. A558

JENSEN, Dave, Director Human Resources, Performance Improvement and Risk Management, Mountain View Hospital, Gadsden, AL, p. A18

JENSEN, Eric P., Chief Executive Officer, Astria Toppenish Hospital, Toppenish, WA, p. A681

JENSEN, Janette, Manager Human Resources, Avera Holy Family Hospital, Estherville, IA, p. A222

JENSEN, Jeff, D.O.
  Vice President, Medical Affairs, Morton Plant Hospital, Clearwater, FL, p. A119
  Vice President, Medical Affairs, Morton Plant North Bay Hospital, New Port Richey, FL, p. A132

JENSEN, Laura J., Vice President Patient Care Services, St. Croix Regional Medical Center, St Croix Falls, WI, p. A706

JENSEN, Mary, Controller, Mountain View Hospital, Gadsden, AL, p. A18

JENSEN, Michael, Chief Executive Officer, Davis Hospital And Medical Center, Layton, UT, p. A648

JENSEN, Neal, Chief Executive Officer, Cobre Valley Regional Medical Center, Globe, AZ, p. A30

JENSEN, Pamela M.
  President, Promedica Fostoria Community Hospital, Fostoria, OH, p. A483
  President, Promedica Memorial Hospital, Fremont, OH, p. A483

JENSEN, Paul, M.D., Chief of Staff, Regional Health Services Of Howard County, Cresco, IA, p. A220

JENSEN, Ron, D.O., Chief Medical Officer and Vice President, Baylor Scott & White Medical Center – Grapevine, Grapevine, TX, p. A608

JENSEN, Ryan, Chief Executive Officer, Desert Springs Hospital Medical Center, Las Vegas, NV, p. A395

JENSEN, Sherry, Chief Financial Officer, Halifax Regional Medical Center, Roanoke Rapids, NC, p. A461

JENSEN, Tom, Chief Executive Officer, Grays Harbor Community Hospital, Aberdeen, WA, p. A670

JENSEN, Troy, Director Human Resources, Healthsouth Rehabilitation Hospital Of Utah, Sandy, UT, p. A653

JENSEN, Twyla, Director Human Resources, Pioneers Medical Center, Meeker, CO, p. A104

JENTZ, Amy, M.D., Chief of Staff, Sparrow Ionia Hospital, Ionia, MI, p. A314

JEPPESEN, Kelly, Chief Medical Officer, San Juan Health Service District, Monticello, UT, p. A649

JEPSEN, Christinia, R.N., Chief Nursing Executive, Memorial Community Hospital And Health System, Blair, NE, p. A383

JEPSON, Brian, President, Ohiohealth Riverside Methodist Hospital, Columbus, OH, p. A480

JEPSON, Mark, Vice President, Silver Cross Hospital, New Lenox, IL, p. A191

JERDEE, Amy L., President, St. Francis Regional Medical Center, Shakopee, MN, p. A340

JERGER, Greg, Chief Financial Officer, Memorial Health Care Systems, Seward, NE, p. A391

JERINA, Anthony T., Chief Nursing Officer, Hereford Regional Medical Center, Hereford, TX, p. A610

JERNIGAN, Pam, Chief Financial Officer, Unity Medical Center, Manchester, TN, p. A573

JESCH, Doug, Director Human Resources, Starke Hospital, Knox, IN, p. A208

JESIOLOWSKI, Craig A, President, Holy Family Hospital, Methuen, MA, p. A300

JESIOLOWSKI, Craig A., President, Holy Family Hospital, Methuen, MA, p. A300

JESSOP, Reuben, Chief Operating Officer, Northern Utah Rehabilitation Hospital, South Ogden, UT, p. A653

JESSUP, Daniel
  Chief Financial Officer, Legacy Silverton Medical Center, Silverton, OR, p. A518
  Chief Financial Officer, Wallowa Memorial Hospital, Enterprise, OR, p. A512

JESTER, Denise, Chief Financial Officer, Nanticoke Memorial Hospital, Seaford, DE, p. A114
JESTILA–PELTOLA, Gail, Chief Financial Officer, Baraga County Memorial Hospital, L'Anse, MI, p. A316
JESURASA, Jebashini, Vice President, Chief Information Technology Officer, Brookdale Hospital Medical Center, New York, NY, p. A432
JETER, John, Chief Executive Officer, Johnston Memorial Hospital, Abingdon, VA, p. A656
JETT, Chris, Administrator, Usa Children'S And Women'S Hospital, Mobile, AL, p. A20
JETTERGREN, Tess, Director Clinical Informatics, Essentia Health St. Mary'S Medical Center, Duluth, MN, p. A331
JEUNEHOMME, Patti, Director Human Resources, Hot Springs County Memorial Hospital, Thermopolis, WY, p. A713
JEWETT, Jess, Chief Medical Officer, Cache Valley Hospital, North Logan, UT, p. A649
JEWETT, Lori, Chief Executive Officer, Falmouth Hospital, Falmouth, MA, p. A298
JEWETT, Sherri R., Chief Executive Officer, Valle Vista Health System, Greenwood, IN, p. A205
JEX, Kerri, R.N., Chief Nursing Officer, Bear Valley Community Hospital, Big Bear Lake, CA, p. A53
JEYAKUMAR, Panch, M.D., Chief of Staff, Olympia Medical Center, Los Angeles, CA, p. A68
JEZIORSKE, John J, Director Human Resources, Abilene Regional Medical Center, Abilene, TX, p. A581
JEZSU, Peggy, Chief Nursing Officer, Alvarado Hospital Medical Center, San Diego, CA, p. A83
JIMENEZ, Betzaida, Director Human Resources, Hospital De La Universidad De Puerto Rico/Dr. Federico Trilla, Carolina, PR, p. A715
JIMENEZ, Cristina, Chief Executive Officer, Coral Gables Hospital, Coral Gables, FL, p. A120
JIMENEZ, Edward, Chief Executive Officer, Uf Health Shands Hospital, Gainesville, FL, p. A124
JIMENEZ, Gerson, M.D., Medical Director, Hospital Episcopal San Lucas Guayama, Guayama, PR, p. A716
JIMENEZ, Guillermo, Director Finance, Castaner General Hospital, Castaner, PR, p. A715
JIMENEZ, Ronald, Chief Executive Officer, Adventhealth Palm Coast, Palm Coast, FL, p. A135
JIMESON, Jean–Marie, Manager Human Resources, Kansas Spine And Specialty Hospital, Wichita, KS, p. A248
JIMMERSON, Kevin, Business Manager, Mental Health Institute, Independence, IA, p. A224
JIN, Marvin, M.D., Medical Director, Parkside Psychiatric Hospital And Clinic, Tulsa, OK, p. A509
JIRON, Feliciano, Chief Executive Officer, Valley View Medical Center, Fort Mohave, AZ, p. A29
JIROVEC, David, Director Finance, Ascension Good Samaritan Hospital, Merrill, WI, p. A700
JOBBITT, Patty, Chief Operating Officer, Dmc Rehabilitation Institute Of Michigan, Detroit, MI, p. A310
JOBE, Kenneth Lynn, Director Human Resources, Tyler County Hospital, Woodville, TX, p. A646
JOCHIM, Steven, Administrator, Pocasset Mental Health Center, Pocasset, MA, p. A302
JODWAY, Timothy, Chief Financial Administrator, Beaumont Hospital – Dearborn, Dearborn, MI, p. A309
JOHANNSEN, Lee, M.D., Chief Medical Officer, Central Texas Medical Center, San Marcos, TX, p. A636
JOHANSON, Amanda, Chief Executive Officer, Holly Hill Hospital, Raleigh, NC, p. A460
JOHE, David, M.D., President Medical Staff, Penn Highlands Elk, Saint Marys, PA, p. A540
JOHN, Aleyamma, R.N., Director of Nursing, Kensington Hospital, Philadelphia, PA, p. A535
JOHN, Janene, Chief Human Resource Officer, Broward Health Coral Springs, Coral Springs, FL, p. A120
JOHNS, Dale, Chief Executive Officer, Salt Lake Regional Medical Center, Salt Lake City, UT, p. A652
JOHNS, Dawn, Director Human Resources, Colquitt Regional Medical Center, Moultrie, GA, p. A158
JOHNS, Jeffery, M.D., Medical Director, Vanderbilt Stallworth Rehabilitation Hospital, Nashville, TN, p. A577
JOHNS, Paul, Chief Operating Officer, South Lake Hospital, Clermont, FL, p. A120
JOHNS, Thomas Bradford, M.D., Medical Director, Ridgeview Institute, Smyrna, GA, p. A160
JOHNSEN, Timothy J., President, Integris Baptist Medical Center, Oklahoma City, OK, p. A504
JOHNSON, Aaron, Vice President Patient Care Services and Chief Nursing Officer, Chi St. Alexius Health Devils Lake Hospital, Devils Lake, ND, p. A466
JOHNSON, Alan, Interim Chief Information Officer, United Medical Center, Washington, DC, p. A116
JOHNSON, Allen
Chief Financial Officer, Truman Medical Center–Hospital Hill, Kansas City, MO, p. A363
Chief Financial Officer, Truman Medical Center–Lakewood, Kansas City, MO, p. A363
JOHNSON, Amy R, R.N., Quality Improvement Safety Officer, Star Valley Medical Center, Afton, WY, p. A710
JOHNSON, Angela, Executive Director, Unitypoint Health – Trinity Muscatine, Muscatine, IA, p. A227
JOHNSON, Arlan D., Chief Executive Officer, Howard County Medical Center, Saint Paul, NE, p. A391
JOHNSON, Ashley, Director Human Resource, Mccamey County Hospital District, Mccamey, TX, p. A624
JOHNSON, Ashley L., Chief Operations Officer, Canyon Vista Medical Center, Sierra Vista, AZ, p. A36
JOHNSON, Becky, Director Human Resources, Oakdale Community Hospital, Oakdale, LA, p. A276
JOHNSON, Belinda, R.N., Chief Nursing Officer/Chief Clinical Officer, Russellville Hospital, Russellville, AL, p. A23
JOHNSON, Betty, Associate Administrator, Ochsner Lsu Health Shrevport – Academic Medical Center, Shreveport, LA, p. A278
JOHNSON, Billy, Chief Executive Officer, Coal County General Hospital, Coalgate, OK, p. A498
JOHNSON, Blake, M.D., Chief of Staff, Salt Lake Regional Medical Center, Salt Lake City, UT, p. A652
JOHNSON, Bonnie, R.N., Vice President of Patient Services, Perham Health, Perham, MN, p. A337
JOHNSON, Brandi, Site Manager Technology Information Systems, Spectrum Health Reed City Hospital, Reed City, MI, p. A320
JOHNSON, Brenda
Director Human Resources, Baptist Memorial Hospital–Collierville, Collierville, TN, p. A568
Director Human Resources, North Mississippi Medical Center–West Point, West Point, MS, p. A355
JOHNSON, Bret
Chief Financial Officer, Bon Secours St. Francis Hospital, Charleston, SC, p. A549
Chief Financial Officer, Roper Hospital, Charleston, SC, p. A550
Chief Financial Officer, Roper St. Francis Mount Pleasant Hospital, Mount Pleasant, SC, p. A555
JOHNSON, Brett M., Chief Executive Officer, Northwest Ohio Psychiatric Hospital, Toledo, OH, p. A492
JOHNSON, Brian, M.D., Chief Medical Officer, Aurora Baycare Medical Center, Green Bay, WI, p. A696
JOHNSON, Bryan N, M.D., Chief Medical Officer, Whitman Hospital And Medical Center, Colfax, WA, p. A672
JOHNSON, C Thomas, Vice President Finance and Chief Financial Officer, Southeastern Health, Lumberton, NC, p. A458
JOHNSON, Candace, President and Chief Executive Officer, Roswell Park Comprehensive Cancer Center, Buffalo, NY, p. A424
JOHNSON, Casey R, Chief Financial Officer, Riverwood Healthcare Center, Aitkin, MN, p. A327
JOHNSON, Charles, M.D., Chief of Staff, Renown Regional Medical Center, Reno, NV, p. A397
JOHNSON, Cheryl, Regional Chief Information Officer, St. Joseph Medical Center, Kansas City, MO, p. A363
JOHNSON, Chris, Chief Nursing Officer, Davis Hospital And Medical Center, Layton, UT, p. A648
JOHNSON, Chris, M.D., Chief of Staff, Mercy Hospital Rogers, Rogers, AR, p. A48
JOHNSON, Christina, Chief Executive Officer, Longmont United Hospital, Longmont, CO, p. A103
JOHNSON, Christina, M.D., Vice President and Chief Clinical and Quality Officer, Lutheran Medical Center, Wheat Ridge, CO, p. A106
JOHNSON, Collette, Chief Financial Officer, Palo Alto County Health System, Emmetsburg, IA, p. A222
JOHNSON, Craig A., Chief Executive Officer, Boundary Community Hospital, Bonners Ferry, ID, p. A168
JOHNSON, Craig L., Chief Executive Officer, Vibra Hospital Of Northwestern Indiana, Crown Point, IN, p. A202
JOHNSON, Cynthia J, R.N., Chief Nursing Officer, Los Robles Hospital And Medical Center, Thousand Oaks, CA, p. A91
JOHNSON, Danielle, Chief Operating Officer, Adventhealth Fish Memorial, Orange City, FL, p. A134
JOHNSON, Darren, M.D., Chief of Staff, West Tennessee Healthcare Dyersburg Hospital, Dyersburg, TN, p. A569
JOHNSON, David
Chief Executive Officer, Kindred Hospital–Louisville, Louisville, KY, p. A256
Chief Executive Officer, Navos, Seattle, WA, p. A677
Manager Information Services, Providence Kodiak Island Medical Center, Kodiak, AK, p. A26
JOHNSON, Debra, Chief Administrator, Spectrum Health Lakeland, Saint Joseph, MI, p. A322
JOHNSON, Deeann, Director Human Resources, Saint Thomas River Park Hospital, Mc Minnville, TN, p. A574
JOHNSON, Denise, M.D., Medical Director, Meadville Medical Center, Meadville, PA, p. A531
JOHNSON, Dennis B., President and Chief Executive Officer, Hardin Memorial Health, Elizabethtown, KY, p. A251
JOHNSON, Derek
Chief Executive Officer, Laurel Oaks Behavioral Health Center, Dothan, AL, p. A17
Chief Operating Officer, Franklin Hospital District, Benton, IL, p. A174
JOHNSON, Diana G, Acting Chief Human Resources Officer, Novato Community Hospital, Novato, CA, p. A75
JOHNSON, Dino, R.N., Chief Operating Officer and Chief Nursing Officer, St. Francis Hospital, Federal Way, WA, p. A673
JOHNSON, Douglas E
Chief Financial Officer, Lakeview Hospital, Stillwater, MN, p. A341
Interim Vice President Operations and Chief Financial Officer, Hudson Hospital And Clinic, Hudson, WI, p. A697
JOHNSON, Douglas V., Chief Executive Officer, Stanislaus Surgical Hospital, Modesto, CA, p. A72
JOHNSON, Drew, Chief Financial Officer, Holdenville General Hospital, Holdenville, OK, p. A500
JOHNSON, Earle
Area Information Officer, Kaiser Permanente Panorama City Medical Center, Los Angeles, CA, p. A67
Area Information Officer, Kaiser Permanente Woodland Hills Medical Center, Los Angeles, CA, p. A67
JOHNSON, Eddie, Chief Information Technology Officer, Kansas City Veterans Affairs Medical Center, Kansas City, MO, p. A362
JOHNSON, Elisha, Interim Administrator, United Medical Rehabilitation Hospital, Gretna, LA, p. A268
JOHNSON, Eric M., Director, United Medical Center, Washington, DC, p. A116
JOHNSON, Eunice, M.D., Chief Medical Staff, Kentucky River Medical Center, Jackson, KY, p. A254
JOHNSON, Fred, M.D., Chief Medical Officer, Dignity Health Arizona General Hospital, Laveen, AZ, p. A31
JOHNSON, Gigi, Chief Nursing Officer, Kindred Hospital–Chattanooga, Chattanooga, TN, p. A567
JOHNSON, Greg
IT Coordinator, North Shore Health, Grand Marais, MN, p. A332
Vice President of Operations, Davis Medical Center, Elkins, WV, p. A685
JOHNSON, Greg K, Chief Operating Officer, Colquitt Regional Medical Center, Moultrie, GA, p. A158
JOHNSON, Heather
Director of Finance, Operations and Business Development, Buffalo Hospital, Buffalo, MN, p. A329
Interim President, Buffalo Hospital, Buffalo, MN, p. A329
JOHNSON, Helen, R.N., MSN, Vice President Patient Services, Spectrum Health Ludington Hospital, Ludington, MI, p. A317
JOHNSON, J David, M.D., Chief of Staff, Ut Health Specialty Hospital, Tyler, TX, p. A642
JOHNSON, J. Ronald., Director, Hunter Holmes Mcguire Veterans Affairs Medical Center–Richmond, Richmond, VA, p. A666
JOHNSON, James, Chief Executive Officer, Franklin Hospital District, Benton, IL, p. A174
JOHNSON, Jamie, Director Human Resources, Miners' Colfax Medical Center, Raton, NM, p. A419
JOHNSON, Jamie, R.N., Vice President Nursing, Community Hospital Of Anaconda, Anaconda, MT, p. A374
JOHNSON, Jani L., Chief Executive Officer, Saint Luke'S Hospital Of Kansas City, Kansas City, MO, p. A363
JOHNSON, Jason, Controller, F. W. Huston Medical Center, Winchester, KS, p. A247
JOHNSON, Jay, Chief Financial Officer, Alliancehealth Clinton, Clinton, OK, p. A498
JOHNSON, Jay R., President and Chief Executive Officer, Duncan Regional Hospital, Duncan, OK, p. A498
JOHNSON, Jayne, Director Human Resources, Great Plains Health, North Platte, NE, p. A388
JOHNSON, Jeff, Director Information Systems, Saint Thomas River Park Hospital, Mc Minnville, TN, p. A574
JOHNSON, Jeffrey
Commander, Brooke Army Medical Center, Fort Sam Houston, TX, p. A604
Vice President, Uchealth Memorial Hospital, Colorado Springs, CO, p. A98
JOHNSON, Jimmy, Chief Financial Officer, Blue Mountain Hospital, Blanding, UT, p. A647
JOHNSON, Joe, Chief Executive Officer, Adventhealth Ocala, Ocala, FL, p. A133
JOHNSON, Joel, M.D., Chief Medical Staff, First Care Health Center, Park River, ND, p. A469

JOHNSON, John, M.D.
Chief of Staff, Greenbrier Valley Medical Center, Ronceverte, WV, p. A689
Clinical Director, U. S. Public Health Service Indian Hospital, Crownpoint, NM, p. A417
JOHNSON, Juantina, Chief of Staff, Choctaw Health Center, Philadelphia, MS, p. A352
JOHNSON, Judith, Controller, Encompass Health Rehabilitation Hospital Of Largo, Largo, FL, p. A128
JOHNSON, Juli, President, Parkview Huntington Hospital, Huntington, IN, p. A206
JOHNSON, Katherine, President, Sentara Northern Virginia Medical Center, Woodbridge, VA, p. A669
JOHNSON, Kathi, Chief Financial Officer, Eskenazi Health, Indianapolis, IN, p. A206
JOHNSON, Kathryn
Chief Nursing Officer, Casa Colina Hospital And Health Systems, Pomona, CA, p. A78
Manager Human Resources, Marketing and Public Relations, St. Vincent Jennings Hospital, North Vernon, IN, p. A213
JOHNSON, Kawanda, Director of Nursing, Specialty Hospital Of Meridian, Meridian, MS, p. A351
JOHNSON, Kayla, R.N., Vice President Patient Care Services and Chief Nursing Officer, St. Francis Medical Center, Monroe, LA, p. A274
JOHNSON, Kelly, Director Human Resources, Madison Healthcare Services, Madison, MN, p. A334
JOHNSON, Kelly, R.N., Chief Nursing Officer, St. John Sapulpa, Sapulpa, OK, p. A507
JOHNSON, Kelly M, Chief Nursing Officer, Lucile Salter Packard Children'S Hospital Stanford, Palo Alto, CA, p. A77
JOHNSON, Ken
Chief Physician Executive, Hshs St. Clare Memorial Hospital, Oconto Falls, WI, p. A703
Chief Physician Executive, Hshs St. Mary'S Hospital Medical Center, Green Bay, WI, p. A696
Chief Physician Executive, Hshs St. Nicholas Hospital, Sheboygan, WI, p. A705
Chief Physician Executive, Hshs St. Vincent Hospital, Green Bay, WI, p. A696
President and Chief Executive Officer, Hutchinson Regional Medical Center, Hutchinson, KS, p. A237
JOHNSON, Kendall, Chief Financial Officer, Baton Rouge General Medical Center, Baton Rouge, LA, p. A263
JOHNSON, Kenneth, Vice President, Sts. Mary & Elizabeth Hospital, Louisville, KY, p. A256
JOHNSON, Kerri, Human Resources Operations Consultant, Integris Bass Pavilion, Enid, OK, p. A499
JOHNSON, Kevin, Chief Executive Officer, Mountain View Hospital, Payson, UT, p. A650
JOHNSON, Kristen, Chief Nursing Officer, Southwest Healthcare System, Murrieta, CA, p. A74
JOHNSON, Kyle
Chief Information Officer, The Aroostook Medical Center, Presque Isle, ME, p. A284
Vice President Finance, East Liverpool City Hospital, East Liverpool, OH, p. A482
JOHNSON, Laurie, Director – Human Resources, Ascension Via Christi Hospital, Pittsburg, KS, p. A244
JOHNSON, Lerenda, Interim Chief Executive Officer, Kindred Hospital Seattle–Northgate, Seattle, WA, p. A677
JOHNSON, Linda, R.N., Vice President, Patient Services Risk Management and Chief Nursing Officer, Heart Of The Rockies Regional Medical Center, Salida, CO, p. A105
JOHNSON, Lois, Chief Financial Officer, Twin Cities Community Hospital, Templeton, CA, p. A91
JOHNSON, Margaret M., President, St. Vincent Northwest Region, St. Vincent Kokomo, Kokomo, IN, p. A209
JOHNSON, Marianne, Chief Nursing Officer, Trace Regional Hospital, Houston, MS, p. A348
JOHNSON, Marie
Chief Nursing Officer, Carrus Rehabilitation Hospital, Sherman, TX, p. A637
Chief Nursing Officer, Carrus Specialty Hospital, Sherman, TX, p. A637
JOHNSON, Marisa, M.D., Vice President Medical Affairs, Christus Health Shreveport–Bossier, Shreveport, LA, p. A278
JOHNSON, Mark
Chief Financial Officer, Norwood Hospital, Norwood, MA, p. A302
Chief Information Officer, West Holt Medical Services, Atkinson, NE, p. A382
JOHNSON, Mary, Chief Nursing Officer, Falmouth Hospital, Falmouth, MA, p. A298
JOHNSON, Marylynn, Director of Nursing, Springbrook Behavioral Health System, Travelers Rest, SC, p. A557
JOHNSON, Matthew, President, Mercyone Centerville Medical Center, Centerville, IA, p. A218

JOHNSON, Melissa, Chief Financial Officer, Baptist Medical Center South, Montgomery, AL, p. A21
JOHNSON, Michael, M.D., Medical Director, Salina Surgical Hospital, Salina, KS, p. A245
JOHNSON, Michael A, M.D., Chief of Staff, Bucyrus Hospital, Bucyrus, OH, p. A474
JOHNSON, Michael G., CPA, Chief Financial Officer, Abrom Kaplan Memorial Hospital, Kaplan, LA, p. A270
JOHNSON, Mike, Vice President, Chief Information Officer, Caromont Regional Medical Center, Gastonia, NC, p. A454
JOHNSON, Monte, Vice President, Medical Affairs, St. Francis Regional Medical Center, Shakopee, MN, p. A340
JOHNSON, Nancy, Chief Nursing Officer, Select Specialty Hospital–North Knoxville, Powell, TN, p. A578
JOHNSON, Nanette, Chief Nursing Officer, Orthopaedic Hospital Of Wisconsin, Glendale, WI, p. A695
JOHNSON, Nate, Chief Information Officer, Highlands Regional Medical Center, Sebring, FL, p. A139
JOHNSON, Neil, Chief Operating Officer, Eskenazi Health, Indianapolis, IN, p. A206
JOHNSON, Nikki, Interim Chief Executive Officer, Cooperstown Medical Center, Cooperstown, ND, p. A466
JOHNSON, Pamela
Treasurer and Chief Financial Officer, Finger Lakes Hospital, Geneva, NY, p. A428
Treasurer and Chief Financial Officer, Soldiers And Sailors Memorial Hospital Of Yates County, Penn Yan, NY, p. A441
JOHNSON, Pamela, R.N., Chief Nursing Officer, Mccurtain Memorial Hospital, Idabel, OK, p. A501
JOHNSON, Pamela O., MS, R.N., Chief Nursing Officer, Mayo Clinic Hospital – Rochester, Rochester, MN, p. A338
JOHNSON, Patricia, R.N., Senior Vice President, Woman'S Hospital, Baton Rouge, LA, p. A264
JOHNSON, Patrick, Director Human Resources, Pondera Medical Center, Conrad, MT, p. A375
JOHNSON, Penny, Chief Financial Officer, Adventhealth Central Texas, Killeen, TX, p. A618
JOHNSON, Peri, Human Resources Director, West Central Georgia Regional Hospital, Columbus, GA, p. A151
JOHNSON, Peter A, Interim Chief Information Officer, Monadnock Community Hospital, Peterborough, NH, p. A402
JOHNSON, Phillip, Vice President, Chief Human Resources Officer, St. Luke'S Regional Medical Center, Boise, ID, p. A168
JOHNSON, Ralph
Chief Information Officer, Franklin Memorial Hospital, Farmington, ME, p. A283
Chief Information Officer, Southern Maine Health Care – Biddeford Medical Center, Biddeford, ME, p. A282
JOHNSON, Randall, Administrator, Beacon Behavioral Hospital, Bunkie, LA, p. A265
JOHNSON, Rashard
President, Advocate South Suburban Hospital, Hazel Crest, IL, p. A185
President, Advocate Trinity Hospital, Chicago, IL, p. A176
JOHNSON, Ric, Associate Administrator, Mountain View Hospital, Payson, UT, p. A650
JOHNSON, Richard, M.D., Chief of Medical Staff, Chi St. Alexius Health Devils Lake Hospital, Devils Lake, ND, p. A466
JOHNSON, Rick, Chief Executive Officer, Spire Cane Creek Rehabilitation Hospital, Martin, TN, p. A573
JOHNSON, Robb, Director Operations, Hamilton Center, Terre Haute, IN, p. A215
JOHNSON, Roger, M.D., Chief of Staff, Cheyenne Veterans Affairs Medical Center, Cheyenne, WY, p. A711
JOHNSON, Ronald W., President and Chief Executive Officer, Shore Medical Center, Somers Point, NJ, p. A412
JOHNSON, Russell W., President and Chief Executive Officer, Lmh Health, Lawrence, KS, p. A239
JOHNSON, Ryan K, Controller, Spectrum Health United Hospital, Greenville, MI, p. A313
JOHNSON, Sam, M.D., Chief Medical Officer, Northeast Georgia Medical Center, Gainesville, GA, p. A154
JOHNSON, Scott H., Vice President Finance and Chief Financial Officer, St. Luke'S Hospital, Chesterfield, MO, p. A358
JOHNSON, Sean, Chief Executive Officer, Tyler Holmes Memorial Hospital, Winona, MS, p. A355
JOHNSON, Sharon, Director Health Information Management, Western State Hospital, Staunton, VA, p. A668
JOHNSON, Shelia B., Director of Nursing, St. Landry Extended Care Hospital, Opelousas, LA, p. A276
JOHNSON, Shelly, Chief Operating Officer, Spectrum Health Gerber Memorial, Fremont, MI, p. A312
JOHNSON, Sheryl, Chief Information Officer, Swedishamerican – A Division Of Uw Health, Rockford, IL, p. A195

JOHNSON, Shirley, MS, R.N., Senior Vice President Nursing and Patient Care Services, Chief Nursing Officer, Roswell Park Comprehensive Cancer Center, Buffalo, NY, p. A424
JOHNSON, Shrea, Director Human Resources, Alliance Health Center, Meridian, MS, p. A351
JOHNSON, Stacy, Chief Executive Officer, Loring Hospital, Sac City, IA, p. A229
JOHNSON, Steven P., President, Upmc Susquehanna Williamsport, Williamsport, PA, p. A545
JOHNSON, Sy
Executive Vice President, Chief Operating Officer, Renown Regional Medical Center, Reno, NV, p. A397
Executive Vice President, Chief Operating Officer, Renown South Meadows Medical Center, Reno, NV, p. A397
JOHNSON, Talicia, Director Human Resources, Brentwood Hospital, Shreveport, LA, p. A278
JOHNSON, Tamatha, Director Human Resources, Rmc–Stringfellow Memorial Hospital, Anniston, AL, p. A13
JOHNSON, Thomas, Director Information Systems, Penn Highlands Brookville, Brookville, PA, p. A521
JOHNSON, Timothy, President and Chief Executive Officer, Eaton Rapids Medical Center, Eaton Rapids, MI, p. A311
JOHNSON, Todd, Chief Financial Officer, Longview Regional Medical Center, Longview, TX, p. A621
JOHNSON, Tom, Chief Human Resource Officer, Minneapolis Veterans Affairs Health Care System, Minneapolis, MN, p. A336
JOHNSON, Trudy, R.N., Chief Nursing Officer, Santa Clara Valley Medical Center, San Jose, CA, p. A87
JOHNSON, Vern, Director Information Technology, Sullivan County Memorial Hospital, Milan, MO, p. A365
JOHNSON, Vernon, Administrator, Dale Medical Center, Ozark, AL, p. A22
JOHNSON, Victoria, R.N., Nursing Director of Surgical and Medical Services, The Healthcenter, Kalispell, MT, p. A378
JOHNSON, Wade C., Chief Executive Officer, St. Peter'S Hospital, Helena, MT, p. A377
JOHNSON, William, Director Information Systems, Shoals Hospital, Muscle Shoals, AL, p. A22
JOHNSON, William F, Chief Medical Officer, Tennova Healthcare – Cleveland, Cleveland, TN, p. A568
JOHNSON, William Micah, Administrator and Chief Nursing Officer, Christus St. Michael Health System, Texarkana, TX, p. A640
JOHNSON–HATCHER, Dawn, Chief Financial Officer, Christus Ochsner Lake Area Hospital, Lake Charles, LA, p. A272
JOHNSON–MEKOTA, Judith, Director, Iowa City Veterans Affairs Health Care System, Iowa City, IA, p. A224
JOHNSON–MILLER, Kimberly, Chief Financial Officer, Carl Vinson Veterans Affairs Medical Center, Dublin, GA, p. A152
JOHNSON–THREAT, Yvette, Vice President Medical Affairs, Medstar Southern Maryland Hospital Center, Clinton, MD, p. A289
JOHNSRUD, Carolyn, Manager Human Resources, Missouri River Medical Center, Fort Benton, MT, p. A376
JOHNSRUD, Jill, Director of Nursing, Essentia Health–Graceville, Graceville, MN, p. A332
JOHNSTON, Christopher, Chief Administrative Officer, Peacehealth United General Medical Center, Sedro, WA, p. A679
JOHNSTON, Diann, R.N., MSN, Vice President of Patient Care Services, Monmouth Medical Center, Long Branch Campus, Long Branch, NJ, p. A407
JOHNSTON, Don, Chief Information Officer, San Joaquin General Hospital, French Camp, CA, p. A59
JOHNSTON, John, Chief Medical Officer, Specialty Hospital Of Meridian, Meridian, MS, p. A351
JOHNSTON, Lori, Chief Information Officer, Promedica Flower Hospital, Sylvania, OH, p. A491
JOHNSTON, Michael Eric., President and Chief Executive Officer, Mclaren Thumb Region, Bad Axe, MI, p. A307
JOHNSTON, Michael V, M.D., Chief Medical Officer and Senior Vice President Medical Programs, Kennedy Krieger Institute, Baltimore, MD, p. A286
JOHNSTON, Mike
Chief Executive Officer, Decatur County Hospital, Leon, IA, p. A225
Director Facilities Operations, Union General Hospital, Blairsville, GA, p. A148
JOHNSTON, Monte, Manager Human Resources, Coquille Valley Hospital, Coquille, OR, p. A512
JOHNSTON, Patricia, Vice President Information Services, Texas Health Harris Methodist Hospital Azle, Azle, TX, p. A586
JOHNSTON, Phyllis M., Vice President, Catawba Valley Medical Center, Hickory, NC, p. A456
JOHNSTON, Scott, Chief of Staff, Onslow Memorial Hospital, Jacksonville, NC, p. A457

JOHNSTON, Susan, Vice President Human Resources, East Alabama Medical Center, Opelika, AL, p. A22
JOHNSTON, Susanne, Manager Human Resources, Lincoln County Medical Center, Ruidoso, NM, p. A420
JOHNSTON, Word, Medical Director, Covington County Hospital, Collins, MS, p. A346
JOHNSTONE, Jennifer, Chief Clinical Officer, Kindred Hospital Rome, Rome, GA, p. A159
JOHRENDT, JT, Information Technology Network Specialist, Edgerton Hospital And Health Services, Edgerton, WI, p. A694
JOICE, Jason, M.D., Chief Medical Staff, Hillcrest Hospital Pryor, Pryor, OK, p. A506
JOLLEY, Colby, D.O., Acting Chief of Staff, Haxtun Hospital District, Haxtun, CO, p. A102
JOLLEY, Sherry, Director of Operations and Nursing, Red Bay Hospital, Red Bay, AL, p. A23
JOLLY, Gaye, President and Chief Administrative Officer, Leconte Medical Center, Sevierville, TN, p. A579
JONASON, Anna, Ph.D., R.N., Chief Nursing Officer, Colleton Medical Center, Walterboro, SC, p. A558
JONES, Adrienne, Director Human Resources, Brookdale Hospital Medical Center, New York, NY, p. A432
JONES, Alesia, Chief Human Resources Officer, University Of Alabama Hospital, Birmingham, AL, p. A15
JONES, Allan, Controller, Encompass Health Rehabilitation Hospital Of Jonesboro, Jonesboro, AR, p. A44
JONES, America, Chief Executive Officer, Kindred Hospital El Paso, El Paso, TX, p. A602
JONES, Anetra, R.N., M.P.H.
Chief Nursing Officer, La Porte Hospital, La Porte, IN, p. A209
Chief Nursing Officer, Starke Hospital, Knox, IN, p. A208
JONES, Austin, CPA, Chief Financial Officer, Physicians Surgical Hospital – Quail Creek, Amarillo, TX, p. A582
JONES, Beth
Chief Operating Officer, Reeves Memorial Medical Center, Bernice, LA, p. A264
Director of Nursing, Reeves Memorial Medical Center, Bernice, LA, p. A264
JONES, Bill
Chief Executive Officer, Jackson County Hospital District, Edna, TX, p. A601
Chief Financial Officer, Florida State Hospital, Chattahoochee, FL, p. A119
JONES, Brain, Director of Information Technology, Multicare Valley Hospital, Spokane Valley, WA, p. A600
JONES, Carol, Controller and Manager Business Office, Coryell Health, Gatesville, TX, p. A607
JONES, Carol S., MSN, R.N., Interim Chief Nursing Officer, Morristown Medical Center, Morristown, NJ, p. A408
JONES, Carolyn, R.N., MSN, Chief Nursing Officer, Box Butte General Hospital, Alliance, NE, p. A382
JONES, Charlene, Chief Nursing Officer, Peterson Healthcare And Rehabilitation Hospital, Wheeling, WV, p. A690
JONES, Chris, Chief Executive Officer, Vibra Hospital Of Northern California, Redding, CA, p. A80
JONES, Christian, Chief Operating Officer, Poplar Bluff Regional Medical Center, Poplar Bluff, MO, p. A367
JONES, Connie, Director Human Resources, Community Behavioral Health Hospital – Rochester, Rochester, MN, p. A338
JONES, Dale, Administrator, Noland Hospital Montgomery, Montgomery, AL, p. A21
JONES, Dana R., R.N., MSN, Chief Nursing Officer and Chief Operating Officer, Springhill Medical Center, Springhill, LA, p. A279
JONES, Danny L., Jr, Chief Executive Officer, St. Francis Hospital, Columbus, GA, p. A150
JONES, Darrell, Chief Executive Officer, Select Specialty Hospital–Pittsburgh/Upmc, Pittsburgh, PA, p. A537
JONES, David
Chief Executive Officer, Encompass Health Rehabilitation Hospital Of Round Rock, Round Rock, TX, p. A632
Chief Financial Officer, Alexian Brothers Behavioral Health Hospital, Hoffman Estates, IL, p. A186
Service Chief, Riverside Shore Memorial Hospital, Onancock, VA, p. A664
JONES, David, M.D., Chief Medical Officer, Beauregard Health System, De Ridder, LA, p. A266
JONES, David C., Administrator, North Caddo Medical Center, Vivian, LA, p. A280
JONES, Debbie, Director of Nursing, Brookhaven Hospital, Tulsa, OK, p. A508
JONES, Deborah, Controller, Sca Houston Hospital For Specialized Surgery, Houston, TX, p. A613
JONES, Derrick, Chief Executive Officer, Lovelace Unm Rehabilitation Hospital, Albuquerque, NM, p. A416
JONES, Don, M.D., Chief Medical Officer, Marshall Medical Center North, Guntersville, AL, p. A19
JONES, Donald J., Administrator, Fayette Medical Center, Fayette, AL, p. A18
JONES, Douglas A, Chief Operating Officer, Forrest General Hospital, Hattiesburg, MS, p. A348
JONES, Elaine, M.D., President Medical Staff, Roger Williams Medical Center, Providence, RI, p. A548
JONES, Elizabeth
Chief Executive Officer, Southwestern Medical Center, Lawton, OK, p. A501
Chief Operating Officer, Lake Cumberland Regional Hospital, Somerset, KY, p. A260
JONES, Evan, Executive Vice President and Chief Financial Officer, Lakeland Regional Health Medical Center, Lakeland, FL, p. A127
JONES, Evelyn, R.N., Vice President Nursing Services, St. Bernard Hospital And Health Care Center, Chicago, IL, p. A180
JONES, Florence, President, Methodist Healthcare Memphis Hospitals, Memphis, TN, p. A575
JONES, Greg, Chief Financial Officer, Wayne Memorial Hospital, Jesup, GA, p. A155
JONES, Holly A, Administrative Director Nursing Services, Illini Community Hospital, Pittsfield, IL, p. A193
JONES, Jace, Interim Chief Executive Officer, Brownwood Regional Medical Center, Brownwood, TX, p. A590
JONES, Janice G, Interim Chief Financial Officer, Controller and Compliance Officer, Mercy Regional Medical Center, Ville Platte, LA, p. A280
JONES, Jason L., R.N., Chief Nursing Officer, Fannin Regional Hospital, Blue Ridge, GA, p. A148
JONES, Jeff, Director Human Resources, Greene Memorial Hospital, Xenia, OH, p. A494
JONES, Jeffrey, Chief Financial Officer, Moses H. Cone Memorial Hospital, Greensboro, NC, p. A455
JONES, Jeremy A., Chief Executive Officer, Arbuckle Memorial Hospital, Sulphur, OK, p. A508
JONES, Joshua, Director Human Resources, Evanston Regional Hospital, Evanston, WY, p. A711
JONES, Joyce, Director Human Resources, Encompass Health Rehabilitation Hospital Of Kingsport, Kingsport, TN, p. A572
JONES, Judy, Chief Clinical Officer, Arkansas Surgical Hospital, North Little Rock, AR, p. A46
JONES, Julie L., Chief Executive Officer, Community Hospital–Fairfax, Fairfax, MO, p. A360
JONES, Karen, Administrative Director Human Resources, Marion General Hospital, Marion, IN, p. A211
JONES, Karin, Interim Chief Nursing Officer, Healthsouth Rehabilitation Hospital Of New Mexico, Albuquerque, NM, p. A416
JONES, Karol, Chief Nursing Officer, Huntsville Hospital, Huntsville, AL, p. A19
JONES, Kathy, Director Human Resources, Jackson Medical Center, Jackson, AL, p. A20
JONES, Keith, Chief Information Officer, Fulton State Hospital, Fulton, MO, p. A360
JONES, Ken M, Chief Operating Officer, Ucsf Medical Center, San Francisco, CA, p. A86
JONES, Kenneth, President, Amita Health Saint Francis Hospital Evanston, Evanston, IL, p. A182
JONES, Kimberly, Director Human Resources, Spine Hospital Of Louisiana (Formally The Neuromedical Center Surgical Hospital), Baton Rouge, LA, p. A264
JONES, Kyle, Chief Financial Officer, Marshall Medical Center, Lewisburg, TN, p. A573
JONES, Lance, Chief Executive Officer, Lewis–Gale Medical Center, Boones Mill, VA, p. A657
JONES, Liston, M.D., Medical Director, Springhill Memorial Hospital, Mobile, AL, p. A20
JONES, Louis, Director Management Information Systems, Adventhealth Heart Of Florida, Davenport, FL, p. A121
JONES, M Steven, President, University Hospitals Geauga Medical Center, Chardon, OH, p. A475
JONES, M Steven.
President, Uh Portage Medical Center, Ravenna, OH, p. A490
President, University Hospitals Conneaut Medical Center, Conneaut, OH, p. A480
President, University Hospitals Geauga Medical Center, Chardon, OH, p. A475
President, University Hospitals Geneva Medical Center, Geneva, OH, p. A484
JONES, Mark, Chief Financial Officer, Hill Country Memorial Hospital, Fredericksburg, TX, p. A606
JONES, Mark A., President, Orlando Regional Medical Center, Orlando, FL, p. A134
JONES, Marsha, R.N.
Director Nursing, Baptist Medical Center Yazoo, Yazoo City, MS, p. A355
Director of Nursing, Baptist Medical Center Yazoo, Yazoo City, MS, p. A355
JONES, Marshall, Senior Vice President Human Resources, Maricopa Integrated Health System, Phoenix, AZ, p. A33
JONES, Matthew, Vice President Support Services and Facilities, The University Of Vermont Health Network – Alice Hyde Medical Center, Malone, NY, p. A430
JONES, Maud, Manager Medical Records, Tops Surgical Specialty Hospital, Houston, TX, p. A614
JONES, MaxAnne, Director Human Resources, Rock Prairie Behavioral Health, College Station, TX, p. A593
JONES, Melinda, R.N., Chief Nursing Officer, Morehouse General Hospital, Bastrop, LA, p. A263
JONES, Mike, Executive Director, Marshall Medical Center, Placerville, CA, p. A78
JONES, Mitchell, Director Information Technology, Little River Memorial Hospital, Ashdown, AR, p. A39
JONES, Pam, MSN, R.N., Associate Hospital Director and Chief Nursing Officer, Vanderbilt University Medical Center, Nashville, TN, p. A577
JONES, Pamela K., Executive Director of Finance, Baptist Health Corbin, Corbin, KY, p. A250
JONES, Pat, Director Information Systems, Merit Health River Oaks, Flowood, MS, p. A346
JONES, Patrice I., R.N., MSN, Vice President and Chief Nursing Officer, Uf Health Jacksonville, Jacksonville, FL, p. A126
JONES, Philip L, Chief Financial Officer, Curahealth Nashville, Nashville, TN, p. A576
JONES, Phyllis, Chief Human Resources, Wm. Jennings Bryan Dorn Veterans Affairs Medical Center, Columbia, SC, p. A552
JONES, Rachel, Chief Financial Officer, Watsonville Community Hospital, Watsonville, CA, p. A94
JONES, Reginald, Business Manager, Georgia Regional Hospital At Atlanta, Decatur, GA, p. A152
JONES, Reid F., Chief Executive Officer, University Of Alabama Hospital, Birmingham, AL, p. A15
JONES, Rex, Chief Executive Officer, Magnolia Regional Medical Center, Magnolia, AR, p. A45
JONES, Richard, M.D., Medical Director, Encompass Health Rehabilitation Hospital Of Richardson, Richardson, TX, p. A631
JONES, Richard W, Chief Financial Officer, Reading Hospital, West Reading, PA, p. A544
JONES, Rita A., Chief Executive Officer, Dundy County Hospital, Benkelman, NE, p. A383
JONES, Rob, Director of Nursing and Operations, Physicians' Medical Center, New Albany, IN, p. A212
JONES, Robert, Director Management Information Systems, St. Joseph Mercy Oakland, Pontiac, MI, p. A320
JONES, Roger, M.D., Interim Chief of Staff, Tennessee Valley Healthcare System, Nashville, TN, p. A577
JONES, Ruth, Chief Clinical Officer, Regency Hospital Of Northwest Arkansas – Springdale, Springdale, AR, p. A49
JONES, Ruth Ann, Ed.D., MSN, R.N.
Senior Vice President, Chief Nursing Officer, University Of Maryland Shore Medical Center At Chestertown, Chestertown, MD, p. A289
Senior Vice President, Chief Nursing Officer, University Of Maryland Shore Medical Center At Easton, Easton, MD, p. A290
JONES, Ryan, Chief Executive Officer, Alliance Community Hospital, Alliance, OH, p. A471
JONES, Sarah, Chief Nurse Executive, Metropolitan St. Louis Psychiatric Center, Saint Louis, MO, p. A369
JONES, Scott
President and Chief Executive Officer, Midwestern Regional Medical Center, Zion, IL, p. A198
Vice President and Facility Executive, Atrium Health'S Carolinas Medical Center, Charlotte, NC, p. A451
JONES, Scott R., Chief Operating Officer, Prisma Health Hillcrest Hospital, Simpsonville, SC, p. A557
JONES, Sean, Director Human Resources, Merit Health Central, Jackson, MS, p. A349
JONES, Shannon, M.D., Medical Director and Attending Psychiatrist, Evansville Psychiatric Children Center, Evansville, IN, p. A203
JONES, Sharon, Chief Financial Officer, Evergreen Medical Center, Evergreen, AL, p. A17
JONES, Sherry J, Chief Financial Officer, Crestwood Medical Center, Huntsville, AL, p. A19
JONES, Staci, R.N., Chief Nursing Officer, Methodist Mckinney Hospital, Mckinney, TX, p. A624
JONES, Stacy, Chief Nursing Officer, Encompass Health Rehabilitation Hospital Of Morgantown, Morgantown, WV, p. A687
JONES, Stephanie, R.N., Chief Nursing Officer, Redmond Regional Medical Center, Rome, GA, p. A159
JONES, Stephen K, M.D., Vice President Medical Staff Affairs, St. Rose Dominican Hospitals – Rose De Lima Campus, Henderson, NV, p. A394

JONES, Steven K, M.D., Medical Director, Advocate Eureka Hospital, Eureka, IL, p. A182
JONES, Theresa L., Manager Human Resources, St. Luke Community Healthcare, Ronan, MT, p. A379
JONES, Tim, Chief Executive Officer, Heart Of Texas Memorial Hospital, Brady, TX, p. A589
JONES, Timothy P., Chief Operating Officer, Concord Hospital, Concord, NH, p. A399
JONES, Tom, Chief Information Officer, Fitzgibbon Hospital, Marshall, MO, p. A365
JONES, Tracey, Director Human Resources, Jackson Park Hospital And Medical Center, Chicago, IL, p. A177
JONES, Traci
- Chief Financial Officer, Usa Children'S And Women'S Hospital, Mobile, AL, p. A20
- Chief Financial Officer, Usa Health University Hospital, Mobile, AL, p. A21

JONES, Tracie, Director Information Services, Missouri Baptist Medical Center, Saint Louis, MO, p. A369
JONES, Vera A., Chief Operating Officer, Copley Hospital, Morrisville, VT, p. A654
JONES, Vernita, Site Manager, Phs Santa Fe Indian Hospital, Santa Fe, NM, p. A420
JONES, Vickie, Interim Chief Executive Officer, Highland–Clarksburg Hospital, Clarksburg, WV, p. A684
JONES, Wendy, Interim Chief Financial Officer, Northern Light Blue Hill Hospital, Blue Hill, ME, p. A282
JONES, William, M.D., Chief Medical Officer, City Hospital At White Rock, Dallas, TX, p. A596
JONES, William G., M.D., Chief Medical Officer, Baylor Scott & White Medical Center – Sunnyvale, Sunnyvale, TX, p. A639
JONES, Yameeka, Chief Executive Officer, Select Specialty Hospital – San Diego, San Diego, CA, p. A84
JONES, Yvette A, Health Information Management Director, Putnam Community Medical Center, Palatka, FL, p. A135
JONGSMA, Michael, R.N., Chief Nursing Officer, Providence Little Company Of Mary Medical Center – Torrance, Torrance, CA, p. A92
JONTZ, Doug, Senior Vice President Human Resources, Mercy Medical Center – Cedar Rapids, Cedar Rapids, IA, p. A218
JORDAN, Amy, Chief Nursing Officer/Vice President of Nursing, Adventhealth Gordon, Calhoun, GA, p. A149
JORDAN, Andrew, M.D., Chief of Staff, Vanderbilt Wilson County Hospital, Lebanon, TN, p. A573
JORDAN, Eric, Chief Executive Officer, Jasper General Hospital, Bay Springs, MS, p. A344
JORDAN, Gary W., Chief Executive Officer, Cherokee Regional Medical Center, Cherokee, IA, p. A219
JORDAN, Heather, Director Human Resources, Chi St. Luke'S Health Memorial Livingston, Livingston, TX, p. A621
JORDAN, Ken, Chief Financial Officer, Fountain Valley Regional Hospital And Medical Center, Fountain Valley, CA, p. A58
JORDAN, Manley, M.D., Chief Medical Officer, Lake Charles Memorial Hospital, Lake Charles, LA, p. A272
JORDAN, Marie Kim, R.N., Senior Vice President and Chief Nursing Officer, Lehigh Valley Hospital, Allentown, PA, p. A519
JORDAN, Patrick, Chief Operating Officer, Dartmouth–Hitchcock Medical Center, Lebanon, NH, p. A400
JORDAN, Quincy, M.D., Chief of Staff, Flint River Community Hospital, Montezuma, GA, p. A157
JORDAN, Rhonda R, Chief Human Resources Officer, Virtua Marlton, Marlton, NJ, p. A408
JORDAN, Terry, M.D., Chief of Staff, Alliance Health Center, Meridian, MS, p. A351
JORDAN, Traci S., MS, R.N., Chief Nursing Officer, Ochsner Lsu Health Shreveport – Monroe Medical Center, Monroe, LA, p. A274
JORDEN BEST, Rosemary, Director Human Resources, Tyrone Hospital, Tyrone, PA, p. A542
JORDEN–ELLIS, Danielle, Director, Bon Secours Baltimore Health System, Baltimore, MD, p. A286
JORE, Bernie, Chief Nursing Officer, Ascension St. Mary'S Of Michigan, Saginaw, MI, p. A321
JORGENSEN, Jacob, Chief Information Officer, Floyd Valley Healthcare, Le Mars, IA, p. A225
JORGENSEN, Steven C., Chief Executive Officer, St. Mary'S Regional Medical Center, Lewiston, ME, p. A283
JOSEPH, Heather, Chief Executive Officer, Cedar Ridge Hospital, Oklahoma City, OK, p. A503
JOSEPH, James, M.D., President Medical Staff, Geisinger–Bloomsburg Hospital, Bloomsburg, PA, p. A521
JOSEPH, Jason, Vice President, Information Services, Spectrum Health – Butterworth Hospital, Grand Rapids, MI, p. A313
JOSEPH–TAYLOR, Terri, Chief Human Resource Manager, Ochsner Medical Center – North Shore, Slidell, LA, p. A279
JOSEPHSON, Louis, President and Chief Executive Officer, Brattleboro Retreat, Brattleboro, VT, p. A654
JOSHI, Maulik, Executive Vice President, Integrated Care Delivery and Chief Operating Officer, Anne Arundel Medical Center, Annapolis, MD, p. A286
JOSHI, Nirmal, M.D., Senior Vice President Medical Affairs and Chief Medical Officer, Upmc Pinnacle Harrisburg, Harrisburg, PA, p. A527
JOSLIN, Charlie, M.D., Chief of Staff, Ellinwood District Hospital, Ellinwood, KS, p. A234
JOSLYN, E Allen, M.D., Chief Medical Officer, Centra Bedford Memorial Hospital, Bedford, VA, p. A656
JOSLYN, J Scott, Senior Vice President and Chief Information Officer, Memorialcare, Saddleback Memorial Medical Center, Laguna Hills, CA, p. A63
JOUD, Mohammad A, M.D., Chief of Staff, Bayfront Health Brooksville, Brooksville, FL, p. A119
JOUDEH, Jalal, M.D.
- Chief Medical Officer, Specialty Rehabilitation Hospital Of Coushatta, Coushatta, LA, p. A266
- Chief of Staff, Dequincy Memorial Hospital, Dequincy, LA, p. A267

JOURDEN, Marti, FACHE, Chief Quality Officer, Ssm Health St. Anthony Hospital – Oklahoma City, Oklahoma City, OK, p. A505
JOY, Michelle L, FACHE, Chief Operating Officer, Carson Tahoe Health, Carson City, NV, p. A393
JOY, Michelle L., Chief Executive Officer, Carson Tahoe Continuing Care Hospital, Carson City, NV, p. A393
JOY, Mike, Administrator, Finance, Ascension Via Christi Hospital, Pittsburg, KS, p. A244
JOY, Roland Eugene, Vice President and Chief Nursing Officer, Adventhealth Hendersonville, Hendersonville, NC, p. A456
JOY, Susan, Chief Nursing Officer, Hillside Rehabilitation Hospital, Warren, OH, p. A493
JOYAL, Shirley, Director Information Systems, Regional Medical Center Of San Jose, San Jose, CA, p. A86
JOYCE, Allyson, Vice President Human Resources, Mclaren Caro Region, Caro, MI, p. A308
JOYCE, Maria, Chief Financial Officer, National Institutes Of Health Clinical Center, Bethesda, MD, p. A289
JOYCE, William F., D.O., Chief of Staff, Bates County Memorial Hospital, Butler, MO, p. A357
JOYNER, Jeff, President, Aurelia Osborn Fox Memorial Hospital, Oneonta, NY, p. A440
JOYNER, Ken, Vice President of Employee Services, Aurora Medical Center – Bay Area, Marinette, WI, p. A699
JOYNER, Thomas, Chief Financial Officer, Lakeside Behavioral Health System, Memphis, TN, p. A575
JUAREZ, Edward, M.D., Chief Medical Officer, Kindred Hospital El Paso, El Paso, TX, p. A602
JUAREZ, Elizabeth, M.D., Chief Medical Officer, Harlingen Medical Center, Harlingen, TX, p. A609
JUAREZ, Rose, Chief Civilian Personnel Branch, Brooke Army Medical Center, Fort Sam Houston, TX, p. A604
JUBAS, John, Vice President Finance, The Children'S Institute Of Pittsburgh, Pittsburgh, PA, p. A537
JUCHNOWICZ, Jean E, Director Human Resources, Merit Health Natchez, Natchez, MS, p. A352
JUDD, Martin H., Regional President and Chief Executive Officer, Amita Health Saints Mary & Elizabeth Medical Center, Chicago, IL, p. A176
JUDD, Russell V., Chief Executive Officer, Kern Medical Center, Bakersfield, CA, p. A52
JUDLIN, Karen Ann, Director Human Resources, St. Charles Parish Hospital, Luling, LA, p. A272
JUDYCKI–CREPEAULT, Christine, Chief Financial Officer, Adcare Hospital Of Worcester, Worcester, MA, p. A305
JUHL, Valerie, Director of Health, Madelia Community Hospital, Madelia, MN, p. A334
JULE, Janet, Chief Nurse Executive, Kaiser Permanente Antioch Medical Center, Antioch, CA, p. A50
JULIAN, Bell, Associate Executive Director and Chief Financial Officer, James Cancer Hospital And Solove Research Institute, Columbus, OH, p. A479
JULIAN, Steve, President, Sentara Obici Hospital, Suffolk, VA, p. A668
JULIAN, Steve, M.D., Vice President Medical Affairs, Sentara Obici Hospital, Suffolk, VA, p. A668
JULIANA, Rich, Director Human Resources, Silver Hill Hospital, New Canaan, CT, p. A109
JUMP, Beth, Chief Information Officer, Logansport Memorial Hospital, Logansport, IN, p. A210
JUMPING EAGLE, Sara, Clinical Director, Standing Rock Service Unit, Fort Yates Hospital, Indian Health Service, Dhhs, Fort Yates, ND, p. A467
JUNEAU, Cindy K, Chief Nursing Officer, Manger Quality and Risk, Avoyelles Hospital, Marksville, LA, p. A273
JUNEAU, James B, Chief Financial Officer, Opelousas General Health System, Opelousas, LA, p. A276
JUNEAU, Tina Louise, Director Human Resources, Bunkie General Hospital, Bunkie, LA, p. A265
JUNG, Darra, Director of Nursing, Union General Hospital, Farmerville, LA, p. A267
JUNGELS, Trisha, R.N., Chief Nursing Officer and Vice President Clinical Services, Jamestown Regional Medical Center, Jamestown, ND, p. A468
JUNGWIRTH, Scott, Chief Human Resources Officer, Providence Alaska Medical Center, Anchorage, AK, p. A25
JUNIS, Jennifer, President, Osf St. Mary Medical Center, Galesburg, IL, p. A183
JUNKINS, Curt M., Chief Executive Officer, Navarro Regional Hospital, Corsicana, TX, p. A594
JUNO, Russell, M.D., Chief of Staff, St. Mark'S Medical Center, La Grange, TX, p. A619
JURCZYK, John A., Senior Vice President and President, St. Joseph Hospital, Nashua, NH, p. A401
JURGENS, Chad, Chief Executive Officer, Jefferson Community Health And Life, Fairbury, NE, p. A384
JURIS, Susan V., President, University Hospitals Ahuja Medical Center, Beachwood, OH, p. A473
JURKUS, Patti
- Director Human Resources, Carilion New River Valley Medical Center, Christiansburg, VA, p. A658
- Vice President and Chief Executive Officer, Centra Bedford Memorial Hospital, Bedford, VA, p. A656

JURY, Tina M., MSN, Chief Nursing Officer, Anmed Health Medical Center, Anderson, SC, p. A549
JUST, Lisa, President, Aurora Medical Center Kenosha, Kenosha, WI, p. A697
JUST, Paula
- Chief Human Resources Officer, Health First Cape Canaveral Hospital, Cocoa Beach, FL, p. A120
- Chief Human Resources Officer, Health First Holmes Regional Medical Center, Melbourne, FL, p. A129
- Chief Human Resources Officer, Health First Palm Bay Hospital, Palm Bay, FL, p. A135
- Chief Human Resources Officer, Health First Viera Hospital, Melbourne, FL, p. A129

JUSTICE, Jay D.
- Chief Human Resource Officer, Adena Medical Center, Chillicothe, OH, p. A475
- Chief Human Resources Officer, Adena Pike Medical Center, Waverly, OH, p. A493

JUSTICE, Kansas, Senior Vice President and Chief Operating Officer, Pikeville Medical Center, Pikeville, KY, p. A259
JUSTICE, Kim, Vice President Planning and Operations, Atlantic General Hospital, Berlin, MD, p. A288
JUSTIN, Patrick, Chief Financial Officer, United Hospital District, Blue Earth, MN, p. A328
JUSTIN–TANNER, Karen, R.N., Chief Nursing Officer, Fairbanks Memorial Hospital, Fairbanks, AK, p. A26
JUSTUS, Jason, Vice President Finance and Chief Financial Officer, Pomerene Hospital, Millersburg, OH, p. A488
JUTILA, Kathy, M.D., Chief of Staff, Wheatland Memorial Healthcare, Harlowton, MT, p. A377
JYRKAS, Wade A, Director Computer Information Systems, Lake Region Healthcare, Fergus Falls, MN, p. A332

K

KABERLINE, Gene, Chief Financial Officer, Susan B. Allen Memorial Hospital, El Dorado, KS, p. A234
KABITZKE–GROTH, Terry, R.N., Chief Nursing Officer, Aurora Medical Center In Washington County, Hartford, WI, p. A697
KACHIGION, Claudia, M.D., Medical Director, Alton Mental Health Center, Alton, IL, p. A173
KADDOURI, Sami, M.D., Medical Director, Cornerstone Of Medical Arts Center Hospital, Fresh Meadows, NY, p. A428
KADIVAR, Aryan, M.D., Chief Medical Officer, Southwestern Medical Center, Lawton, OK, p. A501
KAFKA, Rich, M.D., Chief Medical Officer, Avera Gregory Hospital, Gregory, SD, p. A561
KAHL, Larry, Chief Operating Officer, Mid–Columbia Medical Center, The Dalles, OR, p. A518
KAHL, Vicky, Director Human Resources, Valley Regional Medical Center, Brownsville, TX, p. A590
KAHLE, Russ, Chief Information Officer, Logan County Hospital, Oakley, KS, p. A242
KAHLE, Ty
- Assistant Vice President Human Resources, Methodist Hospital Union County, Morganfield, KY, p. A258
- Vice President Human Resources, Methodist Hospital, Henderson, KY, p. A253

KAHLER, John G., M.D., Radiologist, Bryan W. Whitfield Memorial Hospital, Demopolis, AL, p. A17

KAHLY–MCMAHON, Heidi
Interim Vice President Human Resources, Genesis Medical Center, Davenport, Davenport, IA, p. A220
Vice President Human Resources, Genesis Medical Center, Silvis, Silvis, IL, p. A196

KAHN, Jalil, M.D., Chief of Staff, Atrium Medical Center Of Corinth, Corinth, TX, p. A594

KAHN, Maureen A., President and Chief Executive Officer, Blessing Hospital, Quincy, IL, p. A194

KAHO, Clint
President, Baptist Health La Grange, La Grange, KY, p. A254
Vice President, Baptist Health Louisville, Louisville, KY, p. A256

KAHRS, Amy, Director of Finance, Franklin County Memorial Hospital, Franklin, NE, p. A384

KAINO, Linda, Chief Nursing Officer, Ocean Beach Hospital, Ilwaco, WA, p. A674

KAISER, Brenda, Director Human Resources, University Of Kansas Health System Great Bend Campus, Great Bend, KS, p. A235

KAISER, James, Site Director Information Technology, Upper Valley Medical Center, Troy, OH, p. A492

KAISER, Janet, R.N., Chief Nursing Officer, Kansas Medical Center, Andover, KS, p. A232

KAISER, Ken, Coordinator Information Systems, Grant Regional Health Center, Lancaster, WI, p. A698

KAISER, Russell, Interim Chief Executive Officer and Chief Nursing Officer, The Colony Er Hospital, The Colony, TX, p. A640

KAJIWARA, Gary K, President and Chief Executive Officer, Kuakini Medical Center, Honolulu, HI, p. A164

KAJIWARA, Gary K., President and Chief Executive Officer, Kuakini Medical Center, Honolulu, HI, p. A164

KAKAVAS, Connie, Chief Human Resources Officer, Summit Healthcare Regional Medical Center, Show Low, AZ, p. A36

KAKUDA, James, M.D., Chief of Staff, Pali Momi Medical Center, Aiea, HI, p. A164

KALAFUS, Lisa, MSN, R.N., Chief Nursing Officer, Gaylord Hospital, Wallingford, CT, p. A111

KALAJAINEN, Kimberly
Vice President Operations and Chief Information Officer, Lawrence + Memorial Hospital, New London, CT, p. A110
Vice President, Operations and Information Technology, Chief Information Officer, Westerly Hospital, Westerly, RI, p. A548

KALANIHUIA, Janice, President, Molokai General Hospital, Kaunakakai, HI, p. A166

KALAR, Cathy, Chief Financial Officer, Broaddus Hospital, Philippi, WV, p. A690

KALAVAR, Jagadeesh S, M.D., Chief of Staff, Michael E. Debakey Veterans Affairs Medical Center, Houston, TX, p. A613

KALCHIK, Kevin, Chief Financial Officer, War Memorial Hospital, Sault Sainte Marie, MI, p. A322

KALE, Debra
Director Human Resources, Atrium Health Kings Mountain, Kings Mountain, NC, p. A457
Vice President Human Resources, Atrium Health Cleveland, Shelby, NC, p. A462

KALEEL, Reza
Chief Executive Officer, Kadlec Regional Medical Center, Richland, WA, p. A677
Executive Vice President and Chief Operating Officer, St. Mary'S Hospital And Medical Center, Grand Junction, CO, p. A101

KALINA, Andrea, Vice President External Affairs and Chief Human Resources Officer, St. Clair Hospital, Pittsburgh, PA, p. A537

KALINSKI, Cami, Director Financial Services, Frances Mahon Deaconess Hospital, Glasgow, MT, p. A376

KALKA, Gina, R.N., Chief Nursing Officer, Pecos County Memorial Hospital, Fort Stockton, TX, p. A604

KALKOWSKI, Kelly, Chief Executive Officer, Niobrara Valley Hospital, Lynch, NE, p. A387

KALKUT, Gary, M.D., Senior Vice President and Chief Medical Officer, Brookdale Hospital Medical Center, New York, NY, p. A432

KALL, Greg, Chief Information Officer, Summa Health System, Akron, OH, p. A471

KALLEVIG, Daryl, Chief Information Officer, Riverwood Healthcare Center, Aitkin, MN, p. A327

KALMAN, Jill, Executive Director, Brookdale Hospital Medical Center, New York, NY, p. A432

KALSMAN, Stephen L., Area Finance Officer, Kaiser Permanente San Jose Medical Center, San Jose, CA, p. A86

KALTENBACH, Gretchen, R.N., Chief Operating Officer, Genesis Behavioral Hospital, Breaux Bridge, LA, p. A265

KALUA, Patricia, Chief Nurse Executive, Kona Community Hospital, Kealakekua, HI, p. A166

KAMBER, Sean, Chief Executive Officer, Medical City Weatherford, Weatherford, TX, p. A644

KAMBEROS, Peter N, Chief Operating Officer, Thorek Memorial Hospital, Chicago, IL, p. A180

KAMBEROV, Denis, M.D., Chief of Staff, De Soto Regional Health System, Mansfield, LA, p. A273

KAMBIC, Phillip M., President and Chief Executive Officer, Riverside Medical Center, Kankakee, IL, p. A187

KAMBOJ, Pradeep, M.D., Chief Medical Staff, Adventist Health – Tulare, Tulare, CA, p. A92

KAMENS, Eric, Regional Director Information Systems, Shriners Hospitals For Children–Springfield, Springfield, MA, p. A303

KAMERMAYER, Angela K, MS, Chief Nursing Officer, Integris Health Edmond, Edmond, OK, p. A499

KAMGUIA, Rebecca, Administrative Director Human Resources, Bon Secours Memorial Regional Medical Center, Mechanicsville, VA, p. A662

KAMIKAWA, Cynthia, President, North Hawaii Community Hospital, Kamuela, HI, p. A165

KAMINSKI, Gene, Vice President Human Resources and Hospitality Services, Mclaren Northern Michigan, Petoskey, MI, p. A319

KAMINSKI, Tammy
Director Human Resources, Alaska Regional Hospital, Anchorage, AK, p. A25
Vice President Human Relations, Riverside Community Hospital, Riverside, CA, p. A81

KAMINSKI, Toni, Director Human Resources, Medical Center Enterprise, Enterprise, AL, p. A17

KAMMERER, James M., Vice President Support Services, Great River Health System, West Burlington, IA, p. A231

KAMMERUD, Shawn, Manager Information Services, Osceola Medical Center, Osceola, WI, p. A703

KAMOWSKI, David, Vice President and Chief Information Officer, Temple University Hospital, Philadelphia, PA, p. A536

KAMPHUIS, Jan, Ph.D., R.N., Executive Vice President and Chief Nurse Executive, Sanford Bismarck, Bismarck, ND, p. A465

KAMPSCHNIEDER, Carol, Vice President Clinical and Regulatory Services, St. Francis Memorial Hospital, West Point, NE, p. A392

KAMPWERTH, Dennis, Director Management Information Systems, Gateway Regional Medical Center, Granite City, IL, p. A184

KAMRAN, Khurram, M.D.
Vice President Medical Affairs, Promedica Toledo Hospital, Toledo, OH, p. A492
Vice President Physician Services, Winter Haven Hospital, Winter Haven, FL, p. A144

KANAPARTI, V.R., M.D., Director Medical Services, Kalamazoo Psychiatric Hospital, Kalamazoo, MI, p. A316

KANDOW, Casey
Chief Operating Officer, Mclaren Greater Lansing, Lansing, MI, p. A316
Interim President and Chief Executive Officer, Mclaren Greater Lansing, Lansing, MI, p. A316

KANE, Addy, Chief Financial Officer, Roger Williams Medical Center, Providence, RI, p. A548

KANE, Audrey, Interim Chief Financial Officer, Prowers Medical Center, Lamar, CO, p. A103

KANE, Kelli R, Director of Finance, Barnes–Kasson County Hospital, Susquehanna, PA, p. A542

KANE, Nancy, Assistant Vice President Finance LifeBridge Health, Northwest Hospital, Randallstown, MD, p. A293

KANE, Robert E.
Chief Administrative Officer, Upmc Susquehanna Divine Providence Campus, Williamsport, PA, p. A545
Chief Executive Officer, Upmc Susquehanna Sunbury, Sunbury, PA, p. A542

KANE, Steve, Director Information Technology, Lower Bucks Hospital, Bristol, PA, p. A521

KANE, Thomas, R.N., Vice President Patient Services and Chief Nursing Officer, Munson Healthcare Manistee Hospital, Manistee, MI, p. A317

KANE, Trisha, Director Human Resources, Continuecare Hospital At Hendrick Medical Center, Abilene, TX, p. A581

KANIA, Kathy, Associate Executive Director and Chief Information Officer, Brookdale Hospital Medical Center, New York, NY, p. A432

KANNADAY, Colleen
President, Advocate Bromenn Medical Center, Normal, IL, p. A191
President, Advocate Eureka Hospital, Eureka, IL, p. A182

KANTELAS, Sandra Jean, Chief Nursing Officer, University Hospitals Elyria Medical Center, Elyria, OH, p. A482

KANTOS, Craig A., Chief Executive Officer, Coteau Des Prairies Hospital, Sisseton, SD, p. A564

KANUCH, James A
Vice President Finance, Allegheny Valley Hospital, Natrona Heights, PA, p. A533
Vice President Finance, West Penn Hospital, Pittsburgh, PA, p. A538

KANWAL, Neeraj
Interim President, Metro Region, Promedica Bay Park Hospital, Oregon, OH, p. A489
Interim President, Metro Region, Promedica Flower Hospital, Sylvania, OH, p. A491
Interim President, Metro Region, Promedica Toledo Hospital, Toledo, OH, p. A492

KAPER, Jonathan, Chief Medical Officer, Beaumont Hospital – Trenton, Trenton, MI, p. A324

KAPLAN, Alan, Chief Executive Officer, University Hospital, Madison, WI, p. A698

KAPLAN, Gary, Chairman and Chief Executive Officer, Virginia Mason Medical Center, Seattle, WA, p. A679

KAPLAN, Ronald, Chief Financial Officer, North Philadelphia Health System, Philadelphia, PA, p. A536

KAPLAN, Tamra, PharmD, Chief Operating Officer, Memorialcare, Miller Children'S & Women'S Hospital Long Beach, Long Beach, CA, p. A65

KAPLANIS, Gene, Director Information Technology, Alaska Regional Hospital, Anchorage, AK, p. A25

KAPRE, Sheela, M.D., Chief Medical Officer, San Joaquin General Hospital, French Camp, CA, p. A59

KARA, Amynah, M.D., Chief Medical Officer, Baylor Scott & White Emergency Hospital–Aubrey, Aubrey, TX, p. A584

KARADJOFF, Peter, Interim President, Henry Ford Wyandotte Hospital, Wyandotte, MI, p. A325

KARAM, Annah, Director Human Resources, San Gorgonio Memorial Hospital, Banning, CA, p. A52

KARAM, Chris, President and Chief Executive Officer, Senior Vice President Group Operations, Christus St. Frances Cabrini Hospital, Alexandria, LA, p. A262

KARAM, Christopher J, Chief Operating Officer, Saint Joseph Health System, Mishawaka, IN, p. A211

KARAM, Christopher J., President, Plymouth Medical Center, Plymouth, IN, p. A213

KARANJA, Diana, R.N., Director of Nursing, St. John Vianney Hospital, Downingtown, PA, p. A524

KARANJAI, Rajohn, M.D., Chief Medical Officer, Sidney Health Center, Sidney, MT, p. A380

KARCZ, Chrisi, Chief Nursing Officer, Van Matre Encompass Health, Rockford, IL, p. A195

KARDOW, Vivian
Chief Human Resources Officer, Memorial Hermann – Texas Medical Center, Houston, TX, p. A612
Chief Human Resources Officer, Tirr Memorial Hermann, Houston, TX, p. A614

KAREL, Thomas L, Vice President Organization and Talent Effectiveness, Mercy Health Saint Mary'S, Grand Rapids, MI, p. A313

KARG, Gary, Interim Vice President Finance, Christus St. Frances Cabrini Hospital, Alexandria, LA, p. A262

KARIM, Parvez, M.D., Chief Medical Officer, Allegiance Specialty Hospital Of Greenville, Greenville, MS, p. A347

KARL, Don
Chief Operating Officer, Las Palmas Medical Center, El Paso, TX, p. A602
Interim Chief Executive Officer, Las Palmas Medical Center, El Paso, TX, p. A602

KARL, Thomas P., President, Parkland Health Center – Farmington Community, Farmington, MO, p. A360

KARMACH, Izabela, Administrator, San Diego County Psychiatric Hospital, San Diego, CA, p. A84

KARMACH, Izabela, R.N., Administrator, San Diego County Psychiatric Hospital, San Diego, CA, p. A84

KARN, Cielette, M.D., Chief of Staff, Sagewest Health Care At Riverton, Riverton, WY, p. A712

KARNER, Diana M., R.N., MSN
Chief Nursing Executive, California Pacific Medical Center– St. Luke'S Campus, San Francisco, CA, p. A85
Chief Nursing Officer, California Pacific Medical Center, San Francisco, CA, p. A85

KARNS, Kristopher, Chief Executive Officer, Cornerstone Hospital Of Oklahoma–Shawnee, Shawnee, OK, p. A507

KARP, Bob, M.D., Chief Medical Officer, United Hospital District, Blue Earth, MN, p. A328

KARRE, Kris, Director Finance and Accounting, Unitypoint Health–Keokuk, Keokuk, IA, p. A225

KARSOS, Felicia, President and Chief Executive Officer, Hudson Regional Hospital, Secaucus, NJ, p. A412

KARSOS, Felicia, R.N., Chief Nursing Officer, Hudson Regional Hospital, Secaucus, NJ, p. A412

KARSTEN, Margo
Chief Executive Officer, Banner Fort Collins Medical Center, Fort Collins, CO, p. A100

Chief Executive Officer, Mckee Medical Center, Loveland, CO, p. A104

Chief Executive Officer, North Colorado Medical Center, Greeley, CO, p. A101

KARSTEN, Paul H, Vice President Finance and Chief Financial Officer, Pine Rest Christian Mental Health Services, Grand Rapids, MI, p. A313

KARSTETTER, James M., R.N., Vice President & Chief Nursing Officer, Western Maryland Regional Medical Center, Cumberland, MD, p. A290

KASIRYE, Yusuf, M.D., Chief of Staff, Flambeau Hospital, Park Falls, WI, p. A703

KASITZ, Todd, Vice President Finance, Newton Medical Center, Newton, KS, p. A241

KASNIC, Tracey A

Chief Nursing Officer, Confluence Health/Wenatchee Valley Hospital, Wenatchee, WA, p. A682

Senior Vice President Inpatient and Chief Nursing Officer, Confluence Health/Central Washington Hospital, Wenatchee, WA, p. A682

KASPER, Katie, Chief Clinical Officer, Uh Avon Rehabilitation Hospital, Avon, OH, p. A472

KASPER, Yobi, Chief Information Officer, Advanced Diagnostics Hospital, Houston, TX, p. A610

KASS, Andrew J A, M.D., Assistant Superintendent, Albert J. Solnit Psychiatric Center – South Campus, Middletown, CT, p. A109

KASSAB, Jerry, President and Chief Executive Officer, Aspire Health Partners, Orlando, FL, p. A134

KASSAHN, Kristine, Chief Executive Officer, Fresno Surgical Hospital, Fresno, CA, p. A59

KASSER, Michael

Chief Financial Officer, Herrin Hospital, Herrin, IL, p. A185

Vice President Chief Financial Officer and Treasurer, Memorial Hospital Of Carbondale, Carbondale, IL, p. A175

KASSIS, Charles, President, Mercy Medical Center Merced, Merced, CA, p. A71

KASSIS, Maher, M.D., Chief Medical Staff, Mercy Health – Marcum And Wallace, Irvine, KY, p. A254

KASTEN, Gina, Manager Human Resources, Aspirus Ontonagon Hospital, Inc., Ontonagon, MI, p. A319

KATEN–BAHENSKY, Donna, Director, West Palm Beach Veterans Affairs Medical Center, West Palm Beach, FL, p. A144

KATES, Josh, Information Technology Analyst, Andrew Mcfarland Mental Health Center, Springfield, IL, p. A196

KATHRINS, Richard J., President and Chief Executive Officer, Bacharach Institute For Rehabilitation, Pomona, NJ, p. A411

KATNENI, Jitendra P., M.D., Medical Director, Select Specialty Hospital–Flint, Flint, MI, p. A311

KATO, Laura

Vice President Human Resources, St. Francis Medical Center, Lynwood, CA, p. A70

Vice President of Human Resources, San Antonio Regional Hospital, Upland, CA, p. A93

KATSCHKE, R William, M.D., Medical Director, Grover C. Dils Medical Center, Caliente, NV, p. A393

KATZ, Jeffrey, M.D., Chief Medical Officer, Memorial Hermann – Texas Medical Center, Houston, TX, p. A612

KATZ, Michelle, Director Human Resources, Encompass Health Nittany Valley Rehabilitation Hospital, Pleasant Gap, PA, p. A539

KATZ, Richard, M.D., Vice President Medical Affairs, Mt. Washington Pediatric Hospital, Baltimore, MD, p. A287

KATZ, Robert, M.D., Chief of Staff, Columbus Community Hospital, Columbus, TX, p. A593

KATZ, Yair

Chief Financial Officer, Memorialcare, Long Beach Memorial Medical Center, Long Beach, CA, p. A65

Chief Financial Officer, Memorialcare, Miller Children'S & Women'S Hospital Long Beach, Long Beach, CA, p. A65

KAUFFMAN, Angie, Chief Executive Officer, South Texas Spine And Surgical Hospital, San Antonio, TX, p. A635

KAUFMAN, Cheryl

Director Health Information Management, Adventhealth Dade City, Dade City, FL, p. A121

Information Technology Technician, Coteau Des Prairies Hospital, Sisseton, SD, p. A564

KAUFMAN, Dan, Director Information Services, Paulding County Hospital, Paulding, OH, p. A489

KAUFMAN, Irvin A, M.D., Chief Medical Officer, Rady Children'S Hospital – San Diego, San Diego, CA, p. A84

KAUFMAN, Robert

Director Financial Services, Central State Hospital, Petersburg, VA, p. A664

Fiscal Officer, Hiram W. Davis Medical Center, Petersburg, VA, p. A665

KAUFMAN, Samuel, Chief Executive Officer, Henderson Hospital, Henderson, NV, p. A394

KAUFMAN, Seth, M.D., Chief Medical Officer, Northbay Medical Center, Fairfield, CA, p. A57

KAUPA, Michael, Executive Vice President and Chief Operating Officer, Park Nicollet Methodist Hospital, Saint Louis Park, MN, p. A339

KAUTZ, Peter, Chief Executive Officer, Meadowbrook Rehabilitation Hospital, Gardner, KS, p. A235

KAUTZ, Terri, Manager Human Resources, Weiser Memorial Hospital, Weiser, ID, p. A172

KAUZLARICH, Sidney A., M.D., Medical Director, Douglas County Community Mental Health Center, Omaha, NE, p. A389

KAVALIER, MaryJo, Administrator, Mercyone Cedar Falls Medical Center, Cedar Falls, IA, p. A218

KAVANAGH, Darina, R.N., MSN, Chief Nursing Officer, Good Samaritan Hospital, San Jose, CA, p. A86

KAVANAGH, Sean, Director Information Technology, Pondera Medical Center, Conrad, MT, p. A375

KAVANAUGH, Paul B., President and Chief Executive Officer, Community Care Hospital, New Orleans, LA, p. A275

KAVANAUGH, Samantha, Chief Financial Officer, Riverview Psychiatric Center, Augusta, ME, p. A281

KAVTARADZE, David, M.D., Chief of Staff, Crisp Regional Hospital, Cordele, GA, p. A151

KAY, Kirk, Chief Financial Officer, Veterans Affairs Nebraska–Western Iowa Health Care System, Omaha, NE, p. A390

KAY, Robert W, Senior Vice President and Chief Financial Officer, Memorial Medical Center, Springfield, IL, p. A196

KAY–GARCIA, Lisa, Chief Information Officer, Kearny County Hospital, Lakin, KS, p. A238

KAYE, Jessie, Chief Executive Officer, Prairie View, Newton, KS, p. A242

KAYGA, Alicia R., R.N., Chief Nursing Officer, Brownwood Regional Medical Center, Brownwood, TX, p. A590

KAYROUZ, Thomas, M.D., Chief Medical Officer, Anmed Health Medical Center, Anderson, SC, p. A549

KAYSER, Sonya J, Human Resources Officer, Avera Marshall Regional Medical Center, Marshall, MN, p. A335

KAZMIERCZAK, Sara Marie, R.N., Director of Nursing, North Valley Health Center, Warren, MN, p. A342

KAZMIERCZAK, Stanley, Controller, Amita Health Saint Joseph Hospital, Chicago, IL, p. A176

KA'AKIMAKA, Holly, Director Human Resources, Hilo Medical Center, Hilo, HI, p. A164

KEANE, Dennis M., Vice President Finance and Chief Financial Officer, St. John'S Riverside Hospital, Yonkers, NY, p. A448

KEANE, Fran, Vice President Human Resources, Centrastate Healthcare System, Freehold, NJ, p. A406

KEANE, Merry Ann, Chief Administrative Officer, Peacehealth Peace Island Medical Center, Friday Harbor, WA, p. A673

KEANE, Valerie E, FACHE, Chief Nursing Executive, Sentara Northern Virginia Medical Center, Woodbridge, VA, p. A669

KEARNEY, Elizabeth, R.N., Chief Nursing Officer, Mountain Vista Medical Center, Mesa, AZ, p. A31

KEARNEY, Karen

Vice President Inpatient Rehabilitation Services, Allied Services Rehabilitation Hospital, Scranton, PA, p. A540

Vice President Inpatient Rehabilitation Services, John Heinz Institute Of Rehabilitation Medicine, Wilkes, PA, p. A545

KEARNEY, Lynn, Vice President Nursing, Robert Wood Johnson University Hospital Somerset, Somerville, NJ, p. A412

KEARNEY, M Clark, Vice President Human Resources, Saint Mary'S Hospital, Waterbury, CT, p. A111

KEARNS, Debbie

Chief Executive Officer, Community Hospital, Oklahoma City, OK, p. A505

Chief Executive Officer, Northwest Surgical Hospital, Oklahoma City, OK, p. A504

KEASTER, Lorna, Interim Chief Nursing Officer, Hshs Holy Family Hospital In Greenville, Greenville, IL, p. A184

KEATING, Todd, Chief Financial Officer, University Of Vermont Medical Center, Burlington, VT, p. A654

KEATON, Tony, Director Information Systems, Roane General Hospital, Spencer, WV, p. A689

KECK, Paul, President and Chief Executive Officer, Lindner Center Of Hope, Mason, OH, p. A487

KEDDINGTON, Richard, Chief Executive Officer, Watertown Regional Medical Center, Watertown, WI, p. A707

KEE, Agnes, Financial Manager, Gallup Indian Medical Center, Gallup, NM, p. A418

KEE, Robert, Chief Information Officer, Brookdale Hospital Medical Center, New York, NY, p. A432

KEEF, Shaun, Chief Financial Officer, Eastern Oklahoma Medical Center, Poteau, OK, p. A506

KEEFE, Eileen, Chief Nursing Officer, Parkland Medical Center, Derry, NH, p. A399

KEEFER, Katrina, Chief Executive Officer, Augusta University Medical Center, Augusta, GA, p. A147

KEEFER, Russ, Chief Human Resources Officer, Trios Health, Kennewick, WA, p. A674

KEEGAN, Justin, Director Support Services, Avera Gregory Hospital, Gregory, SD, p. A561

KEEL, Barry L., Administrator, North Mississippi Medical Center–West Point, West Point, MS, p. A355

KEEL, Patricia, Senior Vice President and Chief Financial Officer, St. Jude Children'S Research Hospital, Memphis, TN, p. A575

KEELE, Paula

Manager Information Systems, Osf Heart Of Mary Medical Center, Urbana, IL, p. A197

Manager Information Systems, Osf Sacred Heart Medical Center, Danville, IL, p. A180

KEELE, Ryan, Chief Executive Officer, Northern Utah Rehabilitation Hospital, South Ogden, UT, p. A653

KEELER, Dave, Chief Financial Officer, Pipestone County Medical Center Avera, Pipestone, MN, p. A338

KEELER, Jason, Executive Vice President and Chief Operating Officer, University Of Chicago Medical Center, Chicago, IL, p. A180

KEELER, Jean M., President and Chief Executive Officer, Grand View Health, Sellersville, PA, p. A541

KEELER, Karl, President, Mercyone Des Moines Medical Center, Des Moines, IA, p. A221

KEELEY, Katherine, M.D., Chief of Staff, Sunrise Hospital And Medical Center, Las Vegas, NV, p. A396

KEELINE, Leah, Clinical Informatics Specialist, Catalina Island Medical Center, Avalon, CA, p. A51

KEELING, Kathy, Director of Nursing, Rehabilitation Hospital Of Rhode Island, North Smithfield, RI, p. A547

KEELING, Kevin, Chief Financial Officer, St. Lucie Medical Center, Port St Lucie, FL, p. A137

KEELING, Michele A., Vice President and Administrator, Saint Francis Hospital Muskogee, Muskogee, OK, p. A502

KEELING, Terri, Vice President Information Systems, Upmc Mckeesport, Mckeesport, PA, p. A531

KEEN, Kris, Chief Information Officer, Cameron Memorial Community Hospital, Angola, IN, p. A199

KEEN, Michael, Senior Vice President and Chief Financial Officer, Grand View Health, Sellersville, PA, p. A541

KEEN, Scott R., Chief Executive Officer, Honorhealth Rehabilitation Hospital, Scottsdale, AZ, p. A35

KEENAN, Bob, Chief Medical Officer, H. Lee Moffitt Cancer Center And Research Institute, Tampa, FL, p. A141

KEENAN, Kevin, M.D., Physician Advisor, East Cooper Medical Center, Mount Pleasant, SC, p. A555

KEENAN, Nancy C, R.N., Senior Vice President and Chief Nursing Officer, Houston Methodist Willowbrook Hospital, Houston, TX, p. A612

KEENAN, Richard, Senior Vice President Finance and Chief Financial Officer, Valley Hospital, Ridgewood, NJ, p. A412

KEENE, Emilie, FACHE, Interim Chief Operating Officer, Prisma Health Baptist Parkridge Hospital, Columbia, SC, p. A551

KEENE, Kimberly, Chief Executive Officer, St. Bernard Parish Hospital, Chalmette, LA, p. A265

KEENER, Vicki, Administrative Assistant and Director Human Resources, Little River Memorial Hospital, Ashdown, AR, p. A39

KEEPSEAGLE, Joelle, Director of Nursing, Standing Rock Service Unit, Fort Yates Hospital, Indian Health Service, Dhhs, Fort Yates, ND, p. A467

KEESBURY, Drew

Chief Financial Officer, La Porte Hospital, La Porte, IN, p. A209

Chief Financial Officer, Starke Hospital, Knox, IN, p. A208

KEEVER, Jerry, Administrator, Sharkey–Issaquena Community Hospital, Rolling Fork, MS, p. A354

KEFALAS, George, Chief Medical Officer, Aultman Specialty Hospital, Canton, OH, p. A474

KEGLEY, Carl J, System Director Information Technology, Fairbanks Memorial Hospital, Fairbanks, AK, p. A26

KEGLEY, Glen, Chief Operating Officer, Hutchinson Health, Hutchinson, MN, p. A333

KEGLEY, Shawn, Director Information Services, Research Medical Center, Kansas City, MO, p. A362

KEHIAYAN, Nancy, Director of Nursing, Colorado Mental Health Institute At Fort Logan, Denver, CO, p. A98

KEHRBERG, Mark W, M.D.

Chief Medical Officer, Ascension Calumet Hospital, Chilton, WI, p. A693

Senior Vice President and Chief Medical Officer, Ascension Northeast Wisconsin Mercy Hospital, Oshkosh, WI, p. A703

KEHUS, Frank, Associate Director for Operations, Marion Veterans Affairs Medical Center, Marion, IL, p. A188

KEIL, James, M.D., Chief Medical Officer, Niobrara Valley Hospital, Lynch, NE, p. A387

KEIM, Thomas, Chief Executive Officer, Ste. Genevieve County Memorial Hospital, Ste Genevieve, MO, p. A372

KEIRNS, Melody, Manager Human Resources, F. W. Huston Medical Center, Winchester, KS, p. A247
KEISER, Trish, Comptroller, Avera Gregory Hospital, Gregory, SD, p. A561
KEISTER, Catharine L, Chief Nursing Officer, Upmc Susquehanna Sunbury, Sunbury, PA, p. A542
KEITH, Bridgette, Director Human Resources, Healthsouth Northern Kentucky Rehabilitation Hospital, Edgewood, KY, p. A251
KEITH, Christopher, Chief Executive Officer, Select Specialty Hospital–Wichita, Wichita, KS, p. A248
KEITH, Darlene, Chief Information Systems, Alleghany Memorial Hospital, Sparta, NC, p. A462
KEITH, David N., President and Chief Executive Officer, Mcalester Regional Health Center, Mcalester, OK, p. A502
KEITH, Jeannie, Director Patient Care Services and Nurse Executive, Shriners Hospitals For Children–Houston, Houston, TX, p. A613
KEITH, Lorraine
Chief Nursing Officer, St. Vincent'S Medical Center Riverside, Jacksonville, FL, p. A126
Chief Nursing Officer, St. Vincent'S Medical Center Southside, Jacksonville, FL, p. A126
KELBAUGH, Brian, Chief Financial Officer, Summersville Regional Medical Center, Summersville, WV, p. A689
KELBLY, Kevin, Senior Vice President Finance and Corporate Fiscal Affairs, Carroll Hospital Center, Westminster, MD, p. A293
KELL, Douglas B, Chief Financial Officer, Scottsdale Liberty Hospital, Scottsdale, AZ, p. A36
KELLAR, Brian, Chief Executive Officer, Banner Casa Grande Medical Center, Casa Grande, AZ, p. A28
KELLAR, Mark, R.N., Interim Chief Nursing Officer, Our Lady Of The Angels Hospital, Bogalusa, LA, p. A264
KELLAR, Richard A., President, Aurora West Allis Medical Center, West Allis, WI, p. A708
KELLEHER, Cynthia, President and Chief Executive Officer, University Of Maryland Rehabilitation & Orthopaedic Institute, Baltimore, MD, p. A288
KELLEHER, Mary, Vice President Human Resources, Holyoke Medical Center, Holyoke, MA, p. A299
KELLEHER, Mary Lou, R.N., MSN, Vice President, Nursing, Franciscan Children'S, Brighton, MA, p. A296
KELLEHER, Michael, Chief Medical Officer, Ann & Robert H. Lurie Children'S Hospital Of Chicago, Chicago, IL, p. A176
KELLEHER, William H, Director, Veterans Affairs Boston Healthcare System Brockton Division, Brockton, MA, p. A297
KELLENBARGER, Lance, Site Director Information Systems, St. Catherine Hospital, Garden City, KS, p. A235
KELLER, Allen, Director Human Resources, Sumner Regional Medical Center, Wellington, KS, p. A247
KELLER, Anita M., R.N., MSN, Chief Nursing Officer, Johnson Memorial Hospital, Franklin, IN, p. A204
KELLER, Ann, Supervisor Health Information Management, Walton Rehabilitation Hospital, Augusta, GA, p. A148
KELLER, Christine, Chief Administrative Officer, Bluffton Hospital, Bluffton, OH, p. A473
KELLER, Diane R., Chief Executive Officer, Memorial Community Health, Aurora, NE, p. A382
KELLER, Gretchen, Director Health Information, Neosho Memorial Regional Medical Center, Chanute, KS, p. A233
KELLER, James
Chief Information Officer, Ascension Borgess–Lee Hospital, Dowagiac, MI, p. A310
Director Human Resources, Nea Baptist Memorial Hospital, Jonesboro, AR, p. A44
KELLER, James, M.D., Vice President, Medical Management, Advocate Trinity Hospital, Chicago, IL, p. A176
KELLER, Jill, R.N., MSN, Vice President for Nursing Services, Quality and Risk Management, Waynesboro Hospital, Waynesboro, PA, p. A543
KELLER, Jim, Site Director Information Services, Mercy Health Saint Mary'S, Grand Rapids, MI, p. A313
KELLER, Justin, Chief Information Officer, Murray County Medical Center, Slayton, MN, p. A340
KELLER, Ken, President and Chief Executive Officer, Bakersfield Memorial Hospital, Bakersfield, CA, p. A52
KELLER, Marsha, Director Human Resources, Upmc Kane, Kane, PA, p. A528
KELLER, Maryalice, Vice President Brand and Talent Management, Unity Hospital, Rochester, NY, p. A443
KELLER, Patricia, MSN, R.N., Nurse Administrator, Mayo Clinic Health System – Northland In Barron, Barron, WI, p. A692
KELLER, Ruey, Acting Chief Information Officer, Va San Diego Healthcare System, San Diego, CA, p. A84
KELLER, Stewart, M.D., Medical Director, Mesa Springs, Fort Worth, TX, p. A605
KELLER, Thomas W., President and Chief Executive Officer, Ozarks Medical Center, West Plains, MO, p. A373
KELLER, Wendy, Director Health Information Management, Atrium Medical Center Of Corinth, Corinth, TX, p. A594
KELLERMAN, Laurie, MSN, Chief Clinical Officer, Marshall Browning Hospital, Du Quoin, IL, p. A181
KELLERMAN, Scott, Chief Financial Officer, Ely–Bloomenson Community Hospital, Ely, MN, p. A331
KELLEY, Brent, Director Information Technology, Nor–Lea Hospital District, Lovington, NM, p. A419
KELLEY, Danny, Administrative Director, Health Information Technology, Norman Regional Health System, Norman, OK, p. A503
KELLEY, Jalinda, Secretary of Interior Services, Chickasaw Nation Medical Center, Ada, OK, p. A496
KELLEY, James, Chief Human Resources Officer, Desert Regional Medical Center, Palm Springs, CA, p. A76
KELLEY, Janice, Chief Financial Officer, Marshall County Hospital, Benton, KY, p. A249
KELLEY, Julie, M.D., Chief of Staff, Red Bud Regional Hospital, Red Bud, IL, p. A194
KELLEY, Lewis, Chief Operating Officer, Union General Hospital, Blairsville, GA, p. A148
KELLEY, Mary, Director Human Resources, The Outer Banks Hospital, Nags Head, NC, p. A459
KELLEY, Neal, Vice President and Chief Operating Officer, Ascension Seton Hays, Kyle, TX, p. A618
KELLEY, Patti, MSN, R.N., Vice President, Nursing and Chief Nursing Officer, Ssm Health Saint Louis University Hospital, Saint Louis, MO, p. A370
KELLEY, Randall
President, Spectrum Health Gerber Memorial, Fremont, MI, p. A312
President, Spectrum Health Ludington Hospital, Ludington, MI, p. A317
KELLEY, Sarah Jo, Executive Director of Human Resources and Support Services, Ste. Genevieve County Memorial Hospital, Ste Genevieve, MO, p. A372
KELLEY, Sharon, Chief Financial Officer, Clifton Springs Hospital And Clinic, Clifton Springs, NY, p. A426
KELLEY, Steven L., President and Chief Executive Officer, Ellenville Regional Hospital, Ellenville, NY, p. A427
KELLEY, Sue, Chief Financial Officer, Cordell Memorial Hospital, Cordell, OK, p. A498
KELLEY, Thomas J., Executive Vice President and Chief Financial Officer, Froedtert South – Kenosha Medical Center, Kenosha, WI, p. A697
KELLEY, Vicky, Chief Financial Officer, Dequincy Memorial Hospital, Dequincy, LA, p. A267
KELLEY, Warren, Chief Information Officer, Reynolds Memorial Hospital, Glen Dale, WV, p. A685
KELLIHER, Brandon, Chief Information Officer, Great Plains Health, North Platte, NE, p. A388
KELLOGG, Benjamin, M.D., Chief of Staff, Rhea Medical Center, Dayton, TN, p. A569
KELLOGG, Jason, M.D., Chief of Staff, Newport Bay Hospital, Newport Beach, CA, p. A74
KELLOGG, Susan, Administrator Patient Care Services, Carthage Area Hospital, Carthage, NY, p. A425
KELLS, Anne, Interim Chief Financial Officer, Appleton Area Health Services, Appleton, MN, p. A327
KELLUM, Craig, Director Management Information Systems, Cape Fear Valley – Bladen County Hospital, Elizabethtown, NC, p. A454
KELLY, Brian
Acting Chief Fiscal Service, San Francisco Va Medical Center, San Francisco, CA, p. A85
Vice President Finance, Advocate South Suburban Hospital, Hazel Crest, IL, p. A185
KELLY, Brian, M.D., Vice President Medical Affairs and Medical Director, Sturdy Memorial Hospital, Attleboro, MA, p. A294
KELLY, Brian E., M.D., President Medical Staff, Saint Elizabeth'S Medical Center, Wabasha, MN, p. A342
KELLY, Charlene, Chief Nursing Officer, Kane County Hospital, Kanab, UT, p. A648
KELLY, Charles, D.O., Vice President Medical Affairs and Chief Medical Officer, Henry Ford Macomb Hospitals, Clinton Township, MI, p. A309
KELLY, Colan, Chief Financial Officer, Southeastern Kentucky Medical Center, Pineville, KY, p. A259
KELLY, Dan, R.N., Chief Nursing Officer, Memorial Hermann Memorial City Medical Center, Houston, TX, p. A613
KELLY, Daniel R., Chief Executive Officer, Mckenzie County Healthcare System, Watford City, ND, p. A470
KELLY, Diane, Chief Operating Officer, Greenwich Hospital, Greenwich, CT, p. A108
KELLY, Edward, Chief Executive Officer and President, Milford Regional Medical Center, Milford, MA, p. A301
KELLY, James J., Senior Vice President and Chief Financial Officer, Uf Health Shands Hospital, Gainesville, FL, p. A124
KELLY, James P., Administrator, Community Behavioral Health Hospital – Annandale, Annandale, MN, p. A327
KELLY, Jennifer, Chief Executive Officer, Perimeter Behavioral Hospital Of West Memphis, West Memphis, AR, p. A49
KELLY, Jim, Chief Operating Officer, Nantucket Cottage Hospital, Nantucket, MA, p. A301
KELLY, John, R.N., Chief Nursing Officer and Chief Operating Officer, Umass Memorial–Marlborough Hospital, Marlborough, MA, p. A300
KELLY, Kecia, R.N., Chief Nurse Executive, Kaiser Permanente Medical Center, Honolulu, HI, p. A164
KELLY, Laurence E., President and Chief Executive Officer, Nathan Littauer Hospital And Nursing Home, Gloversville, NY, p. A428
KELLY, Leo, Vice President Medical Management, Advocate Lutheran General Hospital, Park Ridge, IL, p. A192
KELLY, Mark
Administrator, Regional One Health Extended Care Hospital, Memphis, TN, p. A575
Vice President Finance, St. Francis Medical Center, Trenton, NJ, p. A413
KELLY, Maura, Vice President Fiscal Services, Pen Bay Medical Center, Rockport, ME, p. A285
KELLY, Melissa, Chief Executive Officer and Chief Financial Officer, Pender Community Hospital, Pender, NE, p. A391
KELLY, Michael
Vice President Operations, Missouri Baptist Medical Center, Saint Louis, MO, p. A369
Vice President, Christian Hospital, Saint Louis, MO, p. A369
KELLY, Patrick J., Director, Minneapolis Veterans Affairs Health Care System, Minneapolis, MN, p. A336
KELLY, Peter, President, Putnam Hospital Center, Carmel, NY, p. A425
KELLY, Ray, R.N., MSN, Vice President Chief Nursing Officer, Texas Health Harris Methodist Hospital Hurst–Euless–Bedford, Bedford, TX, p. A588
KELLY, Robert E, President, Brookdale Hospital Medical Center, New York, NY, p. A432
KELLY, Shannon, Director Human Resources, Arbor Health, Morton Hospital, Morton, WA, p. A675
KELLY, Stephen, M.D., Chief Medical Officer, Ssm Health St. Mary'S Hospital – St. Louis, Saint Louis, MO, p. A370
KELLY, Steve, Interim Chief Executive Officer, Austin Oaks Hospital, Austin, TX, p. A585
KELLY, Teresa M, MSN, R.N., Chief Nursing Officer, Chestnut Hill Hospital, Philadelphia, PA, p. A534
KELLY, Virginia, Chief Financial Officer, Eastside Psychiatric Hospital, Tallahassee, FL, p. A140
KELMAN, Gregory, M.D., Area Medical Director, Kaiser Permanente Woodland Hills Medical Center, Los Angeles, CA, p. A67
KELTNER, Burt, Administrator, Prairie Community Hospital, Terry, MT, p. A380
KEM, Mark, Vice President Finance and Chief Financial Officer, Chandler Regional Medical Center, Chandler, AZ, p. A28
KEMKER, S E, M.D., President Medical Staff, St. Vincent Salem Hospital, Salem, IN, p. A214
KEMMERER, Jan, Director of Nursing, Mitchell County Hospital Health Systems, Beloit, KS, p. A232
KEMP, Marlo, Vice President and Chief Financial Officer, Roseland Community Hospital, Chicago, IL, p. A179
KEMP, Susie, Chief Financial Officer, Fulton State Hospital, Fulton, MO, p. A360
KEMPF, Gary L., Administrator, Houston Methodist Continuing Care Hospital, Katy, TX, p. A617
KEMPIAK, Matthew, Director Human Resources and Administrative Services, Memorial Hospital Of Gardena, Gardena, CA, p. A60
KEMPINSKI, Paul D.
Chief Executive Officer, Children'S Mercy Hospital Kansas City, Kansas City, MO, p. A362
Chief Executive Officer, Children'S Mercy Hospital Kansas, Overland Park, KS, p. A243
KEMPTON, Matthew, Chief Executive Officer and Administrator, Stephens Memorial Hospital, Breckenridge, TX, p. A589
KENAGY, John Jay, Ph.D.
Senior Vice President and Chief Information Officer, Legacy Meridian Park Medical Center, Tualatin, OR, p. A518
Senior Vice President and Chief Information Officer, Legacy Mount Hood Medical Center, Gresham, OR, p. A513
KENAGY, Rob, President and Chief Executive Officer, Stormont Vail Health, Topeka, KS, p. A246
KENAGY, Rob, M.D., Senior Vice President and Chief Medical Officer, Stormont Vail Health, Topeka, KS, p. A246

KENDALL, Abigail, Chief Nursing Officer, Lake Granbury Medical Center, Granbury, TX, p. A608

KENDALL, Anthony
Vice President Human Resources, Baptist Health Extended Care Hospital, Little Rock, AR, p. A44
Vice President Human Resources, Baptist Health Medical Center–Arkadelphia, Arkadelphia, AR, p. A39
Vice President Human Resources, Baptist Health Medical Center–Little Rock, Little Rock, AR, p. A44
Vice President Human Resources, Baptist Health Rehabilitation Institute, Little Rock, AR, p. A45

KENDALL, Clint, R.N., Chief Nursing Officer, Clinch Valley Medical Center, Richlands, VA, p. A665

KENDALL, Dorothy, Medical Director, William J. Mccord Adolescent Treatment Facility, Orangeburg, SC, p. A556

KENDLE, Melinda
Director Fiscal Management, Evansville State Hospital, Evansville, IN, p. A203
Manager Business Office, Evansville Psychiatric Children Center, Evansville, IN, p. A203

KENDLER, Lisa
Chief Financial Officer, Memorial Hermann Memorial City Medical Center, Houston, TX, p. A613
Chief Financial Officer, Memorial Hermann Sugar Land Hospital, Sugar Land, TX, p. A638

KENDRICK, Donovan, M.D., Chief Medical Officer, Baptist Medical Center South, Montgomery, AL, p. A21

KENDRICK, Ray, Chief Human Resources Officer, Memorial Hospital Miramar, Miramar, FL, p. A132

KENINGER, Luke, Information Technology Client Leader, Winona Health, Winona, MN, p. A343

KENNEDY, Anita J, Vice President Operations, Methodist Hospital Of Sacramento, Sacramento, CA, p. A82

KENNEDY, Carol, Chief Clinical Officer, Barrett Hospital & Healthcare, Dillon, MT, p. A376

KENNEDY, Connie, Director Human Resources, Marlette Regional Hospital, Marlette, MI, p. A317

KENNEDY, Darla, Chief Information Officer, Foothill Regional Medical Center, Tustin, CA, p. A92

KENNEDY, Diana, Director Human Resources, Meadowview Regional Medical Center, Maysville, KY, p. A257

KENNEDY, Eric, Chief Executive Officer, Arbour Hospital, Boston, MA, p. A294

KENNEDY, Jack L, R.N., MS, Vice President and Chief Nursing Officer, Pratt Regional Medical Center, Pratt, KS, p. A244

KENNEDY, Jessica, D.O., Chief Medical Officer, Adair County Health System, Greenfield, IA, p. A223

KENNEDY, Jill M, R.N., Vice President, Ambulatory Patient Care Services, Bon Secours Memorial Regional Medical Center, Mechanicsville, VA, p. A662

KENNEDY, John, M.D., Vice President of Medical Affairs, Mercy Health – Fairfield Hospital, Fairfield, OH, p. A483

KENNEDY, Kay, Chief Nurse Executive, Wellstar Cobb Hospital, Austell, GA, p. A148

KENNEDY, Kimberly, Manager Human Resources, Osf Saint Paul Medical Center, Mendota, IL, p. A189

KENNEDY, Larkin, Chief Executive Officer, Rush Foundation Hospital, Meridian, MS, p. A351

KENNEDY, Nancy A., M.D., Chief Medical Officer, Highpoint Health, Lawrenceburg, IN, p. A210

KENNEDY, Peter, Chief Operating Officer, Northside Hospital, Saint Petersburg, FL, p. A138

KENNEDY, R. Scott, M.D., Chief Medical Officer and Safety Officer, Olympic Medical Center, Port Angeles, WA, p. A676

KENNEDY, Ryan
Chief Financial Officer, Holy Name Medical Center, Teaneck, NJ, p. A413
Chief Operating Officer, Kingman Regional Medical Center, Kingman, AZ, p. A30

KENNEDY, TaDren, Administrator, Walthall County General Hospital, Tylertown, MS, p. A354

KENNEDY, Tiffany, Chief Nursing Officer, Breckinridge Memorial Hospital, Hardinsburg, KY, p. A253

KENNEDY, Timea, Director Human Resources, St. Mary–Corwin Medical Center, Pueblo, CO, p. A105

KENNEDY, Todd S., President and Chief Executive Officer, Providence Hospital, Mobile, AL, p. A20

KENNEMER, Darline, Controller, Methodist Rehabilitation Hospital, Dallas, TX, p. A597

KENNETT, Jerry, M.D., Chief Medical Officer, Boone Hospital Center, Columbia, MO, p. A359

KENNEY, Mary Ellen, Chief Human Services, Manchester Veterans Affairs Medical Center, Manchester, NH, p. A401

KENNEY, Ronda, Chief Operating Officer, Eastern State Hospital, Medical Lake, WA, p. A675

KENNEY, Stephen F., Chief Financial Officer, The University Of Vermont Health Network Central Vermont Medical Center, Berlin, VT, p. A654

KENNINGTON, Lynn, Chief Financial Officer, Alaska Regional Hospital, Anchorage, AK, p. A25

KENNISON, Barbara, Director Clinical Services, Aurora Behavioral Healthcare San Diego, San Diego, CA, p. A83

KENNY, Carolyn, Executive Vice President Clinical Care, Children'S Healthcare Of Atlanta, Atlanta, GA, p. A146

KENNY, Virginia, Chief Nursing Officer, Hancock Medical Center, Bay Saint Louis, MS, p. A344

KENSINGER, Brooke, Chief Executive Officer, Mercyone Elkader Medical Center, Elkader, IA, p. A222

KENT, Alan, Chief Executive Officer, Meadows Regional Medical Center, Vidalia, GA, p. A162

KENT, David, Chief Operating Officer, Southeastern Regional Medical Center, Newnan, GA, p. A158

KENT, David, M.D., Chief Medical Officer, Safe Haven Hospital Of Treasure Valley, Boise, ID, p. A167

KENT, Mary, Administrator, Johnson County Hospital, Tecumseh, NE, p. A392

KENT, Robert, President and Chief Executive Officer, Western Reserve Hospital, Cuyahoga Falls, OH, p. A481

KENTERA, Amy, Chief Information Officer, Conifer Park, Glenville, NY, p. A428

KENTFIELD, Melinda Johanna, R.N., Director of Nursing and Interim Chief Nursing Officer, Methodist Fremont Health, Fremont, NE, p. A385

KENTON, Bart, Chief Financial Officer, Holton Community Hospital, Holton, KS, p. A237

KENWOOD, Linda S, R.N., MSN, Chief Nursing Officer and Chief Operating Officer, Shore Medical Center, Somers Point, NJ, p. A412

KEOWN, Janet, Vice President Human Resources, Behavioral Health Network, Natchaug Hospital, Mansfield Center, CT, p. A108

KEPLINGER, Ron, Chief Information Officer, Western Maryland Hospital Center, Hagerstown, MD, p. A291

KEPNER, Donald L, Chief Financial Officer, Ashtabula County Medical Center, Ashtabula, OH, p. A472

KEPPLER, Edward L., M.D., Chief Medical Officer, Marion General Hospital, Marion, IN, p. A211

KEPPNER, Brandon, Administrator, Laureate Psychiatric Clinic And Hospital, Tulsa, OK, p. A508

KEPSHIRE, Bob, Administrator and Chief Nursing Officer, University Hospital Mcduffie, Thomson, GA, p. A161

KEPSHIRE, Bob, R.N., MS, Administrator and Chief Nursing Officer, University Hospital Mcduffie, Thomson, GA, p. A161

KERBS, Curtis, Regional Chief Information Officer, Memorial Hospital, North Conway, NH, p. A402

KERCHENSKI, Marlene, Chief Nurse, U. S. Air Force Hospital, Hampton, VA, p. A660

KERI, Alison, Director Human Resources, Hiawatha Community Hospital, Hiawatha, KS, p. A236

KERIAN–MASTERS, RN, Carol, Chief Nursing Officer, Regional Health Services Of Howard County, Cresco, IA, p. A220

KERLIN, Kerry, Chief Information Officer, Roswell Park Comprehensive Cancer Center, Buffalo, NY, p. A424

KERMEN, John, D.O., Chief Medical Staff, Mendocino Coast District Hospital, Fort Bragg, CA, p. A58

KERN, Daniel, Chief Executive Officer, Strategic Behavioral Health – Wilmington, Leland, NC, p. A457

KERN, Douglas W., Chief Executive Officer, Northcoast Behavioral Healthcare, Northfield, OH, p. A488

KERN, Howard P.
Chief Operating Officer, Sentara Princess Anne Hospital, Virginia Beach, VA, p. A668
President and Chief Operating Officer, Sentara Leigh Hospital, Norfolk, VA, p. A664

KERNAN, Jacqueline D., President, Osf Saint Luke Medical Center, Kewanee, IL, p. A187

KERNDL, John, Executive Vice President and Chief Financial Officer, Beaumont Hospital – Royal Oak, Royal Oak, MI, p. A321

KERNELL, Shane, Chief Executive Officer, Graham Regional Medical Center, Graham, TX, p. A608

KERNIVAN, Lorna, Chief Operating Officer, Palms West Hospital, Loxahatchee, FL, p. A128

KERNS, Elizabeth, Senior Vice President and Chief Information Officer, Lakeland Regional Health Medical Center, Lakeland, FL, p. A127

KEROACK, Mark A., President and Chief Executive Officer, Baystate Health, Baystate Medical Center, Springfield, MA, p. A303

KERR, Jeff, M.D., Chief Medical Officer, Baylor Scott & White Medical Center At – Mckinney, Mckinney, TX, p. A624

KERR, Karen
President, Bartow Regional Medical Center, Bartow, FL, p. A117
President, South Florida Baptist Hospital, Plant City, FL, p. A137

KERR, Michael D, Chief Executive Officer, Promise Hospital Of East Los Angeles, Los Angeles, CA, p. A68

KERR, Michael D.
Chief Executive Officer, Kindred Hospital South Bay, Gardena, CA, p. A60
Chief Executive Officer, Promise Hospital Of East Los Angeles, Los Angeles, CA, p. A68

KERRINS, David, Vice President Information Services and Chief Information Officer, Dameron Hospital, Stockton, CA, p. A90

KERSCHEN, Susan, MS, R.N., Vice President and Chief Nursing Officer, Good Samaritan Medical Center, Lafayette, CO, p. A102

KERSTETTER, Kathleen, R.N., MSN, Chief Clinical Officer, Acuity Specialty Hospital Of New Jersey, Atlantic City, NJ, p. A403

KERSTING, Clay, M.D., Chief Medical Staff, Newport Hospital And Health Services, Newport, WA, p. A675

KERSWILL, Randy, M.D., Medical Director, Winnebago Mental Health Institute, Winnebago, WI, p. A709

KERWOOD, Christine, Chief Nursing Officer, East Ohio Regional Hospital, Martins Ferry, OH, p. A486

KERWOOD, Lori A, Director Human Resources, Cooley Dickinson Hospital, Northampton, MA, p. A301

KESSEL, Jennifer, Chief Executive Officer, Aultman Orrville Hospital, Orrville, OH, p. A489

KESSLER, Alexander, M.D., Chief of Staff, Northside Hospital–Cherokee, Canton, GA, p. A149

KESSLER, David, M.D., Clinical Director, U. S. Public Health Service Indian Hospital, Zuni, NM, p. A421

KESSLER, Jeffrey R, Vice President Information Services, Dana–Farber Cancer Institute, Boston, MA, p. A295

KESSLER, John E., Chief Executive Officer, Sarah D. Culbertson Memorial Hospital, Rushville, IL, p. A195

KESSLER, Joseph, Executive Vice President and Chief Financial Officer, Kaleida Health, Buffalo, NY, p. A424

KESSNER, Jennifer, Financial Director, Roosevelt Medical Center, Culbertson, MT, p. A375

KESTER, Bonnie J, R.N., MSN, Vice President Patient Care Services and Chief Nursing Officer, Nantucket Cottage Hospital, Nantucket, MA, p. A301

KESTERSON, Matt
Director Information Services, Wadley Regional Medical Center At Hope, Hope, AR, p. A43
Director Information Services, Wadley Regional Medical Center, Texarkana, TX, p. A640

KETCH, Lynn
Human Resources Recruiter Generalist, Integris Canadian Valley Hospital, Yukon, OK, p. A510
Regional Director Integris Southwest Medical Center, Integris Southwest Medical Center, Oklahoma City, OK, p. A504

KETCHAM, Krista, Chief Financial Officer, Buena Vista Regional Medical Center, Storm Lake, IA, p. A230

KETCHAM, Michael
Chief Medical Officer, Mountain View Regional Medical Center, Norton, VA, p. A664
President, Medical Staff, Lonesome Pine Hospital, Big Stone Gap, VA, p. A656

KETCHEM, Tami, Human Resource Director, Up Health System–Bell, Ishpeming, MI, p. A315

KETTERHAGEN, James P, M.D., Senior Vice President and Chief Medical Officer, Jewish Hospital, Louisville, KY, p. A256

KETTERLING, Kimberly A., R.N., Vice President Patient Care Services, Chi Oakes Hospital, Oakes, ND, p. A469

KETTERMAN, Patricia P., President and Chief Administrative Officer, Claiborne Medical Center, Tazewell, TN, p. A580

KETTLER, Paul, M.D., Vice President Medical Affairs, Fairview Ridges Hospital, Burnsville, MN, p. A329

KETTNER, Mark, Interim Chief Executive Officer, Eastern State Hospital, Medical Lake, WA, p. A675

KEY, Jennifer, Chief Nursing Officer, Piedmont Newnan Hospital, Newnan, GA, p. A158

KEY, Lora, Chief Executive Officer, Sabetha Community Hospital, Sabetha, KS, p. A244

KEYONNIE, Christine, CPA, Chief Financial Officer, Tuba City Regional Health Care Corporation, Tuba City, AZ, p. A37

KEYS, Janice C., Senior Vice President, Chief Nurse Executive, Erlanger Medical Center, Chattanooga, TN, p. A567

KHADE, Kashmira, Coordinator Non–Clinical Services, Behavioral Center Of Michigan, Warren, MI, p. A324

KHALEGHI, Trisha
Chief Executive Officer, Sharp Mesa Vista Hospital, San Diego, CA, p. A84
Senior Vice President and Chief Executive Officer, Sharp Mesa Vista Hospital, San Diego, CA, p. A84

KHALIQUE, Tania, Director Human Resources, Select Specialty Hospital – San Diego, San Diego, CA, p. A84

KHAN, Atique, M.D., Medical Director, University Behavioral Health Of Denton, Denton, TX, p. A599
KHAN, Dan, M.D., Chief Medical Officer, Yoakum County Hospital, Denver City, TX, p. A600
KHAN, Faraz, Chief Financial Officer, Doctors Hospital Of Laredo, Laredo, TX, p. A619
KHAN, Humayun, M.D., Chief Medical Officer, Hshs Sacred Heart Hospital, Eau Claire, WI, p. A694
KHAN, Sarfraz, Medical Director, Meridian Health Services, Muncie, IN, p. A212
KHAN, Shahbaz, M.D., Medical Director, Two Rivers Behavioral Health System, Kansas City, MO, p. A363
KHAN, Waheed, M.D., President Medical Staff, Summers County Arh Hospital, Hinton, WV, p. A685
KHANCHANDANI, Ashok, Chief Financial Officer, Oroville Hospital, Oroville, CA, p. A76
KHANDELWAL, Ashish, M.D., Medical Director, Healthsouth Rehabilitation Hospital Of Middletown, Middletown, DE, p. A113
KHANNA, Rajive
Chief Executive Officer, Grace Hospital, Cleveland, OH, p. A477
Chief Executive Officer, Specialty Hospital Of Lorain, Amherst, OH, p. A471
KHARONOV, Arthur, Vice President Nursing, Columbus Hospital Ltach, Newark, NJ, p. A409
KHATAMI, Manoochehr, M.D., Medical Director, Hickory Trail Hospital, Desoto, TX, p. A600
KHATUA, Sanjeeb, M.D., Chief Medical Officer and Vice President, Edward Hospital, Naperville, IL, p. A190
KHAVKIN, Lisa, Vice President Human Resources, Huntington Hospital, Huntington, NY, p. A429
KHDOUR, Adel, M.D., Chief Medical Officer, Indiana University Health White Memorial Hospital, Monticello, IN, p. A211
KHEMKA, Hemant
Chief Financial Officer, Surgery Specialty Hospitals Of America, Pasadena, TX, p. A628
Chief Operating Officer, Surgery Specialty Hospitals Of America, Pasadena, TX, p. A628
KHIAMI, Ahmad, Chief of Staff, Beckley Arh Hospital, Beckley, WV, p. A683
KHIM FUGATE, Guay, Chief Operations Officer, Kindred Hospital Riverside, Perris, CA, p. A78
KHOERL, Thomas, Vice President Finance, Spectrum Health Big Rapids Hospital, Big Rapids, MI, p. A307
KHOO, Alex, Interim Area Finance Officer, Kaiser Permanente San Francisco Medical Center, San Francisco, CA, p. A85
KIBAR, Nizar, M.D., Chief Medical Staff, Kiowa County Memorial Hospital, Greensburg, KS, p. A236
KIBBY, Rosalinda, Superintendent and Administrator, Columbia Basin Hospital, Ephrata, WA, p. A673
KIDA, Sue, Chief Executive Officer, Kessler Institute For Rehabilitation, West Orange, NJ, p. A414
KIDD, David, Manager Human Resources, Sentara Careplex Hospital, Hampton, VA, p. A660
KIDD, Monica, Administrator, Parkview Hospital, Wheeler, TX, p. A645
KIDD, Sabrina, M.D., Chief Medical Officer, Sonoma Valley Hospital, Sonoma, CA, p. A90
KIDD, Thomas J., Chief Executive Officer, Macon Community Hospital, Lafayette, TN, p. A572
KIDDER, David M., D.O., Chief Medical Officer, Garfield County Health Center, Jordan, MT, p. A378
KIDDER, Suzanne F, Human Resources Officer, Opelousas General Health System, Opelousas, LA, p. A276
KIEBZAK, Stanley F, R.N., Chief Nursing Officer, Encompass Health Rehabilitation Hospital The Vintage, Houston, TX, p. A611
KIEDROWSKI, Brian, M.D., Chief Medical Director, Miami Jewish Home And Hospital For Aged, Miami, FL, p. A130
KIEFER, William
Chief Nursing Officer, Tmc Bonham Hospital, Bonham, TX, p. A589
Chief Operating Officer, Rehoboth Mckinley Christian Health Care Services, Gallup, NM, p. A418
KIEFFER, Kelley
Chief Nursing Officer, Banner Baywood Medical Center, Mesa, AZ, p. A31
Chief Nursing Officer, Banner Heart Hospital, Mesa, AZ, p. A31
KIEHL, Tiffany, Chief Executive Officer, Mid–America Rehabilitation Hospital, Shawnee Mission, KS, p. A245
KIEHLE, Jessica, R.N., Chief Nursing Officer, Abilene Regional Medical Center, Abilene, TX, p. A581
KIELY, Sharon, M.D., Senior Vice President Medical Affairs and Chief Medical Officer, Stamford Hospital, Stamford, CT, p. A111
KIERNAN, Richard
Regional Chief Human Resources Officer, Monmouth Medical Center, Southern Campus, Lakewood, NJ, p. A407
Vice President Human Resources, Monmouth Medical Center, Long Branch Campus, Long Branch, NJ, p. A407
KIGER, Tom, Director Information Systems, Trinity Health System, Steubenville, OH, p. A491
KIGHT, Sheila, Director Human Resources, Tristar Horizon Medical Center, Dickson, TN, p. A569
KILARSKI, David J., Chief Executive Officer, Firsthealth Moore Regional Hospital, Pinehurst, NC, p. A460
KILBORN, Mark, Director Information Systems, Springhill Memorial Hospital, Mobile, AL, p. A20
KILE, Steven E, Vice President Human Resources, Indiana University Health North Hospital, Carmel, IN, p. A201
KILEY, David, Vice President, Community Hospital South, Indianapolis, IN, p. A206
KILGORE, Julie, Vice President, Human Resources, Broadlawns Medical Center, Des Moines, IA, p. A221
KILLINGSWORTH, Meri, Chief Operating Officer, Hereford Regional Medical Center, Hereford, TX, p. A610
KILMER, Michael T., Director, Grand Junction Veterans Health Care System, Grand Junction, CO, p. A101
KILPACK, Lee, Chief Executive Officer, Marian Center, Salt Lake City, UT, p. A651
KILPATRICK, Von
Chief Nursing Officer, South Peninsula Hospital, Homer, AK, p. A26
Chief Nursing Officer, St. Vincent General Hospital District, Leadville, CO, p. A103
KIM, Donald, M.D., Chief Medical Officer, Memorial Regional Hospital, Hollywood, FL, p. A124
KIM, Eric, Chief Information Officer, Las Encinas Hospital, Pasadena, CA, p. A77
KIM, Eugene P., M.D., Chief Medical Officer, St. Jude Medical Center, Fullerton, CA, p. A60
KIM, Hyon Su, M.D., Medical Director, Northlake Behavioral Health System, Mandeville, LA, p. A273
KIM, John, Chief Financial Officer, Anchor Hospital, Atlanta, GA, p. A145
KIMBALL, Kevin, Director Information Technology, Brooks Memorial Hospital, Dunkirk, NY, p. A427
KIMBALL, Mark E., Chief Executive Officer, Erlanger Western Carolina Hospital, Murphy, NC, p. A459
KIMBALL, Tim, Chief Nursing Officer, Northwest Health Physicians' Specialty Hospital, Fayetteville, AR, p. A41
KIMBLE, Becky, R.N., Chief Nursing Officer, Encompass Health Rehabilitation Hospital Of Jonesboro, Jonesboro, AR, p. A44
KIMBLE, D. Gay, Chief Human Resource Officer, Susan B. Allen Memorial Hospital, El Dorado, KS, p. A234
KIMBLE, Robert J., Chief Financial Officer, William R. Sharpe, Jr. Hospital, Weston, WV, p. A690
KIMBRELL, Jason, Chief Executive Officer, Highlands Regional Medical Center, Sebring, FL, p. A139
KIMBREW, Missey, Director Human Resources, Grafton City Hospital, Grafton, WV, p. A685
KIMBRO, George, Vice President Finance, Angel Medical Center, Franklin, NC, p. A454
KIMBROUGH, Pam, M.D., Vice President Medical Affairs, Mercy Hospital Ardmore, Ardmore, OK, p. A496
KIMMEL, Kyle, Chief Financial Officer, Bacon County Hospital And Health System, Alma, GA, p. A145
KIMMEL, Stephen, Chief Financial Officer, Cook Children'S Medical Center, Fort Worth, TX, p. A604
KIMMES, Robert P., Chief Executive Officer, Skyline Hospital, White Salmon, WA, p. A682
KIMMET, Jackie, Chief Human Resource Officer, River'S Edge Hospital And Clinic, Saint Peter, MN, p. A340
KIMPLE, Robin, Director Information Services, Wellspan Gettysburg Hospital, Gettysburg, PA, p. A526
KIMZEY, Mike, Chief Executive Officer, Onecore Health, Oklahoma City, OK, p. A505
KINARD, Tifani, Administrator and Chief Nursing Officer, Polk Medical Center, Cedartown, GA, p. A149
KINCAID, Kevin, Chief Executive Officer, Knoxville Hospital & Clinics, Knoxville, IA, p. A225
KINCAID, Steve, Information Technology Manager, Eastern State Hospital, Lexington, KY, p. A255
KINDER, Barbara, R.N., Chief Clinical Officer, Clark Regional Medical Center, Winchester, KY, p. A261
KINDRED, Deanne, Vice President Finance, Baylor Scott & White Medical Center – Plano, Plano, TX, p. A629
KINDSCHI, Mark, Director Human Resources, Edgerton Hospital And Health Services, Edgerton, WI, p. A694
KING, Abner
Chief Executive Officer, Syringa Hospital And Clinics, Grangeville, ID, p. A169
Chief Operating Officer, Steele Memorial Medical Center, Salmon, ID, p. A172
KING, Beth, Chief Financial Officer, Jersey Community Hospital, Jerseyville, IL, p. A186
KING, Brent R, Chief Medical Officer and Chief Physician, Alfred I. Dupont Hospital For Children, Wilmington, DE, p. A114
KING, Bruce, President and Chief Executive Officer, New London Hospital, New London, NH, p. A401
KING, Chris, Director Information Services, Ohiohealth Marion General Hospital, Marion, OH, p. A486
KING, Christopher, Director Operations and Administrative Services, Matheny Medical And Educational Center, Peapack, NJ, p. A410
KING, Donna, R.N., FACHE, Vice President Clinical Operations and Chief Nursing Executive, Advocate Illinois Masonic Medical Center, Chicago, IL, p. A176
KING, Doug, M.D., Director Clinical Services, Western Mental Health Institute, Bolivar, TN, p. A566
KING, Glenn, R.N., MSN
Vice President and Chief Nursing Officer, Midmichigan Medical Center–Gladwin, Gladwin, MI, p. A312
Vice President, Chief Nursing Officer, Midmichigan Medical Center–Clare, Clare, MI, p. A309
KING, Janine, M.D., Chief of Staff, East Los Angeles Doctors Hospital, Los Angeles, CA, p. A66
KING, Jay, Vice President Human Resources, Mercy Hospitals Of Bakersfield, Bakersfield, CA, p. A52
KING, Jo Nell, Director of Nursing, Northlake Behavioral Health System, Mandeville, LA, p. A273
KING, Joanie, Chief Financial Officer, Carteret Health Care, Morehead City, NC, p. A458
KING, JoAnne, Chief Operating Officer, Adventhealth Palm Coast, Palm Coast, FL, p. A135
KING, Katie, R.N., Chief Nursing Officer, Mountain View Hospital, Payson, UT, p. A650
KING, Katrina, R.N., Senior Director, Nursing, Novant Health Huntersville Medical Center, Huntersville, NC, p. A456
KING, Kim, Director Human Resources and Public Relations, Baptist Memorial Hospital–Carroll County, Huntingdon, TN, p. A571
KING, Levi J., Director Human Resources, Conway Behavioral Health Hospital, Conway, AR, p. A40
KING, Louie
Chief Executive Officer, Benefis Teton Medical Center, Choteau, MT, p. A375
President, Harry Bold Nursing Home Administrator, Missouri River Medical Center, Fort Benton, MT, p. A376
KING, Micheal, Controller, Spectrum Health Pennock, Hastings, MI, p. A314
KING, Patrick, Administrator, Bastrop Rehabilitation Hospital, Monroe, LA, p. A274
KING, Paul, M.D., Medical Director, Parkwood Behavioral Health System, Olive Branch, MS, p. A352
KING, Paul A, Executive Director, Michigan Medicine, Ann Arbor, MI, p. A306
KING, Paul A., President and Chief Executive Officer, Lucile Salter Packard Children'S Hospital Stanford, Palo Alto, CA, p. A77
KING, Ray, M.D., Senior Vice President, Medical Affairs and Chief Medical Officer, Henry Ford Allegiance Health, Jackson, MI, p. A315
KING, Sam, Chief Financial Officer, Renown Regional Medical Center, Reno, NV, p. A397
KING, Sammy, Controller, Encompass Health Rehabilitation Hospital Of Ocala, Ocala, FL, p. A133
KING, Sandra, Chief Nursing Officer, Sagamore Children'S Psychiatric Center, Dix Hills, NY, p. A427
KING, Shari, Interim Vice President of Operations, Unitypoint Health – Marshalltown, Marshalltown, IA, p. A226
KING, Tamara, R.N., MSN, Chief Nurse Executive, Shepherd Center, Atlanta, GA, p. A147
KING, Val, Chief Information Officer, Val Verde Regional Medical Center, Del Rio, TX, p. A599
KINGHAM, Darrell L, CPA, Vice President Finance, Beauregard Health System, De Ridder, LA, p. A266
KINGRY, Jennifer, Chief Financial Officer, St. Vincent'S Blount, Oneonta, AL, p. A22
KINGSLEY, Christi, Vice President Human Resources, West Calcasieu Cameron Hospital, Sulphur, LA, p. A279
KINGSTON, Eileen M, R.N., Nurse Executive, Associate Director Patient Care, Veterans Affairs Nebraska–Western Iowa Health Care System, Omaha, NE, p. A390
KINGSTON, Mary Beth, Ph.D., R.N., MSN, Executive Vice President and Chief Nursing Officer, Aurora Medical Center Of Oshkosh, Oshkosh, WI, p. A703
KINGSTON, Mary E., Chief Executive, Peacehealth Sacred Heart Medical Center At Riverbend, Springfield, OR, p. A518
KINGSTON, Peggy, Chief Executive Officer, Select Specialty Hospital–Pontiac, Pontiac, MI, p. A320
KINKAID, Steve, Director Information Systems, St. Luke'S – Gnaden Huetten Campus, Lehighton, PA, p. A530

KINLEN, Thomas, Superintendent, Larned State Hospital, Larned, KS, p. A238
KINMAN, Amanda, Director of Finance, Saint Joseph Mount Sterling, Mount Sterling, KY, p. A258
KINNAIRD, Adriene, Chief Executive Officer, Select Specialty Hospital Midtown Atlanta, Atlanta, GA, p. A147
KINNEER, James W, Vice President Organizational Development, Indiana Regional Medical Center, Indiana, PA, p. A528
KINNEMAN, Mary, R.N., MSN, Chief Nursing Officer, Vice President Patient Care Services, Norwood Hospital, Norwood, MA, p. A302
KINNEY, Janet, Chief Operating Officer, Northwest Florida Community Hospital, Chipley, FL, p. A119
KINSALA, Edeli, Chief Executive Officer, Sonora Behavioral Health Hospital, Tucson, AZ, p. A38
KINSEL, Mike, Controller, Federal Medical Center, Lexington, KY, p. A255
KINSELLA, Daniel F
Executive Vice President Information Technology, Northwestern Medicine Delnor Hospital, Geneva, IL, p. A184
Vice President and Chief Information Officer, Northwestern Medicine Central Dupage Hospital, Winfield, IL, p. A198
KINSEY, Daniel, M.D., Medical Director, Oaklawn Psychiatric Center, Goshen, IN, p. A205
KINSEY, Wayne
Chief Executive Officer, Promise Hospital Of Phoenix, Mesa, AZ, p. A32
Chief Executive Officer, Promise Hospital Of Salt Lake, Salt Lake City, UT, p. A652
KINSLOW, Kathleen, President, Jefferson Health Northeast, Philadelphia, PA, p. A535
KINTZ, Ronald J
Chief Financial Officer, Ira Davenport Memorial Hospital, Bath, NY, p. A423
Senior Vice President Finance and Chief Financial Officer, St. Joseph'S Hospital, Elmira, NY, p. A427
Vice President and Treasurer, Arnot Ogden Medical Center, Elmira, NY, p. A427
KINYON, Craig C., President and Chief Executive Officer, Reid Health, Richmond, IN, p. A214
KINYON, David, Vice President of Operations and Outpatient Services, Asante Three Rivers Medical Center, Grants Pass, OR, p. A513
KINZIC, Elizabeth, M.D., Chief of Staff, Share Medical Center, Alva, OK, p. A496
KINZIE, Wesley, M.D., Chief of Staff, Stanislaus Surgical Hospital, Modesto, CA, p. A72
KIO, Kenneth, Manager Human Resources, Albany Stratton Veterans Affairs Medical Center, Albany, NY, p. A422
KIPP, Kris M, Executive Director, Patient Services and Chief Nursing Officer, James Cancer Hospital And Solove Research Institute, Columbus, OH, p. A479
KIRACOFE, Darin, Director Information Resource Management, Broughton Hospital, Morganton, NC, p. A458
KIRALY, Denise G, Director, Human Resources and Organization Development, Lima Memorial Health System, Lima, OH, p. A485
KIRBOW, Keith, R.N., Vice President and Chief Nursing Officer, Christus Good Shepherd Medical Center–Marshall, Marshall, TX, p. A623
KIRBY, Adrienne, President and Executive Chair, Cooper University Health Care, Camden, NJ, p. A404
KIRBY, Brendan, M.D., Medical Director, Riverview Psychiatric Center, Augusta, ME, p. A281
KIRBY, Elizabeth A
Senior Director Human Resources, Aurora Baycare Medical Center, Green Bay, WI, p. A696
Senior Director Human Resources, Aurora Medical Center – Manitowoc County, Two Rivers, WI, p. A707
KIRBY, James M., II, President and Chief Executive Officer, Margaret R. Pardee Memorial Hospital, Hendersonville, NC, p. A456
KIRBY, John, Senior Vice President and Chief Financial Officer, Virtua Memorial, Mount Holly, NJ, p. A408
KIRBY, Juliana Kay, R.N., MSN, Chief Nursing Officer, Adventist Health Medical Center – Tehachapi Valley, Tehachapi, CA, p. A91
KIRBY, Penny V, MSN, Chief Nursing Officer, Livingston Regional Hospital, Livingston, TN, p. A573
KIRBY, Ruby, Administrator, Bolivar General Hospital, Bolivar, TN, p. A566
KIRBY, Tracy
Assistant Vice President Business Relationship Management, Chi St. Vincent Hot Springs, Hot Springs, AR, p. A43
Assistant Vice President Business Relationship Management, Chi St. Vincent Infirmary Medical Center, Little Rock, AR, p. A45
Assistant Vice President Business Relationship Management, Chi St. Vincent Morrilton, Morrilton, AR, p. A46
KIRCH, Cyndi
Vice President Human Resources, Mercy General Hospital, Sacramento, CA, p. A82
Vice President Human Resources, Methodist Hospital Of Sacramento, Sacramento, CA, p. A82
KIRCHER, Janelle, Chief Executive Officer, Kindred Hospital–Denver, Denver, CO, p. A99
KIRCHNER, Kent, M.D., Chief of Staff, G.V. (Sonny) Montgomery Veterans Affairs Medical Center, Jackson, MS, p. A348
KIRCHNER, Susan M, Director Human Resources, Four Winds Hospital, Saratoga Springs, NY, p. A443
KIRISITS, Christopher, Chief Nursing Officer, Rochester Psychiatric Center, Rochester, NY, p. A442
KIRITANI, Tracy, Vice President and Chief Financial Officer, Clovis Community Medical Center, Clovis, CA, p. A55
KIRK, Darlene, Manager Finance, U. S. Public Health Service Indian Hospital, Crownpoint, NM, p. A417
KIRK, Donald, M.D., Chief of Staff, Star Valley Medical Center, Afton, WY, p. A710
KIRK, H Lee., Jr, Administrator, Shriners Hospitals For Children–Springfield, Springfield, MA, p. A303
KIRK, J. Douglas, M.D., Chief Medical Officer, University Of California, Davis Medical Center, Sacramento, CA, p. A82
KIRK, Jean, Chief Financial Officer, Bennett County Hospital And Nursing Home, Martin, SD, p. A561
KIRK, Paul, Vice President, Woman'S Hospital, Baton Rouge, LA, p. A264
KIRK, Peggy, Senior Vice President Clinical Operations, Shirley Ryan Abilitylab, Chicago, IL, p. A179
KIRK, Roger L, President and Chief Executive Officer, Bethesda Hospital East, Boynton Beach, FL, p. A118
KIRK, Roger L., President and Chief Executive Officer, Bethesda Hospital East, Boynton Beach, FL, p. A118
KIRK, Vanessa, Director of Nursing, Kiowa County Memorial Hospital, Greensburg, KS, p. A236
KIRK, Warren J., Chief Executive Officer, Doctors Medical Center Of Modesto, Modesto, CA, p. A72
KIRKBRIDE, James B., President and Chief Executive Officer, Susan B. Allen Memorial Hospital, El Dorado, KS, p. A234
KIRKER, Donna, R.N., MS, Vice President Patient Services and Chief Nursing Officer, Glens Falls Hospital, Glens Falls, NY, p. A428
KIRKER, Lynda I, Chief Financial Officer, Flagler Hospital, Saint Augustine, FL, p. A138
KIRKHAM, Brett, Chief Operating Officer, Integris Deaconess, Oklahoma City, OK, p. A504
KIRKHAM, Paul, Chief Executive Officer, Newport News Behavioral Health Center, Newport News, VA, p. A663
KIRKLAND–ROSE, Tina, Coordinator Human Resources, Select Specialty Hospital–Lexington, Lexington, KY, p. A255
KIRKLEY, Scott, M.D., BJC Chief Medical Officer Group Liaison, Parkland Health Center – Farmington Community, Farmington, MO, p. A360
KIRKPATRICK, Brett, Executive Director, Mccullough–Hyde Memorial Hospital/Trihealth, Oxford, OH, p. A489
KIRKPATRICK, Kyle
Chief Executive Officer, Baylor Scott & White Emergency Hospital – Burleson, Burleson, TX, p. A590
Chief Executive Officer, Baylor Scott & White Emergency Hospital – Rockwall, Rockwall, TX, p. A631
Chief Executive Officer, Baylor Scott & White Emergency Hospital–Aubrey, Aubrey, TX, p. A584
Chief Executive Officer, Baylor Scott & White Emergency Medical Center– Cedar Park, Cedar Park, TX, p. A592
KIRKS, Linda, Vice President and Chief Financial Officer, Christus Santa Rosa Health System, San Antonio, TX, p. A633
KIRMAN, Lynn, R.N., Chief Nursing Officer, St. John'S Medical Center And Living Center, Jackson, WY, p. A711
KIRSHNER, Arthur N, Chief Information Management, Winn Army Community Hospital, Hinesville, GA, p. A154
KIRSHNER, David L., Chief Financial Officer, Strong Memorial Hospital Of The University Of Rochester, Rochester, NY, p. A443
KIRSTEIN, Susan N., R.N., MSN, Chief Nursing Officer, Broadlawns Medical Center, Des Moines, IA, p. A221
KIRTON, Carl, Ph.D., Chief Nursing Officer, University Hospital, Newark, NJ, p. A409
KISACKY, Christina A, Vice President, Operations, Uhs Chenango Memorial Hospital, Norwich, NY, p. A440
KISER, Greg, Chief Executive Officer, Three Rivers Medical Center, Louisa, KY, p. A255
KISER, Harrison, Chief Operating Officer, Saint Thomas West Hospital, Nashville, TN, p. A577
KISER, James R., II, Chief Executive Officer, Montrose Memorial Hospital, Montrose, CO, p. A104
KISER, Pamela, R.N., MS, Chief Nursing Executive and Vice President of Nursing, St. John Medical Center, Tulsa, OK, p. A510
KISHNER, Janice, R.N., FACHE, Chief Clinical Officer, St. Bernard Parish Hospital, Chalmette, LA, p. A265
KISKADDON, Robert, M.D., Chief Medical Officer, Margaret R. Pardee Memorial Hospital, Hendersonville, NC, p. A456
KISNER, Angela, Director Human Resources and Coordinator Medical Staff, Landmark Hospital Of Cape Girardeau, Cape Girardeau, MO, p. A357
KISS, Meredith, Administrator, Elgin Mental Health Center, Elgin, IL, p. A182
KISSNER, Michael, Chief Executive Officer, Encompass Health Rehabilitation Hospital Of Treasure Coast, Vero Beach, FL, p. A143
KISTLER, Beckie, Director of Finance, Chi Our Lady Of Peace, Louisville, KY, p. A256
KISTNER, Kasondra, Chief Executive Officer, Warm Springs Rehabilitation Hospital Of San Antonio, San Antonio, TX, p. A635
KITCH, Barrett, M.D., Senior Vice President, Clinical Affairs and Chief Medical Officer, Emerson Hospital, Concord, MA, p. A298
KITCHEN, Steven, M.D., Chief Medical Officer, Phoebe Putney Memorial Hospital, Albany, GA, p. A145
KITTNER, Bonnie, R.N., Chief Nursing Officer, Mendocino Coast District Hospital, Fort Bragg, CA, p. A58
KJERGAARD, Holly, Chief Nursing Officer, Audubon County Memorial Hospital And Clinics, Audubon, IA, p. A217
KJOSA, Ann Marie, R.N., MSN, Chief Nursing Officer, Eastern Idaho Regional Medical Center, Idaho Falls, ID, p. A169
KLAMFOTH, William, Administrator, Christus Southeast Texas Orthopedic Specialty Center, Beaumont, TX, p. A587
KLANN, Andrew, D.O., Chief of Staff, Southwest Health, Platteville, WI, p. A703
KLARKOWSKI, Troy, Administrator and Chief Executive Officer, U. S. Public Health Service Indian Hospital–Sells, Sells, AZ, p. A36
KLASEK, Chance, CPA, Chief Financial Officer, Jefferson Community Health And Life, Fairbury, NE, p. A384
KLASKO, Stephen K, President, Thomas Jefferson University Hospitals, Philadelphia, PA, p. A536
KLASS, Cheryl, President, Kaleida Health, Buffalo, NY, p. A424
KLASSEN, Brad, Information Technology Coordinator, Sanford Worthington Medical Center, Worthington, MN, p. A343
KLASSEN, Karen, Controller, Encompass Health Rehabilitation Hospital Of Chattanooga, Chattanooga, TN, p. A567
KLAUSTERMEIER, Lisa, R.N., MSN, Chief Nursing Officer, Anderson Hospital, Maryville, IL, p. A188
KLAWITTER, Kyle, Vice President Human Resources, Summa Health System, Akron, OH, p. A471
KLAY, Chris, President and Chief Executive Officer, Hshs St. Joseph'S Hospital, Breese, IL, p. A174
KLEAM, Douglas V., President, St. Bernardine Medical Center, San Bernardino, CA, p. A83
KLEAS, Tara, Area Director Human Resources, Encompass Health Rehabilitation Hospital Of Fort Worth, Fort Worth, TX, p. A605
KLEEN, Kathy, Chief Nursing Officer, Tri–County Hospital, Wadena, MN, p. A342
KLEFFMAN, Angela, Director of Ancillary Services, Bigfork Valley Hospital, Bigfork, MN, p. A328
KLEHN, Paul, Chief Information Technology Officer, Liberty Hospital, Liberty, MO, p. A364
KLEIN, Aron
Vice President Finance, Advocate Bromenn Medical Center, Normal, IL, p. A191
Vice President of Finance, Advocate Eureka Hospital, Eureka, IL, p. A182
KLEIN, Barbara, R.N., Director of Nursing, Arms Acres, Carmel, NY, p. A425
KLEIN, Bernard, Chief Executive, Providence Holy Cross Medical Center, Mission Hills, CA, p. A71
KLEIN, Cindy, Chief Executive Officer, Lamb Healthcare Center, Littlefield, TX, p. A620
KLEIN, Cindy C, Vice President Human Resources, Peacehealth St. Joseph Medical Center, Bellingham, WA, p. A670
KLEIN, David, Ph.D., Vice President Operations, Behavioral Health Network, Natchaug Hospital, Mansfield Center, CT, p. A108
KLEIN, David G., President, Saint Francis Memorial Hospital, San Francisco, CA, p. A85
KLEIN, Diany, Vice President Human Resources, Community Memorial Hospital, Ventura, CA, p. A93
KLEIN, Edward A, Chief Financial Officer, Johnston Health, Smithfield, NC, p. A462

KLEIN, Jacqueline, Chief Financial Officer, Marshfield Medical Center – Rice Lake, Rice Lake, WI, p. A704
KLEIN, Jillyn, Chief Operating Officer, Howard County Medical Center, Saint Paul, NE, p. A391
KLEIN, Julie, Chief Operating Officer, Mckee Medical Center, Loveland, CO, p. A104
KLEIN, Kenneth, M.D., Vice President Medical Affairs, Beloit Health System, Beloit, WI, p. A692
KLEIN, Kyle, Assistant Chief Financial Officer, Mercy Health – West Hospital, Cincinnati, OH, p. A476
KLEIN, Perry, Chief Engineering, Mann–Grandstaff Veterans Affairs Medical Center, Spokane, WA, p. A679
KLEIN, Terrence, Vice President and Chief Operating Officer, Franciscan Health Crawfordsville, Crawfordsville, IN, p. A202
KLEIN, Terrence, Ph.D., Vice President and Chief Operating Officer, Franciscan Health Crawfordsville, Crawfordsville, IN, p. A202
KLEINBECK, Seth M., M.D., Chief of Staff, Baptist Health Medical Center–Stuttgart, Stuttgart, AR, p. A49
KLEINE, Doug, IT Director, St. Mary Medical Center, Apple Valley, CA, p. A51
KLEINHANZL, Thomas A., President and Chief Executive Officer, Frederick Regional Health System, Frederick, MD, p. A290
KLEINSASSER, Dustin, Information Technology and BioMed, Fall River Hospital, Hot Springs, SD, p. A561
KLEINSMITH, Carmen, MSN, R.N., Vice President, Chief Nurse Executive, Unitypoint Health – St. Luke'S Hospital, Cedar Rapids, IA, p. A218
KLEINSTEUBER, Kathy, Chief Executive Officer, Rehabilitation Hospital Of Savannah, Savannah, GA, p. A160
KLENKE, Lisa R., Chief Executive Officer, Mercer Health, Coldwater, OH, p. A478
KLENNER, Susan, Chief Nursing Officer and Vice President of Hospital Operations, Olmsted Medical Center, Rochester, MN, p. A338
KLEPIN, Michael R, Administrator, Hunt Regional Medical Center, Greenville, TX, p. A608
KLESS, Adam
Chief Nursing Officer, Highlands Regional Medical Center, Sebring, FL, p. A139
Chief Nursing Officer, Raulerson Hospital, Okeechobee, FL, p. A133
KLESSENS, Thomas
Chief Financial Officer, Landmark Medical Center, Woonsocket, RI, p. A548
Chief Financial Officer, Rehabilitation Hospital Of Rhode Island, North Smithfield, RI, p. A547
KLEVEN, Brian, Chief Financial Officer, St. Rose Dominican Hospitals – Siena Campus, Henderson, NV, p. A394
KLIEWER, Chad, Information Technology Specialist, Mercy Hospital Kingfisher, Kingfisher, OK, p. A501
KLIMEK, David
Chief Human Resources Officer, Miami County Medical Center, Paola, KS, p. A243
Vice President Human Resources, Olathe Medical Center, Olathe, KS, p. A242
KLIMP, Mary J., Interim Administrator, Mayo Clinic Health System In New Prague, New Prague, MN, p. A336
KLINE, Brian S, Vice President and Chief Financial Officer, Penn Highlands Dubois, Dubois, PA, p. A524
KLINE, Burke, Chief Executive Officer, Greeley County Health Services, Tribune, KS, p. A246
KLINE, Daniel B, Vice President, Site Administrator, St. Joseph'S University Medical Center, Paterson, NJ, p. A410
KLINE, Donald E., President and Chief Executive Officer, Mercy Health – St. Elizabeth Youngstown Hospital, Youngstown, OH, p. A495
KLINE, Jack, M.D., Chief of Staff, Mercyone New Hampton Medical Center, New Hampton, IA, p. A227
KLINE, Julie, R.N., Senior Vice President Patient Services, Adventist Health Sonora, Sonora, CA, p. A90
KLINE, Mark W, M.D., Physician in Chief, Texas Children'S Hospital, Houston, TX, p. A614
KLINE, Melissa, Chief Nursing Officer, Metrohealth Medical Center, Cleveland, OH, p. A478
KLINGA, Maria, Director Management Information Systems, Silver Hill Hospital, New Canaan, CT, p. A109
KLINGEMAN, Jennifer, Director of Nursing, Chester Mental Health Center, Chester, IL, p. A176
KLINGENBERG, Pat, Director Human Resources, Towner County Medical Center, Cando, ND, p. A465
KLINGLER, Stacie, R.N., Vice President of Patient Services, Franciscan Health Rensselear, Rensselaer, IN, p. A214
KLINGSEIS, Robert, Director Information Systems, Desert Regional Medical Center, Palm Springs, CA, p. A76
KLINK, Sheryl, Chief Financial Officer, Piedmont Hospital, Atlanta, GA, p. A146
KLINKNER, Donna M, Chief Financial Officer, Madelia Community Hospital, Madelia, MN, p. A334
KLOCK, Kathy, R.N., Senior Vice President Clinical Operations and Human Resources, Gundersen Lutheran Medical Center, La Crosse, WI, p. A697
KLOCKMAN, Dena, Chief Financial Officer, Ogallala Community Hospital, Ogallala, NE, p. A388
KLOCKO, Daniel, Vice President Human Resources, Kootenai Health, Coeur D'Alene, ID, p. A169
KLOECKNER, Vicki, Director Human Resources, Hshs Holy Family Hospital In Greenville, Greenville, IL, p. A184
KLOEWER, Ron, Chief Information Officer, Montgomery County Memorial Hospital, Red Oak, IA, p. A228
KLOPFER, Anthony Rudy., Director, Veterans Affairs Eastern Kansas Health Care System, Topeka, KS, p. A246
KLOPP, Amanda, Director, Innovation and Clinical Integration, Penn State Health St. Joseph, Reading, PA, p. A539
KLOPPE, William, Chief Financial Officer, Geary Community Hospital, Junction City, KS, p. A237
KLOSTERMEIER, Janice, Senior Vice President and Chief Financial Officer, Valley Presbyterian Hospital, Los Angeles, CA, p. A70
KLUESNER, Kevin, Chief Administrative Officer, Ascension Southeast Wisconsin Hospital – St. Joseph'S Campus, Milwaukee, WI, p. A700
KLUGE, Thomas S.
President, Hampshire Memorial Hospital, Romney, WV, p. A689
President, War Memorial Hospital, Berkeley Springs, WV, p. A683
KLUGHERZ, Greg, Vice President Corporate Services and Chief Financial Officer, St. Cloud Hospital, Saint Cloud, MN, p. A339
KMETZ, Thomas D., Interim Chief Executive Officer, Johns Hopkins All Children'S Hospital, Saint Petersburg, FL, p. A138
KNACKSTEDT, Cameron, D.O., Chief Medical Staff, Harlan County Health System, Alma, NE, p. A382
KNACKSTEDT, Nathan, D.O., Chief of Staff, Clara Barton Hospital, Hoisington, KS, p. A236
KNAK, Roger, Administrator and Chief Executive Officer, Fairview Regional Medical Center, Fairview, OK, p. A500
KNAPHEIDE, Debbie, Site Administrator, Chief Nursing Officer and Chief Operating Officer, Carondelet Holy Cross Hospital, Nogales, AZ, p. A32
KNAPHEIDE, Debbie, MSN, Site Administrator, Chief Nursing Officer and Chief Operating Officer, Carondelet Holy Cross Hospital, Nogales, AZ, p. A32
KNAPIK, Steven, M.D., Chief of Staff, Bear Valley Community Hospital, Big Bear Lake, CA, p. A53
KNAPP, Brian A, Vice President Operations, Fairview Ridges Hospital, Burnsville, MN, p. A329
KNE, Tanya, M.D., Chief Medical Officer, Banner Desert Medical Center, Mesa, AZ, p. A31
KNECHT, Brian J, Chief Operating Officer, Regional Medical Center Of San Jose, San Jose, CA, p. A86
KNECHT, John, Chief Medical Staff, Linton Hospital, Linton, ND, p. A468
KNEDLER, Marie E., Interim President, Chi Health Creighton University Medical Center – Bergan Mercy, Omaha, NE, p. A388
KNEELAND, Misty, Chief Medical Staff, Medical Center Of South Arkansas, El Dorado, AR, p. A41
KNEISEL, Kristin, Interim Director, Information Services, Alice Peck Day Memorial Hospital, Lebanon, NH, p. A400
KNEPP, Gary, D.O., Regional Chief Medical Officer and Chief Quality Officer, Unitypoint Health – Peoria, Peoria, IL, p. A193
KNEPP, Keith
President and Chief Executive Officer, Unitypoint Health – Peoria, Peoria, IL, p. A193
President and Chief Executive Officer, Unitypoint Health – Proctor, Peoria, IL, p. A193
President and Chief Executive Officer, Unitypoint Health–Pekin Hospital, Pekin, IL, p. A193
KNIEVEL, Lon, Chief Executive Officer, Osmond General Hospital, Osmond, NE, p. A390
KNIFFIN, Fred, M.D., Chief Medical Officer, Porter Medical Center, Middlebury, VT, p. A654
KNIGHT, Beth, Chief Nursing Officer, Nacogdoches Memorial Hospital, Nacogdoches, TX, p. A626
KNIGHT, Bethany, M.D., Chief of Staff, Izard County Medical Center, Calico Rock, AR, p. A40
KNIGHT, Christopher D., Vice President Finance and Chief Financial Officer, Reid Health, Richmond, IN, p. A214
KNIGHT, Deana, Chief Executive Officer, Select Specialty Hospital–Greensboro, Greensboro, NC, p. A455
KNIGHT, Don, Assistant Administrator and Risk Manager, Teche Regional Medical Center, Morgan City, LA, p. A274
KNIGHT, Jennifer, Manager Human Resources, Waynesboro Hospital, Waynesboro, PA, p. A543
KNIGHT, Kimber, Chief Financial Officer, Braxton County Memorial Hospital, Gassaway, WV, p. A685
KNIGHT, Laura, Chief Nursing Officer, Merit Health Central, Jackson, MS, p. A349
KNIGHT, Mark T, Executive Vice President and Chief Financial Officer, Jackson Health System, Miami, FL, p. A130
KNIGHT, Michael, M.D., Medical Director, Hampstead Hospital, Hampstead, NH, p. A400
KNIGHT, Reginald Q., Chief Medical Officer, Aurelia Osborn Fox Memorial Hospital, Oneonta, NY, p. A440
KNIGHT, Ricardo, Interim Medical Director, Van Matre Encompass Health, Rockford, IL, p. A195
KNIGHT, Ronny, President and Chief Executive Officer, The Connecticut Hospice, Branford, CT, p. A107
KNIGHT, Terry, Public Information Officer and Administrative Assistant, California Mens Colony Correctional Treatment Center, San Luis Obispo, CA, p. A87
KNIGHT, Warren, Chief Financial Officer, Baton Rouge Behavioral Hospital, Baton Rouge, LA, p. A263
KNIGHT, Wayne
Chief Financial Officer, Indiana University Health Frankfort, Frankfort, IN, p. A204
Director Finance, St. Vincent Clay Hospital, Brazil, IN, p. A200
KNIGHT, Wesley, Chief Financial Officer, Ut Health Henderson, Henderson, TX, p. A610
KNIPP, Cindi, Director Human Resources, Rooks County Health Center, Plainville, KS, p. A244
KNISLEY, Shane, Chief Operating Officer, Mercy Health – Fairfield Hospital, Fairfield, OH, p. A483
KNITT, Lori, Chief Nursing Officer, Aurora Sheboygan Memorial Medical Center, Sheboygan, WI, p. A705
KNOBLOCH, Stanley, Director Fiscal Services, Sanford Luverne Medical Center, Luverne, MN, p. A334
KNOCKE, Michael, Chief Information Officer, Kansas Spine And Specialty Hospital, Wichita, KS, p. A248
KNODE, Scott, Chief Financial Officer, Veterans Memorial Hospital, Waukon, IA, p. A231
KNOEPFFLER, Susan, R.N., Vice President Nursing, Huntington Hospital, Huntington, NY, p. A429
KNOEPFLEIN, Susan, Chief Nurse Executive, Fulton State Hospital, Fulton, MO, p. A360
KNOEPFLER, David, M.D., Chief Medical Officer, Overlake Medical Center, Bellevue, WA, p. A670
KNOERL, Thomas, Vice President Finance, Spectrum Health Reed City Hospital, Reed City, MI, p. A320
KNORR, Kelly, Chief Financial Officer, First Hospital Wyoming Valley, Kingston, PA, p. A528
KNOWLES, B K, D.O., Chief of Staff, Pershing Memorial Hospital, Brookfield, MO, p. A357
KNOWLES, Christy, Chief Human Resources Officer, Coosa Valley Medical Center, Sylacauga, AL, p. A23
KNOWLES, John, Director Human Resources, Clinch Valley Medical Center, Richlands, VA, p. A665
KNOWLES, Robert, M.D., Chief of Staff, Saint Thomas Highlands Hospital, Sparta, TN, p. A579
KNOWLES–SMITH, Peter, M.D., Medical Director, Bennett County Hospital And Nursing Home, Martin, SD, p. A561
KNOX, Dennis M., Chief Executive Officer, Mid–Columbia Medical Center, The Dalles, OR, p. A518
KNOX, Jody, Chief Operating Officer, Kindred Hospital Rancho, Rancho Cucamonga, CA, p. A79
KNOX, John, Senior Vice President and Chief Information Officer, Atrium Health University City, Charlotte, NC, p. A451
KNOX, Jud, Chief Executive Officer, York Hospital, York, ME, p. A285
KNOX, Roland, Chief Executive Officer, Northern Cochise Community Hospital, Willcox, AZ, p. A38
KNOX, Stacey A., Administrator, Rock County Hospital, Bassett, NE, p. A382
KNUDSEN, Jessica, Chief Operating Officer and Director Performance Improvement and Risk Management, Holly Hill Hospital, Raleigh, NC, p. A460
KNUDSEN, Mark, Director Fiscal Services, Shriners Hospitals For Children–Portland, Portland, OR, p. A516
KNUDSEN, Matthew, Director, Information Systems, Sheppard Pratt Health System, Baltimore, MD, p. A288
KNUDSON, Jenny, Controller, Hiawatha Community Hospital, Hiawatha, KS, p. A236
KNUDTEN, Kristine, M.D., Vice President Medical Affairs, Glencoe Regional Health, Glencoe, MN, p. A332
KNUTH, Kerry, Chief Operating Officer, Mercy Hospital Of Defiance, Defiance, OH, p. A481
KNUTSON, Holly, Manager Information Technology, Kittson Memorial Healthcare Center, Hallock, MN, p. A333
KNUTSON, John P, M.D., Chief Medical Staff, Delta County Memorial Hospital, Delta, CO, p. A98

KNUTSON, Larry, Director Finance, Centracare Health–Long Prairie, Long Prairie, MN, p. A334

KNYCH, Stephen, M.D., Chief Medical Officer, Adventhealth Fish Memorial, Orange City, FL, p. A134

KO, Dicken S.C., M.D., Vice President of Medical Affairs and Chief Medical Officer, St. Elizabeth'S Medical Center, Brockton, MA, p. A296

KO, Tommy, M.D., Chief Medical Officer, St. Joseph Medical Center, Kansas City, MO, p. A363

KOBELJA, Mark A., Director, Walter Reed National Military Medical Center, Bethesda, MD, p. A289

KOCH, Eric, Chief Nursing Officer, Northern Montana Health Care, Havre, MT, p. A377

KOCH, Holly, Chief Financial Officer, Girard Medical Center, Girard, KS, p. A235

KOCH, Jamie, R.N., Chief Nursing Officer, Thayer County Health Services, Hebron, NE, p. A386

KOCH, Joseph G., Chief Executive Officer, Meadowview Regional Medical Center, Maysville, KY, p. A257

KOCHIE, Daniel A, CPA, Chief Financial Officer, Samaritan Hospital – Main Campus, Troy, NY, p. A445

KOCHIS, Mary Ellen, MSN, R.N., Administrator Nursing Operations, Beaumont Hospital – Dearborn, Dearborn, MI, p. A309

KOCIOLA, Matthew, Senior Vice President and Chief Financial Officer, Upmc Somerset Hospital, Somerset, PA, p. A541

KOCOUREK, Cathie A., President, Aurora Medical Center – Manitowoc County, Two Rivers, WI, p. A707

KOCSIS, Dana
   Vice President Nursing and Operations, Cleveland Clinic Akron General Lodi Hospital, Lodi, OH, p. A485
   Vice President, Nursing and Operations, Cleveland Clinic Akron General Lodi Hospital, Lodi, OH, p. A485

KOCSIS, Violet, Chief Human Resources Officer, Hunterdon Healthcare, Flemington, NJ, p. A406

KOCZENT, Kurt, Executive Vice President and Chief Operating Officer, F. F. Thompson Hospital, Canandaigua, NY, p. A425

KODROFF, Kurt, Chief Executive Officer, Brookdale Hospital Medical Center, New York, NY, p. A432

KOEBKE, Troy L
   Director Human Resources Management, Bellin Hospital, Green Bay, WI, p. A696
   Director Human Resources, Bellin Psychiatric Center, Green Bay, WI, p. A696
   Human Resource Director, Bellin Health Oconto Hospital, Oconto, WI, p. A702

KOEHLER, Amy, Director Human Resources, Hshs Good Shepherd Hospital, Shelbyville, IL, p. A195

KOELE, Craig, Chief Executive Officer, Cornerstone Hospital Of Oklahoma–Muskogee, Muskogee, OK, p. A502

KOENIG, Donald E.
   Chief Operating Officer, Mercy Health – St. Joseph Warren Hospital, Warren, OH, p. A493
   Executive Vice President and Regional Chief Operating Officer, President, St. Elizabeth Youngstown Hospital, Mercy Health – St. Elizabeth Youngstown Hospital, Youngstown, OH, p. A495

KOENIG, Harris F., President and Chief Executive Officer, San Antonio Regional Hospital, Upland, CA, p. A93

KOENIG, Lori, Assistant Finance Director, Cleveland Clinic Avon Hospital, Avon, OH, p. A472

KOENIG, Mary, Chief Financial Officer, Vernon Memorial Healthcare, Elk Mound, WI, p. A694

KOEPKE, Eldon, Chief Financial Officer, Mitchell County Hospital Health Systems, Beloit, KS, p. A232

KOEPKE, Jennifer, R.N., Vice President of Patient Care Services and Chief Nursing Officer, Western Missouri Medical Center, Warrensburg, MO, p. A372

KOEPPEL-OLSEN, Carol, Vice President, Patient Care Services, Winter Haven Hospital, Winter Haven, FL, p. A144

KOERNER, Jill, Manager Employee Relations, Weisman Children'S Rehabilitation Hospital, Marlton, NJ, p. A408

KOERNIG, Felissa, President and Chief Operating Officer, Guthrie Towanda Memorial Hospital, Towanda, PA, p. A542

KOESSL, Brenda, R.N., Director of Nursing Services, Frances Mahon Deaconess Hospital, Glasgow, MT, p. A376

KOESTER, Jean, Manager Human Resources, Limestone Medical Center, Groesbeck, TX, p. A608

KOESTERER, Susan, Vice President, Finance, Alton Memorial Hospital, Alton, IL, p. A173

KOETTING, Edward, Chief Financial Officer, Bedford Veterans Affairs Medical Center, Edith Nourse Rogers Memorial Veterans Hospital, Bedford, MA, p. A294

KOHANKE, Crystal H, Group Vice President, Human Resources, Christus Santa Rosa Health System, San Antonio, TX, p. A633

KOHL, Randy T., Deputy Director, Health Services, Nebraska Penal And Correctional Hospital, Lincoln, NE, p. A387

KOHLENBERG, Chris, Chief Financial Officer, Lafayette Surgical Specialty Hospital, Lafayette, LA, p. A271

KOHLER, Douglas, M.D., Vice President Medical Operations, Marymount Hospital, Garfield Heights, OH, p. A483

KOHLER, Tracy
   Chief Executive Officer, Kindred Hospital Tomball, Tomball, TX, p. A641
   Chief Executive Officer, Kindred Hospital–Houston Northwest, Houston, TX, p. A612

KOHR, Kathy, Chief Financial Officer, Midmichigan Medical Center – West Branch, West Branch, MI, p. A325

KOHRER, Tammy, Director of Nursing–Acute, Wahiawa General Hospital, Wahiawa, HI, p. A166

KOINZAN, Leigh Jean, Director Finance, Boys Town National Research Hospital, Omaha, NE, p. A388

KOKJOHN, Bradley J, Chief Financial Officer, Fort Madison Community Hospital, Fort Madison, IA, p. A223

KOKJOHN, Vicki, Director Employee Relations, Fort Madison Community Hospital, Fort Madison, IA, p. A223

KOLACZ, Nicole, Chief Nursing Officer, Aultman Hospital, Canton, OH, p. A474

KOLB, Andy, Chief Executive Officer, Lillian M. Hudspeth Memorial Hospital, Sonora, TX, p. A637

KOLB, Edward, M.D., Medical Director, Boys Town National Research Hospital, Omaha, NE, p. A388

KOLB, Pat, Manager Information Technology, Mcleod Health Clarendon, Manning, SC, p. A555

KOLHEDE, Deborah, Vice President and Chief Operating Officer, St. Mary'S Medical Center, San Francisco, CA, p. A86

KOLLMEYER, Sherry, Vice President Human Resources, Youth Villages Inner Harbour Campus, Douglasville, GA, p. A152

KOLMAN, Bret, Chief Executive Officer, Centerpoint Medical Center, Independence, MO, p. A361

KOLODZIEJCYK, Wanda S, Director Human Resources, Cuero Community Hospital, Cuero, TX, p. A595

KOLODZIEJCZYK, Clayton, Chief Financial Officer, Meadowview Regional Medical Center, Maysville, KY, p. A257

KOLOSKY, John A, Executive Vice President and Chief Operating Officer, H. Lee Moffitt Cancer Center And Research Institute, Tampa, FL, p. A141

KOLSETH, Shelley V, Chief Financial Officer, Memorial Hospital Of Tampa, Tampa, FL, p. A141

KOMAN, Stuart, President and Chief Executive Officer, Walden Behavioral Care, Waltham, MA, p. A304

KOMANDURI, Ramanujam, M.D., Chief of Staff, Veterans Affairs Southern Nevada Healthcare System, North Las Vegas, NV, p. A396

KOMAR, Ellen M, R.N., Vice President Patient Care Services and Chief Nursing Officer, Stamford Hospital, Stamford, CT, p. A111

KOME, Hunter, Campus President, Prisma Health Oconee Memorial Hospital, Seneca, SC, p. A557

KOMINS, Jeff, M.D., Chief Medical Officer, Mercy Fitzgerald Hospital, Darby, PA, p. A524

KOMORNIK, Jeffrey, Director Human Resources, Milford Hospital, Milford, CT, p. A109

KONARSKI, Debbie, Interim Chief Financial Officer, Pottstown Hospital, Pottstown, PA, p. A539

KONECNE, Robin, Manager Human Resources, Kit Carson County Health Service District, Burlington, CO, p. A97

KONG, Mei, Chief Operating Officer, Brookdale Hospital Medical Center, New York, NY, p. A432

KONGARA, Rama, Chief Financial Officer, St. James Behavioral Health Hospital, Gonzales, LA, p. A267

KONIECZEK, Raymond, Chief Human Resources Officer, John F. Kennedy Memorial Hospital, Indio, CA, p. A62

KONKEL, Robert, Manager Finance, James A. Haley Veterans' Hospital–Tampa, Tampa, FL, p. A141

KONSAVAGE, Christian, M.D., Chief of Staff, Cumberland County Hospital, Burkesville, KY, p. A250

KOOIMAN, Thomas, Chief Executive Officer, Granite Falls Health, Granite Falls, MN, p. A333

KOOKEN, Kyron J., Chief Executive Officer, Kindred Hospital Dallas Central, Dallas, TX, p. A596

KOON, Rion, Chief Information Management Division, William Beaumont Army Medical Center, El Paso, TX, p. A603

KOOP, Steven, M.D., Chief Medical Officer, Medical Director, Gillette Children'S Specialty Healthcare, Saint Paul, MN, p. A339

KOOVAKADA, Philip, Chief Executive Officer, Nacogdoches Medical Center, Nacogdoches, TX, p. A625

KOOYMAN, James, Human Resources Manager, Seneca Healthcare District, Chester, CA, p. A54

KOPEL, Samuel, M.D., Medical Director, Brookdale Hospital Medical Center, New York, NY, p. A432

KOPFLE, Sue, Chief Human Resources Officer, University Of Missouri Health Care, Columbia, MO, p. A359

KOPIN, Jeffrey D., Senior Vice President and Chief Medical Officer, Northwestern Medicine Lake Forest Hospital, Lake Forest, IL, p. A187

KOPITNIK, Thomas, Acting Chief Executive Officer, Mountain View Regional Hospital, Casper, WY, p. A710

KOPPELMAN, Benjamin
   Interim President, Chi Lakewood Health, Baudette, MN, p. A328
   President, Chi St. Joseph'S Health, Park Rapids, MN, p. A337

KOPPENHAVER, Colleen, Interim Chief Financial Officer, Amita Health Resurrection Medical Center, Chicago, IL, p. A176

KOPPERUD, Gordon, Director Operations, Sanford Westbrook Medical Center, Westbrook, MN, p. A342

KORBEL, Tamara, Director Management Information Systems, Ridgeview Medical Center, Waconia, MN, p. A342

KORDAHL, Rebecca, R.N., Associate Director, Patient Care Services, William S. Middleton Memorial Veterans Hospital, Madison, WI, p. A699

KORDUCKI, Stanley R., President, Wood County Hospital, Bowling Green, OH, p. A473

KORDUPEL, Maureen
   Director Information Technology Relationship Manager, Mercy Health – St. Elizabeth Boardman Hospital, Boardman, OH, p. A473
   Director Relationship Manager, Mercy Health – St. Elizabeth Youngstown Hospital, Youngstown, OH, p. A495

KORF, Rick, Chief Financial Officer, Yuma District Hospital, Yuma, CO, p. A106

KORICH, Frank
   Senior Vice President, Operations, Finger Lakes Hospital, Geneva, NY, p. A428
   Senior Vice President, Operations, Soldiers And Sailors Memorial Hospital Of Yates County, Penn Yan, NY, p. A441

KORICH, Frank, FACHE, Senior Vice President, Operations, Finger Lakes Hospital, Geneva, NY, p. A428

KORKMAS, Ross, Chief Executive Officer, Palo Pinto General Hospital, Mineral Wells, TX, p. A625

KORN, Roy, M.D., Medical Director, Cobleskill Regional Hospital, Cobleskill, NY, p. A426

KORNBLATT, Lynne R, Chief Human Resources Officer, Einstein Medical Center Philadelphia, Philadelphia, PA, p. A534

KORNFIELD, Lee, M.D., Medical Director, St. Luke'S Rehabilitation Hospital, Boise, ID, p. A168

KOROLY, Marla, M.D., Chief Medical Officer and Senior Vice President Medical Affairs, Northern Westchester Hospital, Mount Kisco, NY, p. A432

KOROM, Nancy K
   Chief Nursing Officer and Vice President, Children'S Hospital Of Wisconsin–Fox Valley, Neenah, WI, p. A702
   Chief Nursing Officer and Vice President, Children'S Hospital Of Wisconsin, Milwaukee, WI, p. A701

KORPELA, Donita, R.N., Director of Patient Care Services, Mercy Hospital, Moose Lake, MN, p. A336

KORPIEL, Michael, Chief Executive Officer, Mercy San Juan Medical Center, Carmichael, CA, p. A54

KORRELL, Charlene, Chief Executive Officer, Weisbrod Memorial County Hospital, Eads, CO, p. A100

KORTE, Fred, Chief Financial Officer, Mclaren Flint, Flint, MI, p. A311

KORTH, Paul
   Chief Executive Officer, Cookeville Regional Medical Center, Cookeville, TN, p. A568
   Chief Financial Officer, Cookeville Regional Medical Center, Cookeville, TN, p. A568

KORTH–WHITE, Kirsten, President, Munson Healthcare Grayling Hospital, Grayling, MI, p. A313

KOSANOVICH, John, M.D., Executive Vice President Physician Enterprise and Chief Executive Officer, Covenant Medical Group, Covenant Healthcare, Saginaw, MI, p. A321

KOSANOVICH, John P, President, Watertown Regional Medical Center, Watertown, WI, p. A707

KOSE, William H, M.D., Vice President Quality and Medical Affairs, Bluffton Hospital, Bluffton, OH, p. A473

KOSEK, Kevin, Associate Director Operations, Iowa City Veterans Affairs Health Care System, Iowa City, IA, p. A224

KOSIER, Douglas D., Chief Executive Officer, Mason District Hospital, Havana, IL, p. A185

KOSLOW, Howard B, President and Chief Executive Officer, Promise Hospital Of Miss Lou, Vidalia, LA, p. A279

KOSMAN, Beth, Director Health Information Management, Ringgold County Hospital, Mount Ayr, IA, p. A226

KOSNIK, Linda, R.N., MSN, Chief Nursing Officer and Vice President, Patient Care Services, Sinai Hospital Of Baltimore, Baltimore, MD, p. A287

KOSNOSKY, David, M.D., Chief Medical Officer, University Hospitals Geauga Medical Center, Chardon, OH, p. A475

KOSTER, Tracy, Director Human Resources, Carlinville Area Hospital, Carlinville, IL, p. A175

KOSTERS, Gregory J, D.O., Chief Medical Officer, Osceola Community Hospital, Sibley, IA, p. A229

KOSTOK, Barbara, Manager Human Resources, Punxsutawney Area Hospital, Punxsutawney, PA, p. A539
KOSTURKO, MaryEllen, R.N., Senior Vice President Patient Care Operations and Chief Nursing Officer, Bridgeport Hospital, Bridgeport, CT, p. A107
KOSYLA, Gail, Chief Financial Officer and Senior Vice President Strategy, Hunterdon Healthcare, Flemington, NJ, p. A406
KOTIL, Drew, Director Information Technology, Crete Area Medical Center, Crete, NE, p. A384
KOTIN, Kathy, Chief Financial Officer, Banner – University Medical Center Phoenix, Phoenix, AZ, p. A33
KOTRBA, Mitchell, Chief Financial Officer, North Valley Health Center, Warren, MN, p. A342
KOTTENBROOK, Susan, Chief Executive Officer, Red River Behavioral Center, Bossier City, LA, p. A265
KOTTMANN, Bill, President and Chief Executive Officer, Edward Hospital, Naperville, IL, p. A190
KOUNS, Jaccel, Vice President and Executive Director, Montefiore Mount Vernon, Mount Vernon, NY, p. A432
KOUNTZ, David, M.D., Senior Vice President Medical Affairs, Hackensack Meridian Health Jersey Shore University Medical Center, Neptune, NJ, p. A408
KOUSKOLEKAS, Anthony, President, Pelham Medical Center, Greer, SC, p. A554
KOUTOUZOS, Connie L., Chief Executive Officer, Aspirus Iron River Hospitals & Clinics, Inc., Iron River, MI, p. A315
KOVAC, John, Facility Chief Information Officer, Veterans Affairs Pittsburgh Healthcare System, Pittsburgh, PA, p. A538
KOVACH, Andrew L, Vice President Human Resources and Chief Administrative Officer, Newton Medical Center, Newton, NJ, p. A410
KOVACS, Tina, Chief Financial Officer, Saint Francis Hospital–Bartlett, Bartlett, TN, p. A566
KOVAL, Matthew, M.D., Vice President Medical Affairs, Kidspeace Children'S Hospital, Orefield, PA, p. A533
KOVALSKI, Jerry, Director Information Systems, Madera Community Hospital, Madera, CA, p. A70
KOWALSKI, Brad, Director Information Technology, Marcus Daly Memorial Hospital, Hamilton, MT, p. A377
KOWALSKI, David, Chief Executive Officer, Kindred Hospital–La Mirada, La Mirada, CA, p. A63
KOWALSKI, Patrick A, Chief Financial Officer, Mercy Health – Anderson Hospital, Cincinnati, OH, p. A476
KOWNACKI, Dawn, Director Human Resources, Brooke Glen Behavioral Hospital, Fort Washington, PA, p. A526
KOWNACKI, Hamila
Chief Operating Officer, California Pacific Medical Center–St. Luke'S Campus, San Francisco, CA, p. A85
Chief Operating Officer, California Pacific Medical Center, San Francisco, CA, p. A85
KOZAI, Gerald T., President and Chief Executive Officer, St. Francis Medical Center, Lynwood, CA, p. A70
KOZAR, Michael A., Chief Executive Officer, Northwest Florida Community Hospital, Chipley, FL, p. A119
KOZEL, Kenneth D.
President and Chief Executive Officer, University Of Maryland Shore Medical Center At Chestertown, Chestertown, MD, p. A289
President and Chief Executive Officer, University Of Maryland Shore Medical Center At Dorchester, Cambridge, MD, p. A289
President and Chief Executive Officer, University Of Maryland Shore Medical Center At Easton, Easton, MD, p. A290
KOZEL, Mary Ann, Chief Fiscal, Wilmington Veterans Affairs Medical Center, Wilmington, DE, p. A114
KOZIK, Kelly, Director Human Resources, Encompass Health Reading Rehabilitation Hospital, Reading, PA, p. A539
KOZIKUSKI, Courtney, Chief Financial Officer, Stillwater Medical Perry, Perry, OK, p. A506
KOZIN, Scott, M.D., Chief of Staff, Shriners Hospitals For Children–Philadelphia, Philadelphia, PA, p. A536
KOZIOL, Michael J, Chief Financial Officer, Holyoke Medical Center, Holyoke, MA, p. A299
KRABILL, Emma, Chief Executive Officer, Scenic Mountain Medical Center, Big Spring, TX, p. A588
KRABLIN, Brett, M.D., Chief of Staff, Mercy Hospital Kingfisher, Kingfisher, OK, p. A501
KRAEGER, Russell, Interim Chief Executive Officer, St. Alexius Hospital – Broadway Campus, Saint Louis, MO, p. A370
KRAFT, Chris, Director Information Systems, York General, York, NE, p. A392
KRAFVE, Jake Matthew, Chief Financial Officer, Royal Oaks Hospital, Windsor, MO, p. A373
KRAHN, Lois E., Interim Chief Executive Officer, Mayo Clinic Hospital, Phoenix, AZ, p. A33
KRAHNERT, John F, M.D., Chief Medical Officer, Firsthealth Moore Regional Hospital, Pinehurst, NC, p. A460
KRAJEWSKI, David, Senior Vice President and Chief Financial Officer, Sinai Hospital Of Baltimore, Baltimore, MD, p. A287
KRAMER, Blake, Chief Executive Officer, Franklin Medical Center, Winnsboro, LA, p. A280
KRAMER, Danette, Chief Financial Officer, Regional Medical Center, Manchester, IA, p. A226
KRAMER, Janie, Chief Operating Officer, Sharp Memorial Hospital, San Diego, CA, p. A84
KRAMER, Karen, R.N., Vice President and System Chief Nursing Officer, Cox Medical Centers, Springfield, MO, p. A371
KRAMER, Kathryn, M.D., President Medical Staff, Unitypoint Health–Pekin Hospital, Pekin, IL, p. A193
KRAMER, Kevin, Chief Executive Officer, Modoc Medical Center, Alturas, CA, p. A50
KRAMER, Lynette, M.D., Chief Medical Officer, Boone County Health Center, Albion, NE, p. A382
KRAMER, Michael, Chief Executive Officer, Mercy Health – West Hospital, Cincinnati, OH, p. A476
KRAMER, Susan, Director of Human Resources, Levi Hospital, Hot Springs National Park, AR, p. A43
KRAMPITS, Carrie, Director Human Resources, Mckenzie Health System, Sandusky, MI, p. A322
KRANZ, Karl, M.D., Chief of Staff, Cascade Medical Center, Leavenworth, WA, p. A674
KRASON, Jane E., Chief Executive Officer, Appalachian Behavioral Healthcare, Athens, OH, p. A472
KRASS, Todd, Chief Executive Officer, Belton Regional Medical Center, Belton, MO, p. A356
KRAUKLIS, Gene
Regional Vice President Human Resources, Aurora Lakeland Medical Center, Elkhorn, WI, p. A694
Regional Vice President Human Resources, Aurora Medical Center Burlington, Burlington, WI, p. A693
KRAUS, Jason, Director Human Resources, Magruder Memorial Hospital, Port Clinton, OH, p. A490
KRAUS, John, M.D., Chief Medical Officer, Bryn Mawr Rehabilitation Hospital, Malvern, PA, p. A530
KRAUSE, Donna, Chief Information Officer, Harry S. Truman Memorial Veterans Hospital, Columbia, MO, p. A359
KRAUSE, Jason, R.N., Director of Nursing, River Oaks Hospital, New Orleans, LA, p. A275
KRAUSE, Jill A., Director, Kalamazoo Psychiatric Hospital, Kalamazoo, MI, p. A316
KRAUSE, Kim, Director Human Resources, Baylor Scott & White Heart & Vascular Hospital–Dallas, Dallas, TX, p. A595
KRAUSE, Steven, Manager Information Technology, Franciscan Healthcare Munster, Munster, IN, p. A212
KRAUSE, Wade, M.D., Chief Medical Officer, Connally Memorial Medical Center, Floresville, TX, p. A604
KRAUTSCHEID, Steven P, Ancillary Services Administrator, Tuality Healthcare, Hillsboro, OR, p. A513
KRAVETZ, Michael, M.D., Medical Director, Encompass Health Valley Of The Sun Rehabilitation Hospital, Glendale, AZ, p. A30
KRAVETZ, Todd, Chief of Staff, Wickenburg Community Hospital, Wickenburg, AZ, p. A38
KREATSOULAS, Nicholas, Vice President Medical Affairs, Mercy Health – St. Joseph Warren Hospital, Warren, OH, p. A493
KREBS, Christine
Director of Nursing, Ascension Sacred Heart Hospital, Tomahawk, WI, p. A707
Director or Nursing, Ascension St. Mary'S Hospital, Rhinelander, WI, p. A704
KREBS, Cindy, District Director Human Resources, Matagorda Regional Medical Center, Bay City, TX, p. A587
KREBS, George, M.D., Chief Medical Officer, Broughton Hospital, Morganton, NC, p. A458
KREBS, Mary Jane, President, Spring Harbor Hospital, Westbrook, ME, p. A285
KREBSBACH, Mayla, Chief Executive Officer, Vista Del Mar Hospital, Ventura, CA, p. A94
KREELEY, Chris, Director Nursing, Kessler Marlton Rehabilitation, Marlton, NJ, p. A408
KREHBIEL, Rod, M.D., Chief of Staff, Klickitat Valley Health, Goldendale, WA, p. A673
KREIDER, David, Controller, Wellspan Ephrata Community Hospital, Ephrata, PA, p. A525
KREIDLER, Marlene, Executive Director Human Resources, Adventist Health Bakersfield, Bakersfield, CA, p. A52
KREITINGER, Tate J., Chief Executive Officer, The Healthcenter, Kalispell, MT, p. A378
KREITZER, Teri, Director Human Resources, Saint Francis Medical Center, Cape Girardeau, MO, p. A357
KREJCI, Kathy Blair, Chief Nursing Officer, Marshall Medical Center, Placerville, CA, p. A78
KRELL, G Christopher, M.D., Chief of Staff, South Lincoln Medical Center, Kemmerer, WY, p. A711
KRELSTEIN, Michael, M.D., Medical Director, San Diego County Psychiatric Hospital, San Diego, CA, p. A84
KREN, John, Chief Financial Officer, St. John'S Medical Center And Living Center, Jackson, WY, p. A711
KRESHON, James, M.D., Medical Director, Encompass Health Harmarville Rehabilitation Hospital, Pittsburgh, PA, p. A537
KRETSCHMAN, Robin, MSN, R.N., Vice President Patient Care Services, Marshfield Medical Center, Marshfield, WI, p. A699
KRETSCHMER, Suzanne, Chief Executive Officer, Chg Cornerstone Hospital Conroe, Conroe, TX, p. A593
KRETZ, Blake, President, Texas Health Arlington Memorial Hospital, Arlington, TX, p. A583
KRETZINGER, Curt, Chief Operating Officer, Mosaic Life Care At St. Joseph – Medical Center, Saint Joseph, MO, p. A368
KRETZSCHMER, Kendra, Patient Care System Leader, Scheurer Hospital, Pigeon, MI, p. A319
KREUTNER, Ron, Chief Financial Officer, San Joaquin General Hospital, French Camp, CA, p. A59
KREUTZER, Kevin, Chief Financial Officer, Russell Regional Hospital, Russell, KS, p. A244
KREUZ, Betsy, Chief Financial Officer, Upmc Altoona, Altoona, PA, p. A520
KREUZER, Jay E., Chief Executive Officer, Kona Community Hospital, Kealakekua, HI, p. A166
KRHOVSKY, David, M.D., Vice President, Medical Affairs, Spectrum Health – Butterworth Hospital, Grand Rapids, MI, p. A313
KRIEGER, Cathy, Human Resources Director, Greene County Medical Center, Jefferson, IA, p. A225
KRIEGER, Mark, Vice President and Chief Financial Officer, Barnes–Jewish Hospital, Saint Louis, MO, p. A369
KRIEGER, Tim, Director Information Systems, Harnett Health System, Dunn, NC, p. A452
KRIER, Jennifer, Vice President Human Resources, Wesley Healthcare Center, Wichita, KS, p. A248
KRILICH, Chad, M.D.
Chief Med Officer–AMC/CMC, Multicare Auburn Medical Center, Auburn, WA, p. A670
Chief Medical Officer, Santa Rosa Memorial Hospital, Santa Rosa, CA, p. A89
KRINKE, Susan, Chief Executive Officer, Kindred Hospital Lima, Lima, OH, p. A485
KRIPAKARAN, Kasturi, M.D., Medical Director, Andrew Mcfarland Mental Health Center, Springfield, IL, p. A196
KRIPINSKI, Laura, Chief Nursing Officer, Forks Community Hospital, Forks, WA, p. A673
KRISHNAN, Radha, M.D., Chief Medical Officer, Antelope Valley Hospital, Lancaster, CA, p. A64
KRISHNASWAMY, Jaikumar, President, Baylor Scott & White Medical Center – Centennial, Frisco, TX, p. A606
KRISTEL, John, President and Chief Executive Officer, Good Shepherd Rehabilitation Hospital, Allentown, PA, p. A510
KRMPOTIC, Debra J., Chief Executive Officer, Banner Thunderbird Medical Center, Glendale, AZ, p. A30
KRODEL, Scott, Vice President Information Systems, Johnson Memorial Hospital, Franklin, IN, p. A204
KROESE, Brandi, Director Operations, West Springs Hospital, Grand Junction, CO, p. A101
KROESE, Robert D, FACHE, Chief Executive Officer, Pella Regional Health Center, Pella, IA, p. A228
KROESE, Robert D., Chief Executive Officer, Pella Regional Health Center, Pella, IA, p. A228
KROLICKI, Karen, Director, Human Resources, Beaumont Hospital – Taylor, Taylor, MI, p. A323
KROMER, Harold, Director Site Information Systems, Advocate Condell Medical Center, Libertyville, IL, p. A188
KRONENBERG, Seth, M.D., Chief Medical Officer, Crouse Health, Syracuse, NY, p. A445
KROSOFF, Mary June, Chief Human Resources Officer, Highlands Hospital, Connellsville, PA, p. A523
KROUSE, Donald, M.D., Chief of Staff, Trinity Hospital, Weaverville, CA, p. A94
KROUSE, Michael
Chief Information Officer Information Services, Ohiohealth Grady Memorial Hospital, Delaware, OH, p. A482
Chief Information Officer, Ohiohealth Doctors Hospital, Columbus, OH, p. A479
Chief Information Officer, Ohiohealth Grant Medical Center, Columbus, OH, p. A479
Chief Information Officer, Ohiohealth Riverside Methodist Hospital, Columbus, OH, p. A480
Senior Vice President Chief Information Officer, Ohiohealth Dublin Methodist Hospital, Dublin, OH, p. A482
KRUEGER, Christine, M.D., Chief of Staff, Munising Memorial Hospital, Munising, MI, p. A318
KRUEGER, Ellen, Director Human Resources, Chadron Community Hospital And Health Services, Chadron, NE, p. A384
KRUEGER, Eric, Chief Financial Officer, Mercy Hospital And Medical Center, Chicago, IL, p. A178

KRUEGER, James G., Chief Executive Officer, Brookdale Hospital Medical Center, New York, NY, p. A432
KRUEGER, Justin, President, Mercy Health – Clermont Hospital, Batavia, OH, p. A472
KRUEGER, Mary, Commanding Officer, Tripler Army Medical Center, Honolulu, HI, p. A165
KRUG, Robert J., Chief Executive Officer, Mount Sinai Rehabilitation Hospital, Hartford, CT, p. A108
KRUGEL, Gary M, Chief Financial Officer, Norwegian American Hospital, Chicago, IL, p. A179
KRUGER, Dale K., Chief Executive Officer, Mahnomen Health Center, Mahnomen, MN, p. A334
KRUGER, George, CPA, Chief Financial Officer, Comanche County Memorial Hospital, Lawton, OK, p. A501
KRUMMEL, Dere, Director Information Systems, Ochsner Medical Center – Kenner, Kenner, LA, p. A270
KRUMREY, Arthur J, Chief Information Officer, Loyola University Medical Center, Maywood, IL, p. A189
KRUMWIED, Robert D., President and Chief Executive Officer, Regional Mental Health Center, Merrillville, IN, p. A211
KRUPALA, Judith, R.N., Chief Nursing Officer, Cuero Community Hospital, Cuero, TX, p. A595
KRUSE, Joseph J
  Chief Administrative Officer, Mayo Clinic Health System – Franciscan Healthcare In Sparta, Sparta, WI, p. A705
  Executive Vice President, Mayo Clinic Health System – Franciscan Healthcare In La Crosse, La Crosse, WI, p. A698
KRUSE, Marcia, R.N., Director Nursing, Logan County Hospital, Oakley, KS, p. A242
KRUSE, Victoria, Manager Human Resources, Franklin General Hospital, Hampton, IA, p. A223
KRUSIE, Kathleen R, President, Community Hospital East, Indianapolis, IN, p. A206
KRUSIE, Kathleen R., President, Community Hospital North, Indianapolis, IN, p. A206
KRUYER–COLLINS, Emyle, Chief Human Resources Officer, Unity Medical & Surgical Hospital, Mishawaka, IN, p. A211
KRUZEL, Janet, Business Office Manager, Centracare Health–Melrose, Melrose, MN, p. A335
KRUZICK, Michael, Acting Chief Financial Officer, Norwalk Hospital, Norwalk, CT, p. A110
KRUZNER, Melinda, Chief Financial Officer, Lexington Medical Center, West Columbia, SC, p. A558
KRYSTOWIAK, Thomas P
  Chief Financial Officer, Thedacare Medical Center–Berlin, Berlin, WI, p. A692
  Vice President Finance, Theda Care Medical Center – Wild Rose, Wild Rose, WI, p. A708
KRZASTEK, Sue, Vice President Human Resources, Augusta Health, Fishersville, VA, p. A659
KRZYMOWSKI, David, M.D., Chief of Staff, Sanpete Valley Hospital, Mount Pleasant, UT, p. A649
KUBALA, Joseph
  Chief Financial Officer, St. Vincent Jennings Hospital, North Vernon, IN, p. A213
  Director Financial and Support Services, St. Vincent Salem Hospital, Salem, IN, p. A214
KUBALL, Lana, Director Administrative Services, Lucas County Health Center, Chariton, IA, p. A219
KUBE, Don, M.D., Chief Medical Officer, Dickinson County Healthcare System, Iron Mountain, MI, p. A314
KUBIAK, Phillip J., President, Hampstead Hospital, Hampstead, NH, p. A400
KUBICEK, Jim, Vice President, Operations, Rogers Memorial Hospital, Inc., Oconomowoc, WI, p. A702
KUBOTA, Andrea, R.N., MSN, Director Patient Care Services and Nurse Executive, Shriners Hospitals For Children–Honolulu, Honolulu, HI, p. A165
KUBOUSHEK, David, Chief, Fiscal Service, Durham Veterans Affairs Medical Center, Durham, NC, p. A453
KUCERA, Kim, Chief Operating Officer, Mille Lacs Health System, Onamia, MN, p. A337
KUCICH, Vincent, FACHE, FACS, M.D.
  Chief Medical Officer, Osf Heart Of Mary Medical Center, Urbana, IL, p. A197
  Chief Medical Officer, Osf Sacred Heart Medical Center, Danville, IL, p. A180
KUCKEWICH, Mike, Director Information Systems, Terre Haute Regional Hospital, Terre Haute, IN, p. A215
KUCZORA, Paul, Chief Executive Officer, Grant–Blackford Mental Health Center, Marion, IN, p. A211
KUDER, Merlin, Chief Information Officer, Hamilton County Hospital, Syracuse, KS, p. A246
KUDLA, Angela, MSN, R.N., Chief Nursing Officer, Select Specialty Hospital–Downriver, Wyandotte, MI, p. A325
KUEHLER, Sheila, R.N., Director of Nursing, Knox County Hospital, Knox City, TX, p. A618
KUEHLER, Stephen A., Administrator, Knox County Hospital, Knox City, TX, p. A618
KUEHN, David, Chief Financial Officer, Marshfield Medical Center – Ladysmith, Ladysmith, WI, p. A698
KUENNEN, Patrice, Chief Executive Officer, Gundersen Palmer Lutheran Hospital And Clinics, West Union, IA, p. A231
KUENY, Patrick, Chief Operating Officer, Lee'S Summit Medical Center, Lee'S Summit, MO, p. A364
KUEPERS, Kathleen, Chief Executive Officer, Memorial Hospital Of Lafayette County, Darlington, WI, p. A693
KUESTERSTEFFEN, Vicki, Director and Chief Executive Officer, J. D. Mccarty Center For Children With Developmental Disabilities, Norman, OK, p. A503
KUEVEN, John, Senior Vice President and President, Wellstar Paulding Hospital, Hiram, GA, p. A154
KUHAR, Peggy A, R.N., MSN, Chief Nursing Officer, University Hospitals Geauga Medical Center, Chardon, OH, p. A475
KUHARICH, Ryan, Chief Executive Officer, Aultman Specialty Hospital, Canton, OH, p. A474
KUHLMAN, Ian, Manager Information Technology, Hshs Good Shepherd Hospital, Shelbyville, IL, p. A195
KUHN, Anita, Controller, Texas County Memorial Hospital, Houston, MO, p. A361
KUHN, Brenda, Ph.D., R.N., FACHE
  Chief Nursing Officer, Greene Memorial Hospital, Xenia, OH, p. A494
  Chief Nursing Officer, Kettering Medical Center, Kettering, OH, p. A485
KUHN, Keith, Chief Executive Officer, Haven Behavioral Senior Care Of Dayton, Dayton, OH, p. A481
KUHN, Marguerite, M.D., Vice President Medical Affairs, Midmichigan Medical Center–Midland, Midland, MI, p. A318
KUHN, Mark, Chief Executive Officer, Hammond–Henry Hospital, Geneseo, IL, p. A184
KUHN, Steve, Chief Financial Officer, River Park Hospital, Huntington, WV, p. A686
KUHNS, Jay, Vice President Human Resources, Johns Hopkins All Children'S Hospital, Saint Petersburg, FL, p. A138
KUHRT, Sharon, Chief Nursing Officer, New England Rehabilitation Hospital Of Portland, Portland, ME, p. A284
KUIPER, Evert J., President and Chief Executive Officer, Hshs St. John'S Hospital, Springfield, IL, p. A196
KUKELHAN, Alison, Manager Human Resources, Adams Memorial Hospital, Decatur, IN, p. A202
KULHANEK, Linda, Chief Financial Officer, Memorial Hermann Katy Hospital, Katy, TX, p. A617
KULICK, Daniel, M.D., Chief of Staff, Marlette Regional Hospital, Marlette, MI, p. A317
KULIK, Alec G, Administrator, Cleveland Clinic Children'S Hospital For Rehabilitation, Cleveland, OH, p. A477
KULISZ, Michael, D.O.
  Chief Medical Officer, Northwestern Medicine Kishwaukee Hospital, Dekalb, IL, p. A181
  Vice President, Chief Medical Officer, Northwestern Medicine Valley West Hospital, Sandwich, IL, p. A195
KULLMAN, Betsy, R.N., MSN, Executive Vice President and Chief Nursing Officer, Medical Center At Bowling Green, Bowling Green, KY, p. A250
KULMA, Mariarose, R.N., Vice President Patient Services, Ut Health Tyler, Tyler, TX, p. A642
KUMAR, Deborah W, MSN, Chief Nursing Officer, Adventhealth Carrollwood, Tampa, FL, p. A141
KUMAR, Jaya, M.D., Chief Medical Officer, Medical City Mckinney, Mckinney, TX, p. A624
KUMAR, Nanda, M.D., Chief of Staff, Vibra Hospital Of Northern California, Redding, CA, p. A80
KUMMER, Margaret, Chief Human Resource Officer, Citizens Medical Center, Colby, KS, p. A233
KUNDU, Nabarun, Chief Executive Officer, Regency Hospital Of Columbus, Columbus, OH, p. A480
KUNERT, Alicia, Executive Director, Conway Regional Rehabilitation Hospital, Conway, AR, p. A40
KUNES, Courtney, Director Human Resources, Upmc Susquehanna Lock Haven, Lock Haven, PA, p. A530
KUNKEL, Elisabeth J., M.D., Professor, Pennsylvania State College of Medicine, Pennsylvania Psychiatric Institute, Harrisburg, PA, p. A526
KUNNAPPILLY, Chester, Interim Chief Executive Officer, San Mateo Medical Center, San Mateo, CA, p. A87
KUNSTLING, Ted, M.D., Chief Medical Officer, Duke Raleigh Hospital, Raleigh, NC, p. A460
KUNZ, Donna
  System Director Human Resources, Saint Luke'S Cushing Hospital, Leavenworth, KS, p. A239
  System Director Human Resources, Saint Luke'S North Hospital – Barry Road, Kansas City, MO, p. A363
  System Director Human Resources, Saint Luke'S South Hospital, Overland Park, KS, p. A243
KUNZA, Mary Kay, Manager Human Resources, Mercy Hospital Lincoln, Troy, MO, p. A372
KUOPUS, Lisa, Chief Nursing Officer, Legent Orthopedic + Spine, San Antonio, TX, p. A633
KUPER, Kandi, Chief Nursing Officer, Kit Carson County Health Service District, Burlington, CO, p. A97
KUPFERSTEIN, Ron, Chief Executive Officer, Monrovia Memorial Hospital, Monrovia, CA, p. A72
KUPLEN, Carol, President and Chief Executive Officer, St. Luke'S University Hospital – Bethlehem Campus, Bethlehem, PA, p. A520
KUPPLER, Sylvia, Chief Financial Officer, Belmont Pines Hospital, Youngstown, OH, p. A495
KURAITIS, Kestutis V, M.D., Chief of Staff, Pioneers Memorial Healthcare District, Brawley, CA, p. A53
KURCAB, Jeff, Chief Financial Officer, Lewisgale Hospital Pulaski, Pulaski, VA, p. A665
KUROKI, Helen, Senior Vice President and Chief Medical Officer, Chi Memorial, Chattanooga, TN, p. A567
KURRA, Shankar, M.D., Senior Vice President Medical Affairs, Fisher–Titus Medical Center, Norwalk, OH, p. A488
KURTZ, Kris, Chief Financial Officer, Metro Health – University Of Michigan Health, Wyoming, MI, p. A325
KURTZ, Maria
  Director Human Resources, Lutheran Hospital Of Indiana, Fort Wayne, IN, p. A204
  Director Human Resources, Orthopaedic Hospital Of Lutheran Health Network, Fort Wayne, IN, p. A204
KURTZ, Thomas F, Chief Operating Officer, Georgia Regional Hospital At Savannah, Savannah, GA, p. A160
KURTZ, Thomas M., President and Chief Executive Officer, Chan Soon–Shiong Medical Center, Windber, PA, p. A545
KURTZ, Tom, Vice President Information Services and Chief Information Officer, Memorial Healthcare, Owosso, MI, p. A319
KURZ, Kenneth R, M.D., Chief of Staff, Midstate Medical Center, Meriden, CT, p. A108
KURZ, Sharon H., Chief Executive Officer, St. Elias Specialty Hospital, Anchorage, AK, p. A25
KUSHNER, Michael S., Senior Vice President and Chief Talent Officer, Nicklaus Children'S Hospital, Miami, FL, p. A131
KUSLER, Julie, Manager Information Services, Avera St. Luke'S Hospital, Aberdeen, SD, p. A559
KUSNIERZ, William J., Vice President and Chief Financial Officer, Springfield Regional Medical Center, Springfield, OH, p. A491
KUTCH, John M., President, Trinity Health, Minot, ND, p. A469
KUTILEK, Richard J, Chief Operating Officer, Brookdale Hospital Medical Center, New York, NY, p. A432
KUTNER, Jean, M.D., Chief Medical Officer, University Of Colorado Hospital, Aurora, CO, p. A96
KUVSHINOFF, Boris, M.D., Chief Medical Officer, Roswell Park Comprehensive Cancer Center, Buffalo, NY, p. A424
KUYKENDALL, Jana, Chief Executive Officer, Post Acute/ Warm Springs Specialty Hospital Of Luling, Luling, TX, p. A623
KUZAS, Betsy, Executive Vice President and Chief Operating Officer, Phoenix Children'S Hospital, Phoenix, AZ, p. A34
KUZEE, Ann, Executive Director Human Resources, Riverview Health, Noblesville, IN, p. A213
KWIATEK, Susan, Executive Director, Glen Cove Hospital, Glen Cove, NY, p. A428
KWIESIELEWICZ, Nancy
  Human Resources Manager, Ascension Good Samaritan Hospital, Merrill, WI, p. A700
  Human Resources Manager, Ascension Saint Clare'S Hospital, Weston, WI, p. A708
KYHNELL, Koreen H, Vice President Human Resources, Indiana University Health Arnett Hospital, Lafayette, IN, p. A209
KYLER, Yvonne
  Director Human Resources, Texas Health Arlington Memorial Hospital, Arlington, TX, p. A583
  Director Human Resources, Texas Health Heart & Vascular Hospital Arlington, Arlington, TX, p. A584
KYWI, Alberto
  Chief Information Officer, Goleta Valley Cottage Hospital, Santa Barbara, CA, p. A88
  Chief Information Officer, Santa Barbara Cottage Hospital, Santa Barbara, CA, p. A88

L

LA CAVA, Joseph, Chief Nursing Officer and Director of Anesthesia, Desoto Memorial Hospital, Arcadia, FL, p. A117
LA CROIX, Kent, Chief Information Officer, Schoolcraft Memorial Hospital, Manistique, MI, p. A317

LABADIE, Wendy, Chief Human Resource Officer, Banner Estrella Medical Center, Phoenix, AZ, p. A33
LABAGNARA, James, M.D., Vice President Medical Affairs, St. Joseph'S University Medical Center, Paterson, NJ, p. A410
LABARBERA, Sonja, President and Chief Executive Officer, Gaylord Hospital, Wallingford, CT, p. A111
LABARGE, Robert J., President and Chief Executive Officer, Sturgis Hospital, Sturgis, MI, p. A323
LABELLE, Douglas, M.D., Chief Medical Officer, Up Health System–Bell, Ishpeming, MI, p. A315
LABELLE, James, M.D.
Chief Medical Officer, Scripps Green Hospital, La Jolla, CA, p. A62
Chief Medical Officer, Scripps Memorial Hospital–La Jolla, La Jolla, CA, p. A63
LABONTE, Karen Y, Chief Nursing Officer, Northwest Medical Center – Springdale, Springdale, AR, p. A48
LABONTE, Robin, Leader Financial Care, York Hospital, York, ME, p. A285
LABOUCHARDIERE, Mark, Interim Facility Administrator, Lincoln Regional Center, Lincoln, NE, p. A387
LABRIOLA, Suzanne M., D.O., Chief Medical Officer, Allegheny Valley Hospital, Natrona Heights, PA, p. A533
LABRIOLA, Terri, Human Resources Officer, Sierra Nevada Memorial Hospital, Grass Valley, CA, p. A61
LABRUM, Chad, Chief Financial Officer, Ashley Regional Medical Center, Vernal, UT, p. A653
LACAZE, Todd, Chief Financial Officer, Riverside Community Hospital, Riverside, CA, p. A81
LACEFIELD, Gayla, Director Human Resources, Howard Memorial Hospital, Nashville, AR, p. A46
LACEY, Carmen, President, Charles A. Cannon Memorial Hospital, Newland, NC, p. A459
LACEY, Carmen, MSN, R.N., President and Director of Patient Care Services, Charles A. Cannon Memorial Hospital, Newland, NC, p. A459
LACEY, Paul, M.D., Chief Medical Staff, North Valley Hospital, Tonasket, WA, p. A681
LACHANCE, Eric, Chief Financial Officer, Adventhealth Ocala, Ocala, FL, p. A133
LACHAPELLE, Diana, Chief Executive Officer, Encompass Health Rehabilitation Hospital Of Concord, Concord, NH, p. A399
LACHER, Paula A, MSN, R.N., Chief Nursing Officer, West Penn Hospital, Pittsburgh, PA, p. A538
LACHINA, Ignazio, M.D., Medical Director, Encompass Health Rehabilitation Hospital Of Cypress, Houston, TX, p. A611
LACHNEY, Cheryl, Director of Nursing, Compass Behavioral Center Of Alexandria, Alexandria, LA, p. A262
LACHOWSKY, John, M.D., Chief Medical Officer, Mercy Hospital Ozark, Ozark, AR, p. A47
LACINA, Amy, R.N., Director of Nursing, North Shore Health, Grand Marais, MN, p. A332
LACKEY, Lori, Chief Financial Officer, Sabetha Community Hospital, Sabetha, KS, p. A244
LACKMAN, Vickie, Human Resource Director, Peninsula Region, Harrison Medical Center, Bremerton, WA, p. A670
LACKNEY, Christopher J, Director Human Resources, Grace Cottage Hospital, Townshend, VT, p. A655
LACOT, Ivette, Director Human Resources, Hospital Episcopal San Lucas Guayama, Guayama, PR, p. A716
LACY, Angela, Director of Nursing, Bolivar General Hospital, Bolivar, TN, p. A566
LACY, Julie, Chief Financial Officer, Crete Area Medical Center, Crete, NE, p. A384
LACY, Tyson, Chief Executive Officer and Superintendent, Lincoln Hospital, Davenport, WA, p. A672
LADAROLA, Sandra, Chief Nursing Officer, Waterbury Hospital, Waterbury, CT, p. A112
LADD, Bill, Director Information Services, Western Missouri Medical Center, Warrensburg, MO, p. A372
LADEVICH, Michael, Interim Chief Executive Officer, Murray County Medical Center, Slayton, MN, p. A340
LADWIG, Michael, M.D., Chief of Staff, Marion Veterans Affairs Medical Center, Marion, IL, p. A188
LADY, Brian, Administrator and Chief Executive Officer, Concho County Hospital, Eden, TX, p. A601
LAFERNEY, Jimmy, M.D., Vice President Medical Staff Affairs, Baylor Scott & White Medical Center–Frisco, Frisco, TX, p. A606
LAFFEY, Leah, Chief Executive Officer, Encompass Health Rehabilitation Hospital Of Sewickley, Sewickley, PA, p. A541
LAFLAMME, Christine, R.N., MSN, Chief Nursing Officer, Ascension Seton Smithville, Smithville, TX, p. A637
LAFRANCOIS, Gregory, President, The Aroostook Medical Center, Presque Isle, ME, p. A284
LAFRANCOIS, Mary, Vice President Human Resources, Christus Spohn Hospital Corpus Christi Memorial, Corpus Christi, TX, p. A594
LAGASSE, David A, Senior Vice President Fiscal Affairs, Mclean Hospital, Belmont, MA, p. A294
LAGNESE, John, M.D., Vice President Medical Affairs, Upmc St. Margaret, Pittsburgh, PA, p. A538
LAGROU, Robert, D.O., Medical Director, Henry Ford Kingswood Hospital, Ferndale, MI, p. A311
LAGUNA, Joanne, Vice President of Hospital Operations and Chief Nursing Officer, Marina Del Rey Hospital, Marina Del Rey, CA, p. A71
LAHAYE, Daniel, Manager, Savoy Medical Center, Mamou, LA, p. A273
LAHOOD, Amy, R.N., Director of Nursing, Vermilion Behavioral Health Systems – North Campus, Lafayette, LA, p. A271
LAHOUT, Brenda, Chief Nurse Executive, Danville State Hospital, Danville, PA, p. A523
LAHTI, Molly, Director Human Resources, Parkland Medical Center, Derry, NH, p. A399
LAI, Iris, Chief Executive Officer, Alhambra Hospital Medical Center, Alhambra, CA, p. A50
LAIBINIS, Walter, M.D., Chief Medical Officer, Upmc Susquehanna Soldiers + Sailors, Wellsboro, PA, p. A544
LAIGN, Michael B., President and Chief Executive Officer, Holy Redeemer Hospital, Meadowbrook, PA, p. A531
LAIL, Steve, Chief Executive Officer, Down East Community Hospital, Machias, ME, p. A284
LAIOSA, Sarah, M.D., Chief Medical Staff, Harney District Hospital, Burns, OR, p. A511
LAIRD, Alan, M.D., Chief Medical Officer, Orange City Area Health System, Orange City, IA, p. A227
LAIRD, David, Chief Executive Officer, St. David'S Medical Center, Austin, TX, p. A586
LAIRD, Jeff, Controller, Stephens County Hospital, Toccoa, GA, p. A162
LAIRD, Laci, Chief Executive Officer, Oceans Behavioral Hospital Lufkin, Lufkin, TX, p. A622
LAIRD, Shaw, Chief Information Officer, Musc Health Chester Medical Center, Chester, SC, p. A550
LAISTER, Judy K, Director, Human Resources, Methodist Mansfield Medical Center, Mansfield, TX, p. A623
LAKE, Chandra, Associate Director, Sheridan Veterans Affairs Medical Center, Sheridan, WY, p. A712
LAKE, Monica, Chief Nursing Officer, Louisiana Extended Care Hospital Of Lafayette, Lafayette, LA, p. A271
LAKE, Nathan, Vice President Human Resources, Prairie Lakes Healthcare System, Watertown, SD, p. A565
LAKE, Peter M, M.D., Chief Medical Officer, Rogers Memorial Hospital, Inc., Oconomowoc, WI, p. A702
LAKE, Ryan, Director Information Technology, Glencoe Regional Health, Glencoe, MN, p. A332
LAKEY, Travis, Chief Financial Officer, Mayers Memorial Hospital District, Fall River Mills, CA, p. A58
LALAS, Angela, Senior Vice President, Finance, Loma Linda University Children'S Hospital, Loma Linda, CA, p. A64
LALIBERTE, John, Chief Information Officer, St. Vincent'S Blount, Oneonta, AL, p. A22
LALIOTIS, Anna, Chief Executive Officer, Mesilla Valley Hospital, Las Cruces, NM, p. A418
LALLY, Robert P, Vice President Finance, Medstar Franklin Square Medical Center, Baltimore, MD, p. A288
LAM, Shiva, M.D., Executive Medical Director, Austin Lakes Hospital, Austin, TX, p. A585
LAM, Thomas, Chief Medical Officer, Garfield Medical Center, Monterey Park, CA, p. A73
LAMADELEINE, Joseph, Chief Financial Officer, Veterans Affairs Connecticut Healthcare System, West Haven, CT, p. A112
LAMANTEER, Mike, M.D., Senior Vice President Medical Affairs, Bsa Hospital, Llc, Amarillo, TX, p. A582
LAMARCHE, Heather, Manager Human Resources, Amg Specialty Hospital–Lafayette, Lafayette, LA, p. A270
LAMARCHE, Maximo, M.D., Chief Medical Officer, Amg Specialty Hospital–Lafayette, Lafayette, LA, p. A270
LAMB, Andrew, M.D., Chief of Staff, Alamance Regional Medical Center, Burlington, NC, p. A450
LAMB, Cindy, Director Human Resources, Marias Medical Center, Shelby, MT, p. A380
LAMB, Deanna, Director Human Resources, Central Carolina Hospital, Sanford, NC, p. A462
LAMB, Hope, Manager Human Resources, Kimble Hospital, Junction, TX, p. A617
LAMB, Joshua, Vice President Operations, Christus Health Shreveport–Bossier, Shreveport, LA, p. A278
LAMB, Mollee, Manager Human Resources, Lds Hospital, Salt Lake City, UT, p. A651
LAMB–PAGONE, Jerilynn, Nurse Executive, Connecticut Valley Hospital, Middletown, CT, p. A109
LAMBERT, Amand, Director Human Resources, Allen Parish Community Healthcare, Kinder, LA, p. A270
LAMBERT, Barbara, Director Healthcare Compliance, Eastern State Hospital, Williamsburg, VA, p. A668
LAMBERT, Cheryl, Chief Financial Officer, Acuity Specialty Hospital Of New Jersey, Atlantic City, NJ, p. A403
LAMBERT, James M., Chief Executive Officer, Memorial Hospital And Manor, Bainbridge, GA, p. A148
LAMBERT, Karen A., President, Advocate Good Shepherd Hospital, Barrington, IL, p. A174
LAMBERT, Lynn, Chief Financial Officer, Harnett Health System, Dunn, NC, p. A452
LAMBERT, Paul, M.D., Chief of Staff, Boise Veterans Affairs Medical Center, Boise, ID, p. A167
LAMBERT, Suzanne, R.N., Regional Chief Nursing Officer and Support Services, Amita Health Saints Mary & Elizabeth Medical Center, Chicago, IL, p. A176
LAMBETH, Laura, Chief Executive Officer, Ashe Memorial Hospital, Jefferson, NC, p. A457
LAMBRECHT, Craig, President and Chief Executive Officer, Kalispell Regional Healthcare, Kalispell, MT, p. A378
LAMEBULL, Charlotte, Administrative Officer, Fort Belknap Service Unit, Harlem, MT, p. A377
LAMEN, Drake M., President, Chief Executive Officer and Chief Medical Officer, Uhs Chenango Memorial Hospital, Norwich, NY, p. A440
LAMERS, Jamon
Director Finance, Ascension Eagle River Hospital, Eagle River, WI, p. A694
Director Finance, Ascension Sacred Heart Hospital, Tomahawk, WI, p. A707
Director Finance, Ascension St. Mary'S Hospital, Rhinelander, WI, p. A704
Director Finance, Howard Young Medical Center, Woodruff, WI, p. A709
LAMEY, Mark, Commander, U. S. Air Force Regional Hospital, Elmendorf Afb, AK, p. A26
LAMEY, Rebecca, Vice President Human Resources, Mainegeneral Medical Center, Augusta, ME, p. A281
LAMLE, Sandra, Chief Financial Officer, Okeene Municipal Hospital, Okeene, OK, p. A503
LAMMERS, Sandra, Coordinator Human Resources and Finance, Chi Health Mercy Corning, Corning, IA, p. A219
LAMONT, Jennifer
Chief Financial Officer, West Suburban Medical Center, Oak Park, IL, p. A192
Chief Financial Officer, Westlake Hospital, Melrose Park, IL, p. A189
LAMORELLA, Vincent M, Chief Financial Officer, Clarion Hospital, Clarion, PA, p. A522
LAMOUREUX, John P., Commander, Dwight David Eisenhower Army Medical Center, Fort Gordon, GA, p. A153
LAMOUREUX, Laurie, Director of Finance, Cooley Dickinson Hospital, Northampton, MA, p. A301
LAMPE, Michael, M.D., Chief of Staff, Kossuth Regional Health Center, Algona, IA, p. A217
LAMPE, Tammy K, Director Human Resources, Edwards County Medical Center, Kinsley, KS, p. A238
LAMPIE, Abbie, Director of Nursing, Kirkbride Center, Philadelphia, PA, p. A535
LAMPLEY, Danny, Chief Operating Officer, Harrisburg Medical Center, Harrisburg, IL, p. A184
LAMPLEY, Joseph, D.O., Chief of Staff, Fisher County Hospital District, Rotan, TX, p. A632
LAMPTON, Lucius, M.D., Medical Director, Beacham Memorial Hospital, Magnolia, MS, p. A350
LANCASTER, Brian, Executive Director Information Management, Nebraska Medicine – Bellevue, Bellevue, NE, p. A383
LANCASTER, Penny, Controller, Cascade Medical Center, Cascade, ID, p. A168
LANCASTER, William, Administrator, Compass Behavioral Center Of Alexandria, Alexandria, LA, p. A262
LANCTIN, Henri, M.D., Chief of Staff, Prairie Lakes Healthcare System, Watertown, SD, p. A565
LAND, Steve, Senior Administrator, Wamego Health Center, Wamego, KS, p. A247
LAND, Susann, M.D., Chief Medical Officer, Texas Health Harris Methodist Hospital Hurst–Euless–Bedford, Bedford, TX, p. A588
LANDERS, Alice, Administrative Director Operations, Texas Health Harris Methodist Hospital Hurst–Euless–Bedford, Bedford, TX, p. A588
LANDERS, Kimberly A., MS, R.N., Vice President Patient Care Services, Morris Hospital & Healthcare Centers, Morris, IL, p. A190
LANDERS, Lalah, R.N., Director of Nursing, Saunders Medical Center, Wahoo, NE, p. A392
LANDINI, Kristin
Vice President Human Resources, Advocate South Suburban Hospital, Hazel Crest, IL, p. A185
Vice President, Human Resources, Advocate Trinity Hospital, Chicago, IL, p. A176

LANDIS, Janie, Chief Financial Officer, Russell County Hospital, Russell Springs, KY, p. A260

LANDMAN, Adam, M.D., Chief Information Officer, Brigham And Women'S Hospital, Boston, MA, p. A295

LANDMAN, Paul, Director Human Resources, Ellwood City Medical Center, Llc, Ellwood City, PA, p. A525

LANDOLL, Therese, Interim Chief Financial Officer, Community Memorial Healthcare, Marysville, KS, p. A240

LANDON, Anna, Chief Nursing Officer, Mercy Hospital Washington, Washington, MO, p. A373

LANDRAU, Erika, Director Human Resources, Encompass Health Rehabilitation Hospital Of Manati, Manati, PR, p. A717

LANDRENEAU, John Derrick
Director of Nursing and Marketing Manager, Baton Rouge Rehabilitation Hospital, Baton Rouge, LA, p. A263
Director of Nursing, Baton Rouge Rehabilitation Hospital, Baton Rouge, LA, p. A263

LANDRETH, Jonathan, Administrator, United Medical Rehabilitation Hospital, Hammond, LA, p. A268

LANDRETH, Kathy, Chief Executive Officer, Bath Community Hospital, Hot Springs, VA, p. A661

LANDRETH, Sandy, Director Human Resources, Seiling Regional Medical Center, Seiling, OK, p. A507

LANDRETH, Shannan, Information Systems, Livingston Hospital And Healthcare Services, Salem, KY, p. A260

LANDRUM, David, Chief Police Services, Atascadero State Hospital, Atascadero, CA, p. A51

LANDRY, Adam, Director of Information Systems, Northern Maine Medical Center, Fort Kent, ME, p. A283

LANDRY, Candy, Chief Human Resource Officer, Eastside Psychiatric Hospital, Tallahassee, FL, p. A140

LANDRY, Crystal, Chief Executive Officer, Penobscot Valley Hospital, Lincoln, ME, p. A283

LANDRY, Donna F., Chief Operating Officer, Our Lady Of Lourdes Regional Medical Center, Lafayette, LA, p. A271

LANDRY, Lisa G., Human Resources Director, Redington–Fairview General Hospital, Skowhegan, ME, p. A285

LANDRY, Nobie, Chief Financial Officer, Prevost Memorial Hospital, Donaldsonville, LA, p. A267

LANDRY, Ray A., Chief Executive Officer, Abbeville General Hospital, Abbeville, LA, p. A262

LANDRY NUNEZ, Lexis, Chief Executive Officer, St. Catherine Memorial Hospital, New Orleans, LA, p. A276

LANDSMAN, Joseph, President and Chief Executive Officer, University Of Tennessee Medical Center, Knoxville, TN, p. A572

LANDSTROM, John, Director Human Resources, Rml Specialty Hospital, Hinsdale, IL, p. A186

LANE, Andrea, Chief Financial Officer, Conway Behavioral Health Hospital, Conway, AR, p. A40

LANE, Andrew, Chief Financial Officer, Medical City Fort Worth, Fort Worth, TX, p. A605

LANE, Charles A., Chief Medical Officer, Anderson Hospital, Maryville, IL, p. A188

LANE, Diron
Director Information Systems, Lewisgale Hospital Montgomery, Blacksburg, VA, p. A656
Director Information Systems, Lewisgale Hospital Pulaski, Pulaski, VA, p. A665

LANE, Kevin, Vice President Information Systems, Silver Cross Hospital, New Lenox, IL, p. A191

LANE, Kevin, D.O., Chief of Staff, Hardeman County Memorial Hospital, Quanah, TX, p. A630

LANE, Kim, Chief Fiscal Service, Overton Brooks Veterans Affairs Medical Center, Shreveport, LA, p. A278

LANE, Mike, Chief Operating Officer, Twin Cities Community Hospital, Templeton, CA, p. A91

LANE, Richard, Chief Financial Officer, Mid–America Rehabilitation Hospital, Shawnee Mission, KS, p. A245

LANE, Sonia, Interim Chief Nursing Officer, Uc Irvine Medical Center, Orange, CA, p. A76

LANEAUX, Eleanor, Director Information Systems, Placentia–Linda Hospital, Placentia, CA, p. A78

LANER, Richard, Manager Information Systems, Miners' Colfax Medical Center, Raton, NM, p. A419

LANEY, Samuel Mark., Chief Executive Officer, Mosaic Life Care At St. Joseph – Medical Center, Saint Joseph, MO, p. A368

LANG, Cyndi, Director Information Services, French Hospital Medical Center, San Luis Obispo, CA, p. A87

LANG, Gary, M.D., Clinical Director, Claremore Indian Hospital, Claremore, OK, p. A498

LANG, Gordon, M.D., Chief of Staff, Trego County–Lemke Memorial Hospital, Wakeeney, KS, p. A247

LANG, Jeff, Chief Executive Officer, Coquille Valley Hospital, Coquille, OR, p. A512

LANG, John Christopher., Chief Executive Officer, Cass Regional Medical Center, Harrisonville, MO, p. A361

LANG, Joseph, M.D., Chief of Staff, Carolinas Continuecare Hospital At Pineville, Charlotte, NC, p. A451

LANG, Linda, Chief Human Resources Officer, Marinhealth Medical Center, Greenbrae, CA, p. A61

LANG, Nicholas P, M.D., Chief Medical Officer, Uams Medical Center, Little Rock, AR, p. A45

LANG, Richard, Ed.D., Vice President and Chief Information Officer, Doylestown Hospital, Doylestown, PA, p. A524

LANG, Richard T, Chief Financial Officer, Gouverneur Hospital, Gouverneur, NY, p. A428

LANGAN, Lynn, Chief Nursing Officer, Quillen Rehabilitation Hospital, Johnson City, TN, p. A571

LANGBEHN, Cody, Administrator, St. Luke'S Wood River Medical Center, Ketchum, ID, p. A170

LANGBEHN, Jennifer, Medical Director, Mayo Clinic Health System In Saint James, Saint James, MN, p. A339

LANGBERG, Michael L, M.D., Senior Vice President Medical Affairs and Chief Medical Officer, Cedars–Sinai Medical Center, Los Angeles, CA, p. A66

LANGDON, Ashlee, Controller, Yalobusha General Hospital, Water Valley, MS, p. A355

LANGE, Connie, R.N., Vice President Quality, Inpatient and Community Services, Lakes Regional Healthcare, Spirit Lake, IA, p. A230

LANGENBERG, Shannon, Director Human Resources, Jackson County Regional Health Center, Maquoketa, IA, p. A226

LANGENFELD, John, Medical Records Coordinator, Arizona Orthopedic Surgical Hospital, Chandler, AZ, p. A28

LANGFORD, Scott
Administrator, Beaver Valley Hospital, Beaver, UT, p. A647
Administrator, Milford Valley Memorial Hospital, Milford, UT, p. A648

LANGFORD, Terrie, Director Human Resources, Baylor Scott & White Surgical Hospital–Sherman, Sherman, TX, p. A636

LANGHOFF, Erik, Director, Brookdale Hospital Medical Center, New York, NY, p. A432

LANGLAND, Robert, Senior Vice President and Chief Financial Officer, Stormont Vail Health, Topeka, KS, p. A246

LANGLEY, Kim
Business Partner, Promedica Bixby Hospital, Adrian, MI, p. A306
Business Partner, Promedica Herrick Hospital, Tecumseh, MI, p. A323

LANGLITZ, Sara, Controller, Kindred Hospital Houston Medical Center, Houston, TX, p. A612

LANGLOIS, John, Chief Executive Officer, Riverview Regional Medical Center, Gadsden, AL, p. A18

LANGMEAD, Paula A., Chief Executive Officer, Springfield Hospital Center, Sykesville, MD, p. A293

LANGSTON, David L
Corporate Vice President Human Resources, Ut Health Rehabilitation Hospital, Tyler, TX, p. A642
Corporate Vice President Human Resources, Ut Health Specialty Hospital, Tyler, TX, p. A642

LANGSTON, Phillip W., Administrator, Lawrence County Hospital, Monticello, MS, p. A351

LANIER, Donna, R.N., Chief Nursing Officer, Delta Medical Center, Memphis, TN, p. A574

LANIER, Mary, Vice President, Post Acute Services and Site Administrator, California Pacific Medical Center–Davies Campus, San Francisco, CA, p. A85

LANIER, Regina, MSN, R.N., Senior Vice President and Chief Nursing Officer, Onslow Memorial Hospital, Jacksonville, NC, p. A457

LANKOWICZ, Andrew, President, Chi St. Alexius Health Devils Lake Hospital, Devils Lake, ND, p. A466

LANKOWICZ, Genevieve, M.D., Chief Medical Officer, Saint Joseph Health System, Mishawaka, IN, p. A211

LANNING, John, Chief Operating Officer, Kearney Regional Medical Center, Kearney, NE, p. A386

LANNOYE, Craig, Vice President Operations, Wilson Memorial Hospital, Sidney, OH, p. A491

LANOUE, Cheryl, Chief Financial Officer, Ottawa County Health Center, Minneapolis, KS, p. A241

LANSDOWNE, Lynn, Administrator Human Resources, Lehigh Valley Hospital – Pocono, East Stroudsburg, PA, p. A524

LANTOS, Phyllis R, Executive Vice President, Corporate Chief Financial Officer and Treasurer, Brookdale Hospital Medical Center, New York, NY, p. A432

LANTZY, William, Chief Financial Officer, Dmc Huron Valley–Sinai Hospital, Commerce Township, MI, p. A309

LANZ, April, Interim Administrator, Mayo Clinic Health System In Waseca, Waseca, MN, p. A342

LANZA, Nicholas, Controller, St. Mary'S General Hospital, Passaic, NJ, p. A410

LAPERLE, Linda M, Vice President Administrative Services, Androscoggin Valley Hospital, Berlin, NH, p. A399

LAPHAM, Lisa, President and Chief Executive Officer, Healthsource Saginaw, Inc., Saginaw, MI, p. A321

LAPLANT, Dawn, Manager Health Information Management, Brown County Community Treatment Center, Green Bay, WI, p. A696

LAPLANTE, Lisa, Interim Chief Executive Officer, Evergreenhealth Monroe, Monroe, WA, p. A675

LAPOSTA, Mary Jo, Ph.D., R.N., Senior Vice President Patient Care and Organizational Excellence, Saratoga Hospital, Saratoga Springs, NY, p. A444

LAPPEN, Michael, Chief Executive Officer, Milwaukee County Behavioral Health Division, Milwaukee, WI, p. A701

LARA, Anne, Chief Information Officer, Union Hospital, Elkton, MD, p. A290

LARA, Sergio, M.D., Chief Medical Officer, Covenant Hospital Plainview, Plainview, TX, p. A629

LARAMIE, Robert, Chief Information Officer, Beverly Hospital, Beverly, MA, p. A294

LARAMIE, Wayne, Vice President Nursing, Ssm Health St. Clare Hospital – Fenton, Fenton, MO, p. A360

LARCAS, John, M.D., Acting Medical Director, Choate Mental Health Center, Anna, IL, p. A173

LAREAU, Daniel, Executive Director, Operations and Information, St. Vincent Carmel Hospital, Carmel, IN, p. A201

LAREAU, Kim, Vice President and Chief Information Officer, Regions Hospital, Saint Paul, MN, p. A340

LARET, Mark R., Chief Executive Officer, Ucsf Medical Center, San Francisco, CA, p. A86

LARIMER, Cynthia, M.D., Chief of Staff, Lake Butler Hospital Hand Surgery Center, Lake Butler, FL, p. A127

LARIMORE, Rhonda
Vice President Human Resources, Upmc Magee–Womens Hospital, Pittsburgh, PA, p. A538
Vice President, Human Resources, Upmc Children'S Hospital Of Pittsburgh, Pittsburgh, PA, p. A538

LARISCY, Christopher, M.D., Chief of Staff, Davis Regional Medical Center, Statesville, NC, p. A462

LARISCY, Robin Barton, M.D., Medical Director, Mary S Harper Geriatric Psychiatry Center, Tuscaloosa, AL, p. A24

LARIVEE, Theresa M., Chief Executive Officer, Pennsylvania Hospital, Philadelphia, PA, p. A536

LARIVIERE, Beckye, Controller, Encompass Health Rehabilitation Hospital Of Charleston, Charleston, SC, p. A550

LARKIN, Kevin
Regional Chief Financial Officer, Amita Health Mercy Medical Center, Aurora, IL, p. A173
Regional Chief Financial Officer, Amita Health Saint Joseph Hospital, Elgin, IL, p. A182

LARKIN, Kim, Chief Information Officer, Washington County Hospital, Nashville, IL, p. A191

LARKIN–SKINNER, Melissa, Chief Executive Officer, Centerstone Hospital, Bradenton, FL, p. A118

LARMER, Jennifer, R.N., Chief Clinical Officer, Lincoln Hospital, Davenport, WA, p. A672

LARMORE, Mark, Chief Financial Officer, Ohio State University Wexner Medical Center, Columbus, OH, p. A479

LARNER, Cheryl, Chief Financial Officer, Sentara Careplex Hospital, Hampton, VA, p. A660

LAROSA, Vincent
Director of Information Systems, Landmark Medical Center, Woonsocket, RI, p. A548
Director of Information Technology Services, Rehabilitation Hospital Of Rhode Island, North Smithfield, RI, p. A547

LAROWE, Mary E., President and Chief Executive Officer, Brooks Memorial Hospital, Dunkirk, NY, p. A427

LARRIMORE, Kenneth, Administrator, Grove Hill Memorial Hospital, Grove Hill, AL, p. A19

LARRISON, Robert G., Jr, President, Atrium Health'S Carolinas Rehabilitation, Charlotte, NC, p. A451

LARSEN, Bill, Vice President Human Resources, Driscoll Children'S Hospital, Corpus Christi, TX, p. A594

LARSEN, Catherine M, Director Marketing, Sutter Tracy Community Hospital, Tracy, CA, p. A92

LARSEN, Donald, M.D., Chief Medical Officer, Providence Saint John'S Health Center, Santa Monica, CA, p. A89

LARSEN, Kevin, Associate Vice President, Business and Ancillary Services, Uconn, John Dempsey Hospital, Farmington, CT, p. A108

LARSEN, Ryan C., Chief Executive Officer, Community Medical Center, Inc., Falls City, NE, p. A384

LARSON, Alan
Chief Executive Officer, Sovah Health–Danville, Danville, VA, p. A658
Market President, Sovah Health–Martinsville, Martinsville, VA, p. A662

LARSON, Bill, Vice President Finance and Chief Financial Officer, Torrance Memorial Medical Center, Torrance, CA, p. A92

LARSON, Derek, Information Technology Network, Lakes Regional Healthcare, Spirit Lake, IA, p. A230

LARSON, Erick, Vice President and Chief Information Officer, Mid–Columbia Medical Center, The Dalles, OR, p. A518
LARSON, Jennifer, M.D., Chief of Staff, Blue Ridge Regional Hospital, Spruce Pine, NC, p. A462
LARSON, Jon, M.D., Medical Director, Encompass Health Rehabilitation Institute Of Tucson, Tucson, AZ, p. A37
LARSON, Karla, Director Human Resources, Stevens Community Medical Center, Morris, MN, p. A336
LARSON, Kay, R.N., Chief Nursing Officer, Essentia Health St. Mary'S – Detroit Lakes, Detroit Lakes, MN, p. A330
LARSON, Michael, Vice President Chief Information Officer, Midmichigan Medical Center–Clare, Clare, MI, p. A309
LARSON, Mike, Chief Operating Officer, Essentia Health St. Joseph'S Medical Center, Brainerd, MN, p. A329
LARSON, Pamela, Division Director Financial Services, Hutchinson Health, Hutchinson, MN, p. A333
LARSON, Rodney, M.D., Medical Director, Fall River Hospital, Hot Springs, SD, p. A561
LARSON, Ronald, Chief Financial Officer, Va San Diego Healthcare System, San Diego, CA, p. A84
LARSON, Scott, M.D., Vice President Medical Affairs and Chief Medical Officer, Bronson Methodist Hospital, Kalamazoo, MI, p. A315
LARSON, Scott C., Chief Executive Officer, Sanford Canton–Inwood Medical Center, Canton, SD, p. A559
LARSON, Shelly, Chief Financial Officer, Hot Springs County Memorial Hospital, Thermopolis, WY, p. A713
LARSON, Steve, M.D., Director Information Systems, Mercyone Siouxland Medical Center, Sioux City, IA, p. A230
LARSON, Tammy, Chief Financial Officer, Towner County Medical Center, Cando, ND, p. A465
LARSON, Tracy, MS, Vice President Patient Care Services and Chief Nursing Officer, Mercyone Siouxland Medical Center, Sioux City, IA, p. A230
LARSON, Walt, Vice President Finance, Adventist Healthtillamook, Tillamook, OR, p. A518
LARSON, Wendy, Chief Clinical Officer, Promise Hospital Of Phoenix, Mesa, AZ, p. A32
LASATER, Laci, R.N., Chief Nursing Officer, Christus Spohn Hospital Kleberg, Kingsville, TX, p. A618
LASCANO, Terrance, Administrative Officer, U. S. Public Health Service Indian Hospital, Cass Lake, MN, p. A330
LASECKI, Cynthia, M.D., Chief Medical Officer, Bellin Hospital, Green Bay, WI, p. A696
LASHBROOK, Amy, Chief Financial Officer, Community Hospital Of Bremen, Bremen, IN, p. A200
LASHER, Karen, Chief Nursing Officer, Vanderbilt Stallworth Rehabilitation Hospital, Nashville, TN, p. A577
LASHKARI, Haady, Chief Administrative Officer, Ojai Valley Community Hospital, Ojai, CA, p. A75
LASKER, Rose, Director Information Services, Bluefield Regional Medical Center, Bluefield, WV, p. A683
LASKOWSKI, Rose, Director, Caro Center, Caro, MI, p. A308
LASKOWSKI, Rose, R.N., Director, Caro Center, Caro, MI, p. A308
LASKY, John, Vice President, Chief Human Resources Officer, Temple University Hospital, Philadelphia, PA, p. A536
LASOTA, John, Assistant Finance Officer, Clement J. Zablocki Veterans Affairs Medical Center, Milwaukee, WI, p. A701
LATEEF, Omar, Chief Executive Officer, Rush University Medical Center, Chicago, IL, p. A179
LATER, Elizabeth B., R.N., Chief Nursing Officer, Ogden Regional Medical Center, Ogden, UT, p. A650
LATIBEAUDIERE, Jorge, Chief Financial Officer, Lea Regional Medical Center, Hobbs, NM, p. A418
LATIMER, Kevin, Chief Executive Officer, Childress Regional Medical Center, Childress, TX, p. A592
LATIMER, Timothy, Chief Financial Officer, University Of Kansas Health System Great Bend Campus, Great Bend, KS, p. A235
LATIOLAIS, Ryan J, Director Information Systems, Our Lady Of Lourdes Regional Medical Center, Lafayette, LA, p. A271
LATNEY, Cynthia, Chief Nursing Officer, Penrose–St. Francis Health Services, Colorado Springs, CO, p. A98
LATO, Barb, Chief Nursing Officer, Aspirus Medford Hospital & Clinics, Inc., Medford, WI, p. A699
LATREILLE, William, M.D., Chief Medical Officer, The University Of Vermont Health Network – Alice Hyde Medical Center, Malone, NY, p. A430
LATTANZI, Katie, Chief Operating Officer, St. David'S Round Rock Medical Center, Round Rock, TX, p. A632
LATTERNER, Renee, Director Human Resources, Adventhealth Lake Wales, Lake Wales, FL, p. A127
LATTO, Janet B., Chief Nursing Officer and Disaster Officer, Pacifica Hospital Of The Valley, Los Angeles, CA, p. A68
LATUCHIE, Richard
Chief Information Officer, Spearfish Regional Hospital, Spearfish, SD, p. A564
Vice President Business Development, Rapid City Regional Hospital, Rapid City, SD, p. A563
LATULIPPE, Steve, President Medical Staff, East Liverpool City Hospital, East Liverpool, OH, p. A482
LAU, James, M.D., Area Medical Director, Kaiser Permanente Panorama City Medical Center, Los Angeles, CA, p. A67
LAUBENTHAL, Sherrie L, R.N., Chief Nursing Officer, Clarinda Regional Health Center, Clarinda, IA, p. A219
LAUDON, Larry A., Administrator, Community Behavioral Health Hospital – Bemidji, Bemidji, MN, p. A328
LAUE, Edward, M.D., Chief Medical Officer, Texas Health Huguley Hospital Fort Worth South, Burleson, TX, p. A590
LAUE, Jerry
Administrator, St. Vincent Clay Hospital, Brazil, IN, p. A200
Administrator, St. Vincent Dunn Hospital, Bedford, IN, p. A200
LAUER, Bill, Chief Information Officer, Morris County Hospital, Council Grove, KS, p. A234
LAUF, Michael K., President and Chief Executive Officer, Cape Cod Hospital, Hyannis, MA, p. A299
LAUFFER, Daniel
President and Chief Executive Officer, Saint Francis Hospital, Charleston, WV, p. A684
President and Chief Executive Officer, Thomas Memorial Hospital, South Charleston, WV, p. A689
LAUFLE, Chuck, Director of Information Services, San Luis Valley Health, Alamosa, CO, p. A96
LAUGHLIN, Jennifer, Chief Information Officer, Watertown Regional Medical Center, Watertown, WI, p. A707
LAUGHLIN, Warren, Vice President Human Resources, Longmont United Hospital, Longmont, CO, p. A103
LAUKAITIS, Fran, President, Methodist Charlton Medical Center, Dallas, TX, p. A597
LAUNIUS, Billie, Director Business Finance, Dallas County Medical Center, Fordyce, AR, p. A42
LAUREANO, Prudencio A., Chief Executive Officer, Hospital Universitario Dr. Ramon Ruiz Arnau, Bayamon, PR, p. A715
LAURENTS, W Robert, CPA, Chief Financial Officer, Madison Parish Hospital, Tallulah, LA, p. A279
LAURETANO, Arthur, M.D., Chief Medical Officer, Lowell General Hospital, Lowell, MA, p. A300
LAURETO, Rose Ann
Chief Information Officer, Promedica Fostoria Community Hospital, Fostoria, OH, p. A483
Chief Information Officer, Promedica Toledo Hospital, Toledo, OH, p. A492
Corporate Vice President Information Resources, Promedica Bay Park Hospital, Oregon, OH, p. A489
LAURIDSEN, Amy, Director Human Resources, Northern Colorado Rehabilitation Hospital, Johnstown, CO, p. A102
LAURIN, George M, Interim Director Human Resources, Crisp Regional Hospital, Cordele, GA, p. A151
LAUTER, Keith A.
Chief Financial Officer, Franciscan Health Carmel, Carmel, IN, p. A201
Regional Chief Financial Officer, Franciscan Health Indianapolis, Indianapolis, IN, p. A207
Vice President Finance, Franciscan Health Crawfordsville, Crawfordsville, IN, p. A202
LAUTEREN, Mark, Chief Information Officer, Usa Health University Hospital, Mobile, AL, p. A21
LAUTNER, Marty, Vice President Finance and Chief Financial Officer, Cardinal Hill Rehabilitation Hospital, Lexington, KY, p. A254
LAUVE, Lisa R., R.N., Regional Chief Nursing Executive and Chief Operating Officer, Christus St. Frances Cabrini Hospital, Alexandria, LA, p. A262
LAUVER, David, M.D., Chief Division Hospital Based Care, Central Maine Medical Center, Lewiston, ME, p. A283
LAUZAU, Paul, Controller, Beaumont Hospital – Trenton, Trenton, MI, p. A324
LAVELLE, John P., M.D., Chief Medical Officer, Parkview Hospital, Wheeler, TX, p. A645
LAVELY, Patricia A, FACHE, Senior Vice President and Chief Information Officer, Gwinnett Hospital System, Lawrenceville, GA, p. A156
LAVENDER, John Kenneth, Chief Information Officer, Lincoln County Health System, Fayetteville, TN, p. A569
LAVERY FRASCA, Denise Anne, MSN, R.N., Vice President Patient Care Services and Chief Nursing Officer, Jeanes Hospital, Philadelphia, PA, p. A535
LAVIGNETTE, Brooke, Director of Nursing, Sycamore Springs Hospital, Lafayette, IN, p. A210
LAVIOLETTE, Judy, M.D.
Chief Medical Officer, Texas Health Harris Methodist Hospital Azle, Azle, TX, p. A586
Chief Medical Officer, Texas Health Harris Methodist Hospital Cleburne, Cleburne, TX, p. A592
LAVOIE, Brad, Chief Financial Officer, Coastal Harbor Treatment Center, Savannah, GA, p. A160
LAW, Charles, Ph.D., Chief Operating Officer, Catawba Hospital, Catawba, VA, p. A657
LAW, Johnny, Area Information Officer, Kaiser Permanente Oakland Medical Center, Oakland, CA, p. A75
LAWHORN, David, M.D., Chief Medical Officer, Shoshone Medical Center, Kellogg, ID, p. A169
LAWHORN, Renee, Director Medical Records, Ut Health Carthage, Carthage, TX, p. A591
LAWHORNE, Thomas
Chief Financial Officer, Regional Medical Center Bayonet Point, Hudson, FL, p. A125
Interim Chief Executive Officer, Regional Medical Center Bayonet Point, Hudson, FL, p. A125
LAWLER, Anne, Director Human Resources, North Mississippi Medical Center–Hamilton, Hamilton, AL, p. A19
LAWLER, Kay, Business Office Manager, North Mississippi Medical Center–West Point, West Point, MS, p. A355
LAWLER, Patrick, Chief Executive Officer, Youth Villages Inner Harbour Campus, Douglasville, GA, p. A152
LAWLESS, JoBeth, Chief Nursing Officer, Nursing Services and Director Emergency Management Services, Lucas County Health Center, Chariton, IA, p. A219
LAWLESS, Rosalie, Director Human Resources, Fairlawn Rehabilitation Hospital, Worcester, MA, p. A305
LAWONN, Kenneth
Senior Vice President and Chief Information Officer, Chi Health Mercy Corning, Corning, IA, p. A219
Senior Vice President and Chief Information Officer, Chi Health Schuyler, Schuyler, NE, p. A391
Senior Vice President and Chief Information Officer, Sharp Grossmont Hospital, La Mesa, CA, p. A63
Senior Vice President and Chief Information Officer, Sharp Memorial Hospital, San Diego, CA, p. A84
Senior Vice President Information Systems, Sharp Mesa Vista Hospital, San Diego, CA, p. A84
LAWRASON, Jock, M.D., Chief Medical Officer, Nantucket Cottage Hospital, Nantucket, MA, p. A301
LAWRENCE, Glenda, R.N., Chief Nursing Officer, Red River Hospital, Llc, Wichita Falls, TX, p. A646
LAWRENCE, Jonathan I.
President and Chief Executive Officer, St. Joseph'S Hospital, Elmira, NY, p. A427
System Chief Operating Officer, Arnot Ogden Medical Center, Elmira, NY, p. A427
LAWRENCE, Kelcey, Manager Information Technology, Union County General Hospital, Clayton, NM, p. A417
LAWRENCE, Mark, Director Information Systems, Saint Francis Hospital–Bartlett, Bartlett, TN, p. A566
LAWRENCE, Michael, Chief Financial Officer, Ingalls Memorial Hospital, Harvey, IL, p. A185
LAWRENCE, Paige, Assistant Administrator, University Of Mississippi Medical Center Holmes County, Lexington, MS, p. A350
LAWRENCE, Sandra A J, Executive Vice President and Chief Financial Officer, Children'S Mercy Hospital Kansas, Overland Park, KS, p. A243
LAWRENCE, Stephanie
Chief Financial Officer, Kentfield Rehabilitation And Specialty Hospital, Kentfield, CA, p. A62
Chief Financial Officer, Vibra Specialty Hospital Of Portland, Portland, OR, p. A516
LAWRENCE, Tiffany, Vice President of Finance, Sanford Medical Center Fargo, Fargo, ND, p. A467
LAWRENSON, Victoria
Chief Operating Officer, Bullock County Hospital, Union Springs, AL, p. A24
Chief Operating Officer, Crenshaw Community Hospital, Luverne, AL, p. A20
LAWS, Stephanie, Vice President, Administrator, Union Hospital Clinton, Clinton, IN, p. A201
LAWSON, Alvin R., Chief Executive Officer, Encompass Health Rehabilitation Hospital Of Parkersburg, Parkersburg, WV, p. A688
LAWSON, Beth, Chief Nursing Officer, Union Medical Center, Union, SC, p. A558
LAWSON, Chad, Chief Information Officer, St. Anthony Regional Hospital, Carroll, IA, p. A218
LAWSON, David C., Senior Vice President Human Resources, St. Clare Hospital, Lakewood, WA, p. A674
LAWSON, Eric, Chief Executive Officer, North Florida Regional Medical Center, Gainesville, FL, p. A123
LAWSON, Jessica, Director of Nursing, Greenwood Regional Rehabilitation Hospital, Greenwood, SC, p. A554
LAWSON, Judy, Director Information Services, Norton Community Hospital, Norton, VA, p. A664
LAWSON, Kelly, Chief Nursing Officer, Williamsburg Regional Hospital, Kingstree, SC, p. A554
LAWSON, Linda B., Chief Nursing Officer, The Hospitals Of Providence Transmountain Campus, El Paso, TX, p. A603
LAWSON, Michael, President and Chief Operating Officer, Ohiohealth Grant Medical Center, Columbus, OH, p. A479

LAWSON, Penny, Human Resource Director, Quillen Rehabilitation Hospital, Johnson City, TN, p. A571

LAWSON, Ralph E, Executive Vice President and Chief Financial Officer, Baptist Health South Florida, Baptist Hospital Of Miami, Miami, FL, p. A130

LAWSON, Sandra K., Interim Director Fiscal Services, Shriners Hospitals For Children–St. Louis, Saint Louis, MO, p. A370

LAWSON, T Douglas., Chief Executive Officer, Baylor St. Luke'S Medical Center, Houston, TX, p. A610

LAWTON, Geoff
Interim Chief Executive Officer, Littleton Adventist Hospital, Littleton, CO, p. A103
Vice President Operations, Littleton Adventist Hospital, Littleton, CO, p. A103

LAY, A K, M.D., Chief Medical Officer, Jasper General Hospital, Bay Springs, MS, p. A344

LAYFIELD, Michael G., Interim Chief Executive Officer, Optim Medical Center – Screven, Sylvania, GA, p. A161

LAYMAN, Benjamin, President, Ssm Health St. Mary'S Hospital Janesville, Monroe, WI, p. A702

LAYNE, Kristine, R.N., Chief Nursing Officer, Riverwood Healthcare Center, Aitkin, MN, p. A327

LAYTON, Ann, M.D., Chief of Staff, North Metro Medical Center, Jacksonville, AR, p. A43

LAYUGAN, Melvin, Director Human Resources, Horizon Specialty Hospital, Las Vegas, NV, p. A395

LAZARUS, David, M.D., Medical Director Clinical Affairs, Newton Medical Center, Newton, NJ, p. A410

LAZENBY, John, M.D., Chief Medical Officer, Memorial Hospital Jacksonville, Jacksonville, FL, p. A125

LAZO, Nelson, Chief Executive Officer, Baptist Health South Florida, Doctors Hospital, Coral Gables, FL, p. A120

LAZO, Wendy, President, St. Luke's Hospital – Miners Campus, Coaldale, PA, p. A522

LAZROFF, Gary, Vice President Human Resources, St. John Medical Center, Westlake, OH, p. A494

LAZZARO, Frank A., Chief Human Resources Officer, Phelps Health, Rolla, MO, p. A368

LE, Emily, Director Information Technology and Services, Woman'S Hospital Of Texas, Houston, TX, p. A615

LE, Jennifer, Chief Financial Officer, Southern Hills Hospital And Medical Center, Las Vegas, NV, p. A395

LE, Tuan
Chief Executive Officer, Christus Dubuis Hospital Of Beaumont, Beaumont, TX, p. A587
Chief Executive Officer, Continuecare Hospital At Baptist Health Corbin, Corbin, KY, p. A250

LEA, Hampton P S., Acting Chief Executive Officer, Eastern Louisiana Mental Health System, Jackson, LA, p. A269

LEA, Katie, Chief Nursing Officer, Saline Memorial Hospital, Benton, AR, p. A39

LEA, Rich, Vice President Operations, Euclid Hospital, Euclid, OH, p. A482

LEACH, Craig, President and Chief Executive Officer, Torrance Memorial Medical Center, Torrance, CA, p. A92

LEACH, Dana, Director Human Resources, Alliancehealth Midwest, Midwest City, OK, p. A502

LEACH, Deonca, Director, Human Resources, Atrium Health'S Carolinas Rehabilitation, Charlotte, NC, p. A451

LEACH, Leslie, Administrator, Pam Specialty Hospital Of Lufkin, Lufkin, TX, p. A622

LEACH, Ryan, Chief Information Officer, Hshs St. John'S Hospital, Springfield, IL, p. A196

LEACH, Todd, Vice President and Chief Information Officer, University Of Texas Medical Branch, Galveston, TX, p. A607

LEACH, Travis, President, Saint Alphonsus Medical Center – Nampa, Nampa, ID, p. A170

LEADBETTER, Dan, Information Technology Systems Site Lead, Chi Lakewood Health, Baudette, MN, p. A328

LEADBETTER, Raymond J., Revenue Cycle Consultant, Appling Healthcare System, Baxley, GA, p. A148

LEAHY, Mary
Chief Executive Officer, Bon Secours Community Hospital, Port Jervis, NY, p. A442
Chief Executive Officer, Good Samaritan Regional Medical Center, Suffern, NY, p. A445
Chief Executive Officer, St. Anthony Community Hospital, Warwick, NY, p. A446

LEAHY, Mary P, Regional Vice President, Chief Human Resources Officer, St. Joseph Hospital, Orange, CA, p. A76

LEAHY, Rosanne, Vice President Nursing Services, Carolinaeast Health System, New Bern, NC, p. A459

LEAKE, Neta F, Administrative Assistant Human Resources, West Feliciana Parish Hospital, Saint Francisville, LA, p. A277

LEAKE, Sandy, MSN, R.N., Associate Director, Nursing and Patient Care Services, Atlanta Veterans Affairs Medical Center, Decatur, GA, p. A151

LEAKEY, Kim, R.N., Chief Nursing Officer, Lafayette Regional Health Center, Lexington, MO, p. A364

LEAL, Carlos, Director Information Technology, Valley Regional Medical Center, Brownsville, TX, p. A590

LEAL, Enrique A, M.D., Chief of Staff, Sweeny Community Hospital, Sweeny, TX, p. A639

LEAL, Joseph M, M.D., Chief of Staff, Glendive Medical Center, Glendive, MT, p. A376

LEAMING, Larry E., Chief Executive Officer, Estes Park Medical Center, Estes Park, CO, p. A100

LEAMON, Jim, Chief Financial Officer, Jfk Medical Center, Atlantis, FL, p. A117

LEAR, Richard
Director Information Systems, St. David'S Medical Center, Austin, TX, p. A586
Director Information Systems, St. David'S South Austin Medical Center, Austin, TX, p. A586

LEARSON, Jerome, Manager Information Technology and Chief Security Officer, Palo Verde Hospital, Blythe, CA, p. A53

LEARY, Edward B.
Chief Executive Officer, Vibra Hospital Of Southeastern Massachusetts, New Bedford, MA, p. A301
Interim Chief Executive Officer, Vibra Hospital Of Western Massachusetts, Springfield, MA, p. A304

LEASE, Faye, Director of Nursing, Reeves County Hospital, Pecos, TX, p. A628

LEASE–HOMEYER, Cheryl, Lead Information Technology Business Partner, Mercy Hospital Carthage, Carthage, MO, p. A358

LEASURE, Sandie, Senior Vice President Human Resources, O'Bleness Memorial Hospital, Athens, OH, p. A472

LEATHERS, Cynthia, R.N., Chief Nursing Officer, Integris Bass Baptist Health Center, Enid, OK, p. A499

LEAVITT, Jared, Chief Operating Officer, Kern Medical Center, Bakersfield, CA, p. A52

LEBEAU, Michael, President, Sanford Bismarck, Bismarck, ND, p. A465

LEBEAU, Michelle
President and Chief Operating Officer, The University Of Vermont Health Network–Champlain Valley Physicians Hospital, Plattsburgh, NY, p. A441
President, The University Of Vermont Health Network – Alice Hyde Medical Center, Malone, NY, p. A430

LEBER, Ian, M.D., Chief Medical Officer, Hackensack Meridian Health Bayshore Community Hospital, Holmdel, NJ, p. A406

LEBLANC, Fernis, Chief Operating Officer, Ochsner St. Anne General Hospital, Raceland, LA, p. A277

LEBLANC, Julie, Director of Nursing, Memorial Specialty Hospital, Lake Charles, LA, p. A272

LEBLANC, Karen, Director, Applications, Samaritan Hospital – Main Campus, Troy, NY, p. A445

LEBOWITZ, Howard, M.D., Chief Medical Officer, Specialty Hospital Of Central Jersey, Lakewood, NJ, p. A407

LEBRON, Juan, M.D., Medical Director, Sea Pines Rehabilitation Hospital, Melbourne, FL, p. A129

LEBRON, Sonia M, Human Resources Specialist, Industrial Hospital, San Juan, PR, p. A719

LECATES, William W, M.D., Vice President Medical Affairs and Medical Director, Bassett Medical Center, Cooperstown, NY, p. A426

LECATES, William W., President, Bassett Medical Center, Cooperstown, NY, p. A426

LECHICH, Anthony, M.D., Chief Medical Officer, Brookdale Hospital Medical Center, New York, NY, p. A432

LECHNER, David, M.D., Chief Medical Officer and Vice President Innovation, Community Medical Center, Missoula, MT, p. A378

LECHUGA, Mario, Director Human Resources, Turquoise Lodge Hospital, Albuquerque, NM, p. A417

LECKELT, Mitchell D., Chief Executive Officer, Up Health System–Bell, Ishpeming, MI, p. A315

LECKER, Marijo, Vice President, Sentara Martha Jefferson Hospital, Charlottesville, VA, p. A657

LECKEY, Scott, Chief Financial Officer, Banner Desert Medical Center, Mesa, AZ, p. A31

LEDBETTER, Joy, Regional Chief Human Resources Officer, Unitypoint Health – Peoria, Peoria, IL, p. A193

LEDBETTER, Thomas Glenn, M.D., Chief Medical Officer, Baylor Scott & White Medical Center–Waxahachie, Waxahachie, TX, p. A644

LEDDEN, Edwin L, Assistant Administrator and Director Human Resources, Henry County Medical Center, Paris, TN, p. A578

LEDELL, Michelle
Director Human Resource, Fairview Ridges Hospital, Burnsville, MN, p. A329
Director Human Resources, Fairview Southdale Hospital, Edina, MN, p. A331

LEDERER, Jane, R.N., Ed.D., Vice President and Chief Nursing Officer, Brookdale Hospital Medical Center, New York, NY, p. A432

LEDERMAN, Joel, Director Information Systems, Promedica Coldwater Regional Hospital, Coldwater, MI, p. A309

LEDERMAN, Mark, Chief Information Officer, Brookdale Hospital Medical Center, New York, NY, p. A432

LEDFORD, Keith, M.D., Chief of Staff, Scenic Mountain Medical Center, Big Spring, TX, p. A588

LEE, Byong, Chief Information Officer, Limestone Medical Center, Groesbeck, TX, p. A608

LEE, Cheryl, Human Resources Director, North Alabama Medical Center, Florence, AL, p. A18

LEE, Cheryl D, R.N., MSN, Vice President of Patient Care Services and Chief Nursing Officer, University Of Maryland Rehabilitation & Orthopaedic Institute, Baltimore, MD, p. A288

LEE, Clare, Chief Operating Officer, Mercy General Hospital, Sacramento, CA, p. A82

LEE, Darren W.
President and Chief Executive Officer, St. John'S Pleasant Valley Hospital, Camarillo, CA, p. A53
President and Chief Executive Officer, St. John'S Regional Medical Center, Oxnard, CA, p. A76

LEE, David, Chief Executive Officer, Otto Kaiser Memorial Hospital, Kenedy, TX, p. A617

LEE, Dennis, Vice President and Chief Information Officer, Cabell Huntington Hospital, Huntington, WV, p. A685

LEE, Eric A., President and Chief Executive Officer, Jennie Stuart Medical Center, Hopkinsville, KY, p. A253

LEE, Francis, M.D., Chief Medical Officer, Calais Regional Hospital, Calais, ME, p. A282

LEE, James R, M.D., Chief of Staff, Hamilton General Hospital, Hamilton, TX, p. A609

LEE, James Y., Hospital Administrator, Kaiser Permanente Medical Center, Honolulu, HI, p. A164

LEE, Jenny, Human Resources Generalist, Essentia Health–Graceville, Graceville, MN, p. A332

LEE, John Paul, M.D., Chief of Staff, Lackey Memorial Hospital, Forest, MS, p. A347

LEE, Joshua, M.D., Chief Medical Officer, Loyola University Medical Center, Maywood, IL, p. A189

LEE, Karen
Director Human Resources, Gallup Indian Medical Center, Gallup, NM, p. A418
Interim Administrator, Creek Nation Community Hospital, Okemah, OK, p. A503

LEE, Karen, MSN, R.N., Chief Nursing Officer, Belton Regional Medical Center, Belton, MO, p. A356

LEE, Kenneth, Division Chair, Human Resource Advisory, Mayo Clinic Health System In Eau Claire, Eau Claire, WI, p. A694

LEE, Kim, Chief Operating Officer, Faith Community Hospital, Jacksboro, TX, p. A616

LEE, Kristina, Director Human Resources, Chi St. Joseph Health Grimes Hospital, Navasota, TX, p. A626

LEE, Kwon, Chief Information Officer, Pennsylvania Hospital, Philadelphia, PA, p. A536

LEE, Loretta, Acting Chief Nursing Officer, Baylor St. Luke'S Medical Center, Houston, TX, p. A610

LEE, Lori L, Vice President Nursing, Nanticoke Memorial Hospital, Seaford, DE, p. A114

LEE, Michael, President, Weeks Medical Center, Lancaster, NH, p. A400

LEE, Michael D, Chief Human Resources Officer, Adirondack Health, Saranac Lake, NY, p. A443

LEE, Mihi, Chief Financial Officer, Coast Plaza Hospital, Norwalk, CA, p. A74

LEE, Mike, R.N., Chief Nursing Officer, Matagorda Regional Medical Center, Bay City, TX, p. A587

LEE, Nancy, R.N., MSN, Vice President Patient Care Services and Chief Nursing Officer, Stanford Health Care, Palo Alto, CA, p. A77

LEE, Nathan W, Chief Executive Officer, Mary Breckinridge Arh Hospital, Hyden, KY, p. A254

LEE, Pamela R., Chief Operating Officer, Ozarks Medical Center, West Plains, MO, p. A373

LEE, Randy, M.D., Senior Vice President Medical Affairs, Community Hospital South, Indianapolis, IN, p. A206

LEE, Reginald, Chief Executive Officer, Vibra Hospital Of Southeastern Michigan, Llc, Lincoln Park, MI, p. A317

LEE, Ryan, Chief Operating Officer, West Boca Medical Center, Boca Raton, FL, p. A118

LEE, S. Kwon, M.D., Chief of Staff, Vibra Hospital Of Sacramento, Folsom, CA, p. A58

LEE, Stacey, Chief Executive Officer, Johnson Memorial Health Services, Dawson, MN, p. A330

LEE, Terri
Chief Information Officer, Higgins General Hospital, Bremen, GA, p. A148

Chief Information Officer, Tanner Medical Center–Villa Rica, Villa Rica, GA, p. A162

LEE, Thomas G, Chief Financial Officer, Medicine Lodge Memorial Hospital, Medicine Lodge, KS, p. A241

LEE, W. Bryan, Chief Executive Officer, Our Lady Of Lourdes Regional Medical Center, Lafayette, LA, p. A271

LEE, W. Bryan., Chief Executive Officer, Our Lady Of Lourdes Regional Medical Center, Lafayette, LA, p. A271

LEE, Wendy, Chief Nursing Officer, Regional Rehabilitation Hospital, Phenix City, AL, p. A22

LEE–EDDIE, Deborah M., Interim President and Chief Executive Officer, Jewish Hospital, Louisville, KY, p. A256

LEEGSTRA, Ruurd, Chief Financial Officer, Silver Hill Hospital, New Canaan, CT, p. A109

LEEK, Dustin, Vice President of Enterprise Technology Services, Health First Holmes Regional Medical Center, Melbourne, FL, p. A129

LEEKA, Andrew B., President and Chief Executive Officer, Good Samaritan Hospital, Los Angeles, CA, p. A66

LEEMING, Rosemary, M.D., Chief Medical Officer, Uh Regional Hospitals, Cleveland, OH, p. A478

LEEPER, Doug, Chief Information Officer, Kaweah Delta Medical Center, Visalia, CA, p. A94

LEEPER, Kevin, Chief Executive Officer, Morris County Hospital, Council Grove, KS, p. A234

LEESMAN, Keenan, Director Information Systems, Abraham Lincoln Memorial Hospital, Lincoln, IL, p. A188

LEFEVRE, Denise, Chief Information Officer, Oroville Hospital, Oroville, CA, p. A76

LEFF, Marc, Vice President Human Resources, St. John'S Riverside Hospital, Yonkers, NY, p. A448

LEFKOW, Frances, Director Human Resources, La Rabida Children'S Hospital, Chicago, IL, p. A178

LEFTERIS, Chad T., Chief Operating Officer, Uc Irvine Medical Center, Orange, CA, p. A76

LEFTON, Ray, Chief Financial Officer, Jeanes Hospital, Philadelphia, PA, p. A535

LEFTON, Ruth, Chief Operating Officer, Einstein Medical Center Philadelphia, Philadelphia, PA, p. A534

LEFTWICH, Hal W., Chief Executive Officer, Big South Fork Medical Center, Oneida, TN, p. A578

LEFTWITCH, Billy, Director, Information Technology, Wellstone Regional Hospital, Jeffersonville, IN, p. A208

LEGASPI, Johnson, Director Information Systems, Alhambra Hospital Medical Center, Alhambra, CA, p. A50

LEGAY, Jeff, Chief Financial Officer, Chatham Hospital, Siler City, NC, p. A462

LEGEND, Rachel, Chief Executive Officer, Arbour–Fuller Hospital, Attleboro, MA, p. A294

LEGER, Lynn, Director Information Systems, Ridgeview Institute, Smyrna, GA, p. A160

LEGG, Alyce, Vice President Human Resources, University Hospitals Samaritan Medical Center, Ashland, OH, p. A472

LEGG, Debra Lynn, Associate Director Patient Care Services and Nurse Executive, Beckley Veterans Affairs Medical Center, Beckley, WV, p. A683

LEGGETT, G Raymond., III, President and Chief Executive Officer, Carolinaeast Health System, New Bern, NC, p. A459

LEGGETT, Sandra, Chief Operating Officer, Atchison Hospital, Atchison, KS, p. A232

LEGLEITER, Brenda, Chief Executive Officer, Rush County Memorial Hospital, La Crosse, KS, p. A238

LEGRAND, Kila, Chief Nursing Officer, Sanford Aberdeen Medical Center, Aberdeen, SD, p. A559

LEHMAN, Andy
  Senior Vice President Technology & Analytics, Greene Memorial Hospital, Xenia, OH, p. A494
  Senior Vice President Technology and Analytics, Fort Hamilton Hospital, Hamilton, OH, p. A484
  Senior Vice President Technology and Analytics, Grandview Medical Center, Dayton, OH, p. A481
  Senior Vice President Technology and Analytics, Kettering Medical Center, Kettering, OH, p. A485
  Senior Vice President Technology and Analytics, Sycamore Medical Center, Miamisburg, OH, p. A487
  Vice President Information Systems, Soin Medical Center, Beavercreek, OH, p. A473

LEHMAN, Brennan, Chief Information Officer, Mosaic Life Care At St. Joseph – Medical Center, Saint Joseph, MO, p. A368

LEHMAN, James, M.D.
  Vice President Medical Affairs, Mercyone Cedar Falls Medical Center, Cedar Falls, IA, p. A218
  Vice President Medical Affairs, Mercyone Oelwein Medical Center, Oelwein, IA, p. A227
  Vice President Medical Affairs, Mercyone Waterloo Medical Center, Waterloo, IA, p. A231

LEHMAN, Ronda, PharmD, Chief Operating Officer, SRPS, Mercy Health – St. Rita'S Medical Center, Lima, OH, p. A485

LEHMAN, Sandi, Chief Financial Officer, Humboldt General Hospital, Winnemucca, NV, p. A398

LEHMAN, Travis, M.D., Medical Director, Wilbarger General Hospital, Vernon, TX, p. A643

LEHN, Toby, Director of Nurses, Concho County Hospital, Eden, TX, p. A601

LEHNHOF-WATTS, Laurie
  Administrator and Chief Nursing Officer, Ut Health Rehabilitation Hospital, Tyler, TX, p. A642
  Administrator and Chief Nursing Officer, Ut Health Specialty Hospital, Tyler, TX, p. A642

LEIBMAN, Maurice, M.D., Chief Medical Officer, Memorial Hermann Greater Heights Hospital, Houston, TX, p. A612

LEICHMAN, Ann Marie, MSN, R.N., Senior Vice President Patient Care Services and Chief Nursing Officer, Valley Hospital, Ridgewood, NJ, p. A412

LEIDY, R. Grant, Chief Financial Officer, Deborah Heart And Lung Center, Browns Mills, NJ, p. A404

LEIF, Sue, R.N., Director Human Resources, Annie Jeffrey Memorial County Health Center, Osceola, NE, p. A390

LEIGHTON, Heather, Director, Revenue Cycle and Privacy Officer, Upper Connecticut Valley Hospital, Colebrook, NH, p. A399

LEIGHTON, Martha, Senior Vice President and Chief Nursing Officer, Elliot Hospital, Manchester, NH, p. A401

LEIGHTON, Richard, Financial Application Analyst, Unity Medical & Surgical Hospital, Mishawaka, IN, p. A211

LEINEN, Rick J, Chief Financial Officer, Montgomery County Memorial Hospital, Red Oak, IA, p. A228

LEININGER, Bethany, Manager Human Resource, Hillcrest Hospital Cushing, Cushing, OK, p. A498

LEISHER, George
  Chief Human Resources Officer, Antelope Valley Hospital, Lancaster, CA, p. A64
  Vice President Human Resources, Hollywood Presbyterian Medical Center, Los Angeles, CA, p. A67

LEISHER, Karla, Business Office Manager, Beaver County Memorial Hospital, Beaver, OK, p. A497

LEISING, Elizabeth, Chief Nursing Officer and Vice President Patient Services, Margaret Mary Health, Batesville, IN, p. A199

LEIST, Frank, Human Resources Manager, Piedmont Mountainside Hospital, Jasper, GA, p. A155

LEIST, Vincent, President and Chief Executive Officer, North Arkansas Regional Medical Center, Harrison, AR, p. A42

LEITERMAN, Gretchen, Chief Operating Officer, Ssm Health Saint Louis University Hospital, Saint Louis, MO, p. A370

LEITNER, Mark, Administrator, Ut Health Henderson, Henderson, TX, p. A610

LEJEUNE, Lucille, Assistant Administrator and Chief Financial Officer, Acadia–St. Landry Hospital, Church Point, LA, p. A265

LEJSEK, Shari, Administrator, Patients' Hospital Of Redding, Redding, CA, p. A70

LELAND, Joni, Director Human Resources, Gonzales Healthcare Systems, Gonzales, TX, p. A608

LEM, Alan
  Vice President Finance, Fairview Ridges Hospital, Burnsville, MN, p. A329
  Vice President Finance, Fairview Southdale Hospital, Edina, MN, p. A331

LEMAIRE, Joseph M
  Executive Vice President Finance and Partner Company Operations, Hackensack Meridian Health Bayshore Community Hospital, Holmdel, NJ, p. A406
  Executive Vice President Finance, Hackensack Meridian Health Riverview Medical Center, Red Bank, NJ, p. A412
  Executive Vice President, Hackensack Meridian Health Southern Ocean Medical Center, Manahawkin, NJ, p. A408

LEMANSKI, Dennis R, D.O., Senior Vice President Medical Affairs and Medical Education/CMO, Henry Ford Wyandotte Hospital, Wyandotte, MI, p. A325

LEMASTERS, Debra J, Director Human Resources, Woodlawn Hospital, Rochester, IN, p. A214

LEMASTERS, Ryan, Chief Operating Officer, Timpanogos Regional Hospital, Orem, UT, p. A650

LEMAY, Catherine, Vice President Finance, Millinocket Regional Hospital, Millinocket, ME, p. A284

LEMAY, Robert Raymond, R.N., Chief Nursing Officer, The Physicians Centre Hospital, Bryan, TX, p. A590

LEMBCKE, Brad, M.D., Vice President Medical Staff Affairs, Baylor University Medical Center, Dallas, TX, p. A596

LEMEL, Mark, Chief of Staff, Transylvania Regional Hospital, Brevard, NC, p. A450

LEMIEUX, Harry, Chief Information Officer, Harrington Hospital, Southbridge, MA, p. A303

LEMIEUX, Kandie, Administrative Assistant and Director Human Resources, Northern Rockies Medical Center, Cut Bank, MT, p. A375

LEMKE, Michelle, Administrator Human Resources and Support Services, Ridgecrest Regional Hospital, Ridgecrest, CA, p. A80

LEMLE, Trent, Chief Financial Officer, Fayette County Memorial Hospital, Washington Court House, OH, p. A493

LEMMER, Donn J, Chief Financial Officer and Chief Operating Officer, Munson Healthcare Manistee Hospital, Manistee, MI, p. A317

LEMMERMAN, Deborah, Chief People Officer, Hebrew Rehabilitation Center, Roslindale, MA, p. A302

LEMMON, Don, Chief Executive Officer, Providence Seaside Hospital, Seaside, OR, p. A518

LEMMONS, Joe, D.O., Chief of Staff, Lehigh Regional Medical Center, Lehigh Acres, FL, p. A128

LEMOINE, Kirk, Chief Executive Officer, Bienville Medical Center, Arcadia, LA, p. A263

LEMON, Brian J.
  President, Northwestern Medicine Central Dupage Hospital, Winfield, IL, p. A198
  President, Northwestern Medicine Marianjoy Rehabilitation Hospital, Wheaton, IL, p. A198

LEMON, Marc, Chief Executive Officer, Kindred Hospital Denver South, Denver, CO, p. A99

LEMON, Rita, Director Human Resources, Avera Queen Of Peace Hospital, Mitchell, SD, p. A562

LEMON, Thomas R., Chief Executive Officer, Munson Healthcare Otsego Memorial Hospital, Gaylord, MI, p. A312

LEMONTE, David, Vice President and Chief Operating Officer, Christus Spohn Hospital Kleberg, Kingsville, TX, p. A618

LENA, Ela C
  Administrator and Vice President Operations, Bethesda Hospital East, Boynton Beach, FL, p. A118
  Interim System Chief Nursing Officer, Bethesda Hospital East, Boynton Beach, FL, p. A118

LENAHAN, Kevin
  Director Corporate Accounting, Budgets, Grants and Reimbursements, Newton Medical Center, Newton, NJ, p. A410
  Vice President Finance and Chief Financial Officer, Overlook Medical Center, Summit, NJ, p. A413

LENAMOND, Kevin, Information Management Service Line Executive, Michael E. Debakey Veterans Affairs Medical Center, Houston, TX, p. A613

LENARZ, Sandy, Chief Nursing Officer, Grand Itasca Clinic And Hospital, Grand Rapids, MN, p. A333

LENCHUS, Joshua D., Chief Medical Officer, Broward Health Medical Center, Fort Lauderdale, FL, p. A122

LENDARIS, Nia, MS, R.N., Regional Vice President Patient Care, Adventist Health St. Helena, Saint Helena, CA, p. A82

LENFANT, Rodney, Chief Financial Officer, Oakbend Medical Center, Richmond, TX, p. A631

LENGFELDER, Valerie, M.D., Chief of Staff, Powell Valley Healthcare, Powell, WY, p. A712

LENIOR, Frank, Vice President Human Resources, St. Dominic–Jackson Memorial Hospital, Jackson, MS, p. A349

LENKO, Paul, Section Head Information Technology, Mayo Clinic Hospital, Phoenix, AZ, p. A33

LENNARTZ, Randal P., President and Chief Executive Officer, Highland District Hospital, Hillsboro, OH, p. A484

LENNON, Colin, Chief Financial Officer, Richard L. Roudebush Veterans Affairs Medical Center, Indianapolis, IN, p. A207

LENNON, Roslyn J, R.N., MS, Chief Nursing Officer, West Suburban Medical Center, Oak Park, IL, p. A192

LENTENBRINK, Laura, Vice President, Human Resources, Ascension Borgess Hospital, Kalamazoo, MI, p. A315

LENTZ, Darrell, President, Aspirus Wausau Hospital, Inc., Wausau, WI, p. A708

LENTZ, Matt, R.N., Director of Patient Services, Brown County Hospital, Ainsworth, NE, p. A382

LENZ, Jan, Chief Nursing Officer, Athens–Limestone Hospital, Athens, AL, p. A13

LENZA, Robert, Chief Executive Officer, Methodist Hospital, San Antonio, TX, p. A634

LENZO, Julie, Director Business Office, Amg Specialty Hospital–Albuquerque, Albuquerque, NM, p. A416

LEO, Elizabeth, Chief Human Resources Officer, Moses Taylor Hospital, Scranton, PA, p. A540

LEON, Daniel, Chief Financial Officer, Sherman Oaks Hospital, Los Angeles, CA, p. A69

LEON, Edwin, Chief Executive Officer, Pampa Regional Medical Center, Pampa, TX, p. A627

LEON, Luis, Chief Operating Officer, Desert Valley Hospital, Victorville, CA, p. A94

LEONARD, Anne, R.N., Chief Nursing Officer, Tristar Greenview Regional Hospital, Bowling Green, KY, p. A250

LEONARD, Barry, Vice President of Finance, Encompass Health Rehabilitation Hospital Of Braintree, Braintree, MA, p. A296

LEONARD, Beckie, R.N., Chief Nursing Officer, Foundation Surgical Hospital Of San Antonio, San Antonio, TX, p. A634

LEONARD, Bruce, M.D., Medical Director and Chief of Psychiatry, Colorado Mental Health Institute At Fort Logan, Denver, CO, p. A98

LEONARD, Donavan, Chief Financial Officer, Baptist Memorial Hospital–Booneville, Booneville, MS, p. A345

LEONARD, Edward F, Executive Vice President and Chief Operating Officer, White Plains Hospital Center, White Plains, NY, p. A448

LEONARD, James C., President and Chief Executive Officer, Carle Foundation Hospital, Urbana, IL, p. A197

LEONARD, Jayne, M.D., Family Medicine, Ashe Memorial Hospital, Jefferson, NC, p. A457

LEONARD, Julie
Chief Executive Officer, Garfield County Public Hospital District, Pomeroy, WA, p. A676
Chief Financial Officer, Garfield County Public Hospital District, Pomeroy, WA, p. A676

LEONARD, Kevin, Vice President, Finance, Henry Ford Allegiance Health, Jackson, MI, p. A315

LEONARD, Mark, Vice President Finance, Beaumont Hospital – Troy, Troy, MI, p. A324

LEONARD, Mark T.
Chief Executive Officer, Dickenson Community Hospital, Clintwood, VA, p. A658
Chief Executive Officer, Norton Community Hospital, Norton, VA, p. A664
Interim Chief Executive Officer, Lonesome Pine Hospital, Big Stone Gap, VA, p. A656
Interim Chief Executive Officer, Mountain View Regional Medical Center, Norton, VA, p. A664

LEONARD, Robert, Director Information Services, Sierra Vista Regional Medical Center, San Luis Obispo, CA, p. A87

LEONARD, Steven E., President and Chief Executive Officer, Peninsula Regional Medical Center, Salisbury, MD, p. A293

LEONARD, William H., President, Atrium Health University City, Charlotte, NC, p. A451

LEONDAR, Kimberly, Director Human Resources, Texas Health Harris Methodist Hospital Stephenville, Stephenville, TX, p. A638

LEONELIS, Lisa, Chief Information Officer, Veterans Affairs Salt Lake City Health Care System, Salt Lake City, UT, p. A652

LEOPARD, Erik, Manager Human Resource, Methodist Hospital For Surgery, Addison, TX, p. A581

LEOPARD, Jimmy, Chief Executive Officer, Wagoner Community Hospital, Wagoner, OK, p. A510

LEOPOLD, Michael, Chief Operating Officer, Broward Health Coral Springs, Coral Springs, FL, p. A120

LEPAK, Jason, M.D.
Medical Director, St. John Broken Arrow, Broken Arrow, OK, p. A497
Medical Director, St. John Sapulpa, Sapulpa, OK, p. A507

LEPPER, Dale, Chief Information Officer, Antelope Valley Hospital, Lancaster, CA, p. A64

LEPPKE, Ben, Chief Information Officer, Satanta District Hospital And Long Term Care, Satanta, KS, p. A245

LEQUEUX, Veronica, Vice President Human Resources, Blake Medical Center, Bradenton, FL, p. A118

LERASH, Terrance, President and Chief Executive Officer, Scheurer Hospital, Pigeon, MI, p. A319

LERCH, Gail, R.N.
Executive Vice President Human Resources, Straub Medical Center, Honolulu, HI, p. A165
Vice President Human Resources, Pali Momi Medical Center, Aiea, HI, p. A164
Vice President, Kapiolani Medical Center For Women & Children, Honolulu, HI, p. A164

LERCH, Shawn, Chief Executive Officer, Sauk Prairie Healthcare, Prairie Du Sac, WI, p. A704

LERMA, Robert J., Chief Executive Officer, Austin Lakes Hospital, Austin, TX, p. A585

LERNER, Jerome, M.D., Medical Director, Sierra Tucson, Tucson, AZ, p. A38

LEROY, Michael
Senior Vice President and Chief Information Officer, Dmc – Detroit Receiving Hospital, Detroit, MI, p. A310
Senior Vice President and Chief Information Officer, Dmc Harper University Hospital, Detroit, MI, p. A310

LESCH, Jason, Chief Financial Officer, Auburn Community Hospital, Auburn, NY, p. A423

LESCHER, Mary, Chief Clinical Officer, Doctor'S Memorial Hospital, Perry, FL, p. A136

LESHER, Jennifer, Chief Financial Officer, Upmc Susquehanna Lock Haven, Lock Haven, PA, p. A530

LESIAK, Cindy, Vice President Patient Care Services and Director of Nursing, Boone County Health Center, Albion, NE, p. A382

LESINS, Ross, Chief Information Officer, Casa Colina Hospital And Health Systems, Pomona, CA, p. A78

LESKO, Joan, Director Technical Support and Services, Kidspeace Children'S Hospital, Orefield, PA, p. A533

LESLIE, Andrea M.
President, Spectrum Health Big Rapids Hospital, Big Rapids, MI, p. A307
President, Spectrum Health Reed City Hospital, Reed City, MI, p. A320
President, Spectrum Health United Hospital, Greenville, MI, p. A313

LESLIE, Bruce W, M.D., Chief of Staff, Grant Memorial Hospital, Petersburg, WV, p. A688

LESLIE, Desdemona, Finance Officer, U. S. Public Health Service Indian Hospital–Whiteriver, Whiteriver, AZ, p. A38

LESLIE, Donald P, M.D., Medical Director, Shepherd Center, Atlanta, GA, p. A147

LESLIE, Kelly, Chief Financial Officer, Ferry County Memorial Hospital, Republic, WA, p. A677

LESLIE, Steve, Chief Financial Officer, Fairbanks Memorial Hospital, Fairbanks, AK, p. A26

LESMEISTER, Danielle, Chief Executive Officer, Prairie Ridge Hospital And Health Services, Elbow Lake, MN, p. A331

LESNIAK, Jacklynn, R.N., MS, Vice President Patient Care Services and Chief Nursing Officer, Midwestern Regional Medical Center, Zion, IL, p. A198

LESNICK, Kelly, Resource Manager Flight Commander, Wright Patterson Medical Center, Wright, OH, p. A494

LESNIEWSKI, Amy, Associate Director Patient Care Services, Alexandria Veterans Affairs Health Care System, Pineville, LA, p. A277

LESSMANN, Eric, Chief of Staff, South Sunflower County Hospital, Indianola, MS, p. A348

LESTER, Lisa, Chief Nursing Officer, Encompass Health Rehabilitation Hospital Of Princeton, Princeton, WV, p. A688

LESTER, Ron, Chief Human Resources, Cheyenne Veterans Affairs Medical Center, Cheyenne, WY, p. A711

LESTER, Wade K.
Administrator, Mid–Jefferson Extended Care Hospital, Nederland, TX, p. A626
Chief Executive Officer, Riverside Hospital Of Louisiana, Alexandria, LA, p. A262

LESTER, William, M.D., Vice President Medical Affairs, Cardinal Hill Rehabilitation Hospital, Lexington, KY, p. A254

LETCHWORTH, Mike, Manager Information Systems, Cherry Hospital, Goldsboro, NC, p. A455

LETEXIER, Lisa, Interim Chief Executive Officer, Pembina County Memorial Hospital And Wedgewood Manor, Cavalier, ND, p. A466

LETHI, Scott, R.N., FACHE, Chief Nursing Officer, Fort Duncan Regional Medical Center, Eagle Pass, TX, p. A600

LEU, Christopher, President, Texas Health Harris Methodist Hospital Stephenville, Stephenville, TX, p. A638

LEUBNER, Kristel, D.O., Chief of Staff, Chi St. Joseph Health Burleson Hospital, Caldwell, TX, p. A591

LEUDECKE, Amelia, Director Human Resources, Encompass Health Rehabilitation Hospital Of Round Rock, Round Rock, TX, p. A632

LEUNG, Lawrence, M.D., Chief of Staff, Va Palo Alto Health Care System, Palo Alto, CA, p. A77

LEURCK, Mary P, Human Resources Director, Adventist Medical Center – Hinsdale, Hinsdale, IL, p. A186

LEVANGER, Nathan, M.D., Chief of Staff, Teton Valley Health Care, Driggs, ID, p. A169

LEVECK, Dianna, Chief Human Resources Officer, Genesis Healthcare System, Zanesville, OH, p. A495

LEVEILLEE, Mary, Senior Vice President Patient Care Services and Chief Nursing Officer, Butler Hospital, Providence, RI, p. A547

LEVELING, Jim, Director Information Technology, Kansas City Orthopaedic Institute, Leawood, KS, p. A239

LEVENDOFSKY, Randy, Director Information Technology, Thayer County Health Services, Hebron, NE, p. A386

LEVER, Roger, M.D., President Medical Staff, The Outer Banks Hospital, Nags Head, NC, p. A459

LEVERING, Theresa, Director Human Resources, Doctors Hospital Of Sarasota, Sarasota, FL, p. A139

LEVESQUE, David, Director, Information Systems, New Hampshire Hospital, Concord, NH, p. A399

LEVI, Dina, Director, Business Development, Psychiatric Institute Of Washington, Washington, DC, p. A116

LEVI, John, Director Human Resources, St. Lawrence Rehabilitation Center, Lawrenceville, NJ, p. A407

LEVIN, Alan M., MSN, R.N., Chief Nursing Officer, Brookdale Hospital Medical Center, New York, NY, p. A432

LEVINE, Larry L., President and Chief Executive Officer, Blythedale Children'S Hospital, Valhalla, NY, p. A446

LEVINE, Robert V, Executive Vice President and Chief Operating Officer, Brookdale Hospital Medical Center, New York, NY, p. A432

LEVINE, Stuart M., President and Chief Medical Officer, Medstar Harbor Hospital, Baltimore, MD, p. A287

LEVINSON, Adam, Associate Director, Information Services, Rutgers University Behavioral Healthcare, Piscataway, NJ, p. A411

LEVIS, Randolph, Chief Financial Officer, Saint Vincent Hospital, Erie, PA, p. A525

LEVISON, Julie, Director Human Resources, Providence Medford Medical Center, Medford, OR, p. A515

LEVITAN, Kenneth, Chief Administrative Officer, Einstein Medical Center Montgomery, East Norriton, PA, p. A524

LEVITOW, John, Vice President Patient Care Services and Chief Nursing Officer, Frisbie Memorial Hospital, Rochester, NH, p. A402

LEVITZ, Michele, Director Finance, St. Luke'S Hospital – Miners Campus, Coaldale, PA, p. A522

LEVY, Becky
Chief Financial Officer, Paradise Valley Hospital, National City, CA, p. A74
Chief Financial Officer, Shasta Regional Medical Center, Redding, CA, p. A80
Chief Operating Officer, Shasta Regional Medical Center, Redding, CA, p. A80

LEVY, Dana, Chief Nursing Officer, University Of Maryland Charles Regional Medical Center, La Plata, MD, p. A291

LEVY, Jennifer C., Director Human Resources, Texas Institute For Surgery At Texas Health Presbyterian Dallas, Dallas, TX, p. A598

LEVY, Scott S, M.D., Vice President and Chief Medical Officer, Doylestown Hospital, Doylestown, PA, p. A524

LEVY, Susan M, M.D., Vice President Medical Affairs, Levindale Hebrew Hospital And Nursing, Baltimore, MD, p. A286

LEWANDOWSKI, James, Vice President Human Resources, Perry Memorial Hospital, Princeton, IL, p. A194

LEWANDOWSKI, Jim, Interim Director of Human Resources, Carson Tahoe Health, Carson City, NV, p. A393

LEWANDOWSKI, Terri, Director Financial Services, Ascension Our Lady Of Victory Hospital, Stanley, WI, p. A706

LEWELLEN, Patsy, Interim Chief Nursing Officer, Moberly Regional Medical Center, Moberly, MO, p. A365

LEWELLEN, Thomas, D.O., Chief of Staff, Delta Memorial Hospital, Dumas, AR, p. A41

LEWERKE, Jane, Manager Human Resources, Northern Arizona Veterans Affairs Health Care System, Prescott, AZ, p. A34

LEWIS, Alene, R.N., Chief Nursing Officer, Raleigh General Hospital, Beckley, WV, p. A683

LEWIS, Angela, Senior Vice President Administration, Cookeville Regional Medical Center, Cookeville, TN, p. A568

LEWIS, Barbara, Chief Nursing Officer, Alliancehealth Seminole, Seminole, OK, p. A507

LEWIS, Brandon, Director of Information Technology, Ivinson Memorial Hospital, Laramie, WY, p. A711

LEWIS, Brinsley, Chief Executive Officer, Kindred Hospital Chicago–Northlake, Northlake, IL, p. A191

LEWIS, Caren, R.N., Chief Nursing Officer, Lawrence + Memorial Hospital, New London, CT, p. A110

LEWIS, Carlisle, Senior Vice President Legal and Human Resources, Sharp Mesa Vista Hospital, San Diego, CA, p. A84

LEWIS, Christine, Assistant Administrator, Finance, Hermann Area District Hospital, Hermann, MO, p. A361

LEWIS, Colleen, Director Human Resources, Texas Neurorehab Center, Austin, TX, p. A586

LEWIS, Courtney, Director Human Resources, Houston Methodist Baytown Hospital, Baytown, TX, p. A587

LEWIS, Craig, Chief Financial Officer, Sentara Albemarle Medical Center, Elizabeth City, NC, p. A453

LEWIS, Dana, Director Clinical Services, Southern Kentucky Rehabilitation Hospital, Bowling Green, KY, p. A250

LEWIS, Daniel
Chief Medical Officer, Greeneville Community Hospital West, Greeneville, TN, p. A570
Executive Vice President and Chief Operating Officer, Metrohealth Medical Center, Cleveland, OH, p. A478

LEWIS, Darlene, Vice President Human Resources, Canton–Potsdam Hospital, Potsdam, NY, p. A442

LEWIS, Dave, Director Information Services, Mosaic Medical Center – Maryville, Maryville, MO, p. A365

LEWIS, Dennis, M.D., Chief of Staff, Ashley Regional Medical Center, Vernal, UT, p. A653

LEWIS, Doug
Chief Financial Officer, St. Luke'S Rehabilitation Hospital, Boise, ID, p. A168
Chief Financial Officer, Wheatland Memorial Healthcare, Harlowton, MT, p. A377

LEWIS, Douglas, Chief Financial Officer, Boulder City Hospital, Boulder City, NV, p. A393

LEWIS, Eric, Chief Executive Officer, Olympic Medical Center, Port Angeles, WA, p. A676

LEWIS, Gerry
Chief Information Officer, Ascension Seton Highland Lakes, Burnet, TX, p. A590
Chief Information Officer, Ascension Seton Williamson, Round Rock, TX, p. A632
LEWIS, Gordon, Chief Executive Officer, Burnett Medical Center, Grantsburg, WI, p. A695
LEWIS, Irvan Wick, Vice President Human Resources, Mt. Graham Regional Medical Center, Safford, AZ, p. A35
LEWIS, J Steve, Director Finance, Youth Villages Inner Harbour Campus, Douglasville, GA, p. A152
LEWIS, Jacob, Chief Financial Officer, Mark Twain Medical Center, San Andreas, CA, p. A83
LEWIS, Jeff, Administrator, Waukesha County Mental Health Center, Waukesha, WI, p. A707
LEWIS, John I., President and Chief Executive Officer, Acmh Hospital, Kittanning, PA, p. A528
LEWIS, Kent, Director Information Services, Southwestern Medical Center, Lawton, OK, p. A501
LEWIS, Lawrence E., Chief Executive Officer, Pioneers Memorial Healthcare District, Brawley, CA, p. A53
LEWIS, Luther J., Chief Executive Officer, St. Bernards Five Rivers, Pocahontas, AR, p. A47
LEWIS, Marcus, Chief Executive Officer and Administrator, First Care Health Center, Park River, ND, p. A469
LEWIS, Marie, Human Resources Liaison, Veterans Affairs St. Louis Health Care System, Saint Louis, MO, p. A371
LEWIS, Nicholas P., Chief Executive Officer, Hardin Medical Center, Savannah, TN, p. A579
LEWIS, Pam, Chief Compliance Officer, William R. Sharpe, Jr. Hospital, Weston, WV, p. A690
LEWIS, Paul, Chief Executive Officer, Holy Rosary Healthcare, Miles City, MT, p. A378
LEWIS, Paula, Interim Chief Nursing Officer, St. Bernards Five Rivers, Pocahontas, AR, p. A47
LEWIS, Rebecca, President, Grandview Medical Center, Dayton, OH, p. A481
LEWIS, Robin, Chief Financial Officer, Kiowa District Healthcare, Kiowa, KS, p. A238
LEWIS, Ron, President, Spectrum Health Zeeland Community Hospital, Zeeland, MI, p. A326
LEWIS, Rosalind, R.N., MSN, Director of Ancillary Services, Community Healthcare System, Onaga, KS, p. A242
LEWIS, Sharon, Director Information Systems, Forbes Hospital, Monroeville, PA, p. A532
LEWIS, Sheila, Administrator, Harmon Memorial Hospital, Hollis, OK, p. A500
LEWIS, Sherlyn, Manager Finance, The Orthopedic Specialty Hospital, Murray, UT, p. A649
LEWIS, Stephen, Chief Executive Officer, Chase County Community Hospital, Imperial, NE, p. A386
LEWIS, Thomas D, Chief Operating Officer, Clifton T. Perkins Hospital Center, Jessup, MD, p. A291
LEWIS, Vicki, President and Chief Executive Officer, Coffee Regional Medical Center, Douglas, GA, p. A152
LEWIS, Vickie, Chief Executive Officer, Central Florida Behavioral Hospital, Orlando, FL, p. A134
LEWIS–TAYLOR, Tracey, Chief Operating Officer, Stanford Health Care – Valleycare, Pleasanton, CA, p. A78
LEWISTON, Jamie, R.N., MSN, Chief Nursing Officer, Aurora Psychiatric Hospital, Wauwatosa, WI, p. A708
LEYDEN, Andrea, Chief Nursing Officer, Washington County Hospital And Clinics, Washington, IA, p. A230
LI, Eric, M.D., Chief Medical Officer, United Medical Center, Washington, DC, p. A116
LI, Ronald, Vice President Management Information Systems, New Bridge Medical Center, Paramus, NJ, p. A410
LI, Stephen, Vice President Management Information Systems, Jersey City Medical Center, Jersey City, NJ, p. A407
LI, Xiao H., M.D., Chief of Staff, Surgery Specialty Hospitals Of America, Pasadena, TX, p. A628
LIANG, Bonnie, Divisional Finance Officer, Sutter Maternity And Surgery Center Of Santa Cruz, Santa Cruz, CA, p. A89
LIBBY, Kenneth, Vice President Finance, Vcu Health Community Memorial Hospital, South Hill, VA, p. A667
LIBCKE, Julia, R.N., MSN
Chief Nursing Officer, Mclaren Macomb, Mount Clemens, MI, p. A318
VP Patient Care Services, Dmc – Rehabilitation Institute Of Michigan, Detroit, MI, p. A310
LIBERATORE, Kristi, Vice President and Chief Financial Officer, St. Joseph Hospital, Orange, CA, p. A76
LICHIUS, Sylvia Marie, R.N., Chief Nursing Officer, Morrill County Community Hospital, Bridgeport, NE, p. A383
LICHTENFELS, Suellen, Vice President and Chief Nursing Officer, Upmc Somerset Hospital, Somerset, PA, p. A541
LICHTENWALNER, Tom, Vice President Finance, St. Luke'S University Hospital – Bethlehem Campus, Bethlehem, PA, p. A520
LICHTY, Scott, M.D., Physician, Sanford Sheldon Medical Center, Sheldon, IA, p. A229
LICINA, Leonard, Chief Executive Officer, Sutter Health Kahi Mohala, Ewa Beach, HI, p. A164
LIDDELL, Sean, Manager Regional Service Information Technology, Unitypoint Health – Trinity Muscatine, Muscatine, IA, p. A227
LIDHOLM, Helen, Chief Executive Officer, Saint Mary'S Regional Medical Center, Reno, NV, p. A397
LIEBER, Alan R., President, Overlook Medical Center, Summit, NJ, p. A413
LIEBERMAN, Jeffrey A., Executive Director, Brookdale Hospital Medical Center, New York, NY, p. A432
LIEBERMAN, Steven L, M.D., Chief of Staff, Veterans Affairs New Jersey Health Care System, East Orange, NJ, p. A405
LIEBERS, David, M.D., Chief Medical Officer and Vice President Medical Affairs, Ellis Hospital, Schenectady, NY, p. A444
LIEBMAN, Jeffrey H., Chief Executive Officer, Roger Williams Medical Center, Providence, RI, p. A548
LIEFER, Alan, M.D., President Medical Staff, Memorial Hospital, Chester, IL, p. A176
LIESCHING, Timothy, M.D., Chief Medical Officer, Lahey Hospital & Medical Center, Burlington, Burlington, MA, p. A297
LIESEN, Daniel, M.D., Chief Medical Officer, Vista Health, Waukegan, IL, p. A198
LIESMANN, George, M.D., Chief Medical Officer, Blessing Hospital, Quincy, IL, p. A194
LIETTE, Cindy, Vice President Patient Care Services, Mercer Health, Coldwater, OH, p. A478
LIEZERT, Timothy, Medical Center Director, Orlando Va Medical Center, Orlando, FL, p. A134
LIFFERTH, Geoffrey, M.D., Chief Medical Officer, Sumner Regional Medical Center, Gallatin, TN, p. A570
LIGHT, Asher, M.D., Medical Director, Baylor Scott & White Institute For Rehabilitation–Fort Worth, Fort Worth, TX, p. A604
LIGHT, Gary, Vice President and Chief Information Officer, Memorial Hospital And Health Care Center, Jasper, IN, p. A208
LIGHT, Laura, Director Human Resources, St. David'S North Austin Medical Center, Austin, TX, p. A586
LIGHTBOURNE, Olieth, Chief Nursing Officer, Streamwood Behavioral Health Center, Streamwood, IL, p. A197
LIGHTCAP, Debora, Director Human Resources, Mercy Medical Center, Roseburg, OR, p. A517
LIGHTFOOT, William M, M.D., Vice President Medical Services, Providence Hospital, Mobile, AL, p. A20
LIGON, Kim, Director Information Services, Dch Regional Medical Center, Tuscaloosa, AL, p. A24
LIGON, Lynda, Chief Nursing Officer, Warm Springs Medical Center, Warm Springs, GA, p. A162
LIKES, Randle L, M.D., Chief Medical Officer, Timpanogos Regional Hospital, Orem, UT, p. A650
LILES, Jerry, D.O., Chief Medical Officer, Christus Spohn Hospital Alice, Alice, TX, p. A581
LILES, Richard A, M.D., Medical Director, Encompass Health Rehabilitation Hospital Of Largo, Largo, FL, p. A128
LILJEBERT, Sam, Chief Executive Officer, St. Theresa Specialty Hospital, Kenner, LA, p. A270
LILLEBOE, Linda, R.N., MSN, Director Operations, Carson Valley Medical Center, Gardnerville, NV, p. A394
LILLEY, Jeffrey, Chief Executive Officer, Princeton Community Hospital, Princeton, WV, p. A688
LILLY, Ryan S., Director, Maine Veterans Affairs Medical Center, Augusta, ME, p. A281
LIM, Rosemarie, M.D., Chief Medical Officer, Paradise Valley Hospital, National City, CA, p. A74
LIMA, Robert, Director Information Systems, Pappas Rehabilitation Hospital For Children, Canton, MA, p. A297
LIMBAGA, Aries, R.N., Chief Nursing Officer, Rancho Los Amigos National Rehabilitation Center, Downey, CA, p. A56
LIMBAUGH, Jason K, Vice President and Chief Financial Officer, Wellstar Atlanta Medical Center, Atlanta, GA, p. A147
LIMBOCKER, Jeff, Chief Financial Officer, Our Lady Of The Lake Regional Medical Center, Baton Rouge, LA, p. A264
LIMM, Whitney, M.D., Executive Vice President and Chief Physician Executive, The Queen'S Medical Center, Honolulu, HI, p. A165
LIN, Dean Q., Regional President, Hackensack Meridian Health Ocean Medical Center, Brick Township, NJ, p. A404
LIN, George, M.D., Physician Advisor, Hackensack Meridian Health Pascack Valley Medical Center, Westwood, NJ, p. A415
LIN, James Y, D.O., Chief of Staff, Lecom Health Millcreek Community Hospital, Erie, PA, p. A525
LINAFELTER, Robb, Chief Executive Officer, Lincoln Surgical Hospital, Lincoln, NE, p. A387
LINARES, Manuel, President and Chief Executive Officer, Touro Infirmary, New Orleans, LA, p. A276
LINCK, Cindy, Chief Nursing Officer, Cornerstone Hospital Of Oklahoma–Shawnee, Shawnee, OK, p. A507
LINCKS, Brad, R.N., Chief Nursing Officer and Vice President, Chi Our Lady Of Peace, Louisville, KY, p. A256
LIND, Jonathan, Chief Operating Officer, Swedish Covenant Hospital, Chicago, IL, p. A180
LIND, Mark, Chief Information Officer, Mammoth Hospital, Mammoth Lakes, CA, p. A70
LIND, Sharon
Chief Executive Officer, Banner Goldfield Medical Center, Apache Junction, AZ, p. A28
Chief Executive Officer, Banner Ironwood Medical Center, San Tan Valley, AZ, p. A35
LIND, Trent, Chief Executive Officer, Eastside Medical Center, Snellville, GA, p. A160
LINDBERG, Bob, Chief Operating Officer, Cumberland Healthcare, Cumberland, WI, p. A693
LINDBERG, Chris, Chief Information Officer, Milwaukee County Behavioral Health Division, Milwaukee, WI, p. A701
LINDBERG, Michael, M.D., Chief Medical Officer, Monadnock Community Hospital, Peterborough, NH, p. A402
LINDBERG, Steven, Chief Administrative Officer, Mayo Clinic Health System – Red Cedar In Menomonie, Menomonie, WI, p. A700
LINDELL, Jonathan, Director Information Technology, Miracle Mile Medical Center, Los Angeles, CA, p. A68
LINDEMAN, Barry K, Director Human Resources, Cardinal Hill Rehabilitation Hospital, Lexington, KY, p. A254
LINDEMAN, Gretchen, Director of Human Resources, Monterey Park Hospital, Monterey Park, CA, p. A73
LINDEMANN, Fran, Director Finance, Kell West Regional Hospital, Wichita Falls, TX, p. A645
LINDEMANN, Steve, Chief Financial Officer, Brookings Health System, Brookings, SD, p. A559
LINDEN, Kelly, Chief Executive Officer, Providence Saint Joseph Medical Center, Burbank, CA, p. A53
LINDER, James, Chief Executive Officer, Nebraska Medicine – Nebraska Medical Center, Omaha, NE, p. A389
LINDFORS, Teresa, Chief Nursing Officer and Vice President, Patient Services, Stoughton Hospital Association, Stoughton, WI, p. A706
LINDQUIST, James
Chief Nursing Officer, Hackensack Meridian Health Jfk Johnson Rehabilitation Institute, Edison, NJ, p. A405
Chief Nursing Officer, Hackensack Meridian Health Jfk Medical Center, Edison, NJ, p. A405
LINDQUIST, Peter, Vice President and Chief Nursing Officer, Providence Hospital, Mobile, AL, p. A20
LINDQUIST, Steve, Assistant Vice President, Behavioral Health, Avera Mckennan Hospital And University Health Center, Sioux Falls, SD, p. A563
LINDSAY, Kelly, Chief Operating Officer, Coliseum Medical Centers, Macon, GA, p. A156
LINDSAY–BELL, Davida, Area Human Resources Leader, Kaiser Permanente Antioch Medical Center, Antioch, CA, p. A50
LINDSAY–WOOD, Elizabeth, Interim Chief Information Officer, Overlook Medical Center, Summit, NJ, p. A413
LINDSEY, Don, Vice President and Chief Information Officer, Tallahassee Memorial Healthcare, Tallahassee, FL, p. A141
LINDSEY, Hugh, M.D., Chief Medical Officer, Hayes Green Beach Memorial Hospital, Charlotte, MI, p. A308
LINDSEY, Jay, Chief Executive Officer, Plano Surgical Hospital, Plano, TX, p. A629
LINDSEY, Kim, Chief Human Resources Officer, Lourdes Hospital, Paducah, KY, p. A259
LINDSEY, Robbie, Chief Information Officer, Twin Lakes Regional Medical Center, Leitchfield, KY, p. A254
LINDSEY, Tony, M.D., Chief of Staff, University Of North Carolina Hospitals, Chapel Hill, NC, p. A451
LINDSTROM, David, M.D., Vice President Medical Affairs, Promedica Bay Park Hospital, Oregon, OH, p. A489
LINES, Brian
Chief Executive Officer, Lone Peak Hospital, Draper, UT, p. A647
Chief Operating Officer, Ogden Regional Medical Center, Ogden, UT, p. A650
LING, Lori, Information Technician, Windom Area Hospital, Windom, MN, p. A343
LINGEN, Tom, M.D., Chief of Staff, Cumberland Healthcare, Cumberland, WI, p. A693
LINGLE, Dan, Chief Nursing Officer, Banner Casa Grande Medical Center, Casa Grande, AZ, p. A28
LINGLE, David, Directors Council Chairman and Chief of Staff, Vidant Roanoke–Chowan Hospital, Ahoskie, NC, p. A449
LINGO, Jessica, Human Resource Generalist, Story County Medical Center, Nevada, IA, p. A227

LINHARES, James, Chief Executive Officer, Bridgepoint Hospital Capitol Hill, Washington, DC, p. A115

LINK, Nathan, M.D., Medical Director, Brookdale Hospital Medical Center, New York, NY, p. A432

LINKENHOKER, Ellen Y, Chief Nursing Officer, Lewisgale Hospital Montgomery, Blacksburg, VA, p. A656

LINN, Steven C, M.D.
Chief Medical Officer, Inspira Medical Center–Elmer, Elmer, NJ, p. A405
Chief Medical Officer, Inspira Medical Center–Vineland, Vineland, NJ, p. A413

LINNELL, Jon E., Chief Executive Officer, North Valley Health Center, Warren, MN, p. A342

LINNINGTON, Darryl, Chief Financial Officer, Mcalester Regional Health Center, Mcalester, OK, p. A502

LINSCHEID, Carol, Vice President Human Resources, Enloe Medical Center, Chico, CA, p. A54

LINSCOTT, Jason, CPA, Chief Financial Officer, Texas Health Presbyterian Hospital Of Rockwall, Rockwall, TX, p. A631

LINSE, Margaret, Administrative Secretary and Director Human Resources, West Holt Medical Services, Atkinson, NE, p. A382

LINSKEY, Chris, M.D., Acting Chief Medical Officer, Guidance Center, Flagstaff, AZ, p. A29

LINSTROM, Joseph, Vice President Operations, Suburban Hospital, Bethesda, MD, p. A289

LINTON, Dwight, Director Human Resources, Detar Healthcare System, Victoria, TX, p. A643

LINTZ, Gordon, President and Chief Administrative Officer, Morristown–Hamblen Healthcare System, Morristown, TN, p. A576

LINVILLE, Kimberly, Chief Nursing Officer, Grant Memorial Hospital, Petersburg, WV, p. A688

LINZMAN, Rob, D.O., Chief of Staff, Jefferson County Hospital, Waurika, OK, p. A510

LIPE, Curt, Vice President, Chief Financial Officer, Osf St. Mary Medical Center, Galesburg, IL, p. A183

LIPINSKI, Gary, M.D., Chief Medical Officer, Amita Health Saint Joseph Medical Center, Joliet, IL, p. A187

LIPMAN, Brian, M.D., Medical Director and Medical Staff Services, Oconomowoc Memorial Hospital, Oconomowoc, WI, p. A702

LIPMAN, Henry D
Senior Vice President, Financial Strategy and External Relations, Franklin Regional Hospital, Franklin, NH, p. A400
Senior Vice President, Financial Strategy and External Relations, Lakes Region General Hospital, Laconia, NH, p. A400

LIPNER, Zach, Vice President Human Resources, Newark Beth Israel Medical Center, Newark, NJ, p. A409

LIPPERT, Brandt, Vice President Human Resources, Adena Greenfield Medical Center, Greenfield, OH, p. A484

LIPPINCOTT, Ken, M.D., Chief of Staff, North Mississippi State Hospital, Tupelo, MS, p. A354

LIPSCOMB, Teresa, Director Human Resources, Springbrook Behavioral Health System, Travelers Rest, SC, p. A557

LIPSCOMB, Tiffiny J, Manager Human Resources, Intermountain Medical Center, Murray, UT, p. A649

LIPSCOMB, Tracy, CPA, Vice President Financial Services and Chief Financial Officer, Garrett Regional Medical Center, Oakland, MD, p. A292

LIPSON, Wayne, M.D., Chief Physician Executive, Baptist Health Madisonville, Madisonville, KY, p. A257

LIPTAK, Valenda M., Chief Executive Officer, Western Massachusetts Hospital, Westfield, MA, p. A305

LIPTON, Pat
Director Team Resources, South Florida Baptist Hospital, Plant City, FL, p. A137
Director Team Resources, St. Joseph'S Hospital, Tampa, FL, p. A142

LIRAKIS, Kathy, R.N., Chief Nursing Officer, Northern Light Blue Hill Hospital, Blue Hill, ME, p. A282

LIRIO, Ruel R., M.D., Clinical Physician Advisor, Spectrum Health Zeeland Community Hospital, Zeeland, MI, p. A326

LISA, Mark P.
Chief Executive Officer, Sierra Vista Regional Medical Center, San Luis Obispo, CA, p. A87
Chief Executive Officer, Twin Cities Community Hospital, Templeton, CA, p. A91

LISELL, Susan C, Vice President of Clinical Services, Lifecare Medical Center, Roseau, MN, p. A339

LISKA, Lee Ann, Chief Executive Officer, Augusta University Medical Center, Augusta, GA, p. A147

LISKO, Stuart, Vice President, Chief Financial Officer and Compliance Officer, Levi Hospital, Hot Springs National Park, AR, p. A43

LISKOV, David, M.D., Medical Director, First Hospital Wyoming Valley, Kingston, PA, p. A528

LISONBEE, Rod, Chief Financial Officer, Utah Valley Hospital, Provo, UT, p. A651

LISS, Rita, Vice President Fiscal Services and Chief Financial Officer, Boone County Health Center, Albion, NE, p. A382

LIST, Alan F., President and Chief Executive Officer, H. Lee Moffitt Cancer Center And Research Institute, Tampa, FL, p. A141

LISTER, Jack, Director Human Resources, Greeneville Community Hospital West, Greeneville, TN, p. A570

LISTI, Daniel, Chief Executive Officer, Shelby Baptist Medical Center, Alabaster, AL, p. A13

LISTON, Allison, Director, Human Resources, Cedar Crest Hospital And Residential Treatment Center, Belton, TX, p. A588

LISTON, John, Chief Operating Officer, Mclaren Port Huron, Port Huron, MI, p. A320

LITAKER, Thomas, Regional Vice President and Chief Financial Officer, Cascade Valley Hospital, Arlington, WA, p. A670

LITER, Jennifer Lynn, Vice President of Inpatient Services, King'S Daughters' Health, Madison, IN, p. A210

LITKA, Calvin, R.N., Director of Nursing, Horsham Clinic, Ambler, PA, p. A520

LITOVITZ, Gary, M.D., Medical Director, Dominion Hospital, Falls Church, VA, p. A658

LITSINGER, James, CPA
Chief Operating Officer, Sheltering Arms Hospital South, Midlothian, VA, p. A663
Vice President and Chief Financial Officer, Sheltering Arms Rehabilitation Hospital, Mechanicsville, VA, p. A662

LITTERER, Karen, R.N., MSN, Administrator and Chief Operating Officer, Ascension Seton Highland Lakes, Burnet, TX, p. A590

LITTLE, Christopher M, Vice President and Chief Financial Officer, Ellwood City Medical Center, Llc, Ellwood City, PA, p. A525

LITTLE, Denise, Director Human Resources, St. Elizabeth Community Hospital, Red Bluff, CA, p. A79

LITTLE, Gary, M.D., Medical Director, George Washington University Hospital, Washington, DC, p. A115

LITTLE, James P, M.D., Medical Director, Encompass Health Rehabilitation Hospital Of Kingsport, Kingsport, TN, p. A572

LITTLE, Lisa, Chief Nursing Officer, Washington County Hospital, Nashville, IL, p. A191

LITTLE, Lou, President and Chief Executive Officer, Sparrow Specialty Hospital, Lansing, MI, p. A316

LITTLE, Monica, Coordinator Human Resources, Kindred Rehabilitation Hospital Clear Lake, Webster, TX, p. A645

LITTLE, Suzanne, Human Resources Specialist, Columbia Basin Hospital, Ephrata, WA, p. A673

LITTLE, William, Chief Executive Officer, Carolina Pines Regional Medical Center, Hartsville, SC, p. A554

LITTLEDEER, Lenora, R.N., Director of Nursing, Lawton Indian Hospital, Lawton, OK, p. A501

LITTLEFIELD, Karen, Director Human Resources, Waldo County General Hospital Maine Health, Belfast, ME, p. A282

LITTLEJOHN, Edward, Chief Operating Officer, Fountain Valley Regional Hospital And Medical Center, Fountain Valley, CA, p. A58

LITTLEJOHN, Matthew, Chief Executive Officer, Tennova Newport Medical Center, Newport, TN, p. A578

LITTLEJOHN, Traxler, Human Resources Director, Encompass Health Rehabilitation Hospital Of Charleston, Charleston, SC, p. A550

LITTLEPAGE, Dana, Interim Chief Nursing Officer, St. John'S Pleasant Valley Hospital, Camarillo, CA, p. A53

LITTRELL, Angela P., CPA, Chief Financial Officer and Chief Operating Officer, Fitzgibbon Hospital, Marshall, MO, p. A365

LITTRELL, Mark
Chief Executive Officer, Lincoln Prairie Behavioral Health Center, Springfield, IL, p. A196
Group Director, The Pavilion, Champaign, IL, p. A175

LIU, Marsha, Executive Vice President and Chief Financial Officer, Northwest Community Hospital, Arlington Heights, IL, p. A173

LIUZZA, Jed M, Chief Human Resources Officer, Ou Medical Center, Oklahoma City, OK, p. A505

LIUZZO, Gary, Director Information Systems, Scotland Health Care System, Laurinburg, NC, p. A457

LIVELY, Corey, Chief Executive Officer, Great Plains Regional Medical Center, Elk City, OK, p. A499

LIVELY, David, Chief Nursing Officer, Atoka County Medical Center, Atoka, OK, p. A496

LIVERMAN, Brett, Chief Financial Officer, Alleghany Memorial Hospital, Sparta, NC, p. A462

LIVERSAGE, Lavonne, Director, Fargo Veterans Affairs Health Care System, Fargo, ND, p. A466

LIVESAY, William, D.O., Medical Director, Encompass Health Rehabilitation Hospital Of Charleston, Charleston, SC, p. A550

LIVIN, Lee, Chief Financial Officer, Yavapai Regional Medical Center, Prescott, AZ, p. A35

LIVINGSTON, Carolyn, Director Human Resources, Salt Lake Regional Medical Center, Salt Lake City, UT, p. A652

LIVINGSTON, Charles
Administrator, Dakota Plains Surgical Center, Aberdeen, SD, p. A559
Chief Executive Officer, Midwest Surgical Hospital, Omaha, NE, p. A389

LIVINGSTON, Denise, Director Human Resources, St. Mary Medical Center, Long Beach, CA, p. A65

LIVINGSTON, Keith
Senior Vice President and Chief Information Officer, Thedacare Regional Medical Center–Appleton, Appleton, WI, p. A691
Senior Vice President and Chief Information Officer, Thedacare Regional Medical Center–Neenah, Neenah, WI, p. A702

LIVINGSTON, Richard, M.D., Medical Director, Valley Behavioral Health System, Barling, AR, p. A39

LIVINGSTON, Sam, Information Resource Consultant, G. Werber Bryan Psychiatric Hospital, Columbia, SC, p. A551

LIVSEY, Don, Vice President and Chief Information Officer, Ucsf Benioff Children'S Hospital Oakland, Oakland, CA, p. A75

LIZZA, Beth, Chief Nursing Officer, Ohio Valley Surgical Hospital, Springfield, OH, p. A491

LLANO, Manuel R., Chief Executive Officer, Fort Lauderdale Hospital, Fort Lauderdale, FL, p. A122

LLEWELLYN, Michael R, Chief Operating Officer, Laguna Honda Hospital And Rehabilitation Center, San Francisco, CA, p. A85

LLOYD, Richard, D.O., Chief of Staff, Harbor Beach Community Hospital, Harbor Beach, MI, p. A314

LLOYD, Russell E., Director, Wilkes–Barre Veterans Affairs Medical Center, Wilkes, PA, p. A545

LOBBAN, Victoria, Vice President Finance, New England Sinai Hospital And Rehabilitation Center, Stoughton, MA, p. A304

LOCEY, Vicky, R.N., MSN, Chief Operating Officer and Chief Nursing Executive, Kaiser Permanente Santa Rosa Medical Center, Santa Rosa, CA, p. A89

LOCHALA, Richard, Chief of Staff, Mena Regional Health System, Mena, AR, p. A46

LOCK, Lesa, Chief Nursing Officer, Valley View Medical Center, Fort Mohave, AZ, p. A29

LOCKARD, Dennis, FACHE, Chief Financial Officer, Coshocton Regional Medical Center, Coshocton, OH, p. A480

LOCKCUFF, Todd, Chief Financial Officer, Inova Alexandria Hospital, Alexandria, VA, p. A656

LOCKE, Cheryl, Vice President and Chief Human Resource Officer, Wake Forest Baptist Medical Center, Winston, NC, p. A464

LOCKE, Christopher, Chief Executive Officer, Saint Francis Hospital–Bartlett, Bartlett, TN, p. A566

LOCKE, Marianne, R.N., MSN, Associate Director Patient Care Services, Edward Hines, Jr. Veterans Affairs Hospital, Hines, IL, p. A185

LOCKE, Stuart, Chief Executive Officer, Southern Kentucky Rehabilitation Hospital, Bowling Green, KY, p. A250

LOCKERD, Marie Paul, M.D., Chief Medical Officer, Sanford Jackson Medical Center, Jackson, MN, p. A333

LOCKETT, Kevin, Interim Chief Financial Officer, Mayo Clinic Hospital In Florida, Jacksonville, FL, p. A125

LOCKEY, Chris, Chief Executive Officer, Sun Behavioral Kentucky, Erlanger, KY, p. A251

LOCKHART, Jimmy Wayne, M.D., Medical Director, Encompass Health Rehabilitation Hospital Of Treasure Coast, Vero Beach, FL, p. A143

LOCKLEAR, Ann, Vice President, Human Resources, Scotland Health Care System, Laurinburg, NC, p. A457

LOCKRIDGE, Michael, Chief Financial Officer, Northern Louisiana Medical Center, Ruston, LA, p. A277

LOCKWOOD, Melissa, Chief Executive Officer, Preston Memorial Hospital, Kingwood, WV, p. A686

LOE, Cindy, R.N., Director of Nursing, Essentia Health Northern Pines Medical Center, Aurora, MN, p. A328

LOEB, Amy E, Ed.D., R.N., Chief Nursing Officer, Peconic Bay Medical Center, Riverhead, NY, p. A442

LOEFFELHOLZ, Tim, Account Executive Information Technology, Unitypoint Health – Finley Hospital, Dubuque, IA, p. A222

LOELIGER, Eric, Vice President of Medical Affairs, Asante Three Rivers Medical Center, Grants Pass, OR, p. A513

LOEPP, Robert A., Jr, Chief Executive Officer, Amg Specialty Hospital–Wichita, Wichita, KS, p. A247

LOERA, Arnold, M.D., Clinical Director, Bristol Bay Area Health Corporation, Dillingham, AK, p. A26

LOERINC, Albert, M.D., Medical Director, Vibra Hospital Of Southeastern Massachusetts, New Bedford, MA, p. A301
LOESCHER, Cori, R.N., Chief Nursing Officer and Vice President of Patient Care Services, Brigham And Women'S Faulkner Hospital, Boston, MA, p. A295
LOEWENSTEIN, Howard, Chief Information Resource Management Services, Jesse Brown Veterans Affairs Medical Center, Chicago, IL, p. A177
LOFFING, David, Chief Operating Officer, University Of Illinois Hospital & Health Sciences System, Chicago, IL, p. A180
LOFTIS, Dennis
Senior Vice President and Chief Information Officer, Riverside Regional Medical Center, Newport News, VA, p. A663
Senior Vice President of Information Systems, Coastal Virginia Rehabilitation, Newport News, VA, p. A663
LOFTIS, Michelle, Human Resources Officer, Ferry County Memorial Hospital, Republic, WA, p. A677
LOFTON, Veronica, Acting Chief Executive Officer, Twin Valley Behavioral Healthcare, Columbus, OH, p. A480
LOFTUS, John, M.D., Chief of Staff, Kaiser Permanente Oakland Medical Center, Oakland, CA, p. A75
LOFTUS, Mary Virginia, Chief Nursing Officer, Specialists Hospital – Shreveport, Shreveport, LA, p. A278
LOFTUS, Philip, Ph.D.
Chief Information Officer, Aurora West Allis Medical Center, West Allis, WI, p. A708
Vice President and Chief Information Officer, Aurora Medical Center Of Oshkosh, Oshkosh, WI, p. A703
Vice President and Chief Information Officer, Aurora Psychiatric Hospital, Wauwatosa, WI, p. A708
Vice President and Chief Information Officer, Aurora St. Luke'S Medical Center, Milwaukee, WI, p. A701
LOFTUS, Terry, M.D., Chief Medical Officer, Medical City Fort Worth, Fort Worth, TX, p. A605
LOFURNO, Justin A, Director Human Resources, Providence Hospital, Columbia, SC, p. A551
LOGAN, Angela, Chief Nursing Officer, Lutheran Hospital Of Indiana, Fort Wayne, IN, p. A204
LOGAN, Ann P., Chief Operating Officer, Carepoint Health Hoboken University Medical Center, Hoboken, NJ, p. A406
LOGAN, Ann P., R.N., Ph.D., Chief Operating Officer, Carepoint Health Hoboken University Medical Center, Hoboken, NJ, p. A406
LOGAN, Denise, Director Human Resources, Specialty Rehabilitation Hospital Of Coushatta, Coushatta, LA, p. A266
LOGAN, John, M.D., Chief Medical Officer, Methodist Hospital, Henderson, KY, p. A253
LOGAN, Renee, Chief Financial Officer, Murray County Medical Center, Slayton, MN, p. A340
LOGAN–OWENS, Michelle, Chief Operating Officer, Prisma Health Tuomey Hospital, Sumter, SC, p. A557
LOGAR, Michael, Assistant Superintendent, Larue D. Carter Memorial Hospital, Indianapolis, IN, p. A207
LOGDSON, David, Chief Nursing Officer, Twin Lakes Regional Medical Center, Leitchfield, KY, p. A254
LOGOZZO, Vince, Director Information Technology, Aultman Orrville Hospital, Orrville, OH, p. A489
LOGSDON, Terri
Chief Financial Officer, Covington Behavioral Health, Covington, LA, p. A266
Chief Financial Officer, Hickory Trail Hospital, Desoto, TX, p. A600
LOGUE, Amy Antani, Ph.D., Vice President Human Resources, Advocate Condell Medical Center, Libertyville, IL, p. A188
LOH, Marcel C., Chief Executive Officer, Providence Saint John'S Health Center, Santa Monica, CA, p. A89
LOHMAN, Eric, M.D., Chief of Staff, Meadowview Regional Medical Center, Maysville, KY, p. A257
LOHN, Eric
Chief Financial Officer, Lake View Hospital, Two Harbors, MN, p. A341
Vice President and Chief Financial Officer, St. Luke'S Hospital, Duluth, MN, p. A331
LOHR, Daniel E, Regional Vice President Finance, Windham Hospital, Willimantic, CT, p. A112
LOHRMAN, Joseph W, Chief Executive Officer, Annie Jeffrey Memorial County Health Center, Osceola, NE, p. A390
LOHRMAN, Joseph W., Chief Executive Officer, Annie Jeffrey Memorial County Health Center, Osceola, NE, p. A390
LOHSTRETER, Thomas, M.D., Chief of Staff, Kittson Memorial Healthcare Center, Hallock, MN, p. A333
LOKKEN, Christine, Chief Financial Officer, Bigfork Valley Hospital, Bigfork, MN, p. A328
LOLLEY, Tim, MSN, Chief Nursing Officer, Merit Health Madison, Canton, MS, p. A345
LOLLIS, Sylvia, Director Human Resources, Osceola Regional Medical Center, Kissimmee, FL, p. A126
LOLLO, Trisha, President, Barnes–Jewish West County Hospital, Saint Louis, MO, p. A369
LOMAN, Sarah, Director Human Resources, Penobscot Valley Hospital, Lincoln, ME, p. A283
LOMBA, Maria R, Medical Director, New Braunfels Regional Rehabilitation Hospital, New Braunfels, TX, p. A626
LOMBARD, Lisa, Chief Medical Officer, Ohiohealth Rehabilitation Hospital, Columbus, OH, p. A479
LOMBARDO, Alan, Associate Director, Hunter Holmes Mcguire Veterans Affairs Medical Center–Richmond, Richmond, VA, p. A666
LOMEO, Jody, Chief Executive Officer, Kaleida Health, Buffalo, NY, p. A424
LONES, Malachi, Interim Administrator, Hamilton County Hospital, Syracuse, KS, p. A246
LONEY, Chris, Director Personnel, Thomas B. Finan Center, Cumberland, MD, p. A290
LONG, Amy, Administrator, Mayo Clinic Health System In Fairmont, Fairmont, MN, p. A331
LONG, Angela S, Vice President Clinical Services and Chief Nursing Officer, Southeastern Ohio Regional Medical Center, Cambridge, OH, p. A474
LONG, Brian, President and Chief Executive Officer, Memorial Healthcare, Owosso, MI, p. A319
LONG, Dennis, Director Human Resources, Western Missouri Medical Center, Warrensburg, MO, p. A372
LONG, Erik, Controller, Baptist Health South Florida, South Miami Hospital, Miami, FL, p. A130
LONG, Floyd R, Chief Executive Officer, Brookdale Hospital Medical Center, New York, NY, p. A432
LONG, Gloria, Chief Operating Officer, Guam Regional Medical City, Dededo, GU, p. A714
LONG, Gregory L, M.D.
Chief Medical Officer, Thedacare Regional Medical Center–Appleton, Appleton, WI, p. A691
Chief Medical Officer, Thedacare Regional Medical Center–Neenah, Neenah, WI, p. A702
LONG, Gretchen, Manager Human Resources, Shriners Hospitals For Children – Cincinnati, Cincinnati, OH, p. A476
LONG, Jeremy
Chief Information Officer, St. Vincent Heart Center, Indianapolis, IN, p. A206
Manager Information Systems, St. Vincent Salem Hospital, Salem, IN, p. A214
LONG, Jonathan Ray, M.D., Chief of Staff, Weatherford Regional Hospital, Weatherford, OK, p. A510
LONG, Judy M, R.N., MS, Chief Nursing Officer and Chief Operating Officer, Appling Healthcare System, Baxley, GA, p. A148
LONG, Karen, R.N., FACHE, Vice President Nursing, Bayfront Health St. Petersburg, Saint Petersburg, FL, p. A138
LONG, Kimberly C., Chief Executive Officer, Vibra Hospital Of Sacramento, Folsom, CA, p. A58
LONG, Michelle
Regional Human Resource Manager, Abraham Lincoln Memorial Hospital, Lincoln, IL, p. A188
Regional Human Resource Manager, Taylorville Memorial Hospital, Taylorville, IL, p. A197
LONG, Mike, Chief Financial Officer, Powell Valley Healthcare, Powell, WY, p. A712
LONG, Richard, M.D., Chief Medical Officer, Upmc Hamot, Erie, PA, p. A525
LONG, Stephanie, President and Chief Executive Officer, River Bend Hospital, West Lafayette, IN, p. A216
LONG, Steven V., President and Chief Executive Officer, Hancock Regional Hospital, Greenfield, IN, p. A205
LONG, Theresa, Chief Executive Officer, Danville State Hospital, Danville, PA, p. A523
LONGABAUGH, James, M.D., Chief Medical Staff, Sabetha Community Hospital, Sabetha, KS, p. A244
LONGACRE, Mark E, FACHE, Chief Operating Officer, Orthonebraska Hospital, Omaha, NE, p. A390
LONGDO, Derrick, Director Information Systems, Marshfield Medical Center – Neillsville, Neillsville, WI, p. A702
LONGEST, Bruce, M.D., President Medical Staff, Baptist Memorial Hospital – Calhoun, Calhoun City, MS, p. A345
LONGEST, Sonya, M.D., Chief Medical Officer, Walter B. Jones Alcohol And Drug Abuse Treatment Center, Greenville, NC, p. A455
LONGLEY, Frank, Business Partner Information Technology, Cleveland Clinic, Medina Hospital, Medina, OH, p. A487
LONGLEY, Michael, M.D., Chief Medical Officer, Adventhealth North Pinellas, Tarpon Springs, FL, p. A142
LONGMORE, David, Chief Information Officer, Wilkes–Barre Veterans Affairs Medical Center, Wilkes, PA, p. A545
LONGMUIR, Bryan, Chief Resource Management, Madigan Army Medical Center, Tacoma, WA, p. A680
LONGMUIR, Marla, M.D., Chief Medical Officer, Mountrail County Medical Center, Stanley, ND, p. A469
LONGNECKER, Stacy, Chief of Staff, Ortonville Area Health Services, Ortonville, MN, p. A337
LONGO, Joseph, Chief Information Officer, Parkland Health & Hospital System, Dallas, TX, p. A597
LONGO, Marybeth, Manager Human Resources, Trenton Psychiatric Hospital, Trenton, NJ, p. A413
LONGTIN, Brett
Chief Financial Officer, Lake Region Healthcare, Fergus Falls, MN, p. A332
Chief Financial Officer, Prairie Ridge Hospital And Health Services, Elbow Lake, MN, p. A331
LONGWELL, Connie, Chief Executive Officer, Elkhorn Valley Rehabilitation Hospital, Casper, WY, p. A710
LONGWORTH, David L., Chief Executive Officer, Lahey Hospital & Medical Center, Burlington, Burlington, MA, p. A297
LONIS, Robert M, CPA, Chief Financial Officer, Lincoln County Health System, Fayetteville, TN, p. A569
LONIS, Robert M., Interim Chief Executive Officer, Lincoln County Health System, Fayetteville, TN, p. A569
LOOMIS, Greg, Interim President and Chief Operating Officer, Mercy Health Hackley Campus, Muskegon, MI, p. A318
LOOMIS, Randy, Chief Financial Officer, Dallas County Hospital, Perry, IA, p. A228
LOONEY, Zane, Chief Information Officer, St. Bernard Parish Hospital, Chalmette, LA, p. A265
LOOSBROCK, Tammy, Senior Director, Sanford Luverne Medical Center, Luverne, MN, p. A334
LOOSEMORE, Tim
Director, Franciscan Health Crown Point, Crown Point, IN, p. A202
Regional Director Information Systems, Franciscan Health Michigan City, Michigan City, IN, p. A211
LOOSLI, Angela, Assistant Administrator, Operations, State Hospital South, Blackfoot, ID, p. A167
LOPACHIN, Vicki, M.D., Chief Medical Officer, Brookdale Hospital Medical Center, New York, NY, p. A432
LOPAS, Mary, Chief Information Officer, Door County Medical Center, Sturgeon Bay, WI, p. A706
LOPES, Michelle Anne, MSN, R.N., Senior Vice President, Patient Care Services & Chief Nursing Officer, John Muir Medical Center, Walnut Creek, Walnut Creek, CA, p. A94
LOPEZ, Augustine, Chief Financial Officer, Salinas Valley Memorial Healthcare System, Salinas, CA, p. A83
LOPEZ, Cesar, R.N., Director of Nurses, Chi St. Joseph Health Grimes Hospital, Navasota, TX, p. A626
LOPEZ, David S, FACHE, Executive Vice President and Chief Operating Officer, Parkland Health & Hospital System, Dallas, TX, p. A597
LOPEZ, Enrique, M.D., Medical Director, Larry B. Zieverink, Sr. Alcoholism Treatment Center, Raleigh, NC, p. A460
LOPEZ, Ericca, Director Human Resources, Canyon Ridge Hospital, Chino, CA, p. A54
LOPEZ, Ivonne, Director Human Resources, Hospital Oriente, Humacao, PR, p. A716
LOPEZ, Jose, M.D., Medical Staff President, Indiana University Health Paoli Hospital, Paoli, IN, p. A213
LOPEZ, Leonard H, Chief Operating Officer, Hopi Health Care Center, Keams Canyon, AZ, p. A30
LOPEZ, Leonardo, President Medical Staff, Osf Saint Paul Medical Center, Mendota, IL, p. A189
LOPEZ, Lesbia, Chief Nursing Officer, Doctors' Center Hospital San Juan, San Juan, PR, p. A718
LOPEZ, Lisa M, Director Human Resources, San Joaquin General Hospital, French Camp, CA, p. A59
LOPEZ, Maria Rose, R.N., Chief of Nursing, Nix Health Care System, San Antonio, TX, p. A634
LOPEZ, Maritza, M.D., Chief of Staff, Sanford Canby Medical Center, Canby, MN, p. A329
LOPEZ, Rene, Chief Executive Officer, Knapp Medical Center, Weslaco, TX, p. A645
LOPEZ, Robert, Chief Medical Officer, Highland Community Hospital, Picayune, MS, p. A353
LOPEZ, Rodrigo, Interim President and Chief Executive Officer, Children'S Hospital And Medical Center, Omaha, NE, p. A389
LOPEZ, Rosalio J, M.D., Senior Vice President and Chief Medical Officer, Pih Health Hospital – Whittier, Whittier, CA, p. A95
LOPEZ, Steve Kelley, Chief Financial Officer, Colorado River Medical Center, Needles, CA, p. A74
LOPEZ, Steve Kelley., Chief Executive Officer, Colorado River Medical Center, Needles, CA, p. A74
LOPEZ, Steven, M.D., Chief Medical Officer, Palmetto Lowcountry Behavioral Health, Charleston, SC, p. A550
LOPEZ, Susan Nordstrom., President, Advocate Illinois Masonic Medical Center, Chicago, IL, p. A176
LOPEZ, Trish, Area Chief Financial Officer, Kaiser Permanente Fontana Medical Center, Fontana, CA, p. A58

LOPEZ, Valerie, CPA, Chief Financial Officer, Uvalde Memorial Hospital, Uvalde, TX, p. A643

LOPEZ-CEPERO, Joe, Chief Nursing Officer, Good Samaritan Medical Center, West Palm Beach, FL, p. A144

LOPREATO, Elayne
Chief Clinical Officer, Kindred Hospital The Palm Beaches, Riviera Beach, FL, p. A137
Chief Executive Officer, Kindred Hospital The Palm Beaches, Riviera Beach, FL, p. A137

LORAH, Kelly M., Chief Executive Officer, Lower Bucks Hospital, Bristol, PA, p. A521

LORD, David, President, Osf St. Francis Hospital And Medical Group, Escanaba, MI, p. A311

LORD, Gregory D, M.D., Chief Medical Officer, Leesville Rehabilitation Hospital, Leesville, LA, p. A272

LORD, Jeff, Director of Nursing, Connecticut Veterans Home And Hospital, Rocky Hill, CT, p. A110

LORD, Robert L., President and Chief Executive Officer, Cleveland Clinic Martin North Hospital, Stuart, FL, p. A140

LORENTZ, Derick, Chief Financial Officer, Goodland Regional Medical Center, Goodland, KS, p. A235

LORENZ, Paul E., Chief Executive Officer, Santa Clara Valley Medical Center, San Jose, CA, p. A87

LORENZ, Todd, Chief Executive Officer, Pam Rehabilitation Hospital Of Beaumont, Beaumont, TX, p. A587

LORENZEN, Shelli, Chief Human Resources Officer, Manning Regional Healthcare Center, Manning, IA, p. A226

LORENZO, Heather, M.D., Vice President and Chief Medical Officer, Meritus Medical Center, Hagerstown, MD, p. A291

LORIMER, Lee, Regional Director Human Resources, Mckay-Dee Hospital, Ogden, UT, p. A649

LORISH, Tom, Interim Chief Executive, Providence Medford Medical Center, Medford, OR, p. A515

LORMAN, William J, Ph.D., Clinical Director, Livengrin Foundation, Bensalem, PA, p. A520

LORMAND, Jared, Vice President Information Technology, Opelousas General Health System, Opelousas, LA, p. A276

LORTON, Donald E, Executive Vice President, Centra Bedford Memorial Hospital, Bedford, VA, p. A656

LOSITO, Glenna, R.N., MSN, Chief Nursing Officer, Cibola General Hospital, Grants, NM, p. A418

LOTHE, Eric L, FACHE
Executive Vice President and Chief Operating Officer, Unitypoint Health – Iowa Methodist Medical Center, Des Moines, IA, p. A221
Senior Vice President and Chief Operating Officer, Unitypoint Health–Iowa Lutheran Hospital, Des Moines, IA, p. A221

LOTT, Benjamin, Chief Executive Officer, Copiah County Medical Center, Hazlehurst, MS, p. A348

LOTT, Cynthia, Director Human Resources, Northern Virginia Mental Health Institute, Falls Church, VA, p. A659

LOTT, Laura, Administrative Director, Eastern Louisiana Mental Health System, Jackson, LA, p. A269

LOTT, Rodney, Director Management Information Systems and Facility Operations, Baylor Scott & White Medical Center – Llano, Llano, TX, p. A621

LOTZE, Eberhard, M.D., Chief Medical Officer, Woman'S Hospital Of Texas, Houston, TX, p. A615

LOUBERT, Cheryl, M.D., Chief Medical Staff, Midmichigan Medical Center–Gladwin, Gladwin, MI, p. A312

LOUDEN CORBETT, Jeanette L, Chief Human Resources Officer, Highland Hospital, Oakland, CA, p. A75

LOUGHERY, Vicki, R.N., MS, Chief Nursing Officer, Monadnock Community Hospital, Peterborough, NH, p. A402

LOUGHRAN, Lisa, Chief Nursing Officer, Gunnison Valley Hospital, Gunnison, CO, p. A101

LOUGHRAN, Michael, Vice President Human Resources, Kennedy Krieger Institute, Baltimore, MD, p. A286

LOUK, Rodney, Vice President Information Systems, Washington Hospital, Washington, PA, p. A543

LOUKATOS, George, M.D., President Medical Staff Affairs, Merit Health Biloxi, Biloxi, MS, p. A344

LOVATO, Anthony, Director Information Technology, Coon Memorial Hospital, Dalhart, TX, p. A595

LOVDAHL, Brian A., Chief Executive Officer, Ccm Health, Montevideo, MN, p. A336

LOVE, Alex, Acting Manager Human Resources, Alexandria Veterans Affairs Health Care System, Pineville, LA, p. A277

LOVE, Bianca, Assistant Administrator Human Resources, Trinity Hospital Twin City, Dennison, OH, p. A482

LOVE, E Clifford, Director Fiscal Services, Eastern State Hospital, Williamsburg, VA, p. A668

LOVE, Glenn Neil, M.D., Medical Director, Hilton Head Hospital, Hilton Head Island, SC, p. A554

LOVE, Matthew
Chief Financial Officer, Nicklaus Children'S Hospital, Miami, FL, p. A131
Interim Chief Executive Officer, Nicklaus Children'S Hospital, Miami, FL, p. A131

LOVE, Tami, Chief Financial Officer, Memorial Hospital Of Sweetwater County, Rock Springs, WY, p. A712

LOVE, Tim, Director Information Services, Reid Health, Richmond, IN, p. A214

LOVE, Valerie, Manager Business Office, Heatherhill Care Communities, Chardon, OH, p. A475

LOVEJOY, David, Chief Operations Officer, Riverview Psychiatric Center, Augusta, ME, p. A281

LOVEJOY, Leslie, R.N., Ph.D., Chief Nursing and Quality Officer, Sonoma Valley Hospital, Sonoma, CA, p. A90

LOVEJOY, Rob
Chief Operating Officer, Sanford Thief River Falls Behavioral Health Center, Thief River Falls, MN, p. A341
Director, Operations, Sanford Medical Center Thief River Falls, Thief River Falls, MN, p. A341

LOVELACE, Alan, Vice President and Chief Financial Officer, Stillwater Medical Center, Stillwater, OK, p. A507

LOVELACE, Christina, Director Human Resources, Gunnison Valley Hospital, Gunnison, CO, p. A101

LOVELESS, Craig, Chief Executive Officer, Prowers Medical Center, Lamar, CO, p. A103

LOVELESS, Jane Doll, Vice President, Chief Information Officer, Grand View Health, Sellersville, PA, p. A541

LOVELESS, Kurt, Chief Executive Officer, The Core Institute Specialty Hospital, Phoenix, AZ, p. A34

LOVELESS, Steve, President and Chief Executive Officer, St. Vincent Healthcare, Billings, MT, p. A374

LOVELL, Charles D., Jr, Chief Executive Officer, Barbourville Arh Hospital, Barbourville, KY, p. A249

LOVELL, Mark, Vice President and Chief Financial Officer, Prisma Health Tuomey Hospital, Sumter, SC, p. A557

LOVELL, Stephanie, Vice President and General Counsel, Boston Medical Center, Boston, MA, p. A295

LOVELL, Terrence, Vice President Human Resources, Union Hospital, Elkton, MD, p. A290

LOVELLETTE, Teresa A, Manager Human Resources, Herrin Hospital, Herrin, IL, p. A185

LOVERA, Carlos, Director Information Systems, Montrose Memorial Hospital, Montrose, CO, p. A104

LOVERING, Keith, Information Technician, Miller County Hospital, Colquitt, GA, p. A150

LOVERING, Richard, Corporate Vice President Human Resources and Organizational Development, Atlanticare Regional Medical Center, Atlantic City, NJ, p. A403

LOVERN, Ed, Chief Operating Officer, Piedmont Hospital, Atlanta, GA, p. A146

LOVERSO, Felice L., President and Chief Executive Officer, Casa Colina Hospital And Health Systems, Pomona, CA, p. A78

LOVETT, Chad, Chief Executive Officer, Kindred Hospital–Greensboro, Greensboro, NC, p. A455

LOVING, David E., Chief Executive Officer, St. Luke'S Des Peres Hospital, Saint Louis, MO, p. A370

LOVING, Tonya, Director of Human Resources, Uva-Healthsouth Rehabilitation Hospital, Charlottesville, VA, p. A657

LOVINGER, Warren, M.D., Chief Medical Officer, Nevada Regional Medical Center, Nevada, MO, p. A366

LOVINGOOD, Toni, Chief Operating Officer, Erlanger Western Carolina Hospital, Murphy, NC, p. A459

LOVRICH, John
Chief Financial Officer, Catalina Island Medical Center, Avalon, CA, p. A51
Chief Financial Officer, Glenn Medical Center, Willows, CA, p. A95

LOW, Kern, M.D.
Chief Medical Officer, St. Mary–Corwin Medical Center, Pueblo, CO, p. A105
Chief Medical Officer, St. Thomas More Hospital, Canon City, CO, p. A97

LOW, Lewis, M.D.
Chief Medical Officer, Legacy Mount Hood Medical Center, Gresham, OR, p. A513
Senior Vice President and Chief Medical Officer, Legacy Meridian Park Medical Center, Tualatin, OR, p. A518
Senior Vice President and Chief Medical Officer, Legacy Salmon Creek Medical Center, Vancouver, WA, p. A681

LOW, Melissa, Chief Executive Officer, Amg Specialty Hospital, San Antonio, TX, p. A633

LOWE, Bren, Chief Executive Officer, Star Valley Medical Center, Afton, WY, p. A710

LOWE, E Rick, FACHE, Operations Support Risk Management and Compliance, St. Francis Hospital, Columbus, GA, p. A150

LOWE, E Rick., Chief Executive Officer, Select Specialty Hospital–Augusta, Augusta, GA, p. A147

LOWE, Joe, Director Management Information Systems, Cumberland Medical Center, Crossville, TN, p. A568

LOWE, Kristen, Chief Executive Officer, Post Acute/Warm Springs Specialty Hospital Of San Antonio, San Antonio, TX, p. A635

LOWE, Lavah Boyers, Chief Nursing Officer, Avista Adventist Hospital, Louisville, CO, p. A104

LOWE, Rob, Director, Healthcare Information Management, Onslow Memorial Hospital, Jacksonville, NC, p. A457

LOWE, Scott
Director Human Resource, Mcalester Regional Health Center, Mcalester, OK, p. A502
Market Chief Executive Officer, Physicians Regional – Pine Ridge, Naples, FL, p. A132

LOWELL, David, M.D., Chief Medical Officer, Spaulding Rehabilitation Hospital Cape Cod, East Sandwich, MA, p. A298

LOWENTHAL, David, M.D., Clinical Director, Brookdale Hospital Medical Center, New York, NY, p. A432

LOWENTHAL, Steve B, M.D., M.P.H., FACS, Senior Vice President Medical Affairs and Chief Medical Officer, Rush-Copley Medical Center, Aurora, IL, p. A174

LOWERY, Elizabeth, Interim Director, Amarillo Veterans Affairs Health Care System, Amarillo, TX, p. A582

LOWERY, John, M.D., Deputy Commander Clinical Services, General Leonard Wood Army Community Hospital, Fort Leonard Wood, MO, p. A360

LOWERY, Josh, Director of Human Resources, Baptist Memorial Hospital–North Mississippi, Oxford, MS, p. A352

LOWMAN, LeeAnn, Director Human Resources, Lake Taylor Transitional Care Hospital, Norfolk, VA, p. A664

LOWREY, Linda, Human Resources Officer, Atmore Community Hospital, Atmore, AL, p. A14

LOWRY, Claudia Jean, R.N., Director of Nursing, Community Howard Specialty Hospital, Kokomo, IN, p. A209

LOWRY, David, M.D., Chief Medical Officer, Caldwell Unc Health Care, Lenoir, NC, p. A457

LOY, Michael, Interim Chief Executive Officer, North Central Health Care, Wausau, WI, p. A708

LOYA, John R, Vice President Human Resources and Organizational Development, Columbus Regional Hospital, Columbus, IN, p. A201

LOYA, Theresa, R.N., Chief Nursing Officer, John C. Fremont Healthcare District, Mariposa, CA, p. A71

LOYA, Velma, Administrative Human Resource Coordinator, Rice Medical Center, Eagle Lake, TX, p. A600

LOYD, Chris, Director Human Resources, Methodist Richardson Medical Center, Richardson, TX, p. A631

LOYD, Stephana, Vice President, Chief Nursing Officer, Baptist Health Medical Center – Conway, Conway, AR, p. A40

LOYKE, Christopher, Chief Medical Officer, University Hospitals Parma Medical Center, Parma, OH, p. A489

LOYO–RODRIGUEZ, Raul J, Administrative Analyst III, San Diego County Psychiatric Hospital, San Diego, CA, p. A84

LOZADA, Leonardo J, M.D., Chief Physician Executive, Saint Luke'S North Hospital – Barry Road, Kansas City, MO, p. A363

LOZANO, Elias B., Executive Officer, Tripler Army Medical Center, Honolulu, HI, p. A165

LOZANO, Melanie, Chief Financial Officer, Concho County Hospital, Eden, TX, p. A601

LOZANO, Michelle, Chief Executive Officer, Lifecare Hospitals Of San Antonio, San Antonio, TX, p. A634

LOZAR, Beverly, Chief Nursing Executive, St. Vincent Charity Medical Center, Cleveland, OH, p. A478

LOZIER, Tim, Director Human Resources, Vibra Specialty Hospital At Desoto, Desoto, TX, p. A600

LUBARSKY, Neil, Senior Vice President, Finance and Chief Financial Officer, Thomas Jefferson University Hospitals, Philadelphia, PA, p. A536

LUBIN, Bertram, President and Chief Executive Officer, Ucsf Benioff Children'S Hospital Oakland, Oakland, CA, p. A75

LUBINSKY, Jeanie, Chief Financial Officer, Mayo Clinic Health System – Red Cedar In Menomonie, Menomonie, WI, p. A700

LUBITZ, Robert, M.D., Vice President of Medical Affairs, Wellstar Kennestone Hospital, Marietta, GA, p. A157

LUCAS, Benny Lee, Chief Nursing Executive, St. Joseph'S Behavioral Health Center, Stockton, CA, p. A90

LUCAS, Bob, Vice President Operations, King'S Daughters Medical Center, Ashland, KY, p. A249

LUCAS, Christine, Chief of Staff, Union County Hospital, Anna, IL, p. A173

LUCAS, Denise, R.N., MSN, Vice President Clinical Services and Chief Nursing Officer, Margaret R. Pardee Memorial Hospital, Hendersonville, NC, p. A456

LUCAS, Kasey, Chief Executive Officer, Hospital Administrator, Salem Memorial District Hospital, Salem, MO, p. A371

LUCAS, Kelly, Chief Information Officer, Sampson Regional Medical Center, Clinton, NC, p. A452

LUCAS, Marshall, M.D., Medical Director, Cypress Creek Hospital, Houston, TX, p. A611

LUCCHESI, Michael, M.D., Chief Medical Officer; Chair, Emergency Medicine, Brookdale Hospital Medical Center, New York, NY, p. A432

LUCE, Glenda, Chief Nursing Officer, Memorial Hospital Of Gardena, Gardena, CA, p. A60

LUCE, Paul W., Vice President Operations, Miami County Medical Center, Paola, KS, p. A243

LUCE, Randall, R.N., Director of Nursing, Rock Springs, Georgetown, TX, p. A607

LUCENA, Ann, Chief Executive Officer, San Ramon Regional Medical Center, San Ramon, CA, p. A88

LUCENA, Yelitza, Executive Director, Hospital Metropolitano Dr. Susoni, Arecibo, PR, p. A715

LUCERO, Brenda, Chief Clinical Officer, Cornerstone Hospital Of Houston At Clearlake, Webster, TX, p. A644

LUCERO, Lupe, Manager Business Office, Presbyterian Espanola Hospital, Espanola, NM, p. A418

LUCEY, Jeffery, M.D., Clinical Director, Brookdale Hospital Medical Center, New York, NY, p. A432

LUCHSINGER, Catherine, MSN, Chief Nursing Officer, Halifax Health Medical Center Of Daytona Beach, Daytona Beach, FL, p. A121

LUCIA, Sandra J, Director Health Information and Corporate Compliance Officer, Hampstead Hospital, Hampstead, NH, p. A400

LUCIANO, Lisa, D.O., Medical Director, Hackensack Meridian Health Shore Rehabilitation Institute, Brick, NJ, p. A403

LUCIER, Robbyn, Director Human Resources, Up Health System–Portage, Hancock, MI, p. A314

LUCKE, Kim, Vice President Finance, Northern Montana Health Care, Havre, MT, p. A377

LUCORE, Charles, President, St. Francis Hospital, The Heart Center, Roslyn, NY, p. A443

LUDFORD, Brad, Chief Financial Officer, Bozeman Health, Bozeman, MT, p. A375

LUDWIG, John A., President and Chief Operating Officer, Hshs St. Joseph'S Hospital, Highland, IL, p. A185

LUDWIG, Walter, President and Chief Executive Officer, Kenmore Mercy Hospital, Kenmore, NY, p. A430

LUDWIGSEN, Kevin, Chief Information Officer, Southeastern Ohio Regional Medical Center, Cambridge, OH, p. A474

LUEBBERING, Tom, Vice President Finance, Capital Region Medical Center, Jefferson City, MO, p. A361

LUEBCKE, Diane, R.N., Director Nursing, Community Memorial Healthcare, Marysville, KS, p. A240

LUECHT, Jackie
Chief Human Resources Officer, Mercyone North Iowa Medical Center, Mason City, IA, p. A226
Director, Human Resources, Mercyone New Hampton Medical Center, New Hampton, IA, p. A227

LUEDDERS, Keith, Chief Operations Officer, Tri Valley Health System, Cambridge, NE, p. A383

LUEDERS, Kathy, R.N., Director of Nursing–Acute Care, Saint Elizabeth'S Medical Center, Wabasha, MN, p. A342

LUEHRS, Bill, Chief Human Resources Officer, Northshore University Health System, Evanston, IL, p. A182

LUEHRS, Paul R, Chief Operating Officer, Mercy San Juan Medical Center, Carmichael, CA, p. A54

LUELLEN, John, M.D.
Chief Operating Officer, Heritage Valley Health System, Beaver, PA, p. A520
Chief Operating Officer, Sewickley Valley Hospital, (A Division Of Valley Medical Facilities), Sewickley, PA, p. A541

LUFF, Brian, Chief Executive Officer, Quillen Rehabilitation Hospital, Johnson City, TN, p. A571

LUFFEY, Michelle L, MSN, R.N., Chief Nursing Officer, Fairmont Regional Medical Center, Fairmont, WV, p. A685

LUFKIN, Kirk, M.D., VPMA, Mclaren Northern Michigan, Petoskey, MI, p. A319

LUGER, Gerald, M.D., President Medical Staff, Gottlieb Memorial Hospital, Melrose Park, IL, p. A189

LUGO, Cesar, Director Human Resources, Victor Valley Global Medical Center, Victorville, CA, p. A94

LUHRS, Jason J., Vice President Fiscal Services, Westfields Hospital And Clinic, New Richmond, WI, p. A702

LUKE, Leslie Paul., President and Chief Executive Officer, St. Joseph'S Hospital Health Center, Syracuse, NY, p. A445

LUKENS, Tammy, Director Information, Kosciusko Community Hospital, Warsaw, IN, p. A216

LUKER, Patricia A., President, Osf Holy Family Medical Center, Monmouth, IL, p. A189

LUKISH, Kris, Human Resources Officer, Chippenham Hospital, Richmond, VA, p. A666

LULICH, Diane, Director Human Resources, Memorial Medical Center Of Ashland, Ashland, WI, p. A691

LULL, Todd, Director Information Technology, Southwest Health, Platteville, WI, p. A703

LULOFF, Lynn, Chief Financial Officer, Winneshiek Medical Center, Decorah, IA, p. A221

LUMIA, Beth A., Acting Medical Center Director, Chillicothe Veterans Affairs Medical Center, Chillicothe, OH, p. A475

LUMPKINS, Deborah, MSN, Chief Nursing Officer, Maury Regional Hospital, Columbia, TN, p. A568

LUMPP, Karen, Senior Vice President and Chief Financial Officer, Trinitas Regional Medical Center, Elizabeth, NJ, p. A405

LUMSDEN, Chris A., President and Chief Executive Officer, Northern Hospital Of Surry County, Mount Airy, NC, p. A459

LUNA, Raul D., Chief Nurse Executive, El Paso Psychiatric Center, El Paso, TX, p. A602

LUNA, Tony, M.D., Chief of Staff, Minneola District Hospital, Minneola, KS, p. A241

LUND, Dennis, M.D., Chief Medical Officer, Lucile Salter Packard Children'S Hospital Stanford, Palo Alto, CA, p. A77

LUND, Elizabeth, M.D., Chief of Staff, West Tennessee Healthcare Volunteer Hospital, Martin, TN, p. A574

LUNDAL, David, Senior Vice President Information Systems and Chief Information Officer, Amita Health Holy Family Medical Center, Des Plaines, IL, p. A181

LUNDBERG, Lanetta, Vice President Culture and People, Peacehealth Ketchikan Medical Center, Ketchikan, AK, p. A26

LUNDBLAD, Jackie, Chief Financial Officer, Wickenburg Community Hospital, Wickenburg, AZ, p. A38

LUNDE, Susan, R.N., Director of Nursing, Fallon Medical Complex, Baker, MT, p. A374

LUNDQUIST, David W., President and Chief Executive Officer, Rome Memorial Hospital, Rome, NY, p. A443

LUNDY, Kelly, Chief Information Officer, Peacehealth St. Joseph Medical Center, Bellingham, WA, p. A670

LUNDY, Marcel, Chief Information Officer, Putnam General Hospital, Eatonton, GA, p. A153

LUNDY, Noah, Director of Human Resources, Northern Light Maine Coast Hospital, Ellsworth, ME, p. A283

LUNDY–PAINE, Robert, Director Information Systems, Alameda Hospital, Alameda, CA, p. A50

LUNN, William, President and Chief Executive Officer, Tulane Health System, New Orleans, LA, p. A276

LUNNEBORG, Brandi, Chief Executive Officer, Phoebe Sumter Medical Center, Americus, GA, p. A145

LUNNEY, Kathleen, MS, R.N., Vice President Patient Care Services and Chief Nursing Officer, Nyack Hospital, Nyack, NY, p. A440

LUNSFORD, Cindy, Executive Vice President and Chief Operating Officer, Peninsula Regional Medical Center, Salisbury, MD, p. A293

LUNSFORD, Kaye W, System Director Human Resources, St. Vincent'S Medical Center Southside, Jacksonville, FL, p. A126

LUNT, Kimberly, Controller, Encompass Health Rehabilitation Hospital Of Spring Hill, Brooksville, FL, p. A119

LUNTZ, Adam, Chief Financial Officer, Aultman Orrville Hospital, Orrville, OH, p. A489

LUOMA, Michael, M.D., Chief of Staff, Aspirus Keweenaw Hospital, Inc., Laurium, MI, p. A316

LUPINACCI, Michael, M.D., Medical Director, Encompass Health Rehabilitation Hospital Of Mechanicsburg, Mechanicsburg, PA, p. A531

LUSKIN–HAWK, Roberta
Chief Executive, Redwood Memorial Hospital, Fortuna, CA, p. A58
Chief Executive, St. Joseph Hospital, Eureka, CA, p. A57

LUSSIER, Shirley G, Vice President Human Resources, Northeast Rehabilitation Hospital, Salem, NH, p. A402

LUSTERIO, Efren, Director of Nursing, Behavioral Center Of Michigan, Warren, MI, p. A324

LUTES, Adrianne, Chief Executive Officer, Select Specialty Hospital Daytona Beach, Daytona Beach, FL, p. A121

LUTES, Michael, President, Atrium Health Union, Monroe, NC, p. A458

LUTHER, Lori, CPA, Chief Operating Officer, Indiana University Health Ball Memorial Hospital, Muncie, IN, p. A212

LUTHER, Tracie, Director Employee and Labor Relations, Brooks Memorial Hospital, Dunkirk, NY, p. A427

LUTHER, Vera, M.D., Chief of Staff, Sabine County Hospital, Hemphill, TX, p. A609

LUTKENHAUS, Tiffany, Chief Nursing Officer, Muenster Memorial Hospital, Muenster, TX, p. A625

LUTZ, Barbara, Vice President Human Resources, Heart Of The Rockies Regional Medical Center, Salida, CO, p. A105

LUTZ, Denise, Chief Human Resources Officer, Chi St. Alexius Health – Dickinson Medical Center, Dickinson, ND, p. A466

LUTZ, Don, Director Information Technology, Easton Hospital, Easton, PA, p. A524

LUTZ, Kevin, DPM, Chief Operating Officer, Grant, Ohiohealth Grant Medical Center, Columbus, OH, p. A479

LUTZ, Terry, Chief Financial Officer, Scheurer Hospital, Pigeon, MI, p. A319

LUX, Teresa M., President and Chief Operating Officer, Community Memorial Hospital, Menomonee Falls, WI, p. A700

LYDICK, Bryan, Chief Executive Officer, Carris Health – Redwood, Redwood Falls, MN, p. A338

LYDON, Jean, MS, R.N., System Vice President Operations, Chief Nursing Officer, Elmhurst Hospital, Elmhurst, IL, p. A182

LYLE, Janet, Chief Human Resources and Allied Health Services, Springfield Hospital, Springfield, VT, p. A655

LYLE, Jeffrey, Chief Executive Officer, Falls Community Hospital And Clinic, Marlin, TX, p. A623

LYMAN, Jeremy, Chief Executive Officer, Blue Mountain Hospital, Blanding, UT, p. A647

LYNAM, Sheila, M.D., Chief Medical Officer, Peacehealth St. John Medical Center, Longview, WA, p. A674

LYNCE, Danialle
Business Partner Human Resources, University Hospitals Conneaut Medical Center, Conneaut, OH, p. A480
Business Partner Human Resources, University Hospitals Geneva Medical Center, Geneva, OH, p. A484
Manager Human Resources, University Hospitals Geauga Medical Center, Chardon, OH, p. A475

LYNCH, Becky, Manager Business Entity Management and Information Systems, Osf St. Mary Medical Center, Galesburg, IL, p. A183

LYNCH, Cecelia, R.N., MS, Vice President Patient Care Services and Chief Nursing Officer, Lowell General Hospital, Lowell, MA, p. A300

LYNCH, Danile, Chief Operating Officer, Saint Luke Institute, Silver Spring, MD, p. A293

LYNCH, Elizabeth A, Vice President Human Resources, The Hospital Of Central Connecticut, New Britain, CT, p. A109

LYNCH, Ernest C., III, President and Chief Executive Officer, Medical City Mckinney, Mckinney, TX, p. A624

LYNCH, G Michael, M.D., Chief Medical Officer, Inova Fair Oaks Hospital, Fairfax, VA, p. A658

LYNCH, James
Interim Chief Executive Officer, Beaumont Hospital – Grosse Pointe, Grosse Pointe, MI, p. A313
Interim President, Beaumont Hospital – Troy, Troy, MI, p. A324

LYNCH, James, M.D., Senior Vice President and Chief Medical Officer, Beaumont Hospital – Troy, Troy, MI, p. A324

LYNCH, Jim, Chief Executive Officer, Fairbanks Memorial Hospital, Fairbanks, AK, p. A26

LYNCH, John, Vice President and Chief Information Officer, Faxton St. Luke'S Healthcare, Utica, NY, p. A446

LYNCH, John, M.D., Vice President and Chief Medical Officer, Barnes–Jewish Hospital, Saint Louis, MO, p. A369

LYNCH, Lisa, Chief Financial Officer, Illinois Valley Community Hospital, Peru, IL, p. A193

LYNCH, Marc, D.O., Chief of Staff, Kindred Hospital–Ontario, Ontario, CA, p. A76

LYNCH, Megan, Manager Human Resources, Johnson Memorial Health Services, Dawson, MN, p. A330

LYNCH, Michael T., M.D., Chief Medical Officer, Alice Peck Day Memorial Hospital, Lebanon, NH, p. A400

LYNCH, Torie A, Manager Human Resources, Central Montana Medical Center, Lewistown, MT, p. A378

LYNCH, William, Executive Vice President and Chief Operating Officer, Brookdale Hospital Medical Center, New York, NY, p. A432

LYNCH–KILIC, Cathy, Vice President Human Resources, St. Mary'S General Hospital, Passaic, NJ, p. A410

LYND, Samuel, Administrator and Chief Executive Officer, Baptist Memorial Hospital–Tipton, Covington, TN, p. A568

LYNE, Marjorie, Associate Director for Patient Care Services, Hunter Holmes Mcguire Veterans Affairs Medical Center–Richmond, Richmond, VA, p. A666

LYNN, Christina, M.D., Medical Director, Three Rivers Behavioral Health, West Columbia, SC, p. A558

LYNN, Jason, Director Finance, St. Vincent'S St. Clair, Pell City, AL, p. A22

LYNN, Priscilla, President, Saint Alphonsus Medical Center – Baker City, Baker City, OR, p. A511

LYNN, Samuel, Director Human Resources, Northwest Texas Healthcare System, Amarillo, TX, p. A582

LYNSKEY, Jeanne, Vice President and Chief Financial Officer, Milford Regional Medical Center, Milford, MA, p. A301

LYON, Tami, Director Human Resources, Community Memorial Hospital, Burke, SD, p. A559

LYONS, Althea C, Vice President Human Resources and Development, Beverly Hospital, Beverly, MA, p. A294

LYONS, Denise, Chief Nursing Officer, Cumberland Hall Hospital, Hopkinsville, KY, p. A253

LYONS, Jim
Chief Clinic Officer, Hutchinson Health, Hutchinson, MN, p. A333
President, Hutchinson Health, Hutchinson, MN, p. A333

LYONS, Lenny
Administrator, Delta Community Medical Center, Delta, UT, p. A647
Administrator, Fillmore Community Hospital, Fillmore, UT, p. A648

LYONS, Michael
Regional Director Information Services, Shriners Hospitals For Children–Galveston, Galveston, TX, p. A607
Regional Information Systems Director, Shriners Hospitals For Children–Shreveport, Shreveport, LA, p. A278

LYONS, Timothy, M.D., Chief Medical Officer, Adventist Health St. Helena, Saint Helena, CA, p. A82

LYREN, Joseph, Chief Financial Officer, Ohiohealth Medcentral Mansfield Hospital, Mansfield, OH, p. A486

LYSAGHT, Marcia C, R.N., MSN, Associate Director Patient Care Services, Miami Veterans Affairs Healthcare System, Miami, FL, p. A130

LYSAGHT, William, Chief Financial Officer, Kindred Hospital Las Vegas–Sahara, Henderson, NV, p. A394

LYTHGOE, Derek
Chief Financial Officer, Banner Baywood Medical Center, Mesa, AZ, p. A31
Chief Financial Officer, Banner Heart Hospital, Mesa, AZ, p. A31

L'ITALIEN, Mark, Director Information Services, Salem Regional Medical Center, Salem, OH, p. A490

M

MAAS, Vernon, M.D., Vice President, Medical Affairs, St. Vincent Evansville, Evansville, IN, p. A203

MAASS, Judith, Chief Executive Officer, Lac–Olive View–Ucla Medical Center, Los Angeles, CA, p. A68

MABRY, Jerry D., Chief Executive Officer, National Park Medical Center, Hot Springs, AR, p. A43

MACAFEE, Francis M, Vice President Finance and Chief Financial Officer, Guthrie Corning Hospital, Corning, NY, p. A426

MACAFFEE, Laurie, Director of Nursing, Willow Springs Center, Reno, NV, p. A397

MACARONAS, Thomas, Chief Financial Officer, Labette Health, Parsons, KS, p. A243

MACATOL, Matthew, M.D., President Medical Staff, Marietta Memorial Hospital, Marietta, OH, p. A486

MACDONALD, Joan, R.N., MSN, Chief Nursing Officer, Aurelia Osborn Fox Memorial Hospital, Oneonta, NY, p. A440

MACDONALD, Laurie, Vice President Finance, Penn Highlands Elk, Saint Marys, PA, p. A540

MACDONALD, Neil, Vice President, Operations, Medstar Union Memorial Hospital, Baltimore, MD, p. A287

MACDONELL, Jean, Interim Chief Executive Officer, Grand Itasca Clinic And Hospital, Grand Rapids, MN, p. A333

MACDOUGALL, David, Chief Financial Officer, United Health Services Hospitals–Binghamton, Binghamton, NY, p. A424

MACE, T. Paul, Chief Medical Officer, Garden Park Medical Center, Gulfport, MS, p. A347

MACEVOY, Bonnie, Chief of Staff, Mad River Community Hospital, Arcata, CA, p. A51

MACFADYEN, James, M.D., Medical Director, St. John Vianney Hospital, Downingtown, PA, p. A524

MACH, Robert, Chief Executive Officer, Select Specialty Hospital–Battle Creek, Battle Creek, MI, p. A307

MACHADO, James, President, St. Vincent'S Medical Center Clay County, Middleburg, FL, p. A132

MACHADO, Richard, President and Chief Executive Officer, Hospital Hermanos Melendez, Bayamon, PR, p. A715

MACHORRO, Vicky, R.N., Chief Nursing Officer, Kittitas Valley Healthcare, Ellensburg, WA, p. A672

MACIAS–HOAG, Annette, R.N., Vice President, Health System and Service Line Operations Interim Associate Chief Nursing & Patient Care Services Office, University Of Texas Medical Branch, Galveston, TX, p. A607

MACIEL, Maureen, M.D., Chief of Staff, Shriners Hospitals For Children–Tampa, Tampa, FL, p. A142

MACK, Charles, Vice President Finance and Chief Financial Officer, Merit Health Natchez, Natchez, MS, p. A352

MACK, Kristina, Manager, Human Resources, San Dimas Community Hospital, San Dimas, CA, p. A85

MACK, Winnie, Interim President and Chief Executive Officer, Nassau University Medical Center, East Meadow, NY, p. A427

MACKAY, Cristal, Chief Operating Officer, Banner Desert Medical Center, Mesa, AZ, p. A31

MACKENROTH, Robin D., Chief Operating Officer, Kaiser Permanente Riverside Medical Center, Riverside, CA, p. A81

MACKENZIE, Susan, Medical Center Director, Providence Veterans Affairs Medical Center, Providence, RI, p. A547

MACKETT, Charles, M.D., Senior Vice President and Chief Medical Officer, Cleveland Clinic Indian River Hospital, Vero Beach, FL, p. A143

MACKEY, Denise, Administrator, Hale Ho'Ola Hamakua, Honokaa, HI, p. A164

MACKIN, Stephen, President, Mercy Hospital St. Louis, Saint Louis, MO, p. A368

MACKINNON, Paul, R.N., Chief Operating Officer, Umass Memorial Healthalliance–Clinton Hospital, Leominster, MA, p. A300

MACKSOOD, Dan, Regional Senior Vice President and Chief Financial Officer, Good Samaritan Hospital Medical Center, West Islip, NY, p. A447

MACLAUGHLIN, Jeremy, Director Human Resources, Citizens Memorial Hospital, Bolivar, MO, p. A356

MACLEAN, Scott, Administrator, Vibra Hospital Of Western Massachusetts, Springfield, MA, p. A304

MACLENNAN, Alex, Chief Human Resources Officer, Tahoe Forest Hospital District, Truckee, CA, p. A92

MACLEOD, Deborah, MS, R.N., Vice President Nursing and Patient Care Services, Mid Coast Hospital, Brunswick, ME, p. A282

MACNEILL, Bruce, Chief Financial Officer, Kindred Hospital Seattle–Northgate, Seattle, WA, p. A677

MACNICOL, Daniel, Chief Executive Officer, Encompass Health Rehabilitation Hospital Of Dallas, Dallas, TX, p. A596

MACOGAY, Melissa, Vice President and Chief Nursing Officer, Johns Hopkins All Children'S Hospital, Saint Petersburg, FL, p. A138

MACPHEE, Alan, Chief Executive Officer, Kahuku Medical Center, Kahuku, HI, p. A165

MACRI, Fredrick, Executive Vice President, Rhode Island Hospital, Providence, RI, p. A548

MADAN, Sunil, M.D., Chief Medical Officer and Chief Population Health Officer, Doctors Community Hospital, Lanham, MD, p. A291

MADDEN, Ann Marie, MS, R.N., Vice President of Patient Care Services and Chief Nursing Officer, Moses H. Cone Memorial Hospital, Greensboro, NC, p. A455

MADDEN, R. Craig, Director Employee Relations, Reynolds Memorial Hospital, Glen Dale, WV, p. A685

MADDEN RICE, Ann, President, Abbott Northwestern Hospital, Minneapolis, MN, p. A335

MADDOX, Dale, Chief Financial Officer, Medical Center Of South Arkansas, El Dorado, AR, p. A41

MADDOX, Jamie, Chief Nursing Officer, Christus Mother Frances Hospital – Jacksonville, Jacksonville, TX, p. A616

MADER, Elaine, M.D., Chief of Staff, Integris Miami Hospital, Miami, OK, p. A502

MADER, Frank, Director Information Services, East Liverpool City Hospital, East Liverpool, OH, p. A482

MADER, Vikki, Director Health Information Services, Pratt Regional Medical Center, Pratt, KS, p. A244

MADIGAN, Catherine, Chief Nursing Officer, University Of North Carolina Hospitals, Chapel Hill, NC, p. A451

MADIGAN, Patrick, Interim Chief Executive Officer, Cheyenne Regional Medical Center, Cheyenne, WY, p. A710

MADKINS, Catrina, Controller and Chief Financial Officer, Encompass Health Rehabilitation Hospital Of Plano, Plano, TX, p. A629

MADRID, Melissa, R.N., Chief Nursing Officer, Harper County Community Hospital, Buffalo, OK, p. A497

MADSEN, Greg T., Chief Executive Officer, Carilion Stonewall Jackson Hospital, Lexington, VA, p. A661

MAEKAWA, Steve, Chief Financial Officer, Garfield Medical Center, Monterey Park, CA, p. A73

MAENIUS, Linda, Chief Financial Officer, Laurel Ridge Treatment Center, San Antonio, TX, p. A634

MAERTENS, Mary B., President and Chief Executive Officer, Avera Marshall Regional Medical Center, Marshall, MN, p. A335

MAES, Jillian, Director Marketing and Public Relations, St. Thomas More Hospital, Canon City, CO, p. A97

MAES, Stephen, Director Information Systems, Franciscan Health Olympia Fields, Olympia Fields, IL, p. A192

MAESTAS, Sadie, Interim Chief Nursing Officer, Copper Queen Community Hospital, Bisbee, AZ, p. A28

MAGDANGAL, Connie, Executive Vice President and Chief Financial Officer, New Bridge Medical Center, Paramus, NJ, p. A410

MAGEE, Becky, Chief Information Officer, Washington Regional Medical Center, Fayetteville, AR, p. A42

MAGEE, James L., Executive Director, Piggott Community Hospital, Piggott, AR, p. A47

MAGEE, Robert A
Director Human Resources, Shriners Hospitals For Children–Galveston, Galveston, TX, p. A607
Director Human Resources, Shriners Hospitals For Children–Houston, Houston, TX, p. A613

MAGEE, William F, Chief Financial Officer, Alliance Healthcare System, Holly Springs, MS, p. A348

MAGES, Michael, Chief Executive Officer, Ashland Health Center, Ashland, KS, p. A232

MAGESTRO, Ben, Chief Operating Officer, North Central Surgical Center, Dallas, TX, p. A597

MAGGARD, Amanda
Chief Executive Officer, Adventhealth Dade City, Dade City, FL, p. A121
Chief Executive Officer, Adventhealth Zephyrhills, Zephyrhills, FL, p. A144

MAGHAZEHE, Al
President and Chief Executive Officer, Capital Health Medical Center–Hopewell, Pennington, NJ, p. A410
President and Chief Executive Officer, Capital Health Regional Medical Center, Trenton, NJ, p. A413

MAGID, Philip, Director Fiscal Services, Shriners Hospitals For Children–Chicago, Chicago, IL, p. A179

MAGILL, Marc, Medical Center Director, Jesse Brown Veterans Affairs Medical Center, Chicago, IL, p. A177

MAGNER, Johanna, Interim Chief Nursing Officer, Saint Michael'S Medical Center, Newark, NJ, p. A409

MAGNER, Kile, Administrator, Ellinwood District Hospital, Ellinwood, KS, p. A234

MAGNUSON, Johna, Director Nursing, Hillsboro Community Hospital, Hillsboro, KS, p. A236

MAGOON, Patrick M., President and Chief Executive Officer, Ann & Robert H. Lurie Children'S Hospital Of Chicago, Chicago, IL, p. A176

MAGU, Bharat, M.D., Chief Medical Officer, Yuma Regional Medical Center, Yuma, AZ, p. A38

MAGUIRE, Christina, Senior Vice President and Chief Operating Officer, Mount Desert Island Hospital, Bar Harbor, ME, p. A281

MAGUIRE, David L, M.D., Vice President Medical Affairs, Baystate Wing Hospital, Palmer, MA, p. A302

MAGUIRE, Kimberly, Chief Nursing Officer, Mercy Health Hackley Campus, Muskegon, MI, p. A318

MAGUREAN, Vickie
Chief Financial Officer, Englewood Community Hospital, Englewood, FL, p. A122
Chief Financial Officer, Fawcett Memorial Hospital, Port Charlotte, FL, p. A137
Chief Financial Officer, Seven Rivers Regional Medical Center, Crystal River, FL, p. A120

MAGUTA, Sam, Coordinator Information Systems, Devereux Advanced Behavioral Health Georgia, Kennesaw, GA, p. A155

MAHAN, Michelle K, Senior Vice President and Chief Financial Officer, Frederick Regional Health System, Frederick, MD, p. A290

MAHAN, Vic
Chief Information Officer, Chino Valley Medical Center, Chino, CA, p. A54
Director Information Systems, Garden Grove Hospital And Medical Center, Garden Grove, CA, p. A60
Director Information Technology, La Palma Intercommunity Hospital, La Palma, CA, p. A63
Director Information Technology, West Anaheim Medical Center, Anaheim, CA, p. A50

MAHAR, Priscilla, Chief Operating Officer, Spectrum Health United Hospital, Greenville, MI, p. A313

MAHER, Donna, R.N., Chief Operating Officer, Morton Hospital And Medical Center, Taunton, MA, p. A304

MAHER, John P, Executive Vice President and Chief Financial Officer, Nassau University Medical Center, East Meadow, NY, p. A427

MAHER, Sean, Director Human Resources, Devereux Children'S Behavioral Health Center, Malvern, PA, p. A530

MAHER, Thomas, Chief Executive Officer and Administrator, Boulder City Hospital, Boulder City, NV, p. A393

MAHERA, Tina, M.D., Chief Medical Officer, Garfield Park Hospital, Chicago, IL, p. A177

MAHESHWARI, Narendra, M.D., Chief of Staff, Broward Health North, Deerfield Beach, FL, p. A121

MAHEUX, Diane, Vice President Finance, Memorial Hospital, North Conway, NH, p. A402

MAHIDA, Chaitanya, M.D., Chief of Staff, Oak Valley Hospital District, Oakdale, CA, p. A75

MAHL, Morgan G, Director Human Resources, St. Luke'S Hospital – Warren Campus, Phillipsburg, NJ, p. A411

MAHLE, Thomas J., Chief Executive Officer, Las Encinas Hospital, Pasadena, CA, p. A77

MAHMOOD, Ahsan, M.D., Chief Medical Officer, Hamilton Center, Terre Haute, IN, p. A215

MAHMOOD, Khalid, President and Chairman, Crescent Medical Center Lancaster, Lancaster, TX, p. A619

MAHNEKE, Suzette, Associate Vice President of Nursing, Adventist Medical Center Glenoaks, Glendale Heights, IL, p. A184

MAHONE, William, President and Chief Executive Officer, Halifax Regional Medical Center, Roanoke Rapids, NC, p. A461

MAHONEY, Bryan, Chief Financial Officer, Columbia Memorial Hospital, Hudson, NY, p. A429

MAHONEY, James, Chief Information Officer, Upmc Memorial, York, PA, p. A546

MAHONEY, Nicole, Chief Financial Officer, Pioneer Memorial Hospital, Heppner, OR, p. A513

MAHONEY, William K., President and Senior Vice President, Community Hospital Group, Cox Medical Center Branson, Branson, MO, p. A357

MAHR–CHAN, Lydia, Director of Human Resources, Chinese Hospital, San Francisco, CA, p. A85

MAIBERGER, Michael J., President, Miami Valley Hospital, Dayton, OH, p. A481

MAIDEN, Phillip G, M.D., Medical Director, Belmont Pines Hospital, Youngstown, OH, p. A495

MAIER, Cindy, R.N., Director of Nursing, Ness County Hospital District No 2, Ness City, KS, p. A241

MAIER, Curtis, Administrator, St. Luke'S Jerome, Jerome, ID, p. A169

MAIER, Walter M., Chief of Staff, San Bernardino Mountains Community Hospital District, Lake Arrowhead, CA, p. A63

MAIETTA, Carol, Vice President Human Resources and Chief Learning Officer, St. Vincent'S East, Birmingham, AL, p. A15

MAIJALA, Jussi, Vice President, Human Resources, Phelps Memorial Hospital Center, Sleepy Hollow, NY, p. A444

MAIN, Cleo, Finance Officer, Blackfeet Community Hospital, Saint Mary, MT, p. A380

MAINES, Stephanie, Chief Nursing Officer, Crossroads Community Hospital, Mount Vernon, IL, p. A190

MAIZE, Makyla, Director Information Services, Washington County Hospital And Clinics, Washington, IA, p. A230

MAJAUSKAS, Joel, Chief Information Officer, Clifton Springs Hospital And Clinic, Clifton Springs, NY, p. A426

MAJCHRZAK, John, Chief Financial Officer, Touchette Regional Hospital, Centreville, IL, p. A175

MAJDALANI, Elias, Director Management Information Systems, Mildred Mitchell–Bateman Hospital, Huntington, WV, p. A686

MAJERUS, Michelle, Chief Information Officer, Olmsted Medical Center, Rochester, MN, p. A338

MAJESKI, Denise, MSN, R.N., Vice President Operations and Chief Nurse Executive, Northwestern Medicine Lake Forest Hospital, Lake Forest, IL, p. A187

MAJETICH, Stephen D, CPA, Chief Financial Officer, Southwestern Vermont Medical Center, Bennington, VT, p. A654

MAJHAIL, Ruby, Chief Financial Officer, St. Luke'S Behavioral Health Center, Phoenix, AZ, p. A34

MAJOR, Aprille, Director Human Resources, Foothill Regional Medical Center, Tustin, CA, p. A92

MAJOR, Kerry, R.N., MSN, Chief Nursing Officer, Cleveland Clinic Florida, Weston, FL, p. A144

MAJOR, Pattie, Chief Financial Officer, Paul B. Hall Regional Medical Center, Paintsville, KY, p. A259

MAJORS, Ed, Chief Executive Officer, Newman Memorial Hospital, Shattuck, OK, p. A507

MAJORS, Valerie, Director Information Services, Western State Hospital, Hopkinsville, KY, p. A253

MAK, David, Chief Financial Officer, El Campo Memorial Hospital, El Campo, TX, p. A601

MAKAROFF, Jason, Chief Operating Officer and Associate Vice President, Adventist Healthcare Physical Health And Rehabilitation, Rockville, MD, p. A293

MAKELA, Taylor, Director Information Technology, Baraga County Memorial Hospital, L'Anse, MI, p. A316

MAKEPEACE, Anne, Director Human Resources, New Ulm Medical Center, New Ulm, MN, p. A337

MAKI, Jacquelyn, Chief Nursing Officer, Oakleaf Surgical Hospital, Altoona, WI, p. A691

MAKI, Richard, R.N., Vice President Nursing and Chief Nursing Officer, Anna Jaques Hospital, Newburyport, MA, p. A301

MAKIEVSKY, Inna, Interim Chief Nursing Officer, Adventist Health And Rideout, Marysville, CA, p. A71

MAKORO, Leslie, Director Information management Systems, Merit Health Natchez, Natchez, MS, p. A352

MAKOSKY, Michael D., Chief Executive Officer, Fulton County Medical Center, Mc Connellsburg, PA, p. A531

MAKSOUD, Jane, R.N.
Senior Vice President Human Resources and Labor Relations, Mount Sinai Health System, Brookdale Hospital Medical Center, New York, NY, p. A432
Senior Vice President Human Resources and Labor Relations, Brookdale Hospital Medical Center, New York, NY, p. A432

MAKSYMOW, Michael, Vice President Information Systems, Beebe Healthcare, Lewes, DE, p. A113

MAKUNDA, Beejadi, M.D., Chief Medical Officer, Heatherhill Care Communities, Chardon, OH, p. A475

MALAER, Gary, Chief Executive Officer, Detar Healthcare System, Victoria, TX, p. A643

MALAKAR, Crystal, Team Leader Inpatient Nursing, Bellin Psychiatric Center, Green Bay, WI, p. A696

MALAKOFF, Stacey, Executive Vice President and Chief Financial Officer, Brookdale Hospital Medical Center, New York, NY, p. A432

MALAMED, Michael, M.D., Chief of Staff, Sherman Oaks Hospital, Los Angeles, CA, p. A69

MALAN, Glen, Vice President Information Technology and Chief Information Officer, Northwest Community Hospital, Arlington Heights, IL, p. A173

MALANEY, Scott C., President and Chief Executive Officer, Blanchard Valley Hospital, Findlay, OH, p. A483

MALCOLM, Dru, Vice President and Chief Nursing Officer, Johnson City Medical Center, Johnson City, TN, p. A571

MALCOLMSON, James F, M.D., Chief of Staff, Sierra Vista Hospital, Truth Or Consequences, NM, p. A421

MALDONADO, Diraida, Chief Executive Officer, Hospital De La Universidad De Puerto Rico/Dr. Federico Trilla, Carolina, PR, p. A715

MALENSEK, Frank, M.D., Chief Medical Officer, St. Vincent'S East, Birmingham, AL, p. A15

MALEY, Shelley, Director Human Resources, St. Luke'S Hospital – Quakertown Campus, Quakertown, PA, p. A539

MALIK, Azfar, M.D.
Chief Medical Officer, Centerpointe Hospital, Saint Charles, MO, p. A368
Chief Medical Officer, Signature Psychiatric Hospital, Kansas City, MO, p. A363

MALIK, Chuck
Director Information Systems, Advocate Good Shepherd Hospital, Barrington, IL, p. A174
Director Information Systems, Advocate Illinois Masonic Medical Center, Chicago, IL, p. A176

MALIN, Seth, M.D., President Medical and Dental Staff, Delaware County Memorial Hospital, Drexel Hill, PA, p. A524

MALINA, Joanne J, M.D., Chief of Staff, Veterans Affairs Hudson Valley Health Care System, Montrose, NY, p. A431

MALINDZAK, Edward, Chief Human Resources Officer, Oconomowoc Memorial Hospital, Oconomowoc, WI, p. A702

MALJOVEC, John, M.D., Medical Director, Warren General Hospital, Warren, PA, p. A543

MALKO, Jennifer, Market Chief Executive Officer, Lifecare Hospitals Of Pittsburgh, Pittsburgh, PA, p. A537

MALLETT, Belinda, R.N., MS, Vice President, Patient Care and Clinical Services, Soin Medical Center, Beavercreek, OH, p. A473

MALLETT, Conrad L., Jr, Chief Executive Officer, Dmc – Sinai–Grace Hospital, Detroit, MI, p. A310

MALLETT, Teresa, Chief Financial Officer, Madison Regional Health System, Madison, SD, p. A561

MALLICOAT, Robert E., Chief Executive Officer, Complex Care Hospital At Ridgelake, Sarasota, FL, p. A139

MALLIK, Subodh, M.D., Chief of Staff, Pecos County Memorial Hospital, Fort Stockton, TX, p. A604

MALLING, Timothy, M.D., Chief of Staff, Centracare Health–Paynesville, Paynesville, MN, p. A337

MALLONEE, Teresa, Director Human Resources, Angel Medical Center, Franklin, NC, p. A454

MALLORY, Brenda, M.D., Medical Director, Penn State Hershey Rehabilitation Hospital, Hummelstown, PA, p. A527

MALLOY, Patrick C., M.D., Chief of Staff, Brookdale Hospital Medical Center, New York, NY, p. A432

MALLOY, Peter, Chief Information Officer, Cheshire Medical Center, Keene, NH, p. A400

MALM, Brad, Director Human Resources and Education, Lindsborg Community Hospital, Lindsborg, KS, p. A240

MALMSTROM, Ron, Information Research Specialist, Parsons State Hospital And Training Center, Parsons, KS, p. A243

MALONE, Donald A., Jr, President, Lutheran Hospital, Cleveland, OH, p. A478

MALONE, Ginger, Chief Nursing Officer, Ssm Health St. Mary'S Hospital, Madison, WI, p. A698

MALONE, Meredith, Chief Financial Officer, West Tennessee Healthcare Dyersburg Hospital, Dyersburg, TN, p. A569

MALONE, Michael, Vice President and Chief Human Resources Officer, Virginia Hospital Center, Arlington, VA, p. A656

MALONE, Patty, M.D., Chief Medical Officer, Ocean Beach Hospital, Ilwaco, WA, p. A674

MALONEY, Christopher, M.D., Senior Vice President, Medical Affairs and Chief Medical Officer, Children'S Hospital And Medical Center, Omaha, NE, p. A389

MALONEY, Jay, M.D., Chief of Staff, Cabinet Peaks Medical Center, Libby, MT, p. A378

MALONEY, Patrick J.
Chief Executive Officer, Franciscan Health Dyer, Dyer, IN, p. A202
Chief Executive Officer, Franciscan Health Hammond, Hammond, IN, p. A205
Chief Executive Officer, Franciscan Healthcare Munster, Munster, IN, p. A212

MALONEY, Paul V, Vice President Finance, Behavioral Health Network, Natchaug Hospital, Mansfield Center, CT, p. A108

MALONEY, Robert, Chief Operating Officer, Mercy Health – Anderson Hospital, Cincinnati, OH, p. A476

MALOTT, Deanna, Director Human Resources, Henry Community Health, New Castle, IN, p. A212

MALOTT, Gregg, Chief Financial Officer, Pulaski Memorial Hospital, Winamac, IN, p. A216

MALOTTE, Rebecca, Executive Director and Chief Nursing Officer, Deaconess Gateway Hospital, Newburgh, IN, p. A213

MALSED, Brad, Area Chief Financial Officer, Kaiser Permanente Los Angeles Medical Center, Los Angeles, CA, p. A67

MALSEED, Timothy James, Chief Information Officer, Keck Hospital Of Usc, Los Angeles, CA, p. A67

MALSEED, TJ, Vice President and Chief Information Officer, Children'S Hospital Los Angeles, Los Angeles, CA, p. A66

MALYSZEK, Richard, M.D., Chief of Staff, Pikes Peak Regional Hospital, Woodland Park, CO, p. A106

MAMBOURG, Rolland, M.D., Vice President Medical Affairs, Mercy Health Saint Mary'S, Grand Rapids, MI, p. A313

MANAKAS, Christopher, Chief Information Officer, Fort Healthcare, Fort Atkinson, WI, p. A695

MANAS, Julie
Regional President, St. Vincent Carmel Hospital, Carmel, IN, p. A201
Regional President, St. Vincent Fishers Hospital, Fishers, IN, p. A203

MANCHUR, Richard, President, Grandview Medical Center, Dayton, OH, p. A481

MANDAL, Alan, Vice President Financial Operations, Scripps Memorial Hospital–La Jolla, La Jolla, CA, p. A63

MANDAL, Konoy, M.D., Medical Director, Centennial Peaks Hospital, Louisville, CO, p. A104

MANDANAS, Renato, M.D., Chief Medical Officer, Oswego Hospital, Oswego, NY, p. A441

MANDERINO, Michelle, Chief Human Resources, North Florida/South Georgia Veteran'S Health System, Gainesville, FL, p. A123

MANDHAN, Narain, M.D., Chief Medical Officer, Kirby Medical Center, Monticello, IL, p. A190

MANDI, Deepak, M.D., Chief of Staff, West Palm Beach Veterans Affairs Medical Center, West Palm Beach, FL, p. A144

MANDRACCHIA, Vincent, DPM, Chief Medical Officer, Broadlawns Medical Center, Des Moines, IA, p. A221

MANESTRINA, Robert, Vice President Human Resources, Inspira Medical Center–Woodbury, Woodbury, NJ, p. A415

MANFREDI, Susan, R.N., Vice President and Chief Nursing Officer, Uw Medicine/Northwest Hospital & Medical Center, Seattle, WA, p. A678

MANFREDO, John, Chief Operating Officer, Norman Regional Health System, Norman, OK, p. A503

MANGIN, Paul, Vice President Finance, Mercyone Clinton Medical Center, Clinton, IA, p. A219

MANGINI, Susan A, MSN, R.N., Chief Nursing Officer, Metrowest Medical Center, Framingham, MA, p. A298

MANGIONE, Ellen, M.D., Chief of Staff, Veterans Affairs Eastern Colorado Health Care System, Denver, CO, p. A99

MANGONA, John, Vice President, Chief Information Officer and Compliance Officer, Saratoga Hospital, Saratoga Springs, NY, p. A444

MANGUM, Lisa, Chief Nursing Officer, North Canyon Medical Center, Gooding, ID, p. A169

MANGUM, Rozanne, Administrative Assistant and Director Human Resources, Grover C. Dils Medical Center, Caliente, NV, p. A393

MANIATIS, Theodore, M.D., Medical Director, Brookdale Hospital Medical Center, New York, NY, p. A432

MANKER, Marcia
Chief Executive Officer, Memorialcare, Orange Coast Memorial Medical Center, Fountain Valley, CA, p. A58
Chief Executive Officer, Memorialcare, Saddleback Memorial Medical Center, Laguna Hills, CA, p. A63

MANKINS, Mark L, M.D., Chief of Staff, Hamilton Hospital, Olney, TX, p. A627

MANKOSKI, Susan, Vice President Human Resources, Ssm Health St. Mary'S Hospital – Jefferson City, Jefferson City, MO, p. A361

MANLAGNIT, Maybelle, Senior Accounting Officer, Metropolitan State Hospital, Norwalk, CA, p. A75

MANLEY, John, Director Information Systems, Jackson General Hospital, Ripley, WV, p. A689

MANN, Brian, Chief Executive Officer, Select Specialty Hospital–Danville, Danville, PA, p. A523

MANN, Corey, Director Human Resources, Memorial Health Care Systems, Seward, NE, p. A391

MANN, Erin, R.N., Chief Nursing Officer, Mccamey County Hospital District, Mccamey, TX, p. A624

MANN, Julie D, Vice President and Chief Administrative Officer, Katherine Shaw Bethea Hospital, Dixon, IL, p. A181

MANN, Karen, R.N., Chief Nursing Officer, Shoshone Medical Center, Kellogg, ID, p. A169

MANN, Lori, R.N., MSN, Chief Nursing Officer, Rusk Rehabilitation Hospital, Columbia, MO, p. A359

MANN, Rex, M.D., Chief Medical Officer, Ochiltree General Hospital, Perryton, TX, p. A628

MANN, Rhonda, Chief Nursing Officer, Franklin Woods Community Hospital, Johnson City, TN, p. A571

MANN, Todd, Chief Executive Officer, South Texas Health System, Edinburg, TX, p. A601

MANNI, Joseph, Executive Vice President and Chief Operating Officer, Deborah Heart And Lung Center, Browns Mills, NJ, p. A404

MANNICH, Andy, Regional Administrator, Georgia Regional Hospital At Savannah, Savannah, GA, p. A160

MANNING, Angela, Director Health Information Services, Encompass Health Rehabilitation Hospital Of Sunrise, Sunrise, FL, p. A140

MANNING, Austin Lane, Chief Operating Officer, Los Robles Hospital And Medical Center, Thousand Oaks, CA, p. A91

MANNING, Claude, Chief Financial Officer, Palacios Community Medical Center, Palacios, TX, p. A627

MANNING, Donald, M.D., Clinical Director, Georgia Regional Hospital At Savannah, Savannah, GA, p. A160

MANNING, James, Administrator, Pathway Rehabilitation Hospital, Bossier City, LA, p. A265

MANNING, JoAnn, Chief Financial Officer, Emory Johns Creek Hospital, Johns Creek, GA, p. A155

MANNING, Kevin, Chief Nursing Officer, Kingwood Medical Center, Kingwood, TX, p. A618

MANNING, Kimberly, Chief Nursing Officer, Washington County Hospital, Plymouth, NC, p. A460

MANNING, Laura, Administrative Director, Guthrie Corning Hospital, Corning, NY, p. A426

MANNING, Lori, Administrator Human Resources, Western State Hospital, Tacoma, WA, p. A681

MANNION, Stephen, Assistant Vice President Information Systems Customer Service, Medstar Franklin Square Medical Center, Baltimore, MD, p. A288

MANNIX, Mary N., President and Chief Executive Officer, Augusta Health, Fishersville, VA, p. A659

MANNS, Bill, President, St. Joseph Mercy Ann Arbor, Ypsilanti, MI, p. A325

MANNY, Martin, Director, I.S., Providence St. Mary Medical Center, Walla Walla, WA, p. A681

MANOHARA, Anand, Chief Operating Officer, Good Samaritan Hospital, Bakersfield, CA, p. A52

MANSEAU, Jani, Vice President Operations and Chief Nursing Officer, Scottsdale Liberty Hospital, Scottsdale, AZ, p. A36

MANSFIELD, Deena, Director Human Resources, Ashley Regional Medical Center, Vernal, UT, p. A653

MANSFIELD, Jerry A, Ph.D., R.N., Executive Chief Nursing Officer & Chief Patient Experience Officer, Musc Health Of Medical University Of South Carolina, Charleston, SC, p. A550

MANSKE, Kristin, Chief Executive Officer, Greenwood Regional Rehabilitation Hospital, Greenwood, SC, p. A554

MANSKE, Lou Ann, Vice President Human Resources, Madonna Rehabilitation Hospital, Lincoln, NE, p. A387

MANSON, David, Manager Human Resources, Santa Clara Valley Medical Center, San Jose, CA, p. A87

MANSON, Kelly, Chief Financial Officer, Veterans Affairs Sierra Nevada Health Care System, Reno, NV, p. A397

MANSON, Lisa, Director Ambulatory Services, Guttenberg Municipal Hospital, Guttenberg, IA, p. A223

MANSON, Stephanie, Chief Operating Officer, Our Lady Of The Lake Regional Medical Center, Baton Rouge, LA, p. A264

MANSON, William T, III, Chief Executive Officer, Anmed Health Medical Center, Anderson, SC, p. A549

MANSON, William T., III, Chief Executive Officer, Anmed Health Medical Center, Anderson, SC, p. A549

MANSTEDT, Chase, Chief Financial Officer, Saunders Medical Center, Wahoo, NE, p. A392

MANSUKHANI, Martin, Chief Financial Officer, Desert Valley Hospital, Victorville, CA, p. A94

MANSURE, John F., President, Prisma Health Greer Memorial Hospital, Greer, SC, p. A554

MANTERNACH, Paul, M.D., Senior Vice President Physician Integration, Mercyone North Iowa Medical Center, Mason City, IA, p. A226

MANTOOTH, Charles, President and Chief Executive Officer, Watauga Medical Center, Boone, NC, p. A450

MANUBENS, Claudio, M.D., Chief of Staff, Adventhealth Heart Of Florida, Davenport, FL, p. A121

MANUEL, Shasta, Executive Director Finance, Ssm Health St. Anthony Hospital – Oklahoma City, Oklahoma City, OK, p. A505

MANUEL, Wendy, Vice President and Chief Financial Officer, Rehabilitation Hospital Of The Pacific, Honolulu, HI, p. A165

MANZO, Arnold D, Vice President Human Resources, Saint Barnabas Medical Center, Livingston, NJ, p. A407

MANZO–LUNA, Hilda, Chief Nursing Officer, La Palma Intercommunity Hospital, La Palma, CA, p. A63

MANZOOR, Amir, M.D., Medical Director, Select Specialty Hospital–Panama City, Panama City, FL, p. A136

MAPARA, Anupam, M.D., Chief of Staff, Sutter Delta Medical Center, Antioch, CA, p. A50

MAPLES, Michael, M.D., Vice President and Chief Medical Officer, Mississippi Baptist Medical Center, Jackson, MS, p. A349

MAPPIN, F Gregory, M.D., Vice President Medical Affairs and Chief Medical Officer, Self Regional Healthcare, Greenwood, SC, p. A554

MARAAN, Sheila, Director of Nursing, Brynn Marr Hospital, Jacksonville, NC, p. A456

MARANDI, Hossain, President and Chief Executive Officer, St. Vincent Indianapolis Hospital, Indianapolis, IN, p. A208

MARANO, Deena, Human Resources Director, Community Hospital Of San Bernardino, San Bernardino, CA, p. A83

MARAS, Greg, Vice President Human Resources, Meadville Medical Center, Meadville, PA, p. A531

MARASA, Richard, M.D., President Medical Staff, Springfield Hospital, Springfield, VT, p. A655

MARBLE, Kevin, Director Information Technology, Oklahoma Forensic Center, Vinita, OK, p. A510

MARCANO, Norma, Chief Operating Officer, San Juan City Hospital, San Juan, PR, p. A719

MARCANTEL, Bill, Chief Information Systems, Allen Parish Community Healthcare, Kinder, LA, p. A270

MARCEAUX, Caroline, MSN, R.N., Chief Nursing Officer, Acadia General Hospital, Crowley, LA, p. A266

MARCELIN, Fitzgerald, M.D., Chief of Staff, Southern Virginia Regional Medical Center, Emporia, VA, p. A658

MARCHANT, Joseph, Administrator, Bibb Medical Center, Centreville, AL, p. A16

MARCHETTI, Mark E., President and Chief Executive Officer, Mt. Graham Regional Medical Center, Safford, AZ, p. A35

MARCHIK, Katie A
Chief Financial Officer, Unitypoint Health – Trinity Rock Island, Rock Island, IL, p. A194
Vice President, Consolidated Services, UnityPoint Health and Chief Financial Officer, Trinity Regional Health System, Unitypoint Health – Trinity Muscatine, Muscatine, IA, p. A227

MARCIANO, Paolo G, M.D., Chief Medical Officer, Beaumont Hospital – Dearborn, Dearborn, MI, p. A309

MARCO, James E, Interim Vice President, Human Resources, Oswego Hospital, Oswego, NY, p. A441

MARCOTTE, Eric, M.D., Chief Medical Officer, Riverview Health, Noblesville, IN, p. A213

MARCOTTE, Lynn, Chief Financial Officer, Mclaren Oakland, Pontiac, MI, p. A320

MARCOTTE, Melissa, Chief Financial Officer, Rainy Lake Medical Center, International Falls, MN, p. A333

MARCOVICI, Mia, M.D., Chief Medical Officer, Norristown State Hospital, Norristown, PA, p. A533

MARCOWITZ, David, M.D., Chief of Staff, Lucas County Health Center, Chariton, IA, p. A219

MARCRUM, Jennifer, Chief Financial Officer, Sumner County Hospital District 1, Caldwell, KS, p. A233

MARCUCCI, John, M.D., Vice President Medical Affairs, Baylor Scott & White Medical Center – Plano, Plano, TX, p. A629

MARCUM, Amie, Human Resources Coordinator, Continuecare Hospital At Baptist Health Corbin, Corbin, KY, p. A250

MARCUS, Shannon, Chief Executive Officer, Three Rivers Behavioral Health, West Columbia, SC, p. A558

MARCZEWSKI, Les, M.D., Chief Medical Officer, Loring Hospital, Sac City, IA, p. A229

MARDY, Paul, Chief Information Technology Officer, Tennessee Valley Healthcare System, Nashville, TN, p. A577

MAREK, Kyle, Chief Information Officer, Carteret Health Care, Morehead City, NC, p. A458

MAREK, Rick, Vice President Medical Information Systems, Warm Springs Rehabilitation Hospital Of San Antonio, San Antonio, TX, p. A635

MARGENAU, Randall, Chief Information Officer, William S. Middleton Memorial Veterans Hospital, Madison, WI, p. A699

MARGER, Brian, Chief Executive Officer, Tristar Summit Medical Center, Hermitage, TN, p. A570

MARGOLIS, Marilyn, Chief Executive Officer, Emory Johns Creek Hospital, Johns Creek, GA, p. A155

MARGULIS, Richard T., President and Chief Executive Officer, Long Island Community Hospital, Patchogue, NY, p. A441

MARIANI, Marilyn, R.N., Chief Nursing Officer, Lakeview Hospital, Bountiful, UT, p. A647

MARIANI, Meleah, Chief Nursing Officer, Spectrum Health Gerber Memorial, Fremont, MI, p. A312

MARICN, Tanya, Interim Vice President Human Resources, Mercy Hospital Springfield, Springfield, MO, p. A371

MARIETTA, John, M.D., Chief Medical Officer, St. David'S Medical Center, Austin, TX, p. A586

MARIETTA, Megan, Chief Executive Officer, West Houston Medical Center, Houston, TX, p. A614

MARIETTA, Richard, M.D., Medical Director, Hca Houston Healthcare Clear Lake, League City, TX, p. A620

MARIGOMEN, Nancy Ann, R.N., Director of Nursing, Milwaukee County Behavioral Health Division, Milwaukee, WI, p. A701

MARIN, Loyman, Chief Human Resources, Miami Veterans Affairs Healthcare System, Miami, FL, p. A130

MARIN, Octavio, Vice President Long Term Care and Ambulatory Care Services, Brookdale Hospital Medical Center, New York, NY, p. A432

MARINARO, Jon, M.D., Chief Medical Officer, Kindred Hospital–Albuquerque, Albuquerque, NM, p. A416

MARINELLO, Anthony, Chief Operating Officer, University Medical Center, Las Vegas, NV, p. A396

MARINI, Frank, Senior Vice President and Chief Information Officer, Tmc Healthcare, Tucson, AZ, p. A38

MARINO, A Michael, M.D., Senior Vice President Medical Administration, Greenwich Hospital, Greenwich, CT, p. A108

MARINO, Christopher, M.D., Chief of Staff, Memphis Veterans Affairs Medical Center, Memphis, TN, p. A575

MARINO, Joseph, Chief Financial Officer, Suburban Community Hospital, Norristown, PA, p. A533

MARINO, Marchita H, Vice President Human Resources, Rockledge Regional Medical Center, Rockledge, FL, p. A138

MARINOFF, Peter, President, Paul Oliver Memorial Hospital, Frankfort, MI, p. A312

MARION, Amy, Chief Human Resource Officer, Walter B. Jones Alcohol And Drug Abuse Treatment Center, Greenville, NC, p. A455

MARION, Kristie, Chief Nurse Executive, Memorial Hospital Los Banos, Los Banos, CA, p. A70

MARIOTTI, Denise J., Chief Human Resource Officer, Hospital Of The University Of Pennsylvania, Philadelphia, PA, p. A535

MARIS, Peter, Director Human Resources, Brookdale Hospital Medical Center, New York, NY, p. A432

MARKENSON, David, M.D., Chief Medical Officer, Sky Ridge Medical Center, Lone Tree, CO, p. A103

MARKER, John, MSN, R.N., Chief Nursing Officer, Medical City North Hills, North Richland Hills, TX, p. A626

MARKESINO, Patricia A, FACHE, Chief Nurse Executive and Chief Operating Officer, Providence Willamette Falls Medical Center, Oregon City, OR, p. A515

MARKGRAF, SHRM–SCP, SPHR, Janelle K., Director Human Resources and Off Campus Services, Aspirus Langlade Hospital, Antigo, WI, p. A691

MARKHAM, Barbara, Chief Financial Officer, Glendive Medical Center, Glendive, MT, p. A376

MARKHAM, Chad, Chief Operating Officer, Unitypoint Health – St. Lukes'S Sioux City, Sioux City, IA, p. A230

MARKHAM, Kevin, Chief Financial Officer, Eastpointe Hospital, Daphne, AL, p. A16

MARKOS, Dennis R., Chief Executive Officer, Ed Fraser Memorial Hospital And Baker Community Health Center, Macclenny, FL, p. A128

MARKOS, Valerie, Chief Nursing Officer, Ed Fraser Memorial Hospital And Baker Community Health Center, Macclenny, FL, p. A128

MARKOWITZ, Christine, Chief Financial Officer, East Georgia Regional Medical Center, Statesboro, GA, p. A161

MARKOWITZ, Stuart, M.D., Chief Medical Officer, Hartford Hospital, Hartford, CT, p. A108

MARKOWSKI, Stan, Chief Financial Officer, Palmetto Lowcountry Behavioral Health, Charleston, SC, p. A550

MARKS, Craig J., Chief Executive Officer, Prosser Memorial Health, Prosser, WA, p. A676

MARKS, Jerry, Vice President Finance, Decatur County Memorial Hospital, Greensburg, IN, p. A205

MARKS, Kimberly W., Chief Executive Officer, Southampton Memorial Hospital, Franklin, VA, p. A659

MARKS, Kindra, Chief Executive Officer, Regency Hospital Of Columbus, Columbus, OH, p. A480

MARKS, Marie, Chief Nursing Officer, Lake Norman Regional Medical Center, Mooresville, NC, p. A458
MARKS, Michael, M.D., Chief of Staff, Norwalk Hospital, Norwalk, CT, p. A110
MARKS, Michelle, Medical Director, Cleveland Clinic Children'S Hospital For Rehabilitation, Cleveland, OH, p. A477
MARKS, Peter, Vice President & Chief Information Officer, Wakemed Raleigh Campus, Raleigh, NC, p. A461
MARKS, Stanley, M.D., FACS
Chief Medical Officer, Memorial Hospital Miramar, Miramar, FL, p. A132
Chief Medical Officer, Memorial Hospital Pembroke, Pembroke Pines, FL, p. A136
MARKSTROM, Susan, M.D., Chief of Staff, St. Cloud Veterans Affairs Health Care System, Saint Cloud, MN, p. A339
MARKUS, Stacey, Chief Nursing Officer, Williamson Memorial Hospital, Williamson, WV, p. A690
MARLATT, Pam, Business Systems Director, Essentia Health St. Joseph'S Medical Center, Brainerd, MN, p. A329
MARLER, Ruth, Chief Nursing Officer and Chief Operating Officer, Johnston Health, Smithfield, NC, p. A462
MARLER, Steven R, Assistant Administrator, Parkland Health Center – Farmington Community, Farmington, MO, p. A360
MARLEY, Charles, D.O., Vice President Medical Affairs, Wellspan Gettysburg Hospital, Gettysburg, PA, p. A526
MARLEY, Lee, VP/Information Services Chief Application Officer, Presbyterian Hospital, Albuquerque, NM, p. A417
MARLEY, Michael, Chief Information Officer, Veterans Affairs Central Western Massachusetts Healthcare System, Leeds, MA, p. A300
MARLOW, Gary P, Chief Financial Officer, Beverly Hospital, Beverly, MA, p. A294
MARLOWE, Justin, Information Technology Director, Shands Live Oak Regional Medical Center, Live Oak, FL, p. A128
MARMANDE, Susanne, Administrator, Infirmary Long Term Acute Care Hospital, Mobile, AL, p. A20
MARNEY, Terri A, R.N., Director of Nursing, Plains Regional Medical Center, Clovis, NM, p. A417
MARON, Michael, President and Chief Executive Officer, Holy Name Medical Center, Teaneck, NJ, p. A413
MARONEY, Gerry, Chief Information Officer and Security Officer, Gaylord Hospital, Wallingford, CT, p. A111
MAROSTICA, Tony, Chief Compliance and Human Resource Officer, Spanish Peaks Regional Health Center, Walsenburg, CO, p. A106
MAROTTA, Diane, Vice President Human Resources, John T. Mather Memorial Hospital, Port Jefferson, NY, p. A441
MAROUN, Christiane, M.D., Chief of Staff, Lifescape, Sioux Falls, SD, p. A563
MARQUES, John, Vice President Human Resources, Banner – University Medical Center Tucson, Tucson, AZ, p. A37
MARQUES, Tony, Director Information Systems, Grace Cottage Hospital, Townshend, VT, p. A655
MARQUSEE, Joanne, President and Chief Executive Officer, Cooley Dickinson Hospital, Northampton, MA, p. A301
MARR, Debbie, Administrative Assistant and Director Human Resources, Fredonia Regional Hospital, Fredonia, KS, p. A235
MARRAN, Mary, President and Chief Operating Officer, Butler Hospital, Providence, RI, p. A547
MARRERO, Jamie L, M.D., Medical Director, Encompass Health Rehabilitation Hospital Of Manati, Manati, PR, p. A717
MARRERO, Jose, Director Finance, San Jorge Children'S Hospital, Santurce, PR, p. A719
MARRERO, Norma, Executive Administrator, Doctors' Center Hospital San Juan, San Juan, PR, p. A718
MARRONI, Denise
Chief Financial Officer, Providence Centralia Hospital, Centralia, WA, p. A671
Chief Financial Officer, Providence St. Peter Hospital, Olympia, WA, p. A676
MARRUFO, Gabriel, Chief Financial Officer, Methodist Stone Oak Hospital, San Antonio, TX, p. A634
MARSEE, DeWayne, Director Information Systems, Mercer Health, Coldwater, OH, p. A478
MARSH, Amy, Chief Financial Officer, Fairfield Memorial Hospital, Fairfield, IL, p. A183
MARSH, J. Michael., President and Chief Executive Officer, Overlake Medical Center, Bellevue, WA, p. A670
MARSH, Leslie, Chief Executive Officer, Lexington Regional Health Center, Lexington, NE, p. A386
MARSH, Linda, Vice President Financial Services and Chief Financial Officer, Alhambra Hospital Medical Center, Alhambra, CA, p. A50
MARSH, Mark A., President, Health Central Hospital, Ocoee, FL, p. A133
MARSH, Mitch, Interim Executive Director, Brookdale Hospital Medical Center, New York, NY, p. A432
MARSH, Rob, Chief Executive Officer, San Jose Behavorial Health, San Jose, CA, p. A86
MARSH, Toby, MSN, R.N., Interim Chief Patient Care Services Officer, University Of California, Davis Medical Center, Sacramento, CA, p. A82
MARSH, Wallace, Director of Information Technology, Willow Springs Center, Reno, NV, p. A397
MARSHAK, Glenn, M.D., Chief of Staff, Mission Community Hospital, Los Angeles, CA, p. A68
MARSHALL, Deborah K, Vice President Public Relations, Good Samaritan Regional Medical Center, Suffern, NY, p. A445
MARSHALL, Erika, Interim Chief Nursing Officer, Calais Regional Hospital, Calais, ME, p. A282
MARSHALL, James I., President and Chief Executive Officer, Uintah Basin Medical Center, Roosevelt, UT, p. A651
MARSHALL, Jerry, Director Information Services, Information Technology Security Officer, United Regional Health Care System, Wichita Falls, TX, p. A646
MARSHALL, Joe, Chief Operating Officer, Lillian M. Hudspeth Memorial Hospital, Sonora, TX, p. A637
MARSHALL, Judy, Director Human Resources, Holy Cross Hospital, Taos, NM, p. A421
MARSHALL, Julie, Assistant Vice President Quality and Risk Management, The University Of Vermont Health Network – Alice Hyde Medical Center, Malone, NY, p. A430
MARSHALL, Kenneth P., Chief Operating Officer, University Of Louisville Hospital, Louisville, KY, p. A257
MARSHALL, Michael, Vice President Finance and Chief Financial Officer, Anderson Hospital, Maryville, IL, p. A188
MARSHALL, Patricia, Assistant Administrator Human Resources, Washington Health System Greene, Waynesburg, PA, p. A543
MARSHALL, Penny, Chief Nursing Officer, Bear River Valley Hospital, Tremonton, UT, p. A653
MARSHALL, Robert L., Jr, Chief Executive Officer, Bolivar Medical Center, Cleveland, MS, p. A346
MARSHALL, Ryan, Chief Financial Officer, Doctors Hospital Of Manteca, Manteca, CA, p. A70
MARSHBURN, Deborah, Chief Nursing Executive, Cape Fear Valley Medical Center, Fayetteville, NC, p. A454
MARSICO, Nick, Vice President and Chief Operating Officer, Magruder Memorial Hospital, Port Clinton, OH, p. A490
MARSO, Paul, Vice President Human Resources, Avera St. Mary'S Hospital, Pierre, SD, p. A562
MARSTON, Shawn, Director Human Resources, Newport News Behavioral Health Center, Newport News, VA, p. A663
MARTANIUK, Jean, Director Human Resources, Mt. Ascutney Hospital And Health Center, Windsor, VT, p. A655
MARTE, Maria, Administrator, Doctor'S Center Of Bayamon, Bayamon, PR, p. A715
MARTELL, Gustavo, M.D., Chief Medical Officer, The Hospitals Of Providence Transmountain Campus, El Paso, TX, p. A603
MARTENS, Angela, Chief Financial Officer, Cumberland Healthcare, Cumberland, WI, p. A693
MARTENS, Troy, Chief Operating Officer, Unitypoint Health – Trinity Regional Medical Center, Fort Dodge, IA, p. A222
MARTHONE, Frances, Chief Nursing Officer, Mercy Medical Center, Springfield, MA, p. A303
MARTI, Maria L, Director Fiscal Services, Auxilio Mutuo Hospital, San Juan, PR, p. A718
MARTIN, Adam
Chief Executive Officer, Southern Tennessee Regional Health System–Lawrenceburg, Lawrenceburg, TN, p. A573
Chief Operating Officer, Wythe County Community Hospital, Wytheville, VA, p. A669
MARTIN, Amanda, Manager Human Resources, Ohio Valley Surgical Hospital, Springfield, OH, p. A491
MARTIN, Andrew Shane., Administrator, Good Shepherd Specialty Hospital, Bethlehem, PA, p. A520
MARTIN, Angelia, M.D., Chief of Staff, Mosaic Medical Center – Albany, Albany, MO, p. A356
MARTIN, Barbara, Chief Nursing Officer, Mercy St. Vincent Medical Center, Toledo, OH, p. A492
MARTIN, Brent, Administrator, Lifecare Hospitals Of Shreveport–Willis Knighton, Shreveport, LA, p. A278
MARTIN, Brian, Vice President Medical Affairs, Upmc Children'S Hospital Of Pittsburgh, Pittsburgh, PA, p. A538
MARTIN, Bruce A, Vice President Human Resources, Carolinaeast Health System, New Bern, NC, p. A459
MARTIN, Carmen, Associate Administrator, Auxilio Mutuo Hospital, San Juan, PR, p. A718
MARTIN, Cary, Chief Executive Officer, Houston Medical Center, Warner Robins, GA, p. A163
MARTIN, Charity, Controller and Regional Business Officer Manager, Greenwood Regional Rehabilitation Hospital, Greenwood, SC, p. A554
MARTIN, Cheryl
Chief Information Officer, Kingman Regional Medical Center, Kingman, AZ, p. A30
Chief Information Officer, Prisma Health Tuomey Hospital, Sumter, SC, p. A557
MARTIN, Christine M, Vice President and Chief Financial Officer, Atrium Health Cleveland, Shelby, NC, p. A462
MARTIN, Clifford G, M.D.
Regional Vice President and Chief Medical Officer, Osf Holy Family Medical Center, Monmouth, IL, p. A189
Regional Vice President and Chief Medical Officer, Osf Saint Luke Medical Center, Kewanee, IL, p. A187
Regional Vice President and Chief Medical Officer, Osf St. Mary Medical Center, Galesburg, IL, p. A183
MARTIN, Connie, Vice President and Chief Support Officer, Methodist Medical Center Of Oak Ridge, Oak Ridge, TN, p. A578
MARTIN, Corey, M.D., Director Medical Affairs, Buffalo Hospital, Buffalo, MN, p. A329
MARTIN, Cyndie, Director, Coal County General Hospital, Coalgate, OK, p. A498
MARTIN, David, Assistant Administrator, Multicare Valley Hospital, Spokane Valley, WA, p. A680
MARTIN, David W, M.D., Vice President Chief Medical Officer, Ascension Seton Medical Center Austin, Austin, TX, p. A584
MARTIN, Deanna, Chief Executive Officer, Encompass Health Rehabilitation Hospital Of Rock Hill, Rock Hill, SC, p. A556
MARTIN, Deborah
Regional Vice President Human Resources, Cascade Valley Hospital, Arlington, WA, p. A670
Regional Vice President Human Resources, Skagit Regional Health, Mount Vernon, WA, p. A675
MARTIN, Debra, Chief Nursing Officer, Hamilton General Hospital, Hamilton, TX, p. A609
MARTIN, Doug, Chief Executive Officer, Houston County Community Hospital, Erin, TN, p. A569
MARTIN, Garland, M.D., Chief of Staff, Appling Healthcare System, Baxley, GA, p. A148
MARTIN, Gregg
Chief Information Officer, Arnot Ogden Medical Center, Elmira, NY, p. A427
Chief Information Officer, Ira Davenport Memorial Hospital, Bath, NY, p. A423
Chief Information Officer, St. Joseph'S Hospital, Elmira, NY, p. A427
MARTIN, Harvey C, M.D., Medical Director, Red River Hospital, Llc, Wichita Falls, TX, p. A646
MARTIN, Holly
Director Human Resource, Iowa Specialty Hospital–Belmond, Belmond, IA, p. A217
Human Resources Leader, Iowa Specialty Hospital–Clarion, Clarion, IA, p. A219
MARTIN, Jackie, Chief Financial Officer, Saint Luke'S Cushing Hospital, Leavenworth, KS, p. A239
MARTIN, James, Chief Information Officer, River Park Hospital, Huntington, WV, p. A686
MARTIN, James D
Chief Financial Officer, Hawthorn Children Psychiatric Hospital, Saint Louis, MO, p. A369
Chief Financial Officer, Metropolitan St. Louis Psychiatric Center, Saint Louis, MO, p. A369
Chief Financial Officer, St. Louis Psychiatric Rehabilitation Center, Saint Louis, MO, p. A370
MARTIN, Janice S, R.N., Chief Nursing Officer, Davis Regional Medical Center, Statesville, NC, p. A462
MARTIN, Jason, M.D., Medical Director, Ascension Seton Northwest, Austin, TX, p. A584
MARTIN, Jeanene R, M.P.H.
Senior Vice President Human Resources and Chief People Officer, Wakemed Cary Hospital, Cary, NC, p. A450
Senior Vice President Human Resources, Wakemed Raleigh Campus, Raleigh, NC, p. A461
MARTIN, Jeffrey H, M.D., Chief of Staff, Erlanger Western Carolina Hospital, Murphy, NC, p. A459
MARTIN, Jeremy, Chief Support Services Officer, St. James Parish Hospital, Lutcher, LA, p. A273
MARTIN, Jessica, Director Human Resources, Logan Regional Medical Center, Logan, WV, p. A686
MARTIN, Jessie, R.N., Chief Nursing Executive, Community Memorial Hospital, Turtle Lake, ND, p. A469
MARTIN, Josh
Chief Executive Officer, Summit Pacific Medical Center, Elma, WA, p. A672
Chief Operating Officer, Summit Pacific Medical Center, Elma, WA, p. A672
MARTIN, Karen, Chief Nursing Officer, Musc Health Lancaster Medical Center, Lancaster, SC, p. A555
MARTIN, Karen, R.N., MSN, Chief Nursing Officer, Marshall Medical Center, Lewisburg, TN, p. A573
MARTIN, Keith, M.D., Chief Medical Officer, Fhn Memorial Hospital, Freeport, IL, p. A183
MARTIN, Kelly, Chief Financial Officer, Fairchild Medical Center, Yreka, CA, p. A95

MARTIN, Kelly K, Human Resource Officer, Texas Health Presbyterian Hospital Plano, Plano, TX, p. A630

MARTIN, Kenneth A, M.D., Chief of Staff, Arkansas Surgical Hospital, North Little Rock, AR, p. A46

MARTIN, Kevin, Administrator, Shriners Hospitals For Children–Salt Lake City, Salt Lake City, UT, p. A652

MARTIN, Kevin P., M.D., Chief Medical Officer, Four Winds Hospital, Saratoga Springs, NY, p. A443

MARTIN, Konnie, Chief Executive Officer, San Luis Valley Health, Alamosa, CO, p. A96

MARTIN, Kory Lann, M.D., Chief of Staff, Seymour Hospital, Seymour, TX, p. A636

MARTIN, Kristina, Chief Information Officer, Curry General Hospital, Gold Beach, OR, p. A513

MARTIN, Leslee, Manager Information Technology, Hshs St. Elizabeth'S Hospital, O'Fallon, IL, p. A192

MARTIN, Marlana, Director Human Resources, Benewah Community Hospital, Saint Maries, ID, p. A171

MARTIN, Mary, MSN, R.N., Chief Nursing Officer, Hshs St. Nicholas Hospital, Sheboygan, WI, p. A705

MARTIN, Matthew, Director Resource Management, Naval Hospital Oak Harbor, Oak Harbor, WA, p. A675

MARTIN, Nick, Chief Information Officer, Minidoka Memorial Hospital, Rupert, ID, p. A171

MARTIN, Nikki, Chief Financial Officer, Christus Southeast Texas Jasper Memorial, Jasper, TX, p. A616

MARTIN, Patrick, Director Information Systems, Brookdale Hospital Medical Center, New York, NY, p. A432

MARTIN, Patrick, M.D., Medical Director, Wilmington Treatment Center, Wilmington, NC, p. A464

MARTIN, Patsy, Manager Human Resources, Select Rehabilitation Hospital Of Denton, Denton, TX, p. A599

MARTIN, Paul, Chief Medical Officer, Grandview Medical Center, Dayton, OH, p. A481

MARTIN, Paul J, Director Human Resources, Kaiser Permanente Los Angeles Medical Center, Los Angeles, CA, p. A67

MARTIN, Ric, Information Specialist, Madison State Hospital, Madison, IN, p. A211

MARTIN, Richard A, MSN, R.N., Senior Vice President and Chief Nursing Officer, Hoag Memorial Hospital Presbyterian, Newport Beach, CA, p. A74

MARTIN, Sabrina, Chief Executive Officer, Rehabilitation Hospital Of Southern New Mexico, Las Cruces, NM, p. A419

MARTIN, Sharon E, M.D., Ph.D., President Medical Staff, Fulton County Medical Center, Mc Connellsburg, PA, p. A531

MARTIN, Sheila, Chief Nursing Officer, Cmh Regional Health System, Wilmington, OH, p. A494

MARTIN, Sherri, M.D., President Medical Staff, Adventhealth Shawnee Mission, Shawnee Mission, KS, p. A245

MARTIN, Stacy L, Director Human Resources, Grant Regional Health Center, Lancaster, WI, p. A698

MARTIN, Susan, Vice President Finance, Middlesex Hospital, Middletown, CT, p. A109

MARTIN, Tom, Senior Vice President, Strategy and Information Technology Officer, Evergreenhealth, Kirkland, WA, p. A674

MARTIN, Tracie, M.D., Chief Medical Officer, Mercyone Oakland Medical Center, Oakland, NE, p. A388

MARTIN, Val, Director Financial Management Services Center, Veterans Affairs Salt Lake City Health Care System, Salt Lake City, UT, p. A652

MARTIN, W. Carl, Chief Operating Officer, Providence Hospital, Columbia, SC, p. A551

MARTIN, Wendy, Chief Financial Officer, Shands Starke Regional Medical Center, Starke, FL, p. A140

MARTIN–LINNARD, Tamara, R.N., Chief Clinical Officer, Great Plains Health, North Platte, NE, p. A388

MARTIN–PRATT, Diane, Director Information Systems, Niagara Falls Memorial Medical Center, Niagara Falls, NY, p. A439

MARTINEZ, Albino, Director Budget and Finance, Miners' Colfax Medical Center, Raton, NM, p. A419

MARTINEZ, Angel, R.N., Director Patient Care Services, Shriners Hospitals For Children–Galveston, Galveston, TX, p. A607

MARTINEZ, Darlene, Director Finance, New Mexico Behavioral Health Institute At Las Vegas, Las Vegas, NM, p. A419

MARTINEZ, Eddie, Chief Financial Officer, El Paso Ltac Hospital, El Paso, TX, p. A602

MARTINEZ, Edward, Chief Information Officer, Nicklaus Children'S Hospital, Miami, FL, p. A131

MARTINEZ, Eleanor, Chief Nursing Officer, Alhambra Hospital Medical Center, Alhambra, CA, p. A50

MARTINEZ, Francisco, Executive Director, Hospital San Antonio, Mayaguez, PR, p. A717

MARTINEZ, Frank, Senior Vice President Human Resources, East Jefferson General Hospital, Metairie, LA, p. A273

MARTINEZ, Jason, Director Information Technology, West Valley Medical Center, Caldwell, ID, p. A168

MARTINEZ, Jeanine, Director Human Resources, Putnam General Hospital, Eatonton, GA, p. A153

MARTINEZ, Jorge I., Executive Director, Hospital Perea, Mayaguez, PR, p. A717

MARTINEZ, Jose, M.D., Chief Medical Officer, Northwest Medical Center, Margate, FL, p. A129

MARTINEZ, Josue, Coordinator Information Systems, University Hospital, San Juan, PR, p. A719

MARTINEZ, Katherine, Chief Nursing Officer, North Central Surgical Center, Dallas, TX, p. A597

MARTINEZ, Kathryn J, Chief Nursing Officer, Fhn Memorial Hospital, Freeport, IL, p. A183

MARTINEZ, Leanne, Chief Executive Officer and Administrator, Fisher County Hospital District, Rotan, TX, p. A632

MARTINEZ, Lee, Chief Information Officer, Cooley Dickinson Hospital, Northampton, MA, p. A301

MARTINEZ, Louisa, Director of Nursing, Frio Regional Hospital, Pearsall, TX, p. A628

MARTINEZ, Maria, Chief Nursing Officer, La Paz Regional Hospital, Parker, AZ, p. A32

MARTINEZ, Michelle
Chief Executive Officer, U. S. Public Health Service Indian Hospital–Whiteriver, Whiteriver, AZ, p. A38
Controller, Healthsouth Rehabilitation Hospital Of New Mexico, Albuquerque, NM, p. A416

MARTINEZ, Ozalina, R.N., Director of Nursing, Northeastern Health System Sequoyah, Sallisaw, OK, p. A507

MARTINEZ, Regina M, Director Human Resources, La Paz Regional Hospital, Parker, AZ, p. A32

MARTINEZ, Rosette, Acting Chief Executive Officer, Lemuel Shattuck Hospital, Jamaica Plain, MA, p. A299

MARTINEZ, Suzanne, Director Human Resources, Centennial Peaks Hospital, Louisville, CO, p. A104

MARTINEZ, Terri, Chief Financial Officer, Plains Memorial Hospital, Dimmitt, TX, p. A600

MARTINEZ, Tina, Director Human Resources, J. D. Mccarty Center For Children With Developmental Disabilities, Norman, OK, p. A503

MARTINEZ, Virginia, Director Human Resources, Copper Queen Community Hospital, Bisbee, AZ, p. A28

MARTINEZ, Yolanda, Chief Fiscal Services, Edward Hines, Jr. Veterans Affairs Hospital, Hines, IL, p. A185

MARTINEZ, Yvette, Director Human Resources, Sutter Auburn Faith Hospital, Auburn, CA, p. A51

MARTINEZ–NIETO, Arlene, M.D., Chief Medical Officer, First Hospital Panamericano, Cidra, PR, p. A716

MARTING, Bill, Senior Vice President and Chief Financial Officer, The University Of Kansas Hospital, Kansas City, KS, p. A238

MARTINSON, Erling, M.D., Medical Director, Nelson County Health System, Mcville, ND, p. A468

MARTINSON, Tiffany, Director Human Resources, Norton Sound Regional Hospital, Nome, AK, p. A26

MARTOCCIO, Debora, R.N., Chief Operating Officer, Adventhealth Connerton, Land O'Lakes, FL, p. A127

MARTORANO, Ann, Chief Operating Officer, Halifax Health Medical Center Of Daytona Beach, Daytona Beach, FL, p. A121

MARTUCCI, Kathleen, Chief Operating Officer, Helen Hayes Hospital, West Haverstraw, NY, p. A447

MARTZ, Dean
Chief Medical Officer, Providence Holy Family Hospital, Spokane, WA, p. A679
Chief Medical Officer, Providence Sacred Heart Medical Center & Children'S Hospital, Spokane, WA, p. A680

MARTZ, Michael, Chief Information Officer, Ohio Valley Medical Center, Wheeling, WV, p. A690

MARVIN, Ryan, Support Services Director, Rawlins County Health Center, Atwood, KS, p. A232

MARX, Edward, Chief Information Officer, Cleveland Clinic, Cleveland, OH, p. A477

MARX, Kenneth, Chief Financial Officer, Ranken Jordan Pediatric Bridge Hospital, Maryland Heights, MO, p. A365

MARX, Tomasine, Chief Financial Officer and Chief Operating Officer, Ascension Crittenton Hospital Medical Center, Rochester, MI, p. A320

MARX, Troy, Human Resources Director, Upland Hills Health, Dodgeville, WI, p. A693

MARZELLA, Robert, Chief Operations Officer, Upstate University Hospital, Syracuse, NY, p. A445

MARZOLF, Steve, R.N., Chief Nursing Officer, Spectrum Health Pennock, Hastings, MI, p. A314

MASE, Kerin A., President and Chief Executive Officer, Marian Regional Medical Center, Santa Maria, CA, p. A89

MASHAK–EKERN, Jane, Fiscal Officer, Va Medical Center, Tomah, WI, p. A706

MASI, George V., Chief Executive Officer, Harris Health System, Houston, TX, p. A611

MASIELLO, Matthew, M.D., Chief Medical Officer, The Children'S Institute Of Pittsburgh, Pittsburgh, PA, p. A537

MASKELL, Denise, Chief Information Officer, Springfield Hospital Center, Sykesville, MD, p. A293

MASON, Bill A., Chief Executive Officer, Meadow Wood Behavioral Health System, New Castle, DE, p. A113

MASON, Drew, Chief Executive Officer, Grandview Medical Center, Birmingham, AL, p. A14

MASON, H F, M.D., Chief Medical Officer, Baptist Memorial Hospital–Union County, New Albany, MS, p. A352

MASON, Jeffrey, President and Chief Executive Officer, Glencoe Regional Health, Glencoe, MN, p. A332

MASON, Jill K, MS, R.N., Chief Nursing Officer, Blessing Hospital, Quincy, IL, p. A194

MASON, John, Chief Information Officer, Hill Country Memorial Hospital, Fredericksburg, TX, p. A606

MASON, Kathy, Chief Operating Officer, Atrium Medical Center Of Corinth, Corinth, TX, p. A594

MASON, Kathy, R.N., MSN, Chief Nursing Officer, Lifecare Hospitals Of Dallas, Dallas, TX, p. A596

MASON, Kay, Chief Financial Officer, Texas Health Heart & Vascular Hospital Arlington, Arlington, TX, p. A584

MASON, Keith, Chief Executive Officer, Bailey Medical Center, Owasso, OK, p. A506

MASON, Phyllis, M.D., Chief Medical Officer, Natchitoches Regional Medical Center, Natchitoches, LA, p. A274

MASON, Rhonda, Vice President of Patient Care Services, Tri–State Memorial Hospital, Clarkston, WA, p. A671

MASON, Sandra, MSN, R.N., Director Nursing Services and Senior Nurse Executive, Robert E. Bush Naval Hospital, Twentynine Palms, CA, p. A92

MASON, Stacie, Vice President and Chief Financial Officer, Integris Grove Hospital, Grove, OK, p. A500

MASON, William R, Chief Operating Officer, Brooke Glen Behavioral Hospital, Fort Washington, PA, p. A526

MASON–JONES, Taryn, Chief Nurse Executive, Norristown State Hospital, Norristown, PA, p. A533

MASOOD, Shahid, M.D., Clinical Director, Mildred Mitchell–Bateman Hospital, Huntington, WV, p. A686

MASSA, Rhonda, Director of Nursing, Clarion Psychiatric Center, Clarion, PA, p. A522

MASSAAD, Aziz, M.D., Medical Staff President, Down East Community Hospital, Machias, ME, p. A284

MASSELLA, Joan, Administrative Vice President and Chief Nursing Officer, St. Clair Hospital, Pittsburgh, PA, p. A537

MASSENGALE, David
Chief Financial Officer, Methodist Hospital Union County, Morganfield, KY, p. A258
Vice President and Chief Financial Officer, Methodist Hospital, Henderson, KY, p. A253

MASSENGILL, Leigh, Chief Executive Officer, Medical Center Of Trinity, Trinity, FL, p. A143

MASSEY, Gina, Vice President Human Resources, Clarity Child Guidance Center, San Antonio, TX, p. A633

MASSEY, Rocco K., Community Chief Executive Officer, Beckley Arh Hospital, Beckley, WV, p. A683

MASSEY, Steven, President and Chief Executive Officer, Westfields Hospital And Clinic, New Richmond, WI, p. A702

MASSEY, Tami, M.D., Chief of Medical Staff, Edgefield County Healthcare, Edgefield, SC, p. A552

MASSEY, Terry, Chief Fiscal Services, Beckley Veterans Affairs Medical Center, Beckley, WV, p. A683

MASSIELLO, Martin, Executive Vice President and Chief Operating Officer, Eisenhower Medical Center, Rancho Mirage, CA, p. A79

MASSIMILLA, John P, FACHE, Vice President and Chief Operating Officer, Chambersburg Hospital, Chambersburg, PA, p. A522

MASSINI, Stephen M., Chief Executive Officer, Penn State Milton S. Hershey Medical Center, Hershey, PA, p. A527

MASSMAN, Patty, Director of Nursing, Granite Falls Health, Granite Falls, MN, p. A333

MASSOUH, Rafik, M.D., Chief of Staff, Mercy Allen Hospital, Oberlin, OH, p. A489

MAST, Delvin, R.N., Director of Nursing, Weatherford Regional Hospital, Weatherford, OK, p. A510

MAST, Duane, M.D., Medical Director, Hocking Valley Community Hospital, Logan, OH, p. A485

MAST, Joelle, Ph.D., M.D., Chief Medical Officer, Blythedale Children'S Hospital, Valhalla, NY, p. A446

MAST, Nathan, Chief Executive Officer, Vibra Hospital Of Mahoning Valley, Boardman, OH, p. A473

MASTER, Moiz, M.D., Medical Director of Quality, Piedmont Mountainside Hospital, Jasper, GA, p. A155

MASTERS, Emily, Chief Human Relations Officer, Windom Area Hospital, Windom, MN, p. A343

MASTERS, Ken, Director Information Technology, Chambers Memorial Hospital, Danville, AR, p. A41

MASTERS, Kim, M.D., Medical Director, Saint Simons By–The–Sea Hospital, Saint Simons Island, GA, p. A159

MASTERS, Regina, R.N., MSN, Director of Nursing, Continuing Care Hospital, Lexington, KY, p. A255
MASTERSON, David J., President, Sentara Williamsburg Regional Medical Center, Williamsburg, VA, p. A669
MASTERSON, Paul, Chief Financial Officer, Genesis Healthcare System, Zanesville, OH, p. A495
MASTERSON, Sammie, Director Human Resources, Harney District Hospital, Burns, OR, p. A511
MASTROIANNI, Anthony, Regional Vice President Finance, The William W. Backus Hospital, Norwich, CT, p. A110
MASTROIANNI, Thomas, Administrative Director of Human Resources, Halifax Regional Medical Center, Roanoke Rapids, NC, p. A461
MASTROMANNO, Christopher
    Chief Operating Officer, Brookdale Hospital Medical Center, New York, NY, p. A432
    Interim Chief Executive Officer, Brookdale Hospital Medical Center, New York, NY, p. A432
MATA, Maribel, Director Information Services, Doctors Hospital Of Laredo, Laredo, TX, p. A619
MATA-GUERRERO, Rita, Director of Nursing, Weslaco Regional Rehabilitation Hospital, Weslaco, TX, p. A645
MATAI, Divya, Chief Financial Officer, Northwest Texas Healthcare System, Amarillo, TX, p. A582
MATAMOROS, Mary L., Chief Executive Officer, Seaside Behavioral Center, New Orleans, LA, p. A276
MATEJICKA, Anthony, D.O., M.P.H., Vice President, Chief Medical Officer, Nyack Hospital, Nyack, NY, p. A440
MATEJKA, Cheryl
    Chief Financial Officer, Mercy Hospital St. Louis, Saint Louis, MO, p. A368
    Chief Financial Officer, Mercy Hospital Washington, Washington, MO, p. A373
MATENAER, Thomas M, Chief Financial Officer, Banner Gateway Medical Center, Gilbert, AZ, p. A29
MATHAI, George, M.D., Chief of Staff, Three Rivers Hospital, Waverly, TN, p. A580
MATHAI, Matt, M.D., Medical Director, Select Specialty Hospital–Milwaukee, Milwaukee, WI, p. A701
MATHEIS, Tracey
    Chief Financial Officer, Moberly Regional Medical Center, Moberly, MO, p. A365
    Chief Operating Officer, Moberly Regional Medical Center, Moberly, MO, p. A365
MATHER, Kelly, Chief Executive Officer, Sonoma Valley Hospital, Sonoma, CA, p. A90
MATHER, Martha S, Chief Operating Officer and Vice President, Chi Our Lady Of Peace, Louisville, KY, p. A256
MATHERS, Larry, M.D., Chief of Staff, Tennova Newport Medical Center, Newport, TN, p. A578
MATHES, Lisa L, Human Resources Director, Southwest Medical Center, Liberal, KS, p. A239
MATHEW, Finny
    President, Integris Bass Baptist Health Center, Enid, OK, p. A499
    President, Integris Bass Pavilion, Enid, OK, p. A499
MATHEWS, Christine, R.N., MSN, Vice President Nursing Services, Geisinger–Lewistown Hospital, Lewistown, PA, p. A530
MATHEWS, Gary, M.D., Medical Doctor, Beaver County Memorial Hospital, Beaver, OK, p. A497
MATHEWS, Nimmy, Acting Director Quality Management, San Carlos Apache Healthcare Corporation, Peridot, AZ, p. A32
MATHEWS, Paul G., Administrator, Hardtner Medical Center, Olla, LA, p. A276
MATHEWS, Thomas, Vice President, Finance, Mercy Hospital Joplin, Joplin, MO, p. A362
MATHEWSON, Patricia, Chief Nursing Officer, Adventist Health – Tulare, Tulare, CA, p. A92
MATHIAS, Matt
    Chief Executive Officer, Stonesprings Hospital Center, Dulles, VA, p. A658
    Chief Operating Officer, Lewisgale Hospital Montgomery, Blacksburg, VA, p. A656
MATHIEU, Angie, System Director Information Technology and Regional Chief Information Officer, The William W. Backus Hospital, Norwich, CT, p. A110
MATHIEU, Lori, MSN, Chief Nursing Officer, Glenwood Regional Medical Center, West Monroe, LA, p. A280
MATHIS, Alison, Chief Nursing Officer, Copiah County Medical Center, Hazlehurst, MS, p. A348
MATHIS, Ashley, Privacy Officer, Columbus Community Hospital, Columbus, TX, p. A593
MATHIS, Jane, Chief Financial Officer, Baylor Scott & White Surgical Hospital Fort Worth, Fort Worth, TX, p. A604
MATHIS, Patricia, Associate Director Patient Care Service, Richard L. Roudebush Veterans Affairs Medical Center, Indianapolis, IN, p. A207

MATHIS, Rebecca
    Chief Financial Officer, Adventist Medical Center Bolingbrook, Bolingbrook, IL, p. A174
    Chief Financial Officer, Adventist Medical Center Lagrange, La Grange, IL, p. A187
    Vice President and Chief Financial Officer, Adventist Medical Center – Hinsdale, Hinsdale, IL, p. A186
MATHIS, Richard C., Chief Executive Officer, North Runnels Hospital, Winters, TX, p. A646
MATHIS, Robin, Director Human Resources, Methodist Healthcare Olive Branch Hospital, Olive Branch, MS, p. A352
MATHISEN, Arthur, President, Memorial Hospital, North Conway, NH, p. A402
MATHUR, Ashish, M.D., Chief of Staff, Siloam Springs Regional Hospital, Siloam Springs, AR, p. A48
MATHUR, Tanmay, Chief Executive Officer, Covington Behaviorial Health, Covington, LA, p. A266
MATHURIN, Emile, M.D., Medical Director, Encompass Health Rehabilitation Hospital Of Humble, Humble, TX, p. A615
MATHURIN, Venra, Vice President Human Resources, Brookdale Hospital Medical Center, New York, NY, p. A432
MATIS, Sue, Director Human Resources, North Central Health Care, Wausau, WI, p. A708
MATLACK, Victoria L.
    Director and Human Resources Business Partner, Ohiohealth Dublin Methodist Hospital, Dublin, OH, p. A482
    Director and Human Resources Business Partner, Ohiohealth Grady Memorial Hospital, Delaware, OH, p. A482
MATNEY, James L., President and Chief Executive Officer, Colquitt Regional Medical Center, Moultrie, GA, p. A158
MATNEY, Patty, Human Resources Consultant, Saint Thomas Hickman Hospital, Centerville, TN, p. A567
MATNEY, Tim, Chief Financial Officer, Logan Regional Medical Center, Logan, WV, p. A686
MATOS, Patricia, Chief Nursing Officer, Stewart & Lynda Resnick Neuropsychiatric Hospital At Ucla, Los Angeles, CA, p. A69
MATSINGER, John, D.O., Chief Medical Officer, Virtua Marlton, Marlton, NJ, p. A408
MATT, Robert Lawrence, Vice President and Chief Operating Officer, Hancock Regional Hospital, Greenfield, IN, p. A205
MATTER, Stephanie, Manager Human Resources, Lifecare Hospitals Of Wisconsin, Pewaukee, WI, p. A703
MATTERN, Bonnie, Director Human Resources, Chi St. Alexius Health Devils Lake Hospital, Devils Lake, ND, p. A466
MATTERN, Joe, M.D., Chief Medical Officer, Jefferson Healthcare, Port Townsend, WA, p. A676
MATTERN, Karen, Director of Human Resources, Shriners Hospitals For Children–Spokane, Spokane, WA, p. A680
MATTES, Bryan, Associate Administrator, Crossridge Community Hospital, Wynne, AR, p. A49
MATTES, Dennis, Chief Executive Officer, Select Specialty Hospital–Milwaukee, Milwaukee, WI, p. A701
MATTEUCCI, Dolly
    Executive Director, Napa State Hospital, Napa, CA, p. A74
    Superintendent, Oregon State Hospital, Salem, OR, p. A517
MATTHEI, Ruth, R.N., MS, Chief Nursing Officer, Westlake Hospital, Melrose Park, IL, p. A189
MATTHEW, Mathew, M.D., Chief Medical Officer, Nazareth Hospital, Philadelphia, PA, p. A535
MATTHEWS, Adora, M.D., Medical Director, Encompass Health Rehabilitation Hospital Of Florence, Florence, SC, p. A552
MATTHEWS, Bryan C., Medical Center Director, Veterans Affairs Gulf Coast Veterans Health Care System, Biloxi, MS, p. A344
MATTHEWS, Carol, Director Human Resources, Saline Memorial Hospital, Benton, AR, p. A39
MATTHEWS, Clinton, President and Chief Executive Officer, Reading Hospital Rehabilitation At Wyomissing, Wyomissing, PA, p. A545
MATTHEWS, Deborah
    Chief Nursing Officer, Tanner Medical Center–Carrollton, Carrollton, GA, p. A149
    Senior Vice President, Tanner Medical Center–Villa Rica, Villa Rica, GA, p. A162
MATTHEWS, Edward, Chief Financial Officer, San Dimas Community Hospital, San Dimas, CA, p. A85
MATTHEWS, Gwen, Chief Executive Officer, Ukiah Valley Medical Center, Ukiah, CA, p. A93
MATTHEWS, Judith, Nurse Executive, Riverside Tappahannock Hospital, Tappahannock, VA, p. A668
MATTHEWS, Kristopher, Chief Operating Officer, Decatur Health Systems, Oberlin, KS, p. A242
MATTHEWS, Lauren, Chief Financial Officer, Piedmont Newton Hospital, Covington, GA, p. A151

MATTHEWS, Lori
    Vice President Information Technology System, Banner Baywood Medical Center, Mesa, AZ, p. A31
    Vice President, Information Technology System, Banner Heart Hospital, Mesa, AZ, p. A31
MATTHEWS, Melissa, Director Human Resources, Dahl Memorial Healthcare Association, Ekalaka, MT, p. A376
MATTHEWS, Michael, Vice President Human Resources, Holland Hospital, Holland, MI, p. A314
MATTHEWS, Oliver, M.D., Chief Medical Officer, North Alabama Medical Center, Florence, Al., p. A18
MATTHEWS, Ted, Chief Executive Officer, Eastland Memorial Hospital, Eastland, TX, p. A600
MATTHEY, Michael, Facility Chief Information Officer, Louis A. Johnson Veterans Affairs Medical Center, Clarksburg, WV, p. A684
MATTHIAS, Mark, M.D., Vice President of Medical Affairs, St. Cloud Hospital, Saint Cloud, MN, p. A339
MATTHIESSEN, Matthew
    Chief Executive Officer, John C. Fremont Healthcare District, Mariposa, CA, p. A71
    Chief Financial Officer, John C. Fremont Healthcare District, Mariposa, CA, p. A71
MATTICE, Gloria, R.N., Director Patient Care, George C Grape Community Hospital, Hamburg, IA, p. A223
MATTINGLY, Marty, Chief Human Resources Officer, St. Vincent Evansville, Evansville, IN, p. A203
MATTISON, Denise, Director Finance and Accounting Services, Mayo Clinic Health System In Eau Claire, Eau Claire, WI, p. A694
MATTLY, Sheila, Chief Nursing Officer, Wayne County Hospital, Corydon, IA, p. A220
MATTNER, Matthew, Chief Operating Officer, Lutheran Hospital, Cleveland, OH, p. A478
MATTSON, Jodi, Director of Nursing, Cedar Springs Hospital, Colorado Springs, CO, p. A97
MATTSON, Wayne, Management Information Systems Specialist, Rogers Memorial Hospital, Inc., Oconomowoc, WI, p. A702
MATUS, Jose, M.D., Director Medical, Carrus Rehabilitation Hospital, Sherman, TX, p. A637
MATUSZKIEWICZ, Marcin, M.D., Chief of Staff and Medical Director, Jerold Phelps Community Hospital, Garberville, CA, p. A60
MATZENBACHER, Elaine, Chief Financial Officer, Washington County Hospital, Nashville, IL, p. A191
MATZIGKEIT, Linda, Senior Vice President Human Resources, Children'S Healthcare Of Atlanta, Atlanta, GA, p. A146
MAUCK, Lynn, R.N., Chief Operating Officer and Chief Nursing Officer, Fishermen'S Hospital, Marathon, FL, p. A129
MAURER, Gregory L., Chief Executive Officer, Sheridan Memorial Hospital, Plentywood, MT, p. A379
MAURER, Jackie, Fiscal Officer, Julian F. Keith Alcohol And Drug Abuse Treatment Center, Black Mountain, NC, p. A450
MAURER, Linda, Vice President Patient Care Services, Wilson Memorial Hospital, Sidney, OH, p. A491
MAURER, Marsha L., R.N., MS, Chief Nursing Officer Patient Care Services, Beth Israel Deaconess Medical Center, Boston, MA, p. A294
MAURICE, Timothy, Chief Financial Officer, University Of California, Davis Medical Center, Sacramento, CA, p. A82
MAURIN, Michael J, Chief Financial Officer, Southern Surgical Hospital, Slidell, LA, p. A279
MAVROMATIS, Lou, Vice President Information Technology, Medstar Southern Maryland Hospital Center, Clinton, MD, p. A289
MAVROS, George, Chief Operating Officer, Citrus Memorial Health System, Inverness, FL, p. A125
MAXIE, Bryan K., Administrator, Highland Community Hospital, Picayune, MS, p. A353
MAXSON, Diana, Director Human Resources, University Hospital Summerville, Augusta, GA, p. A147
MAXWELL, Dale, Executive Vice President and Chief Financial Officer, Presbyterian Hospital, Albuquerque, NM, p. A417
MAXWELL, Jody, Manager Business Office, Smith County Memorial Hospital, Smith Center, KS, p. A246
MAXWELL, Ronnie, Director Information Systems, Glenwood Regional Medical Center, West Monroe, LA, p. A280
MAY, Brandon
    Chief Executive Officer, Doctors Hospital Of Manteca, Manteca, CA, p. A70
    Chief Operating Officer, The Hospitals Of Providence East Campus, El Paso, TX, p. A602
MAY, David, Chief of Staff, Richland Hospital, Richland Center, WI, p. A704
MAY, Kevin B
    Chief Financial Officer, Watauga Medical Center, Boone, NC, p. A450
    System Director Finance, Charles A. Cannon Memorial Hospital, Newland, NC, p. A459

MAY, Robin, Director Information Systems, Platte County Memorial Hospital, Wheatland, WY, p. A713

MAY, Ronald B, M.D., Vice President Medical Affairs, Carolinaeast Health System, New Bern, NC, p. A459

MAY, Scott, Area Director Technology, Kaiser Permanente Santa Clara Medical Center, Santa Clara, CA, p. A88

MAY, Sonja, Director Human Resources, Morton County Health System, Elkhart, KS, p. A234

MAY, Todd, M.D., Chief Medical Officer, Zuckerberg San Francisco General Hospital And Trauma Center, San Francisco, CA, p. A86

MAY, Troy, Chief Information Officer, University Of Louisville Hospital, Louisville, KY, p. A257

MAY, William J., Administrator, Hawaii State Hospital, Kaneohe, HI, p. A166

MAYBEN, Casey, Chief Nursing Officer, Ut Health Pittsburg, Pittsburg, TX, p. A628

MAYEAUX, Rachel, Chief Executive Officer, Amg Specialty Hospital–Lafayette, Lafayette, LA, p. A270

MAYER, David, Chief of Staff, Wayne County Hospital, Monticello, KY, p. A258

MAYER, Karen M, Ph.D., R.N., FACHE, Senior Vice President Patient Care Services, Rush Oak Park Hospital, Oak Park, IL, p. A191

MAYER, Peter, Director Information Systems, Bakersfield Heart Hospital, Bakersfield, CA, p. A52

MAYER, William, M.D., Vice President Medical Staff Services, St. Mary'S Healthcare, Amsterdam, NY, p. A422

MAYES, Libby, Human Resource Director, Ephraim Mcdowell Regional Medical Center, Danville, KY, p. A251

MAYEWSKI, Raymond, M.D.
Chief Medical Officer, Highland Hospital, Rochester, NY, p. A442
Chief Medical Officer, Strong Memorial Hospital Of The University Of Rochester, Rochester, NY, p. A443

MAYFIELD, Michael Bradley, M.D., Chief of Staff, Chicot Memorial Medical Center, Lake Village, AR, p. A44

MAYFIELD, William, M.D., Chief of Staff, Tristar Stonecrest Medical Center, Smyrna, TN, p. A579

MAYHLE, Douglas, M.D., Medical Director, Nicholas H. Noyes Memorial Hospital, Dansville, NY, p. A426

MAYLE, Connie, Vice President Administrative Services, Upmc Horizon, Farrell, PA, p. A526

MAYNARD, Bob, Chief Information Officer, Fairview Regional Medical Center, Fairview, OK, p. A500

MAYO, Andrew, Chief Executive Officer and Managing Director, North Star Behavioral Health System, Anchorage, AK, p. A25

MAYO, Hal, Chief Financial Officer, Liberty Dayton Regional Medical Center, Liberty, TX, p. A620

MAYO, Jim, M.D., Clinical Director, Cherry Hospital, Goldsboro, NC, p. A455

MAYO, Michael A., President, Baptist Medical Center Jacksonville, Jacksonville, FL, p. A125

MAYO, Randy, Director Information Technology, William Newton Hospital, Winfield, KS, p. A248

MAYO, Robert, M.D.
Chief Medical Officer, Rochester General Hospital, Rochester, NY, p. A442
Executive Vice President, Chief Medical Officer, Rochester Regional Health, Newark–Wayne Community Hospital, Newark, NY, p. A439

MAYO, Sarah, Vice President Financial Services, Unc Lenoir Healthcare, Kinston, NC, p. A457

MAYORGA, Oliver, M.D.
Chief Medical Officer, Lawrence + Memorial Hospital, New London, CT, p. A110
Chief Medical Officer, Westerly Hospital, Westerly, RI, p. A548

MAYS, Christine
Chief Operating Officer and Chief Nurse Executive, Chi Saint Joseph East, Lexington, KY, p. A254
Chief Operating Officer and Chief Nurse Executive, Chi Saint Joseph Health, Lexington, KY, p. A255

MAYS, Dawn, Chief Nursing Officer, Scott Memorial Health, Scottsburg, IN, p. A214

MAYS, Raymond, M.D., Medical Director, River Crest Hospital, San Angelo, TX, p. A632

MAYS, Sherrie, MSN, R.N., Vice President and Chief Nursing Officer, Baptist Health Corbin, Corbin, KY, p. A250

MAYSENT, Patty, Chief Executive Officer, Uc San Diego Health, San Diego, CA, p. A84

MAYSILLES, Nancy, R.N., Chief Nursing Officer, Medical Center Of Trinity, Trinity, FL, p. A143

MAYSON, Mark J, M.D., Medical Director, Prisma Health Baptist Hospital, Columbia, SC, p. A551

MAZANEC, Lori
Chief Executive Officer, Box Butte General Hospital, Alliance, NE, p. A382
Chief Operating Officer, Box Butte General Hospital, Alliance, NE, p. A382

MAZEK, Mariusz, Vice President Information Technology and Chief Information Officer, Roseland Community Hospital, Chicago, IL, p. A179

MAZOUR, Linda, M.D., President, Franklin County Memorial Hospital, Franklin, NE, p. A384

MAZUREK, Michele A, Interim Vice President Patient Care Services and Chief Nursing Officer, Mount Sinai Hospital, Chicago, IL, p. A178

MAZZA, Mary, Director Human Resources, Encompass Health Rehabilitation Hospital Of Western Massachusetts, Ludlow, MA, p. A300

MAZZARELLA, Frank, M.D., Chief Medical Officer, Clara Maass Medical Center, Belleville, NJ, p. A403

MAZZARELLI, Anthony J, JD, M.D., Co–President, Cooper University Health Care, Camden, NJ, p. A404

MAZZO, Joseph, Chief Executive Officer, John Randolph Medical Center, Hopewell, VA, p. A661

MAZZOLA, Joe, D.O., Senior Vice President Medical Affairs and Chief Medical Officer, Carolinas Healthcare System Blue Ridge, Morganton, NC, p. A459

MAZZOLA, Joseph, M.D., Chief Medical Officer, Osceola Regional Medical Center, Kissimmee, FL, p. A126

MAZZONI, Dean, President and Chief Executive Officer, Franciscan Health Michigan City, Michigan City, IN, p. A211

MAZZUCA, Darryl, Director Management Information Systems, Little Company Of Mary Hospital And Health Care Centers, Evergreen Park, IL, p. A183

MBENGA, Saul, Manager Information Technology, Alliance Healthcare System, Holly Springs, MS, p. A348

MC KELLAR, Grey, Chief Operating Officer and Director of Performance Improvement and Risk, Kingwood Pines Hospital, Kingwood, TX, p. A618

MCADAMS, David, Chief Financial Officer, Lindner Center Of Hope, Mason, OH, p. A487

MCADOO, Jackie, Chief Financial Officer, Grady Memorial Hospital, Chickasha, OK, p. A498

MCAFEE, Thomas J., President, North Region, Northwestern Medicine Lake Forest Hospital, Lake Forest, IL, p. A187

MCALISTER, Julene, Administrator, Accord Rehabiliation Hospital, Plaquemine, LA, p. A277

MCALISTER, Michael, Chief Executive Officer, Select Specialty Hospital – Dallas Downtown, Dallas, TX, p. A598

MCALISTER, Stephanie, Controller, Tippah County Hospital, Ripley, MS, p. A354

MCALLISTER, Guy, Vice President and Chief Information Officer, Tift Regional Medical Center, Tifton, GA, p. A162

MCALLISTER, Ric, Chief Executive Officer, Windsor–Laurelwood Center For Behavioral Medicine, Willoughby, OH, p. A494

MCALLISTER, Yvonne, Senior Director Human Resources, Southern Maine Health Care – Biddeford Medical Center, Biddeford, ME, p. A282

MCALOON, Richard, Vice President Human Resources, Hartford Hospital, Hartford, CT, p. A108

MCANDREWS, Kevin
Vice President Human Resources, Nexus Specialty Hospital, Shenandoah, TX, p. A636
Vice President, Human Resources, Nexus Specialty Hospital The Woodlands, The Woodlands, TX, p. A641

MCARTHUR, Ronald L., Chief Executive Officer, Summit Healthcare Regional Medical Center, Show Low, AZ, p. A36

MCARTOR, Dana, R.N., Director of Nursing, Perkins County Health Services, Grant, NE, p. A385

MCASKILL, L. Craig, M.D., Chief Medical Officer, Englewood Community Hospital, Englewood, FL, p. A122

MCAULIFFE, Gregory, M.D.
Chief Medical Officer, San Luis Valley Health Conejos County Hospital, La Jara, CO, p. A102
Chief Medical Officer, San Luis Valley Health, Alamosa, CO, p. A96

MCAULIFFE, John, M.D., Medical Director, Sauk Prairie Healthcare, Prairie Du Sac, WI, p. A704

MCAVOY, Tim, M.D., Medical Director, Rehabilitation Hospital Of Wisconsin, Waukesha, WI, p. A707

MCBEE, Jeff, Administrator, Presbyterian Hospital, Albuquerque, NM, p. A417

MCBEE, John, Chief of Staff, Chi St. Anthony Hospital, Pendleton, OR, p. A515

MCBREARTY, Michael, M.D., Vice President Medical Affairs, Thomas Hospital, Fairhope, AL, p. A18

MCBRIDE, Anne, Chief Executive Officer, Regional Hospital For Respiratory And Complex Care, Burien, WA, p. A671

MCBRIDE, Brandon, Operations Officer, Logan Regional Hospital, Logan, UT, p. A648

MCBRIDE, Dina, Chief Operating Officer and Director Human Resources, East Adams Rural Healthcare, Ritzville, WA, p. A677

MCBRIDE, Grace, Regional Chief Nursing Officer, Amita Health Mercy Medical Center, Aurora, IL, p. A173

MCBRIDE, Lamar, Chief Executive Officer, Vibra Hospital Of Denver, Thornton, CO, p. A106

MCBRIDE, Thomas Y, Executive Vice President and Chief Financial Officer, Gwinnett Hospital System, Lawrenceville, GA, p. A156

MCBROOM, Robert, M.D., Medical Director, Promise Hospital Of Wichita Falls, Wichita Falls, TX, p. A645

MCBRYDE, Robin, Chief Information Officer, Alexandria Veterans Affairs Health Care System, Pineville, LA, p. A277

MCCAA, Karen, R.N., Vice President Patient Care Services and Chief Nursing Officer, Baptist Medical Center South, Montgomery, AL, p. A21

MCCABE, Mary, Chief Financial Officer, North Colorado Medical Center, Greeley, CO, p. A101

MCCABE, Patrick, Senior Vice President Finance and Chief Financial Officer, Bridgeport Hospital, Bridgeport, CT, p. A107

MCCABE, Patrick G., Jr, President and Chief Executive Officer, Levi Hospital, Hot Springs National Park, AR, p. A43

MCCABE, Steve, Chief Executive Officer, Hill Crest Behavioral Health Services, Birmingham, AL, p. A14

MCCAFFERTY, Michael, Chief Executive Officer, Sheridan Memorial Hospital, Sheridan, WY, p. A712

MCCAFFREY, Anne E., President and Chief Executive Officer, Eastern Niagara Hospital, Lockport, NY, p. A430

MCCAFFREY, Roberta A, R.N., Vice President and Chief Nursing Officer, Methodist Hospital Of Southern California, Arcadia, CA, p. A51

MCCAHILL, Connie, President and Chief Executive Officer, Cameron Memorial Community Hospital, Angola, IN, p. A199

MCCAHILL, Mary, Chief Nursing Officer, Thorek Memorial Hospital, Chicago, IL, p. A180

MCCAIN, Rebecca J., Chief Executive Officer, Electra Memorial Hospital, Electra, TX, p. A603

MCCALL, Harlo, Chief Executive Officer, Encompass Health Rehabilitation Hospital Of Texarkana, Texarkana, TX, p. A640

MCCALL, Lee, Chief Executive Officer, Neshoba County General Hospital, Philadelphia, MS, p. A353

MCCALL, Pam, Director Human Resources, Heatherhill Care Communities, Chardon, OH, p. A475

MCCALLISTER, Bob, Director Human Resources, Baptist Memorial Hospital–Golden Triangle, Columbus, MS, p. A346

MCCALLISTER, Darla, Chief Financial Officer, Lakeside Women'S Hospital, Oklahoma City, OK, p. A504

MCCALLISTER, Dianne, M.D., Chief Medical Officer, Medical Center Of Aurora, Aurora, CO, p. A96

MCCALLISTER, Sean, Chief Executive Officer, Johnson County Healthcare Center, Buffalo, WY, p. A710

MCCAMMON, Colleen, Chief Executive Officer, Westpark Springs, Richmond, TX, p. A631

MCCAMPBELL, Kellie, Coordinator Human Resources, Kindred Hospital–Chattanooga, Chattanooga, TN, p. A567

MCCAMPBELL, Marcia, M.D., Chief Medical Officer, Shasta Regional Medical Center, Redding, CA, p. A80

MCCANDLESS, David, Vice President Medical Affairs, Upmc Northwest, Seneca, PA, p. A541

MCCANN, Barbara, Director Human Resources, Sunrise Canyon Hospital, Lubbock, TX, p. A622

MCCANN, Kyle, Chief Operating Officer, St. Joseph'S Hospital, Savannah, GA, p. A160

MCCANN, Lew, Director Management Information Systems, Osf Holy Family Medical Center, Monmouth, IL, p. A189

MCCARTAN, Mary E, Manager Human Resources, Va Long Beach Healthcare System, Long Beach, CA, p. A65

MCCARTER, Alyssa, Chief Financial Officer, W. J. Mangold Memorial Hospital, Lockney, TX, p. A621

MCCARTER, Scott, Chief Information Officer, Karmanos Cancer Center, Detroit, MI, p. A310

MCCARTHY, Barbara, Chief Executive Officer, Specialty Hospital Jacksonville, Jacksonville, FL, p. A126

MCCARTHY, Brian, Director Information Systems, Salem Medical Center, Salem, NJ, p. A412

MCCARTHY, Cynthia L, Chief Nursing Officer, Texas Health Harris Methodist Hospital Stephenville, Stephenville, TX, p. A638

MCCARTHY, Maureen, M.D., Chief of Staff, Phoenix Veterans Affairs Health Care System, Phoenix, AZ, p. A34

MCCARTHY, Rick, Chief Information Officer, White Plains Hospital Center, White Plains, NY, p. A448

MCCARTHY, Sandra Mac
Chief Nursing Officer, Arnot Ogden Medical Center, Elmira, NY, p. A427
Chief Nursing Officer, St. Joseph'S Hospital, Elmira, NY, p. A427

MCCARTHY, Tim, President Puerto Rico Division, First Hospital Panamericano, Cidra, PR, p. A716

MCCARTY, Daniel P, Chief Operating Officer, Orange City Area Health System, Orange City, IA, p. A227

MCCARTY, Jacob M., Chief Executive Officer, Kindred Hospital–San Francisco Bay Area, San Leandro, CA, p. A87

MCCARTY, Melany, R.N., Chief Clinical Officer, Vibra Hospital Of Amarillo, Amarillo, TX, p. A582

MCCARTY, Tim, Chief Information Officer, Oakbend Medical Center, Richmond, TX, p. A631

MCCARTY, Wendy, Director Human Resources, Hillsboro Community Hospital, Hillsboro, KS, p. A236

MCCARY, Steve C., Administrator, Riverside Doctors' Hospital Williamsburg, Williamsburg, VA, p. A669

MCCASLIN, Anna, Chief Financial Officer, Orthonebraska Hospital, Omaha, NE, p. A390

MCCASLIN, Jami, Director Human Resources, Providence Hood River Memorial Hospital, Hood River, OR, p. A513

MCCAULEY, Cynthia, Chief Financial Officer, Good Samaritan Medical Center, West Palm Beach, FL, p. A144

MCCAULEY, Dudley, Controller, Lincoln County Medical Center, Ruidoso, NM, p. A420

MCCAULEY, Jason, Administrator, Jane Phillips Nowata Health Center, Nowata, OK, p. A503

MCCAULEY, Sue E, Director Finance, Mercyone Primghar Medical Center, Primghar, IA, p. A228

MCCAWLEY, Thomas J, Vice President, Beloit Health System, Beloit, WI, p. A692

MCCHESNEY, Lisa D, R.N., Senior Director Information Systems, Upmc Hamot, Erie, PA, p. A525

MCCLAIN, James, Deputy Director, Clement J. Zablocki Veterans Affairs Medical Center, Milwaukee, WI, p. A701

MCCLAIN, Richard, M.D., Chief Medical Officer, Chickasaw Nation Medical Center, Ada, OK, p. A496

MCCLAIN, Tami, Human Resources Operations Specialist, Leconte Medical Center, Sevierville, TN, p. A579

MCCLANAHAN, Cary, Chief Information Officer, Northeastern Health System Sequoyah, Sallisaw, OK, p. A507

MCCLARIGAN, Linda, R.N., Chief Nursing Officer, Adirondack Health, Saranac Lake, NY, p. A443

MCCLASKEY, Cynthia, Director, Southwestern Virginia Mental Health Institute, Marion, VA, p. A662

MCCLEARY, Heather, Director Human Resources, Coulee Medical Center, Grand Coulee, WA, p. A673

MCCLEESE, Randy
Chief Information Officer, Methodist Hospital Union County, Morganfield, KY, p. A258
Chief Information Officer, Methodist Hospital, Henderson, KY, p. A253
Vice President Information Services and Chief Information Officer, St. Claire Healthcare, Morehead, KY, p. A258

MCCLELLAN, Ashley
Chief Executive Officer, Research Medical Center, Kansas City, MO, p. A362
Chief Executive Officer, Woman'S Hospital Of Texas, Houston, TX, p. A615

MCCLELLAN, Kathryn, Chief Information Officer, Memorial Health, Savannah, GA, p. A160

MCCLELLAND, Patricia, Director Human Resources, South Texas Health System, Edinburg, TX, p. A601

MCCLELLAND, Scott, Administrator, Sage Rehabilitation Hospital, Baton Rouge, LA, p. A264

MCCLINTIC, James, M.D., Vice President Medical Affairs, St. Anthony'S Hospital, Saint Petersburg, FL, p. A138

MCCLINTICK, Cliff, Chief Information Officer, Lindner Center Of Hope, Mason, OH, p. A487

MCCLOSKEY, Louis, Chief Human Resources, Wilmington Veterans Affairs Medical Center, Wilmington, DE, p. A114

MCCLUNG, Lyle, M.D., Chief of Staff, Carilion Stonewall Jackson Hospital, Lexington, VA, p. A661

MCCLURE, Kenneth, M.D., Chief of Staff, Longview Regional Medical Center, Longview, TX, p. A621

MCCLURG, Cathy, Director Human Resources, William Newton Hospital, Winfield, KS, p. A248

MCCLURG, Chris, Vice President Finance and Chief Financial Officer, St. Claire Healthcare, Morehead, KY, p. A258

MCCLUSKEY, Diane M, Chief Human Resources Officer, Twin Cities Community Hospital, Templeton, CA, p. A91

MCCLUSKEY, Scott Elton, Chief Financial Officer, Tyler County Hospital, Woodville, TX, p. A646

MCCLUSKEY, Tabb, M.D., Chief Medical Officer, Hendricks Community Hospital Association, Hendricks, MN, p. A333

MCCLUSKEY, Zachary
Chief Executive Officer, Chippenham Hospital, Richmond, VA, p. A666
Interim Chief Executive Officer, Chippenham Hospital, Richmond, VA, p. A666

MCCLUSKY, Derek, M.D., Chief of Staff, Northern Louisiana Medical Center, Ruston, LA, p. A277

MCCLYMONT, Troy, Chief Information Technology Officer, Sheridan Memorial Hospital, Plentywood, MT, p. A379

MCCOBB, David, Chief Information Officer, Foothill Presbyterian Hospital, Glendora, CA, p. A60

MCCOIC, Kristie, Clinic Operations Officer and Director Human Resources, Gundersen St. Joseph'S Hospital And Clinics, Hillsboro, WI, p. A697

MCCOLL, Karen, M.D., Chief Medical Officer, Meadows Regional Medical Center, Vidalia, GA, p. A162

MCCOLLUM, Joann, Chief Nursing Officer, Bolivar Medical Center, Cleveland, MS, p. A346

MCCOLLUM, Kathleen, Senior Vice President, Clinical Integration and Chief Operating Officer, University Of Maryland Baltimore Washington Medical Center, Glen Burnie, MD, p. A291

MCCOLM, Denni, Chief Information Officer, Citizens Memorial Hospital, Bolivar, MO, p. A356

MCCOMB, Canise A, Director Human Resources, Graham Hospital Association, Canton, IL, p. A175

MCCONKEY, Teresa L, MSN, R.N., Vice President of Nursing and Chief Nursing Officer, Graham Hospital Association, Canton, IL, p. A175

MCCONNACHIE, Angela, Chief Executive Officer and Chief Nursing Officer, Deckerville Community Hospital, Deckerville, MI, p. A309

MCCONNELL, George, Director, Earle E. Morris Alcohol And Drug Treatment Center, Columbia, SC, p. A551

MCCONNELL, Linda M, R.N., MSN, FACHE, Associate Medical Center Director Patient Care Services, James H. Quillen Veterans Affairs Medical Center, Mountain Home, TN, p. A576

MCCONNELL, Patrick G, Chief Financial Officer, West Park Hospital, Cody, WY, p. A711

MCCONNELL, Ron, Chief Operating Officer, Upmc Altoona, Altoona, PA, p. A520

MCCONNELL, William, President and Chief Executive Officer, Mercy Regional Medical Center, Durango, CO, p. A99

MCCORMACK, J. David., Chief Executive Officer, Vaughan Regional Medical Center, Selma, AL, p. A23

MCCORMACK, Jane, R.N., MSN, Vice President, Chief Nursing Officer and Nursing and Patient Care Services, Unity Hospital, Rochester, NY, p. A443

MCCORMACK–MILLER, Linda, Chief Nursing Officer, Faxton St. Luke'S Healthcare, Utica, NY, p. A446

MCCORMICK, Brad, Chief Financial Officer, Natchitoches Regional Medical Center, Natchitoches, LA, p. A274

MCCORMICK, Daniel, President and Chief Executive Officer, Franciscan Health Crown Point, Crown Point, IN, p. A202

MCCORMICK, Dee Dawn, Director Personnel and Human Resources, Coon Memorial Hospital, Dalhart, TX, p. A595

MCCORMICK, Jason, Interim Chief Financial Officer, Melissa Memorial Hospital, Holyoke, CO, p. A102

MCCORMICK, Jayne, M.D., Chief Medical Officer CDS, Presbyterian Hospital, Albuquerque, NM, p. A417

MCCORMICK, John, President and Chief Executive Officer, Oak Valley Hospital District, Oakdale, CA, p. A76

MCCORMICK, Martha, Chief Executive Officer, Unity Medical Center, Manchester, TN, p. A573

MCCORMICK, Pam, Director Human Resources, Permian Regional Medical Center, Andrews, TX, p. A583

MCCOWN, Fran, Administrator, Haskell Memorial Hospital, Haskell, TX, p. A609

MCCOY, Adriene
Chief Human Resource Officer, Baptist Health South Florida, Baptist Hospital Of Miami, Miami, FL, p. A130
Corporate Vice President, Baptist Health South Florida, Homestead Hospital, Homestead, FL, p. A125

MCCOY, Andrea C.S., M.D., Chief Medical Officer, Cape Regional Health System, Cape May Court House, NJ, p. A404

MCCOY, Doug
Chief Executive Officer, Kindred Hospital Las Vegas–Sahara, Henderson, NV, p. A394
Chief Executive Officer, Kindred Hospital Seattle–Northgate, Seattle, WA, p. A677

MCCOY, Janice M, MS, R.N., Chief Clinical Officer, Promise Hospital Of Florida At The Villages, Oxford, FL, p. A135

MCCOY, Jessica, Director Human Resources, Cedar Springs Hospital, Colorado Springs, CO, p. A97

MCCOY, Josh, Administrator, Adena Greenfield Medical Center, Greenfield, OH, p. A484

MCCOY, Melissa, Vice President and Chief Financial Officer, West Virginia University Hospitals, Morgantown, WV, p. A687

MCCOY, Michael Jerry, M.D., Chief Medical Officer, Great River Health System, West Burlington, IA, p. A231

MCCOY, Mike, Chief Executive Officer, Chambers Memorial Hospital, Danville, AR, p. A41

MCCOY, Shawn W., Chief Executive Officer, Deaconess Midtown Hospital, Evansville, IN, p. A203

MCCOY, Stephanie, President and Chief Executive Officer, Jackson General Hospital, Ripley, WV, p. A689

MCCOY, Tara, Chief Executive Officer, Good Samaritan Medical Center, West Palm Beach, FL, p. A144

MCCRACKEN, Gail, M.D., Medical Director, Baptist Health Extended Care Hospital, Little Rock, AR, p. A44

MCCRACKEN, Mark, M.D., Chief of Staff, East Georgia Regional Medical Center, Statesboro, GA, p. A161

MCCRAW, Elizabeth, Vice President, Human Resources, Caromont Regional Medical Center, Gastonia, NC, p. A454

MCCRAW, Nicki, Assistant Vice President Human Resources, Uw Medicine/Harborview Medical Center, Seattle, WA, p. A678

MCCREA, Kim, Chief Human Resources Officer, Ortonville Area Health Services, Ortonville, MN, p. A337

MCCREA, Yvette, Chief Human Resources, Winn Army Community Hospital, Hinesville, GA, p. A154

MCCREADY, David O., President, Brigham And Women'S Faulkner Hospital, Boston, MA, p. A295

MCCREARY, Michael, Chief of Services, Mercy Hospital Washington, Washington, MO, p. A373

MCCREARY, William, Vice President and Chief Information Officer, The University Of Toledo Medical Center, Toledo, OH, p. A492

MCCRIMMON, Scott, Manager Information Technology, Northern Arizona Veterans Affairs Health Care System, Prescott, AZ, p. A34

MCCROSKEY, Mark, Vice President Operations, Northeastern Health System, Tahlequah, OK, p. A508

MCCUE, Jennifer, Director Patient Care, Summersville Regional Medical Center, Summersville, WV, p. A689

MCCUE, Raymond, M.D., Vice President, Medical Affairs and Chief Medical Officer, Chesapeake Regional Medical Center, Chesapeake, VA, p. A657

MCCUE, Robert N, Vice President Finance, Mid Coast Hospital, Brunswick, ME, p. A282

MCCUE, Steven, Chief Financial Officer, Umass Memorial–Marlborough Hospital, Marlborough, MA, p. A300

MCCULLEY, Becky, Chief Operations Officer, University Of Texas Southwestern Medical Center, Dallas, TX, p. A598

MCCULLEY, Larry W., President and Chief Executive Officer, Touchette Regional Hospital, Centreville, IL, p. A175

MCCULLOCH, Greg, CPA, Vice President of Finance and Chief Financial Officer, Adventist Health Sonora, Sonora, CA, p. A90

MCCULLOCH, Liz, Chief Information Resource Management Systems, Cheyenne Veterans Affairs Medical Center, Cheyenne, WY, p. A711

MCCULLOUGH, Barbara A, Vice President Human Resources, Washington Hospital, Washington, PA, p. A543

MCCULLOUGH, Bobby, Chief Executive Officer, Memorial Satilla Health, Waycross, GA, p. A163

MCCULLOUGH, Erin, Chief Clinical Officer, Kindred Hospital–Philadelphia, Philadelphia, PA, p. A535

MCCULLOUGH, Mary Kelly, Associate Director Patient Care Services, Lexington Veterans Affairs Medical Center, Lexington, KY, p. A255

MCCULLOUGH, Patrick, M.D., Chief Medical Services, Summit Behavioral Healthcare, Cincinnati, OH, p. A476

MCCULLOUGH, Wadra, Chief Nursing Officer, Wellstar Spalding Regional Hospital, Griffin, GA, p. A154

MCCULLY, Michael, Chief Operating Officer, Northport Veterans Affairs Medical Center, Northport, NY, p. A439

MCCUNE, Becky, Director Human Resources, Community Relations and Education, Coffeyville Regional Medical Center, Coffeyville, KS, p. A233

MCCURDY, Brent, Director Management Information, St. Croix Regional Medical Center, St Croix Falls, WI, p. A706

MCCURDY, Judy, R.N., Vice President and Chief Nursing Officer, St. Vincent Medical Center, Los Angeles, CA, p. A69

MCCUTCHAN, Matt, Chief Financial Officer, Greater Regional Medical Center, Creston, IA, p. A220

MCCUTCHEON, Edna I.
Chief Executive Officer, Norristown State Hospital, Norristown, PA, p. A533
Chief Executive Officer, Torrance State Hospital, Torrance, PA, p. A542

MCDADE, Len, Chief Executive Officer, Extended Care Hospital, New Orleans, LA, p. A275

MCDANALD, Matt, M.D., Chief Medical Officer, Baptist Health La Grange, La Grange, KY, p. A254

MCDANEL, Joyce
Vice President Human Resources and Education, Unitypoint Health – Iowa Methodist Medical Center, Des Moines, IA, p. A221
Vice President Human Resources and Education, Unitypoint Health–Iowa Lutheran Hospital, Des Moines, IA, p. A221

MCDANIEL, Amy, Chief Executive Officer, Iowa Specialty Hospital–Belmond, Belmond, IA, p. A217

MCDANIEL, Donald E, Chief Financial Officer, Paris Regional Medical Center, Paris, TX, p. A628

MCDANIEL, Hilton, President, Piedmont Geriatric Hospital, Burkeville, VA, p. A657
MCDANIEL, Kim, Director Human Resources, Encompass Health Rehabilitation Hospital Of Montgomery, Montgomery, AL, p. A21
MCDANIEL, LaDonna, Financial Manager, Prattville Baptist Hospital, Prattville, AL, p. A23
MCDANIEL, Randy, Information Systems Director, Jackson Purchase Medical Center, Mayfield, KY, p. A257
MCDANIEL, Suzie Q, Chief Human Resource Officer, Bay Area Hospital, Coos Bay, OR, p. A512
MCDANNALD, E.R., Interim Chief Executive Officer, Taylor Regional Hospital, Hawkinsville, GA, p. A154
MCDAVID, Clarence, Vice President Human Resources, Rose Medical Center, Denver, CO, p. A99
MCDERMOTT, James, M.D., Chief of Staff, Sedan City Hospital, Sedan, KS, p. A245
MCDERMOTT, Mary, MS, MSN, R.N., Senior Vice President Patient Care Services and Chief Nursing Officer, Phelps Memorial Hospital Center, Sleepy Hollow, NY, p. A444
MCDERMOTT, Michael P.
President and Chief Executive Officer, Mary Washington Hospital, Fredericksburg, VA, p. A659
President and Chief Executive Officer, Stafford Hospital, Stafford, VA, p. A667
MCDERMOTT–LORD, Sheila, Chief Executive Officer, Haven Behavioral Senior Care Of Albuquerque, Albuquerque, NM, p. A416
MCDEVITT, Robert J, M.D., Chief of Staff, Wilson Memorial Hospital, Sidney, OH, p. A491
MCDONAGH, Andrew, M.D., Chief Medical Officer, Aurora West Allis Medical Center, West Allis, WI, p. A708
MCDONALD, Amanda, MSN, Chief Nurse Executive, Kerrville State Hospital, Kerrville, TX, p. A617
MCDONALD, Carl, Senior Director, Human Resources, Cleveland Clinic Florida, Weston, FL, p. A144
MCDONALD, Connie, Chief Financial Officer, Marion Veterans Affairs Medical Center, Marion, IL, p. A188
MCDONALD, Edward A, Chief Financial Officer, Adventist Health St. Helena, Vallejo, CA, p. A93
MCDONALD, Elizabeth, Director Human Resources, Wayne Memorial Hospital, Honesdale, PA, p. A527
MCDONALD, Frederick Joseph., Commanding Officer, Naval Hospital Oak Harbor, Oak Harbor, WA, p. A675
MCDONALD, Gary
Associate Administrator Human Resources, Stone County Medical Center, Mountain View, AR, p. A46
Chief Facilities and Personnel Officer, White River Medical Center, Batesville, AR, p. A39
MCDONALD, Gregory, Vice President Finance and Chief Financial Officer, Roswell Park Comprehensive Cancer Center, Buffalo, NY, p. A424
MCDONALD, Holly, Controller, Boundary Community Hospital, Bonners Ferry, ID, p. A168
MCDONALD, Jeff, Information Technology Manager, Adventhealth Wauchula, Wauchula, FL, p. A143
MCDONALD, John
Chief Executive Officer, Lee'S Summit Medical Center, Lee'S Summit, MO, p. A364
Chief Operating Officer, Northwest Texas Healthcare System, Amarillo, TX, p. A582
MCDONALD, John, M.D., Chief Medical Officer, Medical City North Hills, North Richland Hills, TX, p. A626
MCDONALD, Larry, Director Human Resources, Miami Jewish Home And Hospital For Aged, Miami, FL, p. A130
MCDONALD, Mark, President and Chief Executive Officer, Institute For Orthopaedic Surgery, Lima, OH, p. A485
MCDONALD, Mark, M.D., President and Chief Executive Officer, Institute For Orthopaedic Surgery, Lima, OH, p. A485
MCDONALD, Michael S., Jr, Chief Executive Officer, Friends Hospital, Philadelphia, PA, p. A534
MCDONALD, Shari, Vice President Patient Care Services, Mercy Hospital, Buffalo, NY, p. A424
MCDONALD, Shelly, Chief Human Resources Officer, Ness County Hospital District No 2, Ness City, KS, p. A241
MCDONALD, Stanton B, M.D., Medical Director, Heber Valley Hospital, Heber City, UT, p. A648
MCDONALD, Stuart, M.D., President Medical Staff, Kindred Hospital–Fort Worth, Fort Worth, TX, p. A605
MCDONALD, Susan, Vice President, Medical Affairs, Sentara Rmh Medical Center, Harrisonburg, VA, p. A660
MCDONALD, Tedd, M.D., Chief Medical Officer, Banner Churchill Community Hospital, Fallon, NV, p. A393
MCDONALD–PINKETT, Shelly, Chief Medical Officer, Howard University Hospital, Washington, DC, p. A115
MCDONNELL, M. Therese, M.D., Interim Vice President Patient Safety, Quality and Medical Affairs, Sibley Memorial Hospital, Washington, DC, p. A116
MCDONNELL, Michael, M.D., Chief Medical Officer, Mercy Hospital And Medical Center, Chicago, IL, p. A178
MCDONNELL, Nancy, Manager Information Systems, Illinois Valley Community Hospital, Peru, IL, p. A193
MCDONNELL, Stephen C, Chief Financial Officer, Chesapeake Regional Medical Center, Chesapeake, VA, p. A657
MCDOUGLE, Mark, Executive Vice President and Chief Operating Officer, Brookdale Hospital Medical Center, New York, NY, p. A432
MCDOWELL, Arthur V, M.D., Vice President Clinical Affairs, Middlesex Hospital, Middletown, CT, p. A109
MCDOWELL, Jean, Chief Financial Officer, Kindred Hospital–Dallas, Dallas, TX, p. A596
MCDOWELL, Paul L
Deputy Chief Financial Officer, Mission Hospital, Asheville, NC, p. A449
Vice President Finance and Chief Financial Officer, King'S Daughters Medical Center, Ashland, KY, p. A249
MCDOWELL, Richard, Chief Financial Officer, Ridge Behavioral Health System, Lexington, KY, p. A255
MCDOWELL, Richard, M.D., Medical Director, Kona Community Hospital, Kealakekua, HI, p. A166
MCDOWELL, Wendy, R.N., Director of Nursing, Weisbrod Memorial County Hospital, Eads, CO, p. A100
MCDOWN, Missy, Director Information Systems, Ascension Via Christi Hospital, Pittsburg, KS, p. A244
MCDRURY, Martha M, R.N., Chief Operating Officer and Chief Nursing Officer, Holy Family Hospital, Methuen, MA, p. A300
MCEACHERN, John, Controller, Sebastian River Medical Center, Sebastian, FL, p. A139
MCEACHIN, Brenda, Human Resources Director, Jeff Davis Hospital, Hazlehurst, GA, p. A154
MCELDOWNEY, Erin, Manager Human Resources, Haven Senior Horizons, Phoenix, AZ, p. A33
MCELMURRAY, Dodie, Interim Chief Executive Officer and Chief Operating Officer, West Jefferson Medical Center, Marrero, LA, p. A273
MCELRATH, Matthew
Chief Human Resources Officer, Keck Hospital Of Usc, Los Angeles, CA, p. A67
Chief Human Resources Officer, Usc Norris Comprehensive Cancer Center, Los Angeles, CA, p. A69
MCELROY, Kevin, Chief Human Resources Officer, Mackinac Straits Health System, Inc., Saint Ignace, MI, p. A321
MCENTEE, Chris, Network Specialist, Van Buren County Hospital, Keosauqua, IA, p. A225
MCENTEE, Kara, Chief Financial Officer, Van Buren County Hospital, Keosauqua, IA, p. A225
MCENTIRE, Ann, MSN, R.N., Chief Nursing Officer, Citizens Baptist Medical Center, Talladega, AL, p. A23
MCEUEN, Jacqueline, Coordinator Human Resources, Chi St. Joseph Health Bellville Hospital, Bellville, TX, p. A588
MCEWAN, Kevin K, MSN, R.N., Chief Nursing Officer, Down East Community Hospital, Machias, ME, p. A284
MCEWEN, Michelle, President and Chief Executive Officer, Speare Memorial Hospital, Plymouth, NH, p. A402
MCFADDEN, Krista, Interim Chief Executive Officer, Hillside Rehabilitation Hospital, Warren, OH, p. A493
MCFADYEN, David M., Administrator, St. Luke'S Regional Medical Center, Boise, ID, p. A168
MCFALL, Cathy, Human Resources Manager, Kiowa County Memorial Hospital, Greensburg, KS, p. A236
MCFALL, Michael, Chief Financial Officer, Kindred Rehabilitation Hospital Clear Lake, Webster, TX, p. A645
MCFALL, Vicky, Chief Executive Officer, Monroe County Medical Center, Tompkinsville, KY, p. A261
MCFALL–ROBERTS, Ebuni, Director Human Resources, Holly Hill Hospital, Raleigh, NC, p. A460
MCFARLAND, Kenneth D., Chief Executive Officer, Fountain Valley Regional Hospital And Medical Center, Fountain Valley, CA, p. A58
MCFARLAND, Nita, Director of Nursing, Kingman Community Hospital, Kingman, KS, p. A238
MCFARLAND, Rhonda
Director Human Resources, Atrium Health Anson, Wadesboro, NC, p. A463
Director Human Resources, Atrium Health Union, Monroe, NC, p. A458
MCFARLAND, Rodney, M.D., Medical Director, Freeman Neosho Hospital, Neosho, MO, p. A366
MCFARLAND, Tracee, Chief Financial Officer, Claiborne Medical Center, Tazewell, TN, p. A580
MCFARLANE, Michael
Chief Human Resource Officer, St. Louis Psychiatric Rehabilitation Center, Saint Louis, MO, p. A370
Director Human Resource, Hawthorn Children Psychiatric Hospital, Saint Louis, MO, p. A369
Director Human Resources, Metropolitan St. Louis Psychiatric Center, Saint Louis, MO, p. A369
MCFERRAN, Virginia, Chief Information Officer, Ucla Medical Center–Santa Monica, Santa Monica, CA, p. A89
MCGAHAN, Thomas P., M.D., Chief Medical Officer, Emory Saint Joseph'S Hospital Of Atlanta, Atlanta, GA, p. A146
MCGAHEY, Nikki, Information Officer, Jefferson County Hospital, Waurika, OK, p. A510
MCGARIGLE, Kristine, R.N., Vice President Patient Care, Ascension Good Samaritan Hospital, Merrill, WI, p. A700
MCGARVEY, Missy, Chief Information Officer, Twin Valley Behavioral Healthcare, Columbus, OH, p. A480
MCGEACHEY, Edward J, President and Chief Executive Officer, Southern Maine Health Care – Biddeford Medical Center, Biddeford, ME, p. A282
MCGEE, Angela, Vice President Nursing Services, Aultman Orrville Hospital, Orrville, OH, p. A489
MCGEE, Genemarie, R.N., MS, Chief Nursing Officer, Sentara Leigh Hospital, Norfolk, VA, p. A664
MCGEE, Jessica
Chief Financial Officer, Amg Specialty Hospital–Lafayette, Lafayette, LA, p. A270
Chief Financial Officer, Sage Specialty Hospital (Ltac), Denham Springs, LA, p. A267
MCGEE, Kevin, Chief Executive Officer, River Point Behavioral Health, Jacksonville, FL, p. A125
MCGEE, Mark F, M.D., Chief Clinical Officer, Appalachian Behavioral Healthcare, Athens, OH, p. A472
MCGEE, Terry, Chief Operations Officer, Central State Hospital, Milledgeville, GA, p. A157
MCGEEHAN, Paul, M.D., Chief Medical Staff, Lecom Corry Memorial Hospital, Corry, PA, p. A523
MCGETTIGAN, Ryan, Chief Information Officer, Coatesville Veterans Affairs Medical Center, Coatesville, PA, p. A523
MCGHEE, Kenneth, Vice President and Chief Financial Officer, Loretto Hospital, Chicago, IL, p. A178
MCGHEE, Michael, M.D., Medical Director, Unity Psychiatric Care–Clarksville, Clarksville, TN, p. A568
MCGIBBON, Monica, Chief Nursing Officer, Brookdale Hospital Medical Center, New York, NY, p. A432
MCGILL, Brittini, MSN, R.N., Chief Nursing Officer, Norman Regional Health System, Norman, OK, p. A503
MCGILL, Martha, Executive Vice President and Chief Operating Officer, Nicklaus Children'S Hospital, Miami, FL, p. A131
MCGILL, Rusty, System Director Information Technology, Indiana University Health Arnett Hospital, Lafayette, IN, p. A209
MCGILL, Steve, Vice President Finance and Chief Financial Officer, Wabash General Hospital, Mount Carmel, IL, p. A190
MCGILL, Thomas, M.D., Chief Information Officer, Butler Health System, Butler, PA, p. A521
MCGILL, Timothy W., Chief Executive Officer, Livingston Regional Hospital, Livingston, TN, p. A573
MCGILVRAY, Greg, Chief Financial Officer, Medical Center Enterprise, Enterprise, AL, p. A17
MCGIMSEY, Erika, Controller, Jewish Hospital–Shelbyville, Shelbyville, KY, p. A260
MCGINLEY, Mary Ann, Ph.D., Senior Vice President, Patient Services and Chief Nursing Officer, Thomas Jefferson University Hospitals, Philadelphia, PA, p. A536
MCGINNIS, Christina, Director Information Technology, Menorah Medical Center, Overland Park, KS, p. A243
MCGINNIS, Jeff, M.D., President Medical Staff, Saint Joseph Mount Sterling, Mount Sterling, KY, p. A258
MCGINNIS, Paula, Chief Executive Officer, St. Joseph'S Hospital, Tampa, FL, p. A142
MCGIRL, John, Chief Human Resources Officer, Nch Baker Hospital, Naples, FL, p. A132
MCGLADE, James, Director Human Resources, United Hospital, Saint Paul, MN, p. A340
MCGLEW, Timothy, Chief Executive Officer, Kern Valley Healthcare District, Lake Isabella, CA, p. A63
MCGLON, Tracy, Director Human Resources, Gulf Coast Regional Medical Center, Panama City, FL, p. A135
MCGLYNN, Mia, Director Management Information Systems, Plantation General Hospital, Plantation, FL, p. A137
MCGOLDRICK, Margaret M., President, Abington Hospital, Abington, PA, p. A519
MCGOVERN, Charles, Chief of Staff, Margaret Mary Health, Batesville, IN, p. A199
MCGOVERN, Joanne, MSN, R.N., Chief Nursing Officer, Cancer Treatment Centers Of America–Eastern Regional Medical Center, Philadelphia, PA, p. A534
MCGOVERN, Julia, Vice President Human Resources, Chilton Medical Center, Pompton Plains, NJ, p. A411
MCGOVERN, Julie, Vice President Human Resources, Anne Arundel Medical Center, Annapolis, MD, p. A286
MCGOVERN, Kimberly, Manager Human Resources, Hackettstown Medical Center, Hackettstown, NJ, p. A406
MCGOVERN, Pam, Director Technology, Huggins Hospital, Wolfeboro, NH, p. A402

MCGOVERN, Sandra, Chief Nursing Officer, Up Health System–Bell, Ishpeming, MI, p. A315
MCGOWEN, Bernard A, M.D., Medical Director, Kindred Hospital Tarrant County–Arlington, Arlington, TX, p. A583
MCGOWIN, Norman F, M.D., Chief of Staff, Regional Medical Center Of Central Alabama, Greenville, AL, p. A19
MCGRAIL, David, Vice President Finance, Carney Hospital, Boston, MA, p. A295
MCGRAIL, Robert, Chief Executive Officer, Midmichigan Medical Center – West Branch, West Branch, MI, p. A325
MCGRATH, Denise B., Chief Executive Officer, Sea Pines Rehabilitation Hospital, Melbourne, FL, p. A129
MCGRATH, John, Chief Information Officer, Mclaren Port Huron, Port Huron, MI, p. A320
MCGRATH, Kelly, Chief Medical Officer, Clearwater Valley Hospital And Clinics, Orofino, ID, p. A170
MCGRATH, Lynn, M.D., Vice President Medical Affairs, Deborah Heart And Lung Center, Browns Mills, NJ, p. A404
MCGRAW, Belinda
Director Human Resources, Boulder City Hospital, Boulder City, NV, p. A393
Director Human Resources, Complex Care Hospital At Tenaya, Las Vegas, NV, p. A394
MCGRAW, Karin L., Director, Veterans Affairs Pittsburgh Healthcare System, Pittsburgh, PA, p. A538
MCGRAW, Kathleen, M.D., Chief Medical Officer, Brattleboro Memorial Hospital, Brattleboro, VT, p. A654
MCGRAW, Scott, M.D., Medical Director, Baylor Surgical Hospital At Las Colinas, Irving, TX, p. A616
MCGREEVY, John
Chief Executive Officer, Christus Mother Frances Hospital – Tyler, Tyler, TX, p. A642
President, Methodist Southlake Hospital, Southlake, TX, p. A637
MCGREGOR, Catherine, Deputy Director Facility and Administrative Services, Capital District Psychiatric Center, Albany, NY, p. A422
MCGREGOR, Julie
Director Human Resources, Sts. Mary & Elizabeth Hospital, Louisville, KY, p. A256
Vice President and Chief People Officer, Jewish Hospital, Louisville, KY, p. A256
MCGREGOR, Robert, M.D., Chief Medical Officer, Akron Children'S Hospital, Akron, OH, p. A471
MCGREW, David S, Chief Financial Officer, San Mateo Medical Center, San Mateo, CA, p. A87
MCGREW, Deborah A, Vice President and Chief Operating Officer, University Of Texas Medical Branch, Galveston, TX, p. A607
MCGREW, Diane, Chief Nurse Executive, Montgomery County Memorial Hospital, Red Oak, IA, p. A228
MCGRIFF, Marchelle M, Chief Nursing Executive, Sutter Medical Center, Sacramento, Sacramento, CA, p. A82
MCGUF, Lisa, Controller, Healthsouth Northern Kentucky Rehabilitation Hospital, Edgewood, KY, p. A251
MCGUFFIN, Patty, Chief Nursing Officer, Allen County Regional Hospital, Iola, KS, p. A237
MCGUIGAN, Kevin, M.D., Medical Director, St. Lawrence Rehabilitation Center, Lawrenceville, NJ, p. A407
MCGUILL, Gail, R.N., MSN, Chief Nursing Officer and Administrative Director of Patient Care Services, Shriners Hospitals For Children–Salt Lake City, Salt Lake City, UT, p. A652
MCGUINNESS, Patrick, Chief Information Management, Keller Army Community Hospital, West Point, NY, p. A447
MCGUIRE, Ann M., Regional Vice President Human Resources, Indiana University Health Ball Memorial Hospital, Muncie, IN, p. A212
MCGUIRE, Cynthia, President and Chief Executive Officer, Monadnock Community Hospital, Peterborough, NH, p. A402
MCGUIRE, Patrick, Chief Financial Officer, Michigan Market, Ascension Macomb–Oakland Hospital, Warren, MI, p. A324
MCGUIRE, Shane, Chief Executive Officer, Columbia County Health System, Dayton, WA, p. A672
MCGUIRK, Christina Marie, R.N., Chief Nursing Officer, Health Central Hospital, Ocoee, FL, p. A133
MCGUIRL, Mary, Director Information Systems, Oneida Healthcare, Oneida, NY, p. A440
MCGURK, Kevin, Controller, Bellin Psychiatric Center, Green Bay, WI, p. A696
MCHARDY, Bryson, M.D., President Medical Staff, Hannibal Regional Hospital, Hannibal, MO, p. A361
MCHUGH, Matthew, Director Information Services, Vaughan Regional Medical Center, Selma, AL, p. A23
MCHUGH, Ryan, M.D., Chief of Staff, The Medical Center Of Southeast Texas, Port Arthur, TX, p. A630
MCHUGH, William, M.D., Medical Director and Chief Medical Officer, Trinitas Regional Medical Center, Elizabeth, NJ, p. A405
MCILROY, Gail, Director Medical Records, Promise Hospital Of Wichita Falls, Wichita Falls, TX, p. A645
MCILVAIN, Spencer, Director of Human Resources, Peterson Healthcare And Rehabilitation Hospital, Wheeling, WV, p. A690
MCILWAIN, T Pinckney, M.D., Vice President and Chief Medical Officer, Charleston Area Medical Center, Charleston, WV, p. A684
MCINERNEY, Terry, Director of Nursing, Inpatient, Navos, Seattle, WA, p. A677
MCINTOSH, Craig, Chief Information Officer, Northwest Specialty Hospital, Post Falls, ID, p. A171
MCINTOSH, Eric D., Vice President Human Resources, Upmc Jameson, New Castle, PA, p. A533
MCINTOSH, Ernasha, Interim Director of Nursing, Sage Memorial Hospital, Ganado, AZ, p. A29
MCINTOSH, Joe, Director Management Information Systems, Logansport State Hospital, Logansport, IN, p. A210
MCINTOSH, Tyler, Chief Financial Officer, Creek Nation Community Hospital, Okemah, OK, p. A503
MCINTYRE, Cindy, R.N., Administrative Director Clinical Services, Magee General Hospital, Magee, MS, p. A350
MCINTYRE, Daniel J., President, Charlotte Hungerford Hospital, Torrington, CT, p. A111
MCIWAIN, John, Director Human Resources, Wayne Memorial Hospital, Jesup, GA, p. A155
MCKAIN, Rick, Chief Executive Officer, Anderson County Hospital, Garnett, KS, p. A235
MCKALE, Brigitte, MSN, FACHE, Vice President and Chief Nurse Executive, Pali Momi Medical Center, Aiea, HI, p. A164
MCKAY, Amy, Chief Nursing Officer, Mid–America Rehabilitation Hospital, Shawnee Mission, KS, p. A245
MCKAY, Daniel E., Chief Executive Officer, Ephraim Mcdowell Regional Medical Center, Danville, KY, p. A251
MCKAY, Danny H., Administrator, Noxubee General Hospital, Macon, MS, p. A350
MCKAY, Michael, Chief Information Officer, Wickenburg Community Hospital, Wickenburg, AZ, p. A38
MCKAY, Rebecca, Director Human Resources, Sweeny Community Hospital, Sweeny, TX, p. A639
MCKAY, Ronda, R.N., Vice President Patient Care Services, Chief Nursing Officer, Community Hospital, Munster, IN, p. A212
MCKEE, Debra, R.N., Chief Clinical Officer and Chief Nursing Officer, Joint Township District Memorial Hospital, Saint Marys, OH, p. A490
MCKEE, Michele, Vice President and Chief Financial Officer, St. Louis Children'S Hospital, Saint Louis, MO, p. A370
MCKEE, Robert J, Vice President Human Resources, Penn Highlands Dubois, Dubois, PA, p. A524
MCKEE, Willis P, M.D., Chief Medical Officer, Frankfort Regional Medical Center, Frankfort, KY, p. A252
MCKEEBY, Ben, Senior Vice President and Chief Information Officer, Grady Memorial Hospital, Atlanta, GA, p. A146
MCKEEBY, Jon W, Chief Information Officer, National Institutes Of Health Clinical Center, Bethesda, MD, p. A289
MCKEEN, Marcia, Director Human Resources, Twin Valley Behavioral Healthcare, Columbus, OH, p. A480
MCKELDIN, Pat, Human Resource Business Partner, Kaiser Permanente Manteca Medical Center, Manteca, CA, p. A71
MCKENDREE, Rodney, Senior Vice President and Chief Financial Officer, Nemours Children'S Hospital, Orlando, FL, p. A134
MCKENNA, Dennis, M.D., Interim Vice President Medical Affairs, Albany Medical Center, Albany, NY, p. A422
MCKENNA, Donald, President and Chief Executive Officer, Jupiter Medical Center, Jupiter, FL, p. A126
MCKENNA, John F., Chief Executive Officer and Managing Director, Rockford Center, Newark, DE, p. A113
MCKENNA, Quinn, Chief Operating Officer, Stanford Health Care, Palo Alto, CA, p. A77
MCKENNERY, Kay, Interim Chief Executive Officer, Hickory Trail Hospital, Desoto, TX, p. A600
MCKENNEY, Jennifer, M.D., Chief Medical Officer, Fredonia Regional Hospital, Fredonia, KS, p. A235
MCKENZIE, Christine, Director Human Resources, Davis Regional Medical Center, Statesville, NC, p. A462
MCKENZIE, Jackie, Director Administrative Services, Beacham Memorial Hospital, Magnolia, MS, p. A350
MCKENZIE, Kimberly, Interim Chief Executive Officer, Harbor–Ucla Medical Center, Torrance, CA, p. A91
MCKENZIE, Kimberly, R.N., MSN, Chief Nursing Officer and Chief Operations Officer, Harbor–Ucla Medical Center, Torrance, CA, p. A91
MCKENZIE, Margaret, President, South Pointe Hospital, Warrensville Heights, OH, p. A493
MCKENZIE, Sandra D., Executive Vice President and Chief Operating Officer, Hamilton Medical Center, Dalton, GA, p. A151
MCKENZIE, Troy, Chief information Officer, Faith Community Hospital, Jacksboro, TX, p. A616
MCKEON, John, Vice President Human Resources, Brookdale Hospital Medical Center, New York, NY, p. A432
MCKEON, Sean, Director, Information Technology, Franciscan Children'S, Brighton, MA, p. A296
MCKEOWN, Colleen
Senior Vice President and Area Manager, Kaiser Permanente Antioch Medical Center, Antioch, CA, p. A50
Senior Vice President and Area Manager, Kaiser Permanente Walnut Creek Medical Center, Walnut Creek, CA, p. A94
MCKERNAN, James E., Chief Operating Officer, Bronson Battle Creek Hospital, Battle Creek, MI, p. A307
MCKERNAN, Kathleen S., Director Information Systems, Pioneers Memorial Healthcare District, Brawley, CA, p. A53
MCKEVETT, Timothy M., President and Chief Executive Officer, Beloit Health System, Beloit, WI, p. A692
MCKIBBEN, Leeanna, R.N., MSN
Vice President Patient Services and Chief Nursing Officer, Upmc Mckeesport, Mckeesport, PA, p. A531
Vice President Patient Services and Chief Nursing Officer, Upmc Mercy, Pittsburgh, PA, p. A538
MCKIBBEN, Sean, President and Chief Operating Officer, Mount Carmel, Columbus, OH, p. A479
MCKIDDY, Paul, Director Information Technology, Monroe County Medical Center, Tompkinsville, KY, p. A261
MCKIE, Kathy, Director Human Resources, Montrose Memorial Hospital, Montrose, CO, p. A104
MCKILLIP, Ed, Vice President Finance, Riddle Hospital, Media, PA, p. A531
MCKIMMY, Doyle L., Chief Executive Officer, Jewell County Hospital, Mankato, KS, p. A240
MCKINLEY, Alton, Chief Financial Officer, Veterans Affairs North Texas Health Care System, Dallas, TX, p. A598
MCKINLEY, Bryan, Chief Financial Officer, St. Mark'S Hospital, Salt Lake City, UT, p. A652
MCKINLEY, Ivy
Director Human Resources, Amita Health Holy Family Medical Center, Des Plaines, IL, p. A181
Regional Human Resources Officer, Community First Medical Center, Chicago, IL, p. A177
Regional Lead Human Resources, Amita Health Resurrection Medical Center, Chicago, IL, p. A176
MCKINLEY, John, Director, Information Technology, Community Mental Health Center, Lawrenceburg, IN, p. A210
MCKINLEY, Mike, Information Security Officer, West Texas Veterans Affairs Health Care System, Big Spring, TX, p. A588
MCKINLEY, Ronald, Ph.D., Vice President Human Resources and Employee Services, University Of Texas Medical Branch, Galveston, TX, p. A607
MCKINNEY, Brenda, Chief Executive Officer, Reeves County Hospital, Pecos, TX, p. A628
MCKINNEY, Bruce, Business Officer, Administrative Services, Central Prison Hospital, Raleigh, NC, p. A460
MCKINNEY, Dan, Administrator, Hermann Area District Hospital, Hermann, MO, p. A361
MCKINNEY, Dana, Chief Nursing Officer, Select Specialty Hospital–Madison, Madison, WI, p. A698
MCKINNEY, Daniel, Chief Executive Officer, South Baldwin Regional Medical Center, Foley, AL, p. A18
MCKINNEY, James, Warden, Iowa Medical And Classification Center, Coralville, IA, p. A219
MCKINNEY, Jillyan, Chief Executive Officer, Avista Adventist Hospital, Louisville, CO, p. A104
MCKINNEY, Rachael, Chief Executive Officer, Sutter Davis Hospital, Davis, CA, p. A56
MCKINNEY, Rex, President and Chief Executive Officer, Decatur County Memorial Hospital, Greensburg, IN, p. A205
MCKINNEY, Thomas
President, Christus Spohn Hospital Alice, Alice, TX, p. A581
President, Christus Spohn Hospital Kleberg, Kingsville, TX, p. A618
MCKINNON, Mark, M.D., Chief of Staff, North Runnels Hospital, Winters, TX, p. A646
MCKINNON, Ron, Chief Information Officer, Ellis Hospital, Schenectady, NY, p. A444
MCKINSTRY, Merissa, Chief Operating Officer, Columbus Dublin Springs, Dublin, OH, p. A482
MCKNIGHT, David, Chief Executive Officer, Spotsylvania Regional Medical Center, Fredericksburg, VA, p. A659
MCKNIGHT, Stephanie, Hospital Nursing Manager, Sanford Bagley Medical Center, Bagley, MN, p. A328
MCKNIGHT, Tim, M.D., Chief of Staff, Trinity Hospital Twin City, Dennison, OH, p. A482

MCKOY, Lori, Business Partner, Pender Memorial Hospital, Burgaw, NC, p. A450

MCKULA, Tim, Vice President Information Systems and Chief Information Officer, Shirley Ryan Abilitylab, Chicago, IL, p. A179

MCKUNE, Jeff, Chief Health Informatics Officer, Phelps Health, Rolla, MO, p. A368

MCLAIN, Allen, M.D., Chief of Staff, Grisell Memorial Hospital District One, Ransom, KS, p. A244

MCLAIN, John R., Chief Executive Officer, Starr Regional Medical Center, Athens, TN, p. A566

MCLANE, Kerry
Chief Executive Officer, Select Specialty Hospital–Muskegon, Muskegon, MI, p. A318
Interim Chief Executive Officer, Select Specialty Hospital–Omaha, Omaha, NE, p. A390

MCLARIN, Benita, Chief Operating Officer, Santa Clara Valley Medical Center, San Jose, CA, p. A87

MCLARTY, Walter L
Chief Human Resources Officer, Bethesda North Hospital, Cincinnati, OH, p. A475
Chief Human Resources Officer, Good Samaritan Hospital, Cincinnati, OH, p. A476

MCLAUGHLIN, Amy, CPA, Chief Financial Officer, Manning Regional Healthcare Center, Manning, IA, p. A226

MCLAUGHLIN, Cathy, R.N., MSN, Chief Nursing Officer, Medical City Arlington, Arlington, TX, p. A583

MCLAUGHLIN, Dan C.
Chief Executive Officer, Menifee Valley Medical Center, Sun City, CA, p. A91
Chief Hospital Executive Officer, Hemet Valley Medical Center, Hemet, CA, p. A61

MCLAUGHLIN, Kathryn, Chief Nursing Officer, Hemet Valley Medical Center, Hemet, CA, p. A61

MCLAUGHLIN, Leslie, Director of Business Development, Michiana Behavioral Health Center, Plymouth, IN, p. A213

MCLAUGHLIN, Maribeth, R.N., Vice President Patient Care Services, Upmc Magee–Womens Hospital, Pittsburgh, PA, p. A538

MCLAUGHLIN, Mederic D., Executive Director, Veritas Collaborative, Atlanta, GA, p. A147

MCLAUGHLIN, Pamela, Chief Financial Officer, Encompass Health Rehabilitation Hospital Of Austin, Austin, TX, p. A585

MCLAUGHLIN, Rebecca, Chief Human Resource Officer, Banner Goldfield Medical Center, Apache Junction, AZ, p. A28

MCLAUGHLIN, Sherry, Director Human Resources, Forrest City Medical Center, Forrest City, AR, p. A42

MCLAURIN, Monty E., Chief Executive Officer, Northwest Market, Indian Path Medical Center, Kingsport, TN, p. A572

MCLAWS, Douglas, D.O., Chief Medical Officer, Manning Regional Healthcare Center, Manning, IA, p. A226

MCLEAN, Anthony
Market President, St. Francis Hospital, Federal Way, WA, p. A673
President, Highline Medical Center, Burien, WA, p. A671

MCLEAN, Chris, Chief Administrative Officer, Methodist Healthcare Memphis Hospitals, Memphis, TN, p. A575

MCLEAN, Cindy J, R.N., MSN, Director of Nursing, Central Prison Hospital, Raleigh, NC, p. A460

MCLEAN, Georgia, Director Human Resources, Mount Sinai Medical Center, Miami Beach, FL, p. A131

MCLEAN, Robb, M.D., Chief Medical Officer, Unm Sandoval Regional Medical Center, Inc., Rio Rancho, NM, p. A419

MCLENDON, Carla
Director Human Resources, Appling Healthcare System, Baxley, GA, p. A148
Director Information Resource Management Services, Charles George Veterans Affairs Medical Center, Asheville, NC, p. A449

MCLENDON, John
Senior Vice President and Chief Information Officer, Adventist Medical Center Bolingbrook, Bolingbrook, IL, p. A174
Vice President and Chief Information Officer, Johns Hopkins All Children'S Hospital, Saint Petersburg, FL, p. A138

MCLENDON, Tom, Administrator, Evergreen Medical Center, Evergreen, AL, p. A17

MCLEOD, Les, Director of Nursing Services, Blue Mountain Hospital District, John Day, OR, p. A514

MCLEOD, Margie, Director Information Technology, North Canyon Medical Center, Gooding, ID, p. A169

MCLEOD, Michael, M.D., Chief Medical Officer, Cuero Community Hospital, Cuero, TX, p. A595

MCLEOD, Sheldon
Chief Executive Officer, Brookdale Hospital Medical Center, New York, NY, p. A432
Chief Operating Officer, Brookdale Hospital Medical Center, New York, NY, p. A432

MCLIN, Robert D., President and Chief Executive Officer, Good Samaritan Hospital, Vincennes, IN, p. A216

MCLOONE, Mark, Chief Executive Officer, Suburban Community Hospital, Norristown, PA, p. A533

MCLOONE, Paul, M.D.
Chief Medical Officer, Unitypoint Health – Trinity Bettendorf, Bettendorf, IA, p. A217
Chief Medical Officer, Unitypoint Health – Trinity Rock Island, Rock Island, IL, p. A194

MCMACKIN, Ann, President, Vassar Brothers Medical Center, Poughkeepsie, NY, p. A442

MCMAHAN, Steve, M.D., Chief Medical Officer, Glenwood Regional Medical Center, West Monroe, LA, p. A280

MCMAHON, Alisha, Director Human Resources, Mountrail County Medical Center, Stanley, ND, p. A469

MCMAHON, Andrew, Chief Fiscal Officer, Veterans Affairs Central Western Massachusetts Healthcare System, Leeds, MA, p. A300

MCMAHON, Chris, Chief Operating Officer, The Medical Center Of Southeast Texas, Port Arthur, TX, p. A630

MCMAHON, Elaine, Administrator, Kwajalein Hospital, Kwajalein Island, MH, p. A714

MCMAHON, Eugene
Senior Vice President and Chief Medical Officer, Capital Health Medical Center–Hopewell, Pennington, NJ, p. A410
Senior Vice President and Chief Medical Officer, Capital Health Regional Medical Center, Trenton, NJ, p. A413

MCMAHON, Leigh, MS, R.N., Senior Vice President Patient Care Services and Chief Nursing Officer, White Plains Hospital Center, White Plains, NY, p. A448

MCMAHON, Nancy, Vice President Human Resources, Miriam Hospital, Providence, RI, p. A547

MCMANAMAN, Craig, M.D., Chief of Staff, Mclaren Thumb Region, Bad Axe, MI, p. A307

MCMANMON, Kristin, President, Ascension All Saints, Racine, WI, p. A704

MCMANUS, Doug, Chief Medical Officer, Aurora Medical Center Grafton, Grafton, WI, p. A695

MCMANUS, Michael T
Chief Operating Officer, Memorial Hospital East, Shiloh, IL, p. A196
Chief Operating Officer, Memorial Hospital, Belleville, IL, p. A174

MCMANUS, Ronald, Senior Vice President Clinical Services and Business Entities, Peconic Bay Medical Center, Riverhead, NY, p. A442

MCMASTER, Sandra
Regional Chief Information Officer, Kauai Veterans Memorial Hospital, Waimea, HI, p. A166
Regional Chief Information Officer, Samuel Mahelona Memorial Hospital, Kapaa, HI, p. A166

MCMATH, Mark W
Chief Information Officer, Indiana University Health Bloomington Hospital, Bloomington, IN, p. A200
Chief Information Officer, Methodist Healthcare Memphis Hospitals, Memphis, TN, p. A575

MCMENAMIN, Anneliese, Senior Vice President Information Technology and Program Services, Jefferson Stratford Hospital, Stratford, NJ, p. A413

MCMICHEN, Diane, Director Human Resources, Dekalb Regional Medical Center, Fort Payne, AL, p. A18

MCMILLAN, Deborah, Director Human Resources, Glenn Medical Center, Willows, CA, p. A95

MCMILLAN, Donn
Chief Information Officer, Peacehealth Sacred Heart Medical Center University District, Eugene, OR, p. A512
Senior Director, IST Client Liaison, Peacehealth Southwest Medical Center, Vancouver, WA, p. A681

MCMILLAN, Douglas A., Administrator and Chief Executive Officer, West Park Hospital, Cody, WY, p. A711

MCMILLAN, Jon R, Chief Financial Officer, Banner Lassen Medical Center, Susanville, CA, p. A91

MCMILLAN, Sheila, Chief Financial Officer, Park Nicollet Methodist Hospital, Saint Louis Park, MN, p. A339

MCMILLEN, Eric, Chief Executive Officer, Ochsner Medical Center – Baton Rouge, Baton Rouge, LA, p. A263

MCMILLIN, Lori, Administrator, Mercy Hospital Tishomingo, Tishomingo, OK, p. A508

MCMILLION, Kelley, Chief Nursing Officer, Clay County Memorial Hospital, Henrietta, TX, p. A610

MCMINN, Ken, Director Information Technology, Scotland County Hospital, Memphis, MO, p. A365

MCMINN, Melvin, Director Human Resources, Wernersville State Hospital, Wernersville, PA, p. A544

MCMINOWAY, Kelly, R.N., Vice President, Nursing, Baptist Health Floyd, New Albany, IN, p. A212

MCMULLAN, Cheryl, Chief Financial Officer, Baylor Scott & White Medical Center–Waxahachie, Waxahachie, TX, p. A644

MCMULLAN, Heidi, R.N., Chief Nursing Officer, Wellspan Philhaven, Mount Gretna, PA, p. A532

MCMULLAN, Rosemary, Chief Human Resources, Mayo Clinic Hospital In Florida, Jacksonville, FL, p. A125

MCMULLIN, John, Chief Financial Officer, Rehoboth Mckinley Christian Health Care Services, Gallup, NM, p. A418

MCMURRAY, Rob, Chief Financial Officer, Christiana Care Health System, Newark, DE, p. A113

MCMURRAY, Sharon, Director, Human Resources, Rock Springs, Georgetown, TX, p. A607

MCMURREN, Mary Anne, Chief Administrative Officer, Peacehealth Sacred Heart Medical Center University District, Eugene, OR, p. A512

MCMURREY, Jean Ann, R.N., MSN, Chief Nursing Officer, Southern Tennessee Regional Health System–Winchester, Winchester, TN, p. A580

MCNABB, Dana, Human Resources Manager, Field Memorial Community Hospital, Centreville, MS, p. A345

MCNABB, Teresita, R.N., FACHE, Vice President Nursing Services, Terrebonne General Medical Center, Houma, LA, p. A269

MCNAIR, Lisa, CPA, Senior Vice President and Chief Financial Officer, Chi St. Joseph Regional Health Center, Bryan, TX, p. A590

MCNAIR, Rebekah, Director Human Resources, Encompass Health Rehabilitation Hospital Of Chattanooga, Chattanooga, TN, p. A567

MCNAIR, Scott, Chief Financial Officer, Neshoba County General Hospital, Philadelphia, MS, p. A353

MCNALLY, Joseph, M.D., Medical Director, Streamwood Behavioral Health Center, Streamwood, IL, p. A197

MCNALLY, Kathy, Chief Nursing Officer, Healthsouth Rehabilitation Hospital At Drake, Cincinnati, OH, p. A476

MCNALLY, Lou–Ann, Executive Director Human Resources and Staff Development, Claxton–Hepburn Medical Center, Ogdensburg, NY, p. A440

MCNAMARA, John, M.D., Senior Vice President, Chief Medical Officer, Torrance Memorial Medical Center, Torrance, CA, p. A92

MCNAMARA, Marilyn, M.D., Chief Medical Officer, Southwest General Health Center, Middleburg Heights, OH, p. A487

MCNAMARA, Mike, Chief Information Officer, Mee Memorial Hospital, King City, CA, p. A62

MCNAMARA, Steve, Chief Financial Officer, Memorialcare, Orange Coast Memorial Medical Center, Fountain Valley, CA, p. A58

MCNAMARA, Thomas, D.O., Vice President Medical Affairs, Wellstar Cobb Hospital, Austell, GA, p. A148

MCNAMARA, Timothy M
Senior Vice President Human Resources, Bradford Regional Medical Center, Bradford, PA, p. A521
Senior Vice President Human Resources, Olean General Hospital, Olean, NY, p. A440

MCNAMEE, Hugar, D.O., Chief Medical Officer, Adventhealth Zephyrhills, Zephyrhills, FL, p. A144

MCNATT, James, Chief Financial Officer, Baylor Scott & White Medical Center – Carrollton, Carrollton, TX, p. A591

MCNAUGHTON, Kathy, Chief Information Officer, Nemaha County Hospital, Auburn, NE, p. A382

MCNAUGHTON, Richard, Chief Information Management Service, Maine Veterans Affairs Medical Center, Augusta, ME, p. A281

MCNEA, Melvin, Chief Executive Officer, Great Plains Health, North Platte, NE, p. A388

MCNEAR, Michael, M.D., Chief Medical Officer, Jersey Community Hospital, Jerseyville, IL, p. A186

MCNEECE, Steve, Interim Chief Executive Officer, Mineral Community Hospital, Superior, MT, p. A380

MCNEEL, Jacob, D.O., Chief of Staff, Plateau Medical Center, Oak Hill, WV, p. A688

MCNEEL, Wakelin, M.D., Medical Director, Bhc Alhambra Hospital, Rosemead, CA, p. A81

MCNEIL, Ane, Vice President Human Resources, St. Joseph Mercy Oakland, Pontiac, MI, p. A320

MCNEIL, Karen, President, University Hospitals Samaritan Medical Center, Ashland, OH, p. A472

MCNEILL, Michael, Chief Financial Management, New Mexico Veterans Affairs Health Care System – Raymond G. Murphy Medical Center, Albuquerque, NM, p. A417

MCNEY, Jim, Senior Vice President Finance and Chief Financial Officer, North Kansas City Hospital, North Kansas City, MO, p. A366

MCNICHOLS, Janiece, Chief Financial Officer, St. Mary–Corwin Medical Center, Pueblo, CO, p. A105

MCNULTY, Bruce, Chief Medical Officer, Swedish Covenant Hospital, Chicago, IL, p. A180

MCNULTY, Stephanie, Chief Operating Officer, St. Petersburg General Hospital, Saint Petersburg, FL, p. A139

MCNULTY, Timothy, Director Human Resources, Spring Harbor Hospital, Westbrook, ME, p. A285

MCNUTT, Elena, Chief Nursing Officer, Desert Springs Hospital Medical Center, Las Vegas, NV, p. A395
MCNUTT, Mike, Assistant Administrator, Covenant Hospital Plainview, Plainview, TX, p. A629
MCNUTT, Pamela
Senior Vice President and Chief Information Officer, Methodist Dallas Medical Center, Dallas, TX, p. A597
Senior Vice President and Chief Information Officer, Methodist Mansfield Medical Center, Mansfield, TX, p. A623
Senior Vice President and Chief Information Officer, Methodist Richardson Medical Center, Richardson, TX, p. A631
Vice President Information Systems, Methodist Charlton Medical Center, Dallas, TX, p. A597
MCPEAK, Sara, Chief Nursing Officer, Carlinville Area Hospital, Carlinville, IL, p. A175
MCPHERSON, Jason, Chief Executive Officer, Rock Springs, Georgetown, TX, p. A607
MCPHERSON, Lon, M.D., Senior Vice President Medical Affairs and Chief Quality Officer, Adventhealth Ocala, Ocala, FL, p. A133
MCPHERSON, Rhonda, Vice President Human Resources, Fayette Regional Health System, Connersville, IN, p. A201
MCPHERSON, Valarie, MSN, Chief Nursing Executive, California Hospital Medical Center, Los Angeles, CA, p. A66
MCQUAID, David P., Chief Operating Officer, Ohio State University Wexner Medical Center, Columbus, OH, p. A479
MCQUAID, David P., FACHE, Chief Operating Officer, Ohio State University Wexner Medical Center, Columbus, OH, p. A479
MCQUAIDE, Ben, M.D., Chief of Staff, Clark Regional Medical Center, Winchester, KY, p. A261
MCQUILLEN, Paul, M.D., Chief Medical Officer, Jane Phillips Medical Center, Bartlesville, OK, p. A497
MCQUISTAN, Bob, Vice President Finance, York General, York, NE, p. A392
MCQUISTON, Mike, Administrative Director Human Resources, Wise Health System, Decatur, TX, p. A598
MCRAE, Ashley, Chief Clinical Officer, Kindred Hospital North Florida, Green Cove Springs, FL, p. A124
MCRAE, Colin, Chief Executive Officer, Tennova Healthcare–Jefferson Memorial Hospital, Jefferson City, TN, p. A571
MCREYNOLDS, John, Chief Operating Officer, North Valley Hospital, Tonasket, WA, p. A681
MCRIMMON, Dana, Chief Financial Officer, Mesilla Valley Hospital, Las Cruces, NM, p. A418
MCROBERTS, Kevin G, FACHE, Senior Vice President of Operations, Lake Regional Health System, Osage Beach, MO, p. A366
MCTAGGART, Jac
Chief Executive Officer, Sanford Hillsboro Medical Center, Hillsboro, ND, p. A468
Chief Executive Officer, Sanford Mayville Medical Center, Mayville, ND, p. A468
MCTIGRIT, Chris, Manager Information Technology, Delta Memorial Hospital, Dumas, AR, p. A41
MCTIGUE, Mary, Vice President Patient Care Services and Chief Nursing Officer, Trinitas Regional Medical Center, Elizabeth, NJ, p. A405
MCTIGUE, Michael
Chief Information Officer, Clara Maass Medical Center, Belleville, NJ, p. A403
Chief Information Officer, Saint Barnabas Medical Center, Livingston, NJ, p. A407
MCVAY, Tara, Chief Nursing Officer, Logansport Memorial Hospital, Logansport, IN, p. A210
MCVEIGH, Kevin, Chief Human Resources Officer, Banner Desert Medical Center, Mesa, AZ, p. A31
MCVEY, Eric A, M.D., Executive Vice President Medical Affairs and Quality, St. Dominic–Jackson Memorial Hospital, Jackson, MS, p. A349
MCVEY, Lynn, Chief Operating Officer, Hudson Regional Hospital, Secaucus, NJ, p. A412
MCVEY, Marian Lorraine, Chief Nursing Officer, Prisma Health North Greenville Ltach, Travelers Rest, SC, p. A557
MCVEY, Patrick, Chief Executive Officer, Kindred Hospital North Florida, Green Cove Springs, FL, p. A124
MCWAY, Jacob, Senior Vice President and Chief Financial Officer, Cox Medical Centers, Springfield, MO, p. A371
MCWEY, Russ, M.D., Vice President and Chief Information Officer, Virginia Hospital Center, Arlington, VA, p. A656
MCWHERTER, Joe, Chief Financial Officer, Baptist Memorial Hospital–Desoto, Southaven, MS, p. A354
MCWILLIAMS, Jill, Chief Nursing Officer, Sierra Nevada Memorial Hospital, Grass Valley, CA, p. A61
MEACHAM, Byanka, Director Human Resources, Montgomery County Emergency Service, Norristown, PA, p. A533
MEACHEM, Michelle, Director Human Resources, The University Of Vermont Health Network Elizabethtown Community Hospital, Elizabethtown, NY, p. A427
MEAD, Linda, Director Human Resources, Margaretville Hospital, Margaretville, NY, p. A431
MEAD, Richard, Senior Director Human Resources, Saint Francis Memorial Hospital, San Francisco, CA, p. A85
MEAD, Rick, Human Resources Leader, Kaiser Permanente Oakland Medical Center, Oakland, CA, p. A75
MEADE, Andrew, Chief Executive Officer, Select Specialty Hospital–Longview, Longview, TX, p. A621
MEADE, Robert C., Chief Executive Officer, Doctors Hospital Of Sarasota, Sarasota, FL, p. A139
MEADE, Stephanie, R.N., Chief Nursing Officer, Mercy Health – West Hospital, Cincinnati, OH, p. A476
MEADE, Teresa, R.N., Chief Nursing Officer, Boone Memorial Hospital, Madison, WV, p. A687
MEADOWS, Barbara, Chief Financial Manager, Captain James A. Lovell Federal Health Care Center, North Chicago, IL, p. A191
MEADOWS, Danny, M.D., Medical Director, Logansport State Hospital, Logansport, IN, p. A210
MEADOWS, Hal, M.D., Chief Medical Officer, Banner Lassen Medical Center, Susanville, CA, p. A91
MEADOWS, Nancy, Chief Financial Officer, Methodist Hospital, San Antonio, TX, p. A634
MEADOWS, Sheila M, Chief Human Resources Officer, Mission Hospital, Asheville, NC, p. A449
MEADOWS, Theresa, Chief Information Officer, Cook Children'S Medical Center, Fort Worth, TX, p. A604
MEANS, Dennis, M.D., Vice President Medical Affairs, Carilion New River Valley Medical Center, Christiansburg, VA, p. A658
MEANS, Paul, M.D., President Medical Staff, Highlands Hospital, Connellsville, PA, p. A523
MEARNS, Stephanie, Vice President Patient Care Services and Chief Nurse Executive, Seton Medical Center, Daly City, CA, p. A56
MEARS, Edith, Chief Executive Officer, Regional General Hospital, Williston, FL, p. A144
MEARS, Terry, Director Information Systems, Duke Regional Hospital, Durham, NC, p. A452
MECHAM, Cindy, Health Information Director, Mountain View Hospital, Payson, UT, p. A650
MEDAGLIA, Guy A., President and Chief Executive Officer, Saint Anthony Hospital, Chicago, IL, p. A179
MEDEIROS, Ron, Director Applied Information Technology, Worcester Recovery Center And Hospital, Worcester, MA, p. A305
MEDEROS, Ana J., Chief Executive Officer, Palmetto General Hospital, Hialeah, FL, p. A124
MEDINA, Alberto, Information Technology Senior Consultant, Hospital Manati Medical Center, Manati, PR, p. A717
MEDINA, Betsmari, Director Human Resources, Dr. Ramon E. Betances Hospital–Mayaguez Medical Center Branch, Mayaguez, PR, p. A717
MEDINA, Ed, M.D., Medical Director, Phillips County Hospital, Malta, MT, p. A378
MEDINA, Eleanor, M.D., Chief Medical Officer, Behavioral Center Of Michigan, Warren, MI, p. A324
MEDINA, Luz D, Controller, Hospital Hermanos Melendez, Bayamon, PR, p. A715
MEDINA, Marco, Chief Information Officer, Stanton County Hospital, Johnson, KS, p. A237
MEDINA, Obdulia, Associate Director for Administrative Support, Clinical Management and Ambulatory Care, Ashford Presbyterian Community Hospital, San Juan, PR, p. A718
MEDINA, Shelby, Chief Executive Officer, Windom Area Hospital, Windom, MN, p. A343
MEDINA CRUZ, Victor L., Administrator, Hospital Cuidado Agudo Especializado En Pacientes Politraumatizados, San Juan, PR, p. A718
MEDLAND, Jacqueline, President and Chief Nursing Officer, Highlands–Cashiers Hospital, Highlands, NC, p. A456
MEDLEY, Adron, M.D., Chief Medical Staff, Northern Rockies Medical Center, Cut Bank, MT, p. A375
MEDLEY, Barry, Director Information Systems, Cook Medical Center–A Campus Of Tift Regional Medical Center, Adel, GA, p. A145
MEDLEY, Dennis
Chief Executive Officer and Administrator, Physicians' Medical Center, New Albany, IN, p. A212
Chief Executive Officer, Physicians' Medical Center, New Albany, IN, p. A212
MEDLEY, Wathen, M.D., Chief Medical Officer, Owensboro Health Regional Hospital, Owensboro, KY, p. A258
MEDLIN, John, Chief Nursing Officer, North Carolina Specialty Hospital, Durham, NC, p. A453
MEDLIN, Marcia, Chief Executive Officer, Select Specialty Hospital–Camp Hill, Camp Hill, PA, p. A521
MEDLIN, Marsha, Senior Vice President of Clinical and Operations, Pam Specialty Hospital Of Covington, Covington, LA, p. A266
MEDLOCK, Darci, Manager Human Resources, St. Vincent Dunn Hospital, Bedford, IN, p. A200
MEDOVICH, Lisa, Chief Financial Officer, Peterson Regional Medical Center, Kerrville, TX, p. A618
MEEKER, Brian, D.O., President Medical Staff, Virginia Gay Hospital, Vinton, IA, p. A230
MEEKER, Chris, M.D., Chief Medical Officer, Sanford Bismarck, Bismarck, ND, p. A465
MEEKER, Christina, Director Human Resources, Strategic Behavioral Health – Raleigh, Garner, NC, p. A454
MEEKINS, Lance, Chief Executive Officer, Nocona General Hospital, Nocona, TX, p. A626
MEEKINS, Michelle, Manager Human Resources, Sentara Virginia Beach General Hospital, Virginia Beach, VA, p. A668
MEEKS, Deborah, Chief Nursing Officer, Harlingen Medical Center, Harlingen, TX, p. A609
MEENK, Susan
Vice President Human Resources, Providence St. Peter Hospital, Olympia, WA, p. A676
Vice President Service Area, Providence Centralia Hospital, Centralia, WA, p. A671
MEESE, John, Acting Director, Gallup Indian Medical Center, Gallup, NM, p. A418
MEESE, Larry R., Jr, Chief Executive Officer, Lane Regional Medical Center, Zachary, LA, p. A280
MEESIG, Deborah, M.D., Chief of Staff, Chillicothe Veterans Affairs Medical Center, Chillicothe, OH, p. A475
MEGEHEE, Mark, Vice President and Chief Information Officer, Decatur Morgan Hospital, Decatur, AL, p. A16
MEGGS, Christi, Director, Musc Health Marion Medical Center, Mullins, SC, p. A556
MEGLEMRE, Amy J, R.N., MSN, Senior Vice President and Chief Nursing Officer, Olathe Medical Center, Olathe, KS, p. A242
MEGLI, Cami, Controller, Morrison Community Hospital, Morrison, IL, p. A190
MEGLIOLA, Donna M, Assistant Vice President, Johnson Memorial Medical Center, Stafford Springs, CT, p. A111
MEGOW, Kimberly, M.D., Chief Medical Officer, South Georgia Medical Center, Valdosta, GA, p. A162
MEGUIAR, Ramon V, M.D., Chief Medical Officer, Memorial Health, Savannah, GA, p. A160
MEHAFFEY, M. Beth, Senior Vice President Human Resources, Baptist Medical Center Jacksonville, Jacksonville, FL, p. A125
MEHINDRU, Vinay, M.D.
Medical Director, Rockledge Regional Medical Center, Rockledge, FL, p. A138
Vice President/Chief Medical Officer, Adventhealth Waterman, Tavares, FL, p. A142
MEHLHAUS, Brian, M.D., Chief of Staff, Boone County Hospital, Boone, IA, p. A218
MEHR, Nicholle, Vice President Operations, Mclaren Oakland, Pontiac, MI, p. A320
MEHTA, Kalpana, Chief Fiscal Services, Jesse Brown Veterans Affairs Medical Center, Chicago, IL, p. A177
MEHTA, Sonia, M.D., Chief Medical Officer, Loretto Hospital, Chicago, IL, p. A178
MEHTA, Umesh, M.D., Interim Chief Medical Officer, Hackensack Meridian Health Carrier Clinic, Belle Mead, NJ, p. A403
MEIDINGER, Sue, Manager Business Office, Linton Hospital, Linton, ND, p. A468
MEIER, Suzanne S, System Director, Compensation and Human Resources Technology, Memorial Hermann Memorial City Medical Center, Houston, TX, p. A613
MEIERGERD, Jean, Chief Information Officer, St. Francis Memorial Hospital, West Point, NE, p. A392
MEIERS, Dawn, Coordinator Medical Staff and Personnel Services, Southeast Michigan Surgical Hospital, Warren, MI, p. A324
MEIGS, Jeffrey L, Chief Financial Officer, Louis A. Weiss Memorial Hospital, Chicago, IL, p. A178
MEIGS, John, M.D., Chief of Staff, Bibb Medical Center, Centreville, AL, p. A16
MEINDEL, Nympha, R.N., Chief Information Officer, North Shore University Hospital, Manhasset, NY, p. A430
MEINKE, Kenneth, Senior Vice President Administrative Services, Finance and Chief Financial Officer, Spartanburg Medical Center – Church Street Campus, Spartanburg, SC, p. A557
MEINKE, Victor E, Chief Financial Officer, Jewish Home Of San Francisco, San Francisco, CA, p. A85
MEINKOTH, Jennifer
Executive Director I.S., Memorial Hospital East, Shiloh, IL, p. A196
Executive Director, IS, Memorial Hospital, Belleville, IL, p. A174
MEISINGER, Alan, Chief Financial Officer, Herington Municipal Hospital, Herington, KS, p. A236

MEISNER, Anne, President and Chief Executive Officer, Southeastern Regional Medical Center, Newnan, GA, p. A158

MEKHAEL, Hani, M.D., Chief Staff, Havenwyck Hospital, Auburn Hills, MI, p. A306

MELAHN, William L, M.D., Vice President Medical Affairs and Chief Medical Officer, St. Claire Healthcare, Morehead, KY, p. A258

MELAN, Kristen, Director Human Resources Administration, Good Shepherd Specialty Hospital, Bethlehem, PA, p. A520

MELANCON, Eric, Chief of Staff, Teche Regional Medical Center, Morgan City, LA, p. A274

MELAND, Jeff, M.D., Vice President, Chief Medical Officer, Northfield Hospital And Clinics, Northfield, MN, p. A337

MELARAGNO, Robert, Vice President Finance, O'Bleness Memorial Hospital, Athens, OH, p. A472

MELBOURNE, John, M.D., Medical Director, Conifer Park, Glenville, NY, p. A428

MELBY, Gina, Chief Executive Officer, Jfk Medical Center, Atlantis, FL, p. A117

MELBY, Larry, Chief Executive Officer, Select Specialty Hospital–Palm Beach, Lake Worth, FL, p. A127

MELBY, Rachel, Vice President, Chief Financial Officer, Crawford County Memorial Hospital, Denison, IA, p. A221

MELCHER, Nancy, Chief Nursing Officer, Wellstar North Fulton Hospital, Roswell, GA, p. A159

MELCHIOR, Eric L, Executive Vice President and Chief Financial Officer, Greater Baltimore Medical Center, Baltimore, MD, p. A288

MELCHIORRE, Lisa, Chief Operating Officer and Chief Nursing Officer, St. Luke'S Elmore, Mountain Home, ID, p. A170

MELCHIORRE, Lisa, R.N., MS, Chief Operating Officer and Chief Nursing Officer, St. Luke'S Elmore, Mountain Home, ID, p. A170

MELEAR, Brian, Chief Executive Officer, Raulerson Hospital, Okeechobee, FL, p. A133

MELENDEZ, Alma, Controller, Dimmit Regional Hospital, Carrizo Springs, TX, p. A591

MELENDEZ, Jose, M.D., Chief Medical Officer, Uchealth Memorial Hospital, Colorado Springs, CO, p. A98

MELENDEZ, Pedro
Chief Executive Director, Hospital Menonita De Cayey, Cayey, PR, p. A716
Chief Executive Officer, Centro De Salud Conductual Menonita–Cima, Aibonito, PR, p. A714
Chief Executive Officer, Mennonite General Hospital, Aibonito, PR, p. A715
Executive Director, Hospital Menonita De Caguas, Caguas, PR, p. A715

MELINE, Brenda, Manager Human Resources, Patients' Hospital Of Redding, Redding, CA, p. A79

MELL, Kevin, Vice President Operations, Medstar Montgomery Medical Center, Olney, MD, p. A292

MELLETT, David, Chief Financial Officer, Harrison Memorial Hospital, Cynthiana, KY, p. A251

MELLGREN, Gustave, M.D., Chief of Staff, Glacial Ridge Health System, Glenwood, MN, p. A332

MELLO, Brett, Chief Information Officer, Cayuga Medical Center At Ithaca, Ithaca, NY, p. A429

MELLO, Paul, Manager Data Processing, Metropolitan State Hospital, Norwalk, CA, p. A75

MELLOWS, George, Facility Director, Hawthorn Center, Northville, MI, p. A319

MELNIKOFF, Jean, Vice President Human Resources, Kaiser Permanente Medical Center, Honolulu, HI, p. A164

MELO, Kathleen, Administrator, The Willough At Naples, Naples, FL, p. A132

MELTON, Anne, Chief Nursing Officer, Sumner Regional Medical Center, Gallatin, TN, p. A570

MELTON, Chad, Chief Executive Officer, Fauquier Hospital, Warrenton, VA, p. A668

MELTON, Josh, Chief Information Officer, St. Bernards Medical Center, Jonesboro, AR, p. A44

MELTVEDT, Robert, M.D., Vice President Medical Affairs, Warren Memorial Hospital, Front Royal, VA, p. A660

MELTZER, David B, Chief Financial Officer, Texas Health Presbyterian Hospital Denton, Denton, TX, p. A599

MELVILLE, Carol, Director Human Resources, West Houston Medical Center, Houston, TX, p. A614

MELVIN, Susan, D.O., Chief Medical Officer, Memorialcare, Long Beach Memorial Medical Center, Long Beach, CA, p. A65

MENA, Theodore, Chief Executive Officer, Select Specialty Hospital–Orlando, Orlando, FL, p. A134

MENDELOWITZ, Susan, R.N., FACHE, Executive Vice President and Chief Operating Officer, New Bridge Medical Center, Paramus, NJ, p. A410

MENDEZ, Alex A, Executive Vice President of Operations and Chief Financial Officer, Mount Sinai Medical Center, Miami Beach, FL, p. A131

MENDEZ, Kim K, Ed.D., R.N., Chief Nurse Officer, Brookdale Hospital Medical Center, New York, NY, p. A432

MENDEZ, Lincoln S., Chief Executive Officer, Boca Raton Regional Hospital, Boca Raton, FL, p. A118

MENDEZ, Nicholas Paul., Chief Executive Officer, Pam Specialty Hospital Of Hammond, Hammond, LA, p. A268

MENDEZ, Samantha, Human Resources, Scottsdale Liberty Hospital, Scottsdale, AZ, p. A36

MENDIOLA–BALDERAS, Rosie L, Director Information Systems, South Texas Health System, Edinburg, TX, p. A601

MENDIZABAL, Oscar, Chief Nursing Officer, Highlands Rehabilitation Hospital, El Paso, TX, p. A602

MENDOZA, Carlos, Controller, Baptist Memorial Rehabilitation Hospital, Germantown, TN, p. A570

MENDOZA, Christopher, Chief Executive Officer, Alliancehealth Ponca City, Ponca City, OK, p. A506

MENDOZA, Dana, Chief Information Officer, Maui Memorial Medical Center, Wailuku, HI, p. A166

MENDOZA, Joseph
Chief Financial Officer, Hillcrest Hospital Cushing, Cushing, OK, p. A498
Chief Financial Officer, Hillcrest Hospital Henryetta, Henryetta, OK, p. A500
Chief Financial Officer, Hillcrest Medical Center, Tulsa, OK, p. A508

MENDOZA, Joseph, M.D., Medical Director, Porterville Developmental Center, Porterville, CA, p. A78

MENDOZA, Yolanda, Director Human Resources, Rehabilitation Hospital Of Southern New Mexico, Las Cruces, NM, p. A419

MENDYKA, Nick, Chief Financial Officer, University Of Virginia Medical Center, Charlottesville, VA, p. A657

MENEFEE, Jason J, Chief Financial Officer, Mccamey County Hospital District, Mccamey, TX, p. A624

MENEN, Michael, M.D., Chief Medical Officer, Bon Secours St. Francis Medical Center, Midlothian, VA, p. A662

MENGENHAUSEN, Jeff, Chief Executive Officer, Madelia Community Hospital, Madelia, MN, p. A334

MENGLE, Scott, Vice President Human Resources, Penn State Health St. Joseph, Reading, PA, p. A539

MENKES, Jeffrey, President and Chief Executive Officer, Burke Rehabilitation Hospital, White Plains, NY, p. A447

MENNONNA, Guy, Senior Vice President Human Resources, New Bridge Medical Center, Paramus, NJ, p. A410

MENON, Rema, M.D., Clinical Director, Parsons State Hospital And Training Center, Parsons, KS, p. A243

MENSCH, Alan, M.D., Senior Vice President Medical Affairs, Plainview Hospital, Plainview, NY, p. A441

MENSEN, Amy, Chief Administrative Officer, Regional Medical Center, Manchester, IA, p. A226

MENTGEN, John, President and Chief Executive Officer, Regional West Medical Center, Scottsbluff, NE, p. A391

MENTHCOAST, Lynn, Chief Fiscal Service, Tennessee Valley Healthcare System, Nashville, TN, p. A577

MENTINK, Terri, Chief Financial Officer, Mercyone Oakland Medical Center, Oakland, NE, p. A388

MENTZEL, Bridget, Director Human Resources, Mercy Health – West Hospital, Cincinnati, OH, p. A476

MENTZER, Larry, Chief Human Resources Officer, Veterans Affairs Roseburg Healthcare System, Roseburg, OR, p. A517

MENZEL, Colette, Ph.D., Chief Operating Officer and Chief Financial Officer, Antelope Valley Hospital, Lancaster, CA, p. A64

MENZIE, Sue, R.N., Director Patient Care, Sierra Tucson, Tucson, AZ, p. A38

MERCADO, Felix V., Chief Financial Officer, Lawrence General Hospital, Lawrence, MA, p. A299

MERCADO, Gloria, Director of Nursing, Mennonite General Hospital, Aibonito, PR, p. A715

MERCADO, Leda Marta R, Chief Operating Officer, Hospital Menonita De Cayey, Cayey, PR, p. A716

MERCER, David, Coordinator Information Systems, Baptist Memorial Hospital–Union City, Union City, TN, p. A580

MERCER, Shawna, Director Human Resources, Kansas Neurological Institute, Topeka, KS, p. A246

MERCER, William, M.D., Director, Peterson Healthcare And Rehabilitation Hospital, Wheeling, WV, p. A690

MERCHANT, Deven, M.D., Chief Medical Executive, Sutter Davis Hospital, Davis, CA, p. A56

MERCULIEFF, Leatha N., Hospital Administrator, Wrangell Medical Center, Wrangell, AK, p. A27

MERCURI, Ralph, Vice President and Chief Financial Officer, Major Hospital, Shelbyville, IN, p. A214

MEREDITH, Katie, Chief Nursing Officer, Select Specialty Hospital–Lexington, Lexington, KY, p. A255

MEREDITH, Keith, Chief Operating Officer, Salem Regional Medical Center, Salem, OH, p. A490

MEREK, Gloria, Director of Nursing, Springfield Hospital Center, Sykesville, MD, p. A293

MERIDA, Andy, Director Management Information Systems, Fayette Regional Health System, Connersville, IN, p. A201

MERILLO, Myra, Supervisor Health Information Management, Encompass Health Rehabilitation Hospital Of Spring Hill, Brooksville, FL, p. A119

MERINGOLO, Francis, Vice President Human Resources, Umass Memorial–Marlborough Hospital, Marlborough, MA, p. A300

MERIWETHER, Wayne, Chief Executive Officer, Twin Lakes Regional Medical Center, Leitchfield, KY, p. A254

MERK, Richard
Director Human Resources, Allegiance Behavioral Health Center Of Plainview, Plainview, TX, p. A629
Executive Vice President, Allegiance Behavioral Health Center Of Plainview, Plainview, TX, p. A629

MERKEL, Rebecca, Privacy Officer, Franciscan Health Carmel, Carmel, IN, p. A201

MERKLE, John F., Medical Center Director, Tuscaloosa Veterans Affairs Medical Center, Tuscaloosa, AL, p. A24

MERKLEY, Jason R., Chief Executive Officer, Brookings Health System, Brookings, SD, p. A559

MERKLIN, Paul, Vice President Finance and Chief Financial Officer, Adventhealth Manchester, Manchester, KY, p. A257

MERRIFIELD, Matt, Chief Operating Officer, Aiken Regional Medical Centers, Aiken, SC, p. A549

MERRIGAN, Mary C, Manager Public Relations, Sanford Vermillion Medical Center, Vermillion, SD, p. A564

MERRILL, Cheryl Bhima, MSN, R.N., Senior Vice President Patient Care Services and Chief Nursing Officer, North Shore Medical Center, Salem, MA, p. A303

MERRILL, Chuck, M.D., Vice President Medical Affairs, Marian Regional Medical Center, Santa Maria, CA, p. A89

MERRILL, Doug, Executive Vice President Chief Medical and Academic Officer, Renown Rehabilitation Hospital, Reno, NV, p. A397

MERRILL, Rick W., System President and Chief Executive Officer, Cook Children'S Medical Center, Fort Worth, TX, p. A604

MERRILL, Stacie, Chief Nursing Officer, Baylor Scott & White Surgical Hospital Fort Worth, Fort Worth, TX, p. A604

MERRITT, Becky A, Director Human Resources, Houston Methodist Clear Lake Hospital, Nassau Bay, TX, p. A626

MERRITT, Belinda, M.D., Medical Director, Spire Cane Creek Rehabilitation Hospital, Martin, TN, p. A573

MERRITT, Bradley, M.D., Medical Director, Christus Trinity Mother Frances Rehabilitation Hospital, A Partner Of Encompass Health, Tyler, TX, p. A642

MERRITT, Janet, Chief Financial Officer, St. Vincent Williamsport Hospital, Williamsport, IN, p. A216

MERRITT, Tim E., Chief Executive Officer, Summitridge Hospital, Lawrenceville, GA, p. A156

MERRITT, Trevor, Director Human Resources, Star Valley Medical Center, Afton, WY, p. A710

MERRY, Duane, Chief Information Officer, Little Falls Hospital, Little Falls, NY, p. A430

MERRYMAN, Mary, Regional Director Information Management, Christus Health Shreveport–Bossier, Shreveport, LA, p. A278

MERRYMAN, Scott
Chief Financial Officer, Christus Coushatta Health Care Center, Coushatta, LA, p. A266
Chief Financial Officer, Christus Health Shreveport–Bossier, Shreveport, LA, p. A278
Chief Financial Officer, Christus Ochsner St. Patrick Hospital Southwest Louisiana, Lake Charles, LA, p. A272

MERRYWELL, Paul, Chief Information Officer, Sycamore Shoals Hospital, Elizabethton, TN, p. A569

MERSON, John, M.D., Chief of Staff, John Muir Medical Center, Concord, Concord, CA, p. A55

MERSON, Wendy, Chief Executive Officer, Windmoor Healthcare Of Clearwater, Clearwater, FL, p. A120

MESA, Gustavo, Chief Information Officer, San Juan City Hospital, San Juan, PR, p. A719

MESAROS, Dennis, Administrator, St. Luke'S Regional Medical Center, Boise, ID, p. A168

MESIC, John, M.D., Chief Medical Officer, Sutter Auburn Faith Hospital, Auburn, CA, p. A51

MESICK, Marc, Vice President and Chief Financial Officer, Ellis Hospital, Schenectady, NY, p. A444

MESKAN, Paula, R.N., Chief Nursing Officer, River'S Edge Hospital And Clinic, Saint Peter, MN, p. A340

MESORAS, Amber, Chief Human Resources Officer, Veterans Affairs Pittsburgh Healthcare System, Pittsburgh, PA, p. A538

MESSA–GILL, Nicole, Manager Human Resources, Northlake Behavioral Health System, Mandeville, LA, p. A273

MESSELT, Mary Jo
Manager Human Resources, Mercy Hospital Watonga, Watonga, OK, p. A510
Senior Human Resources Manager, Mercy Hospital Logan County, Guthrie, OK, p. A500

MESSER, Kelly, Director of Finance, Devereux Hospital And Children'S Center Of Florida, Melbourne, FL, p. A129
MESSER, Mark, D.O., Clinical Director, Terrell State Hospital, Terrell, TX, p. A640
MESSERSMITH, Scott E, Director Human Resources, Columbus Community Hospital, Columbus, NE, p. A384
MESSINA, Arlene, R.N., MSN, Director of Nursing, Riverside Doctors' Hospital Williamsburg, Williamsburg, VA, p. A669
MESSINA, Daniel J., President and Chief Executive Officer, Brookdale Hospital Medical Center, New York, NY, p. A432
MESSMAN, Catherine, Chief Financial Officer, Mills–Peninsula Health Services, Burlingame, CA, p. A53
MESTAS, Lisa, Associate Administrator and System Chief Nursing Officer, Usa Health University Hospital, Mobile, AL, p. A21
MESTER, Sulynn, R.N., Chief Nursing Officer, Childress Regional Medical Center, Childress, TX, p. A592
MESZLER, Lori A., Chief Financial Officer, Helen Hayes Hospital, West Haverstraw, NY, p. A447
METCALF, Angie L, Vice President and Chief Human Resource Officer, Cleveland Clinic Martin North Hospital, Stuart, FL, p. A140
METCALF, Chris, Director of Nursing, Utah State Hospital, Provo, UT, p. A650
METCALF, Kathleen, Chief Information Officer, University Hospitals Samaritan Medical Center, Ashland, OH, p. A472
METCALF, Peter, M.D., President Medical Staff, Genesis Medical Center, Silvis, Silvis, IL, p. A196
METHE, Joan, Chief Information Officer, Mercy Medical Center, Springfield, MA, p. A303
METHVEN, Jeffrey M, Vice President Ambulatory Services and Chief Human Resources Officer, Saratoga Hospital, Saratoga Springs, NY, p. A444
METHVIN, Jeff, Manager Information Technology, St. Luke Hospital And Living Center, Marion, KS, p. A240
METIKO, Olushola, M.D., Medical Director, Central Prison Hospital, Raleigh, NC, p. A460
METINKO, Andrew, M.D., Chief Medical Officer, The Hsc Pediatric Center, Washington, DC, p. A116
METIVIER, Roberta, Vice President Human Resources and Administrator, Western Main Nursing Home, Stephens Memorial Hospital, Norway, ME, p. A284
METRO, Michelle, Vice President Nursing, Cloud County Health Center, Concordia, KS, p. A234
METTEAUER, Kenneth, Chief Financial Officer, Redmond Regional Medical Center, Rome, GA, p. A159
METZ, Amy, Chief Executive Officer, Regency Hospital Of Florence, Florence, SC, p. A553
METZ, Bruce, Ph.D., Senior Vice President and Chief Information Officer, Lahey Hospital & Medical Center, Burlington, Burlington, MA, p. A297
METZ, Carl, Vice President, Ephraim Mcdowell Fort Logan Hospital, Stanford, KY, p. A261
METZGER, Alysha, Director Human Resources, Hill Country Memorial Hospital, Fredericksburg, TX, p. A606
METZGER, Cynthia, Chief Nursing and Operations Officer, Little River Memorial Hospital, Ashdown, AR, p. A39
METZGER, Terry
Chief Financial Officer, St. Vincent Seton Specialty Hospital, Indianapolis, IN, p. A208
Vice President, Finance, St. Vincent Indianapolis Hospital, Indianapolis, IN, p. A208
MEUER, Lynn, Interim Chief Nursing Officer, Sibley Memorial Hospital, Washington, DC, p. A116
MEURER, Bryan, Director Information Systems, Mat–Su Regional Medical Center, Palmer, AK, p. A27
MEURER, Lynn, MSN, R.N., Interim Chief Nursing Officer, Wellstar Kennestone Hospital, Marietta, GA, p. A157
MEWHIRTER, Michael, President, Fort Hamilton Hospital, Hamilton, OH, p. A484
MEYER, Anthony, M.D., Medical Director, Aurora Psychiatric Hospital, Wauwatosa, WI, p. A708
MEYER, Barb, Executive Director of Nursing, Gibson Area Hospital And Health Services, Gibson City, IL, p. A184
MEYER, Cameron, CPA, Chief Financial Officer, Excelsior Springs Hospital, Excelsior Springs, MO, p. A359
MEYER, Cheryl, Director Human Resources, Gundersen Palmer Lutheran Hospital And Clinics, West Union, IA, p. A231
MEYER, Cheryl, MSN, Director of Nursing, Haven Behavioral Senior Care Of Dayton, Dayton, OH, p. A481
MEYER, Daniel T, President, Aurora Baycare Medical Center, Green Bay, WI, p. A696
MEYER, Daniel T., President, Aurora Baycare Medical Center, Green Bay, WI, p. A696
MEYER, Francis, Vice President Information Systems Technology, Kaleida Health, Buffalo, NY, p. A424
MEYER, Gordon, Director Human Resources, Surgeons Choice Medical Center, Southfield, MI, p. A323
MEYER, Jeffrey K., Interim Chief Executive Officer, Osceola Medical Center, Osceola, WI, p. A703
MEYER, Joe S, Chief Financial Officer, Scott County Hospital, Scott City, KS, p. A245
MEYER, Karen, Vice President Finance and Chief Financial Officer, Rush Memorial Hospital, Rushville, IN, p. A214
MEYER, Kurt A
Chief Human Resource Officer, Saint Joseph Health System, Mishawaka, IN, p. A211
Chief Human Resources Officer, Plymouth Medical Center, Plymouth, IN, p. A213
MEYER, Mark, Chief Financial Officer, Grady Memorial Hospital, Atlanta, GA, p. A146
MEYER, Michele C., Chief Executive Officer, Washington County Memorial Hospital, Potosi, MO, p. A367
MEYER, Michele C., R.N., Vice President of Operations, Mercy Hospital Jefferson, Festus, MO, p. A360
MEYER, Morgan, Chief Financial Officer, Howard County Medical Center, Saint Paul, NE, p. A391
MEYER, Nate, Director Finance, Alomere Health, Alexandria, MN, p. A327
MEYER, Robert L., President and Chief Executive Officer, Phoenix Children'S Hospital, Phoenix, AZ, p. A34
MEYER, Roger, M.D., Chief of Staff, Friend Community Healthcare System, Friend, NE, p. A385
MEYER, Timothy, M.D., Chief of Staff, Marshfield Medical Center – Neillsville, Neillsville, WI, p. A702
MEYER, Traci, Director Human Resources, Canyon Vista Medical Center, Sierra Vista, AZ, p. A36
MEYER, Wessel H., M.D., Chief of Staff, Veterans Affairs Central California Health Care System, Fresno, CA, p. A60
MEYERHOEFER, Todd, M.D., Vice President Medical Affairs, Cleveland Clinic Union Hospital, Dover, OH, p. A482
MEYERS, Audrey, President and Chief Executive Officer, Valley Hospital, Ridgewood, NJ, p. A412
MEYERS, Betty, Chief Financial Officer, Crook County Medical Services District, Sundance, WY, p. A713
MEYERS, J Cullen., Chief Executive Officer, Pam Specialty Hospital Of Covington, Covington, LA, p. A266
MEYERS, Larry, Chief Information Officer, Wilson Memorial Hospital, Sidney, OH, p. A491
MEYERS, Mark S., M.D., Chief of Staff, Battle Mountain General Hospital, Battle Mountain, NV, p. A393
MEYERS, Russell, President and Chief Executive Officer, Midland Memorial Hospital, Midland, TX, p. A624
MEYERS, William, Chief Information Officer, St. Luke'S Hospital, Chesterfield, MO, p. A358
MEZA, Eduardo, M.D., Medical Director, Prairie St. John'S, Fargo, ND, p. A466
MEZA, Lourdes, Coordinator Human Resources, West Covina Medical Center, West Covina, CA, p. A94
MEZOFF, Adam, M.D., Vice President and Chief Medical Officer, Dayton Children's Hospital, Dayton, OH, p. A481
MHERABI, Nader, Senior Vice President and Vice Dean, Chief Information Officer, Brookdale Hospital Medical Center, New York, NY, p. A432
MIANO, Christena, Vice President, Human Resources, Medical Center Of Trinity, Trinity, FL, p. A143
MICAN, Deborah, R.N., Chief Nursing Officer, Capital Health Medical Center–Hopewell, Pennington, NJ, p. A410
MICCOLI, Vincent, Executive Director, Brookdale Hospital Medical Center, New York, NY, p. A432
MICHAEL, Amy J, Chief Operating Officer, Sullivan County Memorial Hospital, Milan, MO, p. A365
MICHAEL, Elizabeth, R.N., MS, Vice President Patient Care Services and Chief Nursing Officer, Stillwater Medical Center, Stillwater, OK, p. A507
MICHAELS, Stephen T., M.D., Chief Operating Officer and Chief Medical Officer, Medstar St. Mary'S Hospital, Leonardtown, MD, p. A292
MICHALEK, Debra, Chief Financial Officer, Fayette Regional Health System, Connersville, IN, p. A201
MICHALSKI, Carrie, President and Chief Executive Officer, Riverview Health, Crookston, MN, p. A330
MICHEL, Diane, Senior Vice President, Chief Nursing Officer, Children'S Hospital, New Orleans, LA, p. A275
MICHEL, George J, Chief Operating Officer, Larkin Community Hospital–South Miami Campus, South Miami, FL, p. A140
MICHEL, Randall, M.D., Chief of Staff, Lompoc Valley Medical Center, Lompoc, CA, p. A64
MICHEL–OGBORN, Deborah, Chief Information Resource Management, North Florida/South Georgia Veteran'S Health System, Gainesville, FL, p. A123
MICHELE, Margorie, Chief Human Resources Officer, Penn Presbyterian Medical Center, Philadelphia, PA, p. A536
MICHELEN, Jeannith
Chief Implementation Officer, Brookdale Hospital Medical Center, New York, NY, p. A432
Senior Associate Executive Director, Brookdale Hospital Medical Center, New York, NY, p. A432
MICHELL, Pamela W, R.N., Vice President, Chief Nursing Officer, Adventhealth Ocala, Ocala, FL, p. A133
MICHELSON, Soad, M.D., Senior Medical Director, Clarity Child Guidance Center, San Antonio, TX, p. A633
MICHENER, Scott, M.D., Chief Medical Officer, Comanche County Memorial Hospital, Lawton, OK, p. A501
MICHL, Michelle, Director Human Resources, Mercy Medical Center Mount Shasta, Mount Shasta, CA, p. A73
MICKIEWICZ, Nanette, President, Dominican Hospital, Santa Cruz, CA, p. A88
MIDDENDORF, Bruce, M.D., Chief Medical Officer, St. Mary'S Health Care System, Athens, GA, p. A145
MIDDLEBROOKS, Mark, M.D., Medical Director, Noland Hospital Birmingham, Birmingham, AL, p. A15
MIDDLETON, Jackie, Vice President Human Resources, Methodist Dallas Medical Center, Dallas, TX, p. A597
MIDDLETON, James, MSN, R.N., Chief Nursing Officer, Knox Community Hospital, Mount Vernon, OH, p. A488
MIDDLETON, Robert Eldon, MSN, R.N., Chief Nursing Officer, Gerald Champion Regional Medical Center, Alamogordo, NM, p. A416
MIDGETT, Steve, R.N., Chief Nursing Officer, Encompass Health Rehabilitation Hospital Of Sugar Land, Sugar Land, TX, p. A638
MIDKIFF, Stephen L., Chief Executive Officer, Lake Norman Regional Medical Center, Mooresville, NC, p. A458
MIDTLIEN, Tonia, Information Systems Support Specialist, Gundersen Boscobel Area Hospital And Clinics, Boscobel, WI, p. A692
MIEDLER, Michael, M.D., Chief Medical Officer, Continuing Care Hospital, Lexington, KY, p. A255
MIESNER, Gail, Chief Financial Officer, Memorial Hospital, Chester, IL, p. A176
MIGLIETTA, Steve, Chief Financial Officer, Orlando Regional Medical Center, Orlando, FL, p. A134
MIGOYA, Carlos A., President and Chief Executive Officer, Jackson Health System, Miami, FL, p. A130
MIHALAKAKOS, Paul, M.D., Chief of Staff, Aurora Medical Center – Manitowoc County, Two Rivers, WI, p. A707
MIHALJEVIC, Tomislav, President and Chief Executive Officer, Cleveland Clinic, Cleveland, OH, p. A477
MIKELL, Evarista, Assistant Finance Officer, William S. Middleton Memorial Veterans Hospital, Madison, WI, p. A699
MIKHAIL, Ashraf, M.D., Medical Director, Brynn Marr Hospital, Jacksonville, NC, p. A456
MIKI, Nobuyuki, M.D., Vice President Medical Services and Chief Medical Officer, Kuakini Medical Center, Honolulu, HI, p. A164
MIKITARIAN, George, Jr, President and Chief Executive Officer, Parrish Medical Center, Titusville, FL, p. A143
MIKITKA, Joseph, Vice President Human Resources, St. Luke'S Sacred Heart Campus, Allentown, PA, p. A519
MIKKELSEN, Kallie, Vice President Nursing, Memorial Hospital Of Sweetwater County, Rock Springs, WY, p. A712
MIKKELSON, Tom, M.D.
Interim Chief Operating Officer, Touchette Regional Hospital, Centreville, IL, p. A175
Vice President Medical Affairs, Touchette Regional Hospital, Centreville, IL, p. A175
MIKLAVIC, Kirk
Director Human Resources, Bridgton Hospital, Bridgton, ME, p. A282
Director, Human Resources, Central Maine Medical Center, Lewiston, ME, p. A283
MIKLOS, Maggie, Director Human Resources, Northside Hospital, Saint Petersburg, FL, p. A138
MIKOS, Kathleen A, Vice President and Chief Nursing Officer, Ingalls Memorial Hospital, Harvey, IL, p. A185
MIKOS, Ken, Director Information Technology, Wilbarger General Hospital, Vernon, TX, p. A643
MIKULIC, Jeannie, Director Human Resources, Providence Portland Medical Center, Portland, OR, p. A516
MILAM, Wendy, Chief Nursing Officer, Encompass Health Rehabilitation Hospital Of Ocala, Ocala, FL, p. A133
MILAN, Isabel, R.N., Chief Nursing Officer, Lac+Usc Medical Center, Los Angeles, CA, p. A68
MILAND, Shelly
Chief Financial Officer, Texas Health Specialty Hospital, Fort Worth, TX, p. A606
Group Finance Officer, Texas Health Harris Methodist Hospital Cleburne, Cleburne, TX, p. A592
Group Financial Officer, Texas Health Harris Methodist Hospital Fort Worth, Fort Worth, TX, p. A605
MILANES, Carlos, Chief Executive Officer, Edgefield County Healthcare, Edgefield, SC, p. A552
MILANO, Arthur D, Vice President Human Resources, Berkshire Medical Center, Pittsfield, MA, p. A302
MILATOVICH, Natasha, Association Vice President Human Resources, Adventist Health White Memorial, Los Angeles, CA, p. A66

MILAZZO, John, Chief Financial Officer, Merit Health River Region, Vicksburg, MS, p. A355

MILBRANDT, David, M.D., Vice President Medical Affairs, Fairview Lakes Health Services, Wyoming, MN, p. A343

MILBURN, Sandra, Director Human Resources, Encompass Health Rehabilitation Hospital Of Memphis, Memphis, TN, p. A574

MILBURN, Sharon, Chief Nursing Officer, Summers County Arh Hospital, Hinton, WV, p. A685

MILES, Ben, President, Parkview Regional Medical Center, Fort Wayne, IN, p. A204

MILES, Dana, Chief Nursing Officer and Chief Clinical Officer, Delta Memorial Hospital, Dumas, AR, p. A41

MILES, John, Chief Financial Officer, Piedmont Newnan Hospital, Newnan, GA, p. A158

MILES, Karen, M.D., Medical Director, Strategic Behavioral Health – Raleigh, Garner, NC, p. A454

MILES, Kerry
Chief Information Officer, Providence St. Peter Hospital, Olympia, WA, p. A676
Site Director, Providence Centralia Hospital, Centralia, WA, p. A671

MILES, Lee Ann, Chief Financial Officer, Harrison County Community Hospital, Bethany, MO, p. A356

MILES, Paul V
Chief Operating Officer, Morgan County Arh Hospital, West Liberty, KY, p. A261
Vice President Administration, Whitesburg Arh Hospital, Whitesburg, KY, p. A261

MILETO, Dottie, Chief Nursing Officer, Adventhealth Heart Of Florida, Davenport, FL, p. A121

MILHALTSES, Dean, Chief Operating Officer, Brookdale Hospital Medical Center, New York, NY, p. A432

MILIAN, Tony, Chief Financial Officer, Larkin Community Hospital–Palm Springs Campus, Hialeah, FL, p. A124

MILICEVIC, Heather, Director Human Resources, Western Reserve Hospital, Cuyahoga Falls, OH, p. A481

MILIUS, Hank A., Chief Executive Officer, Meridian Health Services, Muncie, IN, p. A212

MILLAN, Wilfredo Rabelo, Chief Operating Officer, Cardiovascular Center Of Puerto Rico And The Caribbean, San Juan, PR, p. A718

MILLARD, Kathleen, Acting Director Nursing, Kalamazoo Psychiatric Hospital, Kalamazoo, MI, p. A316

MILLEN, Peter S, Chief Medical Officer MHSATS, Community Behavioral Health Hospital – Rochester, Rochester, MN, p. A338

MILLER, Alicia, Director Human Resources, Aspen Valley Hospital, Aspen, CO, p. A96

MILLER, Andy, Chief Financial Officer, Memorial Hospital Jacksonville, Jacksonville, FL, p. A125

MILLER, Barbara, Manager Business Office, Regional General Hospital, Williston, FL, p. A144

MILLER, Bob
President, Aurora Lakeland Medical Center, Elkhorn, WI, p. A694
President, Aurora Medical Center Burlington, Burlington, WI, p. A693

MILLER, Brent R, Manager Human Resources, Brown County Community Treatment Center, Green Bay, WI, p. A696

MILLER, Brian, Chief Executive Officer, Dewitt Hospital, Dewitt, AR, p. A41

MILLER, Carol R, R.N., Chief Nursing Officer, Reynolds Memorial Hospital, Glen Dale, WV, p. A685

MILLER, Carrie, Director Human Resources, Promedica Defiance Regional Hospital, Defiance, OH, p. A482

MILLER, Chad J., President and Chief Executive Officer, Morrow County Hospital, Mount Gilead, OH, p. A488

MILLER, Chandra, Director of Nursing, John J. Pershing Veterans Affairs Medical Center, Poplar Bluff, MO, p. A367

MILLER, Che', M.D., Chief of Staff, Duncan Regional Hospital, Duncan, OK, p. A498

MILLER, Chris K., Chief Financial Officer, Highland Hospital, Charleston, WV, p. A684

MILLER, Christine
Chief Human Resources Management Services, Maine Veterans Affairs Medical Center, Augusta, ME, p. A281
General Counsel and Vice President Human Resources, Upmc Hanover, Hanover, PA, p. A526

MILLER, Cindy, Chief Executive Officer, Pam Specialty Hospital Of Wilkes–Barre, Wilkes Barre, PA, p. A544

MILLER, Clint, Chief Nursing Officer, Spooner Health, Spooner, WI, p. A705

MILLER, Connie, Vice President Human Resources, Overland Park Regional Medical Center, Overland Park, KS, p. A243

MILLER, Daniel
Chief Executive Officer, Methodist Hospital, San Antonio, TX, p. A634
Human Resources Business Partner, University Hospitals Parma Medical Center, Parma, OH, p. A489

Vice President Human Resources, University Hospitals Elyria Medical Center, Elyria, OH, p. A482

MILLER, Debra, Administrator, Crosbyton Clinic Hospital, Crosbyton, TX, p. A595

MILLER, Derek, Senior Vice President and Chief Financial Officer, Southeast Alabama Medical Center, Dothan, AL, p. A17

MILLER, Diane, Administrator, Peterson Healthcare And Rehabilitation Hospital, Wheeling, WV, p. A690

MILLER, Dillon D, M.D., Chief Medical Officer, Fannin Regional Hospital, Blue Ridge, GA, p. A148

MILLER, Dionne, Chief Operating Officer, Sutter Roseville Medical Center, Roseville, CA, p. A81

MILLER, Duane
Chief Financial Officer, Chi St. Luke'S Health Memorial Livingston, Livingston, TX, p. A621
Chief Financial Officer, Integris Bass Baptist Health Center, Enid, OK, p. A499
Chief Financial Officer, Pam Specialty Hospital Of Lufkin, Lufkin, TX, p. A622

MILLER, Dyrek, M.D., Chief Medical Staff, Vidant Duplin Hospital, Kenansville, NC, p. A457

MILLER, Elaine G, Director of Nursing, Oaklawn Psychiatric Center, Goshen, IN, p. A205

MILLER, Elizabeth, Director of Nursing, Harlan County Health System, Alma, NE, p. A382

MILLER, Esteban, Chief Medical Officer, Black River Memorial Hospital, Black River Falls, WI, p. A692

MILLER, Gary L
Regional Director Information Systems, Plymouth Medical Center, Plymouth, IN, p. A213
Senior Director Information Systems, Saint Joseph Health System, Mishawaka, IN, p. A211

MILLER, Gene, Interim Chief Executive Officer, Jellico Community Hospital, Jellico, TN, p. A571

MILLER, George, President and Chief Executive Officer, Loretto Hospital, Chicago, IL, p. A178

MILLER, Greg, Senior Vice President Operations, Uf Health Jacksonville, Jacksonville, FL, p. A126

MILLER, Hope, Director of Medical Records, Peterson Healthcare And Rehabilitation Hospital, Wheeling, WV, p. A690

MILLER, J D, M.D.
Chief Medical Officer, Hazard Arh Regional Medical Center, Hazard, KY, p. A253
Vice President Medical Affairs, Morgan County Arh Hospital, West Liberty, KY, p. A261
Vice President Medical Affairs, Tug Valley Arh Regional Medical Center, South Williamson, KY, p. A260

MILLER, James, Chief Executive Officer, Glen Oaks Hospital, Greenville, TX, p. A608

MILLER, James L, Chief Financial Officer, Baptist Medical Center Yazoo, Yazoo City, MS, p. A355

MILLER, Jane E.
Director Human Resources, Avera Creighton Hospital, Creighton, NE, p. A384
Human Resources Officer, Avera Sacred Heart Hospital, Yankton, SD, p. A565

MILLER, Jason R., Chief Financial Officer, The Medical Center Of Southeast Texas, Port Arthur, TX, p. A630

MILLER, Jeff, Chief Operating Officer, Citizens Memorial Hospital, Bolivar, MO, p. A356

MILLER, Jeff, M.D., Chief of Staff, Parkview Wabash Hospital, Wabash, IN, p. A216

MILLER, Jon, Director Accounting and Information Services, Hancock Regional Hospital, Greenfield, IN, p. A205

MILLER, Joshua, Director Information Systems, Joint Township District Memorial Hospital, Saint Marys, OH, p. A490

MILLER, Joy, Chief Nursing Officer, Cornerstone Hospital Of Little Rock, Little Rock, AR, p. A45

MILLER, Julie, Chief Operating Officer, Williamson Medical Center, Franklin, TN, p. A570

MILLER, Karen, Chief Financial Officer, San Juan Regional Medical Center, Farmington, NM, p. A418

MILLER, Kay J, R.N., MSN, Chief Nursing Officer, Uchealth Memorial Hospital, Colorado Springs, CO, p. A98

MILLER, Keith, Chief Operating Officer, Daviess Community Hospital, Washington, IN, p. A216

MILLER, Ken, Chief Financial Officer, Beaufort Memorial Hospital, Beaufort, SC, p. A549

MILLER, Kevin
President, Chi Health Lakeside, Omaha, NE, p. A389
President, Chi Health Midlands, Papillion, NE, p. A390

MILLER, Kris, Senior Human Resources Business Partner, Spectrum Health Reed City Hospital, Reed City, MI, p. A320

MILLER, Krista, R.N., Chief Nursing Officer, Shriners Hospitals For Children–Philadelphia, Philadelphia, PA, p. A536

MILLER, Laurie, Administrative Assistant, Sakakawea Medical Center, Hazen, ND, p. A467

MILLER, Leanne R, Director Human Resources, Community Hospital, Mccook, NE, p. A387

MILLER, Lisa, Director Human Resources, Hendry Regional Medical Center, Clewiston, FL, p. A120

MILLER, Maria, Controller, Beaumont Hospital – Grosse Pointe, Grosse Pointe, MI, p. A313

MILLER, Mark
Chief Executive Officer, West Hills Hospital And Medical Center, Los Angeles, CA, p. A70
Chief Financial Officer, Freeman Regional Health Services, Freeman, SD, p. A561
Director Information Systems, Perry County Memorial Hospital, Tell City, IN, p. A215

MILLER, Mark A., Chief Executive Officer, Harlan County Health System, Alma, NE, p. A382

MILLER, Mary, Vice President Finance and Business Development, Mt. Washington Pediatric Hospital, Baltimore, MD, p. A287

MILLER, Mary Beth, M.D., Chief of Staff, Cheyenne County Hospital, Saint Francis, KS, p. A244

MILLER, Mathew, M.D., Vice President and Chief Medical Officer, St. Joseph Hospital, Eureka, CA, p. A57

MILLER, Michael J
Director Human Resources, Barnes–Jewish St. Peters Hospital, Saint Peters, MO, p. A371
Director Human Resources, Progress West Hospital, O'Fallon, MO, p. A366

MILLER, Michele A, R.N., MSN, Vice President, Acute and Nursing Services, Rutgers University Behavioral Healthcare, Piscataway, NJ, p. A411

MILLER, Michelle, Chief Human Resources, Placentia–Linda Hospital, Placentia, CA, p. A78

MILLER, Nicole, Director Human Resources, Riverside Shore Memorial Hospital, Onancock, VA, p. A664

MILLER, Patrick, Technology Coordinator, San Bernardino Mountains Community Hospital District, Lake Arrowhead, CA, p. A63

MILLER, Paul, Director of Operations, Sanford Chamberlain Medical Center, Chamberlain, SD, p. A560

MILLER, Peter S, Chief Financial Officer, North Vista Hospital, North Las Vegas, NV, p. A396

MILLER, Phil, Chief Information Officer, Unity Health White County Medical Center, Searcy, AR, p. A48

MILLER, Redonda G., President, Johns Hopkins Hospital, Baltimore, MD, p. A286

MILLER, Richard, Administrator Finance, Banner Thunderbird Medical Center, Glendale, AZ, p. A30

MILLER, Richard B., Ph.D., Vice President Hospital Affairs and Chief Financial Officer, Brookdale Hospital Medical Center, New York, NY, p. A432

MILLER, Rick
Chief Financial Officer, District One Hospital, Faribault, MN, p. A332
Director, Operations and Finance, District One Hospital, Faribault, MN, p. A332
President and Chief Operating Officer, Nationwide Children'S Hospital, Columbus, OH, p. A479

MILLER, Rod, Chief Information Technology, Community Hospital, Torrington, WY, p. A713

MILLER, Ryan, Administrator, Christus Southeast Texas Hospital – St. Elizabeth, Beaumont, TX, p. A587

MILLER, Sam, Chief Executive Officer, North Sunflower Medical Center, Ruleville, MS, p. A354

MILLER, Shane
Chief Information Officer, Hshs St. Clare Memorial Hospital, Oconto Falls, WI, p. A703
Chief Information Officer, Hshs St. Mary'S Hospital Medical Center, Green Bay, WI, p. A696
Chief Information Officer, Hshs St. Nicholas Hospital, Sheboygan, WI, p. A705
Chief Information Officer, Hshs St. Vincent Hospital, Green Bay, WI, p. A696

MILLER, Stacy, Entity Human Resources Officer, Texas Health Presbyterian Hospital Dallas, Dallas, TX, p. A598

MILLER, Steve, Director Information Systems, Baptist Medical Center South, Montgomery, AL, p. A21

MILLER, Susan, Financial Administrator, Faulkton Area Medical Center, Faulkton, SD, p. A560

MILLER, Suzanne, R.N., MSN, Senior Director Patient Care Services and Nursing, St. Luke'S Wood River Medical Center, Ketchum, ID, p. A170

MILLER, Tamara, Chief Executive Officer and Administrator, Madison Regional Health System, Madison, SD, p. A561

MILLER, Ted, Vice President and Chief Financial Officer, Memorial Hospital And Health Care Center, Jasper, IN, p. A208

MILLER, Thomas, Chief Executive Officer, University Of Louisville Hospital, Louisville, KY, p. A257

MILLER, Thomas, M.D., Medical Director, University Of Utah Health, Salt Lake City, UT, p. A652

MILLER, Valerie L, MSN, R.N., Director of Nursing, Major Hospital, Shelbyville, IN, p. A214
MILLER, Weston, M.D., Chief Medical Officer, Abbeville General Hospital, Abbeville, LA, p. A262
MILLER, William, Coordinator Management Information Systems, Livengrin Foundation, Bensalem, PA, p. A520
MILLER–BALFOUR, Pam, Director Human Resources, Socorro General Hospital, Socorro, NM, p. A421
MILLER–COLLETTE, Melody M, Director Human Resources, North Okaloosa Medical Center, Crestview, FL, p. A120
MILLICAN, Sharon, Associate Director, Patient Care Services, South Texas Veterans Health Care System, San Antonio, TX, p. A635
MILLIS, David, M.D., Clinical Director, Thomas B. Finan Center, Cumberland, MD, p. A290
MILLS, Amanda, Chief Nursing Officer, Mcleod Loris Seacoast Hospital, Loris, SC, p. A555
MILLS, Aundrea, Chief Nursing Officer, Sovah Health–Danville, Danville, VA, p. A658
MILLS, Craig
Chief Financial Officer, Heber Valley Hospital, Heber City, UT, p. A648
Vice President Human Resources, Peacehealth Sacred Heart Medical Center University District, Eugene, OR, p. A512
MILLS, Dennis, Chief Human Resources Officer, San Ramon Regional Medical Center, San Ramon, CA, p. A88
MILLS, Gene, Director Information Technology, Scenic Mountain Medical Center, Big Spring, TX, p. A588
MILLS, Jerry, Chief Human Resources Management Services, San Francisco Va Medical Center, San Francisco, CA, p. A85
MILLS, Jim, Regional Director Information Technology, Sutter Medical Center, Sacramento, Sacramento, CA, p. A82
MILLS, John, Chief Operating Officer, Cleveland Clinic Avon Hospital, Avon, OH, p. A472
MILLS, John C, Senior Vice President Operations, Cleveland Clinic Fairview Hospital, Cleveland, OH, p. A477
MILLS, Kalen M, Director Human Resources, Southern Coos Hospital And Health Center, Bandon, OR, p. A511
MILLS, Marianne, R.N., Chairperson, Stanton County Hospital, Johnson, KS, p. A237
MILLS, Scott, M.D., Vice President Medical Staff Administration and Chief Medical Officer, Mid Coast Hospital, Brunswick, ME, p. A202
MILLS, Sean
Chief Financial Officer, Our Lady Of Lourdes Memorial Hospital, Inc., Binghamton, NY, p. A424
Chief Financial Officer, Samaritan Medical Center, Watertown, NY, p. A447
MILLS, Tylie, Chief Executive Officer, Pike County Memorial Hospital, Louisiana, MO, p. A364
MILLS, Vicki L, Chief Financial Officer, Anderson County Hospital, Garnett, KS, p. A236
MILLS, William, M.D.
Senior Vice President Quality and Professional Affairs, Bradford Regional Medical Center, Bradford, PA, p. A521
Senior Vice President Quality and Professional Affairs, Olean General Hospital, Olean, NY, p. A440
MILLS–MATHEWS, Marcy, Director Human Resources, Palms West Hospital, Loxahatchee, FL, p. A128
MILLSAP, Debra, Director of Nursing, River Crest Hospital, San Angelo, TX, p. A632
MILLSAPS, Janet
Chief Human Resources Officer, Harris Regional Hospital, Sylva, NC, p. A463
Vice President Human Resources, Haywood Regional Medical Center, Clyde, NC, p. A452
MILLSAPS, Jarrett B., Jr, Chief Executive Officer, Parkridge Medical Center, Chattanooga, TN, p. A567
MILNE, C Dean, D.O., Medical Director, Complex Care Hospital At Tenaya, Las Vegas, NV, p. A394
MILNER, Mark W, Chief Nursing Officer, Ephraim Mcdowell Regional Medical Center, Danville, KY, p. A251
MILNER, Rene, Chief Medical Officer, Osceola Medical Center, Osceola, WI, p. A703
MILONE, Sheri, Chief Executive Officer and Administrator, Lovelace Women'S Hospital, Albuquerque, NM, p. A416
MILOVICH, David, Vice President Human Resources, Saint Mary'S Regional Medical Center, Reno, NV, p. A397
MILSTEIN, Marc E., Vice President Information Resources, University Of Texas Southwestern Medical Center, Dallas, TX, p. A598
MILTON, Kerry K., R.N., Chief Nursing Officer, St. Tammany Parish Hospital, Covington, LA, p. A266
MILTON, Paul A, Executive Vice President and Chief Operating Officer, Ellis Hospital, Schenectady, NY, p. A444
MILTON, Paul A., President and Chief Executive Officer, Ellis Hospital, Schenectady, NY, p. A444
MILTON, S. Byron, M.D., Medical Director, Emory Rehabilitation Hospital, Atlanta, GA, p. A146
MILUS, Lori, R.N., MSN, Director of Nursing, Aurora Behavioral Health System West, Glendale, AZ, p. A30
MILVET, Robert W., Jr, Chief Executive Officer, Grant Memorial Hospital, Petersburg, WV, p. A688
MIMS, Krystal, Chief Executive Officer, Sagecrest Hospital Of Grapevine, Grapevine, TX, p. A608
MIMS, Staci, Chief Nursing Officer, Dorminy Medical Center, Fitzgerald, GA, p. A153
MIMS, Tammy
Chief Executive Officer, Jeff Davis Hospital, Hazlehurst, GA, p. A154
Interim Chief Executive Officer, Liberty Regional Medical Center, Hinesville, GA, p. A154
MINARD, Keith, Chief Information Officer, Chinese Hospital, San Francisco, CA, p. A85
MINCEY, Wallace D, Chief Executive Officer, Clinch Memorial Hospital, Homerville, GA, p. A155
MINDEN, Philip, President, St. Joseph'S Hospital, Tampa, FL, p. A142
MINEAR, Michael N., Senior Vice President and Chief Information Officer, Lehigh Valley Hospital, Allentown, PA, p. A519
MINEAU, Francine, Chief Nursing Officer, Baton Rouge Behavioral Hospital, Baton Rouge, LA, p. A263
MINER, Bill, M.D., Chief of Staff, Huron Regional Medical Center, Huron, SD, p. A561
MINER, Edwina A R.N., Chief Nursing Officer, Ennis Regional Medical Center, Ennis, TX, p. A603
MINER, Greg, Administrator, Dunes Surgical Hospital, Dakota Dunes, SD, p. A560
MINER, John, Chief Financial Officer, Kindred Hospital Central Tampa, Tampa, FL, p. A141
MINGLE, Regina, Senior Vice President and Chief Leadership Officer, Penn Medicine Lancaster General Hospital, Lancaster, PA, p. A529
MINGS, William, M.D., Medical Director, Carl Albert Community Mental Health Center, Mcalester, OK, p. A502
MINGUS, Linda, Director Human Resources, Aurora Medical Center Of Oshkosh, Oshkosh, WI, p. A703
MINIER, Lori, Chief Financial Officer, Benewah Community Hospital, Saint Maries, ID, p. A171
MINIER, Mary, President, Indiana University Health White Memorial Hospital, Monticello, IN, p. A211
MINIOR, Devin, M.D., Chief Medical Officer, Banner Casa Grande Medical Center, Casa Grande, AZ, p. A28
MINISSALE, Joseph, President, Methodist Mckinney Hospital, Mckinney, TX, p. A624
MINKS, Michael H.
Chief Information Officer VI, Ascension Seton Medical Center Austin, Austin, TX, p. A584
Chief Information Officer VI, Dell Seton Medical Center At The University Of Texas, Austin, TX, p. A585
Chief Information Officer, Ascension Seton Edgar B. Davis Hospital, Luling, TX, p. A622
Chief Information Officer, Ascension Seton Northwest, Austin, TX, p. A584
Chief Information Officer, Ascension Seton Shoal Creek, Austin, TX, p. A585
MINNICK, Paul E, R.N., MSN, Senior Vice President and Chief Operating Officer, Virtua Voorhees, Voorhees, NJ, p. A414
MINNICK, Peggy, Chief Executive Officer, Bhc Alhambra Hospital, Rosemead, CA, p. A81
MINNIS, Rosanne, Business Officer, Rochester Psychiatric Center, Rochester, NY, p. A442
MINON, Maria, M.D.
Vice President Medical Affairs and Chief Medical Officer, Children'S Hospital Of Orange County, Orange, CA, p. A76
Vice President Medical Affairs and Chief Medical Officer, Choc Children'S At Mission Hospital, Mission Viejo, CA, p. A72
MINOR, Amy, Chief Nursing Officer, Troy Regional Medical Center, Troy, AL, p. A23
MINOR, Athena, Chief Nursing Officer, Ohio County Hospital, Hartford, KY, p. A253
MINOR, Beverly, Chief Human Resources, Schleicher County Medical Center, Eldorado, TX, p. A603
MINOR, Blaine, M.D., Chief of Staff, Adventhealth Murray, Chatsworth, GA, p. A150
MINSHEW, Tony L., Vice President, Patient Care Services, Conway Medical Center, Conway, SC, p. A552
MINSINGER, Linda, Vice President Hospital Division, Gifford Medical Center, Randolph, VT, p. A655
MINSKY, Bart R, Interim Vice President Human Resources, Adventist Health And Rideout, Marysville, CA, p. A71
MINTEER, Laura, Chief Human Resource Officer, Meritus Medical Center, Hagerstown, MD, p. A291
MINTON, Tamra, R.N., MSN, Vice President Patient Care Services and Chief Nursing Officer, Upmc East, Monroeville, PA, p. A532
MINTONYE, Traci, Chief Financial Officer, River Hospital, Alexandria Bay, NY, p. A422
MINTZ, Michael, M.D., Chief Medical Officer, South Texas Surgical Hospital, Corpus Christi, TX, p. A594
MIRABELLA, Ilene, Director Human Resources, Vibra Hospital Of Southeastern Massachusetts, New Bedford, MA, p. A301
MIRANDA, Ada S, M.D., Medical Director, Hospital Metropolitano Dr. Susoni, Arecibo, PR, p. A715
MIRANDA, Casey D., Executive Vice President and Chief Operating Officer, Jackson County Memorial Hospital, Altus, OK, p. A496
MIRANDA, Ivette, Chief Executive Officer, Healthsouth Rehabilitation Hospital At Martin Health, Stuart, FL, p. A140
MIRANDA, Kim, Chief Financial Officer, St. Elizabeth Community Hospital, Red Bluff, CA, p. A79
MIRANDA, Kimberly
Chief Financial Officer, Mercy Medical Center Mount Shasta, Mount Shasta, CA, p. A73
Regional Vice President Finance and Chief Financial Officer, Mercy Medical Center Redding, Redding, CA, p. A79
MIRANDA, Lisa, Vice President Operations, University Medical Center, New Orleans, LA, p. A275
MIRANDA, Michael, Chief of Staff, Mercy Hospital Booneville, Booneville, AR, p. A40
MIRANDA, Samuel, Chief Nursing Officer, Good Shepherd Specialty Hospital, Bethlehem, PA, p. A520
MIRANDA, Vicki, Vice President Human Resources, Dominican Hospital, Santa Cruz, CA, p. A88
MIRANDA, Victor Hernandez, M.D., Chief of Staff, Mennonite General Hospital, Aibonito, PR, p. A715
MIRZA, Irfan, Chief Financial Officer, Plantation General Hospital, Plantation, FL, p. A137
MIRZABEGIAN, Edward
Chief Executive Officer, Antelope Valley Hospital, Lancaster, CA, p. A64
Chief Executive Officer, West Anaheim Medical Center, Anaheim, CA, p. A50
MISHKIND, Steven, M.D., Chief of Staff, Desoto Memorial Hospital, Arcadia, FL, p. A117
MISHLER, Sheila, Chief Executive Officer, St. Vincent Indianapolis Hospital, Indianapolis, IN, p. A208
MISITI, Joseph, M.D., President Medical Staff, Medina Memorial Hospital, Medina, NY, p. A431
MISKIMEN, Theresa, M.D., Vice President Medical Services, Rutgers University Behavioral Healthcare, Piscataway, NJ, p. A411
MISRA, Sahana, Acting Chief of Staff, Va Portland Healthcare System, Portland, OR, p. A516
MISSERITTI, Colomba, Director Human Resources, Rochester Psychiatric Center, Rochester, NY, p. A442
MITCHAM, Debbie, Chief Financial Officer, Northside Hospital, Atlanta, GA, p. A146
MITCHELL, Adonna, Director Fiscal Services, North Mississippi Medical Center–Eupora, Eupora, MS, p. A346
MITCHELL, Andrew J., President and Chief Executive Officer, Peconic Bay Medical Center, Riverhead, NY, p. A442
MITCHELL, Barbara
Director Human Resources, Oasis Behavioral Health – Chandler, Chandler, AZ, p. A28
Senior Vice President Marketing and Human Resources, Uw Medicine/Valley Medical Center, Renton, WA, p. A677
MITCHELL, Bridgett, Chief Clinical Officer, Advanced Specialty Hospital Of Toledo, Toledo, OH, p. A492
MITCHELL, Camelia, M.D., Medical Director, Texas Rehabilitation Hospital Of Arlington, Arlington, TX, p. A584
MITCHELL, Dave, Manager Information Services, Spectrum Health Gerber Memorial, Fremont, MI, p. A312
MITCHELL, David
Chief Executive Officer, Baptist Emergency Hospital, San Antonio, TX, p. A633
Interim Chief Executive Officer, Baptist Emergency Hospital, San Antonio, TX, p. A633
MITCHELL, Douglas W, Vice President and Chief Nursing Officer, West Virginia University Hospitals, Morgantown, WV, p. A687
MITCHELL, Elizabeth C, Chief Operating Officer, Specialty Hospital Of Meridian, Meridian, MS, p. A351
MITCHELL, Elizabeth C., Chief Executive Officer and Chief Operating Officer, Specialty Hospital Of Meridian, Meridian, MS, p. A351
MITCHELL, Errol, Chief Financial Officer, Integris Canadian Valley Hospital, Yukon, OK, p. A510
MITCHELL, Heath, Chief Operating Officer, Memorial Hospital, Seminole, TX, p. A636
MITCHELL, Ivan, Chief Operating Officer, Great Plains Health, North Platte, NE, p. A388

MITCHELL, Jack C., Chief Executive Officer, Encompass Health Rehabilitation Hospital, A Partner Of Washington Regional, Fayetteville, AR, p. A41

MITCHELL, Jenifer, R.N., Director of Nursing Services, Mineral Community Hospital, Superior, MT, p. A380

MITCHELL, Jodie, Facility Financial Director, Sturgis Regional Hospital, Sturgis, SD, p. A564

MITCHELL, Joe J., Chief Executive Officer, Acadia General Hospital, Crowley, LA, p. A266

MITCHELL, Karen, Vice President Patient Care Services, Children'S Hospital Of The King'S Daughters, Norfolk, VA, p. A663

MITCHELL, Kathy
Chief Nursing Officer, Owensboro Health Muhlenberg Community Hospital, Greenville, KY, p. A252
Director Human Resources, Marshfield Medical Center – Rice Lake, Rice Lake, WI, p. A704

MITCHELL, Kathy, R.N., Chief Nursing Officer, Doctors Hospital Of Sarasota, Sarasota, FL, p. A139

MITCHELL, Kent, Chief Financial Officer, Hamilton Memorial Hospital District, Mcleansboro, IL, p. A189

MITCHELL, Leah, R.N., Interim Chief Information Officer, Salem Hospital, Salem, OR, p. A517

MITCHELL, Marsha, Director Human Resources, Fleming County Hospital, Flemingsburg, KY, p. A251

MITCHELL, Mary S, Chief Resource Management Services, Birmingham Veterans Affairs Medical Center, Birmingham, AL, p. A14

MITCHELL, Morris, Director Human Resources, Poplar Springs Hospital, Petersburg, VA, p. A665

MITCHELL, Naomi, Director Human Resources, Kentucky River Medical Center, Jackson, KY, p. A254

MITCHELL, Perry, M.D., Chief of Staff, Little Colorado Medical Center, Winslow, AZ, p. A38

MITCHELL, Rebekah, Chief Financial Officer, Madison County Health Care System, Winterset, IA, p. A231

MITCHELL, Rhonda K, Director Human Resources, Stonewall Jackson Memorial Hospital, Weston, WV, p. A690

MITCHELL, Richard R, Director Information Technology, Eagleville Hospital, Eagleville, PA, p. A524

MITCHELL, Sarah, Director Finance, Mary S Harper Geriatric Psychiatry Center, Tuscaloosa, AL, p. A24

MITCHELL, Scot, Chief Executive Officer and Administrator, Cordova Community Medical Center, Cordova, AK, p. A25

MITCHELL, Steve, Chief Operating Officer, Memorial Medical Center, Modesto, CA, p. A72

MITCHELL, Timothy, R.N., Chief Nursing Officer, Complex Care Hospital At Ridgelake, Sarasota, FL, p. A139

MITCHELL, Walton F., III, Director, Catawba Hospital, Catawba, VA, p. A657

MITCHELL, William, Chief Executive Officer and Administrator, Kindred Hospital Riverside, Perris, CA, p. A78

MITCHELL SANCHEZ, Lexi, D.O., Chief of Staff, Clay County Memorial Hospital, Henrietta, TX, p. A610

MITCHUM, Linda, Director of Nursing, William J. Mccord Adolescent Treatment Facility, Orangeburg, SC, p. A556

MITHUN, Robert, M.D., Physician in Chief, Kaiser Permanente San Francisco Medical Center, San Francisco, CA, p. A85

MITRICK, Joseph M., President, Baptist Medical Center Beaches, Jacksonville Beach, FL, p. A126

MITRY, Norman F.
President and Chief Executive Officer, Heritage Valley Health System, Beaver, PA, p. A520
President and Chief Executive Officer, Sewickley Valley Hospital, (A Division Of Valley Medical Facilities), Sewickley, PA, p. A541

MITTAL, Vikrant, M.D., Chief Medical Officer, Danville State Hospital, Danville, PA, p. A523

MIX, Sherry, Chief Executive Officer and Administrator, The Neuromedical Center Rehabilitation Hospital, Baton Rouge, LA, p. A264

MIXON, Robin, Administrator, North Mississippi Medical Center–Eupora, Eupora, MS, p. A346

MIYAMOTO, Faye, Assistant Vice President Human Resources, Rehabilitation Hospital Of The Pacific, Honolulu, HI, p. A165

MIYASAWA, Patricia, CPA, Director Fiscal Service, Shriners Hospitals For Children–Honolulu, Honolulu, HI, p. A165

MIYAUCHI, Kimberly, R.N., Chief Nursing Officer, Kingman Regional Medical Center, Kingman, AZ, p. A30

MIZE, William D, Chief Operating Officer, Trousdale Medical Center, Hartsville, TN, p. A570

MIZELL, Philip L, M.D., Medical Director, The Bridgeway, North Little Rock, AR, p. A47

MIZER, Alison, Chief Financial Officer, St. Anthony North Health Campus, Westminster, CO, p. A106

MIZIA, Robert, Director Information Systems and Chief Information Officer, Inspira Medical Center–Woodbury, Woodbury, NJ, p. A415

MIZONO, Gary, M.D., Physician–in–Chief, Kaiser Permanente San Rafael Medical Center, San Rafael, CA, p. A87

MLAWSKY, Karen, Senior Vice President and Chief Operations Officer, Tmc Healthcare, Tucson, AZ, p. A38

MMEJE, Ikenna, Chief Operating Officer, Memorialcare, Long Beach Memorial Medical Center, Long Beach, CA, p. A65

MO, Lin H, President, Brookdale Hospital Medical Center, New York, NY, p. A432

MOAD, Sharon, Human Resources Director Health Information Management, Elkview General Hospital, Hobart, OK, p. A500

MOAK, Jennifer, Business Office Manager, Lawrence County Hospital, Monticello, MS, p. A351

MOAKLER, Thomas J., Chief Executive Officer, Houlton Regional Hospital, Houlton, ME, p. A283

MOATS, Susan K., R.N.
Vice President Patient Care Services and Chief Nursing Officer, Baylor Scott & White The Heart Hospital Plano, Plano, TX, p. A629
Vice President Patient Care Services and Chief Nursing Officer, Baylor Scott & White The Heart Hospital–Denton, Denton, TX, p. A599

MOAWAD, Gerald, Chief Medical Officer, Bridgepoint Hospital Capitol Hill, Washington, DC, p. A115

MOCK, Jesse, Chief Executive Officer, University Of Kansas Health System Great Bend Campus, Great Bend, KS, p. A235

MOCK, Presley, M.D., Chief of Staff, Texas Institute For Surgery At Texas Health Presbyterian Dallas, Dallas, TX, p. A598

MOE, Jonathan
Chief Operating Officer, Shenandoah Medical Center, Shenandoah, IA, p. A229
President, Chi Health Missouri Valley, Missouri Valley, IA, p. A226

MOEEN, Farida, Chief Executive Officer, United Memorial Medical Care, Houston, TX, p. A614

MOEEN, Farida, M.D., Chief Executive Officer, United Memorial Medical Care, Houston, TX, p. A614

MOELLER, Deborah A, R.N., MS, Interim Chief Nursing Officer, Baylor Scott & White Medical Center – Sunnyvale, Sunnyvale, TX, p. A639

MOEN, Belinda, R.N., MSN, Interim Director of Nursing, Mountrail County Medical Center, Stanley, ND, p. A469

MOEN, Daniel P., President, St. Francis Medical Center, Trenton, NJ, p. A413

MOEN, Larry, Chief Financial Officer, Coteau Des Prairies Hospital, Sisseton, SD, p. A564

MOFFA, Salvatore, M.D., Vice President, Medical Affairs and Chief Medical Officer, Robert Wood Johnson University Hospital Somerset, Somerville, NJ, p. A412

MOFFAT, Jeanne, Manager Information Technology, Keefe Memorial Hospital, Cheyenne Wells, CO, p. A97

MOFFAT, Jennifer, Staff Accountant, Regional West Garden County, Oshkosh, NE, p. A390

MOFFATT, Dan, Chief Information Officer, Sanford Bemidji Medical Center, Bemidji, MN, p. A328

MOFFET, Chris, Director Information Services, Bob Wilson Memorial Grant County Hospital, Ulysses, KS, p. A247

MOFFITT, Brenda L., Chief Nursing Officer, Memorial Health System, Abilene, KS, p. A232

MOFFITT SOD, Rhonda, Chief Nursing Officer, First Hospital Wyoming Valley, Kingston, PA, p. A528

MOGERMAN, Shauna, Chief Executive Officer, Roxbury Treatment Center, Shippensburg, PA, p. A541

MOGG, Cassie, Chief Financial Officer, Covenant Hospital Plainview, Plainview, TX, p. A629

MOHAMED, Antonia, Acting Chief Information Officer, Birmingham Veterans Affairs Medical Center, Birmingham, AL, p. A14

MOHAMMED, Ehtaisham, M.D., Chief Medical Officer, Ridgeview Sibley Medical Center, Arlington, MN, p. A327

MOHAN, Amit, President and Chief Executive Officer, Barlow Respiratory Hospital, Los Angeles, CA, p. A66

MOHAN, Rajesh, M.D., Chief Medical Officer, Monmouth Medical Center, Southern Campus, Lakewood, NJ, p. A407

MOHANDAS, Arjun, M.D., Chief of Staff, Ascension Seton Edgar B. Davis Hospital, Luling, TX, p. A622

MOHLER, Brittany, Director Human Resources, Essentia Health–Deer River, Deer River, MN, p. A330

MOHNK, Richard, Vice President Corporate Services, Bayhealth Medical Center, Dover, DE, p. A113

MOHNKERN, Pearl, Vice President and Director Human Resources, Christus St. Vincent Regional Medical Center, Santa Fe, NM, p. A420

MOHR, Amanda, Chief Nursing Officer, Greater Regional Medical Center, Creston, IA, p. A220

MOHR, Amy, Coordinator Human Resources, Forest Health Medical Center, Ypsilanti, MI, p. A325

MOHR, Angela, R.N., MS, Vice President Nursing and Chief Operating Officer, Ssm Health St. Anthony Hospital – Shawnee, Shawnee, OK, p. A507

MOHR, Catherine, R.N., MSN, Chief Nursing Officer, Guthrie Robert Packer Hospital, Sayre, PA, p. A540

MOHR, Liz, Assistant Chief Financial Officer, Mercy Health – Fairfield Hospital, Fairfield, OH, p. A483

MOHR, Steve, Senior Vice President and Chief Financial Officer, Huntington Memorial Hospital, Pasadena, CA, p. A77

MOISAN, Terrence, Chief Executive Officer, Palos Health, Palos Heights, IL, p. A192

MOK, Michelle, Chief Financial Officer, Redlands Community Hospital, Redlands, CA, p. A80

MOKDESSI, Margot, Interim Chief Financial Officer, Vermilion Behavioral Health Systems – North Campus, Lafayette, LA, p. A271

MOKRY, Deborah, Chief Nurse Executive, St. Louis Psychiatric Rehabilitation Center, Saint Louis, MO, p. A370

MOL, Stacy E, CPA, Director Finance, Spencer Hospital, Spencer, IA, p. A230

MOLACEK, Shane, Chief Information Officer, Valley County Health System, Ord, NE, p. A390

MOLELUS, Elena, Manager Human Resources, Santa Barbara County Psychiatric Health Facility, Santa Barbara, CA, p. A88

MOLINA, Isabel, M.D., Chief Medical Officer, Lamb Healthcare Center, Littlefield, TX, p. A620

MOLINA, Luis F., Chief Executive Officer and Administrator, Community Hospital, Munster, IN, p. A212

MOLINARO, Frank L.
Chief Executive Officer, Abrazo Central Campus, Phoenix, AZ, p. A32
Chief Executive Officer, Abrazo Scottsdale Campus, Phoenix, AZ, p. A32

MOLITOR, Margie, Chief Executive Officer, Hot Springs County Memorial Hospital, Thermopolis, WY, p. A713

MOLL, Ben, Assistant Chief Financial Officer, Nashoba Valley Medical Center, Ayer, MA, p. A294

MOLL, Eric, Chief Executive Officer, Mason General Hospital And Family Of Clinics, Shelton, WA, p. A679

MOLL, Gudrun, R.N., MSN, Chief Nursing Officer, San Antonio Regional Hospital, Upland, CA, p. A93

MOLL, Jeffrey, M.D., Medical Director, Clarion Psychiatric Center, Clarion, PA, p. A522

MOLL, Michael A., M.D., Chief Medical Officer and Chief of Staff, Spanish Peaks Regional Health Center, Walsenburg, CO, p. A106

MOLLER, Dan, M.D., Chief Medical Officer, Willis–Knighton Medical Center, Shreveport, LA, p. A278

MOLLER, Lynn, Chief Financial Officer, Weston County Health Services, Newcastle, WY, p. A712

MOLLOHAN, Joan, Vice President Human Resources, Ochsner Medical Center, New Orleans, LA, p. A275

MOLLOY, Kevin, Senior Vice President and Chief Operating Officer, Brookdale Hospital Medical Center, New York, NY, p. A432

MOLLOY, Reuben D, Chief Information Officer, Governor Juan F. Luis Hospital, Christiansted, VI, p. A720

MOLNAR, Becky, Director of Finance, Cleveland Clinic, Medina Hospital, Medina, OH, p. A487

MOLT, Brianna, Human Resources Director, Genoa Medical Facilities, Genoa, NE, p. A385

MOLYNEUX, Phyllis, Associate Administrator Human Resources and Education, Williamson Medical Center, Franklin, TN, p. A570

MOMEYER, Polly, Manager Human Resources, Lecom Health Millcreek Community Hospital, Erie, PA, p. A525

MONAGHAN, Aimee, Chief Executive Officer, Compass Behavioral Center Of Lafayette, Lafayette, LA, p. A270

MONAHAN, Jane, Vice President Ministry, Spiritual Care and Human Resources, Monroe Clinic, Monroe, WI, p. A701

MONASTERIO, Eugene A, M.D., Medical Director, Children'S Hospital Of Richmond At Vcu–Brook Road Campus, Richmond, VA, p. A666

MONCHER, Daniel J, Vice President and Chief Financial Officer, Firelands Regional Health System, Sandusky, OH, p. A490

MONCHER, Daniel J., Interim President and Chief Executive Officer, Firelands Regional Health System, Sandusky, OH, p. A490

MONCRIEF, William, ORH IT Client Executive, Surgeons Choice Medical Center, Southfield, MI, p. A323

MONCZEWSKI, Ted, Vice President Human Resources, St. Vincent Charity Medical Center, Cleveland, OH, p. A478

MONDA, Cam, D.O., Medical Director, Greenwood Regional Rehabilitation Hospital, Greenwood, SC, p. A554

MONETTE, Steven, Chief Financial Officer, Brattleboro Retreat, Brattleboro, VT, p. A654

MONGE, Candice, R.N., Chief Nurse Executive Officer, Marian Regional Medical Center, Santa Maria, CA, p. A89

MONGE, Jacqualyn
Director of Nursing, Ascension Eagle River Hospital, Eagle River, WI, p. A694
Director of Nursing, Howard Young Medical Center, Woodruff, WI, p. A709

MONGELL, Mitchell P., Chief Executive Officer, Fort Walton Beach Medical Center, Fort Walton Beach, FL, p. A123

MONGER, Shelton, Director Information Technology, Wayne Healthcare, Greenville, OH, p. A484

MONIACI, Cathy, Administrator, Shriners Hospitals For Children–Houston, Houston, TX, p. A613

MONJE, Mary Anne
Chief Financial Officer and Chief Operating Officer, Whittier Hospital Medical Center, Whittier, CA, p. A95
Chief Financial Officer, Ahmc Anaheim Regional Medical Center, Anaheim, CA, p. A50
Chief Operations Officer, Ahmc Anaheim Regional Medical Center, Anaheim, CA, p. A50

MONJESKY, Kimberly, Chief Executive Officer, Pikes Peak Regional Hospital, Woodland Park, CO, p. A106

MONKRES, Paula, Administrative Assistant and Director Human Resources, Nocona General Hospital, Nocona, TX, p. A626

MONROE, Ame, Director Human Resources, Rolling Plains Memorial Hospital, Sweetwater, TX, p. A639

MONROE, Lori, Director of Nursing, Winnebago Mental Health Institute, Winnebago, WI, p. A709

MONROE, Temple, Director Nursing Operations, Wilson Medical Center, Neodesha, KS, p. A241

MONROIG, Domingo, Executive Director, Castaner General Hospital, Castaner, PR, p. A715

MONROY–MILLER, Cherry, M.D., Acting Medical Director, Greystone Park Psychiatric Hospital, Morris Plains, NJ, p. A408

MONSANTO, Monte, Chief Information Systems, Russell County Hospital, Russell Springs, KY, p. A260

MONSRUD, Michele, Director Human Resources, Piedmont Walton Hospital, Monroe, GA, p. A157

MONTAGNESE, Robert A., President and Chief Executive Officer, Licking Memorial Hospital, Newark, OH, p. A488

MONTALBO, Tripp, Chief Executive Officer, Hca Houston Healthcare Clear Lake, League City, TX, p. A620

MONTALVO, Eladio, Chief Executive Officer, Fort Duncan Regional Medical Center, Eagle Pass, TX, p. A600

MONTALVO, Jose, M.D., Medical Director, Hospital Del Maestro, San Juan, PR, p. A718

MONTANA, Jennifer, Manager Human Resources, Community Memorial Hospital, Hamilton, NY, p. A429

MONTANA–RHODES, Lou, Vice President of Patient Care Services, Vidant Beaufort Hospital, Washington, NC, p. A463

MONTANIO, John, Chief Financial Officer, Longleaf Hospital, Alexandria, LA, p. A262

MONTANO, Maxine, R.N., Chief Nursing Officer, Rolling Plains Memorial Hospital, Sweetwater, TX, p. A639

MONTANO, Mayra, Director Information Systems, Hospital Metropolitano Dr. Susoni, Arecibo, PR, p. A715

MONTANTE, Carl, Director Information Systems and Information Technology, Shriners Hospitals For Children–Portland, Portland, OR, p. A516

MONTANYE, Richard, Director Information Systems, Hunt Regional Medical Center, Greenville, TX, p. A608

MONTANYE–IRELAND, Cherelle, Chief Administrative Officer, Peacehealth St. John Medical Center, Longview, WA, p. A674

MONTELONGO, Rick J., Chief Executive Officer, St. Mark'S Medical Center, La Grange, TX, p. A619

MONTENEGRO, Diana, Director Human Resources, Baptist Health South Florida, South Miami Hospital, Miami, FL, p. A130

MONTER, Brian, President, Uh Regional Hospitals, Cleveland, OH, p. A478

MONTESI, Michael W., M.D., Chief of Staff, North Sunflower Medical Center, Ruleville, MS, p. A354

MONTESINO–KING, Becky, MS, R.N., MSN, Vice President and Chief Nursing Officer, Baptist Health South Florida, Baptist Hospital Of Miami, Miami, FL, p. A130

MONTGOMERY, Brigett, Director Human Resource, Lawrence Memorial Hospital, Walnut Ridge, AR, p. A49

MONTGOMERY, Daniel, Chief Financial Officer, Specialists Hospital – Shreveport, Shreveport, LA, p. A278

MONTGOMERY, Jennifer
Chief Financial Officer, Washakie Medical Center, Worland, WY, p. A713
President and Chief Executive Officer, Mclaren Port Huron, Port Huron, MI, p. A320

MONTGOMERY, Mark, M.D., Chief Medical Officer, Texas Health Harris Methodist Hospital Southwest Fort Worth, Fort Worth, TX, p. A606

MONTGOMERY, Mary Jim, R.N., MSN, FACHE, Chief Operating Officer, Crisp Regional Hospital, Cordele, GA, p. A151

MONTGOMERY, Peggy, Director Medical Records, Arrowhead Behavioral Health Hospital, Maumee, OH, p. A487

MONTGOMERY, Roxie, Director of Nursing, Jane Todd Crawford Hospital, Greensburg, KY, p. A252

MONTGOMERY, Susan, Chief Nursing Officer, Asante Ashland Community Hospital, Ashland, OR, p. A511

MONTGOMERY, Tina, Chief Financial Officer, Sidney Health Center, Sidney, MT, p. A380

MONTMENY, Richard, Vice President Professional Services, On–Site Administrator, St. John'S Pleasant Valley Hospital, Camarillo, CA, p. A53

MONTOUR, Vina, Director Information Technology, U. S. Public Health Service Phoenix Indian Medical Center, Phoenix, AZ, p. A34

MONTOYA, Alfred, Director, Manchester Veterans Affairs Medical Center, Manchester, NH, p. A401

MONTOYA, Brooke, Director Human Resources, Lake Granbury Medical Center, Granbury, TX, p. A608

MONTOYA, Lillian, President and Chief Executive Officer, Christus St. Vincent Regional Medical Center, Santa Fe, NM, p. A420

MONTOYA, Lionel J., Chief Financial Officer, Spanish Peaks Regional Health Center, Walsenburg, CO, p. A106

MONZINGO, Ashley, Human Resources, Accounts Payable and Payroll, Tops Surgical Specialty Hospital, Houston, TX, p. A614

MONZON, Rogelio, Chief Financial Officer, Good Samaritan Hospital, Bakersfield, CA, p. A52

MOODY, Christy, R.N., Chief Nursing Officer, Carolina Pines Regional Medical Center, Hartsville, SC, p. A554

MOODY, Crystal R, Director Human Resources, Izard County Medical Center, Calico Rock, AR, p. A40

MOODY, David, Vice President Human Resources, Salina Regional Health Center, Salina, KS, p. A245

MOODY, James, Chief Financial Officer, Donalsonville Hospital, Donalsonville, GA, p. A152

MOODY, Vicky, Director Human Resources, Houlton Regional Hospital, Houlton, ME, p. A283

MOON, Bob, Chief Financial Officer, Christus St. Vincent Regional Medical Center, Santa Fe, NM, p. A420

MOON, David, Director Information Systems, Lake City Community Hospital, Lake City, SC, p. A555

MOON, Diane, Chief Financial Officer, Adventist Health And Rideout, Marysville, CA, p. A71

MOON, James, Chief Financial Officer, Pana Community Hospital, Pana, IL, p. A192

MOON, John, Associate Director, Veterans Affairs Eastern Kansas Health Care System, Topeka, KS, p. A246

MOONEY, Claire Bradley, R.N., Vice President and Chief Nursing Officer, Jennersville Hospital, West Grove, PA, p. A544

MOONEY, Claire Bradley., President and Chief Executive Officer, Jennersville Hospital, West Grove, PA, p. A544

MOONEY, Melissa, Director Human Resources, Mercy Rehabilitation Hospital Springfield, Springfield, MO, p. A372

MOONEY, Robert W, M.D., Medical Director, Willingway Hospital, Statesboro, GA, p. A161

MOONEY, Susan E., President and Chief Executive Officer, Alice Peck Day Memorial Hospital, Lebanon, NH, p. A400

MOORE, Amy, Human Resources, Hamilton Hospital, Olney, TX, p. A627

MOORE, Ben, III, President and Chief Executive Officer, River Hospital, Alexandria Bay, NY, p. A422

MOORE, Betty, Business Manager, North Mississippi Medical Center–Iuka, Iuka, MS, p. A348

MOORE, Bill, Chief Human Resources, El Centro Regional Medical Center, El Centro, CA, p. A57

MOORE, Brandon, Administrator and Chief Executive Officer, Park Place Surgical Hospital, Lafayette, LA, p. A271

MOORE, Brett, CPA, Assistant Administrator Finance, Sutter Amador Hospital, Jackson, CA, p. A62

MOORE, Brian, President and Chief Executive Officer, Bay Area Hospital, Coos Bay, OR, p. A512

MOORE, C Thomas, FACHE, Chief Financial Officer, Delta Regional Medical Center, Greenville, MS, p. A347

MOORE, Carrie, Director Human Resources, Meadowbrook Rehabilitation Hospital, Gardner, KS, p. A235

MOORE, Cecelia B, CPA, Associate Vice Chancellor Finance, Vanderbilt University Medical Center, Nashville, TN, p. A577

MOORE, Christie, Director Human Resources, Encompass Health Rehabilitation Hospital Of The Mid–Cities, Bedford, TX, p. A588

MOORE, Christy, Chief Nursing Officer, Medical Center Barbour, Eufaula, AL, p. A17

MOORE, Dana, Chief Information Officer, Children'S Hospital Colorado, Aurora, CO, p. A96

MOORE, Deborah, Director Human Resources, Walter P. Reuther Psychiatric Hospital, Westland, MI, p. A325

MOORE, Diane C., Chief Financial Officer, Memorial Medical Center, Port Lavaca, TX, p. A630

MOORE, Edward H., President and Chief Executive Officer, Harrington Hospital, Southbridge, MA, p. A303

MOORE, Elizabeth, Chief Operating Officer, Silver Hill Hospital, New Canaan, CT, p. A109

MOORE, Emily, Director Human Resources and Information Technology, Haskell Memorial Hospital, Haskell, TX, p. A609

MOORE, Ethel L, M.D., Director of Medical Affairs, Fort Belknap Service Unit, Harlem, MT, p. A377

MOORE, Harold, Chief Information Technology Officer, Spartanburg Medical Center – Church Street Campus, Spartanburg, SC, p. A557

MOORE, Jason H, Vice President and Chief Operating Officer, Tallahassee Memorial Healthcare, Tallahassee, FL, p. A141

MOORE, Jeffrey Steve, Chief Financial Officer, Fort Walton Beach Medical Center, Fort Walton Beach, FL, p. A123

MOORE, Jody Dewen, District Director Human Resources, Kindred Hospital–San Diego, San Diego, CA, p. A83

MOORE, John, President, South Lake Hospital, Clermont, FL, p. A120

MOORE, John, M.D.
Medical Director, Granite County Medical Center, Philipsburg, MT, p. A379
Vice President Medical Affairs, Ssm Health Depaul Hospital – St. Louis, Bridgeton, MO, p. A357

MOORE, John G, Vice President and Chief Financial Officer, Atrium Health Union, Monroe, NC, p. A458

MOORE, Kandi, Administrator, Specialists Hospital – Shreveport, Shreveport, LA, p. A278

MOORE, Karen, Vice President Information Technology and Chief Information Officer, Southern Regional Medical Center, Riverdale, GA, p. A159

MOORE, Karen O., FACHE, Senior Vice President Operations and Chief Nursing Officer, Lawrence General Hospital, Lawrence, MA, p. A299

MOORE, Keri, Vice President Human Resources and Support Services, Presbyterian–St. Luke'S Medical Center, Denver, CO, p. A99

MOORE, Kermit, R.N., Chief Operating Officer and Chief Nursing Officer, Nemaha County Hospital, Auburn, NE, p. A382

MOORE, Kyna, R.N.
Chief Nursing Officer, Pocahontas Memorial Hospital, Buckeye, WV, p. A683
Director of Nursing, Bath Community Hospital, Hot Springs, VA, p. A661

MOORE, Leigh, Administrative Assistant Human Resources, H. C. Watkins Memorial Hospital, Quitman, MS, p. A353

MOORE, Linda, Manager Human Resources, Seymour Hospital, Seymour, TX, p. A636

MOORE, Margaret, Director Business Office, Sabine County Hospital, Hemphill, TX, p. A609

MOORE, Matthew, Director of Financial Reporting, Effingham Hospital, Springfield, GA, p. A160

MOORE, Melinda, Director Human Resources, Multicare Deaconess Hospital, Spokane, WA, p. A679

MOORE, Michael, Director Information Systems, Troy Regional Medical Center, Troy, AL, p. A23

MOORE, Mike, President and Chief Operating Officer, Jane Phillips Medical Center, Bartlesville, OK, p. A497

MOORE, Nolda, Director Data Processing, Memorial Hospital And Manor, Bainbridge, GA, p. A148

MOORE, Patricia J, Director Human Resource, Valley Behavioral Health System, Barling, AR, p. A39

MOORE, Paul, Chief Information Officer, Connecticut Mental Health Center, New Haven, CT, p. A109

MOORE, Paul, R.N., Chief Clinical Officer, Mercy Rehabilitation Hospital Springfield, Springfield, MO, p. A372

MOORE, Paula, R.N., Chief Clinical Officer, Hugh Chatham Memorial Hospital, Elkin, NC, p. A454

MOORE, Randy, Chief Information Officer, Banner Lassen Medical Center, Susanville, CA, p. A91

MOORE, Rick
Chief Information Officer, Bethesda North Hospital, Cincinnati, OH, p. A475
Chief Information Officer, Good Samaritan Hospital, Cincinnati, OH, p. A476

MOORE, Robin A., Chief Human Resources Officer, Concord Hospital, Concord, NH, p. A399

MOORE, Ronald E, R.N., MSN, Vice President Professional Practice and Chief Nursing Officer, Charleston Area Medical Center, Charleston, WV, p. A684

MOORE, Samuel, Chief Financial Officer, University Of Kansas Health System St. Francis Campus, Topeka, KS, p. A246

MOORE, Sandee, Chief Operating Officer, Eastern Idaho Regional Medical Center, Idaho Falls, ID, p. A169

MOORE, Saunya, Chief Financial Officer, Parkside Psychiatric Hospital And Clinic, Tulsa, OK, p. A509

MOORE, Shari, Chief Executive Officer, Methodist Rehabilitation Hospital, Dallas, TX, p. A597

MOORE, Steve, Chief Financial Officer, Southern Tennessee Regional Health System–Winchester, Winchester, TN, p. A580

MOORE, Susan, MS, R.N., Chief Nursing Officer, Gothenburg Health, Gothenburg, NE, p. A385
MOORE, Sylvia, Vice President and Chief Operating Officer, Southeast Hospital, Cape Girardeau, MO, p. A358
MOORE, Tim
  Chief Accounting Officer and Vice President Ancillary Services and Finance, Blessing Hospital, Quincy, IL, p. A194
  Vice President Finance, Illini Community Hospital, Pittsfield, IL, p. A193
MOORE, Vernon, Senior Vice President Chief Business and Finance, Ut Health North Campus Tyler, Tyler, TX, p. A642
MOORE, VonDa, Administrator, Mercy Hospital Berryville, Berryville, AR, p. A39
MOORE, Warren E., President and Chief Executive Officer, Children'S Specialized Hospital, New Brunswick, NJ, p. A409
MOORE, Wayne, Interim Administrator, Christus Southeast Texas Jasper Memorial, Jasper, TX, p. A616
MOORE, William, Chief Information Officer, Parrish Medical Center, Titusville, FL, p. A143
MOORE-CONNELLY, Marci, M.D., Vice President Chief Medical Officer, Memorial Hospital Of Carbondale, Carbondale, IL, p. A175
MOORE-HARDY, Cynthia, President and Chief Executive Officer, Lake Health, Concord Township, OH, p. A480
MOORE-JONES, Debra, Chief Executive Officer, Parkside Psychiatric Hospital And Clinic, Tulsa, OK, p. A509
MOOREHOUSE, Brett, Chief Executive Officer, Ranken Jordan Pediatric Bridge Hospital, Maryland Heights, MO, p. A365
MOORER, Thad, Chief Information Officer, Eastside Psychiatric Hospital, Tallahassee, FL, p. A140
MOORHEAD, David, M.D., Chief Medical Officer, Adventhealth Orlando, Orlando, FL, p. A134
MOORMAN, Gary L., D.O., Chief Medical Officer and Senior Vice President Medical Affairs, Promedica Monroe Regional Hospital, Monroe, MI, p. A318
MORA, Debbie, Director, Southwest General Hospital, San Antonio, TX, p. A635
MORACA, Lynn, Director Human Resources, Cleveland Clinic Akron General Lodi Hospital, Lodi, OH, p. A485
MORAHAN, John, Vice President Finance, St. Joseph Hospital, Bethpage, NY, p. A423
MORAHAN, John R, President and Chief Executive Officer, Penn State Health St. Joseph, Reading, PA, p. A539
MORAHAN, John R., President and Chief Executive Officer, Penn State Health St. Joseph, Reading, PA, p. A539
MORALES, Autumn, Chief Medical Staff Officer, Clarinda Regional Health Center, Clarinda, IA, p. A219
MORALES, Daniza
  Chief Information Officer, Hospital Menonita De Cayey, Cayey, PR, p. A716
  Manager Information System, Mennonite General Hospital, Aibonito, PR, p. A715
MORALES, Elsie, Chief Financial Officer, Hospital Universitario Dr. Ramon Ruiz Arnau, Bayamon, PR, p. A715
MORALES, Joel, Chief Financial Officer, Fort Duncan Regional Medical Center, Eagle Pass, TX, p. A600
MORALES, John R, Chief Financial Officer, John H. Stroger Jr. Hospital Of Cook County, Chicago, IL, p. A177
MORALES, Kathryn
  Director of Finance, Hampshire Memorial Hospital, Romney, WV, p. A689
  Director of Finance, War Memorial Hospital, Berkeley Springs, WV, p. A683
MORALES, Kristin, Chief Operating Officer, Harrington Hospital, Southbridge, MA, p. A303
MORALES, Marilyn, Chief Executive Officer, Hospital Buen Samaritano, Aguadilla, PR, p. A714
MORALES, Trish, Director Human Resources, Lakewood Ranch Medical Center, Bradenton, FL, p. A118
MORAN, Alina, Chief Executive Officer, Brookdale Hospital Medical Center, New York, NY, p. A432
MORAN, Debbie
  Executive Director, Carl Albert Community Mental Health Center, Mcalester, OK, p. A502
  Executive Director, Jim Taliaferro Community Mental Health, Lawton, OK, p. A501
MORAN, Mary, M.D., Pediatrician In Chief, St. Christopher'S Hospital For Children, Philadelphia, PA, p. A536
MORAN, Michael Francis., President and Chief Administrative Officer, Baystate Wing Hospital, Palmer, MA, p. A302
MORAN, Tim, Chief Executive Officer, Chino Valley Medical Center, Chino, CA, p. A54
MORAN, Timothy M., Chief Executive Officer, Glenn Medical Center, Willows, CA, p. A95
MORANDEIRA, Ana, Director Marketing, San Juan Capestrano Hospital, San Juan, PR, p. A719

MORASKO, Jerome
  Chief Executive Officer, Bucyrus Hospital, Bucyrus, OH, p. A474
  President and Chief Executive Officer, Avita Ontario Hospital, Ontario, OH, p. A489
  President and Chief Executive Officer, Galion Hospital, Galion, OH, p. A483
MORASKO, Robert A., Chief Executive Officer, Heart Of The Rockies Regional Medical Center, Salida, CO, p. A105
MORAVICK, Donna, Executive Director, Southside Hospital, Bay Shore, NY, p. A423
MORDACH, John P, Senior Vice President and Chief Financial Officer, Rush University Medical Center, Chicago, IL, p. A179
MORDECAI, Steve, Director Human Resources, Griffin Hospital, Derby, CT, p. A107
MOREFIELD, Terri, Deputy Chief Human Resources Division, Bassett Army Community Hospital, Fort Wainwright, AK, p. A26
MOREH, Swenda
  Interim Chief Executive Officer, Bridgepoint Hospital National Harbor, Washington, DC, p. A115
  Vice President and Chief Operating Officer, Bridgepoint Hospital National Harbor, Washington, DC, p. A115
MOREIN, Sandy, Chief Nursing Officer, Iberia Medical Center, New Iberia, LA, p. A274
MORELAND, Janet, Administrator, Lakeside Medical Center, Belle Glade, FL, p. A117
MORELAND, John, M.D., Chief Medical Officer, Marcus Daly Memorial Hospital, Hamilton, MT, p. A377
MORELAND, Tresha, MS, Regional Vice President Human Resources, Dameron Hospital, Stockton, CA, p. A90
MORELL, Ixel, Chief Operating Officer, Sierra Vista Hospital, Sacramento, CA, p. A82
MORELLI, Gerald, Director Human Resources, Philadelphia Veterans Affairs Medical Center, Philadelphia, PA, p. A536
MORENO, Debbie, R.N., Patient Care Executive, Adventist Health Lodi Memorial, Lodi, CA, p. A64
MORENO, Jorge, Director Information Technology Operations, Canyon Vista Medical Center, Sierra Vista, AZ, p. A36
MORENO, Robin
  Chief Financial Officer, North Texas State Hospital, Wichita Falls Campus, Wichita Falls, TX, p. A645
  Financial Officer, North Texas State Hospital, Vernon, TX, p. A643
MORENO, Sandra, Chief Nursing Officer, Orange County Global Medical Center, Inc., Santa Ana, CA, p. A88
MORETTE, Joseph M, Executive Vice President, Methodist Rehabilitation Center, Jackson, MS, p. A349
MOREY, Scott David, Chief Nursing Officer, Abrazo West Campus, Goodyear, AZ, p. A30
MORGAN, Bradley, Vice President of Operations, Baylor Scott & White The Heart Hospital–Denton, Denton, TX, p. A599
MORGAN, Charlene, Chief Nursing Officer, Henderson County Community Hospital, Lexington, TN, p. A573
MORGAN, David, Vice President and Chief Financial Officer, Bristol Bay Area Health Corporation, Dillingham, AK, p. A26
MORGAN, Dennis P, Chief of Staff, Baptist Memorial Hospital–North Mississippi, Oxford, MS, p. A352
MORGAN, Derek
  Vice President Human Resources, Kettering Medical Center, Kettering, OH, p. A485
  Vice President Human Resources, Sycamore Medical Center, Miamisburg, OH, p. A487
MORGAN, Eric, Chief Executive Officer, Prattville Baptist Hospital, Prattville, AL, p. A23
MORGAN, James, M.D., Chief Medical Officer, Memorial Hospital Of Converse County, Douglas, WY, p. A711
MORGAN, Janelle, Interim Director of Nursing, Howard County Medical Center, Saint Paul, NE, p. A391
MORGAN, Jeff, Director Information Systems, Northeastern Nevada Regional Hospital, Elko, NV, p. A393
MORGAN, Jeffrey H., Vice President Finance and Chief Financial Officer, Brooks Memorial Hospital, Dunkirk, NY, p. A427
MORGAN, John, Chief Executive Officer, Jackson Parish Hospital, Jonesboro, LA, p. A269
MORGAN, Julie, Director of Nursing, St. Helena Parish Hospital, Greensburg, LA, p. A268
MORGAN, Kelly C., President and Chief Executive Officer, Mercy Medical Center, Roseburg, OR, p. A517
MORGAN, Lois, R.N., MSN, Vice President and Chief Nursing Officer, Gibson General Hospital, Princeton, IN, p. A214
MORGAN, Loretta Y, Director Human Resources, Connally Memorial Medical Center, Floresville, TX, p. A604
MORGAN, Lori J., President and Chief Executive Officer, Huntington Memorial Hospital, Pasadena, CA, p. A77
MORGAN, Mace, Director Information Systems, Minden Medical Center, Minden, LA, p. A274
MORGAN, MacGregor, Chief Executive Officer, Curahealth Hospital Stoughton, Stoughton, MA, p. A304

MORGAN, Marguerite J., Administrator, Florida State Hospital, Chattahoochee, FL, p. A119
MORGAN, Mark E., Medical Center Director, Jack C. Montgomery Veterans Affairs Medical Center, Muskogee, OK, p. A502
MORGAN, Matthew, Associate Administrator, Hillcrest Hospital – South, Tulsa, OK, p. A508
MORGAN, Nyle, Chief Information Officer, Sheridan Memorial Hospital, Sheridan, WY, p. A712
MORGAN, Rose, MS, R.N., Vice President Patient Care Services, Princeton Community Hospital, Princeton, WV, p. A688
MORGAN, Shawn, Finance Officer, Northern Navajo Medical Center, Shiprock, NM, p. A420
MORGAN, Susan, Director of Nursing Services, Prairie Community Hospital, Terry, MT, p. A380
MORGAN, Teresa
  Assistant Vice President Human Resources, Shannon Medical Center, San Angelo, TX, p. A633
  Chief Financial Officer, Mcgehee Hospital, Mcgehee, AR, p. A45
MORGAN-FINE, Richard, IT Director, Clarinda Regional Health Center, Clarinda, IA, p. A219
MORGESE, Vincent, M.D., Executive Vice President, Chief Operating Officer and Chief Medical Officer, Queen Of The Valley Medical Center, Napa, CA, p. A74
MORIN, Robert J., Vice President Finance and Chief Financial Officer, Sturgis Hospital, Sturgis, MI, p. A323
MORIN-SCRIBNER, Nicole, Director Human Resources, St. Mary'S Regional Medical Center, Lewiston, ME, p. A283
MORISCO, Antonietta, M.D., Medical Director, Chairman Anesthesiology, Brookdale Hospital Medical Center, New York, NY, p. A432
MORITZ, Mary, Administrator Human Resources, Humboldt County Memorial Hospital, Humboldt, IA, p. A224
MORK, David L., Jr
  Chief Executive Officer, Roosevelt Warm Springs Rehabilitation And Specialty Hospitals – Ltac, Warm Springs, GA, p. A162
  Chief Executive Officer, Roosevelt Warm Springs Rehabilitation Hospital – Rehab, Warm Springs, GA, p. A162
MORKRID, Shirley, Chief Nursing Officer, Liberty Medical Center, Chester, MT, p. A375
MORLOCK, Paul J, FACHE, Vice President Human Resources and Occupational Health, Children'S Hospital Of The King'S Daughters, Norfolk, VA, p. A663
MORON, David, M.D., Clinical Director, Rio Grande State Center/South Texas Health Care System, Harlingen, TX, p. A609
MORONY, David, Chief Financial Officer, Casa Colina Hospital And Health Systems, Pomona, CA, p. A78
MORQUECHO, Adam, Director Information Technology, Huntington Beach Hospital, Huntington Beach, CA, p. A62
MORREALE, Daniel
  Chief Information Officer, Hunterdon Healthcare, Flemington, NJ, p. A406
  Vice President and Chief Information Officer, Brookdale Hospital Medical Center, New York, NY, p. A432
MORREALE, Gene, President and Chief Executive Officer, Oneida Healthcare, Oneida, NY, p. A440
MORRELL, Dan, Manager Information Systems, Sierra Vista Hospital, Truth Or Consequences, NM, p. A421
MORRELL, Jeffrey F., Chief Executive Officer, Intermountain Hospital, Boise, ID, p. A167
MORRIONE, Thomas, Medical Director, New England Rehabilitation Hospital Of Portland, Portland, ME, p. A284
MORRIS, Alexander, Corporate Director Human Resources, Fort Washington Medical Center, Oxen Hill, MD, p. A292
MORRIS, Barbara, R.N., Chief Nursing Officer, Pam Rehabilitation Hospital Of Beaumont, Beaumont, TX, p. A587
MORRIS, Christi, Director of Nursing, Bayside Community Hospital, Anahuac, TX, p. A583
MORRIS, Christopher
  Director Human Resources, Ascension Southeast Wisconsin Hospital – Elmbrook Campus, Brookfield, WI, p. A693
  Senior Director, Human Resources, Ascension Southeast Wisconsin Hospital – St. Joseph'S Campus, Milwaukee, WI, p. A700
MORRIS, Clayton, Medical Director, Griffin Memorial Hospital, Norman, OK, p. A503
MORRIS, Debbie M, Director Human Resources, Marcus Daly Memorial Hospital, Hamilton, MT, p. A377
MORRIS, Debra D., R.N., MSN, Chief Nursing Officer, Great Plains Regional Medical Center, Elk City, OK, p. A499
MORRIS, Dennis, Area Finance Officer, Kaiser Permanente Oakland Medical Center, Oakland, CA, p. A75
MORRIS, Donald, Vice President Human Resources, Hillcrest Medical Center, Tulsa, OK, p. A508

MORRIS, Douglas
Chief Financial Officer, Eden Springs Health Care Center, Green Springs, OH, p. A484
Chief Financial Officer, Vibra Hospital Of Northwestern Indiana, Crown Point, IN, p. A202
Chief Financial Officer, Vibra Hospital Of Southeastern Michigan, Llc, Lincoln Park, MI, p. A317
MORRIS, Janet, Director Human Resources, Encompass Rehabilitation Hospital Of Lakeview, Elizabethtown, KY, p. A251
MORRIS, Janice, Accountant, Crossridge Community Hospital, Wynne, AR, p. A49
MORRIS, Jarrett L
Controller and Chief Information Officer, Atrium Health Lincoln, Lincolnton, NC, p. A458
Controller, Atrium Health Lincoln, Lincolnton, NC, p. A458
MORRIS, Jerry
Administrator, Higgins General Hospital, Bremen, GA, p. A148
Administrator, Tanner Medical Center/East Alabama, Wedowee, AL, p. A24
MORRIS, Jim
Vice President Finance, Baptist Health La Grange, La Grange, KY, p. A254
Vice President Finance, Baptist Health Louisville, Louisville, KY, p. A256
MORRIS, Jonathan B, M.D.
Senior Vice President and Chief Information Officer, Wellstar Cobb Hospital, Austell, GA, p. A148
Senior Vice President and Chief Information Officer, Wellstar Kennestone Hospital, Marietta, GA, p. A157
MORRIS, Lisa, Vice President Human Resources, Swedish Medical Center, Englewood, CO, p. A100
MORRIS, Luke P
Assistant Vice President Talent, American Fork Hospital, American Fork, UT, p. A647
Assistant Vice President Talent, Utah Valley Hospital, Provo, UT, p. A651
MORRIS, Marsha, Manager Information Services, Fairview Park Hospital, Dublin, GA, p. A152
MORRIS, Mary, Chief Financial Officer, Purcell Municipal Hospital, Purcell, OK, p. A506
MORRIS, Nerissa E., Senior Vice President and Chief Human Resource Officer, Cincinnati Children'S Hospital Medical Center, Cincinnati, OH, p. A475
MORRIS, Philip, Chief Operating Officer, West Houston Medical Center, Houston, TX, p. A614
MORRIS, R Randall, Administrator, West Carroll Memorial Hospital, Oak Grove, LA, p. A276
MORRIS, Scott, Vice President Information Systems, Eskenazi Health, Indianapolis, IN, p. A206
MORRIS, Tony, Business Manager, Mental Health Institute, Cherokee, IA, p. A219
MORRIS, Will, Director Information Technology, Panola Medical Center, Batesville, MS, p. A344
MORRISON, Deane, Chief Information Officer, Concord Hospital, Concord, NH, p. A399
MORRISON, Dereck, Assistant Administrator, Bryan W. Whitfield Memorial Hospital, Demopolis, AL, p. A17
MORRISON, Devin
Director Administration, Naval Hospital Pensacola, Pensacola, FL, p. A136
Director for Administration, Naval Hospital Pensacola, Pensacola, FL, p. A136
MORRISON, Dianne, Director Human Resources, Mizell Memorial Hospital, Opp, AL, p. A22
MORRISON, Greta M., Assistant Chief Nursing Officer, Russell County Medical Center, Lebanon, VA, p. A661
MORRISON, J. E., M.D., M.P.H., Chief Medical Officer, Baylor Scott & White Medical Center – Hillcrest, Waco, TX, p. A644
MORRISON, Kathy E, Executive Director Human Resources, St. Catherine Hospital, Garden City, KS, p. A235
MORRISON, Kevin, Chief Financial Officer, Dickenson Community Hospital, Clintwood, VA, p. A658
MORRISON, Maureen, Vice President, Finance, Advocate Trinity Hospital, Chicago, IL, p. A176
MORRISON, Michael, Chief Financial Officer, Tristar Skyline Medical Center, Nashville, TN, p. A577
MORRISON, Sarah, President and Chief Executive Officer, Shepherd Center, Atlanta, GA, p. A147
MORRISSETT, Barbara, Vice President Human Resources, St. Mary'S Medical Center, San Francisco, CA, p. A86
MORRISSETTE, Daniel, Chief Financial Officer, Stanford Health Care, Palo Alto, CA, p. A77
MORRISSEY, Moira, Chief Operating Officer and General Counsel, Four Winds Hospital, Katonah, NY, p. A429
MORRISSEY, Una E, R.N., MSN, Senior Vice President Operations, Chief Operating Officer and Chief Nursing Officer, Brookdale Hospital Medical Center, New York, NY, p. A432

MORROW, Charles, M.D., Chief Medical Officer, Spartanburg Medical Center – Church Street Campus, Spartanburg, SC, p. A557
MORROW, Ginger, Executive Vice President Human Resources, Christus Good Shepherd Medical Center–Marshall, Marshall, TX, p. A623
MORROW, Jennifer, Director Human Resources, San Joaquin Valley Rehabilitation Hospital, Fresno, CA, p. A59
MORROW, Laurie, Executive Director Human Resources, Washington Regional Medical Center, Fayetteville, AR, p. A42
MORROW, Pat, Director Human Resources, Walker Baptist Medical Center, Jasper, AL, p. A20
MORROW, Randy, Vice President and Chief Operating Officer, Boone Hospital Center, Columbia, MO, p. A359
MORROW, Sarah, Vice President Human Resources, Capital Region Medical Center, Jefferson City, MO, p. A361
MORROW, W. Robert, M.D., Executive Vice President and Chief Medical Officer, Children'S Medical Center Dallas, Dallas, TX, p. A596
MORSCHAUSER, Roberta, Administrator, Brown County Community Treatment Center, Green Bay, WI, p. A696
MORSE, Brad S., Interim Chief Executive Officer, Mccurtain Memorial Hospital, Idabel, OK, p. A501
MORSE, Craig, Chief Financial Officer, Carlsbad Medical Center, Carlsbad, NM, p. A417
MORSE, Douglas E., Chief Executive Officer and Administrator, Hansen Family Hospital, Iowa Falls, IA, p. A225
MORSE, Jason, Director Information Technology, Cumberland Healthcare, Cumberland, WI, p. A693
MORSTAD, Joan, Director Information Systems, Coliseum Medical Centers, Macon, GA, p. A156
MORTENSEN, Lorrie, MSN, R.N., Director, Patient Care, Floyd Valley Healthcare, Le Mars, IA, p. A225
MORTENSEN, Shane
Chief Financial Officer, San Luis Valley Health Conejos County Hospital, La Jara, CO, p. A102
Chief Financial Officer, San Luis Valley Health, Alamosa, CO, p. A96
MORTENSON, June, R.N., Director of Nursing, Power County Hospital District, American Falls, ID, p. A167
MORTINSEN, Roy, M.D., Chief of Staff, Sanford Vermillion Medical Center, Vermillion, SD, p. A564
MORTON, David, M.D., Clinical Director, West Central Georgia Regional Hospital, Columbus, GA, p. A151
MORTON, Leslie, Manager Human Resources, Riverview Regional Medical Center, Gadsden, AL, p. A18
MORTON, Lucas
Regional Chief Financial Officer, Osf Heart Of Mary Medical Center, Urbana, IL, p. A197
Regional Chief Financial Officer, Osf Sacred Heart Medical Center, Danville, IL, p. A180
MORTON, Robert, M.D., Medical Director, Rolling Hills Hospital, Ada, OK, p. A496
MORTON, Stephanie, Chief Information Officer, Providence Alaska Medical Center, Anchorage, AK, p. A25
MORTON, Steve, M.D., Chief Medical Officer, Continuecare Hospital At Baptist Health Corbin, Corbin, KY, p. A250
MORTON ROWE, Laura, Director of Human Resources, Providence Saint John'S Health Center, Santa Monica, CA, p. A89
MORTOZA, Angela, Chief Executive Officer, Dallas County Hospital, Perry, IA, p. A228
MOSBY, Charmaine T, Area Director Health Information Management, Promise Hospital Baton Rouge – Main Campus, Baton Rouge, LA, p. A264
MOSCA, Philip, M.D., President, Medical Staff, Integris Southwest Medical Center, Oklahoma City, OK, p. A504
MOSCATO, Mary K., President, Hebrew Rehabilitation Center, Roslindale, MA, p. A302
MOSCHKAU, Don, Senior Director Human Resources, University of Minnesota Medical Center, Fairview, Minneapolis, MN, p. A336
MOSCOSO, Ricardo, M.D., Medical Director, University Hospital, San Juan, PR, p. A719
MOSEL, Lindy, Director of Nursing, Memorial Community Health, Aurora, NE, p. A382
MOSELY, Chisty, Director Information Management, Saint Simons By–The–Sea Hospital, Saint Simons Island, GA, p. A159
MOSER, Cindy, Director Human Resources, Allegheny Valley Hospital, Natrona Heights, PA, p. A533
MOSER, Joseph, M.D., Chief Medical Officer, University Of Maryland Charles Regional Medical Center, La Plata, MD, p. A291
MOSER, Kevin, Vice President of Operations, Baptist Health Madisonville, Madisonville, KY, p. A257
MOSER, Neal, M.D., Medical Director, Healthsouth Northern Kentucky Rehabilitation Hospital, Edgewood, KY, p. A251

MOSESIAN, Robert, Controller, Encompass Health Rehabilitation Hospital Of Bakersfield, Bakersfield, CA, p. A52
MOSHER, Guy W
Manager Information Systems, Finger Lakes Hospital, Geneva, NY, p. A428
Manager Information Systems, Soldiers And Sailors Memorial Hospital Of Yates County, Penn Yan, NY, p. A441
MOSHIER, John, Director Human Resources, Clara Barton Hospital, Hoisington, KS, p. A236
MOSHIRPUR, Jasmin, M.D.
Chief Medical Officer, Brookdale Hospital Medical Center, New York, NY, p. A432
Dean and Medical Director, Brookdale Hospital Medical Center, New York, NY, p. A432
MOSHOFSKY, Bill, M.D., Chief of Staff, Peacehealth Sacred Heart Medical Center University District, Eugene, OR, p. A512
MOSIER, Dawn, Director Human Resources, Encompass Health Rehabilitation Institute Of Tucson, Tucson, AZ, p. A37
MOSIER, John, D.O., Chief of Staff, Herington Municipal Hospital, Herington, KS, p. A236
MOSKOWITZ, Samuel E., President, Medstar Franklin Square Medical Center, Baltimore, MD, p. A288
MOSLEY, J. Christopher., Chief Executive Officer, Cartersville Medical Center, Cartersville, GA, p. A149
MOSLEY, Tonja
Chief Financial Officer, Adventhealth Heart Of Florida, Davenport, FL, p. A121
Chief Financial Officer, Wellington Regional Medical Center, Wellington, FL, p. A143
MOSMEYER, Kathleen C, Director Human Resources, Citizens Medical Center, Victoria, TX, p. A643
MOSS, Austin, Vice President Human Resources, Jennie Stuart Medical Center, Hopkinsville, KY, p. A253
MOSS, Barry, Chief Executive Officer, Merit Health Central, Jackson, MS, p. A349
MOSS, Bradley, Administrator, Unity Psychiatric Care–Huntsville, Huntsville, AL, p. A19
MOSS, C Renee, M.D., Chief Medical Officer, Coastal Virginia Rehabilitation, Newport News, VA, p. A663
MOSS, Jennifer, MS, R.N., Chief Clinical Officer, Kirby Medical Center, Monticello, IL, p. A190
MOSS, Keith A, Vice President & Chief Medical Informatics Officers, Riverside Medical Center, Kankakee, IL, p. A187
MOSS, Misty, Director Business Administration, Logansport State Hospital, Logansport, IN, p. A210
MOSS, Ray, Vice President and Chief Information Officer, Henry Mayo Newhall Hospital, Valencia, CA, p. A92
MOSS, Shelby, Human Resource Officer, Sheridan County Health Complex, Hoxie, KS, p. A237
MOSS, Stuart, Chief Financial Officer, Kessler Marlton Rehabilitation, Marlton, NJ, p. A408
MOSS, Tyler, Chief Financial Officer, Milford Valley Memorial Hospital, Milford, UT, p. A648
MOST, Kevin, D.O., Vice President Medical Affairs, Northwestern Medicine Central Dupage Hospital, Winfield, IL, p. A198
MOSTOFI, Ann R, MSN, R.N., Vice President Patient Care and Chief Nursing Officer, Eisenhower Medical Center, Rancho Mirage, CA, p. A79
MOTAKEF, Shahin
President, Baylor Scott & White Continuing Care Hospital–Temple, Temple, TX, p. A639
President, Baylor Scott & White Medical Center – Temple, Temple, TX, p. A639
MOTEJZIK, Thomas, Director Information Systems, Carlsbad Medical Center, Carlsbad, NM, p. A417
MOTONAGA, Gregg, M.D., Chief of Staff, Central Peninsula Hospital, Soldotna, AK, p. A27
MOTT, Daman, MSN, Chief Nursing Officer, Doctors Hospital Of Laredo, Laredo, TX, p. A619
MOTT, Joseph, Chief Executive Officer, Intermountain Medical Center, Murray, UT, p. A649
MOTT, William, Chief Operating Officer, Ascension Macomb–Oakland Hospital, Warren, MI, p. A324
MOTTE, Michael J., Chief Executive Officer, St. Alexius Hospital – Broadway Campus, Saint Louis, MO, p. A370
MOUGHAN, Jennifer L, Chief Human Resources Officer, Our Lady Of Lourdes Medical Center, Camden, NJ, p. A404
MOUISSET, Rena B, Director Human Resources and Contract Compliance, St. Martin Hospital, Breaux Bridge, LA, p. A265
MOULTON, Susan, Director Health Information Management, Spring Harbor Hospital, Westbrook, ME, p. A285
MOUNIE, Mike, Director Finance, Sentara Obici Hospital, Suffolk, VA, p. A668

MOUNTAIN, J Michael, Chief Financial Officer, Rivervalley Behavioral Health Hospital, Owensboro, KY, p. A259

MOUSA, Ayman, Chief Executive Officer, Pacifica Hospital Of The Valley, Los Angeles, CA, p. A68

MOUSA, Cindy, Director Human Resources, Touro Infirmary, New Orleans, LA, p. A276

MOUSTAKAKIS, John, Senior Vice President Information Systems and Chief Information Officer, Westchester Medical Center, Valhalla, NY, p. A446

MOVSESIAN, Gregory, M.D., Acting Chief of Staff, Aleda E. Lutz Veterans Affairs Medical Center, Saginaw, MI, p. A321

MOWAN, Chris, Chief Executive Officer, Medical City Dallas, Dallas, TX, p. A597

MOYA, Linda, Director Human Resources, Mesilla Valley Hospital, Las Cruces, NM, p. A418

MOYER, Dale, Vice President Information Systems, Evangelical Community Hospital, Lewisburg, PA, p. A530

MOYER, Debra, R.N.
    Chief Nurse Executive, Unitypoint Health–Iowa Lutheran Hospital, Des Moines, IA, p. A221
    Chief Nursing Executive and Vice President Nursing Services, Unitypoint Health – Iowa Methodist Medical Center, Des Moines, IA, p. A221

MOYER, Douglas J., President, Sentara Rmh Medical Center, Harrisonburg, VA, p. A660

MOYER, Karen W, R.N., Senior Vice President and Chief Nursing Officer, Mount Sinai Medical Center, Miami Beach, FL, p. A131

MOYER, William, President, St. Luke'S University Hospital – Bethlehem Campus, Bethlehem, PA, p. A520

MRAMOR, Joann, Director Human Resources, Seven Rivers Regional Medical Center, Crystal River, FL, p. A120

MUCARIA, Jaclyn, President, Brookdale Hospital Medical Center, New York, NY, p. A432

MUCK, Erin, Vice President, Clinical Nursing, Crawford County Memorial Hospital, Denison, IA, p. A221

MUDEN, Todd, Section Head Information Management, Mayo Clinic Health System – Northland In Barron, Barron, WI, p. A692

MUDRY, Janel, Chief Operating Officer, Washington Health System Greene, Waynesburg, PA, p. A543

MUELLER, Arthur, Director Management Information Systems, Cuero Community Hospital, Cuero, TX, p. A595

MUELLER, Charles, M.D., Chief of Staff, Texas County Memorial Hospital, Houston, MO, p. A361

MUELLER, Donald, Vice President and CEO, Erlanger Medical Center, Chattanooga, TN, p. A567

MUELLER, Eric, Chief Executive Officer and Market Chief Executive Officer, Vibra Hospital Of Amarillo, Amarillo, TX, p. A582

MUELLER, Karen, R.N., Chief Nursing Officer, Mount Desert Island Hospital, Bar Harbor, ME, p. A281

MUELLER, Michael E, Chief Financial Officer, Health Central Hospital, Ocoee, FL, p. A133

MUELLER, Paul, Chief Financial Officer, Sparta Community Hospital, Sparta, IL, p. A196

MUELLER, Paul A., Chief Executive Officer, Hospital Division, Rogers Memorial Hospital, Inc., Oconomowoc, WI, p. A702

MUELLER, Paul S., Regional Vice President, Mayo Clinic Health System – Franciscan Healthcare In La Crosse, La Crosse, WI, p. A698

MUGGLI, David D.
    Chief Executive Officer, Select Specialty Hospital– Cincinnati, Cincinnati, OH, p. A476
    Interim Chief Executive Officer, Select Specialty Hospital – Cincinnati North, Cincinnati, OH, p. A476

MUHAMMAD, Mark, Manager Human Resources, Michael E. Debakey Veterans Affairs Medical Center, Houston, TX, p. A613

MUHS, David, Chief Financial Officer, Henry County Health Center, Mount Pleasant, IA, p. A227

MUILENBURG, Jeff, Chief of Staff, Memorial Community Health, Aurora, NE, p. A382

MUIR, Brian, Chief of Staff, Minidoka Memorial Hospital, Rupert, ID, p. A171

MULDER, Doris, Vice President Nursing, Beloit Health System, Beloit, WI, p. A692

MULDERIG, Marsha L., R.N., MSN, Chief Nursing Officer, Crisp Regional Hospital, Cordele, GA, p. A151

MULDOON, Sean R, M.D.
    Chief Medical Officer, Kindred Hospital–New Jersey Morris County, Dover, NJ, p. A404
    Senior Vice President and Chief Medical Officer–Kindred Healthcare, Hospital Division, Kindred Hospital Northland, Kansas City, MO, p. A362

MULIS, Becky, Director of Health Information Management Systems, Four County Counseling Center, Logansport, IN, p. A210

MULKEY, Peter, Chief Executive Officer, Clinch Valley Medical Center, Richlands, VA, p. A665

MULLEN, Thomas R., President and Chief Executive Officer, Mercy Medical Center, Baltimore, MD, p. A288

MULLENAX, Paul, Business Manager, Wyoming State Hospital, Evanston, WY, p. A711

MULLENDER, Monica, Director of Nursing, Osborne County Memorial Hospital, Osborne, KS, p. A242

MULLENS, Allen, M.D., Chief Medical Staff, Norton Community Hospital, Norton, VA, p. A664

MULLER, Donna L., Interim Chief Financial Officer, Upmc Hanover, Hanover, PA, p. A526

MULLER, Lynn, Chief Financial Officer, North Metro Medical Center, Jacksonville, AR, p. A43

MULLER, Oz, Director Human Resources, Porter Adventist Hospital, Denver, CO, p. A99

MULLERY CHHR, Barbara M, Vice President Administration, Robert Wood Johnson University Hospital Rahway, Rahway, NJ, p. A411

MULLIGAN, Marie, R.N., MSN, Vice President Nursing, John T. Mather Memorial Hospital, Port Jefferson, NY, p. A441

MULLINAX, Bradley, Chief Administrative Officer, Saint Thomas Dekalb Hospital, Smithville, TN, p. A579

MULLINGS, Donna, Director of Nursing, Assumption Community Hospital, Napoleonville, LA, p. A274

MULLINS, Bandy, M.D., Chief of Staff, Summersville Regional Medical Center, Summersville, WV, p. A689

MULLINS, Brad, Director Information Technology, Gove County Medical Center, Quinter, KS, p. A244

MULLINS, Bryan, Chief Operating Officer, Johnston Memorial Hospital, Abingdon, VA, p. A656

MULLINS, Cindy, Director Information Technology, Saint Mary'S Regional Medical Center, Reno, NV, p. A397

MULLINS, Dustin
    Chief Human Resources, Bayne–Jones Army Community Hospital, Fort Polk, LA, p. A267
    Chief Resource Management, Bayne–Jones Army Community Hospital, Fort Polk, LA, p. A267

MULLINS, Erin, D.O., Chief Medical Staff, Dickenson Community Hospital, Clintwood, VA, p. A658

MULLINS, Michelle, Chief Information Officer, Oklahoma Heart Hospital, Oklahoma City, OK, p. A505

MULLIS, Jeffrey
    Interim Chief Financial Officer, Bayfront Health Port Charlotte, Port Charlotte, FL, p. A137
    Interim Chief Financial Officer, Piedmont Walton Hospital, Monroe, GA, p. A157

MULROONEY, JoAnn M, R.N., Chief Operating Officer, Trinity Health System, Steubenville, OH, p. A491

MULTACH, Mark, M.D., Chief Medical Officer, Mount Sinai Hospital, Chicago, IL, p. A178

MULTACK, Richard, D.O., Vice President Medical Management, Advocate South Suburban Hospital, Hazel Crest, IL, p. A185

MULVEHILL, Mitchell, Group Financial Officer, Texas Health Harris Methodist Hospital Southlake, Southlake, TX, p. A637

MULVEY, Lee, Human Resource Officer, Texas Health Harris Methodist Hospital Hurst–Euless–Bedford, Bedford, TX, p. A588

MUMFORD, Stephen, Chief Operating Officer, Baton Rouge General Medical Center, Baton Rouge, LA, p. A263

MUMOLIE, Gina
    Senior Vice President and Chief Nurse Executive, Inspira Medical Center–Woodbury, Woodbury, NJ, p. A415
    Senior Vice President Hospital Administration, Capital Health Regional Medical Center, Trenton, NJ, p. A413

MUMPOWER, Rebecca, Director Marketing, Mesilla Valley Hospital, Las Cruces, NM, p. A418

MUNA, Esther L., Chief Executive Officer, Commonwealth Health Center, Saipan, MP, p. A714

MUNCHEL, Bryan, Senior Vice President and Chief Information Officer, Pam Specialty Hospital Of Covington, Covington, LA, p. A266

MUNGOVAN, Sandy, Chief Information Officer, Harbor–Ucla Medical Center, Torrance, CA, p. A91

MUNHOLLAND, Cleta
    Administrator, Louisiana Extended Care Hospital West Monroe, West Monroe, LA, p. A280
    Administrator, Specialty Hospital, Monroe, LA, p. A274
    Interim Administrator, Christus Dubuis Hospital Of Hot Springs, Hot Springs National Park, AR, p. A43

MUNIR, Amjad, M.D., Medical Director, Encompass Health Rehabilitation Hospital Of Chattanooga, Chattanooga, TN, p. A567

MUNLEY, William, Administrator, Shriners Hospitals For Children–Greenville, Greenville, SC, p. A554

MUNOZ, Alejandro, M.D., Chief Medical Officer, Cedar Crest Hospital And Residential Treatment Center, Belton, TX, p. A588

MUNOZ, Astro, Executive Director, First Hospital Panamericano, Cidra, PR, p. A716

MUNOZ, Thalia H., Chief Executive Officer, Starr County Memorial Hospital, Rio Grande City, TX, p. A631

MUNSHI, Imtiaz A, M.D., Chief of Staff, Richard L. Roudebush Veterans Affairs Medical Center, Indianapolis, IN, p. A207

MUNSON, Bill, Vice President and Chief Financial Officer, Boulder Community Health, Boulder, CO, p. A96

MUNSON, Jennifer, Chief Financial Officer, Three Rivers Hospital, Brewster, WA, p. A671

MUNSON, John, Vice President and Chief Financial Officer, St. Anthony Regional Hospital, Carroll, IA, p. A218

MUNSON, Kris, Director Human Resources, Arbour H. R. I. Hospital, Brookline, MA, p. A297

MUNTEFERING, Denise, Vice President Patient Care Services, Avera St. Benedict Health Center, Parkston, SD, p. A562

MUNTZ, Dana M.
    Chief Executive Officer, St. Vincent Jennings Hospital, North Vernon, IN, p. A213
    Chief Executive Officer, St. Vincent Salem Hospital, Salem, IN, p. A214

MUNTZ, Tim, President and Chief Executive Officer, St. Margaret'S Hospital, Spring Valley, IL, p. A196

MUNYAN, Lori, Director, Human Resources, Healthsouth Rehabilitation Hospital Of Toms River, Toms River, NJ, p. A413

MURANSKY, Ed, Owner, Surgical Hospital At Southwoods, Youngstown, OH, p. A495

MURCHISON, Sandra, Director Medical Records, Coosa Valley Medical Center, Sylacauga, AL, p. A23

MURDAUGH, Laura, Finance Director, William J. Mccord Adolescent Treatment Facility, Orangeburg, SC, p. A556

MURDOCH, William, M.D., Medical Director, Loma Linda University Behavioral Medicine Center, Redlands, CA, p. A80

MURDOCK, Guy, Vice President Human Resources, Healthbridge Children'S Hospital Of Houston, Houston, TX, p. A611

MURDOCK, Holly, Human Resources Coordinator, Kindred Hospital Rome, Rome, GA, p. A159

MURDOCK, Mark, Medical Center Director, Cincinnati Veterans Affairs Medical Center, Cincinnati, OH, p. A476

MURDOCK–LANGAN, Patricia, M.D.
    Chief Medical Officer, Chi Health Lakeside, Omaha, NE, p. A389
    Chief Medical Officer, Chi Health Midlands, Papillion, NE, p. A390

MURILLO, Jeremias, M.D., Chief Medical Officer, Newark Beth Israel Medical Center, Newark, NJ, p. A409

MURIN, William J, Chief Human Resources Officer, Uc San Diego Health, San Diego, CA, p. A84

MURO, Deborah, Chief Information Officer, El Camino Hospital, Mountain View, CA, p. A73

MURPHREE, Shari, Chief Executive Officer, Willow Crest Hospital, Miami, OK, p. A502

MURPHY, Brian
    Chief Executive Officer, Valley View Hospital, Glenwood Springs, CO, p. A101
    Senior Director Admissions and Referral Services, Hebrew Rehabilitation Center, Roslindale, MA, p. A302

MURPHY, Bruce, President and Chief Executive Officer, Arkansas Heart Hospital, Little Rock, AR, p. A44

MURPHY, Charles J, Associate Vice President Human Resources, Strong Memorial Hospital Of The University Of Rochester, Rochester, NY, p. A443

MURPHY, Christine, MS, Chief Operating Officer, Cypress Grove Behavioral Health, Bastrop, LA, p. A263

MURPHY, Colleen, M.D., Chief of Staff, Clay County Hospital, Flora, IL, p. A183

MURPHY, Dee, Vice President Human Resources, Southwest General Health Center, Middleburg Heights, OH, p. A487

MURPHY, Elizabeth A, R.N., FACHE, Vice President for Patient Care Services, Mercy Health Saint Mary'S, Grand Rapids, MI, p. A313

MURPHY, Evelyn, Chief Nursing Officer, St. Mary'S Sacred Heart Hospital, Lavonia, GA, p. A156

MURPHY, J Patrick, Chief Financial Officer, North Baldwin Infirmary, Bay Minette, AL, p. A14

MURPHY, James M., M.D., Chief Medical Officer Regional Development and Outpatient Services, New London Hospital, New London, NH, p. A401

MURPHY, John B, M.D., Vice President Medical Affairs and Chief Medical Officer, Rhode Island Hospital, Providence, RI, p. A548

MURPHY, John M, President and Chief Executive Officer, Western Connecticut Health Network, Danbury Hospital, Danbury, CT, p. A107

MURPHY, John M., President, Danbury Hospital, Danbury, CT, p. A107

MURPHY, Julie, Chief Financial Officer, Saint Luke'S North Hospital – Barry Road, Kansas City, MO, p. A363

MURPHY, Kathy, Site Manager, Mescalero Public Health Service Indian Hospital, Mescalero, NM, p. A419

MURPHY, Kelly, Vice President Human Resources, Colorado Canyons Hospital And Medical Center, Fruita, CO, p. A101

MURPHY, Kevin, Director, Information Technology Services, Bayfront Health St. Petersburg, Saint Petersburg, FL, p. A138

MURPHY, Kyle, Director Information Technology, Mayhill Hospital, Denton, TX, p. A599

MURPHY, Linda, Chief Financial Officer, Osborne County Memorial Hospital, Osborne, KS, p. A242

MURPHY, Lionel
Chief Executive Officer and Administrator, Bethesda Rehabilitation Hospital, Baton Rouge, LA, p. A263
Chief Executive Officer, Southeast Regional Medical Center, Kentwood, LA, p. A270

MURPHY, Margaret M, Chief Executive Officer, Kindred Hospital–Philadelphia, Philadelphia, PA, p. A535

MURPHY, Marie, Director Human Resources, Effingham Hospital, Springfield, GA, p. A160

MURPHY, Mary S, MSN
Regional Chief Nursing Officer, Adventist Medical Center Lagrange, La Grange, IL, p. A187
Vice President and Chief Nursing Officer, Adventist Medical Center – Hinsdale, Hinsdale, IL, p. A186

MURPHY, Matthew, Chief Financial Officer, Compass Memorial Healthcare, Marengo, IA, p. A226

MURPHY, Maureen, M.D., Director of Medical Affairs, Ssm Health St. Clare Hospital–Baraboo, Baraboo, WI, p. A692

MURPHY, Michael, M.D., JD, Chief Medical Officer, Sharp Grossmont Hospital, La Mesa, CA, p. A63

MURPHY, Michael D., Chief Executive Officer, Abilene Regional Medical Center, Abilene, TX, p. A581

MURPHY, Nancy, Vice President, Human Resources, Franciscan Children'S, Brighton, MA, p. A296

MURPHY, Paul, Chief Information Officer, Lane Regional Medical Center, Zachary, LA, p. A280

MURPHY, Peter J., Senior Vice President and Chief Operating Officer, Franciscan Health Mooresville, Mooresville, IN, p. A211

MURPHY, Richard J., President and Chief Executive Officer, South Nassau Communities Hospital, Oceanside, NY, p. A440

MURPHY, Rita, Director Human Resources, Cobre Valley Regional Medical Center, Globe, AZ, p. A30

MURPHY, Sheryl, Chief Nursing Officer and Director of Clinical Services, Peacehealth Peace Island Medical Center, Friday Harbor, WA, p. A673

MURPHY, Steve
Director Information Systems, Ssm Health St. Mary'S Hospital Centralia, Centralia, IL, p. A175
FM–East Region IS, Good Samaritan Regional Health Center, Mount Vernon, IL, p. A190

MURPHY, Steven, Executive Director, Devereux Hospital And Children'S Center Of Florida, Melbourne, FL, p. A129

MURPHY, Terry
Director Information Services, Phoenixville Hospital, Phoenixville, PA, p. A537
President and Chief Executive Officer, Bayhealth Medical Center, Dover, DE, p. A113

MURPHY, Theresa, Chief Nursing Officer, Usc Verdugo Hills Hospital, Glendale, CA, p. A60

MURPHY, Timothy, Vice President Human Resources, Mercy Hospital Joplin, Joplin, MO, p. A362

MURPHY, Timothy, R.N., Chief Nursing Officer, Encompass Health Rehabilitation Hospital Of Desert Canyon, Las Vegas, NV, p. A395

MURPHY, Tom, Chief Executive Officer, Minidoka Memorial Hospital, Rupert, ID, p. A171

MURPHY–FROBISH, Erin, Vice President Human Resources, Morris Hospital & Healthcare Centers, Morris, IL, p. A190

MURPHY–MIJARES, Monique, Chief Information Officer, Valley View Medical Center, Fort Mohave, AZ, p. A29

MURRAY, Alexander, Interim Associate Director, Veterans Affairs Gulf Coast Veterans Health Care System, Biloxi, MS, p. A344

MURRAY, Beverly, Director of Human Resources, Providence Tarzana Medical Center, Los Angeles, CA, p. A69

MURRAY, Brian, Chief Financial Officer, Gunnison Valley Hospital, Gunnison, UT, p. A648

MURRAY, Brian, M.D., Medical Director, Erie County Medical Center, Buffalo, NY, p. A424

MURRAY, Cindy, R.N., Chief Nursing Officer and Chief Operating Officer, Baylor Scott & White Medical Center–Waxahachie, Waxahachie, TX, p. A644

MURRAY, Denise R., Chief Executive Officer, Anmed Health Rehabilitation Hospital, Anderson, SC, p. A549

MURRAY, Diana, Director Information Systems, Grand River Hospital District, Rifle, CO, p. A105

MURRAY, Kent, M.D., Chief of Staff, Robert J. Dole Veterans Affairs Medical Center, Wichita, KS, p. A248

MURRAY, Kevin, M.D., Director Medical Services, Lake Taylor Transitional Care Hospital, Norfolk, VA, p. A664

MURRAY, Kevin J, Senior Vice President, John T. Mather Memorial Hospital, Port Jefferson, NY, p. A441

MURRAY, Lorraine, Chief Executive Officer, Post Acute Medical Specialty Hospital Of Texarkana – North, Texarkana, TX, p. A640

MURRAY, Marisa, CPA, Director Finance, Hshs St. Francis Hospital, Litchfield, IL, p. A188

MURRAY, Michael, Chief Financial Officer, Christus Dubuis Hospital Of Paris, Paris, TX, p. A627

MURRAY, Sherri, Chief Financial Officer, Montgomery General Hospital, Montgomery, WV, p. A687

MURRAY, Susan
Chief Operating Officer, The Queen'S Medical Center, Honolulu, HI, p. A165
Director Information Services, Trident Medical Center, Charleston, SC, p. A550

MURRAY, Wesley E., Chief Executive Officer, Texas County Memorial Hospital, Houston, MO, p. A361

MURRELL, Joseph, Chief Executive Officer, Wayne County Hospital, Monticello, KY, p. A258

MURRILL, Michael, President and Chief Executive Officer, Adventist Medical Center Lagrange, La Grange, IL, p. A187

MURROW, Carol, Vice President Business Development, Cox Medical Center Branson, Branson, MO, p. A357

MURRY, Jim, Chief Information Officer, Stony Brook University Hospital, Stony Brook, NY, p. A444

MURT, Mary Lou, R.N., Senior Vice President Nursing, Monongahela Valley Hospital, Monongahela, PA, p. A532

MURTHY, Anandhi, Chief Medical Officer, Harrison Community Hospital, Cadiz, OH, p. A474

MURTHY, Bangalore, M.D., Director Medical Staff, Jackson Park Hospital And Medical Center, Chicago, IL, p. A177

MURTHY, Krishna, M.D., Chief of Medical Staff, Gibson General Hospital, Princeton, IN, p. A214

MURZYN, Derek
Chief Executive Officer, Carolinas Continuecare Hospital At University, Charlotte, NC, p. A451
Market Chief Executive Officer, Carolinas Continuecare Hospital At Pineville, Charlotte, NC, p. A451

MUSACK, Scott, Chief Information Officer, Silver Lake Medical Center, Los Angeles, CA, p. A69

MUSANTE, David, M.D., Medical Director, North Carolina Specialty Hospital, Durham, NC, p. A453

MUSGRAVE, Chelsea, Director of Human Resources, Clay County Hospital, Flora, IL, p. A183

MUSICH, Trisha E., R.N., Chief Nursing Officer, Amita Health Saint Francis Hospital Evanston, Evanston, IL, p. A182

MUSOIU, Robert, Director Human Resources, Fairfield Memorial Hospital, Fairfield, IL, p. A183

MUSSI, Alexis
Chief Operating Officer, Southern Hills Hospital And Medical Center, Las Vegas, NV, p. A395
Interim Chief Executive Officer, Southern Hills Hospital And Medical Center, Las Vegas, NV, p. A395

MUSSI, Natalie, President and Chief Executive Officer, Los Robles Hospital And Medical Center, Thousand Oaks, CA, p. A91

MUSSMAN, Rebekah, President and Chief Executive Officer, Crete Area Medical Center, Crete, NE, p. A384

MUSSO, Lewis C, Vice President Human Resources, Trinity Health System, Steubenville, OH, p. A491

MUSTACCHIA, Michele, Chief Human Resources Officer, Banner Gateway Medical Center, Gilbert, AZ, p. A29

MUSTARD, Ruth W., R.N., MSN, Associate Director Nursing and Patient Services, Wm. Jennings Bryan Dorn Veterans Affairs Medical Center, Columbia, SC, p. A552

MUSTIAN, J. Perry, President and Chief Executive Officer, John D. Archbold Memorial Hospital, Thomasville, GA, p. A161

MUSUNURU, J.R., Executive Director, Fond Du Lac County Mental Health Center, Fond Du Lac, WI, p. A695

MUTHU, Karthik, Chief Executive Officer, Encompass Health Rehabilitation Hospital Of Ocala, Ocala, FL, p. A133

MUTTERER, Michael, Senior Vice President and Chief Nursing Officer, Riverside Medical Center, Kankakee, IL, p. A187

MUTZIGER, John, M.D., Chief Medical Officer, Laird Hospital, Union, MS, p. A354

MWANIKI, Mary, Chief Financial Officer, Encompass Health Rehabilitation Hospital Of The Mid–Cities, Bedford, TX, p. A588

MWEBE, David, M.D., Chief of Staff, Osmond General Hospital, Osmond, NE, p. A390

MYATT, Kevin A, Senior Vice President Human Resources, Yale–New Haven Hospital, New Haven, CT, p. A110

MYCROFT, Tina, Senior Vice President, Chief Financial Officer, Evergreenhealth, Kirkland, WA, p. A674

MYDLER, Todd, M.D., Vice President and Chief Medical Officer, Good Samaritan Medical Center, Lafayette, CO, p. A102

MYER, Amber, Director Medical Technology, Throckmorton County Memorial Hospital, Throckmorton, TX, p. A641

MYERS, Becky, Human Resources Specialist, Illini Community Hospital, Pittsfield, IL, p. A193

MYERS, Chrissy, R.N., Director of Nursing, Unity Psychiatric Care–Clarksville, Clarksville, TN, p. A568

MYERS, Douglas, Executive Vice President and Chief Financial Officer, Phoenix Children'S Hospital, Phoenix, AZ, p. A34

MYERS, Ed, Administrator, Shriners Hospitals For Children–Philadelphia, Philadelphia, PA, p. A536

MYERS, Gabby, Human Resources Director, Advanced Diagnostics Hospital, Houston, TX, p. A610

MYERS, Grace, MSN, Vice President, Nurse Executive, Sentara Princess Anne Hospital, Virginia Beach, VA, p. A668

MYERS, Jeffrey D., President and Chief Executive Officer, Hamilton Medical Center, Dalton, GA, p. A151

MYERS, Jerry, Chief Executive Officer and Medical Director, Kell West Regional Hospital, Wichita Falls, TX, p. A645

MYERS, Joseph, Interim Administrator, J. C. Blair Memorial Hospital, Huntingdon, PA, p. A527

MYERS, Josette M., Chief Executive Officer, Encompass Health Rehabilitation Hospital Of Mechanicsburg, Mechanicsburg, PA, p. A531

MYERS, Julie
Chief Executive Officer, Kindred Hospital–La Mirada, La Mirada, CA, p. A63
Chief Executive Officer, Kindred Hospital–Westminster, Westminster, CA, p. A94

MYERS, Karen, Vice President Financial Services, Stoughton Hospital Association, Stoughton, WI, p. A706

MYERS, Kathy R, MS, R.N., Chief Nursing Officer, Tennova Healthcare–Lafollette Medical Center, La Follette, TN, p. A572

MYERS, Kevin
Director Information Systems, Lake Granbury Medical Center, Granbury, TX, p. A608
Director Information Technology, Wilson Medical Center, Neodesha, KS, p. A241

MYERS, Kimberly, Director Human Resources, Guthrie County Hospital, Guthrie Center, IA, p. A223

MYERS, Lisa, Director Human Resources, Heritage Oaks Hospital, Sacramento, CA, p. A81

MYERS, Mary, R.N., MSN, Chief Nursing Officer, St. Vincent Indianapolis Hospital, Indianapolis, IN, p. A208

MYERS, Michael D., Chief Executive Officer, Veterans Memorial Hospital, Waukon, IA, p. A231

MYERS, Michelle F., Director Human Resources, Adventhealth Wauchula, Wauchula, FL, p. A143

MYERS, Paul, M.D., Neonatologist and Chief Medical Officer, Children'S Hospital Of Wisconsin–Fox Valley, Neenah, WI, p. A702

MYERS, Philip, M.D., Vice President Medical Affairs, University Hospitals Samaritan Medical Center, Ashland, OH, p. A472

MYERS, Randy, Chief Information Officer, Rehoboth Mckinley Christian Health Care Services, Gallup, NM, p. A418

MYERS, Robert T, Chief Operating Officer, Goshen Health, Goshen, IN, p. A205

MYERS, Rosemary, Manager, Team Resources, Winter Haven Hospital, Winter Haven, FL, p. A144

MYERS, Russ, Chief Executive Officer, Virginia Mason Memorial, Yakima, WA, p. A682

MYERS, Shane P, Chief Operating Officer, Iberia Medical Center, New Iberia, LA, p. A274

MYERS, Sheri, Vice President Patient Care Services, Mclaren Central Michigan, Mount Pleasant, MI, p. A318

MYERS, Stephen, Chief Executive Officer, Providence Hospital Of North Houston, Houston, TX, p. A613

MYERS, Theresa, Personnel Director, Fallon Medical Complex, Baker, MT, p. A374

MYERS, William, Chief Executive Officer, Montgomery County Emergency Service, Norristown, PA, p. A533

MYHRE, Tracy, R.N., MSN, Chief Nursing Officer, Tomah Memorial Hospital, Tomah, WI, p. A706

MYLAVARAPU, Sarada, M.D., Chief Medical Officer, Woodland Healthcare, Woodland, CA, p. A95

MYSTER, Jennifer, President, Park Nicollet Methodist Hospital, Saint Louis Park, MN, p. A339

N

NABEL, Elizabeth, President, Brigham And Women'S Hospital, Boston, MA, p. A295

NABULSHI, Sari A., M.D., Chief Medical Officer, Medical Center Health System, Odessa, TX, p. A627

NACEY, Marley, Director Finance, Sentara Virginia Beach General Hospital, Virginia Beach, VA, p. A668

NACHIMUTHU, Anbu, Chief Financial Officer, Atrium Medical Center Of Corinth, Corinth, TX, p. A594

NACHTIGAL, Amy, Chief Financial Officer, Saint Luke'S Hospital Of Kansas City, Kansas City, MO, p. A363

NACHTRIEB, Han, Vice President Human Resources, Seattle Cancer Care Alliance, Seattle, WA, p. A678

NACION, Glenn, Vice President Human Resources, Trinitas Regional Medical Center, Elizabeth, NJ, p. A405

NADEAU, Barbara, Chief Human Resources Management Service, White River Junction Veterans Affairs Medical Center, White River Junction, VT, p. A655

NADEAU, Stephen, Senior Vice President Human Resources, Gwinnett Hospital System, Lawrenceville, GA, p. A156

NADER, Daniel, D.O., Chief of Staff, Southwestern Regional Medical Center, Tulsa, OK, p. A509

NADER, Keoni, Director Human Resources, Louis A. Weiss Memorial Hospital, Chicago, IL, p. A178

NADER, Rick Lee, Chief Financial Officer, Haxtun Hospital District, Haxtun, CO, p. A102

NADKARNI, Manasi, M.D., Vice President Medical Affairs, Unitypoint Health – Trinity Muscatine, Muscatine, IA, p. A227

NADLE, Patricia A, R.N., Chief Nursing Officer, St. Joseph Health Services Of Rhode Island, North Providence, RI, p. A547

NADLER, Tammy R, Chief Financial Officer, Golden Valley Memorial Healthcare, Clinton, MO, p. A358

NADOLNY, Stephanie, Vice President of Hospital Operations, Spaulding Rehabilitation Hospital Cape Cod, East Sandwich, MA, p. A298

NAEGLER, Rick, Chief Executive Officer, Lake City Medical Center, Lake City, FL, p. A127

NAFZIGER, Laurie N., President and Chief Executive Officer, Oaklawn Psychiatric Center, Goshen, IN, p. A205

NAFZIGER, Steve, M.D., Vice President Medical Affairs, Parkview Medical Center, Pueblo, CO, p. A104

NAG, Pratip, Vice President, Chief Medical Officer, Katherine Shaw Bethea Hospital, Dixon, IL, p. A181

NAGARAJ, Alaka, M.D., Medical Director, Regency Hospital Of Minneapolis, Golden Valley, MN, p. A332

NAGARAJ, Raghava, Chief Medical Officer, Wake Forest Baptist Health–Lexington Medical Center, Lexington, NC, p. A458

NAGATOSHI, Holly, R.N., Chief Nursing Officer, San Dimas Community Hospital, San Dimas, CA, p. A85

NAGLE, Melissa
  Chief Executive Officer, Continuecare Hospital At Madisonville, Madisonville, KY, p. A257
  Chief Nursing Officer, Continuecare Hospital At Madisonville, Madisonville, KY, p. A257

NAGLER, Richard, M.D., Chief of Staff, Mayo Clinic Health System – Northland In Barron, Barron, WI, p. A692

NAGOWSKI, Michael, Chief Executive Officer, Cape Fear Valley Medical Center, Fayetteville, NC, p. A454

NAGY, Jeff, Chief Financial Officer, River Bend Hospital, West Lafayette, IN, p. A216

NAGY, Linda J., MSN, R.N., Chief Nursing Officer, Brattleboro Retreat, Brattleboro, VT, p. A654

NAGY, Ryan, President and Chief Medical Officer, Indiana University Health University Hospital, Indianapolis, IN, p. A207

NAHAPETIAN, Arby, M.D., Vice President Medical Affairs and Quality, Adventist Health Glendale, Los Angeles, CA, p. A65

NAHM, Christopher, M.D., Chief Medical Officer, Livingston Regional Hospital, Livingston, TN, p. A573

NAIBERK, Donald T., Administrator and Chief Executive Officer, Butler County Health Care Center, David City, NE, p. A384

NAIL, Cheryl, R.N., Chief Nursing Officer, City Hospital At White Rock, Dallas, TX, p. A596

NAIR, Chand, M.D., Medical Director, Brooke Glen Behavioral Hospital, Fort Washington, PA, p. A526

NAIR, Vijayachandran, M.D., Chief of Staff, John J. Pershing Veterans Affairs Medical Center, Poplar Bluff, MO, p. A367

NAJIEB, LaDonna, Service Area Director Human Resources, Providence Saint Joseph Medical Center, Burbank, CA, p. A53

NAJJAR, Maher, M.D., Medical Director, Kindred Hospital Chicago–Northlake, Northlake, IL, p. A191

NAJJAR, Milad, Information Technology, Scottsdale Liberty Hospital, Scottsdale, AZ, p. A36

NAKAMOTO, Kenneth, M.D., Vice President Medical Affairs, Pomona Valley Hospital Medical Center, Pomona, CA, p. A78

NAKAMURA, Bridget, Director Information Systems, Simi Valley Hospital, Simi Valley, CA, p. A89

NAKASUJI, Jody, Chief Financial Officer, Harbor–Ucla Medical Center, Torrance, CA, p. A91

NALDI, Robert, Chief Financial Officer, Brookdale Hospital Medical Center, New York, NY, p. A432

NALL, Brian, Chief Executive Officer, North Country Hospital And Health Center, Newport, VT, p. A654

NALL, Wes
  Chief Financial Officer, Monroe County Hospital, Monroeville, AL, p. A21
  Interim Chief Executive Officer, Monroe County Hospital, Monroeville, AL, p. A21

NALLEY, Leanna W, Director Human Resources, Texas Health Harris Methodist Hospital Southwest Fort Worth, Fort Worth, TX, p. A606

NANCE, Christi, R.N., MSN, Chief Nursing Officer, Northwest Specialty Hospital, Post Falls, ID, p. A171

NAPIER, Frank, Interim Chief Financial Officer, Cobre Valley Regional Medical Center, Globe, AZ, p. A30

NAPIERKOWSKI, Daniel
  President, Euclid Hospital, Euclid, OH, p. A482
  President, Marymount Hospital, Garfield Heights, OH, p. A483

NAPOLITANO, Mary Pat, Director Human Resources, Specialty Hospital Of Central Jersey, Lakewood, NJ, p. A407

NAPPER, Rick D., Chief Executive Officer, Medical Center Health System, Odessa, TX, p. A627

NARAMORE, G Harold, M.D., Chief Medical Officer and In house Legal Counsel, Blount Memorial Hospital, Maryville, TN, p. A574

NARANG, Steve, Chief Executive Officer, Banner – University Medical Center Phoenix, Phoenix, AZ, p. A33

NARANJO, Maria, Director Human Resources, Memorial Hospital West, Pembroke Pines, FL, p. A136

NARROW, Ann, Director of Nursing, River Hospital, Alexandria Bay, NY, p. A422

NASEM, Charles D., Chief Executive Officer, Select Specialty Hospital–Tulsa Midtown, Tulsa, OK, p. A509

NASER, Bashar, Chief Financial Officer, Gerald Champion Regional Medical Center, Alamogordo, NM, p. A416

NASET–PAYNE, Janet, MS, R.N., Chief Nursing Officer, Van Diest Medical Center, Webster City, IA, p. A231

NASH, Daniel J, Chief Information Officer, Citrus Valley Medical Center–Inter Community Campus, Covina, CA, p. A56

NASH, Ernest
  Chief Financial Officer, South Texas Rehabilitation Hospital, Brownsville, TX, p. A589
  Chief Financial Officer, Weslaco Regional Rehabilitation Hospital, Weslaco, TX, p. A645

NASH, Gayle, R.N., M.P.H., Chief Nursing Officer, Mountainview Regional Medical Center, Las Cruces, NM, p. A419

NASH, Jacqueline, Controller, Beaumont Hospital, Wayne, Wayne, MI, p. A324

NASH, John D., President and Chief Executive Officer, Franciscan Children'S, Brighton, MA, p. A296

NASH, Mary G, Ph.D., R.N., Chief Nursing Officer, Ohio State University Wexner Medical Center, Columbus, OH, p. A479

NASH, Robert, M.D., Chief of Staff, Carle Richland Memorial Hospital, Olney, IL, p. A192

NASH, Sandra, Chief Fiscal Service, James H. Quillen Veterans Affairs Medical Center, Mountain Home, TN, p. A576

NASH, Tim, M.D., Chief of Staff, Board Vice Chairman, Marshall Medical Center, Lewisburg, TN, p. A573

NASHID, Nadia, M.D., Chief of Staff, Windham Hospital, Willimantic, CT, p. A112

NASLUND, Kevin, Manager Information Technology, Cherokee Regional Medical Center, Cherokee, IA, p. A219

NASRALLAH, Fadi, M.D., Vice President Medical Affairs, Christus Mother Frances Hospital – Tyler, Tyler, TX, p. A642

NASSIEF, Raymond, Senior Vice President, Hospital Operations and Support Services, John Muir Medical Center, Walnut Creek, Walnut Creek, CA, p. A94

NASSTROM, Jeff, D.O., Chief of Staff, Mitchell County Regional Health Center, Osage, IA, p. A228

NAST, Ed, M.D., Chief Medical Officer, Oak Hill Hospital, Brooksville, FL, p. A119

NATAL, Yesenia, Coordinator Human Resources, Hospital Pavia Arecibo, Arecibo, PR, p. A715

NATCHER, Charles, Chief Financial Officer, Kindred Hospital– Los Angeles, Los Angeles, CA, p. A67

NATELSON, Richard, M.D., Chief of Staff, Steele Memorial Medical Center, Salmon, ID, p. A172

NATEMAN, Barry, Manager Human Resources, French Hospital Medical Center, San Luis Obispo, CA, p. A87

NATH, Dilip, Sc.D., Associate Chief Information Officer, Brookdale Hospital Medical Center, New York, NY, p. A432

NATH, Pravene, Chief Information Officer, Stanford Health Care, Palo Alto, CA, p. A77

NATHANSON, Andrea, Director Finance, Baystate Franklin Medical Center, Greenfield, MA, p. A299

NATHEM, Joanne, MSN, R.N., Chief Clinical and Nursing Officer, Waverly Health Center, Waverly, IA, p. A231

NATRAJAN, Sunil, M.D., Medical Director, Curahealth Tucson, Tucson, AZ, p. A37

NAU, James, Manager Computer and Applications Support, Delaware Psychiatric Center, New Castle, DE, p. A113

NAUMAN, Michael B
  Chief Information Officer and Corporate Vice President, Children'S Hospital Of Wisconsin–Fox Valley, Neenah, WI, p. A702
  Chief Information Officer, Children'S Hospital Of Wisconsin, Milwaukee, WI, p. A701

NAUMOWICH, Sarah
  President, Morton Plant North Bay Hospital, New Port Richey, FL, p. A132
  President, St. Joseph'S Hospital, Tampa, FL, p. A142

NAVA, Madeline, Chief Executive Officer, Plantation General Hospital, Plantation, FL, p. A137

NAVARRO, Beth Ann, Chief Clinical Officer, Kindred Hospital–Sycamore, Sycamore, IL, p. A197

NAVARRO, Ramomita, Director Human Resources, University Hospital, San Juan, PR, p. A719

NAVARRO, Tess, Chief Financial Officer, Laguna Honda Hospital And Rehabilitation Center, San Francisco, CA, p. A85

NAVAS, Manuel, M.D., Medical Director, Hospital San Pablo Del Este, Fajardo, PR, p. A716

NAWROCKI, Bernie
  Administrative Director Finance, Promedica Bixby Hospital, Adrian, MI, p. A306
  Administrative Director Finance, Promedica Herrick Hospital, Tecumseh, MI, p. A323

NAWROCKI, Edward, President, St. Luke'S Hospital – Anderson Campus, Easton, PA, p. A525

NAYAK, Yeshavanth, M.D., Interim Chief Medical Officer, Community Medical Center, Toms River, NJ, p. A413

NAZ, Haroon, Chief Executive Officer, Pinnacle Hospital, Crown Point, IN, p. A202

NAZARIAN, Alexander, CPA
  Chief Financial Officer, Kirby Medical Center, Monticello, IL, p. A190
  Director Information Technology, Kirby Medical Center, Monticello, IL, p. A190

NAZARIO, Uriel, M.D., Chief of Medical Staff, Kindred Hospital North Florida, Green Cove Springs, FL, p. A124

NAZE, Jesse, Chief Financial Officer, Fall River Hospital, Hot Springs, SD, p. A561

NAZEER, Imran, M.D., Chief of Staff, Woodland Heights Medical Center, Lufkin, TX, p. A622

NAZIR, Tariq, Interim Director Information Technology, Signature Psychiatric Hospital, Kansas City, MO, p. A363

NDOMEA, Feisal, Director Case Management, Kindred Hospital Sugar Land, Sugar Land, TX, p. A638

NDOW, Emmanuel, Chief Information Officer, Marion General Hospital, Marion, IN, p. A211

NEAL, Bob, Information Technology, Sparrow Ionia Hospital, Ionia, MI, p. A314

NEAL, Greg, President, Bristol Regional Medical Center, Bristol, TN, p. A566

NEAL, Kaley, Chief Financial Officer, Shenandoah Medical Center, Shenandoah, IA, p. A229

NEAL, Robert, Manager Information Technology Services, Newman Memorial Hospital, Shattuck, OK, p. A507

NEAL, Roger, Chief Operating Officer, Duncan Regional Hospital, Duncan, OK, p. A498

NEAL, Terrell, R.N., Chief Operating Officer and Chief Nursing Officer, St. Charles Parish Hospital, Luling, LA, p. A272

NEAL, Thomas, Chief Executive Officer, Berwick Hospital Center, Berwick, PA, p. A520

NEALE, Debra, R.N., Chief Nursing Officer, O'Connor Hospital, Delhi, NY, p. A426

NEALON, Matthew, Vice President, Chief Financial Officer, University Of Cincinnati Medical Center, Cincinnati, OH, p. A477

NEAPOLITAN, David, Chief Financial Officer, Emanuel Medical Center, Turlock, CA, p. A92

NEAR, Holly, Chief Administrative Officer, Harsha Behavioral Center, Terre Haute, IN, p. A215

NEAT, Gary
  Chief Information Officer, Ephraim Mcdowell Regional Medical Center, Danville, KY, p. A251
  Director Information Systems, Ephraim Mcdowell Fort Logan Hospital, Stanford, KY, p. A261

NECAS, Kevin, Chief Financial Officer, University Of Missouri Health Care, Columbia, MO, p. A359

NEEB, Verette, R.N., MSN, Chief Nursing Officer, Baylor Scott & White Medical Center–Uptown, Dallas, TX, p. A595

NEECE, Patrick, Chief Information Officer, Jefferson Regional Medical Center, Pine Bluff, AR, p. A47
NEEDHAM, Kim, Assistant Chief Executive Officer, Vista Health, Waukegan, IL, p. A198
NEEDHAM, Tammy, Chief Nursing Officer, Chatham Hospital, Siler City, NC, p. A462
NEEDLES, Kim, Manager Business Office, Patients' Hospital Of Redding, Redding, CA, p. A79
NEELAGARU, Narasimhulu, M.D., Chief of Staff, Northridge Medical Center, Commerce, GA, p. A151
NEELY, Denise, Vice President and Chief Nursing Officer, Bronson Methodist Hospital, Kalamazoo, MI, p. A315
NEELY, Jill, Chief Financial Officer, Titusville Area Hospital, Titusville, PA, p. A542
NEELY, K. Dale., Chief Executive Officer, Encompass Health Rehabilitation Hospital Of Tallahassee, Tallahassee, FL, p. A140
NEELY, Kathy E., R.N.
Interim Vice President Patient Care Services, Chi St. Vincent Infirmary Medical Center, Little Rock, AR, p. A45
Interim Vice President Patient Care Services, Chi St. Vincent Morrilton, Morrilton, AR, p. A46
NEELY, Randall, CEO, Simpson General Hospital, Mendenhall, MS, p. A351
NEENAN, Sharon, Interim Chief Nursing Officer, Grant, Ohiohealth Grant Medical Center, Columbus, OH, p. A479
NEERGHEEN, Chabilal, M.D., Medical Director, Western Massachusetts Hospital, Westfield, MA, p. A305
NEESEN, Cindy, Director of Information Technology, Butler County Health Care Center, David City, NE, p. A384
NEET, Bradley D, Chief Executive Officer, Southwest Healthcare System, Murrieta, CA, p. A74
NEET, Bradley D., Chief Executive Officer, Southwest Healthcare System, Murrieta, CA, p. A74
NEFCY, Christine
Chief Medical Officer, Munson Healthcare, Munson Medical Center, Traverse City, MI, p. A323
Chief Medical Officer, Mckay–Dee Hospital, Ogden, UT, p. A649
NEFF, Kris, Chief Operating Officer, Samaritan Healthcare, Moses Lake, WA, p. A675
NEFF, Mark J., President and Chief Executive Officer, St. Claire Healthcare, Morehead, KY, p. A258
NEFF, Richard, M.D., Interim Chief Medical Officer, Flagstaff Medical Center, Flagstaff, AZ, p. A29
NEFF, William, M.D., Chief Medical Officer, Uchealth Medical Center Of The Rockies, Loveland, CO, p. A104
NEGRÓN, Manuel, Chief Information Technology Service, Veterans Affairs Caribbean Healthcare System, San Juan, PR, p. A719
NEIGER, Kelly, Chief Financial Officer, Barton Memorial Hospital, South Lake Tahoe, CA, p. A90
NEIKIRK, Richard, Chief Executive Officer, Cumberland County Hospital, Burkesville, KY, p. A250
NEIL, Eric, Interim Chief Information Officer, Uw Medicine/ Northwest Hospital & Medical Center, Seattle, WA, p. A678
NEIL, William, Vice President and Chief Information Officer, Cleveland Clinic Indian River Hospital, Vero Beach, FL, p. A143
NEILSEN SWANSON, Verbelee, Administrator, Adventhealth Orlando, Orlando, FL, p. A134
NEILSON, Carol, CPA, Controller, Encompass Health Rehabilitation Hospital Of Sugar Land, Sugar Land, TX, p. A638
NEILSON, Erinn, Chief Nursing Officer, Minidoka Memorial Hospital, Rupert, ID, p. A171
NEILSON, Karen, Administrator, Safe Haven Hospital Of Pocatello, Pocatello, ID, p. A171
NEILSON, Richard, Director of Information Services, Timpanogos Regional Hospital, Orem, UT, p. A650
NEIMAN, Carla A, Chief Financial Officer, Clark Fork Valley Hospital, Plains, MT, p. A379
NEISWONGER, Randy, Chief Executive Officer, Up Health System–Portage, Hancock, MI, p. A314
NEITZEL, Monte, Chief Executive Officer, Greater Regional Medical Center, Creston, IA, p. A220
NELKIN MCCORMICK, Elizabeth, MSN, R.N., Senior Vice President and Chief Nursing Officer, Brookdale Hospital Medical Center, New York, NY, p. A432
NELL, Sergio, Director Information Systems, Watsonville Community Hospital, Watsonville, CA, p. A94
NELLSCH, Verner, M.D., Chief of Staff, Chi St. Luke'S Health Memorial Livingston, Livingston, TX, p. A621
NELSON, Allison
Chief Financial Officer, Sanford Canby Medical Center, Canby, MN, p. A329
Chief Financial Officer, Sanford Clear Lake Medical Center, Clear Lake, SD, p. A560
NELSON, Barbara J, Ph.D., R.N., Chief Nursing Executive, Sutter Roseville Medical Center, Roseville, CA, p. A81
NELSON, Bill, Chief Executive Officer, Mille Lacs Health System, Onamia, MN, p. A337
NELSON, Carol, Director Human Resources, Montevista Hospital, Las Vegas, NV, p. A395
NELSON, Cory D., Administrator, Sioux Center Health, Sioux Center, IA, p. A229
NELSON, David, FACHE
Chief Financial Officer, Hshs Sacred Heart Hospital, Eau Claire, WI, p. A694
Divisional Chief Financial Officer, Hshs St. Joseph'S Hospital, Chippewa Falls, WI, p. A693
NELSON, David, M.D., Medical Director, Barlow Respiratory Hospital, Los Angeles, CA, p. A66
NELSON, David A., President and Chief Executive Officer, Chi St. Francis Health, Breckenridge, MN, p. A329
NELSON, Dawn, Director Human Resources, Sagewest Health Care At Riverton, Riverton, WY, p. A712
NELSON, Diane, R.N., Chief Nursing Officer, Kindred Hospital–Albuquerque, Albuquerque, NM, p. A416
NELSON, Elaine, R.N., MSN, Chief Nursing Officer, Texas Health Harris Methodist Hospital Fort Worth, Fort Worth, TX, p. A605
NELSON, Gina, Chief Financial Officer, Renown South Meadows Medical Center, Reno, NV, p. A397
NELSON, Jack, Vice President Finance and Chief Financial Officer, Ohio Valley Hospital, Mckees Rocks, PA, p. A531
NELSON, Jackie, Director Human Resources, Hansford Hospital, Spearman, TX, p. A637
NELSON, James J, Senior Vice President Finance and Strategic Planning, Fort Healthcare, Fort Atkinson, WI, p. A695
NELSON, Jamie, Vice President and Chief Information Officer, Brookdale Hospital Medical Center, New York, NY, p. A432
NELSON, Jennifer, Senior Human Resource Business Partner, Spectrum Health United Hospital, Greenville, MI, p. A313
NELSON, Jodi, Interim Chief Executive Officer, St. Luke'S Medical Center, Crosby, ND, p. A466
NELSON, Joseph, M.D., President Medical Staff, Lewis–Gale Medical Center, Boones Mill, VA, p. A657
NELSON, Julia, Vice President of Human Resources, Northern Hospital Of Surry County, Mount Airy, NC, p. A459
NELSON, Katey, Director Human Resources, Sevier Valley Hospital, Richfield, UT, p. A651
NELSON, Kathy
Chief Financial Officer, Marshall Medical Center North, Guntersville, AL, p. A19
Chief Financial Officer, Marshall Medical Center South, Boaz, AL, p. A15
NELSON, Kellie, Director Human Resources, Aurora Medical Center Kenosha, Kenosha, WI, p. A697
NELSON, Kenneth E, R.N., Chief Nursing Officer, Hshs St. Vincent Hospital, Green Bay, WI, p. A696
NELSON, Kerri, Chief Financial Officer, Spectrum Health Ludington Hospital, Ludington, MI, p. A317
NELSON, Lucy, Director Finance, Vice President, Maniilaq Health Center, Kotzebue, AK, p. A26
NELSON, Lynn M., R.N., R.N., Chief Nursing Officer and Chief Operating Officer, St. John'S Riverside Hospital, Yonkers, NY, p. A448
NELSON, Marlin Pete, Vice President Fiscal Services, Divine Savior Healthcare, Portage, WI, p. A704
NELSON, Martha
Chief Financial Officer, Antelope Memorial Hospital, Neligh, NE, p. A388
Chief Financial Officer, Niobrara Valley Hospital, Lynch, NE, p. A387
NELSON, Melissa, Assistant Administrator, Baptist Memorial Hospital For Women, Memphis, TN, p. A574
NELSON, Meredith, Chief Financial Officer, Willamette Valley Medical Center, Mcminnville, OR, p. A514
NELSON, Michael
Chief Financial Officer, Select Specialty Hospital Midtown Atlanta, Atlanta, GA, p. A147
Executive Vice President and Chief Financial Officer, Pomona Valley Hospital Medical Center, Pomona, CA, p. A78
NELSON, Nan, Senior Vice President Finance, Aurora St. Luke'S Medical Center, Milwaukee, WI, p. A701
NELSON, Nancy, Director Human Resources, Intermountain Hospital, Boise, ID, p. A167
NELSON, Nick, Director Support Services, Adams Memorial Hospital, Decatur, IN, p. A202
NELSON, Peggy, Chief Executive Officer, Encompass Health Rehabilitation Hospital Of Desert Canyon, Las Vegas, NV, p. A395
NELSON, Raymond, Acting Chief Information Resource Management, Fargo Veterans Affairs Health Care System, Fargo, ND, p. A466
NELSON, Richard, Chief of Human Resources Management Services, Central Arkansas Veterans Healthcare System, Little Rock, AR, p. A45
NELSON, RimaAnn O., Director, Phoenix Veterans Affairs Health Care System, Phoenix, AZ, p. A34
NELSON, Robin, Chief Financial Officer, Gundersen St. Joseph'S Hospital And Clinics, Hillsboro, WI, p. A697
NELSON, Selena, Chief Financial Officer, Fallon Medical Complex, Baker, MT, p. A374
NELSON, Siri, Chief Executive Officer, Renown South Meadows Medical Center, Reno, NV, p. A397
NELSON, Stewart R
Vice President and Chief Financial Officer, Sentara Halifax Regional Hospital, South Boston, VA, p. A667
Vice President and Chief Financial Officer, Sentara Martha Jefferson Hospital, Charlottesville, VA, p. A657
Vice President and Chief Financial Officer, Sentara Rmh Medical Center, Harrisonburg, VA, p. A660
NELSON, Suzanne, R.N., Director of Nursing, Salt Lake Behavioral Health, Salt Lake City, UT, p. A652
NELSON, Tricia, Chief Financial Officer, Riverwoods Behavioral Health System, Riverdale, GA, p. A159
NELSON, Trudy, Chief Human Resource Officer, Niobrara Valley Hospital, Lynch, NE, p. A387
NELSON–JONES, Susan, Director Human Resources, Adventist Health Medical Center – Tehachapi Valley, Tehachapi, CA, p. A91
NEMECHEK, Victor, M.D., Chief of Staff and Chief Medical Officer, Sheridan County Health Complex, Hoxie, KS, p. A237
NEMETH, Jim
Chief Financial Officer, Monroe Clinic, Monroe, WI, p. A701
Senior Vice President of Patient Care Services and Chief Nursing Officer, Memorial Healthcare, Owosso, MI, p. A319
NEMI, Neil, Administrator Facility Information Center, Richard H. Hutchings Psychiatric Center, Syracuse, NY, p. A445
NEONAKIS, Stephanie W, Manager Human Resources, Uh Regional Hospitals, Cleveland, OH, p. A478
NERMOE, Bryan, Executive Vice President, Sanford Bemidji Medical Center, Bemidji, MN, p. A328
NERO, Theresa R, R.N., MS, Chief Nursing Officer, Kaiser Permanente San Jose Medical Center, San Jose, CA, p. A86
NESBITT, William, President, Texas Health Heart & Vascular Hospital Arlington, Arlington, TX, p. A584
NESMITH, Nikki
Chief Executive Officer and Chief Nursing Officer, Evans Memorial Hospital, Claxton, GA, p. A150
Chief Nursing Officer, Evans Memorial Hospital, Claxton, GA, p. A150
NESPOLI, John L, President, St. Luke'S – Gnaden Huetten Campus, Lehighton, PA, p. A530
NESPOLI, John L., President, St. Luke'S – Gnaden Huetten Campus, Lehighton, PA, p. A530
NESS, David L, Vice President Operations, Unitypoint Health – Grinnell Regional Medical Center, Grinnell, IA, p. A223
NESS, Joe, Chief Operating Officer, Ohsu Hospital, Portland, OR, p. A516
NESS, Jon, Chief Executive Officer, Kootenai Health, Coeur D'Alene, ID, p. A169
NESSEL, Mark
Chief Operating Officer, Our Lady Of Lourdes Medical Center, Camden, NJ, p. A404
Executive Vice President and Chief Operating Officer, Lourdes Medical Center Of Burlington County, Willingboro, NJ, p. A415
NESSELRODT, Derek, Director Information Systems, Grant Memorial Hospital, Petersburg, WV, p. A688
NESTER, Brian A., President and Chief Executive Officer, Lehigh Valley Hospital, Allentown, PA, p. A519
NESTER, Darlene E.
Chief Human Resources Officer, Hilton Head Hospital, Hilton Head Island, SC, p. A554
Market Chief Human Resources Officer, Coastal Carolina Hospital, Hardeeville, SC, p. A554
NESTER, Michael, Administrator, H. C. Watkins Memorial Hospital, Quitman, MS, p. A353
NESTER WOLFE, Cheryl R., President and Chief Executive Officer, Salem Hospital, Salem, OR, p. A517
NESTLER, Nicole, Division Director Human Resources, Chi Mercy Health, Valley City, ND, p. A469
NETTERVILLE, Chad, Administrator and Chief Executive Officer, Field Memorial Community Hospital, Centreville, MS, p. A345
NETTLES, Angela F, Vice President, Human Resources and Support Services, Kershawhealth, Camden, SC, p. A549
NETTLES, Robert, Director Human Resources, Mountainview Hospital, Las Vegas, NV, p. A395
NETZER, Craig, M.D., President Medical Staff, Wilcox Medical Center, Lihue, HI, p. A166
NEUBERT, Todd, Chief Executive Officer, Riverton Hospital, Riverton, UT, p. A651

NEUENDORF, Deborah, Vice President Administration, New York–Presbyterian/Hudson Valley Hospital, Cortlandt Manor, NY, p. A426
NEUENDORF, James, M.D., Medical Director, Saint Joseph'S Medical Center, Yonkers, NY, p. A448
NEUENDORF, Michael, Chief Executive Officer, Princeton Baptist Medical Center, Birmingham, AL, p. A15
NEUFELD, Ellis, M.D., Chief Medical Officer, St. Jude Children'S Research Hospital, Memphis, TN, p. A575
NEUFELDER, Daniel, President, Indiana University Health Arnett Hospital, Lafayette, IN, p. A209
NEUGENT, Kevin, Chief Information Officer, Hayes Green Beach Memorial Hospital, Charlotte, MI, p. A308
NEUJAHR, Elias
Chief Executive Officer, Children'S Hospital Of Richmond At Vcu–Brook Road Campus, Richmond, VA, p. A666
Chief Executive Officer, Vcu Medical Center, Richmond, VA, p. A666
NEUMAN, Keith A.
Chief Information Officer, Lutheran Hospital Of Indiana, Fort Wayne, IN, p. A204
Chief Information Officer, Orthopaedic Hospital Of Lutheran Health Network, Fort Wayne, IN, p. A204
NEUMAN, Michael J, Vice President Finance, Kennedy Krieger Institute, Baltimore, MD, p. A286
NEUMANN, Jamie, Director Human Resources, Iroquois Memorial Hospital And Resident Home, Watseka, IL, p. A197
NEUMEISTER, Daniel P, Senior Vice President and Chief Operating Officer, Searhc Mt. Edgecumbe Hospital, Sitka, AK, p. A27
NEUNER, Kathy, R.N., Chief Nursing Officer, Clark Memorial Health, Jeffersonville, IN, p. A208
NEUVIRTH, Stephanie, Chief Human Resource and Diversity Officer, City Of Hope'S Helford Clinical Research Hospital, Duarte, CA, p. A57
NEVAREZ, Domingo, Chief Executive Officer, Hospital Metropolitan, San Juan, PR, p. A719
NEVERS, Rick L., Interim President, Aspirus Keweenaw Hospital, Inc., Laurium, MI, p. A316
NEVILLE, Bette, R.N., MSN, Vice President and Chief Nursing Officer, Northern Light Mercy Hospital, Portland, ME, p. A284
NEVILLE, Lawrence, Chief Medical Officer, Peacehealth Southwest Medical Center, Vancouver, WA, p. A681
NEVILLE, Michelle, Chief Executive Officer, Highland Ridge Hospital, Midvale, UT, p. A648
NEVILLE, Ryan T., President and Chief Executive Officer, Marshfield Medical Center – Neillsville, Neillsville, WI, p. A702
NEVIN, James, M.D., Vice President Medical Management, Advocate Bromenn Medical Center, Normal, IL, p. A191
NEVIN, Janice E., Chief Executive Officer, Christiana Care Health System, Newark, DE, p. A113
NEVINS, Norm, Manager Human Resources, Kansas Medical Center, Andover, KS, p. A232
NEWBURN, Lorance, M.D., Medical Chief of Staff, Saunders Medical Center, Wahoo, NE, p. A392
NEWBY, Doug, Chief Information Officer, Highlands Medical Center, Scottsboro, AL, p. A23
NEWBY, Glenda, Chief Executive Officer, Dallas Regional Medical Center, Mesquite, TX, p. A624
NEWBY, Jennifer, Operations Director Support Services and Finance, Memorial Community Hospital And Health System, Blair, NE, p. A383
NEWBY, Nancy M., President and Chief Executive Officer, Washington County Hospital, Nashville, IL, p. A191
NEWCOMB, James, M.D.
Vice President Medical Affairs, Slidell Memorial Hospital, Slidell, LA, p. A279
Vice President Medical, Ochsner Medical Center – North Shore, Slidell, LA, p. A279
NEWCOMB, Michael, D.O.
Senior Vice President and Chief Operating Officer, Legacy Meridian Park Medical Center, Tualatin, OR, p. A518
Senior Vice President and Chief Operating Officer, Legacy Mount Hood Medical Center, Gresham, OR, p. A513
Senior Vice President and Chief Operating Officer, Legacy Salmon Creek Medical Center, Vancouver, WA, p. A681
NEWCOMER, Jeremy, Director Information Services, Elmira Psychiatric Center, Elmira, NY, p. A427
NEWCOMER, Peter, M.D., Chief Medical Officer, University Hospital, Madison, WI, p. A698
NEWELL, Dan, Chief Financial Officer, Highlands Medical Center, Scottsboro, AL, p. A23
NEWELL, Janice
Chief Information Officer, Swedish Medical Center–Cherry Hill Campus, Seattle, WA, p. A678
Chief Information Officer, Swedish Medical Center–First Hill, Seattle, WA, p. A678
NEWELL, Richard, Chief Executive Officer, Pottstown Hospital, Pottstown, PA, p. A539
NEWEY, Mark, D.O., Chief of Staff, Mercy Hospital Healdton, Healdton, OK, p. A500
NEWHOUSE, Chuck, M.D., Chief of Staff, Boundary Community Hospital, Bonners Ferry, ID, p. A168
NEWHOUSE, Paul R., President, Union Medical Center, Union, SC, p. A558
NEWLAND, Judy, Chief Nursing Officer, Incline Village Community Hospital, Incline Village, NV, p. A394
NEWLAND, Judy, R.N., Chief Operating Officer, Tahoe Forest Hospital District, Truckee, CA, p. A92
NEWMAN, Billy, Department Head, Naval Hospital Lemoore, Lemoore, CA, p. A64
NEWMAN, Carlotta Hannah, Human Resources Manager, Northeast Georgia Medical Center Barrow, Winder, GA, p. A163
NEWMAN, Christopher, M.D., Vice President Medical Affairs and Chief Medical Officer, Penn State Health St. Joseph, Reading, PA, p. A539
NEWMAN, Cynthia, Manager Human Resources, Petersburg Medical Center, Petersburg, AK, p. A27
NEWMAN, Dan, Chief Executive Officer, Houston Methodist Clear Lake Hospital, Nassau Bay, TX, p. A626
NEWMAN, Edith, Interim Administrator, John J. Madden Mental Health Center, Hines, IL, p. A185
NEWMAN, John B., President, Aurora Medical Center Of Oshkosh, Oshkosh, WI, p. A703
NEWMAN, JW, Chief Operating Officer, Medical City Fort Worth, Fort Worth, TX, p. A605
NEWMAN, Karen, Ed.D., MSN, R.N., Vice President and Chief Nursing Officer, Baptist Health Louisville, Louisville, KY, p. A256
NEWMAN, Kurt, President and Chief Executive Officer, Children'S National Health System, Washington, DC, p. A115
NEWMAN, Mark, Executive Vice President of Health Affairs, University Of Kentucky Albert B. Chandler Hospital, Lexington, KY, p. A255
NEWMAN, Richard, Chief Human Resources Officer, Olympic Medical Center, Port Angeles, WA, p. A676
NEWMAN, Sonya, R.N., Chief Nursing Officer, Blount Memorial Hospital, Maryville, TN, p. A574
NEWMAN, Thomas M
Chief Financial Officer, Upmc Passavant, Pittsburgh, PA, p. A538
Vice President Finance, Upmc St. Margaret, Pittsburgh, PA, p. A538
NEWMILLER, Vicki, Chief Executive Officer, Great Falls Clinic Hospital, Great Falls, MT, p. A377
NEWPOWER, Nicole, Coordinator Human Resources, Kindred Hospital–Fort Worth, Fort Worth, TX, p. A605
NEWQUIST, Dennis, Director Information Systems, Abilene Regional Medical Center, Abilene, TX, p. A581
NEWSOM, Cynthia, Chief Executive Officer, Vibra Hospital Of Boise, Boise, ID, p. A168
NEWSOM, Terri T., Vice President of Finance and Chief Financial Officer, Prisma Health Greenville Memorial Hospital, Greenville, SC, p. A553
NEWSOME, Samuel C, M.D., Chief of Staff, Lifebrite Community Hospital Of Stokes, Danbury, NC, p. A452
NEWSWANGER, Jeff, M.D., Chief Medical Officer, Adventhealth Manchester, Manchester, KY, p. A257
NEWTON, Gail, R.N., MSN, Vice President Patient Care Services, St. Luke'S Hospital – Warren Campus, Phillipsburg, NJ, p. A411
NEWTON, Jennifer, R.N., Chief Nursing Officer, Neosho Memorial Regional Medical Center, Chanute, KS, p. A233
NEWTON, Keith, Chief Executive Officer, Northern Louisiana Medical Center, Ruston, LA, p. A277
NEWTON, Steven R., President, Baylor University Medical Center, Dallas, TX, p. A596
NEWTON, Susan, Chief Operating Officer, Broward Health North, Deerfield Beach, FL, p. A121
NEWTON, Terri, Chief Nursing Officer, Lakewood Regional Medical Center, Lakewood, CA, p. A64
NEWTON, Wilma, Executive Vice President and Chief Financial Officer, St. Vincent'S Birmingham, Birmingham, AL, p. A15
NEZBETH, Jacqueline, Human Resources Officer, Select Specialty Hospital Of Southeast Ohio, Newark, OH, p. A488
NG, Anthony, M.D., Vice President and Chief Medical Officer, The Acadia Hospital, Bangor, ME, p. A281
NG, Hong–Kin, M.D., Chief Medical Officer, Roane General Hospital, Spencer, WV, p. A689
NG, Thomas T., Chief Information Officer, Collingsworth General Hospital, Wellington, TX, p. A645
NG, Vincent
Director, Veterans Affairs Boston Healthcare System Brockton Division, Brockton, MA, p. A297
Director, Veterans Affairs Boston Healthcare System, West Roxbury, MA, p. A304
NGIRAISUI, Clarinda, Director, Human Resources, Commonwealth Health Center, Saipan, MP, p. A714
NGUYEN, Abby, R.N., Chief Nursing Officer, Genesis Healthcare System, Zanesville, OH, p. A495
NGUYEN, Bach, Director Information Systems, Northwest Texas Healthcare System, Amarillo, TX, p. A582
NGUYEN, Harry, Medical Director, The Woods At Parkside, Gahanna, OH, p. A483
NGUYEN, Nga, Manager Human Resources and Organizational Development, Glendale Memorial Hospital And Health Center, Glendale, CA, p. A60
NIBLOCK, Jenny, Chief Clinical Officer, Citizens Medical Center, Colby, KS, p. A233
NICASTRO, Pamela, Director Human Resources, Brylin Hospitals, Buffalo, NY, p. A424
NICAUD, Kent, President and Chief Executive Officer, Memorial Hospital At Gulfport, Gulfport, MS, p. A347
NICHELSON, Kathleen, Director Human Resources, Horsham Clinic, Ambler, PA, p. A520
NICHOLAS, Angela, Vice President, Medical Affairs, Einstein Medical Center Montgomery, East Norriton, PA, p. A524
NICHOLAS, Chris, Administrator of Rehabilitation Hospital, Renown Rehabilitation Hospital, Reno, NV, p. A397
NICHOLAS, David, Chief Executive Officer, St. John Rehabilitation Hospital, Broken Arrow, OK, p. A497
NICHOLS, Amanda, M.D., Chief of Staff, Sistersville General Hospital, Sistersville, WV, p. A689
NICHOLS, Barbara, President and Chief Executive Officer, Lecom Corry Memorial Hospital, Corry, PA, p. A523
NICHOLS, Bryan
Chief Financial Officer, Baylor Scott & White The Heart Hospital Plano, Plano, TX, p. A629
Chief Financial Officer, Baylor Scott & White The Heart Hospital–Denton, Denton, TX, p. A599
NICHOLS, Christopher, Chief Executive Officer, Fillmore County Hospital, Geneva, NE, p. A385
NICHOLS, Cynthia, Chief Executive Officer, Lakeland Community Hospital, Haleyville, AL, p. A19
NICHOLS, Donna, R.N., Chief Nursing Officer, Goodall–Witcher Hospital Authority, Clifton, TX, p. A592
NICHOLS, Greg, Chief Executive Officer, East Alabama Medical Center, Opelika, AL, p. A22
NICHOLS, Gretchen, President, Legacy Mount Hood Medical Center, Gresham, OR, p. A513
NICHOLS, Laura L, Director Human Resources, Hancock Regional Hospital, Greenfield, IN, p. A205
NICHOLS, Michael, Chief Information Officer, Masonicare Health Center, Wallingford, CT, p. A111
NICHOLS, Nathan, Director of Finance, Sterling Regional Medcenter, Sterling, CO, p. A105
NICHOLS, Randy
Chief Financial Officer, Great River Medical Center, Blytheville, AR, p. A39
Chief Financial Officer, South Mississippi County Regional Medical Center, Osceola, AR, p. A47
NICHOLS, Robin, Interim Chief Financial Officer, Emory Decatur Hospital, Decatur, GA, p. A152
NICHOLS, Suzanne, Director Human Resources, Muleshoe Area Medical Center, Muleshoe, TX, p. A625
NICHOLSON, Britain, M.D., Chief Medical Officer, Massachusetts General Hospital, Boston, MA, p. A295
NICHOLSON, Charles, Vice President, Medical Affairs, Sentara Albemarle Medical Center, Elizabeth City, NC, p. A453
NICHOLSON, Chrissy, Vice President of Human Resources, Delta Regional Medical Center, Greenville, MS, p. A347
NICHOLSON, Cindy, Director Human Resources, Shelby Baptist Medical Center, Alabaster, AL, p. A13
NICHOLSON, Debra, Manager Finance, Central Alabama Veterans Health Care System, Montgomery, AL, p. A21
NICHOLSON, H. Stacy, M.D., M.P.H., Physician in Chief, Phoenix Children'S Hospital, Phoenix, AZ, p. A34
NICHOLSON, Jack, Chief Executive Officer, Kindred Hospital–Louisville, Louisville, KY, p. A256
NICHOLSON, Kristin, Coordinator Human Resources, Genesis Medical Center, Dewitt, De Witt, IA, p. A220
NICHOLSON, Molly, MS, R.N.
Chief Nurse Executive, Osf Heart Of Mary Medical Center, Urbana, IL, p. A197
Vice President of Patient Care/Chief Nurse Executive, Osf Sacred Heart Medical Center, Danville, IL, p. A180
NICHOSON, Julia, M.D., Chief Medical Officer, Drew Memorial Health System, Monticello, AR, p. A46
NICKEL, Jennifer, Chief Executive Officer, Pam Rehabilitation Hospital Of Victoria, Victoria, TX, p. A643
NICKEL, Kathleen, Director Communications, Mercy Medical Center, Roseburg, OR, p. A517
NICKELL, Angela, Executive Director, Sequel Pomegranate Health Systems, Columbus, OH, p. A480

NICKELL, Jerry, Vice President Human Resource and Mission, Saint Alphonsus Medical Center – Baker City, Baker City, OR, p. A511
NICKELS, John, M.D., President Medical Staff, Grace Hospital, Cleveland, OH, p. A477
NICKENS, John R., IV, President and Chief Executive Officer, Children'S Hospital, New Orleans, LA, p. A275
NICKENS, Wesley, M.D., Chief of Staff, Collingsworth General Hospital, Wellington, TX, p. A645
NICKRAND, Tami, Director Information Technology, Harbor Beach Community Hospital, Harbor Beach, MI, p. A314
NICKS, Bret, M.D., Chief Medical Officer and Chief of Staff, Wake Forest Baptist Health–Davie Medical Center, Bermuda Run, NC, p. A449
NICOLAY, Donald, M.D., Chief Medical Officer, Community Hospital, Grand Junction, CO, p. A101
NICOLL, C. Diana, M.D., Ph.D., Chief of Staff, San Francisco Va Medical Center, San Francisco, CA, p. A85
NICOLSON, Lynne T, M.D., Medical Director, Sunnyview Rehabilitation Hospital, Schenectady, NY, p. A444
NICOSIA, Chris, Chief Financial Officer, Corpus Christi Medical Center, Corpus Christi, TX, p. A594
NIECE, Pamela S, Director Human Resources, Orem Community Hospital, Orem, UT, p. A650
NIEDERPRUEM, Mark L., Administrator, Shriners Hospitals For Children–Chicago, Chicago, IL, p. A179
NIELSEN, Gwen, Manager Human Resources, Indianhead Medical Center, Shell Lake, WI, p. A705
NIELSEN, Helen V
Director Human Resources, Lovelace Medical Center, Albuquerque, NM, p. A416
Director Human Resources, Lovelace Unm Rehabilitation Hospital, Albuquerque, NM, p. A416
NIELSEN, Kristine, Manager Human Resources, Memorial Community Hospital And Health System, Blair, NE, p. A383
NIELSEN, Randy, Director Information Technology, Arbor Health, Morton Hospital, Morton, WA, p. A675
NIELSEN, Wayne, Director Human Resources, Ocala Regional Medical Center, Ocala, FL, p. A133
NIELSON, Curtis, Chief Financial Officer, South Lincoln Medical Center, Kemmerer, WY, p. A711
NIELSON, Lars, M.D., Chief Medical Officer, Weeks Medical Center, Lancaster, NH, p. A400
NIELSON, Lori, Regional Finance Director, Park City Hospital, Park City, UT, p. A650
NIELSON, P Douglas, M.D., Chief of Staff, Kahuku Medical Center, Kahuku, HI, p. A165
NIELSON, Yvonne, Chief Nursing Officer, Director Quality Management and Regulatory Compliance, Mountain West Medical Center, Tooele, UT, p. A653
NIEMALA, Amanda, Director of Information Services, Bigfork Valley Hospital, Bigfork, MN, p. A328
NIEMANN, Lynne, Director Nurses and Patient Care, Community Memorial Hospital, Sumner, IA, p. A230
NIEMUTH, Trisha, Market Chief Executive Officer, Lifecare Hospitals Of Pittsburgh, Pittsburgh, PA, p. A537
NIENHUIS, Jamie, Chief Nursing Officer, Cavalier County Memorial Hospital And Clinics, Langdon, ND, p. A468
NIERMAN, Peter, M.D., Chief Medical Officer, Chicago Lakeshore Hospital, Chicago, IL, p. A177
NIERMAN, Stephen A., President, Winter Haven Hospital, Winter Haven, FL, p. A144
NIERMANN, Michelle, President and Chief Executive Officer, Unitypoint Health – St. Luke'S Hospital, Cedar Rapids, IA, p. A218
NIERSTEDT, Kelly
President, Orlando Regional Medical Center, Orlando, FL, p. A134
President, Osf Saint Francis Medical Center, Peoria, IL, p. A193
NIES, Lynn, Human Resources Officer, Erie Veterans Affairs Medical Center, Erie, PA, p. A525
NIESE, Mel, Chief Fiscal Service, Va Palo Alto Health Care System, Palo Alto, CA, p. A77
NIESSINK, Henry
Regional Director Information Technology Services, Mercy Medical Center Redding, Redding, CA, p. A79
Senior Manager Information Technology Systems, St. Elizabeth Community Hospital, Red Bluff, CA, p. A79
NIEVES, Deborah, Director Management Information Systems, Hospital San Francisco, San Juan, PR, p. A719
NIEVES, Erick, M.D., Medical Director, Hospital San Carlos Borromeo, Moca, PR, p. A717
NIEVES, James F., Executive Director, San Juan City Hospital, San Juan, PR, p. A719
NIGG, Nicole, Chief Executive Officer, Mercyone Clive Rehabilitation Hospital, Clive, IA, p. A219
NIGH, Andrew, M.D., Chief of Staff, Indiana University Health West Hospital, Avon, IN, p. A199
NIGHMAN, Mike, Facility Coordinator Information Systems, Shelby Baptist Medical Center, Alabaster, AL, p. A13
NIGHTINGALE, Judi, R.N., Dr.PH, Chief Nursing Officer, Riverside University Health System–Medical Center, Moreno Valley, CA, p. A73
NIGRIN, Daniel, M.D., Vice President Information Services and Chief Information Officer, Boston Children'S Hospital, Boston, MA, p. A295
NIHALANI, Sunil, M.D., Chief Medical Staff, Adventhealth Lake Wales, Lake Wales, FL, p. A127
NIJOKA, Monica, Chief Nursing Officer, Baton Rouge General Medical Center, Baton Rouge, LA, p. A263
NIKOLIC, Srbo, Chief Financial Officer, Hartgrove Hospital, Chicago, IL, p. A177
NILES, Heather, Director Human Resources Operations, Mercyhealth Hospital And Medical Center – Harvard, Harvard, IL, p. A184
NILSSON, Keith, Chief Financial Officer, Cleveland Clinic Florida, Weston, FL, p. A144
NIMMO, Ben, M.D., Medical Director, Pinnacle Pointe Hospital, Little Rock, AR, p. A45
NIMMO, Brian, Director, Huntington Veterans Affairs Medical Center, Huntington, WV, p. A686
NIMS, Carrie, Director of Nursing, Post Acute/Warm Springs Specialty Hospital Of San Antonio, San Antonio, TX, p. A635
NINNEMAN, David, Associate Director, Cincinnati Veterans Affairs Medical Center, Cincinnati, OH, p. A476
NIPPER, Nathan
Chief Operating Officer, Piedmont Fayette Hospital, Fayetteville, GA, p. A153
Vice President and Chief Operating Officer, Piedmont Newnan Hospital, Newnan, GA, p. A158
NIPPERT, Kathi, Acting Chief Human Resources Officer, Kansas City Veterans Affairs Medical Center, Kansas City, MO, p. A362
NISH, Paulette, Chief Nursing Officer, Geisinger Jersey Shore Hospital, Jersey Shore, PA, p. A528
NISKANEN, Grant, M.D., Vice President Medical Affairs, Sky Lakes Medical Center, Klamath Falls, OR, p. A514
NISSEN, Beth, Director Human Resources, Troy Regional Medical Center, Troy, AL, p. A23
NIX, Alisha, Director Human Resources, Wilbarger General Hospital, Vernon, TX, p. A643
NIX, Angela, Administrator, Veterans Affairs North Texas Health Care System, Dallas, TX, p. A598
NIX, Do, Chief Information Officer, Madison Valley Medical Center, Ennis, MT, p. A376
NIX, Julie, Vice President and Administrator, Baptist Health Rehabilitation Institute, Little Rock, AR, p. A45
NIXDORF, David L, Director Support Services, Frances Mahon Deaconess Hospital, Glasgow, MT, p. A376
NIXON, James, Chief Operating Officer, Meadows Regional Medical Center, Vidalia, GA, p. A162
NIXON, Myra, Director Human Resources, Encompass Health Rehabilitation Hospital Of Concord, Concord, NH, p. A399
NIZAMI, Nassar, Chief Information Officer, Thomas Jefferson University Hospitals, Philadelphia, PA, p. A536
NNAJI, Felix, Chief Medical Staff, Bolivar General Hospital, Bolivar, TN, p. A566
NOAK, Amy, Director Human Resources, St. David'S Round Rock Medical Center, Round Rock, TX, p. A632
NOAKES, Timothy J, Chief Financial Officer, Memorial Hospital Los Banos, Los Banos, CA, p. A70
NOBLE, Angela, Director of Nursing, West Feliciana Parish Hospital, Saint Francisville, LA, p. A277
NOBLE, Damien, Director Information Technology and System, Colleton Medical Center, Walterboro, SC, p. A558
NOBLE, Dave, Director of Nursing, Livingston Healthcare, Livingston, MT, p. A378
NOBLE, Lloyd, Chief Executive Officer, Anchor Hospital, Atlanta, GA, p. A145
NOBLE, Mallie S., Administrator, Mary Breckinridge Arh Hospital, Hyden, KY, p. A254
NOBLES, Diane, Nurse Executive, East Mississippi State Hospital, Meridian, MS, p. A351
NOBLES, Sharon
Chief Financial Officer, North Mississippi Medical Center – Tupelo, Tupelo, MS, p. A354
Interim Chief Financial Officer, Baptist Hospital, Pensacola, FL, p. A136
NOBLES, Trent, Chief Executive Officer, Southside Regional Medical Center, Petersburg, VA, p. A665
NOCITA, Suzanne, Senior Vice President and Chief Human Resource Officer, Children'S Hospital And Medical Center, Omaha, NE, p. A389
NOCKOWITZ, Richard, M.D., Medical Director, Ohio Hospital For Psychiatry, Columbus, OH, p. A479
NOE, Sharon, Chief Executive Officer, Cobalt Rehabilitation Hospital, Surprise, AZ, p. A36
NOEL, Bill, Chief Operating Officer, Grand River Hospital District, Rifle, CO, p. A105
NOEL, Philip J., III, Chief Executive Officer, Ottumwa Regional Health Center, Ottumwa, IA, p. A228
NOEL, Vicki, Vice President Human Resources, Southern Ohio Medical Center, Portsmouth, OH, p. A490
NOESS, Bobbi, Director of Nursing, Bowdle Hospital, Bowdle, SD, p. A559
NOFFSINGER, Sandy, Executive Assistant, Risk Manager and Director Marketing, Dundy County Hospital, Benkelman, NE, p. A383
NOGLER, Wendy, Director Human Resources, Lincoln County Health System, Fayetteville, TN, p. A569
NOKELS, Kevin J., President and Chief Executive Officer, St. Luke'S Hospital, Duluth, MN, p. A331
NOKES, Gregory, Vice President Human Resources, Middlesex Hospital, Middletown, CT, p. A109
NOLAN, Douglas, M.D., Medical Director, Cherokee Nation W.W. Hastings Indian Hospital, Tahlequah, OK, p. A508
NOLAN, Heather, Director Information Services, Northern Louisiana Medical Center, Ruston, LA, p. A277
NOLAN, Jennifer
President and Chief Executive Officer, Chi Flaget Memorial Hospital, Bardstown, KY, p. A249
President and Chief Executive Officer, Chi Our Lady Of Peace, Louisville, KY, p. A256
NOLAN, Joe, Chief Operating Officer, Saint Clare'S Denville Hospital, Denville, NJ, p. A404
NOLAN, Matthew, Chief Operating Officer, The University Of Vermont Health Network Elizabethtown Community Hospital, Elizabethtown, NY, p. A427
NOLAN, Patrick, Vice President Finance and Chief Financial Officer, Gillette Children'S Specialty Healthcare, Saint Paul, MN, p. A339
NOLAN, Patrick B, Chief Operating Officer, Inspira Medical Center–Woodbury, Woodbury, NJ, p. A415
NOLAN, Rosemary, R.N., MSN, JD, Chief Operating Officer, Temple University Hospital, Philadelphia, PA, p. A536
NOLAN, Roz, Interim Chief Nursing Officer, Community Hospital Of San Bernardino, San Bernardino, CA, p. A83
NOLAND, Pam, Director of Nursing, Northern Cochise Community Hospital, Willcox, AZ, p. A38
NOLASCO, Wanda, Chief Nursing Officer, Fairmount Behavioral Health System, Philadelphia, PA, p. A534
NOLD, Pam, Chief Nurse Executive, Northwest Missouri Psychiatric Rehabilitation Center, Saint Joseph, MO, p. A368
NOLEN, Benny, President and Chief Executive Officer, Methodist Hospital, Henderson, KY, p. A253
NOLES, Coy, Chief Financial Officer Consultant, Hamilton Hospital, Olney, TX, p. A627
NOLL, David, Director, Adventist Health St. Helena, Saint Helena, CA, p. A82
NOLL, Gerald A, Chief Financial Officer, Rogers Memorial Hospital, Inc., Oconomowoc, WI, p. A702
NOLL, Keith D., President, Wellspan York Hospital, York, PA, p. A546
NOLLEY, Dexter, Chief Human Resources Officer, Duke Regional Hospital, Durham, NC, p. A452
NOLT, Lori, Director Information Technology, Wellspan Philhaven, Mount Gretna, PA, p. A532
NOLTE, Darlene R, Chief Human Resource Officer, Saint Francis Hospital Vinita, Vinita, OK, p. A510
NONNEMAN, Lisa, Director Information Technology Services, Mary Lanning Healthcare, Hastings, NE, p. A385
NOONAN, Anna T., President and Chief Operating Officer, The University Of Vermont Health Network Central Vermont Medical Center, Berlin, VT, p. A654
NOONAN, Kathryn, Director Information Management, Lemuel Shattuck Hospital, Jamaica Plain, MA, p. A299
NOONE, Thomas, M.D., Chief Medical Officer, Bayfront Health Port Charlotte, Port Charlotte, FL, p. A137
NOPWASKEY, Cristen, Chief Information Officer, Weirton Medical Center, Weirton, WV, p. A690
NORBURY, Denise
Regional Chief Executive Officer, Center For Behavioral Medicine, Kansas City, MO, p. A362
Regional Executive Officer, Northwest Missouri Psychiatric Rehabilitation Center, Saint Joseph, MO, p. A368
NORBY, Michael, Chief Financial Officer, Harris Health System, Houston, TX, p. A611
NORD, Gay
Chief Executive Officer, West Florida Hospital, Pensacola, FL, p. A136
President, Baylor St. Luke'S Medical Center Mcnair Campus, Houston, TX, p. A610
NORD, Stanley K, Chief Financial Officer, West Houston Medical Center, Houston, TX, p. A614

NORDAHL, Richard E., Senior Director, Sanford Sheldon Medical Center, Sheldon, IA, p. A229

NORDBERG, Traci, Chief Human Resources Officer, Vanderbilt University Medical Center, Nashville, TN, p. A577

NORDBY, Betsy, Director of Human Resources, St. Croix Regional Medical Center, St Croix Falls, WI, p. A706

NORDBY, Shawn A, Chief Financial Officer, Mary Lanning Healthcare, Hastings, NE, p. A385

NORDELL, Cindy, Chief Nursing Officer, Healthsouth Rehabilitation Hospital Of Colorado Springs, Colorado Springs, CO, p. A97

NORDENG, Rod, Administrator, Floyd County Medical Center, Charles City, IA, p. A219

NORDIN, Danna, Director Human Resources, Anchor Hospital, Atlanta, GA, p. A145

NORDLAND, Thomas, Chief Medical Officer, Fort Healthcare, Fort Atkinson, WI, p. A695

NORDLUND, Judy, R.N., Chief Nursing Officer, Trinity Hospital, Weaverville, CA, p. A94

NORDLUND, Sarah, Director of Nursing, Garfield County Health Center, Jordan, MT, p. A378

NORDSTROM, Janice, Director Human Resources, Landmark Hospital Of Joplin, Joplin, MO, p. A362

NORDSTROM, Katie, Director Human Resources, Beartooth Billings Clinic, Red Lodge, MT, p. A379

NORDWICK, Thomas, Chief Executive Officer, Uvalde Memorial Hospital, Uvalde, TX, p. A643

NORDYKE, Charles, Chief Executive Officer, Clarinda Regional Health Center, Clarinda, IA, p. A219

NORDYKE, Melissa, Chief Financial Officer, Ascension Seton Smithville, Smithville, TX, p. A637

NOREEN, James, M.D., Chief Medical Officer, Regina Hospital, Hastings, MN, p. A333

NORELDIN, Mohsen, M.D., President Medical Staff, Athol Hospital, Athol, MA, p. A294

NORELL, Brett, Interim Chief Executive Officer, Holy Family Memorial, Manitowoc, WI, p. A699

NOREM, Ashley, Chief Information Systems, Starke Hospital, Knox, IN, p. A208

NOREM, Julie, MSN, Chief Nursing Officer, Rochelle Community Hospital, Rochelle, IL, p. A194

NOREN, Tom, M.D., Chief Medical Officer, Up Health System–Marquette, Marquette, MI, p. A317

NORGAARD, Margaret B.
Chief Executive Officer, Poplar Community Hospital, Poplar, MT, p. A379
Chief Executive Officer, Trinity Hospital, Wolf Point, MT, p. A381

NORICK, Laurence, M.D., Clinical Director, U. S. Public Health Service Indian Hospital, Parker, AZ, p. A32

NORKO, Michael A, Acting Chief Executive Officer, Connecticut Valley Hospital, Middletown, CT, p. A109

NORMAN, Andrea, Chief Executive Officer, Valley Behavioral Health System, Barling, AR, p. A39

NORMAN, Daniel, Regional Service Manager, Unitypoint Health – Allen Hospital, Waterloo, IA, p. A231

NORMAN, Debbie, Director Human Resources, Central Louisiana Surgical Hospital, Alexandria, LA, p. A262

NORMAN, Debbie, MSN, R.N., Chief Nursing Officer, Elkview General Hospital, Hobart, OK, p. A500

NORMAN, Jimmy, Chief Financial Officer, Mountain Lakes Medical Center, Clayton, GA, p. A150

NORMAN, Laura, Chief Development and Information Officer, Windhaven Psychiatric Hospital, Prescott Valley, AZ, p. A35

NORMAN, Lori, Chief Financial Officer, Encompass Health Rehabilitation Hospital Of Gadsden, Gadsden, AL, p. A18

NORMAN, Michael L, Executive Vice President and Chief Operating Officer, Landmark Hospital Of Cape Girardeau, Cape Girardeau, MO, p. A357

NORMAN, Robin, Senior Vice President and Chief Financial Officer, Virginia Hospital Center, Arlington, VA, p. A656

NORMINGTON–SLAY, Jeremy
Chief Executive Officer, Ascension Good Samaritan Hospital, Merrill, WI, p. A700
President, North Central Region, Ascension Saint Clare'S Hospital, Weston, WI, p. A708
President, North Central Region, Ascension St. Michael'S Hospital, Stevens Point, WI, p. A706
President, Ascension Our Lady Of Victory Hospital, Stanley, WI, p. A706

NORQUEST, Cathy, Director Human Resources, York General, York, NE, p. A392

NORRICK, Michael, Director of Campus Operations, Prisma Health Laurens County Hospital, Clinton, SC, p. A550

NORRIS, David, Chief Medical Staff, Sweetwater Hospital, Sweetwater, TN, p. A580

NORRIS, Lucy, Administrator Interim Chief Nursing Officer, Multicare Good Samaritan Hospital, Puyallup, WA, p. A677

NORRIS, Robert, Chief Executive Officer, Huntington Creek Recovery Center, Shickshinny, PA, p. A541

NORTH, Ralene, Chief Nurse Executive, Massena Memorial Hospital, Massena, NY, p. A431

NORTHCUTT, Lynn, Chief Information Officer, Musc Health Florence Medical Center, Florence, SC, p. A553

NORTHERN, Gail M., Director Human Resources, Blue Mountain Hospital, Blanding, UT, p. A647

NORTHUP, Carol, R.N., Chief Nursing Officer and Chief Operating Officer, J. Arthur Dosher Memorial Hospital, Southport, NC, p. A462

NORTHUP, Jeffrey, D.O., Chief Medical Officer, Knox Community Hospital, Mount Vernon, OH, p. A488

NORTON, Andrew J, M.D.
Chief Medical Officer, Bryn Mawr Hospital, Bryn Mawr, PA, p. A521
Chief Medical Officer, Paoli Hospital, Paoli, PA, p. A533

NORTON, Bill, Chief Nursing Officer, Rehoboth Mckinley Christian Health Care Services, Gallup, NM, p. A418

NORTON, Carole, Chief Nursing Officer, Stonewall Jackson Memorial Hospital, Weston, WV, p. A690

NORTON, Debbie, Chief Financial Officer, Medical Center Barbour, Eufaula, AL, p. A17

NORTON, Julie, Vice President, Operational Finance, Avera Mckennan Hospital And University Health Center, Sioux Falls, SD, p. A563

NORTON, Lizette O, Vice President, Human Resources, Loma Linda University Children'S Hospital, Loma Linda, CA, p. A64

NORTON, Meg, Executive Vice President and Chief Administrative Officer, Rady Children'S Hospital – San Diego, San Diego, CA, p. A84

NORTON, Robert G, President, North Shore Medical Center, Salem, MA, p. A303

NORTON, Susan, Vice President Human Resources, Augusta University Medical Center, Augusta, GA, p. A147

NORVILLE, Amy, Vice President Support Services, St. Luke'S Hospital, Columbus, NC, p. A452

NORWOOD, William, Vice President, Human Resources, Brattleboro Memorial Hospital, Brattleboro, VT, p. A654

NOSACKA, David
Chief Financial Officer, Hshs St. Elizabeth'S Hospital, O'Fallon, IL, p. A192
Southern Illinois Division Chief Financial Officer, Hshs St. Joseph'S Hospital, Highland, IL, p. A185

NOSACKA, Mark, Chief Executive Officer, Piedmont Medical Center, Rock Hill, SC, p. A556

NOSBISCH, Don, Director Human Resources, Floyd County Medical Center, Charles City, IA, p. A219

NOSEWORTHY, Ed, Chief Executive Officer, Adventhealth Daytona Beach, Daytona Beach, FL, p. A121

NOSKIN, Gary, Senior Vice President and Chief Medical Officer, Northwestern Memorial Hospital, Northwestern Memorial Hospital, Chicago, IL, p. A178

NOSKO, Jeannine Burnat, Vice President Patient Care, Aspirus Wausau Hospital, Inc., Wausau, WI, p. A708

NOSTRANT, Hunter, Chief Financial Officer, Helen Newberry Joy Hospital, Newberry, MI, p. A319

NOTEMAN, Laurali, Director Human Resources, Kane County Hospital, Kanab, UT, p. A648

NOTTER, Pat, R.N., Chief Nursing Officer and Director Quality, Melissa Memorial Hospital, Holyoke, CO, p. A102

NOTTINGHAM, Cheryl, Chief Financial Officer, Atlantic General Hospital, Berlin, MD, p. A288

NOUNA, Nabil, M.D., Chief of Staff, Allegan General Hospital, Allegan, MI, p. A306

NOVAK, Charles, M.D., Chief Medical Officer, Intermountain Hospital, Boise, ID, p. A167

NOVAK, Christopher, Chief Operating Officer, Alexian Brothers Behavioral Health Hospital, Hoffman Estates, IL, p. A186

NOVAK, Georgene, Director Human Resources, Littleton Regional Healthcare, Littleton, NH, p. A401

NOVAK, Jerald, Chief People Officer, University Of Vermont Medical Center, Burlington, VT, p. A654

NOVAK, Kristen, Manager Human Resources, River Falls Area Hospital, River Falls, WI, p. A705

NOVAK, Matthew
President, Mease Countryside Hospital, Safety Harbor, FL, p. A138
President, Mease Dunedin Hospital, Dunedin, FL, p. A122

NOVAK, Michael
Vice President and Chief Operating Officer, Nyack Hospital, Nyack, NY, p. A440
Vice President, Operations and Chief Information Officer, Saint Mary'S Hospital, Waterbury, CT, p. A111

NOVELLO, Regina, R.N., Chief Operating Officer, Healdsburg District Hospital, Healdsburg, CA, p. A61

NOVICK, Peggy, Vice President, Clinical Support and Outpatient Services, Milford Regional Medical Center, Milford, MA, p. A301

NOVITSKY, Mark, M.D., Corporate Medical Director, Kirkbride Center, Philadelphia, PA, p. A535

NOVOA LOYOLA, Jose E, M.D., Medical Director, Cardiovascular Center Of Puerto Rico And The Caribbean, San Juan, PR, p. A718

NOVOSEL, Stacie, Vice President, Human Resources, South Bay Hospital, Sun City Center, FL, p. A140

NOWACHEK, Debra S., Director Human Resources, Unitypoint Health – Grinnell Regional Medical Center, Grinnell, IA, p. A223

NOWICKI, Becky, Director Human Resources, Michiana Behavioral Health Center, Plymouth, IN, p. A213

NOWICKI, Michelle, R.N., MSN, Chief Nurse Executive, Kaiser Permanente Baldwin Park Medical Center, Baldwin Park, CA, p. A51

NOWLIN, Jeffrey D., President and Chief Operating Officer, St. John Medical Center, Tulsa, OK, p. A510

NOWLIN, Patricia
Director Accounting, Pinnacle Regional Hospital, Boonville, MO, p. A357
Director Human Resources, Pinnacle Regional Hospital, Boonville, MO, p. A357

NOWLING, Tara, Director Human Resources, Monroe County Hospital, Monroeville, AL, p. A21

NOYES, Vikki, Executive Vice President and Chief Operating Officer, Confluence Health/Central Washington Hospital, Wenatchee, WA, p. A682

NUAKO, Kofi, M.D., President Medical Staff, Baptist Memorial Hospital–Union City, Union City, TN, p. A580

NUDD, Brandon M., Chief Executive Officer, Castle Rock Adventist Hospital, Castle Rock, CO, p. A97

NUGENT, Shelly, R.N., Director Nurses and Infection Control, Louisiana Extended Care Hospital West Monroe, West Monroe, LA, p. A280

NUGENT, Victoria, Chief Nursing Officer, Dignity Health Arizona General Hospital, Laveen, AZ, p. A31

NUMMI, Lisa, MSN, R.N., Chief Operating Officer, Blake Medical Center, Bradenton, FL, p. A118

NUNEZ, Humberto F., M.D., Chief Medical Officer, Mission Regional Medical Center, Mission, TX, p. A625

NUNEZ, Michael, Chief Financial Officer, University Medical Center Of El Paso, El Paso, TX, p. A603

NUNEZ, Milton, Executive Director, Brookdale Hospital Medical Center, New York, NY, p. A432

NUNEZ, Sheila, Director Human Resources, Eastern New Mexico Medical Center, Roswell, NM, p. A420

NUNN, Brian, Chief Executive Officer, Encompass Health Rehabilitation Hospital Of Florence, Florence, SC, p. A552

NUNN, Chalmers, M.D., Chief Medical Officer and Senior Vice President, Centra Lynchburg General Hospital, Lynchburg, VA, p. A662

NUNNELLY, Sarah, Executive Vice President and Chief Operating Officer, East Alabama Medical Center, Opelika, AL, p. A22

NURU, Betty, Director Human Resources, Millwood Hospital, Arlington, TX, p. A583

NURY, Alex, Chief Information Officer, Providence Tarzana Medical Center, Los Angeles, CA, p. A69

NUSBAUM, Neil, M.D., Chief of Staff, Veterans Affairs Central Western Massachusetts Healthcare System, Leeds, MA, p. A300

NUSS, Suzanne Langan, Ph.D., R.N., Chief Nursing Officer, Nebraska Medicine – Nebraska Medical Center, Omaha, NE, p. A389

NUSSBAUM, Joseph, M.D., Chief of Staff, California Hospital Medical Center, Los Angeles, CA, p. A66

NUSSBAUM, Mark, Vice President Operations, Marymount Hospital, Garfield Heights, OH, p. A483

NUTTER, Robert, President, Littleton Regional Healthcare, Littleton, NH, p. A401

NWOKIKE, Jerome, M.D., Medical Director, Spring Mountain Treatment Center, Las Vegas, NV, p. A396

NYAMU, Samuel, M.D., Chief Medical Officer, Sanford Aberdeen Medical Center, Aberdeen, SD, p. A559

NYBERG, Becky T, Chief Financial Officer, Bloomington Meadows Hospital, Bloomington, IN, p. A200

NYIKES, Debra, Director Finance and Chief Financial Officer, Cleveland Clinic Children'S Hospital For Rehabilitation, Cleveland, OH, p. A477

NYKAMP, Robert, Vice President and Chief Operating Officer, Pine Rest Christian Mental Health Services, Grand Rapids, MI, p. A313

NYLUND, Barbara, M.D., Chief of Staff, Novato Community Hospital, Novato, CA, p. A75

NYMOEN, Gary, Chief Financial Officer, Hialeah Hospital, Hialeah, FL, p. A124

NYSTROM, Dale, M.D., Chief Medical Officer, Physician, Hawarden Regional Healthcare, Hawarden, IA, p. A224

O

O CONNOR, Joyce, Chief Operating Officer, Taunton State Hospital, Taunton, MA, p. A304
OAKES, Julie P, R.N., Manager Risk and Quality, Ocean Beach Hospital, Ilwaco, WA, p. A674
OAKES FERRUCCI, Susan, MS, Vice President Patient Services and Chief Nursing Officer, Cobleskill Regional Hospital, Cobleskill, NY, p. A426
OAKLEY, Lisa, Chief Financial Officer, Harper County Community Hospital, Buffalo, OK, p. A497
OAKLEY, Sarah G, Vice President Nursing, North Kansas City Hospital, North Kansas City, MO, p. A366
OAKS, Dana C., Chief Executive Officer, University Hospital And Medical Center, Tamarac, FL, p. A141
OAXACA, Norma, Director Human Resources, Peak Behavioral Health Services, Santa Teresa, NM, p. A420
OBANDO, Alisha, Director of Nursing, Chadron Community Hospital And Health Services, Chadron, NE, p. A384
OBERHEU, Todd, Administrator, Lincoln County Medical Center, Ruidoso, NM, p. A420
OBERMIER, Jenny, Senior Vice President, Chief Operating Officer and Chief Nursing Officer, York General, York, NE, p. A392
OBERSTAR, Joel V., Chief Executive Officer and Chief Medical Officer, Prairiecare – Brooklyn Park, Brooklyn Park, MN, p. A329
OBEY, Bianca A., Chief Financial Officer, Alexandria Veterans Affairs Health Care System, Pineville, LA, p. A277
OBEY, Cleveland, Administrator, Compass Behavioral Center Of Houma, Houma, LA, p. A268
OBORNY, Jane, Chief Financial Officer, Rush County Memorial Hospital, La Crosse, KS, p. A238
OCASIO, J Manuel, Vice President Human Resources, Holy Cross Hospital, Silver Spring, MD, p. A293
OCEGUERA, Louis, M.D., Medical Director, Little Falls Hospital, Little Falls, NY, p. A430
OCHOA, Mark S, M.D., Deputy Commander, Clinical Services, Irwin Army Community Hospital, Junction City, KS, p. A237
OCHOA, Monica, Chief Executive Officer, Georgetown Behavioral Health Institute, Georgetown, TX, p. A607
OCHOA, Nikki, Interim Chief Financial Officer, St. Joseph'S Medical Center, Stockton, CA, p. A91
OCHSENDORF, Derrick, Manager Information Technology and Systems, Johnson Memorial Health Services, Dawson, MN, p. A330
ODATO, David, Chief Administrative and Chief Human Resources Officer, Ucsf Medical Center, San Francisco, CA, p. A86
ODEGAARD, Daniel, Chief Executive Officer, Caldwell Medical Center, Princeton, KY, p. A260
ODELL, Cheryl, R.N., Chief Nursing Officer, Sharp Mesa Vista Hospital, San Diego, CA, p. A84
ODELL, Michelle, Director of Public Affairs, Kaiser Permanente South Sacramento Medical Center, Sacramento, CA, p. A82
ODEN, Greg, Chief Medical Officer, Merit Health Central, Jackson, MS, p. A349
ODEN, Ryan, D.O., Chief of Staff, Arbuckle Memorial Hospital, Sulphur, OK, p. A508
ODETOYINBO, Adedapo, M.D., Chief Medical Office, Emory Johns Creek Hospital, Johns Creek, GA, p. A155
ODLE, Susan, Administrator, St. Joseph Memorial Hospital, Murphysboro, IL, p. A190
ODOM, Jake, Chief Information Officer, Trinity Hospital, Weaverville, CA, p. A94
ODOM, Jennifer, Interim Director Human Resources, Flowers Hospital, Dothan, AL, p. A17
ODOM, Lee Ann, Division President, Beaumont Hospital – Taylor, Taylor, MI, p. A323
ODOM, Robbin, R.N., MSN, Chief Nursing Officer, Christus Ochsner Lake Area Hospital, Lake Charles, LA, p. A272
ODOM, Terry, Chief Executive Officer, Powell Valley Healthcare, Powell, WY, p. A712
ODUWOLE, Adedapo, M.D., Medical Director, Lighthouse Behavioral Health Hospital, Conway, SC, p. A552
OEHL, Varonica, Chief Financial Officer, Fort Lauderdale Hospital, Fort Lauderdale, FL, p. A122
OEHLKE, Tammy, Director Human Resources, St. Mark'S Medical Center, La Grange, TX, p. A619
OEHMKE, Brittni, Administrator, Hanover Hospital, Hanover, KS, p. A236
OEMCKE, Barbara A., Director, Northern Arizona Veterans Affairs Health Care System, Prescott, AZ, p. A34
OETTING, Phyllis, Director Human Resources, Mitchell County Hospital Health Systems, Beloit, KS, p. A232

OETZEL, Gerald P, Chief Financial Officer, Temple University Hospital, Philadelphia, PA, p. A536
OFFUTT, Dan, Manager Finance, Knox County Hospital, Knox City, TX, p. A618
OFSTEDAL, Jeff, Manager Information Technology, Glacial Ridge Health System, Glenwood, MN, p. A332
OGASAWARA, Keith, M.D., Associate Medical Director and Professional Chief of Staff, Kaiser Permanente Medical Center, Honolulu, HI, p. A164
OGAWA, Quin
  Chief Financial Officer, Sutter Health Kahi Mohala, Ewa Beach, HI, p. A164
  Vice President Finance and Chief Financial Officer, Kuakini Medical Center, Honolulu, HI, p. A164
OGDEN, Judy, Director Information Technology, Franklin Medical Center, Winnsboro, LA, p. A280
OGDEN, Lesley
  Chief Executive Officer, Samaritan North Lincoln Hospital, Lincoln City, OR, p. A514
  Chief Executive Officer, Samaritan Pacific Communities Hospital, Newport, OR, p. A515
OGDEN, Michael L., President and Chief Executive Officer, Little Falls Hospital, Little Falls, NY, p. A430
OGIER, Katie, Director of Nursing, Rock County Hospital, Bassett, NE, p. A382
OGILVIE, Richard, Chief Information Officer, Southwestern Vermont Medical Center, Bennington, VT, p. A654
OGLESBY, Lorie A., Director of Human Resources, Baptist Health Madisonville, Madisonville, KY, p. A257
OGLESBY, Lorri, Chief Nursing Officer, Encompass Health Rehabilitation Hospital Of Texarkana, Texarkana, TX, p. A640
OGORZALEK, Ed, Chief Financial Officer, Rutland Regional Medical Center, Rutland, VT, p. A655
OGRINC, Mary L, R.N., MS, Chief Nursing Officer, Senior Vice President Patient Care Services, Lake Health, Concord Township, OH, p. A480
OGROD, Eugene, M.D., Chief Medical Officer, Kingwood Medical Center, Kingwood, TX, p. A618
OH, Christina E., Chief Executive Officer, Abrazo West Campus, Goodyear, AZ, p. A30
OHASHI, Curtis, Chief Executive Officer, Montevista Hospital, Las Vegas, NV, p. A395
OHL, Connie, Acting Chief Human Resources, Veterans Affairs Illiana Health Care System, Danville, IL, p. A180
OHMART, Dean, Vice President Financial Services and Chief Financial Officer, Western Missouri Medical Center, Warrensburg, MO, p. A372
OHRT, James M, M.D., Director Medical Staff, Henderson Health Care Services, Henderson, NE, p. A386
OJEDA, Guadalupe, R.N., Chief Nursing Officer, West Covina Medical Center, West Covina, CA, p. A94
OJOMO, Karanita, M.D., Chief of Staff, Lewisgale Hospital Pulaski, Pulaski, VA, p. A665
OKABE, David
  Executive Vice President, Chief Financial Officer and Treasurer, Pali Momi Medical Center, Aiea, HI, p. A164
  Executive Vice President, Chief Financial Officer and Treasurer, Straub Medical Center, Honolulu, HI, p. A165
  Executive Vice President, Chief Financial Officer and Treasurer, Wilcox Medical Center, Lihue, HI, p. A166
  Senior Vice President, Chief Financial Officer and Treasurer, Kapiolani Medical Center For Women & Children, Honolulu, HI, p. A164
OKEN, Jeffrey, Vice President of Medical Affairs, Northwestern Medicine Marianjoy Rehabilitation Hospital, Wheaton, IL, p. A198
OKESON, Keith, President and Chief Executive Officer, Lifecare Medical Center, Roseau, MN, p. A339
OKEY, Suzi, Director of Nursing, Southwest Health, Platteville, WI, p. A703
OKONIEWSKI, Susan, M.D., Chief of Staff, Chi St. Gabriel'S Health, Little Falls, MN, p. A334
OKSENDAHL, Elaine, Director Human Resources and Risk Management, Schick Shadel Hospital, Seattle, WA, p. A678
OKUHARA, Mary, Chief Human Resource Officer, Lakewood Regional Medical Center, Lakewood, CA, p. A64
OKUNO-JONES, Susan K, Vice President Patient Care Services and Chief Nursing Executive, Advocate Good Samaritan Hospital, Downers Grove, IL, p. A181
OLANDER, Scott, Chief Financial Officer, Evergreenhealth Monroe, Monroe, WA, p. A675
OLASON, Roxanne, R.N., FACHE, Vice President and Chief Nursing Officer, Skagit Regional Health, Mount Vernon, WA, p. A675
OLDER, Michael, M.D., President Medical Staff, Nashoba Valley Medical Center, Ayer, MA, p. A294
OLDHAM, Jennie, Director Human Resources, Goodall–Witcher Hospital Authority, Clifton, TX, p. A592

OLDHAM, Lawrence, Chief Financial Officer, Arise Austin Medical Center, Austin, TX, p. A584
OLDHAM, Marriner, M.D., Chief Medical Officer, U. S. Air Force Regional Hospital, Elmendorf Afb, AK, p. A26
OLDS, Debbie D, R.N., MSN, Director of Nursing, Willis-Knighton Medical Center, Shreveport, LA, p. A278
OLEJNICZAK, David R
  Chief Operating Officer, Hshs St. John'S Hospital, Springfield, IL, p. A196
  Chief Operating Officer, Metro Health – University Of Michigan Health, Wyoming, MI, p. A325
OLEKSYK, Mike, M.D., Vice President and Chief Medical Officer, Baptist Hospital, Pensacola, FL, p. A136
OLESTON, Caryn Lynn, FACHE, MSN, R.N.
  Chief Nursing Officer, Mercyhealth Hospital And Medical Center – Harvard, Harvard, IL, p. A184
  Chief Nursing Officer, Mercyhealth Hospital And Medical Center – Walworth, Lake Geneva, WI, p. A698
OLESZAK, Randy, Director Fiscal Services, Milwaukee County Behavioral Health Division, Milwaukee, WI, p. A701
OLEY, Edwin M., President and Chief Executive Officer, Mercy Regional Medical Center, Lorain, OH, p. A486
OLIGSCHLAEGER, David, Medical Staff President, Hshs Good Shepherd Hospital, Shelbyville, IL, p. A195
OLIND, Shelby, Interim Chief Executive Officer, Community Hospital, Torrington, WY, p. A713
OLINDE, Chad E., Administrator and Chief Executive Officer, Pointe Coupee General Hospital, New Roads, LA, p. A276
OLINGER, Richard P, Chief Financial Officer, Lecom Health Millcreek Community Hospital, Erie, PA, p. A525
OLINSKI, Janis, R.N., Vice President Clinical Services, Harrison Community Hospital, Cadiz, OH, p. A474
OLIPHANT, Gerald P, Executive Vice President and Chief Operating Officer, Good Samaritan Hospital, Cincinnati, OH, p. A476
OLIPHANT, Jenny, Executive Vice President and Chief Operating Officer, Bethesda North Hospital, Cincinnati, OH, p. A475
OLIPHANT, Phillip, Chief Information Officer, U. S. Air Force Regional Hospital, Elmendorf Afb, AK, p. A26
OLIVARES, Rafael, Controller, Starr County Memorial Hospital, Rio Grande City, TX, p. A631
OLIVAREZ, Lorenzo, Senior Vice President and Chief Financial Officer, Bsa Hospital, Llc, Amarillo, TX, p. A582
OLIVAS, Ray, Chief Fiscal Service, West Texas Veterans Affairs Health Care System, Big Spring, TX, p. A588
OLIVE, Alan C., Chief Executive Officer, Northern Nevada Medical Center, Sparks, NV, p. A398
OLIVENCIA, Humberto, M.D., Medical Director, Hospital Perea, Mayaguez, PR, p. A717
OLIVER, David, Director Information Systems, King'S Daughters Medical Center, Ashland, KY, p. A249
OLIVER, Diane, R.N., MSN, Chief Nursing Officer, Parkwest Medical Center, Knoxville, TN, p. A572
OLIVER, Doug, Chief Financial Officer, Windhaven Psychiatric Hospital, Prescott Valley, AZ, p. A35
OLIVER, Michelle
  Chief Nursing Executive, Hshs Good Shepherd Hospital, Shelbyville, IL, p. A195
  Chief Nursing Officer, Hshs St. Mary'S Hospital, Decatur, IL, p. A181
OLIVER, Rick, Information Technology, Hamilton Hospital, Olney, TX, p. A627
OLIVER, Rosalie
  Chief Financial Officer, Adventhealth Sebring, Sebring, FL, p. A139
  Senior Vice President and Chief Financial Officer, Adventhealth Wauchula, Wauchula, FL, p. A143
OLIVER, Vincent, Administrator, Island Hospital, Anacortes, WA, p. A670
OLIVERA, Sue, Vice President, Aultman Hospital, Canton, OH, p. A474
OLIVERAS, Freddy, Chief Information Officer, Martin County Hospital District, Stanton, TX, p. A638
OLIVERAS LAGUNA, Ana, Administrator, Caribbean Medical Center, Fajardo, PR, p. A716
OLIVIER, Athan J., III, Administrator and Chief Executive Officer, Iberia Rehabilitation Hospital, New Iberia, LA, p. A275
OLIVIER, Edward
  Chief Financial Officer, Martha'S Vineyard Hospital, Oak Bluffs, MA, p. A302
  Chief Financial Officer, Northern Light Ca Dean Hospital, Greenville, ME, p. A283
OLLI, Cindy, R.N., Chief Nursing Officer, Schoolcraft Memorial Hospital, Manistique, MI, p. A317
OLLIE, Edwin J, Executive Vice President and Chief Financial Officer, New Hanover Regional Medical Center, Wilmington, NC, p. A464
OLLSON, Joanne, Vice President Human Resources, Baystate Noble Hospital, Westfield, MA, p. A304

OLM–SHIPMAN, Bobby
Chief Executive Officer, Saint Luke'S South Hospital, Overland Park, KS, p. A243
President and Chief Executive Officer, Saint Luke'S Cushing Hospital, Leavenworth, KS, p. A239
OLMSTEAD, David, Director, Human Resources, City Hospital At White Rock, Dallas, TX, p. A596
OLMSTEAD, Linda, Director, Human Resources, Uw Medicine/Northwest Hospital & Medical Center, Seattle, WA, p. A678
OLNEY, Garry M.
Chief Executive Officer, Providence Little Company Of Mary Medical Center – Torrance, Torrance, CA, p. A92
Chief Executive Officer, Providence Little Company Of Mary Medical Center San Pedro, Los Angeles, CA, p. A69
OLS, Timothy A.
Chief Executive Officer, Baylor Scott & White Medical Center – Llano, Llano, TX, p. A621
President, Baylor Scott & White Medical Center – Marble Falls, Marble Falls, TX, p. A623
OLSCAMP, Karen E., President and Chief Executive Officer, University Of Maryland Baltimore Washington Medical Center, Glen Burnie, MD, p. A291
OLSEN, Debbie, Human Resource Partner, Sparrow Ionia Hospital, Ionia, MI, p. A314
OLSEN, Jennifer, M.D., Chief of Staff, North Canyon Medical Center, Gooding, ID, p. A169
OLSEN, Karen M, R.N., Chief Nursing Officer, Mission Hospital, Asheville, NC, p. A449
OLSEN, Ryan, Chief Operating Officer, Memorialcare, Saddleback Memorial Medical Center, Laguna Hills, CA, p. A63
OLSEN, Sabrina, Chief Financial Officer, Duke University Hospital, Durham, NC, p. A453
OLSON, Cheryl, Vice President, Palomar Medical Center Poway, Poway, CA, p. A79
OLSON, Craig, Director Information Technology, Southwestern Regional Medical Center, Tulsa, OK, p. A509
OLSON, Dave, Director of Nursing, Montana State Hospital, Warm Springs, MT, p. A380
OLSON, Diana
Chief Human Resources Officer, Mercy Health – Willard Hospital, Willard, OH, p. A494
Director Human Resources, Mercy Tiffin Hospital, Tiffin, OH, p. A491
OLSON, Eric, Chief Financial Officer, Providence Portland Medical Center, Portland, OR, p. A516
OLSON, Erik, Chief Executive Officer, Renown Regional Medical Center, Reno, NV, p. A397
OLSON, Forrest, M.D., Chief Medical Officer, Enloe Medical Center, Chico, CA, p. A54
OLSON, John L., M.D., Medical Director, Marshfield Medical Center – Rice Lake, Rice Lake, WI, p. A704
OLSON, Joni, Chief Executive Officer, Gundersen Tri–County Hospital And Clinics, Whitehall, WI, p. A708
OLSON, Kevin, Director Information Systems, Ssm Health St. Anthony Hospital – Oklahoma City, Oklahoma City, OK, p. A505
OLSON, Kristi, Chief Executive Officer, St. Thomas More Hospital, Canon City, CO, p. A97
OLSON, Lacey, M.D., Chief Medical Staff, Sanford Chamberlain Medical Center, Chamberlain, SD, p. A560
OLSON, Lynn R, Director Human Resources, Hendricks Community Hospital Association, Hendricks, MN, p. A333
OLSON, Marcia
Business Office Manager, Webster County Community Hospital, Red Cloud, NE, p. A391
Director Finance and Controller, Spearfish Regional Hospital, Spearfish, SD, p. A564
OLSON, MariBeth, R.N., Vice President Patient Care Services, Mercy Hospital, Coon Rapids, MN, p. A330
OLSON, Mark, Interim Chief Information Officer, Behavioral Health Network, Natchaug Hospital, Mansfield Center, CT, p. A108
OLSON, Mark, M.D., Chief of Staff, Lincoln Community Hospital And Nursing Home, Hugo, CO, p. A102
OLSON, Michael R., Chief Executive Officer, Citizens Medical Center, Victoria, TX, p. A643
OLSON, Tim
Senior Vice President Finance, Thedacare Regional Medical Center–Appleton, Appleton, WI, p. A691
Senior Vice President Finance, Thedacare Regional Medical Center–Neenah, Neenah, WI, p. A702
OLSON, Tracy L, Human Resource Officer, Avera St. Luke'S Hospital, Aberdeen, SD, p. A559
OLSZYK, Mark, M.D., Vice President Medical Affairs and Chief Medical Officer, Carroll Hospital Center, Westminster, MD, p. A293
OMAN, Michelle, D.O.
Chief Medical Officer, Essentia Health Northern Pines Medical Center, Aurora, MN, p. A328

Chief Medical Officer, Essentia Health–Virginia, Virginia, MN, p. A341
OMOLARA, Khar, M.D., Chief Medical Staff, Jefferson County Hospital, Fayette, MS, p. A346
OMRAN, Yasser, M.D., President Medical Staff, Pomerene Hospital, Millersburg, OH, p. A488
OMTA, Stephen R, Chief Operating Officer, Peacehealth St. Joseph Medical Center, Bellingham, WA, p. A670
OMURA, David, Director, Wm. Jennings Bryan Dorn Veterans Affairs Medical Center, Columbia, SC, p. A552
ONDRUSEK, Ashley, Chief Executive Officer, Post Acute/Warm Springs Specialty Hospital Of New Braunfels, New Braunfels, TX, p. A626
ONEAL, Karen, Chief Financial Officer, Burke Medical Center, Waynesboro, GA, p. A163
ONEILL, Steve, Chief Information Officer, Brookdale Hospital Medical Center, New York, NY, p. A432
ONG, Hannah, Director, Medical Affairs, Saint Elizabeths Hospital, Washington, DC, p. A116
ONG, Richard B, Chief Information Officer, Saint Vincent Hospital, Erie, PA, p. A525
ONI, Buki, M.D., Chief Medical Officer, Kenmare Community Hospital, Kenmare, ND, p. A468
ONIFATHER, Jeff, Chief Financial Officer, Cornerstone Of Medical Arts Center Hospital, Fresh Meadows, NY, p. A428
ONO, Craig, M.D., Chief of Staff, Shriners Hospitals For Children–Honolulu, Honolulu, HI, p. A165
ONOFRE, Bonnie, Chief Nursing Officer, South Lake Hospital, Clermont, FL, p. A120
OPBROEK, Steve, Manager Information Technology, Skyline Hospital, White Salmon, WA, p. A682
OPHAUG, Courtney, Chief Executive Officer, Banner Estrella Medical Center, Phoenix, AZ, p. A33
OPHEIKENS, Robyn, Assistant Administrator Human Resources, St. Mark'S Hospital, Salt Lake City, UT, p. A652
OPPONG, Bernard, D.O., Chief of Staff, Madison Health, London, OH, p. A486
OPRANDI, Allison, M.D., Chief Medical Officer, Aultman Hospital, Canton, OH, p. A474
OPRISKO, Judy P
Vice President Human Resources, John Heinz Institute Of Rehabilitation Medicine, Wilkes, PA, p. A545
Vice President, Allied Services Rehabilitation Hospital, Scranton, PA, p. A540
OPSETH, Gregory, Chief Nursing Officer, Guthrie County Hospital, Guthrie Center, IA, p. A223
OPSTEDAHL, DeeAnna, R.N., Vice President Patient Care Services, Chi St. Alexius Health – Dickinson Medical Center, Dickinson, ND, p. A466
OPSUT, Jennifer, Interim Chief Operating Officer, West Valley Medical Center, Caldwell, ID, p. A168
OQUENDO, Tanja, Chief Human Resources Officer, Chi Flaget Memorial Hospital, Bardstown, KY, p. A249
ORAVEC, Jon, Vice President, Human Resources, Howard County General Hospital, Columbia, MD, p. A290
ORAZINE, Jay, Director Information Services, Baptist Health Paducah, Paducah, KY, p. A259
ORCUTT, David, Chief Executive Officer, Lake Granbury Medical Center, Granbury, TX, p. A608
ORDYNA, Daniel, Chief Executive Officer, Portneuf Medical Center, Pocatello, ID, p. A171
ORE, Ruta, Director Human Resources, Pottstown Hospital, Pottstown, PA, p. A539
OREAR, Kathy, Director Human Resources, Newman Regional Health, Emporia, KS, p. A234
OREGEL, Omar, Controller, Kindred Hospital–Ontario, Ontario, CA, p. A76
ORELLANA, Feliipe, Chief Medical Officer, Barnes–Jewish St. Peters Hospital, Saint Peters, MO, p. A371
OREN, Cole, R.N., Chief Nursing Officer, Select Specialty Hospital–Durham, Durham, NC, p. A453
OREOL, Harry, Acting Chief Executive Officer, Patton State Hospital, Patton, CA, p. A77
ORFANIDIS, Deanna, Chief Nursing Officer, Mt. Ascutney Hospital And Health Center, Windsor, VT, p. A655
ORIOL, Albert, Vice President Information Management and Chief Information Officer, Rady Children'S Hospital – San Diego, San Diego, CA, p. A84
ORLANDI, Mary, Manager Human Resources, Carney Hospital, Boston, MA, p. A295
ORLANDO, Anthony T, Senior Vice President Finance, Englewood Hospital And Medical Center, Englewood, NJ, p. A405
ORLANDO, Kristin, Director Operations, Mid–Hudson Forensic Psychiatric Center, New Hampton, NY, p. A432
ORLANDO, Lorraine, Vice President Human Resources, Brookdale Hospital Medical Center, New York, NY, p. A432
ORMAN, Bernard A., Jr, Chief Executive Officer, Samaritan Hospital, Macon, MO, p. A365

ORMOND, Evalyn, Chief Executive Officer, Union General Hospital, Farmerville, LA, p. A267
ORMOND, Jack, Chief Financial Officer, Cuba Memorial Hospital, Cuba, NY, p. A426
ORMOND, John (Jack) T., Director Finance and Revenue, Wyoming County Community Hospital, Warsaw, NY, p. A446
ORNELAS, Henry
Chief Operating Officer, Lac+Usc Medical Center, Los Angeles, CA, p. A68
Chief Operating Officer, Salinas Valley Memorial Healthcare System, Salinas, CA, p. A83
OROZCO, Jorge, Chief Executive Officer, Rancho Los Amigos National Rehabilitation Center, Downey, CA, p. A56
ORR, Karen
Administrator and Chief Nursing Officer, Providence Medical Center, Kansas City, KS, p. A238
Chief Nursing Officer, Providence Medical Center, Kansas City, KS, p. A238
ORR, Natassia, Chief Operating Officer, Broward Health Medical Center, Fort Lauderdale, FL, p. A122
ORR, Stephanie, Chief Nursing Officer, Steele Memorial Medical Center, Salmon, ID, p. A172
ORRICK, Charles H., Administrator, Donalsonville Hospital, Donalsonville, GA, p. A152
ORSINI, John
Executive Vice President and Chief Financial Officer, Northwestern Medicine Central Dupage Hospital, Winfield, IL, p. A198
Executive Vice President and Chief Financial Officer, Northwestern Medicine Delnor Hospital, Geneva, IL, p. A184
Senior Vice President, Chief Financial Officer, Northwestern Medicine Kishwaukee Hospital, Dekalb, IL, p. A181
ORSINI, Thomas J., President and Chief Executive Officer, Lake Taylor Transitional Care Hospital, Norfolk, VA, p. A664
ORT, Linda, Chief Financial Officer, Piggott Community Hospital, Piggott, AR, p. A47
ORTEGA, Becky, Manager Human Resources, Avista Adventist Hospital, Louisville, CO, p. A104
ORTEGA, Cesar, M.D., Chief of Staff, United Memorial Medical Care, Houston, TX, p. A614
ORTEGA, Debbie, Chief Human Resource Officer and Vice President Administrative Services, Huntington Memorial Hospital, Pasadena, CA, p. A77
ORTEGA, Jose, Chief Operating Officer, Greater El Monte Community Hospital, South El Monte, CA, p. A90
ORTEGO, Ashley, Director Human Resources and Marketing, Springhill Medical Center, Springhill, LA, p. A279
ORTH, Angela P., Executive Officer, Randolph Hospital, Asheboro, NC, p. A449
ORTH, Charam, Director Human Resources, Frances Mahon Deaconess Hospital, Glasgow, MT, p. A376
ORTHAUS, Denis, Director Human Resources, Wellspan Philhaven, Mount Gretna, PA, p. A532
ORTIZ, Andrew, Senior Vice President, Human Resources and Organization Development, Cedars–Sinai Medical Center, Los Angeles, CA, p. A66
ORTIZ, Bienvenido, Coordinator Information Systems, Hospital De Damas, Ponce, PR, p. A717
ORTIZ, Blas, Assistant Superintendent and Public Information Officer, Rio Grande State Center/South Texas Health Care System, Harlingen, TX, p. A609
ORTIZ, Edson, Chief Information Officer, Hospital Pavia Yauco, Yauco, PR, p. A720
ORTIZ, Evelyn Padilla
Director Human Resources, Hospital Menonita De Cayey, Cayey, PR, p. A716
Director Human Resources, Mennonite General Hospital, Aibonito, PR, p. A715
ORTIZ, Francisco, M.D., Chief of Staff, Jackson County Hospital District, Edna, TX, p. A601
ORTIZ, Jose O, Chief Financial Officer, Ryder Memorial Hospital, Humacao, PR, p. A716
ORTIZ, Migdalia, Director Human Resources, Hospital San Carlos Borromeo, Moca, PR, p. A717
ORTIZ, Nancy, Director Human Resource and Marketing, Frio Regional Hospital, Pearsall, TX, p. A628
ORTIZ, Norma, M.D., Medical Director, Hospital Hermanos Melendez, Bayamon, PR, p. A715
ORTIZ BAEZ, Felix, Administrator, I. Gonzalez Martinez Oncologic Hospital, Hato Rey, PR, p. A716
ORTO, Victoria K, R.N., Chief Nursing and Patient Care Services Officer, Duke Regional Hospital, Durham, NC, p. A452
ORTOLANI, Philip A, Vice President Operations, Mid Coast Hospital, Brunswick, ME, p. A282
ORTON, Wendy, Chief Nursing Officer, Alleghany Memorial Hospital, Sparta, NC, p. A462

OSANTOSKI, Tina, Director Human Resources, Harbor Beach Community Hospital, Harbor Beach, MI, p. A314
OSARIO, Cesar, Specialist Information Technology, Cedar Crest Hospital And Residential Treatment Center, Belton, TX, p. A588
OSBERG, Art, M.D., Chief Medical Officer, Ocala Regional Medical Center, Ocala, FL, p. A133
OSBORN, Kim, Chief Financial Officer, Sequoia Hospital, Redwood City, CA, p. A80
OSBORN, Melodie
Vice President and Chief Nursing Officer, Transitional Care Services, Renown Rehabilitation Hospital, Reno, NV, p. A397
Vice President and Chief Nursing Officer, Transitional Care Services, Renown South Meadows Medical Center, Reno, NV, p. A397
OSBORN, Tom, D.O., Chief Medical Staff, Holdenville General Hospital, Holdenville, OK, p. A500
OSBORNE, Anna, Chief Human Resources Management Service, West Texas Veterans Affairs Health Care System, Big Spring, TX, p. A588
OSBORNE, Phil, Director Information Technology, Bourbon Community Hospital, Paris, KY, p. A259
OSBURN, Jerry, Chief Executive Officer, Yoakum County Hospital, Denver City, TX, p. A600
OSCADAL, Martin
Senior Vice President Human Resources, St. Elizabeth Florence, Florence, KY, p. A252
Senior Vice President Human Resources, St. Elizabeth Fort Thomas, Fort Thomas, KY, p. A252
Vice President Human Resources, St. Elizabeth Edgewood, Edgewood, KY, p. A251
OSE, Peggy, FACHE, MSN, R.N., Chief Nursing Officer, Aspirus Riverview Hospital And Clinics, Inc., Wisconsin Rapids, WI, p. A709
OSEGARD, Jeff, Chief Information Officer, Cass County Memorial Hospital, Atlantic, IA, p. A217
OSEHOBO, Philip, M.D., Chief Medical Officer, Wellstar Spalding Regional Hospital, Griffin, GA, p. A154
OSER, William F., M.D.
Chief Medical Officer, Hackensack Meridian Health Jfk Johnson Rehabilitation Institute, Edison, NJ, p. A405
Senior Vice President and Chief Medical Officer, Hackensack Meridian Health Jfk Medical Center, Edison, NJ, p. A405
OSINSKI, Kathleen, Chief Human Resources Service, John D. Dingell Veterans Affairs Medical Center, Detroit, MI, p. A310
OSKIN, Jeffrey L., Vice President and Administrator, Charleston Area Medical Center, Charleston, WV, p. A684
OSLIN, Dave, M.D., Chief of Staff, Philadelphia Veterans Affairs Medical Center, Philadelphia, PA, p. A536
OSOWSKI, Angela, Chief Nursing Officer, Lifecare Hospitals Of Wisconsin, Pewaukee, WI, p. A703
OSSELLO, Susan, Chief Financial Officer, Granite County Medical Center, Philipsburg, MT, p. A379
OSTASZEWSKI, Patricia, Chief Executive Officer, Healthsouth Rehabilitation Hospital Of Toms River, Toms River, NJ, p. A413
OSTASZEWSKI, Patricia, MS, Chief Executive Officer, Healthsouth Rehabilitation Hospital Of Toms River, Toms River, NJ, p. A413
OSTBERG, Melissa, Chief Financial Officer, Marias Medical Center, Shelby, MT, p. A380
OSTBLOOM, Jan, Human Resources Consultant, Chi Our Lady Of Peace, Louisville, KY, p. A256
OSTEEN, Tom J, Director Area Technology, Kaiser Permanente Manteca Medical Center, Manteca, CA, p. A71
OSTENSON, Scott, Chief Financial Officer, Jacobson Memorial Hospital Care Center, Elgin, ND, p. A466
OSTER, Kurt, Human Resources Officer, Carl Vinson Veterans Affairs Medical Center, Dublin, GA, p. A152
OSTERBERG, Valerie, Chief Financial Officer, Sanford Vermillion Medical Center, Vermillion, SD, p. A564
OSTERHOUT, David, Assistant Superintendent and Chief Financial Officer, El Paso Psychiatric Center, El Paso, TX, p. A602
OSTERLY, Eric, Chief Financial Officer, Adventhealth Fish Memorial, Orange City, FL, p. A134
OSTLIG, Jane, Chief Medical Officer, Sanford Mayville Medical Center, Mayville, ND, p. A468
OSTRANDER, Maria DC, R.N., MSN, Chief Nurse Executive, San Antonio State Hospital, San Antonio, TX, p. A635
OSTREM, Jill, Senior Vice President and Chief Operating Officer, Jefferson Stratford Hospital, Stratford, NJ, p. A413
OSTROW, Peter, M.D., President Medical Staff, Beth Israel Deaconess Hospital–Needham Campus, Needham, MA, p. A301
OSWAL, Arvind, Interim Chief Financial Officer, Arrowhead Regional Medical Center, Colton, CA, p. A55
OSWALD, Traci L
Vice President of Human Resources, Galion Hospital, Galion, OH, p. A483
Vice President, Chief Human Resources, Avita Ontario Hospital, Ontario, OH, p. A489
OTERO, Jorge Torres., Executive Director, Hospital Del Maestro, San Juan, PR, p. A718
OTHOLE, Jean, Chief Executive Officer, U. S. Public Health Service Indian Hospital, Zuni, NM, p. A421
OTOMO, Ellen, Interim Hospital Administrator, Chicago–Read Mental Health Center, Chicago, IL, p. A177
OTOTT, Kelly, R.N., Chief Nursing Officer, Washington County Hospital, Washington, KS, p. A247
OTT, Darin, D.O., Chief of Staff, Kane County Hospital, Kanab, UT, p. A648
OTT, Eugene J., Jr, Chief Executive Officer, Eagleville Hospital, Eagleville, PA, p. A524
OTT, Laurie, Vice President Human Resources and President University Health Care Foundation, University Hospital, Augusta, GA, p. A147
OTT, Mark, M.D., Regional Chief Medical Director, Intermountain Medical Center, Murray, UT, p. A649
OTT, Pamela, Vice President Finance, Aurora Sheboygan Memorial Medical Center, Sheboygan, WI, p. A705
OTTATI, David
Regional Chief Executive Officer, Adventhealth New Smyrna Beach, New Smyrna Beach, FL, p. A133
Regional Chief Executive Officer, Adventhealth Orlando, Orlando, FL, p. A134
OTTE, Elaine, Chief Operating Officer, Clarinda Regional Health Center, Clarinda, IA, p. A219
OTTEMAN, Diane, Chief Executive Officer, Kindred Chicago–Central Hospital, Chicago, IL, p. A178
OTTEN, Sharon A., Vice President Nursing, Advocate South Suburban Hospital, Hazel Crest, IL, p. A185
OTTENBACHER, John, Chief of Staff, Bowdle Hospital, Bowdle, SD, p. A559
OTTENS, Mark, Chief Nursing Officer, Baptist Memorial Hospital–North Mississippi, Oxford, MS, p. A352
OTTMAR, Kellie, Manager Information Services, East Adams Rural Healthcare, Ritzville, WA, p. A677
OTTO, Sara, Chief Compliance Officer, North Canyon Medical Center, Gooding, ID, p. A169
OTTO, Steve, Chief Executive Officer, Tristar Skyline Medical Center, Nashville, TN, p. A577
OTTOLINO, Joseph
Chief Executive Officer, West Suburban Medical Center, Oak Park, IL, p. A192
Chief Executive Officer, Westlake Hospital, Melrose Park, IL, p. A189
OUBRE, Chris, Information Technology Director, Garden Park Medical Center, Gulfport, MS, p. A347
OUELETTE, Lisa, Director Human Resources, Beaumont Hospital – Troy, Troy, MI, p. A334
OUELLETTE, Demetra, Chief Operating Officer, Rehabilitation Hospital Of Rhode Island, North Smithfield, RI, p. A547
OUNGST, Laurie
Vice President and Chief Operating Officer, Ascension St. Mary'S Hospital, Rhinelander, WI, p. A704
Vice President, Operations, Ascension Eagle River Hospital, Eagle River, WI, p. A694
Vice President, Operations, Ascension Sacred Heart Hospital, Tomahawk, WI, p. A707
Vice President, Operations, Howard Young Medical Center, Woodruff, WI, p. A709
OURS, Matt, Chief Executive Officer and Managing Director, Rivendell Behavioral Health, Bowling Green, KY, p. A250
OUSEY, Tracy, Director Human Resources, Washington County Hospital And Clinics, Washington, IA, p. A230
OUTHIER, Amy, Director Health Information Management, Weatherford Regional Hospital, Weatherford, OK, p. A510
OUTLAW, Debbie, R.N., Director Patient Care Services, Coastal Virginia Rehabilitation, Newport News, VA, p. A663
OVANDO, Benjamin, Chief Operations Officer, Rancho Los Amigos National Rehabilitation Center, Downey, CA, p. A56
OVERBEY, William J., Chief Executive Officer, Kansas Rehabilitation Hospital, Topeka, KS, p. A246
OVERBY, Roger, Executive Director Information Systems, Greene County Medical Center, Jefferson, IA, p. A225
OVERCASH, Jenny, Director Human Resources, Encompass Health Rehabilitation Hospital Of Huntington, Huntington, WV, p. A686
OVERSTREET, Alyson, Chief Financial Officer, Washington County Hospital, Chatom, AL, p. A16
OVERSTREET, Amy, Director Human Resources, Trousdale Medical Center, Hartsville, TN, p. A570
OVERTON, Camie, Chief Executive Officer, Curahealth Tucson, Tucson, AZ, p. A37
OVERTON, Deana, Director Human Resources, Mitchell County Hospital, Colorado City, TX, p. A593
OVERTON, Saundra, R.N., Chief Nursing Officer, Royal Oaks Hospital, Windsor, MO, p. A373
OVESON, Mark, M.D., Chief Medical Staff, Central Valley Medical Center, Nephi, UT, p. A649
OWEN, Sabrina, Human Resources Officer, Veterans Affairs Central Iowa Health Care System, Des Moines, IA, p. A221
OWEN, Sandra, Director Fiscal and Accounting, Hospital District 6 – Harper Campus, Harper, KS, p. A236
OWENS, Beverly, Controller, Rehabilitation Hospital, Navicent Health, Macon, GA, p. A157
OWENS, Brian, Chief Operating Officer, Lindner Center Of Hope, Mason, OH, p. A487
OWENS, Craig A., President, Wellstar Douglas Hospital, Douglasville, GA, p. A152
OWENS, Daniel, Chief Executive Officer, Emory University Hospital Midtown, Atlanta, GA, p. A146
OWENS, Diane, Assistant Administrator, St. David'S Medical Center, Austin, TX, p. A586
OWENS, Mark, M.D., Vice President Medical Affairs, Mercy San Juan Medical Center, Carmichael, CA, p. A54
OWENS, Maxwell, FACHE, Chief Financial Officer, Huntsville Memorial Hospital, Huntsville, TX, p. A615
OWENS, Nancy, Administrator, Christus Dubuis Hospital Of Fort Smith, Fort Smith, AR, p. A42
OWENS, Paul, M.D., Chief Medical Officer, Hackettstown Medical Center, Hackettstown, NJ, p. A406
OWENS, Rick, Administrator, D. W. Mcmillan Memorial Hospital, Brewton, AL, p. A15
OWENS, Royce Bramer, Chief Operating Officer, Baylor Scott & White Medical Center – Llano, Llano, TX, p. A621
OWENS, Stephanie, Manager Human Resources, Mcdowell Arh Hospital, Mcdowell, KY, p. A258
OWENS, Thomas, President, Duke University Hospital, Durham, NC, p. A453
OWENSBY, Terri, R.N., Chief Nursing Executive, Kaiser Permanente South Sacramento Medical Center, Sacramento, CA, p. A82
OWINGS, Karen, MSN, Vice President, Patient Care Services, Medstar Union Memorial Hospital, Baltimore, MD, p. A287
OWINGS, Raymond C., Interim Chief Financial Officer, Unc Rockingham Health Care, Eden, NC, p. A453
OWINGS, Thomas, Chief Executive Officer, Wesley Healthcare Center, Wichita, KS, p. A248
OWREY, Donald R.
President, Upmc Horizon, Farrell, PA, p. A526
President, Upmc Jameson, New Castle, PA, p. A533
OXENDALE, Sharon, President and Chief Operating Officer, Multicare Tacoma General Hospital, Tacoma, WA, p. A680
OXFORD, Michelle, Chief Operating Officer, Acting Chief Executive Officer, Bakersfield Heart Hospital, Bakersfield, CA, p. A52
OXFORD, Tammy, Director Human Resources, Bob Wilson Memorial Grant County Hospital, Ulysses, KS, p. A247
OXLEY, Dawn, R.N., Associate Director Patient Care Services and Nurse Executive, Iowa City Veterans Affairs Health Care System, Iowa City, IA, p. A224
OXLEY, James, D.O., Vice President Medical Affairs, Orange Regional Medical Center, Middletown, NY, p. A431
OXLEY, Scott, President, The Acadia Hospital, Bangor, ME, p. A281
OXTON, Alice, Director Information Technology, Sentara Obici Hospital, Suffolk, VA, p. A668
OZBURN, Thomas H., Chief Executive Officer, Parkridge Medical Center, Chattanooga, TN, p. A567
OZEL, A Deniz, M.D., Chief Medical Officer, Northeast Rehabilitation Hospital, Salem, NH, p. A402
OZMENT, Mary, Chief Nursing Officer, Hillcrest Hospital Pryor, Pryor, OK, p. A506
OZUAH, Philip O., M.D., Ph.D., Executive Vice President and Chief Operating Officer, Brookdale Hospital Medical Center, New York, NY, p. A432
O'BRIEN, Beth, Chief Executive Officer, Baylor Scott & White Medical Center – Carrollton, Carrollton, TX, p. A591
O'BRIEN, Daniel R., Vice President and Chief Financial Officer, Community Hospital, Munster, IN, p. A212
O'BRIEN, Elizabeth, Chief Financial Officer, Northern Nevada Adult Mental Health Services, Sparks, NV, p. A398
O'BRIEN, Jane E, M.D., Medical Director, Franciscan Children'S, Brighton, MA, p. A296
O'BRIEN, John, Chief Executive Officer, Manning Regional Healthcare Center, Manning, IA, p. A226
O'BRIEN, Karen, Director Human Resources, Gerald Champion Regional Medical Center, Alamogordo, NM, p. A416
O'BRIEN, Kelly, Chief Operating Officer, Hackensack Meridian Health Riverview Medical Center, Red Bank, NJ, p. A412
O'BRIEN, Kevin, Chief Financial Officer, Share Medical Center, Alva, OK, p. A496
O'BRIEN, Laureen, Chief Information Officer, Providence Newberg Medical Center, Newberg, OR, p. A515

O'BRIEN, Renee, Director Human Resources, Greater Binghamton Health Center, Binghamton, NY, p. A423

O'BRIEN–PARADIS, Katie, M.D., Chief Medical Officer, Chi Oakes Hospital, Oakes, ND, p. A469

O'BRYANT, G. Mark., President and Chief Executive Officer, Tallahassee Memorial Healthcare, Tallahassee, FL, p. A141

O'CONNELL, Brian, Director Information Services, North Star Behavioral Health System, Anchorage, AK, p. A25

O'CONNELL, Melody M, Director Human Resources, St. Bernard Parish Hospital, Chalmette, LA, p. A265

O'CONNELL, Tim, Chief Financial Officer, Lincoln Hospital, Davenport, WA, p. A672

O'CONNOR, Alice M, Chief Executive Officer, Kindred Hospital–New Jersey Morris County, Dover, NJ, p. A404

O'CONNOR, Betty, Chief Nursing Officer, Crouse Health, Syracuse, NY, p. A445

O'CONNOR, Colleen, Director Human Resources, Centerstone Hospital, Bradenton, FL, p. A118

O'CONNOR, David, Executive Vice President and Chief Financial Officer, Caromont Regional Medical Center, Gastonia, NC, p. A454

O'CONNOR, Dennis, M.D., Medical Director, Ira Davenport Memorial Hospital, Bath, NY, p. A423

O'CONNOR, James
    Chief Administrative Officer, St. Catherine Of Siena Medical Center, Smithtown, NY, p. A444
    President, St. Charles Hospital, Port Jefferson, NY, p. A441

O'CONNOR, Kathy
    Vice President Finance and Controller, St. Joseph Mercy Livingston Hospital, Howell, MI, p. A314
    Vice President Finance, St. Joseph Mercy Ann Arbor, Ypsilanti, MI, p. A325

O'CONNOR, Kevin, D.O., President, Medical Staff, Spectrum Health United Hospital, Greenville, MI, p. A313

O'CONNOR, Michael F, Senior Vice President Finance, Wellspan York Hospital, York, PA, p. A546

O'CONNOR, Michael P, M.D., Chief Medical Officer, Banner Baywood Medical Center, Mesa, AZ, p. A31

O'CONNOR, Thomas, President, United Hospital, Saint Paul, MN, p. A340

O'CONNOR, Tim, Area Finance Officer, Kaiser Permanente Santa Clara Medical Center, Santa Clara, CA, p. A88

O'CONNOR, Timothy P., Executive Vice President and Chief Financial Officer, Lahey Hospital & Medical Center, Burlington, Burlington, MA, p. A297

O'CONNOR–SNYDER, Judy, Chief Nursing Officer, Mercy Hospital Lebanon, Lebanon, MO, p. A364

O'DEA, Edward, Executive Vice President and Chief Financial Officer, Lehigh Valley Hospital, Allentown, PA, p. A519

O'DELL, Darrell, Director Information Services, Good Samaritan Hospital, San Jose, CA, p. A86

O'DELL, Michael, Chief Financial Officer, Sheridan County Health Complex, Hoxie, KS, p. A237

O'DONNELL, Jan, Chief Nursing Officer, South Texas Surgical Hospital, Corpus Christi, TX, p. A594

O'DONNELL, John, Director of Information Technology Services, Spartanburg Medical Center – Mary Black, Spartanburg, SC, p. A557

O'DONNELL, Michael F., CPA, Chief Financial Officer, Peconic Bay Medical Center, Riverhead, NY, p. A442

O'DONNELL, Patrick W., President and Chief Executive Officer, Chambersburg Hospital, Chambersburg, PA, p. A522

O'DONOGHUE, Brian, M.D., Chief Medical Officer, Breckinridge Memorial Hospital, Hardinsburg, KY, p. A253

O'FLANAGAN, Jayne, Director Human Resources, Incline Village Community Hospital, Incline Village, NV, p. A394

O'GORMAN, Victoria, Administrator, Kaiser Permanente Fremont Medical Center, Fremont, CA, p. A59

O'HARA, Denise, Vice President Human Resources, Wilson Medical Center, Wilson, NC, p. A464

O'HARA, Kathleen, Vice President Human Resources, Erie County Medical Center, Buffalo, NY, p. A424

O'HARA, Michael
    Senior Executive Director Human Resources, Houston Medical Center, Warner Robins, GA, p. A163
    Senior Executive Director, Perry Hospital, Perry, GA, p. A158

O'HAVER, Tim, Chief Operating Officer, St. Joseph Medical Center, Tacoma, WA, p. A681

O'HERN, Mark
    President, Upmc East, Monroeville, PA, p. A532
    President, Upmc Mckeesport, Mckeesport, PA, p. A531

O'KEEFE, James M., President and Chief Executive Officer, Mile Bluff Medical Center, Mauston, WI, p. A699

O'KEEFE, John
    Chief Executive Officer, Select Specialty Hospital–Gulfport, Gulfport, MS, p. A348
    Chief Nursing Officer, Day Kimball Hospital, Putnam, CT, p. A110

O'KEEFE, Kathy
    Executive Director, Pilgrim Psychiatric Center, Brentwood, NY, p. A424
    Interim Executive Director, Sagamore Children'S Psychiatric Center, Dix Hills, NY, p. A427

O'KEEFE, Sharon L, President, University of Chicago Medical Center, University Of Chicago Medical Center, Chicago, IL, p. A180

O'KEEFE, Sharon L., President, University Of Chicago Medical Center, Chicago, IL, p. A180

O'KEEFE, Trish, President, Morristown Medical Center, Morristown, NJ, p. A408

O'KELLEY, J. Shannon, Chief Operating Officer, Ronald Reagan Ucla Medical Center, Los Angeles, CA, p. A69

O'LAIRE, Beth, Manager Human Resources, Ascension Calumet Hospital, Chilton, WI, p. A693

O'LEARY, Bill, Chief Executive Officer, Pondera Medical Center, Conrad, MT, p. A375

O'LEARY, Daniel H, M.D., Chief Medical Officer, Umass Memorial Healthalliance–Clinton Hospital, Leominster, MA, p. A300

O'LEARY, Kevin J, Senior Vice President and Chief Financial Officer, Exeter Hospital, Exeter, NH, p. A400

O'LEARY, Megan A, Vice President Human Resources and Rehabilitation Services, Mckenzie–Willamette Medical Center, Springfield, OR, p. A518

O'LOUGHLIN, James F., Chief Executive Officer, Aiken Regional Medical Centers, Aiken, SC, p. A549

O'MALLEY, Constance, President, Beaumont Hospital – Farmington Hills, Farmington Hills, MI, p. A311

O'MALLEY, John F., President, St. Joseph Mercy Livingston Hospital, Howell, MI, p. A314

O'MALLEY, Jon P., Chief Executive Officer, Select Specialty Hospital–Macomb County, Mount Clemens, MI, p. A318

O'MALLEY, Mary Jo, R.N., MS, Vice President Diagnostics and Support Services, Oconomowoc Memorial Hospital, Oconomowoc, WI, p. A702

O'MALLEY, Trevor, Site Manager, Amita Health Saint Joseph Hospital, Elgin, IL, p. A182

O'NEAL, Charlotte, Vice President Human Resources, Research Medical Center, Kansas City, MO, p. A362

O'NEAL, Jessica
    Chief Executive Officer, Medical City Dallas, Dallas, TX, p. A597
    Chief Operating Officer, West Florida Hospital, Pensacola, FL, p. A136

O'NEAL, Karen, Chief Executive Officer, Candler County Hospital, Metter, GA, p. A157

O'NEAL, Lewis Stephen, R.N., MSN, Chief Nursing Officer, Chi Saint Joseph London, London, KY, p. A255

O'NEAL, Michael, Chief Executive Officer, George C Grape Community Hospital, Hamburg, IA, p. A223

O'NEIL, Alan, Chief Executive Officer, Unity Medical Center, Grafton, ND, p. A467

O'NEIL, Jeremy, Administrator, Providence Valdez Medical Center, Valdez, AK, p. A27

O'NEIL, John, Chief Executive Officer, Pickens County Medical Center, Carrollton, AL, p. A16

O'NEIL, Patrick, Senior Vice President Medical Affairs, Lake Regional Health System, Osage Beach, MO, p. A366

O'NEIL, Terry, Chief Information Technology, Nazareth Hospital, Philadelphia, PA, p. A535

O'NEILL, Beth, Chief Nursing Officer, Morgan Memorial Hospital, Madison, GA, p. A157

O'NEILL, Jennifer A, R.N., Chief Nursing Officer, Vice President Patient Care Services, Saint Barnabas Medical Center, Livingston, NJ, p. A407

O'NEILL, Lynn, R.N., Chief Nursing Officer, Medical City Lewisville, Lewisville, TX, p. A620

O'NEILL, Melissa, Vice President Human Resources, Advocate Sherman Hospital, Elgin, IL, p. A182

O'NEILL, Michael, M.D., Chief Medical Officer, Eastside Medical Center, Snellville, GA, p. A160

O'NEILL, Stephan, Vice President Information Services, Hartford Hospital, Hartford, CT, p. A108

O'REAR, Caleb F., Chief Executive Officer, Alta Vista Regional Hospital, Las Vegas, NM, p. A419

O'REILLY, Frank, Director, Dr. J. Corrigan Mental Health Center, Fall River, MA, p. A298

O'REILLY, Terrance, Chief Executive Officer, Dallas Behavioral Healthcare Hospital, Desoto, TX, p. A600

O'ROURKE, Jane, R.N., Chief Nursing Officer, Vice President Operations, St. Peter'S Hospital, Albany, NY, p. A422

O'ROURKE, Michael
    Regional Human Resource Officer, Amita Health Mercy Medical Center, Aurora, IL, p. A173
    Regional Human Resources Lead, Amita Health Saint Joseph Hospital, Elgin, IL, p. A182

O'SHEA, James, Chief Operating Officer, Baton Rouge Behavioral Hospital, Baton Rouge, LA, p. A263

O'STEEN, Neil, Director Information Technology, Bacon County Hospital And Health System, Alma, GA, p. A145

O'STEEN, Tony, Chief Financial Officer, Meadows Regional Medical Center, Vidalia, GA, p. A162

O'SULLIVAN, Barbara, M.D., M.P.H., Medical Director, Brookdale Hospital Medical Center, New York, NY, p. A432

O'SULLIVAN, Colin, Interim Chief Executive Officer, Cornerstone Hospital Of Houston At Clearlake, Webster, TX, p. A644

O'SULLIVAN, Paul
    Chief Executive Officer, Memorial Hermann Greater Heights Hospital, Houston, TX, p. A612
    Chief Executive Officer, Memorial Hermann Memorial City Medical Center, Houston, TX, p. A613

O'TOOL, Nick, Vice President Operational Finance, Chi Health Lakeside, Omaha, NE, p. A389

P

PAASCH, Michael
    Regional Chief Information Officer, Ssm Health St. Mary'S Hospital – St. Louis, Saint Louis, MO, p. A370
    Regional Vice President and Chief Information Officer, Ssm Cardinal Glennon Children'S Hospital, Saint Louis, MO, p. A370
    Vice President, Regional Chief Information Officer, Ssm Health St. Clare Hospital – Fenton, Fenton, MO, p. A360

PABLO, Gary M., M.D., Chief Medical Officer, Sacred Heart Hospital On The Emerald Coast, Miramar Beach, FL, p. A132

PABON, Jose O, Director Operations, Wilma N. Vazquez Medical Center, Vega Baja, PR, p. A720

PABON–RAMIREZ, Felix, Chief Information Officer, St. Charles Hospital, Port Jefferson, NY, p. A441

PACCA, Richard, M.D., Chief of Staff, Granville Health System, Oxford, NC, p. A460

PACCAPANICCIA, Dominic, Chief Operating Officer, Indiana Regional Medical Center, Indiana, PA, p. A528

PACE, Dewane, President and Chief Executive Officer, Haxtun Hospital District, Haxtun, CO, p. A102

PACE, Kathleen, MSN, R.N., Chief Nursing Officer, Englewood Community Hospital, Englewood, FL, p. A122

PACE, Kelly, Director Human Resource, Strategic Behavioral Health – Wilmington, Leland, NC, p. A457

PACEK, Thomas
    Vice President Information Systems and Chief Information Officer, Inspira Medical Center–Elmer, Elmer, NJ, p. A405
    Vice President Information Systems and Chief Information Officer, Inspira Medical Center–Vineland, Vineland, NJ, p. A413

PACEY, Amy, Vice President Human Resources, Good Samaritan Medical Center, Lafayette, CO, p. A102

PACHECO, Robert W, Vice President Finance, Women & Infants Hospital Of Rhode Island, Providence, RI, p. A548

PACHUCKI, James J., Chief Financial Officer, Upmc Susquehanna Sunbury, Sunbury, PA, p. A542

PACINI, Jenna, Human Resources Specialist, Belmont Behavioral Hospital, Philadelphia, PA, p. A534

PACK, Natalie, Chief Financial Officer, St. David'S North Austin Medical Center, Austin, TX, p. A586

PACK, William, Chief Financial Officer, Memorial Hermann – Texas Medical Center, Houston, TX, p. A612

PACKER, Eric, Chief Executive Officer, Cedar City Hospital, Cedar City, UT, p. A647

PACKER, Lee, Administrator, South Florida State Hospital, Hollywood, FL, p. A124

PACKER, Steven J., President and Chief Executive Officer, Community Hospital Of The Monterey Peninsula, Monterey, CA, p. A73

PACURA, Lori, President, Holy Cross Hospital, Chicago, IL, p. A177

PACYNA, Andrew
    Acting Director, Veterans Affairs Ann Arbor Healthcare System, Ann Arbor, MI, p. A306
    Deputy Director, Louis Stokes Cleveland Veterans Affairs Medical Center, Cleveland, OH, p. A478

PADDEN, Ernest C, Chief Financial Officer, Bon Secours Maryview Medical Center, Portsmouth, VA, p. A665

PADDOCK, Steve, Director of Information Services, Gibson General Hospital, Princeton, IN, p. A214

PADEN, Tawnya, Director Human Resources, Weatherford Regional Hospital, Weatherford, OK, p. A510

PADGETT, Martin
Acting Chief Executive Officer, Scott Memorial Health, Scottsburg, IN, p. A214
President and Chief Executive Officer, Clark Memorial Health, Jeffersonville, IN, p. A208

PADGETT, Shirley, Director Human Resources, Cook Medical Center–A Campus Of Tift Regional Medical Center, Adel, GA, p. A145

PADILLA, Ami, Director Human Resources, Arroyo Grande Community Hospital, Arroyo Grande, CA, p. A51

PADILLA, Gregory, Administrator, Coast Plaza Hospital, Norwalk, CA, p. A74

PADILLA, Kathy, Director of Nursing, Marcus Daly Memorial Hospital, Hamilton, MT, p. A377

PADULA, Judy, MSN, R.N., Vice President Patient Care Services and Chief Nursing Officer, St. Joseph'S University Medical Center, Paterson, NJ, p. A410

PAFFORD, Roger, M.D., Medical Director, Mineral Community Hospital, Superior, MT, p. A380

PAGANA, Charles C M.D., Chief Medical Officer, Upmc Susquehanna Sunbury, Sunbury, PA, p. A542

PAGANELLI, Deborah, Chief Executive Officer, Lifecare Hospitals Of Dallas, Dallas, TX, p. A596

PAGE, Alison, Chief Executive Officer, Western Wisconsin Health, Baldwin, WI, p. A691

PAGE, Bob, Chief Executive Officer, The University Of Kansas Hospital, Kansas City, KS, p. A238

PAGE, Cynthia, FACHE, Chief Operating Officer, Oss Orthopaedic Hospital, York, PA, p. A546

PAGE, Deborah, Chief Human Resources Officer, Duke University Hospital, Durham, NC, p. A453

PAGE, Heather, MSN, Director of Nursing, Chi St. Joseph Health Burleson Hospital, Caldwell, TX, p. A591

PAGE, Keith Allen., President and Chief Executive Officer, Anderson Hospital, Maryville, IL, p. A188

PAGE, Nancy E., MS, R.N., Chief Nursing Officer, Upstate University Hospital, Syracuse, NY, p. A445

PAGE, Pattie, Director Marketing and Public Relations, Eastside Medical Center, Snellville, GA, p. A160

PAGE, Robert, Chief Information and Technology Officer, Memphis Veterans Affairs Medical Center, Memphis, TN, p. A575

PAGE, Rodger, President, Mercy Medical Center Mount Shasta, Mount Shasta, CA, p. A73

PAGE, Sue, Director Human Resources, Monroe County Medical Center, Tompkinsville, KY, p. A261

PAGE, Susan M., President and Chief Executive Officer, Pratt Regional Medical Center, Pratt, KS, p. A244

PAGE, William E, CPA, Chief Financial Officer, Franklin Medical Center, Winnsboro, LA, p. A280

PAGELER, Robert
Chief Information Officer, Confluence Health/Central Washington Hospital, Wenatchee, WA, p. A682
Chief Information Officer, Confluence Health/Wenatchee Valley Hospital, Wenatchee, WA, p. A682

PAGET, Cindy, Chief Human Resources Officer, Forks Community Hospital, Forks, WA, p. A673

PAGLIUZZA, Greg, Chief Financial Officer, Unitypoint Health – Trinity Bettendorf, Bettendorf, IA, p. A217

PAGNINI, Janie, Administrator Accounting, Atascadero State Hospital, Atascadero, CA, p. A51

PAGUAGA, Ana, Director of Human Resources, Coral Gables Hospital, Coral Gables, FL, p. A120

PAHE, Gary, Manager Human Resources, Sage Memorial Hospital, Ganado, AZ, p. A29

PAHL, Jodi, Chief Nurse Executive, Mercy Health – St. Rita'S Medical Center, Lima, OH, p. A485

PAI, Ajith, President, Texas Health Harris Methodist Hospital Cleburne, Cleburne, TX, p. A592

PAIGE, Peter G, Chief Medical Officer, Jackson Health System, Miami, FL, p. A130

PAINE, Lincoln, M.D., Medical Director, River Oaks Hospital, New Orleans, LA, p. A275

PAINE, Russ, Human Resources Officer, Erlanger Western Carolina Hospital, Murphy, NC, p. A459

PAINTER, Jeff, Manager Information Technology, Summit Pacific Medical Center, Elma, WA, p. A672

PAIRISH, Katherine, Chief Financial Officer, Eastern Plumas Health Care, Portola, CA, p. A79

PALADINO, James, Controller, New England Rehabilitation Hospital Of Portland, Portland, ME, p. A284

PALAZZOLO, Chris
Health System President and Chief Executive Officer Mid–Michigan, Ascension St. Mary'S Of Michigan, Saginaw, MI, p. A321
President and Chief Executive Officer, Ascension Crittenton Hospital Medical Center, Rochester, MI, p. A320
President and Chief Executive Officer, Ascension Genesys Hospital, Grand Blanc, MI, p. A312
President and Chief Executive Officer, Ascension Standish Hospital, Standish, MI, p. A323

PALERMO, Robert, Vice President Finance, Hackensack Meridian Health Ocean Medical Center, Brick Township, NJ, p. A404

PALETTA, Lisa A., Chief Executive Officer, Alta View Hospital, Sandy, UT, p. A652

PALETTA, Lisa A., R.N., FACHE, Chief Nursing Officer, Utah Valley Hospital, Provo, UT, p. A651

PALICKA, Martha, Director Information Systems, Bartlett Regional Hospital, Juneau, AK, p. A26

PALIGO, Terry, Chief Financial Officer, Union County Hospital, Anna, IL, p. A173

PALKOWSKI, Chris, M.D., Physician in Chief, Kaiser Permanente Sacramento Medical Center, Sacramento, CA, p. A81

PALLIN, Angel, Senior Vice President of Operations, Mount Sinai Medical Center, Miami Beach, FL, p. A131

PALMER, Charles, Director Information Technology, Nanticoke Memorial Hospital, Seaford, DE, p. A114

PALMER, Debra L, MS, R.N., Chief Human Resources Officer and Corporate Compliance Officer, Fairfield Medical Center, Lancaster, OH, p. A485

PALMER, Janel M, Director Human Resources, Greenwood County Hospital, Eureka, KS, p. A235

PALMER, Justin, Administrator, John C. Stennis Memorial Hospital, De Kalb, MS, p. A346

PALMER, Katie, Manager Human Resources, Sanford Aberdeen Medical Center, Aberdeen, SD, p. A559

PALMER, Keith, Assistant Administrator, Winkler County Memorial Hospital, Kermit, TX, p. A617

PALMER, Kelly, D.O., Medical Director, State Hospital South, Blackfoot, ID, p. A167

PALMER, Stephanie, Chief Nursing Officer, Encompass Health Valley Of The Sun Rehabilitation Hospital, Glendale, AZ, p. A30

PALMER, Trisha, Director, St. James Healthcare, Butte, MT, p. A375

PALMIER, Michael L, Chief Human Resources Management, Overton Brooks Veterans Affairs Medical Center, Shreveport, LA, p. A278

PALMUCCI, Jeffrey, Chief Executive Officer, Vanderbilt Stallworth Rehabilitation Hospital, Nashville, TN, p. A577

PALO, Alan, Chief Financial Officer, Sarah D. Culbertson Memorial Hospital, Rushville, IL, p. A195

PALUMBO, Christopher M., Chief Executive Officer, Nebraska Spine Hospital, Omaha, NE, p. A389

PALUMBO, Michael, D.O., Vice President Medical Affairs and Chief Education, Northern Light Inland Hospital, Waterville, ME, p. A285

PALUMBO, Michael, M.D., Executive Vice President and Medical Director, White Plains Hospital Center, White Plains, NY, p. A448

PAM, Brower, Chief Financial Officer, Christus Spohn Hospital Corpus Christi Memorial, Corpus Christi, TX, p. A594

PAMPERIEN, Linda, Chief Financial Officer, Texas County Memorial Hospital, Houston, MO, p. A361

PANDL, Therese B.
President and Chief Executive Officer, Hshs St. Mary'S Hospital Medical Center, Green Bay, WI, p. A696
President and Chief Executive Officer, Hshs St. Vincent Hospital, Green Bay, WI, p. A696

PANDO, Terry, R.N., Associate Executive Director and Chief Nursing Officer, Brookdale Hospital Medical Center, New York, NY, p. A432

PANDOLPH, Philip E., Chief Executive Officer, Meadville Medical Center, Meadville, PA, p. A531

PANDYA, Kamel, Director Information Services, San Antonio Regional Hospital, Upland, CA, p. A93

PANDYA, Sherrie, Administrator, Kane County Hospital, Kanab, UT, p. A648

PANKEY, De'Niro, Director Information Systems, Corona Regional Medical Center, Corona, CA, p. A55

PANKEY, Susan Kay, Chief Nursing Officer, Davis County Hospital, Bloomfield, IA, p. A218

PANKOW, Thomas, Chief Information Officer, Jackson Park Hospital And Medical Center, Chicago, IL, p. A177

PANKOWSKI, Charles, Manager Human Resources, Select Specialty Hospital–Columbus, Columbus, OH, p. A480

PANLASIGUI, Bonnie, Chief Operating Officer, St. Mary Medical Center, Long Beach, CA, p. A65

PANNELL, Kenneth
Chief Financial Officer, College Station Medical Center, College Station, TX, p. A592
Chief Financial Officer, Western Arizona Regional Medical Center, Bullhead City, AZ, p. A28

PANNULLO, Ava, M.D., Vice President Medical Services and Physician in Chief, Hebrew Senior Care, West Hartford, CT, p. A112

PANSA, Leonard F, Senior Vice President Human Resources and Administrative Services, Mercy Medical Center, Springfield, MA, p. A303

PANZA, Louis J., Jr, President and Chief Executive Officer, Monongahela Valley Hospital, Monongahela, PA, p. A532

PAOLINELLI, Karen, Chief Executive Officer, Madera Community Hospital, Madera, CA, p. A70

PAOLUCCI, Benjamin, D.O., Chief of Staff, Southeast Michigan Surgical Hospital, Warren, MI, p. A324

PAPA, AnnMarie, R.N., Vice President and Chief Nursing Officer, Einstein Medical Center Montgomery, East Norriton, PA, p. A524

PAPADAKOS, James, Chief Financial Officer, Signature Healthcare Brockton Hospital, Brockton, MA, p. A296

PAPALIA, Fern, Director of Nursing, Essex County Hospital Center, Cedar Grove, NJ, p. A404

PAPALIA, John, Chief Executive Officer, Encompass Health Rehabilitation Hospital Of Erie, Erie, PA, p. A525

PAPALIA, Mark, President, Upmc Kane, Kane, PA, p. A528

PAPE, Becky A., Chief Executive Officer, Good Samaritan Regional Medical Center, Corvallis, OR, p. A512

PAPKA, Lauren, Chief Administrative Officer, St. Mary'S Sacred Heart Hospital, Lavonia, GA, p. A156

PAPPAN, Clayton, Director Human Resources and Marketing, South Central Kansas Medical Center, Arkansas City, KS, p. A232

PAPPAS, Kirk, M.D., Physician–in–Chief, Kaiser Permanente Santa Rosa Medical Center, Santa Rosa, CA, p. A89

PAPPAS, Michael, Chief Fiscal Service Officer, Louis Stokes Cleveland Veterans Affairs Medical Center, Cleveland, OH, p. A478

PAPPAS, Sheryl L, Chief Financial Officer, Sanford Webster Medical Center, Webster, SD, p. A565

PAPPAS, Theron, Director Management Information Systems, Holy Family Memorial, Manitowoc, WI, p. A699

PAQUETTE, Julie, M.D., Chief Medical Officer, Providence Seaside Hospital, Seaside, OR, p. A518

PARADIS, Brian, Chief Operating Officer, Adventhealth Orlando, Orlando, FL, p. A134

PARADIS, James, President, Paoli Hospital, Paoli, PA, p. A533

PARADIS, Jeanne, Director Information Services, The Acadia Hospital, Bangor, ME, p. A281

PARAUDA, Martina A, Director, Brookdale Hospital Medical Center, New York, NY, p. A432

PARAUDA, Martina A., Director, Brookdale Hospital Medical Center, New York, NY, p. A432

PARAVATE, Chris, Chief Information Officer, Northeast Georgia Medical Center, Gainesville, GA, p. A154

PARAVISINI, Nilda, Director Human Resources, Hospital Manati Medical Center, Manati, PR, p. A717

PARCEL, Jim, Director Information Technology, Maury Regional Hospital, Columbia, TN, p. A568

PARCHMENT, Deborah, Executive Director, Brookdale Hospital Medical Center, New York, NY, p. A432

PARDEE, Wendy Ann., President and Chief Executive Officer, The Children'S Institute Of Pittsburgh, Pittsburgh, PA, p. A537

PARDUE, Helen, Interim Chief Nursing Officer, Johnson County Community Hospital, Mountain City, TN, p. A576

PAREEK, Yogesh, M.D., Clinical Director, Brown County Community Treatment Center, Green Bay, WI, p. A696

PARENT, Paula A.
Chief Nursing Officer and Director of Human Resources, Cary Medical Center, Caribou, ME, p. A282
Chief Nursing Officer, Cary Medical Center, Caribou, ME, p. A282

PARET, Jason, Chief Executive Officer, Catalina Island Medical Center, Avalon, CA, p. A51

PARHAM, Eva, R.N., Chief Nurse Executive, Central State Hospital, Petersburg, VA, p. A664

PARHAM, Tracy
Chief Information Officer, University Of North Carolina Hospitals, Chapel Hill, NC, p. A451
Health Care System Chief Information Officer, Unc Rex Health Care, Raleigh, NC, p. A460

PARIGI, John S, Interim Chief Financial Officer, Healdsburg District Hospital, Healdsburg, CA, p. A61

PARIS, David, Chief Executive Officer, Perry County General Hospital, Richton, MS, p. A353

PARIS, Karen, Controller, Crittenden County Hospital, Marion, KY, p. A257

PARIS, Sherri, Chief Operating Officer, Providence Milwaukie Hospital, Milwaukie, OR, p. A515

PARIS, Trevor, M.D., Medical Director, Brooks Rehabilitation Hospital, Jacksonville, FL, p. A125

PARISI, James
Chief Executive Officer, Chi St. Luke'S Health–Lakeside Hospital, The Woodlands, TX, p. A640
Chief Executive Officer, Chi St. Luke'S Health–The Woodlands Hospital, The Woodlands, TX, p. A640

PARISKY, Yuri, M.D., Chief of Staff, Mammoth Hospital, Mammoth Lakes, CA, p. A70

PARK, Bockhi
Chief Executive Officer, Encino Hospital Medical Center, Los Angeles, CA, p. A66
Chief Executive Officer, Sherman Oaks Hospital, Los Angeles, CA, p. A69
PARK, Denten
Chief Executive Officer, Northwest Health Physicians' Specialty Hospital, Fayetteville, AR, p. A41
Chief Executive Officer, Northwest Medical Center – Springdale, Springdale, AR, p. A48
PARK, Gary L
Chief Executive Officer, University Of North Carolina Hospitals, Chapel Hill, NC, p. A451
President, University Of North Carolina Hospitals, Chapel Hill, NC, p. A451
PARK, Gary L., President, University Of North Carolina Hospitals, Chapel Hill, NC, p. A451
PARK, Jessica, Director Accounting, Penn Highlands Brookville, Brookville, PA, p. A521
PARK, Rustin, Director of Nursing, Seven Hills Hospital, Henderson, NV, p. A394
PARK, Theron
Chief Executive Officer, Chi St. Joseph Health Bellville Hospital, Bellville, TX, p. A588
Chief Executive Officer, Chi St. Joseph Health Burleson Hospital, Caldwell, TX, p. A591
Chief Executive Officer, Chi St. Joseph Health Grimes Hospital, Navasota, TX, p. A626
Chief Executive Officer, Chi St. Joseph Health Madison Hospital, Madisonville, TX, p. A623
Chief Executive Officer, Chi St. Joseph Regional Health Center, Bryan, TX, p. A590
PARKE, Carol, Chief Operating Officer, SUN Kentucky, Sun Behavioral Kentucky, Erlanger, KY, p. A251
PARKER, Audrey, Budget Analyst, Twelve Clans Unity Hospital, Winnebago, NE, p. A392
PARKER, Charisse, Director Human Resources, Tennova Healthcare–Shelbyville, Shelbyville, TN, p. A579
PARKER, Cindy, Chief Financial Officer and Director Human Resources, Throckmorton County Memorial Hospital, Throckmorton, TX, p. A641
PARKER, Cynthia, R.N., Administrator and Director of Nursing, Carson Tahoe Continuing Care Hospital, Carson City, NV, p. A393
PARKER, David, VP Information Technology, Magnolia Regional Health Center, Corinth, MS, p. A346
PARKER, Deanna, Director Human Resources, J. Arthur Dosher Memorial Hospital, Southport, NC, p. A462
PARKER, Donald J., President and Chief Executive Officer, Hackensack Meridian Health Carrier Clinic, Belle Mead, NJ, p. A403
PARKER, Janie, Chief Financial Officer, Hardin County General Hospital, Rosiclare, IL, p. A195
PARKER, Jim, Chief Executive Officer, Webster County Memorial Hospital, Webster Springs, WV, p. A690
PARKER, Michael, M.D., Chief of Staff, Sharon Hospital, Sharon, CT, p. A110
PARKER, Ralph, Chief Nursing Officer, Olympic Medical Center, Port Angeles, WA, p. A676
PARKER, Richard, President, Hillcrest Hospital, Hillcrest Hospital, Cleveland, OH, p. A477
PARKER, Robert, Chief Executive Officer, Lake Cumberland Regional Hospital, Somerset, KY, p. A260
PARKER, Sandra K, M.D., Chief Medical Officer, Eastpointe Hospital, Daphne, AL, p. A16
PARKER, Theresa M, Regional Finance Director, Transylvania Regional Hospital, Brevard, NC, p. A450
PARKER, Thomas
Chief Executive Officer, Mammoth Hospital, Mammoth Lakes, CA, p. A70
President, Upper Valley Medical Center, Troy, OH, p. A492
PARKER, Tina, Director Human Resources, Encompass Health Rehabilitation Hospital Midland Odessa, Midland, TX, p. A624
PARKER, Travis, Director Human Resources, Southwest Health System, Cortez, CO, p. A98
PARKER, Valerie, M.D., Clinical Director, U. S. Public Health Service Indian Hospital, Rosebud, SD, p. A563
PARKEY, Kasey, Coordinator Payroll and Benefits, Pam Specialty Hospital Of Corpus Christi South, Corpus Christi, TX, p. A594
PARKHILL, Cherie, Chief Financial Officer, Crosbyton Clinic Hospital, Crosbyton, TX, p. A595
PARKHURST, James E., President and Chief Executive Officer, Newport Bay Hospital, Newport Beach, CA, p. A74
PARKHURST, Jennifer, Chief Financial Officer, City Of Hope'S Helford Clinical Research Hospital, Duarte, CA, p. A57
PARKHURST, Phyllis, Vice President Support Services, Newport Bay Hospital, Newport Beach, CA, p. A74

PARKINSON, Justin, M.D., President Medical Staff, Jordan Valley Medical Center West Valley Campus, West Valley City, UT, p. A653
PARKINSON, Michelle A, Director Human Resources, Prairie St. John'S, Fargo, ND, p. A466
PARKS, Amanda, Chief Nursing Officer, Lifebrite Community Hospital Of Stokes, Danbury, NC, p. A452
PARKS, Audrey, Chief Information Officer, Salinas Valley Memorial Healthcare System, Salinas, CA, p. A83
PARKS, Cary, Chief Information Resource Management, Hampton Veterans Affairs Medical Center, Hampton, VA, p. A660
PARKS, Dave, Chief Information Officer, Three Rivers Health, Three Rivers, MI, p. A323
PARKS, Ginger, Director Human Resources, Cape Fear Valley – Bladen County Hospital, Elizabethtown, NC, p. A454
PARKS, Jody, Administrator, Ottawa County Health Center, Minneapolis, KS, p. A241
PARKS, Kathi, Director of Nursing, South Lincoln Medical Center, Kemmerer, WY, p. A711
PARKS, Kelvin L., Interim Director, Veterans Health Care System Of The Ozarks, Fayetteville, AR, p. A41
PARKS, Kyle, M.D., Chief of Staff, Evans Memorial Hospital, Claxton, GA, p. A150
PARKS, Michelle, Administrator, Rivervalley Behavioral Health Hospital, Owensboro, KY, p. A259
PARKS, Peggy, R.N., Chief Nursing Officer, Northeast Regional Medical Center, Kirksville, MO, p. A363
PARKS, Sherry, R.N., MS, Chief Nursing Officer, Saint Alphonsus Regional Medical Center, Boise, ID, p. A168
PARKS, Vicki, Chief Financial Officer, Jackson Purchase Medical Center, Mayfield, KY, p. A257
PARMER, David N, Chief Executive Officer, Baptist Hospitals Of Southeast Texas, Beaumont, TX, p. A587
PARMER, David N., Chief Executive Officer, Baptist Hospitals Of Southeast Texas, Beaumont, TX, p. A587
PARMER, Michael, Chief Medical Officer, Carepartners Health Services, Asheville, NC, p. A449
PARNEL, George, Chief Financial Officer, Clifton T. Perkins Hospital Center, Jessup, MD, p. A291
PARNELL, Linda, Chief Nursing Officer, Musc Health Marion Medical Center, Mullins, SC, p. A556
PARNELL, Sally A., Interim Chief Executive Officer, Arkansas Continued Care Hospital, Jonesboro, AR, p. A43
PAROD, Daniel A., President, St. Vincent Evansville, Evansville, IN, p. A203
PAROSKI, Margaret, M.D., Executive Vice President and Chief Medical Officer, Kaleida Health, Buffalo, NY, p. A424
PARR, James
Chief Financial Officer, Salem Health West Valley, Dallas, OR, p. A512
Chief Financial Officer, Salem Hospital, Salem, OR, p. A517
PARR, Lynnette, Chief Financial Officer, Down East Community Hospital, Machias, ME, p. A284
PARRA, Kristin, Chief Nursing Officer, Yuma Rehabilitation Hospital, A Partnership Of Encompass Health And Yrmc, Yuma, AZ, p. A38
PARRA, Michelle, Director Human Resources, Kindred Hospital South Bay, Gardena, CA, p. A60
PARRADO, Carlos, M.D., Chief Medical Officer, Roosevelt Warm Springs Rehabilitation And Specialty Hospitals – Ltac, Warm Springs, GA, p. A162
PARRINELLO, Kathleen M, Ph.D., Chief Operating Officer, Strong Memorial Hospital Of The University Of Rochester, Rochester, NY, p. A443
PARRISH, Becky, Director Human Resources, Southern Virginia Regional Medical Center, Emporia, VA, p. A658
PARRISH, Carl, Chief Fiscal Service, James E. Van Zandt Veterans Affairs Medical Center, Altoona, PA, p. A519
PARRISH, Denise, Interim Chief Administrative Officer, Ascension Northeast Wisconsin Mercy Hospital, Oshkosh, WI, p. A703
PARRISH, Suann, Chief Financial Officer, Yoakum County Hospital, Denver City, TX, p. A600
PARRISH, Todd, M.D., Chief of Staff, Ut Health Jacksonville, Jacksonville, TX, p. A616
PARRY, Kayla, Manager Human Resources, Ivinson Memorial Hospital, Laramie, WY, p. A711
PARRY, Mary, Vice President Operations and Chief Operating Officer, Oneida Healthcare, Oneida, NY, p. A440
PARRY, Timothy, R.N., Chief Operating Officer, Highland District Hospital, Hillsboro, OH, p. A484
PARSI, Kia, M.D.
Chief Medical Officer, Chi St. Joseph Regional Health Center, Bryan, TX, p. A590
Chief Medical Officer, Chi St. Joseph'S Health, Park Rapids, MN, p. A337
PARSLEY, George N, Chief Operating Officer, Detar Healthcare System, Victoria, TX, p. A643

PARSON, Charlynne, Nurse Executive, Moccasin Bend Mental Health Institute, Chattanooga, TN, p. A567
PARSONS, Beth, Administrator, Christus Dubuis Hospital Of Alexandria, Alexandria, LA, p. A262
PARSONS, Brad, Administrator and Chief Executive Officer, Nea Baptist Memorial Hospital, Jonesboro, AR, p. A44
PARSONS, Brent, Chief Executive Officer, Bluffton Regional Medical Center, Bluffton, IN, p. A200
PARSONS, John, R.N., Chief Nursing Officer, Trustpoint Rehabilitation Hospital Of Lubbock, Lubbock, TX, p. A622
PARSONS, Terri L., Administrator, Advanced Care Hospital Of White County, Searcy, AR, p. A48
PARTEE, Paris I, Associate Administrator and Director Human Resources, John H. Stroger Jr. Hospital Of Cook County, Chicago, IL, p. A177
PARTENZA, John, Vice President and Treasurer, Northern Westchester Hospital, Mount Kisco, NY, p. A432
PARTHEMORE, Warrenette, Director Human Resources, Promedica Memorial Hospital, Fremont, OH, p. A483
PARTIN, James R, M.D., Chief Medical Director, Hill Country Memorial Hospital, Fredericksburg, TX, p. A606
PARTON, Gerald L., Chief Executive Officer, East Jefferson General Hospital, Metairie, LA, p. A273
PARTRIDGE, Susan, Director Human Resources, Nantucket Cottage Hospital, Nantucket, MA, p. A301
PARUCH, Randy J, Director, Information Systems, Holland Hospital, Holland, MI, p. A314
PASCASCIO, Dellone, Chief Nursing Officer, Lac–Olive View–Ucla Medical Center, Los Angeles, CA, p. A68
PASCASIO, Robert A., Chief Executive Officer, Palacios Community Medical Center, Palacios, TX, p. A627
PASCO, Teri, Director Human Resources, East Liverpool City Hospital, East Liverpool, OH, p. A482
PASCUAL, Bolivar, M.D., Medical Director, Essex County Hospital Center, Cedar Grove, NJ, p. A404
PASCUZZI, Robert, Chief Financial Officer, Mercy San Juan Medical Center, Carmichael, CA, p. A54
PASQUALE, Mark
Chief Information Officer, Integris Baptist Medical Center, Oklahoma City, OK, p. A504
Chief Information Officer, Integris Southwest Medical Center, Oklahoma City, OK, p. A504
PASS, Christian
Interim Chief Financial Officer, John Muir Medical Center, Concord, Concord, CA, p. A55
Senior Vice President & Chief Financial Officer, John Muir Medical Center, Walnut Creek, Walnut Creek, CA, p. A94
Senior Vice President and Chief Financial Officer, John Muir Behavioral Health Center, Concord, CA, p. A55
PASSAFARO, David, Chief Executive Officer, New England Baptist Hospital, Boston, MA, p. A296
PASSANNANTE, Anthony, Jr, President, Hackensack Meridian Health Palisades Medical Center, North Bergen, NJ, p. A410
PASSARELLI, Theresa, Human Resources Generalist, Warm Springs Medical Center, Warm Springs, GA, p. A162
PASSMANN, Frederic K, M.D., Chief of Staff, Stonewall Memorial Hospital, Aspermont, TX, p. A584
PASSMORE, Gary, Chief Information Officer, Endless Mountain Health Systems, Montrose, PA, p. A532
PASTERNAK, Lewis Reuven., Chief Executive Officer, Stony Brook University Hospital, Stony Brook, NY, p. A444
PASTIAN, Andre, R.N., MSN, Chief Nursing Officer, Boulder City Hospital, Boulder City, NV, p. A393
PASTOR, Robert, II, Chief Executive Officer, Rainy Lake Medical Center, International Falls, MN, p. A333
PASTORE, Raymond, M.D., Chief Medical Officer, Brookdale Hospital Medical Center, New York, NY, p. A432
PASTRANA, Guillermo, Executive Director, Hospital Pavia–Hato Rey, San Juan, PR, p. A719
PASZTOR, Barbara J., R.N.
Vice President Nursing and Patient Care Services, Bluffton Hospital, Bluffton, OH, p. A473
Vice President Patient Care Services and Chief Nursing Officer, Blanchard Valley Hospital, Findlay, OH, p. A483
PATCHELL, Lee, Lead Human Resources Business Partner, Presbyterian Hospital, Albuquerque, NM, p. A417
PATE, John, M.D., Chief Medical Officer, Tri–County Hospital, Wadena, MN, p. A342
PATE, Lois, R.N., Chief Nursing Officer, Island Hospital, Anacortes, WA, p. A670
PATE, Warren, Chief Financial Officer, South Bay Hospital, Sun City Center, FL, p. A140
PATEL, Amita, M.D., Medical Director, Haven Behavioral Senior Care Of Dayton, Dayton, OH, p. A481
PATEL, Bimal, President, Hartford Hospital, Hartford, CT, p. A108
PATEL, Binesh, M.D., Chief Medical Officer, Mclaren Flint, Flint, MI, p. A311

PATEL, Deepak, M.D., Medical Director, Cumberland Hall Hospital, Hopkinsville, KY, p. A253

PATEL, Dilip, M.D., Chief of Staff, Greater El Monte Community Hospital, South El Monte, CA, p. A90

PATEL, Fatma, M.D., Vice President Medical Affairs, Niagara Falls Memorial Medical Center, Niagara Falls, NY, p. A439

PATEL, Govind, M.D., Medical Director, Encompass Health Rehabilitation Hospital Of Morgantown, Morgantown, WV, p. A687

PATEL, Hema, Director Medical Records, Riverwoods Behavioral Health System, Riverdale, GA, p. A159

PATEL, Hiral, Chief Executive Officer, Tulane Health System, New Orleans, LA, p. A276

PATEL, Malini, M.D., Medical Director, Elgin Mental Health Center, Elgin, IL, p. A182

PATEL, Malisha
Senior Vice President and Chief Executive Officer, Memorial Hermann Greater Heights Hospital, Houston, TX, p. A612
Senior Vice President and Chief Executive Officer, Memorial Hermann Sugar Land Hospital, Sugar Land, TX, p. A638

PATEL, Natu M, M.D., Chief of Staff, Phoebe Worth Medical Center, Sylvester, GA, p. A161

PATEL, Nirav, M.D.
Chief of Staff, Los Alamitos Medical Center, Los Alamitos, CA, p. A65
Interim Chief Medical Officer, Ssm Health Saint Louis University Hospital, Saint Louis, MO, p. A370

PATEL, Paryus, M.D., Chief Medical Officer, Centinela Hospital Medical Center, Inglewood, CA, p. A62

PATEL, Prakash Chandra, M.D., Chief of Staff, Kindred Hospital–La Mirada, La Mirada, CA, p. A63

PATEL, Pravin, M.D., Acting President and Chief Executive Officer, Southern Virginia Mental Health Institute, Danville, VA, p. A658

PATEL, Pravinchandra, M.D., Chief Medical Officer, Barnes–Kasson County Hospital, Susquehanna, PA, p. A542

PATEL, Raj, M.D., Medical Director, Lifecare Hospitals Of Chester County, West Chester, PA, p. A544

PATEL, Rajesh, M.D., Chief of Staff, Upmc Susquehanna Lock Haven, Lock Haven, PA, p. A530

PATEL, Rakesh, D.O., Medical Director, Encompass Health Rehabilitation Hospital Of Altoona, Altoona, PA, p. A519

PATEL, Shailesh, M.D., Medical Director, Anchor Hospital, Atlanta, GA, p. A145

PATEL, Shalin, M.D., Chief Medical Officer, Memorial Hermann Rehabilitation Hospital – Katy, Katy, TX, p. A617

PATEL, Sharad, M.D., Medical Director, Adventhealth Connerton, Land O'Lakes, FL, p. A127

PATEL, Shatish, M.D., Chief Medical Officer, Atrium Medical Center, Stafford, TX, p. A638

PATEL, Tanay M., M.D., Chief of Staff, Golden Plains Community Hospital, Borger, TX, p. A589

PATEL, Viraj, M.D., Chief Medical Officer, Unity Medical & Surgical Hospital, Mishawaka, IN, p. A211

PATER, Tom, Chief Financial Officer, Rml Specialty Hospital, Hinsdale, IL, p. A186

PATHAK, Ajay, President, Osf Healthcare Saint Anthony'S Health Center, Alton, IL, p. A173

PATHAK, Rajiv, Chief of Staff, Marshall Medical Center, Placerville, CA, p. A78

PATIL, Steve, Chief Financial Officer, W. G. (Bill) Heffner Veterans Affairs Medical Center, Salisbury, NC, p. A461

PATILLO, Laura, Manager Human Resources, Fresno Surgical Hospital, Fresno, CA, p. A59

PATIN, Al, R.N., Senior Vice President and Chief Operating Officer, Lafayette General Medical Center, Lafayette, LA, p. A271

PATINO, Beth, Chief Information Officer, Emory Decatur Hospital, Decatur, GA, p. A152

PATMAS, Michael, M.D., Chief Medical Officer, Gritman Medical Center, Moscow, ID, p. A170

PATONAI, Steven D., Interim Chief Executive Officer, Lake Chelan Community Hospital And Clinics, Chelan, WA, p. A671

PATRIAS, Thomas, FACHE, Chief Operating Officer, Tulane Health System, New Orleans, LA, p. A276

PATRICIO, Mars, Chief Financial Officer, Seven Hills Hospital, Henderson, NV, p. A394

PATRICK, Ann M, Vice President Human Resources, Northwest Community Hospital, Arlington Heights, IL, p. A173

PATRICK, Calvin, Director Information Services, Adventhealth New Smyrna Beach, New Smyrna Beach, FL, p. A133

PATRICK, Chad, President and Chief Executive Officer, Orange Park Medical Center, Orange Park, FL, p. A134

PATRICK, Christian C, M.D., Chief Medical Officer, Baptist Memorial Hospital – Memphis, Memphis, TN, p. A574

PATRICK, Devin, Manager Human Resources, Utah State Hospital, Provo, UT, p. A650

PATRICK, Lisa, Chief Operating Officer, Caldwell Memorial Hospital, Columbia, LA, p. A265

PATRICK, Ronald, Chief Financial Officer, Northwest Medical Center, Tucson, AZ, p. A37

PATRICK, Sandra, Chief Financial Officer, Three Rivers Hospital, Waverly, TN, p. A580

PATRICK, Sean, Director Information Systems, Gifford Medical Center, Randolph, VT, p. A655

PATRIZIO, Eugene, Chief Executive Officer, Memorial Medical Center, Modesto, CA, p. A72

PATRONIS, Michael, Chief Executive Officer, Springhill Medical Center, Springhill, LA, p. A279

PATTEN, William D., Jr, Chief Executive Officer, Holy Cross Hospital, Taos, NM, p. A421

PATTERSON, Anthony, Chief Operating Officer, University Of Alabama Hospital, Birmingham, AL, p. A15

PATTERSON, Barbara, Chief Financial Officer, Provident Hospital Of Cook County, Chicago, IL, p. A179

PATTERSON, Betsy B, MSN, R.N., Chief Nursing Officer, Baylor Scott & White Medical Center – Llano, Llano, TX, p. A621

PATTERSON, Camie, Chief Operating Officer, Manatee Memorial Hospital, Bradenton, FL, p. A118

PATTERSON, Christina, Chief Financial Officer, Saint Thomas River Park Hospital, Mc Minnville, TN, p. A574

PATTERSON, Dave, Chief Information Officer, Memorial Hospital Of Converse County, Douglas, WY, p. A711

PATTERSON, David, Director Human Resources, Parkside Psychiatric Hospital And Clinic, Tulsa, OK, p. A509

PATTERSON, Debbie, Director Health Information Management, Wesley Rehabilitation Hospital, Wichita, KS, p. A248

PATTERSON, Devasha, Director of Human Resources, Northwest Mississippi Medical Center, Clarksdale, MS, p. A345

PATTERSON, Diane, Senior Vice President, Chief Operating Officer and Chief Nursing Officer, Virginia Mason Memorial, Yakima, WA, p. A682

PATTERSON, Jan, Chief Nursing Officer, Avera St. Luke'S Hospital, Aberdeen, SD, p. A559

PATTERSON, Jeff, Chief Executive Officer, Abrazo Arrowhead Campus, Glendale, AZ, p. A30

PATTERSON, Karen, Deputy Director Operations, Elmira Psychiatric Center, Elmira, NY, p. A427

PATTERSON, Larry R., Deputy Commander Administration, Bayne–Jones Army Community Hospital, Fort Polk, LA, p. A267

PATTERSON, Lisa, Director Human Resources, Pointe Coupee General Hospital, New Roads, LA, p. A276

PATTERSON, Marcia, Chief Financial Officer, Valley Regional Medical Center, Brownsville, TX, p. A590

PATTERSON, Marcia, MSN, R.N., Chief Nursing Officer, Nor-Lea Hospital District, Lovington, NM, p. A419

PATTERSON, Maria, Manager Health Information Management, Canyon Ridge Hospital, Chino, CA, p. A54

PATTERSON, Mark, M.D., Chief Medical Officer, Greeneville Community Hospital East, Greeneville, TN, p. A570

PATTERSON, Melanie, R.N., Vice President Patient Care Services and Chief Nursing Officer, Children'S Hospital Of Orange County, Orange, CA, p. A76

PATTERSON, Michael C., Chief Executive Officer, Flint River Community Hospital, Montezuma, GA, p. A157

PATTERSON, Michael N., Chief Executive Officer, Havasu Regional Medical Center, Lake Havasu City, AZ, p. A31

PATTERSON, Mike, Director of Operations, Northside Hospital–Cherokee, Canton, GA, p. A149

PATTERSON, Philip A., President, Providence Healthcare Network, Waco, TX, p. A644

PATTERSON, Renee A., Vice President Employment and Training Services, Rogers Memorial Hospital, Inc., Oconomowoc, WI, p. A702

PATTERSON, Robert, Vice President Human Resources and Rehabilitation Services, The University Of Vermont Health Network Central Vermont Medical Center, Berlin, VT, p. A654

PATTERSON, Russ
Director Information Technology, St. Rose Dominican Hospitals – Siena Campus, Henderson, NV, p. A394
Site Manager Information Technology, St. Rose Dominican Hospitals – San Martin Campus, Las Vegas, NV, p. A396

PATTERSON, Sam, Chief Financial Officer, Bay Area Hospital, Coos Bay, OR, p. A512

PATTERSON, Steve, Chief Executive Officer, Select Specialty Hospital–Springfield, Springfield, MO, p. A372

PATTERSON, Stuart, M.D., Chief of Staff, Bartow Regional Medical Center, Bartow, FL, p. A117

PATTERSON, Todd, Chief Executive Officer, Washington County Hospital And Clinics, Washington, IA, p. A230

PATTERSON, Tony, Chief Financial Officer, Ephraim Mcdowell James B. Haggin Memorial Hospital, Harrodsburg, KY, p. A253

PATTI, Rosa, Chief Financial Officer, Cameron Regional Medical Center, Cameron, MO, p. A357

PATTON, Christina, Chief Financial Officer, Colorado Plains Medical Center, Fort Morgan, CO, p. A100

PATTON, Daniel, Director Information Systems, Henrico Doctors' Hospital, Richmond, VA, p. A666

PATTON, David J., President, Upmc St. Margaret, Pittsburgh, PA, p. A538

PATTON, Joy, Director Information Technology, Pampa Regional Medical Center, Pampa, TX, p. A627

PATTON, Kevin, Chief Executive Officer, Old Vineyard Behavioral Health Services, Winston, NC, p. A464

PATTON, Meghan
Vice President Human Resources, Abington Hospital, Abington, PA, p. A519
Vice President Human Resources, Abington–Lansdale Hospital Jefferson Health, Lansdale, PA, p. A529

PATTON, Melissa, MSN, Director of Nursing, Columbus Dublin Springs, Dublin, OH, p. A482

PATTON, Pat, Chief Executive Officer, Hospital District 6 – Harper Campus, Harper, KS, p. A236

PATTON, Sally K, R.N., MS, Chief Nursing Officer, New London Hospital, New London, NH, p. A401

PAUL, Adam, Chief Financial Officer, Prairie Lakes Healthcare System, Watertown, SD, p. A565

PAUL, Allison Kay, R.N., Chief Nursing Officer, Hshs St. John'S Hospital, Springfield, IL, p. A196

PAUL, Darrick, Chief People Officer, Musc Health Of Medical University Of South Carolina, Charleston, SC, p. A550

PAUL, Donn, Chief Human Resources, Lackey Memorial Hospital, Forest, MS, p. A347

PAUL, Lise, Vice President Reimbursement and Network Planning, Hebrew Rehabilitation Center, Roslindale, MA, p. A302

PAUL, Mary
Chief Information Officer, Ascension Columbia St. Mary'S Hospital Milwaukee, Milwaukee, WI, p. A700
Chief Information Officer, Ascension Columbia St. Mary'S Hospital Ozaukee, Mequon, WI, p. A700
Vice President and Chief Information Officer, Ascension Columbia St. Mary'S Milwaukee Hospital, Milwaukee, WI, p. A700

PAUL, West, M.D., Ph.D.
Senior Vice President and Chief Quality and Medical Staff Officer, Wakemed Raleigh Campus, Raleigh, NC, p. A461
Senior Vice President, Chief Quality and Medical Staff Officer, Wakemed Cary Hospital, Cary, NC, p. A450

PAULEY, Clarence, Senior Vice President and Chief Human Resources Officer, University Of Cincinnati Medical Center, Cincinnati, OH, p. A477

PAULS, Scott R, Director Information Technology, HealthNet Connect, Guttenberg Municipal Hospital, Guttenberg, IA, p. A223

PAULSEN, Susan, Director Human Resources, Northridge Hospital Medical Center, Los Angeles, CA, p. A66

PAULSON, Adam, Director Finance, Centracare Health–Melrose, Melrose, MN, p. A335

PAULSON, Erik, Director of Finance, J. D. Mccarty Center For Children With Developmental Disabilities, Norman, OK, p. A503

PAULSON, Gordon, Manager Human Resources, Glacial Ridge Health System, Glenwood, MN, p. A332

PAULSON, Sybil K., Administrator, North Oaks Rehabilitation Hospital, Hammond, LA, p. A268

PAULUS, Terresa Ann
Chief Nursing Officer, Banner Goldfield Medical Center, Apache Junction, AZ, p. A28
Chief Nursing Officer, Banner Ironwood Medical Center, San Tan Valley, AZ, p. A35

PAUTLER, J. Stephen, FACHE, Chief Operating Officer, Peterson Regional Medical Center, Kerrville, TX, p. A618

PAVALONIS, Diane, Chief Nurse Executive, Western State Hospital, Staunton, VA, p. A668

PAVIA, Antoine, M.D., Medical Director, Hospital Pavia Arecibo, Arecibo, PR, p. A715

PAVIK, Sarah, Director Human Resources and Guest Services, Inova Loudoun Hospital, Leesburg, VA, p. A661

PAVILANIS, Charlotte J, R.N., Vice President of Clinical Services and Chief Nursing Officer, Sturgis Hospital, Sturgis, MI, p. A323

PAVLATOS, Thales, Medical Director, Ohio Valley Surgical Hospital, Springfield, OH, p. A491

PAWAR, Ganesh, M.D., Chief of Staff, Marshfield Medical Center – Ladysmith, Ladysmith, WI, p. A698

PAWLEK, Kenny, Chief Operating Officer, Usc Verdugo Hills Hospital, Glendale, CA, p. A60

PAWLOSKI, Paula, Chief Nursing Officer, Lifecare Hospitals Of Pittsburgh, Pittsburgh, PA, p. A537

PAWLOWICZ, James E, Director Human Resources, Shriners Hospitals For Children–Chicago, Chicago, IL, p. A179

PAWLOWSKI, Phil, Chief Financial Officer, Glenbeigh Hospital And Outpatient Centers, Rock Creek, OH, p. A490

PAWOLA, Ken, Chief Operating Officer, Rml Specialty Hospital, Hinsdale, IL, p. A186

PAXSON, Gary, Administrator, White River Medical Center, Batesville, AR, p. A39

PAXTON, Douglas V., Director, Veterans Affairs Roseburg Healthcare System, Roseburg, OR, p. A517

PAYNE, Angel, Clinical Director, Director of Nursing, Sonora Behavioral Health Hospital, Tucson, AZ, p. A38

PAYNE, Ellen, Chief Operating Officer, Georgetown Behavioral Health Institute, Georgetown, TX, p. A607

PAYNE, James, Director Information Systems, Southern Tennessee Regional Health System–Winchester, Winchester, TN, p. A580

PAYNE, Jason, Executive Vice President and Chief Operating Officer, Rush Foundation Hospital, Meridian, MS, p. A351

PAYNE, Judy H., Chief Executive Officer, Turning Point Hospital, Moultrie, GA, p. A158

PAYNE, Keela, Director Human Resources, Hamilton General Hospital, Hamilton, TX, p. A609

PAYNE, Kenneth G, Chief Financial Officer, Holzer Medical Center, Gallipolis, OH, p. A483

PAYNE, Michael, M.D., Chief of Staff, Dallas County Medical Center, Fordyce, AR, p. A42

PAYNE, Rick, Director Information Systems, Santa Rosa Medical Center, Milton, FL, p. A132

PAYNE, Steven, Chief Financial Officer, Jordan Valley Medical Center West Valley Campus, West Valley City, UT, p. A653

PAYTON, Becky J, Vice President Human Resources, Mercy Hospital Oklahoma City, Oklahoma City, OK, p. A504

PAZDERNIK, Mary, Chief Financial Officer, Mahnomen Health Center, Mahnomen, MN, p. A334

PEA, Richard, Director Human Resources, Memorial Hospital And Health Care Center, Jasper, IN, p. A208

PEABODY, Kim, Chief Operating Officer, The Brook Hospital – Kmi, Louisville, KY, p. A257

PEACE, Lother E., III, President and Chief Executive Officer, Russell Medical, Alexander City, AL, p. A13

PEACH, Larry, Chief Financial Officer, Jefferson County Health Center, Fairfield, IA, p. A222

PEACH, Susan M., Chief Executive Officer, Sumner Regional Medical Center, Gallatin, TN, p. A570

PEACOCK, Tammy, Facility Director, Northern Virginia Mental Health Institute, Falls Church, VA, p. A659

PEAL, Chip, Chief Executive Officer, Frankfort Regional Medical Center, Frankfort, KY, p. A252

PEARCE, Charles T, Chief Financial and Information Officer, The Healthcenter, Kalispell, MT, p. A378

PEARCE, Darren, Executive Director, Rehabilitation Hospital, Navicent Health, Macon, GA, p. A157

PEARCE, Margaret, R.N., Ph.D., Chief Nursing Officer, University Of Utah Health, Salt Lake City, UT, p. A652

PEARCH, William, Chief Information Officer, Yukon–Kuskokwim Delta Regional Hospital, Bethel, AK, p. A25

PEARCY, Joetta J, Director, Human Resources, Glendive Medical Center, Glendive, MT, p. A376

PEARCY, Steve, Director Human Resources, Community Hospital North, Indianapolis, IN, p. A206

PEARLMAN, Helen, Nurse Executive, Minneapolis Veterans Affairs Health Care System, Minneapolis, MN, p. A336

PEARSON, Bruce, Senior Vice President and Chief Operating Officer, Honorhealth Scottsdale Thompson Peak Medical Center, Scottsdale, AZ, p. A36

PEARSON, Christine, Chief Financial Officer, Anmed Health Medical Center, Anderson, SC, p. A549

PEARSON, Dawn, Director Human Resources, Healthsouth Rehabilitation Hospital Of Vineland, Vineland, NJ, p. A413

PEARSON, Frank P., Commanding Officer, Naval Hospital Camp Pendleton, Camp Pendleton, CA, p. A54

PEARSON, Gregory, Chief Executive Officer, Minden Medical Center, Minden, LA, p. A274

PEARSON, Jeff
Chief Information Officer, Christus Mother Frances Hospital – Jacksonville, Jacksonville, TX, p. A616
Vice President and Chief Information Officer, Christus Mother Frances Hospital – Tyler, Tyler, TX, p. A642

PEARSON, Kellie T., Chief Human Resource Officer, St. Christopher'S Hospital For Children, Philadelphia, PA, p. A536

PEARSON, Madelyn, R.N., Senior Vice President Patient Care Services and Chief Nursing Officer, Brigham And Women'S Hospital, Boston, MA, p. A295

PEARSON, Marshall, Director Management Information Systems, St. David'S North Austin Medical Center, Austin, TX, p. A586

PEARSON, Nancy, MSN, R.N., Director, Nursing, Novant Health Thomasville Medical Center, Thomasville, NC, p. A463

PEARSON, Susan, M.D., Chief Medical Officer, Mayo Clinic Health System In Mankato, Mankato, MN, p. A334

PEART, Blake, Administrator, Kindred Hospital–Mansfield, Mansfield, TX, p. A623

PEART, Carol, Chief Financial Officer, Chicago Lakeshore Hospital, Chicago, IL, p. A177

PEBURN, Eric, Chief Financial Officer, Halifax Health Medical Center Of Daytona Beach, Daytona Beach, FL, p. A121

PECHOUS, Bryan, M.D., Vice President Medical Affairs, Unitypoint Health – Finley Hospital, Dubuque, IA, p. A222

PECK, Amy, R.N., Chief Nursing Officer, Memorial Regional Health, Craig, CO, p. A98

PECK, Bob, Chief Financial Officer, Wesley Rehabilitation Hospital, Wichita, KS, p. A248

PECK, Darin, M.D., Chief of Staff, Northern Light Ca Dean Hospital, Greenville, ME, p. A283

PECK, Kay E., Chief Executive Officer, Encompass Health Rehabilitation Hospital Of Modesto, Modesto, CA, p. A72

PECK, Michael D, Assistant Administrator, Caribou Memorial Hospital And Living Center, Soda Springs, ID, p. A172

PECK, Robert C, M.D., Chief Medical Officer, Mayo Clinic Health System In Eau Claire, Eau Claire, WI, p. A694

PEDANO, Andrea D, D.O., Chief Medical Officer, Suburban Community Hospital, Norristown, PA, p. A533

PEDERSEN, Darren, Coordinator Information Technology, Weisman Children'S Rehabilitation Hospital, Marlton, NJ, p. A408

PEDERSEN, Paul E, M.D., Vice President and Chief Medical Officer, Osf St. Joseph Medical Center, Bloomington, IL, p. A174

PEDERSON, Bryan, Human Resources Manager, Tri–County Hospital, Wadena, MN, p. A342

PEDERSON, Karn, Manager Health Information Management, Mckenzie County Healthcare System, Watford City, ND, p. A470

PEDERSON, Randall K., Chief Executive Officer, Tioga Medical Center, Tioga, ND, p. A469

PEDLEY, Joe, CPA, Vice President and Chief Financial Officer, Lmh Health, Lawrence, KS, p. A239

PEDLOW, Bernadette R, Senior Vice President Business and Chief Operating Officer, Albany Medical Center, Albany, NY, p. A422

PEDRETTI, Jennalee, Vice President Operations, Regional Health Services Of Howard County, Cresco, IA, p. A220

PEDROZA, Fernando, Vice President Information Technology, Uchealth Poudre Valley Hospital, Fort Collins, CO, p. A100

PEEBLES, Wanda V., Chief Nursing Officer, Jps Health Network, Fort Worth, TX, p. A605

PEEK, Chris, Chief Executive Officer, Caromont Regional Medical Center, Gastonia, NC, p. A454

PEEK, Scott, FACHE, Chief Operating Officer, Baylor University Medical Center, Dallas, TX, p. A596

PEELER, Cindy K, R.N., Chief Nursing Officer, Adair County Health System, Greenfield, IA, p. A223

PEELGREN, Jim, Chief Information Officer, Adventist Health – Tulare, Tulare, CA, p. A92

PEEPLES, Jonnitra, Chief Human Resource Officer, Vibra Hospital Of Richmond, Richmond, VA, p. A666

PEER, Julianne, President, Penn Highlands Brookville, Brookville, PA, p. A521

PEERY, Lori, Chief Human Resource Management Services, Va Palo Alto Health Care System, Palo Alto, CA, p. A77

PEET, Fred, Chief Information Officer, Yuma Regional Medical Center, Yuma, AZ, p. A38

PEGE, Diane, M.D., Vice President Medical Affairs, Sutter Lakeside Hospital, Lakeport, CA, p. A64

PEGLOW, Robert, Interim Chief Administrative Officer, Saint Thomas Stones River Hospital, Woodbury, TN, p. A580

PEIFFER, Paul, Chief Financial Officer and Vice President, Jackson Hospital And Clinic, Montgomery, AL, p. A21

PEIL, Michael, M.D., Chief Medical Director, Kindred Hospital Peoria, Peoria, IL, p. A193

PEIPERT, John, Interim President and Chief Executive Officer, Hshs St. Francis Hospital, Litchfield, IL, p. A188

PEIPERT, John, R.N., Chief Nursing Officer, Hshs St. Francis Hospital, Litchfield, IL, p. A188

PEKOFSKE, Robert, Vice President Finance, Advocate Christ Medical Center, Oak Lawn, IL, p. A191

PELEUSES, John, Interim Chief Executive Officer, Sonoma West Medical Center, Sebastopol, CA, p. A89

PELFREY, Joy S, R.N., MSN, Vice President and Chief Nursing Officer, Cabell Huntington Hospital, Huntington, WV, p. A685

PELHAM, Wesley, Chief Information Officer, Florida State Hospital, Chattahoochee, FL, p. A119

PELKOWSKI, Margaret, R.N., Vice President Patient Care Services, Brookdale Hospital Medical Center, New York, NY, p. A432

PELLEGRIN, Kimberley, Director, Human Resources, Red River Hospital, Llc, Wichita Falls, TX, p. A646

PELLEGRINO, Ron, Chief Operating Officer, West Virginia University Hospitals, Morgantown, WV, p. A687

PELLICONE, John T, M.D., Chief Medical Officer, Brookdale Hospital Medical Center, New York, NY, p. A432

PELOT, Jeff, Interim Chief Information Officer, Denver Health, Denver, CO, p. A98

PELTIER, Glenn, Chief Financial Officer, Christus Mother Frances Hospital – Winnsboro, Winnsboro, TX, p. A646

PELTIER, Robert, M.D.
Chief Medical Officer, North Oaks Medical Center, Hammond, LA, p. A268
Senior Vice President, Chief Medical Officer, North Oaks Health System, North Oaks Rehabilitation Hospital, Hammond, LA, p. A268

PELTON, Ed, Chief of Staff, Chadron Community Hospital And Health Services, Chadron, NE, p. A384

PELUSO, Joseph J., Chief Executive Officer, Tyrone Hospital, Tyrone, PA, p. A542

PEMBERTON, Edith, Chief Financial Officer, East Morgan County Hospital, Brush, CO, p. A97

PEMBERTON, Stacy, Chief Nursing Officer, Grand River Hospital District, Rifle, CO, p. A105

PEMELTON, Debbie, Director Human Resources, Weslaco Regional Rehabilitation Hospital, Weslaco, TX, p. A645

PENA, Carolina, Assistant Director Administrator, Larkin Community Hospital–South Miami Campus, South Miami, FL, p. A140

PENA, Jessica, Manager Finance, Christus Spohn Hospital Kleberg, Kingsville, TX, p. A618

PENA, Julie, Director Finance, Community Howard Specialty Hospital, Kokomo, IN, p. A209

PENA, Rafael, Chief Executive Officer, Kindred Hospital–Brea, Brea, CA, p. A53

PENA, Terry, Chief Operating Officer and Chief Nursing Officer, San Bernardino Mountains Community Hospital District, Lake Arrowhead, CA, p. A63

PENCO, Kris, Director Information Systems, Coffeyville Regional Medical Center, Coffeyville, KS, p. A233

PENDER, Carol, Assistant Vice President Human Resources, Walden Behavioral Care, Waltham, MA, p. A304

PENDER, Debra, MS, R.N., Vice President Nursing, Mercy Hospital Ardmore, Ardmore, OK, p. A496

PENDERGRAFT, Tina, Chief Nursing Officer, Satanta District Hospital And Long Term Care, Satanta, KS, p. A245

PENDLETON, Gretchen, Director Human Resources, Suburban Community Hospital, Norristown, PA, p. A533

PENDLETON, Timothy, M.D., President Medical Staff, Penn Highlands Brookville, Brookville, PA, p. A521

PENICK, Lisa, R.N., Chief Nursing Officer, Carroll County Memorial Hospital, Carrollton, KY, p. A250

PENLAND, Jennifer, Controller, Kindred Hospital Tarrant County–Arlington, Arlington, TX, p. A583

PENN, Nicholas A., Chief Financial Officer, Hopedale Medical Complex, Hopedale, IL, p. A186

PENN, Shelia, Facility Director, Bryce Hospital, Tuscaloosa, AL, p. A24

PENNACCHIO, Suzanne, MSN, R.N., Chief Nursing Officer, Brookdale Hospital Medical Center, New York, NY, p. A432

PENNER, Jerome, Chief Executive Officer, Murray–Calloway County Hospital, Murray, KY, p. A258

PENNEY, Cindy L, R.N., Vice President Nursing, Mercyone Iowa City Medical Center, Iowa City, IA, p. A224

PENNEY, Jan, R.N., Vice President and Chief Nursing Officer, Midmichigan Medical Center–Midland, Midland, MI, p. A318

PENNINGTON, Brian Keith., President and Chief Executive Officer, Medical West, Bessemer, AL, p. A14

PENNINGTON, Kim, Chief Executive Officer, Select Specialty Hospital–Lexington, Lexington, KY, p. A255

PENNINGTON, Stephen G., Chief Executive Officer, East Georgia Regional Medical Center, Statesboro, GA, p. A161

PENNINO, Jackie, Director Human Resources, Old Vineyard Behavioral Health Services, Winston, NC, p. A464

PENNISSON, Jay M, Chief Financial Officer, Brookwood Baptist Medical Center, Birmingham, AL, p. A14

PENOVICH, Carrie L, Chief Clinical Services Officer, Aurora Medical Center – Manitowoc County, Two Rivers, WI, p. A707

PENUEL, Jennifer, Director Human Resources, Madison Medical Center, Fredericktown, MO, p. A360

PEOPLES, Kathleen K, R.N., MS, Vice President of Nursing, St. Vincent Kokomo, Kokomo, IN, p. A209

PEOPLES, Kyle, Director Technology Management Services, Springfield Hospital, Springfield, VT, p. A655

PEOPLES, Lynn, Interim Chief Nursing Officer, Person Memorial Hospital, Roxboro, NC, p. A461

PEOPLES, Phyllis L., President and Chief Executive Officer, Terrebonne General Medical Center, Houma, LA, p. A269

PEPE, Joseph, President and Chief Executive Officer, Catholic Medical Center, Manchester, NH, p. A401

PEPPEL, David
Executive Director, Elmira Psychiatric Center, Elmira, NY, p. A427
Executive Director, Greater Binghamton Health Center, Binghamton, NY, p. A423

PEPPER, L. Douglas, M.D., President, Medical Staff, Monongahela Valley Hospital, Monongahela, PA, p. A532

PEPPLER, Lisa, Financial Manager, Parkview Whitley Hospital, Columbia City, IN, p. A201

PERAL, Sherry, Manager Information Systems, Oak Valley Hospital District, Oakdale, CA, p. A75

PERALEZ, Jesse, Chief Executive Officer, Nix Health Care System, San Antonio, TX, p. A634

PERALTA, Pennie, R.N., VP, Nursing & Chief Nursing Officer, Bon Secours St. Francis Hospital, Charleston, SC, p. A549

PERCELLO, Thomas, Chief Financial Officer, Community Medical Center, Toms River, NJ, p. A413

PEREA, Ely, Director and Chief Executive Officer, Covenant Specialty Hospital, Lubbock, TX, p. A621

PEREACE, Vicki, Manager Human Resources, William Bee Ririe Hospital, Ely, NV, p. A393

PERECKO, Gary L., President, Riddle Hospital, Media, PA, p. A531

PEREIRA, Raul Ramos, M.D., Medical Director, Ryder Memorial Hospital, Humacao, PR, p. A716

PEREL, Michael
Regional Chief Financial Officer, Kauai Veterans Memorial Hospital, Waimea, HI, p. A166
Regional Chief Financial Officer, Samuel Mahelona Memorial Hospital, Kapaa, HI, p. A166

PEREZ, Carmen, Director Human Resources, Doctors' Center Hospital San Juan, San Juan, PR, p. A718

PEREZ, David, Vice President and Chief Information Officer, Eisenhower Medical Center, Rancho Mirage, CA, p. A79

PEREZ, Edwin, M.D., Chief of Medical Staff, Marshall County Hospital, Benton, KY, p. A249

PEREZ, Francisco, Manager Management Information Systems, Hospital De La Universidad De Puerto Rico/Dr. Federico Trilla, Carolina, PR, p. A715

PEREZ, Joe, Associate Director, South Texas Veterans Health Care System, San Antonio, TX, p. A635

PEREZ, Lisa, R.N., Director Nursing, Meadowbrook Rehabilitation Hospital, Gardner, KS, p. A235

PEREZ, Mercedes, Vice President Nursing, Larkin Community Hospital–South Miami Campus, South Miami, FL, p. A140

PEREZ, Nina, R.N., MSN, Chief Nursing Officer, North Okaloosa Medical Center, Crestview, FL, p. A120

PEREZ, Tony, M.D., President Medical Staff, Jewish Hospital–Shelbyville, Shelbyville, KY, p. A260

PEREZ, III, Miguel, Chief Information Officer, Driscoll Children's Hospital, Corpus Christi, TX, p. A594

PEREZ-GUERRA, Francisco, Chief Executive Officer, Gundersen Moundview Hospital & Clinics, Friendship, WI, p. A695

PEREZ-MIR, Ernesto, Vice President, Chief Nursing Officer, Brookdale Hospital Medical Center, New York, NY, p. A432

PERI, Gil, President and Chief Operating Officer, Connecticut Children's Medical Center, Hartford, CT, p. A108

PERJON, Cindy, Associate Director, Southwest Connecticut Mental Health System, Bridgeport, CT, p. A107

PERKERSON, Robyn, Administrator, Lifecare Hospitals Of North Carolina, Rocky Mount, NC, p. A461

PERKERSON, Robyn, R.N., Administrator, Lifecare Hospitals Of North Carolina, Rocky Mount, NC, p. A461

PERKES, Neil C, Operations Officer, Logan Regional Hospital, Logan, UT, p. A648

PERKET, William, Vice President Human Resources, North Country Hospital And Health Center, Newport, VT, p. A654

PERKINS, Brett, M.D., Chief Medical Staff, Madison County Memorial Hospital, Madison, FL, p. A128

PERKINS, Chris, Director Information Services, Clinch Valley Medical Center, Richlands, VA, p. A665

PERKINS, Dan
Corporate Director Human Resources, Cornerstone Hospital–West Monroe, West Monroe, LA, p. A280
Vice President of Human Resources, Solara Hospital Harlingen, Harlingen, TX, p. A609

PERKINS, Jeanne, Vice President Nursing and Interim Manager Human Resources, Bucyrus Hospital, Bucyrus, OH, p. A474

PERKINS, Kathryn, M.D.
Chief Medical Officer, Banner Boswell Medical Center, Sun City, AZ, p. A36
Chief Medical Officer, Banner Thunderbird Medical Center, Glendale, AZ, p. A30

PERKINS, Lewis L., R.N., MSN, Chief Nursing Officer, Integris Baptist Medical Center, Oklahoma City, OK, p. A504

PERKINS, Mike, Vice President and Administrator, Baptist Health Medical Center – North Little Rock, North Little Rock, AR, p. A46

PERKINS, Richard, Chief Financial Officer, Baylor Scott & White Medical Center – Hillcrest, Waco, TX, p. A644

PERKINS, Sherry B., President and Chief Executive Officer, University Of Maryland Capital Region Health Prince George'S Hospital Center, Cheverly, MD, p. A289

PERKINS, Tom, Chief Information Officer, Shannon Medical Center, San Angelo, TX, p. A633

PERKINS–PEPPERS, Andrea, Chief Information Officer, Forks Community Hospital, Forks, WA, p. A673

PERL, Lawrence, M.D., Chief Medical Officer, Columbia Memorial Hospital, Hudson, NY, p. A429

PERLA, Salvatore, President, Norwood Hospital, Norwood, MA, p. A302

PERLICH, Gwynn, Chief Operating Officer, St. Vincent Evansville, Evansville, IN, p. A203

PERLSTEIN, David A., President and Chief Executive Officer, Brookdale Hospital Medical Center, New York, NY, p. A432

PERMANN, Darcy, Manager Business Office, Landmann–Jungman Memorial Hospital Avera, Scotland, SD, p. A563

PERNICE, Paul, Vice President Finance, Beebe Healthcare, Lewes, DE, p. A113

PERRA, Scott H.
Chief Executive Officer, St. Elizabeth Medical Center, Utica, NY, p. A446
President and Chief Executive Officer, Faxton St. Luke'S Healthcare, Utica, NY, p. A446

PERRAS, Joseph L., President and Chief Executive Officer, Mt. Ascutney Hospital And Health Center, Windsor, VT, p. A655

PERRIGOT, Keri, Manager Human Resources, Cassia Regional Hospital, Burley, ID, p. A168

PERRIN, Cynthia K., President and Chief Executive Officer, Texas Health Presbyterian Hospital Of Rockwall, Rockwall, TX, p. A631

PERRINE, Vicki, FACHE, Chief Operating Officer, Claxton Hepburn Medical Center, Ogdensburg, NY, p. A440

PERRITT, Daniel, Chief Financial Officer, Sunrise Hospital And Medical Center, Las Vegas, NV, p. A396

PERROTTE, Kenneth, Director Operations, Rockland Children'S Psychiatric Center, Orangeburg, NY, p. A440

PERROTTI, Paul R, CPA, Chief Financial Officer, Wellstar West Georgia Medical Center, Lagrange, GA, p. A155

PERRY, Carol, R.N., Vice President and Chief Nursing Officer, Stormont Vail Health, Topeka, KS, p. A246

PERRY, Cheryl
Chief Financial Officer, Integris Baptist Medical Center, Oklahoma City, OK, p. A504
Chief Financial Officer, Vibra Hospital Of Southeastern Massachusetts, New Bedford, MA, p. A301
Executive Director Human Resources, Paris Regional Medical Center, Paris, TX, p. A628

PERRY, Cynthia, M.D., Chief of Staff, Stephens Memorial Hospital, Breckenridge, TX, p. A589

PERRY, Darrin Keith, Chief Information Officer and Senior Vice President, St. Jude Children'S Research Hospital, Memphis, TN, p. A575

PERRY, Doug, M.D., Chief of Staff, Baptist Medical Center Leake, Carthage, MS, p. A345

PERRY, Faye, Chief Nursing Officer, Tennova Healthcare–Clarksville, Clarksville, TN, p. A568

PERRY, Jan, R.N., Vice President Patient Care Services, Community Medical Center, Missoula, MT, p. A378

PERRY, Jeff
Director Information Technology, St. John'S Pleasant Valley Hospital, Camarillo, CA, p. A53
Director Information Technology, St. John'S Regional Medical Center, Oxnard, CA, p. A76

PERRY, Jeffery, President and Chief Executive Officer, Atchison Hospital, Atchison, KS, p. A232

PERRY, Karen, Chief Information Resource Management Services, James H. Quillen Veterans Affairs Medical Center, Mountain Home, TN, p. A576

PERRY, Kathleen, Senior Vice President and Chief Information Officer, Mercy Medical Center, Baltimore, MD, p. A288

PERRY, Matthew, Director Information Systems, Andalusia Health, Andalusia, AL, p. A13

PERRY, Matthew J., President and Chief Executive Officer, Genesis Healthcare System, Zanesville, OH, p. A495

PERRY, Melanie A., Chief Executive Officer, Washington County Hospital, Plymouth, NC, p. A460

PERRY, Michael, Chief Executive Officer, Michiana Behavioral Health Center, Plymouth, IN, p. A213

PERRY, Nini, Chief Nursing Officer, Georgetown Behavioral Health Institute, Georgetown, TX, p. A607

PERRY, Rhonda S., Chief Financial Officer, Medical Center, Navicent Health, Macon, GA, p. A156

PERRY, Robert Keith, Senior Vice President, Chief Information Officer, Carilion Franklin Memorial Hospital, Rocky Mount, VA, p. A667

PERRY, Sally, Chief Executive Officer, Coastal Harbor Treatment Center, Savannah, GA, p. A160

PERRY, Sharon, Chief Nursing Officer, Emanuel Medical Center, Turlock, CA, p. A92

PERRY, Shaun, Chief Information Officer, Mcgehee Hospital, Mcgehee, AR, p. A45

PERRY, Solette, Regional Director Human Resources, Kauai Veterans Memorial Hospital, Waimea, HI, p. A166

PERRY, Stacey, Director, Nursing, Hamilton County Hospital, Syracuse, KS, p. A246

PERRY, Teresa J, Chief Financial Officer, Up Health System–Bell, Ishpeming, MI, p. A315

PERRY, Tim, Executive Director of Human Resources, Baptist Health Corbin, Corbin, KY, p. A250

PERRY, V Mark, Chief Financial Officer, Adventist Health Portland, Portland, OR, p. A516

PERRYMAN, Mike, Chief Financial Officer, Baptist Memorial Hospital–Union City, Union City, TN, p. A580

PERSE, David F., President and Chief Executive Officer, St. Vincent Charity Medical Center, Cleveland, OH, p. A478

PERSICHILLI, Judith M., Acting President and Chief Executive Officer, University Hospital, Newark, NJ, p. A409

PERSILY, Cynthia A., Chief Executive Officer, Highland Hospital, Charleston, WV, p. A684

PERSING, Tamara F., Chief Nursing Officer, Evangelical Community Hospital, Lewisburg, PA, p. A530

PERT, Robert M, Vice President Finance and Chief Financial Officer, United Regional Health Care System, Wichita Falls, TX, p. A646

PERUGINO, Tony, Assistant Vice President Decision Support, Vassar Brothers Medical Center, Poughkeepsie, NY, p. A442

PESCHEL, Colleen, Director Human Resources, Sutter Medical Center, Sacramento, Sacramento, CA, p. A82

PESKIN, Ted, M.D., Acute Care Medical Director, Hilo Medical Center, Hilo, HI, p. A164

PESONEN–JOHNSON, Alice, Chief Nursing Officer, Chi St. Francis Health, Breckenridge, MN, p. A329

PESTLE, Janet K., R.N., MSN, Chief Nursing Officer, United Hospital, Saint Paul, MN, p. A340

PETER, David, M.D.
Senior Vice President Medical Affairs and Chief Medical Director, Cleveland Clinic Akron General, Akron, OH, p. A471
Senior Vice President Medical Affairs and Chief Medical Officer, Cleveland Clinic Akron General Lodi Hospital, Lodi, OH, p. A485

PETER, Douglas G, M.D., Chief Medical Officer, Gallup Indian Medical Center, Gallup, NM, p. A418

PETER, Jan D, Vice President Fiscal Services and Chief Financial Officer, Good Shepherd Health Care System, Hermiston, OR, p. A513

PETER, John, M.D., Vice President Medical Affairs, Ssm Cardinal Glennon Children'S Hospital, Saint Louis, MO, p. A370

PETER, Sherma, M.D., Chief of Staff, Optim Medical Center – Screven, Sylvania, GA, p. A161

PETERMAN, John, Vice President and Administrator, Riverside Shore Memorial Hospital, Onancock, VA, p. A664

PETERMAN, Tammy, R.N., MS, Executive Vice President, Chief Operating Officer and Chief Nursing Officer, The University Of Kansas Hospital, Kansas City, KS, p. A238

PETERMEIER, Jill, Senior Executive Human Resources, Unitypoint Health – Marshalltown, Marshalltown, IA, p. A226

PETERS, Amy, R.N.
Chief Nursing Officer, Truman Medical Center–Hospital Hill, Kansas City, MO, p. A363
Chief Nursing Officer, Truman Medical Center–Lakewood, Kansas City, MO, p. A363

PETERS, Bruce
Chief Executive Officer, Mercy Hospitals Of Bakersfield, Bakersfield, CA, p. A52
Vice President and Chief Operating Officer, Bakersfield Memorial Hospital, Bakersfield, CA, p. A52

PETERS, Candace, R.N., Director of Nursing, Webster County Community Hospital, Red Cloud, NE, p. A391

PETERS, Connie, President, Chi Health Schuyler, Schuyler, NE, p. A391

PETERS, Dave, Chief Human Resources Officer, Veterans Affairs Nebraska–Western Iowa Health Care System – Lincoln, Lincoln, NE, p. A387

PETERS, Gerald, Vice President Information Technologies and Chief Information Officer, Lake Health, Concord Township, OH, p. A480

PETERS, Holli, Director Health Information Management, Holton Community Hospital, Holton, KS, p. A237

PETERS, Jan, Vice President Human Resources, Saint Vincent Hospital, Worcester, MA, p. A305

PETERS, Mary
  Chief Information Officer, Womack Army Medical Center, Fort Bragg, NC, p. A454
  Chief Nursing Officer, Unitypoint Health – Finley Hospital, Dubuque, IA, p. A222
PETERS, Patrick, Chief Executive Officer, Guthrie County Hospital, Guthrie Center, IA, p. A223
PETERS, Suzanne K, Vice President Human Resources, Munson Medical Center, Traverse City, MI, p. A323
PETERS, Violeta, Chief Executive Officer and Interim Center Director, Specialty Hospital Of Central Jersey, Lakewood, NJ, p. A407
PETERS, Wayne, Administrator, Southern Virginia Mental Health Institute, Danville, VA, p. A658
PETERSEN, Brenda, Human Resources, Sanford Wheaton Medical Center, Wheaton, MN, p. A342
PETERSEN, Debbie, R.N., Chief Operating Officer and Chief Nursing Officer, Spalding Rehabilitation Hospital, Aurora, CO, p. A96
PETERSEN, Julie, Chief Executive Officer, Kittitas Valley Healthcare, Ellensburg, WA, p. A672
PETERSEN, Richard W, President and Chief Executive Officer, Maine Medical Center, Portland, ME, p. A284
PETERSEN, Richard W., President and Chief Executive Officer, Maine Medical Center, Portland, ME, p. A284
PETERSEN, Susan, Human Resources, Lincoln Community Hospital And Nursing Home, Hugo, CO, p. A102
PETERSEN, Tina, Chief Nursing Officer, Hillcrest Hospital Cushing, Cushing, OK, p. A498
PETERSON, Alison, Vice President Medical Affairs, United Hospital, Saint Paul, MN, p. A340
PETERSON, Anne, Vice President Human Resources and Support Services, Licking Memorial Hospital, Newark, OH, p. A488
PETERSON, Bill, Director Human Resources, Saint Francis Hospital Muskogee, Muskogee, OK, p. A502
PETERSON, Brent A., Administrator, Cherry County Hospital, Valentine, NE, p. A392
PETERSON, Brett, Director of Information Services, Adventhealth North Pinellas, Tarpon Springs, FL, p. A142
PETERSON, Carrie, Director of Nursing, Henderson Health Care Services, Henderson, NE, p. A386
PETERSON, Chad, Chief Information Officer, Northwood Deaconess Health Center, Northwood, ND, p. A469
PETERSON, Cheryl, Business Office Manager, Surgical Institute Of Reading, Wyomissing, PA, p. A545
PETERSON, Dan, Chief Administrative Officer, Sutter Lakeside Hospital, Lakeport, CA, p. A64
PETERSON, David, Senior Vice President, Chief Technology Officer, Erlanger Medical Center, Chattanooga, TN, p. A567
PETERSON, Denise, President and Chief Executive Officer, Hebrew Senior Care, West Hartford, CT, p. A112
PETERSON, Douglas R., President and Chief Executive Officer, Adventhealth Durand, Durand, WI, p. A694
PETERSON, Eric, Director, Ogden Regional Medical Center, Ogden, UT, p. A650
PETERSON, Erica
  Chief Executive Officer and Chief Financial Officer, Sanford Chamberlain Medical Center, Chamberlain, SD, p. A560
  Chief Executive Officer, Sanford Chamberlain Medical Center, Chamberlain, SD, p. A560
PETERSON, Gary, M.D., Vice President Medical Affairs and Chief Medical Officer, St. Luke'S Hospital, Duluth, MN, p. A331
PETERSON, James Kevin, Human Resources Leader, Kaiser Permanente South Sacramento Medical Center, Sacramento, CA, p. A82
PETERSON, Jeff, M.D., Chief of Staff, Essentia Health Ada, Ada, MN, p. A327
PETERSON, Jeffrey, M.D., Medical Director, Cooperstown Medical Center, Cooperstown, ND, p. A466
PETERSON, Jim, Chief Financial Officer, Steele Memorial Medical Center, Salmon, ID, p. A172
PETERSON, Josilyn, Chief Financial Officer, Ballinger Memorial Hospital, Ballinger, TX, p. A586
PETERSON, Judy, R.N., Chief Nursing Officer, Ut Health Carthage, Carthage, TX, p. A591
PETERSON, Julie, Chief Financial Officer, Sutter Delta Medical Center, Antioch, CA, p. A50
PETERSON, Kathy, Director Information Services, Osf Saint Anthony Medical Center, Rockford, IL, p. A195
PETERSON, Katie, R.N., Chief Nursing Officer, Pender Community Hospital, Pender, NE, p. A391
PETERSON, Larry, Chief Financial Officer, Allen County Regional Hospital, Iola, KS, p. A237
PETERSON, Linda, M.D., Vice President Medical Affairs, Mclaren Greater Lansing, Lansing, MI, p. A316
PETERSON, Mackenzie, M.D., Chief of Staff, Anderson County Hospital, Garnett, KS, p. A235

PETERSON, Margaret R., President, California Hospital Medical Center, Los Angeles, CA, p. A66
PETERSON, Michael, President, Androscoggin Valley Hospital, Berlin, NH, p. A399
PETERSON, Michael, FACHE, Chief Operating Officer, Northlight Sebasticook Valley Hospital, Pittsfield, ME, p. A284
PETERSON, Michael, M.D., Chief of Staff, Southeastern Kentucky Medical Center, Pineville, KY, p. A259
PETERSON, Natalie
  Director of Human Resources, Jenkins County Medical Center, Millen, GA, p. A157
  Director of Human Resources, Optim Medical Center – Screven, Sylvania, GA, p. A161
PETERSON, Robert, I, Chief Executive Officer, Millinocket Regional Hospital, Millinocket, ME, p. A284
PETERSON, Robert, CPA, Chief Financial Officer, Hackettstown Medical Center, Hackettstown, NJ, p. A406
PETERSON, Ron
  Chief Information Officer, Pottstown Hospital, Pottstown, PA, p. A539
  President and Chief Executive Officer, Baxter Regional Medical Center, Mountain Home, AR, p. A46
PETERSON, Scott, Vice President of People and Organizational Development, Peninsula Regional Medical Center, Salisbury, MD, p. A293
PETERSON, Scott, M.D., President Medical Staff, Avera Flandreau Hospital, Flandreau, SD, p. A561
PETERSON, Scott J., Chief Executive Officer, Encompass Health Rehabilitation Hospital Of Franklin, Franklin, TN, p. A569
PETERSON, Seth, Director Information Services, Coshocton Regional Medical Center, Coshocton, OH, p. A480
PETERSON, Shelley, R.N., Vice President Patient Services and Chief Nursing Officer, St. Mary'S Hospital And Medical Center, Grand Junction, CO, p. A101
PETERSON, Steve, M.D., Chief of Staff, Chi Health Plainview, Plainview, NE, p. A391
PETERSON, Steven, Chief Information Officer, Vice President of Operations, Garrett Regional Medical Center, Oakland, MD, p. A292
PETERSON, Tim, M.D., Chief of Staff, Meeker Memorial Hospital, Litchfield, MN, p. A334
PETERSON HALL, Jesse, President, Northshore University Health System, Evanston, IL, p. A182
PETIK, Jason, Chief Executive Officer, Sidney Regional Medical Center, Sidney, NE, p. A391
PETITT, Michael
  Director of Finance, Ascension Southeast Wisconsin Hospital – Elmbrook Campus, Brookfield, WI, p. A693
  Director of Finance, Ascension Southeast Wisconsin Hospital – St. Joseph'S Campus, Milwaukee, WI, p. A700
PETRE, Patrick A., Chief Executive Officer, Garfield Medical Center, Monterey Park, CA, p. A73
PETRICK, Teresa G, President, Upmc Passavant, Pittsburgh, PA, p. A538
PETRIK, Jennifer, Interim Chief Nursing Officer, Multicare Deaconess Hospital, Spokane, WA, p. A679
PETRILLO, Mary Ann, R.N., MSN, Acting Associate Director Nursing and Patient Clinical Services, Bedford Veterans Affairs Medical Center, Edith Nourse Rogers Memorial Veterans Hospital, Bedford, MA, p. A294
PETRILLO, Nancy, Director Human Resources, Matheny Medical And Educational Center, Peapack, NJ, p. A410
PETRINA, Robert
  Chief Financial Officer, Alta Bates Summit Medical Center, Berkeley, CA, p. A52
  Interim Chief Financial Officer, Santa Rosa Memorial Hospital, Santa Rosa, CA, p. A89
PETRINI, Julie A., Chief Executive Officer, Alta Bates Summit Medical Center, Berkeley, CA, p. A52
PETRINI, Lindsey, Chief Operating Officer, Wellstar North Fulton Hospital, Roswell, GA, p. A159
PETRITZ, Jennifer J, Director Human Resources, University Of Washington Medical Center, Seattle, WA, p. A678
PETROVICH, Lawrence, M.D., Chief Medical Officer, York Hospital, York, ME, p. A285
PETROWER, Stacey, President, New York–Presbyterian/ Hudson Valley Hospital, Cortlandt Manor, NY, p. A426
PETRY, Fernando, M.D., Vice President and Chief Medical Officer, Cleveland Clinic Martin North Hospital, Stuart, FL, p. A140
PETRY, Gary, M.D., Chief of Staff, St. Vincent General Hospital District, Leadville, CO, p. A103
PETTEY, Robbie, Chief Financial Officer, National Park Medical Center, Hot Springs, AR, p. A43
PETTIGREW, Dennis, Chief Operating Officer, Saint Michael'S Medical Center, Newark, NJ, p. A409
PETTIGREW, Rob, Director Information Technology, Wyoming Medical Center, Casper, WY, p. A710

PETTIJOHN, Kim, R.N., MSN, Chief Nursing Officer, Spine Hospital Of Louisiana (Formally The Neuromedical Center Surgical Hospital), Baton Rouge, LA, p. A264
PETTIJOHN, Trent, M.D.
  Chief Medical Officer, Baylor Scott & White The Heart Hospital Plano, Plano, TX, p. A629
  Chief Medical Officer, Baylor Scott & White The Heart Hospital–Denton, Denton, TX, p. A599
PETTINATO, Jim, Director Patient Care Services, Wayne Memorial Hospital, Honesdale, PA, p. A527
PETTIT, Amy, R.N., Vice President Nursing Services and Chief Nursing Officer, Schneck Medical Center, Seymour, IN, p. A214
PETTIT, Donny, Chief Financial Officer, Coon Memorial Hospital, Dalhart, TX, p. A595
PETTIT, Harlan, M.D., Chief of Medical Staff, Fishermen'S Hospital, Marathon, FL, p. A129
PETTITE, Shirley F, Chief Human Resources Officer, Tennessee Valley Healthcare System, Nashville, TN, p. A577
PETTREY, Lisa J., Chief Executive Officer, Select Specialty Hospital–Columbus, Columbus, OH, p. A480
PETTY, Jane, Director Human Resources, Southern Tennessee Regional Health System–Pulaski, Pulaski, TN, p. A578
PETTY, Russ, M.D., Chief of Staff, Towner County Medical Center, Cando, ND, p. A465
PETULA, Ronald J.
  Chief Financial Officer, Good Shepherd Rehabilitation Hospital, Allentown, PA, p. A519
  Chief Financial Officer, Good Shepherd Specialty Hospital, Bethlehem, PA, p. A520
  Vice President Finance, Good Shepherd Penn Partners Specialty Hospital At Rittenhouse, Philadelphia, PA, p. A534
PFAFF, Joni, Chief Nursing Officer, Grisell Memorial Hospital District One, Ransom, KS, p. A244
PFAFF, Tony, Chief Executive Officer, Deer Lodge Medical Center, Deer Lodge, MT, p. A376
PFALTZGRAFF, George, Chief Medical Officer, Hansen Family Hospital, Iowa Falls, IA, p. A225
PFAU, Ben, Chief Facility and Information Officer, Bay Area Hospital, Coos Bay, OR, p. A512
PFAU, Beth, M.D., Chief Medical Officer, Larue D. Carter Memorial Hospital, Indianapolis, IN, p. A207
PFEFFER, Amy, Chief Financial Officer, Sturdy Memorial Hospital, Attleboro, MA, p. A294
PFEFFER, Daniel William, Chief Nurse Executive, Weisman Children'S Rehabilitation Hospital, Marlton, NJ, p. A408
PFEFFER, Michael, M.D.
  Chief Information Officer, Ronald Reagan Ucla Medical Center, Los Angeles, CA, p. A69
  Chief Medical Informatics Officer, UCLA Health, Stewart & Lynda Resnick Neuropsychiatric Hospital At Ucla, Los Angeles, CA, p. A69
PFEFFER, Stacey, Senior Vice President Human Resources, Nyu Winthrop Hospital, Mineola, NY, p. A431
PFEIFER, Mark P, M.D., Senior Vice President and Chief Medical Officer, University Of Louisville Hospital, Louisville, KY, p. A257
PFEIFFER, James A., President and Chief Executive Officer, Self Regional Healthcare, Greenwood, SC, p. A554
PFEIFFER, Margaret, R.N., MSN, Vice President Patient Care Services, Good Samaritan Hospital, Los Angeles, CA, p. A66
PFISTER, Joann M, Director Human Resources, Providence Willamette Falls Medical Center, Oregon City, OR, p. A515
PFISTER, Pam, Chief Executive Officer, Morrison Community Hospital, Morrison, IL, p. A190
PFISTER, Scott, Director Finance, Providence St. Vincent Medical Center, Portland, OR, p. A517
PFLEIGER, Dennis, President and Chief Operating Officer, St. Luke'S Hospital – Quakertown Campus, Quakertown, PA, p. A539
PFRANK, Kym, Senior Vice President and Chief Operating Officer, Union Hospital, Terre Haute, IN, p. A215
PHAM, Bong, Chief Medical Officer, Kit Carson County Health Service District, Burlington, CO, p. A97
PHAM, K, M.D., Chief of Staff, Winkler County Memorial Hospital, Kermit, TX, p. A617
PHELAN, Cynthia, Vice President Human Resources, Lawrence General Hospital, Lawrence, MA, p. A299
PHELPS, Britton, Chief Executive Officer, Merit Health Madison, Canton, MS, p. A345
PHELPS, Craig, M.D., Chief of Staff, Great Plains Regional Medical Center, Elk City, OK, p. A499
PHELPS, David E., President and Chief Executive Officer, Berkshire Medical Center, Pittsfield, MA, p. A302
PHELPS, Gail, R.N., Chief Nursing Officer, Haxtun Hospital District, Haxtun, CO, p. A102

PHELPS, Joel, President and Chief Operating Officer, Salina Regional Health Center, Salina, KS, p. A245
PHELPS, Kathleen, Director Human Resources, Treasure Valley Hospital, Boise, ID, p. A168
PHELPS, Lisa, Senior Vice President, Human Resources, Phoenix Children'S Hospital, Phoenix, AZ, p. A34
PHELPS, Michael
President and Chief Executive Officer, Ridgeview Medical Center, Waconia, MN, p. A342
President and Chief Executive Officer, Ridgeview Sibley Medical Center, Arlington, MN, p. A327
PHETTEPLACE, Danial, Director Information Technology, Gundersen St. Joseph'S Hospital And Clinics, Hillsboro, WI, p. A697
PHILIP, Neena S., R.N., Vice President of Patient Care Services and Chief Nursing Officer, Carepoint Health Hoboken University Medical Center, Hoboken, NJ, p. A406
PHILIPS, Grady W., III, President, Winchester Medical Center, Winchester, VA, p. A669
PHILLIPS, Alan M, Controller, Encompass Health Nittany Valley Rehabilitation Hospital, Pleasant Gap, PA, p. A539
PHILLIPS, Barry, Executive Director Human Resources, Camden General Hospital, Camden, TN, p. A566
PHILLIPS, Bill, Vice President Information Services, University Health System, San Antonio, TX, p. A635
PHILLIPS, Bobby, Chief Nursing Officer, Medical Center Enterprise, Enterprise, AL, p. A17
PHILLIPS, Courtney, Chief Executive Officer, South Sunflower County Hospital, Indianola, MS, p. A348
PHILLIPS, David D., Chief Executive Officer and Administrator, Barnesville Hospital, Barnesville, OH, p. A472
PHILLIPS, David L.
Chief Operating Officer, St. John Broken Arrow, Broken Arrow, OK, p. A497
President and Chief Operating Officer, St. John Owasso, Owasso, OK, p. A506
PHILLIPS, Donna, President, Bryn Mawr Rehabilitation Hospital, Malvern, PA, p. A530
PHILLIPS, Eddie, M.D.
Chief Medical Affairs, Baptist Health Medical Center – North Little Rock, North Little Rock, AR, p. A46
Chief Medical Officer, Baptist Health Medical Center–Arkadelphia, Arkadelphia, AR, p. A39
PHILLIPS, Frank, M.D., Chief of Staff, Cherokee Medical Center, Gaffney, SC, p. A553
PHILLIPS, Glenn, Director Information Systems, Gadsden Regional Medical Center, Gadsden, AL, p. A18
PHILLIPS, Heath, Chief Executive Officer, Flowers Hospital, Dothan, AL, p. A17
PHILLIPS, Jan P., R.N., Chief Nursing Officer, Central Carolina Hospital, Sanford, NC, p. A462
PHILLIPS, John, Vice President Information Services, Chi St. Joseph Regional Health Center, Bryan, TX, p. A590
PHILLIPS, John E., President, Methodist Dallas Medical Center, Dallas, TX, p. A597
PHILLIPS, Jonathan, Interim Administrator, Ochsner Lsu Health Shreveport – Monroe Medical Center, Monroe, LA, p. A274
PHILLIPS, Kelly, M.D., M.P.H., Clinical Director and Chief Staff, Spring Grove Hospital Center, Baltimore, MD, p. A288
PHILLIPS, Kimberly A, Chief Financial Officer, The Children'S Home Of Pittsburgh, Pittsburgh, PA, p. A537
PHILLIPS, Lionel J, Vice President Financial Services, Fauquier Hospital, Warrenton, VA, p. A668
PHILLIPS, Mike, Chief Executive Officer, Wyoming Behavioral Institute, Casper, WY, p. A710
PHILLIPS, Monie, Director Clinical Informatics, Jackson Parish Hospital, Jonesboro, LA, p. A269
PHILLIPS, Paul, Chief Financial Officer, Taylor Regional Hospital, Campbellsville, KY, p. A250
PHILLIPS, Robert, M.D., Ph.D., FACC, Executive Vice President and Chief Medical Officer, Houston Methodist Hospital, Houston, TX, p. A612
PHILLIPS, Robert A., Chief Executive Officer, Walker Baptist Medical Center, Jasper, AL, p. A20
PHILLIPS, Sarah, Manager Human Resources, Morgan Memorial Hospital, Madison, GA, p. A157
PHILLIPS, Steve, Information Officer, Greene County General Hospital, Linton, IN, p. A210
PHILLIPS, Tammy, Director, Information Systems, Texas Health Presbyterian Hospital Dallas, Dallas, TX, p. A598
PHILLIPS, Traci, Superintendent, Big Spring State Hospital, Big Spring, TX, p. A588
PHINNEY, Cody, Administrator, Northern Nevada Adult Mental Health Services, Sparks, NV, p. A398
PHIPPS, Emily, Director Human Resources, Oklahoma Center For Orthopedic And Multi–Specialty Surgery, Oklahoma City, OK, p. A504
PHIPPS, Jackie G, Director Human Resources, Johnston Memorial Hospital, Abingdon, VA, p. A656
PHIPPS ADAMS, Holly, Vice President of Human Resources, Carroll Hospital Center, Westminster, MD, p. A293
PIANALTO, Eric, Chief Executive Officer, Mercy Hospital Rogers, Rogers, AR, p. A48
PIATKOWSKI, Shannon, Director Information Technology, Blake Medical Center, Bradenton, FL, p. A118
PIAZZA, Doreen, Acting Executive Director, Brookdale Hospital Medical Center, New York, NY, p. A432
PIAZZA, Kenneth P., Medical Center Director, Bath Veterans Affairs Medical Center, Bath, NY, p. A423
PIAZZA, Tony, Director Human Resources, Titus Regional Medical Center, Mount Pleasant, TX, p. A625
PICAZA, Jose, M.D., Chief of Staff, Unicoi County Memorial Hospital, Erwin, TN, p. A569
PICCIONE, Elizabeth, M.D., Chief Medical Officer, Upmc Jameson, New Castle, PA, p. A533
PICCIONE, Jennifer, Chief Nursing and Clinical Services Officer, Madison Health, London, OH, p. A486
PICHE, Glenn, Chief Executive Officer, Landmark Hospital Of Columbia, Columbia, MO, p. A359
PICKARD, Bert, Chief Financial Officer, North Mississippi Medical Center Gilmore–Amory, Amory, MS, p. A344
PICKEL, Joseph, Director Resource Management, Walter Reed National Military Medical Center, Bethesda, MD, p. A289
PICKENS, Gayle, Chief Executive Officer, Putnam County Memorial Hospital, Unionville, MO, p. A372
PICKENS, Ramona, Chief Operating Officer, East Cooper Medical Center, Mount Pleasant, SC, p. A555
PICKENS, Regina, Chief Financial Officer, Grafton City Hospital, Grafton, WV, p. A685
PICKER, Josephine, MSN, R.N., Director of Nursing, Asheville Specialty Hospital, Asheville, NC, p. A449
PICKERING, David, System Director, Applications, Linden Oaks Hospital, Naperville, IL, p. A190
PICKETT, C. Judson, Chief of Staff, University Hospital Summerville, Augusta, GA, p. A147
PICKETT, H. Andrew, M.D., Medical Staff President, Excelsior Springs Hospital, Excelsior Springs, MO, p. A359
PICKETT, Lisa C, M.D., Chief Medical Officer, Duke University Hospital, Durham, NC, p. A453
PICKLER, Nancy, Director of Human Resources, Encompass Health Rehabilitation Hospital Of East Valley, Mesa, AZ, p. A31
PICOU, Timothy, Manager Information Technology, Lower Umpqua Hospital District, Reedsport, OR, p. A517
PIEDRAFITE, JoAnn, R.N., Chief Nursing Officer, Saint Vincent Hospital, Worcester, MA, p. A305
PIEFFER, Paul
Chief Operating Officer, Great River Medical Center, Blytheville, AR, p. A39
Chief Operating Officer, South Mississippi County Regional Medical Center, Osceola, AR, p. A47
PIEH, Samuel
Chief Operating Officer, Dmc Huron Valley–Sinai Hospital, Commerce Township, MI, p. A309
Chief Operating Officer, Saint Francis Hospital, Memphis, TN, p. A575
PIEPER, Blaine, Chief Executive Officer, Ohio County Hospital, Hartford, KY, p. A253
PIERCE, Bonnie, MSN, R.N., Associate Director for Patient Care Services, Jack C. Montgomery Veterans Affairs Medical Center, Muskogee, OK, p. A502
PIERCE, Christy, Director of Human Resources, Katherine Shaw Bethea Hospital, Dixon, IL, p. A181
PIERCE, Felicia, R.N.
Chief Nursing Officer, Great River Medical Center, Blytheville, AR, p. A39
Chief Nursing Officer, South Mississippi County Regional Medical Center, Osceola, AR, p. A47
PIERCE, James, Administrator, Community Behavioral Health Hospital – Rochester, Rochester, MN, p. A338
PIERCE, Jeff M
Chief Human Resource Officer, Marshall Medical Center, Lewisburg, TN, p. A573
Manager Human Resources, Wayne Medical Center, Waynesboro, TN, p. A580
PIERCE, Jennifer, Administrative Director of Finance, Ssm Health St. Anthony Hospital – Shawnee, Shawnee, OK, p. A507
PIERCE, John, Acting President, Rapid City Regional Hospital, Rapid City, SD, p. A563
PIERCE, Kenneth, Chief Financial Officer, Brookhaven Hospital, Tulsa, OK, p. A508
PIERCE, Laura, Director Human Resources, Memorial Medical Center, Las Cruces, NM, p. A418
PIERCE, Margaret H., Executive Director, Kaiser Permanente Baldwin Park Medical Center, Baldwin Park, CA, p. A51
PIERCE, Pamela, Deputy Chief Executive Officer, Windhaven Psychiatric Hospital, Prescott Valley, AZ, p. A35
PIERCE, Pat, Director Information Systems, Lakewood Regional Medical Center, Lakewood, CA, p. A64
PIERCE, Reid, M.D., Chief Medical Officer, Jefferson Regional Medical Center, Pine Bluff, AR, p. A47
PIERCE, Sherri, R.N., Chief Nursing Officer, Sweeny Community Hospital, Sweeny, TX, p. A639
PIERCE, Tiffany, Director Human Resources, Wellstone Regional Hospital, Jeffersonville, IN, p. A208
PIERDON, Steven, M.D., Executive Vice President and Chief Medical Officer, Geisinger Wyoming Valley Medical Center, Wilkes Barre, PA, p. A544
PIERESCHI, Giovanni
Vice President Enterprise Information and Chief Information Officer, Hima San Pablo Caguas, Caguas, PR, p. A715
Vice President Management Information Systems, Hospital Hima De Humacao, Humacao, PR, p. A716
PIERLUISI, Guillermo, Vice President of Medical Affairs, Wellstar Paulding Hospital, Hiram, GA, p. A154
PIERRE, Andre, Chief Financial Officer, Forest View Psychiatric Hospital, Grand Rapids, MI, p. A312
PIERRE, Letonia, Coordinator Human Resources, Assumption Community Hospital, Napoleonville, LA, p. A274
PIERSON, Cindy, Interim Chief Nursing Officer, Highlands–Cashiers Hospital, Highlands, NC, p. A456
PIERSON, Jerome, Chief Medical Officer, Mercyone Siouxland Medical Center, Sioux City, IA, p. A230
PIERSON, Kim, R.N., Chief Nursing Officer, Wilbarger General Hospital, Vernon, TX, p. A643
PIERSON, Kyle A., Chief Financial Officer, Roane General Hospital, Spencer, WV, p. A689
PIERSON, Lois K., Chief Financial Officer, University Of Texas Harris County Psychiatric Center, Houston, TX, p. A614
PIETRYKOWSKI, Susan, Commander, U. S. Air Force Hospital, Hampton, VA, p. A660
PIETSCH, Al, CPA, Senior Vice President and Chief Financial Officer, University Of Maryland Baltimore Washington Medical Center, Glen Burnie, MD, p. A291
PIETSCH, Brandon E., Administrator, Centracare Health–Paynesville, Paynesville, MN, p. A337
PIETZ, Gerald, Vice President Finance, Mercy Hospital, Coon Rapids, MN, p. A330
PIFKO, Duane, Interim Director Financial Services, Daniel Drake Center For Post Acute Care, Cincinnati, OH, p. A476
PIGG, Russell, Chief Executive Officer, North Alabama Medical Center, Florence, AL, p. A18
PIGOTT, John, M.D., Chief Medical Officer, Tulane Health System, New Orleans, LA, p. A276
PIKE, David, Interim Chief Financial Officer, Memorial Hospital Of Carbon County, Rawlins, WY, p. A712
PIKE, Irving, M.D., Senior Vice President and Chief Medical Officer, John Muir Medical Center, Walnut Creek, Walnut Creek, CA, p. A94
PIKE, Pauline, Chief Operating Officer, Beverly Hospital, Beverly, MA, p. A294
PIKE, Randi, Director of Nursing, Pioneer Medical Center, Big Timber, MT, p. A374
PIKE, Ronald F, M.D., Medical Director, Adcare Hospital Of Worcester, Worcester, MA, p. A305
PIKE, Tim, M.D., Chief Medical Officer, Portsmouth Regional Hospital, Portsmouth, NH, p. A402
PIKER, John F, M.D., Medical Director, Villa Feliciana Medical Complex, Jackson, LA, p. A269
PIKULA, Shirley, MSN, Associate Director Patient Center Care, San Francisco Va Medical Center, San Francisco, CA, p. A85
PIL, Pieter, M.D., Chief Medical Staff, Martha'S Vineyard Hospital, Oak Bluffs, MA, p. A302
PILANT, Jason B., President and Chief Administrative Officer, Roane Medical Center, Harriman, TN, p. A570
PILCHER, Shane, Administrative Director Information Systems, Siskin Hospital For Physical Rehabilitation, Chattanooga, TN, p. A567
PILE, Larry, Director Human Resources, Deaconess Midtown Hospital, Evansville, IN, p. A203
PILE, Mindi L., Chief Operations Officer, Summit Medical Center, Casper, WY, p. A710
PILEGGI, Anne, Administrator and Associate Vice President, Christus Mother Frances Hospital – Jacksonville, Jacksonville, TX, p. A616
PILGRIM, Patti, Chief Financial Officer, Sutter Davis Hospital, Davis, CA, p. A56
PILLION, Scott, Chief Executive Officer, Helen Newberry Joy Hospital, Newberry, MI, p. A319
PILLOT, Juan, M.D., Medical Director, Hospital Pavia Yauco, Yauco, PR, p. A720
PILNEY, Jeffrey, Chief Medical Officer, Pocahontas Memorial Hospital, Buckeye, WV, p. A683

PILON, Michele, President and Chief Nursing Officer, Transylvania Regional Hospital, Brevard, NC, p. A450

PILOT, Dave, Chief Financial Officer, Essentia Health St. Joseph'S Medical Center, Brainerd, MN, p. A329

PINA, Joseph, Chief Executive Officer, Inova Mount Vernon Hospital, Alexandria, VA, p. A656

PINA, Julie A., Assistant Vice President Patient Care Services and Chief Nursing Officer, Driscoll Children'S Hospital, Corpus Christi, TX, p. A594

PINE, Richard M., President and Chief Executive Officer, Livengrin Foundation, Bensalem, PA, p. A520

PINEIRO, Carlos M, President, Hospital Hima De Humacao, Humacao, PR, p. A716

PINELLE, Brian, R.N., Chief Nursing Officer, Gulf Coast Regional Medical Center, Panama City, FL, p. A135

PINER, Thomas J., Director for Resources Management, Naval Medical Center San Diego, San Diego, CA, p. A83

PINERO, Efrain, Administrator, Hospital Oriente, Humacao, PR, p. A716

PINETTE, Jameson, Chief Executive Officer, Arbour H. R. I. Hospital, Brookline, MA, p. A297

PINKELMAN, Janet M, Director Human Resources, Faith Regional Health Services, Norfolk, NE, p. A388

PINKERTON, Jay, Chief Medical Officer, George Regional Hospital, Lucedale, MS, p. A350

PINKOSKY, Frank
   Executive Vice President, Guthrie Troy Community Hospital, Troy, PA, p. A542
   Senior Vice President, Guthrie Robert Packer Hospital, Sayre, PA, p. A540

PINO, Elena, Chief Operating Officer and Chief Nursing Officer, Mesa Hills Specialty Hospital, El Paso, TX, p. A602

PINO, Joseph, M.D., Chief Medical Officer, Regional Medical Center Bayonet Point, Hudson, FL, p. A125

PINON, Richard, Chief Medical Officer, Eastern New Mexico Medical Center, Roswell, NM, p. A420

PINSKY, Karen, M.D., Chief Medical Information Officer, Penn Medicine Chester County Hospital, West Chester, PA, p. A544

PINTER, Tabatha, Director of Nursing, George Regional Hospital, Lucedale, MS, p. A350

PINTO, Frank, Chief Information Officer, The Hospital Of Central Connecticut, New Britain, CT, p. A109

PIO RODA, Claro M, Dr.PH, Vice President, Finance and Chief Financial Officer, Howard County General Hospital, Columbia, MD, p. A290

PIPER, Angel, Chief Executive Officer, Ohio Hospital For Psychiatry, Columbus, OH, p. A479

PIPER, Burt, Chief Operating Officer, Ephraim Mcdowell Regional Medical Center, Danville, KY, p. A251

PIPER, Kevin, Director Information Systems, Adventhealth Deland, Deland, FL, p. A121

PIPER, Vicky, Vice President Human Resources, Loyola University Medical Center, Maywood, IL, p. A189

PIPGRASS, Michele, Chief Fiscal Service, Oklahoma City Veterans Affairs Medical Center, Oklahoma City, OK, p. A504

PIPKINS, David, Chief Executive Officer and Administrator, Kate Dishman Rehabilitation Hospital, Beaumont, TX, p. A587

PIPPIN, Kim, Chief Nursing Officer, Select Specialty Hospital–Augusta, Augusta, GA, p. A147

PIRO, Michael J, Chief Information Officer, Brookdale Hospital Medical Center, New York, NY, p. A432

PIRRI, Christine, Vice President Human Resources, Little Falls Hospital, Little Falls, NY, p. A430

PIRTLE, Kathleen, Director Human Resources, Encompass Health Rehabilitation Hospital Of Wichita Falls, Wichita Falls, TX, p. A645

PIRTLE, Randy B, Chief Financial Officer, King'S Daughters Medical Center, Brookhaven, MS, p. A345

PISANO, Thomas, M.D., Chief Professional Services, Connecticut Valley Hospital, Middletown, CT, p. A109

PISCIOTTA, Michael J., Chief Executive Officer, Southern Surgical Hospital, Slidell, LA, p. A279

PISICOTTA, Robert, Chief Nursing Officer, Baylor Scott & White Continuing Care Hospital–Temple, Temple, TX, p. A639

PISPISA, D. Patricia, Senior Vice President, Patient Care Services and Chief Nursing Officer, Eastern Long Island Hospital, Greenport, NY, p. A428

PISTERS, Peter, President, University Of Texas M.D. Anderson Cancer Center, Houston, TX, p. A614

PISZCZATOSKI, Thomas J, Chief Human Resource Officer, St. Mary'S Medical Center, West Palm Beach, FL, p. A144

PITCHER, Ellen, Chief Nursing Officer and Chief Operating Officer, El Paso Children'S Hospital, El Paso, TX, p. A601

PITCHER, Kerry
   Administrator, Lanai Community Hospital, Lanai City, HI, p. A166

Chief Executive Officer, Kula Hospital, Kula, HI, p. A166

PITMAN, David R, Vice President Finance, Medstar Harbor Hospital, Baltimore, MD, p. A287

PITTMAN, Cyndi, Chief Financial Officer, Baptist Memorial Hospital – Memphis, Memphis, TN, p. A574

PITTMAN, Jennifer, Chief Financial Officer, Shelby Baptist Medical Center, Alabaster, AL, p. A13

PITTMAN, Jeremy, Chief Financial Officer, Castle Rock Adventist Hospital, Castle Rock, CO, p. A97

PITTMAN, Michael, Chief Nursing Officer, Sovah Health–Martinsville, Martinsville, VA, p. A662

PITTMAN, Scott M, Chief Operating Officer, Buchanan General Hospital, Grundy, VA, p. A660

PITTS, Celeste, Chief Financial Officer, Upper Connecticut Valley Hospital, Colebrook, NH, p. A399

PITTS, Lynn, Director Human Resources, Calhoun–Liberty Hospital, Blountstown, FL, p. A118

PITTS, Robert, Executive Director, Wilmington Treatment Center, Wilmington, NC, p. A464

PITTS, Sherry J., Chief Executive Officer, Merit Health Woman'S Hospital, Flowood, MS, p. A347

PITZ, Kenneth, M.D., Chief of Staff, St. Francis Memorial Hospital, West Point, NE, p. A392

PITZER, Jeremy, Chief Executive Officer, River Place Behavioral Health, La Place, LA, p. A270

PIVONKA, Mary, Director Quality Management, Rockland Children'S Psychiatric Center, Orangeburg, NY, p. A440

PIZ, Tom, Director Human Resources, Fremont Hospital, Fremont, CA, p. A58

PIZARRO, Hugo A, Vice President Human Resources, Brookdale Hospital Medical Center, New York, NY, p. A432

PIZZI, Chris, Chief Operating Officer and Chief Financial Officer, Providence Medford Medical Center, Medford, OR, p. A515

PIZZINO, Mary, Chief Information Officer, Effingham Hospital, Springfield, GA, p. A160

PLAGGEMEYER, Rikki, Director Acute Care Nursing, Sturgis Regional Hospital, Sturgis, SD, p. A564

PLAISANCE, Stephen, Chief Financial Officer, Meeker Memorial Hospital, Litchfield, MN, p. A334

PLAKUN, Eric M., Medical Center Director and Chief Executive Officer, Austen Riggs Center, Stockbridge, MA, p. A304

PLAMANN, Joy, R.N., Chief Nursing and Operating Officer, St. Cloud Hospital, Saint Cloud, MN, p. A339

PLAMONDON, Richard, Vice President Finance and Chief Financial Officer, St. Joseph Hospital, Nashua, NH, p. A401

PLANO, Crystal, Controller, St. Vincent Dunn Hospital, Bedford, IN, p. A200

PLANT, Steven L, Chief Financial Officer, Cottage Hospital, Woodsville, NH, p. A402

PLASEK, James, M.D., Chief of Staff, Memorial Health Care Systems, Seward, NE, p. A391

PLASKETT, Darice S., Interim Chief Executive Officer, Governor Juan F. Luis Hospital, Christiansted, VI, p. A720

PLASS, Mary Ellen, MS, R.N., Senior Vice President and Chief Nursing Officer, Columbia Memorial Hospital, Hudson, NY, p. A429

PLATE, James, M.D., Chief of Staff, Kimball Health Services, Kimball, NE, p. A386

PLATEL, Raylene, M.D., Chief Medical Officer, Citrus Memorial Health System, Inverness, FL, p. A125

PLATER, Queenie C.
   Vice President, Human Resources National Capital Region Johns Hopkins Medicine, Sibley Memorial Hospital, Washington, DC, p. A116
   Vice President, Human Resources National Capital Region Johns Hopkins Medicine, Suburban Hospital, Bethesda, MD, p. A289

PLATT, Dwayne, M.D., Chief Medical Officer, Conemaugh Meyersdale Medical Center, Meyersdale, PA, p. A532

PLATT, James, Chief Executive Officer, Jackson Hospital, Marianna, FL, p. A129

PLATZ, Scott, Director Finance, Uh Regional Hospitals, Cleveland, OH, p. A478

PLAUTH, William, M.D., Vice President Operations and Chief Medical Officer, Mercy Regional Medical Center, Durango, CO, p. A99

PLAVIAK, David J, Interim Chief Financial Officer, Novant Health Uva Health System Culpeper Medical Center, Culpeper, VA, p. A658

PLAVIN, Joshua, M.D., Medical Director Medicine Division, Gifford Medical Center, Randolph, VT, p. A655

PLAZA, Marta Rivera., Chief Executive Officer and Managing Director, San Juan Capestrano Hospital, San Juan, PR, p. A719

PLEDGER, Michelle, Coordinator Human Resources, Grady General Hospital, Cairo, GA, p. A149

PLEMEL, Jeff, Director Health Information, Ccm Health, Montevideo, MN, p. A336

PLEMMONS, Debra, Chief Nursing Officer, Middle Park Medical Center–Kremmling, Kremmling, CO, p. A102

PLESKOW, Eric D., President and Chief Executive Officer, Brylin Hospitals, Buffalo, NY, p. A424

PLESS, Katy, Director of Human Resources, Carepartners Health Services, Asheville, NC, p. A449

PLOPPER, Michael, M.D., Chief Medical Officer, Sharp Mesa Vista Hospital, San Diego, CA, p. A84

PLOSZEK, Judith M., Chief Financial Officer, Tampa General Hospital, Tampa, FL, p. A142

PLOSZEK, Michael A., President, Advocate Condell Medical Center, Libertyville, IL, p. A188

PLUARD, Dennis, Vice President Finance and Operations, Sarah Bush Lincoln Health Center, Mattoon, IL, p. A188

PLUMLEE, Steve, Chief Executive Officer, Select Specialty Hospital–North Knoxville, Powell, TN, p. A578

PLUMMER, Debra, Chief Executive Officer, Kindred Hospital Bay Area–Tampa, Tampa, FL, p. A141

PLUMMER, Donald, Senior Vice President, Operations, Legent Orthopedic + Spine, San Antonio, TX, p. A633

PLUMMER, Doug, Chief Operating Officer, Sabine Medical Center, Many, LA, p. A273

PLUNKETT, Alicia, Chief Nurse Executive, Parkwood Behavioral Health System, Olive Branch, MS, p. A352

PLYMELL, Shane, Chief Executive Officer, Shannon Medical Center, San Angelo, TX, p. A633

PLYWACZYNSKI, Russell J., CPA, Director of Finance, St. Joseph'S Hospital Of Buckhannon, Buckhannon, WV, p. A684

POBLETE, Ronald, M.D., President Medical and Dental Staff, St. Mary'S General Hospital, Passaic, NJ, p. A410

POCCHIARI, Michael, Director Human Resources, Garden Park Medical Center, Gulfport, MS, p. A347

POCOCK, Donald, Vice–President Medical Affairs, Carteret Health Care, Morehead City, NC, p. A458

PODE, Maureen, Co–Interim Executive Director, Brookdale Hospital Medical Center, New York, NY, p. A432

PODESTA, Charles H, Chief Information Officer, Uc Irvine Medical Center, Orange, CA, p. A76

PODGES, Christopher J, Vice President Outpatient Services and Chief Information Officer, Munson Medical Center, Traverse City, MI, p. A323

PODNOS, Yale D., M.D., Chief Medical Officer, West Hills Hospital And Medical Center, Los Angeles, CA, p. A70

PODOLSKY, Daniel
   President, University Of Texas Southwestern Medical Center, Dallas, TX, p. A598
   President, William P. Clements, Jr. University Hospital, Dallas, TX, p. A598

PODZIMEK, Marcia, Chief Human Resources Officer, Wagner Community Memorial Hospital Avera, Wagner, SD, p. A565

POE, Dale
   Vice President and Chief Financial Officer, Hawkins County Memorial Hospital, Rogersville, TN, p. A579
   Vice President Finance and Operations, Holston Valley Medical Center, Kingsport, TN, p. A572

POE, Terri Lyn, Interim Chief Nursing Officer, University Of Alabama Hospital, Birmingham, AL, p. A15

POEHLER, Kathy, Vice President, Human Resources, University Of Maryland Baltimore Washington Medical Center, Glen Burnie, MD, p. A291

POEST, Scott, Chief Information Officer, Lake Regional Health System, Osage Beach, MO, p. A366

POFAHL, Barnetta, Director Human Resources, Wagoner Community Hospital, Wagoner, OK, p. A510

POFF, Heather, Director Human Resources, Princeton Community Hospital, Princeton, WV, p. A688

POFFENBARGER, John, Director Fiscal Services, Northern Virginia Mental Health Institute, Falls Church, VA, p. A659

POGAS, George, CPA, Senior Vice President and Chief Financial Officer, Witham Health Services, Lebanon, IN, p. A210

POGLIANO, Chris, M.D., Chief Medical Staff, Aspirus Ironwood Hospitals & Clinics, Inc., Ironwood, MI, p. A315

POGUE, Rick, Vice President, Human Resources, Brookdale Hospital Medical Center, New York, NY, p. A432

POHAR, Mark, Executive Director, Margaretville Hospital, Margaretville, NY, p. A431

POHJALA, Eric
   Chief Financial Officer, Upmc Susquehanna Soldiers + Sailors, Wellsboro, PA, p. A544
   Executive Vice President and Chief Financial Officer, Upmc Susquehanna Muncy, Muncy, PA, p. A532
   Executive Vice President and Chief Financial Officer, Upmc Susquehanna Williamsport, Williamsport, PA, p. A545

POHL, Ann–Marie J, Vice President and Chief Nursing Officer, Lima Memorial Health System, Lima, OH, p. A485

POHL, David F., M.D., Chief of Staff, Cornerstone Hospital Of Austin, Austin, TX, p. A585

POHL, David L., M.D., Chief of Staff, Hillcrest Hospital – South, Tulsa, OK, p. A508

POHLMAN, John, Vice President Finance and Administration, St. Catherine Of Siena Medical Center, Smithtown, NY, p. A444

POIROT, Diane, Vice President Human Resources, Harris Health System, Houston, TX, p. A611

POISKER, Karen C, MSN, Vice President Patient Care Services and Chief Nursing Officer, Peninsula Regional Medical Center, Salisbury, MD, p. A293

POISSON, Keith R, Executive Vice President and Chief Operating Officer, Greater Baltimore Medical Center, Baltimore, MD, p. A288

POLAND, David, Chief Financial Officer, Grove City Medical Center, Grove City, PA, p. A526

POLASHEK, Maurene, Chief Financial Officer, Oro Valley Hospital, Oro Valley, AZ, p. A32

POLEGA, Steve, Chief Nursing Officer, Metro Health – University Of Michigan Health, Wyoming, MI, p. A325

POLENZ, Scott, Chief Administrative Officer, Marshfield Medical Center – Eau Claire Hospital, Eau Claire, WI, p. A694

POLHILL, James, M.D., Chief Medical Officer, Jefferson Hospital, Louisville, GA, p. A156

POLIKAITIS, Audrius, Chief Information Officer, University Of Illinois Hospital & Health Sciences System, Chicago, IL, p. A180

POLING, Rodney, M.D., Medical Director, Unity Psychiatric Care–Columbia, Columbia, TN, p. A568

POLING, Susan, Director Human Resources, King'S Daughters' Health, Madison, IN, p. A210

POLIS, Nikki S, Ph.D., Chief Nurse Executive, Methodist Healthcare Memphis Hospitals, Memphis, TN, p. A575

POLISKNOWSKI, John, Chief Nursing Officer, Northside Hospital, Saint Petersburg, FL, p. A138

POLITE, Elmer, Chief Financial Officer, Coliseum Northside Hospital, Macon, GA, p. A156

POLITIS, Christos, M.D., Chief Medical Officer, Memorial Hospital Of Tampa, Tampa, FL, p. A141

POLITO, Janine, Chief Human Resources Officer, Banner Ironwood Medical Center, San Tan Valley, AZ, p. A35

POLIVKA, Maureen, Chief Nursing Officer, Hill Country Memorial Hospital, Fredericksburg, TX, p. A606

POLIZZI, Arturo
President and Chief Executive Officer, Christ Hospital, Cincinnati, OH, p. A475
President and Chief Executive Officer, Promedica Toledo Hospital, Toledo, OH, p, A492

POLIZZOTTO, Mike, Chief Medical Officer, Swedishamerican – A Division Of Uw Health, Rockford, IL, p. A195

POLK, Brent, M.D., Chair Department of Pediatrics and Vice President Academic Affairs, Children'S Hospital Los Angeles, Los Angeles, CA, p. A66

POLK, Claire, Chief Financial Officer, Lake Norman Regional Medical Center, Mooresville, NC, p. A458

POLK, Monica, M.D., Chief Medical Officer, Salt Lake Behavioral Health, Salt Lake City, UT, p. A652

POLKOW, Craig, Vice President, Finance, St. Vincent Evansville, Evansville, IN, p. A203

POLLACK, Neil, Senior Administrator, Brookdale Hospital Medical Center, New York, NY, p. A432

POLLAK, Erich, M.D., Chief of Staff, West Covina Medical Center, West Covina, CA, p. A94

POLLARD, Amy, President and Chief Executive Officer, Nicholas H. Noyes Memorial Hospital, Dansville, NY, p. A426

POLLARD, Anthony, D.O., Chief Medical Officer, Amg Specialty Hospital – Las Vegas, Las Vegas, NV, p. A394

POLLMAN, Brian, Chief Medical Officer, Hutchinson Health, Hutchinson, MN, p. A333

POLLOCK, Jeffrey, Chief Information Officer, Wentworth–Douglass Hospital, Dover, NH, p. A399

POLO, James A, M.D., Chief Medical Officer, Western State Hospital, Tacoma, WA, p. A681

POLO, Therese, Medical Staff President, Carlinville Area Hospital, Carlinville, IL, p. A175

POLSELLI, Donna, Chief Operating Officer, Franciscan Children'S, Brighton, MA, p. A296

POLSTER, Peggy, Manager Personnel and Administrative Assistant, Falls Community Hospital And Clinic, Marlin, TX, p. A623

POLTAWSKY, Jeffrey S, Senior Vice President, University Hospital, Madison, WI, p. A698

POLTAWSKY, Jeffrey S., President and Market Leader, Multicare Mary Bridge Children'S Hospital And Health Center, Tacoma, WA, p. A680

POLUNAS, David M., Director, Colorado Mental Health Institute At Fort Logan, Denver, CO, p. A98

POLZIN, Greg
Chief Financial Officer, Iowa Specialty Hospital–Belmond, Belmond, IA, p. A217
Chief Financial Officer, Iowa Specialty Hospital–Clarion, Clarion, IA, p. A219

POMMETT, Francis A, Chief Operating Officer, Shands Lake Shore Regional Medical Center, Lake City, FL, p. A127

PONCE, Agustin, Supervisor Maintenance, Castaner General Hospital, Castaner, PR, p. A715

PONCE, Joseph A, Chief Information Management, Dwight David Eisenhower Army Medical Center, Fort Gordon, GA, p. A153

PONCE, Martha, Director Information Technologies and Telecommunications, Providence Saint John'S Health Center, Santa Monica, CA, p. A89

PONCZOCHA, John, Chief Executive Officer, Select Specialty Hospital–Downriver, Wyandotte, MI, p. A325

POND, Dwight, TIS Boise, Saint Alphonsus Regional Medical Center, Boise, ID, p. A168

POND–BELL, Michele, R.N., Nurse Administrator, Cassia Regional Hospital, Burley, ID, p. A168

PONDER, Beverly K, Executive Assistant and Human Resources Coordinator, Covington County Hospital, Collins, MS, p. A346

PONDER, David, Information Technology Officer, Claremore Indian Hospital, Claremore, OK, p. A498

PONETA, Jan, Director Information Services, Mercy Hospital Jefferson, Festus, MO, p. A360

PONOZZO, Nancy Lynn, MSN, R.N., Chief Nursing Officer, Aspirus Iron River Hospitals & Clinics, Inc., Iron River, MI, p. A315

PONTICELLO, Nat, Vice President Human Resources, Valley Children'S Healthcare, Madera, CA, p. A70

PONTIOUS, Becky, Human Resources/Accounting, Loring Hospital, Sac City, IA, p. A229

PONTIOUS, Michael, M.D., Chief of Staff, St. Mary'S Regional Medical Center, Enid, OK, p. A499

PONTON, Elyonel, Executive Director, Hospital Episcopal San Lucas Guayama, Guayama, PR, p. A716

POOK, Lots, Chief Information Officer, National Jewish Health, Denver, CO, p. A99

POOLE, Andrew J., Interim Chief Financial Officer, Oaklawn Hospital, Marshall, MI, p. A317

POOLE, Robert, Chief Executive Officer, Regency Hospital Of Northwest Arkansas – Springdale, Springdale, AR, p. A49

POOLE–ADAMS, Veronica, R.N., Vice President, Chief Operating Officer and Chief Nursing Executive, Atrium Health Cleveland, Shelby, NC, p. A462

POORE, Caleb, Chief Financial Officer, Callaway District Hospital, Callaway, NE, p. A383

POORE, Justin, D.O., Chief Medical Staff, Cloud County Health Center, Concordia, KS, p. A234

POORE, Luke David., Chief Executive Officer, Kearney County Health Services, Minden, NE, p. A387

POORE, Timothy T., Chief Executive Officer, Encompass Health Rehabilitation Hospital Of Northwest Tucson, Tucson, AZ, p. A37

POOS, Joshua, M.D., President Medical Staff, Community Hospital Of Staunton, Staunton, IL, p. A197

POPE, Alan R, M.D.
Chief Medical Officer, Our Lady Of Lourdes Medical Center, Camden, NJ, p. A404
Vice President, Medical Affairs, Lourdes Medical Center Of Burlington County, Willingboro, NJ, p. A415

POPE, Alice H, Chief Financial Officer, Honorhealth Scottsdale Thompson Peak Medical Center, Scottsdale, AZ, p. A36

POPE, Brad W, Vice President Human Resources, Chi Memorial, Chattanooga, TN, p. A567

POPE, Eddie, Chief Information Officer, Lackey Memorial Hospital, Forest, MS, p. A347

POPE, James W., President and Chief Executive Officer, Van Wert County Hospital, Van Wert, OH, p. A493

POPE, Jayne E., Chief Executive Officer, Hill Country Memorial Hospital, Fredericksburg, TX, p. A606

POPE, Richard, Vice President Human Resources, Jackson County Memorial Hospital, Altus, OK, p. A496

POPE, Robert A., Director I, St. Vincent Anderson, Anderson, IN, p. A199

POPE, Susan, Director Human Resources, Wills Memorial Hospital, Washington, GA, p. A163

POPHAN, Cameron, Chief Financial Officer, Hca Houston Healthcare Northwest, Houston, TX, p. A611

POPKIN, Steven
Chief Executive Officer, Lompoc Valley Medical Center, Lompoc, CA, p. A64
Chief Executive Officer, Parkview Community Hospital Medical Center, Riverside, CA, p. A81

POPLAWSKI, Christine, Chief Financial Officer, Cherokee Medical Center, Gaffney, SC, p. A553

POPLI, Anand, Medical Director, Porter–Starke Services, Valparaiso, IN, p. A216

POPOWYCZ, Alex
Chief Information Officer, Health First Viera Hospital, Melbourne, FL, p. A129
Senior Vice President and Chief Information Officer, Health First Cape Canaveral Hospital, Cocoa Beach, FL, p. A120

Senior Vice President and Chief Information Officer, Health First Palm Bay Hospital, Palm Bay, FL, p. A135

POPP, Adam, Director Information Systems, Avera St. Benedict Health Center, Parkston, SD, p. A562

POPP, Jason, Chief of Medical Staff, Rochelle Community Hospital, Rochelle, IL, p. A194

POPP, Susan, Controller, Kindred Hospital–Fort Worth, Fort Worth, TX, p. A605

POPPEN, Jeffrey, Chief Financial Officer, Sanford Aberdeen Medical Center, Aberdeen, SD, p. A559

POPPERT, Dale, M.D., Chief of Staff, Kaiser Permanente Antioch Medical Center, Antioch, CA, p. A50

POPPY, Bill, Chief Information Officer, Virginia Mason Medical Center, Seattle, WA, p. A679

POQUETTE, Gary R., Chief Executive Officer, Mimbres Memorial Hospital, Deming, NM, p. A418

PORADA, John, Chief Financial Officer, Tristar Southern Hills Medical Center, Nashville, TN, p. A577

PORCELLI, Cheri, MSN, R.N., Chief Nursing Officer, Deer'S Head Hospital Center, Salisbury, MD, p. A293

PORCO, Albert, Director Management Information Systems, Hackensack Meridian Health Palisades Medical Center, North Bergen, NJ, p. A410

PORTCHY, Mindy, Manager Human Resources, Summit Pacific Medical Center, Elma, WA, p. A672

PORTER, Bruce, Chief Financial Officer, Red River Hospital, Llc, Wichita Falls, TX, p. A646

PORTER, Cedric, M.D., President Medical Staff, Emanuel Medical Center, Swainsboro, GA, p. A161

PORTER, Daniel J., Senior Vice President and Chief Financial Officer, J. Arthur Dosher Memorial Hospital, Southport, NC, p. A462

PORTER, Glen, Vice President Human Resources, Essentia Health St. Mary'S Medical Center, Duluth, MN, p. A331

PORTER, Greg, Chief Financial Officer, Rio Grande Hospital, Del Norte, CO, p. A98

PORTER, Heather Renee, Chief Clinical Officer, Newton Medical Center, Newton, KS, p. A241

PORTER, James, Chief Financial Officer, Brookdale Hospital Medical Center, New York, NY, p. A432

PORTER, James P, Chief Financial Officer, St. Bernard Hospital And Health Care Center, Chicago, IL, p. A180

PORTER, Jim, Chief Financial Officer, Southern Virginia Regional Medical Center, Emporia, VA, p. A658

PORTER, Jody, R.N., Senior Vice President Patient Care Services and Chief Nursing Officer, Greater Baltimore Medical Center, Baltimore, MD, p. A288

PORTER, Lance, Chief Executive Officer, Banner Payson Medical Center, Payson, AZ, p. A32

PORTER, Laura, Executive Director, Good Shepherd Penn Partners Specialty Hospital At Rittenhouse, Philadelphia, PA, p. A534

PORTER, Lisa, Director Human Resources, Leadership and Education, Veterans Affairs Salt Lake City Health Care System, Salt Lake City, UT, p. A652

PORTER, Mary, M.D., Medical Staff President, Grande Ronde Hospital, La Grande, OR, p. A514

PORTER, Sharon, Chief Financial Officer, Pappas Rehabilitation Hospital For Children, Canton, MA, p. A297

PORTER, Stephen D., Chief Executive Officer, Piedmont Fayette Hospital, Fayetteville, GA, p. A153

PORTER, T J, Director Human Resources, Bennett County Hospital And Nursing Home, Martin, SD, p. A561

PORTERFIELD, Liza, Chief Financial Officer, Regional Medical Center, Orangeburg, SC, p. A556

PORTMAN, Angela, Chief Executive Officer, Breckinridge Memorial Hospital, Hardinsburg, KY, p. A253

PORTNER, Barry, M.D., Chief of Staff, Prowers Medical Center, Lamar, CO, p. A103

PORWOLL, Amy, Vice President of Information Systems, St. Cloud Hospital, Saint Cloud, MN, p. A339

POSCH, Tim B, Business Manager and Director Personnel, Parsons State Hospital And Training Center, Parsons, KS, p. A243

POSECAI, Scott J, Executive Vice President and Chief Financial Officer, Ochsner Medical Center, New Orleans, LA, p. A275

POSEY, Dawn, Chief Operating Officer, Promise Hospital Of Vicksburg, Vicksburg, MS, p. A355

POSEY, Richard B, Director Human Resources, Prisma Health Baptist Easley Hospital, Easley, SC, p. A552

POSPISIL, Matt E., Vice President Perioperative Services, Nebraska Medicine – Bellevue, Bellevue, NE, p. A383

POSS, Rick, Interim Chief Executive Officer, Wheatland Memorial Healthcare, Harlowton, MT, p. A377

POST, Daniel J., Interim President, Loyola University Medical Center, Maywood, IL, p. A189

POST, Eleanor, R.N., Chief Nursing Officer, Piedmont Rockdale Hospital, Conyers, GA, p. A151

POST, Gwen, R.N., Chief Nursing Officer, Sanford Worthington Medical Center, Worthington, MN, p. A343

POST, John, M.D., Medical Director, Morrill County Community Hospital, Bridgeport, NE, p. A383

POST, Kimberly
  Senior Vice President and Chief Clinical Officer, Honorhealth Scottsdale Thompson Peak Medical Center, Scottsdale, AZ, p. A36
  Senior Vice President and Chief Executive Officer, Honorhealth Scottsdale Osborn Medical Center, Scottsdale, AZ, p. A35

POST, Michael, Chief Executive Officer, Clarion Psychiatric Center, Clarion, PA, p. A522

POSTERNACK, Charles, M.D., Vice President, Boca Raton Regional Hospital, Boca Raton, FL, p. A118

POSTON, Anne, Director of Human Resources/Compliance, Lake City Community Hospital, Lake City, SC, p. A555

POSTON, Sharon, President and Chief Executive Officer, Williamsburg Regional Hospital, Kingstree, SC, p. A554

POSTULKA, Carol, Administrative Coordinator, Avera Gregory Hospital, Gregory, SD, p. A561

POTEATE, Kathy, Interim Director Human Resources, Hugh Chatham Memorial Hospital, Elkin, NC, p. A454

POTEETE, Robin, Manager Human Resources, Hawkins County Memorial Hospital, Rogersville, TN, p. A579

POTEMPA, Debra, Vice President, Mercyhealth Hospital And Trauma Center – Janesville, Janesville, WI, p. A697

POTITADKUL, Wendy, Chief Information Officer, Sunrise Canyon Hospital, Lubbock, TX, p. A622

POTTER, Carolyn
  Chief Human Resources Officer, Mclaren Bay Region, Bay City, MI, p. A307
  Vice President Human Resources, Mclaren Bay Special Care, Bay City, MI, p. A307
  Vice President Human Resources, Mclaren Central Michigan, Mount Pleasant, MI, p. A318

POTTER, Val, Director Human Resources, St. Vincent Salem Hospital, Salem, IN, p. A214

POTTORFF, Kelly, Chief Executive Officer, Cheyenne County Hospital, Saint Francis, KS, p. A244

POTTS, Mary Ann, Director Personnel, Community Hospitals And Wellness Centers, Bryan, OH, p. A474

POULSON, Rhonda, Chief Nursing Officer and Vice President of Clinical Operations, Chi Memorial, Chattanooga, TN, p. A567

POUND, Steve, Vice President Human Resources, St. Joseph'S Hospital, Savannah, GA, p. A160

POUND, Terry, Chief Financial Officer, Hospital District No 1 Of Rice County, Lyons, KS, p. A240

POUND, Veronica, Administrator, Socorro General Hospital, Socorro, NM, p. A421

POUND, Veronica, R.N., Interim Administrator and Director of Patient Care, Socorro General Hospital, Socorro, NM, p. A421

POVICH, Mark, D.O., Medical Director, Osf St. Francis Hospital And Medical Group, Escanaba, MI, p. A311

POWE, Lee, Director Management Information Systems, Hugh Chatham Memorial Hospital, Elkin, NC, p. A454

POWEL, Linda J., M.D., Medical Director, Odessa Memorial Healthcare Center, Odessa, WA, p. A675

POWELL, Adam, Program Manager, Marion Veterans Affairs Medical Center, Marion, IL, p. A188

POWELL, Candy, Administrator, Collingsworth General Hospital, Wellington, TX, p. A645

POWELL, Charles
  Chief Financial Officer, Arkansas Surgical Hospital, North Little Rock, AR, p. A46
  Interim Chief Executive Officer, Lubbock Heart & Surgical Hospital, Lubbock, TX, p. A622
  President, Sts. Mary & Elizabeth Hospital, Louisville, KY, p. A256

POWELL, D Jerome, M.D., Chief Information Officer, Strong Memorial Hospital Of The University Of Rochester, Rochester, NY, p. A443

POWELL, Hannah, Chief Nursing Officer, Mercy Hospital Kingfisher, Kingfisher, OK, p. A501

POWELL, Holly, Administrator, Continuecare Hospital At Medical Center (Odessa), Odessa, TX, p. A626

POWELL, Jackie, Director Human Resources, Pemiscot Memorial Health System, Hayti, MO, p. A361

POWELL, James R, Associate Administrator, Banner Gateway Medical Center, Gilbert, AZ, p. A29

POWELL, Jimmy, Manager Human Resources, Harry S. Truman Memorial Veterans Hospital, Columbia, MO, p. A359

POWELL, Josh, Facility Controller, Cox Monett Hospital, Monett, MO, p. A366

POWELL, Karen S., Vice President, Human Resources, Mary Free Bed Rehabilitation Hospital, Grand Rapids, MI, p. A312

POWELL, Kay, Director Human Resources, Christus Southeast Texas Jasper Memorial, Jasper, TX, p. A616

POWELL, Michelle, Chief Executive Officer, Select Rehabilitation Hospital Of Denton, Denton, TX, p. A599

POWELL, Parker, Chief Executive Officer, Glendive Medical Center, Glendive, MT, p. A376

POWELL, Tammy, President, Ssm Health St. Anthony Hospital – Oklahoma City, Oklahoma City, OK, p. A505

POWELL, Traci, Director Human Resources, Encompass Health Rehabilitation Hospital Of Panama City, Panama City, FL, p. A135

POWELL, Virginia, Director Finance, Wilmington Treatment Center, Wilmington, NC, p. A464

POWELL–STAFFORD, Valerie L., Chief Executive Officer, Northside Hospital, Saint Petersburg, FL, p. A138

POWER, Bob, Vice President Information Services, Good Samaritan Regional Medical Center, Corvallis, OR, p. A512

POWER, Robert
  Chief Information Officer, Samaritan Pacific Communities Hospital, Newport, OR, p. A515
  Vice President Information Services, Samaritan Lebanon Community Hospital, Lebanon, OR, p. A514

POWERS, Anthony, Interim President and Vice President of Patient Services, Baptist Health Corbin, Corbin, KY, p. A250

POWERS, Barbara, R.N., Chief Nursing Officer, Austin Lakes Hospital, Austin, TX, p. A585

POWERS, Brent, M.D., Vice President/Chief Medical Officer, Lexington Medical Center, West Columbia, SC, p. A558

POWERS, Jamekia, Assistant Director Human Resources, Georgia Regional Hospital At Savannah, Savannah, GA, p. A160

POWERS, Judi, Chief Executive Officer, Advanced Care Hospital Of Montana, Billings, MT, p. A374

POWERS, Kelli, Chief Financial Officer, Huntsville Hospital, Huntsville, AL, p. A19

POWERS, Mary, R.N., MSN
  Senior Vice President and Chief Nursing Officer, Manchester Memorial Hospital, Manchester, CT, p. A108
  Senior Vice President and Chief Nursing Officer, Rockville General Hospital, Vernon, CT, p. A111

POWERS, Peter, Chief Executive Officer, St. Anthony Hospital, Lakewood, CO, p. A103

POWERS, Ryan J., Vice President Finance, Spectrum Health Zeeland Community Hospital, Zeeland, MI, p. A326

POWERS, Tim, Chief Executive Officer, North Canyon Medical Center, Gooding, ID, p. A169

POWRIE, Raymond, M.D., Senior Vice President Quality and Clinical Effectiveness, Women & Infants Hospital Of Rhode Island, Providence, RI, p. A548

POYNTER, Carmen, Director Human Resources, Rockcastle Regional Hospital And Respiratory Care Center, Mount Vernon, KY, p. A258

POYTHRESS, Antoine
  Chief Financial Officer, Washington County Regional Medical Center, Sandersville, GA, p. A159
  Interim Chief Executive Officer, Washington County Regional Medical Center, Sandersville, GA, p. A159

PRABHAKARAN, Madhan, M.D., Chief Medical Officer, Palo Alto County Health System, Emmetsburg, IA, p. A222

PRACHEIL, Michael, Chief Financial Officer, Gothenburg Health, Gothenburg, NE, p. A385

PRACHT, Matthew, Vice President Finance, Scotland Health Care System, Laurinburg, NC, p. A457

PRADA, Janina
  Director Information Services, University Medical Center Of El Paso, El Paso, TX, p. A603
  Director Information Technology, El Paso Children'S Hospital, El Paso, TX, p. A601

PRAFKA, David, Ed.D., Director of Human Resources, Vidant Edgecombe Hospital, Tarboro, NC, p. A463

PRAKASH, Amitabh, M.D., Chief Medical Officer, Ahmc Anaheim Regional Medical Center, Anaheim, CA, p. A50

PRAKASH, Vijay, Information Technology Officer, Essex County Hospital Center, Cedar Grove, NJ, p. A404

PRANTE, Melissa, Chief Financial Officer, Kimball Health Services, Kimball, NE, p. A386

PRATER, Jeffrey, Chief Executive Officer, Carson Valley Medical Center, Gardnerville, NV, p. A394

PRATER, Judith, Director of Nursing, Pike County Memorial Hospital, Louisiana, MO, p. A364

PRATER, Marsha A., Ph.D., R.N., Senior Vice President and Chief Nursing Officer, Memorial Medical Center, Springfield, IL, p. A196

PRATER, Robin, Director Human Resources, Rusk Rehabilitation Hospital, Columbia, MO, p. A359

PRATHER, Jean, Director of Human Resources, Greene County General Hospital, Linton, IN, p. A210

PRATHER, Rachael, Chief Nursing Officer, Ferrell Hospital, Eldorado, IL, p. A181

PRATT, Audra, Chief Human Resource Officer, St. Vincent Indianapolis Hospital, Indianapolis, IN, p. A208

PRATT, Bailey, Chief Financial Officer, Saint Thomas Rutherford Hospital, Murfreesboro, TN, p. A576

PRATT, Dustin, M.D., Chief of Staff, Childress Regional Medical Center, Childress, TX, p. A592

PRATT, Lisa D., Vice President, Human Resources, Mclean Hospital, Belmont, MA, p. A294

PRATT, MaryEllen, Chief Executive Officer, St. James Parish Hospital, Lutcher, LA, p. A273

PRATT, Ramona, Chief Operating Officer, Pih Health Hospital – Downey, Downey, CA, p. A56

PRATT, Timothy J, M.D., Vice President Medical Affairs and Chief Medical Officer, Ssm Health St. Clare Hospital – Fenton, Fenton, MO, p. A360

PRATT, Troy, Information Technology Site Director, Covenant Medical Center, Lubbock, TX, p. A621

PREAU, William, M.D., Medical Director, Avala, Covington, LA, p. A266

PRECOURT, Justin, Chief Nursing Officer, Umass Memorial Medical Center, Worcester, MA, p. A305

PREISINGER, Andrea, Director Human Resources, Menninger Clinic, Houston, TX, p. A613

PREMO, Mark, Senior Director HC Intelligence, Providence Portland Medical Center, Portland, OR, p. A516

PRENTISS, Kristin, Chief Financial Officer, Specialty Hospital Of Central Jersey, Lakewood, NJ, p. A407

PRESCOTT, Tina, Vice President, Hospital Services, Jackson–Madison County General Hospital, Jackson, TN, p. A571

PRESNELL, Elizabeth, Assistant Vice President of Finance, St. Luke'S Hospital, Columbus, NC, p. A452

PRESS, Robert, M.D., Senior Vice President, Vice Dean and Chief Hospital Operations, Brookdale Hospital Medical Center, New York, NY, p. A432

PRESSMAN, Sean, Chief Executive Officer, Lewisgale Hospital Pulaski, Pulaski, VA, p. A665

PRESTEGAARD, Benjamin, Chief Medical Officer, Uh Portage Medical Center, Ravenna, OH, p. A490

PRESTON, Tara
  Director Human Resources, Bingham Memorial Hospital, Blackfoot, ID, p. A167
  Director Human Resources, Mountain River Birthing And Surgery Center, Blackfoot, ID, p. A167

PRESTON, Venicea Austin., Administrator, Cypress Grove Behavioral Health, Bastrop, LA, p. A263

PRESTRIDGE, Tim, Interim Chief Financial Officer, Logan Memorial Hospital, Russellville, KY, p. A260

PRETE, Mark, M.D., Vice President Medical Affairs, Charlotte Hungerford Hospital, Torrington, CT, p. A111

PRETTYMAN, Edgar E., Chief Executive Officer, Texas Neurorehab Center, Austin, TX, p. A586

PRETZLAFF, Robert, M.D.
  Chief Medical Officer, St. Rose Dominican Hospitals – San Martin Campus, Las Vegas, NV, p. A396
  Chief Medical Officer, St. Rose Dominican Hospitals – Siena Campus, Henderson, NV, p. A394

PREWITT, Connie F, Chief Financial Officer, Billings Clinic, Billings, MT, p. A374

PREWITT, Margaret Elizabeth, Vice President Patient Services and Chief Nursing Officer, St. Catherine Hospital, Garden City, KS, p. A235

PRIBITKIN, Edmund A., M.D., Chief Medical Officer, Thomas Jefferson University Hospitals, Philadelphia, PA, p. A536

PRICE, Bernard J, Chief Human Resources Officer, Medical Center, Navicent Health, Macon, GA, p. A156

PRICE, Connie, M.D., Chief Medical Officer, Denver Health, Denver, CO, p. A98

PRICE, David
  Chief Executive Officer, Honorhealth Deer Valley Medical Center, Phoenix, AZ, p. A33
  Chief Executive Officer, Honorhealth Scottsdale Thompson Peak Medical Center, Scottsdale, AZ, p. A36

PRICE, James, Hospital Administrator, State Hospital South, Blackfoot, ID, p. A167

PRICE, John, Chief Financial Officer, King'S Daughters' Health, Madison, IN, p. A210

PRICE, John Stephen, M.D., Chief of Staff, Fairview Regional Medical Center, Fairview, OK, p. A500

PRICE, Kelley, R.N., Chief Nursing Officer, Battle Mountain General Hospital, Battle Mountain, NV, p. A393

PRICE, Kevin A
  Vice President and Chief Operating Officer, Sparrow Clinton Hospital, Saint Johns, MI, p. A322
  Vice President and Chief Operating Officer, Sparrow Ionia Hospital, Ionia, MI, p. A314

PRICE, Kim, Chief Executive Officer, Franklin General Hospital, Hampton, IA, p. A223

PRICE, Kyle, Chief Executive Officer, Memorial Hermann Greater Heights Hospital, Houston, TX, p. A612

PRICE, Larry, Chief Executive Officer, Limestone Medical Center, Groesbeck, TX, p. A608

PRICE, Lori, President, Gottlieb Memorial Hospital, Melrose Park, IL, p. A189

PRICE, Lorraine B, Associate Director, Hampton Veterans Affairs Medical Center, Hampton, VA, p. A660

PRICE, Manuel, Director Information Systems, Brookwood Baptist Medical Center, Birmingham, AL, p. A14

PRICE, Meredith, Vice President Fiscal Services and Chief Financial Officer, St. Joseph'S Hospital Health Center, Syracuse, NY, p. A445

PRICE, Mindy, Chief Executive Officer, Rosebud Health Care Center, Forsyth, MT, p. A376

PRICE, Norman M., Chief Executive Officer, Southwest Mississippi Regional Medical Center, Mccomb, MS, p. A350

PRICE, Sam, Executive Vice President Finance/Chief Financial Officer, East Alabama Medical Center, Opelika, AL, p. A22

PRICE, Shari, Director Information Services, Baptist Health Louisville, Louisville, KY, p. A256

PRICE, Terry, Director Information Technology, Great Plains Regional Medical Center, Elk City, OK, p. A499

PRICE, Tonya, Chief Nursing Officer, Wilson N. Jones Regional Medical Center, Sherman, TX, p. A637

PRICE, Walter, Director Information Technology, Newport Hospital And Health Services, Newport, WA, p. A675

PRICE-YONTS, Melody, Chief Executive Officer, Acoma–Canoncito–Laguna Hospital, Acoma, NM, p. A416

PRICKEL, Trisha, Information Systems Director, Margaret Mary Health, Batesville, IN, p. A199

PRIDDY, Ernest C, Chief Financial Officer, Old Vineyard Behavioral Health Services, Winston, NC, p. A464

PRIDDY, Steven, M.D., VP of Physician Affairs/Chief Medical Officer, St. Vincent Carmel Hospital, Carmel, IN, p. A201

PRIDEAUX, Heather, Chief Financial Officer, Rawlins County Health Center, Atwood, KS, p. A232

PRIDGEN, Kim
  Chief Financial Officer, Houston County Community Hospital, Erin, TN, p. A569
  Chief Financial Officer, Northcrest Medical Center, Springfield, TN, p. A579

PRIDGEN, Parker, Chief Financial Officer, Central Texas Medical Center, San Marcos, TX, p. A636

PRIES, Kathleen M, Director Human Resources, Nazareth Hospital, Philadelphia, PA, p. A535

PRIEST, David, Director Information Systems, Munson Healthcare Charlevoix Hospital, Charlevoix, MI, p. A308

PRIEST, Geoff, M.D., Chief Medical Officer, Unitypoint Health Meriter, Madison, WI, p. A698

PRIEST, Mike, M.D., Chief of Staff, Pawhuska Hospital, Pawhuska, OK, p. A506

PRIETTO, Carlos, President and Chief Executive Officer, Hoag Orthopedic Institute, Irvine, CA, p. A62

PRIHODA, Matt, M.D., Chief of Staff, Washington County Hospital And Clinics, Washington, IA, p. A230

PRILUTSKY, Michael, President and Chief Executive Officer, Jersey City Medical Center, Jersey City, NJ, p. A407

PRIMACK, Matthew Lee., President, Advocate Christ Medical Center, Oak Lawn, IL, p. A191

PRINCE, Clay, M.D., Chief Medical Officer, Madison Memorial Hospital, Rexburg, ID, p. A171

PRINCE, Kem, Manager of Finance, Parkview Noble Hospital, Kendallville, IN, p. A208

PRINCE, Michele, Chief Operating Officer, Lewis County General Hospital, Lowville, NY, p. A430

PRINCE, Sue, Director Information Systems, Northern Westchester Hospital, Mount Kisco, NY, p. A432

PRINCIPE, Adam, Chief Executive Officer, Select Specialty Hospital Pensacola, Pensacola, FL, p. A136

PRINCIPE, Hector Cintron, M.D., Director, Hospital Universitario Dr. Ramon Ruiz Arnau, Bayamon, PR, p. A715

PRINGLE–MILLER, Letitia, Administrative Director, Prisma Health Tuomey Hospital, Sumter, SC, p. A557

PRINTY, Wayne, Chief Financial Officer and Senior Vice President Finance, Lincolnhealth, Damariscotta, ME, p. A282

PRIORE, Jacqueline, Chief Nursing Officer, Samaritan Hospital – Main Campus, Troy, NY, p. A445

PRISELAC, Thomas M., President and Chief Executive Officer, Cedars–Sinai Medical Center, Los Angeles, CA, p. A66

PRISTER, James R, President and Chief Executive Officer, Rml Specialty Hospital, Hinsdale, IL, p. A186

PRISTER, James R., President and Chief Executive Officer, Rml Specialty Hospital, Hinsdale, IL, p. A186

PRITCHARD, Jason, Chief Financial Officer, Hackensack Meridian Health Pascack Valley Medical Center, Westwood, NJ, p. A415

PRITCHARD, Jeff, Chief Executive Officer, Beckett Springs, West Chester, OH, p. A494

PRITCHARD, Joann, Chief Financial Officer, Erie Veterans Affairs Medical Center, Erie, PA, p. A525

PRITCHETT, Greg, Chief Financial Officer, Cuero Community Hospital, Cuero, TX, p. A595

PRITTS, Robert, Chief Executive Officer, Ssm Select Rehabilitation Hospital, Richmond Heights, MO, p. A367

PRIVETT, David, Deputy Director, Western New York Children'S Psychiatric Center, West Seneca, NY, p. A447

PROBASCO, Brent, Chief Financial Officer, Cass Regional Medical Center, Harrisonville, MO, p. A361

PROBST, Nancy, R.N., Chief Nursing Officer, Bigfork Valley Hospital, Bigfork, MN, p. A328

PROBUS, Kimberly, Chief Nursing Officer, Opelousas General Health System, Opelousas, LA, p. A276

PROCHASKA, Jodi, Chief Financial Officer, Butler County Health Care Center, David City, NE, p. A384

PROCHILO, John F., Jr, Chief Executive Officer, Northeast Rehabilitation Hospital, Salem, NH, p. A402

PROCHNOW, Bryan, Chief Financial Officer, Matagorda Regional Medical Center, Bay City, TX, p. A587

PROCTOR, Brandy, Director of Nursing, North Star Behavioral Health System, Anchorage, AK, p. A25

PROCTOR, Jason J., Chief Operating Officer, Christus Mother Frances Hospital – Tyler, Tyler, TX, p. A642

PROCTOR, Quinn, Director Human Resources, Claremore Indian Hospital, Claremore, OK, p. A498

PROCTOR, Sandra, R.N., MS, Chief Nurse Executive, Memorial Medical Center, Modesto, CA, p. A72

PROCTOR, Scott, Chief Executive Officer, Safe Haven Hospital Of Treasure Valley, Boise, ID, p. A167

PROCTOR, Stephen, Director of Human Resources/Risk, Russellville Hospital, Russellville, AL, p. A23

PROFOTA, Lori, Chief Nursing Officer, Copley Hospital, Morrisville, VT, p. A654

PRONGER, Derk F.
  Chief Operating Officer, Munson Medical Center, Traverse City, MI, p. A323
  Interim President and Chief Executive Officer, Munson Medical Center, Traverse City, MI, p. A323

PRONI, John, CPA, Manager Finance and Operations, Baycare Alliant Hospital, Dunedin, FL, p. A122

PROPP, Elizabeth R, Vice President Finance and Chief Financial Officer, Dameron Hospital, Stockton, CA, p. A90

PROSKOCIL, Danielle, Director Human Resources, Valley County Health System, Ord, NE, p. A390

PROSPER, Charles, Chief Executive Officer, Alta Bates Summit Medical Center – Summit Campus, Oakland, CA, p. A75

PROSSER, Alita, Chief Financial Officer, Baylor Scott & White Medical Center – Temple, Temple, TX, p. A639

PROSSER, Edna, Chief Nursing Officer, Ozark Health Medical Center, Clinton, AR, p. A40

PROSSER, Joseph, M.D., Chief Medical Officer, Texas Health Harris Methodist Hospital Fort Worth, Fort Worth, TX, p. A605

PROUD, James, Vice President Human Resources and Marketing, Uniontown Hospital, Uniontown, PA, p. A543

PROUJANSKY, Roy, Chief Executive Officer, Alfred I. Dupont Hospital For Children, Wilmington, DE, p. A114

PROVENZANO, Jeff
  Vice President and Chief Financial Officer, Midmichigan Medical Center–Clare, Clare, MI, p. A309
  Vice President and Chief Financial Officer, Midmichigan Medical Center–Gladwin, Gladwin, MI, p. A312
  Vice President and Chief Financial Officer, Midmichigan Medical Center–Gratiot, Alma, MI, p. A306

PROVENZANO, Stacey, Chief Operating Officer, Greystone Park Psychiatric Hospital, Morris Plains, NJ, p. A408

PROVINCE, Steven, President and Chief Executive Officer, Adventist Medical Center – Hinsdale, Hinsdale, IL, p. A186

PROVOST, Deborah A, Chief Nursing Officer, Baystate Franklin Medical Center, Greenfield, MA, p. A299

PRUESS, Mark, M.D., Chief Medical Staff, Sparta Community Hospital, Sparta, IL, p. A196

PRUETT–BAER, Karen, Senior Nurse Executive, Naval Hospital Oak Harbor, Oak Harbor, WA, p. A675

PRUITT, Jeffrey, M.D., Chief of Staff, Mercy Hospital Of Defiance, Defiance, OH, p. A481

PRUKOP, Jeff, Director Professional Services, Jackson County Hospital District, Edna, TX, p. A601

PRUNCHUNAS, Edward M, Executive Vice President and Chief Financial Officer, Cedars–Sinai Medical Center, Los Angeles, CA, p. A66

PRUNOSKE, Mark, Chief Financial Officer and Senior Vice President Finance, F. F. Thompson Hospital, Canandaigua, NY, p. A425

PRUSATIS, Michael, Vice President Finance, Dmc – Sinai–Grace Hospital, Detroit, MI, p. A310

PRYBYLO, Mary, President and Chief Executive Officer, St. Joseph Hospital, Bangor, ME, p. A281

PRYOR, David, President, Athens–Limestone Hospital, Athens, AL, p. A13

PRYOR, Vincent, Senior Vice President and Chief Financial Officer, Silver Cross Hospital, New Lenox, IL, p. A191

PRZESTRZELSKI, David, Associate Director, Patient Care Services and Chief Nursing Executive, Charles George Veterans Affairs Medical Center, Asheville, NC, p. A449

PRZYBYLSKI, David, Controller, Sparrow Specialty Hospital, Lansing, MI, p. A316

PSAILA, Justin P, M.D., Vice President Medical Affairs, St. Luke'S Hospital – Anderson Campus, Easton, PA, p. A525

PSCODNA, Susan, Director Human Resources, Mercy Hospital Of Defiance, Defiance, OH, p. A481

PU, Steve, D.O., Chief Medical Officer, Poplar Bluff Regional Medical Center, Poplar Bluff, MO, p. A367

PUCHBAUER, Aaron, President, Hshs Good Shepherd Hospital, Shelbyville, IL, p. A195

PUCKETT, Clay, Assistant Administrator and Chief Information Officer, Blount Memorial Hospital, Maryville, TN, p. A574

PUCKETT, Kristi, Director Human Resources, Grande Ronde Hospital, La Grande, OR, p. A514

PUCKETT, Mark, Chief Executive Officer, Brentwood Springs, Newburgh, IN, p. A212

PUCLIK, Becky, Division Chief People Officer, Hshs St. John'S Hospital, Springfield, IL, p. A196

PUENTES, Francisco, Human Resource Officer, San Diego County Psychiatric Hospital, San Diego, CA, p. A84

PUFFENBERGER, James, Vice President and Chief Financial Officer, Mercy Hospital Of Defiance, Defiance, OH, p. A481

PUFFENBERGER, Sheila, Manager Information Technology, Hillsdale Hospital, Hillsdale, MI, p. A314

PUGACH, Judy, Chief Nursing Officer, Pih Health Hospital – Downey, Downey, CA, p. A56

PUGH, Larry, Vice President and Chief Financial Officer, Beverly Hospital, Montebello, CA, p. A72

PUGH, Marcia, Chief Executive Officer, Greene County Health System, Eutaw, AL, p. A17

PUGH, Melodee, Director Human Resources, Navarro Regional Hospital, Corsicana, TX, p. A594

PUGH, Ryan, Chief Financial Officer, Western Plains Medical Complex, Dodge City, KS, p. A234

PUGH, William H, Senior Vice President Corporate Finance and Chief Financial Officer, Upmc Pinnacle Harrisburg, Harrisburg, PA, p. A527

PUGSLEY, Tim, Chief Information Officer, Orthonebraska Hospital, Omaha, NE, p. A390

PUHL, Cathy A., Vice President Human Resources, Chambersburg Hospital, Chambersburg, PA, p. A522

PUKALA, Shirley, R.N., Assistant Administrator Operations, St. Lawrence Rehabilitation Center, Lawrenceville, NJ, p. A407

PULASKI, Jason, Controller, Encompass Health Reading Rehabilitation Hospital, Reading, PA, p. A539

PULEO, Mark, Vice President and Chief Human Resources Officer, Henry Mayo Newhall Hospital, Valencia, CA, p. A93

PULIDO, Michael, Chief Administrative Officer, Mosaic Life Care At St. Joseph – Medical Center, Saint Joseph, MO, p. A368

PULLARKAT, Sajit, Chief Executive Officer and Managing Director, Centennial Hills Hospital Medical Center, Las Vegas, NV, p. A394

PULLEN, Connie, R.N., Chief Nursing Officer, Willamette Valley Medical Center, Mcminnville, OR, p. A514

PULLIAM, Elizabeth, Chief Financial Officer, Christus Mother Frances Hospital – Jacksonville, Jacksonville, TX, p. A616

PULLIN, Dennis W.
  President and Chief Executive Officer, Virtua Marlton, Marlton, NJ, p. A408
  President and Chief Executive Officer, Virtua Memorial, Mount Holly, NJ, p. A408
  President and Chief Executive Officer, Virtua Voorhees, Voorhees, NJ, p. A414

PULLINS, Ruth
  Chief Human Resources Officer, Truman Medical Center–Hospital Hill, Kansas City, MO, p. A363
  Chief Human Resources Officer, Truman Medical Center–Lakewood, Kansas City, MO, p. A363

PULLMAN, Debbie, Director Finance, Avera Hand County Memorial Hospital, Miller, SD, p. A562

PULLMAN, Jayson, Chief Executive Officer, Hawarden Regional Healthcare, Hawarden, IA, p. A224

PULVER, Dayna, Director of Nursing, Friend Community Healthcare System, Friend, NE, p. A385

PUMMEL, Keely, Director, Financial Operations, Ohiohealth Dublin Methodist Hospital, Dublin, OH, p. A482

PUMPHREY, Robbin K, Chief Nursing Officer, Jackson Hospital, Marianna, FL, p. A129

PUNG, Margaret, R.N., Chief Nursing Officer, University Of Texas Harris County Psychiatric Center, Houston, TX, p. A614

PUNJABI, Rishab, Chief Financial Officer, Kindred Hospital–La Mirada, La Mirada, CA, p. A63

PUORTO, Charlene, Chief Nursing Officer, Capital District Psychiatric Center, Albany, NY, p. A422

PURCELL, Deborah, Director of Information Technology, Caldwell Unc Health Care, Lenoir, NC, p. A457

PURCELL, Terrance J., Director Information Services, Lea Regional Medical Center, Hobbs, NM, p. A418

PURDY, Bruce, M.D., Chief of Staff, Muleshoe Area Medical Center, Muleshoe, TX, p. A625

PURINGTON, Denise, Vice President and Chief Information Officer, Elliot Hospital, Manchester, NH, p. A401

PURINTON, Sandy, Chief Nursing Officer, Trego County–Lemke Memorial Hospital, Wakeeney, KS, p. A247

PURMONT, Tiffany, Supervisor Medical Records, Monroe County Hospital, Forsyth, GA, p. A153

PUROHIT, Divyesh, M.D., Chief of Staff, Sullivan County Community Hospital, Sullivan, IN, p. A215

PUROHIT, Kumar, Chief Financial Officer, Rockford Center, Newark, DE, p. A113

PUROHIT, Shamb, Chief Financial Officer, Colquitt Regional Medical Center, Moultrie, GA, p. A158

PURRINGTON, Janice, Coordinator Medical Records, Avera Hand County Memorial Hospital, Miller, SD, p. A562

PURSLEY, Roger, Chief Executive Officer, Western Mental Health Institute, Bolivar, TN, p. A566

PURTLE, Mark, M.D.
Vice President Medical Affairs, Unitypoint Health – Iowa Methodist Medical Center, Des Moines, IA, p. A221
Vice President Medical Affairs, Unitypoint Health–Iowa Lutheran Hospital, Des Moines, IA, p. A221

PURUSHOTHAM, Sanjay, Executive Director Information Systems, Bon Secours Baltimore Health System, Baltimore, MD, p. A286

PURVANCE, Clint, President and Chief Executive Officer, Barton Memorial Hospital, South Lake Tahoe, CA, p. A90

PURVES, Stephen A., President and Chief Executive Officer, Maricopa Integrated Health System, Phoenix, AZ, p. A33

PURVIS, Jay, President and Chief Executive Officer, Wabash General Hospital, Mount Carmel, IL, p. A190

PURVIS, Kevin, Chief Information Officer, Community Howard Regional Health, Kokomo, IN, p. A209

PURVIS, Michael L.
Chief Executive Officer, Cook Medical Center–A Campus Of Tift Regional Medical Center, Adel, GA, p. A145
Chief Executive Officer, Novato Community Hospital, Novato, CA, p. A75

PURVIS, Mike, Chief Administrative Officer, Sutter Santa Rosa Regional Hospital, Santa Rosa, CA, p. A89

PUSHARD, Roland, Director of Nursing, Riverview Psychiatric Center, Augusta, ME, p. A281

PUSTINA, Karl, Vice President Finance, Upland Hills Health, Dodgeville, WI, p. A693

PUSZKARSKA, Lucyna M., M.D., Medical Director, Riveredge Hospital, Forest Park, IL, p. A183

PUTHOFF, Timothy, Chief Executive Officer, Brookwood Baptist Medical Center, Birmingham, AL, p. A14

PUTNAM, Mark, M.D., Medical Director, Haven Behavioral Hospital Of Eastern Pennsylvania, Reading, PA, p. A539

PUTNAM, Maureen M, Director Human Resources, Oss Orthopaedic Hospital, York, PA, p. A546

PUTNAM, Stewart C, Executive Vice President and Chief Operating Officer, Unity Hospital, Rochester, NY, p. A443

PUTNAM, Timothy L., President and Chief Executive Officer, Margaret Mary Health, Batesville, IN, p. A199

PUTZ, Kim, R.N., Director, Nursing Hospital, Ridgeview Le Sueur Medical Center, Le Sueur, MN, p. A334

PUVOGEL, LuAnn, Chief Executive Officer, Salina Surgical Hospital, Salina, KS, p. A245

PUZO, Thomas C., President and Chief Executive Officer, Cornerstone Of Medical Arts Center Hospital, Fresh Meadows, NY, p. A428

PUZZUTO, David, M.D., Vice President Medical Affairs and Chief Medical Officer, Waterbury Hospital, Waterbury, CT, p. A112

PYGON, Bernard, M.D., Chief Medical Officer, University Of Illinois Hospital & Health Sciences System, Chicago, IL, p. A180

PYLE, Diana, Director Human Resources and Executive Assistant to Chief Executive Officer, Cedar County Memorial Hospital, El Dorado Springs, MO, p. A359

PYLE, Julia, R.N., Chief Nursing Officer, Newman Regional Health, Emporia, KS, p. A234

PYLE, Rick, Director Information Systems, Harrisburg Medical Center, Harrisburg, IL, p. A184

PYLE FARRELL, Martha, Vice President Human Resources and General Counsel, Massachusetts Eye And Ear, Boston, MA, p. A295

PYNE, Mel
Chief Executive Officer, Emanuel Medical Center, Swainsboro, GA, p. A161
Regional Chief Executive Officer, Dorminy Medical Center, Fitzgerald, GA, p. A153

PYRAH, Scott, Director Information Systems, St. Luke'S Rehabilitation Hospital, Boise, ID, p. A168

Q

QUACKENBUSH, Kirk, M.D., Chief of Staff, Platte Valley Medical Center, Brighton, CO, p. A97

QUAGLIERI, Mike, Chief Financial Officer, North Central Surgical Center, Dallas, TX, p. A597

QUALLS, Brenda, Chief Financial Officer, Navicent Health Baldwin, Milledgeville, GA, p. A157

QUALLS, Hugh, Administrator, Mount Grant General Hospital, Hawthorne, NV, p. A394

QUALLS, Paul E., Chief Executive Officer, Post Acute Medical Specialty Hospital Of Milwaukee, Greenfield, WI, p. A696

QUAMMEN, Becky, Chief Information Officer, Howard University Hospital, Washington, DC, p. A115

QUANCE, Daniel, Chief Financial Officer, Fairmont Regional Medical Center, Fairmont, WV, p. A685

QUARANTE, Dino, CPA, Chief Financial Officer, Oasis Behavioral Health – Chandler, Chandler, AZ, p. A28

QUARLES, Christopher, M.D., Director Medical Services, Naval Hospital Jacksonville, Jacksonville, FL, p. A125

QUATE, Becky, Vice President Nursing and Patient Care Services, Iredell Health System, Statesville, NC, p. A463

QUATROCHE, Thomas J., Jr, President and Chief Executive Officer, Erie County Medical Center, Buffalo, NY, p. A424

QUATTROCCHI, Robert, President and Chief Executive Officer, Northside Hospital, Atlanta, GA, p. A146

QUEBEDEAUX, Jay, Chief Executive Officer, Mena Regional Health System, Mena, AR, p. A46

QUEBODEAUX, Bryce, Chief Executive Officer, Abrom Kaplan Memorial Hospital, Kaplan, LA, p. A270

QUEEN, Sharon H, R.N., Chief Nursing Officer, Piedmont Walton Hospital, Monroe, GA, p. A157

QUENAN, James, M.D., Chief Medical Officer, Amery Hospital And Clinic, Amery, WI, p. A691

QUESNEL, Brenda, R.N., Vice President of Patient Care and Chief Nursing Officer, West Calcasieu Cameron Hospital, Sulphur, LA, p. A279

QUICCI, London, Chief Operating Officer, Dmc – Sinai–Grace Hospital, Detroit, MI, p. A310

QUICHOCHO, Vince, Manager Information Systems, Guam Memorial Hospital Authority, Tamuning, GU, p. A714

QUIGLEY, Stephen J., Chief Executive Officer, Southwood Psychiatric Hospital, Pittsburgh, PA, p. A537

QUILLIN, Gayla, Administrator, Parmer Medical Center, Friona, TX, p. A606

QUIN, Matt, Interim Chief Operating Officer, Women & Infants Hospital Of Rhode Island, Providence, RI, p. A548

QUIN, Robert, Regional Vice President Finance, and Chief Financial Officer, Unitypoint Health – Peoria, Peoria, IL, p. A193

QUINLAN, Christine, MS, R.N., Chief Nursing Officer, Alexian Brothers Behavioral Health Hospital, Hoffman Estates, IL, p. A186

QUINLAN, Patrick J, M.D., Chief Executive Officer, Ochsner Clinic Foundation & International Services, Exec. Director Ochsner Center for Community, Ochsner Medical Center, New Orleans, LA, p. A275

QUINLIVAN, John, Chief Executive Officer, Redmond Regional Medical Center, Rome, GA, p. A159

QUINLIVAN, Kathy, Director Management Information Systems, Avera Sacred Heart Hospital, Yankton, SD, p. A565

QUINN, Clifton, Chief Executive Officer, Select Specialty Hospital–Birmingham, Birmingham, AL, p. A15

QUINN, Donna, Vice President Operations, Driscoll Children'S Hospital, Corpus Christi, TX, p. A594

QUINN, Jennifer, Quality and Safety Coordinator, Thedacare Medical Center–Shawano, Shawano, WI, p. A705

QUINN, Judith, Vice President Patient Care Services, Cape Cod Hospital, Hyannis, MA, p. A299

QUINN, Mary Ann
Administrative Assistant, Casey County Hospital, Liberty, KY, p. A255
Administrative Assistant, Jane Todd Crawford Hospital, Greensburg, KY, p. A252

QUINN, Mary Anna, Executive Vice President, Chief Administrative Officer, St. Jude Children'S Research Hospital, Memphis, TN, p. A575

QUINN, Paul, Information Systems Manager, Kern Valley Healthcare District, Lake Isabella, CA, p. A63

QUINN, Tim, M.D., Executive Vice President and Chief of Clinical Operations and President Mercy Care Management, Mercy Medical Center – Cedar Rapids, Cedar Rapids, IA, p. A218

QUINONES, Yolanda, Director Finance, I. Gonzalez Martinez Oncologic Hospital, Hato Rey, PR, p. A716

QUINONEZ, Yolanda, Chief Financial Officer, Hospital De La Universidad De Puerto Rico/Dr. Federico Trilla, Carolina, PR, p. A715

QUINT–BOUZID, Marjorie, Chief Nursing Officer and Vice President Patient Care Services, Fort Washington Medical Center, Oxen Hill, MD, p. A292

QUINTANA, Francisco, Warden, Federal Medical Center, Lexington, KY, p. A255

QUINTO, Mike, Chief Information Officer, Watauga Medical Center, Boone, NC, p. A450

QUINTON, J. Ben., Administrator, William Newton Hospital, Winfield, KS, p. A248

QUINTYNE, Stephen, Chief Executive Officer, The Vines, Ocala, FL, p. A133

QUIRICONI, Stephan F
Chief Financial Officer, Bon Secours St. Mary'S Hospital, Richmond, VA, p. A665
Vice President Finance, Bon Secours Memorial Regional Medical Center, Mechanicsville, VA, p. A662
Vice President, Finance, Bon Secours St. Francis Medical Center, Midlothian, VA, p. A662

QUIRKE, David, Vice President Information Services, Frederick Regional Health System, Frederick, MD, p. A290

QUIST, Robert, Interim Chief Executive Officer, Memorial Hospital Of Carbon County, Rawlins, WY, p. A712

QUITO, Arturo L, M.D., Chief of Staff, Erlanger Bledsoe Hospital, Pikeville, TN, p. A578

QUO, Justin, Chief of Staff, Chi Lakewood Health, Baudette, MN, p. A328

QVISTGAARD, Guy C, Chief Executive Officer, Highland Hospital, Oakland, CA, p. A75

R

RAAUM, Elizabeth, Manger Business Office, Roosevelt Medical Center, Culbertson, MT, p. A375

RABAGO, Janie, Chief Accountant, San Antonio State Hospital, San Antonio, TX, p. A635

RABEL, Jonas, President, Integris Miami Hospital, Miami, OK, p. A502

RABIDEAU, Ray, M.D., Senior Vice President and Chief Medical Officer, Memorial Hospital, North Conway, NH, p. A402

RABIN, Barry, M.D., Regional Medical Director, Linden Oaks Hospital, Naperville, IL, p. A190

RABINE, Traci, Vice President Clinic Operations, Prairie Lakes Healthcare System, Watertown, SD, p. A565

RABINOWITZ, Jordy, Senior Vice President Human Resources Operations, Westchester Medical Center, Valhalla, NY, p. A446

RABNER, Barry S., President and Chief Executive Officer, Princeton Healthcare System, Penn Medicine Princeton Medical Center, Plainsboro, NJ, p. A411

RABON, Catherine, M.D., Chief Medical Officer, Mcleod Health Clarendon, Manning, SC, p. A555

RABORN, Janelle, Chief Operating Officer, Lovelace Women'S Hospital, Albuquerque, NM, p. A416

RACHAL, Paul, M.D., Chief Medical Officer, Pointe Coupee General Hospital, New Roads, LA, p. A276

RACHUIG, Sue, Director Information Services, Tulane Health System, New Orleans, LA, p. A276

RACICOT, Mark, Chief Executive Officer, North Shore Medical Center, Miami, FL, p. A131

RACKLIFFE, David, Assistant Vice President Information Services, Bristol Hospital, Bristol, CT, p. A107

RACZEK, James, M.D., Sr. Vice President of Operations and Chief Medical Officer, Northern Light Eastern Maine Medical Center, Bangor, ME, p. A281

RADANDT, Jeremiah, President, Children'S Medical Center Plano, Plano, TX, p. A629

RADCLIFF, Joey, Chief Financial Officer, St. Bernards Five Rivers, Pocahontas, AR, p. A47

RADCLIFFE, Eric, M.D., Medical Director, United Hospital Center, Bridgeport, WV, p. A683

RADEMACHER, Frank
Director, Information Systems, St. Joseph Mercy Livingston Hospital, Howell, MI, p. A314

Senior Director Information Systems, St. Joseph Mercy Ann Arbor, Ypsilanti, MI, p. A325
RADER, Herbert, M.D., Advisor for Medical Affairs, Brookdale Hospital Medical Center, New York, NY, p. A432
RADFORD, Angie, R.N., Director of Nursing, Wills Memorial Hospital, Washington, GA, p. A163
RADFORD, Jeffrey, Chief Executive Officer, Select Specialty Hospital–Tri Cities, Bristol, TN, p. A566
RADKE, Erma, Director of Operations, Oakleaf Surgical Hospital, Altoona, WI, p. A691
RADNER, Allen, M.D., Chief Medical Officer, Salinas Valley Memorial Healthcare System, Salinas, CA, p. A83
RADOTICH, Maureen, Director Human Resources, Providence Valdez Medical Center, Valdez, AK, p. A27
RADTKE, Lisa, Chief Administrative Officer, Winneshiek Medical Center, Decorah, IA, p. A221
RADUNSKY, Daniel, M.D., Medical Staff President, Union County General Hospital, Clayton, NM, p. A417
RADZEVICH, Jason, Vice President Finance, Beth Israel Deaconess Hospital Plymouth, Plymouth, MA, p. A302
RAETHEL, Kathryn A., President and Chief Executive Officer, Adventist Health Castle, Kailua, HI, p. A165
RAETZ, Elizabeth A, R.N., MSN, Vice President Nursing and Chief Nursing Officer, Chi Health St Elizabeth, Lincoln, NE, p. A387
RAFALA, Paula, Director, Human Resources, Memorial Medical Center, Modesto, CA, p. A72
RAFFERTY, Joyce, Vice President Finance, The University Of Vermont Health Network–Champlain Valley Physicians Hospital, Plattsburgh, NY, p. A441
RAFFERTY, Patrick W, Executive Vice President and Chief Operating Officer, Community Regional Medical Center, Fresno, CA, p. A59
RAFFETY, Leannette, Administrative Generalist, Stroud Regional Medical Center, Stroud, OK, p. A508
RAFFOUL, John, Chief Executive Officer, Adventist Health White Memorial, Los Angeles, CA, p. A66
RAFUS, Matthew, Chief Information Officer, White River Junction Veterans Affairs Medical Center, White River Junction, VT, p. A655
RAGAIN, Michael, M.D., Chief Medical Officer and Senior Vice President, University Medical Center, Lubbock, TX, p. A622
RAGAN, Donna, R.N., Chief Nursing Officer, Shands Live Oak Regional Medical Center, Live Oak, FL, p. A128
RAGAS, Rene J., Chief Operating Officer, Our Lady Of The Angels Hospital, Bogalusa, LA, p. A264
RAGER, Claudia, R.N., Vice President Patient Care Services, Conemaugh Memorial Medical Center, Johnstown, PA, p. A528
RAGGIO, Sharon, President and Chief Executive Officer, West Springs Hospital, Grand Junction, CO, p. A101
RAGLAND, Jane, President Medical Staff, Christus Mother Frances Hospital – Jacksonville, Jacksonville, TX, p. A616
RAGLE, Bertha, Director Personnel, Crossridge Community Hospital, Wynne, AR, p. A49
RAGONA, Robert A, Senior Vice President Finance and Chief Financial Officer, Eastern Long Island Hospital, Greenport, NY, p. A428
RAGONESE–GREEN, Virginia, Chief Nursing Officer, Encompass Health Rehabilitation Hospital Of Northwest Tucson, Tucson, AZ, p. A37
RAGSDALE, Sarah, R.N., Chief Nursing Officer, Smith County Memorial Hospital, Smith Center, KS, p. A246
RAGUKAS, Judith, Interim Chief Nursing Officer, Tyler Memorial Hospital, Tunkhannock, PA, p. A542
RAHDERT, Richard, M.D., Medical Director, River Bend Hospital, West Lafayette, IN, p. A216
RAHIJA, David, President, Northshore University Health System, Evanston, IL, p. A182
RAHMAN, Randy
Chief Information Officer, Miami County Medical Center, Paola, KS, p. A243
Vice President and Chief Information Officer, Olathe Medical Center, Olathe, KS, p. A242
RAHMAN, Syed, M.D., Chief of Staff, Horizon Specialty Hospital, Las Vegas, NV, p. A395
RAHN, Kevin, President Medical Staff, Orthopaedic Hospital Of Lutheran Health Network, Fort Wayne, IN, p. A204
RAINA, Suresh, M.D., Vice President Medical Staff and Chief Medical Officer, Hackensack Meridian Health Palisades Medical Center, North Bergen, NJ, p. A410
RAINBOLT, Mike, Chief Financial Officer, Rivendell Behavioral Health Services Of Arkansas, Benton, AR, p. A39
RAINEY, Jackie, Chief Financial Officer, Little River Memorial Hospital, Ashdown, AR, p. A39
RAINEY, Mark J, Director Human Resources, Texas Health Presbyterian Hospital Kaufman, Kaufman, TX, p. A617
RAINEY, Michelle L., Senior Vice President and Chief Nursing Officer, Pikeville Medical Center, Pikeville, KY, p. A259
RAINS, Celeste, D.O., Chief of Staff, Logan County Hospital, Oakley, KS, p. A242
RAINS, Debbie, Coordinator Health Information Management, Erlanger Bledsoe Hospital, Pikeville, TN, p. A578
RAINS, Della, Chief Nursing Officer, Continuecare Hospital At Baptist Health Corbin, Corbin, KY, p. A250
RAINS, Jeff G., Chief Executive Officer, Baptist Medical Center East, Montgomery, AL, p. A21
RAINS, Jon–Michael
Chief Executive Officer, Carrus Rehabilitation Hospital, Sherman, TX, p. A637
Chief Executive Officer, Carrus Specialty Hospital, Sherman, TX, p. A637
RAINS, Paul, President, St. Joseph'S Behavioral Health Center, Stockton, CA, p. A90
RAINS, Ronald, Chief Executive Officer, University Behavioral Health Of Denton, Denton, TX, p. A599
RAINS, Steve, Director Information Services, Mckee Medical Center, Loveland, CO, p. A104
RAISNER, Gary, Chief Operating Officer, Norristown State Hospital, Norristown, PA, p. A533
RAJEWSKI, Frank A, Chief Financial Officer, Rooks County Health Center, Plainville, KS, p. A244
RAJPARA, Suresh, M.D., Chief Medical Officer, Jerome Golden Center For Behavioral Health, Inc., West Palm Beach, FL, p. A144
RAJU, Vasudeva, M.D., Chief, Long Term Acute Care Medicine, Brookdale Hospital Medical Center, New York, NY, p. A432
RAK, Roger, Director Human Resources, South Shore Hospital, Chicago, IL, p. A179
RAKES, Lori, Chief Operating Officer, Cartersville Medical Center, Cartersville, GA, p. A149
RAKES–STEPHENS, Kim, M.D., Chief Medical Staff, Colleton Medical Center, Walterboro, SC, p. A558
RAKOV, Robert, M.D., Chief Medical Officer, Cogdell Memorial Hospital, Snyder, TX, p. A637
RALSTIN, Char, Director of Nursing, Haven Senior Horizons, Phoenix, AZ, p. A33
RAMA–BANAAG, Gemma, R.N., MSN, Chief Nursing Officer, Paradise Valley Hospital, National City, CA, p. A74
RAMAGE, Gary, M.D., Chief Medical Officer, Mckenzie County Healthcare System, Watford City, ND, p. A470
RAMAN, Jayashree, Vice President and Chief Information Officer, Reading Hospital, West Reading, PA, p. A544
RAMAZANI, Regina
Chief Financial Officer, Garden Park Medical Center, Gulfport, MS, p. A347
Chief Financial Officer, Tulane Health System, New Orleans, LA, p. A276
Chief Operating Officer, Garden Park Medical Center, Gulfport, MS, p. A347
RAMEY, Rita, Director Information Systems, Buchanan General Hospital, Grundy, VA, p. A660
RAMEY, Robert L., President, Baptist Health Madisonville, Madisonville, KY, p. A257
RAMEY, Steve, Chief Financial Officer, Southampton Memorial Hospital, Franklin, VA, p. A659
RAMIREZ, Ana, Director of Nursing, Mesa Springs, Fort Worth, TX, p. A605
RAMIREZ, Arthur L., M.D.
Medical Director, El Paso Behavioral Health System, El Paso, TX, p. A601
Medical Director, Mesilla Valley Hospital, Las Cruces, NM, p. A418
RAMIREZ, Corazon, Chief Executive Officer, Saint Camillus Medical Center, Hurst, TX, p. A615
RAMIREZ, Eddy, Assistant Vice President Business Development, Ochsner Medical Center – Kenner, Kenner, LA, p. A270
RAMIREZ, Harvey, Chief Information Officer, Coleman County Medical Center, Coleman, TX, p. A592
RAMIREZ, Jaime, Chief Executive Officer, Mccamey County Hospital District, Mccamey, TX, p. A624
RAMIREZ, Jolene Elizabeth, R.N., Chief Nursing Officer, Vice President Nursing Services, Aurora Medical Center – Manitowoc County, Two Rivers, WI, p. A707
RAMIREZ, Omar, Chief Executive Officer, Los Angeles Community Hospital At Los Angeles, Los Angeles, CA, p. A68
RAMIREZ, Ruben, M.D., Chief of Staff, Monterey Park Hospital, Monterey Park, CA, p. A73
RAMIREZ, Susan, Chief Nursing Officer, Encompass Health Rehabilitation Hospital Of Las Vegas, Las Vegas, NV, p. A395
RAMIREZ, Venus V., Executive Director, Hospital San Pablo Del Este, Fajardo, PR, p. A716
RAMIREZ, Willie, Manager Labor Relations, Laguna Honda Hospital And Rehabilitation Center, San Francisco, CA, p. A85
RAMLO, Ricki, Chief Operating Officer and Human Resources, Jamestown Regional Medical Center, Jamestown, ND, p. A468
RAMLOCHAN, Tara, Chief Executive Officer, Meade District Hospital, Meade, KS, p. A240
RAMON, Maggie, Chief Financial Officer, Cochran Memorial Hospital, Morton, TX, p. A625
RAMOS, Eduardo, M.D., Medical Director, Encompass Health Rehabilitation Hospital Of San Juan, San Juan, PR, p. A718
RAMOS, Eric, M.D., Division Chief Medical Officer, Southern Hills Hospital And Medical Center, Las Vegas, NV, p. A395
RAMOS, Gracie, Chief Human Resources Officer, Ogallala Community Hospital, Ogallala, NE, p. A388
RAMOS, Holly, R.N., Chief Clinical Officer, Kindred Hospital–Ontario, Ontario, CA, p. A76
RAMOS, Jessie, Manager Human Resources, Skyline Hospital, White Salmon, WA, p. A682
RAMOS, Jet, Head Staff Administration, Naval Hospital Camp Pendleton, Camp Pendleton, CA, p. A54
RAMOS, Raymond, FACHE, Chief Operating Officer, Doctors Hospital Of Laredo, Laredo, TX, p. A619
RAMPAT, Ananda, Chief Financial Officer, Northwest Medical Center, Margate, FL, p. A129
RAMPP, Randal D, M.D., Chief Medical Officer, Saint Thomas River Park Hospital, Mc Minnville, TN, p. A574
RAMSAMY, Dev, Chief Financial Officer, St. Rose Dominican Hospitals – San Martin Campus, Las Vegas, NV, p. A396
RAMSER, Emmett, Chief Administrative Officer, Norton Children'S Hospital, Louisville, KY, p. A256
RAMSEY, Antonina, Senior Vice President and Chief Human Resource Officer, Henry Ford Hospital, Detroit, MI, p. A310
RAMSEY, David L., President and Chief Executive Officer, Charleston Area Medical Center, Charleston, WV, p. A684
RAMSEY, Kristin, R.N., Senior Vice President and Chief Nursing Executive, Northwestern Memorial Hospital, Northwestern Memorial Hospital, Chicago, IL, p. A178
RAMSEY, Lisa, Chief Financial Officer, Prairie View, Newton, KS, p. A242
RAMSEY, Rance, Chief Executive Officer, Martin County Hospital District, Stanton, TX, p. A638
RAMSEY, Rhonda, Controller, Healthsouth Deaconess Rehabilitation Hospital, Evansville, IN, p. A203
RAMSEY, Ross, M.D., Chief of Staff, Scheurer Hospital, Pigeon, MI, p. A319
RAMSEY, Roy M., Executive Director, Bradford Health Services At Warrior Lodge, Warrior, AL, p. A24
RAMSEY, Thomas, Chief Financial Officer, Hancock Medical Center, Bay Saint Louis, MS, p. A344
RAMSEY, Tom, Chief Financial Officer, Morehouse General Hospital, Bastrop, LA, p. A263
RAMTHUN, Jane, Chief Financial Officer, Story County Medical Center, Nevada, IA, p. A227
RANA, Chaula, M.D., Medical Director, Encompass Health Rehabilitation Hospital Of San Antonio, San Antonio, TX, p. A634
RANCK, Sonja, MSN, R.N., Chief Operating Officer and Chief Nursing Officer, Mercyone Newton Medical Center, Newton, IA, p. A227
RANCOURT, Lindsay, Director of Nursing, Upper Connecticut Valley Hospital, Colebrook, NH, p. A399
RANDALL, Andrea, Interim Chief Executive Officer, Haskell County Community Hospital, Stigler, OK, p. A507
RANDALL, Bryan J
Vice President Finance and Chief Financial Officer, Heritage Valley Health System, Beaver, PA, p. A520
Vice President Finance and Chief Financial Officer, Sewickley Valley Hospital, (A Division Of Valley Medical Facilities), Sewickley, PA, p. A541
RANDALL, Cherry, Business Officer, Greater Binghamton Health Center, Binghamton, NY, p. A423
RANDALL, Jody, Chief Executive Officer/Chief Nursing Officer, Woodlands Specialty Hospital, The Woodlands, TX, p. A641
RANDLE, Emily, Vice President Operations, Memorialcare, Orange Coast Memorial Medical Center, Fountain Valley, CA, p. A58
RANDOLPH, Arianne, Director Human Resources, Pikes Peak Regional Hospital, Woodland Park, CO, p. A106
RANDOLPH, Bonnie, M.D., Chief of Staff, Community Hospital, Torrington, WY, p. A713
RANDOLPH, Joseph, M.D., Chairman Medical Executive Committee, Orthoindy Hospital, Indianapolis, IN, p. A207
RANDOLPH, Karsten, Executive Vice President and Chief Financial Officer, Adventhealth Shawnee Mission, Shawnee Mission, KS, p. A245
RANDOLPH, Linda, Director Personnel Services, Washington County Hospital, Chatom, AL, p. A16
RANDOLPH, Mark, President, Ochsner Lsu Health Shreveport – Academic Medical Center, Shreveport, LA, p. A278
RANEY, Hollie, Director of Nursing, Dallas County Medical Center, Fordyce, AR, p. A42

RANEY, Lance C., Commander, Womack Army Medical Center, Fort Bragg, NC, p. A454
RANGE, Bonny, MSN, Chief Nursing Officer, Holy Family Memorial, Manitowoc, WI, p. A699
RANKIN, Charlotte, R.N., Chief Operating Officer, Mercy Hospital Rogers, Rogers, AR, p. A48
RANKIN, Cynthia, Chief Nursing Officer, Lovelace Unm Rehabilitation Hospital, Albuquerque, NM, p. A416
RANNEY, Timothy, M.D., Chief Medical Officer, Seton Medical Center, Daly City, CA, p. A56
RANSOM, Natalie
Chief Nursing Officer, Mountainview Hospital, Las Vegas, NV, p. A395
Chief Nursing Officer, North Florida Regional Medical Center, Gainesville, FL, p. A123
RANSOM, Ric A., Chief Operating Officer, Prisma Health Greenville Memorial Hospital, Greenville, SC, p. A553
RAO, Kalapala, M.D., Medical Director, Encompass Health Rehabilitation Hospital Of Parkersburg, Parkersburg, WV, p. A688
RAPENSKE, Jennifer, Manager Financial Services, Mercyone New Hampton Medical Center, New Hampton, IA, p. A227
RAPP, Catherine, R.N., MS, Vice President Nursing, Oconomowoc Memorial Hospital, Oconomowoc, WI, p. A702
RAPP, David, Chief Information Officer, Wheeling Hospital, Wheeling, WV, p. A690
RAPP, Ron, Vice President Finance, Upmc Cole, Coudersport, PA, p. A523
RAPPACH, Shannon, Chief Fiscal Services, Dayton Veterans Affairs Medical Center, Dayton, OH, p. A481
RASCHKE, Judy, Director Human Resources, Pipestone County Medical Center Avera, Pipestone, MN, p. A338
RASHID, Harun, Vice President and Chief Information Officer, Akron Children'S Hospital, Akron, OH, p. A471
RASHILLA, Matt, Chief Information and Application Officer, Monongahela Valley Hospital, Monongahela, PA, p. A532
RASK, Brenda, Vice President Operations, Chi St Alexius Health Carrington Medical Center, Carrington, ND, p. A465
RASKE, Jamie, Information Technology Lead, Avera St. Mary'S Hospital, Pierre, SD, p. A562
RASMUSSEN, Diane, Director Human Resources, Cambridge Medical Center, Cambridge, MN, p. A329
RASMUSSEN, Jeanell, R.N., Vice President Patient Care Services and Chief Nursing Officer, Harrison Medical Center, Bremerton, WA, p. A670
RASMUSSEN, John, Vice President for Information Technology, Medstar Georgetown University Hospital, Washington, DC, p. A115
RASMUSSEN, Rick, Chief Executive Officer, Northwest Specialty Hospital, Post Falls, ID, p. A171
RASMUSSEN, Scott, Director Human Resources, Lincoln Regional Center, Lincoln, NE, p. A387
RASMUSSON, Duane, Vice President Human Resources, St. Cloud Hospital, Saint Cloud, MN, p. A339
RASNICK, Laura Lynn, Administrator, Parkland Health Center–Bonne Terre, Bonne Terre, MO, p. A356
RASOOL, Chaudri, D.O., Chief of Staff, Gundersen Palmer Lutheran Hospital And Clinics, West Union, IA, p. A231
RASOR, Linda, Chief Executive Officer, Plains Memorial Hospital, Dimmitt, TX, p. A600
RASTER, Robert, M.D., Medical Director, Michiana Behavioral Health Center, Plymouth, IN, p. A213
RATAJ, Marianne, Chief Nursing Officer, Mercy Hospital Fort Smith, Fort Smith, AR, p. A42
RATCLIFF, David, M.D., Chief Medical Affairs, Washington Regional Medical Center, Fayetteville, AR, p. A42
RATCLIFF, Paul, Director Information Services, Baylor Scott & White Medical Center – Carrollton, Carrollton, TX, p. A591
RATCLIFFE, Alma, M.D., Executive Vice President Medical Staff and Business Development, Saint Clare'S Denville Hospital, Denville, NJ, p. A404
RATH, Kevin, Vice President and Executive Director, Amita Health Hoffman Estates, Hoffman Estates, IL, p. A186
RATH, Megan, Chief Financial Officer, Wishek Community Hospital And Clinics, Wishek, ND, p. A470
RATHGABER, Scott W., Chief Executive Officer, Gundersen Lutheran Medical Center, La Crosse, WI, p. A697
RATLIFF, Ada
Chief Executive Officer, Claiborne County Medical Center, Port Gibson, MS, p. A353
Chief Information Officer, Claiborne County Medical Center, Port Gibson, MS, p. A353
RATLIFF, Bonnie, Chief Information Officer, Columbia Memorial Hospital, Hudson, NY, p. A429
RATLIFF, Kim, Director Health Information Management, Southwestern Virginia Mental Health Institute, Marion, VA, p. A662
RATLIFF, Maggie, Vice President Information Systems, Sarah Bush Lincoln Health Center, Mattoon, IL, p. A188
RATLIFF, Simon
Chief Operating Officer, Logan Regional Medical Center, Logan, WV, p. A686
Interim Chief Executive Officer, Logan Regional Medical Center, Logan, WV, p. A686
RATLIFF, Steve, Director Information Technology, Guadalupe Regional Medical Center, Seguin, TX, p. A636
RATLIFF, Tammy, Chief Executive Officer, Regency Hospital Of Greenville, Greenville, SC, p. A553
RATNASAMY, Suthanthira M., Chief Executive Officer, Kindred Hospital Bay Area–Tampa, Tampa, FL, p. A141
RATTLE, John, Chief Financial Officer, West Springs Hospital, Grand Junction, CO, p. A101
RATTRAY, Cindy Stewart, Director Human Resources, Jewish Hospital–Shelbyville, Shelbyville, KY, p. A260
RAU, John, President and Chief Executive Officer, Stevens Community Medical Center, Morris, MN, p. A336
RAU, Robin, Chief Executive Officer, Miller County Hospital, Colquitt, GA, p. A150
RAUB, Jessica, Director Health Information Management, Seven Hills Hospital, Henderson, NV, p. A394
RAUCH, Rhonda, Chief Nursing Officer, Lovelace Regional Hospital – Roswell, Roswell, NM, p. A420
RAUCH, Scott C, Vice President Human Resources, Reid Health, Richmond, IN, p. A214
RAUCH, Scott L., President and Psychiatrist in Chief, Mclean Hospital, Belmont, MA, p. A294
RAUEN, Rebecca A., Director Human Resources, Maple Grove Hospital, Maple Grove, MN, p. A335
RAUH, Bradley W., Vice President, Chief Operating Officer, Southwest General Health Center, Middleburg Heights, OH, p. A487
RAUH, Cindy, R.N., Vice President and Chief Nursing Officer, Duncan Regional Hospital, Duncan, OK, p. A498
RAUNER, Mary Ellen, R.N., Chief Nursing Officer, Suburban Community Hospital, Norristown, PA, p. A533
RAUPERS, Deb, MSN, R.N.
Chief Nursing Officer, Guthrie Corning Hospital, Corning, NY, p. A426
Vice President Patient Services and Chief Nursing Officer, Cayuga Medical Center At Ithaca, Ithaca, NY, p. A429
RAUTIO, Wendy, Chief Financial Officer, Munising Memorial Hospital, Munising, MI, p. A318
RAVELING, Lynn, Chief Financial Officer, Pocahontas Community Hospital, Pocahontas, IA, p. A228
RAWLEY, Jennifer, Chief Executive Officer, Select Specialty Hospital–Durham, Durham, NC, p. A453
RAWLINGS, Linda, Director Human Resources and Personnel, Three Rivers Hospital, Waverly, TN, p. A580
RAWLINGS, Michael, Interim Chief Operating Officer, Brookdale Hospital Medical Center, New York, NY, p. A432
RAWLINGS, Patrick
Chief Human Resource Officer, Saint Francis Hospital, Charleston, WV, p. A684
Human Resources Director, Thomas Memorial Hospital, South Charleston, WV, p. A689
RAWLINGS, Sheri, Chief Information Officer, San Juan Regional Medical Center, Farmington, NM, p. A418
RAWSON, Richard, Chief Executive Officer, Adventist Health And Rideout, Marysville, CA, p. A71
RAWSON, Richard L, President and Chief Executive Officer, Adventist Medical Center – Hanford, Hanford, CA, p. A61
RAY, Beverly, Director Human Resources, West Tennessee Healthcare Dyersburg Hospital, Dyersburg, TN, p. A569
RAY, Brenda, Director Human Resources, Huntsville Memorial Hospital, Huntsville, TX, p. A615
RAY, Denise, Chief Executive Officer, Piedmont Mountainside Hospital, Jasper, GA, p. A155
RAY, Diane, R.N., FACHE, Senior Vice President and Chief Operating Officer; Network Chief Nursing Officer, St. Luke'S Hospital, Chesterfield, MO, p. A358
RAY, Donald, Vice President Operations, University Of Maryland Medical Center Midtown Campus, Baltimore, MD, p. A287
RAY, Elaine, Administrator, Choate Mental Health Center, Anna, IL, p. A173
RAY, Evan, Chief Executive Officer, St. Vincent'S Birmingham, Birmingham, AL, p. A15
RAY, Jerilyn, Manager Human Resources, St. Elizabeth Hospital, Enumclaw, WA, p. A672
RAY, Joel, MSN, Vice President and Chief Nursing Officer, Unc Rex Health Care, Raleigh, NC, p. A460
RAY, Kirk M., President and Chief Executive Officer, Mclaren Greater Lansing, Lansing, MI, p. A316
RAY, Marge, Director Information Systems, Mercyone Waterloo Medical Center, Waterloo, IA, p. A231
RAY, Marilyn, MSN, Chief Nursing Officer, Upson Regional Medical Center, Thomaston, GA, p. A161
RAY, Rachel, Chief Financial Officer, Unity Medical Center, Grafton, ND, p. A467
RAY, Roger A, M.D., Executive Vice President and Chief Medical Officer, Atrium Health'S Carolinas Medical Center, Charlotte, NC, p. A451
RAYBOURN, Gina, Director Health Information, Ellett Memorial Hospital, Appleton City, MO, p. A356
RAYLS, Kim, Director Human Resources, Twin Lakes Regional Medical Center, Leitchfield, KY, p. A254
RAYMER, Chris Lee.
Chief Executive Officer, Great River Medical Center, Blytheville, AR, p. A39
Chief Executive Officer, South Mississippi County Regional Medical Center, Osceola, AR, p. A47
RAYMOND, Greg, Regional Vice President, Southern Colorado, Children'S Hospital Colorado, Aurora, CO, p. A96
RAYMOND, Heather, Area Public Relations Director, Kaiser Permanente Fontana Medical Center, Fontana, CA, p. A58
RAYMOND, Jane, Vice President and Chief Operating Officer, Reston Hospital Center, Reston, VA, p. A665
RAYMOND, Katherine, Chief Nursing Officer, St. Rose Dominican Hospitals – San Martin Campus, Las Vegas, NV, p. A396
RAYMOND, Mindy, Vice President Human Resources, Boca Raton Regional Hospital, Boca Raton, FL, p. A118
RAYMOND, Scott, Director Information Systems, Memorialcare, Orange Coast Memorial Medical Center, Fountain Valley, CA, p. A58
RAYNER, Thomas J, Senior Vice President and Chief Operating Officer, Kaweah Delta Medical Center, Visalia, CA, p. A94
RAYNES, Anthony, M.D., Psychiatrist in Chief, Arbour H. R. I. Hospital, Brookline, MA, p. A297
RAYNES, Scott
President, Baptist Hospital, Pensacola, FL, p. A136
President, Gulf Breeze Hospital, Gulf Breeze, FL, p. A124
RAYNOR, Robert, Human Resources Director, Park Royal Hospital, Fort Myers, FL, p. A123
RAYUDU, Subbu, M.D., Chief of Staff, Alliance Healthcare System, Holly Springs, MS, p. A348
RAZMIC, Tammy, Associate Administrator Finance and Chief Financial Officer, Inova Mount Vernon Hospital, Alexandria, VA, p. A656
RAZO, Virginia, Chief Executive Officer, Curry General Hospital, Gold Beach, OR, p. A513
REA, Jerry A., Superintendent, Parsons State Hospital And Training Center, Parsons, KS, p. A243
REA, Noel, Interim Chief Executive Officer, South Peninsula Hospital, Homer, AK, p. A26
READ, Eddie, Interim Chief Financial Officer, Val Verde Regional Medical Center, Del Rio, TX, p. A599
READ, John, Chief Nursing Officer, Allegiance Specialty Hospital Of Greenville, Greenville, MS, p. A347
READ, Paul, R.N., MSN, Vice President and Chief Nursing Officer, Springhill Memorial Hospital, Mobile, AL, p. A20
READ, Richard, Chief Financial Officer, Central Florida Regional Hospital, Sanford, FL, p. A139
READER, G. Whitney, M.D., Chief Medical Officer, Kansas Medical Center, Andover, KS, p. A232
READING, Jared, M.D., Chief of Staff, Uvalde Memorial Hospital, Uvalde, TX, p. A643
READINGER, Phillip, Chief Executive Officer, Select Specialty Hospital–St. Louis, Saint Charles, MO, p. A368
REALE, Kelli, Vice President Human Resources, Upmc Mckeesport, Mckeesport, PA, p. A531
REAM, Tom, Regional Chief Information Officer, Sutter Auburn Faith Hospital, Auburn, CA, p. A51
REAMER, Roger J., Chief Executive Officer, Memorial Health Care Systems, Seward, NE, p. A391
REAMES, Jim, Director Human Resources, Bayfront Health St. Petersburg, Saint Petersburg, FL, p. A138
REANDEAU, Michael, Chief Information Officer, Mills–Peninsula Health Services, Burlingame, CA, p. A53
REASONER, Vanessa, Chief Executive Officer, Grace Medical Center, Lubbock, TX, p. A622
REASY, Stephanie
Administrator and Chief Executive Officer, Avera De Smet Memorial Hospital, De Smet, SD, p. A560
Administrator and Chief Executive Officer, Avera Weskota Memorial Hospital, Wessington Springs, SD, p. A565
REBERRY, Darinda, President and Chief Executive Officer, Western Missouri Medical Center, Warrensburg, MO, p. A372
REBLOCK, Kimberly, M.D., Chief Operating Officer, The Children'S Home Of Pittsburgh, Pittsburgh, PA, p. A537
REBOCK, Michael, Chief Medical Officer, Beaumont Hospital – Farmington Hills, Farmington Hills, MI, p. A311
RECA, Thomas, Deputy Executive Director and Chief Financial Officer, Brookdale Hospital Medical Center, New York, NY, p. A432
RECHNER, Paula, M.D., Chief Medical Officer, War Memorial Hospital, Sault Sainte Marie, MI, p. A322

RECHSTEINER, Hans, M.D., Chief of Staff, Burnett Medical Center, Grantsburg, WI, p. A695

RECKDENWALD, Jeanine, Vice President Human Resources and Support Services, Bristol Hospital, Bristol, CT, p. A107

RECKERT, Sandy, Director Communications and Public Affairs, Johns Hopkins Bayview Medical Center, Baltimore, MD, p. A286

RECTOR, Fax, Director Information Technology, Upmc Susquehanna Sunbury, Sunbury, PA, p. A542

RECTOR, Jeanne, Chief Nursing Officer, Carroll County Memorial Hospital, Carrollton, MO, p. A358

RECUPERO, David, Chief Financial Officer, San Gorgonio Memorial Hospital, Banning, CA, p. A52

REDD, Brook, M.D., Chief of Staff, Sanford Medical Center Thief River Falls, Thief River Falls, MN, p. A341

REDD, Dakota, R.N., Chief Clinical Officer, Kindred Hospital–St. Louis, Saint Louis, MO, p. A369

REDDEN, Chase, Chief Financial Officer, Palms Of Pasadena Hospital, Saint Petersburg, FL, p. A138

REDDING, Georgia, Director Human Resources, Forbes Hospital, Monroeville, PA, p. A532

REDDING, Lisa, Manager Human Resources, Morgan County Arh Hospital, West Liberty, KY, p. A261

REDDY, Aravind, M.D., Chief of Staff, Iroquois Memorial Hospital And Resident Home, Watseka, IL, p. A197

REDDY, Challa, M.D., President Medical Staff, Mayo Regional Hospital, Dover, ME, p. A283

REDDY, Sridhar, M.D., Chief Medical Officer, Lake Huron Medical Center, Port Huron, MI, p. A320

REDHORSE–CHARLEY, Gloria, Director Human Resources, Northern Navajo Medical Center, Shiprock, NM, p. A420

REDING, Janeen K., Ed.D., Market Vice President of Human Resources, Chi St. Anthony Hospital, Pendleton, OR, p. A515

REDINGTON, James, M.D., Chief of Staff, Bath Community Hospital, Hot Springs, VA, p. A661

REDLER, Kathleen A., Director Patient Care Services, Shriners Hospitals For Children–Shreveport, Shreveport, LA, p. A278

REDMON, Gary, Chief Financial Officer, Methodist Hospital South, Jourdanton, TX, p. A616

REDMOND, Paula, Controller, Encompass Health Rehabilitation Hospital Of Tustin, Tustin, CA, p. A92

REDRICK, Heather, Chief Nursing Officer, Emory Johns Creek Hospital, Johns Creek, GA, p. A155

REECE, Brandon, Chief Executive Officer, Floyd Cherokee Medical Center, Centre, AL, p. A16

REECE, Mike, Chief Executive Officer, Fulton Medical Center, Fulton, MO, p. A360

REECE, Morris A, EVP/COO, Laird Hospital, Union, MS, p. A354

REECER, Jeff, Chief Executive Officer, Texas Health Presbyterian Hospital Denton, Denton, TX, p. A599

REED, Alex
Chief Information Officer, Avita Ontario Hospital, Ontario, OH, p. A489
Chief Information Officer, Galion Hospital, Galion, OH, p. A483

REED, Catherine, MSN, R.N., Chief Nursing Officer, Cedar Crest Hospital And Residential Treatment Center, Belton, TX, p. A588

REED, Chris, Director of Nursing, Pam Specialty Hospital Of Victoria North, Victoria, TX, p. A643

REED, Cindy, Director Community Relations, Austin State Hospital, Austin, TX, p. A585

REED, David Ashton, M.D., Chief Medical Officer, Louisiana Extended Care Hospital Of Lafayette, Lafayette, LA, p. A271

REED, Fred, M.D., Chief of Staff, Lincoln Hospital, Davenport, WA, p. A672

REED, Gloria, Leader Human Resources, Ssm Health Depaul Hospital – St. Louis, Bridgeton, MO, p. A357

REED, Helen, Director Health Information, North Mississippi Medical Center–Eupora, Eupora, MS, p. A346

REED, James K.
Chief Executive Officer, Albany Memorial Hospital, Albany, NY, p. A422
Chief Executive Officer, Samaritan Hospital – Main Campus, Troy, NY, p. A445
Chief Executive Officer, St. Peter'S Hospital, Albany, NY, p. A422

REED, Jason, Chief Executive Officer, Beacham Memorial Hospital, Magnolia, MS, p. A350

REED, John E, M.D., Medical Director, Baptist Memorial Hospital–Golden Triangle, Columbus, MS, p. A346

REED, Kathleen, Manager Human Resources, Missouri Baptist Sullivan Hospital, Sullivan, MO, p. A372

REED, Kirby, Director Information Systems, Franciscan Health Rensselaer, Rensselaer, IN, p. A214

REED, Laura, R.N.
Chief Nursing Executive, Bethesda Hospital, Saint Paul, MN, p. A339
Chief Nursing Executive, St. John'S Hospital, Maplewood, MN, p. A335

REED, Leslie, Chief Financial Officer, Wright Memorial Hospital, Trenton, MO, p. A372

REED, Linda
Vice President and Chief Information Officer, St. Joseph'S University Medical Center, Paterson, NJ, p. A410
Vice President Information Systems and Chief Information Officer, Newton Medical Center, Newton, NJ, p. A410

REED, Lorrie, Chief Financial Officer, Osceola Community Hospital, Sibley, IA, p. A229

REED, Margaret M, R.N., Chief Nursing Officer, Altru Health System, Grand Forks, ND, p. A467

REED, Pamela R., Chief Executive Officer, Kindred Hospital Melbourne, Melbourne, FL, p. A129

REED, Renee
Director Human Resources, Ascension Via Christi Hospital, Manhattan, Manhattan, KS, p. A240
Director Human Resources, Wamego Health Center, Wamego, KS, p. A247

REED, Tim, Vice President and Chief Financial Officer, Virginia Mason Memorial, Yakima, WA, p. A682

REED, Tina, Director of Human Resources, Encompass Health Rehabilitation Hospital Of Modesto, Modesto, CA, p. A72

REED, Tracy Collings, Vice President Patient Care Services, Chief Nursing Officer, Siskin Hospital For Physical Rehabilitation, Chattanooga, TN, p. A567

REED, Zachary, Chief Operating Officer, Henrico Doctors' Hospital, Richmond, VA, p. A666

REEDER, Austin, Chief Executive Officer, St. Charles Parish Hospital, Luling, LA, p. A272

REEDER, Carol, R.N., Chief Nursing Officer, St. Joseph Hospital, Eureka, CA, p. A57

REEDER, Janet Lee, MSN, Chief Nurse Executive, Kaiser Westside Medical Center, Hillsboro, OR, p. A513

REEDER, Wendy, R.N., Chief Nursing Officer, Harrison Memorial Hospital, Cynthiana, KY, p. A251

REEDY, James Christopher, Chief Nursing Officer, Sutter Delta Medical Center, Antioch, CA, p. A50

REEDY, Janet, Manager Human Resources, St. Thomas More Hospital, Canon City, CO, p. A97

REEFER, John C, M.D., Director, Butler Health System, Butler, PA, p. A521

REEL, Micah, Director of Bio–Med, Potomac Valley Hospital, Keyser, WV, p. A686

REEL, Stephanie L, Senior Vice President Information Services, Johns Hopkins Hospital, Baltimore, MD, p. A286

REES, Adam, President, Essentia Health St. Joseph'S Medical Center, Brainerd, MN, p. A329

REES, Jeff, Director Information Systems, Bacharach Institute For Rehabilitation, Pomona, NJ, p. A411

REES, Matthew, Administrator, Jerold Phelps Community Hospital, Garberville, CA, p. A60

REES, Stephen G., M.D., Vice President Medical Affairs, Lafayette General Medical Center, Lafayette, LA, p. A271

REESE, Bert
Chief Information Officer, Sentara Leigh Hospital, Norfolk, VA, p. A664
Chief Information Officer, Sentara Norfolk General Hospital, Norfolk, VA, p. A664
Chief Information Officer, Sentara Princess Anne Hospital, Virginia Beach, VA, p. A668

REESE, Jeff, Chief Financial Officer, Rusk Rehabilitation Hospital, Columbia, MO, p. A359

REESE, Jeffrey, Chief Executive Officer, Van Matre Encompass Health, Rockford, IL, p. A195

REESE, Kathie, Regional Administrator and Chief Executive Officer, Christus Dubuis Hospital Of Paris, Paris, TX, p. A627

REESE, Maryann, President and Chief Executive Officer, Saint Francis Medical Center, Cape Girardeau, MO, p. A357

REESE, Mike, Chief Financial Officer, Ou Medical Center, Oklahoma City, OK, p. A505

REESE, Todd, Director Human Performance, Adventist Health Castle, Kailua, HI, p. A165

REETZ, Brenda, Chief Executive Officer, Greene County General Hospital, Linton, IN, p. A210

REETZ, Renee, Director Human Resources, Ascension Standish Hospital, Standish, MI, p. A323

REEVE, Jay A., President and Chief Executive Officer, Eastside Psychiatric Hospital, Tallahassee, FL, p. A140

REEVES, Cory, Chief Financial Officer, Adventhealth Gordon, Calhoun, GA, p. A149

REEVES, Danny, Chief Financial Officer, Penrose–St. Francis Health Services, Colorado Springs, CO, p. A98

REEVES, Katy, Vice President Human Resources, Fauquier Hospital, Warrenton, VA, p. A668

REEVES, Kaylene, Director, Tahoe Pacific Hospitals, Sparks, NV, p. A398

REEVES, Matthew, D.O., Chief Medical Officer, Atrium Medical Center, Middletown, OH, p. A487

REEVES, Mike
Chief Information Officer, St. John Owasso, Owasso, OK, p. A506
Vice President, St. John Medical Center, Tulsa, OK, p. A510

REEVES, Pamela J., Director, John D. Dingell Veterans Affairs Medical Center, Detroit, MI, p. A310

REEVES, Steve, M.D., Chief Medical Staff, Greater Regional Medical Center, Creston, IA, p. A220

REEVES, Susan A, Chief Nursing Executive, Dartmouth–Hitchcock Medical Center, Lebanon, NH, p. A400

REEVES, Timothy, Administrator, Bucktail Medical Center, Renovo, PA, p. A540

REEVES, Valerie, Chief Financial Officer, Integris Miami Hospital, Miami, OK, p. A502

REFFNER, Gina, Chief Financial Officer, Little Colorado Medical Center, Winslow, AZ, p. A38

REFNESS, Kristen, Director, Financial Operations, Linden Oaks Hospital, Naperville, IL, p. A190

REGAN, Timothy, President and Chief Medical Officer, Lakeland Regional Health Medical Center, Lakeland, FL, p. A127

REGAN, Timothy, M.D., President and Chief Medical Officer, Lakeland Regional Health Medical Center, Lakeland, FL, p. A127

REGEN, Debbie, R.N., Chief Nursing Officer, Hackensack Meridian Health Mountainside Medical Center, Montclair, NJ, p. A408

REGIER, Donald, M.D., Chief Medical Officer, Sedgwick County Health Center, Julesburg, CO, p. A102

REGIER, Marion, Chief Executive Officer, Hillsboro Community Hospital, Hillsboro, KS, p. A236

REGIER, Steve, Chief Financial Officer, Kearney Regional Medical Center, Kearney, NE, p. A386

REGISTER, Kellie, Director of Nursing, Clinch Memorial Hospital, Homerville, GA, p. A155

REGULA, John
Chief Information Officer, Allied Services Rehabilitation Hospital, Scranton, PA, p. A540
Chief Information Officer, John Heinz Institute Of Rehabilitation Medicine, Wilkes, PA, p. A545

REHBEIN, Beth, Chief Nursing and Quality Officer, Story County Medical Center, Nevada, IA, p. A227

REHM, Janice, Manager Human Resources, Usa Children'S And Women'S Hospital, Mobile, AL, p. A20

REHM, Micah, Chief Nursing Officer, Forrest General Hospital, Hattiesburg, MS, p. A348

REHMER, Patricia, President, Natchaug Hospital, Mansfield Center, CT, p. A108

REHN, Lindsay, Executive Director of Financial Operations, Wellstar Paulding Hospital, Hiram, GA, p. A154

REHN, Ronald G.
Chief Executive Officer, Providence Mount Carmel Hospital, Colville, WA, p. A672
Chief Executive Officer, Providence St. Joseph'S Hospital, Chewelah, WA, p. A671

REICH, David I, M.D., President and Chief Operating Officer, Brookdale Hospital Medical Center, New York, NY, p. A432

REICH, David L., President and Chief Operating Officer, Brookdale Hospital Medical Center, New York, NY, p. A432

REICH, Joanne, R.N., Chief Nursing Officer, Jersey City Medical Center, Jersey City, NJ, p. A407

REICH, Joel R, M.D.
Senior Vice President Medical Affairs, Manchester Memorial Hospital, Manchester, CT, p. A108
Senior Vice President Medical Affairs, Rockville General Hospital, Vernon, CT, p. A111

REICHARD, Steve, Manager Information Systems, Brigham City Community Hospital, Brigham City, UT, p. A647

REICHERT, Don, Vice President Associate Chief Information Officer, Metrohealth Medical Center, Cleveland, OH, p. A478

REICHERT, James, Chief Medical Officer, Mercer Health, Coldwater, OH, p. A478

REICHFIELD, Michael L., President, Ohiohealth Doctors Hospital, Columbus, OH, p. A479

REICHLE, Paula, Senior Vice President and Chief Operating Officer, Sparrow Hospital, Lansing, MI, p. A316

REICHMAN, Joseph, M.D., Vice President Medical Affairs and Clinical Effectiveness, Hackensack Meridian Health Riverview Medical Center, Red Bank, NJ, p. A412

REID, Bernadette, Vice President, Information Technology and Chief Information Officer, Torrance Memorial Medical Center, Torrance, CA, p. A92

REID, Bev, Chief Financial Officer, St. Luke Hospital And Living Center, Marion, KS, p. A240

REID, Dereesa, Administrator, Shriners Hospitals For Children–Portland, Portland, OR, p. A516

REID, Jim, Vice President and Chief Information Officer, Covenant Children'S Hospital, Lubbock, TX, p. A621

REID, Kelly, Human Resources Director, South Mississippi State Hospital, Purvis, MS, p. A353

REID, Kenneth G., President and Chief Executive Officer, Carlinville Area Hospital, Carlinville, IL, p. A175

REID, Patricia, Director of Nursing, Marion General Hospital, Columbia, MS, p. A346

REID, Richard, Vice President Chief Finance Officer, Sparrow Carson Hospital, Carson City, MI, p. A308

REID, Stephanie, R.N., Vice President of Patient Care Services and Chief Nursing Officer, Carroll Hospital Center, Westminster, MD, p. A293

REIDER, Rochelle, Vice President Patient Care, Avera Queen Of Peace Hospital, Mitchell, SD, p. A562

REIDY, Margaret, M.D., Vice President Medical Affairs, Upmc Presbyterian, Pittsburgh, PA, p. A538

REILLY, Brian M, Chief Financial Officer, Robert Wood Johnson University Hospital, New Brunswick, NJ, p. A409

REILLY, Janelle, Chief Executive Officer, Chi Memorial, Chattanooga, TN, p. A567

REILLY, Joanne, Administrator, Hudson County Meadowview Psychiatric Hospital, Secaucus, NJ, p. A412

REILLY, John, M.D., Vice President Medical Affairs and Chief Medical Officer, Mercy Medical Center, Rockville Centre, NY, p. A443

REILLY, Robert, Vice President and Chief Financial Officer, Anne Arundel Medical Center, Annapolis, MD, p. A286

REILLY, Theresa, MSN, R.N., Senior Vice President Patient Services and Chief Nursing Officer, Abington Hospital, Abington, PA, p. A519

REILLY, Tiffany, Director Human Resources, Lifescape, Sioux Falls, SD, p. A563

REIMER, Arlo, M.D., Chief of Staff, Kearny County Hospital, Lakin, KS, p. A238

REIMER, Ronda, R.N., Chief Nursing Officer and Assistant Administrator, Franklin General Hospital, Hampton, IA, p. A223

REIN, Mitchell S, M.D., Chief Medical Officer, North Shore Medical Center, Salem, MA, p. A303

REINBOTH, Thomas, Chief Financial Officer, Roxborough Memorial Hospital, Philadelphia, PA, p. A536

REINER, Mark, Chief Medical Office, Executive, St. Anthony'S Rehabilitation Hospital, Lauderdale Lakes, FL, p. A128

REINERT, Brenda, Director Human Resources, Tomah Memorial Hospital, Tomah, WI, p. A706

REINERT, Chad, Chief Information Officer, Hamilton General Hospital, Hamilton, TX, p. A609

REINHARD, Diane, R.N., Vice President of Patient Care Services, Craig Hospital, Englewood, CO, p. A100

REINHARD, Russ, Chief Executive, Providence Willamette Falls Medical Center, Oregon City, OR, p. A515

REINHARDT, Tom, Chief Executive Officer, Cascade Medical Center, Cascade, ID, p. A168

REINKE, Bradley, M.D., Vice President Medical Affairs and Chief Medical Officer, Dameron Hospital, Stockton, CA, p. A90

REINKE, N Sue, Vice President Human Resources, Geisinger–Lewistown Hospital, Lewistown, PA, p. A530

REINKE, Peggy, Administrator, Chi Lisbon Health, Lisbon, ND, p. A468

REINKING, Cheryl, R.N., MS, Chief Nursing Officer, El Camino Hospital, Mountain View, CA, p. A73

REISELT, Doug
Vice President and Chief Information Officer, Baptist Memorial Hospital – Memphis, Memphis, TN, p. A574
Vice President and Chief Information Officer, Baptist Memorial Hospital–Collierville, Collierville, TN, p. A568

REISING, Robyn, R.N., Chief Nursing Officer, Decatur Memorial Hospital, Decatur, IL, p. A180

REISMAN, Ernestine O, Vice President Human Resources, Down East Community Hospital, Machias, ME, p. A284

REISS, Deanna, Hospital Director of Nursing, Devereux Children'S Behavioral Health Center, Malvern, PA, p. A530

REITZ, Brent, President, Adventist Healthcare Physical Health And Rehabilitation, Rockville, MD, p. A293

REITZ, Robert, Chief Executive Officer, Fulton State Hospital, Fulton, MO, p. A360

REITZEL, David, Chief Information Officer, Brookdale Hospital Medical Center, New York, NY, p. A432

REKOWSKI, Christian
Information Technology Director, Jenkins County Medical Center, Millen, GA, p. A157
Information Technology Manager, Optim Medical Center – Screven, Sylvania, GA, p. A161

RELPH, Daren, Chief Executive Officer, Wayne County Hospital, Corydon, IA, p. A220

REMALEY, Anne, Vice President Human Resources, Acmh Hospital, Kittanning, PA, p. A528

REMARK, Megan, President and Chief Executive Officer, Regions Hospital, Saint Paul, MN, p. A340

REMBIS, Michael A., Chief Executive Officer, Maui Memorial Medical Center, Wailuku, HI, p. A166

REMBOLD, Abbey
Human Resources Senior Generalist, Hampshire Memorial Hospital, Romney, WV, p. A689
Human Resources Senior Generalist, War Memorial Hospital, Berkeley Springs, WV, p. A683
Manager, Human Resource Business Partnerships, Valley Health Shenandoah Memorial Hospital, Woodstock, VA, p. A669

REMIGIO, Odalys, Assistant Vice President, Finance, Baptist Health South Florida, West Kendall Baptist Hospital, Miami, FL, p. A130

REMILLARD, John R, President and Chief Executive Officer, The University Of Vermont Health Network Elizabethtown Community Hospital, Elizabethtown, NY, p. A427

REMILLARD, John R., President and Chief Executive Officer, The University Of Vermont Health Network Elizabethtown Community Hospital, Elizabethtown, NY, p. A427

REMINGTON, Amanda
Director Human Resources, Wellstar Spalding Regional Hospital, Griffin, GA, p. A154
Director Human Resources, Wellstar Sylvan Grove Hospital, Jackson, GA, p. A155

REMLEY, Richard, Chief Executive Officer, Southcoast Behavioral Health, Dartmouth, MA, p. A298

REMSPECHER, Mark, Director Human Resources, Southeast Missouri Mental Health Center, Farmington, MO, p. A360

RENDA, Nick, Chief Financial Officer, Merit Health Woman'S Hospital, Flowood, MS, p. A347

RENDER–LEACH, Cynthia, Director Human Resources, Highland Community Hospital, Picayune, MS, p. A353

RENEAU, John D., Medical Director, Encompass Health Rehabilitation Hospital Of Las Vegas, Las Vegas, NV, p. A395

RENFREE, Mark, Chief Financial Officer, La Rabida Children'S Hospital, Chicago, IL, p. A178

RENIER, Hugh, M.D.
Vice President Medical Affairs, Essentia Health Duluth, Duluth, MN, p. A331
Vice President Medical Affairs, Essentia Health St. Mary'S Medical Center, Duluth, MN, p. A331

RENKIEWICZ, Ginger L, Chief Clinical Officer, Chief Nursing Executive, and Chief Quality Officer, Unitypoint Health – Trinity Rock Island, Rock Island, IL, p. A194

RENN, Amy Katherine, Interim Administrator, Patient Care and Nursing, Ascension Via Christi Hospital, Pittsburg, KS, p. A244

RENNEKER, James M, FACHE, MSN, R.N., Vice President and Chief Nursing Officer, Methodist Hospitals, Gary, IN, p. A205

RENNER, Dianne, Director Human Resources, Logansport State Hospital, Logansport, IN, p. A210

RENNING, Kathryn, Director of Nursing, Cherry County Hospital, Valentine, NE, p. A392

RENO, Kelly, R.N., Chief Nursing Officer, Menorah Medical Center, Overland Park, KS, p. A243

RENO, Mike, Chief Operating Officer, Hill Country Memorial Hospital, Fredericksburg, TX, p. A606

RENO, William, M.D., President Medical Staff, Merit Health Wesley, Hattiesburg, MS, p. A348

RENSHAW, Dee, Chief Executive Officer, Hillcrest Hospital Henryetta, Henryetta, OK, p. A500

RENTAS, Margarita, R.N., Nursing Director, Castaner General Hospital, Castaner, PR, p. A715

RENTSCH, Richard E, President, Stroud Regional Medical Center, Stroud, OK, p. A508

REOHR, Sara, Regional Controller, West Gables Rehabilitation Hospital, Miami, FL, p. A131

REPAC, Kimberly S, Senior Vice President and Chief Financial Officer, Western Maryland Regional Medical Center, Cumberland, MD, p. A290

REPASS, Lois, Quality Assurance Specialist and Coordinator Performance Improvement, Northern Nevada Adult Mental Health Services, Sparks, NV, p. A398

REPETTI, Gregory George., III, Chief Executive Officer, Multicare Valley Hospital, Spokane Valley, WA, p. A680

REPKO, Keith D., Director, Veterans Affairs St. Louis Health Care System, Saint Louis, MO, p. A371

REPPY, William, President, Lehigh Valley Hospital – Schuylkill, Pottsville, PA, p. A539

REPTA, Shirley, Chief Executive Officer, The Pavilion At Williamsburg Place, Williamsburg, VA, p. A669

RESENDEZ, James R., Chief Executive Officer, Doctors Hospital Of Laredo, Laredo, TX, p. A619

RESETAR, Gayle L, Vice President and Chief Operating Officer, Tidelands Georgetown Memorial Hospital, Georgetown, SC, p. A553

RESLER, Lori, R.N., Chief Nurse, Sullivan County Community Hospital, Sullivan, IN, p. A215

RESSLER, David, Chief Executive Officer, Aspen Valley Hospital, Aspen, CO, p. A96

RESSLER, Dennis, Vice President, Finance and Chief Financial Officer, Hendricks Regional Health, Danville, IN, p. A202

RESTREPO, Nicolas, M.D., Vice President Medical Affairs, Winchester Medical Center, Winchester, VA, p. A669

RESTUCCIA, Michael, Chief Information Officer, Hospital Of The University Of Pennsylvania, Philadelphia, PA, p. A535

RESTUM, William, Chief Executive Officer, Dmc – Rehabilitation Institute Of Michigan, Detroit, MI, p. A310

RETALIC, Tammy B., R.N., MS, Chief Nursing Officer, Hebrew Rehabilitation Center, Roslindale, MA, p. A302

RETHAMEL, Terry, Director of Support Services, Newport News Behavioral Health Center, Newport News, VA, p. A663

RETHORST, Richard, Chief of Medical Staff, Franklin Hospital District, Benton, IL, p. A174

RETTGER, Linda, M.D., President Medical Staff, Upmc Kane, Kane, PA, p. A528

RETTIG, Jeffrey, D.O., Chief of Staff, Limestone Medical Center, Groesbeck, TX, p. A608

RETTIG, Linda, Director Financial Services, Washington County Hospital, Washington, KS, p. A247

REULAND, Charles B., Sc.D.
Executive Vice President and Chief Operating Officer, Johns Hopkins Bayview Medical Center, Baltimore, MD, p. A286
Executive Vice President and Chief Operations Officer, Johns Hopkins Hospital, Baltimore, MD, p. A286

REUST, Michele, Controller, Memorial Hospital Of Texas County, Guymon, OK, p. A500

REUTTINGER, H. Rex, D.O., Chief Medical Officer, Administration, Garden City Hospital, Garden City, MI, p. A312

REVELS, Beverly, Director Human Resources, Sutter Amador Hospital, Jackson, CA, p. A62

REVELS, Tonya, Senior Strategic Business Partner, Mcdowell Hospital, Marion, NC, p. A458

REVERMAN, Larry, Director Information Systems, Clark Memorial Health, Jeffersonville, IN, p. A208

REVIEL, Jackie, Chief Executive Officer, Allen Parish Community Healthcare, Kinder, LA, p. A270

REWERTS, Karen
System Vice President Finance, Ssm Health St. Joseph – St. Charles, Saint Charles, MO, p. A368
System Vice President of Finance, Ssm Cardinal Glennon Children'S Hospital, Saint Louis, MO, p. A370
System Vice President of Finance, Ssm Health St. Mary'S Hospital – St. Louis, Saint Louis, MO, p. A370

REXFORD, Linda, Director Human Resources, Weeks Medical Center, Lancaster, NH, p. A400

REXWINKLE, Lori, Chief Executive Officer, Coffeyville Regional Medical Center, Coffeyville, KS, p. A233

REYES, Anthony, Information Technology Director, Commonwealth Health Center, Saipan, MP, p. A714

REYES, Glenda, Chief Financial Officer, Northwest Medical Center, Winfield, AL, p. A24

REYES, Marco, Executive Director, Hospital Psiquiatrico Metropolitano, Cabo Rojo, PR, p. A715

REYES, Netonua, MSN, Chief Operating Officer and Chief Nursing Officer, Broward Health Imperial Point, Fort Lauderdale, FL, p. A122

REYES, Raul, M.D., Medical Director, San Juan City Hospital, San Juan, PR, p. A719

REYES, Roxanne, Director of Nursing, Cornerstone Regional Hospital, Edinburg, TX, p. A601

REYKA, Michael, Chief Executive Officer, Western Maryland Hospital Center, Hagerstown, MD, p. A291

REYMAN, Reed, President, Chi St. Alexius Health – Dickinson Medical Center, Dickinson, ND, p. A466

REYNA, Krista, Chief Nursing Officer, Mcbride Orthopedic Hospital, Oklahoma City, OK, p. A504

REYNGOUDT, Mark
Chief Financial Officer, Brandywine Hospital, Coatesville, PA, p. A523
Chief Financial Officer, Upmc Carlisle, Carlisle, PA, p. A522

REYNOLDS, Angela D, Chief Financial Officer, Lewis–Gale Medical Center, Boones Mill, VA, p. A657

REYNOLDS, Denise, Chief Nursing Officer, Memorial Hospital Miramar, Miramar, FL, p. A132

REYNOLDS, Doug, Area Finance Officer, Kaiser Permanente Redwood City Medical Center, Redwood City, CA, p. A80

REYNOLDS, Ian, Chief Medical Officer, Advanced Diagnostics Hospital, Houston, TX, p. A610

REYNOLDS, James B, M.D., Medical Director, Northwest Missouri Psychiatric Rehabilitation Center, Saint Joseph, MO, p. A368

REYNOLDS, Jay, M.D., Chief Medical Officer and Chief Clinical Officer, The Aroostook Medical Center, Presque Isle, ME, p. A284
REYNOLDS, Katelyn, Manager Human Resources, Greeley County Health Services, Tribune, KS, p. A246
REYNOLDS, Lennetta M, Administrative Supervisor, Community Behavioral Health Hospital – Annandale, Annandale, MN, p. A327
REYNOLDS, Mike
Chief Financial Officer, Delta Medical Center, Memphis, TN, p. A574
Chief Financial Officer, Newberry County Memorial Hospital, Newberry, SC, p. A556
REYNOLDS, Paul, M.D., Medical Director, Coleman County Medical Center, Coleman, TX, p. A592
REYNOLDS, Ray, Chief Executive Officer, Glen Rose Medical Center, Glen Rose, TX, p. A607
REYNOLDS, Robert, Director Information Systems, Mary Rutan Hospital, Bellefontaine, OH, p. A473
REYNOLDS, Ronald J., President, Upmc Susquehanna Lock Haven, Lock Haven, PA, p. A530
REYNOLDS, Scott, Vice President Finance, Mercy Hospital Springfield, Springfield, MO, p. A371
REYNOLDS, Teresa, Chief Operating Officer, Haywood Regional Medical Center, Clyde, NC, p. A452
REYNOLDS, Todd, Chief Information Officer, Memorial Medical Center Of Ashland, Ashland, WI, p. A691
REYNOLDS, Vance V., Chief Executive Officer, Musc Health Florence Medical Center, Florence, SC, p. A553
REYNOLDS–GOSSETTE, Youdie, Controller, Wilma N. Vazquez Medical Center, Vega Baja, PR, p. A720
REZAC, Julie A, R.N., Chief Operating Officer, Saunders Medical Center, Wahoo, NE, p. A392
RHEINHEIMER, Rick, Chief Clinical Officer, Kindred Hospital–Chattanooga, Chattanooga, TN, p. A567
RHINE, Kathleen, President and Chief Executive Officer, Mount Nittany Medical Center, State College, PA, p. A541
RHINEHART, Jennie R., Administrator and Chief Executive Officer, Community Hospital, Tallassee, AL, p. A23
RHOADES, Charles E., Chief Executive Officer, Kansas City Orthopaedic Institute, Leawood, KS, p. A239
RHOADES, Mark, Vice President and Chief Human Resources Officer, Duncan Regional Hospital, Duncan, OK, p. A498
RHOADES, Shelly, Chief Financial Officer, Clarion Psychiatric Center, Clarion, PA, p. A522
RHOADS, Jack, M.D., Medical Director, Landmark Hospital Of Joplin, Joplin, MO, p. A362
RHOADS, Pam, Chief Financial Officer, Fairfax Behavioral Health, Kirkland, WA, p. A674
RHODES, David, M.D., Senior Vice President Medical Affairs and Chief Medical Officer, Rapides Regional Medical Center, Alexandria, LA, p. A262
RHODES, Helen, R.N., Associate Director Operations, Veterans Affairs Northern Indiana Health Care System, Fort Wayne, IN, p. A204
RHODES, Tracey, Coordinator Human Resources, Evergreen Medical Center, Evergreen, AL, p. A17
RHONE, Steve, R.N., MS, Vice President Patient Care Services, Beebe Healthcare, Lewes, DE, p. A113
RHYNALDS, Kayla, Interim Chief Financial Officer, Kearney County Health Services, Minden, NE, p. A387
RHYNE, Craig, M.D., FACS
Chief Medical Officer, Covenant Children'S Hospital, Lubbock, TX, p. A621
Chief Medical Officer, Covenant Medical Center, Lubbock, TX, p. A621
RHYNE, Dennis, M.D., Acting Medical Director, Fairbanks, Indianapolis, IN, p. A206
RHYNE, Tim, Personnel Officer, Ventura County Medical Center, Ventura, CA, p. A93
RIAL, Joanne, Chief Financial Officer, Cumberland Hospital For Children And Adolescents, New Kent, VA, p. A663
RIALS, Joe, Director Fiscal Services, North Mississippi State Hospital, Tupelo, MS, p. A354
RIALS, Loren
Chief Financial Officer, Musc Health Florence Medical Center, Florence, SC, p. A553
Chief Financial Officer, Musc Health Marion Medical Center, Mullins, SC, p. A556
RIANO, Omaira D., Chief Nursing Officer, Encompass Health Rehabilitation Hospital Of Sunrise, Sunrise, FL, p. A140
RIBA, Chris, Director Human Resources, Western Wisconsin Health, Baldwin, WI, p. A691
RICARDO, Jennifer, Director of Human Resources, Westchester General Hospital, Miami, FL, p. A131
RICCI, Lynn, President and Chief Executive Officer, Hospital For Special Care, New Britain, CT, p. A109
RICCIARDI, Patrice, Director Human Resources, Columbus Hospital Ltach, Newark, NJ, p. A409
RICCIO, Dustin
President Eastern Region, Newark–Wayne Community Hospital, Newark, NY, p. A439
President, Clifton Springs Hospital And Clinic, Clifton Springs, NY, p. A426
RICCIO, John A., M.D., Chief Medical Officer, Auburn Community Hospital, Auburn, NY, p. A423
RICCIONI, Michel
Chief Financial Officer, North Hawaii Community Hospital, Kamuela, HI, p. A165
Chief Financial Officer, Petaluma Valley Hospital, Petaluma, CA, p. A78
Chief Financial Officer, St. Joseph Hospital, Eureka, CA, p. A57
Chief Financial Officer, The Queen'S Medical Center, Honolulu, HI, p. A165
Vice President and Chief Financial Officer, Northern California Region, Queen Of The Valley Medical Center, Napa, CA, p. A74
RICCITELLI, Anthony, Chief Operating Officer, Worcester Recovery Center And Hospital, Worcester, MA, p. A305
RICE, Aimee, Human Resources Manager, Riverview Psychiatric Center, Augusta, ME, p. A281
RICE, Amy
Chief Financial Officer, Helena Regional Medical Center, Helena, AR, p. A43
Interim Chief Executive Officer, Helena Regional Medical Center, Helena, AR, p. A43
RICE, Bernard
Chief Compliance Officer, Rangely District Hospital, Rangely, CO, p. A105
Chief Information Officer, Nemours Children'S Hospital, Orlando, FL, p. A134
RICE, Carolyn, M.D., Director Medical Services, Naval Hospital Pensacola, Pensacola, FL, p. A136
RICE, Cathy, Director Support Services, Clifton–Fine Hospital, Star Lake, NY, p. A444
RICE, Craig, Director Information Technology, Schneck Medical Center, Seymour, IN, p. A214
RICE, James W., Director, Oscar G. Johnson Veterans Affairs Medical Center, Iron Mountain, MI, p. A315
RICE, Mark, CPA, Chief Financial Officer, Geisinger Jersey Shore Hospital, Jersey Shore, PA, p. A520
RICE, Mark J., Administrator, Ruston Regional Specialty Hospital, Ruston, LA, p. A277
RICE, Peter, M.D., Medical Director, Peacehealth Ketchikan Medical Center, Ketchikan, AK, p. A26
RICE, Tim, President and Chief Executive Officer, Lakewood Health System, Staples, MN, p. A341
RICH, Anna, Chief Financial Officer, Complex Care Hospital At Tenaya, Las Vegas, NV, p. A394
RICH, Bill, Chief Executive Officer, Tennova Healthcare–Shelbyville, Shelbyville, TN, p. A579
RICH, Judy F., President and Chief Executive Officer, Tmc Healthcare, Tucson, AZ, p. A38
RICH, Kori, Chief Executive Officer, The Physicians Centre Hospital, Bryan, TX, p. A590
RICH, Philip, M.D., Chief Medical Officer, West Hills Hospital, Reno, NV, p. A397
RICH, Travis, Chief Executive Officer, Highlands Rehabilitation Hospital, El Paso, TX, p. A602
RICHARD, Andrea J., M.D., Chief Medical Officer, Warren State Hospital, Warren, PA, p. A543
RICHARD, Angelique, R.N., Ph.D., Vice President Clinical Nursing, Chief Nursing Officer and Associate Dean for Practice, College of Nursing, Rush University Medical Center, Chicago, IL, p. A179
RICHARD, Brandi, Chief Nursing Officer, Michiana Behavioral Health Center, Plymouth, IN, p. A213
RICHARD, Brent, Administrative Director Information Systems, Southern Ohio Medical Center, Portsmouth, OH, p. A490
RICHARD, Christina, Market Chief Executive Officer, Kindred Hospital Tarrant County–Arlington, Arlington, TX, p. A583
RICHARD, Thomas, Director Budget and Revenue Cycle, Carris Health – Redwood, Redwood Falls, MN, p. A338
RICHARD, Tim, IT Coordinator, Crawford Memorial Hospital, Robinson, IL, p. A194
RICHARDS, Craig A., Chief Executive Officer, Mildred Mitchell–Bateman Hospital, Huntington, WV, p. A686
RICHARDS, Frank
Chief Information Officer, Geisinger Medical Center, Danville, PA, p. A523
Chief Information Officer, Geisinger Wyoming Valley Medical Center, Wilkes Barre, PA, p. A544
RICHARDS, Jaena, Chief Financial Officer, Deer Lodge Medical Center, Deer Lodge, MT, p. A376
RICHARDS, Jon, Chief Financial Officer, Tennova Newport Medical Center, Newport, TN, p. A578
RICHARDS, Jonathan, Chief Financial Officer, David Grant Usaf Medical Center, Travis Afb, CA, p. A92
RICHARDS, Judith, Director of Nursing, Adcare Hospital Of Worcester, Worcester, MA, p. A305
RICHARDS, Kelly, MSN
Senior Vice President and Chief Nursing Officer, Mercyone Cedar Falls Medical Center, Cedar Falls, IA, p. A218
Senior Vice President and Chief Nursing Officer, Mercyone Oelwein Medical Center, Oelwein, IA, p. A227
Senior Vice President and Chief Nursing Officer, Mercyone Waterloo Medical Center, Waterloo, IA, p. A231
RICHARDS, Kyle, Chief Executive Officer, Lake Region Healthcare, Fergus Falls, MN, p. A332
RICHARDS, Mandy, R.N., MSN, System Chief Nursing Officer, Allina Health Vice President of Care, Abbott Northwestern Hospital, Minneapolis, MN, p. A335
RICHARDS, Nate, Director Information Technology, Mitchell County Hospital Health Systems, Beloit, KS, p. A232
RICHARDS, Sheila K, Human Resources Director, Dallas Medical Center, Dallas, TX, p. A596
RICHARDS, Stanlee, R.N., MS, Chief Nurse Executive, Brookdale Hospital Medical Center, New York, NY, p. A432
RICHARDS, Suzanne
Chief Executive Officer, Hahnemann University Hospital, Philadelphia, PA, p. A534
Chief Executive Officer, St. Christopher'S Hospital For Children, Philadelphia, PA, p. A536
RICHARDS, Thom, Director Information Technology, Knoxville Hospital & Clinics, Knoxville, IA, p. A225
RICHARDSON, Crystal, Chief Nursing Officer, Vibra Hospital Of Richmond, Richmond, VA, p. A666
RICHARDSON, David, M.D., Chief of Staff, Delta Medical Center, Memphis, TN, p. A574
RICHARDSON, Denise, R.N., MSN, Senior Vice President and Chief Nursing Officer, Brookdale Hospital Medical Center, New York, NY, p. A432
RICHARDSON, Dorothy, Director Human Resources, Van Matre Encompass Health, Rockford, IL, p. A195
RICHARDSON, Dwayne, Chief Operating Officer, Placentia–Linda Hospital, Placentia, CA, p. A78
RICHARDSON, Greg H, Assistant Administrator Human Resources, Piedmont Newton Hospital, Covington, GA, p. A151
RICHARDSON, Irene, Chief Executive Officer, Memorial Hospital Of Sweetwater County, Rock Springs, WY, p. A712
RICHARDSON, James, Chief Medical Officer, Holy Cross Hospital, Chicago, IL, p. A177
RICHARDSON, Judy, M.D., President Medical Staff, Mid-Columbia Medical Center, The Dalles, OR, p. A518
RICHARDSON, Karen K., Senior Vice President and Chief Financial Officer, Providence Healthcare Network, Waco, TX, p. A644
RICHARDSON, Keith, President and Chief Executive Officer, East Liverpool City Hospital, East Liverpool, OH, p. A482
RICHARDSON, Kevin, M.D., Chief of Staff, Southwest Mississippi Regional Medical Center, Mccomb, MS, p. A350
RICHARDSON, Kirk
Vice President, Chief Operating Officer and Chief Nursing Officer, Bronson South Haven Hospital, South Haven, MI, p. A322
Vice President, Chief Operating Officer, and Chief Nursing Officer, Bronson Lakeview Hospital, Paw Paw, MI, p. A319
RICHARDSON, Kirk, R.N., Vice President, Chief Operating Officer, and Chief Nursing Officer, Bronson Lakeview Hospital, Paw Paw, MI, p. A319
RICHARDSON, Nathaniel, Jr, President, Decatur Morgan Hospital, Decatur, AL, p. A16
RICHARDSON, Pamela, Business Manager, Central Regional Hospital, Butner, NC, p. A450
RICHARDSON, Paul McKinley, Chief Medical Officer, Conway Medical Center, Conway, SC, p. A552
RICHARDSON, Robert, Information Technology Administrator, Porter Regional Hospital, Valparaiso, IN, p. A215
RICHARDSON, Rodney, Director of Information Technology, Baptist Health Corbin, Corbin, KY, p. A250
RICHARDSON, Sarah, Director Information Systems, Belton Regional Medical Center, Belton, MO, p. A356
RICHARDSON, Stanley, Coordinator Human Resources and Payroll Benefits, Kindred Hospital–San Antonio, San Antonio, TX, p. A634
RICHARDSON, Terika, President, Advocate Lutheran General Hospital, Park Ridge, IL, p. A192
RICHARDSON, Terrie, Coordinator Human Resources, Select Specialty Hospital–Augusta, Augusta, GA, p. A147
RICHARDSON, Timothy J, M.D., Chief of Staff, Maine Veterans Affairs Medical Center, Augusta, ME, p. A281
RICHARDSON, Todd, Chief Information Officer, Aspirus Medford Hospital & Clinics, Inc., Medford, WI, p. A699

RICHASON, Amie A
Vice President Human Resources, Leesburg Regional Medical Center, Leesburg, FL, p. A128
Vice President Human Resources, The Villages Regional Hospital, The Villages, FL, p. A142
RICHAUD, Benjamin, Interim Chief Executive Officer, Merit Health River Region, Vicksburg, MS, p. A355
RICHBOURG, Gail A, Director Human Resources, Mcleod Health Clarendon, Manning, SC, p. A555
RICHBURG, Melanie, Chief Executive Officer, Lynn County Hospital District, Tahoka, TX, p. A639
RICHCREEK, Keith, Manager Technical Services, Lafayette Regional Health Center, Lexington, MO, p. A364
RICHENS, Ken, Chief Information Officer, Central Valley Medical Center, Nephi, UT, p. A649
RICHER, R David, Chief Executive Officer, Cleveland Clinic Rehabilitation Hospital, Avon, OH, p. A472
RICHERT, Ed, M.D., Chief of Staff, Modoc Medical Center, Alturas, CA, p. A50
RICHETTI, Michael, Chief Financial Officer, Chilton Medical Center, Pompton Plains, NJ, p. A411
RICHHART, David, Chief Financial Officer, North Valley Hospital, Whitefish, MT, p. A381
RICHMAN, Craig, M.D., Medical Director, Meadows Psychiatric Center, Centre Hall, PA, p. A522
RICHMAN, Jonathan, M.D., Chief of Staff, Chase County Community Hospital, Imperial, NE, p. A386
RICHMAN, Timothy, President and Chief Executive Officer, Ascension Southeast Wisconsin Hospital – Elmbrook Campus, Brookfield, WI, p. A693
RICHMOND, Andy, Director Information Technology, Choctaw Memorial Hospital, Hugo, OK, p. A501
RICHMOND, Brett M., President and Chief Executive Officer, Methodist Fremont Health, Fremont, NE, p. A385
RICHMOND, Craig, Senior Vice President and Chief Financial Officer, Metrohealth Medical Center, Cleveland, OH, p. A478
RICHMOND, Ira, Associate Director Patient Care Services, Veterans Affairs Pittsburgh Healthcare System, Pittsburgh, PA, p. A538
RICHOUX, Jacquelyn, Chief Financial Officer, Lady Of The Sea General Hospital, Cut Off, LA, p. A266
RICHTER, Daniel, M.D., Chief of Staff, Chi Health Missouri Valley, Missouri Valley, IA, p. A226
RICHTER, Thomas V., Chief Executive Officer, Pioneer Memorial Hospital And Health Services, Viborg, SD, p. A565
RICK, Bob, Vice President Information Technology, Usmd Hospital At Arlington, Arlington, TX, p. A584
RICKARD, Sheryl, Chief Executive Officer, Bonner General Hospital, Sandpoint, ID, p. A172
RICKENS, Chris, R.N., MS, Senior Vice President and Chief Nursing Officer, Upmc Altoona, Altoona, PA, p. A520
RICKS, Edward, Vice President and Chief Information Officer, Beaufort Memorial Hospital, Beaufort, SC, p. A549
RICKS, Loretha, Human Resources Supervisor, Southampton Memorial Hospital, Franklin, VA, p. A659
RICKS, Michael, Chief Operating Officer, Hoag Memorial Hospital Presbyterian, Newport Beach, CA, p. A74
RICO, Carrie, Chief Human Resource Officer, Keefe Memorial Hospital, Cheyenne Wells, CO, p. A97
RICO, Richard, Vice President and Chief Financial Officer, Sky Lakes Medical Center, Klamath Falls, OR, p. A514
RIDALL, Jackie, Director Human Resources, Berwick Hospital Center, Berwick, PA, p. A520
RIDDER, Terri, Director Human Resources, St. Francis Memorial Hospital, West Point, NE, p. A392
RIDDLE, Kent, Chief Executive Officer, Mary Free Bed Rehabilitation Hospital, Grand Rapids, MI, p. A312
RIDGE, Frederick R., M.D., Chief of Staff, Greene County General Hospital, Linton, IN, p. A210
RIDGE, Lisa, Chief Executive Officer, Van Diest Medical Center, Webster City, IA, p. A231
RIDLEN, Deborah, CPA, Vice President Finance and Chief Financial Officer, Schneck Medical Center, Seymour, IN, p. A214
RIDLEY, John, Executive Vice President & Chief Operating Officer, Decatur Memorial Hospital, Decatur, IL, p. A180
RIDLEY, Pam, Director Information Systems, Henry County Medical Center, Paris, TN, p. A578
RIDLEY, Zena, Director Human Resources, Harbor Oaks Hospital, New Baltimore, MI, p. A318
RIDNER, Sheila, R.N., Director of Nursing, Unity Psychiatric Care–Columbia, Columbia, TN, p. A568
RIEBER, Dan, Chief Financial Officer, Uchealth Memorial Hospital, Colorado Springs, CO, p. A98
RIEBER, Jim, Director Information Systems, Perham Health, Perham, MN, p. A337
RIECHERS, Thomas, M.D., Chief Medical Staff, Mercy Hospital Washington, Washington, MO, p. A373
RIECK, Amy, Human Resources Officer, Greater Regional Medical Center, Creston, IA, p. A220
RIEDEL, Sherry, Chief Financial Management Service, John D. Dingell Veterans Affairs Medical Center, Detroit, MI, p. A310
RIEDLINGER, Floyd, Director Human Resources, West Jefferson Medical Center, Marrero, LA, p. A273
RIEDLINGER, Joann, Vice President Nursing and Manager Information Systems, Bucyrus Hospital, Bucyrus, OH, p. A474
RIEG, Kevin, M.D., President Medical Staff, Ascension Via Christi Rehabilitation Hospital, Wichita, KS, p. A247
RIEGER, Bill, Chief Information Officer, Flagler Hospital, Saint Augustine, FL, p. A138
RIEGER, Tim, Chief Financial Officer, Mercy Health – St. Rita'S Medical Center, Lima, OH, p. A485
RIEGERT, Patricia, Director Fiscal Services, Danville State Hospital, Danville, PA, p. A523
RIEKE, Diane, Director Patient Care Services, Patients' Hospital Of Redding, Redding, CA, p. A79
RIEKS, Katie, Chief Nursing Officer, Hansen Family Hospital, Iowa Falls, IA, p. A225
RIER, Kirk, Chief Operating Officer, Iowa Specialty Hospital–Clarion, Clarion, IA, p. A219
RIES, Heather, MSN, R.N., Chief Nursing Officer, Regional Medical Center, Manchester, IA, p. A226
RIESER, Michael, M.D., Medical Director, Ridge Behavioral Health System, Lexington, KY, p. A255
RIETMAN, Cheryl, Chief Administrative Officer, Deaconess Midtown Hospital, Evansville, IN, p. A203
RIETSEMA, Wouter, M.D., Chief Quality and Information Officer, The University Of Vermont Health Network–Champlain Valley Physicians Hospital, Plattsburgh, NY, p. A441
RIEVES, Cheryl, Chief Nurse Executive Lorain Region, Mercy Allen Hospital, Oberlin, OH, p. A489
RIFFLE, Virginia, Vice President Patient Care Services, Samaritan North Lincoln Hospital, Lincoln City, OR, p. A514
RIFKIN, Scott, Chief Executive Officer, Anaheim Global Medical Center, Anaheim, CA, p. A50
RIGAS, Warren Alston, Executive Vice President and Chief Operating Officer, Floyd Medical Center, Rome, GA, p. A159
RIGDON, Alice W., Vice President Finance, Saint Joseph Hospital, Denver, CO, p. A99
RIGDON, Edward, M.D., Chief Medical Officer, Merit Health Rankin, Brandon, MS, p. A345
RIGDON, Pam, Director Nursing, Laird Hospital, Union, MS, p. A354
RIGGIN, Andrew, Chief Executive Officer, Bennett County Hospital And Nursing Home, Martin, SD, p. A561
RIGGLE, Vikki, Director Human Resources, Eastern Louisiana Mental Health System, Jackson, LA, p. A269
RIGGS, Jennifer, R.N., Chief Nurse Officer, Mainegeneral Medical Center, Augusta, ME, p. A281
RIGNEY, Alice, Chief Human Resources Officer, Abbeville Area Medical Center, Abbeville, SC, p. A549
RIGSBEE CARROLL, Cristina, Chief Operating Officer, Granville Health System, Oxford, NC, p. A460
RIGSBY, Diane, Chief Information Officer, Capital Hospice, Arlington, VA, p. A656
RILEY, Colleen, M.D., Medical Director, Laguna Honda Hospital And Rehabilitation Center, San Francisco, CA, p. A85
RILEY, Daniel, Chief Financial Officer, West Jefferson Medical Center, Marrero, LA, p. A273
RILEY, James, Chief Operating Officer, Piedmont Medical Center, Rock Hill, SC, p. A556
RILEY, Jennifer, Vice President Operations, Memorial Regional Health, Craig, CO, p. A98
RILEY, Jim, Director Information Technology, Wagoner Community Hospital, Wagoner, OK, p. A510
RILEY, Joe B., President and Chief Executive Officer, Jackson Hospital And Clinic, Montgomery, AL, p. A21
RILEY, Kenneth, Director Information Systems, Baystate Wing Hospital, Palmer, MA, p. A302
RILEY, Linzie, Interim Human Resource Manager, Lifecare Hospitals Of Dallas, Dallas, TX, p. A596
RILEY, Mike, President and Chief Operating Officer, Novant Health Huntersville Medical Center, Huntersville, NC, p. A456
RILEY, Randy
Chief Financial Officer, Center For Behavioral Medicine, Kansas City, MO, p. A362
Fiscal and Administrative Manager, Northwest Missouri Psychiatric Rehabilitation Center, Saint Joseph, MO, p. A368
RILEY, Robert, Interim Chief Financial Officer, East Jefferson General Hospital, Metairie, LA, p. A273
RILEY, Susan, Director Human Resources, Encompass Health Rehabilitation Hospital Of Miami, Cutler Bay, FL, p. A120
RILEY, Wayne J., President, Brookdale Hospital Medical Center, New York, NY, p. A432
RILEY, William, M.D., Chief of Staff, Memorial Hermann Sugar Land Hospital, Sugar Land, TX, p. A638
RILEY–BROWN, Michelle, President, Texas Children'S Hospital, Houston, TX, p. A614
RINALDI, Anthony, Executive Vice President, Fairview Hospital, Great Barrington, MA, p. A299
RINALDI, Blythe, Vice President, Mayo Clinic Health System – Northland In Barron, Barron, WI, p. A692
RINDELS, Doris, Vice President Operations, Unitypoint Health – Grinnell Regional Medical Center, Grinnell, IA, p. A223
RINDFLEISCH, Jody, Manager Human Resources, Carris Health – Redwood, Redwood Falls, MN, p. A338
RINDLISBACHER, Diane, Manager Information Systems, Orem Community Hospital, Orem, UT, p. A650
RINEHART, Linda, Director Human Resources, Encompass Health Rehabilitation Hospital Of Treasure Coast, Vero Beach, FL, p. A143
RINEHART, Rick, Vice President, Chief Information Officer, Carle Foundation Hospital, Urbana, IL, p. A197
RING, Brian K, Chief Operating Officer, Henry Community Health, New Castle, IN, p. A212
RING, Caroline A, Chief Nursing Officer, Spectrum Health Big Rapids Hospital, Big Rapids, MI, p. A307
RINGE, Kathy, Director Human Resources, Sage Rehabilitation Hospital, Baton Rouge, LA, p. A264
RINGER, Dave, M.D., Chief of Staff, St. Mary'S Good Samaritan Hospital, Greensboro, GA, p. A154
RINGO, Jonathan, President and Chief Operating Officer, Sinai Hospital Of Baltimore, Baltimore, MD, p. A287
RINKE, Joseph
Director Human Resources, Streamwood Behavioral Health Center, Streamwood, IL, p. A197
Director of Human Resources, Riveredge Hospital, Forest Park, IL, p. A183
RINKENBERGER, Sean, Chief Financial Officer, St. Andrew'S Health Center, Bottineau, ND, p. A465
RINKER, John M., Chief Medical Officer, Osf Saint James – John W. Albrecht Medical Center, Pontiac, IL, p. A194
RINKS, Kevin, Chief Executive Officer, Jackson–Madison County General Hospital, Jackson, TN, p. A571
RION, Trey, Chief Information Officer, West Calcasieu Cameron Hospital, Sulphur, LA, p. A279
RIOS, Cindy, Chief Financial Officer, Alliancehealth Durant, Durant, OK, p. A499
RIOS, Damaris, Executive Nursing Director, Hospital Metropolitano Dr. Susoni, Arecibo, PR, p. A715
RIOS, Jose C, Director Information Services, Adventhealth Murray, Chatsworth, GA, p. A150
RIOS, Margot, R.N., Chief Nursing Officer, Christus Spohn Hospital Alice, Alice, TX, p. A581
RIOS, Mary, R.N., Interim Director of Nursing, Cordova Community Medical Center, Cordova, AK, p. A25
RIPPERGER, Ted, Administrative Director Human Resources, Atrium Medical Center, Middletown, OH, p. A487
RIPPEY, Wesley E, M.D., Chief Medical Officer, Adventist Health Portland, Portland, OR, p. A516
RIPSCH, Sue, Senior Vice President & Chief Operating Officer, Javon Bea Hospital–Rockton, Rockford, IL, p. A194
RISBY, Emile, M.D., Clinical Director, Georgia Regional Hospital At Atlanta, Decatur, GA, p. A152
RISHA, Holly, Administrative Director Human Resources, College Hospital Cerritos, Cerritos, CA, p. A54
RISINGER, Jeff, Director Human Resources, Uams Medical Center, Little Rock, AR, p. A45
RISK, Carl W., II, President, Elkhart General Hospital, Elkhart, IN, p. A202
RISKA, Marilouise, Chief Executive Officer, Select Specialty Hospital–Downriver, Wyandotte, MI, p. A325
RISLOW, Deb, Chief Information Officer, Gundersen Lutheran Medical Center, La Crosse, WI, p. A697
RISOVI, Carol, Human Resources, Chi St Alexius Health Carrington Medical Center, Carrington, ND, p. A465
RISSE, Thomas, Chief Financial Officer and Vice President Business Services, Kaiser Permanente Medical Center, Honolulu, HI, p. A164
RITCHEY, Jim, Director Human Resources, Sky Ridge Medical Center, Lone Tree, CO, p. A103
RITCHIE, Bruce, Vice President of Finance and Chief Financial Officer, Peninsula Regional Medical Center, Salisbury, MD, p. A293
RITCHIE, Eric, M.D., Clinical Director, Chinle Comprehensive Health Care Facility, Chinle, AZ, p. A29
RITCHIE, Jill, Director of Nursing, Ellinwood District Hospital, Ellinwood, KS, p. A234
RITCHIE, Jim, Director Management Information Systems, South Shore Hospital, Chicago, IL, p. A179

RITENOUR, Chad W.M., M.D., Chief Medical Officer, Emory University Hospital, Atlanta, GA, p. A146

RITON, John, Director Information Services, Memorial Hospital Of Tampa, Tampa, FL, p. A141

RITTENOUR, Melanie, Director Human Resources, Paulding County Hospital, Paulding, OH, p. A489

RITTER, Jane, R.N., Vice President, Patient Care and Clinical Services, United Regional Health Care System, Wichita Falls, TX, p. A646

RITTER, Robert G, FACHE, Associate Director, Harry S. Truman Memorial Veterans Hospital, Columbia, MO, p. A359

RITTMAN, Todd, Director of Nursing, Larue D. Carter Memorial Hospital, Indianapolis, IN, p. A207

RITZUS, Michael, Chief Executive Officer, Elmore Community Hospital, Wetumpka, AL, p. A24

RIVAS, Eloy, Director of Information Systems, Venice Regional Bayfront Health, Venice, FL, p. A143

RIVAS, Jose, M.D., Chief of Staff, Community Hospital Of Huntington Park, Huntington Park, CA, p. A62

RIVAS, Ramon Rodriguez, M.D., Medical Director, Hospital San Cristobal, Coto Laurel, PR, p. A716

RIVERA, Angela, Chief Nursing Officer, Beckley Arh Hospital, Beckley, WV, p. A683

RIVERA, Anthony, Director Human Resources, Hartgrove Hospital, Chicago, IL, p. A177

RIVERA, Ashley, Chief Financial Officer and Chief Executive Officer, Kittson Memorial Healthcare Center, Hallock, MN, p. A333

RIVERA, Christina, Director Human Resources, Southwest General Hospital, San Antonio, TX, p. A635

RIVERA, Cristina, Chief Executive Officer, Rio Grande Regional Hospital, Mcallen, TX, p. A623

RIVERA, Edgar, Chief Information Officer, Brownfield Regional Medical Center, Brownfield, TX, p. A589

RIVERA, Enrique, Chief Financial Officer, Bella Vista Hospital, Mayaguez, PR, p. A717

RIVERA, Ivonne, Director Finance, Hospital Oriente, Humacao, PR, p. A716

RIVERA, Jamie, Chief Financial Officer, Hospital Pavia Arecibo, Arecibo, PR, p. A715

RIVERA, Joe, Chief Information Technology Officer, Laredo Medical Center, Laredo, TX, p. A620

RIVERA, Jose Garcia, Director Human Resources, Hospital Buen Samaritano, Aguadilla, PR, p. A714

RIVERA, Luis, Director Human Resources, San Juan Capestrano Hospital, San Juan, PR, p. A719

RIVERA, Maria, Director Human Resources, Westside Regional Medical Center, Plantation, FL, p. A137

RIVERA, Zamarys, R.N., Chief Nursing Officer, Encompass Health Rehabilitation Hospital Of San Juan, San Juan, PR, p. A718

RIVERA MALDONADO, Luis, Executive Director, Bella Vista Hospital, Mayaguez, PR, p. A717

RIVERA-POL, Noriselle, Vice President Finance, Hospital Manati Medical Center, Manati, PR, p. A717

RIVERS, Eric, Chief Information Officer, Mission Community Hospital, Los Angeles, CA, p. A68

RIVERS, Jan, Director Human Resources, Ochsner Medical Center – Baton Rouge, Baton Rouge, LA, p. A263

RIVERS, Ken, Chief Operating Officer, Fontana Medical Center, Kaiser Permanente Fontana Medical Center, Fontana, CA, p. A58

RIVERS, Nikki, R.N., Regional Chief Nursing Officer, South Market, Ascension Seton Hays, Kyle, TX, p. A618

RIVES, Patricia, Chief Executive Officer, Community Hospital Of Huntington Park, Huntington Park, CA, p. A62

RIVOIRE, John
Administrator, Bridgepoint Continuing Care Hospital, Marrero, LA, p. A273
Administrator, Louisiana Extended Care Hospital Of Natchitoches, Natchitoches, LA, p. A274

RIZK, Magdy, M.D., Chief of Staff, West Houston Medical Center, Houston, TX, p. A614

RIZK, Norman, M.D., Chief Medical Officer, Stanford Health Care, Palo Alto, CA, p. A77

RIZK, Rob, Director Information Technology, Good Shepherd Health Care System, Hermiston, OR, p. A513

RIZKALLA, Nasseem, M.D., Chief Medical Officer, Aspirus Iron River Hospitals & Clinics, Inc., Iron River, MI, p. A315

RIZZO, Frank, Chief Financial Officer, Central Region, North Shore University Hospital, Manhasset, NY, p. A430

RIZZO, Theresa, Administrator, Franklin County Memorial Hospital, Franklin, NE, p. A384

ROACH, Crystal, Chief Financial Officer, Trustpoint Rehabilitation Hospital Of Lubbock, Lubbock, TX, p. A622

ROACH, David, Vice President Information Systems, Kadlec Regional Medical Center, Richland, WA, p. A677

ROACH, Dee A, M.D., Chief of Staff, Mitchell County Hospital, Colorado City, TX, p. A593

ROACH, Donna
Chief Information Officer, Ascension Via Christi St. Francis, Mulvane, KS, p. A241
Chief Information Officer, Sacred Heart Hospital Pensacola, Pensacola, FL, p. A136

ROACH, Geoff, Director Human Resources, Barrett Hospital & Healthcare, Dillon, MT, p. A376

ROACH, Maureen, Senior Chief Financial Officer, Kindred Hospital–St. Louis, Saint Louis, MO, p. A369

ROACH, Renee
System Vice President, Human Resources, Ssm Health St. Clare Hospital – Fenton, Fenton, MO, p. A360
System Vice President, Ssm Health St. Joseph Hospital – Lake Saint Louis, Lake Saint Louis, MO, p. A364

ROACH, Steven P, Interim President, Umass Memorial Healthalliance–Clinton Hospital, Leominster, MA, p. A300

ROACH, Steven P.
Interim Chief Executive Officer, Umass Memorial Healthalliance–Clinton Hospital, Leominster, MA, p. A300
President and Chief Executive Officer, Umass Memorial–Marlborough Hospital, Marlborough, MA, p. A300

ROADER, Charles, Vice President Finance, Edgerton Hospital And Health Services, Edgerton, WI, p. A694

ROAN, Linda Lyn, Chief Nursing Officer, East Morgan County Hospital, Brush, CO, p. A97

ROANHORSE, Anslem, Chief Executive Officer, U. S. Public Health Service Indian Hospital, Crownpoint, NM, p. A417

ROARK, Chris, Chief Information Officer, Stillwater Medical Center, Stillwater, OK, p. A507

ROARK, Robert R, Director Human Resources, Greeneville Community Hospital East, Greeneville, TN, p. A570

ROARTY, Maureen, Executive Vice President Human Resources, Nassau University Medical Center, East Meadow, NY, p. A427

ROB, Lee, Director Human Resources, Monroe Regional Hospital, Aberdeen, MS, p. A344

ROBB, Joy, Vice President Human Resources, Prairie View, Newton, KS, p. A242

ROBBINS, Dan, Information Technology and Account Executive, St. Vincent Medical Center, Los Angeles, CA, p. A69

ROBBINS, Donald, Chief Executive Officer, Lawrence County Memorial Hospital, Lawrenceville, IL, p. A187

ROBBINS, Donald, M.D., Chief Staff, Hills & Dales General Hospital, Cass City, MI, p. A308

ROBBINS, Joe, M.D., Vice President Medical Affairs, Sentara Williamsburg Regional Medical Center, Williamsburg, VA, p. A669

ROBBINS, Shannon, Chief Operating Officer, Ohio Hospital For Psychiatry, Columbus, OH, p. A479

ROBEANO, Karen, R.N., Chief Nursing Officer and Vice President Patient Care Services, Firsthealth Moore Regional Hospital, Pinehurst, NC, p. A460

ROBEL, Susan M, R.N., Executive Vice President and Chief Nursing Officer, Geisinger Medical Center, Danville, PA, p. A523

ROBERGE, Jeremy
Chief Financial Officer, Huggins Hospital, Wolfeboro, NH, p. A402
Director Reimbursement, Androscoggin Valley Hospital, Berlin, NH, p. A399
President and Chief Executive Officer, Huggins Hospital, Wolfeboro, NH, p. A402

ROBERSON, Ed, Director Information Systems, Hca Houston Healthcare Northwest, Houston, TX, p. A611

ROBERSON, Joe, Chief Executive Officer, Encompass Health Rehabilitation Hospital Of Abilene, Abilene, TX, p. A581

ROBERSON, Lynda, Senior Program Director, Rusk State Hospital, Rusk, TX, p. A632

ROBERSON, Meika, M.D., Chief Medical Officer, Carepoint Health Hoboken University Medical Center, Hoboken, NJ, p. A406

ROBERSON, Scotty, Assistant Administrator and Chief Nursing Officer, Usa Children'S And Women'S Hospital, Mobile, AL, p. A20

ROBERT, Jeffery, Chief Operating Officer, Swedish/Issaquah, Issaquah, WA, p. A674

ROBERT, Thomas W., Senior Vice President of Finance and Chief Financial Officer, Mercy Medical Center, Springfield, MA, p. A303

ROBERTS, Allyson, CPA, Chief Financial Officer, Nor–Lea Hospital District, Lovington, NM, p. A419

ROBERTS, Andrew, Interim Chief Human Resources Officer, Veterans Affairs Gulf Coast Veterans Health Care System, Biloxi, MS, p. A344

ROBERTS, Barbara, Chief Financial Officer, Robley Rex Veterans Affairs Medical Center, Louisville, KY, p. A256

ROBERTS, Bert, Controller, Miracle Mile Medical Center, Los Angeles, CA, p. A68

ROBERTS, Brad, Network Administrator, Swisher Memorial Healthcare System, Tulia, TX, p. A642

ROBERTS, Cassidi, R.N., Chief Nursing Officer, Medical City Mckinney, Mckinney, TX, p. A624

ROBERTS, Cathy, Vice President Mission Integration and Human Resources, Mercy Regional Medical Center, Durango, CO, p. A99

ROBERTS, Charles, M.D.
Executive Vice President and Executive Medical Director, Children'S Mercy Hospital Kansas City, Kansas City, MO, p. A362
Medical Director, Children'S Mercy Hospital Kansas, Overland Park, KS, p. A243

ROBERTS, Curt L., Chief Executive Officer, Cornerstone Hospital Of Austin, Austin, TX, p. A585

ROBERTS, Cyndi, Director Human Resources, Medical City Fort Worth, Fort Worth, TX, p. A605

ROBERTS, David, M.D., Chief Medical Officer, Jackson–Madison County General Hospital, Jackson, TN, p. A571

ROBERTS, David J., President, North Shore Medical Center, Salem, MA, p. A303

ROBERTS, Deborah, R.N., Chief Nursing Officer, The Core Institute Specialty Hospital, Phoenix, AZ, p. A34

ROBERTS, Debra, Director of Human Resources, Chi St. Luke'S Health–Lakeside Hospital, The Woodlands, TX, p. A640

ROBERTS, Jason
Director Information System, Carson Valley Medical Center, Gardnerville, NV, p. A394
Director of Information Services, Barton Memorial Hospital, South Lake Tahoe, CA, p. A90

ROBERTS, Jeff, Director Information Technology, Pinckneyville Community Hospital, Pinckneyville, IL, p. A193

ROBERTS, Jeffrey, Chief Executive Officer, Encompass Health Rehabilitation Hospital Of East Valley, Mesa, AZ, p. A31

ROBERTS, Kathryn, Director Human Resources, Mercy Medical Center–Dubuque, Dubuque, IA, p. A222

ROBERTS, Kenneth D., President, John T. Mather Memorial Hospital, Port Jefferson, NY, p. A441

ROBERTS, Kevin A.
President and Chief Executive Officer, Adventhealth Central Texas, Killeen, TX, p. A618
President and Chief Executive Officer, Adventhealth Rollins Brook, Lampasas, TX, p. A619

ROBERTS, Kim, Chief Strategy Officer, Lucile Salter Packard Children'S Hospital Stanford, Palo Alto, CA, p. A77

ROBERTS, Krista, Chief Executive Officer, St. Mary'S Regional Medical Center, Enid, OK, p. A499

ROBERTS, Laurel, Interim Chief Executive Officer, Rolling Hills Hospital, Franklin, TN, p. A569

ROBERTS, Laurel, R.N., MSN, Chief Nursing Officer, Rolling Hills Hospital, Franklin, TN, p. A569

ROBERTS, Mark, Chief Operating Officer, Memorial Satilla Health, Waycross, GA, p. A163

ROBERTS, Matthew S., Chief Executive Officer, Raleigh General Hospital, Beckley, WV, p. A683

ROBERTS, Michael, Chief Information Officer, Highlands Arh Regional Medical Center, Prestonsburg, KY, p. A259

ROBERTS, Nancy, Chief Operating Officer, Providence St. Vincent Medical Center, Portland, OR, p. A517

ROBERTS, Pamela W., Chief Executive Officer, Henderson County Community Hospital, Lexington, TN, p. A573

ROBERTS, Paul L., Director, Cheyenne Veterans Affairs Medical Center, Cheyenne, WY, p. A711

ROBERTS, Paula, Chief Nursing Officer, Cumberland Hospital For Children And Adolescents, New Kent, VA, p. A663

ROBERTS, Phillip G, Vice President Finance and Chief Financial Officer, Columbus Community Hospital, Inc., Columbus, WI, p. A693

ROBERTS, Rob, Director Information Technology, Benson Hospital, Benson, AZ, p. A28

ROBERTS, Robert C
Senior Vice President Financial Services, Baptist Health Medical Center – North Little Rock, North Little Rock, AR, p. A46
Senior Vice President Financial Services, Baptist Health Medical Center–Little Rock, Little Rock, AR, p. A44
Senior Vice President, Baptist Health Rehabilitation Institute, Little Rock, AR, p. A45
Vice President and Chief Financial Officer, Baptist Health Medical Center–Arkadelphia, Arkadelphia, AR, p. A39
Vice President, Baptist Health Extended Care Hospital, Little Rock, AR, p. A44

ROBERTS, Robin, Executive Director of Patient Services, Greeneville Community Hospital West, Greeneville, TN, p. A570

ROBERTS, Roslyn, Manager, Northside Hospital–Cherokee, Canton, GA, p. A149

ROBERTS, Sally, R.N., Director of Nursing, Abrom Kaplan Memorial Hospital, Kaplan, LA, p. A270

ROBERTS, Shayna Brooke, Director Human Resources, Northeastern Health System Sequoyah, Sallisaw, OK, p. A507

ROBERTS, Teresa, Chief Financial Officer, Ringgold County Hospital, Mount Ayr, IA, p. A226

ROBERTSHAW, Hazel, R.N., Ph.D., Chief Nursing Officer, Vice President Patient Services, F. F. Thompson Hospital, Canandaigua, NY, p. A425

ROBERTSON, Carla, Chief Operating Officer and Chief Financial Officer, Saline Memorial Hospital, Benton, AR, p. A39

ROBERTSON, Casey, Chief Executive Officer, Longview Regional Medical Center, Longview, TX, p. A621

ROBERTSON, Darcy, Chief Financial Officer, Page Hospital, Page, AZ, p. A32

ROBERTSON, Elizabeth, Area Controller, Encompass Health Rehabilitation Hospital Of Dallas, Dallas, TX, p. A596

ROBERTSON, John L., Administrator, West Central Georgia Regional Hospital, Columbus, GA, p. A151

ROBERTSON, Larry, President, Texas Health Center For Diagnostic & Surgery, Plano, TX, p. A630

ROBERTSON, Laura, Chief Executive Officer, Banner Desert Medical Center, Mesa, AZ, p. A31

ROBERTSON, Michael, Chief Executive Officer, Piedmont Newnan Hospital, Newnan, GA, p. A158

ROBERTSON, Misty, R.N., Chief Nursing Officer, Bonner General Hospital, Sandpoint, ID, p. A172

ROBERTSON, Steve
Executive Vice President and Chief Information Officer, Straub Medical Center, Honolulu, HI, p. A165
Executive Vice President Revenue Cycle Management and Chief Information Officer, Wilcox Medical Center, Lihue, HI, p. A166
Senior Vice President, Pali Momi Medical Center, Aiea, HI, p. A164
Vice President, Kapiolani Medical Center For Women & Children, Honolulu, HI, p. A164

ROBERTSTAD, John R., Chief Executive Officer, Rehabilitation Hospital Of Wisconsin, Waukesha, WI, p. A707

ROBESON, Gail, Vice President Patient Services, Huron Regional Medical Center, Huron, SD, p. A561

ROBICHAUX, Andre', Administrator, Jennings Senior Care Hospital, Jennings, LA, p. A269

ROBICHAUX, Jody, Chief Executive Officer, Amg Specialty Hospital–Houma, Houma, LA, p. A268

ROBICHAUX, Martha, Chief Human Resources Officer, John C. Fremont Healthcare District, Mariposa, CA, p. A71

ROBICHEAUX, James Warren., Chief Executive Officer, Matagorda Regional Medical Center, Bay City, TX, p. A587

ROBIN, Nikki, Chief Operating Officer, Mid–Jefferson Extended Care Hospital, Nederland, TX, p. A626

ROBINSON, Aaron, President and Chief Executive Officer, South County Hospital, Wakefield, RI, p. A548

ROBINSON, Adam M.
Acting Director, Washington Dc Veterans Affairs Medical Center, Washington, DC, p. A116
Director, Veterans Affairs Maryland Health Care System–Baltimore Division, Baltimore, MD, p. A288

ROBINSON, Alan, Chief Financial Officer, Logan Regional Hospital, Logan, UT, p. A648

ROBINSON, Anitra, Human Resources Director, Healthsouth Rehabilitation Hospital Of Middletown, Middletown, DE, p. A113

ROBINSON, Anthony, Manager, Human Resources, Mercy Hospital Of Folsom, Folsom, CA, p. A58

ROBINSON, Bradley, Chief Financial Officer, Evans U. S. Army Community Hospital, Fort Carson, CO, p. A100

ROBINSON, Cliff, M.D., Chief of Staff, Central Alabama Veterans Health Care System, Montgomery, AL, p. A21

ROBINSON, Dakota, Interim Chief Financial Officer and Controller, North Caddo Medical Center, Vivian, LA, p. A280

ROBINSON, David, President Medical and Dental Staff, Community Hospital, Munster, IN, p. A212

ROBINSON, David, D.O., Medical Director, St. Joseph'S Behavioral Health Center, Stockton, CA, p. A90

ROBINSON, Elena, Chief Human Resources Officer, Hima San Pablo Caguas, Caguas, PR, p. A715

ROBINSON, Girard, M.D., Senior Vice President Medical and Clinical Affairs, Spring Harbor Hospital, Westbrook, ME, p. A285

ROBINSON, Glenn A., President, Baylor Scott & White Medical Center – Hillcrest, Waco, TX, p. A644

ROBINSON, Herbert, M.D., Vice President, Chief Medical Information Officer, North Oaks Health System, North Oaks Rehabilitation Hospital, Hammond, LA, p. A268

ROBINSON, James L., III, President, Amita Health Saint Joseph Hospital, Chicago, IL, p. A176

ROBINSON, Jeanne, Director Human Resources, Inova Fair Oaks Hospital, Fairfax, VA, p. A658

ROBINSON, Jennifer, Administrator, Unity Psychiatric Care–Clarksville, Clarksville, TN, p. A568

ROBINSON, Jennifer B, Vice President Human Resources, St. Petersburg General Hospital, Saint Petersburg, FL, p. A139

ROBINSON, Mark
Associate Administrator and Chief Financial Officer, Hazel Hawkins Memorial Hospital, Hollister, CA, p. A61
Chief Executive Officer, St. Mark'S Hospital, Salt Lake City, UT, p. A652

ROBINSON, Mary, Chief Nursing Officer and Vice President Patient Care Services, Texas Health Harris Methodist Hospital Southwest Fort Worth, Fort Worth, TX, p. A606

ROBINSON, Paul H, M.D., Medical Director, American Fork Hospital, American Fork, UT, p. A647

ROBINSON, Phil, Chief Financial Officer, Saint Agnes Medical Center, Fresno, CA, p. A59

ROBINSON, Phillip D., President, Lankenau Medical Center, Wynnewood, PA, p. A546

ROBINSON, Raymond, Chief Executive Officer, Pembroke Hospital, Pembroke, MA, p. A302

ROBINSON, Ronald R.
Chief Executive Officer and Chief Medical Officer, Goodland Regional Medical Center, Goodland, KS, p. A235
Chief Executive Officer and Chief Medical Officer, Rawlins County Health Center, Atwood, KS, p. A232

ROBINSON, Ronald R., M.D., M.P.H., FACHE
Chief Executive Officer and Chief Medical Officer, Goodland Regional Medical Center, Goodland, KS, p. A235
Chief Executive Officer and Chief Medical Officer, Rawlins County Health Center, Atwood, KS, p. A232

ROBINSON, Stephen, Jr, Chief Executive Officer, Ochsner Medical Center – Kenner, Kenner, LA, p. A270

ROBINSON, Susan Beth, Vice President Human Resources, St. Mary'S Medical Center, Huntington, WV, p. A686

ROBINSON, Tim, Chief Executive Officer, Nationwide Children'S Hospital, Columbus, OH, p. A479

ROBINSON, Trena, Director, Human Resources, Central Texas Rehabilitation Hospital, Austin, TX, p. A585

ROBINSON, Vance, Chief Information Officer, Iberia Medical Center, New Iberia, LA, p. A274

ROBINSON, William, Director Human Resources, Encompass Health Rehabilitation Hospital Of Erie, Erie, PA, p. A525

ROBINSON, William J, Senior Vice President and Chief Financial Officer, Uf Health Rehab Hospital, Gainesville, FL, p. A124

ROBISON, Bruce, Vice President and Chief Information Officer, Cox Medical Centers, Springfield, MO, p. A371

ROBISON, John, Chief Executive Officer, Clifton T. Perkins Hospital Center, Jessup, MD, p. A291

ROBISON, Keith, Chief Information Officer, Upmc Chautauqua Wca, Jamestown, NY, p. A429

ROBISON, Neely, Director Human Resources, The Bridgeway, North Little Rock, AR, p. A47

ROBISON, Rob, Director Information Technology, Medical Center Of South Arkansas, El Dorado, AR, p. A41

ROBISON, Ryan, Chief Nursing Officer, Sanpete Valley Hospital, Mount Pleasant, UT, p. A649

ROBISON, Wendell, M.D., Chief of Staff, Sheridan Veterans Affairs Medical Center, Sheridan, WY, p. A712

ROBITAILLE, Mark E, President and Chief Executive Officer, Cleveland Clinic Martin North Hospital, Stuart, FL, p. A140

ROBL, Chris, Human Resources, Ellinwood District Hospital, Ellinwood, KS, p. A234

ROBLES, Burt, Vice President Information Services, Guthrie Robert Packer Hospital, Sayre, PA, p. A540

ROCA, Robert, M.D., Vice President Medical Affairs, Sheppard Pratt Health System, Baltimore, MD, p. A288

ROCHA, Israel, Jr, Chief Executive Officer, Brookdale Hospital Medical Center, New York, NY, p. A432

ROCHA, Julie, Vice President Human Resources, Mercy Medical Center Merced, Merced, CA, p. A71

ROCHELEAU, John, Vice President Business Support and Information Technology, Bellin Hospital, Green Bay, WI, p. A696

ROCHER, Leslie, Senior Vice President and Chief Medical Officer, Beaumont Hospital – Royal Oak, Royal Oak, MI, p. A321

ROCHESTER, Charmaine, Vice President Finance, Bon Secours–Depaul Medical Center, Norfolk, VA, p. A663

ROCHIER, Dennis, Chief Medical Officer, Renown South Meadows Medical Center, Reno, NV, p. A397

ROCK, Betty Ann, Vice President Nursing and Chief Nursing Officer, Uniontown Hospital, Uniontown, PA, p. A543

ROCK, Brian, Director of Information Systems, Vcu Health Community Memorial Hospital, South Hill, VA, p. A667

ROCK, David, Executive Vice President and Chief Operating Officer, Brookdale Hospital Medical Center, New York, NY, p. A432

ROCKWELL, Jane, Director Support Services, North Metro Medical Center, Jacksonville, AR, p. A43

ROCKWELL, Karla, Director of Nursing, Doctors Memorial Hospital, Bonifay, FL, p. A118

ROCKWOOD, John D., President, Medstar National Rehabilitation Hospital, Washington, DC, p. A115

ROCKWOOD, Sylvia, Director Human Resources, Upmc Carlisle, Carlisle, PA, p. A522

RODDEN, Celeste, Chief Information Officer, Hillcrest Hospital Claremore, Claremore, OK, p. A498

RODDY, Thomas, Chief Operating Officer, Saint Thomas Rutherford Hospital, Murfreesboro, TN, p. A576

RODEBUSH, Anthony, Chief Operating Officer, St. Mary'S Regional Medical Center, Enid, OK, p. A499

RODEN, George
Vice President Human Resources, Mercy Hospital Aurora, Aurora, MO, p. A356
Vice President Human Resources, Mercy Hospital Cassville, Cassville, MO, p. A358

RODENBAUGH, Cathy, Director Human Resources, Holy Rosary Healthcare, Miles City, MT, p. A378

RODENFELS, Cheryl, System Vice President, IT Operations, Amita Health Saints Mary & Elizabeth Medical Center, Chicago, IL, p. A176

RODER, Darla, Chief Operating Officer, Cavalier County Memorial Hospital And Clinics, Langdon, ND, p. A468

RODERICK, Travis W., Chief Executive Officer, Premier Surgical Institute, Galena, KS, p. A235

RODEWALD, Amanda, Interim Chief Financial Officer, Daviess Community Hospital, Washington, IN, p. A216

RODGE, Mark, Director Information Systems, Eaton Rapids Medical Center, Eaton Rapids, MI, p. A311

RODGERS, April, Vice President, Human Resources, Holy Name Medical Center, Teaneck, NJ, p. A413

RODGERS, Bruce C., Chief Administrative Officer, Salem Health West Valley, Dallas, OR, p. A512

RODGERS, Dondie, Interim Chief Nursing Officer, Memorial Hospital Of Texas County, Guymon, OK, p. A500

RODGERS, Jamie, Chief Executive Officer, Choctaw Regional Medical Center, Ackerman, MS, p. A344

RODGERS, Lee, M.D., Vice President Quality, United Regional Health Care System, Wichita Falls, TX, p. A646

RODIER, James Barton, M.D., Chief Quality Officer, Health Central Hospital, Ocoee, FL, p. A133

RODIS, John F., President, Saint Francis Hospital And Medical Center, Hartford, CT, p. A108

RODOWICZ, Darlene, Chief Financial Officer, Berkshire Medical Center, Pittsfield, MA, p. A302

RODRIGUES, Pablo, M.D., Medical Director, Vibra Hospital Of Amarillo, Amarillo, TX, p. A582

RODRIGUEZ, Alex
Vice President and Chief Information Officer, St. Elizabeth Edgewood, Edgewood, KY, p. A251
Vice President and Chief Information Officer, St. Elizabeth Florence, Florence, KY, p. A252
Vice President and Chief Information Officer, St. Elizabeth Fort Thomas, Fort Thomas, KY, p. A252

RODRIGUEZ, Betsy, Vice President Human Resources, Barnes–Jewish Hospital, Saint Louis, MO, p. A369

RODRIGUEZ, Candie, Director Human Resources, Hospital San Cristobal, Coto Laurel, PR, p. A716

RODRIGUEZ, Edgardo, Director Management Information Systems, Auxilio Mutuo Hospital, San Juan, PR, p. A718

RODRIGUEZ, Heather, Chief Nursing Officer, Fresno Heart And Surgical Hospital, Fresno, CA, p. A59

RODRIGUEZ, Jaime, Chief Financial Officer, San Juan City Hospital, San Juan, PR, p. A719

RODRIGUEZ, Joe, Chief Executive Officer, South Texas Health System, Edinburg, TX, p. A601

RODRIGUEZ, Jose Luis., Chief Executive Officer, Hospital Pavia–Santurce, San Juan, PR, p. A719

RODRIGUEZ, Jose O, M.D., Medical Director, Castaner General Hospital, Castaner, PR, p. A715

RODRIGUEZ, Laura, Director Medical Records, Hospital Del Maestro, San Juan, PR, p. A718

RODRIGUEZ, Leticia, Chief Executive Officer, Ward Memorial Hospital, Monahans, TX, p. A625

RODRIGUEZ, Lizzette, Director Finance, Hospital San Francisco, San Juan, PR, p. A719

RODRIGUEZ, Marco, Chief Financial Officer, Valley Baptist Medical Center–Harlingen, Harlingen, TX, p. A609

RODRIGUEZ, Mario, Chief Executive Officer, New Braunfels Regional Rehabilitation Hospital, New Braunfels, TX, p. A626

RODRIGUEZ, Maritza, Chief Financial Officer, Hospital Metropolitan, San Juan, PR, p. A719

RODRIGUEZ, Miguel, Medical Director, Caribbean Medical Center, Fajardo, PR, p. A716

RODRIGUEZ, Onel, Chief Financial Officer, Broward Health Coral Springs, Coral Springs, FL, p. A120

RODRIGUEZ, Oscar, Chief Fiscal Officer, Veterans Affairs Caribbean Healthcare System, San Juan, PR, p. A719

RODRIGUEZ, Patricia M., Senior Vice President and Area Manager, Kaiser Permanente South Sacramento Medical Center, Sacramento, CA, p. A82
RODRIGUEZ, Ramon J., President and Chief Executive Officer, Brookdale Hospital Medical Center, New York, NY, p. A432
RODRIGUEZ, Rufus, M.D., Medical Director, Mayo Clinic Health System In Fairmont, Fairmont, MN, p. A331
RODRIGUEZ, Sara
Chief Financial Officer, Kindred Hospital Sugar Land, Sugar Land, TX, p. A638
Human Resources, Ascension Seton Smithville, Smithville, TX, p. A637
RODRIGUEZ, Tammy, Vice President of Patient Care Services, Adventhealth Rollins Brook, Lampasas, TX, p. A619
RODRIGUEZ, Tomas, Chief Information Technology Officer, First Hospital Panamericano, Cidra, PR, p. A716
RODRIGUEZ, Tony, Director Human Resources, South Texas Rehabilitation Hospital, Brownsville, TX, p. A589
RODRIGUEZ, Vilma, Director Human Resources, Hospital San Pablo Del Este, Fajardo, PR, p. A716
RODRIGUEZ, Wilfredo, M.D., Chief of Staff, Battle Creek Veterans Affairs Medical Center, Battle Creek, MI, p. A307
RODRIGUEZ, Yelitza Sanchez., Executive Director, Metropolitano De La Montana, Utuado, PR, p. A720
RODRIGUEZ COLLAZO, Jose Luis, Executive Director, Hospital Pavia Arecibo, Arecibo, PR, p. A715
RODRIGUEZ SCHMIDT, Myriam T, Director Human Resources, Cardiovascular Center Of Puerto Rico And The Caribbean, San Juan, PR, p. A718
RODRIQUEZ, Daisy, Director Human Resources, Fort Duncan Regional Medical Center, Eagle Pass, TX, p. A600
RODRIQUEZ, Monica, Director of Human Resources, Stewart & Lynda Resnick Neuropsychiatric Hospital At Ucla, Los Angeles, CA, p. A69
ROE, Daniel, M.D., Chief Operating Officer, Copper Queen Community Hospital, Bisbee, AZ, p. A28
ROE, Timothy J., President and Chief Executive Officer, Rehabilitation Hospital Of The Pacific, Honolulu, HI, p. A165
ROEBACK, Jason, Chief Operating Officer, Saint Vincent Hospital, Erie, PA, p. A525
ROEBKEN, Curtis, M.D., Chief Medical Staff, Kentfield Rehabilitation And Specialty Hospital, Kentfield, CA, p. A62
ROEBUCK, Amanda, Chief Executive Officer, Genoa Medical Facilities, Genoa, NE, p. A385
ROEDER, Donna, Chief Financial Officer, Jackson County Regional Health Center, Maquoketa, IA, p. A226
ROEDERER, Chris, Senior Vice President Human Resources, Tampa General Hospital, Tampa, FL, p. A142
ROEHR, Richard
Chief Operating Officer, Adventist Medical Center Bolingbrook, Bolingbrook, IL, p. A174
Vice President and Chief Operating Officer, Adventist Medical Center Glenoaks, Glendale Heights, IL, p. A184
ROEHRLE, Andreas, Director Finance, Sentara Williamsburg Regional Medical Center, Williamsburg, VA, p. A669
ROESER, William
Interim President and Chief Executive Officer, Sparrow Carson Hospital, Carson City, MI, p. A308
President and Chief Executive Officer, Sparrow Ionia Hospital, Ionia, MI, p. A314
ROESLER, Bruce E., Chief Executive Officer, Richland Hospital, Richland Center, WI, p. A704
ROETMAN, James D., President and Chief Executive Officer, Pocahontas Community Hospital, Pocahontas, IA, p. A228
ROEVER, Judy, MSN, R.N., Chief Nursing Officer, Scenic Mountain Medical Center, Big Spring, TX, p. A588
ROFFELSEN, Michael S.
Chief Executive Officer, Encompass Health Rehabilitation Hospital Of Sunrise, Sunrise, FL, p. A140
Chief Executive Officer, Kindred Hospital South Florida–Fort Lauderdale, Fort Lauderdale, FL, p. A123
ROGALSKI, Robert, Chief Executive Officer, Excela Health Westmoreland Hospital, Greensburg, PA, p. A526
ROGALSKI, Ted, Administrator, Genesis Medical Center–Aledo, Aledo, IL, p. A173
ROGAN, Edie, Manager Human Resources, Eastern State Hospital, Williamsburg, VA, p. A668
ROGERS, Aaron, Chief Executive Officer, Trinity Hospital, Weaverville, CA, p. A94
ROGERS, B. Carter, Chief of Staff, Piedmont Newton Hospital, Covington, GA, p. A151
ROGERS, Carrie, Chief Nursing Officer, Southern Tennessee Regional Health System–Lawrenceburg, Lawrenceburg, TN, p. A573
ROGERS, Cathy M, Manager Human Resources, Prisma Health Laurens County Hospital, Clinton, SC, p. A550
ROGERS, David, Chief Executive Officer, Ortonville Area Health Services, Ortonville, MN, p. A337
ROGERS, Doris, Vice President Human Resources, Saint Luke'S Hospital Of Kansas City, Kansas City, MO, p. A363
ROGERS, Eric, Chief Information Officer, Hebrew Rehabilitation Center, Roslindale, MA, p. A302
ROGERS, Gregory H., President, Midmichigan Medical Center–Midland, Midland, MI, p. A318
ROGERS, James H., Chief Executive Officer, Cornerstone Hospital Of Little Rock, Little Rock, AR, p. A45
ROGERS, Jared
President and Chief Executive Officer, Osf Heart Of Mary Medical Center, Urbana, IL, p. A197
President and Chief Executive Officer, Osf Sacred Heart Medical Center, Danville, IL, p. A180
ROGERS, Jeremy, Chief Financial Officer, St. Francis Medical Center, Monroe, LA, p. A274
ROGERS, Jerry, R.N., Director Nurses and Infection Control, Specialty Hospital, Monroe, LA, p. A274
ROGERS, Joseph J, Vice President and Chief Operating Officer, Redwood Memorial Hospital, Fortuna, CA, p. A58
ROGERS, Kathy, Vice President Marketing, San Luis Valley Health Conejos County Hospital, La Jara, CO, p. A102
ROGERS, LaDonna, Executive Vice President Human Resources, T. J. Samson Community Hospital, Glasgow, KY, p. A252
ROGERS, Lucy, Chief Information Resource Management Systems, Veterans Affairs North Texas Health Care System, Dallas, TX, p. A598
ROGERS, Mark G
Interim Vice President Finance and Chief Financial Officer, Genesis Medical Center, Davenport, Davenport, IA, p. A220
Interim Vice President Finance and Chief Financial Officer, Genesis Medical Center, Silvis, Silvis, IL, p. A196
Vice President, Finance and Chief Financial Officer, Genesis Medical Center–Aledo, Aledo, IL, p. A173
ROGERS, Matt, Chief Financial Officer, Wellspan Philhaven, Mount Gretna, PA, p. A532
ROGERS, Michael, Vice President Fiscal Services, Brattleboro Memorial Hospital, Brattleboro, VT, p. A654
ROGERS, Patricia, Director of Nursing, Dahl Memorial Healthcare Association, Ekalaka, MT, p. A376
ROGERS, Randy, Chief Executive Officer, Garden Park Medical Center, Gulfport, MS, p. A347
ROGERS, Rich, Vice President Information Services, Prisma Health Greenville Memorial Hospital, Greenville, SC, p. A553
ROGERS, Richard, M.D., Chief Medical Officer, Saint Thomas Rutherford Hospital, Murfreesboro, TN, p. A576
ROGERS, Robert I, M.D., Medical Director, Canton–Potsdam Hospital, Potsdam, NY, p. A442
ROGERS, Seth, Controller, Encompass Health Rehabilitation Hospital Of Modesto, Modesto, CA, p. A72
ROGERS, Sherry L, MS, R.N., Chief Nursing Officer, Redington–Fairview General Hospital, Skowhegan, ME, p. A285
ROGERS, Tammy, Director Human Resources, Mt. San Rafael Hospital, Trinidad, CO, p. A106
ROGERS, Tracy, Chief Executive Officer, North Tampa Behavioral Health, Wesley Chapel, FL, p. A143
ROGERS, Valerie J, Director of Nursing, Cherokee Nation W.W. Hastings Indian Hospital, Tahlequah, OK, p. A508
ROGERS, William, Chief Medical Officer, North Mississippi Medical Center Gilmore–Amory, Amory, MS, p. A344
ROGOLS, Kevin L., Administrator, Kalkaska Memorial Health Center, Kalkaska, MI, p. A316
ROGOZ, Brian, Vice President Finance and Treasurer, The Hospital Of Central Connecticut, New Britain, CT, p. A109
ROHAN, Colleen, Director Human Resources, Little Company Of Mary Hospital And Health Care Centers, Evergreen Park, IL, p. A183
ROHAN, Patrick, Chief Operating Officer, Plantation General Hospital, Plantation, FL, p. A137
ROHLEDER, Scott, Chief Information Officer, Hays Medical Center, Hays, KS, p. A236
ROHMAN, Cindy, R.N., MS, Vice President/Chief Nursing Officer, Lexington Medical Center, West Columbia, SC, p. A558
ROHMAN, Ryan, MSN, R.N.
Chief Operating Officer, Uchealth Medical Center Of The Rockies, Loveland, CO, p. A104
Chief Operating Officer, Uchealth Poudre Valley Hospital, Fort Collins, CO, p. A100
ROHRBACH, Dan D., President, Southwest Health, Platteville, WI, p. A703
ROHRBACK, Allen, Chief Executive Officer, Madison Valley Medical Center, Ennis, MT, p. A376
ROHRBACK, Jenny, Director Human Resource, Ruby Valley Medical Center, Sheridan, MT, p. A380
ROHRER, Harry, Chief Financial Officer, University Of Miami Hospital And Clinics, Miami, FL, p. A131
ROHRER, John J., Director, William S. Middleton Memorial Veterans Hospital, Madison, WI, p. A699
ROHRICH, George A., Chief Executive Officer, River'S Edge Hospital And Clinic, Saint Peter, MN, p. A340
ROIZ, JoAnn, Director Human Resources, Encompass Health Rehabilitation Hospital Of Tustin, Tustin, CA, p. A92
ROJAS, Curtis, Interim Chief Financial Officer, Connally Memorial Medical Center, Floresville, TX, p. A604
ROKER, Christopher, Chief Executive Officer, Brookdale Hospital Medical Center, New York, NY, p. A432
ROKOSZ, Gregory, D.O., Senior Vice President Medical and Academic Affairs, Saint Barnabas Medical Center, Livingston, NJ, p. A407
ROLAND, Brian, Chief Executive Officer, Muenster Memorial Hospital, Muenster, TX, p. A625
ROLAND, John, R.N., Chief Operating Officer and Chief Nursing Officer, Bleckley Memorial Hospital, Cochran, GA, p. A150
ROLDAN, Lanyce, Chief Nursing Officer, Penn Medicine Lancaster General Hospital, Lancaster, PA, p. A529
ROLEK, Jim, Chief Human Resources Officer, Vice President, Clara Maass Medical Center, Belleville, NJ, p. A403
ROLEY, Margaret, Chief Nursing Officer, South Baldwin Regional Medical Center, Foley, AL, p. A18
ROLFE, David, Chief Information Officer, Madonna Rehabilitation Hospital, Lincoln, NE, p. A387
ROLFF, Christi, Director Business Development, San Joaquin Valley Rehabilitation Hospital, Fresno, CA, p. A59
ROLING, Robin, FACHE, MS, R.N., Chief Operating Officer, Cheyenne Regional Medical Center, Cheyenne, WY, p. A710
ROLLI, Molli Martha, M.D., Medical Director, Mendota Mental Health Institute, Madison, WI, p. A698
ROLLING, Andy, Director of Finance, Regina Hospital, Hastings, MN, p. A333
ROLLINS, David W, Chief Financial Officer, Mt. San Rafael Hospital, Trinidad, CO, p. A106
ROLLINS, James
Chief Financial Officer, Arbour H. R. I. Hospital, Brookline, MA, p. A297
Chief Financial Officer, Arbour–Fuller Hospital, Attleboro, MA, p. A294
ROLLINS, Larry, Supervisor Information Technology, Mccamey County Hospital District, Mccamey, TX, p. A624
ROLLINS, Skip, Chief Information Officer, Freeman Health System, Joplin, MO, p. A362
ROLSEN, Timothy, Chief Executive Officer, Regency Hospital Cleveland East, Warrensville Heights, OH, p. A493
ROMAN, Eloy, M.D., Chief of Staff, Palmetto General Hospital, Hialeah, FL, p. A124
ROMAN, Jody, Chief Human Resource Officer, Hillside Rehabilitation Hospital, Warren, OH, p. A493
ROMAN, Linda K, Administrator, Coast Plaza Hospital, Norwalk, CA, p. A74
ROMAN, Marina, M.D., Medical Director, Hospital De La Universidad De Puerto Rico/Dr. Federico Trilla, Carolina, PR, p. A715
ROMANELLO, Marcus, Chief Medical Officer, Fort Hamilton Hospital, Hamilton, OH, p. A484
ROMANIA, Matt, Director of Nursing, Upmc Susquehanna Soldiers + Sailors, Wellsboro, PA, p. A544
ROMANICK, Odile, Chief information Officer, Day Kimball Hospital, Putnam, CT, p. A110
ROMANIELLO, Guy, Director Fiscal Services, Belmont Behavioral Hospital, Philadelphia, PA, p. A534
ROMANO, C. James, M.D., Chief Medical Officer, St. Francis Medical Center, Trenton, NJ, p. A413
ROMANO, Jean, Chief Nursing Officer, Good Shepherd Penn Partners Specialty Hospital At Rittenhouse, Philadelphia, PA, p. A534
ROMANO, Sara, R.N., Vice President, Mountain View Hospital, Gadsden, AL, p. A18
ROMANOWSKI, Ellen, Chief Nursing Officer, Encompass Health Rehabilitation Hospital Of Miami, Cutler Bay, FL, p. A120
ROMANS, Alan, Director Information Technology, Ashland Health Center, Ashland, KS, p. A232
ROMEO, John, Chief Information Officer, Mercy Hospital And Medical Center, Chicago, IL, p. A178
ROMER, Douglas, Executive Director Patient Care Services, Grande Ronde Hospital, La Grande, OR, p. A514
ROMERO, Brenda, Hospital Chief, Presbyterian Espanola Hospital, Espanola, NM, p. A418
ROMERO, Edward, Chief Financial Officer, Rehabilitation Hospital Of Fort Wayne, Fort Wayne, IN, p. A204
ROMERO, Frank, M.D.
Chief Medical Officer, Cox Medical Centers, Springfield, MO, p. A371
Vice President Medical Affairs and Chief Medical Officer, Cox Monett Hospital, Monett, MO, p. A366
ROMERO, Matt, Chief Financial Officer, Oak Hill Hospital, Brooksville, FL, p. A119

ROMIG, Glenn, Chief Financial Officer, Largo Medical Center, Largo, FL, p. A128

ROMINE, Andrew, Chief Executive Officer, Rockledge Regional Medical Center, Rockledge, FL, p. A138

ROMITO, Edmund J, Chief Information Officer, Genesis Healthcare System, Zanesville, OH, p. A495

RONAN, Barry P., President and Chief Executive Officer, Western Maryland Regional Medical Center, Cumberland, MD, p. A290

RONAN, John
President, Northern Light Blue Hill Hospital, Blue Hill, ME, p. A282
President, Northern Light Maine Coast Hospital, Ellsworth, ME, p. A283

RONCA, Cyndi, Director Human Resources, Twin Cities Hospital, Niceville, FL, p. A133

RONDE, Christa, Assistant Chief Financial Officer, Palo Verde Hospital, Blythe, CA, p. A53

RONKE, Lisa, Director Finance, St. Michael'S Hospital Avera, Tyndall, SD, p. A564

RONNISCH, Kim, R.N., Vice President Nursing and Operations, Ascension River District Hospital, East China, MI, p. A311

ROOD, Mandy, Vice President Human Resources, Hayes Green Beach Memorial Hospital, Charlotte, MI, p. A308

ROODMAN, Richard D., Chief Executive Officer, Uw Medicine/Valley Medical Center, Renton, WA, p. A677

ROOF, Marie, Executive Vice President Information Systems, Vibra Specialty Hospital Of Portland, Portland, OR, p. A516

ROOKER, Mark, Chief Operations and Information Officer, Susan B. Allen Memorial Hospital, El Dorado, KS, p. A234

ROONERY, Nicole, Chief Nursing Officer, Ivinson Memorial Hospital, Laramie, WY, p. A711

ROONEY, Al, Director Information Systems, St. Vincent Healthcare, Billings, MT, p. A374

ROONEY, David, Administrator Operations, Winneshiek Medical Center, Decorah, IA, p. A221

ROONEY, Thomas, Chief Information Resource Management, Veterans Affairs Hudson Valley Health Care System, Montrose, NY, p. A431

ROOP, Terri, Director Patient Care Services, Dickenson Community Hospital, Clintwood, VA, p. A658

ROOS, Joel A., Commanding Officer, Naval Medical Center San Diego, San Diego, CA, p. A83

ROOSA, Carol, Vice President Information Services and Chief Information Officer, Athol Hospital, Athol, MA, p. A294

ROOSE, Robert, M.D., Chief Medical Officer, Mercy Medical Center, Springfield, MA, p. A303

ROOT, Jim, Vice President Human Resources, Saint Elizabeth'S Medical Center, Wabasha, MN, p. A342

ROOT, Rodney Mark, D.O., Vice President Medical Affairs, Bakersfield Memorial Hospital, Bakersfield, CA, p. A52

ROPER, Anne, Interim Chief Executive Officer, Fairlawn Rehabilitation Hospital, Worcester, MA, p. A305

ROPER, Embra, Chief Medical Officer, Regional Hospital For Respiratory And Complex Care, Burien, WA, p. A671

ROPER, Sandra, Chief Human Resources, General Leonard Wood Army Community Hospital, Fort Leonard Wood, MO, p. A360

ROQUE, Lee Ann, Director of Human Resources, Spartanburg Medical Center – Mary Black, Spartanburg, SC, p. A557

ROSA–TOLEDO, Luis R, M.D., Medical Director, Hospital Manati Medical Center, Manati, PR, p. A717

ROSAAEN, Nancy, Chief Executive Officer, Mccone County Health Center, Circle, MT, p. A375

ROSADO, Jose S., Executive Director, Hospital Manati Medical Center, Manati, PR, p. A717

ROSALES, Alvina, R.N., Chief Nursing Officer, Tuba City Regional Health Care Corporation, Tuba City, AZ, p. A37

ROSATI, Rosemarie, Chief Operating Officer, Rutgers University Behavioral Healthcare, Piscataway, NJ, p. A411

ROSBOROUGH, Brian S, M.D., Chief Medical Officer, Osf Saint Elizabeth Medical Center, Ottawa, IL, p. A192

ROSBURG, Deb, Chief Financial Officer, Franklin General Hospital, Hampton, IA, p. A223

ROSCOE, Joan, Chief Information Officer, Winchester Medical Center, Winchester, VA, p. A669

ROSE, Cheryl, Human Resources Director, Fulton County Medical Center, Mc Connellsburg, PA, p. A531

ROSE, Hugh, Vice President Fiscal Management, Palos Health, Palos Heights, IL, p. A192

ROSE, Julia, R.N., Director of Nursing, Braxton County Memorial Hospital, Gassaway, WV, p. A685

ROSE, Kim, Chief Information Technology, Crouse Health, Syracuse, NY, p. A445

ROSE, Laura L, Chief Financial Officer, St. Vincent Anderson, Anderson, IN, p. A199

ROSE, Mary R, R.N., Chief Clinical Officer, Promedica Coldwater Regional Hospital, Coldwater, MI, p. A309

ROSE, May, Director Human Resources, Memorial Hospital, Chester, IL, p. A176

ROSE, Michael S., President and Chief Executive Officer, Southern New Hampshire Medical Center, Nashua, NH, p. A401

ROSE, Michaell, Chief Operating Officer, St. Joseph'S Medical Center, Stockton, CA, p. A91

ROSE, Richard T, Associate Director, Manchester Veterans Affairs Medical Center, Manchester, NH, p. A401

ROSE, Robert, M.D., Chief Medical Officer, Upper Connecticut Valley Hospital, Colebrook, NH, p. A399

ROSE, Robin, R.N., Chief Operating and Clinical Officer, Gibson Area Hospital And Health Services, Gibson City, IL, p. A184

ROSE, Silvia, Director Patient Care Services, Vidant Bertie Hospital, Windsor, NC, p. A464

ROSE, Steven A, President and Chief Executive Officer, Nanticoke Memorial Hospital, Seaford, DE, p. A114

ROSELLO, Patricia M., Chief Executive Officer, Baptist Health South Florida, Baptist Hospital Of Miami, Miami, FL, p. A130

ROSEMORE, Michael, M.D., Medical Director, Encompass Health Lakeshore Rehabilitation Hospital, Birmingham, AL, p. A14

ROSEN, Barry, M.D., Vice President Medical Management, Advocate Good Shepherd Hospital, Barrington, IL, p. A174

ROSEN, Jules, M.D., Chief Medical Officer, West Springs Hospital, Grand Junction, CO, p. A101

ROSEN, Michael, M.D., Chief Medical Officer, Havasu Regional Medical Center, Lake Havasu City, AZ, p. A31

ROSEN, Raymond, FACHE, Vice President Operations, Wellspan York Hospital, York, PA, p. A546

ROSENA, Robens, Director Information Systems, Delray Medical Center, Delray Beach, FL, p. A121

ROSENBALM, Jennifer, Manager Business Office, Veterans Affairs Nebraska–Western Iowa Health Care System, Omaha, NE, p. A390

ROSENBAUM, Robert, Vice President Operations, Vassar Brothers Medical Center, Poughkeepsie, NY, p. A442

ROSENBAUM, Victor, Chief Operating Officer, Alaska Regional Hospital, Anchorage, AK, p. A25

ROSENBERG, Andrew, M.D., Chief Information Officer, Michigan Medicine, Ann Arbor, MI, p. A306

ROSENBERG, Julie, Administrator, Essentia Health–Graceville, Graceville, MN, p. A332

ROSENBERG, Patricia, R.N., MSN, Chief Nursing Officer, Palm Beach Gardens Medical Center, Palm Beach Gardens, FL, p. A135

ROSENBERG, Steven, Chief Financial Officer, Danbury Hospital, Danbury, CT, p. A107

ROSENBERG, Stuart E., President, Johnson Memorial Medical Center, Stafford Springs, CT, p. A111

ROSENBERGER, Robert, Chief Financial Officer, Adena Medical Center, Chillicothe, OH, p. A475

ROSENBERGER–SLAMPACK, Janie, Chief Executive Officer, Curahealth Heritage Valley, Beaver, PA, p. A520

ROSENBLATT, Michael, M.D., Medical Director, Kindred Rehabilitation Hospital Clear Lake, Webster, TX, p. A645

ROSENBLOOM, Mark, M.D., Vice President of Medical Affairs, Health First Holmes Regional Medical Center, Melbourne, FL, p. A129

ROSENBURG, Deborah L, Vice President Human Resources, Chesapeake Regional Medical Center, Chesapeake, VA, p. A657

ROSENBURG, Jeffrey M., Chief Medical Officer, Sierra Nevada Memorial Hospital, Grass Valley, CA, p. A61

ROSENCRANCE, Daris, Chief Financial Officer, Stonewall Jackson Memorial Hospital, Weston, WV, p. A690

ROSENCRANCE, Gregory, Chief Executive Officer, Cleveland Clinic Indian River Hospital, Vero Beach, FL, p. A143

ROSENDAHL, Lisa, Director Human Resources, St. Cloud Veterans Affairs Health Care System, Saint Cloud, MN, p. A339

ROSENFELD, Merryll, Vice President, Human Resources, Catholic Medical Center, Manchester, NH, p. A401

ROSENSTEIN, Gaynor, Vice President Operations, Bon Secours Community Hospital, Port Jervis, NY, p. A442

ROSENTHAL, Benjamin, Information Systems Director, South Sunflower County Hospital, Indianola, MS, p. A348

ROSENTHAL, Philip P, Executive Director, Brookdale Hospital Medical Center, New York, NY, p. A432

ROSENTHAL, Raul, M.D., Interim Chief of Staff, Cleveland Clinic Florida, Weston, FL, p. A144

ROSEQUIST, Helen, Manager Information Systems, Warren General Hospital, Warren, PA, p. A543

ROSETTA, Kathy, Chief Nursing Officer, Laurel Ridge Treatment Center, San Antonio, TX, p. A634

ROSHAN, Payman
Chief Operating Officer, Kaiser Permanente Baldwin Park Medical Center, Baldwin Park, CA, p. A51
Senior Vice President and Area Manager, Kaiser Permanente Panorama City Medical Center, Los Angeles, CA, p. A67

ROSHETKO, Chet, Chief Nursing Officer, Eastern State Hospital, Medical Lake, WA, p. A675

ROSILES, Nancy, Director Human Resources, Encompass Health Rehabilitation Hospital Of Arlington, Arlington, TX, p. A583

ROSKE, Jeff, D.O., Chief Medical Staff, Community Memorial Hospital, Sumner, IA, p. A230

ROSKOVSKI, Stephanie, Chief Operating Officer, Butler Health System, Butler, PA, p. A521

ROSLER, Andrea P, Vice President Human Resources, Huntsville Hospital, Huntsville, AL, p. A19

ROSS, Charles, M.D., Vice President Medical Affairs, Chilton Medical Center, Pompton Plains, NJ, p. A411

ROSS, Christopher J., Chief Information Technology Officer, Mayo Clinic Hospital – Rochester, Rochester, MN, p. A338

ROSS, Darrell, Chief Nursing Officer, Dequincy Memorial Hospital, Dequincy, LA, p. A267

ROSS, Denzil
Administrator, Lovelace Medical Center, Albuquerque, NM, p. A416
Chief Operating Officer, Lovelace Medical Center, Albuquerque, NM, p. A416

ROSS, Douglas B., President, Chi St. Vincent Hot Springs, Hot Springs, AR, p. A43

ROSS, Hoyt, Chief Executive Officer, Promise Hospital Of Florida At The Villages, Oxford, FL, p. A135

ROSS, Jacqueline, Chief Human Resources Officer, Mann–Grandstaff Veterans Affairs Medical Center, Spokane, WA, p. A679

ROSS, Jay
Chief Financial Officer, Chi St. Joseph'S Health, Park Rapids, MN, p. A337
Vice President of Finance, Chi Lakewood Health, Baudette, MN, p. A328

ROSS, Jeffrey, M.D.
Chief of Staff, King'S Daughters Medical Center, Brookhaven, MS, p. A345
Medical Director, Amg Specialty Hospital–Albuquerque, Albuquerque, NM, p. A416

ROSS, Joan, Senior Vice President and Chief Operating Officer, St. Vincent Charity Medical Center, Cleveland, OH, p. A478

ROSS, John, Vice President, Franciscan Health Mooresville, Mooresville, IN, p. A211

ROSS, Johnny Shane, Executive Medical Director, Encompass Health Rehabilitation Hospital Of Austin, Austin, TX, p. A585

ROSS, Karen, Chief Executive Officer, Allegiance Specialty Hospital Of Kilgore, Kilgore, TX, p. A618

ROSS, Laurie, Chief Nursing Officer, Southampton Memorial Hospital, Franklin, VA, p. A659

ROSS, Phil, Chief Executive Officer, Surgical Hospital Of Oklahoma, Oklahoma City, OK, p. A505

ROSS, Randall W., President and Chief Executive Officer, Mercy Hospital Of Folsom, Folsom, CA, p. A58

ROSS, Robert, Chief Operating Officer, Medstar Washington Hospital Center, Washington, DC, p. A116

ROSS, Samuel Lee., Chief Executive Officer, Bon Secours Baltimore Health System, Baltimore, MD, p. A286

ROSS, Shana, Vice President Human Resources, Bayhealth Medical Center, Dover, DE, p. A113

ROSS, Zeff, Executive Vice President and Chief Executive Officer, Memorial Regional Hospital, Hollywood, FL, p. A124

ROSS–COLE, Melissa, Director Human Resources, Regency Hospital Of Northwest Arkansas – Springdale, Springdale, AR, p. A49

ROSS–SPANG, Carol, Chief Human Resources Officer, Methodist Healthcare Memphis Hospitals, Memphis, TN, p. A575

ROSSI, Alfred N., Chief Executive Officer, Hopedale Medical Complex, Hopedale, IL, p. A186

ROSSI, Coleen, Director Quality Services, Healthsouth Rehabilitation Hospital Of Toms River, Toms River, NJ, p. A413

ROSSI, Lawrence, M.D., Clinical Director, Trenton Psychiatric Hospital, Trenton, NJ, p. A413

ROSSI, Mark F, Chief Operating Officer and General Counsel, Hopedale Medical Complex, Hopedale, IL, p. A186

ROSSMANN, Barbara W., President and Chief Executive Officer, Henry Ford Macomb Hospitals, Clinton Township, MI, p. A309

ROSSMANN, Samuel H., Chief Executive Officer, Tops Surgical Specialty Hospital, Houston, TX, p. A614

ROSVOLD, Robert, Director Finance, Virtua Voorhees, Voorhees, NJ, p. A414

ROTENBERRY–BAGGETT, Katie, Administrative Assistant and Human Resources, Yalobusha General Hospital, Water Valley, MS, p. A355

ROTERT, Angela Lynne, Chief Clinical Officer, Kindred Hospital–Indianapolis, Indianapolis, IN, p. A207

ROTGER, Lindsey, Chief Nursing Officer, Spire Cane Creek Rehabilitation Hospital, Martin, TN, p. A573
ROTH, Anna M., Chief Executive Officer, Contra Costa Regional Medical Center, Martinez, CA, p. A71
ROTH, Chad, Director Information Services, Prairie View, Newton, KS, p. A242
ROTH, Dan, M.D., Vice President Medical Affairs, Mercy Health – Anderson Hospital, Cincinnati, OH, p. A476
ROTH, Diane, Chief Financial Officer, Piedmont Rockdale Hospital, Conyers, GA, p. A151
ROTH, Edward J., III, President and Chief Executive Officer, Aultman Hospital, Canton, OH, p. A474
ROTH, Eugene, Vice President Information Services, Mercy Hospital St. Louis, Saint Louis, MO, p. A368
ROTH, Jessica, R.N., Chief Clinical Officer, Tri Valley Health System, Cambridge, NE, p. A383
ROTH, Mark A., Chief Financial Officer, Mountain Valley Regional Rehabilitation Hospital, Prescott Valley, AZ, p. A35
ROTH, Norman G., President, Greenwich Hospital, Greenwich, CT, p. A108
ROTH, Randy, Chief Medical Officer, Singing River Health System, Pascagoula, MS, p. A352
ROTH–MALLEK, Nancy, Vice President of Finance, Aspirus Riverview Hospital And Clinics, Inc., Wisconsin Rapids, WI, p. A709
ROTHBERG, Kathryn, Director Human Resources, Evergreenhealth Monroe, Monroe, WA, p. A675
ROTHBERGER, Richard, Corporate Executive Vice President and Chief Financial Officer, Scripps Green Hospital, La Jolla, CA, p. A62
ROTHENBERGER, David, Chief Financial Officer, Summit Healthcare Regional Medical Center, Show Low, AZ, p. A36
ROTHERMICH, Anthony, Administrator, Mercy Hospital Lincoln, Troy, MO, p. A372
ROTHERMICH, Michael, M.D., Chief of Staff, Hermann Area District Hospital, Hermann, MO, p. A361
ROTHFIELD, Kenneth, M.D., Chief Medical Officer, Medical City Dallas, Dallas, TX, p. A597
ROTHMAN, Marc, M.D., Medical Director, Friends Hospital, Philadelphia, PA, p. A534
ROTHSCHILD, Marylee, Chief of Staff, Robley Rex Veterans Affairs Medical Center, Louisville, KY, p. A256
ROTHSCHILD, Marylee, M.D., Chief of Staff, Robley Rex Veterans Affairs Medical Center, Louisville, KY, p. A256
ROTSTED, Scott T., Chief Executive Officer, California Rehabilitation Institute, Los Angeles, CA, p. A66
ROTY, Christopher, President, Baptist Health Paducah, Paducah, KY, p. A259
ROUGH, Vicki, Chief Nursing Officer, Highlands Hospital, Connellsville, PA, p. A523
ROUILLARD, Smita, M.D., Physician in Chief, Kaiser Permanente Fresno Medical Center, Fresno, CA, p. A59
ROULEAU, Greg, Vice President Nursing, Mercy Medical Center Merced, Merced, CA, p. A71
ROUND, Laurie, MS, R.N., Chief Nurse Executive, Advocate Bromenn Medical Center, Normal, IL, p. A191
ROUNDS, Jason
Chief Executive Officer, Christus St. Michael Health System, Texarkana, TX, p. A640
Chief Operating Officer and Administrator, Christus St. Michael Health System, Texarkana, TX, p. A640
ROUNDY, Ann, Vice President Employee Services, Columbus Community Hospital, Inc., Columbus, WI, p. A693
ROUNSLEY, Joan, Director Human Resources, Geisinger Jersey Shore Hospital, Jersey Shore, PA, p. A528
ROUNSLEY, Karen, Controller, Healthsouth Chesapeake Rehabilitation Hospital, Salisbury, MD, p. A293
ROUSSE, Michael, M.D., Chief Medical Officer, Northeastern Vermont Regional Hospital, Saint Johnsbury, VT, p. A655
ROUSSEAU, Mickie, Director Human Resources, Terrebonne General Medical Center, Houma, LA, p. A269
ROUSSEL, Steve
Chief Financial Officer, Baylor Scott & White Medical Center At – Mckinney, Mckinney, TX, p. A624
Vice President Finance, Baylor Scott & White Medical Center–Irving, Irving, TX, p. A616
ROUSSELLE, Karen, Administrator, Omega Hospital, Metairie, LA, p. A273
ROUSSOS, Michael, Administrator, University Health System, San Antonio, TX, p. A635
ROUTH, Lori, R.N., Nurse Administrator, Mayo Clinic Health System – Albert Lea And Austin, Albert Lea, MN, p. A327
ROUX, Roger, Chief Financial Officer, Rady Children'S Hospital – San Diego, San Diego, CA, p. A84
ROUZER, Cindy, Director Human Resources, Spooner Health, Spooner, WI, p. A705
ROVITO, Kevin, Chief Financial Officer, Jackson Hospital, Marianna, FL, p. A129
ROW, Tracy, Manager Business Office, Fredonia Regional Hospital, Fredonia, KS, p. A235
ROW, Tyler, Director Information Technology, Fredonia Regional Hospital, Fredonia, KS, p. A235
ROWAN, Cary, Chief Financial Officer, Astria Sunnyside Hospital, Sunnyside, WA, p. A680
ROWAN, Mark, Interim Chief Information Officer, Rome Memorial Hospital, Rome, NY, p. A443
ROWAN, R C, Director Human Resources, Neosho Memorial Regional Medical Center, Chanute, KS, p. A233
ROWE, Chad, Human Resource Director, Aspirus Keweenaw Hospital, Inc., Laurium, MI, p. A316
ROWE, Jeanne M, M.D., Chief Medical Officer, Shore Medical Center, Somers Point, NJ, p. A412
ROWE, Melissa S., Chief Executive Officer, Grover C. Dils Medical Center, Caliente, NV, p. A393
ROWE, Mike, M.D., Chief of Staff, Fayette Regional Health System, Connersville, IN, p. A201
ROWE, Paul W, Director Information Technology, St. Francis Hospital, Wilmington, DE, p. A114
ROWE, Richard M.
Chief Executive Officer, Garden Grove Hospital And Medical Center, Garden Grove, CA, p. A60
Chief Executive Officer, Huntington Beach Hospital, Huntington Beach, CA, p. A62
ROWE, Scott, Chief Executive Officer, Encompass Health Rehabilitation Hospital Of Chattanooga, Chattanooga, TN, p. A567
ROWE, Wilma, M.D., Senior Vice President Medical Affairs, Mercy Medical Center, Baltimore, MD, p. A288
ROWELL, Julie, R.N., Chief Nursing Officer, Thomas Hospital, Fairhope, AL, p. A18
ROWEN, Lisa, R.N.
Chief Nursing Officer, University Of Maryland Medical Center Midtown Campus, Baltimore, MD, p. A287
Senior Vice President and Chief Nursing Officer, University Of Maryland Medical Center, Baltimore, MD, p. A287
ROWLAND, Claire, Director Human Resources, Vermilion Behavioral Health Systems – North Campus, Lafayette, LA, p. A271
ROWLAND, Michael, M.D., Vice President Medical Affairs, Franklin Memorial Hospital, Farmington, ME, p. A283
ROWLAND, Nick
Chief Executive Officer, Pushmataha Hospital, Antlers, OK, p. A496
Chief Operating Officer, Pushmataha Hospital, Antlers, OK, p. A496
Interim Chief Executive Officer, Choctaw Memorial Hospital, Hugo, OK, p. A501
ROWLAND, Robert, M.D., Medical Director, Encompass Health Rehabilitation Hospital Of Tallahassee, Tallahassee, FL, p. A140
ROWLAND, Ruby, Strategic Partner, Highlands–Cashiers Hospital, Highlands, NC, p. A456
ROWLAND, Ted, Chief of Medical Staff, Atoka County Medical Center, Atoka, OK, p. A496
ROWLANDS, Dewey R, Vice President and Chief Financial Officer, Rome Memorial Hospital, Rome, NY, p. A443
ROWLEY, Charla, Chief Financial Officer, Southwest Mississippi Regional Medical Center, Mccomb, MS, p. A350
ROWLEY, Mike, Chief Executive Officer, Springbrook Behavioral Health System, Travelers Rest, SC, p. A557
ROY, Joel, Manager Information Systems, The Brook Hospital – Kmi, Louisville, KY, p. A257
ROY, Linda, R.N., Chief Nursing Officer, Walter B. Jones Alcohol And Drug Abuse Treatment Center, Greenville, NC, p. A455
ROY, Rock, Professional Services Director, Power County Hospital District, American Falls, ID, p. A167
ROY, Schindelheim, M.D., Chief of Staff, Mee Memorial Hospital, King City, CA, p. A62
ROYAL, Keli, Chief Human Resources Officer, Shenandoah Medical Center, Shenandoah, IA, p. A229
ROYAL, Shawanna, R.N., Director Nursing, Strategic Behavioral Health – Raleigh, Garner, NC, p. A454
ROYAL, Ty, Executive Director of Human Resources and Support Services, Gibson Area Hospital And Health Services, Gibson City, IL, p. A184
ROYE, G. Dean, M.D., Senior Vice President of Medical Affairs and Chief Medical Officer, Miriam Hospital, Providence, RI, p. A547
ROYNE, Sharon, Senior Vice President: Human Resources, Highline Medical Center, Burien, WA, p. A671
ROYSTER, Kirsten, President and Chief Operating Officer, Novant Health Medical Park Hospital, Winston, NC, p. A464
ROZELL, Becky, Vice President, Human Resources, Madison Health, London, OH, p. A486
ROZENBOOM, Steve, Chief Financial Officer, Holy Cross Hospital, Taos, NM, p. A421
ROZENFELD, Jon, President, Ssm Health St. Mary'S Hospital, Madison, WI, p. A698
ROZIER, Derek, Chief Financial Officer, Liberty Regional Medical Center, Hinesville, GA, p. A154
ROZNOVSKY, Karen, Director Human Resources, Yoakum Community Hospital, Yoakum, TX, p. A646
RUBANO, Kathleen A, MSN, R.N., Chief Nursing Officer, Corpus Christi Medical Center, Corpus Christi, TX, p. A594
RUBAR, Jackie, Administrative Assistant and Director Human Resources, Leesville Rehabilitation Hospital, Leesville, LA, p. A272
RUBE, David M, M.D., Clinical Director, Brookdale Hospital Medical Center, New York, NY, p. A432
RUBEN, Wanda, R.N., Chief Nursing Officer, Garden Grove Hospital And Medical Center, Garden Grove, CA, p. A60
RUBENS, Deborah, Director Human Resources, Shriners Hospitals For Children–Northern California, Sacramento, CA, p. A82
RUBERG, Greg, President and Chief Executive Officer, Lake View Hospital, Two Harbors, MN, p. A341
RUBERTE, Henry, Administrator, Hospital San Gerardo, San Juan, PR, p. A719
RUBERTI, Charlene, Director Information Technology Development, Ancora Psychiatric Hospital, Hammonton, NJ, p. A406
RUBIN, Nancy, Vice President Human Resources, Motion Picture And Television Fund Hospital And Residential Services, Los Angeles, CA, p. A68
RUBIN, Randy, Senior Vice President and Chief Financial Officer, Mercyone Des Moines Medical Center, Des Moines, IA, p. A221
RUBIN, Vincent, Chief Financial Officer, Southern California Hospital At Culver City, Culver City, CA, p. A56
RUBINATE, Donna, R.N., Chief Operating Officer, Good Samaritan Medical Center, Brockton, MA, p. A296
RUBINO, Mark, President, Forbes Hospital, Monroeville, PA, p. A532
RUBINO, Mark, M.D., Chief Medical Officer, Forbes Hospital, Monroeville, PA, p. A532
RUBINSTEIN, Mitchell, M.D.
Chief Medical Officer, Palms Of Pasadena Hospital, Saint Petersburg, FL, p. A138
Chief Medical Officer, St. Petersburg General Hospital, Saint Petersburg, FL, p. A139
RUBIO, Felipe, M.D., Medical Director, Kindred Hospital–Dayton, Dayton, OH, p. A481
RUBLE, Justin
Director Human Resources, Jefferson Medical Center, Ranson, WV, p. A689
Director, Human Resources, Berkeley Medical Center, Martinsburg, WV, p. A687
RUBY, Blaine, M.D., Chief of Staff, Johnson County Healthcare Center, Buffalo, WY, p. A710
RUCH, Jordan, Vice President and Chief Information Officer, Robert Wood Johnson University Hospital Somerset, Somerville, NJ, p. A412
RUCHTI, Robert D., Chief Executive Officer, Buchanan General Hospital, Grundy, VA, p. A660
RUCKER, Alisa, Vice President Finance and Chief Financial Officer, Washington Hospital, Washington, PA, p. A543
RUCKER, Genifer, President, Christus Spohn Hospital Beeville, Beeville, TX, p. A588
RUCKER, Jodi, MSN, R.N., Vice President Patient Care Services and Chief Nursing Officer, Promedica Memorial Hospital, Fremont, OH, p. A483
RUCKER, Rick, Chief Operating Officer, Highland Hospital, Charleston, WV, p. A684
RUDBERG, Susan, M.D., Chief Medical Officer, Range Regional Health Services, Hibbing, MN, p. A333
RUDD, Adam, Chief Executive Officer, Largo Medical Center, Largo, FL, p. A128
RUDD, Barry, Chief Information Officer, Memorial Satilla Health, Waycross, GA, p. A163
RUDD, Jedd, Director of Ancillary Services and Safety, Mad River Community Hospital, Arcata, CA, p. A51
RUDD, John B., President and Chief Executive Officer, Cayuga Medical Center At Ithaca, Ithaca, NY, p. A429
RUDDEN, Elizabeth, Vice President Human Resources, Connecticut Children'S Medical Center, Hartford, CT, p. A108
RUDE, Erik G., Commander, William Beaumont Army Medical Center, El Paso, TX, p. A603
RUDEK, Charles M.
Chief Information Officer, Upmc Jameson, New Castle, PA, p. A533
Chief Information Officer, Upmc St. Margaret, Pittsburgh, PA, p. A538
RUDISILL, Joe, Chief Operating Officer, Regional Medical Center Bayonet Point, Hudson, FL, p. A125
RUDITZ, Bettiann S, MS, R.N., Chief Nursing Officer, Broward Health North, Deerfield Beach, FL, p. A121

RUDOLPH, Dawn, President and Chief Executive Officer, St. Vincent'S Medical Center, Bridgeport, CT, p. A107

RUDQUIST, Debra, President and Chief Executive Officer, Amery Hospital And Clinic, Amery, WI, p. A691

RUDY, Bret, Executive Director and Senior Vice President, Brookdale Hospital Medical Center, New York, NY, p. A432

RUDZIK, Carrie, Chief Administrative Officer, Eastern State Hospital, Lexington, KY, p. A255

RUDZIK, Donna, Director Human Resources, Christus Mother Frances Hospital – Sulphur Springs, Sulphur Springs, TX, p. A638

RUE, Loring, M.D., Senior Vice President, Quality Patient Safety and Clinical Effectiveness, University Of Alabama Hospital, Birmingham, AL, p. A15

RUE, Robert, Chief Financial Officer, Ellenville Regional Hospital, Ellenville, NY, p. A427

RUECKERT, Sebastian, M.D.
Chief Medical Officer, Christian Hospital, Saint Louis, MO, p. A369
Vice President and Chief Medical Officer, Alton Memorial Hospital, Alton, IL, p. A173

RUEDISUELI, Amy, Vice President of Finance, Mckenzie Health System, Sandusky, MI, p. A322

RUEGG, Mary Kaye, Chief Nursing Officer, Mackinac Straits Health System, Inc., Saint Ignace, MI, p. A321

RUELLO, Rocky, Vice President Human Resources, Mercy Hospital St. Louis, Saint Louis, MO, p. A368

RUFF, Robin, Chief Financial Officer, Pikes Peak Regional Hospital, Woodland Park, CO, p. A106

RUFF, Victoria, M.D., Medical Director, Select Specialty Hospital–Columbus, Columbus, OH, p. A480

RUFFIN, Marshall, Chief Information Officer, Inova Fair Oaks Hospital, Fairfax, VA, p. A658

RUFFING, Cindy, Director Human Resources, Siloam Springs Regional Hospital, Siloam Springs, AR, p. A48

RUFFOLO, Joseph A., President and Chief Executive Officer, Niagara Falls Memorial Medical Center, Niagara Falls, NY, p. A439

RUGE, Randy
Chief Executive Officer, Paulding County Hospital, Paulding, OH, p. A489
Chief Operating Officer, Paulding County Hospital, Paulding, OH, p. A489

RUGGIERO, Joanne, Interim Chief Nursing Officer, Pennsylvania Hospital, Philadelphia, PA, p. A536

RUGGIERO, Mike, Interim Chief Executive Officer, Lane County Hospital, Dighton, KS, p. A234

RUGGIERO, Taren, R.N., MSN, Vice President and Chief Nursing Officer, Holy Cross Hospital, Fort Lauderdale, FL, p. A122

RUIZ, Irene, Area Human Resources Director, Kaiser Permanente Fontana Medical Center, Fontana, CA, p. A58

RUIZ, Javier, M.D.
Medical Director, Intracare North Hospital, Houston, TX, p. A612
Medical Director, Kingwood Pines Hospital, Kingwood, TX, p. A618

RUIZ, Kathleen, M.D., Associate Director Patient Care Services, Veterans Affairs Caribbean Healthcare System, San Juan, PR, p. A719

RUIZ, Patricia, R.N., Chief Nursing Officer, Brookdale Hospital Medical Center, New York, NY, p. A432

RUIZ, Tony, Senior Vice President, Chief Operating Officer, Medical Center Health System, Odessa, TX, p. A627

RULAND, Jyl
Chief Financial Officer, Clearwater Valley Hospital And Clinics, Orofino, ID, p. A170
Chief Financial Officer, St. Mary'S Hospital, Cottonwood, ID, p. A169

RULLI, Sheila, Director Human Resources, Kidspeace Children'S Hospital, Orefield, PA, p. A533

RUMMEL, Jennifer
Director Human Resources, Freestone Medical Center, Fairfield, TX, p. A603
Director Human Resources, Ut Health Athens, Athens, TX, p. A584

RUMPH, Jerald W., Chief Executive Officer, Mercy Rehabilitation Hospital St. Louis, Chesterfield, MO, p. A358

RUNKLE, Thomas, MS, Ph.D., Chief Operating Officer, St. Christopher'S Hospital For Children, Philadelphia, PA, p. A536

RUNNELS, Clay, Vice President Chief Medical Officer Washington County, Johnson City Medical Center, Johnson City, TN, p. A571

RUNYAN, Mark
Director Information Services, Salt Lake Regional Medical Center, Salt Lake City, UT, p. A652
Director Information Systems, Jordan Valley Medical Center West Valley Campus, West Valley City, UT, p. A653

RUNYON, Annette, Vice President and Administrator, Medical Center At Franklin, Franklin, KY, p. A252

RUPA, Maitra, M.D., Acting Medical Director, Chester Mental Health Center, Chester, IL, p. A176

RUPERT, Chris, Chief Executive Officer, Options Behavioral Health System, Indianapolis, IN, p. A207

RUPERT, Duke, Chief Operating Officer, Allegheny General Hospital, Pittsburgh, PA, p. A537

RUPERT, James M., Chief Fiscal Services, Battle Creek Veterans Affairs Medical Center, Battle Creek, MI, p. A307

RUPERT, Michael J, Chief Financial Officer, Va Long Beach Healthcare System, Long Beach, CA, p. A65

RUPP, Connie, MSN, R.N., Executive Vice President and Chief Nursing Officer, Regional West Medical Center, Scottsbluff, NE, p. A391

RUPP, Robert, President, Integris Grove Hospital, Grove, OK, p. A500

RUPPERT, Jennifer, Chief Financial Officer, Iowa City Veterans Affairs Health Care System, Iowa City, IA, p. A224

RUPPERT SCHILLER, Kerri
Senior Vice President and Chief Financial Officer, Children'S Hospital Of Orange County, Orange, CA, p. A76
Senior Vice President and Chief Financial Officer, Choc Children'S At Mission Hospital, Mission Viejo, CA, p. A72

RUSCH, Brett, Acting Director, White River Junction Veterans Affairs Medical Center, White River Junction, VT, p. A655

RUSH, Andrew G., Chief Executive Officer, Upmc Somerset Hospital, Somerset, PA, p. A541

RUSH, Ann Marie, Chief Financial Officer, Penobscot Valley Hospital, Lincoln, ME, p. A283

RUSH, Christopher, Chief Financial Officer, Specialty Hospital Of Meridian, Meridian, MS, p. A351

RUSH, Cindy, Director Human Resources, Clay County Medical Center, Clay Center, KS, p. A233

RUSH, Ed, President and Chief Executive Officer, Iredell Health System, Statesville, NC, p. A463

RUSH, Jeff, Chief Financial Officer, Rutherford Regional Health System, Rutherfordton, NC, p. A461

RUSH, Matthew, President and Chief Executive Officer, Hayes Green Beach Memorial Hospital, Charlotte, MI, p. A308

RUSHIN, Denise, Director Human Resources, Poplar Bluff Regional Medical Center, Poplar Bluff, MO, p. A367

RUSHING, Derek, Chief Executive Officer, Uchealth Grandview Hospital, Colorado Springs, CO, p. A98

RUSHING, Heath
Senior Vice President and Chief Executive Officer, Memorial Hermann – Texas Medical Center, Houston, TX, p. A612
Senior Vice President and Chief Executive Officer, Memorial Hermann Katy Hospital, Katy, TX, p. A617

RUSHING, R Lynn., Chief Executive Officer, Brook Lane Health Services, Hagerstown, MD, p. A291

RUSHING, Randy, Chief Financial Officer, Massac Memorial Hospital, Metropolis, IL, p. A189

RUSHLOW, David, Vice President Medical Affairs, Mayo Clinic Health System – Franciscan Healthcare In La Crosse, La Crosse, WI, p. A698

RUSK, Scott, M.D., Chief Medical Officer, St. Joseph Hospital, Orange, CA, p. A76

RUSNACZYK, John, Senior Vice President and Chief Financial Officer, St. Vincent Charity Medical Center, Cleveland, OH, p. A478

RUSNAK, Greg, Executive Vice President and Chief Operating Officer, Prisma Health Greenville Memorial Hospital, Greenville, SC, p. A553

RUSS, Nicole L, Director Colleague Relations, Alliance Community Hospital, Alliance, OH, p. A471

RUSSELL, Bill, Senior Chief Information Officer, Mission Hospital, Mission Viejo, CA, p. A72

RUSSELL, Brant, R.N., Chief Operating Officer, Ascension St. John Hospital, Detroit, MI, p. A309

RUSSELL, Brett, Finance Business Partner Specialist, Eastern State Hospital, Lexington, KY, p. A255

RUSSELL, Dardanella, Chief Human Resources Management Service, Veterans Affairs Hudson Valley Health Care System, Montrose, NY, p. A431

RUSSELL, David, President and Chief Executive Officer, Adventist Health Portland, Portland, OR, p. A516

RUSSELL, Donald
AMITA Health Senior Vice President and Chief Human Resources Officer, Adventist Medical Center Glenoaks, Glendale Heights, IL, p. A184
Senior Vice President and Chief Human Resources Officer, Amita Health Elk Grove Village, Elk Grove Village, IL, p. A182
Senior Vice President and Chief Human Resources Officer, Amita Health Hoffman Estates, Hoffman Estates, IL, p. A186

RUSSELL, Erin, Controller, Kindred Hospital–San Antonio, San Antonio, TX, p. A634

RUSSELL, Freda, Chief Executive Officer and Chief Nursing Officer, Three Rivers Hospital, Waverly, TN, p. A580

RUSSELL, Freda, R.N., Chief Executive Officer and Chief Nursing Officer, Three Rivers Hospital, Waverly, TN, p. A580

RUSSELL, Georgette, Vice President of Talent & Organizational Effectiveness, Sparrow Carson Hospital, Carson City, MI, p. A308

RUSSELL, John D., President and Chief Executive Officer, Columbus Community Hospital, Inc., Columbus, WI, p. A693

RUSSELL, Jon
Senior Vice President & Chief Information Officer, John Muir Medical Center, Walnut Creek, Walnut Creek, CA, p. A94
Senior Vice President and Chief Information Officer, John Muir Medical Center, Concord, Concord, CA, p. A55

RUSSELL, Karen M, Director of Employee Relations, Osf Saint Elizabeth Medical Center, Ottawa, IL, p. A192

RUSSELL, Kathy, R.N., Chief Nursing Officer, Bluegrass Community Hospital, Versailles, KY, p. A261

RUSSELL, Kendrick, Chief Human Resources Officer, Abrazo Scottsdale Campus, Phoenix, AZ, p. A32

RUSSELL, Kimberly, Chief Nursing Officer, Mercy Hospital Booneville, Booneville, AR, p. A40

RUSSELL, Laurie, Director Human Resources, Lea Regional Medical Center, Hobbs, NM, p. A418

RUSSELL, Linda, Vice President and Chief Nursing Officer, Self Regional Healthcare, Greenwood, SC, p. A554

RUSSELL, Michelle L., Administrator, Community Howard Specialty Hospital, Kokomo, IN, p. A209

RUSSELL, Patti, Vice President Nursing, Masonicare Health Center, Wallingford, CT, p. A111

RUSSELL, Robert, Chief Executive Officer, Encompass Health Rehabilitation Hospital Of Shelby County, Pelham, AL, p. A22

RUSSELL, Robert J, Associate Executive Director Operations, Penn Presbyterian Medical Center, Philadelphia, PA, p. A536

RUSSELL, Shelly
Chief Executive Officer, Mitchell County Regional Health Center, Osage, IA, p. A228
Chief Nursing Officer, Mitchell County Regional Health Center, Osage, IA, p. A228

RUSSELL, Sherrie
AMITA Health Senior Vice President and Chief Information Officer, Adventist Medical Center Glenoaks, Glendale Heights, IL, p. A184
Senior Vice President & Chief Information Officer, Amita Health Elk Grove Village, Elk Grove Village, IL, p. A182
Senior Vice President and Chief Information Officer, Amita Health Hoffman Estates, Hoffman Estates, IL, p. A186
Vice President and Chief Information Officer, Alexian Brothers Behavioral Health Hospital, Hoffman Estates, IL, p. A186

RUSSELL, Susan
Chief Financial Officer, Och Regional Medical Center, Starkville, MS, p. A354
Chief Nursing Officer, Singing River Health System, Pascagoula, MS, p. A352

RUSSELL–JENKINS, Shane, M.D., Medical Director, Windhaven Psychiatric Hospital, Prescott Valley, AZ, p. A35

RUSSO, Arthur, M.D., Director Medical Affairs, Harrington Hospital, Southbridge, MA, p. A303

RUSSO, Kimberly
Chief Executive Officer, George Washington University Hospital, Washington, DC, p. A115
Chief Operating Officer, George Washington University Hospital, Washington, DC, p. A115

RUSSO, Mike, Vice President Information Systems, Chi St. Joseph Health Grimes Hospital, Navasota, TX, p. A626

RUSSO, Paul M., Director, Bay Pines Veterans Affairs Healthcare System, Bay Pines, FL, p. A117

RUST, Jeff, Information Technology Systems Site Manager, Chi St. Alexius Health – Williston Medical Center, Williston, ND, p. A470

RUST, Steve, Director, Human Resources, Scripps Memorial Hospital–Encinitas, Encinitas, CA, p. A57

RUTH, Daniel R., President and Chief Executive Officer, Jewish Home Of San Francisco, San Francisco, CA, p. A85

RUTH, Ed, President, Mercy Allen Hospital, Oberlin, OH, p. A489

RUTH, Joseph, Executive Vice President and Chief Operating Officer, Sparrow Hospital, Lansing, MI, p. A316

RUTHERFORD, Eddie, Director of Pharmacy, Tyler Holmes Memorial Hospital, Winona, MS, p. A355

RUTHERFORD, Jeremiah, Chief Medical Officer, Cornerstone Hospital Of Oklahoma–Muskogee, Muskogee, OK, p. A502

RUTHERFORD, Peter
Chief Executive Officer, Confluence Health/Central Washington Hospital, Wenatchee, WA, p. A682
Chief Executive Officer, Confluence Health/Wenatchee Valley Hospital, Wenatchee, WA, p. A682

RUTHERFORD, Ronald, Chief Information Officer, Beth Israel Deaconess Hospital Plymouth, Plymouth, MA, p. A302

RUTHERFORD, Theresa, President and Chief Executive Officer, Hshs St. Anthony'S Memorial Hospital, Effingham, IL, p. A181

RUTHS, Steve, M.D., Chief Medical Officer, Vista Del Mar Hospital, Ventura, CA, p. A94

RUTKOWSKI, Jennifer, R.N., MSN, Vice President Professional Services, Grant Regional Health Center, Lancaster, WI, p. A698

RUTKOWSKI, Jim, Chief Financial Officer, United Hospital Center, Bridgeport, WV, p. A683

RUTLEDGE, Debra K, R.N., Vice President Nursing Services, Chi Health Plainview, Plainview, NE, p. A391

RUTLEDGE, Rebel, Director Human Resources, Grady Memorial Hospital, Chickasha, OK, p. A498

RUWOLDT, Steven T, Chief Operating Officer, Memorial Medical Center, Las Cruces, NM, p. A418

RYAN, Chris, Chief Information Officer, Auburn Community Hospital, Auburn, NY, p. A423

RYAN, Christie, Chief Nursing Officer, Encompass Health Rehabilitation Hospital Of Sewickley, Sewickley, PA, p. A541

RYAN, Christina M, R.N., Chief Executive Officer and Chief Nursing Officer, The Women'S Hospital, Newburgh, IN, p. A213

RYAN, Christina M., Chief Executive Officer, The Women'S Hospital, Newburgh, IN, p. A213

RYAN, Connie, Chief Nursing Officer, Select Specialty Hospital–Tulsa Midtown, Tulsa, OK, p. A509

RYAN, David P., Vice President Human Resources, Melrosewakefield Healthcare, Melrose, MA, p. A300

RYAN, Debora, R.N., Vice President Patient Care, St. Francis Regional Medical Center, Shakopee, MN, p. A340

RYAN, Dennis, Senior Vice President and Chief Financial Officer, Children'S Hospital Of The King'S Daughters, Norfolk, VA, p. A663

RYAN, Emily, Chief Executive Officer, Medical Behavioral Hospital Of Mishawaka, Knox, IN, p. A209

RYAN, Frank, Chief Financial Officer, Manchester Veterans Affairs Medical Center, Manchester, NH, p. A401

RYAN, Jacqueline, Director Human Resources, Mayo Clinic Health System In Lake City, Lake City, MN, p. A334

RYAN, Jeffrey
  Chief Operating Officer, Cancer Treatment Centers Of America–Eastern Regional Medical Center, Philadelphia, PA, p. A534
  Senior Vice President, Finance and Business Development, Cancer Treatment Centers Of America–Eastern Regional Medical Center, Philadelphia, PA, p. A534

RYAN, John Jack, M.D., Chief Medical Officer, Surgeons Choice Medical Center, Southfield, MI, p. A323

RYAN, Kimberly, President, Wellstar Atlanta Medical Center, Atlanta, GA, p. A147

RYAN, Lisa M, Coordinator Human Resources, Hampstead Hospital, Hampstead, NH, p. A400

RYAN, Maria, Chief Executive Officer, Cottage Hospital, Woodsville, NH, p. A402

RYAN, Mike, Director of Information Services, Gunnison Valley Hospital, Gunnison, UT, p. A648

RYAN, Patrice
  Vice President Human Resources, Goleta Valley Cottage Hospital, Santa Barbara, CA, p. A88
  Vice President Human Resources, Santa Barbara Cottage Hospital, Santa Barbara, CA, p. A88
  Vice President Human Resources, Santa Ynez Valley Cottage Hospital, Solvang, CA, p. A90

RYAN, Patrick G., Chief Executive Officer, Promise Hospital Of Fort Myers, Fort Myers, FL, p. A123

RYAN, Patrick J., Chief Human Resources Officer, Helen Hayes Hospital, West Haverstraw, NY, p. A447

RYAN, Rebecca, Interim Director Human Resources and Employee Health, Ukiah Valley Medical Center, Ukiah, CA, p. A93

RYAN, Robert, M.D., Chief Medical Officer, Guadalupe Regional Medical Center, Seguin, TX, p. A636

RYAN, Sharon, Regional Controller, Select Specialty Hospital–Macomb County, Mount Clemens, MI, p. A318

RYAN, Tim, Chief Financial Officer, Centennial Peaks Hospital, Louisville, CO, p. A104

RYAN, William, Vice President and Chief Financial Officer, Uf Health Jacksonville, Jacksonville, FL, p. A126

RYBA, Janice L., Chief Executive Officer, St. Mary Medical Center, Hobart, IN, p. A206

RYBA, Thomas L., Chief Executive Officer, Lighthouse Behavioral Health Hospital, Conway, SC, p. A552

RYBA, Tomi S., President and Chief Executive Officer, Regional Medical Center Of San Jose, San Jose, CA, p. A86

RYBICKI, Cathy, Chief Operating Officer, Spectrum Health Reed City Hospital, Reed City, MI, p. A320

RYBOLT, Andrew, Chief Financial Officer, El Paso Children'S Hospital, El Paso, TX, p. A601

RYCKMAN, George, D.O., Chief of Staff, Paul Oliver Memorial Hospital, Frankfort, MI, p. A312

RYDER, Doug, President, Holy Cross Germantown Hospital, Germantown, MD, p. A290

RYDER, Jeff, Director Information Systems, Saint Joseph Mount Sterling, Mount Sterling, KY, p. A258

RYDER, Natalie, Chief Administrative Officer, Ascension Borgess–Lee Hospital, Dowagiac, MI, p. A310

RYDER, Ronald, D.O., President of the Medical Staff, Robert Wood Johnson University Hospital At Hamilton, Hamilton, NJ, p. A406

RYERSE, David, Chief Executive Officer, Stillwater Billings Clinic, Columbus, MT, p. A375

RYKOWSKI, Margaret A., Acting Chief Executive Officer, Laguna Honda Hospital And Rehabilitation Center, San Francisco, CA, p. A85

RYLAND, Jennifer M, R.N., Chief Administrative Officer, Jackson Medical Center, Jackson, AL, p. A20

RYLAND, Jennifer M., Chief Executive Officer, Jackson Medical Center, Jackson, AL, p. A20

RYLE, Barry W., Chief Information Officer, Oswego Hospital, Oswego, NY, p. A441

RYMER, Brandy, Coordinator Human Resources, Adventhealth Murray, Chatsworth, GA, p. A150

RYON, Joel, M.D., Chief of Staff, Henry County Health Center, Mount Pleasant, IA, p. A227

RYS, Jan, Chief Executive Officer, Straith Hospital For Special Surgery, Southfield, MI, p. A323

RYSTROM, Jennifer, R.N., Chief Nursing Officer, West Holt Medical Services, Atkinson, NE, p. A382

RZOMP, Kimberly
  Vice President and Chief Financial Officer, Chambersburg Hospital, Chambersburg, PA, p. A522
  Vice President Finance, Waynesboro Hospital, Waynesboro, PA, p. A543

S

SAAD, Michael, Vice President and Chief Information Officer, University Of Tennessee Medical Center, Knoxville, TN, p. A572

SAADAT, Annette, Human Resources Business Partner, Saint Joseph Mount Sterling, Mount Sterling, KY, p. A258

SAALFELD, Thomas, Senior Vice President and Chief Operating Officer, St. Elizabeth Fort Thomas, Fort Thomas, KY, p. A252

SAARI, Heidi L, Director Human Resources, Upper Connecticut Valley Hospital, Colebrook, NH, p. A399

SAAVEDRA, JayLynn, Chief Information Officer, U. S. Public Health Service Indian Hospital, Parker, AZ, p. A32

SABANDIT, Elizabeth, Director Human Resources, Alhambra Hospital Medical Center, Alhambra, CA, p. A50

SABELLA, Deborah, Chief Executive Officer, Landmark Hospital Of Cape Girardeau, Cape Girardeau, MO, p. A357

SABHARRWAL, Parajeet, Chief Executive Officer, Minimally Invasive Surgery Hospital, Lenexa, KS, p. A239

SABIA, John, M.D., Vice President Medical Affairs, Northern Dutchess Hospital, Rhinebeck, NY, p. A442

SABOTTA, John, Director Information Systems, St. Margaret'S Hospital, Spring Valley, IL, p. A196

SACHARSKI, Steve, Chief Financial Officer, Havenwyck Hospital, Auburn Hills, MI, p. A306

SACHDEV, Aruna, M.D., Medical Director, Pappas Rehabilitation Hospital For Children, Canton, MA, p. A297

SACHDEV, Vish, M.D., Chief Medical Officer, Brookwood Baptist Medical Center, Birmingham, AL, p. A14

SACHDEVA, Sandeep, M.D., Vice President Medical Affairs, Swedish/Edmonds, Edmonds, WA, p. A672

SACHS, Henry T, M.D., Medical Director, Emma Pendleton Bradley Hospital, East Providence, RI, p. A547

SACHTJEN, Mistie, Chief Executive Officer, Community Memorial Hospital, Burke, SD, p. A559

SACHTLEBEN, Michael, President, Medstar Georgetown University Hospital, Washington, DC, p. A115

SACK, Michael V, Chief Executive Officer, Melrosewakefield Healthcare, Melrose, MA, p. A300

SACKETT, John, President SGMC and Executive Vice President and Chief Operating Officer, Adventist Healthcare Shady Grove Medical Center, Rockville, MD, p. A293

SACKETT, Walter, President, Sycamore Medical Center, Miamisburg, OH, p. A487

SACKMANN, Charles, M.D., Chief of Staff, East Adams Rural Healthcare, Ritzville, WA, p. A677

SACKRISON, Jeffrey
  President, Vidant Bertie Hospital, Windsor, NC, p. A464
  President, Vidant Chowan Hospital, Edenton, NC, p. A453

SADA, Judy, Chief Financial Officer, Memorial Hospital Miramar, Miramar, FL, p. A132

SADLER, Cindy, Chief Nursing Officer, Iron County Medical Center, Pilot Knob, MO, p. A367

SADLER, Donna, Director Human Resources, Arkansas State Hospital, Little Rock, AR, p. A44

SADLER, Joy, Director Human Resources, Bear River Valley Hospital, Tremonton, UT, p. A653

SADLER BELL, Kelli S, R.N.
  Vice President, Chief Nursing Officer, Novant Health Charlotte Orthopaedic Hospital, Charlotte, NC, p. A451
  Vice President, Chief Nursing Officer, Novant Health Presbyterian Medical Center, Charlotte, NC, p. A451

SADOFF, Jennifer, Chief Executive Officer, Moab Regional Hospital, Moab, UT, p. A648

SADR, Farrokh, M.D., Chief Medical Officer, St. Luke'S Sacred Heart Campus, Allentown, PA, p. A519

SADRO, Cheryl A, Executive Vice President Chief Business and Finance Officer, University Of Texas Medical Branch, Galveston, TX, p. A607

SAENZ, Luis J Rodriquez, M.D., Medical Director, Hospital Menonita De Cayey, Cayey, PR, p. A716

SAENZ, Melanie, Regional Human Resources Officer, Amita Health Saints Mary & Elizabeth Medical Center, Chicago, IL, p. A176

SAFFA, Steve, Director Human Resources, University Of Kansas Health System St. Francis Campus, Topeka, KS, p. A246

SAFLEY, Thomas, Chief Financial Officer, St. Joseph Regional Medical Center, Lewiston, ID, p. A170

SAFYER, Steven M., President and Chief Executive Officer, Brookdale Hospital Medical Center, New York, NY, p. A432

SAGE, Kelly, Chief Nursing Officer, Hshs St. Anthony'S Memorial Hospital, Effingham, IL, p. A181

SAGER, Kelly, President and Chief Executive Officer, Hshs Holy Family Hospital In Greenville, Greenville, IL, p. A184

SAGMIT, Rodney, Chief Information Management, Va Long Beach Healthcare System, Long Beach, CA, p. A65

SAHA, Sanjay K, Chief Operating Officer, Sibley Memorial Hospital, Washington, DC, p. A116

SAHLOLBEI, Hossain, M.D., Chief of Staff, Palo Verde Hospital, Blythe, CA, p. A53

SAHLSTROM, Christopher, M.D., Chief of Staff, Mat–Su Regional Medical Center, Palmer, AK, p. A27

SAHMAUNT, Sarabeth, Supervisory Accountant, Lawton Indian Hospital, Lawton, OK, p. A501

SAIA, Carrie L., Chief Executive Officer, Holton Community Hospital, Holton, KS, p. A237

SAINBERT, Wilmino, Chief Human Resources Management Service, Northport Veterans Affairs Medical Center, Northport, NY, p. A439

SAINTZ, Jeffrey, Vice President Human Resources, Titusville Area Hospital, Titusville, PA, p. A542

SAIYED, Ashfaq, M.D., Medical Director, Irwin County Hospital, Ocilla, GA, p. A158

SAIZ, Claudia, Chief Executive Officer, Advanced Care Hospital Of Southern New Mexico, Las Cruces, NM, p. A418

SAJID, Muhammad W., M.D., Medical Director, Lincoln Trail Behavioral Health System, Radcliff, KY, p. A260

SAKALOSKY, Matt, Director Information Services and Chief Information Officer, Methodist Fremont Health, Fremont, NE, p. A385

SAKOVITS, Steven, Vice President Information Systems and Chief Information Officer, Stamford Hospital, Stamford, CT, p. A111

SALAKI, Jana, Regional Director Human Resources, Wellspan Ephrata Community Hospital, Ephrata, PA, p. A525

SALAMANCA, Mary, Director Human Resources, Encompass Health Rehabilitation Hospital Of Spring Hill, Brooksville, FL, p. A119

SALAMONE, Joanna, Senior Vice President Clinical Services and Chief Nursing Officer, Southern Maine Health Care – Biddeford Medical Center, Biddeford, ME, p. A282

SALANDI, John, Chief Executive Officer, Landmark Hospital Of Savannah, Savannah, GA, p. A160

SALAS, Dawn, Controller, Healthsouth Rehabilitation Hospital At Martin Health, Stuart, FL, p. A140

SALAS, Victor, M.D., President Medical Staff, Unitypoint Health – Jones Regional Medical Center, Anamosa, IA, p. A217

SALAWAY, Tarek, R.N., Chief Operating Officer, Usc Norris Comprehensive Cancer Center, Los Angeles, CA, p. A69

SALAZAR, Eloisa, Chief Financial Officer, South Texas Veterans Health Care System, San Antonio, TX, p. A635

SALAZAR, Leanne, Chief Operating Officer, Oak Hill Hospital, Brooksville, FL, p. A119

SALAZAR, Linda C, Information Technology Leader, Kaiser Permanente Baldwin Park Medical Center, Baldwin Park, CA, p. A51

SALAZAR, Pamela, M.D., Chief of Staff, Walton Rehabilitation Hospital, Augusta, GA, p. A148

SALAZAR, Serafin, M.D., Chief of Staff, Parkview Community Hospital Medical Center, Riverside, CA, p. A81

SALCEDO, Martha, Interim Director Human Resources, Whittier Hospital Medical Center, Whittier, CA, p. A95

SALCEDO, Nydimar, Chief Human Resources Officer, Castaner General Hospital, Castaner, PR, p. A715

SALDANHA, Glenn J., Chief Operating Officer, Palms Of Pasadena Hospital, Saint Petersburg, FL, p. A138

SALDIVAR, Antoninette, Vice President, Human Resources, Bridgepoint Hospital National Harbor, Washington, DC, p. A115

SALDIVAR, Duke, Chief Executive Officer, Warm Springs Rehabilitation Hospital Of Kyle, Kyle, TX, p. A619

SALEEBY, Manhal, M.D., Chief of Staff, Vcu Health Community Memorial Hospital, South Hill, VA, p. A667

SALEEM, David, Director Information Technology, Greystone Park Psychiatric Hospital, Morris Plains, NJ, p. A408

SALEM, Gary, M.D., Vice President Medical Affairs, Mclaren Lapeer Region, Lapeer, MI, p. A316

SALEM, Michael, President and Chief Executive Officer, National Jewish Health, Denver, CO, p. A99

SALGADO, Joe, M.D., Chief of Staff, Artesia General Hospital, Artesia, NM, p. A417

SALINAS, Amaro, Assistant Administrator and Human Resource Officer, Starr County Memorial Hospital, Rio Grande City, TX, p. A631

SALINAS, Daniel, M.D., Senior Vice President and Chief Medical Officer, Children'S Healthcare Of Atlanta, Atlanta, GA, p. A146

SALINAS, Noe
Vice President Information Technology, Nexus Specialty Hospital The Woodlands, The Woodlands, TX, p. A641
Vice President Information Technology, Nexus Specialty Hospital, Shenandoah, TX, p. A636

SALING, Christopher, Manager Human Resources, Park City Hospital, Park City, UT, p. A650

SALISBURY, Dennis, M.D., Vice President for Medical Affairs, St. James Healthcare, Butte, MT, p. A375

SALISBURY, Renee A, Director Human Resources, Osf Saint Luke Medical Center, Kewanee, IL, p. A187

SALISBURY, Tracy
Director Human Resources, Hiram W. Davis Medical Center, Petersburg, VA, p. A665
Regional Manager Human Resources, Central State Hospital, Petersburg, VA, p. A664

SALLER, William, Chief Financial Officer, Rio Grande Regional Hospital, Mcallen, TX, p. A623

SALLEY, Wanda, Vice President Human Resources, West Florida Hospital, Pensacola, FL, p. A136

SALLIS, Tom, Director Information Systems, Baptist Health – Fort Smith, Fort Smith, AR, p. A42

SALLOUM, Fadi, M.D., Medical Director, Select Specialty Hospital–Pontiac, Pontiac, MI, p. A320

SALMAN, Wael, M.D., Vice President Medical Affairs, Memorial Healthcare, Owosso, MI, p. A319

SALMANULLAH, Muhammad, Chief Medical Director, Encompass Health Rehabilitation Hospital Of Concord, Concord, NH, p. A399

SALOM, Ira, M.D., Clinical Director, Northern Navajo Medical Center, Shiprock, NM, p. A420

SALOME, Jenny, Chief Financial Officer and Assistant Administrator, Northwest Hills Surgical Hospital, Austin, TX, p. A586

SALOMON, Kathryn, Director Human Resources, Kona Community Hospital, Kealakekua, HI, p. A166

SALTAFORMAGGIO, Cheri, Chief Executive Officer, St. Charles Surgical Hospital, New Orleans, LA, p. A276

SALTER, Cherry B, Director of Nursing, Hardtner Medical Center, Olla, LA, p. A276

SALTONSTALL, Christine, Chief Financial Officer, Kindred Hospital–Baldwin Park, Baldwin Park, CA, p. A51

SALTZGABER, Lee, Chief Medical Officer, Gerald Champion Regional Medical Center, Alamogordo, NM, p. A416

SALVADOR, Ed, Chief Financial Officer, St. Jude Medical Center, Fullerton, CA, p. A60

SALVATI, Mario, Director Fiscal Services, Shriners Hospitals For Children–Philadelphia, Philadelphia, PA, p. A536

SALVI, Donna, Chief Nursing Officer, Watsonville Community Hospital, Watsonville, CA, p. A94

SALVINO, Sonia, Vice President Finance, University Hospitals Cleveland Medical Center, Cleveland, OH, p. A478

SALVITTI, Alfred P, Chief Financial Officer, Eagleville Hospital, Eagleville, PA, p. A524

SALVO, Stephen, Vice President Human Resources, Anna Jaques Hospital, Newburyport, MA, p. A301

SALWAN, Manav, Medical Director, Kindred Hospital–Sycamore, Sycamore, IL, p. A197

SALY, David, Director, Information Services, Largo Medical Center, Largo, FL, p. A128

SALYER, Steven, Chief Operating Officer, Up Health System–Marquette, Marquette, MI, p. A317

SALZMAN, Shona, Chief Operating Officer, William Newton Hospital, Winfield, KS, p. A248

SAMBASIVAN, Venkataraman, M.D., Chief Medical Officer, Lourdes Medical Center, Pasco, WA, p. A676

SAMILO, Nick, Vice President Fiscal Services and Chief Financial Officer, Atrium Health Stanly, Albemarle, NC, p. A449

SAMMARCO, Michael, M.D., Chief Financial Officer, Erie County Medical Center, Buffalo, NY, p. A424

SAMMONS, Craig, Chief Financial Officer, Sky Ridge Medical Center, Lone Tree, CO, p. A103

SAMMONS, Jacquelyn, Supervisor, Child And Adolescent Behavioral Health Services, Willmar, MN, p. A342

SAMMS, Caswell, Network Chief Financial Officer, Brookdale Hospital Medical Center, New York, NY, p. A432

SAMORA, Martha, Chief Executive Officer, Encompass Health Rehabilitation Hospital Of Bakersfield, Bakersfield, CA, p. A52

SAMPAGA, Arthur, Assistant Director Nursing, Hilo Medical Center, Hilo, HI, p. A164

SAMPSON, Arthur J., President, Miriam Hospital, Providence, RI, p. A547

SAMPSON, Bob
Senior Vice President, Human Resources, Evergreenhealth, Kirkland, WA, p. A674
Vice President Human Resources, Redwood Memorial Hospital, Fortuna, CA, p. A58

SAMPSON, Jill, Director Human Resources, Lemuel Shattuck Hospital, Jamaica Plain, MA, p. A299

SAMS, Alfred, President and Chief Executive Officer, St. Andrew'S Health Center, Bottineau, ND, p. A465

SAMS, Carla, R.N., Director of Nursing, Cypress Grove Behavioral Health, Bastrop, LA, p. A263

SAMS, James C., Chief of Staff, Mckenzie Health System, Sandusky, MI, p. A322

SAMSON, Ley, Director Management Information Systems, Hca Houston Healthcare Clear Lake, League City, TX, p. A620

SAMUDRALA, Siresha, M.D., Medical Director, Mercy Rehabilitation Hospital St. Louis, Chesterfield, MO, p. A358

SAMUEL, Nicole, Chief Financial Officer, Sierra Vista Hospital, Sacramento, CA, p. A82

SAMUELS, Christopher, Chief of Staff, Skyline Hospital, White Salmon, WA, p. A682

SAMUELSON, Kimberly, Director of Information Management, Highland–Clarksburg Hospital, Clarksburg, WV, p. A684

SAMUELSON, Melissa A, R.N.
Vice President and Chief Nursing Officer, Mercy Health – Anderson Hospital, Cincinnati, OH, p. A476
Vice President and Chief Nursing Officer, Mercy Health – Clermont Hospital, Batavia, OH, p. A472

SAMYN, Mike, Vice President, Finance and Chief Financial Officer, St. Mary Mercy Hospital, Livonia, MI, p. A317

SAMZ, Jeff, Chief Operating Officer, Huntsville Hospital, Huntsville, AL, p. A19

SAN FILIPPO, Bruce, M.D., Chief Medical Officer, Memorial Medical Center, Las Cruces, NM, p. A418

SANBORN, Michael, President, Baylor Scott & White All Saints Medical Center – Fort Worth, Fort Worth, TX, p. A604

SANBORN, Randall, Director Information Systems, Garden City Hospital, Garden City, MI, p. A312

SANCHEZ, Alvaro, M.D., Chief Medical Officer, Ridgeview Medical Center, Waconia, MN, p. A342

SANCHEZ, Antonio, Executive Director, Northport Veterans Affairs Medical Center, Northport, NY, p. A439

SANCHEZ, Arnaldo Rodriguez, M.D., Chief Operating Officer, Hospital Episcopal San Lucas Guayama, Guayama, PR, p. A716

SANCHEZ, Emalie, Director Human Resources, Baylor Scott & White Medical Center–Uptown, Dallas, TX, p. A595

SANCHEZ, Esperanza, Chief Clinical Officer, Kindred Hospital–La Mirada, La Mirada, CA, p. A63

SANCHEZ, Freddie, Director Information Systems, Fountain Valley Regional Hospital And Medical Center, Fountain Valley, CA, p. A58

SANCHEZ, John, Vice President Human Resources, White Plains Hospital Center, White Plains, NY, p. A448

SANCHEZ, Jose R., President and Chief Executive Officer, Norwegian American Hospital, Chicago, IL, p. A179

SANCHEZ, Jose', Chief Nursing Officer, Chg Hospital Tucson, Llc, Tucson, AZ, p. A37

SANCHEZ, Nancy, Senior Vice President and Vice Dean Human Resources, Brookdale Hospital Medical Center, New York, NY, p. A432

SANCHEZ, Rebecca, R.N., M.P.H., Director of Nursing, Texas Center For Infectious Disease, San Antonio, TX, p. A635

SANCHEZ–BICKLEY, Michelle
Chief Human Resources Officer, Renown Regional Medical Center, Reno, NV, p. A397
Vice President Human Resources, Renown Rehabilitation Hospital, Reno, NV, p. A397
Vice President Human Resources, Renown South Meadows Medical Center, Reno, NV, p. A397

SANCHEZ–RICO, Gloria, Chief Nursing Officer and Vice President, Huntington Memorial Hospital, Pasadena, CA, p. A77

SAND, Michelle, R.N., MSN, Vice President and Chief Nursing Officer, Cascade Valley Hospital, Arlington, WA, p. A670

SANDAGER, Brian, Chief Information Officer, Lowell General Hospital, Lowell, MA, p. A300

SANDBERG, Susan, Chief Executive Officer, Melrosewakefield Healthcare, Melrose, MA, p. A300

SANDBERG, Todd, Chief Executive Officer, Riverwood Healthcare Center, Aitkin, MN, p. A327

SANDBULTE, Nyla H, R.N., Director of Nursing, Sanford Luverne Medical Center, Luverne, MN, p. A334

SANDEFUR, Gwen, President, Spectrum Health Hospital Group, Spectrum Health – Butterworth Hospital, Grand Rapids, MI, p. A313

SANDER, Cindy, Coordinator Human Resources, Kindred Hospital–St. Louis, Saint Louis, MO, p. A369

SANDERS, Amy, Chief Human Resources, Captain James A. Lovell Federal Health Care Center, North Chicago, IL, p. A191

SANDERS, Carolyn Lucey, Senior Vice President Patient Services and Chief Nursing Officer, University Of Colorado Hospital, Aurora, CO, p. A96

SANDERS, David, Chief Financial Officer, Springhill Medical Center, Springhill, LA, p. A279

SANDERS, David S., Chief Executive Officer, Fannin Regional Hospital, Blue Ridge, GA, p. A148

SANDERS, Gale H, Director, Gadsden Regional Medical Center, Gadsden, AL, p. A18

SANDERS, Harv, Chief Financial Officer, Rhea Medical Center, Dayton, TN, p. A569

SANDERS, Jeff, Senior Vice President, Chief Operating Officer, Maine Medical Center, Portland, ME, p. A284

SANDERS, Jeffrey, M.D., Chief of Staff, Carson Tahoe Health, Carson City, NV, p. A393

SANDERS, Kelly B., Vice President Human Resources, Good Shepherd Health Care System, Hermiston, OR, p. A513

SANDERS, Kenneth, Administrator and Chief Executive Officer, Dallas County Medical Center, Fordyce, AR, p. A42

SANDERS, Kimberly, Chief Nursing Officer, Baptist Memorial Hospital–Carroll County, Huntingdon, TN, p. A571

SANDERS, Kris, Chief Financial Officer, Methodist Healthcare Olive Branch Hospital, Olive Branch, MS, p. A352

SANDERS, Kyle
Chief Financial Officer, Nea Baptist Memorial Hospital, Jonesboro, AR, p. A44
President, Sebastian River Medical Center, Sebastian, FL, p. A139

SANDERS, Michael B., President and Chief Executive Officer, Monroe Clinic, Monroe, WI, p. A701

SANDERS, Michael R, MS, Chief Operating Officer, Promise Hospital Baton Rouge – Main Campus, Baton Rouge, LA, p. A264

SANDERS, R. Bradley, D.O., Executive Medical Director, Alvarado Parkway Institute Behavioral Health System, La Mesa, CA, p. A63

SANDERS, Robert, M.D., Chief Medical Officer, Texoma Medical Center, Denison, TX, p. A599

SANDERS, Sheila M, Chief Information Officer, Emory University Hospital, Atlanta, GA, p. A146

SANDERS, Steve, Chief Financial Officer, Washington County Hospital And Clinics, Washington, IA, p. A230

SANDERS, Susie Sherrod, Chief Financial Officer, Cherry Hospital, Goldsboro, NC, p. A455

SANDHU, Rohinder, M.D., President of the Medical Staff, San Antonio Regional Hospital, Upland, CA, p. A93

SANDIFER, Ron, Chief Information Officer, Community Memorial Hospital, Ventura, CA, p. A93

SANDIN, James H, M.D., Assistant Administrator Medical Affairs, Hunt Regional Medical Center, Greenville, TX, p. A608

SANDLES, Christopher R., Medical Center Director, South Texas Veterans Health Care System, San Antonio, TX, p. A635

SANDLIN, Michael, M.D., Chief of Staff, Muscogee Creek Nation Medical Center, Okmulgee, OK, p. A506

SANDMANN, Patty, Senior Director of Nursing, Burgess Health Center, Onawa, IA, p. A227

SANDS, Dennis, Chief Medical Officer, Osf Healthcare Saint Anthony'S Health Center, Alton, IL, p. A173

SANDS, Mark, M.D., Chief Medical Officer, Stony Brook University Hospital, Stony Brook, NY, p. A444

SANDS, Sherry, R.N., Chief Nursing Officer, Southern Tennessee Regional Health System–Pulaski, Pulaski, TN, p. A578

SANDS, Tiffany, Manager Health Information, Arbuckle Memorial Hospital, Sulphur, OK, p. A508

SANDS, Tom, Interim Chief Executive Officer, Carney Hospital, Boston, MA, p. A295

SANDSTROM, C Bruce, Vice President and Chief Financial Officer, The Aroostook Medical Center, Presque Isle, ME, p. A284

SANDUJA, Sourabh, Administrator, Altus Baytown Hospital, Baytown, TX, p. A587

SANFORD, Debbie F, Administrator, Forrest General Hospital, Hattiesburg, MS, p. A348

SANFORD, Lisa, VP Patient Care/CNO, Holy Rosary Healthcare, Miles City, MT, p. A378

SANFORD, Ricca, Director Human Resources, Regional West Garden County, Oshkosh, NE, p. A390

SANFORD, Sharon K, Director Human Resources, Jersey Community Hospital, Jerseyville, IL, p. A186

SANFORD, Stacy, Chief Executive Officer, Oceans Behavioral Hospital Abilene, Abilene, TX, p. A581

SANGER, David, M.D., Chief Medical Officer, University Of Kansas Health System Pawnee Valley Campus, Larned, KS, p. A239

SANGER, Ken, R.N., Chief Nursing Officer and Chief Operations Officer, Lake Huron Medical Center, Port Huron, MI, p. A320

SANGER, Neal, Vice President Information Services, Mayo Clinic Health System – Franciscan Healthcare In La Crosse, La Crosse, WI, p. A698

SANGHI, Harishankar, M.D., Clinical Director, St. Lawrence Psychiatric Center, Ogdensburg, NY, p. A440

SANKARAN, Jaya, M.D., Chief of Staff, Ascension Standish Hospital, Standish, MI, p. A323

SANKE, Kristina, Chief Financial Officer, Orchard Hospital, Gridley, CA, p. A61

SANKOORIKAL, Joseph, M.D., Chief Medical Staff, Kansas Rehabilitation Hospital, Topeka, KS, p. A246

SANKS, Claude, Chief Medical Staff, Effingham Hospital, Springfield, GA, p. A160

SANNUTO, John
Chief Executive Officer, Clearvista Health And Wellness, Lorain, OH, p. A486
Chief Executive Officer, Wellbridge Healthcare Greater Dallas, Plano, TX, p. A630

SANSOM, Christine R, Chief Nursing Officer, Mclaren Port Huron, Port Huron, MI, p. A320

SANSONE, John, Vice President, Human Resources, Monadnock Community Hospital, Peterborough, NH, p. A402

SANTA ANA, Coleen F., President, Sentara Albemarle Medical Center, Elizabeth City, NC, p. A453

SANTANA, Leticia, Administrator Medical Records, Hospital Hermanos Melendez, Bayamon, PR, p. A715

SANTANGELO, Craig, Director Information Services, Medical City Arlington, Arlington, TX, p. A583

SANTANGELO, Joe, M.D., Vice President of Medical Affairs, Munson Healthcare Cadillac Hospital, Cadillac, MI, p. A308

SANTANGELO, John, Director Information Technology, Cleveland Clinic Florida, Weston, FL, p. A144

SANTARELLI, James, M.D., President Medical Staff, Aurora Medical Center Kenosha, Kenosha, WI, p. A697

SANTIAGO, Alejandro, Director Finance, Doctors' Center Hospital San Juan, San Juan, PR, p. A718

SANTIAGO, Julio, M.D., Chief of Staff, Genesis Medical Center–Aledo, Aledo, IL, p. A173

SANTIAGO, Manuel, Chief Information Officer, Hospital Metropolitan, San Juan, PR, p. A719

SANTIAGO, Orlando, Human Resources Officer, Hospital Del Maestro, San Juan, PR, p. A718

SANTIAGO, Sugehi, Director, Hospital San Francisco, San Juan, PR, p. A719

SANTIAGO, Ubaldo, M.D., Chairman, Doctors' Center Hospital San Juan, San Juan, PR, p. A718

SANTIESTEBAN, Nancy, Director Patient Care Services, Presbyterian Espanola Hospital, Espanola, NM, p. A418

SANTILLI, Robert J., Chief Executive Officer, Gunnison Valley Hospital, Gunnison, CO, p. A101

SANTINA, Ray, Director Information Systems, Psychiatric Institute Of Washington, Washington, DC, p. A116

SANTISTEVAN, Vivian, Chief Human Resources, Tsehootsooi Medical Center, Fort Defiance, AZ, p. A29

SANTMAN, Kim D, Vice President Finance, St. Margaret'S Hospital, Spring Valley, IL, p. A196

SANTORA, Judith
Chief Human Resource Officer, Lutheran Hospital, Cleveland, OH, p. A478
Human Resources Business Partner, Marymount Hospital, Garfield Heights, OH, p. A483

SANTOS, Alfred, Chief Executive Officer, Encompass Health Rehabilitation Hospital Of Northern Virginia, Aldie, VA, p. A656

SANTOS, Daniel, Director Ancillary Services, Pacifica Hospital Of The Valley, Los Angeles, CA, p. A68

SANTOS, David
President and Chief Executive Officer, Adventist Health Clear Lake, Clearlake, CA, p. A54
President Chief Executive Officer, Adventist Health Clear Lake, Clearlake, CA, p. A54

SANTOS, Deborah, R.N., Chief Nursing Officer, Encompass Health Rehabilitation Hospital Of Western Massachusetts, Ludlow, MA, p. A300

SANTOS, Gloria N, R.N., MS
Chief Nursing Officer, Adventhealth Sebring, Sebring, FL, p. A139
Vice President and Chief Nursing Officer, Adventhealth Wauchula, Wauchula, FL, p. A143

SANTOS, Ismael, Director Human Resources, Valle Vista Health System, Greenwood, IN, p. A205

SANTOS, Lori
Chief Financial Officer, St. Peter'S Hospital, Albany, NY, p. A422
Vice President Finance, Albany Memorial Hospital, Albany, NY, p. A422

SANTUCCI, James, Chief Operating Officer, Desert Regional Medical Center, Palm Springs, CA, p. A76

SANTULLI, Patricia, Director Human Resources, Elmira Psychiatric Center, Elmira, NY, p. A427

SANVILLE, David, Chief Financial Officer, Mt. Ascutney Hospital And Health Center, Windsor, VT, p. A655

SANWARI, Murtaza, Senior Vice President and Area Manager, Kaiser Permanente Woodland Hills Medical Center, Los Angeles, CA, p. A67

SANZONE, Frank, Manager Information Technology, Ascension Brighton Center For Recovery, Brighton, MI, p. A307

SAPMAZ, Cagri, Information Technology Director, Bolivar Medical Center, Cleveland, MS, p. A346

SAPORITO, Angie, Administrator, Mercy Hospital Columbus, Columbus, KS, p. A233

SAPORITO, Joann L., R.N., Vice President Nursing Services, Oak Valley Hospital District, Oakdale, CA, p. A75

SAPP, Tracy, Director Human Resources, Encompass Health Rehabilitation Hospital Of Ocala, Ocala, FL, p. A133

SAPPENFIELD, Debra, R.N., Chief Nursing Officer, Hemphill County Hospital, Canadian, TX, p. A591

SAPPINGTON-CRITTENDEN, Shana, Chief Operating Officer, Westside Regional Medical Center, Plantation, FL, p. A137

SARBACHER, James, Chief Information Officer, State Hospital North, Orofino, ID, p. A171

SARDANA, Sadhana, M.D., Clinical Director, Rockland Children'S Psychiatric Center, Orangeburg, NY, p. A440

SARDELLA, Jeff, Director Information Technology, Terrebonne General Medical Center, Houma, LA, p. A269

SARDONE, Frank J, President and Chief Executive Officer, Bronson Methodist Hospital, Kalamazoo, MI, p. A315

SARDONE, Frank J.
President and Chief Executive Officer, Bronson Battle Creek Hospital, Battle Creek, MI, p. A307
President and Chief Executive Officer, Bronson Methodist Hospital, Kalamazoo, MI, p. A315

SARDUY, Innette Mary, M.P.H., R.N., Associate Director Patient Care Services and Nurse Executive, Louis Stokes Cleveland Veterans Affairs Medical Center, Cleveland, OH, p. A478

SARGENT, Kimberly, Vice President Patient Services, St. Luke'S Hospital – Miners Campus, Coaldale, PA, p. A522

SARGENT, Kurt, CPA
Vice President Operational Finance, Chi St. Alexius Health Devils Lake Hospital, Devils Lake, ND, p. A466
Vice President, Operational Finance, Chi St Alexius Health Carrington Medical Center, Carrington, ND, p. A465

SARGENT, Reed
Assistant Administrator Finance, Cedar City Hospital, Cedar City, UT, p. A647
Assistant Administrator Finance, Garfield Memorial Hospital, Panguitch, UT, p. A650

SARGENT, Teresa, Vice President Human Resources, Saint Alphonsus Regional Medical Center, Boise, ID, p. A168

SARIAN, Michael, Interim Chief Executive Officer, La Palma Intercommunity Hospital, La Palma, CA, p. A63

SARMENTO, Joann, Manager Human Resources, Fairchild Medical Center, Yreka, CA, p. A95

SARNECKI, Adrienne, R.N.
Chief Nurse Executive, Spaulding Hospital For Continuing Medical Care Cambridge, Cambridge, MA, p. A297
Chief Nursing Officer, Spaulding Rehabilitation Hospital Cape Cod, East Sandwich, MA, p. A298

SARNECKI, Robert, Interim Chief Information Officer, Children'S Of Alabama, Birmingham, AL, p. A14

SAROFIN, Michelle, Superintendent, Albert J. Solnit Psychiatric Center – South Campus, Middletown, CT, p. A109

SARROS, Steven, Vice President and Chief Information Officer, Baptist Hospital, Pensacola, FL, p. A136

SARROUI, B, M.D., Chief of Staff, Advanced Specialty Hospital Of Toledo, Toledo, OH, p. A492

SARTAIN, Jarred, M.D., President Medical Staff, North Mississippi Medical Center–Hamilton, Hamilton, AL, p. A19

SARTAIN, Lisa M., Vice President, Human Resources, Bellevue Hospital, Bellevue, OH, p. A473

SARVEPALLI, Raghu, M.D., Vice President of Medical Affairs, Ascension St. Mary'S Of Michigan, Saginaw, MI, p. A321

SARVER, Troy, R.N., Chief Nursing Officer, Texas Orthopedic Hospital, Houston, TX, p. A614

SAS, Mary, Director of Clinical Services, Hampshire Memorial Hospital, Romney, WV, p. A689

SASSER, Kelley, Director Information Systems, Adventhealth Zephyrhills, Zephyrhills, FL, p. A144

SATHER, Sonia, M.D., President Medical Staff, Spencer Hospital, Spencer, IA, p. A230

SATTAR, Parhez, Senior Director Information Technology, Grande Ronde Hospital, La Grande, OR, p. A514

SATTERWHITE, Glenda, Director of Nursing, Oklahoma Forensic Center, Vinita, OK, p. A510

SAUDE, Aaron, Chief Executive Officer, Bigfork Valley Hospital, Bigfork, MN, p. A328

SAUDER, Chris, Vice President and Chief Financial Officer, Adventhealth Carrollwood, Tampa, FL, p. A141

SAUER, Bernie, Director Information Technology, San Gabriel Valley Medical Center, San Gabriel, CA, p. A86

SAUER, Mary R, R.N., Chief Nursing Officer, Cleveland Clinic Avon Hospital, Avon, OH, p. A472

SAUERBREI, Teresa, Chief Nursing Officer, Compass Memorial Healthcare, Marengo, IA, p. A226

SAUERS, Preston, Chief Financial Officer, Ellsworth County Medical Center, Ellsworth, KS, p. A234

SAUM, Anita, Director Human Resources, Encompass Health Rehabilitation Hospital Of Tinton Falls, Tinton Falls, NJ, p. A413

SAUNDERS, John R, M.D., Senior Vice President Medical Affairs and Chief Medical Officer, Greater Baltimore Medical Center, Baltimore, MD, p. A288

SAUNDERS, Jonathan, Chief Financial Officer, Baylor Scott & White Medical Center – Trophy Club, Trophy Club, TX, p. A641

SAUNDERS, Kevin, Human Resources Officer III, Arrowhead Regional Medical Center, Colton, CA, p. A55

SAUNDERS, Kristi K, Director and Compliance Officer, Calais Regional Hospital, Calais, ME, p. A282

SAUNDERS, M Patricia, R.N., MS, Vice President Nursing, Upmc Hanover, Hanover, PA, p. A526

SAUNDERS, Ninfa M., President and Chief Executive Officer, Medical Center, Navicent Health, Macon, GA, p. A156

SAURO, Anthony, Chief Information Officer, Pointe Coupee General Hospital, New Roads, LA, p. A276

SAUS, Heather, Human Resource Generalist, Edwin Shaw Rehab, Cuyahoga Falls, OH, p. A480

SAUSEDO, Rhonda, Chief Nursing Officer, Placentia–Linda Hospital, Placentia, CA, p. A78

SAUTER, Michael, M.D., Chief Medical Officer, St. Charles Hospital, Port Jefferson, NY, p. A441

SAVAGE, Elizabeth, Senior Vice President and Chief Human Resource Officer and Vice President Community Health and Wellness, Winchester Medical Center, Winchester, VA, p. A669

SAVAGE, Ginny, Director of Human Resources, Carolina Center For Behavioral Health, Greer, SC, p. A554

SAVAGE, Heather, Director Human Resources, The Rehabilitation Institute Of St. Louis, Saint Louis, MO, p. A371

SAVAGE, Jeanne, M.D., Chief Medical Officer, Willamette Valley Medical Center, Mcminnville, OR, p. A514

SAVAGE, Steve, Chief Executive Officer, Stonecrest Center, Detroit, MI, p. A310

SAVITSKY, Marian, R.N., Chief Nursing Officer, Sky Ridge Medical Center, Lone Tree, CO, p. A103

SAVOY, F. Peter., III, Chief Executive Officer, Byrd Regional Hospital, Leesville, LA, p. A272

SAVOY, Greg, M.D., Chief Medical Officer, Savoy Medical Center, Mamou, LA, p. A273

SAWA, Kendall, R.N., Chief Operating Officer, Providence Portland Medical Center, Portland, OR, p. A516

SAWALLISH, Trevor, Senior Vice President Clinical Operations and Chief Operating Officer, Children'S Hospitals And Clinics Of Minnesota, Minneapolis, MN, p. A335

SAWDEY, Don, M.D., Medical Director, Daniels Memorial Healthcare Center, Scobey, MT, p. A380

SAWICKI, Mitzi, Director of Nursing, Havenwyck Hospital, Auburn Hills, MI, p. A306

SAWYER, Anne, Chief Financial Officer, Wayne County Hospital, Monticello, KY, p. A258

SAWYER, Colleen A.
Executive Director, Mohawk Valley Psychiatric Center, Utica, NY, p. A446
Executive Director, Richard H. Hutchings Psychiatric Center, Syracuse, NY, p. A445

SAWYER, Holly, Director and Human Resources Business Partner, Piedmont Fayette Hospital, Fayetteville, GA, p. A153

SAWYER, Joseph T., Jr, President, Guthrie Robert Packer Hospital, Sayre, PA, p. A540

SAWYER, Regina, Vice President Chief Nursing Officer, Kaweah Delta Medical Center, Visalia, CA, p. A94

SAWYER, Scott, Chief Financial Officer, Community Medical Center, Inc., Falls City, NE, p. A384

SAWYER, Stephen, Chief Financial Officer, Norton Community Hospital, Norton, VA, p. A664

SAWYER, Steve, Chief Financial Officer, Indian Path Medical Center, Kingsport, TN, p. A572

SAWYER, Sydney, Chief Executive Officer, Lackey Memorial Hospital, Forest, MS, p. A347

SAXON, Kathy, R.N., Vice President Patient Care Services, Adventist Healthtillamook, Tillamook, OR, p. A518

SAXTON, Beth, Chief Executive Officer, Yuma District Hospital, Yuma, CO, p. A106

SAYAH, Assaad, Interim Chief Executive Officer, Cambridge Health Alliance, Cambridge, MA, p. A297

SAYAH, Assaad, M.D., Chief Medical Officer, Cambridge Health Alliance, Cambridge, MA, p. A297

SAYLER, Elizabeth, M.D., Chief of Staff, Lead–Deadwood Regional Hospital, Deadwood, SD, p. A560

SAYLER, Roger, Finance Officer, Fargo Veterans Affairs Health Care System, Fargo, ND, p. A466

SAYLES, Debbie A, R.N., Vice President and Chief Nursing Officer, Texas Scottish Rite Hospital For Children, Dallas, TX, p. A598

SAYLOR, Richard F, M.D., Chief Medical Officer, Pottstown Hospital, Pottstown, PA, p. A539

SAYRE, Amy, Director Human Resources, Pershing Memorial Hospital, Brookfield, MO, p. A357

SAYRE, Cindy, Ph.D., R.N., Chief Nursing Officer, University Of Washington Medical Center, Seattle, WA, p. A678

SBARDELLA, Steven P., M.D., FABC, President Clinical Operations and Chief Medical Officer, Melrosewakefield Healthcare, Melrose, MA, p. A300

SCAFIDDI, Darlene, R.N., MSN, Vice President Nursing and Patient Care Services, Pomona Valley Hospital Medical Center, Pomona, CA, p. A78

SCAGLIONE, Kim, Vice President Human Resources, Baptist Health Louisville, Louisville, KY, p. A256

SCALES, Melisa, Director of Nursing, Parkview Hospital, Wheeler, TX, p. A645

SCALFARI, Patricia A, Vice President Nursing, Medstar Southern Maryland Hospital Center, Clinton, MD, p. A289

SCALLION, Jessika, Administrator, Beacon Behavioral Hospital Northshore, Lacombe, LA, p. A270

SCAMARDO, Luke P, M.D., Chief of Staff, Chi St. Joseph Health Grimes Hospital, Navasota, TX, p. A626

SCAMINACI, Peter
President, Mercy Medical Center, Rockville Centre, NY, p. A443
President, St. Joseph Hospital, Bethpage, NY, p. A423

SCANLON, Donald
Chief Corporate Services, Mount Sinai Health System, Brookdale Hospital Medical Center, New York, NY, p. A432
Chief Financial Officer, Brookdale Hospital Medical Center, New York, NY, p. A432

SCANLON, John, DPM, Chief Medical Officer, Chestnut Hill Hospital, Philadelphia, PA, p. A534

SCANLON, Kerri, MSN, Chief Nursing Officer, North Shore University Hospital, Manhasset, NY, p. A430

SCANNELL, Donna, Vice President Information Technology, Kaiser Permanente Medical Center, Honolulu, HI, p. A164

SCANZERA, Christopher A, Vice President and Chief Information Officer, Atlanticare Regional Medical Center, Atlantic City, NJ, p. A403

SCARBORO, Parrish, Chief Executive Officer, San Dimas Community Hospital, San Dimas, CA, p. A85

SCARBROUGH, Keith, Director, Information Systems, Saint Francis Hospital, Memphis, TN, p. A575

SCARLATTI, Shirley K, Associate Chief Nursing Officer, Parkridge Medical Center, Chattanooga, TN, p. A567

SCARLETT, Kamesha, Chief Information Resource Management, Veterans Affairs New Jersey Health Care System, East Orange, NJ, p. A405

SCARMATO, Victor, M.D., Acting Medical Director, Nassau University Medical Center, East Meadow, NY, p. A427

SCARPINO, David
President and Chief Executive Officer, Health Alliance Hospital – Broadway Campus, Kingston, NY, p. A430
President and Chief Executive Officer, Health Alliance Hospital – Mary'S Avenue Campus, Kingston, NY, p. A430

SCARROW, Lloyd, Chief Executive Officer, Edgewood Surgical Hospital, Transfer, PA, p. A542

SCEPANSKI, Theresa, Vice President People and Organizational Development, University Health System, San Antonio, TX, p. A635

SCERCY, Charles, Corporate Director, Mary Washington Hospital, Fredericksburg, VA, p. A659

SCHAAB, Ben, Vice President, Chief Financial Officer, Cgh Medical Center, Sterling, IL, p. A197

SCHAACK, Ann, Chief Executive Officer, Willow Springs Center, Reno, NV, p. A397

SCHAACK, Gregory J, CPA
Vice President and Chief Financial Officer, Candler Hospital, Savannah, GA, p. A160
Vice President and Chief Financial Officer, St. Joseph'S Hospital, Savannah, GA, p. A160

SCHADE, Sue, Interim Chief Information Officer, University Hospitals Cleveland Medical Center, Cleveland, OH, p. A478

SCHAEF, Toby, Director Information Technology, Memorial Hospital Of Carbon County, Rawlins, WY, p. A712

SCHAEFER, Becky, Chief Financial Officer, University Of Utah Neuropsychiatric Institute, Salt Lake City, UT, p. A652

SCHAEFER, Debra, Chief Nursing Officer, Windsor–Laurelwood Center For Behavioral Medicine, Willoughby, OH, p. A494

SCHAEFER, Jamie, Vice President Finance, Avera Sacred Heart Hospital, Yankton, SD, p. A565

SCHAEFER, Kevin, Manager Information Services, River'S Edge Hospital And Clinic, Saint Peter, MN, p. A340

SCHAEFER, Matthew, Chief Operating Officer, Children'S Hospital, New Orleans, LA, p. A275

SCHAEFER, Michael J, Executive Vice President and Chief Financial Officer, Methodist Charlton Medical Center, Dallas, TX, p. A597

SCHAEFER, Michelle, Chief Financial Officer, Lillian M. Hudspeth Memorial Hospital, Sonora, TX, p. A637

SCHAEFER, Stephen, Chief Executive Officer, Healthsouth Rehabilitation Hospital Of Colorado Springs, Colorado Springs, CO, p. A97

SCHAEFFER, Andre, M.D., Chief of Staff, Union General Hospital, Blairsville, GA, p. A148

SCHAEFFER, Richard, Vice President Information Systems and Chief Information Officer, St. Clair Hospital, Pittsburgh, PA, p. A537

SCHAETTI, Susan
Chief Executive Officer, Kindred Hospital Tarrant County–Arlington, Arlington, TX, p. A583
Chief Executive Officer, Kindred Hospital–Fort Worth, Fort Worth, TX, p. A605

SCHAFER, Laurie, Chief Nursing Officer, San Juan Health Service District, Monticello, UT, p. A649

SCHAFER, Michael, Chief Executive Officer and Administrator, Spooner Health, Spooner, WI, p. A705

SCHAFER, Mona, Regional Manager Human Resources, Milbank Area Hospital Avera, Milbank, SD, p. A562

SCHAFFER, John, R.N., Director of Nursing, Clifton–Fine Hospital, Star Lake, NY, p. A444

SCHAFFER, Megan, Administrative Assistant, Surgical Institute Of Reading, Wyomissing, PA, p. A545

SCHAFFER, Renee, Coordinator Human Resources, Select Specialty Hospital–Wichita, Wichita, KS, p. A248

SCHAFFNER, Leroy, Interim Chief Executive Officer, Ochiltree General Hospital, Perryton, TX, p. A628

SCHAFFNER, Richard
Executive Vice President and Chief Operating Officer, Beebe Healthcare, Lewes, DE, p. A113
Interim Chief Executive Officer, Beebe Healthcare, Lewes, DE, p. A113

SCHAFSNITZ, Patricia, Director of Nursing Services, Mckenzie Health System, Sandusky, MI, p. A322

SCHALES, Marion, Chief Financial Officer, Highland Hospital, Oakland, CA, p. A75

SCHALL, Dee, R.N., Chief Nursing Officer, Baptist Health Medical Center–Hot Spring County, Malvern, AR, p. A45

SCHALSKI, Paula, Director Human Resources, Pushmataha Hospital, Antlers, OK, p. A496

SCHALTZ, Linda, MSN, R.N., Chief Nursing Officer, Spectrum Health United Hospital, Greenville, MI, p. A313

SCHAMP, Cindy K., President, Baylor Scott & White Medical Center–Irving, Irving, TX, p. A616

SCHANDL, Brian, Chief Information Officer, Marshall Browning Hospital, Du Quoin, IL, p. A181

SCHANEL, Judith A, Chief Operating Officer, Moses H. Cone Memorial Hospital, Greensboro, NC, p. A455

SCHANWALD, Pamela R., Chief Executive Officer, The Children'S Home Of Pittsburgh, Pittsburgh, PA, p. A537

SCHAPP, Susan, Vice President Finance and Treasurer, Charlotte Hungerford Hospital, Torrington, CT, p. A111

SCHARBER, Laurel, Administrative Assistant and Coordinator Human Resources, Kindred Hospital–Ontario, Ontario, CA, p. A76

SCHARENBROCK, Chris, M.D., Chief Medical Staff, David Grant Usaf Medical Center, Travis Afb, CA, p. A92

SCHARFF, Tom, Director Information Services, University Hospital And Medical Center, Tamarac, FL, p. A141

SCHARNBERG, Cathi Rae, R.N., M.P.H., Vice President Patient Services, Avera Holy Family Hospital, Estherville, IA, p. A222

SCHARNHORST, Alicia, Human Resources and Administrative Assistant, Garfield County Public Hospital District, Pomeroy, WA, p. A676

SCHARR, Vickie, Chief Financial Officer, Bakersfield Heart Hospital, Bakersfield, CA, p. A52

SCHATTSCHNEIDER, Tami, Chief Nursing Officer, St. Agnes Hospital, Fond Du Lac, WI, p. A695

SCHAUF, Jeffrey, Director Information Systems, Wesley Healthcare Center, Wichita, KS, p. A248

SCHAUF, Kyle, M.D., President Medical Staff, Integris Grove Hospital, Grove, OK, p. A500

SCHAWL, Bud, Chief Executive Officer, Kindred Hospital–Albuquerque, Albuquerque, NM, p. A416

SCHEAFFEL, Margaret M.
Chief Nursing Officer, Carilion Franklin Memorial Hospital, Rocky Mount, VA, p. A667
Chief Nursing Officer, Carilion Roanoke Memorial Hospital, Roanoke, VA, p. A667

SCHEERER, Dan, M.D., Chief Medical Officer, Genesis Healthcare System, Zanesville, OH, p. A495

SCHEETZ, Allison, M.D., Medical Director, Rehabilitation Hospital, Navicent Health, Macon, GA, p. A157

SCHEFFLER, Robert, Chief Executive Officer, Haven Behavioral Hospital Of Eastern Pennsylvania, Reading, PA, p. A539

SCHEFFLER, Tom, Chief Fiscal Officer, Veterans Affairs Maryland Health Care System–Baltimore Division, Baltimore, MD, p. A288

SCHEINBART, Lee, M.D.
Vice President Medical Affairs, Health First Community Hospitals, Health First Cape Canaveral Hospital, Cocoa Beach, FL, p. A120
Vice President Medical Affairs, Health First Community Hospitals, Health First Palm Bay Hospital, Palm Bay, FL, p. A135

SCHEINBLUM, Richard, Chief Financial Officer, Monadnock Community Hospital, Peterborough, NH, p. A402

SCHELBAR, E Joe, M.D., Medical Director, Select Specialty Hospital–Tulsa Midtown, Tulsa, OK, p. A509

SCHELL, James, M.D., Vice President Medical Affairs, Saint Francis Medical Center, Cape Girardeau, MO, p. A357

SCHELL, Jonathan, Chief Nursing Officer, Drew Memorial Health System, Monticello, AR, p. A46

SCHEMER, Tonia, Interim Chief Human Resources, St. Joseph Mercy Livingston Hospital, Howell, MI, p. A314

SCHENKER, Amy, Human Resources Director, Shriners Hospitals For Children–Tampa, Tampa, FL, p. A142

SCHEPICI, Denise, Chief Executive Officer and President, Martha'S Vineyard Hospital, Oak Bluffs, MA, p. A302

SCHEPMANN, Jane, Vice President and Chief Nursing Officer, Clara Barton Hospital, Hoisington, KS, p. A236

SCHEPPERS, Levi, Chief Executive Officer, Orthonebraska Hospital, Omaha, NE, p. A390

SCHEPPERS, Lisa, Chief Medical Officer, Regional West Medical Center, Scottsbluff, NE, p. A391

SCHER, Kathleen, Ed.D., R.N., Chief Nursing Officer, Brookdale Hospital Medical Center, New York, NY, p. A432

SCHERER, Timothy, M.D., Chief Medical Officer, Southern New Hampshire Medical Center, Nashua, NH, p. A401

SCHERLER, Jay, Vice President Finance and Chief Information Officer, Providence Healthcare Network, Waco, TX, p. A644

SCHERLING, Adam, President, Grundy County Memorial Hospital, Grundy Center, IA, p. A223

SCHERNECK, Michael D., President and Chief Executive Officer, Southeast Georgia Health System Brunswick Campus, Brunswick, GA, p. A148

SCHERPF, John
Chief Executive Officer, Banner – University Medical Center South, Tucson, AZ, p. A37
Chief Executive Officer, Banner – University Medical Center Tucson, Tucson, AZ, p. A37

SCHEVING, Travis, Chief Financial Officer, Holy Rosary Healthcare, Miles City, MT, p. A378
SCHEXNAYDER, Glenn, M.D., Chief of Staff, Prevost Memorial Hospital, Donaldsonville, LA, p. A267
SCHEY, David, Chief Financial Officer, Brook Lane Health Services, Hagerstown, MD, p. A291
SCHICK, Eric
Chief Financial Officer, Saint Francis Hospital South, Tulsa, OK, p. A509
Senior Vice President and Chief Financial Officer, Saint Francis Health System, Saint Francis Hospital, Tulsa, OK, p. A509
Senior Vice President, Chief Administrative Officer and Chief Financial Officer, Laureate Psychiatric Clinic And Hospital, Tulsa, OK, p. A508
SCHIEBER, Steven M.
Chief Executive Officer, Hedrick Medical Center, Chillicothe, MO, p. A358
Interim Chief Executive Officer, Wright Memorial Hospital, Trenton, MO, p. A372
SCHIEFELBEIN, Shelia, Coordinator Human Resources, Northwest Florida Community Hospital, Chipley, FL, p. A119
SCHIERECK, Stacie, Director Management Services, Mendota Mental Health Institute, Madison, WI, p. A698
SCHIESL, Troy, Director Information Services, Bellin Psychiatric Center, Green Bay, WI, p. A696
SCHIESLER, Hannah, Interim Assistant Director Human Resources, Baptist Hospitals Of Southeast Texas, Beaumont, TX, p. A587
SCHILLER, Ann Mattia, Vice President Human Resources, College Medical Center, Long Beach, CA, p. A65
SCHILLER, Jonathan, Chief Executive Officer, Catskill Regional Medical Center, Harris, NY, p. A429
SCHILLING, Helen, M.D., Medical Director, Kindred Rehabilitation Hospital Northeast Houston, Humble, TX, p. A615
SCHIMEROWSKI, Deb
Regional Chief Financial Officer, Amita Health St. Mary'S Hospital, Kankakee, IL, p. A187
Regional Finance Officer, Amita Health Saint Joseph Medical Center, Joliet, IL, p. A187
SCHIMMING, Christopher, M.D., Medical Director, Mayo Clinic Health System In Waseca, Waseca, MN, p. A342
SCHIMMING, Michael B
Director Financial Services, Shriners Hospitals For Children–Galveston, Galveston, TX, p. A607
Director Fiscal Services, Shriners Hospitals For Children–Houston, Houston, TX, p. A613
SCHIPPER, Brad J., Chief Operating Officer, Sanford Usd Medical Center, Sioux Falls, SD, p. A564
SCHIPPER, Jody, Director of Nursing, Grundy County Memorial Hospital, Grundy Center, IA, p. A223
SCHLABACH, Michael, M.D., Chief Medical Officer, Baylor Scott & White Hospital Medical Center – Brenham, Brenham, TX, p. A589
SCHLADER, Rod G., President and Chief Executive Officer, Mercyone North Iowa Medical Center, Mason City, IA, p. A226
SCHLAGER, Robert, M.D., Chief Medical Officer, Northlight Sebasticook Valley Hospital, Pittsfield, ME, p. A284
SCHLAGGER, Bradley, President and Chief Executive Officer, Kennedy Krieger Institute, Baltimore, MD, p. A286
SCHLANGEN, Greg, R.N., Chief Operating Officer, Carolina Center For Behavioral Health, Greer, SC, p. A554
SCHLECHTER, Sandy, Chief Executive Officer, Bowdle Hospital, Bowdle, SD, p. A559
SCHLEETER, Larry C, Chief Human Resources Officer, Memorial Health, Marysville, OH, p. A486
SCHLEGEL, Patricia, Executive Director Finance, Ridgeview Le Sueur Medical Center, Le Sueur, MN, p. A334
SCHLEICHER, Larry, Manager Information Services, Warner Hospital And Health Services, Clinton, IL, p. A180
SCHLEIF, John V, Senior Vice President and Chief Operating Officer, Henry Mayo Newhall Hospital, Valencia, CA, p. A93
SCHLENKER, Jim, Chief Operating Officer, Good Shepherd Health Care System, Hermiston, OR, p. A513
SCHLESKE, Brenda, Administrator, Community Behavioral Health Hospital – Fergus Falls, Fergus Falls, MN, p. A332
SCHLESSMAN, Alissa, Administrator, Beaver County Memorial Hospital, Beaver, OK, p. A497
SCHLEY, Kurt, Market Chief Executive Officer, Chi St. Alexius Health, Bismarck, ND, p. A465
SCHLICHTMAN, Beth A, Manager Human Resources, Brodstone Memorial Hospital, Superior, NE, p. A392
SCHLICHTMANN, Phyllis J., Chief Executive Officer, Kessler Marlton Rehabilitation, Marlton, NJ, p. A408
SCHLIECH, Roxane K, Chief Financial Officer, Gundersen Tri-County Hospital And Clinics, Whitehall, WI, p. A708
SCHLUETER, Ann, Chief Operating Officer, Community Hospital–Fairfax, Fairfax, MO, p. A360
SCHLUNTZ, Ana, Director of Human Resources, Harlan County Health System, Alma, NE, p. A382
SCHLUTER, Robin M., Chief Executive Officer, Regional Health Services Of Howard County, Cresco, IA, p. A220
SCHMACKER, Eric, Chief Executive Officer, Baptist Medical Center, San Antonio, TX, p. A633
SCHMAEDECKE, Dena, Vice President Human Resources, North Suburban Medical Center, Thornton, CO, p. A105
SCHMEDEMANN, Isabel, Chief Executive Officer and Administrator, Herington Municipal Hospital, Herington, KS, p. A236
SCHMID, Nancy A, R.N., MS, Associate Director Patient Care Services, Coatesville Veterans Affairs Medical Center, Coatesville, PA, p. A523
SCHMIDT, Allen J, M.D., President, Medical Staff, Decatur Morgan Hospital, Decatur, AL, p. A16
SCHMIDT, Anne, Vice President of Patient Care Services and Chief Nursing Officer, South County Hospital, Wakefield, RI, p. A548
SCHMIDT, Barbara, Chief Executive Officer, Mesa Springs, Fort Worth, TX, p. A605
SCHMIDT, Bobbi, Chief Nursing Officer, Select Specialty Hospital–Cincinnati, Cincinnati, OH, p. A476
SCHMIDT, Constance, FACHE, R.N., Vice President Patient Care Services and Chief Nursing Officer, St. Mary–Corwin Medical Center, Pueblo, CO, p. A105
SCHMIDT, Harry M., President and Chief Executive Officer, Passavant Area Hospital, Jacksonville, IL, p. A186
SCHMIDT, Janie, Director of Nursing, Greeley County Health Services, Tribune, KS, p. A246
SCHMIDT, Joan E, Director Human Resources, Eden Springs Health Care Center, Green Springs, OH, p. A484
SCHMIDT, Mark C.
President, Custer Regional Hospital, Custer, SD, p. A560
President, Lead–Deadwood Regional Hospital, Deadwood, SD, p. A560
SCHMIDT, Milan, Medical Director, North Shore Health, Grand Marais, MN, p. A332
SCHMIDT, Richard O, Jr, President and Chief Executive Officer, Froedtert South – Kenosha Medical Center, Kenosha, WI, p. A697
SCHMIDT, Richard O., Jr, President and Chief Executive Officer, Froedtert South – Kenosha Medical Center, Kenosha, WI, p. A697
SCHMIDT, Robert F, Director Human Resources, Hocking Valley Community Hospital, Logan, OH, p. A485
SCHMIDT, Rosanne, R.N., Chief Nursing Officer, Chi St. Alexius Health, Bismarck, ND, p. A465
SCHMIDT, Steve, Director Information Systems, Evans Memorial Hospital, Claxton, GA, p. A150
SCHMIDT, Veronica, President and Chief Executive Officer, Jennie M. Melham Memorial Medical Center, Broken Bow, NE, p. A383
SCHMIDT, William
Chief Executive Officer, Thedacare Medical Center–Shawano, Shawano, WI, p. A705
President and Chief Executive Officer, Thedacare Medical Center–New London, New London, WI, p. A702
SCHMIDTBERGER, Sheryl, Chief Financial Officer, Alliancehealth Ponca City, Ponca City, OK, p. A506
SCHMIEDT, Jason, Chief Financial Officer, Clinch Valley Medical Center, Richlands, VA, p. A665
SCHMIER, Joseph, Interim Director Human Resources, North Valley Hospital, Whitefish, MT, p. A381
SCHMIESING, Karee, Director of Nursing, Sleepy Eye Medical Center, Sleepy Eye, MN, p. A340
SCHMITS, Peggy, Director, Nursing Operations, New Braunfels Regional Rehabilitation Hospital, New Braunfels, TX, p. A626
SCHMITT, John, Senior Vice President and Chief Financial Officer, Brookdale Hospital Medical Center, New York, NY, p. A432
SCHMITT, Joseph
Chief Financial Officer, Va Greater Los Angeles Healthcare System, Los Angeles, CA, p. A70
Chief Information Officer, St. Elizabeth'S Medical Center, Brockton, MA, p. A296
Senior Vice President Finance and Chief Financial Officer, Henry Ford Hospital, Detroit, MI, p. A310
SCHMITT, Karl, M.D., Chief of Staff, St. Elizabeth Edgewood, Edgewood, KY, p. A251
SCHMITT, Peggy, President and Chief Executive Officer, North Kansas City Hospital, North Kansas City, MO, p. A366
SCHMITT, Robert C., II, Chief Executive Officer, Gibson Area Hospital And Health Services, Gibson City, IL, p. A184
SCHMITT, Thomas M., Chief Executive Officer, Kansas Spine And Specialty Hospital, Wichita, KS, p. A248
SCHMITT, Zach, Chief Financial Officer, Red Bud Regional Hospital, Red Bud, IL, p. A194
SCHMITZ, Bonnie
Chief Financial Officer, Ripon Medical Center, Ripon, WI, p. A705
Chief Financial Officer, Waupun Memorial Hospital, Waupun, WI, p. A707
Vice President and Chief Financial Officer, St. Agnes Hospital, Fond Du Lac, WI, p. A695
SCHMITZ, Christopher, Associate Vice President, Director Human Resources, Stoughton Hospital Association, Stoughton, WI, p. A706
SCHMITZ, Douglas, Director of Nursing, Long–Term Acute Care Hospital, Mosaic Life Care At St. Joseph, Saint Joseph, MO, p. A368
SCHMITZ, Jessica, Director of Nursing, Roosevelt Medical Center, Culbertson, MT, p. A375
SCHMITZ, Joseph, Chief Financial Officer, St. Cloud Veterans Affairs Health Care System, Saint Cloud, MN, p. A339
SCHMOTZER, Dave, Chief Financial Officer, Bryn Mawr Rehabilitation Hospital, Malvern, PA, p. A530
SCHMOYER, Leah, Human Resources Director, Buffalo Hospital, Buffalo, MN, p. A329
SCHMUS, Angie, Chief Information Technology, Aleda E. Lutz Veterans Affairs Medical Center, Saginaw, MI, p. A321
SCHNABEL, Annette, President and Chief Executive Officer, Perry Memorial Hospital, Princeton, IL, p. A194
SCHNACK, Tim H.
Chief Financial Officer, Chi Health Immanuel, Omaha, NE, p. A389
Chief Financial Officer, Chi Health Plainview, Plainview, NE, p. A391
Chief Financial Officer, Chi Health Schuyler, Schuyler, NE, p. A391
Vice President Financial Services, Chi Health Creighton University Medical Center – Bergan Mercy, Omaha, NE, p. A388
Vice President Operations Finance, Chi Health St. Mary'S, Nebraska City, NE, p. A388
SCHNEDLER, Lisa W., President and Chief Executive Officer, Upland Hills Health, Dodgeville, WI, p. A693
SCHNEIDER, Barbara, Chief Executive Officer, Foothill Regional Medical Center, Tustin, CA, p. A92
SCHNEIDER, Brenda, Chief Financial Officer, Skyline Hospital, White Salmon, WA, p. A682
SCHNEIDER, Brian, Chief Financial Officer, Dupont Hospital, Fort Wayne, IN, p. A203
SCHNEIDER, Carol L., President and Chief Executive Officer, Mercy Hospital And Medical Center, Chicago, IL, p. A178
SCHNEIDER, Frank, Chief Executive Officer, Gateway Rehabilitation Hospital, Florence, KY, p. A251
SCHNEIDER, Gina, Director Human Resources, Northwest Specialty Hospital, Post Falls, ID, p. A171
SCHNEIDER, Jennifer S., Vice President of Finance, Saint Francis Hospital And Medical Center, Hartford, CT, p. A108
SCHNEIDER, Jessie, Director Human Resources, Community Memorial Healthcare, Marysville, KS, p. A240
SCHNEIDER, John, Human Resources Director, Putnam Community Medical Center, Palatka, FL, p. A135
SCHNEIDER, John, M.D., Medical Director, Milwaukee County Behavioral Health Division, Milwaukee, WI, p. A701
SCHNEIDER, Sally Ann., Chief Executive Officer, Smokey Point Behavioral Hospital, Marysville, WA, p. A674
SCHNEIDER, Shanon, Chief Information Officer, Greeley County Health Services, Tribune, KS, p. A246
SCHNEIDER, Stacie A, Director Human Resources, Aurora Sheboygan Memorial Medical Center, Sheboygan, WI, p. A705
SCHNEIDER, Stephen, Manager Information Services, Alaska Psychiatric Institute, Anchorage, AK, p. A25
SCHNEIDER, Steve, Manager Behavioral Services and Director Operations, New Ulm Medical Center, New Ulm, MN, p. A337
SCHNEIDER, Steven E., President, Saint Mary'S Hospital, Waterbury, CT, p. A111
SCHNEIDER, Thomas D, D.O., Chief of Staff, Jack C. Montgomery Veterans Affairs Medical Center, Muskogee, OK, p. A502
SCHNEIDER, Valerie, Director Human Resources, Gove County Medical Center, Quinter, KS, p. A244
SCHNELL, Dawn
Chief Nursing Officer and Interim Senior Director, Sanford Jackson Medical Center, Jackson, MN, p. A333
Chief Nursing Officer, Sanford Jackson Medical Center, Jackson, MN, p. A333
SCHNIEDERS, Michael H., President, Chi Health Good Samaritan, Kearney, NE, p. A386
SCHNIER, Martin, D.O., Chief of Staff, West Texas Veterans Affairs Health Care System, Big Spring, TX, p. A588

SCHNITTKER, Kira, Director of Nursing, St. Vincent'S Blount, Oneonta, AL, p. A22

SCHNOOR, Jeff, Director Information Systems, Swedish Medical Center, Englewood, CO, p. A100

SCHOELLER, Betsy V, Director Human Resources and Education, Mary Greeley Medical Center, Ames, IA, p. A217

SCHOEN, Greg, M.D., Regional Medical Director, Fairview Northland Medical Center, Princeton, MN, p. A338

SCHOENDALER, Hannah, Chief Nursing Officer, Sheridan County Health Complex, Hoxie, KS, p. A237

SCHOENECKER, Perry L, M.D., Chief of Staff, Shriners Hospitals For Children–St. Louis, Saint Louis, MO, p. A370

SCHOENER, Timothy E
Chief Information Officer, Upmc Susquehanna Muncy, Muncy, PA, p. A532
Senior Vice President and Chief Information Officer, Upmc Susquehanna Soldiers + Sailors, Wellsboro, PA, p. A544
Vice President and Chief Information Officer, Upmc Susquehanna Williamsport, Williamsport, PA, p. A545

SCHOENIG, Thomas
Chief Information Officer, Adventist Medical Center Lagrange, La Grange, IL, p. A187
Chief Information Officer, Jupiter Medical Center, Jupiter, FL, p. A126
Regional Chief Information Officer, Texas Health Huguley Hospital Fort Worth South, Burleson, TX, p. A590

SCHOENIG, Tom, Regional Director Information Services, Valley Hospital Medical Center, Las Vegas, NV, p. A396

SCHOETTLE, Steve, M.D., Chief Medical Staff, Ozark Health Medical Center, Clinton, AR, p. A40

SCHOFIELD, Joseph, Chief Operating Officer, Suburban Community Hospital, Norristown, PA, p. A533

SCHOFIELD, Sherry, Director Human Resources, Sovah Health–Martinsville, Martinsville, VA, p. A662

SCHOLEFIELD, Robert, MS, R.N., Executive Vice President and Chief Operating Officer, Faxton St. Luke'S Healthcare, Utica, NY, p. A446

SCHOLL, Shyanne, Interim Human Resources Director, Friend Community Healthcare System, Friend, NE, p. A385

SCHOLZ, Suzanne, Director Medical Records, Horsham Clinic, Ambler, PA, p. A520

SCHONEBERY, Jeremy, Director Information Technology, Heart Of America Medical Center, Rugby, ND, p. A469

SCHONS, Jeri, R.N., Chief Nursing Officer, Sanford Tracy Medical Center, Tracy, MN, p. A341

SCHOOL, Peggy, Director of Nursing, Thedacare Medical Center–New London, New London, WI, p. A702

SCHOOLER, Rick, Vice President and Chief Information Officer, Orlando Regional Medical Center, Orlando, FL, p. A134

SCHOONOVER, Michele, Chief Executive Officer, Virginia Gay Hospital, Vinton, IA, p. A230

SCHOPP, Mary Ellen, Senior Vice President Human Resources, Rush University Medical Center, Chicago, IL, p. A179

SCHOR, Mark, Chief Executive Officer, Belmont Behavioral Hospital, Philadelphia, PA, p. A534

SCHORER, Emily
Senior Vice President Human Resources, Cape Cod Hospital, Hyannis, MA, p. A299
Vice President, Human Resources, Falmouth Hospital, Falmouth, MA, p. A298

SCHOTT, Connie, Vice President, Human Resources, Ozarks Medical Center, West Plains, MO, p. A373

SCHOTTEL, Roxanne, Chief Executive Officer, Washington County Hospital, Washington, KS, p. A247

SCHOWENGERDT, Daniel, M.D., Chief of Staff, Comanche County Hospital, Coldwater, KS, p. A233

SCHRADER, Guillermo, M.D., Acting Medical Director, Eastern State Hospital, Williamsburg, VA, p. A668

SCHRAEDER, David, Director Information Systems, Russell Regional Hospital, Russell, KS, p. A244

SCHRAMM, Michael, Chief Executive Officer, Rice Memorial Hospital, Willmar, MN, p. A342

SCHRAMM, Steven R, Chief Financial Officer, Mountain View Hospital, Payson, UT, p. A650

SCHRANK, Kenton, M.D., President Medical Staff, Wilson N. Jones Regional Medical Center, Sherman, TX, p. A637

SCHRANT, Benjamin, M.D., Chief of Staff, Northeast Regional Medical Center, Kirksville, MO, p. A363

SCHREFFLER, Mary Jane, Director Human Resources, Meadows Psychiatric Center, Centre Hall, PA, p. A522

SCHREIBER, Anne, Manager Human Resources, Fairfax Behavioral Health, Kirkland, WA, p. A674

SCHREIBER, Elizabeth, R.N., Director Patient Care Services, Flambeau Hospital, Park Falls, WI, p. A703

SCHREIER, Garett E., R.N., Associate Director, Nursing and Patient Care Services, Ralph H. Johnson Veterans Affairs Medical Center, Charleston, SC, p. A550

SCHREINER, David L., President and Chief Executive Officer, Katherine Shaw Bethea Hospital, Dixon, IL, p. A181

SCHREINER, Jim, Chief Information Officer, Graham Hospital Association, Canton, IL, p. A175

SCHRIER, Erick, Supervisor Information Technology, Van Diest Medical Center, Webster City, IA, p. A231

SCHROCK, Bonnie W, FACHE, Chief Operating Officer, Baptist Health Paducah, Paducah, KY, p. A259

SCHRODER, Loren D, Chief Financial Officer, Phelps Memorial Health Center, Holdrege, NE, p. A386

SCHROEDER, Brian D., M.D., Senior Vice President and Chief Medical Officer, Sparrow Hospital, Lansing, MI, p. A316

SCHROEDER, Catherine, Deputy Chief Information Officer, Brigham And Women'S Faulkner Hospital, Boston, MA, p. A295

SCHROEDER, Cygnet, D.O., Medical Director, Encompasss Health Rehabilitation Hospital Of Fort Smith, Fort Smith, AR, p. A42

SCHROEDER, Destiny, Information Systems Director, Rawlins County Health Center, Atwood, KS, p. A232

SCHROEDER, Heather, R.N., Vice President Nursing, Aurora Baycare Medical Center, Green Bay, WI, p. A696

SCHROEDER, Joanne, President, Munson Healthcare Charlevoix Hospital, Charlevoix, MI, p. A308

SCHROEDER, Rick, Chief Executive Officer, North Big Horn Hospital District, Lovell, WY, p. A712

SCHROEDL, Greg, M.D., Vice President, Medical and Chief Medical Officer, Uw Medicine/Northwest Hospital & Medical Center, Seattle, WA, p. A678

SCHROEPPEL, Stacie, Director of Human Resources, Baptist Memorial Rehabilitation Hospital, Germantown, TN, p. A570

SCHROYER, Mike K., President, St. Vincent Anderson, Anderson, IN, p. A199

SCHRUMPF, Jason, President, Missouri Delta Medical Center, Sikeston, MO, p. A371

SCHUBACH, Michael, Chief People Officer, Carroll County Memorial Hospital, Carrollton, MO, p. A358

SCHUCK, Eric, M.D., Chief Medical Officer, Tristar Southern Hills Medical Center, Nashville, TN, p. A577

SCHUCK, Jennifer, Associate Administrator, Emory University Hospital, Atlanta, GA, p. A146

SCHUCKMAN, Tim, Chief Financial Officer, Jennie M. Melham Memorial Medical Center, Broken Bow, NE, p. A383

SCHUE, Janine
Executive Vice President, Chief Human Resources Officer, Rochester Regional Health, Newark–Wayne Community Hospital, Newark, NY, p. A439
Senior Vice President Human Resources, Rochester General Hospital, Rochester, NY, p. A442

SCHUELER, Joe, Chief Financial Officer, Morrow County Hospital, Mount Gilead, OH, p. A488

SCHUERCH, Timothy, President and Chief Executive Officer, Maniilaq Health Center, Kotzebue, AK, p. A26

SCHUESSLER, Dwight, Chief Information Officer, Iowa City Veterans Affairs Health Care System, Iowa City, IA, p. A224

SCHUITEMAN, Jackson, Chief Financial Officer, Sioux Center Health, Sioux Center, IA, p. A229

SCHULER, Allison, R.N., Chief Nursing Officer, Baptist Medical Center Attala, Kosciusko, MS, p. A350

SCHULER, Kathy, R.N., MS, Chief Operating Officer and Chief Nursing Officer, Winchester Hospital, Winchester, MA, p. A305

SCHULHOF, Alicia
President and Chief Executive Officer, Indiana University Health North Hospital, Carmel, IN, p. A201
President and Chief Executive Officer, Indiana University Health University Hospital, Indianapolis, IN, p. A207

SCHULTE, Mark, President, Sturgis Regional Hospital, Sturgis, SD, p. A564

SCHULTES, Jeremy, Administrator and Chief Executive Officer, Philip Health Services, Philip, SD, p. A562

SCHULTHEIS, Hal, Director Information Systems, Tristar Hendersonville Medical Center, Hendersonville, TN, p. A570

SCHULTZ, Bradley, Chief Financial Officer, Wesley Healthcare Center, Wichita, KS, p. A248

SCHULTZ, David W.
President, Peninsula Region, Harrison Medical Center, Bremerton, WA, p. A670
President, Peninsula Region, St. Anthony Hospital, Gig Harbor, WA, p. A673

SCHULTZ, Jacky, President, Suburban Hospital, Bethesda, MD, p. A289

SCHULTZ, Jim, Chief Executive Officer, Edgerton Hospital And Health Services, Edgerton, WI, p. A694

SCHULTZ, Kurt
Chief Financial Officer, Cornerstone Hospital–West Monroe, West Monroe, LA, p. A280
Chief Financial Officer, Solara Hospital Harlingen, Harlingen, TX, p. A609
Group Chief Financial Officer, Chg Hospital Tucson, Llc, Tucson, AZ, p. A37

SCHULTZ, Mary Kay, Director Human Resources, Sturgis Hospital, Sturgis, MI, p. A323

SCHULTZ, Merrilee, Chief Finance, Sanford Usd Medical Center, Sioux Falls, SD, p. A564

SCHULTZ, Rachelle H., President and Chief Executive Officer, Winona Health, Winona, MN, p. A343

SCHULTZ, Sharon A, Chief Nurse Executive and Vice President, Tri–City Medical Center, Oceanside, CA, p. A75

SCHULTZ, Teresa L, R.N., Vice President of Patient Care, Rogers Memorial Hospital, Inc., Oconomowoc, WI, p. A702

SCHULTZ, Vince, M.D., Chief Medical Officer, Munson Healthcare Grayling Hospital, Grayling, MI, p. A313

SCHULZ, Ken, Chief Operating Officer, North Dakota State Hospital, Jamestown, ND, p. A468

SCHULZ, Leah, Director of Nursing, North Dakota State Hospital, Jamestown, ND, p. A468

SCHULZ, Marcie, Director Patient Care, Sakakawea Medical Center, Hazen, ND, p. A467

SCHULZ, Susan G, Director Patient Care Services, Beaumont Hospital – Trenton, Trenton, MI, p. A324

SCHUMACHER, Ann
President, Chi Health Immanuel, Omaha, NE, p. A389
President, Chi Health Mercy Council Bluffs, Council Bluffs, IA, p. A220

SCHUMACHER, Debbie
Chief Human Resource Officer, Clearwater Valley Hospital And Clinics, Orofino, ID, p. A170
Chief Human Resource Officer, St. Mary'S Hospital, Cottonwood, ID, p. A169

SCHUMACHER, Kevin, Director of Information Systems, Lifecare Medical Center, Roseau, MN, p. A339

SCHUMACHER, Larry P, Chief Executive Officer, Chi Memorial, Chattanooga, TN, p. A567

SCHUMACHER, Paul, Chief Operating Officer, Mcleod Health Clarendon, Manning, SC, p. A555

SCHUMACHER, Rodney, Interim Chief Executive Officer, San Angelo Community Medical Center, San Angelo, TX, p. A632

SCHUMANN, Vera, Director of Finance and Controller, North Shore Health, Grand Marais, MN, p. A332

SCHURKAMP, Christine, Senior Human Resources Business Partner, Spectrum Health Gerber Memorial, Fremont, MI, p. A312

SCHUSTER, Carol E, R.N., Chief Nursing Officer and Vice President Patient Care Services, Franciscan Health Crown Point, Crown Point, IN, p. A202

SCHUSTER, Christine C., President and Chief Executive Officer, Emerson Hospital, Concord, MA, p. A298

SCHUSTER, Janet, Chief Nursing Officer, Lutheran Hospital, Cleveland, OH, p. A478

SCHUSTER, Jolene, Chief Financial Officer, Grisell Memorial Hospital District One, Ransom, KS, p. A244

SCHUSTER, Lexie, Vice President Human Resources, Good Samaritan Hospital, Los Angeles, CA, p. A66

SCHUSTER, Todd, Administrator, Saint Francis Hospital Vinita, Vinita, OK, p. A510

SCHUSTER, Tony, M.D.
Vice President of Physician Services, Mease Countryside Hospital, Safety Harbor, FL, p. A138
Vice President of Physician Services, Mease Dunedin Hospital, Dunedin, FL, p. A122

SCHWAB, Bob, M.D., Chief Medical Officer, Texas Health Presbyterian Hospital Allen, Allen, TX, p. A582

SCHWAB, Caryn A, Executive Director, Brookdale Hospital Medical Center, New York, NY, p. A432

SCHWAB, Eric, Chief Executive Officer, Select Specialty Hospital–Laurel Highlands, Latrobe, PA, p. A529

SCHWABENBAUER, Mary Ann, Director Information Technology, Penn Highlands Elk, Saint Marys, PA, p. A540

SCHWAEGEL, Glen
Chief Financial Officer, Progress West Hospital, O'Fallon, MO, p. A366
Vice President and Chief Financial Officer, Barnes–Jewish St. Peters Hospital, Saint Peters, MO, p. A371

SCHWAGER, Mary A, Director Human Resources, Antelope Memorial Hospital, Neligh, NE, p. A388

SCHWALL, Garry, Chief Operating Officer, Nyu Winthrop Hospital, Mineola, NY, p. A431

SCHWAN, Joni, Director Human Resources, Excelsior Springs Hospital, Excelsior Springs, MO, p. A359

SCHWAN, Karin, Chief Nursing Officer, Vice President Patient Care Services, University Hospitals Samaritan Medical Center, Ashland, OH, p. A472

SCHWANER, Charles, Chief Financial Officer, Doctors Hospital Of Sarasota, Sarasota, FL, p. A139

SCHWANKE, Daniel, President, Promedica Monroe Regional Hospital, Monroe, MI, p. A318

SCHWARM, Tony, President, Missouri Baptist Sullivan Hospital, Sullivan, MO, p. A372

SCHWARTZ, Ave, Chief Information Officer, Austen Riggs Center, Stockbridge, MA, p. A304
SCHWARTZ, David, M.D.
Chief Medical Officer, Saint Francis Hospital–Bartlett, Bartlett, TN, p. A566
Chief Medical Officer, Saint Francis Hospital, Memphis, TN, p. A575
SCHWARTZ, David M, D.O., Vice President, Medical Affairs, Sentara Northern Virginia Medical Center, Woodbridge, VA, p. A669
SCHWARTZ, Jack, Director Information Technology, Kittitas Valley Healthcare, Ellensburg, WA, p. A672
SCHWARTZ, Jonathon, M.D., Chief Medical Officer, Spaulding Hospital For Continuing Medical Care Cambridge, Cambridge, MA, p. A297
SCHWARTZ, Kenneth V, M.D., Medical Director, Griffin Hospital, Derby, CT, p. A107
SCHWARTZ, Kim, Assistant Administrator Human Resources and Operations, Boone County Hospital, Boone, IA, p. A218
SCHWARTZ, Michael, M.D., Chief of Staff, College Hospital Costa Mesa, Costa Mesa, CA, p. A55
SCHWARTZ, Mitchell B, M.D., Chief Medical Officer, Anne Arundel Medical Center, Annapolis, MD, p. A286
SCHWARTZ, Peggy, Vice President Human Resources, Wayne Healthcare, Greenville, OH, p. A484
SCHWARTZ, Peter, Director of Information Systems, Hackensack Meridian Health Carrier Clinic, Belle Mead, NJ, p. A403
SCHWARTZ, Roberta, Executive Vice President, Houston Methodist Hospital, Houston, TX, p. A612
SCHWARTZ, Ronald, M.D., Medical Director, Masonicare Health Center, Wallingford, CT, p. A111
SCHWARTZ, Sharon, Director Medical Records, Baylor Scott & White Hospital Medical Center – Brenham, Brenham, TX, p. A589
SCHWARTZ, Stephanie L., Vice President AHS and President CMC, Chilton Medical Center, Pompton Plains, NJ, p. A411
SCHWARZ, John, Vice President Administration, Lankenau Medical Center, Wynnewood, PA, p. A546
SCHWARZBACH, Jerry, M.D., Medical Director, Ut Health Rehabilitation Hospital, Tyler, TX, p. A642
SCHWARZKOPF, Ruth, Chief Nursing Officer, West Boca Medical Center, Boca Raton, FL, p. A118
SCHWEBLER, Michael W., President and Chief Executive Officer, Highpoint Health, Lawrenceburg, IN, p. A210
SCHWECHHEIMER, Betsy L, Chief Operating Officer, Tewksbury Hospital, Tewksbury, MA, p. A304
SCHWEICKHARDT, Mary Jo, Vice President Human Resources, Medstar Georgetown University Hospital, Washington, DC, p. A115
SCHWEIGERT, Nicole, Director Human Resources, Texas Health Presbyterian Hospital Flower Mound, Flower Mound, TX, p. A604
SCHWEIGHART, Karen, Administrator, Andrew Mcfarland Mental Health Center, Springfield, IL, p. A196
SCHWEIKART, Jay
Chief Financial Officer, Kindred Hospital Chicago–Northlake, Northlake, IL, p. A191
Chief Financial Officer, Kindred Hospital–Sycamore, Sycamore, IL, p. A197
SCHWEITZER, Michael, M.D., Chief Medical Officer, St. Vincent Healthcare, Billings, MT, p. A374
SCHWIEGER, Kay, Chief Human Resources Officer, Clement J. Zablocki Veterans Affairs Medical Center, Milwaukee, WI, p. A701
SCHWIND, David, Chief Financial Officer, Capital Hospice, Arlington, VA, p. A656
SCHWINGLER, Joyce, Chief Financial Officer, Eureka Community Health Services Avera, Eureka, SD, p. A560
SCIARRA, Michael, M.D., Chief Medical Officer, Hudson Regional Hospital, Secaucus, NJ, p. A412
SCIARRO, Jason, President and Chief Operating Officer, Northwestern Medicine Mchenry, Mchenry, IL, p. A189
SCIMECA, Paul, Senior Vice President Operations and Chief Operating Officer, Glens Falls Hospital, Glens Falls, NY, p. A428
SCIONTI, Jeff, Chief Executive Officer, Parkland Medical Center, Derry, NH, p. A399
SCIOSCIA, Angela, M.D., Chief Medical Officer, Uc San Diego Health, San Diego, CA, p. A84
SCLAMA, Tony, M.D., Vice President Medical Affairs, Medstar Franklin Square Medical Center, Baltimore, MD, p. A288
SCOGGIN, Terry
Chief Executive Officer, Titus Regional Medical Center, Mount Pleasant, TX, p. A625
Chief Financial Officer, Titus Regional Medical Center, Mount Pleasant, TX, p. A625
SCOGGINS, James
Director of Nursing, Arkansas State Hospital, Little Rock, AR, p. A44
Interim Chief Executive Officer, Arkansas State Hospital, Little Rock, AR, p. A44
SCOGGINS, Mib, Chief Executive Officer, Mcleod Health Cheraw, Cheraw, SC, p. A550
SCOGNA, Stephen, President and Chief Executive Officer, Northwest Community Hospital, Arlington Heights, IL, p. A173
SCORZELLI, Gerard, Chief Financial Officer, Albany Stratton Veterans Affairs Medical Center, Albany, NY, p. A422
SCOTFORD, Lucrecia, Executive Vice President and Chief Operations Officer, Bristol Bay Area Health Corporation, Dillingham, AK, p. A26
SCOTT, Colleen M, Vice President Finance, Waterbury Hospital, Waterbury, CT, p. A112
SCOTT, Cullen, Chief Executive Officer, Northwest Hills Surgical Hospital, Austin, TX, p. A586
SCOTT, Damien, Chief Information Officer, Emanuel Medical Center, Swainsboro, GA, p. A161
SCOTT, Daniel, Director of Information Systems, Good Samaritan Hospital, Vincennes, IN, p. A216
SCOTT, David W., President and Chief Executive Officer, Ohio Valley Hospital, Mckees Rocks, PA, p. A531
SCOTT, Doug, Corporate Director Human Resources, Rmc Anniston, Anniston, AL, p. A13
SCOTT, Ernie, Director Human Resources, Natchitoches Regional Medical Center, Natchitoches, LA, p. A274
SCOTT, Henry, Executive Director, Technical Services, Piedmont Newnan Hospital, Newnan, GA, p. A158
SCOTT, James, M.D.
Vice President Medical Affairs, Candler Hospital, Savannah, GA, p. A160
Vice President Medical Affairs, St. Joseph'S Hospital, Savannah, GA, p. A160
SCOTT, Jeffrey, Chief Information Officer, St. Vincent Kokomo, Kokomo, IN, p. A209
SCOTT, Jennifer, Director of Informatics, Carepartners Health Services, Asheville, NC, p. A449
SCOTT, Jo Ellen, R.N., MS, Senior Vice President of Patient Care Services and Chief Nursing Officer, Indiana University Health Tipton Hospital, Tipton, IN, p. A215
SCOTT, Julie, Chief Nursing Officer, Encompass Health Rehabilitation Hospital Of York, York, PA, p. A546
SCOTT, Karen M, Vice President Patient Care, Adventist Health Howard Memorial, Willits, CA, p. A95
SCOTT, Lanell, Chief Executive Officer, Christus Santa Rosa Health System, San Antonio, TX, p. A633
SCOTT, Lincoln, Vice President Human Resources, Southeast Hospital, Cape Girardeau, MO, p. A358
SCOTT, M Daryl, Assistant Vice President, Jefferson Regional Medical Center, Pine Bluff, AR, p. A47
SCOTT, Margie A., Director, Central Arkansas Veterans Healthcare System, Little Rock, AR, p. A45
SCOTT, Martha Lynn, Chief Patient Care Officer, Covington County Hospital, Collins, MS, p. A346
SCOTT, Monica, Chief Financial Officer, Great Plains Regional Medical Center, Elk City, OK, p. A499
SCOTT, Paul, M.D., Chief of Staff, Hudson Hospital And Clinic, Hudson, WI, p. A697
SCOTT, Rhonda A, Ph.D., R.N., Chief Operating Officer, Grady Memorial Hospital, Atlanta, GA, p. A146
SCOTT, Robert F, Vice President and Chief Human Resources Officer, Memorial Medical Center, Springfield, IL, p. A196
SCOTT, Sam, Vice President Financial Services, St. Dominic–Jackson Memorial Hospital, Jackson, MS, p. A349
SCOTT, Sharon, Health Information Director, Allegiance Specialty Hospital Of Greenville, Greenville, MS, p. A347
SCOTT, Steve, Chief Operating Officer, Sheridan Community Hospital, Sheridan, MI, p. A322
SCOTT, Steven M., President, Ssm Health Saint Louis University Hospital, Saint Louis, MO, p. A370
SCOTT, Susan, Chief Nurse Executive, Ventura County Medical Center, Ventura, CA, p. A93
SCOTT, Thomas W., Senior Vice President and Chief Operating Officer, Centrastate Healthcare System, Freehold, NJ, p. A406
SCOTT, Tina, Acting Health Director, Choctaw Health Center, Philadelphia, MS, p. A352
SCOTT, Todd, Chief Financial Officer, Vibra Hospital Of Sacramento, Folsom, CA, p. A58
SCOTT, Travis
Chief Executive Officer, Lawton Indian Hospital, Lawton, OK, p. A501
Service Unit Director, U. S. Public Health Service Indian Hospital, Pine Ridge, SD, p. A562
SCOTT, Veronica, Business Office Manager, Inspire Specialty Hospital, Midwest City, OK, p. A502
SCOTT, William, Chief Financial Officer, Promise Hospital Of Overland Park, Overland Park, KS, p. A243
SCOTT, William, M.D., Vice President Medical Affairs, Regional Medical Center Of San Jose, San Jose, CA, p. A86
SCOTT, William P, M.D., Chief of Staff, River Valley Medical Center, Dardanelle, AR, p. A41
SCOTTO, Dan, Director Information Technology, Eastern Long Island Hospital, Greenport, NY, p. A428
SCOUFOS, Jennifer, M.D., Chief of Staff, Northeastern Health System Sequoyah, Sallisaw, OK, p. A507
SCOVILL, Terry, Chief Executive Officer, Intracare North Hospital, Houston, TX, p. A612
SCOWN, Kent, Director Operations and Information Services, Jerold Phelps Community Hospital, Garberville, CA, p. A60
SCREMIN, Karen, Vice President Finance, Lutheran Medical Center, Wheat Ridge, CO, p. A106
SCRIVO, Joseph A, Director Human Resources, Mercy Hospital, Buffalo, NY, p. A424
SCROGGIN, Christy, Chief Operating Officer, Conway Regional Rehabilitation Hospital, Conway, AR, p. A40
SCROGGINS, Todd, Chief Financial Officer, Wise Health System, Decatur, TX, p. A598
SCROGGS, Amy, Chief Nursing Officer, Delano Regional Medical Center, Delano, CA, p. A56
SCRUGGS, Sherry, Administrator, Milan General Hospital, Milan, TN, p. A576
SCUDDER, Angela K., MSN, R.N., Vice President Patient Care Services, Highpoint Health, Lawrenceburg, IN, p. A210
SCUDERI, Denise, Vice President Patient Care Services, Mayo Regional Hospital, Dover, ME, p. A283
SCULL, Stephen W, Vice President Ethics and Compliance officer, Rapides Regional Medical Center, Alexandria, LA, p. A262
SCULLY, Charles
Chief Information Officer, Honorhealth Scottsdale Thompson Peak Medical Center, Scottsdale, AZ, p. A36
Chief Information Officer, Renown Regional Medical Center, Reno, NV, p. A397
SCULLY, Kem, Chief Executive Officer and Chief Nursing Officer, Purcell Municipal Hospital, Purcell, OK, p. A506
SCULLY, Trish
Director Human Resources, Taunton State Hospital, Taunton, MA, p. A304
Manager Employment Services, Pappas Rehabilitation Hospital For Children, Canton, MA, p. A297
SCZYGELSKI, Sidney C, Senior Vice President Finance and Chief Financial Officer, Aspirus Wausau Hospital, Inc., Wausau, WI, p. A708
SEAGER, Jerry, Assistant Vice President and Chief Financial Officer, Inova Fair Oaks Hospital, Fairfax, VA, p. A658
SEAGO, Terri, Chief Financial Officer, Baptist Memorial Hospital–Collierville, Collierville, TN, p. A568
SEAGRAM, Patricia, Vice President Human Resources, Henry Ford Allegiance Health, Jackson, MI, p. A315
SEAGROVES, Matthew, Chief Financial Officer, Bayfront Health Brooksville, Brooksville, FL, p. A119
SEAHORN, Martha, Chief Nursing Officer, Gadsden Regional Medical Center, Gadsden, AL, p. A18
SEAL, John
Director Human Resources, Riverside Medical Center, Franklinton, LA, p. A267
Interim Chief Financial Officer Director Human Resources, Riverside Medical Center, Kankakee, IL, p. A187
SEAL, Ronald T., Chief Executive Officer, Texoma Medical Center, Denison, TX, p. A599
SEALE, Corey A, Chief Operating Officer, Kaiser Permanente Moreno Valley Medical Center, Moreno Valley, CA, p. A73
SEALE, Jonathan, Chief Information Officer, Erie Veterans Affairs Medical Center, Erie, PA, p. A525
SEALS, Robert, D.O., Medical Director, Sparrow Carson Hospital, Carson City, MI, p. A308
SEAMON, Robert L., Chief Executive Officer, Copper Queen Community Hospital, Bisbee, AZ, p. A28
SEARLE, Anne, Chief Information Officer, Penn Medicine Princeton Medical Center, Plainsboro, NJ, p. A411
SEARLS, Barbara, Chief Financial Officer, Searhc Mt. Edgecumbe Hospital, Sitka, AK, p. A27
SEARLS, Gary, Chief Financial Officer, Brandon Regional Hospital, Brandon, FL, p. A119
SEARS, Erin Clare, Associate Director of Operations, Providence Veterans Affairs Medical Center, Providence, RI, p. A547
SEARS, Marilyn, Chief Financial Officer, Hshs Good Shepherd Hospital, Shelbyville, IL, p. A195
SEARS, Tina, Director Patient Care Services, Sullivan County Memorial Hospital, Milan, MO, p. A365
SEASE, Peggy, Vice President Human Resources, Dch Regional Medical Center, Tuscaloosa, AL, p. A24
SEATON, Tracy, Director of Nursing, Taylorville Memorial Hospital, Taylorville, IL, p. A197

SEAVER, Roger E., President and Chief Executive Officer, Henry Mayo Newhall Hospital, Valencia, CA, p. A93

SEBEK, Brenda Jean, R.N., Administrator, Chi Health St. Mary'S, Nebraska City, NE, p. A388

SEBENALER, Ginette, Associate Chief Financial Officer, Aspen Valley Hospital, Aspen, CO, p. A96

SECKINGER, Mark R., President, O'Bleness Memorial Hospital, Athens, OH, p. A472

SECOR, April, R.N., Chief Nursing Officer, Hillcrest Hospital Henryetta, Henryetta, OK, p. A500

SECOR, Diane K, Director Human Resources, Lawrence Medical Center, Moulton, AL, p. A21

SECURRO, Matthew J., Vice President, Human Resources, Conway Medical Center, Conway, SC, p. A552

SEDA, Jolene R., Vice President People and Culture, Virginia Mason Memorial, Yakima, WA, p. A682

SEEDER, Rachael, Controller, Santiam Hospital, Stayton, OR, p. A518

SEELEY, Kevin, Chief Information Officer, Mike O'Callaghan Federal Hospital, Nellis Afb, NV, p. A396

SEELEY, Pam, Chief Nursing Officer, Elmira Psychiatric Center, Elmira, NY, p. A427

SEELEY, Steven, Vice President, Chief Operating Officer, Chief Nursing Officer, Jupiter Medical Center, Jupiter, FL, p. A126

SEELY, Paula, Manager Human Resources, Kossuth Regional Health Center, Algona, IA, p. A217

SEEMS, Steven, Director of Information Technology, Phillips County Health Systems, Phillipsburg, KS, p. A243

SEESE, Rebecca, Chief Operating Officer, U. S. Air Force Regional Hospital, Elmendorf Afb, AK, p. A26

SEESEE, Alan, Chief Executive Officer, Capital Regional Medical Center, Tallahassee, FL, p. A140

SEEVER, Jennifer, Regional Chief Financial Officer, Sedan City Hospital, Sedan, KS, p. A245

SEGAL, Jonathan, Chief Financial Officer, Brookdale Hospital Medical Center, New York, NY, p. A432

SEGAL, Rebecca, Chief Executive Officer, Rutherford Regional Health System, Rutherfordton, NC, p. A461

SEGAL, Stanton, M.D., Chief Medical Officer, Jefferson Health Northeast, Philadelphia, PA, p. A535

SEGAL, Tanya, Director, Easton Hospital, Easton, PA, p. A524

SEGALLA, Domenic, Chief Operating Officer and Chief Financial Officer, Clara Maass Medical Center, Belleville, NJ, p. A403

SEGAWA, Lance
Chief Executive Officer, Kauai Veterans Memorial Hospital, Waimea, HI, p. A166
Chief Executive Officer, Samuel Mahelona Memorial Hospital, Kapaa, HI, p. A166

SEGER, LaDonna, Director Information Services, Saint Luke'S North Hospital – Barry Road, Kansas City, MO, p. A363

SEGIN, Robert
Chief Financial Officer, Virtua Memorial, Mount Holly, NJ, p. A408
Executive Vice President & Chief Financial Officer, Virtua Marlton, Marlton, NJ, p. A408

SEGUR, Jennifer, Chief Nursing Officer and Chief Clinical Officer, Adventhealth North Pinellas, Tarpon Springs, FL, p. A142

SEGURA, Mario, Director of Nursing, Starr County Memorial Hospital, Rio Grande City, TX, p. A631

SEHNERT, Laura, Chief Medical Officer, Uchealth Yampa Valley Medical Center, Steamboat Springs, CO, p. A105

SEHRT, Lori
Associate Chief Financial Officer Northern Colorado, Banner Fort Collins Medical Center, Fort Collins, CO, p. A100
Chief Financial Officer, Mckee Medical Center, Loveland, CO, p. A104

SEIBERT, Jenee, Chief Finance Officer, Fulton County Health Center, Wauseon, OH, p. A493

SEIBOLD, Spencer Garrett, M.D., Chief of Medical Staff, Power County Hospital District, American Falls, ID, p. A167

SEID, Lynette, Area Chief Financial Officer, Kaiser Permanente San Diego Medical Center, San Diego, CA, p. A83

SEIDL, Doris A, Vice President Human Resources, Mclaren Port Huron, Port Huron, MI, p. A320

SEIDMAN, Robert
Chief Operating Officer, Health Alliance Hospital – Broadway Campus, Kingston, NY, p. A430
Chief Operating Officer, Health Alliance Hospital – Mary'S Avenue Campus, Kingston, NY, p. A430

SEIFER, Jill, Vice President Human Resources, Oaklawn Psychiatric Center, Goshen, IN, p. A205

SEIFERT, Debra A, Director Human Resources, Lake Huron Medical Center, Port Huron, MI, p. A320

SEILER, Gregory A, Chief Executive Officer, Methodist Hospital, San Antonio, TX, p. A634

SEIM, Kay E., Chief Executive Officer, Aurora Santa Rosa Hospital, Santa Rosa, CA, p. A89

SEIM, Lori, R.N., Director Nursing Services, First Care Health Center, Park River, ND, p. A469

SEIP, Jeffrey, M.D., Chief Medical Staff, Hi–Desert Medical Center, Joshua Tree, CA, p. A62

SEIPLE, Donald, President, St. Luke'S Monroe, Stroudsburg, PA, p. A542

SEIRER, Jeff, Interim Chief Financial Officer, Ascension Via Christi St. Francis, Mulvane, KS, p. A241

SEITZ, Kimberly A, Area Human Resources Leader, Kaiser Permanente Redwood City Medical Center, Redwood City, CA, p. A80

SEITZ, Tawnya, Chief Financial Officer, Lincoln County Hospital, Lincoln, KS, p. A240

SELBY, Eric, R.N., Chief Nursing Officer, Chicot Memorial Medical Center, Lake Village, AR, p. A44

SELBY, Victoria, Vice President, Ancillary and Support Services, Community Hospital Of San Bernardino, San Bernardino, CA, p. A83

SELF, Chris, Chief Executive Officer, Adventhealth Manchester, Manchester, KY, p. A257

SELFRIDGE, Tara, Manager Human Resources, Purcell Municipal Hospital, Purcell, OK, p. A506

SELHORST, Sonya, R.N., Administrator and Chief Nursing Officer, Mercy Hospital Of Defiance, Defiance, OH, p. A481

SELIG, Doug R, MSN, R.N., Vice President of Patient Services, Parkview Huntington Hospital, Huntington, IN, p. A206

SELIGA, Patricia, R.N., Chief Nursing Officer, Moses Taylor Hospital, Scranton, PA, p. A540

SELIGMAN, Joel, President and Chief Executive Officer, Northern Westchester Hospital, Mount Kisco, NY, p. A432

SELIGMAN, Morris H, M.D., Chief Medical Officer and Chief Medical Information Officer, Sycamore Shoals Hospital, Elizabethton, TN, p. A569

SELL, Paula, Director Human Resources, Allen County Regional Hospital, Iola, KS, p. A237

SELL, Teri, Payroll and Personnel Coordinator, Jennie M. Melham Memorial Medical Center, Broken Bow, NE, p. A383

SELLE, Ginger, Vice President Patient Care Services, Ssm Health St. Clare Hospital–Baraboo, Baraboo, WI, p. A692

SELLE, Justin, Chief Executive Officer, Hshs St. Nicholas Hospital, Sheboygan, WI, p. A705

SELLERS, Laura, Director Information Systems, Youth Villages Inner Harbour Campus, Douglasville, GA, p. A152

SELLERS, Liz, Chief Executive Officer, Benewah Community Hospital, Saint Maries, ID, p. A171

SELLERS, Mary, Chief Information Officer, Navos, Seattle, WA, p. A677

SELLHEIM, Kevin, Administrator, Sleepy Eye Medical Center, Sleepy Eye, MN, p. A340

SELLS, Matt, Chief Executive Officer, Shenandoah Medical Center, Shenandoah, IA, p. A229

SELMAN, David, Chief Executive Officer, Select Specialty Hospital–Phoenix Downtown, Phoenix, AZ, p. A34

SELMAN, J Peter., Chief Executive Officer, Baptist Medical Center South, Montgomery, AL, p. A21

SELMON, Patricia, Director Public Relations and Chief Human Resources, Jefferson County Hospital, Fayette, MS, p. A346

SELNER, Ralph, Chief Executive Officer, Kindred Hospital Central Tampa, Tampa, FL, p. A141

SELPH, Wendy, Director Human Resources, Dodge County Hospital, Eastman, GA, p. A153

SELSOR, Doug, Director Finance, Select Rehabilitation Hospital Of Denton, Denton, TX, p. A599

SELTZER, Paul, M.D., Chief of Staff, Jfk Medical Center North Campus, West Palm Beach, FL, p. A144

SELVAM, A Panneer, M.D., Chief of Staff, Northern Arizona Veterans Affairs Health Care System, Prescott, AZ, p. A34

SELVIDGE, Sandra, Chief Fiscal Service, Cincinnati Veterans Affairs Medical Center, Cincinnati, OH, p. A476

SELZ, Timothy P, Vice President, Orange Regional Medical Center, Middletown, NY, p. A431

SELZER, Stephen R., Market Chief Executive Officer, Providence Hospital, Columbia, SC, p. A551

SEMELSBERGER, Kimberly, CPA, Chief Financial Officer, Conemaugh Nason Medical Center, Roaring Spring, PA, p. A540

SEMERDJIAN, Nancy, R.N., Chief Nursing Officer, Northshore University Health System, Evanston, IL, p. A182

SEMERE, Jana
Chief Nursing Officer, Leonard J. Chabert Medical Center, Houma, LA, p. A268
Chief Nursing Officer, Ochsner St. Anne General Hospital, Raceland, LA, p. A277

SEMEYN, Janice, D.O., President, Medical Staff, Clarion Hospital, Clarion, PA, p. A522

SEMINARO, Anthony J.
Chief Financial Officer, Mercy Health – St. Elizabeth Youngstown Hospital, Youngstown, OH, p. A495
Chief Financial Youngstown, Mercy Health – St. Elizabeth Boardman Hospital, Boardman, OH, p. A473

SEMINGSON, John H., Chief Executive Officer, Ruby Valley Medical Center, Sheridan, MT, p. A380

SEMRAD, Louis, Chief Executive Officer, Jefferson Hospital, Louisville, GA, p. A156

SEMRAU, Clint, Chief of Staff, Western Wisconsin Health, Baldwin, WI, p. A691

SENDAYDIEGO, Fe, Director Information Systems, Sonoma Valley Hospital, Sonoma, CA, p. A90

SENGER, Joshua
Chief Financial Officer, Chi St. Francis Health, Breckenridge, MN, p. A329
Vice President, Operational Finance, Chi Mercy Health, Valley City, ND, p. A469

SENGER, Richard, Chief Financial Officer, Portsmouth Regional Hospital, Portsmouth, NH, p. A402

SENGER, Tricia, Chief Financial Officer, St. Luke'S Elmore, Mountain Home, ID, p. A170

SENKER, Margaret, Chief Information Officer, Veterans Affairs Western New York Healthcare System–Buffalo Division, Buffalo, NY, p. A425

SENKER, Thomas J., President, Medstar Montgomery Medical Center, Olney, MD, p. A292

SENN, Sheila, Chief Clinical and Administrative Officer, Community First Medical Center, Chicago, IL, p. A177

SENNEFF, Robert G., President and Chief Executive Officer, Graham Hospital Association, Canton, IL, p. A175

SENNETT, Paul, Chief Financial Officer, Centinela Hospital Medical Center, Inglewood, CA, p. A62

SENNISH, James, Vice President Human Resources, Firelands Regional Health System, Sandusky, OH, p. A490

SENSAT, Marsha, R.N., Chief Nursing Officer, Pikes Peak Regional Hospital, Woodland Park, CO, p. A106

SEPP, Howard W., Jr, Vice–President and Administrator, Southeast Georgia Health System Camden Campus, Saint Marys, GA, p. A159

SEQUIN, Shannon, MSN, Chief Nursing Officer, Select Specialty Hospital–Saginaw, Saginaw, MI, p. A321

SERENO, Joseph, Chief Financial Officer, Lovelace Women'S Hospital, Albuquerque, NM, p. A416

SERFLING, G Aubrey., President and Chief Executive Officer, Eisenhower Medical Center, Rancho Mirage, CA, p. A79

SERGEANT, Lindy, Medical Staff President, Community Hospital Of Bremen, Bremen, IN, p. A200

SERKETICH, Steve, Manager Information Services, Aurora Sheboygan Memorial Medical Center, Sheboygan, WI, p. A705

SERLE, John, President and Chief Executive Officer, Lourdes Medical Center, Pasco, WA, p. A676

SERNYAK, Michael, Director, Connecticut Mental Health Center, New Haven, CT, p. A109

SERRANO, Jorge L Matta., Administrator, Auxilio Mutuo Hospital, San Juan, PR, p. A718

SERRANO, Lorenzo, Chief Executive Officer, Winkler County Memorial Hospital, Kermit, TX, p. A617

SERZAN, Megan, Director of Quality, Compliance, Risk & Safety, Asheville Specialty Hospital, Asheville, NC, p. A449

SESSIONS, Jerry W., M.D., Chief Medical Staff, Springhill Medical Center, Springhill, LA, p. A279

SESSLER, Connie, Director Human Resources, St. Luke'S Hospital, Maumee, OH, p. A487

SESTERHENN, Steven, Vice President, Unitypoint Health – Allen Hospital, Waterloo, IA, p. A231

SETHI, Sanjiv, M.D., Medical Director, Fulton State Hospital, Fulton, MO, p. A360

SETHNEY, Julie, R.N., Vice President Patient Care, Fairview Ridges Hospital, Burnsville, MN, p. A329

SETLIFF, Chad, President and Chief Operating Officer, Novant Health Forsyth Medical Center, Winston, NC, p. A464

SETO, Colbert, Chief Information Officer, Rehabilitation Hospital Of The Pacific, Honolulu, HI, p. A165

SETTLE, Andrea, Director Human Resources, Taylor Regional Hospital, Campbellsville, KY, p. A250

SETTLES, Allicia, Chief Nursing Officer, Ut Health Quitman, Quitman, TX, p. A630

SETTLES, April, Chief Financial Officer, Greene County General Hospital, Linton, IN, p. A210

SETZER, Jeffery, Administrator Information Systems, J. D. Mccarty Center For Children With Developmental Disabilities, Norman, OK, p. A503

SETZER, Randy R, Financial Services Manager, Waukesha County Mental Health Center, Waukesha, WI, p. A707

SETZKORN–MEYER, Marsha, Director Public Relations and Marketing, Hillsboro Community Hospital, Hillsboro, KS, p. A236

SEVCO, Mark
Chief Operating Officer, Upmc Pinnacle Harrisburg, Harrisburg, PA, p. A527
President, Upmc Children'S Hospital Of Pittsburgh, Pittsburgh, PA, p. A538

SEVILLA, Mark, Executive Director, Yale–New Haven Hospital, New Haven, CT, p. A110

SEVILLIAN, Clarence, President and Chief Executive Officer, Mclaren Bay Region, Bay City, MI, p. A307

SEWATSKY, Mary, M.D., Chief Medical Officer, Moses Taylor Hospital, Scranton, PA, p. A540

SEWELL, Lance, Chief Financial Officer, South Lake Hospital, Clermont, FL, p. A120

SEWICK, Alayne, Vice President Human Resources, Medical City Mckinney, Mckinney, TX, p. A624

SEXTON, Charles, Manager Human Resources, Cumberland Medical Center, Crossville, TN, p. A568

SEXTON, Cindy, Chief Financial Officer, St. David'S Round Rock Medical Center, Round Rock, TX, p. A632

SEXTON, Kevin, Director Information Systems, Raleigh General Hospital, Beckley, WV, p. A683

SEXTON, William P., Chief Executive Officer, Crossing Rivers Health Medical Center, Prairie Du Chien, WI, p. A704

SEYMOUR, Barbara, Vice President of Nursing, Health First Holmes Regional Medical Center, Melbourne, FL, p. A129

SEYMOUR, Claudette, Director Personnel, Memphis Mental Health Institute, Memphis, TN, p. A575

SEYMOUR, Jose, Chief Information Resource Management, James A. Haley Veterans' Hospital–Tampa, Tampa, FL, p. A141

SEYMOUR, Robert, Chief Financial Officer/Senior Director Finance, Grande Ronde Hospital, La Grande, OR, p. A514

SEYMOUR, Ryan
Chief Executive Officer, Baylor Scott & White Institute For Rehabilitation–Fort Worth, Fort Worth, TX, p. A604
Chief Executive Officer, Baylor Scott & White Institute For Rehabilitation–Frisco, Frisco, TX, p. A606

SEYMOUR, Sally, Chief Operating Officer, Medical Center Of Trinity, Trinity, FL, p. A143

SGARLATA, Lisa, MSN
Chief Patient Care Officer, Cape Coral Hospital, Cape Coral, FL, p. A119
Chief Patient Care Officer, Gulf Coast Medical Center, Fort Myers, FL, p. A123

SHACKELFORD, Gerald, Staff Support Specialist, Texas Center For Infectious Disease, San Antonio, TX, p. A635

SHACKELFORD, J. Larry., President and Chief Executive Officer, Washington Regional Medical Center, Fayetteville, AR, p. A42

SHACKELFORD, Paul, M.D., Chief Medical Officer, Vidant Medical Center, Greenville, NC, p. A455

SHACKLETON, Carol, M.D., Medical Director, Gothenburg Health, Gothenburg, NE, p. A385

SHADENSACK, Don, Vice President Clinical Services, Osf St. Mary Medical Center, Galesburg, IL, p. A183

SHADOWENS, Karen, Director Finance and Chief Financial Officer, West Chester Hospital, West Chester, OH, p. A494

SHAFER, Kenny, Chief Operating Officer, Johnson City Medical Center, Johnson City, TN, p. A571

SHAFER, Robert
Vice President Finance, Mercy Medical Center–Dubuque, Dubuque, IA, p. A222
Vice President Finance, Mercy Medical Center–Dyersville, Dyersville, IA, p. A222

SHAFER, Timothy, M.D., Medical Director, Grace Cottage Hospital, Townshend, VT, p. A655

SHAFFER, Jeraldene, MSN, Chief Nursing Officer, Roseland Community Hospital, Chicago, IL, p. A179

SHAFICI, Khaled, M.D., President Medical Staff, Cornerstone Hospital–West Monroe, West Monroe, LA, p. A280

SHAFIU, Mohamed, M.D., Chief of Staff, Val Verde Regional Medical Center, Del Rio, TX, p. A599

SHAH, Beena, M.D., Chief of Staff and Chief Medical Officer, Anaheim Global Medical Center, Anaheim, CA, p. A50

SHAH, Jayendra H, M.D., Chief Medical Officer, Southern Arizona Veterans Affairs Health Care System, Tucson, AZ, p. A38

SHAH, Paresh, Director Information Systems, Reston Hospital Center, Reston, VA, p. A665

SHAH, Syed, M.D., Chief of Staff, Pioneer Memorial Hospital And Health Services, Viborg, SD, p. A565

SHAH, Vital, M.D., Associate Director and Chief Medical Officer, Central State Hospital, Louisville, KY, p. A256

SHAHAN, Matthew, Chief Executive Officer, West River Regional Medical Center, Hettinger, ND, p. A468

SHAHI, Niloo, Chief Operating Officer, Lac–Olive View–Ucla Medical Center, Los Angeles, CA, p. A68

SHAHNAM, Melissa Shreves, Director Human Resources, Mon Health Medical Center, Morgantown, WV, p. A687

SHAHRYAR, Syed, M.D., Medical Director, Promise Hospital Of Phoenix, Mesa, AZ, p. A32

SHAHZADA, Kamran, M.D., Chief Medical Staff, South Central Kansas Medical Center, Arkansas City, KS, p. A232

SHAIFFER, Mandy, Chief Nursing Officer, Mt. San Rafael Hospital, Trinidad, CO, p. A106

SHAKOOR, Arif, Chief of Staff, Raulerson Hospital, Okeechobee, FL, p. A133

SHALLOCK, James R, Chief Financial Officer, Memorial Hermann Greater Heights Hospital, Houston, TX, p. A612

SHAMBURG, Steffen, M.D., Chief of Staff, Hiawatha Community Hospital, Hiawatha, KS, p. A236

SHAMMAS, Karen, Chief Executive Officer, Curahealth Phoenix, Phoenix, AZ, p. A33

SHANAHAN, Thomas
Chief Financial Officer and Senior Vice President, Hackensack Meridian Health Raritan Bay Medical Center, Perth Amboy, NJ, p. A411
Chief Operating Officer, Hackensack Meridian Health Raritan Bay Medical Center, Perth Amboy, NJ, p. A411
Vice President, Human Resources, Children'S Hospital Of Wisconsin–Fox Valley, Neenah, WI, p. A702
Vice President, Human Resources, Children'S Hospital Of Wisconsin, Milwaukee, WI, p. A701

SHAND, Natalie, M.D., Vice President Integrative Medicine and Chief Medical Officer, Scottsdale Liberty Hospital, Scottsdale, AZ, p. A36

SHANLEY, Diane, Deputy Service Unit Director, U. S. Public Health Service Indian Hospital–Sells, Sells, AZ, p. A36

SHANLEY, Linda L., Vice President, Chief Information Officer, Saint Francis Hospital And Medical Center, Hartford, CT, p. A108

SHANNON, David A., Interim Chief Executive Officer, Three Rivers Health, Three Rivers, MI, p. A323

SHANNON, Greg
Chief Executive Officer, First Hospital Wyoming Valley, Kingston, PA, p. A528
Chief Executive Officer, Two Rivers Behavioral Health System, Kansas City, MO, p. A363
Chief Human Resources Officer, Golden Valley Memorial Healthcare, Clinton, MO, p. A358

SHANNON, John Jay.
Chief Executive Officer, John H. Stroger Jr. Hospital Of Cook County, Chicago, IL, p. A177
Chief Executive Officer, Provident Hospital Of Cook County, Chicago, IL, p. A179

SHANNON, Lori, President, St Vincent Heart Center, Indianapolis, IN, p. A206

SHANNON, Patrick, Chief Operating Officer, Baptist Hospitals Of Southeast Texas, Beaumont, TX, p. A587

SHANNON, Richard, M.D., Chief of Staff, Montrose Memorial Hospital, Montrose, CO, p. A104

SHANNON, Scott, Director Finance, Socorro General Hospital, Socorro, NM, p. A421

SHAPE, Amy, Information Technology, North Dakota State Hospital, Jamestown, ND, p. A468

SHAPIRO, David, M.D.
Vice President Medical Affairs and Chief Medical Officer, Ascension Columbia St. Mary'S Hospital Milwaukee, Milwaukee, WI, p. A700
Vice President Medical Affairs and Chief Medical Officer, Ascension Columbia St. Mary'S Hospital Ozaukee, Mequon, WI, p. A700
Vice President Medical Affairs and Chief Medical Officer, Ascension Columbia St. Mary'S Milwaukee Hospital, Milwaukee, WI, p. A700

SHAPIRO, Louis A., President and Chief Executive Officer, Brookdale Hospital Medical Center, New York, NY, p. A432

SHAPIRO, Marc, M.D., Chief Medical Officer, Adventist Health Clear Lake, Clearlake, CA, p. A54

SHAPIRO, Steven D, M.D.
Chief Medical Officer, Bon Secours St. Francis Hospital, Charleston, SC, p. A549
Chief Medical Officer, Roper St. Francis Mount Pleasant Hospital, Mount Pleasant, SC, p. A555
Vice President Medical Affairs, Roper Hospital, Charleston, SC, p. A550

SHAPPLEY, Robert, Chief Operating Officer, Lakewood Regional Medical Center, Lakewood, CA, p. A64

SHARANGPANI, Rojesh, M.D., Chief of Staff, Capital Medical Center, Olympia, WA, p. A676

SHARKEY, Linda, R.N., MSN, Vice President Patient Care Services and Chief Nurse Executive, Fauquier Hospital, Warrenton, VA, p. A668

SHARLOW, Joseph, M.D., Chief of Staff, Ste. Genevieve County Memorial Hospital, Ste Genevieve, MO, p. A372

SHARMA, Adhi, M.D., Senior Vice President, Medical Affairs and Chief Medical Officer, South Nassau Communities Hospital, Oceanside, NY, p. A440

SHARMA, Aika, M.D., President Medical Staff, Alameda Hospital, Alameda, CA, p. A50

SHARMA, Chandra, M.D., Chief of Staff, Welch Community Hospital, Welch, WV, p. A690

SHARMA, Roger, Executive Vice President/Chief Financial Officer, Citrus Valley Medical Center–Inter Community Campus, Covina, CA, p. A56

SHARMA, Satish C, M.D., Chief of Staff, Providence Veterans Affairs Medical Center, Providence, RI, p. A547

SHARON, Joesph P., Associate Director, Wilkes–Barre Veterans Affairs Medical Center, Wilkes, PA, p. A545

SHARON, Sandy, Senior Vice President and Area Manager, Kaiser Permanente Sacramento Medical Center, Sacramento, CA, p. A81

SHARP, Alan
Chief Financial Officer, Saint Thomas Dekalb Hospital, Smithville, TN, p. A579
Chief Financial Officer, Saint Thomas Stones River Hospital, Woodbury, TN, p. A580

SHARP, Cheryl, Chief Financial Office, Miami County Medical Center, Paola, KS, p. A243

SHARP, Cindy, M.D., Chief Medical Officer, Madison Valley Medical Center, Ennis, MT, p. A376

SHARP, Gina, President and Chief Executive Officer, Linden Oaks Hospital, Naperville, IL, p. A190

SHARP, Greg, M.D., Senior Vice President and Chief Medical Officer, Arkansas Children'S Hospital, Little Rock, AR, p. A44

SHARP, John K, Chief Financial Officer, Seton Medical Center Harker Heights, Harker Heights, TX, p. A609

SHARP, Julie, Supervisor Human Resources, Chase County Community Hospital, Imperial, NE, p. A386

SHARP, Mike, Interim Director, Wellstar Atlanta Medical Center, Atlanta, GA, p. A147

SHARP, Patrick, Chief Executive Officer, Range Regional Health Services, Hibbing, MN, p. A333

SHARP, Rebecca, Chief Financial Officer, Wagoner Community Hospital, Wagoner, OK, p. A510

SHARP, Richard, M.D., Medical Director, Christus St. Michael Rehabilitation Hospital, Texarkana, TX, p. A640

SHARP, Stacy, Coordinator Human Resources, Atoka County Medical Center, Atoka, OK, p. A496

SHARP, Tanya, President and Chief Executive Officer, Boone County Health Center, Albion, NE, p. A382

SHARP, Tony, Supervisor Information System, Sweetwater Hospital, Sweetwater, TN, p. A580

SHARPE, Deborah, R.N., Director of Nursing, West Springs Hospital, Grand Junction, CO, p. A101

SHARPTON, Debra, Director of Nursing, Devereux Advanced Behavioral Health Georgia, Kennesaw, GA, p. A155

SHARUM, Melinda
Director Human Resources, Mercy Hospital Ardmore, Ardmore, OK, p. A496
Director Human Resources, Mercy Hospital Healdton, Healdton, OK, p. A500

SHATRAW, Thomas, Director Human Resources, Samaritan Medical Center, Watertown, NY, p. A447

SHAUGHNESSY, John, Chief Financial Officer, Mcleod Health Clarendon, Manning, SC, p. A555

SHAUGHNESSY, Mary
Vice President Finance, Spaulding Hospital For Continuing Medical Care Cambridge, Cambridge, MA, p. A297
Vice President Finance, Spaulding Rehabilitation Hospital Cape Cod, East Sandwich, MA, p. A298
Vice President Finance, Spaulding Rehabilitation Hospital, Charlestown, MA, p. A298

SHAUINGER, Beckie, Chief Executive Officer, Fairfax Behavioral Health, Kirkland, WA, p. A674

SHAULL, Heather, Chief Financial Officer, Adair County Health System, Greenfield, IA, p. A223

SHAULL, Ty, President and Chief Executive Officer, Wyandot Memorial Hospital, Upper Sandusky, OH, p. A492

SHAUNESSY, Celia, Vice President Human Resources, Ascension St. Michael'S Hospital, Stevens Point, WI, p. A706

SHAVER, Chris
Vice President Human Resources, Covenant Children'S Hospital, Lubbock, TX, p. A621
Vice President Human Resources, Covenant Medical Center, Lubbock, TX, p. A621
Vice President Human Resources, Covenant Specialty Hospital, Lubbock, TX, p. A621

SHAVER, Jennifer
Director of Nursing, Gouverneur Hospital, Gouverneur, NY, p. A428
Director of Nursing, Lewis County General Hospital, Lowville, NY, p. A430

SHAVER, John, Chief Financial Officer, Baystate Noble Hospital, Westfield, MA, p. A304

SHAVER, Robert D, M.D., Vice President Medical Affairs, Wellspan Good Samaritan Hospital, Lebanon, PA, p. A530

SHAW, David, Director Information Technology, Forrest City Medical Center, Forrest City, AR, p. A42

SHAW, David B., Chief Executive Officer and Administrator, Nor–Lea Hospital District, Lovington, NM, p. A419

SHAW, Douglas A., Chief Executive Officer, Mad River Community Hospital, Arcata, CA, p. A51

SHAW, Greg, Vice President, Finance, Aspirus Medford Hospital & Clinics, Inc., Medford, WI, p. A699

SHAW, Howard, M.D., Chief Medical Officer, Medical City Denton, Denton, TX, p. A599

SHAW, Jan, Director Personnel, River Bend Hospital, West Lafayette, IN, p. A216

SHAW, Jean, Chief Financial Officer, Valley Regional Hospital, Claremont, NH, p. A399

SHAW, John C, M.D., Medical Director, Southern Indiana Rehabilitation Hospital, New Albany, IN, p. A212

SHAW, Kendra, Chief Information Officer, Western Wisconsin Health, Baldwin, WI, p. A691

SHAW, Kimberly
 Chief Operating Officer, St. Rose Dominican Hospitals – Siena Campus, Henderson, NV, p. A394
 Vice President Patient Care and Chief Nursing Executive, Mercy Medical Center Redding, Redding, CA, p. A79

SHAW, Mandy, M.D., Chief of Staff, Sidney Regional Medical Center, Sidney, NE, p. A391

SHAW, Patrick D., Chief Executive Officer, Grafton City Hospital, Grafton, WV, p. A685

SHAW, Violet, R.N., Director of Nursing, Grafton City Hospital, Grafton, WV, p. A685

SHAWGO, Darla, Director Human Resources, Sparta Community Hospital, Sparta, IL, p. A196

SHAWN, D.J., Director Human Resources, Alliancehealth Madill, Madill, OK, p. A501

SHEA, Drew, Chief Financial Officer, City Hospital At White Rock, Dallas, TX, p. A596

SHEA, Natalie, Chief Nursing Officer, Mercyone Elkader Medical Center, Elkader, IA, p. A222

SHEAR, Larry, Administrative Assistant, Norwood Health Center, Marshfield, WI, p. A699

SHEARER, Christopher, M.D., Chief Medical Officer, Honorhealth John C. Lincoln Medical Center, Phoenix, AZ, p. A33

SHEARER, Laura, R.N., MSN, Senior Vice President and Chief Nursing Officer, Phoebe Putney Memorial Hospital, Albany, GA, p. A145

SHEARER, Ron, M.D., Regional Medical Director, Peacehealth Peace Harbor Medical Center, Florence, OR, p. A512

SHEARS, Ann Marie, Vice President Patient Care Services, Robert Wood Johnson University Hospital Rahway, Rahway, NJ, p. A411

SHECKLER, Robert L., Administrator, Avera Gettysburg Hospital, Gettysburg, SD, p. A561

SHEEHAN, John C.
 Interim President and Chief Executive Officer, Unitypoint Health – Trinity Bettendorf, Bettendorf, IA, p. A217
 Interim President and Chief Executive Officer, Unitypoint Health – Trinity Rock Island, Rock Island, IL, p. A194

SHEEHAN, Karen, Vice President and Chief Information Officer, Swedish Covenant Hospital, Chicago, IL, p. A180

SHEEHAN, Terrence P, M.D., Medical Director, Adventist Healthcare Physical Health And Rehabilitation, Rockville, MD, p. A293

SHEEHY, Earl Nielsen., Chief Executive Officer, Ray County Memorial Hospital, Richmond, MO, p. A367

SHEERIN, Rick
 Chief Financial Officer, Polk Medical Center, Cedartown, GA, p. A149
 Vice President Fiscal Services, Floyd Medical Center, Rome, GA, p. A159

SHEETS, Cindy, Vice President Information Systems and Chief Information Officer, Ohiohealth Medcentral Mansfield Hospital, Mansfield, OH, p. A486

SHEETS, Jim, Chief Executive Officer and Administrator, Lds Hospital, Salt Lake City, UT, p. A651

SHEFFIELD, Aubrey, Administrative Assistant Human Resources and Public Relations, Grove Hill Memorial Hospital, Grove Hill, AL, p. A19

SHEFFIELD, Loretta, Chief Executive Officer, Select Specialty Hospital–Miami, Miami, FL, p. A131

SHEFFIELD, Nichol, Chief Executive Officer, Pacific Grove Hospital, Riverside, CA, p. A81

SHEFIELD, Jennifer, M.D., Chief of Staff, West River Regional Medical Center, Hettinger, ND, p. A468

SHEFTE, David H., Chief Executive Officer, Healthsouth Rehabilitation Hospital Of Littleton, Littleton, CO, p. A103

SHEGOLEV, Igor, Vice President Human Resources, Carondelet St. Joseph'S Hospital, Tucson, AZ, p. A37

SHEHAN, Mary, Chief Executive Officer, Louis A. Weiss Memorial Hospital, Chicago, IL, p. A178

SHEHATA, Nady, M.D., Vice President Medical Affairs, Sisters Of Charity Hospital Of Buffalo, Buffalo, NY, p. A425

SHEHI, G Michael, M.D., Medical Director, Mountain View Hospital, Gadsden, AL, p. A18

SHEHI, G Michael., Chief Executive Officer, Mountain View Hospital, Gadsden, AL, p. A18

SHEHI, Jay, Chief Executive Officer, Alliance Health Center, Meridian, MS, p. A351

SHEIKH, Arsalan, Chief of Medicine, Bon Secours Baltimore Health System, Baltimore, MD, p. A286

SHEIKH, Azad, Chief Medical Officer, Adventist Health And Rideout, Marysville, CA, p. A71

SHEINBEIN, David, Chief Medical Officer, Banner – University Medical Center South, Tucson, AZ, p. A37

SHELAK, Matt, Chief Executive Officer, Roxborough Memorial Hospital, Philadelphia, PA, p. A536

SHELBURNE, John D, M.D., Chief of Staff, Durham Veterans Affairs Medical Center, Durham, NC, p. A453

SHELBY, Dennis R., Chief Executive Officer, Wilson Medical Center, Neodesha, KS, p. A241

SHELBY, Joyce, Manager Human Resources, Hardin County General Hospital, Rosiclare, IL, p. A195

SHELDEN, Diana, Chief Nursing Officer, Stone County Medical Center, Mountain View, AR, p. A46

SHELDON, Lyle Ernest.
 President and Chief Executive Officer, University Of Maryland Harford Memorial Hospital, Havre De Grace, MD, p. A291
 President and Chief Executive Officer, University Of Maryland Upper Chesapeake Medical Center, Bel Air, MD, p. A288

SHELDON, Mo P., Chief Executive Officer and Administrator, Odessa Memorial Healthcare Center, Odessa, WA, p. A675

SHELFORD, Dave, Assistant Superintendent, Richmond State Hospital, Richmond, IN, p. A214

SHELL, John, M.D., Chief Medical Officer, Coffey County Hospital, Burlington, KS, p. A233

SHELL, Steve, Chief Executive Officer, Reno Behavioral Healthcare Hospital, Reno, NV, p. A397

SHELLENBERGER, David, President, St. John Vianney Hospital, Downingtown, PA, p. A524

SHELLS, Tammy, Chief Nursing Officer, Belmont Pines Hospital, Youngstown, OH, p. A495

SHELT, Elizabeth, Civilian Personnel Officer, Dwight David Eisenhower Army Medical Center, Fort Gordon, GA, p. A153

SHELTON, Amy, Chief Nursing Officer, St. Vincent'S East, Birmingham, AL, p. A15

SHELTON, Angela, Chief Financial Officer, Jack Hughston Memorial Hospital, Phenix City, AL, p. A22

SHELTON, Carol, Director Human Resources, Lovelace Women'S Hospital, Albuquerque, NM, p. A416

SHELTON, Darlene, Coordinator Team Resources, Baycare Alliant Hospital, Dunedin, FL, p. A122

SHELTON, Jared, Chief Executive Officer, Texas Health Presbyterian Hospital Allen, Allen, TX, p. A582

SHELTON, Kathy, Director Human Resources, Ut Health Pittsburg, Pittsburg, TX, p. A628

SHELTON, Mark, Chief of Staff, Winn Parish Medical Center, Winnfield, LA, p. A280

SHELTON, Richard, M.D., Chief Medical Officer, Baptist Health Richmond, Richmond, KY, p. A260

SHELTON, Tom, Coordinator of Nursing Services, Porterville Developmental Center, Porterville, CA, p. A78

SHENDELL–FALIK, Nancy, President, Baystate Medical Center, Springfield, MA, p. A303

SHENDELL–FALIK, Nancy, R.N., Senior Vice President, Chief Operating Officer and Chief Nursing Officer, Baystate Medical Center, Springfield, MA, p. A303

SHENEFIELD, Jason, Senior Vice President and Chief Operating Officer, Phelps Health, Rolla, MO, p. A368

SHENGLE, Lori, Director Information Technology, Morrill County Community Hospital, Bridgeport, NE, p. A383

SHEPARD, Bridget, Vice President Human Resources, Wabash General Hospital, Mount Carmel, IL, p. A190

SHEPARD, Karen, Senior Vice President and Chief Financial Officer, St. Charles Prineville, Prineville, OR, p. A517

SHEPARD, Megan, Director Clinical Services, Odessa Memorial Healthcare Center, Odessa, WA, p. A675

SHEPARD, Sheila, Controller, Encompass Health Rehabilitation Hospital Of Humble, Humble, TX, p. A615

SHEPARDSON, Dean, Chief Financial Officer, Banner Estrella Medical Center, Phoenix, AZ, p. A33

SHEPARDSON, Heather S, Vice President Human Resources, Carilion Roanoke Memorial Hospital, Roanoke, VA, p. A667

SHEPHARD, Bryan, Chief Financial Officer, Tristar Summit Medical Center, Hermitage, TN, p. A570

SHEPHARD, Russ, Senior Systems Analyst, West Tennessee Healthcare Dyersburg Hospital, Dyersburg, TN, p. A569

SHEPHERD, Laura, Director Human Resources, Texas Health Huguley Hospital Fort Worth South, Burleson, TX, p. A590

SHEPHERD, Linda M., Chief Nursing Officer, Johnston Memorial Hospital, Abingdon, VA, p. A656

SHEPHERD, Lisa, M.D., Chief of Staff, Buena Vista Regional Medical Center, Storm Lake, IA, p. A230

SHEPHERD, Thomas, Executive Vice President and Chief Operating Officer, Gwinnett Hospital System, Lawrenceville, GA, p. A156

SHEPLER, Mary, R.N., Vice President and Chief Nursing Officer, Saint Joseph Hospital, Denver, CO, p. A99

SHEPPARD, Ballard, Chief Executive Officer, Rivendell Behavioral Health Services Of Arkansas, Benton, AR, p. A39

SHEPPARD, Sandy, Vice President Patient Services, Wake Forest Baptist Health – Wilkes Medical Center, North Wilkesboro, NC, p. A459

SHEPPARD, Sharon, Manager Human Resources, Sycamore Shoals Hospital, Elizabethton, TN, p. A569

SHEPPARD, Varinya, R.N., Chief Nursing Officer, St. Elizabeth Medical Center, Utica, NY, p. A446

SHERBONDY, Beverly, Assistant Vice President, Human Resources, Jeanes Hospital, Philadelphia, PA, p. A535

SHERBONDY, Lori, Director Human Resources, Battle Mountain General Hospital, Battle Mountain, NV, p. A393

SHERER, Janet, Chief of Patient Care Services, Springfield Hospital, Springfield, VT, p. A655

SHERER, Susan, Chief Information Resource Management, Dayton Veterans Affairs Medical Center, Dayton, OH, p. A481

SHERIDAN, Cheryl, R.N., Senior Vice President Patient Care Services, Rochester General Hospital, Rochester, NY, p. A442

SHERIDAN, Elizabeth
 Chief Operating Officer and Chief Nursing Executive, Inspira Medical Center–Elmer, Elmer, NJ, p. A405
 Chief Operating Officer and Chief Nursing Executive, Inspira Medical Center–Vineland, Vineland, NJ, p. A413

SHERIDAN, Kolbe, Chief Operating Officer, Heartland Regional Medical Center, Marion, IL, p. A188

SHERIDAN, Phil, Chief Executive Officer, Centerpointe Hospital Of Columbia, Columbia, MO, p. A359

SHERIF, Ali, M.D., Chief of Staff, Lea Regional Medical Center, Hobbs, NM, p. A418

SHERMAN, Angelina, R.N., MSN, Chief Nursing Officer, The Rehabilitation Institute Of St. Louis, Saint Louis, MO, p. A371

SHERMAN, Frederick C, M.D., Chief Medical Officer, The Children'S Home Of Pittsburgh, Pittsburgh, PA, p. A537

SHERMAN, Sheila, Vice President Patient Care Services, Vail Health, Vail, CO, p. A106

SHERMAN, Stephanie, Chief Human Resources Officer, West Boca Medical Center, Boca Raton, FL, p. A118

SHERON, William E., Chief Executive Officer, Wooster Community Hospital, Wooster, OH, p. A494

SHERRILL, Angela
 Chief Information Officer, Laird Hospital, Union, MS, p. A354
 Corporate Director Information System, Rush Foundation Hospital, Meridian, MS, p. A351
 Corporate Director Information System, Specialty Hospital Of Meridian, Meridian, MS, p. A351

SHERROD, Michael, Chief Executive Officer, Tristar Greenview Regional Hospital, Bowling Green, KY, p. A250

SHERROD, Rhonda Kay.
 Chief Executive Officer, Shands Lake Shore Regional Medical Center, Lake City, FL, p. A127
 Chief Executive Officer, Shands Live Oak Regional Medical Center, Live Oak, FL, p. A128

SHERRON, Tammy M., Vice President Finance, Carolinaeast Health System, New Bern, NC, p. A459

SHERRY, Bernie, Senior Vice President, Ascension Healthcare, Ministry, Midwest Orthopedic Specialty Hospital, Franklin, WI, p. A695

SHERRY, Mark A., Regional Director Human Resource Strategic Services, Austin/Round Rock Region, Baylor Scott & White Medical Center – Round Rock, Round Rock, TX, p. A632

SHERWIN, Charles H., President, Midmichigan Medical Center – Alpena, Alpena, MI, p. A306

SHERWOOD, Edward J, Chief Executive Officer, Cornerstone Hospital Of Austin, Austin, TX, p. A585

SHERWOOD, Jennifer L, Division, Human Resource Business Partner, Banner – University Medical Center South, Tucson, AZ, p. A37

SHERWOOD, Matthew M, Chief Financial Officer, Unity Medical & Surgical Hospital, Mishawaka, IN, p. A211

SHETTLESWORTH, Amanda, Director Human Resources, Bloomington Meadows Hospital, Bloomington, IN, p. A200

SHETTY, Atul, Chief of Staff, Weirton Medical Center, Weirton, WV, p. A690

SHEW, Angel, Director Area Technology, Kaiser Permanente South San Francisco, South San Francisco, CA, p. A90

SHEWBRIDGE, Richard K., President, Cleveland Clinic, Medina Hospital, Medina, OH, p. A487

SHEYKA, Patricia, Chief Nursing Officer, Gila Regional Medical Center, Silver City, NM, p. A420

SHIBINETTE, Lori, Chief Executive Officer, New Hampshire Hospital, Concord, NH, p. A399

SHICKOLOVICH, William, Chief Information Officer, Tufts Medical Center, Boston, MA, p. A296

SHIELDS, Charlie
  Chief Executive Officer, Truman Medical Center–Lakewood, Kansas City, MO, p. A363
  President and Chief Executive Officer, Truman Medical Center–Hospital Hill, Kansas City, MO, p. A363

SHIELDS, Diane, Chief Human Resources Officer, Midmichigan Medical Center – Alpena, Alpena, MI, p. A306

SHIELDS, Stuart, Director, G. Werber Bryan Psychiatric Hospital, Columbia, SC, p. A551

SHIELDS, Todd, Administrator, St. Charles Prineville, Prineville, OR, p. A517

SHIFF, Mary Treacy, Chief Financial Officer, Kindred Chicago–Central Hospital, Chicago, IL, p. A178

SHIFFERMILLER, William, M.D., Vice President Medical Affairs, Nebraska Methodist Hospital, Omaha, NE, p. A389

SHIHADY, Sharon, Director Human Resources, Spire Cane Creek Rehabilitation Hospital, Martin, TN, p. A573

SHIKIAR, Mindy, MSN, Chief Operating Officer, Boca Raton Regional Hospital, Boca Raton, FL, p. A118

SHILKAITIS, Mary, Vice President Patient Care and Chief Nursing Officer, Rush–Copley Medical Center, Aurora, IL, p. A174

SHILLING, Stacy, Controller, Chi St. Vincent Sherwood Rehabilitation Hospital, Sherwood, AR, p. A48

SHIM, Eunmee, R.N., MSN, Vice President Operations, Adventist Healthcare Shady Grove Medical Center, Rockville, MD, p. A293

SHIMAMOTO, Kevin, Vice President and Chief Informational Officer, Valley Children'S Healthcare, Madera, CA, p. A70

SHIMP, David, Chief Executive Officer, Las Palmas Medical Center, El Paso, TX, p. A602

SHINAGAWA, Nathan, Chief Operating Officer, Banner Del E. Webb Medical Center, Sun City West, AZ, p. A36

SHINER, Cindy, Manager Human Resources, Lebanon Veterans Affairs Medical Center, Lebanon, PA, p. A529

SHINGLETON, Kathy J., Ed.D., Vice President, Human Resources, Virginia Mason Medical Center, Seattle, WA, p. A679

SHINICK, Mary K, Vice President Human Resources, Nyack Hospital, Nyack, NY, p. A440

SHININGER, Kimberly R, Manger, Human Resources, Parkview Wabash Hospital, Wabash, IN, p. A216

SHIPLEY, Carolyn, R.N., Chief Nursing Officer, Roane Medical Center, Harriman, TN, p. A570

SHIPLEY, Janice, M.D., Chief Medical Officer, Cibola General Hospital, Grants, NM, p. A418

SHIPLEY, Kurt, Chief Financial Officer, Jordan Valley Medical Center, West Jordan, UT, p. A653

SHIPP, Geraldine H, Director of Risk Management, Sampson Regional Medical Center, Clinton, NC, p. A452

SHIRAH, Anita, Director Human Resources, Usa Health University Hospital, Mobile, AL, p. A21

SHIRLEY, Christian, Director Human Resources, Geisinger Encompass Health Rehabilitation Hospital, Danville, PA, p. A523

SHIRLEY, Douglas E., Senior Executive Vice President and Chief Financial Officer, Cooper University Health Care, Camden, NJ, p. A404

SHIRLEY, Steve, Chief Information Officer, Parkview Medical Center, Pueblo, CO, p. A104

SHIVELY, Lori, Vice President of Finance, Munson Healthcare Grayling Hospital, Grayling, MI, p. A313

SHIVERY, Toni M
  Vice President Human Resources, University Of Maryland Harford Memorial Hospital, Havre De Grace, MD, p. A291
  Vice President Human Resources, University Of Maryland Upper Chesapeake Medical Center, Bel Air, MD, p. A288

SHMERLING, James E., President and Chief Executive Officer, Connecticut Children'S Medical Center, Hartford, CT, p. A108

SHOBE, Franklin, Administrator and Chief Executive Officer, Black Hills Surgical Hospital, Rapid City, SD, p. A563

SHOBE, Susan, Director Administration and Support Services, Alton Mental Health Center, Alton, IL, p. A173

SHOCK, Ernest, Chief Nursing Officer, Abbeville Area Medical Center, Abbeville, SC, p. A549

SHOCKEY, Kathryn L, Director Human Resources, Lead–Deadwood Regional Hospital, Deadwood, SD, p. A560

SHOCKLEY, Mary, Human Resources Director, Russell Medical, Alexander City, AL, p. A13

SHOCKNEY, Brian T., President, Indiana University Health Bloomington Hospital, Bloomington, IN, p. A200

SHOEMAKER, Matt, D.O., Vice President and Chief Medical Officer, Southeast Hospital, Cape Girardeau, MO, p. A358

SHOENER, Carl, Chief Information Officer, Lehigh Valley Hospital – Hazleton, Hazleton, PA, p. A527

SHOFNER, Connie, Chief Nursing Officer, Carlsbad Medical Center, Carlsbad, NM, p. A417

SHOLTIS, Bridget, Chief Financial Officer, Mclaren Port Huron, Port Huron, MI, p. A320

SHOMAKER, Susan, Director Information Management Systems, J. Arthur Dosher Memorial Hospital, Southport, NC, p. A462

SHOOK, Susan, Interim Chief Executive Officer, Adventhealth Murray, Chatsworth, GA, p. A150

SHOOK, Teressia, Chief Financial Officer, Clinch Memorial Hospital, Homerville, GA, p. A155

SHOR, Joel, M.D., Chief of Staff, Bluefield Regional Medical Center, Bluefield, WV, p. A683

SHORES, Larry, M.D., Executive Medical Director, Cedar Springs Hospital, Colorado Springs, CO, p. A97

SHORT, M Andrew, Vice President Information Services, Samaritan Medical Center, Watertown, NY, p. A447

SHORT, Penny, R.N., Chief Operating Officer, Nanticoke Memorial Hospital, Seaford, DE, p. A114

SHORT, Peter H, M.D., Senior Vice President Medical Affairs, Beverly Hospital, Beverly, MA, p. A294

SHORT, Ted, Chief Financial Officer, Fairview Park Hospital, Dublin, GA, p. A152

SHORT, W L, M.D., Chief Medical Officer, Memorial Health System, Abilene, KS, p. A232

SHOUKAIR, Sami, M.D., Chief Medical Officer, La Palma Intercommunity Hospital, La Palma, CA, p. A63

SHOUP, Barbara, R.N., Chief Nursing Officer, Ascension Brighton Center For Recovery, Brighton, MI, p. A307

SHOUP, Emily, Director Nursing Services, Roundup Memorial Healthcare, Roundup, MT, p. A380

SHOUSE, Shellie, Chief Financial Officer, Bluegrass Community Hospital, Versailles, KY, p. A261

SHOWALTER, Amy J, R.N.
  Chief Operating Officer, Sheltering Arms Hospital South, Midlothian, VA, p. A663
  Chief Operating Officer, Sheltering Arms Rehabilitation Hospital, Mechanicsville, VA, p. A662

SHOWALTER, Will, Senior Vice President Information Technology, Holston Valley Medical Center, Kingsport, TN, p. A572

SHOWALTER, William, Senior Vice President and Chief Information Officer, Information Technology Services, Wake Forest Baptist Health–Davie Medical Center, Bermuda Run, NC, p. A449

SHOWS, Carla
  Human Resource and Payroll Clerk, George Regional Hospital, Lucedale, MS, p. A350
  Payroll Clerk, Greene County Hospital, Leakesville, MS, p. A350

SHRAKE, Kevin L., Chief Executive Officer, Kindred Hospital–St. Louis, Saint Louis, MO, p. A369

SHREEVE, Susan, Chief Financial Officer, Research Medical Center, Kansas City, MO, p. A362

SHRESTHA, Sanjeeb, M.D., Chief Medical Staff, Medical City Weatherford, Weatherford, TX, p. A644

SHREVE, Susan, Executive Director Information Technology, Boone Memorial Hospital, Madison, WV, p. A687

SHREWSBURY, Kim, Vice President and Chief Financial Officer, Decatur Morgan Hospital, Decatur, AL, p. A16

SHRIDE, Chris, President, Amita Health St. Mary'S Hospital, Kankakee, IL, p. A187

SHRIVASTAVA, Rakesh, M.D., Chief Medical Officer, Cornerstone Hospital Of Oklahoma–Shawnee, Shawnee, OK, p. A507

SHRIVER, Debra, R.N., MSN, Chief Nurse Executive, Unitypoint Health – Trinity Regional Medical Center, Fort Dodge, IA, p. A222

SHRIVER, Kren K, M.D., Clinical Director, Capital District Psychiatric Center, Albany, NY, p. A422

SHROADES, David W, Vice President Technology Services, Alliance Community Hospital, Alliance, OH, p. A471

SHROCK, Lynda J, Vice President Human Resources, Logansport Memorial Hospital, Logansport, IN, p. A210

SHROFF, Divya, Chief Medical Officer, Tristar Ashland City Medical Center, Ashland City, TN, p. A566

SHROFF, Rajendra, M.D., Administrative Medical Director, Ssm Health St. Mary'S Hospital Centralia, Centralia, IL, p. A175

SHUART, Jeffery, M.D., Chief of Staff, Blackwell Regional Hospital, Blackwell, OK, p. A497

SHUFFLEBARGER, Tom, Chief Operating Officer, Children'S Of Alabama, Birmingham, AL, p. A14

SHUFORD, Little, Health Information Manager, Kindred Hospital–Greensboro, Greensboro, NC, p. A455

SHUGARMAN, Mark D., Administrator, Shriners Hospitals For Children – Cincinnati, Cincinnati, OH, p. A476

SHUGART, Susan C, Chief Operating Officer, Carolina Pines Regional Medical Center, Hartsville, SC, p. A554

SHUGART, Susan C., Chief Executive Officer, Kershawhealth, Camden, SC, p. A549

SHUGHART, Deborah A, Chief Financial Officer, Fulton County Medical Center, Mc Connellsburg, PA, p. A531

SHUGRUE, Dianne, President and Chief Executive Officer, Glens Falls Hospital, Glens Falls, NY, p. A428

SHULER, Conrad K, M.D., Chief Medical Officer, Prisma Health Oconee Memorial Hospital, Seneca, SC, p. A557

SHULIK, David, Vice President and Chief Financial Officer, Upmc Horizon, Farrell, PA, p. A526

SHULL, Jennifer, R.N., Chief Nursing Officer, Adventhealth Fish Memorial, Orange City, FL, p. A134

SHULTS, Randi L., Chief Executive Officer, North Carolina Specialty Hospital, Durham, NC, p. A453

SHUMAKER, Bradley, Chief Medical Officer, Orange Park Medical Center, Orange Park, FL, p. A134

SHUMAN, Betty, Director Human Resources, Wesley Rehabilitation Hospital, Wichita, KS, p. A248

SHUMAN, Daniel, D.O., Chief Medical Officer, Ashland Health Center, Ashland, KS, p. A232

SHUMATE, Karen J, R.N., Chief Operating Officer, Lmh Health, Lawrence, KS, p. A239

SHUMATE, Kim, Human Resources Officer, Ohio State University Wexner Medical Center, Columbus, OH, p. A479

SHUMWAY, Barbara, Director Human Resources, North Big Horn Hospital District, Lovell, WY, p. A712

SHUPERT, Charlene
  Director Staff Services, Carrus Rehabilitation Hospital, Sherman, TX, p. A637
  Director Staff Services, Carrus Specialty Hospital, Sherman, TX, p. A637

SHUPP, Susan, Chief Human Resources Officer, Nemaha County Hospital, Auburn, NE, p. A382

SHUSHTARI, J. Kevin, M.D., Chief Medical Officer, Hospital For Special Care, New Britain, CT, p. A109

SHUTE, Keith M, M.D., Senior Vice President Medical Affairs and Clinical Services, Androscoggin Valley Hospital, Berlin, NH, p. A399

SHYSHKA, Susan, Associate Director, Va Greater Los Angeles Healthcare System, Los Angeles, CA, p. A70

SIAL, Ajay, Chief Financial Officer, UC Irvine Health, Uc Irvine Medical Center, Orange, CA, p. A76

SIAL, Jay, Chief Financial Officer, Loyola University Medical Center, Maywood, IL, p. A189

SIBBITT, Stephen, M.D., Chief Medical Officer, Baylor Scott & White Medical Center – Temple, Temple, TX, p. A639

SIBLEY, Beth, Director of Nursing, Sage Rehabilitation Hospital, Baton Rouge, LA, p. A264

SIBLEY, Jeri, Director Revenue Cycle, Riverside Tappahannock Hospital, Tappahannock, VA, p. A668

SICA, Vincent A., President and Chief Executive Officer, Desoto Memorial Hospital, Arcadia, FL, p. A117

SICHTS, Pam, Director Human Resources, Sycamore Springs Hospital, Lafayette, IN, p. A210

SICILIA, Bruce, M.D., Medical Director, Encompass Health Rehabilitation Hospital Of York, York, PA, p. A546

SIDDIQI, Ather, M.D.
  Medical Director, Nexus Specialty Hospital The Woodlands, The Woodlands, TX, p. A641
  Medical Director, Nexus Specialty Hospital, Shenandoah, TX, p. A636

SIDDIQI, Syed, M.D., President Medical Staff, Raleigh General Hospital, Beckley, WV, p. A683

SIDDIQUI, Joseph, Vice President Human Resources, The Aroostook Medical Center, Presque Isle, ME, p. A284

SIDES, Tim, Chief Financial Officer, Valle Vista Health System, Greenwood, IN, p. A205

SIDMAN, Robert, M.D., Regional Vice President, Medical Affairs, The William W. Backus Hospital, Norwich, CT, p. A110

SIDONE, LeighAnn, MSN, R.N., Chief Nursing Officer, Suburban Hospital, Bethesda, MD, p. A289

SIEBENALER, Christopher, Regional Senior Vice President and Chief Executive Officer, Houston Methodist Sugar Land Hospital, Sugar Land, TX, p. A638

SIEBERT, Matt, Assistant Administrator Ancillary Services, Hermann Area District Hospital, Hermann, MO, p. A361

SIEDLECKI, Cathy, Director Human Resources, Carthage Area Hospital, Carthage, NY, p. A425

SIEG, Greg, Director Information Technology, Healthsource Saginaw, Inc., Saginaw, MI, p. A321

SIEGEL, Fredric, M.D., Chief of Staff, Desert View Hospital, Pahrump, NV, p. A397

SIEGEL, Lesley, M.D., Medical Director, Albert J. Solnit Psychiatric Center – South Campus, Middletown, CT, p. A109

SIEGEL, Tiffany, Chief Nursing Officer, Fulton County Health Center, Wauseon, OH, p. A493

SIEGELMAN, Gary M., M.D., MSC, Senior Vice President and Chief Medical Officer, Bayhealth Medical Center, Dover, DE, p. A113

SIEGFRIED, Carole A, MSN, R.N., Campus Nurse Executive, Prisma Health Richland Hospital, Columbia, SC, p. A551

SIEGLE, Lora, M.D., Chief Medical Officer, Morris County Hospital, Council Grove, KS, p. A234

SIEGLEN, Linda, M.D., Chief Medical Officer, Mission Hospital, Mission Viejo, CA, p. A72

SIEGMAN, Ira, M.D., Chief Medical Officer, Northside Hospital, Saint Petersburg, FL, p. A138

SIEGRIST, Steve, Director of Human Resources, Mesa View Regional Hospital, Mesquite, NV, p. A396

SIEK, Terry, MSN, R.N., Chief Nursing Officer, Hays Medical Center, Hays, KS, p. A236

SIEMERS, Thomas R., Chief Executive Officer, J. Arthur Dosher Memorial Hospital, Southport, NC, p. A462

SIEVERT, Deana, MSN, R.N., Chief Nursing Officer, Promedica Toledo Hospital, Toledo, OH, p. A492

SIEWERT, Charles
Director Human Resources, Buffalo Psychiatric Center, Buffalo, NY, p. A424
Director Human Resources, Western New York Children'S Psychiatric Center, West Seneca, NY, p. A447

SIFERS, Carl, Director Information Technology and System Services, Centerpoint Medical Center, Independence, MO, p. A361

SIFFRING, Connie K., Chief Executive Officer, Select Specialty Hospital – Lincoln, Lincoln, NE, p. A387

SIFRI, Christi, Chief Nursing Executive, Regional Hospital For Respiratory And Complex Care, Burien, WA, p. A671

SIGEL, Heather, Director of Clinical Services, War Memorial Hospital, Berkeley Springs, WV, p. A683

SIGLER, Wes
Chief Executive Officer, University Of Mississippi Medical Center Grenada, Grenada, MS, p. A347
Chief Executive Officer, University Of Mississippi Medical Center Holmes County, Lexington, MS, p. A350

SIGNOR, Kristin, Director Finance, Sunnyview Rehabilitation Hospital, Schenectady, NY, p. A444

SIGREST, Marion, M.D., Chief of Staff, Baptist Medical Center Yazoo, Yazoo City, MS, p. A355

SILARD, Kathleen A., President and Chief Executive Officer, Stamford Hospital, Stamford, CT, p. A111

SILAS, Maria, Manager Human Resources, Brookdale Hospital Medical Center, New York, NY, p. A432

SILBER, Steven, M.D., Senior Vice President Medical Affairs, Brookdale Hospital Medical Center, New York, NY, p. A432

SILLS, Doug, Chief Executive Officer, Santa Rosa Medical Center, Milton, FL, p. A132

SILLS, John T, Chief Information Officer, Health Central Hospital, Ocoee, FL, p. A133

SILLYMAN, Bryce, Chief Operating Officer, Pottstown Hospital, Pottstown, PA, p. A539

SILSBEE, Dave, Chief Information Officer, Cary Medical Center, Caribou, ME, p. A282

SILVA, Carmen, R.N., Chief Operating Officer, Doctors Hospital Of Manteca, Manteca, CA, p. A70

SILVA, Francisco, Financial Director, Hospital Metropolitano Dr. Susoni, Arecibo, PR, p. A715

SILVA, Shawn, Chief Executive Officer, Heritage Oaks Hospital, Sacramento, CA, p. A81

SILVA–STEELE, Jamie A., President and Chief Executive Officer, Unm Sandoval Regional Medical Center, Inc., Rio Rancho, NM, p. A419

SILVEIRA, Mike, Human Resources Leader, Kaiser Permanente Fresno Medical Center, Fresno, CA, p. A59

SILVER, Michael R., M.D.
Chief Information Officer, Rush Oak Park Hospital, Oak Park, IL, p. A191
Vice President Medical Affairs, Rush Oak Park Hospital, Oak Park, IL, p. A191

SILVER, Timothy, M.D., Medical Director, SAH–S, Sheltering Arms Hospital South, Midlothian, VA, p. A663

SILVERIA, Rich, Executive Vice President and Chief Financial Officer, University Of Chicago Medical Center, Chicago, IL, p. A180

SILVERMAN, Daniel C, M.D.
Chief Medical Officer, Acute Care Troy, Samaritan Hospital – Main Campus, Troy, NY, p. A445
Vice President and Chief Medical Officer, Sinai Hospital Of Baltimore, Baltimore, MD, p. A287

SILVERSTEIN, Douglas M, President, Northshore University Health System, Evanston, IL, p. A182

SILVERSTEIN, Joel, M.D., Chief Medical Officer, Copley Hospital, Morrisville, VT, p. A654

SILVERSTEIN, Kenneth L, M.D., Chief Clinical Officer, Christiana Care Health System, Newark, DE, p. A113

SILVERTHORNE, Samuel, Chief Information Officer, U. S. Air Force Medical Center Keesler, Keesler Afb, MS, p. A349

SILVESTRI, Scott, Chief Financial Officer, Hospital Financial Operations, Guthrie Robert Packer Hospital, Sayre, PA, p. A540

SILVEUS, Patrick, M.D., Medical Director, Kosciusko Community Hospital, Warsaw, IN, p. A216

SILVEY, Christie, Director People Services, Hshs St. Joseph'S Hospital, Highland, IL, p. A185

SILVIA, Charles B, M.D., Chief Medical Officer and Vice President Medical Affairs, Peninsula Regional Medical Center, Salisbury, MD, p. A293

SIM, Carol, President and Chief Executive Officer, Siskin Hospital For Physical Rehabilitation, Chattanooga, TN, p. A567

SIMCHUK, Cathy J, Chief Operating Officer, Providence Holy Family Hospital, Spokane, WA, p. A679

SIMIA, Greg
Chief Financial Officer, Hshs St. Clare Memorial Hospital, Oconto Falls, WI, p. A703
Chief Financial Officer, Hshs St. Mary'S Hospital Medical Center, Green Bay, WI, p. A696
Chief Financial Officer, Hshs St. Nicholas Hospital, Sheboygan, WI, p. A705
Chief Financial Officer, Hshs St. Vincent Hospital, Green Bay, WI, p. A696

SIMKINS, Palma, Chief Human Resources Management Services, Battle Creek Veterans Affairs Medical Center, Battle Creek, MI, p. A307

SIMMONS, Angela L., Chief Executive Officer, Encompass Health Rehabilitation Hospital Of Humble, Humble, TX, p. A615

SIMMONS, Barbara
Chief Executive Officer, Plantation General Hospital, Plantation, FL, p. A137
Chief Executive Officer, Westside Regional Medical Center, Plantation, FL, p. A137

SIMMONS, Brad
Chief Operating Officer, Saint Luke'S Hospital Of Kansas City, Kansas City, MO, p. A363
Chief Operating Officer, University Of California, Davis Medical Center, Sacramento, CA, p. A82
Interim Chief Executive Officer, University Of California, Davis Medical Center, Sacramento, CA, p. A82

SIMMONS, Daniel F, Senior Vice President and Treasurer, Monongahela Valley Hospital, Monongahela, PA, p. A532

SIMMONS, Dorlynn, Chief Executive Officer, Mescalero Public Health Service Indian Hospital, Mescalero, NM, p. A419

SIMMONS, Dwayne, Interim Chief Information Officer, Montefiore St. Luke'S Cornwall, Newburgh, NY, p. A439

SIMMONS, Eileen
Chief Financial Officer, UPMC Hospital Network, Upmc Mercy, Pittsburgh, PA, p. A538
Chief Financial Officer, Upmc Magee–Womens Hospital, Pittsburgh, PA, p. A538
Chief Financial Officer, Upmc Presbyterian, Pittsburgh, PA, p. A538

SIMMONS, Jeanette, Chief Operating Officer, Center For Behavioral Medicine, Kansas City, MO, p. A362

SIMMONS, Jodi, Chief Nursing Officer, Hillcrest Medical Center, Tulsa, OK, p. A508

SIMMONS, Kermit C., Chief Executive Officer, Louisiana Extended Care Hospital Of Lafayette, Lafayette, LA, p. A271

SIMMONS, Leslie, President, Carroll Hospital Center, Westminster, MD, p. A293

SIMMONS, Randy, Chief Executive Officer, Pinnacle Regional Hospital, Boonville, MO, p. A357

SIMMONS, Rickie, Controller, Kindred Hospital North Florida, Green Cove Springs, FL, p. A124

SIMMONS, Taquisa, Interim Director, Hampton Veterans Affairs Medical Center, Hampton, VA, p. A660

SIMMS, Miquel Noelani, R.N., Chief Nursing Officer, North Hawaii Community Hospital, Kamuela, HI, p. A165

SIMODEJKA, John E, Marketing Chief Executive Officer, Select Specialty Hospital–Camp Hill, Camp Hill, PA, p. A521

SIMODEJKA, John E., Chief Executive Officer, Select Specialty Hospital–Camp Hill, Camp Hill, PA, p. A521

SIMON, Anha, Director Human Resources, Riceland Medical Center, Winnie, TX, p. A646

SIMON, Ashley, Chief Financial Officer, Kansas Surgery And Recovery Center, Wichita, KS, p. A248

SIMON, Brenda, Chief Executive Officer, Northern Colorado Rehabilitation Hospital, Johnstown, CO, p. A102

SIMON, Daniel I., President, University Hospitals Cleveland Medical Center, Cleveland, OH, p. A478

SIMON, Joan M., R.N., FACHE, Chief Nursing Officer, Kootenai Health, Coeur D'Alene, ID, p. A169

SIMON, Kareen, Vice President of Operations, Wheeling Hospital, Wheeling, WV, p. A690

SIMON, Kenneth B, M.D., Chief of Staff, Veterans Affairs Gulf Coast Veterans Health Care System, Biloxi, MS, p. A344

SIMON, Keri, Executive Director, University Of Missouri Health Care, Columbia, MO, p. A359

SIMON, Lloyd, M.D., Medical Director, Eastern Long Island Hospital, Greenport, NY, p. A428

SIMON, Mark, System Chief Information Officer, Benefis Health System, Great Falls, MT, p. A377

SIMON, Patricia, Chief Nursing Officer, Encompass Health Rehabilitation Hospital Of Charleston, Charleston, SC, p. A550

SIMON, Richard, M.D., Chief of Staff, Uconn, John Dempsey Hospital, Farmington, CT, p. A108

SIMON, Stuart, M.D., Medical Director, North Central Surgical Center, Dallas, TX, p. A597

SIMON, Teresa, Director Information Systems, Nacogdoches Medical Center, Nacogdoches, TX, p. A625

SIMON, Thresa, M.D., Medical Director, Poplar Springs Hospital, Petersburg, VA, p. A665

SIMONEAUX, Katherine
Administrator, Oceans Behavioral Hospital Of Crowley, Rayne, LA, p. A277
Administrator, Oceans Behavioral Hospital Of Opelousas, Opelousas, LA, p. A276

SIMONIN, Steven J., President and Chief Executive Officer, Iowa Specialty Hospital–Clarion, Clarion, IA, p. A219

SIMONS, Janice, Chief Executive Officer, Medina Regional Hospital, Hondo, TX, p. A610

SIMONS, Preston, Chief Information Officer, Aurora Medical Center – Manitowoc County, Two Rivers, WI, p. A707

SIMONSEN, Carolyn, President and Interim Chief Executive Officer, Meritus Medical Center, Hagerstown, MD, p. A291

SIMONSON, John F, M.D., President Medical Staff, Memorial Community Hospital And Health System, Blair, NE, p. A383

SIMONSON, Paul, Vice President, Trinity Health, Minot, ND, p. A469

SIMPSON, Brenda, Chief Nursing Officer, Northeast Georgia Medical Center, Gainesville, GA, p. A154

SIMPSON, Brenda, R.N., Chief Nursing Officer, Largo Medical Center, Largo, FL, p. A128

SIMPSON, Chris, Chief Executive Officer, Cornerstone Hospital–West Monroe, West Monroe, LA, p. A280

SIMPSON, Greg, Chief Nursing Officer, St. Joseph Medical Center, Kansas City, MO, p. A363

SIMPSON, Julie, Vice President Human Resources, University Of Tennessee Medical Center, Knoxville, TN, p. A572

SIMPSON, Keith J, Chief Operating Officer, Jennings American Legion Hospital, Jennings, LA, p. A269

SIMPSON, Laura, Director Human Resources, Sabine County Hospital, Hemphill, TX, p. A609

SIMPSON, Lee A., Chief Executive Officer, Landmark Hospital Of Joplin, Joplin, MO, p. A362

SIMPSON, Mark, Chief Executive Officer, Welch Community Hospital, Welch, WV, p. A690

SIMPSON, Mikael, Chief Executive Officer, Kindred Rehabilitation Hospital Clear Lake, Webster, TX, p. A645

SIMPSON, Rae, R.N., Chief Nursing Officer, Western State Hospital, Tacoma, WA, p. A681

SIMPSON, Robert, Vice President Operations, Methodist Richardson Medical Center, Richardson, TX, p. A631

SIMPSON, Ryan
President and Chief Executive Officer, Medical Center Of Aurora, Aurora, CO, p. A96
President and Chief Executive Officer, Spalding Rehabilitation Hospital, Aurora, CO, p. A96

SIMPSON, Shawndra, Interim Chief Executive Officer, Sutter Surgical Hospital – North Valley, Yuba City, CA, p. A95

SIMPSON, Sheila, Vice President Human Resources, Palmetto Lowcountry Behavioral Health, Charleston, SC, p. A550

SIMPSON, Steve, Chief Executive Officer, Northeastern Nevada Regional Hospital, Elko, NV, p. A393

SIMPSON–TUGGLE, Deloris, Vice President Human Resources and Organizational Development and Chief Human Resources Officer, Greater Baltimore Medical Center, Baltimore, MD, p. A288

SIMS, Anthony, M.D., Chief of Staff, Dekalb Regional Medical Center, Fort Payne, AL, p. A18

SIMS, Blake, Chief Executive Officer, Northern Colorado Long Term Acute Hospital, Johnstown, CO, p. A102

SIMS, Brian, Chief Executive Officer, Lucas County Health Center, Chariton, IA, p. A219

SIMS, Charles, M.D., Chief of Staff, Chi St. Luke'S Health–The Woodlands Hospital, The Woodlands, TX, p. A640

SIMS, Jason, Facility Information Security Officer, Medical City North Hills, North Richland Hills, TX, p. A626
SIMS, Jason, M.D., Chief Medical Officer, Cleveland Area Hospital, Cleveland, OK, p. A498
SIMS, Jeffrey, Chief Executive Officer, Heartland Behavioral Healthcare, Massillon, OH, p. A487
SIMS, Jyric, Chief Executive Officer, Medical City Fort Worth, Fort Worth, TX, p. A605
SIMS, Mark E., Chief Executive Officer, Grand Strand Regional Medical Center, Myrtle Beach, SC, p. A556
SIMS, William, M.D., Medical Director, Elkview General Hospital, Hobart, OK, p. A500
SIMZYK, Monica
Regional Chief Human Resources Officer, Amita Health St. Mary'S Hospital, Kankakee, IL, p. A187
Regional Human Resource Officer, Amita Health Saint Joseph Medical Center, Joliet, IL, p. A187
SINCICH, Robert, Vice President Human Resources, Trumbull Memorial Hospital, Warren, OH, p. A493
SINCLAIR, Bradley, Chief Financial Officer, Touro Infirmary, New Orleans, LA, p. A276
SINCLAIR, Elyria, Director Human Resources, Crestwood Medical Center, Huntsville, AL, p. A19
SINCLAIR, Kathy, Vice President Human Resources, Spartanburg Medical Center – Church Street Campus, Spartanburg, SC, p. A557
SINCLAIR, Laura, Director Human Resources, Kansas City Orthopaedic Institute, Leawood, KS, p. A239
SINCLAIR, Noreen, Human Resources Administrator, Connecticut Veterans Home And Hospital, Rocky Hill, CT, p. A110
SINCLAIR–CHUNG, Opal, R.N., MS, Chief Nursing Officer, Deputy Executive Director, Brookdale Hospital Medical Center, New York, NY, p. A432
SINCOCK, Gregory M, Information Technology Leader, Kaiser Permanente West Los Angeles Medical Center, Los Angeles, CA, p. A67
SINDELAR, Michael, Vice President and Chief Financial Officer, Methodist Fremont Health, Fremont, NE, p. A385
SINDLINGER, Julie A, Director of Human Resources, Weston County Health Services, Newcastle, WY, p. A712
SINEK, James J., President, Boone Hospital Center, Columbia, MO, p. A359
SINGER, John, Chief Operating Officer, Munson Healthcare Charlevoix Hospital, Charlevoix, MI, p. A308
SINGH, Amandeep, Chief Medical Officer, Monroe Hospital, Bloomington, IN, p. A200
SINGH, Amarjit, President and Chief Executive Officer, Brunswick Psych Center, Amityville, NY, p. A422
SINGH, Brij, Medical Staff Director, Kindred Hospital Rome, Rome, GA, p. A159
SINGH, Gagandeep, M.D., Chief Medical Officer Behavioral Health, Banner Behavioral Health Hospital – Scottsdale, Scottsdale, AZ, p. A35
SINGH, Gurmant, Chief of Staff, Good Samaritan Hospital, Bakersfield, CA, p. A52
SINGH, Himanshu, M.D., Associate Director, Veterans Affairs Ann Arbor Healthcare System, Ann Arbor, MI, p. A306
SINGH, Manish, Chief Executive Officer, Doctor'S Hospital At Renaissance, Edinburg, TX, p. A601
SINGH, Vijayant, M.D., Chief Medical Officer, Carepoint Health Bayonne Medical Center, Bayonne, NJ, p. A403
SINGLES, James L, Chief Financial Officer, Marlette Regional Hospital, Marlette, MI, p. A317
SINGLETARY–TWYMAN, Michelle, Chief Nursing Officer, Rockford Center, Newark, DE, p. A113
SINGLETON, Al, M.D., Chief Psychiatry and Chief Medical Staff, Colorado Mental Health Institute At Pueblo, Pueblo, CO, p. A104
SINGLETON, Doris, Chief Executive Officer, Conway Behavioral Health Hospital, Conway, AR, p. A40
SINGLETON, Roy, Director Computer Information Systems, Palmdale Regional Medical Center, Palmdale, CA, p. A77
SINHA, Sunil K., M.D., FACHE, Chief Medical Officer, Bon Secours Memorial Regional Medical Center, Mechanicsville, VA, p. A662
SINIARD, Sandra, Vice President of Patient Care Services, Chi Memorial Hospital – Georgia, Fort Oglethorpe, GA, p. A153
SINICKAS, Robert, Director Information Services, Northwestern Medicine Marianjoy Rehabilitation Hospital, Wheaton, IL, p. A198
SINICROPE, Frank J, Vice President Financial Services, Princeton Community Hospital, Princeton, WV, p. A688
SINISI, Albert, Director Information Systems, Pontiac General Hospital, Pontiac, MI, p. A320
SINK, Kristi M., President, University Hospitals Elyria Medical Center, Elyria, OH, p. A482
SINNOTT, Daniel J., President and Chief Executive Officer, St. Francis Hospital, Wilmington, DE, p. A114
SINNOTT, James, M.D., Chief Medical Staff, Coquille Valley Hospital, Coquille, OR, p. A512
SINNOTT, Lisa M, Director Human Resources, Acuity Specialty Hospital Of Southern New Jersey, Willingboro, NJ, p. A415
SINOPOLI, Angelo, M.D., Vice President Clinical Integration and Chief Medical Officer, Prisma Health Greenville Memorial Hospital, Greenville, SC, p. A553
SINOTTE, Brian, Chief Executive Officer, Up Health System–Marquette, Marquette, MI, p. A317
SINYARD, Robert, M.D.
Chief Medical Officer, Piedmont Athens Regional Medical Center, Athens, GA, p. A145
Chief Medical Officer, Piedmont Walton Hospital, Monroe, GA, p. A157
SIOSON, Stephanie
Director Human Resources, Garden Grove Hospital And Medical Center, Garden Grove, CA, p. A60
Director Human Resources, Huntington Beach Hospital, Huntington Beach, CA, p. A62
Director Human Resources, La Palma Intercommunity Hospital, La Palma, CA, p. A63
Director Human Resources, West Anaheim Medical Center, Anaheim, CA, p. A50
SIOUFI, Habib, M.D., Chief Medical Officer, Umass Memorial–Marlborough Hospital, Marlborough, MA, p. A300
SIPEK, John, Supervisor Client Services, Aurora Medical Center In Washington County, Hartford, WI, p. A697
SIREK, David, Chief Information Officer, Myrtue Medical Center, Harlan, IA, p. A224
SIRK, Donald, Director Information Systems, Medstar St. Mary'S Hospital, Leonardtown, MD, p. A292
SIROIS, Peter, Chief Executive Officer, Northern Maine Medical Center, Fort Kent, ME, p. A283
SIROTTA, Ted
Chief Financial Officer, Vail Health, Vail, CO, p. A106
Senior Vice President and Chief Financial Officer, Henry Mayo Newhall Hospital, Valencia, CA, p. A93
SISILLO, Sabato, M.D.
Chief Medical Officer, Providence Medical Center, Kansas City, KS, p. A238
Chief Medical Officer, Saint John Hospital, Leavenworth, KS, p. A239
SISK, Bryan W., Associate Director Patient and Nursing Services, Central Texas Veterans Health Care System, Temple, TX, p. A640
SISK, Glenn C., President, Coosa Valley Medical Center, Sylacauga, AL, p. A23
SISK, Jack, Chief Financial Officer, Punxsutawney Area Hospital, Punxsutawney, PA, p. A539
SISK, Lori
Chief Executive Officer, Sanford Canby Medical Center, Canby, MN, p. A329
Chief Executive Officer, Sanford Clear Lake Medical Center, Clear Lake, SD, p. A560
SISK, Rodney, Chief Financial Officer, University Hospital Summerville, Augusta, GA, p. A147
SISK, Susan, Chief Financial Officer, Chi St. Alexius Health, Bismarck, ND, p. A465
SISLER, Debbie, Director, Human Resource, Vidant Roanoke–Chowan Hospital, Ahoskie, NC, p. A449
SISON, Joseph, M.D., Medical Director, Heritage Oaks Hospital, Sacramento, CA, p. A81
SISSON, William G., President, Baptist Health Lexington, Lexington, KY, p. A254
SISTO, Steven A., Senior Vice President and Chief Operating Officer, Methodist Hospital Of Southern California, Arcadia, CA, p. A51
SISTRUNK, Heather, Chief Executive Officer, Merit Health Rankin, Brandon, MS, p. A345
SITLINGER, James, Chief Human Resources Management, Charles George Veterans Affairs Medical Center, Asheville, NC, p. A449
SITTIG, Kevin, M.D., Senior Associate Dean and Chief Medical Officer, Ochsner Lsu Health Shrevport – Academic Medical Center, Shreveport, LA, p. A278
SIU, Max, Chief Information Officer, Hackensack Meridian Health Mountainside Medical Center, Montclair, NJ, p. A408
SIVAK, Steven, M.D., Chief Medical Officer, Einstein Physicians Philadelphia, Einstein Medical Center Philadelphia, Philadelphia, PA, p. A534
SIVEK, Carla, Director, Coatesville Veterans Affairs Medical Center, Coatesville, PA, p. A523
SIVLEY, Susanna S, Chief Personnel Officer, Highlands Medical Center, Scottsboro, AL, p. A23
SIWEK, Steven M., President and Chief Executive Officer, Scottsdale Liberty Hospital, Scottsdale, AZ, p. A36
SIX, Deborah, Coordinator Data Processing, Wayne Memorial Hospital, Jesup, GA, p. A155
SIX, Stephanie, Chief Executive Officer, Northeastern Health System Sequoyah, Sallisaw, OK, p. A507
SJOBERG, Rochelle, Director Human Resources, Ely–Bloomenson Community Hospital, Ely, MN, p. A331
SKABELUND, Hoyt, Chief Executive Officer, Platte County Memorial Hospital, Wheatland, WY, p. A713
SKAGGS, Lynda, Chief Nursing Officer, Fleming County Hospital, Flemingsburg, KY, p. A251
SKALA, Pat, Chief Information Officer, Laguna Honda Hospital And Rehabilitation Center, San Francisco, CA, p. A85
SKALSKI, Eileen, Chief Nursing Officer, Encompass Health Harmarville Rehabilitation Hospital, Pittsburgh, PA, p. A537
SKARKA, Kathy, MSN, R.N., Executive Vice President Patient Care Services, Nassau University Medical Center, East Meadow, NY, p. A427
SKARULIS, Patricia, Senior Vice President and Chief Information Systems Officer, Brookdale Hospital Medical Center, New York, NY, p. A432
SKARZYNSKI, Joseph, M.D., Medical Director, Brookdale Hospital Medical Center, New York, NY, p. A432
SKEEN, Steven, R.N., Chief Nursing Officer, Mizell Memorial Hospital, Opp, AL, p. A22
SKEENS, Henrietta, Chief Financial Officer, Lower Keys Medical Center, Key West, FL, p. A126
SKELDON, Timothy
Chief Financial Officer, Thomas Memorial Hospital, South Charleston, WV, p. A689
Senior Vice President and Chief Financial Officer, Parrish Medical Center, Titusville, FL, p. A143
SKELTON, Jenny, System Integration Manager, The Women'S Hospital, Newburgh, IN, p. A213
SKELTON, Katie, MSN, R.N., Vice President Nursing and Chief Nursing Officer, St. Joseph Hospital, Orange, CA, p. A76
SKELTON, Meaghan, Chief Executive Officer, Valir Rehabilitation Hospital, Oklahoma City, OK, p. A505
SKIBBA, Joshua, Chief Medical Officer, Ohio County Hospital, Hartford, KY, p. A253
SKIDMORE, Jocelyn, Director Finance, Mosaic Medical Center – Maryville, Maryville, MO, p. A365
SKIDMORE, Kim, Chief Executive Officer, Izard County Medical Center, Calico Rock, AR, p. A40
SKIEM, Paul, Senior Vice President Human Resources, Amita Health Saint Francis Hospital Evanston, Evanston, IL, p. A182
SKILLINGS, Charles E., President and Chief Executive Officer, Ssm Health St. Anthony Hospital – Shawnee, Shawnee, OK, p. A507
SKILLINGS, Lois N., President and Chief Executive Officer, Mid Coast Hospital, Brunswick, ME, p. A282
SKILLINGS, Michelle, Chief Nursing Officer, Franklin Foundation Hospital, Franklin, LA, p. A267
SKINNER, Christopher, Chief of Staff, Spectrum Health Big Rapids Hospital, Big Rapids, MI, p. A307
SKINNER, Eileen F., Administrator, Shriners Hospitals For Children–Boston, Boston, MA, p. A296
SKINNER, Gary, Director Information Technology, Rehabilitation Hospital Of Indiana, Indianapolis, IN, p. A207
SKINNER, Gwendolyn, Operational Vice President, Devereux Advanced Behavioral Health Georgia, Kennesaw, GA, p. A155
SKINNER, Kellcie, Controller, Newman Memorial Hospital, Shattuck, OK, p. A507
SKINNER, Kristina, Director Quality, Sanpete Valley Hospital, Mount Pleasant, UT, p. A649
SKINNER, Marjorie, Director Finance, Pershing General Hospital, Lovelock, NV, p. A396
SKINNER, Richard, Chief Information Technology Officer, University Of Virginia Medical Center, Charlottesville, VA, p. A657
SKIPPER, Kymberli, Manager Human Resources, Prattville Baptist Hospital, Prattville, AL, p. A23
SKIPPER, Michelle, Director Human Resources, Kaiser Permanente Riverside Medical Center, Riverside, CA, p. A81
SKJOLDEN, Jessica, M.D., Chief of Staff, St. Andrew'S Health Center, Bottineau, ND, p. A465
SKLAMBERG, Todd, President, Sunrise Hospital And Medical Center, Las Vegas, NV, p. A396
SKLAR, Joel, M.D., Chief Medical Officer, Marinhealth Medical Center, Greenbrae, CA, p. A61
SKLIRIS, Demetre, Chief Medical Officer, Avera Dells Area Hospital, Dell Rapids, SD, p. A560
SKOWRON, Paul, Chief Executive Officer, Warner Hospital And Health Services, Clinton, IL, p. A180
SKRINDE, Tracie, Senior Human Resources Partner, Peacehealth United General Medical Center, Sedro, WA, p. A679
SKRIPPS, Michele M., Chief Executive Officer, Encompass Health Rehabilitation Hospital Of Charleston, Charleston, SC, p. A550
SKULA, Erika, President and Chief Executive Officer, Adventhealth Carrollwood, Tampa, FL, p. A141

SKULA, Joe, Director Human Resources, Adventhealth Manchester, Manchester, KY, p. A257

SKVARENINA, Michael, Assistant Vice President Information Systems, Holy Name Medical Center, Teaneck, NJ, p. A413

SLABA, Bryan, Chief Executive Officer, Wagner Community Memorial Hospital Avera, Wagner, SD, p. A565

SLABIK, Shauna, Chief Financial Officer, Sanford Mayville Medical Center, Mayville, ND, p. A468

SLACK, Randy, Chief Financial Officer, Nacogdoches Medical Center, Nacogdoches, TX, p. A625

SLADKY, Todd J., Chief Financial Officer and Vice President Finance, Great River Health System, West Burlington, IA, p. A231

SLAGLE, Julie A, R.N., MSN, Vice President Patient Care Services, Sidney Regional Medical Center, Sidney, NE, p. A391

SLATE, Sonny, Chief Operating Officer, Georgia Regional Hospital At Atlanta, Decatur, GA, p. A152

SLATER, Craig M, M.D., Chief Medical Officer, Atrium Health Union, Monroe, NC, p. A458

SLATER, Mark, Director Information Systems, Baylor Scott & White Medical Center – Lake Pointe, Rowlett, TX, p. A632

SLATER–NESUOLD, Stephanie, Director of Nursing, Landmark Hospital Of Joplin, Joplin, MO, p. A362

SLATON, Brenda, Superintendent, Rusk State Hospital, Rusk, TX, p. A632

SLATTERY, Greg, Vice President Information, Community Hospitals And Wellness Centers, Bryan, OH, p. A474

SLATTERY, Robert, Vice President of Operations, Bridgton Hospital, Bridgton, ME, p. A282

SLATTERY, Susan L, Director Human Resources, Unitypoint Health – St. Luke'S Hospital, Cedar Rapids, IA, p. A218

SLATTMAN, Robin, Chief Nursing Officer, Memorial Health, Marysville, OH, p. A486

SLAVIN, Kevin J, President and Chief Executive Officer, St. Joseph'S University Medical Center, Paterson, NJ, p. A410

SLAVIN, Kevin J., President and Chief Executive Officer, St. Joseph'S University Medical Center, Paterson, NJ, p. A410

SLAVIN, Peter L., President, Massachusetts General Hospital, Boston, MA, p. A295

SLAWITSKY, Bruce, Vice President Human Resources, Brookdale Hospital Medical Center, New York, NY, p. A432

SLAYMAN, Aubree, Director Patient Services, Miami County Medical Center, Paola, KS, p. A243

SLAYTON, Val, M.D., Vice President Medical Affairs, Sts. Mary & Elizabeth Hospital, Louisville, KY, p. A256

SLEDGE, Cynthia Moore, M.D., Medical Director, Bryce Hospital, Tuscaloosa, AL, p. A24

SLEDGE, Tasha, Director Human Resources, Texas Health Harris Methodist Hospital Southlake, Southlake, TX, p. A637

SLEDGE, Thomas, Chief Executive Officer, North Texas Medical Center, Gainesville, TX, p. A607

SLEDGE, Tom, Chief Operating Officer, Northwest Medical Center – Springdale, Springdale, AR, p. A48

SLEE, Kim, Chief Operating Officer, Fulton County Medical Center, Mc Connellsburg, PA, p. A531

SLEEPER, Justin, Vice President Clinical Operations, Behavioral Health Network, Natchaug Hospital, Mansfield Center, CT, p. A108

SLEIME, Melanie, Director Human Resources, Memorial Hospital, North Conway, NH, p. A402

SLEITER, Michelle, Chief Executive Officer, Humboldt County Memorial Hospital, Humboldt, IA, p. A224

SLENSZAK, David, Director, Information Services, Williamsburg Regional Hospital, Kingstree, SC, p. A554

SLESSOR, Steve Robert., Chief Executive Officer, Buchanan County Health Center, Independence, IA, p. A224

SLICK, Lois, Director Human Resources, Lifecare Medical Center, Roseau, MN, p. A339

SLIDER, Carol, Chief Nursing Officer, Titus Regional Medical Center, Mount Pleasant, TX, p. A625

SLIGER, Susan, Director Human Resources, War Memorial Hospital, Sault Sainte Marie, MI, p. A322

SLITER, Elizabeth, M.D., Chairman Medical Staff, Decatur Health Systems, Oberlin, KS, p. A242

SLIVA, Paul, Chief Information Officer, Boone County Hospital, Boone, IA, p. A218

SLIWA, James, M.D., Chief Medical Officer, Shirley Ryan Abilitylab, Chicago, IL, p. A179

SLIWINSKI, Jeff, Chief Financial Officer, Hca Houston Healthcare Clear Lake, League City, TX, p. A620

SLIWINSKI, Ron, Chief of Hospital Division, University Hospital, Madison, WI, p. A698

SLOAN, Brian, Chief Operating Officer, Duke Raleigh Hospital, Raleigh, NC, p. A460

SLOAN, Patrick, Chief Financial Officer, Memorial Satilla Health, Waycross, GA, p. A163

SLOAN, Prudence, Coordinator Human Resources, Select Specialty Hospital–Pittsburgh/Upmc, Pittsburgh, PA, p. A537

SLOAN, Ronald A., President, The Outer Banks Hospital, Nags Head, NC, p. A459

SLOAN, Steve, Chief Financial Officer, Lake Cumberland Regional Hospital, Somerset, KY, p. A260

SLOCUM, Brandon H, Senior Vice President and Chief Financial Officer, Medical West, Bessemer, AL, p. A14

SLOCUM, Gregg Y, Chief Financial Officer, Valley Forge Medical Center And Hospital, Norristown, PA, p. A533

SLONIM, Sheryl A, Executive Vice President and Chief Nursing Officer, Holy Name Medical Center, Teaneck, NJ, p. A413

SLONINA, Marrianne, Director Human Resources, Georgetown Community Hospital, Georgetown, KY, p. A252

SLOPER, Carol, Manager Information Technology, Cheyenne County Hospital, Saint Francis, KS, p. A244

SLUCK, Jeana, R.N., Executive Director Nursing Clinical Inpatient Departments, Allied Services Rehabilitation Hospital, Scranton, PA, p. A540

SLUSHER, Carlene, Director Finance, Seneca Healthcare District, Chester, CA, p. A54

SLUSHER, Michael, Community Chief Executive Officer, Middlesboro Arh Hospital, Middlesboro, KY, p. A258

SLUSHER, W. James (Jamie), M.D., Chief of Staff, Jackson Parish Hospital, Jonesboro, LA, p. A269

SLUTSKER, Vladimir, Medical Director, Encompass Health Rehabilitation Hospital Of Gadsden, Gadsden, AL, p. A18

SLYTER, Mark F.
President and Chief Executive Officer, East Valley, Dignity Health Arizona General Hospital, Laveen, AZ, p. A31
President and Chief Operating Officer, Chandler Regional Medical Center, Chandler, AZ, p. A28
President and Chief Operating Officer, Mercy Gilbert Medical Center, Gilbert, AZ, p. A29

SLYTER, Mark F., FACHE
President and Chief Operating Officer, Chandler Regional Medical Center, Chandler, AZ, p. A28
President and Chief Operating Officer, Mercy Gilbert Medical Center, Gilbert, AZ, p. A29

SMAJSTRLA, Julie, Director Nursing, Seymour Hospital, Seymour, TX, p. A636

SMALE, Cindy, Director, Human Resources, Iredell Health System, Statesville, NC, p. A463

SMALL, Becky
Chief Human Resources Officer, Kindred Hospital–Aurora, Aurora, CO, p. A96
Chief Nursing Officer, North Texas Medical Center, Gainesville, TX, p. A607

SMALL, Donna, R.N., Chief Nursing Officer, St. Mary'S Medical Center, West Palm Beach, FL, p. A144

SMALL, Jonathan, Chief Operations Information and Technology, John D. Dingell Veterans Affairs Medical Center, Detroit, MI, p. A310

SMALL, Terry L., Assistant Chief Executive Officer, William R. Sharpe, Jr. Hospital, Weston, WV, p. A690

SMALLEY, Ben, Administrator, Cassia Regional Hospital, Burley, ID, p. A168

SMALLWOOD, Ravae, IS Coordinator, Chi Health Missouri Valley, Missouri Valley, IA, p. A226

SMARR, Susan, M.D., Physician–in–Chief, Kaiser Permanente Santa Clara Medical Center, Santa Clara, CA, p. A88

SMART, Dan, Chief Information Management Officer, Permian Regional Medical Center, Andrews, TX, p. A583

SMART, George J, Vice President Finance and Information Technology, Midmichigan Medical Center – Alpena, Alpena, MI, p. A306

SMART, Joanne F, M.D., Director Medical Affairs, Indiana University Health Bedford Hospital, Bedford, IN, p. A199

SMART, Melissa, Communication ad Public Relations Specialist, Texas Health Presbyterian Hospital Denton, Denton, TX, p. A599

SMART, Paul, CPA, Chief Financial Officer, Franklin County Medical Center, Preston, ID, p. A171

SMART, Robert M., Chief Executive Officer, Encompass Health Rehabilitation Hospital Of The Mid–Cities, Bedford, TX, p. A588

SMART, Stephanie, Chief Nursing Officer, United Hospital Center, Bridgeport, WV, p. A683

SMENDIK, Douglas, M.D., Hospital Medical Director, Spectrum Health Pennock, Hastings, MI, p. A314

SMIDT, Jessica, R.N., Director of Nursing, Pipestone County Medical Center Avera, Pipestone, MN, p. A338

SMIGA, Lance, Chief Financial Officer, Jackson County Hospital District, Edna, TX, p. A601

SMILEY, Christy, Leader Human Resources, Ssm Health St. Mary'S Hospital – Audrain, Mexico, MO, p. A365

SMITH, Agnes A, MSN, R.N., Chief Nursing Officer, Twin County Regional Healthcare, Galax, VA, p. A660

SMITH, Alan H
Chief Financial Officer, Huntington Beach Hospital, Huntington Beach, CA, p. A62
Chief Financial Officer, La Palma Intercommunity Hospital, La Palma, CA, p. A63

SMITH, Andrew
Chief Financial Officer, Blake Medical Center, Bradenton, FL, p. A118
Chief Information Management, Madigan Army Medical Center, Tacoma, WA, p. A680

SMITH, Ann, Senior Vice President, Inpatient Services and Interim Chief Administrative Officer, University Of Cincinnati Medical Center, Cincinnati, OH, p. A477

SMITH, Anton C., Administrator, Shriners Hospitals For Children–Honolulu, Honolulu, HI, p. A165

SMITH, Barbara H, Senior Vice President & Chief Operating Officer, Robert Wood Johnson University Hospital At Hamilton, Hamilton, NJ, p. A406

SMITH, Bennie
Chief Information Officer, Lady Of The Sea General Hospital, Cut Off, LA, p. A266
Director Human Resources and Risk Management, Lady Of The Sea General Hospital, Cut Off, LA, p. A266

SMITH, Bernie, Chief Financial Officer, Guthrie Troy Community Hospital, Troy, PA, p. A542

SMITH, Bethany
Controller, Spire Cane Creek Rehabilitation Hospital, Martin, TN, p. A573
Director of Finance, Chi Oakes Hospital, Oakes, ND, p. A469

SMITH, Betsy, Chief Nursing Officer, Effingham Hospital, Springfield, GA, p. A160

SMITH, Beverly Bzdek, Chief Nursing Officer, Southside Regional Medical Center, Petersburg, VA, p. A665

SMITH, Blythe, Administrative Assistant, Faulkton Area Medical Center, Faulkton, SD, p. A560

SMITH, Bobby, Vice President Physician Services and Quality, Illinois Valley Community Hospital, Peru, IL, p. A193

SMITH, Bradley, President and Chief Executive Officer, Rush Memorial Hospital, Rushville, IN, p. A214

SMITH, Brenda, Director Financial Services, Alliance Health Center, Meridian, MS, p. A351

SMITH, Brent, Chief Executive Officer, Comanche County Memorial Hospital, Lawton, OK, p. A501

SMITH, Brian
Chief Financial Officer, Beth Israel Deaconess Hospital–Needham Campus, Needham, MA, p. A301
Director of Operations, Wamego Health Center, Wamego, KS, p. A247

SMITH, C David, M.D., Chief Medical Officer, Jay Hospital, Jay, FL, p. A126

SMITH, Candace Susan, Chief Nursing Officer, Manatee Memorial Hospital, Bradenton, FL, p. A118

SMITH, Carl, Director Information Systems, King'S Daughters Medical Center, Brookhaven, MS, p. A345

SMITH, Carol, Vice President Patient Care and Chief Nursing Officer, Tift Regional Medical Center, Tifton, GA, p. A162

SMITH, Carol A, R.N., Director Operations and Nursing, Novant Health Medical Park Hospital, Winston, NC, p. A464

SMITH, Carole, Senior Human Resource Business Partner, Banner Del E. Webb Medical Center, Sun City West, AZ, p. A36

SMITH, Cheryl, Manager Human Resources, New Braunfels Regional Rehabilitation Hospital, New Braunfels, TX, p. A626

SMITH, Chris, Chief Information Officer, Falls Community Hospital And Clinic, Marlin, TX, p. A623

SMITH, Connie, Chief Executive Officer, Medical Center At Bowling Green, Bowling Green, KY, p. A250

SMITH, Dan
Director Human Resources, Austin Lakes Hospital, Austin, TX, p. A585
Director Human Resources, Memorial Hospital, Carthage, IL, p. A175

SMITH, Danelle, Chief Executive Officer, Twelve Clans Unity Hospital, Winnebago, NE, p. A392

SMITH, Daniel
Chief Financial Officer, Palo Pinto General Hospital, Mineral Wells, TX, p. A625
Chief Financial Officer, Tops Surgical Specialty Hospital, Houston, TX, p. A614

SMITH, Daniel B
Chief Financial Officer, Samaritan Pacific Communities Hospital, Newport, OR, p. A515
Vice President Finance, Good Samaritan Regional Medical Center, Corvallis, OR, p. A512
Vice President Finance, Samaritan Albany General Hospital, Albany, OR, p. A511
Vice President Finance, Samaritan Lebanon Community Hospital, Lebanon, OR, p. A514

SMITH, Darrin, Chief Operating Officer, Parkview Medical Center, Pueblo, CO, p. A104

SMITH, Darwin K, Vice President Human Resources, Cleveland Clinic Union Hospital, Dover, OH, p. A482

SMITH, David
Chief Executive Officer, Baylor Scott & White Institute For Rehabilitation – Dallas, Dallas, TX, p. A595
President and Chief Executive Officer, Grant Regional Health Center, Lancaster, WI, p. A698
SMITH, David, D.O., Chief of Staff, Madison County Health Care System, Winterset, IA, p. A231
SMITH, Debra, Chief Nursing Officer, Encompass Health Rehabilitation Hospital Of Kingsport, Kingsport, TN, p. A572
SMITH, Denise
Director Health Information, Encompass Health Rehabilitation Hospital Of Chattanooga, Chattanooga, TN, p. A567
Director People Services, Hshs St. Mary'S Hospital, Decatur, IL, p. A181
SMITH, Diana B, Chief Financial Officer, Promise Hospital Of Dallas, Dallas, TX, p. A598
SMITH, Dianne, Director Personnel and Human Resources, Potomac Valley Hospital, Keyser, WV, p. A686
SMITH, Dick, Director Human Resources, West Park Hospital, Cody, WY, p. A711
SMITH, Dirkland T., Chief Executive Officer, Faulkton Area Medical Center, Faulkton, SD, p. A560
SMITH, Donald, President Medical Staff, Bellevue Hospital, Bellevue, OH, p. A473
SMITH, Donna M, Chief Nursing Officer, Barstow Community Hospital, Barstow, CA, p. A52
SMITH, Donna P., R.N., Vice President Chief Operating Officer and Chief Nursing Officer, Clifton Springs Hospital And Clinic, Clifton Springs, NY, p. A426
SMITH, Donnie
Chief Human Resources Officer, Laird Hospital, Union, MS, p. A354
Director Human Resources, Rush Foundation Hospital, Meridian, MS, p. A351
Director of Human Resources, Specialty Hospital Of Meridian, Meridian, MS, p. A351
SMITH, Doug
Chief Financial Officer, Mckay-Dee Hospital, Ogden, UT, p. A649
Chief Financial Officer, Sun Behavioral Houston, Houston, TX, p. A614
SMITH, Edward, Chief of Staff, Mackinac Straits Health System, Inc., Saint Ignace, MI, p. A321
SMITH, Edward H., President and Chief Executive Officer, St. Anthony Regional Hospital, Carroll, IA, p. A218
SMITH, Eric, Chief Financial Officer, Bayfront Health St. Petersburg, Saint Petersburg, FL, p. A138
SMITH, Ericka, Chief Operating Officer, Monterey Park Hospital, Monterey Park, CA, p. A73
SMITH, Erin, Chief Operating Officer, East Georgia Regional Medical Center, Statesboro, GA, p. A161
SMITH, Eugene, Chief Information Officer, Maniilaq Health Center, Kotzebue, AK, p. A26
SMITH, G. Todd, Chief Executive Officer, Mercy Medical Center Redding, Redding, CA, p. A79
SMITH, Gary, Chief Operating Officer, Aurelia Osborn Fox Memorial Hospital, Oneonta, NY, p. A440
SMITH, Gene, Chief Executive Officer, North Alabama Specialty Hospital, Athens, AL, p. A14
SMITH, Geoffrey, Chief Financial Officer, Lebanon Veterans Affairs Medical Center, Lebanon, PA, p. A529
SMITH, Gia, Chief Executive Officer, Central Valley Specialty Hospital, Modesto, CA, p. A72
SMITH, Greg, Chief Medical Officer, Lake Region Healthcare, Fergus Falls, MN, p. A332
SMITH, Gregory
Chief Executive Officer, Fort Belknap Service Unit, Harlem, MT, p. A377
Senior Vice President and Chief Information Officer, Ascension Southeast Wisconsin Hospital – Franklin Campus, Franklin, WI, p. A695
Senior Vice President and Chief Information Officer, Ascension Southeast Wisconsin Hospital – St. Francis Campus, Milwaukee, WI, p. A700
Senior Vice President and Chief Information Officer, Midwest Orthopedic Specialty Hospital, Franklin, WI, p. A695
SMITH, Gretchen, Vice President of Operations, Risk and Compliance, and Chief Operating Officer, Rush Memorial Hospital, Rushville, IN, p. A214
SMITH, Harley, Chief Executive Officer, Tmc Bonham Hospital, Bonham, TX, p. A589
SMITH, Heather
Chief Operating Officer, Welch Community Hospital, Welch, WV, p. A690
President, Conemaugh Meyersdale Medical Center, Meyersdale, PA, p. A532
SMITH, Holt, Chief Financial Officer, Musc Health Lancaster Medical Center, Lancaster, SC, p. A555

SMITH, Jack, Acting Chief Information Resources Management Service, Veterans Affairs Sierra Nevada Health Care System, Reno, NV, p. A397
SMITH, Jackie, R.N., Chief Nursing Officer, Holdenville General Hospital, Holdenville, OK, p. A500
SMITH, James E.
Superintendent, North Texas State Hospital, Wichita Falls Campus, Wichita Falls, TX, p. A645
Superintendent, North Texas State Hospital, Vernon, TX, p. A643
SMITH, Jameson, President, Saint Joseph Hospital, Denver, CO, p. A99
SMITH, Jamie, Supervisor Health Information Management Systems, Encompass Health Rehabilitation Hospital Of Sewickley, Sewickley, PA, p. A541
SMITH, Janet
Chief Financial Officer, Troy Regional Medical Center, Troy, AL, p. A23
Chief Financial Officer, Wiregrass Medical Center, Geneva, AL, p. A18
SMITH, Jared M., Chief Executive Officer, Broward Health Coral Springs, Coral Springs, FL, p. A120
SMITH, Jason
Chief Medical Officer, Beaver Dam Community Hospitals, Beaver Dam, WI, p. A692
Chief Operating Officer, Piedmont Athens Regional Medical Center, Athens, GA, p. A145
SMITH, Jay, Director Information Systems, Brownwood Regional Medical Center, Brownwood, TX, p. A590
SMITH, Jeanna, Administrative Assistant and Human Resources Officer, Polk Medical Center, Cedartown, GA, p. A149
SMITH, Jeff, Chief Information Officer, Holy Cross Hospital, Fort Lauderdale, FL, p. A122
SMITH, Jeffrey A., M.D.
Executive Vice President Hospital Operations and Chief Operating Officer, Cedars-Sinai Medical Center, Los Angeles, CA, p. A66
Senior Vice President and Chief Medical Officer, Aurora St. Luke'S Medical Center, Milwaukee, WI, p. A701
SMITH, Jesse, Director of Nursing, Keefe Memorial Hospital, Cheyenne Wells, CO, p. A97
SMITH, Jim, Director Information Systems, Washington County Memorial Hospital, Potosi, MO, p. A367
SMITH, Jo Beth
Chief Operating Officer, Medical Arts Hospital, Lamesa, TX, p. A619
Vice President Human Resources, Decatur County Hospital, Leon, IA, p. A225
SMITH, JoAnn P., R.N., Chief Nursing Officer, and Vice President Patient Care Services, Unc Rockingham Health Care, Eden, NC, p. A453
SMITH, Joanne C., President and Chief Executive Officer, Shirley Ryan Abilitylab, Chicago, IL, p. A179
SMITH, Jodi, Administrative Assistant Human Resources, Eureka Springs Hospital, Eureka Springs, AR, p. A41
SMITH, Jon, Chief Financial Officer, Lost Rivers Medical Center, Arco, ID, p. A167
SMITH, Jonathan, Assistant Administrator and Chief Financial Officer, Blount Memorial Hospital, Maryville, TN, p. A574
SMITH, Joseph S., Chief Executive Officer, Boone County Hospital, Boone, IA, p. A218
SMITH, Julia
Chief Financial Officer, Kindred Hospital Rome, Rome, GA, p. A159
Chief Financial Officer, Kindred Hospital–Chattanooga, Chattanooga, TN, p. A567
Chief Financial Officer, Vibra Hospital Of Charleston, Mt. Pleasant, SC, p. A555
SMITH, Julie
Director Human Resources, Encompass Health Lakeshore Rehabilitation Hospital, Birmingham, AL, p. A14
Senior Human Resources Strategic Partner, Providence Milwaukie Hospital, Milwaukie, OR, p. A515
SMITH, Julie, R.N., MSN, Director of Nursing, Jersey Community Hospital, Jerseyville, IL, p. A186
SMITH, Karen S, Director Information Services, Chilton Medical Center, Pompton Plains, NJ, p. A411
SMITH, Karla, Director Human Resources, St. Peter'S Hospital, Helena, MT, p. A377
SMITH, Karyl, Director Human Resources, Harbor–Ucla Medical Center, Torrance, CA, p. A91
SMITH, Kathy A., MSN, R.N., Nurse Executive, Summit Behavioral Healthcare, Cincinnati, OH, p. A476
SMITH, Kelli, M.D., Chief of Staff, Magee General Hospital, Magee, MS, p. A350
SMITH, Kenneth P, Chief of Staff, John C. Fremont Healthcare District, Mariposa, CA, p. A71
SMITH, Kevin, D.O., Chief of Staff, Munson Healthcare Otsego Memorial Hospital, Gaylord, MI, p. A312

SMITH, Kevin L, Area Finance Officer, Kaiser Permanente South Sacramento Medical Center, Sacramento, CA, p. A82
SMITH, Kevin M, Director Human Resources, Indian Path Medical Center, Kingsport, TN, p. A572
SMITH, Kris, Controller, Chi St. Joseph Health Rehabilitation Hospital, An Affiliate Of Encompass Health, Bryan, TX, p. A590
SMITH, Kyle, Director Information Systems, Iredell Health System, Statesville, NC, p. A463
SMITH, Lana, Human Resources Director, Ashe Memorial Hospital, Jefferson, NC, p. A457
SMITH, Larry, Senior Vice President and Chief Financial Officer, Uw Medicine/Valley Medical Center, Renton, WA, p. A677
SMITH, Laura
Chief Nursing Officer and Director of Infection Control, Ellett Memorial Hospital, Appleton City, MO, p. A356
Vice President Finance and Chief Financial Officer, Milford Hospital, Milford, CT, p. A109
SMITH, LaVonne, Director Health Information Technology, Tomah Memorial Hospital, Tomah, WI, p. A706
SMITH, Leanne, Chief Financial Officer, Windsor–Laurelwood Center For Behavioral Medicine, Willoughby, OH, p. A494
SMITH, Leora, Information System and Health Information Management Team Leader, Phelps Memorial Health Center, Holdrege, NE, p. A386
SMITH, Linda C, M.D., Medical Director, Pam Rehabilitation Hospital Of Beaumont, Beaumont, TX, p. A587
SMITH, Linda T, Director Human Resources, Clay County Hospital, Ashland, AL, p. A13
SMITH, Linda V, Vice President Human Resources, Central Florida Regional Hospital, Sanford, FL, p. A139
SMITH, Lori, Chief Financial Officer, North Big Horn Hospital District, Lovell, WY, p. A712
SMITH, Lori J., Vice President Human Resources, St. Bernards Medical Center, Jonesboro, AR, p. A44
SMITH, Lorie, Director Human Resources, Conemaugh Nason Medical Center, Roaring Spring, PA, p. A540
SMITH, Lorraine, Chief Executive Officer, Monroe County Hospital, Forsyth, GA, p. A153
SMITH, Lory Beth, Manager Human Resource, South Texas Surgical Hospital, Corpus Christi, TX, p. A594
SMITH, M. Scott, President, St. Anthony'S Hospital, Saint Petersburg, FL, p. A138
SMITH, Marisa, Director, Hca Houston Healthcare Tomball, Tomball, TX, p. A641
SMITH, Mark
Director Human Resources, Providence Holy Family Hospital, Spokane, WA, p. A679
Director Human Resources, Providence Sacred Heart Medical Center & Children'S Hospital, Spokane, WA, p. A680
Director Nursing Operations, Northern Colorado Rehabilitation Hospital, Johnstown, CO, p. A102
SMITH, Mark, M.D., Chief Medical Officer, Methodist Richardson Medical Center, Richardson, TX, p. A631
SMITH, Mark T., President and Chief Operating Officer, Multicare Auburn Medical Center, Auburn, WA, p. A670
SMITH, Marsh, Manager Health Information, University Behavioral Health Of Denton, Denton, TX, p. A599
SMITH, Martha, Chief Executive Officer, Kapiolani Medical Center For Women & Children, Honolulu, HI, p. A164
SMITH, Martha, R.N., Chief Nursing Officer, New Orleans East Hospital, New Orleans, LA, p. A275
SMITH, Mary Clare.
Director, Western State Hospital, Staunton, VA, p. A668
Interim Facility Director, Commonwealth Center For Children And Adolescents, Staunton, VA, p. A667
SMITH, Matt, Interim Chief Executive Officer, Bourbon Community Hospital, Paris, KY, p. A259
SMITH, Matthew, M.D., Vice President Medical Affairs and Chief Medical Officer, Baylor Scott & White Medical Center – Carrollton, Carrollton, TX, p. A591
SMITH, Megan, M.D., Chief Medical Staff, Community Memorial Hospital, Burke, SD, p. A559
SMITH, Melinda, Chief Information Systems, H. C. Watkins Memorial Hospital, Quitman, MS, p. A353
SMITH, Melissa
Controller, Select Specialty Hospital–Jackson, Jackson, MS, p. A349
Interim Vice President Human Resources, North Memorial Health Hospital, Robbinsdale, MN, p. A338
SMITH, Michael, Director of Nursing, Cypress Creek Hospital, Houston, TX, p. A611
SMITH, Michelle, Coordinator Human Resources, Baton Rouge Rehabilitation Hospital, Baton Rouge, LA, p. A263
SMITH, Michelle T, R.N., MSN, FACHE, Vice President Nursing Chief Nursing Officer Chief Experience Officer, Prisma Health Greenville Memorial Hospital, Greenville, SC, p. A553

SMITH, Mickey, Chief Executive Officer, Oak Hill Hospital, Brooksville, FL, p. A119

SMITH, Mike
Chief Information Officer, Cape Coral Hospital, Cape Coral, FL, p. A119
Chief Information Officer, Gulf Coast Medical Center, Fort Myers, FL, p. A123
Chief Information Officer, Lee Memorial Hospital, Fort Myers, FL, p. A123

SMITH, Missy, Coordinator Human Resources, Scotland County Hospital, Memphis, MO, p. A365

SMITH, Mona R., Chief Nursing Officer, Santa Cruz Valley Regional Hospital, Green Valley, AZ, p. A30

SMITH, Moneca, Chief Nursing Officer, The University Of Toledo Medical Center, Toledo, OH, p. A492

SMITH, Nadine, Director Human Resources, Reeves County Hospital, Pecos, TX, p. A628

SMITH, Neil, President, Cleveland Clinic Fairview Hospital, Cleveland, OH, p. A477

SMITH, Nekisha, Chief Operating Officer, Riverland Medical Center, Ferriday, LA, p. A267

SMITH, Nelson, Chief Executive Officer, Poplar Springs Hospital, Petersburg, VA, p. A665

SMITH, Nicholas T., Chief Executive Officer, Larkin Community Hospital–Palm Springs Campus, Hialeah, FL, p. A124

SMITH, Nicole, Director Human Resources, Hi–Desert Medical Center, Joshua Tree, CA, p. A62

SMITH, Norine, Chief Executive Officer, Red Lake Indian Health Service Hospital, Red Lake, MN, p. A338

SMITH, Oliver, President and Chief Executive Officer, Paris Community Hospital, Paris, IL, p. A192

SMITH, Pam, Chief Nursing Officer, Encompass Health Rehabilitation Hospital Of Richardson, Richardson, TX, p. A631

SMITH, Pamela, Commander, U. S. Air Force Regional Hospital, Eglin Afb, FL, p. A122

SMITH, Patricia, Chief Nursing Officer, Prisma Health Oconee Memorial Hospital, Seneca, SC, p. A557

SMITH, Patrick, Director Information Technology, Clay County Hospital, Ashland, AL, p. A13

SMITH, Patrick, M.D., Chief Medical Officer, Abrazo Arrowhead Campus, Glendale, AZ, p. A30

SMITH, Peg, Vice President and Chief Nursing Officer, Chandler Regional Medical Center, Chandler, AZ, p. A28

SMITH, Phyllis, Vice President Human Resources, Northeastern Health System, Tahlequah, OK, p. A508

SMITH, Phyllis J., Associate Director, Birmingham Veterans Affairs Medical Center, Birmingham, AL, p. A14

SMITH, Randall, Executive Vice President, Jackson Park Hospital And Medical Center, Chicago, IL, p. A177

SMITH, Rebecca T, Chief Operating Officer and Chief Nursing Officer, Caldwell Unc Health Care, Lenoir, NC, p. A457

SMITH, Rhonda
Applications Support Manager, Uh Portage Medical Center, Ravenna, OH, p. A490
Chief Nursing Officer, Benewah Community Hospital, Saint Maries, ID, p. A171
Director Human Resources, Shriners Hospitals For Children–Portland, Portland, OR, p. A516

SMITH, Rich
Vice President Human Resources, Kaiser Sunnyside Medical Center, Clackamas, OR, p. A512
Vice President Human Resources, Kaiser Westside Medical Center, Hillsboro, OR, p. A513

SMITH, Richard
Administrator, Plains Regional Medical Center, Clovis, NM, p. A417
Chief of Staff, Carroll County Memorial Hospital, Carrollton, MO, p. A358

SMITH, Richard C.
Chief Financial Officer, Hackensack Meridian Health Jfk Johnson Rehabilitation Institute, Edison, NJ, p. A405
Senior Vice President and Chief Financial Officer, Hackensack Meridian Health Jfk Medical Center, Edison, NJ, p. A405
Senior Vice President Finance, Hackensack Meridian Health Shore Rehabilitation Institute, Brick, NJ, p. A403

SMITH, Rick
Chief Financial Officer, Mason General Hospital And Family Of Clinics, Shelton, WA, p. A679
Chief Operating Officer, Health Central Hospital, Ocoee, FL, p. A133
Director Human Resources, Cibola General Hospital, Grants, NM, p. A418
Senior Vice President Human Resources and Chief Administrative Officer, Vail Health, Vail, CO, p. A106

SMITH, Robert M., Director, Va San Diego Healthcare System, San Diego, CA, p. A84

SMITH, Robert T., M.D.
Chief Medical Officer, Kettering Medical Center, Kettering, OH, p. A485

Chief Medical Officer, Sycamore Medical Center, Miamisburg, OH, p. A487

SMITH, Robin C, Chief Nursing Officer, Indiana University Health White Memorial Hospital, Monticello, IN, p. A211

SMITH, Rodney, Vice President and Administrator, Herrin Hospital, Herrin, IL, p. A185

SMITH, Ruth, Division Human Resources Business Partner, Banner Lassen Medical Center, Susanville, CA, p. A91

SMITH, Ryan K, Senior Vice President Information Technology, Banner – University Medical Center South, Tucson, AZ, p. A37

SMITH, Ryan K., Chief Executive Officer, Memorial Hospital Of Converse County, Douglas, WY, p. A711

SMITH, Scott, M.D., Chief Medical Officer, Adams Memorial Hospital, Decatur, IN, p. A202

SMITH, Scott M., Chief Executive Officer, Western Plains Medical Complex, Dodge City, KS, p. A234

SMITH, Sherry, Manager Human Resources, Dallas County Hospital, Perry, IA, p. A228

SMITH, Shirley M, Chief Financial Officer, Andalusia Health, Andalusia, AL, p. A13

SMITH, Sid, Director Information Resources, Larned State Hospital, Larned, KS, p. A238

SMITH, Skip, Vice President Finance, Iredell Health System, Statesville, NC, p. A463

SMITH, Stacey, R.N., Director of Nursing, Jefferson Hospital, Louisville, GA, p. A156

SMITH, Stephen
President and Chief Operating Officer, Novant Health Uva Health System Haymarket Medical Center, Haymarket, VA, p. A661
President and Chief Operating Officer, Novant Health Uva Health System Prince William Medical Center, Manassas, VA, p. A662
President, Selby General Hospital, Marietta, OH, p. A486

SMITH, Steve
Assistant Vice President Finance, Chi St. Gabriel'S Health, Little Falls, MN, p. A334
Chief Financial Officer, Kansas Heart Hospital, Wichita, KS, p. A247

SMITH, Steve, M.D., Chief of Staff, Providence Kodiak Island Medical Center, Kodiak, AK, p. A26

SMITH, Steven, Chief Information Officer, Northshore University Health System, Evanston, IL, p. A182

SMITH, Steven L., Chief Executive Officer, Huntsville Memorial Hospital, Huntsville, TX, p. A615

SMITH, Suzanne E, R.N., MSN, Chief Nursing Officer, San Juan Regional Medical Center, Farmington, NM, p. A418

SMITH, Taylor, Chief Financial Officer, Eureka Springs Hospital, Eureka Springs, AR, p. A41

SMITH, Teresa, Chief Financial Officer, Memorial Hospital, Carthage, IL, p. A175

SMITH, Terrance, M.D., Chairman Medical Staff, Sanford Clear Lake Medical Center, Clear Lake, SD, p. A560

SMITH, Terri, Chief Operating Officer, Sacred Heart Hospital Pensacola, Pensacola, FL, p. A136

SMITH, Thomas, M.D., Vice President Medical Affairs, Hutchinson Regional Medical Center, Hutchinson, KS, p. A237

SMITH, Tiffani, Chief Human Resources Officer, Stonesprings Hospital Center, Dulles, VA, p. A658

SMITH, Tim
Chief Executive Officer, Iroquois Memorial Hospital And Resident Home, Watseka, IL, p. A197
Senior Vice President and Chief Executive Officer, Sharp Memorial Hospital, San Diego, CA, p. A84

SMITH, Todd A., Chief Executive Officer, Aurora Charter Oak Hospital, Covina, CA, p. A55

SMITH, Toni, Chief Nursing Officer, Kern Medical Center, Bakersfield, CA, p. A52

SMITH, Tonya
Chief Financial Officer, Usmd Hospital At Arlington, Arlington, TX, p. A584
President, Munson Healthcare Cadillac Hospital, Cadillac, MI, p. A308

SMITH, Tracy, Director Human Resources, Mercy St. Francis Hospital, Mountain View, MO, p. A366

SMITH, Trevor, Chief Management Information Services, Gunnison Valley Hospital, Gunnison, CO, p. A101

SMITH, Tripp, Chief Executive Officer, Encompass Health Rehabilitation Hospital Of Largo, Largo, FL, p. A128

SMITH, Trisha, Chief Financial Officer, Mimbres Memorial Hospital, Deming, NM, p. A418

SMITH, Tyson, M.D., Chief Medical Officer, Haywood Regional Medical Center, Clyde, NC, p. A452

SMITH, Vanessa, Chief Human Resources Officer, Community Medical Center, Toms River, NJ, p. A413

SMITH, Vincent, Chief Information Officer, Brookdale Hospital Medical Center, New York, NY, p. A432

SMITH, Wade, Chief Operating Officer, Drew Memorial Health System, Monticello, AR, p. A46

SMITH, Wendell, Chief Operating Officer, St. James Behavioral Health Hospital, Gonzales, LA, p. A267

SMITH, William E., M.D., Chief of Staff, Cullman Regional Medical Center, Cullman, AL, p. A16

SMITH–HILL, Janet
Executive Vice President and Chief HR Officer, Novant Health Matthews Medical Center, Matthews, NC, p. A458
Executive Vice President and Chief Human Resource Officer, Novant Health Charlotte Orthopaedic Hospital, Charlotte, NC, p. A451
Executive Vice President and Chief Human Resource Officer, Novant Health Medical Park Hospital, Winston, NC, p. A464
Executive Vice President and Chief Human Resource Officer, Novant Health Rowan Medical Center, Salisbury, NC, p. A461
Executive Vice President and Chief Human Resource Officer, Novant Health Thomasville Medical Center, Thomasville, NC, p. A463
Executive Vice President and Chief Human Resources Officer, Novant Health Brunswick Medical Center, Bolivia, NC, p. A450
Executive Vice President and Chief Human Resources, Novant Health Huntersville Medical Center, Huntersville, NC, p. A456
Senior Vice President Human Resources, Novant Health Forsyth Medical Center, Winston, NC, p. A464
Senior Vice President Human Resources, Novant Health Presbyterian Medical Center, Charlotte, NC, p. A451

SMITH–ZUBA, Lorraina, R.N., MSN, Chief Nursing Officer, Porter Medical Center, Middlebury, VT, p. A654

SMITHERS, John, Network Specialist, River Hospital, Alexandria Bay, NY, p. A422

SMITHHART, Paula, Director Human Resources, Coryell Health, Gatesville, TX, p. A607

SMITHSON, Pamela, R.N., Vice President Nursing, Davis Medical Center, Elkins, WV, p. A685

SMITHSON, Tracey, MSN, R.N., Chief Nursing Officer, Eastside Medical Center, Snellville, GA, p. A160

SMITTLE, Tammy
Chief Executive Officer, Arise Austin Medical Center, Austin, TX, p. A584
Chief Executive Officer, The Hospital At Westlake Medical Center, Austin, TX, p. A586

SMOAK, Tim, Administrator, Mcleod Medical Center Darlington, Darlington, SC, p. A552

SMOCK, Tait, Manager Information Systems, Pella Regional Health Center, Pella, IA, p. A228

SMOKER, Bret, M.D., Clinical Director, Phs Santa Fe Indian Hospital, Santa Fe, NM, p. A420

SMOKOVITZ, Ryan, Chief Executive Officer, Healthsouth Rehabilitation Hospital At Drake, Cincinnati, OH, p. A476

SMOLIK, Trisha, R.N., MSN, Chief Nursing Officer, Select Specialty Hospital – Lincoln, Lincoln, NE, p. A387

SMORRA, Colleen, Assistant Administrator, Hackensack Meridian Health Pascack Valley Medical Center, Westwood, NJ, p. A415

SMOTHERS, Kevin, M.D., Vice President Chief Medical Officer, Adventist Healthcare Shady Grove Medical Center, Rockville, MD, p. A293

SMOTHERS, Mark, M.D., Chief Medical Officer, University Of Mississippi Medical Center Holmes County, Lexington, MS, p. A350

SMOTHERS, Stephen, Director Information Systems, Medical Center Enterprise, Enterprise, AL, p. A17

SMYTH, Thomas, President and Chief Executive Officer, University Of Maryland St. Joseph Medical Center, Towson, MD, p. A293

SNAPP, Jeremy, Director Information Systems, Lindsborg Community Hospital, Lindsborg, KS, p. A240

SNAPP, William R
Executive Vice President Finance and Chief Financial Officer, Ephraim Mcdowell Regional Medical Center, Danville, KY, p. A251
Vice President and Chief Financial Officer, Ephraim Mcdowell Fort Logan Hospital, Stanford, KY, p. A261

SNAVELY, Gretchen, Director Human Resources, Holton Community Hospital, Holton, KS, p. A237

SNEAD, Joseph, Chief of Medical Staff, Stonewall Jackson Memorial Hospital, Weston, WV, p. A690

SNEATH, Roger, Chief Financial Officer, Aurora Medical Center – Bay Area, Marinette, WI, p. A699

SNEDEGAR, Michael, Chief Financial Officer, Bourbon Community Hospital, Paris, KY, p. A259

SNEED, Farron, Chief Operating Officer, Hillcrest Medical Center, Tulsa, OK, p. A508

SNEFF, Mark, Vice President Human Resources, Good Shepherd Penn Partners Specialty Hospital At Rittenhouse, Philadelphia, PA, p. A534

SNELGROVE, Steven C., President, Howard County General Hospital, Columbia, MD, p. A290

SNELL, Dan, Chief Medical Officer, Portneuf Medical Center, Pocatello, ID, p. A171

SNELL, Peggy, Chief Finance Officer, Cherry County Hospital, Valentine, NE, p. A392

SNENK, Don, Chief Financial Officer, Mercy Fitzgerald Hospital, Darby, PA, p. A524

SNIDE, Jeaniffr P., Chief Nursing Officer, Crete Area Medical Center, Crete, NE, p. A384

SNIDER, Charles, Vice President Human Resources, Oak Hill Hospital, Brooksville, FL, p. A119

SNIDER, Cheryl, Director Human Resources, St. Vincent General Hospital District, Leadville, CO, p. A103

SNIDER, Glenn R, M.D., Chief of Staff, Louis A. Johnson Veterans Affairs Medical Center, Clarksburg, WV, p. A684

SNIDER, Glenn R., Interim Director, Louis A. Johnson Veterans Affairs Medical Center, Clarksburg, WV, p. A684

SNIDER, Tim, Senior Vice President for Finance, Upper Valley Medical Center, Troy, OH, p. A492

SNIDER, Timothy, Manager Information Systems, Fannin Regional Hospital, Blue Ridge, GA, p. A148

SNIPES, Rob, Administrator, Optim Medical Center – Tattnall, Reidsville, GA, p. A158

SNODGRASS, Donald R., M.D., Chief Medical Officer, Mary Lanning Healthcare, Hastings, NE, p. A385

SNODGRASS, Elizabeth, Chief Executive Officer, Livingston Hospital And Healthcare Services, Salem, KY, p. A260

SNODGRASS, Liz, Chief Financial Officer, Trigg County Hospital, Cadiz, KY, p. A250

SNOOK, Joel, Chief Financial Officer, Westchester General Hospital, Miami, FL, p. A131

SNOW, Dorothy, M.D., Chief of Staff, Veterans Affairs Maryland Health Care System–Baltimore Division, Baltimore, MD, p. A288

SNOW, Jason T
Director Human Resources, Hshs St. Joseph'S Hospital, Breese, IL, p. A174
Director People Services, Hshs St. Elizabeth'S Hospital, O'Fallon, IL, p. A192

SNOW, John, Chief Executive Officer, Granville Health System, Oxford, NC, p. A460

SNOW, Meldon L., Chief Executive Officer, Logan County Hospital, Oakley, KS, p. A242

SNOW, Ryan
Director Human Resources, Habersham Medical Center, Demorest, GA, p. A152
Administrator, Chatuge Regional Hospital And Nursing Home, Hiawassee, GA, p. A154

SNOWDON, Susan, Director Information Technology, Four Winds Hospital, Saratoga Springs, NY, p. A443

SNYDER, Alice, Vice President, Chief Nursing Officer, Osf St. Mary Medical Center, Galesburg, IL, p. A183

SNYDER, Bill, Chief Executive Officer, Denver Springs, Englewood, CO, p. A100

SNYDER, Bobby, Chief Executive Officer, Inspire Specialty Hospital, Midwest City, OK, p. A502

SNYDER, David, M.D., Chief of Staff, Emory Long–Term Acute Care, Decatur, GA, p. A152

SNYDER, John, Executive Vice President and System Chief Operating Officer, Carle Foundation Hospital, Urbana, IL, p. A197

SNYDER, Kristi, Vice President Human Resources, Charleston Area Medical Center, Charleston, WV, p. A684

SNYDER, Kristine, Chief Operating Officer, Fulton County Health Center, Wauseon, OH, p. A493

SNYDER, Kyle C., Chief Administrative Officer, Geisinger Holy Spirit, Camp Hill, PA, p. A521

SNYDER, Leah, Director Health Information Services, Loring Hospital, Sac City, IA, p. A229

SNYDER, Mary E, Chief Operations Officer, Montrose Memorial Hospital, Montrose, CO, p. A104

SNYDER, Matthew, R.N., Director of Nursing, Johnson County Hospital, Tecumseh, NE, p. A392

SNYDER, Norman, M.D., Medical Director, Vantage Point Of Northwest Arkansas, Fayetteville, AR, p. A41

SNYDER, R Brad, Chief Operating Officer, Torrance State Hospital, Torrance, PA, p. A542

SNYDER, Renae, Chief Financial Officer, Sakakawea Medical Center, Hazen, ND, p. A467

SNYDER, Ron, Chief Operating Officer, Ohiohealth Hardin Memorial Hospital, Kenton, OH, p. A485

SNYDER, Sheree, Manager Human Resources, Hillcrest Hospital Henryetta, Henryetta, OK, p. A500

SNYDER, Steve, Chief Financial Officer, Ohio Hospital For Psychiatry, Columbus, OH, p. A479

SNYDER, Tom, Interim Chief Executive Officer, Community Memorial Hospital, Redfield, SD, p. A563

SNYDER, Tony, Administrator and Chief Executive Officer, Pomerene Hospital, Millersburg, OH, p. A488

SNYDER, Vicky, Chief Operating Officer, Cleveland Clinic, Medina Hospital, Medina, OH, p. A487

SOARES, Brian, Chief Executive Officer, Kindred Hospital South Florida–Fort Lauderdale, Fort Lauderdale, FL, p. A123

SOARES, Jair C., Executive Director, University Of Texas Harris County Psychiatric Center, Houston, TX, p. A614

SOBECK, Brenda, Director of Human Resources, Jones Memorial Hospital, Wellsville, NY, p. A447

SODERLING, Marcia, R.N., Hospital Nurse Executive, Legacy Mount Hood Medical Center, Gresham, OR, p. A513

SOEKEN, Charles
Director Information Technology, Providence Medical Center, Kansas City, KS, p. A238
Director Information Technology, Saint John Hospital, Leavenworth, KS, p. A239

SOEKORO, Julie, Chief Financial Officer, Grandview Medical Center, Birmingham, AL, p. A14

SOGARD, Matt, Chief Executive Officer, Overland Park Regional Medical Center, Overland Park, KS, p. A243

SOGLIN, David, Chief Medical Officer, La Rabida Children'S Hospital, Chicago, IL, p. A178

SOHN, Steven, M.D., President Medical Staff, Dallas County Hospital, Perry, IA, p. A228

SOILEAU, D. Kirk., Chief Executive Officer, Natchitoches Regional Medical Center, Natchitoches, LA, p. A274

SOIMAN, Erika, CPA, Chief Financial Officer, Brookdale Hospital Medical Center, New York, NY, p. A432

SOKOLA, Thomas P., Chief Administrative Officer, Geisinger Medical Center, Danville, PA, p. A523

SOLAIMAN, Shereen, Vice President Human Resources, Ohiohealth Riverside Methodist Hospital, Columbus, OH, p. A480

SOLARE, Frank A., Chief Executive Officer, Kindred Hospital Northwest Indiana, Hammond, IN, p. A205

SOLA', Ivan', President Medical Staff, Upmc Carlisle, Carlisle, PA, p. A522

SOLBERG, Bradley V., President, Osf Saint James – John W. Albrecht Medical Center, Pontiac, IL, p. A194

SOLBERG, Don, M.D., Chief Medical Officer, Kittitas Valley Healthcare, Ellensburg, WA, p. A672

SOLCHER, Barry, M.D., Chief of Staff, The Physicians Centre Hospital, Bryan, TX, p. A590

SOLDO, Stephen, M.D., Chief Medical Officer, Saint Agnes Medical Center, Fresno, CA, p. A59

SOLE, Kelly, Chief Operating Officer, Appalachian Behavioral Healthcare, Athens, OH, p. A472

SOLER, Eddie, Chief Financial Officer, Adventhealth Orlando, Orlando, FL, p. A134

SOLEO, Jason, Manager Information Systems, St. James Mercy Hospital, Hornell, NY, p. A429

SOLHEIM, John H., Chief Executive Officer, Trios Health, Kennewick, WA, p. A674

SOLIE, Carol M, M.D., Chief Medical Officer, Wyoming Medical Center, Casper, WY, p. A710

SOLIMAN, Russell, Director Information Services, Amita Health St. Mary'S Hospital, Kankakee, IL, p. A187

SOLIN, Andrea
Chief Financial Officer, Lovelace Unm Rehabilitation Hospital, Albuquerque, NM, p. A416
Chief Financial Officer, Lovelace Westside Hospital, Albuquerque, NM, p. A416

SOLINSKI, Ruth, Senior Director Human Resources, Up Health System–Marquette, Marquette, MI, p. A317

SOLIS, Gloria, R.N., MSN, Chief Nursing Officer, Saint Luke'S East Hospital, Lee'S Summit, MO, p. A364

SOLIVAN, Jose E
Chief Financial Officer, Hospital Menonita De Cayey, Cayey, PR, p. A716
Chief Financial Officer, Mennonite General Hospital, Aibonito, PR, p. A715

SOLIZ, Mindy
Director Human Resource Strategy, Christus Spohn Hospital Kleberg, Kingsville, TX, p. A618
Director Human Resources, Christus Spohn Hospital Alice, Alice, TX, p. A581

SOLLENBERGER, Donna K, Executive Vice President and Chief Executive Officer, University Of Texas Medical Branch, Galveston, TX, p. A607

SOLLENBERGER, Donna K., Executive Vice President and Chief Executive Officer, University Of Texas Medical Branch, Galveston, TX, p. A607

SOLLIS, Jeff, Chief Executive Officer, Eastern Idaho Regional Medical Center, Idaho Falls, ID, p. A169

SOLOMON, John, Director, South Carolina Department Of Corrections Hospital, Columbia, SC, p. A551

SOLOMON, Oliver, M.D., Chief Medical Officer, Glendora Community Hospital, Glendora, CA, p. A61

SOLOMON, Tina, Executive Director Finance, Winter Haven Hospital, Winter Haven, FL, p. A144

SOLOMON–OWENS, Felicia, Director Human Resources, Fayette Medical Center, Fayette, AL, p. A18

SOLORIO, Roberta, Vice President, Chief Human Resource Officer, Midland Memorial Hospital, Midland, TX, p. A624

SOLORZANO, Rosa, Interim Director Human Resources, Astria Toppenish Hospital, Toppenish, WA, p. A681

SOLOW, Jodie Sartor, Director of Human Resources, Chatham Hospital, Siler City, NC, p. A462

SOLTIS, Les, Director – Human Resources, St. Francis Hospital, Federal Way, WA, p. A673

SOMERS, Tyrel, M.D., Chief Medical Officer, Russell Regional Hospital, Russell, KS, p. A244

SOMMERS, Belinda, Chief Information Officer, Lake Charles Memorial Hospital, Lake Charles, LA, p. A272

SOMMERS, Dorene M., Associate Director Patient Care Services, Erie Veterans Affairs Medical Center, Erie, PA, p. A525

SONATORE, Carol, D.O., Medical Director, Healthsouth Rehabilitation Hospital Of Toms River, Toms River, NJ, p. A413

SONDAG, Timothy, Senior Nursing Officer, Hopedale Medical Complex, Hopedale, IL, p. A186

SONDERMAN, Betty, Manager Human Resources, Ridgeview Institute, Smyrna, GA, p. A160

SONDERMAN, Thomas, M.D., Vice President and Chief Medical Officer, Columbus Regional Hospital, Columbus, IN, p. A201

SONEL, Ali, M.D., Chief of Staff, Veterans Affairs Pittsburgh Healthcare System, Pittsburgh, PA, p. A538

SONENREICH, Steven D., President and Chief Executive Officer, Mount Sinai Medical Center, Miami Beach, FL, p. A131

SONG, Daniel, Chief Financial Officer, Monterey Park Hospital, Monterey Park, CA, p. A73

SONGER, Lucille, Chief Nursing Officer, Athol Hospital, Athol, MA, p. A294

SONGY, David, President and Chief Executive Officer, Saint Luke Institute, Silver Spring, MD, p. A293

SONI, Anita, M.D., Chief Medical Officer, Brookdale Hospital Medical Center, New York, NY, p. A432

SONNENBERG, Martha, M.D., Chief of Staff, Southern California Hospital At Culver City, Culver City, CA, p. A56

SONNENBERG, Stephanie
Director Information Technology, Promedica Bixby Hospital, Adrian, MI, p. A306
Director Information Technology, Promedica Herrick Hospital, Tecumseh, MI, p. A323

SONNENBERG, William, M.D., President Medical Staff, Titusville Area Hospital, Titusville, PA, p. A542

SONNENSCHEIN, Silvia, M.D., Chief of Staff, Kohala Hospital, Kohala, HI, p. A166

SONTZ, Jennifer
Director Human Resources, Evansville Psychiatric Children Center, Evansville, IN, p. A203
Director Human Resources, Evansville State Hospital, Evansville, IN, p. A203

SOOHOO, Richard, Chief Financial Officer, Sutter Medical Center, Sacramento, Sacramento, CA, p. A82

SOPER, Brent, Chief Financial Officer, Adventist Health Bakersfield, Bakersfield, CA, p. A52

SOPIARZ, Ed, Chief Financial Officer, University Behavioral Health Of Denton, Denton, TX, p. A599

SOPKO, Joseph A., M.D., Chief Medical Officer, St. Vincent Charity Medical Center, Cleveland, OH, p. A478

SOPT, Michael, M.D., Chief of Staff, Brooks County Hospital, Quitman, GA, p. A158

SORBELLO, Bud, Director Management Information Systems, New York–Presbyterian/Hudson Valley Hospital, Cortlandt Manor, NY, p. A426

SORENSEN, Bonny
Chief Financial Officer, Wadley Regional Medical Center At Hope, Hope, AR, p. A43
Chief Financial Officer, Wadley Regional Medical Center, Texarkana, TX, p. A640

SORENSEN, Damon, Chief Financial Officer, Mclaren Bay Region, Bay City, MI, p. A307

SORENSEN, Vanessa, Chief Nursing Officer, Summit Medical Center, Casper, WY, p. A710

SORENSON, Chris
Chief Health Information Officer, Sheltering Arms Hospital South, Midlothian, VA, p. A663
Chief Information Officer, Sheltering Arms Rehabilitation Hospital, Mechanicsville, VA, p. A662

SORENSON, Dennis, Supervisor Information Technology, Bronson South Haven Hospital, South Haven, MI, p. A322

SORENSON, Eric C, Chief Financial Officer, Veterans Affairs Loma Linda Healthcare System, Loma Linda, CA, p. A64
SORENSON, Sheri, Manager Business Office, Highland Ridge Hospital, Midvale, UT, p. A648
SORENSON, Tawnya, Director of Nursing, Kittson Memorial Healthcare Center, Hallock, MN, p. A333
SORRELL, Dierdra, Chief Executive Officer, Clifton–Fine Hospital, Star Lake, NY, p. A444
SORRELL, Rachel, Chief Financial Officer, Tsehootsooi Medical Center, Fort Defiance, AZ, p. A29
SORRELL, Ralph W, Chief Financial Officer, Adena Greenfield Medical Center, Greenfield, OH, p. A484
SORRELLS, Dwane, Chief Information Officer, Choctaw Nation Health Care Center, Talihina, OK, p. A508
SOSA, Phillip
Chief Financial Officer, El Paso Behavioral Health System, El Paso, TX, p. A601
Interim Chief Executive Officer, El Paso Behavioral Health System, El Paso, TX, p. A601
SOSA–GUERRERO, Sandra, Chief Executive Officer, Larkin Community Hospital–South Miami Campus, South Miami, FL, p. A140
SOSEBEE, Tonya, Chief Operating and Nursing Officer, Texas Health Harris Methodist Hospital Azle, Azle, TX, p. A586
SOSEBEE, Tonya, MSN, R.N., Chief Operating and Nursing Officer, Texas Health Harris Methodist Hospital Azle, Azle, TX, p. A586
SOSNOW, Peter L, Medical Director, O'Connor Hospital, Delhi, NY, p. A426
SOTERAKIS, Jack, M.D., Executive Vice President Medical Affairs, St. Francis Hospital, The Heart Center, Roslyn, NY, p. A443
SOTO, Ciria, Director Human Resources, Sonora Behavioral Health Hospital, Tucson, AZ, p. A38
SOTO, Itza, MSN, Nursing Executive, Ashford Presbyterian Community Hospital, San Juan, PR, p. A718
SOTO, Juan Carlos, Director Information Systems, Hospital San Carlos Borromeo, Moca, PR, p. A717
SOTOIZAGUIRRE, Felix, Chief Financial Officer, Wellstar North Fulton Hospital, Roswell, GA, p. A159
SOTOS, Steven, M.D., President Medical Staff, Lifecare Hospitals Of Pittsburgh, Pittsburgh, PA, p. A537
SOUDERS, Stuart, Chief, Human Resources, William S. Middleton Memorial Veterans Hospital, Madison, WI, p. A699
SOUKUP, Paul, Chief Financial Officer, St. Luke Community Healthcare, Ronan, MT, p. A379
SOULAR, Dan, M.D., Vice President, Medical Affairs, Grand Itasca Clinic And Hospital, Grand Rapids, MN, p. A333
SOULE, Joyce, R.N., MSN, Chief Nursing Officer, Medical City Dallas, Dallas, TX, p. A597
SOURBEER, Jay C., Commanding Officer, Robert E. Bush Naval Hospital, Twentynine Palms, CA, p. A92
SOUTHER, Geoffrey C, Chief Operating Officer, New Hampshire Hospital, Concord, NH, p. A399
SOUTHERLAND, David, Vice President of Operations, Petaluma Valley Hospital, Petaluma, CA, p. A78
SOUTHERN, Joel, Chief Executive Officer, Northwest Mississippi Medical Center, Clarksdale, MS, p. A345
SOUTHWICK, Mitch, Chief Operating Officer, Mclaren Bay Region, Bay City, MI, p. A307
SOUTHWICK, William, Chief Executive Officer, Banner Behavioral Health Hospital – Scottsdale, Scottsdale, AZ, p. A35
SOUTHWORTH, Scott, M.D., Medical Director, South Davis Community Hospital, Bountiful, UT, p. A647
SOUZA, Beatrix, Chief Executive Officer, Buffalo Psychiatric Center, Buffalo, NY, p. A424
SOUZA, Darlene, Vice President, St. Joseph Health Services Of Rhode Island, North Providence, RI, p. A547
SOUZA, Greg, Vice President Human Resources, Lucile Salter Packard Children'S Hospital Stanford, Palo Alto, CA, p. A77
SOUZA, Jim, Chief Medical Officer, St. Luke'S Regional Medical Center, Boise, ID, p. A168
SOUZA, Liz, Coordinator Nursing Services, Atascadero State Hospital, Atascadero, CA, p. A51
SOUZA, Michael
Chief Executive Officer, Landmark Medical Center, Woonsocket, RI, p. A548
Chief Executive Officer, Rehabilitation Hospital Of Rhode Island, North Smithfield, RI, p. A547
SOVETSKHY, Ed, Director Information Services, Portsmouth Regional Hospital, Portsmouth, NH, p. A402
SOWDERS, Dale, President and Chief Executive Officer, Holland Hospital, Holland, MI, p. A314
SOWELL, Ronald G., FACHE
Chief Financial Officer, Medical Center At Scottsville, Scottsville, KY, p. A260
Executive Vice President and Chief Financial Officer, The Medical Center At Caverna, Horse Cave, KY, p. A253
Executive Vice President, Chief Financial Officer, The Medical Center Albany, Albany, KY, p. A249
Executive Vice President, Commonwealth Regional Specialty Hospital, Bowling Green, KY, p. A249
Executive Vice President, Medical Center At Bowling Green, Bowling Green, KY, p. A250
Executive Vice President, Medical Center At Franklin, Franklin, KY, p. A252
SOWELL, Vincent, Chief Nursing Officer, Otto Kaiser Memorial Hospital, Kenedy, TX, p. A617
SOWERS, Chuck, Vice President Finance and Chief Financial Officer, Mercy Gilbert Medical Center, Gilbert, AZ, p. A29
SOWIZRAL, Shirley, Chief Executive Officer, Wernersville State Hospital, Wernersville, PA, p. A544
SPACK, Paula, R.N., MSN, Vice President Nursing, Punxsutawney Area Hospital, Punxsutawney, PA, p. A539
SPACKMAN, Jared
Chief Financial Officer, Davis Hospital And Medical Center, Layton, UT, p. A648
Chief Operating Officer, Davis Hospital And Medical Center, Layton, UT, p. A648
SPACONE, Celia, M.D., Director Operations, Buffalo Psychiatric Center, Buffalo, NY, p. A424
SPADONI, Robert S, Vice President of Hospital Operations, Rush Oak Park Hospital, Oak Park, IL, p. A191
SPAGNA, Lauren, Marketing Director, West Boca Medical Center, Boca Raton, FL, p. A118
SPAHLINGER, David, President, Michigan Medicine, Ann Arbor, MI, p. A306
SPAHR, Kristen, Director of Marketing, Desoto Memorial Hospital, Arcadia, FL, p. A117
SPAIN, Jeanine R., R.N., MS
Vice President, Chief Operating Officer and Chief Nursing Officer, Unitypoint Health – Peoria, Peoria, IL, p. A193
Vice President, Chief Operating Officer and Chief Nursing Officer, Unitypoint Health – Proctor, Peoria, IL, p. A193
Vice President, Chief Operating Officer and Chief Nursing Officer, Unitypoint Health–Pekin Hospital, Pekin, IL, p. A193
SPAIN, Steve, Chief Operating Officer, Larned State Hospital, Larned, KS, p. A238
SPAIN, Tom, Director Operations Finance, Community Memorial Hospital, Turtle Lake, ND, p. A469
SPALDING, Cathy, Vice President of Operations, Jewish Hospital, Louisville, KY, p. A256
SPANBAUER, Lisa, Financial Program Supervisor, Winnebago Mental Health Institute, Winnebago, WI, p. A709
SPANGHER, Guido, M.D., Clinical Director, Big Spring State Hospital, Big Spring, TX, p. A588
SPANGLER, Mark, M.D., Chief Medical Officer, Gibson Area Hospital And Health Services, Gibson City, IL, p. A184
SPANGLER, Michael, Health Information Management Services Supervisor, Encompass Health Rehabilitation Hospital Of Tallahassee, Tallahassee, FL, p. A140
SPANGLER, Wendell J, M.D., Chief of Staff, Paulding County Hospital, Paulding, OH, p. A489
SPANN, Debbie, Director Human Resources, Morehouse General Hospital, Bastrop, LA, p. A263
SPANN, Lori, Director Human Resources, Iberia Medical Center, New Iberia, LA, p. A274
SPANO, Dennis, M.D., Medical Director, Mayo Clinic Health System In Lake City, Lake City, MN, p. A334
SPANO, Jason, Director of Information Technology, Prowers Medical Center, Lamar, CO, p. A103
SPARE, John, Accountant, Parsons State Hospital And Training Center, Parsons, KS, p. A243
SPARER, Cynthia, Senior Vice President and Executive Director Women's & Children, Yale–New Haven Hospital, New Haven, CT, p. A110
SPARGER, Kathy, R.N., MSN, Chief Nursing Officer, Baptist Health South Florida, South Miami Hospital, Miami, FL, p. A130
SPARKMAN, Dena C., Community Chief Executive Officer, Whitesburg Arh Hospital, Whitesburg, KY, p. A261
SPARKMAN, Jill, Director Human Resources, Odessa Regional Medical Center, Odessa, TX, p. A627
SPARKS, Dennis W.
Vice President Human Resources, Saint Michael'S Medical Center, Newark, NJ, p. A409
Vice President of Human Resources, Saint Francis Hospital And Medical Center, Hartford, CT, p. A108
SPARKS, Gary R.
Administrator, Crossridge Community Hospital, Wynne, AR, p. A49
Interim President, Lawrence Memorial Hospital, Walnut Ridge, AR, p. A49
SPARKS, Holly H., Chief Clinical Officer, South Sunflower County Hospital, Indianola, MS, p. A348
SPARKS, Jason, Director, Human Resources, Healthsouth Rehabilitation Hospital At Drake, Cincinnati, OH, p. A476
SPARKS, Jennifer, Human Resources Generalist, Complex Care Hospital At Ridgelake, Sarasota, FL, p. A139
SPARKS, Lisa, R.N., Chief Nursing Officer and Vice President Patient Care Services, Indiana University Health West Hospital, Avon, IN, p. A199
SPARKS, Wendy, Chief Operating Officer, North Colorado Medical Center, Greeley, CO, p. A101
SPARLING, Nicki, Manager Human Resources, Major Hospital, Shelbyville, IN, p. A214
SPARROW, Francis D, M.D., Medical Director, Wellspan Philhaven, Mount Gretna, PA, p. A532
SPARROW, Robert T., M.D., Vice President, Chief Medical Officer, Osf Saint Francis Medical Center, Peoria, IL, p. A193
SPARTA, Mark, President, Hackensack Meridian Health Hackensack University Medical Center, Hackensack, NJ, p. A406
SPARTZ, Dale A, Chief Human Resources Officer, University Of Utah Health, Salt Lake City, UT, p. A652
SPATH, Deborah, R.N., MSN, Associate Director Patient and Nurses Services, Albany Stratton Veterans Affairs Medical Center, Albany, NY, p. A422
SPEARE, Mark, Senior Associate Director Patient Relations and Human Resources, Ucla Medical Center–Santa Monica, Santa Monica, CA, p. A89
SPEARS, David, D.O., Chief of Staff, Selby General Hospital, Marietta, OH, p. A486
SPEARS, Gina, Chief Financial Officer, Thomas B. Finan Center, Cumberland, MD, p. A290
SPEARS, Kevin, Chief Executive Officer, Stone County Medical Center, Mountain View, AR, p. A46
SPEARS, LaLana, Supervisor Accounting, Claremore Indian Hospital, Claremore, OK, p. A498
SPEARS, Michael, Human Resource Leader, Ssm Health St. Anthony Hospital – Shawnee, Shawnee, OK, p. A507
SPEAS, Ryan, Director Finance, Livingston Healthcare, Livingston, MT, p. A378
SPEASE, Dorothy, Manager Business Office, Douglas County Memorial Hospital, Armour, SD, p. A559
SPECK, Michelle, Senior Vice President Human Resources, Usmd Hospital At Fort Worth, Fort Worth, TX, p. A606
SPECK, Michelle A
Vice President Human Resources, Upmc Altoona, Altoona, PA, p. A520
Vice President Human Resources, Upmc Bedford Memorial, Everett, PA, p. A526
SPECKMAN, Kelly Ann, Chief Financial Officer, Kearny County Hospital, Lakin, KS, p. A238
SPEEK, Timothy, Director of Nursing, Glenn Medical Center, Willows, CA, p. A95
SPEELMAN, Steven, Director Information Systems, Novant Health Uva Health System Culpeper Medical Center, Culpeper, VA, p. A658
SPEER, Kevin, President and Chief Executive Officer, Hendricks Regional Health, Danville, IN, p. A202
SPEER–SMITH, Carol, R.N., Chief Nursing Officer, Oroville Hospital, Oroville, CA, p. A76
SPEIER, Ryan, Vice President Administration, Kvc Prairie Ridge Psychiatric Hospital, Kansas City, KS, p. A238
SPEIGHT, Marianne, Vice President Information System and Chief Information Officer, Cincinnati Children'S Hospital Medical Center, Cincinnati, OH, p. A475
SPELL, Kenneth R., Chief Executive Officer, Baptist Health South Florida, Homestead Hospital, Homestead, FL, p. A125
SPELL, Nicole
Director Human Resources, Vidant Bertie Hospital, Windsor, NC, p. A464
Director Human Resources, Vidant Chowan Hospital, Edenton, NC, p. A453
SPELLBERG, Brad, M.D., Chief Medical Officer, Lac+Usc Medical Center, Los Angeles, CA, p. A68
SPELLMAN, Warren K., Chief Executive Officer, Grady Memorial Hospital, Chickasha, OK, p. A498
SPELLMEIER, Rhonda, R.N., Director of Nursing, Sabetha Community Hospital, Sabetha, KS, p. A244
SPELLS–WILSON, Debbie, R.N., Chief Operating Officer and Chief Nursing Officer, Conemaugh Miners Medical Center, Hastings, PA, p. A527
SPENCE, Andre, Chief Medical Staff, Sanford Bagley Medical Center, Bagley, MN, p. A328
SPENCE, Ben
Chief Financial Officer, Cape Coral Hospital, Cape Coral, FL, p. A119
Chief Financial Officer, Gulf Coast Medical Center, Fort Myers, FL, p. A123
Chief Financial Officer, Lee Memorial Hospital, Fort Myers, FL, p. A123
SPENCE, Karie, Director Human Resources, Miller County Hospital, Colquitt, GA, p. A150

SPENCE, Karla, Director of Nursing, St. Andrew'S Health Center, Bottineau, ND, p. A465

SPENCE, Monte, Chief Operating Officer, Rehabilitation Hospital Of Indiana, Indianapolis, IN, p. A207

SPENCE, Sheldon, Director of Revenue Cycle, IT, Memorial Hospital of Texas County, Guymon, OK, p. A500

SPENCE, Steven Walter, M.D., Chief Medical Officer, Jackson Hospital, Marianna, FL, p. A129

SPENCE, Terri
 Chief Information Officer, Bon Secours Maryview Medical Center, Portsmouth, VA, p. A665
 Chief Information Officer, Bon Secours St. Mary'S Hospital, Richmond, VA, p. A665
 Vice President and Regional Chief Information Officer, Bon Secours St. Francis Medical Center, Midlothian, VA, p. A662
 Vice President Information Services, Bon Secours Mary Immaculate Hospital, Newport News, VA, p. A663

SPENCER, Erich, Chief Human Resource Officer, Fairview Northland Medical Center, Princeton, MN, p. A338

SPENCER, Jim, Director Information System, Mcleod Health Cheraw, Cheraw, SC, p. A550

SPENCER, Marie, Chief Nursing Officer and Senior Administrator, Burke Rehabilitation Hospital, White Plains, NY, p. A447

SPENCER, Mike, Chief Information Officer, Henry Community Health, New Castle, IN, p. A212

SPENCER, Misti, Director Inpatient Services, Selby General Hospital, Marietta, OH, p. A486

SPENCER, Rachelle, Chief Executive Officer, Healthsouth Rehabilitation Hospital Of New Mexico, Albuquerque, NM, p. A416

SPENCER, Sarah, M.D., Chief of Staff, South Peninsula Hospital, Homer, AK, p. A26

SPENCER, Scott, Chief Financial Officer, South Shore Hospital, Chicago, IL, p. A179

SPENCER, Susan, Chief Financial Officer, Samaritan Hospital, Macon, MO, p. A365

SPENCER, Todd, M.D., Chief Medical Staff, Adventist Medical Center–Reedley, Reedley, CA, p. A80

SPERDUTI, Karen, Chief Operating Officer, Saint Camillus Medical Center, Hurst, TX, p. A615

SPERLING, Deanna, President and Chief Executive Officer, Rwjbarnabas Health Behavioral Health Center And Network, Toms River, NJ, p. A413

SPERLING, Louis J, Vice President Human Resources, Rhode Island Hospital, Providence, RI, p. A548

SPERLING, Walter, M.D., Medical Director, Ellenville Regional Hospital, Ellenville, NY, p. A427

SPERRAZZA, John, Chief Operating Officer, Sisters Of Charity Hospital Of Buffalo, Buffalo, NY, p. A425

SPERRING, Jeff, Chief Executive Officer, Seattle Children'S Hospital, Seattle, WA, p. A678

SPICER, Joan G, R.N., Chief Nursing Officer, San Mateo Medical Center, San Mateo, CA, p. A87

SPICER, Michael J., President and Chief Executive Officer, Saint Joseph'S Medical Center, Yonkers, NY, p. A448

SPICER, Randy, Information Technology Supervisor, Central State Hospital, Louisville, KY, p. A256

SPICER, Sam, M.D., Vice President Medical Affairs, New Hanover Regional Medical Center, Wilmington, NC, p. A464

SPIDLE, Tara, Chief Financial Officer, Decatur County Hospital, Leon, IA, p. A225

SPIEGEL, Kevin M., Chief Executive Officer, Erlanger Medical Center, Chattanooga, TN, p. A567

SPIER, Deborah, Administrator, Oceans Behavioral Hospital Of Greater New Orleans, Kenner, LA, p. A270

SPIGEL, Michael, Executive Vice President & Chief Operating Officer, Brooks Rehabilitation Hospital, Jacksonville, FL, p. A125

SPIGNER, Jason, Vice President Human Resources, Advocate Good Shepherd Hospital, Barrington, IL, p. A174

SPIKE, Jennifer, Director Human Resources, St. James Mercy Hospital, Hornell, NY, p. A429

SPILLERS, David S., Chief Executive Officer, Huntsville Hospital, Huntsville, AL, p. A19

SPILSBURY, Lauren, R.N., MSN, Vice President for Patient Care Services, Redlands Community Hospital, Redlands, CA, p. A80

SPINA, Lori, Vice President Human Resources, Good Samaritan Hospital Medical Center, West Islip, NY, p. A447

SPINALE, Joseph W, D.O., Chief Medical Officer, St. Joseph'S Hospital Health Center, Syracuse, NY, p. A445

SPINGOS, Maria, Director of Nursing, Fort Lauderdale Hospital, Fort Lauderdale, FL, p. A122

SPISSO, Johnese, Chief Executive Officer, Ronald Reagan Ucla Medical Center, Los Angeles, CA, p. A69

SPITSER, Christy
 Vice President Finance and Business Development, Chi Saint Joseph London, London, KY, p. A255

 Vice President Finance, Chi Saint Joseph Berea, Berea, KY, p. A249

SPIVEY, Amy, Chief Medical Officer, Mccullough–Hyde Memorial Hospital/Trihealth, Oxford, OH, p. A489

SPIVEY, Courtney, Chief Nursing Officer, Hardin County General Hospital, Rosiclare, IL, p. A195

SPIVEY, David A., President and Chief Executive Officer, St. Mary Mercy Hospital, Livonia, MI, p. A317

SPLITT, Richie
 President and Chief Executive Office, Norman Regional Health System, Norman, OK, p. A503
 President and Chief Executive Officer, Norman Regional Health System, Norman, OK, p. A503

SPOELMA, Susan G, MSN, R.N., Chief Nursing Officer, Healdsburg District Hospital, Healdsburg, CA, p. A61

SPONSLER, Betsy A, Chief Financial Officer, Valley Hospital Medical Center, Las Vegas, NV, p. A396

SPOON, Barry, M.D., Chief of Staff, Mercy St. Francis Hospital, Mountain View, MO, p. A366

SPOONER, Allan M., President and Chief Executive Officer, Franciscan Health Olympia Fields, Olympia Fields, IL, p. A192

SPOONER, Jennifer, Controller, Encompass Health Rehabilitation Hospital Of Tallahassee, Tallahassee, FL, p. A140

SPOOR, David, R.N., Vice President, Patient Care Services and Chief Nursing Officer, Sturdy Memorial Hospital, Attleboro, MA, p. A294

SPORE, Larry, Chief Financial Officer, Lawrence County Memorial Hospital, Lawrenceville, IL, p. A187

SPRADLIN, John, Information Systems Director, Franklin Foundation Hospital, Franklin, LA, p. A267

SPRAGUE, F. Remington, M.D., Chief Medical Officer, Mercy Health Hackley Campus, Muskegon, MI, p. A318

SPRAKER, Larissa, Vice President Business Development and Chief Strategy Officer, Mercy Gilbert Medical Center, Gilbert, AZ, p. A29

SPRANGER, Lance, Chief Information Officer, St. John'S Medical Center And Living Center, Jackson, WY, p. A711

SPRATT, Kelly, President, Cambridge Medical Center, Cambridge, MN, p. A329

SPRAY, William R, Interim Chief Executive Officer, Southern Tennessee Regional Health System–Winchester, Winchester, TN, p. A580

SPRAY, William R., Chief Executive Officer, Southern Tennessee Regional Health System–Winchester, Winchester, TN, p. A580

SPREER–ALBERT, Frances, Chief Financial Officer and Executive Vice President, Albany Medical Center, Albany, NY, p. A422

SPRIGGS, Larry Floyd, CPA, Controller, Encompass Health Rehabilitation Hospital Of San Antonio, San Antonio, TX, p. A634

SPRINGATE, Brian, Chief Executive Officer, Fleming County Hospital, Flemingsburg, KY, p. A251

SPRINGER, Amy, Medical Director, Webster County Community Hospital, Red Cloud, NE, p. A391

SPRINGER, Madge, Director Human Resources, Adventhealth Waterman, Tavares, FL, p. A142

SPRINGER, Rebecca, MSN, R.N., Chief Nursing Officer, Hendry Regional Medical Center, Clewiston, FL, p. A120

SPRINGER, Theresa, Chief Financial Officer, Osf Holy Family Medical Center, Monmouth, IL, p. A189

SPRINGMANN, Tressa
 Vice President and Chief Information Officer, Levindale Hebrew Hospital And Nursing, Baltimore, MD, p. A286
 Vice President and Chief Information Officer, Northwest Hospital, Randallstown, MD, p. A293

SPRINKEL, George, Chief Financial Officer, Tennova Healthcare–Clarksville, Clarksville, TN, p. A568

SPRINKLE, Patricia, Vice President, Human Resources, Bluffton Regional Medical Center, Bluffton, IN, p. A200

SPROTT, Kendell R., Chief Executive Officer, Matheny Medical And Educational Center, Peapack, NJ, p. A410

SPROUT, Merry, R.N., Chief Nursing Officer, Antelope Memorial Hospital, Neligh, NE, p. A388

SPROWL, Chris, M.D., Vice President, Peacehealth St. Joseph Medical Center, Bellingham, WA, p. A670

SPRYS, Michael, D.O., Chief of Staff, Medical Arts Hospital, Lamesa, TX, p. A619

SPUHLER, Richard, Chief Executive Officer, Brigham City Community Hospital, Brigham City, UT, p. A647

SPURLOCK, James, D.O., Chief of Staff, Saint Thomas Stones River Hospital, Woodbury, TN, p. A580

SPURLOCK, Steve, Director Information Systems, Buena Vista Regional Medical Center, Storm Lake, IA, p. A230

SPYKERMAN, Connie, Chief Nursing Officer, Pelham Medical Center, Greer, SC, p. A554

SPYROW, Florence (Flo), Chief Administrative Officer, Flagstaff Medical Center, Flagstaff, AZ, p. A29

SQUIRES, Danny
 Chief Financial Officer, Wake Forest Baptist Health–Davie Medical Center, Bermuda Run, NC, p. A449
 Vice President and Chief Financial Officer, Wake Forest Baptist Health–Lexington Medical Center, Lexington, NC, p. A458

SQUIRES, Elizabeth, R.N., Chief Nursing Officer, Encompass Health Rehabilitation Hospital Of Tallahassee, Tallahassee, FL, p. A140

SQUIRES, Paula C, Senior Vice President, Chief Human Resources Officer and Chief Human Resources Officer, Baystate Medical Center, Springfield, MA, p. A303

SQUIRES, Teresa, R.N., Chief Nursing Officer, Lake District Hospital, Lakeview, OR, p. A514

SRAON, Karandeep, Interim Director, Aleda E. Lutz Veterans Affairs Medical Center, Saginaw, MI, p. A321

SREBINSKI, Ron, Chief Financial Officer, Mclaren Caro Region, Caro, MI, p. A308

SRIBNICK, Wayne, M.D., Senior Vice President and Chief Medical Officer, Providence Hospital, Columbia, SC, p. A551

SRINIVASAN, Parthasarathy, M.D., President Medical Staff, Galesburg Cottage Hospital, Galesburg, IL, p. A183

SRIPADA, Subra
 Exec. Vice President, Chief Transformation Officer and Chief Information Officer, Beaumont Hospital – Taylor, Taylor, MI, p. A323
 Executive Vice President, Chief Transformation Officer and Chief Information Officer, Beaumont Hospital – Dearborn, Dearborn, MI, p. A309
 Executive Vice President, Chief Transformation Officer and Chief Information Officer, Beaumont Hospital – Trenton, Trenton, MI, p. A324
 Executive Vice President, Chief Transformation Officer and Chief Information Officer, Beaumont Hospital, Wayne, Wayne, MI, p. A324
 Executive Vice President, Chief Transportation Officer and Chief Information Officer, Beaumont Hospital – Farmington Hills, Farmington Hills, MI, p. A311
 Executive Vice President, Chief Transportation Officer and Chief Information Officer, Beaumont Hospital – Grosse Pointe, Grosse Pointe, MI, p. A313
 Executive Vice President, Chief Transportation Officer and Chief Information Officer, Beaumont Hospital – Royal Oak, Royal Oak, MI, p. A321
 Executive Vice President, Chief Transportation Officer and Chief Information Officer, Beaumont Hospital – Troy, Troy, MI, p. A324

SRIVASTAVA, Mohit, M.D., Chief of Staff, Bunkie General Hospital, Bunkie, LA, p. A265

ST CLAIR, Jeffery M., President and Chief Executive Officer, Springhill Memorial Hospital, Mobile, AL, p. A20

ST PIERRE, Jay, Chief Financial Officer, North Florida Regional Medical Center, Gainesville, FL, p. A123

ST. AUBYN, Lisa, Chief Executive Officer, Signature Psychiatric Hospital, Kansas City, MO, p. A363

ST. LOUIS, Charles, Director of Patient Care Services, Sutter Health Kahi Mohala, Ewa Beach, HI, p. A164

ST. PETER, Colette, Senior Manager Human Resources, Mercy Hospital Carthage, Carthage, MO, p. A358

ST. PE', Laurin, Administrator – Singing River Hospital, Singing River Health System, Pascagoula, MS, p. A352

STAATS, Jason, Chief Executive Officer, Cumberland Hall Hospital, Hopkinsville, KY, p. A253

STABRYLA, Della, Director of Nursing, Ellwood City Medical Center, Llc, Ellwood City, PA, p. A525

STACEY, Brian, Chief Financial Officer, Brookdale Hospital Medical Center, New York, NY, p. A432

STACEY, Susan, Chief Nursing Officer, Providence Sacred Heart Medical Center & Children'S Hospital, Spokane, WA, p. A680

STACIE, Beverly, Director Human Resources, Clifton T. Perkins Hospital Center, Jessup, MD, p. A291

STACKHOUSE, Jenni, Chief Financial Officer, River Point Behavioral Health, Jacksonville, FL, p. A125

STACKHOUSE, Rebecca J., Medical Center Director, Salem Veterans Affairs Medical Center, Salem, VA, p. A667

STACKHOUSE, Sharon, Assistant Administrator and Director Risk Management, Peachford Behavioral Health System, Atlanta, GA, p. A146

STACY, Doug, Director Information Technology, Up Health System–Marquette, Marquette, MI, p. A317

STADHEIM, Barbara, Chief Nursing Officer, West River Regional Medical Center, Hettinger, ND, p. A468

STADHEIM, Nathan, Chief Financial Officer, West River Regional Medical Center, Hettinger, ND, p. A468

STADLER, James J, M.D., Associate Administrator Medical Services, Guam Memorial Hospital Authority, Tamuning, GU, p. A714

STADLER, Thomas, M.D., Vice President Medical Affairs and Chief Medical Officer, Madonna Rehabilitation Hospital, Lincoln, NE, p. A387

STAFFORD, Tom, Chief Information Officer, Halifax Health Medical Center Of Daytona Beach, Daytona Beach, FL, p. A121

STAFFORD, Walt, Director Information Technology, Chatuge Regional Hospital And Nursing Home, Hiawassee, GA, p. A154

STAGG, Kevin, Executive Vice President Finance and Chief Financial Officer, Christian Health Care Center, Wyckoff, NJ, p. A415

STAGGS, Nathan, Interim Chief Executive Officer, Anson General Hospital, Anson, TX, p. A583

STAHL, Anthony
Chief Executive Officer, Central Texas Medical Center, San Marcos, TX, p. A636
Vice President, Adventhealth Sebring, Sebring, FL, p. A139

STAHL, Daniel, D.O., Chief Medical Officer, Rush Memorial Hospital, Rushville, IN, p. A214

STAHL, Kathy, Chief Nursing Officer, Wheeling Hospital, Wheeling, WV, p. A690

STAHL, Pam, Regional Chief Human Resources Officer, Providence Holy Cross Medical Center, Mission Hills, CA, p. A71

STAHL, Sherri, R.N., Senior Vice President Hospital Services, Chambersburg Hospital, Chambersburg, PA, p. A522

STAHL, Steven J, Director Human Resources, Columbia County Health System, Dayton, WA, p. A672

STAHL, William D, Chief Operating Officer, Rooks County Health Center, Plainville, KS, p. A244

STAHLKUPPE, Robert F M.D., Chief of Staff, Chatuge Regional Hospital And Nursing Home, Hiawassee, GA, p. A154

STAHULAK, Brian M, R.N., Chief Nursing Officer, Ann & Robert H. Lurie Children'S Hospital Of Chicago, Chicago, IL, p. A176

STAIGER, Tom, Medical Director, University Of Washington Medical Center, Seattle, WA, p. A678

STAIGL, Christine, Chief Nursing Officer, Tristar Skyline Medical Center, Nashville, TN, p. A577

STALCUP, Connie, Manager Information Systems, Erlanger Western Carolina Hospital, Murphy, NC, p. A459

STALCUP, Linda, Chief Executive Officer, Stevens County Hospital, Hugoton, KS, p. A237

STALKER, Neil, M.D., Chief of Staff, Dukes Memorial Hospital, Peru, IN, p. A213

STALL, Kristi, Chief Human Resources Officer, Mahnomen Health Center, Mahnomen, MN, p. A334

STALLINGS, Jay, Chief Executive Officer, Washakie Medical Center, Worland, WY, p. A713

STALLINGS, Terry, M.D., Chief Medical Officer, West Florida Hospital, Pensacola, FL, p. A136

STALLINGS–SICARD, Lori, R.N., Chief Nursing Officer, Dmc Huron Valley–Sinai Hospital, Commerce Township, MI, p. A309

STALLWORTH, David, M.D., Chief of Staff, Monroe County Hospital, Monroeville, AL, p. A21

STALLWORTH, Monica, M.D., Chief of Staff, Western Maryland Hospital Center, Hagerstown, MD, p. A291

STALLWORTH, Terresa, M.D., Clinical Director, San Antonio State Hospital, San Antonio, TX, p. A635

STALNAKER, Avah, Chief Executive Officer, Stonewall Jackson Memorial Hospital, Weston, WV, p. A690

STALNAKER, Kevin P, CPA, Assistant Chief Executive Officer, Stonewall Jackson Memorial Hospital, Weston, WV, p. A690

STAMAS, Peter, M.D., Vice President Medical Affairs, Marshfield Medical Center, Marshfield, WI, p. A699

STAMM, Pam, Chief Nursing Officer, Throckmorton County Memorial Hospital, Throckmorton, TX, p. A641

STAMOPOULOS, Marion, Vice President Human Resources, Deborah Heart And Lung Center, Browns Mills, NJ, p. A404

STAMOS, George D., M.D., Chief Medical Officer, Overland Park Regional Medical Center, Overland Park, KS, p. A243

STANBRO, Dave
Director Human Resources, Arnot Ogden Medical Center, Elmira, NY, p. A427
Director Human Resources, Ira Davenport Memorial Hospital, Bath, NY, p. A423
Director Human Resources, St. Joseph'S Hospital, Elmira, NY, p. A427

STANDARD, Heather, Chief Nursing Officer, Northeast Georgia Medical Center Barrow, Winder, GA, p. A163

STANDEFFER, Luke, Administrator, Dch Regional Medical Center, Tuscaloosa, AL, p. A24

STANDER, Paul, M.D., Chief Medical Officer, Banner – University Medical Center Phoenix, Phoenix, AZ, p. A33

STANDIFORD, Steven B., M.D., Chief of Staff, Cancer Treatment Centers Of America–Eastern Regional Medical Center, Philadelphia, PA, p. A534

STANDLEE, Cynthia, R.N., Chief Nursing Officer, Estes Park Medical Center, Estes Park, CO, p. A100

STANEK, Janet, Senior Vice President and Chief Operating Officer, Stormont Vail Health, Topeka, KS, p. A246

STANFORD, Brion, Director Human Resources, New Orleans East Hospital, New Orleans, LA, p. A275

STANFORD, Tracy
Director Human Resources, Baylor Scott & White All Saints Medical Center – Fort Worth, Fort Worth, TX, p. A604
Director Human Resources, Baylor Scott & White The Heart Hospital Plano, Plano, TX, p. A629
Director Human Resources, Baylor Scott & White The Heart Hospital–Denton, Denton, TX, p. A599

STANGE, Della G, Director Human Resources, Southwest Healthcare System, Murrieta, CA, p. A74

STANGE KOLO, Tracey
Vice President Human Resources, Upmc St. Margaret, Pittsburgh, PA, p. A538
Vice President, Human Resources, Upmc Mercy, Pittsburgh, PA, p. A538

STANGL, Abbey, Chief Financial Officer, Cass County Memorial Hospital, Atlantic, IA, p. A217

STANHILL, Keith, Chief Human Resources Officer, Saint Francis Hospital, Memphis, TN, p. A575

STANIC, Steve M
Vice President and Chief Information Officer, Mississippi Baptist Medical Center, Jackson, MS, p. A349
Vice President and Chief Information Officer, Select Specialty Hospital – Belhaven, Jackson, MS, p. A349

STANKO, Shelley, M.D., Chief Medical Officer, Chi Saint Joseph London, London, KY, p. A255

STANLEY, Cassandra, Director Personnel, Eastern Shore Hospital Center, Cambridge, MD, p. A289

STANLEY, Donna K, R.N., Chief Nursing Officer, Ut Health Henderson, Henderson, TX, p. A610

STANLEY, James, Interim Chief Operating Officer, Galesburg Cottage Hospital, Galesburg, IL, p. A183

STANLEY, Jeff, Chief Executive Officer, Cavalier County Memorial Hospital And Clinics, Langdon, ND, p. A468

STANLEY, Jennifer, M.D., Chief Medical Officer, St. Vincent Jennings Hospital, North Vernon, IN, p. A213

STANLEY, Mark, Director Fiscal Services, Middle Tennessee Mental Health Institute, Nashville, TN, p. A576

STANSBERY, Shawn, M.D., Chief of Staff, Wood County Hospital, Bowling Green, OH, p. A473

STANSBURY, Bill, Chief Financial Officer, Jackson Parish Hospital, Jonesboro, LA, p. A269

STANSBURY, Kevin M., Chief Executive Officer, Lincoln Community Hospital And Nursing Home, Hugo, CO, p. A102

STANSKI, Vickie, Financial Manager, Parkview Lagrange Hospital, Lagrange, IN, p. A210

STANTON, Lowell, Chief Financial Officer, Houston Methodist Sugar Land Hospital, Sugar Land, TX, p. A638

STANTON, Melanie, R.N.
Chief Nursing Officer, Sycamore Shoals Hospital, Elizabethton, TN, p. A569
Chief Nursing Officer, Unicoi County Memorial Hospital, Erwin, TN, p. A569

STANTON, Mike, D.O., Medical Director, Baylor Scott & White Medical Center – Trophy Club, Trophy Club, TX, p. A641

STANUSH, Chris, Director Information Management, San Antonio State Hospital, San Antonio, TX, p. A635

STANZIONE, Dominick, President and Chief Executive Officer, Brookdale Hospital Medical Center, New York, NY, p. A432

STAPLES, Janet, Vice President Human Resources, South Central Regional Medical Center, Laurel, MS, p. A350

STAPLES–EVANS, Helen, Chief Nursing Officer, LLUCH, Loma Linda University Children'S Hospital, Loma Linda, CA, p. A64

STAPLETON, Carla J., Director Human Resources, Paul B. Hall Regional Medical Center, Paintsville, KY, p. A259

STAPLETON, Kathleen, Chief Financial Officer, Prisma Health Baptist Easley Hospital, Easley, SC, p. A552

STAPLETON, Michael, President and Chief Executive Officer, F. F. Thompson Hospital, Canandaigua, NY, p. A425

STAPLETON, Robert, Director Administration, Richard H. Hutchings Psychiatric Center, Syracuse, NY, p. A445

STARA, Jeanne, R.N., MSN, Chief Nursing Officer, Alliancehealth Ponca City, Ponca City, OK, p. A506

STARCK, Rebecca, President, Cleveland Clinic Avon Hospital, Avon, OH, p. A472

STARK, David, Chief Financial Officer, Lancaster Rehabilitation Hospital, Lancaster, PA, p. A528

STARK, David A.
President and Chief Executive Officer, Unitypoint Health – Iowa Methodist Medical Center, Des Moines, IA, p. A221
President and Chief Executive Officer, Unitypoint Health–Iowa Lutheran Hospital, Des Moines, IA, p. A221

STARK, Donna, Director Human Resources, Baylor Scott & White Medical Center – Grapevine, Grapevine, TX, p. A608

STARK, Patricia Ann, R.N., CNO, Adventhealth Deland, Deland, FL, p. A121

STARK, Sharon, R.N., Manager Clinical Information Systems, Methodist Mckinney Hospital, Mckinney, TX, p. A624

STARK, Steve Lee., Chief Executive Officer, Orchard Hospital, Gridley, CA, p. A61

STARKEBAUM, Gordon, M.D., Chief of Staff, Veterans Affairs Puget Sound Health Care System, Seattle, WA, p. A678

STARKES, Henry, M.D., Medical Director, Orchard Hospital, Gridley, CA, p. A61

STARLING, James F, M.D., Chief Medical Officer, Sovah Health–Danville, Danville, VA, p. A658

STARLING, Susan, President and Chief Executive Officer, Mercy Health – Marcum And Wallace, Irvine, KY, p. A254

STARNES, Gregory D., Chief Executive Officer, Fayette County Hospital, Vandalia, IL, p. A197

STARR, Erin L., Chief Nursing Officer, Jefferson Community Health And Life, Fairbury, NE, p. A384

STARR, Kay, Manager Human Resources, Vernon Memorial Healthcare, Elk Mound, WI, p. A694

STASI, Joseph P, Chief Financial Officer, Saint Luke'S East Hospital, Lee'S Summit, MO, p. A364

STASKIN, David, Director Human Resources, Encompass Health Rehabilitation Hospital Of Mechanicsburg, Mechanicsburg, PA, p. A531

STASNEY, Amy, Chief Executive Officer, Cornerstone Hospital Of Houston At Clearlake, Webster, TX, p. A644

STASTNY, Mark, Vice President and Chief Information Officer, Children'S Hospital And Medical Center, Omaha, NE, p. A389

STATEN, Gary L., Chief Executive Officer, Trace Regional Hospital, Houston, MS, p. A348

STATES, Chuck, Director Information Systems, Punxsutawney Area Hospital, Punxsutawney, PA, p. A539

STATON, Donna, Chief Information Officer, Fauquier Hospital, Warrenton, VA, p. A668

STATON, John, Senior Vice President Operations, Olathe Medical Center, Olathe, KS, p. A242

STATON, Paul
Chief Financial Officer, Ronald Reagan Ucla Medical Center, Los Angeles, CA, p. A69
Chief Financial Officer, Ucla Medical Center–Santa Monica, Santa Monica, CA, p. A89

STATZ, Chris, Chief Financial Officer, Lincoln Prairie Behavioral Health Center, Springfield, IL, p. A196

STATZ, Linda Taplin, System Director, Employee Experience, Ssm Health St. Mary'S Hospital, Madison, WI, p. A698

STAUB, David, M.D., Chief of Staff, Coteau Des Prairies Hospital, Sisseton, SD, p. A564

STAUB, Julie, Chief Human Resources Officer, Jackson Health System, Miami, FL, p. A130

STAUDINGER, Michael, M.D., Chief of Staff, Theda Care Medical Center – Wild Rose, Wild Rose, WI, p. A708

STAUFFER, Karla, Executive Director People Resources, Billings Clinic, Billings, MT, p. A374

STAUFFER, Keith, Regional Chief Information Officer, Chi St Alexius Health Carrington Medical Center, Carrington, ND, p. A465

STAUSS, Laura, Director of Human Resources, Huggins Hospital, Wolfeboro, NH, p. A402

STAVELEY, Melinda, President and Chief Executive Officer, Santa Barbara Cottage Hospital, Santa Barbara, CA, p. A88

STEAD, William, Associate Vice Chancellor Health Affairs, Director Informatics Center and Chief Strategy and Information Officer, Vanderbilt University Medical Center, Nashville, TN, p. A577

STEADHAM, Mark B., President and Chief Executive Officer, Morris Hospital & Healthcare Centers, Morris, IL, p. A190

STEAGALL, Susan, Vice President Information Services, Vcu Medical Center, Richmond, VA, p. A666

STEARNS, Charles, Area Information Officer, Kaiser Westside Medical Center, Hillsboro, OR, p. A513

STEARNS, Zebediah, M.D., Chief of Staff, Mercy Regional Medical Center, Ville Platte, LA, p. A280

STEC, Julianne, Chief Operating Officer, Mercy Hospital Fort Smith, Fort Smith, AR, p. A42

STECKEL, Cindy, Ph.D., R.N., Vice President Chief Nurse and Operations Executive, Scripps Memorial Hospital–La Jolla, La Jolla, CA, p. A63

STECKER, Tim, Chief Financial Officer, Kindred Hospital–Denver, Denver, CO, p. A99

STEED, Robert A, Director Information Systems, Capital Regional Medical Center, Tallahassee, FL, p. A140

STEEL, Diana, Vice President Human Resources, West Hills Hospital And Medical Center, Los Angeles, CA, p. A70

STEELE, Anthony, M.D., Chief Medical Officer, Witham Health Services, Lebanon, IN, p. A210

STEELE, Chrys, Director Information Systems, Musc Health Lancaster Medical Center, Lancaster, SC, p. A555
STEELE, David, Vice President Chief Information Officer, Leesburg Regional Medical Center, Leesburg, FL, p. A128
STEELE, Erik N, D.O., Senior Vice President and Chief Medical Officer, Summa Health System, Akron, OH, p. A471
STEELE, Mark, M.D.
Chief Medical Officer, Truman Medical Center–Hospital Hill, Kansas City, MO, p. A363
Chief Medical Officer, Truman Medical Center–Lakewood, Kansas City, MO, p. A363
STEELE, Michael, M.D., Chief of Staff, Perry County Memorial Hospital, Perryville, MO, p. A367
STEELE, Robert, President, Mercy Hospital Springfield, Springfield, MO, p. A371
STEELE, Sherri, Chief Nursing Officer, Providence Medford Medical Center, Medford, OR, p. A515
STEELE, Terry L, Vice President Finance and Chief Financial Officer, Holland Hospital, Holland, MI, p. A314
STEELE, Tina, Chief Executive Officer and Chief Financial Officer, Fairfax Community Hospital, Fairfax, OK, p. A499
STEELE, Wes, M.D., Chief of Staff, Fairmont Regional Medical Center, Fairmont, WV, p. A685
STEELMAN, Jeffrey, Director Information Systems, Lewisgale Hospital Alleghany, Low Moor, VA, p. A661
STEELY, Karen
Administrator, Adventhealth Murray, Chatsworth, GA, p. A150
Chief Operating Officer, Adventhealth Gordon, Calhoun, GA, p. A149
Chief Operating Officer, Adventhealth Murray, Chatsworth, GA, p. A150
STEEN, Jon, Director Human Resources, Davis Medical Center, Elkins, WV, p. A685
STEFFEN, Elizabeth, Director Information Technology, Seneca Healthcare District, Chester, CA, p. A54
STEFFEN, Lorri, Director of Nursing, Osage Beach Center For Cognitive Disorders, Osage Beach, MO, p. A366
STEFFENS, Aaron, Chief Operating Officer, Mercy Hospital Oklahoma City, Oklahoma City, OK, p. A504
STEFFIN, Renee, Chief Nursing Officer, Cuyuna Regional Medical Center, Crosby, MN, p. A330
STEFL, William, Director Information Systems, Mercy Health Hackley Campus, Muskegon, MI, p. A318
STEGALL, Christopher A, Regional Chief Financial Officer and Chief Operating Officer, Promise Hospital Of Vicksburg, Vicksburg, MS, p. A355
STEGER, Elizabeth, FACHE, R.N., Chief Nursing Officer, Ascension Seton Medical Center Austin, Austin, TX, p. A584
STEGGE, Sherri, Director Human Resources, Kaiser Permanente Vallejo Medical Center, Vallejo, CA, p. A93
STEHMER, Marie F, Senior Director of Human Resources, Peacehealth Sacred Heart Medical Center At Riverbend, Springfield, OR, p. A518
STEICHEN, Barry L
Executive Vice President and Chief Operating Officer, Saint Francis Health System, Saint Francis Hospital, Tulsa, OK, p. A509
Executive Vice President and Chief Operating Officer, Saint Francis Hospital South, Tulsa, OK, p. A509
STEICHEN, Elizabeth, Human Resources, Lewis And Clark Specialty Hospital, Yankton, SD, p. A565
STEICHEN, Terry, Business Officer, Lewis And Clark Specialty Hospital, Yankton, SD, p. A565
STEIGMAN, Don S
Chief Executive Officer, Jackson Health System, Miami, FL, p. A130
Chief Operating Officer, Jackson Health System, Miami, FL, p. A130
STEIGMEYER, Robert P., President and Chief Executive Officer, Concord Hospital, Concord, NH, p. A399
STEIN, Brad, Chief Financial Officer, Medical City Mckinney, Mckinney, TX, p. A624
STEIN, Cathy, Chief Inpatient Services, Sagamore Children'S Psychiatric Center, Dix Hills, NY, p. A427
STEIN, Eric H., President, Cobleskill Regional Hospital, Cobleskill, NY, p. A426
STEIN, Keith L, M.D.
Chief Medical Officer, Baptist Medical Center Beaches, Jacksonville Beach, FL, p. A126
Senior Vice President Medical Affairs and Chief Medical Officer, Baptist Medical Center Jacksonville, Jacksonville, FL, p. A125
STEIN, Patrick, M.D., Clinical Director, Western New York Children'S Psychiatric Center, West Seneca, NY, p. A447
STEIN, Paul, Chief Operating Officer, Mainegeneral Medical Center, Augusta, ME, p. A281
STEIN, Richard, M.D., Chief Medical Officer, Aurora Medical Center – Bay Area, Marinette, WI, p. A699
STEIN, Robert, Chief Executive Officer, Kindred Hospital Houston Medical Center, Houston, TX, p. A612
STEIN, Robert, M.D., Vice President Medical Management, Advocate Christ Medical Center, Oak Lawn, IL, p. A191
STEIN, Sandra, Chief Human Resources Management, Veterans Affairs Central California Health Care System, Fresno, CA, p. A60
STEIN, Sheldon J., President and Chief Executive Officer, Mt. Washington Pediatric Hospital, Baltimore, MD, p. A287
STEINBERG, James P, M.D., Chief Medical Officer, Emory University Hospital Midtown, Atlanta, GA, p. A146
STEINBLOCK, Matthew, Director Information Systems, Syracuse Area Health, Syracuse, NE, p. A392
STEINER, Scott
Chief Executive Officer, Dmc – Detroit Receiving Hospital, Detroit, MI, p. A310
Chief Executive Officer, Dmc Harper University Hospital, Detroit, MI, p. A310
Chief Executive Officer, Phoebe Putney Memorial Hospital, Albany, GA, p. A145
STEINER, Thomas K., Interim Chief Executive Officer, Burke Medical Center, Waynesboro, GA, p. A163
STEINES, Brian D, Chief Financial Officer, Northeast Georgia Medical Center, Gainesville, GA, p. A154
STEINES, Jeanne, D.O., Medical Director, Connecticut Mental Health Center, New Haven, CT, p. A109
STEINGALL, Patricia, MS, R.N., R.N., MS, Vice President, Patient Care Services, Hunterdon Healthcare, Flemington, NJ, p. A406
STEINHART, Curt, M.D., Chief Medical Officer, Ou Medical Center, Oklahoma City, OK, p. A505
STEINKE, Paul
Chief Financial Officer, St. Bernardine Medical Center, San Bernardino, CA, p. A83
President and Chief Executive Officer, Cgh Medical Center, Sterling, IL, p. A197
STEINKE, Paul, D.O., President and Chief Executive Officer, Cgh Medical Center, Sterling, IL, p. A197
STEINMANN, Robin, Administrative Director Human Resources, Anderson Hospital, Maryville, IL, p. A188
STEINSICK, Bill, M.D., Chief Medical Staff, Asante Ashland Community Hospital, Ashland, OR, p. A511
STEINWACHS, Lynn R., Vice President and Administrator, Methodist Hospital Union County, Morganfield, KY, p. A258
STELL, G Max, M.D., Medical Director, Minden Medical Center, Minden, LA, p. A274
STELLER, Wayne, Vice President Chief Nursing Officer, The Acadia Hospital, Bangor, ME, p. A281
STELLING, Jonathan, M.D., Vice President Medical Affairs, Chi Health St. Mary'S, Nebraska City, NE, p. A388
STELTENPOHL, Robert, Vice President, Southern Indiana Rehabilitation Hospital, New Albany, IN, p. A212
STELTER, Carolyn, M.D., Chief of Staff, Ridgeview Le Sueur Medical Center, Le Sueur, MN, p. A334
STELZER, Jason, Director Human Resources, Ssm Health St. Clare Hospital–Baraboo, Baraboo, WI, p. A692
STENCEL, Lindsay, Chief Administrative Officer, Baptist Memorial Hospital–Collierville, Collierville, TN, p. A568
STENDEL–FREELS, Robin, Coordinator Human Resources, Amg Specialty Hospital–Albuquerque, Albuquerque, NM, p. A416
STENERSON, David, Vice President and Chief Financial Officer, Osf Saint Anthony Medical Center, Rockford, IL, p. A195
STENGER, George S., D.O., Chief of Staff, Okeene Municipal Hospital, Okeene, OK, p. A503
STENGER, John D, Acting Associate Director, Charlie Norwood Veterans Affairs Medical Center, Augusta, GA, p. A147
STENGER, Michael J, Chief Executive Officer, Western Arizona Regional Medical Center, Bullhead City, AZ, p. A28
STENGER, Sandra, Acting Chief Human Resources, Cincinnati Veterans Affairs Medical Center, Cincinnati, OH, p. A476
STENNETT, Kevin T, M.D., Chief of Staff, W. J. Mangold Memorial Hospital, Lockney, TX, p. A621
STENSON, James, Chief Information Officer, Syracuse Veterans Affairs Medical Center, Syracuse, NY, p. A445
STENSRUD, Kirk A., Chief Executive Officer, Glacial Ridge Health System, Glenwood, MN, p. A332
STEPANSKY, David, M.D., Chief Medical Officer, Phoenixville Hospital, Phoenixville, PA, p. A537
STEPHENS, Brian, President and Chief Executive Officer, Door County Medical Center, Sturgeon Bay, WI, p. A706
STEPHENS, Carrie, Director Information Technology, Saunders Medical Center, Wahoo, NE, p. A392
STEPHENS, Debra, Director Personnel, Riverland Medical Center, Ferriday, LA, p. A267
STEPHENS, Eddy, Vice President Information Technology, Mobile Infirmary Medical Center, Mobile, AL, p. A20
STEPHENS, Ellen, Vice President Information Services, Mercy Hospital Oklahoma City, Oklahoma City, OK, p. A504
STEPHENS, Heather, Director of Information Health Technology, Ssm Health St. Clare Hospital–Baraboo, Baraboo, WI, p. A692
STEPHENS, Jeremy, Vice President and Chief Human Resources Officer, St. Joseph Mercy Chelsea, Chelsea, MI, p. A308
STEPHENS, Kathy, Vice President of Patient Care, Decatur County Memorial Hospital, Greensburg, IN, p. A205
STEPHENS, Larry
Chief Financial Officer, Collingsworth General Hospital, Wellington, TX, p. A645
Chief Financial Officer, Kimble Hospital, Junction, TX, p. A617
Chief Financial Officer, Sabine County Hospital, Hemphill, TX, p. A609
Chief Financial Officer, Schleicher County Medical Center, Eldorado, TX, p. A603
STEPHENS, Linda, R.N., Chief Nursing Officer, Memorial Hermann Northeast, Humble, TX, p. A615
STEPHENS, Maria, Director Human Resources, Education and Occupational Health and Wellness, Vcu Health Community Memorial Hospital, South Hill, VA, p. A667
STEPHENS, Mike, Chief Financial Officer, Nch Baker Hospital, Naples, FL, p. A132
STEPHENS, Norman F., Interim Chief Executive Officer, Vista Health, Waukegan, IL, p. A198
STEPHENS, Peggy, Superintendent and Medical Director, Madison State Hospital, Madison, IN, p. A211
STEPHENS, Peggy, M.D., Superintendent and Medical Director, Madison State Hospital, Madison, IN, p. A211
STEPHENS, Royce
Chief Financial Officer, Riverton Hospital, Riverton, UT, p. A651
Director Finance, Intermountain Medical Center, Murray, UT, p. A649
STEPHENS, Ruth M., Chief Executive Officer, Pawnee County Memorial Hospital And Rural Health Clinic, Pawnee City, NE, p. A390
STEPHENS, Terry A., Chief Executive Officer, River Park Hospital, Huntington, WV, p. A686
STEPHENSON, Ben, M.D., Chief of Staff, Phillips County Health Systems, Phillipsburg, KS, p. A243
STEPHENSON, Darlene
Chief Executive Officer, Bon Secours Mary Immaculate Hospital, Newport News, VA, p. A663
Vice President Operations, Bon Secours Mary Immaculate Hospital, Newport News, VA, p. A663
STEPHENSON, Michelle, R.N., Executive Vice President & Chief Operations Officer, Ann & Robert H. Lurie Children'S Hospital Of Chicago, Chicago, IL, p. A176
STEPHENSON, Ron, Chief Operating Officer, Long Island Community Hospital, Patchogue, NY, p. A441
STEPHENSON, Steve R., President and Chief Operating Officer, Unitypoint Health – Iowa Methodist Medical Center, Des Moines, IA, p. A221
STEPP, Dana, Human Resources Officer, Mercy Health – Marcum And Wallace, Irvine, KY, p. A254
STERBACH, Maureen, Vice President Human Resources, St. Joseph'S Hospital And Medical Center, Phoenix, AZ, p. A34
STERN, Barry, President and Chief Executive Officer, Brookdale Hospital Medical Center, New York, NY, p. A432
STERNBERG, Paul, M.D., Professor and Chairman, Vanderbilt University Medical Center, Nashville, TN, p. A577
STERUD, Brian, Chief Information Officer, Faith Regional Health Services, Norfolk, NE, p. A388
STESNEY–RIDENOUR, Christine, President, Beaumont Hospital – Trenton, Trenton, MI, p. A324
STETTHEIMER, Timothy, Vice President and Chief Information Officer, St. Vincent'S Birmingham, Birmingham, AL, p. A15
STEVEN, Eva, Chief Financial Officer, Roosevelt General Hospital, Portales, NM, p. A419
STEVENS, Ann Marie., Chief Executive Officer, Tyler Memorial Hospital, Tunkhannock, PA, p. A542
STEVENS, Ben, Chief Financial Officer, Buchanan County Health Center, Independence, IA, p. A224
STEVENS, Bryan N
Chief Financial Officer, Field Memorial Community Hospital, Centreville, MS, p. A345
Interim Chief Financial Officer, Copiah County Medical Center, Hazlehurst, MS, p. A348
STEVENS, Chris E, Chief Information Officer, Billings Clinic, Billings, MT, p. A374
STEVENS, Emily, Chief Nursing Officer, Mat–Su Regional Medical Center, Palmer, AK, p. A27
STEVENS, Eric, Chief Executive Officer, Adventhealth Sebring, Sebring, FL, p. A139

STEVENS, Jeffrey, Executive Vice President and Chief Human Resource Officer, Thomas Jefferson University Hospitals, Philadelphia, PA, p. A536

STEVENS, Kelly, Manager Human Resources, St. Joseph Memorial Hospital, Murphysboro, IL, p. A190

STEVENS, Lisa, Chief Clinical Officer and Chief Operating Officer, Vibra Hospital Of Northern California, Redding, CA, p. A80

STEVENS, Lori A, MSN, R.N., Interim Chief Nursing Officer, Verde Valley Medical Center, Cottonwood, AZ, p. A29

STEVENS, Mark
  Director Human Resources, St. Luke'S Jerome, Jerome, ID, p. A169
  Senior Director Human Resources, St. Luke'S Magic Valley Medical Center, Twin Falls, ID, p. A172

STEVENS, Mark, M.D., Chief Medical Staff, Marion General Hospital, Columbia, MS, p. A346

STEVENS, Rick, President, Christian Hospital, Saint Louis, MO, p. A369

STEVENS, Rodney, East Central Region Director of Nursing Practice, Indiana University Health Blackford Hospital, Hartford City, IN, p. A206

STEVENS, Scot, Assistant Administrator, Salt Lake Regional Medical Center, Salt Lake City, UT, p. A652

STEVENS, Shelbourn, President and Chief Operating Officer, Novant Health Brunswick Medical Center, Bolivia, NC, p. A450

STEVENS, Susan
  Director Human Resources, The Healthcenter, Kalispell, MT, p. A378
  Human Resources Strategic Business Partner, Transylvania Regional Hospital, Brevard, NC, p. A450
  Information Technology Specialist, Fallon Medical Complex, Baker, MT, p. A374

STEVENS, Tammy, Chief Executive Officer, Madison County Memorial Hospital, Madison, FL, p. A128

STEVENS, Tom, Director Personnel, Unc Rockingham Health Care, Eden, NC, p. A453

STEVENS, Vicki, Human Resources Executive, Northfield Hospital And Clinics, Northfield, MN, p. A337

STEVENSON, Angelia, Manager Finance, Tuscaloosa Veterans Affairs Medical Center, Tuscaloosa, AL, p. A24

STEVENSON, Brett, Controller, Kindred Hospital Northland, Kansas City, MO, p. A362

STEVENSON, John, M.D., Senior Vice President and Chief Medical Officer, South Shore Hospital, South Weymouth, MA, p. A303

STEVERSON, Denise, Director Human Resources, Dorminy Medical Center, Fitzgerald, GA, p. A153

STEVES, Sonja
  Senior Vice President Human Resources and Marketing, Legacy Emanuel Medical Center, Portland, OR, p. A516
  Senior Vice President Human Resources, Legacy Mount Hood Medical Center, Gresham, OR, p. A513
  Senior Vice President Human Resources, Legacy Salmon Creek Medical Center, Vancouver, WA, p. A681
  Vice President Human Resources and Marketing, Legacy Meridian Park Medical Center, Tualatin, OR, p. A518
  Vice President Marketing, Legacy Good Samaritan Medical Center, Portland, OR, p. A516

STEWARD, Rachel, Director Human Resources, Hillcrest Hospital – South, Tulsa, OK, p. A508

STEWARD, Todd E.
  Acting Chief Executive Officer, St. David'S South Austin Medical Center, Austin, TX, p. A586
  Chief Executive Officer, St. David'S Medical Center, Austin, TX, p. A586

STEWART, Anne, Vice President and Chief Nursing Officer, Beaumont Hospital – Grosse Pointe, Grosse Pointe, MI, p. A313

STEWART, Brandi, R.N., Vice President and Chief Nursing Officer, Integris Grove Hospital, Grove, OK, p. A500

STEWART, Caroline
  Chief Nursing Officer, Citrus Memorial Health System, Inverness, FL, p. A125
  Chief Nursing Officer, Fort Walton Beach Medical Center, Fort Walton Beach, FL, p. A123

STEWART, Christine R., Chief Executive Officer, Russellville Hospital, Russellville, AL, p. A23

STEWART, Clint
  Chief Financial Officer, Blue Ridge Regional Hospital, Spruce Pine, NC, p. A462
  Regional Director of Finance East, Mcdowell Hospital, Marion, NC, p. A458

STEWART, Daniel, M.D., Vice President Medical Affairs, Bronson Battle Creek Hospital, Battle Creek, MI, p. A307

STEWART, David K, Senior Vice President and Chief Financial Officer, Mercy Medical Center, Canton, OH, p. A474

STEWART, Douglas, President, Unity Hospital, Rochester, NY, p. A443

STEWART, Greg, Chief Executive Officer, Wellstone Regional Hospital, Jeffersonville, IN, p. A208

STEWART, Hedda, Director Human Resources, Neshoba County General Hospital, Philadelphia, MS, p. A353

STEWART, Jane, Director Information Services, Jfk Medical Center, Atlantis, FL, p. A117

STEWART, Jessi, Director Human Resources, Rockford Center, Newark, DE, p. A113

STEWART, John, Director Finance, Burke Rehabilitation Hospital, White Plains, NY, p. A447

STEWART, Kelly, Director of Human Resources, Community Mental Health Center, Lawrenceburg, IN, p. A210

STEWART, Kendall, M.D., Chief Medical Officer, Southern Ohio Medical Center, Portsmouth, OH, p. A490

STEWART, Larry D., Chief Medical Officer and Vice President, Medical Affairs, Perry Hospital, Perry, GA, p. A158

STEWART, Marc, M.D., Vice President and Medical Director, Seattle Cancer Care Alliance, Seattle, WA, p. A678

STEWART, Marty, Chief Information Officer, Anmed Health Medical Center, Anderson, SC, p. A549

STEWART, Michael K., Chief Executive Officer, Saline Memorial Hospital, Benton, AR, p. A39

STEWART, Pamela, Director of Nursing, Washington County Regional Medical Center, Sandersville, GA, p. A159

STEWART, Patty
  Chief Financial Officer, Gonzales Healthcare Systems, Gonzales, TX, p. A608
  Interim Chief Executive Officer, Gonzales Healthcare Systems, Gonzales, TX, p. A608

STEWART, Paul, M.D., Medical Director, Kindred Hospital Las Vegas–Sahara, Henderson, NV, p. A394

STEWART, Paul R., President and Chief Executive Officer, Sky Lakes Medical Center, Klamath Falls, OR, p. A514

STEWART, Ronnelle, Chief Human Resources Officer, Brookwood Baptist Medical Center, Birmingham, AL, p. A14

STEWART, Roxane, Chief Financial Officer, Magnolia Regional Medical Center, Magnolia, AR, p. A45

STEWART, Russell L, D.O., Medical Director, Braxton County Memorial Hospital, Gassaway, WV, p. A685

STEWART, Scott, Manager Information Services, Rochelle Community Hospital, Rochelle, IL, p. A194

STEWART, Scott, M.D., Vice President Medical Management, Good Samaritan Medical Center, Brockton, MA, p. A296

STEWART, Stephen, M.D., Vice President Medical Affairs, Ssm Health St. Mary'S Hospital – Jefferson City, Jefferson City, MO, p. A361

STEWART, Stephen C., Chief Executive Officer, Holdenville General Hospital, Holdenville, OK, p. A500

STEWART, Tim, Chief Information Officer, Abbeville Area Medical Center, Abbeville, SC, p. A549

STIEKES, Robert, Chief Operating Officer, Wilkes–Barre General Hospital, Wilkes, PA, p. A545

STIFF, Patrick, Coordinator Information Technology, Madison County Memorial Hospital, Madison, FL, p. A128

STIFFARM, Garland, Chief Executive Officer, Blackfeet Community Hospital, Saint Mary, MT, p. A380

STIFFARM, Kevin J., Chief Executive Officer, Indian Health Service Hospital, Rapid City, SD, p. A563

STIKELEATHER, Janie, Director Marketing and Community Relations, Davis Regional Medical Center, Statesville, NC, p. A462

STILES, Geoffrey, M.D., Chief Medical Officer, Sharp Memorial Hospital, San Diego, CA, p. A84

STILGENBAUER, Mike, Director Finance, Marymount Hospital, Garfield Heights, OH, p. A483

STILLER, Brian G., Director Medical Center, Veterans Affairs Western New York Healthcare System–Buffalo Division, Buffalo, NY, p. A425

STILLWELL, Michelle, Chief Financial Officer, Claiborne Memorial Medical Center, Homer, LA, p. A268

STILSON, Dwain, Chief Financial Officer, Mosaic Life Care At St. Joseph – Medical Center, Saint Joseph, MO, p. A368

STILTNER, Wanda B., Director Human Resources, Buchanan General Hospital, Grundy, VA, p. A660

STIMPSON, Dan, Chief Financial Officer, Banner Del E. Webb Medical Center, Sun City West, AZ, p. A36

STIMPSON, Jared, Chief Financial Officer, Central Carolina Hospital, Sanford, NC, p. A462

STIMSON, Judi
  Chief Financial Officer, Desert Regional Medical Center, Palm Springs, CA, p. A76
  Chief Financial Officer, Palm Beach Gardens Medical Center, Palm Beach Gardens, FL, p. A135

STIMSON, Michael, Chief Nursing Officer, Adventhealth Waterman, Tavares, FL, p. A142

STINES, Chris
  President, Chi St. Vincent Infirmary Medical Center, Little Rock, AR, p. A45

President, Chi St. Vincent Medical Center–North, Sherwood, AR, p. A48

STINGLEY, Susan D, Chief Nursing Officer, Kearny County Hospital, Lakin, KS, p. A238

STINNETT, Thomas, M.D., Chief Medical Officer, Conway Behavioral Health Hospital, Conway, AR, p. A40

STINSON, Katy, Director Information Services, Alliancehealth Durant, Durant, OK, p. A499

STINSON, Martha, Director of Information Technology, Palms West Hospital, Loxahatchee, FL, p. A128

STINSON, Michael, Human Resources Coordinator, Select Specialty Hospital–Durham, Durham, NC, p. A453

STIPE, Christopher R., Chief Executive Officer, Manhattan Surgical, Manhattan, KS, p. A240

STITH, Melanie
  Vice President Human Resources, Roper Hospital, Charleston, SC, p. A550
  Vice President Human Resources, Roper St. Francis Mount Pleasant Hospital, Mount Pleasant, SC, p. A555

STITT, Bobby
  Administrator, Mercy Hospital Logan County, Guthrie, OK, p. A500
  Administrator, Mercy Hospital Watonga, Watonga, OK, p. A510

STITT, Patrick, Director of Information Systems, Fishermen'S Hospital, Marathon, FL, p. A129

STOBER, Karick, Chief Financial Officer, Pam Specialty Hospital Of Covington, Covington, LA, p. A266

STOCK, Constance, M.D., Chief Medical Officer, Sturgis Regional Hospital, Sturgis, SD, p. A564

STOCK, Greg K., Chief Executive Officer, Thibodaux Regional Medical Center, Thibodaux, LA, p. A279

STOCK, Lesa, R.N., Chief Clinical Officer, Citizens Memorial Hospital, Bolivar, MO, p. A356

STOCK, Neil, Director Technology and Facilities, Mercy Regional Medical Center, Durango, CO, p. A99

STOCKARD, Herbert, M.D., Chief Medical Officer, Mercy St. Anne Hospital, Toledo, OH, p. A492

STOCKER, Trena, Chief Nursing Executive, Mercy Health – Marcum And Wallace, Irvine, KY, p. A254

STOCKHAUSEN, Christopher, Chief Financial Officer, Upmc Mckeesport, Mckeesport, PA, p. A531

STOCKS, Gregory, M.D., Chief of Staff, Texas Orthopedic Hospital, Houston, TX, p. A614

STOCKTON, David Bradley, Chief Operating Officer, Redmond Regional Medical Center, Rome, GA, p. A159

STOCKTON, Kevin, Chief Executive Officer, Northwest Medical Center, Tucson, AZ, p. A37

STOCKTON, Linda, Interim Chief Executive Officer, Seven Rivers Regional Medical Center, Crystal River, FL, p. A120

STOCKTON, Rick, Chief Executive Officer, Promise Hospital Of Louisiana – Shreveport Campus, Shreveport, LA, p. A278

STODDARD, Mark R., Chief Executive Officer, Central Valley Medical Center, Nephi, UT, p. A649

STOFFERSON, Laura, Chief Nursing Officer, Shenandoah Medical Center, Shenandoah, IA, p. A229

STOGSDILL, Don, Chief Medical Officer, St. Vincent Heart Center, Indianapolis, IN, p. A206

STOGSDILL, Vicki, R.N., MSN, Chief Nursing Officer, Owensboro Health Regional Hospital, Owensboro, KY, p. A258

STOJAKOVICH, Edward R
  Chief Financial Officer, Dominion Hospital, Falls Church, VA, p. A658
  Chief Financial Officer, Reston Hospital Center, Reston, VA, p. A665

STOKER, Rick, Director Management Information Systems, Tristar Horizon Medical Center, Dickson, TN, p. A569

STOKER, Vicki, Chief Nursing Officer, University Behavioral Health Of Denton, Denton, TX, p. A599

STOKES, Eric, Vice President of Operations, Decatur County Memorial Hospital, Greensburg, IN, p. A205

STOKES, Gary L., Interim Chief Executive Officer, Nacogdoches Memorial Hospital, Nacogdoches, TX, p. A626

STOKES, Laura
  Director Human Resources, Roosevelt Warm Springs Rehabilitation And Specialty Hospitals – Ltac, Warm Springs, GA, p. A162
  Director Human Resources, Roosevelt Warm Springs Rehabilitation Hospital – Rehab, Warm Springs, GA, p. A162

STOKES, Letha, Chief Executive Officer, Medical Arts Hospital, Lamesa, TX, p. A619

STOKES, Priscilla, MS, R.N., Vice President Patient Care and Hospital Operations, Unitypoint Health – St. Lukes'S Sioux City, Sioux City, IA, p. A230

STOKES, Richard W, CPA, Chief Financial Officer, Gila Regional Medical Center, Silver City, NM, p. A420

STOKES, Tina, Manager Human Resources, Regency Hospital Of Florence, Florence, SC, p. A553

STOKOE, Shelby
Chief Financial Officer, Providence Holy Family Hospital, Spokane, WA, p. A679
Senior Director Finance, Providence Sacred Heart Medical Center & Children'S Hospital, Spokane, WA, p. A680

STOLDT, Garrick J, Vice President and Chief Financial Officer, Saint Peter'S University Hospital, New Brunswick, NJ, p. A409

STOLLAR, Joseph Randall, Chief Information Officer, Johnson County Hospital, Tecumseh, NE, p. A392

STOLLER, Theo, Chief Executive Officer, Jacobson Memorial Hospital Care Center, Elgin, ND, p. A466

STOLS, Natalie, Interim Chief Executive Officer, Amg Physical Rehabilitation Hospital, Covington, LA, p. A266

STOLTMAN, Erin, Administrator, Essentia Health Ada, Ada, MN, p. A327

STOLTZ, Kyla, Vice President Human Resources, Centerpoint Medical Center, Independence, MO, p. A361

STOLYAR, Edward B., D.O., Divisional Chief Informational Officer, Brookdale Hospital Medical Center, New York, NY, p. A432

STOMBERG, LeAnn, Chief Financial Officer, Minneapolis Veterans Affairs Health Care System, Minneapolis, MN, p. A336

STONE, Connie, R.N., Chief Nursing Officer, Medstar Montgomery Medical Center, Olney, MD, p. A292

STONE, Dan, Senior Community Chief Executive Officer, Hazard Arh Regional Medical Center, Hazard, KY, p. A253

STONE, Darlene, Vice President Human Resources, Baptist Hospital, Pensacola, FL, p. A136

STONE, Duncan, D.D.S., Chief Medical Staff, Mississippi State Hospital, Whitfield, MS, p. A355

STONE, Jeanette, Vice President Operations, Baptist Health South Florida, South Miami Hospital, Miami, FL, p. A130

STONE, Jill, Manager Human Resources, Lynn County Hospital District, Tahoka, TX, p. A639

STONE, Joanna, Chief Nursing Officer, Livingston Hospital And Healthcare Services, Salem, KY, p. A260

STONE, Levi Ross, R.N., Chief Nursing Officer and Chief Operating Officer, Odessa Regional Medical Center, Odessa, TX, p. A627

STONE, Loren, Chief Executive Officer, Endless Mountain Health Systems, Montrose, PA, p. A532

STONE, Matt, President and Chief Executive Officer, Baptist Medical Center, San Antonio, TX, p. A633

STONE, Patricia, R.N., MSN, Senior Vice President Operations and Chief Nursing Officer, Adventist Health White Memorial, Los Angeles, CA, p. A66

STONE, Richard, Manager, Technical Services, Uhs Chenango Memorial Hospital, Norwich, NY, p. A440

STONE, Robert, President and Chief Executive Officer, City Of Hope'S Helford Clinical Research Hospital, Duarte, CA, p. A57

STONE, Ronald W, Regional Chief Human Resource Officer, Brookdale Hospital Medical Center, New York, NY, p. A432

STONE, Sam, Operations Administrator, Essentia Health–Virginia, Virginia, MN, p. A341

STONE, Susan
Director Human Resources, Claiborne Medical Center, Tazewell, TN, p. A580
Senior Vice President and Chief Executive Officer, Sharp Coronado Hospital And Healthcare Center, Coronado, CA, p. A55

STONE, Terry, Chief Financial Officer and Chief Information Officer, Willapa Harbor Hospital, South Bend, WA, p. A679

STONE, Thomas J., Chief Executive Officer, Doctor'S Memorial Hospital, Perry, FL, p. A136

STONE, Timothy D., Jr, President and Chief Executive Officer, Decatur Memorial Hospital, Decatur, IL, p. A180

STONEBURNER, Marianna, R.N., Chief Nursing Officer, Upmc Jameson, New Castle, PA, p. A533

STONER, Jamey, Chief Financial Officer, Frye Regional Medical Center, Hickory, NC, p. A456

STONER, Steve, Chief Information Officer, Richard L. Roudebush Veterans Affairs Medical Center, Indianapolis, IN, p. A207

STONESTREET, Jana S, R.N., Ph.D., Chief Nursing Officer, Tulane Health System, New Orleans, LA, p. A276

STOPPER, Jim, CPA, Chief Financial Officer, Evangelical Community Hospital, Lewisburg, PA, p. A530

STOPPLER, Maria, Chief Executive Officer, Granite County Medical Center, Philipsburg, MT, p. A379

STOREY, Kam, Director Human Resources, Sebastian River Medical Center, Sebastian, FL, p. A139

STOREY, Kevin L.
Vice President and Administrator, Baptist Health Medical Center–Heber Springs, Heber Springs, AR, p. A43
Vice President and Administrator, Baptist Health Medical Center–Stuttgart, Stuttgart, AR, p. A49

STORFJELL, Judith, Ph.D., R.N., Senior Vice President and Chief Nursing Officer, Loma Linda University Medical Center, Loma Linda, CA, p. A64

STORM, Dave, Director Business Support, Hshs St. Anthony'S Memorial Hospital, Effingham, IL, p. A181

STORR, Katie, Director of Human Resources, Mississippi State Hospital, Whitfield, MS, p. A355

STORRS, Elaine, Chief Nursing Officer, Springfield Regional Medical Center, Springfield, OH, p. A491

STORTO, David E., President, Spaulding Rehabilitation Hospital, Charlestown, MA, p. A298

STOTLER, Sherry, R.N., MSN, Chief Nursing Officer, Maricopa Integrated Health System, Phoenix, AZ, p. A33

STOTTLEMYRE, Georgan L., Chief Human Relations Officer, Northern Inyo Hospital, Bishop, CA, p. A53

STOTTS, Vicki, Coordinator Human Resources, Flint River Community Hospital, Montezuma, GA, p. A157

STOUGH, Joe, Interim President, Mobile Infirmary Medical Center, Mobile, AL, p. A20

STOUT, Amanda, Chief Nursing Officer, Minneola District Hospital, Minneola, KS, p. A241

STOUT, Bess, Director Human Resources, Tennova Healthcare–Lafollette Medical Center, La Follette, TN, p. A572

STOUT, Cindy, Chief Executive Officer, El Paso Children'S Hospital, El Paso, TX, p. A601

STOUT, Deana
Vice President Financial Services, Medstar Good Samaritan Hospital, Baltimore, MD, p. A286
Vice President, Finance, Medstar Union Memorial Hospital, Baltimore, MD, p. A287

STOUT, Kimberly Dawn, Chief Nursing Officer and Chief Operating Officer, Mcalester Regional Health Center, Mcalester, OK, p. A502

STOUT, Patsy, Director Personnel, Richland Parish Hospital, Delhi, LA, p. A267

STOUT–TORRES, Sherri, R.N., Chief Nursing Executive, Sutter Maternity And Surgery Center Of Santa Cruz, Santa Cruz, CA, p. A89

STOVALL, Henry, President, Sacred Heart Hospital Pensacola, Pensacola, FL, p. A136

STOVALL, Richard G, Senior Vice President Fiscal Services and Chief Financial Officer, Southern Regional Medical Center, Riverdale, GA, p. A159

STOVALL, Shella D., Interim Director, Veterans Affairs Salt Lake City Health Care System, Salt Lake City, UT, p. A652

STOVER, Benny, Vice President Finance, Mercy Hospital Rogers, Rogers, AR, p. A48

STOVER, George M., Chief Executive Officer, Hospital District No 1 Of Rice County, Lyons, KS, p. A240

STOVER, Nick, Director Information Systems, Plateau Medical Center, Oak Hill, WV, p. A688

STOVER, Patricia A, Administrator Nursing, Doylestown Hospital, Doylestown, PA, p. A524

STOVER, Raymond
President and Chief Executive Officer, Midmichigan Medical Center–Clare, Clare, MI, p. A309
President and Chief Executive Officer, Midmichigan Medical Center–Gladwin, Gladwin, MI, p. A312

STOVER, Theresa, Chief Human Resource Officer, Edgefield County Healthcare, Edgefield, SC, p. A552

STOVER, Tim, Interim Chief Executive Officer, Ascension Borgess Hospital, Kalamazoo, MI, p. A315

STOWE, Mary
Senior Vice President and Chief Nursing Officer, Children'S Medical Center Dallas, Dallas, TX, p. A596
Senior Vice President and Chief Nursing Officer, Children'S Medical Center Plano, Plano, TX, p. A629

STOWELL, Dana A, Chief Information Officer, Mccurtain Memorial Hospital, Idabel, OK, p. A501

STOWMAN, Amber, Controller, Chi Lisbon Health, Lisbon, ND, p. A468

STOY, Gale, Manager Information Systems, Mid Coast Hospital, Brunswick, ME, p. A282

STOYANOFF, Pamela
Executive Vice President and Chief Operating Officer, Methodist Charlton Medical Center, Dallas, TX, p. A597
Executive Vice President and Chief Operating Officer, Methodist Dallas Medical Center, Dallas, TX, p. A597

STRABEL, Elizabeth, M.D., Chief Medical Staff, Divine Savior Healthcare, Portage, WI, p. A704

STRACHAN, Ronald
Chief Information Officer, Mclaren Bay Region, Bay City, MI, p. A307
Chief Information Officer, Mclaren Flint, Flint, MI, p. A311

STRACK, Kirk, Vice President and Chief Financial Officer, Clark Memorial Health, Jeffersonville, IN, p. A208

STRADER, Lynn, Chief Financial Officer, Chippenham Hospital, Richmond, VA, p. A666

STRADER, Yvonne M, Chief Nursing Officer, Providence St. Mary Medical Center, Walla Walla, WA, p. A681

STRADI, Silvia, Chief Nursing Officer, Palms West Hospital, Loxahatchee, FL, p. A128

STRADTMAN, Jackie, Director Human Resources, Chi St. Joseph Health Burleson Hospital, Caldwell, TX, p. A591

STRAHAN, Greg
Chief Operating Officer, Owensboro Health Regional Hospital, Owensboro, KY, p. A258
Interim Chief Executive Officer, Owensboro Health Regional Hospital, Owensboro, KY, p. A258

STRAIN, Donna, Director Human Resources, Ray County Memorial Hospital, Richmond, MO, p. A367

STRAIN, Lynn, R.N., MSN, Chief Nursing Officer, Slidell Memorial Hospital, Slidell, LA, p. A279

STRAMOWSKI, Mallary, Chief Human Resources Officer, Select Specialty Hospital–Madison, Madison, WI, p. A698

STRAND, Eric, Director Information Services, North Florida Regional Medical Center, Gainesville, FL, p. A123

STRASSER, Michael, Vice President and Chief Financial Officer, Mercy Medical Center Merced, Merced, CA, p. A71

STRASSNER III, Lawrence F, Ph.D., FACHE, R.N., MS, Senior Vice President Operations and Chief Nursing Officer, Medstar Franklin Square Medical Center, Baltimore, MD, p. A288

STRATON, Sam, Chief Nursing Officer, Saint Thomas West Hospital, Nashville, TN, p. A577

STRATTON, James
Regional Vice President Finance, Ssm Health St. Mary'S Hospital – Audrain, Mexico, MO, p. A365
Vice President Finance, Ssm Health St. Mary'S Hospital – Jefferson City, Jefferson City, MO, p. A361

STRATTON, Joseph, Chief Executive Officer, Geary Community Hospital, Junction City, KS, p. A237

STRATTON, Mary, Director Human Resources, River Park Hospital, Huntington, WV, p. A686

STRAUGHAN, Janet, Manager Human Resources, Highlands Rehabilitation Hospital, El Paso, TX, p. A602

STRAUGHAN, John, Director Information Technology, Wallowa Memorial Hospital, Enterprise, OR, p. A512

STRAUMAN, Karen S, R.N., Chief Nurse Executive, Kaiser Permanente Fresno Medical Center, Fresno, CA, p. A59

STRAUMANIS, John P., M.D., Vice President Medical Affairs and Chief Medical Officer, University Of Maryland Rehabilitation & Orthopaedic Institute, Baltimore, MD, p. A288

STRAUSBAUGH, Andrew, Chief Administrative Officer, Norton Hospital, Louisville, KY, p. A256

STRAUSS, Alan
Chief Financial Officer, Carondelet Holy Cross Hospital, Nogales, AZ, p. A32
Chief Financial Officer, Carondelet St. Joseph'S Hospital, Tucson, AZ, p. A37

STRAUSS, Karen, Chief Human Resources Officer, Promedica Flower Hospital, Sylvania, OH, p. A491

STRAWN, Keith A, Vice President Human Resources, New Hanover Regional Medical Center, Wilmington, NC, p. A464

STRAWSER, Debbie A, Director Human Resources, Lindner Center Of Hope, Mason, OH, p. A487

STRAYHORN, Shelly, R.N.
Chief Nursing Officer, Wadley Regional Medical Center At Hope, Hope, AR, p. A43
Chief Nursing Officer, Wadley Regional Medical Center, Texarkana, TX, p. A640

STRBICH, Steve, D.O., Chief of Staff, Spectrum Health Ludington Hospital, Ludington, MI, p. A317

STREATER, Vivian
Chief Nursing Officer and Co–Acting Chief Executive Officer, Broughton Hospital, Morganton, NC, p. A458
Co–Acting Chief Executive Officer, Broughton Hospital, Morganton, NC, p. A458

STRECKER, Kevin
President, Ascension Via Christi Rehabilitation Hospital, Wichita, KS, p. A247
President, Ascension Via Christi St. Francis, Mulvane, KS, p. A241

STRECKER, Robert, M.D., Chief of Staff, Colorado River Medical Center, Needles, CA, p. A74

STREDNEY, Thomas, Chief Human Resources Management Service, Aleda E. Lutz Veterans Affairs Medical Center, Saginaw, MI, p. A321

STREET, Rex, Senior Vice President and Chief Financial Officer, Alamance Regional Medical Center, Burlington, NC, p. A450

STREET, Scott, Chief Executive Officer, Medical Center Of South Arkansas, El Dorado, AR, p. A41

STREETER, Alan W, Chief Financial Officer, Beatrice Community Hospital And Health Center, Beatrice, NE, p. A383

STREETER, Matthew, Chief Financial Officer, Southwest Health, Platteville, WI, p. A703

STREETER, Maxine, Administrator, Reception And Medical Center, Lake Butler, FL, p. A127

STREETER, Robert, M.D., Vice President Medical Affairs, Mercy Medical Center Merced, Merced, CA, p. A71

STREICH, Rebecca, Manager Human Resources and Education Manager, Hutchinson Health, Hutchinson, MN, p. A333

STREIT, Loren, Director Human Resources, Geary Community Hospital, Junction City, KS, p. A237

STREJC, Irene T, M.P.H., R.N., Vice President, Nursing, Methodist Richardson Medical Center, Richardson, TX, p. A631

STRICKER, Sean, Chief Executive Officer, Regency Hospital Of Minneapolis, Golden Valley, MN, p. A332

STRICKER, Steven, M.D., Physician in Chief, Kaiser Permanente Vallejo Medical Center, Vallejo, CA, p. A93

STRICKLAND, David, Area Information Officer, Kaiser Permanente Los Angeles Medical Center, Los Angeles, CA, p. A67

STRICKLAND, Lee, Regional Director Information Technology, Adventhealth Hendersonville, Hendersonville, NC, p. A456

STRICKLAND, Morris S, Chief Financial Officer, Helen Keller Hospital, Sheffield, AL, p. A23

STRICKLER, David
Chief Financial Officer, Nexus Specialty Hospital The Woodlands, The Woodlands, TX, p. A641
Chief Financial Officer, Nexus Specialty Hospital, Shenandoah, TX, p. A636

STRICKLER, Stephen Todd, Director of Nursing, Sistersville General Hospital, Sistersville, WV, p. A689

STRICKLING, Keith
Chief Accountant, Jay Hospital, Jay, FL, p. A126
Chief Financial Officer, Atmore Community Hospital, Atmore, AL, p. A14

STRIEBICH, Shannon, Chief Executive Officer, St. Joseph Mercy Oakland, Pontiac, MI, p. A320

STRIKE, Helen J.
President, Regina Hospital, Hastings, MN, p. A333
President, River Falls Area Hospital, River Falls, WI, p. A705

STRING, Sherrie
Senior Vice President Human Resources, Hackensack Meridian Health Bayshore Community Hospital, Holmdel, NJ, p. A406
Senior Vice President Human Resources, Hackensack Meridian Health Ocean Medical Center, Brick Township, NJ, p. A404
Senior Vice President Human Resources, Hackensack Meridian Health Riverview Medical Center, Red Bank, NJ, p. A412

STRINGFELLOW, Grace, M.D., Chief of Staff, Veterans Affairs Nebraska–Western Iowa Health Care System, Omaha, NE, p. A390

STRINGOS, Gust, M.D., Medical Staff Director, Redington–Fairview General Hospital, Skowhegan, ME, p. A285

STRIPLIN, Elizabeth, Chief Financial Officer, Rehabilitation Hospital Of Southern New Mexico, Las Cruces, NM, p. A419

STRITTMATTER, Julie, Director Human Resources, Baylor University Medical Center, Dallas, TX, p. A596

STROBEL, Deb, R.N., Chief Nursing Officer, Russell Regional Hospital, Russell, KS, p. A244

STROBEL, Jane, Vice President and Chief Financial Officer, Mercy Regional Medical Center, Durango, CO, p. A99

STROBEL, Rand
Regional Chief Information Officer, Information Technology Services, Harrison Medical Center, Bremerton, WA, p. A670
Regional Chief Information Officer, St. Francis Hospital, Federal Way, WA, p. A673
Vice President Information Technology and Compliance, St. Joseph Medical Center, Tacoma, WA, p. A681

STRODE, Marc, Chief Executive Officer, Methodist Stone Oak Hospital, San Antonio, TX, p. A634

STROH, Rhonda, Chief Human Resources Officer, Community Memorial Hospital, Redfield, SD, p. A563

STROHECKER, Sharon, R.N., MSN, Vice President Clinical Operations and Chief Nursing Officer, Penn State Health St. Joseph, Reading, PA, p. A539

STROHLA, Patti, R.N., Chief Nursing Officer, Franklin Regional Hospital, Franklin, NH, p. A400

STROM, Lisa, Director Information Systems, North Big Horn Hospital District, Lovell, WY, p. A712

STROMBERG, Audrey, Administrator, Roosevelt Medical Center, Culbertson, MT, p. A375

STRONG, David, Chief Financial Officer/Vice President Finance, Cox Medical Center Branson, Branson, MO, p. A357

STRONG, Melissa D, Chief Nursing Officer, Mason General Hospital And Family Of Clinics, Shelton, WA, p. A679

STRONG, Tanya, Manager Information Technology, Harney District Hospital, Burns, OR, p. A511

STROSS, Daniel
Chief Information Officer, Ascension Genesys Hospital, Grand Blanc, MI, p. A312
Chief Information Officer, Ascension St. Joseph Hospital, Tawas City, MI, p. A323
Chief Information Officer, Ascension St. Mary'S Of Michigan, Saginaw, MI, p. A321

STROTHER, James, Site Director Information Technology Systems, Mercyone Des Moines Medical Center, Des Moines, IA, p. A221

STROTHKAMP, Brad, Chief Information Systems, Lakeland Behavioral Health System, Springfield, MO, p. A371

STROUCKEN, Christian, Chief Operating Officer, Carney Hospital, Boston, MA, p. A295

STROUD, Justin, Chief Financial Officer, Merit Health Central, Jackson, MS, p. A349

STROUD, Teresa, Chief Financial Officer, Salem Township Hospital, Salem, IL, p. A195

STROUP, Jeff, Chief Operating Officer, Oklahoma State University Medical Center, Tulsa, OK, p. A509

STROUSE, Thomas, M.D., Medical Director and Professor of Clinical Psych, Stewart & Lynda Resnick Neuropsychiatric Hospital At Ucla, Los Angeles, CA, p. A69

STRUB, Lisa, Chief Operating Officer, Centennial Peaks Hospital, Louisville, CO, p. A104

STRUYK, Douglas A., President and Chief Executive Officer, Christian Health Care Center, Wyckoff, NJ, p. A415

STRZELECKI, Sarah, Ed.D., R.N., Chief Nursing Officer, Phoenixville Hospital, Phoenixville, PA, p. A537

STRZEMPKO, Stanley, M.D., Vice President Medical Affairs and Chief Medical Officer, Baystate Noble Hospital, Westfield, MA, p. A304

STUART, Danna, M.D., Chief Medical Officer, Newman Memorial Hospital, Shattuck, OK, p. A507

STUART, Philip J., Administrator and Chief Executive Officer, Tomah Memorial Hospital, Tomah, WI, p. A706

STUART, Robin, Chief Executive Officer, Morrill County Community Hospital, Bridgeport, NE, p. A383

STUBBS, Don, Vice President Human Resources, Candler Hospital, Savannah, GA, p. A160

STUBBS, Kay, Chief Nursing Officer, Northwest Medical Center, Tucson, AZ, p. A37

STUBITSCH, Brian, M.D., Chief Medical Officer, Edgerton Hospital And Health Services, Edgerton, WI, p. A694

STUCKY, Nancy, Director Human Resources and Public Relations, Kingman Community Hospital, Kingman, KS, p. A238

STUCZYNSKI, Joseph, Assistant Administrator Finance and Support, Memorial Hospital Pembroke, Pembroke Pines, FL, p. A136

STUDEBAKER, Shelly, Human Resources Assistant, Clinch Memorial Hospital, Homerville, GA, p. A155

STUDER, Tim, President Medical Staff, Perham Health, Perham, MN, p. A337

STUDLEY, Jason A., President, Sentara Halifax Regional Hospital, South Boston, VA, p. A667

STUENKEL, Kurt, President and Chief Executive Officer, Floyd Medical Center, Rome, GA, p. A159

STUEVE, Angela, M.D., Chief Medical Officer, Nemaha Valley Community Hospital, Seneca, KS, p. A245

STUEVE, Jo W., Executive Vice President and Co–Chief Operating Officer, Children'S Mercy Hospital Kansas City, Kansas City, MO, p. A362

STUHLMILLER, Michael, Chief Financial Officer, Mann–Grandstaff Veterans Affairs Medical Center, Spokane, WA, p. A679

STULTS, Cynthia S., Executive Assistant and Human Resources Director, Rangely District Hospital, Rangely, CO, p. A105

STULTS, Kim, Director, Information Systems, Bellevue Hospital, Bellevue, OH, p. A473

STUMBO, Kathy, President, Arh Our Lady Of The Way, Martin, KY, p. A257

STUMME, Sarah, Director Human Resources, Owatonna Hospital, Owatonna, MN, p. A337

STUMP, Lisa, Interim Chief Information Officer, Yale–New Haven Hospital, New Haven, CT, p. A110

STUMP, Tammie, Chief Executive Officer, Union County General Hospital, Clayton, NM, p. A417

STUMP, Veronica, Director of Nursing, Carilion Giles Community Hospital, Pearisburg, VA, p. A664

STUMPO, Barbara J, R.N., Vice President Patient Care Services, Griffin Hospital, Derby, CT, p. A107

STUNKARD, Jill, R.N., MSN, Associate Chief Nurse Executive and Interim Chief Nursing Officer, Einstein Medical Center Philadelphia, Philadelphia, PA, p. A534

STURGEON, Jim, Area Director Human Resources, Kindred Hospital Las Vegas–Sahara, Henderson, NV, p. A394

STURGILL, Lori, Vice President Business Partnership, Mercy Hospital Springfield, Springfield, MO, p. A371

STURGIS, Gayle, R.N., Nurse Administrator, Heber Valley Hospital, Heber City, UT, p. A648

STURGIS, Jonathan, Chief Financial Officer, Houston Methodist Baytown Hospital, Baytown, TX, p. A587

STURGIS, Paul
Chief Human Resource Officer, Sparrow Specialty Hospital, Lansing, MI, p. A316
Director Human Resources, Dmc – Rehabilitation Institute Of Michigan, Detroit, MI, p. A310
Vice President and Chief Human Resources Officer, Sparrow Hospital, Lansing, MI, p. A316

STURLER, Kelly, Chief Nursing Officer, Mckee Medical Center, Loveland, CO, p. A104

STURSA, Robin, Chief Information Officer, St. Vincent Charity Medical Center, Cleveland, OH, p. A478

STUWE, Shannon, Director of Nursing, Faulkton Area Medical Center, Faulkton, SD, p. A560

STYER, Brent
Chief Information Officer, Summers County Arh Hospital, Hinton, WV, p. A685
Director Information Technology, Whitesburg Arh Hospital, Whitesburg, KY, p. A261

STYLES, Kelly R, Vice President and Chief Information Officer, Connecticut Children'S Medical Center, Hartford, CT, p. A108

STYRON, Stacie, Chief Nursing Officer, Lamb Healthcare Center, Littlefield, TX, p. A620

SUAREZ, Irma, Deputy Executive Director, Brookdale Hospital Medical Center, New York, NY, p. A432

SUAREZ, Lauren, Chief Executive Officer, Encompass Health Rehabilitation Hospital Of Austin, Austin, TX, p. A585

SUAREZ, Orlando, Director Information Technology, Larkin Community Hospital–South Miami Campus, South Miami, FL, p. A140

SUBBIAH, Varadarajan, M.D., Chief Medical Officer, Arrowhead Regional Medical Center, Colton, CA, p. A55

SUBIA, Corina, Director Human Resources, Ward Memorial Hospital, Monahans, TX, p. A625

SUBLER, Jeffrey R., Vice President Support Services, Wayne Healthcare, Greenville, OH, p. A484

SUBLETTE, Elizabeth, Director Finance, Providence Willamette Falls Medical Center, Oregon City, OR, p. A515

SUBRAMANIAN, Aarti, Vice President and Chief Financial Officer, Psychiatric Institute Of Washington, Washington, DC, p. A116

SUCATO, Daniel J, M.D., MS, Chief of Staff, Texas Scottish Rite Hospital For Children, Dallas, TX, p. A598

SUCHER, Therese O, Senior Vice President Operations, Southern Regional Medical Center, Riverdale, GA, p. A159

SUDAK, Mariellena, Vice President and Chief Nursing Officer, Palomar Medical Center, Escondido, CA, p. A57

SUDAK, Mariellena, R.N., MSN, Vice President and Chief Nursing Officer, Palomar Medical Center, Escondido, CA, p. A57

SUDBURY, Russ, M.D., President Medical Staff, Ascension Sacred Heart Hospital, Tomahawk, WI, p. A707

SUDDUTH, Anthony G., Interim Chief Executive Officer, Southwest Health System, Cortez, CO, p. A98

SUDICKY, Mary, Chief Financial Officer, St. Mary Medical Center, Hobart, IN, p. A206

SUDOLCAN, Joseph, M.D., Medical Director, Reagan Memorial Hospital, Big Lake, TX, p. A588

SUEHS, JoAnne, Manager Human Resources, Chapman Global Medical Center, Orange, CA, p. A76

SUGAR, Bev, Associate Administrator and Director Human Resources, Inova Mount Vernon Hospital, Alexandria, VA, p. A656

SUGDEN, Elizabeth, M.D., Chief Medical Officer, St. Luke'S Jerome, Jerome, ID, p. A169

SUGG, Amy, Director Human Resources, Scott Regional Hospital, Morton, MS, p. A352

SUGGS, Heather, Manager Human Resources, Jay Hospital, Jay, FL, p. A126

SUHR, Nancy, Manager Human Resources, Pender Community Hospital, Pender, NE, p. A391

SUITTER, Marie, Chief Financial Officer, The Acadia Hospital, Bangor, ME, p. A281

SUKENIK, Richard, CPA, Vice President Finance and Chief Financial Officer, Chan Soon–Shiong Medical Center, Windber, PA, p. A545

SUKIN, Debra F., Regional Senior Vice President and Chief Executive Officer, Houston Methodist The Woodlands Hospital, The Woodlands, TX, p. A641

SULIT, Teresa, Director of Human Resources, Seven Hills Hospital, Henderson, NV, p. A394

SULLIVAN, Christopher, M.D., Chief Medical Officer, Centerpoint Medical Center, Independence, MO, p. A361

SULLIVAN, Daniel, D.O., Chief Medical Officer, Vice President Medical Administration, Elmhurst Hospital, Elmhurst, IL, p. A182

SULLIVAN, Danita S., R.N., Chief Nursing Officer, Touro Infirmary, New Orleans, LA, p. A276

SULLIVAN, David, Director Human Resources, Ohiohealth Doctors Hospital, Columbus, OH, p. A479

SULLIVAN, Denis, Chief Human Resources Management, Veterans Affairs Black Hills Health Care System, Fort Meade, SD, p. A561

SULLIVAN, Donald, M.D., Medical Director, Encompass Health Rehabilitation Hospital Of North Memphis, Memphis, TN, p. A574

SULLIVAN, Gregory, Manager Human Resources, Girard Medical Center, Girard, KS, p. A235

SULLIVAN, James, M.D., Chief Medical Officer, Butler Hospital, Providence, RI, p. A547

SULLIVAN, Jennie, Chief Executive Officer, Wray Community District Hospital, Wray, CO, p. A106

SULLIVAN, John, M.D., Chief Medical Officer, St. Clair Hospital, Pittsburgh, PA, p. A537

SULLIVAN, Katherine, Director, Human Resources, Moab Regional Hospital, Moab, UT, p. A648

SULLIVAN, Kathleen, M.D., Chief of Staff, Memorialcare, Saddleback Memorial Medical Center, Laguna Hills, CA, p. A63

SULLIVAN, Lowery, M.D., Chief Medical Officer, Northwestern Medical Center, Saint Albans, VT, p. A655

SULLIVAN, Martha, Chief Information Officer, Harrison Memorial Hospital, Cynthiana, KY, p. A251

SULLIVAN, Mary Patricia, R.N., MSN, Chief Nursing Officer, Overlook Medical Center, Summit, NJ, p. A413

SULLIVAN, Michael, M.D.
Chief Medical Officer, Northern Maine Medical Center, Fort Kent, ME, p. A283
Medical Director Emergency Services, Peacehealth Peace Island Medical Center, Friday Harbor, WA, p. A673

SULLIVAN, Patrick L, Chief Operating Officer, Brookdale Hospital Medical Center, New York, NY, p. A432

SULLIVAN, Peter, Chief Executive Officer, Riverside Medical Center, Franklinton, LA, p. A267

SULLIVAN, Staci, R.N., Chief Nursing Officer, Lane Regional Medical Center, Zachary, LA, p. A280

SULLIVAN, Theresa, Chief Executive Officer, Samaritan Healthcare, Moses Lake, WA, p. A675

SULLIVAN, Thomas, Vice President Fiscal Services, Harrington Hospital, Southbridge, MA, p. A303

SULLIVAN, William, Chief Financial Officer, Mount Auburn Hospital, Cambridge, MA, p. A297

SULLIVAN SMITH, Mary, R.N., MS, Senior Vice President, Chief Operating Officer and Chief Nursing Officer, New England Baptist Hospital, Boston, MA, p. A296

SULLIVANT, Laura, Area Chief Information Officer, Kaiser Permanente San Diego Medical Center, San Diego, CA, p. A83

SULSER, Jamey, Director Human Resources, South Davis Community Hospital, Bountiful, UT, p. A647

SULU, Dorothy, Budget Analyst, Hopi Health Care Center, Keams Canyon, AZ, p. A30

SULZEN, Jessica, Director Human Resources, Belton Regional Medical Center, Belton, MO, p. A356

SUMMERLIN, Craig, Chief Human Resources Officer, Singing River Health System, Pascagoula, MS, p. A352

SUMMERLIN, Valerie, R.N., MS, Chief Nursing Officer, Adventist Healthcare Physical Health And Rehabilitation, Rockville, MD, p. A293

SUMMERS, Barbara L., Ph.D., R.N., Vice President Nursing Practice and Chief Nursing Officer, University Of Texas M.D. Anderson Cancer Center, Houston, TX, p. A614

SUMMERS, Curtis, Chief Executive Officer, Summit Medical Center, Edmond, OK, p. A499

SUMMERS, Debra, Chief Nursing Officer, Calhoun–Liberty Hospital, Blountstown, FL, p. A118

SUMMERS, Jeff, M.D., Medical Director, Select Specialty Hospital–North Knoxville, Powell, TN, p. A578

SUMMERS, Kelly, Chief Information Officer, Maricopa Integrated Health System, Phoenix, AZ, p. A33

SUMMERS, Paul
Interim Chief Financial Officer, Uhs Delaware Valley Hospital, Walton, NY, p. A446
President and Chief Executive Officer, Uhs Delaware Valley Hospital, Walton, NY, p. A446

SUMMERS–MAIN, Theresa, President, Genesis Medical Center, Silvis, Silvis, IL, p. A196

SUMMERSON, Tonya, Chief Clinical Officer, Dallas County Hospital, Perry, IA, p. A228

SUMMERVILLE, Wendell, Chief Financial Officer, Bryce Hospital, Tuscaloosa, AL, p. A24

SUMNER, Donna, Director, Human Resources and Organizational Development, St. Joseph Medical Center, Kansas City, MO, p. A363

SUMNER, Jack R, Assistant Administrator Finance, Providence Newberg Medical Center, Newberg, OR, p. A515

SUMNER, John, Chief Executive Officer, Trigg County Hospital, Cadiz, KY, p. A250

SUMPTER, Nikki, Senior Vice President Human Resources, Jps Health Network, Fort Worth, TX, p. A605

SUMRA, K S, M.D., Chief of Staff, Pembina County Memorial Hospital And Wedgewood Manor, Cavalier, ND, p. A466

SUMRALL, Mary Ellen, Chief Nursing Officer, Baptist Memorial Hospital–Golden Triangle, Columbus, MS, p. A346

SUMTER, Rob
Executive Vice President and Chief Operating Officer, Regional One Health, Memphis, TN, p. A575
Executive Vice President and Chief Operation Officer, Regional One Health, Memphis, TN, p. A575

SUN RHODES, Neil, M.D., Chief Medical Officer, Blackfeet Community Hospital, Saint Mary, MT, p. A380

SUND, Lynn A.
Chief Nursing Executive, Saint Francis Hospital South, Tulsa, OK, p. A509
Senior Vice President, Administrator and Chief Nursing Executive, Laureate Psychiatric Clinic And Hospital, Tulsa, OK, p. A508
Senior Vice President, Chief Nurse Executive, Saint Francis Health System and Administrator, Saint Francis Hospital, Saint Francis Hospital, Tulsa, OK, p. A509

SUNDARAMOORTHY, Abirammy, M.D., Chief Medical Officer, University Hospitals Conneaut Medical Center, Conneaut, OH, p. A480

SUNDBERG, Nita, Director Human Resources, Three Rivers Behavioral Health, West Columbia, SC, p. A558

SUNDBLOM, Karin, MSN, R.N., Chief Nursing Officer, Saint Luke'S Cushing Hospital, Leavenworth, KS, p. A239

SUNDERLIN, Tammy, Director of Nursing, Auburn Community Hospital, Auburn, NY, p. A423

SUNDGERG, Karl, Chief Executive Officer, South Lincoln Medical Center, Kemmerer, WY, p. A711

SUNDIN, Jon, M.D., Medical Director, The Orthopedic Specialty Hospital, Murray, UT, p. A649

SUNDRUD, Diane
Director Human Resources, Essentia Health Fosston, Fosston, MN, p. A332
Human Resource Service Partner, Essentia Health St. Mary'S – Detroit Lakes, Detroit Lakes, MN, p. A330

SUNGA, Marcos N, M.D., Chief of Staff, Hardin County General Hospital, Rosiclare, IL, p. A195

SUNQUIST, Joanne
Chief Information Officer East Region, St. Joseph'S Hospital, Saint Paul, MN, p. A340
Chief Information Officer, Woodwinds Health Campus, Woodbury, MN, p. A343

SUNTAY, Renato, Chief Financial Officer, Meadville Medical Center, Meadville, PA, p. A531

SUNTHA, Mohan
President and Chief Executive Officer, University Of Maryland Medical Center Midtown Campus, Baltimore, MD, p. A287
President and Chief Executive Officer, University Of Maryland Medical Center, Baltimore, MD, p. A287

SUNTRAPAK, Todd A., President and Chief Executive Officer, Valley Children'S Healthcare, Madera, CA, p. A70

SUPPLEE, Linda, Chief Executive Officer, Select Specialty Hospital Of Southeast Ohio, Newark, OH, p. A488

SURBER, Randy, Chief Executive Officer, Adventhealth Sebring, Sebring, FL, p. A139

SURBER, Shannon, Chief Operating Officer, Peacehealth Sacred Heart Medical Center At Riverbend, Springfield, OR, p. A518

SURCOUF, Shelli, Chief Financial Officer, Georgetown Behavioral Health Institute, Georgetown, TX, p. A607

SURESH, Srinivasan, M.D., Chief Medical Information Officer, Upmc Children'S Hospital Of Pittsburgh, Pittsburgh, PA, p. A538

SURGUY, Jean, Vice President, Chief Nursing Officer, Mile Bluff Medical Center, Mauston, WI, p. A699

SURKALA, Karen, Chief Executive Officer, Select Specialty Hospital–Erie, Erie, PA, p. A525

SURL, Deepak, Chief Information Officer, Eastern New Mexico Medical Center, Roswell, NM, p. A420

SURO, Marta R Mercado, Chief Operating Officer, Mennonite General Hospital, Aibonito, PR, p. A715

SUROWITZ, Dale, Chief Executive, Providence Tarzana Medical Center, Los Angeles, CA, p. A69

SURRATT, Shawn, M.D., Chief of Staff, Memorial Hospital And Manor, Bainbridge, GA, p. A148

SURROCK, Lester, Chief Financial Officer, Mission Regional Medical Center, Mission, TX, p. A625

SUSI, Jeffrey L, President and Chief Executive Officer, Cleveland Clinic Indian River Hospital, Vero Beach, FL, p. A143

SUSICK, Nancy, President, Beaumont Hospital – Royal Oak, Royal Oak, MI, p. A321

SUSIE–LATTNER, Debra, M.D., Vice President Medical Management, Advocate Condell Medical Center, Libertyville, IL, p. A188

SUSSMAN, Andrew, M.D., Chief Operating Officer, Umass Memorial Medical Center, Worcester, MA, p. A305

SUSSMAN, Howard, M.D., Chief Medical Officer, St. Joseph Hospital, Bethpage, NY, p. A423

SUSTERICH, Tim, Chief Financial Officer and Chief Operating Officer, Memorial Healthcare, Owosso, MI, p. A319

SUTARIA, Saumya, Chief Operating Officer, Hca Houston Healthcare Tomball, Tomball, TX, p. A641

SUTARIA, Saumya, M.D., Chief Operating Officer, Hca Houston Healthcare Tomball, Tomball, TX, p. A641

SUTER, Brian, Chief Financial Officer, Mayo Clinic Health System In Fairmont, Fairmont, MN, p. A331

SUTER, Lorenzo, Chief Executive Officer, Dupont Hospital, Fort Wayne, IN, p. A203

SUTER, Mia, Chief Administration Officer, Owensboro Health Regional Hospital, Owensboro, KY, p. A258

SUTHERLAND, Shea, Chief Financial Officer, Merit Health Madison, Canton, MS, p. A345

SUTIKA, John, President, Penn Highlands Dubois, Dubois, PA, p. A524

SUTKUS, Amy, M.D., Medical Staff President, Santiam Hospital, Stayton, OR, p. A518

SUTTLES, Mary Anne, Chief Nursing Officer, St. Francis Medical Center, Trenton, NJ, p. A413

SUTTON, Andrew
Chief Human Resources Officer, Coatesville Veterans Affairs Medical Center, Coatesville, PA, p. A523
Chief, Human Resources Management Service, James A. Haley Veterans' Hospital–Tampa, Tampa, FL, p. A141

SUTTON, Angie, Chief Financial Officer, Genoa Medical Facilities, Genoa, NE, p. A385

SUTTON, Elaine, Chief Information Officer, Pershing Memorial Hospital, Brookfield, MO, p. A357

SUTTON, Fred, M.D., Chief Medical Officer, Harris Health System, Houston, TX, p. A611

SUTTON, Janet, D.O., Medical Director, Mclaren Bay Special Care, Bay City, MI, p. A307

SUTTON, Jeffrey, Chief Information Officer, Lexington Veterans Affairs Medical Center, Lexington, KY, p. A255

SUTTON, Jesse, Senior Vice President and Chief Financial Officer, Texas Health Huguley Hospital Fort Worth South, Burleson, TX, p. A590

SUTTON, Julie, Director Performance Improvement, State Hospital South, Blackfoot, ID, p. A167

SUTTON, Michael, Chief Financial Officer, Chi Memorial, Chattanooga, TN, p. A567

SUTTON, Michele Kidd., President and Chief Executive Officer, North Oaks Medical Center, Hammond, LA, p. A268

SUTTON, Rhonda, Director Human Resources, Richland Hospital, Richland Center, WI, p. A704

SUTTON, Richard O., Chief Executive Officer, Southeast Alabama Medical Center, Dothan, AL, p. A17

SUTTON, Thomas, Associate Director, North Florida/South Georgia Veteran'S Health System, Gainesville, FL, p. A123

SUTTON–WALLACE, Pamela, Chief Executive Officer, University Of Virginia Medical Center, Charlottesville, VA, p. A657

SUVER, James A., Chief Executive Officer, Ridgecrest Regional Hospital, Ridgecrest, CA, p. A80

SUZUKI, Daniel, M.D., Medical Director, Las Encinas Hospital, Pasadena, CA, p. A77

SVARC, Mackenzie, Finance Director, Friend Community Healthcare System, Friend, NE, p. A385

SVEC, David, M.D., Chief Medical Officer, Stanford Health Care – Valleycare, Pleasanton, CA, p. A78

SVENDSEN, Mark Deyo, M.D., Medical Director, Mayo Clinic Health System – Red Cedar In Menomonie, Menomonie, WI, p. A700

SWAGERTY, Jill, Director Human Resources, Union County General Hospital, Clayton, NM, p. A417

SWAIN, Art, Vice President Support Services, Joint Township District Memorial Hospital, Saint Marys, OH, p. A490

SWANDAL, Dianne, R.N., MSN, Vice President Patient Care, St. Joseph Hospital, Bangor, ME, p. A281

SWANGER, Cae, Chief Information Officer, Riverside Community Hospital, Riverside, CA, p. A81

SWANGER, Carol, Chief Nursing Officer, Kansas Rehabilitation Hospital, Topeka, KS, p. A246

SWANK, Colleen, Chief Medical Officer, Altru Health System, Grand Forks, ND, p. A467

SWANK, Georgia, Chief Nursing Officer, Ridge Behavioral Health System, Lexington, KY, p. A255

SWANSBORO, Pam, R.N., Chief Nursing Officer, Conemaugh Meyersdale Medical Center, Meyersdale, PA, p. A532

SWANSON, Julie, Coordinator Human Resources, Encompass Health Rehabilitation Hospital Of Parkersburg, Parkersburg, WV, p. A688

SWANSON, Kerry, Regional President, President Good Samaritan, Good Samaritan Regional Health Center, Mount Vernon, IL, p. A190

SWARTOUT, Paula, Human Resources Manager, Dickinson County Healthcare System, Iron Mountain, MI, p. A314

SWARTWOOD, Peggy, Assistant Vice President, Finance and Controller, Uhs Chenango Memorial Hospital, Norwich, NY, p. A440

SWARTWOOD, Philip, Director Information Systems, Grove City Medical Center, Grove City, PA, p. A526

SWARTZ, Edward, Chief Financial Officer, Spring Grove Hospital Center, Baltimore, MD, p. A288

SWARTZ, Michael J., Interim Director, Veterans Affairs Western New York Healthcare System–Batavia Division, Batavia, NY, p. A423

SWAYNE, Angela, M.D., Chief Medical Officer, Piedmont Fayette Hospital, Fayetteville, GA, p. A153

SWEARINGEN, Angela, Vice President Finance, St. Mary'S Medical Center, Huntington, WV, p. A686

SWEAT, Holli, Associate Administrator and Chief Nursing Officer, Memorial Satilla Health, Waycross, GA, p. A163

SWEAT, Kendra, Director Human Resources, Power County Hospital District, American Falls, ID, p. A167

SWEENEY, Janey, Chief Nursing Officer, Suncoast Behavioral Health Center, Bradenton, FL, p. A119

SWEENEY, Karen, Vice President, Chief Nursing Officer, Mercy Hospital Ada, Ada, OK, p. A496

SWEENEY, Michael
Chief Informatics Officer, Jeanes Hospital, Philadelphia, PA, p. A535
Chief Information Officer, Fox Chase Cancer Center–American Oncologic Hospital, Philadelphia, PA, p. A534

SWEENEY, Shaun, Vice President Patient Care Services, Hackensack Meridian Health Carrier Clinic, Belle Mead, NJ, p. A403

SWEET, Mary, Administrator, Kiowa County Memorial Hospital, Greensburg, KS, p. A236

SWEET, Renae, Chief Financial Officer, Surprise Valley Health Care District, Cedarville, CA, p. A54

SWEET, Terrance J., Director Information Technology, Winnebago Mental Health Institute, Winnebago, WI, p. A709

SWEETAPPLE, Carolyn, Executive Director, South Oaks Hospital, Amityville, NY, p. A422

SWEHA, Amir, M.D., Vice President Medical Administration, Methodist Hospital Of Sacramento, Sacramento, CA, p. A82

SWEITZER, Gregory, Chief Medical Officer, Wright Patterson Medical Center, Wright, OH, p. A494

SWENSON, Daniel J., Administrator, Centracare Health–Long Prairie, Long Prairie, MN, p. A334

SWENSON, Jennifer, President and Chief Executive Officer, Simi Valley Hospital, Simi Valley, CA, p. A89

SWENSON, Nena, Financial Manager, Tahoe Pacific Hospitals, Sparks, NV, p. A398

SWENSON, Nina, Director Business Services, Newport Bay Hospital, Newport Beach, CA, p. A74

SWENSON, Paula C., R.N., Vice President and Chief Nursing Officer, St. Catherine Hospital, East Chicago, IN, p. A202

SWENSON, Warren, Chief Financial Officer, United Medical Rehabilitation Hospital, Hammond, LA, p. A268

SWICK, Michael D., President and Chief Executive Officer, Lima Memorial Health System, Lima, OH, p. A485

SWIDERSKI, Tom, Chief Financial Officer, Orthopaedic Hospital Of Wisconsin, Glendale, WI, p. A695

SWIFT, Brian M, Senior Administrator Plant Operations, Burke Rehabilitation Hospital, White Plains, NY, p. A447

SWIFT, David, Chief Human Resources Officer, Penn State Milton S. Hershey Medical Center, Hershey, PA, p. A527

SWIFT, Kyle, Chief Executive Officer, Woodland Heights Medical Center, Lufkin, TX, p. A622

SWIFT, Nick, Chief Financial Officer, Maury Regional Hospital, Columbia, TN, p. A568

SWIFT, Patrick T., Chief Executive Officer, Select Specialty Hospital–Northeast New Jersey, Rochelle Park, NJ, p. A412

SWIGER, Jared, Director Information Systems, Ashtabula County Medical Center, Ashtabula, OH, p. A472

SWINDELL, Terry
Chief Financial Officer, Camden General Hospital, Camden, TN, p. A566
Controller, Bolivar General Hospital, Bolivar, TN, p. A566

SWINDLE, Patrick
Administrator, Ut Health Quitman, Quitman, TX, p. A630
Interim Chief Executive Officer, Ut Health Pittsburg, Pittsburg, TX, p. A628

SWINDLER, Diana, Chief Financial Officer, Tri Valley Health System, Cambridge, NE, p. A383

SWINGLE, Dale, Vice President Information Services, Guthrie Troy Community Hospital, Troy, PA, p. A542

SWINT, Ken
Director Finance, Promedica Defiance Regional Hospital, Defiance, OH, p. A482
Vice President Finance and Chief Financial Officer, Promedica Fostoria Community Hospital, Fostoria, OH, p. A483

SWINT, Patricia
Director Information Management Systems, Promedica Defiance Regional Hospital, Defiance, OH, p. A482
Director Information Technology, St. Luke'S Hospital, Maumee, OH, p. A487

SWISHER, Kay, Chief Nursing Officer, Prisma Health Laurens County Hospital, Clinton, SC, p. A550

SWISSHELM, Patricia, Acting Chief Fiscal Service, Lexington Veterans Affairs Medical Center, Lexington, KY, p. A255

SWOFFORD, William, M.D., Chief of Staff, Miller County Hospital, Colquitt, GA, p. A150

SY, Annette
Chief Nursing Officer, Keck Hospital Of Usc, Los Angeles, CA, p. A67
Chief Nursing Officer, Usc Norris Comprehensive Cancer Center, Los Angeles, CA, p. A69

SYED, Imran, Manager Technology Information Services, Spectrum Health Zeeland Community Hospital, Zeeland, MI, p. A326

SYED, Mamoon
Vice President Human Resources, Children'S Hospital Of Orange County, Orange, CA, p. A76
Vice President Human Resources, Rady Children'S Hospital – San Diego, San Diego, CA, p. A84

SYKES, Angel, Director Human Resources, Memorial Hospital And Manor, Bainbridge, GA, p. A148

SYKES, Christina, Director Human Resources, Labette Health, Parsons, KS, p. A243

SYKES, Lee, Human Resources Director, Lifebrite Community Hospital Of Stokes, Danbury, NC, p. A452

SYKES, Lisa
Director Information Services, Atrium Health Union, Monroe, NC, p. A458
IS/Communications Director, Atrium Health Anson, Wadesboro, NC, p. A463
Manager, Information Services, Atrium Health Cabarrus, Concord, NC, p. A452

SYKES, Rebecca S
Chief Information Officer, Mercy Health – Fairfield Hospital, Fairfield, OH, p. A483
Chief Information Officer, Mercy St. Anne Hospital, Toledo, OH, p. A492
Senior Vice President Resource Management, Chief Information Officer, Mercy Health – St. Charles Hospital, Oregon, OH, p. A489

SYLSBERRY, Angelia, Chief Nursing Officer, Pam Rehabilitation Hospital Of Tulsa, Tulsa, OK, p. A509

SYLVESTER, Joy L., Administrator, People Services, South Lake Hospital, Clermont, FL, p. A120

SYLVIA–HUTCHINSON, Doreen M, Vice President Operations and Chief Nurse Executive, Fairview Hospital, Great Barrington, MA, p. A299

SYNDERGAARD, Christy, Vice President Nursing, Cherokee Regional Medical Center, Cherokee, IA, p. A219

SYNNESTVEDT, Eric, Director Information Technology, Southside Regional Medical Center, Petersburg, VA, p. A665

SYPIEN, Troy
Director Information Technology and Systems, Medical City Dallas, Dallas, TX, p. A597
Director Information Technology and Systems, Tristar Skyline Medical Center, Nashville, TN, p. A577

SZABO, Sandor, M.D., Ph.D., M.P.H., Chief of Staff, Va Long Beach Healthcare System, Long Beach, CA, p. A65

SZAPOR, Ann, Vice President and Chief Nursing Officer, Memorial Hermann Greater Heights Hospital, Houston, TX, p. A612

SZCZEPANSKI, Bernadette S, Senior Vice President, Human Resources, Northwestern Medicine Mchenry, Mchenry, IL, p. A189

SZCZUROWSKI, Richard, Director Human Resources, Norristown State Hospital, Norristown, PA, p. A533

SZEKELY, Lauraine, R.N., Senior Vice President, Patient Care, Northern Westchester Hospital, Mount Kisco, NY, p. A432

SZEWCZYK, Edwin, Chief Financial Officer, Wetzel County Hospital, New Martinsville, WV, p. A687

SZKLANY, Chelsea, Hospital Administrator, Southern Nevada Adult Mental Health Services, Las Vegas, NV, p. A395

SZOSTEK, Joshua, Chief Financial Officer, Specialty Hospital Jacksonville, Jacksonville, FL, p. A126

SZUMEL, Richard C., Chief Executive Officer, Union Hospital, Elkton, MD, p. A290

SZURA, Kathleen, R.N., Chief Nursing Officer, Encompass Health Rehabilitation Hospital Of Bakersfield, Bakersfield, CA, p. A52

SZYSKA, Julie, Chief Executive Officer and Managing Director, Havenwyck Hospital, Auburn Hills, MI, p. A306

T

TAAFFE, Janette, Vice President, Human Resource, St. Luke'S Hospital, Chesterfield, MO, p. A358

TABAK, Jeremy, M.D., President Medical Staff, Baptist Health South Florida, South Miami Hospital, Miami, FL, p. A130

TABB, Kevin, Chief Executive Officer, Beth Israel Deaconess Medical Center, Boston, MA, p. A294

TABIBI, Wasae S, M.D., President Medical Staff, Plaza Specialty Hospital, Houston, TX, p. A613

TABOR, J. Britton, Executive Vice President, Chief Financial Officer, Erlanger Medical Center, Chattanooga, TN, p. A567

TABOR, Jeffrey, Director Human Resources, Jackson General Hospital, Ripley, WV, p. A689

TABOR, Susan, Interim Chief Executive Officer, Red River Behavioral Health System, Grand Forks, ND, p. A467

TABOR, Tammie, Chief Executive Officer, Vibra Rehabilitation Hospital Of Amarillo, Amarillo, TX, p. A582

TABORA, Knaya, Chief Operating Officer and Chief Nursing Officer, Colorado River Medical Center, Needles, CA, p. A74

TABUENCA, Arnold, M.D., Medical Director, Riverside University Health System–Medical Center, Moreno Valley, CA, p. A73

TACHIBANA, Charleen, R.N., Senior Vice President and Chief Nursing Officer, Virginia Mason Medical Center, Seattle, WA, p. A679

TACKITT, Sue, Chief Nursing Officer, Connally Memorial Medical Center, Floresville, TX, p. A604

TADURAN, Virgilio, M.D., Chief Medical Officer, Satanta District Hospital And Long Term Care, Satanta, KS, p. A245

TADYCH, Michael C., Director, Veterans Affairs Puget Sound Health Care System, Seattle, WA, p. A678

TAFFE, Patrick, Vice President Information Services, North Memorial Health Hospital, Robbinsdale, MN, p. A338

TAFOYA, Debbie, Vice President and Chief Information Officer, Huntington Memorial Hospital, Pasadena, CA, p. A77

TAFT, Kenneth L, Executive Vice President and Chief Operating Officer, Bronson Methodist Hospital, Kalamazoo, MI, p. A315

TAFUR, Mario, M.D., Chief of Staff, St. Luke'S Behavioral Health Center, Phoenix, AZ, p. A34

TAGGART, Travis, Director Information Technology, Rivervalley Behavioral Health Hospital, Owensboro, KY, p. A259

TAGGE, Gordon, M.D., President Medical Staff, Three Rivers Hospital, Brewster, WA, p. A671

TAHAN, Pamela S., Chief Executive Officer, Wellington Regional Medical Center, Wellington, FL, p. A143

TAHBO, Robin, Financial Management Officer, U. S. Public Health Service Indian Hospital, Parker, AZ, p. A32

TAHIR, Fahad
Chief Executive Officer, Saint Thomas Midtown Hospital, Nashville, TN, p. A577
Chief Executive Officer, Saint Thomas West Hospital, Nashville, TN, p. A577

TAILLEFER, Marguerite, M.D., Acting President Medical Staff, Sarah D. Culbertson Memorial Hospital, Rushville, IL, p. A195

TAKACS, Susan, Market Chief Operating Officer, Physicians Regional – Pine Ridge, Naples, FL, p. A132

TAKES, Kay
President, Mercy Medical Center–Dubuque, Dubuque, IA, p. A222
President, Mercy Medical Center–Dyersville, Dyersville, IA, p. A222

TAKEUCHI, Susi, Chief Human Resources and Organization Development Officer, Ronald Reagan Ucla Medical Center, Los Angeles, CA, p. A69

TALBERT, Adrienne, Interim Administrator, Prisma Health North Greenville Ltach, Travelers Rest, SC, p. A557

TALBERT, Bradley S., President and Chief Executive Officer, Memorial Hospital Jacksonville, Jacksonville, FL, p. A125

TALBOT, Angela, Manager Human Resources, Hamilton County Hospital, Syracuse, KS, p. A246

TALBOT, Jack, Director, Human Resources, West Chester Hospital, West Chester, OH, p. A494

TALBOT, Lisa, Director Human Resources, St. David'S South Austin Medical Center, Austin, TX, p. A586
TALBOT, Tom, Chief Executive Officer, Community Mental Health Center, Lawrenceburg, IN, p. A210
TALBOTT, Ellen E, MSN, R.N., Vice President Patient Care Services, Mclaren Bay Region, Bay City, MI, p. A307
TALBOTT, Sarah, Chief Nursing Officer, Sanford Chamberlain Medical Center, Chamberlain, SD, p. A560
TALLEY, Cyndi, Director Information Systems, Tristar Greenview Regional Hospital, Bowling Green, KY, p. A250
TALLEY, Linda, MS, R.N., Vice President and Chief Nursing Officer, Children'S National Health System, Washington, DC, p. A115
TALLEY, Rockey, M.D., Chief Medical Officer, Alliancehealth Midwest, Midwest City, OK, p. A502
TALLEY, Stephanie S.
Chief Human Resource Officer, The Hospitals Of Providence Sierra Campus, El Paso, TX, p. A603
Chief Human Resource Officer, The Hospitals Of Providence Transmountain Campus, El Paso, TX, p. A603
Director Human Resources, Baylor Scott & White Medical Center – Centennial, Frisco, TX, p. A606
Market Chief Human Resource Officer, The Hospitals Of Providence Memorial Campus, El Paso, TX, p. A602
TALLEY, Tracey, Chief Financial and Information Officer, Kalispell Regional Healthcare, Kalispell, MT, p. A378
TALLON, Joe, Vice President Finance, Salina Regional Health Center, Salina, KS, p. A245
TALLON, Richard, Chief Financial Officer, Jefferson County Hospital, Waurika, OK, p. A510
TAM, David A, M.D., FACHE, Chief Operating Officer, Providence Saint John'S Health Center, Santa Monica, CA, p. A89
TAMANAHA, Nona, Vice President Human Resources, The Queen'S Medical Center, Honolulu, HI, p. A165
TAMAYO, Loree, Chief Executive Officer, Coon Memorial Hospital, Dalhart, TX, p. A595
TAMBURELLO, Leonardo, Chief Financial Officer, Brookdale Hospital Medical Center, New York, NY, p. A432
TAMMARO, Vincent, Chief Financial Officer, Yale–New Haven Hospital, New Haven, CT, p. A110
TAMMINEN, John, M.D., President Medical Staff, Carilion Giles Community Hospital, Pearisburg, VA, p. A664
TAN, Bradford, M.D., Chief Medical Officer, Midwestern Regional Medical Center, Zion, IL, p. A198
TANAKA, Steven, Chief Information Officer, Palomar Medical Center Poway, Poway, CA, p. A79
TANCREDO, Beth, Director Operations, South Florida Baptist Hospital, Plant City, FL, p. A137
TANDE, Brett, Chief Financial Officer, Santa Ynez Valley Cottage Hospital, Solvang, CA, p. A90
TANDON, Satwant, M.D., Director of Clinical Services, Oklahoma Forensic Center, Vinita, OK, p. A510
TANDY, Gary R, Chief Financial Officer, Pershing Memorial Hospital, Brookfield, MO, p. A357
TANDY, William C., Chief Information Officer, Upmc Hanover, Hanover, PA, p. A526
TANEBAUM, Cynthia, Director Information Services, Medstar Harbor Hospital, Baltimore, MD, p. A287
TANEJA, K. Singh, Chief Operating Officer, Saint Elizabeths Hospital, Washington, DC, p. A116
TANEY, Amy, Chief Human Resource Officer, Highland Hospital, Rochester, NY, p. A442
TANG, Francis, Chief Information Officer, Rancho Los Amigos National Rehabilitation Center, Downey, CA, p. A56
TANG, Shirley, R.N., Chief Nursing Officer, Monterey Park Hospital, Monterey Park, CA, p. A73
TANGEMAN, Todd
Chief Operating Officer and Chief Human Resource Officer, Newton Medical Center, Newton, KS, p. A241
Chief Operating Officer, Newton Medical Center, Newton, KS, p. A241
TANGUAY, Denis, Chief Information Officer, Central Maine Medical Center, Lewiston, ME, p. A283
TANJUAKIO, Robert, Chief Information Resources Management, Edward Hines, Jr. Veterans Affairs Hospital, Hines, IL, p. A185
TANKEL, Nancy, R.N., Chief Nurse Executive, Kaiser Permanente Woodland Hills Medical Center, Los Angeles, CA, p. A67
TANNENBAUM, Scott, M.D., Medical Director, Encompass Health Rehabilitation Hospital Of Sunrise, Sunrise, FL, p. A140
TANNER, Ashley, Director of Nursing, Wiregrass Medical Center, Geneva, AL, p. A18
TANNER, Douglas, President, Atmore Community Hospital, Atmore, AL, p. A14
TANNER, James, M.D., Chief Medical Officer, Northwest Medical Center – Springdale, Springdale, AR, p. A48
TANNOS, Paul, Chief Financial Officer, The Physicians Centre Hospital, Bryan, TX, p. A590
TANTHOREY, Geoff, Director, Information Systems, Granville Health System, Oxford, NC, p. A460
TANZELLA, Richard, Chief Executive Officer, Piedmont Rockdale Hospital, Conyers, GA, p. A151
TAPLETT, Dean, Controller, Quincy Valley Medical Center, Quincy, WA, p. A677
TAPLIN, Tyrrell, Chief Executive Officer, Encompass Health Rehabilitation Hospital Of Arlington, Arlington, TX, p. A583
TAPP, Gina
Director Human Resources, Samaritan North Lincoln Hospital, Lincoln City, OR, p. A514
Director Human Resources, Samaritan Pacific Communities Hospital, Newport, OR, p. A515
TAPPER, Shane, Director Management Information Systems, Fort Madison Community Hospital, Fort Madison, IA, p. A223
TARAR, Ahmad, M.D., Medical Director, Heartland Behavioral Health Services, Nevada, MO, p. A366
TARASOVICH, James
Chief Financial Officer, Mayo Clinic Health System In Saint James, Saint James, MN, p. A339
Chief Financial Officer, Mayo Clinic Health System In Springfield, Springfield, MN, p. A341
TARBAY, Amy, Director Nursing Services, Naval Hospital Pensacola, Pensacola, FL, p. A136
TARBET, Joyce, M.D., Chief Medical Officer, Murray County Medical Center, Slayton, MN, p. A340
TARDIF, Kathleen, Director of Human Resources, Central Regional Hospital, Butner, NC, p. A450
TAROLA, Robert, Chief Financial Officer, Little Company Of Mary Hospital And Health Care Centers, Evergreen Park, IL, p. A183
TARRANT, Jeffrey S., Chief Executive Officer, Upson Regional Medical Center, Thomaston, GA, p. A161
TARRANT, Maureen, President and Chief Executive Officer, Presbyterian–St. Luke'S Medical Center, Denver, CO, p. A99
TARULLI, Pamela, Senior Vice President Human Resources, Good Samaritan Regional Medical Center, Suffern, NY, p. A445
TARVER, Dennis, Director Information Technology, Elkview General Hospital, Hobart, OK, p. A500
TARVER, Jeanette, Director of Finance, Sonoma Valley Hospital, Sonoma, CA, p. A90
TARVER, Rebecca, Chief Nursing Officer, Bates County Memorial Hospital, Butler, MO, p. A357
TASSEY, Karen, FACHE, Chief Operating Officer, Columbia Memorial Hospital, Hudson, NY, p. A429
TASSIN, Bruce J., President, CHI Saint Joseph Health, Lexington, KY, p. A255
TASSO, Tina, Manager Human Resources, The Orthopedic Specialty Hospital, Murray, UT, p. A649
TATE, Charlene, M.D., Chief Medical Staff and Clinical Services, Eleanor Slater Hospital, Cranston, RI, p. A547
TATE, Charles, Director Information Technology, Lallie Kemp Medical Center, Independence, LA, p. A269
TATE, James, M.D., Chief of Staff, Patients' Hospital Of Redding, Redding, CA, p. A79
TATE, Jean, Vice President Human Resources, Riverview Health, Crookston, MN, p. A330
TATE, Joel W., Chief Executive Officer, Clay County Hospital, Ashland, AL, p. A13
TATE, Mary Lou, Chief Financial Officer, Morris Hospital & Healthcare Centers, Morris, IL, p. A190
TATE CURTI, Joseph, Chief Operating Officer, Elliot Hospital, Manchester, NH, p. A401
TATRO, Chad, Supervisor Information Systems, Northeast Regional Medical Center, Kirksville, MO, p. A363
TATRO, Mary, Chief Nursing Officer, Millinocket Regional Hospital, Millinocket, ME, p. A284
TATU, Ryan, Chief Executive Officer, Texoma Medical Center, Denison, TX, p. A599
TAUL, Kelly, Business Manager, Meadowbrook Rehabilitation Hospital, Gardner, KS, p. A235
TAUNER, Gary, Chief Operating Officer, St. John'S Medical Center And Living Center, Jackson, WY, p. A711
TAUNTON, David, M.D., Chief of Staff, Texas Health Harris Methodist Hospital Southlake, Southlake, TX, p. A637
TAUPIN, Michel, M.D., Chief Medical Officer, Abington–Lansdale Hospital Jefferson Health, Lansdale, PA, p. A529
TAVARY, James, Chief Executive Officer, Wickenburg Community Hospital, Wickenburg, AZ, p. A38
TAVELLA, Christopher
Acting Executive Director, Rockland Children'S Psychiatric Center, Orangeburg, NY, p. A440
Executive Director, Rockland Psychiatric Center, Orangeburg, NY, p. A441
TAWNEY, Michael W, D.O., Vice President Medical Affairs, Mclaren Port Huron, Port Huron, MI, p. A320
TAYLOR, Adam, Manager Information Technology, Northern Inyo Hospital, Bishop, CA, p. A53
TAYLOR, Adrienne, Director of Health Information Management, Northwest Mississippi Medical Center, Clarksdale, MS, p. A345
TAYLOR, Al, Vice President and Administrator, Memorial Hospital Of Carbondale, Carbondale, IL, p. A175
TAYLOR, Alice, Chief Executive Officer, Broward Health North, Deerfield Beach, FL, p. A121
TAYLOR, Allison H, R.N., Chief Nursing Officer and Vice President Clinical Services, Sampson Regional Medical Center, Clinton, NC, p. A452
TAYLOR, Amy, Chief Financial Officer, Oklahoma Center For Orthopedic And Multi–Specialty Surgery, Oklahoma City, OK, p. A504
TAYLOR, Anthony, Manager Information Technology, Cherokee Indian Hospital, Cherokee, NC, p. A452
TAYLOR, Beth, Vice President, Human Resources, Newton–Wellesley Hospital, Newton Lower Falls, MA, p. A301
TAYLOR, Brenda, Director Information Systems, Texas Health Harris Methodist Hospital Cleburne, Cleburne, TX, p. A592
TAYLOR, Brett, Manager Information, Van Wert County Hospital, Van Wert, OH, p. A493
TAYLOR, Carol M., Regional Director Clinical Operations, Kaiser Permanente Capitol Hill Campus, Seattle, WA, p. A677
TAYLOR, Cecilia, Chief Financial Officer, Midwestern Regional Medical Center, Zion, IL, p. A198
TAYLOR, Cherie, Chief Executive Officer, Northern Rockies Medical Center, Cut Bank, MT, p. A375
TAYLOR, Cheryl, R.N., Director of Nursing, Henry Ford Kingswood Hospital, Ferndale, MI, p. A311
TAYLOR, Christina, Director Human Resources, The Brook Hospital – Kmi, Louisville, KY, p. A257
TAYLOR, Dana Shantel, Director Organizational Development, Fairfield Memorial Hospital, Fairfield, IL, p. A183
TAYLOR, Deborah, Chief Information Officer, Chatham Hospital, Siler City, NC, p. A462
TAYLOR, Debra, Chief Nursing Officer, Paris Regional Medical Center, Paris, TX, p. A628
TAYLOR, Dwayne, Chief Executive Officer, Sycamore Shoals Hospital, Elizabethton, TN, p. A569
TAYLOR, Dylan, Chief Administrative Officer, Aspirus Ontonagon Hospital, Inc., Ontonagon, MI, p. A319
TAYLOR, Ernest Lee, M.D., Vice President Medical Affairs, St. Mary'S Medical Center, Huntington, WV, p. A686
TAYLOR, Eulon Ross, Clinical Director, North Texas State Hospital, Wichita Falls Campus, Wichita Falls, TX, p. A645
TAYLOR, Faye M, R.N., Director of Nursing, Stephens County Hospital, Toccoa, GA, p. A162
TAYLOR, Gregory W, M.D., Vice President and Chief Operating Officer, High Point Medical Center, High Point, NC, p. A456
TAYLOR, Heather, Human Resources Manager, Tippah County Hospital, Ripley, MS, p. A354
TAYLOR, Heidi, President, Morton Hospital And Medical Center, Taunton, MA, p. A304
TAYLOR, Janey, Chief Information and Technology, Overton Brooks Veterans Affairs Medical Center, Shreveport, LA, p. A278
TAYLOR, Jay, M.D., Chief of Medical Staff, Pondera Medical Center, Conrad, MT, p. A375
TAYLOR, Jeff, Vice President Finance, St. Luke'S Regional Medical Center, Boise, ID, p. A168
TAYLOR, Jeremy, Director Information Services, Saint Francis Hospital, Charleston, WV, p. A684
TAYLOR, Jim, Chief Business Office, North Florida/South Georgia Veteran'S Health System, Gainesville, FL, p. A123
TAYLOR, Joel
Chief Executive Officer, Coastal Carolina Hospital, Hardeeville, SC, p. A554
Chief Information Officer, Carepoint Health Bayonne Medical Center, Bayonne, NJ, p. A403
Chief Information Officer, Carepoint Health Hoboken University Medical Center, Hoboken, NJ, p. A406
TAYLOR, Judd
Chief Financial Officer, Eastern Idaho Regional Medical Center, Idaho Falls, ID, p. A169
Chief Financial Officer, Ogden Regional Medical Center, Ogden, UT, p. A650
TAYLOR, Julia, Area Director Human Resources, Vibra Hospital Of Charleston, Mt. Pleasant, SC, p. A555
TAYLOR, Julie, Chief Executive Officer, Alaska Regional Hospital, Anchorage, AK, p. A25
TAYLOR, Kendra, President and Chief Executive Officer, Salem Township Hospital, Salem, IL, p. A195
TAYLOR, Konnie, Chief Financial Officer, Carl Albert Community Mental Health Center, Mcalester, OK, p. A502

TAYLOR, Kristie, Chief Financial Officer, Southern Tennessee Regional Health System–Lawrenceburg, Lawrenceburg, TN, p. A573

TAYLOR, Lora, Director Human Resources and Compliance Officer, Unitypoint Health–Keokuk, Keokuk, IA, p. A225

TAYLOR, Marc, IS Director, Mountain West Medical Center, Tooele, UT, p. A653

TAYLOR, Marcia, Chief Executive Officer, Select Specialty Hospital–Memphis, Memphis, TN, p. A575

TAYLOR, Meredith, Controller, South Sunflower County Hospital, Indianola, MS, p. A348

TAYLOR, Merle, Vice President Operations, Upmc St. Margaret, Pittsburgh, PA, p. A538

TAYLOR, Michael
  Chief Information Officer, Bon Secours St. Francis Hospital, Charleston, SC, p. A549
  Vice President Finance, Northridge Hospital Medical Center, Los Angeles, CA, p. A68
  Vice President Financial Services and Chief Financial Officer, St. Rose Hospital, Hayward, CA, p. A61

TAYLOR, Michael V
  Senior Vice President Human Resources, Sentara Leigh Hospital, Norfolk, VA, p. A664
  Vice President Human Resources, Sentara Princess Anne Hospital, Virginia Beach, VA, p. A668

TAYLOR, Mimi
  Corporate Vice President Information Technology, Baptist Health South Florida, Baptist Hospital Of Miami, Miami, FL, p. A130
  Corporate Vice President Information Technology, Baptist Health South Florida, Homestead Hospital, Homestead, FL, p. A125
  Vice President Information Technology, Baptist Health South Florida, Mariners Hospital, Tavernier, FL, p. A142
  Vice President Information Technology, Baptist Health South Florida, South Miami Hospital, Miami, FL, p. A130

TAYLOR, Nathan, Director of Nursing, Heartland Behavioral Health Services, Nevada, MO, p. A366

TAYLOR, Nick, Chief Executive Officer, Baylor Scott & White Medical Center–Uptown, Dallas, TX, p. A595

TAYLOR, Patrick, President and Chief Executive Officer, Holy Cross Hospital, Fort Lauderdale, FL, p. A122

TAYLOR, Paul, Administrator, Ozarks Community Hospital, Gravette, AR, p. A42

TAYLOR, Randy, Chief Information Technology Officer, Stillwater Medical Perry, Perry, OK, p. A506

TAYLOR, Renae, Chief Nursing Officer, Southeastern Health, Lumberton, NC, p. A458

TAYLOR, Richard, Chief Financial Officer, Western Mental Health Institute, Bolivar, TN, p. A566

TAYLOR, Robbie, Director Human Resources, North Sunflower Medical Center, Ruleville, MS, p. A354

TAYLOR, Robert, Director Information Services, St. Christopher'S Hospital For Children, Philadelphia, PA, p. A536

TAYLOR, Ross, M.D., Clinical Director, Austin State Hospital, Austin, TX, p. A585

TAYLOR, Sarah, Chief Human Resources, National Jewish Health, Denver, CO, p. A99

TAYLOR, Scott J., President and Chief Executive Officer, St. Catherine Hospital, Garden City, KS, p. A235

TAYLOR, Scotty, Information Technology Director, East Mississippi State Hospital, Meridian, MS, p. A351

TAYLOR, Sharon, Human Resources Director, Allegiance Specialty Hospital Of Greenville, Greenville, MS, p. A347

TAYLOR, Sheri, Director Human Resources, Union General Hospital, Farmerville, LA, p. A267

TAYLOR, Stacy, Chief Financial Officer, Nemaha County Hospital, Auburn, NE, p. A382

TAYLOR, Steve, Chief Information Officer, Anderson Regional Health System South, Meridian, MS, p. A351

TAYLOR, Steven E.
  Chief Executive Officer, Blackwell Regional Hospital, Blackwell, OK, p. A497
  Chief Executive Officer, Stillwater Medical Perry, Perry, OK, p. A506

TAYLOR, Steven L., Chief Executive Officer, Harrison County Hospital, Corydon, IN, p. A201

TAYLOR, Sue O., Vice President Nursing, Vidant Duplin Hospital, Kenansville, NC, p. A457

TAYLOR, Susan L., Chief Executive Officer, College Hospital Costa Mesa, Costa Mesa, CA, p. A55

TAYLOR, Todd, Chief Executive Officer, Stafford County Hospital, Stafford, KS, p. A246

TAYLOR, Tracy, Chief Nurse Executive, Fairfield Memorial Hospital, Fairfield, IL, p. A183

TAYLOR, Tyler, Chief Executive Officer, Wayne Medical Center, Waynesboro, TN, p. A580

TAYLOR, Tyrone, Chief Financial Officer, Veterans Affairs New Jersey Health Care System, East Orange, NJ, p. A405

TAYLOR, Venus, Director Human Resources, Bhc Alhambra Hospital, Rosemead, CA, p. A81

TAYLOR, Wes, Chief Operating Officer, Havasu Regional Medical Center, Lake Havasu City, AZ, p. A31

TEAFF, Sarah, Chief Operating Officer, St. Luke Community Healthcare, Ronan, MT, p. A379

TEAGUE, Dean, Chief Executive Officer, Calverthealth Medical Center, Prince Frederick, MD, p. A293

TEAGUE, Lara Ellen, R.N., Chief Nursing Officer, Lillian M. Hudspeth Memorial Hospital, Sonora, TX, p. A637

TEAHL, Bradley, Director Human Resources, Encompass Health Rehabilitation Hospital Of York, York, PA, p. A546

TEAL, Barbara, R.N., Associate Director Patient Care Services and Nurse Executive, Sioux Falls Veterans Affairs Health Care System, Sioux Falls, SD, p. A564

TEAL, Cydney, M.D., Vice President Medical Affairs, Union Hospital, Elkton, MD, p. A290

TEAS, Gregory, M.D., Chief Medical Officer, Alexian Brothers Behavioral Health Hospital, Hoffman Estates, IL, p. A186

TEATER, Phyllis, Chief Information Officer, Ohio State University Wexner Medical Center, Columbus, OH, p. A479

TEATSORTH, Neil, Vice President Human Resources, Norwegian American Hospital, Chicago, IL, p. A179

TEBBE, James, M.D., Vice President Medical Affairs, Ochsner Medical Center – Kenner, Kenner, LA, p. A270

TEDDER, Cookie, Human Resources Manager, Texas Health Center For Diagnostic & Surgery, Plano, TX, p. A630

TEDESCO, Art, Interim Chief Financial Officer, Gaylord Hospital, Wallingford, CT, p. A111

TEEL, David R., Financial Officer, Terrell State Hospital, Terrell, TX, p. A640

TEETER, Stephen, Business Manager, Hawaii State Hospital, Kaneohe, HI, p. A166

TEFFETELLER, Scott L., Senior Vice President and President of East Region, Community Hospital East, Indianapolis, IN, p. A206

TEICHMEIER, Laura, Director Human Resources, Memorial Community Health, Aurora, NE, p. A382

TEIGEN, Seth R.
  Chief Executive Officer, Mission Hospital, Mission Viejo, CA, p. A72
  President, Ascension Southeast Wisconsin Hospital – Franklin Campus, Franklin, WI, p. A695
  President, Ascension Southeast Wisconsin Hospital – St. Francis Campus, Milwaukee, WI, p. A700

TEITELBAUM, Karen
  Chief Executive Officer, Schwab Rehabilitation Hospital, Chicago, IL, p. A179
  President and Chief Executive Officer, Mount Sinai Hospital, Chicago, IL, p. A178

TEJADA, Vanessa, Director Human Resources, Encompass Health Rehabilitation Hospital Of San Antonio, San Antonio, TX, p. A634

TEJEDA, Nicholas R, Market Chief Executive Officer, The Hospitals Of Providence Memorial Campus, El Paso, TX, p. A602

TEJEDA, Nicholas R., Market Chief Executive Officer, The Hospitals Of Providence Memorial Campus, El Paso, TX, p. A602

TELHIARD, Nicole, MSN, Chief Nursing Officer, Our Lady Of The Lake Regional Medical Center, Baton Rouge, LA, p. A264

TELITZ, Rita, Chief Administrative Officer, Marshfield Medical Center – Ladysmith, Ladysmith, WI, p. A698

TELL, Marjorie, Vice President Information Technology, Aspirus Riverview Hospital And Clinics, Inc., Wisconsin Rapids, WI, p. A709

TELLES, Ron
  Chief Financial Officer, Whidbeyhealth, Coupeville, WA, p. A672
  Interim Chief Executive Officer, Whidbeyhealth, Coupeville, WA, p. A672

TELLOR, Tammy, Acting Director Human Resources, Choate Mental Health Center, Anna, IL, p. A173

TELLY, Joel, Chief Executive Officer, Healthbridge Children'S Hospital Of Houston, Houston, TX, p. A611

TELTHORSTER, M.ED, Marcia M, Vice President Human Resources, Penn Medicine Princeton Medical Center, Plainsboro, NJ, p. A411

TEMPELMEYER, Zak, M.D., Chief Medical Staff, Syracuse Area Health, Syracuse, NE, p. A392

TEMPEST, Wendy, Director Human Resources, Vibra Hospital Of Northern California, Redding, CA, p. A80

TEMPLE, Amber L, Director Human Resources, Morrison Community Hospital, Morrison, IL, p. A190

TEMPLE, Gina, Chief Executive Officer, Baptist Medical Center, San Antonio, TX, p. A633

TEMPLE, Richard, Chief Information Officer, Deborah Heart And Lung Center, Browns Mills, NJ, p. A404

TEMPLETON, Gary, M.D., Medical Director, Regency Hospital Of Northwest Arkansas – Springdale, Springdale, AR, p. A49

TEMPLETON, Parker A., Chief Executive Officer, Iberia Medical Center, New Iberia, LA, p. A274

TEMPLETON, Sheryl, Chief Financial Officer, Scotland County Hospital, Memphis, MO, p. A365

TEMPLETON, William, M.D., Medical Director, Clark Memorial Health, Jeffersonville, IN, p. A208

TEMPLIN, Nancy, Vice President Finance and Chief Financial Officer, Johns Hopkins All Children'S Hospital, Saint Petersburg, FL, p. A138

TENEWITZ, Edward, M.D., Chief of Staff, Healthmark Regional Medical Center, Defuniak Springs, FL, p. A121

TENGERES, Michael A.
  Chief Financial Officer, Crouse Health, Syracuse, NY, p. A445
  Corporate Vice President and Chief Financial Officer, Bassett Medical Center, Cooperstown, NY, p. A426

TENHENGEL–DEVILLE, Michelle, Chief Executive Officer, Regency Hospital Of South Atlanta, East Point, GA, p. A153

TENHOUSE, Steven D., Chief Executive Officer, Kirby Medical Center, Monticello, IL, p. A190

TENNEY, Ralph
  Chief Information Officer, Ascension Crittenton Hospital Medical Center, Rochester, MI, p. A320
  Chief Information Officer, Ascension Macomb–Oakland Hospital, Warren, MI, p. A324
  Chief Information Officer, Ascension St. John Hospital, Detroit, MI, p. A309

TENNISON, Gary, M.D., Chief of Staff, Crawford Memorial Hospital, Robinson, IL, p. A194

TENNYSON, Ruby, Director Administration, Naval Hospital Jacksonville, Jacksonville, FL, p. A125

TENREIRO, Edgardo J, Chief Executive Officer and Chief Operating Officer, Baton Rouge General Medical Center, Baton Rouge, LA, p. A263

TENREIRO, Edgardo J., Chief Executive Officer and Chief Operating Officer, Baton Rouge General Medical Center, Baton Rouge, LA, p. A263

TEPEDINO, Miguel, M.D., Chief Medicine, Lake City Medical Center, Lake City, FL, p. A127

TEPPER, Gil, Chief Executive Officer, Miracle Mile Medical Center, Los Angeles, CA, p. A68

TEPPER, Gil, M.D., Chief of Staff, Miracle Mile Medical Center, Los Angeles, CA, p. A68

TER HORST, Thomas C, Vice President Human Resources, Aurora St. Luke'S Medical Center, Milwaukee, WI, p. A701

TERBUSH, Jennifer, Vice President, Patient Services, Hills & Dales General Hospital, Cass City, MI, p. A308

TERI, Anthony, Director Information Technology, Hackensack Meridian Health Pascack Valley Medical Center, Westwood, NJ, p. A415

TERPSTRA, Kelli, R.N., Senior Director, Our Children'S House, Dallas, TX, p. A597

TERRELL, Jay, Manager Management Information Systems, Riverview Regional Medical Center, Gadsden, AL, p. A18

TERRESON, Gregg, Chief Financial Officer, Cascade Behavioral Hospital, Tukwila, WA, p. A681

TERRINONI, Gary G., President and Chief Executive Officer, Brookdale Hospital Medical Center, New York, NY, p. A432

TERRY, Darrell K., Sr, President and Chief Executive Officer, Newark Beth Israel Medical Center, Newark, NJ, p. A409

TERRY, Micheal, President and Chief Executive Officer, Salina Regional Health Center, Salina, KS, p. A245

TERRY, Randi, Site Director Management Information Systems, Munson Healthcare Cadillac Hospital, Cadillac, MI, p. A308

TERRY, Richard, Vice President & Chief Information Officer, Sparrow Carson Hospital, Carson City, MI, p. A308

TERRY, Teresa, Director Human Resource, Payroll, Fisher County Hospital District, Rotan, TX, p. A632

TERRY–WILLIAMS, Teresa, R.N., Chief Nursing Officer, Pennsylvania Psychiatric Institute, Harrisburg, PA, p. A526

TERSHAKOVEC, George R., M.D., President Medical Staff, Baptist Health South Florida, Homestead Hospital, Homestead, FL, p. A125

TERTEL, Jenifer K, Director Human Resources, Medical City Dallas, Dallas, TX, p. A597

TERWILLIGER, James G, Executive Vice President and Chief Operating Officer, Dana–Farber Cancer Institute, Boston, MA, p. A295

TERWILLIGER, Michael, Chief Financial Officer, Friends Hospital, Philadelphia, PA, p. A534

TERZANO, Valerie, MSN, R.N., Senior Vice President Nursing, Nyu Winthrop Hospital, Mineola, NY, p. A431

TESKE, Mark, Chief Financial Officer, Hill Crest Behavioral Health Services, Birmingham, AL, p. A14

TESSARZIK, Connie, Business Manager, Albert J. Solnit Psychiatric Center – South Campus, Middletown, CT, p. A109

TESSLER, Nicolette B, Chief Executive Officer of Behavioral Health Hospital, Jackson Health System, Miami, FL, p. A130
TESTA, Nick, M.D., Chief Medical Officer, Providence Saint Joseph Medical Center, Burbank, CA, p. A53
TESTER, Shawn, Chief Executive Officer, Northeastern Vermont Regional Hospital, Saint Johnsbury, VT, p. A655
TETZ, Warren, Senior Vice President and Chief Operating Officer, Adventist Health Glendale, Los Angeles, CA, p. A65
TEUBNER, Sandra, Chief Financial Officer, St. Aloisius Medical Center, Harvey, ND, p. A467
TEUFEL, George, Vice President Finance, Advocate Good Shepherd Hospital, Barrington, IL, p. A174
TEVES, Alicia, Coordinator Human Resources, Molokai General Hospital, Kaunakakai, HI, p. A166
TEW, Brian, Chief Information Officer, Catskill Regional Medical Center, Harris, NY, p. A429
TEWARI, Arun, M.D., Chief Medical Officer, Henry Community Health, New Castle, IN, p. A212
TEWKSBURY, Randy E, Senior Vice President Finance and Chief Financial Officer, Mount Nittany Medical Center, State College, PA, p. A541
THACKER, Adam, Chief Operating Officer, Good Samaritan Hospital, Vincennes, IN, p. A216
THACKER, Roland, Chief Financial Officer, Piedmont Columbus Regional Northside, Columbus, GA, p. A150
THAKOR, Pratapji, M.D., Chief of Staff, South Mississippi County Regional Medical Center, Osceola, AR, p. A47
THAKUR, Abhash, M.D., Chief of Staff, Greenwood Leflore Hospital, Greenwood, MS, p. A347
THALER, Klaus, FACS, M.D., Chief Medical Officer, Houston Methodist Baytown Hospital, Baytown, TX, p. A587
THAMA, Todd, Chief Operating Officer, Fairfax Behavioral Health, Kirkland, WA, p. A674
THAMES, Stephen, Chief Financial Officer, Allen Parish Community Healthcare, Kinder, LA, p. A270
THAMES, Thomas B., President, Sentara Princess Anne Hospital, Virginia Beach, VA, p. A668
THARP, Beth S., President and Chief Executive Officer, Community Hospital Of Anderson & Madison County, Anderson, IN, p. A199
THARP, Stephen
Medical Director, Indiana University Health Frankfort, Frankfort, IN, p. A204
Regional Chief Medical Officer, St. Vincent Clay Hospital, Brazil, IN, p. A200
THAUNG, Htin, M.D., Chief Medical Officer, Ward Memorial Hospital, Monahans, TX, p. A625
THAYER, Charles, M.D., Chief Medical Officer, Morton Hospital And Medical Center, Taunton, MA, p. A304
THAYER, Gilbert M., M.D., Chief Medical Staff, Hardin Medical Center, Savannah, TN, p. A579
THAYER, Kendra, MSN, R.N., Chief Nursing Officer, Vice President Clinical Services, Garrett Regional Medical Center, Oakland, MD, p. A292
THEIRING, James, Chief Executive Officer, Mission Community Hospital, Los Angeles, CA, p. A68
THEISEN, Janet
Chief Information Officer, Sanford Tracy Medical Center, Tracy, MN, p. A341
Chief Information Officer, Sanford Westbrook Medical Center, Westbrook, MN, p. A342
THELEN, Deann, Chief Executive Officer, Jackson–Madison County General Hospital, Jackson, TN, p. A571
THELEN, Raymond Scott, Vice President and Chief Financial Officer, Masonicare Health Center, Wallingford, CT, p. A111
THEOBALD, Terry, Chief Information Officer, Ventura County Medical Center, Ventura, CA, p. A93
THEODOROU, Andreas, Chief Medical Officer, Banner – University Medical Center Tucson, Tucson, AZ, p. A37
THEOHARES, Nick, Executive Director, Operations, St. Vincent Anderson, Anderson, IN, p. A199
THERADY, Agnes, MSN, FACHE
Vice President and Chief Nursing Officer, Franciscan Health Carmel, Carmel, IN, p. A201
Vice President and Chief Nursing Officer, Franciscan Health Indianapolis, Indianapolis, IN, p. A207
Vice President and Chief Nursing Officer, Franciscan Health Mooresville, Mooresville, IN, p. A211
THERIAC, Gary, Director Information Technology, Lawrence County Memorial Hospital, Lawrenceville, IL, p. A187
THERRIEN, Charles D., President, Northern Light Mercy Hospital, Portland, ME, p. A284
THERRIEN, Tinna, R.N., Chief Information Officer and Senior Director Ancillary Services, Gothenburg Health, Gothenburg, NE, p. A385
THETFORD, Carol, Chief Nursing Officer, Baptist Memorial Hospital For Women, Memphis, TN, p. A574
THEUS, Will, M.D., Chief of Staff, Adventhealth Gordon, Calhoun, GA, p. A149
THIBERT, Kimberly, R.N., MSN, Vice President Patient Care Services and Chief Nursing Officer, Samaritan Medical Center, Watertown, NY, p. A447
THIBODEAU, Helene, R.N., MSN, Vice President Patient Care Services, Northeast Rehabilitation Hospital, Salem, NH, p. A402
THIBODEAU, Jan, Director Human Resources, Encompass Health Rehabilitation Hospital Of Princeton, Princeton, WV, p. A688
THIBODEAUX, Anita, Chief Nursing Officer, Beauregard Health System, De Ridder, LA, p. A266
THIBODEAUX, Annette, Director Human Resources, Savoy Medical Center, Mamou, LA, p. A273
THIBODEAUX, Douglas, M.D., Chief Medical Officer, Oakbend Medical Center, Richmond, TX, p. A631
THIEL, David, M.D., Medical Director, Mayo Clinic Hospital In Florida, Jacksonville, FL, p. A125
THIEL, Stefanie
Senior Human Resources Business Partner, Saint Alphonsus Medical Center – Nampa, Nampa, ID, p. A170
Senior Human Resources Business Partner, Saint Alphonsus Medical Center – Ontario, Ontario, OR, p. A515
THIELEMIER, Kevin, Director Human Resources, Arkansas Methodist Medical Center, Paragould, AR, p. A47
THIELEN, Kent, Chief Executive Officer, Mayo Clinic Hospital In Florida, Jacksonville, FL, p. A125
THIELEN, Kurt, Associate Director, Minneapolis Veterans Affairs Health Care System, Minneapolis, MN, p. A336
THIELK, Colleen, MSN, R.N., Chief Nursing Officer, Palms Of Pasadena Hospital, Saint Petersburg, FL, p. A138
THIELKE, Jayne, Chief Financial Officer, Swift County – Benson Health Services, Benson, MN, p. A328
THIEME, Ron, Ph.D., Chief Knowledge and Information Officer, Community Hospital North, Indianapolis, IN, p. A206
THIES, Dana, Director of Nursing, Meadows Psychiatric Center, Centre Hall, PA, p. A522
THILGES, Michael, Chief Financial Officer, Clarke County Hospital, Osceola, IA, p. A228
THILL, Jennifer, Chief of Staff, Mid–Valley Hospital, Omak, WA, p. A676
THIRUMALAREDDY, Joseph, M.D., Chief of Staff, Wishek Community Hospital And Clinics, Wishek, ND, p. A470
THOELE, Theresa, Director Human Resources, Coffey County Hospital, Burlington, KS, p. A233
THOENDEL, Victor, M.D., Chief Medical Officer, Butler County Health Care Center, David City, NE, p. A384
THOMAN, Dawn, Vice President Human Resources, Cloud County Health Center, Concordia, KS, p. A234
THOMAN, Michele, R.N., Chief Nursing Officer, Nch Baker Hospital, Naples, FL, p. A132
THOMAS, Andrea, Chief Operating Officer, St. Cloud Regional Medical Center, Saint Cloud, FL, p. A138
THOMAS, Andrew, M.D., Chief Medical Officer, Ohio State University Wexner Medical Center, Columbus, OH, p. A479
THOMAS, Anthony, Chief Executive Officer, Rooks County Health Center, Plainville, KS, p. A244
THOMAS, Brian E., Administrator, Alton Mental Health Center, Alton, IL, p. A173
THOMAS, Brian N., President and Chief Executive Officer, Jefferson Regional Medical Center, Pine Bluff, AR, p. A47
THOMAS, Brook, Chief Financial Officer, West Boca Medical Center, Boca Raton, FL, p. A118
THOMAS, Calvin, Chief Operating Officer, St. Lucie Medical Center, Port St Lucie, FL, p. A137
THOMAS, Chris, President and Chief Executive Officer, Community Hospital, Grand Junction, CO, p. A101
THOMAS, Christina, Chief Executive Officer, Caribou Memorial Hospital And Living Center, Soda Springs, ID, p. A172
THOMAS, Clay, Chief Operating Officer, Covenant Children'S Hospital, Lubbock, TX, p. A621
THOMAS, Curt, Administrator, Ness County Hospital District No 2, Ness City, KS, p. A241
THOMAS, David, President Medical Staff, Riddle Hospital, Media, PA, p. A531
THOMAS, Deana, Vice President Finance and Chief Financial Officer, North Arkansas Regional Medical Center, Harrison, AR, p. A42
THOMAS, Debora, Chief Financial Officer, Adventhealth Daytona Beach, Daytona Beach, FL, p. A121
THOMAS, Debra A., Vice President of Patient Care Services and Chief Nursing Officer, Penn Highlands Brookville, Brookville, PA, p. A521
THOMAS, Denise, Chief Financial Officer, Spring View Hospital, Lebanon, KY, p. A254
THOMAS, Dennis, Chief Nursing Officer, Hardeman County Memorial Hospital, Quanah, TX, p. A630
THOMAS, Frank D., Chief Executive Officer, Citizens Baptist Medical Center, Talladega, AL, p. A23
THOMAS, Gene, Vice President, Information Systems, Chief Information Officer, Memorial Hospital At Gulfport, Gulfport, MS, p. A347
THOMAS, George, M.D., Chief of Staff, Palo Pinto General Hospital, Mineral Wells, TX, p. A625
THOMAS, Gina, Chief Nursing Officer & Director of Patient Care Services, Carle Richland Memorial Hospital, Olney, IL, p. A192
THOMAS, Jayne
Chief Nursing Officer, Integris Deaconess, Oklahoma City, OK, p. A504
Chief Nursing Officer, Southwestern Medical Center, Lawton, OK, p. A501
THOMAS, Jeff, Chief Financial Officer, Heartland Regional Medical Center, Marion, IL, p. A188
THOMAS, Jennifer, Chief Operating Officer and Director of Public Relations, Lake Butler Hospital Hand Surgery Center, Lake Butler, FL, p. A127
THOMAS, Jill, Director of Nursing, Western State Hospital, Hopkinsville, KY, p. A253
THOMAS, John, Chief Operating Officer, San Mateo Medical Center, San Mateo, CA, p. A87
THOMAS, John A., M.D., Chief Medical Staff, Culberson Hospital, Van Horn, TX, p. A643
THOMAS, Keith, M.D., Chief of Staff, Blue Mountain Hospital District, John Day, OR, p. A514
THOMAS, Kirk E, Chief Administrative Officer, Geisinger–Lewistown Hospital, Lewistown, PA, p. A530
THOMAS, Kirk E., Chief Administrative Officer, Geisinger–Lewistown Hospital, Lewistown, PA, p. A530
THOMAS, Maggie, Vice President Human Resources and Practice Management, South County Hospital, Wakefield, RI, p. A548
THOMAS, Michael
Associate Administrator, Wayne County Hospital, Corydon, IA, p. A220
Chief Executive Officer, Encompass Health Rehabilitation Hospital Of San Antonio, San Antonio, TX, p. A634
THOMAS, Michael S, President and Chief Administrative Officer, John Muir Medical Center, Concord, Concord, CA, p. A55
THOMAS, Michael S., President and Chief Administrative Officer, John Muir Medical Center, Concord, Concord, CA, p. A55
THOMAS, Nicky, Director Human Resources, Baptist Memorial Hospital–Union City, Union City, TN, p. A580
THOMAS, Nicole B., President, Baptist Medical Center Jacksonville, Jacksonville, FL, p. A125
THOMAS, Patricia F, Chief Nursing Officer, Sentara Halifax Regional Hospital, South Boston, VA, p. A667
THOMAS, Paula, Vice President Patient Services, Upmc Bedford Memorial, Everett, PA, p. A526
THOMAS, Phillip, Director Human Resources, Jackson Parish Hospital, Jonesboro, LA, p. A269
THOMAS, Ron, M.D., Chief Medical Officer, Adventhealth Palm Coast, Palm Coast, FL, p. A135
THOMAS, Russell, M.D., Chief of Staff, Rice Medical Center, Eagle Lake, TX, p. A600
THOMAS, Ruth, Chief Operating Officer, Mercy Fitzgerald Hospital, Darby, PA, p. A524
THOMAS, Sarah, Director of Human Resources, Healthsouth Rehabilitation Hospital Of Littleton, Littleton, CO, p. A103
THOMAS, Scott, Administrative Director Human Resources and Communications, Granville Health System, Oxford, NC, p. A460
THOMAS, Shawn M., Director Human Resources, Banner Payson Medical Center, Payson, AZ, p. A32
THOMAS, Spencer, Chief Executive Officer, Central Carolina Hospital, Sanford, NC, p. A462
THOMAS, Sue, Manager Human Resources, Beckley Arh Hospital, Beckley, WV, p. A683
THOMAS, Sylvia, Chief Nursing Officer, Jack Hughston Memorial Hospital, Phenix City, AL, p. A22
THOMAS, Twilla, Chief Nursing Officer, Pampa Regional Medical Center, Pampa, TX, p. A627
THOMAS, William, M.D., Medical Director Clinical and Internal Affairs, Molokai General Hospital, Kaunakakai, HI, p. A166
THOMAS, Wilson A., Chief Executive Officer, Southern Virginia Regional Medical Center, Emporia, VA, p. A658
THOMAS–BOYD, Sharon, Chief Operating Officer, Oaklawn Hospital, Marshall, MI, p. A317
THOMAS–FOLDS, Lana, System Director Human Resources, Jack Hughston Memorial Hospital, Phenix City, AL, p. A22
THOMAS–WILLIAMS, Jovita, Senior Vice President of Human Resources, Massachusetts General Hospital, Boston, MA, p. A295
THOMASON, Scott, Chief Nursing Officer, Lakeside Behavioral Health System, Memphis, TN, p. A575
THOMMAN, Connie, Director of Nursing, Covenant Hospital–Levelland, Levelland, TX, p. A620

THOMPSON, Aaron, M.D., Chief of Staff, Arkansas Methodist Medical Center, Paragould, AR, p. A47
THOMPSON, Alan, M.D., President Medical Staff, Warm Springs Medical Center, Warm Springs, GA, p. A162
THOMPSON, Amy, Chief Executive Officer, Covenant Children'S Hospital, Lubbock, TX, p. A621
THOMPSON, Becki, President, Chi Oakes Hospital, Oakes, ND, p. A469
THOMPSON, Belinda, Coordinator Human Resources, Healthsouth Chesapeake Rehabilitation Hospital, Salisbury, MD, p. A293
THOMPSON, Bobby, Director Information Technology, Stephens Memorial Hospital, Breckenridge, TX, p. A589
THOMPSON, Cathy, Manager Human Resources, Paris Community Hospital, Paris, IL, p. A192
THOMPSON, Chad
Chief Executive Officer, Morton County Health System, Elkhart, KS, p. A234
Chief Financial Officer, Lallie Kemp Medical Center, Independence, LA, p. A269
THOMPSON, Charles, M.D., Chief Medical Officer, Nacogdoches Medical Center, Nacogdoches, TX, p. A625
THOMPSON, Charolette, Chief Financial Officer, Reeves Memorial Medical Center, Bernice, LA, p. A264
THOMPSON, Cheryl
Chief Nursing Officer, Garden Park Medical Center, Gulfport, MS, p. A347
Facility Director Human Resources, Connecticut Valley Hospital, Middletown, CT, p. A109
THOMPSON, Chris
Chief Financial Officer, Delta Community Medical Center, Delta, UT, p. A647
Chief Financial Officer, Fillmore Community Hospital, Fillmore, UT, p. A648
Chief Financial Officer, Sanpete Valley Hospital, Mount Pleasant, UT, p. A649
Chief Financial Officer, Sevier Valley Hospital, Richfield, UT, p. A651
THOMPSON, Cindy, Chief Financial Officer, Northwest Surgical Hospital, Oklahoma City, OK, p. A504
THOMPSON, Craig, Chief Executive Officer, Golden Valley Memorial Healthcare, Clinton, MO, p. A358
THOMPSON, Craig B., President and Chief Executive Officer, Brookdale Hospital Medical Center, New York, NY, p. A432
THOMPSON, Dale, Chief Financial Officer, Mclaren Greater Lansing, Lansing, MI, p. A316
THOMPSON, David, Chief Financial Officer, Central Maine Medical Center, Lewiston, ME, p. A283
THOMPSON, David, M.D., Chief of Staff, Richardson Medical Center, Rayville, LA, p. A277
THOMPSON, David M., Chief Executive Officer, Sutter Tracy Community Hospital, Tracy, CA, p. A92
THOMPSON, Debbie, Chief Financial Officer, Sweetwater Hospital, Sweetwater, TN, p. A580
THOMPSON, Douglas, Chief Information Officer, Upson Regional Medical Center, Thomaston, GA, p. A161
THOMPSON, Dwight, Chief Financial Officer, Altru Health System, Grand Forks, ND, p. A467
THOMPSON, Greg
Chief Medical Officer, Gundersen Lutheran Medical Center, La Crosse, WI, p. A697
Corporate Director, Human Resources, Orlando Regional Medical Center, Orlando, FL, p. A134
THOMPSON, Heath, Administrator, Singing River Health System, Pascagoula, MS, p. A352
THOMPSON, Ian, Jr, President, Christus Santa Rosa Health System, San Antonio, TX, p. A633
THOMPSON, Ivan, Vice President, Chief Human Resource Officer, University Of Texas Southwestern Medical Center, Dallas, TX, p. A598
THOMPSON, James H., Owner and Chief Executive Officer, Healthmark Regional Medical Center, Defuniak Springs, FL, p. A121
THOMPSON, John W, M.D., Chief of Staff, Eastern Louisiana Mental Health System, Jackson, LA, p. A269
THOMPSON, Julie
Chief Operating Officer and Chief Nursing Officer, Bluffton Regional Medical Center, Bluffton, IN, p. A200
Manager Personnel and Payroll, Mayers Memorial Hospital District, Fall River Mills, CA, p. A58
THOMPSON, Kim, Vice President and Chief Financial Officer, Ozarks Medical Center, West Plains, MO, p. A373
THOMPSON, Lennis, Vice President and Chief Financial Officer, Hardin Memorial Health, Elizabethtown, KY, p. A251
THOMPSON, Linda
Chief Operating Officer, Fairfax Community Hospital, Fairfax, OK, p. A499
Senior Vice President, Human Resources and Service Excellence, New England Baptist Hospital, Boston, MA, p. A296
THOMPSON, Lisa, MSN, R.N., Director of Nursing, Hiawatha Community Hospital, Hiawatha, KS, p. A236
THOMPSON, Lori L, Manager Human Resources, Orthonebraska Hospital, Omaha, NE, p. A390
THOMPSON, Marion A., Chief Executive Officer, Allen County Regional Hospital, Iola, KS, p. A237
THOMPSON, Mark
Market Chief Financial Officer Northern Region and Chief Financial Officer, Mercy Health – St. Charles Hospital, Oregon, OH, p. A489
System Chief Financial Officer, Thedacare Regional Medical Center–Neenah, Neenah, WI, p. A702
Vice President Financial Services, Rapid City Regional Hospital, Rapid City, SD, p. A563
THOMPSON, Nate, Chief Executive Officer, Story County Medical Center, Nevada, IA, p. A227
THOMPSON, Ormand P., President, Thomas Hospital, Fairhope, AL, p. A18
THOMPSON, Pamela, Chief Operations Officer, Huhukam Memorial Hospital, Sacaton, AZ, p. A35
THOMPSON, Patti, Chief Operating Officer, San Luis Valley Health, Alamosa, CO, p. A96
THOMPSON, Patty, Area Compliance Officer, Kaiser Permanente Fresno Medical Center, Fresno, CA, p. A59
THOMPSON, Randell, Chief Nursing Officer, Plateau Medical Center, Oak Hill, WV, p. A688
THOMPSON, Randy, Chief Executive Officer, Encompass Health Rehabilitation Hospital Of Montgomery, Montgomery, AL, p. A21
THOMPSON, Reanna, R.N., Chief Operating Officer and Chief Nursing Officer, Pih Health Hospital – Whittier, Whittier, CA, p. A95
THOMPSON, Ronnie, Chief Financial Officer, Belton Regional Medical Center, Belton, MO, p. A356
THOMPSON, Sarah, Director Health Information Management, Hardtner Medical Center, Olla, LA, p. A276
THOMPSON, Scott, Chief Executive Officer, Russell County Hospital, Russell Springs, KY, p. A260
THOMPSON, Selva, R.N., Chief Nurse Executive, Gallup Indian Medical Center, Gallup, NM, p. A418
THOMPSON, Sheila, Director Human Resources, Hamilton Memorial Hospital District, Mcleansboro, IL, p. A189
THOMPSON, Stacey, Superintendent, Austin State Hospital, Austin, TX, p. A585
THOMPSON, Stuart, Vice President Human Resources, Memorial Hospital Jacksonville, Jacksonville, FL, p. A125
THOMPSON, Tim
Senior Vice President and Chief Informatics Officer, St. Anthony'S Hospital, Saint Petersburg, FL, p. A138
Senior Vice President, Chief Information Officer, South Florida Baptist Hospital, Plant City, FL, p. A137
Senior Vice President, Informant Services and Chief Information Officer, Mease Countryside Hospital, Safety Harbor, FL, p. A138
Senior Vice President, Information Services and Chief Information Officer, Mease Dunedin Hospital, Dunedin, FL, p. A122
THOMPSON, Timothy
Senior Vice President and Chief Information Officer, Morton Plant Hospital, Clearwater, FL, p. A119
Senior Vice President and Chief Information Officer, Morton Plant North Bay Hospital, New Port Richey, FL, p. A132
THOMPSON, Tina H, Coordinator Human Resources, Firsthealth Montgomery Memorial Hospital, Troy, NC, p. A463
THOMPSON, Trinise, Director Human Resources, St. Luke'S Medical Center, Phoenix, AZ, p. A34
THOMPSON, Vera, Director Human Resources, Brookdale Hospital Medical Center, New York, NY, p. A432
THOMPSON, Wayne, Executive Vice President and Chief Information Officer, Mount Nittany Medical Center, State College, PA, p. A541
THOMPSON, Wayne D., Interim Chief Executive Officer, Panola Medical Center, Batesville, MS, p. A344
THOMPSON, Wesley, M.D., President Medical Staff, Fairfield Memorial Hospital, Fairfield, IL, p. A183
THOMPSON, William, Chief Financial Officer, Mississippi Baptist Medical Center, Jackson, MS, p. A349
THOMPSON, William, M.D., Chief Medical Officer, Saint Thomas Midtown Hospital, Nashville, TN, p. A577
THOMPSON–COOK, Timothy, Chief Operating Officer, Contra Costa Regional Medical Center, Martinez, CA, p. A71
THOMSEN, Sue, Chief Financial Officer, New Braunfels Regional Rehabilitation Hospital, New Braunfels, TX, p. A626
THOMSEN, Vicki
Director Human Resources, Aurora Behavioral Health System East, Tempe, AZ, p. A36
Director Human Resources, Aurora Behavioral Health System West, Glendale, AZ, p. A30
THOMSON, Doug, M.D., Chief Medical Officer, Commonwealth Regional Specialty Hospital, Bowling Green, KY, p. A249
THOMSON, Nicole, Chief Financial Officer, Saint Louise Regional Hospital, Gilroy, CA, p. A60
THOMSON, Steven, M.D., Medical Director, Heartland Behavioral Healthcare, Massillon, OH, p. A487
THORDARSON, Heidar, Chief Financial Officer, Adventist Health Castle, Kailua, HI, p. A165
THORE, Joe, Chief Operating Officer, Ashe Memorial Hospital, Jefferson, NC, p. A457
THORELL, Nicole, R.N., MSN, Chief Nursing Officer, Lexington Regional Health Center, Lexington, NE, p. A386
THORESON, Scott D.
Administrator, Mayo Clinic Health System In Saint James, Saint James, MN, p. A339
Administrator, Mayo Clinic Health System In Springfield, Springfield, MN, p. A341
THORN, Eugene A, Vice President Finance and Chief Financial Officer, Cleveland Clinic Union Hospital, Dover, OH, p. A482
THORN, Margaret, Interim Director of Nursing, Red Bay Hospital, Red Bay, AL, p. A23
THORN, Mark, FACHE, Executive Director, Finance, Mercy Hospital Lincoln, Troy, MO, p. A372
THORNBRUGH, Mitchell
Acting Chief Information Officer, Cherokee Nation W.W. Hastings Indian Hospital, Tahlequah, OK, p. A508
Administrative Officer, Cherokee Nation W.W. Hastings Indian Hospital, Tahlequah, OK, p. A508
THORNBURY, Neil
Chief Executive Officer, T. J. Samson Community Hospital, Glasgow, KY, p. A252
Chief Executive Officer, T.J. Health Columbia, Columbia, KY, p. A250
THORNE, Dana, Administrator Human Resources, Valley Hospital Medical Center, Las Vegas, NV, p. A396
THORNELL, Louise, Chief Nursing Officer, Christus St. Michael Health System, Texarkana, TX, p. A640
THORNELL, Timothy, Chief Executive Officer, Lea Regional Medical Center, Hobbs, NM, p. A418
THORNSBERRY, Michael, M.D., Chief Medical Officer, Texas Health Specialty Hospital, Fort Worth, TX, p. A606
THORNTON, Carol, Director Human Resources, Cherry Hospital, Goldsboro, NC, p. A455
THORNTON, Cayetano, Chief Information Officer, Walter Reed National Military Medical Center, Bethesda, MD, p. A289
THORNTON, Daryl W, Chief Operating Officer, Kansas Medical Center, Andover, KS, p. A232
THORNTON, Jan, Chief Nursing Officer, Bay Medical Sacred Heart, Panama City, FL, p. A135
THORNTON, Jillisa, Director of Nursing, Coastal Harbor Treatment Center, Savannah, GA, p. A160
THORNTON, Laird, Director Information Systems, Alta Vista Regional Hospital, Las Vegas, NM, p. A419
THORNTON, Matt, Chief Executive Officer, Liberty Dayton Regional Medical Center, Liberty, TX, p. A620
THORPE, Judith, R.N., MSN, Vice President and Chief Nursing Officer, Umass Memorial Healthalliance–Clinton Hospital, Leominster, MA, p. A300
THORPE, Linda, Chief Executive Officer, East Morgan County Hospital, Brush, CO, p. A97
THORPE, Wendy, Area Director Information Systems, St. Joseph Hospital, Eureka, CA, p. A57
THORSEN, Erik, Chief Executive Officer, Columbia Memorial Hospital, Astoria, OR, p. A511
THORWALD, Robert, Chief Information Officer, Washington Hospital Healthcare System, Fremont, CA, p. A59
THOTAKURA, Raj, M.D., Medical Director, Old Vineyard Behavioral Health Services, Winston, NC, p. A464
THRASHER, Amanda, Director Nursing, Ellsworth County Medical Center, Ellsworth, KS, p. A234
THRASHER, Kimberly, Controller, Encompass Health Lakeshore Rehabilitation Hospital, Birmingham, AL, p. A14
THRASHER, Sherri, Executive Human Resources Partner, Spectrum Health Pennock, Hastings, MI, p. A314
THREEWITS, Sheree, Director Human Resources, Manatee Memorial Hospital, Bradenton, FL, p. A118
THRIFT, William Kyle, Chief Nursing Officer, Brandon Regional Hospital, Brandon, FL, p. A119
THULI, Karen, Information Systems Coordinator, Upland Hills Health, Dodgeville, WI, p. A693
THUN, Todd, Director Human Resources, Montana State Hospital, Warm Springs, MT, p. A380
THUN, Tracey, Director Business and Support Services, Montana State Hospital, Warm Springs, MT, p. A380
THUNELL, Adam, Chief Operating Officer and Vice President Operations, Community Memorial Hospital, Ventura, CA, p. A93
THURBER, Joe, Director Information Technology, Central Regional Hospital, Butner, NC, p. A450

THURMER, DeAnn
President and Chief Nursing Officer, Ripon Medical Center, Ripon, WI, p. A705
President and Chief Nursing Officer, Waupun Memorial Hospital, Waupun, WI, p. A707
THURSTON, Thomas, M.D., Medical Director, J. D. Mccarty Center For Children With Developmental Disabilities, Norman, OK, p. A503
THYGESON, Cindy, M.D., Director Medical Affairs, Sutter Center For Psychiatry, Sacramento, CA, p. A82
THYNE, Shannon, Chief Medical Officer, Lac–Olive View–Ucla Medical Center, Los Angeles, CA, p. A68
TIBBITS, Dick, Vice President and Chief Operating Officer, Adventhealth Tampa, Tampa, FL, p. A141
TIBBITS, Richard M, Vice President and Chief Operating Officer, Loma Linda University Medical Center–Murrieta, Murrieta, CA, p. A73
TICE, Evan, Director Information Technology and Systems, Sky Ridge Medical Center, Lone Tree, CO, p. A103
TICE, Heidi, Chief Financial Officer, Cheyenne County Hospital, Saint Francis, KS, p. A244
TICE, Kirk C., President and Chief Executive Officer, Robert Wood Johnson University Hospital Rahway, Rahway, NJ, p. A411
TICE, Linda, Director Information Systems, Sagewest Health Care At Riverton, Riverton, WY, p. A712
TICHENOR, John, Chief Financial Officer, Ohio County Hospital, Hartford, KY, p. A253
TICHENOR, Rick, Chief Executive Officer, Accel Rehabilitation Hospital Of Plano, Plano, TX, p. A629
TIDWELL, Jan, Chief Nursing Officer, Cartersville Medical Center, Cartersville, GA, p. A149
TIDWELL, Tim, Human Resources Director, Wiregrass Medical Center, Geneva, AL, p. A18
TIDWELL, Wesley, Chief Operating Officer, Memorial Hermann Greater Heights Hospital, Houston, TX, p. A612
TIEDE, Brad, Director Information Systems, Memorial Community Health, Aurora, NE, p. A382
TIEDT, Douglas, M.D., Chief of Staff, Musc Health Lancaster Medical Center, Lancaster, SC, p. A555
TIEDT, Jerry, Director Information Systems, Waverly Health Center, Waverly, IA, p. A231
TIEFENTHALER, Brenda Marie, R.N., MSN, Vice President Patient Care and Informatics, Spencer Hospital, Spencer, IA, p. A230
TIEMENS, Linda, Chief Executive Officer, Vibra Hospital Of Richmond, Richmond, VA, p. A666
TIERNAN, Kelley, Chief Financial Officer, Claxton–Hepburn Medical Center, Ogdensburg, NY, p. A440
TIERNEY, Gregory, M.D., President, BMG and BHS Chief Medical Officer, Benefis Health System, Great Falls, MT, p. A377
TIERNEY, Mark A, Chief Financial Officer, Manatee Memorial Hospital, Bradenton, FL, p. A118
TIETJEN, Patricia, M.D., Vice President, Medical Affairs, Danbury Hospital, Danbury, CT, p. A107
TIGGELAAR, Tom
Vice President Finance ad Chief Financial Officer, Mayo Clinic Health System – Franciscan Healthcare In Sparta, Sparta, WI, p. A705
Vice President Finance, Mayo Clinic Health System – Franciscan Healthcare In La Crosse, La Crosse, WI, p. A698
TILGHMAN, Bradley, Controller, Encompass Health Rehabilitation Hospital Of Panama City, Panama City, FL, p. A135
TILLER, Debra, Director Personnel and Administrative Secretary, Healthmark Regional Medical Center, Defuniak Springs, FL, p. A121
TILLER, Jaconna Joni, Chief Nursing Officer, Alliancehealth Midwest, Midwest City, OK, p. A502
TILLETT, Grant, Chief Information Officer, Prairie Lakes Healthcare System, Watertown, SD, p. A565
TILLMAN, Jill, Assistant Chief Executive Officer, Brandywine Hospital, Coatesville, PA, p. A523
TILLMAN, Kanner
Chief Financial Officer, Corona Regional Medical Center, Corona, CA, p. A55
Chief Financial Officer, Encino Hospital Medical Center, Los Angeles, CA, p. A66
TILLMAN, Michael C., President and Chief Executive Officer, United Hospital Center, Bridgeport, WV, p. A683
TILLMAN, Pamela P., Administrator, Lifebrite Community Hospital Of Stokes, Danbury, NC, p. A452
TILLMAN, Randy, M.D., Chief Medical Staff, Promise Hospital Of Miss Lou, Vidalia, LA, p. A279
TILLMAN–TAYLOR, Susan, Manager Human Resources, Hackensack Meridian Health Southern Ocean Medical Center, Manahawkin, NJ, p. A408
TILSON, Natalie, Controller, Encompass Health Rehabilitation Hospital Of Kingsport, Kingsport, TN, p. A572
TIMANUS, Anthony, Chief Executive Officer, Avera Gregory Hospital, Gregory, SD, p. A561
TIMBERS, Christopher, Vice President and Chief Information Officer, Northbay Medical Center, Fairfield, CA, p. A57
TIMBERS, Christopher T, Chief Information Officer, Sibley Memorial Hospital, Washington, DC, p. A116
TIMLIN, Marie, R.N., Chief Nursing Officer, Uchealth Yampa Valley Medical Center, Steamboat Springs, CO, p. A105
TIMM, Doreen, MSN, Senior Director and Chief Nursing Officer, Javon Bea Hospital–Rockton, Rockford, IL, p. A194
TIMM, Karen, R.N., MSN, Vice President Patient Services, St. Anthony Regional Hospital, Carroll, IA, p. A218
TIMM, Mark, Executive Director Human Resources, Yavapai Regional Medical Center, Prescott, AZ, p. A35
TIMM, Matt, M.D., Medical Director, Pender Community Hospital, Pender, NE, p. A391
TIMMER, Kari, Chief Financial Officer, Hegg Health Center Avera, Rock Valley, IA, p. A229
TIMMERMAN, Jo, Manager Accounting, Norwood Health Center, Marshfield, WI, p. A699
TIMMONS, William
Chief Executive Officer, Los Ninos Hospital, Phoenix, AZ, p. A33
President and Chief Executive Officer, Hacienda Children'S Hospital, Mesa, AZ, p. A31
TIMPE, Ron, Chief Financial Officer, Floyd County Medical Center, Charles City, IA, p. A219
TINAGERO, Doris, Executive Director, University Of New Mexico Hospitals, Albuquerque, NM, p. A417
TINCH, Roberta, Chief Operations Officer, Spotsylvania Regional Medical Center, Fredericksburg, VA, p. A659
TINCHER, Pat, Director Finance, Aspirus Langlade Hospital, Antigo, WI, p. A691
TINDALL, Shedale, Chief Nursing Officer, The Pavilion At Williamsburg Place, Williamsburg, VA, p. A669
TINDLE, Jeff A., Chief Executive Officer, Carroll County Memorial Hospital, Carrollton, MO, p. A358
TINDLE, Tim, Chief Information Officer, Harris Health System, Houston, TX, p. A611
TINGSTAD, Jonathan, Vice President and Chief Financial Officer, Seattle Cancer Care Alliance, Seattle, WA, p. A678
TINNERELLO, Jeremy M., President, Glenwood Regional Medical Center, West Monroe, LA, p. A280
TINNERELLO, Jeremy M., MSN, R.N., President, Glenwood Regional Medical Center, West Monroe, LA, p. A280
TINNESZ, Thomas, M.D., Chief Medical Officer, Chambers Memorial Hospital, Danville, AR, p. A41
TINNEY, Sean, FACHE, Chief Operating Officer, Medical West, Bessemer, AL, p. A14
TINSA, Udom, M.D., Medical Director, Ashley Medical Center, Ashley, ND, p. A465
TINSLEY, Cassie, Director, Human Resources, Powell Valley Healthcare, Powell, WY, p. A712
TINSLEY, Edward D., III, Regional Administrator, Mcleod Loris Seacoast Hospital, Loris, SC, p. A555
TINSLEY, Nancy M., President, Advocate Good Samaritan Hospital, Downers Grove, IL, p. A181
TIPPIN, Russell, Chief Executive Officer and Administrator, Permian Regional Medical Center, Andrews, TX, p. A583
TIPPS, Linda, Director Human Resources, Southern Tennessee Regional Health System–Winchester, Winchester, TN, p. A580
TIPTON, Maggie, Chief Information Officer, Unicoi County Memorial Hospital, Erwin, TN, p. A569
TIPTON, Peggy, Chief Operating Officer and Chief Nursing Officer, Oklahoma Heart Hospital, Oklahoma City, OK, p. A505
TIPTON, Regina, Director of Operations, Rehabilitation Hospital, Navicent Health, Macon, GA, p. A157
TIRA, Cheryl, Director Information Systems, Columbus Community Hospital, Columbus, NE, p. A384
TIRADO, Norma, Vice President, Human Resources and Health Information Technology, Lakeland Hospital, Watervliet, Watervliet, MI, p. A324
TIRMAN, Kerry, Chief Executive Officer, Slidell Memorial Hospital, Slidell, LA, p. A279
TISDALE, Willis E, Director Human Resources, Shriners Hospitals For Children–Greenville, Greenville, SC, p. A554
TISDALL, Renae, Chief Financial Officer, Mobridge Regional Hospital, Mobridge, SD, p. A562
TISSIER, Becky, Chief Fiscal Service, Veterans Affairs Illiana Health Care System, Danville, IL, p. A180
TITO, David, M.D., President Medical Staff, Riverside Community Hospital, Riverside, CA, p. A81
TITSWORTH, Sue, Director Human Resources, Coleman County Medical Center, Coleman, TX, p. A592
TITTLE, JoDee, Chief Executive Officer, Plumas District Hospital, Quincy, CA, p. A79
TITUS, Monica B., Chief Executive Officer, Acuity Specialty Hospital Of New Jersey, Atlantic City, NJ, p. A403
TOALSON, Jason, Chief Executive Officer, Cottonwood Springs Hospital, Olathe, KS, p. A242
TOBEY, Shelley R, R.N., MS, Chief Operating Officer and Chief Nursing Officer, Texas Health Presbyterian Hospital Flower Mound, Flower Mound, TX, p. A604
TOBIN, Hugh, Chief Financial Officer, Davis Regional Medical Center, Statesville, NC, p. A462
TOBIN, Ryan, President and Chief Executive Officer, Rose Medical Center, Denver, CO, p. A99
TOBIN–PAYNE, Cindy, Director, Magee Rehabilitation Hospital, Philadelphia, PA, p. A535
TOBLER, Randy, Chief Executive Officer, Scotland County Hospital, Memphis, MO, p. A365
TOBLER, Randy, M.D., Chief Medical Officer, Scotland County Hospital, Memphis, MO, p. A365
TOCCO–BRADLEY, Rosalie, Ph.D., M.D.
Chief Medical Officer, St. Joseph Mercy Ann Arbor, Ypsilanti, MI, p. A325
Chief Medical Officer, St. Joseph Mercy Livingston Hospital, Howell, MI, p. A314
TODD, David, M.D., President Medical Staff, Pam Specialty Hospital Of Lufkin, Lufkin, TX, p. A622
TODD, Kimberly, Chief Nursing Officer, Alliancehealth Clinton, Clinton, OK, p. A498
TODD, Mark, Senior Systems Administrator, Hamilton Memorial Hospital District, Mcleansboro, IL, p. A189
TODD, Nate, Chief Financial Officer, Central Arkansas Veterans Healthcare System, Little Rock, AR, p. A45
TODD, Robbie, Director Information Technology, Horn Memorial Hospital, Ida Grove, IA, p. A224
TODD, Steve J., Chief Executive Officer, St. Luke Community Healthcare, Ronan, MT, p. A379
TODOROW, Thomas, Chief Financial Officer and Executive Vice President, Children'S Hospital Of Philadelphia, Philadelphia, PA, p. A534
TOEDT, Michael E, M.D., Director Clinical Services, Cherokee Indian Hospital, Cherokee, NC, p. A452
TOFANI, Barbara F., R.N., MSN, Senior Vice President and Chief Nursing Officer, Cincinnati Children'S Hospital Medical Center, Cincinnati, OH, p. A475
TOJINO, Allan, Director, Information Systems, Paradise Valley Hospital, National City, CA, p. A74
TOKAR, Andrew, Chief Financial Officer, Overlake Medical Center, Bellevue, WA, p. A670
TOL, Daryl, President and Chief Executive Officer, Adventhealth Orlando, Orlando, FL, p. A134
TOLBERT, James, Director Information Systems, Saint Francis Hospital Muskogee, Muskogee, OK, p. A502
TOLEDO, Iris, Chief Nursing Officer, Hospital Pavia Arecibo, Arecibo, PR, p. A715
TOLINE, Tyler, Chief Executive Officer, Saunders Medical Center, Wahoo, NE, p. A392
TOLLEFSON, Sue, Coordinator Payroll Personnel, Granite Falls Health, Granite Falls, MN, p. A333
TOLLEY, Cherie, Chief Executive Officer, Willingway Hospital, Statesboro, GA, p. A161
TOLMIE, John Kerr., Chief Executive Officer, Howard University Hospital, Washington, DC, p. A115
TOLSON, Rick
Chief Administrative Officer and Chief Human Resources Officer, Christ Hospital, Cincinnati, OH, p. A475
Divisional Chief People Officer, Hshs St. Joseph'S Hospital, Chippewa Falls, WI, p. A693
TOMAS, George, Director Information Services, Griffin Hospital, Derby, CT, p. A107
TOMASESKI, Gina, Chief Executive Officer, Icare Rehabilitation Hospital, Flower Mound, TX, p. A604
TOMASO, Nancy, Vice President, Patient Care Services, Milford Regional Medical Center, Milford, MA, p. A301
TOME, Michael, M.D., Medical Director, Kaiser Permanente Los Angeles Medical Center, Los Angeles, CA, p. A67
TOMLIN, Jeffrey, Chief Executive Officer, Evergreenhealth, Kirkland, WA, p. A674
TOMLIN, Kerry W, Associate Administrator, Clay County Hospital, Ashland, AL, p. A13
TOMLIN, Teresa, Administrator, Sumner County Hospital District 1, Caldwell, KS, p. A233
TOMLIN, Teresa, R.N., Chief Nursing Officer, Hospital District 6 – Harper Campus, Harper, KS, p. A236
TOMLINSON, Charles M, M.D., Chief Medical Officer, Atrium Health Cleveland, Shelby, NC, p. A462
TOMLINSON, David, Executive Vice President Chief Financial Officer and Chief Information Officer, Northwestern Medicine Mchenry, Mchenry, IL, p. A189
TOMLINSON, Sallie, Manager Human Resources, Arbuckle Memorial Hospital, Sulphur, OK, p. A508

TOMORY, Gerald, M.D.
Regional Medical Director, Kauai Veterans Memorial Hospital, Waimea, HI, p. A166
Regional Medical Director, Samuel Mahelona Memorial Hospital, Kapaa, HI, p. A166

TOMPKINS, Charles, M.D., Chief of Staff, Crenshaw Community Hospital, Luverne, AL, p. A20

TOMPKINS, Kim, Director Information Services, Detar Healthcare System, Victoria, TX, p. A643

TOMPKINS, Misti, Employee Relations Director, Osf St. Joseph Medical Center, Bloomington, IL, p. A174

TOMPKINS, Tommy, Vice President, Finance and Chief Financial Officer, Yukon–Kuskokwim Delta Regional Hospital, Bethel, AK, p. A25

TOMSU, Karen, MSN, R.N., Chief Nursing Officer, Baptist Hospitals Of Southeast Texas, Beaumont, TX, p. A587

TONER, Tina, Chief Nursing Officer, Jefferson Healthcare, Port Townsend, WA, p. A676

TONEY, Patty, R.N., MSN, Chief Nurse Executive, Christus Santa Rosa Health System, San Antonio, TX, p. A633

TONG, Cheryl, Corporate Chief Financial Officer, Community Hospital Of Huntington Park, Huntington Park, CA, p. A62

TONGATE, Scott A., Chief Financial Officer, Macon Community Hospital, Lafayette, TN, p. A572

TONJES, Ken, Chief Financial Officer, Peacehealth Ketchikan Medical Center, Ketchikan, AK, p. A26

TONN, Deb L, Vice President Patient Care, Campbell County Health, Gillette, WY, p. A711

TONNU, Lannie, Senior Vice President and Chief Financial Officer, Children'S Hospital Los Angeles, Los Angeles, CA, p. A66

TOOKE, Ryan, Chief Executive Officer, Dahl Memorial Healthcare Association, Ekalaka, MT, p. A376

TOOLE, LaDon, Chief Executive Officer, Dodge County Hospital, Eastman, GA, p. A153

TOOLE, Trish, Vice President Administrative Services, Hackensack Meridian Health Carrier Clinic, Belle Mead, NJ, p. A403

TOON, William, Chief Information Officer, Baptist Hospitals Of Southeast Texas, Beaumont, TX, p. A587

TOOTLE, Julie, Chief Executive Officer, Ellett Memorial Hospital, Appleton City, MO, p. A356

TOPOLEWSKI, Ted, Chief Executive Officer, Madison Parish Hospital, Tallulah, LA, p. A279

TOPPEN, Jacki, Director of Nursing, Prairie St. John'S, Fargo, ND, p. A466

TORBETT, Russell B, Director Human Resources, Creek Nation Community Hospital, Okemah, OK, p. A503

TORCHIA, Jude, Chief Executive Officer, Orthocolorado Hospital, Lakewood, CO, p. A102

TORCHIA NEA–BC, Lisa F, MSN, R.N., Vice President and Chief Nursing Officer, Geisinger Holy Spirit, Camp Hill, PA, p. A521

TORGE, Andrew, Director Human Resources, Shasta Regional Medical Center, Redding, CA, p. A80

TORMANEN, John, Director Mission and Human Resources, Chi St. Joseph'S Health, Park Rapids, MN, p. A337

TORO PALACIOS, Belinda L., Executive Director, Doctors Center, Manati, PR, p. A716

TORONTOW, R. John, M.D., Chief Medical Staff, Cedar County Memorial Hospital, El Dorado Springs, MO, p. A359

TOROSSIAN, Lynn M., President and Chief Executive Officer, Henry Ford West Bloomfield Hospital, West Bloomfield, MI, p. A324

TORRES, Anthony, Manager Information Technology, Blue Mountain Hospital, Blanding, UT, p. A647

TORRES, Anthony, M.D., Chief Medical Officer, Yavapai Regional Medical Center, Prescott, AZ, p. A35

TORRES, Jose M., Executive Director, St. Luke'S Episcopal Hospital, Ponce, PR, p. A717

TORRES, Maribel, Chief Nursing Officer, Hialeah Hospital, Hialeah, FL, p. A124

TORRES, Mayra, CPA, Chief Financial Officer, Ashford Presbyterian Community Hospital, San Juan, PR, p. A718

TORRES, Tammy, Chief Executive Officer, Salem Medical Center, Salem, NJ, p. A412

TORRES, Victor, Information Technology Specialist Administrator, El Paso Behavioral Health System, El Paso, TX, p. A601

TORRES AYALA, Eugenio, Director Information Systems, Cardiovascular Center Of Puerto Rico And The Caribbean, San Juan, PR, p. A718

TORRICO, Pat, Chief Nursing Officer, Osf Saint Elizabeth Medical Center, Ottawa, IL, p. A192

TORSCH, Peter, Chief Financial Officer, St. Charles Parish Hospital, Luling, LA, p. A272

TORTELLA, Anthony, Chief Financial Officer, Fairmount Behavioral Health System, Philadelphia, PA, p. A534

TOSTEBERG, Chris, Superintendent, Mental Health Institute, Cherokee, IA, p. A219

TOSTENSON, Brad, Chief Information Officer, Essentia Health–Graceville, Graceville, MN, p. A332

TOSTI, Debra, Chief Executive Officer, Tewksbury Hospital, Tewksbury, MA, p. A304

TOTAH, Sam, Chief Operating Officer, Kaiser Permanente San Diego Medical Center, San Diego, CA, p. A83

TOUCHSTONE, Pat, Chief Nursing Officer, Crane Memorial Hospital, Crane, TX, p. A595

TOUPS, Sharon A, Senior Vice President and Chief Operating Officer, St. Tammany Parish Hospital, Covington, LA, p. A266

TOURE', Joahd, M.D., Chief Medical Officer, Adirondack Health, Saranac Lake, NY, p. A443

TOURIGNY, Barry
Human Resources Director, Johnson City Medical Center, Johnson City, TN, p. A571
Vice President Human Resources and Organizational Development, Cabell Huntington Hospital, Huntington, WV, p. A685

TOUSIGNANT, Grace, R.N., MSN
Chief Nursing Officer, Aspirus Ironwood Hospitals & Clinics, Inc., Ironwood, MI, p. A315
Chief Nursing Officer, Aspirus Keweenaw Hospital, Inc., Laurium, MI, p. A316

TOUVELLE, Cynthia, R.N., Senior Director Care Management and Chief Nursing Officer, Barnesville Hospital, Barnesville, OH, p. A472

TOWERY, O B, M.D., Chief of Staff, John Muir Behavioral Health Center, Concord, CA, p. A55

TOWLE, Sonya, Director Human Resources, Mercy Hospital, Moose Lake, MN, p. A336

TOWN, Alex
Chief Financial Officer, Samaritan Healthcare, Moses Lake, WA, p. A675
Vice President Finance, Tri–State Memorial Hospital, Clarkston, WA, p. A671

TOWNDROW, Geraldine, R.N., Senior Vice President Nursing, Lutheran Medical Center, Wheat Ridge, CO, p. A106

TOWNE, Jana, Nurse Executive, U. S. Public Health Service Indian Hospital–Whiteriver, Whiteriver, AZ, p. A38

TOWNER, Chad, Chief Executive Officer, Saint Joseph Health System, Mishawaka, IN, p. A211

TOWNES, Tim, Director Information Systems, Grandview Medical Center, Birmingham, AL, p. A14

TOWNLEY, Nancy, R.N., Senior Vice President Operations, United Regional Health Care System, Wichita Falls, TX, p. A646

TOWNLEY, Patricia, Director Operations, Chi Health Creighton University Medical Center – Bergan Mercy, Omaha, NE, p. A388

TOWNSEND, Alan, Interim Chief Financial Officer, Jps Health Network, Fort Worth, TX, p. A605

TOWNSEND, Cathy, Chief Nursing Officer, Banner – University Medical Center South, Tucson, AZ, p. A37

TOWNSEND, Dona E, Chief Nursing Officer, Navarro Regional Hospital, Corsicana, TX, p. A594

TOWNSEND, Gary, Chief Information Officer, Hurley Medical Center, Flint, MI, p. A311

TOWNSEND, Michael, Chief Information Officer, James Cancer Hospital And Solove Research Institute, Columbus, OH, p. A479

TOWNSEND, Mike, Interim Director Health Information Systems, Grady Memorial Hospital, Chickasha, OK, p. A498

TOWNSEND, Sammuel, LAN Administrator, University Of Mississippi Medical Center Holmes County, Lexington, MS, p. A350

TOWNSEND, Tanya, Senior Vice President, Chief Information Officer (part of LCMC), Children'S Hospital, New Orleans, LA, p. A275

TOY, Linda, Director Information Systems, Havasu Regional Medical Center, Lake Havasu City, AZ, p. A31

TOY, Stanley, Jr, Chief Executive Officer, Greater El Monte Community Hospital, South El Monte, CA, p. A90

TRABAL, Milton, Chief Financial Officer, Clarinda Regional Health Center, Clarinda, IA, p. A219

TRAC, Vincent, Chief Executive Officer, Kindred Hospital–Ontario, Ontario, CA, p. A76

TRACEY, Karen, Chief Human Resources, Select Specialty Hospital–Greensboro, Greensboro, NC, p. A455

TRACY, Allen R, Senior Vice President and Chief Financial Officer, St. John Medical Center, Westlake, OH, p. A494

TRACY, Larry A., Jr, President, Memorial Hospital Of South Bend, South Bend, IN, p. A215

TRACY, Pat, Administrator, Ridgeview Behavioral Hospital, Middle Point, OH, p. A487

TRACY, Thomas, Chief Medical Officer, Penn State Milton S. Hershey Medical Center, Hershey, PA, p. A527

TRACY, Timothy J., Senior Director, Sanford Vermillion Medical Center, Vermillion, SD, p. A564

TRACZ, Robert B, CPA, Senior Vice President and Chief Financial Officer, Lake Health, Concord Township, OH, p. A480

TRAHAN, Jennifer Lynch, Assistant Vice President Human Resources, Our Lady Of Lourdes Regional Medical Center, Lafayette, LA, p. A271

TRAHAN, Leslie T., Chief Executive Officer, South Cameron Memorial Hospital, Cameron, LA, p. A265

TRAHAN, Thomas, M.D., Chief of Medical Staff, Lane Regional Medical Center, Zachary, LA, p. A280

TRAIL, Alan, Director Information Systems, Owensboro Health Muhlenberg Community Hospital, Greenville, KY, p. A252

TRAINER, Michael, Chief Financial Officer, Akron Children'S Hospital, Akron, OH, p. A471

TRAINOR, Karyn, Director Human Resources, Providence St. Patrick Hospital, Missoula, MT, p. A379

TRAINOR, Paul, Senior Vice President Finance and Chief Financial Officer, Southern New Hampshire Medical Center, Nashua, NH, p. A401

TRAISTER, Lynne, Controller, Encompass Health Rehabilitation Hospital Of Tinton Falls, Tinton Falls, NJ, p. A413

TRAMMELL, Patrick, Chief Executive Officer, Dekalb Regional Medical Center, Fort Payne, AL, p. A18

TRAMP, Francis G., President, Burgess Health Center, Onawa, IA, p. A227

TRAN, Ann, Chief Financial Officer, Pike County Memorial Hospital, Louisiana, MO, p. A364

TRAN, Khiem, M.D., Acting Chief of Staff, Veterans Affairs Illiana Health Care System, Danville, IL, p. A180

TRAN, Lac, Senior Vice President Information Services, Rush University Medical Center, Chicago, IL, p. A179

TRAN, Richard, Director Information Technology, Galesburg Cottage Hospital, Galesburg, IL, p. A183

TRAN, Thanh, Chief Executive Officer, North Central Surgical Center, Dallas, TX, p. A597

TRANCHINA, Scott, Administrator, Cobalt Rehabilitation Hospital Of New Orleans, New Orleans, LA, p. A275

TRANSIER, Rhonda, Financial Officer, Rusk State Hospital, Rusk, TX, p. A632

TRANTALIS, Carolyn, R.N., MSN
Chief Operating Officer, East Region, Windham Hospital, Willimantic, CT, p. A112
Regional Vice President, Clinical Services and Operations, The William W. Backus Hospital, Norwich, CT, p. A110

TRANTHAM, Susan, Director Human Resources, Encompass Health Rehabilitation Hospital Of Florence, Florence, SC, p. A552

TRAPNELL, Kerry A., Chief Executive Officer, Elbert Memorial Hospital, Elberton, GA, p. A153

TRAPP, John, Vice President Medical Affairs, Bryan Medical Center, Lincoln, NE, p. A386

TRAVIS, Calee, R.N., Chief Nursing Officer, Baylor Scott & White Medical Center – Centennial, Frisco, TX, p. A606

TRAVIS, David A
Chief Financial Officer, Freestone Medical Center, Fairfield, TX, p. A603
Chief Financial Officer, Ut Health Athens, Athens, TX, p. A584

TRAVIS, Dee Dee, Vice President Community Relations, Calais Regional Hospital, Calais, ME, p. A282

TRAVIS, Sara, Chief Nursing Officer and Assistant Administrator, Palo Alto County Health System, Emmetsburg, IA, p. A222

TRAWICK, Thomas S., Chief Executive Officer, Christus Health Shreveport–Bossier, Shreveport, LA, p. A278

TRAYLOR, Desiree, Chief Information Officer, Chickasaw Nation Medical Center, Ada, OK, p. A496

TRAYLOR, Jerri Sue, Director Human Resources, The Women'S Hospital, Newburgh, IN, p. A213

TRAYNOR, Karen, Chief Financial Officer, Richland Hospital, Richland Center, WI, p. A704

TRCZINSKI, Judi, Vice President and Chief Human Resources Officer, Hospital For Special Care, New Britain, CT, p. A109

TREACY, Nancy, Director Finance, Cambridge Medical Center, Cambridge, MN, p. A329

TREACY–SHIFF, Mary, Vice President Finance, Advocate Good Samaritan Hospital, Downers Grove, IL, p. A181

TREADWAY, Michael G, Controller, Christus Trinity Mother Frances Rehabilitation Hospital, A Partner Of Encompass Health, Tyler, TX, p. A642

TREADWELL, Karen, Director Human Resources, Lake Martin Community Hospital, Dadeville, AL, p. A16

TREASE, Kevin, Chief Information Officer, Antelope Memorial Hospital, Neligh, NE, p. A388

TREASURE, Angela, Chief Nursing Officer, Portneuf Medical Center, Pocatello, ID, p. A171

TREASURE, Jeffrey
Chief Financial Officer, Northern Arizona Healthcare, Flagstaff Medical Center, Flagstaff, AZ, p. A29
Chief Financial Officer, Northern Arizona Healthcare, Verde Valley Medical Center, Cottonwood, AZ, p. A29

TREASURE, Martin, Director Human Resources, Lehigh Valley Hospital – Schuylkill, Pottsville, PA, p. A539
TREECE, Amy, M.D., Medical Director, Prisma Health North Greenville Ltach, Travelers Rest, SC, p. A557
TREGLOWN, Brad, Director Information Systems, Redmond Regional Medical Center, Rome, GA, p. A159
TREHAN, Rajeev, M.D., M.P.H., Chief of Staff, Veterans Affairs Eastern Kansas Health Care System, Topeka, KS, p. A246
TREITLER, Scot, Chief Operating Officer, Cypress Pointe Surgical Hospital, Hammond, LA, p. A268
TREMAINE, Lisa, Manager Human Resources, Carson Valley Medical Center, Gardnerville, NV, p. A394
TREMBLE, Nakia, Chief Executive Officer, Kindred Hospital Indianapolis North, Indianapolis, IN, p. A207
TREMONTI, Carl
Chief Financial Officer, Mease Countryside Hospital, Safety Harbor, FL, p. A138
Chief Financial Officer, Mease Dunedin Hospital, Dunedin, FL, p. A122
Chief Financial Officer, Morton Plant Hospital, Clearwater, FL, p. A119
Chief Financial Officer, Morton Plant North Bay Hospital, New Port Richey, FL, p. A132
Chief Financial Officer, South Florida Baptist Hospital, Plant City, FL, p. A137
Chief Financial Officer, St. Anthony'S Hospital, Saint Petersburg, FL, p. A138
TREMONTI, Yvette, Chief Financial Officer, H. Lee Moffitt Cancer Center And Research Institute, Tampa, FL, p. A141
TRENDE, Gary D, FACHE, Associate Director, Tuscaloosa Veterans Affairs Medical Center, Tuscaloosa, AL, p. A24
TRENSCHEL, Robert, President and Chief Executive Officer, Yuma Regional Medical Center, Yuma, AZ, p. A38
TRENT, Cindy, Manager Personnel, Fall River Hospital, Hot Springs, SD, p. A561
TRESSLER, Carrie, Vice President of Nursing and Chief Nursing Officer, Rush Memorial Hospital, Rushville, IN, p. A214
TRETINA, Mike, Senior Vice President and Chief Financial Officer, Bayhealth Medical Center, Dover, DE, p. A113
TRETTER, Stan, M.D., Chief Medical Officer, Memorial Hospital And Health Care Center, Jasper, IN, p. A208
TREVATHAN, Dave, Director Information Systems, Rose Medical Center, Denver, CO, p. A99
TREVINO, Jorge, Chief Executive Officer, City Hospital At White Rock, Dallas, TX, p. A596
TREVINO, Malissa, Director Human Resources, Pecos County Memorial Hospital, Fort Stockton, TX, p. A604
TREVINO, Paul, Chief Executive Officer, Christus Southeast Texas Hospital – St. Elizabeth, Beaumont, TX, p. A587
TREVISANI, Michael F, M.D., Senior Vice President and Chief Medical Officer, Faxton St. Luke'S Healthcare, Utica, NY, p. A446
TRIANA, Rudy, M.D., Chief of Staff, Jackson Purchase Medical Center, Mayfield, KY, p. A257
TRICKEY, Donna, R.N., Chief Nursing Officer, Fairview Park Hospital, Dublin, GA, p. A152
TRIEBES, David G., Chief Executive Officer, Samaritan Albany General Hospital, Albany, OR, p. A511
TRIGG, Terry, Director Human Resources, Merit Health Wesley, Hattiesburg, MS, p. A348
TRIMBLE, Deborah, Chief Executive Officer, Paul B. Hall Regional Medical Center, Paintsville, KY, p. A259
TRIMBLE, Donald, CPA, Chief Financial Officer, Vibra Specialty Hospital At Desoto, Desoto, TX, p. A600
TRIMBLE, Lisa, Controller, Healthsouth Rehabilitation Hospital Of Middletown, Middletown, DE, p. A113
TRIMM, Robert, Administrator, North Mississippi Medical Center–Hamilton, Hamilton, AL, p. A19
TRIMMER, Mary R, Interim Chief Operating Officer, Mount Carmel, Columbus, OH, p. A479
TRIMMER, Matthew, Director Information Services, Holy Cross Hospital, Silver Spring, MD, p. A293
TRINCHETTO, Thomas, M.D., Chief Medical Officer, Doctors Hospital Of Sarasota, Sarasota, FL, p. A139
TRINH, Khiet, M.D., Chief Medical Officer, Bon Secours St. Mary'S Hospital, Richmond, VA, p. A665
TRIPLETT, Daniel, Acting Chief Operating Officer, Springfield Hospital Center, Sykesville, MD, p. A293
TRIPLETT, John, D.O., President Medical Staff, Arh Our Lady Of The Way, Martin, KY, p. A257
TRIPP, Gina, Director Information Systems, Tirr Memorial Hermann, Houston, TX, p. A614
TRIPP, Kelly, Chief Executive Officer, Ten Broeck Tennessee Treatment Facility, Cookeville, TN, p. A568
TRIPPEL, Donald E, Chief Financial Officer, Hugh Chatham Memorial Hospital, Elkin, NC, p. A454
TRITTIN, Kim, Manager Human Resources, Mayo Clinic Health System In Red Wing, Red Wing, MN, p. A338
TRIVEDI, Harsh, President and Chief Executive Officer, Sheppard Pratt Health System, Baltimore, MD, p. A288
TRIVETTE, Chastity, Chief Executive Officer, Johnson County Community Hospital, Mountain City, TN, p. A576
TRIVETTE, Theresa, R.N., Chief Nursing Officer, Adventhealth Tampa, Tampa, FL, p. A141
TROCINO, Mark, Chief Information Officer, Emory Hillandale Hospital, Lithonia, GA, p. A156
TROGMAN, Richard, FACHE, Chief Operating Officer, Kaiser Permanente Woodland Hills Medical Center, Los Angeles, CA, p. A67
TROLLOPE, Grant, Chief Financial Officer, Northeastern Nevada Regional Hospital, Elko, NV, p. A393
TROMBATORE, Beverly, R.N., Director Managed Information Systems, Matagorda Regional Medical Center, Bay City, TX, p. A587
TROMBLEE, Julie, R.N., Chief Nursing Officer, The University Of Vermont Health Network Elizabethtown Community Hospital, Elizabethtown, NY, p. A427
TROMPETER, Dawn, President, Osf Saint Paul Medical Center, Mendota, IL, p. A189
TRONCONE, Michael T, Chief Human Resources Officer, Brookdale Hospital Medical Center, New York, NY, p. A432
TROSIN, Jill A., R.N., MSN, Vice President Patient Care Services, Chief Nursing Officer, St. Luke'S Hospital, Maumee, OH, p. A487
TROTTER, Wally, Director Human Resources, Mountain View Hospital, Payson, UT, p. A650
TROTTIER, Timothy R., Chief Executive Officer, Spring View Hospital, Lebanon, KY, p. A254
TROUBLEFIELD, David G, Director, Human Resources, Hemphill County Hospital, Canadian, TX, p. A591
TROUP, Bill, M.D., Chief of Staff, Stanton County Hospital, Johnson, KS, p. A237
TROUP, Matthew, President and Chief Executive Officer, Conway Regional Medical Center, Conway, AR, p. A40
TROUT, Gene, Chief Financial Officer, Weirton Medical Center, Weirton, WV, p. A690
TROUTMAN, Gary, CPA, Chief Financial Officer, Baptist Hospitals Of Southeast Texas, Beaumont, TX, p. A587
TROWHILL, Jan, Director Health Information Management Systems, Spire Cane Creek Rehabilitation Hospital, Martin, TN, p. A573
TROXELL, Larry, Chief Executive Officer, Comanche County Medical Center, Comanche, TX, p. A593
TROY, Patrick J, R.N., MSN, Associate Director Patient Care Services, Veterans Affairs New Jersey Health Care System, East Orange, NJ, p. A405
TROY, Peggy N.
President and Chief Executive Officer, Children'S Hospital Of Wisconsin–Fox Valley, Neenah, WI, p. A702
President and Chief Executive Officer, Children'S Hospital Of Wisconsin, Milwaukee, WI, p. A701
TROYER, David, Chief Information Officer, Veterans Affairs Northern Indiana Health Care System, Fort Wayne, IN, p. A204
TROYER, Devin, M.D., Medical Director, Encompass Health Rehabilitation Hospital Of Columbia, Columbia, SC, p. A551
TROYO–SAUVIAC, Glynda, Chief Executive Officer, Vibra Hospital Of Central Dakotas, Mandan, ND, p. A468
TRUE, Terry, M.D., Chief of Staff, Shoals Hospital, Muscle Shoals, AL, p. A22
TRUEBLOOD, Susan
Chief Executive Officer, Georgia Regional Hospital At Atlanta, Decatur, GA, p. A152
Regional Hospital Administrator, Central State Hospital, Milledgeville, GA, p. A157
TRUELOVE, Lynn, Chief Executive Officer, Stone County Hospital, Wiggins, MS, p. A355
TRUESDALE, Fred A, Administrator, North Mississippi Medical Center–Iuka, Iuka, MS, p. A348
TRUESDALE, Fred A., Jr, Administrator, North Mississippi Medical Center–Iuka, Iuka, MS, p. A348
TRUESDELL, Shannon, Chief Operating Officer, Marshall Medical Center, Placerville, CA, p. A78
TRUITT, Louise
Human Resource Director, Coliseum Northside Hospital, Macon, GA, p. A156
Vice President Human Resources, Capital Regional Medical Center, Tallahassee, FL, p. A140
TRUJILLO, Jesse, Chief Information Officer, St. Mark'S Hospital, Salt Lake City, UT, p. A652
TRUMAN, Julia
Chief Operating Officer, Multicare Tacoma General Hospital, Tacoma, WA, p. A680
Vice President Human Resources, Fort Walton Beach Medical Center, Fort Walton Beach, FL, p. A123
TRUMAN, Lisa, Chief Nursing Officer, Sea Pines Rehabilitation Hospital, Melbourne, FL, p. A129
TRUMAN, Mark, Vice President of Operations, Baptist Health Floyd, New Albany, IN, p. A212
TRYON, Ellen, R.N., Chief Nursing Officer, Adventist Health Portland, Portland, OR, p. A516
TSAI, James, President, Brookdale Hospital Medical Center, New York, NY, p. A432
TSALATE, Cynthia, Human Resource Specialist, U. S. Public Health Service Indian Hospital, Zuni, NM, p. A421
TSAMBIRAS, Petros, M.D., Chief of Staff, Adventhealth Dade City, Dade City, FL, p. A121
TSAO, Sean, Director Information Technology, Blue Mountain Hospital District, John Day, OR, p. A514
TSE, Graham, M.D., Chief Medical Officer, Memorialcare, Miller Children'S & Women'S Hospital Long Beach, Long Beach, CA, p. A65
TSENG, Allen, Chief Operations Officer, Memorial Hermann Memorial City Medical Center, Houston, TX, p. A613
TSUNEISHI, Lani, Nursing Services Manager, Hawaii State Hospital, Kaneohe, HI, p. A166
TUBBS, John, M.D.
Chief of Staff, Rock County Hospital, Bassett, NE, p. A382
Chief of Staff, West Holt Medical Services, Atkinson, NE, p. A382
TUBBS, Mary Beth, Chief Nursing Officer, Astria Sunnyside Hospital, Sunnyside, WA, p. A680
TUBERVILLE, Abby, Human Resource Manager, Fillmore County Hospital, Geneva, NE, p. A385
TUCK, Greg, Area Information Officer, Kaiser Permanente San Jose Medical Center, San Jose, CA, p. A86
TUCKER, Albert, Chief Financial Officer, Miami Veterans Affairs Healthcare System, Miami, FL, p. A130
TUCKER, Amy, M.D., Chief Medical Officer, Upstate University Hospital, Syracuse, NY, p. A445
TUCKER, Andy, Chief Financial Officer, South Mississippi State Hospital, Purvis, MS, p. A353
TUCKER, Bruce, Acting Director, Canandaigua Veterans Affairs Medical Center, Canandaigua, NY, p. A425
TUCKER, Cathy, Director Human Resources, Iraan General Hospital, Iraan, TX, p. A615
TUCKER, Denis, Chief Information Officer, Wilkes–Barre General Hospital, Wilkes, PA, p. A545
TUCKER, Gary C., President and Chief Executive Officer, Mount St. Mary'S Hospital And Health Center, Lewiston, NY, p. A430
TUCKER, Ian, M.D., Vice President Medical Affairs, Johnson Memorial Medical Center, Stafford Springs, CT, p. A111
TUCKER, Jessie Lee, III, Chief Executive Officer, Methodist Healthcare Memphis Hospitals, Memphis, TN, p. A575
TUCKER, John
Chief Executive Officer, Mt. San Rafael Hospital, Trinidad, CO, p. A106
Chief Nursing Executive, Center For Behavioral Medicine, Kansas City, MO, p. A362
TUCKER, Joseph B, Senior Vice President and Chief Financial Officer, Fort Washington Medical Center, Oxen Hill, MD, p. A292
TUCKER, Joseph B., Interim President and Chief Executive Officer, Fort Washington Medical Center, Oxen Hill, MD, p. A292
TUCKER, Mona, Vice President Human Resources, Bsa Hospital, Llc, Amarillo, TX, p. A582
TUCKER, Rebecca
Chief Financial Officer, Memorial Hermann Northeast, Humble, TX, p. A615
President, Texas Health Harris Methodist Hospital Southwest Fort Worth, Fort Worth, TX, p. A606
TUCKER, Ron, Business Office Manager, Kiowa County Memorial Hospital, Greensburg, KS, p. A236
TUCKER, Sarah, Chief Nursing Officer, Bradley County Medical Center, Warren, AR, p. A49
TUCKER, Theresa, Human Resources Officer, Sioux Center Health, Sioux Center, IA, p. A229
TUDELA, John M, M.D., Director of Medical Affairs, Commonwealth Health Center, Saipan, MP, p. A714
TUDOR, Brandon, Chief Executive Officer, Encompass Health Rehabilitation Hospital Of Plano, Plano, TX, p. A629
TUDOR, Nathan, Chief Executive Officer, El Campo Memorial Hospital, El Campo, TX, p. A601
TUER, Patrick, Interim Chief Executive Officer, Select Specialty Hospital–Mckeesport, Mckeesport, PA, p. A531
TULLIER, Debbie, Chief Executive Officer, Lake Pines Hospital, Kenner, LA, p. A270
TULLIS, Bea, Chief Financial Officer and Budget Officer, Broughton Hospital, Morganton, NC, p. A458
TULLMAN, Stephen M., Chief Executive Officer, Phoenixville Hospital, Phoenixville, PA, p. A537
TUMA, Bonnie, Human Resources Team Lead, National Institutes Of Health Clinical Center, Bethesda, MD, p. A289
TUMA, Roman, Chief Medical Officer, Easton Hospital, Easton, PA, p. A524

TUMLIN, Richard, Chief Administrative Officer, Saint Thomas Highlands Hospital, Sparta, TN, p. A579

TUMMONS, Coleen, Chief Executive Officer, Gove County Medical Center, Quinter, KS, p. A244

TUMMURU, Ramireddy K, M.D., Chief Medical Officer, Porter Regional Hospital, Valparaiso, IN, p. A215

TUNGATE, Rex A.
Chief Executive Officer, Casey County Hospital, Liberty, KY, p. A255
Chief Executive Officer, Jane Todd Crawford Hospital, Greensburg, KY, p. A252

TUNNELL, Richard, Chief Information Officer, University Hospital, Newark, NJ, p. A409

TUNSON, Lynn, Manager Medical Records, Complex Care Hospital At Tenaya, Las Vegas, NV, p. A394

TUPPER, David, Chief Executive Officer, Solara Hospital Mcallen, Mcallen, TX, p. A623

TUPPONCE, David, President, Central Maine Medical Center, Lewiston, ME, p. A283

TURBAK, Shelly, R.N., Chief Nursing Officer, Prairie Lakes Healthcare System, Watertown, SD, p. A565

TUREK, Beth, Site Manager Information Systems, Advocate South Suburban Hospital, Hazel Crest, IL, p. A185

TUREK, Derrill Kent, R.N., Chief Nursing Officer, Blue Mountain Hospital, Blanding, UT, p. A647

TURK, Edward, Vice President Finance, Scripps Mercy Hospital, San Diego, CA, p. A84

TURKAL–BARRETT, Kari, Flight Commander Resource Management Officer, Mike O'Callaghan Federal Hospital, Nellis Afb, NV, p. A396

TURLEY, Mary Ann, D.O., Medical Director, Honorhealth Deer Valley Medical Center, Phoenix, AZ, p. A33

TURLEY, Matt, Interim Director Information Systems, Greenbrier Valley Medical Center, Ronceverte, WV, p. A689

TURMAN, Tracy, Administrator, Uva Transitional Care Hospital, Charlottesville, VA, p. A657

TURNA, Tarlochan, M.D., Medical Director, Mayo Clinic Health System In Cannon Falls, Cannon Falls, MN, p. A329

TURNAGE, Richard, Chief Executive Officer, Uams Medical Center, Little Rock, AR, p. A45

TURNBULL, James, Chief Information Officer, University Of Utah Health, Salt Lake City, UT, p. A652

TURNBULL, Rosie, Director Human Resources, St. Lawrence Psychiatric Center, Ogdensburg, NY, p. A440

TURNER, Barbara, Director of Nursing, Austen Riggs Center, Stockbridge, MA, p. A304

TURNER, Bill, Vice President Human Resources, Valir Rehabilitation Hospital, Oklahoma City, OK, p. A505

TURNER, Brenda C
Chief Human Resources Officer, Palomar Medical Center Poway, Poway, CA, p. A79
Chief Human Resources Officer, Palomar Medical Center, Escondido, CA, p. A57

TURNER, Chad, Chief Financial Officer, Star Valley Medical Center, Afton, WY, p. A710

TURNER, Cindy R, Chief Executive Officer, Bacon County Hospital And Health System, Alma, GA, p. A145

TURNER, Cindy R., Chief Executive Officer, Bacon County Hospital And Health System, Alma, GA, p. A145

TURNER, Dale, Chief Operating Officer, Reedsburg Area Medical Center, Reedsburg, WI, p. A704

TURNER, Farrell, Chief Executive Officer, Medical Center Barbour, Eufaula, AL, p. A17

TURNER, Howard D., Chief Executive Officer, Abbeville Area Medical Center, Abbeville, SC, p. A549

TURNER, Jeff, Chief Executive Officer, Moore County Hospital District, Dumas, TX, p. A600

TURNER, Karen, Chief Nursing Officer, Seneca Healthcare District, Chester, CA, p. A54

TURNER, Karissa, Vice President Operations, Wabash General Hospital, Mount Carmel, IL, p. A190

TURNER, Kelly, Senior Vice President Finance and Chief Financial Officer, Adventist Health Glendale, Los Angeles, CA, p. A65

TURNER, Kevin, M.D., Medical Director, Pathways Of Tennessee, Jackson, TN, p. A571

TURNER, Mark
Director Information Systems, Beverly Hospital, Montebello, CA, p. A72
Manager Information Technology, Ojai Valley Community Hospital, Ojai, CA, p. A75

TURNER, Mark J.
President, Memorial Hospital East, Shiloh, IL, p. A196
President, Memorial Hospital Belleville, Belleville, IL, p. A174

TURNER, Mark S., Chief Executive Officer, Capital Medical Center, Olympia, WA, p. A676

TURNER, Marquita, Chief Operating Officer and Chief Nursing Officer, Atrium Medical Center, Middletown, OH, p. A487

TURNER, Maurita, Team Leader Health Information Systems Services, Chi St. Joseph Health Madison Hospital, Madisonville, TX, p. A623

TURNER, Melissa, Senior Vice President Human Resources, Bridgeport Hospital, Bridgeport, CT, p. A107

TURNER, Michael
Chief Information Officer, Plaza Specialty Hospital, Houston, TX, p. A613
Director Human Resources, Moberly Regional Medical Center, Moberly, MO, p. A365

TURNER, Nancy, Director Communications, Sutter Roseville Medical Center, Roseville, CA, p. A81

TURNER, Peggy, Assistant Vice President and Director of Nursing, Unity Health White County Medical Center, Searcy, AR, p. A48

TURNER, Ralph, Chief Operating Officer, Cleveland Clinic Indian River Hospital, Vero Beach, FL, p. A143

TURNER, Randy, Chief Human Resource Management Services, Boise Veterans Affairs Medical Center, Boise, ID, p. A167

TURNER, Robert A., Chief Executive Officer, Ad Hospital East, Houston, TX, p. A610

TURNER, Sara, Director Human Resources, Alvarado Hospital Medical Center, San Diego, CA, p. A83

TURNER, Saundra G, Director Human Resources, Mercy Hospital Jefferson, Festus, MO, p. A360

TURNER, Scott, Chief Operating Officer, University Of Iowa Hospitals And Clinics, Iowa City, IA, p. A224

TURNER, Sherrilyn, Director Human Resources, Southeast Colorado Hospital District, Springfield, CO, p. A105

TURNER, Spencer, President, Texas Health Presbyterian Hospital Flower Mound, Flower Mound, TX, p. A604

TURNER, Steve, Director Information Technology, Salem Township Hospital, Salem, IL, p. A195

TURNER, Teri, Chief Nursing Officer, Haskell Memorial Hospital, Haskell, TX, p. A609

TURNER, Tiffany, MSN, R.N., Vice President of Nursing and Chief Nursing Officer, Paris Community Hospital, Paris, IL, p. A192

TURNER, Will, President, Baylor Scott & White Medical Center–Waxahachie, Waxahachie, TX, p. A644

TURNEY, Amanda, Director Human Resources, Cochran Memorial Hospital, Morton, TX, p. A625

TURNEY, Brian, Chief Executive Officer, Kingman Regional Medical Center, Kingman, AZ, p. A30

TURNEY, David, Chief Information Officer, Cochran Memorial Hospital, Morton, TX, p. A625

TURNEY, Larry, Administrator, Cochran Memorial Hospital, Morton, TX, p. A625

TURNQUIST, Carrie, Director Human Resources, Buena Vista Regional Medical Center, Storm Lake, IA, p. A230

TURO, Albert, Vice President Human Resources, St. Mary'S Healthcare, Amsterdam, NY, p. A422

TURPEN, Brad, Interim Chief Executive Officer, Valor Health, Emmett, ID, p. A169

TURPIN, Debra, R.N., MSN, Vice President Patient Care Services and Chief Nursing Officer, Alton Memorial Hospital, Alton, IL, p. A173

TURPIN, James
Chief of Staff, Ephraim Mcdowell Fort Logan Hospital, Stanford, KY, p. A261
Human Resources, Breckinridge Memorial Hospital, Hardinsburg, KY, p. A253

TURQUEZA, Sandra
Human Resources Business Partner, Chi Saint Joseph Berea, Berea, KY, p. A249
Senior Human Resources Business Partner, Chi Saint Joseph London, London, KY, p. A255

TURSKY, Martin, President and Chief Executive Officer, Mclaren Central Michigan, Mount Pleasant, MI, p. A318

TURSO, Janet, Controller, Healthsouth Rehabilitation Hospital Of Toms River, Toms River, NJ, p. A413

TURTON, Jonathan, Chief Executive Officer, Broward Health Medical Center, Fort Lauderdale, FL, p. A122

TUSA, Edward A, Chief Financial Officer, Mayo Clinic Health System In Cannon Falls, Cannon Falls, MN, p. A329

TUSCANY, Joanne E
Director Human Resources, Ascension St. John Hospital, Detroit, MI, p. A309
Senior Director Human Resources, Ascension Macomb–Oakland Hospital, Warren, MI, p. A324

TUSTEN, Jay, Chief Executive Officer, Stanton County Hospital, Johnson, KS, p. A237

TUSTIN, Bill, Chief Operating Officer, Piedmont Columbus Regional Midtown, Columbus, GA, p. A150

TUTT, Michael, M.D., Chief Medical Officer, Tsehootsooi Medical Center, Fort Defiance, AZ, p. A29

TUTTLE, Casey, Director Information Technology, Sistersville General Hospital, Sistersville, WV, p. A689

TUTTLE, Kathryn, R.N., Director of Nursing, Memorial Medical Center Of Ashland, Ashland, WI, p. A691

TVEIT, Charles B., Chief Executive Officer, Lake District Hospital, Lakeview, OR, p. A514

TWARDY, Cindi, Manager Human Resources, Meeker Memorial Hospital, Litchfield, MN, p. A334

TWEED, Frances, Executive Director and Administrator, New Mexico Behavioral Health Institute At Las Vegas, Las Vegas, NM, p. A419

TWEHOUS, Debra, Medical Director, Fairlawn Rehabilitation Hospital, Worcester, MA, p. A305

TWIDWELL, Lisa, Administrator, Madison Medical Center, Fredericktown, MO, p. A360

TWIGG, Nicole, Director Human Resources, Brook Lane Health Services, Hagerstown, MD, p. A291

TWIGG, Spencer, Chief Executive Officer, Musc Health Marion Medical Center, Mullins, SC, p. A556

TYE, Angie, Director Human Resources, Waverly Health Center, Waverly, IA, p. A231

TYK, Robert C., Interim Chief Executive Officer, Artesia General Hospital, Artesia, NM, p. A417

TYLER, Holley, R.N., Chief Nursing Officer, Woman'S Hospital Of Texas, Houston, TX, p. A615

TYLER, James E., Chief Executive Officer, Smyth County Community Hospital, Marion, VA, p. A662

TYLER, Kevin L, M.D., President Medical Staff, Penn Highlands Clearfield, Clearfield, PA, p. A522

TYLER, Philene, Chief Finance Officer, Chinle Comprehensive Health Care Facility, Chinle, AZ, p. A29

TYLER, Richard, Corporate Director Human Resources, Conway Regional Medical Center, Conway, AR, p. A40

TYLER, Rick, M.D., Vice President Medical Affairs, Christus Southeast Texas Hospital – St. Elizabeth, Beaumont, TX, p. A587

TYLER, Rob, Chief Financial Officer, West Oaks Hospital, Houston, TX, p. A615

TYLER, Tanya, Vice President Human Resources, Chi St. Luke'S Health Memorial Lufkin, Lufkin, TX, p. A622

TYNES, L Lee, M.D., Ph.D., Medical Director, Central Louisiana State Hospital, Pineville, LA, p. A277

TYO, Joanne, Chief Financial Officer, Carolinas Continuecare Hospital At Pineville, Charlotte, NC, p. A451

TYRA, Diana, Director Health Information, Kentucky River Medical Center, Jackson, KY, p. A254

TYRA, J Allen., Chief Executive, North Mississippi Medical Center Gilmore–Amory, Amory, MS, p. A344

TYRELL, Wade, Chief Executive Officer and Chief Nursing Officer, Sterling Regional Medcenter, Sterling, CO, p. A105

TYRRELL, Wade Alan, Chief Executive Officer and Chief Nursing Officer, Sterling Regional Medcenter, Sterling, CO, p. A105

TYSON, Rhoda, Chief Information Officer, Central Alabama Veterans Health Care System, Montgomery, AL, p. A21

U

UBER, Charlotte M., Chief Executive Officer, Warren State Hospital, Warren, PA, p. A543

UDALL, Ben, M.D., Chief of Staff, Kimble Hospital, Junction, TX, p. A617

UDOVICH, Christopher, M.D., Chief of Staff, Silver Cross Hospital, New Lenox, IL, p. A191

UFFER, Mark H., Chief Executive Officer, Corona Regional Medical Center, Corona, CA, p. A55

UGHOUWA, Ejiro, M.D., Chief of Staff, Allen Parish Community Healthcare, Kinder, LA, p. A270

UGWUEKE, Michael, President and Chief Executive Officer, Methodist Healthcare Memphis Hospitals, Memphis, TN, p. A575

UHARRIET, Bart, Director Information Services, Mississippi State Hospital, Whitfield, MS, p. A355

UHL, Michael, President, Atrium Medical Center, Middletown, OH, p. A487

UHLIR, Tricia, Chief Executive Officer, Fall River Hospital, Hot Springs, SD, p. A561

ULERY, Brian
Chief Operating Officer, Thomas Memorial Hospital, South Charleston, WV, p. A689
Senior Vice President and Chief Operating Officer, Saint Francis Hospital, Charleston, WV, p. A684

ULETT, John, Vice President and Chief Information Officer, Centrastate Healthcare System, Freehold, NJ, p. A406

ULFERTS, Wendy, Vice President and Chief Nursing Officer, Maple Grove Hospital, Maple Grove, MN, p. A335

ULI, James
Chief Financial Officer, Loma Linda University Medical Center–Murrieta, Murrieta, CA, p. A73

Chief Financial Officer, Providence Saint John'S Health Center, Santa Monica, CA, p. A89
ULIBARRI, Laura, M.D., Chief of Staff, Catalina Island Medical Center, Avalon, CA, p. A51
ULLRICH, John, M.D., Chief of Staff, Ivinson Memorial Hospital, Laramie, WY, p. A711
ULMER, Becky, R.N., Director of Nursing, Jasper General Hospital, Bay Springs, MS, p. A344
ULMER, Carlton, Chief Executive Officer, Medical City Plano, Plano, TX, p. A629
ULMER, Carol, Chief Executive Officer, Select Specialty Hospital–Sioux Falls, Sioux Falls, SD, p. A564
ULREICH, Shawn, MSN, R.N., Vice President Clinical Operations and Chief Nursing Executive, Spectrum Health – Butterworth Hospital, Grand Rapids, MI, p. A313
ULREY, Chris, Director Management Information Systems, St. Luke'S Behavioral Health Center, Phoenix, AZ, p. A34
ULRICH, Alan
  Chief Financial Officer, Bartlett Regional Hospital, Juneau, AK, p. A26
  Chief Financial Officer, Guam Memorial Hospital Authority, Tamuning, GU, p. A714
ULRICH, James P., Jr, Chief Executive Officer, York General, York, NE, p. A392
ULSETH, Randy, Chief Executive Officer, Firstlight Health System, Mora, MN, p. A336
ULVELING, Kyle, M.D., Chief of Staff, St. Anthony Regional Hospital, Carroll, IA, p. A218
UMHAU, John, M.D., Clinical Director, U. S. Public Health Service Indian Hospital–Whiteriver, Whiteriver, AZ, p. A38
UNDERDAHL, Steve, President and Chief Executive Officer, Northfield Hospital And Clinics, Northfield, MN, p. A337
UNDERHILL, Robert, Director of Business Services, Central State Hospital, Louisville, KY, p. A256
UNDERWOOD, Debbie, Manager Human Resources, Plains Memorial Hospital, Dimmitt, TX, p. A600
UNDERWOOD, Jerri C, R.N., Chief Nursing Officer, Parkridge Medical Center, Chattanooga, TN, p. A567
UNDERWOOD, Kelsey N, Director of Nursing, Gundersen Tri-County Hospital And Clinics, Whitehall, WI, p. A708
UNDERWOOD, Ken, Chief Executive Officer, Hazel Hawkins Memorial Hospital, Hollister, CA, p. A61
UNDERWOOD, Martha, Chief Human Resources Officer, Saint Thomas Midtown Hospital, Nashville, TN, p. A577
UNDERWOOD, Phillip, Chief Executive Officer, Kindred Hospital–Dayton, Dayton, OH, p. A481
UNDERWOOD, Vickie, Director Human Resources, Wyandot Memorial Hospital, Upper Sandusky, OH, p. A492
UNDERWOOD, Virgil, Chief Executive Officer, Boone Memorial Hospital, Madison, WV, p. A687
UNDLIN, Cassie, Chief Operating Officer, Navos, Seattle, WA, p. A677
UNELL, Deonna, Chief Executive Officer, Baylor Surgical Hospital At Las Colinas, Irving, TX, p. A616
UNG, David
  Director, Information Technology, California Hospital Medical Center, Los Angeles, CA, p. A66
  Site Director, St. Mary Medical Center, Long Beach, CA, p. A65
UNGER, Henry D., M.D., Senior Vice President and Chief Medical Officer, Holy Redeemer Hospital, Meadowbrook, PA, p. A531
UNGER, Kevin L.
  President and Chief Executive Officer, Uchealth Medical Center Of The Rockies, Loveland, CO, p. A104
  President and Chief Executive Officer, Uchealth Poudre Valley Hospital, Fort Collins, CO, p. A100
UNHEE, Kim, President, Mount Carmel St. Ann'S, Westerville, OH, p. A494
UNITAN, Carol, M.D., Chief Medical Officer, Kaiser Westside Medical Center, Hillsboro, OR, p. A513
UNRUH, Greg, Chief Executive Officer, Citizens Medical Center, Colby, KS, p. A233
UNZEN, John, Chief Financial Officer, Mille Lacs Health System, Onamia, MN, p. A337
UPCHURCH, Jim, M.D., Chief Medical Officer, Crow/Northern Cheyenne Hospital, Crow Agency, MT, p. A375
UPCRAFT, Jeffrey, Director Information Services, Southwest Healthcare System, Murrieta, CA, p. A74
UPFIELD, Jaclyn, Chief Operating Officer, G. Werber Bryan Psychiatric Hospital, Columbia, SC, p. A551
UPSHAW, Joy, Chief Nursing Officer, Oklahoma State University Medical Center, Tulsa, OK, p. A509
UPTON, Carol, Interim Chief Executive Officer, Merit Health Wesley, Hattiesburg, MS, p. A348
UPTON, Daniel, Vice President and Chief Financial Officer, Doylestown Hospital, Doylestown, PA, p. A524
UPTON, Matthew
  Chief Medical Information Officer, Thomas Memorial Hospital, South Charleston, WV, p. A689
  Chief Medical Officer and Chief Medical Information Officer, Saint Francis Hospital, Charleston, WV, p. A684
URADNIK, Michael, Chief Executive Officer, Cascade Behavioral Hospital, Tukwila, WA, p. A681
URAIZEE, Rizwan A., Chief Financial Officer, Kedren Community Mental Health Center, Los Angeles, CA, p. A67
URBAN, Frank, Chief Financial Officer, Southwood Psychiatric Hospital, Pittsburgh, PA, p. A537
URBAN, Josh, Chief Executive Officer, Memorial Hermann Northeast, Humble, TX, p. A615
URBAN, Louise
  President and Chief Executive Officer, Canonsburg Hospital, Canonsburg, PA, p. A522
  President and Chief Executive Officer, Jefferson Hospital, Jefferson Hills, PA, p. A528
URBAN, Thomas S., President and Chief Executive Officer, Mercy Health – Fairfield Hospital, Fairfield, OH, p. A483
URBANCSIK, Don
  Director Finance, Euclid Hospital, Euclid, OH, p. A482
  Director Finance, Lutheran Hospital, Cleveland, OH, p. A478
URBANSKI, Pamela A R.N., MSN, Chief Nursing Officer, Senior Vice President, Patient Care Services, Promedica Monroe Regional Hospital, Monroe, MI, p. A318
URBINA, Ana, Chief Financial Officer, Atrium Medical Center, Stafford, TX, p. A638
URBISTONDO, Lisa, Chief Financial Officer, Medical Center Of Peach County, Navicent Health, Bryon, GA, p. A149
URDANETA, Alfonso, M.D., President Medical Staff, Washington County Hospital, Nashville, IL, p. A191
URISH, Abigail R., M.D., Chief of Staff, Rangely District Hospital, Rangely, CO, p. A105
URLAUB, Charles J., President and Chief Executive Officer, Mercy Hospital, Buffalo, NY, p. A424
URQUHART, Mary, R.N., Vice President Patient Care, Brattleboro Memorial Hospital, Brattleboro, VT, p. A654
URQUHART, Mary Beth, Vice President Patient Care Services and Director of Quality, New England Sinai Hospital And Rehabilitation Center, Stoughton, MA, p. A304
URQUHART, Mary Beth., Interim President, Vice President Patient Care Services and Chief Nursing Officer, New England Sinai Hospital And Rehabilitation Center, Stoughton, MA, p. A304
URQUHART, Teresa C., Chief Executive Officer, Palm Beach Gardens Medical Center, Palm Beach Gardens, FL, p. A135
USELMAN, Krista, Chief Executive Officer, Encompass Health Rehabilitation Hospital The Vintage, Houston, TX, p. A611
USELMAN, Melissa, Chief Financial Officer, Gundersen Boscobel Area Hospital And Clinics, Boscobel, WI, p. A692
UTECHT, Tom, M.D
  Chief Medical and Quality Officer, Community Regional Medical Center, Fresno, CA, p. A59
  Corporate Chief Quality Officer, Fresno Heart And Surgical Hospital, Fresno, CA, p. A60
  Senior Vice President and Chief Quality Officer, Community Behavioral Health Center, Fresno, CA, p. A59
UTLEY, Donna, Vice President Human Resources, Mercy San Juan Medical Center, Carmichael, CA, p. A54
UTLEY, Renee, Chief Financial Officer, Hamilton Center, Terre Haute, IN, p. A215
UTTENDORFSKY, Rob, Director Information Management, Lewis County General Hospital, Lowville, NY, p. A430
UTTER, Camille, R.N., Chief Nursing Officer, Scotland Health Care System, Laurinburg, NC, p. A457
UTTERBACK, Julie, Chief Financial Officer, Roane Medical Center, Harriman, TN, p. A570
UYEMURA, Monte, M.D., Chief of Staff, Wray Community District Hospital, Wray, CO, p. A106

V

VAAGENES, Carl P., Chief Executive Officer, Alomere Health, Alexandria, MN, p. A327
VAALER, Mark, M.D., Chief Medical Officer, South Florida Baptist Hospital, Plant City, FL, p. A137
VACCARO, Stacey, Chief Operating Officer, The Children'S Institute Of Pittsburgh, Pittsburgh, PA, p. A537
VACHON, Scott, Director Information Technology, Littleton Regional Healthcare, Littleton, NH, p. A401
VADYAK, Karen, Chief Nursing Officer, Easton Hospital, Easton, PA, p. A524
VAEZAZIZI, Reza, M.D., Chief of Staff, Southwest Healthcare System, Murrieta, CA, p. A74
VAGUE, Jeff, Regional Manager Information Systems, Mercy Hospitals Of Bakersfield, Bakersfield, CA, p. A52
VAHLBERG, Susan, Director Employee and Community Relations, Valor Health, Emmett, ID, p. A169
VAIL, B J, Director Information Systems, Morehouse General Hospital, Bastrop, LA, p. A263
VAIL, Bryan, Chief Information Officer, Clement J. Zablocki Veterans Affairs Medical Center, Milwaukee, WI, p. A701
VAIL, Lisa M, R.N., Chief Nursing Officer and Vice President of Patient Care Services, Bryan Medical Center, Lincoln, NE, p. A386
VAIL, Ronald, M.D., Chief of Staff, Lower Umpqua Hospital District, Reedsport, OR, p. A517
VAILLANCOURT, Alex, Chief Information Officer, Christ Hospital, Cincinnati, OH, p. A475
VAILLANCOURT, Stacy, Vice President Marketing, Communications, Advocacy and Human Resources, Saint Agnes Medical Center, Fresno, CA, p. A59
VALDENEGRO, Maria, Chief Financial Officer, Meadow Wood Behavioral Health System, New Castle, DE, p. A113
VALDERAZ, Leonard, Administrator, Sunrise Canyon Hospital, Lubbock, TX, p. A622
VALDESPINO, Gustavo A., President and Chief Executive Officer, Valley Presbyterian Hospital, Los Angeles, CA, p. A70
VALDEZ, J. Alex, President and Chief Executive Officer, Christus St. Vincent Regional Medical Center, Santa Fe, NM, p. A420
VALENCERINA, Madeline, Chief Operating Officer, Kedren Community Mental Health Center, Los Angeles, CA, p. A67
VALENTE, Anthony, M.D., Vice President Medical Affairs, Lehigh Valley Hospital – Hazleton, Hazleton, PA, p. A527
VALENTE, T. J., M.D., Medical Director, Lifestream Behavioral Center, Leesburg, FL, p. A128
VALENTIN, Carlos, Chief Financial Officer, St. Luke'S Episcopal Hospital, Ponce, PR, p. A717
VALENTIN, Leonardo, Chief Executive Officer, Professional Hospital Guaynabo, Guaynabo, PR, p. A716
VALENTINE, Lisa R, Chief Executive Officer, Trident Medical Center, Charleston, SC, p. A550
VALENTINE, Mark
  President, Baylor Scott & White The Heart Hospital Plano, Plano, TX, p. A629
  President, Baylor Scott & White The Heart Hospital–Denton, Denton, TX, p. A599
VALENTINI, Rudolph, M.D., Chief Medical Officer, Dmc – Children'S Hospital Of Michigan, Detroit, MI, p. A309
VALENTO, Jessica, Director Information Systems, Range Regional Health Services, Hibbing, MN, p. A333
VALLA, Nancy, R.N., Chief Nursing Officer, St. Mary Medical Center, Long Beach, CA, p. A65
VALLE, Bernardo, Vice President Human Resources, Usmd Hospital At Arlington, Arlington, TX, p. A584
VALLE, David, Chief Information Officer, Hospital Pavia Arecibo, Arecibo, PR, p. A715
VALLE, Karla, Area Chief Financial Officer, Kaiser Permanente Panorama City Medical Center, Los Angeles, CA, p. A67
VALLELY, Ian, Information Technology Site Leader, Sequoia Hospital, Redwood City, CA, p. A80
VALLIDO, Gabe, Chief Information Officer, Naval Hospital Camp Pendleton, Camp Pendleton, CA, p. A54
VALLIERE, George, Chief Executive Officer, Claremore Indian Hospital, Claremore, OK, p. A498
VAN BREE, Margaret M., President, Rhode Island Hospital, Providence, RI, p. A548
VAN BUSKIRK, George F, M.D., Chief of Staff, Bay Pines Veterans Affairs Healthcare System, Bay Pines, FL, p. A117
VAN BUSKIRK, Kryder, Medical Staff President at EMRMC, Ephraim Mcdowell Regional Medical Center, Danville, KY, p. A251
VAN CAMP, Keith, Vice President Information Services, St. Dominic–Jackson Memorial Hospital, Jackson, MS, p. A349
VAN CLEAVE, Bruce L, M.D., Senior Vice President and Chief Medical Officer, Aurora Medical Center Of Oshkosh, Oshkosh, WI, p. A703
VAN CLEAVE, Chad, Chief Financial Officer, Columbus Community Hospital, Columbus, NE, p. A384
VAN DECAR, Tama, M.D., Chief Medical Officer, Fort Walton Beach Medical Center, Fort Walton Beach, FL, p. A123
VAN DER VEER, Jon, D.O., Vice President Medical Affairs, Greene County Medical Center, Jefferson, IA, p. A225
VAN DRIEL, Allen, Administrator, Smith County Memorial Hospital, Smith Center, KS, p. A246
VAN DUREN, Michael, M.D., Chief Medical Officer, Bay Area Hospital, Coos Bay, OR, p. A512
VAN DYK, Holly, M.D., Interim Chief Medical Officer, Tuba City Regional Health Care Corporation, Tuba City, AZ, p. A37
VAN EECKHOUT, Barbara, M.D., Chief of Staff, Los Alamos Medical Center, Los Alamos, NM, p. A419
VAN EPERN, Keri, Manager Human Resources, Aspirus Ironwood Hospitals & Clinics, Inc., Ironwood, MI, p. A315

VAN ESSENDELFT, Seth
Vice President and Chief Financial Officer, Lawrence + Memorial Hospital, New London, CT, p. A110
Vice President and Chief Financial Officer, Westerly Hospital, Westerly, RI, p. A548
VAN ETTEN, Mark, M.D., Chief of Staff, Spooner Health, Spooner, WI, p. A705
VAN GENDEREN, Nathan, Executive Vice President and Chief Financial Officer, Mercy Medical Center – Cedar Rapids, Cedar Rapids, IA, p. A218
VAN HOET, Jim, Chief Financial Officer, Coffey County Hospital, Burlington, KS, p. A233
VAN HOUDEN, Charles, M.D., Chief Medical Officer, Neosho Memorial Regional Medical Center, Chanute, KS, p. A233
VAN HYNING, Jill, Director Human Resources, Carle Richland Memorial Hospital, Olney, IL, p. A192
VAN KAMPEN, Cindy, Chief Nursing Officer, North Ottawa Community Hospital, Grand Haven, MI, p. A312
VAN LEEUWE, Matthew, Chief Operating Officer, Abilene Regional Medical Center, Abilene, TX, p. A581
VAN MEETEREN, Robert, President and Chief Executive Officer, Reedsburg Area Medical Center, Reedsburg, WI, p. A704
VAN METER, Rex, President, Integris Deaconess, Oklahoma City, OK, p. A504
VAN NATTA, Timothy, M.D., Chief Medical Officer, Harbor–Ucla Medical Center, Torrance, CA, p. A91
VAN NORMAN, Steven, M.D., Medical Director, Dixie Regional Medical Center, Saint George, UT, p. A651
VAN RYBROEK, Greg, Chief Executive Officer, Mendota Mental Health Institute, Madison, WI, p. A698
VAN SCOYK, Mitch, Manager Information Systems, Delta County Memorial Hospital, Delta, CO, p. A98
VAN VICKLE, Robin, Chief Financial Officer, Bristow Medical Center, Bristow, OK, p. A497
VAN VOLKENBURG, Mark, Chief Executive Officer, Encompass Health Harmarville Rehabilitation Hospital, Pittsburgh, PA, p. A537
VAN VRANKEN, Arthur, M.D., Chief Medical Officer, Essentia Health–Graceville, Graceville, MN, p. A332
VAN VRANKEN, Ross, Executive Director, University Of Utah Neuropsychiatric Institute, Salt Lake City, UT, p. A652
VAN WHY, Susan, Director Human Resources, St. Luke'S Hospital – Miners Campus, Coaldale, PA, p. A522
VAN WINKLE, James, M.D., Chief of Staff, Unity Medical Center, Manchester, TN, p. A573
VAN WINKLE, Melanie, Chief Financial Officer, Mammoth Hospital, Mammoth Lakes, CA, p. A70
VAN ZANTEN, Lorinda, Chief Executive, Providence Newberg Medical Center, Newberg, OR, p. A515
VANATOR, John, CPA
Chief Financial Officer, Indiana University Health Ball Memorial Hospital, Muncie, IN, p. A212
Chief Financial Officer, Indiana University Health Blackford Hospital, Hartford City, IN, p. A206
VANBOEKEL, Tony, Director Information Systems, Shasta Regional Medical Center, Redding, CA, p. A80
VANCE, Derek
President, Chi Health Nebraska Heart, Lincoln, NE, p. A386
President, Chi Health St Elizabeth, Lincoln, NE, p. A387
VANCE, Ellen B
Chief Human Resource Officer, Sheltering Arms Rehabilitation Hospital, Mechanicsville, VA, p. A662
Chief Human Resources Officer, Sheltering Arms Hospital South, Midlothian, VA, p. A663
VANCE, Mark, M.D., Chief Medical Officer, Quincy Valley Medical Center, Quincy, WA, p. A677
VANCE, Ruth, Director Information Systems, Quincy Valley Medical Center, Quincy, WA, p. A677
VANCE, Stacie
Chief Nursing Officer and Vice President Operations, Orthoindy Hospital, Indianapolis, IN, p. A207
Chief Nursing Officer and, Orthoindy Hospital, Indianapolis, IN, p. A207
VANCE, Steven
Chief Financial Officer, Dixie Regional Medical Center, Saint George, UT, p. A651
Information Technology Director, Lake District Hospital, Lakeview, OR, p. A514
VANCOURT, Bernie
Chief Operating Officer, Aurora Medical Center – Bay Area, Marinette, WI, p. A699
Interim Chief Nursing Officer, Aurora Medical Center – Bay Area, Marinette, WI, p. A699
VANDENBARK, Heather, Human Resources Specialist, State Hospital North, Orofino, ID, p. A171
VANDENBERG, Andra, Director Human Resources, Butler County Health Care Center, David City, NE, p. A384
VANDENBOSCH, Dan, Chief Information Officer, Madison County Health Care System, Winterset, IA, p. A231

VANDER, Allen, M.D., Chief Medical Staff, Thibodaux Regional Medical Center, Thibodaux, LA, p. A279
VANDER KOLK, Keith, President and Chief Executive Officer, Saint Agnes Healthcare, Baltimore, MD, p. A287
VANDERBEEK, Sam, Chief Information Officer, W. J. Mangold Memorial Hospital, Lockney, TX, p. A621
VANDERHOOFT, J Eric, M.D., President Medical Staff, St. Mark'S Hospital, Salt Lake City, UT, p. A652
VANDERLINDEN, Mark A, Chief Financial Officer, Greene County Medical Center, Jefferson, IA, p. A225
VANDERMARK, Jay H, Chief Financial Officer, Veterans Affairs Northern Indiana Health Care System, Fort Wayne, IN, p. A204
VANDERMEER, Nick, Director Information Systems, Banner Payson Medical Center, Payson, AZ, p. A32
VANDERPOL, Antoinette, Chief of Staff, Avera St. Benedict Health Center, Parkston, SD, p. A562
VANDERPOOL, Lee, Vice President, Dominican Hospital, Santa Cruz, CA, p. A88
VANDERSCHAAFF, Trixie, Chief Nursing Officer, St. Anthony Summit Medical Center, Frisco, CO, p. A100
VANDERSLICE, Douglas M, Senior Vice President and Chief Financial Officer, Boston Children'S Hospital, Boston, MA, p. A295
VANDERSTEEG, James, Chief Executive Officer, Parkwest Medical Center, Knoxville, TN, p. A572
VANDERSTEK, Eliott R, Chief Fiscal Service, Veterans Affairs Eastern Colorado Health Care System, Denver, CO, p. A99
VANDERSTOUW, Karl, Vice President Information Systems, Unc Lenoir Healthcare, Kinston, NC, p. A457
VANDERVLIET, William, M.D., Vice President Medical Affairs, Holland Hospital, Holland, MI, p. A314
VANDERWEGE, Larry, Administrator, Lindsborg Community Hospital, Lindsborg, KS, p. A240
VANDEUSEN, Leya, Interim Chief Financial Officer, Hillsdale Hospital, Hillsdale, MI, p. A314
VANDEWEGE, Dana, Director Human Resources, Capital Medical Center, Olympia, WA, p. A676
VANDONKELAAR, Rodney
Chief Financial Officer, Carolina Pines Regional Medical Center, Hartsville, SC, p. A554
Chief Financial Officer, Saint Thomas Highlands Hospital, Sparta, TN, p. A579
VANDORT, Patti J, MSN, R.N., Vice President Nursing/Chief Nursing Officer, Holland Hospital, Holland, MI, p. A314
VANDRUFF, John, M.D., Chief of Staff, Banner Payson Medical Center, Payson, AZ, p. A32
VANDYKE, Yvonne, R.N., MSN, Chief Nursing Officer, Texas Market, Ascension Seton Northwest, Austin, TX, p. A584
VANEK, James, Chief Executive Officer, Columbus Community Hospital, Columbus, TX, p. A593
VANES, Wendell, Chief Financial Officer, Saint Mary'S Regional Medical Center, Russellville, AR, p. A48
VANHAREN, James, M.D., Medical Director, Forest View Psychiatric Hospital, Grand Rapids, MI, p. A312
VANHORN, Jeffrey, Chief Executive Officer, Star Medical Center, Plano, TX, p. A629
VANHOUWELING, Mason, Chief Executive Officer, University Medical Center, Las Vegas, NV, p. A396
VANHOY, Michael, Director of Quality, Uva–Healthsouth Rehabilitation Hospital, Charlottesville, VA, p. A657
VANMETER, David, Acting Director, Miami Veterans Affairs Healthcare System, Miami, FL, p. A130
VANNATTER, Mistie, Chief Nursing Officer, Advanced Care Hospital Of White County, Searcy, AR, p. A48
VANNETT, Vince, Director Human Resources, Jellico Community Hospital, Jellico, TN, p. A571
VANO, Ann
Vice President Human Resources, Ascension Of Providence Hospital, Southfield Campus, Southfield, MI, p. A322
Vice President, Human Resources, Ascension Crittenton Hospital Medical Center, Rochester, MI, p. A320
VANOSDOL, Thomas J.
Chief Executive Officer, St. Vincent'S Medical Center Riverside, Jacksonville, FL, p. A126
Chief Executive Officer, St. Vincent'S Medical Center Southside, Jacksonville, FL, p. A126
VANSANT, Scott, M.D., Chief Medical Officer, Central State Hospital, Milledgeville, GA, p. A157
VANSTRIEN, Amy, Director Talent Operations, Midwestern Regional Medical Center, Zion, IL, p. A198
VANTONGEREN, Teri, Director Information Services, Spectrum Health Pennock, Hastings, MI, p. A314
VANWALLAGHEN, Brenda, Interim Chief Nursing Officer, Dmc – Children'S Hospital Of Michigan, Detroit, MI, p. A309
VANWICHEN, Ward C., Chief Executive Officer, Phillips County Hospital, Malta, MT, p. A378
VANWYHE, Brenda, Senior Vice President Finance and Chief Financial Officer, Rush–Copley Medical Center, Aurora, IL, p. A174

VARELA, Alberto M., President, Inspira Ponce, Ponce, PR, p. A717
VARELA, Nancy, Director Human Resources, Patton State Hospital, Patton, CA, p. A77
VARGA, Patrick, Chief Operating Officer, Mercy Medical Center Redding, Redding, CA, p. A79
VARGAS, Idelfonso, Executive Director, Dr. Ramon E. Betances Hospital–Mayaguez Medical Center Branch, Mayaguez, PR, p. A717
VARGAS, Jose L, M.D., Medical Director, West Gables Rehabilitation Hospital, Miami, FL, p. A131
VARGAS, Margie, Chief Human Resources Officer, Memorial Regional Hospital, Hollywood, FL, p. A124
VARGAS, Marisol, Director Finance, Hospital Del Maestro, San Juan, PR, p. A718
VARGAS, Nancy
Chief Human Resources, St. Joseph'S Behavioral Health Center, Stockton, CA, p. A90
Director Human Resources, Mark Twain Medical Center, San Andreas, CA, p. A83
Vice President Human Resources, St. Joseph'S Medical Center, Stockton, CA, p. A91
VARGAS–MAHAR, Monica, Chief Executive Officer, The Hospitals Of Providence East Campus, El Paso, TX, p. A602
VARGHESE, Roy, M.D., Chief of Staff, Mary Breckinridge Arh Hospital, Hyden, KY, p. A254
VARGHESE, Shibu, Vice President Human Resources, University Of Texas M.D. Anderson Cancer Center, Houston, TX, p. A614
VARIALE, Vincenzo, Chief Executive Officer, North Vista Hospital, North Las Vegas, NV, p. A396
VARIAN, Grant, M.D., Medical Director, Mary Rutan Hospital, Bellefontaine, OH, p. A473
VARK, Lawrence, M.D., Chief Medical Officer, Creek Nation Community Hospital, Okemah, OK, p. A503
VARLEY, Kevin
Chief Financial Officer, Curahealth Heritage Valley, Beaver, PA, p. A520
Chief Financial Officer, Curahealth Pittsburgh, Oakdale, PA, p. A533
Chief Financial Officer, Kindred Hospital South Philadelphia, Philadelphia, PA, p. A535
VARNADO, Anjanette, M.D., Chief Medical Officer, St. Helena Parish Hospital, Greensburg, LA, p. A268
VARNADO, Darryl, Executive Vice President and Chief People Officer, Children'S National Health System, Washington, DC, p. A115
VARNADO, Donna, Vice President Finance, Cypress Pointe Surgical Hospital, Hammond, LA, p. A268
VARNADO, Kim, R.N., Chief Nursing Officer, Highland Community Hospital, Picayune, MS, p. A353
VARNADOE, Milo, Director Information Systems, Warm Springs Medical Center, Warm Springs, GA, p. A162
VARNADORE, Jennifer, Administrator, Christus Health Shreveport–Bossier, Shreveport, LA, p. A278
VARNAM, Jessica, Chief of Staff, Grant Regional Health Center, Lancaster, WI, p. A698
VARNELL, Misti, Chief Executive Officer, Kindred Hospital–Dallas, Dallas, TX, p. A596
VARNER, Terry, Administrator, Yalobusha General Hospital, Water Valley, MS, p. A355
VARNEY, Tim, R.N., Chief Nursing Officer, Select Specialty Hospital–Ann Arbor, Ypsilanti, MI, p. A325
VARTANIAN, Sarkis, Chief Nursing Officer, Whittier Hospital Medical Center, Whittier, CA, p. A95
VARTELAS, Helene M., Chief Executive Officer, Connecticut Valley Hospital, Middletown, CT, p. A109
VASCONCELLOS, Jacques, Director, Operations, Winter Haven Hospital, Winter Haven, FL, p. A144
VASEK, Barbara, Director Information Technology, Yoakum Community Hospital, Yoakum, TX, p. A646
VASHISHTA, Ashok, M.D., Vice President Medical Affairs, Mclaren Central Michigan, Mount Pleasant, MI, p. A318
VASIL, Kathleen, Vice President Finance, St. Charles Hospital, Port Jefferson, NY, p. A441
VASILE, Ann, M.D., Medical Director, Encompass Health Rehabilitation Hospital Of Tustin, Tustin, CA, p. A92
VASQUEZ, Alberto, Administrator, Garfield Memorial Hospital, Panguitch, UT, p. A650
VASQUEZ, Arthur, President, Indiana University Health West Hospital, Avon, IN, p. A199
VASQUEZ, Carlos, Vice President and Chief Operating Officer, Franciscan Health Rensselear, Rensselaer, IN, p. A214
VASQUEZ, Christann
Executive Vice President and Chief Operating Officer, University Health System, San Antonio, TX, p. A635
President and Chief Executive Officer, Ascension Seton Medical Center Austin, Austin, TX, p. A584

President and Chief Executive Officer, Ascension Seton Shoal Creek, Austin, TX, p. A585
President, Dell Seton Medical Center At The University Of Texas, Austin, TX, p. A585
VASQUEZ, George
Chief Technology Officer, Clovis Community Medical Center, Clovis, CA, p. A55
Corporate Chief Information Officer, Fresno Heart And Surgical Hospital, Fresno, CA, p. A59
Vice President Information Services, Community Behavioral Health Center, Fresno, CA, p. A59
VASQUEZ, Jill, Manager Human Resources, Spectrum Health Ludington Hospital, Ludington, MI, p. A317
VASQUEZ, Kenneth, Associate Director, Jfk Medical Center North Campus, West Palm Beach, FL, p. A144
VASQUEZ, Nelson, Vice President Finance, Jackson Park Hospital And Medical Center, Chicago, IL, p. A177
VASQUEZ, Stacy J.
Chief Executive Officer, Birmingham Veterans Affairs Medical Center, Birmingham, AL, p. A14
Director, Beckley Veterans Affairs Medical Center, Beckley, WV, p. A683
VASS, Paula, Vice President Clinical Operations, Walden Behavioral Care, Waltham, MA, p. A304
VASTOLA, David, Medical Director, Searhc Mt. Edgecumbe Hospital, Sitka, AK, p. A27
VASUNAGA, Amy, Chief Nurse Executive, Leahi Hospital, Honolulu, HI, p. A164
VATH, Richard, M.D., Vice President Medical Affairs, Our Lady Of The Lake Regional Medical Center, Baton Rouge, LA, p. A264
VATSAVAI, Sundararama R, M.D., Medical Director, Baton Rouge Rehabilitation Hospital, Baton Rouge, LA, p. A263
VAUGHAN, Alan, Director Information Technology, Share Medical Center, Alva, OK, p. A496
VAUGHAN, Amanda
Chief Financial Officer, Bob Wilson Memorial Grant County Hospital, Ulysses, KS, p. A247
Chief Financial Officer, St. Catherine Hospital, Garden City, KS, p. A235
Interim Administrator, Bob Wilson Memorial Grant County Hospital, Ulysses, KS, p. A247
VAUGHAN, Brandon, Chief Financial Officer and Vice President Finance, Jamestown Regional Medical Center, Jamestown, ND, p. A468
VAUGHAN, Page H.
Chief Executive Officer, Musc Health Chester Medical Center, Chester, SC, p. A550
Chief Executive Officer, Musc Health Lancaster Medical Center, Lancaster, SC, p. A555
VAUGHAN, Peggy, M.D.
Senior Vice President Medical Affairs, University Of Maryland Harford Memorial Hospital, Havre De Grace, MD, p. A291
Senior Vice President Medical Affairs, University Of Maryland Upper Chesapeake Medical Center, Bel Air, MD, p. A288
VAUGHAN, Rob, Chief Financial Officer, Carilion New River Valley Medical Center, Christiansburg, VA, p. A658
VAUGHN, Barbara, R.N., Chief Nursing Officer, Baylor Scott & White Medical Center – Carrollton, Carrollton, TX, p. A591
VAUGHN, Debbie, Chief Nursing Officer, The Medical Center Of Southeast Texas, Port Arthur, TX, p. A630
VAUGHN, Joseph, Director, W. G. (Bill) Heffner Veterans Affairs Medical Center, Salisbury, NC, p. A461
VAUGHN, Kerry, Chief Information Officer, St. Mary'S Health Care System, Athens, GA, p. A145
VAUGHN, Kevin P, Chief Financial Officer, Kansas Spine And Specialty Hospital, Wichita, KS, p. A248
VAUGHN, Michael, Director of Nursing, Southeast Rehabilitation Hospital, Lake Village, AR, p. A44
VAUGHN, Sandy
Director Information Services, Baylor Scott & White All Saints Medical Center – Fort Worth, Fort Worth, TX, p. A604
Director Information Systems, Baylor Scott & White Medical Center – Grapevine, Grapevine, TX, p. A608
VAUGHN, Sharma, Chief Nursing Officer, Rangely District Hospital, Rangely, CO, p. A105
VAUGHN, Ted W, Director Human Resources, Unitypoint Health – Trinity Regional Medical Center, Fort Dodge, IA, p. A222
VAUGHN, Vickie, Chief Nursing Officer, Tennova Healthcare–Shelbyville, Shelbyville, TN, p. A579
VAUTER, Rebecca, Facility Director, Central State Hospital, Petersburg, VA, p. A664
VAVARUTSOS, Tony, Director Information Systems, Thorek Memorial Hospital, Chicago, IL, p. A180
VAZIRI, H Kevin., President, Woodland Healthcare, Woodland, CA, p. A95
VAZQUEZ, Barbara
Chief Nursing Officer, Palmetto General Hospital, Hialeah, FL, p. A124
Chief Nursing Officer, The Hospitals Of Providence Memorial Campus, El Paso, TX, p. A602
VAZQUEZ, Brunilda, Medical Director, Hospital De Psiquiatria, San Juan, PR, p. A718
VAZQUEZ, Emilio, M.D., Chief Medical Officer, Dekalb Health, Auburn, IN, p. A199
VAZQUEZ, Francisco, Director, Michael E. Debakey Veterans Affairs Medical Center, Houston, TX, p. A613
VEACH, Jamie, Chief Operating Officer, Clay County Hospital, Flora, IL, p. A183
VEAL, Bonita Wells, Chief Nursing Officer, Anaheim Global Medical Center, Anaheim, CA, p. A50
VEDRAL–BARON, Jennifer, Health System Director, Tennessee Valley Healthcare System, Nashville, TN, p. A577
VEERAMACHANENI, Harish, M.D., Chief of Staff, Wayne Medical Center, Waynesboro, TN, p. A580
VEESER, Tom, Chief Nursing Officer, Ascension St. Michael'S Hospital, Stevens Point, WI, p. A706
VEGA, James, Director Information Systems, Palm Beach Gardens Medical Center, Palm Beach Gardens, FL, p. A135
VEGA, Jane, Executive Director, Industrial Hospital, San Juan, PR, p. A719
VEGA, Maria, Director Human Resources, Auxilio Mutuo Hospital, San Juan, PR, p. A718
VEGA, Mary, R.N., MSN, Vice President Nursing, St. Margaret'S Hospital, Spring Valley, IL, p. A196
VEGA, Oscar, M.D., Chief Medical Officer, Las Palmas Medical Center, El Paso, TX, p. A602
VEGA, Zoraida, MSN, R.N., Chief Nursing Officer, St. Luke'S Episcopal Hospital, Ponce, PR, p. A717
VEILLETTE, Michael D.
Senior Vice President and Chief Financial Officer, Manchester Memorial Hospital, Manchester, CT, p. A108
Senior Vice President and Chief Financial Officer, Rockville General Hospital, Vernon, CT, p. A111
VEILLEUX, Jeffrey
Executive Vice President and Chief Financial Officer, Swedish Medical Center–First Hill, Seattle, WA, p. A678
Senior Vice President and Chief Financial Officer, Swedish Medical Center–Cherry Hill Campus, Seattle, WA, p. A678
VEILLON, Paul, CPA
Chief Financial Officer, Christus Dubuis Hospital Of Fort Smith, Fort Smith, AR, p. A42
Chief Financial Officer, Christus Dubuis Hospital Of Hot Springs, Hot Springs National Park, AR, p. A43
VEIT, Amanda, R.N., Chief Nursing Officer, Presbyterian–St. Luke'S Medical Center, Denver, CO, p. A99
VELA, Javier, Director Information Technology, Baylor Scott & White Medical Center–Uptown, Dallas, TX, p. A595
VELA, Manuel, President and Chief Executive Officer, Valley Baptist Medical Center–Harlingen, Harlingen, TX, p. A609
VELASCO, Paul, IT Manager, Kit Carson County Health Service District, Burlington, CO, p. A97
VELASQUEZ, Alfred T
Area Information Officer, Kaiser Permanente Moreno Valley Medical Center, Moreno Valley, CA, p. A73
Area Information Officer, Kaiser Permanente Riverside Medical Center, Riverside, CA, p. A81
VELASQUEZ, Lin, Vice President Human Resources, Saint Louise Regional Hospital, Gilroy, CA, p. A60
VELEZ, Luz M, Director–Administration of Nursing Services, Hospital San Carlos Borromeo, Moca, PR, p. A717
VELEZ, Pablo, Chief Executive Officer, Sharp Chula Vista Medical Center, Chula Vista, CA, p. A54
VELEZ, Raul
Director Information Systems, Huntsville Memorial Hospital, Huntsville, TX, p. A615
Information Technology Director, North Alabama Medical Center, Florence, AL, p. A18
VENABLE, Brett, Commander, Keller Army Community Hospital, West Point, NY, p. A447
VENABLE, Mark, Interim Director Human Resources, Shriners Hospitals For Children–St. Louis, Saint Louis, MO, p. A370
VENABLE, Robert, M.D., Chief Medical Staff, Washington County Hospital, Plymouth, NC, p. A460
VENDETTI, Marilouise, M.D., Chief Medical Officer, Atlanticare Regional Medical Center, Atlantic City, NJ, p. A403
VENEZIANO, Terri, Interim Chief Nursing Officer, Columbus Regional Healthcare System, Whiteville, NC, p. A463
VENGCO, Joel L., MS, Vice President, Chief Information Officer, Baystate Medical Center, Springfield, MA, p. A303
VENHUIZEN, Pamela, Chief Human Resources Officer, Cooperstown Medical Center, Cooperstown, ND, p. A466
VENOIT, Jon–Paul
Chief Operating Officer, Masonicare Health Center, Wallingford, CT, p. A111
President and Chief Executive Officer, Masonicare Health Center, Wallingford, CT, p. A111
VENTURA, Rosemary, M.D., Chief Nursing Informatics Officer, Brookdale Hospital Medical Center, New York, NY, p. A432
VENTURA, Sylvia A, R.N., MS, Chief Nursing Officer, Olympia Medical Center, Los Angeles, CA, p. A68
VENTURELLA, James, Vice President Information Technology, West Virginia University Hospitals, Morgantown, WV, p. A687
VENUTO, Frank, Chief Human Capital Officer, Nebraska Medicine – Nebraska Medical Center, Omaha, NE, p. A389
VERA, Luis F, M.D., Medical Director, Kensington Hospital, Philadelphia, PA, p. A535
VERAGIWALA, Jignesh, Chief of Staff, Mercy Hospital Logan County, Guthrie, OK, p. A500
VERBUS, John R, Senior Vice President and Chief Operating Officer, Frederick Regional Health System, Frederick, MD, p. A290
VERCHER, Gretchen, Chief Nursing Officer, Encompass Health Rehabilitation Hospital Of Montgomery, Montgomery, AL, p. A21
VERDEJA, Juan–Carlos, M.D., President of Medical Staff, Baptist Health South Florida, West Kendall Baptist Hospital, Miami, FL, p. A130
VERDON, Chris, Director Finance, Phillips Eye Institute, Minneapolis, MN, p. A336
VERFURTH, Larry, D.O., Executive Vice President and Chief Medical Officer, Christus Good Shepherd Medical Center–Marshall, Marshall, TX, p. A623
VERGA, Joseph P., Chief Executive Officer, Guam Memorial Hospital Authority, Tamuning, GU, p. A714
VERGARA, Aimee, Chief Executive Officer, Hospital For Extended Recovery, Norfolk, VA, p. A663
VERGONIO, Merlinda, Chief Information Management and Technology, U. S. Air Force Hospital, Hampton, VA, p. A660
VERGOS, Katherine, President, St. Agnes Hospital, Fond Du Lac, WI, p. A695
VERINDER, David, President and Chief Executive Officer, Sarasota Memorial Health Care System, Sarasota, FL, p. A139
VERMA, Virendar, M.D., Medical Director, Encompass Health Rehabilitation Hospital Of Jonesboro, Jonesboro, AR, p. A44
VERMILLION, Kerry, Senior Vice President Finance and Chief Financial Officer, Gulf Breeze Hospital, Gulf Breeze, FL, p. A124
VERMULEN, Peter, Director Information Technology, Schick Shadel Hospital, Seattle, WA, p. A678
VERRET, Dean, Vice President Financial Services, Terrebonne General Medical Center, Houma, LA, p. A269
VERRETTE, Paul, M.D., Chief Medical Officer, St. Bernard Parish Hospital, Chalmette, LA, p. A265
VERRETTE, Paula, M.D., Senior Vice President Quality and Physician Services and Chief Medical Officer, Huntington Memorial Hospital, Pasadena, CA, p. A77
VERRILL, Alan, M.D., President Medical Staff, Bridgton Hospital, Bridgton, ME, p. A282
VERTIN, Amy, M.D., Chief of Staff, Crete Area Medical Center, Crete, NE, p. A384
VETTER, Norman, Chief Executive Officer, Division of Substance Abuse and Mental Health, Delaware Psychiatric Center, New Castle, DE, p. A113
VETTER, Rich, M.D., Associate Chief, Essentia Health St. Mary'S – Detroit Lakes, Detroit Lakes, MN, p. A330
VIALL, John, M.D., Vice President Medical Affairs, Holzer Medical Center, Gallipolis, OH, p. A483
VIATOR, Dionne, CPA, FACHE, Chief Financial Officer, Iberia Medical Center, New Iberia, LA, p. A274
VIBETO, Brett, M.D., Chief of Staff, Chi St. Alexius Health – Williston Medical Center, Williston, ND, p. A470
VIBHAKAR, Neel, M.D., Senior Vice President and Chief Medical Officer, University Of Maryland Baltimore Washington Medical Center, Glen Burnie, MD, p. A291
VICE, Jeff
Chief Operating Officer and Interim Chief Executive Officer, Starke Hospital, Knox, IN, p. A208
Chief Operating Officer, Starke Hospital, Knox, IN, p. A208
VICENS–RIVERA, Enrique A., Jr, Chief Executive Officer, Encompass Health Rehabilitation Hospital Of Miami, Cutler Bay, FL, p. A120
VICENT, Leonardo, III, Executive Director, Brookdale Hospital Medical Center, New York, NY, p. A432
VICENTE, Oscar, Chief Financial Officer, Palmetto General Hospital, Hialeah, FL, p. A124
VICENTI, Darren, M.D., Clinical Director, Hopi Health Care Center, Keams Canyon, AZ, p. A30
VICK, Dan J., M.D., Vice President of Medical Affairs and Chief Medical Officer, Oneida Healthcare, Oneida, NY, p. A440

VICKERS, Cynthia, R.N., Assistant Administrator for Nursing Services, Memorial Hospital And Manor, Bainbridge, GA, p. A148

VICKERS, Dave, Chief Financial Officer, Los Alamitos Medical Center, Los Alamitos, CA, p. A65

VICKERS, Don, Chief Executive Officer, Cleveland Emergency Hospital, Cleveland, TX, p. A592

VICKERS, Kathy, Director Human Resources, Vantage Point Of Northwest Arkansas, Fayetteville, AR, p. A41

VICKERY, Ian, Director Information Technology, D. W. Mcmillan Memorial Hospital, Brewton, AL, p. A15

VICKERY, Tim, Chief Information Officer, St. Mary'S Sacred Heart Hospital, Lavonia, GA, p. A156

VICKROY, Joseph, M.D., Medical Director, Healthsouth Rehabilitation Hospital Of Utah, Sandy, UT, p. A653

VICKS, Ray, Senior Vice President, Finance and Chief Financial Officer, The Hsc Pediatric Center, Washington, DC, p. A116

VICTORIA, Mario, M.D., Vice President, Medical Affairs, Samaritan Medical Center, Watertown, NY, p. A447

VIDONI–CLARK, Clotilde, Ph.D., R.N., Chief Nursing Executive, Saint Elizabeths Hospital, Washington, DC, p. A116

VIEIRA, Jeanette, Chief Executive, Providence Hood River Memorial Hospital, Hood River, OR, p. A513

VIEIRA, Terri
President, Northern Light Ca Dean Hospital, Greenville, ME, p. A283
President, Northlight Sebasticook Valley Hospital, Pittsfield, ME, p. A284

VIELKIND, James
Chief Financial Officer, Cobleskill Regional Hospital, Cobleskill, NY, p. A426
Chief Financial Officer, Little Falls Hospital, Little Falls, NY, p. A430

VIENNEAU, Marie E., President and Chief Executive Officer, Mayo Regional Hospital, Dover, ME, p. A283

VIERLING, Taryn, Chief Nursing Officer, Select Specialty Hospital Of Southeast Ohio, Newark, OH, p. A488

VIG, Vibha, Chief of Staff, Merit Health Madison, Canton, MS, p. A345

VIGIL, Kevin, Director Information Systems, Los Alamos Medical Center, Los Alamos, NM, p. A419

VIGILANTE, Sarah, Manager Human Resources, Mammoth Hospital, Mammoth Lakes, CA, p. A70

VIGNA, Greg A., M.D., Medical Director, Encompass Health Rehabilitation Hospital Of Modesto, Modesto, CA, p. A72

VIGNERI, Joseph, M.D., Chief Medical Officer, Summit Medical Center, Casper, WY, p. A710

VILANOVA, Lynda, Director Patient Care Services, Shriners Hospitals For Children–Spokane, Spokane, WA, p. A680

VILAR, Ramon J., Administrator, Wilma N. Vazquez Medical Center, Vega Baja, PR, p. A720

VILHAUER, Beverly, Chief Executive Officer, Wishek Community Hospital And Clinics, Wishek, ND, p. A470

VILLA, Alex, Chief Executive Officer, Tennova Healthcare–Clarksville, Clarksville, TN, p. A568

VILLA, Jo Ellen, Chief Executive Officer, Community Hospital Of Anaconda, Anaconda, MT, p. A374

VILLA, Maria, Interim Chief Nursing Officer, Kendall Regional Medical Center, Miami, FL, p. A130

VILLAFRANCO, Brenda
Administrator, Memorial Hermann First Colony Hospital, Sugar Land, TX, p. A638
Administrator, Memorial Hermann Tomball Hospital, Tomball, TX, p. A641

VILLAFUERTE, Herbert
Chief Operating Officer and Chief Nursing Officer, Garfield Medical Center, Monterey Park, CA, p. A73
Chief Operating Officer/Chief Nursing Officer, Garfield Medical Center, Monterey Park, CA, p. A73

VILLANI, Travis A., Chief Executive Officer and Administrator, Physicians' Hospital In Anadarko, Anadarko, OK, p. A496

VILLANO, Jeremi, M.D., Chief of Staff, Crook County Medical Services District, Sundance, WY, p. A713

VILLARREAL, Xavier, Chief Executive Officer, Hillcrest Medical Center, Tulsa, OK, p. A508

VILLARRUZ, Alex, Chief Executive Officer, Healthbridge Children'S Hospital, Orange, CA, p. A76

VILLEGAS, Lorraine, Manager Human Resources, Paradise Valley Hospital, National City, CA, p. A74

VILLEGAS, William, Vice President Finance, Fort Hamilton Hospital, Hamilton, OH, p. A484

VILUMS, Karlis, Chief Financial Officer, Broadlawns Medical Center, Des Moines, IA, p. A221

VINAS, Elmo, Director Human Resources, Franklin Foundation Hospital, Franklin, LA, p. A267

VINCENT, Cynthia, Vice President Finance and Operations, St. Francis Regional Medical Center, Shakopee, MN, p. A340

VINCENT, David, Director Information Systems, Canonsburg Hospital, Canonsburg, PA, p. A522

VINCENT, Joan M, MSN, MS, R.N., Vice President Patient Care Services and Chief Nurse Executive, Adventist Healthcare Shady Grove Medical Center, Rockville, MD, p. A293

VINCENT, Julie S., R.N., MSN, Chief Nursing Officer, Sycamore Medical Center, Miamisburg, OH, p. A487

VINCENT, Larry, Director Human Resources, Delta County Memorial Hospital, Delta, CO, p. A98

VINCENT, Laurence Marie, Chief Nursing Officer, University Hospital And Clinics, Lafayette, LA, p. A271

VINCENT, Mitchell S, Vice President Organizational Support, Range Regional Health Services, Hibbing, MN, p. A333

VINCENT, Paula, President and Chief Operating Officer, Novant Health Presbyterian Medical Center, Charlotte, NC, p. A451

VINCENT, Shawn, Interim Chief Operating Officer, Augusta University Medical Center, Augusta, GA, p. A147

VINCENZ, Felix T, Chief Operating Officer, St. Louis Psychiatric Rehabilitation Center, Saint Louis, MO, p. A370

VINCIFORA, Teresa, Chief Operating Officer, Benson Hospital, Benson, AZ, p. A28

VINCIGUERRA, Tracy, Chief Executive Officer, Encompass Health Rehabilitation Hospital Of Morgantown, Morgantown, WV, p. A687

VINSANT, George O'Neal, M.D., Chief Medical Officer, Tennova Healthcare–Lafollette Medical Center, La Follette, TN, p. A572

VIOLETTE, Brenda, M.D., Director Medical Staff, Firelands Regional Health System, Sandusky, OH, p. A490

VIOLI, Ronald L., Chief Executive Officer, Wheeling Hospital, Wheeling, WV, p. A690

VIRGEN, Tomas, R.N., MSN, Chief Operating Officer, El Centro Regional Medical Center, El Centro, CA, p. A57

VIRGIL, Cindy L, MSN, R.N., Senior Vice President Patient Care Services, Indiana Regional Medical Center, Indiana, PA, p. A528

VIRJI, Ayaz, M.D., Chief of Staff, Johnson Memorial Health Services, Dawson, MN, p. A330

VIRKLER, Joe, Chief Information Officer, Carthage Area Hospital, Carthage, NY, p. A425

VISCONI, Deborah D., President and Chief Executive Officer, New Bridge Medical Center, Paramus, NJ, p. A410

VISH, Nancy, President, Baylor Scott & White Heart & Vascular Hospital–Dallas, Dallas, TX, p. A595

VISSER, Jessica, R.N., Vice President Patient Care Services and Chief Nursing Officer, Mount St. Mary'S Hospital And Health Center, Lewiston, NY, p. A430

VISSERS, Robert, President and Chief Executive Officer, Boulder Community Health, Boulder, CO, p. A96

VITAL, Dale, Chief Nursing Officer, Memorialcare, Orange Coast Memorial Medical Center, Fountain Valley, CA, p. A58

VITALE–NOLEN, Roberta A, Administrator, Patient Care Services, New Hampshire Hospital, Concord, NH, p. A399

VITALI, Joe, Director Information Technology, Parkside Psychiatric Hospital And Clinic, Tulsa, OK, p. A509

VITALI, Vincent S, Chief Information Officer, Rml Specialty Hospital, Hinsdale, IL, p. A186

VITIELLO, Jon, Senior Vice President, Finance Operations and Analytics, Mercy Hospital Oklahoma City, Oklahoma City, OK, p. A504

VITOLAS, Victor, Acting Chief Information Technology Services, Central Texas Veterans Health Care System, Temple, TX, p. A640

VIVIANO, Paul S., President and Chief Executive Officer, Children'S Hospital Los Angeles, Los Angeles, CA, p. A66

VIVIT, Romeo, Chief Surgeon, U. S. Public Health Service Indian Hospital, Rosebud, SD, p. A563

VIVODA, Michael
Senior Vice President Human Resources, Northwestern Medicine Valley West Hospital, Sandwich, IL, p. A195
Senior Vice President, Administration, Northwestern Memorial Hospital, Chicago, IL, p. A178
Senior Vice President, Human Resources, Northwestern Medicine Kishwaukee Hospital, Dekalb, IL, p. A181

VIZCARRA, Edred T., M.D., Chief of Staff, St. Luke Community Healthcare, Ronan, MT, p. A379

VLAHAVAS, Beth, R.N., MSN, Vice President Patient Care Services and Chief Nursing Officer, Mercy Medical Center, Rockville Centre, NY, p. A443

VLARS, Scott, Chief Information Technology Services, Wilmington Veterans Affairs Medical Center, Wilmington, DE, p. A114

VLODARCHYK, Coreen, R.N., Vice President, Patient Care Services and Chief Nursing Officer, Barnes–Jewish Hospital, Saint Louis, MO, p. A369

VLOSICH, Kristopher Wade., Director, Oklahoma City Veterans Affairs Medical Center, Oklahoma City, OK, p. A504

VOCCA, Lori A, Vice President Human Resources, Providence Regional Medical Center Everett, Everett, WA, p. A673

VOECKS, Barbara, Chief Information Officer, Ortonville Area Health Services, Ortonville, MN, p. A337

VOELKEL, Jonathon, Chief Executive Officer, Reagan Memorial Hospital, Big Lake, TX, p. A588

VOELKER, Justin, Chief Financial Officer, Multicare Valley Hospital, Spokane Valley, WA, p. A680

VOELKER, Thomas, M.D., Chief Medical Officer, Aspirus Riverview Hospital And Clinics, Inc., Wisconsin Rapids, WI, p. A709

VOGE, Chris, Chief of Staff, French Hospital Medical Center, San Luis Obispo, CA, p. A87

VOGEL, Clay, Administrator and Chief Executive Officer, Coleman County Medical Center, Coleman, TX, p. A592

VOGELSANG, Mark, Director Information Services, Providence Holy Family Hospital, Spokane, WA, p. A679

VOGENTIZ, William, M.D., Medical Director, Anmed Health Rehabilitation Hospital, Anderson, SC, p. A549

VOGT, Dennis, Director Information Technology, Madison Health, London, OH, p. A486

VOGT, Sam, Manager Human Resources, Hebrew Senior Care, West Hartford, CT, p. A112

VOHS, Lester, Manager Information Systems, Cass Regional Medical Center, Harrisonville, MO, p. A361

VOIGT, Jordan, Administrator, Genesis Medical Center, Davenport, Davenport, IA, p. A220

VOISARD, Victor, Director Human Resources, San Gabriel Valley Medical Center, San Gabriel, CA, p. A86

VOISELLE, Dana, Director Human Resources and Community Relations, Baptist Medical Center Beaches, Jacksonville Beach, FL, p. A126

VOKOUN, Cory, Chief Nursing Officer, Nevada Regional Medical Center, Nevada, MO, p. A366

VOLINSKI, Douglas R, Vice President and Chief Financial Officer, Duncan Regional Hospital, Duncan, OK, p. A498

VOLK, Charles T., M.D., Regional Chief Medical Officer, Christus Spohn Hospital Corpus Christi Memorial, Corpus Christi, TX, p. A594

VOLKERDING, Elizabeth, Director Workforce Excellence, San Juan Regional Medical Center, Farmington, NM, p. A418

VOLKERT, Brent, Director Information Technology, Ferrell Hospital, Eldorado, IL, p. A181

VOLLER, Kristi, Director of Nursing, Mobridge Regional Hospital, Mobridge, SD, p. A562

VOLLMER, Kris, Director Patient Care Services, Avera Tyler Hospital, Tyler, MN, p. A341

VOLOCH, Bill, President and Chief Executive Officer, Wesley Healthcare Center, Wichita, KS, p. A248

VOLOVIC, Mark, Vice President and Chief Information Officer, Indiana Regional Medical Center, Indiana, PA, p. A528

VOLPE, Buddy, Director Human Resources, Peterson Regional Medical Center, Kerrville, TX, p. A618

VOLPE, Michele M., Chief Executive Officer, Penn Presbyterian Medical Center, Philadelphia, PA, p. A536

VON ARX, Michelle, Chief Executive Officer, Penn State Hershey Rehabilitation Hospital, Hummelstown, PA, p. A527

VON BEHREN, Rachel, Director Financial Services, Unitypoint Health – Jones Regional Medical Center, Anamosa, IA, p. A217

VONACHEN, April, Chief Financial Officer and Vice President Financial Services, Cumberland Medical Center, Crossville, TN, p. A568

VONK, Brandon
Administrator, Bear River Valley Hospital, Tremonton, UT, p. A653
Nurse Administrator, Lds Hospital, Salt Lake City, UT, p. A651

VOOYS, Nathan, Chief Executive Officer, Terre Haute Regional Hospital, Terre Haute, IN, p. A215

VOS, Helen, R.N., Interim Chief Nursing Officer, Peacehealth Southwest Medical Center, Vancouver, WA, p. A681

VOSHELL, Shane, Director Human Resources, Adventist Health Portland, Portland, OR, p. A516

VOSS, Daryle, President and Chief Executive Officer, Mercy Hospital Ardmore, Ardmore, OK, p. A496

VOSS, Peter, M.D., Chief Medical Officer, Indiana University Health Ball Memorial Hospital, Muncie, IN, p. A212

VOSS, Robert, Chief Financial Officer, Laredo Specialty Hospital, Laredo, TX, p. A620

VOSS, Wayne M., Chief Executive Officer, Houston Methodist West Hospital, Houston, TX, p. A612

VOSSBERG, Brad, M.D., Chief Rehabilitation, Community Howard Specialty Hospital, Kokomo, IN, p. A209

VOSSLER, Jeffrey W, Chief Financial Officer, Joint Township District Memorial Hospital, Saint Marys, OH, p. A490

VOWELL, Christy, D.O., Chief of Staff, North Mississippi Medical Center–Eupora, Eupora, MS, p. A346

VOZOS, Frank J., Chief Executive Officer, MMC Southern Campus, Monmouth Medical Center, Southern Campus, Lakewood, NJ, p. A407

VRANA, Daniel A
Area Controller, Encompass Health Rehabilitation Hospital Of Sewickley, Sewickley, PA, p. A541
Controller, Encompass Health Harmarville Rehabilitation Hospital, Pittsburgh, PA, p. A537
VRBA, Frank, Chief Information Officer, Annie Jeffrey Memorial County Health Center, Osceola, NE, p. A390
VRBAS, Laken, R.N., Director of Nursing, Dundy County Hospital, Benkelman, NE, p. A383
VROBEL, Matthew, Vice President, Medical Operations, Cleveland Clinic, Medina Hospital, Medina, OH, p. A487
VRONKO, Jeremy, Manager, Information Services, Spectrum Health Ludington Hospital, Ludington, MI, p. A317
VROTSOS, Darlene, R.N., Senior Vice President and Chief Nursing Officer, Virginia Hospital Center, Arlington, VA, p. A656
VUCHAK, Jerry
Vice President Healthcare Delivery, Barnes–Jewish Hospital, Saint Louis, MO, p. A369
Vice President Information Systems, Barnes–Jewish West County Hospital, Saint Louis, MO, p. A369
VUKICH, David, M.D., Senior Vice President, Chief Medical Officer and Chief Quality Officer, Uf Health Jacksonville, Jacksonville, FL, p. A126
VUKSTA, Jeanne, Chief Financial Officer, Bacharach Institute For Rehabilitation, Pomona, NJ, p. A411
VUTRANO, Frank A, Chief Financial Officer, Brookdale Hospital Medical Center, New York, NY, p. A432
VYZOUREK, Treg, Chief Executive Officer, Brodstone Memorial Hospital, Superior, NE, p. A392

W

WAALA, Shelly, Vice President Patient Care Services and Chief Nursing Officer, St. Joseph'S Hospital, West Bend, WI, p. A708
WACHOWIAK, Darrell, Associate Vice President Operations, Promedica Bay Park Hospital, Oregon, OH, p. A489
WACK, Mark, Chief Financial Officer, Memorial Hospital At Gulfport, Gulfport, MS, p. A347
WADDELL, Kathy, Administrator, Wayne General Hospital, Waynesboro, MS, p. A355
WADDELL, Lesa, Director Human Resources, Compass Memorial Healthcare, Marengo, IA, p. A226
WADE, Bruce, Vice President Human Resources, Indiana University Health Bedford Hospital, Bedford, IN, p. A199
WADE, Cynthia, R.N., Executive Vice President and Chief Operating Officer, Lincolnhealth, Damariscotta, ME, p. A282
WADE, Donna, Senior Director Human Resources, Comanche County Memorial Hospital, Lawton, OK, p. A501
WADE, Glenn, Director Information Systems, Saint Thomas Highlands Hospital, Sparta, TN, p. A579
WADE, Hong, Chief Financial Officer, Sweeny Community Hospital, Sweeny, TX, p. A639
WADE, Hope, Chief Operating Officer, Christus St. Vincent Regional Medical Center, Santa Fe, NM, p. A420
WADE, Jacqueline, Director, Desert Willow Treatment Center, Las Vegas, NV, p. A395
WADE, Jonathan O., Chief Executive Officer, Jersey Community Hospital, Jerseyville, IL, p. A186
WADE, Kathy, Chief Human Resource Officer, Winona Health, Winona, MN, p. A343
WADE, Susan, Vice President, Hendrick Health System, Abilene, TX, p. A581
WADEWITZ, Martin, Chief Operations Officer/ Vice President, Operations, Angel Medical Center, Franklin, NC, p. A454
WADLE, Don
Interim Director Human Resources, Portneuf Medical Center, Pocatello, ID, p. A171
Vice President Clinical and Support Services, Portneuf Medical Center, Pocatello, ID, p. A171
WADSWORTH, Barbara A, MSN, R.N., FACHE, Chief Nursing Officer, Bryn Mawr Hospital, Bryn Mawr, PA, p. A523
WAFFORD, Marty, Under Secretary of Support and Programs, Chickasaw Nation Medical Center, Ada, OK, p. A496
WAFLE, Sue, Director, Human Resources, Mile Bluff Medical Center, Mauston, WI, p. A699
WAGERS, Rick, Senior Executive Vice President and Chief Financial Officer, Regional One Health, Memphis, TN, p. A575
WAGGENER, Yvonne, Chief Financial Officer, San Bernardino Mountains Community Hospital District, Lake Arrowhead, CA, p. A63
WAGGONER, Jeff, M.D., Chief of Staff, Weisbrod Memorial County Hospital, Eads, CO, p. A100

WAGGONER, Michelle, Chief Executive Officer, Community Memorial Hospital, Hicksville, OH, p. A484
WAGLEY, Ronnie, Market Chief Executive Officer, Select Specialty Hospital–Gainesville, Gainesville, FL, p. A123
WAGMEISTER, Lee, M.D., President Medical Staff, Deaconess Gateway Hospital, Newburgh, IN, p. A213
WAGNER, Dale, Chief Financial Officer, Kindred Hospital–Westminster, Westminster, CA, p. A94
WAGNER, David, South Florida Market Chief Executive Officer, Kindred Hospital South Florida–Fort Lauderdale, Fort Lauderdale, FL, p. A123
WAGNER, David D, Chief Information Management Service, Veterans Affairs Gulf Coast Veterans Health Care System, Biloxi, MS, p. A344
WAGNER, David S., Chief Executive Officer, Pearland Medical Center, Pearland, TX, p. A628
WAGNER, Elaina, Director Human Resources, Astria Sunnyside Hospital, Sunnyside, WA, p. A680
WAGNER, Fred, Chief Financial Officer, Osf St. Francis Hospital And Medical Group, Escanaba, MI, p. A311
WAGNER, Gwendolyn Dianne, R.N., MSN, Chief Nursing Officer, Mission Community Hospital, Los Angeles, CA, p. A68
WAGNER, Janet, Chief Executive Officer, Mills–Peninsula Health Services, Burlingame, CA, p. A53
WAGNER, Jefferey, Director, Information Technology, Lake Huron Medical Center, Port Huron, MI, p. A320
WAGNER, Linda, Chief Financial Officer, Sanford Worthington Medical Center, Worthington, MN, p. A343
WAGNER, Linda S., Chief Executive Officer, Seneca Healthcare District, Chester, CA, p. A54
WAGNER, Lynne, R.N., Chief Nursing Officer, Rose Medical Center, Denver, CO, p. A99
WAGNER, Randall J, Chief Operating Officer, Mercy Health Saint Mary'S, Grand Rapids, MI, p. A313
WAGNER, Renee, M.D., Chief Medical Officer, Fairfield Medical Center, Lancaster, OH, p. A485
WAGNER, Russell R, Executive Vice President and Chief Financial Officer, Holy Redeemer Hospital, Meadowbrook, PA, p. A531
WAGNER, Sarah, Human Resources Officer, Memorial Hospital Of Texas County, Guymon, OK, p. A500
WAGNER, Sherrie A, Manager Human Resources, The Core Institute Specialty Hospital, Phoenix, AZ, p. A34
WAGNER, Suzie, Director Human Resources, Encompass Health Rehabilitation Hospital Of Alexandria, Alexandria, LA, p. A262
WAGNER, Terry, Chief Information Officer, Upstate University Hospital, Syracuse, NY, p. A445
WAGNER, Terry, R.N., Chief Operating Officer, Pocahontas Memorial Hospital, Buckeye, WV, p. A683
WAGNER, Timothy, M.D., Chief Medical Staff, Yoakum Community Hospital, Yoakum, TX, p. A646
WAGNER, Tom, Interim Vice President Finance, Avera St. Mary'S Hospital, Pierre, SD, p. A562
WAGNER, Vanessa, Chief Financial Officer, Lawrence Memorial Hospital, Walnut Ridge, AR, p. A49
WAGNON, LaNell, Director Medical Records, Comanche County Hospital, Coldwater, KS, p. A233
WAGNON, William, Chief Executive Officer, Henrico Doctors' Hospital, Richmond, VA, p. A666
WAGONER, Craig
Chief Executive Officer, Community Behavioral Health Center, Fresno, CA, p. A59
Chief Executive Officer, Community Regional Medical Center, Fresno, CA, p. A59
WAGONER, Dean, Director Human Resources, Good Samaritan Hospital, Vincennes, IN, p. A216
WAGONER, Renee, R.N., Director of Nursing, Gove County Medical Center, Quinter, KS, p. A244
WAHAB, Amir J., M.D., Medical Staff President, Abraham Lincoln Memorial Hospital, Lincoln, IL, p. A188
WAHL, Josephine Sclafani, R.N., MS, FACHE, VP, Patient Care Services & CNO, Henry Ford Wyandotte Hospital, Wyandotte, MI, p. A325
WAHL, Tony, Chief Executive Officer, Baylor Scott & White Texas Spine & Joint Hospital–Tyler, Tyler, TX, p. A642
WAHLERS, Brenda, M.D., Chief of Staff, Upmc Cole, Coudersport, PA, p. A523
WAHLUND, Keith, Vice President Human Resources, Essentia Health Fargo, Fargo, ND, p. A466
WAIBEL, David, M.D., Medical Director, Clarks Summit State Hospital, Clarks Summit, PA, p. A522
WAIDE, Mary Beth, Chief Executive Officer, Deer'S Head Hospital Center, Salisbury, MD, p. A293
WAIN, Matthew, Chief Operating Officer, Musc Health Of Medical University Of South Carolina, Charleston, SC, p. A550
WAIND, Mark, Chief Information Officer, Altru Health System, Grand Forks, ND, p. A467

WAIT, Wendy, Chief Financial Officer, Montgomery County Emergency Service, Norristown, PA, p. A533
WAITE, Douglas, M.D., Chief Medical Officer, Saint Vincent Hospital, Worcester, MA, p. A305
WAITE, Douglas D
Senior Vice President and Chief Financial Officer, Ascension Seton Highland Lakes, Burnet, TX, p. A590
Senior Vice President and Chief Financial Officer, Ascension Seton Williamson, Round Rock, TX, p. A632
WAITES, Alan, Chief Financial Officer, Gove County Medical Center, Quinter, KS, p. A244
WAJDA, David, Chief Financial Officer, Nazareth Hospital, Philadelphia, PA, p. A535
WAKEFIELD, Brett
Director Human Resources, Thorek Memorial Hospital, Chicago, IL, p. A180
Vice President Human Resources, Gottlieb Memorial Hospital, Melrose Park, IL, p. A189
WAKEFIELD, Jeff, CPA, Vice President and Chief Financial Officer, Marion General Hospital, Marion, IN, p. A211
WAKEFIELD, Mamie
Chief Financial Officer, Miriam Hospital, Providence, RI, p. A547
Senior Vice President and Chief Financial Officer, Rhode Island Hospital, Providence, RI, p. A548
Vice President Finance and Chief Financial Officer, Emma Pendleton Bradley Hospital, East Providence, RI, p. A547
WAKEM, Jennifer, Chief Financial Officer, University Medical Center, Las Vegas, NV, p. A396
WAKEMAN, Daniel L., President, St. Luke'S Hospital, Maumee, OH, p. A487
WAKIM, Tina, Vice President Information, Northside Hospital, Atlanta, GA, p. A146
WALAS, Steven, Chief Executive Officer, Healthsouth Chesapeake Rehabilitation Hospital, Salisbury, MD, p. A293
WALCEK, Peter, Vice President Finance, Wentworth–Douglass Hospital, Dover, NH, p. A399
WALCH, Tina, M.D., Medical Director, South Oaks Hospital, Amityville, NY, p. A422
WALCZAK, Laura, President, Ssm Health St. Clare Hospital–Baraboo, Baraboo, WI, p. A692
WALCZYK-JOERS, Barbara, President and Chief Executive Officer, Gillette Children'S Specialty Healthcare, Saint Paul, MN, p. A339
WALD, Barry, Chief Financial Officer, Wake Forest Baptist Health – Wilkes Medical Center, North Wilkesboro, NC, p. A459
WALDBART, Andy, Department Manager, Heart Of The Rockies Regional Medical Center, Salida, CO, p. A105
WALDBILLIG, Karla, Director Human Resources, Unitypoint Health – Finley Hospital, Dubuque, IA, p. A222
WALDBILLIG, Kurt, Chief Executive Officer, Meeker Memorial Hospital, Litchfield, MN, p. A334
WALDEN, Anita, Vice President and Chief Nursing Officer, Decatur Morgan Hospital, Decatur, AL, p. A16
WALDERA, John, Director Information Technology, Gundersen Tri–County Hospital And Clinics, Whitehall, WI, p. A708
WALDO, Bruce
Chief Executive Officer, Aurora Behavioral Health System East, Tempe, AZ, p. A36
Chief Executive Officer, Aurora Behavioral Health System West, Glendale, AZ, p. A30
WALDO, Gail, Director Information Technology, Piedmont Rockdale Hospital, Conyers, GA, p. A151
WALDRON, Michele, Senior Vice President and Chief Financial Officer, Valley Children'S Healthcare, Madera, CA, p. A70
WALDRON, Ray, Director Information Technology, Gordon Memorial Health Services, Gordon, NE, p. A385
WALDRON, Sheila, Finance Manager, Providence Milwaukie Hospital, Milwaukie, OR, p. A515
WALDROP, Catherine M.
Administrator, Southeast Rehabilitation Hospital, Lake Village, AR, p. A44
Administrator, Sterlington Rehabilitation Hospital, Bastrop, LA, p. A263
WALDROP, Cathy, Director, Hospital Nursing Services, North Mississippi Medical Center–Pontotoc, Pontotoc, MS, p. A353
WALI, Jyotika, M.D., Chief of Staff, Kindred Hospital–Brea, Brea, CA, p. A53
WALIGURA, R Curtis, D.O., Vice President Medical Affairs, Chief Medical Officer, Upmc Mckeesport, Mckeesport, PA, p. A531
WALK, Rex D., Chief Executive Officer, Phillips County Health Systems, Phillipsburg, KS, p. A243
WALKENHORST, Debbie G
Network Vice President, Ssm Cardinal Glennon Children'S Hospital, Saint Louis, MO, p. A370
System Vice President Talent Management, Ssm Health St. Joseph – St. Charles, Saint Charles, MO, p. A368

WALKER, Alene, Director Human Resources, Quincy Valley Medical Center, Quincy, WA, p. A677

WALKER, Alexander J., Executive Vice President Operations and Strategic Development, Catholic Medical Center, Manchester, NH, p. A401

WALKER, Amy, MSN, Chief Nursing Officer, Delta Regional Medical Center, Greenville, MS, p. A347

WALKER, Angela, Manager Human Resources, Aspire Hospital, Conroe, TX, p. A593

WALKER, Angela, M.D., Medical Director, Healthsouth Rehabilitation Hospital Of New Mexico, Albuquerque, NM, p. A416

WALKER, Annette, Associate Director, John D. Dingell Veterans Affairs Medical Center, Detroit, MI, p. A310

WALKER, Beth
Chief Executive Officer, Ochsner Medical Center, New Orleans, LA, p. A275
Chief Information Officer, Emanuel Medical Center, Turlock, CA, p. A92
President, Firsthealth Montgomery Memorial Hospital, Troy, NC, p. A463

WALKER, C O, M.D., Chief of Staff, Donalsonville Hospital, Donalsonville, GA, p. A152

WALKER, Candace, Chief Financial Officer, East Central Regional Hospital, Augusta, GA, p. A147

WALKER, Carol, Chief Financial Officer, Oklahoma Heart Hospital, Oklahoma City, OK, p. A505

WALKER, Cass
Vice President Administrative & Support Services, Franklin Regional Hospital, Franklin, NH, p. A400
Vice President Administrative & Support Services, Lakes Region General Hospital, Laconia, NH, p. A400

WALKER, Charles, Director Information Technology, Kimball Health Services, Kimball, NE, p. A386

WALKER, Cheri, R.N., Chief Nursing Officer, King'S Daughters Medical Center, Brookhaven, MS, p. A345

WALKER, Christopher, Chief Nursing Officer and Operating Officer, Sharp Coronado Hospital And Healthcare Center, Coronado, CA, p. A55

WALKER, Codie, Chief Financial Officer, Salem Veterans Affairs Medical Center, Salem, VA, p. A667

WALKER, Dan, Chief Nursing Officer, Lincoln Community Hospital And Nursing Home, Hugo, CO, p. A102

WALKER, David, Interim Chief Executive Officer, George E. Weems Memorial Hospital, Apalachicola, FL, p. A117

WALKER, David M., Medical Center Director, G.V. (Sonny) Montgomery Veterans Affairs Medical Center, Jackson, MS, p. A348

WALKER, Donna, Chief Nurse Executive, Weeks Medical Center, Lancaster, NH, p. A400

WALKER, Durwin, M.D., Chief Medical Officer, Sage Specialty Hospital (Ltac), Denham Springs, LA, p. A267

WALKER, Gerri H., President and Chief Executive Officer, North Philadelphia Health System, Philadelphia, PA, p. A536

WALKER, Gregory J., Chief Executive Officer, Wentworth–Douglass Hospital, Dover, NH, p. A399

WALKER, Imani, M.D., Medical Director, Gateways Hospital And Mental Health Center, Los Angeles, CA, p. A66

WALKER, Jan
Director Human Resources, Centra Lynchburg General Hospital, Lynchburg, VA, p. A662
Director Human Resources, Glenwood Regional Medical Center, West Monroe, LA, p. A280

WALKER, Janice L, R.N., System Chief Nursing Executive, Senior Vice President, Baylor Scott & White All Saints Medical Center – Fort Worth, Fort Worth, TX, p. A604

WALKER, Jeff E., Chief Operating Officer, City Of Hope'S Helford Clinical Research Hospital, Duarte, CA, p. A57

WALKER, Jeremy Tyler, Vice President and Chief Financial Officer, Hendrick Health System, Abilene, TX, p. A581

WALKER, John, Chief Operating Officer, Medical City Denton, Denton, TX, p. A599

WALKER, Jon W., M.D., Chief Medical Officer, Wise Health System, Decatur, TX, p. A598

WALKER, Karen, Chief Executive Officer, Oakwood Springs, Oklahoma City, OK, p. A504

WALKER, Kathy, Chief Financial Officer, Trinity Hospital, Weaverville, CA, p. A94

WALKER, Kimberly, Director of Human Resources, Northcrest Medical Center, Springfield, TN, p. A579

WALKER, Kristie E, M.P.H., Director of Human Resources, Wythe County Community Hospital, Wytheville, VA, p. A669

WALKER, LeRoy, Vice President Human Resources, Emory Decatur Hospital, Decatur, GA, p. A152

WALKER, Linda, Chief Executive Officer, Val Verde Regional Medical Center, Del Rio, TX, p. A599

WALKER, Lynette, R.N., Ph.D., Vice President Human Resources, Baptist Health Lexington, Lexington, KY, p. A254

WALKER, Mary, Manager Information Technology, Encompass Health Rehabilitation Hospital Of Wichita Falls, Wichita Falls, TX, p. A645

WALKER, Matthew, Chief Executive Officer and Administrator, William Bee Ririe Hospital, Ely, NV, p. A393

WALKER, Melissa, CPA, Chief Financial Officer, North Texas Medical Center, Gainesville, TX, p. A607

WALKER, Nicole
Chief Executive Officer, First Surgical Hospital, Bellaire, TX, p. A588
Chief Executive Officer, Hermann Drive Surgical Hospital, Houston, TX, p. A611

WALKER, Pandora, Director, Human Resources, Beaumont Hospital – Grosse Pointe, Grosse Pointe, MI, p. A313

WALKER, Randy
Chief Nursing Officer, Hillcrest Hospital Claremore, Claremore, OK, p. A498
Director Nursing Services, State Hospital South, Blackfoot, ID, p. A167
Vice President, Methodist Dallas Medical Center, Dallas, TX, p. A597

WALKER, Robert, M.D., Medical Director, Encompass Health Rehabilitation Hospital Of Princeton, Princeton, WV, p. A688

WALKER, Robert L., President and Chief Executive Officer, Texas Scottish Rite Hospital For Children, Dallas, TX, p. A598

WALKER, Robin, Chief Nursing Officer, Field Memorial Community Hospital, Centreville, MS, p. A345

WALKER, Samuel, Director of IT, Pocahontas Memorial Hospital, Buckeye, WV, p. A683

WALKER, Scott, Chief Financial Officer, Southeastern Regional Medical Center, Newnan, GA, p. A158

WALKER, Tim, Manager Information Services, Peacehealth Ketchikan Medical Center, Ketchikan, AK, p. A26

WALKER, Todd, President, Prisma Health Baptist Easley Hospital, Easley, SC, p. A552

WALKER, Troy, Director Finance, Ssm Health St. Clare Hospital–Baraboo, Baraboo, WI, p. A692

WALKER, Tyree, Chief Human Resources Officer, Vidant Medical Center, Greenville, NC, p. A455

WALKER, Virginia, Vice President Nursing Services and Chief Nursing Officer, Kuakini Medical Center, Honolulu, HI, p. A164

WALL, Daniel J., President and Chief Executive Officer, Emma Pendleton Bradley Hospital, East Providence, RI, p. A547

WALL, Debbie, Chief Nursing Officer, Cherry Hospital, Goldsboro, NC, p. A455

WALL, Doug, M.D.
Vice President Medical Affairs, Novant Health Uva Health System Prince William Medical Center, Manassas, VA, p. A662
Vice President of Medical Affairs, Novant Health Uva Health System Haymarket Medical Center, Haymarket, VA, p. A661

WALL, Heather, Chief Nursing Officer, Peacehealth Sacred Heart Medical Center At Riverbend, Springfield, OR, p. A518

WALL, Kathryn S
Executive Vice President Human Resources and Organizational Development, Stafford Hospital, Stafford, VA, p. A667
Executive Vice President, Human Resources and Organizational Development, Mary Washington Hospital, Fredericksburg, VA, p. A659

WALL, Lorraine, Chief Operating Officer, Olympic Medical Center, Port Angeles, WA, p. A676

WALLACE, Brad, Director Information Services, Grays Harbor Community Hospital, Aberdeen, WA, p. A670

WALLACE, Carolyn, Director Human Resources, Connecticut Mental Health Center, New Haven, CT, p. A109

WALLACE, Cynthia, M.D., Medical Director, Vibra Specialty Hospital Of Portland, Portland, OR, p. A516

WALLACE, David, Chief Executive Officer, Mat–Su Regional Medical Center, Palmer, AK, p. A27

WALLACE, Dianne, County Information Manager, Douglas County Community Mental Health Center, Omaha, NE, p. A389

WALLACE, Donna Geiken, Chief Operating Officer and Chief Financial Officer, Christus Mother Frances Hospital – Sulphur Springs, Sulphur Springs, TX, p. A638

WALLACE, Glenn, Chief Executive Officer, Medical City Alliance, Fort Worth, TX, p. A605

WALLACE, Kathleen, Administrator and Chief Executive Officer, Lifecare Hospitals Of Dallas, Dallas, TX, p. A596

WALLACE, Kristina, Chief Executive Officer, Ou Medical Center, Oklahoma City, OK, p. A505

WALLACE, Mark, Chief Financial Officer, Cumberland Hall Hospital, Hopkinsville, KY, p. A253

WALLACE, Mark A., President and Chief Executive Officer, Texas Children'S Hospital, Houston, TX, p. A614

WALLACE, Mark T, Director Human Resources, Adventist Health Lodi Memorial, Lodi, CA, p. A64

WALLACE, Martha, Administrator, California Mens Colony Correctional Treatment Center, San Luis Obispo, CA, p. A87

WALLACE, Melanie, Manager Human Resources, Sutter Tracy Community Hospital, Tracy, CA, p. A92

WALLACE, Michael S., President and Chief Executive Officer, Fort Healthcare, Fort Atkinson, WI, p. A695

WALLACE, Nancy
Division Senior Vice President, Chief Human Resource Officer, Chi Health Lakeside, Omaha, NE, p. A389
Division Senior Vice President, Chief Human Resource Officer, Chi Health Midlands, Papillion, NE, p. A390
Senior Vice President Human Resources, Chi Health Mercy Council Bluffs, Council Bluffs, IA, p. A220
Senior Vice President, Chief Human Resources Officer, Chi Health St Elizabeth, Lincoln, NE, p. A387
Vice President Human Resources, CHI Health, Chi Health Saint Francis, Grand Island, NE, p. A385
Vice President Human Resources, Chi Health Creighton University Medical Center – Bergan Mercy, Omaha, NE, p. A388
Vice President Human Resources, Chi Health Immanuel, Omaha, NE, p. A389
Vice President Human Resources, Chi Health Schuyler, Schuyler, NE, p. A391

WALLACE, Penny, Chief Financial Officer, Guadalupe Regional Medical Center, Seguin, TX, p. A636

WALLACE, Tabatha, Director Human Resources, Adventhealth Dade City, Dade City, FL, p. A121

WALLACE–MOORE, Patrice, Chief Executive Officer and Executive Director, Arms Acres, Carmel, NY, p. A425

WALLEN, Carla, Manager Human Resources, Cass Regional Medical Center, Harrisonville, MO, p. A361

WALLENTINE, Jeffrey, Chief of Staff, Mountain View Hospital, Payson, UT, p. A650

WALLER, Ernie, Director Information Technology, Ed Fraser Memorial Hospital And Baker Community Health Center, Macclenny, FL, p. A128

WALLER, Kenneth, Fiscal Administrator, Deer'S Head Hospital Center, Salisbury, MD, p. A293

WALLER, Matthew, Chief Executive Officer, Liberty Medical Center, Chester, MT, p. A375

WALLER, Raymond A., Director and Administrator, Ascension Brighton Center For Recovery, Brighton, MI, p. A307

WALLINE, Linda K, R.N., Ph.D., MSN, Vice President Nursing, Columbus Community Hospital, Columbus, NE, p. A384

WALLING, Vernon, M.D.
Chief Medical Officer, Sun Behavioral Houston, Houston, TX, p. A614
Executive Medical Director, West Oaks Hospital, Houston, TX, p. A615

WALLINGA, Joel, Chief Financial Officer, Veterans Affairs Ann Arbor Healthcare System, Ann Arbor, MI, p. A306

WALLINGA, Melvin, M.D., Medical Director, St. Michael'S Hospital Avera, Tyndall, SD, p. A564

WALLIS, Pam B, MSN, Vice President Nursing Services, Magnolia Regional Health Center, Corinth, MS, p. A346

WALLMAN, Gerald H., Administrator, West Covina Medical Center, West Covina, CA, p. A94

WALLS, Craig, M.D., Ph.D., Chief Medical Officer, Natividad Medical Center, Salinas, CA, p. A82

WALLS, Martha Delaney, R.N., MSN, Chief Nursing Officer, Crestwood Medical Center, Huntsville, AL, p. A19

WALLS, Randy, Manager Information Services, Fairbanks, Indianapolis, IN, p. A206

WALLS, Ron, M.D., Executive Vice President and Chief Operating Officer, Brigham And Women'S Hospital, Boston, MA, p. A295

WALLSCHLAEGER, Erich, Chief Financial Officer, Cedar Park Regional Medical Center, Cedar Park, TX, p. A592

WALRATH, Andrea, Chief Operating Officer, Forest Health Medical Center, Ypsilanti, MI, p. A325

WALRAVEN, Jeff, Chief Executive Officer, Lindsay Municipal Hospital, Lindsay, OK, p. A501

WALSER, Bill, Coordinator Technology, Cameron Regional Medical Center, Cameron, MO, p. A357

WALSH, Brad, M.D., Chief of Staff, Ashley County Medical Center, Crossett, AR, p. A40

WALSH, Catherine, Interim Nursing Executive, Mercy Regional Medical Center, Lorain, OH, p. A486

WALSH, Daniel P., Vice President, Information Systems and Technology Northern Division, Abington Hospital, Abington, PA, p. A519

WALSH, Debbie, MSN, Chief Operating Officer, Maui Memorial Medical Center, Wailuku, HI, p. A166

WALSH, Gerard W., Chief Executive Officer, Brookdale Hospital Medical Center, New York, NY, p. A432
WALSH, John, Chief Fiscal Services, Veterans Affairs Hudson Valley Health Care System, Montrose, NY, p. A431
WALSH, Kate, President and Chief Executive Officer, Boston Medical Center, Boston, MA, p. A295
WALSH, Katherine, MS, R.N., Dr.PH, Vice President and Chief Nursing Officer, Houston Methodist Hospital, Houston, TX, p. A612
WALSH, Ken, Chief Financial Officer, St. Luke'S Medical Center, Phoenix, AZ, p. A34
WALSH, Kim, Chief Nursing Officer, Signature Healthcare Brockton Hospital, Brockton, MA, p. A296
WALSH, Len, Executive Vice President and Chief Operating Officer, Brookdale Hospital Medical Center, New York, NY, p. A432
WALSH, Linda, R.N., MSN, Vice President Chief Nursing Executive, Hackensack Meridian Health Bayshore Community Hospital, Holmdel, NJ, p. A406
WALSH, Marcia S, M.P.H., Chief Operating Officer, Community Healthcare System, Onaga, KS, p. A242
WALSH, Marilyn J, Vice President Human Resources, Kent County Memorial Hospital, Warwick, RI, p. A548
WALSH, Mary, R.N., MSN, Vice President Patient Care Services and Chief Nursing Officer, Brookdale Hospital Medical Center, New York, NY, p. A432
WALSH, Michael
Senior Vice President Finance and Chief Financial Officer, Abington Hospital, Abington, PA, p. A519
Senior Vice President Finance and Chief Financial Officer, Abington–Lansdale Hospital Jefferson Health, Lansdale, PA, p. A529
WALSH, Michele M, Chief Nursing Officer, St. Mary'S Healthcare, Amsterdam, NY, p. A422
WALSTON, John, Chief Information Officer, Southern Arizona Veterans Affairs Health Care System, Tucson, AZ, p. A38
WALTER, Gayle, Director of Nursing, Thomas B. Finan Center, Cumberland, MD, p. A290
WALTER, Melissa, Director Human Resources, Clarinda Regional Health Center, Clarinda, IA, p. A219
WALTER, Stephen
Senior Vice President and Chief Financial Officer, Community Behavioral Health Center, Fresno, CA, p. A59
Senior Vice President and Chief Financial Officer, Community Regional Medical Center, Fresno, CA, p. A59
WALTERS, Cindy, Chief Executive Officer, Acadia–St. Landry Hospital, Church Point, LA, p. A265
WALTERS, Jane, Director of Nursing, Mendota Mental Health Institute, Madison, WI, p. A698
WALTERS, Julie, Chief Nursing Officer, Hillsdale Hospital, Hillsdale, MI, p. A314
WALTERS, Kevin, Chief Financial Officer, St. Rose Dominican Hospitals – Rose De Lima Campus, Henderson, NV, p. A394
WALTERS, Leah, R.N., Director of Nursing, Mountain Valley Regional Rehabilitation Hospital, Prescott Valley, AZ, p. A35
WALTERS, Leslie, MSN, Chief Nursing Officer, Clarion Hospital, Clarion, PA, p. A522
WALTERS, Todd, Director of UHC Information Technology Services, Ochsner Lsu Health Shreveport – Monroe Medical Center, Monroe, LA, p. A274
WALTHALL, Wayne, Vice President and Chief Financial Officer, St. John Medical Center, Tulsa, OK, p. A510
WALTHER, Diane, Controller, Henry County Hospital, Napoleon, OH, p. A488
WALTON, Amy E., M.D., Chief Medical Officer, Ascension Seton Shoal Creek, Austin, TX, p. A585
WALTON, Dawn, Chief Financial Officer, Children'S Of Alabama, Birmingham, AL, p. A14
WALTON, Gary, M.D., Chief Medical Officer, Hill Hospital Of Sumter County, York, AL, p. A24
WALTON, Georgian, Director Human Resources, Elbert Memorial Hospital, Elberton, GA, p. A153
WALTON, Linda, R.N., MSN, Chief Nursing Officer, Cleveland Clinic Indian River Hospital, Vero Beach, FL, p. A143
WALTZ, Dan, Vice President and Chief Information Officer, Midmichigan Medical Center–Gladwin, Gladwin, MI, p. A312
WALZ, Rachel A, Director Patient Care, Centracare Health–Paynesville, Paynesville, MN, p. A337
WAMPLER, Andrew
Chief Financial Officer, Franklin Woods Community Hospital, Johnson City, TN, p. A571
Chief Financial Officer, Margaret R. Pardee Memorial Hospital, Hendersonville, NC, p. A456
WAMPLER, Beth A, R.N., Chief Nursing Officer, Fayette Regional Health System, Connersville, IN, p. A201
WAMSLEY, Marie, Chief Financial Officer, Memorial Hospital Of Lafayette County, Darlington, WI, p. A693
WANG, William Norberto, M.D., Chief Operating Officer, Brookdale Hospital Medical Center, New York, NY, p. A432
WANG, MD, Shu–Ming, Vice President Medical Affairs, Chi Health Saint Francis, Grand Island, NE, p. A385
WANGSMO, Gary L, Chief Financial Officer, Mee Memorial Hospital, King City, CA, p. A62
WANGSNESS, Erik
Chief Executive Officer, Adventhealth Wesley Chapel, Wesley Chapel, FL, p. A143
President, Adventist Healthcare Washington Adventist Hospital, Takoma Park, MD, p. A293
WANLY, Bahaa, Interim Chief Operating Officer, Salem Hospital, Salem, OR, p. A517
WANNER, David
Chief Information Officer, Trinity Health, Minot, ND, p. A469
Director Information Technology, Kenmare Community Hospital, Kenmare, ND, p. A468
WAPPELHORST, Andrea, Chief Nursing Officer, Tops Surgical Specialty Hospital, Houston, TX, p. A614
WAR, Melissa, Chief Executive Officer, Mountain'S Edge Hospital, Las Vegas, NV, p. A395
WARBURTON, John B., Chief Executive Officer, Riverwoods Behavioral Health System, Riverdale, GA, p. A159
WARD, Brook, Executive Vice President, Washington Hospital, Washington, PA, p. A543
WARD, Celia F, Controller and Chief Financial Officer, Doctors Memorial Hospital, Bonifay, FL, p. A118
WARD, Charlotte, Entity Financial Officer, Texas Health Harris Methodist Hospital Southwest Fort Worth, Fort Worth, TX, p. A606
WARD, Chris
Chief Nursing Officer, Comanche County Memorial Hospital, Lawton, OK, p. A501
Director Management Information Systems, Dorminy Medical Center, Fitzgerald, GA, p. A153
WARD, David M, Chief Financial Officer and Chief Acquisition Officer, Cabell Huntington Hospital, Huntington, WV, p. A685
WARD, Dillon, Management Information Systems Specialist, Tennova Healthcare–Latollette Medical Center, La Follette, TN, p. A572
WARD, Elizabeth S.
Chief Financial Officer, Tidelands Georgetown Memorial Hospital, Georgetown, SC, p. A553
Chief Financial Officer, Tidelands Waccamaw Community Hospital, Murrells Inlet, SC, p. A556
WARD, Henry J., Interim President, Westfield Memorial Hospital, Westfield, NY, p. A447
WARD, Jeffery, Director Human Resources, Cedar Park Regional Medical Center, Cedar Park, TX, p. A592
WARD, Julie, Vice President Finance, Northeastern Health System, Tahlequah, OK, p. A508
WARD, Julie, MSN, R.N., Chief Nursing Officer, St. Joseph'S Hospital And Medical Center, Phoenix, AZ, p. A34
WARD, Julie R., MSN, R.N., Vice President Patient Care Services, Hutchinson Regional Medical Center, Hutchinson, KS, p. A237
WARD, Kevin, Chief Operating Officer, Jewish Home Of San Francisco, San Francisco, CA, p. A85
WARD, Kevin J, Vice President and Chief Financial Officer, Brookdale Hospital Medical Center, New York, NY, p. A432
WARD, Kimberly J, Chief Nurse Officer, St. Luke'S Rehabilitation Institute, Spokane, WA, p. A680
WARD, Lesli, Vice President Human Resources, Uf Health Jacksonville, Jacksonville, FL, p. A126
WARD, Lisa, Director Information Systems, Columbus Regional Healthcare System, Whiteville, NC, p. A463
WARD, Lorna J, MSN, R.N., Chief Nursing Officer, Novant Health Brunswick Medical Center, Bolivia, NC, p. A450
WARD, Louis James, Chief Operating Officer, Mayers Memorial Hospital District, Fall River Mills, CA, p. A58
WARD, Louis James., Interim Chief Executive Officer, Mayers Memorial Hospital District, Fall River Mills, CA, p. A58
WARD, Mark, M.D., Chief of Staff, Roundup Memorial Healthcare, Roundup, MT, p. A380
WARD, Michael
Chief Executive Officer, Encompass Health Rehabilitation Hospital Of Las Vegas, Las Vegas, NV, p. A395
Director Information Services, Anderson Hospital, Maryville, IL, p. A188
WARD, Mike
Chief Information Officer, Morristown–Hamblen Healthcare System, Morristown, TN, p. A576
Covenant Health, Senior Vice President and Chief Information Officer, Methodist Medical Center Of Oak Ridge, Oak Ridge, TN, p. A578
Senior Vice President Chief Information Officer, Roane Medical Center, Harriman, TN, p. A570
WARD, Rhonda, R.N., MSN, Chief Nursing Officer, Littleton Adventist Hospital, Littleton, CO, p. A103
WARD, Rory, Chief Financial Officer, Pushmataha Hospital, Antlers, OK, p. A496
WARD, Silva, Director Human Resources, Center For Behavioral Medicine, Kansas City, MO, p. A362
WARD, Stormy, Chief Nurse Executive, Big Spring State Hospital, Big Spring, TX, p. A588
WARD, Virginia, Human Resources Officer, Robert E. Bush Naval Hospital, Twentynine Palms, CA, p. A92
WARDA, Paul, Chief Financial Officer, Medstar Georgetown University Hospital, Washington, DC, p. A115
WARDEN, Michael S, Senior Vice President Information Technology, Banner – University Medical Center Phoenix, Phoenix, AZ, p. A33
WARDLOW, Marlon, Chief Operating Officer, Parkview Regional Medical Center, Fort Wayne, IN, p. A204
WARDROP, Daniel, M.D., Medical Director, Heart Of The Rockies Regional Medical Center, Salida, CO, p. A105
WARE, Bobbie K., Chief Executive Officer, Mississippi Baptist Medical Center, Jackson, MS, p. A349
WARE, Bobbie K., R.N., FACHE, Vice President Patient Care and Chief Nursing Officer, Mississippi Baptist Medical Center, Jackson, MS, p. A349
WARE, Dana, M.D., Chief of Staff, Seneca Healthcare District, Chester, CA, p. A54
WARE, John, Director of Human Resources, Venice Regional Bayfront Health, Venice, FL, p. A143
WARE, Judy
Chief Financial Officer, Putnam General Hospital, Eatonton, GA, p. A153
Director Human Resources, Johnson Memorial Hospital, Franklin, IN, p. A204
WARE, Judy King, Chief Financial Officer, Monroe County Hospital, Forsyth, GA, p. A153
WARE, Kathy, Director of Nursing, Daniels Memorial Healthcare Center, Scobey, MT, p. A380
WARE, Risa, Commander, Irwin Army Community Hospital, Junction City, KS, p. A237
WAREING, Colleen, Vice President Patient Care Services, Atlantic General Hospital, Berlin, MD, p. A288
WARFIELD, William, Chief Human Resources Management, Veterans Affairs Boston Healthcare System, West Roxbury, MA, p. A304
WARING, Lance, Director Human Resources, Texas Health Harris Methodist Hospital Azle, Azle, TX, p. A586
WARLICK, Mark
Chief Information Officer, Elkhart General Hospital, Elkhart, IN, p. A202
Chief Information Officer, Memorial Hospital Of South Bend, South Bend, IN, p. A215
WARLITNER, Todd, Vice President Business Operations, The Outer Banks Hospital, Nags Head, NC, p. A459
WARM, Ira, Senior Vice President Human Resources, Brookdale Hospital Medical Center, New York, NY, p. A432
WARMAN, Debbie, Vice President Human Resources, Metrohealth Medical Center, Cleveland, OH, p. A478
WARMBOLD, Steve, Director Information Management Service Line, Veterans Affairs St. Louis Health Care System, Saint Louis, MO, p. A371
WARMERDAM, David, Chief Financial Officer, Brynn Marr Hospital, Jacksonville, NC, p. A456
WARNER, Grady, Director of Information Technology, Burgess Health Center, Onawa, IA, p. A227
WARNER, John, Chief Executive Officer, University Of Texas Southwestern Medical Center, Dallas, TX, p. A598
WARNER, John, M.D., Chief Executive Officer, Interim Chief Medical Officer, University Of Texas Southwestern Medical Center, Dallas, TX, p. A598
WARNER, Norma, Area Director Health Information Management, Kindred Hospital–Fort Worth, Fort Worth, TX, p. A605
WARNER, Petra, Chief of Staff, Shriners Hospitals For Children – Cincinnati, Cincinnati, OH, p. A476
WARNER LYNN, Lynne, Administrator, Ephraim Mcdowell James B. Haggin Memorial Hospital, Harrodsburg, KY, p. A253
WARNER–PACHECO, Paula, Chief Human Resources, Rio Grande Hospital, Del Norte, CO, p. A98
WARNING, Kendra, Chief Financial Officer, Davis County Hospital, Bloomfield, IA, p. A218
WARNOCK, Dawn, Director Medical Records, Taylor Regional Hospital, Hawkinsville, GA, p. A154
WARREN, Brent, President Medical Staff, Iredell Health System, Statesville, NC, p. A463
WARREN, Charlene, R.N., Chief Nursing Officer, Greenbrier Valley Medical Center, Ronceverte, WV, p. A689
WARREN, Danny, Chief Financial Officer, Venice Regional Bayfront Health, Venice, FL, p. A143
WARREN, Denise Wilder, R.N.
Executive Vice President and Chief Operating Officer, Wakemed Cary Hospital, Cary, NC, p. A450
Executive Vice President and Chief Operating Officer, Wakemed Raleigh Campus, Raleigh, NC, p. A461

Index of Health Care Professionals / Warren

WARREN, Gidgett, Director of Nursing, T.J. Health Columbia, Columbia, KY, p. A250
WARREN, Jana, Human Resources Business Partner, Piedmont Henry Hospital, Stockbridge, GA, p. A161
WARREN, Karen, Fiscal Officer, Porterville Developmental Center, Porterville, CA, p. A78
WARREN, Linda, Director Human Resources, Cogdell Memorial Hospital, Snyder, TX, p. A637
WARREN, Lynn, Interim Chief Executive Officer, Group Vice President NueHealth, Methodist Hospital For Surgery, Addison, TX, p. A581
WARREN, Sarah, Coordinator Human Resources, Hickory Trail Hospital, Desoto, TX, p. A600
WARREN, Seth, President and Chief Executive Officer, Riverview Health, Noblesville, IN, p. A213
WARREN, Shanna, Director Human Resources, Medical City Plano, Plano, TX, p. A629
WARREN, Terri, Chief Financial Officer, Adventhealth Waterman, Tavares, FL, p. A142
WARREN, Wm. Michael., Jr, President and Chief Executive Officer, Children'S Of Alabama, Birmingham, AL, p. A14
WARRENER, Gerald, M.D., Chief Medical Officer, Parkview Noble Hospital, Kendallville, IN, p. A208
WARRIN, Richard, Chief Operating Officer, Musc Health Lancaster Medical Center, Lancaster, SC, p. A555
WARRINER, Ken, Market Chief Financial Officer, Physicians Regional – Pine Ridge, Naples, FL, p. A132
WARRNER, Judy, Chief Operating Officer, Northridge Medical Center, Commerce, GA, p. A151
WARSING, Tracy, M.D., Site Leader Chief of Staff, Mayo Clinic Health System – Franciscan Healthcare In Sparta, Sparta, WI, p. A705
WARTELLE, Scott, Chief Financial Officer, Sierra Vista Regional Medical Center, San Luis Obispo, CA, p. A87
WAS, Gregory J., Chief Executive Officer, White Mountain Regional Medical Center, Springerville, AZ, p. A36
WASEK, Arthur A, Director Human Resources, Panola Medical Center, Batesville, MS, p. A344
WASHBURN, Geoff, Vice President Human Resources, Los Robles Hospital And Medical Center, Thousand Oaks, CA, p. A91
WASHBURN, Geoffrey A., Vice President, Regional Medical Center Bayonet Point, Hudson, FL, p. A125
WASHBURN, Kimberly D, Director Human Resources, Snoqualmie Valley Hospital District, Snoqualmie, WA, p. A679
WASHBURN, Tonya, M.D., Medical Director, Valir Rehabilitation Hospital, Oklahoma City, OK, p. A505
WASHECKA, James, Chief Financial Officer, Hillcrest Hospital – South, Tulsa, OK, p. A508
WASHINGTON, Carolyn, Director of Human Resources, United Memorial Medical Care, Houston, TX, p. A614
WASHINGTON, Glen A., Chief Executive Officer, Pleasant Valley Hospital, Point Pleasant, WV, p. A688
WASHINGTON, Stephanie
  Director Community Relations and Human Resources, Baptist Medical Center Yazoo, Yazoo City, MS, p. A355
  Human Resources Director, Baptist Medical Center Attala, Kosciusko, MS, p. A350
WASHINGTON, Tarra, Chief Executive Officer, Kindred Hospital–New Jersey Morris County, Dover, NJ, p. A404
WASHINGTON, Vindell, M.D., Vice President Performance Excellence and Technology, Our Lady Of The Lake Regional Medical Center, Baton Rouge, LA, p. A264
WASILICK, Tamara, Director Operations, Kidspeace Children'S Hospital, Orefield, PA, p. A533
WATERBURY, Brad, Director Human Resources, Bonner General Hospital, Sandpoint, ID, p. A172
WATERS, Bill, M.D., Chief Medical Officer, Higgins General Hospital, Bremen, GA, p. A148
WATERS, Danny, Director, Information Services, Palms Of Pasadena Hospital, Saint Petersburg, FL, p. A138
WATERS, Eric, Vice President Operations, Pen Bay Medical Center, Rockport, ME, p. A285
WATERS, Gina, Director Human Resources, Evans Memorial Hospital, Claxton, GA, p. A150
WATERS, Jerod, Chief Nursing Officer, Chickasaw Nation Medical Center, Ada, OK, p. A496
WATERS, Karen, Chief Nursing Officer, St. Vincent Warrick, Boonville, IN, p. A200
WATERS, Laura M, Vice President Human Resources, Garrett Regional Medical Center, Oakland, MD, p. A292
WATERS, Nancy, Interim Chief Information Officer, High Point Medical Center, High Point, NC, p. A456
WATERS, Stephen F, M.D., Medical Director, Atlantic General Hospital, Berlin, MD, p. A288
WATERS, William, M.D.
  Chief Medical Officer, Tanner Medical Center–Carrollton, Carrollton, GA, p. A149
  Executive Vice President, Tanner Medical Center–Villa Rica, Villa Rica, GA, p. A162
WATHEN, Cheryl A, Interim Chief Financial Officer, Deaconess Midtown Hospital, Evansville, IN, p. A203
WATHEN, Susan R, Vice President Human Resources, Hannibal Regional Hospital, Hannibal, MO, p. A361
WATKINS, Anne Marie, R.N., Chief Nurse Executive, Kaiser Permanente San Diego Medical Center, San Diego, CA, p. A83
WATKINS, James, M.D., President Medical Staff, Providence Willamette Falls Medical Center, Oregon City, OR, p. A515
WATKINS, Jonathan, Chief Executive Officer, Broward Health Imperial Point, Fort Lauderdale, FL, p. A122
WATKINS, Joycelyn, R.N., Chief Nursing Officer, Magnolia Regional Medical Center, Magnolia, AR, p. A45
WATKINS, Michael, Chief Operating Officer, North Oaks Medical Center, Hammond, LA, p. A268
WATKINS, Michelle, Human Resources Manager, Greenwood Regional Rehabilitation Hospital, Greenwood, SC, p. A554
WATKINS, Pamela, Chief Financial Officer, Atlanta Veterans Affairs Medical Center, Decatur, GA, p. A151
WATKINS, Paul, President, Northridge Hospital Medical Center, Los Angeles, CA, p. A68
WATKINS, Rolanda, Chief Human Resources Management Service, Dayton Veterans Affairs Medical Center, Dayton, OH, p. A481
WATKINS, Steve, Chief Executive Officer, Lifescape, Sioux Falls, SD, p. A563
WATRIDGE, Donna, R.N.
  Chief Nursing Officer, Hackettstown Medical Center, Hackettstown, NJ, p. A406
  Director of Operations, Hackettstown Medical Center, Hackettstown, NJ, p. A406
WATRY, Margaret, Director of Patient Care Services and Nurse Executive, Phillips Eye Institute, Minneapolis, MN, p. A336
WATSON, B Keith, M.D., Chief Medical Staff, North Mississippi Medical Center–West Point, West Point, MS, p. A355
WATSON, Barbara K, Chief Nursing Officer, Osceola Regional Medical Center, Kissimmee, FL, p. A126
WATSON, Betty A, Chief Financial Officer, Syringa Hospital And Clinics, Grangeville, ID, p. A169
WATSON, Cheryl, Chief Information Officer, Howard County Medical Center, Saint Paul, NE, p. A391
WATSON, Dalph, Director of Human Resources, Beaumont Hospital – Farmington Hills, Farmington Hills, MI, p. A311
WATSON, Deagan, Chief Executive Officer, River Oaks Hospital, New Orleans, LA, p. A275
WATSON, Dean, M.D., Chief Medical Officer, Tallahassee Memorial Healthcare, Tallahassee, FL, p. A141
WATSON, Deborah, Senior Vice President and Chief Operating Officer, Bayhealth Medical Center, Dover, DE, p. A113
WATSON, Deborah, R.N.
  Chief Nursing Officer, Providence Mount Carmel Hospital, Colville, WA, p. A672
  Chief Nursing Officer, Providence St. Joseph'S Hospital, Chewelah, WA, p. A671
WATSON, Deidre L, Director Human Resources, Belmont Pines Hospital, Youngstown, OH, p. A495
WATSON, Dolores, Director Health Information Management, Arms Acres, Carmel, NY, p. A425
WATSON, H Alan., Chief Executive Officer, Maury Regional Hospital, Columbia, TN, p. A568
WATSON, Heath
  Controller, Encompass Health Rehabilitation Hospital Of Dothan, Dothan, AL, p. A17
  Controller, Encompass Health Rehabilitation Hospital Of Montgomery, Montgomery, AL, p. A21
WATSON, James B., President, Schuyler Hospital, Montour Falls, NY, p. A431
WATSON, Kathy, Administrator and Chief Nursing Officer, Saint Thomas Hospital For Spinal Surgery, Nashville, TN, p. A576
WATSON, Lisa, Chief Executive Officer, Chi St. Vincent Sherwood Rehabilitation Hospital, Sherwood, AR, p. A48
WATSON, Luke, M.D., Chief of Staff, College Medical Center, Long Beach, CA, p. A65
WATSON, Lynn, Interim Chief Nursing Officer, Amita Health Saint Joseph Medical Center, Joliet, IL, p. A187
WATSON, Margie, Chief Nursing Officer, Sabine County Hospital, Hemphill, TX, p. A609
WATSON, Michael, M.D., Chief of Staff, Memorial Hospital, Seminole, TX, p. A636
WATSON, Nancy, Director Human Resources, Mercy Hospital, Coon Rapids, MN, p. A330
WATSON, Nathan, M.D., Chief of Staff, Carrus Specialty Hospital, Sherman, TX, p. A637
WATSON, Rob, M.D., Chief Medical Officer, Baylor Scott & White Medical Center – Round Rock, Round Rock, TX, p. A632
WATSON, Scott, Administrator, Mercy Hospital Carthage, Carthage, MO, p. A358
WATSON, Shane, Chief Executive Officer, Red Bud Regional Hospital, Red Bud, IL, p. A194
WATSON, Susan, MSN, R.N., Vice President, Bronson Battle Creek Hospital, Battle Creek, MI, p. A307
WATSON, Teresa C, Vice President Administration, Atrium Health Lincoln, Lincolnton, NC, p. A458
WATSON, Thelma Ruth, M.D., Medical Director, Schneider Regional Medical Center, Saint Thomas, VI, p. A720
WATSON, Thomas, M.D., Chief of Staff, Mayers Memorial Hospital District, Fall River Mills, CA, p. A58
WATSON, Trey, Network Administrator, Sumner County Hospital District 1, Caldwell, KS, p. A233
WATSON, Vicki, Manager Human Resources, Select Specialty Hospital–Jackson, Jackson, MS, p. A349
WATT, Andrew, M.D., Vice President, Information Technology & Services, Chief Information Officer, Chief Medical Information Officer, Southern New Hampshire Medical Center, Nashua, NH, p. A401
WATT, Ella, Chief Financial Officer, University Of New Mexico Hospitals, Albuquerque, NM, p. A417
WATTENBARGER, J. Michael, M.D., Chief of Staff, Shriners Hospitals For Children–Greenville, Greenville, SC, p. A554
WATTENBARGER, Mike
  Chief Information Officer, Lifecare Hospitals Of Pittsburgh, Pittsburgh, PA, p. A537
  Chief Information Officer, Lifecare Hospitals Of San Antonio, San Antonio, TX, p. A634
WATTOO, Dost, M.D., Chief of Staff, Valley Hospital Medical Center, Las Vegas, NV, p. A396
WATTS, Blake, Chief Operating Officer, Piedmont Rockdale Hospital, Conyers, GA, p. A151
WATTS, Chris
  President, Barnes–Jewish St. Peters Hospital, Saint Peters, MO, p. A371
  President, Progress West Hospital, O'Fallon, MO, p. A366
WATTS, Dawn, Chief Executive Officer, Encompasss Health Rehabilitation Hospital Of Fort Smith, Fort Smith, AR, p. A42
WATTS, Gail, Director, St. Vincent Medical Center, Los Angeles, CA, p. A69
WATTS, Lynda, Vice President, Chief Nursing Officer, Fort Sanders Regional Medical Center, Knoxville, TN, p. A572
WATTS–JOHNSON, Christine M, Assistant Vice President, Madera Community Hospital, Madera, CA, p. A70
WAY, Dee, Director Human Resources, Jerold Phelps Community Hospital, Garberville, CA, p. A60
WAYNE, Denise, Chief Executive Officer, Pioneer Specialty Hospital, Pontiac, MI, p. A320
WAYNE, Jason, Network Administrator, Suburban Community Hospital, Norristown, PA, p. A533
WAYTULA, Elizabeth, Chief Executive Officer, Cornerstone Hospital Of Oklahoma–Muskogee, Muskogee, OK, p. A502
WEATHERFORD, Cynthia, Administrator and Director of Nursing, Mercy St. Francis Hospital, Mountain View, MO, p. A366
WEATHERFORD, Dennis, Chief Executive Officer, Putnam County Hospital, Greencastle, IN, p. A205
WEATHERLY, Daniel R, Chief Operating Officer, Cape Fear Valley Medical Center, Fayetteville, NC, p. A454
WEATHERSBY, Mae C, R.N., Chief Clinical Officer, Vibra Specialty Hospital At Desoto, Desoto, TX, p. A600
WEATHERWAX, Lisa, R.N., Chief Nursing Officer, Iowa Specialty Hospital–Belmond, Belmond, IA, p. A217
WEATHERWAX, Marlene, Vice President and Chief Financial Officer, Columbus Regional Hospital, Columbus, IN, p. A201
WEAVER, Angie L, Director Human Resources, North Mississippi Medical Center Gilmore–Amory, Amory, MS, p. A344
WEAVER, Colin, Chief Executive Officer, Brynn Marr Hospital, Jacksonville, NC, p. A456
WEAVER, Daryl W., Chief Executive Officer, Baptist Medical Center Leake, Carthage, MS, p. A345
WEAVER, Douglas K., Chief Executive Officer, Hillcrest Hospital Pryor, Pryor, OK, p. A506
WEAVER, Greg, Chief Operating Officer, Coteau Des Prairies Hospital, Sisseton, SD, p. A564
WEAVER, Harry, M.D., Chief of Staff, Covenant Hospital–Levelland, Levelland, TX, p. A620
WEAVER, Jason, Director Information Systems, Southern Tennessee Regional Health System–Lawrenceburg, Lawrenceburg, TN, p. A573
WEAVER, Jeff, Chief Financial Officer, Medical Arts Hospital, Lamesa, TX, p. A619
WEAVER, Joe, Chief Executive Officer, Rmc–Stringfellow Memorial Hospital, Anniston, AL, p. A13
WEAVER, Judy K., Chief Executive Officer, Acuity Specialty Hospitals Ohio Valley, Steubenville, OH, p. A491
WEAVER, Kimberli, Chief Nursing Officer, Regional Medical Center Of Central Alabama, Greenville, AL, p. A19

WEAVER, Rudolph D, Vice President Human Resources, Southwestern Vermont Medical Center, Bennington, VT, p. A654
WEAVER, Sabrina, Director of Human Resources, Marshall Medical Center North, Guntersville, AL, p. A19
WEAVER, William, Chief Executive Officer, Brentwood Hospital, Shreveport, LA, p. A278
WEBB, Amy, Chief Operating Officer, Cascade Medical Center, Leavenworth, WA, p. A674
WEBB, Charles L., Jr, Chief Executive Officer, Lincoln Trail Behavioral Health System, Radcliff, KY, p. A260
WEBB, Darrallyn, R.N., Chief Nursing Officer, Conway Regional Rehabilitation Hospital, Conway, AR, p. A40
WEBB, David, Chief Financial Officer, Baptist Memorial Hospital–Golden Triangle, Columbus, MS, p. A346
WEBB, Dee, Vice President Human Resources, St. Bernardine Medical Center, San Bernardino, CA, p. A83
WEBB, Donald, Chief Executive Officer, Williamson Medical Center, Franklin, TN, p. A570
WEBB, Glenn T., M.D., Medical Director, Ten Broeck Tennessee Treatment Facility, Cookeville, TN, p. A568
WEBB, Jeffrey D, CPA, Chief Financial Officer, Franciscan Health Rensselear, Rensselaer, IN, p. A214
WEBB, Joseph, Chief Executive Officer, Nashville General Hospital, Nashville, TN, p. A576
WEBB, Kimberly, Chief Financial Officer, Kootenai Health, Coeur D'Alene, ID, p. A169
WEBB, Linda, R.N., Chief Nursing Executive, Pulaski Memorial Hospital, Winamac, IN, p. A216
WEBB, Lisa
Vice President for Operational Finance, Chi Health Good Samaritan, Kearney, NE, p. A386
Vice President Operational Finance, Chi Health Saint Francis, Grand Island, NE, p. A385
WEBB, Melanie R
Vice President Human Resources, Hca Houston Healthcare Northwest, Houston, TX, p. A611
Vice President Human Resources, Park Plaza Hospital, Houston, TX, p. A613
WEBB, Paula, Chief Financial Officer and Compliance Officer, Lake Butler Hospital Hand Surgery Center, Lake Butler, FL, p. A127
WEBB, Renick, M.D., Chief Medical Director, Central Louisiana Surgical Hospital, Alexandria, LA, p. A262
WEBB, Rhonda, Chief Executive Officer, Pagosa Springs Medical Center, Pagosa Springs, CO, p. A104
WEBB, Steven B., President and Chief Executive Officer, Unity Health White County Medical Center, Searcy, AR, p. A48
WEBB, William, Assistant Superintendent, Eastern Shore Hospital Center, Cambridge, MD, p. A289
WEBB–HAPGOOD, Judy, Chief Executive Officer, Select Specialty Hospital–Oklahoma City, Oklahoma City, OK, p. A505
WEBBER, Cathy, Director of Health Information Management, Franklin County Memorial Hospital, Franklin, NE, p. A384
WEBBER, Denise, President and Chief Executive Officer, Stillwater Medical Center, Stillwater, OK, p. A507
WEBBER, Joyce, Chief Financial Officer, Spalding Rehabilitation Hospital, Aurora, CO, p. A96
WEBER, Andrew, Vice President and Administrator, Charleston Area Medical Center, Charleston, WV, p. A684
WEBER, Ann, M.D., Chief Medical Officer, North Florida Regional Medical Center, Gainesville, FL, p. A123
WEBER, Carmen, Administrator, Eureka Community Health Services Avera, Eureka, SD, p. A560
WEBER, Deborah, Chief Human Resource Officer, Northeast Georgia Medical Center, Gainesville, GA, p. A154
WEBER, Frank, Chief Executive Officer, Select Specialty Hospital–Charleston, Charleston, WV, p. A684
WEBER, Gordon, Chief Operating Officer, Clarks Summit State Hospital, Clarks Summit, PA, p. A522
WEBER, Lauren, Administrator, Oceans Behavioral Hospital Longview, Longview, TX, p. A621
WEBER, Mark, M.D., President Medical Staff, Midmichigan Medical Center – West Branch, West Branch, MI, p. A325
WEBER, Pete M., President and Chief Executive Officer, Adventhealth Gordon, Calhoun, GA, p. A149
WEBER, Rebecca
Senior Vice President and Chief Information Officer, Hackensack Meridian Health Bayshore Community Hospital, Holmdel, NJ, p. A406
Senior Vice President and Chief Information Officer, Hackensack Meridian Health Jersey Shore University Medical Center, Neptune, NJ, p. A408
Senior Vice President and Chief Information Officer, Hackensack Meridian Health Ocean Medical Center, Brick Township, NJ, p. A404
Senior Vice President and Chief Information Officer, Hackensack Meridian Health Southern Ocean Medical Center, Manahawkin, NJ, p. A408
Senior Vice President Information Technology, Hackensack Meridian Health Riverview Medical Center, Red Bank, NJ, p. A412
WEBER, Stephen, M.D., Chief Medical Officer, University Of Chicago Medical Center, Chicago, IL, p. A180
WEBER, Trish, R.N., FACHE, Vice President Operations and Chief Nursing Officer, Franciscan Health Michigan City, Michigan City, IN, p. A211
WEBER, Wilson, Chief Operating Officer, Continuecare Hospital At Baptist Health Corbin, Corbin, KY, p. A250
WEBSTER, Cindy, Vice President Financial Services, Licking Memorial Hospital, Newark, OH, p. A488
WEBSTER, Gwen, M.D., President Medical Staff, Texas Health Presbyterian Hospital Plano, Plano, TX, p. A630
WEBSTER, Janice, Director Human Resources, West Oaks Hospital, Houston, TX, p. A615
WEBSTER, Jeffrey, Administrator, Harris Health System, Houston, TX, p. A611
WEBSTER, Kathleen, R.N., MSN, Vice President Patient Services, New York–Presbyterian/Hudson Valley Hospital, Cortlandt Manor, NY, p. A426
WEBSTER, Mark
President and Chief Executive Officer, Cortland Regional Medical Center, Cortland, NY, p. A426
Vice President Finance, New York–Presbyterian/Hudson Valley Hospital, Cortlandt Manor, NY, p. A426
WEBSTER, Nancy, Administrator and Chief Operating Officer, St. Luke'S Rehabilitation Institute, Spokane, WA, p. A680
WEBSTER, Richard, President, Thomas Jefferson University Hospitals, Philadelphia, PA, p. A536
WECKENBORG, Janet, Vice President Operations, Capital Region Medical Center, Jefferson City, MO, p. A361
WECKESSER, Kim, Director Human Resources, Munson Healthcare Manistee Hospital, Manistee, MI, p. A317
WEDDLE, Chari, Chief Human Resource Management Service, Richard L. Roudebush Veterans Affairs Medical Center, Indianapolis, IN, p. A207
WEDGEWORTH, Joyce, Financial Clerk, Hill Hospital Of Sumter County, York, AL, p. A24
WEDGWORTH, Megan, Chief Executive Officer, Vantage Point Of Northwest Arkansas, Fayetteville, AR, p. A41
WEE, Donald, Chief Executive Officer, Tri–State Memorial Hospital, Clarkston, WA, p. A671
WEED, Warren
Director Associate Relations, Merit Health Woman'S Hospital, Flowood, MS, p. A347
Director Human Resources, Merit Health River Oaks, Flowood, MS, p. A346
WEEDEN, Gerard, Chief Medical Officer, Vibra Hospital Of Richmond, Richmond, VA, p. A666
WEEKS, Doug, FACHE, Executive Vice President and Chief Operations Officer, Baptist Health Medical Center – North Little Rock, North Little Rock, AR, p. A46
WEEKS, Ed, Manager Information Services, Paris Community Hospital, Paris, IL, p. A192
WEELDREYER, Jim, Manager Information Technology, Pershing General Hospital, Lovelock, NV, p. A396
WEEMS, Reva S, Director Human Resources, Gateway Regional Medical Center, Granite City, IL, p. A184
WEEMS, Taylor, Vice President, Chief Information Officer, Midland Memorial Hospital, Midland, TX, p. A624
WEG, Jennifer, Executive Director, Sanford Worthington Medical Center, Worthington, MN, p. A343
WEGHORST, George, M.D., Chief Medical Officer, Providence Newberg Medical Center, Newberg, OR, p. A515
WEGLARZ, Ron, Chief Executive Officer and Managing Director, Streamwood Behavioral Health Center, Streamwood, IL, p. A197
WEGLEITNER, Theodore, Chief Executive Officer and President, Lakeview Hospital, Stillwater, MN, p. A341
WEHBEH, Wehbeh, M.D., Chief Medical Officer, Brookdale Hospital Medical Center, New York, NY, p. A432
WEHE, Brad
Chief Executive Officer, Altru Health System, Grand Forks, ND, p. A467
Chief Operating Officer, Altru Health System, Grand Forks, ND, p. A467
WEHLING, Ed, Chief Medical Staff, Decatur County Hospital, Leon, IA, p. A225
WEHLING, Robert D, Interim Chief Financial Officer, Saint Alphonsus Medical Center – Baker City, Baker City, OR, p. A511
WEHMEYER, Jeffrey, Director Information Technology, Hermann Area District Hospital, Hermann, MO, p. A361
WEHNER, Jill, Vice President Financial Services, Harbor Beach Community Hospital, Harbor Beach, MI, p. A314
WEHRMEISTER, Erica, Chief Operating Officer, St. Vincent Indianapolis Hospital, Indianapolis, IN, p. A208
WEIDEMANN, Donald, Acting Administrator, Regional West Garden County, Oshkosh, NE, p. A390
WEIDER, Will
Chief Information Officer, Ascension Calumet Hospital, Chilton, WI, p. A693
Chief Information Officer, Ascension Northeast Wisconsin Mercy Hospital, Oshkosh, WI, p. A703
Chief Information Officer, Ascension Northeast Wisconsin St. Elizabeth Hospital, Appleton, WI, p. A691
Chief Information Officer, Ascension St. Michael'S Hospital, Stevens Point, WI, p. A706
Chief Information Officer, Marshfield Medical Center, Marshfield, WI, p. A699
WEIDNER, Deborah, Medical Director, Natchaug Hospital, Mansfield Center, CT, p. A108
WEIDNER, Peter, Director Information Technology, St. John'S Riverside Hospital, Yonkers, NY, p. A448
WEIGEL, Cherry, Director Health Information Management, Rc Hospital And Clinics, Olivia, MN, p. A337
WEIL, David S., Senior Vice President and Administrator, Saint Francis Hospital South, Tulsa, OK, p. A509
WEILAND, David, M.D., Chief Medical Officer, Largo Medical Center, Largo, FL, p. A128
WEIMER, Linn, Chief Information Officer, Adena Medical Center, Chillicothe, OH, p. A475
WEINER, Gary
Chief Information Officer, St. Catherine Hospital, East Chicago, IN, p. A202
Vice President Information Technology and Chief Information Officer, St. Mary Medical Center, Hobart, IN, p. A206
Vice President Information Technology, Chief Information Officer, Community Hospital, Munster, IN, p. A212
WEINER, Jerome, M.D., Senior Vice President Medical Affairs, Good Samaritan Hospital Medical Center, West Islip, NY, p. A447
WEINER, Richard I., Chief Executive Officer and Chief Medical Officer, Winchester Hospital, Winchester, MA, p. A305
WEINER, Richard I., M.D., Chief Executive Officer and Chief Medical Officer, Winchester Hospital, Winchester, MA, p. A305
WEINGART, Steve, Chief Financial Officer, Los Alamos Medical Center, Los Alamos, NM, p. A419
WEINGARTNER, Ronald, Vice President Administration, St. Charles Hospital, Port Jefferson, NY, p. A441
WEINKRANTZ, Alan, Chief Financial Officer, Finance, Rutgers University Behavioral Healthcare, Piscataway, NJ, p. A411
WEINMANN, Shannon, Human Resources Manager, Community Medical Center, Inc., Falls City, NE, p. A384
WEINREIS, Brian, Vice President Operations and Finance, Abbott Northwestern Hospital, Minneapolis, MN, p. A335
WEINSTEIN, Barry S, Chief Financial Officer, Four Winds Hospital, Katonah, NY, p. A429
WEINSTEIN, Brian, M.D., Chief of Staff, Westside Regional Medical Center, Plantation, FL, p. A137
WEINSTEIN, Freddie, M.D., Chief Medical Officer, Dominican Hospital, Santa Cruz, CA, p. A90
WEINSTEIN, Gary B., President and Chief Executive Officer, Washington Hospital, Washington, PA, p. A543
WEINSTEIN, Todd S, M.D., Chief of Staff, Logansport Memorial Hospital, Logansport, IN, p. A210
WEIR, Elizabeth, Site Administrator and Vice President of Nursing, Ira Davenport Memorial Hospital, Bath, NY, p. A423
WEIR, Tim W., Chief Executive Officer, Olmsted Medical Center, Rochester, MN, p. A338
WEIS, Brian, M.D., Chief Medical Officer, Northwest Texas Healthcare System, Amarillo, TX, p. A582
WEIS, Charles
Chief Financial Officer, Mount Sinai Hospital, Chicago, IL, p. A178
Chief Financial Officer, Schwab Rehabilitation Hospital, Chicago, IL, p. A179
Executive Vice President and Chief Financial Officer, Holy Cross Hospital, Chicago, IL, p. A177
WEIS, Harry, Chief Executive Officer, Tahoe Forest Hospital District, Truckee, CA, p. A92
WEIS, Maurine, MSN, R.N., Vice President Nursing and Chief Nursing Officer, Promedica Flower Hospital, Sylvania, OH, p. A491
WEIS, Robert
Director Information Systems, Bingham Memorial Hospital, Blackfoot, ID, p. A167
Director Information Technology, Mountain River Birthing And Surgery Center, Blackfoot, ID, p. A167
WEISENFREUND, Jochanan, M.D., Senior Vice President Academic and Medical Affairs, Brookdale Hospital Medical Center, New York, NY, p. A432
WEISER, Marcus, D.O., Chief of Staff, Community Healthcare System, Onaga, KS, p. A242
WEISFIELD, Phyllis, Chief Executive Officer and Managing Director, Horsham Clinic, Ambler, PA, p. A520

WEISHAPL, Natasha, Manager Business Office and Human Resources, Decatur Health Systems, Oberlin, KS, p. A242

WEISKITTEL, Scott, Chief Operating Officer, Trident Medical Center, Charleston, SC, p. A550

WEISNER, Brad, Executive Vice President and Chief Operating Officer, Nash Unc Health Care, Rocky Mount, NC, p. A461

WEISS, Anthony, M.D., Chief Medical Officer, Beth Israel Deaconess Medical Center, Boston, MA, p. A294

WEISS, David, M.D., Vice President, Medical Operations, Peninsula Region, Harrison Medical Center, Bremerton, WA, p. A670

WEISS, Gary, Chief Financial Officer, Northshore University Health System, Evanston, IL, p. A182

WEISS, Patrice M, Executive Vice President, Administration, Carilion Franklin Memorial Hospital, Rocky Mount, VA, p. A667

WEISS, Phyllis, Director Human Resources, Alameda Hospital, Alameda, CA, p. A50

WEISS, Terri, Chief Financial Officer, Encompass Health Rehabilitation Hospital Vision Park, Shenandoah, TX, p. A636

WEISSENBERGER, Ralf, Director Information Systems, Adventist Health White Memorial, Los Angeles, CA, p. A66

WEISSER, Lisa, Supervisor Finance, Wagner Community Memorial Hospital Avera, Wagner, SD, p. A565

WEISSINGER, Drew, Chief Financial Officer, North Sunflower Medical Center, Ruleville, MS, p. A354

WEISSLER, Jonathan, M.D., Chief Medical Officer, Lifecare Hospitals Of Dallas, Dallas, TX, p. A596

WEISTREICH, Tracy, Ph.D., R.N., Associate Director Patient Care Services/Nurse Executive, Veterans Affairs Roseburg Healthcare System, Roseburg, OR, p. A517

WEISUL, Jonathan, M.D., Vice President Medical Affairs and Chief Medical Officer, Christus Coushatta Health Care Center, Coushatta, LA, p. A266

WELANDER, Jennifer, CPA
Senior Vice President Finance and Chief Financial Officer, St. Charles Bend, Bend, OR, p. A511
Senior Vice President Finance and Chief Financial Officer, St. Charles Redmond, Redmond, OR, p. A517

WELCH, Abbey, Director Human Resources, Harmon Memorial Hospital, Hollis, OK, p. A500

WELCH, Andrew
Director, New Mexico Veterans Affairs Health Care System – Raymond G. Murphy Medical Center, Albuquerque, NM, p. A417
Interim Director, Veterans Affairs Loma Linda Healthcare System, Loma Linda, CA, p. A64

WELCH, Bryant, Chief Human Resources, Washington Hospital Healthcare System, Fremont, CA, p. A59

WELCH, David
Chief Executive Officer, Simpson General Hospital, Mendenhall, MS, p. A351
Director Information Technology, Simpson General Hospital, Mendenhall, MS, p. A351

WELCH, David, M.D., Medical Director, Clifton–Fine Hospital, Star Lake, NY, p. A444

WELCH, Denise, Chief Financial Officer, Arbuckle Memorial Hospital, Sulphur, OK, p. A508

WELCH, Donald E, Chief Operating Officer, Adventhealth Zephyrhills, Zephyrhills, FL, p. A144

WELCH, Douglas, Chief Executive Officer, Doctors Hospital, Augusta, GA, p. A147

WELCH, Gary A., Assistant to the Chief Executive Officer and Administrative Director Support Systems, Bon Secours Memorial Regional Medical Center, Mechanicsville, VA, p. A662

WELCH, Nicole, Chief Human Resources Officer, Fairbanks Memorial Hospital, Fairbanks, AK, p. A26

WELCH, Rosemary C, R.N., Vice President and Chief Nursing Officer, Medstar National Rehabilitation Hospital, Washington, DC, p. A115

WELCH, Sherri, R.N., Chief Nursing Officer, College Station Medical Center, College Station, TX, p. A592

WELCH, Thomas, M.D., Chief Medical Officer, Mercy St. Vincent Medical Center, Toledo, OH, p. A492

WELCH, Tony
Senior Vice President and Chief Human Resources Officer, Phoebe Putney Memorial Hospital, Albany, GA, p. A145
Vice President Human Resources, Southeast Alabama Medical Center, Dothan, AL, p. A17

WELDAY, Doug, Senior Vice President Finance, Spectrum Health – Butterworth Hospital, Grand Rapids, MI, p. A313

WELDON, James, Chief Information Officer, North Mississippi Medical Center – Tupelo, Tupelo, MS, p. A354

WELDY, Alan, Vice President Human Resources, Compliance and Legal Services, Goshen Health, Goshen, IN, p. A205

WELKIE, Katy, MBA, Chief Executive Officer, Primary Children'S Hospital, Salt Lake City, UT, p. A652

WELLBROCK, Jenna, Chief Nursing Officer, Gateway Rehabilitation Hospital, Florence, KY, p. A251

WELLING, Lynn, M.D., Chief Medical Officer, Sharp Chula Vista Medical Center, Chula Vista, CA, p. A54

WELLING, Michele, M.D., Chief of Staff, Bluegrass Community Hospital, Versailles, KY, p. A261

WELLMAN, Amanda, MSN, R.N., Chief Nursing Officer, Select Specialty Hospital–Omaha, Omaha, NE, p. A390

WELLMAN, James, Senior Director Information Services, Comanche County Memorial Hospital, Lawton, OK, p. A501

WELLMAN, Sonia I., Chief Executive Officer, Memorial Hospital Of Tampa, Tampa, FL, p. A141

WELLMANN, Jane, Chief Financial Officer, Baylor Scott & White Hospital Medical Center – Brenham, Brenham, TX, p. A589

WELLS, A Shane, Chief Financial Officer, Cornerstone Hospital Of Houston At Clearlake, Webster, TX, p. A644

WELLS, Carol, R.N., MSN, Chief Nursing Officer, Central Louisiana Surgical Hospital, Alexandria, LA, p. A262

WELLS, Craig, Chief Information Officer, George C Grape Community Hospital, Hamburg, IA, p. A223

WELLS, Crystal, Administrator, Grady General Hospital, Cairo, GA, p. A149

WELLS, Dale W., Chief Financial and Operating Officer, Alliance Community Hospital, Alliance, OH, p. A471

WELLS, Daren, Chief Executive Officer, Cache Valley Hospital, North Logan, UT, p. A649

WELLS, James, Chief Nursing Officer, Merit Health Biloxi, Biloxi, MS, p. A344

WELLS, Jason
Chief Human Resources Management Service, Fargo Veterans Affairs Health Care System, Fargo, ND, p. A466
President and Chief Executive Officer, Adventist Health Howard Memorial, Willits, CA, p. A95

WELLS, Jimmy, Chief Nursing and Administrative Officer, Westside Surgical Hospital, Houston, TX, p. A615

WELLS, Jonathan, Supervisor Information Technology, Kansas Surgery And Recovery Center, Wichita, KS, p. A248

WELLS, Mallory Gulley, CPA, Chief Financial Officer, Richardson Medical Center, Rayville, LA, p. A277

WELLS, Mary Ellen
Administrator, Centracare Health–Monticello, Monticello, MN, p. A336
Interim Chief Executive Officer, Swift County – Benson Health Services, Benson, MN, p. A328

WELLS, Pamela, R.N., MSN, Chief Nursing Officer, Sharp Memorial Hospital, San Diego, CA, p. A84

WELLS, Robert, M.D., Chief Medical Officer, Providence Portland Medical Center, Portland, OR, p. A516

WELLS, Roxie Cannon., President, Hoke Hospital, Raeford, NC, p. A460

WELLS, Scott E, MSN, R.N., Vice President Patient Care Services, Caromont Regional Medical Center, Gastonia, NC, p. A454

WELLS, Valerie, Manager Human Resources, Encompass Health Rehabilitation Hospital The Woodlands, Conroe, TX, p. A593

WELSER, Jeremy, Director Information Systems, Bonner General Hospital, Sandpoint, ID, p. A172

WELSH, J. Luckey., Jr, Chief Executive Officer, Cherry Hospital, Goldsboro, NC, p. A455

WELSH, Joyce, R.N., MS, Vice President of Clinical Services and Chief Nursing Officer, Emerson Hospital, Concord, MA, p. A298

WELTON, George, Chief Executive Officer, Encompass Health Rehabilitation Hospital Of Altamonte Springs, Altamonte Springs, FL, p. A117

WELTON, Jill, President and Chief Executive Officer, Glendale Memorial Hospital And Health Center, Glendale, CA, p. A60

WELTON, Mark, M.D.
Chief Medical Officer, Bethesda Hospital, Saint Paul, MN, p. A339
Chief Medical Officer, St. John'S Hospital, Maplewood, MN, p. A335

WEMPE, John M, M.D., Chief of Staff, Sioux Falls Veterans Affairs Health Care System, Sioux Falls, SD, p. A564

WENDELL, David, Manager, Information Systems, St. Mary'S Medical Center, Huntington, WV, p. A686

WENDELL, Sean, Chief Executive Officer, Beacon Behavioral Hospital – New Orleans, New Orleans, LA, p. A275

WENDT, Alvin, Acting Chief Executive Officer, Dignity Health East Valley Rehabilitation Hospital, Chandler, AZ, p. A28

WENGER, Cheryl, Manager Health Information and Quality Assurance, Hiawatha Community Hospital, Hiawatha, KS, p. A236

WENGER, Jill, Chief Human Resources Officer, Atchison Hospital, Atchison, KS, p. A232

WENGER–KELLER, David, M.D., Chief of Staff, Fort Madison Community Hospital, Fort Madison, IA, p. A223

WENTWORTH, Cynthia, Chief Human Resource Officer, East Morgan County Hospital, Brush, CO, p. A97

WENTZ, Amber, Director of Clinical Information Systems & Clinical Informatics, Mercyone Newton Medical Center, Newton, IA, p. A227

WENTZ, Jim, Chief Financial Officer, Chi Flaget Memorial Hospital, Bardstown, KY, p. A249

WENTZ, Robert J., President and Chief Executive Officer, Oroville Hospital, Oroville, CA, p. A76

WENTZEL, Chris, M.D., Interim Medical Director, Guthrie Corning Hospital, Corning, NY, p. A426

WENZEL, Matthew, President and Chief Executive Officer, Great River Health System, West Burlington, IA, p. A231

WERFT, Ronald C.
President and Chief Executive Officer, Goleta Valley Cottage Hospital, Santa Barbara, CA, p. A88
President and Chief Executive Officer, Santa Barbara Cottage Hospital, Santa Barbara, CA, p. A88
President and Chief Executive Officer, Santa Ynez Valley Cottage Hospital, Solvang, CA, p. A90

WERKIN, Dave, Vice President Finance and Chief Financial Officer, Trinity Health System, Steubenville, OH, p. A491

WERNER, John W., Chief Executive Officer, Brown County Hospital, Ainsworth, NE, p. A382

WERNER, Kurt, M.D., Chief of Staff, Veterans Affairs Montana Health Care System, Fort Harrison, MT, p. A376

WERNER, Tiffany
Senior Human Resource Business Partner, Banner Baywood Medical Center, Mesa, AZ, p. A31
Senior Human Resource Business Partner, Banner Heart Hospital, Mesa, AZ, p. A31

WERNKE, Chris, Chief Operating Officer, Dominican Hospital, Santa Cruz, CA, p. A88

WERRBACH, John P., President and Chief Executive Officer, Amita Health Elk Grove Village, Elk Grove Village, IL, p. A182

WERTH–SWEENEY, Stacey, Facility Operating Officer, Lincoln Regional Center, Lincoln, NE, p. A387

WERTHMAN, Ronald J, Senior Vice President Finance, Chief Financial Officer and Treasurer, Johns Hopkins Hospital, Baltimore, MD, p. A286

WERTZ, Jackie, Director Human Resources, George C Grape Community Hospital, Hamburg, IA, p. A223

WESCOATT, Sampson, Manager Information Technology, Molokai General Hospital, Kaunakakai, HI, p. A166

WESCOTT, Lisle
President, Ssm Health St. Joseph – St. Charles, Saint Charles, MO, p. A368
President, Ssm Health St. Joseph Hospital – Lake Saint Louis, Lake Saint Louis, MO, p. A364

WESENER DIECK, Jill, Human Resources Operations Manager, Gundersen Tri–County Hospital And Clinics, Whitehall, WI, p. A708

WESLEY, Deb, MSN, Chief Nursing Officer, Children'S Of Alabama, Birmingham, AL, p. A14

WESLEY, Jim, Senior Vice President and Chief Information Officer, John Muir Behavioral Health Center, Concord, CA, p. A55

WESLEY, Mary Lou, R.N., Senior Vice President and Chief Nursing Officer, Sparrow Hospital, Lansing, MI, p. A316

WESOLOWSKI, Paul J, Chief Operating Officer, Vcu Medical Center, Richmond, VA, p. A666

WESP, Clyde, M.D., Chief Medical Officer, Valley Presbyterian Hospital, Los Angeles, CA, p. A70

WESSELS, Jana, Associate Vice President Human Resources, University Of Iowa Hospitals And Clinics, Iowa City, IA, p. A224

WESSON, Jim D, President and Administrator, Christus Santa Rosa Health System, San Antonio, TX, p. A633

WEST, Andrea, MS, Vice President of Human Resources, Columbus Regional Healthcare System, Whiteville, NC, p. A463

WEST, Brenda, Vice President, Information Services and Interim Chief Information Officer, Einstein Medical Center Philadelphia, Philadelphia, PA, p. A534

WEST, Brenda, R.N., MSN, Chief Nursing Officer, Evergreenhealth Monroe, Monroe, WA, p. A675

WEST, Bridgette, Director Patient Access Services, Cobleskill Regional Hospital, Cobleskill, NY, p. A426

WEST, Charles, M.D., Chief Medical Officer, Randolph Hospital, Asheboro, NC, p. A449

WEST, Christopher, Chief Executive Officer, Seven Hills Hospital, Henderson, NV, p. A394

WEST, Darren, M.D., Interim Chief Medical Officer, Banner Ironwood Medical Center, San Tan Valley, AZ, p. A35

WEST, James R.
President and Chief Executive Officer, Pih Health Hospital – Downey, Downey, CA, p. A56
President and Chief Executive Officer, Pih Health Hospital – Whittier, Whittier, CA, p. A95

WEST, Jennifer, R.N., Chief Nursing Officer, South Texas Spine And Surgical Hospital, San Antonio, TX, p. A635
WEST, Judith M, Senior Vice President Human Resources and Chief Human Resources Officer, Maine Medical Center, Portland, ME, p. A284
WEST, Melissa, Chief Financial Officer, Cedar Crest Hospital And Residential Treatment Center, Belton, TX, p. A588
WEST, Michael, Manager Systems Account, New England Sinai Hospital And Rehabilitation Center, Stoughton, MA, p. A304
WEST, Michael C, M.D., Chief of Staff, Mccurtain Memorial Hospital, Idabel, OK, p. A501
WEST, Steve, M.D., Chief Medical Officer, Capital Regional Medical Center, Tallahassee, FL, p. A140
WEST, Tamara, R.N., MSN, Vice President Patient Care, Nicholas H. Noyes Memorial Hospital, Dansville, NY, p. A426
WESTENFELDER, Grant, M.D., Chief Medical Officer, Midwest Medical Center, Galena, IL, p. A183
WESTER, K Scott., President and Chief Executive Officer, Our Lady Of The Lake Regional Medical Center, Baton Rouge, LA, p. A264
WESTER, Scott, President and Chief Executive Officer, Our Lady Of The Lake Regional Medical Center, Baton Rouge, LA, p. A264
WESTERCHIL, Beth, Chief Nursing Officer, Byrd Regional Hospital, Leesville, LA, p. A272
WESTERFIELD, Jerry D., M.D., Chief of Medical Staff, Russell County Hospital, Russell Springs, KY, p. A260
WESTERHEIDE, Karen, Chief Financial Officer, Veterans Affairs St. Louis Health Care System, Saint Louis, MO, p. A371
WESTERMAN, Mandy, Chief Executive Officer, West Oaks Hospital, Houston, TX, p. A615
WESTFALL, Gay, Senior Vice President Human Resources, Kaiser Permanente Sacramento Medical Center, Sacramento, CA, p. A81
WESTFALL, Roger, Director, Western State Hospital, Hopkinsville, KY, p. A253
WESTIN, Robert, M.D., Chief Medical Officer, Cuyuna Regional Medical Center, Crosby, MN, p. A330
WESTMAN, Ken, Chief Executive Officer, Barrett Hospital & Healthcare, Dillon, MT, p. A376
WESTMORELAND, Penny
Chief Financial Officer, Lakeland Community Hospital, Haleyville, AL, p. A19
Chief Financial Officer, Red Bay Hospital, Red Bay, AL, p. A23
Chief Financial Officer, Russellville Hospital, Russellville, AL, p. A23
WESTON, Betty, Chief Human Resources Officer, U. S. Public Health Service Phoenix Indian Medical Center, Phoenix, AZ, p. A34
WESTON, Dana, Chief Executive Officer, Unc Rockingham Health Care, Eden, NC, p. A453
WESTON, Lori, Administrator, Park City Hospital, Park City, UT, p. A650
WESTON, Susan, CPA, Chief Financial Officer, Mountrail County Medical Center, Stanley, ND, p. A469
WESTON, Terry, M.D., Vice President Physician Services, Ohiohealth Medcentral Mansfield Hospital, Mansfield, OH, p. A486
WESTON–HALL, Patricia, Chief Executive Officer, Glenbeigh Hospital And Outpatient Centers, Rock Creek, OH, p. A490
WESTOVER, Teresa, Director Human Resources, North Texas Medical Center, Gainesville, TX, p. A607
WESTPHAL, Chris, Chief Information Technology Officer, Southeast Colorado Hospital District, Springfield, CO, p. A105
WESTPHAL, James, M.D., AMHD Medical Director, Hawaii State Hospital, Kaneohe, HI, p. A166
WESTPHAL, Laura R., R.N., Vice President Patient Care Services, Adventist Health Castle, Kailua, HI, p. A165
WESTPHAL, Susan, Assistant Administrator, Patient Care Services, Fairchild Medical Center, Yreka, CA, p. A95
WESTRUM, Jennifer, Administrator, Community Behavioral Health Hospital – Alexandria, Alexandria, MN, p. A327
WESTRY, Tanza, Chief Financial Officer, Hunter Holmes Mcguire Veterans Affairs Medical Center–Richmond, Richmond, VA, p. A666
WESTWOOD, Denise P, Chief Nursing Officer, Weirton Medical Center, Weirton, WV, p. A690
WETHAL, Robert, R.N., Vice President and Chief Nursing Officer, Mercy Medical Center–Dubuque, Dubuque, IA, p. A222
WETMORE, Melanie, MSN, R.N., Chief Nursing Officer, Regional Medical Center Bayonet Point, Hudson, FL, p. A125
WETTON, Darlene, Chief Executive Officer, Temecula Valley Hospital, Temecula, CA, p. A91
WETZ, Staci, Chief Financial Officer, Shannon Medical Center, San Angelo, TX, p. A633
WETZEL, James L, M.D., Senior Vice President, Chief Medical Officer, Olathe Medical Center, Olathe, KS, p. A242
WETZEL, Lou, M.D., Chief of Staff, The University Of Kansas Hospital, Kansas City, KS, p. A238
WEYMOUTH, Linda, Chief Financial Officer, Suncoast Behavioral Health Center, Bradenton, FL, p. A119
WHALEN, David, Chief Executive Officer, Twin Cities Hospital, Niceville, FL, p. A133
WHALEN, Eileen, President and Chief Operating Officer, University Of Vermont Medical Center, Burlington, VT, p. A654
WHALEN, Patti, Manager Human Resources, Wichita County Health Center, Leoti, KS, p. A239
WHALEN, Thomas, Vice President Finance, Good Samaritan Medical Center, Brockton, MA, p. A296
WHALEN, Thomas V., M.D., Chief Medical Officer, Lehigh Valley Hospital, Allentown, PA, p. A519
WHALEY, Joseph, Chief, Human Resources Management Service, Fayetteville Veterans Affairs Medical Center, Fayetteville, NC, p. A454
WHALEY, Mary, Director of Acute Care, Johnson County Healthcare Center, Buffalo, WY, p. A710
WHARTON, Joe H, M.D., Chief of Staff, Bradley County Medical Center, Warren, AR, p. A49
WHEAT, Ken, Senior Vice President and Chief Financial Officer, Eisenhower Medical Center, Rancho Mirage, CA, p. A79
WHEAT, Terry, R.N., M.P.H., Director of Patient Care Services, Shriners Hospitals For Children–Chicago, Chicago, IL, p. A179
WHEATLEY, Bernard, Chief Executive Officer, Schneider Regional Medical Center, Saint Thomas, VI, p. A720
WHEATLEY, Jane, Chief Executive Officer, Taylor Regional Hospital, Campbellsville, KY, p. A250
WHEATLEY, Richard, Chief Information Officer, Cape Regional Health System, Cape May Court House, NJ, p. A404
WHEATLEY, Samuel N, Chief Medical Officer, Columbus Regional Healthcare System, Whiteville, NC, p. A463
WHEATLEY, Sonya, Human Resources Manager, Central State Hospital, Louisville, KY, p. A256
WHEATLEY, Stephen J., Director of Operations, Franciscan Health Carmel, Carmel, IN, p. A201
WHEATON, David, Director Human Resources, Northern Light Blue Hill Hospital, Blue Hill, ME, p. A282
WHEATON, Tammy H., Interim Chief Nursing Officer, Union County Hospital, Anna, IL, p. A173
WHEELAN, Kevin, M.D., Medical Director, Baylor Scott & White Heart & Vascular Hospital–Dallas, Dallas, TX, p. A595
WHEELER, Brent, Vice President of Operations, Mclaren Flint, Flint, MI, p. A311
WHEELER, Cambria, Communications and Marketing, Adventist Health Clear Lake, Clearlake, CA, p. A54
WHEELER, Dane, Chief Financial Officer, Adams Memorial Hospital, Decatur, IN, p. A202
WHEELER, Dawne, Chief Executive Officer, Select Specialty Hospital–Akron, Akron, OH, p. A471
WHEELER, Frankie, Director, Human Resources, Saint Elizabeths Hospital, Washington, DC, p. A116
WHEELER, James A, Vice President Human Relations and Community Development, Androscoggin Valley Hospital, Berlin, NH, p. A399
WHEELER, Kim, R.N., Director of Nursing, Kingwood Pines Hospital, Kingwood, TX, p. A618
WHEELER, Lynette, MSN, Chief Operating Officer, Truman Medical Center–Lakewood, Kansas City, MO, p. A363
WHEELER, Newman, Chief Financial Officer and Chief Operating Officer, Covenant Hospital–Levelland, Levelland, TX, p. A620
WHEELER, Pamela R, Director Human Resources, Scott County Hospital, Scott City, KS, p. A245
WHEELER, Penny Ann, M.D., President and Chief Medical Officer, Abbott Northwestern Hospital, Minneapolis, MN, p. A335
WHEELER, Philip, Director Finance, Mercy Health – Clermont Hospital, Batavia, OH, p. A472
WHEELER, Rebecca, Director Finance, Kaiser Permanente Baldwin Park Medical Center, Baldwin Park, CA, p. A51
WHEELER, Robert
Controller, Encompass Health Rehabilitation Hospital Of Florence, Florence, SC, p. A552
Vice President Human Resources, South Shore Hospital, South Weymouth, MA, p. A303
WHEELER, William, M.D., Chief of Staff, Benewah Community Hospital, Saint Maries, ID, p. A171
WHEELER, Zachariah P, Senior Vice President Human Resources, John D. Archbold Memorial Hospital, Thomasville, GA, p. A161
WHEELER–MOORE, Juanita, Director Financial Services, Four Winds Hospital, Saratoga Springs, NY, p. A443
WHEELES, Locke, Information Technology Manager, Field Memorial Community Hospital, Centreville, MS, p. A345
WHEELUS, Matthew
Chief Operating Officer, Spring Valley Hospital Medical Center, Las Vegas, NV, p. A396
Vice President, Chief Operating Officer, Harrison Medical Center, Bremerton, WA, p. A670
WHELAN, Laurie A, Senior Vice President Finance and Chief Financial Officer, Hospital For Special Care, New Britain, CT, p. A109
WHELAN, Thomas, Chief Executive Officer, Cibola General Hospital, Grants, NM, p. A418
WHERRY, Robin, Risk Manager and Director Quality Assurance and Health Information Management, Encompass Health Rehabilitation Hospital Of Morgantown, Morgantown, WV, p. A687
WHICHARD, Forrest, Chief Financial Officer, Ochsner Medical Center – North Shore, Slidell, LA, p. A279
WHICHARD, Nick, Chief Information Officer, St. Luke'S Hospital, Columbus, NC, p. A452
WHIDDON, William, Chief Financial Officer, Woodland Heights Medical Center, Lufkin, TX, p. A622
WHILDEN, Sean
Chief Financial Officer, Houston Medical Center, Warner Robins, GA, p. A163
Chief Financial Officer, Perry Hospital, Perry, GA, p. A158
WHILEY, Karen
Vice President Patient Care Services, Fairview Lakes Health Services, Wyoming, MN, p. A343
Vice President Patient Care Services, Fairview Northland Medical Center, Princeton, MN, p. A338
WHILLOCK, Mary C, R.N., MS, Associate Nursing Officer and Chief Operating Officer, Adventhealth Carrollwood, Tampa, FL, p. A141
WHIPKEY, Jared, Chief Financial Officer, Santa Rosa Medical Center, Milton, FL, p. A132
WHIPPLE, C Cynthia, Director of Nursing, Upmc Susquehanna Muncy, Muncy, PA, p. A532
WHIPPLE, James, Chief Executive Officer, Marshall Medical Center, Placerville, CA, p. A78
WHIPPLE, Jennifer, Director Nursing, Lane County Hospital, Dighton, KS, p. A234
WHIPPLE, Michael, Chief Financial Officer, Mercy St. Anne Hospital, Toledo, OH, p. A492
WHISENHUNT, Mickey, Interim Chief Nursing Officer, Regional Medical Center, Orangeburg, SC, p. A556
WHITACRE, James, Chief Executive Officer, Landmark Hospital Of Southwest Florida, Naples, FL, p. A132
WHITAKER, Catherine, MSN, R.N., Vice President and Chief Nursing Officer, University Of Maryland Baltimore Washington Medical Center, Glen Burnie, MD, p. A291
WHITAKER, Charles, Director Information Technology, Madison Parish Hospital, Tallulah, LA, p. A279
WHITAKER, Chasity, Administrative Assistant, Madison Parish Hospital, Tallulah, LA, p. A279
WHITAKER, Cynthia, Chief Nursing Officer, Henry County Medical Center, Paris, TN, p. A578
WHITAKER, Doris, Vice President and Manager, Mercy Hospital Booneville, Booneville, AR, p. A40
WHITAKER, Jimmy, Director Information Systems, Central Carolina Hospital, Sanford, NC, p. A462
WHITAKER, Neil, M.D., Chief Medical Director, Orem Community Hospital, Orem, UT, p. A650
WHITAKER, Robert, Chief Executive Officer, Kiowa District Healthcare, Kiowa, KS, p. A238
WHITAKER, Stephanie, Chief Nursing Officer, Baptist Health – Fort Smith, Fort Smith, AR, p. A42
WHITE, Alexander, Vice President Medical Affairs, Carney Hospital, Boston, MA, p. A295
WHITE, Andrea, Chief Executive Officer, Kindred Hospital–Chattanooga, Chattanooga, TN, p. A567
WHITE, Beverly, Facility Director, Mary S Harper Geriatric Psychiatry Center, Tuscaloosa, AL, p. A24
WHITE, Brian
Director Strategic Operations, Vidant Chowan Hospital, Edenton, NC, p. A453
Director Strategic Planning, Vidant Bertie Hospital, Windsor, NC, p. A464
WHITE, Bruce, Administrator, Covenant Hospital–Levelland, Levelland, TX, p. A620
WHITE, Bruce D., Chief Executive Officer, Knox Community Hospital, Mount Vernon, OH, p. A488
WHITE, C K, M.D., Chief Medical Officer, North Mississippi Medical Center – Tupelo, Tupelo, MS, p. A354
WHITE, Catherine, Chief Financial Officer, Harney District Hospital, Burns, OR, p. A511
WHITE, Cindy, CPA, Vice President of Operations, Integris Canadian Valley Hospital, Yukon, OK, p. A510

WHITE, Darrell, Administrator and Chief Nursing Officer, Tristar Ashland City Medical Center, Ashland City, TN, p. A566

WHITE, Darrell, R.N., Administrator and Chief Nursing Officer, Tristar Ashland City Medical Center, Ashland City, TN, p. A566

WHITE, Darryl, M.D., Chief of Staff, Freestone Medical Center, Fairfield, TX, p. A603

WHITE, Deborah, Human Resource Coordinator, Faith Community Hospital, Jacksboro, TX, p. A616

WHITE, Denise, Administrator, Beacon Behavioral Hospital, Lutcher, LA, p. A272

WHITE, Denise, MSN
Chief Nurse Executive, Atrium Health Anson, Wadesboro, NC, p. A463
Chief Nurse Executive, Atrium Health Union, Monroe, NC, p. A458

WHITE, Diane, Chief Clinical Officer and Chief Nursing Officer, Bridgepoint Hospital National Harbor, Washington, DC, p. A115

WHITE, Diane K., MSN, R.N., Chief Clinical Officer, Kindred Hospital South Philadelphia, Philadelphia, PA, p. A535

WHITE, Gary B, M.D., Chief Medical Staff, Uintah Basin Medical Center, Roosevelt, UT, p. A651

WHITE, Grant, Chief Executive Officer, Southeastern Kentucky Medical Center, Pineville, KY, p. A259

WHITE, Harold, Vice Chancellor, Ochsner Lsu Health Shrevport – Academic Medical Center, Shreveport, LA, p. A278

WHITE, J B, Director Information Systems, Merit Health River Region, Vicksburg, MS, p. A355

WHITE, Jason, M.D., Chief Medical Officer, Mclaren Bay Region, Bay City, MI, p. A307

WHITE, Jean, Vice President Finance, Avera Heart Hospital Of South Dakota, Sioux Falls, SD, p. A563

WHITE, Jeffrey G., Interim Chief Executive Officer, Copley Hospital, Morrisville, VT, p. A654

WHITE, Jennifer, Chief of Staff, Mayo Clinic Health System In Springfield, Springfield, MN, p. A341

WHITE, Jim, Chief Information Officer, Lompoc Valley Medical Center, Lompoc, CA, p. A64

WHITE, Joanne, Chief Information Officer, Wood County Hospital, Bowling Green, OH, p. A473

WHITE, Joel, Chief Operating Officer, Select Specialty Hospital–Omaha, Omaha, NE, p. A390

WHITE, John D, Chief Financial Officer, Wythe County Community Hospital, Wytheville, VA, p. A669

WHITE, Joseph, President and Chief Executive Officer, Lowell General Hospital, Lowell, MA, p. A300

WHITE, Josh, Chief Medical Officer, Deckerville Community Hospital, Deckerville, MI, p. A309

WHITE, Karen
Chief Nursing Officer, Central Montana Medical Center, Lewistown, MT, p. A378
Interim Vice President of Human Resources, Navos, Seattle, WA, p. A677

WHITE, Kelli, Director, Human Resources, Centerpointe Hospital, Saint Charles, MO, p. A368

WHITE, Kelly Lynn, Vice President of Patient Care and Chief Nursing Officer, North Memorial Health Hospital, Robbinsdale, MN, p. A338

WHITE, Kendall, Chief Information Officer, Mount Auburn Hospital, Cambridge, MA, p. A297

WHITE, Kevin A., Administrator, Medicine Lodge Memorial Hospital, Medicine Lodge, KS, p. A241

WHITE, Kishah, Director Human Resources, Bon Secours St. Mary'S Hospital, Richmond, VA, p. A665

WHITE, Knicole S, Vice–President, Human Resources, Kendall Regional Medical Center, Miami, FL, p. A130

WHITE, Lindy P., Vice President and Chief Executive Officer, Holston Valley Medical Center, Kingsport, TN, p. A572

WHITE, Mary–Louise, Chief Operating Officer, Dr. Solomon Carter Fuller Mental Health Center, Boston, MA, p. A295

WHITE, Mike, Chief Financial Officer, Hansen Family Hospital, Iowa Falls, IA, p. A225

WHITE, Nate, Executive Vice President, Sanford Medical Center Fargo, Fargo, ND, p. A467

WHITE, Nathan, Chief Information Officer, Charles A. Cannon Memorial Hospital, Newland, NC, p. A459

WHITE, Pam, Chief Nursing Officer, North Mississippi Medical Center–West Point, West Point, MS, p. A355

WHITE, Pamela K., R.N., MSN, Chief Nursing Officer, Mayo Clinic Health System In Eau Claire, Eau Claire, WI, p. A694

WHITE, Patricia, Vice President Human Resources, Seton Medical Center, Daly City, CA, p. A56

WHITE, Patty, President, St. Joseph'S Hospital And Medical Center, Phoenix, AZ, p. A34

WHITE, Patty, R.N., Director Patient Care Services, Lecom Corry Memorial Hospital, Corry, PA, p. A523

WHITE, Randall, President and Chief Executive Officer, Fayette Regional Health System, Connersville, IN, p. A201

WHITE, Randy, Chief Nursing Officer, Baptist Memorial Hospital–Union County, New Albany, MS, p. A352

WHITE, Sabrina, Coordinator Human Resources, Select Specialty Hospital–Charleston, Charleston, WV, p. A684

WHITE, Sam R, Chief Nursing Officer, Gateway Regional Medical Center, Granite City, IL, p. A184

WHITE, Shawna, Chief Information Officer, Magee Rehabilitation Hospital, Philadelphia, PA, p. A535

WHITE, Shelia, Director Human Resources, Bon Secours–Richmond Community Hospital, Richmond, VA, p. A666

WHITE, Shirley, Director Human Resources, Ashley County Medical Center, Crossett, AR, p. A40

WHITE, Tania A, Director Human Resources, Loretto Hospital, Chicago, IL, p. A178

WHITE, Trina, President and Chief Executive Officer, Sutter Maternity And Surgery Center Of Santa Cruz, Santa Cruz, CA, p. A89

WHITE, Vicki, Chief Nursing Officer, Santa Rosa Memorial Hospital, Santa Rosa, CA, p. A89

WHITE, Vicki, R.N., MS, Chief Nurse Executive, Mills–Peninsula Health Services, Burlingame, CA, p. A53

WHITE, Vickie, Director of Nursing, Unitypoint Health–Keokuk, Keokuk, IA, p. A225

WHITE, Wesley D, Chief Financial Officer, Teton Valley Health Care, Driggs, ID, p. A169

WHITE, Woody, Interim Chief Financial Officer, Allegan General Hospital, Allegan, MI, p. A306

WHITE HOUSE, Judy, Vice President Human Resources, St. Mary'S Hospital And Medical Center, Grand Junction, CO, p. A101

WHITE WAGNER, Joanie, Chief Executive Officer, Martin General Hospital, Williamston, NC, p. A463

WHITE–JACOBS, Mary Beth, Chief Executive Officer, Black River Memorial Hospital, Black River Falls, WI, p. A692

WHITE–TREVINO, Karen, Chief Nursing Officer, West Florida Hospital, Pensacola, FL, p. A136

WHITED, Brian
President and Chief Executive Officer, Mayo Clinic Health System In Lake City, Lake City, MN, p. A334
President and Chief Executive Officer, Mayo Clinic Health System In Red Wing, Red Wing, MN, p. A338
Vice Chair Mayo Clinic Health System, Mayo Clinic Health System In Cannon Falls, Cannon Falls, MN, p. A329

WHITED, Steve, Chief Executive Officer, Minnie Hamilton Healthcare Center, Grantsville, WV, p. A685

WHITEHEAD, Alva W, M.D., Vice President Medical Services, Mcleod Regional Medical Center, Florence, SC, p. A552

WHITEHEAD, Noemi, Administrative Director Human Resources, Sutter Delta Medical Center, Antioch, CA, p. A50

WHITEHOUSE, Alan, Chief Information Officer, Wellstar West Georgia Medical Center, Lagrange, GA, p. A155

WHITEHURST, Rob, Chief, Office of Information and Technology, Veterans Affairs Ann Arbor Healthcare System, Ann Arbor, MI, p. A306

WHITELEY, Earl S., Chief Executive Officer, Jenkins County Medical Center, Millen, GA, p. A157

WHITESEL, Carol, MSN, R.N., Vice President Patient Care Services and Chief Nursing Officer, Community Hospital Of Anderson & Madison County, Anderson, IN, p. A199

WHITESIDE, Anne, Vice President Nursing, Winchester Medical Center, Winchester, VA, p. A669

WHITESIDE, John, Chief Executive Officer, Los Alamos Medical Center, Los Alamos, NM, p. A419

WHITESIDE, Patrick, Manager Information Services, Spectrum Health Big Rapids Hospital, Big Rapids, MI, p. A307

WHITFIELD, Bruce, Chief Executive Officer and Chief Financial Officer, Cabinet Peaks Medical Center, Libby, MT, p. A378

WHITFIELD, Bruce, CPA, Chief Executive Officer and Chief Financial Officer, Cabinet Peaks Medical Center, Libby, MT, p. A378

WHITFIELD, Jay, Chief Financial Officer, Baylor University Medical Center, Dallas, TX, p. A596

WHITING, Barbara, Director Health Information Management, Promise Hospital Of Vicksburg, Vicksburg, MS, p. A355

WHITIS, Matt, Chief Medical Officer, Mahaska Health Partnership, Oskaloosa, IA, p. A228

WHITLATCH, Kristie, President, King'S Daughters Medical Center, Ashland, KY, p. A249

WHITLEY, Carolynn, Chief Nursing Officer, Chi St. Vincent Sherwood Rehabilitation Hospital, Sherwood, AR, p. A48

WHITLEY, Darla, Manager Health Information Technology, Syringa Hospital And Clinics, Grangeville, ID, p. A169

WHITLEY, Kay L., President and Chief Executive Officer, Spanish Peaks Regional Health Center, Walsenburg, CO, p. A106

WHITLEY, Myra, Vice President, Human Resources, Columbus Specialty Hospital, Columbus, GA, p. A150

WHITLEY, Pam, R.N.
Chief Nursing Officer and Chief Operating Officer, Medical City Green Oaks Hospital, Dallas, TX, p. A597
Chief Operating Officer and Chief Nursing Officer, Medical City Green Oaks Hospital, Dallas, TX, p. A597

WHITMER, David, Director, Carl Vinson Veterans Affairs Medical Center, Dublin, GA, p. A152

WHITMEYER, Mary, Chief Executive Officer, Sca Houston Hospital For Specialized Surgery, Houston, TX, p. A613

WHITMORE, Ray B, Chief Financial Officer, Mccurtain Memorial Hospital, Idabel, OK, p. A501

WHITMORE, Robin, Chief Nursing Officer, Midmichigan Medical Center–Gratiot, Alma, MI, p. A306

WHITMORE, Stewart, Chief Financial Officer, Putnam Community Medical Center, Palatka, FL, p. A135

WHITNEY, Donald, Director Human Resources, Kindred Hospital–Albuquerque, Albuquerque, NM, p. A416

WHITNUM, Rhonda, Director Health Improvement Management, Prague Community Hospital, Prague, OK, p. A506

WHITSON, Charles P, CPA, Senior Vice President Finance, Lake Charles Memorial Hospital, Lake Charles, LA, p. A272

WHITT, Alicia, R.N., Chief Nursing Officer, Stephens Memorial Hospital, Breckenridge, TX, p. A589

WHITT, Horace, Chief Executive Officer and Chief Operating Officer, Refugio County Memorial Hospital, Refugio, TX, p. A630

WHITT, Stevan, M.D., Chief Medical Officer, University Of Missouri Health Care, Columbia, MO, p. A359

WHITTAKER, Kelly, Vice President Nursing, Mclaren Caro Region, Caro, MI, p. A308

WHITTAKER, Shawn, Chief Nursing Officer, Miller County Hospital, Colquitt, GA, p. A150

WHITTAKER, Sheena, M.D., Chief Medical Officer, Northern Light Maine Coast Hospital, Ellsworth, ME, p. A283

WHITTEMORE, Marjorie, Director Human Resources, Rio Grande Regional Hospital, Mcallen, TX, p. A623

WHITTEMORE, Scott
Chief Financial Officer and Chief of Ancillary Services, Springfield Hospital, Springfield, VT, p. A655
Chief Financial Officer, University Of Mississippi Medical Center Grenada, Grenada, MS, p. A347
Chief Financial Officer, University Of Mississippi Medical Center Holmes County, Lexington, MS, p. A350

WHITTEN, Jacquelyn, MSN, R.N., Chief Nursing Executive, Vice President of Nursing, Advocate Trinity Hospital, Chicago, IL, p. A176

WHITTINGTON, Billie, Interim Chief Executive Officer and Director Risk Management and Quality Assurance, Northlake Behavioral Health System, Mandeville, LA, p. A273

WHITTINGTON, Bruce, Vice President Human Resources, University Of Kansas Health System Pawnee Valley Campus, Larned, KS, p. A239

WHITTINGTON, Dorothy, Chief Financial Officer, Ochsner Lsu Health Shreveport – Monroe Medical Center, Monroe, LA, p. A274

WHITTINGTON, Hilary, Chief Financial Officer, Jefferson Healthcare, Port Townsend, WA, p. A676

WHITTINGTON, Laurie A, Chief Operating Officer, Memorial Health, Marysville, OH, p. A486

WHITTINGTON, Michael, Chief Executive Officer and Administrator, Hood Memorial Hospital, Amite, LA, p. A262

WHITTINGTON, Shane, Chief Financial Officer, Caldwell Medical Center, Princeton, KY, p. A260

WHITTINGTON–GEPPERT, Kelley, Director Human Resources, Munson Healthcare Cadillac Hospital, Cadillac, MI, p. A308

WHITTON, Beth, Director Human Resources, Ocean Beach Hospital, Ilwaco, WA, p. A674

WHOLLEY, Diane, Director Fiscal Services, Bridgewater State Hospital, Bridgewater, MA, p. A296

WHORLEY, Chris, Chief Information Officer, Nashville General Hospital, Nashville, TN, p. A576

WHYBROW, Peter, Chief Executive Officer, Stewart & Lynda Resnick Neuropsychiatric Hospital At Ucla, Los Angeles, CA, p. A69

WHYTE, Brett, M.D., Chief of Medical Staff, Winona Health, Winona, MN, p. A343

WIATREK, Joseph, Director Information Technology, Otto Kaiser Memorial Hospital, Kenedy, TX, p. A617

WIBBENMEYER, Christopher, Director Human Resources, Perry County Memorial Hospital, Perryville, MO, p. A367

WIBBENS, Cheryl, M.D., Vice President Medical Staff Affairs, Memorial Hospital Of South Bend, South Bend, IN, p. A215

WIBBLESMAN, Christopher, M.D., Chief of Staff, Colorado Canyons Hospital And Medical Center, Fruita, CO, p. A101

WIBORG, Shelley, MS, R.N.
Chief Nursing Officer, Osf Saint Luke Medical Center, Kewanee, IL, p. A187
Director of Nursing, Osf Holy Family Medical Center, Monmouth, IL, p. A189

WICKE, Julius, Vice President Finance and Hospital Financial Officer, Baylor Scott & White Heart & Vascular Hospital–Dallas, Dallas, TX, p. A595

WICKE, Regina, Chief Financial Officer, Columbus Community Hospital, Columbus, TX, p. A593

WICKENS, Amy Lynn, Executive Director Human Resources, Decatur County Memorial Hospital, Greensburg, IN, p. A205

WICKER, Kenneth R., Chief Executive Officer, Bayfront Health Brooksville, Brooksville, FL, p. A119

WICKIZER, Boyd, M.D., Chief Medical Officer, Southside Regional Medical Center, Petersburg, VA, p. A665

WICKLANDER, Jeff, President, North Memorial Health Hospital, Robbinsdale, MN, p. A338

WICKLINE, Melissa, Director Marketing, Greenbrier Valley Medical Center, Ronceverte, WV, p. A689

WICKLUND, Grant, President and Chief Executive Officer, Lutheran Medical Center, Wheat Ridge, CO, p. A106

WIDEMAN, Jeff, Director Information Systems, North Mississippi Medical Center Gilmore–Amory, Amory, MS, p. A344

WIDGER, Judy, M.D., Chief of Staff, Healdsburg District Hospital, Healdsburg, CA, p. A61

WIDICK, Brent, Superintendent, Kansas Neurological Institute, Topeka, KS, p. A246

WIDNER, Eric W., Division President, Beaumont Hospital, Wayne, Wayne, MI, p. A324

WIDRA, Linda S, FACHE, Ph.D., R.N., Chief Operating Officer, Lakewood Ranch Medical Center, Bradenton, FL, p. A118

WIECZOREK, Pawel, Director Information Technology, Brylin Hospitals, Buffalo, NY, p. A424

WIEDELL, Tom, Chief Financial Officer, Brown County Hospital, Ainsworth, NE, p. A382

WIEMAN, Jason S., Director, Fort Belvoir Community Hospital, Fort Belvoir, VA, p. A659

WIENS, Ron, Chief Financial Officer, Shodair Children'S Hospital, Helena, MT, p. A377

WIENTJES, Keri, Director Human Resources, Mobridge Regional Hospital, Mobridge, SD, p. A562

WIERZBICKI, Barb, Manager Human Resources, Select Specialty Hospital–Downriver, Wyandotte, MI, p. A325

WIESMAN, David H, Interim Chief Financial Officer, Fayette County Hospital, Vandalia, Il , p. A197

WIESMANN, Marie, Vice President of Nursing and Chief Nursing Officer, Fort Healthcare, Fort Atkinson, WI, p. A695

WIESNER, Jerry, Administrator and Chief Executive Officer, Southwest Healthcare Services, Bowman, ND, p. A465

WIEWORA, Ron, M.D., Chief Medical Officer, Lakeside Medical Center, Belle Glade, FL, p. A117

WIGGINS, Carla, Director Human Resources, Livingston Hospital And Healthcare Services, Salem, KY, p. A260

WIGGINS, John, Chief Financial Officer, Evans Memorial Hospital, Claxton, GA, p. A150

WIGGINS, Marjorie, Senior Vice President, Chief Nursing Officer, Maine Medical Center, Portland, ME, p. A284

WIGGINS, Michael, President, Methodist Healthcare Memphis Hospitals, Memphis, TN, p. A575

WIGHTMAN, Lori, Chief Executive Officer, Bothwell Regional Health Center, Sedalia, MO, p. A371

WIGINGTON, Yvonne, Vice President, Chief Financial Officer, Wyoming Medical Center, Casper, WY, p. A710

WIGMAN, Cathryn, Director Human Resources, Encompass Health Rehabilitation Hospital Of Braintree, Braintree, MA, p. A296

WIIK, Jennifer, Chief Nursing Officer, Ortonville Area Health Services, Ortonville, MN, p. A337

WIJAYA, Joanne, MSN, R.N., Chief Operating Officer and Risk Manager, Hampton Behavioral Health Center, Westampton, NJ, p. A415

WIJEWARDANE, Chamath, Chief Information Technology Officer, Och Regional Medical Center, Starkville, MS, p. A354

WILBANKS, John F, FACHE
Chief Operating Officer, Baptist Medical Center Beaches, Jacksonville Beach, FL, p. A126
Chief Operating Officer, Baptist Medical Center Jacksonville, Jacksonville, FL, p. A125

WILBUR, Bruce, M.D., Chief Medical Officer, Good Samaritan Hospital, San Jose, CA, p. A86

WILBUR, Thomas W., Chief Executive Officer and Superintendent, Newport Hospital And Health Services, Newport, WA, p. A675

WILBURN, Sue, Vice President Human Resources and Organizational Development, East Tennessee Children'S Hospital, Knoxville, TN, p. A572

WILCHER, Greta
Senior Vice President and Chief Financial Officer, Mercy Hospital Fort Smith, Fort Smith, AR, p. A42
Senior Vice President and Chief Financial Officer, Mercy Hospital Waldron, Waldron, AR, p. A49

WILCOX, Bill, Chief Information Technology Officer, Bristol Bay Area Health Corporation, Dillingham, AK, p. A26

WILCOX, Byron, Chief Financial Management Officer, Standing Rock Service Unit, Fort Yates Hospital, Indian Health Service, Dhhs, Fort Yates, ND, p. A467

WILCOX, David, Chief Financial Officer, Regional Medical Center Of Central Alabama, Greenville, AL, p. A19

WILCOX, Jack
Chief Financial Officer, Ennis Regional Medical Center, Ennis, TX, p. A603
Chief Financial Officer, Parkview Regional Hospital, Mexia, TX, p. A624

WILCOX, John, Chief Information Officer, Ozarks Medical Center, West Plains, MO, p. A373

WILCOX, Kyle M, Vice President Finance, Unitypoint Health – Grinnell Regional Medical Center, Grinnell, IA, p. A223

WILCOX, Robert, Chief Financial Officer, Munson Healthcare Charlevoix Hospital, Charlevoix, MI, p. A308

WILCZEK, Joseph, Chief Executive Officer, St. Elizabeth Hospital, Enumclaw, WA, p. A672

WILCZEK, Vincent Scot, Controller, Pratt Regional Medical Center, Pratt, KS, p. A244

WILDA, Joshua, Chief Information Officer, Metro Health – University Of Michigan Health, Wyoming, MI, p. A325

WILDE, Gary, President and Chief Executive Officer, Community Memorial Hospital, Ventura, CA, p. A93

WILDER, Janet, Director Human Resources, Barbourville Arh Hospital, Barbourville, KY, p. A249

WILDER, Susan
Director Financial Services, Roosevelt Warm Springs Rehabilitation And Specialty Hospitals – Ltac, Warm Springs, GA, p. A162
Director Financial Services, Roosevelt Warm Springs Rehabilitation Hospital – Rehab, Warm Springs, GA, p. A162

WILDHAGEN, Quentin, Systems Administrator, Izard County Medical Center, Calico Rock, AR, p. A40

WILEY, Chuck, Manager Information Systems, Harrison County Hospital, Corydon, IN, p. A201

WILEY, Donald J., President and Chief Executive Officer, St. Joseph'S Medical Center, Stockton, CA, p. A91

WILEY, George, Chief Financial Officer, Desert Springs Hospital Medical Center, Las Vegas, NV, p. A395

WILEY, Mark, Manager Information Systems Development, Upmc Bedford Memorial, Everett, PA, p. A526

WILEY, Ronette, R.N., Executive Vice President and Chief Operating Officer, Bassett Medical Center, Cooperstown, NY, p. A420

WILFER, James, Chief Executive Officer, Red River Hospital, Llc, Wichita Falls, TX, p. A646

WILFONG, Mario, Vice President Finance and Administration, Upmc Bedford Memorial, Everett, PA, p. A526

WILHELM, Connie, Chief Financial Officer, Swisher Memorial Healthcare System, Tulia, TX, p. A642

WILHELM, Paul, M.D., Chief of Staff, Kiowa District Healthcare, Kiowa, KS, p. A238

WILHITE, James, Director Systems Information, North Mississippi State Hospital, Tupelo, MS, p. A354

WILHITE, Jerald, Administrator Human Resources, Heartland Behavioral Healthcare, Massillon, OH, p. A487

WILHOITE, David, CPA, Senior Vice President Finance and Chief Financial Officer, Trousdale Medical Center, Hartsville, TN, p. A570

WILK, Leonard, President and Chief Executive Officer, Amita Health Hoffman Estates, Hoffman Estates, IL, p. A186

WILKE, Kris, Manager Health Information, Granite Falls Health, Granite Falls, MN, p. A333

WILKEN, Thomas
Senior Vice President and Chief Human Resources Officer, Christus Mother Frances Hospital – Tyler, Tyler, TX, p. A642
Vice President Human Resources, Ascension Seton Williamson, Round Rock, TX, p. A632

WILKENS, Gregory, M.D., Chief of Staff, Jellico Community Hospital, Jellico, TN, p. A571

WILKENS, Katy, Chief Nursing Officer and Vice President, Northern Arizona Healthcare, Flagstaff Medical Center, Flagstaff, AZ, p. A29

WILKER, Johnathan, Vice President Finance and Chief Financial Officer, Faith Regional Health Services, Norfolk, NE, p. A388

WILKERSON, Jacquelyn, R.N., Chief Nursing Officer, Conway Regional Medical Center, Conway, AR, p. A40

WILKERSON–UDDYBACK, Patricia, M.D.
Chief Medical Officer, Dmc – Detroit Receiving Hospital, Detroit, MI, p. A310
Chief Medical Officer, Dmc Harper University Hospital, Detroit, MI, p. A310

WILKES, Chris, MS, Executive Director, Human Resources, Blount Memorial Hospital, Maryville, TN, p. A574

WILKES, Margaret, Chief Fiscal Officer, Charles George Veterans Affairs Medical Center, Asheville, NC, p. A449

WILKIE, Chance, Information Technology Specialist, Indian Health Service – Quentin N. Burdick Memorial Health Care Facility, Belcourt, ND, p. A465

WILKIE, Paula, Chief Financial Officer, Presentation Medical Center, Rolla, ND, p. A469

WILKINS, Joseph, Chief Executive Officer, Wythe County Community Hospital, Wytheville, VA, p. A669

WILKINS, Michael, President, Mount Carmel, Columbus, OH, p. A479

WILKINSON, Kyle, Chief Financial Officer, Morgan Memorial Hospital, Madison, GA, p. A157

WILKINSON, Mark, M.D., Chief Medical Officer, Indian Path Medical Center, Kingsport, TN, p. A572

WILKS, Angela, Finance Director, Missouri Baptist Sullivan Hospital, Sullivan, MO, p. A372

WILL, DeDe, Director Finance, Douglas County Community Mental Health Center, Omaha, NE, p. A389

WILL, Jeoff
Chief Operating Office, Acute Care Services, Bethesda Hospital, Saint Paul, MN, p. A339
Chief Operating Officer, Acute Care Services, Bethesda Hospital, Saint Paul, MN, p. A339
Chief Operating Officer, Acute Care Services, Fairview Ridges Hospital, Burnsville, MN, p. A329
Chief Operating Officer, Acute Care Services, Fairview Southdale Hospital, Edina, MN, p. A331

WILL, Nicole, Human Resources Officer, Herington Municipal Hospital, Herington, KS, p. A236

WILLAMS, Mike, Chief Information Officer, Fhn Memorial Hospital, Freeport, IL, p. A183

WILLARD, Cheri, Interim Chief Executive Officer, Evanston Regional Hospital, Evanston, WY, p. A711

WILLARD, Cheri, MSN, R.N., Chief Nursing Officer, Evanston Regional Hospital, Evanston, WY, p. A711

WILLARD, Craig, Director Information Technology and Systems, Frankfort Regional Medical Center, Frankfort, KY, p. A252

WILLCOXON, Phil, Chief Executive Officer, Delta Medical Center, Memphis, TN, p. A574

WILLE, Lesley A., Executive Director, Kaiser Permanente South Bay Medical Center, Los Angeles, CA, p. A67

WILLEMSEN, Jane, President and Chief Administrative Officer, John Muir Medical Center, Walnut Creek, Walnut Creek, CA, p. A94

WILLERT, Todd, Chief Executive Officer, Community Healthcare System, Onaga, KS, p. A242

WILLET, Terry, Chief Financial Officer, Allen Parish Community Healthcare, Kinder, LA, p. A270

WILLETT, Richard, Chief Executive Officer, Redington–Fairview General Hospital, Skowhegan, ME, p. A285

WILLETT, Simon, Director Administrative Operations, South Texas Veterans Health Care System, San Antonio, TX, p. A635

WILLETT, Vita M.
Executive Director, Kaiser Permanente Riverside Medical Center, Riverside, CA, p. A81
Senior Vice President, Area Manager, Kaiser Permanente Moreno Valley Medical Center, Moreno Valley, CA, p. A73

WILLEY, Randy, Business Manager, Lincoln Regional Center, Lincoln, NE, p. A387

WILLHITE, Jean, Director Human Resources, Sutter Solano Medical Center, Vallejo, CA, p. A93

WILLIAMS, Adrian, Chief Executive Officer, Serenity Springs Specialty Hospital, Ruston, LA, p. A277

WILLIAMS, Alec, Chief Information Officer, Southwest General Health Center, Middleburg Heights, OH, p. A487

WILLIAMS, Amber, Vice President and Chief Financial Officer, Southwest Medical Center, Liberal, KS, p. A239

WILLIAMS, Antoinette, Chief Nursing Officer, John H. Stroger Jr. Hospital Of Cook County, Chicago, IL, p. A177

WILLIAMS, Arthur, M.D., Medical Director, Encompass Health Rehabilitation Hospital Of Braintree, Braintree, MA, p. A296

WILLIAMS, Avilla, President, Integris Health Edmond, Edmond, OK, p. A499

WILLIAMS, Bernett, Interim Chief Human Resource Officer, Akron Children'S Hospital, Akron, OH, p. A471

WILLIAMS, Beth, R.N., Chief Nursing Officer, Conway Behavioral Health Hospital, Conway, AR, p. A40

WILLIAMS, Beverly, R.N., Chief Nursing Officer, Washington County Memorial Hospital, Potosi, MO, p. A367

WILLIAMS, Bob, President and Chief Executive Officer, Bsa Hospital, Llc, Amarillo, TX, p. A582

WILLIAMS, Brian, Web Services and Information Technology Manager, St. Joseph'S Hospital Of Buckhannon, Buckhannon, WV, p. A684

WILLIAMS, Brian A., Chief Executive Officer, Labette Health, Parsons, KS, p. A243

WILLIAMS, Brit, M.D., President Medical Staff, Warner Hospital And Health Services, Clinton, IL, p. A180

WILLIAMS, Bryan, R.N., Vice President Patient Care Services, Chi St. Vincent Hot Springs, Hot Springs, AR, p. A43

WILLIAMS, CarolAnn, Chief Financial Officer, Massachusetts Eye And Ear, Boston, MA, p. A295

WILLIAMS, Catherine, M.D., Medical Director, Lewis County General Hospital, Lowville, NY, p. A430

WILLIAMS, Cecille, Assistant Administrator, Shamrock General Hospital, Shamrock, TX, p. A636

WILLIAMS, Charles E., President and Chief Executive Officer, Regional Medical Center, Orangeburg, SC, p. A556

WILLIAMS, Chris J., FACHE, Vice President Operations, Perry Memorial Hospital, Princeton, IL, p. A194

WILLIAMS, Christine, Chief Financial Officer, University Medical Center, New Orleans, LA, p. A275

WILLIAMS, Christopher, M.D., Chief of Staff, Pioneers Medical Center, Meeker, CO, p. A104

WILLIAMS, Craig T., President, St. Elizabeth'S Medical Center, Brockton, MA, p. A296

WILLIAMS, Damita, Ed.D., R.N., MSN, Chief Nursing Officer, Medical City Fort Worth, Fort Worth, TX, p. A605

WILLIAMS, Dan, Vice President Finance and Support, Liberty Hospital, Liberty, MO, p. A364

WILLIAMS, Dana, Chief Financial Officer, Baptist Memorial Hospital–North Mississippi, Oxford, MS, p. A352

WILLIAMS, Dana D., Chief Executive Officer, Jennings American Legion Hospital, Jennings, LA, p. A269

WILLIAMS, Danielle, Assistant Administrator, Caldwell Memorial Hospital, Columbia, LA, p. A265

WILLIAMS, Darek, Director Human Resources, Elgin Mental Health Center, Elgin, IL, p. A182

WILLIAMS, Darlene, Administrator, Chi St. Luke'S Health Memorial San Augustine, San Augustine, TX, p. A636

WILLIAMS, David, Director Information Technology, Franklin Hospital District, Benton, IL, p. A174

WILLIAMS, David L, M.D., Chief Medical Officer, St. Vincent Kokomo, Kokomo, IN, p. A209

WILLIAMS, Dionne, Director Human Resources, Vaughan Regional Medical Center, Selma, AL, p. A23

WILLIAMS, Douglas
Senior Vice President, Administrator, Saint Francis Hospital, Tulsa, OK, p. A509
Vice President, Saint Francis Heart Hospital, Saint Francis Hospital, Tulsa, OK, p. A509

WILLIAMS, Erica, Assistant Chief Executive Officer, South Cameron Memorial Hospital, Cameron, LA, p. A265

WILLIAMS, Frank L., Executive Vice President/ Medical Director, Kedren Community Mental Health Center, Los Angeles, CA, p. A67

WILLIAMS, Greg
Chief Financial Officer, Pih Health Hospital – Downey, Downey, CA, p. A56
Chief Financial Officer, Pih Health Hospital – Whittier, Whittier, CA, p. A95

WILLIAMS, Jackie, Director Human Resources, Merit Health Madison, Canton, MS, p. A345

WILLIAMS, James
Chief Executive Officer, Pearl River County Hospital, Poplarville, MS, p. A353
Vice President and Chief Nursing Officer, Mclaren Flint, Flint, MI, p. A311

WILLIAMS, James, M.D., Chief of Staff, Thedacare Medical Center–Waupaca, Waupaca, WI, p. A707

WILLIAMS, James R., Chief Financial Officer, Minden Medical Center, Minden, LA, p. A274

WILLIAMS, Jason, Director Information Systems, Olympia Medical Center, Los Angeles, CA, p. A68

WILLIAMS, Jeanette
Chief Executive Officer, Kindred Hospital–Aurora, Aurora, CO, p. A96
Chief Executive Officer, Pam Rehabilitation Hospital Of Centennial Hills, Las Vegas, NV, p. A395

WILLIAMS, Jeremy, Chief Financial Officer, Banner Boswell Medical Center, Sun City, AZ, p. A36

WILLIAMS, Joan, Administrative Assistant/Human Resources, Lamb Healthcare Center, Littlefield, TX, p. A620

WILLIAMS, John
Administrator and Chief Executive Officer, Nell J. Redfield Memorial Hospital, Malad City, ID, p. A170
Chief Financial Officer, Upson Regional Medical Center, Thomaston, GA, p. A161
Chief Information Officer, Bay Pines Veterans Affairs Healthcare System, Bay Pines, FL, p. A117

WILLIAMS, John D, Chief Financial Officer, Veterans Affairs Gulf Coast Veterans Health Care System, Biloxi, MS, p. A344

WILLIAMS, Joyce, Consultant Human Resources and Organizational Development, Memorial Hermann Rehabilitation Hospital – Katy, Katy, TX, p. A617

WILLIAMS, Julie
Chief Financial Officer, Muenster Memorial Hospital, Muenster, TX, p. A625
Chief Financial Officer, Smith County Memorial Hospital, Smith Center, KS, p. A246

WILLIAMS, Kathy, Chief Nursing Officer, Eastern New Mexico Medical Center, Roswell, NM, p. A420

WILLIAMS, Kenneth, Chief Information Officer, Fayetteville Veterans Affairs Medical Center, Fayetteville, NC, p. A454

WILLIAMS, Kim, Chief Executive Officer, Providence Regional Medical Center Everett, Everett, WA, p. A673

WILLIAMS, Kristy, Manager Finance, John J. Pershing Veterans Affairs Medical Center, Poplar Bluff, MO, p. A367

WILLIAMS, L Dale, M.D., Vice President and Chief Medical Director, High Point Medical Center, High Point, NC, p. A456

WILLIAMS, Laci, Director Human Resources, Kearny County Hospital, Lakin, KS, p. A238

WILLIAMS, Lana R, Chief Nursing Officer, Arkansas Methodist Medical Center, Paragould, AR, p. A47

WILLIAMS, Linda, Director of Nursing, Villa Feliciana Medical Complex, Jackson, LA, p. A269

WILLIAMS, Lorie, R.N., Vice President Nursing, Samaritan Pacific Communities Hospital, Newport, OR, p. A515

WILLIAMS, Lynn
Vice President Human Resources, Commonwealth Regional Specialty Hospital, Bowling Green, KY, p. A249
Vice President Human Resources, Medical Center At Bowling Green, Bowling Green, KY, p. A250
Vice President Human Resources, Medical Center At Scottsville, Scottsville, KY, p. A260
Vice President, Human Resources, The Medical Center Albany, Albany, KY, p. A249
Vice President, Human Resources, The Medical Center At Caverna, Horse Cave, KY, p. A253

WILLIAMS, Margaret, Chief Financial Officer, Baptist Memorial Hospital For Women, Memphis, TN, p. A574

WILLIAMS, Margo L, R.N., Chief Nursing Officer, Anderson County Hospital, Garnett, KS, p. A235

WILLIAMS, Mary, Director Human Resources, Medina Memorial Hospital, Medina, NY, p. A431

WILLIAMS, Matthew, Chief Executive Officer, Olympia Medical Center, Los Angeles, CA, p. A68

WILLIAMS, Matthew, R.N., Chief Financial Officer, Olympia Medical Center, Los Angeles, CA, p. A68

WILLIAMS, Michael, Chief Information Officer, Lmh Health, Lawrence, KS, p. A239

WILLIAMS, Michael D, Vice President and Administrator, Charleston Area Medical Center, Charleston, WV, p. A684

WILLIAMS, Michael F., Chief Financial Officer, Limestone Medical Center, Groesbeck, TX, p. A608

WILLIAMS, Michael L, FACHE, Vice President Human Resources, Community Howard Regional Health, Kokomo, IN, p. A209

WILLIAMS, Michelle, Administrator, Sedan City Hospital, Sedan, KS, p. A245

WILLIAMS, Mickey, Manager Information Technology, Moccasin Bend Mental Health Institute, Chattanooga, TN, p. A567

WILLIAMS, Nancy M., Administrator, Brooks County Hospital, Quitman, GA, p. A158

WILLIAMS, Nichelle, Director, Hiram W. Davis Medical Center, Petersburg, VA, p. A665

WILLIAMS, Nicole
Chief Operating Officer, Columbia Memorial Hospital, Astoria, OR, p. A511
Director of Human Resources Operations, Dmc Huron Valley–Sinai Hospital, Commerce Township, MI, p. A309

WILLIAMS, Pamela, Vice President, Ridgeview Le Sueur Medical Center, Le Sueur, MN, p. A334

WILLIAMS, Pamela G, Director Human Resources, Unity Health White County Medical Center, Searcy, AR, p. A48

WILLIAMS, Perry E., Sr, Administrator and Chief Executive Officer, Alliance Healthcare System, Holly Springs, MS, p. A348

WILLIAMS, Qiana, Director, Human Resource Business Partner, Grant, Ohiohealth Grant Medical Center, Columbus, OH, p. A479

WILLIAMS, R D, Chief Executive Officer, Hendry Regional Medical Center, Clewiston, FL, p. A120

WILLIAMS, Randy, Director Management Information Systems, Maria Parham Medical Center, Henderson, NC, p. A455

WILLIAMS, Reginald, M.D., Medical Staff President, Curry General Hospital, Gold Beach, OR, p. A513

WILLIAMS, Rich, Director Human Resources, Upson Regional Medical Center, Thomaston, GA, p. A161

WILLIAMS, Richard, Chief Operating Officer, Southwest Mississippi Regional Medical Center, Mccomb, MS, p. A350

WILLIAMS, Robert, Chief Executive Officer, Encompass Health Rehabilitation Hospital Of Princeton, Princeton, WV, p. A688

WILLIAMS, Robert J., M.D., Chief Medical Staff, Wills Memorial Hospital, Washington, GA, p. A163

WILLIAMS, Roberta A, Director of Nursing, U. S. Public Health Service Indian Hospital, Cass Lake, MN, p. A330

WILLIAMS, Roby D., Administrator, Hardin County General Hospital, Rosiclare, IL, p. A195

WILLIAMS, Rodney W, M.D., JD, MS, Vice President Medical Affairs, Good Samaritan Regional Medical Center, Suffern, NY, p. A445

WILLIAMS, Sabrina, Interim Vice President Human Resources, Brigham And Women'S Hospital, Boston, MA, p. A295

WILLIAMS, Sandra, Chief Financial Officer, Cape Fear Valley Medical Center, Fayetteville, NC, p. A454

WILLIAMS, Scott
Chief Executive Officer, Centerpointe Hospital, Saint Charles, MO, p. A368
Chief Executive Officer, Rehabilitation Hospital Of Northwest Ohio, Toledo, OH, p. A492
Chief Operating Officer, Cookeville Regional Medical Center, Cookeville, TN, p. A568

WILLIAMS, Sean J., President and Chief Executive Officer, Mercyone Iowa City Medical Center, Iowa City, IA, p. A224

WILLIAMS, Shane, Director Information Systems, Davis Hospital And Medical Center, Layton, UT, p. A648

WILLIAMS, Sharon, Vice President Finance and Information Technology, Avera Marshall Regional Medical Center, Marshall, MN, p. A335

WILLIAMS, Sheila, Vice President and Administrator, Baptist Health Medical Center–Hot Spring County, Malvern, AR, p. A45

WILLIAMS, Sheri, Chief Operating Officer, Guadalupe Regional Medical Center, Seguin, TX, p. A636

WILLIAMS, Stephanie
Coordinator Human Resources, Kindred Rehabilitation Hospital Northeast Houston, Humble, TX, p. A615
Market Director Human Resources, Lake Norman Regional Medical Center, Mooresville, NC, p. A458

WILLIAMS, Stephanie, R.N., Chief Nursing Officer, Washington Hospital Healthcare System, Fremont, CA, p. A59

WILLIAMS, Sue Ann, Chief Executive Officer, Southeast Health Center Of Stoddard County, Dexter, MO, p. A359

WILLIAMS, Susan, M.D.
Chief Medical Officer, Conemaugh Memorial Medical Center, Johnstown, PA, p. A528
Chief Medical Officer, Conemaugh Miners Medical Center, Hastings, PA, p. A527

WILLIAMS, Susan, R.N., Chief Nursing Officer, Baptist Health Medical Center–Stuttgart, Stuttgart, AR, p. A49

WILLIAMS, Teresa
Regional Administrator, Mercy Hospital Booneville, Booneville, AR, p. A40
Regional Administrator, Mercy Hospital Ozark, Ozark, AR, p. A47
Regional Administrator, Mercy Hospital Paris, Paris, AR, p. A47
Regional Administrator, Mercy Hospital Waldron, Waldron, AR, p. A49

WILLIAMS, Thaddeus, Controller, Encompass Health Rehabilitation Hospital Of North Memphis, Memphis, TN, p. A574

WILLIAMS, Todd, Chief Financial Officer, Siloam Springs Regional Hospital, Siloam Springs, AR, p. A48

WILLIAMS, Tom, Vice President Employee and Community Development, Lake Regional Health System, Osage Beach, MO, p. A366

WILLIAMS, Tricia, Chief Executive Officer, Fremont Hospital, Fremont, CA, p. A58

WILLIAMS, Wade, Chief Information Officer, Unc Rockingham Health Care, Eden, NC, p. A453

WILLIAMS, Wendell H, M.D., Medical Director, Specialty Hospital Jacksonville, Jacksonville, FL, p. A126

WILLIAMSON, Alan, M.D., Chief Medical Officer, Eisenhower Medical Center, Rancho Mirage, CA, p. A79

WILLIAMSON, Barry, President Medical Staff, Southeastern Health, Lumberton, NC, p. A458

WILLIAMSON, John, Human Resources Site Manager, Baptist Health South Florida, Mariners Hospital, Tavernier, FL, p. A142

WILLIAMSON, Johnny, M.D., Chief Medical Officer, Hartgrove Hospital, Chicago, IL, p. A177

WILLIAMSON, Judy, Administrator, Layton Hospital, Layton, UT, p. A648

WILLIAMSON, Sharon, Chief Information Technology, Robert J. Dole Veterans Affairs Medical Center, Wichita, KS, p. A248

WILLIE, David, Chief Financial Officer, Yuma Regional Medical Center, Yuma, AZ, p. A38

WILLIFORD, Sandy, Chief Health Information Management and Revenue Administration, Charlie Norwood Veterans Affairs Medical Center, Augusta, GA, p. A147
WILLINGHAM, John, Chief Executive Officer and Managing Director, Carolina Center For Behavioral Health, Greer, SC, p. A554
WILLIS, Bill, Director Information Technology, River Point Behavioral Health, Jacksonville, FL, p. A125
WILLIS, Danielle S., CPA, Interim Chief Financial Officer, Manager Finance, New Orleans East Hospital, New Orleans, LA, p. A275
WILLIS, Darrell, M.D., Chief of Staff, Dr. Dan C. Trigg Memorial Hospital, Tucumcari, NM, p. A421
WILLIS, Debby, Chief Executive Officer, Crestwyn Behavioral Health, Memphis, TN, p. A574
WILLIS, Jayne, Vice President, System Chief Nurse Executive, Orlando Regional Medical Center, Orlando, FL, p. A134
WILLIS, Jonathon, Director Information Services, Tennova Healthcare–Shelbyville, Shelbyville, TN, p. A579
WILLIS, Joshua, Chief Executive Officer, West Florida Community Care Center, Milton, FL, p. A132
WILLIS, Joy, Acting Chief Fiscal Service, G.V. (Sonny) Montgomery Veterans Affairs Medical Center, Jackson, MS, p. A348
WILLIS, Kathy, M.D., Medical Director, Lallie Kemp Medical Center, Independence, LA, p. A269
WILLIS, Raymond, IT Manager, Choctaw Health Center, Philadelphia, MS, p. A352
WILLIS, Robert, Director Human Resources, North Shore Health, Grand Marais, MN, p. A332
WILLIS, Sandra, Director of Human Resources, Citizens Baptist Medical Center, Talladega, AL, p. A23
WILLIS, Toni, M.D., Medical Director, Encompass Health Rehabilitation Hospital Of The Mid–Cities, Bedford, TX, p. A588
WILLIS, Wendy L, Vice President Human Resources, Children'S Hospital, New Orleans, LA, p. A275
WILLMANN, Adam, President and Chief Executive Officer, Goodall–Witcher Hospital Authority, Clifton, TX, p. A592
WILLMON, Brian, M.D., Medical Director, Plains Regional Medical Center, Clovis, NM, p. A417
WILLMORE, Lois, Supervisor Health Information Management, Cedar County Memorial Hospital, El Dorado Springs, MO, p. A359
WILLOUGHBY, Kirsten, Director of Nursing, Big Horn County Memorial Hospital, Hardin, MT, p. A377
WILLS, Andrea, R.N., Chief Nursing Executive, Munising Memorial Hospital, Munising, MI, p. A318
WILLS, Andy, M.D., Medical Director, Colquitt Regional Medical Center, Moultrie, GA, p. A158
WILLS, Kim, Chief Operating Officer, Cook Medical Center–A Campus Of Tift Regional Medical Center, Adel, GA, p. A145
WILLS, Laura S.
Administrator, Noland Hospital Birmingham, Birmingham, AL, p. A15
Administrator, Noland Hospital Shelby, Alabaster, AL, p. A13
WILLS, Michele, Registered Health Information Administrator, Caro Center, Caro, MI, p. A308
WILLS, Robert, M.D., Chief Medical Officer, Arise Austin Medical Center, Austin, TX, p. A584
WILLS, Shannon, Director Human Resources, Delray Medical Center, Delray Beach, FL, p. A121
WILLS, Tom, R.N., Chief Operating Officer, Merit Health Central, Jackson, MS, p. A349
WILLSHER, Jay, Chief Operating Officer, Unitypoint Health – Trinity Bettendorf, Bettendorf, IA, p. A217
WILLSIE, Brett, Vice President Human Resources, Sentara Northern Virginia Medical Center, Woodbridge, VA, p. A669
WILLWERTH, Deborah J., Chief Executive Officer, Upmc Lititz, Lititz, PA, p. A530
WILLYARD, Deborah, R.N., MSN, Chief Nursing Officer, Pella Regional Health Center, Pella, IA, p. A228
WILMOT, Joan, Chief Finance Officer, White River Junction Veterans Affairs Medical Center, White River Junction, VT, p. A655
WILMOTH, Donna, Vice President Patient Care Services and Chief Nursing Officer, Sentara Williamsburg Regional Medical Center, Williamsburg, VA, p. A669
WILMS, Mike, Director Information Systems, Regional Medical Center Bayonet Point, Hudson, FL, p. A125
WILSON, Ada, Chief Executive Officer, Jefferson County Hospital, Fayette, MS, p. A346
WILSON, Alice, FACHE, Vice President Administration, St. Luke'S Hospital – Warren Campus, Phillipsburg, NJ, p. A411
WILSON, Amy, M.D., Medical Director, Baylor Scott & White Institute For Rehabilitation – Dallas, Dallas, TX, p. A595
WILSON, Bill, Chief Financial Officer, North Carolina Specialty Hospital, Durham, NC, p. A453
WILSON, Bobbie, Director Human Resources, Crete Area Medical Center, Crete, NE, p. A384
WILSON, Carolyn, Chief Operating Officer, Beaumont Hospital – Dearborn, Dearborn, MI, p. A309
WILSON, Carolyn, R.N.
Chief Operating Officer, Beaumont Hospital – Farmington Hills, Farmington Hills, MI, p. A311
Chief Operating Officer, Beaumont Hospital – Grosse Pointe, Grosse Pointe, MI, p. A313
Chief Operating Officer, Beaumont Hospital – Royal Oak, Royal Oak, MI, p. A321
Chief Operating Officer, Beaumont Hospital – Taylor, Taylor, MI, p. A323
Chief Operating Officer, Beaumont Hospital – Trenton, Trenton, MI, p. A324
Chief Operating Officer, Beaumont Hospital – Troy, Troy, MI, p. A324
Chief Operating Officer, Beaumont Hospital, Wayne, Wayne, MI, p. A324
WILSON, Charlene J, Vice President Human Resources, St. Francis Hospital, Wilmington, DE, p. A114
WILSON, Chase, Chief Financial Officer, Sycamore Shoals Hospital, Elizabethton, TN, p. A569
WILSON, Christopher, M.D., Inpatient Medical Director, South Texas Rehabilitation Hospital, Brownsville, TX, p. A589
WILSON, Christy, Chief Financial Officer, Merit Health Rankin, Brandon, MS, p. A345
WILSON, Clifford, Chief Operating Officer, Southern Tennessee Regional Health System–Winchester, Winchester, TN, p. A580
WILSON, Colleen, Chief Nursing Officer, Southern Inyo Healthcare District, Lone Pine, CA, p. A65
WILSON, Craig, Chief Medical Officer, St. Vincent Fishers Hospital, Fishers, IN, p. A203
WILSON, Cynthia, Director, NDI Advanced Treatment Center, Nursing and BHRA Unit Services, Neurodiagnostic Institute And Advanced Treatment Center, Indianapolis, IN, p. A207
WILSON, David C., President, North Mississippi Medical Center – Tupelo, Tupelo, MS, p. A354
WILSON, David R, M.D., Chief of Staff, St. Vincent'S Blount, Oneonta, AL, p. A22
WILSON, Deb, Director Human Resources, Kalispell Regional Healthcare, Kalispell, MT, p. A378
WILSON, Debra, Vice President and Chief Nursing Officer, Saint Luke'S Hospital Of Kansas City, Kansas City, MO, p. A363
WILSON, Dottie D, Director Human Resources, Pickens County Medical Center, Carrollton, AL, p. A16
WILSON, Eleanor, R.N., MSN, Vice President and Chief Operating Officer, Doylestown Hospital, Doylestown, PA, p. A524
WILSON, Elizabeth M, Coordinator Human Resources, Select Specialty Hospital – Cincinnati North, Cincinnati, OH, p. A476
WILSON, Erin, Human Resource Director, Bear Valley Community Hospital, Big Bear Lake, CA, p. A53
WILSON, Fiore, Director Information Systems, Castleview Hospital, Price, UT, p. A650
WILSON, Hamlin J
Senior Vice President Human Resources, Bristol Regional Medical Center, Bristol, TN, p. A566
Senior Vice President Human Resources, Holston Valley Medical Center, Kingsport, TN, p. A572
WILSON, Jason, Administrator and Chief Executive Officer, American Fork Hospital, American Fork, UT, p. A647
WILSON, Jeffrey, Chief Executive Officer, Methodist Hospital, San Antonio, TX, p. A634
WILSON, Jodi, President and Chief Operating Officer, Diley Ridge Medical Center, Canal Winchester, OH, p. A474
WILSON, John R
Chief Operating Officer, Murray–Calloway County Hospital, Murray, KY, p. A258
Vice President, Human Resources, Murray–Calloway County Hospital, Murray, KY, p. A258
WILSON, John W., Chief Executive Officer, Friend Community Healthcare System, Friend, NE, p. A385
WILSON, Kari, R.N., Chief Nursing Officer, Ssm Health St. Mary'S Hospital – Audrain, Mexico, MO, p. A365
WILSON, Kathey, Acting Chief Executive Officer, U. S. Public Health Service Indian Hospital, Rosebud, SD, p. A563
WILSON, Kim, Human Resources Coordinator, Cordova Community Medical Center, Cordova, AK, p. A25
WILSON, Kimberly P, Director Human Resources, University Of Kentucky Albert B. Chandler Hospital, Lexington, KY, p. A255
WILSON, Lawrence, M.D., Vice President, Chief Medical Officer, Midland Memorial Hospital, Midland, TX, p. A624
WILSON, Lerae, Vice President Patient Services and Chief Nursing Officer, St. Claire Healthcare, Morehead, KY, p. A258
WILSON, Loretta, Administrator, Hill Hospital Of Sumter County, York, AL, p. A24
WILSON, Mallory, Administrative Assistant and Human Resources Coordinator, Select Specialty Hospital–North Knoxville, Powell, TN, p. A578
WILSON, Margaret G., Acting Director, Lebanon Veterans Affairs Medical Center, Lebanon, PA, p. A529
WILSON, Nadine, Manager, Human Resources, Jerome Golden Center For Behavioral Health, Inc., West Palm Beach, FL, p. A144
WILSON, Nancy, Chief Financial Officer, Parkview Community Hospital Medical Center, Riverside, CA, p. A81
WILSON, Nathan, R.N., Vice President and Chief Nursing Officer, Baptist Health La Grange, La Grange, KY, p. A254
WILSON, Nicole, Manager Human Resources, St. Theresa Specialty Hospital, Kenner, LA, p. A270
WILSON, Patricia, Senior Vice President Human Resources, Englewood Hospital And Medical Center, Englewood, NJ, p. A405
WILSON, Regina, R.N., Director of Nursing, Share Medical Center, Alva, OK, p. A496
WILSON, Robert, D.O., Director Medical Services, Eagleville Hospital, Eagleville, PA, p. A524
WILSON, Robert E
Vice President and Chief Information Officer, Crozer–Chester Medical Center, Upland, PA, p. A543
Vice President and Chief Information Officer, Delaware County Memorial Hospital, Drexel Hill, PA, p. A524
WILSON, Roy, M.D., Medical Director, St. Louis Psychiatric Rehabilitation Center, Saint Louis, MO, p. A370
WILSON, Sara, Director Human Resources, Cheyenne County Hospital, Saint Francis, KS, p. A244
WILSON, Shea, Chief Nursing Officer, T. J. Samson Community Hospital, Glasgow, KY, p. A252
WILSON, Sherry, R.N., Chief Nursing Officer, Mayers Memorial Hospital District, Fall River Mills, CA, p. A58
WILSON, Sondra Dianne., Chief Executive Officer, Tyler County Hospital, Woodville, TX, p. A646
WILSON, Stephan A, Chief Financial Officer, Montrose Memorial Hospital, Montrose, CO, p. A104
WILSON, Stephan A., Chief Financial Officer, Lifescape, Sioux Falls, SD, p. A563
WILSON, Tammie, R.N., MSN, Chief Nursing Officer, Fayette County Memorial Hospital, Washington Court House, OH, p. A493
WILSON, Terrance E., President and Chief Executive Officer, Franciscan Health Lafayette East, Lafayette, IN, p. A209
WILSON, Tracy, Chief Executive Officer, Kindred Rehabilitation Hospital Northeast Houston, Humble, TX, p. A615
WILSON, Vicki, Human Resources Director, Dixie Regional Medical Center, Saint George, UT, p. A651
WILSON, William, M.D., Chief Medical Officer, Uc Irvine Medical Center, Orange, CA, p. A76
WILSON–NEIL, Carla, FACHE, Chief Operating Officer, Spectrum Health Pennock, Hastings, MI, p. A314
WILSON–STUBBS, Yolande, President, Amita Health Holy Family Medical Center, Des Plaines, IL, p. A181
WILTERMOOD, Michael C., President and Chief Executive Officer, Enloe Medical Center, Chico, CA, p. A54
WILTROUT, Kristy, R.N., Chief Operating Officer, Vernon Memorial Healthcare, Elk Mound, WI, p. A694
WILTROUT, Terry, President, Washington Health System Greene, Waynesburg, PA, p. A543
WILVER, Donald
Vice President Human Resources, Upmc Susquehanna Muncy, Muncy, PA, p. A532
Vice President Human Resources, Upmc Susquehanna Williamsport, Williamsport, PA, p. A545
WIMMER, Keri, R.N., Patient Care Director, Centracare Health–Melrose, Melrose, MN, p. A335
WIMSATT, Michael, Director Human Resources, Piedmont Geriatric Hospital, Burkeville, VA, p. A657
WINBERY, Ben, Chief Financial Officer, Vantage Point Of Northwest Arkansas, Fayetteville, AR, p. A41
WINBUSH, Joyce O., Chief Nursing Officer, Star Medical Center, Plano, TX, p. A629
WINCHESTER, Matthew, Chief Executive Officer, Highland Springs Hospital, Highland Hills, OH, p. A484
WINDAS, Allison Leigh, Director of Patient Care Services–Nurse Executive, Shriners Hospitals For Children–Greenville, Greenville, SC, p. A554
WINDHAM, Joel
Vice President Human Resources, Anderson Regional Health System South, Meridian, MS, p. A351
Vice President Human Resources, Anderson Regional Health System, Meridian, MS, p. A351
WINDHAM, Michael D., Chief Executive Officer, Northwest Medical Center, Winfield, AL, p. A24
WINDHAM, William, Chief Executive Officer, Lewisgale Hospital Alleghany, Low Moor, VA, p. A661

WINDLAND, J Michael, M.D., Chief of Staff, Southern Tennessee Regional Health System–Pulaski, Pulaski, TN, p. A578
WINDOLOVICH, Winona, Associate Chief Information Officer, Zuckerberg San Francisco General Hospital And Trauma Center, San Francisco, CA, p. A86
WINDROW, Matthew, M.D., Chief of Staff, Medina Regional Hospital, Hondo, TX, p. A610
WINDSOR, Bonnie, Senior Vice President Human Resources, Johns Hopkins Hospital, Baltimore, MD, p. A286
WINEGARNER, Rodney, Chief Financial Officer, Mercy Hospitals Of Bakersfield, Bakersfield, CA, p. A52
WINEKAUF, Glen, Chief Executive Officer, Horn Memorial Hospital, Ida Grove, IA, p. A224
WINENGER, John, Interim Chief Executive Officer, Unitypoint Health–Keokuk, Keokuk, IA, p. A225
WINFREE, Kersey, M.D., Chief Medical Officer, Ssm Health St. Anthony Hospital – Oklahoma City, Oklahoma City, OK, p. A505
WING, Lilly, Chief Nursing Officer, Three Rivers Behavioral Health, West Columbia, SC, p. A558
WING, Yakesun, Business Strategy and Finance Leader, Kaiser Permanente Walnut Creek Medical Center, Walnut Creek, CA, p. A94
WINGATE, Phyllis A., President, Atrium Health Cabarrus, Concord, NC, p. A452
WINGET, Mary, Director Human Resources, Minden Medical Center, Minden, LA, p. A274
WINGFIELD, Gena, Senior Vice President and Chief Financial Officer, Arkansas Children'S Hospital, Little Rock, AR, p. A44
WINIGER, Cecilia, Community Outreach and Communication Manager, Adventist Health Howard Memorial, Willits, CA, p. A95
WINK, Jeri, Director Human Resources, Grandview Medical Center, Birmingham, AL, p. A14
WINKELMAN, Dan, President and Chief Executive Officer, Yukon–Kuskokwim Delta Regional Hospital, Bethel, AK, p. A25
WINKLER, Gordon W., Administrator and Chief Executive Officer, Ringgold County Hospital, Mount Ayr, IA, p. A226
WINN, Ann M, M.D., R.N., FACHE, Chief Nursing Officer, Methodist Stone Oak Hospital, San Antonio, TX, p. A634
WINN, Cameron, Director Information Services, Ashley Regional Medical Center, Vernal, UT, p. A653
WINN, Eleyce, Chief Executive Officer, Regency Hospital Of Northwest Indiana, East Chicago, IN, p. A202
WINN, Holly, FACHE, Chief Operating Officer, Black River Memorial Hospital, Black River Falls, WI, p. A692
WINNER, Douglas, Chief Financial Officer, Acute Care Operations, Ascension Of Providence Hospital, Southfield Campus, Southfield, MI, p. A322
WINNETT, Steve, Chief Executive Officer, Advanced Diagnostics Hospital, Houston, TX, p. A610
WINNIK, Mitchell, Chief Operating Officer, Corona Regional Medical Center, Corona, CA, p. A55
WINSETT, Gracia, Chief Financial Officer, Wellstone Regional Hospital, Jeffersonville, IN, p. A208
WINSTON, Bob, M.D., Medical Director, Vermilion Behavioral Health Systems – North Campus, Lafayette, LA, p. A271
WINSTON, Patricia A, FACHE, MS, R.N., Vice President, Chief Administrative Officer and Chief Operating Officer, Brookdale Hospital Medical Center, New York, NY, p. A432
WINT, Jesse, Director of Nursing, Hardin Medical Center, Savannah, TN, p. A579
WINTER, Jon R., D.O., Chief of Staff, Camden General Hospital, Camden, TN, p. A566
WINTER, Melissa, R.N., MSN, Chief Operating Officer and Chief Nursing Officer, Baylor Scott & White Medical Center At – Mckinney, Mckinney, TX, p. A624
WINTER CLARK, Jan, Chief Executive Officer, Summit Medical Center, Casper, WY, p. A710
WINTER–CLARK, Jan, Chief Executive Officer, Bristow Medical Center, Bristow, OK, p. A497
WINTERS, Heidi, Business Partner Human Resources, Chi Health Missouri Valley, Missouri Valley, IA, p. A226
WINTERS, Janice, Controller, Pickens County Medical Center, Carrollton, AL, p. A16
WINTERS, Mary, Interim Chief Nursing Officer, St. James Healthcare, Butte, MT, p. A375
WINTERS, Shane, Chief Information Officer, Jersey Community Hospital, Jerseyville, IL, p. A186
WINTHROP, Michael, President, Bellevue Hospital, Bellevue, OH, p. A473
WIRJO, Jonathan, M.D., Medical Director, Seven Hills Hospital, Henderson, NV, p. A394
WIRTHGEN, Doug
Chief Information Officer, Va Palo Alto Health Care System, Palo Alto, CA, p. A77
Facility Chief Information Officer, Veterans Affairs Loma Linda Healthcare System, Loma Linda, CA, p. A64
WIRTZ, David
Senior LAN Administrator, Evansville State Hospital, Evansville, IN, p. A203
Supervisor Information Technology, Evansville Psychiatric Children Center, Evansville, IN, p. A203
WISE, Claude, Chief Executive Officer, Valley Hospital Medical Center, Las Vegas, NV, p. A396
WISE, Dan, Manager Information Technology, Sarah D. Culbertson Memorial Hospital, Rushville, IL, p. A195
WISE, Elizabeth, President and Chief Executive Officer, Lehigh Valley Hospital – Pocono, East Stroudsburg, PA, p. A524
WISE, Elizabeth, R.N., MS, Chief Nursing Officer and Vice President, Patient Care Services, Saint Peter'S University Hospital, New Brunswick, NJ, p. A409
WISE, Josh, Director Information Technology, Lawrence Memorial Hospital, Walnut Ridge, AR, p. A49
WISE, Kim, Director Human Resources, Bronson South Haven Hospital, South Haven, MI, p. A322
WISE, Teresa, R.N., Chief Nursing Officer, Mena Regional Health System, Mena, AR, p. A46
WISE, Toby, Chief Nursing Officer, Winn Parish Medical Center, Winnfield, LA, p. A280
WISEMAN, Josh, Chief Financial Officer, Va Portland Healthcare System, Portland, OR, p. A516
WISEMANN, Jacob, Chief Financial Officer, Parkland Medical Center, Derry, NH, p. A399
WISEMORE, Donna S, R.N., Vice President and Chief Nursing Officer, Dekalb Health, Auburn, IN, p. A199
WISLER, Tam, Director Human Resources, Columbus Dublin Springs, Dublin, OH, p. A482
WISMANN, Andrea, M.D., Chief of Staff, Southeast Colorado Hospital District, Springfield, CO, p. A105
WISMER, Doug, Chief Financial Officer, Thayer County Health Services, Hebron, NE, p. A386
WISNER, Donna, Chief Financial Officer, Warner Hospital And Health Services, Clinton, IL, p. A180
WISNIESKI, Thomas, Director, North Florida/South Georgia Veteran'S Health System, Gainesville, FL, p. A123
WISNIEWSKI, Cass, Interim Chief Financial Officer, Hurley Medical Center, Flint, MI, p. A311
WISNOSKI, Joseph, Chief Financial Officer, John T. Mather Memorial Hospital, Port Jefferson, NY, p. A441
WISSMAN, Sheryl, M.D., Chief Medical Officer, Ascension Crittenton Hospital Medical Center, Rochester, MI, p. A320
WISWELL, Ashleigh, Chief Operations Officer, Moore County Hospital District, Dumas, TX, p. A600
WITCHER–BOATENG, Bernetta, Ph.D., Director Quality Improvement Services and Compliance, Southwest Connecticut Mental Health System, Bridgeport, CT, p. A107
WITENSKE, James, Chief Information Officer, Jefferson Hospital, Jefferson Hills, PA, p. A528
WITHAM, Val
Director Health Information, Avera Flandreau Hospital, Flandreau, SD, p. A561
Director of Health Information, Avera Dells Area Hospital, Dell Rapids, SD, p. A560
WITHERELL, Jodi, Vice President Patient Care and Quality, Brooks Memorial Hospital, Dunkirk, NY, p. A427
WITHERSPOON, Lynn, Vice President and Chief Information Officer, Ochsner Medical Center, New Orleans, LA, p. A275
WITHINGTON, Amber, R.N., Chief Clinical Officer, Rawlins County Health Center, Atwood, KS, p. A232
WITKOP, Kimberly, Interim Chief Executive Officer, Snoqualmie Valley Hospital District, Snoqualmie, WA, p. A679
WITKOP, Kimberly, M.D., Chief Medical Officer, Snoqualmie Valley Hospital District, Snoqualmie, WA, p. A679
WITKOWICZ, Victor J, Senior Vice President and Chief Financial Officer, Madonna Rehabilitation Hospital, Lincoln, NE, p. A387
WITMER, Bruce, M.D., Medical Director, Fresno Surgical Hospital, Fresno, CA, p. A59
WITT, Cheryl M, Human Resources Director, Kaiser Permanente Moreno Valley Medical Center, Moreno Valley, CA, p. A73
WITT, David, Chief Financial Officer, Meadows Psychiatric Center, Centre Hall, PA, p. A522
WITT, David A, Vice President Finances, Houston Methodist Clear Lake Hospital, Nassau Bay, TX, p. A626
WITT, Jana, Chief Executive Officer, Cedar County Memorial Hospital, El Dorado Springs, MO, p. A359
WITT, Laura, Administrator Human Resources, Banner Thunderbird Medical Center, Glendale, AZ, p. A30
WITT, Lori, Site Finance Director, Mercy Health – Marcum And Wallace, Irvine, KY, p. A254
WITT, Sarah, Director Human Resources, Richmond State Hospital, Richmond, IN, p. A214
WITT, Stephen, President and Chief Executive Officer, College Hospital Cerritos, Cerritos, CA, p. A54
WITT, Ty, M.D., Chief Medical Officer, Lake Chelan Community Hospital And Clinics, Chelan, WA, p. A671
WITTE, Kari, Director Patient Care, Windom Area Hospital, Windom, MN, p. A343
WITTE, Russell, Director Information Technology, Citizens Medical Center, Victoria, TX, p. A643
WITTENSTEIN, Robin D., Chief Executive Officer, Denver Health, Denver, CO, p. A98
WITTHAUS, Patricia, Director Information Services, Valley Regional Hospital, Claremont, NH, p. A399
WITTMAN, Thomas, Chief Information Officer, Jewish Hospital, Louisville, KY, p. A256
WITTWER, Julie, Chief Financial Officer, South Texas Surgical Hospital, Corpus Christi, TX, p. A594
WLEKLINSKI, Maria, Chief Nursing Officer, Siloam Springs Regional Hospital, Siloam Springs, AR, p. A48
WODARZ, Christopher A., Chief, Resource Management Division, Tripler Army Medical Center, Honolulu, HI, p. A165
WODICKA, Mary Jo, Vice President Human Resources, Ascension All Saints, Racine, WI, p. A704
WOELKERS, Joe, Executive Vice President and Chief Staff, Ut Health North Campus Tyler, Tyler, TX, p. A642
WOELTJEN, Bill, Chief Financial Officer, Sarasota Memorial Health Care System, Sarasota, FL, p. A139
WOEN, Linda, Director Human Resources, Yuma Rehabilitation Hospital, A Partnership Of Encompass Health And Yrmc, Yuma, AZ, p. A38
WOHLFARDT, Diana, Director Human Resources, Nashville General Hospital, Nashville, TN, p. A576
WOHLFORD, Steve, Chief Operating Officer, Johnson Memorial Hospital, Franklin, IN, p. A204
WOHLMAN, John, Manager Information Systems, Shoshone Medical Center, Kellogg, ID, p. A169
WOISKE, Edward, M.D., Chief Medical Officer, Avera Marshall Regional Medical Center, Marshall, MN, p. A335
WOITALEWICZ, Rebecca, Chief Financial Officer, Children'S Hospitals And Clinics Of Minnesota, Minneapolis, MN, p. A335
WOJNO, Kathy, Administrator, Memorial Hospital Of Gardena, Gardena, CA, p. A60
WOJNO, Kathy, R.N., MSN, Vice President Nursing Services and Chief Nursing Officer, Beverly Hospital, Montebello, CA, p. A72
WOJTALEWICZ, Jeanette, Chief Financial Officer, Chi Health Mercy Council Bluffs, Council Bluffs, IA, p. A220
WOJTOWICZ, Linda, Chief Executive Officer, Benson Hospital, Benson, AZ, p. A28
WOLAK, Robert, Chief Information Resource Management Service, G.V. (Sonny) Montgomery Veterans Affairs Medical Center, Jackson, MS, p. A348
WOLBERS, Chad, President and Chief Executive Officer, Unitypoint Health – Finley Hospital, Dubuque, IA, p. A222
WOLCOTT, Daniel, President and Chief Executive Officer, Adventist Health Lodi Memorial, Lodi, CA, p. A64
WOLD, Lynn, President and Chief Executive Officer, Unitypoint Health – St. Lukes'S Sioux City, Sioux City, IA, p. A230
WOLESKE, Chris, President and Chief Executive Officer, Bellin Hospital, Green Bay, WI, p. A696
WOLF, Brenda J., President and Chief Executive Officer, La Rabida Children'S Hospital, Chicago, IL, p. A178
WOLF, Chris, Director Information Technology, Clay County Medical Center, Clay Center, KS, p. A233
WOLF, Gregory A, Director Information Systems, Shriners Hospitals For Children–Honolulu, Honolulu, HI, p. A165
WOLF, Heather, Human Resources Business Partner, Mercyone Newton Medical Center, Newton, IA, p. A227
WOLF, Jack, Vice President Information Systems, Brookdale Hospital Medical Center, New York, NY, p. A432
WOLF, Manuela, President and Chief Executive Officer, Memorial Community Hospital And Health System, Blair, NE, p. A383
WOLF, Marc, Assistant Vice President Human Resources, Brookdale Hospital Medical Center, New York, NY, p. A432
WOLF, Ned H., Chief Administrative Officer, Marshfield Medical Center, Marshfield, WI, p. A699
WOLF, Randall, Vice President Finance, Perry County Memorial Hospital, Perryville, MO, p. A367
WOLF, Robin, Chief Nursing Officer, Complex Care Hospital At Tenaya, Las Vegas, NV, p. A394
WOLF, Stephanne, Chief Nursing Officer, Morris County Hospital, Council Grove, KS, p. A234
WOLF, Tricia, Director Information Technology, Oss Orthopaedic Hospital, York, PA, p. A546
WOLFE, Anita, Chief Nurse Executive, Multicare Tacoma General Hospital, Tacoma, WA, p. A680
WOLFE, Brian, Chief of Staff, Allen County Regional Hospital, Iola, KS, p. A237
WOLFE, Cathy Allyson, Chief Nursing Officer, Parkview Wabash Hospital, Wabash, IN, p. A216

WOLFE, Darryl, Chief Financial Officer, Olympic Medical Center, Port Angeles, WA, p. A676
WOLFE, John, Chief Financial Officer, Saint Elizabeth'S Medical Center, Wabasha, MN, p. A342
WOLFE, Lisa, President, Chi Health Mercy Corning, Corning, IA, p. A219
WOLFE, Lois, Director Human Resources, Geisinger–Community Medical Center, Scranton, PA, p. A540
WOLFE, Philip R., President and Chief Executive Officer, Gwinnett Hospital System, Lawrenceville, GA, p. A156
WOLFE, Phillip, Vice President of Professional Operations, Good Samaritan Hospital, Los Angeles, CA, p. A66
WOLFE, Phillip R., Chief Executive Officer, Kindred Hospital–Los Angeles, Los Angeles, CA, p. A67
WOLFE, Scott A., Chief Financial Officer, Piedmont Fayette Hospital, Fayetteville, GA, p. A153
WOLFE, Scott R., President, St. Luke'S Hospital – Warren Campus, Phillipsburg, NJ, p. A411
WOLFE, Sean, Vice President Finance and Chief Financial Officer, Community Hospital, Mccook, NE, p. A387
WOLFE, Stephen A., President and Chief Executive Officer, Indiana Regional Medical Center, Indiana, PA, p. A528
WOLFE, Teresa E, Manager Human Resources, Kansas Heart Hospital, Wichita, KS, p. A247
WOLFENBARGER, Carol C., President, Mcdowell Hospital, Marion, NC, p. A458
WOLFF, David, Director Information Technology, Newberry County Memorial Hospital, Newberry, SC, p. A556
WOLFF, Holly, Chief Executive Officer, Ashley Medical Center, Ashley, ND, p. A465
WOLFF, Patrice P
Director Information Services, Westfields Hospital And Clinic, New Richmond, WI, p. A702
Director Management Information Systems, Amery Hospital And Clinic, Amery, WI, p. A691
WOLFGANG, Tony, Chief Financial Officer, Coatesville Veterans Affairs Medical Center, Coatesville, PA, p. A523
WOLKART, Kristin, President and Chief Executive Officer, St. Francis Medical Center, Monroe, LA, p. A274
WOLOSZYN, Daniel B., Chief Executive Officer, Rehabilitation Hospital Of Indiana, Indianapolis, IN, p. A207
WOLOWITZ, Julie, Vice President, Imaging, Lab, Spectrum Health – Butterworth Hospital, Grand Rapids, MI, p. A313
WOLTEMATH, Kelli, D.O., Chief Medical Staff, George C Grape Community Hospital, Hamburg, IA, p. A223
WOLTERMAN, Robert K., Chief Executive Officer, Ochsner Medical Center, New Orleans, LA, p. A275
WOLTHER, Eunice, Public Information Officer, Colorado Mental Health Institute At Pueblo, Pueblo, CO, p. A104
WOLTHOFF, Matt, Chief Executive Officer, Harlingen Medical Center, Harlingen, TX, p. A609
WOLTHUIZEN, Dianne, Director Human Resources, Sanford Sheldon Medical Center, Sheldon, IA, p. A229
WOLZ, John, M.D., Chief Medical Staff, Yuma District Hospital, Yuma, CO, p. A106
WOMACK, James, Administrator, Mitchell County Hospital, Camilla, GA, p. A149
WONG, Anne Marie, M.D., Chief Medical Officer, Grays Harbor Community Hospital, Aberdeen, WA, p. A670
WONG, Art, Chief Financial Officer, Heritage Oaks Hospital, Sacramento, CA, p. A81
WONG, Bryan, M.D., Medical Director, Ventura County Medical Center, Ventura, CA, p. A93
WONG, Davies, M.D., Medical Director, Kindred Hospital–San Diego, San Diego, CA, p. A83
WONG, Dionne, Vice President and Chief Human Resources Officer, Broward Health Medical Center, Fort Lauderdale, FL, p. A122
WONG, Karen, Chief Human Resources Officer, Mee Memorial Hospital, King City, CA, p. A62
WONG, Lily, Director Psychiatry, Jps Health Network, Fort Worth, TX, p. A605
WONG, Philip, Chief Executive Officer, Gateways Hospital And Mental Health Center, Los Angeles, CA, p. A66
WONG, Philip, PsyD, Chief Operating Officer, Gateways Hospital And Mental Health Center, Los Angeles, CA, p. A66
WONG, Wesley, M.D., Acting Vice President Medical and Academic Affairs, Community Hospital North, Indianapolis, IN, p. A206
WONNACOTT, Matthew, M.D., Chief Medical Officer, Barton Memorial Hospital, South Lake Tahoe, CA, p. A90
WONSER, Matt, Director, Information Services, Providence Regional Medical Center Everett, Everett, WA, p. A673
WOOD, Aaron C., Chief Executive Officer and Administrator, Sanpete Valley Hospital, Mount Pleasant, UT, p. A649
WOOD, Brian, Director Human Resources, Southern Hills Hospital And Medical Center, Las Vegas, NV, p. A395
WOOD, Bud, Chief Human Resources Officer, Saint Thomas West Hospital, Nashville, TN, p. A577
WOOD, Cathy, Vice President, Human Resources, Memorial Hospital At Gulfport, Gulfport, MS, p. A347
WOOD, Clyde, Chief Executive Officer, Tennova North Knoxville Medical Center, Powell, TN, p. A578
WOOD, David P., Director, Boise Veterans Affairs Medical Center, Boise, ID, p. A167
WOOD, Drew, Director Information Technology, Eureka Springs Hospital, Eureka Springs, AR, p. A41
WOOD, Gregory C., President and Chief Executive Officer, Scotland Health Care System, Laurinburg, NC, p. A457
WOOD, Jim
Chief Administrative Officer, Confluence Health/Central Washington Hospital, Wenatchee, WA, p. A682
Chief Human Resources Officer, Confluence Health/ Wenatchee Valley Hospital, Wenatchee, WA, p. A682
WOOD, Joann, M.D., Chief Medical Officer, Baptist Memorial Hospital–Desoto, Southaven, MS, p. A354
WOOD, John, Chief Executive Officer, Central Texas Rehabilitation Hospital, Austin, TX, p. A585
WOOD, Joseph, Vice President and Chief Information Officer, Long Island Community Hospital, Patchogue, NY, p. A441
WOOD, Joyce, Vice President Organizational Improvement and Chief Nursing Officer, Riverview Health, Noblesville, IN, p. A213
WOOD, Lawrence, M.D., Chief Medical Officer, Littleton Adventist Hospital, Littleton, CO, p. A103
WOOD, Phillip E., Chief Information Officer, Cape Fear Valley Medical Center, Fayetteville, NC, p. A454
WOOD, Richard, Chief Financial Officer, Seton Medical Center, Daly City, CA, p. A56
WOOD, Sandy, MSN, R.N., Vice President Patient Services and Chief Nursing Officer, O'Bleness Memorial Hospital, Athens, OH, p. A472
WOOD, Thomas, M.D., Chief Medical Officer, Page Hospital, Page, AZ, p. A32
WOOD, Tina
Chief Operating Officer, Dmc Harper University Hospital, Detroit, MI, p. A310
Chief Operations Officer, Dmc – Detroit Receiving Hospital, Detroit, MI, p. A310
WOOD, Troy, Chief Executive Officer, Lakeview Hospital, Bountiful, UT, p. A647
WOOD, William, M.D., Vice President Medical Affairs, St. Joseph Hospital, Bangor, ME, p. A281
WOODALL, Jay, Chief Executive Officer, Corpus Christi Medical Center, Corpus Christi, TX, p. A594
WOODALL, Lois, Director Human Resources, Lighthouse Behavioral Health Hospital, Conway, SC, p. A552
WOODARD, Andy, President and Chief Executive Officer, Forrest General Hospital, Hattiesburg, MS, p. A348
WOODARD, James, Chief Nursing Officer, St. Thomas More Hospital, Canon City, CO, p. A97
WOODARD, Victor, Manager Information Technology, Dodge County Hospital, Eastman, GA, p. A103
WOODDELL, Mike, Director Information Services, Fairmont Regional Medical Center, Fairmont, WV, p. A685
WOODHOUSE, Janice, Director of Nursing, Missouri River Medical Center, Fort Benton, MT, p. A376
WOODRICH, John T., President and Chief Operating Officer, Bryan Medical Center, Lincoln, NE, p. A386
WOODROW, Victoria, Chief Executive Officer, Hamilton Memorial Hospital District, Mcleansboro, IL, p. A189
WOODRUFF, Kathy, R.N., MSN, Chief Nursing Officer, Marshall Medical Center North, Guntersville, AL, p. A19
WOODRUFF, Stephen, M.D., Chief Medical Officer, Nea Baptist Memorial Hospital, Jonesboro, AR, p. A44
WOODS, Bob, Chief Information Officer, Stanford Health Care – Valleycare, Pleasanton, CA, p. A78
WOODS, Brian, Human Resources Director, Andalusia Health, Andalusia, AL, p. A13
WOODS, Cheryl, Chief Nursing Officer, Ochsner Medical Center – North Shore, Slidell, LA, p. A279
WOODS, Dan, Chief Executive Officer, El Camino Hospital, Mountain View, CA, p. A73
WOODS, Duane L, Chief Financial Officer, Fisher–Titus Medical Center, Norwalk, OH, p. A488
WOODS, Fred, Chief Financial Officer, The Bridgeway, North Little Rock, AR, p. A47
WOODS, Jennifer, R.N., MSN, Chief Nursing Officer, Mclaren Northern Michigan, Petoskey, MI, p. A319
WOODS, Josh, Director Information Systems, Camden Clark Medical Center, Parkersburg, WV, p. A688
WOODS, Julia, R.N., MSN, Vice President and Chief Nursing Officer, Saint Luke'S South Hospital, Overland Park, KS, p. A243
WOODS, Marc Anthony, Assistant Chief Nurse Executive, Eastern State Hospital, Lexington, KY, p. A255
WOODS, Matthew, Vice President Finance, Winchester Hospital, Winchester, MA, p. A305
WOODS, Rashawn, Vice President Human Resources, Barlow Respiratory Hospital, Los Angeles, CA, p. A66
WOODS, Rebecca, Chief Information Officer, Porter Medical Center, Middlebury, VT, p. A654
WOODS, Regetta, Chief Nursing Officer and Chief Clinical Officer, Promise Hospital Of Miss Lou, Vidalia, LA, p. A279
WOODS, Suzanne
Chief Executive Officer, Medical Center Enterprise, Enterprise, AL, p. A17
Senior Vice President of Nursing, Memorial Hospital Jacksonville, Jacksonville, FL, p. A125
WOODS, Theresa L, MSN, R.N., FACHE, Chief Nursing Officer, Jennings American Legion Hospital, Jennings, LA, p. A269
WOODS, Trina, Administrator, Noland Hospital Anniston, Anniston, AL, p. A13
WOODS, Willard, M.D., Chief Medical Officer, Platte County Memorial Hospital, Wheatland, WY, p. A713
WOODSON, Joshua, Chief Executive Officer, Cedar Crest Hospital And Residential Treatment Center, Belton, TX, p. A588
WOODSON, Leslie, Chief Nursing Officer, Mesa View Regional Hospital, Mesquite, NV, p. A396
WOODSON, Stephen, D.O., Chief of Staff, Haskell County Community Hospital, Stigler, OK, p. A507
WOODWARD, Ashley, Director Financial Services, Valley County Health System, Ord, NE, p. A390
WOODWARD, Martin D, Director Acute Care Services, Larry B. Zieverink, Sr. Alcoholism Treatment Center, Raleigh, NC, p. A460
WOODWARD, Martin D., Director Acute Care Services, Larry B. Zieverink, Sr. Alcoholism Treatment Center, Raleigh, NC, p. A460
WOODWARD, Russell, M.D., Chief Medical Officer, Methodist Hospital, San Antonio, TX, p. A634
WOODYARD, Nancy, Chief Financial Officer, Neosho Memorial Regional Medical Center, Chanute, KS, p. A233
WOOLDRIDGE, Joseph, Chief Financial Officer, Brownwood Regional Medical Center, Brownwood, TX, p. A590
WOOLLEY, Diane, Vice President Human Resources, Waterbury Hospital, Waterbury, CT, p. A112
WOOLLEY, Jacqueline
Vice President Human Resources, Southern New Hampshire Medical Center, Nashua, NH, p. A401
Vice President Human Resources, St. Joseph Hospital, Nashua, NH, p. A401
WOOLLEY, Russell, Chief Operating Officer, Highline Medical Center, Burien, WA, p. A671
WOOLLEY, Sheila, R.N., M.P.H., Vice President, Patient Care Services, Wentworth–Douglass Hospital, Dover, NH, p. A399
WOOLSTENHULME, Daren, Chief Financial Officer, Salt Lake Behavioral Health, Salt Lake City, UT, p. A652
WOOTEN, Scott
Senior Vice President and Chief Financial Officer, Baptist Medical Center Beaches, Jacksonville Beach, FL, p. A126
Senior Vice President and Chief Financial Officer, Baptist Medical Center Jacksonville, Jacksonville, FL, p. A125
WOOTEN, Terrence, Vice President of Operations, Support Services, Mission Hospital, Mission Viejo, CA, p. A72
WOOTON, Lore, M.D., Chief of Medical Staff, Weiser Memorial Hospital, Weiser, ID, p. A172
WOOTTON, Aaron, Vice President, Health Information Systems and Chief Information Officer, Henry Ford Allegiance Health, Jackson, MI, p. A315
WORATSCHEK, Alan, System Director of Information Services, Desert Springs Hospital Medical Center, Las Vegas, NV, p. A395
WORD, Jenni, R.N., Chief Nursing Officer, Wallowa Memorial Hospital, Enterprise, OR, p. A512
WORDEN, Beth, Director Nursing Services, Mcpherson Hospital, Mcpherson, KS, p. A240
WORDEN, Connie, Chief Human Resources Officer, Fountain Valley Regional Hospital And Medical Center, Fountain Valley, CA, p. A58
WORDEN, Kieth Anne, Director Human Resources, Mildred Mitchell–Bateman Hospital, Huntington, WV, p. A686
WORKMAN, Donovan, Director Human Capital Management, Appalachian Behavioral Healthcare, Athens, OH, p. A472
WORKMAN, Jessika M, Chief Nursing Officer, Wesley Rehabilitation Hospital, Wichita, KS, p. A248
WORKMAN, Madison, Chief Operating Officer, Coral Gables Hospital, Coral Gables, FL, p. A120
WORLEY, Stella
Director of Finance, Keefe Memorial Hospital, Cheyenne Wells, CO, p. A97
Interim Chief Executive Officer, Keefe Memorial Hospital, Cheyenne Wells, CO, p. A97
WORMAN, Scott, Chief of Staff, Tri–City Medical Center, Oceanside, CA, p. A75

WORRELL, James W, Chief Financial Officer, Pioneers Medical Center, Meeker, CO, p. A104

WORSLEY, Thomas, Chief Executive Officer, Spearfish Regional Hospital, Spearfish, SD, p. A564

WORSOWICZ, Gregory, M.D., Medical Director, Rusk Rehabilitation Hospital, Columbia, MO, p. A359

WORTHAM, Christopher, Chief Executive Officer, Encompass Health Rehabilitation Hospital Midland Odessa, Midland, TX, p. A624

WORTHAM, Turner, Chief Financial Officer, Grand Strand Regional Medical Center, Myrtle Beach, SC, p. A556

WORTHY, David, M.D., Vice President and Chief Medical Officer, Baptist Health Corbin, Corbin, KY, p. A250

WOZNIKAITIS, Linda, Chief Financial Officer, Southwest Connecticut Mental Health System, Bridgeport, CT, p. A107

WRAALSTAD, Kimber L., Administrator, North Shore Health, Grand Marais, MN, p. A332

WRAGGE, Jean, Chief Nursing Officer, Limestone Medical Center, Groesbeck, TX, p. A608

WRATCHFORD, R. Austin, Chief Operating Officer, Parkview Regional Hospital, Mexia, TX, p. A624

WRAY, Christine R.
President, Medstar Southern Maryland Hospital Center, Clinton, MD, p. A289
President, Medstar St. Mary'S Hospital, Leonardtown, MD, p. A292

WRAY, Dean, Vice President Finance, Southern Ohio Medical Center, Portsmouth, OH, p. A490

WRAY, Thomas, Director Information, Geisinger–Bloomsburg Hospital, Bloomsburg, PA, p. A521

WREN, Jason
Chief Executive Officer, Wise Health System, Decatur, TX, p. A598
President and Chief Executive Officer, Wise Health System, Decatur, TX, p. A598

WREN, Mark A, M.D., Medical Director, Encompass Health Rehabilitation Hospital Of Texarkana, Texarkana, TX, p. A640

WREN, Timothy, Chief Financial Officer, Abbeville Area Medical Center, Abbeville, SC, p. A549

WRIBORG, Sara, Chief Executive Officer, Ochsner Rehabilitaton Hospital West Campus, Jefferson, LA, p. A269

WRIGHT, Albert L., Jr, President and Chief Executive Officer, West Virginia University Hospitals, Morgantown, WV, p. A687

WRIGHT, Ann L, R.N., MSN, Assistant Central Delivery System CNO, Presbyterian Hospital, Albuquerque, NM, p. A417

WRIGHT, April, Human Resources Officer, Collingsworth General Hospital, Wellington, TX, p. A645

WRIGHT, Brady, Information Technology Network Administrator, Washington County Hospital, Chatom, AL, p. A16

WRIGHT, Calvin, Chief Information Officer, Hutchinson Regional Medical Center, Hutchinson, KS, p. A237

WRIGHT, Carlene, Chief Financial Officer, Vibra Hospital Of Amarillo, Amarillo, TX, p. A582

WRIGHT, Carol, Chief Nursing Officer, Alliancehealth Madill, Madill, OK, p. A501

WRIGHT, Charles, Chief Financial Officer, Ashe Memorial Hospital, Jefferson, NC, p. A457

WRIGHT, Coleby, Chief Executive Officer, Cross Creek Hospital, Austin, TX, p. A585

WRIGHT, Connie, Vice President Human Resources, Texas Scottish Rite Hospital For Children, Dallas, TX, p. A598

WRIGHT, Creighton, M.D., Vice President Medical Administration, Mercy Health – West Hospital, Cincinnati, OH, p. A476

WRIGHT, Dan, Vice President Human Resources, Children'S Mercy Hospital Kansas, Overland Park, KS, p. A243

WRIGHT, Daniel, Director Information Technology, Saint Alphonsus Medical Center – Nampa, Nampa, ID, p. A170

WRIGHT, Debra J., Chief Executive Officer, Howard Memorial Hospital, Nashville, AR, p. A46

WRIGHT, Dustin, Chief Executive Officer, Floyd Valley Healthcare, Le Mars, IA, p. A225

WRIGHT, Fran, Director of Nursing, Broadwater Health Center, Townsend, MT, p. A380

WRIGHT, Jennifer
Vice President Human Resources, Christus St. Michael Rehabilitation Hospital, Texarkana, TX, p. A640
Vice President Regional Human Resources, Christus St. Michael Health System, Texarkana, TX, p. A640

WRIGHT, Joe
Chief Financial Officer, Mitchell County Hospital, Colorado City, TX, p. A593
Interim Chief Executive Officer, Memorial Hospital, Seminole, TX, p. A636

WRIGHT, Jordan, Chief Executive Officer, St. Elizabeth Community Hospital, Red Bluff, CA, p. A79

WRIGHT, Julie M, Director Human Resources, Ridgeview Psychiatric Hospital And Center, Oak Ridge, TN, p. A578

WRIGHT, Krista, Director Human Resources, Indiana University Health Frankfort, Frankfort, IN, p. A204

WRIGHT, Linda
Chief Financial Officer, Encompass Health Rehabilitation Hospital Of Alexandria, Alexandria, LA, p. A262
Director Information, Ottawa County Health Center, Minneapolis, KS, p. A241

WRIGHT, Mark
Chief Financial Officer, Aultman Specialty Hospital, Canton, OH, p. A474
Vice President, Aultman Hospital, Canton, OH, p. A474

WRIGHT, Mark J., Chief Financial Officer, Aurelia Osborn Fox Memorial Hospital, Oneonta, NY, p. A440

WRIGHT, Mary, Vice President Nursing Services and Chief Nursing Officer, Cortland Regional Medical Center, Cortland, NY, p. A426

WRIGHT, Mary Lynne, President, Huntsville Hospital, Huntsville, AL, p. A19

WRIGHT, Maura, Chief Nursing Officer, Southern Hills Hospital And Medical Center, Las Vegas, NV, p. A395

WRIGHT, Nancy, M.D., Chief Medical Staff, Alta Vista Regional Hospital, Las Vegas, NM, p. A419

WRIGHT, Peter J.
President, Bridgton Hospital, Bridgton, ME, p. A282
President, Rumford Hospital, Rumford, ME, p. A285

WRIGHT, Phillip L., Chief Executive Officer, Select Specialty Hospital Hampton Roads, Newport News, VA, p. A663

WRIGHT, Philoron A., FACHE, Chief Operating Officer, Adventhealth Ocala, Ocala, FL, p. A133

WRIGHT, Robert
Senior Human Resource Advisor, East Ohio Regional Hospital, Martins Ferry, OH, p. A486
Senior Human Resource Advisor, Ohio Valley Medical Center, Wheeling, WV, p. A690

WRIGHT, Robert N., Chief Executive Officer, Newman Regional Health, Emporia, KS, p. A234

WRIGHT, Rory, M.D., President Medical Staff, Orthopaedic Hospital Of Wisconsin, Glendale, WI, p. A695

WRIGHT, Sharon, R.N., Vice President and Chief Nursing Officer, Hardin Memorial Health, Elizabethtown, KY, p. A251

WRIGHT, Stephanie, Director Human Resources Management, Va San Diego Healthcare System, San Diego, CA, p. A84

WRIGHT, Stuart M, CPA, Chief Financial Officer, Upstate University Hospital, Syracuse, NY, p. A445

WRIGHT, Terri, Vice President and Chief Nursing Officer, Warren Memorial Hospital, Front Royal, VA, p. A660

WRIGHT, Tom, Director Human Resources, Kindred Hospital Riverside, Perris, CA, p. A78

WRIGHT, Trevor
Chief Operating Officer, Loma Linda University Children'S Hospital, Loma Linda, CA, p. A64
Chief Operating Officer, Loma Linda University Medical Center, Loma Linda, CA, p. A64

WRIGHT–WHITAKER, Ruth, Director Information Services, Chi Memorial Hospital – Georgia, Fort Oglethorpe, GA, p. A153

WRINN, Denise, Vice President Finance and Chief Financial Officer, Cortland Regional Medical Center, Cortland, NY, p. A426

WROBLEWSKI, Edmund, M.D.
Vice President Medical Affairs and Chief Medical Officer, Goleta Valley Cottage Hospital, Santa Barbara, CA, p. A88
Vice President Medical Affairs and Chief Medical Officer, Santa Barbara Cottage Hospital, Santa Barbara, CA, p. A88
Vice President Medical Affairs and Chief Medical Officer, Santa Ynez Valley Cottage Hospital, Solvang, CA, p. A90

WROGG, Frank, Director Information Technology, Mayo Clinic Health System – Red Cedar In Menomonie, Menomonie, WI, p. A700

WU, Kenneth, M.D., Medical Director, Kessler Marlton Rehabilitation, Marlton, NJ, p. A408

WUCHTER, Greg, Chief Executive Officer, Select Specialty Hospital–Savannah, Savannah, GA, p. A160

WUENSCHEL, Diedra, D.O., President Medical Staff, Coryell Health, Gatesville, TX, p. A607

WUNDERWALD, Wendie, R.N., Vice President Patient Care Services, Samaritan Lebanon Community Hospital, Lebanon, OR, p. A514

WURGLER, Brad D, Chief Financial Officer, Perham Health, Perham, MN, p. A337

WURTZEL, Leann, Director Human Resources, Mayo Clinic Health System – Red Cedar In Menomonie, Menomonie, WI, p. A700

WYATT, Christopher B., President, Cox Barton County Memorial Hospital, Lamar, MO, p. A364

WYATT, Christy, R.N., Interim Chief Nursing Officer, Jackson Parish Hospital, Jonesboro, LA, p. A269

WYATT, Jana, Chief Executive Officer, Mizell Memorial Hospital, Opp, AL, p. A22

WYBLE, Karen O., Chief Executive Officer, St. Martin Hospital, Breaux Bridge, LA, p. A265

WYDICK, Sue, Director Human Resources, Ohio County Hospital, Hartford, KY, p. A253

WYDRA, Lana, Vice President Human Resources, Nathan Littauer Hospital And Nursing Home, Gloversville, NY, p. A428

WYER, Jolena, R.N., Chief Nursing Officer, Oklahoma Center For Orthopedic And Multi–Specialty Surgery, Oklahoma City, OK, p. A504

WYERS, Michael, Chief Financial Officer, Medical Center Of Trinity, Trinity, FL, p. A143

WYLER, Allyson, Vice President, Operations, Advocate Lutheran General Hospital, Park Ridge, IL, p. A192

WYLIE, Eugene, Chief Human Resources Officer, Veterans Affairs Loma Linda Healthcare System, Loma Linda, CA, p. A64

WYLIE, Patrick, Director Information Systems, Petaluma Valley Hospital, Petaluma, CA, p. A78

WYMAN, David, President and Chief Executive Officer, Brookdale Hospital Medical Center, New York, NY, p. A432

WYMER, Melanie, Director Human Resources, Highland District Hospital, Hillsboro, OH, p. A484

WYNN, Katherine, Director Human Resource, Oklahoma Heart Hospital, Oklahoma City, OK, p. A505

WYNN, Paige
Administrator, Irwin County Hospital, Ocilla, GA, p. A158
Chief Financial Officer, Dorminy Medical Center, Fitzgerald, GA, p. A153

WYNNE, Scott, Chief Information Officer Director, Bleckley Memorial Hospital, Cochran, GA, p. A150

WYSE, Debbie, Controller, Quillen Rehabilitation Hospital, Johnson City, TN, p. A571

WYSOCKI, Greg, Chief Financial Officer, Austin Lakes Hospital, Austin, TX, p. A585

WYSONG–HARDER, Alyson, Chief Executive Officer, Heartland Behavioral Health Services, Nevada, MO, p. A366

Y

YABUT, Eduardo, M.D., Medical Director, North Dakota State Hospital, Jamestown, ND, p. A468

YAEGER, Eric, M.D.
Chief Medical Officer, Kindred Hospital–Aurora, Aurora, CO, p. A96
Medical Director, Kindred Hospital–Denver, Denver, CO, p. A99

YAHNER, Michael, Chief Financial Officer, Torrance State Hospital, Torrance, PA, p. A542

YAKE, Laurie B., Vice President Finance, Aurora Medical Center Kenosha, Kenosha, WI, p. A697

YAKLIN, Shelleye, President and Chief Executive Officer, North Ottawa Community Hospital, Grand Haven, MI, p. A312

YAKOVENKO, Gene, Director of Finance, Amita Health Holy Family Medical Center, Des Plaines, IL, p. A181

YAKULIS, Paul, MS, R.N., Senior Vice President Human Resources, Lankenau Medical Center, Wynnewood, PA, p. A546

YALLOWITZ, Joseph, M.D., Vice President and Chief Medical Officer, Valley Hospital, Ridgewood, NJ, p. A412

YAMADA, Jeff, Vice President, Virginia Mason Memorial, Yakima, WA, p. A682

YANES, John C., Chief Executive Officer, Andalusia Health, Andalusia, AL, p. A13

YANEZ, Maria J, Chief Financial Officer, Baptist Health South Florida, Doctors Hospital, Coral Gables, FL, p. A120

YANGA, Ismael David, M.D., Chief Medical Officer, Ascension Brighton Center For Recovery, Brighton, MI, p. A307

YANIK, Sahin, M.D.
Vice President Medical Administration, St. John'S Regional Medical Center, Oxnard, CA, p. A76
Vice President Medical Associate, St. John'S Pleasant Valley Hospital, Camarillo, CA, p. A53

YANKTON, Nikki, Director Human Resources, Oakleaf Surgical Hospital, Altoona, WI, p. A691

YANNI, Anthony, M.D., Vice President Medical Affairs, Regional Hospital Of Scranton, Reading, PA, p. A540

YAP, Elvy, Director of Finance, Rush Oak Park Hospital, Oak Park, IL, p. A191

YAP, Eric, Chief Executive Officer, Ohiohealth Rehabilitation Hospital, Columbus, OH, p. A479

YAP, Winston, M.D., Chief Medical Officer, Carroll County Memorial Hospital, Carrollton, KY, p. A250

YARBOROUGH, Dianne, Director of Information Technology, Baylor Scott & White Medical Center – Centennial, Frisco, TX, p. A606

YARBROUGH, Michelle, Coordinator Human Resources, Allegiance Specialty Hospital Of Kilgore, Kilgore, TX, p. A618

YARBROUGH, Ruth, Vice President, Javon Bea Hospital–Rockton, Rockford, IL, p. A194

YARLING, John, M.D., Medical Director, Four County Counseling Center, Logansport, IN, p. A210

YARMEL, Jeffrey N, Chief Operating Officer, St. Mary Medical Center, Langhorne, PA, p. A529

YARN, Jayce, Director Information Technology, Marias Medical Center, Shelby, MT, p. A380

YAROCH, Julie
President, Promedica Bixby Hospital, Adrian, MI, p. A306
President, Promedica Herrick Hospital, Tecumseh, MI, p. A323

YARRISH, Barbara, President, Wellspan Surgery And Rehabillitation Hospital, York, PA, p. A546

YATES, Ann C, R.N., MSN, Chief Nursing Officer, St. Vincent Mercy Hospital, Elwood, IN, p. A203

YATES, Ann C., Administrator and Chief Nursing Officer, St. Vincent Mercy Hospital, Elwood, IN, p. A203

YATES, Brent, Chief Executive Officer, Encompass Health Rehabilitation Hospital Of Richardson, Richardson, TX, p. A631

YATES, Jackie, R.N., Nurse Executive, Mississippi State Hospital, Whitfield, MS, p. A355

YATES, Jeremy, Chief Executive Officer, Healthsouth Northern Kentucky Rehabilitation Hospital, Edgewood, KY, p. A251

YATES, Katie, Chief Financial Officer, South Sunflower County Hospital, Indianola, MS, p. A348

YATES, Ralph, D.O.
Chief Medical Officer, Salem Health West Valley, Dallas, OR, p. A512
Chief Medical Officer, Salem Hospital, Salem, OR, p. A517

YATES, Randy, M.D., Chief Medical Officer, Straub Medical Center, Honolulu, HI, p. A165

YATES, Vinson
President, Ohiohealth Medcentral Mansfield Hospital, Mansfield, OH, p. A486
President, Ohiohealth Medcentral Shelby Hospital, Shelby, OH, p. A491

YAI SAT TIE, Clyde, Administrative Officer, U. S. Public Health Service Indian Hospital, Zuni, NM, p. A421

YAWORSKY, Jason
Chief Information Officer, Bradford Regional Medical Center, Bradford, PA, p. A521
Senior Vice President Information Systems and Chief Information Officer, Olean General Hospital, Olean, NY, p. A440

YAZAWA, Albert, M.D., Regional Medical Director, Leahi Hospital, Honolulu, HI, p. A164

YBARRA, Farra, R.N., Chief Nursing Officer, Coal County General Hospital, Coalgate, OK, p. A498

YEAGER, Angela, Director Information Technology, Palacios Community Medical Center, Palacios, TX, p. A627

YEAGER, Dianne, Chief Executive Officer, Crane Memorial Hospital, Crane, TX, p. A595

YEAGER, Kerry, Director Information Technology, Berwick Hospital Center, Berwick, PA, p. A520

YEAGER, Kevin, Vice President Fiscal Services, Holzer Medical Center – Jackson, Jackson, OH, p. A484

YEARY, John M., Chief Executive Officer, Freestone Medical Center, Fairfield, TX, p. A603

YEATES, Alan H, Vice President Fiscal Services, Wyandot Memorial Hospital, Upper Sandusky, OH, p. A492

YEATES, Diane, Chief Operating Officer, Terrebonne General Medical Center, Houma, LA, p. A269

YEATS, Melania, M.D., Chief Medical Officer, San Juan Regional Medical Center, Farmington, NM, p. A418

YEE, Martin, M.D., Medical Director, Encompass Health Rehabilitation Hospital Of East Valley, Mesa, AZ, p. A31

YEH, Ada
Chief Executive Officer, Chapman Global Medical Center, Orange, CA, p. A76
Chief Executive Officer, South Coast Global Medical Center, Santa Ana, CA, p. A88
Chief Operating Officer and Chief Nursing Officer, Chapman Global Medical Center, Orange, CA, p. A76

YEHL, Warren, Chief Executive Officer, Eastern New Mexico Medical Center, Roswell, NM, p. A420

YEHLEN, Lorraine, R.N., Vice President Patient Care Services, Dch Regional Medical Center, Tuscaloosa, AL, p. A24

YELENICK, Lori, Chief Financial Officer, Iroquois Memorial Hospital And Resident Home, Watseka, IL, p. A197

YELKEN, Kari, R.N., Director of Nursing, Franklin County Memorial Hospital, Franklin, NE, p. A384

YELVINGTON, Fleury, Administrator, Shriners Hospitals For Children–Tampa, Tampa, FL, p. A142

YETMAN, Robert, M.D., Medical Director, Healthbridge Children'S Hospital Of Houston, Houston, TX, p. A611

YETTER, Tad A., M.D., President Medical Staff, Mason District Hospital, Havana, IL, p. A185

YEUNG, Christopher A., M.D., Chief of Staff, The Core Institute Specialty Hospital, Phoenix, AZ, p. A34

YHI FN, David, Chief Operating Officer, Inspira Medical Center–Elmer, Elmer, NJ, p. A405

YI, Brenda, Director Medical Resource Management and Chief Financial Officer, U. S. Air Force Medical Center Keesler, Keesler Afb, MS, p. A349

YIM, Janet, Director Information Services, St. Mary Mercy Hospital, Livonia, MI, p. A317

YIN, Khin, Medical Director, Rehabilitation Hospital Of Rhode Island, North Smithfield, RI, p. A547

YINGLING, Barbara, R.N., Vice President Patient Care Services and Chief Nursing Officer, Mercy Medical Center, Canton, OH, p. A474

YITTA, Prasad, M.D., Medical Director, River Hospital, Alexandria Bay, NY, p. A422

YOCHELSON, Michael R, M.D., Vice President and Medical Director, Medstar National Rehabilitation Hospital, Washington, DC, p. A115

YOCHUM, Richard E., President and Chief Executive Officer, Pomona Valley Hospital Medical Center, Pomona, CA, p. A78

YODER, Cathy, Chief Financial Officer, St. Joseph'S Hospital, Tampa, FL, p. A142

YODER, Lamont M.
Chief Executive Officer, Banner Baywood Medical Center, Mesa, AZ, p. A31
Chief Executive Officer, Banner Gateway Medical Center, Gilbert, AZ, p. A29
Chief Executive Officer, Banner Heart Hospital, Mesa, AZ, p. A31

YODER, Leslie, Executive Director, Finance, Community Hospital South, Indianapolis, IN, p. A206

YOE, Adam, Chief Executive Officer, Encompass Health Rehabilitation Hospital Of North Memphis, Memphis, TN, p. A574

YOO, George, M.D., Chief Medical Officer, Karmanos Cancer Center, Detroit, MI, p. A310

YOON, Chris, M.D., Medical Director, Encompass Health Rehabilitation Hospital Of Bakersfield, Bakersfield, CA, p. A52

YORK, Christopher, President, Baylor Scott & White Medical Center – Grapevine, Grapevine, TX, p. A608

YORK, Don, Vice President and Chief Human Resource Officer, Sky Lakes Medical Center, Klamath Falls, OR, p. A514

YORK, Linda, Director Human Resource, Memorial Hospital Of Converse County, Douglas, WY, p. A711

YORK, Russell W, Vice President and Chief Financial Officer, Select Specialty Hospital – Belhaven, Jackson, MS, p. A349

YOSHII, Brian, Vice President Information Technology and Chief Information Officer, The Queen'S Medical Center, Honolulu, HI, p. A165

YOUNADAM, Sandro, M.D., Chief Medical Officer, Ottumwa Regional Health Center, Ottumwa, IA, p. A228

YOUNG, Aaron, Chief Information Officer, Summit Healthcare Regional Medical Center, Show Low, AZ, p. A36

YOUNG, Abby, Chief Nursing Officer, Iowa Specialty Hospital–Clarion, Clarion, IA, p. A219

YOUNG, Angela, Human Resources Officer, Chillicothe Veterans Affairs Medical Center, Chillicothe, OH, p. A475

YOUNG, Anita, Chief Operating Officer, Adventhealth Waterman, Tavares, FL, p. A142

YOUNG, Anthony
Chief Executive Officer, Teche Regional Medical Center, Morgan City, LA, p. A274
Information Services Specialist, Chester Mental Health Center, Chester, IL, p. A176

YOUNG, Barry, Director Human Resources, Western Mental Health Institute, Bolivar, TN, p. A566

YOUNG, Bev, Director Human Resources, Frankfort Regional Medical Center, Frankfort, KY, p. A252

YOUNG, Bryce A
Chief Operating Officer, Hays Medical Center, Hays, KS, p. A236
Chief Operating Officer, University Of Kansas Health System Pawnee Valley Campus, Larned, KS, p. A239

YOUNG, C. Ray, M.D., Chief Medical Officer, Bourbon Community Hospital, Paris, KY, p. A259

YOUNG, Chris, Chief Executive Officer, Allegiance Behavioral Health Centers Of Monroe, West Monroe, LA, p. A280

YOUNG, Christine, MSN, R.N., Vice President of Patient Services and Chief Nursing Officer, Akron Children'S Hospital, Akron, OH, p. A471

YOUNG, David, Senior Vice President Planning and Technology, Trousdale Medical Center, Hartsville, TN, p. A570

YOUNG, Debra, R.N., MSN, Vice President, Patient Services and Chief Nursing Officer, Up Health System–Portage, Hancock, MI, p. A314

YOUNG, Duke, Chief Executive Officer, Kimble Hospital, Junction, TX, p. A617

YOUNG, Eric, Director Information Technology and Systems, South Bay Hospital, Sun City Center, FL, p. A140

YOUNG, Eric, M.D., Chief of Staff, Veterans Affairs Ann Arbor Healthcare System, Ann Arbor, MI, p. A306

YOUNG, Eric L
Chief Financial Officer, Selby General Hospital, Marietta, OH, p. A486
Vice President Finance and Chief Financial Officer, Marietta Memorial Hospital, Marietta, OH, p. A486

YOUNG, Gladys, M.D., Chief of Staff, Liberty Medical Center, Chester, MT, p. A375

YOUNG, J Phillip, Chief Executive Officer, Baptist Medical Center, San Antonio, TX, p. A633

YOUNG, James, M.D., Chief of Staff, Mcgehee Hospital, Mcgehee, AR, p. A45

YOUNG, Jeffrey, Chief Human Resource Officer, South Texas Veterans Health Care System, San Antonio, TX, p. A635

YOUNG, Jeffrey D, Chief Information Officer, Children'S Hospitals And Clinics Of Minnesota, Minneapolis, MN, p. A335

YOUNG, Jeremie, M.D., Chief of Staff, Regional General Hospital, Williston, FL, p. A144

YOUNG, John E., Interim Chief Executive Officer, Columbus Regional Healthcare System, Whiteville, NC, p. A463

YOUNG, Joyce, Ph.D., R.N.
Vice President, Patient Services and Chief Nursing Officer, St. Joseph Mercy Ann Arbor, Ypsilanti, MI, p. A325
Vice President, Patient Services and Chief Nursing Officer, St. Joseph Mercy Livingston Hospital, Howell, MI, p. A314

YOUNG, Lisa, CPA
Chief Financial Officer, Continuecare Hospital At Baptist Health Corbin, Corbin, KY, p. A250
Chief Financial Officer, Continuecare Hospital At Hendrick Medical Center, Abilene, TX, p. A581

YOUNG, Martha, Director Human Resources, Cumberland County Hospital, Burkesville, KY, p. A250

YOUNG, Mary, Director Human Resources, Colorado Mental Health Institute At Pueblo, Pueblo, CO, p. A104

YOUNG, Mary C., Chief Executive Officer, Moccasin Bend Mental Health Institute, Chattanooga, TN, p. A567

YOUNG, Mary Lou
Acting Administrator, Continuecare Hospital At Baptist Health Paducah, Paducah, KY, p. A259
Chief Nursing Officer, Continuecare Hospital At Baptist Health Paducah, Paducah, KY, p. A259

YOUNG, Michael, Chief Financial Officer, Mad River Community Hospital, Arcata, CA, p. A51

YOUNG, Michael A., Chief Executive Officer, Temple University Hospital, Philadelphia, PA, p. A536

YOUNG, Pam, Director Human Resources, Davis County Hospital, Bloomfield, IA, p. A218

YOUNG, Patty, R.N., Chief Nursing Officer, Ashland Health Center, Ashland, KS, p. A232

YOUNG, Rhonda, Human Resource Director, Encompass Health Rehabilitation Hospital Of Gadsden, Gadsden, AL, p. A18

YOUNG, Richard T., Director, Walter P. Reuther Psychiatric Hospital, Westland, MI, p. A325

YOUNG, Roberta, Vice President Nursing, Sanford Medical Center Fargo, Fargo, ND, p. A467

YOUNG, Sabrina
Administrative Support Director, South Mississippi State Hospital, Purvis, MS, p. A353
Director, South Mississippi State Hospital, Purvis, MS, p. A353

YOUNG, Shalen, Chief Financial Officer, Arizona Orthopedic Surgical Hospital, Chandler, AZ, p. A28

YOUNG, Sheila, Vice President Human Resources, Mobile Infirmary Medical Center, Mobile, AL, p. A20

YOUNG, Stephanie, Associate Director, Aleda E. Lutz Veterans Affairs Medical Center, Saginaw, MI, p. A321

YOUNG, Terry, Chief Information Officer, Plains Memorial Hospital, Dimmitt, TX, p. A600

YOUNG, Theresa M, Senior Vice President Human Resources, Nemours Children'S Hospital, Orlando, FL, p. A134

YOUNG, William, Chief Information Officer, Berkshire Medical Center, Pittsfield, MA, p. A302

YOUNG, William A., Jr, President and Chief Executive Officer, Southwest General Health Center, Middleburg Heights, OH, p. A487

YOUNGBLOOD, Carrie, Director of Human Resources, Kittitas Valley Healthcare, Ellensburg, WA, p. A672

YOUNGBLOOD, Erin R, Chief Human Resources Officer, Behavioral Center Of Michigan, Warren, MI, p. A324

YOUNGMAN, Darrell, D.O., Chief Medical Officer, Ascension Via Christi St. Francis, Mulvane, KS, p. A241

YOUNGS, Patsy, President, Texas Health Presbyterian Hospital Kaufman, Kaufman, TX, p. A617

YOUREE, Ben, Chief Executive Officer, Tennova North Knoxville Medical Center, Powell, TN, p. A578

YOURTEE, Edward, M.D., Chief Medical Officer, Parkland Medical Center, Derry, NH, p. A399

YOURZEK, Tari, Chief Nursing Officer, Boundary Community Hospital, Bonners Ferry, ID, p. A168

YOUSAITIS, Zoe, Director Human Resources, Eagleville Hospital, Eagleville, PA, p. A524

YOUSO, Michael, Chief Executive Officer, Mercy Hospital, Moose Lake, MN, p. A336

YOUSSEF, Moudy, M.D., Chief Medical Officer, Fairchild Medical Center, Yreka, CA, p. A95

YOUSUF, Faraaz, President and Chief Operating Officer, Northwest Hospital, Randallstown, MD, p. A293

YU, Henry
　Vice President Finance and Chief Financial Officer, California Pacific Medical Center–St. Luke'S Campus, San Francisco, CA, p. A85
　Vice President Finance and Chief Financial Officer, California Pacific Medical Center, San Francisco, CA, p. A85

YUHAS, Joel P., President and Chief Executive Officer, Uchealth Memorial Hospital, Colorado Springs, CO, p. A98

YUHAS, John, D.O., Medical Director, Eden Springs Health Care Center, Green Springs, OH, p. A484

YUNGMANN, Michael, President and Chief Executive Officer, Lourdes Hospital, Paducah, KY, p. A259

YUNUSOV, Ed
　Chief Information Officer, Brookdale Hospital Medical Center, New York, NY, p. A432
　Coordinator Facility Information Center, Brookdale Hospital Medical Center, New York, NY, p. A432

YUST, Randall C.
　Chief Financial Officer NCR, Indiana University Health Tipton Hospital, Tipton, IN, p. A215
　Chief Operating Officer and Chief Financial Officer, Indiana University Health North Hospital, Carmel, IN, p. A201

Z

ZAAS, David William., Chief Executive Officer, Duke Raleigh Hospital, Raleigh, NC, p. A460

ZABAWSKI, Denise, Vice President Information Services and Chief Information Officer, Nationwide Children'S Hospital, Columbus, OH, p. A479

ZABEL, Sarah, Vice President, Operations, Swedish/Edmonds, Edmonds, WA, p. A672

ZABIELSKI, Gerald C, M.D., Chief Medical Staff, Wright Memorial Hospital, Trenton, MO, p. A372

ZACHARIASEN, Keith, Chief Financial Officer, Wamego Health Center, Wamego, KS, p. A247

ZACHARY, Kevin, Chief Executive Officer, Colorado Plains Medical Center, Fort Morgan, CO, p. A100

ZACHRY, Jan, R.N., Vice President Administrator and Chief Operations Executive, Scripps Memorial Hospital–Encinitas, Encinitas, CA, p. A57

ZACIEWSKI, Gary, Chief Executive Officer, Regency Hospital Of Toledo, Sylvania, OH, p. A491

ZAFEREO, Carolyn, Chief Accounting Officer, Citizens Medical Center, Victoria, TX, p. A643

ZAFONTE, Ross, D.O., Chief, Physical Medicine and Rehabilitation and Vice President Medical Affairs, Research and Education, Spaulding Rehabilitation Hospital, Charlestown, MA, p. A298

ZAGERMAN, Robert, Chief Financial Officer, Brooke Glen Behavioral Hospital, Fort Washington, PA, p. A526

ZAHN, Chip, Chief Operating Officer, Medical City Las Colinas, Irving, TX, p. A616

ZAID, Ahmad, Chief Executive Officer, Atrium Medical Center, Stafford, TX, p. A638

ZAJEC, Doris A., Director Human Resources, South Pointe Hospital, Warrensville Heights, OH, p. A493

ZAJIC, Holly, Chief Operating Officer, Ivinson Memorial Hospital, Laramie, WY, p. A711

ZAJICEK, Tammy, Director of Nursing, Jackson County Hospital District, Edna, TX, p. A601

ZAKAI, Aminadav, M.D., Medical Director, Arbour–Fuller Hospital, Attleboro, MA, p. A294

ZAKHARY, M. George, M.D., Chief of Staff, Jackson County Memorial Hospital, Altus, OK, p. A496

ZALDIVAR, Rogelio, M.D., Medical Director, Westchester General Hospital, Miami, FL, p. A131

ZALESKI, Theodore, M.D., Vice President Clinical Effectiveness, Hackensack Meridian Health Southern Ocean Medical Center, Manahawkin, NJ, p. A408

ZALUD, Nicolette, Customer Site Manager, Mclaren Central Michigan, Mount Pleasant, MI, p. A318

ZALUSKI, Heather, M.D., President Medical Staff, Shodair Children'S Hospital, Helena, MT, p. A377

ZAMBITO, John, M.D., Chief of Staff, Astria Regional Medical Center, Yakima, WA, p. A682

ZAMBITO, Paolo, R.N., Chief Operating Officer, East Jefferson General Hospital, Metairie, LA, p. A273

ZAMBRANA, David, Senior Vice President and Chief Executive Officer, Jackson Health System, Miami, FL, p. A130

ZAMBRELLO, Sally, Chief Information Officer, Carondelet St. Joseph'S Hospital, Tucson, AZ, p. A37

ZAMORA DE AGUERO, Hilde, Human Resources Site Director, Baptist Health South Florida, West Kendall Baptist Hospital, Miami, FL, p. A130

ZAMPINI, Maria, Chief Operating Officer, University Medical Center Of El Paso, El Paso, TX, p. A603

ZANE, Kristi, Chief Human Resources Officer, Crawford Memorial Hospital, Robinson, IL, p. A194

ZANI, Carl, Chief Technology Director, Memorial Health, Marysville, OH, p. A486

ZANIS, Tina, Director Information Systems, Lehigh Valley Hospital – Schuylkill, Pottsville, PA, p. A539

ZANNI, David M., Administrator, Adena Pike Medical Center, Waverly, OH, p. A493

ZANT, Dan, M.D., Chief of Staff, Morgan Memorial Hospital, Madison, GA, p. A157

ZARAK, Tamie, Director Human Resources, Marshfield Medical Center – Neilsville, Neillsville, WI, p. A702

ZARECKY, Dan, Chief Executive Officer, Peak View Behavioral Health, Colorado Springs, CO, p. A97

ZAREMA, Claudette A., M.D., Medical Officer, Alaska Psychiatric Institute, Anchorage, AK, p. A25

ZAREN, Douglas, Administrator and CEO, Memorial Regional Hospital, Hollywood, FL, p. A124

ZAUNER, Janiece
　Chief Nursing Officer, Providence Seaside Hospital, Seaside, OR, p. A518
　Chief Operating Officer, Providence Seaside Hospital, Seaside, OR, p. A518

ZAUNER, Mike, Chief Executive Officer, Sierra Vista Hospital, Sacramento, CA, p. A82

ZAVATCHEN, Nancy, Director Information Technology, Cullman Regional Medical Center, Cullman, AL, p. A16

ZAVODNICK, Jacquelyn, M.D., Medical Director, Devereux Children'S Behavioral Health Center, Malvern, PA, p. A530

ZAWACKI, Brenda, Chief Operating Manager, Providence Kodiak Island Medical Center, Kodiak, AK, p. A26

ZDEBLICK, Mick, Chief Executive Officer, Asante Rogue Regional Medical Center, Medford, OR, p. A515

ZDRODOWSKI, Michael, Vice President of Operations and Ambulatory Services, Munson Healthcare Cadillac Hospital, Cadillac, MI, p. A308

ZECHMAN, David M., President and Chief Executive Officer, Mclaren Northern Michigan, Petoskey, MI, p. A319

ZEDNICEK, Allison, Chief Executive Officer, Desert Parkway Behavioral Healthcare Hospital, Las Vegas, NV, p. A395

ZEHM, Laura, Vice President and Chief Financial Officer, Community Hospital Of The Monterey Peninsula, Monterey, CA, p. A73

ZEHNER, Douglas A, Chief Financial Officer, Newark Beth Israel Medical Center, Newark, NJ, p. A409

ZEIGLER, Michele
　Vice President and Chief Information Officer, Chambersburg Hospital, Chambersburg, PA, p. A522
　Vice President Information Services, Waynesboro Hospital, Waynesboro, PA, p. A543

ZEISEL, Henry
　Chief Financial Officer, Northern Region, Amita Health Elk Grove Village, Elk Grove Village, IL, p. A182
　Chief Financial Officer, Northern Region, Amita Health Hoffman Estates, Hoffman Estates, IL, p. A186

ZEITLER, Irvin, D.O., Vice President Medical Affairs, Shannon Medical Center, San Angelo, TX, p. A633

ZEITLER, Jenny, Network Administrator, North Okaloosa Medical Center, Crestview, FL, p. A120

ZELENKA, Anthony
　President and Chief Executive Officer, Jefferson Medical Center, Ranson, WV, p. A689

President and Chief Operating Officer, Berkeley Medical Center, Martinsburg, WV, p. A687

ZELIN, Mira, D.O., Medical Director, Encompass Health Rehabilitation Hospital Of Spring Hill, Brooksville, FL, p. A119

ZELL, John R, Chief Financial Officer, Osf St. Joseph Medical Center, Bloomington, IL, p. A174

ZELLER, Brad, Vice President Operations, Hayward Area Memorial Hospital And Water'S Edge, Hayward, WI, p. A697

ZELLER, Paul, Vice President Human Resources, Medstar Southern Maryland Hospital Center, Clinton, MD, p. A289

ZELLER, Sonya M., R.N., Vice President, Chief Operating Officer and Chief Nursing Officer, Indiana University Health Paoli Hospital, Paoli, IN, p. A213

ZEMAN, Brian, Chief Human Resources, Salem Veterans Affairs Medical Center, Salem, VA, p. A667

ZENDER, Dale, President Hospital Services NW, Peacehealth St. Joseph Medical Center, Bellingham, WA, p. A670

ZENGER, Andrew, Chief Operating Officer, Medical City Mckinney, Mckinney, TX, p. A624

ZENGOTITA, Jamie, M.D., Chief Medical Staff, Mercy Hospital Cassville, Cassville, MO, p. A358

ZENN, Michael B., Chief Executive Officer, University Of Illinois Hospital & Health Sciences System, Chicago, IL, p. A180

ZENNA, Rita, R.N., Vice President Patient Care Services, Deborah Heart And Lung Center, Browns Mills, NJ, p. A404

ZENONE, Michael J, Chief Financial Officer, Emerald Coast Behavioral Hospital, Panama City, FL, p. A135

ZEPHIER, Michelle, Human Resource Specialist, U. S. Public Health Service Indian Hospital, Rosebud, SD, p. A563

ZEPS, Joseph, Vice President Finance, Tomah Memorial Hospital, Tomah, WI, p. A706

ZERINGUE, Rhonda, R.N., Chief Nursing Officer, St. James Parish Hospital, Lutcher, LA, p. A273

ZERRER, Lana, M.D., Chief of Staff, Harry S. Truman Memorial Veterans Hospital, Columbia, MO, p. A359

ZEVENBERGEN, Glenn, Chief Executive Officer, Hegg Health Center Avera, Rock Valley, IA, p. A229

ZEWE, Jeff S, R.N.
　Chief Operating Officer, Bradford Regional Medical Center, Bradford, PA, p. A521
　Senior Vice President, Chief Operating Officer, Olean General Hospital, Olean, NY, p. A440

ZEYNELOGLU, Nejat, Vice President and Chief Quality Medical Officer, Long Island Community Hospital, Patchogue, NY, p. A441

ZHANG, Jian Q, MSN, Chief Operating Officer, Chinese Hospital, San Francisco, CA, p. A85

ZHANG, Jian Q., Chief Executive Officer, Chinese Hospital, San Francisco, CA, p. A85

ZHIRKIN, Georgii, Chief Financial Officer, Community Mental Health Center, Lawrenceburg, IN, p. A210

ZIEGLER, John C, FACHE
　Vice President Human Resources, Memorial Hospital East, Shiloh, IL, p. A196
　Vice President Human Resources, Memorial Hospital, Belleville, IL, p. A174

ZIELAZINSKI, Mark, Chief Information and Technology Integration Officer, Marinhealth Medical Center, Greenbrae, CA, p. A61

ZIELINSKI, Sharon
　Chief Information Resource Officer, Veterans Affairs Maryland Health Care System–Baltimore Division, Baltimore, MD, p. A288
　Manager Health Information, Encompass Health Rehabilitation Hospital Of Erie, Erie, PA, p. A525

ZIEMAN, Michael A., Administrator, Gulfport Behavioral Health System, Gulfport, MS, p. A347

ZIEMER, Patrick C., Chief Executive Officer, Alvarado Parkway Institute Behavioral Health System, La Mesa, CA, p. A63

ZIEMIANSKI, Karen, R.N., MS, Senior Vice President Nursing, Erie County Medical Center, Buffalo, NY, p. A424

ZIENIEWICZ, Stephen P., President and Chief Executive Officer, Saint Barnabas Medical Center, Livingston, NJ, p. A407

ZIEROLD, Bob, Senior Vice President Human Resources, Christian Health Care Center, Wyckoff, NJ, p. A415

ZIGLOR, Danyale
　Assistant Director Human Resources, Wellstar Douglas Hospital, Douglasville, GA, p. A152
　Assistant Vice President Human Resources, Wellstar Cobb Hospital, Austell, GA, p. A148

ZILE, Ron, M.D., Chief of Staff, Highland District Hospital, Hillsboro, OH, p. A484

ZILKOW, Jon, Chief Financial Officer, Southwest Healthcare System, Murrieta, CA, p. A74

ZILLER, Andrew, M.D., Chief Medical Officer, Rose Medical Center, Denver, CO, p. A99

ZILLMAN, Sally E., Interim Vice President, Patient Care Services, Ascension Saint Clare'S Hospital, Weston, WI, p. A708

ZIMA, Cheryl F, Vice President Human Resources Ministry Health Care, Marshfield Medical Center, Marshfield, WI, p. A699

ZIMMEL, Robert, Senior Vice President Human Resources, St. Luke'S University Hospital – Bethlehem Campus, Bethlehem, PA, p. A520

ZIMMER, Jan, R.N., MSN, R.N., MS, Chief Nursing Officer, West Tennessee Healthcare Dyersburg Hospital, Dyersburg, TN, p. A569

ZIMMERLY, Kara, Manager Human Resources, Promedica Bay Park Hospital, Oregon, OH, p. A489

ZIMMERMAN, Aimee, R.N., Chief Operations Officer, Logan County Hospital, Oakley, KS, p. A242

ZIMMERMAN, Anne, Senior Director Patient Care Services and Chief Nursing Officer, Mercy Tiffin Hospital, Tiffin, OH, p. A491

ZIMMERMAN, David, M.D., Chief of Staff, Swain Community Hospital, Bryson City, NC, p. A450

ZIMMERMAN, Don, Director Human Resources, Morris County Hospital, Council Grove, KS, p. A234

ZIMMERMAN, Joanna, Regional Chief Financial Officer, Monmouth Medical Center, Southern Campus, Lakewood, NJ, p. A407

ZIMMERMAN, Keith, Chief Executive Officer, Medical City Arlington, Arlington, TX, p. A583

ZIMMERMAN, Michael
    Human Resource Officer, Osf Heart Of Mary Medical Center, Urbana, IL, p. A197
    Human Resource Officer, Osf Sacred Heart Medical Center, Danville, IL, p. A180

ZIMMERMAN, Nancy, Administrator, Comanche County Hospital, Coldwater, KS, p. A233

ZIMMERMAN, Shelley, Chief Executive Officer, Sycamore Springs Hospital, Lafayette, IN, p. A210

ZIMMERMANN, Deb, R.N., Chief Nursing Officer and Vice President Patient Care Services, Vcu Medical Center, Richmond, VA, p. A666

ZIMMERMANN, Wayne, Chief Operating Officer, Brookdale Hospital Medical Center, New York, NY, p. A432

ZINAMAN, Michael, M.D., Acting Chief Medical Officer, Brookdale Hospital Medical Center, New York, NY, p. A432

ZINK, Jayne, Director of Nursing, Ohio Hospital For Psychiatry, Columbus, OH, p. A479

ZINK, Summer, Chief Financial Officer, Ellinwood District Hospital, Ellinwood, KS, p. A234

ZINKER, Dena, MSN, R.N., Vice President Patient Services, Colquitt Regional Medical Center, Moultrie, GA, p. A158

ZINKULA, Lisa, Chief Financial Officer, Grundy County Memorial Hospital, Grundy Center, IA, p. A223

ZINN, David, M.D., Vice President Medical Affairs, Rmc Anniston, Anniston, AL, p. A13

ZINN, Troy, Chief Executive Officer, Cameron Hospital, Cameron, TX, p. A591

ZINNER, Barbara, Chief Nursing Officer, Marymount Hospital, Garfield Heights, OH, p. A483

ZINNI, Melissa, Chief Financial Officer, Hampton Behavioral Health Center, Westampton, NJ, p. A415

ZINSMEISTER, Mary Sue, Chief Nursing Officer, Rockledge Regional Medical Center, Rockledge, FL, p. A138

ZIOBRO, Ronald
    Chief Operating Officer, Easton Hospital, Easton, PA, p. A524
    Interim Chief Executive Officer, Moses Taylor Hospital, Scranton, PA, p. A540
    Interim Chief Executive Officer, Regional Hospital Of Scranton, Reading, PA, p. A540

ZIOLKOWSKI, David, Chief Executive Officer, Person Memorial Hospital, Roxboro, NC, p. A461

ZIRBSER, Glenn, Senior Vice President Finance and Chief Financial Officer, Jefferson Stratford Hospital, Stratford, NJ, p. A413

ZIRGER, Marion, Chief Financial Officer, Minneola District Hospital, Minneola, KS, p. A241

ZIRKELBACH, Mark
    Chief Information Officer, Loma Linda University Children'S Hospital, Loma Linda, CA, p. A64
    Chief Information Officer, Loma Linda University Medical Center, Loma Linda, CA, p. A64

ZIRKELBACK, Mark, Chief Information Officer, Loma Linda University Behavioral Medicine Center, Redlands, CA, p. A80

ZIRKLE, Isaiah, Chief Operating Officer, West Hills Hospital And Medical Center, Los Angeles, CA, p. A70

ZIRKLE, William, Manager Information Systems, Sentara Halifax Regional Hospital, South Boston, VA, p. A667

ZISKIN, Robert, Chief Information Officer, Northport Veterans Affairs Medical Center, Northport, NY, p. A439

ZOCH, Jeremy
    Chief Executive, St. Joseph Hospital, Orange, CA, p. A76
    Executive Vice President and Chief Operating Officer, St. Joseph Hospital, Orange, CA, p. A76

ZOESCH, Jim, Information Technology Director, Prosser Memorial Health, Prosser, WA, p. A676

ZOGELMAN, Sharon, Director Human Resources, St. Luke Hospital And Living Center, Marion, KS, p. A240

ZOLKIWSKY, Walter R, M.D.
    Chief Medical Officer, Reston Hospital Center, Reston, VA, p. A665
    Chief Medical Officer, Stonesprings Hospital Center, Dulles, VA, p. A658

ZOMCHECK, Daniel, Interim Director, Captain James A. Lovell Federal Health Care Center, North Chicago, IL, p. A191

ZOMCHEK, Daniel, Chief Executive Officer and Medical Center Director, Clement J. Zablocki Veterans Affairs Medical Center, Milwaukee, WI, p. A701

ZOOK, Danette, Chief Financial Officer, Mercyone North Iowa Medical Center, Mason City, IA, p. A226

ZOOK, Lori, Chief Financial Officer, River'S Edge Hospital And Clinic, Saint Peter, MN, p. A340

ZORZA, Elizabeth, Assistant Administrator, Osf St. Francis Hospital And Medical Group, Escanaba, MI, p. A311

ZOUCHA, Larry, Chief Information Officer, Boone County Health Center, Albion, NE, p. A382

ZUANICH, Elizabeth
    Chief Financial Officer, Providence Little Company Of Mary Medical Center – Torrance, Torrance, CA, p. A92
    Chief Financial Officer, Providence Little Company Of Mary Medical Center San Pedro, Los Angeles, CA, p. A69

ZUBER, Steven, Vice President, Methodist Jennie Edmundson Hospital, Council Bluffs, IA, p. A220

ZUEL, Sally, Vice President Human Resources, Union Hospital, Terre Haute, IN, p. A215

ZUHD, Dajani, M.D., President Medical Staff, Punxsutawney Area Hospital, Punxsutawney, PA, p. A539

ZUKOWSKI, Andrew, Chief Financial Officer, Unc Rex Health Care, Raleigh, NC, p. A460

ZULIANI, Michael E., Chief Executive Officer, Encompass Health Rehabilitation Hospital Of Huntington, Huntington, WV, p. A686

ZULTANKY, Lynne, Director Corporate Communications and Media Relations, Bon Secours–Depaul Medical Center, Norfolk, VA, p. A663

ZUMPANO, Anthony, Chief Financial Officer, Penn Presbyterian Medical Center, Philadelphia, PA, p. A536

ZUMSTEIN, James F., M.D., Chief of Medicine, Jack Hughston Memorial Hospital, Phenix City, AL, p. A22

ZUTZ–WICZEK, Sandy, Chief Operating Officer, Firstlight Health System, Mora, MN, p. A336

ZVANUT, Michelle, Vice President Human Resources, Boone Hospital Center, Columbia, MO, p. A359

ZWANZIGER, Marcia, Vice President Finance, Huron Regional Medical Center, Huron, SD, p. A561

ZWEIFEL, Mary A.
    President and Chief Executive Officer, Sheltering Arms Hospital South, Midlothian, VA, p. A663
    President and Chief Executive Officer, Sheltering Arms Rehabilitation Hospital, Mechanicsville, VA, p. A662

ZWENG, Thomas
    Executive Vice President and Chief Medical Officer, Novant Health Brunswick Medical Center, Bolivia, NC, p. A450
    Executive Vice President and Chief Medical Officer, Novant Health Charlotte Orthopaedic Hospital, Charlotte, NC, p. A451
    Executive Vice President and Chief Medical Officer, Novant Health Forsyth Medical Center, Winston, NC, p. A464
    Executive Vice President and Chief Medical Officer, Novant Health Huntersville Medical Center, Huntersville, NC, p. A456
    Executive Vice President and Chief Medical Officer, Novant Health Matthews Medical Center, Matthews, NC, p. A458
    Executive Vice President and Chief Medical Officer, Novant Health Medical Park Hospital, Winston, NC, p. A464
    Executive Vice President and Chief Medical Officer, Novant Health Presbyterian Medical Center, Charlotte, NC, p. A451
    Executive Vice President and Chief Medical Officer, Novant Health Rowan Medical Center, Salisbury, NC, p. A461
    Executive Vice President and Chief Medical Officer, Novant Health Thomasville Medical Center, Thomasville, NC, p. A463

ZWICKER, Mike, Chief Executive Officer, St. Aloisius Medical Center, Harvey, ND, p. A467

ZWIEFEL, Laura, Chief Executive Officer, Hancock County Health System, Britt, IA, p. A218

ZWIEG, Faye, R.N., Vice President and Chief Nursing Officer, Aurora St. Luke'S Medical Center, Milwaukee, WI, p. A701

ZWINGER, Glenn, Manager Information Systems Services, Veterans Affairs Puget Sound Health Care System, Seattle, WA, p. A678

ZYCH, Anita, Director of Nursing, Arrowhead Behavioral Health Hospital, Maumee, OH, p. A487

ZYLA, Jeffrey, Chief Financial Officer, Abrazo Scottsdale Campus, Phoenix, AZ, p. A32

AHA Membership Categories

The American Hospital Association is primarily an organization of hospitals and related institutions. Its object, according to its bylaws, is "to promote high–quality health care and health services for all the people through leadership in the development of public policy, leadership in the representation and advocacy of hospital and health care organization interests, and leadership in the provision of services to assist hospitals and health care organizations in meeting the health care needs of their communities."

Institutional Members

Hospitals or health services organizations or systems which provide a continuum of integrated, community health resources and which include at least one licensed hospital that is owned, leased, managed or religiously sponsored

Institutional members include hospitals, health care systems, integrated delivery systems, and physician hospital organizations (PHOs) and health maintenance organizations (HMOs) wholly or partially owned by or owning a member hospital or system. An Institutional member hospital, health care system or integrated delivery system may, at its discretion and upon approval of a membership application by the Association chief executive officer, extend membership to the health care provider organizations, other than a hospital that it owns, leases, or fully controls.

Freestanding Health Care Provider Organizations

These are health provider organizations, other than registered hospitals, that provide patient care services, including, but not limited to, ambulatory, preventive, rehabilitative, specialty, post–acute and continuing care, as well as physician groups, health insurance services, and staff and group model health maintenance organizations without a hospital component. Freestanding Health Care Provider Organizations members are not owned or controlled by an Institutional member hospital, health care system or integrated delivery system member. They may, however, be part of an organization eligible for, but not holding, Institutional membership.

Other Organizations

This category includes organizations interested in the objectives of the American Hospital Association, but not eligible for Institutional or Freestanding Health Care Provider Organization Membership. Organizations eligible for Other membership shall include, but not be limited to, associations, societies, foundations, corporations, educational and academic institutions, companies, government agencies, international health providers, and organizations having an interest in and a desire to support the objectives of the Association.

Provisional Members

Hospitals that are in the planning or construction stage and that, on completion, will be eligible for institutional membership. Provisional membership may also be granted to applicant institutions that cannot, at present, meet the requirements of Institutional or Freestanding Health Care Provider Organization membership.

Government Institution Group Members

Groups of government hospitals operated by the same unit of government may obtain institutional membership under a group plan. Membership dues are based on a special schedule set forth in the bylaws of the AHA.

Other Institutional Members

Other Institutional Members

Hospitals

Canada

U.S. hospitals and hospitals in areas associated with the U.S. that are Institutional members of the American Hospital Association are included in the list of hospitals in section A. Canadian Institutional members of the American Hospital Association are listed below.

ALBERTA

Lamont: LAMONT HEALTH CARE CENTRE, P O Bag 10, Zip T0B 2R0; tel. 780/895–2211; Harold James, Executive Director

MANITOBA

Winnipeg: RIVERVIEW HEALTH CENTRE, 1 Morley Avenue East, Zip R3L 2P4; tel. 204/452–3411; Norman R. Kasian, President and Chief Executive Officer

ONTARIO

Renfrew: RENFREW VICTORIA HOSPITAL, 499 Raglan Street North, Zip K7V 1P6, tel. 613/432–4851; Randy V. Penney, President and Chief Executive Officer

Thornhill: SHOULDICE HOSPITAL, 7750 Bayview Avenue, Zip L3T 4A3; tel. 905/889–1125; John Hughes, Chief Administrative Officer

---

Associated University Programs in Health Administration

IOWA

Iowa City: DEPARTMENT OF HEALTH MANAGEMENT AND POLICY, UNIVERSITY OF IOWA, 105 River Street, N232A CPHB, Zip 52246; tel. 319/384–3830; Keith Mueller, Professor and Head

MARYLAND

Bethesda: NAVY MEDICINE PROFESSIONAL DEVELOPMENT CENTER, Naval Medicine, Education and Training Command, 8901 Wisconsin Avenue, Building 1, Zip 20889-5611; tel. 301/295–1251; Commander DuWayne Griepentrog, Director Administration

MISSOURI

Columbia: UNIVERSITY OF MISSOURI, HEALTH MANAGEMENT AND INFORMATICS, CE707 Clinical Support and Education Building, DC 00600, One Hospital Drive, Zip 65212; tel. 573/882–6179; Eduardo Simoes; Chair

TEXAS

San Antonio: ARMY-BAYLOR UNIVERSITY PROGRAM IN HEALTH CARE ADMINISTRATION, 3151 Scott Road, Bldg 2841, Zip 78234–6135; tel. 210/221–6443; Lieutenant Colonel M Nicholas Coppola, Program Director

Sheppard AFB: U.S. AIR FORCE SCHOOL OF HEALTH CARE SCIENCES, Building 1900, MST/114, Academic Library, Zip 76311; tel. 817/851–2511

PUERTO RICO

San Juan: SCHOOL OF PUBLIC HEALTH, P O Box 5067, Zip 00936; tel. 809/767–9626; Orlando Nieves, Dean

Hospital Schools
of Nursing

PENNSYLVANIA

New Castle: JAMESON HOSPITAL School of Nursing

Nonhospital Preacute and Postacute Care Facilities

CALIFORNIA

Winterhaven: U. S. PUBLIC HEALTH SERVICE INDIAN HOSPITAL, P O Box 1368, Zip 85366–1368; tel. 760/572–0217; Geniel Harrison, Clinic Director

DELAWARE

Newark: HEALTH CARE CENTER AT CHRISTIANA, 200 Hygeia Drive, Zip 19714; tel. 302/623–0100; Douglas P. Azar, Senior Vice President, Medical Group

FLORIDA

Jacksonville: NEMOURS CHILDREN'S CLINIC, 807 Children's Way, Zip 32207; tel. 904/390–3600; William A. Cover, Administrator

GEORGIA

Calhoun: ALLIANT HEALTH PLANS, INC., 401 South Wall Street, Ste 201, Zip 30701; tel. 706/629–8848; Judy Pair, Chief Executive Officer

GEORGIA HEALTH PLUS, 401 South Wall Street, Ste 201, Zip 30701; tel. 706/629–1833;

Rome: CENTREX, 420 East Second Avenue, Zip 30161; tel. 706/235–1006; Dee B. Russell, Chief Executive Officer

COMMUNITY HOSPICECARE, P O Box 233, Zip 30162–0233; tel. 706/232–0807; Kurt Stuenkel, President and Chief Executive Officer

FLOYD HOME HEALTH AGENCY, P O Box 6248, Zip 30162–6248; tel. 706/802–4600; Kurt Stuenkel, President and Chief Executive Officer

FLOYD MEDICAL OUTPATIENT SURGERY, P O Box 233, Zip 30162–0233; tel. 706/802–2070; Kurt Stuenkel, President and Chief Executive Officer

FLOYD REHABILITATION CENTER, P O Box 233, Zip 30162–0233; tel. 706/802–2091; Kurt Stuenkel, President and Chief Executive Officer

HAWAII

Honolulu: MALUHIA HOSPITAL, 1027 Hala Drive, Zip 96817; tel. 808/832–5874; Derek Akiyoshi, Chief Executive Officer

ILLINOIS

Oak Forest: OAK FOREST HEALTH CENTER OF COOK COUNTY, 15900 South Cicero Avenue, Zip 60452–4006; tel. 708/687–7200;

MAINE

Damariscotta: COVE'S EDGE, 26 Schooner Street, Zip 4543; tel. 207/563–4645; Judy McGuire, Administrator

MILES MEDICAL GROUP, INC., 35 Miles Street, Zip 4543; tel. 207/563–1234; Stacey Miller-Friant, Vice President, Physician Services

Kennebunk: SOUTHERN MAINE HEALTH AND HOME SERVICES, P O Box 739, Zip 4043; tel. 207/985–4767; Elaine Brady, Executive Director

MARYLAND

Baltimore: ST. AGNES HEALTH SERVICES, 900 Caton Avenue, Zip 21229; tel. 410/368–2945; Peter Clay, Senior Vice President Managed Care

ST. AGNES HOME CARE AND HOSPICE, 3421 Benson Avenue, Suite G100, Zip 21227; tel. 410/368–2825; Robin Dowell, Director

Ellicott City: ST. AGNES NURSING AND REHABILITATION CENTER, 3000 North Ridge Road, Zip 21043; tel. 410/461–7577; Barbara A. Gustke, Administrator Extended Care Facility

MASSACHUSETTS

Boston: JOSLIN DIABETES CENTER, One Joslin Place, Zip 2215; tel. 617/732–2400; John L. Brooks, President and Chief Executive Officer

Springfield: BAY STATE VISITING NURSE ASSOCIATION AND HOSPICE, 50 Maple Street, Zip 1105; tel. 413/781–5070; Ruth Odgren, President

MICHIGAN

Big Rapids: MECOSTA HEALTH SERVICES, 650 Linden Street, Zip 49307; tel. 231/796–3200; Gail Bullard, Director

Sault Sainte Marie: SAULT SAINTE MARIE TRIBAL HEALTH AND HUMAN SERVICES CENTER, 2864 Ashmun Street, Zip 49783; tel. 906/495–5651; Russell Vizina, Division Director Health

MISSOURI

Independence: SURGI-CARE CENTER OF INDEPENDENCE, 2311 Redwood Avenue, Zip 64057; tel. 816/373–7995;

NEBRASKA

North Platte: GREAT PLAINS PHO, INC., P O Box 1167, Zip 69103; tel. 308/535–7496; Todd Hlavaty, Chairman

NEW JERSEY

Jersey City: ST. FRANCIS HOSPITAL, 25 McWilliams Place, Zip 07302–1698; tel. 201/418–1000;

Millburn: ATLANTIC HOME CARE AND HOSPICE, 33 Bleeker Street, Zip 7041; tel. 973/379–8400; Susan Quinn, Administrator

Morristown: ALLIANCE IMAGING CENTER, 65 Maple Street, Zip 7960; tel. 973/267–5700; Barbara Picorale, Administrator

Succasunna: DIALYSIS CENTER OF NORTHWEST NEW JERSEY, 170 Righter Road, Zip 7876; tel. 973/584–1117; Carol Cahill, Administrator

NEW MEXICO

Albuquerque: ALBUQUERQUE IHS HEALTH CENTER, 801 Vassar Drive NE, Zip 87106–2799; tel. 505/248–4000; Maria Rickert, Chief Executive Officer

NEW YORK

Tuckahoe: HOME NURSING ASSOCIATION OF WESTCHESTER, 69 Main Street, Zip 10707; tel. 919/961–2818; Mary Wehrberger, Director

NORTH CAROLINA

Jefferson: AMH SEGRAVES CARE CENTER, 200 Hospital Avenue, Zip 28640; tel. 336/246–7101;

Wilson: WILMED NURSING CARE CENTER, 1705 Tarboro Street SW, Zip 27893–3428; tel. 252/399–8998; Randy Smithey, Administrator

OHIO

Cleveland: METROHEALTH CENTER FOR SKILLED NURSING CARE, 4229 Pearl Road, Zip 44109; tel. 216/957–3675; Yvette Bozman, Administrator

OKLAHOMA

Clinton: U. S. PUBLIC HEALTH SERVICE INDIAN HOSPITAL, Route 1, Box 3060, Zip 73601–9303; tel. 580/323–2884;

Eufaula: EUFALA INDIAN HEALTH CENTER, 800 Forest Avenue, Zip 74432; tel. 918/689–2547; Shelly Crow, Health System Administrator

Okmulgee: OKMULGEE INDIAN HEALTH SYSTEM, 1313 East 20th, Zip 74447; tel. 918/758–1926; Kara Lee, Administrator

Sapulpa: SAPULPA INDIAN HEALTH CENTER, 1125 East Clevelend, Zip 74066; tel. 918/224–9310; Sid Daniels, Acting Administrator

PENNSYLVANIA

Warminster: ABINGTON MEMORIAL HEALTH CENTER - WARMINSTER CAMPUS, 225 Newtown Road, Zip 18974–5221; tel. 215/441–6600; Kathleen Farrell, Executive Director

TEXAS

Dallas: SURGICARE OF TRAVIS CENTER, INC., 13355 Noel Road, Suite 650, Zip 75240–6694; tel. 713/520–1782;

Houston: GRAMERCY OUTPATIENT SURGERY CENTER. LTD., 2727 Gramercy, Zip 77025; tel. 713/660–6900; Hamel Patel, Administrator

Houston: WEST HOUSTON SURGICARE, 970 Campbell Road, Zip 77024; tel. 713/461–3547;

Webster: BAY AREA SURGICARE CENTER, 502 Medical Center Boulevard, Zip 77598; tel. 281/332–2433; Carol Simons, Administrator

WISCONSIN

Green Bay: UNITY HOSPICE, P O Box 28345, Zip 54324–8345; tel. 920/494–0225; Donald Seibel, Executive Director

Provisional Hospitals

This listing includes organizations that, as of September 16, 2015, were in the planning or construction stage and that, on completion, will be eligible for Institutional membership. Some hospitals are granted provisional membership for reasons related to other Association requirements. Hospitals classified as provisional members for reasons other than being under construction are indicated by a bullet (●).

TEXAS

Houston: BAYLOR ST. LUKE'S MEDICAL CENTER MCNAIR CAMPUS, One Baylor Plaza, BCM 100, Zip 77030–3411; tel. 713/798–4951; Paul Klotman, M.D., President

Marble Falls: WAYNE & EILEEN HURD REGIONAL MEDICAL CENTER – SCOTT & WHITE, 800 West Highway 71, Zip 78654; tel. 830/598–1204; Eric N. Looper, Chief Executive Officer

GUAM

Dededo: GUAM REGIONAL MEDICAL CITY, P.O. Box 3830, Zip 96932; tel. 671/649–4764; Gloria Long, Chief Operating Officer

Associate Members

Ambulatory Centers and Home Care Agencies

UNITED STATES

NEW YORK

MIDTOWN SURGERY CENTER, 305 East 47th Street, Zip 10017–2303; tel. 212/751–2100; Julia Ferguson, Director, Operations

PENNSYLVANIA

WILLS EYE HOSPITAL, 840 Walnut Street, Philadelphia, Zip 19107–5109; tel. 215/928–3000; Joseph P. Bilson, Executive Director

Blue Cross Plans

UNITED STATES

ARIZONA

BLUE CROSS AND BLUE SHIELD OF ARIZONA, Box 13466, Phoenix, Zip 85002–3466; tel. 602/864–4541; Vishu Jhaveri; Senior Vice President and Chief Medical Officer

The members listed in bold are Associate Advantage members © 2019 AHA Guide

Other Members

UNITED STATES

Architecture

DEVENNEY GROUP ARCHITECTS, 201 West Indian School Road, Phoenix, Arizona Zip 85013–3203; tel: 602/943–8950, Julie Barkenbush, Chief Executive Officer; devenneygroup.com

MATTHEI AND COLIN ASSOCIATES, 332 South Michigan Avenue, Suite 614, Chicago, Illinois Zip 60604; tel: 312/939–4002, Randall Bacidore, Principal; mca–architecture.com/

MESSER CONSTRUCTION COMPANY, 643 West Court Street, Cincinnati, Ohio Zip 45203–1511; tel: 513/242–1541, Peter Bergman, Vice President; messer.com

Bank

HEALTHCARE ASSOCIATES CREDIT UNION, 1151 East Warrenville Road, Naperville, Illinois Zip 60563; tel: 630/276–5771, Jennifer Kleinhenz, Senior Vice President Strategic Initiatives; hacu.org

TD BANK, 2130 Centre Park West Drive, 2nd Floor, West Palm Beach, Florida Zip 33409–6411; tel: 561/352–2086, Colleen Mullaney, Senior Vice President; tdbank.com

Communication Systems Org

AVAILITY, LLC, 750 Old Hickory Boulevard, Building 2 Suite 270, Brentwood, Tennessee Zip 37027–4528; tel: 615/760–3361, Ashleigh Eisinger, Events and Social Media Specialist; availity.com

Construction Firm

POETTKER CONSTRUCTION COMPANY, 308 South Germantown Road, Breese, Illinois Zip 62230; tel: 618/526–7213, Curtis C. Rommerskirchen, Brand Ambassador for Healthcare Facility Services; poettkerconstruction.com

Consulting Firm

AON RISK SOLUTIONS, 5600 West 83rd Street, 8200 Tower, Minneapolis, Minnesota Zip 55402–3721; tel: 952/807–0768, James Craig Nelson, Senior Vice President; stratford360.com

ARAMARK, 10510 Twin Lakes Boulevard, Charlotte, North Carolina Zip 28269–7658; tel: 704/948–4774, Tom Elmore, Director, Industry Relations; aramark.com

AVIVA HEALTHCARE SOLUTIONS, 98 Golden Eye Lane, Port Monmouth, New Jersey Zip 07758–1647; tel: 800/530–5728, Thomas Bojko, President and Managing Partner; avivahealthsolutions.com

CARE TECH SOLUTIONS, 901 Wilshire Drive, Suite 100, Troy, Michigan Zip 48084; tel: 248/823–0950, Jody Meehan, Vice President, Marketing, Communications, and Government Affairs; caretech.com/

CARERISE|CARERISE INDEX, PO Box 880, Mandeville, Louisiana Zip 70470–0880; tel: 985/727–4740, Tim G Goux, Founder; carerise.com

CLEARWATER COMPLIANCE LLC, 106 Windward Point, Hendersonville, Tennessee Zip 37075–5108; tel: 615/800–7988, Kathy S. Ebbert, Chief Operating Officer; clearwatercompliance.com

CREATE PPO, 317 6th Avenue, Suite 1440, Des Moines, Iowa Zip 50309–4131; tel: 515/657–4888, Clayton R. Copple, President and Chief Executive Officer; createppo.com

DRAFFIN TUCKER, 5 Concourse Parkway, Suite 1250, Atlanta, Georgia Zip 30328–5350; tel: 404/220–8484, Sarah Dekutowski, Partner; https://draffin–tucker.com/

EASTER HEALTHCARE CONSULTING, 518 Neilwood Drive, Nashville, Tennessee Zip 37205–3026; tel: 615/424–3642, James G Easter (Jim), Principal and Chief Executive Officer; easterhealthcare.com

ERNST & YOUNG, 150 Fourth Avenue North, Suite 1400, Nashville, Tennessee Zip 37219–2409; tel: 615/252–8254, Chris Barber, US Health Brand, Marketing and Communications Leader; ey.com

GOLDMAN, SACHS AND COMPANY, 200 West Street, New York, New York Zip 10282–2198; tel: 212/902–1000, Cynthia Rivera, Public Sector and Infrastructure Banking

HEALTHCARE CHAPLAINCY NETWORK, INC., 65 Broadway, 12th Floor, New York, New York Zip 10010; tel: 212/644–1111, Eric J. Hall, President and Chief Executive Officer; healthcarechaplaincy.org

HEALTHCARESOURCE, 100 Sylvan Road, Suite 100, Woburn, Massachusetts Zip 01801–1851; tel: 800/691–3737, Sean Parlin, Strategic Alliances Manager; healthcaresource.com

HEALTHEQUITY, INC., 15 West Scenic Pointe Drive, Suite 100, Draper, Utah Zip 84020–6120; tel: 801/727–1000, Stephen Neeleman, Founder and Vice Chairman; healthequity.com

INTERNATIONAL CITIES MANAGEMENT ASSOCIATION–RETIREMENT CORPORATION, 777 North Capitol Street NE, Washington, District of Columbia Zip 20002–4239; tel: 866/265–5126, Kevin F. Orr, Senior Director; icmarc.org

KAUFMAN HALL, 5202 Old Orchard Road, Suite N700, Skokie, Illinois Zip 60077; tel: 847/441–8780, Jason H Sussman, Partner; kaufmanhall.com

LATHAM AND WATKINS, LLP, 633 West 5th Street, Ste 4000, Los Angeles, California Zip 90071; tel: 213/485–1234, Daniel K Settelmayer, Partner; lw.com

MCDONALD HOPKINS, LLC, 600 Superior Avenue East, Suite 2100, Cleveland, Ohio Zip 44114–2690; tel: 216/348–5400, Richard S Cooper, Member; mcdonaldhopkins.com

MCKESSON CORPORATION, 1 Post Street, 33rd Floor, San Francisco, California Zip 94104–5203; tel: 404/338–2985, Anastasia Agapoff, Assistant Manager, Library Operations; mckesson.com/

MILESTONE HEALTHCARE, LLC, 275 West Campbell Road, Suite 300, Richardson, Texas Zip 75080–3560; tel: 800/926–2388, George Thompson, General Manager; milestonehealth.com

NATIONAL CENTER FOR HEALTH STATISTICS, 3311 Toledo Road, Hyattsville, Maryland Zip 20782–2064; tel: 800/232–4636, Monica Deckers, Lead Admin Officer; cdc.gov

NATIONAL MEDICAL FUNDING SERVICES, INC., 1101 Wootton Parkway, 10th Floor, Rockville, Maryland Zip 20852–1059; tel: 301/433–7515, Sandy Waterman, Chief Executive Officer; medx.health

NAVEX GLOBAL, 6000 Meadows Road, Suite 200, Lake Oswego, Oregon Zip 97035–3172; tel: 503/924–1640, Stephen J. Molen, Vice President Strategic Solutions; navexglobal.com

NEWRISTICS, 8777 East Via de Ventura #188, Scottsdale, Arizona Zip 85258; tel: 480/947–8078, Cheryl Palay, Senior Vice President; hsmgroup.com

PROTIVITI, INC., 13727 Noel Road, Suite 800, Dallas, Texas Zip 75240–1336; tel: 214/395–1662, Richard Williams, Managing Director and Global Healthcare Industry Practice; protiviti.com

RYCAN, P O Box 306, Marshall, Minnesota Zip 56258–0306; tel: 800/201–3324, Marg Louwagie, Administrative Assistant; rycan.com

STRATA DECISION TECHNOLOGY; tel: 312/726–1227, Dan Michelson, Chief Executive Officer; stratadecision.com

STROUDWATER ASSOCIATES, 50 Sewall Street, Suite 102, Portland, Maine Zip 04102–2646; tel: 207/221–8255, Marc Voyvodich, Chief Executive Officer; stroudwater.com/

SULLIVAN COTTER & ASSOCIATES, INC, 7733 Forsyth Boulevard, Suite 1100, Clayton, Missouri Zip 63105; tel: 312/564–5883, Sean C. Butler, Director of Client Experience; sullivancotter.com

SYMPLR, 315 Capitol Street, Suite 100, Houston, Texas Zip 77002–2826; tel: 281/863–9500, Rick Pleczko, Chief Executive Officer; vcsdatabase.com

TEAMHEALTH, 265 Brookview Centre Way, Suite 400, Knoxville, Tennessee Zip 37919; tel: 865/293–5486, Leif Murphy, Chief Executive Officer; teamhealth.com

THE CHARTIS GROUP, 220 West Kinzie Street, 5th Floor, Chicago, Illinois Zip 60654–4912; tel: 312/932–3068, Celine White, Manager of Financial Operations; chartis.com

THE QUAMMEN GROUP, INC., 151 Southhall Lane, Suite 168, Maitland, Florida Zip 32751–7486; tel: 407/539–2015, Alexandra Robertson, Director of Marketing; quammengroup.com

VERRAS HEALTHCARE INTERNATIONAL; tel: 888/791–5556, Robert T. Langston, Partner; verras.com/

VIIAD SYSTEMS LLC, 1170 Wheeler Way, Suite 200, Langhorne, Pennsylvania Zip 19047–3243; tel: 866/498–4423, Tricia Bradley, Director, Sales and Marketing Support; viiad.com

WESTERN HEALTHCARE ALLIANCE, 715 Horizon Drive, Suite 401, Grand Junction, Colorado Zip 81506–8731; tel: 970/683–5223, Carolyn Bruce, Chief Executive Officer; wha1.org

XANITOS, INC., 3809 West Chester Pike, Suite 210, Newtown Square, Pennsylvania Zip 19073–2304; tel: 484/654–2300, Graeme A Crothall, Chairman and Chief Executive Officer; xanitos.com

Educational Services

NATIONAL RURAL HEALTH RESOURCE CENTER, 525 South Lake Avenue, Suite 320, Duluth, Minnesota Zip 55802, tel: 218/727 9390, Sally Buck, Chief Executive Officer; ruralcenter.org

PUBLISHING CONCEPTS INC.; tel: 800/561–4686, Gregg Jones, Education and Careers Director; pcipublishing.com

Hospice

HOSPICE OF THE VALLEY, 1510 East Flower Street, Phoenix, Arizona Zip 85014–5698; tel: 602/530–6900, Rachel Behrendt, Senior Vice President, Operations; hov.org

Information Systems

CERNER CORPORATION, 2800 Rockcreek Parkway, Kansas City, Missouri Zip 64117; tel: 816/221–1024, Laurel Vine, Program Manager, Industry Events; cerner.com

EVOLENT, 540 West Madison Street, Suite 1500, Chicago, Illinois Zip 60661; tel: 312/273–6623, Kevin Weinstein, Chief Marketing Officer; valencehealth.com

FLEMING AOD, Inc., 816 Thayer Avenue, Floor 3rd, Silver Spring, Maryland Zip 20910–4508; tel: 202/872–1033, Mary Dalrymple, Managing Director; aod.cx

IMPRIVATA, INC., 10 Maguire Road Building 4, Lexington, Massachusetts Zip 02421–3110; tel: 781/674–2700, Ed Gaudel, Chief Marketing Officer; imprivata.com

KPMG LLP, 200 East Randolph Street, Suite 5500, Chicago, Illinois Zip 60601–6607; tel: 312/665–2073, Edward J Giniat, National Line of Business Leader, Healthcare and Pharmaceuticals Practice; https://home.kpmg.com/us/en/home.html?cid=M-00002211&gclid=CKfszoeUrtACFZSFaQod82wE4g

MEDHOST, 6100 West Plano Parkway, Suite 3100, Plano, Texas Zip 75093–8342; tel: 888/218–4678, Leslie LaFon, Departmental Segment Manager; medhost.com

REAL TIME MEDICAL SYSTEMS, LLC, 901 Elkridge Landing Road, Linthicum Heights, Maryland Zip 21090–2920; tel: 203/249–0404, Joan Neuscheler, Chief Executive Officer; realtimemed.com

Insurance Broker

BOSTON MUTUAL LIFE INSURANCE COMPANY, 120 Royall Street, Canton, Massachusetts Zip 2021; tel: 781/828–7000, Peter Tillson, Vice President; bostonmutual.com

CONSTELLATION, 7701 France Avenue South, Suite 500, Minneapolis, Minnesota Zip 55435–3201; tel: 952/838–6700, Holly Freeman, Manager; mmicgroup.com

Ironshore, 300 South Wacker Drive, Chicago, Illinois Zip 60606–6680; tel: 312/496–7535, Daniel R Nash, Senior Vice President Field Operations and Business Development; ironshore.com

LTC SOLUTIONS, 14715 North East 95th Street, Suite 200, Redmond, Washington Zip 98052; tel: 877/286–2852, Christine McCullugh, President; ltc-solutions.com

THE ALLEN J. FLOOD COMPANIES, INC., 2 Madison Avenue, Larchmont, New York Zip 10538; tel: 914/834–9326, Allen J Flood, President; ajfusa.com

Managed Care/Utilization

CENTENE CORPORATION, 111 East Capitol Street, Suite 500, Jackson, Mississippi Zip 39201; tel: 601/519–6119, K. Michael Bailey, Corporate Vice President; centene.com

Manufacturer/Supplier

3M, 3M CENTER, Building 275–4E–01, Saint Paul, Minnesota Zip 55144–1000; tel: 612/733–8183, Donald R Brewer, Director Medical–Surgical Markets; 3m.com

GE HEALTHCARE, 9900 West Innovation Drive, RP–2177, Wauwatosa, Wisconsin Zip 53226–4856; tel: 262/290–8769, Kimberly Rutherford, Business Partner and Director, Advertising & Promotion US–Canada Region; www3.gehealthcare.com

HILL–ROM, 1069 State Route 46 East, Batesville, Indiana Zip 47006–9167; tel: 812/934–7958, Thomas J Jeffers, Director Government Relations; hill-rom.com

Metro Hospital Assn

HOSPITAL ASSOCIATION OF SOUTHERN CALIFORNIA, 515 South Figueroa Street, Suite 1300, Los Angeles, California Zip 90071–3300; tel: 213/538–0700, George W Greene, President and Chief Executive Officer; hasc.org

Other Health Related

CENTER FOR MEDICAL INTEROPERABILITY, 618 Church Street Suite 220, Nashville, Tennessee Zip 37219–2453; tel: 202/617–6009, Kerry McDermott, Vice President for Public Policy and Communications; medicalinteroperability.org

Other

A3–ASHLEY ADVERTISING AGENCY, 2825 Soni Drive, Trooper, Pennsylvania Zip 19403–1275; tel: 610/631–5500, Frank Gussoni, President; ashleyadvertising.com

ACADEMIC PARTNERSHIP LLC, 600 North Pearl Street, Suite 900, Dallas, Texas Zip 75201; tel: 682/305–3063, Nimisha Savani, Vertical Chief Healthcare; aphealthcareedge.com

AMC HEALTH, INC., 39 Broadway, Suite 540, New York, New York Zip 10006; tel: 877/776–1746, Joanna Haskin, Vice President Partner Development; amchealth.com

AMERICAN ASSOCIATION FOR WOUND CARE MANAGEMENT, 4109 Glenrose Street, Kensington, Maryland Zip 20895–3718; tel: 301/933–2200, Jule Crider, Executive Director; aawcm.org

AMERICAN ASSOCIATION OF NURSE ANESTHETISTS, 222 South Prospect Avenue, Park Ridge, Illinois Zip 60068–4001; tel: 847/655–1100, Randall Moore, Chief Executive Officer; aana.com

AMERICAN BOARD OF MEDICAL SPECIALTIES, 353 North Clark Street, Suite 1400, Chicago, Illinois Zip 60654–3454; tel: 312/436–2626, Richard D Hawkins, President and Chief Executive Officer; abms.org

AMERICAN COLLEGE OF HEALTHCARE EXECUTIVES, 300 South Riverside Plaza, Suite 1900, Chicago, Illinois Zip 60606–6613; tel: 312/424–2800, Deborah Bowen, President and Chief Executive Officer; ache.org

AMERICAN HEALTH INFORMATION MANAGEMENT ASSOCIATION, 233 North Michigan Avenue, Suite 2150, Chicago, Illinois Zip 60601–5806; tel: 312/233–1100, David A Sweet, Director Library Services; ahima.org

AMERICAN SOCIETY OF ANESTHESIOLOGISTS, 1061 American Lane, Schaumburg, Illinois Zip 60173; tel: 847/268–9160, Paul Pomerantz, Chief Executive Officer; asahq.org

AMN HEALTHCARE, INC., 12400 High Bluff Drive, Suite 100, San Diego, California Zip 92130–3581; tel: 866/871–8519, Steve Wehn, Senior Vice President of Corporate Development; amnhealthcare.com

APOGEE PHYSICIANS, 15059 North Scottsdale Road, Suite 600, Scottsdale, Arizona Zip 85254–2685; tel: 602/778–3600, Michael Gregory, Chairman; apogeephysicians.com

ARENA, 502 South Sharp Street, Suite 2300, Baltimore, Maryland Zip 21201–2445; tel: 888/444–0693, Michael Finn, Vice President, Marketing; arena.io

ARIS RADIOLOGY, 5655 Hudson Drive, Suite 210, Hudson, Ohio Zip 44236; tel: 330/655–3800, Stacey Christofferson, Sales and Marketing; arisradiology.com

ASSOCIATION OF PERIOPERATIVE REGISTERED NURSES, 2170 South Parker Road, Suite 400, Denver, Colorado Zip 80231; tel: 303/755–6304, Linda Kay Groah, Executive Director and Chief Executive Officer; aorn.org

AVATAR SOLUTIONS, 25 East Washington Street, Suite 600, Chicago, Illinois Zip 60602; tel: 312/236–7170, Jeffrey Brady, Chief Executive Officer; hrsolutionsinc.com

BACTES, 8344 Clairemont Mesa Boulevard, Suite 201, San Diego, California Zip 92111–1327; tel: 858/244–1811, Rae Danell, Marketing Coordinator; bactes.com

BLUE CROSS AND BLUE SHIELD ASSOCIATION, 225 North Michigan Avenue, Chicago, Illinois Zip 60601–7680; tel: 312/297–6000, Scott P Serota, President and Chief Executive Officer; bcbs.com

BOARDVANTAGE, 4300 Bohannon Drive, Suite 110, Menlo Park, California Zip 94025; tel: 650/330–2444, Virginia Portillo, Conference and Events Coordinator; boardvantage.com

CANON SOLUTIONS AMERICA, INC., 300 Commerce Square Boulevard, Burlington, New Jersey Zip 08016–1270; tel: 847/706–3411, Paul T Murphy, Director Strategic Contract Support; solutions.canon.com

CAPROCK EMERGENCY HOSPITAL, 1630 Briarcrest Drive, Suite 100, Bryan, Texas Zip 77802–2709; tel: 979/314–2323, Lon Young, Chief Medical Officer; caprocker.com

CARECENTRIX, 20 Church Street, Floor 12th, Hartford, Connecticut Zip 06103–1246; tel: 800/808–1902, Sherl Brand, Senior Vice President Strategic Solutions; carecentrix.com

CERTIPHI SCREENING, INC., 1105 Industrial Highway, Southampton, Pennsylvania Zip 18966; tel: 888/260–1370, Tony D'Orazio, CEO; certiphi.com

CHANGE HEALTHCARE, 3535 Piedmont Road, Suite 800, Atlanta, Georgia Zip 30305–1543; tel: 404/279–5029, Kim R. Williams, Chief Financial Officer; changehealthcare.com

CISCO SYSTEMS, 165 Needletree Lane, Glastonbury, Connecticut Zip 6033; tel: 860/657–8127, Michael Haymaker, Director Healthcare Industry Marketing; cisco.com

COMPREHENSIVE PHARMACY SERVICES, 6409 North Quail Hollow Road, Memphis, Tennessee Zip 38120–1414; tel: 901/748–0470, Walker Upshaw, Chief Development Officer; cpspharm.com

CROSS COUNTRY HEALTHCARE, 5201 Congress Avenue, Boca Raton, Florida Zip 33487–3629; tel: 800/347–2264, Robert Murphy, President Workforce Solutions; crosscountryhealthcare.com

CYRACOM, 5780 North Swan Road, Tucson, Arizona Zip 85718–4527; tel: 800/713–4950, Jeremy Woan, President and Chief Executive Officer; cyracom.com

DISH, PO Box 5096524, Englewood, Colorado Zip 80112–5905; tel: 720/514–6019, Steven Wilson, Manager; dish.com

FIRST AMERICAN EQUIPMENT FINANCE, 255 Woodcliff Drive, Fairport, New York Zip 14450–4219; tel: 585/643–3266, Lori Dennis, Senior Vice President; faef.com

GALLAGHER BENEFIT SERVICES, 6525 Morrison Boulevard, Suite 200, Charlotte, North Carolina Zip 28211–3532; tel: 877/332–2265, James Craig Nelson, Senior Vice President; bfbgallagher.com

GOZIO HEALTH, 75 5th Street NW, Suite 2220, Atlanta, Georgia Zip 30308–1019; tel: 772/444–6946, Barbara Kragor, Vice President Sales and Customer Experience; goziohealth.com

HEALTHCARE REVENUE SOLUTIONS, 4851 Keller Springs Road, Suite 228, Addison, Texas Zip 75001; tel: 972/546–6491, Andre Kus, Chief Executive Officer; healthcarerevenuesolutions.org

HEALTHGRID, 4203 Vineland Road, Suite K6, Orlando, Florida Zip 32811; tel: 855/624–2844, Raj Toleti, Founder and Chief Executive Officer; healthgrid.com

HEALTHWAYS, INC, 701 Cool Springs Boulevard, Franklin, Tennessee Zip 37067–2697; tel: 800/327–3822, Karen Meyer, Principal; healthways.com

HMS, 355 Quartermaster Court, Jeffersonville, Indiana Zip 47130–3670; tel: 812/704–5747, Rich Flaherty, Vice President Sales and Marketing; hms.com

HOOPER, LUNDY & BOOKMAN, INC., 1875 Century Park East, Suite 1600, Los Angeles, California Zip 90067; tel: 310/551–8111, Lloyd Bookman, Partner; health–law.com

HOSPITALRECRUITING.COM, 899 South College Mall Road, Suite 395, Bloomington, Indiana Zip 47401–6301; tel: 800/244–7236, Michael Jones, Managing Partner; hospitalrecruiting.com

HYLAND SOFTWARE, INC., 28500 Clemens Road, Westlake, Ohio Zip 44145; tel: 440/788–5814, Michael Kortan, Director Health Care Solutions; onbase.com

IMALOGIX, 1150 First Avenue, Suite 450, King Of Prussia, Pennsylvania Zip 19406–1363; tel: 855/681–9100, David Steigerwalt, Product Manager; imalogix.com

INNOVATIVE CAPITAL LLC, 1489 Baltimore Pike, Building 400, Springfield, Pennsylvania Zip 19064–3958; tel: 610/543–2490, Alan P Richman, President and Chief Executive Officer; innovativecapital.com

INTALERE; tel: 877/711–5700, Laurie McGrath, Vice President Marketing; amerinet–gpo.com

INTELLICENTRICS, INC., 1420 Lakeside Parkway, Suite 110, Flower Mound, Texas Zip 75028; tel: 972/316–6209, Nimisha Savani, Chief Marketing Officer; intellicentrics.com

INTERACTIVE HEALTH SOLUTIONS, 3800 North Wilke Road, Suite 155, Arlington Heights, Illinois Zip 60004–1278; tel: 847/754–2698, Joseph O'Brien, President; interactivesolutions.com

IP SERVICES, 2896 Crescent Avenue, Suite 201, Eugene, Oregon Zip 97408–7422; tel: 541/343–5974, Mark Allers, Vice President Business Development; ipservices.com

JEWISH GUILD HEALTHCARE, 15 West 65th Street, New York, New York Zip 10023; tel: 212/769–6200, Alan R Morse, President and Chief Executive Officer; jgb.org

LANGUAGE LINE SOLUTIONS, One Lower Ragsdale Drive, Building 2, Monterey, California Zip 93940; tel: 800/752–6096, Suzanne duMont–Perez, Government Relations and Channel Manager; languageline.com

MEDICAL INFORMATION TECHNOLOGY, INC.; tel: 781/821–3000, Lynn Robblee, Supervisor of Event Coordination and Memberships; meditech.com

MEDISOLV, INC., 10440 Little Patuxent Parkway, Suite 1000, Columbia, Maryland Zip 21044–3630; tel: 443/539–0505, Erin Heilman, Marketing Specialist; medisolv.com

MEDNAX SERVICES INC., 1301 Concord Terrace, Sunrise, Florida Zip 33323–2843; tel: 954/384–0175, Roger J Medel, President; mednax.com

MODERN HEALTHCARE, 150 North Michigan Avenue, 17th Floor, Chicago, Illinois Zip 60601–3806; tel: 312/649–5491, Fawn Lopez, Publisher; modernhealthcare.com

MUCH SHELIST, 191 North Wacker Drive, Chicago, Illinois Zip 60606–1615; tel: 312/521–2000, Ned Milenkovich, Partner; muchshelist.com

NATIONAL COUNCIL OF STATE BOARDS OF NURSING, 111 East Wacker Drive, 29th Floor, Chicago, Illinois Zip 60601–4277; tel: 312/525–3600, David Charles Benton, Chief Executive Officer; ncsbn.org

OB HOSPITALIST GROUP, tel: 800/967–2289, Guy Kohn, Director, Marketing; obhg.com

PLANON CORPORATION, 45 Braintree Hill Office Park, Suite 400, Braintree, Massachusetts Zip 02184–8730; tel: 781/356–0999, Ellen Schwier, Marketing Manager; planonsoftware.com

*The members listed in **bold** are Associate Advantage members*

PROASSURANCE, 100 Brookwood Place, Birmingham, Alabama Zip 35209–6811; tel: 205/877–4400, W Stancil Starnes, Chairman, Chief Executive Officer; proassurance.com

PROMED HEALTHCARE FINANCING, 1001 Woodward Avenue, Suite 1700, Detroit, Michigan Zip 48226–1904; tel: 631/707–4347, Dan De Chiaro, Director of Operations; promedhcf.com

QUARLES AND BRADY LLP, 300 North LaSalle Street, Suite 4000, Chicago, Illinois Zip 60654–3422; tel: 312/715–2751, Susan Stewart, Director, Client Relations; quarles.com

RRS, 416 Longshore Drive, Ann Arbor, Michigan Zip 48103; tel: 800/517–9634, Nicole Chardoul, Partner and Vice President; recycle.com

SAN–I–PAK, INC., PO Box 1183, Tracy, California Zip 95378; tel: 209/836–2310, Kristy Coleman, Project Manager; sanipak.com

SIMPLEX GRINNELL, 50 Technology Drive, Westminster, Massachusetts Zip 1441; tel: 978/731–8486, Suzanne Rahall, Marketing Manager, Healthcare Communications; simplexgrinnell.com

SUBWAY, 325 Bic Drive, Milford, Connecticut Zip 6461; tel: 800/888–4848, Joanne Kilgore, Global Account Manager; subway.com

TANDEM HOSPITAL PARTNERS, 1415 Louisiana Street, Houston, Texas Zip 77002–7360; tel: 713/999–0837, Debora Simmons, Chief Quality Officer and Chief Nursing Officer; tandemhospitalpartners.com

THE AMERICAN COLLEGE OF OBSTETRICIANS AND GYNECOLOGISTS, 409 12th Street, SW, Washington, District of Columbia Zip 20024–2188; tel: 202/638–5577, Hal Lawrence, Executive Vice President; acog.org

THE CPI GROUP, 7400 East Orchard Road, Suite 270, Englewood, Colorado Zip 80111; tel: 303/504–9999, John Van Gulik, Business Development Manager; thecpigroup.net

THE WALKER COMPANY, 31090 SW Boones Bend Road, Wilsonville, Oregon Zip 97070–6412; tel: 503/694–8539, Larry W Walker, Principal; walkercompany.com

TRACE SECURITY, 6300 Corporate Boulevard, Baton Rouge, Louisiana Zip 70809–1097; tel: 877/275–3009, Marissa Adams, Marketing Coordinator; tracesecurity.com

TRANSAMERICA RETIREMENT SOLUTIONS, 4 Manhattanville Road, Purchase, New York Zip 10577; tel: 914/697–8952, Peter Kunkel, President and Chief Executive Officer; https://www.trsretire.com

TRAPOLLO, 13900 Lincoln Park Drive, 5th Floor, Herndon, Virginia Zip 20171; tel: 866/807–5047, Lisa Majdi, Marketing Director; trapollo.com

UBS, 315 Deaderick Street, Nashville, Tennessee Zip 37238–3000; tel: 615/393–7549, Whit Mayo, Managing Director; ubs.com

UNIFORM DATA SYSTEM FOR MEDICAL REHABILITATION, 270 Northpointe Parkway, Suite 300, Amherst, New York Zip 14228; tel: 716/817–7800, Troy Hillman, Manager, Analytical Services Group; udsmr.org

USDTL, 1700 South Mount Prospect Road, Des Plaines, Illinois Zip 60018–1804; tel: 847/375–0770, Catharine Steccato, Vice President Business Development; usdtl.com

VANGUARD MODULAR BUILDING SYSTEMS, LLC, 3 Great Valley Parkway, Suite 170, Malvern, Pennsylvania Zip 19355–1417; tel: 610/240–8686, Mark Meyers, Vice President, Marketing Services; vanguardmodular.com

VERISYS CORPORATION, 1001 North Fairfax Avenue, Suite 640, Alexandria, Virginia Zip 22314–1798; tel: 703/535–1471, John Benson, Chief Operating Officer; verisys.com/

VESTAGEN TECHNICAL TEXTILES, INC., tel: 407/781–2395, Brian Crawford, Chief Business Officer; vestagen.com

VIGILANZ CORPORATION, 5775 Wayzata Boulevard, Suite 970, Minneapolis, Minnesota Zip 55416–2669; tel: 855/525–9078, David Goldsteen, Chairman and Chief Executive Officer; vigilanzcorp.com

VITAS HEALTHCARE, 201 South Biscayne Boulevard, Suite 400, Miami, Florida Zip 33131; tel: 305/374–4143, Drew Landmeier, Chief Marketing Officer; vistas.com

VIZIENT, 799 9th Street Northwest, Suite 210, Washington, District of Columbia Zip 20001–5325; tel: 202/354–2600, Shoshana Krilow, Vice President Public Policy and Government Relations; https://www.vizientinc.com/

WELLTOWER, INC., 4500 Dorr Street, Toledo, Ohio Zip 43615–4040; tel: 419/247–2800, Rachel Watson, Assistant Vice President; welltower.com

WITT/KIEFFER, 2015 Spring Rd, Ste 510, Oak Brook, Illinois Zip 60523; tel: 630/990–1370, James Gauss, Chairman of Board Services; wittkieffer.com/

YOURCARE UNIVERSE, INC, 6550 Carothers Parkway, Suite 100, Franklin, Tennessee Zip 37067; tel: 844/641–6800, Lauren Douglass, Brand Manager; yourcareuniverse.com

Recruitment Services

DOCCAFE.COM, tel: 574/453–3131, Briana Wick, Digital Marketing Director; doccafe.com

Regional Health Care Assn

TEXAS ORGANIZATION OF RURAL & COMMUNITY HOSPITALS, P O Box 203878, Austin, Texas Zip 78720–3878; tel: 512/873–0045, John Henderson, Chief Executive Officer; torchnet.org

CANADA

Provincial Hospital Assn

ONTARIO HOSPITAL ASSOCIATION, 200 Front Street West, Suite 2800, Toronto, Ontario Zip M5V 3L1; tel: 416/205–1300, Hazim Hassan, Vice President, Business Planning and Strategy; oha.com

BAHAMAS

Other

PRINCESS MARGARET HOSPITAL, P O Box N–8200, Nassau, tel: 242/322–2861, Mary Elizabeth Lightbourne–Walker, Hospital Administrator; phabahamas.org

BAHRAIN

Other

INTERNATIONAL HOSPITAL OF BAHRAIN, P O Box 1084, Manama, tel: 11/759–8222, F. S. Zeerah, President; ihb.net/

BRAZIL

Other

HOSPITAL SAMARITANO, RUA CONSELHEIRO BROTERO, 1486, Sao Paulo, Zip 01232–010; tel: 551/821–5300, Luiz Alberto Oliveira De Luca, Corporate Superintendent; samaritano.com.br

COLOMBIA

Other

ASOCIACION COLOMBIANA DE HOSPITALES Y CLINICAS, Carrera 4, No 73–15, Bogota, Juan Carlos Giraldo Valencia, Director General; achc.org.co

DOMINICAN REPUBLIC

Other

UNITED TELEMEDICINE NETWORK–HOSPITAL CHARLES DE GAULLE, Av Charles de Gaulle #43, Santo Domingo, Zip 11509; tel: 829/345–9335, Horacio Stagno, Commercial Director; hospitalunited.com

GEORGIA

Other

BOKHUA MEMORIAL CARDIOVASCULAR CENTER, Chachava 1 Street, Tbilisi, Zip 159, Giorgi Kipiani, Director

INNOVA MEDICAL CENTER, 7A Sandra Euli Street, Tbilisi, Zip 105, Giorgi Kipiani, Director; innovamedical.ge

MARITIME HOSPITAL JSC, Melikishrin 102B, Batumi, Zip 60100, Tamari Kachlishvili, Medical Director; mh.com.ge

MEDI CLUB GEORGIA, 22A, Tashkenti Street, Tbilisi, Zip 160; tel: 995/225–1991, Nugzar Abramishvili, General Director; mediclubgeorgia.ge

TBILISI CENTRAL HOSPITAL, Chachava Street 1, Tbilisi, Zip 159, Ivane Martiashuili, Co–founder; tch.ge

ZHORDANIA CLINIC, Chachava N1, Tbilisi, Zip 159, Tamar Kobiashvili, Director

JORDAN

Other

SPECIALTY HOSPITAL, P O Box 930186, Amman, Zip 11193, Fawzi Al–Hammouri, General Manager; specialty-hospital.com

LEBANON

Other

SAINT GEORGE HOSPITAL UNIVERSITY MEDICAL CENTER, P O Box 166378, Beirut, Zip 1100–2807; tel: 961/158–5700, Dimitri Haddad, Director; stgeorgehospital.org

MEXICO

Other

SHRINERS HOSPITAL FOR CHILDREN, Av Del Iman 257, Col Pedregal de Santa Ursula, Delegacion Coyoacan, Mexico City, Zip 4600; tel: 525/424–7850, Mariano Gonzalez Lugo, Administrator; shrinershospitalsforchildren.org/locations/mexicocity

MYANMAR

Other

ASIA ROYAL GENERAL HOSPITAL, 14 Baho Street, Sanchaung Township, Yangon, Zip 11162; tel: 951/153–8055, Myat Thu, Managing Director; asiaroyalmedical.com

NIGERIA

Consulting Firm

PETALICE MEDICAL CENTRE, 5/7 Marickson Hospital Way, Uyo, Akwa Ibom State, Zip 520241, Cletus Bassey, Archbishop

PANAMA

Other

CLINICA HOSPITAL SAN FERNANDO, S. A., Dept PTY 1663, P O Box 25207, Miami, Florida Zip 33102–5207; tel: 507/305–6399, Jose Manuel Teran Sitton, Medical Director; hospitalsanfernando.com

PERU

Other

BRITISH AMERICAN HOSPITAL, Avenue Alfredo Salazar 3 Era, Lima 27, tel: 511/712–3000, Gonzalo Garrido–Lecca, Director; angloamericana.com.pe

PHILIPPINES

Other

ST. LUKE'S MEDICAL CENTER, 279 East Rodriguez Sr Boulevard, Quezon City, tel: 632/723–0101, Edgardo R Cortez, President and Chief Executive Officer; stluke.com.ph/home

SAUDI ARABIA

Other

ABDUL RAHMAN AL MISHARI GENERAL HOSPITAL, OLAYA, P.O. Box 56929, Riyadh, Zip 11564; tel: 11/465–7700, Abdul Rahman Al Mishari, President; drabdulrahmanalmishari.com.sa/

MUHAMMAD SALEH BASHARAHIL HOSPITAL, P O Box 10505, Madinah Road, Omora Gadida, Makkah, tel: 9/520–4444, Turki M Basharahil, General Manager; msbasharahil.com/

NABIL AL KADI CONSULTANT ENGINEERS, Dammam, Damman, Taufik Ridani, Chief Executive Officer

SPAIN

Information Systems

SIGESA, S.A., CALLE GUATEMALA, 14, 4b, Madrid, Zip 28016; tel: 349/345–4018, Francisco Alvarez, Chief Financial Officer; sigesa.com

TURKEY

Other

ARTE CERRAHI HASTENESI, 1920 Cad. No:61 Cayyolu, Ankara, Zip 6810; tel: 903/236–1001, Oguz Engiz, Chief Executive Officer; artesaglik.com

UNITED ARAB EMIRATES

Other

AMERICAN HOSPITAL–DUBAI, Oud Metha Road, P.O. Box 5566, Dubai, tel: 11/336–7777, Saeed M Almulla, Chairman; https://www.ahdubai.com/en/

UNITED KINGDOM

Other

FINANSCO HEALTHCARE, 11A Blacka Moor Road, Sheffield, tel: 448/225–3844, Rukhsar Khan, Chief Executive Officer; finansco.com

B

Health Care Systems, Networks and Alliances

B2   Introduction

   3   Statistics for Multihospital Health Care Systems and their Hospitals

   4   Health Care Systems and their Hospitals

150   Headquarters of Health Care Systems, Geographically

159   Networks and their Hospitals

175   Alliances

Section B

Introduction

This section includes listings for networks, health care systems and alliances.

Health Care Systems

To reflect the diversity that exists among health care organizations, this publication uses the term health care system to identify both multihospital and diversified single hospital systems.

Multihospital Systems

A multihospital health care system is two or more hospitals owned, leased, sponsored, or contract managed by a central organization.

Single Hospital Systems

Single, freestanding member hospitals may be categorized as health care systems by bringing into membership three or more, and at least 25 percent, of their owned or leased non–hospital preacute and postacute health care organizations. (For purposes of definition, health care delivery is the availability of professional healthcare staff during all hours of the organization's operations). Organizations provide, or provide and finance, diagnostic, therapeutic, and/or consultative patient or client services that normally precede or follow acute, inpatient, hospitalization; or that serve to prevent or substitute for such hospitalization. These services are provided in either a freestanding facility not eligible for licensure as a hospital under state statue or through one that is a subsidiary of a hospital.

The first part of this section is an alphabetical list of health care systems which are listed under the system by state. Data for this section were compiled from the 2018 *Annual Survey* and the membership information base as published in section A of the *AHA Guide*.

One of the following codes appears after the name of each system listed to indicate the type of organizational control reported by that system:

CC Catholic (Roman) church–related system, not–for–profit

CO Other church–related system, not–for–profit

NP Other not–for–profit system, including nonfederal, governmental systems

IO Investor–owned, for profit system

FG Federal Government

One of the following codes appears after the name of each hospital to indicate how that hospital is related to the system:

O Owned

L Leased

S Sponsored

CM Contract–managed

Health System Classification System

An identification system for Health Systems was developed jointly by the American Hospital Association's Health Research and Education Trust and Health Forum, and the University of California-Berkeley.[1] A health system is assigned to one of five categories based on how much they differentiate and centralized their hospital services, physician arrangements, and provider-based insurance products. Differentiation refers to the number of different products or services that the organization offers. Centralization refers to whether decision-making and service delivery emanate from the system level more so than individual hospitals.

Categories:

Centralized Health System: A delivery system in which the system centrally organizes individual hospital service delivery, physician arrangements, and insurance product development. The number of different products/services that are offered across the system is moderate.

Centralized Physician/Insurance Health System: A delivery system with highly centralized physician arrangements and insurance product development. Within this group, hospital services are relatively decentralized with individual hospitals having discretion over the array of services they offer. The number of different products/services that are offered across the system is moderate.

Moderately Centralized Health System: A delivery system that is distinguished by the presence of both centralized and decentralized activity for hospital services, physician arrangements, and insurance product development. For example, a system within this group may have centralized care of expensive, high technology services, such as open heart surgery, but allows individual hospitals to provide an array of other health services based on local needs. The number of different products/services that are offered across the system is moderate.

Decentralized Health System: A delivery system with a high degree of decentralized of hospital services, physician arrangements, and insurance product development. Within this group, systems may lack an overarching structure for coordination. Service and product differentiation is high, which may explain why centralization is hard to achieve. In this group, the system may simply service a role in sharing information and providing administrative support to highly developed local delivery systems centered around hospitals.

Independent Hospital System: A delivery system with limited differentiation in hospital services, physician arrangements, and insurance product development. These systems are largely horizontal affiliations of autonomous hospitals.

No Assignment: For some systems sufficient data from the Annual Survey were not available to determine a cluster assignment.

The second part of this section lists health care systems indexed geographically by state and city. Every effort has been made to be as inclusive and accurate as possible. However, as in all efforts of this type, there may be omissions. For further information, write to the Section for Health Care Systems, American Hospital Association, 155 N. Wacker Drive, Chicago, IL 60606.

Networks

The *AHA Guide* shows listings of networks. A network is defined as a group of hospitals, physicians, other providers, insurers and/or community agencies that work together to coordinate and deliver a broad spectrum of services to their community. Organizations listed represent the lead or hub of the network activity. Networks are listed by state, then alphabetically by name including participating partners.

The network identification process has purposely been designed to capture networks of varying organization type. Sources include but are not limited to the following: *AHA Annual Survey*, national, state and metropolitan associations, national news and periodical searches, and the networks and their health care providers themselves. Therefore, networks are included regardless of whether a hospital or healthcare system is the network lead. When an individual hospital does appear in the listing, it is indicative of the role the hospital plays as the network lead. In addition, the network listing is not mutually exclusive of the hospital, health care system or alliance listings within this publication.

Networks are very fluid in their composition as goals evolve and partners change. Therefore, some of the networks included in this listing may have dissolved, reformed, or simply been renamed as this section was being produced for publication.

The network identification process is an ongoing and responsive initiative. As more information is collected and validated, it will be made available in other venues, in addition to the *AHA Guide*. For more information concerning the network identification process, please contact The American Hospital Association Resource Center at 312/422–2050.

Alliances

An alliance is a formal organization, usually owned by shareholders/members, that works on behalf of its individual members in the provision of services and products and in the promotion of activities and ventures. The organization functions under a set of bylaws or other written rules to which each member agrees to abide.

Alliances are listed alphabetically by name. Its members are listed alphabetically by state, city, and then by member name.

[1]Bazzoli, CJ; Shortell, SM; Dubbs, N; Chan, C; and Kralovec, P; "A Taxonomy of Health networks and Systems: Bringing Order Out of Chaos" *Health Services Research*, February; 1999

Statistics for Health Care Systems and their Hospitals

The following tables describing health care systems refers to information in section B of the 2020 *AHA Guide*.

Table 1 shows the number of health care systems by type of control. Table 2 provides a breakdown of the number of systems that own, lease, sponsor or contract manage hospitals within each control category. Table 3 gives the number of hospitals and beds in each control category as well as total hospitals and beds. Finally, Table 4 shows the percentage of hospitals and beds in each control category.

For more information on health care systems, please write to the Section for Health Care Systems, 155 N. Wacker Drive, Chicago, Illinois 60606 or call 312/422–3000.

Table 1. Multihospital Health Care Systems, by Type of Organizaton Control

Type of Control	Code	Number of Systems
Catholic (Roman) church–related	CC	26
Other church–related	CO	7
Subtotal, church–related		33
Other not–for–profit	NP	310
Subtotal, not–for–profit		343
Investor Owned	IO	80
Federal Government	FG	5
Total		428

Table 2. Multihospital Health Care Systems, by Type of Ownership and Control

Type of Ownership	Catholic Church–Related (CC)	Other Church–Related (CO)	Total Church–Related (CC + CO)	Other Not–for–Profit (NP)	Total Not–for–Profit (CC, CO, + NP)	Investor–Owned (IO)	Federal Govern–ment (FG)	All Systems
Systems that only own, lease or sponsor	18	6	24	185	209	17	4	230
Systems that only contract–manage	0	0	0	13	13	5	0	18
Systems that manage, own, lease, or sponsor	8	1	9	112	121	58	1	180
Total	26	7	33	310	343	80	5	428

Table 3. Hospitals and Beds in Multihospital Health Care Systems, by Type of Ownership and Control

Type of Ownership	Catholic Church–Related (CC)		Other Church–Related (CO)		Total Church–Related (CC + CO)		Other Not–for–Profit (NP)		Total Not–for–Profit (CC, CO, + NP)		Investor–Owned (IO)		Federal Govern–ment (FG)		All Systems	
	H	B	H	B	H	B	H	B	H	B	H	B	H	B	H	B
Owned, leased or sponsored	572	102,790	79	18,194	651	120,984	1,661	354,862	2,312	475,846	1,365	164,493	203	38,668	3,880	679,007
Contract–managed	43	2,442	3	485	46	2,927	128	9,283	174	12,210	104	5,712	0	0	278	17,922
Total	615	105,232	82	18,679	697	123,911	1,789	364,145	2,486	488,056	1,469	170,205	203	38,668	4,158	696,929

H = hospitals; B = beds.

Table 4. Hospitals and Beds in Multihospital Health Care Systems, by Type of Ownership and Control as a Percentage of All Systems

Type of Ownership	Catholic Church–Related (CC)		Other Church–Related (CO)		Total Church–Related (CC + CO)		Other Not–for–Profit (NP)		Total Not–for–Profit (CC, CO, + NP)		Investor–Owned (IO)		Federal Govern–ment (FG)		All Systems	
	H	B	H	B	H	B	H	B	H	B	H	B	H	B	H	B
Owned, leased or sponsored	14.7	15.1	2.0	2.7	16.8	17.8	42.8	52.3	59.6	70.1	35.2	24.2	5.2	5.7	99.9	100
Contract managed	15.5	13.6	1.1	2.7	16.6	16.3	46.0	52.3	62.6	68.1	37.4	24.2	0	5.7	100	98.5
Total	10.8	15.1	1.4	2.7	12.3	17.8	58.4	52.3	70.6	70.0	25.8	24.2	3.6	5.7	100	100

H = hospitals; B = beds.

*Please note that figures may not always equal the provided subtotal or total percentages due to rounding.

0091: ACADIA HEALTHCARE COMPANY, INC. (IO)
830 Crescent Centre Drive, Suite 610, Franklin, TN, Zip 37067–7323; tel. 615/861–6000; Debra Osteen, Chief Executive Officer
(Decentralized Health System)

ARIZONA: OASIS BEHAVIORAL HEALTH – CHANDLER (O, 47 beds) 2190 North Grace Boulevard, Chandler, AZ, Zip 85225–3416; tel. 480/917–9301; James Gallagher, Chief Executive Officer

SONORA BEHAVIORAL HEALTH HOSPITAL (O, 106 beds) 6050 North Corona Road, #3, Tucson, AZ, Zip 85704–1096; tel. 520/469–8700; Edeli Kinsala, Chief Executive Officer

ARKANSAS: CONWAY BEHAVIORAL HEALTH HOSPITAL (O, 60 beds) 2255 Sturgis Road, Conway, AR, Zip 72034–8029; tel. 501/858–3048; Doris Singleton, Chief Executive Officer
Web address: www.conwaybh.com

RIVERVIEW BEHAVIORAL HEALTH (O, 62 beds) 701 Arkansas Boulevard, Texarkana, AR, Zip 71854–2105; tel. 870/772–5028; Allison De Bruycker, Chief Executive Officer

VALLEY BEHAVIORAL HEALTH SYSTEM (O, 114 beds) 10301 Mayo Drive, Barling, AR, Zip 72923–1660; tel. 479/494–5700; Andrea Norman, Chief Executive Officer
Web address: www.valleybehavioral.com

VANTAGE POINT OF NORTHWEST ARKANSAS (O, 114 beds) 4253 North Crossover Road, Fayetteville, AR, Zip 72703–4596; tel. 479/521–5731; Megan Wedgworth, Chief Executive Officer
Web address: www.vantagepointnwa.com

CALIFORNIA: PACIFIC GROVE HOSPITAL (O, 68 beds) 5900 Brockton Avenue, Riverside, CA, Zip 92506–1862; tel. 951/275–8400; Nichol Sheffield, Chief Executive Officer

SAN JOSE BEHAVORIAL HEALTH (O, 80 beds) 455 Silicon Valley Boulevard, San Jose, CA, Zip 95138–1858; tel. 888/210–2484; Rob Marsh, Chief Executive Officer
Web address: www.sanjosebh.com

DELAWARE: MEADOW WOOD BEHAVIORAL HEALTH SYSTEM (O, 53 beds) 575 South Dupont Highway, New Castle, DE, Zip 19720–4606; tel. 302/328–3330; Bill A. Mason, Chief Executive Officer
Web address: www.meadowwoodhospital.com

FLORIDA: NORTH TAMPA BEHAVIORAL HEALTH (O, 78 beds) 29910 State Road 56, Wesley Chapel, FL, Zip 33543–8800; tel. 813/922–3300; Tracy Rogers, Chief Executive Officer
Web address: www.northtampabehavioralhealth.com

PARK ROYAL HOSPITAL (O, 114 beds) 9241 Park Royal Drive, Fort Myers, FL, Zip 33908–9204; tel. 239/985–2700; Michael Ham, Chief Executive Officer

GEORGIA: GREENLEAF BEHAVIORAL HEALTH HOSPITAL (O, 73 beds) 2209 Pineview Drive, Valdosta, GA, Zip 31602–7316; tel. 229/247–4357; Bryan D. Adams, Chief Executive Officer
Web address: www.greenleafcounseling.net

LAKEVIEW BEHAVIORAL HEALTH (O, 70 beds) 1 Technology Parkway South, Norcross, GA, Zip 30092–2928; tel. 678/713–2600; Bill Anderson, Chief Executive Officer

RIVERWOODS BEHAVIORAL HEALTH SYSTEM (O, 75 beds) 233 Medical Center Drive, Riverdale, GA, Zip 30274–2640; tel. 770/991–8500; John B. Warburton, Chief Executive Officer
Web address: www.riverwoodsbehavioral.com

INDIANA: OPTIONS BEHAVIORAL HEALTH SYSTEM (O, 84 beds) 5602 Caito Drive, Indianapolis, IN, Zip 46226–1346; tel. 317/544–4340; Chris Rupert, Chief Executive Officer
Web address: www.optionsbehavioralhealthsystem.com/

LOUISIANA: COVINGTON BEHAVIORIAL HEALTH (O, 60 beds) 201 Greenbrier Boulevard, Covington, LA, Zip 70433–7236; tel. 985/893–2970; Tanmay Mathur, Chief Executive Officer
Web address: www.greenbrierhospital.com/

LONGLEAF HOSPITAL (O, 92 beds) 44 Versailles Boulevard, Alexandria, LA, Zip 71303–3960; tel. 318/445–5111; Claire Hick, Chief Executive Officer

RIVER PLACE BEHAVIORAL HEALTH (O, 82 beds) 500 Rue De Sante, La Place, LA, Zip 70068–5418; tel. 985/303–2327; Jeremy Pitzer, Chief Executive Officer
Web address: www.riverplacebh.com

VERMILION BEHAVIORAL HEALTH SYSTEMS – NORTH CAMPUS (O, 78 beds) 2520 North University Avenue, Lafayette, LA, Zip 70507–5306; tel. 337/234–5614; Stephanie Hrdlicka, Chief Executive Officer

MASSACHUSETTS: SOUTHCOAST BEHAVIORAL HEALTH (O, 120 beds) 581 Faunce Corner Road, Dartmouth, MA, Zip 02747–1242; tel. 888/210–2475; Richard Remley, Chief Executive Officer
Web address: www.southcoastbehavioral.com

MICHIGAN: HARBOR OAKS HOSPITAL (O, 99 beds) 35031 23 Mile Road, New Baltimore, MI, Zip 48047–3649; tel. 586/725–5777; Briana Jacob, Chief Executive Officer
Web address: www.harboroaks.com

STONECREST CENTER (O, 162 beds) 15000 Gratiot Avenue, Detroit, MI, Zip 48205–1973; tel. 313/245–0600; Steve Savage, Chief Executive Officer

MISSOURI: LAKELAND BEHAVIORAL HEALTH SYSTEM (O, 206 beds) 440 South Market Street, Springfield, MO, Zip 65806–2026; tel. 417/865–5581; Nathan Duncan, Chief Executive Officer
Web address: www.lakeland-hospital.com

NEVADA: SEVEN HILLS HOSPITAL (O, 134 beds) 3021 West Horizon Ridge Parkway, Henderson, NV, Zip 89052–3990; tel. 702/646–5000; Christopher West, Chief Executive Officer

OHIO: OHIO HOSPITAL FOR PSYCHIATRY (O, 130 beds) 880 Greenlawn Avenue, Columbus, OH, Zip 43223–2616; tel. 614/449–9664; Angel Piper, Chief Executive Officer
Web address: www.ohiohospitalforpsychiatry.com/

TEN LAKES CENTER (O, 16 beds) 819 North First Street, 3rd Floor, Dennison, OH, Zip 44621–1003; tel. 740/922–7499; Debra C. Gardner, R.N., MSN, Administrator
Web address: www.tenlakescenter.com/

OKLAHOMA: ROLLING HILLS HOSPITAL (O, 108 beds) 1000 Rolling Hills Lane, Ada, OK, Zip 74820–9415; tel. 580/436–3600; Dennis Gober, Interim Chief Executive Officer
Web address: www.rollinghillshospital.com

PENNSYLVANIA: BELMONT BEHAVIORAL HOSPITAL (O, 171 beds) 4200 Monument Road, Philadelphia, PA, Zip 19131–1625; tel. 215/877–2000; Mark Schor, Chief Executive Officer

SOUTHWOOD PSYCHIATRIC HOSPITAL (O, 156 beds) 2575 Boyce Plaza Road, Pittsburgh, PA, Zip 15241–3925; tel. 412/257–2290; Stephen J. Quigley, Chief Executive Officer
Web address: www.southwoodhospital.com

PUERTO RICO: SAN JUAN CAPESTRANO HOSPITAL (O, 158 beds) Rural Route 2, Box 11, San Juan, PR, Zip 926; tel. 787/625–2900; Marta Rivera. Plaza, Chief Executive Officer and Managing Director

SOUTH CAROLINA: REBOUND BEHAVIORAL HEALTH (O, 42 beds) 134 East Rebound Road, Lancaster, SC, Zip 29720–7712; tel. 877/959–5063; Patricia Hamilton, Chief Executive Officer
Web address: www.reboundbehavioralhealth.com

TENNESSEE: CRESTWYN BEHAVIORAL HEALTH (O, 60 beds) 9485 Crestwyn Hills Cove, Memphis, TN, Zip 38125–8515; tel. 901/248–1500; Debby Willis, Chief Executive Officer
Web address: www.crestwynbh.com

DELTA MEDICAL CENTER (O, 167 beds) 3000 Getwell Road, Memphis, TN, Zip 38118–2299; tel. 901/369–8100; Phil Willcoxon, Chief Executive Officer
Web address: www.deltamedcenter.com

TRUSTPOINT HOSPITAL (O, 101 beds) 1009 North Thompson Lane, Murfreesboro, TN, Zip 37129–4351; tel. 615/867–1111; Beth Goodner, Chief Executive Officer

For explanation of codes following names, see page B2.
★ Indicates Type III membership in the American Hospital Association.

TEXAS: CROSS CREEK HOSPITAL (O, 90 beds) 8402 Cross Park Drive, Austin, TX, Zip 78754; tel. 512/215–3900; Coleby Wright, Chief Executive Officer
Web address: www.cornerstonehealthcaregroup.com

RED RIVER HOSPITAL, LLC (O, 96 beds) 1505 Eighth Street, Wichita Falls, TX, Zip 76301–3106; tel. 940/322–3171; James Wilfer, Chief Executive Officer

UTAH: HIGHLAND RIDGE HOSPITAL (O, 83 beds) 7309 South 180 West, Midvale, UT, Zip 84047–3769; tel. 801/569–2153; Michelle Neville, Chief Executive Officer
Web address: www.highlandridgehospital.com

WASHINGTON: CASCADE BEHAVIORAL HOSPITAL (O, 63 beds) 12844 Military Road South, Tukwila, WA, Zip 98168–3045; tel. 206/244–0180; Michael Uradnik, Chief Executive Officer
Web address: www.cascadebh.com

Owned, leased, sponsored:	38 hospitals	3672 beds
Contract-managed:	0 hospitals	0 beds
Totals:	38 hospitals	3672 beds

★0640: ACUITYHEALTHCARE, LP (IO)
10200 Mallard Creek Road, Suite 300, Charlotte, NC, Zip 28262–9705; tel. 704/887–7280; Edwin H. Cooper Jr, President and Chief Executive Officer
(Independent Hospital System)

NEW JERSEY: ACUITY SPECIALTY HOSPITAL OF NEW JERSEY (O, 30 beds) 1925 Pacific Avenue, 7th Floor, 5 Wellness, Atlantic City, NJ, Zip 08401–6713; tel. 609/441–2122; Monica B. Titus, R.N., Chief Executive Officer

ACUITY SPECIALTY HOSPITAL OF SOUTHERN NEW JERSEY (O, 53 beds) 218 A Sunset Road, Willingboro, NJ, Zip 08046–1110, Mailing Address: 220 Sunset Road, Zip 08046–1110, tel. 609/835–3650; Garrett Arneson, FACHE, R.N., Chief Executive Officer
Web address: www.willingboro.acuityhealthcare.net

OHIO: ACUITY SPECIALTY HOSPITALS OHIO VALLEY (O, 52 beds) 380 Summit Avenue, 3rd Floor, Steubenville, OH, Zip 43952–2667; tel. 740/283–7600; Judy K. Weaver, MS, Chief Executive Officer
Web address: www.acuityhealthcare.net

Owned, leased, sponsored:	3 hospitals	135 beds
Contract-managed:	0 hospitals	0 beds
Totals:	3 hospitals	135 beds

0895: ADENA HEALTH SYSTEM (NP)
272 Hospital Road, Chillicothe, OH, Zip 45601–9031, Mailing Address: PO Box 802846, Kansas City, MO, Zip 64180–2846, tel. 740/779–7500; Jeff Graham, President and Chief Executive Officer
(Independent Hospital System)

OHIO: ADENA GREENFIELD MEDICAL CENTER (O, 25 beds) 550 Mirabeau Street, Greenfield, OH, Zip 45123–1617; tel. 937/981–9400; Josh McCoy, Administrator
Web address: www.adena.org

ADENA MEDICAL CENTER (O, 236 beds) 272 Hospital Road, Chillicothe, OH, Zip 45601–9031; tel. 740/779–7500; Jeff Graham, President and Chief Executive Officer

ADENA PIKE MEDICAL CENTER (O, 25 beds) 100 Dawn Lane, Waverly, OH, Zip 45690–9138; tel. 740/947–2186; David M. Zanni, Administrator
Web address: www.adena.org

Owned, leased, sponsored:	3 hospitals	286 beds
Contract-managed:	0 hospitals	0 beds
Totals:	3 hospitals	286 beds

★4165: ADVENTHEALTH (CO)
900 Hope Way, Altamonte Springs, FL, Zip 32714–1502; tel. 407/357–1000; Terry Shaw, President and Chief Executive Officer
(Decentralized Health System)

COLORADO: AVISTA ADVENTIST HOSPITAL (O, 108 beds) 100 Health Park Drive, Louisville, CO, Zip 80027–9583; tel. 303/673–1000; Jillyan McKinney, Chief Executive Officer

CASTLE ROCK ADVENTIST HOSPITAL (O, 53 beds) 2350 Meadows Boulevard, Castle Rock, CO, Zip 80109–8405; tel. 720/455–5000; Brandon M. Nudd, Chief Executive Officer
Web address: www.castlerockhospital.org

LITTLETON ADVENTIST HOSPITAL (O, 176 beds) 7700 South Broadway Street, Littleton, CO, Zip 80122–2628; tel. 303/730–8900; Geoff Lawton, Interim Chief Executive Officer

PARKER ADVENTIST HOSPITAL (O, 167 beds) 9395 Crown Crest Boulevard, Parker, CO, Zip 80138–8573; tel. 303/269–4000; Michael Goebel, Chief Executive Officer
Web address: www.parkerhospital.org

PORTER ADVENTIST HOSPITAL (O, 250 beds) 2525 South Downing Street, Denver, CO, Zip 80210–5876; tel. 303/778–1955; Todd Folkenberg, Chief Executive Officer
Web address: www.porterhospital.org/poh/home/

FLORIDA: ADVENTHEALTH CARROLLWOOD (O, 96 beds) 7171 North Dale Mabry Highway, Tampa, FL, Zip 33614–2665; tel. 813/932–2222; Erika Skula, President and Chief Executive Officer
Web address: https://www.floridahospital.com/carrollwood

ADVENTHEALTH CONNERTON (O, 50 beds) 9441 Health Center Drive, Land O'Lakes, FL, Zip 34637–5837; tel. 813/903–3701; Brian Adams, President and Chief Executive Officer

ADVENTHEALTH DADE CITY (O, 120 beds) 13100 Fort King Road, Dade City, FL, Zip 33525–5294; tel. 352/521–1100; Amanda Maggard, Chief Executive Officer
Web address: www.floridahospital.com/dade-city

ADVENTFAITH DAYTONA BEACH (O, 326 beds) 301 Memorial Medical Parkway, Daytona Beach, FL, Zip 32117–5167; tel. 386/676–6000; Ed Noseworthy, Chief Executive Officer
Web address: www.floridahospitalmemorial.org

ADVENTHEALTH DELAND (O, 164 beds) 701 West Plymouth Avenue, DeLand, FL, Zip 32720–3236; tel. 386/943–4522; Lorenzo Brown, Chief Executive Officer

ADVENTHEALTH FISH MEMORIAL (O, 175 beds) 1055 Saxon Boulevard, Orange City, FL, Zip 32763–8468; tel. 386/917–5000; Robert Deininger, Chief Executive Officer
Web address: www.fhfishmemorial.org

ADVENTHEALTH HEART OF FLORIDA (O, 193 beds) 40100 Highway 27, Davenport, FL, Zip 33837–5906; tel. 863/422–4971; Brian Adams, Chief Executive Officer
Web address: www.heartofflorida.com

ADVENTHEALTH LAKE WALES (O, 150 beds) 410 South 11th Street, Lake Wales, FL, Zip 33853–4256; tel. 863/676–1433; Brian Adams, Chief Executive Officer
Web address: www.lakewalesmedicalcenter.com

ADVENTHEALTH NEW SMYRNA BEACH (O, 95 beds) 401 Palmetto Street, New Smyrna Beach, FL, Zip 32168–7399; tel. 386/424–5000; David Ottati, Regional Chief Executive Officer
Web address: https://www.floridahospital.com/new-smyrna

ADVENTHEALTH NORTH PINELLAS (O, 187 beds) 1395 South Pinellas Avenue, Tarpon Springs, FL, Zip 34689–3790; tel. 727/942–5000; Jason Dunkel, President and Chief Executive Officer
Web address: www.fhnorthpinellas.com/

ADVENTHEALTH OCALA (O, 300 beds) 1500 SW 1st Avenue, Ocala, FL, Zip 34471–6504, Mailing Address: P.O. Box 6000, Zip 34478–6000, tel. 352/351–7200; Joe Johnson, FACHE, Chief Executive Officer

ADVENTHEALTH ORLANDO (O, 2875 beds) 601 East Rollins Street, Orlando, FL, Zip 32803–1248; tel. 407/303–6611; Daryl Tol, President and Chief Executive Officer
Web address: www.floridahospital.com/orlando

ADVENTHEALTH PALM COAST (O, 99 beds) 60 Memorial Medical Parkway, Palm Coast, FL, Zip 32164–5980; tel. 386/586–2000; Ronald Jimenez, M.D., Chief Executive Officer

ADVENTHEALTH SEBRING (O, 197 beds) 4200 Sun'n Lake Boulevard, Sebring, FL, Zip 33872–1986, Mailing Address: P.O. Box 9400, Zip 33871–9400, tel. 863/314–4466; Randy Surber, Chief Executive Officer
Web address: www.floridahospital.com/heartland/our-location

For explanation of codes following names, see page B2.
★ Indicates Type III membership in the American Hospital Association.

ADVENTHEALTH TAMPA (O, 536 beds) 3100 East Fletcher Avenue, Tampa, FL, Zip 33613–4688; tel. 813/971–6000; Denyse Bales-Chubb, Chief Executive Officer
Web address: www.floridahospital.com/tampa

ADVENTHEALTH WATERMAN (O, 269 beds) 1000 Waterman Way, Tavares, FL, Zip 32778–5266; tel. 352/253–3333; Abel Biri, Chief Executive Officer

ADVENTHEALTH WAUCHULA (O, 25 beds) 533 West Carlton Street, Wauchula, FL, Zip 33873–3407; tel. 863/773–3101; Denise Grimsley, R.N., Vice President and Administrator
Web address: www.fh.floridahospital.com/heartland/home.aspx

ADVENTHEALTH WESLEY CHAPEL (O, 145 beds) 2600 Bruce B Downs Bouelvard, Wesley Chapel, FL, Zip 33544–9207; tel. 813/929–5000; Erik Wangsness, Chief Executive Officer

ADVENTHEALTH ZEPHYRHILLS (O, 149 beds) 7050 Gall Boulevard, Zephyrhills, FL, Zip 33541–1399; tel. 813/788–0411; Amanda Maggard, Chief Executive Officer
Web address: www.fhzeph.org

GEORGIA: ADVENTHEALTH GORDON (O, 83 beds) 1035 Red Bud Road, Calhoun, GA, Zip 30701–2082, Mailing Address: P.O. Box 12938, Zip 30703–7013, tel. 706/629–2895; Pete M. Weber, President and Chief Executive Officer

ADVENTHEALTH MURRAY (O, 12 beds) 707 Old Dalton Ellijay Road, Chatsworth, GA, Zip 30705–2060, Mailing Address: P.O. Box 1406, Zip 30705–1406, tel. 706/695–4564; Karen Steely, Administrator
Web address: www.murraymedical.org/

ILLINOIS: ADVENTIST MEDICAL CENTER – HINSDALE (O, 261 beds) 120 North Oak Street, Hinsdale, IL, Zip 60521–3890; tel. 630/856–6001; Steven Province, President and Chief Executive Officer
Web address: www.AMITAhealth.org

ADVENTIST MEDICAL CENTER BOLINGBROOK (O, 134 beds) 500 Remington Boulevard, Bolingbrook, IL, Zip 60440–4906; tel. 630/312–5000; Bruce C. Christian, Chief Executive Officer

ADVENTIST MEDICAL CENTER GLENOAKS (O, 138 beds) 701 Winthrop Avenue, Glendale Heights, IL, Zip 60139–1403; tel. 630/545–8000; Bruce C. Christian, President and Chief Executive Officer
Web address: www.AMITAHealth.org

ADVENTIST MEDICAL CENTER LAGRANGE (O, 200 beds) 5101 South Willow Spring Road, La Grange, IL, Zip 60525–2600; tel. 708/245–9000; Michael Murrill, President and Chief Executive Officer
Web address: www.keepingyouwell.com

KANSAS: ADVENTHEALTH SHAWNEE MISSION (O, 397 beds) 9100 West 74th Street, Shawnee Mission, KS, Zip 66204–4004, Mailing Address: Box 2923, Zip 66201–1323, tel. 913/676–2000; Sam D. Huenergardt, Chief Executive Officer
Web address: www.shawneemission.org

KENTUCKY: ADVENTHEALTH MANCHESTER (O, 63 beds) 210 Marie Langdon Drive, Manchester, KY, Zip 40962–6388; tel. 606/598–5104; Chris Self, Chief Executive Officer

NORTH CAROLINA: ADVENTHEALTH HENDERSONVILLE (O, 86 beds) 100 Hospital Drive, Hendersonville, NC, Zip 28792–5272; tel. 828/684–8501; Jimm Bunch, President and Chief Executive Officer
Web address: www.parkridgehealth.org

TEXAS: ADVENTHEALTH CENTRAL TEXAS (O, 177 beds) 2201 South Clear Creek Road, Killeen, TX, Zip 76549–4110; tel. 254/526–7523; Kevin A. Roberts, FACHE, President and Chief Executive Officer

ADVENTHEALTH ROLLINS BROOK (O, 35 beds) 608 North Key Avenue, Lampasas, TX, Zip 76550–1106, Mailing Address: P.O. Box 589, Zip 76550–0032, tel. 512/556–3682; Kevin A. Roberts, FACHE, President and Chief Executive Officer
Web address: www.mplex.org

CENTRAL TEXAS MEDICAL CENTER (O, 111 beds) 1301 Wonder World Drive, San Marcos, TX, Zip 78666–7544; tel. 512/353–8979; Anthony Stahl, Ph.D., FACHE, Chief Executive Officer
Web address: www.ctmc.org

TEXAS HEALTH HUGULEY HOSPITAL FORT WORTH SOUTH (C, 193 beds) 11801 South Freeway, Burleson, TX, Zip 76028–7021, Mailing Address: P.O. Box 6337, Fort Worth, Zip 76115–0337, tel. 817/293–9110; Kenneth A. Finch, President and Chief Executive Officer

WISCONSIN: ADVENTHEALTH DURAND (O, 25 beds) 1220 Third Avenue West, Durand, WI, Zip 54736–1600, Mailing Address: P.O. Box 224, Zip 54736–0224, tel. 715/672–4211; Douglas R. Peterson, President and Chief Executive Officer
Web address: www.chippewavalleyhospital.com/

Owned, leased, sponsored:	37 hospitals	8627 beds
Contract-managed:	1 hospitals	193 beds
Totals:	38 hospitals	8820 beds

★0235: ADVENTIST HEALTH (CO)
One Adventist Health Way, Roseville, CA, Zip 95661–3266, Mailing Address: P.O. Box 619002, Zip 95661–9002, tel. 916/406–0000; Scott Reiner, Chief Executive Officer
(Decentralized Health System)

CALIFORNIA: ADVENTIST HEALTH – TULARE (L, 103 beds) 869 North Cherry Street, Tulare, CA, Zip 93274–2287; tel. 559/688–0821; Randy Dodd, President
Web address: www.tulareregional.org

ADVENTIST HEALTH BAKERSFIELD (O, 223 beds) 2615 Chester Avenue, Bakersfield, CA, Zip 93301–2014, Mailing Address: P.O. Box 2615, Zip 93303–2615, tel. 661/395–3000; Sharlet Briggs, Ph.D., Market Chief Executive Officer and President

ADVENTIST HEALTH CLEAR LAKE (O, 25 beds) 15630 18th Avenue, Clearlake, CA, Zip 95422–9336, Mailing Address: P.O. Box 6710, Zip 95422, tel. 707/994–6486; David Santos, President and Chief Executive Officer
Web address: www.adventisthealth.org

ADVENTIST HEALTH GLENDALE (O, 462 beds) 8700 Beverly Blvd, NT-3138, Los Angeles, CA, Zip 90048, Mailing Address: 1509 Wilson Terrace, Glendale, Zip 91206–4098, tel. 818/409–8000; Alice H. Issai, President
Web address: www.glendaleadventist.com

ADVENTIST HEALTH HOWARD MEMORIAL (L, 25 beds) One Marcela Drive, Willits, CA, Zip 95490–4298; tel. 707/459–6801; Jason Wells, President and Chief Executive Officer
Web address: www.howardhospital.com

ADVENTIST HEALTH LODI MEMORIAL (O, 190 beds) 975 South Fairmont Avenue, Lodi, CA, Zip 95240–5118, Mailing Address: P.O. Box 3004, Zip 95241–1908, tel. 209/334–3411; Daniel Wolcott, President and Chief Executive Officer

ADVENTIST HEALTH MEDICAL CENTER – TEHACHAPI VALLEY (C, 24 beds) 115 West 'E' Street, Tehachapi, CA, Zip 93561–1607, Mailing Address: P.O. Box 1900, Zip 93581–1900, tel. 661/823–3000; David Eastman, Interim Chief Executive Officer
Web address: www.tvhd.org

ADVENTIST HEALTH SONORA (O, 152 beds) 1000 Greenley Road, Sonora, CA, Zip 95370–4819; tel. 209/536–5000; Michelle Fuentes, President

ADVENTIST HEALTH ST. HELENA (O, 81 beds) 10 Woodland Road, Saint Helena, CA, Zip 94574–9554; tel. 707/963–3611; Steven Herber, M.D., FACS, President and Chief Executive Officer
Web address: www.sthelenahospital.org

ADVENTIST HEALTH ST. HELENA (O, 61 beds) 525 Oregon Street, Vallejo, CA, Zip 94590–3201; tel. 707/648–2200; Steven Herber, M.D., FACS, President and Chief Executive Officer
Web address: www.sthelenahospitals.org/location/center-for-behavioral-health

ADVENTIST HEALTH WHITE MEMORIAL (O, 353 beds) 1720 Cesar Chavez Avenue, Los Angeles, CA, Zip 90033–2414; tel. 323/268–5000; John Raffoul, Chief Executive Officer

ADVENTIST HEALTH AND RIDEOUT (O, 219 beds) 726 Fourth Street, Marysville, CA, Zip 95901–5600; tel. 530/749–4300; Richard Rawson, Chief Executive Officer
Web address: www.frhg.org

ADVENTIST MEDICAL CENTER – HANFORD (O, 199 beds) 115 Mall Drive, Hanford, CA, Zip 93230–3513; tel. 559/582–9000; Wayne Ferch, President and Chief Executive Officer
Web address: www.adventisthealthcv.com/hospital_newhanfordhospital.aspx

ADVENTIST MEDICAL CENTER-REEDLEY (L, 49 beds) 372 West Cypress Avenue, Reedley, CA, Zip 93654–2199; tel. 559/638–8155; Wayne Ferch, President and Chief Executive Officer
Web address: www.skdh.org

For explanation of codes following names, see page B2.
★ Indicates Type III membership in the American Hospital Association.

CENTRAL VALLEY GENERAL HOSPITAL (O, 49 beds) 1025 North Douty Street, Hanford, CA, Zip 93230–3722, Mailing Address: P.O. Box 480, Zip 93232–2113, tel. 559/583–2100; Wayne Ferch, President and Chief Executive Officer

SIMI VALLEY HOSPITAL (O, 144 beds) 2975 North Sycamore Drive, Simi Valley, CA, Zip 93065–1277; tel. 805/955–6000; Jennifer Swenson, President and Chief Executive Officer
Web address: www.simivalleyhospital.com

UKIAH VALLEY MEDICAL CENTER (O, 50 beds) 275 Hospital Drive, Ukiah, CA, Zip 95482–4531; tel. 707/462–3111; Gwen Matthews, R.N., MSN, Chief Executive Officer
Web address: www.adventisthealth.org

HAWAII: ADVENTIST HEALTH CASTLE (O, 160 beds) 640 Ulukahiki Street, Kailua, HI, Zip 96734–4454; tel. 808/263–5500; Kathryn A. Raethel, R.N., M.P.H., President and Chief Executive Officer
Web address: www.castlemed.org

OREGON: ADVENTIST HEALTH PORTLAND (O, 169 beds) 10123 SE Market Street, Portland, OR, Zip 97216–2599; tel. 503/257–2500; David Russell, President and Chief Executive Officer

ADVENTIST HEALTHTILLAMOOK (L, 25 beds) 1000 Third Street, Tillamook, OR, Zip 97141–3430; tel. 503/842–4444; David Butler, President and Chief Executive Officer
Web address: https://www.adventisthealth.org/tillamook/

Owned, leased, sponsored:	19 hospitals	2739 beds
Contract-managed:	1 hospitals	24 beds
Totals:	20 hospitals	2763 beds

0214: ADVENTIST HEALTHCARE (NP)
820 West Diamond Avenue, Suite 600, Gaithersburg, MD, Zip 20878–1419; tel. 301/315–3185; Terry Forde, President and Chief Executive Officer
(Independent Hospital System)

MARYLAND: ADVENTIST HEALTHCARE PHYSICAL HEALTH AND REHABILITATION (O, 77 beds) 9909 Medical Center Drive, Rockville, MD, Zip 20850–6361; tel. 240/864–6000; Brent Reitz, President

ADVENTIST HEALTHCARE SHADY GROVE MEDICAL CENTER (O, 523 beds) 9901 Medical Center Drive, Rockville, MD, Zip 20850–3395; tel. 240/826–6000; John Sackett, President SGMC and Executive Vice President and Chief Operating Officer
Web address: www.adventisthealthcare.com

ADVENTIST HEALTHCARE WASHINGTON ADVENTIST HOSPITAL (O, 230 beds) 7600 Carroll Avenue, Takoma Park, MD, Zip 20912–6392; tel. 301/891–7600; Erik Wangsness, President
Web address: www.adventisthealthcare.com

Owned, leased, sponsored:	3 hospitals	830 beds
Contract-managed:	0 hospitals	0 beds
Totals:	3 hospitals	830 beds

★1032: ADVOCATE AURORA HEALTH (NP)
3075 Highland Parkway, Suite 600, Downers Grove, IL, Zip 60515–5563; tel. 630/929–8700; Jim Skogsbergh, President and Chief Executive Officer
(Decentralized Health System)

ILLINOIS: ADVOCATE BROMENN MEDICAL CENTER (O, 203 beds) 1304 Franklin Avenue, Normal, IL, Zip 61761–3558, Mailing Address: P.O. Box 2850, Bloomington, Zip 61702–2850, tel. 309/454–1400; Colleen Kannaday, FACHE, President
Web address: www.advocatehealth.com

ADVOCATE CHRIST MEDICAL CENTER (O, 767 beds) 4440 West 95th Street, Oak Lawn, IL, Zip 60453–2699; tel. 708/684–8000; Matthew Lee. Primack, President
Web address: www.advocatehealth.com/christ

ADVOCATE CONDELL MEDICAL CENTER (O, 286 beds) 801 South Milwaukee Avenue, Libertyville, IL, Zip 60048–3199; tel. 847/362–2900; Michael A. Ploszek, President

ADVOCATE EUREKA HOSPITAL (O, 11 beds) 101 South Major Street, Eureka, IL, Zip 61530–1246; tel. 309/467–2371; Colleen Kannaday, FACHE, President
Web address: www.advocatehealth.com/eureka/

ADVOCATE GOOD SAMARITAN HOSPITAL (O, 288 beds) 3815 Highland Avenue, Downers Grove, IL, Zip 60515–1590; tel. 630/275–5900; Nancy M. Tinsley, R.N., FACHE, President

ADVOCATE GOOD SHEPHERD HOSPITAL (O, 176 beds) 450 West Highway 22, Barrington, IL, Zip 60010–1919; tel. 847/381–0123; Karen A. Lambert, President
Web address: www.advocatehealth.com/gshp/

ADVOCATE ILLINOIS MASONIC MEDICAL CENTER (O, 335 beds) 836 West Wellington Avenue, Chicago, IL, Zip 60657–5147; tel. 773/975–1600; Susan Nordstrom. Lopez, President

ADVOCATE LUTHERAN GENERAL HOSPITAL (O, 629 beds) 1775 Dempster Street, Park Ridge, IL, Zip 60068–1174; tel. 847/723–2210; Terika Richardson, M.P.H., President
Web address: www.advocatehealth.com/luth/

ADVOCATE SHERMAN HOSPITAL (O, 255 beds) 1425 North Randall Road, Elgin, IL, Zip 60123–2300; tel. 847/742–9800; Linda Deering, MSN, R.N., President
Web address: www.advocatehealth.com/sherman

ADVOCATE SOUTH SUBURBAN HOSPITAL (O, 217 beds) 17800 South Kedzie Avenue, Hazel Crest, IL, Zip 60429–0989; tel. 708/799–8000; Rashard Johnson, President
Web address: www.advocatehealth.com/ssub/

ADVOCATE TRINITY HOSPITAL (O, 174 beds) 2320 East 93rd Street, Chicago, IL, Zip 60617–3909; tel. 773/967–2000; Rashard Johnson, President

WISCONSIN: AURORA BAYCARE MEDICAL CENTER (O, 167 beds) 2845 Greenbrier Road, Green Bay, WI, Zip 54311–6519, Mailing Address: P.O. Box 8900, Zip 54308–8900, tel. 920/288–8000; Daniel T. Meyer, President
Web address: www.aurorabaycare.com

AURORA LAKELAND MEDICAL CENTER (O, 67 beds) W3985 County Road NN, Elkhorn, WI, Zip 53121–4389; tel. 262/741–2000; Bob Miller, President
Web address: www.aurorahealthcare.org

AURORA MEDICAL CENTER – BAY AREA (O, 59 beds) 3003 University Drive, Marinette, WI, Zip 54143–4110; tel. 715/735–6621; Edward A. Harding, FACHE, President and Chief Executive Officer
Web address: www.bamc.org

AURORA MEDICAL CENTER – MANITOWOC COUNTY (O, 62 beds) 5000 Memorial Drive, Two Rivers, WI, Zip 54241–3900, Mailing Address: 2845 Greenbrier Road, Green Bay, Zip 54311–8900, tel. 920/794–5000; Cathie A. Kocourek, President
Web address: www.aurorahealthcare.org

AURORA MEDICAL CENTER BURLINGTON (O, 55 beds) 252 McHenry Street, Burlington, WI, Zip 53105–1828; tel. 262/767–6000; Bob Miller, President

AURORA MEDICAL CENTER GRAFTON (O, 127 beds) 975 Port Washington Road, Grafton, WI, Zip 53024–9201; tel. 262/329–1000; David Graebner, President
Web address: www.aurorahealthcare.org

AURORA MEDICAL CENTER KENOSHA (O, 79 beds) 10400 75th Street, Kenosha, WI, Zip 53142–7884; tel. 262/948–5600; Lisa Just, President

AURORA MEDICAL CENTER SUMMIT (O, 91 beds) 36500 Aurora Drive, Summit, WI, Zip 53066–4899; tel. 262/434–1000; Michael Bergmann, President
Web address: www.aurorahealthcare.org

AURORA MEDICAL CENTER IN WASHINGTON COUNTY (O, 34 beds) 1032 East Sumner Street, Hartford, WI, Zip 53027–1698; tel. 262/673–2300; David Graebner, President
Web address: www.aurorahealthcare.org

AURORA MEDICAL CENTER OF OSHKOSH (O, 72 beds) 855 North Westhaven Drive, Oshkosh, WI, Zip 54904–7668; tel. 920/456–6000; John B. Newman, President

AURORA PSYCHIATRIC HOSPITAL (O, 91 beds) 1220 Dewey Avenue, Wauwatosa, WI, Zip 53213–2598; tel. 414/454–6600; Peter Carlson, President, Behavioral Health Services
Web address: www.aurorahealthcare.org

Section B

For explanation of codes following names, see page B2.
★ Indicates Type III membership in the American Hospital Association.

AURORA SHEBOYGAN MEMORIAL MEDICAL CENTER (O, 127 beds) 2629 North Seventh Street, Sheboygan, WI, Zip 53083–4998; tel. 920/451–5000; David Graebner, President

AURORA SINAI MEDICAL CENTER (O, 202 beds) 945 North 12th Street, Milwaukee, WI, Zip 53233–1337, Mailing Address: P.O. Box 342, Zip 53201–0342, tel. 414/219–2000; Jessica Bauer, President
Web address: www.aurorahealthcare.org

AURORA ST. LUKE'S MEDICAL CENTER (O, 711 beds) 2900 West Oklahoma Avenue, Milwaukee, WI, Zip 53215–4330, Mailing Address: P.O. Box 2901, Zip 53201–2901, tel. 414/649–6000; Marie Golanowski, R.N., MS, President

AURORA WEST ALLIS MEDICAL CENTER (O, 218 beds) 8901 West Lincoln Avenue, West Allis, WI, Zip 53227–2409, Mailing Address: P.O. Box 27901, Zip 53227–0901, tel. 414/328–6000; Richard A. Kellar, President
Web address: www.aurorahealthcare.org

Owned, leased, sponsored:	26 hospitals	5503 beds
Contract-managed:	0 hospitals	0 beds
Totals:	26 hospitals	5503 beds

0312: AHMC & HEALTHCARE, INC. (IO)
55 South Raymond Avenue, Suite 105, Alhambra, CA, Zip 91801–7101; tel. 626/457–9600; Jonathan Wu, M.D., President and Chairman
(Independent Hospital System)

CALIFORNIA: AHMC ANAHEIM REGIONAL MEDICAL CENTER (O, 223 beds) 1111 West La Palma Avenue, Anaheim, CA, Zip 92801–2881; tel. 714/774–1450; Richard Castro, Chief Executive Officer

ALHAMBRA HOSPITAL MEDICAL CENTER (O, 144 beds) 100 South Raymond Avenue, Alhambra, CA, Zip 91801–3199, Mailing Address: P.O. Box 510, Zip 91802–2510, tel. 626/570–1606; Iris Lai, Chief Executive Officer
Web address: www.alhambrahospital.com

GARFIELD MEDICAL CENTER (O, 195 beds) 525 North Garfield Avenue, Monterey Park, CA, Zip 91754–1205; tel. 626/573–2222; Patrick A. Petre, Chief Executive Officer
Web address: www.garfieldmedicalcenter.com

GREATER EL MONTE COMMUNITY HOSPITAL (O, 117 beds) 1701 Santa Anita Avenue, South El Monte, CA, Zip 91733–3411; tel. 626/579–7777; Stanley Toy Jr, M.D., Chief Executive Officer
Web address: www.greaterelmonte.com

MONTEREY PARK HOSPITAL (O, 101 beds) 900 South Atlantic Boulevard, Monterey Park, CA, Zip 91754–4780; tel. 626/570–9000; Philip A. Cohen, Chief Executive Officer

PARKVIEW COMMUNITY HOSPITAL MEDICAL CENTER (O, 193 beds) 3865 Jackson Street, Riverside, CA, Zip 92503–3998; tel. 951/688–2211; Steven Popkin, Chief Executive Officer
Web address: www.pchmc.org

SAN GABRIEL VALLEY MEDICAL CENTER (O, 273 beds) 438 West Las Tunas Drive, San Gabriel, CA, Zip 91776–1216, Mailing Address: P.O. Box 1507, Zip 91778–1507, tel. 626/289–5454; Jonathon F. Aquino, Chief Executive Officer
Web address: www.sgvmc.org

WHITTIER HOSPITAL MEDICAL CENTER (O, 100 beds) 9080 Colima Road, Whittier, CA, Zip 90605–1600; tel. 562/945–3561; Richard Castro, Chief Executive Officer
Web address: www.whittierhospital.com

Owned, leased, sponsored:	8 hospitals	1346 beds
Contract-managed:	0 hospitals	0 beds
Totals:	8 hospitals	1346 beds

0225: ALAMEDA HEALTH SYSTEM (NP)
15400 Foothill Boulevard, San Leandro, CA, Zip 94578–1009; tel. 510/677–7920; Delvecchio Finley, Chief Executive Officer
(Moderately Centralized Health System)

CALIFORNIA: ALAMEDA HOSPITAL (O, 215 beds) 2070 Clinton Avenue, Alameda, CA, Zip 94501–4397; tel. 510/522–3700; Delvecchio Finley, Chief Executive Officer
Web address: www.alamedahealthsystem.org

HIGHLAND HOSPITAL (O, 372 beds) 1411 East 31st Street, Oakland, CA, Zip 94602–1018; tel. 510/437–4800; Delvecchio Finley, Chief Executive Officer
Web address: www.alamedahealthsystem.org

SAN LEANDRO HOSPITAL (O, 48 beds) 13855 East 14th Street, San Leandro, CA, Zip 94578–2600; tel. 510/357–6500; James E T. Jackson, M.P.H., Chief Administrative Officer
Web address: www.sanleandrohospital.org

Owned, leased, sponsored:	3 hospitals	635 beds
Contract-managed:	0 hospitals	0 beds
Totals:	3 hospitals	635 beds

1020: ALECTO HEALTHCARE (IO)
16310 Bake Parkway, Suite 200, Irvine, CA, Zip 92618–4684; tel. 323/932–5963; Lex Reddy, Chief Executive Officer
(Independent Hospital System)

CALIFORNIA: OLYMPIA MEDICAL CENTER (O, 204 beds) 5900 West Olympic Boulevard, Los Angeles, CA, Zip 90036–4671; tel. 310/657–5900; Matthew Williams, R.N., Chief Executive Officer

ST. ROSE HOSPITAL (C, 150 beds) 27200 Calaroga Avenue, Hayward, CA, Zip 94545–4383; tel. 510/264–4000; Aman Dhuper, President and Chief Executive Officer
Web address: www.srhca.org

OHIO: EAST OHIO REGIONAL HOSPITAL (O, 120 beds) 90 North Fourth Street, Martins Ferry, OH, Zip 43935–1648; tel. 740/633–1100; Jennifer Coello, Chief Operating Officer
Web address: www.ovmc-eorh.com

TEXAS: WILSON N. JONES REGIONAL MEDICAL CENTER (O, 109 beds) 500 North Highland Avenue, Sherman, TX, Zip 75092–7354; tel. 903/870–4611; Glenn Carney, Chief Executive Officer

WEST VIRGINIA: FAIRMONT REGIONAL MEDICAL CENTER (O, 144 beds) 1325 Locust Avenue, Fairmont, WV, Zip 26554–1435; tel. 304/367–7100; Robert S. Adcock, Chief Executive Officer
Web address: www.frmcwv.com

OHIO VALLEY MEDICAL CENTER (O, 169 beds) 2000 Eoff Street, Wheeling, WV, Zip 26003–3870; tel. 304/234–0123; Daniel C. Dunmyer, Chief Executive Officer
Web address: www.ovmc-eorh.com

Owned, leased, sponsored:	5 hospitals	746 beds
Contract-managed:	1 hospitals	150 beds
Totals:	6 hospitals	896 beds

★0199: ALLEGHENY HEALTH NETWORK (NP)
30 Isabella Street, Suite 300, Pittsburgh, PA, Zip 15212–5862; tel. 412/359–3131; Cynthia Hundorfean, President and Chief Executive Officer
(Independent Hospital System)

NEW YORK: WESTFIELD MEMORIAL HOSPITAL (O, 4 beds) 189 East Main Street, Westfield, NY, Zip 14787–1195; tel. 716/326–4921; Henry J. Ward, Interim President
Web address: www.wmhinc.org

PENNSYLVANIA: ALLEGHENY GENERAL HOSPITAL (O, 384 beds) 320 East North Avenue, Pittsburgh, PA, Zip 15212–4756; tel. 412/359–3131; Jeffrey Cohen, M.D., President
Web address: www.wpahs.org/locations/allegheny-general-hospital

ALLEGHENY VALLEY HOSPITAL (O, 77 beds) 1301 Carlisle Street, Natrona Heights, PA, Zip 15065–1152; tel. 724/224–5100; Jeffrey Carlson, Interim Chief Executive Officer
Web address: www.wpahs.org

CANONSBURG HOSPITAL (O, 42 beds) 100 Medical Boulevard, Canonsburg, PA, Zip 15317–9762; tel. 724/745–6100; Louise Urban, R.N., President and Chief Executive Officer

FORBES HOSPITAL (O, 285 beds) 2570 Haymaker Road, Monroeville, PA, Zip 15146–3513; tel. 412/858–2000; Mark Rubino, M.D., President
Web address: www.ahn.org

For explanation of codes following names, see page B2.
★ *Indicates Type III membership in the American Hospital Association.*

Section B

JEFFERSON HOSPITAL (O, 242 beds) 565 Coal Valley Road, Jefferson Hills, PA, Zip 15025–3703, Mailing Address: Box 18119, Pittsburgh, Zip 15236–0119, tel. 412/469–5000; Louise Urban, R.N., President and Chief Executive Officer

SAINT VINCENT HOSPITAL (O, 251 beds) 232 West 25th Street, Erie, PA, Zip 16544–0002; tel. 814/452–5000; Christopher Clark, D.O., President and Chief Executive Officer
Web address: www.svhs.org

WEST PENN HOSPITAL (O, 238 beds) 4800 Friendship Avenue, Pittsburgh, PA, Zip 15224–1722; tel. 412/578–5000; Ronald J. Andro, R.N., MS, President and Chief Executive Officer
Web address: www.wpahs.org

Owned, leased, sponsored:	8 hospitals	1523 beds
Contract-managed:	0 hospitals	0 beds
Totals:	8 hospitals	1523 beds

0413: ALLEGIANCE HEALTH MANAGEMENT (IO)

504 Texas Street, Suite 200, Shreveport, LA, Zip 71101–3526; tel. 318/226–8202; Rock Bordelon, President and Chief Executive Officer
(Independent Hospital System)

ARKANSAS: EUREKA SPRINGS HOSPITAL (O, 15 beds) 24 Norris Street, Eureka Springs, AR, Zip 72632–3541; tel. 479/253–7400
Web address: www.eurekaspringshospital.com

NORTH METRO MEDICAL CENTER (O, 113 beds) 1400 West Braden Street, Jacksonville, AR, Zip 72076–3788; tel. 501/985–7000; Dale Anderson, R.N., Chief Executive Officer
Web address: www.northmetromed.com

RIVER VALLEY MEDICAL CENTER (O, 35 beds) 200 North Third Street, Dardanelle, AR, Zip 72834–3802, Mailing Address: P.O. Box 578, Zip 72834–0578, tel. 479/229–4677; Vicki Andert, R.N., Chief Executive Officer

LOUISIANA: BIENVILLE MEDICAL CENTER (O, 21 beds) 1175 Pine Street, Suite 200, Arcadia, LA, Zip 71001–3122; tel. 318/263–4700; Kirk Lemoine, Chief Executive Officer
Web address: www.bienvillemedicalcenter.net/

BYRD REGIONAL HOSPITAL (O, 60 beds) 1020 West Fertitta Boulevard, Leesville, LA, Zip 71446–4645; tel. 337/239–9041; F. Peter. Savoy III, Chief Executive Officer
Web address: www.byrdregional.com

MERCY REGIONAL MEDICAL CENTER (O, 109 beds) 800 East Main Street, Ville Platte, LA, Zip 70586–4618; tel. 337/363–5684; Calvin Green, Chief Executive Officer
Web address: www.mercyregionalmedicalcenter.com

MINDEN MEDICAL CENTER (O, 161 beds) 1 Medical Plaza Place, Minden, LA, Zip 71055–3330, Mailing Address: P.O. Box 5003, Zip 71058–5003, tel. 318/377–2321; Gregory Pearson, Chief Executive Officer
Web address: www.mindenmedicalcenter.com

SABINE MEDICAL CENTER (O, 24 beds) 240 Highland Drive, Many, LA, Zip 71449–3718; tel. 318/256–5691; Chris Beddoe, Chief Executive Officer

MISSISSIPPI: ALLEGIANCE SPECIALTY HOSPITAL OF GREENVILLE (O, 39 beds) 300 South Washington Avenue, 3rd Floor, Greenville, MS, Zip 38701–4719; tel. 662/332–7344; Vearnail Herzog, Chief Executive Officer
Web address: www.ahmgt.com

TEXAS: ALLEGIANCE BEHAVIORAL HEALTH CENTER OF PLAINVIEW (O, 20 beds) 2601 Dimmit Road, Suite 400, Suite 400, Plainview, TX, Zip 79072–1833; tel. 806/296–9191; Angie Alexander, Chief Executive Officer
Web address: www.ahmgt.com

ALLEGIANCE SPECIALTY HOSPITAL OF KILGORE (O, 60 beds) 1612 South Henderson Boulevard, Kilgore, TX, Zip 75662–3594; tel. 903/984–3505; Karen Ross, Chief Executive Officer

Owned, leased, sponsored:	11 hospitals	657 beds
Contract-managed:	0 hospitals	0 beds
Totals:	11 hospitals	657 beds

0317: ALLIANT MANAGEMENT SERVICES (IO)

2650 Eastpoint Parkway, Suite 300, Louisville, KY, Zip 40223–5164; tel. 502/992–3525; Stephen E. Fischer, Regional Vice President, Finance
(Moderately Centralized Health System)

FLORIDA: CALHOUN-LIBERTY HOSPITAL (C, 25 beds) 20370 NE Burns Avenue, Blountstown, FL, Zip 32424–1045, Mailing Address: P.O. Box 419, Zip 32424–0419, tel. 850/674–5411; Charles E. Durant Jr, FACHE, Chief Executive Officer
Web address: www.calhounlibertyhospital.com

NORTHWEST FLORIDA COMMUNITY HOSPITAL (C, 59 beds) 1360 Brickyard Road, Chipley, FL, Zip 32428–6303, Mailing Address: P.O. Box 889, Zip 32428–0889, tel. 850/638–1610; Michael A. Kozar, Chief Executive Officer
Web address: www.nfch.org

ILLINOIS: FAYETTE COUNTY HOSPITAL (O, 110 beds) 650 West Taylor Street, Vandalia, IL, Zip 62471–1296; tel. 618/283–1231; Gregory D. Starnes, Chief Executive Officer
Web address: www.fayettecountyhospital.org

GIBSON AREA HOSPITAL AND HEALTH SERVICES (C, 67 beds) 1120 North Melvin Street, Gibson City, IL, Zip 60936–1477, Mailing Address: P.O. Box 429, Zip 60936–0429, tel. 217/784–4251; Robert C. Schmitt II, CPA, FACHE, Chief Executive Officer

PARIS COMMUNITY HOSPITAL (C, 25 beds) 721 East Court Street, Paris, IL, Zip 61944–2460; tel. 217/465–4141; Oliver Smith, President and Chief Executive Officer
Web address: www.pariscommunityhospital.com

WABASH GENERAL HOSPITAL (C, 25 beds) 1418 College Drive, Mount Carmel, IL, Zip 62863–2638; tel. 618/262–8621; Jay Purvis, President and Chief Executive Officer

INDIANA: PERRY COUNTY MEMORIAL HOSPITAL (C, 25 beds) 8885 State Road 237, Tell City, IN, Zip 47586–2750; tel. 812/547–7011; Brian J. Herwig, President and Chief Executive Officer
Web address: www.pchospital.org

KENTUCKY: BRECKINRIDGE MEMORIAL HOSPITAL (C, 43 beds) 1011 Old Highway 60, Hardinsburg, KY, Zip 40143–2597; tel. 270/756–7000; Angela Portman, Chief Executive Officer
Web address: www.breckinridgehealth.org/

CARROLL COUNTY MEMORIAL HOSPITAL (C, 25 beds) 309 11th Street, Carrollton, KY, Zip 41008–1400; tel. 502/732–4321; Harry Hays, Chief Executive Officer

TWIN LAKES REGIONAL MEDICAL CENTER (C, 75 beds) 910 Wallace Avenue, Leitchfield, KY, Zip 42754–2414; tel. 270/259–9400; Wayne Meriwether, Chief Executive Officer
Web address: www.tlrmc.com

Owned, leased, sponsored:	1 hospitals	110 beds
Contract-managed:	9 hospitals	369 beds
Totals:	10 hospitals	479 beds

★0041: ALLINA HEALTH (NP)

2925 Chicago Avenue, Minneapolis, MN, Zip 55407–1321, Mailing Address: P.O. Box 43, Zip 55440–0043, tel. 612/262–5000; Penny Ann. Wheeler, M.D., Chief Executive Officer
(Moderately Centralized Health System)

MINNESOTA: ABBOTT NORTHWESTERN HOSPITAL (O, 685 beds) 800 East 28th Street, Minneapolis, MN, Zip 55407–3799; tel. 612/863–4000; Ann Madden Rice, President
Web address: www.abbottnorthwestern.com

BUFFALO HOSPITAL (O, 44 beds) 303 Catlin Street, Buffalo, MN, Zip 55313–1947; tel. 763/682–1212; Heather Johnson, Interim President

CAMBRIDGE MEDICAL CENTER (O, 58 beds) 701 South Dellwood Street, Cambridge, MN, Zip 55008–1920; tel. 763/689–7700; Kelly Spratt, President
Web address: www.allina.com/ahs/cambridge.nsf

For explanation of codes following names, see page B2.
★ Indicates Type III membership in the American Hospital Association.

DISTRICT ONE HOSPITAL (O, 42 beds) 200 State Avenue, Faribault, MN, Zip 55021–6345; tel. 507/334–6451; David L. Albrecht, President
Web address: www.allinahealth.org/District-One-Hospital/

MERCY HOSPITAL (O, 471 beds) 4050 Coon Rapids Boulevard, Coon Rapids, MN, Zip 55433–2586; tel. 763/236–6000; Sara J. Criger, President

NEW ULM MEDICAL CENTER (O, 44 beds) 1324 Fifth Street North, New Ulm, MN, Zip 56073–1553; tel. 507/217–5000; Toby Freier, President
Web address: www.newulmmedicalcenter.com

OWATONNA HOSPITAL (O, 42 beds) 2250 NW 26th Street, Owatonna, MN, Zip 55060–5503; tel. 507/451–3850; David L. Albrecht, President
Web address: www.owatonnahospital.com

PHILLIPS EYE INSTITUTE (O, 8 beds) 2215 Park Avenue, Minneapolis, MN, Zip 55404–3756; tel. 612/775–8800; Daniel S. Conrad, M.D., President

REGINA HOSPITAL (O, 43 beds) 1175 Nininger Road, Hastings, MN, Zip 55033–1098; tel. 651/480–4100; Helen J. Strike, R.N., President
Web address: www.reginamedical.org

ST. FRANCIS REGIONAL MEDICAL CENTER (O, 89 beds) 1455 St Francis Avenue, Shakopee, MN, Zip 55379–3380; tel. 952/428–3000; Amy L. Jerdee, R.N., President
Web address: www.stfrancis-shakopee.com

UNITED HOSPITAL (O, 379 beds) 333 North Smith Avenue, Saint Paul, MN, Zip 55102–2389; tel. 651/241–8000; Thomas O'Connor, President

WISCONSIN: RIVER FALLS AREA HOSPITAL (O, 18 beds) 1629 East Division Street, River Falls, WI, Zip 54022–1571; tel. 715/425–6155; Helen J. Strike, R.N., President
Web address: www.allina.com

Owned, leased, sponsored:	12 hospitals	1923 beds
Contract-managed:	0 hospitals	0 beds
Totals:	12 hospitals	1923 beds

0877: ALTAPOINTE HEALTH SYSTEMS (IO)

5750-A Southland Drive, Mobile, AL, Zip 36693–3316; tel. 251/473–4423; J. Tuerk. Schlesinger, Chief Executive Officer

ALABAMA: BAYPOINTE BEHAVIORAL HEALTH (O, 60 beds) 5800 Southland Drive, Mobile, AL, Zip 36693–3313; tel. 251/661–0153; Jarett Crum, Hospital Director
Web address: www.altapointe.org

EASTPOINTE HOSPITAL (O, 50 beds) 7400 Roper Lane, Daphne, AL, Zip 36526–5274; tel. 251/378–6500; Philip L. Cusa, Hospital Director
Web address: www.altapointe.org/eastpointe.php

Owned, leased, sponsored:	2 hospitals	110 beds
Contract-managed:	0 hospitals	0 beds
Totals:	2 hospitals	110 beds

1043: AMERICAN ACADEMIC HEALTH SYSTEM (IO)

1500 Market Street, Centre Square Suite 24th Floor, Philadelphia, PA, Zip 19102–2100; tel. 215/255–3500; Joel Freedman, Chief Executive Officer

PENNSYLVANIA: HAHNEMANN UNIVERSITY HOSPITAL (O, 496 beds) 230 North Broad Street, Philadelphia, PA, Zip 19102–1192; tel. 215/762–7000; Suzanne Richards, R.N., M.P.H., FACHE, Chief Executive Officer
Web address: www.hahnemannhospital.com

ST. CHRISTOPHER'S HOSPITAL FOR CHILDREN (O, 121 beds) 3601 A Street, Philadelphia, PA, Zip 19134–1043; Mailing Address: 160 E. Erie Avenue, Zip 19134–1011, tel. 215/427–5000; Suzanne Richards, R.N., M.P.H., FACHE, Chief Executive Officer
Web address: www.stchristophershospital.com

Owned, leased, sponsored:	2 hospitals	617 beds
Contract-managed:	0 hospitals	0 beds
Totals:	2 hospitals	617 beds

2295: AMERICAN PROVINCE OF LITTLE COMPANY OF MARY SISTERS (CO)

9350 South California Avenue, Evergreen Park, IL, Zip 60805–2595; tel. 708/229–5095, Sister; Carol Pacini, Region Leader
(Moderately Centralized Health System)

ILLINOIS: LITTLE COMPANY OF MARY HOSPITAL AND HEALTH CARE CENTERS (O, 231 beds) 2800 West 95th Street, Evergreen Park, IL, Zip 60805–2795; tel. 708/422–6200; John Hanlon, M.D., President and Chief Executive Officer
Web address: www.lcmh.org

INDIANA: MEMORIAL HOSPITAL AND HEALTH CARE CENTER (O, 137 beds) 800 West Ninth Street, Jasper, IN, Zip 47546–2516; tel. 812/996–2345; E Kyle. Bennett, President and Chief Executive Officer

Owned, leased, sponsored:	2 hospitals	368 beds
Contract-managed:	0 hospitals	0 beds
Totals:	2 hospitals	368 beds

0644: AMG INTEGRATED HEALTHCARE MANAGEMENT (IO)

101 La Rue France, Suite 500, Lafayette, LA, Zip 70508–3144; tel. 337/269–9828; Timothy W. Howard, Chief Executive Officer
(Independent Hospital System)

KANSAS: AMG SPECIALTY HOSPITAL-WICHITA (O, 26 beds) 8080 East Pawnee Street, Wichita, KS, Zip 67207–5475; tel. 316/682–0004; Robert A. Loepp Jr, FACHE, Chief Executive Officer
Web address: www.amgwichita.com/

LOUISIANA: AMG PHYSICAL REHABILITATION HOSPITAL (O, 24 beds) 5025 Keystone Boulevard, Suite 200, Covington, LA, Zip 70433; tel. 985/888–0301; Natalie Stols, Interim Chief Executive Officer
Web address: www.amgcovingtonprh.com/

AMG SPECIALTY HOSPITAL-HOUMA (O, 40 beds) 629 Dunn Street, Houma, LA, Zip 70360–4707; tel. 985/274–0001; Jody Robichaux, R.N., Chief Executive Officer

AMG SPECIALTY HOSPITAL-LAFAYETTE (O, 18 beds) 310 Youngsville Highway, Lafayette, LA, Zip 70508–4524; tel. 337/839–9880; Rachel Mayeaux, Chief Executive Officer
Web address: www.amglafayette.com

AMG SPECIALTY HOSPITAL-ZACHARY (O, 16 beds) 4601 McHugh Road, Building B, Zachary, LA, Zip 70791–5348; tel. 225/683–1600; April Ebeling, Chief Executive Officer
Web address: www.amgzachary.com/

LAFAYETTE PHYSICAL REHABILITATION HOSPITAL (O, 32 beds) 307 Polly Lane, Lafayette, LA, Zip 70508–4960; tel. 337/314–1111; Bruce J. Bartels, Interim Chief Executive Officer

THE NEUROMEDICAL CENTER REHABILITATION HOSPITAL (O, 23 beds) 10101 Park Rowe Avenue, Suite 500, Baton Rouge, LA, Zip 70810–1685; tel. 225/906–2999; Sherry Mix, Chief Executive Officer and Administrator
Web address: www.theneuromedicalcenter.com

NEVADA: AMG SPECIALTY HOSPITAL – LAS VEGAS (O, 24 beds) 4015 Mcleod Drive, Las Vegas, NV, Zip 89121–4305; tel. 702/433–2200; Kenneth D'Amico, Chief Executive Officer

NEW MEXICO: AMG SPECIALTY HOSPITAL-ALBUQUERQUE (O, 24 beds) 235 Elm Street NE, Albuquerque, NM, Zip 87102–3672; tel. 505/842–5550; Kendra Camp, R.N., Chief Executive Officer
Web address: www.amgalbuquerque.com/

OKLAHOMA: AMG MERCY (O, 30 beds) 4300 West Memorial Road, 2nd Floor, Oklahoma City, OK, Zip 73120–8304; tel. 405/936–5822; Eric Heflin, Chief Executive Officer
Web address: www.https://amgmercy.com/

TEXAS: AMG SPECIALTY HOSPITAL (O, 30 beds) 718 Lexington Avenue, San Antonio, TX, Zip 78212–4768; tel. 210/572–4600; Melissa Low, Chief Executive Officer
Web address: www.southtexas.acuityhealthcare.net/

Owned, leased, sponsored:	11 hospitals	287 beds
Contract-managed:	0 hospitals	0 beds
Totals:	11 hospitals	287 beds

For explanation of codes following names, see page B2.
★ Indicates Type III membership in the American Hospital Association.

★0389: ANMED HEALTH (NP)
800 North Fant Street, Anderson, SC, Zip 29621–5793;
tel. 864/512–1000; William T. Manson III, FACHE, Chief Executive
Officer
(Independent Hospital System)

SOUTH CAROLINA: ANMED HEALTH CANNON (O, 26 beds) 123 W G Acker
Drive, Pickens, SC, Zip 29671–2739, Mailing Address: P.O. Box 188,
Zip 29671–0188, tel. 864/878–4791; Brandon Clary, President and Chief
Executive Officer
Web address: www.cannonhospital.org

ANMED HEALTH MEDICAL CENTER (O, 376 beds) 800 North Fant Street,
Anderson, SC, Zip 29621–5793; tel. 864/512–1000; William T. Manson III,
FACHE, Chief Executive Officer

Owned, leased, sponsored:	2 hospitals	402 beds
Contract-managed:	0 hospitals	0 beds
Totals:	2 hospitals	402 beds

★0866: APPALACHIAN REGIONAL HEALTHCARE SYSTEM (NP)
336 Deerfield Road, Boone, NC, Zip 28607–5008, Mailing
Address: P.O. Box 2600, Zip 28607–2600, tel. 828/262–4100;
Charles Mantooth, President and Chief Executive Officer
(Independent Hospital System)

NORTH CAROLINA: BLOWING ROCK REHABILITATION & DAVANT EXTENDED
CARE CENTER (C, 72 beds) 418 Chestnut Street, Blowing Rock, NC,
Zip 28605–0148, Mailing Address: P.O. Box 148, Zip 28605–0148,
tel. 828/295–3136; Elizabeth Hayes, R.N., Interim Administrator

CHARLES A. CANNON MEMORIAL HOSPITAL (C, 31 beds) 434 Hospital Drive,
Newland, NC, Zip 28646, Mailing Address: P.O. Box 767, Linville, Zip 28646–
0767, tel. 828/737–7000; Carmen Lacey, MSN, R.N., President
Web address: www.https://apprhs.org/locations/cannon-memorial-hospital

WATAUGA MEDICAL CENTER (C, 99 beds) 336 Deerfield Road, Boone,
NC, Zip 28607–5008, Mailing Address: P.O. Box 2600, Zip 28607–2600,
tel. 828/262–4100; Charles Mantooth, President and Chief Executive Officer
Web address: www.https://apprhs.org/contact-us

Owned, leased, sponsored:	0 hospitals	0 beds
Contract-managed:	3 hospitals	202 beds
Totals:	3 hospitals	202 beds

0146: APPALACHIAN REGIONAL HEALTHCARE, INC. (NP)
2260 Executive Drive, Lexington, KY, Zip 40505–4810, Mailing
Address: P.O. Box 8086, Zip 40533–8086, tel. 859/226–2440;
Joseph Grossman, President and Chief Executive Officer
(Moderately Centralized Health System)

KENTUCKY: ARH OUR LADY OF THE WAY (O, 25 beds) 11203 Main Street,
Martin, KY, Zip 41649; tel. 606/285–6400; Kathy Stumbo, President
Web address: www.saintjosephmartin.org

HARLAN ARH HOSPITAL (O, 103 beds) 81 Ball Park Road, Harlan, KY,
Zip 40831–1792; tel. 606/573–8100; Donald R. Fields, Community Chief
Executive Officer

HAZARD ARH REGIONAL MEDICAL CENTER (O, 358 beds) 100 Medical Center
Drive, Hazard, KY, Zip 41701–9421; tel. 606/439–6600; Dan Stone, Senior
Community Chief Executive Officer
Web address: www.arh.org

HIGHLANDS ARH REGIONAL MEDICAL CENTER (O, 139 beds) 5000 Kentucky
Route 321, Prestonsburg, KY, Zip 41653–1273, Mailing Address: P.O. Box
668, Zip 41653–0668, tel. 606/886–8511; Trena F. Hall, Interim Chief
Executive Officer
Web address: www.hrmc.org

MARY BRECKINRIDGE ARH HOSPITAL (O, 25 beds) 130 Kate Ireland Drive,
Hyden, KY, Zip 41749–9071, Mailing Address: P.O. Box 447-A, Zip 41749–
0717, tel. 606/672–2901; Mallie S. Noble, Administrator

MCDOWELL ARH HOSPITAL (O, 25 beds) Route 122, McDowell, KY,
Zip 41647, Mailing Address: P.O. Box 247, Zip 41647–0247, tel. 606/377–
3400; Russell Barker, Community Chief Executive Officer
Web address: www.arh.org

MIDDLESBORO ARH HOSPITAL (O, 73 beds) 3600 West Cumberland
Avenue, Middlesboro, KY, Zip 40965–2614, Mailing Address: P.O. Box 340,
Zip 40965–0340, tel. 606/242–1100; Michael Slusher, Community Chief
Executive Officer
Web address: www.arh.org/middlesboro

MORGAN COUNTY ARH HOSPITAL (L, 25 beds) 476 Liberty Road, West
Liberty, KY, Zip 41472–2049, Mailing Address: P O Box 579, Zip 41472–
0579, tel. 606/743–3186; Stephen M. Gavalchik, FACHE, Community Chief
Executive Officer
Web address: www.arh.org

TUG VALLEY ARH REGIONAL MEDICAL CENTER (O, 123 beds) 260 Hospital
Drive, South Williamson, KY, Zip 41503–4072; tel. 606/237–1710; Timothy
A. Hatfield, Community Chief Executive Officer

WHITESBURG ARH HOSPITAL (O, 89 beds) 240 Hospital Road, Whitesburg, KY,
Zip 41858–7627; tel. 606/633–3500; Dena C. Sparkman, Community Chief
Executive Officer
Web address: www.arh.org/whitesburg

WEST VIRGINIA: BECKLEY ARH HOSPITAL (O, 160 beds) 306 Stanaford Road,
Beckley, WV, Zip 25801–3142; tel. 304/255–3000; Rocco K. Massey,
Community Chief Executive Officer

SUMMERS COUNTY ARH HOSPITAL (L, 25 beds) Terrace Street, Hinton,
WV, Zip 25951–2407, Mailing Address: Drawer 940, Zip 25951–0940,
tel. 304/466–1000; Wesley Dangerfield, Community Chief Executive Officer
Web address: www.arh.org

Owned, leased, sponsored:	12 hospitals	1170 beds
Contract-managed:	0 hospitals	0 beds
Totals:	12 hospitals	1170 beds

★0104: ARCHBOLD MEDICAL CENTER (NP)
910 South Broad Street, Thomasville, GA, Zip 31792–6113;
tel. 229/228–2739; J. Perry Mustian, President and Chief Executive Officer
(Moderately Centralized Health System)

GEORGIA: BROOKS COUNTY HOSPITAL (L, 25 beds) 903 North Court
Street, Quitman, GA, Zip 31643–1315, Mailing Address: P.O. Box
5000, Zip 31643–5000, tel. 229/263–4171; Nancy M. Williams, R.N.,
Administrator
Web address: www.archbold.org

GRADY GENERAL HOSPITAL (L, 48 beds) 1155 Fifth Street SE, Cairo,
GA, Zip 39828–3142, Mailing Address: P.O. Box 360, Zip 39828–0360,
tel. 229/377–1150; Crystal Wells, Administrator

JOHN D. ARCHBOLD MEMORIAL HOSPITAL (O, 320 beds) 915 Gordon
Avenue, Thomasville, GA, Zip 31792–6614, Mailing Address: P.O. Box 1018,
Zip 31799–1018, tel. 229/228–2000; J. Perry Mustian, President and Chief
Executive Officer
Web address: www.archbold.org

MITCHELL COUNTY HOSPITAL (L, 181 beds) 90 East Stephens Street,
Camilla, GA, Zip 31730–1836, Mailing Address: P.O. Box 639, Zip 31730–
0639, tel. 229/336–5284; James Womack, Administrator

Owned, leased, sponsored:	4 hospitals	582 beds
Contract-managed:	0 hospitals	0 beds
Totals:	4 hospitals	582 beds

★0069: ARDENT HEALTH SERVICES (IO)
1 Burton Hills Boulevard, Suite 250, Nashville, TN, Zip 37215–
6195; tel. 615/296–3000; David T. Vandewater, President and
Chief Executive Officer
(Decentralized Health System)

IDAHO: PORTNEUF MEDICAL CENTER (O, 175 beds) 777 Hospital Way,
Pocatello, ID, Zip 83201–5175; tel. 208/239–1000; Daniel Ordyna, Chief
Executive Officer

KANSAS: UNIVERSITY OF KANSAS HEALTH SYSTEM ST. FRANCIS CAMPUS
(O, 242 beds) 1700 SW 7th Street, Topeka, KS, Zip 66606–1690;
tel. 785/295–8000; Steven Anderson, Chief Executive Officer
Web address: www.stfrancistopeka.org

For explanation of codes following names, see page B2.
★ Indicates Type III membership in the American Hospital Association.

Section B

NEW JERSEY: HACKENSACK MERIDIAN HEALTH MOUNTAINSIDE MEDICAL CENTER (O, 202 beds) 1 Bay Avenue, Montclair, NJ, Zip 07042–4898; tel. 973/429–6000; John A. Fromhold, FACHE, President and Chief Executive Officer

HACKENSACK MERIDIAN HEALTH PASCACK VALLEY MEDICAL CENTER (O, 128 beds) 250 Old Hook Road, Westwood, NJ, Zip 07675–3123; tel. 201/383–1035; Emily L. Holliman, Chief Executive Officer
Web address: www.hackensackumcpv.com/

NEW MEXICO: LOVELACE MEDICAL CENTER (O, 247 beds) 601 Martin Luther King Avenue NE, Albuquerque, NM, Zip 87102–3619; tel. 505/727–8000; Troy Greer, Chief Executive Officer

LOVELACE REGIONAL HOSPITAL – ROSWELL (O, 26 beds) 117 East 19th Street, Roswell, NM, Zip 88201–5151; tel. 575/627–7000; Heather L. Harper, FACHE, Chief Executive Officer
Web address: www.lovelace.com

LOVELACE UNM REHABILITATION HOSPITAL (O, 52 beds) 505 Elm Street NE, Albuquerque, NM, Zip 87102–2500; tel. 505/727–4700; Derrick Jones, Chief Executive Officer
Web address: www.lovelace.com

LOVELACE WESTSIDE HOSPITAL (O, 80 beds) 10501 Golf Course Road NW, Albuquerque, NM, Zip 87114–5000, Mailing Address: P.O. Box 25555, Zip 87125–0555, tel. 505/727–8000; Amy Blasing, Chief Executive Officer

LOVELACE WOMEN'S HOSPITAL (O, 78 beds) 4701 Montgomery Boulevard NE, Albuquerque, NM, Zip 87109–1251, Mailing Address: P.O. Box 25555, Zip 87125–0555, tel. 505/727–7800; Sheri Milone, Chief Executive Officer and Administrator
Web address: www.lovelace.com/albuquerque-hospital/lovelace-womens-hospital#.UDZ17KDhf48

OKLAHOMA: BAILEY MEDICAL CENTER (O, 37 beds) 10502 North 110th East Avenue, Owasso, OK, Zip 74055–6655; tel. 918/376–8000; Keith Mason, Chief Executive Officer
Web address: www.baileymedicalcenter.com

HILLCREST HOSPITAL – SOUTH (O, 164 beds) 8801 South 101st East Avenue, Tulsa, OK, Zip 74133–5716; tel. 918/294–4000; Bennett Geister, Chief Executive Officer

HILLCREST HOSPITAL CLAREMORE (O, 67 beds) 1202 North Muskogee Place, Claremore, OK, Zip 74017–3036; tel. 918/341–2556; David Chaussard, Chief Executive Officer
Web address: www.hillcrestclaremore.com

HILLCREST HOSPITAL CUSHING (O, 99 beds) 1027 East Cherry Street, Cushing, OK, Zip 74023–4101; tel. 918/225–2915; Kevin Hawk, Chief Executive Officer
Web address: www.hillcrestcushing.com/

HILLCREST HOSPITAL HENRYETTA (O, 37 beds) 2401 West Main Street, Henryetta, OK, Zip 74437–3893, Mailing Address: P.O. Box 1269, Zip 74437–1269, tel. 918/650–1100; Dee Renshaw, Chief Executive Officer
Web address: www.hillcresthenryetta.com/

HILLCREST HOSPITAL PRYOR (O, 22 beds) 111 North Bailey Street, Pryor, OK, Zip 74361–4201; tel. 918/825–1600; Douglas K. Weaver, FACHE, Chief Executive Officer
Web address: www.hillcrestpryor.com/

HILLCREST MEDICAL CENTER (O, 510 beds) 1120 South Utica Avenue, Tulsa, OK, Zip 74104–4090; tel. 918/579–1000; Xavier Villarreal, FACHE, Chief Executive Officer
Web address: www.hillcrestmedicalcenter.com

TULSA SPINE AND SPECIALTY HOSPITAL (O, 21 beds) 6901 South Olympia Avenue, Tulsa, OK, Zip 74132–1843; tel. 918/388–5701; Trent Gastineau, Chief Executive Officer

TEXAS: BSA HOSPITAL, LLC (O, 355 beds) 1600 Wallace Boulevard, Amarillo, TX, Zip 79106–1799; tel. 806/212–2000; Bob Williams, President and Chief Executive Officer
Web address: www.bsahs.org

PHYSICIANS SURGICAL HOSPITAL – QUAIL CREEK (O, 41 beds) 6819 Plum Creek, Amarillo, TX, Zip 79124–1602; tel. 806/354–6100; Todd Greene, Chief Executive Officer
Web address: www.physurg.com

SETON MEDICAL CENTER HARKER HEIGHTS (O, 83 beds) 850 West Central Texas Expressway, Harker Heights, TX, Zip 76548–1890; tel. 254/690–0900; Zachary K. Dietze, Chief Executive Officer
Web address: www.setonharkerheights.net

UT HEALTH ATHENS (O, 127 beds) 2000 South Palestine Street, Athens, TX, Zip 75751–5610; tel. 903/676–1000; Scott Campbell, Interim Chief Executive Officer

UT HEALTH CARTHAGE (O, 23 beds) 409 Cottage Road, Carthage, TX, Zip 75633–1466; tel. 903/693–3841; Gary Mikeal. Hudson, Administrator
Web address: www.https://uthealthcarthage.com/

UT HEALTH HENDERSON (O, 41 beds) 300 Wilson Street, Henderson, TX, Zip 75652–5956; tel. 903/657–7541; Mark Leitner, FACHE, Administrator

UT HEALTH JACKSONVILLE (O, 38 beds) 501 South Ragsdale Street, Jacksonville, TX, Zip 75766–2413; tel. 903/541–5000; DeLeigh Haley, Chief Executive Officer
Web address: www.https://uthealthjacksonville.com/

UT HEALTH PITTSBURG (O, 25 beds) 2701 Highway 271 North, Pittsburg, TX, Zip 75686–1032; tel. 903/946–5000; Patrick Swindle, Interim Chief Executive Officer
Web address: www.https://uthealthpittsburg.com/

UT HEALTH QUITMAN (O, 25 beds) 117 Winnsboro Street, Quitman, TX, Zip 75783–2144, Mailing Address: P.O. Box 1000, Zip 75783–1000, tel. 903/763–6300; Patrick Swindle, Administrator
Web address: www.https://uthealthquitman.com/

UT HEALTH REHABILITATION HOSPITAL (O, 49 beds) 701 Olympic Plaza Circle, Tyler, TX, Zip 75701–1950, Mailing Address: P.O. Box 7530, Zip 75711–7530, tel. 903/596–3000; Laurie Lehnhof-Watts, Administrator and Chief Nursing Officer
Web address: www.https://uthealthrehab.com/

UT HEALTH SPECIALTY HOSPITAL (O, 36 beds) 1000 South Beckham, 5th Floor, Tyler, TX, Zip 75701–1908, Mailing Address: P.O. Box 7018, Zip 75711–7018, tel. 903/596–3600; Laurie Lehnhof-Watts, Administrator and Chief Nursing Officer
Web address: www.https://uthealtheasttexas.com/locations/ut-health-east-texas-specialty-hospital

UT HEALTH TYLER (O, 399 beds) 1000 South Beckham Street, Tyler, TX, Zip 75701–1908, Mailing Address: Box 6400, Zip 75711–6400, tel. 903/597–0351; Vicki R. Briggs, Chief Executive Officer

Owned, leased, sponsored:	29 hospitals	3429 beds
Contract-managed:	0 hospitals	0 beds
Totals:	29 hospitals	3429 beds

0809: ARNOT HEALTH (NP)
600 Roe Avenue, Elmira, NY, Zip 14905–1629; tel. 607/737–4100; Jonathan I. Lawrence, President and Chief Executive Officer
(Independent Hospital System)

NEW YORK: ARNOT OGDEN MEDICAL CENTER (O, 266 beds) 600 Roe Avenue, Elmira, NY, Zip 14905–1629; tel. 607/737–4100; Jonathan I. Lawrence, System Chief Operating Officer

IRA DAVENPORT MEMORIAL HOSPITAL (O, 135 beds) 7571 State Route 54, Bath, NY, Zip 14810–9590; tel. 607/776–8500; Elizabeth Weir, MSN, R.N., Site Administrator and Vice President of Nursing
Web address: www.arnothealth.org

ST. JOSEPH'S HOSPITAL (O, 141 beds) 555 St. Joseph's Boulevard, Elmira, NY, Zip 14901–3223; tel. 607/733–6541; Jonathan I. Lawrence, President and Chief Executive Officer
Web address: www.arnothealth.org

Owned, leased, sponsored:	3 hospitals	542 beds
Contract-managed:	0 hospitals	0 beds
Totals:	3 hospitals	542 beds

★0094: ASANTE HEALTH SYSTEM (NP)
2650 Siskiyou Boulevard, Suite 200, Medford, OR, Zip 97504–8170; tel. 541/789–4100; Scott A. Kelly, President and Chief Executive Officer
(Centralized Health System)

OREGON: ASANTE ASHLAND COMMUNITY HOSPITAL (O, 38 beds) 280 Maple Street, Ashland, OR, Zip 97520–1593; tel. 541/201–4000; Sheila Clough, Chief Executive Officer
Web address: www.ashlandhospital.org

For explanation of codes following names, see page B2.
★ Indicates Type III membership in the American Hospital Association.

ASANTE ROGUE REGIONAL MEDICAL CENTER (O, 337 beds) 2825 East Barnett Road, Medford, OR, Zip 97504–8332; tel. 541/789–7000; Mick Zleblick, Chief Executive Officer
Web address: www.asante.org

ASANTE THREE RIVERS MEDICAL CENTER (O, 121 beds) 500 SW Ramsey Avenue, Grants Pass, OR, Zip 97527–5554; tel. 541/472–7000; Win Howard, Chief Executive Officer

Owned, leased, sponsored:	3 hospitals	496 beds
Contract-managed:	0 hospitals	0 beds
Totals:	3 hospitals	496 beds

★**0198: ASCENSION HEALTHCARE** (CC)
101 South Hanley Road, Suite 450, Saint Louis, MO, Zip 63105–3406; tel. 314/733–8000; Joseph R. Impicciche, JD, President and Chief Executive Officer
(Decentralized Health System)

ALABAMA: PROVIDENCE HOSPITAL (S, 305 beds) 6801 Airport Boulevard, Mobile, AL, Zip 36608–3785, Mailing Address: P.O. Box 850429, Zip 36685–0429, tel. 251/633–1000; Todd S. Kennedy, President and Chief Executive Officer
Web address: www.providencehospital.org

ST. VINCENT'S BIRMINGHAM (S, 409 beds) 810 St Vincent's Drive, Birmingham, AL, Zip 35205–1695, Mailing Address: P.O. Box 12407, Zip 35202–2407, tel. 205/939–7000; Evan Ray, FACHE, Chief Executive Officer

ST. VINCENT'S BLOUNT (S, 25 beds) 150 Gilbreath, Oneonta, AL, Zip 35121–2827, Mailing Address: P.O. Box 1000, Zip 35121–0013, tel. 205/274–3000; Suzannah Campbell, President
Web address: www.stvhs.com

ST. VINCENT'S CHILTON HOSPITAL (L, 36 beds) 2030 Lay Dam Road, Clanton, AL, Zip 35045; tel. 205/258–4400; John Shanon. Hamilton, Administrator

ST. VINCENT'S EAST (S, 362 beds) 50 Medical Park East Drive, Birmingham, AL, Zip 35235–9987; tel. 205/838–3000; Suzannah Campbell, President
Web address: www.stvhs.com

ST. VINCENT'S ST. CLAIR (S, 40 beds) 7063 Veterans Parkway, Pell City, AL, Zip 35125–1499; tel. 205/814–2105; Suzannah Campbell, President
Web address: www.stvhs.com

CONNECTICUT: ST. VINCENT'S MEDICAL CENTER (S, 352 beds) 2800 Main Street, Bridgeport, CT, Zip 06606–4292; tel. 203/576–6000; Dawn Rudolph, President and Chief Executive Officer

FLORIDA: BAY MEDICAL SACRED HEART (O, 15 beds) 615 North Bonita Avenue, Panama City, FL, Zip 32401–3600, Mailing Address: P.O. Box 59515, Zip 32412–0515, tel. 850/769–1511; Heath Evans, President
Web address: www.baymedical.org

SACRED HEART HOSPITAL PENSACOLA (S, 440 beds) 5151 North Ninth Avenue, Pensacola, FL, Zip 32504–8795, Mailing Address: P.O. Box 2700, Zip 32513–2700, tel. 850/416–7000; Henry Stovall, President
Web address: www.https://healthcare.ascension.org/Locations/Florida/FLPEN/Pensacola-Sacred-Heart-Hospital-Pensacola

SACRED HEART HOSPITAL ON THE EMERALD COAST (S, 76 beds) 7800 Highway 98 West, Miramar Beach, FL, Zip 32550; tel. 850/278–3000; Roger L. Hall, President

SACRED HEART HOSPITAL ON THE GULF (S, 12 beds) 3801 East Highway 98, Port St Joe, FL, Zip 32456–5318; tel. 850/229–5600; Roger L. Hall, President
Web address: www.sacred-heart.org/gulf/

ST. VINCENT'S MEDICAL CENTER CLAY COUNTY (O, 106 beds) 1670 St. Vincent's Way, Middleburg, FL, Zip 32068–8427, Mailing Address: 1670 St. Vincents Way, Zip 32068–8447, tel. 904/602–1000; James Machado, President
Web address: www.jaxhealth.com/

ST. VINCENT'S MEDICAL CENTER RIVERSIDE (S, 482 beds) 1 Shircliff Way, Jacksonville, FL, Zip 32204–4748, Mailing Address: P.O. Box 2982, Zip 32203–2982, tel. 904/308–7300; Thomas J. VanOsdol, Chief Executive Officer

ST. VINCENT'S MEDICAL CENTER SOUTHSIDE (S, 289 beds) 4201 Belfort Road, Jacksonville, FL, Zip 32216–1431; tel. 904/296–3700; Thomas J. VanOsdol, Chief Executive Officer
Web address: www.jaxhealth.com

ILLINOIS: AMITA HEALTH ELK GROVE VILLAGE (O, 401 beds) 800 Biesterfield Road, Elk Grove Village, IL, Zip 60007–3397; tel. 847/437–5500; John P. Werrbach, President and Chief Executive Officer
Web address: www.AMITAHealth.org

AMITA HEALTH HOFFMAN ESTATES (O, 298 beds) 1555 Barrington Road, Hoffman Estates, IL, Zip 60169–1019; tel. 847/843–2000; Leonard Wilk, President and Chief Executive Officer
Web address: www.AMITAHealth.org

AMITA HEALTH HOLY FAMILY MEDICAL CENTER (O, 178 beds) 100 North River Road, Des Plaines, IL, Zip 60016–1255; tel. 847/297–1800; Yolande Wilson-Stubbs, President

AMITA HEALTH MERCY MEDICAL CENTER (O, 292 beds) 1325 North Highland Avenue, Aurora, IL, Zip 60506–1449; tel. 630/859–2222; Michael L. Brown, Regional President and Chief Executive Officer
Web address: www.presencehealth.org/mercy/

AMITA HEALTH RESURRECTION MEDICAL CENTER (O, 337 beds) 7435 West Talcott Avenue, Chicago, IL, Zip 60631–3746; tel. 773/774–8000; Robert Dahl, President and Chief Executive Officer
Web address: www.presencehealth.org

AMITA HEALTH SAINT FRANCIS HOSPITAL EVANSTON (O, 215 beds) 355 Ridge Avenue, Evanston, IL, Zip 60202–3399; tel. 847/316–4000; Kenneth Jones, President
Web address: www.reshealth.org

AMITA HEALTH SAINT JOSEPH HOSPITAL (O, 361 beds) 2900 North Lake Shore Drive, Chicago, IL, Zip 60657–6274; tel. 773/665–3000; James L. Robinson III, President

AMITA HEALTH SAINT JOSEPH HOSPITAL (O, 184 beds) 77 North Airlite Street, Elgin, IL, Zip 60123–4912; tel. 847/695–3200; Michael L. Brown, Regional President and Chief Executive Officer
Web address: www.provena.org

AMITA HEALTH SAINT JOSEPH MEDICAL CENTER (O, 485 beds) 333 North Madison Street, Joliet, IL, Zip 60435–8200; tel. 815/725–7133; Robert J. Erickson, President
Web address: www.presencehealth.org/stjoes

AMITA HEALTH SAINTS MARY & ELIZABETH MEDICAL CENTER (O, 495 beds) 2233 West Division Street, Chicago, IL, Zip 60622–3086; tel. 312/770–2000; Martin H. Judd, Regional President and Chief Executive Officer

AMITA HEALTH ST. MARY'S HOSPITAL (O, 182 beds) 500 West Court Street, Kankakee, IL, Zip 60901–3661; tel. 815/937–2400; Chris Shride, President
Web address: www.presencehealth.org/presence-st-marys-hospital-kankakee

ALEXIAN BROTHERS BEHAVIORAL HEALTH HOSPITAL (O, 141 beds) 1650 Moon Lake Boulevard, Hoffman Estates, IL, Zip 60169–1010; tel. 847/882–1600; Clayton Ciha, President and Chief Executive Officer

OUR LADY OF THE RESURRECTION-LONG TERM CARE (O, 50 beds) 5645 West Addison Street, Chicago, IL, Zip 60634

RESURRECTION NURSING PAVILION (O, 295 beds) 1001 North Greenwood, Park Ridge, IL, Zip 60068; Patricia Tiernan, Administrator

INDIANA: DAVIESS COMMUNITY HOSPITAL (C, 72 beds) 1314 East Walnut Street, Washington, IN, Zip 47501–2860, Mailing Address: P.O. Box 760, Zip 47501–0760, tel. 812/254–2760; Tracy Conroy, Chief Executive Officer
Web address: www.dchosp.org

ST. VINCENT ANDERSON (S, 154 beds) 2015 Jackson Street, Anderson, IN, Zip 46016–4339; tel. 765/649–2511; Mike K. Schroyer, FACHE, MSN, R.N., President

ST. VINCENT CARMEL HOSPITAL (S, 111 beds) 13500 North Meridian Street, Carmel, IN, Zip 46032–1456; tel. 317/582–7000; Julie Manas, Regional President
Web address: https://www.stvincent.org

ST. VINCENT CLAY HOSPITAL (S, 25 beds) 1206 East National Avenue, Brazil, IN, Zip 47834–2797, Mailing Address: 1206 East National Ave, Zip 47834–0489, tel. 812/442–2500; Jerry Laue, Administrator

ST. VINCENT DUNN HOSPITAL (S, 35 beds) 1600 23rd Street, Bedford, IN, Zip 47421–4704; tel. 812/275–3331; Jerry Laue, Administrator
Web address: www.stvincent.org/St-Vincent-Dunn/Default.aspx

ST. VINCENT EVANSVILLE (S, 468 beds) 3700 Washington Avenue, Evansville, IN, Zip 47714–0541; tel. 812/485–4000; Daniel A. Parod, President

For explanation of codes following names, see page B2.
★ Indicates Type III membership in the American Hospital Association.

ST. VINCENT FISHERS HOSPITAL (S, 46 beds) 13861 Olio Road, Fishers, IN, Zip 46037–3487; tel. 317/415–9000; Julie Manas, Regional President
Web address: www.stvincent.org

ST. VINCENT HEART CENTER (S, 80 beds) 10580 North Meridian Street, Indianapolis, IN, Zip 46290–1028; tel. 317/583–5000; Lori Shannon, President

ST. VINCENT INDIANAPOLIS HOSPITAL (S, 840 beds) 2001 West 86th Street, Indianapolis, IN, Zip 46260–1991, Mailing Address: P.O. Box 40970, Zip 46240–0970, tel. 317/338–2345; Joel Feldman, Regional President
Web address: www.stvincent.org

ST. VINCENT JENNINGS HOSPITAL (S, 17 beds) 301 Henry Street, North Vernon, IN, Zip 47265–1097; tel. 812/352–4200; Dana M. Muntz, Chief Executive Officer
Web address: www.stvincent.org

ST. VINCENT KOKOMO (S, 129 beds) 1907 West Sycamore Street, Kokomo, IN, Zip 46901–4197; tel. 765/452–5611; Margaret M. Johnson, President, St. Vincent Northwest Region

ST. VINCENT MERCY HOSPITAL (S, 12 beds) 1331 South 'A' Street, Elwood, IN, Zip 46036–1942; tel. 765/552–4600; Ann C. Yates, R.N., MSN, Administrator and Chief Nursing Officer
Web address: www.stvincent.org

ST. VINCENT RANDOLPH HOSPITAL (S, 18 beds) 473 Greenville Avenue, Winchester, IN, Zip 47394–9436; tel. 765/584–0004; Carla Fouse, Administrator and Chief Nursing Officer
Web address: www.stvincent.org

ST. VINCENT SALEM HOSPITAL (S, 25 beds) 911 North Shelby Street, Salem, IN, Zip 47167–1694; tel. 812/883–5881; Dana M. Muntz, Chief Executive Officer

ST. VINCENT SETON SPECIALTY HOSPITAL (S, 74 beds) 8050 Township Line Road, Indianapolis, IN, Zip 46260–2478; tel. 317/415–8500; Joel Feldman, Regional President
Web address: www.stvincent.org/

ST. VINCENT WARRICK (S, 35 beds) 1116 Millis Avenue, Boonville, IN, Zip 47601–2204; tel. 812/897–4800; Kathy J. Hall, Administrator
Web address: www.stmarys.org/warrick

ST. VINCENT WILLIAMSPORT HOSPITAL (S, 16 beds) 412 North Monroe Street, Williamsport, IN, Zip 47993–1049; tel. 765/762–4000; Jane Craigin, Chief Executive Officer
Web address: www.stvincent.org

KANSAS: ASCENSION VIA CHRISTI HOSPITAL ON ST. TERESA (O, 49 beds) 14800 West St. Teresa, Wichita, KS, Zip 67235–9602; tel. 316/796–7000; Robyn Chadwick, President
Web address: www.via-christi.org/st-teresa

ASCENSION VIA CHRISTI HOSPITAL, MANHATTAN (O, 96 beds) 1823 College Avenue, Manhattan, KS, Zip 66502–3346; tel. 785/776–3322; Robert C. Copple, FACHE, Senior Administrator

ASCENSION VIA CHRISTI HOSPITAL (O, 89 beds) 1 Mt. Carmel Way, Pittsburg, KS, Zip 66762–7587; tel. 620/231–6100; Randall R. Cason, FACHE, Senior Administrator
Web address: www.viachristi.org/pittsburg

ASCENSION VIA CHRISTI REHABILITATION HOSPITAL (O, 58 beds) 1151 North Rock Road, Wichita, KS, Zip 67206–1262; tel. 316/634–3400; Kevin Strecker, President

ASCENSION VIA CHRISTI ST. FRANCIS (O, 647 beds) 211 N College Ave, Mulvane, KS, Zip 67110, Mailing Address: 929 North St Francis Street, Wichita, Zip 67214–3882, tel. 316/268–5000; Kevin Strecker, President
Web address: www.via-christi.org

MARYLAND: SAINT AGNES HEALTHCARE (S, 367 beds) 900 Caton Avenue, Baltimore, MD, Zip 21229–5201; tel. 667/234–6000; Keith Vander Kolk, President and Chief Executive Officer

MICHIGAN: ASCENSION BORGESS HOSPITAL (S, 422 beds) 1521 Gull Road, Kalamazoo, MI, Zip 49048–1640; tel. 269/226–7000; Tim Stover, M.D., Interim Chief Executive Officer
Web address: www.borgess.com

ASCENSION BORGESS-LEE HOSPITAL (S, 25 beds) 420 West High Street, Dowagiac, MI, Zip 49047–1943; tel. 269/782–8681; Natalie Ryder, Chief Administrative Officer
Web address: www.borgess.com

ASCENSION BRIGHTON CENTER FOR RECOVERY (S, 99 beds) 12851 Grand River Road, Brighton, MI, Zip 48116–8506; tel. 810/227–1211; Raymond A. Waller, Director and Administrator

ASCENSION CRITTENTON HOSPITAL MEDICAL CENTER (O, 226 beds) 1101 West University Drive, Rochester, MI, Zip 48307–1831; tel. 248/652–5000; Chris Palazzolo, President and Chief Executive Officer
Web address: www.crittenton.com

ASCENSION GENESYS HOSPITAL (S, 427 beds) One Genesys Parkway, Grand Blanc, MI, Zip 48439–8066; tel. 810/606–5000; Chris Palazzolo, President and Chief Executive Officer

ASCENSION MACOMB-OAKLAND HOSPITAL (S, 535 beds) 11800 East 12 Mile Road, Warren, MI, Zip 48093–3472; tel. 586/573–5000; Terry Hamilton, President
Web address: www.stjohnprovidence.org/macomb-oakland/

ASCENSION RIVER DISTRICT HOSPITAL (S, 18 beds) 4100 River Road, East China, MI, Zip 48054–2909; tel. 810/329–7111; Robert E. Hoban, President
Web address: www.stjohnprovidence.org/RiverDistrict/

ASCENSION ST. JOHN HOSPITAL (S, 592 beds) 22101 Moross Road, Detroit, MI, Zip 48236–2148; tel. 313/343–4000; Robert E. Hoban, President

ASCENSION ST. JOSEPH HOSPITAL (S, 20 beds) 200 Hemlock Street, Tawas City, MI, Zip 48763–9237, Mailing Address: P.O. Box 659, Zip 48764–0659, tel. 989/362–3411; Jan Jacob, R.N., Interim Administrator
Web address: www.sjhsys.org

ASCENSION ST. MARY'S OF MICHIGAN (S, 279 beds) 800 South Washington Avenue, Saginaw, MI, Zip 48601–2594; tel. 989/907–8000; Chris Palazzolo, Health System President and Chief Executive Officer Mid-Michigan

ASCENSION STANDISH HOSPITAL (S, 64 beds) 805 West Cedar Street, Standish, MI, Zip 48658–9526; tel. 989/846–4521; Chris Palazzolo, President and Chief Executive Officer
Web address: www.stmarysofmichigan.org/standish

ASCENSION OF PROVIDENCE HOSPITAL, SOUTHFIELD CAMPUS (S, 628 beds) 16001 West Nine Mile Road, Southfield, MI, Zip 48075; tel. 248/849–3400; Joseph R. Hurshe, President

MINNESOTA: SAINT ELIZABETH'S MEDICAL CENTER (O, 153 beds) 1200 Grant Boulevard West, Wabasha, MN, Zip 55981–1042; tel. 651/565–4531; Thomas Crowley, President and Chief Executive Officer
Web address: www.stelizabethswabasha.org

NEW YORK: OUR LADY OF LOURDES MEMORIAL HOSPITAL, INC. (S, 154 beds) 169 Riverside Drive, Binghamton, NY, Zip 13905–4246; tel. 607/798–5111; Kathryn Connerton, President and Chief Executive Officer

ST. MARY'S HEALTHCARE (S, 290 beds) 427 Guy Park Avenue, Amsterdam, NY, Zip 12010–1054; tel. 518/842–1900; Victor Giulianelli, FACHE, President and Chief Executive Officer
Web address: www.smha.org

OKLAHOMA: JANE PHILLIPS MEDICAL CENTER (O, 114 beds) 3500 East Frank Phillips Boulevard, Bartlesville, OK, Zip 74006–2411; tel. 918/333–7200; Mike Moore, President and Chief Operating Officer
Web address: www.jpmc.org

JANE PHILLIPS NOWATA HEALTH CENTER (O, 15 beds) 237 South Locust Street, Nowata, OK, Zip 74048–3660; tel. 918/273–3102; Jason McCauley, Administrator
Web address: www.jpmc.org

ST. JOHN BROKEN ARROW (O, 44 beds) 1000 West Boise Circle, Broken Arrow, OK, Zip 74012–4900; tel. 918/994–8100; David L. Phillips, Chief Operating Officer

ST. JOHN MEDICAL CENTER (O, 523 beds) 1923 South Utica Avenue, Tulsa, OK, Zip 74104–6502; tel. 918/744–2345; Jeffrey D. Nowlin, President and Chief Operating Officer
Web address: www.sjmc.org

ST. JOHN OWASSO (O, 36 beds) 12451 East 100th Street North, Owasso, OK, Zip 74055–4600; tel. 918/274–5000; David L. Phillips, President and Chief Operating Officer

ST. JOHN SAPULPA (O, 25 beds) 1004 East Bryan Avenue, Sapulpa, OK, Zip 74066–4513, Mailing Address: P.O. Box 1368, Zip 74067–1368, tel. 918/224–4280; Michael Christian, Chief Operating Officer
Web address: www.stjohnhealthsystem.com/sapulpa

For explanation of codes following names, see page B2.
★ Indicates Type III membership in the American Hospital Association.

TENNESSEE: SAINT THOMAS DEKALB HOSPITAL (O, 56 beds) 520 West Main Street, Smithville, TN, Zip 37166–1138, Mailing Address: P.O. Box 640, Zip 37166–0640, tel. 615/215–5000; Bradley Mullinax, Chief Administrative Officer

SAINT THOMAS HICKMAN HOSPITAL (S, 65 beds) 135 East Swan Street, Centerville, TN, Zip 37033–1417; tel. 931/729–4271; Kevin Campbell, Chief Executive Officer
Web address: www.sths.com/hickman

SAINT THOMAS HIGHLANDS HOSPITAL (O, 60 beds) 401 Sewell Road, Sparta, TN, Zip 38583–1299; tel. 931/738–9211; Richard Tumlin, Chief Administrative Officer
Web address: www.whitecountyhospital.com

SAINT THOMAS HOSPITAL FOR SPINAL SURGERY (S, 23 beds) 2011 Murphy Avenue, Suite 400, Nashville, TN, Zip 37203–2065; tel. 615/341–7500; Kathy Watson, R.N., Administrator and Chief Nursing Officer

SAINT THOMAS MIDTOWN HOSPITAL (S, 425 beds) 2000 Church Street, Nashville, TN, Zip 37236–0002; tel. 615/284–5555; Fahad Tahir, Chief Executive Officer
Web address: www.sths.com

SAINT THOMAS RIVER PARK HOSPITAL (O, 85 beds) 1559 Sparta Street, Mc Minnville, TN, Zip 37110–1316; tel. 931/815–4000; Dale Humphrey, Chief Executive Officer

SAINT THOMAS RUTHERFORD HOSPITAL (S, 286 beds) 1700 Medical Center Parkway, Murfreesboro, TN, Zip 37129–2245; tel. 615/396–4100; Gordon B. Ferguson, President and Chief Executive Officer
Web address: www.mtmc.org

SAINT THOMAS STONES RIVER HOSPITAL (O, 60 beds) 324 Doolittle Road, Woodbury, TN, Zip 37190–1139; tel. 615/563–4001; Robert Peglow, Interim Chief Administrative Officer
Web address: www.stonesriverhospital.com

SAINT THOMAS WEST HOSPITAL (S, 395 beds) 4220 Harding Road, Nashville, TN, Zip 37205–2095, Mailing Address: P.O. Box 380, Zip 37202–0380, tel. 615/222–2111; Fahad Tahir, Chief Executive Officer

TEXAS: ASCENSION SETON EDGAR B. DAVIS HOSPITAL (S, 25 beds) 130 Hays Street, Luling, TX, Zip 78648–3207; tel. 830/875–7000; Scott O. Fuller, President and Chief Executive Officer
Web address: www.seton.net/locations/edgar_davis/

ASCENSION SETON HAYS (O, 142 beds) 6001 Kyle Parkway, Kyle, TX, Zip 78640–6112; tel. 512/504–5000; Katherine Henderson, President and Chief Executive Officer
Web address: www.seton.net/locations/seton_medical_center_hays/

ASCENSION SETON HIGHLAND LAKES (S, 19 beds) 3201 South Water Street, Burnet, TX, Zip 78611–4510, Mailing Address: P.O. Box 1219, Zip 78611–7219, tel. 512/715–3000; Scott O. Fuller, President and Chief Executive Officer

ASCENSION SETON MEDICAL CENTER AUSTIN (S, 382 beds) 1201 West 38th Street, Austin, TX, Zip 78705–1006; tel. 512/324–1000; Christann Vasquez, President and Chief Executive Officer
Web address: www.seton.net/locations/smc/

ASCENSION SETON NORTHWEST (S, 117 beds) 11113 Research Boulevard, Austin, TX, Zip 78759–5236; tel. 512/324–6000; Katherine Henderson, President and Chief Executive Officer

ASCENSION SETON SHOAL CREEK (S, 94 beds) 3501 Mills Avenue, Austin, TX, Zip 78731–6391; tel. 512/324–2000; Christann Vasquez, President and Chief Executive Officer
Web address: www.seton.net

ASCENSION SETON SMITHVILLE (O, 5 beds) 1201 Hill Road, Smithville, TX, Zip 78957; tel. 512/237–3214; Scott O. Fuller, President and Chief Executive Officer

ASCENSION SETON SOUTHWEST (S, 11 beds) 7900 F M 1826, Building 1, Austin, TX, Zip 78737–1407; tel. 512/324–9000; Katherine Henderson, President and Chief Executive Officer
Web address: www.seton.net

ASCENSION SETON WILLIAMSON (S, 126 beds) 201 Seton Parkway, Round Rock, TX, Zip 78665–8000; tel. 512/324–4000; Katherine Henderson, President and Chief Executive Officer
Web address: www.seton.net/williamson

DELL CHILDREN'S MEDICAL CENTER OF CENTRAL TEXAS (S, 189 beds) 4900 Mueller Boulevard, Austin, TX, Zip 78723–3079; tel. 512/324–0000; Debra M. Brown, Vice President, Chief Nursing Officer and Chief Operating Officer

DELL SETON MEDICAL CENTER AT THE UNIVERSITY OF TEXAS (O, 195 beds) 1500 Red River Street, Austin, TX, Zip 78701; tel. 512/324–7000; Christann Vasquez, President
Web address: www.seton.net/locations/dell-seton/

PROVIDENCE HEALTHCARE NETWORK (S, 284 beds) 6901 Medical Parkway, Waco, TX, Zip 76712–7998, Mailing Address: P.O. Box 2589, Zip 76702–2589, tel. 254/751–4000; Philip A. Patterson, President
Web address: www.providence.net

WISCONSIN: ASCENSION ALL SAINTS (O, 278 beds) 3801 Spring Street, Racine, WI, Zip 53405–1690; tel. 262/687–4011; Kristin McManmon, President
Web address: www.allsaintshealth.com

ASCENSION CALUMET HOSPITAL (O, 15 beds) 614 Memorial Drive, Chilton, WI, Zip 53014–1597; tel. 920/849–2386; Jenny Derks, Chief Administrative Officer

ASCENSION COLUMBIA ST. MARY'S HOSPITAL MILWAUKEE (S, 288 beds) 2301 North Lake Drive, Milwaukee, WI, Zip 53211–4508; tel. 414/291–1000; Travis Andersen, Chief Executive Officer
Web address: www.columbia-stmarys.org

ASCENSION COLUMBIA ST. MARY'S HOSPITAL OZAUKEE (S, 112 beds) 13111 North Port Washington Road, Mequon, WI, Zip 53097–2416; tel. 262/243–7300; Kelly Elkins, President and Chief Executive Officer
Web address: www.columbia-stmarys.org

ASCENSION COLUMBIA ST. MARY'S MILWAUKEE HOSPITAL (S, 31 beds) 2323 North Lake Drive, Milwaukee, WI, Zip 53211–4508, Mailing Address: 2301 North Lake Drive, Zip 53211–4508, tel. 414/585–1000; Kelly Elkins, President and Chief Executive Officer

ASCENSION EAGLE RIVER HOSPITAL (O, 14 beds) 201 Hospital Road, Eagle River, WI, Zip 54521–8835; tel. 715/479–7411; Sandra L. Anderson, President
Web address: www.ministryhealth.org

ASCENSION GOOD SAMARITAN HOSPITAL (O, 10 beds) 601 South Center Avenue, Merrill, WI, Zip 54452–3404; tel. 715/536–5511; Jeremy Normington-Slay, FACHE, Chief Executive Officer
Web address: www.ministryhealth.org

ASCENSION NORTHEAST WISCONSIN MERCY HOSPITAL (O, 120 beds) 500 South Oakwood Road, Oshkosh, WI, Zip 54904–7944; tel. 920/223–2000; Denise Parrish, Interim Chief Administrative Officer
Web address: www.affinityhealth.org

ASCENSION NORTHEAST WISCONSIN ST. ELIZABETH HOSPITAL (O, 190 beds) 1506 South Oneida Street, Appleton, WI, Zip 54915–1305; tel. 920/738–2000; Monica Hilt, President and Regional Vice President

ASCENSION OUR LADY OF VICTORY HOSPITAL (O, 6 beds) 1120 Pine Street, Stanley, WI, Zip 54768–1297; tel. 715/644–5571; Jeremy Normington-Slay, FACHE, President
Web address: www.ministryhealth.org

ASCENSION SACRED HEART HOSPITAL (O, 8 beds) 401 West Mohawk Drive, Tomahawk, WI, Zip 54487–2274; tel. 715/453–7700; Sandra L. Anderson, President and Chief Executive Officer
Web address: www.ministryhealth.org

ASCENSION SAINT CLARE'S HOSPITAL (O, 60 beds) 3400 Ministry Parkway, Weston, WI, Zip 54476–5220; tel. 715/393–3000; Jeremy Normington-Slay, FACHE, President, North Central Region

ASCENSION SOUTHEAST WISCONSIN HOSPITAL – ELMBROOK CAMPUS (O, 122 beds) 19333 West North Avenue, Brookfield, WI, Zip 53045–4198; tel. 262/785–2000; Timothy Richman, President and Chief Executive Officer
Web address: https://www.mywheaton.org

ASCENSION SOUTHEAST WISCONSIN HOSPITAL – FRANKLIN CAMPUS (O, 44 beds) 10101 South 27th Street, Franklin, WI, Zip 53132–7209; tel. 414/325–4700; Seth R. Teigen, President

ASCENSION SOUTHEAST WISCONSIN HOSPITAL – ST. FRANCIS CAMPUS (O, 152 beds) 3237 South 16th Street, Milwaukee, WI, Zip 53215; tel. 414/647–5000; Seth R. Teigen, President
Web address: www.mywheaton.org/stfrancis

ASCENSION SOUTHEAST WISCONSIN HOSPITAL – ST. JOSEPH'S CAMPUS (O, 370 beds) 5000 West Chambers Street, Milwaukee, WI, Zip 53210–1650; tel. 414/447–2000; Kevin Kluesner, Chief Administrative Officer

ASCENSION ST. MARY'S HOSPITAL (O, 64 beds) 2251 North Shore Drive, Rhinelander, WI, Zip 54501–6710; tel. 715/361–2000; Sandra L. Anderson, President
Web address: www.ministryhealth.org

For explanation of codes following names, see page B2.
★ Indicates Type III membership in the American Hospital Association.

ASCENSION ST. MICHAEL'S HOSPITAL (O, 35 beds) 900 Illinois Avenue, Stevens Point, WI, Zip 54481–3196; tel. 715/346–5000; Jeremy Normington-Slay, FACHE, President, North Central Region
Web address: www.ministryhealth.org/SMH/home.nws

HOWARD YOUNG MEDICAL CENTER (O, 50 beds) 240 Maple Street, Woodruff, WI, Zip 54568–9190, Mailing Address: P.O. Box 470, Zip 54568–0470, tel. 715/356–8000; Sandra L. Anderson, President and Chief Executive Officer
Web address: www.ministryhealth.org

MIDWEST ORTHOPEDIC SPECIALTY HOSPITAL (O, 16 beds) 10101 South 27th Street, 2nd Floor, Franklin, WI, Zip 53132–7209; tel. 414/817–5800; Bernie Sherry, Senior Vice President, Ascension Healthcare, Ministry

Owned, leased, sponsored:	112 hospitals	19972 beds
Contract-managed:	1 hospitals	72 beds
Totals:	113 hospitals	20044 beds

★0519: ASPIRUS, INC. (NP)
2200 Westwood Drive, Wausau, WI, Zip 54401–7806; tel. 715/847–2118; Matthew Heywood, Chief Executive Officer
(Moderately Centralized Health System)

MICHIGAN: ASPIRUS IRON RIVER HOSPITALS & CLINICS, INC. (O, 12 beds) 1400 West Ice Lake Road, Iron River, MI, Zip 49935–9526; tel. 906/265–6121; Connie L. Koutouzos, R.N., MSN, Chief Executive Officer

ASPIRUS IRONWOOD HOSPITALS & CLINICS, INC. (O, 25 beds) N10561 Grand View Lane, Ironwood, MI, Zip 49938–9622; tel. 906/932–2525; Paula L. Chermside, Chief Executive Officer
Web address: www.aspirus.org

ASPIRUS KEWEENAW HOSPITAL, INC. (O, 25 beds) 205 Osceola Street, Laurium, MI, Zip 49913–2134; tel. 906/337–6500; Rick L. Nevers, Interim President
Web address: www.aspirus.org

ASPIRUS ONTONAGON HOSPITAL, INC. (O, 56 beds) 601 South Seventh Street, Ontonagon, MI, Zip 49953–1459; tel. 906/884–8000; Dylan Taylor, Chief Administrative Officer
Web address: www.aspirus.org

WISCONSIN: ASPIRUS LANGLADE HOSPITAL (O, 24 beds) 112 East Fifth Avenue, Antigo, WI, Zip 54409–2796; tel. 715/623–2331; Andrew J. Barth, Executive Director
Web address: www.aspirus.org

ASPIRUS MEDFORD HOSPITAL & CLINICS, INC. (O, 93 beds) 135 South Gibson Street, Medford, WI, Zip 54451; tel. 715/748–8100; Dale Hustedt, Chief Executive Officer
Web address: www.aspirus.org

ASPIRUS RIVERVIEW HOSPITAL AND CLINICS, INC. (O, 75 beds) 410 Dewey Street, Wisconsin Rapids, WI, Zip 54494–4715, Mailing Address: P.O. Box 8080, Zip 54495–8080, tel. 715/423–6060; Todd Burch, Chief Executive Officer
Web address: www.aspirus.org

ASPIRUS WAUSAU HOSPITAL, INC. (O, 247 beds) 333 Pine Ridge Boulevard, Wausau, WI, Zip 54401–4187; tel. 715/847–2121; Darrell Lentz, President

Owned, leased, sponsored:	8 hospitals	557 beds
Contract-managed:	0 hospitals	0 beds
Totals:	8 hospitals	557 beds

1031: ASTRIA HEALTH (NP)
1806 Yakima Valley Highway, Sunnyside, WA, Zip 98944–2263; tel. 509/837–1330; John Gallagher, President and Chief Executive Officer
(Independent Hospital System)

WASHINGTON: ASTRIA REGIONAL MEDICAL CENTER (O, 167 beds) 110 South Ninth Avenue, Yakima, WA, Zip 98902–3315; tel. 509/575–5000; Jeff Egbert, Interim Chief Executive Officer

ASTRIA SUNNYSIDE HOSPITAL (O, 25 beds) 1016 Tacoma Avenue, Sunnyside, WA, Zip 98944–2263, Mailing Address: P.O. Box 719, Zip 98944–0719, tel. 509/837–1500; Brian P. Gibbons Jr, Chief Executive Officer
Web address: www.astria.health/

ASTRIA TOPPENISH HOSPITAL (O, 48 beds) 502 West Fourth Avenue, Toppenish, WA, Zip 98948–1616, Mailing Address: P.O. Box 672, Zip 98948–0672, tel. 509/865–3105; Eric P. Jensen, Chief Executive Officer
Web address: www.astria.health/

Owned, leased, sponsored:	3 hospitals	240 beds
Contract-managed:	0 hospitals	0 beds
Totals:	3 hospitals	240 beds

★0865: ATLANTIC HEALTH SYSTEM (NP)
475 South Street, Morristown, NJ, Zip 07960–6459, Mailing Address: P.O. Box 1905, Zip 07962–1905, tel. 973/660–3270; Brian A. Gragnolati, FACHE, President and Chief Executive Officer
(Decentralized Health System)

NEW JERSEY: CHILTON MEDICAL CENTER (O, 133 beds) 97 West Parkway, Pompton Plains, NJ, Zip 07444–1696; tel. 973/831–5000; Stephanie L. Schwartz, FACHE, Vice President AHS and President CMC
Web address: www.chiltonmemorial.org

HACKETTSTOWN MEDICAL CENTER (O, 80 beds) 651 Willow Grove Street, Hackettstown, NJ, Zip 07840–1799; tel. 908/852–5100; Joseph DiPaolo, FACHE, President

MORRISTOWN MEDICAL CENTER (O, 695 beds) 100 Madison Avenue, Morristown, NJ, Zip 07960–6136; tel. 973/971–5000; Trish O'Keefe, Ph.D., R.N., President
Web address: www.atlantichealth.org/Morristown/

NEWTON MEDICAL CENTER (O, 148 beds) 175 High Street, Newton, NJ, Zip 07860–1004; tel. 973/383–2121; Joseph DiPaolo, FACHE, President
Web address: www.atlantichealth.org/newton/

OVERLOOK MEDICAL CENTER (O, 384 beds) 99 Beauvoir Avenue, Summit, NJ, Zip 07901–3533; tel. 908/522–2000; Alan R. Lieber, President
Web address: www.atlantichealth.org/Overlook

Owned, leased, sponsored:	5 hospitals	1440 beds
Contract-managed:	0 hospitals	0 beds
Totals:	5 hospitals	1440 beds

★0705: ATRIUM HEALTH (NP)
1000 Blythe Boulevard, Charlotte, NC, Zip 28203–5871, Mailing Address: PO Box 32861, Zip 28232–2861, tel. 704/355–2000; Eugene A. Woods, FACHE, President and Chief Executive Officer
(Centralized Health System)

NORTH CAROLINA: ATRIUM HEALTH ANSON (O, 15 beds) 2301 US Highway 74 W, Wadesboro, NC, Zip 28170–7554, Mailing Address: 2301 U.S Highway 74 West, Zip 28170, tel. 704/994–4500; Dave Anderson, FACHE, Vice President and Administrator
Web address: www.carolinashealthcare.org/anson

ATRIUM HEALTH CABARRUS (O, 455 beds) 920 Church Street North, Concord, NC, Zip 28025–2983; tel. 704/403–3000; Phyllis A. Wingate, FACHE, President

ATRIUM HEALTH CLEVELAND (L, 177 beds) 201 East Grover Street, Shelby, NC, Zip 28150–3917; tel. 980/487–3000; Brian Gwyn, President and Chief Executive Officer
Web address: www.clevelandregional.org

ATRIUM HEALTH KINGS MOUNTAIN (O, 53 beds) 706 West King Street, Kings Mountain, NC, Zip 28086–2708; tel. 980/487–5000; Brian Gwyn, President and Chief Executive Officer

ATRIUM HEALTH LINCOLN (O, 101 beds) 433 McAlister Road, Lincolnton, NC, Zip 28092–4147, Mailing Address: PO Box 677, Zip 28093–0677, tel. 980/212–2000; Peter W. Acker, President and Chief Executive Officer
Web address: www.carolinashealthcare.org/lincoln

ATRIUM HEALTH PINEVILLE (O, 250 beds) 10628 Park Road, Charlotte, NC, Zip 28210–8407; tel. 704/667–1000

ATRIUM HEALTH STANLY (C, 109 beds) 301 Yadkin Street, Albemarle, NC, Zip 28001–3441, Mailing Address: P.O. Box 1489, Zip 28002–1489, tel. 704/984–4000; Brian Freeman, President
Web address: www.stanly.org

For explanation of codes following names, see page B2.
★ Indicates Type III membership in the American Hospital Association.

ATRIUM HEALTH UNION (L, 231 beds) 600 Hospital Drive, Monroe, NC, Zip 28112–6000, Mailing Address: P.O. Box 5003, Zip 28111–5003, tel. 980/993–3100; Michael Lutes, President
Web address: www.carolinashealthcare.org/union

ATRIUM HEALTH UNIVERSITY CITY (O, 100 beds) 8800 North Tryon Street, Charlotte, NC, Zip 28262–3300, Mailing Address: P.O. Box 560727, Zip 28256–0727, tel. 704/863–6000; William H. Leonard, President

ATRIUM HEALTH'S CAROLINAS MEDICAL CENTER (O, 1291 beds) 1000 Blythe Boulevard, Charlotte, NC, Zip 28203–5871, Mailing Address: P.O. Box 32861, Zip 28232–2861, tel. 704/355–2000; Christopher Bowe, FACHE, Interim Chief Executive Officer
Web address: www.carolinashealthcare.org/cmc

ATRIUM HEALTH'S CAROLINAS REHABILITATION (O, 150 beds) 1100 Blythe Boulevard, Charlotte, NC, Zip 28203–5864; tel. 704/355–4300; Robert G. Larrison Jr, President
Web address: www.carolinashealthcare.org/rehabilitation

CAROLINAS HEALTHCARE SYSTEM BLUE RIDGE (C, 156 beds) 2201 South Sterling Street, Morganton, NC, Zip 28655–4058; tel. 828/580–5000; Kathy C. Bailey, Ph.D., FACHE, President and Chief Executive Officer
Web address: www.blueridgehealth.org

COLUMBUS REGIONAL HEALTHCARE SYSTEM (C, 85 beds) 500 Jefferson Street, Whiteville, NC, Zip 28472–3634; tel. 910/642–8011; John E. Young, Interim Chief Executive Officer
Web address: www.crhealthcare.org/

SCOTLAND HEALTH CARE SYSTEM (C, 104 beds) 500 Lauchwood Drive, Laurinburg, NC, Zip 28352–5599; tel. 910/291–7000; Gregory C. Wood, President and Chief Executive Officer

ST. LUKE'S HOSPITAL (C, 35 beds) 101 Hospital Drive, Columbus, NC, Zip 28722–6418; tel. 828/894–3311; Michelle Fortune, R.N., Chief Executive Officer
Web address: www.saintlukeshospital.com

Owned, leased, sponsored:	10 hospitals	2823 beds
Contract-managed:	5 hospitals	489 beds
Totals:	15 hospitals	3312 beds

0859: AULTMAN HEALTH FOUNDATION (NP)
2600 Sixth Street SW, Canton, OH, Zip 44710–1702; tel. 330/363–6192; Edward J. Roth III, President and Chief Executive Officer
(Moderately Centralized Health System)

OHIO: ALLIANCE COMMUNITY HOSPITAL (O, 202 beds) 200 East State Street, Alliance, OH, Zip 44601–4936; tel. 330/596–6000; Ryan Jones, Chief Executive Officer
Web address: www.achosp.org

AULTMAN HOSPITAL (O, 532 beds) 2600 Sixth Street SW, Canton, OH, Zip 44710–1702; tel. 330/452–9911; Edward J. Roth III, President and Chief Executive Officer
Web address: www.aultman.com

AULTMAN ORRVILLE HOSPITAL (O, 25 beds) 832 South Main Street, Orrville, OH, Zip 44667–2208; tel. 330/682–3010; Jennifer Kessel, Chief Executive Officer
Web address: www.aultmanorrville.org

AULTMAN SPECIALTY HOSPITAL (O, 30 beds) 2600 Sixth Street, SW, Canton, OH, Zip 44710–1702; tel. 330/363–4000; Ryan Kuharich, Chief Executive Officer

Owned, leased, sponsored:	4 hospitals	789 beds
Contract-managed:	0 hospitals	0 beds
Totals:	4 hospitals	789 beds

0869: AVANTI HOSPITALS (IO)
222 North Sepulveda Boulevard, Suite 950, El Segundo, CA, Zip 90245–5614; tel. 310/356–0550; Michael A. Rembis, FACHE, Corporate Chief Executive Officer
(Independent Hospital System)

CALIFORNIA: COAST PLAZA HOSPITAL (O, 123 beds) 13100 Studebaker Road, Norwalk, CA, Zip 90650–2500; tel. 562/868–3751; Gregory Padilla, Administrator

COMMUNITY HOSPITAL OF HUNTINGTON PARK (O, 81 beds) 2623 East Slauson Avenue, Huntington Park, CA, Zip 90255–2926; tel. 323/583–1931; Patricia Rives, R.N., MSN, Chief Executive Officer
Web address: www.avantihospitals.com/community-hospital-of-huntington-park

EAST LOS ANGELES DOCTORS HOSPITAL (O, 127 beds) 4060 Whittier Boulevard, Los Angeles, CA, Zip 90023–2526; tel. 323/268–5514; Gerald B. Clute, Chief Executive Officer
Web address: www.avantihospitals.com

MEMORIAL HOSPITAL OF GARDENA (O, 172 beds) 1145 West Redondo Beach Boulevard, Gardena, CA, Zip 90247–3528; tel. 310/532–4200; Kathy Wojno, R.N., MSN, Administrator

Owned, leased, sponsored:	4 hospitals	503 beds
Contract-managed:	0 hospitals	0 beds
Totals:	4 hospitals	503 beds

★5255: Avera Health (CC)
3900 West Avera Drive, Suite 300, Sioux Falls, SD, Zip 57108–5721; tel. 605/322–4700; Bob Sutton, President and Chief Executive Officer
(Decentralized Health System)

IOWA: AVERA HOLY FAMILY HOSPITAL (O, 25 beds) 826 North Eighth Street, Estherville, IA, Zip 51334–1598; tel. 712/362–2631; Deborah L. Herzberg, R.N., MS, FACHE, Administrator

AVERA MERRILL PIONEER HOSPITAL (L, 11 beds) 1100 South 10th Avenue, Rock Rapids, IA, Zip 51246–2020; tel. 712/472–5400; Craig Hohn, Chief Executive Officer
Web address: https://www.avera.org

FLOYD VALLEY HEALTHCARE (C, 25 beds) 714 Lincoln Street NE, Le Mars, IA, Zip 51031–3314; tel. 712/546–7871; Dustin Wright, Chief Executive Officer

HEGG HEALTH CENTER AVERA (C, 85 beds) 1202 21st Avenue, Rock Valley, IA, Zip 51247–1497; tel. 712/476–8000; Glenn Zevenbergen, Chief Executive Officer
Web address: www.hegghc.org

LAKES REGIONAL HEALTHCARE (C, 30 beds) 2301 Highway 71 South, Spirit Lake, IA, Zip 51360–0159; tel. 712/336–1230; Jason Harrington, FACHE, President and Chief Executive Officer
Web address: www.lakeshealth.org

OSCEOLA COMMUNITY HOSPITAL (C, 25 beds) 600 Ninth Avenue North, Sibley, IA, Zip 51249–1012, Mailing Address: P.O. Box 258, Zip 51249–0258, tel. 712/754–2574; Ben Davis, Chief Executive Officer

SIOUX CENTER HEALTH (O, 88 beds) 1101 9th Street SE, Sioux Center, IA, Zip 51250; tel. 712/722–8107; Cory D. Nelson, Administrator
Web address: www.siouxcenterhealth.org

MINNESOTA: AVERA MARSHALL REGIONAL MEDICAL CENTER (O, 111 beds) 300 South Bruce Street, Marshall, MN, Zip 56258–3900; tel. 507/532–9661; Mary B. Maertens, FACHE, President and Chief Executive Officer

AVERA TYLER HOSPITAL (C, 39 beds) 240 Willow Street, Tyler, MN, Zip 56178–1166; tel. 507/247–5521; Allen Anderson, Administrator
Web address: www.avera.org

PIPESTONE COUNTY MEDICAL CENTER AVERA (C, 18 beds) 916 4th Avenue SW, Pipestone, MN, Zip 56164–1890; tel. 507/825–5811; Bradley D. Burris, Chief Executive Officer

NEBRASKA: AVERA CREIGHTON HOSPITAL (O, 70 beds) 1503 Main Street, Creighton, NE, Zip 68729–3007, Mailing Address: P.O. Box 186, Zip 68729–0186, tel. 402/358–5700; Todd Consbruck, Chief Executive Officer
Web address: www.avera.org/creighton/

AVERA ST. ANTHONY'S HOSPITAL (O, 25 beds) 300 North Second Street, O'Neill, NE, Zip 68763–1514, Mailing Address: P.O. Box 270, Oneill, Zip 68763–0270, tel. 402/336–2611; Todd Consbruck, President and Chief Executive Officer
Web address: www.avera.org/st-anthonys

SOUTH DAKOTA: AVERA DE SMET MEMORIAL HOSPITAL (L, 6 beds) 306 Prairie Avenue SW, De Smet, SD, Zip 57231–2285, Mailing Address: P.O. Box 160, Zip 57231–0160, tel. 605/854–6100; Stephanie Reasy, Administrator and Chief Executive Officer

Section B

For explanation of codes following names, see page B2.
★ Indicates Type III membership in the American Hospital Association.

AVERA DELLS AREA HOSPITAL (L, 23 beds) 909 North Iowa Avenue, Dell Rapids, SD, Zip 57022–1231; tel. 605/428–5431; Scott James. Hargens, Administrator and Chief Executive Officer
Web address: www.avera.org/dell-rapids/

AVERA FLANDREAU HOSPITAL (L, 18 beds) 214 North Prairie Street, Flandreau, SD, Zip 57028–1243; tel. 605/997–2433; Scott James. Hargens, Administrator and Chief Executive Officer
Web address: www.avera.org/flandreau-medical/

AVERA GETTYSBURG HOSPITAL (O, 55 beds) 606 East Garfield Avenue, Gettysburg, SD, Zip 57442–1398; tel. 605/765–2480; Robert L. Sheckler, Administrator
Web address: www.avera.org/st-marys-pierre/gettysburg-hospital/

AVERA GREGORY HOSPITAL (O, 65 beds) 400 Park Avenue, Gregory, SD, Zip 57533–1302, Mailing Address: P.O. Box 408, Zip 57533–0408, tel. 605/835–8394; Anthony Timanus, Chief Executive Officer
Web address: www.gregoryhealthcare.org

AVERA HAND COUNTY MEMORIAL HOSPITAL (L, 15 beds) 300 West Fifth Street, Miller, SD, Zip 57362–1238; tel. 605/853–2421; Bryan Breitling, Administrator
Web address: www.avera.org

AVERA HEART HOSPITAL OF SOUTH DAKOTA (O, 53 beds) 4500 West 69th Street, Sioux Falls, SD, Zip 57108–8148; tel. 605/977–7000; Michael Gibbs, President

AVERA MCKENNAN HOSPITAL AND UNIVERSITY HEALTH CENTER (O, 500 beds) 1325 South Cliff Avenue, Sioux Falls, SD, Zip 57105–1007, Mailing Address: P.O. Box 5045, Zip 57117–5045, tel. 605/322–8000; David Flicek, President and Chief Executive Officer
Web address: www.averamckennan.org

AVERA QUEEN OF PEACE HOSPITAL (O, 159 beds) 525 North Foster, Mitchell, SD, Zip 57301–2999; tel. 605/995–2000; Thomas A. Clark, Regional President and Chief Executive Officer

AVERA SACRED HEART HOSPITAL (O, 286 beds) 501 Summit Avenue, Yankton, SD, Zip 57078–3855; tel. 605/668–8000; Douglas R. Ekeren, Regional President and Chief Executive Officer
Web address: www.averasacredheart.com

AVERA ST. BENEDICT HEALTH CENTER (O, 99 beds) 401 West Glynn Drive, Parkston, SD, Zip 57366–9605; tel. 605/928–3311; Rita Blasius, President and Chief Executive Officer

AVERA ST. LUKE'S HOSPITAL (O, 212 beds) 305 South State Street, Aberdeen, SD, Zip 57401–4527; tel. 605/622–5000; Todd Forkel, President and Chief Executive Officer
Web address: www.avera.org/st-lukes-hospital/

AVERA ST. MARY'S HOSPITAL (O, 110 beds) 801 East Sioux Avenue, Pierre, SD, Zip 57501–3323; tel. 605/224–3100; Todd Forkel, Interim Chief Executive Officer
Web address: www.avera.org/st-marys-pierre/

AVERA WESKOTA MEMORIAL HOSPITAL (L, 23 beds) 604 First Street NE, Wessington Springs, SD, Zip 57382–2166; tel. 605/539–1201; Stephanie Reasy, Administrator and Chief Executive Officer
Web address: www.averaweskota.org

EUREKA COMMUNITY HEALTH SERVICES AVERA (C, 4 beds) 410 Ninth Street, Eureka, SD, Zip 57437–2182, Mailing Address: P.O. Box 517, Zip 57437–0517, tel. 605/284–2661; Carmen Weber, Administrator

LANDMANN-JUNGMAN MEMORIAL HOSPITAL AVERA (C, 12 beds) 600 Billars Street, Scotland, SD, Zip 57059–2026; tel. 605/583–2226; Melissa Gale, Chief Executive Officer
Web address: www.ljmh.org

MARSHALL COUNTY HEALTHCARE CENTER AVERA (C, 18 beds) 413 Ninth Street, Britton, SD, Zip 57430–2274; tel. 605/448–2253; Nick Fosness, Chief Executive Officer
Web address: www.avera.org

MILBANK AREA HOSPITAL AVERA (L, 25 beds) 301 Flynn Drive, Milbank, SD, Zip 57252–1508; tel. 605/432–4538; Natalie Gauer, Administrator

PLATTE HEALTH CENTER AVERA (C, 61 beds) 601 East Seventh, Platte, SD, Zip 57369–2123, Mailing Address: P.O. Box 200, Zip 57369–0200, tel. 605/337–3364; Mark Burket, Chief Executive Officer
Web address: www.phcavera.org

ST. MICHAEL'S HOSPITAL AVERA (C, 25 beds) 410 West 16th Avenue, Tyndall, SD, Zip 57066–2318; tel. 605/589–2152; Carol Deurmier, Chief Executive Officer
Web address: www.stmichaels-bhfp.org

WAGNER COMMUNITY MEMORIAL HOSPITAL AVERA (C, 20 beds) 513 Third Street SW, Wagner, SD, Zip 57380–9675, Mailing Address: P.O. Box 280, Zip 57380–0280, tel. 605/384–3611; Bryan Slaba, Chief Executive Officer
Web address: www.avera.org/wagnerhospital

Owned, leased, sponsored:	20 hospitals	1891 beds
Contract-managed:	13 hospitals	450 beds
Totals:	33 hospitals	2341 beds

★**0633: AVITA HEALTH SYSTEM** (NP)
269 Portland Way South, Galion, OH, Zip 44833–2399; tel. 419/468–4841; Jerome Morasko, President and Chief Executive Officer
(Independent Hospital System)

OHIO: AVITA ONTARIO HOSPITAL (O, 26 beds) 715 Richland Mall, Ontario, OH, Zip 44906–3802; tel. 567/307–7666; Jerome Morasko, President and Chief Executive Officer

BUCYRUS HOSPITAL (O, 25 beds) 629 North Sandusky Avenue, Bucyrus, OH, Zip 44820–1821; tel. 419/562–4677; Jerome Morasko, Chief Executive Officer
Web address: www.bchonline.org

GALION HOSPITAL (O, 35 beds) 269 Portland Way South, Galion, OH, Zip 44833–2399; tel. 419/468–4841; Jerome Morasko, President and Chief Executive Officer
Web address: www.avitahs.org

Owned, leased, sponsored:	3 hospitals	86 beds
Contract-managed:	0 hospitals	0 beds
Totals:	3 hospitals	86 beds

1033: BALLAD HEALTH (NP)
303 Med Tech Parkway, Johnson City, TN, Zip 37604–2391; tel. 833/822–5523; Alan M. Levine, President and Chief Executive Officer
(Centralized Health System)

TENNESSEE: BRISTOL REGIONAL MEDICAL CENTER (O, 306 beds) 1 Medical Park Boulevard, Bristol, TN, Zip 37620–7430; tel. 423/844–1121; Greg Neal, FACHE, President
Web address: www.wellmont.org

FRANKLIN WOODS COMMUNITY HOSPITAL (O, 102 beds) 300 MedTech Parkway, Johnson City, TN, Zip 37604–2277; tel. 423/302–1000; Patricia Baise, R.N., FACHE, Chief Executive Officer
Web address: www.msha.com

GREENEVILLE COMMUNITY HOSPITAL EAST (O, 121 beds) 1420 Tusculum Boulevard, Greeneville, TN, Zip 37745–5825; tel. 423/787–5000; Tammy Albright, Chief Executive Officer

GREENEVILLE COMMUNITY HOSPITAL WEST (O, 92 beds) 401 Takoma Avenue, Greeneville, TN, Zip 37743–4647; tel. 423/639–3151; Tammy Albright, President
Web address: www.takoma.org

HANCOCK COUNTY HOSPITAL (O, 10 beds) 1519 Main Street, Sneedville, TN, Zip 37869–3657; tel. 423/733–5000; Rebecca Beck, President

HAWKINS COUNTY MEMORIAL HOSPITAL (O, 22 beds) 851 Locust Street, Rogersville, TN, Zip 37857–2407, Mailing Address: P.O. Box 130, Zip 37857–0130, tel. 423/921–7000; Regina Day, Chief Executive Officer
Web address: www.wellmont.org

HOLSTON VALLEY MEDICAL CENTER (O, 345 beds) 130 West Ravine Street, Kingsport, TN, Zip 37660–3837, Mailing Address: P.O. Box 238, Zip 37662–0238, tel. 423/224–4000; Lindy P. White, Vice President and Chief Executive Officer

INDIAN PATH MEDICAL CENTER (O, 160 beds) 2000 Brookside Drive, Kingsport, TN, Zip 37660–4627; tel. 423/857–7000; Monty E. McLaurin, Chief Executive Officer, Northwest Market
Web address: www.msha.com

JOHNSON CITY MEDICAL CENTER (O, 585 beds) 400 North State of Franklin Road, Johnson City, TN, Zip 37604–6094; tel. 423/431–6111; Stan Hickson, FACHE, Chief Executive Officer
Web address: www.msha.com

For explanation of codes following names, see page B2.
★ Indicates Type III membership in the American Hospital Association.

JOHNSON COUNTY COMMUNITY HOSPITAL (O, 2 beds) 1901 South Shady Street, Mountain City, TN, Zip 37683–2271; tel. 423/727–1100; Chastity Trivette, Chief Executive Officer

SYCAMORE SHOALS HOSPITAL (O, 74 beds) 1501 West Elk Avenue, Elizabethton, TN, Zip 37643–2874; tel. 423/542–1300; Dwayne Taylor, Chief Executive Officer
Web address: www.msha.com

UNICOI COUNTY MEMORIAL HOSPITAL (O, 94 beds) 2030 Temple Hill Road, Erwin, TN, Zip 37650, Mailing Address: P.O. Box 802, Zip 37650–0802, tel. 423/743–3141; Eric Carroll, Chief Executive Officer
Web address: www.msha.com

VIRGINIA: DICKENSON COMMUNITY HOSPITAL (O, 11 beds) 312 Hospital Drive, Clintwood, VA, Zip 24228, Mailing Address: P.O. Box 1440, Zip 24228–1440, tel. 276/926–0300; Mark T. Leonard, Chief Executive Officer

JOHNSTON MEMORIAL HOSPITAL (O, 116 beds) 16000 Johnston Memorial Drive, Abingdon, VA, Zip 24211–7659; tel. 276/258–1000; John Jeter, Chief Executive Officer
Web address: www.jmh.org

LONESOME PINE HOSPITAL (O, 32 beds) 1990 Holton Avenue East, Big Stone Gap, VA, Zip 24219–3350; tel. 276/523–3111; Mark T. Leonard, Interim Chief Executive Officer
Web address: www.wellmont.org

MOUNTAIN VIEW REGIONAL MEDICAL CENTER (O, 70 beds) 310 Third Street NE, Norton, VA, Zip 24273–1137; tel. 276/679–9100; Mark T. Leonard, Interim Chief Executive Officer
Web address: www.wellmont.org

NORTON COMMUNITY HOSPITAL (O, 70 beds) 100 15th Street NW, Norton, VA, Zip 24273–1616; tel. 276/679 9600; Mark T. Leonard, Chief Executive Officer

RUSSELL COUNTY MEDICAL CENTER (O, 78 beds) 58 Carroll Street, Lebanon, VA, Zip 24266, Mailing Address: P.O. Box 3600, Zip 24266–0200, tel. 276/883–8000; Stephen K. Givens, Assistant Vice President and Administrator
Web address: www.mountainstateshealth.com/rcmc

SMYTH COUNTY COMMUNITY HOSPITAL (O, 153 beds) 245 Medical Park Drive, Marion, VA, Zip 24354, Mailing Address: P.O. Box 880, Zip 24354–0880, tel. 276/378–1000; James E. Tyler, Chief Executive Officer
Web address: www.msha.com/scch

Owned, leased, sponsored:	19 hospitals	2443 beds
Contract-managed:	0 hospitals	0 beds
Totals:	19 hospitals	2443 beds

★0194: BANNER HEALTH (NP)
2901 North Central Avenue Suite 160, Phoenix, AZ, Zip 85012–2702, Mailing Address: P.O. Box 25489, Zip 85002–5489, tel. 602/747–4000; Peter S. Fine, FACHE, President and Chief Executive Officer
(Centralized Health System)

ARIZONA: BANNER – UNIVERSITY MEDICAL CENTER PHOENIX (O, 727 beds) 1111 East McDowell Road, Phoenix, AZ, Zip 85006–2666, Mailing Address: P.O. Box 2989, Zip 85062–2989, tel. 602/239–2000; Steve Narang, M.D., Chief Executive Officer
Web address: www.bannerhealth.com/Locations/Arizona/Banner+Good+Samaritan+Medical+Center

BANNER – UNIVERSITY MEDICAL CENTER SOUTH (O, 167 beds) 2800 East Ajo Way, Tucson, AZ, Zip 85713–6289; tel. 520/874–2000; John Scherpf, Chief Executive Officer
Web address: www.bannerhealth.com

BANNER – UNIVERSITY MEDICAL CENTER TUCSON (O, 439 beds) 1501 North Campbell Avenue, Tucson, AZ, Zip 85724–5128; tel. 520/694–0111; John Scherpf, Chief Executive Officer
Web address: https://www.bannerhealth.com/locations/tucson/banner-university-medical-center-tucson

BANNER BAYWOOD MEDICAL CENTER (O, 359 beds) 6644 East Baywood Avenue, Mesa, AZ, Zip 85206–1797; tel. 480/321–2000; Lamont M. Yoder, R.N., MSN, FACHE, Chief Executive Officer

BANNER BEHAVIORAL HEALTH HOSPITAL – SCOTTSDALE (O, 124 beds) 7575 East Earll Drive, Scottsdale, AZ, Zip 85251–6915; tel. 480/941–7500; William Southwick, MS, R.N., R.N., Chief Executive Officer
Web address: https://www.bannerhealth.com/locations/scottsdale/banner-behavioral-health-hospital

BANNER BOSWELL MEDICAL CENTER (O, 436 beds) 10401 West Thunderbird Blvd, Sun City, AZ, Zip 85351–3004, Mailing Address: P.O. Box 1690, Zip 85372–1690, tel. 623/832–4000; Debbie Flores, Interim Chief Executive Officer
Web address: www.bannerhealth.com/locations/sun-city/banner-boswell-medical-center

BANNER CASA GRANDE MEDICAL CENTER (O, 123 beds) 1800 East Florence Boulevard, Casa Grande, AZ, Zip 85122–5399; tel. 520/381–6300; Brian Kellar, Chief Executive Officer

BANNER DEL E. WEBB MEDICAL CENTER (O, 390 beds) 14502 West Meeker Boulevard, Sun City West, AZ, Zip 85375–5299; tel. 623/524–4000; Debbie Flores, Chief Executive Officer
Web address: www.bannerhealth.com/Locations/Arizona/Banner+Del+Webb+Medical+Center/

BANNER DESERT MEDICAL CENTER (O, 595 beds) 1400 South Dobson Road, Mesa, AZ, Zip 85202–4707; tel. 480/412–3000; Laura Robertson, R.N., Chief Executive Officer

BANNER ESTRELLA MEDICAL CENTER (O, 293 beds) 9201 West Thomas Road, Phoenix, AZ, Zip 85037–3332; tel. 623/327–4000; Courtney Ophaug, FACHE, Chief Executive Officer
Web address: www.bannerhealth.com/Locations/Arizona/Banner+Estrella+Medical+Center/

BANNER GATEWAY MEDICAL CENTER (O, 177 beds) 1900 North Higley Road, Gilbert, AZ, Zip 85234–1604; tel. 480/543–2000; Lamont M. Yoder, R.N., MSN, FACHE, Chief Executive Officer
Web address: www.bannerhealth.com/Locations/Arizona/Banner+Gateway+Medical+Center/

BANNER GOLDFIELD MEDICAL CENTER (O, 20 beds) 2050 West Southern Avenue, Apache Junction, AZ, Zip 85120–7305; tel. 480/733–3300; Sharon Lind, MSN, FACHE, Chief Executive Officer
Web address: www.bannerhealth.com/Locations/Arizona/Banner+Goldfield+Medical+Center/_Welcome to Banner+Goldfield.htm

BANNER HEART HOSPITAL (O, 111 beds) 6750 East Baywood Avenue, Mesa, AZ, Zip 85206–1749; tel. 480/854–5000; Lamont M. Yoder, R.N., MSN, FACHE, Chief Executive Officer

BANNER IRONWOOD MEDICAL CENTER (O, 53 beds) 37000 North Gantzel Road, San Tan Valley, AZ, Zip 85140–7303; tel. 480/394–4000; Sharon Lind, MSN, FACHE, Chief Executive Officer
Web address: www.bannerhealth.com/Locations/Arizona/Banner+Ironwood/

BANNER PAYSON MEDICAL CENTER (O, 25 beds) 807 South Ponderosa Street, Payson, AZ, Zip 85541–5599, tel. 928/474 3222; Lance Porter, Chief Executive Officer
Web address: www.paysonhospital.com

BANNER THUNDERBIRD MEDICAL CENTER (O, 475 beds) 5555 West Thunderbird Road, Glendale, AZ, Zip 85306–4696; tel. 602/865–5555; Debra J. Krmpotic, R.N., Chief Executive Officer

PAGE HOSPITAL (C, 25 beds) 501 North Navajo Drive, Page, AZ, Zip 86040, Mailing Address: P.O. Box 1447, Zip 86040–1447, tel. 928/645–2424; Susan Eubanks, Chief Executive Officer
Web address: www.bannerhealth.com/Locations/Arizona/Page+Hospital

CALIFORNIA: BANNER LASSEN MEDICAL CENTER (O, 25 beds) 1800 Spring Ridge Drive, Susanville, CA, Zip 96130–6100; tel. 530/252–2000; Catherine S. Harshbarger, R.N., Chief Executive Officer
Web address: https://www.bannerhealth.com/locations/susanville/banner-lassen-medical-center

COLORADO: BANNER FORT COLLINS MEDICAL CENTER (O, 23 beds) 4700 Lady Moon Drive, Fort Collins, CO, Zip 80528–4426; tel. 970/821–4000; Margo Karsten, Ph.D., MSN, Chief Executive Officer

EAST MORGAN COUNTY HOSPITAL (L, 19 beds) 2400 West Edison Street, Brush, CO, Zip 80723–1640; tel. 970/842–6200; Linda Thorpe, Chief Executive Officer
Web address: www.emchbrush.com

MCKEE MEDICAL CENTER (O, 96 beds) 2000 Boise Avenue, Loveland, CO, Zip 80538–4281; tel. 970/669–4640; Margo Karsten, Ph.D., MSN, Chief Executive Officer
Web address: www.mckeeloveland.com

For explanation of codes following names, see page B2.
★ Indicates Type III membership in the American Hospital Association.

NORTH COLORADO MEDICAL CENTER (L, 236 beds) 1801 16th Street, Greeley, CO, Zip 80631–5154; tel. 970/352–4121; Margo Karsten, Ph.D., MSN, Chief Executive Officer

STERLING REGIONAL MEDCENTER (O, 25 beds) 615 Fairhurst Street, Sterling, CO, Zip 80751–4523; tel. 970/522–0122; Wade Tyrell, Chief Executive Officer and Chief Nursing Officer
Web address: https://www.bannerhealth.com/locations/sterling/sterling-regional-medcenter

NEBRASKA: OGALLALA COMMUNITY HOSPITAL (L, 18 beds) 2601 North Spruce Street, Ogallala, NE, Zip 69153–2465; tel. 308/284–4011; Drew H. Dostal, R.N., FACHE, Chief Executive Officer
Web address: https://www.bannerhealth.com/locations/ogallala/ogallala-community-hospital

NEVADA: BANNER CHURCHILL COMMUNITY HOSPITAL (O, 25 beds) 801 East Williams Avenue, Fallon, NV, Zip 89406–3052; tel. 775/423–3151; Robert H. Carnahan II, R.N., Chief Executive Officer

WYOMING: COMMUNITY HOSPITAL (O, 20 beds) 2000 Campbell Drive, Torrington, WY, Zip 82240–1597; tel. 307/532–4181; Shelby Olind, Interim Chief Executive Officer
Web address: www.bannerhealth.com/Locations/Wyoming/Community+Hospital/

PLATTE COUNTY MEMORIAL HOSPITAL (L, 25 beds) 201 14th Street, Wheatland, WY, Zip 82201–3201, Mailing Address: P.O. Box 848, Zip 82201–0848, tel. 307/322–3636; Hoyt Skabelund, Chief Executive Officer
Web address: https://www.bannerhealth.com/locations/wheatland/platte-county-memorial-hospital

WASHAKIE MEDICAL CENTER (L, 18 beds) 400 South 15th Street, Worland, WY, Zip 82401–3531, Mailing Address: P.O. Box 700, Zip 82401–0700, tel. 307/347–3221; Jay Stallings, Chief Executive Officer
Web address: www.washakiemedicalcenter.com

Owned, leased, sponsored:	27 hospitals	5044 beds
Contract-managed:	1 hospitals	25 beds
Totals:	28 hospitals	5069 beds

★0315: BAPTIST HEALTH (CO)
2701 Eastpoint Parkway, Louisville, KY, Zip 40223; tel. 502/896–5000; Gerard Colman, Ph.D., Chief Executive Officer
(Centralized Physician/Insurance Health System)

INDIANA: BAPTIST HEALTH FLOYD (O, 244 beds) 1850 State Street, New Albany, IN, Zip 47150–4997; tel. 812/949–5500; Daniel J. Eichenberger, M.D., President and Chief Executive Officer
Web address: www.floydmemorial.com

KENTUCKY: BAPTIST HEALTH CORBIN (O, 273 beds) 1 Trillium Way, Corbin, KY, Zip 40701–8420; tel. 606/528–1212; Anthony Powers, Interim President and Vice President of Patient Services
Web address: www.baptisthealth.com/corbin

BAPTIST HEALTH LA GRANGE (O, 65 beds) 1025 New Moody Lane, La Grange, KY, Zip 40031–9154; tel. 502/222–5388; Clint Kaho, President
Web address: www.baptisthealthlagrange.com

BAPTIST HEALTH LEXINGTON (O, 391 beds) 1740 Nicholasville Road, Lexington, KY, Zip 40503–1499; tel. 859/260–6100; William G. Sisson, FACHE, President
Web address: www.baptisthealthlexington.com

BAPTIST HEALTH LOUISVILLE (O, 500 beds) 4000 Kresge Way, Louisville, KY, Zip 40207–4676; tel. 502/897–8100; Larry W. Gray, President

BAPTIST HEALTH MADISONVILLE (O, 172 beds) 900 Hospital Drive, Madisonville, KY, Zip 42431–1694; tel. 270/825–5100; Robert L. Ramey, President
Web address: www.baptisthealthmadisonville.com

BAPTIST HEALTH PADUCAH (O, 292 beds) 2501 Kentucky Avenue, Paducah, KY, Zip 42003–3200; tel. 270/575–2100; Christopher Roty, President
Web address: www.baptisthealthpaducah.com

BAPTIST HEALTH RICHMOND (O, 58 beds) 801 Eastern Bypass, Richmond, KY, Zip 40475–2405, Mailing Address: P.O. Box 1600, Zip 40476–2603, tel. 859/623–3131; Greg Donavan. Gerard, President
Web address: www.baptisthealthrichmond.com

HARDIN MEMORIAL HEALTH (C, 268 beds) 913 North Dixie Avenue, Elizabethtown, KY, Zip 42701–2503; tel. 270/737–1212; Dennis B. Johnson, President and Chief Executive Officer

Owned, leased, sponsored:	8 hospitals	1995 beds
Contract-managed:	1 hospitals	268 beds
Totals:	9 hospitals	2263 beds

★0005: BAPTIST HEALTH (NP)
841 Prudential Drive, Suite 1601, Jacksonville, FL, Zip 32207–8202; tel. 904/202–2000; Brett McClung, President and Chief Executive Officer
(Moderately Centralized Health System)

FLORIDA: BAPTIST MEDICAL CENTER BEACHES (O, 135 beds) 1350 13th Avenue South, Jacksonville Beach, FL, Zip 32250–3205; tel. 904/627–2900; Joseph M. Mitrick, FACHE, President

BAPTIST MEDICAL CENTER JACKSONVILLE (O, 955 beds) 800 Prudential Drive, Jacksonville, FL, Zip 32207–8202; tel. 904/202–2000; Michael A. Mayo, FACHE, President
Web address: www.e-baptisthealth.com

BAPTIST MEDICAL CENTER NASSAU (O, 52 beds) 1250 South 18th Street, Fernandina Beach, FL, Zip 32034–3098; tel. 904/321–3500; Edward T. Hubel, FACHE, President

Owned, leased, sponsored:	3 hospitals	1142 beds
Contract-managed:	0 hospitals	0 beds
Totals:	3 hospitals	1142 beds

0150: BAPTIST HEALTH (NP)
301 Brown Springs Road, Montgomery, AL, Zip 36117–7005; tel. 334/273–4400; W Russell. Tyner, President and Chief Executive Officer
(Independent Hospital System)

ALABAMA: BAPTIST MEDICAL CENTER EAST (O, 176 beds) 400 Taylor Road, Montgomery, AL, Zip 36117–3512, Mailing Address: P.O. Box 241267, Zip 36124–1267, tel. 334/277–8330; Jeff G. Rains, Chief Executive Officer
Web address: www.baptistfirst.org

BAPTIST MEDICAL CENTER SOUTH (O, 379 beds) 2105 East South Boulevard, Montgomery, AL, Zip 36116–2409, Mailing Address: Box 11010, Zip 36111–0010, tel. 334/288–2100; J Peter. Selman, FACHE, Chief Executive Officer

PRATTVILLE BAPTIST HOSPITAL (O, 50 beds) 124 South Memorial Drive, Prattville, AL, Zip 36067–3619, Mailing Address: P.O. Box 681630, Zip 36068–1638, tel. 334/365–0651; Eric Morgan, Chief Executive Officer
Web address: www.baptistfirst.org/facilities/prattville-baptist-hospital/default.aspx

Owned, leased, sponsored:	3 hospitals	605 beds
Contract-managed:	0 hospitals	0 beds
Totals:	3 hospitals	605 beds

★0355: BAPTIST HEALTH (NP)
9601 Baptist Health Drive, Little Rock, AR, Zip 72205–6321; tel. 501/202–2000; Troy R. Wells, Chief Executive Officer
(Centralized Physician/Insurance Health System)

ARKANSAS: BAPTIST HEALTH – FORT SMITH (O, 272 beds) 1001 Towson Avenue, Fort Smith, AR, Zip 72901–4921, Mailing Address: P.O. Box 2406, Zip 72917–7006, tel. 479/441–4000; Brandon Bullard, Interim Chief Executive Officer
Web address: https://www.sparkshealth.com/

BAPTIST HEALTH – VAN BUREN (O, 39 beds) East Main and South 20th Streets, Van Buren, AR, Zip 72956–5715, Mailing Address: P.O. Box 409, Zip 72957–0409, tel. 479/474–3401; Brandon Bullard, Interim Chief Executive Officer
Web address: https://www.sparkshealth.com/

For explanation of codes following names, see page B2.
★ Indicates Type III membership in the American Hospital Association.

Section B

BAPTIST HEALTH EXTENDED CARE HOSPITAL (O, 55 beds) 9601 Baptist Health Drive, Little Rock, AR, Zip 72205–7202; tel. 501/202–1070; Lee Gentry, FACHE, Vice President and Administrator

BAPTIST HEALTH MEDICAL CENTER – CONWAY (O, 111 beds) 1555 Exchange Avenue, Conway, AR, Zip 72032–7824; tel. 501/585–2000; Tim Bowen, Vice President and Administrator
Web address: www.baptist-health.com/location/baptist-health-medical-center-conway-conway

BAPTIST HEALTH MEDICAL CENTER – NORTH LITTLE ROCK (O, 177 beds) 3333 Springhill Drive, North Little Rock, AR, Zip 72117–2922; tel. 501/202–3000; Mike Perkins, Vice President and Administrator

BAPTIST HEALTH MEDICAL CENTER-ARKADELPHIA (L, 25 beds) 3050 Twin Rivers Drive, Arkadelphia, AR, Zip 71923–4299; tel. 870/245–2622; Tony Hardage, PharmD, Assistant Vice President and Administrator
Web address: www.baptist-health.com/locations/accesspoint. aspx?accessPointID=187

BAPTIST HEALTH MEDICAL CENTER-HEBER SPRINGS (O, 25 beds) 1800 Bypass Road, Heber Springs, AR, Zip 72543–9135; tel. 501/887–3000; Kevin L. Storey, Vice President and Administrator
Web address: www.baptist-health.com/maps-directions/bhmc-heber-springs

BAPTIST HEALTH MEDICAL CENTER-HOT SPRING COUNTY (L, 72 beds) 1001 Schneider Drive, Malvern, AR, Zip 72104–4811; tel. 501/332–1000; Sheila Williams, Vice President and Administrator
Web address: https://www.baptist-health.com/location/baptist-health-medical-center-hot-spring-county-hot-spring-county

BAPTIST HEALTH MEDICAL CENTER-LITTLE ROCK (O, 682 beds) 9601 Baptist Health Drive, Little Rock, AR, Zip 72205–7299; tel. 501/202–2000; Greg Crain, FACHE, Senior Vice President and Administrator

BAPTIST HEALTH MEDICAL CENTER-STUTTGART (I , 41 beds) 1703 North Buerkle Road, Stuttgart, AR, Zip 72160–1905, Mailing Address: P.O. Box 1905, Zip 72160–1905, tel. 870/673–3511; Kevin L. Storey, Vice President and Administrator
Web address: https://www.baptist-health.com/location/baptist-health-medical-center-stuttgart-stuttgart

BAPTIST HEALTH REHABILITATION INSTITUTE (O, 120 beds) 9501 Baptist Health Drive, Little Rock, AR, Zip 72205–6225; tel. 501/202–7000; Julie Nix, Vice President and Administrator

Owned, leased, sponsored:	11 hospitals	1619 beds
Contract-managed:	0 hospitals	0 beds
Totals:	11 hospitals	1619 beds

★0185: BAPTIST HEALTH CARE CORPORATION (NP)
1717 North 'E' Street, Suite 402, Pensacola, FL, Zip 32501–6377, Mailing Address: P.O. Box 17500, Zip 32522–7500, tel. 850/434–4011; Mark T. Faulkner, President
(Centralized Physician/Insurance Health System)

FLORIDA: BAPTIST HOSPITAL (O, 340 beds) 1000 West Moreno Street, Pensacola, FL, Zip 32501–2316, Mailing Address: P.O. Box 17500, Zip 32522–7500, tel. 850/434–4011; Scott Raynes, President
Web address: www.ebaptisthealthcare.org

GULF BREEZE HOSPITAL (O, 65 beds) 1110 Gulf Breeze Parkway, Gulf Breeze, FL, Zip 32561–4884; tel. 850/934–2000; Scott Raynes, President

JAY HOSPITAL (L, 21 beds) 14114 South Alabama Street, Jay, FL, Zip 32565–1219; tel. 850/675–8000; Michael T. Hutchins, Administrator
Web address: www.bhcpns.org/jayhospital/

Owned, leased, sponsored:	3 hospitals	426 beds
Contract-managed:	0 hospitals	0 beds
Totals:	3 hospitals	426 beds

★0122: BAPTIST HEALTH SOUTH FLORIDA (NP)
6855 Red Road, Suite 600, Coral Gables, FL, Zip 33143–3632; tel. 786/662–7111; Brian E. Keeley, President and Chief Executive Officer
(Centralized Health System)

FLORIDA: BAPTIST HEALTH SOUTH FLORIDA, BAPTIST HOSPITAL OF MIAMI (O, 720 beds) 8900 North Kendall Drive, Miami, FL, Zip 33176–2197; tel. 786/596–1960; Patricia M. Rosello, Chief Executive Officer

BAPTIST HEALTH SOUTH FLORIDA, DOCTORS HOSPITAL (O, 126 beds) 5000 University Drive, Coral Gables, FL, Zip 33146–2094; tel. 786/308–3000; Nelson Lazo, Chief Executive Officer
Web address: www.baptisthealth.net

BAPTIST HEALTH SOUTH FLORIDA, HOMESTEAD HOSPITAL (O, 142 beds) 975 Baptist Way, Homestead, FL, Zip 33033–7600; tel. 786/243–8000; Kenneth R. Spell, Chief Executive Officer
Web address: www.baptisthealth.net

BAPTIST HEALTH SOUTH FLORIDA, MARINERS HOSPITAL (O, 25 beds) 91500 Overseas Highway, Tavernier, FL, Zip 33070–2547; tel. 305/434–3000; Rick Freeburg, Chief Executive Officer
Web address: www.baptisthealth.net/en/facilities/mariners-hospital/Pages/default.aspx

BAPTIST HEALTH SOUTH FLORIDA, SOUTH MIAMI HOSPITAL (O, 336 beds) 6200 SW 73rd Street, Miami, FL, Zip 33143–4679; tel. 786/662–4000; William M. Duquette, Chief Executive Officer
Web address: www.baptisthealth.net

BAPTIST HEALTH SOUTH FLORIDA, WEST KENDALL BAPTIST HOSPITAL (O, 133 beds) 9555 SW 162nd Avenue, Miami, FL, Zip 33196–6408; tel. 786/467–2000; Javier Hernandez-Lichtl, Chief Executive Officer

BETHESDA HOSPITAL EAST (O, 481 beds) 2815 South Seacrest Boulevard, Boynton Beach, FL, Zip 33435–7995; tel. 561/737–7733; Roger L. Kirk, President and Chief Executive Officer
Web address: www.bethesdaweb.com

FISHERMEN'S HOSPITAL (O, 25 beds) 3301 Overseas Highway, Marathon, FL, Zip 33050–2329; tel. 305/743–5533; Rick Freeburg, Chief Executive Officer
Web address: www.fishermenshospital.org

Owned, leased, sponsored:	8 hospitals	1988 beds
Contract-managed:	0 hospitals	0 beds
Totals:	8 hospitals	1988 beds

★1625: BAPTIST MEMORIAL HEALTH CARE CORPORATION (NP)
350 North Humphreys Boulevard, Memphis, TN, Zip 38120–2177; tel. 901/227–5117; Jason Little, President and Chief Executive Officer
(Moderately Centralized Health System)

ARKANSAS: NEA BAPTIST MEMORIAL HOSPITAL (O, 228 beds) 4800 East Johnson Avenue, Jonesboro, AR, Zip 72401–8413; tel. 870/936–1000; Brad Parsons, FACHE, Administrator and Chief Executive Officer
Web address: www.neabaptist.com

MISSISSIPPI: BAPTIST MEDICAL CENTER ATTALA (O, 25 beds) 220 Highway 12 West, Kosciusko, MS, Zip 39090–3208, Mailing Address: P.O. Box 887, Zip 39090–0887, tel. 662/289–4311; Robert Coleman, Chief Executive Officer

BAPTIST MEDICAL CENTER LEAKE (O, 25 beds) 1100 Highway 16 E, Carthage, MS, Zip 39051–3809, Mailing Address: P.O. Box 909, Zip 39051–0909, tel. 601/267–1100; Daryl W. Weaver, Chief Executive Officer
Web address: www.mbhs.com/locations/baptist-medical-center-leake/

BAPTIST MEDICAL CENTER YAZOO (O, 25 beds) 823 Grand Avenue, Yazoo City, MS, Zip 39194–3233; tel. 662/746–2261; Robert Coleman, Chief Executive Officer
Web address: www.mbhs.org/locations/baptist-medical-center-yazoo/

BAPTIST MEMORIAL HOSPITAL – CALHOUN (L, 145 beds) 140 Burke-Calhoun City Road, Calhoun City, MS, Zip 38916–9690; tel. 662/628–6611; Collin Cheek, Administrator

BAPTIST MEMORIAL HOSPITAL-BOONEVILLE (L, 66 beds) 100 Hospital Street, Booneville, MS, Zip 38829–3359; tel. 662/720–5000; James Grantham, Administrator and Chief Executive Officer
Web address: www.bmhcc.org/booneville

BAPTIST MEMORIAL HOSPITAL-DESOTO (O, 339 beds) 7601 Southcrest Parkway, Southaven, MS, Zip 38671–4742; tel. 662/772–4000; James Huffman, Chief Executive Officer and Administrator
Web address: www.baptistonline.org/desoto/

Section B

For explanation of codes following names, see page B2.
★ Indicates Type III membership in the American Hospital Association.

BAPTIST MEMORIAL HOSPITAL-GOLDEN TRIANGLE (O, 236 beds) 2520 Fifth Street North, Columbus, MS, Zip 39705–2095, Mailing Address: P.O. Box 1307, Zip 39703–1307, tel. 662/244–1000; Paul Cade, Administrator and Chief Executive Officer

BAPTIST MEMORIAL HOSPITAL-NORTH MISSISSIPPI (O, 172 beds) 2301 South Lamar Boulevard, Oxford, MS, Zip 38655–5373, Mailing Address: P.O. Box 946, Zip 38655–6002, tel. 662/232–8100; William C. Henning, Administrator and Chief Executive Officer
Web address: www.baptistonline.org/north-mississippi/

BAPTIST MEMORIAL HOSPITAL-UNION COUNTY (L, 153 beds) 200 Highway 30 West, New Albany, MS, Zip 38652–3112; tel. 662/538–7631; Walter Grace, Chief Executive Officer and Administrator

MISSISSIPPI BAPTIST MEDICAL CENTER (O, 423 beds) 1225 North State Street, Jackson, MS, Zip 39202–2064; tel. 601/968–1000; Bobbie K. Ware, R.N., FACHE, Chief Executive Officer
Web address: www.mbhs.org

TENNESSEE: BAPTIST MEMORIAL HOSPITAL – MEMPHIS (O, 571 beds) 6019 Walnut Grove Road, Memphis, TN, Zip 38120–2173; tel. 901/226–5000; Dana Dye, R.N., Vice President, Administrator and Chief Executive Officer

BAPTIST MEMORIAL HOSPITAL FOR WOMEN (O, 140 beds) 6225 Humphreys Boulevard, Memphis, TN, Zip 38120–2373; tel. 901/227–9000; Kevin R. Hammeran, Chief Executive Officer and Administrator
Web address: www.baptistonline.org/womens/

BAPTIST MEMORIAL HOSPITAL-CARROLL COUNTY (O, 35 beds) 631 R.B. Wilson Drive, Huntingdon, TN, Zip 38344–1727; tel. 731/986–4461; Susan M. Breeden, Administrator and Chief Executive Officer
Web address: www.baptistonline.org/huntingdon/

BAPTIST MEMORIAL HOSPITAL-COLLIERVILLE (O, 51 beds) 1500 West Poplar Avenue, Collierville, TN, Zip 38017–0601; tel. 901/861–9400; Lindsay Stencel, Chief Administrative Officer

BAPTIST MEMORIAL HOSPITAL-TIPTON (O, 50 beds) 1995 Highway 51 South, Covington, TN, Zip 38019–3635; tel. 901/476–2621; Samuel Lynd, Administrator and Chief Executive Officer
Web address: www.baptistonline.org/tipton/

BAPTIST MEMORIAL HOSPITAL-UNION CITY (O, 63 beds) 1201 Bishop Street, Union City, TN, Zip 38261–5403, Mailing Address: P.O. Box 310, Zip 38281–0310, tel. 731/885–2410; Barry Bondurant, Administrator and Chief Executive Officer
Web address: www.baptistonline.org/union-city/

BAPTIST MEMORIAL REHABILITATION HOSPITAL (O, 49 beds) 1240 South Germantown Road, Germantown, TN, Zip 38138–2226; tel. 901/275–3300; Christopher L. Bariola, Chief Executive Officer

BAPTIST MEMORIAL RESTORATIVE CARE HOSPITAL (O, 30 beds) 6019 Walnut Grove Road, Memphis, TN, Zip 38120–2113; tel. 901/226–4200; Janice Hill, R.N., Administrator
Web address: www.baptistonline.org/restorative-care/

Owned, leased, sponsored:	19 hospitals	2826 beds
Contract-managed:	0 hospitals	0 beds
Totals:	19 hospitals	2826 beds

★0528: BASSETT HEALTHCARE NETWORK (NP)
1 Atwell Road, Cooperstown, NY, Zip 13326–1301; tel. 607/547–3456; William F. Streck, M.D., President and Chief Executive Officer
(Independent Hospital System)

NEW YORK: AURELIA OSBORN FOX MEMORIAL HOSPITAL (O, 184 beds) 1 Norton Avenue, Oneonta, NY, Zip 13820–2629; tel. 607/432–2000; Jeff Joyner, President
Web address: www.bassett.org/ao-fox-hospital/

BASSETT MEDICAL CENTER (O, 152 beds) One Atwell Road, Cooperstown, NY, Zip 13326–1394; tel. 607/547–3456; William W. LeCates, M.D., President

COBLESKILL REGIONAL HOSPITAL (O, 40 beds) 178 Grandview Drive, Cobleskill, NY, Zip 12043–5144; tel. 518/254–3456; Eric H. Stein, FACHE, President
Web address: www.bassett.org

LITTLE FALLS HOSPITAL (O, 25 beds) 140 Burwell Street, Little Falls, NY, Zip 13365–1725; tel. 315/823–1000; Michael L. Ogden, President and Chief Executive Officer
Web address: www.bassett.org

O'CONNOR HOSPITAL (O, 16 beds) 460 Andes Road, State Route 28, Delhi, NY, Zip 13753–7407; tel. 607/746–0300; Scott Bonderoff, President

Owned, leased, sponsored:	5 hospitals	417 beds
Contract-managed:	0 hospitals	0 beds
Totals:	5 hospitals	417 beds

★0918: BAYLOR SCOTT & WHITE HEALTH (NP)
4005 Crutcher Street, Suite 310, Dallas, TX, Zip 75246–1779; tel. 214/820–0111; James H. Hinton, Chief Executive Officer
(Centralized Physician/Insurance Health System)

TEXAS: BAYLOR SCOTT & WHITE ALL SAINTS MEDICAL CENTER – FORT WORTH (O, 377 beds) 1400 Eighth Avenue, Fort Worth, TX, Zip 76104–4192; tel. 817/926–2544; Michael Sanborn, FACHE, MS, President
Web address: www.baylorhealth.com/PhysiciansLocations/AllSaints/Pages/Default.aspx

BAYLOR SCOTT & WHITE CONTINUING CARE HOSPITAL-TEMPLE (O, 48 beds) 546 North Kegley Road, Temple, TX, Zip 76502–4069; tel. 254/215–0900; Shahin Motakef, FACHE, President
Web address: www.sw.org/location/temple-cch

BAYLOR SCOTT & WHITE HOSPITAL MEDICAL CENTER – BRENHAM (O, 53 beds) 700 Medical Parkway, Brenham, TX, Zip 77833–5498; tel. 979/337–5000; Jason Jennings, FACHE, President
Web address: www.swbrenham.org

BAYLOR SCOTT & WHITE HOSPITAL MEDICAL CENTER – COLLEGE STATION (O, 119 beds) 700 Scott & White Drive, College Station, TX, Zip 77845; tel. 979/207–0100; Jason Jennings, FACHE, President
Web address: www.sw.org/location/college-station-hospital

BAYLOR SCOTT & WHITE MEDICAL CENTER – CARROLLTON (L, 89 beds) 4343 North Josey Lane, Carrollton, TX, Zip 75010–4691; tel. 972/394–1010; Beth O'Brien, R.N., Chief Executive Officer

BAYLOR SCOTT & WHITE MEDICAL CENTER – CENTENNIAL (O, 106 beds) 12505 Lebanon Road, Frisco, TX, Zip 75035–8298; tel. 972/963–3333; Jaikumar Krishnaswamy, President
Web address: www.centennialmedcenter.com

BAYLOR SCOTT & WHITE MEDICAL CENTER – GRAPEVINE (O, 270 beds) 1650 West College Street, Grapevine, TX, Zip 76051–3565; tel. 817/481–1588; Christopher York, FACHE, President

BAYLOR SCOTT & WHITE MEDICAL CENTER – HILLCREST (C, 226 beds) 100 Hillcrest Medical Boulevard, Waco, TX, Zip 76712–8897; tel. 254/202–2000; Glenn A. Robinson, FACHE, President
Web address: www.sw.org/hillcrest-medical-center

BAYLOR SCOTT & WHITE MEDICAL CENTER – LAKE POINTE (O, 112 beds) 6800 Scenic Drive, Rowlett, TX, Zip 75088–4552, Mailing Address: P.O. Box 1550, Zip 75030–1550, tel. 972/412–2273; Donas Cole, FACHE, President

BAYLOR SCOTT & WHITE MEDICAL CENTER – LLANO (O, 10 beds) 200 West Ollie Street, Llano, TX, Zip 78643–2628; tel. 325/247–5040; Timothy A. Ols, FACHE, Chief Executive Officer
Web address: www.bwshealth.com

BAYLOR SCOTT & WHITE MEDICAL CENTER – MARBLE FALLS (O, 46 beds) 800 West Highway 71, Marble Falls, TX, Zip 78654; tel. 830/201–8000; Timothy A. Ols, FACHE, President
Web address: www.sw.org/location/marble-falls-hospital

BAYLOR SCOTT & WHITE MEDICAL CENTER – PLANO (O, 124 beds) 4700 Alliance Boulevard, Plano, TX, Zip 75093–5323; tel. 469/814–2000; Jerri Garison, R.N., President

BAYLOR SCOTT & WHITE MEDICAL CENTER – ROUND ROCK (O, 173 beds) 300 University Boulevard, Round Rock, TX, Zip 78665–1032; tel. 512/509–0100; Jay Fox, President
Web address: www.sw.org

BAYLOR SCOTT & WHITE MEDICAL CENTER – TAYLOR (O, 25 beds) 305 Mallard Lane, Taylor, TX, Zip 76574–1208; tel. 512/352–7611; Jay Fox, Chief Executive Officer

For explanation of codes following names, see page B2.
★ Indicates Type III membership in the American Hospital Association.

BAYLOR SCOTT & WHITE MEDICAL CENTER – TEMPLE (O, 640 beds) 2401 South 31st Street, Temple, TX, Zip 76508–0002; tel. 254/724–2111; Shahin Motakef, FACHE, President
Web address: www.sw.org/location/temple-hospital

BAYLOR SCOTT & WHITE MEDICAL CENTER AT – MCKINNEY (O, 143 beds) 5252 West University Drive, McKinney, TX, Zip 75071–7822; tel. 469/764–1000; Kyle Armstrong, President
Web address: www.baylorhealth.com/PhysiciansLocations/McKinney/Pages/Default.aspx

BAYLOR SCOTT & WHITE MEDICAL CENTER-IRVING (L, 233 beds) 1901 North MacArthur Boulevard, Irving, TX, Zip 75061–2220; tel. 972/579–8100; Cindy K. Schamp, FACHE, President

BAYLOR SCOTT & WHITE MEDICAL CENTER-WAXAHACHIE (O, 129 beds) 2400 North I-35E, Waxahachie, TX, Zip 75165; tel. 469/843–4000; Will Turner, President
Web address: www.baylorhealth.com/PhysiciansLocations/Waxahachie/Pages/Default.aspx

BAYLOR UNIVERSITY MEDICAL CENTER (O, 857 beds) 3500 Gaston Avenue, Dallas, TX, Zip 75246–2088; tel. 214/820–0111; Steven R. Newton, FACHE, President
Web address: www.baylorhealth.com/PhysiciansLocations/Dallas/Pages/Default.aspx

Owned, leased, sponsored:	18 hospitals	3554 beds
Contract-managed:	1 hospitals	226 beds
Totals:	19 hospitals	3780 beds

★1095: BAYSTATE HEALTH, INC. (NP)

280 Chestnut Street, Springfield, MA, Zip 01199–0001; tel. 413/794–0000; Mark A. Keroack, M.D., M.P.H., President and Chief Executive Officer
(Centralized Physician/Insurance Health System)

MASSACHUSETTS: BAYSTATE FRANKLIN MEDICAL CENTER (O, 89 beds) 164 High Street, Greenfield, MA, Zip 01301–2613; tel. 413/773–0211; Ronald Bryant, President
Web address: www.baystatehealth.org

BAYSTATE MEDICAL CENTER (O, 734 beds) 759 Chestnut Street, Springfield, MA, Zip 01199 0001; tel. 413/794–0000; Nancy Shendell-Falik, R.N., President
Web address: www.baystatehealth.org/bmc

BAYSTATE NOBLE HOSPITAL (O, 97 beds) 115 West Silver Street, Westfield, MA, Zip 01085–3628; tel. 413/568–2811; Ronald Bryant, President
Web address: www.baystatehealth.org/locations/noble-hospital

BAYSTATE WING HOSPITAL (O, 74 beds) 40 Wright Street, Palmer, MA, Zip 01069–1138; tel. 413/283–7651; Michael Francis. Moran, President and Chief Administrative Officer

Owned, leased, sponsored:	4 hospitals	994 beds
Contract-managed:	0 hospitals	0 beds
Totals:	4 hospitals	994 beds

★0940: BEACON HEALTH SYSTEM (NP)

615 North Michigan Street, South Bend, IN, Zip 46601–1033; tel. 574/647–1000; Kreg Gruber, Chief Executive Officer
(Centralized Physician/Insurance Health System)

INDIANA: ELKHART GENERAL HOSPITAL (O, 230 beds) 600 East Boulevard, Elkhart, IN, Zip 46514–2499, Mailing Address: P.O. Box 1329, Zip 46515–1329, tel. 574/294–2621; Carl W. Risk II, President
Web address: www.egh.org

MEMORIAL HOSPITAL OF SOUTH BEND (O, 418 beds) 615 North Michigan Street, South Bend, IN, Zip 46601–1033; tel. 574/647–1000; Larry A. Tracy Jr, FACHE, President
Web address: www.beaconhealthsystem.org

LOUISIANA: BEACON BEHAVIORAL HOSPITAL (O, 17 beds) 323 Evergreen Street, Bunkie, LA, Zip 71322–1307; tel. 318/346–3143; Randall Johnson, Administrator
Web address: www.beaconbh.com

Owned, leased, sponsored:	3 hospitals	665 beds
Contract-managed:	0 hospitals	0 beds
Totals:	3 hospitals	665 beds

★0953: BEAUMONT HEALTH (NP)

2000 Town Center, Suite 1200, Southfield, MI, Zip 48075–1145, fraser, tel. 248/898–5000; John T. Fox, President and Chief Executive Officer
(Centralized Health System)

MICHIGAN: BEAUMONT HOSPITAL – DEARBORN (O, 571 beds) 18101 Oakwood Boulevard, Dearborn, MI, Zip 48124–4089, Mailing Address: P.O. Box 2500, Zip 48123–2500, tel. 313/593–7000; David Claeys, FACHE, Chief Executive Officer
Web address: www.beaumont.org

BEAUMONT HOSPITAL – FARMINGTON HILLS (O, 288 beds) 28050 Grand River Avenue, Farmington Hills, MI, Zip 48336–5933; tel. 248/471–8000; Constance O'Malley, President
Web address: www.beaumont.org

BEAUMONT HOSPITAL – GROSSE POINTE (O, 280 beds) 468 Cadieux Road, Grosse Pointe, MI, Zip 48230–1507; tel. 313/473–1000; James Lynch, M.D., Interim Chief Executive Officer
Web address: www.beaumont.org

BEAUMONT HOSPITAL – ROYAL OAK (O, 1100 beds) 3601 West Thirteen Mile Road, Royal Oak, MI, Zip 48073–6712; tel. 248/898–5000; Nancy Susick, MSN, President
Web address: www.beaumont.org

BEAUMONT HOSPITAL – TAYLOR (O, 189 beds) 10000 Telegraph Road, Taylor, MI, Zip 48180–3330; tel. 313/295–5000; Lee Ann Odom, Division President
Web address: www.beaumont.org

BEAUMONT HOSPITAL – TRENTON (O, 193 beds) 5450 Fort Street, Trenton, MI, Zip 48183–4625; tel. 734/671–3800; Christine Stesney-Ridenour, FACHE, President
Web address: www.beaumont.org

BEAUMONT HOSPITAL – TROY (O, 520 beds) 44201 Dequindre Road, Troy, MI, Zip 48085–1117; tel. 248/964–5000; James Lynch, M.D., Interim President
Web address: www.beaumont.org

BEAUMONT HOSPITAL, WAYNE (O, 185 beds) 33155 Annapolis Street, Wayne, MI, Zip 48184–2405; tel. 734/467–4000; Eric W. Widner, FACHE, Division President

Owned, leased, sponsored:	8 hospitals	3326 beds
Contract-managed:	0 hospitals	0 beds
Totals:	8 hospitals	3326 beds

0538: BENEFIS HEALTH SYSTEM (NP)

1101 26th Street South, Great Falls, MT, Zip 59405–5161; tel. 406/455–5000; John H. Goodnow, Chief Executive Officer
(Moderately Centralized Health System)

MONTANA: BENEFIS HEALTH SYSTEM (O, 502 beds) 1101 26th Street South, Great Falls, MT, Zip 59405–5104; tel. 406/455–5000; John H. Goodnow, Chief Executive Officer

BENEFIS TETON MEDICAL CENTER (O, 25 beds) 915 4th Street North West, Choteau, MT, Zip 59422–9123; tel. 406/466–5763; Louie King, Chief Executive Officer
Web address: www.tetonmedicalcenter.net

MISSOURI RIVER MEDICAL CENTER (C, 25 beds) 1501 St Charles Street, Fort Benton, MT, Zip 59442–0249, Mailing Address: P.O. Box 249, Zip 59442–0249, tel. 406/622–3331; Louie King, President, Harry Bold Nursing Home Administrator
Web address: www.mrmcfb.org

Owned, leased, sponsored:	2 hospitals	527 beds
Contract-managed:	1 hospitals	25 beds
Totals:	3 hospitals	552 beds

★2435: BERKSHIRE HEALTH SYSTEMS, INC. (NP)

725 North Street, Pittsfield, MA, Zip 01201–4124; tel. 413/447–2750; David E. Phelps, President and Chief Executive Officer
(Moderately Centralized Health System)

For explanation of codes following names, see page B2.
★ Indicates Type III membership in the American Hospital Association.

Section B

MASSACHUSETTS: BERKSHIRE MEDICAL CENTER (O, 275 beds) 725 North ST, Pittsfield, MA, Zip 01201–4124, Mailing Address: 725 North Street, Zip 01201–4124, tel. 413/447–2000; David E. Phelps, President and Chief Executive Officer

FAIRVIEW HOSPITAL (O, 25 beds) 29 Lewis Avenue, Great Barrington, MA, Zip 01230–1713; tel. 413/528–0790; Eugene A. Dellea, President
Web address: www.bhs1.org/body_fh.cfm?id=39

Owned, leased, sponsored:	2 hospitals	300 beds
Contract-managed:	0 hospitals	0 beds
Totals:	2 hospitals	300 beds

★0949: BETH ISRAEL LAHEY HEALTH (NP)
109 Brookline Avenue, Boston, MA, Zip 02215–3903; tel. 617/667–7000; Kevin Tabb, M.D., Chief Executive Officer

MASSACHUSETTS: ANNA JAQUES HOSPITAL (O, 123 beds) 25 Highland Avenue, Newburyport, MA, Zip 01950–3894; tel. 978/463–1000; Mark L. Goldstein, President and Chief Executive Officer
Web address: www.ajh.org

BETH ISRAEL DEACONESS HOSPITAL PLYMOUTH (O, 170 beds) 275 Sandwich Street, Plymouth, MA, Zip 02360–2196; tel. 508/746–2000; Kevin B. Coughlin, President and Chief Executive Officer
Web address: www.bidplymouth.org

BETH ISRAEL DEACONESS HOSPITAL-MILTON (O, 100 beds) 199 Reedsdale Road, Milton, MA, Zip 02186–3926; tel. 617/696–4600; Richard W. Fernandez, President and Chief Executive Officer

BETH ISRAEL DEACONESS HOSPITAL-NEEDHAM CAMPUS (O, 46 beds) 148 Chestnut Street, Needham, MA, Zip 2492; tel. 781/453–3000; John M. Fogarty, President and Chief Executive Officer
Web address: www.bidneedham.org/

BETH ISRAEL DEACONESS MEDICAL CENTER (O, 719 beds) 330 Brookline Avenue, Boston, MA, Zip 02215–5491; tel. 617/667–7000; Kevin Tabb, M.D., Chief Executive Officer

BEVERLY HOSPITAL (O, 320 beds) 85 Herrick Street, Beverly, MA, Zip 01915–1777; tel. 978/922–3000; Philip M. Cormier, Chief Executive Officer
Web address: www.beverlyhospital.org

LAHEY HOSPITAL & MEDICAL CENTER, BURLINGTON (O, 345 beds) 41 Mall Road, Burlington, MA, Zip 01805–0001, Mailing Address: 31 Mall Road, Zip 01805–0001, tel. 781/744–5100; David L. Longworth, M.D., Chief Executive Officer
Web address: www.lahey.org

MOUNT AUBURN HOSPITAL (O, 205 beds) 330 Mount Auburn Street, Cambridge, MA, Zip 02138–5597; tel. 617/492–3500; Jeanette G. Clough, President and Chief Executive Officer
Web address: www.mountauburnhospital.org

NEW ENGLAND BAPTIST HOSPITAL (O, 113 beds) 125 Parker Hill Avenue, Boston, MA, Zip 02120–2847; tel. 617/754–5800; David Passafaro, Chief Executive Officer

WINCHESTER HOSPITAL (O, 197 beds) 41 Highland Avenue, Winchester, MA, Zip 01890–1496; tel. 781/729–9000; Richard I. Weiner, M.D., Chief Executive Officer and Chief Medical Officer
Web address: www.winchesterhospital.org

Owned, leased, sponsored:	10 hospitals	2338 beds
Contract-managed:	0 hospitals	0 beds
Totals:	10 hospitals	2338 beds

★0051: BJC HEALTHCARE (NP)
4901 Forest Park Avenue, Suite 1200, Saint Louis, MO, Zip 63108–1402; tel. 314/286–2000; Richard J. Liekweg, President and Chief Executive Officer
(Centralized Health System)

ILLINOIS: ALTON MEMORIAL HOSPITAL (O, 200 beds) One Memorial Drive, Alton, IL, Zip 62002–6722; tel. 618/463–7311; David A. Braasch, President
Web address: www.altonmemorialhospital.org

MEMORIAL HOSPITAL EAST (O, 94 beds) 1404 Cross Street, Shiloh, IL, Zip 62269–2988; tel. 618/607–1000; Mark J. Turner, FACHE, President
Web address: www.memhospeast.com

MEMORIAL HOSPITAL (O, 304 beds) 4500 Memorial Drive, Belleville, IL, Zip 62226–5399; tel. 618/233–7750; Mark J. Turner, FACHE, President

MISSOURI: BARNES-JEWISH HOSPITAL (O, 1413 beds) 1 Barnes-Jewish Hospital Plaza, Saint Louis, MO, Zip 63110–1003; tel. 314/747–3000; Robert W. Cannon, President
Web address: www.barnesjewish.org

BARNES-JEWISH ST. PETERS HOSPITAL (O, 101 beds) 10 Hospital Drive, Saint Peters, MO, Zip 63376–1659; tel. 636/916–9000; Chris Watts, President
Web address: www.bjsph.org/

BARNES-JEWISH WEST COUNTY HOSPITAL (O, 77 beds) 12634 Olive Boulevard, Saint Louis, MO, Zip 63141–6337; tel. 314/996–8000; Trisha Lollo, President

BOONE HOSPITAL CENTER (L, 311 beds) 1600 East Broadway, Columbia, MO, Zip 65201–5844; tel. 573/815–8000; James J. Sinek, FACHE, President
Web address: www.boone.org

CHRISTIAN HOSPITAL (O, 220 beds) 11133 Dunn Road, Saint Louis, MO, Zip 63136–6119; tel. 314/653–5000; Rick Stevens, President
Web address: www.christianhospital.org

MISSOURI BAPTIST MEDICAL CENTER (O, 449 beds) 3015 North Ballas Road, Saint Louis, MO, Zip 63131–2329; tel. 314/996–5000; John Antes, President
Web address: www.missouribaptist.org

MISSOURI BAPTIST SULLIVAN HOSPITAL (O, 35 beds) 751 Sappington Bridge Road, Sullivan, MO, Zip 63080–2354; tel. 573/468–4186; Tony Schwarm, FACHE, President
Web address: www.missouribaptistsullivan.org

PARKLAND HEALTH CENTER – FARMINGTON COMMUNITY (O, 103 beds) 1101 West Liberty Street, Farmington, MO, Zip 63640–1921; tel. 573/756–6451; Thomas P. Karl, President

PARKLAND HEALTH CENTER-BONNE TERRE (O, 3 beds) 7245 Raider Road, Bonne Terre, MO, Zip 63628; tel. 573/358–1400; Laura Lynn Rasnick, R.N., Administrator
Web address: www.parklandhealthcenter.org

PROGRESS WEST HOSPITAL (O, 74 beds) Two Progress Point Parkway, O'Fallon, MO, Zip 63368–2208; tel. 636/344–1000; Chris Watts, President
Web address: www.progresswest.org

ST. LOUIS CHILDREN'S HOSPITAL (O, 390 beds) One Children's Place, Saint Louis, MO, Zip 63110–1002; tel. 314/454–6000; Peggy Gordin, Acting President
Web address: www.stlouischildrens.org

Owned, leased, sponsored:	14 hospitals	3774 beds
Contract-managed:	0 hospitals	0 beds
Totals:	14 hospitals	3774 beds

★0852: BLANCHARD VALLEY HEALTH SYSTEM (NP)
1900 South Main Street, Findlay, OH, Zip 45840–1214; tel. 419/423–4500; Scott C. Malaney, FACHE, President and Chief Executive Officer
(Centralized Physician/Insurance Health System)

OHIO: BLANCHARD VALLEY HOSPITAL (O, 159 beds) 1900 South Main Street, Findlay, OH, Zip 45840–1214; tel. 419/423–4500; Scott C. Malaney, FACHE, President and Chief Executive Officer

BLUFFTON HOSPITAL (O, 25 beds) 139 Garau Street, Bluffton, OH, Zip 45817–1027; tel. 419/358–9010; Christine Keller, Chief Administrative Officer
Web address: www.bvhealthsystem.org/

Owned, leased, sponsored:	2 hospitals	184 beds
Contract-managed:	0 hospitals	0 beds
Totals:	2 hospitals	184 beds

5085: BON SECOURS MERCY HEALTH (CC)
1505 Marriottsville Road, Marriottsville, MD, Zip 21104–1399; tel. 410/442–5511; Richard Statuto, President and Chief Executive Officer
(Moderately Centralized Health System)

For explanation of codes following names, see page B2.
★ Indicates Type III membership in the American Hospital Association.

KENTUCKY: OUR LADY OF BELLEFONTE HOSPITAL (O, 151 beds) St Christopher Drive, Ashland, KY, Zip 41101, Mailing Address: P.O. Box 789, Zip 41105–0789, tel. 606/833–3333; Kevin Halter, Chief Executive Officer
Web address: www.olbh.com

MARYLAND: BON SECOURS BALTIMORE HEALTH SYSTEM (O, 69 beds) 2000 West Baltimore Street, Baltimore, MD, Zip 21223–1558; tel. 410/362–3000; Samuel Lee. Ross, M.D., MS, Chief Executive Officer

SOUTH CAROLINA: BON SECOURS ST. FRANCIS HEALTH SYSTEM (O, 352 beds) One St Francis Drive, Greenville, SC, Zip 29601–3207; tel. 864/255–1000; Matthew T. Caldwell, President
Web address: www.stfrancishealth.org

VIRGINIA: BON SECOURS MARY IMMACULATE HOSPITAL (O, 238 beds) 2 Bernardine Drive, Newport News, VA, Zip 23602–4499; tel. 757/886–6000; Darlene Stephenson, Chief Executive Officer

BON SECOURS MARYVIEW MEDICAL CENTER (O, 466 beds) 3636 High Street, Portsmouth, VA, Zip 23707–3270; tel. 757/398–2200; Paul Gaden, Chief Executive Officer
Web address: www.bonsecourshamptonroads.com

BON SECOURS MEMORIAL REGIONAL MEDICAL CENTER (O, 251 beds) 8260 Atlee Road, Mechanicsville, VA, Zip 23116–1844; tel. 804/764–6000; Mark M. Gordon, Chief Executive Officer
Web address: www.bonsecours.com

BON SECOURS ST. FRANCIS MEDICAL CENTER (O, 135 beds) 13710 St Francis Boulevard, Midlothian, VA, Zip 23114–3267; tel. 804/594–7300; Chris Accashian, Chief Executive Officer

BON SECOURS ST. MARY'S HOSPITAL (O, 391 beds) 5801 Bremo Road, Richmond, VA, Zip 23226–1907; tel. 804/285–2011; Francine Barr, R.N., MS, Chief Executive Officer
Web address: www.bonsecours.com

BON SECOURS-DEPAUL MEDICAL CENTER (O, 204 beds) 150 Kingsley Lane, Norfolk, VA, Zip 23505–4650; tel. 757/889–5000; Paul Gaden, Chief Executive Officer

BON SECOURS-RICHMOND COMMUNITY HOSPITAL (O, 96 beds) 1500 North 28th Street, Richmond, VA, Zip 23223–5396, Mailing Address: P.O. Box 27184, Zip 23261–7184, tel. 804/225–1700; Mark M. Gordon, Chief Executive Officer
Web address: www.bonsecours.com

RAPPAHANNOCK GENERAL HOSPITAL (O, 35 beds) 101 Harris Drive, Kilmarnock, VA, Zip 22482–3880, Mailing Address: P.O. Box 1449, Zip 22482–1449, tel. 804/435–8000; Chris Accashian, Chief Executive Officer

Owned, leased, sponsored:	11 hospitals	2388 beds
Contract-managed:	0 hospitals	0 beds
Totals:	11 hospitals	2388 beds

2455: BRADFORD HEALTH SERVICES (IO)
2101 Magnolia Avenue South, Suite 518, Birmingham, AL, Zip 35205–2853; tel. 205/251–7753; Jerry W. Crowder, President and Chief Executive Officer

ALABAMA: BRADFORD HEALTH SERVICES AT HUNTSVILLE (O, 84 beds) 1600 Browns Ferry Road, Madison, AL, Zip 35758–9601, Mailing Address: P.O. Box 1488, Zip 35758–0176, tel. 256/461–7272; Bob Hinds, Executive Director
Web address: www.bradfordhealth.com

BRADFORD HEALTH SERVICES AT WARRIOR LODGE (O, 100 beds) 1189 Allbritt Road, Warrior, AL, Zip 35180, Mailing Address: P.O. Box 129, Zip 35180–0129, tel. 205/647–1945; Roy M. Ramsey, Executive Director

Owned, leased, sponsored:	2 hospitals	184 beds
Contract-managed:	0 hospitals	0 beds
Totals:	2 hospitals	184 beds

0352: BRIDGEPOINT HEALTHCARE (IO)
155 Fleet Street, Portsmouth, NH, Zip 03801–4050; tel. 603/570–4888; Marc C. Ferrell, President and Chief Executive Officer
(Independent Hospital System)

DISTRICT OF COLUMBIA: BRIDGEPOINT HOSPITAL CAPITOL HILL (O, 177 beds) 700 Constitution Avenue NE, Washington, DC, Zip 20002–6058; tel. 202/546–5700; James Linhares, Chief Executive Officer
Web address: www.bridgepointhealthcare.com/

BRIDGEPOINT HOSPITAL NATIONAL HARBOR (O, 82 beds) 4601 Martin Luther King Jr Avenue, SW, Washington, DC, Zip 20032–1131; tel. 202/574–5700; Swenda Moreh, Interim Chief Executive Officer
Web address: www.bridgepointhealthcare.com/

Owned, leased, sponsored:	2 hospitals	259 beds
Contract-managed:	0 hospitals	0 beds
Totals:	2 hospitals	259 beds

★0595: BRONSON HEALTHCARE GROUP (NP)
301 John Street, Kalamazoo, MI, Zip 49007–5295; tel. 269/341–6000; Frank J. Sardone, President and Chief Executive Officer
(Centralized Health System)

MICHIGAN: BRONSON BATTLE CREEK HOSPITAL (O, 198 beds) 300 North Avenue, Battle Creek, MI, Zip 49017–3307; tel. 269/245–8000; Frank J. Sardone, President and Chief Executive Officer
Web address: www.bronsonhealth.com

BRONSON LAKEVIEW HOSPITAL (O, 35 beds) 408 Hazen Street, Paw Paw, MI, Zip 49079–1019, Mailing Address: P.O. Box 209, Zip 49079–0209, tel. 269/657–3141; Kirk Richardson, R.N., Vice President, Chief Operating Officer, and Chief Nursing Officer
Web address: www.bronsonhealth.com/lakeview

BRONSON METHODIST HOSPITAL (O, 415 beds) 601 John Street, Kalamazoo, MI, Zip 49007–5346; tel. 269/341–6000; Frank J. Sardone, President and Chief Executive Officer

BRONSON SOUTH HAVEN HOSPITAL (O, 49 beds) 955 South Bailey Avenue, South Haven, MI, Zip 49090–6743; tel. 269/637–5271; Kirk Richardson, R.N., Vice President, Chief Operating Officer and Chief Nursing Officer
Web address: www.sh-hs.org

Owned, leased, sponsored:	4 hospitals	697 beds
Contract-managed:	0 hospitals	0 beds
Totals:	4 hospitals	697 beds

★3115: BROWARD HEALTH (NP)
1800 NW 49th Street, Fort Lauderdale, FL, Zip 33309–3092; tel. 954/355–4400; Gino Santorio, President and Chief Executive Officer

FLORIDA: BROWARD HEALTH CORAL SPRINGS (O, 196 beds) 3000 Coral Hills Drive, Coral Springs, FL, Zip 33065–4108; tel. 954/344–3000; Jared M. Smith, Chief Executive Officer
Web address: www.browardhealth.org

BROWARD HEALTH IMPERIAL POINT (O, 180 beds) 6401 North Federal Highway, Fort Lauderdale, FL, Zip 33308–1495; tel. 954/776–8500; Jonathan Watkins, Chief Executive Officer
Web address: www.browardhealth.org

BROWARD HEALTH MEDICAL CENTER (O, 656 beds) 1600 South Andrews Avenue, Fort Lauderdale, FL, Zip 33316–2510; tel. 954/355–4400; Jonathan Turton, FACHE, Chief Executive Officer

BROWARD HEALTH NORTH (O, 331 beds) 201 East Sample Road, Deerfield Beach, FL, Zip 33064–3502; tel. 954/941–8300; Alice Taylor, R.N., MSN, Chief Executive Officer
Web address: www.browardhealth.org

Owned, leased, sponsored:	4 hospitals	1363 beds
Contract-managed:	0 hospitals	0 beds
Totals:	4 hospitals	1363 beds

★0400: BRYAN HEALTH (NP)
1600 South 48th Street, Lincoln, NE, Zip 68506–1283, Mailing Address: 1600 S 48th ST, Zip 68506–1283, tel. 402/481–1111; Kimberly A. Russel, FACHE, President and Chief Executive Officer
(Moderately Centralized Health System)

For explanation of codes following names, see page B2.
★ Indicates Type III membership in the American Hospital Association.

IOWA: CLARINDA REGIONAL HEALTH CENTER (C, 25 beds) 220 Essie Davison Drive, Clarinda, IA, Zip 51632–2915, Mailing Address: P.O. Box 217, Zip 51632–0217, tel. 712/542–2176; Charles Nordyke, Chief Executive Officer
Web address: www.clarindahealth.com

NEBRASKA: BRYAN MEDICAL CENTER (O, 551 beds) 1600 South 48th Street, Lincoln, NE, Zip 68506–1299; tel. 402/481–1111; John T. Woodrich, President and Chief Operating Officer
Web address: www.bryanhealth.com

CRETE AREA MEDICAL CENTER (O, 24 beds) 2910 Betten Drive, Crete, NE, Zip 68333–3084, Mailing Address: P.O. Box 220, Zip 68333–0220, tel. 402/826–2102; Rebekah Mussman, President and Chief Executive Officer
Web address: www.creteareamedicalcenter.com

MERRICK MEDICAL CENTER (O, 20 beds) 1715 26th Street, Central City, NE, Zip 68826–9620; tel. 308/946–3015; Paul A. Clark, President and Chief Executive Officer

SAUNDERS MEDICAL CENTER (C, 16 beds) 1760 County Road J, Wahoo, NE, Zip 68066–4152; tel. 402/443–4191; Tyler Toline, FACHE, Chief Executive Officer
Web address: www.saundersmedicalcenter.com

Owned, leased, sponsored:	3 hospitals	595 beds
Contract-managed:	2 hospitals	41 beds
Totals:	5 hospitals	636 beds

★9655: BUREAU OF MEDICINE AND SURGERY, DEPARTMENT OF THE NAVY (FG)
7700 Arlington Boulevard, Suite 5126, Falls Church, VA, Zip 22042; tel. 202/762–3701; Bryce H.P. Mendez, Healthcare Policy Analyst
(Independent Hospital System)

CALIFORNIA: NAVAL HOSPITAL CAMP PENDLETON (O, 72 beds) 200 Mercy Circle, Camp Pendleton, CA, Zip 92055–5191, Mailing Address: P.O. Box 555191, Zip 92055–5191, tel. 760/725–1304, Captain; Frank P. Pearson, Commanding Officer

NAVAL HOSPITAL LEMOORE (O, 16 beds) 937 Franklin Avenue, Lemoore, CA, Zip 93246–0001; tel. 559/998–4481, Captain; Kristen Attenbury, Commanding Officer
Web address: www.med.navy.mil/sites/nhlem/Pages/index.aspx

NAVAL MEDICAL CENTER SAN DIEGO (O, 285 beds) 34800 Bob Wilson Drive, San Diego, CA, Zip 92134–5000; tel. 619/532–6400, Captain; Joel A. Roos, Commanding Officer
Web address: www.med.navy.mil/sites/nmcsd/Pages/default.aspx

ROBERT E. BUSH NAVAL HOSPITAL (O, 29 beds) 1145 Sturgis Road, Twentynine Palms, CA, Zip 92278, Mailing Address: Box 788250, MCAGCC, Zip 92278–8250, tel. 760/830–2190, Captain; Jay C. Sourbeer, Commanding Officer
Web address: www.med.navy.mil/sites/nhtp/Pages/default.aspx

FLORIDA: NAVAL HOSPITAL JACKSONVILLE (O, 64 beds) 2080 Child Street, Jacksonville, FL, Zip 32214–5000; tel. 904/542–7300, Commander; Darryl Green, Director Administration
Web address: www.med.navy.mil/SITES/NAVALHOSPITALJAX/Pages/default.aspx

NAVAL HOSPITAL PENSACOLA (O, 28 beds) 6000 West Highway 98, Pensacola, FL, Zip 32512–0003; tel. 850/505–6601, Commander; Devin Morrison, Director Administration
Web address: www.med.navy.mil/sites/pcola/Pages/default.aspx

GUAM: U. S. NAVAL HOSPITAL GUAM (O, 55 beds) Building #50 Farenholt Avenue, Agana, GU, Zip 96910, Mailing Address: PSC 490, Box 208, FPO, Zip 96540, tel. 671/344–9340, Captain; Daniel Cornwell, Command Officer

MARYLAND: WALTER REED NATIONAL MILITARY MEDICAL CENTER (O, 257 beds) 8901 Wisconsin Avenue, Bethesda, MD, Zip 20889–5600; tel. 301/295–4611, Captain; Mark A. Kobelja, MC, USN, Director
Web address: www.wrnmmc.capmed.mil/SitePages/home.aspx

NORTH CAROLINA: NAVAL HOSPITAL CAMP LEJEUNE (O, 117 beds) 100 Brewster Boulevard, Camp Lejeune, NC, Zip 28547–2538, Mailing Address: P.O. Box 10100, Zip 28547–0100, tel. 910/450–4300, Captain; Rick Freedman, Commanding Officer
Web address: www.med.navy.mil/sites/nhcl/Pages/default.aspx

SOUTH CAROLINA: NAVAL HOSPITAL BEAUFORT (O, 20 beds) 1 Pinckney Boulevard, Beaufort, SC, Zip 29902–6122; tel. 843/228–5301, Lieutenant Commander; Willie Brown, Director Administration
Web address: www.med.navy.mil/sites/nhbeaufort/Pages/Welcome_Page.aspx

VIRGINIA: NAVAL MEDICAL CENTER (O, 274 beds) 620 John Paul Jones Circle, Portsmouth, VA, Zip 23708–2197; tel. 757/953–1980, Captain; Matthew Case, MSC, USN, Executive Officer

WASHINGTON: NAVAL HOSPITAL BREMERTON (O, 23 beds) One Boone Road, Bremerton, WA, Zip 98312–1898; tel. 360/475–4000, Captain; Jeffrey Bitterman, Commanding Officer
Web address: www.med.navy.mil/sites/nhbrem/Pages/default.aspx

NAVAL HOSPITAL OAK HARBOR (O, 29 beds) 3475 North Saratoga Street, Oak Harbor, WA, Zip 98278–8800; tel. 360/257–9500, Commander; Frederick Joseph. McDonald, Commanding Officer
Web address: www.med.navy.mil/sites/nhoh/Pages/default.aspx

Owned, leased, sponsored:	13 hospitals	1269 beds
Contract-managed:	0 hospitals	0 beds
Totals:	13 hospitals	1269 beds

0113: CANCER TREATMENT CENTERS OF AMERICA (IO)
1336 Basswood Road, Schaumburg, IL, Zip 60173–4544; tel. 847/342–7400; Rajesh K. Garg, M.D., JD, President and Chief Executive Officer

ARIZONA: WESTERN REGIONAL MEDICAL CENTER (O, 12 beds) 14200 West Celebrate Life way, Goodyear, AZ, Zip 85338–3005; tel. 623/207–3000; Robert Gould, President and Chief Executive Officer

GEORGIA: SOUTHEASTERN REGIONAL MEDICAL CENTER (O, 50 beds) 600 Celebrate Life Parkway, Newnan, GA, Zip 30265–8000; tel. 770/400–6000; Anne Meisner, MSN, President and Chief Executive Officer
Web address: www.cancercenter.com/southeastern-hospital.cfm

ILLINOIS: MIDWESTERN REGIONAL MEDICAL CENTER (O, 72 beds) 2520 Elisha Avenue, Zion, IL, Zip 60099–2587; tel. 847/872–4561; Scott Jones, President and Chief Executive Officer
Web address: www.cancercenter.com

OKLAHOMA: SOUTHWESTERN REGIONAL MEDICAL CENTER (O, 40 beds) 10109 East 79th Street, Tulsa, OK, Zip 74133–4564; tel. 918/286–5000; Jay Foley, President and Chief Executive Officer
Web address: www.cancercenter.com

PENNSYLVANIA: CANCER TREATMENT CENTERS OF AMERICA-EASTERN REGIONAL MEDICAL CENTER (O, 56 beds) 1331 East Wyoming Avenue, Philadelphia, PA, Zip 19124–3808; tel. 215/537–7400; Nancy Hesse, MSN, R.N., President and Chief Executive Officer

Owned, leased, sponsored:	5 hospitals	230 beds
Contract-managed:	0 hospitals	0 beds
Totals:	5 hospitals	230 beds

★0124: CAPE COD HEALTHCARE, INC. (NP)
27 Park Street, Hyannis, MA, Zip 02601–5230; tel. 508/862–5121; Michael K. Lauf, President and Chief Executive Officer
(Centralized Health System)

MASSACHUSETTS: CAPE COD HOSPITAL (O, 259 beds) 27 Park Street, Hyannis, MA, Zip 02601–5230; tel. 508/771–1800; Michael K. Lauf, President and Chief Executive Officer

FALMOUTH HOSPITAL (O, 95 beds) 100 Ter Heun Drive, Falmouth, MA, Zip 02540–2599; tel. 508/548–5300; Lori Jewett, R.N., Chief Executive Officer
Web address: www.capecodhealth.org

Owned, leased, sponsored:	2 hospitals	354 beds
Contract-managed:	0 hospitals	0 beds
Totals:	2 hospitals	354 beds

For explanation of codes following names, see page B2.
★ Indicates Type III membership in the American Hospital Association.

0835: CAPE FEAR VALLEY HEALTH SYSTEM (NP)

1638 Owen Drive, Fayetteville, NC, Zip 28304–3424, Mailing Address: P.O. Box 2000, Zip 28302–2000, tel. 910/615–4000; Michael Nagowski, President and Chief Executive Officer **(Independent Hospital System)**

NORTH CAROLINA: CAPE FEAR VALLEY – BLADEN COUNTY HOSPITAL (O, 25 beds) 501 South Poplar Street, Elizabethtown, NC, Zip 28337–9375, Mailing Address: P.O. Box 398, Zip 28337–0398, tel. 910/862–5100; Mark Cobb, Chief Executive Officer
Web address: www.bchn.org

CAPE FEAR VALLEY MEDICAL CENTER (O, 620 beds) 1638 Owen Drive, Fayetteville, NC, Zip 28304–3431, Mailing Address: P.O. Box 2000, Zip 28302–2000, tel. 910/615–4000; Michael Nagowski, Chief Executive Officer

HARNETT HEALTH SYSTEM (C, 105 beds) 800 Tilghman Drive, Dunn, NC, Zip 28334–5599, Mailing Address: P.O. Box 1706, Zip 28335–1706, tel. 910/892–1000; Kevin Jackson, Interim Chief Executive Officer
Web address: www.myharnetthealth.org/

HIGHSMITH-RAINEY SPECIALTY HOSPITAL (O, 66 beds) 150 Robeson Street, Fayetteville, NC, Zip 28301–5570; tel. 910/615–1000; Kevin Jackson, On Site Administrator
Web address: www.capefearvalley.com

HOKE HOSPITAL (O, 29 beds) 210 Medical Pavilion Drive, Raeford, NC, Zip 28376–9111; tel. 910/904–8000; Roxie Cannon. Wells, M.D., President

Owned, leased, sponsored:	4 hospitals	740 beds
Contract-managed:	1 hospitals	105 beds
Totals:	5 hospitals	845 beds

★0297: CAPITAL HEALTH (NP)

750 Brunswick Avenue, Trenton, NJ, Zip 08638–4143; tel. 609/394–6000; Al Maghazehe, Ph.D., FACHE, President and Chief Executive Officer **(Independent Hospital System)**

NEW JERSEY: CAPITAL HEALTH MEDICAL CENTER-HOPEWELL (O, 171 beds) 1 Capital Way, Pennington, NJ, Zip 08534–2520; tel. 609/303–4000; Al Maghazehe, Ph.D., FACHE, President and Chief Executive Officer
Web address: www.capitalhealth.org

CAPITAL HEALTH REGIONAL MEDICAL CENTER (O, 162 beds) 750 Brunswick Avenue, Trenton, NJ, Zip 08638–4143; tel. 609/394–6000; Al Maghazehe, Ph.D., FACHE, President and Chief Executive Officer
Web address: www.capitalhealth.org

Owned, leased, sponsored:	2 hospitals	333 beds
Contract-managed:	0 hospitals	0 beds
Totals:	2 hospitals	333 beds

★0099: CARE NEW ENGLAND HEALTH SYSTEM (NP)

45 Willard Avenue, Providence, RI, Zip 02905–3218; tel. 401/453–7900; James E. Fanale, M.D., President, Chief Executive Officer and Chief Clinical Officer **(Moderately Centralized Health System)**

RHODE ISLAND: BUTLER HOSPITAL (O, 143 beds) 345 Blackstone Boulevard, Providence, RI, Zip 02906–4829; tel. 401/455–6200; Mary Marran, MS, President and Chief Operating Officer
Web address: www.butler.org

KENT COUNTY MEMORIAL HOSPITAL (O, 320 beds) 455 Tollgate Road, Warwick, RI, Zip 02886–2770; tel. 401/737–7000; Robert Haffey, R.N., President and Chief Operating Officer
Web address: www.kentri.org

WOMEN & INFANTS HOSPITAL OF RHODE ISLAND (O, 247 beds) 101 Dudley Street, Providence, RI, Zip 02905–2499; tel. 401/274–1100; Matt Quin, Interim Chief Operating Officer

Owned, leased, sponsored:	3 hospitals	710 beds
Contract-managed:	0 hospitals	0 beds
Totals:	3 hospitals	710 beds

0931: CAREPOINT HEALTH (IO)

10 Exchange Place, 15th Floor, Jersey City, NJ, Zip 07302–3918; tel. 877/791–7000; Natasha Deckmann, Chief Executive Officer

NEW JERSEY: CAREPOINT HEALTH BAYONNE MEDICAL CENTER (O, 178 beds) 29th Street & Avenue E, Bayonne, NJ, Zip 07002–4699, Mailing Address: 29 East 29 Street, Zip 07002–4699, tel. 201/858–5000; W. Peter Daniels, FACHE, Executive Vice President and Chief Operating Officer

CAREPOINT HEALTH CHRIST HOSPITAL (O, 376 beds) 176 Palisade Avenue, Jersey City, NJ, Zip 07306–1196, Mailing Address: 176 Palisades Avenue, Zip 07306–1196, tel. 201/795–8200; Marie Theresa Duffy, Chief Hospital Executive
Web address: www.carepointhealth.org

CAREPOINT HEALTH HOBOKEN UNIVERSITY MEDICAL CENTER (O, 333 beds) 308 Willow Avenue, Hoboken, NJ, Zip 07030–3889; tel. 201/418–1000; Ann P. Logan, R.N., Ph.D., Chief Operating Officer

Owned, leased, sponsored:	3 hospitals	887 beds
Contract-managed:	0 hospitals	0 beds
Totals:	3 hospitals	887 beds

★0070: CARILION CLINIC (NP)

1906 Belleview Avenue SE, Roanoke, VA, Zip 24014–1838, Mailing Address: P.O. Box 13727, Zip 24036–3727, tel. 540/981–7000; Nancy Howell. Agee, President and Chief Executive Officer **(Moderately Centralized Health System)**

VIRGINIA: CARILION FRANKLIN MEMORIAL HOSPITAL (O, 18 beds) 180 Floyd Avenue, Rocky Mount, VA, Zip 24151–1389; tel. 540/483–5277; Carl T. Cline, Chief Executive Officer
Web address: www.carilionclinic.org/CFMH

CARILION GILES COMMUNITY HOSPITAL (O, 10 beds) 159 Hartley Way, Pearisburg, VA, Zip 24134–2471; tel. 540/921–6000; William Flattery, Vice President and Administrator Western Division

CARILION NEW RIVER VALLEY MEDICAL CENTER (O, 99 beds) 2900 Lamb Circle, Christiansburg, VA, Zip 24073–6344, Mailing Address: P.O. Box 5, Radford, Zip 24143–0005, tel. 540/731–2000; William Flattery, Vice President and Administrator Western Division
Web address: www.carilionclinic.org/Carilion/cnrv

CARILION ROANOKE MEMORIAL HOSPITAL (O, 643 beds) 1906 Belleview Avenue Southeast, Roanoke, VA, Zip 24014–1838, Mailing Address: P.O. Box 13367, Zip 24033–3367, tel. 540/981–7000; Steven C. Arner, President
Web address: www.carilionclinic.org

CARILION STONEWALL JACKSON HOSPITAL (O, 15 beds) 1 Health Circle, Lexington, VA, Zip 24450–2492; tel. 540/458–3300; Greg T. Madsen, Chief Executive Officer

CARILION TAZEWELL COMMUNITY HOSPITAL (O, 4 beds) 141 Ben Bolt Avenue, Tazewell, VA, Zip 24651–9700, Mailing Address: 388 Ben Bolt Avenue, Zip 24651, tel. 276/988–8700; Kathren Dowdy, MSN, Regional Hospital Senior Director
Web address: www.carilionclinic.org

Owned, leased, sponsored:	6 hospitals	789 beds
Contract-managed:	0 hospitals	0 beds
Totals:	6 hospitals	789 beds

★2575: CARLE FOUNDATION (NP)

611 West Park Street, Urbana, IL, Zip 61801–2595; tel. 217/383–3311; James C. Leonard, M.D., President and Chief Executive Officer **(Moderately Centralized Health System)**

ILLINOIS: CARLE FOUNDATION HOSPITAL (O, 436 beds) 611 West Park Street, Urbana, IL, Zip 61801–2529; tel. 217/383–3311; James C. Leonard, M.D., President and Chief Executive Officer
Web address: www.carle.org

CARLE HOOPESTON REGIONAL HEALTH CENTER (O, 13 beds) 701 East Orange Street, Hoopeston, IL, Zip 60942–1801; tel. 217/283–5531; Harry Brockus, Chief Executive Officer

For explanation of codes following names, see page B2.
★ Indicates Type III membership in the American Hospital Association.

CARLE RICHLAND MEMORIAL HOSPITAL (O, 86 beds) 800 East Locust Street, Olney, IL, Zip 62450–2553; tel. 618/395–2131; Harry Brockus, Chief Executive Officer
Web address: www.richlandmemorial.com

Owned, leased, sponsored:	3 hospitals	535 beds
Contract-managed:	0 hospitals	0 beds
Totals:	3 hospitals	535 beds

0656: CARRUS HOSPITALS (IO)

1810 West US Highway 82, Sherman, TX, Zip 75092–7069; tel. 903/870–2600; Ronald E. Dorris, Chief Executive Officer
(Independent Hospital System)

TEXAS: CARRUS REHABILITATION HOSPITAL (O, 24 beds) 1810 West US Highway 82, Suite 100, Sherman, TX, Zip 75092–7069; tel. 903/870–2600; Jon-Michael Rains, Chief Executive Officer
Web address: www.carrushospital.com

CARRUS SPECIALTY HOSPITAL (O, 33 beds) 1810 West US Highway 82, Sherman, TX, Zip 75092–7069; tel. 903/870–2600; Jon-Michael Rains, Chief Executive Officer

Owned, leased, sponsored:	2 hospitals	57 beds
Contract-managed:	0 hospitals	0 beds
Totals:	2 hospitals	57 beds

0903: CATHOLIC HEALTH SERVICES (CC)

4790 North State Road 7, Lauderdale Lakes, FL, Zip 33319–5860; tel. 954/484–1515; Joseph M. Catania, President and Chief Executive Officer

FLORIDA: ST. ANTHONY'S REHABILITATION HOSPITAL (S, 26 beds) 3485 NW 30th Street, Lauderdale Lakes, FL, Zip 33311–1890; tel. 954/739–6233; Joseph M. Catania, Chief Executive Officer

ST. CATHERINE'S REHABILITATION HOSPITAL (S, 60 beds) 1050 NE 125th Street, North Miami, FL, Zip 33161–5881; tel. 305/357–1735; Jaime Gonzalez, Administrator
Web address: www.catholichealthservices.org

Owned, leased, sponsored:	2 hospitals	86 beds
Contract-managed:	0 hospitals	0 beds
Totals:	2 hospitals	86 beds

0233: CATHOLIC HEALTH SERVICES OF LONG ISLAND (CC)

992 North Village Avenue, 1st Floor, Rockville Centre, NY, Zip 11570–1002; tel. 516/705–3700; Alan D. Guerci, M.D., President and Chief Executive Officer
(Centralized Health System)

NEW YORK: GOOD SAMARITAN HOSPITAL MEDICAL CENTER (O, 417 beds) 1000 Montauk Highway, West Islip, NY, Zip 11795–4927; tel. 631/376–3000; Ruth E Hennessey, President
Web address: www.good-samaritan-hospital.org

MERCY MEDICAL CENTER (O, 191 beds) 1000 North Village Avenue, Rockville Centre, NY, Zip 11570–1000; tel. 516/705–2525; Peter Scaminaci, President

ST. CATHERINE OF SIENA MEDICAL CENTER (O, 281 beds) 50 Route 25-A, Smithtown, NY, Zip 11787–1348; tel. 631/862–3000; James O'Connor, Chief Administrative Officer
Web address: www.stcatherines.chsli.org/

ST. CHARLES HOSPITAL (O, 243 beds) 200 Belle Terre Road, Port Jefferson, NY, Zip 11777–1928; tel. 631/474–6000; James O'Connor, President

ST. FRANCIS HOSPITAL, THE HEART CENTER (O, 320 beds) 100 Port Washington Boulevard, Roslyn, NY, Zip 11576–1353; tel. 516/562–6000; Charles Lucore, M.D., President
Web address: www.stfrancisheartcenter.com/index.html

ST. JOSEPH HOSPITAL (S, 128 beds) 4295 Hempstead Turnpike, Bethpage, NY, Zip 11714–5769; tel. 516/579–6000; Peter Scaminaci, President

Owned, leased, sponsored:	6 hospitals	1580 beds
Contract-managed:	0 hospitals	0 beds
Totals:	6 hospitals	1580 beds

★0234: CATHOLIC HEALTH SYSTEM (CC)

144 Genesee Street, Buffalo, NY, Zip 14203–1560; tel. 716/862–2410; Mark A. Sullivan, FACHE, President and Chief Executive Officer
(Independent Hospital System)

NEW YORK: FATHER BAKER MANOR (O, 160 beds) 6400 Powers Road, Orchard Park, NY, Zip 14127; tel. 716/667–0001; Christine Kluckhohn, President, Continuing Care

KENMORE MERCY HOSPITAL (O, 321 beds) 2950 Elmwood Avenue, Kenmore, NY, Zip 14217–1390, Mailing Address: 2950 Elmwood Avenue, Room 4024, Zip 14217–1390, tel. 716/447–6100; Walter Ludwig, President and Chief Executive Officer
Web address: www.chsbuffalo.org

MCAULEY RESIDENCE (O, 160 beds) 1503 Military Road, Kenmore, NY, Zip 14217; tel. 716/447–6600; Christine Kluckhohn, President, Continuing Care

MERCY HOSPITAL (O, 436 beds) 565 Abbott Road, Buffalo, NY, Zip 14220–2095; tel. 716/826–7000; Charles J. Urlaub, President and Chief Executive Officer
Web address: www.chsbuffalo.org

MERCY NURSING FACILITY (O, 74 beds) 565 Abbott Road, Buffalo, NY, Zip 14220; tel. 716/828–2301; Christine Kluckhohn, President, Continuing Care

MOUNT ST. MARY'S HOSPITAL AND HEALTH CENTER (O, 152 beds) 5300 Military Road, Lewiston, NY, Zip 14092–1903; tel. 716/297–4800; Gary C. Tucker, President and Chief Executive Officer
Web address: www.msmh.org

NAZARETH HOME (O, 125 beds) 291 West North Street, Buffalo, NY, Zip 14201; tel. 716/881–2323; Christine Kluckhohn, President, Continuing Care

SISTERS OF CHARITY HOSPITAL OF BUFFALO (O, 388 beds) 2157 Main Street, Buffalo, NY, Zip 14214–2692; tel. 716/862–1000; Martin Boryszak, President and Chief Executive Officer
Web address: www.chsbuffalo.org

ST. CATHERINE LABOURE (O, 80 beds) 2157 Main Street, Buffalo, NY, Zip 14214; tel. 716/862–1451; Christine Kluckhohn, President, Continuing Care

ST. ELIZABETH'S HOME (O, 117 beds) 5539 Broadway, Lancaster, NY, Zip 14086; tel. 716/683–5150; Christine Kluckhohn, President, Continuing Care

ST. FRANCIS OF BUFFALO (O, 120 beds) 34 Benwood Avenue, Buffalo, NY, Zip 14214; tel. 716/862–2500; Christine Kluckhohn, President, Continuing Care

ST. FRANCIS OF WILLIAMSVILLE (O, 142 beds) 147 Reist Street, Williamsville, NY, Zip 14221; tel. 716/633–5400; Christine Kluckhohn, President, Continuing Care

ST. JOSEPH MANOR (O, 22 beds) 2211 West State Street, Olean, NY, Zip 14760; tel. 716/372–7810; Christine Kluckhohn, President, Continuing Care

Owned, leased, sponsored:	13 hospitals	2297 beds
Contract-managed:	0 hospitals	0 beds
Totals:	13 hospitals	2297 beds

★0991: CAYUGA HEALTH SYSTEM (NP)

101 Dates Drive, Ithaca, NY, Zip 14850–1342; tel. 607/274–4011; Martin Stallone, President and Chief Executive Officer
(Independent Hospital System)

NEW YORK: CAYUGA MEDICAL CENTER AT ITHACA (O, 159 beds) 101 Dates Drive, Ithaca, NY, Zip 14850–1342; tel. 607/274–4011; John B. Rudd, President and Chief Executive Officer

For explanation of codes following names, see page B2.
★ Indicates Type III membership in the American Hospital Association.

SCHUYLER HOSPITAL (O, 145 beds) 220 Steuben Street, Montour Falls, NY, Zip 14865–9709; tel. 607/535–7121; James B. Watson, President
Web address: www.schuylerhospital.org

Owned, leased, sponsored:	2 hospitals	304 beds
Contract-managed:	0 hospitals	0 beds
Totals:	2 hospitals	304 beds

★0984: CEDARS-SINAI HEALTH SYSTEM (NP)

8700 Beverly Boulevard, West Hollywood, CA, Zip 90048–1865, Mailing Address: Box 48750, Los Angeles, Zip 90048–0750, tel. 310/423–5000; Thomas M. Priselac, President and Chief Executive Officer
(Moderately Centralized Health System)

CALIFORNIA: CEDARS-SINAI MEDICAL CENTER (O, 885 beds) 8700 Beverly Boulevard, Los Angeles, CA, Zip 90048–1865; tel. 310/423–5000; Thomas M. Priselac, President and Chief Executive Officer
Web address: www.cedars-sinai.edu

MARINA DEL REY HOSPITAL (O, 145 beds) 4650 Lincoln Boulevard, Marina Del Rey, CA, Zip 90292–6306; tel. 310/823–8911; Paulette Heitmeyer, Administrator and Chief Operating Officer
Web address: www.marinahospital.com

TORRANCE MEMORIAL MEDICAL CENTER (O, 444 beds) 3330 Lomita Boulevard, Torrance, CA, Zip 90505–5073; tel. 310/325–9110; Craig Leach, President and Chief Executive Officer
Web address: www.torrancememorial.org

Owned, leased, sponsored:	3 hospitals	1474 beds
Contract-managed:	0 hospitals	0 beds
Totals:	3 hospitals	1474 beds

★2265: CENTRA HEALTH, INC. (NP)

1901 Tate Springs Road, Lynchburg, VA, Zip 24501–1109; tel. 434/200–3000; Andrew Mueller, M.D., President and Chief Executive Officer
(Moderately Centralized Health System)

VIRGINIA: CENTRA LYNCHBURG GENERAL HOSPITAL (O, 1029 beds) 1901 Tate Springs Road, Lynchburg, VA, Zip 24501–1109; tel. 434/200–4700; Michael Elliott, Acting Chief Executive Officer
Web address: www.centrahealth.com

CENTRA SOUTHSIDE COMMUNITY HOSPITAL (O, 86 beds) 800 Oak Street, Farmville, VA, Zip 23901–1199; tel. 434/392–8811; Thomas Angelo, Chief Executive Officer
Web address: www.sch.centrahealth.com/

Owned, leased, sponsored:	2 hospitals	1115 beds
Contract-managed:	0 hospitals	0 beds
Totals:	2 hospitals	1115 beds

★0184: CENTRACARE HEALTH (NP)

1406 Sixth Avenue North, Saint Cloud, MN, Zip 56303–1900; tel. 320/251–2700; Kenneth D. Holmen, M.D., President and Chief Executive Officer
(Moderately Centralized Health System)

MINNESOTA: CENTRACARE HEALTH-LONG PRAIRIE (O, 20 beds) 20 Ninth Street SE, Long Prairie, MN, Zip 56347–1404; tel. 320/732–2141; Daniel J. Swenson, FACHE, Administrator
Web address: www.centracare.com

CENTRACARE HEALTH-MELROSE (O, 89 beds) 525 Main Street West, Melrose, MN, Zip 56352–1043; tel. 320/256–4231; Gerry Gilbertson, FACHE, Administrator
Web address: www.centracare.com

CENTRACARE HEALTH-MONTICELLO (O, 126 beds) 1013 Hart Boulevard, Monticello, MN, Zip 55362–8230; tel. 763/295–2945; Mary Ellen Wells, FACHE, Administrator
Web address: www.centracare.com

CENTRACARE HEALTH-PAYNESVILLE (O, 66 beds) 200 West 1st Street, Paynesville, MN, Zip 56362–1496; tel. 320/243–3767; Brandon E. Pietsch, Administrator
Web address: www.centracare.com

CENTRACARE HEALTH-SAUK CENTRE (O, 85 beds) 425 North Elm Street, Sauk Centre, MN, Zip 56378–1010; tel. 320/352–2221; Delano Christianson, Administrator
Web address: www.centracare.com/hospitals/sauk_centre/index.html

RICE MEMORIAL HOSPITAL (L, 164 beds) 301 Becker Avenue SW, Willmar, MN, Zip 56201–3395; tel. 320/235–4543; Michael Schramm, Chief Executive Officer
Web address: www.ricehospital.com

ST. CLOUD HOSPITAL (O, 471 beds) 1406 Sixth Avenue North, Saint Cloud, MN, Zip 56303–1901; tel. 320/251–2700; Craig J. Broman, FACHE, President

Owned, leased, sponsored:	7 hospitals	1021 beds
Contract-managed:	0 hospitals	0 beds
Totals:	7 hospitals	1021 beds

0856: CENTRAL FLORIDA HEALTH (NP)

600 East Dixie Avenue, Leesburg, FL, Zip 34748–5925; tel. 352/323–5762; Donald G. Henderson, FACHE, Chief Executive Officer

FLORIDA: LEESBURG REGIONAL MEDICAL CENTER (O, 329 beds) 600 East Dixie Avenue, Leesburg, FL, Zip 34748–5999; tel. 352/323–5762; Donald G. Henderson, FACHE, President and Chief Executive Officer

THE VILLAGES REGIONAL HOSPITAL (O, 297 beds) 1451 El Camino Real, The Villages, FL, Zip 32159–0041; tel. 352/751–8000; Donald G. Henderson, FACHE, President and Chief Executive Officer
Web address: www.cfhalliance.org

Owned, leased, sponsored:	2 hospitals	626 beds
Contract-managed:	0 hospitals	0 beds
Totals:	2 hospitals	626 beds

1007: CENTRAL MAINE HEALTHCARE (NP)

300 Main Street, Lewiston, ME, Zip 04240–7027; tel. 207/795–0111; Jeffrey L. Brickman, FACHE, Chief Executive Officer
(Independent Hospital System)

MAINE: BRIDGTON HOSPITAL (O, 22 beds) 10 Hospital Drive, Bridgton, ME, Zip 04009–1148; tel. 207/647–6000; Peter J. Wright, FACHE, President
Web address: www.bridgtonhospital.org

CENTRAL MAINE MEDICAL CENTER (O, 190 beds) 300 Main Street, Lewiston, ME, Zip 04240–7027; tel. 207/795–0111; David Tupponce, M.D., President
Web address: www.cmmc.org

RUMFORD HOSPITAL (O, 25 beds) 420 Franklin Street, Rumford, ME, Zip 04276–2145; tel. 207/369–1000; Peter J. Wright, FACHE, President
Web address: www.rumfordhospital.org

Owned, leased, sponsored:	3 hospitals	237 beds
Contract-managed:	0 hospitals	0 beds
Totals:	3 hospitals	237 beds

1039: CHILDREN'S HEALTH (NP)

1935 Medical District Drive, Dallas, TX, Zip 75235–7701; tel. 214/456–7000; Christopher J. Durovich, President and Chief Executive Officer
(Centralized Health System)

TEXAS: CHILDREN'S MEDICAL CENTER DALLAS (O, 385 beds) 1935 Medical District Drive, Pavilion, 3rd Floor, Dallas, TX, Zip 75235–7701; tel. 214/456–7000; Christopher J. Durovich, President and Chief Executive Officer
Web address: www.childrens.com

For explanation of codes following names, see page B2.
★ Indicates Type III membership in the American Hospital Association.

CHILDREN'S MEDICAL CENTER PLANO (O, 72 beds) 7601 Preston Road, Plano, TX, Zip 75024–3214; tel. 469/303–7000; Jeremiah Radandt, President
Web address: https://www.childrens.com/location-landing/locations-and-directions/childrens-health-plano

OUR CHILDREN'S HOUSE (O, 39 beds) 1340 Empire Central Drive, Dallas, TX, Zip 75247–4022; tel. 214/867–6700; David T. Berry, President, Children's Health Clinical Operations

Owned, leased, sponsored:	3 hospitals	496 beds
Contract-managed:	0 hospitals	0 beds
Totals:	3 hospitals	496 beds

0407: CHILDREN'S HOSPITAL AND HEALTH SYSTEM (NP)
9000 West Wisconsin Avenue, Milwaukee, WI, Zip 53226–4810, Mailing Address: P.O. Box 1997, Zip 53201–1997, tel. 414/226–2000; Peggy N. Troy, President and Chief Executive Officer
(Independent Hospital System)

WISCONSIN: CHILDREN'S HOSPITAL OF WISCONSIN-FOX VALLEY (O, 19 beds) 130 Second Street, Neenah, WI, Zip 54956–2883; tel. 920/969–7900; Peggy N. Troy, President and Chief Executive Officer
Web address: www.chw.org

CHILDREN'S HOSPITAL OF WISCONSIN (O, 184 beds) 9000 West Wisconsin Avenue, Milwaukee, WI, Zip 53226–4810, Mailing Address: P.O. Box 1997, Zip 53201–1997, tel. 414/266–2000; Peggy N. Troy, President and Chief Executive Officer
Web address: www.chw.org

Owned, leased, sponsored:	2 hospitals	203 beds
Contract-managed:	0 hospitals	0 beds
Totals:	2 hospitals	203 beds

★0131: CHRISTIANA CARE HEALTH SYSTEM (NP)
501 West 14th Street, Wilmington, DE, Zip 19801–1013, Mailing Address: P.O. Box 1668, Zip 19899–1668, tel. 302/733–1000; Janice E. Nevin, M.D., M.P.H., Chief Executive Officer
(Independent Hospital System)

DELAWARE: CHRISTIANA CARE HEALTH SYSTEM (O, 1082 beds) 4755 Ogletown-Stanton Road, Newark, DE, Zip 19718–0002, Mailing Address: P.O. Box 6001, Zip 19718, tel. 302/733–1000; Janice E. Nevin, M.D., M.P.H., Chief Executive Officer
Web address: www.christianacare.org

Owned, leased, sponsored:	1 hospitals	1082 beds
Contract-managed:	0 hospitals	0 beds
Totals:	1 hospitals	1082 beds

★0192: CHRISTUS HEALTH (CC)
919 Hidden Ridge Drive, Irving, TX, Zip 75038; tel. 469/282–2000; Ernie W. Sadau, Chief Executive Officer
(Moderately Centralized Health System)

LOUISIANA: CHRISTUS COUSHATTA HEALTH CARE CENTER (O, 25 beds) 1635 Marvel Street, Coushatta, LA, Zip 71019–9022, Mailing Address: P.O. Box 589, Zip 71019–0589, tel. 318/932–2000; Brandon Hillman, R.N., Interim Administrator, Director of Hospital Services
Web address: www.christuscoushatta.org

CHRISTUS HEALTH SHREVEPORT-BOSSIER (O, 200 beds) 1453 East Bert Kouns Industrial Loop, Shreveport, LA, Zip 71105–6800; tel. 318/681–5000; Thomas S. Trawick, M.D., Chief Executive Officer

CHRISTUS OCHSNER LAKE AREA HOSPITAL (O, 88 beds) 4200 Nelson Road, Lake Charles, LA, Zip 70605–4118; tel. 337/474–6370; Kevin Holland, Chief Executive Officer, CHRISTUS Southwestern Louisiana
Web address: www.Lakeareamc.com

CHRISTUS OCHSNER ST. PATRICK HOSPITAL SOUTHWEST LOUISIANA (O, 160 beds) 524 Dr Michael Debakey Drive, Lake Charles, LA, Zip 70601–5799, Mailing Address: P.O. Box 3401, Zip 70602–3401, tel. 337/436–2511; Kevin Holland, Chief Executive Officer, CHRISTUS Southwestern Louisiana

CHRISTUS ST. FRANCES CABRINI HOSPITAL (O, 293 beds) 3330 Masonic Drive, Alexandria, LA, Zip 71301–3899; tel. 318/487–1122; Chris Karam, FACHE, President and Chief Executive Officer, Senior Vice President Group Operations
Web address: www.cabrini.org/

NATCHITOCHES REGIONAL MEDICAL CENTER (C, 91 beds) 501 Keyser Avenue, Natchitoches, LA, Zip 71457–6036, Mailing Address: P.O. Box 2009, Zip 71457–2009, tel. 318/214–4200; D. Kirk. Soileau, FACHE, Chief Executive Officer
Web address: www.nrmchospital.org

SAVOY MEDICAL CENTER (C, 180 beds) 801 Poinciana Avenue, Mamou, LA, Zip 70554–2298; tel. 337/468–5261; Eugene H. Burge Jr, Chief Executive Officer

NEW MEXICO: CHRISTUS ST. VINCENT REGIONAL MEDICAL CENTER (O, 219 beds) 455 Saint Michaels Drive, Santa Fe, NM, Zip 87505–7601, Mailing Address: P.O. Box 2107, Zip 87505, tel. 505/983–3361; Lillian Montoya, President and Chief Executive Officer
Web address: www.stvin.org

TEXAS: CHRISTUS GOOD SHEPHERD MEDICAL CENTER-MARSHALL (O, 438 beds) 811 South Washington Avenue, Marshall, TX, Zip 75670–5336, Mailing Address: P.O. Box 1599, Zip 75671–1599, tel. 903/927–6000; Todd Hancock, President and Chief Executive Officer

CHRISTUS MOTHER FRANCES HOSPITAL – JACKSONVILLE (O, 23 beds) 2026 South Jackson, Jacksonville, TX, Zip 75766–5822; tel. 903/541–4500; Anne Pileggi, Administrator and Associate Vice President
Web address: www.tmfhs.org/jacksonville

CHRISTUS MOTHER FRANCES HOSPITAL – SULPHUR SPRINGS (O, 56 beds) 115 Airport Road, Sulphur Springs, TX, Zip 75482–2105; tel. 903/885–7671; Paul Harvey, President and Chief Executive Officer

CHRISTUS MOTHER FRANCES HOSPITAL – TYLER (O, 446 beds) 800 East Dawson Street, Tyler, TX, Zip 75701–2036; tel. 903/593–8441; Jason J. Proctor, Chief Operating Officer
Web address: www.tmfhc.org

CHRISTUS MOTHER FRANCES HOSPITAL – WINNSBORO (O, 14 beds) 719 West Coke Road, Winnsboro, TX, Zip 75494–3011; tel. 903/342–5227; Paul Harvey, Chief Executive Officer
Web address: www.tmfhs.org

CHRISTUS SANTA ROSA HEALTH SYSTEM (O, 572 beds) 333 North Santa Rosa Street, San Antonio, TX, Zip 78207–3108, Mailing Address: 100 NE Loop 410 Suite 800, Zip 78216–4749, tel. 210/704–2000; Dean Alexander, President and Chief Executive Officer

CHRISTUS SOUTHEAST TEXAS HOSPITAL – ST. ELIZABETH (O, 370 beds) 2830 Calder Avenue, Beaumont, TX, Zip 77702–1809, Mailing Address: P.O. Box 5405, Zip 77726–5405, tel. 409/892–7171; Paul Trevino, Chief Executive Officer
Web address: www.christushospital.org

CHRISTUS SOUTHEAST TEXAS JASPER MEMORIAL (O, 40 beds) 1275 Marvin Hancock Drive, Jasper, TX, Zip 75951–4995; tel. 409/384–5461; Wayne Moore, Interim Administrator

CHRISTUS SPOHN HOSPITAL ALICE (O, 74 beds) 2500 East Main Street, Alice, TX, Zip 78332–4169; tel. 361/661–8000; Thomas McKinney, President
Web address: www.christusspohn.org/locations_alice.htm

CHRISTUS SPOHN HOSPITAL BEEVILLE (O, 49 beds) 1500 East Houston Street, Beeville, TX, Zip 78102–5312; tel. 361/354–2000; Genifer Rucker, President
Web address: www.christusspohn.org

CHRISTUS SPOHN HOSPITAL CORPUS CHRISTI MEMORIAL (O, 518 beds) 2606 Hospital Boulevard, Corpus Christi, TX, Zip 78405–1804, Mailing Address: P.O. Box 5280, Zip 78405, tel. 361/902–4000; Osbert Blow, M.D., Ph.D., FACS, President and Chief Medical Officer

CHRISTUS SPOHN HOSPITAL KLEBERG (O, 50 beds) 1311 General Cavazos Boulevard, Kingsville, TX, Zip 78363–7130; tel. 361/595–1661; Thomas McKinney, President
Web address: www.christusspohn.org

CHRISTUS ST. MICHAEL HEALTH SYSTEM (O, 354 beds) 2600 St Michael Drive, Texarkana, TX, Zip 75503–5220; tel. 903/614–1000; Jason Rounds, Chief Executive Officer
Web address: www.christusstmichael.org

CHRISTUS ST. MICHAEL REHABILITATION HOSPITAL (O, 50 beds) 2400 St Michael Drive, Texarkana, TX, Zip 75503–2374; tel. 903/614–4000; Patrick Flannery, Administrator

For explanation of codes following names, see page B2.
★ Indicates Type III membership in the American Hospital Association.

CHILDREN'S HOSPITAL OF SAN ANTONIO (O, 196 beds) 333 North Santa Rosa Street, San Antonio, TX, Zip 78207; tel. 210/704–2011; Cris Daskevich, Chief Executive Officer
Web address: www.chofsa.org/

KATE DISHMAN REHABILITATION HOSPITAL (O, 27 beds) 2830 Calder Street, 6th Floor, Beaumont, TX, Zip 77702–1809; tel. 409/899–8380; David Pipkins, Chief Executive Officer and Administrator

Owned, leased, sponsored:	22 hospitals	4262 beds
Contract-managed:	2 hospitals	271 beds
Totals:	24 hospitals	4533 beds

★0101: CITRUS VALLEY HEALTH PARTNERS (NP)
210 West San Bernardino Road, Covina, CA, Zip 91723–1515; tel. 626/331–7331; Robert H. Curry, President and Chief Executive Officer

CALIFORNIA: CITRUS VALLEY MEDICAL CENTER-INTER COMMUNITY CAMPUS (O, 314 beds) 210 West San Bernadino Road, Covina, CA, Zip 91723–1515, Mailing Address: P.O. Box 6108, Zip 91722–5108, tel. 626/331–7331; Robert H. Curry, President and Chief Executive Officer
Web address: www.cvhp.org

FOOTHILL PRESBYTERIAN HOSPITAL (O, 71 beds) 250 South Grand Avenue, Glendora, CA, Zip 91741–4218; tel. 626/963–8411; Robert H. Curry, President and Chief Executive Officer
Web address: www.cvhp.org/Our_Facilities/Foothill_Presbyterian.aspx

Owned, leased, sponsored:	2 hospitals	385 beds
Contract-managed:	0 hospitals	0 beds
Totals:	2 hospitals	385 beds

★0212: CLEVELAND CLINIC HEALTH SYSTEM (NP)
9500 Euclid, Cleveland, OH, Zip 44195–5108; tel. 216/444–2200; Tomislav Mihaljevic, M.D., Chief Executive Officer and President
(Centralized Health System)

FLORIDA: CLEVELAND CLINIC FLORIDA (O, 206 beds) 2950 Cleveland Clinic Boulevard, Weston, FL, Zip 33331–3602; tel. 954/659–5000; Wael Barsoum, M.D., President
Web address: www.clevelandclinic.org/florida

CLEVELAND CLINIC INDIAN RIVER HOSPITAL (O, 220 beds) 1000 36th Street, Vero Beach, FL, Zip 32960–6592; tel. 772/567–4311; Gregory Rosencrance, Chief Executive Officer
Web address: https://www.indianrivermedicalcenter.com/

CLEVELAND CLINIC MARTIN NORTH HOSPITAL (O, 509 beds) 200 SE Hospital Avenue, Stuart, FL, Zip 34994–2346, Mailing Address: P.O. Box 9010, Zip 34995–9010, tel. 772/287–5200; Robert L. Lord, JD, President and Chief Executive Officer

OHIO: CLEVELAND CLINIC AKRON GENERAL LODI HOSPITAL (O, 20 beds) 225 Elyria Street, Lodi, OH, Zip 44254–1096; tel. 330/948–1222; Dana Kocsis, Vice President, Nursing and Operations
Web address: www.lodihospital.org

CLEVELAND CLINIC AKRON GENERAL (O, 482 beds) 1 Akron General Avenue, Akron, OH, Zip 44307–2433; tel. 330/344–6000; Brian J. Harte, M.D., President

CLEVELAND CLINIC AVON HOSPITAL (O, 126 beds) 33300 Cleveland Clinic Boulevard, Avon, OH, Zip 44011; tel. 440/695–5000; Rebecca Starck, M.D., President
Web address: www.my.clevelandclinic.org

CLEVELAND CLINIC CHILDREN'S HOSPITAL FOR REHABILITATION (O, 25 beds) 2801 Martin Luther King Jr Drive, Cleveland, OH, Zip 44104–3865; tel. 216/448–6400; Michelle Marks, D.O., Medical Director
Web address: www.my.clevelandclinic.org/childrens-hospital/default.aspx

CLEVELAND CLINIC FAIRVIEW HOSPITAL (O, 460 beds) 18101 Lorain Avenue, Cleveland, OH, Zip 44111–5656; tel. 216/476–7000; Neil Smith, D.O., President
Web address: www.fairviewhospital.org

CLEVELAND CLINIC UNION HOSPITAL (O, 139 beds) 659 Boulevard, Dover, OH, Zip 44622–2077; tel. 330/343–3311; Bruce James, President and Chief Executive Officer
Web address: www.unionhospital.org

CLEVELAND CLINIC, MEDINA HOSPITAL (O, 143 beds) 1000 East Washington Street, Medina, OH, Zip 44256–2170; tel. 330/725–1000; Richard K. Shewbridge, President
Web address: www.medinahospital.org

CLEVELAND CLINIC (O, 1294 beds) 9500 Euclid Avenue, Cleveland, OH, Zip 44195–5108; tel. 216/444–2200; Tomislav Mihaljevic, M.D., President and Chief Executive Officer

EDWIN SHAW REHAB (O, 35 beds) 330 Broadway Street East, Cuyahoga Falls, OH, Zip 44221–3312; tel. 330/436–0910; Geoffrey Hall, Chief Executive Officer
Web address: www.edwinshaw.com

EUCLID HOSPITAL (O, 165 beds) 18901 Lake Shore Boulevard, Euclid, OH, Zip 44119–1090; tel. 216/531–9000; Daniel Napierkowski, M.D., President
Web address: www.euclidhospital.org

HILLCREST HOSPITAL (O, 440 beds) 6780 Mayfield Road, Cleveland, OH, Zip 44124–2203; tel. 440/312–4500; Richard Parker, M.D., President, Hillcrest Hospital
Web address: www.hillcresthospital.org

LUTHERAN HOSPITAL (O, 194 beds) 1730 West 25th Street, Cleveland, OH, Zip 44113–3170; tel. 216/696–4300; Donald A. Malone Jr, President

MARYMOUNT HOSPITAL (O, 277 beds) 12300 McCracken Road, Garfield Heights, OH, Zip 44125–2975; tel. 216/581–0500; Daniel Napierkowski, M.D., President
Web address: www.marymount.org

SOUTH POINTE HOSPITAL (O, 172 beds) 20000 Harvard Road, Warrensville Heights, OH, Zip 44122–6805; tel. 216/491–6000; Margaret McKenzie, M.D., President

Owned, leased, sponsored:	17 hospitals	4907 beds
Contract-managed:	0 hospitals	0 beds
Totals:	17 hospitals	4907 beds

0076: COLLEGE HEALTH ENTERPRISES (IO)
11627 Telegraph Road, Suite 200, Santa Fe Springs, CA, Zip 90670–6814; tel. 562/923–9449; Barry J. Weiss, Chairman of the Board

CALIFORNIA: COLLEGE HOSPITAL CERRITOS (O, 187 beds) 10802 College Place, Cerritos, CA, Zip 90703–1579; tel. 562/924–9581; Stephen Witt, President and Chief Executive Officer

COLLEGE HOSPITAL COSTA MESA (O, 122 beds) 301 Victoria Street, Costa Mesa, CA, Zip 92627–7131; tel. 949/642–2734; Susan L. Taylor, JD, Chief Executive Officer
Web address: www.collegehospitals.com/cosHome

Owned, leased, sponsored:	2 hospitals	309 beds
Contract-managed:	0 hospitals	0 beds
Totals:	2 hospitals	309 beds

0161: COLUMBUS REGIONAL HEALTHCARE SYSTEM (NP)
707 Center Street, Suite 400, Columbus, GA, Zip 31901–1575; tel. 706/660–6100; M. Scott. Hill, Chief Executive Officer
(Independent Hospital System)

GEORGIA: AZALEA TRACE (O, 110 beds) 910 Talbotton Road, Columbus, GA, Zip 31901; tel. 706/323–9513; Todd West, Administrator

HAMILTON HOUSE NURSING CENTER/ADULT LIVING CENTER (O, 128 beds) 1911 Hamilton Road, Columbus, GA, Zip 31901; tel. 706/571–1850; John Sims, Administrator

MARION MEMORIAL NURSING HOME (O, 70 beds) Highway 41, Buena Vista, GA, Zip 31803, Mailing Address: P.O. Box 197, Zip 31803, tel. 229/649–7100; Barbara Mitchell, Administrator

Owned, leased, sponsored:	3 hospitals	308 beds
Contract-managed:	0 hospitals	0 beds
Totals:	3 hospitals	308 beds

For explanation of codes following names, see page B2.
★ Indicates Type III membership in the American Hospital Association.

Section B

★0948: COMMONSPIRIT HEALTH (CC)
444 West Lake Street Suite 2500, Chicago, IL, Zip 60606–0097; tel. 312/741–7000; Lloyd H. Dean, Chief Executive Officer

ARIZONA: CHANDLER REGIONAL MEDICAL CENTER (O, 338 beds) 1955 West Frye Road, Chandler, AZ, Zip 85224–6282; tel. 480/728–3000; Mark F. Slyter, FACHE, President and Chief Operating Officer
Web address: www.chandlerregional.com

DIGNITY HEALTH ARIZONA GENERAL HOSPITAL (O, 16 beds) 7171 South 51st Avenue, Laveen, AZ, Zip 85339–2923; tel. 623/584–5100; Mark F. Slyter, FACHE, President and Chief Executive Officer, East Valley
Web address: www.dignityhealth.org/arizonageneral/

MERCY GILBERT MEDICAL CENTER (S, 198 beds) 3555 South Val Vista Road, Gilbert, AZ, Zip 85297–7323; tel. 480/728–8000; Mark F. Slyter, FACHE, President and Chief Operating Officer

ST. JOSEPH'S HOSPITAL AND MEDICAL CENTER (S, 574 beds) 350 West Thomas Road, Phoenix, AZ, Zip 85013–4496, Mailing Address: P.O. Box 2071, Zip 85001–2071, tel. 602/406–3000; Patty White, R.N., MS, President
Web address: www.stjosephs-phx.org

ARKANSAS: CHI ST. VINCENT HOT SPRINGS (O, 241 beds) 300 Werner Street, Hot Springs, AR, Zip 71913–6406; tel. 501/622–1000; Douglas B. Ross, President
Web address: www.chistvincent.com/Hospitals/st-vincent-hot-springs

CHI ST. VINCENT INFIRMARY MEDICAL CENTER (S, 355 beds) Two St Vincent Circle, Little Rock, AR, Zip 72205–5499; tel. 501/552–3000; Chris Stines, President
Web address: www.chistvincent.com/

CHI ST. VINCENT MEDICAL CENTER-NORTH (S, 68 beds) 2215 Wildwood Avenue, Sherwood, AR, Zip 72120–5089; tel. 501/552–7100; Chris Stines, President

CHI ST. VINCENT MORRILTON (S, 25 beds) 4 Hospital Drive, Morrilton, AR, Zip 72110–4510; tel. 501/977–2300; Leslie Arnold, Chief Executive Officer and Administrator
Web address: www.chistvincent.com/Hospitals/st-vincent-morrilton

CALIFORNIA: BAKERSFIELD MEMORIAL HOSPITAL (O, 401 beds) 420 34th Street, Bakersfield, CA, Zip 93301–2237; tel. 661/327–1792; Ken Keller, President and Chief Executive Officer

CALIFORNIA HOSPITAL MEDICAL CENTER (O, 318 beds) 1401 South Grand Avenue, Los Angeles, CA, Zip 90015–3010; tel. 213/748–2411; Margaret R. Peterson, Ph.D., R.N., President
Web address: www.chmcla.org

COMMUNITY HOSPITAL OF SAN BERNARDINO (O, 379 beds) 1805 Medical Center Drive, San Bernardino, CA, Zip 92411–1214; tel. 909/887–6333; June Collison, President
Web address: www.dignityhealth.org/san-bernardino

DOMINICAN HOSPITAL (S, 223 beds) 1555 Soquel Drive, Santa Cruz, CA, Zip 95065–1794; tel. 831/462–7700; Nanette Mickiewicz, M.D., President

FRENCH HOSPITAL MEDICAL CENTER (O, 72 beds) 1911 Johnson Avenue, San Luis Obispo, CA, Zip 93401–4197; tel. 805/543–5353; Alan Iftiniuk, Chief Executive Officer
Web address: www.frenchmedicalcenter.org

GLENDALE MEMORIAL HOSPITAL AND HEALTH CENTER (O, 334 beds) 1420 South Central Avenue, Glendale, CA, Zip 91204–2594; tel. 818/502–1900; Jill Welton, President and Chief Executive Officer

MARIAN REGIONAL MEDICAL CENTER (S, 286 beds) 1400 East Church Street, Santa Maria, CA, Zip 93454–5906; tel. 805/739–3000; Kerin A. Mase, President and Chief Executive Officer
Web address: www.marianmedicalcenter.org

MARK TWAIN MEDICAL CENTER (O, 25 beds) 768 Mountain Ranch Road, San Andreas, CA, Zip 95249–9998; tel. 209/754–3521; Robert Diehl, President

MERCY GENERAL HOSPITAL (S, 305 beds) 4001 'J' Street, Sacramento, CA, Zip 95819–3600; tel. 916/453–4545; Edmundo Castaneda, President
Web address: www.mercygeneral.org

MERCY HOSPITAL of FOLSOM (S, 106 beds) 1650 Creekside Drive, Folsom, CA, Zip 95630–3400; tel. 916/983–7400; Randall W. Ross, FACHE, President and Chief Executive Officer

MERCY HOSPITALS OF BAKERSFIELD (S, 204 beds) 2215 Truxtun Avenue, Bakersfield, CA, Zip 93301–3698, Mailing Address: P.O. Box 119, Zip 93302–0119, tel. 661/632–5000; Bruce Peters, Chief Executive Officer
Web address: www.mercybakersfield.org

MERCY MEDICAL CENTER MERCED (S, 186 beds) 333 Mercy Avenue, Merced, CA, Zip 95340–8319; tel. 209/564–5000; Charles Kassis, President
Web address: www.mercymercedcares.org

MERCY MEDICAL CENTER MOUNT SHASTA (S, 33 beds) 914 Pine Street, Mount Shasta, CA, Zip 96067–2143; tel. 530/926–6111; Rodger Page, President
Web address: www.mercymtshasta.org

MERCY MEDICAL CENTER REDDING (S, 267 beds) 2175 Rosaline Avenue, Redding, CA, Zip 96001–2549, Mailing Address: P.O. Box 496009, Zip 96049–6009, tel. 530/225–6000; G. Todd. Smith, Chief Executive Officer
Web address: www.mercy.org

MERCY SAN JUAN MEDICAL CENTER (S, 340 beds) 6501 Coyle Avenue, Carmichael, CA, Zip 95608–0306; tel. 916/537–5000; Michael Korpiel, FACHE, Chief Executive Officer

METHODIST HOSPITAL OF SACRAMENTO (O, 329 beds) 7500 Hospital Drive, Sacramento, CA, Zip 95823–5477; tel. 916/423–3000; Phyllis Baltz, Chief Executive Officer
Web address: www.methodistsacramento.org

NORTHRIDGE HOSPITAL MEDICAL CENTER (O, 394 beds) 18300 Roscoe Boulevard, Northridge, CA, Zip 91328–4167; tel. 818/885–8500; Paul Watkins, JD, President

SAINT FRANCIS MEMORIAL HOSPITAL (O, 239 beds) 900 Hyde Street, San Francisco, CA, Zip 94109–4899, Mailing Address: P.O. Box 7726, Zip 94120–7726, tel. 415/353–6000; David G. Klein, M.D., President
Web address: www.saintfrancismemorial.org

SEQUOIA HOSPITAL (O, 114 beds) 170 Alameda De Las Pulgas, Redwood City, CA, Zip 94062–2799; tel. 650/369–5811; Bill Graham, President

SIERRA NEVADA MEMORIAL HOSPITAL (O, 104 beds) 155 Glasson Way, Grass Valley, CA, Zip 95945–5723, Mailing Address: P.O. Box 1029, Zip 95945–1029, tel. 530/274–6000; Brian Evans Esq, M.D., President and Chief Executive Officer
Web address: www.snmh.org

ST. BERNARDINE MEDICAL CENTER (S, 342 beds) 2101 North Waterman Avenue, San Bernardino, CA, Zip 92404–4855; tel. 909/883–8711; Douglas V. Kleam, President
Web address: www.stbernardinemedicalcenter.com

ST. ELIZABETH COMMUNITY HOSPITAL (S, 65 beds) 2550 Sister Mary Columba Drive, Red Bluff, CA, Zip 96080–4397; tel. 530/529–8000; Jordan Wright, Chief Executive Officer

ST. JOHN'S PLEASANT VALLEY HOSPITAL (S, 127 beds) 2309 Antonio Avenue, Camarillo, CA, Zip 93010–1414; tel. 805/389–5800; Darren W. Lee, President and Chief Executive Officer
Web address: www.dignityhealth.org/pleasantvalley

ST. JOHN'S REGIONAL MEDICAL CENTER (S, 139 beds) 1600 North Rose Avenue, Oxnard, CA, Zip 93030–3723; tel. 805/988–2500; Darren W. Lee, President and Chief Executive Officer
Web address: www.stjohnshealth.org

ST. JOSEPH'S BEHAVIORAL HEALTH CENTER (S, 35 beds) 2510 North California Street, Stockton, CA, Zip 95204–5568; tel. 209/461–2000; Paul Rains, R.N., MSN, President
Web address: www.stjosephscanhelp.org

ST. JOSEPH'S MEDICAL CENTER (S, 273 beds) 1800 North California Street, Stockton, CA, Zip 95204–6019, Mailing Address: P.O. Box 213008, Zip 95213–9008, tel. 209/943–2000; Donald J. Wiley, President and Chief Executive Officer
Web address: www.stjosephsCARES.org

ST. MARY MEDICAL CENTER (S, 302 beds) 1050 Linden Avenue, Long Beach, CA, Zip 90813–3321, Mailing Address: P.O. Box 887, Zip 90801–0887, tel. 562/491–9000; Carolyn P. Caldwell, FACHE, President and Chief Executive Officer

ST. MARY'S MEDICAL CENTER (S, 232 beds) 450 Stanyan Street, San Francisco, CA, Zip 94117–1079; tel. 415/668–1000; John P. Allen, President
Web address: www.stmarysmedicalcenter.com

WOODLAND HEALTHCARE (O, 108 beds) 1325 Cottonwood Street, Woodland, CA, Zip 95695–5199; tel. 530/662–3961; H Kevin. Vaziri, President
Web address: www.woodlandhealthcare.org

COLORADO: LONGMONT UNITED HOSPITAL (S, 131 beds) 1950 West Mountain View Avenue, Longmont, CO, Zip 80501–3162, Mailing Address: P.O. Box 1659, Zip 80502–1659, tel. 303/651–5111; Christina Johnson, M.D., Chief Executive Officer

For explanation of codes following names, see page B2.
★ Indicates Type III membership in the American Hospital Association.

MERCY REGIONAL MEDICAL CENTER (S, 82 beds) 1010 Three Springs Boulevard, Durango, CO, Zip 81301–8296; tel. 970/247–4311; William McConnell, Ph.D., President and Chief Executive Officer
Web address: www.mercydurango.org

ORTHOCOLORADO HOSPITAL (O, 48 beds) 11650 West 2nd Place, Lakewood, CO, Zip 80228–1527; tel. 720/321–5000; Jude Torchia, Chief Executive Officer
Web address: www.orthocolorado.org

PENROSE-ST. FRANCIS HEALTH SERVICES (S, 444 beds) 2222 North Nevada Avenue, Colorado Springs, CO, Zip 80907–6799; tel. 719/776–5000; Brian Erling, Interim Chief Executive Officer

ST. ANTHONY HOSPITAL (S, 219 beds) 11600 West Second Place, Lakewood, CO, Zip 80228–1527; tel. 720/321–0000; Peter Powers, Chief Executive Officer
Web address: www.stanthonyhosp.org

ST. ANTHONY NORTH HEALTH CAMPUS (S, 100 beds) 14300 Orchard Parkway, Westminster, CO, Zip 80023–9206; tel. 720/627–0000; Kevin Jenkins, President and Chief Executive Officer
Web address: www.stanthonynorth.org

ST. ANTHONY SUMMIT MEDICAL CENTER (S, 34 beds) 340 Peak One Drive, Frisco, CO, Zip 80443, Mailing Address: P.O. Box 738, Zip 80443–0738, tel. 970/668–3300; Lee Boyles, Chief Executive Officer

ST. MARY-CORWIN MEDICAL CENTER (S, 125 beds) 1008 Minnequa Avenue, Pueblo, CO, Zip 81004–3798; tel. 719/557–4000; Michael Cafasso, Chief Executive Officer
Web address: www.stmarycorwin.org

ST. THOMAS MORE HOSPITAL (S, 25 beds) 1338 Phay Avenue, Canon City, CO, Zip 81212–2302; tel. 719/285–2000; Kristi Olson, Chief Executive Officer

GEORGIA: CHI MEMORIAL HOSPITAL – GEORGIA (O, 35 beds) 100 Gross Crescent Circle, Fort Oglethorpe, GA, Zip 30742–3669; tel. 706/858–2000; Angie Hullander, Administrator and Special Operations
Web address: www.memorial.org/chi-memorial-hospital-georgia

IOWA: CHI HEALTH MERCY CORNING (S, 22 beds) 603 Rosary Drive, Corning, IA, Zip 50841–1683; tel. 641/322–3121; Lisa Wolfe, President
Web address: www.alegent.com

CHI HEALTH MERCY COUNCIL BLUFFS (S, 148 beds) 800 Mercy Drive, Council Bluffs, IA, Zip 51503–3128; tel. 712/328–5000; Ann Schumacher, R.N., MSN, FACHE, President
Web address: www.chihealth.com/chi-health-mercy-council-bluffs

CHI HEALTH MISSOURI VALLEY (S, 16 beds) 631 North Eighth Street, Missouri Valley, IA, Zip 51555–1102; tel. 712/642–2784; Jonathan Moe, President
Web address: www.chihealth.com/chi-health-missouri-valley

KNOXVILLE HOSPITAL & CLINICS (C, 25 beds) 1002 South Lincoln Street, Knoxville, IA, Zip 50138–3155; tel. 641/842–2151; Kevin Kincaid, Chief Executive Officer

MADISON COUNTY HEALTH CARE SYSTEM (C, 25 beds) 300 West Hutchings Street, Winterset, IA, Zip 50273–2109; tel. 515/462–2373; Marcia Hendricks, FACHE, R.N., Chief Executive Officer
Web address: www.madisonhealth.com

MERCY MEDICAL CENTER-DES MOINES (S, 525 beds) 1111 6th Avenue, Des Moines, IA, Zip 50314–2611; tel. 515/247–3121; Karl Keeler, President

MERCYONE CENTERVILLE MEDICAL CENTER (S, 44 beds) 1 St Joseph's Drive, Centerville, IA, Zip 52544–8055; tel. 641/437–4111; Matthew Johnson, President
Web address: www.mercycenterville.org

MERCYONE NEWTON MEDICAL CENTER (O, 26 beds) 204 North Fourth Avenue East, Newton, IA, Zip 50208–3100; tel. 641/792–1273; Laurie A. Conner, FACHE, President
Web address: www.skiffmed.com

KANSAS: BOB WILSON MEMORIAL GRANT COUNTY HOSPITAL (O, 26 beds) 415 North Main Street, Ulysses, KS, Zip 67880–2133; tel. 620/356–1266; Amanda Vaughan, Interim Administrator
Web address: www.bwmgch.com

ST. CATHERINE HOSPITAL (S, 100 beds) 401 East Spruce Street, Garden City, KS, Zip 67846–5679; tel. 620/272–2561; Scott J. Taylor, President and Chief Executive Officer

KENTUCKY: CHI FLAGET MEMORIAL HOSPITAL (S, 42 beds) 4305 New Shepherdsville Road, Bardstown, KY, Zip 40004–9019; tel. 502/350–5000; Jennifer Nolan, President and Chief Executive Officer
Web address: www.kentuckyonehealth.org/flaget

CHI OUR LADY OF PEACE (O, 220 beds) 2020 Newburg Road, Louisville, KY, Zip 40205–1879; tel. 502/479–4500; Jennifer Nolan, President and Chief Executive Officer
Web address: www.kentuckyonehealth.org/our-lady-of-peace

CHI SAINT JOSEPH BEREA (S, 25 beds) 305 Estill Street, Berea, KY, Zip 40403–1909; tel. 859/986–3151; Terrence G. Deis, CPA, FACHE, President

CHI SAINT JOSEPH EAST (S, 150 beds) 150 North Eagle Creek Drive, Lexington, KY, Zip 40509–1805; tel. 859/967–5000; Eric Gilliam, President
Web address: www.sjhlex.org

CHI SAINT JOSEPH HEALTH (S, 307 beds) One St Joseph Drive, Lexington, KY, Zip 40504–3754; tel. 859/278–3436; Bruce J. Tassin, President
Web address: www.sjhlex.org

CHI SAINT JOSEPH LONDON (S, 116 beds) 1001 Saint Joseph Lane, London, KY, Zip 40741–8345; tel. 606/330–6000; Terrence G. Deis, CPA, FACHE, President
Web address: www.saintjosephhealthsystem.org

CONTINUING CARE HOSPITAL (S, 43 beds) 1 Saint Joseph Drive, Lexington, KY, Zip 40504–3742; tel. 859/967–5744; Robert C. Desotelle, President and Chief Executive Officer

JEWISH HOSPITAL-SHELBYVILLE (S, 30 beds) 727 Hospital Drive, Shelbyville, KY, Zip 40065–1699; tel. 502/647–4000; Annessa Baker, Site Executive and Chief Nursing Officer
Web address: www.kentuckyonehealth.org/jewish-hospital-shelbyville

JEWISH HOSPITAL (O, 421 beds) 200 Abraham Flexner Way, Louisville, KY, Zip 40202–1886; tel. 502/587–4011; Deborah M. Lee-Eddie, Interim President and Chief Executive Officer

SAINT JOSEPH MOUNT STERLING (S, 42 beds) 225 Falcon Drive, Mount Sterling, KY, Zip 40353–1158, Mailing Address: P.O. Box 7, Zip 40353–0007, tel. 859/497–5000; Terrence G. Deis, CPA, FACHE, President
Web address: www.sjhlex.org

STS. MARY & ELIZABETH HOSPITAL (O, 170 beds) 1850 Bluegrass Avenue, Louisville, KY, Zip 40215–1199; tel. 502/361–6000; Charles Powell, President

TAYLOR REGIONAL HOSPITAL (C, 90 beds) 1700 Old Lebanon Road, Campbellsville, KY, Zip 42718–9600; tel. 270/465–3561; Jane Wheatley, Chief Executive Officer
Web address: www.trhosp.org

MINNESOTA: CHI LAKEWOOD HEALTH (S, 55 beds) 600 Main Avenue South, Baudette, MN, Zip 56623–2855; tel. 218/634–2120; Benjamin Koppelman, Interim President
Web address: www.lakewoodhealthcenter.org

CHI ST. FRANCIS HEALTH (S, 105 beds) 2400 St Francis Drive, Breckenridge, MN, Zip 56520–1026; tel. 218/643–3000; David A. Nelson, President and Chief Executive Officer
Web address: www.sfcare.org

CHI ST. GABRIEL'S HEALTH (S, 25 beds) 815 Second Street SE, Little Falls, MN, Zip 56345–3596; tel. 320/632–5441; Lee Boyles, President
Web address: www.stgabriels.com

CHI ST. JOSEPH'S HEALTH (S, 25 beds) 600 Pleasant Avenue, Park Rapids, MN, Zip 56470–1431; tel. 218/732–3311; Benjamin Koppelman, President
Web address: www.sjahs.org

NEBRASKA: CHI HEALTH CREIGHTON UNIVERSITY MEDICAL CENTER – BERGAN MERCY (S, 361 beds) 7500 Mercy Road, Omaha, NE, Zip 68124–2319; tel. 402/398–6060; Marie E. Knedler, R.N., FACHE, Interim President
Web address: www.chihealth.com/chi-health-bergan-mercy

CHI HEALTH GOOD SAMARITAN (S, 218 beds) 10 East 31st Street, Kearney, NE, Zip 68847–2926, Mailing Address: P.O. Box 1990, Zip 68848–1990, tel. 308/865–7100; Michael H. Schnieders, FACHE, President

CHI HEALTH IMMANUEL (S, 269 beds) 6901 North 72nd Street, Omaha, NE, Zip 68122–1799; tel. 402/572–2121; Ann Schumacher, R.N., MSN, FACHE, President
Web address: www.alegent.com/immanuel

CHI HEALTH LAKESIDE (S, 137 beds) 6901 N 72nd St, Omaha, NE, Zip 68122, Mailing Address: 16901 Lakeside Hills Court, Zip 68130–2318, tel. 402/717–8000; Kevin Miller, President

CHI HEALTH MIDLANDS (S, 28 beds) 11111 South 84th Street, Papillion, NE, Zip 68046–4122; tel. 402/593–3000; Kevin Miller, President
Web address: www.CHIhealth.com

For explanation of codes following names, see page B2.
★ Indicates Type III membership in the American Hospital Association.

Section B

CHI HEALTH NEBRASKA HEART (S, 54 beds) 7500 South 91st Street, Lincoln, NE, Zip 68526–9437; tel. 402/327–2700; Derek Vance, President

CHI HEALTH PLAINVIEW (S, 15 beds) 704 North Third Street, Plainview, NE, Zip 68769–2047, Mailing Address: P.O. Box 489, Zip 68769–0489, tel. 402/582–4245; Gregory Beckmann, Regional President
Web address: www.alegentcreighton.com/plainview-hospital

CHI HEALTH SAINT FRANCIS (S, 159 beds) 2620 West Faidley Avenue, Grand Island, NE, Zip 68803–4297, Mailing Address: P.O. Box 9804, Zip 68802–9804, tel. 308/384–4600; Edward J. Hannon, FACHE, President

CHI HEALTH SCHUYLER (S, 25 beds) 104 West 17th Street, Schuyler, NE, Zip 68661–1304; tel. 402/352–2441; Connie Peters, R.N., President
Web address: www.alegent.org

CHI HEALTH ST ELIZABETH (S, 258 beds) 555 South 70th Street, Lincoln, NE, Zip 68510–2494; tel. 402/219–8000; Derek Vance, President

CHI HEALTH ST. MARY'S (S, 18 beds) 1301 Grundman Boulevard, Nebraska City, NE, Zip 68410; tel. 402/873–3321; Daniel DeFreece, M.D., Interim President
Web address: www.chihealthstmarys.com

NEVADA: ST. ROSE DOMINICAN HOSPITALS – ROSE DE LIMA CAMPUS (S, 110 beds) 102 East Lake Mead Parkway, Henderson, NV, Zip 89015–5524; tel. 702/616–5000; Teressa Conley, President and Chief Executive Officer

ST. ROSE DOMINICAN HOSPITALS – SAN MARTIN CAMPUS (O, 147 beds) 8280 West Warm Springs Road, Las Vegas, NV, Zip 89113–3612; tel. 702/492–8000; Lawrence Barnard, President and Chief Executive Officer
Web address: www.strosehospitals.org

ST. ROSE DOMINICAN HOSPITALS – SIENA CAMPUS (S, 326 beds) 3001 St Rose Parkway, Henderson, NV, Zip 89052; tel. 702/616–5000; Eugene Bassett, President and Chief Executive Officer

NORTH DAKOTA: CHI LISBON HEALTH (S, 25 beds) 905 Main Street, Lisbon, ND, Zip 58054–4334, Mailing Address: P.O. Box 353, Zip 58054–0353, tel. 701/683–6400; Peggy Reinke, R.N., Administrator
Web address: www.lisbonhospital.com

CHI MERCY HEALTH (S, 19 beds) 570 Chautauqua Boulevard, Valley City, ND, Zip 58072–3199; tel. 701/845–6400; Keith E. Heuser, Market President
Web address: www.mercyhospitalvalleycity.org

CHI OAKES HOSPITAL (S, 20 beds) 1200 North Seventh Street, Oakes, ND, Zip 58474–2502; tel. 701/742–3291; Becki Thompson, President

CHI ST ALEXIUS HEALTH CARRINGTON MEDICAL CENTER (S, 25 beds) 800 North Fourth Street, Carrington, ND, Zip 58421–1217, Mailing Address: P.O. Box 461, Zip 58421–0461, tel. 701/652–3141; Mariann Doeling, R.N., President
Web address: www.carringtonhealthcenter.org

CHI ST. ALEXIUS HEALTH – DICKINSON MEDICAL CENTER (S, 25 beds) 2500 Fairway Street, Dickinson, ND, Zip 58601–4399; tel. 701/456–4000; Reed Reyman, President
Web address: www.stjoeshospital.org

CHI ST. ALEXIUS HEALTH – WILLISTON MEDICAL CENTER (S, 25 beds) 1301 15th Avenue West, Williston, ND, Zip 58801–3896; tel. 701/774–7400; Dan Bjerknes, Market Leader
Web address: www.mercy-williston.org

CHI ST. ALEXIUS HEALTH DEVILS LAKE HOSPITAL (S, 25 beds) 1031 Seventh Street NE, Devils Lake, ND, Zip 58301–2798; tel. 701/662–2131; Andrew Lankowicz, FACHE, President

CHI ST. ALEXIUS HEALTH GARRISON (O, 50 beds) 407 Third Avenue SE, Garrison, ND, Zip 58540–7235; tel. 701/463–2275; Tod Graeber, Administrator
Web address: www.garrisonmh.com

CHI ST. ALEXIUS HEALTH (O, 237 beds) 900 East Broadway, Bismarck, ND, Zip 58501–4586, Mailing Address: P.O. Box 5510, Zip 58506–5510, tel. 701/530–7000; Kurt Schley, Market Chief Executive Officer

COMMUNITY MEMORIAL HOSPITAL (O, 25 beds) 220 Fifth Avenue, Turtle Lake, ND, Zip 58575–4005, Mailing Address: P.O. Box 280, Zip 58575–0280, tel. 701/448–2331; Tod Graeber, Administrator
Web address: www.wrtc.com/cullum/hospital

OHIO: GOOD SAMARITAN HOSPITAL (S, 423 beds) 375 Dixmyth Avenue, Cincinnati, OH, Zip 45220–2489; tel. 513/862–1400; Jamie Easterling, Executive Director, Operations

PROVIDENCE CARE CENTER (O, 138 beds) 2025 Hayes Avenue, Sandusky, OH, Zip 44870; Rick G. Ryan, Administrator and Chief Executive Officer

TRINITY HEALTH SYSTEM (O, 277 beds) 380 Summit Avenue, Steubenville, OH, Zip 43952–2699; tel. 740/283–7000; Matthew Grimshaw, Market Chief Executive Officer
Web address: www.trinityhealth.com

TRINITY HOSPITAL TWIN CITY (O, 12 beds) 819 North First Street, Dennison, OH, Zip 44621–1098; tel. 740/922–2800; Teresa Gagliardi, R.N., Vice President of Hospital Operations and Site Administrator
Web address: www.trinitytwincity.org

OREGON: CHI ST. ANTHONY HOSPITAL (S, 25 beds) 2801 St Anthony Way, Pendleton, OR, Zip 97801–3800; tel. 541/276–5121; Harold S. Geller, Chief Executive Officer

MERCY MEDICAL CENTER (S, 140 beds) 2700 Stewart Parkway, Roseburg, OR, Zip 97471–1281; tel. 541/673–0611; Kelly C. Morgan, President and Chief Executive Officer
Web address: www.mercyrose.org

TENNESSEE: CHI MEMORIAL (S, 405 beds) 2525 De Sales Avenue, Chattanooga, TN, Zip 37404–1161; tel. 423/495–2525; Janelle Reilly, Chief Executive Officer
Web address: www.memorial.org

TEXAS: BAYLOR ST. LUKE'S MEDICAL CENTER MCNAIR CAMPUS (O, 256 beds) One Baylor Plaza, BCM 100, Houston, TX, Zip 77030–3411; tel. 713/798–4951; Gay Nord, President
Web address: www.bcm.edu

BAYLOR ST. LUKE'S MEDICAL CENTER (O, 615 beds) 6720 Bertner Avenue, Houston, TX, Zip 77030–2697, Mailing Address: P.O. Box 20269, Zip 77225–0269, tel. 832/355–1000; T Douglas. Lawson, Ph.D., FACHE, Chief Executive Officer

CHI ST. JOSEPH HEALTH BELLVILLE HOSPITAL (O, 10 beds) 44 North Cummings Street, Bellville, TX, Zip 77418–1347, Mailing Address: P.O. Box 977, Zip 77418–0977, tel. 979/413–7400; Theron Park, Chief Executive Officer
Web address: www.chistjoseph.org/

CHI ST. JOSEPH HEALTH BURLESON HOSPITAL (O, 12 beds) 1101 Woodson Drive, Caldwell, TX, Zip 77836–1052, Mailing Address: P.O. Box 360, Zip 77836–0360, tel. 979/567–3245; Theron Park, Chief Executive Officer
Web address: www.chistjoseph.org/

CHI ST. JOSEPH HEALTH GRIMES HOSPITAL (O, 18 beds) 210 South Judson Street, Navasota, TX, Zip 77868–3704; tel. 936/825–6585; Theron Park, Chief Executive Officer

CHI ST. JOSEPH HEALTH MADISON HOSPITAL (O, 25 beds) 100 West Cross Street, Madisonville, TX, Zip 77864–2432, Mailing Address: Box 698, Zip 77864–0698, tel. 936/348–2631; Theron Park, Chief Executive Officer
Web address: www.st-joseph.org

CHI ST. JOSEPH REGIONAL HEALTH CENTER (O, 222 beds) 2801 Franciscan Drive, Bryan, TX, Zip 77802–2599; tel. 979/776–3777; Theron Park, Chief Executive Officer
Web address: www.st-joseph.org

CHI ST. LUKE'S HEALTH – PATIENTS MEDICAL CENTER (O, 61 beds) 4600 East Sam Houston Parkway South, Pasadena, TX, Zip 77505–3948; tel. 713/948–7000; Steven Foster, Chief Executive Officer

CHI ST. LUKE'S HEALTH BRAZOSPORT (O, 103 beds) 100 Medical Drive, Lake Jackson, TX, Zip 77566–5674; tel. 979/297–4411; Al Guevara Jr, FACHE, President
Web address: www.chistlukesbrazosport.org

CHI ST. LUKE'S HEALTH MEMORIAL LIVINGSTON (O, 66 beds) 1717 Highway 59 Bypass, Livingston, TX, Zip 77351–1257, Mailing Address: P.O. Box 1257, Zip 77351–0022, tel. 936/329–8700; Kristi Froese, R.N., Vice President Clinical Operations
Web address: www.memorialhealth.org

CHI ST. LUKE'S HEALTH MEMORIAL LUFKIN (O, 194 beds) 1201 West Frank Avenue, Lufkin, TX, Zip 75904–3357, Mailing Address: P.O. Box 1447, Zip 75902–1447, tel. 936/634–8111; Monte J. Bostwick, Market Chief Executive Officer
Web address: www.memorialhealth.us/centers/lufkin

CHI ST. LUKE'S HEALTH MEMORIAL SAN AUGUSTINE (O, 9 beds) 511 East Hospital Street, San Augustine, TX, Zip 75972–2121, Mailing Address: P.O. Box 658, Zip 75972–0658, tel. 936/275–3446; Darlene Williams, R.N., Administrator
Web address: www.memorialhealth.org

For explanation of codes following names, see page B2.
★ Indicates Type III membership in the American Hospital Association.

CHI ST. LUKE'S HEALTH-LAKESIDE HOSPITAL (O, 30 beds) 17400 St. Luke's Way, The Woodlands, TX, Zip 77384–8036; tel. 936/266–9000; James Parisi, Chief Executive Officer
Web address: www.stlukeslakeside.com/

CHI ST. LUKE'S HEALTH-THE WOODLANDS HOSPITAL (O, 201 beds) 17200 St. Luke's Way, The Woodlands, TX, Zip 77384–8007; tel. 936/266–2000; James Parisi, Chief Executive Officer

CHI ST. LUKE'S HOSPITAL – THE VINTAGE HOSPITAL (O, 78 beds) 20171 Chasewood Park Drive, Houston, TX, Zip 77070–1437; tel. 832/534–5000; Mario J. Garner, Ed.D., FACHE, Chief Executive Officer
Web address: https://www.chistlukeshealth.org/locations/vintage-hospital

ST. LUKE'S SUGAR LAND HOSPITAL (O, 96 beds) 1317 Lake Pointe Parkway, Sugar Land, TX, Zip 77478–3997; tel. 281/637–7000; Robert A. Heifner, FACHE, Chief Executive Officer

WASHINGTON: HARRISON MEDICAL CENTER (O, 232 beds) 2520 Cherry Avenue, Bremerton, WA, Zip 98310–4229; tel. 360/744–3911; David W. Schultz, FACHE, President, Peninsula Region
Web address: www.chifranciscan.org/harrison

HIGHLINE MEDICAL CENTER (O, 115 beds) 16251 Sylvester Road SW, Burien, WA, Zip 98166–3052; tel. 206/244–9970; Anthony McLean, President

REGIONAL HOSPITAL FOR RESPIRATORY AND COMPLEX CARE (O, 26 beds) 16251 Sylvester Road SW, Burien, WA, Zip 98166–3017; tel. 206/248–4548; Anne McBride, Chief Executive Officer
Web address: www.regionalhospital.org

ST. ANTHONY HOSPITAL (O, 112 beds) 11567 Canterwood Boulevard NW, Gig Harbor, WA, Zip 98332–5812; tel. 253/530–2000; David W. Schultz, FACHE, President, Peninsula Region
Web address: www.chifranciscan.org/

ST. CLARE HOSPITAL (S, 104 beds) 11315 Bridgeport Way SW, Lakewood, WA, Zip 98499–3004; tel. 253/985–1711; Syd Bersante, R.N., President
Web address: www.fhshealth.org

ST. ELIZABETH HOSPITAL (S, 25 beds) 1455 Battersby Avenue, Enumclaw, WA, Zip 98022–3634, Mailing Address: P.O. Box 218, Zip 98022–0218, tel. 360/802 8800; Syd Bersante, R.N., Market President

ST. FRANCIS HOSPITAL (S, 124 beds) 34515 Ninth Avenue South, Federal Way, WA, Zip 98003–6799; tel. 253/944–8100; Anthony McLean, Market President
Web address: www.fhshealth.org

ST. JOSEPH MEDICAL CENTER (S, 366 beds) 1717 South 'J' Street, Tacoma, WA, Zip 98405–3004, Mailing Address: P.O. Box 2197, Zip 98401–2197, tel. 253/426–4101; Syd Bersante, R.N., President

Owned, leased, sponsored:	125 hospitals	19144 beds
Contract-managed:	3 hospitals	140 beds
Totals:	128 hospitals	19284 beds

★0401: COMMUNITY HEALTH NETWORK (NP)
7330 Shadeland Station, Indianapolis, IN, Zip 46256–3957; tel. 317/355–1411; Bryan A. Mills, President and Chief Executive Officer
(Independent Hospital System)

INDIANA: COMMUNITY HOSPITAL EAST (O, 335 beds) 1500 North Ritter Avenue, Indianapolis, IN, Zip 46219–3095; tel. 317/355–1411; Scott L. Teffeteller, Senior Vice President and President of East Region

COMMUNITY HOSPITAL NORTH (O, 343 beds) 7150 Clearvista Drive, Indianapolis, IN, Zip 46256–1695, Mailing Address: 7250 Clearvista Drive, Suite 200, Zip 46256–1695, tel. 317/355–2469; Kathleen R. Krusie, FACHE, President
Web address: www.ecommunity.com/north

COMMUNITY HOSPITAL SOUTH (O, 158 beds) 1402 East County Line Road South, Indianapolis, IN, Zip 46227–0963; tel. 317/887–7000; David Kiley, M.D., Vice President
Web address: www.ecommunity.com

COMMUNITY HOSPITAL OF ANDERSON & MADISON COUNTY (O, 140 beds) 1515 North Madison Avenue, Anderson, IN, Zip 46011–3453; tel. 765/298–4242; Beth S. Tharp, R.N., President and Chief Executive Officer

COMMUNITY HOWARD REGIONAL HEALTH (O, 159 beds) 3500 South Lafountain Street, Kokomo, IN, Zip 46902–3803, Mailing Address: P.O. Box 9011 Zip 46904–9011, tel. 765/453–0702; Joseph Hooper, President and Chief Executive Officer
Web address: www.howardregional.org

COMMUNITY HOWARD SPECIALTY HOSPITAL (O, 30 beds) 829 North Dixon Road, Kokomo, IN, Zip 46901–7709; tel. 765/452–6700; Michelle L. Russell, Administrator

Owned, leased, sponsored:	6 hospitals	1165 beds
Contract-managed:	0 hospitals	0 beds
Totals:	6 hospitals	1165 beds

★0080: COMMUNITY HEALTH SYSTEMS, INC. (IO)
4000 Meridian Boulevard, Franklin, TN, Zip 37067–6325, Mailing Address: P.O. Box 689020, Zip 37068–9020, tel. 615/465–7000; Wayne T. Smith, Chairman, President and Chief Executive Officer
(Decentralized Health System)

ALABAMA: CRESTWOOD MEDICAL CENTER (O, 180 beds) One Hospital Drive, Huntsville, AL, Zip 35801–3403; tel. 256/429–4000; Pamela Hudson, M.D., Chief Executive Officer
Web address: www.crestwoodmedcenter.com

FLOWERS HOSPITAL (O, 147 beds) 4370 West Main Street, Dothan, AL, Zip 36305–4000, Mailing Address: P.O. Box 6907, Zip 36302–6907, tel. 334/793–5000; Heath Phillips, Chief Executive Officer

GADSDEN REGIONAL MEDICAL CENTER (O, 279 beds) 1007 Goodyear Avenue, Gadsden, AL, Zip 35903–1195; tel. 256/494–4000; Corey Ewing, Chief Executive Officer
Web address: www.gadsdenregional.com

GRANDVIEW MEDICAL CENTER (O, 414 beds) 3690 Grandview Parkway, Birmingham, AL, Zip 35243–3326; tel. 205/971-1000; Drew Mason, Chief Executive Officer

MEDICAL CENTER ENTERPRISE (O, 99 beds) 400 North Edwards Street, Enterprise, AL, Zip 36330–2510; tel. 334/347–0584; Suzanne Woods, Chief Executive Officer
Web address: www.mcehospital.com

SOUTH BALDWIN REGIONAL MEDICAL CENTER (L, 112 beds) 1613 North McKenzie Street, Foley, AL, Zip 36535–2299; tel. 251/949–3400; Daniel McKinney, Chief Executive Officer
Web address: www.southbaldwinrmc.com

ALASKA: MAT-SU REGIONAL MEDICAL CENTER (O, 74 beds) 2500 South Woodworth Loop, Palmer, AK, Zip 99645–8984, Mailing Address: P.O. Box 1687, Zip 99645–1687, tel. 907/861–6000; David Wallace, Chief Executive Officer

ARIZONA: NORTHWEST MEDICAL CENTER (O, 258 beds) 6200 North La Cholla Boulevard, Tucson, AZ, Zip 85741–3599; tel. 520/742–9000; Kevin Stockton, Chief Executive Officer
Web address: www.northwestmedicalcenter.com

ORO VALLEY HOSPITAL (O, 146 beds) 1551 East Tangerine Road, Oro Valley, AZ, Zip 85755–6213; tel. 520/901–3500

WESTERN ARIZONA REGIONAL MEDICAL CENTER (O, 106 beds) 2735 Silver Creek Road, Bullhead City, AZ, Zip 86442–8303; tel. 928/763–2273; Michael J Stenger, Chief Executive Officer
Web address: www.warmc.com

ARKANSAS: MEDICAL CENTER OF SOUTH ARKANSAS (L, 121 beds) 700 West Grove Street, El Dorado, AR, Zip 71730–4416; tel. 870/863–2000; Scott Street, Chief Executive Officer
Web address: www.themedcenter.net

NORTHWEST HEALTH PHYSICIANS' SPECIALTY HOSPITAL (O, 20 beds) 3873 North Parkview Drive, Fayetteville, AR, Zip 72703–6286; tel. 479/571–7070; Denten Park, Chief Executive Officer
Web address: www.pshfay.com

NORTHWEST MEDICAL CENTER – SPRINGDALE (O, 345 beds) 609 West Maple Avenue, Springdale, AR, Zip 72764–5394, Mailing Address: P.O. Box 47, Zip 72765–0047, tel. 479/751–5711; Hans Driessnack, Chief Executive Officer

For explanation of codes following names, see page B2.
★ Indicates Type III membership in the American Hospital Association.

Section B

SILOAM SPRINGS REGIONAL HOSPITAL (O, 44 beds) 603 North Progress Avenue, Siloam Springs, AR, Zip 72761–4352; tel. 479/215–3000; Adam Bracks, Chief Executive Officer
Web address: www.ssrh.net

FLORIDA: BAYFRONT HEALTH BROOKSVILLE (L, 120 beds) 17240 Cortez Boulevard, Brooksville, FL, Zip 34601–8921, Mailing Address: P.O. Box 37, Zip 34605–0037, tel. 352/796–5111; Kenneth R. Wicker, Chief Executive Officer

BAYFRONT HEALTH PORT CHARLOTTE (O, 254 beds) 2500 Harbor Boulevard, Port Charlotte, FL, Zip 33952–5000; tel. 941/766–4122; Timothy J. Cerullo, Chief Executive Officer
Web address: www.bayfrontcharlotte.com

BAYFRONT HEALTH PUNTA GORDA (O, 190 beds) 809 East Marion Avenue, Punta Gorda, FL, Zip 33950–3819, Mailing Address: P.O. Box 51–1328, Zip 33951–1328, tel. 941/639–3131; Andrew Emery, Chief Executive Officer

BAYFRONT HEALTH ST. PETERSBURG (O, 382 beds) 701 Sixth Street South, Saint Petersburg, FL, Zip 33701–4891; tel. 727/823–1234; Sharon Hayes, Chief Executive Officer
Web address: www.bayfrontstpete.com

LOWER KEYS MEDICAL CENTER (L, 90 beds) 5900 College Road, Key West, FL, Zip 33040–4396, Mailing Address: P.O. Box 9107, Zip 33041–9107, tel. 305/294–5531; David Clay, Chief Executive Officer

NORTH OKALOOSA MEDICAL CENTER (O, 110 beds) 151 Redstone Avenue SE, Crestview, FL, Zip 32539–6026; tel. 850/689–8100; Ronnie Daves, Chief Executive Officer
Web address: www.northokaloosa.com

PHYSICIANS REGIONAL – PINE RIDGE (O, 193 beds) 6101 Pine Ridge Road, Naples, FL, Zip 34119–3900; tel. 239/348–4000; Scott Lowe, Market Chief Executive Officer

SANTA ROSA MEDICAL CENTER (L, 68 beds) 6002 Berryhill Road, Milton, FL, Zip 32570–5062; tel. 850/626–7762; Doug Sills, Chief Executive Officer
Web address: www.santarosamedicalcenter.org

SEVEN RIVERS REGIONAL MEDICAL CENTER (O, 128 beds) 6201 North Suncoast Boulevard, Crystal River, FL, Zip 34428–6712; tel. 352/795–6560; Linda Stockton, Interim Chief Executive Officer

SHANDS LAKE SHORE REGIONAL MEDICAL CENTER (O, 85 beds) 368 NE Franklin Street, Lake City, FL, Zip 32055–3047; tel. 386/292–8000; Rhonda Kay. Sherrod, R.N., MSN, Chief Executive Officer
Web address: www.shandslakeshore.com

SHANDS LIVE OAK REGIONAL MEDICAL CENTER (O, 25 beds) 1100 SW 11th Street, Live Oak, FL, Zip 32064–3608; tel. 386/362–0800; Rhonda Kay. Sherrod, R.N., MSN, Chief Executive Officer
Web address: www.shandsliveoak.com/

SHANDS STARKE REGIONAL MEDICAL CENTER (O, 49 beds) 922 East Call Street, Starke, FL, Zip 32091–3699; tel. 904/368–2300; John Emery, Chief Executive Officer
Web address: www.shandsstarke.com

ST. CLOUD REGIONAL MEDICAL CENTER (O, 84 beds) 2906 17th Street, Saint Cloud, FL, Zip 34769–6099; tel. 407/892–2135; Brent Burish, Chief Executive Officer

VENICE REGIONAL BAYFRONT HEALTH (O, 221 beds) 540 The Rialto, Venice, FL, Zip 34285–2900; tel. 941/485–7711; Karen Fordham, Chief Executive Officer
Web address: www.veniceregional.com

GEORGIA: EAST GEORGIA REGIONAL MEDICAL CENTER (O, 149 beds) 1499 Fair Road, Statesboro, GA, Zip 30458–1683, Mailing Address: P.O. Box 1048, Zip 30459–1048, tel. 912/486–1000; Stephen G. Pennington, Chief Executive Officer

INDIANA: BLUFFTON REGIONAL MEDICAL CENTER (O, 54 beds) 303 South Main Street, Bluffton, IN, Zip 46714–2503; tel. 260/824–3210; Brent Parsons, Chief Executive Officer
Web address: www.blufftonregional.com

DUKES MEMORIAL HOSPITAL (O, 25 beds) 275 West 12th Street, Peru, IN, Zip 46970–1638; tel. 765/472–8000; Debra Close, Chief Executive Officer
Web address: www.dukesmemorialhosp.com

DUPONT HOSPITAL (O, 131 beds) 2520 East Dupont Road, Fort Wayne, IN, Zip 46825–1675; tel. 260/416–3000; Lorenzo Suter, Chief Executive Officer

KOSCIUSKO COMMUNITY HOSPITAL (O, 72 beds) 2101 East Dubois Drive, Warsaw, IN, Zip 46580–3288; tel. 574/267–3200; Jae Dale, Chief Executive Officer
Web address: www.kch.com

LA PORTE HOSPITAL (O, 91 beds) 1007 Lincolnway, La Porte, IN, Zip 46350–3201, Mailing Address: P.O. Box 250, Zip 46352–0250, tel. 219/326–1234; Ashley Dickinson, Chief Executive Officer

LUTHERAN HOSPITAL OF INDIANA (O, 407 beds) 7950 West Jefferson Boulevard, Fort Wayne, IN, Zip 46804–4140; tel. 260/435–7001
Web address: www.lutheranhospital.com

ORTHOPAEDIC HOSPITAL OF LUTHERAN HEALTH NETWORK (O, 43 beds) 7952 West Jefferson Boulevard, Fort Wayne, IN, Zip 46804–4140; tel. 260/435–2999; Lorie Ailor, Chief Executive Officer

PORTER REGIONAL HOSPITAL (O, 276 beds) 85 East U. S. Highway 6, Valparaiso, IN, Zip 46383–8947; tel. 219/983–8300; Sean T. Dardeau, FACHE, Chief Executive Officer
Web address: www.porterhealth.com

REHABILITATION HOSPITAL OF FORT WAYNE (O, 36 beds) 7970 West Jefferson Boulevard, Fort Wayne, IN, Zip 46804–4140; tel. 260/435–6100; Ryan Cassedy, Chief Administrative Officer

ST. JOSEPH HOSPITAL (O, 182 beds) 700 Broadway, Fort Wayne, IN, Zip 46802–1493; tel. 260/425–3000; Lisa Dolan, Interim Chief Executive Officer
Web address: www.stjoehospital.com

STARKE HOSPITAL (O, 15 beds) 102 East Culver Road, Knox, IN, Zip 46534–2216, Mailing Address: P.O. Box 339, Zip 46534–0339, tel. 574/772–6231; Jeff Vice, Chief Operating Officer and Interim Chief Executive Officer
Web address: www.iuhealth.org/starke/

LOUISIANA: NORTHERN LOUISIANA MEDICAL CENTER (O, 104 beds) 401 East Vaughn Avenue, Ruston, LA, Zip 71270–5950; tel. 318/254–2100; Keith Newton, Chief Executive Officer
Web address: www.northernlouisianamedicalcenter.com

MISSISSIPPI: MERIT HEALTH BILOXI (L, 198 beds) 150 Reynoir Street, Biloxi, MS, Zip 39530–4199, Mailing Address: P.O. Box 128, Zip 39533–0128, tel. 228/432–1571; Robert Calhoun, Chief Executive Officer

MERIT HEALTH CENTRAL (L, 254 beds) 1850 Chadwick Drive, Jackson, MS, Zip 39204–3479, Mailing Address: P.O. Box 59001, Zip 39284–9001, tel. 601/376–1000; Barry Moss, Chief Executive Officer
Web address: www.merithealthcentral.com/

MERIT HEALTH MADISON (L, 43 beds) 161 River Oaks Drive, Canton, MS, Zip 39046–5375, Mailing Address: PO Box 1607, Zip 39046–5375, tel. 601/855–4000; Britton Phelps, Chief Executive Officer

MERIT HEALTH NATCHEZ (O, 136 beds) 54 Seargent 'S' Prentiss Drive, Natchez, MS, Zip 39120–4726; tel. 601/443–2100; Lance Boyd, Chief Executive Officer
Web address: www.natchezregional.com

MERIT HEALTH RANKIN (L, 134 beds) 350 Crossgates Boulevard, Brandon, MS, Zip 39042–2698; tel. 601/825–2811; Heather Sistrunk, R.N., Chief Executive Officer

MERIT HEALTH RIVER OAKS (O, 158 beds) 1030 River Oaks Drive, Flowood, MS, Zip 39232–9553, Mailing Address: P.O. Box 5100, Jackson, Zip 39296–5100, tel. 601/932–1030; L Dwayne. Blaylock, Chief Executive Officer
Web address: https://www.merithealthriveroaks.com/

MERIT HEALTH RIVER REGION (O, 361 beds) 2100 Highway 61 North, Vicksburg, MS, Zip 39183–8211, Mailing Address: P.O. Box 590, Zip 39181–0590, tel. 601/883–5000; Benjamin Richaud, Interim Chief Executive Officer

MERIT HEALTH WESLEY (O, 211 beds) 5001 Hardy Street, Hattiesburg, MS, Zip 39402–1308, Mailing Address: P.O. Box 16509, Zip 39404–6509, tel. 601/268–8000; Carol Upton, Interim Chief Executive Officer
Web address: www.wesley.com

MERIT HEALTH WOMAN'S HOSPITAL (O, 60 beds) 1026 North Flowood Drive, Flowood, MS, Zip 39232–9532, Mailing Address: 1026 North Flowood Drive, Zip 39232, tel. 601/932–1000; Sherry J. Pitts, Chief Executive Officer

MISSOURI: MOBERLY REGIONAL MEDICAL CENTER (O, 99 beds) 1515 Union Avenue, Moberly, MO, Zip 65270–9449; tel. 660/263–8400; Ranee C. Brayton, FACHE, MSN, R.N., Chief Executive Officer
Web address: www.moberlyhospital.com

NORTHEAST REGIONAL MEDICAL CENTER (L, 50 beds) 315 South Osteopathy Street, Kirksville, MO, Zip 63501–6401, Mailing Address: P.O. Box C8502,

---

For explanation of codes following names, see page B2.
★ Indicates Type III membership in the American Hospital Association.

Zip 63501–8599, tel. 660/785–1000; Ranee C. Brayton, FACHE, MSN, R.N., Chief Executive Officer

POPLAR BLUFF REGIONAL MEDICAL CENTER (O, 255 beds) 3100 Oak Grove Road, Poplar Bluff, MO, Zip 63901, Mailing Address: P.O. Box 88, Zip 63902–0088, tel. 573/776–2000; Bryan Bateman, Chief Executive Officer
Web address: www.poplarbluffregional.com

NEW MEXICO: CARLSBAD MEDICAL CENTER (O, 114 beds) 2430 West Pierce Street, Carlsbad, NM, Zip 88220–3597; tel. 575/887–4100; Cathy Hibbs, Chief Executive Officer

EASTERN NEW MEXICO MEDICAL CENTER (O, 149 beds) 405 West Country Club Road, Roswell, NM, Zip 88201–5209; tel. 575/622–8170; Warren Yehl, Chief Executive Officer
Web address: www.enmmc.com

LEA REGIONAL MEDICAL CENTER (O, 99 beds) 5419 North Lovington Highway, Hobbs, NM, Zip 88240–9125, Mailing Address: P.O. Box 3000, Zip 88241–9501, tel. 575/492–5000; Timothy Thornell, FACHE, Chief Executive Officer
Web address: www.learegionalmedical.com

MOUNTAINVIEW REGIONAL MEDICAL CENTER (O, 142 beds) 4311 East Lohman Avenue, Las Cruces, NM, Zip 88011–8255; tel. 575/556–7600; Derrick Cuenca, Chief Executive Officer

NORTH CAROLINA: DAVIS REGIONAL MEDICAL CENTER (O, 130 beds) 218 Old Mocksville Road, Statesville, NC, Zip 28625–1930, Mailing Address: P.O. Box 1823, Zip 28687–1823, tel. 704/873–0281; Matthew Banks, Chief Executive Officer
Web address: www.davisregional.com

LAKE NORMAN REGIONAL MEDICAL CENTER (O, 123 beds) 171 Fairview Road, Mooresville, NC, Zip 28117–9500, Mailing Address: P.O. Box 3250, Zip 28117–3250, tel. 704/660–4000; Stephen L. Midkiff, Chief Executive Officer

OKLAHOMA: ALLIANCEHEALTH CLINTON (O, 49 beds) 100 North 30th Street, Clinton, OK, Zip 73601–3117; tel. 580/323–2363; Landon E. Hise, Chief Executive Officer
Web address: www.alliancehealthclinton.com

ALLIANCEHEALTH DURANT (O, 140 beds) 1800 University Boulevard, Durant, OK, Zip 74701–3006, Mailing Address: P.O. Box 1207, Zip 74702–1207, tel. 580/924–3080; Charles Hall, Interim Chief Executive Officer
Web address: www.alliancehealthdurant.com/

ALLIANCEHEALTH MADILL (O, 25 beds) 901 South Fifth Avenue, Madill, OK, Zip 73446–3640, Mailing Address: P.O. Box 827, Zip 73446–0827, tel. 580/795–3384; Charles Hall, Interim Chief Executive Officer
Web address: www.myalliancehealth.com

ALLIANCEHEALTH MIDWEST (I, 255 beds) 2825 Parklawn Drive, Midwest City, OK, Zip 73110–4258; tel. 405/610–4411; Clay Franklin, Chief Executive Officer
Web address: www.myalliancehealth.com

ALLIANCEHEALTH PONCA CITY (O, 74 beds) 1900 North 14th Street, Ponca City, OK, Zip 74601–2099; tel. 580/765–3321; Christopher Mendoza, Chief Executive Officer
Web address: www.AllianceHealthPoncaCity.com

ALLIANCEHEALTH SEMINOLE (O, 32 beds) 2401 Wrangler Boulevard, Seminole, OK, Zip 74868–1917; tel. 405/303–4000; Damon Brown, Interim Chief Executive Officer
Web address: www.alliancehealthseminole.com/

ALLIANCEHEALTH WOODWARD (L, 40 beds) 900 17th Street, Woodward, OK, Zip 73801–2448; tel. 580/256–5511; Landon E. Hise, Interim Chief Executive Officer
Web address: www.woodwardhospital.com

PENNSYLVANIA: BERWICK HOSPITAL CENTER (O, 101 beds) 701 East 16th Street, Berwick, PA, Zip 18603–2397; tel. 570/759–5000; Thomas Neal, Chief Executive Officer

FIRST HOSPITAL WYOMING VALLEY (O, 149 beds) 562 Wyoming Avenue, Kingston, PA, Zip 18704–3721; tel. 570/552–3900; Greg Shannon, Chief Executive Officer
Web address: www.commonwealthhealth.net/locations/first-hospital

MOSES TAYLOR HOSPITAL (O, 213 beds) 700 Quincy Avenue, Scranton, PA, Zip 18510–1724; tel. 570/770–5000; Ronald Ziobro, Interim Chief Executive Officer
Web address: www.mth.org

REGIONAL HOSPITAL OF SCRANTON (O, 186 beds) 746 Jefferson Avenue, Scranton, PA, Zip 18510–1624; tel. 570/348–7100; Ronald Ziobro, Interim Chief Executive Officer

TYLER MEMORIAL HOSPITAL (O, 44 beds) 5950 State Route 6, Tunkhannock, PA, Zip 18657–7905; tel. 570/836–2161; Ann Marie. Stevens, R.N., Chief Executive Officer
Web address: www.tylermemorialhospital.net

WILKES-BARRE GENERAL HOSPITAL (O, 374 beds) 575 North River Street, Wilkes-Barre, PA, Zip 18764–0001; tel. 570/829–8111; Cornelio R. Catena, President and Chief Executive Officer

SOUTH CAROLINA: MUSC HEALTH CHESTER MEDICAL CENTER (L, 36 beds) 1 Medical Park Drive, Chester, SC, Zip 29706–9769; tel. 803/581–3151; Page H. Vaughan, Chief Executive Officer
Web address: www.chesterregional.com

MUSC HEALTH FLORENCE MEDICAL CENTER (O, 310 beds) 805 Pamplico Highway, Florence, SC, Zip 29505–6050, Mailing Address: P.O. Box 100550, Zip 29502–0550, tel. 843/674–5000; Vance V. Reynolds, FACHE, CPA, Chief Executive Officer

MUSC HEALTH LANCASTER MEDICAL CENTER (O, 176 beds) 800 West Meeting Street, Lancaster, SC, Zip 29720–2298; tel. 803/286–1214; Page H. Vaughan, Chief Executive Officer
Web address: www.springsmemorial.com

MUSC HEALTH MARION MEDICAL CENTER (O, 209 beds) 2829 East Highway 76, Mullins, SC, Zip 29574–6035, Mailing Address: P O Drawer 1150, Marion, Zip 29571–1150, tel. 843/431–2000; Spencer Twigg, Chief Executive Officer

TENNESSEE: TENNOVA HEALTHCARE – CLEVELAND (O, 186 beds) 2305 Chambliss Avenue NW, Cleveland, TN, Zip 37311–3847, Mailing Address: P.O. Box 3060, Zip 37320–3060, tel. 423/559–6000; J. T. Barnhart, Chief Executive Officer
Web address: www.skyridgemedicalcenter.net

TENNOVA HEALTHCARE-CLARKSVILLE (O, 247 beds) 651 Dunlop Lane, Clarksville, TN, Zip 37040–5015, Mailing Address: P.O. Box 31629, Zip 37040–0028, tel. 931/502–1000; Alex Villa, Chief Executive Officer
Web address: www.tennova.com/

TENNOVA HEALTHCARE-HARTON (O, 135 beds) 1801 North Jackson Street, Tullahoma, TN, Zip 37388–8259; tel. 931/393–3000; Richard Ellis, Chief Executive Officer
Web address: www.hartonmedicalcenter.com

TENNOVA HEALTHCARE-JEFFERSON MEMORIAL HOSPITAL (L, 54 beds) 110 Hospital Drive, Jefferson City, TN, Zip 37760–5281; tel. 865/471–2500; Colin McRae, Chief Executive Officer

TENNOVA HEALTHCARE-LAFOLLETTE MEDICAL CENTER (O, 164 beds) 923 East Central Avenue, La Follette, TN, Zip 37766–2768, Mailing Address: P.O. Box 1301, Zip 37766–1301, tel. 423/907–1200; Mark Cain, Chief Executive Officer
Web address: www.tennova.com

TENNOVA HEALTHCARE-SHELBYVILLE (O, 49 beds) 2835 Highway 231 North, Shelbyville, TN, Zip 37160–7327; tel. 931/685–5433; Bill Rich, Chief Executive Officer
Web address: www.Tennova.com

TENNOVA NEWPORT MEDICAL CENTER (O, 47 beds) 435 Second Street, Newport, TN, Zip 37821–3799; tel. 423/625–2200; Matthew Littlejohn, Chief Executive Officer

TENNOVA NORTH KNOXVILLE MEDICAL CENTER (O, 220 beds) 7565 Dannaher Way, Powell, TN, Zip 37849–4029; tel. 865/859–8000; Clyde Wood, Chief Executive Officer

TEXAS: ABILENE REGIONAL MEDICAL CENTER (O, 205 beds) 6250 US Highway 83, Abilene, TX, Zip 79606–5299; tel. 325/428–1000; Michael D. Murphy, FACHE, Chief Executive Officer
Web address: www.abileneregional.com

BROWNWOOD REGIONAL MEDICAL CENTER (O, 153 beds) 1501 Burnet Road, Brownwood, TX, Zip 76801–8520, Mailing Address: P.O. Box 760, Zip 76804–0760, tel. 325/646–8541; Jace Jones, Interim Chief Executive Officer
Web address: www.brmc-cares.com

CEDAR PARK REGIONAL MEDICAL CENTER (O, 108 beds) 1401 Medical Parkway, Cedar Park, TX, Zip 78613–7763; tel. 512/528–7000; Carl Bo"'. Beaudry, Chief Executive Officer

For explanation of codes following names, see page B2.
★ Indicates Type III membership in the American Hospital Association.

Section B

COLLEGE STATION MEDICAL CENTER (O, 167 beds) 1604 Rock Prairie Road, College Station, TX, Zip 77845–8345; tel. 979/764–5100; America S. Farrell, FACHE, Chief Executive Officer
Web address: www.csmedcenter.com

DETAR HEALTHCARE SYSTEM (O, 225 beds) 506 East San Antonio Street, Victoria, TX, Zip 77901–6060, Mailing Address: P.O. Box 2089, Zip 77902–2089, tel. 361/575–7441; Gary Malaer, Chief Executive Officer

HILL REGIONAL HOSPITAL (O, 66 beds) 101 Circle Drive, Hillsboro, TX, Zip 76645–2670; tel. 254/580–8500; Michael J. Ellis, FACHE, Chief Executive Officer
Web address: www.chs.net

LAKE GRANBURY MEDICAL CENTER (L, 73 beds) 1310 Paluxy Road, Granbury, TX, Zip 76048–5655; tel. 817/573–2273; David Orcutt, Chief Executive Officer
Web address: www.lakegranburymedicalcenter.com

LAREDO MEDICAL CENTER (O, 326 beds) 1700 East Saunders Avenue, Laredo, TX, Zip 78041–5474, Mailing Address: P.O. Box 2068, Zip 78044–2068, tel. 956/796–5000; Enrique Gallegos, Chief Executive Officer

LONGVIEW REGIONAL MEDICAL CENTER (O, 224 beds) 2901 North Fourth Street, Longview, TX, Zip 75605–5191, Mailing Address: P.O. Box 14000, Zip 75607–4000, tel. 903/758–1818; Casey Robertson, Chief Executive Officer
Web address: www.longviewregional.com

NAVARRO REGIONAL HOSPITAL (O, 49 beds) 3201 West State Highway 22, Corsicana, TX, Zip 75110–2469; tel. 903/654–6800; Curt M. Junkins, Chief Executive Officer
Web address: www.navarrohospital.com

SAN ANGELO COMMUNITY MEDICAL CENTER (O, 131 beds) 3501 Knickerbocker Road, San Angelo, TX, Zip 76904–7698; tel. 325/949–9511; Rodney Schumacher, Interim Chief Executive Officer

WOODLAND HEIGHTS MEDICAL CENTER (O, 124 beds) 505 South John Redditt Drive, Lufkin, TX, Zip 75904–3157, Mailing Address: P.O. Box 150610, Zip 75904, tel. 936/634–8311; Kyle Swift, Chief Executive Officer
Web address: www.woodlandheights.net

VIRGINIA: SOUTHAMPTON MEMORIAL HOSPITAL (O, 72 beds) 100 Fairview Drive, Franklin, VA, Zip 23851–1238, Mailing Address: P.O. Box 817, Zip 23851–0817, tel. 757/569–6100; Kimberly W. Marks, Chief Executive Officer
Web address: www.smhfranklin.com

SOUTHERN VIRGINIA REGIONAL MEDICAL CENTER (O, 80 beds) 727 North Main Street, Emporia, VA, Zip 23847–1274; tel. 434/348–4400; Wilson A. Thomas, Chief Executive Officer

SOUTHSIDE REGIONAL MEDICAL CENTER (O, 294 beds) 200 Medical Park Boulevard, Petersburg, VA, Zip 23805–9274; tel. 804/765–5000; Trent Nobles, Chief Executive Officer
Web address: www.srmconline.com

WEST VIRGINIA: BLUEFIELD REGIONAL MEDICAL CENTER (O, 92 beds) 500 Cherry Street, Bluefield, WV, Zip 24701–3390; tel. 304/327–1100; Timothy A. Bess, Chief Executive Officer
Web address: https://www.bluefieldregional.net

GREENBRIER VALLEY MEDICAL CENTER (O, 113 beds) 202 Maplewood Avenue, Ronceverte, WV, Zip 24970–1334, Mailing Address: P.O. Box 497, Zip 24970–0497, tel. 304/647–4411; Jim Hobson, Chief Executive Officer
Web address: www.gvmc.com

PLATEAU MEDICAL CENTER (O, 25 beds) 430 Main Street, Oak Hill, WV, Zip 25901–3455; tel. 304/469–8600; Christopher L. Howe, R.N., Chief Executive Officer

Owned, leased, sponsored:	102 hospitals	14687 beds
Contract-managed:	0 hospitals	0 beds
Totals:	102 hospitals	14687 beds

0249: COMMUNITY HEALTHCARE SYSTEM (NP)
901 MacArthur Boulevard, Hammond, IN, Zip 46321–2959; tel. 219/836–1600; Donald P. Fesko, President and Chief Executive Officer
(Independent Hospital System)

INDIANA: COMMUNITY HOSPITAL (O, 510 beds) 901 Macarthur Boulevard, Munster, IN, Zip 46321–2959; tel. 219/836–1600; Luis F. Molina, Chief Executive Officer and Administrator
Web address: www.comhs.org

ST. CATHERINE HOSPITAL (O, 211 beds) 4321 Fir Street, East Chicago, IN, Zip 46312–3097; tel. 219/392–1700; Leo Correa, Chief Executive Officer and Administrator

ST. MARY MEDICAL CENTER (O, 200 beds) 1500 South Lake Park Avenue, Hobart, IN, Zip 46342–6699; tel. 219/942–0551; Janice L. Ryba, JD, Chief Executive Officer
Web address: www.comhs.org

Owned, leased, sponsored:	3 hospitals	921 beds
Contract-managed:	0 hospitals	0 beds
Totals:	3 hospitals	921 beds

★0384: COMMUNITY HOSPITAL CORPORATION (NP)
7800 North Dallas Parkway, Suite 200, Plano, TX, Zip 75024–6116; tel. 972/943–6400; Jim R. Kendrick, President and Chief Executive Officer
(Moderately Centralized Health System)

ARKANSAS: ARKANSAS CONTINUED CARE HOSPITAL (C, 44 beds) 3024 Red Wolf Boulevard, Jonesboro, AR, Zip 72401–7415; tel. 870/819–4040; Sally A. Parnell, R.N., Interim Chief Executive Officer

KENTUCKY: CONTINUECARE HOSPITAL AT BAPTIST HEALTH CORBIN (O, 32 beds) 1 Trillium Way, Lower Level, Corbin, KY, Zip 40701–8727; tel. 606/523–5150; Tuan Le, Chief Executive Officer
Web address: www.continuecare.org

CONTINUECARE HOSPITAL AT BAPTIST HEALTH PADUCAH (O, 37 beds) 2501 Kentucky Avenue, 5th Floor, Paducah, KY, Zip 42003–3813; tel. 270/575–2598; Mary Lou Young, Acting Administrator
Web address: www.continuecare.org/paducah//

CONTINUECARE HOSPITAL AT MADISONVILLE (O, 35 beds) 900 Hospital Drive, 4th Floor, Madisonville, KY, Zip 42431–1644; tel. 270/825–5450; Melissa Nagle, Chief Executive Officer

LOUISIANA: MOREHOUSE GENERAL HOSPITAL (C, 49 beds) 323 West Walnut Avenue, Bastrop, LA, Zip 71220–4521, Mailing Address: P.O. Box 1060, Zip 71221–1060, tel. 318/283–3600; Derrick A. Frazier, FACHE, Chief Executive Officer
Web address: www.mghospital.com

NEW MEXICO: UNION COUNTY GENERAL HOSPITAL (C, 21 beds) 300 Wilson Street, Clayton, NM, Zip 88415–3304, Mailing Address: P.O. Box 489, Zip 88415–0489, tel. 575/374–2585; Tammie Stump, R.N., Chief Executive Officer

NORTH CAROLINA: CAROLINAS CONTINUECARE HOSPITAL AT PINEVILLE (O, 40 beds) 10648 Park Road, Charlotte, NC, Zip 28210; tel. 704/667–8050; Derek Murzyn, Market Chief Executive Officer
Web address: www.continuecare.org/pineville/

CAROLINAS CONTINUECARE HOSPITAL AT UNIVERSITY (O, 35 beds) 8800 North Tryon Street, Charlotte, NC, Zip 28262–3300; tel. 704/863–8300; Derek Murzyn, Chief Executive Officer
Web address: www.continuecare.org/charlotte//

SOUTH CAROLINA: CONTINUECARE HOSPITAL AT PALMETTO HEALTH BAPTIST (O, 35 beds) Taylor at Marion Street, Columbia, SC, Zip 29220, Mailing Address: PO BOX 11069, Zip 29211–1069, tel. 803/296–3757; Thomas P. Harlan, Chief Executive Officer
Web address: www.continuecare.org/palmetto//

TENNESSEE: JELLICO COMMUNITY HOSPITAL (O, 31 beds) 188 Hospital Lane, Jellico, TN, Zip 37762–4400; tel. 423/784–7252; Gene Miller, Interim Chief Executive Officer
Web address: www.jellicohospital.com

TEXAS: BAPTIST HOSPITALS OF SOUTHEAST TEXAS (O, 317 beds) 3080 College Street, Beaumont, TX, Zip 77701–4689, Mailing Address: P.O. Box 1591, Zip 77704–1591, tel. 409/212–5000; David N. Parmer, FACHE, Chief Executive Officer
Web address: www.bhset.net

CONTINUECARE HOSPITAL AT HENDRICK MEDICAL CENTER (O, 23 beds) 1900 Pine Street, 7th Floor, Jones Building, Abilene, TX, Zip 79601–2432; tel. 325/670–6251; Billy Blasingame, Chief Executive Officer
Web address: www.continuecare.org/hendrick/

For explanation of codes following names, see page B2.
★ Indicates Type III membership in the American Hospital Association.

© 2019 AHA Guide

CONTINUECARE HOSPITAL AT MEDICAL CENTER (ODESSA) (O, 25 beds) 500 West Fourth Street, 4th Floor, Odessa, TX, Zip 79761–5001; tel. 432/640–4380; Holly Powell, Administrator

FREESTONE MEDICAL CENTER (C, 14 beds) 125 Newman Street, Fairfield, TX, Zip 75840–1499; tel. 903/389–2121; John M. Yeary, FACHE, Chief Executive Officer
Web address: www.freestonemc.com/

ST. MARK'S MEDICAL CENTER (O, 38 beds) One St Mark's Place, La Grange, TX, Zip 78945; tel. 979/242–2200; Rick J. Montelongo, Chief Executive Officer
Web address: www.smmctx.org

TYLER CONTINUECARE HOSPITAL (O, 51 beds) 800 East Dawson, 4th Floor, Tyler, TX, Zip 75701–2036; tel. 903/531–4080; Stephanie Hyde, R.N., MSN, Chief Executive Officer
Web address: www.continuecare.org

YOAKUM COMMUNITY HOSPITAL (O, 23 beds) 1200 Carl Ramert Drive, Yoakum, TX, Zip 77995–4868; tel. 361/293–2321; Karen Barber, R.N., Chief Executive Officer

Owned, leased, sponsored:	13 hospitals	722 beds
Contract-managed:	4 hospitals	128 beds
Totals:	17 hospitals	850 beds

1085: COMMUNITY MEDICAL CENTERS (NP)
Fresno and Maddy Drive, Fresno, CA, Zip 93721, Mailing Address: P.O. Box 1232, Zip 93715–1232, tel. 559/459–6000; Tim A. Joslin, President and Chief Executive Officer
(Independent Hospital System)

CALIFORNIA: CLOVIS COMMUNITY MEDICAL CENTER (O, 109 beds) 2755 Herndon Avenue, Clovis, CA, Zip 93611–6801; tel. 559/324–4000; Craig Castro, Chief Executive Officer
Web address: www.communitymedical.org

COMMUNITY BEHAVIORAL HEALTH CENTER (O, 61 beds) 7171 North Cedar Avenue, Fresno, CA, Zip 93720–3311; tel. 559/449–8000; Craig Wagoner, Chief Executive Officer

COMMUNITY REGIONAL MEDICAL CENTER (O, 852 beds) 2823 Fresno Street, Fresno, CA, Zip 93721–1324, Mailing Address: P.O. Box 1232, Zip 93715–1232, tel. 559/459–6000; Craig Wagoner, Chief Executive Officer
Web address: www.communitymedical.org

FRESNO HEART AND SURGICAL HOSPITAL (O, 60 beds) 15 East Audubon Drive, Fresno, CA, Zip 93720–1542; tel. 559/433–8000; Ben Armfield, Associate Administrator

Owned, leased, sponsored:	4 hospitals	1082 beds
Contract-managed:	0 hospitals	0 beds
Totals:	4 hospitals	1082 beds

0990: COMMUNITY MEMORIAL HEALTH SYSTEM (NP)
147 North Brent Street, Ventura, CA, Zip 93003–2809; tel. 805/652–5011; Gary Wilde, President and Chief Executive Officer
(Independent Hospital System)

CALIFORNIA: COMMUNITY MEMORIAL HOSPITAL (O, 126 beds) 147 North Brent Street, Ventura, CA, Zip 93003–2809; tel. 805/652–5011; Gary Wilde, President and Chief Executive Officer

OJAI VALLEY COMMUNITY HOSPITAL (O, 66 beds) 1306 Maricopa Highway, Ojai, CA, Zip 93023–3163; tel. 805/646–1401; Haady Lashkari, Chief Administrative Officer
Web address: www.cmhshealth.org/locations/ojai-valley-community-hospital/

Owned, leased, sponsored:	2 hospitals	192 beds
Contract-managed:	0 hospitals	0 beds
Totals:	2 hospitals	192 beds

0909: COMPASS HEALTH (NP)
713 North Avenue L, Crowley, LA, Zip 70526–3832; tel. 337/788–3330; Aimee Monaghan, Chief Executive Officer

LOUISIANA: COMPASS BEHAVIORAL CENTER OF ALEXANDRIA (O, 16 beds) 6410 Masonic Drve, Alexandria, LA, Zip 71301–2319; tel. 318/442–3163; William Lancaster, Administrator

COMPASS BEHAVIORAL CENTER OF HOUMA (O, 20 beds) 4701 West Park Avenue, Houma, LA, Zip 70364–4426; tel. 985/876–1715; Cleveland Obey, Administrator
Web address: www.compasshealthcare.com/site83.php

COMPASS BEHAVIORAL CENTER OF LAFAYETTE (O, 16 beds) 312 Youngsville Highway, Lafayette, LA, Zip 70508; tel. 337/534–4655; Aimee Monaghan, Chief Executive Officer
Web address: www.compasshealthcare.com/site184.php

Owned, leased, sponsored:	3 hospitals	52 beds
Contract-managed:	0 hospitals	0 beds
Totals:	3 hospitals	52 beds

0999: CONCORD HEALTHCARE GROUP (IO)
111 Clifton AVenue, Lakewood, NJ, Zip 8701; tel. 214/396–3462; Joe Neuman, Chief Executive Officer
(Independent Hospital System)

OKLAHOMA: INSPIRE SPECIALTY HOSPITAL (O, 31 beds) 8210 National Avenue, Midwest City, OK, Zip 73110–8518; tel. 405/739–0800; Bobby Snyder, Chief Executive Officer
Web address: www.inspirehospital.com

TEXAS: MESA HILLS SPECIALTY HOSPITAL (O, 32 beds) 2311 North Oregon Street, 5th Floor, El Paso, TX, Zip 79902–3216; tel. 915/545–1823; Jose Huerta, Chief Executive Officer
Web address: www.specialtyhospitalmesahills.com/

Owned, leased, sponsored:	2 hospitals	63 beds
Contract-managed:	0 hospitals	0 beds
Totals:	2 hospitals	63 beds

0950: CONE HEALTH (NP)
1200 North Elm Street, Greensboro, NC, Zip 27401–1004; tel. 336/832–7000; Terry Akin, President and Chief Executive Officer
(Independent Hospital System)

NORTH CAROLINA: ALAMANCE REGIONAL MEDICAL CENTER (O, 197 beds) 1240 Huffman Mill Road, Burlington, NC, Zip 27215–8700, Mailing Address: P.O. Box 202, Zip 27216–0202, tel. 336/538–7000; Preston W. Hammock, President
Web address: www.armc.com

MOSES H. CONE MEMORIAL HOSPITAL (O, 935 beds) 1200 North Elm Street, Greensboro, NC, Zip 27401–1020; tel. 336/832–7000

Owned, leased, sponsored:	2 hospitals	1132 beds
Contract-managed:	0 hospitals	0 beds
Totals:	2 hospitals	1132 beds

0014: CONNECTICUT DEPARTMENT OF MENTAL HEALTH AND ADDICTION SERVICES (NP)
410 Capitol Avenue, Hartford, CT, Zip 06106–1367, Mailing Address: P.O. Box 341431, Zip 06134–1431, tel. 860/418–7000; Miriam Delphin-Rittmon, Ph.D., Commissioner
(Independent Hospital System)

CONNECTICUT: CONNECTICUT MENTAL HEALTH CENTER (O, 32 beds) 34 Park Street, New Haven, CT, Zip 06519–1109, Mailing Address: P.O. Box 1842, Zip 06508–1842, tel. 203/974–7144; Michael Sernyak, M.D., Director
Web address: www.ct.gov/dmhas/cwp/view.asp?a=2906&q=334596

CONNECTICUT VALLEY HOSPITAL (O, 361 beds) 1000 Silver Street, Middletown, CT, Zip 06457–3947; tel. 860/262–5000; Helene M. Vartelas, MSN, Chief Executive Officer

For explanation of codes following names, see page B2.
★ Indicates Type III membership in the American Hospital Association.

SOUTHWEST CONNECTICUT MENTAL HEALTH SYSTEM (O, 62 beds) 1635 Central Avenue, Bridgeport, CT, Zip 06610–2717; tel. 203/551–7400; Alicia Feller, Chief Executive Officer
Web address: www.ct.gov/dmhas/cwp/view.asp?a=2946&q=378936

Owned, leased, sponsored:	3 hospitals	455 beds
Contract-managed:	0 hospitals	0 beds
Totals:	3 hospitals	455 beds

★0016: COOK COUNTY HEALTH AND HOSPITALS SYSTEM (NP)
1900 West Polk Street, Suite 220, Chicago, IL, Zip 60612–3723; tel. 312/864–6820; John Jay. Shannon, M.D., Chief Executive Officer
(Independent Hospital System)

ILLINOIS: JOHN H. STROGER JR. HOSPITAL OF COOK COUNTY (O, 450 beds) 1969 West Ogden Avenue, Chicago, IL, Zip 60612–3714; tel. 312/864–6000; John Jay. Shannon, M.D., Chief Executive Officer
Web address: www.cookcountyhealth.net

PROVIDENT HOSPITAL OF COOK COUNTY (O, 25 beds) 500 East 51st Street, Chicago, IL, Zip 60615–2494; tel. 312/572–2000; John Jay. Shannon, M.D., Chief Executive Officer
Web address: www.ccbhs.org/pages/ProvidentHospitalofCookCounty.htm

Owned, leased, sponsored:	2 hospitals	475 beds
Contract-managed:	0 hospitals	0 beds
Totals:	2 hospitals	475 beds

0905: CORNERSTONE HEALTHCARE GROUP (IO)
2200 Ross Avenue, Suite 5400, Dallas, TX, Zip 75201–7984; tel. 469/621–6700; Steve Jakubcanin, President and Chief Executive Officer
(Independent Hospital System)

ARIZONA: CHG HOSPITAL TUCSON, LLC (O, 32 beds) 7220 East Rosewood Drive, Tucson, AZ, Zip 85710–1350; tel. 520/546–4595; Vanessa Acevedo, Interim Chief Executive Officer

ARKANSAS: CORNERSTONE HOSPITAL OF LITTLE ROCK (O, 30 beds) 2 Saint Vincent Circle, 6th Floor, Little Rock, AR, Zip 72205–5423; tel. 501/265–0600; James H. Rogers, FACHE, Chief Executive Officer
Web address: www.chghospitals.com/littlerock/

LOUISIANA: CORNERSTONE HOSPITAL OF BOSSIER CITY (O, 54 beds) 4900 Medical Drive, Bossier City, LA, Zip 71112–4521; tel. 318/747–9500; Sheri Burnette, R.N., Chief Executive Officer and Administrator
Web address: www.chghospitals.com/

CORNERSTONE HOSPITAL OF SOUTHWEST LOUISIANA (O, 30 beds) 524 Doctor Michael Debakey Drive, Lake Charles, LA, Zip 70601–5725; tel. 337/310–6000; Austin B. Cleveland, Chief Executive Officer

CORNERSTONE HOSPITAL-WEST MONROE (O, 40 beds) 6198 Cypress Street, West Monroe, LA, Zip 71291–9010; tel. 318/396–5600; Chris Simpson, Chief Executive Officer
Web address: www.chghospitals.com/chwm.html

MEMORIAL SPECIALTY HOSPITAL (O, 29 beds) 524 Doctor Michael Debakey Drive, 3rd Floor, Lake Charles, LA, Zip 70601–5725; tel. 337/480–8990; Jeffrey Clark, Administrator
Web address: www.lcmh.com/

OKLAHOMA: CORNERSTONE HOSPITAL OF OKLAHOMA-MUSKOGEE (O, 41 beds) 351 South 40th Street, Muskogee, OK, Zip 74401–4916; tel. 918/682–6161; Elizabeth Waytula, Chief Executive Officer
Web address: www.chghospitals.com/muskogee/

CORNERSTONE HOSPITAL OF OKLAHOMA-SHAWNEE (O, 34 beds) 1900 Gordon Cooper Drive, 2nd Floor, Shawnee, OK, Zip 74801–8603, Mailing Address: P.O. Box 1245, Zip 74802–1245, tel. 405/395–5800; Kristopher Karns, Chief Executive Officer

TEXAS: CHG CORNERSTONE HOSPITAL CONROE (O, 41 beds) 1500 Grand Lake Drive, Conroe, TX, Zip 77304–2891; tel. 936/523–1800; Suzanne Kretschmer, Chief Executive Officer
Web address: www.chghospitals.com/conroe/

CORNERSTONE HOSPITAL OF AUSTIN (O, 86 beds) 4207 Burnet Road, Austin, TX, Zip 78756–3396; tel. 512/706–1900; Curt L. Roberts, Chief Executive Officer

CORNERSTONE HOSPITAL OF HOUSTON AT CLEARLAKE (O, 148 beds) 709 Medical Center Boulevard, Webster, TX, Zip 77598; tel. 281/332–3322; Amy Stasney, R.N., Chief Executive Officer
Web address: www.cornerstonehealthcaregroup.com

CORNERSTONE HOSPITAL-MEDICAL CENTER OF HOUSTON (O, 35 beds) 2001 Hermann Drive, Houston, TX, Zip 77004; tel. 832/649–6200; Guido J. Cubellis, Chief Executive Officer

SOLARA HOSPITAL HARLINGEN (O, 82 beds) 508 Victoria Lane, Harlingen, TX, Zip 78550–3225; tel. 956/425–9600; Cynthia Isaacs, Chief Executive Officer
Web address: www.chghospitals.com/harlingen/

SOLARA HOSPITAL MCALLEN (O, 78 beds) 301 West Expressway 83, 8th Floor, McAllen, TX, Zip 78503–3045; tel. 956/632–4880; David Tupper, Chief Executive Officer

WEST VIRGINIA: CORNERSTONE HOSPITAL OF HUNTINGTON (O, 28 beds) 2900 First Avenue, Two East, Huntington, WV, Zip 25702–1241; tel. 304/399–2600; Cynthia Isaacs, Chief Executive Officer
Web address: www.chghospitals.com

Owned, leased, sponsored:	15 hospitals	788 beds
Contract-managed:	0 hospitals	0 beds
Totals:	15 hospitals	788 beds

★0103: COTTAGE HEALTH (NP)
400 West Pueblo Street, Santa Barbara, CA, Zip 93105–4353, Mailing Address: P.O. Box 689, Zip 93102–0689, tel. 805/569–7290; Ronald C. Werft, President and Chief Executive Officer
(Independent Hospital System)

CALIFORNIA: GOLETA VALLEY COTTAGE HOSPITAL (O, 28 beds) 351 South Patterson Avenue, Santa Barbara, CA, Zip 93111–2496, Mailing Address: Box 6306, Zip 93160–6306, tel. 805/967–3411; Ronald C. Werft, President and Chief Executive Officer
Web address: www.sbch.org

SANTA BARBARA COTTAGE HOSPITAL (O, 363 beds) 400 West Pueblo Street, Santa Barbara, CA, Zip 93105–4390, Mailing Address: P.O. Box 689, Zip 93102–0689, tel. 805/682–7111; Ronald C. Werft, President and Chief Executive Officer

SANTA YNEZ VALLEY COTTAGE HOSPITAL (O, 11 beds) 2050 Viborg Road, Solvang, CA, Zip 93463–2295; tel. 805/688–6431; Ronald C. Werft, President and Chief Executive Officer
Web address: www.cottagehealthsystem.org

Owned, leased, sponsored:	3 hospitals	402 beds
Contract-managed:	0 hospitals	0 beds
Totals:	3 hospitals	402 beds

★5885: COVENANT HEALTH (CC)
100 Ames Pond Drive, Suite 102, Tewksbury, MA, Zip 01876–1240; tel. 978/654–6363; Stephen J. Grubbs, President and Chief Executive Officer
(Independent Hospital System)

MAINE: ST. JOSEPH HOSPITAL (O, 84 beds) 360 Broadway, Bangor, ME, Zip 04401–3979, Mailing Address: P.O. Box 403, Zip 04402–0403, tel. 207/262–1000; Mary Prybylo, President and Chief Executive Officer

ST. MARY'S REGIONAL MEDICAL CENTER (O, 353 beds) 93 Campus Avenue, Lewiston, ME, Zip 04240–6030, Mailing Address: P.O. Box 291, Zip 04243–0291, tel. 207/777–8100; Steven C. Jorgensen, Chief Executive Officer
Web address: www.stmarysmaine.com

NEW HAMPSHIRE: ST. JOSEPH HOSPITAL (O, 135 beds) 172 Kinsley Street, Nashua, NH, Zip 03060–3648; tel. 603/882–3000; John A. Jurczyk, FACHE, Senior Vice President and President
Web address: www.stjosephhospital.com

Owned, leased, sponsored:	3 hospitals	572 beds
Contract-managed:	0 hospitals	0 beds
Totals:	3 hospitals	572 beds

For explanation of codes following names, see page B2.
★ Indicates Type III membership in the American Hospital Association.

Section B

0123: COVENANT HEALTH (NP)
100 Fort Sanders West Boulevard, Knoxville, TN, Zip 37922–3353; tel. 865/531–5555; James VanderSteeg, President and Chief Executive Officer
(Centralized Health System)

TENNESSEE: CLAIBORNE MEDICAL CENTER (L, 105 beds) 1850 Old Knoxville Road, Tazewell, TN, Zip 37879–3625; tel. 423/626–4211; Patricia P. Ketterman, R.N., President and Chief Administrative Officer
Web address: www.claibornehospital.org

CUMBERLAND MEDICAL CENTER (O, 85 beds) 421 South Main Street, Crossville, TN, Zip 38555–5031; tel. 931/484–9511; David V. Bunch, President and Chief Administrative Officer

FORT LOUDOUN MEDICAL CENTER (L, 30 beds) 550 Fort Loudoun Medical Center Drive, Lenoir City, TN, Zip 37772–5673; tel. 865/271–6000; Jeffrey Feike, President and Chief Administrative Officer
Web address: www.covenanthealth.com

FORT SANDERS REGIONAL MEDICAL CENTER (O, 384 beds) 1901 West Clinch Avenue, Knoxville, TN, Zip 37916–2307; tel. 865/541–1111; Keith Altshuler, President and Chief Administrative Officer

LECONTE MEDICAL CENTER (O, 128 beds) 742 Middle Creek Road, Sevierville, TN, Zip 37862–5019, Mailing Address: P.O. Box 8005, Zip 37864–8005, tel. 865/446–7000; Gaye Jolly, FACHE, President and Chief Administrative Officer
Web address: www.lecontemedicalcenter.com

METHODIST MEDICAL CENTER OF OAK RIDGE (O, 210 beds) 990 Oak Ridge Turnpike, Oak Ridge, TN, Zip 37830–6976, Mailing Address: P.O. Box 2529, Zip 37831–2529, tel. 865/835–1000; Jeremy Biggs, President and Chief Administrative Officer

MORRISTOWN-HAMBLEN HEALTHCARE SYSTEM (O, 131 beds) 908 West Fourth North Street, Morristown, TN, Zip 37814–3894, Mailing Address: P.O. Box 1178, Zip 37816–1178, tel. 423/492–9000; Gordon Lintz, President and Chief Administrative Officer
Web address: www.morristownhamblen.com

PARKWEST MEDICAL CENTER (O, 434 beds) 9352 Park West Boulevard, Knoxville, TN, Zip 37923–4325, Mailing Address: P.O. Box 22993, Zip 37933–0993, tel. 865/373–1000; James VanderSteeg, Chief Executive Officer

ROANE MEDICAL CENTER (O, 52 beds) 8045 Roane Medical Center Dr, Harriman, TN, Zip 37748–8333; tel. 865/316–1000; Jason B. Pilant, President and Chief Administrative Officer
Web address: www.roanemedical.com

Owned, leased, sponsored:	9 hospitals	1559 beds
Contract-managed:	0 hospitals	0 beds
Totals:	9 hospitals	1559 beds

★**0036: COVENANT HEALTH SYSTEM** (NP)
3615 19th Street, Lubbock, TX, Zip 79410–1203; tel. 806/725–0447; Richard H. Parks, FACHE, President and Chief Executive Officer

Owned, leased, sponsored:	0 hospitals	0 beds
Contract-managed:	0 hospitals	0 beds
Totals:	0 hospitals	0 beds

0179: COXHEALTH (NP)
1423 North Jefferson Avenue, Springfield, MO, Zip 65802–1988; tel. 417/269–3108; Steven D. Edwards, President and Chief Executive Officer
(Centralized Physician/Insurance Health System)

MISSOURI: COX BARTON COUNTY MEMORIAL HOSPITAL (O, 25 beds) 29 NW First Lane, Lamar, MO, Zip 64759–8105; tel. 417/681–5100; Christopher B. Wyatt, President
Web address: www.bcmh.net

COX MEDICAL CENTER BRANSON (O, 120 beds) 525 Branson Landing Boulevard, Branson, MO, Zip 65616–2052, Mailing Address: P.O. Box 650, Zip 65615–0650, tel. 417/335–7000; William K. Mahoney, FACHE, President and Senior Vice President, Community Hospital Group

COX MEDICAL CENTERS (O, 665 beds) 1423 North Jefferson Street, Springfield, MO, Zip 65802–1988; tel. 417/269–3000; Steven D. Edwards, President and Chief Executive Officer
Web address: www.coxhealth.com

COX MONETT HOSPITAL (O, 25 beds) 801 North Lincoln Avenue, Monett, MO, Zip 65708–1641; tel. 417/235–3144; Darren Bass, President

Owned, leased, sponsored:	4 hospitals	835 beds
Contract-managed:	0 hospitals	0 beds
Totals:	4 hospitals	835 beds

0930: CRC HEALTH GROUP, INC. (IO)
20400 Stevens Creek Boulevard, Suite 600, Cupertino, CA, Zip 95014–2217; tel. 866/540–5240; Jerome E. Rhodes, Chief Executive Officer
(Independent Hospital System)

ARIZONA: SIERRA TUCSON (O, 139 beds) 39580 South Lago Del Oro Parkway, Tucson, AZ, Zip 85739–1091; tel. 520/624–4000; Stephen P. Fahey, Executive Director

NORTH CAROLINA: WILMINGTON TREATMENT CENTER (O, 44 beds) 2520 Troy Drive, Wilmington, NC, Zip 28401–7643; tel. 910/762–2727; Robert Pitts, Executive Director
Web address: www.wilmtreatment.com

Owned, leased, sponsored:	2 hospitals	183 beds
Contract-managed:	0 hospitals	0 beds
Totals:	2 hospitals	183 beds

0960: CURAE HEALTH (NP)
121 Leinart Street, Clinton, TN, Zip 37716–3632, Mailing Address: P.O. Box 358, Zip 37717–0358, tel. 865/269–4074; Steve Clapp, President and Chief Executive Officer
(Moderately Centralized Health System)

ALABAMA: NORTHWEST MEDICAL CENTER (O, 56 beds) 1530 U S Highway 43, Winfield, AL, Zip 35594–5056; tel. 205/487–7000; Michael D. Windham, Chief Executive Officer
Web address: www.northwestmedcenter.com

RUSSELLVILLE HOSPITAL (O, 92 beds) 15155 Highway 43, Russellville, AL, Zip 35653–1975, Mailing Address: P.O. Box 1089, Zip 35653–1089, tel. 256/332–1611; Christine R. Stewart, FACHE, Chief Executive Officer

FLORIDA: SPECIALTY HOSPITAL JACKSONVILLE (O, 62 beds) 4901 Richard Street, Jacksonville, FL, Zip 32207–7328; tel. 904/737–3120; Barbara McCarthy, Chief Executive Officer
Web address: www.specialtyhospitaljax.com

MISSISSIPPI: NORTHWEST MISSISSIPPI MEDICAL CENTER (O, 181 beds) 1970 Hospital Drive, Clarksdale, MS, Zip 38614–7202, Mailing Address: P.O. Box 1218, Zip 38614–1218, tel. 662/627–3211; Joel Southern, R.N., MSN, Chief Executive Officer
Web address: www.merithealthnorthwestms.com

Owned, leased, sponsored:	4 hospitals	391 beds
Contract-managed:	0 hospitals	0 beds
Totals:	4 hospitals	391 beds

1013: CURAHEALTH HOSPITALS (IO)
650 Beebalm Lane, Suite 220, Garland, TX, Zip 75040–2955; tel. 972/414–0070; Ken McGee, President and Chief Operating Officer
(Independent Hospital System)

ARIZONA: CURAHEALTH PHOENIX (O, 58 beds) 40 East Indianola Avenue, Phoenix, AZ, Zip 85012–2059; tel. 602/280–7000; Karen Cawley, Chief Executive Officer
Web address: www.curahealth.com

CURAHEALTH TUCSON (O, 51 beds) 355 North Wilmot Road, Tucson, AZ, Zip 85711–2601; tel. 520/584–4500; Camie Overton, Chief Executive Officer

For explanation of codes following names, see page B2.
★ Indicates Type III membership in the American Hospital Association.

LOUISIANA: CURAHEALTH NEW ORLEANS (O, 80 beds) 3601 Coliseum Street, New Orleans, LA, Zip 70115–3606; tel. 504/899–1555; Kristy Caleyo, Chief Executive Officer
Web address: www.curahealth.com

MASSACHUSETTS: CURAHEALTH HOSPITAL STOUGHTON (O, 111 beds) 909 Sumner Street, 1st Floor, Stoughton, MA, Zip 02072–3396; tel. 781/297–8200; MacGregor Morgan, R.N., Chief Executive Officer

OKLAHOMA: CURAHEALTH HOSPITAL OKLAHOMA CITY (O, 93 beds) 1407 North Robinson Avenue, Oklahoma City, OK, Zip 73103–4823; tel. 405/232–8000; Brenda Hood, Chief Executive Officer
Web address: www.curahealth.com

PENNSYLVANIA: CURAHEALTH HERITAGE VALLEY (O, 35 beds) 1000 Dutch Ridge Road, Beaver, PA, Zip 15009–9727; tel. 724/773–8480; Janie Rosenberger-Slampack, Chief Executive Officer

CURAHEALTH PITTSBURGH (O, 63 beds) 7777 Steubenville Pike, Oakdale, PA, Zip 15071–3409; tel. 412/494–5500; Carol Falo, R.N., Chief Executive Officer
Web address: www.curahealth.com

TENNESSEE: CURAHEALTH NASHVILLE (O, 60 beds) 1412 County Hospital Road, Nashville, TN, Zip 37218–3007; tel. 615/687–2600; Timothy C. Deaton, Chief Executive Officer
Web address: www.curahealth.com

Owned, leased, sponsored:	8 hospitals	551 beds
Contract-managed:	0 hospitals	0 beds
Totals:	8 hospitals	551 beds

★**0864: DAVIS HEALTH SYSTEM** (NP)
Reed Street and Gorman Avenue, Elkins, WV, Zip 26241, Mailing Address: P.O. Box 1697, Zip 26241–1697, tel. 304/636–3300; Vance Jackson, FACHE, President and Chief Executive Officer
(Independent Hospital System)

WEST VIRGINIA: BROADDUS HOSPITAL (O, 72 beds) 1 Healthcare Drive, Philippi, WV, Zip 26416–9405, Mailing Address: P.O. Box 930, Zip 26416–0930, tel. 304/457–1760; Dana L. Gould, Chief Executive Officer
Web address: www.davishealthsystem.org/

DAVIS MEDICAL CENTER (O, 80 beds) Gorman Avenue and Reed Street, Elkins, WV, Zip 26241, Mailing Address: P.O. Box 1484, Zip 26241–1484, tel. 304/636–3300; Vance Jackson, FACHE, Chief Executive Officer

Owned, leased, sponsored:	2 hospitals	152 beds
Contract-managed:	0 hospitals	0 beds
Totals:	2 hospitals	152 beds

1825: DCH HEALTH SYSTEM (NP)
809 University Boulevard East, Tuscaloosa, AL, Zip 35401–2029; tel. 205/759–7111; Bryan N. Kindred, FACHE, President and Chief Executive Officer
(Independent Hospital System)

ALABAMA: DCH REGIONAL MEDICAL CENTER (O, 607 beds) 809 University Boulevard East, Tuscaloosa, AL, Zip 35401–2029; tel. 205/759–7111; Paul Betz, FACHE, Administrator
Web address: www.dchsystem.com

FAYETTE MEDICAL CENTER (L, 167 beds) 1653 Temple Avenue North, Fayette, AL, Zip 35555–1314, Mailing Address: P O Drawer 710, Zip 35555–0710, tel. 205/932–5966; Donald J. Jones, FACHE, Administrator

Owned, leased, sponsored:	2 hospitals	774 beds
Contract-managed:	0 hospitals	0 beds
Totals:	2 hospitals	774 beds

★**0313: DEACONESS HEALTH SYSTEM** (NP)
600 Mary Street, Evansville, IN, Zip 47710–1658; tel. 812/450–5000; Shawn W. McCoy, Chief Executive Officer
(Moderately Centralized Health System)

INDIANA: DEACONESS GATEWAY HOSPITAL (O, 24 beds) 4007 Gateway Boulevard, Newburgh, IN, Zip 47630–8947; tel. 812/842–4784; Rebecca Malotte, Executive Director and Chief Nursing Officer
Web address: www.deaconess.com/

DEACONESS MIDTOWN HOSPITAL (O, 547 beds) 600 Mary Street, Evansville, IN, Zip 47710–1658; tel. 812/450–5000; Shawn W. McCoy, Chief Executive Officer
Web address: www.deaconess.com

GIBSON GENERAL HOSPITAL (C, 70 beds) 1808 Sherman Drive, Princeton, IN, Zip 47670–1043; tel. 812/385–3401; Claudia Eisenmann, Chief Executive Officer
Web address: www.gibsongeneral.com

THE WOMEN'S HOSPITAL (O, 74 beds) 4199 Gateway Boulevard, Newburgh, IN, Zip 47630–8940; tel. 812/842–4200; Christina M. Ryan, R.N., Chief Executive Officer

Owned, leased, sponsored:	3 hospitals	645 beds
Contract-managed:	1 hospitals	70 beds
Totals:	4 hospitals	715 beds

0330: DEKALB REGIONAL HEALTH SYSTEM (NP)
2701 North Decatur Road, Decatur, GA, Zip 30033–5918; tel. 404/501–1000; Robert E. Wilson Esq, Chief Executive Officer

Owned, leased, sponsored:	0 hospitals	0 beds
Contract-managed:	0 hospitals	0 beds
Totals:	0 hospitals	0 beds

★**9495: DEPARTMENT OF THE AIR FORCE** (FG)
1420 Pentagon, Room 4E1084, Washington, DC, Zip 20330–1420; tel. 202/767–4765, Lieutenant General; Thomas Travis, Surgeon General
(Independent Hospital System)

ALASKA: U. S. AIR FORCE REGIONAL HOSPITAL (O, 64 beds) 5955 Zeamer Avenue, Elmendorf AFB, AK, Zip 99506–3702; tel. 907/580–3006, Major; Mark Lamey, Commander
Web address: www.elmendorf.af.mil/

CALIFORNIA: DAVID GRANT USAF MEDICAL CENTER (O, 116 beds) 101 Bodin Circle, Travis AFB, CA, Zip 94535–1809; tel. 707/423–7300, Lieutenant; Michael Higgins, Commander

FLORIDA: U. S. AIR FORCE REGIONAL HOSPITAL (O, 57 beds) 307 Boatner Road, Suite 114, Eglin AFB, FL, Zip 32542–1282; tel. 850/883–8221, Colonel; Pamela Smith, Commander
Web address: www.eglin.af.mil

MISSISSIPPI: U. S. AIR FORCE MEDICAL CENTER KEESLER (O, 56 beds) 301 Fisher Street, Room 1A132, Keesler AFB, MS, Zip 39534–2519; tel. 228/376–2550, Colonel; Thomas Harrell, M.D., Commander
Web address: www.keesler.af.mil

NEVADA: MIKE O'CALLAGHAN FEDERAL HOSPITAL (O, 46 beds) 4700 Las Vegas Boulevard North, Suite 2419, Nellis AFB, NV, Zip 89191–6600; tel. 702/653–2000, Colonel; Christian Benjamin, USAF, MC, Commander

OHIO: WRIGHT PATTERSON MEDICAL CENTER (O, 62 beds) 4881 Sugar Maple Drive, Wright-Patterson AFB, OH, Zip 45433–5529; tel. 937/257–0837, Colonel; Freddie Jenkins, Administrator
Web address: www.wpafb.af.mil/units/wpmc/

VIRGINIA: U. S. AIR FORCE HOSPITAL (O, 65 beds) 77 Nealy Avenue, Hampton, VA, Zip 23665–2040; tel. 757/764–6969, Colonel; Susan Pietrykowski, Commander

Owned, leased, sponsored:	7 hospitals	466 beds
Contract-managed:	0 hospitals	0 beds
Totals:	7 hospitals	466 beds

For explanation of codes following names, see page B2.
★ Indicates Type III membership in the American Hospital Association.

★**9395: DEPARTMENT OF THE ARMY, OFFICE OF THE SURGEON GENERAL** (FG)
5109 Leesburg Pike, Falls Church, VA, Zip 22041–3215; tel. 703/681–3000, Lieutenant General; Nadja Y. West, Surgeon General
(Moderately Centralized Health System)

ALASKA: BASSETT ARMY COMMUNITY HOSPITAL (O, 24 beds) 1060 Gaffney Road, Box 7400, Fort Wainwright, AK, Zip 99703–5001, Mailing Address: 1060 Gaffney Road, Box 7440, Zip 99703–5001, tel. 907/361–4000, Colonel; Constance Jenkins, Commander
Web address: www.alaska.amedd.army.mil

CALIFORNIA: WEED ARMY COMMUNITY HOSPITAL (O, 27 beds) Inner Loop Road and 4th Street, Building 166, Fort Irwin, CA, Zip 92310–5065, Mailing Address: P.O. Box 105109, Zip 92310–5109, tel. 760/380–3108, Colonel; Larry O. France, Commander

COLORADO: EVANS U. S. ARMY COMMUNITY HOSPITAL (O, 68 beds) 1650 Cochrane Circle, Building 7500, Fort Carson, CO, Zip 80913–4613; tel. 719/526–7200, Colonel; Patrick M. Garman, Commander
Web address: www.https://evans.amedd.army.mil/

GEORGIA: DWIGHT DAVID EISENHOWER ARMY MEDICAL CENTER (O, 107 beds) 300 West Hospital Road, Fort Gordon, GA, Zip 30905–5741; tel. 706/787–5811, Colonel; John P. Lamoureux, Commander
Web address: www.ddeamc.amedd.army.mil

MARTIN ARMY COMMUNITY HOSPITAL (O, 57 beds) 7950 Martin Loop, Fort Benning, GA, Zip 31905–5648, Mailing Address: 7950 Martin Loop, B9200, Room 010, Zip 31905–5648, tel. 706/544–2516, Colonel; Marie Dominguez, Commander
Web address: www.martin.amedd.army.mil

WINN ARMY COMMUNITY HOSPITAL (O, 37 beds) 1061 Harmon Avenue, Hinesville, GA, Zip 31314–5641, Mailing Address: 1061 Harmon Avenue, Suite 2311B, Zip 31314–5641, tel. 912/435–6965, Colonel; Kirk W. Eggleston, Commanding Officer

HAWAII: TRIPLER ARMY MEDICAL CENTER (O, 181 beds) 1 Jarret White Road, Honolulu, HI, Zip 96859–5001; tel. 808/433–6661, Colonel; Mary Krueger, Commanding Officer
Web address: www.tamc.amedd.army.mil

KANSAS: IRWIN ARMY COMMUNITY HOSPITAL (O, 44 beds) 600 Caisson Hill Road, Junction City, KS, Zip 66442–7037; tel. 785/239–7000, Colonel; Risa Ware, Commander
Web address: www.iach.amedd.army.mil

KENTUCKY: COLONEL FLORENCE A. BLANCHFIELD ARMY COMMUNITY HOSPITAL (O, 66 beds) 650 Joel Drive, Fort Campbell, KY, Zip 42223–5318; tel. 270/798–8040, Colonel; Telita Crosland, Commander

LOUISIANA: BAYNE-JONES ARMY COMMUNITY HOSPITAL (O, 13 beds) 1585 3rd Street, Building 283, Fort Polk, LA, Zip 71459–5102; tel. 337/531–3928, Colonel; Marla J. Ferguson, Commanding Officer
Web address: www.polk.amedd.army.mil

MARSHALL ISLANDS: KWAJALEIN HOSPITAL (O, 14 beds) U S Army Kwajalein Atoll, Kwajalein Island, MH, Zip 96960, Mailing Address: Box 1702, APO, UNIT, Zip 96555–5000, tel. 805/355–2225; Elaine McMahon, Administrator

MISSOURI: GENERAL LEONARD WOOD ARMY COMMUNITY HOSPITAL (O, 42 beds) 4430 Missouri Avenue, Fort Leonard Wood, MO, Zip 65473–8952, Mailing Address: PO Box 4430, Zip 65473–8952, tel. 573/596–0414, Colonel; Kimberlie Biever, Hospital Commander
Web address: www.glwach.amedd.army.mil/

NEW YORK: KELLER ARMY COMMUNITY HOSPITAL (O, 12 beds) 900 Washington Road, West Point, NY, Zip 10996–1197, Mailing Address: U S Military Academy, Building 900, Zip 10996–1197, tel. 845/938–5169; Brett Venable, Commander

NORTH CAROLINA: WOMACK ARMY MEDICAL CENTER (O, 156 beds) 2817 Reilly Road, Fort Bragg, NC, Zip 28310–7302; tel. 910/907–6000, Colonel; Lance C. Raney, Commander
Web address: www.wamc.amedd.army.mil/

SOUTH CAROLINA: MONCRIEF ARMY COMMUNITY HOSPITAL (O, 60 beds) 4500 Stuart Street, Fort Jackson, SC, Zip 29207–5700; tel. 803/751–2160, Colonel; Traci Crawford, R.N., Commander
Web address: www.moncrief.amedd.army.mil

TEXAS: BROOKE ARMY MEDICAL CENTER (O, 226 beds) 3851 Roger Brookes Drive, Fort Sam Houston, TX, Zip 78234–4501; tel. 210/916–4141, Brigadier General; Jeffrey Johnson, Commander

CARL R. DARNALL ARMY MEDICAL CENTER (O, 109 beds) 36000 Darnall Loop, Fort Hood, TX, Zip 76544–5095; tel. 254/288–8000, Colonel; David R. Gibson, Chief Executive Officer
Web address: www.crdamc.amedd.army.mil

WILLIAM BEAUMONT ARMY MEDICAL CENTER (O, 209 beds) 5005 North Piedras Street, El Paso, TX, Zip 79920–5001; tel. 915/742–2121, Colonel; Erik G. Rude, Commander

VIRGINIA: FORT BELVOIR COMMUNITY HOSPITAL (O, 46 beds) 9300 Dewitt Loop, Fort Belvoir, VA, Zip 22060–5285; tel. 571/231–3224, Colonel; Jason S. Wieman, Director
Web address: www.fbch.capmed.mil/SitePages/Home.aspx

WASHINGTON: MADIGAN ARMY MEDICAL CENTER (O, 200 beds) Fitzsimmons Drive, Building 9040, Tacoma, WA, Zip 98431–1100; tel. 253/968–1110, Colonel; Thomas S. Bundt, Commanding Officer

Owned, leased, sponsored:	20 hospitals	1698 beds
Contract-managed:	0 hospitals	0 beds
Totals:	20 hospitals	1698 beds

★**9295: DEPARTMENT OF VETERANS AFFAIRS** (FG)
810 Vermont Avenue NW, Washington, DC, Zip 20420–0001; tel. 202/273–5781, Honorable; Robert Wilkie, Secretary
(Decentralized Health System)

ALABAMA: BIRMINGHAM VETERANS AFFAIRS MEDICAL CENTER (O, 141 beds) 700 South 19th Street, Birmingham, AL, Zip 35233–1927; tel. 205/933–8101; Stacy J. Vasquez, Chief Executive Officer

CENTRAL ALABAMA VETERANS HEALTH CARE SYSTEM (O, 245 beds) 215 Perry Hill Road, Montgomery, AL, Zip 36109–3798; tel. 334/272–4670; Linda Lake . Boyle, R.N., MSN, Director
Web address: www.centralalabama.va.gov/

TUSCALOOSA VETERANS AFFAIRS MEDICAL CENTER (O, 315 beds) 3701 Loop Road East, Tuscaloosa, AL, Zip 35404–5015; tel. 205/554–2000; John F. Merkle, Medical Center Director
Web address: www.tuscaloosa.va.gov

ARIZONA: NORTHERN ARIZONA VETERANS AFFAIRS HEALTH CARE SYSTEM (O, 147 beds) 500 Highway 89 North, Prescott, AZ, Zip 86313–5000; tel. 928/445–4860; Barbara A. Oemcke, Director

PHOENIX VETERANS AFFAIRS HEALTH CARE SYSTEM (O, 197 beds) 650 East Indian School Road, Phoenix, AZ, Zip 85012–1892; tel. 602/277–5551; RimaAnn O. Nelson, R.N., Director
Web address: www.phoenix.va.gov/

SOUTHERN ARIZONA VETERANS AFFAIRS HEALTH CARE SYSTEM (O, 323 beds) 3601 Sout 6th Avenue, Tucson, AZ, Zip 85723–0002, Mailing Address: 3601 South 6th Avenue, Zip 85723–0002, tel. 520/792–1450; William J. Caron, Director
Web address: www.tucson.va.gov

ARKANSAS: CENTRAL ARKANSAS VETERANS HEALTHCARE SYSTEM (O, 551 beds) 4300 West Seventh Street, Little Rock, AR, Zip 72205–5446; tel. 501/257–1000; Margie A. Scott, M.D., Director
Web address: www.littlerock.va.gov/

VETERANS HEALTH CARE SYSTEM OF THE OZARKS (O, 72 beds) 1100 North College Avenue, Fayetteville, AR, Zip 72703–1944; tel. 479/443–4301; Kelvin L. Parks, Interim Director

CALIFORNIA: SAN FRANCISCO VA MEDICAL CENTER (O, 241 beds) 4150 Clement Street, San Francisco, CA, Zip 94121–1545; tel. 415/221–4810; Bonnie S. Graham, Director
Web address: www.sanfrancisco.va.gov/

VA GREATER LOS ANGELES HEALTHCARE SYSTEM (O, 422 beds) 11301 Wilshire Boulevard, Los Angeles, CA, Zip 90073–1003; tel. 310/478–3711; Ann R. Brown, M.D., Director

VA LONG BEACH HEALTHCARE SYSTEM (O, 356 beds) 5901 East 7th Street, Long Beach, CA, Zip 90822–5201; tel. 562/826–8000; Walt Dannenberg, Director
Web address: www.longbeach.va.gov/

For explanation of codes following names, see page B2.
★ Indicates Type III membership in the American Hospital Association.

VA PALO ALTO HEALTH CARE SYSTEM (O, 755 beds) 3801 Miranda Avenue, Palo Alto, CA, Zip 94304–1207; tel. 650/493–5000; Thomas J. Fitzgerald III, Director

VA SAN DIEGO HEALTHCARE SYSTEM (O, 248 beds) 3350 LaJolla Village Drive, San Diego, CA, Zip 92161–0002; tel. 858/552–8585; Robert M. Smith, M.D., Director
Web address: www.sandiego.va.gov

VETERANS AFFAIRS CENTRAL CALIFORNIA HEALTH CARE SYSTEM (O, 117 beds) 2615 East Clinton Avenue, Fresno, CA, Zip 93703–2223; tel. 559/225–6100; Stephen R. Bauman, Medical Center Director

VETERANS AFFAIRS LOMA LINDA HEALTHCARE SYSTEM (O, 268 beds) 11201 Benton Street, Loma Linda, CA, Zip 92357–1000; tel. 909/825–7084; Andrew Welch, Interim Director
Web address: www.lomalinda.va.gov

COLORADO: GRAND JUNCTION VETERANS HEALTH CARE SYSTEM (O, 23 beds) 2121 North Avenue, Grand Junction, CO, Zip 81501–6428; tel. 970/242–0731; Michael T. Kilmer, DirectorSOUTHERN COLORADO HEALTHCARE SYSTEM (O, 299 beds)Las AnimasCO81054–0390719456–1260StuartCCollyer5139873Director

VETERANS AFFAIRS EASTERN COLORADO HEALTH CARE SYSTEM (O, 271 beds) 1055 Clermont Street, Denver, CO, Zip 80220–3877; tel. 303/399–8020; Sallie Houser-Hanfelder, FACHE, Director
Web address: www.denver.va.gov/

CONNECTICUT: VETERANS AFFAIRS CONNECTICUT HEALTHCARE SYSTEM (O, 197 beds) 950 Campbell Avenue, West Haven, CT, Zip 06516–2770; tel. 203/932–5711; Gerald F. Culliton, Medical Center Director
Web address: www.connecticut.va.gov

DELAWARE: WILMINGTON VETERANS AFFAIRS MEDICAL CENTER (O, 60 beds) 1601 Kirkwood Highway, Wilmington, DE, Zip 19805–4989; tel. 302/994–2511; Robert W. Callahan Jr, Interim Director
Web address: www.va.gov/wilmington

DISTRICT OF COLUMBIA: WASHINGTON DC VETERANS AFFAIRS MEDICAL CENTER (O, 291 beds) 50 Irving Street NW, Washington, DC, Zip 20422–0002; tel. 202/745–8000; Adam M. Robinson, Acting Director
Web address: www.washingtondc.va.gov/

FLORIDA: BAY PINES VETERANS AFFAIRS HEALTHCARE SYSTEM (O, 396 beds) 10000 Bay Pines Boulevard, Bay Pines, FL, Zip 33744–8200, Mailing Address: P.O. Box 5005, Zip 33744–5005, tel. 727/398–6661; Paul M. Russo, FACHE, Director
Web address: www.baypines.va.gov/

JAMES A. HALEY VETERANS' HOSPITAL-TAMPA (O, 499 beds) 13000 Bruce B Downs Boulevard, Tampa, FL, Zip 33612–4745; tel. 813/972–2000; Joe Battle, Director
Web address: www.tampa.va.gov/

MIAMI VETERANS AFFAIRS HEALTHCARE SYSTEM (O, 401 beds) 1201 NW 16th Street, Miami, FL, Zip 33125–1624; tel. 305/575–7000; David VanMeter, FACHE, Acting Director

NORTH FLORIDA/SOUTH GEORGIA VETERAN'S HEALTH SYSTEM (O, 255 beds) 1601 SW Archer Road, Gainesville, FL, Zip 32608–1135; tel. 352/376–1611; Thomas Wisnieski, FACHE, Director
Web address: www.northflorida.va.gov

WEST PALM BEACH VETERANS AFFAIRS MEDICAL CENTER (O, 300 beds) 7305 North Military Trail, West Palm Beach, FL, Zip 33410–6400; tel. 561/422–8262; Donna Katen-Bahensky, Director

GEORGIA: ATLANTA VETERANS AFFAIRS MEDICAL CENTER (O, 239 beds) 1670 Clairmont Road, Decatur, GA, Zip 30033–4004; tel. 404/321–6111; Ann R. Brown, M.D., Director
Web address: www.atlanta.va.gov/

CARL VINSON VETERANS AFFAIRS MEDICAL CENTER (O, 178 beds) 1826 Veterans Boulevard, Dublin, GA, Zip 31021–3620; tel. 478/272–1210; David Whitmer, FACHE, Director
Web address: www.dublin.va.gov/

CHARLIE NORWOOD VETERANS AFFAIRS MEDICAL CENTER (O, 338 beds) 1 Freedom Way, Augusta, GA, Zip 30904–6285; tel. 706/733–0188; Robin E. Jackson, Ph.D., Interim Acting Director

HAWAII: VETERANS AFFAIRS PACIFIC ISLANDS HEALTH CARE SYSTEM (O, 80 beds) 459 Patterson Road, Honolulu, HI, Zip 96819–1522; tel. 808/433–0600; Jennifer S. Gutowski, FACHE, Director
Web address: www.hawaii.va.gov/

IDAHO: BOISE VETERANS AFFAIRS MEDICAL CENTER (O, 87 beds) 500 West Fort Street, Boise, ID, Zip 83702–4598; tel. 208/422–1000; David P. Wood, FACHE, Director

ILLINOIS: CAPTAIN JAMES A. LOVELL FEDERAL HEALTH CARE CENTER (O, 297 beds) 3001 Green Bay Road, North Chicago, IL, Zip 60064–3049; tel. 847/688–1900; Daniel Zomcheck, Interim Director
Web address: www.lovell.fhcc.va.gov

EDWARD HINES, JR. VETERANS AFFAIRS HOSPITAL (O, 485 beds) 5000 South Fifth Avenue, Hines, IL, Zip 60141–3030, Mailing Address: P.O. Box 5000, Zip 60141–5000, tel. 708/202–8387; Steven E. Braverman, M.D., Director
Web address: www.hines.va.gov/

JESSE BROWN VETERANS AFFAIRS MEDICAL CENTER (O, 207 beds) 820 South Damen, Chicago, IL, Zip 60612–3776; tel. 312/569–8387; Marc Magill, MS, Medical Center Director

MARION VETERANS AFFAIRS MEDICAL CENTER (O, 54 beds) 2401 West Main Street, Marion, IL, Zip 62959–1188; tel. 618/997–5311; Jo-Ann M. Ginsberg, R.N., MSN, Director
Web address: www.marion.va.gov

VETERANS AFFAIRS ILLIANA HEALTH CARE SYSTEM (O, 221 beds) 1900 East Main Street, Danville, IL, Zip 61832–5198; tel. 217/554–3000; Diana Carranza, Interim Director

INDIANA: RICHARD L. ROUDEBUSH VETERANS AFFAIRS MEDICAL CENTER (O, 209 beds) 1481 West Tenth Street, Indianapolis, IN, Zip 46202–2884; tel. 317/554–0000; Brian Hancock, M.D., Director
Web address: www.indianapolis.va.gov

VETERANS AFFAIRS NORTHERN INDIANA HEALTH CARE SYSTEM (O, 217 beds) 2121 Lake Avenue, Fort Wayne, IN, Zip 46805–5100; tel. 260/426–5431; Michael Hershmann, Medical Center Director

IOWA: IOWA CITY VETERANS AFFAIRS HEALTH CARE SYSTEM (O, 78 beds) 601 Highway 6 West, Iowa City, IA, Zip 52246–2208; tel. 319/338–0581; Judith Johnson-Mekota, Director
Web address: www.iowacity.va.gov/

VETERANS AFFAIRS CENTRAL IOWA HEALTH CARE SYSTEM (O, 223 beds) 3600 30th Street, Des Moines, IA, Zip 50310–5753; tel. 515/699–5999; Gail L. Graham, Director

KANSAS: ROBERT J. DOLE VETERANS AFFAIRS MEDICAL CENTER (O, 41 beds) 5500 East Kellogg, Wichita, KS, Zip 67218–1607; tel. 316/685–2221; Rick Ament, Chief Executive Officer
Web address: www.wichita.va.gov

VETERANS AFFAIRS EASTERN KANSAS HEALTH CARE SYSTEM (O, 213 beds) 2200 South West Gage Boulevard, Topeka, KS, Zip 66622–0002; tel. 785/350–3111; Anthony Rudy. Klopfer, FACHE, Director

KENTUCKY: LEXINGTON VETERANS AFFAIRS MEDICAL CENTER (O, 45 beds) 1101 Veterans Drive, Lexington, KY, Zip 40502–2235; tel. 859/281–4901; James Belmont, Interim Director
Web address: www.lexington.va.gov/

ROBLEY REX VETERANS AFFAIRS MEDICAL CENTER (O, 116 beds) 800 Zorn Avenue, Louisville, KY, Zip 40206–1499; tel. 502/287–4000; Marylee Rothschild, M.D., Chief of Staff
Web address: www.louisville.va.gov

LOUISIANA: ALEXANDRIA VETERANS AFFAIRS HEALTH CARE SYSTEM (O, 143 beds) 2495 Shreveport Highway, 71 N, Pineville, LA, Zip 71360–4044, Mailing Address: P.O. Box 69004, Alexandria, Zip 71306–9004, tel. 318/473–0010; Peter C. Dancy Jr, FACHE, Director
Web address: www.alexandria.va.gov/

OVERTON BROOKS VETERANS AFFAIRS MEDICAL CENTER (O, 100 beds) 510 East Stoner Avenue, Shreveport, LA, Zip 71101–4295; tel. 318/221–8411; Richard Crockett, Director
Web address: www.shreveport.va.gov/

MAINE: MAINE VETERANS AFFAIRS MEDICAL CENTER (O, 109 beds) 1 VA Center, Augusta, ME, Zip 04330–6719; tel. 207/623–8411; Ryan S. Lilly, Director

MARYLAND: VETERANS AFFAIRS MARYLAND HEALTH CARE SYSTEM-BALTIMORE DIVISION (O, 727 beds) 10 North Greene Street, Baltimore, MD, Zip 21201–1524; tel. 410/605–7001; Adam M. Robinson, Director
Web address: www.maryland.va.gov/

MASSACHUSETTS: BEDFORD VETERANS AFFAIRS MEDICAL CENTER, EDITH NOURSE ROGERS MEMORIAL VETERANS HOSPITAL (O, 324 beds) 200 Springs Road, Bedford, MA, Zip 01730–1198; tel. 781/687–2000; Joan Clifford, R.N., FACHE, Medical Center Director and Chief Executive Officer

For explanation of codes following names, see page B2.
★ Indicates Type III membership in the American Hospital Association.

VETERANS AFFAIRS BOSTON HEALTHCARE SYSTEM BROCKTON DIVISION (O, 375 beds) 940 Belmont Street, Brockton, MA, Zip 02301–5596; tel. 508/583–4500; Vincent Ng, Director
Web address: www.boston.va.gov/

VETERANS AFFAIRS BOSTON HEALTHCARE SYSTEM (O, 361 beds) 1400 VFW Parkway, West Roxbury, MA, Zip 02132–4927; tel. 617/323–7700; Vincent Ng, Director

VETERANS AFFAIRS CENTRAL WESTERN MASSACHUSETTS HEALTHCARE SYSTEM (O, 117 beds) 421 North Main Street, Leeds, MA, Zip 01053–9764; tel. 413/582–3000; John P. Collins, FACHE, Medical Center Director
Web address: www.centralwesternmass.va.gov/

MICHIGAN: ALEDA E. LUTZ VETERANS AFFAIRS MEDICAL CENTER (O, 89 beds) 1500 Weiss Street, Saginaw, MI, Zip 48602–5298; tel. 989/497–2500; Karandeep Sraon, Interim Director
Web address: www.saginaw.va.gov/

BATTLE CREEK VETERANS AFFAIRS MEDICAL CENTER (O, 242 beds) 5500 Armstrong Road, Battle Creek, MI, Zip 49037–7314; tel. 269/966–5600; James Doelling, Executive Director

JOHN D. DINGELL VETERANS AFFAIRS MEDICAL CENTER (O, 209 beds) 4646 John 'R' Street, Detroit, MI, Zip 48201–1932; tel. 313/576–1000; Pamela J. Reeves, M.D., Director
Web address: www.detroit.va.gov/

OSCAR G. JOHNSON VETERANS AFFAIRS MEDICAL CENTER (O, 17 beds) 325 East 'H' Street, Iron Mountain, MI, Zip 49801–4792; tel. 906/774–3300; James W. Rice, Director
Web address: www.ironmountain.va.gov/

VETERANS AFFAIRS ANN ARBOR HEALTHCARE SYSTEM (O, 109 beds) 2215 Fuller Road, Ann Arbor, MI, Zip 48105–2399; tel. 734/769–7100; Andrew Pacyna, Acting Director

MINNESOTA: MINNEAPOLIS VETERANS AFFAIRS HEALTH CARE SYSTEM (O, 309 beds) One Veterans Drive, Minneapolis, MN, Zip 55417–2399; tel. 612/725–2000; Patrick J. Kelly, FACHE, Director
Web address: www.minneapolis.va.gov

ST. CLOUD VETERANS AFFAIRS HEALTH CARE SYSTEM (O, 388 beds) 4801 Veterans Drive, Saint Cloud, MN, Zip 56303–2099; tel. 320/252–1670; Stephen Black, MS, Health Care System Director
Web address: www.stcloud.va.gov

MISSISSIPPI: G.V. (SONNY) MONTGOMERY VETERANS AFFAIRS MEDICAL CENTER (O, 323 beds) 1500 East Woodrow Wilson Drive, Jackson, MS, Zip 39216–5199; tel. 601/362–4471; David M. Walker, M.D., Medical Center Director

VETERANS AFFAIRS GULF COAST VETERANS HEALTH CARE SYSTEM (O, 392 beds) 400 Veterans Avenue, Biloxi, MS, Zip 39531–2410; tel. 228/523–5000; Bryan C. Matthews, Medical Center Director
Web address: www.biloxi.va.gov/

MISSOURI: HARRY S. TRUMAN MEMORIAL VETERANS HOSPITAL (O, 126 beds) 800 Hospital Drive, Columbia, MO, Zip 65201–5275; tel. 573/814–6000; David Isaacks, Director
Web address: www.columbiamo.va.gov

JOHN J. PERSHING VETERANS AFFAIRS MEDICAL CENTER (O, 58 beds) 1500 North Westwood Boulevard, Poplar Bluff, MO, Zip 63901–3318; tel. 573/686–4151; Patricia Hall, MSN, Ph.D., R.N., Director
Web address: www.poplarbluff.va.gov

KANSAS CITY VETERANS AFFAIRS MEDICAL CENTER (O, 157 beds) 4801 East Linwood Boulevard, Kansas City, MO, Zip 64128–2226; tel. 816/861–4700; Kathleen R. Fogarty, MS, Director

VETERANS AFFAIRS ST. LOUIS HEALTH CARE SYSTEM (O, 356 beds) 915 North Grand Boulevard, Saint Louis, MO, Zip 63106–1621; tel. 314/652–4100; Keith D. Repko, Director
Web address: www.stlouis.va.gov/

MONTANA: VETERANS AFFAIRS MONTANA HEALTH CARE SYSTEM (O, 94 beds) 3687 Veterans Drive, Fort Harrison, MT, Zip 59636–9703, Mailing Address: P.O. Box 1500, Zip 59636–1500, tel. 406/442–6410; Paul Gregory, Acting Director

NEBRASKA: VETERANS AFFAIRS NEBRASKA-WESTERN IOWA HEALTH CARE SYSTEM – LINCOLN (O, 132 beds) 600 South 70th Street, Lincoln, NE, Zip 68510–2493; tel. 402/489–3802; Don Burman, Director
Web address: www.nebraska.va.gov/

VETERANS AFFAIRS NEBRASKA-WESTERN IOWA HEALTH CARE SYSTEM (O, 137 beds) 4101 Woolworth Avenue, Omaha, NE, Zip 68105–1873; tel. 402/346–8800; Don Burman, Director
Web address: www.nebraska.va.gov/

NEVADA: VETERANS AFFAIRS SIERRA NEVADA HEALTH CARE SYSTEM (O, 124 beds) 975 Kirman Avenue, Reno, NV, Zip 89502–0993; tel. 775/786–7200; Lisa M. Howard, Director

VETERANS AFFAIRS SOUTHERN NEVADA HEALTHCARE SYSTEM (O, 90 beds) 6900 North Pecos Road, North Las Vegas, NV, Zip 89086–4400; tel. 702/791–9000; William J. Caron, Chief Executive Officer
Web address: www.lasvegas.va.gov/

NEW HAMPSHIRE: MANCHESTER VETERANS AFFAIRS MEDICAL CENTER (O, 90 beds) 718 Smyth Road, Manchester, NH, Zip 03104–4098; tel. 603/624–4366; Alfred Montoya, Director
Web address: www.manchester.va.gov/

NEW JERSEY: VETERANS AFFAIRS NEW JERSEY HEALTH CARE SYSTEM (O, 439 beds) 385 Tremont Avenue, East Orange, NJ, Zip 07018–1095; tel. 973/676–1000; Vincent F. Immiti, FACHE, Director
Web address: www.newjersey.va.gov/

NEW MEXICO: NEW MEXICO VETERANS AFFAIRS HEALTH CARE SYSTEM – RAYMOND G. MURPHY MEDICAL CENTER (O, 203 beds) 1501 San Pedro SE, Albuquerque, NM, Zip 87108–5153; tel. 505/265–1711; Andrew Welch, Director

NEW YORK: ALBANY STRATTON VETERANS AFFAIRS MEDICAL CENTER (O, 121 beds) 113 Holland Avenue, Albany, NY, Zip 12208–3473; tel. 518/626–5000; Darlene DeLancey, Interim Director
Web address: www.albany.va.gov/

BATH VETERANS AFFAIRS MEDICAL CENTER (O, 274 beds) 76 Veterans Avenue, Bath, NY, Zip 14810–0842; tel. 607/664–4000; Kenneth P. Piazza, Medical Center Director
Web address: www.bath.va.gov

CANANDAIGUA VETERANS AFFAIRS MEDICAL CENTER (O, 164 beds) 400 Fort Hill Avenue, Canandaigua, NY, Zip 14424–1159; tel. 585/394–2000; Bruce Tucker, Acting Director
Web address: www.canandaigua.va.gov/

JAMES J. PETERS VETERANS AFFAIRS MEDICAL CENTER (O, 378 beds) 130 West Kingsbridge Road, Bronx, NY, Zip 10468–3904; tel. 718/584–9000; Erik Langhoff, M.D., Ph.D., Director
Web address: www.bronx.va.gov/

NORTHPORT VETERANS AFFAIRS MEDICAL CENTER (O, 254 beds) 79 Middleville Road, Northport, NY, Zip 11768–2200; tel. 631/261–4400; Antonio Sanchez, M.D., Executive Director
Web address: www.northport.va.gov/index.asp

SYRACUSE VETERANS AFFAIRS MEDICAL CENTER (O, 160 beds) 800 Irving Avenue, Syracuse, NY, Zip 13210–2716; tel. 315/425–4400; Judy A. Hayman, Ph.D., Director
Web address: www.syracuse.va.gov/

VETERANS AFFAIRS HUDSON VALLEY HEALTH CARE SYSTEM (O, 270 beds) 2094 Albany Post Road, Montrose, NY, Zip 10548–1454, Mailing Address: P.O. Box 100, Zip 10548–0100, tel. 914/737–4400; Margaret B. Caplan, Director

VETERANS AFFAIRS NEW YORK HARBOR HEALTHCARE SYSTEM (O, 522 beds) 800 Poly Place, Brooklyn, NY, Zip 11209–7104; tel. 718/630–3500; Martina A. Parauda, Director
Web address: www.nyharbor.va.gov

VETERANS AFFAIRS WESTERN NEW YORK HEALTHCARE SYSTEM-BATAVIA DIVISION (O, 128 beds) 222 Richmond Avenue, Batavia, NY, Zip 14020–1288; tel. 585/297–1000; Michael J. Swartz, FACHE, Interim Director
Web address: www.buffalo.va.gov/batavia.asp

VETERANS AFFAIRS WESTERN NEW YORK HEALTHCARE SYSTEM-BUFFALO DIVISION (O, 113 beds) 3495 Bailey Avenue, Buffalo, NY, Zip 14215–1129; tel. 716/834–9200; Brian G. Stiller, Director Medical Center
Web address: www.buffalo.va.gov/index.asp

NORTH CAROLINA: CHARLES GEORGE VETERANS AFFAIRS MEDICAL CENTER (O, 170 beds) 1100 Tunnel Road, Asheville, NC, Zip 28805–2087; tel. 828/298–7911; Cynthia Breyfogle, FACHE, Director
Web address: www.asheville.va.gov/

For explanation of codes following names, see page B2.
★ Indicates Type III membership in the American Hospital Association.

Section B

DURHAM VETERANS AFFAIRS MEDICAL CENTER (O, 251 beds) 508 Fulton Street, Durham, NC, Zip 27705–3897; tel. 919/286–0411; Paul Crews, Director

FAYETTEVILLE VETERANS AFFAIRS MEDICAL CENTER (O, 58 beds) 2300 Ramsey Street, Fayetteville, NC, Zip 28301–3899; tel. 910/488–2120; Webster Carl. Bazemore, M.D., Interim Medical Director
Web address: www.fayettevillenc.va.gov

W. G. (BILL) HEFFNER VETERANS AFFAIRS MEDICAL CENTER (O, 218 beds) 1601 Brenner Avenue, Salisbury, NC, Zip 28144–2559; tel. 704/638–9000; Joseph Vaughn, Director
Web address: www.salisbury.va.gov

NORTH DAKOTA: FARGO VETERANS AFFAIRS HEALTH CARE SYSTEM (O, 65 beds) 2101 Elm Street North, Fargo, ND, Zip 58102; tel. 701/232–3241; Lavonne Liversage, Director
Web address: www.fargo.va.gov/

OHIO: CHILLICOTHE VETERANS AFFAIRS MEDICAL CENTER (O, 295 beds) 17273 State Route 104, Chillicothe, OH, Zip 45601–9718; tel. 740/773–1141; Beth A. Lumia, Acting Medical Center Director

CINCINNATI VETERANS AFFAIRS MEDICAL CENTER (O, 268 beds) 3200 Vine Street, Cincinnati, OH, Zip 45220–2288; tel. 513/475–6300; Mark Murdock, FACHE, Medical Center Director
Web address: www.cincinnati.va.gov/

DAYTON VETERANS AFFAIRS MEDICAL CENTER (O, 486 beds) 4100 West Third Street, Dayton, OH, Zip 45428–9000; tel. 937/268–6511; Jill Dietrich, JD, FACHE, Medical Center Director
Web address: www.dayton.va.gov/

LOUIS STOKES CLEVELAND VETERANS AFFAIRS MEDICAL CENTER (O, 578 beds) 10701 East Boulevard, Cleveland, OH, Zip 44106–1702; tel. 216/791–3800; Susan Fuehrer, Director

OKLAHOMA: JACK C. MONTGOMERY VETERANS AFFAIRS MEDICAL CENTER (O, 89 beds) 1011 Honor Heights Drive, Muskogee, OK, Zip 74401–1318; tel. 918/577–3000; Mark E. Morgan, Medical Center Director
Web address: www.muskogee.va.gov

OKLAHOMA CITY VETERANS AFFAIRS MEDICAL CENTER (O, 192 beds) 921 NE 13th Street, Oklahoma City, OK, Zip 73104–5028; tel. 405/456–1000; Kristopher Wade. Vlosich, Director
Web address: www.oklahoma.va.gov

OREGON: SOUTHERN OREGON-WHITE CITY VETERANS AFFAIRS REHABILITATION CENTER AND CLINICS (O, 1075 beds) 8495 Crater Lake Highway, White City, OR, Zip 97503; tel. 503/826–2111; Frank A. Drake, Director

VA PORTLAND HEALTHCARE SYSTEM (O, 176 beds) 3710 SW U S Veterans Hospital Road, Portland, OR, Zip 97239–2964, Mailing Address: 3710 SW US Veterans Hospital Road, Zip 97207–1034, tel. 503/220–8262; Michael W. Fisher, Director
Web address: www.portland.va.gov/

VETERANS AFFAIRS ROSEBURG HEALTHCARE SYSTEM (O, 88 beds) 913 NW Garden Valley Boulevard, Roseburg, OR, Zip 97471–6513; tel. 541/440–1000; Douglas V. Paxton, Director
Web address: www.roseburg.va.gov/

PENNSYLVANIA: COATESVILLE VETERANS AFFAIRS MEDICAL CENTER (O, 118 beds) 1400 Black Horse Hill Road, Coatesville, PA, Zip 19320–2040; tel. 610/384–7711; Carla Sivek, Director
Web address: www.coatesville.va.gov/

ERIE VETERANS AFFAIRS MEDICAL CENTER (O, 52 beds) 135 East 38th Street, Erie, PA, Zip 16504–1559; tel. 814/860–2576; John Gennaro, FACHE, Director
Web address: www.erie.va.gov/

JAMES E. VAN ZANDT VETERANS AFFAIRS MEDICAL CENTER (O, 68 beds) 2907 Pleasant Valley Boulevard, Altoona, PA, Zip 16602–4305; tel. 877/626–2500; Sigrid Andrew, Director

LEBANON VETERANS AFFAIRS MEDICAL CENTER (O, 213 beds) 1700 South Lincoln Avenue, Lebanon, PA, Zip 17042–7529; tel. 717/272–6621; Margaret G. Wilson, R.N., MSN, Acting Director
Web address: www.lebanon.va.gov

PHILADELPHIA VETERANS AFFAIRS MEDICAL CENTER (O, 291 beds) 3900 Woodland Avenue, Philadelphia, PA, Zip 19104–4594; tel. 215/823–5800; Daniel Hendee, Director
Web address: www.philadelphia.va.gov/

VETERANS AFFAIRS PITTSBURGH HEALTHCARE SYSTEM (O, 549 beds) University Drive, Pittsburgh, PA, Zip 15240–1001; tel. 866/482–7488; Karin L. McGraw, MSN, FACHE, Director

WILKES-BARRE VETERANS AFFAIRS MEDICAL CENTER (O, 165 beds) 1111 East End Boulevard, Wilkes-Barre, PA, Zip 18711–0030; tel. 570/824–3521; Russell E. Lloyd, Director
Web address: www.va.gov/vamcwb

PUERTO RICO: VETERANS AFFAIRS CARIBBEAN HEALTHCARE SYSTEM (O, 422 beds) 10 Casia Street, San Juan, PR, Zip 00921–3201; tel. 787/641–7582; Carlos R. Escobar, FACHE, Director

RHODE ISLAND: PROVIDENCE VETERANS AFFAIRS MEDICAL CENTER (O, 73 beds) 830 Chalkstone Avenue, Providence, RI, Zip 02908–4799; tel. 401/273–7100; Susan Mackenzie, Ph.D., Medical Center Director
Web address: www.providence.va.gov/

SOUTH CAROLINA: RALPH H. JOHNSON VETERANS AFFAIRS MEDICAL CENTER (O, 98 beds) 109 Bee Street, Charleston, SC, Zip 29401–5799; tel. 843/577–5011; Scott R. Isaacks, FACHE, Director and Chief Executive Officer
Web address: www.charleston.va.gov/

WM. JENNINGS BRYAN DORN VETERANS AFFAIRS MEDICAL CENTER (O, 216 beds) 6439 Garners Ferry Road, Columbia, SC, Zip 29209–1639; tel. 803/776–4000; David Omura, Director
Web address: www.columbiasc.va.gov/

SOUTH DAKOTA: SIOUX FALLS VETERANS AFFAIRS HEALTH CARE SYSTEM (O, 92 beds) 2501 West 22nd Street, Sioux Falls, SD, Zip 57105–1305, Mailing Address: P.O. Box 5046, Zip 57117–5046, tel. 605/336–3230; Darwin Goodspeed, Director
Web address: www.siouxfalls.va.gov

VETERANS AFFAIRS BLACK HILLS HEALTH CARE SYSTEM (O, 243 beds) 113 Comanche Road, Fort Meade, SD, Zip 57741–1099; tel. 605/347–2511; Sandra Horsman, Director

TENNESSEE: JAMES H. QUILLEN VETERANS AFFAIRS MEDICAL CENTER (O, 98 beds) Corner of Lamont & Veterans Way, Mountain Home, TN, Zip 37684, Mailing Address: P.O. Box 4000, Zip 37684–4000, tel. 423/926–1171; Dean B. Borsos, Medical Center Director
Web address: www.mountainhome.va.gov/

MEMPHIS VETERANS AFFAIRS MEDICAL CENTER (O, 251 beds) 1030 Jefferson Avenue, Memphis, TN, Zip 38104–2193; tel. 901/523–8990; David K. Dunning, Medical Center Director and Chief Executive Officer

TENNESSEE VALLEY HEALTHCARE SYSTEM (O, 437 beds) 1310 24th Avenue South, Nashville, TN, Zip 37212–2637; tel. 615/327–4751; Jennifer Vedral-Baron, Health System Director
Web address: www.tennesseevalley.va.gov

TEXAS: AMARILLO VETERANS AFFAIRS HEALTH CARE SYSTEM (O, 55 beds) 6010 West Amarillo Boulevard, Amarillo, TX, Zip 79106–1992; tel. 806/355–9703; Elizabeth Lowery, Interim Director
Web address: www.amarillo.va.gov/

CENTRAL TEXAS VETERANS HEALTH CARE SYSTEM (O, 1532 beds) 1901 Veterans Memorial Drive, Temple, TX, Zip 76504–7493; tel. 254/778–4811; Andrew T. Garcia, Interim Director
Web address: www.centraltexas.va.gov/

MICHAEL E. DEBAKEY VETERANS AFFAIRS MEDICAL CENTER (O, 479 beds) 2002 Holcombe Boulevard, Houston, TX, Zip 77030–4298; tel. 713/791–1414; Francisco Vazquez, Director

SOUTH TEXAS VETERANS HEALTH CARE SYSTEM (O, 838 beds) 7400 Merton Minter Boulevard, San Antonio, TX, Zip 78229–4404; tel. 210/617–5300; Christopher R. Sandles, FACHE, Medical Center Director
Web address: www.southtexas.va.gov/

VETERANS AFFAIRS NORTH TEXAS HEALTH CARE SYSTEM (O, 875 beds) 4500 South Lancaster Road, Dallas, TX, Zip 75216–7167; tel. 214/742–8387; Stephen R. Holt, M.D., Director
Web address: www.northtexas.va.gov/

WEST TEXAS VETERANS AFFAIRS HEALTH CARE SYSTEM (O, 149 beds) 300 Veterans Boulevard, Big Spring, TX, Zip 79720–5500, Big Springs, tel. 432/263–7361; Kalautie JangDhari, Director
Web address: www.bigspring.va.gov/about/

UTAH: VETERANS AFFAIRS SALT LAKE CITY HEALTH CARE SYSTEM (O, 123 beds) 500 Foothill Drive, Salt Lake City, UT, Zip 84148–0002; tel. 801/582–1565; Shella D. Stovall, R.N., Interim Director

For explanation of codes following names, see page B2.
★ Indicates Type III membership in the American Hospital Association.

VERMONT: WHITE RIVER JUNCTION VETERANS AFFAIRS MEDICAL CENTER (O, 76 beds) 215 North Main Street, White River Junction, VT, Zip 05009–0001; tel. 802/295–9363; Brett Rusch, M.D., Acting Director
Web address: www.whiteriver.va.gov/

VIRGINIA: HAMPTON VETERANS AFFAIRS MEDICAL CENTER (O, 451 beds) 100 Emancipation Drive, Hampton, VA, Zip 23667–0001; tel. 757/722–9961; Taquisa Simmons, Interim Director
Web address: www.hampton.va.gov/

HUNTER HOLMES MCGUIRE VETERANS AFFAIRS MEDICAL CENTER-RICHMOND (O, 381 beds) 1201 Broad Rock Boulevard, Richmond, VA, Zip 23249–0002; tel. 804/675–5000; J. Ronald. Johnson, Director
Web address: www.richmond.va.gov/

SALEM VETERANS AFFAIRS MEDICAL CENTER (O, 191 beds) 1970 Roanoke Boulevard, Salem, VA, Zip 24153–6478; tel. 540/982–2463; Rebecca J. Stackhouse, Medical Center Director
Web address: www.salem.va.gov

WASHINGTON: MANN-GRANDSTAFF VETERANS AFFAIRS MEDICAL CENTER (O, 68 beds) 4815 North Assembly Street, Spokane, WA, Zip 99205–6197; tel. 509/434–7000; Tracye B. Davis, Interim Medical Center Director

VETERANS AFFAIRS PUGET SOUND HEALTH CARE SYSTEM (O, 416 beds) 1660 South Columbian Way, Seattle, WA, Zip 98108–1597; tel. 206/762–1010; Michael C. Tadych, FACHE, Director
Web address: www.pugetsound.va.gov/

WEST VIRGINIA: BECKLEY VETERANS AFFAIRS MEDICAL CENTER (O, 173 beds) 200 Veterans Avenue, Beckley, WV, Zip 25801–6499; tel. 304/255–2121; Stacy J. Vasquez, Director
Web address: www.beckley.va.gov/

HUNTINGTON VETERANS AFFAIRS MEDICAL CENTER (O, 80 beds) 1540 Spring Valley Drive, Huntington, WV, Zip 25704–9300; tel. 304/429–6741; Brian Nimmo, Director
Web address: www.huntington.va.gov/

LOUIS A. JOHNSON VETERANS AFFAIRS MEDICAL CENTER (O, 71 beds) 1 Medical Center Drive, Clarksburg, WV, Zip 26301–4199; tel. 304/623–3461; Glenn R. Snider, M.D., Interim Director

MARTINSBURG VETERANS AFFAIRS MEDICAL CENTER (O, 557 beds) 510 Butler Avenue, Martinsburg, WV, Zip 25405–9990; tel. 304/263–0811; Timothy J. Cooke, Medical Center Director and Chief Executive Officer
Web address: www.martinsburg.va.gov/

WISCONSIN: CLEMENT J. ZABLOCKI VETERANS AFFAIRS MEDICAL CENTER (O, 637 beds) 5000 West National Avenue, Milwaukee, WI, Zip 53295–0001; tel. 414/384–2000; Daniel Zomchek, Ph.D., Chief Executive Officer and Medical Center Director
Web address: www.milwaukee.va.gov/

VA MEDICAL CENTER (O, 71 beds) 500 East Veterans Street, Tomah, WI, Zip 54660–3105; tel. 608/372–3971; Victoria Brahm, R.N., MSN, Medical Center Director

WILLIAM S. MIDDLETON MEMORIAL VETERANS HOSPITAL (O, 87 beds) 2500 Overlook Terrace, Madison, WI, Zip 53705–2286; tel. 608/256–1901; John J. Rohrer, Director
Web address: www.madison.va.gov

WYOMING: CHEYENNE VETERANS AFFAIRS MEDICAL CENTER (O, 61 beds) 2360 East Pershing Boulevard, Cheyenne, WY, Zip 82001–5392; tel. 307/778–7550; Paul L. Roberts, Director

SHERIDAN VETERANS AFFAIRS MEDICAL CENTER (O, 145 beds) 1898 Fort Road, Sheridan, WY, Zip 82801–8320; tel. 307/672–3473; Pamela Crowell, Director
Web address: www.sheridan.va.gov/

Owned, leased, sponsored:	135 hospitals	34353 beds
Contract-managed:	0 hospitals	0 beds
Totals:	135 hospitals	34353 beds

0845: DEVEREUX (NP)
444 Devereux Drive, Villanova, PA, Zip 19085–1932, Mailing Address: P.O. Box 638, Zip 19085–0638, tel. 610/520–3000; Robert Q. Kreider, President and Chief Executive Officer
(Independent Hospital System)

FLORIDA: DEVEREUX HOSPITAL AND CHILDREN'S CENTER OF FLORIDA (O, 100 beds) 8000 Devereux Drive, Melbourne, FL, Zip 32940–7907; tel. 321/242–9100; Steven Murphy, Executive Director
Web address: www.devereux.org

GEORGIA: DEVEREUX ADVANCED BEHAVIORAL HEALTH GEORGIA (O, 110 beds) 1291 Stanley Road NW, Kennesaw, GA, Zip 30152–4359; tel. 770/427–0147; Gwendolyn Skinner, Operational Vice President

PENNSYLVANIA: DEVEREUX CHILDREN'S BEHAVIORAL HEALTH CENTER (O, 49 beds) 655 Sugartown Road, Malvern, PA, Zip 19355–3303, Mailing Address: 655 Sugartown Rd, Zip 19355–3303, tel. 800/345–1292; Patricia Hillis-Clark, Executive Director
Web address: www.devereux.org

TEXAS: DEVEREUX TEXAS TREATMENT NETWORK (O, 30 beds) 1150 Devereux Drive, League City, TX, Zip 77573–2043; tel. 281/335–1000; Pamela E. Helm, Executive Director
Web address: www.devereux.org

Owned, leased, sponsored:	4 hospitals	289 beds
Contract-managed:	0 hospitals	0 beds
Totals:	4 hospitals	289 beds

0010: DIVISION OF MENTAL HEALTH AND ADDICTION SERVICES, DEPARTMENT OF HUMAN SERVICES, STATE OF NEW JERSEY (NP)
222 South Warren Street, Trenton, NJ, Zip 08608–2306, Mailing Address: P.O. Box 700, Zip 08625–0700, tel. 609/777–0702; Lynn Kovich, Assistant Commissioner
(Independent Hospital System)

NEW JERSEY: ANCORA PSYCHIATRIC HOSPITAL (O, 449 beds) 301 Spring Garden Road, Hammonton, NJ, Zip 08037–9699; tel. 609/561–1700; Joseph Canale, Acting Chief Executive Officer
Web address: https://www.state.nj.us/humanservices/dmhas/resources/services/treatment/aph.html

ARTHUR BRISBANE CHILDREN TREATMENT CENTER (O, 92 beds) County Road 524, Farmingdale, NJ, Zip 7727, Mailing Address: P.O. Box 625, Zip 7727; Vincent Giampeitro, Chief Executive Officer

GREYSTONE PARK PSYCHIATRIC HOSPITAL (O, 542 beds) 59 Koch Avenue, Morris Plains, NJ, Zip 07950–4400; tel. 973/538–1800; Tomika Carter, Chief Executive Officer
Web address: https://www.state.nj.us/humanservices/dmhas/resources/services/treatment/gpph.html

TRENTON PSYCHIATRIC HOSPITAL (O, 431 beds) Route 29 and Sullivan Way, Trenton, NJ, Zip 08628–3425, Mailing Address: P.O. Box 7500, West Trenton, Zip 08628–0500, tel. 609/633–1500; Robyn Caporoso, Chief Executive Officer
Web address: www.state.nj.us/humanservices/dmhs/oshm/tph/

Owned, leased, sponsored:	4 hospitals	1514 beds
Contract-managed:	0 hospitals	0 beds
Totals:	4 hospitals	1514 beds

0536: DIVISION OF MENTAL HEALTH, DEPARTMENT OF HUMAN SERVICES (NP)
319 East Madison Street, S-3B, Springfield, IL, Zip 62701–1035; tel. 217/785–6023; Lorrie Rickman. Jones, Ph.D., Director
(Independent Hospital System)

ILLINOIS: ALTON MENTAL HEALTH CENTER (O, 115 beds) 4500 College Avenue, Alton, IL, Zip 62002–5099; tel. 618/474–3800; Brian E. Thomas, Administrator

ANDREW MCFARLAND MENTAL HEALTH CENTER (O, 142 beds) 901 East Southwind Road, Springfield, IL, Zip 62703–5125; tel. 217/786–6994; Karen Schweighart, R.N., MS, Administrator

CHESTER MENTAL HEALTH CENTER (O, 271 beds) Chester Road, Chester, IL, Zip 62233–0031, Mailing Address: Box 31, Zip 62233–0031, tel. 618/826–4571; Leah Hammel, Acting Administrator

CHICAGO-READ MENTAL HEALTH CENTER (O, 200 beds) 4200 North Oak Park Avenue, Chicago, IL, Zip 60634–1457; tel. 773/794–4000; Ellen Otomo, Interim Hospital Administrator

For explanation of codes following names, see page B2.
★ Indicates Type III membership in the American Hospital Association.

Section B

CHOATE MENTAL HEALTH CENTER (O, 79 beds) 1000 North Main Street, Anna, IL, Zip 62906–1699; tel. 618/833–5161; Elaine Ray, Administrator

ELGIN MENTAL HEALTH CENTER (O, 383 beds) 750 South State Street, Elgin, IL, Zip 60123–7692; tel. 847/742–1040; Meredith Kiss, Administrator
Web address: www.dhs.state.il.us

JOHN J. MADDEN MENTAL HEALTH CENTER (O, 125 beds) 1200 South First Avenue, Hines, IL, Zip 60141–0800; tel. 708/338–7202; Edith Newman, Interim Administrator

Owned, leased, sponsored:	7 hospitals	1315 beds
Contract-managed:	0 hospitals	0 beds
Totals:	7 hospitals	1315 beds

★0861: DUKE LIFEPOINT HEALTHCARE (IO)
330 Seven Springs Way, Brentwood, TN, Zip 37027–5098; tel. 615/920–7000; Jeffrey G. Seraphine, FACHE, President
(Moderately Centralized Health System)

MICHIGAN: UP HEALTH SYSTEM-MARQUETTE (O, 260 beds) 580 West College Avenue, Marquette, MI, Zip 49855–2736; tel. 906/228–9440; Brian Sinotte, Chief Executive Officer
Web address: www.mgh.org

NORTH CAROLINA: CENTRAL CAROLINA HOSPITAL (O, 127 beds) 1135 Carthage Street, Sanford, NC, Zip 27330–4162; tel. 919/774–2100; Spencer Thomas, Chief Executive Officer

FRYE REGIONAL MEDICAL CENTER (O, 271 beds) 420 North Center Street, Hickory, NC, Zip 28601–5049, Mailing Address: 1950 11th Street Crt. NW, Zip 28601, tel. 828/315–5000; Garfield Atchison, Chief Executive Officer
Web address: www.fryemedctr.com

HARRIS REGIONAL HOSPITAL (O, 86 beds) 68 Hospital Road, Sylva, NC, Zip 28779–2722; tel. 828/586–7000; Steve Heatherly, Chief Executive Officer
Web address: www.westcare.org

HAYWOOD REGIONAL MEDICAL CENTER (O, 146 beds) 262 Leroy George Drive, Clyde, NC, Zip 28721–7430; tel. 828/456–7311; Rod Harkleroad, R.N., Chief Executive Officer
Web address: www.haymed.org

MARIA PARHAM MEDICAL CENTER (O, 102 beds) 566 Ruin Creek Road, Henderson, NC, Zip 27536–2927; tel. 252/438–4143; Bert Beard, Chief Executive Officer

PERSON MEMORIAL HOSPITAL (O, 77 beds) 615 Ridge Road, Roxboro, NC, Zip 27573–4629; tel. 336/599–2121; David Ziolkowski, Chief Executive Officer
Web address: www.personhospital.com

RUTHERFORD REGIONAL HEALTH SYSTEM (O, 112 beds) 288 South Ridgecrest Avenue, Rutherfordton, NC, Zip 28139–2838; tel. 828/286–5000; Rebecca Segal, Chief Executive Officer
Web address: www.rutherfordhosp.org

SWAIN COMMUNITY HOSPITAL (O, 25 beds) 45 Plateau Street, Bryson City, NC, Zip 28713–4200; tel. 828/488–2155; Steve Heatherly, Chief Executive Officer

WILSON MEDICAL CENTER (O, 220 beds) 1705 Tarboro Street, SW, Wilson, NC, Zip 27893–3428; tel. 252/399–8040; William E. Caldwell Jr, FACHE, Chief Executive Officer
Web address: www.wilmed.org

PENNSYLVANIA: CONEMAUGH MEMORIAL MEDICAL CENTER (O, 539 beds) 1086 Franklin Street, Johnstown, PA, Zip 15905–4398; tel. 814/534–9000; William E. Caldwell Jr, FACHE, Chief Executive Officer

CONEMAUGH MEYERSDALE MEDICAL CENTER (O, 20 beds) 200 Hospital Drive, Meyersdale, PA, Zip 15552–1249; tel. 814/634–5911; Heather Smith, President
Web address: www.conemaugh.org

CONEMAUGH MINERS MEDICAL CENTER (O, 30 beds) 290 Haida Avenue, Hastings, PA, Zip 16646–5610, Mailing Address: P.O. Box 689, Zip 16646–0689, tel. 814/247–3100; Timothy Harclerode, Chief Executive Officer
Web address: www.conemaugh.org

VIRGINIA: TWIN COUNTY REGIONAL HEALTHCARE (O, 86 beds) 200 Hospital Drive, Galax, VA, Zip 24333–2227; tel. 276/236–8181; Dale Alward, Chief Executive Officer
Web address: www.tcrh.org

Owned, leased, sponsored:	14 hospitals	2101 beds
Contract-managed:	0 hospitals	0 beds
Totals:	14 hospitals	2101 beds

★0190: DUKE UNIVERSITY HEALTH SYSTEM (NP)
201 Trent Drive, Durham, NC, Zip 27710–3037, Mailing Address: P.O. Box 3701, Zip 27710–3701, tel. 919/684–2255; A. Eugene. Washington, M.D., President and Chief Executive Officer
(Centralized Health System)

NORTH CAROLINA: DUKE RALEIGH HOSPITAL (O, 175 beds) 3400 Wake Forest Road, Raleigh, NC, Zip 27609–7373; tel. 919/954–3000; David William. Zaas, M.D., Chief Executive Officer
Web address: www.dukehealthraleigh.org

DUKE REGIONAL HOSPITAL (L, 214 beds) 3643 North Roxboro Street, Durham, NC, Zip 27704–2763; tel. 919/470–4000; Kathleen B. Galbraith, FACHE, President

DUKE UNIVERSITY HOSPITAL (O, 970 beds) 2301 Erwin Road, DUMC Box # 3814, Durham, NC, Zip 27705–4699, Mailing Address: P.O. Box 3814, Zip 27710–3708, tel. 919/684–8111; Thomas Owens, M.D., President
Web address: www.dukehealth.org

Owned, leased, sponsored:	3 hospitals	1359 beds
Contract-managed:	0 hospitals	0 beds
Totals:	3 hospitals	1359 beds

1027: DUNCAN REGIONAL HOSPITAL (NP)
1407 North Whisenant Drive, Duncan, OK, Zip 73533–1650; tel. 580/252–5300; Jay R. Johnson, FACHE, President and Chief Executive Officer
(Independent Hospital System)

OKLAHOMA: DUNCAN REGIONAL HOSPITAL (O, 117 beds) 1407 North Whisenant Drive, Duncan, OK, Zip 73533–1650, Mailing Address: P.O. Box 2000, Zip 73534–2000, tel. 580/252–5300; Jay R. Johnson, FACHE, President and Chief Executive Officer
Web address: www.duncanregional.com

JEFFERSON COUNTY HOSPITAL (L, 25 beds) Highway 70 and 81, Waurika, OK, Zip 73573–3075, Mailing Address: P.O. Box 90, Zip 73573–0090, tel. 580/228–2344; Richard Gillespie, Chief Executive Officer
Web address: www.jeffersoncountyhospital.net

Owned, leased, sponsored:	2 hospitals	142 beds
Contract-managed:	0 hospitals	0 beds
Totals:	2 hospitals	142 beds

★0926: EDWARD-ELMHURST HEALTHCARE (NP)
801 South Washington Street, Naperville, IL, Zip 60540–7430; tel. 630/527–3000; Mary Lou Mastro, FACHE, MS, R.N., System Chief Executive Officer
(Independent Hospital System)

ILLINOIS: EDWARD HOSPITAL (O, 358 beds) 801 South Washington Street, Naperville, IL, Zip 60540–7499; tel. 630/527–3000; Bill Kottmann, President and Chief Executive Officer

ELMHURST HOSPITAL (O, 269 beds) 155 East Brush Hill Road, Elmhurst, IL, Zip 60126–5658; tel. 331/221–1000; Pamela L. Dunley, MS, R.N., Chief Executive Officer
Web address: www.eehealth.org

LINDEN OAKS HOSPITAL (O, 108 beds) 852 South West Street, Naperville, IL, Zip 60540–6400; tel. 630/305–5500; Gina Sharp, FACHE, President and Chief Executive Officer

Owned, leased, sponsored:	3 hospitals	735 beds
Contract-managed:	0 hospitals	0 beds
Totals:	3 hospitals	735 beds

For explanation of codes following names, see page B2.
★ Indicates Type III membership in the American Hospital Association.

1685: EINSTEIN HEALTHCARE NETWORK (NP)

5501 Old York Road, Philadelphia, PA, Zip 19141–3098; tel. 215/456–7890; Barry R. Freedman, President and Chief Executive Officer

PENNSYLVANIA: EINSTEIN MEDICAL CENTER MONTGOMERY (O, 171 beds) 559 West Germantown Pike, East Norriton, PA, Zip 19403–4250; tel. 484/622–1000; Beth Duffy, Chief Operating Officer

EINSTEIN MEDICAL CENTER PHILADELPHIA (O, 499 beds) 5501 Old York Road, Philadelphia, PA, Zip 19141–3098; tel. 215/456–7890; Barry R. Freedman, President and Chief Executive Officer
Web address: www.einstein.edu

Owned, leased, sponsored:	2 hospitals	670 beds
Contract-managed:	0 hospitals	0 beds
Totals:	2 hospitals	670 beds

0879: EMERUS (IO)

10077 Grogan's Mill, Suite 100, The Woodlands, TX, Zip 77380–1022; tel. 281/292–2450; Craig Goguen, Chief Executive Officer

TEXAS: BAPTIST EMERGENCY HOSPITAL (O, 30 beds) 16088 San Pedro, San Antonio, TX, Zip 78232–2249; tel. 210/402–4092; David Mitchell, Interim Chief Executive Officer
Web address: www.baptistemergencyhospital.com

BAYLOR SCOTT & WHITE EMERGENCY HOSPITAL – ROCKWALL (O, 8 beds) 1975 Alpha Drive Suite 100, Rockwall, TX, Zip 75087–4951; tel. 214/294–6200; Kyle Kirkpatrick, Chief Executive Officer

BAYLOR SCOTT & WHITE EMERGENCY HOSPITAL – BURLESON (O, 24 beds) 12500 South Freeway Suite 100, Burleson, TX, Zip 76028–7128; tel. 214/294–6250; Kyle Kirkpatrick, Chief Executive Officer
Web address: www.bayloremc.com/burleson

BAYLOR SCOTT & WHITE EMERGENCY HOSPITAL–AUBREY (O, 40 beds) 26791 Highway 380, Aubrey, TX, Zip 76227; tel. 972/347–2525; Kyle Kirkpatrick, Chief Executive Officer
Web address: www.bemcataubrey.com

MEMORIAL HERMANN FIRST COLONY HOSPITAL (O, 7 beds) 16000 Southwest Freeway, Suite 100, Sugar Land, TX, Zip 77479–2674; tel. 281/277–0911; Brenda Villafranco, Administrator
Web address: www.emerus.com

MEMORIAL HERMANN TOMBALL HOSPITAL (O, 15 beds) 24429 State Highway 249, Tomball, TX, Zip 77375–8214; tel. 281/516–0911, Brenda Villafranco, Administrator

Owned, leased, sponsored:	6 hospitals	124 beds
Contract-managed:	0 hospitals	0 beds
Totals:	6 hospitals	124 beds

★0256: EMORY HEALTHCARE (NP)

1440 Clifton Road NE, Suite 400, Atlanta, GA, Zip 30322–1102; tel. 404/778–5000; Jonathan S. Lewin, M.D., President
(Centralized Health System)

GEORGIA: EMORY DECATUR HOSPITAL (O, 472 beds) 2701 North Decatur Road, Decatur, GA, Zip 30033–5995; tel. 404/501–1000; Jim Forstner, Chief Executive Officer
Web address: www.dekalbmedical.org

EMORY HILLANDALE HOSPITAL (O, 70 beds) 2801 DeKalb Medical Parkway, Lithonia, GA, Zip 30058–4996; tel. 404/501–8000; Jim Forstner, Chief Executive Officer

EMORY JOHNS CREEK HOSPITAL (O, 118 beds) 6325 Hospital Parkway, Johns Creek, GA, Zip 30097–5775; tel. 678/474–7000; Marilyn Margolis, MSN, Chief Executive Officer
Web address: www.emoryjohnscreek.com

EMORY LONG-TERM ACUTE CARE (O, 38 beds) 450 North Candler Street, Decatur, GA, Zip 30030–2671; tel. 404/501–6700; Jim Forstner, Chief Executive Officer
Web address: www.dekalbmedicalcenter.org

EMORY REHABILITATION HOSPITAL (O, 46 beds) 1441 Clifton Road NE, Atlanta, GA, Zip 30322–1004; tel. 404/712–5512; Michael Eric. Garrard, FACHE, Chief Executive Officer
Web address: www.emoryhealthcare.org/rehabilitation

EMORY SAINT JOSEPH'S HOSPITAL OF ATLANTA (O, 273 beds) 5665 Peachtree Dunwoody Road NE, Atlanta, GA, Zip 30342–1701; tel. 678/843–7001; Heather Dexter, Chief Executive Officer

EMORY UNIVERSITY HOSPITAL MIDTOWN (O, 512 beds) 550 Peachtree Street NE, Atlanta, GA, Zip 30308–2247; tel. 404/686–4411; Daniel Owens, Chief Executive Officer
Web address: www.emoryhealthcare.org

EMORY UNIVERSITY HOSPITAL (O, 622 beds) 1364 Clifton Road NE, Atlanta, GA, Zip 30322; tel. 404/712–2000; Bryce D. Gartland, M.D., Chief Executive Officer
Web address: www.emoryhealthcare.org

Owned, leased, sponsored:	8 hospitals	2151 beds
Contract-managed:	0 hospitals	0 beds
Totals:	8 hospitals	2151 beds

★0023: ENCOMPASS HEALTH CORPORATION (IO)

3660 Grandview Parkway, Suite 200, Birmingham, AL, Zip 35243–3332, Mailing Address: 9001 Liberty Parkway, Zip 35242–3332, tel. 205/967–7116; Mark J. Tarr, President and Chief Executive Officer
(Independent Hospital System)

ALABAMA: ENCOMPASS HEALTH LAKESHORE REHABILITATION HOSPITAL (O, 100 beds) 3800 Ridgeway Drive, Birmingham, AL, Zip 35209–5599; tel. 205/868–2000; Michael Bartell, Chief Executive Officer
Web address: www.encompasshealth.com/lakeshorerehab

ENCOMPASS HEALTH REHABILITATION HOSPITAL OF DOTHAN (O, 51 beds) 1736 East Main Street, Dothan, AL, Zip 36301–3040, Mailing Address: P.O. Box 6708, Zip 36302–6708, tel. 334/712–6333; Margaret A. Futch, Chief Executive Officer

ENCOMPASS HEALTH REHABILITATION HOSPITAL OF GADSDEN (O, 44 beds) 801 Goodyear Avenue, Gadsden, AL, Zip 35903–1133; tel. 256/439–5000; Kayla Feazell, Chief Executive Officer
Web address: www.encompasshealth.com/gadsdenrehab

ENCOMPASS HEALTH REHABILITATION HOSPITAL OF MONTGOMERY (O, 70 beds) 4465 Narrow Lane Road, Montgomery, AL, Zip 36116–2900; tel. 334/284–7700; Randy Thompson, Chief Executive Officer
Web address: www.encompasshealth.com/montgomeryrehab

ENCOMPASS HEALTH REHABILITATION HOSPITAL OF SHELBY COUNTY (O, 35 beds) 900 Oak Mountain Commons Lane, Pelham, AL, Zip 35124; tel. 205/216–7600; Robert Russell, Chief Executive Officer
Web address: www.encompasshealth.com/shelbycountyrehab

ENCOMPASS REHABILITATION HOSPITAL OF NORTH ALABAMA (O, 70 beds) 107 Governors Drive SW, Huntsville, AL, Zip 35801–4326; tel. 256/535–2300; Douglas H. Beverly, Chief Executive Officer

REGIONAL REHABILITATION HOSPITAL (O, 58 beds) 3715 Highway 280/431 North, Phenix City, AL, Zip 36867; tel. 334/732–2200; Lora Davis, FACHE, Chief Executive Officer
Web address: www.regionalrehabhospital.com

ARIZONA: ENCOMPASS HEALTH REHABILITATION HOSPITAL OF EAST VALLEY (O, 60 beds) 5652 East Baseline Road, Mesa, AZ, Zip 85206–4713; tel. 480/567–0350; Jeffrey Roberts, Chief Executive Officer

ENCOMPASS HEALTH REHABILITATION HOSPITAL OF NORTHWEST TUCSON (O, 60 beds) 1921 West Hospital Drive, Tucson, AZ, Zip 85704–7806; tel. 520/742–2800; Timothy T. Poore, Chief Executive Officer
Web address: https://www.encompasshealth.com/northwesttucsonrehab

ENCOMPASS HEALTH REHABILITATION HOSPITAL OF SCOTTSDALE (O, 60 beds) 9630 East Shea Boulevard, Scottsdale, AZ, Zip 85260–6267; tel. 480/551–5400; Kenneth Bell, Chief Executive Officer

ENCOMPASS HEALTH REHABILITATION INSTITUTE OF TUCSON (O, 80 beds) 2650 North Wyatt Drive, Tucson, AZ, Zip 85712–6108; tel. 520/325–1300; Jeffrey Christensen, Chief Executive Officer
Web address: https://www.encompasshealth.com/rehabinstituteoftucson

For explanation of codes following names, see page B2.
★ Indicates Type III membership in the American Hospital Association.

ENCOMPASS HEALTH VALLEY OF THE SUN REHABILITATION HOSPITAL (O, 75 beds) 13460 North 67th Avenue, Glendale, AZ, Zip 85304–1042; tel. 623/878–8800; Beth Bacher, Chief Executive Officer

YUMA REHABILITATION HOSPITAL, A PARTNERSHIP OF ENCOMPASS HEALTH AND YRMC (O, 41 beds) 901 West 24th Street, Yuma, AZ, Zip 85364–6384; tel. 928/726–5000; Ian Hodge, Chief Executive Officer
Web address: https://www.encompasshealth.com/yumarehab

ARKANSAS: CHI ST. VINCENT HOT SPRINGS REHABILITATION HOSPITAL (O, 40 beds) 1636 Higdon Ferry Road, Hot Springs, AR, Zip 71913–6912; tel. 501/651–2000; Janette Daniels, Chief Executive Officer
Web address: https://www.encompasshealth.com

CHI ST. VINCENT SHERWOOD REHABILITATION HOSPITAL (O, 80 beds) 2201 Wildwood Avenue, Sherwood, AR, Zip 72120–5074; tel. 501/834–1800; Lisa Watson, Chief Executive Officer

ENCOMPASS HEALTH REHABILITATION HOSPITAL OF JONESBORO (O, 67 beds) 1201 Fleming Avenue, Jonesboro, AR, Zip 72401–4311, Mailing Address: P.O. Box 1680, Zip 72403–1680, tel. 870/932–0440; Donna Harris, Chief Executive Officer
Web address: www.healthsouthjonesboro.com

ENCOMPASS HEALTH REHABILITATION HOSPITAL, A PARTNER OF WASHINGTON REGIONAL (O, 80 beds) 153 East Monte Painter Drive, Fayetteville, AR, Zip 72703–4002; tel. 479/444–2200; Jack C. Mitchell, FACHE, Chief Executive Officer
Web address: https://www.encompasshealth.com/fayettevillerehab

ENCOMPASSS HEALTH REHABILITATION HOSPITAL OF FORT SMITH (O, 60 beds) 1401 South 'J' Street, Fort Smith, AR, Zip 72901–5155; tel. 479/785–3300; Dawn Watts, Chief Executive Officer
Web address: www.healthsouthfortsmith.com

CALIFORNIA: ENCOMPASS HEALTH REHABILITATION HOSPITAL OF BAKERSFIELD (O, 70 beds) 5001 Commerce Drive, Bakersfield, CA, Zip 93309–0689; tel. 661/323–5500; Martha Samora, R.N., FACHE, Chief Executive Officer

ENCOMPASS HEALTH REHABILITATION HOSPITAL OF TUSTIN (O, 48 beds) 14851 Yorba Street, Tustin, CA, Zip 92780–2925; tel. 714/832–9200; Diana Hanyak, Chief Executive Officer
Web address: www.tustinrehab.com

COLORADO: HEALTHSOUTH REHABILITATION HOSPITAL OF COLORADO SPRINGS (O, 60 beds) 325 Parkside Drive, Colorado Springs, CO, Zip 80910–3134; tel. 719/630–8000; Stephen Schaefer, Chief Executive Officer

HEALTHSOUTH REHABILITATION HOSPITAL OF LITTLETON (O, 28 beds) 1001 West Mineral Avenue, Littleton, CO, Zip 80120–4507; tel. 303/334–1100; David H. Shefte, Chief Executive Officer
Web address: www.healthsouthdenver.com

DELAWARE: HEALTHSOUTH REHABILITATION HOSPITAL OF MIDDLETOWN (O, 37 beds) 250 East Hampden Road, Middletown, DE, Zip 19709–5303; tel. 302/464–3400; Mathew Gooch, Chief Executive Officer
Web address: www.healthsouthmiddletown.com

FLORIDA: ENCOMPASS HEALTH REHABILITATION HOSPITAL OF ALTAMONTE SPRINGS (O, 50 beds) 831 South State Road 434, Altamonte Springs, FL, Zip 32714–3502; tel. 407/587–8600; George Welton, Chief Executive Officer
Web address: www.healthsouthaltamontesprings.com

ENCOMPASS HEALTH REHABILITATION HOSPITAL OF LARGO (O, 70 beds) 901 North Clearwater-Largo Road, Largo, FL, Zip 33770–4126; tel. 727/586–2999; Tripp Smith, Chief Executive Officer

ENCOMPASS HEALTH REHABILITATION HOSPITAL OF MIAMI (O, 60 beds) 20601 Old Cutler Road, Cutler Bay, FL, Zip 33189–2400; tel. 305/251–3800; Enrique A. Vicens-Rivera Jr, JD, Chief Executive Officer
Web address: www.healthsouthmiami.com

ENCOMPASS HEALTH REHABILITATION HOSPITAL OF OCALA (O, 60 beds) 2275 SW 22nd Lane, Ocala, FL, Zip 34471–7710; tel. 352/282–4000; Karthik Muthu, Chief Executive Officer
Web address: www.healthsouthocala.com

ENCOMPASS HEALTH REHABILITATION HOSPITAL OF PANAMA CITY (O, 75 beds) 1847 Florida Avenue, Panama City, FL, Zip 32405–4640; tel. 850/914–8600; Tony N. Bennett, Chief Executive Officer

ENCOMPASS HEALTH REHABILITATION HOSPITAL OF SARASOTA (O, 96 beds) 6400 Edgelake Drive, Sarasota, FL, Zip 34240–8813; tel. 941/921–8600; Marcus Braz, Chief Executive Officer
Web address: www.healthsouthsarasota.com

ENCOMPASS HEALTH REHABILITATION HOSPITAL OF SPRING HILL (O, 80 beds) 12440 Cortez Boulevard, Brooksville, FL, Zip 34613–2628; tel. 352/592–4250; Jeffrey Alexander, Chief Executive Officer

ENCOMPASS HEALTH REHABILITATION HOSPITAL OF SUNRISE (O, 126 beds) 4399 North Nob Hill Road, Sunrise, FL, Zip 33351–5899; tel. 954/749–0300; Michael S. Roffelsen, Chief Executive Officer
Web address: www.healthsouthsunrise.com

ENCOMPASS HEALTH REHABILITATION HOSPITAL OF TALLAHASSEE (O, 76 beds) 1675 Riggins Road, Tallahassee, FL, Zip 32308–5315; tel. 850/656–4800; K. Dale. Neely, FACHE, Chief Executive Officer
Web address: www.healthsouthtallahassee.com

ENCOMPASS HEALTH REHABILITATION HOSPITAL OF TREASURE COAST (O, 80 beds) 1600 37th Street, Vero Beach, FL, Zip 32960–4863; tel. 772/778–2100; Michael Kissner, Chief Executive Officer
Web address: www.healthsouthtreasurecoast.com

HEALTHSOUTH REHABILITATION HOSPITAL AT MARTIN HEALTH (O, 54 beds) 5850 SE Community Drive, Stuart, FL, Zip 34997–6420; tel. 772/324–3500; Ivette Miranda, Chief Executive Officer
Web address: www.healthsouthmartin.com

SEA PINES REHABILITATION HOSPITAL (O, 90 beds) 101 East Florida Avenue, Melbourne, FL, Zip 32901–8301; tel. 321/984–4600; Denise B. McGrath, Chief Executive Officer

GEORGIA: REHABILITATION HOSPITAL OF SAVANNAH (O, 50 beds) 6510 Seawright DR, Savannah, GA, Zip 31406–2752; tel. 800/622–7269; Kathy Kleinsteuber, Chief Executive Officer
Web address: www.rehabilitationhospitalsavannah.com

WALTON REHABILITATION HOSPITAL (O, 50 beds) 1355 Independence Drive, Augusta, GA, Zip 30901–1037; tel. 706/724–7746; Eric Crossan, Chief Executive Officer

ILLINOIS: VAN MATRE ENCOMPASS HEALTH (O, 61 beds) 950 South Mulford Road, Rockford, IL, Zip 61108–4274; tel. 815/381–8500; Jeffrey Reese, Chief Executive Officer
Web address: www.healthsouth.com

INDIANA: HEALTHSOUTH DEACONESS REHABILITATION HOSPITAL (O, 103 beds) 4100 Covert Avenue, Evansville, IN, Zip 47714–5567, Mailing Address: P.O. Box 5349, Zip 47716–5349, tel. 812/476–9983; Blake Bunner, Chief Executive Officer

KANSAS: KANSAS REHABILITATION HOSPITAL (O, 57 beds) 1504 SW Eighth Avenue, Topeka, KS, Zip 66606–1632; tel. 785/235–6600; William J. Overbey, Chief Executive Officer
Web address: www.kansasrehabhospital.com

MID-AMERICA REHABILITATION HOSPITAL (O, 98 beds) 5701 West 110th Street, Shawnee Mission, KS, Zip 66211–2503, Overland Park, tel. 913/491–2400; Tiffany Kiehl, Chief Executive Officer

WESLEY REHABILITATION HOSPITAL (O, 65 beds) 8338 West 13th Street North, Wichita, KS, Zip 67212–2984; tel. 316/729–9999; James F. Grocholski, FACHE, Chief Executive Officer
Web address: www.wesleyrehabhospital.com

KENTUCKY: CARDINAL HILL REHABILITATION HOSPITAL (O, 232 beds) 2050 Versailles Road, Lexington, KY, Zip 40504–1405; tel. 859/254–5701; Tara Diebling, Chief Executive Officer

ENCOMPASS REHABILITATION HOSPITAL OF LAKEVIEW (O, 40 beds) 134 Heartland Drive, Elizabethtown, KY, Zip 42701–2778; tel. 270/769–3100; Lori Jarboe, Chief Executive Officer
Web address: www.healthsouthlakeview.com

HEALTHSOUTH NORTHERN KENTUCKY REHABILITATION HOSPITAL (O, 40 beds) 201 Medical Village Drive, Edgewood, KY, Zip 41017–3407; tel. 859/341–2044; Jeremy Yates, Chief Executive Officer
Web address: www.healthsouthkentucky.com

LOUISIANA: ENCOMPASS HEALTH REHABILITATION HOSPITAL OF ALEXANDRIA (O, 47 beds) 104 North Third Street, Alexandria, LA, Zip 71301–8581; tel. 318/449–1370; David Goodson, Chief Executive Officer
Web address: www.healthsouthalexandria.com

MAINE: NEW ENGLAND REHABILITATION HOSPITAL OF PORTLAND (O, 90 beds) 335 Brighton Avenue, Portland, ME, Zip 04102–2363; tel. 207/775–4000; Jeanine Chesley, Chief Executive Officer

For explanation of codes following names, see page B2.
★ Indicates Type III membership in the American Hospital Association.

MARYLAND: HEALTHSOUTH CHESAPEAKE REHABILITATION HOSPITAL (O, 54 beds) 220 Tilghman Road, Salisbury, MD, Zip 21804–1921; tel. 410/546–4600; Steven Walas, Chief Executive Officer
Web address: www.healthsouthchesapeake.com

MASSACHUSETTS: ENCOMPASS HEALTH REHABILITATION HOSPITAL OF BRAINTREE (O, 187 beds) 250 Pond Street, Braintree, MA, Zip 02184–5351; tel. 781/348–2500; Randy Doherty, CPA, Chief Executive Officer

ENCOMPASS HEALTH REHABILITATION HOSPITAL OF NEW ENGLAND (O, 210 beds) Two Rehabilitation Way, Woburn, MA, Zip 01801–6098; tel. 781/935–5050; David Coggins, MS, Chief Executive Officer
Web address: www.newenglandrehab.com

ENCOMPASS HEALTH REHABILITATION HOSPITAL OF WESTERN MASSACHUSETTS (O, 53 beds) 222 State Street, Ludlow, MA, Zip 01056–3437; tel. 413/308–3300; John R. Hunt, Chief Executive Officer

FAIRLAWN REHABILITATION HOSPITAL (O, 110 beds) 189 May Street, Worcester, MA, Zip 01602–4339; tel. 508/791–6351; Anne Roper, Interim Chief Executive Officer
Web address: www.fairlawnrehab.org

MISSISSIPPI: ENCOMPASS HEALTH REHABILITATION HOSPITAL OF GULFPORT (O, 33 beds) 4500 13th Street, Suite 900, Gulfport, MS, Zip 39501–2515; tel. 228/822–6965; Amber Hester, Chief Executive Officer
Web address: www.healthsouthgulfport.com

MISSOURI: RUSK REHABILITATION HOSPITAL (O, 60 beds) 315 Business Loop 70 West, Columbia, MO, Zip 65203–3248; tel. 573/817–2703; John M. Dawes, FACHE, Chief Executive Officer
Web address: www.ruskrehab.com

THE REHABILITATION INSTITUTE OF ST. LOUIS (O, 131 beds) 4455 Duncan Avenue, Saint Louis, MO, Zip 63110–1111; tel. 314/658–3800; Mark Dwyer, FACHE, Chief Executive Officer
Web address: www.rehabinstitutestl.com

NEVADA: ENCOMPASS HEALTH REHABILITATION HOSPITAL OF DESERT CANYON (O, 50 beds) 9175 West Oquendo Road, Las Vegas, NV, Zip 89148–1234; tel. 702/252–7342; Peggy Nelson, Chief Executive Officer

ENCOMPASS HEALTH REHABILITATION HOSPITAL OF HENDERSON (O, 90 beds) 10301 Jeffreys Street, Henderson, NV, Zip 89052–3922; tel. 702/939–9400; Samantha Billig, Chief Executive Officer
Web address: www.hendersonrehabhospital.com

ENCOMPASS HEALTH REHABILITATION HOSPITAL OF LAS VEGAS (O, 79 beds) 1250 South Valley View Boulevard, Las Vegas, NV, Zip 89102–1861; tel. 702/877–8898; Michael Ward, Chief Executive Officer

NEW HAMPSHIRE: ENCOMPASS HEALTH REHABILITATION HOSPITAL OF CONCORD (O, 50 beds) 254 Pleasant Street, Concord, NH, Zip 03301–2508; tel. 603/226–9800; Diana Lachapelle, CPA, Chief Executive Officer
Web address: www.healthsouthrehabconcordnh.com

NEW JERSEY: ENCOMPASS HEALTH REHABILITATION HOSPITAL OF TINTON FALLS (O, 60 beds) 2 Centre Plaza, Tinton Falls, NJ, Zip 07724–9744; tel. 732/460–5320; Jason Dan. Hudson, R.N., Chief Executive Officer
Web address: www.rehabnjtintonfalls.com/

HEALTHSOUTH REHABILITATION HOSPITAL OF TOMS RIVER (O, 92 beds) 14 Hospital Drive, Toms River, NJ, Zip 08755–6470; tel. 732/244–3100; Patricia Ostaszewski, MS, Chief Executive Officer
Web address: www.rehabnjtomsriver.com/

HEALTHSOUTH REHABILITATION HOSPITAL OF VINELAND (O, 41 beds) 1237 West Sherman Avenue, Vineland, NJ, Zip 08360–6920; tel. 856/696–7100; Tammy Feuer, Chief Executive Officer

NEW MEXICO: HEALTHSOUTH REHABILITATION HOSPITAL OF NEW MEXICO (O, 87 beds) 7000 Jefferson Street NE, Albuquerque, NM, Zip 87109–4313; tel. 505/344–9478; Rachelle Spencer, Chief Executive Officer
Web address: www.healthsouthnewmexico.com

OHIO: HEALTHSOUTH REHABILITATION HOSPITAL AT DRAKE (O, 100 beds) 151 West Galbraith Road, Cincinnati, OH, Zip 45216–1015; tel. 513/418–5600; Ryan Smokovitz, Chief Executive Officer
Web address: www.healthsouthatdrake.com

HEALTHSOUTH REHABILITATION HOSPITAL OF DAYTON (O, 50 beds) One Elizabeth Place, Dayton, OH, Zip 45417–3445; tel. 937/424–8200; Lynne Blinco, Chief Executive Officer

OKLAHOMA: ST. JOHN REHABILITATION HOSPITAL (O, 40 beds) 1200 West Albany Drive, Broken Arrow, OK, Zip 74012–8146; tel. 918/744–2338; David Nicholas, Chief Executive Officer
Web address: www.stjohnrehab.com

PENNSYLVANIA: ENCOMPASS HEALTH HARMARVILLE REHABILITATION HOSPITAL (O, 60 beds) 320 Guys Run Road, Pittsburgh, PA, Zip 15238–0460, Mailing Address: P.O. Box 11460, Zip 15238–0460, tel. 412/828–1300; Mark Van Volkenburg, Chief Executive Officer

ENCOMPASS HEALTH NITTANY VALLEY REHABILITATION HOSPITAL (O, 73 beds) 550 West College Avenue, Pleasant Gap, PA, Zip 16823–7401; tel. 814/359–3421; Susan Hartman, Chief Executive Officer
Web address: www.nittanyvalleyrehab.com

ENCOMPASS HEALTH READING REHABILITATION HOSPITAL (O, 60 beds) 1623 Morgantown Road, Reading, PA, Zip 19607–9455; tel. 610/796–6000; Mathew Gooch, Area Chief Executive Officer
Web address: www.healthsouthreading.com

ENCOMPASS HEALTH REHABILITATION HOSPITAL OF ALTOONA (O, 80 beds) 2005 Valley View Boulevard, Altoona, PA, Zip 16602–4598; tel. 814/944–3535; Scott Filler, Chief Executive Officer
Web address: www.healthsouthaltoona.com

ENCOMPASS HEALTH REHABILITATION HOSPITAL OF ERIE (O, 100 beds) 143 East Second Street, Erie, PA, Zip 16507–1501; tel. 814/878–1200; John Papalia, Chief Executive Officer

ENCOMPASS HEALTH REHABILITATION HOSPITAL OF MECHANICSBURG (O, 75 beds) 175 Lancaster Boulevard, Mechanicsburg, PA, Zip 17055 3562; tel. 717/691–3700; Josette M. Myers, Chief Executive Officer
Web address: www.healthsouthpa.com

ENCOMPASS HEALTH REHABILITATION HOSPITAL OF SEWICKLEY (O, 44 beds) 303 Camp Meeting Road, Sewickley, PA, Zip 15143–8322; tel. 412/741–9500; Leah Laffey, R.N., Chief Executive Officer

ENCOMPASS HEALTH REHABILITATION HOSPITAL OF YORK (O, 90 beds) 1850 Normandie Drive, York, PA, Zip 17408–1534; tel. 717/767–6941; Steven Alwine, Chief Executive Officer
Web address: www.healthsouthyork.com

GEISINGER ENCOMPASS HEALTH REHABILITATION HOSPITAL (O, 42 beds) 2 Rehab Lane, Danville, PA, Zip 17821–8498; tel. 570/271–6733; Lorie Dillon, Chief Executive Officer

PUERTO RICO: ENCOMPASS HEALTH REHABILITATION HOSPITAL OF MANATI (O, 40 beds) Carretera 2, Kilometro 47 7, Manati, PR, Zip 674; tel. 787/621–3800; Enid Y. Gonzalez, Chief Executive Officer
Web address: www.healthsouth.com

ENCOMPASS HEALTH REHABILITATION HOSPITAL OF SAN JUAN (O, 32 beds) University Hospital, 3rd Floor, San Juan, PR, Zip 923, Mailing Address: P.O. Box 70344, Zip 923, tel. 707/274 5100; Daniel Del Castillo, Chief Executive Officer

SOUTH CAROLINA: ANMED HEALTH REHABILITATION HOSPITAL (O, 60 beds) 1 Spring Back Way, Anderson, SC, Zip 29621–2676; tel. 864/716–2600; Denise R. Murray, Chief Executive Officer
Web address: www.anmedrehab.com

ENCOMPASS HEALTH REHABILITATION HOSPITAL OF CHARLESTON (O, 49 beds) 9181 Medcom Street, Charleston, SC, Zip 29406–9168; tel. 843/820–7777; Michele M. Skripps, R.N., Chief Executive Officer
Web address: www.healthsouthcharleston.com

ENCOMPASS HEALTH REHABILITATION HOSPITAL OF COLUMBIA (O, 96 beds) 2935 Colonial Drive, Columbia, SC, Zip 29203–6811; tel. 803/254–7777; Chris Daughtry, Chief Executive Officer

ENCOMPASS HEALTH REHABILITATION HOSPITAL OF FLORENCE (O, 88 beds) 900 East Cheves Street, Florence, SC, Zip 29506–2704; tel. 843/679–9000; Brian Nunn, R.N., Chief Executive Officer
Web address: www.healthsouthflorence.com

ENCOMPASS HEALTH REHABILITATION HOSPITAL OF ROCK HILL (O, 50 beds) 1795 Dr. Frank Gaston Boulevard, Rock Hill, SC, Zip 29732–1190; tel. 803/326–3500; Deanna Martin, Chief Executive Officer
Web address: www.healthsouthrockhill.com

TENNESSEE: ENCOMPASS HEALTH REHABILITATION HOSPITAL OF CHATTANOOGA (O, 69 beds) 2412 McCallie Avenue, Chattanooga, TN, Zip 37404–3398; tel. 423/698–0221; Scott Rowe, Chief Executive Officer
Web address: www.healthsouthchattanooga.com

For explanation of codes following names, see page B2.
★ Indicates Type III membership in the American Hospital Association.

ENCOMPASS HEALTH REHABILITATION HOSPITAL OF FRANKLIN (O, 40 beds) 1000 Physicians Way, Franklin, TN, Zip 37067–1471; tel. 615/721–4000; Scott J. Peterson, Chief Executive Officer

ENCOMPASS HEALTH REHABILITATION HOSPITAL OF KINGSPORT (O, 50 beds) 113 Cassel Drive, Kingsport, TN, Zip 37660–3775; tel. 423/246–7240; Troy Clark, Chief Executive Officer
Web address: www.healthsouthkingsport.com

ENCOMPASS HEALTH REHABILITATION HOSPITAL OF MEMPHIS (O, 72 beds) 1282 Union Avenue, Memphis, TN, Zip 38104–3414; tel. 901/722–2000; Stephanie Bridges, Chief Executive Officer
Web address: www.healthsouthmemphis.com

ENCOMPASS HEALTH REHABILITATION HOSPITAL OF NORTH MEMPHIS (O, 50 beds) 4100 Austin Peay Highway, Memphis, TN, Zip 38128–2502; tel. 901/213–5400; Adam Yoe, Chief Executive Officer
Web address: www.healthsouthnorthmemphis.com

QUILLEN REHABILITATION HOSPITAL (O, 31 beds) 2511 Wesley Street, Johnson City, TN, Zip 37601–1723; tel. 423/952–1700; Brian Luff, Chief Executive Officer

SPIRE CANE CREEK REHABILITATION HOSPITAL (O, 40 beds) 180 Mount Pelia Road, Martin, TN, Zip 38237–3812; tel. 731/587–4231; Rick Johnson, Chief Executive Officer
Web address: www.healthsouthcanecreek.com

VANDERBILT STALLWORTH REHABILITATION HOSPITAL (O, 80 beds) 2201 Childrens Way, Nashville, TN, Zip 37212–3165; tel. 615/320–7600; Jeffrey Palmucci, Chief Executive Officer

TEXAS: CHI ST. JOSEPH HEALTH REHABILITATION HOSPITAL, AN AFFILIATE OF ENCOMPASS HEALTH (O, 49 beds) 1600 Joseph Drive, Suite 2000, Bryan, TX, Zip 77802–1502; tel. 979/213–4300; Amy Gray, Chief Executive Officer
Web address: www.encompasshealth.com/locations/stjrehab

CHRISTUS TRINITY MOTHER FRANCES REHABILITATION HOSPITAL, A PARTNER OF ENCOMPASS HEALTH (O, 94 beds) 3131 Troup Highway, Tyler, TX, Zip 75701–8352; tel. 903/510–7000; Sharla Anderson, Chief Executive Officer
Web address: www.tmfrehabhospital.com

ENCOMPASS HEALTH REHABILITATION HOSPITAL MIDLAND ODESSA (O, 80 beds) 1800 Heritage Boulevard, Midland, TX, Zip 79707–9750; tel. 432/520–1600; Christopher Wortham, Chief Executive Officer
Web address: www.healthsouthmidland.com

ENCOMPASS HEALTH REHABILITATION HOSPITAL THE VINTAGE (O, 60 beds) 20180 Chasewood Park Drive, Houston, TX, Zip 77070–1436; tel. 281/205–5100; Krista Uselman, Chief Executive Officer
Web address: www.reliantnwhouston.com

ENCOMPASS HEALTH REHABILITATION HOSPITAL THE WOODLANDS (O, 84 beds) 18550 'IH' 45 South, Conroe, TX, Zip 77384; tel. 281/364–2000; Jennifer Brewer, Chief Executive Officer

ENCOMPASS HEALTH REHABILITATION HOSPITAL VISION PARK (O, 60 beds) 117 Vision Park Boulevard, Shenandoah, TX, Zip 77384–3001; tel. 936/444–1700; Jennifer Brewer, Chief Executive Officer
Web address: www.healthsouthvisionpark.com/

ENCOMPASS HEALTH REHABILITATION HOSPITAL OF ABILENE (O, 60 beds) 6401 Directors Parkway, Abilene, TX, Zip 79606–5869; tel. 325/691–1600; Joe Roberson, Chief Executive Officer

ENCOMPASS HEALTH REHABILITATION HOSPITAL OF ARLINGTON (O, 85 beds) 3200 Matlock Road, Arlington, TX, Zip 76015–2911; tel. 817/468–4000; Tyrrell Taplin, Chief Executive Officer
Web address: www.healthsoutharlington.com

ENCOMPASS HEALTH REHABILITATION HOSPITAL OF AUSTIN (O, 40 beds) 330 West Ben White Boulevard, Austin, TX, Zip 78704; tel. 512/730–4800; Lauren Suarez, Chief Executive Officer
Web address: www.healthsouthaustin.com

ENCOMPASS HEALTH REHABILITATION HOSPITAL OF CITY VIEW (O, 62 beds) 6701 Oakmont Boulevard, Fort Worth, TX, Zip 76132–2957; tel. 817/370–4700; Janell Briscoe, Chief Executive Officer

ENCOMPASS HEALTH REHABILITATION HOSPITAL OF CYPRESS (O, 60 beds) 13031 Wortham Center Drive, Houston, TX, Zip 77065–5662; tel. 832/280–2500; Sheila A. Bollier, Chief Executive Officer
Web address: www.healthsouthcypress.com

ENCOMPASS HEALTH REHABILITATION HOSPITAL OF DALLAS (O, 40 beds) 7930 Northaven Road, Dallas, TX, Zip 75230–3331; tel. 214/706–8200; Daniel MacNicol, Chief Executive Officer

ENCOMPASS HEALTH REHABILITATION HOSPITAL OF FORT WORTH (O, 60 beds) 1212 West Lancaster Avenue, Fort Worth, TX, Zip 76102–4510; tel. 817/870–2336; Janell Briscoe, Chief Executive Officer
Web address: www.healthsouthfortworth.com

ENCOMPASS HEALTH REHABILITATION HOSPITAL OF HUMBLE (O, 60 beds) 19002 McKay Drive, Humble, TX, Zip 77338–5701; tel. 281/446–6148; Angela L. Simmons, Chief Executive Officer

ENCOMPASS HEALTH REHABILITATION HOSPITAL OF PEARLAND (O, 40 beds) 2121 Business Center Drive, Pearland, TX, Zip 77584–2153; tel. 346/907–3000; Michael Cabiro, Chief Executive Officer
Web address: https://www.encompasshealth.com/locations/pearlandrehab

ENCOMPASS HEALTH REHABILITATION HOSPITAL OF PLANO (O, 83 beds) 2800 West 15th Street, Plano, TX, Zip 75075–7526; tel. 972/612–9000; Brandon Tudor, Chief Executive Officer
Web address: www.healthsouthplano.com

ENCOMPASS HEALTH REHABILITATION HOSPITAL OF RICHARDSON (O, 50 beds) 3351 Waterview Parkway, Richardson, TX, Zip 75080–1449; tel. 972/398–5700; Brent Yates, Chief Executive Officer
Web address: www.relianthcp.com

ENCOMPASS HEALTH REHABILITATION HOSPITAL OF ROUND ROCK (O, 51 beds) 1400 Hester's Crossing, Round Rock, TX, Zip 78681–8025; tel. 512/244–4400; David Jones, Chief Executive Officer
Web address: https://www.encompasshealth.com/roundrockrehab

ENCOMPASS HEALTH REHABILITATION HOSPITAL OF SAN ANTONIO (O, 96 beds) 9119 Cinnamon Hill, San Antonio, TX, Zip 78240–5401; tel. 210/691–0737; Michael Thomas, Chief Executive Officer

ENCOMPASS HEALTH REHABILITATION HOSPITAL OF SUGAR LAND (O, 50 beds) 1325 Highway 6, Sugar Land, TX, Zip 77478–4906; tel. 281/276–7574; Nicholas Hardin, FACHE, Chief Executive Officer
Web address: www.healthsouthsugarland.com

ENCOMPASS HEALTH REHABILITATION HOSPITAL OF TEXARKANA (O, 60 beds) 515 West 12th Street, Texarkana, TX, Zip 75501–4416; tel. 903/735–5000; Harlo McCall, Chief Executive Officer

ENCOMPASS HEALTH REHABILITATION HOSPITAL OF WICHITA FALLS (O, 63 beds) 3901 Armory Road, Wichita Falls, TX, Zip 76302–2204; tel. 940/720–5700; Robbi Hudson, Chief Executive Officer
Web address: www.healthsouthwichitafalls.com

ENCOMPASS HEALTH REHABILITATION HOSPITAL OF THE MID-CITIES (O, 60 beds) 2304 State Highway 121, Bedford, TX, Zip 76021–5985; tel. 817/684–2000; Robert M. Smart, Chief Executive Officer
Web address: www.relianthcp.com

UTAH: HEALTHSOUTH REHABILITATION HOSPITAL OF UTAH (O, 105 beds) 8074 South 1300 East, Sandy, UT, Zip 84094–0743; tel. 801/561–3400; Jeff Frandsen, Chief Executive Officer

VIRGINIA: ENCOMPASS HEALTH REHABILITATION HOSPITAL OF FREDERICKSBURG (O, 40 beds) 300 Park Hill Drive, Fredericksburg, VA, Zip 22401–3387; tel. 540/368–7300; David Cashwell, Chief Executive Officer
Web address: www.fredericksburgrehabhospital.com

ENCOMPASS HEALTH REHABILITATION HOSPITAL OF NORTHERN VIRGINIA (O, 60 beds) 24430 Millstream Drive, Aldie, VA, Zip 20105–3098; tel. 703/957–2000; Alfred Santos, Chief Executive Officer
Web address: www.healthsouthnorthernvirginia.com

ENCOMPASS HEALTH REHABILITATION HOSPITAL OF PETERSBURG (O, 53 beds) 95 Medical Park Boulevard, Petersburg, VA, Zip 23805–9233; tel. 804/504–8100; Louis Collier, Chief Executive Officer

ENCOMPASS HEALTH REHABILITATION HOSPITAL OF VIRGINIA (O, 40 beds) 5700 Fitzhugh Avenue, Richmond, VA, Zip 23226–1800; tel. 804/288–5700; Dan Gaskell, Chief Executive Officer
Web address: https://www.encompasshealth.com

REHABILITATION HOSPITAL OF SOUTHWEST VIRGINIA (O, 25 beds) 103 North Street, Bristol, VA, Zip 24201–3201; tel. 276/642–7900; Georgeanne Cole, Chief Executive Officer
Web address: www.rehabilitationhospitalswvirginia.com

UVA-HEALTHSOUTH REHABILITATION HOSPITAL (O, 50 beds) 515 Ray C Hunt Drive, Charlottesville, VA, Zip 22903–2981; tel. 434/244–2000; Barbara Adcock Mohr, Chief Executive Officer

For explanation of codes following names, see page B2.
★ Indicates Type III membership in the American Hospital Association.

Section B

WEST VIRGINIA: ENCOMPASS HEALTH REHABILITATION HOSPITAL OF HUNTINGTON (O, 62 beds) 6900 West Country Club Drive, Huntington, WV, Zip 25705–2000; tel. 304/733–1060; Michael E. Zuliani, Chief Executive Officer
Web address: www.healthsouthhuntington.com

ENCOMPASS HEALTH REHABILITATION HOSPITAL OF MORGANTOWN (O, 96 beds) 1160 Van Voorhis Road, Morgantown, WV, Zip 26505–3437; tel. 304/598–1100; Tracy Vinciguerra, Chief Executive Officer
Web address: www.healthsouthmountainview.com

ENCOMPASS HEALTH REHABILITATION HOSPITAL OF PARKERSBURG (O, 40 beds) 3 Western Hills Drive, Parkersburg, WV, Zip 26105–8122; tel. 304/420–1300; Alvin R. Lawson, FACHE, JD, Chief Executive Officer
Web address: www.healthsouthwesternhills.com

ENCOMPASS HEALTH REHABILITATION HOSPITAL OF PRINCETON (O, 45 beds) 120 Twelfth Street, Princeton, WV, Zip 24740–2352; tel. 304/487–8000; Robert Williams, Chief Executive Officer
Web address: www.healthsouthsouthernhills.com

Owned, leased, sponsored:	124 hospitals	8335 beds
Contract-managed:	0 hospitals	0 beds
Totals:	124 hospitals	8335 beds

0959: EPHRAIM MCDOWELL HEALTH (NP)

217 South Third Street, Danville, KY, Zip 40422–1823; tel. 859/239–1000; Daniel E. McKay, Chief Executive Officer
(Independent Hospital System)

KENTUCKY: EPHRAIM MCDOWELL FORT LOGAN HOSPITAL (O, 25 beds) 110 Metker Trail, Stanford, KY, Zip 40484–1020; tel. 606/365–4600; Ina Louise. Glass, Administrator
Web address: www.fortloganhospital.org

EPHRAIM MCDOWELL JAMES B. HAGGIN MEMORIAL HOSPITAL (O, 25 beds) 464 Linden Avenue, Harrodsburg, KY, Zip 40330–1862; tel. 859/734–5441; Lynne Warner Lynn, R.N., Administrator

EPHRAIM MCDOWELL REGIONAL MEDICAL CENTER (O, 159 beds) 217 South Third Street, Danville, KY, Zip 40422–1823; tel. 859/239–1000; Daniel E. McKay, Chief Executive Officer
Web address: www.emrmc.org

Owned, leased, sponsored:	3 hospitals	209 beds
Contract-managed:	0 hospitals	0 beds
Totals:	3 hospitals	209 beds

0525: ERLANGER HEALTH SYSTEM (NP)

975 East Third Street, Chattanooga, TN, Zip 37403–2147; tel. 423/778–7000; Kevin M. Spiegel, President and Chief Executive Officer
(Centralized Physician/Insurance Health System)

NORTH CAROLINA: ERLANGER WESTERN CAROLINA HOSPITAL (O, 25 beds) 3990 U S Highway 64 East Alt, Murphy, NC, Zip 28906–7917; tel. 828/837–8161; Mark E. Kimball, Chief Executive Officer
Web address: https://www.erlanger.org

TENNESSEE: ERLANGER BLEDSOE HOSPITAL (C, 25 beds) 71 Wheeler Avenue, Pikeville, TN, Zip 37367, Mailing Address: P.O. Box 699, Zip 37367–0699, tel. 423/447–2112; Stephanie Boynton, Administrator
Web address: www.erlanger.org

ERLANGER MEDICAL CENTER (O, 788 beds) 975 East Third Street, Chattanooga, TN, Zip 37403–2147; tel. 423/778–7000; Kevin M. Spiegel, Chief Executive Officer

Owned, leased, sponsored:	2 hospitals	813 beds
Contract-managed:	1 hospitals	25 beds
Totals:	3 hospitals	838 beds

0382: ERNEST HEALTH, INC. (IO)

7770 Jefferson Street NE, Suite 320, Albuquerque, NM, Zip 87109–4386; tel. 505/856–5300; Darby Brockette, Chief Executive Officer
(Independent Hospital System)

ARIZONA: MOUNTAIN VALLEY REGIONAL REHABILITATION HOSPITAL (O, 16 beds) 3700 North Windsong Drive, Prescott Valley, AZ, Zip 86314–1253; tel. 928/759–8800; Judy Baum, Chief Executive Officer
Web address: www.mvrrh.ernesthealth.com

REHABILITATION HOSPITAL OF NORTHERN ARIZONA (O, 40 beds) 1851 North Gemini Drive, Flagstaff, AZ, Zip 86001–1607; tel. 928/774–7070; Judy Baum, Chief Executive Officer, Mountain Valley Regional Rehabilitation Hospital
Web address: www.ernesthealth.com/gallery-item/rehabilitation-hospital-of-northern-arizona/

COLORADO: NORTHERN COLORADO LONG TERM ACUTE HOSPITAL (O, 40 beds) 4401 Union Street, Johnstown, CO, Zip 80534; tel. 970/619–3663; Blake Sims, Chief Executive Officer

NORTHERN COLORADO REHABILITATION HOSPITAL (O, 40 beds) 4401 Union Street, Johnstown, CO, Zip 80534–2800; tel. 970/619–3400; Brenda Simon, Chief Executive Officer
Web address: www.ncrh.ernesthealth.com

IDAHO: NORTHERN IDAHO ADVANCED CARE HOSPITAL (O, 40 beds) 600 North Cecil Road, Post Falls, ID, Zip 83854–6200; tel. 208/262–2800; Una Alderman, Chief Executive Officer

REHABILITATION HOSPITAL OF THE NORTHWEST (O, 25 beds) 3372 East Jenalan Avenue, Post Falls, ID, Zip 83854–7787; tel. 208/262–8700; Darby Brockette, Chief Executive Officer
Web address: www.ernesthealth.com

INDIANA: LAFAYETTE REGIONAL REHABILITATION HOSPITAL (O, 40 beds) 950 Park East Boulevard, Lafayette, IN, Zip 47905–0792; tel. 765/447–4040; Greg Floyd, Chief Executive Officer
Web address: www.lrrh.ernesthealth.com

MONTANA: ADVANCED CARE HOSPITAL OF MONTANA (O, 40 beds) 3528 Gabel Road, Billings, MT, Zip 59102–7307; tel. 406/373–8000; Judi Powers, Chief Executive Officer

NEW MEXICO: ADVANCED CARE HOSPITAL OF SOUTHERN NEW MEXICO (O, 40 beds) 4451 East Lohman Avenue, Las Cruces, NM, Zip 88011–8267; tel. 575/521–6600; Claudia Saiz, Chief Executive Officer
Web address: www.achsnm.ernesthealth.com

REHABILITATION HOSPITAL OF SOUTHERN NEW MEXICO (O, 40 beds) 4441 East Lohman Avenue, Las Cruces, NM, Zip 88011–8267; tel. 575/521–6400; Sabrina Martin, Chief Executive Officer

OHIO: REHABILITATION HOSPITAL OF NORTHWEST OHIO (O, 40 beds) 1455 West Medical Loop, Toledo, OH, Zip 43614; tel. 419/214–6600; Scott Williams, Chief Executive Officer

SOUTH CAROLINA: GREENWOOD REGIONAL REHABILITATION HOSPITAL (O, 54 beds) 1530 Parkway, Greenwood, SC, Zip 29646–4027; tel. 864/330–1800; Kristin Manske, Chief Executive Officer
Web address: www.grrh.ernesthealth.com

TEXAS: LAREDO REHABILITATION HOSPITAL (O, 20 beds) 2005a East Bustamante Street, Laredo, TX, Zip 78041; tel. 956/764–8555; Larisa Higgins, Administrator and Chief Operating Officer

LAREDO SPECIALTY HOSPITAL (O, 40 beds) 2005 Bustamante Street, Laredo, TX, Zip 78041–5470; tel. 956/753–5353; Hanna Huang, Chief Executive Officer
Web address: www.lsh.ernesthealth.com

MESQUITE REHABILITATION INSTITUTE (O, 30 beds) 1023 North Belt Line Road, Mesquite, TX, Zip 75149–1788; tel. 972/216–2400; Brian Abraham, Chief Executive Officer
Web address: www.mesquiterehab.ernesthealth.com/

MESQUITE SPECIALTY HOSPITAL (O, 40 beds) 1024 North Galloway Avenue, Mesquite, TX, Zip 75149–2434; tel. 972/216–2300; Louis Bradley, Chief Executive Officer

NEW BRAUNFELS REGIONAL REHABILITATION HOSPITAL (O, 40 beds) 2041 Sundance Parkway, New Braunfels, TX, Zip 78130–2779; tel. 830/625–6700; Mario Rodriguez, Chief Executive Officer
Web address: www.nbrrh.ernesthealth.com

SOUTH TEXAS REHABILITATION HOSPITAL (O, 40 beds) 425 East Alton Gloor Boulevard, Brownsville, TX, Zip 78526–3361; tel. 956/554–6000; Leo Garza, Chief Executive Officer

TRUSTPOINT REHABILITATION HOSPITAL OF LUBBOCK (O, 72 beds) 4302A Princeton Street, Lubbock, TX, Zip 79415–1304; tel. 806/749–2222; Craig Bragg, Chief Executive Officer
Web address: www.trustpointhospital.com/

For explanation of codes following names, see page B2.
★ Indicates Type III membership in the American Hospital Association.

UTAH: NORTHERN UTAH REHABILITATION HOSPITAL (O, 20 beds) 5825 Harrison Boulevard, South Ogden, UT, Zip 84403–4316; tel. 801/475–5254; Ryan Keele, Chief Executive Officer

UTAH VALLEY SPECIALTY HOSPITAL (O, 40 beds) 306 River Bend Lane, Provo, UT, Zip 84604–5625; tel. 801/226–8880; Brynn Beck, Chief Executive Officer
Web address: www.uvsh.ernesthealth.com

WYOMING: ELKHORN VALLEY REHABILITATION HOSPITAL (O, 41 beds) 5715 East 2nd Street, Casper, WY, Zip 82609–4322; tel. 307/265–0005; Connie Longwell, Chief Executive Officer

Owned, leased, sponsored:	22 hospitals	838 beds
Contract-managed:	0 hospitals	0 beds
Totals:	22 hospitals	838 beds

★0396: ESSENTIA HEALTH (NP)
502 East Second Street, Duluth, MN, Zip 55805–1913; tel. 218/786–8376; David C. Herman, M.D., Chief Executive Officer
(Moderately Centralized Health System)

IDAHO: CLEARWATER VALLEY HOSPITAL AND CLINICS (O, 23 beds) 301 Cedar, Orofino, ID, Zip 83544–9029; tel. 208/476–4555; Lenne Bonner, President

ST. MARY'S HOSPITAL (O, 25 beds) 701 Lewiston Street, Cottonwood, ID, Zip 83522–9750, Mailing Address: P.O. Box 137, Zip 83522–0137, tel. 208/962–3251; Lenne Bonner, President
Web address: www.smh-cvhc.org/getpage.php?name=index

MINNESOTA: ESSENTIA HEALTH ADA (O, 14 beds) 201 9th Street West, Ada, MN, Zip 56510–1279; tel. 218/784–5000; Erin Stoltman, Administrator
Web address: www.essentiahealth.org

ESSENTIA HEALTH DULUTH (O, 154 beds) 502 East Second Street, Duluth, MN, Zip 55805–1982; tel. 218/727–8762; James Garvey, Hospital Operations
Web address: www.smdcmedicalcenter.org

ESSENTIA HEALTH FOSSTON (O, 74 beds) 900 Hilligoss Boulevard SE, Fosston, MN, Zip 56542–1599; tel. 218/435–1133; Kevin Gish, Administrator and Vice President
Web address: www.essentiahealth.org

ESSENTIA HEALTH NORTHERN PINES MEDICAL CENTER (O, 58 beds) 5211 Highway 110, Aurora, MN, Zip 55705–1599; tel. 218/229–2211; Laura Ackman, Chief Operating Officer and Administrator

ESSENTIA HEALTH SANDSTONE (O, 9 beds) 705 Lundorff Drive, Sandstone, MN, Zip 55072–5009; tel. 320/245–2212; Michael D. Hedrix, Administrator and President
Web address: www.pinemedicalcenter.org

ESSENTIA HEALTH ST. JOSEPH'S MEDICAL CENTER (O, 122 beds) 523 North Third Street, Brainerd, MN, Zip 56401–3098; tel. 218/829–2861; Adam Rees, President

ESSENTIA HEALTH ST. MARY'S – DETROIT LAKES (O, 132 beds) 1027 Washington Avenue, Detroit Lakes, MN, Zip 56501–3409; tel. 218/847–5611; Ryan Hill, Interim Administrator
Web address: www.essentiahealth.org

ESSENTIA HEALTH ST. MARY'S MEDICAL CENTER (O, 310 beds) 407 East Third Street, Duluth, MN, Zip 55805–1984; tel. 218/786–4000; James Garvey, Senior Vice President Hospital Practice, Essentia Health East
Web address: www.essentiahealth.org/StMarysMedicalCenter/FindaClinic/Essentia-HealthSt-Marys-Medical-Center-46.aspx

ESSENTIA HEALTH-DEER RIVER (O, 52 beds) 115 10th Avenue NE, Deer River, MN, Zip 56636–8795; tel. 218/246–2900; Marsha Green, Administrator and Chief Operating Officer

ESSENTIA HEALTH-GRACEVILLE (O, 55 beds) 115 West Second Street, Graceville, MN, Zip 56240–4845, Mailing Address: P.O. Box 157, Zip 56240–0157, tel. 320/748–7223; Julie Rosenberg, Administrator
Web address: www.essentiahealth.org/HolyTrinityHospital/FindaClinic/Essentia-HealthHoly-Trinity-Hospital-96.aspx

ESSENTIA HEALTH-VIRGINIA (L, 144 beds) 901 Ninth Street North, Virginia, MN, Zip 55792–2398; tel. 218/741–3340; Sam Stone, Operations Administrator
Web address: www.essentiahealth.org

NORTH DAKOTA: ESSENTIA HEALTH FARGO (O, 137 beds) 3000 32nd Avenue South, Fargo, ND, Zip 58103–6132; tel. 701/364–8000; Al Hurley, Chief Operating Officer
Web address: www.essentiahealth.com

WISCONSIN: ESSENTIA HEALTH ST. MARY'S HOSPITAL OF SUPERIOR (O, 25 beds) 3500 Tower Avenue, Superior, WI, Zip 54880–5395; tel. 715/817–7000; Terry Jacobson, Administrator and Chief Executive Officer

Owned, leased, sponsored:	15 hospitals	1334 beds
Contract-managed:	0 hospitals	0 beds
Totals:	15 hospitals	1334 beds

0951: EVEREST REHABILITATION HOSPITALS, LLC (IO)
5100 Belt Line Road, Suite 310, Dallas, TX, Zip 75254–7559; tel. 469/713–1145; Jay Quintana, Chief Executive Officer and Co-Founder

Owned, leased, sponsored:	0 hospitals	0 beds
Contract-managed:	0 hospitals	0 beds
Totals:	0 hospitals	0 beds

2395: EXCELA HEALTH (NP)
532 West Pittsburgh Street, Greensburg, PA, Zip 15601, Mailing Address: 134 Industrial Park Road, Zip 15601–7328, tel. 724/832–5050; Robert Rogalski, Chief Executive Officer
(Independent Hospital System)

PENNSYLVANIA: EXCELA FRICK HOSPITAL (O, 33 beds) 508 South Church Street, Mount Pleasant, PA, Zip 15666–1790; tel. 724/547–1500; Michael D. Busch, Executive Vice President and Chief Operating Officer
Web address: www.excelahealth.org/PatientsandVisitors/HospitalsFacilities/Hospitals/Frick.aspx

EXCELA HEALTH WESTMORELAND HOSPITAL (O, 270 beds) 532 West Pittsburgh Street, Greensburg, PA, Zip 15601–2282; tel. 724/832–4000; Robert Rogalski, Chief Executive Officer

EXCELA LATROBE AREA HOSPITAL (O, 114 beds) One Mellon Way, Latrobe, PA, Zip 15650–1096; tel. 724/537–1000; Michael D. Busch, Executive Vice President and Chief Operating Officer
Web address: www.excelahealth.org

Owned, leased, sponsored:	3 hospitals	417 beds
Contract-managed:	0 hospitals	0 beds
Totals:	3 hospitals	417 beds

★1325: FAIRVIEW HEALTH SERVICES (NP)
2450 Riverside Avenue, Minneapolis, MN, Zip 55454–1400; tel. 612/672–6141; James Hereford, President and Chief Executive Officer
(Centralized Health System)

MINNESOTA: BETHESDA HOSPITAL (O, 114 beds) 559 Capitol Boulevard, Saint Paul, MN, Zip 55103–2101; tel. 651/232–2000; Jeoff Will, Chief Operating Office, Acute Care Services
Web address: www.healtheast.org

FAIRVIEW LAKES HEALTH SERVICES (O, 37 beds) 5200 Fairview Boulevard, Wyoming, MN, Zip 55092–8013; tel. 651/982–7000; Lia Christiansen, Chief Operating Officer, Acute Care Hospitals

FAIRVIEW NORTHLAND MEDICAL CENTER (O, 23 beds) 911 Northland Drive, Princeton, MN, Zip 55371–2173; tel. 763/389–1313; Lia Christiansen, Chief Operating Officer, Acute Care Hospitals
Web address: www.northland.fairview.org

FAIRVIEW RIDGES HOSPITAL (O, 162 beds) 201 East Nicollet Boulevard, Burnsville, MN, Zip 55337–5799; tel. 952/892–2000; Jeoff Will, Chief Operating Officer, Acute Care Services

FAIRVIEW SOUTHDALE HOSPITAL (O, 316 beds) 6401 France Avenue South, Edina, MN, Zip 55435–2199; tel. 952/924–5000; Jeoff Will, Chief Operating Officer, Acute Care Services
Web address: www.fairview.org

For explanation of codes following names, see page B2.
★ Indicates Type III membership in the American Hospital Association.

GRAND ITASCA CLINIC AND HOSPITAL (O, 49 beds) 1601 Golf Course Road, Grand Rapids, MN, Zip 55744–8648; tel. 218/326–5000; Jean MacDonell, Interim Chief Executive Officer

RANGE REGIONAL HEALTH SERVICES (O, 72 beds) 750 East 34th Street, Hibbing, MN, Zip 55746–4600; tel. 218/262–4881; Patrick Sharp, Chief Executive Officer
Web address: www.range.fairview.org

ST. JOHN'S HOSPITAL (O, 192 beds) 1575 Beam Avenue, Maplewood, MN, Zip 55109–1126; tel. 651/232–7000; Lia Christiansen, Chief Operating Officer, Acute Care Hospitals
Web address: www.stjohnshospital-mn.org

ST. JOSEPH'S HOSPITAL (O, 239 beds) 45 West 10th Street, Saint Paul, MN, Zip 55102–1053; tel. 651/232–3000; Lia Christiansen, Chief Operating Officer, Acute Care Hospitals
Web address: www.healtheast.org

UNIVERSITY OF MINNESOTA MEDICAL CENTER, FAIRVIEW (O, 861 beds) 2450 Riverside Avenue, Minneapolis, MN, Zip 55454–1400; tel. 612/672–6000; John Doherty, Co-President, M Health

WOODWINDS HEALTH CAMPUS (O, 86 beds) 1925 Woodwinds Drive, Woodbury, MN, Zip 55125–4445; tel. 651/232–0228; Lia Christiansen, Chief Operating Officer, Acute Care Hospitals
Web address: www.woodwinds.org

Owned, leased, sponsored:	11 hospitals	2151 beds
Contract-managed:	0 hospitals	0 beds
Totals:	11 hospitals	2151 beds

0814: FAITH REGIONAL HEALTH SERVICES (NP)

2700 West Norfolk Avenue, Norfolk, NE, Zip 68701–4438, Mailing Address: P.O. Box 869, Zip 68702–0869, tel. 402/371–4880; Kelly Driscoll, R.N., FACHE, President and Chief Executive Officer
(Independent Hospital System)

NEBRASKA: FAITH REGIONAL HEALTH SERVICES (O, 194 beds) 2700 West Norfolk Avenue, Norfolk, NE, Zip 68701–4438, Mailing Address: P.O. Box 869, Zip 68702–0869, tel. 402/371–4880; Kelly Driscoll, R.N., FACHE, President and Chief Executive Officer
Web address: www.frhs.org

GENOA MEDICAL FACILITIES (C, 58 beds) 706 Ewing Avenue, Genoa, NE, Zip 68640–3035, Mailing Address: P.O. Box 310, Zip 68640–0310, tel. 402/993–2283; Amanda Roebuck, Chief Executive Officer
Web address: www.genoamedical.org/

NIOBRARA VALLEY HOSPITAL (C, 20 beds) 401 South Fifth Street, Lynch, NE, Zip 68746–0118, Mailing Address: P.O. Box 118, Zip 68746–0118, tel. 402/569–2451; Kelly Kalkowski, Chief Executive Officer

WEST HOLT MEDICAL SERVICES (C, 17 beds) 406 West Neely Street, Atkinson, NE, Zip 68713–4801; tel. 402/925–2811; Jeremy Bauer, Interim Chief Executive Officer
Web address: www.westholtmed.org

Owned, leased, sponsored:	1 hospitals	194 beds
Contract-managed:	3 hospitals	95 beds
Totals:	4 hospitals	289 beds

0397: FINGER LAKES HEALTH (NP)

196 North Street, Geneva, NY, Zip 14456–1651; tel. 315/787–4000; Jose Acevedo, M.D., President and Chief Executive Officer
(Independent Hospital System)

NEW YORK: FINGER LAKES HOSPITAL (O, 132 beds) 196 North Street, Geneva, NY, Zip 14456–1694; tel. 315/787–4000; Frank Korich, FACHE, Senior Vice President, Operations
Web address: www.flhealth.org

SOLDIERS AND SAILORS MEMORIAL HOSPITAL OF YATES COUNTY (O, 189 beds) 418 North Main Street, Penn Yan, NY, Zip 14527–1085; tel. 315/531–2000; Frank Korich, FACHE, Senior Vice President, Operations
Web address: www.flhealth.org

Owned, leased, sponsored:	2 hospitals	321 beds
Contract-managed:	0 hospitals	0 beds
Totals:	2 hospitals	321 beds

1010: FIRST PHYSICIANS CAPITAL GROUP, INC. (IO)

4323 NW 63rd Street Suite 140, Oklahoma City, OK, Zip 73116–1513; tel. 405/246–0218; Sean Kirrane, Chief Executive Officer

OKLAHOMA: CARNEGIE TRI-COUNTY MUNICIPAL HOSPITAL (C, 17 beds) 102 North Broadway, Carnegie, OK, Zip 73015, Mailing Address: P.O. Box 97, Zip 73015–0097, tel. 580/654–1050; Thomas Henton, Chief Executive Officer
Web address: www.carnegiehospital.org/

PHYSICIANS' HOSPITAL IN ANADARKO (C, 25 beds) 1002 Central Boulevard East, Anadarko, OK, Zip 73005–4496; tel. 405/247–2551; Travis A. Villani, FACHE, Chief Executive Officer and Administrator

STROUD REGIONAL MEDICAL CENTER (C, 25 beds) Highway 66 West, Stroud, OK, Zip 74079, Mailing Address: P.O. Box 530, Zip 74079–0530, tel. 918/968–3571; Ed Dyer, Chief Executive Officer
Web address: www.stroudhospital.com/

Owned, leased, sponsored:	0 hospitals	0 beds
Contract-managed:	3 hospitals	67 beds
Totals:	3 hospitals	67 beds

★0243: FIRSTHEALTH OF THE CAROLINAS (NP)

155 Memorial Drive, Pinehurst, NC, Zip 28374–8710, Mailing Address: P.O. Box 3000, Zip 28374–3000, tel. 910/715–1000; Mickey Foster, Chief Executive Officer
(Centralized Physician/Insurance Health System)

NORTH CAROLINA: FIRSTHEALTH MONTGOMERY MEMORIAL HOSPITAL (O, 5 beds) 520 Allen Street, Troy, NC, Zip 27371–2802; tel. 910/571–5000; Beth Walker, R.N., President
Web address: www.firsthealth.org

FIRSTHEALTH MOORE REGIONAL HOSPITAL (O, 362 beds) 155 Memorial Drive, Pinehurst, NC, Zip 28374–8710, Mailing Address: P.O. Box 3000, Zip 28374–3000, tel. 910/715–1000; David J. Kilarski, FACHE, Chief Executive Officer

Owned, leased, sponsored:	2 hospitals	367 beds
Contract-managed:	0 hospitals	0 beds
Totals:	2 hospitals	367 beds

1016: FLOYD HEALTHCARE MANAGEMENT (NP)

304 Turner McCall Boulevard, Rome, GA, Zip 30165–5621, Mailing Address: P.O. Box 233, Zip 30162–0233, tel. 706/509–5000; Kurt Stuenkel, FACHE, President and Chief Executive Officer
(Moderately Centralized Health System)

ALABAMA: FLOYD CHEROKEE MEDICAL CENTER (O, 45 beds) 400 Northwood Drive, Centre, AL, Zip 35960–1023; tel. 256/927–5531; Brandon Reece, Chief Executive Officer
Web address: www.cherokeemedicalcenter.com

GEORGIA: FLOYD MEDICAL CENTER (O, 327 beds) 304 Turner McCall Boulevard, Rome, GA, Zip 30165–5621, Mailing Address: P.O. Box 233, Zip 30162–0233, tel. 706/509–5000; Kurt Stuenkel, FACHE, President and Chief Executive Officer

POLK MEDICAL CENTER (O, 25 beds) 2360 Rockmart Highway, Cedartown, GA, Zip 30125–6029; tel. 770/748–2500; Tifani Kinard, Administrator and Chief Nursing Officer
Web address: www.polkhospital.org

Owned, leased, sponsored:	3 hospitals	397 beds
Contract-managed:	0 hospitals	0 beds
Totals:	3 hospitals	397 beds

0900: FOUNDATION SURGICAL HOSPITAL AFFILIATES (IO)

14000 North Portland Avenue, Suite 204, Oklahoma City, OK, Zip 73134–4002; tel. 405/608–1700; Thomas A. Michaud, Chief Executive Officer
(Independent Hospital System)

For explanation of codes following names, see page B2.
★ Indicates Type III membership in the American Hospital Association.

Section B

TEXAS: BAYLOR SCOTT & WHITE SURGICAL HOSPITAL-SHERMAN (O, 12 beds) 3601 North Calais Street, Sherman, TX, Zip 75090–1785; tel. 903/870–0999; Marc Devorsetz, Chief Executive Officer
Web address: www.heritageparksurgicalhospital.com

FOUNDATION SURGICAL HOSPITAL OF EL PASO (O, 20 beds) 1416 George Dieter Drive, El Paso, TX, Zip 79936–7601; tel. 915/598–4240; Don Burris, Chief Executive Officer

Owned, leased, sponsored:	2 hospitals	32 beds
Contract-managed:	0 hospitals	0 beds
Totals:	2 hospitals	32 beds

5345: FRANCISCAN HEALTH (CC)
1515 Dragoon Trail, Mishawaka, IN, Zip 46544–4710, Mailing Address: P.O. Box 1290, Zip 46546–1290, tel. 574/256–3935; Kevin D. Leahy, President and Chief Executive Officer
(Independent Hospital System)

ILLINOIS: FRANCISCAN HEALTH OLYMPIA FIELDS (O, 206 beds) 20201 South Crawford Avenue, Olympia Fields, IL, Zip 60461–1010; tel. 708/747–4000; Allan M. Spooner, President and Chief Executive Officer

INDIANA: FRANCISCAN HEALTH CARMEL (O, 6 beds) 12188B North Meridian Street, Carmel, IN, Zip 46032–4840; tel. 317/705–4500; Stephen J. Wheatley, Director of Operations
Web address: www.franciscanalliance.org/hospitals/carmel/Pages/default.aspx

FRANCISCAN HEALTH CRAWFORDSVILLE (O, 40 beds) 1710 Lafayette Road, Crawfordsville, IN, Zip 47933–1099; tel. 765/362–2800; Terrence Klein, Ph.D., Vice President and Chief Operating Officer

FRANCISCAN HEALTH CROWN POINT (O, 254 beds) 1201 South Main Street, Crown Point, IN, Zip 46307–8483; tel. 219/738–2100; Daniel McCormick, M.D., President and Chief Executive Officer
Web address: www.franciscanalliance.org

FRANCISCAN HEALTH DYER (O, 341 beds) 24 Joliet Street, Dyer, IN, Zip 46311–1799; tel. 219/865–2141; Patrick J. Maloney, Chief Executive Officer

FRANCISCAN HEALTH HAMMOND (O, 406 beds) 5454 Hohman Avenue, Hammond, IN, Zip 46320–1999; tel. 219/932–2300; Patrick J. Maloney, Chief Executive Officer
Web address: https://www.franciscanhealth.org/healthcare-facilities/franciscan-health-hammond-18

FRANCISCAN HEALTH INDIANAPOLIS (O, 485 beds) 8111 South Emerson Avenue, Indianapolis, IN, Zip 46237–8601; tel. 317/528–5000; James Callaghan III, M.D., President and Chief Executive Officer
Web address: www.stfrancishospitals.org

FRANCISCAN HEALTH LAFAYETTE EAST (O, 203 beds) 1701 South Creasy Lane, Lafayette, IN, Zip 47905–4972; tel. 765/502–4000; Terrance E. Wilson, President and Chief Executive Officer
Web address: www.ste.org

FRANCISCAN HEALTH MICHIGAN CITY (O, 171 beds) 301 West Homer Street, Michigan City, IN, Zip 46360–4358; tel. 219/879–8511; Dean Mazzoni, President and Chief Executive Officer

FRANCISCAN HEALTH MOORESVILLE (O, 115 beds) 1201 Hadley Road, Mooresville, IN, Zip 46158–1789; tel. 317/831–1160; Peter J. Murphy, Senior Vice President and Chief Operating Officer
Web address: www.franciscanalliance.org/hospitals/mooresville/Pages/default.aspx

FRANCISCAN HEALTH RENSSELEAR (O, 46 beds) 1104 East Grace Street, Rensselaer, IN, Zip 47978–3296; tel. 219/866–5141; Carlos Vasquez, Vice President and Chief Operating Officer
Web address: www.franciscanhealth.org

FRANCISCAN HEALTHCARE MUNSTER (O, 32 beds) 701 Superior Avenue, Munster, IN, Zip 46321–4037; tel. 219/924–1300; Patrick J. Maloney, Chief Executive Officer

Owned, leased, sponsored:	12 hospitals	2305 beds
Contract-managed:	0 hospitals	0 beds
Totals:	12 hospitals	2305 beds

★1475: FRANCISCAN MISSIONARIES OF OUR LADY HEALTH SYSTEM, INC. (CC)
4200 Essen Lane, Baton Rouge, LA, Zip 70809–2158; tel. 225/923–2701; Richard Vath, M.D., President and Chief Executive Officer
(Moderately Centralized Health System)

LOUISIANA: ASSUMPTION COMMUNITY HOSPITAL (O, 6 beds) 135 Highway 402, Napoleonville, LA, Zip 70390–2217; tel. 985/369–3600; Christina P. Hockaday, FACHE, Chief Executive Officer
Web address: www.https://ololrmc.com

OUR LADY OF LOURDES REGIONAL MEDICAL CENTER (O, 186 beds) 4801 Ambassador Caffery Parkway, Lafayette, LA, Zip 70508–6917; tel. 337/470–2000; W. Bryan. Lee, Chief Executive Officer

OUR LADY OF THE ANGELS HOSPITAL (O, 57 beds) 433 Plaza Street, Bogalusa, LA, Zip 70427–3793; tel. 985/730–6700; Rene J. Ragas, Chief Operating Officer
Web address: www.oloah.org

OUR LADY OF THE LAKE REGIONAL MEDICAL CENTER (O, 1189 beds) 5000 Hennessy Boulevard, Baton Rouge, LA, Zip 70808–4375; tel. 225/765–6565; K Scott. Wester, FACHE, President and Chief Executive Officer

ST. FRANCIS MEDICAL CENTER (O, 365 beds) 309 Jackson Street, Monroe, LA, Zip 71201–7407, Mailing Address: P.O. Box 1901, Zip 71210–1901, tel. 318/966–4000; Kristin Wolkart, R.N., President and Chief Executive Officer
Web address: www.stfran.com

Owned, leased, sponsored:	5 hospitals	1803 beds
Contract-managed:	0 hospitals	0 beds
Totals:	5 hospitals	1803 beds

★1455: FRANCISCAN SISTERS OF CHRISTIAN CHARITY SPONSORED MINISTRIES, INC. (CC)
1415 South Rapids Road, Manitowoc, WI, Zip 54220–9302; tel. 920/684–7071; Scott McConnaha, FACHE, President and Chief Executive Officer
(Moderately Centralized Health System)

NEBRASKA: ST. FRANCIS MEMORIAL HOSPITAL (O, 25 beds) 430 North Monitor Street, West Point, NE, Zip 68788–1555; tel. 402/372–2404; David J. Ameen, Interim President and Chief Executive Officer
Web address: www.fcswp.org

OHIO: GENESIS HEALTHCARE SYSTEM (O, 321 beds) 2951 Maple Avenue, Zanesville, OH, Zip 43701–1406; tel. 740/454–5000; Matthew J. Perry, President and Chief Executive Officer

WISCONSIN: HOLY FAMILY MEMORIAL (O, 67 beds) 2300 Western Avenue, Manitowoc, WI, Zip 54220–3712, Mailing Address: P.O. Box 1450, Zip 54221–1450, tel. 920/320–2011; Brett Norell, Interim Chief Executive Officer
Web address: www.hfmhealth.org

Owned, leased, sponsored:	3 hospitals	413 beds
Contract-managed:	0 hospitals	0 beds
Totals:	3 hospitals	413 beds

★0271: FREEMAN HEALTH SYSTEM (NP)
1102 West 32nd Street, Joplin, MO, Zip 64804–3503; tel. 417/347–1111; Paula F. Baker, President and Chief Executive Officer
(Moderately Centralized Health System)

MISSOURI: FREEMAN HEALTH SYSTEM (O, 381 beds) 1102 West 32nd Street, Joplin, MO, Zip 64804–3503; tel. 417/347–1111; Paula F. Baker, President and Chief Executive Officer
Web address: www.freemanhealth.com

FREEMAN NEOSHO HOSPITAL (O, 25 beds) 113 West Hickory Street, Neosho, MO, Zip 64850–1705; tel. 417/455–4352; Renee Denton, Chief Operating Officer
Web address: www.freemanhealth.com

For explanation of codes following names, see page B2.
★ Indicates Type III membership in the American Hospital Association.

NEVADA REGIONAL MEDICAL CENTER (C, 71 beds) 800 South Ash Street, Nevada, MO, Zip 64772–3223; tel. 417/667–3355; Steve Branstetter, Chief Executive Officer
Web address: www.nrmchealth.com

Owned, leased, sponsored:	2 hospitals	406 beds
Contract-managed:	1 hospitals	71 beds
Totals:	3 hospitals	477 beds

0924: FROEDTERT HEALTH (NP)
9200 West Wisconsin Avenue, Milwaukee, WI, Zip 53226–3596, Mailing Address: P.O. Box 26099, Zip 53226–0099, tel. 414/805–3000; Catherine A. Jacobson, President and Chief Executive Officer

WISCONSIN: COMMUNITY MEMORIAL HOSPITAL (O, 202 beds) W180 N8085 Town Hall Road, Menomonee Falls, WI, Zip 53051–3518, Mailing Address: P.O. Box 408, Zip 53052–0408, tel. 262/251–1000; Teresa M. Lux, President and Chief Operating Officer
Web address: www.communitymemorial.com

FROEDTERT AND THE MEDICAL COLLEGE OF WISCONSIN FROEDTERT HOSPITAL (O, 604 beds) 9200 West Wisconsin Avenue, Milwaukee, WI, Zip 53226–3596, Mailing Address: P.O. Box 26099, Zip 53226–0099, tel. 414/805–3000; Catherine Buck, MSN, R.N., President
Web address: www.froedtert.com

ST. JOSEPH'S HOSPITAL (O, 70 beds) 3200 Pleasant Valley Road, West Bend, WI, Zip 53095–9274; tel. 262/836–5533; Allen Ericson, President
Web address: www.froedtert.com

Owned, leased, sponsored:	3 hospitals	876 beds
Contract-managed:	0 hospitals	0 beds
Totals:	3 hospitals	876 beds

0182: FUNDAMENTAL LONG TERM CARE HOLDINGS, LLC (IO)
930 Ridgebrook Road, Sparks Glencoe, MD, Zip 21152–9390; tel. 410/773–1000; W Bradley Bennett, President and Chief Executive Officer
(Independent Hospital System)

NEVADA: HARMON MEDICAL AND REHABILITATION HOSPITAL (O, 118 beds) 2170 East Harmon Avenue, Las Vegas, NV, Zip 89119–7840; tel. 702/794–0100; Bonnie Essex. Hillegass, Chief Executive Officer

HORIZON SPECIALTY HOSPITAL (O, 49 beds) 640 Desert Lane, Las Vegas, NV, Zip 89106–4207; tel. 702/382–3155; Darrin Cook, Chief Executive Officer and Administrator
Web address: www.horizonspecialtyhosp.com/

SOUTHERN NEVADA MEDICAL AND REHABILITATION CENTER (O, 100 beds) 2945 Casa Vegas, Las Vegas, NV, Zip 89169–2248; tel. 702/735–7179; Maureen Davis, Administrator

Owned, leased, sponsored:	3 hospitals	267 beds
Contract-managed:	0 hospitals	0 beds
Totals:	3 hospitals	267 beds

★5570: GEISINGER (NP)
100 North Academy Avenue, Danville, PA, Zip 17822–9800; tel. 570/271–6211; Jaewon Ryu, M.D., President and Chief Executive Officer
(Centralized Physician/Insurance Health System)

NEW JERSEY: ATLANTICARE REGIONAL MEDICAL CENTER (O, 533 beds) 1925 Pacific Avenue, Atlantic City, NJ, Zip 08401–6713; tel. 609/441–8994; Lori S. Herndon, R.N., President and Chief Executive Officer

PENNSYLVANIA: GEISINGER HOLY SPIRIT (O, 311 beds) 503 North 21st Street, Camp Hill, PA, Zip 17011–2204; tel. 717/763–2100; Kyle C. Snyder, Chief Administrative Officer
Web address: www.hsh.org

GEISINGER JERSEY SHORE HOSPITAL (O, 25 beds) 1020 Thompson Street, Jersey Shore, PA, Zip 17740–1794; tel. 570/398–0100; Tammy Anderer, Acting President
Web address: www.jsh.org

GEISINGER MEDICAL CENTER (O, 540 beds) 100 North Academy Avenue, Danville, PA, Zip 17822–2201; tel. 570/271–6211; Thomas P. Sokola, Chief Administrative Officer

GEISINGER WYOMING VALLEY MEDICAL CENTER (O, 277 beds) 1000 East Mountain Boulevard, Wilkes Barre, PA, Zip 18711–0027; tel. 570/808–7300; Ronald R. Beer, FACHE, Chief Administrative Officer
Web address: www.geisinger.org

GEISINGER-BLOOMSBURG HOSPITAL (O, 76 beds) 549 Fair Street, Bloomsburg, PA, Zip 17815–1419; tel. 570/387–2100; Lissa Bryan-Smith, Chief Administrative Officer

GEISINGER-COMMUNITY MEDICAL CENTER (O, 213 beds) 1800 Mulberry Street, Scranton, PA, Zip 18510–2369; tel. 570/703–8000; Ronald R. Beer, FACHE, Chief Administrative Officer
Web address: www.geisinger.org/for-patients/locations-directions/gcmc/

GEISINGER-LEWISTOWN HOSPITAL (O, 123 beds) 400 Highland Avenue, Lewistown, PA, Zip 17044–1198; tel. 717/248–5411; Kirk E. Thomas, Chief Administrative Officer

Owned, leased, sponsored:	8 hospitals	2098 beds
Contract-managed:	0 hospitals	0 beds
Totals:	8 hospitals	2098 beds

★0311: GENESIS HEALTH SYSTEM (NP)
1227 East Rusholme Street, Davenport, IA, Zip 52803–2498; tel. 563/421–1000; Douglas P. Cropper, President and Chief Executive Officer
(Centralized Physician/Insurance Health System)

ILLINOIS: GENESIS MEDICAL CENTER, SILVIS (O, 127 beds) 801 Illini Drive, Silvis, IL, Zip 61282–1893; tel. 309/281–4000; Theresa Summers-Main, R.N., President
Web address: www.genesishealth.com

GENESIS MEDICAL CENTER-ALEDO (O, 22 beds) 409 NW Ninth Avenue, Aledo, IL, Zip 61231–1296; tel. 309/582–9100; Ted Rogalski, Administrator

IOWA: GENESIS MEDICAL CENTER, DAVENPORT (O, 368 beds) 1227 East Rusholme Street, Davenport, IA, Zip 52803–2498; tel. 563/421–1000; Jordan Voigt, Administrator
Web address: www.genesishealth.com

GENESIS MEDICAL CENTER, DEWITT (O, 88 beds) 1118 11th Street, De Witt, IA, Zip 52742–1296; tel. 563/659–4200; Curt Coleman, FACHE, Chief Executive Officer
Web address: www.genesishealth.com

JACKSON COUNTY REGIONAL HEALTH CENTER (C, 12 beds) 700 West Grove Street, Maquoketa, IA, Zip 52060–2163; tel. 563/652–2474; Curt Coleman, FACHE, Administrator
Web address: www.jcrhc.org

Owned, leased, sponsored:	4 hospitals	605 beds
Contract-managed:	1 hospitals	12 beds
Totals:	5 hospitals	617 beds

0283: GILLIARD HEALTH SERVICES (IO)
3091 Carter Hill Road, Montgomery, AL, Zip 36111–1801; tel. 334/265–5009; William G. McKenzie, President, Chief Executive Officer and Chairman

ALABAMA: EVERGREEN MEDICAL CENTER (O, 39 beds) 101 Crestview Avenue, Evergreen, AL, Zip 36401–3333, Mailing Address: P.O. Box 706, Zip 36401–0706, tel. 251/578–2480; Tom McLendon, Administrator
Web address: www.evergreenmedical.org

For explanation of codes following names, see page B2.
★ Indicates Type III membership in the American Hospital Association.

Section B

JACKSON MEDICAL CENTER (O, 26 beds) 220 Hospital Drive, Jackson, AL, Zip 36545–2459, Mailing Address: P.O. Box 428, Zip 36545–0428, tel. 251/246–9021; Jennifer M. Ryland, R.N., Chief Executive Officer
Web address: www.jacksonmedicalcenter.org

Owned, leased, sponsored:	2 hospitals	65 beds
Contract-managed:	0 hospitals	0 beds
Totals:	2 hospitals	65 beds

0648: GOOD SHEPHERD REHABILITATION NETWORK (IO)
850 South Fifth Street, Allentown, PA, Zip 18103–3308; tel. 610/776–3100; John Kristel, President and Chief Executive Officer
(Independent Hospital System)

PENNSYLVANIA: GOOD SHEPHERD REHABILITATION HOSPITAL (O, 106 beds) 850 South 5th Street, Allentown, PA, Zip 18103–3308; tel. 610/776–3299; John Kristel, President and Chief Executive Officer
Web address: www.goodshepherdrehab.org

GOOD SHEPHERD SPECIALTY HOSPITAL (O, 32 beds) 2545 Schoenersville Road, 4th Floor, Bethlehem, PA, Zip 18017–7300; tel. 484/884–5051; Andrew Shane. Martin, Administrator

Owned, leased, sponsored:	2 hospitals	138 beds
Contract-managed:	0 hospitals	0 beds
Totals:	2 hospitals	138 beds

★**1535: GREAT PLAINS HEALTH ALLIANCE, INC.** (NP)
250 North Rock Road, Suite 160, Wichita, KS, Zip 67206–2241; tel. 316/685–1523; Dave Dellasega, President and Chief Executive Officer
(Decentralized Health System)

KANSAS: ASHLAND HEALTH CENTER (C, 25 beds) 709 Oak Street, Ashland, KS, Zip 67831–0188, Mailing Address: P.O. Box 188, Zip 67831–0188, tel. 620/635–2241; Michael Mages, Chief Executive Officer
Web address: www.ashlandhc.org

CHEYENNE COUNTY HOSPITAL (L, 16 beds) 210 West First Street, Saint Francis, KS, Zip 67756–3540, Mailing Address: P.O. Box 547, Zip 67756–0547, tel. 785/332–2104; Kelly Pottorff, Chief Executive Officer
Web address: www.cheyennecountyhospital.com

COMANCHE COUNTY HOSPITAL (C, 12 beds) 202 South Frisco Street, Coldwater, KS, Zip 67029–9101, Mailing Address: HC 65, Box 8A, Zip 67029–9500, tel. 620/582–2144; Nancy Zimmerman, R.N., Administrator

ELLINWOOD DISTRICT HOSPITAL (L, 25 beds) 605 North Main Street, Ellinwood, KS, Zip 67526–1440; tel. 620/564–2548; Kile Magner, Administrator
Web address: www.ellinwooddistricthospital.org

FREDONIA REGIONAL HOSPITAL (C, 25 beds) 1527 Madison Street, Fredonia, KS, Zip 66736–1751, Mailing Address: P.O. Box 579, Zip 66736–0579, tel. 620/378–2121; Johnathan Durrett, Chief Executive Officer
Web address: www.fredoniaregionalhospital.org

GRISELL MEMORIAL HOSPITAL DISTRICT ONE (C, 42 beds) 210 South Vermont Avenue, Ransom, KS, Zip 67572–9525; tel. 785/731–2231; David Caudill, Administrator
Web address: www.grisellmemorialhospital.org

KIOWA COUNTY MEMORIAL HOSPITAL (L, 15 beds) 721 West Kansas Avenue, Greensburg, KS, Zip 67054–1633; tel. 620/723–3341; Mary Sweet, Administrator

LANE COUNTY HOSPITAL (C, 25 beds) 235 West Vine, Dighton, KS, Zip 67839–0969, Mailing Address: P.O. Box 969, Zip 67839–0969, tel. 620/397–5321; Mike Ruggiero, Interim Chief Executive Officer
Web address: www.lanecountyhospital.com/

MEDICINE LODGE MEMORIAL HOSPITAL (C, 25 beds) 710 North Walnut Street, Medicine Lodge, KS, Zip 67104–1019; tel. 620/886–3771; Kevin A. White, Administrator
Web address: www.mlmh.net/

MINNEOLA DISTRICT HOSPITAL (C, 54 beds) 212 Main Street, Minneola, KS, Zip 67865–8511, Mailing Address: P.O. Box 127, Zip 67865–0127, tel. 620/885–4264; Deborah Bruner, Chief Executive Officer and Administrator
Web address: www.minneolahealthcare.com

OSBORNE COUNTY MEMORIAL HOSPITAL (C, 25 beds) 424 West New Hampshire Street, Osborne, KS, Zip 67473–2314, Mailing Address: P.O. Box 70, Zip 67473–0070, tel. 785/346–2121; Marianna Harris, Administrator
Web address: www.ocmh.org

OTTAWA COUNTY HEALTH CENTER (L, 35 beds) 215 East Eighth, Minneapolis, KS, Zip 67467–1902, Mailing Address: P.O. Box 290, Zip 67467–0290, tel. 785/392–2122; Jody Parks, Administrator

REPUBLIC COUNTY HOSPITAL (L, 25 beds) 2420 'G' Street, Belleville, KS, Zip 66935–2400; tel. 785/527–2254; David-Paul Cavazos, Chief Executive Officer
Web address: www.rphospital.org

SABETHA COMMUNITY HOSPITAL (L, 25 beds) 14th and Oregon Streets, Sabetha, KS, Zip 66534–0229, Mailing Address: P.O. Box 229, Zip 66534–0229, tel. 785/284–2121; Lora Key, Chief Executive Officer
Web address: www.sabethahospital.com

SATANTA DISTRICT HOSPITAL AND LONG TERM CARE (C, 57 beds) 401 South Cheyenne Street, Satanta, KS, Zip 67870–0159, Mailing Address: P.O. Box 159, Zip 67870–0159, tel. 620/649–2761; Jeremy Clingenpeel, Administrator
Web address: www.satantahospital.org

SMITH COUNTY MEMORIAL HOSPITAL (L, 25 beds) 921 East Highway 36, Smith Center, KS, Zip 66967; tel. 785/282–6845; Allen Van Driel, FACHE, Administrator
Web address: www.gpha.com

TREGO COUNTY-LEMKE MEMORIAL HOSPITAL (C, 62 beds) 320 North 13th Street, Wakeeney, KS, Zip 67672–2099; tel. 785/743–2182; David Augustine, Chief Executive Officer
Web address: www.tclmh.org

WICHITA COUNTY HEALTH CENTER (C, 42 beds) 211 East Earl Street, Leoti, KS, Zip 67861–9620; tel. 620/375–2233; Teresa Clark, Chief Executive Officer and Administrator

NEBRASKA: HARLAN COUNTY HEALTH SYSTEM (C, 19 beds) 717 North Brown Street, Alma, NE, Zip 68920–2132, Mailing Address: P.O. Box 836, Zip 68920–0836, tel. 308/928–2151; Mark A. Miller, FACHE, Chief Executive Officer
Web address: www.harlancountyhealth.com

Owned, leased, sponsored:	7 hospitals	166 beds
Contract-managed:	12 hospitals	413 beds
Totals:	19 hospitals	579 beds

★**0144: GREATER HUDSON VALLEY HEALTH SYSTEM** (NP)
707 East Main Street, Middletown, NY, Zip 10940–2650; tel. 845/333–1000; Scott Batulis, President and Chief Executive Officer
(Centralized Health System)

NEW YORK: CATSKILL REGIONAL MEDICAL CENTER (O, 119 beds) 68 Harris Bushville Road, Harris, NY, Zip 12742–5030, Mailing Address: P.O. Box 800, Zip 12742–0800, tel. 845/794–3300; Jonathan Schiller, Chief Executive Officer
Web address: www.crmcny.org

GROVER M. HERMANN HOSPITAL (O, 15 beds) 8881 Route 97, Callicoon, NY, Zip 12723; tel. 845/887–5530; Rolland Bojo, R.N., Administrator

ORANGE REGIONAL MEDICAL CENTER (O, 340 beds) 707 East Main Street, Middletown, NY, Zip 10940–2650; tel. 845/333–1000; Scott Batulis, President and Chief Executive Officer
Web address: www.ormc.org

Owned, leased, sponsored:	3 hospitals	474 beds
Contract-managed:	0 hospitals	0 beds
Totals:	3 hospitals	474 beds

★**0675: GUTHRIE CLINIC** (NP)
One Guthrie Square, Sayre, PA, Zip 18840–1625; tel. 570/888–5858; Joseph A. Scopelliti, M.D., President and Chief Executive Officer
(Moderately Centralized Health System)

For explanation of codes following names, see page B2.
★ Indicates Type III membership in the American Hospital Association.

NEW YORK: GUTHRIE CORNING HOSPITAL (O, 65 beds) One Guthrie Drive, Corning, NY, Zip 14830–3696; tel. 607/937–7200; Garrett W. Hoover, FACHE, President
Web address: www.corninghospital.com

PENNSYLVANIA: GUTHRIE ROBERT PACKER HOSPITAL (O, 237 beds) 1 Guthrie Square, Sayre, PA, Zip 18840–1698; tel. 570/888–6666; Joseph T. Sawyer Jr, President
Web address: https://www.guthrie.org/location/robert-packer-hospital

GUTHRIE TOWANDA MEMORIAL HOSPITAL (O, 195 beds) 91 Hospital Drive, Towanda, PA, Zip 18848–9702; tel. 570/265–2191; Felissa Koernig, President and Chief Operating Officer
Web address: https://www.guthrie.org/location/guthrie-towanda-memorial-hospital

GUTHRIE TROY COMMUNITY HOSPITAL (O, 25 beds) 275 Guthrie Drive, Troy, PA, Zip 16947; tel. 570/297–2121; Lori Barnett, R.N., MSN, President and Chief Operating Officer

Owned, leased, sponsored:	4 hospitals	522 beds
Contract-managed:	0 hospitals	0 beds
Totals:	4 hospitals	522 beds

★**1003: HACKENSACK MERIDIAN HEALTH** (NP)
343 Thornall Street, 8th Floor, Edison, NJ, Zip 08837–2206, Mailing Address: 343 Thornall Street, Zip 08837–2206, tel. 844/464–9355; Robert C. Garrett, FACHE, Chief Executive Officer
(Centralized Health System)

NEW JERSEY: HACKENSACK MERIDIAN HEALTH BAYSHORE COMMUNITY HOSPITAL (O, 160 beds) 727 North Beers Street, Holmdel, NJ, Zip 07733–1598; tel. 732/739–5900; Timothy J. Hogan, FACHE, President, RMC and BMC
Web address: www.bchs.com

HACKENSACK MERIDIAN HEALTH CARRIER CLINIC (O, 328 beds) 252 County Route 601, Belle Mead, NJ, Zip 08502–0147, Mailing Address: P.O. Box 147, Zip 08502–0147, tel. 908/281–1000; Donald J. Parker, President and Chief Executive Officer

HACKENSACK MERIDIAN HEALTH HACKENSACK UNIVERSITY MEDICAL CENTER (O, 691 beds) 30 Prospect Avenue, Hackensack, NJ, Zip 07601–1914; tel. 201/996–2000; Mark Sparta, President
Web address: www.hackensackumc.org

HACKENSACK MERIDIAN HEALTH JFK JOHNSON REHABILITATION INSTITUTE (O, 94 beds) 65 James Street, Edison, NJ, Zip 8818; tel. 732/321–7050; Anthony Cuzzola, Vice President and Administrator
Web address: www.njrehab.org

HACKENSACK MERIDIAN HEALTH JFK MEDICAL CENTER (O, 360 beds) 65 James Street, Edison, NJ, Zip 8818; tel. 732/321–7000; Raymond F. Fredericks, Central Regional President

HACKENSACK MERIDIAN HEALTH JERSEY SHORE UNIVERSITY MEDICAL CENTER (O, 583 beds) 1945 Route 33, Neptune, NJ, Zip 07754–0397; tel. 732/775–5500; Vito Buccellato, Chief Executive Officer
Web address: www.meridianhealth.com

HACKENSACK MERIDIAN HEALTH OCEAN MEDICAL CENTER (O, 324 beds) 425 Jack Martin Boulevard, Brick Township, NJ, Zip 08724–7732; tel. 732/840–2200; Dean Q. Lin, FACHE, Regional President
Web address: www.meridianhealth.com

HACKENSACK MERIDIAN HEALTH PALISADES MEDICAL CENTER (O, 182 beds) 7600 River Road, North Bergen, NJ, Zip 07047–6217; tel. 201/854–5000; Anthony Passannante Jr, M.D., FACC, President

HACKENSACK MERIDIAN HEALTH RARITAN BAY MEDICAL CENTER (O, 282 beds) 530 New Brunswick Avenue, Perth Amboy, NJ, Zip 08861–3654; tel. 732/442–3700; Thomas Shanahan, Chief Operating Officer
Web address: www.rbmc.org

HACKENSACK MERIDIAN HEALTH RIVERVIEW MEDICAL CENTER (O, 324 beds) 1 Riverview Plaza, Red Bank, NJ, Zip 07701–1864; tel. 732/741–2700; Timothy J. Hogan, FACHE, President, RMC and BMC
Web address: www.riverviewmedicalcenter.com

HACKENSACK MERIDIAN HEALTH SHORE REHABILITATION INSTITUTE (O, 40 beds) 425 Jack Martin Boulevard, Brick, NJ, Zip 08724–7732; tel. 732/836–4500; Kerri Fitzgerald, Executive Director

HACKENSACK MERIDIAN HEALTH SOUTHERN OCEAN MEDICAL CENTER (O, 174 beds) 1140 Route 72 West, Manahawkin, NJ, Zip 08050–2499; tel. 609/597–6011; Regina Foley, R.N., FACHE, Chief Operating Officer
Web address: www.soch.com

Owned, leased, sponsored:	12 hospitals	3542 beds
Contract-managed:	0 hospitals	0 beds
Totals:	12 hospitals	3542 beds

★**0541: HARTFORD HEALTHCARE** (NP)
One State Street, 19th Floor, Hartford, CT, Zip 6103; tel. 860/263–4100; Elliot T. Joseph, Chief Executive Officer
(Centralized Health System)

CONNECTICUT: CHARLOTTE HUNGERFORD HOSPITAL (O, 65 beds) 540 Litchfield Street, Torrington, CT, Zip 06790–6679, Mailing Address: P.O. Box 988, Zip 06790–0988, tel. 860/496–6666; Daniel J. McIntyre, President
Web address: www.charlottehungerford.org

HARTFORD HOSPITAL (O, 912 beds) 80 Seymour Street, Hartford, CT, Zip 06102–8000, Mailing Address: P.O. Box 5037, Zip 06102–5037, tel. 860/545–5000; Bimal Patel, President

MIDSTATE MEDICAL CENTER (O, 97 beds) 435 Lewis Avenue, Meriden, CT, Zip 06451–2101; tel. 203/694–8200; Gary C. Havican, President
Web address: www.midstatemedical.org

NATCHAUG HOSPITAL (O, 57 beds) 189 Storrs Road, Mansfield Center, CT, Zip 06250–1683; tel. 860/456–1311; Patricia Rehmer, MSN, FACHE, President
Web address: www.natchaug.org

THE HOSPITAL OF CENTRAL CONNECTICUT (O, 179 beds) 100 Grand Street, New Britain, CT, Zip 06052–2017, Mailing Address: P.O. Box 100, Zip 06052–2017, tel. 860/224–5011; Gary C. Havican, President

THE WILLIAM W. BACKUS HOSPITAL (O, 184 beds) 326 Washington Street, Norwich, CT, Zip 06360–2740; tel. 860/889–8331; Donna Handley, President
Web address: www.backushospital.org

WINDHAM HOSPITAL (O, 99 beds) 112 Mansfield Avenue, Willimantic, CT, Zip 06226–2040; tel. 860/456–9116; Donna Handley, President
Web address: www.windhamhospital.org

Owned, leased, sponsored:	7 hospitals	1593 beds
Contract-managed:	0 hospitals	0 beds
Totals:	7 hospitals	1593 beds

0637: HAVEN BEHAVIORAL HEALTHCARE (IO)
652 West Iris Drive, Nashville, TN, Zip 37204–3191; tel. 615/250–9500; Kelly Gill, Chief Executive Officer

ARIZONA: HAVEN SENIOR HORIZONS (O, 45 beds) 1201 South 7th Avenue, Suite 200, Phoenix, AZ, Zip 85007–4076; tel. 623/236–2000; Ashley Ellis, Chief Executive Officer

OHIO: HAVEN BEHAVIORAL SENIOR CARE OF DAYTON (O, 32 beds) One Elizabeth Place, 4th Floor Southwest Tower, Dayton, OH, Zip 45417–3445; tel. 937/234–0100; Keith Kuhn, Chief Executive Officer
Web address: www.havenbehavioraldayton.com/

PENNSYLVANIA: HAVEN BEHAVIORAL HOSPITAL OF EASTERN PENNSYLVANIA (O, 48 beds) 145 North 6th Street, 3rd Floor, Reading, PA, Zip 19601–3096; tel. 610/406–4340; Robert Scheffler, Chief Executive Officer

HAVEN BEHAVIORAL HOSPITAL OF PHILADELPHIA (O, 36 beds) Four Falls Building, 3301 Scotts Lane, Philadelphia, PA, Zip 19129–1121; tel. 215/791–6821; Abigail Halloran, Chief Executive Officer
Web address: www.https://philadelphia.havenbehavioral.com

Owned, leased, sponsored:	4 hospitals	161 beds
Contract-managed:	0 hospitals	0 beds
Totals:	4 hospitals	161 beds

★**3555: HAWAII HEALTH SYSTEMS CORPORATION** (NP)
3675 Kilauea Avenue, Honolulu, HI, Zip 96816–2333; tel. 808/733–4151; Linda Rosen, M.D., Chief Executive Officer
(Independent Hospital System)

For explanation of codes following names, see page B2.
★ Indicates Type III membership in the American Hospital Association.

Section B

HAWAII: HALE HO'OLA HAMAKUA (O, 77 beds) 45–547 Plumeria Street, Honokaa, HI, Zip 96727–6902; tel. 808/932–4100; Denise Mackey, Administrator
Web address: www.halehoolahamakua.org

HILO MEDICAL CENTER (O, 199 beds) 1190 Waianuenue Avenue, Hilo, HI, Zip 96720–2089; tel. 808/932–3000; Dan Brinkman, R.N., Chief Executive Officer

KA'U HOSPITAL (O, 21 beds) 1 Kamani Street, Pahala, HI, Zip 96777, Mailing Address: P.O. Box 40, Zip 96777–0040, tel. 808/932–4200; Merilyn Harris, Administrator
Web address: www.hhsc.org

KAUAI VETERANS MEMORIAL HOSPITAL (O, 45 beds) 4643 Waimea Canyon Road, Waimea, HI, Zip 96796, Mailing Address: P.O. Box 337, Zip 96796–0337, tel. 808/338–9431; Lance Segawa, Chief Executive Officer
Web address: www.kvmh.hhsc.org

KOHALA HOSPITAL (O, 28 beds) 54–383 Hospital Road, Kohala, HI, Zip 96755, Mailing Address: P.O. Box 10, Kapaau, Zip 96755–0010, tel. 808/889–6211; Eugene Amar Jr, Administrator

KONA COMMUNITY HOSPITAL (O, 94 beds) 79–1019 Haukapila Street, Kealakekua, HI, Zip 96750–7920; tel. 808/322–9311; Jay E. Kreuzer, FACHE, Chief Executive Officer
Web address: www.kch.hhsc.org

LEAHI HOSPITAL (O, 126 beds) 3675 Kilauea Avenue, Honolulu, HI, Zip 96816–2398; tel. 808/733–8000; Derek Akiyoshi, Chief Executive Officer
Web address: www.hhsc.org

MALUHIA HOSPITAL (O, 146 beds) 1027 Hala Drive, Honolulu, HI, Zip 96817; tel. 808/832–5874; Derek Akiyoshi, Chief Executive Officer

SAMUEL MAHELONA MEMORIAL HOSPITAL (O, 80 beds) 4800 Kawaihau Road, Kapaa, HI, Zip 96746–1971; tel. 808/822–4961; Lance Segawa, Chief Executive Officer
Web address: www.smmh.hhsc.org

Owned, leased, sponsored:	9 hospitals	816 beds
Contract-managed:	0 hospitals	0 beds
Totals:	9 hospitals	816 beds

0266: HAWAII PACIFIC HEALTH (NP)

55 Merchant Street, Honolulu, HI, Zip 96813–4306; tel. 808/949–9355; Raymond P. Vara Jr, President and Chief Executive Officer
(Centralized Health System)

HAWAII: KAPIOLANI MEDICAL CENTER FOR WOMEN & CHILDREN (O, 180 beds) 1319 Punahou Street, Honolulu, HI, Zip 96826–1001; tel. 808/983–6000; Martha Smith, Chief Executive Officer
Web address: www.kapiolani.org

PALI MOMI MEDICAL CENTER (O, 118 beds) 98–1079 Moanalua Road, Aiea, HI, Zip 96701–4713; tel. 808/486–6000; Art Gladstone, R.N., Chief Executive Officer

STRAUB MEDICAL CENTER (O, 121 beds) 888 South King Street, Honolulu, HI, Zip 96813–3097; tel. 808/522–4000; Art Gladstone, R.N., Chief Executive Officer
Web address: www.straubhealth.org

WILCOX MEDICAL CENTER (O, 65 beds) 3–3420 Kuhio Highway, Lihue, HI, Zip 96766–1099; tel. 808/245–1100; Jen Chahanovich, President and Chief Executive Officer

Owned, leased, sponsored:	4 hospitals	484 beds
Contract-managed:	0 hospitals	0 beds
Totals:	4 hospitals	484 beds

★0048: HCA HEALTHCARE (IO)

One Park Plaza, Nashville, TN, Zip 37203–1548; tel. 615/344–5248; Samuel Hazen, President and Chief Executive Officer
(Decentralized Health System)

ALASKA: ALASKA REGIONAL HOSPITAL (O, 132 beds) 2801 Debarr Road, Anchorage, AK, Zip 99508–2997; tel. 907/264–1754; Julie Taylor, FACHE, Chief Executive Officer
Web address: www.alaskaregional.com

CALIFORNIA: GOOD SAMARITAN HOSPITAL (O, 349 beds) 2425 Samaritan Drive, San Jose, CA, Zip 95124–3997, Mailing Address: P.O. Box 240002, Zip 95154–2402, tel. 408/559–2011; Joseph DeSchryver, Chief Executive Officer

LOS ROBLES HOSPITAL AND MEDICAL CENTER (O, 325 beds) 215 West Janss Road, Thousand Oaks, CA, Zip 91360–1899; tel. 805/370–4421; Natalie Mussi, President and Chief Executive Officer
Web address: www.losrobleshospital.com

REGIONAL MEDICAL CENTER OF SAN JOSE (O, 247 beds) 225 North Jackson Avenue, San Jose, CA, Zip 95116–1603; tel. 408/259–5000; Tomi S. Ryba, President and Chief Executive Officer

RIVERSIDE COMMUNITY HOSPITAL (O, 373 beds) 4445 Magnolia Avenue, Riverside, CA, Zip 92501–4199; tel. 951/788–3000; Jacqueline DeSouza-Van Blaricum, President and Chief Executive Officer
Web address: www.riversidecommunityhospital.com

WEST HILLS HOSPITAL AND MEDICAL CENTER (O, 225 beds) 7300 Medical Center Drive, West Hills, CA, Zip 91307–1900; tel. 818/676–4000; Mark Miller, FACHE, Chief Executive Officer

COLORADO: MEDICAL CENTER OF AURORA (O, 261 beds) 1501 South Potomac Street, Aurora, CO, Zip 80012–5411; tel. 303/695–2600; Ryan Simpson, President and Chief Executive Officer
Web address: www.auroramed.com

NORTH SUBURBAN MEDICAL CENTER (O, 139 beds) 9191 Grant Street, Thornton, CO, Zip 80229–4341; tel. 303/451–7800; Daphne G. David, President and Chief Executive Officer
Web address: www.northsuburban.com

PRESBYTERIAN-ST. LUKE'S MEDICAL CENTER (O, 359 beds) 1719 East 19th Avenue, Denver, CO, Zip 80218–1281; tel. 720/754–6000; Maureen Tarrant, President and Chief Executive Officer

ROSE MEDICAL CENTER (O, 282 beds) 4567 East Ninth Avenue, Denver, CO, Zip 80220–3941; tel. 303/320–2121; Ryan Tobin, President and Chief Executive Officer
Web address: www.rosebabies.com

SKY RIDGE MEDICAL CENTER (O, 274 beds) 10101 Ridge Gate Parkway, Lone Tree, CO, Zip 80124–5522; tel. 720/225–1000; Susan Hicks, Chief Executive Officer

SPALDING REHABILITATION HOSPITAL (O, 40 beds) 900 Potomac Steet, Aurora, CO, Zip 80011–6716; tel. 303/367–1166; Ryan Simpson, President and Chief Executive Officer
Web address: www.spaldingrehab.com

SWEDISH MEDICAL CENTER (O, 386 beds) 501 East Hampden Avenue, Englewood, CO, Zip 80113–2702; tel. 303/788–5000; Richard A. Hammett, President and Chief Executive Officer
Web address: www.swedishhospital.com

FLORIDA: AVENTURA HOSPITAL AND MEDICAL CENTER (O, 359 beds) 20900 Biscayne Boulevard, Aventura, FL, Zip 33180–1407; tel. 305/682–7000; Lee B. Chaykin, Chief Executive Officer
Web address: www.aventurahospital.com

BLAKE MEDICAL CENTER (O, 383 beds) 2020 59th Street West, Bradenton, FL, Zip 34209–4669; tel. 941/792–6611; Randy Currin, Chief Executive Officer

BRANDON REGIONAL HOSPITAL (O, 407 beds) 119 Oakfield Drive, Brandon, FL, Zip 33511–5779; tel. 813/681–5551; Bland Eng, Chief Executive Officer
Web address: www.brandonhospital.com

CAPITAL REGIONAL MEDICAL CENTER (O, 198 beds) 2626 Capital Medical Boulevard, Tallahassee, FL, Zip 32308–4499; tel. 850/325–5000; Alan Seesee, Chief Executive Officer
Web address: www.capitalregionalmedicalcenter.com

CENTRAL FLORIDA REGIONAL HOSPITAL (O, 226 beds) 1401 West Seminole Boulevard, Sanford, FL, Zip 32771–6764; tel. 407/321–4500; Trey Abshier, Chief Executive Officer

CITRUS MEMORIAL HEALTH SYSTEM (O, 204 beds) 502 West Highland Boulevard, Inverness, FL, Zip 34452–4754; tel. 352/726–1551; Ralph A. Aleman, President and Chief Executive Officer
Web address: www.citrusmh.com

DOCTORS HOSPITAL OF SARASOTA (O, 168 beds) 5731 Bee Ridge Road, Sarasota, FL, Zip 34233–5056; tel. 941/342–1100; Robert C. Meade, Chief Executive Officer
Web address: www.doctorsofsarasota.com

For explanation of codes following names, see page B2.
★ Indicates Type III membership in the American Hospital Association.

ENGLEWOOD COMMUNITY HOSPITAL (O, 100 beds) 700 Medical Boulevard, Englewood, FL, Zip 34223–3978; tel. 941/475–6571; Michael Ehrat, Chief Executive Officer
Web address: www.englewoodcommunityhospital.com

FAWCETT MEMORIAL HOSPITAL (O, 237 beds) 21298 Olean Boulevard, Port Charlotte, FL, Zip 33952–6765; tel. 941/629–1181; William Hawley, President and Chief Executive Officer

FORT WALTON BEACH MEDICAL CENTER (O, 257 beds) 1000 Mar-Walt Drive, Fort Walton Beach, FL, Zip 32547–6795; tel. 850/862–1111; Mitchell P. Mongell, FACHE, Chief Executive Officer
Web address: www.fwbmc.com

GULF COAST REGIONAL MEDICAL CENTER (O, 176 beds) 449 West 23rd Street, Panama City, FL, Zip 32405–4593, Mailing Address: P.O. Box 15309, Zip 32406–5309, tel. 850/769–8341; Brad Griffin, Chief Executive Officer
Web address: www.egulfcoastmedical.com

HIGHLANDS REGIONAL MEDICAL CENTER (O, 80 beds) 3600 South Highlands Avenue, Sebring, FL, Zip 33870–5495, Mailing Address: Drawer 2066, Zip 33871–2066, tel. 863/385–6101; Jason Kimbrell, Chief Executive Officer
Web address: www.highlandsregional.com

JFK MEDICAL CENTER NORTH CAMPUS (O, 245 beds) 2201 45th Street, West Palm Beach, FL, Zip 33407–2047; tel. 561/842–6141; Patricia Burns, Chief Executive Officer
Web address: www.westpalmhospital.com

JFK MEDICAL CENTER (O, 424 beds) 5301 South Congress Avenue, Atlantis, FL, Zip 33462–1197; tel. 561/965–7300; Gina Melby, Chief Executive Officer

KENDALL REGIONAL MEDICAL CENTER (O, 300 beds) 11750 Bird Road, Miami, FL, Zip 33175–3530; tel. 305/223–3000; Brandon Haushalter, Chief Executive Officer
Web address: www.kendallmed.com

LAKE CITY MEDICAL CENTER (O, 67 beds) 340 NW Commerce Drive, Lake City, FL, Zip 32055–4709; tel. 386/719–9000; Rick Naegler, Chief Executive Officer

LARGO MEDICAL CENTER (O, 243 beds) 201 14th Street SW, Largo, FL, Zip 33770–3133; tel. 727/588–5200; Adam Rudd, Chief Executive Officer
Web address: www.largomedical.com

LAWNWOOD REGIONAL MEDICAL CENTER & HEART INSTITUTE (O, 331 beds) 1700 South 23rd Street, Fort Pierce, FL, Zip 34950–4803; tel. 772/461–4000; Eric Goldman, Chief Executive Officer

MEDICAL CENTER OF TRINITY (O, 276 beds) 9330 State Road 54, Trinity, FL, Zip 34655–1808; tel. 727/834–4900; Leigh Massengill, Chief Executive Officer
Web address: www.medicalcentertrinity.com

MEMORIAL HOSPITAL JACKSONVILLE (O, 410 beds) 3625 University Boulevard South, Jacksonville, FL, Zip 32216–4207; tel. 904/702–6111; Bradley S. Talbert, FACHE, President and Chief Executive Officer

MEMORIAL HOSPITAL OF TAMPA (O, 139 beds) 2901 Swann Avenue, Tampa, FL, Zip 33609–4057; tel. 813/873–6400; Sonia I. Wellman, Chief Executive Officer
Web address: www.memorialhospitaltampa.com

NORTH FLORIDA REGIONAL MEDICAL CENTER (O, 432 beds) 6500 Newberry Road, Gainesville, FL, Zip 32605–4392, Mailing Address: P.O. Box 147006, Zip 32614–7006, tel. 352/333–4000; Eric Lawson, Chief Executive Officer

NORTHSIDE HOSPITAL (O, 217 beds) 6000 49th Street North, Saint Petersburg, FL, Zip 33709–2145; tel. 727/521–4411; Valerie L. Powell-Stafford, Chief Executive Officer
Web address: www.northsidehospital.com

NORTHWEST MEDICAL CENTER (O, 228 beds) 2801 North State Road 7, Margate, FL, Zip 33063–5727; tel. 954/974–0400; Erica Gulrich, Chief Executive Officer

OAK HILL HOSPITAL (O, 280 beds) 11375 Cortez Boulevard, Brooksville, FL, Zip 34613–5409; tel. 352/596–6632; Mickey Smith, Chief Executive Officer
Web address: www.oakhillhospital.com

OCALA REGIONAL MEDICAL CENTER (O, 270 beds) 1431 SW First Avenue, Ocala, FL, Zip 34471–6500, Mailing Address: P.O. Box 2200, Zip 34478–2200, tel. 352/401–1000; Chad Christianson, Chief Executive Officer

ORANGE PARK MEDICAL CENTER (O, 320 beds) 2001 Kingsley Avenue, Orange Park, FL, Zip 32073–5156; tel. 904/639–8500; Chad Patrick, President and Chief Executive Officer
Web address: www.opmedical.com

OSCEOLA REGIONAL MEDICAL CENTER (O, 404 beds) 700 West Oak Street, Kissimmee, FL, Zip 34741–4996; tel. 407/846–2266; Davide M. Carbone, FACHE, Chief Executive Officer

OVIEDO MEDICAL CENTER (O, 64 beds) 8300 Red Bug Lake Road, Oviedo, FL, Zip 32765–6801; tel. 407/890–2273; Kenneth C. Donahey, Chief Executive Officer
Web address: www.oviedomedicalcenter.com

PALMS WEST HOSPITAL (O, 204 beds) 13001 Southern Boulevard, Loxahatchee, FL, Zip 33470–9203; tel. 561/798–3300; Joshua DeTillio, Chief Executive Officer
Web address: www.palmswesthospital.com

PALMS OF PASADENA HOSPITAL (O, 187 beds) 1501 Pasadena Avenue South, Saint Petersburg, FL, Zip 33707–3798; tel. 727/381–1000; Jacob Fisher, Chief Executive Officer
Web address: www.palmspasadena.com

PLANTATION GENERAL HOSPITAL (O, 264 beds) 401 NW 42nd Avenue, Plantation, FL, Zip 33317–2882; tel. 954/587–5010; Madeline Nava, Chief Executive Officer

POINCIANA MEDICAL CENTER (O, 24 beds) 325 Cypress Parkway, Kissimmee, FL, Zip 34758; tel. 407/530–2000; Christopher Cosby, Chief Executive Officer
Web address: www.poincianamedicalcenter.com

PUTNAM COMMUNITY MEDICAL CENTER (O, 99 beds) 611 Zeagler Drive, Palatka, FL, Zip 32177–3810; tel. 386/328–5711; Mark J. Dooley, Chief Executive Officer
Web address: www.pcmcfl.com

RAULERSON HOSPITAL (O, 100 beds) 1796 Highway 441 North, Okeechobee, FL, Zip 34972–1918, Mailing Address: P.O. Box 1307, Zip 34973–1307, tel. 863/763–2151; Brian Melear, Chief Executive Officer

REGIONAL MEDICAL CENTER BAYONET POINT (O, 290 beds) 14000 Fivay Road, Hudson, FL, Zip 34667–7199; tel. 727/869–5400; Thomas Lawhorne, Interim Chief Executive Officer
Web address: www.rmchealth.com

SOUTH BAY HOSPITAL (O, 138 beds) 4016 Sun City Center Blvd, Sun City Center, FL, Zip 33573–5298; tel. 813/634–3301; Daniel Bender, Chief Executive Officer
Web address: www.southbayhospital.com/

ST. LUCIE MEDICAL CENTER (O, 194 beds) 1800 SE Tiffany Avenue, Port St Lucie, FL, Zip 34952–7521; tel. 772/335–4000; Jay Finnegan, Chief Executive Officer

ST. PETERSBURG GENERAL HOSPITAL (O, 219 beds) 6500 38th Avenue North, Saint Petersburg, FL, Zip 33710–1629; tel. 727/384–1414; Janice Balzano, President and Chief Executive Officer
Web address: www.stpetegeneral.com

TWIN CITIES HOSPITAL (O, 65 beds) 2190 Highway 85 North, Niceville, FL, Zip 32578–1045; tel. 850/678–4131; David Whalen, Chief Executive Officer

UNIVERSITY HOSPITAL AND MEDICAL CENTER (O, 317 beds) 7201 North University Drive, Tamarac, FL, Zip 33321–2996; tel. 954/721–2200; Dana C. Oaks, Chief Executive Officer
Web address: www.uhmchealth.com

WEST FLORIDA HOSPITAL (O, 339 beds) 8383 North Davis Highway, Pensacola, FL, Zip 32514–6088; tel. 850/494–4000; Gay Nord, Chief Executive Officer
Web address: www.westfloridahospital.com

WESTSIDE REGIONAL MEDICAL CENTER (O, 224 beds) 8201 West Broward Boulevard, Plantation, FL, Zip 33324–2701; tel. 954/473–6600; Barbara Simmons, R.N., Chief Executive Officer

GEORGIA: CARTERSVILLE MEDICAL CENTER (O, 80 beds) 960 Joe Frank Harris Parkway, Cartersville, GA, Zip 30120–2129; tel. 770/382–1530; J. Christopher. Mosley, Chief Executive Officer
Web address: www.cartersvillemedical.com

COLISEUM MEDICAL CENTERS (O, 227 beds) 350 Hospital Drive, Macon, GA, Zip 31217–3871; tel. 478/765–7000; Stephen J. Daugherty, Chief Executive Officer
Web address: www.coliseumhealthsystem.com

COLISEUM NORTHSIDE HOSPITAL (O, 103 beds) 400 Charter Boulevard, Macon, GA, Zip 31210–4853, Mailing Address: P.O. Box 4627, Zip 31208–4627, tel. 478/757–8200; Greg Caples, Chief Executive Officer
Web address: www.coliseumhealthsystem.com

For explanation of codes following names, see page B2.
★ Indicates Type III membership in the American Hospital Association.

DOCTORS HOSPITAL (O, 307 beds) 3651 Wheeler Road, Augusta, GA, Zip 30909–6426; tel. 706/651–3232; Douglas Welch, Chief Executive Officer

EASTSIDE MEDICAL CENTER (O, 294 beds) 1700 Medical Way, Snellville, GA, Zip 30078–2195; tel. 770/979–0200; Trent Lind, Chief Executive Officer
Web address: www.eastsidemedical.com

FAIRVIEW PARK HOSPITAL (O, 168 beds) 200 Industrial Boulevard, Dublin, GA, Zip 31021–2997, Mailing Address: P.O. Box 1408, Zip 31040–1408, tel. 478/275–2000; Donald R. Avery, FACHE, President and Chief Executive Officer

MEMORIAL HEALTH (O, 508 beds) 4700 Waters Avenue, Savannah, GA, Zip 31404–6283, Mailing Address: P.O. Box 23089, Zip 31403–3089, tel. 912/350–8000; Shayne George, Chief Executive Officer
Web address: www.memorialhealth.com

MEMORIAL SATILLA HEALTH (O, 199 beds) 1900 Tebeau Street, Waycross, GA, Zip 31501–6357, Mailing Address: P.O. Box 139, Zip 31502–0139, tel. 912/283–3030; Bobby McCullough, Chief Executive Officer
Web address: www.memorialsatillahealth.com/

REDMOND REGIONAL MEDICAL CENTER (O, 230 beds) 501 Redmond Road, Rome, GA, Zip 30165–1415, Mailing Address: P.O. Box 107001, Zip 30164–7001, tel. 706/291–0291; John Quinlivan, Chief Executive Officer

IDAHO: EASTERN IDAHO REGIONAL MEDICAL CENTER (O, 280 beds) 3100 Channing Way, Idaho Falls, ID, Zip 83404–7533, Mailing Address: P.O. Box 2077, Zip 83403–2077, tel. 208/529–6111; Jeff Sollis, Chief Executive Officer
Web address: www.eirmc.com

WEST VALLEY MEDICAL CENTER (O, 105 beds) 1717 Arlington, Caldwell, ID, Zip 83605–4802; tel. 208/459–4641; Elizabeth Hunsicker, Chief Executive Officer

INDIANA: TERRE HAUTE REGIONAL HOSPITAL (O, 208 beds) 3901 South Seventh Street, Terre Haute, IN, Zip 47802–5709; tel. 812/232–0021; Nathan Vooys, Chief Executive Officer
Web address: www.regionalhospital.com

KANSAS: MENORAH MEDICAL CENTER (O, 158 beds) 5721 West 119th Street, Overland Park, KS, Zip 66209–3722; tel. 913/498–6000; Phil Buttell, Chief Executive Officer
Web address: www.menorahmedicalcenter.com

OVERLAND PARK REGIONAL MEDICAL CENTER (O, 283 beds) 10500 Quivira Road, Overland Park, KS, Zip 66215–2306, Mailing Address: P.O. Box 15959, Zip 66215–5959, tel. 913/541–5000; Matt Sogard, Chief Executive Officer
Web address: www.oprmc.com

WESLEY HEALTHCARE CENTER (O, 573 beds) 550 North Hillside, Wichita, KS, Zip 67214–4976; tel. 316/962–2000; Bill Voloch, President and Chief Executive Officer
Web address: www.wesleymc.com

KENTUCKY: FRANKFORT REGIONAL MEDICAL CENTER (O, 115 beds) 299 King's Daughters Drive, Frankfort, KY, Zip 40601–4186; tel. 502/875–5240; Chip Peal, Chief Executive Officer

TRISTAR GREENVIEW REGIONAL HOSPITAL (O, 148 beds) 1801 Ashley Circle, Bowling Green, KY, Zip 42104–3362; tel. 270/793–1000; Michael Sherrod, Chief Executive Officer
Web address: www.greenviewhospital.com

LOUISIANA: RAPIDES REGIONAL MEDICAL CENTER (O, 357 beds) 211 4th ST, Alexandria, LA, Zip 71301–8421, Mailing Address: 211 Fourth Street, Zip 71301–8421, tel. 318/769–3000; Jason E. Cobb, FACHE, Chief Executive Officer
Web address: www.rapidesregional.com

TULANE HEALTH SYSTEM (O, 294 beds) 1415 Tulane Avenue, New Orleans, LA, Zip 70112–2600; tel. 504/988–5263; William Lunn, M.D., President and Chief Executive Officer
Web address: www.tuhc.com

MISSISSIPPI: GARDEN PARK MEDICAL CENTER (O, 130 beds) 15200 Community Road, Gulfport, MS, Zip 39503–3085, Mailing Address: P.O. Box 1240, Zip 39502–1240, tel. 228/575–7000; Randy Rogers, FACHE, Chief Executive Officer

MISSOURI: BELTON REGIONAL MEDICAL CENTER (O, 48 beds) 17065 South 71 Highway, Belton, MO, Zip 64012–4631; tel. 816/348–1200; Todd Krass, Chief Executive Officer
Web address: www.beltonregionalmedicalcenter.com

CENTERPOINT MEDICAL CENTER (O, 285 beds) 19600 East 39th Street, Independence, MO, Zip 64057–2301; tel. 816/698–7000; Bret Kolman, CPA, FACHE, Chief Executive Officer
Web address: www.centerpointmedical.com

LAFAYETTE REGIONAL HEALTH CENTER (O, 25 beds) 1500 State Street, Lexington, MO, Zip 64067–1107; tel. 660/259–2203; Darrel Box, Chief Executive Officer
Web address: www.lafayetteregionalhealthcenter.com

LEE'S SUMMIT MEDICAL CENTER (O, 80 beds) 2100 SE Blue Parkway, Lee's Summit, MO, Zip 64063–1007; tel. 816/282–5000; John McDonald, Chief Executive Officer
Web address: www.leessummitmedicalcenter.com

RESEARCH MEDICAL CENTER (O, 472 beds) 2316 East Meyer Boulevard, Kansas City, MO, Zip 64132–1136; tel. 816/276–4000; Ashley McClellan, FACHE, Chief Executive Officer

NEVADA: MOUNTAINVIEW HOSPITAL (O, 340 beds) 3100 North Tenaya Way, Las Vegas, NV, Zip 89128–0436; tel. 702/255–5000; Jeremy Bradshaw, Chief Executive Officer
Web address: www.mountainview-hospital.com

SOUTHERN HILLS HOSPITAL AND MEDICAL CENTER (O, 134 beds) 9300 West Sunset Road, Las Vegas, NV, Zip 89148–4844; tel. 702/880–2100; Alexis Mussi, Interim Chief Executive Officer
Web address: www.southernhillshospital.com

SUNRISE HOSPITAL AND MEDICAL CENTER (O, 668 beds) 3186 South Maryland Parkway, Las Vegas, NV, Zip 89109–2306, Mailing Address: P.O. Box 98530, Zip 89193, tel. 702/731–8000; Todd Sklamberg, President
Web address: www.sunrisehospital.com

NEW HAMPSHIRE: PARKLAND MEDICAL CENTER (O, 82 beds) One Parkland Drive, Derry, NH, Zip 03038–2750; tel. 603/432–1500; Jeff Scionti, Chief Executive Officer
Web address: www.parklandmedicalcenter.com

PORTSMOUTH REGIONAL HOSPITAL (O, 165 beds) 333 Borthwick Avenue, Portsmouth, NH, Zip 03801–7128; tel. 603/436–5110; Dean Carucci, Chief Executive Officer

NORTH CAROLINA: ANGEL MEDICAL CENTER (O, 36 beds) 120 Riverview Street, Franklin, NC, Zip 28734–2612, Mailing Address: P.O. Box 1209, Zip 28744–0569, tel. 828/524–8411; Karen S. Gorby, R.N., MSN, FACHE, Chief Executive Officer and Chief Nursing Officer
Web address: www.angelmed.org

ASHEVILLE SPECIALTY HOSPITAL (O, 34 beds) 428 Biltmore Avenue, 4th Floor, Asheville, NC, Zip 28801–4502; tel. 828/213–5400; Julie A. Dikos, President and Chief Executive Officer

BLUE RIDGE REGIONAL HOSPITAL (O, 21 beds) 125 Hospital Drive, Spruce Pine, NC, Zip 28777–3035; tel. 828/765–4201; Rebecca W. Carter, MSN, R.N., FACHE, President and Chief Nursing Officer
Web address: www.spchospital.org

CAREPARTNERS HEALTH SERVICES (O, 80 beds) 68 Sweeten Creek Road, Asheville, NC, Zip 28803–2318, Mailing Address: P.O. Box 15025, Zip 28813–0025, tel. 828/277–4800; Tracy Buchanan, Chief Executive Officer and President

HIGHLANDS-CASHIERS HOSPITAL (O, 104 beds) 190 Hospital Drive, Highlands, NC, Zip 28741–7600, Mailing Address: P O Drawer 190, Zip 28741–0190, tel. 828/526–1200; Jacqueline Medland, MS, Ph.D., President and Chief Nursing Officer
Web address: www.hchospital.org

MCDOWELL HOSPITAL (O, 30 beds) 430 Rankin Drive, Marion, NC, Zip 28752–6568, Mailing Address: P.O. Box 730, Zip 28752–0730, tel. 828/659–5000; Carol C. Wolfenbarger, FACHE, MSN, President
Web address: www.mission-health.org

MISSION HOSPITAL (O, 763 beds) 509 Biltmore Avenue, Asheville, NC, Zip 28801–4690; tel. 828/213–1111; Jill Hoggard Green, Ph.D., R.N., President

TRANSYLVANIA REGIONAL HOSPITAL (O, 40 beds) 260 Hospital Drive, Brevard, NC, Zip 28712–3378; tel. 828/884–9111; Michele Pilon, President and Chief Nursing Officer
Web address: www.trhospital.org

SOUTH CAROLINA: COLLETON MEDICAL CENTER (O, 131 beds) 501 Robertson Boulevard, Walterboro, SC, Zip 29488–5714; tel. 843/782–2000; Jimmy O. Hiott III, Chief Executive Officer
Web address: www.colletonmedical.com

For explanation of codes following names, see page B2.
★ Indicates Type III membership in the American Hospital Association.

Section B

GRAND STRAND REGIONAL MEDICAL CENTER (O, 371 beds) 809 82nd Parkway, Myrtle Beach, SC, Zip 29572-4607; tel. 843/692-1000; Mark E. Sims, Chief Executive Officer

TRIDENT MEDICAL CENTER (O, 451 beds) 9330 Medical Plaza Drive, Charleston, SC, Zip 29406-9195; tel. 843/797-7000; Todd Gallati, FACHE, President and Chief Executive Officer
Web address: www.tridenthealthsystem.com

TENNESSEE: PARKRIDGE MEDICAL CENTER (O, 464 beds) 2333 McCallie Avenue, Chattanooga, TN, Zip 37404-3258; tel. 423/698-6061; Thomas H. Ozburn, Chief Executive Officer
Web address: www.parkridgemedicalcenter.com

TRISTAR ASHLAND CITY MEDICAL CENTER (O, 12 beds) 313 North Main Street, Ashland City, TN, Zip 37015-1347; tel. 615/792-3030; Darrell White, R.N., Administrator and Chief Nursing Officer

TRISTAR CENTENNIAL MEDICAL CENTER (O, 650 beds) 2300 Patterson Street, Nashville, TN, Zip 37203-1528; tel. 615/342-1000; Scott A. Cihak, President and Chief Executive Officer
Web address: www.tristarcentennial.com

TRISTAR HENDERSONVILLE MEDICAL CENTER (O, 125 beds) 355 New Shackle Island Road, Hendersonville, TN, Zip 37075-2479; tel. 615/338-1000; Regina Bartlett, Chief Executive Officer
Web address: www.hendersonvillemedicalcenter.com

TRISTAR HORIZON MEDICAL CENTER (O, 130 beds) 111 Highway 70 East, Dickson, TN, Zip 37055-2080; tel. 615/446-0446; Dustin Greene, Chief Executive Officer

TRISTAR SKYLINE MEDICAL CENTER (O, 579 beds) 3441 Dickerson Pike, Nashville, TN, Zip 37207-2539; tel. 615/769-2000; Steve Otto, Chief Executive Officer
Web address: www.tristarskyline.com

TRISTAR SOUTHERN HILLS MEDICAL CENTER (O, 87 beds) 391 Wallace Road, Nashville, TN, Zip 37211-4859, Mailing Address: 3441 Dickerson Pike, Zip 37207, tel. 615/781-4000; Joanna J. Conley, FACHE, Chief Executive Officer
Web address: www.tristarsouthernhills.com

TRISTAR STONECREST MEDICAL CENTER (O, 101 beds) 200 StoneCrest Boulevard, Smyrna, TN, Zip 37167-6810; tel. 615/768-2000; Louis Caputo, Chief Executive Officer

TRISTAR SUMMIT MEDICAL CENTER (O, 196 beds) 5655 Frist Boulevard, Hermitage, TN, Zip 37076-2053; tel. 615/316-3000; Brian Marger, Chief Executive Officer
Web address: www.summitmedctr.com

TEXAS: BAYSHORE MEDICAL CENTER (O, 286 beds) 4000 Spencer Highway, Pasadena, TX, Zip 77504-1202; tel. 713/359-2000; Jeanna Bamburg, FACHE, Chief Executive Officer

CORPUS CHRISTI MEDICAL CENTER (O, 424 beds) 3315 South Alameda Street, Corpus Christi, TX, Zip 78411-1883, Mailing Address: P.O. Box 8991, Zip 78468-8991, tel. 361/761-1400; Jay Woodall, FACHE, Chief Executive Officer
Web address: www.ccmedicalcenter.com

HCA HOUSTON HEALTHCARE CLEAR LAKE (O, 584 beds) 620 Power St., League City, TX, Zip 77598-4220, Mailing Address: 500 Medical Center Boulevard, Webster, Zip 77598-4220, tel. 281/332-2511; Todd Caliva, FACHE, Chief Executive Officer

HCA HOUSTON HEALTHCARE CONROE (O, 301 beds) 504 Medical Boulevard, Conroe, TX, Zip 77304, Mailing Address: P.O. Box 1538, Zip 77305-1538, tel. 936/539-1111; Matt Davis, FACHE, Chief Executive Officer
Web address: www.conroeregional.com/

HCA HOUSTON HEALTHCARE NORTHWEST (O, 254 beds) 710 Cypress Creek Parkway, Houston, TX, Zip 77090-3402; tel. 281/440-1000; Scott Davis, Chief Executive Officer

HCA HOUSTON HEALTHCARE TOMBALL (O, 346 beds) 605 Holderrieth Street, Tomball, TX, Zip 77375-6445; tel. 281/401-7500; Saumya Sutaria, M.D., Chief Operating Officer
Web address: www.tomballregionalmedicalcenter.com

KINGWOOD MEDICAL CENTER (O, 559 beds) 22999 U S Highway 59 North, Kingwood, TX, Zip 77339; tel. 281/348-8000; John Corbeil, Chief Executive Officer
Web address: www.kingwoodmedical.com

LAS PALMAS MEDICAL CENTER (O, 546 beds) 1801 North Oregon Street, El Paso, TX, Zip 79902-3591; tel. 915/521-1200; Don Karl, Interim Chief Executive Officer

MEDICAL CITY ALLIANCE (O, 75 beds) 3101 North Tarrant Parkway, Fort Worth, TX, Zip 76177; tel. 817/639-1000; Glenn Wallace, Chief Executive Officer
Web address: www.baylorhealth.com/PhysiciansLocations/BIR/Pages/Default.aspx

MEDICAL CITY ARLINGTON (O, 324 beds) 3301 Matlock Road, Arlington, TX, Zip 76015-2908; tel. 817/465-3241; Keith Zimmerman, Chief Executive Officer

MEDICAL CITY DALLAS (O, 711 beds) 7777 Forest Lane, Dallas, TX, Zip 75230-2598; tel. 972/566-7000; Chris Mowan, Chief Executive Officer
Web address: www.medicalcityhospital.com

MEDICAL CITY DENTON (O, 185 beds) 3535 South I-35 East, Denton, TX, Zip 76210; tel. 940/384-3535; Steven Edgar, FACHE, President and Chief Executive Officer

MEDICAL CITY FORT WORTH (O, 218 beds) 900 Eighth Avenue, Fort Worth, TX, Zip 76104-3902; tel. 817/336-2100; Jyric Sims, FACHE, Chief Executive Officer
Web address: www.medicalcityfortworth.com/about/

MEDICAL CITY GREEN OAKS HOSPITAL (O, 124 beds) 7808 Clodus Fields Drive, Dallas, TX, Zip 75251-2206; tel. 972/991-9504; Thomas M. Collins, President, Chairman and Chief Executive Officer
Web address: www.greenoakspsych.com

MEDICAL CITY LAS COLINAS (O, 72 beds) 6800 North MacArthur Boulevard, Irving, TX, Zip 75039-2422; tel. 972/969-2000; Daniela Decell, Chief Executive Officer

MEDICAL CITY LEWISVILLE (O, 156 beds) 500 West Main, Lewisville, TX, Zip 75057-3699; tel. 972/420-1000; LaSharndra Barbarin, Chief Executive Officer
Web address: www.lewisvillemedical.com

MEDICAL CITY MCKINNEY (O, 222 beds) 4500 Medical Center Drive, McKinney, TX, Zip 75069-1650; tel. 972/547-8000; Ernest C. Lynch III, FACHE, President and Chief Executive Officer
Web address: www.medicalcenterofmckinney.com

MEDICAL CITY NORTH HILLS (O, 140 beds) 4401 Booth Calloway Road, North Richland Hills, TX, Zip 76180-7399; tel. 817/255-1000; Nancy L. Hill, R.N., MSN, Chief Operating Officer

MEDICAL CITY PLANO (O, 472 beds) 3901 West 15th Street, Plano, TX, Zip 75075-7738; tel. 972/596-6800; Carlton Ulmer, Chief Executive Officer
Web address: www.medicalcenterplano.com

MEDICAL CITY WEATHERFORD (O, 82 beds) 713 East Anderson Street, Weatherford, TX, Zip 76086-5705; tel. 682/582-1000; Sean Kamber, Chief Executive Officer
Web address: www.weatherfordregional.com

METHODIST AMBULATORY SURGERY HOSPITAL – NORTHWEST (O, 21 beds) 9150 Huebner Road, Suite 100, San Antonio, TX, Zip 78240-1545; tel. 210/575-5000; Cathy Bump, R.N., Interim Chief Executive Officer
Web address: www.sahealth.com

METHODIST HOSPITAL SOUTH (O, 51 beds) 1905 Highway 97 East, Jourdanton, TX, Zip 78026-1504; tel. 830/769-3515; Pamela Guillory, Interim Chief Executive Officer

METHODIST HOSPITAL (O, 1631 beds) 7700 Floyd Curl Drive, San Antonio, TX, Zip 78229-3993; tel. 210/575-4000; Daniel Miller, FACHE, Chief Executive Officer
Web address: www.sahealth.com

METHODIST STONE OAK HOSPITAL (O, 242 beds) 1139 E Sonterra Boulevard, San Antonio, TX, Zip 78258-4347, Mailing Address: 1139 East Sonterra Boulevard, Zip 78258-4347, tel. 210/638-2100; Marc Strode, Chief Executive Officer
Web address: www.sahealth.com/locations/methodist-stone-oak-hospital/

PARK PLAZA HOSPITAL (O, 139 beds) 1313 Hermann Drive, Houston, TX, Zip 77004-7092; tel. 713/527-5000; Peyton Elliott, Chief Executive Officer

PEARLAND MEDICAL CENTER (O, 53 beds) 11100 Shadow Creek Parkway, Pearland, TX, Zip 77584-7285; tel. 713/770-7000; David S. Wagner, Chief Executive Officer
Web address: www.pearlandmc.com

PLAZA SPECIALTY HOSPITAL (O, 46 beds) 1300 Binz Street, Houston, TX, Zip 77004-7016; tel. 713/285-1000; Peyton Elliott, Chief Executive Officer

RIO GRANDE REGIONAL HOSPITAL (O, 320 beds) 101 East Ridge Road, McAllen, TX, Zip 78503-1299; tel. 956/632-6000; Cristina Rivera, Chief Executive Officer
Web address: www.riohealth.com

For explanation of codes following names, see page B2.
★ Indicates Type III membership in the American Hospital Association.

ST. DAVID'S MEDICAL CENTER (O, 591 beds) 919 East 32nd Street, Austin, TX, Zip 78705–2709, Mailing Address: P.O. Box 4039, Zip 78765–4039, tel. 512/476–7111; Todd E. Steward, FACHE, Chief Executive Officer
Web address: www.stdavids.com

ST. DAVID'S NORTH AUSTIN MEDICAL CENTER (O, 398 beds) 12221 North MoPac Expressway, Austin, TX, Zip 78758–2496; tel. 512/901–1000; Thomas W. Jackson, Chief Executive Officer

ST. DAVID'S ROUND ROCK MEDICAL CENTER (O, 171 beds) 2400 Round Rock Avenue, Round Rock, TX, Zip 78681–4097; tel. 512/341–1000; Jeremy Barclay, Chief Executive Officer
Web address: www.stdavids.com

ST. DAVID'S SOUTH AUSTIN MEDICAL CENTER (O, 290 beds) 901 West Ben White Boulevard, Austin, TX, Zip 78704–6903; tel. 512/447–2211; Todd E. Steward, FACHE, Acting Chief Executive Officer
Web address: www.southaustinmc.com

TEXAS ORTHOPEDIC HOSPITAL (O, 49 beds) 7401 South Main Street, Houston, TX, Zip 77030–4509; tel. 713/799–8600; Eric Becker, Chief Executive Officer

VALLEY REGIONAL MEDICAL CENTER (O, 214 beds) 100A Alton Gloor Boulevard, Brownsville, TX, Zip 78526–3354; tel. 956/350–7101; Art Garza, FACHE, Chief Executive Officer
Web address: www.valleyregionalmedicalcenter.com

WEST HOUSTON MEDICAL CENTER (O, 264 beds) 12141 Richmond Avenue, Houston, TX, Zip 77082–2499; tel. 281/558–3444; Megan Marietta, Chief Executive Officer

WOMAN'S HOSPITAL OF TEXAS (O, 367 beds) 7600 Fannin Street, Houston, TX, Zip 77054–1906; tel. 713/790–1234; Ashley McClellan, FACHE, Chief Executive Officer
Web address: www.womanshospital.com

UTAH: BRIGHAM CITY COMMUNITY HOSPITAL (O, 39 beds) 950 South Medical Drive, Brigham City, UT, Zip 84302–4724; tel. 435/734–9471; Richard Spuhler, Chief Executive Officer
Web address: www.brighamcityhospital.com

CACHE VALLEY HOSPITAL (O, 22 beds) 2380 North 400 East, North Logan, UT, Zip 84341–6000; tel. 435/713–9700; Daren Wells, Chief Executive Officer

LAKEVIEW HOSPITAL (O, 119 beds) 630 East Medical Drive, Bountiful, UT, Zip 84010–4908; tel. 801/299–2200; Troy Wood, Chief Executive Officer
Web address: www.lakeviewhospital.com

LONE PEAK HOSPITAL (O, 32 beds) 1925 South State Street, Draper, UT, Zip 84020; tel. 801/545–8000; Brian Lines, Chief Executive Officer
Web address: www.lonepeakhospital.com

MOUNTAIN VIEW HOSPITAL (O, 114 beds) 1000 East 100 North, Payson, UT, Zip 84651–1600; tel. 801/465–7000; Kevin Johnson, Chief Executive Officer

OGDEN REGIONAL MEDICAL CENTER (O, 167 beds) 5475 South 500 East, Ogden, UT, Zip 84405–6905; tel. 801/479–2111; Mark B. Adams, Chief Executive Officer
Web address: www.ogdenregional.com

ST. MARK'S HOSPITAL (O, 277 beds) 1200 East 3900 South, Salt Lake City, UT, Zip 84124–1390; tel. 801/268–7111; Mark Robinson, FACHE, Chief Executive Officer
Web address: www.stmarkshospital.com

TIMPANOGOS REGIONAL HOSPITAL (O, 106 beds) 750 West 800 North, Orem, UT, Zip 84057–3660; tel. 801/714–6000; Kimball S. Anderson, FACHE, Chief Executive Officer

VIRGINIA: CHIPPENHAM HOSPITAL (O, 765 beds) 7101 Jahnke Road, Richmond, VA, Zip 23225–4044; tel. 804/320–3911; Zachary McCluskey, Interim Chief Executive Officer
Web address: www.cjwmedical.com

DOMINION HOSPITAL (O, 100 beds) 2960 Sleepy Hollow Road, Falls Church, VA, Zip 22044–2030; tel. 703/536–2000; Lee Higginbotham, Chief Executive Officer
Web address: www.dominionhospital.com

HENRICO DOCTORS' HOSPITAL (O, 560 beds) 1602 Skipwith Road, Richmond, VA, Zip 23229–5205; tel. 804/289–4500; William Wagnon, Chief Executive Officer

JOHN RANDOLPH MEDICAL CENTER (O, 112 beds) 411 West Randolph Road, Hopewell, VA, Zip 23860–2938; tel. 804/541–1600; Joseph Mazzo, Chief Executive Officer
Web address: www.johnrandolphmed.com

LEWIS-GALE MEDICAL CENTER (O, 521 beds) 8633 Grassy Hill Rd, Boones Mill, VA, Zip 24065, Mailing Address: 1900 Electric Road, Salem, Zip 24153–7494, tel. 540/776–4000; Lance Jones, Chief Executive Officer

LEWISGALE HOSPITAL ALLEGHANY (O, 146 beds) One ARH Lane, Low Moor, VA, Zip 24457, Mailing Address: P.O. Box 7, Zip 24457–0007, tel. 540/862–6011; William Windham, Chief Executive Officer
Web address: www.alleghanyregional.com

LEWISGALE HOSPITAL MONTGOMERY (O, 89 beds) 3700 South Main Street, Blacksburg, VA, Zip 24060–7081, Mailing Address: P.O. Box 90004, Zip 24062–9004, tel. 540/951–1111; Alan J. Fabian, Chief Executive Officer

LEWISGALE HOSPITAL PULASKI (O, 54 beds) 2400 Lee Highway, Pulaski, VA, Zip 24301–2326, Mailing Address: P.O. Box 759, Zip 24301–0759, tel. 540/994–8100; Sean Pressman, Chief Executive Officer
Web address: www.lewisgale.com/

RESTON HOSPITAL CENTER (O, 222 beds) 1850 Town Center Parkway, Reston, VA, Zip 20190–3219; tel. 703/689–9000; John A. Deardorff, President and Chief Executive, Northern Virginia Market

SPOTSYLVANIA REGIONAL MEDICAL CENTER (O, 100 beds) 4600 Spotsylvania Parkway, Fredericksburg, VA, Zip 22408–7762; tel. 540/498–4000; David McKnight, CPA, Chief Executive Officer
Web address: www.spotsrmc.com

STONESPRINGS HOSPITAL CENTER (O, 124 beds) 24440 Stone Spring Boulevard, Dulles, VA, Zip 20166–2247; tel. 571/349–4000; Matt Mathias, Chief Executive Officer
Web address: www.stonespringshospital.com

Owned, leased, sponsored:	161 hospitals	39569 beds
Contract-managed:	0 hospitals	0 beds
Totals:	161 hospitals	39569 beds

0328: HEALTH FIRST, INC. (NP)
6450 US Highway 1, Rockledge, FL, Zip 32955–5747; tel. 321/434–7000; Steven P. Johnson, Ph.D., President and Chief Executive Officer
(Centralized Health System)

FLORIDA: HEALTH FIRST CAPE CANAVERAL HOSPITAL (O, 144 beds) 701 West Cocoa Beach Causeway, Cocoa Beach, FL, Zip 32931–5595, Mailing Address: P.O. Box 320069, Zip 32932–0069, tel. 321/799–7111; Brett A. Esrock, FACHE, President
Web address: www.health-first.org

HEALTH FIRST HOLMES REGIONAL MEDICAL CENTER (O, 514 beds) 1350 South Hickory Street, Melbourne, FL, Zip 32901–3224; tel. 321/434–7000; Brett A. Esrock, FACHE, Chief Executive Officer
Web address: www.health-first.org

HEALTH FIRST PALM BAY HOSPITAL (O, 120 beds) 1425 Malabar Road NE, Palm Bay, FL, Zip 32907–2506; tel. 321/434–8000; Brett A. Esrock, FACHE, President

HEALTH FIRST VIERA HOSPITAL (O, 84 beds) 8745 North Wickham Road, Melbourne, FL, Zip 32940–5997; tel. 321/434–9164; Brett A. Esrock, FACHE, President
Web address: www.vierahospital.org

Owned, leased, sponsored:	4 hospitals	862 beds
Contract-managed:	0 hospitals	0 beds
Totals:	4 hospitals	862 beds

0307: HEALTH QUEST SYSTEMS, INC. (NP)
1351 Route 55 Ste 200, LaGrangeville, NY, Zip 12540–5108, Mailing Address: 1351 Route 55, Zip 12540–5108, tel. 845/475–9500; Robert Friedberg, President and Chief Executive Officer
(Independent Hospital System)

CONNECTICUT: SHARON HOSPITAL (O, 78 beds) 50 Hospital Hill Road, Sharon, CT, Zip 06069–2096, Mailing Address: P.O. Box 789, Zip 06069–0789, tel. 860/364–4000; Denise George, R.N., Interim Chief Executive Officer

For explanation of codes following names, see page B2.
★ Indicates Type III membership in the American Hospital Association.

NEW YORK: NORTHERN DUTCHESS HOSPITAL (O, 84 beds) 6511 Springbrook Avenue, Rhinebeck, NY, Zip 12572–3709, Mailing Address: P.O. Box 5002, Zip 12572–5002, tel. 845/876–3001; Denise George, R.N., President
Web address: www.health-quest.org/home_nd.cfm?id=9

PUTNAM HOSPITAL CENTER (O, 140 beds) 670 Stoneleigh Avenue, Carmel, NY, Zip 10512–3997; tel. 845/279–5711; Peter Kelly, President

VASSAR BROTHERS MEDICAL CENTER (O, 365 beds) 45 Reade Place, Poughkeepsie, NY, Zip 12601–3947; tel. 845/454–8500; Ann McMackin, President
Web address: www.health-quest.org

Owned, leased, sponsored:	4 hospitals	667 beds
Contract-managed:	0 hospitals	0 beds
Totals:	4 hospitals	667 beds

0342: HEALTHPARTNERS (NP)
8170 33rd Avenue South, Bloomington, MN, Zip 55425–4516; tel. 952/883–7600; Andrea Walsh, President and Chief Executive Officer
(Moderately Centralized Health System)

MINNESOTA: GLENCOE REGIONAL HEALTH (C, 135 beds) 1805 Hennepin Avenue North, Glencoe, MN, Zip 55336–1416; tel. 320/864–3121; Jeffrey Mason, President and Chief Executive Officer
Web address: www.grhsonline.org

HUTCHINSON HEALTH (O, 49 beds) 1095 Highway 15 South, Hutchinson, MN, Zip 55350–3182; tel. 320/234–5000; Jim Lyons, President
Web address: www.hutchhealth.com

LAKEVIEW HOSPITAL (O, 67 beds) 927 Churchill Street West, Stillwater, MN, Zip 55082–6605; tel. 651/439–5330; Theodore Wegleitner, Chief Executive Officer and President
Web address: www.lakeview.org

PARK NICOLLET METHODIST HOSPITAL (O, 365 beds) 6500 Excelsior Boulevard, Saint Louis Park, MN, Zip 55426–4702; tel. 952/993–5000; Jennifer Myster, President

REGIONS HOSPITAL (O, 457 beds) 640 Jackson Street, Saint Paul, MN, Zip 55101–2595, tel. 651/254 3456; Megan Remark, President and Chief Executive Officer
Web address: www.regionshospital.com

WISCONSIN: AMERY HOSPITAL AND CLINIC (O, 16 beds) 265 Griffin Street East, Amery, WI, Zip 54001–1439; tel. 715/268–8000; Debra Rudquist, FACHE, President and Chief Executive Officer

HUDSON HOSPITAL AND CLINIC (O, 24 beds) 405 Stageline Road, Hudson, WI, Zip 54016–7848; tel. 715/531–6000; Thomas Borowski, FACHE, President
Web address: www.hudsonhospital.org

WESTFIELDS HOSPITAL AND CLINIC (O, 25 beds) 535 Hospital Road, New Richmond, WI, Zip 54017–1449; tel. 715/243–2600; Steven Massey, President and Chief Executive Officer
Web address: www.westfieldshospital.com

Owned, leased, sponsored:	7 hospitals	1003 beds
Contract-managed:	1 hospitals	135 beds
Totals:	8 hospitals	1138 beds

★0585: HEALTHTECH MANAGEMENT SERVICES (IO)
5110 Maryland Way Suite 200, Brentwood, TN, Zip 37027–2307; tel. 615/309–6053; Derek Morkel, Chief Executive Officer
(Moderately Centralized Health System)

ARIZONA: COBRE VALLEY REGIONAL MEDICAL CENTER (C, 25 beds) 5880 South Hospital Drive, Globe, AZ, Zip 85501–9454; tel. 928/425–3261; Neal Jensen, Chief Executive Officer

GEORGIA: UPSON REGIONAL MEDICAL CENTER (C, 83 beds) 801 West Gordon Street, Thomaston, GA, Zip 30286–3426, Mailing Address: P.O. Box 1059, Zip 30286–0027, tel. 706/647–8111; Jeffrey S. Tarrant, FACHE, Chief Executive Officer
Web address: www.urmc.org

ILLINOIS: CARLINVILLE AREA HOSPITAL (C, 25 beds) 20733 North Broad Street, Carlinville, IL, Zip 62626–1499; tel. 217/854–3141; Kenneth G. Reid, President and Chief Executive Officer
Web address: www.cahcare.com

HAMMOND-HENRY HOSPITAL (C, 61 beds) 600 North College Avenue, Geneseo, IL, Zip 61254–1099; tel. 309/944–6431; Mark Kuhn, Chief Executive Officer
Web address: www.hammondhenry.com

HILLSBORO AREA HOSPITAL (C, 25 beds) 1200 East Tremont Street, Hillsboro, IL, Zip 62049–1900; tel. 217/532–6111; Rex H. Brown, President and Chief Executive Officer
Web address: www.hillsborohealth.org

LOUISIANA: IBERIA MEDICAL CENTER (C, 123 beds) 2315 East Main Street, New Iberia, LA, Zip 70560–4031, Mailing Address: P.O. Box 13338, Zip 70562–3338, tel. 337/364–0441; Parker A. Templeton, FACHE, Chief Executive Officer
Web address: www.iberiamedicalcenter.com

MONTANA: BARRETT HOSPITAL & HEALTHCARE (C, 18 beds) 600 Mt Highway 91 South, Dillon, MT, Zip 59725–7379; tel. 406/683–3000; Ken Westman, Chief Executive Officer

OREGON: BLUE MOUNTAIN HOSPITAL DISTRICT (C, 62 beds) 170 Ford Road, John Day, OR, Zip 97845–2009; tel. 541/575–1311; Derek Daly, Chief Executive Officer
Web address: www.bluemountainhospital.org

WISCONSIN: GRANT REGIONAL HEALTH CENTER (C, 6 beds) 507 South Monroe Street, Lancaster, WI, Zip 53813–2054; tel. 608/723–2143; David Smith, President and Chief Executive Officer
Web address: www.grantregional.com

SPOONER HEALTH (C, 18 beds) 1280 Chandler Drive, Spooner, WI, Zip 54801–1299; tel. 715/635–2111; Michael Schafer, Chief Executive Officer and Administrator
Web address: www.spoonerhealth.com

TOMAH MEMORIAL HOSPITAL (C, 25 beds) 321 Butts Avenue, Tomah, WI, Zip 54660–1412; tel. 608/372–2181; Philip J. Stuart, Administrator and Chief Executive Officer
Web address: www.tomahhospital.org

WYOMING: HOT SPRINGS COUNTY MEMORIAL HOSPITAL (C, 25 beds) 150 East Arapahoe Street, Thermopolis, WY, Zip 82443–2490; tel. 307/864 3121; Margie Molitor, FACHE, R.N., Chief Executive Officer

Owned, leased, sponsored:	0 hospitals	0 beds
Contract-managed:	12 hospitals	496 beds
Totals:	12 hospitals	496 beds

★9505: HENRY FORD HEALTH SYSTEM (NP)
One Ford Place, Detroit, MI, Zip 48202–3450; tel. 313/876–8708; Wright L. Lassiter III, President and Chief Executive Officer
(Centralized Health System)

MICHIGAN: HENRY FORD ALLEGIANCE HEALTH (O, 404 beds) 205 North East Avenue, Jackson, MI, Zip 49201–1753; tel. 517/205–4800; Paula R. Autry, FACHE, President and Chief Executive Officer
Web address: www.allegiancehealth.org

HENRY FORD ALLEGIANCE SPECIALTY HOSPITAL (O, 44 beds) 110 North Elm Avenue, Jackson, MI, Zip 49202–3595; tel. 517/205–4463; J Mark. Fall, Chief Executive Officer
Web address: www.carelinkofjackson.org

HENRY FORD HOSPITAL (O, 773 beds) 2799 West Grand Boulevard, Detroit, MI, Zip 48202–2608; tel. 313/916–2600; Veronica Hall, R.N., Interim President and Chief Executive Officer

HENRY FORD KINGSWOOD HOSPITAL (O, 94 beds) 10300 West Eight Mile Road, Ferndale, MI, Zip 48220–2100; tel. 248/398–3200; Cathrine Frank, M.D., Chairperson
Web address: www.henryford.com

HENRY FORD MACOMB HOSPITALS (O, 415 beds) 15855 19 Mile Road, Clinton Township, MI, Zip 48038–6324; tel. 586/263–2300; Barbara W. Rossmann, R.N., President and Chief Executive Officer
Web address: www.henryfordmacomb.com

For explanation of codes following names, see page B2.
★ Indicates Type III membership in the American Hospital Association.

© 2019 AHA Guide   Health Care Systems, Networks and Alliances   **B65**

Section B

HENRY FORD WEST BLOOMFIELD HOSPITAL (O, 212 beds) 6777 West Maple Road, West Bloomfield, MI, Zip 48322–3013; tel. 248/661–4100; Lynn M. Torossian, President and Chief Executive Officer

HENRY FORD WYANDOTTE HOSPITAL (O, 334 beds) 2333 Biddle Avenue, Wyandotte, MI, Zip 48192–4668; tel. 734/246–6000; Peter Karadjoff, Interim President
Web address: www.henryfordhealth.org

Owned, leased, sponsored:	7 hospitals	2276 beds
Contract-managed:	0 hospitals	0 beds
Totals:	7 hospitals	2276 beds

0309: HERITAGE VALLEY HEALTH SYSTEM (NP)
1000 Dutch Ridge Road, Beaver, PA, Zip 15009–9727; tel. 724/773–2024; Norman F. Mitry, President and Chief Executive Officer
(Independent Hospital System)

PENNSYLVANIA: HERITAGE VALLEY HEALTH SYSTEM (O, 271 beds) 1000 Dutch Ridge Road, Beaver, PA, Zip 15009–9727; tel. 724/728–7000; Norman F. Mitry, President and Chief Executive Officer
Web address: www.heritagevalley.org

SEWICKLEY VALLEY HOSPITAL, (A DIVISION OF VALLEY MEDICAL FACILITIES) (O, 179 beds) 720 Blackburn Road, Sewickley, PA, Zip 15143–1459; tel. 412/741–6600; Norman F. Mitry, President and Chief Executive Officer
Web address: www.heritagevalley.org

Owned, leased, sponsored:	2 hospitals	450 beds
Contract-managed:	0 hospitals	0 beds
Totals:	2 hospitals	450 beds

1024: HEYWOOD HEALTHCARE (NP)
242 Green Street, Gardner, MA, Zip 01440–1336; tel. 978/632–3420; Winfield S. Brown, FACHE, Chief Executive Officer
(Independent Hospital System)

MASSACHUSETTS: ATHOL HOSPITAL (O, 25 beds) 2033 Main Street, Athol, MA, Zip 01331–3598; tel. 978/249–3511; Winfield S. Brown, FACHE, President and Chief Executive Officer
Web address: www.atholhospital.org

HEYWOOD HOSPITAL (O, 93 beds) 242 Green Street, Gardner, MA, Zip 01440–1373; tel. 978/632–3420; Winfield S. Brown, FACHE, President and Chief Executive Officer
Web address: www.heywood.org

Owned, leased, sponsored:	2 hospitals	118 beds
Contract-managed:	0 hospitals	0 beds
Totals:	2 hospitals	118 beds

1014: HOLZER HEALTH SYSTEM (NP)
500 Burlington Road, Jackson, OH, Zip 45640–9360; tel. 855/446–5937; Michael R. Canady, M.D., Chief Executive Officer
(Independent Hospital System)

OHIO: HOLZER MEDICAL CENTER – JACKSON (O, 24 beds) 500 Burlington Road, Jackson, OH, Zip 45640–9360; tel. 740/288–4625; Michael R. Canady, M.D., Chief Executive Officer

HOLZER MEDICAL CENTER (O, 195 beds) 100 Jackson Pike, Gallipolis, OH, Zip 45631–1563; tel. 740/446–5000; Michael R. Canady, M.D., Interim Chief Executive Officer
Web address: www.holzer.org

Owned, leased, sponsored:	2 hospitals	219 beds
Contract-managed:	0 hospitals	0 beds
Totals:	2 hospitals	219 beds

★0963: HONORHEALTH (NP)
8125 North Hayden Road, Scottsdale, AZ, Zip 85258–2463; tel. 623/580–5800; Todd LaPorte, Chief Executive Officer
(Independent Hospital System)

ARIZONA: HONORHEALTH DEER VALLEY MEDICAL CENTER (O, 204 beds) 19829 North 27th Avenue, Phoenix, AZ, Zip 85027–4002; tel. 623/879–6100; David Price, Chief Executive Officer

HONORHEALTH JOHN C. LINCOLN MEDICAL CENTER (O, 262 beds) 250 East Dunlap Avenue, Phoenix, AZ, Zip 85020–2825; tel. 602/943–2381; Margaret Elizabeth. Griffin, Chief Executive Officer
Web address: www.jcl.com

HONORHEALTH SCOTTSDALE OSBORN MEDICAL CENTER (O, 347 beds) 7400 East Osborn Road, Scottsdale, AZ, Zip 85251–6403; tel. 480/882–4000; Kimberly Post, Senior Vice President and Chief Executive Officer
Web address: www.shc.org

HONORHEALTH SCOTTSDALE SHEA MEDICAL CENTER (O, 427 beds) 9003 East Shea Boulevard, Scottsdale, AZ, Zip 85260–6771; tel. 480/323–3000; Gary E. Baker, Senior Vice President and Chief Executive Officer
Web address: www.shc.org

HONORHEALTH SCOTTSDALE THOMPSON PEAK MEDICAL CENTER (O, 92 beds) 7400 East Thompson Peak Parkway, Scottsdale, AZ, Zip 85255–4109; tel. 480/324–7000; David Price, Chief Executive Officer

Owned, leased, sponsored:	5 hospitals	1332 beds
Contract-managed:	0 hospitals	0 beds
Totals:	5 hospitals	1332 beds

★0642: HOUSTON HEALTHCARE SYSTEM (NP)
1601 Watson Boulevard, Warner Robins, GA, Zip 31093–3431, Mailing Address: P.O. Box 2886, Zip 31099–2886, tel. 478/922–4281; Cary Martin, Chief Executive Officer
(Independent Hospital System)

GEORGIA: HOUSTON MEDICAL CENTER (O, 237 beds) 1601 Watson Boulevard, Warner Robins, GA, Zip 31093–3431, Mailing Address: P.O. Box 2886, Zip 31099–2886, tel. 478/922–4281; Cary Martin, Chief Executive Officer

PERRY HOSPITAL (O, 39 beds) 1120 Morningside Drive, Perry, GA, Zip 31069–2906; tel. 478/987–3600; David Campbell, Administrator
Web address: www.hhc.org

Owned, leased, sponsored:	2 hospitals	276 beds
Contract-managed:	0 hospitals	0 beds
Totals:	2 hospitals	276 beds

★7235: HOUSTON METHODIST (CO)
6565 Fannin Street, D-200, Houston, TX, Zip 77030–2707; tel. 713/441–2221; Marc L. Boom, M.D., Chief Executive Officer
(Centralized Health System)

TEXAS: HOUSTON METHODIST BAYTOWN HOSPITAL (O, 227 beds) 4401 Garth Road, Administration Department, Baytown, TX, Zip 77521–2122; tel. 281/420–8600; David P. Bernard, FACHE, Chief Executive Officer
Web address: www.houstonmethodist.org

HOUSTON METHODIST CLEAR LAKE HOSPITAL (O, 129 beds) 18300 St John Drive, Nassau Bay, TX, Zip 77058–6302; tel. 281/333–5503; Dan Newman, Chief Executive Officer

HOUSTON METHODIST CONTINUING CARE HOSPITAL (O, 58 beds) 701 Fry Road, Katy, TX, Zip 77450–2255; tel. 281/599–5700; Gary L. Kempf, R.N., Administrator
Web address: www.houstonmethodist.org/katy-st-catherine-hospital

HOUSTON METHODIST HOSPITAL (O, 948 beds) 6565 Fannin Street, D200, Houston, TX, Zip 77030–2707; tel. 713/790–3311; Roberta Schwartz, Ph.D., Executive Vice President

HOUSTON METHODIST SUGAR LAND HOSPITAL (O, 321 beds) 16655 SW Freeway, Sugar Land, TX, Zip 77479–2329; tel. 281/274–7000; Christopher Siebenaler, Regional Senior Vice President and Chief Executive Officer
Web address: www.methodisthealth.com

For explanation of codes following names, see page B2.
★ Indicates Type III membership in the American Hospital Association.

HOUSTON METHODIST THE WOODLANDS HOSPITAL (O, 146 beds) 17201 Interstate 45 South, The Woodlands, TX, Zip 77385; tel. 713/790–3333; Debra F. Sukin, Ph.D., Regional Senior Vice President and Chief Executive Officer

HOUSTON METHODIST WEST HOSPITAL (O, 212 beds) 18500 Katy Freeway, Houston, TX, Zip 77094–1110; tel. 832/522–1000; Wayne M. Voss, Chief Executive Officer
Web address: www.methodisthealth.org

HOUSTON METHODIST WILLOWBROOK HOSPITAL (O, 312 beds) 18220 State Highway 249, Houston, TX, Zip 77070–4347; tel. 281/477–1000; Keith Barber, CPA, Chief Executive Officer

Owned, leased, sponsored:	8 hospitals	2353 beds
Contract-managed:	0 hospitals	0 beds
Totals:	8 hospitals	2353 beds

★**5355: HSHS HOSPITAL SISTERS HEALTH SYSTEM** (CC)
4936 LaVerna Road, Springfield, IL, Zip 62707–9797, Mailing Address: P.O. Box 19456, Zip 62794–9456, tel. 217/523–4747; Mary Starmann-Harrison, FACHE, R.N., President and Chief Executive Officer
(Decentralized Health System)

ILLINOIS: HSHS GOOD SHEPHERD HOSPITAL (O, 30 beds) 200 South Cedar Street, Shelbyville, IL, Zip 62565–1838; tel. 217/774–3961; Aaron Puchbauer, President
Web address: www.mysmh.org

HSHS HOLY FAMILY HOSPITAL IN GREENVILLE (O, 42 beds) 200 Healthcare Drive, Greenville, IL, Zip 62246–1154; tel. 618/664–1230; Kelly Sager, R.N., President and Chief Executive Officer

HSHS ST. ANTHONY'S MEMORIAL HOSPITAL (O, 123 beds) 503 North Maple Street, Effingham, IL, Zip 62401–2099; tel. 217/342–2121; Theresa Rutherford, R.N., MS, FACHE, President and Chief Executive Officer
Web address: www.stanthonyshospital.org

HSHS ST. ELIZABETH'S HOSPITAL (O, 224 beds) One St. Elizabeth's Boulevard, O'Fallon, IL, Zip 62269; tel. 618/234–2120; Patricia Fischer, FACHE, R.N., President and Chief Executive Officer

HSHS ST. FRANCIS HOSPITAL (O, 25 beds) 1215 Franciscan Drive, Litchfield, IL, Zip 62056–1799, Mailing Address: P.O. Box 1215, Zip 62056–0999, tel. 217/324–2191; John Peipert, R.N., Interim President and Chief Executive Officer
Web address: www.stfrancis-litchfield.org

HSHS ST. JOHN'S HOSPITAL (O, 404 beds) 800 East Carpenter Street, Springfield, IL, Zip 62769–0002; tel. 217/544–6464; Evert J. Kuiper, President and Chief Executive Officer
Web address: www.st-johns.org

HSHS ST. JOSEPH'S HOSPITAL (O, 65 beds) 9515 Holy Cross Lane, Breese, IL, Zip 62230–3618, Mailing Address: PO Box 99, Zip 62230–0099, tel. 618/526–4511; Chris Klay, President and Chief Executive Officer

HSHS ST. JOSEPH'S HOSPITAL (O, 25 beds) 12866 Troxler Avenue, Highland, IL, Zip 62249–1698; tel. 618/651–2600; John A. Ludwig, President and Chief Operating Officer
Web address: www.stjosephshighland.com

HSHS ST. MARY'S HOSPITAL (O, 230 beds) 1800 East Lake Shore Drive, Decatur, IL, Zip 62521–3883; tel. 217/464–2966; Michael Hicks, President and Chief Executive Officer

WISCONSIN: HSHS SACRED HEART HOSPITAL (O, 205 beds) 900 West Clairemont Avenue, Eau Claire, WI, Zip 54701–6122; tel. 715/717–4121; Andrew Bagnall, President and Chief Executive Officer
Web address: www.sacredhearteauclaire.org

HSHS ST. CLARE MEMORIAL HOSPITAL (O, 20 beds) 855 South Main Street, Oconto Falls, WI, Zip 54154–1296; tel. 920/846–3444; Christopher Brabant, President and Chief Executive Officer
Web address: www.stclarememorial.org

HSHS ST. JOSEPH'S HOSPITAL (O, 102 beds) 2661 County Highway I, Chippewa Falls, WI, Zip 54729–5407; tel. 715/723–1811; Andrew Bagnall, Interim Chief Executive Officer

HSHS ST. MARY'S HOSPITAL MEDICAL CENTER (O, 83 beds) 1726 Shawano Avenue, Green Bay, WI, Zip 54303–3282; tel. 920/498–4200; Therese B. Pandl, President and Chief Executive Officer
Web address: www.stmgb.org

HSHS ST. NICHOLAS HOSPITAL (O, 46 beds) 3100 Superior Avenue, Sheboygan, WI, Zip 53081–1948; tel. 920/459–8300; Justin Selle, Chief Executive Officer
Web address: www.stnicholashospital.org

HSHS ST. VINCENT HOSPITAL (O, 255 beds) 835 South Van Buren Street, Green Bay, WI, Zip 54301–3526, Mailing Address: P.O. Box 13508, Zip 54307–3508, tel. 920/433–0111; Therese B. Pandl, President and Chief Executive Officer

Owned, leased, sponsored:	15 hospitals	1879 beds
Contract-managed:	0 hospitals	0 beds
Totals:	15 hospitals	1879 beds

0907: HUNT REGIONAL HEALTHCARE (NP)
4215 Joe Ramsey Boulevard, Greenville, TX, Zip 75401–7852, Mailing Address: P.O. Box 1059, Zip 75403–1059, tel. 903/408–5000; Richard Carter, Chief Executive Officer
(Independent Hospital System)

TEXAS: HUNT REGIONAL MEDICAL CENTER (O, 167 beds) 4215 Joe Ramsey Boulevard, Greenville, TX, Zip 75401–7899, Mailing Address: P.O. Box 1059, Zip 75403–1059, tel. 903/408–5000; Richard Carter, District Chief Executive Officer
Web address: www.huntregional.org

Owned, leased, sponsored:	1 hospitals	167 beds
Contract-managed:	0 hospitals	0 beds
Totals:	1 hospitals	167 beds

0117: HUNTSVILLE HOSPITAL HEALTH SYSTEM (NP)
101 Sivley Road SW, Huntsville, AL, Zip 35801–4421; tel. 265/256–1000; David S. Spillers, Chief Executive Officer
(Independent Hospital System)

ALABAMA: ATHENS-LIMESTONE HOSPITAL (C, 71 beds) 700 West Market Street, Athens, AL, Zip 35611–2457, Mailing Address: P.O. Box 999, Zip 35612–0999, tel. 256/233–9292; David Pryor, President
Web address: www.athenslimestonehospital.com

DECATUR MORGAN HOSPITAL (O, 110 beds) 1201 Seventh Street SE, Decatur, AL, Zip 35601–3303, Mailing Address: P.O. Box 2239, Zip 35609–2239, tel. 256/341–2000; Nathaniel Richardson Jr, President

HELEN KELLER HOSPITAL (C, 143 beds) 1300 South Montgomery Avenue, Sheffield, AL, Zip 35660–6334, Mailing Address: P.O. Box 610, Zip 35660–0610, tel. 256/386–4196; Kyle Buchanan, President
Web address: www.helenkeller.com

HUNTSVILLE HOSPITAL (O, 948 beds) 101 Sivley Road SW, Huntsville, AL, Zip 35801–4470; tel. 256/265–1000; David S. Spillers, Chief Executive Officer

LAWRENCE MEDICAL CENTER (C, 43 beds) 202 Hospital Street, Moulton, AL, Zip 35650–1218, Mailing Address: P.O. Box 39, Zip 35650–0039, tel. 256/974–2200; Dean A. Griffin, Chief Executive Officer
Web address: www.lawrencemedicalcenter.com

RED BAY HOSPITAL (C, 22 beds) 211 Hospital Road, Red Bay, AL, Zip 35582–3858, Mailing Address: P.O. Box 490, Zip 35582–0490, tel. 256/356–9532; Sherry Jolley, Director of Operations and Nursing
Web address: www.redbayhospital.com

Owned, leased, sponsored:	2 hospitals	1058 beds
Contract-managed:	4 hospitals	279 beds
Totals:	6 hospitals	1337 beds

★**0231: INDIANA UNIVERSITY HEALTH** (NP)
340 West 10th Street, Suite 6100, Indianapolis, IN, Zip 46202–3082, Mailing Address: P.O. Box 1367, Zip 46206–1367, tel. 317/962–2000; Dennis M. Murphy, President and Chief Executive Officer
(Moderately Centralized Health System)

For explanation of codes following names, see page B2.
★ Indicates Type III membership in the American Hospital Association.

Section B

INDIANA: INDIANA UNIVERSITY HEALTH ARNETT HOSPITAL (O, 192 beds) 5165 McCarty Lane, Lafayette, IN, Zip 47905–8764, Mailing Address: P.O. Box 5545, Zip 47903–5545, tel. 765/448–8000; Daniel Neufelder, President
Web address: www.iuhealth.org

INDIANA UNIVERSITY HEALTH BALL MEMORIAL HOSPITAL (O, 344 beds) 2401 West University Avenue, Muncie, IN, Zip 47303–3499; tel. 765/747–3111; Jeffrey C. Bird, M.D., President
Web address: www.iuhealth.org

INDIANA UNIVERSITY HEALTH BEDFORD HOSPITAL (O, 25 beds) 2900 West 16th Street, Bedford, IN, Zip 47421–3583; tel. 812/275–1200; Bradford W. Dykes, President and Chief Executive Officer
Web address: www.iuhealth.org

INDIANA UNIVERSITY HEALTH BLACKFORD HOSPITAL (O, 15 beds) 410 Pilgrim Boulevard, Hartford City, IN, Zip 47348–1897; tel. 765/348–0300; David W. Hyatt, President

INDIANA UNIVERSITY HEALTH BLOOMINGTON HOSPITAL (O, 282 beds) 601 West Second Street, Bloomington, IN, Zip 47403–2317, Mailing Address: P.O. Box 1149, Zip 47402–1149, tel. 812/336–6821; Brian T. Shockney, FACHE, President
Web address: www.iuhealth.org

INDIANA UNIVERSITY HEALTH FRANKFORT (C, 25 beds) 1300 South Jackson Street, Frankfort, IN, Zip 46041–3313; tel. 765/656–3000; Kelly Braverman, President
Web address: www.stvincent.org

INDIANA UNIVERSITY HEALTH JAY HOSPITAL (C, 35 beds) 500 West Votaw Street, Portland, IN, Zip 47371–1322; tel. 260/726–7131; David W. Hyatt, President
Web address: www.jaycountyhospital.com

INDIANA UNIVERSITY HEALTH NORTH HOSPITAL (O, 161 beds) 11700 North Meridian Avenue, Carmel, IN, Zip 46032–4656; tel. 317/688–2000; Alicia Schulhof, President and Chief Executive Officer

INDIANA UNIVERSITY HEALTH PAOLI HOSPITAL (O, 25 beds) 642 West Hospital Road, Paoli, IN, Zip 47454–9672, Mailing Address: P.O. Box 499, Zip 47454–0499, tel. 812/723–2811; Larry Bailey, President
Web address: www.iuhealth.org/paoli

INDIANA UNIVERSITY HEALTH TIPTON HOSPITAL (O, 25 beds) 1000 South Main Street, Tipton, IN, Zip 46072–9799; tel. 765/675–8500; Michael Harlowe, President and Chief Executive Officer
Web address: www.iuhealth.org

INDIANA UNIVERSITY HEALTH UNIVERSITY HOSPITAL (O, 1288 beds) 550 University Boulevard, Indianapolis, IN, Zip 46202–5149, Mailing Address: P.O. Box 1367, Zip 46206–1367, tel. 317/944–5000; Ryan Nagy, M.D., President and Chief Medical Officer

INDIANA UNIVERSITY HEALTH WEST HOSPITAL (O, 127 beds) 1111 North Ronald Reagan Parkway, Avon, IN, Zip 46123–7085; tel. 317/217–3000; Arthur Vasquez, President
Web address: www.iuhealth.org

INDIANA UNIVERSITY HEALTH WHITE MEMORIAL HOSPITAL (O, 25 beds) 720 South Sixth Street, Monticello, IN, Zip 47960–8182; tel. 574/583–7111; Mary Minier, President
Web address: www.iuhealth.org/white-memorial

REHABILITATION HOSPITAL OF INDIANA (O, 83 beds) 4141 Shore Drive, Indianapolis, IN, Zip 46254–2607; tel. 317/329–2000; Daniel B. Woloszyn, Chief Executive Officer

Owned, leased, sponsored:	12 hospitals	2592 beds
Contract-managed:	2 hospitals	60 beds
Totals:	14 hospitals	2652 beds

2025: INFIRMARY HEALTH SYSTEM (NP)
5 Mobile Infirmary Circle, Mobile, AL, Zip 36607–3513; tel. 251/435–5500; D Mark. Nix, President and Chief Executive Officer
(Independent Hospital System)

ALABAMA: ATMORE COMMUNITY HOSPITAL (O, 33 beds) 401 Medical Park Drive, Atmore, AL, Zip 36502–3091; tel. 251/368–2500; Douglas Tanner, President

INFIRMARY LONG TERM ACUTE CARE HOSPITAL (L, 38 beds) 5 Mobile Infirmary Circle, Mobile, AL, Zip 36607–3513, Mailing Address: P.O. Box 2226, Zip 36652–2226, tel. 251/660–5239; Susanne Marmande, Administrator
Web address: www.theinfirmary.com/

MOBILE INFIRMARY MEDICAL CENTER (O, 554 beds) 5 Mobile Infirmary Drive North, Mobile, AL, Zip 36607–3513, Mailing Address: P.O. Box 2144, Zip 36652–2144, tel. 251/435–2400; Joe Stough, Interim President

NORTH BALDWIN INFIRMARY (L, 50 beds) 1815 Hand Avenue, Bay Minette, AL, Zip 36507–4110, Mailing Address: P.O. Box 1409, Zip 36507–1409, tel. 251/937–5521; Benjamin K. Hansert, Administrator
Web address: www.mobileinfirmary.org

THOMAS HOSPITAL (L, 136 beds) 750 Morphy Avenue, Fairhope, AL, Zip 36532–1812, Mailing Address: P.O. Box 929, Zip 36533–0929, tel. 251/928–2375; Ormand P. Thompson, President
Web address: www.thomashospital.com

Owned, leased, sponsored:	5 hospitals	811 beds
Contract-managed:	0 hospitals	0 beds
Totals:	5 hospitals	811 beds

★1305: INOVA HEALTH SYSTEM (NP)
8110 Gatehouse Road, Suite 200 East, Falls Church, VA, Zip 22042–1252; tel. 703/289–2069; J Stephen. Jones, M.D., Chief Executive Officer
(Centralized Health System)

VIRGINIA: INOVA ALEXANDRIA HOSPITAL (O, 318 beds) 4320 Seminary Road, Alexandria, VA, Zip 22304–1535; tel. 703/504–3167; Rina Bansal, Acting President and Chief Nursing Officer
Web address: www.inova.org

INOVA FAIR OAKS HOSPITAL (O, 201 beds) 3600 Joseph Siewick Drive, Fairfax, VA, Zip 22033–1798; tel. 703/391–3600; Donald Brideau, M.D., Chief Executive Officer
Web address: www.inova.org

INOVA FAIRFAX HOSPITAL (O, 1031 beds) 3300 Gallows Road, Falls Church, VA, Zip 22042–3300; tel. 703/776–4001; Susan T. Carroll, FACHE, Acting President
Web address: www.inova.org

INOVA LOUDOUN HOSPITAL (O, 279 beds) 44045 Riverside Parkway, Leesburg, VA, Zip 20176–5101, Mailing Address: P.O. Box 6000, Zip 20177–0600, tel. 703/858–6000; Deborah Addo, Chief Executive Officer

INOVA MOUNT VERNON HOSPITAL (O, 237 beds) 2501 Parker's Lane, Alexandria, VA, Zip 22306–3209; tel. 703/664–7000; Joseph Pina, M.D., Chief Executive Officer
Web address: www.inova.org

Owned, leased, sponsored:	5 hospitals	2066 beds
Contract-managed:	0 hospitals	0 beds
Totals:	5 hospitals	2066 beds

★0151: INSPIRA HEALTH NETWORK (NP)
165 Bridgeton Pike, Mullica Hill, NJ, Zip 8062; tel. 856/641–8000; John A. DiAngelo, President and Chief Executive Officer
(Independent Hospital System)

NEW JERSEY: INSPIRA MEDICAL CENTER-ELMER (O, 96 beds) 501 West Front Street, Elmer, NJ, Zip 08318–2101; tel. 856/363–1000; John A. DiAngelo, President and Chief Executive Officer

INSPIRA MEDICAL CENTER-VINELAND (O, 335 beds) 1505 West Sherman Avenue, Vineland, NJ, Zip 08360–6912; tel. 856/641–8000; John A. DiAngelo, President and Chief Executive Officer
Web address: www.inspirahealthnetwork.org/?id=5280&sid=1

INSPIRA MEDICAL CENTER-WOODBURY (O, 311 beds) 509 North Broad Street, Woodbury, NJ, Zip 08096–1697; tel. 856/845–0100; John A. DiAngelo, President and Chief Executive Officer
Web address: www.inspirahealthnetwork.org/?id=5282&sid=1

Owned, leased, sponsored:	3 hospitals	742 beds
Contract-managed:	0 hospitals	0 beds
Totals:	3 hospitals	742 beds

For explanation of codes following names, see page B2.
★ Indicates Type III membership in the American Hospital Association.

★0305: INTEGRIS HEALTH (NP)

3366 NW Expressway, Suite 800, Oklahoma City, OK, Zip 73112–9756; tel. 405/949–6066; Timothy T. Pehrson, President and Chief Executive Officer
(Moderately Centralized Health System)

OKLAHOMA: INTEGRIS BAPTIST MEDICAL CENTER (O, 597 beds) 3300 NW Expressway, Oklahoma City, OK, Zip 73112–4418; tel. 405/949–3011; Timothy J. Johnsen, MS, President
Web address: www.integrisok.com

INTEGRIS CANADIAN VALLEY HOSPITAL (O, 59 beds) 1201 Health Center Parkway, Yukon, OK, Zip 73099–6381; tel. 405/717–6800; Teresa Gray, President

INTEGRIS DEACONESS (O, 155 beds) 5501 North Portland Avenue, Oklahoma City, OK, Zip 73112–2099; tel. 405/604–6000; Rex Van Meter, President
Web address: www.https://integrisok.com/locations/hospital/integris-deaconess

INTEGRIS GROVE HOSPITAL (O, 58 beds) 1001 East 18th Street, Grove, OK, Zip 74344–2907; tel. 918/786–2243; Robert Rupp, President

INTEGRIS HEALTH EDMOND (O, 40 beds) 4801 Integris Parkway, Edmond, OK, Zip 73034–8864; tel. 405/657–3000; Avilla Williams, MS, President
Web address: www.integrisok.com/edmond

INTEGRIS MIAMI HOSPITAL (O, 57 beds) 200 Second Avenue SW, Miami, OK, Zip 74354–6830; tel. 918/542–6611; Jonas Rabel, President
Web address: www.integrisok.com/miami-hospital

INTEGRIS SOUTHWEST MEDICAL CENTER (O, 275 beds) 4401 South Western, Oklahoma City, OK, Zip 73109–3413; tel. 405/636–7000; Jordan Cash, President
Web address: www.integrisok.com

INTEGRIS BASS BAPTIST HEALTH CENTER (O, 152 beds) 600 South Monroe Street, Enid, OK, Zip 73701–7211, Mailing Address: P.O. Box 3168, Zip 73702–3168, tel. 580/233–2300; Finny Mathew, President

LAKESIDE WOMEN'S HOSPITAL (O, 23 beds) 11200 North Portland Avenue, Oklahoma City, OK, Zip 73120–5045; tel. 405/936–1500; Kelley Brewer, R.N., MSN, President
Web address: www.lakeside-wh.net

Owned, leased, sponsored:	9 hospitals	1416 beds
Contract-managed:	0 hospitals	0 beds
Totals:	9 hospitals	1416 beds

★1815: INTERMOUNTAIN HEALTHCARE, INC. (NP)

36 South State Street, 22nd Floor, Salt Lake City, UT, Zip 84111–1453; tel. 801/442–2000; A. Marc. Harrison, M.D., President and Chief Executive Officer
(Centralized Health System)

IDAHO: CASSIA REGIONAL HOSPITAL (O, 25 beds) 1501 Hiland Avenue, Burley, ID, Zip 83318–2688; tel. 208/678–4444; Ben Smalley, Administrator
Web address: www.cassiaregional.org

UTAH: ALTA VIEW HOSPITAL (O, 58 beds) 9660 South 1300 East, Sandy, UT, Zip 84094–3793; tel. 801/501–2600; Lisa A. Paletta, R.N., FACHE, Chief Executive Officer
Web address: www.intermountainhealthcare.org

AMERICAN FORK HOSPITAL (O, 78 beds) 170 North 1100 East, American Fork, UT, Zip 84003–2096; tel. 801/855–3300; Jason Wilson, Administrator and Chief Executive Officer

BEAR RIVER VALLEY HOSPITAL (O, 13 beds) 905 North 1000 West, Tremonton, UT, Zip 84337–2497; tel. 435/207–4500; Brandon Vonk, Administrator
Web address: www.https://intermountainhealthcare.org/locations/bear-river-valley-hospital/

CEDAR CITY HOSPITAL (O, 48 beds) 1303 North Main Street, Cedar City, UT, Zip 84721–9746; tel. 435/868–5000; Eric Packer, Chief Executive Officer

DELTA COMMUNITY MEDICAL CENTER (O, 31 beds) 126 South White Sage Avenue, Delta, UT, Zip 84624–8937; tel. 435/864–5591; Lenny Lyons, Administrator
Web address: www.ihc.com

DIXIE REGIONAL MEDICAL CENTER (O, 263 beds) 1380 East Medical Center Drive, Saint George, UT, Zip 84790–2123; tel. 435/251–1000; Mitchell Cloward, Administrator
Web address: www.intermountainhealthcare.org

FILLMORE COMMUNITY HOSPITAL (O, 19 beds) 674 South Highway 99, Fillmore, UT, Zip 84631–5013; tel. 435/743–5591; Lenny Lyons, Administrator

GARFIELD MEMORIAL HOSPITAL (C, 15 beds) 200 North 400 East, Panguitch, UT, Zip 84759, Mailing Address: P.O. Box 389, Zip 84759–0389, tel. 435/676–8811; Alberto Vasquez, Administrator
Web address: www.ihc.com/hospitals/garfield

HEBER VALLEY HOSPITAL (O, 19 beds) 1485 South Highway 40, Heber City, UT, Zip 84032–3522; tel. 435/654–2500; Si William. Hutt, Administrator

INTERMOUNTAIN MEDICAL CENTER (O, 502 beds) 5121 South Cottonwood Street, Murray, UT, Zip 84107–5701; tel. 801/507–7000; Joseph Mott, Chief Executive Officer
Web address: www.intermountainhealthcare.org

LDS HOSPITAL (O, 250 beds) Eighth Avenue and 'C' Street, Salt Lake City, UT, Zip 84143–0001; tel. 801/408–1100; Jim Sheets, Chief Executive Officer and Administrator
Web address: www.intermountainhealthcare.org

LAYTON HOSPITAL (O, 43 beds) 201 West Layton Parkway, Layton, UT, Zip 84041–3692; tel. 801/543–6000; Judy Williamson, R.N., Administrator
Web address: www.https://intermountainhealthcare.org/locations/layton-hospital/medical-services/

LOGAN REGIONAL HOSPITAL (O, 137 beds) 1400 North 500 East, Logan, UT, Zip 84341–2455; tel. 435/716–1000; Kyle A. Hansen, Chief Executive Officer

MCKAY-DEE HOSPITAL (O, 310 beds) 4401 Harrison Boulevard, Ogden, UT, Zip 84403–3195; tel. 801/387–2800; Michael A. Clark, Administrator
Web address: www.mckay-dee.org

OREM COMMUNITY HOSPITAL (O, 24 beds) 331 North 400 West, Orem, UT, Zip 84057–1999; tel. 801/224–4080; J. Francis. Gibson, Administrator and Chief Executive Officer
Web address: www.intermountainhealthcare.org

PARK CITY HOSPITAL (O, 37 beds) 900 Round Valley Drive, Park City, UT, Zip 84060–7552; tel. 435/658–7000; Lori Weston, Administrator

PRIMARY CHILDREN'S HOSPITAL (O, 289 beds) 100 North Mario Capecchi Drive, Intermountain Primary Children's Hospital, Environmental Services, Salt Lake City, UT, Zip 84113–1100, tel. 801/662–1000; Katy Welkie MBA, R.N., Chief Executive Officer
Web address: www.intermountainhealthcare.org

RIVERTON HOSPITAL (O, 87 beds) 3741 West 12600 South, Riverton, UT, Zip 84065–7215; tel. 801/285–4000; Todd Neubert, Chief Executive Officer

SANPETE VALLEY HOSPITAL (O, 18 beds) 1100 South Medical Drive, Mount Pleasant, UT, Zip 84647–2222; tel. 435/462–2441; Aaron C. Wood, Chief Executive Officer and Administrator
Web address: www.intermountainhealthcare.com

SEVIER VALLEY HOSPITAL (O, 24 beds) 1000 North Main Street, Richfield, UT, Zip 84701–1857; tel. 435/893–4100; Gary E. Beck, Administrator
Web address: www.sevierhospital.org

THE ORTHOPEDIC SPECIALTY HOSPITAL (O, 40 beds) 5848 South 300 East, Murray, UT, Zip 84107–6121; tel. 801/314–4100; Adam Chandio, Administrator

UTAH VALLEY HOSPITAL (O, 359 beds) 1034 North 500 West, Provo, UT, Zip 84604–3337; tel. 801/357–7850; Maria Black, Interim Administrator
Web address: www.https://intermountainhealthcare.org/locations/utah-valley-hospital/

Owned, leased, sponsored:	22 hospitals	2674 beds
Contract-managed:	1 hospitals	15 beds
Totals:	23 hospitals	2689 beds

★0902: IOWA SPECIALTY HOSPITALS (NP)

1316 South Main Street, Clarion, IA, Zip 50525–2019; tel. 515/532–2811; Steven J. Simonin, Chief Executive Officer
(Independent Hospital System)

For explanation of codes following names, see page B2.
★ Indicates Type III membership in the American Hospital Association.

Section B

IOWA: IOWA SPECIALTY HOSPITAL-BELMOND (C, 22 beds) 403 1st Street SE, Belmond, IA, Zip 50421–1201; tel. 641/444–3223; Amy McDaniel, Chief Executive Officer
Web address: www.iowaspecialtyhospital.com

IOWA SPECIALTY HOSPITAL-CLARION (C, 25 beds) 1316 South Main Street, Clarion, IA, Zip 50525–2019; tel. 515/532–2811; Steven J. Simonin, President and Chief Executive Officer
Web address: www.iowaspecialtyhospital.com

Owned, leased, sponsored:	0 hospitals	0 beds
Contract-managed:	2 hospitals	47 beds
Totals:	2 hospitals	47 beds

★7775: JEFFERSON HEALTH (NP)

925 Chestnut Street, Suite 110, Philadelphia, PA, Zip 19107–4216; tel. 610/225–6200; Stephen K. Klasko, M.D., Chief Executive Officer
(Moderately Centralized Health System)

NEW JERSEY: JEFFERSON STRATFORD HOSPITAL (O, 716 beds) 18 East Laurel Road, Stratford, NJ, Zip 08084–1327; tel. 856/346–6000; Jill Ostrem, Senior Vice President and Chief Operating Officer
Web address: www.kennedyhealth.org

PENNSYLVANIA: ABINGTON HOSPITAL (O, 611 beds) 1200 Old York Road, Abington, PA, Zip 19001–3720; tel. 215/481–2000; Margaret M. McGoldrick, President
Web address: www.abingtonhealth.org

ABINGTON-LANSDALE HOSPITAL JEFFERSON HEALTH (O, 127 beds) 100 Medical Campus Drive, Lansdale, PA, Zip 19446–1200; tel. 215/368–2100; Kathleen Farrell, Chief Administrative Officer
Web address: www.abingtonhealth.org/find-a-location/abington-lansdale-hospital/#.V5dyVVL9yk4

JEFFERSON HEALTH NORTHEAST (O, 450 beds) 10800 Knights Road, Mansion House, Philadelphia, PA, Zip 19114–4200; tel. 215/612–4000; Kathleen Kinslow, Ed.D., President

THOMAS JEFFERSON UNIVERSITY HOSPITALS (O, 888 beds) 111 South 11th Street, Philadelphia, PA, Zip 19107–5084; tel. 215/955–6000; Richard Webster, R.N., President
Web address: www.jefferson.edu

Owned, leased, sponsored:	5 hospitals	2792 beds
Contract-managed:	0 hospitals	0 beds
Totals:	5 hospitals	2792 beds

★0324: JOHN MUIR HEALTH (NP)

1400 Treat Boulevard, Walnut Creek, CA, Zip 94597–2142; tel. 925/941–2100; Calvin K. Knight, President and Chief Executive Officer
(Independent Hospital System)

CALIFORNIA: JOHN MUIR BEHAVIORAL HEALTH CENTER (O, 73 beds) 2740 Grant Street, Concord, CA, Zip 94520–2265; tel. 925/674–4100; Cindy Bolter, Chief Nursing and Operations Officer
Web address: www.johnmuirhealth.com

JOHN MUIR MEDICAL CENTER, CONCORD (O, 207 beds) 2540 East Street, Concord, CA, Zip 94520–1906; tel. 925/682–8200; Michael S. Thomas, President and Chief Administrative Officer
Web address: www.johnmuirhealth.com

JOHN MUIR MEDICAL CENTER, WALNUT CREEK (O, 420 beds) 1601 Ygnacio Valley Road, Walnut Creek, CA, Zip 94598–3194; tel. 925/939–3000; Jane Willemsen, President and Chief Administrative Officer
Web address: https://www.johnmuirhealth.com/

Owned, leased, sponsored:	3 hospitals	700 beds
Contract-managed:	0 hospitals	0 beds
Totals:	3 hospitals	700 beds

★1015: JOHNS HOPKINS HEALTH SYSTEM (NP)

733 North Broadway, BRB 104, Baltimore, MD, Zip 21205–1832; tel. 410/955–5000; Kevin W. Sowers, MSN, R.N., President
(Centralized Physician/Insurance Health System)

DISTRICT OF COLUMBIA: SIBLEY MEMORIAL HOSPITAL (O, 273 beds) 5255 Loughboro Road NW, Washington, DC, Zip 20016–2633; tel. 202/537–4000; Richard O. Davis, Ph.D., President

FLORIDA: JOHNS HOPKINS ALL CHILDREN'S HOSPITAL (O, 259 beds) 501 6th Avenue South, Saint Petersburg, FL, Zip 33701–4634; tel. 727/898–7451; Thomas D. Kmetz, Interim Chief Executive Officer
Web address: www.allkids.org

MARYLAND: HOWARD COUNTY GENERAL HOSPITAL (O, 259 beds) 5755 Cedar Lane, Columbia, MD, Zip 21044–2999; tel. 410/740–7890; Steven C. Snelgrove, President

JOHNS HOPKINS BAYVIEW MEDICAL CENTER (O, 414 beds) 4940 Eastern Avenue, Baltimore, MD, Zip 21224–2780; tel. 410/550–0100; Richard G. Bennett, M.D., President
Web address: www.hopkinsbayview.org

JOHNS HOPKINS HOSPITAL (O, 988 beds) 600 North Wolfe Street, Admin 104, Baltimore, MD, Zip 21287–1629; tel. 410/955–5000; Redonda G. Miller, M.D., President
Web address: www.hopkinsmedicine.org

SUBURBAN HOSPITAL (O, 208 beds) 8600 Old Georgetown Road, Bethesda, MD, Zip 20814–1497; tel. 301/896–3100; Jacky Schultz, MSN, R.N., President
Web address: www.suburbanhospital.org

Owned, leased, sponsored:	6 hospitals	2401 beds
Contract-managed:	0 hospitals	0 beds
Totals:	6 hospitals	2401 beds

★2105: KAISER FOUNDATION HOSPITALS (NP)

One Kaiser Plaza, 27th Floor – Office #2743, Oakland, CA, Zip 94612–3600; tel. 510/271–5910; Bernard J. Tyson, Chairman and Chief Executive Officer
(Decentralized Health System)

CALIFORNIA: KAISER PERMANENTE ANTIOCH MEDICAL CENTER (O, 150 beds) 4501 Sand Creek Road, Antioch, CA, Zip 94531–8687; tel. 925/813–6500; Colleen McKeown, Senior Vice President and Area Manager

KAISER PERMANENTE BALDWIN PARK MEDICAL CENTER (O, 257 beds) 1011 Baldwin Park Boulevard, Baldwin Park, CA, Zip 91706–5806; tel. 626/851–1011; Margaret H. Pierce, Executive Director
Web address: www.kp.org

KAISER PERMANENTE DOWNEY MEDICAL CENTER (O, 352 beds) 9333 Imperial Highway, Downey, CA, Zip 90242–2812; tel. 562/657–9000; James Branchick, R.N., MS, Senior Vice President and Area Manager
Web address: www.kaiserpermanente.org

KAISER PERMANENTE FONTANA MEDICAL CENTER (O, 490 beds) 9961 Sierra Avenue, Fontana, CA, Zip 92335–6794; tel. 909/427–5000; Greg Christian, Senior Vice President, Area Manager – San Bernardino County Area
Web address: www.kaiserpermanente.org

KAISER PERMANENTE FREMONT MEDICAL CENTER (O, 76 beds) 39400 Paseo Padre Parkway, Fremont, CA, Zip 94538–2310; tel. 510/248–3000; Victoria O'Gorman, Administrator

KAISER PERMANENTE FRESNO MEDICAL CENTER (O, 169 beds) 7300 North Fresno Street, Fresno, CA, Zip 93720–2942; tel. 559/448–4500; Debbie Hemker, Senior Vice President and Area Manager
Web address: www.kaiserpermanente.org

KAISER PERMANENTE LOS ANGELES MEDICAL CENTER (O, 528 beds) 4867 Sunset Boulevard, Los Angeles, CA, Zip 90027–5961; tel. 323/783–4011; William N. Grice, Executive Director

KAISER PERMANENTE MANTECA MEDICAL CENTER (O, 213 beds) 1777 West Yosemite Avenue, Manteca, CA, Zip 95337–5187; tel. 209/825–3700; Corwin N. Harper, Senior Vice President and Area Manager
Web address: www.kaiserpermanente.org

KAISER PERMANENTE MORENO VALLEY MEDICAL CENTER (O, 94 beds) 27300 Iris Avenue, Moreno Valley, CA, Zip 92555–4800; tel. 951/243–0811; Vita M. Willett, Senior Vice President, Area Manager

KAISER PERMANENTE OAKLAND MEDICAL CENTER (O, 297 beds) 3600 Broadway, Oakland, CA, Zip 94611–5693; tel. 510/752–1000; Jeffrey A. Collins, M.D., Senior Vice President and Area Manager
Web address: www.kaiserpermanente.org

For explanation of codes following names, see page B2.
★ Indicates Type III membership in the American Hospital Association.

KAISER PERMANENTE ORANGE COUNTY ANAHEIM MEDICAL CENTER (O, 469 beds) 3440 East La Palma Avenue, Anaheim, CA, Zip 92806–2020; tel. 714/644–2000; Mark E. Costa, Executive Director
Web address: www.kp.org

KAISER PERMANENTE PANORAMA CITY MEDICAL CENTER (O, 115 beds) 13652 Cantara Street, Panorama City, CA, Zip 91402–5497; tel. 818/375–2000; Payman Roshan, Senior Vice President and Area Manager
Web address: www.kaiserpermanente.org

KAISER PERMANENTE REDWOOD CITY MEDICAL CENTER (O, 149 beds) 1100 Veterans Boulevard, Redwood City, CA, Zip 94063–2087; tel. 650/299–2000; Michelle Gaskill-Hames, R.N., Senior Vice President & Area Manager

KAISER PERMANENTE RIVERSIDE MEDICAL CENTER (O, 226 beds) 10800 Magnolia Avenue, Riverside, CA, Zip 92505–3000; tel. 951/353–2000; Vita M. Willett, Executive Director
Web address: www.kaiserpermanente.org

KAISER PERMANENTE ROSEVILLE MEDICAL CENTER (O, 340 beds) 1600 Eureka Road, Roseville, CA, Zip 95661–3027; tel. 916/784–4000; Jordan Herget, Senior Vice President and Manager

KAISER PERMANENTE SACRAMENTO MEDICAL CENTER (O, 200 beds) 2025 Morse Avenue, Sacramento, CA, Zip 95825–2100; tel. 916/973–5000; Sandy Sharon, Senior Vice President and Area Manager
Web address: www.kp.org

KAISER PERMANENTE SAN DIEGO MEDICAL CENTER (O, 446 beds) 4647 Zion Avenue, San Diego, CA, Zip 92120–2507; tel. 619/528–5000; Jane Finley, Senior Vice President & Area Manager

KAISER PERMANENTE SAN FRANCISCO MEDICAL CENTER (O, 239 beds) 2425 Geary Boulevard, San Francisco, CA, Zip 94115–3358; tel. 415/833–2000; Ronald Groepper, Senior Vice President and Area Manager
Web address: www.kaiserpermanente.org

KAISER PERMANENTE SAN JOSE MEDICAL CENTER (O, 247 beds) 250 Hospital Parkway, San Jose, CA, Zip 95119–1199; tel. 408/972–7000; Irene Chavez, Senior Vice President and Area Manager
Web address: www.kaiserpermanente.org

KAISER PERMANENTE SAN LEANDRO MEDICAL CENTER (O, 186 beds) 2500 Merced Street, San Leandro, CA, Zip 94577–4201; tel. 510/454–1000; Thomas S. Hanenburg, Senior Vice President and Area Manager

KAISER PERMANENTE SAN RAFAEL MEDICAL CENTER (O, 116 beds) 99 Montecillo Road, San Rafael, CA, Zip 94903–3397; tel. 415/444–2000; Judy Coffey, R.N., Senior Vice President and Area Manager
Web address: www.kaiserpermanente.org

KAISER PERMANENTE SANTA CLARA MEDICAL CENTER (O, 327 beds) 700 Lawrence Expressway, Santa Clara, CA, Zip 95051–5173; tel. 408/851–1000; Christopher L. Doyd, Senior Vice President and Area Manager
Web address: www.kaiserpermanente.org

KAISER PERMANENTE SANTA ROSA MEDICAL CENTER (O, 173 beds) 401 Bicentennial Way, Santa Rosa, CA, Zip 95403–2192; tel. 707/393–4000; Judy Coffey, R.N., Senior Vice President and Area Manager

KAISER PERMANENTE SOUTH BAY MEDICAL CENTER (O, 226 beds) 25825 Vermont Avenue, Harbor City, CA, Zip 90710–3599; tel. 310/325–5111; Lesley A. Wille, Executive Director
Web address: www.kaiserpermanente.org

KAISER PERMANENTE SOUTH SACRAMENTO MEDICAL CENTER (O, 217 beds) 6600 Bruceville Road, Sacramento, CA, Zip 95823–4691; tel. 916/688–2430; Patricia M. Rodriguez, Senior Vice President and Area Manager
Web address: www.kp.org

KAISER PERMANENTE SOUTH SAN FRANCISCO (O, 120 beds) 1200 El Camino Real, South San Francisco, CA, Zip 94080–3208; tel. 650/742–2000; Ronald Groepper, Senior Vice President and Area Manager
Web address: www.kaiserpermanente.org

KAISER PERMANENTE VACAVILLE MEDICAL CENTER (O, 140 beds) 1 Quality Drive, Vacaville, CA, Zip 95688–9494; tel. 707/624–4000; Norair Jemjemian, Senior Vice President and Area Manager

KAISER PERMANENTE VALLEJO MEDICAL CENTER (O, 248 beds) 975 Sereno Drive, Vallejo, CA, Zip 94589–2441; tel. 707/651–1000; Corwin N. Harper, Senior Vice President and Area Manager
Web address: www.kaiserpermanente.org

KAISER PERMANENTE WALNUT CREEK MEDICAL CENTER (O, 233 beds) 1425 South Main Street, Walnut Creek, CA, Zip 94596–5300; tel. 925/295–4000; Colleen McKeown, Senior Vice President and Area Manager

KAISER PERMANENTE WEST LOS ANGELES MEDICAL CENTER (O, 126 beds) 6041 Cadillac Avenue, Los Angeles, CA, Zip 90034–1700; tel. 323/857–2201; Georgina R. Garcia, R.N., Executive Director
Web address: www.kaiserpermanente.org

KAISER PERMANENTE WOODLAND HILLS MEDICAL CENTER (O, 160 beds) 5601 DeSoto Avenue, Woodland Hills, CA, Zip 91367–6798; tel. 818/719–2000; Murtaza Sanwari, Senior Vice President and Area Manager
Web address: www.kaiserpermanente.org

HAWAII: KAISER PERMANENTE MEDICAL CENTER (O, 295 beds) 3288 Moanalua Road, Honolulu, HI, Zip 96819–1469; tel. 808/432–0000; James Y. Lee, Hospital Administrator
Web address: www.kaiserpermanente.org

KULA HOSPITAL (C, 114 beds) 100 Keokea Place, Kula, HI, Zip 96790–7450; tel. 808/878–1221; Kerry Pitcher, Chief Executive Officer

LANAI COMMUNITY HOSPITAL (C, 14 beds) 628 Seventh Street, Lanai City, HI, Zip 96763–0650, Mailing Address: P.O. Box 630650, Zip 96763–0650, tel. 808/565–8450; Kerry Pitcher, Administrator
Web address: https://www.mauihealthsystem.org/lanai-hospital/

MAUI MEMORIAL MEDICAL CENTER (C, 214 beds) 221 Mahalani Street, Wailuku, HI, Zip 96793–2581; tel. 808/244–9056; Michael A. Rembis, FACHE, Chief Executive Officer
Web address: https://www.mauihealthsystem.org/maui-memorial/

OREGON: KAISER SUNNYSIDE MEDICAL CENTER (O, 301 beds) 10180 SE Sunnyside Road, Clackamas, OR, Zip 97015–8970; tel. 503/652–2880; Justin N. Evander, Administrator and Chief Operating Officer

KAISER WESTSIDE MEDICAL CENTER (O, 122 beds) 2875 NE Stucki Avenue, Hillsboro, OR, Zip 97124–5806; tel. 971/310–1000; Brantley Dettmer, Administrator and Chief Operating Officer
Web address: www.kp.org

Owned, leased, sponsored:	34 hospitals	8047 beds
Contract-managed:	3 hospitals	342 beds
Totals:	37 hospitals	8389 beds

0954: KECK MEDICINE OF USC (NP)
1510 San Pablo Street, Suite 600, Los Angeles, CA, Zip 90033–5405; tel. 323/442–8500; Thomas E. Jackiewicz, Senior Vice President and Chief Executive Officer
(Independent Hospital System)

CALIFORNIA: KECK HOSPITAL OF USC (O, 401 beds) 1500 San Pablo Street, Los Angeles, CA, Zip 90033–5313; tel. 323/442–8500; Rodney B. Hanners, Chief Executive Officer
Web address: https://www.keckmedicine.org/

USC NORRIS COMPREHENSIVE CANCER CENTER (O, 60 beds) 1441 Eastlake Avenue, Los Angeles, CA, Zip 90089–0112; tel. 323/865–3000; Rodney B. Hanners, Chief Executive Officer
Web address: www.uscnorriscancerhospital.org

USC VERDUGO HILLS HOSPITAL (O, 154 beds) 1812 Verdugo Boulevard, Glendale, CA, Zip 91208–1409; tel. 818/790–7100; Keith Hobbs, Chief Executive Officer

Owned, leased, sponsored:	3 hospitals	615 beds
Contract-managed:	0 hospitals	0 beds
Totals:	3 hospitals	615 beds

★0258: KETTERING HEALTH NETWORK (NP)
3965 Southern Boulevard, Dayton, OH, Zip 45429–1229; tel. 855/536–7543; Fred M. Manchur, Chief Executive Officer
(Independent Hospital System)

OHIO: FORT HAMILTON HOSPITAL (O, 164 beds) 630 Eaton Avenue, Hamilton, OH, Zip 45013–2770; tel. 513/867–2000; Michael Mewhirter, President
Web address: www.khnetwork.org/forthamilton

GRANDVIEW MEDICAL CENTER (O, 297 beds) 405 West Grand Avenue, Dayton, OH, Zip 45405–4796; tel. 937/723–3200; Rebecca Lewis, President

For explanation of codes following names, see page B2.
★ Indicates Type III membership in the American Hospital Association.

GREENE MEMORIAL HOSPITAL (O, 49 beds) 1141 North Monroe Drive, Xenia, OH, Zip 45385–1600; tel. 937/352–2000; Rick A. Dodds, President
Web address: www.ketteringhealth.org/greene

KETTERING MEDICAL CENTER (O, 422 beds) 3535 Southern Boulevard, Kettering, OH, Zip 45429–1221; tel. 937/298–4331; Terry M. Burns, President

SOIN MEDICAL CENTER (O, 133 beds) 3535 Pentagon Boulevard, Beavercreek, OH, Zip 45431–1705; tel. 937/702–4000; Rick A. Dodds, President
Web address: www.khnetwork.org/soin

SYCAMORE MEDICAL CENTER (O, 168 beds) 4000 Miamisburg-Centerville Road, Miamisburg, OH, Zip 45342–7615; tel. 937/866–0551; Walter Sackett, President
Web address: www.khnetwork.org/sycamore

Owned, leased, sponsored:	6 hospitals	1233 beds
Contract-managed:	0 hospitals	0 beds
Totals:	6 hospitals	1233 beds

★0026: KINDRED HEALTHCARE (IO)
680 South Fourth Street, Louisville, KY, Zip 40202–2412; tel. 502/596–7300; Pete Kalmey, President, Hospital Division
(Independent Hospital System)

ARIZONA: DIGNITY HEALTH EAST VALLEY REHABILITATION HOSPITAL (O, 50 beds) 1515 West Chandler Boulevard, Chandler, AZ, Zip 85224–6141; tel. 602/594–5400; Alvin Wendt, Acting Chief Executive Officer
Web address: www.dignityhealthevrehab.com

CALIFORNIA: KINDRED HOSPITAL RANCHO (O, 55 beds) 10841 White Oak Avenue, Rancho Cucamonga, CA, Zip 91730–3811; tel. 909/581–6400; Victor Carrasco, Chief Executive Officer
Web address: www.khrancho.com

KINDRED HOSPITAL RIVERSIDE (O, 40 beds) 2224 Medical Center Drive, Perris, CA, Zip 92571–2638; tel. 951/436–3535; William Mitchell, Chief Executive Officer and Administrator

KINDRED HOSPITAL SOUTH BAY (O, 84 beds) 1246 West 155th Street, Gardena, CA, Zip 90247–4062; tel. 310/323–5330; Michael D. Kerr, Chief Executive Officer
Web address: www.khsouthbay.com/

KINDRED HOSPITAL-BALDWIN PARK (C, 91 beds) 14148 Francisquito Avenue, Baldwin Park, CA, Zip 91706–6120; tel. 626/388–2700; Fiona Basa-Reyes, Chief Executive Officer

KINDRED HOSPITAL-BREA (O, 48 beds) 875 North Brea Boulevard, Brea, CA, Zip 92821–2699; tel. 714/529–6842; Rafael Pena, Chief Executive Officer
Web address: www.kindredhospitalbrea.com/

KINDRED HOSPITAL-LA MIRADA (O, 216 beds) 14900 East Imperial Highway, La Mirada, CA, Zip 90638–2172; tel. 562/944–1900; David Kowalski, Chief Executive Officer
Web address: www.kindredlamirada.com/

KINDRED HOSPITAL-LOS ANGELES (O, 81 beds) 5525 West Slauson Avenue, Los Angeles, CA, Zip 90056–1067; tel. 310/642–0325; Phillip R. Wolfe, Chief Executive Officer

KINDRED HOSPITAL-ONTARIO (O, 81 beds) 550 North Monterey Avenue, Ontario, CA, Zip 91764–3399; tel. 909/391–0333; Vincent Trac, Chief Executive Officer
Web address: www.khontario.com/

KINDRED HOSPITAL-SAN DIEGO (O, 58 beds) 1940 El Cajon Boulevard, San Diego, CA, Zip 92104–1096; tel. 619/543–4500; Kerry Ashment, Chief Executive Officer

KINDRED HOSPITAL-SAN FRANCISCO BAY AREA (O, 99 beds) 2800 Benedict Drive, San Leandro, CA, Zip 94577–6840; tel. 510/357–8300; Jacob M. McCarty, Chief Executive Officer
Web address: www.kindredhospitalsfba.com

KINDRED HOSPITAL-WESTMINSTER (O, 109 beds) 200 Hospital Circle, Westminster, CA, Zip 92683–3910; tel. 714/893–4541; Julie Myers, Chief Executive Officer
Web address: www.khwestminster.com/

COLORADO: KINDRED HOSPITAL DENVER SOUTH (O, 28 beds) 2525 South Downing Street, 3 South, Denver, CO, Zip 80210–5817; tel. 303/715–7373; Marc Lemon, Chief Executive Officer

KINDRED HOSPITAL-AURORA (O, 23 beds) 700 Potomac Street 2nd Floor, Aurora, CO, Zip 80011–6844; tel. 720/857–8333; Jeanette Williams, Chief Executive Officer
Web address: www.khaurora.com/

KINDRED HOSPITAL-DENVER (O, 68 beds) 1920 High Street, Denver, CO, Zip 80218–1213; tel. 303/320–5871; Janelle Kircher, R.N., MSN, Chief Executive Officer
Web address: www.kh-denver.com

FLORIDA: KINDRED HOSPITAL BAY AREA-TAMPA (O, 73 beds) 4555 South Manhattan Avenue, Tampa, FL, Zip 33611–2397; tel. 813/839–6341; Suthanthira M. Ratnasamy, R.N., FACHE, Chief Executive Officer
Web address: www.khtampa.com/

KINDRED HOSPITAL CENTRAL TAMPA (O, 109 beds) 4801 North Howard Avenue, Tampa, FL, Zip 33603–1411; tel. 813/874–7575; Ralph Selner, Chief Executive Officer

KINDRED HOSPITAL MELBOURNE (O, 60 beds) 765 West Nasa Boulevard, Melbourne, FL, Zip 32901–1815; tel. 321/733–5725; Pamela R. Reed, Chief Executive Officer
Web address: www.khmelbourne.com

KINDRED HOSPITAL NORTH FLORIDA (O, 80 beds) 801 Oak Street, Green Cove Springs, FL, Zip 32043–4317; tel. 904/284–9230; Patrick McVey, Chief Executive Officer

KINDRED HOSPITAL OCALA (O, 31 beds) 1500 SW 1st Avenue, Ocala, FL, Zip 34471–6504; tel. 352/369–0513; Merlene Bhoorasingh, Administrator
Web address: www.kindredocala.com/

KINDRED HOSPITAL SOUTH FLORIDA-FORT LAUDERDALE (O, 123 beds) 1516 East Las Olas Boulevard, Fort Lauderdale, FL, Zip 33301–2399; tel. 954/764–8900; Michael S. Roffelsen, Chief Executive Officer
Web address: www.khfortlauderdale.com/

KINDRED HOSPITAL THE PALM BEACHES (O, 70 beds) 5555 West Blue Heron Boulevard, Riviera Beach, FL, Zip 33418–7813; tel. 561/840–0754; Elayne Lopreato, Chief Executive Officer

GEORGIA: KINDRED HOSPITAL ROME (O, 45 beds) 304 Turner McCall Boulevard, Rome, GA, Zip 30165–5621; tel. 706/378–6800; Al Diaz, M.D., Chief Executive Officer
Web address: www.kindredrome.com

ILLINOIS: KINDRED CHICAGO-CENTRAL HOSPITAL (O, 187 beds) 4058 West Melrose Street, Chicago, IL, Zip 60641–4797; tel. 773/736–7000
Web address: www.khchicagocentral.com

KINDRED HOSPITAL CHICAGO-NORTHLAKE (O, 94 beds) 365 East North Avenue, Northlake, IL, Zip 60164–2628; tel. 708/345–8100; Brinsley Lewis, FACHE, Chief Executive Officer
Web address: www.kindrednorthlake.com/

KINDRED HOSPITAL PEORIA (O, 50 beds) 500 West Romeo B Garrett Avenue, Peoria, IL, Zip 61605–2301; tel. 309/680–1500; Christopher Curry, Chief Executive Officer

KINDRED HOSPITAL-SYCAMORE (O, 69 beds) 225 Edward Street, Sycamore, IL, Zip 60178–2137; tel. 815/895–2144; Jim Cohick, Chief Executive Officer
Web address: www.kindredhospitalsyc.com/

INDIANA: KINDRED HOSPITAL INDIANAPOLIS NORTH (O, 45 beds) 8060 Knue Road, Indianapolis, IN, Zip 46250–1976; tel. 317/813–8900; Nakia Tremble, Chief Executive Officer

KINDRED HOSPITAL NORTHWEST INDIANA (O, 70 beds) 5454 Hohman Avenue, 5th Floor, Hammond, IN, Zip 46320–1931; tel. 219/937–9900; Frank A. Solare, Chief Executive Officer
Web address: www.khnwindiana.com

KINDRED HOSPITAL-INDIANAPOLIS (O, 59 beds) 1700 West 10th Street, Indianapolis, IN, Zip 46222–3802; tel. 317/636–4400; Bryan Chatterton, Chief Executive Officer

KENTUCKY: KINDRED HOSPITAL-LOUISVILLE (O, 117 beds) 1313 Saint Anthony Place, Louisville, KY, Zip 40204–1740; tel. 502/587–7001; Jack Nicholson, Chief Executive Officer
Web address: www.kindredlouisville.com

MISSOURI: KINDRED HOSPITAL NORTHLAND (O, 35 beds) 500 Northwest 68th Street, Kansas City, MO, Zip 64118–2455; tel. 816/420–6300; Laura Inge, MSN, R.N., Chief Executive Officer
Web address: www.khnorthland.com

For explanation of codes following names, see page B2.
★ Indicates Type III membership in the American Hospital Association.

KINDRED HOSPITAL-ST. LOUIS (O, 98 beds) 4930 Lindell Boulevard, Saint Louis, MO, Zip 63108–1510; tel. 314/361–8700; Kevin L. Shrake, Chief Executive Officer
Web address: www.kindredstlouis.com/

MERCY REHABILITATION HOSPITAL ST. LOUIS (O, 90 beds) 14561 North Outer Forty Road, Chesterfield, MO, Zip 63017; tel. 314/881–4000; Jerald W. Rumph, Chief Executive Officer

NEVADA: KINDRED HOSPITAL LAS VEGAS-SAHARA (O, 238 beds) 102 East Mead Parkway, 3rd Floor, Henderson, NV, Zip 89015; tel. 702/871–1418; Doug McCoy, Chief Executive Officer
Web address: www.kindredhospitallvs.com/

NEW JERSEY: KINDRED HOSPITAL-NEW JERSEY MORRIS COUNTY (O, 117 beds) 400 West Blackwell Street, Dover, NJ, Zip 07801–2525; tel. 973/537–3818; Tarra Washington, Chief Executive Officer
Web address: www.khmorriscounty.com/

NEW MEXICO: KINDRED HOSPITAL-ALBUQUERQUE (O, 61 beds) 700 High Street NE, Albuquerque, NM, Zip 87102–2565; tel. 505/242–4444; Bud Schawl, Chief Executive Officer

NORTH CAROLINA: KINDRED HOSPITAL-GREENSBORO (O, 101 beds) 2401 Southside Boulevard, Greensboro, NC, Zip 27406–3311; tel. 336/271–2800; Chad Lovett, Chief Executive Officer
Web address: www.khgreensboro.com

OHIO: KINDRED HOSPITAL LIMA (O, 26 beds) 730 West Market Street, 6th Floor, Lima, OH, Zip 45801–4602; tel. 419/224–1888; Susan Krinke, Chief Executive Officer
Web address: www.khlima.com

KINDRED HOSPITAL-DAYTON (O, 67 beds) 707 South Edwin C Moses Boulevard, Dayton, OH, Zip 45417–3462; tel. 937/222–5963; Phillip Underwood, Chief Executive Officer

UH AVON REHABILITATION HOSPITAL (O, 50 beds) 37900 Chester Road, Avon, OH, Zip 44011–1044; tel. 440/695–7100; Andrew Goldfrach, Chief Executive Officer
Web address: www.uhhospitals.org/uh-avon-rehabilitation-hospital

UH REHABILITATION HOSPITAL (O, 50 beds) 23333 Harvard Road, Beachwood, OH, Zip 44122–6232; tel. 216/593–2200; Mirza Baig, M.D., Medical Director
Web address: www.uhhospitals.org

PENNSYLVANIA: KINDRED HOSPITAL SOUTH PHILADELPHIA (O, 58 beds) 1930 South Broad Street, Philadelphia, PA, Zip 19145–2328; tel. 267/570–5200; Michele S. Basile, Chief Executive Officer

KINDRED HOSPITAL-PHILADELPHIA (O, 52 beds) 6129 Palmetto Street, Philadelphia, PA, Zip 19111–5729; tel. 215/722–8555; Michele S. Basile, Interim Chief Executive Officer
Web address: www.kindredphila.com/

ST. MARY REHABILITATION HOSPITAL (O, 50 beds) 1201 Langhorne Newtown Road, Langhorne, PA, Zip 19047–1201, Mailing Address: 1208 Langhorne Newtown Road, Zip 19047–1234, tel. 267/560–1111; Lisa Haney, Chief Executive Officer
Web address: www.stmaryhealthcare.org

TENNESSEE: KINDRED HOSPITAL-CHATTANOOGA (O, 39 beds) 709 Walnut Street, Chattanooga, TN, Zip 37402–1916; tel. 423/266–7721; Andrea White, Chief Executive Officer
Web address: www.kindredchattanooga.com/

TEXAS: KINDRED HOSPITAL CLEAR LAKE (O, 110 beds) 350 Blossom Street, Webster, TX, Zip 77598; tel. 281/316–7800; Angel Gradney, Chief Executive Officer
Web address: www.khclearlake.com

KINDRED HOSPITAL DALLAS CENTRAL (O, 60 beds) 8050 Meadow Road, Dallas, TX, Zip 75231–3406; tel. 469/232–6500; Kyron J. Kooken, MS, Chief Executive Officer
Web address: www.khdallascentral.com/

KINDRED HOSPITAL EL PASO (O, 52 beds) 1740 Curie Drive, El Paso, TX, Zip 79902–2901; tel. 915/351–9044; America Jones, R.N., Chief Executive Officer

KINDRED HOSPITAL HOUSTON MEDICAL CENTER (O, 105 beds) 6441 Main Street, Houston, TX, Zip 77030–1596; tel. 713/790–0500; Robert Stein, Chief Executive Officer
Web address: www.khhouston.com/

KINDRED HOSPITAL SAN ANTONIO CENTRAL (O, 44 beds) 111 Dallas Street, 4th Floor, San Antonio, TX, Zip 78205–1201; tel. 210/297–7185; Abiola Anyebe, Interim Chief Executive Officer
Web address: www.kindredsanantoniocentral.com/

KINDRED HOSPITAL SUGAR LAND (O, 105 beds) 1550 First Colony Boulevard, Sugar Land, TX, Zip 77479–4000; tel. 281/275–6000; John D. Cross, Chief Executive Officer

KINDRED HOSPITAL TARRANT COUNTY-ARLINGTON (O, 147 beds) 1000 North Cooper Street, Arlington, TX, Zip 76011–5540; tel. 817/548–3400; Christina Richard, Market Chief Executive Officer
Web address: www.kindredhospitalarl.com/

KINDRED HOSPITAL TOMBALL (O, 258 beds) 505 Graham Drive, Tomball, TX, Zip 77375–3368; tel. 281/255–5600; Tracy Kohler, Chief Executive Officer
Web address: www.khtomball.com/

KINDRED HOSPITAL-DALLAS (O, 66 beds) 9525 Greenville Avenue, Dallas, TX, Zip 75243–4116; tel. 214/355–2600; Misti Varnell, Chief Executive Officer
Web address: www.khdallas.com

KINDRED HOSPITAL-FORT WORTH (O, 67 beds) 815 Eighth Avenue, Fort Worth, TX, Zip 76104–2609; tel. 817/332–4812; Susan Schaetti, Chief Executive Officer

KINDRED HOSPITAL-HOUSTON NORTHWEST (O, 84 beds) 11297 Fallbrook Drive, Houston, TX, Zip 77065–4292; tel. 281/897–8114; Tracy Kohler, Chief Executive Officer
Web address: www.khhoustonnw.com/

KINDRED HOSPITAL-MANSFIELD (O, 55 beds) 1802 Highway 157 North, Mansfield, TX, Zip 76063–3923; tel. 817/473–6101; Blake Peart, Administrator

KINDRED HOSPITAL-SAN ANTONIO (O, 59 beds) 3636 Medical Drive, San Antonio, TX, Zip 78229–2183; tel. 210/616–0616; Abiola Anyebe, Interim Chief Executive Officer
Web address: www.khsanantonio.com/

TEXAS REHABILITATION HOSPITAL OF FORT WORTH (O, 66 beds) 425 Alabama Avenue, Fort Worth, TX, Zip 76104–1022; tel. 817/820–3400; Jake Daggett, Chief Executive Officer
Web address: www.texasrehabhospital.com/

WASHINGTON: KINDRED HOSPITAL SEATTLE-NORTHGATE (O, 80 beds) 10631 8th Avenue NE, Seattle, WA, Zip 98125–7213; tel. 206/364–2050; Lerenda Johnson, Interim Chief Executive Officer

WISCONSIN: REHABILITATION HOSPITAL OF WISCONSIN (O, 40 beds) 1625 Coldwater Creek Drive, Waukesha, WI, Zip 53188–8028; tel. 262/521–8800; John R. Robertstad, FACHE, Chief Executive Officer
Web address: www.rehabhospitalwi.com

Owned, leased, sponsored:	61 hospitals	4852 beds
Contract-managed:	1 hospitals	91 beds
Totals:	62 hospitals	4943 beds

0333: KPC HEALTHCARE, INC. (IO)

1301 North Tustin Avenue, Santa Ana, CA, Zip 92705–8619; tel. 714/953–3652
(Independent Hospital System)

CALIFORNIA: ANAHEIM GLOBAL MEDICAL CENTER (O, 188 beds) 1025 South Anaheim Boulevard, Anaheim, CA, Zip 92805–5806; tel. 714/533–6220; Scott Rifkin, Chief Executive Officer

CHAPMAN GLOBAL MEDICAL CENTER (O, 100 beds) 2601 East Chapman Avenue, Orange, CA, Zip 92869–3296; tel. 714/633–0011; Ada Yeh, Chief Executive Officer
Web address: www.Chapman-GMC.com

ORANGE COUNTY GLOBAL MEDICAL CENTER, INC. (O, 282 beds) 1001 North Tustin Avenue, Santa Ana, CA, Zip 92705–3577; tel. 714/953–3500; Ann Abe, Interim Chief Executive Officer
Web address: www.orangecounty-gmc.com

SOUTH COAST GLOBAL MEDICAL CENTER (O, 178 beds) 2701 South Bristol Street, Santa Ana, CA, Zip 92704–6278; tel. 714/754–5454; Ada Yeh, Chief Executive Officer

Owned, leased, sponsored:	4 hospitals	748 beds
Contract-managed:	0 hospitals	0 beds
Totals:	4 hospitals	748 beds

Section B

0911: LAFAYETTE GENERAL HEALTH (NP)

920 West Pinhook Road, Lafayette, LA, Zip 70503–2455; tel. 337/289–7991; David L. Callecod, President and Chief Executive Officer
(Independent Hospital System)

LOUISIANA: ABROM KAPLAN MEMORIAL HOSPITAL (C, 35 beds) 1310 West Seventh Street, Kaplan, LA, Zip 70548–2910; tel. 337/643–8300; Bryce Quebodeaux, Chief Executive Officer
Web address: www.lafayettegeneral.com

ACADIA GENERAL HOSPITAL (C, 140 beds) 1305 Crowley Rayne Highway, Crowley, LA, Zip 70526–8202; tel. 337/783–3222; Joe J. Mitchell, FACHE, Chief Executive Officer

LAFAYETTE GENERAL MEDICAL CENTER (O, 420 beds) 1214 Coolidge Boulevard, Lafayette, LA, Zip 70503–2696, Mailing Address: P.O. Box 52009 OCS, Zip 70505–2009, tel. 337/289–7991; Patrick W. Gandy Jr, CPA, Executive Vice President and Chief Executive Officer
Web address: www.lafayettegeneral.com

LAFAYETTE GENERAL SURGICAL HOSPITAL (C, 10 beds) 1000 West Pinhook Road, Suite 100, Lafayette, LA, Zip 70503–2460; tel. 337/289–8088; Kimberly H. Dooley, R.N., Administrator

ST. MARTIN HOSPITAL (C, 25 beds) 210 Champagne Boulevard, Breaux Bridge, LA, Zip 70517–3700, Mailing Address: P.O. Box 357, Zip 70517–0357, tel. 337/332–2178; Karen O. Wyble, R.N., Chief Executive Officer
Web address: www.stmartinhospital.org

UNIVERSITY HOSPITAL AND CLINICS (L, 52 beds) 2390 West Congress Street, Lafayette, LA, Zip 70506–4298; tel. 337/261–6000; Katherine D. Hebert, MS, Chief Executive Officer
Web address: www.lafayettegeneral.com

Owned, leased, sponsored:	2 hospitals	472 beds
Contract-managed:	4 hospitals	210 beds
Totals:	6 hospitals	682 beds

0393: LANDMARK HOSPITALS (IO)

3255 Independence Street, Cape Girardeau, MO, Zip 63701–4914; tel. 573/335–1091; William K. Kapp III, M.D., President and Chief Executive Officer
(Independent Hospital System)

FLORIDA: LANDMARK HOSPITAL OF SOUTHWEST FLORIDA (O, 50 beds) 1285 Creekside Boulevard East, Naples, FL, Zip 34108; tel. 239/529–1800; James Whitacre, Chief Executive Officer
Web address: www.landmarkhospitals.com/our-hospitals/southwest-florida/

GEORGIA: LANDMARK HOSPITAL OF ATHENS (O, 42 beds) 775 Sunset Drive, Athens, GA, Zip 30606–2211; tel. 706/425–1500; Vivian Goff, R.N., Chief Executive Officer

LANDMARK HOSPITAL OF SAVANNAH (O, 50 beds) 800 East 68th Street, Savannah, GA, Zip 31405–4710; tel. 912/298–1000; John Salandi, Chief Executive Officer
Web address: www.landmarkhospitals.com/savannah

MISSOURI: LANDMARK HOSPITAL OF CAPE GIRARDEAU (O, 30 beds) 3255 Independence Street, Cape Girardeau, MO, Zip 63701–4914; tel. 573/335–1091; Deborah Sabella, R.N., Chief Executive Officer
Web address: www.landmarkhospitals.com

LANDMARK HOSPITAL OF COLUMBIA (O, 23 beds) 604 Old 63 North, Columbia, MO, Zip 65201–6308; tel. 573/499–6600; Glenn Piche, Chief Executive Officer
Web address: www.landmarkhospitals.com

LANDMARK HOSPITAL OF JOPLIN (O, 30 beds) 2040 West 32nd Street, Joplin, MO, Zip 64804–3512; tel. 417/627–1300; Lee A. Simpson, Chief Executive Officer

UTAH: LANDMARK HOSPITAL OF SALT LAKE CITY (O, 38 beds) 4252 South Birkhill Boulevard, Murray, UT, Zip 84107–5715; tel. 801/268–5400; Gina Herchenhahn, Chief Executive Officer
Web address: www.https://landmarkhospitalsaltlake.com/

Owned, leased, sponsored:	7 hospitals	263 beds
Contract-managed:	0 hospitals	0 beds
Totals:	7 hospitals	263 beds

0932: LCMC HEALTH (NP)

200 Henry Clay Avenue, New Orleans, LA, Zip 70118–5720; tel. 504/899–9511; Greg Feirn, CPA, President and Chief Executive Officer
(Moderately Centralized Health System)

LOUISIANA: CHILDREN'S HOSPITAL (O, 210 beds) 200 Henry Clay Avenue, New Orleans, LA, Zip 70118–5720; tel. 504/899–9511; John R. Nickens IV, President and Chief Executive Officer
Web address: www.chnola.org

NEW ORLEANS EAST HOSPITAL (C, 34 beds) 5620 Read Boulevard, New Orleans, LA, Zip 70127–3106, Mailing Address: 5620 Read Blvd, Zip 70127–3106, tel. 504/592–6600; Takeisha C. Davis, M.D., M.P.H., President and Chief Executive Officer
Web address: www.noehospital.org

TOURO INFIRMARY (O, 280 beds) 1401 Foucher Street, New Orleans, LA, Zip 70115–3593; tel. 504/897–7011; Manuel Linares, President and Chief Executive Officer

UNIVERSITY MEDICAL CENTER (O, 324 beds) 2000 Canal Street, New Orleans, LA, Zip 70112–3018; tel. 504/702–3000; Danny Hardman, FACHE, R.N., Chief Executive Officer
Web address: www.umcno.org

WEST JEFFERSON MEDICAL CENTER (C, 229 beds) 1101 Medical Center Boulevard, Marrero, LA, Zip 70072–3191; tel. 504/347–5511; Dodie McElmurray, Interim Chief Executive Officer and Chief Operating Officer
Web address: www.wjmc.org

Owned, leased, sponsored:	3 hospitals	814 beds
Contract-managed:	2 hospitals	263 beds
Totals:	5 hospitals	1077 beds

★0369: LEE HEALTH (NP)

2776 Cleveland Avenue, Fort Myers, FL, Zip 33901–5864, Mailing Address: P.O. Box 2218, Zip 33902–2218, tel. 239/343–2000; Lawrence Antonucci, M.D., President and Chief Executive Officer
(Moderately Centralized Health System)

FLORIDA: CAPE CORAL HOSPITAL (O, 291 beds) 636 Del Prado Boulevard, Cape Coral, FL, Zip 33990–2695; tel. 239/424–2000; Lawrence Antonucci, M.D., President and Chief Executive Officer

GULF COAST MEDICAL CENTER (O, 356 beds) 13681 Doctor's Way, Fort Myers, FL, Zip 33912–4300; tel. 239/343–1000; Lawrence Antonucci, M.D., President and Chief Executive Officer
Web address: www.leememorial.org

LEE MEMORIAL HOSPITAL (O, 803 beds) 2776 Cleveland Avenue, Fort Myers, FL, Zip 33901–5855, Mailing Address: P.O. Box 2218, Zip 33902–2218, tel. 239/343–2000; Lawrence Antonucci, M.D., President and Chief Executive Officer

Owned, leased, sponsored:	3 hospitals	1450 beds
Contract-managed:	0 hospitals	0 beds
Totals:	3 hospitals	1450 beds

★2755: LEGACY HEALTH (NP)

1919 NW Lovejoy Street, Portland, OR, Zip 97209–1503; tel. 503/415–5600; Kathryn G. Correia, President and Chief Executive Officer
(Centralized Health System)

OREGON: LEGACY EMANUEL MEDICAL CENTER (O, 532 beds) 2801 North Gantenbein Avenue, Portland, OR, Zip 97227–1674; tel. 503/413–2200; Trent Green, President

LEGACY GOOD SAMARITAN MEDICAL CENTER (O, 222 beds) 1015 NW 22nd Avenue, Portland, OR, Zip 97210–3099; tel. 503/413–7711; Jonathan Avery, Chief Administrative Officer
Web address: www.legacyhealth.org

LEGACY MERIDIAN PARK MEDICAL CENTER (O, 144 beds) 19300 SW 65th Avenue, Tualatin, OR, Zip 97062–9741; tel. 503/692–1212; Allyson Anderson, President
Web address: www.legacyhealth.org

For explanation of codes following names, see page B2.
★ Indicates Type III membership in the American Hospital Association.

LEGACY MOUNT HOOD MEDICAL CENTER (O, 98 beds) 24800 SE Stark, Gresham, OR, Zip 97030–3378; tel. 503/667–1122; Gretchen Nichols, R.N., President

LEGACY SILVERTON MEDICAL CENTER (O, 47 beds) 139 Breyonna Way, Silverton, OR, Zip 97381, Mailing Address: 342 Fairview Street, Zip 97381–1993, tel. 503/873–1500; Sarah Fronza, President
Web address: www.legacyhealth.org/locations/hospitals/legacy-silverton-medical-center.aspx

WASHINGTON: LEGACY SALMON CREEK MEDICAL CENTER (O, 211 beds) 2211 NE 139th Street, Vancouver, WA, Zip 98686–2742; tel. 360/487–1000; Bryce R. Helgerson, Chief Administrative Officer

Owned, leased, sponsored:	6 hospitals	1254 beds
Contract-managed:	0 hospitals	0 beds
Totals:	6 hospitals	1254 beds

★0370: LEHIGH VALLEY HEALTH NETWORK (NP)
1200 South Cedar Crest Boulevard, Allentown, PA, Zip 18103–6202, Mailing Address: P.O. Box 689, Zip 18105–1556, tel. 610/402–8000; Brian A. Nester, D.O., President and Chief Executive Officer
(Moderately Centralized Health System)

PENNSYLVANIA: LEHIGH VALLEY HOSPITAL – HAZLETON (O, 120 beds) 700 East Broad Street, Hazleton, PA, Zip 18201–6897; tel. 570/501–4000; John R. Fletcher, President
Web address: www.lvhn.org/hazleton/

LEHIGH VALLEY HOSPITAL – POCONO (O, 239 beds) 206 East Brown Street, East Stroudsburg, PA, Zip 18301–3006; tel. 570/421–4000; Elizabeth Wise, President and Chief Executive Officer

LEHIGH VALLEY HOSPITAL – SCHUYLKILL (O, 211 beds) 420 South Jackson Street, Pottsville, PA, Zip 17901–3625; tel. 570/621–5000; William Reppy, President
Web address: www.schuylkillhealth.com

LEHIGH VALLEY HOSPITAL (O, 1052 beds) 1200 South Cedar Crest Boulevard, Allentown, PA, Zip 18103–6248, Mailing Address: P.O. Box 689, Zip 18105–1556, tel. 610/402–8000; Brian A. Nester, D.O., President and Chief Executive Officer

Owned, leased, sponsored:	4 hospitals	1622 beds
Contract-managed:	0 hospitals	0 beds
Totals:	4 hospitals	1622 beds

0632: LHC GROUP (IO)
420 West Pinhook Road, Lafayette, LA, Zip 70503–2131; tel. 337/233–1307; Keith G. Myers, Chairman and Chief Executive Officer
(Independent Hospital System)

ARKANSAS: CHRISTUS DUBUIS HOSPITAL OF FORT SMITH (O, 25 beds) /301 Rogers Avenue, 4th Floor, Fort Smith, AR, Zip 72903–4100; tel. 479/314–4900; Nancy Owens, Administrator
Web address: www.christusdubuis.org/fortsmith

CHRISTUS DUBUIS HOSPITAL OF HOT SPRINGS (O, 27 beds) 300 Werner Street, 3rd Floor East, Hot Springs National Park, AR, Zip 71913–6406; tel. 501/609–4300; Cleta Munholland, Interim Administrator

LOUISIANA: CHRISTUS DUBUIS HOSPITAL OF ALEXANDRIA (O, 25 beds) 3330 Masonic Drive, 4th Floor, Alexandria, LA, Zip 71301–3841; tel. 318/448–4938; Beth Parsons, R.N., Administrator
Web address: www.christusdubuis.org/CHRISTUSDubuisHospitalofAlexandriaLA

EXTENDED CARE HOSPITAL (O, 32 beds) 2614 Jefferson Highway, 2nd Floor, New Orleans, LA, Zip 70121–3828; tel. 504/314–4242; Len McDade, Chief Executive Officer
Web address: www.lhcgroup.com/

LOUISIANA EXTENDED CARE HOSPITAL WEST MONROE (O, 18 beds) 503 McMillan Road, 3rd Floor, West Monroe, LA, Zip 71291–5327; tel. 318/329–4378; Cleta Munholland, Administrator

LOUISIANA EXTENDED CARE HOSPITAL OF LAFAYETTE (O, 42 beds) 2810 Ambassador Caffery Parkway, 6th Floor, Lafayette, LA, Zip 70506–5906; tel. 337/289–8180; Kermit C. Simmons, Chief Executive Officer
Web address: www.lhcgroup.com

LOUISIANA EXTENDED CARE HOSPITAL OF NATCHITOCHES (O, 21 beds) 501 Keyser Avenue, Natchitoches, LA, Zip 71457–6018; tel. 318/354–2044; John Rivoire, R.N., MSN, Administrator
Web address: www.lhcgroup.com

SPECIALTY HOSPITAL (O, 32 beds) 309 Jackson Street, 7th Floor, Monroe, LA, Zip 71201–7407, Mailing Address: P.O. Box 1532, Zip 71210–1532, tel. 318/966–7045; Cleta Munholland, Administrator

ST. LANDRY EXTENDED CARE HOSPITAL (O, 41 beds) 539 East Prudhomme Street, 6th Floor, Opelousas, LA, Zip 70570–6499; tel. 337/948–2251; Biff David, R.N., Administrator
Web address: www.lhcgroup.com

TEXAS: CHRISTUS DUBUIS HOSPITAL OF BEAUMONT (O, 33 beds) 2830 Calder Avenue, 4th Floor, Beaumont, TX, Zip 77702–1809; tel. 409/899–7680; Jason Baker, Administrator
Web address: www.christusdubuis.org/BeaumontandPortArthurSystem-CHRISTUSDubuisHospitalofBeaumont

CHRISTUS DUBUIS HOSPITAL OF PARIS (O, 25 beds) 820 Clarksville Street, 6th Floor, Paris, TX, Zip 75460–6027; tel. 903/737–3600; Kathie Reese, R.N., Regional Administrator and Chief Executive Officer
Web address: www.christusdubuis.org

Owned, leased, sponsored:	11 hospitals	321 beds
Contract-managed:	0 hospitals	0 beds
Totals:	11 hospitals	321 beds

0158: LIFEBRIDGE HEALTH (NP)
2401 West Belvedere Avenue, Baltimore, MD, Zip 21215–5216; tel. 410/601–5134; Neil M. Meltzer, President and Chief Executive Officer
(Moderately Centralized Health System)

MARYLAND: CARROLL HOSPITAL CENTER (O, 146 beds) 200 Memorial Avenue, Westminster, MD, Zip 21157–5799; tel. 410/848–3000; Leslie Simmons, FACHE, R.N., President
Web address: www.carrollhospitalcenter.org

LEVINDALE HEBREW HOSPITAL AND NURSING (O, 490 beds) 2434 West Belvedere Avenue, Baltimore, MD, Zip 21215–5267; tel. 410/601–2400; Deborah Graves, R.N., President and Chief Operating Officer

NORTHWEST HOSPITAL (O, 171 beds) 5401 Old Court Road, Randallstown, MD, Zip 21133–5185; tel. 410/521–2200; Faraaz Yousuf, President and Chief Operating Officer
Web address: www.lifebridgehealth.org

SINAI HOSPITAL OF BALTIMORE (O, 404 beds) 2401 West Belvedere Avenue, Baltimore, MD, Zip 21215–5271; tel. 410/601–9000; Jonathan Ringo, M.D., President and Chief Operating Officer

Owned, leased, sponsored:	4 hospitals	1211 beds
Contract-managed:	0 hospitals	0 beds
Totals:	4 hospitals	1211 beds

0947: LIFEBRITE HOSPITAL GROUP, LLC (IO)
3970 Five Forks Trickum Road SW Suite A, Lilburn, GA, Zip 30047–2339; tel. 678/505–9657; Christian Al. Fletcher, Chief Executive Officer

GEORGIA: LIFEBRITE COMMUNITY HOSPITAL OF EARLY (O, 152 beds) 11740 Columbia Street, Blakely, GA, Zip 39823–2574; tel. 229/723–4241; Ginger Cushing, Chief Executive Officer
Web address: www.pchearly.com

NORTH CAROLINA: LIFEBRITE COMMUNITY HOSPITAL OF STOKES (O, 65 beds) 1570 NC 8 & 89 Highway North, Danbury, NC, Zip 27016, Mailing Address: P.O. Box 10, Zip 27016–0010, tel. 336/593–2831; Pamela P. Tillman, Administrator

Owned, leased, sponsored:	2 hospitals	217 beds
Contract-managed:	0 hospitals	0 beds
Totals:	2 hospitals	217 beds

For explanation of codes following names, see page B2.
★ Indicates Type III membership in the American Hospital Association.

Section B

★0191: LIFECARE MANAGEMENT SERVICES (IO)
5340 Legacy Drive, Suite 150, Plano, TX, Zip 75024–3131; tel. 469/241–2100; James E. Murray, Chief Executive Officer
(Independent Hospital System)

COLORADO: COLORADO ACUTE LONG TERM HOSPITAL (O, 63 beds) 1690 North Meade Street, Denver, CO, Zip 80204–1552; tel. 303/264–6900; Craig Bailey, MS, Chief Executive Officer and Administrator

FLORIDA: COMPLEX CARE HOSPITAL AT RIDGELAKE (O, 40 beds) 6150 Edgelake Drive, Sarasota, FL, Zip 34240–8803; tel. 941/342–3000; Robert E. Mallicoat, Chief Executive Officer
Web address: www.lifecare-hospitals.com/hospital.php?id=23

LOUISIANA: LIFECARE HOSPITALS OF SHREVEPORT-WILLIS KNIGHTON (O, 54 beds) 8001 Youree Drive, Shreveport, LA, Zip 71115–2302; tel. 318/212–2200; Brent Martin, Administrator
Web address: https://www.lifecarehealthpartners.com/region/shreveport

NEVADA: COMPLEX CARE HOSPITAL AT TENAYA (O, 70 beds) 2500 North Tenaya, Las Vegas, NV, Zip 89128–0482; tel. 702/562–2021; Matt Archer, Chief Executive Officer

TAHOE PACIFIC HOSPITALS (O, 60 beds) 2375 East Prater Way, Sparks, NV, Zip 89434; tel. 775/355–5600; Matt Archer, Chief Executive Officer
Web address: www.lifecare-hospitals.com

NORTH CAROLINA: LIFECARE HOSPITALS OF NORTH CAROLINA (O, 43 beds) 1051 Noell Lane, Rocky Mount, NC, Zip 27804–1761; tel. 252/451–2300; Robyn Perkerson, R.N., Administrator
Web address: www.lifecare-hospitals.com

OHIO: LIFECARE HOSPITAL OF DAYTON (O, 44 beds) 4000 Miamisburg-Centerville Road, Miamisburg, OH, Zip 45342–7615; tel. 937/384–8300; William Bryant, Chief Executive Officer
Web address: www.lifecare-hospitals.com

PENNSYLVANIA: LIFECARE HOSPITALS OF CHESTER COUNTY (O, 39 beds) 400 East Marshall Street, West Chester, PA, Zip 19380–5412; tel. 484/826–0400; Janet Biedron, R.N., Chief Executive Officer

LIFECARE HOSPITALS OF PITTSBURGH (O, 196 beds) 225 Penn Avenue, Pittsburgh, PA, Zip 15221–2148; tel. 469/241–2100; Jennifer Malko, Market Chief Executive Officer
Web address: www.lifecare-hospitals.com

TEXAS: LIFECARE HOSPITALS OF DALLAS (O, 156 beds) 1950 Record Crossing Road, Dallas, TX, Zip 75235–6223; tel. 214/640–9600; Deborah Paganelli, FACHE, Chief Executive Officer
Web address: www.lifecare-hospitals.com/hospital/dallas

LIFECARE HOSPITALS OF SAN ANTONIO (O, 62 beds) 8902 Floyd Curl Drive, San Antonio, TX, Zip 78240–1681; tel. 210/690–7000; Michelle Lozano, Chief Executive Officer
Web address: www.lifecare-hospitals.com

WISCONSIN: LIFECARE HOSPITALS OF WISCONSIN (O, 30 beds) 2400 Golf Road, Pewaukee, WI, Zip 53072–5590; tel. 262/524–2600; David Chaudier, Chief Executive Officer

Owned, leased, sponsored:	12 hospitals	857 beds
Contract-managed:	0 hospitals	0 beds
Totals:	12 hospitals	857 beds

★0180: LIFEPOINT HEALTH (IO)
330 Seven Springs Way, Brentwood, TN, Zip 37027–4536; tel. 615/920–7000; David M. Dill, President and Chief Executive Officer
(Decentralized Health System)

ALABAMA: ANDALUSIA HEALTH (O, 88 beds) 849 South Three Notch Street, Andalusia, AL, Zip 36420–5325, Mailing Address: P.O. Box 760, Zip 36420–1214, tel. 334/222–8466; John C. Yanes, Chief Executive Officer
Web address: www.andalusiahealth.com

NORTH ALABAMA MEDICAL CENTER (O, 321 beds) 1701 Veterans Drive, Florence, AL, Zip 35630–6033; tel. 256/629–1000; Russell Pigg, Chief Executive Officer
Web address: www.https://namccares.com/

SHOALS HOSPITAL (O, 137 beds) 201 Avalon Avenue, Muscle Shoals, AL, Zip 35661–2805, Mailing Address: P.O. Box 3359, Zip 35662–3359, tel. 256/386–1600; Kidada Hawkins, Chief Executive Officer
Web address: www.shoalshospital.com

VAUGHAN REGIONAL MEDICAL CENTER (O, 149 beds) 1015 Medical Center Parkway, Selma, AL, Zip 36701–6352; tel. 334/418–4100; J. David. McCormack, Chief Executive Officer

ARIZONA: CANYON VISTA MEDICAL CENTER (O, 100 beds) 5700 East Highway 90, Sierra Vista, AZ, Zip 85635–9110; tel. 520/263–2000; Bob Gomes, FACHE, President and Chief Executive Officer
Web address: www.canyonvistamedicalcenter.com/

HAVASU REGIONAL MEDICAL CENTER (O, 162 beds) 101 Civic Center Lane, Lake Havasu City, AZ, Zip 86403–5683; tel. 928/855–8185; Michael N. Patterson, Chief Executive Officer

VALLEY VIEW MEDICAL CENTER (O, 84 beds) 5330 South Highway 95, Fort Mohave, AZ, Zip 86426–9225; tel. 928/788–2273; Feliciano Jiron, Chief Executive Officer
Web address: www.valleyviewmedicalcenter.net

ARKANSAS: NATIONAL PARK MEDICAL CENTER (O, 181 beds) 1910 Malvern Avenue, Hot Springs, AR, Zip 71901–7799; tel. 501/321–1000; Jerry D. Mabry, FACHE, Chief Executive Officer
Web address: www.nationalparkmedical.com

SAINT MARY'S REGIONAL MEDICAL CENTER (O, 141 beds) 1808 West Main Street, Russellville, AR, Zip 72801–2724; tel. 479/968–2841; James Davidson, Chief Executive Officer
Web address: www.saintmarysregional.com

SALINE MEMORIAL HOSPITAL (O, 133 beds) 1 Medical Park Drive, Benton, AR, Zip 72015–3354; tel. 501/776–6000; Michael K. Stewart, Chief Executive Officer

COLORADO: COLORADO PLAINS MEDICAL CENTER (L, 50 beds) 1000 Lincoln Street, Fort Morgan, CO, Zip 80701–3298; tel. 970/867–3391; Kevin Zachary, Chief Executive Officer
Web address: www.coloradoplainsmedicalcenter.com

GEORGIA: ST. FRANCIS HOSPITAL (O, 331 beds) 2122 Manchester Expressway, Columbus, GA, Zip 31904–6878, Mailing Address: P.O. Box 7000, Zip 31908–7000, tel. 706/596–4000; Danny L. Jones Jr, FACHE, Chief Executive Officer
Web address: www.mystfrancis.com

IDAHO: ST. JOSEPH REGIONAL MEDICAL CENTER (O, 123 beds) 415 Sixth Street, Lewiston, ID, Zip 83501–2431; tel. 208/743–2511; Blain Claypool, Chief Executive Officer

INDIANA: CLARK MEMORIAL HEALTH (O, 185 beds) 1220 Missouri Avenue, Jeffersonville, IN, Zip 47130–3743, Mailing Address: P.O. Box 69, Zip 47131–0600, tel. 812/282–6631; Martin Padgett, President and Chief Executive Officer
Web address: www.clarkmemorial.org

SCOTT MEMORIAL HEALTH (O, 25 beds) 1415 North Gardner Street, Scottsburg, IN, Zip 47170, Mailing Address: Box 430, Zip 47170–0430, tel. 812/752–3456; Martin Padgett, Acting Chief Executive Officer
Web address: www.scottmemorial.com

IOWA: OTTUMWA REGIONAL HEALTH CENTER (O, 101 beds) 1001 Pennsylvania Avenue, Ottumwa, IA, Zip 52501–2186; tel. 641/684–2300; Philip J. Noel III, Chief Executive Officer
Web address: www.ottumwaregionalhealth.com

KANSAS: WESTERN PLAINS MEDICAL COMPLEX (O, 45 beds) 3001 Avenue 'A', Dodge City, KS, Zip 67801–6508, Mailing Address: P.O. Box 1478, Zip 67801–1478, tel. 620/225–8400; Scott M. Smith, Chief Executive Officer
Web address: www.westernplainsmc.com

KENTUCKY: BLUEGRASS COMMUNITY HOSPITAL (O, 17 beds) 360 Amsden Avenue, Versailles, KY, Zip 40383–1286; tel. 859/873–3111; Tommy Haggard, Chief Executive Officer

BOURBON COMMUNITY HOSPITAL (O, 58 beds) 9 Linville Drive, Paris, KY, Zip 40361–2196; tel. 859/987–3600; Matt Smith, Interim Chief Executive Officer
Web address: www.bourbonhospital.com

CLARK REGIONAL MEDICAL CENTER (O, 79 beds) 175 Hospital Drive, Winchester, KY, Zip 40391–9591; tel. 859/745–3500; Aphreikah DuHaney-West, Chief Executive Officer
Web address: www.clarkregional.org

Section B

FLEMING COUNTY HOSPITAL (O, 52 beds) 55 Foundation Drive, Flemingsburg, KY, Zip 41041–9815, Mailing Address: P.O. Box 388, Zip 41041–0388, tel. 606/849–5000; Brian Springate, Chief Executive Officer

GEORGETOWN COMMUNITY HOSPITAL (O, 58 beds) 1140 Lexington Road, Georgetown, KY, Zip 40324–9362; tel. 502/868–1100; William Haugh, Administrator
Web address: www.georgetowncommunityhospital.com

JACKSON PURCHASE MEDICAL CENTER (O, 227 beds) 1099 Medical Center Circle, Mayfield, KY, Zip 42066–1159; tel. 270/251–4100; David Anderson, Chief Executive Officer
Web address: www.jacksonpurchase.com

LAKE CUMBERLAND REGIONAL HOSPITAL (O, 295 beds) 305 Langdon Street, Somerset, KY, Zip 42503–2750, Mailing Address: P.O. Box 620, Zip 42502–0620, tel. 606/679–7441; Robert Parker, Chief Executive Officer
Web address: www.lakecumberlandhospital.com

LOGAN MEMORIAL HOSPITAL (O, 30 beds) 1625 South Nashville Road, Russellville, KY, Zip 42276–8834, Mailing Address: P.O. Box 10, Zip 42276–0010, tel. 270/726–4011; James Bills, Chief Executive Officer

MEADOWVIEW REGIONAL MEDICAL CENTER (O, 100 beds) 989 Medical Park Drive, Maysville, KY, Zip 41056–8750; tel. 606/759–5311; Joseph G. Koch, Chief Executive Officer
Web address: www.meadowviewregional.com

SPRING VIEW HOSPITAL (O, 60 beds) 320 Loretto Road, Lebanon, KY, Zip 40033–1300; tel. 270/692–3161; Timothy R. Trottier, Chief Executive Officer

LOUISIANA: TECHE REGIONAL MEDICAL CENTER (L, 164 beds) 1125 Marguerite Street, Morgan City, LA, Zip 70380–1855, Mailing Address: P.O. Box 2308, Zip 70381–2308, tel. 985/384–2200; Anthony Young, Chief Executive Officer
Web address: www.techeregional.com

MICHIGAN: UP HEALTH SYSTEM-BELL (O, 25 beds) 901 Lakeshore Drive, Ishpeming, MI, Zip 49849–1367; tel. 906/486–4431; Mitchell D. Leckelt, Chief Executive Officer

UP HEALTH SYSTEM-PORTAGE (O, 96 beds) 500 Campus Drive, Hancock, MI, Zip 49930–1569; tel. 906/483–1000; Randy Neiswonger, Chief Executive Officer
Web address: www.portagehealth.org

MISSISSIPPI: BOLIVAR MEDICAL CENTER (L, 129 beds) 901 East Sunflower Road, Cleveland, MS, Zip 38732–2833, Mailing Address: P.O. Box 1380, Zip 38732–1380, tel. 662/846–0061; Robert L. Marshall Jr, FACHE, Chief Executive Officer
Web address: www.bolivarmedical.com

MONTANA: COMMUNITY MEDICAL CENTER (O, 135 beds) 2827 Fort Missoula Road, Missoula, MT, Zip 59804–7408; tel. 406/728–4100; Dean French, M.D., Chief Executive Officer

NEVADA: NORTHEASTERN NEVADA REGIONAL HOSPITAL (O, 75 beds) 2001 Errecart Boulevard, Elko, NV, Zip 89801–8333; tel. 775/738–5151; Steve Simpson, Chief Executive Officer
Web address: www.nnrhospital.com

NEW MEXICO: LOS ALAMOS MEDICAL CENTER (O, 29 beds) 3917 West Road, Los Alamos, NM, Zip 87544–2293; tel. 505/661–9500; John Whiteside, Chief Executive Officer

MEMORIAL MEDICAL CENTER (L, 173 beds) 2450 South Telshor Boulevard, Las Cruces, NM, Zip 88011–5076; tel. 575/522–8641; John Harris, Chief Executive Officer
Web address: www.mmclc.org

OHIO: CMH REGIONAL HEALTH SYSTEM (O, 165 beds) 610 West Main Street, Wilmington, OH, Zip 45177–2125; tel. 937/382–6611; Lance Beus, Chief Executive Officer
Web address: www.cmhregional.com

OKLAHOMA: SOUTHWESTERN MEDICAL CENTER (O, 178 beds) 5602 SW Lee Boulevard, Lawton, OK, Zip 73505–9635; tel. 580/531–4700; Elizabeth Jones, Chief Executive Officer
Web address: www.swmconline.com

OREGON: WILLAMETTE VALLEY MEDICAL CENTER (O, 60 beds) 2700 SE Stratus Avenue, McMinnville, OR, Zip 97128–6255; tel. 503/472–6131; Peter A. Hofstetter, Chief Executive Officer

PENNSYLVANIA: CONEMAUGH NASON MEDICAL CENTER (O, 45 beds) 105 Nason Drive, Roaring Spring, PA, Zip 16673–1202; tel. 814/224–2141; Timothy Harclerode, Chief Executive Officer
Web address: www.nasonhospital.com

SOUTH CAROLINA: CAROLINA PINES REGIONAL MEDICAL CENTER (O, 105 beds) 1304 West Bobo Newsom Highway, Hartsville, SC, Zip 29550–4710; tel. 843/339–2100; William Little, Chief Executive Officer
Web address: www.cprmc.com

KERSHAWHEALTH (O, 110 beds) 1315 Roberts Street, Camden, SC, Zip 29020–3737, Mailing Address: P.O. Box 7003, Zip 29021–7003, tel. 803/432–4311; Susan C. Shugart, Chief Executive Officer

PROVIDENCE HOSPITAL (O, 216 beds) 2435 Forest Drive, Columbia, SC, Zip 29204–2098; tel. 803/865–4500; Stephen R. Selzer, Market Chief Executive Officer
Web address: www.sistersofcharityhealth.org/health-care/providence-hospitals/

TENNESSEE: LIVINGSTON REGIONAL HOSPITAL (O, 82 beds) 315 Oak Street, Livingston, TN, Zip 38570–1728, Mailing Address: P.O. Box 550, Zip 38570–0550, tel. 931/823–5611; Timothy W. McGill, Chief Executive Officer
Web address: www.MyLivingstonHospital.com

RIVERVIEW REGIONAL MEDICAL CENTER (O, 35 beds) 158 Hospital Drive, Carthage, TN, Zip 37030–1096; tel. 615/735–1560; Michael Herman, Chief Executive Officer

SOUTHERN TENNESSEE REGIONAL HEALTH SYSTEM-LAWRENCEBURG (O, 99 beds) 1607 South Locust Avenue, Lawrenceburg, TN, Zip 38464–4011, Mailing Address: P.O. Box 847, Zip 38464–0847, tel. 931/762–6571; Adam Martin, Chief Executive Officer
Web address: www.crocketthospital.com

SOUTHERN TENNESSEE REGIONAL HEALTH SYSTEM-PULASKI (O, 56 beds) 1265 East College Street, Pulaski, TN, Zip 38478–4541; tel. 931/363–7531; James H. Edmondson, Chief Executive Officer
Web address: www.southerntnpulaski.com/

SOUTHERN TENNESSEE REGIONAL HEALTH SYSTEM-WINCHESTER (O, 190 beds) 185 Hospital Road, Winchester, TN, Zip 37398–2404; tel. 931/967–8200; William R. Spray, Chief Executive Officer
Web address: www.southerntennessee.com

STARR REGIONAL MEDICAL CENTER (O, 63 beds) 1114 West Madison Avenue, Athens, TN, Zip 37303–4150, Mailing Address: P.O. Box 250, Zip 37371–0250, tel. 423/745–1411; John R. McLain, Chief Executive Officer

SUMNER REGIONAL MEDICAL CENTER (O, 110 beds) 555 Hartsville Pike, Gallatin, TN, Zip 37066–2400, Mailing Address: P.O. Box 1558, Zip 37066–1558, tel. 615/452–4210; Susan M. Peach, R.N., Chief Executive Officer
Web address: www.mysumnermedical.com

TROUSDALE MEDICAL CENTER (O, 25 beds) 500 Church Street, Hartsville, TN, Zip 37074–1744; tel. 615/374–2221; Michael Herman, Chief Executive Officer
Web address: www.mytrousdalemedical.com

TEXAS: ENNIS REGIONAL MEDICAL CENTER (L, 58 beds) 2201 West Lampasas Street, Ennis, TX, Zip 75119–5644; tel. 972/875–0900; Robert C. Honeycutt, Chief Executive Officer
Web address: www.ennisregional.com

PALESTINE REGIONAL MEDICAL CENTER-EAST (O, 120 beds) 2900 South Loop 256, Palestine, TX, Zip 75801–6958; tel. 903/731–1000; Roy Finch, Chief Executive Officer

PARIS REGIONAL MEDICAL CENTER (O, 171 beds) 865 Deshong Drive, Paris, TX, Zip 75460–9313, Mailing Address: P.O. Box 9070, Zip 75461–9070, tel. 903/785–4521; Steve Hyde, Chief Executive Officer
Web address: www.https://parisregionalmedical.com/

PARKVIEW REGIONAL HOSPITAL (L, 58 beds) 600 South Bonham, Mexia, TX, Zip 76667–3603; tel. 254/562–5332; Robert C. Honeycutt, Chief Executive Officer

UTAH: ASHLEY REGIONAL MEDICAL CENTER (O, 39 beds) 150 West 100 North, Vernal, UT, Zip 84078–2036; tel. 435/789–3342; Ben Cluff, Chief Executive Officer
Web address: www.ashleyregional.com

CASTLEVIEW HOSPITAL (O, 49 beds) 300 North Hospital Drive, Price, UT, Zip 84501–4200; tel. 435/637–4800; Greg Cook, Chief Executive Officer

For explanation of codes following names, see page B2.
★ Indicates Type III membership in the American Hospital Association.

VIRGINIA: CLINCH VALLEY MEDICAL CENTER (O, 95 beds) 6801 Governor G C Peery Highway, Richlands, VA, Zip 24641–2194; tel. 276/596–6000; Peter Mulkey, Chief Executive Officer
Web address: www.clinchvalleymedicalcenter.com

FAUQUIER HOSPITAL (O, 160 beds) 500 Hospital Drive, Warrenton, VA, Zip 20186–3099; tel. 540/316–5000; Chad Melton, Chief Executive Officer
Web address: www.fauquierhealth.org/

SOVAH HEALTH-DANVILLE (O, 250 beds) 142 South Main Street, Danville, VA, Zip 24541–2922; tel. 434/799–2100; Alan Larson, Chief Executive Officer

SOVAH HEALTH-MARTINSVILLE (O, 150 beds) 320 Hospital Drive, Martinsville, VA, Zip 24112–1981, Mailing Address: P.O. Box 4788, Zip 24115–4788, tel. 276/666–7200; Alan Larson, Market President
Web address: www.martinsvillehospital.com

WYTHE COUNTY COMMUNITY HOSPITAL (L, 70 beds) 600 West Ridge Road, Wytheville, VA, Zip 24382–1099; tel. 276/228–0200; Joseph Wilkins, Chief Executive Officer
Web address: www.wcchcares.com

WASHINGTON: CAPITAL MEDICAL CENTER (O, 52 beds) 3900 Capital Mall Drive SW, Olympia, WA, Zip 98502–5026; tel. 360/754–5858; Mark S. Turner, Chief Executive Officer

LOURDES COUNSELING CENTER (O, 20 beds) 1175 Carondelet Drive, Richland, WA, Zip 99354–3300; tel. 509/943–9104; Mark Gregson, Interim Chief Executive Officer
Web address: www.lourdeshealth.net

LOURDES MEDICAL CENTER (O, 53 beds) 520 North Fourth Avenue, Pasco, WA, Zip 99301–5257; tel. 509/547–7704; John Serle, FACHE, President and Chief Executive Officer

TRIOS HEALTH (O, 96 beds) 900 South Auburn Street, Kennewick, WA, Zip 99336–5621, Mailing Address: P.O. Box 6128, Zip 99336–0128, tel. 509/586–6111; John H. Solheim, Chief Executive Officer
Web address: www.trioshealth.org

WEST VIRGINIA: LOGAN REGIONAL MEDICAL CENTER (O, 129 beds) 20 Hospital Drive, Logan, WV, Zip 25601–3452; tel. 304/831–1101; Simon Ratliff, Interim Chief Executive Officer
Web address: www.loganregionalmedicalcenter.com

RALEIGH GENERAL HOSPITAL (O, 229 beds) 1710 Harper Road, Beckley, WV, Zip 25801–3397; tel. 304/256–4100; Matthew S. Roberts, Chief Executive Officer

WISCONSIN: WATERTOWN REGIONAL MEDICAL CENTER (O, 64 beds) 125 Hospital Drive, Watertown, WI, Zip 53098–3303; tel. 920/261–4210; Richard Keddington, Chief Executive Officer
Web address: www.watertownregional.com/Main/Home.aspx

WYOMING: SAGEWEST HEALTH CARE AT RIVERTON (O, 93 beds) 2100 West Sunset Drive, Riverton, WY, Zip 82501–2274; tel. 307/856–4161; Robert Alan. Daugherty, Chief Executive Officer

Owned, leased, sponsored:	69 hospitals	7653 beds
Contract-managed:	0 hospitals	0 beds
Totals:	69 hospitals	7653 beds

0060: LIFESPAN CORPORATION (NP)
167 Point Street, Providence, RI, Zip 02903–4771; tel. 401/444–3500; Timothy J. Babineau, M.D., President and Chief Executive Officer
(Centralized Health System)

RHODE ISLAND: EMMA PENDLETON BRADLEY HOSPITAL (O, 70 beds) 1011 Veterans Memorial Parkway, East Providence, RI, Zip 02915–5099; tel. 401/432–1000; Daniel J. Wall, President and Chief Executive Officer

MIRIAM HOSPITAL (O, 247 beds) 164 Summit Avenue, Providence, RI, Zip 02906–2853; tel. 401/793–2500; Arthur J. Sampson, FACHE, President
Web address: www.lifespan.org

NEWPORT HOSPITAL (O, 104 beds) 11 Friendship Street, Newport, RI, Zip 02840–2299; tel. 401/846–6400; Crista F. Durand, President

RHODE ISLAND HOSPITAL (O, 682 beds) 593 Eddy Street, Providence, RI, Zip 02903–4900; tel. 401/444–4000; Margaret M. Van Bree, Dr.PH, President
Web address: www.rhodeislandhospital.org/

Owned, leased, sponsored:	4 hospitals	1103 beds
Contract-managed:	0 hospitals	0 beds
Totals:	4 hospitals	1103 beds

2175: LOMA LINDA UNIVERSITY ADVENTIST HEALTH SCIENCES CENTER (NP)
11175 Campus Street, Loma Linda, CA, Zip 92350–1700; tel. 909/558–7572; Richard H. Hart, President and Chief Executive Officer
(Centralized Health System)

CALIFORNIA: LOMA LINDA UNIVERSITY BEHAVIORAL MEDICINE CENTER (O, 89 beds) 1710 Barton Road, Redlands, CA, Zip 92373–5304; tel. 909/558–9200; Edward Field, Administrator
Web address: www.llu.edu

LOMA LINDA UNIVERSITY CHILDREN'S HOSPITAL (O, 339 beds) 11234 Anderson Street, Loma Linda, CA, Zip 92354–2804; tel. 909/558–8000; Kerry Heinrich, JD, Chief Executive Officer
Web address: www.llu.edu/lluch

LOMA LINDA UNIVERSITY MEDICAL CENTER-MURRIETA (O, 111 beds) 28062 Baxter Road, Murrieta, CA, Zip 92563–1401; tel. 951/290–4000; Peter Baker, Senior Vice President and Administrator
Web address: www.llumcmurrieta.org

LOMA LINDA UNIVERSITY MEDICAL CENTER (O, 538 beds) 11234 Anderson Street, Loma Linda, CA, Zip 92354–2804, Mailing Address: P.O. Box 2000, Zip 92354–0200, tel. 909/558–4000; Kerry Heinrich, JD, Chief Executive Officer

Owned, leased, sponsored:	4 hospitals	1077 beds
Contract-managed:	0 hospitals	0 beds
Totals:	4 hospitals	1077 beds

5755: LOS ANGELES COUNTY-DEPARTMENT OF HEALTH SERVICES (NP)
313 North Figueroa Street, Room 912, Los Angeles, CA, Zip 90012–2691; tel. 213/240–8101; Mitchell H. Katz, M.D., Director
(Moderately Centralized Health System)

CALIFORNIA: HARBOR-UCLA MEDICAL CENTER (O, 373 beds) 1000 West Carson Street, Torrance, CA, Zip 90502–2059; tel. 310/222–2345; Kimberly McKenzie, R.N., MSN, Interim Chief Executive Officer
Web address: www.harbor-ucla.org

LAC+USC MEDICAL CENTER (O, 664 beds) 2051 Marengo Street, Los Angeles, CA, Zip 90033–1352; tel. 323/409–1000; Dan A. Castillo, FACHE, Chief Executive Officer

LAC-OLIVE VIEW-UCLA MEDICAL CENTER (O, 202 beds) 14445 Olive View Drive, Sylmar, CA, Zip 91342–1438; tel. 818/364–1555; Judith Maass, Chief Executive Officer
Web address: www.dhs.lacounty.gov/wps/portal/dhs/oliveview

RANCHO LOS AMIGOS NATIONAL REHABILITATION CENTER (O, 207 beds) 7601 East Imperial Highway, Downey, CA, Zip 90242–3496; tel. 562/401–7111; Jorge Orozco, Chief Executive Officer

Owned, leased, sponsored:	4 hospitals	1446 beds
Contract-managed:	0 hospitals	0 beds
Totals:	4 hospitals	1446 beds

0047: LOUISIANA STATE HOSPITALS (NP)
628 North 4th Street, Baton Rouge, LA, Zip 70802–5342, Mailing Address: P.O. Box 629, Zip 70821–0628, tel. 225/342–9500; Shelby Price, Chief Executive Officer
(Independent Hospital System)

For explanation of codes following names, see page B2.
★ Indicates Type III membership in the American Hospital Association.

LOUISIANA: CENTRAL LOUISIANA STATE HOSPITAL (O, 120 beds) 242 West Shamrock Avenue, Pineville, LA, Zip 71360–6439, Mailing Address: P.O. Box 5031, Zip 71361–5031, tel. 318/484–6200; Sandra Duck, Administrator
Web address: www.dhh.louisiana.gov/index.cfm/directory/detail/217

EASTERN LOUISIANA MENTAL HEALTH SYSTEM (O, 473 beds) 4502 Highway 10, Jackson, LA, Zip 70748, Mailing Address: P.O. Box 498, Zip 70748–0498, tel. 225/634–0100; Hampton P S. Lea, Acting Chief Executive Officer

Owned, leased, sponsored:	2 hospitals	593 beds
Contract-managed:	0 hospitals	0 beds
Totals:	2 hospitals	593 beds

★0320: LRGHEALTHCARE (NP)

80 Highland Street, Laconia, NH, Zip 03246–3298; tel. 603/524–3211; Kevin Donovan, FACHE, President and Chief Executive Officer
(Independent Hospital System)

NEW HAMPSHIRE: FRANKLIN REGIONAL HOSPITAL (O, 31 beds) 15 Aiken Avenue, Franklin, NH, Zip 03235–1299; tel. 603/934–2060; Kevin Donovan, FACHE, President and Chief Executive Officer

LAKES REGION GENERAL HOSPITAL (O, 90 beds) 80 Highland Street, Laconia, NH, Zip 03246–3298; tel. 603/524–3211; Kevin Donovan, FACHE, President and Chief Executive Officer
Web address: www.lrgh.org

Owned, leased, sponsored:	2 hospitals	121 beds
Contract-managed:	0 hospitals	0 beds
Totals:	2 hospitals	121 beds

0614: MAINEHEALTH (NP)

110 Free Street, Portland, ME, Zip 04101–3537; tel. 207/661–7001; William L. Caron Jr, President
(Moderately Centralized Health System)

MAINE: LINCOLNHEALTH (O, 91 beds) 35 Miles Street, Damariscotta, ME, Zip 04543–4047; tel. 207/563–1234; James W. Donovan, President and Chief Executive Officer

MAINE MEDICAL CENTER (O, 637 beds) 22 Bramhall Street, Portland, ME, Zip 04102–3175; tel. 207/662–0111; Richard W. Petersen, President and Chief Executive Officer
Web address: www.mmc.org

PEN BAY MEDICAL CENTER (O, 151 beds) 6 Glen Cove Drive, Rockport, ME, Zip 04856–4240; tel. 207/921–8000; Mark Fourre, President and Chief Executive Officer
Web address: www.penbayhealthcare.org

SPRING HARBOR HOSPITAL (O, 100 beds) 123 Andover Road, Westbrook, ME, Zip 04092–3850; tel. 207/761–2200; Mary Jane Krebs, FACHE, President
Web address: www.springharbor.org

STEPHENS MEMORIAL HOSPITAL (O, 25 beds) 181 Main Street, Norway, ME, Zip 04268–5664; tel. 207/743–5933; Timothy A. Churchill, President

WALDO COUNTY GENERAL HOSPITAL MAINE HEALTH (O, 25 beds) 118 Northport Avenue, Belfast, ME, Zip 04915–6072, Mailing Address: P.O. Box 287, Zip 04915–0287, tel. 207/338–2500; Mark Fourre, Chief Executive Officer
Web address: www.wcgh.org

NEW HAMPSHIRE: MEMORIAL HOSPITAL (O, 70 beds) 3073 White Mountain Highway, North Conway, NH, Zip 03860–7101; tel. 603/356–5461; Arthur Mathisen, FACHE, President
Web address: www.memorialhospitalnh.org

Owned, leased, sponsored:	7 hospitals	1099 beds
Contract-managed:	0 hospitals	0 beds
Totals:	7 hospitals	1099 beds

1975: MARSHALL HEALTH SYSTEM (NP)

227 Britany Road, Guntersville, AL, Zip 35976–5766; tel. 256/894–6615; Gary R. Gore, Chief Executive Officer
(Independent Hospital System)

ALABAMA: MARSHALL MEDICAL CENTER NORTH (O, 90 beds) 8000 Alabama Highway 69, Guntersville, AL, Zip 35976; tel. 256/753–8000; Cheryl M. Hays, FACHE, Administrator and Chief Operating Officer
Web address: www.mmcenters.com

MARSHALL MEDICAL CENTER SOUTH (O, 114 beds) U S Highway 431 North, Boaz, AL, Zip 35957–0999, Mailing Address: P.O. Box 758, Zip 35957–0758, tel. 256/593–8310; John D. Anderson, FACHE, Administrator
Web address: www.mmcenters.com//index.php/facilities/marshall_south

Owned, leased, sponsored:	2 hospitals	204 beds
Contract-managed:	0 hospitals	0 beds
Totals:	2 hospitals	204 beds

★1022: MARSHFIELD CLINIC HEALTH SYSTEM (NP)

1000 North Oak Avenue, Marshfield, WI, Zip 54449–5703; tel. 800/782–8581; Susan Turney, M.D., MS, Chief Executive Officer
(Moderately Centralized Health System)

WISCONSIN: BEAVER DAM COMMUNITY HOSPITALS (O, 163 beds) 707 South University Avenue, Beaver Dam, WI, Zip 53916–3089; tel. 920/887–7181; Joseph Gilene, Interim Chief Administrative Officer

FLAMBEAU HOSPITAL (O, 25 beds) 98 Sherry Avenue, Park Falls, WI, Zip 54552–1467, Mailing Address: P.O. Box 310, Zip 54552–0310, tel. 715/762–2484; James R. Braun, Chief Administrative Officer and Chief Financial Officer
Web address: www.flambeauhospital.org

MARSHFIELD MEDICAL CENTER – EAU CLAIRE HOSPITAL (O, 44 beds) 2310 Craig Road, Eau Claire, WI, Zip 54701–6128; tel. 715/858–8100; Scott Polenz, CPA, Chief Administrative Officer
Web address: https://www.marshfieldclinic.org/locations/centers/Eau%20Claire%20-%20Marshfield%20Medical%20Center

MARSHFIELD MEDICAL CENTER – LADYSMITH (O, 25 beds) 900 College Avenue West, Ladysmith, WI, Zip 54848–2116; tel. 715/532–5561; Jeff Euclide, R.N., Chief Executive Officer

MARSHFIELD MEDICAL CENTER – NEILSVILLE (O, 16 beds) 216 Sunset Place, Neillsville, WI, Zip 54456–1799; tel. 715/743–3101; Ryan T. Neville, FACHE, President and Chief Executive Officer
Web address: www.memorialmedcenter.org

MARSHFIELD MEDICAL CENTER – RICE LAKE (O, 40 beds) 1700 West Stout Street, Rice Lake, WI, Zip 54868–5000; tel. 715/234–1515; Bradley D. Groseth, Chief Administrative Officer
Web address: www.lakeviewmedical.com

MARSHFIELD MEDICAL CENTER (O, 200 beds) 611 St Joseph Avenue, Marshfield, WI, Zip 54449–1898; tel. 715/387–1713; Ned H. Wolf, Chief Administrative Officer

Owned, leased, sponsored:	7 hospitals	513 beds
Contract-managed:	0 hospitals	0 beds
Totals:	7 hospitals	513 beds

★0523: MARY WASHINGTON HEALTHCARE (NP)

1001 Sam Perry Boulevard, Fredericksburg, VA, Zip 22401–4453; tel. 540/741–3100; Michael P. McDermott, M.D., President and Chief Executive Officer
(Centralized Health System)

VIRGINIA: MARY WASHINGTON HOSPITAL (O, 451 beds) 1001 Sam Perry Boulevard, Fredericksburg, VA, Zip 22401–3354; tel. 540/741–1100; Michael P. McDermott, M.D., President and Chief Executive Officer

STAFFORD HOSPITAL (O, 78 beds) 101 Hospital Center Boulevard, Stafford, VA, Zip 22554–6200; tel. 540/741–9000; Michael P. McDermott, M.D., President and Chief Executive Officer
Web address: www.mwhc.com

Owned, leased, sponsored:	2 hospitals	529 beds
Contract-managed:	0 hospitals	0 beds
Totals:	2 hospitals	529 beds

For explanation of codes following names, see page B2.
★ Indicates Type III membership in the American Hospital Association.

0013: MASSACHUSETTS DEPARTMENT OF MENTAL HEALTH
(NP)

25 Staniford Street, Boston, MA, Zip 02114–2575; tel. 617/626–8123; Joan Mikula, Interim Commissioner

MASSACHUSETTS: DR. J. CORRIGAN MENTAL HEALTH CENTER (O, 16 beds) 49 Hillside Street, Fall River, MA, Zip 02720–5266; tel. 508/235–7200; Frank O'Reilly, Director

TAUNTON STATE HOSPITAL (O, 45 beds) 60 Hodges Avenue Extension, Taunton, MA, Zip 02780–3034, Mailing Address: PO Box 4007, Zip 02780–0997, tel. 508/977–3000; Joyce O Connor, Chief Operating Officer

WORCESTER RECOVERY CENTER AND HOSPITAL (O, 126 beds) 309 Belmont Street, Worcester, MA, Zip 01604–1695; tel. 508/368–3300; Anthony Riccitelli, Chief Operating Officer

Owned, leased, sponsored:	3 hospitals	187 beds
Contract-managed:	0 hospitals	0 beds
Totals:	3 hospitals	187 beds

0280: MASSACHUSETTS DEPARTMENT OF PUBLIC HEALTH
(NP)

250 Washington Street, Boston, MA, Zip 02108–4619; tel. 617/624–6000; Sandra Akers, Bureau Director, Public Health Hospitals

(Independent Hospital System)

MASSACHUSETTS: LEMUEL SHATTUCK HOSPITAL (O, 260 beds) 170 Morton Street, Jamaica Plain, MA, Zip 02130–3735; tel. 617/522–8110; Rosette Martinez, Acting Chief Executive Officer

PAPPAS REHABILITATION HOSPITAL FOR CHILDREN (O, 80 beds) 3 Randolph Street, Canton, MA, Zip 02021–2351; tel. 781/828–2440; Brian V. Devin, Chief Executive Officer
Web address: www.mhsf.us/

TEWKSBURY HOSPITAL (O, 381 beds) 365 East Street, Tewksbury, MA, Zip 01876–1998; tel. 978/851–7321; Debra Tosti, Chief Executive Officer
Web address: www.mass.gov

WESTERN MASSACHUSETTS HOSPITAL (O, 80 beds) 91 East Mountain Road, Westfield, MA, Zip 01085–1801; tel. 413/562–4131; Valenda M. Liptak, Chief Executive Officer
Web address: www.mass.gov/eohhs/gov/departments/dph/programs/western-massachusetts-hospital.html

Owned, leased, sponsored:	4 hospitals	801 beds
Contract-managed:	0 hospitals	0 beds
Totals:	4 hospitals	801 beds

★0882: MAURY REGIONAL HEALTH SYSTEM (NP)

1224 Trotwood Avenue, Columbia, TN, Zip 38401–4802; tel. 931/381–1111; H Alan. Watson, FACHE, Chief Executive Officer

(Independent Hospital System)

TENNESSEE: MARSHALL MEDICAL CENTER (O, 12 beds) 1080 North Ellington Parkway, Lewisburg, TN, Zip 37091–2227, Mailing Address: P.O. Box 1609, Zip 37091–1609, tel. 931/359–6241; Phyllis Brown, Chief Executive Officer
Web address: www.mauryregional.com

MAURY REGIONAL HOSPITAL (O, 219 beds) 1224 Trotwood Avenue, Columbia, TN, Zip 38401–4802; tel. 931/381–1111; H Alan. Watson, FACHE, Chief Executive Officer

WAYNE MEDICAL CENTER (L, 25 beds) 103 J V Mangubat Drive, Waynesboro, TN, Zip 38485–2440, Mailing Address: P.O. Box 580, Zip 38485–0580, tel. 931/722–5411; Tyler Taylor, Chief Executive Officer
Web address: www.mauryregional.com

Owned, leased, sponsored:	3 hospitals	256 beds
Contract-managed:	0 hospitals	0 beds
Totals:	3 hospitals	256 beds

★1875: MAYO CLINIC (NP)

200 First Street SW, Rochester, MN, Zip 55905–0002; tel. 507/284–2511; Gianrico Farrugia, M.D., President

(Decentralized Health System)

ARIZONA: MAYO CLINIC HOSPITAL (O, 280 beds) 5777 East Mayo Boulevard, Phoenix, AZ, Zip 85054–4502; tel. 480/342–2000; Lois E. Krahn, M.D., Interim Chief Executive Officer
Web address: www.mayoclinic.org/arizona/

FLORIDA: MAYO CLINIC HOSPITAL IN FLORIDA (O, 277 beds) 4500 San Pablo Road South, Jacksonville, FL, Zip 32224–1865; tel. 904/953–2000; Kent Thielen, M.D., Chief Executive Officer
Web address: www.mayoclinic.org/jacksonville/

IOWA: FLOYD COUNTY MEDICAL CENTER (C, 25 beds) 800 Eleventh Street, Charles City, IA, Zip 50616–3499; tel. 641/228–6830; Rod Nordeng, Administrator
Web address: www.fcmc.us.com/

WINNESHIEK MEDICAL CENTER (C, 25 beds) 901 Montgomery Street, Decorah, IA, Zip 52101–2325; tel. 563/382–2911; Lisa Radtke, Chief Administrative Officer
Web address: www.winmedical.org

MINNESOTA: MAYO CLINIC HEALTH SYSTEM – ALBERT LEA AND AUSTIN (O, 85 beds) 404 West Fountain Street, Albert Lea, MN, Zip 56007–2473; tel. 507/373–2384; Mark Ciota, M.D., Chief Executive Officer

MAYO CLINIC HEALTH SYSTEM IN CANNON FALLS (O, 15 beds) 32021 County Road 24 Boulevard, Cannon Falls, MN, Zip 55009–1898; tel. 507/263–4221; Brian Whited, M.D., Vice Chair Mayo Clinic Health System
Web address: www.mayoclinichealthsystem.org/locations/cannon-falls

MAYO CLINIC HEALTH SYSTEM IN FAIRMONT (O, 23 beds) 800 Medical Center Drive, Fairmont, MN, Zip 56031–4575; tel. 507/238–8100; Amy Long, Administrator
Web address: www.fairmontmedicalcenter.org

MAYO CLINIC HEALTH SYSTEM IN LAKE CITY (O, 98 beds) 500 West Grant Street, Lake City, MN, Zip 55041–1143; tel. 651/345–3321; Brian Whited, M.D., President and Chief Executive Officer
Web address: www.lakecitymedicalcenter.org

MAYO CLINIC HEALTH SYSTEM IN MANKATO (O, 172 beds) 1025 Marsh Street, Mankato, MN, Zip 56001–4752; tel. 507/625–4031; James Hebl, M.D., Regional Vice President
Web address: www.mayoclinichealthsystem.org

MAYO CLINIC HEALTH SYSTEM IN NEW PRAGUE (O, 19 beds) 301 Second Street NE, New Prague, MN, Zip 56071–1799; tel. 952/758–4431; Mary J. Klimp, FACHE, Interim Administrator
Web address: www.mayoclinichealthsystem.org/locations/new-prague

MAYO CLINIC HEALTH SYSTEM IN RED WING (O, 30 beds) 701 Hewitt Boulevard, Red Wing, MN, Zip 55066–2848, Mailing Address: P.O. Box 95, Zip 55066–0095, tel. 651/267–5000; Brian Whited, M.D., President and Chief Executive Officer
Web address: www.mayoclinichealthsystem.org/locations/red-wing

MAYO CLINIC HEALTH SYSTEM IN SAINT JAMES (O, 8 beds) 1101 Moulton and Parsons Drive, Saint James, MN, Zip 56081–5550; tel. 507/375–3261; Scott D. Thoreson, FACHE, Administrator
Web address: www.mayoclinichealthsystem.org/locations/st-james

MAYO CLINIC HEALTH SYSTEM IN SPRINGFIELD (O, 10 beds) 625 North Jackson Avenue, Springfield, MN, Zip 56087–1714, Mailing Address: P.O. Box 146, Zip 56087–0146, tel. 507/723–6201; Scott D. Thoreson, FACHE, Administrator
Web address: www.mayoclinichealthsystem.org

MAYO CLINIC HEALTH SYSTEM IN WASECA (O, 12 beds) 501 North State Street, Waseca, MN, Zip 56093–2811; tel. 507/835–1210; April Lanz, Interim Administrator
Web address: www.mayoclinichealthsystem.org

MAYO CLINIC HOSPITAL – ROCHESTER (O, 1283 beds) 1216 Second Street SW, Rochester, MN, Zip 55902–1906; tel. 507/255–5123; Kenneth F. Ackerman, FACHE, Hospital Administrator

WISCONSIN: MAYO CLINIC HEALTH SYSTEM – CHIPPEWA VALLEY IN BLOOMER (O, 21 beds) 1501 Thompson Street, Bloomer, WI, Zip 54724–1299; tel. 715/568–2000; Michele Eberle, Vice Chair
Web address: www.bloomermedicalcenter.org

For explanation of codes following names, see page B2.
★ Indicates Type III membership in the American Hospital Association.

Section B

MAYO CLINIC HEALTH SYSTEM – FRANCISCAN HEALTHCARE IN LA CROSSE (O, 132 beds) 700 West Avenue South, La Crosse, WI, Zip 54601–4783; tel. 608/785–0940; Paul S. Mueller, Regional Vice President
Web address: www.franciscanskemp.org

MAYO CLINIC HEALTH SYSTEM – FRANCISCAN HEALTHCARE IN SPARTA (O, 15 beds) 310 West Main Street, Sparta, WI, Zip 54656–2171; tel. 608/269–2132; Kimberly Hawthorne, Administrator
Web address: www.mayoclinichealthsystem.org

MAYO CLINIC HEALTH SYSTEM – NORTHLAND IN BARRON (O, 23 beds) 1222 East Woodland Avenue, Barron, WI, Zip 54812–1798; tel. 715/537–3186; Michele Eberle, Vice Chair

MAYO CLINIC HEALTH SYSTEM – OAKRIDGE IN OSSEO (O, 16 beds) 13025 Eighth Street, Osseo, WI, Zip 54758–7634, Mailing Address: P.O. Box 70, Zip 54758–0070, tel. 715/597–3121; Dean Eide, Vice President
Web address: www.mayoclinichealthsystem.org/locations/osseo

MAYO CLINIC HEALTH SYSTEM – RED CEDAR IN MENOMONIE (O, 25 beds) 2321 Stout Road, Menomonie, WI, Zip 54751–2397; tel. 715/235–5531; Steven Lindberg, Chief Administrative Officer

MAYO CLINIC HEALTH SYSTEM IN EAU CLAIRE (O, 185 beds) 1221 Whipple Street, Eau Claire, WI, Zip 54703–5270, Mailing Address: P.O. Box 4105, Zip 54702, tel. 715/838–3311; Richard Helmers, M.D., Regional Vice President
Web address: www.mhs.mayo.edu

Owned, leased, sponsored:	20 hospitals	2729 beds
Contract-managed:	2 hospitals	50 beds
Totals:	22 hospitals	2779 beds

0252: MCLAREN HEALTH CARE CORPORATION (NP)

3373 Regency Park Drive, Grand Blanc, MI, Zip 48439, Mailing Address: One McLaren Parkway, Zip 48439, tel. 810/342–1100; Philip A. Incarnati, President and Chief Executive Officer
(Centralized Physician/Insurance Health System)

MICHIGAN: MARWOOD MANOR NURSING HOME (O, 106 beds) 1300 Beard Street, Port Huron, MI, Zip 48060; tel. 818/982–2594; Brian Oberly, Administrator

MCLAREN BAY REGION (O, 338 beds) 1900 Columbus Avenue, Bay City, MI, Zip 48708–6831; tel. 989/894–3000; Clarence Sevillian, President and Chief Executive Officer
Web address: www.mclaren.org/bayregion

MCLAREN BAY SPECIAL CARE (O, 21 beds) 3250 East Midland Road, Suite 1, Bay City, MI, Zip 48706–2835; tel. 989/667–6851; Monica Baranski, MS, R.N., President

MCLAREN CARO REGION (O, 25 beds) 401 North Hooper Street, Caro, MI, Zip 48723–1476, Mailing Address: P.O. Box 435, Zip 48723–0435, tel. 989/673–3141; Marc Augsburger, R.N., President and Chief Executive Officer
Web address: www.cch-mi.org

MCLAREN CENTRAL MICHIGAN (O, 78 beds) 1221 South Drive, Mount Pleasant, MI, Zip 48858–3257; tel. 989/772–6700; Martin Tursky, President and Chief Executive Officer
Web address: www.cmch.org

MCLAREN FLINT (O, 371 beds) 401 South Ballenger Highway, Flint, MI, Zip 48532–3685; tel. 810/342–2000; Chad M. Grant, President and Chief Executive Officer

MCLAREN GREATER LANSING (O, 321 beds) 401 West Greenlawn Avenue, Lansing, MI, Zip 48910–2819; tel. 517/975–6000; Kirk M. Ray, President and Chief Executive Officer
Web address: www.mclaren.org

MCLAREN LAPEER REGION (O, 159 beds) 1375 North Main Street, Lapeer, MI, Zip 48446–1350; tel. 810/667–5500; Chris Candela, President and Chief Executive Officer
Web address: www.lapeerregional.org

MCLAREN MACOMB (O, 288 beds) 1000 Harrington Boulevard, Mount Clemens, MI, Zip 48043–2992; tel. 586/493–8000; Thomas M. Brisse, President and Chief Executive Officer
Web address: www.mclaren.org/macomb/macomb.aspx

MCLAREN NORTHERN MICHIGAN (O, 188 beds) 416 Connable Avenue, Petoskey, MI, Zip 49770–2297; tel. 231/487–4000; David M. Zechman, FACHE, President and Chief Executive Officer
Web address: www.northernhealth.org

MCLAREN OAKLAND (O, 253 beds) 50 North Perry Street, Pontiac, MI, Zip 48342–2253; tel. 248/338–5000; Margaret Dimond, Ph.D., President and Chief Executive Officer
Web address: www.mclaren.org/oakland

MCLAREN PORT HURON (O, 186 beds) 1221 Pine Grove Avenue, Port Huron, MI, Zip 48060–3511; tel. 810/987–5000; Jennifer Montgomery, FACHE, R.N., President and Chief Executive Officer
Web address: www.porthuronhospital.org

MCLAREN THUMB REGION (O, 49 beds) 1100 South Van Dyke Road, Bad Axe, MI, Zip 48413–9615; tel. 989/269–9521; Michael Eric. Johnston, President and Chief Executive Officer

Owned, leased, sponsored:	13 hospitals	2383 beds
Contract-managed:	0 hospitals	0 beds
Totals:	13 hospitals	2383 beds

0874: MCLEOD HEALTH (NP)

555 East Cheves Street, Florence, SC, Zip 29506–2617, Mailing Address: P.O. Box 100551, Zip 29502–0551, tel. 843/777–2000; Robert L. Colones, President and Chief Executive Officer
(Centralized Health System)

SOUTH CAROLINA: MCLEOD HEALTH CHERAW (O, 40 beds) 711 Chesterfield Highway, Cheraw, SC, Zip 29520–7002; tel. 843/537–7881; Mib Scoggins, Chief Executive Officer
Web address: www.chesterfieldgeneral.com

MCLEOD HEALTH CLARENDON (C, 49 beds) 10 Hospital Street, Manning, SC, Zip 29102–3153, Mailing Address: P.O. Box 550, Zip 29102–0550, tel. 803/433–3000; Rachel Gainey, Administrator

MCLEOD LORIS SEACOAST HOSPITAL (O, 100 beds) 3655 Mitchell Street, Loris, SC, Zip 29569–2827; tel. 843/716–7000; Edward D. Tinsley III, Regional Administrator
Web address: www.mcleodhealth.org

MCLEOD MEDICAL CENTER DARLINGTON (O, 41 beds) 701 Cashua Ferry Road, Darlington, SC, Zip 29532–8488, Mailing Address: P.O. Box 1859, Zip 29540, tel. 843/395–1100; Tim Smoak, Administrator

MCLEOD MEDICAL CENTER DILLON (O, 34 beds) 301 East Jackson Street, Dillon, SC, Zip 29536–2509, Mailing Address: P.O. Box 1327, Zip 29536–1327, tel. 843/774–4111; Joan Ervin, Administrator
Web address: www.mcleodhealth.org

MCLEOD REGIONAL MEDICAL CENTER (O, 488 beds) 555 East Cheves Street, Florence, SC, Zip 29506–2617, Mailing Address: P.O. Box 100551, Zip 29502–0551, tel. 843/777–2000; Robert L. Colones, President and Chief Executive Officer

Owned, leased, sponsored:	5 hospitals	703 beds
Contract-managed:	1 hospitals	49 beds
Totals:	6 hospitals	752 beds

★1001: MEADVILLE MEDICAL CENTER (NP)

751 Liberty Street, Meadville, PA, Zip 16335–2559; tel. 814/333–5000; Philip E. Pandolph, FACHE, Chief Executive Officer
(Independent Hospital System)

PENNSYLVANIA: MEADVILLE MEDICAL CENTER (O, 232 beds) 751 Liberty Street, Meadville, PA, Zip 16335–2559; tel. 814/333–5000; Philip E. Pandolph, FACHE, Chief Executive Officer

TITUSVILLE AREA HOSPITAL (O, 25 beds) 406 West Oak Street, Titusville, PA, Zip 16354–1404; tel. 814/827–1851; Lee Clinton, FACHE, Chief Executive Officer
Web address: www.titusvillehospital.org

Owned, leased, sponsored:	2 hospitals	257 beds
Contract-managed:	0 hospitals	0 beds
Totals:	2 hospitals	257 beds

For explanation of codes following names, see page B2.
★ Indicates Type III membership in the American Hospital Association.

Section B

0520: MED CENTER HEALTH (NP)

800 Park Street, Bowling Green, KY, Zip 42101–2356; tel. 270/745–1500; Connie Smith, FACHE, MSN, R.N., President and Chief Executive Officer

(Centralized Physician/Insurance Health System)

KENTUCKY: COMMONWEALTH REGIONAL SPECIALTY HOSPITAL (O, 28 beds) 250 Park Drive, 6th Floor, Bowling Green, KY, Zip 42101–1760, Mailing Address: P.O. Box 90010, Zip 42102–9010, tel. 270/796–6200; Christa Atkins, Administrator

Web address: www.commonwealthregionalspecialtyhospital.org

MEDICAL CENTER AT BOWLING GREEN (O, 337 beds) 250 Park Street, Bowling Green, KY, Zip 42101–1795, Mailing Address: P.O. Box 90010, Zip 42102–9010, tel. 270/745–1000; Connie Smith, FACHE, MSN, R.N., Chief Executive Officer

MEDICAL CENTER AT FRANKLIN (O, 25 beds) 1100 Brookhaven Road, Franklin, KY, Zip 42134–2746; tel. 270/598–4800; Annette Runyon, Vice President and Administrator

Web address: www.themedicalcenterfranklin.org

MEDICAL CENTER AT SCOTTSVILLE (O, 135 beds) 456 Burnley Road, Scottsville, KY, Zip 42164–6355; tel. 270/622–2800; Eric Hagan, R.N., Executive Vice President and Administrator

Web address: www.themedicalcenterscottsville.org/

THE MEDICAL CENTER ALBANY (C, 42 beds) 723 Burkesville Road, Albany, KY, Zip 42602–1654; tel. 606/387–8000; Laura Belcher, Administrator

Web address: www.chc.net/services/hospitals/the_medical_center_at_albany.aspx

THE MEDICAL CENTER AT CAVERNA (O, 25 beds) 1501 South Dixie Street, Horse Cave, KY, Zip 42749–1477; tel. 270/786–2191; Alan B. Alexander, FACHE, Vice President and Administrator

Web address: www.TheMedicalCenterCaverna.org

Owned, leased, sponsored:	5 hospitals	550 beds
Contract-managed:	1 hospitals	42 beds
Totals:	6 hospitals	592 beds

★0971: MEDISYS HEALTH NETWORK (NP)

8900 Van Wyck Expressway, Jamaica, NY, Zip 11418–2832; tel. 718/206–6000; Bruce J. Flanz, President and Chief Executive Officer

(Moderately Centralized Health System)

NEW YORK: FLUSHING HOSPITAL MEDICAL CENTER (C, 299 beds) 4500 Parsons Boulevard, Flushing, NY, Zip 11355–2205; tel. 718/670–5000; Bruce J. Flanz, President and Chief Executive Officer

JAMAICA HOSPITAL MEDICAL CENTER (C, 668 beds) 8900 Van Wyck Expressway, Jamaica, NY, Zip 11418–2832; tel. 718/206–6000; Bruce J. Flanz, President and Chief Executive Officer

Web address: www.Jamaicahospital.org

Owned, leased, sponsored:	0 hospitals	0 beds
Contract-managed:	2 hospitals	967 beds
Totals:	2 hospitals	967 beds

★0154: MEDSTAR HEALTH (NP)

10980 Grantchester Way, Columbia, MD, Zip 21044–2665; tel. 410/772–6500; Kenneth A. Samet, President and Chief Executive Officer

(Centralized Health System)

DISTRICT OF COLUMBIA: MEDSTAR GEORGETOWN UNIVERSITY HOSPITAL (O, 409 beds) 3800 Reservoir Road NW, Washington, DC, Zip 20007–2197; tel. 202/444–2000; Michael Sachtleben, President

MEDSTAR NATIONAL REHABILITATION HOSPITAL (O, 137 beds) 102 Irving Street NW, Washington, DC, Zip 20010–2949; tel. 202/877–1000; John D. Rockwood, President

Web address: www.medstarnrh.org

MEDSTAR WASHINGTON HOSPITAL CENTER (O, 745 beds) 110 Irving Street NW, Washington, DC, Zip 20010–3017; tel. 202/877–7000; Gregory J. Argyros, M.D., Senior Vice President and President

MARYLAND: MEDSTAR FRANKLIN SQUARE MEDICAL CENTER (O, 369 beds) 9000 Franklin Square Drive, Baltimore, MD, Zip 21237–3901; tel. 443/777–7000; Samuel E. Moskowitz, President

Web address: www.medstarfranklin.org

MEDSTAR GOOD SAMARITAN HOSPITAL (O, 227 beds) 5601 Loch Raven Boulevard, Baltimore, MD, Zip 21239–2995; tel. 443/444–8000; Bradley Chambers, President and Senior Vice President, MedStar Health

Web address: www.goodsam-md.org

MEDSTAR HARBOR HOSPITAL (O, 127 beds) 3001 South Hanover Street, Baltimore, MD, Zip 21225–1290; tel. 410/350–3200; Stuart M. Levine, M.D., President and Chief Medical Officer

Web address: www.harborhospital.org

MEDSTAR MONTGOMERY MEDICAL CENTER (O, 147 beds) 18101 Prince Philip Drive, Olney, MD, Zip 20832–1512; tel. 301/774–8882; Thomas J. Senker, FACHE, President

Web address: www.medstarmontgomery.org

MEDSTAR SOUTHERN MARYLAND HOSPITAL CENTER (O, 206 beds) 7503 Surratts Road, Clinton, MD, Zip 20735–3358; tel. 301/868–8000; Christine R. Wray, President

MEDSTAR ST. MARY'S HOSPITAL (O, 109 beds) 25500 Point Lookout Road, Leonardtown, MD, Zip 20650–2015, Mailing Address: PO Box 527, Zip 20650–0527, tel. 301/475–6001; Christine R. Wray, President

Web address: www.medstarstmarys.org

MEDSTAR UNION MEMORIAL HOSPITAL (O, 215 beds) 201 East University Parkway, Baltimore, MD, Zip 21218–2895; tel. 410/554–2000; Bradley Chambers, President

Owned, leased, sponsored:	10 hospitals	2691 beds
Contract-managed:	0 hospitals	0 beds
Totals:	10 hospitals	2691 beds

★0086: MEMORIAL HEALTH SYSTEM (NP)

701 North First Street, Springfield, IL, Zip 62781–0001; tel. 217/788–3000; Edgar J. Curtis, FACHE, President and Chief Executive Officer

(Centralized Health System)

ILLINOIS: ABRAHAM LINCOLN MEMORIAL HOSPITAL (O, 25 beds) 200 Stahlhut Drive, Lincoln, IL, Zip 62656–5066; tel. 217/732–2161; Dolan Dalpoas, President and Chief Executive Officer

Web address: www.almh.org

MEMORIAL MEDICAL CENTER (O, 451 beds) 701 North First Street, Springfield, IL, Zip 62781–0001; tel. 217/788–3000; Edgar J. Curtis, FACHE, President and Chief Executive Officer

Web address: www.memorialmedical.com

PASSAVANT AREA HOSPITAL (O, 118 beds) 1600 West Walnut Street, Jacksonville, IL, Zip 62650–1136; tel. 217/245–9541; Harry M. Schmidt, President and Chief Executive Officer

TAYLORVILLE MEMORIAL HOSPITAL (O, 25 beds) 201 East Pleasant Street, Taylorville, IL, Zip 62568–1597; tel. 217/824–3331; Kimberly L. Bourne, Chief Executive Officer

Web address: www.taylorvillememorial.org

Owned, leased, sponsored:	4 hospitals	619 beds
Contract-managed:	0 hospitals	0 beds
Totals:	4 hospitals	619 beds

0998: MEMORIAL HEALTH SYSTEM (NP)

401 Matthew Street, Marietta, OH, Zip 45750–1635; tel. 740/374–1400; J Scott. Cantley, President and Chief Executive Officer

(Independent Hospital System)

OHIO: MARIETTA MEMORIAL HOSPITAL (O, 152 beds) 401 Matthew Street, Marietta, OH, Zip 45750–1699; tel. 740/374–1400; J Scott. Cantley, President and Chief Executive Officer

Web address: www.mhsystem.org

For explanation of codes following names, see page B2.
★ Indicates Type III membership in the American Hospital Association.

SELBY GENERAL HOSPITAL (O, 35 beds) 1106 Colegate Drive, Marietta, OH, Zip 45750–1323; tel. 740/568–2000; Stephen Smith, President
Web address: www.selbygeneral.org

Owned, leased, sponsored:	2 hospitals	187 beds
Contract-managed:	0 hospitals	0 beds
Totals:	2 hospitals	187 beds

★**0083: MEMORIAL HEALTHCARE SYSTEM** (NP)
3501 Johnson Street, Hollywood, FL, Zip 33021–5421; tel. 954/987–2000; Aurelio Fernandez, Chief Executive Officer
(Centralized Health System)

FLORIDA: MEMORIAL HOSPITAL MIRAMAR (O, 178 beds) 1901 SW 172nd Avenue, Miramar, FL, Zip 33029–5592; tel. 954/538–5000; Grisel Fernandez-Bravo, R.N., Administrator and Chief Executive Officer

MEMORIAL HOSPITAL PEMBROKE (L, 186 beds) 7800 Sheridan Street, Pembroke Pines, FL, Zip 33024–2536; tel. 954/883–8482; Mark Doyle, Administrator and Chief Executive Officer
Web address: www.memorialpembroke.com/

MEMORIAL HOSPITAL WEST (O, 382 beds) 703 North Flamingo Road, Pembroke Pines, FL, Zip 33028–1014; tel. 954/436–5000; Leah A. Carpenter, Administrator and Chief Executive Officer

MEMORIAL REGIONAL HOSPITAL (O, 1013 beds) 3501 Johnson Street, Hollywood, FL, Zip 33021–5421; tel. 954/987–2000; Zeff Ross, FACHE, Executive Vice President and Chief Executive Officer
Web address: www.mhs.net

Owned, leased, sponsored:	4 hospitals	1759 beds
Contract-managed:	0 hospitals	0 beds
Totals:	4 hospitals	1759 beds

★**2645: MEMORIAL HERMANN HEALTH SYSTEM** (NP)
929 Gessner, Suite 2700, Houston, TX, Zip 77024–2593; tel. 713/338–5555; David L. Callender, M.D., President and Chief Executive Officer
(Centralized Health System)

TEXAS: MEMORIAL HERMANN – TEXAS MEDICAL CENTER (O, 1075 beds) 6411 Fannin Street, Houston, TX, Zip 77030–1501; tel. 713/704–4000; Gregory Haralson, FACHE, Senior Vice President and Chief Executive Officer

MEMORIAL HERMANN GREATER HEIGHTS HOSPITAL (O, 1380 beds) 1635 North Loop West, Houston, TX, Zip 77008–1532; tel. 713/867–3380; Paul O'Sullivan, FACHE, Chief Executive Officer
Web address: www.memorialhermann.org

MEMORIAL HERMANN KATY HOSPITAL (O, 199 beds) 23900 Katy Freeway, Katy, TX, Zip 77494–1323; tel. 281/644–7000; Heath Rushing, Senior Vice President and Chief Executive Officer
Web address: www.memorialhermann.org/locations/katy/

MEMORIAL HERMANN MEMORIAL CITY MEDICAL CENTER (L, 421 beds) 1760 Barker Cypress Rd, Apt 1412, Houston, TX, Zip 77084, Mailing Address: 921 Gessner Road, Zip 77024–2501, tel. 713/242–3000; Paul O'Sullivan, FACHE, Chief Executive Officer

MEMORIAL HERMANN NORTHEAST (O, 217 beds) 18951 North Memorial Drive, Humble, TX, Zip 77338–4297; tel. 281/540–7700; Josh Urban, Chief Executive Officer
Web address: www.memorialhermann.org/locations/northeast/

MEMORIAL HERMANN REHABILITATION HOSPITAL – KATY (O, 35 beds) 21720 Kingsland Boulevard, 2nd Floor, Katy, TX, Zip 77450–2550; tel. 800/447–3422; Jerry Ashworth, Senior Vice President and Chief Executive Officer
Web address: www.memorialhermann.org/locations/katy-rehab/

MEMORIAL HERMANN SUGAR LAND HOSPITAL (O, 149 beds) 17500 West Grand Parkway South, Sugar Land, TX, Zip 77479–2562; tel. 281/725–5000; Malisha Patel, Senior Vice President and Chief Executive Officer

MEMORIAL HERMANN TOMBALL HOSPITAL (O, 15 beds) 24429 State Highway 249, Tomball, TX, Zip 77375–8214; tel. 281/516–0911; Brenda Villafranco, Administrator
Web address: www.emerus.com/tomball/

TIRR MEMORIAL HERMANN (O, 134 beds) 1333 Moursund Street, Houston, TX, Zip 77030–3405; tel. 713/799–5000; Jerry Ashworth, Senior Vice President and Chief Executive Officer
Web address: www.memorialhermann.org/locations/tirr.html

Owned, leased, sponsored:	9 hospitals	3625 beds
Contract-managed:	0 hospitals	0 beds
Totals:	9 hospitals	3625 beds

0084: MEMORIALCARE (NP)
17360 Brookhurst Street, Fountain Valley, CA, Zip 92708–3720, Mailing Address: P.O. Box 1428, Long Beach, Zip 90801–1428, tel. 714/377–2900; Barry S. Arbuckle, Ph.D., President and Chief Executive Officer
(Centralized Health System)

CALIFORNIA: MEMORIALCARE, LONG BEACH MEMORIAL MEDICAL CENTER (O, 458 beds) 2801 Atlantic Avenue, Long Beach, CA, Zip 90806–1701, Mailing Address: P.O. Box 1428, Zip 90801–1428, tel. 562/933–2000; John Bishop, Chief Executive Officer

MEMORIALCARE, MILLER CHILDREN'S & WOMEN'S HOSPITAL LONG BEACH (O, 371 beds) 2801 Atlantic Avenue, Long Beach, CA, Zip 90806–1701; tel. 562/933–5437; John Bishop, Chief Executive Officer
Web address: www.memorialcare.org

MEMORIALCARE, ORANGE COAST MEMORIAL MEDICAL CENTER (O, 218 beds) 9920 Talbert Avenue, Fountain Valley, CA, Zip 92708–5115; tel. 714/378–7000; Marcia Manker, Chief Executive Officer
Web address: www.memorialcare.org

MEMORIALCARE, SADDLEBACK MEMORIAL MEDICAL CENTER (O, 250 beds) 24451 Health Center Drive, Laguna Hills, CA, Zip 92653–3689; tel. 949/837–4500; Marcia Manker, Chief Executive Officer

Owned, leased, sponsored:	4 hospitals	1297 beds
Contract-managed:	0 hospitals	0 beds
Totals:	4 hospitals	1297 beds

★**5185: MERCY** (CC)
14528 South Outer 40, Suite 100, Chesterfield, MO, Zip 63017–5743; tel. 314/579–6100; Lynn Britton, President and Chief Executive Officer
(Decentralized Health System)

ARKANSAS: MERCY HOSPITAL BERRYVILLE (O, 25 beds) 214 Carter Street, Berryville, AR, Zip 72616–4303; tel. 870/423–3355; VonDa Moore, Administrator
Web address: https://www.mercy.net/newsroom/mercy-hospital-berryville-quick-facts/

MERCY HOSPITAL BOONEVILLE (O, 25 beds) 880 West Main Street, Booneville, AR, Zip 72927–3443; tel. 479/675–2800; Teresa Williams, R.N., Regional Administrator

MERCY HOSPITAL FORT SMITH (O, 352 beds) 7301 Rogers Avenue, Fort Smith, AR, Zip 72903–4189, Mailing Address: P.O. Box 17000, Zip 72917–7000, tel. 479/314–6000; Ryan Gehrig, President
Web address: www.mercy.net/fortsmithar

MERCY HOSPITAL OZARK (O, 25 beds) 801 West River Street, Ozark, AR, Zip 72949–3023; tel. 479/667–4138; Teresa Williams, R.N., Regional Administrator
Web address: https://www.mercy.net/practice/mercy-hospital-ozark/

MERCY HOSPITAL PARIS (O, 16 beds) 500 East Academy, Paris, AR, Zip 72855–4040; tel. 479/963–6101; Teresa Williams, R.N., Regional Administrator

MERCY HOSPITAL ROGERS (O, 194 beds) 2710 Rife Medical Lane, Rogers, AR, Zip 72758–1452; tel. 479/338–8000; Eric Pianalto, Chief Executive Officer
Web address: https://www.mercy.net/practice/mercy-hospital-northwest-arkansas/

MERCY HOSPITAL WALDRON (O, 24 beds) 1341 West 6th Street, Waldron, AR, Zip 72958–7642; tel. 479/637–4135; Teresa Williams, R.N., Regional Administrator
Web address: https://www.mercy.net/practice/mercy-hospital-waldron/

Section B

For explanation of codes following names, see page B2.
★ Indicates Type III membership in the American Hospital Association.

KANSAS: MERCY HOSPITAL COLUMBUS (O, 18 beds) 220 North Pennsylvania Avenue, Columbus, KS, Zip 66725–1110; tel. 620/429–2545; Angie Saporito, Administrator

MISSOURI: MERCY HOSPITAL AURORA (L, 25 beds) 500 Porter Street, Aurora, MO, Zip 65605–2365; tel. 417/678–2122; Nicki Gamet, R.N., Administrator
Web address: www.stjohns.com/aboutus/aurora.aspx

MERCY HOSPITAL CARTHAGE (L, 25 beds) 3125 Dr Russell Smith Way, Carthage, MO, Zip 64836–7402; tel. 417/358–8121; Scott Watson, Administrator
Web address: www.mercy.net

MERCY HOSPITAL CASSVILLE (L, 18 beds) 94 Main Street, Cassville, MO, Zip 65625–1610; tel. 417/847–6000; Nicki Gamet, R.N., Administrator
Web address: www.mercy.net/northwestarar/practice/mercy-hospital-cassville

MERCY HOSPITAL JEFFERSON (O, 204 beds) 1400 US Highway 61 South, Festus, MO, Zip 63028–4100, Mailing Address: P.O. Box 350, Crystal City, Zip 63019–0350, tel. 636/933–1000; Eric Ammons, President

MERCY HOSPITAL JOPLIN (O, 236 beds) 100 Mercy Way, Joplin, MO, Zip 64804–1626; tel. 417/781–2727; Jeremy Drinkwitz, President and Chief Executive Officer
Web address: www.mercy.net/joplinmo

MERCY HOSPITAL LEBANON (O, 58 beds) 100 Hospital Drive, Lebanon, MO, Zip 65536–9210; tel. 417/533–6100; Scott W. Childers, FACHE, Administrator
Web address: www.mercy.net/practice/mercy-hospital-lebanon

MERCY HOSPITAL LINCOLN (L, 25 beds) 1000 East Cherry Street, Troy, MO, Zip 63379–1513; tel. 636/528–8551; Anthony Rothermich, Administrator
Web address: www.mercy.net

MERCY HOSPITAL SOUTH (O, 523 beds) 10010 Kennerly Road, Saint Louis, MO, Zip 63128–2106; tel. 314/525–1000; Sean Hogan, FACHE, President

MERCY HOSPITAL SPRINGFIELD (O, 660 beds) 1235 East Cherokee Street, Springfield, MO, Zip 65804–2263; tel. 417/820–2000; Brent Hubbard, FACHE, President and Chief Operating Officer
Web address: www.mercy.net/springfieldmo

MERCY HOSPITAL ST. LOUIS (O, 859 beds) 615 South New Ballas Road, Saint Louis, MO, Zip 63141–8277; tel. 314/251–6000; Stephen Mackin, President

MERCY HOSPITAL WASHINGTON (O, 148 beds) 901 East Fifth Street, Washington, MO, Zip 63090–3127; tel. 636/239–8000; Eric J. Eoloff, President
Web address: www.mercy.net

MERCY ST. FRANCIS HOSPITAL (O, 20 beds) 100 West Highway 60, Mountain View, MO, Zip 65548–7125; tel. 417/934–7000; Cynthia Weatherford, R.N., Administrator and Director of Nursing

OKLAHOMA: MERCY HEALTH LOVE COUNTY (C, 25 beds) 300 Wanda Street, Marietta, OK, Zip 73448–1200; tel. 580/276–3347; Richard Barker, Administrator and Chief Executive Officer
Web address: www.mercyhealthlovecounty.com

MERCY HOSPITAL ADA (L, 156 beds) 430 North Monte Vista, Ada, OK, Zip 74820–4610; tel. 580/332–2323; Terence Farrell, President

MERCY HOSPITAL ARDMORE (O, 190 beds) 1011 14th Avenue NW, Ardmore, OK, Zip 73401–1828; tel. 580/223–5400; Daryle Voss, FACHE, President and Chief Executive Officer
Web address: www.mercyok.net

MERCY HOSPITAL HEALDTON (L, 22 beds) 3462 Hospital Road, Healdton, OK, Zip 73438–6124, Mailing Address: P.O. Box 928, Zip 73438–0928, tel. 580/229–0701; Nichole Barrett, R.N., Interim Administrator
Web address: www.mercyok.com

MERCY HOSPITAL KINGFISHER (L, 25 beds) 1000 Hospital Cirle, Kingfisher, OK, Zip 73750–5002, Mailing Address: P.O. Box 59, Zip 73750–0059, tel. 405/375–3141; Brian Denton, Administrator
Web address: https://www.mercy.net/practice/mercy-hospital-kingfisher/

MERCY HOSPITAL LOGAN COUNTY (O, 25 beds) 200 South Academy Road, Guthrie, OK, Zip 73044–8727, Mailing Address: P.O. Box 1017, Zip 73044–1017, tel. 405/282–6700; Bobby Stitt, R.N., Administrator

MERCY HOSPITAL OKLAHOMA CITY (O, 349 beds) 4300 West Memorial Road, Oklahoma City, OK, Zip 73120–8362; tel. 405/755–1515; Jim Gebhart Jr, FACHE, President
Web address: www.mercyok.net

MERCY HOSPITAL TISHOMINGO (L, 12 beds) 1000 South Byrd Street, Tishomingo, OK, Zip 73460–3299; tel. 580/371–2327; Lori McMillin, Administrator
Web address: www.mercy.net/

MERCY HOSPITAL WATONGA (L, 25 beds) 500 North Clarence Nash Boulevard, Watonga, OK, Zip 73772–2845, Mailing Address: P.O. Box 370, Zip 73772–0370, tel. 580/623–7211; Bobby Stitt, R.N., Administrator
Web address: www.mercy.net/watongaok/practice/mercy-hospital-watonga

Owned, leased, sponsored:	28 hospitals	4284 beds
Contract-managed:	1 hospitals	25 beds
Totals:	29 hospitals	4309 beds

5155: MERCY HEALTH (CC)

1701 Mercy Health Place, Cincinnati, OH, Zip 45237; tel. 513/639–2800; John M. Starcher, President and Chief Executive Officer
(Moderately Centralized Health System)

KENTUCKY: LOURDES HOSPITAL (O, 281 beds) 1530 Lone Oak Road, Paducah, KY, Zip 42003–7900, Mailing Address: P.O. Box 7100, Zip 42002–7100, tel. 270/444–2444; Michael Yungmann, President and Chief Executive Officer
Web address: www.lourdes-pad.org

MERCY HEALTH – MARCUM AND WALLACE (O, 25 beds) 60 Mercy Court, Irvine, KY, Zip 40336–1331; tel. 606/723–2115; Susan Starling, President and Chief Executive Officer

OHIO: INSTITUTE FOR ORTHOPAEDIC SURGERY (O, 3 beds) 801 Medical Drive, Suite B, Lima, OH, Zip 45804–4030; tel. 419/224–7586; Mark McDonald, M.D., President and Chief Executive Officer
Web address: www.ioshospital.com

MERCY ALLEN HOSPITAL (O, 25 beds) 200 West Lorain Street, Oberlin, OH, Zip 44074–1077; tel. 440/775–1211; Ed Ruth, President
Web address: www.mercyonline.org/mercy_allen_hospital.aspx

MERCY HEALTH – ST. CHARLES HOSPITAL (O, 279 beds) 2600 Navarre Avenue, Oregon, OH, Zip 43616–3297; tel. 419/696–7200; Craig Albers, President and Chief Operating Officer
Web address: www.mercyweb.org

MERCY HEALTH – ANDERSON HOSPITAL (O, 281 beds) 7500 State Road, Cincinnati, OH, Zip 45255–2492; tel. 513/624–4500; Ken James, President and Chief Executive Officer of East Market

MERCY HEALTH – CLERMONT HOSPITAL (O, 147 beds) 3000 Hospital Drive, Batavia, OH, Zip 45103–1921; tel. 513/732–8200; Justin Krueger, FACHE, President
Web address: www.e-mercy.com

MERCY HEALTH – FAIRFIELD HOSPITAL (O, 236 beds) 3000 Mack Road, Fairfield, OH, Zip 45014–5335; tel. 513/870–7000; Thomas S. Urban, FACHE, President and Chief Executive Officer
Web address: www.e-mercy.com

MERCY HEALTH – ST. ELIZABETH BOARDMAN HOSPITAL (O, 217 beds) 8401 Market Street, Boardman, OH, Zip 44512–6777; tel. 330/729–2929; Eugenia Aubel, President, St. Elizabeth Boardman Hospital

MERCY HEALTH – ST. ELIZABETH YOUNGSTOWN HOSPITAL (O, 387 beds) 1044 Belmont Avenue, Youngstown, OH, Zip 44504–1096, Mailing Address: P.O. Box 1790, Zip 44501–1790, tel. 330/746–7211; Donald E. Kline, President and Chief Executive Officer
Web address: www.mercy.com

MERCY HEALTH – ST. JOSEPH WARREN HOSPITAL (O, 140 beds) 667 Eastland Avenue SE, Warren, OH, Zip 44484–4531, Mailing Address: 627 Eastland Avenue, Zip 44484–4531, tel. 330/841–4000; Kathy Cook, FACHE, MSN, President

MERCY HEALTH – ST. RITA'S MEDICAL CENTER (O, 271 beds) 730 West Market Street, Lima, OH, Zip 45801–4602; tel. 419/227–3361; Dale Gisi, President
Web address: www.stritas.org

MERCY HEALTH – WEST HOSPITAL (O, 250 beds) 3300 Mercy Health Boulevard, Cincinnati, OH, Zip 45211–1103; tel. 513/215–5000; Michael Kramer, Chief Executive Officer

For explanation of codes following names, see page B2.
★ Indicates Type III membership in the American Hospital Association.

MERCY HEALTH – WILLARD HOSPITAL (O, 20 beds) 1100 Neal Zick Road, Willard, OH, Zip 44890–9287; tel. 419/964–5000; B Lynn. Detterman, President and Chief Executive Officer
Web address: www.mercyweb.org

MERCY HOSPITAL OF DEFIANCE (O, 23 beds) 1404 East Second Street, Defiance, OH, Zip 43512–2440; tel. 419/782–8444; B Lynn. Detterman, President and Chief Executive Officer

MERCY MEMORIAL HOSPITAL (O, 25 beds) 904 Scioto Street, Urbana, OH, Zip 43078–2200; tel. 937/653–5231; Matthew T. Caldwell, President and Chief Executive Officer
Web address: www.health-partners.org

MERCY REGIONAL MEDICAL CENTER (O, 251 beds) 3700 Kolbe Road, Lorain, OH, Zip 44053–1697; tel. 440/960–4000; Edwin M. Oley, President and Chief Executive Officer

MERCY ST. ANNE HOSPITAL (O, 96 beds) 3404 West Sylvania Avenue, Toledo, OH, Zip 43623–4467; tel. 419/407–2663; Bradley J. Bertke, President and Chief Operating Officer
Web address: www.mercyweb.org

MERCY ST. VINCENT MEDICAL CENTER (O, 370 beds) 2213 Cherry Street, Toledo, OH, Zip 43608–2691; tel. 419/251–3232; Jeffrey Dempsey, President
Web address: www.mercyweb.org

MERCY TIFFIN HOSPITAL (O, 46 beds) 45 St Lawrence Drive, Tiffin, OH, Zip 44883–8310; tel. 419/455–7000; B Lynn. Detterman, President and Chief Executive Officer

SPRINGFIELD REGIONAL MEDICAL CENTER (O, 259 beds) 100 Medical Center Drive, Springfield, OH, Zip 45504–2687; tel. 937/523–1000; Adam Groshans, President
Web address: www.community-mercy.org

THE JEWISH HOSPITAL – MERCY HEALTH (O, 209 beds) 4777 East Galbraith Road, Cincinnati, OH, Zip 45236–2725; tel. 513/686–3000; Patricia Davis-Hagens, R.N., Central Market Leader and President
Web address: www.jewishhospitalcincinnati.com/

Owned, leased, sponsored:	22 hospitals	3841 beds
Contract-managed:	0 hospitals	0 beds
Totals:	22 hospitals	3841 beds

0649: MERCY HEALTH SYSTEM (NP)

1000 Mineral Point Avenue, Janesville, WI, Zip 53548–2940, Mailing Address: P.O. Box 5003, Zip 53547–5003, tel. 608/756–6000; Javon R Bea, President and Chief Executive Officer
(Centralized Physician/Insurance Health System)

ILLINOIS: JAVON BEA HOSPITAL-ROCKTON (O, 288 beds) 2400 North Rockton Avenue, Rockford, IL, Zip 61103–3655; tel. 815/971–5000; Javon R. Bea, President and Chief Executive Officer
Web address: www.rhsnet.org

MERCYHEALTH HOSPITAL AND MEDICAL CENTER – HARVARD (O, 50 beds) 901 Grant Street, Harvard, IL, Zip 60033–1898, Mailing Address: P.O. Box 850, Zip 60033–0850, tel. 815/943–5431; Javon R. Bea, Chief Executive Officer

WISCONSIN: MERCYHEALTH HOSPITAL AND MEDICAL CENTER – WALWORTH (O, 17 beds) N2950 State Road 67, Lake Geneva, WI, Zip 53147–2655; tel. 262/245–0535; Javon R. Bea, President and Chief Executive Officer
Web address: www.mercyhealthsystem.org

MERCYHEALTH HOSPITAL AND TRAUMA CENTER – JANESVILLE (O, 135 beds) 1000 Mineral Point Avenue, Janesville, WI, Zip 53548–2982, Mailing Address: P.O. Box 5003, Zip 53547–5003, tel. 608/756–6000; Javon R. Bea, President and Chief Executive Officer

Owned, leased, sponsored:	4 hospitals	490 beds
Contract-managed:	0 hospitals	0 beds
Totals:	4 hospitals	490 beds

0944: MERCYONE (NP)

1449 NW 128th Street, Clive, IA, Zip 50325–7400; tel. 515/358–9200; Robert P. Ritz, Chief Executive Officer

IOWA: ADAIR COUNTY HEALTH SYSTEM (C, 17 beds) 609 SE Kent Street, Greenfield, IA, Zip 50849–9454; tel. 641/743–2123; Marcia Hendricks, FACHE, R.N., Chief Executive Officer

DALLAS COUNTY HOSPITAL (C, 15 beds) 610 10th Street, Perry, IA, Zip 50220–2221; tel. 515/465–3547; Angela Mortoza, Chief Executive Officer
Web address: www.dallascohospital.org

DAVIS COUNTY HOSPITAL (C, 13 beds) 509 North Madison Street, Bloomfield, IA, Zip 52537–1271; tel. 641/664–2145; Veronica Fuhs, Chief Executive Officer

DECATUR COUNTY HOSPITAL (C, 11 beds) 1405 NW Church Street, Leon, IA, Zip 50144–1299; tel. 641/446–4871; Mike Johnston, Chief Executive Officer
Web address: www.decaturcountyhospital.org

GUTTENBERG MUNICIPAL HOSPITAL (C, 20 beds) 200 Main Street, Guttenberg, IA, Zip 52052–9108, Mailing Address: P.O. Box 550, Zip 52052–0550, tel. 563/252–1121; Tim Ahlers, Chief Executive Officer

MANNING REGIONAL HEALTHCARE CENTER (C, 79 beds) 1550 6th Street, Manning, IA, Zip 51455–1093; tel. 712/655–2072; John O'Brien, Chief Executive Officer
Web address: www.mrhcia.com

MERCYONE IOWA CITY MEDICAL CENTER (C, 223 beds) 500 East Market Street, Iowa City, IA, Zip 52245–2689; tel. 319/339–0300; Sean J. Williams, President and Chief Executive Officer

MONROE COUNTY HOSPITAL AND CLINICS (C, 25 beds) 6580 165th Street, Albia, IA, Zip 52531–8793; tel. 641/932–2134; Veronica Fuhs, Chief Executive Officer
Web address: www.mchalbia.com

RINGGOLD COUNTY HOSPITAL (C, 16 beds) 504 North Cleveland Street, Mount Ayr, IA, Zip 50854–2201; tel. 641/464–3226; Gordon W. Winkler, Administrator and Chief Executive Officer
Web address: www.rchmtayr.org

VAN DIEST MEDICAL CENTER (C, 25 beds) 2350 Hospital Drive, Webster City, IA, Zip 50595–6600, Mailing Address: P.O. Box 430, Zip 50595–0430, tel. 515/832–9400; Lisa Ridge, Chief Executive Officer
Web address: www.vandiestmc.org

WAYNE COUNTY HOSPITAL (C, 25 beds) 417 South East Street, Corydon, IA, Zip 50060–1860, Mailing Address: P.O. Box 305, Zip 50060–0305, tel. 641/872–2260; Daren Relph, Chief Executive Officer

Owned, leased, sponsored:	0 hospitals	0 beds
Contract-managed:	11 hospitals	469 beds
Totals:	11 hospitals	469 beds

★2735: METHODIST HEALTH SYSTEM (NP)

1441 North Beckley Avenue, Dallas, TX, Zip 75203–1201, Mailing Address: P.O. Box 655999, Zip 75265–5999, tel. 214/947–8181; James C. Scoggin Jr, Chief Executive Officer
(Centralized Physician/Insurance Health System)

TEXAS: METHODIST CHARLTON MEDICAL CENTER (O, 292 beds) 3500 West Wheatland Road, Dallas, TX, Zip 75237–3460, Mailing Address: P.O. Box 225357, Zip 75222–5357, tel. 214/947–7777; Fran Laukaitis, R.N., FACHE, President
Web address: www.methodisthealthsystem.org/charlton

METHODIST DALLAS MEDICAL CENTER (O, 390 beds) 1441 North Beckley Avenue, Dallas, TX, Zip 75203–1201, Mailing Address: P.O. Box 655999, Zip 75265–5999, tel. 214/947–8181; John E. Phillips, FACHE, President

METHODIST MANSFIELD MEDICAL CENTER (O, 254 beds) 2700 East Broad Street, Mansfield, TX, Zip 76063–5899; tel. 682/622–2000; Juan Fresquez, President
Web address: www.methodisthealthsystem.org/mansfield

METHODIST RICHARDSON MEDICAL CENTER (O, 226 beds) 2831 East President George Bush Highway, Richardson, TX, Zip 75082–3561; tel. 469/204–1000; E. Kenneth. Hutchenrider Jr, FACHE, President

METHODIST SOUTHLAKE HOSPITAL (O, 12 beds) 421 East State Highway 114, Southlake, TX, Zip 76092; tel. 817/865–4400; John McGreevy, FACHE, President
Web address: www.https://methodistsouthlake.com/

Owned, leased, sponsored:	5 hospitals	1174 beds
Contract-managed:	0 hospitals	0 beds
Totals:	5 hospitals	1174 beds

For explanation of codes following names, see page B2.
★ Indicates Type III membership in the American Hospital Association.

Section B

★9345: METHODIST LE BONHEUR HEALTHCARE (CO)
1211 Union Avenue, Suite 700, Memphis, TN, Zip 38104–6600;
tel. 901/516–0791; Michael Ugwueke, President and Chief
Executive Officer
(Centralized Physician/Insurance Health System)

MISSISSIPPI: METHODIST HEALTHCARE OLIVE BRANCH HOSPITAL (O,
53 beds) 4250 Bethel Road, Olive Branch, MS, Zip 38654–8737;
tel. 662/932–9000; David G. Baytos, President
Web address: www.methodisthealth.org/olivebranch

TENNESSEE: METHODIST HEALTHCARE-MEMPHIS HOSPITALS (O, 1362 beds)
1265 Union Avenue, Memphis, TN, Zip 38104–3415; tel. 901/516–7000;
Michael Ugwueke, President and Chief Executive Officer

Owned, leased, sponsored:	2 hospitals	1415 beds
Contract-managed:	0 hospitals	0 beds
Totals:	2 hospitals	1415 beds

★0001: MIDMICHIGAN HEALTH (NP)
4000 Wellness Drive, Midland, MI, Zip 48670–0001;
tel. 989/839–3000; Diane Postler-Slattery, Ph.D., President and
Chief Executive Officer
(Centralized Physician/Insurance Health System)

MICHIGAN: MIDMICHIGAN MEDICAL CENTER – ALPENA (O, 125 beds) 1501
West Chisholm Street, Alpena, MI, Zip 49707–1401; tel. 989/356–7000;
Charles H. Sherwin, President
Web address: www.alpenaregionalmedicalcenter.org

MIDMICHIGAN MEDICAL CENTER – WEST BRANCH (O, 88 beds) 2463 South
M-30, West Branch, MI, Zip 48661–1199; tel. 989/345–3660; Robert
McGrail, Chief Executive Officer
Web address: www.wbrmc.com

MIDMICHIGAN MEDICAL CENTER-CLARE (O, 49 beds) 703 North McEwan
Street, Clare, MI, Zip 48617–1440; tel. 989/802–5000; Raymond Stover,
President and Chief Executive Officer

MIDMICHIGAN MEDICAL CENTER-GLADWIN (O, 25 beds) 515 Quarter Street,
Gladwin, MI, Zip 48624–1959; tel. 989/426–9286; Raymond Stover,
President and Chief Executive Officer
Web address: www.midmichigan.org

MIDMICHIGAN MEDICAL CENTER-GRATIOT (O, 96 beds) 300 East Warwick
Drive, Alma, MI, Zip 48801–1014; tel. 989/463–1101; Marita Hattem-
Schiffman, President

MIDMICHIGAN MEDICAL CENTER-MIDLAND (O, 270 beds) 4000 Wellness Drive,
Midland, MI, Zip 48670–2000; tel. 989/839–3000; Gregory H. Rogers, President
Web address: www.midmichigan.org

Owned, leased, sponsored:	6 hospitals	653 beds
Contract-managed:	0 hospitals	0 beds
Totals:	6 hospitals	653 beds

0368: MINNESOTA DEPARTMENT OF HUMAN SERVICES (NP)
540 Cedar Street, Saint Paul, MN, Zip 55101–2208, Mailing
Address: P.O. Box 64998, Zip 55164–0998, tel. 651/431–3212;
Anne Barry, Deputy Commissioner
(Independent Hospital System)

MINNESOTA: ANOKA-METROPOLITAN REGIONAL TREATMENT CENTER (O,
200 beds) 3301 Seventh Avenue, Anoka, MN, Zip 55303–4516, Mailing
Address: 3301 Seventh Avenue North, Zip 55303–4516, tel. 651/431–
5000; Wade Brost, Executive Director
Web address: www.health.state.mn.us

COMMUNITY BEHAVIORAL HEALTH HOSPITAL – ALEXANDRIA (O, 16 beds)
1610 8th Avenue East, Alexandria, MN, Zip 56308–2472; tel. 320/335–
6201; Jennifer Westrum, Administrator

COMMUNITY BEHAVIORAL HEALTH HOSPITAL – ANNANDALE (O, 16 beds) 400
Annandale Boulevard, Annandale, MN, Zip 55302–3141; tel. 651/259–3850;
James P. Kelly, FACHE, Administrator
Web address: www.health.state.mn.us

COMMUNITY BEHAVIORAL HEALTH HOSPITAL – BAXTER (O, 16 beds) 14241
Grand Oaks Drive, Baxter, MN, Zip 56425–8749; tel. 218/316–3101; James
Coughenour, Administrator
Web address: www.business.explorebrainerdlakes.com/list/member/
community-behavioral-health-hospital-baxter-8647

COMMUNITY BEHAVIORAL HEALTH HOSPITAL – BEMIDJI (O, 16 beds) 800
Bemidji Avenue North, Bemidji, MN, Zip 56601–3054; tel. 218/308–2400;
Larry A. Laudon, Administrator

COMMUNITY BEHAVIORAL HEALTH HOSPITAL – FERGUS FALLS (O, 16 beds)
1801 West Alcott Avenue, Fergus Falls, MN, Zip 56537–2661, Mailing
Address: P.O. Box 478, Zip 56538–0478, tel. 218/332–5001; Brenda
Schleske, Administrator

COMMUNITY BEHAVIORAL HEALTH HOSPITAL – ROCHESTER (O, 8 beds) 251
Wood Lake Drive SE, Rochester, MN, Zip 55904–5530; tel. 507/206–2561;
James Pierce, Administrator
Web address: www.health.state.mn.us

Owned, leased, sponsored:	7 hospitals	288 beds
Contract-managed:	0 hospitals	0 beds
Totals:	7 hospitals	288 beds

★2475: MISSISSIPPI COUNTY HOSPITAL SYSTEM (NP)
1520 North Division Street, Blytheville, AR, Zip 72315–1448,
Mailing Address: P.O. Box 108, Zip 72316–0108, tel. 870/838–
7300; Chris Lee. Raymer, MSN, Chief Executive Officer

Owned, leased, sponsored:	0 hospitals	0 beds
Contract-managed:	0 hospitals	0 beds
Totals:	0 hospitals	0 beds

0017: MISSISSIPPI STATE DEPARTMENT OF MENTAL HEALTH (NP)
1101 Robert E Lee Building, 239 North Lamar Street, Jackson,
MS, Zip 39201–1101; tel. 601/359–1288; Edwin C. LeGrand III,
Executive Director
(Independent Hospital System)

MISSISSIPPI: EAST MISSISSIPPI STATE HOSPITAL (O, 266 beds) 1818 College
Drive, Meridian, MS, Zip 39307, Mailing Address: Box 4128, West Station,
Zip 39304–4128, tel. 601/482–6186; Charles Carlisle, Director
Web address: www.emsh.state.ms.us

MISSISSIPPI STATE HOSPITAL (O, 316 beds) 3550 Highway 468 West,
Whitfield, MS, Zip 39193–5529, Mailing Address: P.O. Box 157-A, Zip 39193–
0157, tel. 601/351–8000; James G. Chastain, FACHE, Director

NORTH MISSISSIPPI STATE HOSPITAL (O, 50 beds) 1937 Briar Ridge Road,
Tupelo, MS, Zip 38804–5963; tel. 662/690–4200; Paul A. Callens, Ph.D.,
Director
Web address: www.nmsh.state.ms.us

SOUTH MISSISSIPPI STATE HOSPITAL (O, 50 beds) 823 Highway 589, Purvis,
MS, Zip 39475–4194; tel. 601/794–0100; Sabrina Young, Director
Web address: www.smsh.ms.gov/

Owned, leased, sponsored:	4 hospitals	682 beds
Contract-managed:	0 hospitals	0 beds
Totals:	4 hospitals	682 beds

★0970: MON HEALTH SYSTEM (NP)
1200 J. D. Anderson Drive, Morgantown, WV, Zip 26505–3494;
tel. 304/598–1200; David Goldberg, President and Chief Executive
(Independent Hospital System)

WEST VIRGINIA: MON HEALTH MEDICAL CENTER (O, 185 beds) 1200 J D
Anderson Drive, Morgantown, WV, Zip 26505–3486; tel. 304/598–1200;
David Goldberg, President and Chief Executive Officer
Web address: www.mongeneral.com

PRESTON MEMORIAL HOSPITAL (O, 25 beds) 150 Memorial Drive, Kingwood,
WV, Zip 26537–1495; tel. 304/329–1400; Melissa Lockwood, Chief
Executive Officer

For explanation of codes following names, see page B2.
★ Indicates Type III membership in the American Hospital Association.

Section B

STONEWALL JACKSON MEMORIAL HOSPITAL (O, 70 beds) 230 Hospital Plaza, Weston, WV, Zip 26452–8558; tel. 304/269–8000; Avah Stalnaker, Chief Executive Officer
Web address: www.stonewallhospital.com

Owned, leased, sponsored:	3 hospitals	280 beds
Contract-managed:	0 hospitals	0 beds
Totals:	3 hospitals	280 beds

0343: MONTEFIORE HEALTH SYSTEM (NP)

111 East 210th Street, Bronx, NY, Zip 10467–2490; tel. 718/920–4321; Steven M. Safyer, M.D., President and Chief Executive Officer

(Centralized Physician/Insurance Health System)

NEW YORK: BURKE REHABILITATION HOSPITAL (O, 150 beds) 785 Mamaroneck Avenue, White Plains, NY, Zip 10605–2523; tel. 914/597–2500; Jeffrey Menkes, President and Chief Executive Officer

MONTEFIORE MEDICAL CENTER (O, 1553 beds) 111 East 210th Street, Bronx, NY, Zip 10467–2401; tel. 718/920–4321; Steven M. Safyer, M.D., President and Chief Executive Officer
Web address: www.montefiore.org

MONTEFIORE MOUNT VERNON (O, 62 beds) 12 North Seventh Avenue, Mount Vernon, NY, Zip 10550–2098; tel. 914/664–8000; Jaccel Kouns, R.N., MS, Vice President and Executive Director

MONTEFIORE NEW ROCHELLE (O, 301 beds) 16 Guion Place, New Rochelle, NY, Zip 10801–5502; tel. 914/632–5000; Anthony Alfano, Vice President Executive Director
Web address: www.montefiorehealthsystem.org

MONTEFIORE ST. LUKE'S CORNWALL (O, 128 beds) 70 Dubois Street, Newburgh, NY, Zip 12550–4851; tel. 845/561–4400; Joan Cusack-McGuirk, President and Chief Executive Officer

NYACK HOSPITAL (O, 235 beds) 160 North Midland Avenue, Nyack, NY, Zip 10960–1998; tel. 845/348–2000; Mark Geller, M.D., President and Chief Executive Officer
Web address: www.nyackhospital.org

WHITE PLAINS HOSPITAL CENTER (O, 246 beds) 41 East Post Road, White Plains, NY, Zip 10601–4699; tel. 914/681–0600; Susan Fox, President and Chief Executive Officer
Web address: www.wphospital.org

Owned, leased, sponsored:	7 hospitals	2675 beds
Contract-managed:	0 hospitals	0 beds
Totals:	7 hospitals	2675 beds

1335: MORTON PLANT MEASE HEALTH CARE (NP)

2985 Drew Street, Clearwater, FL, Zip 33759, Mailing Address: P.O. Box 210, Zip 33757–0210, tel. 727/462–7000; Glenn D. Waters, FACHE, President

FLORIDA: MORTON PLANT HOSPITAL (O, 710 beds) 300 Pinellas Street, Clearwater, FL, Zip 33756–3804, Mailing Address: P.O. Box 210, Zip 33757–0210, tel. 727/462–7000; Lou Galdieri, R.N., President

MORTON PLANT NORTH BAY HOSPITAL (O, 222 beds) 6600 Madison Street, New Port Richey, FL, Zip 34652–1900; tel. 727/842–8468; Sarah Naumowich, President
Web address: www.mpmhealth.com

MORTON PLANT REHABILITATION CENTER (O, 126 beds) 400 Corbett Street, Belleair, FL, Zip 34640; tel. 813/462–7600; Linda A. Kirk, Administrator

Owned, leased, sponsored:	3 hospitals	1058 beds
Contract-managed:	0 hospitals	0 beds
Totals:	3 hospitals	1058 beds

★0946: MOSAIC LIFE CARE (NP)

5325 Faraon Street, Saint Joseph, MO, Zip 64506–3488; tel. 816/271–6000; Samuel Mark. Laney, M.D., Chief Executive Officer

MISSOURI: LONG-TERM ACUTE CARE HOSPITAL, MOSAIC LIFE CARE AT ST. JOSEPH (O, 41 beds) 5325 Faraon Street, Saint Joseph, MO, Zip 64506–3488; tel. 816/271–6000; Dana Anderson, R.N., Administrator
Web address: https://www.mymosaiclifecare.org/General/Long-Term-Acute-Care-Hospital/

MOSAIC LIFE CARE AT ST. JOSEPH – MEDICAL CENTER (O, 352 beds) 5325 Faraon Street, Saint Joseph, MO, Zip 64506–3488; tel. 816/271–6000; Samuel Mark. Laney, M.D., Chief Executive Officer

MOSAIC MEDICAL CENTER – ALBANY (O, 25 beds) 705 North College Street, Albany, MO, Zip 64402–1433; tel. 660/726–3941; Jon D. Doolittle, Regional President
Web address: www.northwestmedicalcenter.org

MOSAIC MEDICAL CENTER – MARYVILLE (O, 50 beds) 2016 South Main Street, Maryville, MO, Zip 64468–2655; tel. 660/562–2600; Nate Blackford, President

Owned, leased, sponsored:	4 hospitals	468 beds
Contract-managed:	0 hospitals	0 beds
Totals:	4 hospitals	468 beds

★0917: MOUNT SINAI HEALTH SYSTEM (NP)

One Gustave L. Levy Place, New York, NY, Zip 10029; tel. 212/659–8888; Kenneth L. Davis, M.D., President and Chief Executive Officer

(Centralized Health System)

NEW YORK: MOUNT SINAI BETH ISRAEL (O, 537 beds) First Avenue and 16th Street, New York, NY, Zip 10003–3803; tel. 212/420–2000; Jeremy Boal, M.D., President
Web address: www.bethisraelny.org

MOUNT SINAI HOSPITAL (O, 1181 beds) One Gustave L Levy Place, P.O. Box 1068, New York, NY, Zip 10029–0310; tel. 212/241–6500; David L. Reich, M.D., President and Chief Operating Officer
Web address: www.mountsinai.org

MOUNT SINAI WEST (O, 763 beds) 1111 Amsterdam Avenue, New York, NY, Zip 10025–1716; tel. 212/523–4000; Arthur A. Gianelli, M.P.H., President
Web address: www.stlukeshospitalnyc.org

NEW YORK EYE AND EAR INFIRMARY OF MOUNT SINAI (O, 16 beds) 310 East 14th Street, New York, NY, Zip 10003–4201; tel. 212/979–4000; James Tsai, M.D., President

Owned, leased, sponsored:	4 hospitals	2497 beds
Contract-managed:	0 hospitals	0 beds
Totals:	4 hospitals	2497 beds

0952: MOUNTAIN HEALTH NETWORK (IO)

517 9th Street, Huntington, WV, Zip 25701–2020; tel. 304/781–4466; Michael Mullins, President and Chief Executive Officer

WEST VIRGINIA: CABELL HUNTINGTON HOSPITAL (O, 303 beds) 1340 Hal Greer Boulevard, Huntington, WV, Zip 25701–0195; tel. 304/526–2000; Kevin N. Fowler, President and Chief Executive Officer
Web address: www.cabellhuntington.org

PLEASANT VALLEY HOSPITAL (O, 168 beds) 2520 Valley Drive, Point Pleasant, WV, Zip 25550–2031; tel. 304/675–4340; Glen A. Washington, Chief Executive Officer
Web address: www.pvalley.org

ST. MARY'S MEDICAL CENTER (O, 393 beds) 2900 First Avenue, Huntington, WV, Zip 25702–1272; tel. 304/526–1234; Todd Campbell, Chief Executive Officer

Owned, leased, sponsored:	3 hospitals	864 beds
Contract-managed:	0 hospitals	0 beds
Totals:	3 hospitals	864 beds

6555: MULTICARE HEALTH SYSTEM (NP)

315 Martin Luther King Jr Way, Tacoma, WA, Zip 98405–4234, Mailing Address: P.O. Box 5299, Zip 98415–0299, tel. 253/403–1000; William G. Robertson, President and Chief Executive Officer

(Centralized Physician/Insurance Health System)

For explanation of codes following names, see page B2.
★ Indicates Type III membership in the American Hospital Association.

Section B

WASHINGTON: MULTICARE AUBURN MEDICAL CENTER (O, 153 beds) 202 North Division, Plaza One, Auburn, WA, Zip 98001–4908; tel. 253/833–7711; Mark T. Smith, JD, CPA, President and Chief Operating Officer

MULTICARE DEACONESS HOSPITAL (O, 352 beds) 800 West Fifth Avenue, Spokane, WA, Zip 99204–2803, Mailing Address: P.O. Box 248, Zip 99210–0248, tel. 509/458–5800; Laureen Driscoll, President
Web address: https://www.multicare.org/deaconess-hospital/

MULTICARE GOOD SAMARITAN HOSPITAL (O, 362 beds) 401 15th Avenue SE, Puyallup, WA, Zip 98372–3770, Mailing Address: P.O. Box 1247, Zip 98371–0192, tel. 253/697–4000; Christopher Bredeson, President and Chief Operating Officer

MULTICARE MARY BRIDGE CHILDREN'S HOSPITAL AND HEALTH CENTER (O, 75 beds) 317 Martin Luther King Jr Way, Tacoma, WA, Zip 98405–4234, Mailing Address: P.O. Box 5299, Zip 98415–0299, tel. 253/403–1400; Jeffrey S. Poltawsky, President and Market Leader
Web address: www.multicare.org/marybridge

MULTICARE TACOMA GENERAL HOSPITAL (O, 444 beds) 315 Martin Luther King Jr Way, Tacoma, WA, Zip 98405–4234, Mailing Address: P.O. Box 5299, Zip 98415–0299, tel. 253/403–1000; Sharon Oxendale, President and Chief Operating Officer

MULTICARE VALLEY HOSPITAL (O, 123 beds) 12606 East Mission Avenue, Spokane Valley, WA, Zip 99216–1090; tel. 509/924–6650; Gregory George. Repetti III, FACHE, Chief Executive Officer
Web address: www.valleyhospital.org

Owned, leased, sponsored:	6 hospitals	1509 beds
Contract-managed:	0 hospitals	0 beds
Totals:	6 hospitals	1509 beds

★1465: MUNSON HEALTHCARE (NP)

1105 Sixth Street, Traverse City, MI, Zip 49684–2386; tel. 231/935–6703; Edwin Ness, President and Chief Executive Officer

(Centralized Health System)

MICHIGAN: KALKASKA MEMORIAL HEALTH CENTER (C, 112 beds) 419 South Coral Street, Kalkaska, MI, Zip 49646–2503; tel. 231/258–7500; Kevin L. Rogols, FACHE, Administrator

MUNSON HEALTHCARE CADILLAC HOSPITAL (O, 49 beds) 400 Hobart Street, Cadillac, MI, Zip 49601–2389; tel. 231/876–7200; Tonya Smith, President
Web address: www.mercyhealthcadillac.com/welcome-cadillac

MUNSON HEALTHCARE CHARLEVOIX HOSPITAL (O, 25 beds) 14700 Lake Shore Drive, Charlevoix, MI, Zip 49720–1999; tel. 231/547–4024; Joanne Schroeder, President
Web address: www.cah.org

MUNSON HEALTHCARE GRAYLING HOSPITAL (O, 110 beds) 1100 East Michigan Avenue, Grayling, MI, Zip 49738–1312; tel. 989/348–5461; Kirsten Korth-White, President
Web address: https://www.munsonhealthcare.org

MUNSON HEALTHCARE MANISTEE HOSPITAL (O, 45 beds) 1465 East Parkdale Avenue, Manistee, MI, Zip 49660–9709; tel. 231/398–1000; James Barker, Chief Executive Officer
Web address: www.westshoremedcenter.org

MUNSON HEALTHCARE OTSEGO MEMORIAL HOSPITAL (O, 80 beds) 825 North Center Avenue, Gaylord, MI, Zip 49735–1592; tel. 989/731–2100; Thomas R. Lemon, Chief Executive Officer

MUNSON MEDICAL CENTER (O, 442 beds) 1105 Sixth Street, Traverse City, MI, Zip 49684–2386; tel. 231/935–5000; Derk F. Pronger, Interim President and Chief Executive Officer
Web address: www.munsonhealthcare.org

PAUL OLIVER MEMORIAL HOSPITAL (O, 47 beds) 224 Park Avenue, Frankfort, MI, Zip 49635–9658; tel. 231/352–2200; Peter Marinoff, President
Web address: www.munsonhealthcare.org

Owned, leased, sponsored:	7 hospitals	798 beds
Contract-managed:	1 hospitals	112 beds
Totals:	8 hospitals	910 beds

0261: NATIONAL SURGICAL HEALTHCARE (IO)

250 South Wacker Drive, Suite 500, Chicago, IL, Zip 60606–5897; tel. 312/627–8400; David Crane, Chief Executive Officer
(Independent Hospital System)

ARIZONA: ARIZONA SPINE AND JOINT HOSPITAL (O, 23 beds) 4620 East Baseline Road, Mesa, AZ, Zip 85206–4624; tel. 480/832–4770; Todd Greene, Chief Executive Officer

GEORGIA: JENKINS COUNTY MEDICAL CENTER (O, 25 beds) 931 East Winthrope Avenue, Millen, GA, Zip 30442–1839; tel. 478/982–4221; Earl S. Whiteley, FACHE, Chief Executive Officer
Web address: www.https://jenkinsmedicalcenter.com/

OPTIM MEDICAL CENTER – SCREVEN (O, 25 beds) 215 Mims Road, Sylvania, GA, Zip 30467–2097; tel. 912/564–7426; Michael G. Layfield, Interim Chief Executive Officer
Web address: www.optimhealth.com

OPTIM MEDICAL CENTER – TATTNALL (O, 25 beds) 247 South Main Street, Reidsville, GA, Zip 30453–4605; tel. 912/557–1000; Rob Snipes, Administrator

IDAHO: NORTHWEST SPECIALTY HOSPITAL (O, 34 beds) 1593 East Polston Avenue, Post Falls, ID, Zip 83854–5326; tel. 208/262–2300; Rick Rasmussen, Chief Executive Officer
Web address: www.northwestspecialtyhospital.com

LOUISIANA: LAFAYETTE SURGICAL SPECIALTY HOSPITAL (O, 20 beds) 1101 Kaliste Saloom Road, Lafayette, LA, Zip 70508–5705; tel. 337/769–4100; Buffy Domingue, Chief Executive Officer
Web address: www.lafayettesurgical.com

MICHIGAN: SOUTHEAST MICHIGAN SURGICAL HOSPITAL (O, 13 beds) 21230 Dequindre, Warren, MI, Zip 48091–2287; tel. 586/427–1000; Barry Cullen, Chief Executive Officer

NORTH CAROLINA: NORTH CAROLINA SPECIALTY HOSPITAL (O, 18 beds) 3916 Ben Franklin Boulevard, Durham, NC, Zip 27704–2383, Mailing Address: PO Box 15819, Zip 27704–2383, tel. 919/956–9300; Randi L. Shults, Chief Executive Officer
Web address: www.ncspecialty.com

TEXAS: SOUTH TEXAS SPINE AND SURGICAL HOSPITAL (O, 30 beds) 18600 Hardy Oak Boulevard, San Antonio, TX, Zip 78258–4206; tel. 210/507–4090; Angie Kauffman, Chief Executive Officer
Web address: www.southtexassurgical.com

SOUTH TEXAS SURGICAL HOSPITAL (O, 20 beds) 6130 Parkway Drive, Corpus Christi, TX, Zip 78414–2455; tel. 361/993–2000; David G. Covert, Chief Executive Officer
Web address: www.southtexassurgicalhospital.com

WISCONSIN: OAKLEAF SURGICAL HOSPITAL (O, 13 beds) 1000 OakLeaf Way, Altoona, WI, Zip 54701–3016; tel. 715/831–8130; Anne Hargrave-Thomas, Chief Executive Officer

WYOMING: MOUNTAIN VIEW REGIONAL HOSPITAL (O, 23 beds) 6550 East Second Street, Casper, WY, Zip 82609–4321, Mailing Address: P.O. Box 51888, Zip 82605–1888, tel. 307/995–8100; Thomas Kopitnik, Acting Chief Executive Officer
Web address: www.mountainviewregionalhospital.com

Owned, leased, sponsored:	12 hospitals	269 beds
Contract-managed:	0 hospitals	0 beds
Totals:	12 hospitals	269 beds

0923: NAVICENT HEALTH (NP)

777 Hemlock Street, MSC 105, Macon, GA, Zip 31201–2155, Mailing Address: 777 Hemlock Street, Zip 31201–2155, tel. 478/633–1000; Ninfa M. Saunders, President and Chief Executive Officer

(Moderately Centralized Health System)

GEORGIA: MEDICAL CENTER OF PEACH COUNTY, NAVICENT HEALTH (O, 25 beds) 1960 Highway 247 Connector, Bryon, GA, Zip 31008; tel. 478/654–2000; Laura Gentry, Administrator

---

For explanation of codes following names, see page B2.
★ Indicates Type III membership in the American Hospital Association.

MEDICAL CENTER, NAVICENT HEALTH (O, 627 beds) 777 Hemlock Street, Macon, GA, Zip 31201–2155; tel. 478/633–1000; Ninfa M. Saunders, President and Chief Executive Officer
Web address: https://www.navicenthealth.org/

NAVICENT HEALTH BALDWIN (O, 90 beds) 821 North Cobb Street, Milledgeville, GA, Zip 31061–2351, Mailing Address: P.O. Box 690, Zip 31059–0690, tel. 478/454–3505; Todd Dixon, R.N., Chief Executive Officer
Web address: www.navicenthealth.org/nhb/home

REHABILITATION HOSPITAL, NAVICENT HEALTH (O, 58 beds) 3351 Northside Drive, Macon, GA, Zip 31210–2587; tel. 478/201–6500; Regina Tipton, Director of Operations

Owned, leased, sponsored:	4 hospitals	800 beds
Contract-managed:	0 hospitals	0 beds
Totals:	4 hospitals	800 beds

★9265: NEBRASKA METHODIST HEALTH SYSTEM, INC. (CO)
8511 West Dodge Road, Omaha, NE, Zip 68114–3403; tel. 402/354–5411; Stephen L. Goeser, FACHE, President and Chief Executive Officer
(Centralized Physician/Insurance Health System)

IOWA: METHODIST JENNIE EDMUNDSON HOSPITAL (O, 114 beds) 933 East Pierce Street, Council Bluffs, IA, Zip 51503–4652, Mailing Address: P.O. Box 2C, Zip 51502–3002, tel. 712/396–6000; Steven P. Baumert, President and Chief Executive Officer

NEBRASKA: METHODIST FREMONT HEALTH (L, 181 beds) 450 East 23rd Street, Fremont, NE, Zip 68025–2387; tel. 402/721–1610; Brett M. Richmond, President and Chief Executive Officer
Web address: www.fremonthealth.com

NEBRASKA METHODIST HOSPITAL (O, 402 beds) 8303 Dodge Street, Omaha, NE, Zip 68114–4199; tel. 402/354–4000; Josie Abboud, President and Chief Executive Officer
Web address: www.bestcare.org

Owned, leased, sponsored:	3 hospitals	697 beds
Contract-managed:	0 hospitals	0 beds
Totals:	3 hospitals	697 beds

0892: NEMOURS (NP)
10140 Centurion Parkway North, Jacksonville, FL, Zip 32256–0532; tel. 904/697–4100; R. Lawrence. Moss, M.D., President and Chief Executive Officer
(Independent Hospital System)

DELAWARE: ALFRED I. DUPONT HOSPITAL FOR CHILDREN (O, 200 beds) 1600 Rockland Road, Wilmington, DE, Zip 19803–3616, Mailing Address: Box 269, Zip 19899–0269, tel. 302/651–4000; Roy Proujansky, M.D., Chief Executive Officer

FLORIDA: NEMOURS CHILDREN'S HOSPITAL (O, 92 beds) 13535 Nemours Parkway, Orlando, FL, Zip 32827–7402; tel. 407/567–4000; Dana Bledsoe, MS, R.N., President
Web address: www.nemours.org

Owned, leased, sponsored:	2 hospitals	292 beds
Contract-managed:	0 hospitals	0 beds
Totals:	2 hospitals	292 beds

0620: NEUROPSYCHIATRIC HOSPITALS (IO)
1625 East Jefferson Boulevard, Mishawaka, IN, Zip 46545–7103; tel. 574/255–1400; Cameron R. Gilbert, Ph.D., President and Chief Executive Officer

INDIANA: DOCTORS NEUROPSYCHIATRIC HOSPITAL AND RESEARCH INSTITUTE (O, 37 beds) 417 South Whitlock Street, Bremen, IN, Zip 46506–1626; tel. 574/546–0330; Christy Gilbert, Interim Chief Executive Officer

MEDICAL BEHAVIORAL HOSPITAL OF MISHAWAKA (O, 30 beds) 5985 E 200 S, Knox, IN, Zip 46534, Mailing Address: 1625 East Jefferson Boulevard, Mishawaka, Zip 46545–7103, tel. 574/255–1400; Emily Ryan, Chief Executive Officer
Web address: www.physicianshospitalsystem.net/

NEUROPSYCHIATRIC HOSPITAL OF INDIANAPOLIS (O, 50 beds) 6720 Parkdale Place, Indianapolis, IN, Zip 46254–4668; tel. 317/744–9200; Tracy Davis, Chief Executive Officer
Web address: https://www.neuropsychiatrichospitals.net

Owned, leased, sponsored:	3 hospitals	117 beds
Contract-managed:	0 hospitals	0 beds
Totals:	3 hospitals	117 beds

★0213: NEW HANOVER REGIONAL MEDICAL CENTER (NP)
2131 South 17th Street, Wilmington, NC, Zip 28401–7407; tel. 910/343–7040; John H. Gizdic, President and Chief Executive Officer
(Moderately Centralized Health System)

NORTH CAROLINA: NEW HANOVER REGIONAL MEDICAL CENTER (O, 713 beds) 2131 South 17th Street, Wilmington, NC, Zip 28401–7483, Mailing Address: P.O. Box 9000, Zip 28402–9000, tel. 910/343–7000; Andre Boyd Sr, Executive Vice President, Hospital Division
Web address: www.nhrmc.org

PENDER MEMORIAL HOSPITAL (C, 59 beds) 507 East Freemont Street, Burgaw, NC, Zip 28425–5131; tel. 910/259–5451; Ruth Glaser, President
Web address: www.pendermemorial.org

Owned, leased, sponsored:	1 hospitals	713 beds
Contract-managed:	1 hospitals	59 beds
Totals:	2 hospitals	772 beds

0009: NEW YORK STATE OFFICE OF MENTAL HEALTH (NP)
44 Holland Avenue, Albany, NY, Zip 12208–3411; tel. 518/474–7056; Kristin M. Woodlock, R.N., Acting Commissioner
(Independent Hospital System)

NEW YORK: BRONX PSYCHIATRIC CENTER (O, 450 beds) 1500 Waters Place, Bronx, NY, Zip 10461–2796; tel. 718/931–0600; Anita Daniels, Director
Web address: www.omh.ny.gov

BUFFALO PSYCHIATRIC CENTER (O, 240 beds) 400 Forest Avenue, Buffalo, NY, Zip 14213–1298, tel. 716/885–2261; Beatrix Souza, Chief Executive Officer

CAPITAL DISTRICT PSYCHIATRIC CENTER (O, 200 beds) 75 New Scotland Avenue, Albany, NY, Zip 12208–3474; tel. 518/549–6000; William Dickson, Executive Director
Web address: www.omh.ny.gov/omhweb/facilities/cdpc/facility.htm

CENTRAL NEW YORK PSYCHIATRIC CENTER (O, 226 beds) 9005 Old River Road, Marcy, NY, Zip 13403–3000, Mailing Address: P.O. Box 300, Zip 13403–0300, tel. 315/765–3600; Maureen Bosco, Executive Director
Web address: www.omh.ny.gov

CREEDMOOR PSYCHIATRIC CENTER (O, 322 beds) 79–25 Winchester Boulevard, Jamaica, NY, Zip 11427–2128; tel. 718/264–3600; Ann Marie. Barbarotta, Executive Director
Web address: www.omh.ny.gov

ELMIRA PSYCHIATRIC CENTER (O, 61 beds) 100 Washington Street, Elmira, NY, Zip 14901–2898; tel. 607/737–4739; David Peppel, Executive Director

GREATER BINGHAMTON HEALTH CENTER (O, 86 beds) 425 Robinson Street, Binghamton, NY, Zip 13904–1735; tel. 607/724–1391; David Peppel, Executive Director
Web address: www.omh.ny.gov/omhweb/facilities/bipc/facility.htm

KINGSBORO PSYCHIATRIC CENTER (O, 290 beds) 681 Clarkson Avenue, Brooklyn, NY, Zip 11203–2125; tel. 718/221–7395; Deborah Parchment, Executive Director
Web address: www.omh.ny.gov/omhweb/facilities/kbpc/facility/htm

KIRBY FORENSIC PSYCHIATRIC CENTER (O, 193 beds) 600 East 125th Street, New York, NY, Zip 10035–6000; tel. 646/672–5800; Vincent Miccoli, Executive Director
Web address: https://www.omh.ny.gov/omhweb/facilities/krpc/

Section B

MANHATTAN PSYCHIATRIC CENTER-WARD'S ISLAND (O, 745 beds) 600 East 125th Street, New York, NY, Zip 10035–6000; tel. 646/672–6767; Vincent Miccoli, Executive Director
Web address: www.omh.ny.gov

MID-HUDSON FORENSIC PSYCHIATRIC CENTER (O, 285 beds) Route 17M, New Hampton, NY, Zip 10958, Mailing Address: P.O. Box 158, Zip 10958–0158, tel. 845/374–8700; Joseph Freebern, Executive Director

MOHAWK VALLEY PSYCHIATRIC CENTER (O, 614 beds) 1400 Noyes Street, Utica, NY, Zip 13502–3854; tel. 315/738–3800; Colleen A. Sawyer, R.N., MSN, Executive Director
Web address: www.omh.ny.gov/omhweb/facilities/mvpc/facility.htm

NEW YORK CITY CHILDREN'S CENTER (O, 97 beds) 74–03 Commonwealth Boulevard, Jamaica, NY, Zip 11426–1890; tel. 718/264–4506; Kanika Jefferies, Executive Director

NEW YORK STATE PSYCHIATRIC INSTITUTE (O, 58 beds) 1051 Riverside Drive, New York, NY, Zip 10032–1007; tel. 646/774–5000; Jeffrey A. Lieberman, M.D., Executive Director
Web address: www.nyspi.org

PILGRIM PSYCHIATRIC CENTER (O, 569 beds) 998 Crooked Hill Road, Brentwood, NY, Zip 11717–1019; tel. 631/761–3500; Kathy O'Keefe, Executive Director

RICHARD H. HUTCHINGS PSYCHIATRIC CENTER (O, 131 beds) 620 Madison Street, Syracuse, NY, Zip 13210–2319; tel. 315/426–3632; Colleen A. Sawyer, R.N., MSN, Executive Director
Web address: www.omh.ny.gov

ROCHESTER PSYCHIATRIC CENTER (O, 180 beds) 1111 Elmwood Avenue, Rochester, NY, Zip 14620–3005; tel. 585/241–1200; Philip Griffin, Director of Operations

ROCKLAND CHILDREN'S PSYCHIATRIC CENTER (O, 54 beds) 599 Convent Road, Orangeburg, NY, Zip 10962–1162; tel. 845/359–7400; Christopher Tavella, Acting Executive Director
Web address: www.omh.ny.gov/

ROCKLAND PSYCHIATRIC CENTER (O, 525 beds) 140 Old Orangeburg Road, Orangeburg, NY, Zip 10962–1157; tel. 845/359–1000; Christopher Tavella, Executive Director
Web address: www.omh.ny.gov/

SAGAMORE CHILDREN'S PSYCHIATRIC CENTER (O, 54 beds) 197 Half Hollow Road, Dix Hills, NY, Zip 11746–5861; tel. 631/370–1700; Kathy O'Keefe, Interim Executive Director

SOUTH BEACH PSYCHIATRIC CENTER (O, 248 beds) 777 Seaview Avenue, Staten Island, NY, Zip 10305–3409; tel. 718/667–2300; Doreen Piazza, Acting Executive Director
Web address: www.omh.ny.gov/omhweb/facilities/sbpc/facility.htm

ST. LAWRENCE PSYCHIATRIC CENTER (O, 146 beds) 1 Chimney Point Drive, Ogdensburg, NY, Zip 13669–2291; tel. 315/541–2001; Timothy Farrell, Executive Director

WESTERN NEW YORK CHILDREN'S PSYCHIATRIC CENTER (O, 46 beds) 1010 East and West Road, West Seneca, NY, Zip 14224–3602; tel. 716/677–7000; Kathe Hayes, Executive Director
Web address: www.omh.ny.gov

Owned, leased, sponsored:	23 hospitals	5820 beds
Contract-managed:	0 hospitals	0 beds
Totals:	23 hospitals	5820 beds

★0142: NEWYORK-PRESBYTERIAN (NP)
525 East 68th Street, Box 182, New York, NY, Zip 10065; tel. 212/746–3745; Steven J. Corwin, M.D., President and Chief Executive Officer
(Centralized Health System)

NEW YORK: NEW YORK-PRESBYTERIAN HOSPITAL (O, 2586 beds) 525 East 68th Street, New York, NY, Zip 10065–4870; tel. 212/746–5454; Steven J. Corwin, M.D., President and Chief Executive Officer
Web address: www.nyp.org

NEW YORK-PRESBYTERIAN QUEENS (O, 491 beds) 56–45 Main Street, Flushing, NY, Zip 11355–5045; tel. 718/670–1231; Jaclyn Mucaria, President
Web address: www.nyhq.org

NEW YORK-PRESBYTERIAN/HUDSON VALLEY HOSPITAL (O, 128 beds) 1980 Crompond Road, Cortlandt Manor, NY, Zip 10567–4182; tel. 914/737–9000; Stacey Petrower, President
Web address: www.hvhc.org

NEWYORK-PRESBYTERIAN BROOKLYN METHODIST HOSPITAL (O, 591 beds) 506 Sixth Street, Brooklyn, NY, Zip 11215–3609; tel. 718/780–3000; Robert Guimento, President

Owned, leased, sponsored:	4 hospitals	3796 beds
Contract-managed:	0 hospitals	0 beds
Totals:	4 hospitals	3796 beds

0353: NEXUS HEALTH SYSTEMS (IO)
One Riverway, Suite 600, Houston, TX, Zip 77056–1993; tel. 713/355–6111; John W. Cassidy, M.D., President, Chief Executive Officer and Chief Medical Officer
(Independent Hospital System)

CALIFORNIA: HEALTHBRIDGE CHILDREN'S HOSPITAL (O, 27 beds) 393 South Tustin Street, Orange, CA, Zip 92866–2501; tel. 714/289–2400; Alex Villarruz, Chief Executive Officer

TEXAS: HEALTHBRIDGE CHILDREN'S HOSPITAL OF HOUSTON (O, 40 beds) 2929 Woodland Park Drive, Houston, TX, Zip 77082–2687; tel. 281/293–7774; Joel Telly, Chief Executive Officer
Web address: www.healthbridgehouston.com/

NEXUS SPECIALTY HOSPITAL (O, 76 beds) 123 Vision Park Boulevard, Shenandoah, TX, Zip 77384–3001; tel. 281/364–0317; Eric Cantrell, Chief Executive Officer

Owned, leased, sponsored:	3 hospitals	143 beds
Contract-managed:	0 hospitals	0 beds
Totals:	3 hospitals	143 beds

1021: NOBILIS HEALTH CORPORATION (IO)
11700 Katy Freeway Suite 300, Houston, TX, Zip 77079–1218; tel. 713/355–8614; Harry Fleming, Chief Executive Officer
(Independent Hospital System)

ARIZONA: SCOTTSDALE LIBERTY HOSPITAL (O, 12 beds) 17500 North Perimeter Drive, Scottsdale, AZ, Zip 85255–7808; tel. 480/586–2300; Steven M. Siwek, M.D., President and Chief Executive Officer

TEXAS: FIRST SURGICAL HOSPITAL (O, 19 beds) 4801 Bissonnet, Bellaire, TX, Zip 77401–4028; tel. 713/275–1111; Nicole Walker, Chief Executive Officer
Web address: www.firststreethospital.com

HERMANN DRIVE SURGICAL HOSPITAL (O, 25 beds) 2001 Hermann Drive, Houston, TX, Zip 77004–7643; tel. 713/285–5500; Nicole Walker, Chief Executive Officer
Web address: www.nobilishealth.com/our-facilities/houston/

PLANO SURGICAL HOSPITAL (O, 26 beds) 2301 Marsh Lane, Plano, TX, Zip 75093–8497; tel. 972/820–2600; Jay Lindsey, Chief Executive Officer
Web address: www.nobilishealth.com/our-facilities/dallas/

Owned, leased, sponsored:	4 hospitals	82 beds
Contract-managed:	0 hospitals	0 beds
Totals:	4 hospitals	82 beds

0349: NOLAND HEALTH SERVICES, INC. (NP)
600 Corporate Parkway, Suite 100, Birmingham, AL, Zip 35242–5451; tel. 205/783–8484; Gary M. Glasscock, President and Chief Executive Officer

ALABAMA: NOLAND HOSPITAL ANNISTON (O, 38 beds) 400 East 10th Street, 4th Fl, Anniston, AL, Zip 36207–4716; tel. 256/741–6141; Trina Woods, Administrator
Web address: www.nolandhealth.com

NOLAND HOSPITAL BIRMINGHAM (O, 45 beds) 50 Medical Park East Drive, 8th Floor, Birmingham, AL, Zip 35235; tel. 205/808–5100; Laura S. Wills, Administrator

For explanation of codes following names, see page B2.
★ Indicates Type III membership in the American Hospital Association.

Section B

NOLAND HOSPITAL DOTHAN (O, 38 beds) 1108 Ross Clark Circle, 4th Floor, Dothan, AL, Zip 36301–3022; tel. 334/699–4300; Kaye Burk, Administrator **Web address:** www.nolandhealth.com

NOLAND HOSPITAL MONTGOMERY (O, 65 beds) 1725 Pine Street, 5 North, Montgomery, AL, Zip 36106–1109; tel. 334/240–0532; Dale Jones, Administrator

NOLAND HOSPITAL SHELBY (O, 52 beds) 1000 First Street North, 3rd Floor, Alabaster, AL, Zip 35007–8703; tel. 205/620–8641; Laura S. Wills, Administrator **Web address:** www.nolandhospitals.com

NOLAND HOSPITAL TUSCALOOSA (O, 32 beds) 809 University Blvd E, 4th Fl, Tuscaloosa, AL, Zip 35401–2029; tel. 205/759–7241; Jack Gibson, Administrator

Owned, leased, sponsored:	6 hospitals	270 beds
Contract-managed:	0 hospitals	0 beds
Totals:	6 hospitals	270 beds

1030: NORTH COUNTRY HEALTHCARE (NP)

600 Saint Johnsbury Road, Littleton, NH, Zip 03561–3442; tel. 603/444–9000; Thomas Mee, R.N., Chief Executive Officer **(Moderately Centralized Health System)**

Owned, leased, sponsored:	0 hospitals	0 beds
Contract-managed:	0 hospitals	0 beds
Totals:	0 hospitals	0 beds

0887: NORTH MEMORIAL HEALTH CARE (NP)

3300 Oakdale Avenue North, Robbinsdale, MN, Zip 55422–2926; tel. 763/520–5200; J. Kevin. Croston, M.D., Chief Executive Officer **(Centralized Physician/Insurance Health System)**

MINNESOTA: MAPLE GROVE HOSPITAL (C, 108 beds) 9875 Hospital Drive, Maple Grove, MN, Zip 55369–4648; tel. 763/581–1000; Andrew S. Cochrane, Chief Executive Officer **Web address:** www.maplegrovehospital.org

NORTH MEMORIAL HEALTH HOSPITAL (O, 358 beds) 3300 Oakdale Avenue North, Robbinsdale, MN, Zip 55422–2926, tel. 763/520 5200; Jeff Wicklander, President **Web address:** www.northmemorial.com

Owned, leased, sponsored:	1 hospitals	358 beds
Contract-managed:	1 hospitals	108 beds
Totals:	2 hospitals	466 beds

★0032: NORTH MISSISSIPPI HEALTH SERVICES, INC. (NP)

830 South Gloster Street, Tupelo, MS, Zip 38801–4996; tel. 662/377–3136; M. Shane. Spees, President and Chief Executive Officer **(Centralized Physician/Insurance Health System)**

ALABAMA: NORTH MISSISSIPPI MEDICAL CENTER-HAMILTON (O, 15 beds) 1256 Military Street South, Hamilton, AL, Zip 35570–5003; tel. 205/921–6200; Robert Trimm, Administrator **Web address:** www.nmhs.net

MISSISSIPPI: NORTH MISSISSIPPI MEDICAL CENTER – TUPELO (O, 747 beds) 830 South Gloster Street, Tupelo, MS, Zip 38801–4934; tel. 662/377–3000; David C. Wilson, President **Web address:** www.nmhs.net

NORTH MISSISSIPPI MEDICAL CENTER GILMORE-AMORY (O, 95 beds) 1105 Earl Frye Boulevard, Amory, MS, Zip 38821–5500, Mailing Address: P.O. Box 459, Zip 38821–0459, tel. 662/256–7111; J Allen. Tyra, Chief Executive

NORTH MISSISSIPPI MEDICAL CENTER-EUPORA (O, 73 beds) 70 Medical Plaza, Eupora, MS, Zip 39744–4018; tel. 662/258–6221; Robin Mixon, Administrator **Web address:** www.nmhs.net/eupora

NORTH MISSISSIPPI MEDICAL CENTER-IUKA (O, 48 beds) 1777 Curtis Drive, Iuka, MS, Zip 38852–1001, Mailing Address: P.O. Box 860, Zip 38852–0860, tel. 662/423–6051; Fred A. Truesdale Jr, Administrator

NORTH MISSISSIPPI MEDICAL CENTER-PONTOTOC (L, 69 beds) 176 South Main Street, Pontotoc, MS, Zip 38863–3311, Mailing Address: P.O. Box 790, Zip 38863–0790, tel. 662/488–7640; Leslia Carter, Administrator **Web address:** www.nmhs.net

NORTH MISSISSIPPI MEDICAL CENTER-WEST POINT (O, 49 beds) 835 Medical Center Drive, West Point, MS, Zip 39773–9320; tel. 662/495–2300; Barry L. Keel, Administrator **Web address:** www.nmhs.net/westpoint

Owned, leased, sponsored:	7 hospitals	1096 beds
Contract-managed:	0 hospitals	0 beds
Totals:	7 hospitals	1096 beds

0867: NORTH OAKS HEALTH SYSTEM (NP)

15790 Paul Vega MD Drive, Hammond, LA, Zip 70403–1436, Mailing Address: P.O. Box 2668, Zip 70404–2668, tel. 985/345–2700; Michele Kidd. Sutton, FACHE, President and Chief Executive Officer **(Independent Hospital System)**

LOUISIANA: NORTH OAKS MEDICAL CENTER (O, 231 beds) 15790 Paul Vega, MD, Drive, Hammond, LA, Zip 70403–1436, Mailing Address: P.O. Box 2668, Zip 70404–2668, tel. 985/345–2700; Michele Kidd. Sutton, FACHE, President and Chief Executive Officer **Web address:** www.northoaks.org

NORTH OAKS REHABILITATION HOSPITAL (O, 27 beds) 1900 South Morrison Boulevard, Hammond, LA, Zip 70403–5742; tel. 985/542–7777; Sybil K. Paulson, R.N., MSN, Administrator

Owned, leased, sponsored:	2 hospitals	258 beds
Contract-managed:	0 hospitals	0 beds
Totals:	2 hospitals	258 beds

1018: NORTHEAST GEORGIA HEALTH SYSTEM (NP)

743 Spring Street NE, Gainesville, GA, Zip 30501–3715; tel. 770/219–9000; Carol H. Burrell, President and Chief Executive Officer **(Centralized Physician/Insurance Health System)**

GEORGIA: NORTHEAST GEORGIA MEDICAL CENTER BARROW (O, 30 beds) 316 North Broad Street, Winder, GA, Zip 30680–2150, Mailing Address: P.O. Box 688, Zip 30680–0688, tel. 770/867–3400; Chad Hatfield, Chief Executive Officer **Web address:** www.barrowregional.com

NORTHEAST GEORGIA MEDICAL CENTER BRASELTON (O, 100 beds) 1400 River Place, Braselton, GA, Zip 30517–5600; tel. 770/219–9000; Carol H. Burrell, Chief Executive Officer

NORTHEAST GEORGIA MEDICAL CENTER (O, 887 beds) 743 Spring Street NE, Gainesville, GA, Zip 30501–3899; tel. 770/219–3553; Carol H. Burrell, Chief Executive Officer **Web address:** www.nghs.com

Owned, leased, sponsored:	3 hospitals	1017 beds
Contract-managed:	0 hospitals	0 beds
Totals:	3 hospitals	1017 beds

★0281: NORTHERN ARIZONA HEALTHCARE (NP)

1200 North Beaver Street, Flagstaff, AZ, Zip 86001–3118; tel. 928/779–3366; Florence (Flo). Spyrow, President and Chief Executive Officer **(Moderately Centralized Health System)**

ARIZONA: FLAGSTAFF MEDICAL CENTER (O, 264 beds) 1200 North Beaver Street, Flagstaff, AZ, Zip 86001–3118; tel. 928/779–3366; Florence (Flo). Spyrow, Chief Administrative Officer

For explanation of codes following names, see page B2.
★ Indicates Type III membership in the American Hospital Association.

Section B

VERDE VALLEY MEDICAL CENTER (O, 98 beds) 269 South Candy Lane, Cottonwood, AZ, Zip 86326–4170; tel. 928/639–6000; Barbara Firminger, Chief Administrative Officer
Web address: www.https://nahealth.com/

Owned, leased, sponsored:	2 hospitals	362 beds
Contract-managed:	0 hospitals	0 beds
Totals:	2 hospitals	362 beds

★**0555: NORTHERN LIGHT HEALTH** (NP)
43 Whiting Hill Road, Brewer, ME, Zip 04412–1005; tel. 207/973–7045; M. Michelle. Hood, FACHE, President and Chief Executive Officer
(Moderately Centralized Health System)

MAINE: NORTHERN LIGHT BLUE HILL HOSPITAL (O, 23 beds) 57 Water Street, Blue Hill, ME, Zip 04614–5231, Mailing Address: P.O. Box 1029, Zip 04614–1029, tel. 207/374–3400; John Ronan, President

NORTHERN LIGHT CA DEAN HOSPITAL (O, 50 beds) 364 Pritham Avenue, Greenville, ME, Zip 04441–1395, Mailing Address: P.O. Box 1129, Zip 04441–1129, tel. 207/695–5200; Terri Vieira, President
Web address: www.cadean.org

NORTHERN LIGHT EASTERN MAINE MEDICAL CENTER (O, 385 beds) 489 State Street, Bangor, ME, Zip 04401–6674, Mailing Address: P.O. Box 404, Zip 04402–0404, tel. 207/973–7000; Timothy Dentry, Interim President

NORTHERN LIGHT INLAND HOSPITAL (O, 29 beds) 200 Kennedy Memorial Drive, Waterville, ME, Zip 04901–4595; tel. 207/861–3000; John Dalton, President
Web address: www.inlandhospital.org

NORTHERN LIGHT MAINE COAST HOSPITAL (O, 52 beds) 50 Union Street, Ellsworth, ME, Zip 04605–1599; tel. 207/664–5311; John Ronan, President

NORTHERN LIGHT MERCY HOSPITAL (O, 104 beds) 144 State Street, Portland, ME, Zip 04101–3795; tel. 207/879–3000; Charles D. Therrien, President
Web address: www.https://northernlighthealth.org/Mercy-Hospital

NORTHLIGHT SEBASTICOOK VALLEY HOSPITAL (O, 25 beds) 447 North Main Street, Pittsfield, ME, Zip 04967–3707; tel. 207/487–4000; Terri Vieira, President
Web address: www.sebasticookvalleyhealth.org

THE ACADIA HOSPITAL (O, 68 beds) 268 Stillwater Avenue, Bangor, ME, Zip 04401–3945, Mailing Address: P.O. Box 422, Zip 04402–0422, tel. 207/973–6100; Scott Oxley, President

THE AROOSTOOK MEDICAL CENTER (O, 120 beds) 140 Academy Street, Presque Isle, ME, Zip 04769–3171, Mailing Address: P.O. Box 151, Zip 04769–0151, tel. 207/768–4000; Gregory LaFrancois, President
Web address: www.tamc.org

Owned, leased, sponsored:	9 hospitals	856 beds
Contract-managed:	0 hospitals	0 beds
Totals:	9 hospitals	856 beds

★**0410: NORTHSIDE HEALTHCARE SYSTEM** (NP)
1000 Johnson Ferry Road NE, Atlanta, GA, Zip 30342–1611; tel. 404/851–8000; Robert Quattrocchi, President and Chief Executive Officer

GEORGIA: NORTHSIDE HOSPITAL-CHEROKEE (O, 122 beds) 450 Northside Cherokee Boulevard, Canton, GA, Zip 30115–8015, Mailing Address: P.O. Box 906, Zip 30169–0906, tel. 770/720–5100; William M. Hayes, Chief Executive Officer

NORTHSIDE HOSPITAL-FORSYTH (O, 325 beds) 1200 Northside Forsyth Drive, Cumming, GA, Zip 30041–7659; tel. 770/844–3200; Lynn Jackson, Administrator
Web address: www.northside.com

NORTHSIDE HOSPITAL (O, 639 beds) 1000 Johnson Ferry Road NE, Atlanta, GA, Zip 30342–1611; tel. 404/851–8000; Robert Quattrocchi, President and Chief Executive Officer

Owned, leased, sponsored:	3 hospitals	1086 beds
Contract-managed:	0 hospitals	0 beds
Totals:	3 hospitals	1086 beds

★**0062: NORTHWELL HEALTH** (NP)
2000 Marcus Avenue, New Hyde Park, NY, Zip 11042; tel. 516/465–8100; Michael J. Dowling, President and Chief Executive Officer
(Centralized Health System)

NEW YORK: GLEN COVE HOSPITAL (O, 119 beds) 101 St Andrews Lane, Glen Cove, NY, Zip 11542–2254; tel. 516/674–7300; Susan Kwiatek, R.N., Executive Director

HUNTINGTON HOSPITAL (O, 280 beds) 270 Park Avenue, Huntington, NY, Zip 11743–2799; tel. 631/351–2000; Nick Fitterman, M.D., Executive Director
Web address: www.https://huntington.northwell.edu

JOHN T. MATHER MEMORIAL HOSPITAL (O, 248 beds) 75 North Country Road, Port Jefferson, NY, Zip 11777–2190; tel. 631/473–1320; Kenneth D. Roberts, President
Web address: www.matherhospital.com

LENOX HILL HOSPITAL (O, 440 beds) 100 East 77th Street, New York, NY, Zip 10075–1850; tel. 212/434–2000; Jill Kalman, M.D., Executive Director

LONG ISLAND JEWISH MEDICAL CENTER (O, 1522 beds) 270–05 76th Avenue, New Hyde Park, NY, Zip 11040–1496; tel. 718/470–7000; Michael Goldberg, Executive Director
Web address: www.lij.edu

NORTH SHORE UNIVERSITY HOSPITAL (O, 813 beds) 300 Community Drive, Manhasset, NY, Zip 11030–3816; tel. 516/562–0100; Alessandro Bellucci, M.D., Executive Director
Web address: https://www.northwell.edu/find-care/locations/north-shore-university-hospital

NORTHERN WESTCHESTER HOSPITAL (O, 195 beds) 400 East Main Street, Mount Kisco, NY, Zip 10549–3477, Mailing Address: 400 East Main Street, G-02, Zip 10549–3477, tel. 914/666–1200; Joel Seligman, President and Chief Executive Officer
Web address: www.nwhc.net

PECONIC BAY MEDICAL CENTER (O, 110 beds) 1300 Roanoke Avenue, Riverhead, NY, Zip 11901–2031; tel. 631/548–6000; Andrew J. Mitchell, President and Chief Executive Officer
Web address: www.pbmchealth.org

PHELPS MEMORIAL HOSPITAL CENTER (O, 153 beds) 701 North Broadway, Sleepy Hollow, NY, Zip 10591–1020; tel. 914/366–3000; Daniel Blum, President

PLAINVIEW HOSPITAL (O, 150 beds) 888 Old Country Road, Plainview, NY, Zip 11803–4978; tel. 516/719–3000; Michael Fener, Executive Director
Web address: https://www.planview.com/

SOUTH OAKS HOSPITAL (O, 202 beds) 400 Sunrise Highway, Amityville, NY, Zip 11701–2508; tel. 631/264–4000; Carolyn Sweetapple, Ph.D., CPA, R.N., Executive Director

SOUTHSIDE HOSPITAL (O, 278 beds) 301 East Main Street, Bay Shore, NY, Zip 11706–8458; tel. 631/968–3000; Donna Moravick, R.N., MSN, Executive Director
Web address: https://www.northwell.edu/find-care/locations/southside-hospital

STATEN ISLAND UNIVERSITY HOSPITAL (O, 627 beds) 475 Seaview Avenue, Staten Island, NY, Zip 10305–3436; tel. 718/226–9000; Brahim Ardolic, M.D., Chief Executive Officer
Web address: www.siuh.edu

Owned, leased, sponsored:	13 hospitals	5137 beds
Contract-managed:	0 hospitals	0 beds
Totals:	13 hospitals	5137 beds

★**0024: NORTHWESTERN MEMORIAL HEALTHCARE** (NP)
251 East Huron Street, Chicago, IL, Zip 60611–2908; tel. 312/926–2000; Dean M. Harrison, President and Chief Executive Officer
(Centralized Health System)

ILLINOIS: NORTHWESTERN MEDICINE CENTRAL DUPAGE HOSPITAL (O, 419 beds) 25 North Winfield Road, Winfield, IL, Zip 60190; tel. 630/933–1600; Brian J. Lemon, President
Web address: www.nm.org

For explanation of codes following names, see page B2.
★ Indicates Type III membership in the American Hospital Association.

NORTHWESTERN MEDICINE DELNOR HOSPITAL (O, 142 beds) 300 Randall Road, Geneva, IL, Zip 60134–4200; tel. 630/208–3000; Maureen A. Bryant, FACHE, President
Web address: www.nm.org

NORTHWESTERN MEDICINE KISHWAUKEE HOSPITAL (O, 98 beds) 1 Kish Hospital Drive, DeKalb, IL, Zip 60115–9602, Mailing Address: P.O. Box 707, Zip 60115–0707, tel. 815/756–1521; Jay Anderson, President

NORTHWESTERN MEDICINE LAKE FOREST HOSPITAL (O, 120 beds) 1000 North Westmoreland Road, Lake Forest, IL, Zip 60045–1696, Mailing Address: 1000 N Westmoreland Road, Zip 60045–1658, tel. 847/234–5600; Thomas J. McAfee, President, North Region
Web address: www.nm.org

NORTHWESTERN MEDICINE MARIANJOY REHABILITATION HOSPITAL (O, 127 beds) 26 West 171 Roosevelt Road, Wheaton, IL, Zip 60187–0795, Mailing Address: P.O. Box 795, Zip 60187–0795, tel. 630/909–8000; Brian J. Lemon, President
Web address: www.marianjoy.org

NORTHWESTERN MEDICINE MCHENRY (O, 326 beds) 4201 Medical Center Drive, McHenry, IL, Zip 60050–8409; tel. 815/344–5000; Michael S. Eesley, Chief Executive Officer

NORTHWESTERN MEDICINE VALLEY WEST HOSPITAL (O, 25 beds) 1302 North Main Street, Sandwich, IL, Zip 60548–2587; tel. 815/786–8484; Jay Anderson, President
Web address: www.nm.org

NORTHWESTERN MEMORIAL HOSPITAL (O, 894 beds) 251 East Huron Street, Chicago, IL, Zip 60611–2908; tel. 312/926–2000; Julie L. Creamer, President, Northwestern Memorial Hospital and Senior Vice President Northwestern Memorial HealthCare

Owned, leased, sponsored:	8 hospitals	2151 beds
Contract-managed:	0 hospitals	0 beds
Totals:	8 hospitals	2151 beds

★2285: NORTON HEALTHCARE (NP)
4967 US Highway 42, Suite 100, Louisville, KY, Zip 40222–6363, Mailing Address: P.O. Box 35070, Zip 40232–5070, tel. 502/629–8000; Russell Cox, President and Chief Executive Officer
(Centralized Health System)

KENTUCKY: NORTON CHILDREN'S HOSPITAL (O, 279 beds) 231 East Chestnut Street, Louisville, KY, Zip 40202–1821; tel. 502/629–6000; Emmett Ramser, Chief Administrative Officer
Web address: www.kosairchildrens.com/

NORTON HOSPITAL (O, 1232 beds) 200 East Chestnut Street, Louisville, KY, Zip 40202–1800, Mailing Address: P.O. Box 35070, Zip 40232–5070, tel. 502/629–8000; Matthew Ayers, Chief Administrative Officer

Owned, leased, sponsored:	2 hospitals	1511 beds
Contract-managed:	0 hospitals	0 beds
Totals:	2 hospitals	1511 beds

★0139: NOVANT HEALTH (NP)
2085 Frontis Plaza Boulevard, Winston Salem, NC, Zip 27103–5614; tel. 336/718–5600; Carl S. Armato, President and Chief Executive Officer
(Independent Hospital System)

NORTH CAROLINA: ASHE MEMORIAL HOSPITAL (C, 25 beds) 200 Hospital Avenue, Jefferson, NC, Zip 28640–9244; tel. 336/846–7101; Laura Lambeth, Chief Executive Officer
Web address: www.ashememorial.org

HALIFAX REGIONAL MEDICAL CENTER (C, 142 beds) 250 Smith Church Road, Roanoke Rapids, NC, Zip 27870–4914, Mailing Address: P.O. Box 1089, Zip 27870–1089, tel. 252/535–8011; William Mahone, President and Chief Executive Officer
Web address: www.halifaxmedicalcenter.org

NOVANT HEALTH BRUNSWICK MEDICAL CENTER (O, 54 beds) 240 Hospital Drive NE, Bolivia, NC, Zip 28422–8346; tel. 910/721–1000; Shelbourn Stevens, President and Chief Operating Officer
Web address: https://www.novanthealth.org

NOVANT HEALTH CHARLOTTE ORTHOPAEDIC HOSPITAL (O, 31 beds) 1901 Randolph Road, Charlotte, NC, Zip 28207–1195; tel. 704/316–2000; Jason Bernd, President and Chief Operating Officer

NOVANT HEALTH FORSYTH MEDICAL CENTER (O, 740 beds) 3333 Silas Creek Parkway, Winston-Salem, NC, Zip 27103–3090; tel. 336/718–5000; Chad Setliff, President and Chief Operating Officer
Web address: https://www.novanthealth.org

NOVANT HEALTH HUNTERSVILLE MEDICAL CENTER (O, 91 beds) 10030 Gilead Road, Huntersville, NC, Zip 28078–7545, Mailing Address: P.O. Box 3508, Zip 28070–3508, tel. 704/316–4000; Mike Riley, President and Chief Operating Officer

NOVANT HEALTH MATTHEWS MEDICAL CENTER (O, 117 beds) 1500 Matthews Township Parkway, Matthews, NC, Zip 28105–4656; tel. 704/384–6500; Roland R. Bibeau, President and Chief Operating Officer
Web address: https://www.novanthealth.org

NOVANT HEALTH MEDICAL PARK HOSPITAL (O, 21 beds) 1950 South Hawthorne Road, Winston-Salem, NC, Zip 27103–3993; tel. 336/718–0600; Kirsten Royster, President and Chief Operating Officer
Web address: www.novanthealth.org

NOVANT HEALTH PRESBYTERIAN MEDICAL CENTER (O, 440 beds) 200 Hawthorne Lane, Charlotte, NC, Zip 28204–2528, Mailing Address: P.O. Box 33549, Zip 28233–3549, tel. 704/384–4000; Paula Vincent, MSN, President and Chief Operating Officer

NOVANT HEALTH ROWAN MEDICAL CENTER (O, 149 beds) 612 Mocksville Avenue, Salisbury, NC, Zip 28144–2799; tel. 704/210–5000; Dari Caldwell, R.N., Ph.D., FACHE, President and Chief Operating Officer
Web address: https://www.novanthealth.org/rowan-medical-center.aspx

NOVANT HEALTH THOMASVILLE MEDICAL CENTER (O, 87 beds) 207 Old Lexington Road, Thomasville, NC, Zip 27360–3428, Mailing Address: P.O. Box 789, Zip 27361–0789, tel. 336/472–2000; Jon D. Applebaum, President and Chief Operating Officer
Web address: www.thomasvillemedicalcenter.org

VIRGINIA: NOVANT HEALTH UVA HEALTH SYSTEM CULPEPER MEDICAL CENTER (O, 68 beds) 501 Sunset Lane, Culpeper, VA, Zip 22701–3917, Mailing Address: P.O. Box 592, Zip 22701–0500, tel. 540/829–4100; Jeff Hotmanski, President and Chief Operating Officer

NOVANT HEALTH UVA HEALTH SYSTEM HAYMARKET MEDICAL CENTER (O, 18 beds) 15225 Heathcote Boulevard, Haymarket, VA, Zip 20155–4023, Mailing Address: 14535 John Marshall Hwy, Gainesville, Zip 20155–4023, tel. 571/284–1000; Stephen Smith, President and Chief Operating Officer
Web address: www.novanthealth.org

NOVANT HEALTH UVA HEALTH SYSTEM PRINCE WILLIAM MEDICAL CENTER (O, 87 beds) 8700 Sudley Road, Manassas, VA, Zip 20110–4418, Mailing Address: P.O. Box 2610, Zip 20108–0867, tel. 703/369–8000; Stephen Smith, President and Chief Operating Officer
Web address: www.pwhs.org

Owned, leased, sponsored:	12 hospitals	1903 beds
Contract-managed:	2 hospitals	167 beds
Totals:	14 hospitals	2070 beds

★3075: NYC HEALTH + HOSPITALS (NP)
125 Worth Street, Room 514, New York, NY, Zip 10013–4006; tel. 212/788–3321; Mitchell H. Katz, M.D., Chief Executive Officer
(Decentralized Health System)

NEW YORK: NYC HEALTH + HOSPITALS / BELLEVUE (O, 722 beds) 462 First Avenue, New York, NY, Zip 10016–9198; tel. 212/562–4141; William Hicks, Chief Executive Officer
Web address: www.nyc.gov/bellevue

NYC HEALTH + HOSPITALS / CONEY ISLAND (O, 381 beds) 2601 Ocean Parkway, Brooklyn, NY, Zip 11235–7795; tel. 718/616–3000; William A. Brown, FACHE, Chief Executive Officer

NYC HEALTH + HOSPITALS / ELMHURST (O, 506 beds) 79–01 Broadway, Elmhurst, NY, Zip 11373–1329; tel. 718/334–4000; Israel Rocha Jr, Chief Executive Officer
Web address: www.nyc.gov/html/hhc/ehc/html/home/home.shtml

Section B

For explanation of codes following names, see page B2.
★ Indicates Type III membership in the American Hospital Association.

NYC HEALTH + HOSPITALS / GOUVERNEUR (O, 196 beds) 227 Madison Street, New York, NY, Zip 10002; tel. 212/238-7000; Martha Adams Sullivan, Chief Executive Officer

NYC HEALTH + HOSPITALS / HARLEM (O, 258 beds) 506 Lenox Avenue, New York, NY, Zip 10037-1802; tel. 212/939-1000; Ebone' Carrington, Chief Executive Officer and Chief Operating Officer
Web address: www.nyc.gov/html/hhc/harlem

NYC HEALTH + HOSPITALS / HENRY J CARTER SPECIALTY HOSPITAL AND MEDICAL CENTER (O, 365 beds) 1752 Park Avenue, New York, NY, Zip 10035; tel. 646/686-0000; Robert K. Hughes, Executive Director

NYC HEALTH + HOSPITALS / JACOBI (O, 388 beds) 1400 Pelham Parkway South, Bronx, NY, Zip 10461-1197; tel. 718/918-5000; Christopher Mastromanno, Interim Chief Executive Officer
Web address: www.nyc.gov/html/hhc/jacobi/home.html

NYC HEALTH + HOSPITALS / KINGS COUNTY (O, 544 beds) 451 Clarkson Avenue, Brooklyn, NY, Zip 11203-2054; tel. 718/245-3131; Sheldon Mcleod, Chief Executive Officer

NYC HEALTH + HOSPITALS / LINCOLN (O, 347 beds) 234 East 149th Street, Bronx, NY, Zip 10451-5504, Mailing Address: 234 East 149th Street, Room 923, Zip 10451-5504, tel. 718/579-5700; Milton Nunez, Executive Director
Web address: www.nyc.gov/html/hhc/lincoln

NYC HEALTH + HOSPITALS / METROPOLITAN (O, 273 beds) 1901 First Avenue, New York, NY, Zip 10029-7404; tel. 212/423-6262; Alina Moran, Chief Executive Officer
Web address: www.nyc.gov/html/hhc/mhc/html/home/home.shtml

NYC HEALTH + HOSPITALS / NORTH CENTRAL BRONX (O, 142 beds) 3424 Kossuth Avenue, Bronx, NY, Zip 10467-2489; tel. 718/519-3500; Maureen Pode, Co-Interim Executive Director

NYC HEALTH + HOSPITALS / QUEENS (O, 259 beds) 82-68 164th Street, Jamaica, NY, Zip 11432-1104; tel. 718/883-3000; Christopher Roker, Chief Executive Officer
Web address: www.nyc.gov/html/hhc/qhc/html/home/home.shtml

NYC HEALTH + HOSPITALS / SEA VIEW (O, 304 beds) 460 Brielle Avenue, Staten Island, NY, Zip 10314; tel. 212/390-8181; Jane M. Lyons, Executive Director

NYC HEALTH + HOSPITALS / WOODHULL (O, 274 beds) 760 Broadway, Brooklyn, NY, Zip 11206-5383; tel. 718/963-8000; Gregory Calliste, Ph.D., FACHE, Chief Executive Officer
Web address: www.nyc.gov/html/hhc

Owned, leased, sponsored:	14 hospitals	4959 beds
Contract-managed:	0 hospitals	0 beds
Totals:	14 hospitals	4959 beds

1026: NYU LANGONE HEALTH (NP)

550 First Avenue, New York, NY, Zip 10016-6402; tel. 646/929-7870; Robert I. Grossman, M.D., Chief Executive Officer
(Moderately Centralized Health System)

NEW YORK: NYU LANGONE HOSPITALS (O, 1152 beds) 550 First Avenue, New York, NY, Zip 10016-6402; tel. 212/263-7300; Robert I. Grossman, M.D., Chief Executive Officer
Web address: www.nyumedicalcenter.org

NYU WINTHROP HOSPITAL (O, 511 beds) 259 First Street, Mineola, NY, Zip 11501-3957; tel. 516/663-0333; John F. Collins, President and Chief Executive Officer

Owned, leased, sponsored:	2 hospitals	1663 beds
Contract-managed:	0 hospitals	0 beds
Totals:	2 hospitals	1663 beds

0616: OCEANS HEALTHCARE (IO)

2720 Rue de Jardin, Suite 100, Lake Charles, LA, Zip 70605-4050; tel. 337/721-1900; Jason Reed, President and Chief Executive Officer
(Independent Hospital System)

LOUISIANA: OCEANS BEHAVIORAL HOSPITAL OF ALEXANDRIA (O, 24 beds) 2621 North Bolton Avenue, Alexandria, LA, Zip 71303-4506; tel. 318/448-8473; Ben Cooper, Administrator
Web address: www.obha.info/

OCEANS BEHAVIORAL HOSPITAL OF BATON ROUGE (O, 20 beds) 11135 Florida Boulevard, Baton Rouge, LA, Zip 70815-2013; tel. 225/356-7030; Valerie Dalton, R.N., Administrator
Web address: www.obhbr.info/

OCEANS BEHAVIORAL HOSPITAL OF BROUSSARD (O, 38 beds) 418 Albertson Parkway, Broussard, LA, Zip 70518-4971; tel. 337/237-6444; Amy Dysart-Credeur, Administrator

OCEANS BEHAVIORAL HOSPITAL OF DE RIDDER (O, 20 beds) 1420 Blankenship Drive, Deridder, LA, Zip 70634-4604; tel. 337/460-9472; Stuart Archer, Chief Executive Officer, Oceans Healthcare
Web address: www.obhd.info/

OCEANS BEHAVIORAL HOSPITAL OF GREATER NEW ORLEANS (O, 30 beds) 716 Village Road, Kenner, LA, Zip 70065-2751; tel. 504/464-8895; Deborah Spier, Administrator
Web address: www.obhgno.info/

OCEANS BEHAVIORAL HOSPITAL OF KENTWOOD (O, 16 beds) 921 Avenue G, Kentwood, LA, Zip 70444-2636; tel. 985/229-0717; Marty Dean, Administrator

OCEANS BEHAVIORAL HOSPITAL OF LAKE CHARLES (O, 40 beds) 4250 5th Avenue, Lake Charles, LA, Zip 70607-3900; tel. 337/474-7581; Nicholas D. Guillory, MSN, Administrator
Web address: www.obhlc.info/

OCEANS BEHAVIORAL HOSPITAL OF OPELOUSAS (O, 20 beds) 1310 Heather Drive, Opelousas, LA, Zip 70570-7714; tel. 337/948-8820; Katherine Simoneaux, Administrator
Web address: www.obho.info/

TEXAS: OCEANS BEHAVIORAL HEALTH CENTER PERMIAN BASIN (O, 58 beds) 3300 South FM 1788, Midland, TX, Zip 79706-2601; tel. 432/561-5915; Lorie Dunnam, Chief Executive Officer
Web address: www.oceanspermianbasin.com/

OCEANS BEHAVIORAL HOSPITAL ABILENE (O, 90 beds) 4225 Woods Place, Abilene, TX, Zip 79602-7991; tel. 325/691-0030; Stacy Sanford, Chief Executive Officer
Web address: www.oceansabilene.com

OCEANS BEHAVIORAL HOSPITAL KATY (O, 48 beds) 455 Park Grove Lane, Katy, TX, Zip 77450-1572; tel. 281/492-8888; Stuart Archer, Chief Executive Officer

OCEANS BEHAVIORAL HOSPITAL LONGVIEW (O, 24 beds) 615 Clinic Drive, Longview, TX, Zip 75605-5172; tel. 903/212-3105; Lauren Weber, Administrator
Web address: www.oceanslongview.com/

OCEANS BEHAVIORAL HOSPITAL LUFKIN (O, 24 beds) 302 Gobblers Knob Road, Lufkin, TX, Zip 75904-5419; tel. 936/632-2276; Laci Laird, Chief Executive Officer

Owned, leased, sponsored:	13 hospitals	452 beds
Contract-managed:	0 hospitals	0 beds
Totals:	13 hospitals	452 beds

★0359: OCHSNER HEALTH SYSTEM (NP)

1514 Jefferson Highway, New Orleans, LA, Zip 70121-2429; tel. 800/874-8984; Warner L. Thomas, FACHE, President and Chief Executive Officer
(Centralized Health System)

LOUISIANA: LEONARD J. CHABERT MEDICAL CENTER (C, 78 beds) 1978 Industrial Boulevard, Houma, LA, Zip 70363-7094; tel. 985/873-2200; Timothy J. Allen, FACHE, Chief Executive Officer
Web address: www.ochsner.org/locations/leonard_j_chabert_medical_center/

OCHSNER MEDICAL CENTER – BATON ROUGE (O, 152 beds) 17000 Medical Center Drive, Baton Rouge, LA, Zip 70816-3224; tel. 225/752-2470; Eric McMillen, FACHE, Chief Executive Officer

OCHSNER MEDICAL CENTER – KENNER (O, 110 beds) 180 West Esplanade Avenue, Kenner, LA, Zip 70065-6001; tel. 504/468-8600; Stephen Robinson Jr, FACHE, Chief Executive Officer
Web address: https://www.ochsner.org/locations/ochsner-medical-center-kenner/

OCHSNER MEDICAL CENTER – NORTH SHORE (L, 163 beds) 100 Medical Center Drive, Slidell, LA, Zip 70461-5520; tel. 985/649-7070; John J. Herman, FACHE, Chief Executive Officer
Web address: https://www.ochsner.org/locations/ochsner-medical-center-north-shore/

For explanation of codes following names, see page B2.
★ Indicates Type III membership in the American Hospital Association.

OCHSNER MEDICAL CENTER (O, 934 beds) 1514 Jefferson Highway, New Orleans, LA, Zip 70121–2429; tel. 504/842–3000; Robert K. Wolterman, Chief Executive Officer

OCHSNER ST. ANNE GENERAL HOSPITAL (O, 35 beds) 4608 Highway 1, Raceland, LA, Zip 70394–2623; tel. 985/537–6841; Timothy J. Allen, FACHE, Chief Executive Officer
Web address: www.ochsner.org/locations/ochsner-st-anne

SLIDELL MEMORIAL HOSPITAL (C, 175 beds) 1001 Gause Boulevard, Slidell, LA, Zip 70458–2987; tel. 985/280–2200; Kerry Tirman, JD, FACHE, Chief Executive Officer
Web address: www.slidellmemorial.org

ST. BERNARD PARISH HOSPITAL (C, 40 beds) 8000 West Judge Perez Drive, Chalmette, LA, Zip 70043–1668; tel. 504/826–9500; Kimberly Keene, R.N., Chief Executive Officer

ST. CHARLES PARISH HOSPITAL (C, 59 beds) 1057 Paul Maillard Road, Luling, LA, Zip 70070–4349, Mailing Address: P.O. Box 87, Zip 70070–0087, tel. 985/785–6242; Austin Reeder, M.P.H., Chief Executive Officer
Web address: https://www.ochsner.org/locations/st-charles-parish-hospital/

MISSISSIPPI: HANCOCK MEDICAL CENTER (C, 102 beds) 149 Drinkwater Boulevard, Bay Saint Louis, MS, Zip 39520–1658, Bay St Louis, tel. 228/467–8600; Alan Hodges, Chief Executive Officer

Owned, leased, sponsored:	5 hospitals	1394 beds
Contract-managed:	5 hospitals	454 beds
Totals:	10 hospitals	1848 beds

0537: OHIO DEPARTMENT OF MENTAL HEALTH (NP)
30 East Broad Street, 8th Floor, Columbus, OH, Zip 43215–3430; tel. 614/466–2297; Tracy Plouck, Director
(Independent Hospital System)

OHIO: APPALACHIAN BEHAVIORAL HEALTHCARE (O, 224 beds) 100 Hospital Drive, Athens, OH, Zip 45701–2301; tel. 740/594–5000; Jane E. Krason, R.N., Chief Executive Officer
Web address: www.mh.state.oh.us

HEARTLAND BEHAVIORAL HEALTHCARE (O, 152 beds) 3000 Erie Stree South, Massillon, OH, Zip 44646–7993, Mailing Address: 3000 Erie Street South, Zip 44646–7976, tel. 330/833–3135, Jeffrey Sims, Chief Executive Officer
Web address: www.mh.state.oh.us/lbhs/bhos/hoh.html

NORTHCOAST BEHAVIORAL HEALTHCARE (O, 258 beds) 1756 Sagamore Road, Northfield, OH, Zip 44067–1086; tel. 330/467–7131; Douglas W. Kern, Chief Executive Officer

NORTHWEST OHIO PSYCHIATRIC HOSPITAL (O, 112 beds) 930 Detroit Avenue, Toledo, OH, Zip 43614–2701; tel. 419/381–1881; Brett M. Johnson, Chief Executive Officer
Web address: www.mh.state.oh.us/

SUMMIT BEHAVIORAL HEALTHCARE (O, 291 beds) 1101 Summit Road, Cincinnati, OH, Zip 45237–2652; tel. 513/948–3600; Elizabeth Banks, Chief Executive Officer
Web address: www.mh.state.oh.us/

TWIN VALLEY BEHAVIORAL HEALTHCARE (O, 178 beds) 2200 West Broad Street, Columbus, OH, Zip 43223–1297; tel. 614/752–0333; Veronica Lofton, Acting Chief Executive Officer
Web address: www.mh.state.oh.us/ibhs/bhos/tvbh.html

Owned, leased, sponsored:	6 hospitals	1215 beds
Contract-managed:	0 hospitals	0 beds
Totals:	6 hospitals	1215 beds

★0251: OHIO STATE UNIVERSITY HEALTH SYSTEM (NP)
370 West Ninth Avenue, Columbus, OH, Zip 43210–1238; tel. 614/685–9015; David P. McQuaid, FACHE, Chief Executive Officer
(Centralized Physician/Insurance Health System)

OHIO: JAMES CANCER HOSPITAL AND SOLOVE RESEARCH INSTITUTE (O, 308 beds) 460 West Tenth Avenue, Columbus, OH, Zip 43210–1240; tel. 614/293–3300; William Farrar, M.D., Interim Chief Executive Officer
Web address: www.https://cancer.osu.edu/

OHIO STATE UNIVERSITY WEXNER MEDICAL CENTER (O, 1091 beds) 410 West 10th Avenue, Columbus, OH, Zip 43210–1240; tel. 614/293–8000; David P. McQuaid, FACHE, Chief Operating Officer
Web address: www.medicalcenter.osu.edu

Owned, leased, sponsored:	2 hospitals	1399 beds
Contract-managed:	0 hospitals	0 beds
Totals:	2 hospitals	1399 beds

★0162: OHIOHEALTH (NP)
180 East Broad Street, Columbus, OH, Zip 43215–3707; tel. 614/544–4455; Stephen Markovich, M.D., President and Chief Executive Officer
(Moderately Centralized Health System)

OHIO: BERGER HEALTH SYSTEM (L, 56 beds) 600 North Pickaway Street, Circleville, OH, Zip 43113–1447; tel. 740/474–2126; Tim A. Colburn, President and Chief Executive Officer
Web address: www.bergerhealth.com

MORROW COUNTY HOSPITAL (C, 23 beds) 651 West Marion Road, Mount Gilead, OH, Zip 43338–1027; tel. 419/946–5015; Chad J. Miller, President and Chief Executive Officer
Web address: www.morrowcountyhospital.com

O'BLENESS MEMORIAL HOSPITAL (O, 76 beds) 55 Hospital Drive, Athens, OH, Zip 45701–2302; tel. 740/593–5551; Mark R. Seckinger, President

OHIOHEALTH DOCTORS HOSPITAL (O, 195 beds) 5100 West Broad Street, Columbus, OH, Zip 43228–1607; tel. 614/544–1000; Michael L. Reichfield, President
Web address: www.ohiohealth.com

OHIOHEALTH DUBLIN METHODIST HOSPITAL (O, 114 beds) 7500 Hospital Drive, Dublin, OH, Zip 43016–8518; tel. 614/544–8000; Steve Bunyard, President

OHIOHEALTH GRADY MEMORIAL HOSPITAL (O, 61 beds) 561 West Central Avenue, Delaware, OH, Zip 43015–1410; tel. 740/615–1000; Steve Bunyard, President
Web address: www.ohiohealth.com

OHIOHEALTH GRANT MEDICAL CENTER (O, 471 beds) 111 South Grant Avenue, Columbus, OH, Zip 43215–1898; tel. 614/566–9000; Michael Lawson, President and Chief Operating Officer

OHIOHEALTH HARDIN MEMORIAL HOSPITAL (O, 25 beds) 921 East Franklin Street, Kenton, OH, Zip 43326–2099; tel. 419/673–0761; Ron Snyder, Chief Operating Officer
Web address: www.hardinmemorial.org

OHIOHEALTH MARION GENERAL HOSPITAL (O, 174 beds) 1000 McKinley Park Drive, Marion, OH, Zip 43302–6397; tel. 740/383–8400; Curtis Gingrich, M.D., Chief Operating Officer
Web address: www.ohiohealth.com/mariongeneral

OHIOHEALTH MEDCENTRAL MANSFIELD HOSPITAL (O, 249 beds) 335 Glessner Avenue, Mansfield, OH, Zip 44903–2265; tel. 419/526–8000; Vinson Yates, President

OHIOHEALTH MEDCENTRAL SHELBY HOSPITAL (O, 25 beds) 199 West Main Street, Shelby, OH, Zip 44875–1490; tel. 419/342–5015; Vinson Yates, President
Web address: www.medcentral.org/body.cfm?id=153

OHIOHEALTH RIVERSIDE METHODIST HOSPITAL (O, 753 beds) 3535 Olentangy River Road, Columbus, OH, Zip 43214–3998; tel. 614/566–5000; Brian Jepson, President

Owned, leased, sponsored:	11 hospitals	2199 beds
Contract-managed:	1 hospitals	23 beds
Totals:	12 hospitals	2222 beds

0018: OKLAHOMA DEPARTMENT OF MENTAL HEALTH AND SUBSTANCE ABUSE SERVICES (NP)
1200 NE 13th Street, Oklahoma City, OK, Zip 73117–1022, Mailing Address: P.O. Box 53277, Zip 73152–3277, tel. 405/522–3908; Terri White, Commissioner
(Independent Hospital System)

For explanation of codes following names, see page B2.
★ Indicates Type III membership in the American Hospital Association.

OKLAHOMA: GRIFFIN MEMORIAL HOSPITAL (O, 120 beds) 900 East Main Street, Norman, OK, Zip 73071–5305, Mailing Address: P.O. Box 151, Zip 73070–0151, tel. 405/573–6600; Henry Hartsell, Ph.D., Executive Director
Web address: www.odmhsas.org

NORTHWEST CENTER FOR BEHAVIORAL HEALTH (O, 24 beds) 1 Mi East Highway 270, Fort Supply, OK, Zip 73841, Mailing Address: 1222 10th Street, Suite 211, Woodward, Zip 73801–3156, tel. 580/766–2311; Cathy Billings, Interim Executive Director

OKLAHOMA FORENSIC CENTER (O, 200 beds) 24800 South 4420 Road, Vinita, OK, Zip 74301–5544, Mailing Address: P.O. Box 69, Zip 74301–0069, tel. 918/256–7841; Kevan Finley, Chief Executive Officer
Web address: www.odmhsas.org

Owned, leased, sponsored:	3 hospitals	344 beds
Contract-managed:	0 hospitals	0 beds
Totals:	3 hospitals	344 beds

3355: ORLANDO HEALTH (NP)

1414 Kuhl Avenue, Orlando, FL, Zip 32806–2093; tel. 321/843–7000; David W. Strong, President and Chief Executive Officer
(Moderately Centralized Health System)

FLORIDA: HEALTH CENTRAL HOSPITAL (O, 439 beds) 10000 West Colonial Drive, Ocoee, FL, Zip 34761–3499; tel. 407/296–1000; Mark A. Marsh, President
Web address: www.healthcentral.org

ORLANDO REGIONAL MEDICAL CENTER (O, 1331 beds) 52 West Underwood Street, Orlando, FL, Zip 32806; tel. 407/841–5111; Mark A. Jones, President

SOUTH LAKE HOSPITAL (O, 170 beds) 1900 Don Wickham Drive, Clermont, FL, Zip 34711–1979; tel. 352/394–4071; John Moore, President
Web address: www.southlakehospital.com

Owned, leased, sponsored:	3 hospitals	1940 beds
Contract-managed:	0 hospitals	0 beds
Totals:	3 hospitals	1940 beds

★5335: OSF HEALTHCARE (CC)

800 NE Glen Oak Avenue, Peoria, IL, Zip 61603–3200; tel. 309/655–2850; Robert Sehring, Chief Executive Officer
(Moderately Centralized Health System)

ILLINOIS: OSF HEALTHCARE SAINT ANTHONY'S HEALTH CENTER (O, 140 beds) 1 Saint Anthony's Way, Alton, IL, Zip 62002–4579, Mailing Address: PO Box 340, Zip 62002–0340, tel. 618/465–2571; Ajay Pathak, President

OSF HEART OF MARY MEDICAL CENTER (O, 181 beds) 1400 West Park Street, Urbana, IL, Zip 61801–2396, Mailing Address: P.O. Box 6259, Peoria, Zip 61601, tel. 217/337–2000; Jared Rogers, M.D., President and Chief Executive Officer
Web address: www.presencehealth.org/covenant

OSF HOLY FAMILY MEDICAL CENTER (O, 23 beds) 1000 West Harlem Avenue, Monmouth, IL, Zip 61462–1007; tel. 309/734–3141; Patricia A. Luker, President
Web address: www.osfholyfamily.org

OSF SACRED HEART MEDICAL CENTER (O, 117 beds) 812 North Logan, Danville, IL, Zip 61832–3788; tel. 217/443–5000; Jared Rogers, M.D., President and Chief Executive Officer

OSF SAINT ANTHONY MEDICAL CENTER (O, 235 beds) 5666 East State Street, Rockford, IL, Zip 61108–2425; tel. 815/226–2000; Paula A. Carynski, MS, R.N., President
Web address: www.osfhealth.com

OSF SAINT ELIZABETH MEDICAL CENTER (O, 87 beds) 1100 East Norris Drive, Ottawa, IL, Zip 61350–1687; tel. 815/433–3100; Kenneth Beutke, President

OSF SAINT FRANCIS MEDICAL CENTER (O, 629 beds) 530 NE Glen Oak Avenue, Peoria, IL, Zip 61637–0001; tel. 309/655–2000; Robert G. Anderson Jr, President
Web address: www.osfsaintfrancis.org

OSF SAINT JAMES – JOHN W. ALBRECHT MEDICAL CENTER (O, 42 beds) 2500 West Reynolds, Pontiac, IL, Zip 61764–9774; tel. 815/842–2828; Bradley V. Solberg, FACHE, President
Web address: www.osfsaintjames.org

OSF SAINT LUKE MEDICAL CENTER (O, 25 beds) 1051 West South Street, Kewanee, IL, Zip 61443–8354, Mailing Address: P.O. Box 747, Zip 61443–0747, tel. 309/852–7500; Jacqueline D. Kernan, President

OSF SAINT PAUL MEDICAL CENTER (O, 25 beds) 1401 East 12th Street, Mendota, IL, Zip 61342–9216; tel. 815/539–7461; Dawn Trompeter, President
Web address: https://www.osfhealthcare.org/saint-paul

OSF ST. JOSEPH MEDICAL CENTER (O, 149 beds) 2200 East Washington Street, Bloomington, IL, Zip 61701–4323; tel. 309/662–3311; Lynn Fulton, President

OSF ST. MARY MEDICAL CENTER (O, 71 beds) 3333 North Seminary Street, Galesburg, IL, Zip 61401–1299; tel. 309/344–3161; Jennifer Junis, MSN, R.N., President
Web address: www.osfstmary.org

SAINT CLARE HOME (O, 0 beds) 5533 North Galena Road, Peoria Heights, IL, Zip 61614–4499; tel. 309/682–5428; Candy Conover, Administrator

ST. ANTHONY'S CONTINUING CARE CENTER (O, 179 beds) 767 30th Street, Rock Island, IL, Zip 61201, Sister; Mary Anthony. Mazzaferri, Administrator

MICHIGAN: OSF ST. FRANCIS HOSPITAL AND MEDICAL GROUP (O, 25 beds) 3401 Ludington Street, Escanaba, MI, Zip 49829–1377; tel. 906/786–3311; David Lord, President
Web address: www.osfstfrancis.org

Owned, leased, sponsored:	15 hospitals	1928 beds
Contract-managed:	0 hospitals	0 beds
Totals:	15 hospitals	1928 beds

0982: OWENSBORO HEALTH (NP)

1201 Pleasant Valley Road, Owensboro, KY, Zip 42303–9811; tel. 270/417–2000; Greg Strahan, Interim Chief Executive Officer
(Moderately Centralized Health System)

KENTUCKY: OWENSBORO HEALTH MUHLENBERG COMMUNITY HOSPITAL (O, 105 beds) 440 Hopkinsville Street, Greenville, KY, Zip 42345–1172, Mailing Address: P.O. Box 387, Zip 42345–0378, tel. 270/338–8000; Ed Heath, FACHE, Chief Executive Officer
Web address: www.mchky.org

OWENSBORO HEALTH REGIONAL HOSPITAL (O, 360 beds) 1201 Pleasant Valley Road, Owensboro, KY, Zip 42303; tel. 270/417–2000; Greg Strahan, Interim Chief Executive Officer

Owned, leased, sponsored:	2 hospitals	465 beds
Contract-managed:	0 hospitals	0 beds
Totals:	2 hospitals	465 beds

0367: PACER HEALTH CORPORATION (IO)

14100 Palmetto Frontage Road, Suite 110, Miami Lakes, FL, Zip 33016; tel. 305/828–7660; Rainier Gonzalez, Chairman and Chief Executive Officer

KENTUCKY: BARBOURVILLE ARH HOSPITAL (O, 25 beds) 80 Hospital Drive, Barbourville, KY, Zip 40906–7363, Mailing Address: P.O. Box 10, Zip 40906–0010, tel. 606/546–4175; Charles D. Lovell Jr, FACHE, Chief Executive Officer
Web address: www.knoxcohospital.com

Owned, leased, sponsored:	1 hospitals	25 beds
Contract-managed:	0 hospitals	0 beds
Totals:	1 hospitals	25 beds

★5235: PALLOTTINE HEALTH SERVICES (CC)

2900 First Avenue, Huntington, WV, Zip 25702–1241; tel. 304/526–1234; Michael G. Sellards, Chief Executive Officer
(Independent Hospital System)

Owned, leased, sponsored:	0 hospitals	0 beds
Contract-managed:	0 hospitals	0 beds
Totals:	0 hospitals	0 beds

For explanation of codes following names, see page B2.
★ Indicates Type III membership in the American Hospital Association.

★**7555: PALOMAR HEALTH** (NP)
456 East Grand Avenue, Escondido, CA, Zip 92025–3319;
tel. 760/740–6393; Diane Hansen, Chief Executive Officer
(Independent Hospital System)

CALIFORNIA: PALOMAR MEDICAL CENTER POWAY (O, 201 beds) 15615 Pomerado Road, Poway, CA, Zip 92064–2460; tel. 858/613–4000; Cheryl Olson, Vice President
Web address: www.pph.org

PALOMAR MEDICAL CENTER (O, 403 beds) 2185 West Citracado Parkway, Escondido, CA, Zip 92029–4159; tel. 760/739–3000; Mariellena Sudak, R.N., MSN, Vice President and Chief Nursing Officer

Owned, leased, sponsored:	2 hospitals	604 beds
Contract-managed:	0 hospitals	0 beds
Totals:	2 hospitals	604 beds

★**0159: PARKVIEW HEALTH** (NP)
10501 Corporate Drive, Fort Wayne, IN, Zip 46845–1700;
tel. 260/373–7001; Michael J. Packnett, President and Chief Executive Officer

(Centralized Physician/Insurance Health System)

INDIANA: PARKVIEW ORTHO HOSPITAL (O, 37 beds) 11130 Parkview Circle Drive, Fort Wayne, IN, Zip 46845–1735; tel. 260/672–5000; Julie Fleck, Chief Operating Officer
Web address: www.parkview.com

PARKVIEW HUNTINGTON HOSPITAL (O, 36 beds) 2001 Stults Road, Huntington, IN, Zip 46750–1291; tel. 260/355–3000; Juli Johnson, MSN, R.N., President
Web address: www.parkview.com

PARKVIEW LAGRANGE HOSPITAL (O, 25 beds) 207 North Townline Road, LaGrange, IN, Zip 46761–1325; tel. 260/463–9000; Jordi K. Disler, President
Web address: www.parkview.com

PARKVIEW NOBLE HOSPITAL (O, 31 beds) 401 Sawyer Road, Kendallville, IN, Zip 46755–2568; tel. 260/347–8700; Gary W. Adkins, President
Web address: www.parkview.com

PARKVIEW REGIONAL MEDICAL CENTER (O, 753 beds) 11109 Parkview Plaza Drive, Fort Wayne, IN, Zip 46845–1701; tel. 260/266–1000; Ben Miles, President
Web address: www.parkview.com

PARKVIEW WABASH HOSPITAL (O, 18 beds) 10 John Kissinger Drive, Wabash, IN, Zip 46992–1648; tel. 260/563–3131; Marilyn J. Custer-Mitchell, President

PARKVIEW WHITLEY HOSPITAL (O, 30 beds) 1260 East State Road 205, Columbia City, IN, Zip 46725–9492; tel. 260/248–9000; Scott F. Gabriel, President
Web address: www.parkview.com

Owned, leased, sponsored:	7 hospitals	930 beds
Contract-managed:	0 hospitals	0 beds
Totals:	7 hospitals	930 beds

★**1785: PARTNERS HEALTHCARE SYSTEM, INC.** (NP)
800 Boylston Street, Suite 1150, Boston, MA, Zip 02199–8123;
tel. 617/278–1004; Anne Klibanski, M.D., Chief Executive Officer
(Decentralized Health System)

MASSACHUSETTS: BRIGHAM AND WOMEN'S FAULKNER HOSPITAL (O, 125 beds) 1153 Centre Street, Boston, MA, Zip 02130–3446; tel. 617/983–7000; David O. McCready, President

BRIGHAM AND WOMEN'S HOSPITAL (O, 781 beds) 75 Francis Street, Boston, MA, Zip 02115–6110; tel. 617/732–5500; Elizabeth Nabel, M.D., President
Web address: www.brighamandwomens.org

COOLEY DICKINSON HOSPITAL (O, 56 beds) 30 Locust Street, Northampton, MA, Zip 01060–2093, Mailing Address: P.O. Box 5001, Zip 01061–5001, tel. 413/582–2000; Joanne Marquese, President and Chief Executive Officer
Web address: www.cooleydickinson.org

MARTHA'S VINEYARD HOSPITAL (O, 86 beds) One Hospital Road, Oak Bluffs, MA, Zip 2557, Mailing Address: P.O. Box 1477, Zip 02557–1477, tel. 508/693–0410; Denise Schepici, M.P.H., Chief Executive Officer and President
Web address: www.mvhospital.com/

MASSACHUSETTS EYE AND EAR (O, 41 beds) 243 Charles Street, Boston, MA, Zip 02114–3002; tel. 617/523–7900; John R. Fernandez, President and Chief Executive Officer

MASSACHUSETTS GENERAL HOSPITAL (O, 1032 beds) 55 Fruit Street, Boston, MA, Zip 02114–2696; tel. 617/726–2000; Peter L. Slavin, M.D., President
Web address: www.massgeneral.org

MCLEAN HOSPITAL (O, 217 beds) 115 Mill Street, Belmont, MA, Zip 02478–1064; tel. 617/855–2000; Scott L. Rauch, M.D., President and Psychiatrist in Chief
Web address: www.mcleanhospital.org

NANTUCKET COTTAGE HOSPITAL (O, 19 beds) 57 Prospect Street, Nantucket, MA, Zip 02554–2799; tel. 508/825–8100; Jeannette Ives. Erickson, Interim President and Chief Executive Officer

NEWTON-WELLESLEY HOSPITAL (O, 220 beds) 2014 Washington Street, Newton Lower Falls, MA, Zip 02462–1699; tel. 617/243–6000; Michael R. Jaff, D.O., President
Web address: www.nwh.org

NORTH SHORE MEDICAL CENTER (O, 362 beds) 81 Highland Avenue, Salem, MA, Zip 01970–2714; tel. 978/741–1200; David J. Roberts, M.D., President

SPAULDING HOSPITAL FOR CONTINUING MEDICAL CARE CAMBRIDGE (O, 118 beds) 1575 Cambridge Street, Cambridge, MA, Zip 02138–4308; tel. 617/876–4344; Maureen Banks, FACHE, MS, R.N., President
Web address: www.spauldingnetwork.org

SPAULDING REHABILITATION HOSPITAL CAPE COD (O, 60 beds) 311 Service Road, East Sandwich, MA, Zip 02537–1370; tel. 508/833–4000; Maureen Banks, FACHE, MS, R.N., President

SPAULDING REHABILITATION HOSPITAL (O, 132 beds) 300 First Avenue, Charlestown, MA, Zip 02129–3109; tel. 617/952–5000; David E. Storto, President
Web address: www.spauldingrehab.org

NEW HAMPSHIRE: WENTWORTH-DOUGLASS HOSPITAL (O, 142 beds) 789 Central Avenue, Dover, NH, Zip 3820; tel. 603/742–5252; Gregory J. Walker, Chief Executive Officer

Owned, leased, sponsored:	14 hospitals	3391 beds
Contract-managed:	0 hospitals	0 beds
Totals:	14 hospitals	3391 beds

★**5415: PEACEHEALTH** (CC)
1115 SE 164th Avenue, Vancouver, WA, Zip 98683;
tel. 360/729–1000; Elizabeth Dunne, President and Chief Executive Officer
(Moderately Centralized Health System)

ALASKA: PEACEHEALTH KETCHIKAN MEDICAL CENTER (L, 54 beds) 3100 Tongass Avenue, Ketchikan, AK, Zip 99901–5746; tel. 907/225–5171; Edward E. Freysinger, Chief Administrative Officer
Web address: www.peacehealth.org

OREGON: PEACEHEALTH COTTAGE GROVE COMMUNITY MEDICAL CENTER (O, 14 beds) 1515 Village Drive, Cottage Grove, OR, Zip 97424–9700; tel. 541/942–0511; Tim Herrmann, R.N., Administrator

PEACEHEALTH PEACE HARBOR MEDICAL CENTER (O, 21 beds) 400 Ninth Street, Florence, OR, Zip 97439–7398; tel. 541/997–8412; Jason F. Hawkins, Chief Administrative Officer
Web address: www.peacehealth.org

PEACEHEALTH SACRED HEART MEDICAL CENTER UNIVERSITY DISTRICT (O, 93 beds) 1255 Hilyard Street, Eugene, OR, Zip 97401–3700, Mailing Address: P.O. Box 10905, Zip 97440–2905, tel. 541/686–7300; Mary Anne McMurren, R.N., Chief Administrative Officer

PEACEHEALTH SACRED HEART MEDICAL CENTER AT RIVERBEND (O, 379 beds) 3333 Riverbend Drive, Springfield, OR, Zip 97477–8800; tel. 541/222–7300; Mary E. Kingston, FACHE, R.N., Chief Executive
Web address: www.peacehealth.org

WASHINGTON: PEACEHEALTH PEACE ISLAND MEDICAL CENTER (O, 10 beds) 1117 Spring Street, Friday Harbor, WA, Zip 98250–9782; tel. 360/378–2141; Merry Ann Keane, Chief Administrative Officer

For explanation of codes following names, see page B2.
★ Indicates Type III membership in the American Hospital Association.

PEACEHEALTH SOUTHWEST MEDICAL CENTER (O, 436 beds) 400 NE Mother Joseph Place, Vancouver, WA, Zip 98664–3200, Mailing Address: P.O. Box 1600, Zip 98668–1600, tel. 360/256–2000; Sean Gregory, Chief Executive
Web address: www.peacehealth.org

PEACEHEALTH ST. JOHN MEDICAL CENTER (O, 180 beds) 1615 Delaware Street, Longview, WA, Zip 98632–2367, Mailing Address: P.O. Box 3002, Zip 98632–0302, tel. 360/414–2000; Cherelle Montanye-Ireland, Chief Administrative Officer

PEACEHEALTH ST. JOSEPH MEDICAL CENTER (O, 255 beds) 2901 Squalicum Parkway, Bellingham, WA, Zip 98225–1851; tel. 360/734–5400; Dale Zender, President Hospital Services NW
Web address: www.peacehealth.org

PEACEHEALTH UNITED GENERAL MEDICAL CENTER (C, 25 beds) 2000 Hospital Drive, Sedro-Woolley, WA, Zip 98284–4327; tel. 360/856–6021; Christopher Johnston, Chief Administrative Officer
Web address: www.peacehealth.org/united-general

Owned, leased, sponsored:	9 hospitals	1442 beds
Contract-managed:	1 hospitals	25 beds
Totals:	10 hospitals	1467 beds

0989: PENN STATE HERSHEY HEALTH SYSTEM (NP)
500 University Drive, Hershey, PA, Zip 17033–2360; tel. 717/531–8521; Stephen M. Massini, Chief Executive Officer
(Independent Hospital System)

PENNSYLVANIA: PENN STATE HEALTH ST. JOSEPH (O, 180 beds) 2500 Bernville Road, Reading, PA, Zip 19605–9453, Mailing Address: P.O. Box 316, Zip 19603–0316, tel. 610/378–2000; John R. Morahan, President and Chief Executive Officer
Web address: www.thefutureofhealthcare.org

PENN STATE MILTON S. HERSHEY MEDICAL CENTER (O, 528 beds) 500 University Drive, Hershey, PA, Zip 17033–2360, Mailing Address: P.O. Box 850, Zip 17033–0850, tel. 717/531–8521; Stephen M. Massini, Chief Executive Officer
Web address: www.pennstatehershey.org/

Owned, leased, sponsored:	2 hospitals	708 beds
Contract-managed:	0 hospitals	0 beds
Totals:	2 hospitals	708 beds

★0314: PHOEBE PUTNEY HEALTH SYSTEM (NP)
417 Third Avenue, Albany, GA, Zip 31701–1943; tel. 229/312–1000; Scott Steiner, FACHE, Chief Executive Officer
(Independent Hospital System)

GEORGIA: PHOEBE PUTNEY MEMORIAL HOSPITAL (O, 461 beds) 417 West Third Avenue, Albany, GA, Zip 31701–1943, Mailing Address: P.O. Box 3770, Zip 31706–3770, tel. 229/312–4100; Scott Steiner, FACHE, Chief Executive Officer
Web address: www.phoebeputney.com

PHOEBE SUMTER MEDICAL CENTER (O, 44 beds) 126 Highway, 280 West, Americus, GA, Zip 31719, Mailing Address: 126 Highway 280 West, Zip 31719, tel. 229/924–6011; Brandi Lunneborg, Chief Executive Officer

PHOEBE WORTH MEDICAL CENTER (O, 18 beds) 807 South Isabella Street, Sylvester, GA, Zip 31791–7554, Mailing Address: P.O. Box 545, Zip 31791–0545, tel. 229/776–6961; Kim Gilman, Chief Executive Officer
Web address: www.phoebeputney.com

SOUTHWEST GEORGIA REGIONAL MEDICAL CENTER (O, 25 beds) 361 Randolph Street, Cuthbert, GA, Zip 39840–6127; tel. 229/732–2181; Kim Gilman, Chief Executive Officer and Chief Nursing Officer

Owned, leased, sponsored:	4 hospitals	548 beds
Contract-managed:	0 hospitals	0 beds
Totals:	4 hospitals	548 beds

0043: PHYSICIANS FOR HEALTHY HOSPITALS (IO)
1117 East Devonshire Avenue, Hemet, CA, Zip 92543–3083; tel. 951/652–2811; Joel M. Bergenfeld, Chief Executive Officer

CALIFORNIA: HEMET VALLEY MEDICAL CENTER (O, 238 beds) 1117 East Devonshire Avenue, Hemet, CA, Zip 92543–3083; tel. 951/652–2811; Dan C. McLaughlin, Chief Hospital Executive Officer

MENIFEE VALLEY MEDICAL CENTER (O, 84 beds) 28400 McCall Boulevard, Sun City, CA, Zip 92585–9537; tel. 951/679–8888; Dan C. McLaughlin, Chief Executive Officer
Web address: www.valleyhealthsystem.com

Owned, leased, sponsored:	2 hospitals	322 beds
Contract-managed:	0 hospitals	0 beds
Totals:	2 hospitals	322 beds

0310: PIEDMONT HEALTHCARE (NP)
1800 Howell Mill Road NW, Suite 850, Roswell, GA, Zip 30076, Atlanta, tel. 404/425–1314; Kevin Brown, President and Chief Executive Officer
(Moderately Centralized Health System)

GEORGIA: PIEDMONT ATHENS REGIONAL MEDICAL CENTER (O, 345 beds) 1199 Prince Avenue, Athens, GA, Zip 30606–2797; tel. 706/475–7000; Michael Burnett, Chief Executive Officer
Web address: https://www.piedmont.org/locations/piedmont-athens

PIEDMONT COLUMBUS REGIONAL MIDTOWN (O, 510 beds) 710 Center Street, Columbus, GA, Zip 31901–1527, Mailing Address: P.O. Box 951, Zip 31902–0951, tel. 706/571–1000; M. Scott. Hill, President and Chief Executive Officer
Web address: www.columbusregional.com

PIEDMONT COLUMBUS REGIONAL NORTHSIDE (O, 100 beds) 100 Frist Court, Columbus, GA, Zip 31909–3578, Mailing Address: P.O. Box 7188, Zip 31908–7188, tel. 706/494–2100; M. Scott. Hill, President and Chief Executive Officer

PIEDMONT FAYETTE HOSPITAL (O, 221 beds) 1255 Highway 54 West, Fayetteville, GA, Zip 30214–4526; tel. 770/719–7000; Stephen D. Porter, Chief Executive Officer
Web address: www.piedmont.org

PIEDMONT HENRY HOSPITAL (L, 236 beds) 1133 Eagle's Landing Parkway, Stockbridge, GA, Zip 30281–5099; tel. 678/604–1000; Deborah Armstrong, Chief Executive Officer
Web address: www.piedmont.org

PIEDMONT HOSPITAL (O, 512 beds) 1968 Peachtree Road NW, Atlanta, GA, Zip 30309–1281; tel. 404/605–5000; Patrick M. Battey, FACS, M.D., Chief Executive Officer

PIEDMONT MOUNTAINSIDE HOSPITAL (O, 52 beds) 1266 Highway 515 South, Jasper, GA, Zip 30143–4872; tel. 706/692–2441; Denise Ray, Chief Executive Officer
Web address: https://www.piedmont.org

PIEDMONT NEWNAN HOSPITAL (O, 146 beds) 745 Poplar Road, Newnan, GA, Zip 30265–1618; tel. 770/400–1000; Michael Robertson, Chief Executive Officer

PIEDMONT NEWTON HOSPITAL (O, 103 beds) 5126 Hospital Drive, Covington, GA, Zip 30014–2567; tel. 770/786–7053; Eric Bour, M.D., FACS, Chief Executive Officer
Web address: www.newtonmedical.com

PIEDMONT ROCKDALE HOSPITAL (O, 158 beds) 1412 Milstead Avenue NE, Conyers, GA, Zip 30012–3877; tel. 770/918–3000; Richard Tanzella, Chief Executive Officer
Web address: www.rockdalemedicalcenter.org

PIEDMONT WALTON HOSPITAL (O, 52 beds) 2151 West Spring Street, Monroe, GA, Zip 30655–3115, Mailing Address: PO BOX 1346, Zip 30655–1346, tel. 770/267–8461; Larry W. Ebert Jr, Chief Executive Officer

Owned, leased, sponsored:	11 hospitals	2435 beds
Contract-managed:	0 hospitals	0 beds
Totals:	11 hospitals	2435 beds

★0958: PIH HEALTH (NP)
12401 Washington Boulevard, Whittier, CA, Zip 90602–1006; tel. 562/698–0811; James R. West, President and Chief Executive Officer
(Moderately Centralized Health System)

For explanation of codes following names, see page B2.
★ Indicates Type III membership in the American Hospital Association.

CALIFORNIA: PIH HEALTH HOSPITAL – DOWNEY (O, 156 beds) 11500 Brookshire Avenue, Downey, CA, Zip 90241–4917; tel. 562/904–5000; James R. West, President and Chief Executive Officer
Web address: www.PIHHealth.org

PIH HEALTH HOSPITAL – WHITTIER (O, 236 beds) 12401 Washington Boulevard, Whittier, CA, Zip 90602–1099; tel. 562/698–0811; James R. West, President and Chief Executive Officer
Web address: www.PIHHealth.org

Owned, leased, sponsored:	2 hospitals	392 beds
Contract-managed:	0 hospitals	0 beds
Totals:	2 hospitals	392 beds

★0617: POST ACUTE MEDICAL, LLC (IO)
1828 Good Hope Road, Suite 102, Enola, PA, Zip 17025–1233; tel. 717/731–9660; Anthony F. Misitano, President and Chief Executive Officer
(Independent Hospital System)

LOUISIANA: PAM SPECIALTY HOSPITAL OF COVINGTON (O, 58 beds) 20050 Crestwood Boulevard, Covington, LA, Zip 70433–5207; tel. 985/875–7525; J Cullen. Meyers, Chief Executive Officer
Web address: www.postacutemedical.com

PAM SPECIALTY HOSPITAL OF HAMMOND (O, 40 beds) 42074 Veterans Avenue, Hammond, LA, Zip 70403–1408; tel. 985/902–8148; Nicholas Paul. Mendez, Chief Executive Officer

NEVADA: PAM REHABILITATION HOSPITAL OF CENTENNIAL HILLS (O, 44 beds) 6166 North Durango Drive, Las Vegas, NV, Zip 89149; tel. 725/223–4100; Jeanette Williams, Chief Executive Officer
Web address: www.postacutemedical.com/facilities/find-facility/rehabilitation-hospitals/pam-rehabilitation-hospital-centennial-hills

OKLAHOMA: PAM REHABILITATION HOSPITAL OF TULSA (O, 41 beds) 10020 East 91st Street, Tulsa, OK, Zip 74133; tel. 918/893–2400; Thomas Biby, Chief Executive Officer
Web address: www.warmsprings.org/our-facilities/outpatient-rehabilitation

POST ACUTE MEDICAL SPECIALTY HOSPITAL OF TULSA (O, 60 beds) 3219 South 79th East Avenue, Tulsa, OK, Zip 74145–1343; tel. 918/663–8183; Ian Cooper, Chief Executive Officer

PENNSYLVANIA: PAM SPECIALTY HOSPITAL OF WILKES-BARRE (O, 36 beds) 575 North River Street, 7th Floor, Wilkes Barre, PA, Zip 18702–2634; tel. 570/208–3310; Cindy Miller, Chief Executive Officer
Web address: www.warmsprings.org/our-facilities/hospitals/post-acute-medical-specialty-hospital-wilkes-barre/

TEXAS: PAM REHABILITATION HOSPITAL OF BEAUMONT (O, 61 beds) 3340 Plaza 10 Boulevard, Beaumont, TX, Zip 77707–2551; tel. 409/835–0835; Todd Lorenz, Chief Executive Officer
Web address: www.postacutemedical.com/our-facilities/outpatient-rehabilitation/rehabilitation-hospital-beaumont/

PAM REHABILITATION HOSPITAL OF VICTORIA (O, 26 beds) 101 James Coleman Drive, Victoria, TX, Zip 77904–3147; tel. 361/220–7900; Jennifer Nickel, Chief Executive Officer

PAM SPECIALTY HOSPITAL OF CORPUS CHRISTI SOUTH (O, 74 beds) 6226 Saratoga Boulevard, Corpus Christi, TX, Zip 78414–3421; tel. 361/986–1600; Hector Bernal, Chief Executive Officer
Web address: www.postacutemedical.com

PAM SPECIALTY HOSPITAL OF LUFKIN (O, 26 beds) 1201 West Frank Avenue, D5, Lufkin, TX, Zip 75904–3357, Mailing Address: P.O. Box 1447, Zip 75902–1447, tel. 936/639–7530; Leslie Leach, Administrator

PAM SPECIALTY HOSPITAL OF VICTORIA NORTH (O, 26 beds) 102 Medical Drive, Victoria, TX, Zip 77904–3101; tel. 361/576–6200; Christina Adrean, Chief Executive Officer
Web address: www.warmsprings.org

PAM SPECIALTY HOSPITAL OF VICTORIA SOUTH (O, 23 beds) 506 East San Antonio Street, 3rd Floor, Victoria, TX, Zip 77901–6060; tel. 361/575–1445; Christina Adrean, Chief Executive Officer

POST ACUTE MEDICAL SPECIALTY HOSPITAL OF CORPUS CHRISTI – NORTH (O, 41 beds) 600 Elizabeth Street, 3rd Floor, Corpus Christi, TX, Zip 78404–2235; tel. 361/881–3223; Hector Bernal, Chief Executive Officer
Web address: www.postacutemedical.com/our-facilities/hospitals/post-acute-medical-specialty-hospital-corpus-christi/

POST ACUTE MEDICAL SPECIALTY HOSPITAL OF TEXARKANA – NORTH (O, 30 beds) 2400 St Michael Drive, 2nd Floor, Texarkana, TX, Zip 75503–2372; tel. 903/614–7600; Lorraine Murray, Chief Executive Officer

POST ACUTE REHABILITATION HOSPITAL OF ALLEN (O, 40 beds) 1001 Raintree Circle, Allen, TX, Zip 75013–4912; tel. 972/908–2015; Jennifer Beuerlein, Chief Executive Officer
Web address: www.warmsprings.org

POST ACUTE/WARM SPRINGS SPECIALTY HOSPITAL OF LULING (O, 34 beds) 200 Memorial Drive, Luling, TX, Zip 78648–3213; tel. 830/875–8400; Jana Kuykendall, Chief Executive Officer

POST ACUTE/WARM SPRINGS SPECIALTY HOSPITAL OF NEW BRAUNFELS (O, 40 beds) 1445 Hanz Drive, New Braunfels, TX, Zip 78130–2567; tel. 830/627–7600; Ashley Ondrusek, Chief Executive Officer
Web address: www.warmsprings.org/locations/hos/h1/

POST ACUTE/WARM SPRINGS SPECIALTY HOSPITAL OF SAN ANTONIO (O, 26 beds) 5418 N Loop 1604 W, San Antonio, TX, Zip 78247; tel. 210/921–3550; Kristen Lowe, Chief Executive Officer

WARM SPRINGS REHABILITATION HOSPITAL OF KYLE (O, 36 beds) 5980 Kyle Parkway, Kyle, TX, Zip 78640–2400; tel. 512/262–0821; Duke Saldivar, FACHE, Chief Executive Officer
Web address: www.warmsprings.org/our-facilities/outpatient-rehabilitation/warm-springs-rehabilitation-center-kyle/

WARM SPRINGS REHABILITATION HOSPITAL OF SAN ANTONIO (O, 139 beds) 5101 Medical Drive, San Antonio, TX, Zip 78229–4801; tel. 210/616–0100; Debra Bornmann, Chief Executive Officer
Web address: www.postacutemedical.com/our-facilities/hospitals/warm-springs-rehabilitation-hospital-san-antonio/

WISCONSIN: POST ACUTE MEDICAL SPECIALTY HOSPITAL OF MILWAUKEE (O, 56 beds) 5017 South 110Th Street, Greenfield, WI, Zip 53228–3131; tel. 414/427–8282; Paul E. Qualls, Chief Executive Officer
Web address: www.postacutemedical.com/

Owned, leased, sponsored:	21 hospitals	957 beds
Contract-managed:	0 hospitals	0 beds
Totals:	21 hospitals	957 beds

0240: PREFERRED MANAGEMENT CORPORATION (IO)
120 West MacArthur, Suite 121, Shawnee, OK, Zip 74804–2005; tel. 405/878–0202; Donald Freeman, President and Chief Executive Officer
(Independent Hospital System)

OKLAHOMA: ARBUCKLE MEMORIAL HOSPITAL (C, 13 beds) 2011 West Broadway Street, Sulphur, OK, Zip 73086–4221, Mailing Address: P.O. Box 1109, Zip 73086–0109, tel. 580/622–2161; Jeremy A. Jones, Chief Executive Officer
Web address: www.arbucklehospital.com/

TEXAS: COLEMAN COUNTY MEDICAL CENTER (L, 25 beds) 310 South Pecos Street, Coleman, TX, Zip 76834–4159; tel. 325/625–2135; Clay Vogel, Administrator and Chief Executive Officer
Web address: www.colemantexas.org/hospital.html

COLLINGSWORTH GENERAL HOSPITAL (L, 13 beds) 1013 15th Street, Wellington, TX, Zip 79095–3703, Mailing Address: P.O. Box 1112, Zip 79095–1112, tel. 806/447–2521; Candy Powell, Administrator

CULBERSON HOSPITAL (L, 14 beds) Eisenhower-Farm Market Road 2185, Van Horn, TX, Zip 79855, Mailing Address: P.O. Box 609, Zip 79855–0609, tel. 432/283–2760; Rick Gray, Chief Executive Officer
Web address: www.culbersonhospital.org

KIMBLE HOSPITAL (O, 15 beds) 349 Reid Road, Junction, TX, Zip 76849–3049; tel. 325/446–3321; Duke Young, Chief Executive Officer

MULESHOE AREA MEDICAL CENTER (L, 25 beds) 708 South First Street, Muleshoe, TX, Zip 79347–3627; tel. 806/272–4524; Dennis Fleenor, R.N., Administrator
Web address: www.mahdtx.org

PARMER MEDICAL CENTER (C, 15 beds) 1307 Cleveland Street, Friona, TX, Zip 79035–1121; tel. 806/250–2754; Gayla Quillin, Administrator

SABINE COUNTY HOSPITAL (L, 25 beds) 2301 Worth Street, Hemphill, TX, Zip 75948–7216, Mailing Address: P.O. Box 750, Zip 75948–0750, tel. 409/787–3300; Jerry Howell, Administrator
Web address: www.sabinecountyhospital.com/

Section B

For explanation of codes following names, see page B2.
★ Indicates Type III membership in the American Hospital Association.

SCHLEICHER COUNTY MEDICAL CENTER (L, 14 beds) 102 North US Highway 277, Eldorado, TX, Zip 76936–4010; tel. 325/853–2507; Paul Burke, Administrator

Owned, leased, sponsored:	7 hospitals	131 beds
Contract-managed:	2 hospitals	28 beds
Totals:	9 hospitals	159 beds

★0977: PREMIER HEALTH (NP)

110 North Main Street Suite 390, Dayton, OH, Zip 45402–3720; tel. 937/499–9401; Mary H. Boosalis, President and Chief Executive Officer
(Centralized Physician/Insurance Health System)

OHIO: ATRIUM MEDICAL CENTER (O, 284 beds) One Medical Center Drive, Middletown, OH, Zip 45005–1066; tel. 513/424–2111; Michael Uhl, President
Web address: www.PremierHealth.com

MIAMI VALLEY HOSPITAL (O, 516 beds) One Wyoming Street, Dayton, OH, Zip 45409–2793; tel. 937/208–8000; Michael J. Maiberger, President

UPPER VALLEY MEDICAL CENTER (O, 78 beds) 3130 North County Road 25A, Troy, OH, Zip 45373–1309; tel. 937/440–4000; Thomas Parker, President
Web address: www.uvmc.com

Owned, leased, sponsored:	3 hospitals	878 beds
Contract-managed:	0 hospitals	0 beds
Totals:	3 hospitals	878 beds

★3505: PRESBYTERIAN HEALTHCARE SERVICES (NP)

9521 San Mateo Blvd. NE, Albuquerque, NM, Zip 87113, Mailing Address: P.O. Box 26666, Zip 87125–6666, tel. 505/841–1234; Dale Maxwell, Chief Executive Officer
(Centralized Physician/Insurance Health System)

NEW MEXICO: DR. DAN C. TRIGG MEMORIAL HOSPITAL (L, 10 beds) 301 East Miel De Luna Avenue, Tucumcari, NM, Zip 88401–3810, Mailing Address: P.O. Box 608, Zip 88401–0608, tel. 575/461–7000; Troy Clark, Interim Administrator

LINCOLN COUNTY MEDICAL CENTER (L, 25 beds) 211 Sudderth Drive, Ruidoso, NM, Zip 88345–6043, Mailing Address: P.O. Box 8000, Zip 88355–8000, tel. 575/257–8200; Todd Oberheu, Administrator
Web address: www.phs.org

PLAINS REGIONAL MEDICAL CENTER (O, 80 beds) 2100 North Doctor Martin Luther King Boulevard, Clovis, NM, Zip 88101–9412, Mailing Address: P.O. Box 1688, Zip 88102–1688, tel. 575/769–2141; Richard Smith, Administrator

PRESBYTERIAN ESPANOLA HOSPITAL (O, 46 beds) 1010 Spruce Street, Espanola, NM, Zip 87532–2746; tel. 505/753–7111; Brenda Romero, Hospital Chief
Web address: www.phs.org

PRESBYTERIAN HOSPITAL (O, 644 beds) 1100 Central Avenue SE, Albuquerque, NM, Zip 87106–4934, Mailing Address: P.O. Box 26666, Zip 87125–6666, tel. 505/841–1234; Devon Hyde, Vice President, Chief Administrative Officer

SOCORRO GENERAL HOSPITAL (O, 24 beds) 1202 Highway 60 West, Socorro, NM, Zip 87801–3914, Mailing Address: P.O. Box 1009, Zip 87801–1009, tel. 575/835–1140; Veronica Pound, R.N., Administrator
Web address: www.phs.org

Owned, leased, sponsored:	6 hospitals	829 beds
Contract-managed:	0 hospitals	0 beds
Totals:	6 hospitals	829 beds

★0357: PRIME HEALTHCARE (IO)

3300 East Guasti Road, Ontario, CA, Zip 91761–8655; tel. 909/235–4400; Prem Reddy, M.D., Chairman, President and Chief Executive Officer
(Moderately Centralized Health System)

ALABAMA: RIVERVIEW REGIONAL MEDICAL CENTER (O, 280 beds) 600 South Third Street, Gadsden, AL, Zip 35901–5399; tel. 256/543–5200; John Langlois, Chief Executive Officer
Web address: www.riverviewregional.com

CALIFORNIA: ALVARADO HOSPITAL MEDICAL CENTER (O, 137 beds) 6655 Alvarado Road, San Diego, CA, Zip 92120–5208; tel. 619/287–3270; Robin Gomez, R.N., MSN, Administrator

CENTINELA HOSPITAL MEDICAL CENTER (O, 369 beds) 555 East Hardy Street, Inglewood, CA, Zip 90301–4011, Mailing Address: P.O. Box 720, Zip 90312–6720, tel. 310/673–4660; Linda Bradley, Chief Executive Officer
Web address: www.centinelamed.com

CHINO VALLEY MEDICAL CENTER (O, 112 beds) 5451 Walnut Avenue, Chino, CA, Zip 91710–2672; tel. 909/464–8600; Tim Moran, Chief Executive Officer

DESERT VALLEY HOSPITAL (O, 110 beds) 16850 Bear Valley Road, Victorville, CA, Zip 92395–5795; tel. 760/241–8000; Fred Hunter, R.N., Chief Executive Officer
Web address: www.dvmc.com

ENCINO HOSPITAL MEDICAL CENTER (O, 78 beds) 16237 Ventura Boulevard, Encino, CA, Zip 91436–2272; tel. 818/995–5000; Bockhi Park, Chief Executive Officer
Web address: www.encinomed.com

GARDEN GROVE HOSPITAL AND MEDICAL CENTER (O, 167 beds) 12601 Garden Grove Boulevard, Garden Grove, CA, Zip 92843–1959; tel. 714/537–5160; Richard M. Rowe, PharmD, Chief Executive Officer
Web address: www.gardengrovehospital.com

GLENDORA COMMUNITY HOSPITAL (O, 128 beds) 150 West Route 66, Glendora, CA, Zip 91740–6207; tel. 626/852–5000; Sofia Abrina, R.N., Chief Executive Officer
Web address: www.evhmc.com

HUNTINGTON BEACH HOSPITAL (O, 102 beds) 17772 Beach Boulevard, Huntington Beach, CA, Zip 92647–6896; tel. 714/843–5000; Richard M. Rowe, PharmD, Chief Executive Officer
Web address: www.hbhospital.com

LA PALMA INTERCOMMUNITY HOSPITAL (O, 140 beds) 7901 Walker Street, La Palma, CA, Zip 90623–1764; tel. 714/670–7400; Michael Sarian, Interim Chief Executive Officer
Web address: www.lapalmaintercommunityhospital.com

MONTCLAIR HOSPITAL MEDICAL CENTER (O, 102 beds) 5000 San Bernardino Street, Montclair, CA, Zip 91763–2326; tel. 909/625–5411; Sofia Abrina, R.N., Administrator
Web address: www.montclair-hospital.com

PARADISE VALLEY HOSPITAL (O, 256 beds) 2400 East Fourth Street, National City, CA, Zip 91950–2099; tel. 619/470–4321; William J. Comer, Chief Executive Officer
Web address: www.paradisevalleyhospital.org

SAN DIMAS COMMUNITY HOSPITAL (O, 101 beds) 1350 West Covina Boulevard, San Dimas, CA, Zip 91773–3219; tel. 909/599–6811; Parrish Scarboro, Chief Executive Officer
Web address: www.sandimashospital.com/

SHASTA REGIONAL MEDICAL CENTER (O, 100 beds) 1100 Butte Street, Redding, CA, Zip 96001–0853, Mailing Address: P.O. Box 496072, Zip 96049–6072, tel. 530/244–5400; Casey Fatch, Chief Executive Officer

SHERMAN OAKS HOSPITAL (O, 90 beds) 4929 Van Nuys Boulevard, Sherman Oaks, CA, Zip 91403–1777; tel. 818/981–7111; Bockhi Park, Chief Executive Officer
Web address: www.shermanoakshospital.com

WEST ANAHEIM MEDICAL CENTER (O, 219 beds) 3033 West Orange Avenue, Anaheim, CA, Zip 92804–3183; tel. 714/827–3000; Edward Mirzabegian, Chief Executive Officer

FLORIDA: LEHIGH REGIONAL MEDICAL CENTER (O, 53 beds) 1500 Lee Boulevard, Lehigh Acres, FL, Zip 33936–4835; tel. 239/369–2101; Gary C. Bell, LFACHE, Chief Executive Officer
Web address: www.lehighregional.com

GEORGIA: SOUTHERN REGIONAL MEDICAL CENTER (O, 331 beds) 11 Upper Riverdale Road SW, Riverdale, GA, Zip 30274–2615; tel. 770/991–8000; Charlotte W. Dupre, Chief Executive Officer

For explanation of codes following names, see page B2.
★ Indicates Type III membership in the American Hospital Association.

INDIANA: MONROE HOSPITAL (O, 32 beds) 4011 South Monroe Medical Park Boulevard, Bloomington, IN, Zip 47424; tel. 812/825–1111; Nancy Bakewell, Administrator
Web address: www.monroehospital.com

KANSAS: PROVIDENCE MEDICAL CENTER (O, 215 beds) 8929 Parallel Parkway, Kansas City, KS, Zip 66112–1689; tel. 913/596–4000; Karen Orr, Administrator and Chief Nursing Officer
Web address: www.providencekc.com

SAINT JOHN HOSPITAL (O, 58 beds) 3500 South Fourth Street, Leavenworth, KS, Zip 66048–5043; tel. 913/680–6000; Paula Ellis, Administrator
Web address: www.providence-health.org/sjh

MICHIGAN: GARDEN CITY HOSPITAL (O, 152 beds) 6245 Inkster Road, Garden City, MI, Zip 48135–4001; tel. 734/421–3300; Saju George, Chief Executive Officer

LAKE HURON MEDICAL CENTER (O, 119 beds) 2601 Electric Avenue, Port Huron, MI, Zip 48060–6518; tel. 810/985–1500; Jay De los Reyes, Chief Executive Officer
Web address: www.mymercy.us

MISSOURI: ST. JOSEPH MEDICAL CENTER (O, 171 beds) 1000 Carondelet Drive, Kansas City, MO, Zip 64114–4673; tel. 816/942–4400; Jodi Fincher, R.N., Administrator
Web address: www.stjosephkc.com/

ST. MARY'S MEDICAL CENTER (O, 83 beds) 201 Northwest R D Mize Road, Blue Springs, MO, Zip 64014–2518; tel. 816/228–5900; Drew Grossman, Chief Executive Officer

NEVADA: NORTH VISTA HOSPITAL (O, 177 beds) 1409 East Lake Mead Boulevard, North Las Vegas, NV, Zip 89030–7197; tel. 702/649–7711; Vincenzo Variale, Chief Executive Officer
Web address: www.northvistahospital.com

SAINT MARY'S REGIONAL MEDICAL CENTER (O, 293 beds) 235 West Sixth Street, Reno, NV, Zip 89503–4548; tel. 775/770–3000; Helen Lidholm, Chief Executive Officer

NEW JERSEY: SAINT CLARE'S DENVILLE HOSPITAL (O, 412 beds) 25 Pocono Road, Denville, NJ, Zip 07834–2954; tel. 973/625–6000; Brian Finestein, Chief Executive Officer
Web address: www.saintclares.org

SAINT MICHAEL'S MEDICAL CENTER (O, 162 beds) 111 Central Avenue, Newark, NJ, Zip 07102–1909; tel. 973/877–5350; Robert C. Iannaccone, JD, Chief Executive Officer
Web address: www.smmcnj.org

ST. MARY'S GENERAL HOSPITAL (O, 287 beds) 350 Boulevard, Passaic, NJ, Zip 07055–2840; tel. 973/365–4300; Edward Condit, President and Chief Executive Officer
Web address: www.smh-passaic.org

OHIO: COSHOCTON REGIONAL MEDICAL CENTER (O, 44 beds) 1460 Orange Street, Coshocton, OH, Zip 43812–2229, Mailing Address: P.O. Box 1330, Zip 43812–6330, tel. 740/622–6411; Stephanie Conn, Administrator and Chief Nursing Officer
Web address: https://www.coshoctonhospital.org

EAST LIVERPOOL CITY HOSPITAL (O, 120 beds) 425 West Fifth Street, East Liverpool, OH, Zip 43920–2498; tel. 330/385–7200; Keith Richardson, President and Chief Executive Officer
Web address: www.elch.org

PENNSYLVANIA: LOWER BUCKS HOSPITAL (O, 104 beds) 501 Bath Road, Bristol, PA, Zip 19007–3190; tel. 215/785–9200; Kelly M. Lorah, FACHE, Chief Executive Officer

ROXBOROUGH MEMORIAL HOSPITAL (O, 140 beds) 5800 Ridge Avenue, Philadelphia, PA, Zip 19128–1737; tel. 215/483–9900; Matt Shelak, Chief Executive Officer
Web address: www.roxboroughmemorial.com

SUBURBAN COMMUNITY HOSPITAL (O, 126 beds) 2701 DeKalb Pike, Norristown, PA, Zip 19401–1820; tel. 610/278–2000; Mark McLoone, Chief Executive Officer

RHODE ISLAND: LANDMARK MEDICAL CENTER (O, 140 beds) 115 Cass Avenue, Woonsocket, RI, Zip 02895–4731; tel. 401/769–4100; Michael Souza, Chief Executive Officer
Web address: www.landmarkmedcenter.com

REHABILITATION HOSPITAL OF RHODE ISLAND (O, 70 beds) 116 Eddie Dowling Highway, North Smithfield, RI, Zip 02896–7327; tel. 401/766–0800; Michael Souza, Chief Executive Officer

TEXAS: DALLAS MEDICAL CENTER (O, 71 beds) Seven Medical Parkway, Dallas, TX, Zip 75234–7823, Mailing Address: P.O. Box 819094, Zip 75381–9094, tel. 972/247–1000; J. T. Barnhart, Chief Executive Officer
Web address: www.dallasmedcenter.com

DALLAS REGIONAL MEDICAL CENTER (O, 127 beds) 1011 North Galloway Avenue, Mesquite, TX, Zip 75149–2433; tel. 214/320–7000; Glenda Newby, Chief Executive Officer

HARLINGEN MEDICAL CENTER (O, 88 beds) 5501 South Expressway 77, Harlingen, TX, Zip 78550–3213; tel. 956/365–1000; Matt Wolthoff, Chief Executive Officer
Web address: www.harlingenmedicalcenter.com

KNAPP MEDICAL CENTER (O, 186 beds) 1401 East Eighth Street, Weslaco, TX, Zip 78596–6640, Mailing Address: P.O. Box 1110, Zip 78599–1110, tel. 956/968–8567; Rene Lopez, Chief Executive Officer

MISSION REGIONAL MEDICAL CENTER (O, 228 beds) 900 South Bryan Road, Mission, TX, Zip 78572–6613; tel. 956/323–9103; Kane A. Dawson, Chief Executive Officer
Web address: www.missionrmc.org

PAMPA REGIONAL MEDICAL CENTER (O, 72 beds) One Medical Plaza, Pampa, TX, Zip 79065; tel. 806/665–3721; Edwin Leon, Chief Executive Officer
Web address: www.prmctx.com

Owned, leased, sponsored:	43 hospitals	6552 beds
Contract-managed:	0 hospitals	0 beds
Totals:	43 hospitals	6552 beds

★**4155: PRISMA HEALTH – MIDLANDS** (NP)
1301 Taylor Street, Suite 9-A, Columbia, SC, Zip 29201–2942, Mailing Address: P.O. Box 2266, Zip 29202–2266, tel. 803/296–2100; Mark O'Halla, President and Chief Executive Officer, Prisma Health
(Centralized Health System)

SOUTH CAROLINA: PRISMA HEALTH BAPTIST HOSPITAL (O, 401 beds) Taylor at Marion Street, Columbia, SC, Zip 29220–0001; tel. 803/296–5010; Michael N. Bundy, Chief Operating Officer
Web address: www.palmettohealth.org

PRISMA HEALTH BAPTIST PARKRIDGE HOSPITAL (O, 76 beds) 400 Palmetto Health Parkway, Columbia, SC, Zip 29212–1760, Mailing Address: P.O. Box 2266, Zip 29202–2266, tel. 803/907–7000; Michael N. Bundy, Chief Operating Officer
Web address: www.palmettohealth.org

PRISMA HEALTH RICHLAND HOSPITAL (O, 674 beds) Five Richland Medical Park Drive, Columbia, SC, Zip 29203–6897; tel. 803/434–7000; Jay Hamm, R.N., FACHE, Chief Operating Officer

PRISMA HEALTH TUOMEY HOSPITAL (O, 219 beds) 129 North Washington Street, Sumter, SC, Zip 29150–4983; tel. 803/774–9000; Michelle Logan-Owens, Ph.D., R.N., Chief Operating Officer
Web address: www.tuomey.com

Owned, leased, sponsored:	4 hospitals	1370 beds
Contract-managed:	0 hospitals	0 beds
Totals:	4 hospitals	1370 beds

★**1555: PRISMA HEALTH – UPSTATE** (NP)
701 Grove Road, Greenville, SC, Zip 29605–5611; tel. 864/455–7000; Spence Taylor, M.D., President of Prisma Health Upstate
(Centralized Health System)

SOUTH CAROLINA: PRISMA HEALTH GREENVILLE MEMORIAL HOSPITAL (O, 814 beds) 701 Grove Road, Greenville, SC, Zip 29605–4295; tel. 864/455–7000; Ric A. Ransom, Chief Operating Officer

PRISMA HEALTH GREER MEMORIAL HOSPITAL (O, 70 beds) 830 South Buncombe Road, Greer, SC, Zip 29650–2400; tel. 864/797–8000; John F. Mansure, FACHE, President
Web address: www.ghs.org

For explanation of codes following names, see page B2.
★ Indicates Type III membership in the American Hospital Association.

PRISMA HEALTH HILLCREST HOSPITAL (O, 43 beds) 729 SE Main Street, Simpsonville, SC, Zip 29681–3280; tel. 864/454–6100; Scott R. Jones, FACHE, Chief Operating Officer
Web address: www.ghs.org

PRISMA HEALTH LAURENS COUNTY HOSPITAL (L, 71 beds) 22725 Highway 76 East, Clinton, SC, Zip 29325–7527, Mailing Address: P O Drawer 976, Zip 29325–0976, tel. 864/833–9100; Justin Benfield, Southern Region Chief Operating Officer

PRISMA HEALTH OCONEE MEMORIAL HOSPITAL (L, 256 beds) 298 Memorial Drive, Seneca, SC, Zip 29672–9499; tel. 864/882–3351; Hunter Kome, Campus President
Web address: www.oconeemed.org

PRISMA HEALTH PATEWOOD HOSPITAL (O, 72 beds) 175 Patewood Drive, Greenville, SC, Zip 29615–3570; tel. 864/797–1000; Tim Brookshire, Chief Operating Officer

Owned, leased, sponsored:	6 hospitals	1326 beds
Contract-managed:	0 hospitals	0 beds
Totals:	6 hospitals	1326 beds

★0153: PROHEALTH CARE, INC. (NP)

N17 W24100 Riverwood Drive, Suite 130, Waukesha, WI, Zip 53188; tel. 262/928–2242; Susan A. Edwards, President and Chief Executive Officer
(Centralized Health System)

WISCONSIN: OCONOMOWOC MEMORIAL HOSPITAL (O, 58 beds) 791 Summit Avenue, Oconomowoc, WI, Zip 53066–3896; tel. 262/569–9400; Susan A. Edwards, President and Chief Executive Officer
Web address: www.prohealthcare.org/locations/locations-v2-detail/?id=1123

WAUKESHA MEMORIAL HOSPITAL (O, 262 beds) 725 American Avenue, Waukesha, WI, Zip 53188–5099; tel. 262/928–1000; Susan A. Edwards, Chief Executive Officer
Web address: www.prohealthcare.org/locations/locations-v2-detail/?id=1119

Owned, leased, sponsored:	2 hospitals	320 beds
Contract-managed:	0 hospitals	0 beds
Totals:	2 hospitals	320 beds

★0197: PROMEDICA HEALTH SYSTEM (NP)

100 Madison Avenue, Toledo, OH, Zip 43604–1516; tel. 567/585–9601; Randall D. Oostra, FACHE, President and Chief Executive Officer
(Centralized Physician/Insurance Health System)

MICHIGAN: PROMEDICA BIXBY HOSPITAL (O, 66 beds) 818 Riverside Avenue, Adrian, MI, Zip 49221–1446; tel. 517/265–0900; Julie Yaroch, D.O., President
Web address: www.promedica.org

PROMEDICA COLDWATER REGIONAL HOSPITAL (O, 62 beds) 274 East Chicago Street, Coldwater, MI, Zip 49036–2041; tel. 517/279–5400; Randy DeGroot, President and Chief Executive Officer
Web address: www.chcbc.com

PROMEDICA HERRICK HOSPITAL (O, 25 beds) 500 East Pottawatamie Street, Tecumseh, MI, Zip 49286–2018; tel. 517/424–3000; Julie Yaroch, D.O., President
Web address: www.promedica.org

PROMEDICA MONROE REGIONAL HOSPITAL (O, 100 beds) 718 North Macomb Street, Monroe, MI, Zip 48162–7815; tel. 734/240–8400; Daniel Schwanke, President

OHIO: PROMEDICA BAY PARK HOSPITAL (O, 44 beds) 2801 Bay Park Drive, Oregon, OH, Zip 43616–4920; tel. 419/690–7900; Neeraj Kanwal, M.D., Interim President, Metro Region
Web address: www.promedica.org

PROMEDICA DEFIANCE REGIONAL HOSPITAL (O, 35 beds) 1200 Ralston Avenue, Defiance, OH, Zip 43512–1396; tel. 419/783–6955; Doug Bush, President
Web address: www.promedica.org

PROMEDICA FLOWER HOSPITAL (O, 245 beds) 5200 Harroun Road, Sylvania, OH, Zip 43560–2196; tel. 419/824–1444; Neeraj Kanwal, M.D., Interim President, Metro Region
Web address: www.promedica.org

PROMEDICA FOSTORIA COMMUNITY HOSPITAL (O, 25 beds) 501 Van Buren Street, Fostoria, OH, Zip 44830–1534, Mailing Address: P.O. Box 907, Zip 44830–0907, tel. 419/435–7734; Pamela M. Jensen, FACHE, President

PROMEDICA MEMORIAL HOSPITAL (O, 76 beds) 715 South Taft Avenue, Fremont, OH, Zip 43420–3237; tel. 419/332–7321; Pamela M. Jensen, FACHE, President
Web address: https://www.promedica.org

PROMEDICA TOLEDO HOSPITAL (O, 560 beds) 2142 North Cove Boulevard, Toledo, OH, Zip 43606–3896; tel. 419/291–4000; Neeraj Kanwal, M.D., Interim President, Metro Region
Web address: www.promedica.org

Owned, leased, sponsored:	10 hospitals	1238 beds
Contract-managed:	0 hospitals	0 beds
Totals:	10 hospitals	1238 beds

0230: PROMISE HEALTHCARE (IO)

999 Yamato Road, 3rd Floor, Boca Raton, FL, Zip 33431–4477; tel. 561/869–3100; Peter R. Baronoff, Chief Executive Officer
(Independent Hospital System)

ARIZONA: PROMISE HOSPITAL OF PHOENIX (L, 40 beds) 433 East 6th Street, Mesa, AZ, Zip 85203–7104; tel. 480/427–3000; Wayne Kinsey, Chief Executive Officer

CALIFORNIA: PROMISE HOSPITAL OF EAST LOS ANGELES (L, 213 beds) 443 South Soto Street, Los Angeles, CA, Zip 90033–4398; tel. 323/261–1181; Michael D. Kerr, Chief Executive Officer
Web address: www.promiseeastla.com

KANSAS: PROMISE HOSPITAL OF OVERLAND PARK (O, 104 beds) 6509 West 103rd Street, Overland Park, KS, Zip 66212–1728; tel. 913/649–3701; Kristen Barrett, Chief Executive Officer
Web address: www.promise-overlandpark.com

LOUISIANA: PROMISE HOSPITAL BATON ROUGE – MAIN CAMPUS (L, 39 beds) 5130 Mancuso Lane, Baton Rouge, LA, Zip 70809–3583; tel. 225/490–9600; Kiley P. Cedotal, FACHE, Chief Executive Officer
Web address: www.promise-batonrouge.com

PROMISE HOSPITAL OF LOUISIANA – SHREVEPORT CAMPUS (O, 146 beds) 1800 Irving Place, Shreveport, LA, Zip 71101–4608; tel. 318/425–4096; Rick Stockton, Chief Executive Officer

PROMISE HOSPITAL OF MISS LOU (O, 40 beds) 209 Front Street, Vidalia, LA, Zip 71373–2837; tel. 318/336–6500; Michael Harrell, R.N., Chief Executive Officer
Web address: www.promise-misslou.com

MISSISSIPPI: PROMISE HOSPITAL OF VICKSBURG (L, 33 beds) 1111 North Frontage Road, 2nd Floor, Vicksburg, MS, Zip 39180–5102; tel. 601/619–3526; Michael Harrell, R.N., Chief Executive Officer

TEXAS: PROMISE HOSPITAL OF DALLAS (O, 66 beds) 7955 Harry Hines Boulevard, Dallas, TX, Zip 75235–3305; tel. 214/637–0000; Louis P. Bradley Jr, Chief Executive Officer
Web address: www.promise-dallas.com/

PROMISE HOSPITAL OF WICHITA FALLS (O, 31 beds) 1103 Grace Street, Wichita Falls, TX, Zip 76301–4414; tel. 940/720–6633; Louis P. Bradley Jr, Chief Executive Officer
Web address: www.promise-wichitafalls.com

UTAH: PROMISE HOSPITAL OF SALT LAKE (O, 41 beds) 8 Avenue, C Street, Salt Lake City, UT, Zip 84143; tel. 801/408–7110; Wayne Kinsey, Chief Executive Officer

Owned, leased, sponsored:	10 hospitals	753 beds
Contract-managed:	0 hospitals	0 beds
Totals:	10 hospitals	753 beds

For explanation of codes following names, see page B2.
★ Indicates Type III membership in the American Hospital Association.

© 2019 AHA Guide

1012: PROSPECT MEDICAL HOLDINGS (IO)
10780 California Route 2 #400, Los Angeles, CA, Zip 90025; tel. 714/796–5900; Mitchell Lew, M.D., President
(Independent Hospital System)

CALIFORNIA: FOOTHILL REGIONAL MEDICAL CENTER (O, 42 beds) 14662 Newport Avenue, Tustin, CA, Zip 92780–6064; tel. 714/838–9600; Barbara Schneider, R.N., Chief Executive Officer

LOS ANGELES COMMUNITY HOSPITAL AT LOS ANGELES (O, 180 beds) 4081 East Olympic Boulevard, Los Angeles, CA, Zip 90023–3330; tel. 323/267–0477; Omar Ramirez, Chief Executive Officer
Web address: www.altacorp.com/altacorp/our-hospitals/lach-menu.html

SOUTHERN CALIFORNIA HOSPITAL AT CULVER CITY (O, 239 beds) 3828 Delmas Terrace, Culver City, CA, Zip 90232–6806; tel. 310/836–7000; Sean Fowler, Chief Executive Officer
Web address: www.sch-culvercity.com

SOUTHERN CALIFORNIA AT HOLLYWOOD (O, 45 beds) 6245 De Longpre Avenue, Los Angeles, CA, Zip 90028–9001; tel. 323/462–2271; Bruce P. Grimshaw, FACHE, Chief Executive Officer

CONNECTICUT: MANCHESTER MEMORIAL HOSPITAL (O, 156 beds) 71 Haynes Street, Manchester, CT, Zip 06040–4188; tel. 860/646–1222; Michael F. Collins, Chief Executive Officer
Web address: www.echn.org

ROCKVILLE GENERAL HOSPITAL (O, 47 beds) 31 Union Street, Vernon, CT, Zip 06066–3160; tel. 860/872–0501; Michael F. Collins, Chief Executive Officer
Web address: www.echn.org

WATERBURY HOSPITAL (O, 183 beds) 64 Robbins Street, Waterbury, CT, Zip 06708–2600; tel. 203/573–6000; Peter J. Adamo, President and Chief Executive Officer
Web address: www.waterburyhospital.org

NEW JERSEY: EAST ORANGE GENERAL HOSPITAL (O, 143 beds) 300 Central Avenue, East Orange, NJ, Zip 07018–2897; tel. 973/672–8400; Paige Dworak, FACHE, Chief Executive Officer
Web address: www.evh.org

PENNSYLVANIA: CROZER-CHESTER MEDICAL CENTER (O, 384 beds) One Medical Center Boulevard, Upland, PA, Zip 19013–3995; tel. 610/447–2000; Michael Curran, President
Web address: www.crozer.org

DELAWARE COUNTY MEMORIAL HOSPITAL (O, 168 beds) 501 North Lansdowne Avenue, Drexel Hill, PA, Zip 19026–1114; tel. 610/284–8100; Robert Haffey, R.N., President
Web address: www.crozer.org

RHODE ISLAND: ROGER WILLIAMS MEDICAL CENTER (O, 86 beds) 825 Chalkstone Avenue, Providence, RI, Zip 02908–4735; tel. 401/456–2000; Jeffrey H. Liebman, Chief Executive Officer

ST. JOSEPH HEALTH SERVICES OF RHODE ISLAND (O, 125 beds) 200 High Service Avenue, North Providence, RI, Zip 02904–5199; tel. 401/456–3000; John J. Holiver, Chief Executive Officer
Web address: www.saintjosephri.com

TEXAS: NIX HEALTH CARE SYSTEM (O, 228 beds) 414 Navarro Street, San Antonio, TX, Zip 78205–2516; tel. 210/271–1800; Jesse Peralez, Chief Executive Officer

Owned, leased, sponsored:	13 hospitals	2026 beds
Contract-managed:	0 hospitals	0 beds
Totals:	13 hospitals	2026 beds

★1006: PROVIDENCE ST. JOSEPH HEALTH (CC)
1801 Lind Avenue Southwest, 9016, Renton, WA, Zip 98057–9016, Mailing Address: 181 Lind Avenue Southwest, 9016, Zip 98057–9016, tel. 425/525–3698; Rodney F. Hochman, M.D., President and Chief Executive Officer
(Decentralized Health System)

ALASKA: PROVIDENCE ALASKA MEDICAL CENTER (O, 401 beds) 3200 Providence Drive, Anchorage, AK, Zip 99508–4615, Mailing Address: P.O. Box 196604, Zip 99519–6604, tel. 907/562–2211; Ella M. Goss, MSN, R.N., Chief Executive Officer
Web address: www.alaska.providence.org/locations/p/pamc

PROVIDENCE KODIAK ISLAND MEDICAL CENTER (L, 6 beds) 1915 East Rezanof Drive, Kodiak, AK, Zip 99615–6602; tel. 907/486–3281; Regina L. Bishop, Administrator
Web address: www.providence.org

PROVIDENCE SEWARD MEDICAL CENTER (C, 6 beds) 417 First Avenue, Seward, AK, Zip 99664, Mailing Address: P.O. Box 365, Zip 99664–0365, tel. 907/224–5205; Don Hanna, Interim Chief Executive Officer
Web address: www.providence.org

PROVIDENCE VALDEZ MEDICAL CENTER (C, 21 beds) 911 Meals Avenue, Valdez, AK, Zip 99686–0550, Mailing Address: P.O. Box 550, Zip 99686–0550, tel. 907/835–2249; Jeremy O'Neil, Administrator
Web address: www.providence.org/alaska

CALIFORNIA: HOAG MEMORIAL HOSPITAL PRESBYTERIAN (O, 588 beds) One Hoag Drive, Newport Beach, CA, Zip 92663–4120, Mailing Address: P.O. Box 6100, Zip 92658–6100, tel. 949/764–4624; Robert Braithwaite, President and Chief Executive Officer

MISSION HOSPITAL (O, 296 beds) 27700 Medical Center Road, Mission Viejo, CA, Zip 92691–6474; tel. 949/364–1400; Seth R. Teigen, Chief Executive Officer
Web address: www.mission4health.com

PROVIDENCE HOLY CROSS MEDICAL CENTER (O, 377 beds) 15031 Rinaldi Street, Mission Hills, CA, Zip 91345–1207; tel. 818/365–8051; Bernard Klein, M.D., Chief Executive
Web address: www.https://california.providence.org/holy-cross/Pages/default.aspx

PROVIDENCE LITTLE COMPANY OF MARY MEDICAL CENTER – TORRANCE (O, 386 beds) 4101 Torrance Boulevard, Torrance, CA, Zip 90503–4664; tel. 310/540–7676; Garry M. Olney, Chief Executive Officer
Web address: www.providence.org

PROVIDENCE LITTLE COMPANY OF MARY MEDICAL CENTER SAN PEDRO (O, 318 beds) 1300 West Seventh Street, San Pedro, CA, Zip 90732–3505; tel. 310/832–3311; Garry M. Olney, Chief Executive Officer

PROVIDENCE SAINT JOHN'S HEALTH CENTER (O, 228 beds) 2121 Santa Monica Boulevard, Santa Monica, CA, Zip 90404–2091; tel. 310/829–5511; Marcel C. Loh, FACHE, Chief Executive Officer
Web address: www.providence.org/saintjohns

PROVIDENCE SAINT JOSEPH MEDICAL CENTER (O, 383 beds) 501 South Buena Vista Street, Burbank, CA, Zip 91505–4866; tel. 818/843–5111; Kelly Linden, Chief Executive Officer

PROVIDENCE TARZANA MEDICAL CENTER (O, 229 beds) 18321 Clark Street, Tarzana, CA, Zip 91356–3521; tel. 818/881–0800; Dale Surowitz, Chief Executive
Web address: www.providence.org/tarzana.com

QUEEN OF THE VALLEY MEDICAL CENTER (O, 208 beds) 1000 Trancas Street, Napa, CA, Zip 94558–2906, Mailing Address: P.O. Box 2340, Zip 94558–0688, tel. 707/252–4411; Larry Coomes, Chief Executive Officer

REDWOOD MEMORIAL HOSPITAL (O, 25 beds) 3300 Renner Drive, Fortuna, CA, Zip 95540–3198; tel. 707/725–3361; Roberta Luskin-Hawk, M.D., Chief Executive
Web address: www.redwoodmemorial.org/

SANTA ROSA MEMORIAL HOSPITAL (O, 278 beds) 1165 Montgomery Drive, Santa Rosa, CA, Zip 95405–4897, Mailing Address: P.O. Box 522, Zip 95402–0522, tel. 707/546–3210; Tyler Hedden, Interim Chief Executive Officer

ST. JOSEPH HOSPITAL (O, 153 beds) 2700 Dolbeer Street, Eureka, CA, Zip 95501–4799; tel. 707/445–8121; Roberta Luskin-Hawk, M.D., Chief Executive
Web address: www.stjosepheureka.org

ST. JOSEPH HOSPITAL (O, 379 beds) 1100 West Stewart Drive, Orange, CA, Zip 92868–3849, Mailing Address: P.O. Box 5600, Zip 92863–5600, tel. 714/633–9111; Jeremy Zoch, Chief Executive
Web address: www.sjo.org

ST. JUDE MEDICAL CENTER (O, 320 beds) 101 East Valencia Mesa Drive, Fullerton, CA, Zip 92835–3875; tel. 714/992–3000; Brian Helleland, Chief Executive Officer

ST. MARY MEDICAL CENTER (O, 212 beds) 18300 Highway 18, Apple Valley, CA, Zip 92307–2206, Mailing Address: P.O. Box 7025, Zip 92307–0725, tel. 760/242–2311; Randall Castillo, Chief Executive Officer
Web address: www.stmaryapplevalley.com/

For explanation of codes following names, see page B2.
★ Indicates Type III membership in the American Hospital Association.

Section B

MONTANA: GRANITE COUNTY MEDICAL CENTER (C, 25 beds) 310 Sansome Street, Philipsburg, MT, Zip 59858–0729, Mailing Address: P.O. Box 729, Zip 59858–0729, tel. 406/859–3271; Maria Stoppler, Chief Executive Officer

PROVIDENCE ST. JOSEPH MEDICAL CENTER (O, 22 beds) 6 Thirteenth Avenue East, Polson, MT, Zip 59860–5315, Mailing Address: P.O. Box 1010, Zip 59860–1010, tel. 406/883–5377; Devin Huntley, Chief Operating Officer
Web address: www.saintjoes.org

PROVIDENCE ST. PATRICK HOSPITAL (O, 183 beds) 500 West Broadway, Missoula, MT, Zip 59802–4096, Mailing Address: P.O. Box 4587, Zip 59806–4587, tel. 406/543–7271; Joyce Dombrouski, R.N., Chief Executive Officer

OREGON: PROVIDENCE HOOD RIVER MEMORIAL HOSPITAL (O, 25 beds) 810 12th Street, Hood River, OR, Zip 97031–1587, Mailing Address: P.O. Box 149, Zip 97031–0055, tel. 541/386–3911; Jeanette Vieira, Chief Executive
Web address: www.providence.org/hoodriver

PROVIDENCE MEDFORD MEDICAL CENTER (O, 138 beds) 1111 Crater Lake Avenue, Medford, OR, Zip 97504–6241; tel. 541/732–5000; Tom Lorish, M.D., Interim Chief Executive
Web address: www.providence.org

PROVIDENCE MILWAUKIE HOSPITAL (O, 60 beds) 10150 SE 32nd Avenue, Milwaukie, OR, Zip 97222–6516; tel. 503/513–8300; Keith Hyde, Chief Executive
Web address: www.providence.org

PROVIDENCE NEWBERG MEDICAL CENTER (O, 40 beds) 1001 Providence Drive, Newberg, OR, Zip 97132–7485; tel. 503/537–1555; Lorinda Van Zanten, MSN, Chief Executive
Web address: www.phsor.org

PROVIDENCE PORTLAND MEDICAL CENTER (O, 407 beds) 4805 NE Glisan Street, Portland, OR, Zip 97213–2933; tel. 503/215–5526; Krista Farnham, Chief Executive
Web address: www.providence.org

PROVIDENCE SEASIDE HOSPITAL (O, 25 beds) 725 South Wahanna Road, Seaside, OR, Zip 97138–7735; tel. 503/717–7000; Don Lemmon, Chief Executive Officer
Web address: www.providence.org

PROVIDENCE ST. VINCENT MEDICAL CENTER (O, 528 beds) 9205 SW Barnes Road, Portland, OR, Zip 97225–6661; tel. 503/216–1234; Janice Burger, Chief Executive

PROVIDENCE WILLAMETTE FALLS MEDICAL CENTER (O, 111 beds) 1500 Division Street, Oregon City, OR, Zip 97045–1597; tel. 503/656–1631; Russ Reinhard, Chief Executive
Web address: www.providence.org/pwfmc

TEXAS: COVENANT CHILDREN'S HOSPITAL (O, 201 beds) 4015 22nd Place, Lubbock, TX, Zip 79410; tel. 806/725–1011; Amy Thompson, M.D., Chief Executive Officer
Web address: www.covenanthealth.org/About-Us/Facilities/Childrens-Hospital.aspx

COVENANT HOSPITAL PLAINVIEW (O, 68 beds) 2601 Dimmitt Road, Plainview, TX, Zip 79072–1833; tel. 806/296–5531; Robert Copeland, Interim Chief Executive Officer

COVENANT HOSPITAL-LEVELLAND (L, 26 beds) 1900 South College Avenue, Levelland, TX, Zip 79336–6508; tel. 806/894–4963; Bruce White, Administrator
Web address: www.covenanthospitallevelland.com/

COVENANT MEDICAL CENTER (O, 380 beds) 3615 19th Street, Lubbock, TX, Zip 79410–1203, Mailing Address: P.O. Box 1201, Zip 79408–1201, tel. 806/725–0000; Walt Cathey, Chief Executive Officer
Web address: www.covenanthealth.org

COVENANT SPECIALTY HOSPITAL (O, 56 beds) 3815 20th Street, Lubbock, TX, Zip 79410–1235; tel. 806/725–9200; Ely Perea, Director and Chief Executive Officer
Web address: www.covenanthealth.org/view/Facilities/Specialty_Hospital

GRACE MEDICAL CENTER (O, 43 beds) 2412 50th Street, Lubbock, TX, Zip 79412–2494; tel. 806/788–4100; Vanessa Reasoner, Chief Executive Officer

WASHINGTON: KADLEC REGIONAL MEDICAL CENTER (O, 260 beds) 888 Swift Boulevard, Richland, WA, Zip 99352–3514; tel. 509/946–4611; Reza Kaleel, Chief Executive Officer
Web address: https://www.kadlec.org

PROVIDENCE CENTRALIA HOSPITAL (O, 91 beds) 914 S Scheuber RD, Centralia, WA, Zip 98531–9027, Mailing Address: 914 South Scheuber Road, Zip 98531–9027, tel. 360/736–2803; Medrice Coluccio, R.N., Southwest Region Chief Executive

PROVIDENCE HOLY FAMILY HOSPITAL (O, 191 beds) 5633 North Lidgerwood Street, Spokane, WA, Zip 99208–1224; tel. 509/482–0111; Peggy M. Currie, R.N., Chief Operating Officer
Web address: www.providence.org

PROVIDENCE MOUNT CARMEL HOSPITAL (O, 25 beds) 982 East Columbia Avenue, Colville, WA, Zip 99114–3352; tel. 509/685–5100; Ronald G. Rehn, Chief Executive Officer

PROVIDENCE REGIONAL MEDICAL CENTER EVERETT (O, 530 beds) 1321 Colby Avenue, Everett, WA, Zip 98201–1665, Mailing Address: P.O. Box 1147, Zip 98206–1147, tel. 425/261–2000; Kim Williams, R.N., MS, Chief Executive Officer
Web address: www.providence.org

PROVIDENCE SACRED HEART MEDICAL CENTER & CHILDREN'S HOSPITAL (O, 656 beds) 101 West Eighth Avenue, Spokane, WA, Zip 99204–2364, Mailing Address: P.O. Box 2555, Zip 99220–2555, tel. 509/474–3131; Peggy M. Currie, R.N., Chief Operating Officer
Web address: www.shmc.org

PROVIDENCE ST. JOSEPH'S HOSPITAL (O, 55 beds) 500 East Webster Street, Chewelah, WA, Zip 99109–9523; tel. 509/935–8211; Ronald G. Rehn, Chief Executive Officer

PROVIDENCE ST. MARY MEDICAL CENTER (O, 92 beds) 401 W Poplar Street, Walla Walla, WA, Zip 99362–2846, Mailing Address: P.O. Box 1477, Zip 99362–0312, tel. 509/897–3320; Susan Blackburn, Chief Administrative Officer
Web address: www.washington.providence.org/hospitals/st-mary/

PROVIDENCE ST. PETER HOSPITAL (O, 349 beds) 413 Lilly Road NE, Olympia, WA, Zip 98506–5166; tel. 360/491–9480; Medrice Coluccio, R.N., Chief Executive Officer

ST. LUKE'S REHABILITATION INSTITUTE (O, 72 beds) 711 South Cowley Street, Spokane, WA, Zip 99202–1388; tel. 509/473–6000; Nancy Webster, Administrator and Chief Operating Officer
Web address: www.st-lukes.org

SWEDISH MEDICAL CENTER-CHERRY HILL CAMPUS (O, 208 beds) 500 17th Avenue, Seattle, WA, Zip 98122–5711; tel. 206/320–2000; June Altaras, R.N., Chief Executive Officer

SWEDISH MEDICAL CENTER-FIRST HILL (O, 689 beds) 747 Broadway, Seattle, WA, Zip 98122–4307; tel. 206/386–6000; June Altaras, R.N., Chief Executive Officer
Web address: www.swedish.org

SWEDISH/EDMONDS (O, 185 beds) 21601 76th Avenue West, Edmonds, WA, Zip 98026–7506; tel. 425/640–4000; Sarah Zabel, Vice President, Operations
Web address: www.swedish.org

SWEDISH/ISSAQUAH (O, 153 beds) 751 NE Blakely Drive, Issaquah, WA, Zip 98029–6201; tel. 425/313–4000; Guy Hudson, Chief Executive Officer
Web address: www.swedish.org/issaquah

WHITMAN HOSPITAL AND MEDICAL CENTER (C, 25 beds) 1200 West Fairview Street, Colfax, WA, Zip 99111–9579; tel. 509/397–3435; Hank Hanigan, FACHE, Chief Executive Officer

Owned, leased, sponsored:	47 hospitals	10656 beds
Contract-managed:	4 hospitals	77 beds
Totals:	51 hospitals	10733 beds

★0011: PUERTO RICO DEPARTMENT OF HEALTH (NP)
Building 'A' – Medical Center, San Juan, PR, Zip 936, Mailing Address: Call Box 70184, Zip 936, tel. 787/765–2929; Rafael Rodriguez. Mercado, Secretary of Health
(Independent Hospital System)

PUERTO RICO: CARDIOVASCULAR CENTER OF PUERTO RICO AND THE CARIBBEAN (O, 139 beds) Americo Miranda Centro Medico, San Juan, PR, Zip 936, Mailing Address: P.O. Box 366528, Zip 00936–6528, tel. 787/754–8500; Carlos Cabrera, Executive Director

HOSPITAL UNIVERSITARIO DR. RAMON RUIZ ARNAU (O, 101 beds) Avenue Laurel #100, Santa Juanita, Bayamon, PR, Zip 956; tel. 787/787–5151; Prudencio A. Laureano, Chief Executive Officer
Web address: www.salud.gov.pr/Dept-de-Salud/Pages/Nuestros-Hospitales.aspx

For explanation of codes following names, see page B2.
★ Indicates Type III membership in the American Hospital Association.

UNIVERSITY HOSPITAL (O, 220 beds) Nineyas 869 Rio Piedras, San Juan, PR, Zip 922, Mailing Address: P.O. Box 2116, Zip 922, tel. 787/754–0101; Jorge Matta. Gonzalez, Executive Director

UNIVERSITY PEDIATRIC HOSPITAL (O, 145 beds) Barrio Monacenno, Carretera 22, Rio Piedras, PR, Zip 935, Mailing Address: P.O. Box 191079, San Juan, Zip 00910–1070, tel. 787/777–3535; Gloria Hernandez, Executive Director
Web address: www.md.rcm.upr.edu/pediatrics/university_pediatric_hospital. php

Owned, leased, sponsored:	4 hospitals	605 beds
Contract-managed:	0 hospitals	0 beds
Totals:	4 hospitals	605 beds

★0002: QHR (IO)

1573 Mallory Lane, Suite 200, Brentwood, TN, Zip 37027, Mailing Address: 1573 Mallory Lane, Suite 200, Zip 37027, tel. 800/233–1470; Bob Vento, President and Chief Executive Officer

(Decentralized Health System)

CALIFORNIA: BEAR VALLEY COMMUNITY HOSPITAL (C, 30 beds) 41870 Garstin Drive, Big Bear Lake, CA, Zip 92315, Mailing Address: P.O. Box 1649, Zip 92315–1649, tel. 909/866–6501; John P. Friel, Chief Executive Officer

COLORADO: ARKANSAS VALLEY REGIONAL MEDICAL CENTER (C, 106 beds) 1100 Carson Avenue, La Junta, CO, Zip 81050–2799; tel. 719/383–6000; Lynn Crowell, Chief Executive Officer
Web address: www.avrmc.org

COMMUNITY HOSPITAL (C, 78 beds) 2351 G Road, Grand Junction, CO, Zip 81505; tel. 970/242–0920; Chris Thomas, FACHE, President and Chief Executive Officer
Web address: www.yourcommunityhospital.com

MONTROSE MEMORIAL HOSPITAL (C, 60 beds) 800 South Third Street, Montrose, CO, Zip 81401–4212; tel. 970/249–2211; James R. Kiser II, Chief Executive Officer

PIONEERS MEDICAL CENTER (C, 45 beds) 100 Pioneers Medical Center Drive, Meeker, CO, Zip 81641 3181; tel. 970/878–5047; Kenneth Harman, Chief Executive Officer
Web address: www.pioneershospital.org

PROWERS MEDICAL CENTER (C, 25 beds) 401 Kendall Drive, Lamar, CO, Zip 81052–3993; tel. 719/336–4343; Craig Loveless, Chief Executive Officer

SOUTHEAST COLORADO HOSPITAL DISTRICT (C, 79 beds) 373 East Tenth Avenue, Springfield, CO, Zip 81073–1699; tel. 719/523–4501; David Engel, Chief Executive Officer and Administrator
Web address: www.sechosp.org

SPANISH PEAKS REGIONAL HEALTH CENTER (C, 140 beds) 23500 U S Highway 160, Walsenburg, CO, Zip 81089–9524; tel. 719/738–5100; Kay L. Whitley, President and Chief Executive Officer
Web address: www.sprhc.org

VALLEY VIEW HOSPITAL (C, 49 beds) 1906 Blake Avenue, Glenwood Springs, CO, Zip 81601–4259; tel. 970/945–6535; Brian Murphy, M.D., Chief Executive Officer

FLORIDA: HENDRY REGIONAL MEDICAL CENTER (C, 25 beds) 524 West Sagamore Avenue, Clewiston, FL, Zip 33440–3514; tel. 863/902–3000; R D Williams, Chief Executive Officer
Web address: www.hendryregional.org

JACKSON HOSPITAL (C, 68 beds) 4250 Hospital Drive, Marianna, FL, Zip 32446–1917, Mailing Address: P.O. Box 1608, Zip 32447–5608, tel. 850/526–2200; James Platt, Chief Executive Officer
Web address: www.jacksonhosp.com

IDAHO: BENEWAH COMMUNITY HOSPITAL (C, 19 beds) 229 South Seventh Street, Saint Maries, ID, Zip 83861–1803; tel. 208/245–5551; Liz Sellers, R.N., MSN, Chief Executive Officer

GRITMAN MEDICAL CENTER (C, 25 beds) 700 South Main Street, Moscow, ID, Zip 83843–3056; tel. 208/882–4511; Kara Besst, President and Chief Executive Officer
Web address: www.gritman.org

STEELE MEMORIAL MEDICAL CENTER (C, 18 beds) 203 South Daisy Street, Salmon, ID, Zip 83467–4709; tel. 208/756–5600; Jeanine Gentry, Chief Executive Officer
Web address: www.steelemh.org

ILLINOIS: CRAWFORD MEMORIAL HOSPITAL (C, 63 beds) 1000 North Allen Street, Robinson, IL, Zip 62454–1167; tel. 618/544–3131; Douglas Florkowski, Chief Executive Officer
Web address: www.crawfordmh.net

LAWRENCE COUNTY MEMORIAL HOSPITAL (C, 25 beds) 2200 West State Street, Lawrenceville, IL, Zip 62439–1852; tel. 618/943–1000; Donald Robbins, Chief Executive Officer

MEMORIAL HOSPITAL (C, 18 beds) 1454 North County Road 2050, Carthage, IL, Zip 62321–3551, Mailing Address: P.O. Box 160, Zip 62321–0160, tel. 217/357–8500; Ada Bair, Chief Executive Officer
Web address: www.mhtlc.org

INDIANA: SULLIVAN COUNTY COMMUNITY HOSPITAL (C, 25 beds) 2200 North Section Street, Sullivan, IN, Zip 47882–7523, Mailing Address: P.O. Box 10, Zip 47882–0010, tel. 812/268–4311; Michelle Franklin, Chief Executive Officer

IOWA: BOONE COUNTY HOSPITAL (C, 25 beds) 1015 Union Street, Boone, IA, Zip 50036–4821; tel. 515/432–3140; Joseph S. Smith, Chief Executive Officer
Web address: www.boonehospital.com

WASHINGTON COUNTY HOSPITAL AND CLINICS (C, 68 beds) 400 East Polk Street, Washington, IA, Zip 52353–1237, Mailing Address: P.O. Box 909, Zip 52353–0909, tel. 319/653–5481; Todd Patterson, Chief Executive Officer
Web address: www.wchc.org

KANSAS: COFFEYVILLE REGIONAL MEDICAL CENTER (C, 87 beds) 1400 West Fourth, Coffeyville, KS, Zip 67337–3306; tel. 620/251–1200; Lori Rexwinkle, Chief Executive Officer
Web address: https://www.crmcinc.org

GREELEY COUNTY HEALTH SERVICES (C, 50 beds) 506 Third Street, Tribune, KS, Zip 67879–9684, Mailing Address: P.O. Box 338, Zip 67879–0338, tel. 620/376–4221; Burke Kline, Chief Executive Officer
Web address: www.mygchs.com

NEOSHO MEMORIAL REGIONAL MEDICAL CENTER (C, 25 beds) 629 South Plummer, Chanute, KS, Zip 66720–1928, Mailing Address: P.O. Box 426, Zip 66720–0426, tel. 620/431–4000; Dennis Franks, FACHE, Chief Executive Officer

WILSON MEDICAL CENTER (C, 15 beds) 2600 Ottawa Road, Neodesha, KS, Zip 66757–1897, Mailing Address: P.O. Box 360, Zip 66757–0360, tel. 620/325–2611; Dennis R. Shelby, Chief Executive Officer
Web address: www.wilsonmedical.org

KENTUCKY: CALDWELL MEDICAL CENTER (C, 25 beds) 100 Medical Center Drive, Princeton, KY, Zip 42445–2430, Mailing Address: P.O. Box 410, Zip 42445–0410, tel. 270/365–0300; Daniel Odegaard, FACHE, Chief Executive Officer

JENNIE STUART MEDICAL CENTER (C, 139 beds) 320 West 18th Street, Hopkinsville, KY, Zip 42240–1965, Mailing Address: P.O. Box 2400, Zip 42241–2400, tel. 270/887–0100; Eric A. Lee, President and Chief Executive Officer
Web address: www.jsmc.org

OHIO COUNTY HOSPITAL (C, 30 beds) 1211 Main Street, Hartford, KY, Zip 42347–1619; tel. 270/298–7411; Blaine Pieper, Chief Executive Officer

LOUISIANA: FRANKLIN FOUNDATION HOSPITAL (C, 22 beds) 1097 Northwest Boulevard, Franklin, LA, Zip 70538–3407, Mailing Address: P.O. Box 577, Zip 70538–0577, tel. 337/828–0760; Stephanie A. Guidry, Chief Executive Officer
Web address: www.franklinfoundation.org

LANE REGIONAL MEDICAL CENTER (C, 179 beds) 6300 Main Street, Zachary, LA, Zip 70791–4037; tel. 225/658–4000; Larry R. Meese Jr, FACHE, Chief Executive Officer
Web address: www.lanermc.org

THIBODAUX REGIONAL MEDICAL CENTER (C, 154 beds) 602 North Acadia Road, Thibodaux, LA, Zip 70301–4847, Mailing Address: P.O. Box 1118, Zip 70302–1118, tel. 985/447–5500; Greg K. Stock, FACHE, Chief Executive Officer

Section B

For explanation of codes following names, see page B2.
★ Indicates Type III membership in the American Hospital Association.

MAINE: CARY MEDICAL CENTER (C, 49 beds) 163 Van Buren Road, Suite 1, Caribou, ME, Zip 04736–3567; tel. 207/498–3111; Kris A. Doody, R.N., Chief Executive Officer
Web address: www.carymedicalcenter.org

MICHIGAN: ALLEGAN GENERAL HOSPITAL (C, 25 beds) 555 Linn Street, Allegan, MI, Zip 49010–1524; tel. 269/673–8424; Gerald J. Barbini, President and Chief Executive Officer
Web address: www.aghosp.org

THREE RIVERS HEALTH (C, 60 beds) 701 South Health Parkway, Three Rivers, MI, Zip 49093–8352; tel. 269/278–1145; David A. Shannon, Interim Chief Executive Officer
Web address: www.threerivershealth.org

MINNESOTA: RAINY LAKE MEDICAL CENTER (C, 25 beds) 1400 Highway 71, International Falls, MN, Zip 56649–2189; tel. 218/283–4481; Robert Pastor II, R.N., Chief Executive Officer
Web address: www.rainylakemedical.com

RIVER'S EDGE HOSPITAL AND CLINIC (C, 17 beds) 1900 North Sunrise Drive, Saint Peter, MN, Zip 56082–5376; tel. 507/931–2200; George A. Rohrich, FACHE, Chief Executive Officer
Web address: www.rehc.org

RIVERVIEW HEALTH (C, 49 beds) 323 South Minnesota Street, Crookston, MN, Zip 56716–1601; tel. 218/281–9200; Carrie Michalski, President and Chief Executive Officer

MISSISSIPPI: KING'S DAUGHTERS MEDICAL CENTER (C, 79 beds) 427 Highway 51 North, Brookhaven, MS, Zip 39601–2350, Mailing Address: P.O. Box 948, Zip 39602–0948, tel. 601/833–6011; Alvin Hoover, FACHE, Chief Executive Officer
Web address: www.kdmc.org

MAGNOLIA REGIONAL HEALTH CENTER (C, 200 beds) 611 Alcorn Drive, Corinth, MS, Zip 38834–9321; tel. 662/293–1000; Ronny Humes, Chief Executive Officer
Web address: www.mrhc.org

MONTANA: CABINET PEAKS MEDICAL CENTER (C, 25 beds) 209 Health Park Drive, Libby, MT, Zip 59923–2130; tel. 406/283–7000; Bruce Whitfield, CPA, Chief Executive Officer and Chief Financial Officer

KALISPELL REGIONAL HEALTHCARE (C, 178 beds) 310 Sunnyview Lane, Kalispell, MT, Zip 59901–3129; tel. 406/752–5111; Craig Lambrecht, M.D., President and Chief Executive Officer
Web address: www.krmc.org

MARIAS MEDICAL CENTER (C, 21 beds) 640 Park Drive, Shelby, MT, Zip 59474–1663, Mailing Address: P.O. Box 915, Zip 59474–0915, tel. 406/434–3200; Jessica Brusven, Chief Executive Officer
Web address: www.mmcmt.org

NORTH VALLEY HOSPITAL (C, 25 beds) 1600 Hospital Way, Whitefish, MT, Zip 59937–7849; tel. 406/863–3500; Kevin Abel, Chief Executive Officer

NORTHERN ROCKIES MEDICAL CENTER (C, 29 beds) 802 Second Street SE, Cut Bank, MT, Zip 59427–3329; tel. 406/873–2251; Cherie Taylor, Chief Executive Officer
Web address: www.nrmcinc.org

PONDERA MEDICAL CENTER (C, 79 beds) 805 Sunset Boulevard, Conrad, MT, Zip 59425–1717, Mailing Address: P.O. Box 668, Zip 59425–0668, tel. 406/271–3211; Bill O'Leary, Chief Executive Officer

THE HEALTHCENTER (C, 28 beds) 320 Sunnyview Lane, Kalispell, MT, Zip 59901–3129; tel. 406/751–7550; Tate J. Kreitinger, Chief Executive Officer
Web address: www.krmc.org

NEBRASKA: PHELPS MEMORIAL HEALTH CENTER (C, 25 beds) 1215 Tibbals Street, Holdrege, NE, Zip 68949–1255; tel. 308/995–2211; Mark Harrel, Chief Executive Officer
Web address: www.phelpsmemorial.com

NEW HAMPSHIRE: ANDROSCOGGIN VALLEY HOSPITAL (C, 25 beds) 59 Page Hill Road, Berlin, NH, Zip 03570–3531; tel. 603/752–2200; Michael Peterson, FACHE, President

LITTLETON REGIONAL HEALTHCARE (C, 25 beds) 600 Saint Johnsbury Road, Littleton, NH, Zip 03561–3442; tel. 603/444–9000; Robert Nutter, President
Web address: www.littletonhospital.org

UPPER CONNECTICUT VALLEY HOSPITAL (C, 12 beds) 181 Corliss Lane, Colebrook, NH, Zip 03576–3207; tel. 603/237–4971; Scott Colby, President

WEEKS MEDICAL CENTER (C, 25 beds) 173 Middle Street, Lancaster, NH, Zip 03584–3508; tel. 603/788–4911; Michael Lee, President
Web address: www.weeksmedical.org

NEW MEXICO: CIBOLA GENERAL HOSPITAL (C, 25 beds) 1016 East Roosevelt Avenue, Grants, NM, Zip 87020–2118; tel. 505/287–4446; Thomas Whelan, Chief Executive Officer

HOLY CROSS HOSPITAL (C, 25 beds) 1397 Weimer Road, Taos, NM, Zip 87571–6253; tel. 575/758–8883; William D. Patten Jr, Chief Executive Officer
Web address: www.taoshospital.org

SIERRA VISTA HOSPITAL (C, 15 beds) 800 East Ninth Avenue, Truth or Consequences, NM, Zip 87901–1961; tel. 575/894–2111; David Faulkner, Interim Chief Executive Officer

NEW YORK: ADIRONDACK HEALTH (C, 120 beds) 2233 State Route 86, Saranac Lake, NY, Zip 12983–5644, Mailing Address: P.O. Box 471, Zip 12983–0471, tel. 518/891–4141; Sylvia Getman, President and Chief Executive Officer
Web address: www.adirondackhealth.org

OHIO: KNOX COMMUNITY HOSPITAL (C, 71 beds) 1330 Coshocton Road, Mount Vernon, OH, Zip 43050–1495; tel. 740/393–9000; Bruce D. White, Chief Executive Officer
Web address: www.kch.org

WOOSTER COMMUNITY HOSPITAL (C, 152 beds) 1761 Beall Avenue, Wooster, OH, Zip 44691–2342; tel. 330/263–8100; William E. Sheron, Chief Executive Officer
Web address: www.woosterhospital.org

PENNSYLVANIA: CLARION HOSPITAL (C, 66 beds) One Hospital Drive, Clarion, PA, Zip 16214–8501; tel. 814/226–9500; Steven T. Davis, Chief Executive Officer

SOUTH CAROLINA: ABBEVILLE AREA MEDICAL CENTER (C, 25 beds) 420 Thomson Circle, Abbeville, SC, Zip 29620–5656, Mailing Address: P.O. Box 887, Zip 29620–0887, tel. 864/366–5011; Howard D. Turner, Chief Executive Officer
Web address: www.abbevilleareamc.com

NEWBERRY COUNTY MEMORIAL HOSPITAL (C, 54 beds) 2669 Kinard Street, Newberry, SC, Zip 29108–2911, Mailing Address: P.O. Box 497, Zip 29108–0497, tel. 803/276–7570; Bruce A. Baldwin, Chief Executive Officer
Web address: www.newberryhospital.org

REGIONAL MEDICAL CENTER (C, 283 beds) 3000 St Matthews Road, Orangeburg, SC, Zip 29118–1442; tel. 803/395–2200; Charles E. Williams, FACHE, President and Chief Executive Officer
Web address: www.trmchealth.org

TIDELANDS GEORGETOWN MEMORIAL HOSPITAL (C, 136 beds) 606 Black River Road, Georgetown, SC, Zip 29440–3368, Mailing Address: Drawer 421718, Zip 29442–4203, tel. 843/527–7000; Bruce P. Bailey, Chief Executive Officer

TIDELANDS WACCAMAW COMMUNITY HOSPITAL (C, 169 beds) 4070 Highway 17 Bypass, Murrells Inlet, SC, Zip 29576–5033, Mailing Address: P O Drawer 3350, Zip 29576–2673, tel. 843/652–1000; Bruce P. Bailey, Chief Executive Officer
Web address: www.tidelandswaccamawcommunity.org

SOUTH DAKOTA: HURON REGIONAL MEDICAL CENTER (C, 30 beds) 172 Fourth Street SE, Huron, SD, Zip 57350–2590; tel. 605/353–6200; David Dick, Chief Executive Officer
Web address: www.huronregional.org

TENNESSEE: MACON COMMUNITY HOSPITAL (C, 25 beds) 204 Medical Drive, Lafayette, TN, Zip 37083–1799, Mailing Address: P.O. Box 378, Zip 37083–0378, tel. 615/666–2147; Thomas J. Kidd, CPA, Chief Executive Officer

RHEA MEDICAL CENTER (C, 25 beds) 9400 Rhea County Highway, Dayton, TN, Zip 37321–7922; tel. 423/775–1121; David Bixler, Chief Executive Officer
Web address: www.rheamedical.org

TEXAS: GONZALES HEALTHCARE SYSTEMS (C, 33 beds) 1110 Sarah Dewitt Drive, Gonzales, TX, Zip 78629–3311, Mailing Address: P.O. Box 587, Zip 78629–0587, tel. 830/672–7581; Patty Stewart, Interim Chief Executive Officer

For explanation of codes following names, see page B2.
★ Indicates Type III membership in the American Hospital Association.

Section B

MATAGORDA REGIONAL MEDICAL CENTER (C, 58 beds) 104 7th Street, Bay City, TX, Zip 77414–4853; tel. 979/245–6383; James Warren. Robicheaux, FACHE, Chief Executive Officer
Web address: www.matagordaregional.org

WILBARGER GENERAL HOSPITAL (C, 27 beds) 920 Hillcrest Drive, Vernon, TX, Zip 76384–3196; tel. 940/552–9351; Dennis D. Jack, FACHE, Chief Executive Officer

VERMONT: NORTHWESTERN MEDICAL CENTER (C, 55 beds) 133 Fairfield Street, Saint Albans, VT, Zip 05478–1726; tel. 802/524–5911; Jill Berry. Bowen, Chief Executive Officer
Web address: www.northwesternmedicalcenter.org

WYOMING: MEMORIAL HOSPITAL OF CARBON COUNTY (C, 25 beds) 2221 West Elm Street, Rawlins, WY, Zip 82301–5108, Mailing Address: P.O. Box 460, Zip 82301–0460, tel. 307/324–2221; Robert Quist, Interim Chief Executive Officer

WEST PARK HOSPITAL (C, 112 beds) 707 Sheridan Avenue, Cody, WY, Zip 82414–3409; tel. 307/527–7501; Douglas A. McMillan, Administrator and Chief Executive Officer
Web address: www.westparkhospital.org

Owned, leased, sponsored:	0 hospitals	0 beds
Contract-managed:	71 hospitals	4249 beds
Totals:	71 hospitals	4249 beds

★0040: QUEEN'S HEALTH SYSTEMS (NP)
1301 Punchbowl Street, Honolulu, HI, Zip 96813–2402; tel. 808/535–5448; Arthur A. Ushijima, FACHE, President and Chief Executive Officer
(Moderately Centralized Health System)

HAWAII: MOLOKAI GENERAL HOSPITAL (O, 15 beds) 280 Home Olu Place, Kaunakakai, HI, Zip 96748–0408, Mailing Address: P.O. Box 408, Zip 96748–0408, tel. 808/553–5331; Janice Kalanihuia, President
Web address: www.queens.org

NORTH HAWAII COMMUNITY HOSPITAL (O, 35 beds) 67–1125 Mamalahoa Highway, Kamuela, HI, Zip 96743–8496; tel. 808/885–4444; Cynthia Kamikawa, R.N., M3N, President

THE QUEEN'S MEDICAL CENTER (O, 637 beds) 1301 Punchbowl Street, Honolulu, HI, Zip 96813–2499; tel 808/691–5100; Jill Hoggard Green, Ph.D., R.N., Chief Executive Officer
Web address: www.queensmedicalcenter.org

Owned, leased, sponsored:	3 hospitals	687 beds
Contract-managed:	0 hospitals	0 beds
Totals:	3 hospitals	687 beds

★0981: QUORUM HEALTH (IO)
1573 Mallory Lane, Suite 100, Brentwood, TN, Zip 37027; tel. 615/221–1400; Robert D. Fish, Chief Executive Officer
(Moderately Centralized Health System)

ALABAMA: DEKALB REGIONAL MEDICAL CENTER (O, 115 beds) 200 Medical Center Drive, Fort Payne, AL, Zip 35968–3458, Mailing Address: P.O. Box 680778, Zip 35968–1608, tel. 256/845–3150; Patrick Trammell, Chief Executive Officer
Web address: www.dekalbregional.com

ARKANSAS: FORREST CITY MEDICAL CENTER (L, 55 beds) 1601 Newcastle Road, Forrest City, AR, Zip 72335–2218; tel. 870/261–0000; Kevin Decker, Chief Executive Officer
Web address: www.forrestcitymedicalcenter.com

HELENA REGIONAL MEDICAL CENTER (L, 105 beds) 1801 Martin Luther King Drive, Helena, AR, Zip 72342, Mailing Address: P.O. Box 788, Zip 72342–0788, tel. 870/338–5800; Amy Rice, Interim Chief Executive Officer
Web address: www.helenarmc.com

CALIFORNIA: BARSTOW COMMUNITY HOSPITAL (L, 30 beds) 820 East Mountain View Street, Barstow, CA, Zip 92311–3004; tel. 760/256–1761; Matthew H. Blevins, Chief Executive Officer

WATSONVILLE COMMUNITY HOSPITAL (O, 106 beds) 75 Nielson Street, Watsonville, CA, Zip 95076–2468; tel. 831/724–4741; Audra Earle, FACHE, Chief Executive Officer
Web address: www.watsonvillehospital.com

GEORGIA: FANNIN REGIONAL HOSPITAL (O, 50 beds) 2855 Old Highway 5, Blue Ridge, GA, Zip 30513–6248; tel. 706/632–3711; David S. Sanders, Chief Executive Officer
Web address: www.fanninregionalhospital.com

ILLINOIS: CROSSROADS COMMUNITY HOSPITAL (O, 31 beds) 8 Doctors Park Road, Mount Vernon, IL, Zip 62864–6224; tel. 618/244–5500; Amanda J. Basso, Chief Executive Officer
Web address: www.crossroadshospital.com

GALESBURG COTTAGE HOSPITAL (O, 119 beds) 695 North Kellogg Street, Galesburg, IL, Zip 61401–2885; tel. 309/343–8131; James Flynn, Chief Executive Officer

GATEWAY REGIONAL MEDICAL CENTER (O, 127 beds) 2100 Madison Avenue, Granite City, IL, Zip 62040–4799; tel. 618/798–3000; M Edward. Cunningham, Chief Executive Officer
Web address: www.gatewayregional.net

HEARTLAND REGIONAL MEDICAL CENTER (O, 92 beds) 3333 West DeYoung, Marion, IL, Zip 62959–5884; tel. 618/998–7000; Melisa Adkins, Chief Executive Officer
Web address: www.heartlandregional.com

METROSOUTH MEDICAL CENTER (O, 285 beds) 12935 South Gregory Street, Blue Island, IL, Zip 60406–2470; tel. 708/597–2000; John D. Baird, Chief Executive Officer

RED BUD REGIONAL HOSPITAL (O, 140 beds) 325 Spring Street, Red Bud, IL, Zip 62278–1105; tel. 618/282–3831; Shane Watson, Chief Executive Officer
Web address: www.redbudregional.com

UNION COUNTY HOSPITAL (L, 47 beds) 517 North Main Street, Anna, IL, Zip 62906–1696; tel. 618/833–4511; James R. Farris, FACHE, Chief Executive Officer

VISTA HEALTH (O, 190 beds) 1324 North Sheridan Road, Waukegan, IL, Zip 60085–2161; tel. 847/360–3000; Norman F. Stephens, Interim Chief Executive Officer
Web address: www.vistahealth.com

KENTUCKY: KENTUCKY RIVER MEDICAL CENTER (L, 54 beds) 540 Jett Drive, Jackson, KY, Zip 41339–9622; tel. 606/666–6000; John Ballard, Ph.D., Chief Executive Officer
Web address: www.kentuckyrivermc.com

PAUL B. HALL REGIONAL MEDICAL CENTER (O, 72 beds) 625 James S. Trimble Boulevard, Paintsville, KY, Zip 41240–0000; tel. 606/789–3511; Deborah Trimble, R.N., Chief Executive Officer
Web address: www.pbhrmc.com

THREE RIVERS MEDICAL CENTER (O, 90 beds) 2485 Highway 644, Louisa, KY, Zip 41230–9242, Mailing Address: P.O. Box 769, Zip 41230 0769, tel. 606/638–9451; Greg Kiser, Chief Executive Officer

NEVADA: MESA VIEW REGIONAL HOSPITAL (O, 25 beds) 1299 Bertha Howe Avenue, Mesquite, NV, Zip 89027–7500; tel. 702/346–8040; Ned Hill, Chief Executive Officer
Web address: www.mesaviewhospital.com

NEW MEXICO: ALTA VISTA REGIONAL HOSPITAL (O, 54 beds) 104 Legion Drive, Las Vegas, NM, Zip 87701–4804; tel. 505/426–3500; Caleb F. O'Rear, Chief Executive Officer

MIMBRES MEMORIAL HOSPITAL (O, 75 beds) 900 West Ash Street, Deming, NM, Zip 88030–4098, Mailing Address: P.O. Box 710, Zip 88031–0710, tel. 575/546–5800; Gary R. Poquette, FACHE, Chief Executive Officer
Web address: www.mimbresmemorial.com

NORTH CAROLINA: MARTIN GENERAL HOSPITAL (L, 49 beds) 310 South McCaskey Road, Williamston, NC, Zip 27892–2150, Mailing Address: P.O. Box 1128, Zip 27892–1128, tel. 252/809–6300; Joanie White Wagner, Chief Executive Officer
Web address: www.martingeneral.com

OREGON: MCKENZIE-WILLAMETTE MEDICAL CENTER (O, 112 beds) 1460 'G' Street, Springfield, OR, Zip 97477–4197; tel. 541/726–4400; David Elgarico, Chief Executive Officer

---

For explanation of codes following names, see page B2.
★ Indicates Type III membership in the American Hospital Association.

TENNESSEE: HENDERSON COUNTY COMMUNITY HOSPITAL (O, 45 beds) 200 West Church Street, Lexington, TN, Zip 38351–2038; tel. 731/968–3646; Pamela W. Roberts, Chief Executive Officer
Web address: www.hendersoncchospital.com

TEXAS: BIG BEND REGIONAL MEDICAL CENTER (O, 25 beds) 2600 Highway 118 North, Alpine, TX, Zip 79830–2002; tel. 432/837–3447; Rick Flores, Interim Chief Executive Officer
Web address: www.bigbendhealthcare.com

UTAH: MOUNTAIN WEST MEDICAL CENTER (O, 44 beds) 2055 North Main Street, Tooele, UT, Zip 84074–9819; tel. 435/843–3600; Philip Eaton, Interim Chief Executive Officer

WYOMING: EVANSTON REGIONAL HOSPITAL (O, 42 beds) 190 Arrowhead Drive, Evanston, WY, Zip 82930–9266; tel. 307/789–3636; Cheri Willard, MSN, R.N., Interim Chief Executive Officer
Web address: www.evanstonregionalhospital.com

Owned, leased, sponsored:	26 hospitals	2179 beds
Contract-managed:	0 hospitals	0 beds
Totals:	26 hospitals	2179 beds

★8495: REGIONAL HEALTH (NP)

353 Fairmont Boulevard, Rapid City, SD, Zip 57701–7375, Mailing Address: P.O. Box 6000, Zip 57709–6000, tel. 605/719–1000; Paulette Davidson, FACHE, President and Chief Executive Officer
(Moderately Centralized Health System)

SOUTH DAKOTA: CUSTER REGIONAL HOSPITAL (L, 87 beds) 1039 Montgomery Street, Custer, SD, Zip 57730–1397; tel. 605/673–2229; Mark C. Schmidt, President
Web address: www.regionalhealth.com

LEAD-DEADWOOD REGIONAL HOSPITAL (O, 7 beds) 61 Charles Street, Deadwood, SD, Zip 57732–1303; tel. 605/717–6000; Mark C. Schmidt, President
Web address: www.regionalhealth.com

PHILIP HEALTH SERVICES (C, 48 beds) 503 West Pine Street, Philip, SD, Zip 57567–3300, Mailing Address: P.O. Box 790, Zip 57567–0790, tel. 605/859–2511; Jeremy Schultes, Administrator and Chief Executive Officer
Web address: www.philiphealthservices.com/

RAPID CITY REGIONAL HOSPITAL (O, 375 beds) 353 Fairmont Boulevard, Rapid City, SD, Zip 57701–7393, Mailing Address: P.O. Box 6000, Zip 57709–6000, tel. 605/755–1000; John Pierce, Acting President

SPEARFISH REGIONAL HOSPITAL (O, 35 beds) 1440 North Main Street, Spearfish, SD, Zip 57783–1504; tel. 605/644–4000; Thomas Worsley, Chief Executive Officer
Web address: www.regionalhealth.com/Our-Locations/Regional-Hospitals/Spearfish-Regional-Hospital.aspx

STURGIS REGIONAL HOSPITAL (O, 109 beds) 949 Harmon Street, Sturgis, SD, Zip 57785–2452; tel. 605/720–2400; Mark Schulte, FACHE, President
Web address: www.regionalhealth.org/Our-Locations/Regional-Hospitals/Sturgis-Regional-Hospital.aspx

WYOMING: CROOK COUNTY MEDICAL SERVICES DISTRICT (C, 16 beds) 713 Oak Street, Sundance, WY, Zip 82729, Mailing Address: P.O. Box 517, Zip 82729–0517, tel. 307/283–3501; Nathan Hough, Chief Executive Officer

WESTON COUNTY HEALTH SERVICES (C, 70 beds) 1124 Washington Boulevard, Newcastle, WY, Zip 82701–2972; tel. 307/746–4491; Maureen K. Cadwell, Chief Executive Officer
Web address: www.wchs-wy.org

Owned, leased, sponsored:	5 hospitals	613 beds
Contract-managed:	3 hospitals	134 beds
Totals:	8 hospitals	747 beds

1019: REGIONAL MEDICAL CENTER (NP)

400 East 10th Street, Anniston, AL, Zip 36207–4716; tel. 256/235–5121; Louis A. Bass, President and Chief Executive Officer
(Independent Hospital System)

ALABAMA: RMC ANNISTON (O, 118 beds) 400 East Tenth Street, Anniston, AL, Zip 36207–4716, Mailing Address: P.O. Box 2208, Zip 36202–2208, tel. 256/235–5121; Louis A. Bass, Chief Executive Officer
Web address: www.rmccares.org

RMC-STRINGFELLOW MEMORIAL HOSPITAL (O, 88 beds) 301 East 18th Street, Anniston, AL, Zip 36207–3952; tel. 256/235–8900; Joe Weaver, Chief Executive Officer
Web address: www.stringfellowmemorial.com

Owned, leased, sponsored:	2 hospitals	206 beds
Contract-managed:	0 hospitals	0 beds
Totals:	2 hospitals	206 beds

★2625: RENOWN HEALTH (NP)

50 West Liberty Street, Suite 1100, Reno, NV, Zip 89501–1951; tel. 775/982–5529; Anthony D. Slonim, M.D., Dr.PH, President and Chief Executive Officer
(Centralized Health System)

NEVADA: RENOWN REGIONAL MEDICAL CENTER (O, 667 beds) 1155 Mill Street, Reno, NV, Zip 89502–1576; tel. 775/982–4100; Erik Olson, Chief Executive Officer

RENOWN REHABILITATION HOSPITAL (O, 62 beds) 1495 Mill Street, Reno, NV, Zip 89502–1479; tel. 775/982–3500; Chris Nicholas, Administrator of Rehabilitation Hospital
Web address: www.renown.org

RENOWN SOUTH MEADOWS MEDICAL CENTER (O, 76 beds) 10101 Double 'R' Boulevard, Reno, NV, Zip 89521–5931; tel. 775/982–7000; Siri Nelson, Chief Executive Officer
Web address: www.renown.org

Owned, leased, sponsored:	3 hospitals	805 beds
Contract-managed:	0 hospitals	0 beds
Totals:	3 hospitals	805 beds

★0964: RIDGEVIEW MEDICAL CENTER (IO)

500 South Maple Street, Waconia, MN, Zip 55387–1752; tel. 952/442–2191; Michael Phelps, President and Chief Executive Officer
(Independent Hospital System)

MINNESOTA: RIDGEVIEW LE SUEUR MEDICAL CENTER (O, 49 beds) 621 South Fourth Street, Le Sueur, MN, Zip 56058–2298; tel. 507/665–3375; Pamela Williams, Vice President
Web address: www.mvhc.org

RIDGEVIEW MEDICAL CENTER (O, 108 beds) 500 South Maple Street, Waconia, MN, Zip 55387–1791; tel. 952/442–2191; Michael Phelps, President and Chief Executive Officer
Web address: www.ridgeviewmedical.org

RIDGEVIEW SIBLEY MEDICAL CENTER (L, 6 beds) 601 West Chandler Street, Arlington, MN, Zip 55307–2127; tel. 507/964–2271; Michael Phelps, President and Chief Executive Officer

Owned, leased, sponsored:	3 hospitals	163 beds
Contract-managed:	0 hospitals	0 beds
Totals:	3 hospitals	163 beds

4810: RIVERSIDE HEALTH SYSTEM (NP)

701 Town Center Drive, Suite 1000, Newport News, VA, Zip 23606–4286; tel. 757/534–7000; William B. Downey, President and Chief Executive Officer
(Centralized Health System)

VIRGINIA: RIVERSIDE DOCTORS' HOSPITAL WILLIAMSBURG (O, 16 beds) 1500 Commonwealth Avenue, Williamsburg, VA, Zip 23185–5229; tel. 757/585–2200; Steve C. McCary, Administrator

---

For explanation of codes following names, see page B2.
★ Indicates Type III membership in the American Hospital Association.

RIVERSIDE REGIONAL MEDICAL CENTER (O, 307 beds) 500 J Clyde Morris Boulevard, Newport News, VA, Zip 23601–1929; tel. 757/594–2000; Michael J. Doucette, Senior Vice President and Administrator
Web address: https://www.riversideonline.com/rrmc/index.cfm

RIVERSIDE SHORE MEMORIAL HOSPITAL (O, 22 beds) 20480 Market Street, Onancock, VA, Zip 23417–4309, Mailing Address: P.O. Box 430, Zip 23417, tel. 757/302–2100; John Peterman, Vice President and Administrator

RIVERSIDE TAPPAHANNOCK HOSPITAL (O, 16 beds) 618 Hospital Road, Tappahannock, VA, Zip 22560–5000; tel. 804/443–3311; Esther Muscari. Desimini, Administrator
Web address: https://www.riversideonline.com

RIVERSIDE WALTER REED HOSPITAL (O, 30 beds) 7519 Hospital Drive, Gloucester, VA, Zip 23061–4178, Mailing Address: P.O. Box 1130, Zip 23061–1130, tel. 804/693–8800; Esther Muscari. Desimini, Interim Administrator

Owned, leased, sponsored:	5 hospitals	391 beds
Contract-managed:	0 hospitals	0 beds
Totals:	5 hospitals	391 beds

★0046: ROCHESTER REGIONAL HEALTH (NP)

1425 Portland Avenue, 5th Floor, Rochester, NY, Zip 14621–3001; tel. 585/922–4000; Eric Bieber, M.D., President and Chief Executive Officer
(Centralized Health System)

NEW YORK: CLIFTON SPRINGS HOSPITAL AND CLINIC (O, 179 beds) 2 Coulter Road, Clifton Springs, NY, Zip 14432–1189; tel. 315/462–9561; Dustin Riccio, M.D., President

NEWARK-WAYNE COMMUNITY HOSPITAL (O, 289 beds) 1200 Driving Park Avenue, Newark, NY, Zip 14513–1057, Mailing Address: P.O. Box 111, Zip 14513–0111, tel. 315/332–2022; Dustin Riccio, M.D., President Eastern Region
Web address: www.rochesterregional.org

ROCHESTER GENERAL HOSPITAL (O, 528 beds) 1425 Portland Avenue, Rochester, NY, Zip 14621–3099; tel. 585/922–4000; Kevin John. Casey, President
Web address: https://www.rochesterregional.org/

UNITED MEMORIAL MEDICAL CENTER (O, 133 beds) 127 North Street, Batavia, NY, Zip 14020–1631; tel. 585/343–6030; Daniel P. Ireland, FACHE, President

UNITY HOSPITAL (O, 451 beds) 1555 Long Pond Road, Rochester, NY, Zip 14626–4182; tel. 585/723–7000; Douglas Stewart, PsyD, President
Web address: www.unityhealth.org

Owned, leased, sponsored:	5 hospitals	1580 beds
Contract-managed:	0 hospitals	0 beds
Totals:	5 hospitals	1580 beds

1044: ROPER ST. FRANCIS HEALTHCARE (NP)

125 Doughty Street, Suite 760, Charleston, SC, Zip 29403–5785; tel. 843/402–2273; Lorraine Lutton, President and Chief Executive Officer

SOUTH CAROLINA: BON SECOURS ST. FRANCIS HOSPITAL (O, 160 beds) 2095 Henry Tecklenburg Drive, Charleston, SC, Zip 29414–5733; tel. 843/402–1000; W. Anthony. Jackson, Chief Executive Officer
Web address: www.rsfh.com/

ROPER HOSPITAL (O, 305 beds) 316 Calhoun Street, Charleston, SC, Zip 29401–1125; tel. 843/724–2000; W. Anthony. Jackson, Chief Executive Officer

ROPER ST. FRANCIS MOUNT PLEASANT HOSPITAL (O, 73 beds) 3500 Highway 17 North, Mount Pleasant, SC, Zip 29466–9123, Mailing Address: 3500 North Highway 17, Zip 29466–9123, tel. 843/606–7000; W. Anthony. Jackson, Chief Executive Officer
Web address: www.rsfh.com/mount-pleasant-hospital

Owned, leased, sponsored:	3 hospitals	538 beds
Contract-managed:	0 hospitals	0 beds
Totals:	3 hospitals	538 beds

0348: RURAL COMMUNITY HOSPITALS OF AMERICA (IO)

1100 Main Street, Suite 2350, Kansas City, MO, Zip 64105–5186; tel. 816/474–7800; Paul L. Nusbaum, President and Co-Owner
(Independent Hospital System)

KANSAS: HILLSBORO COMMUNITY HOSPITAL (O, 15 beds) 701 South Main Street, Hillsboro, KS, Zip 67063–1553; tel. 620/947–3114; Marion Regier, Chief Executive Officer
Web address: www.hchks.com

NORTH CAROLINA: WASHINGTON COUNTY HOSPITAL (O, 25 beds) 958 U S Highway 64 East, Plymouth, NC, Zip 27962–9591, Mailing Address: PO Box 707, Zip 27962–9591, tel. 252/793–4135; Melanie A. Perry, Chief Executive Officer

OKLAHOMA: DRUMRIGHT REGIONAL HOSPITAL (O, 15 beds) 610 West Bypass, Drumright, OK, Zip 74030–5957; tel. 918/382–2300; Micheal Christensen, Interim Chief Executive Officer
Web address: www.drumrighthospital.com/

FAIRFAX COMMUNITY HOSPITAL (O, 15 beds) 40 Hospital Road, Fairfax, OK, Zip 74637–5084; tel. 918/642–3291; Tina Steele, Chief Executive Officer and Chief Financial Officer

HASKELL COUNTY COMMUNITY HOSPITAL (O, 20 beds) 401 Northwest 'H' Street, Stigler, OK, Zip 74462–1625; tel. 918/967–4682; Andrea Randall, Interim Chief Executive Officer
Web address: www.haskellhospital.com

PRAGUE COMMUNITY HOSPITAL (O, 15 beds) 1322 Klabzuba Avenue, Prague, OK, Zip 74864–9005, Mailing Address: P.O. Box S, Zip 74864–1090, tel. 405/567–4922; Shelly Dyer, Interim Chief Executive Officer

Owned, leased, sponsored:	6 hospitals	105 beds
Contract-managed:	0 hospitals	0 beds
Totals:	6 hospitals	105 beds

★0109: RURAL HEALTH GROUP (IO)

48 West 1500 North, Nephi, UT, Zip 84648–8900; tel. 435/623–4224; Mark R. Stoddard, President and Chairman
(Independent Hospital System)

UTAH: CENTRAL VALLEY MEDICAL CENTER (L, 27 beds) 48 West 1500 North, Nephi, UT, Zip 84648–8900; tel. 435/623–3000; Mark R. Stoddard, Chief Executive Officer
Web address: www.cvmed.net

Owned, leased, sponsored:	1 hospitals	27 beds
Contract-managed:	0 hospitals	0 beds
Totals:	1 hospitals	27 beds

0220: RUSH HEALTH SYSTEMS (NP)

1314 19th Avenue, Meridian, MS, Zip 39301–4116; tel. 601/483–0011; Larkin Kennedy, President and Chief Executive Officer
(Independent Hospital System)

ALABAMA: CHOCTAW GENERAL HOSPITAL (O, 25 beds) 401 Vanity Fair Avenue, Butler, AL, Zip 36904–3032; tel. 205/459–9100; J W. Cowan, Administrator
Web address: www.choctawgeneral.com/cgh/

MISSISSIPPI: H. C. WATKINS MEMORIAL HOSPITAL (O, 25 beds) 605 South Archusa Avenue, Quitman, MS, Zip 39355–2331; tel. 601/776–6925; Michael Nester, Administrator
Web address: www.watkinsmemorialhospital.com/hcwmh/

JOHN C. STENNIS MEMORIAL HOSPITAL (O, 25 beds) 14365 Highway 16 West, De Kalb, MS, Zip 39328–7974; tel. 769/486–1000; Justin Palmer, Administrator
Web address: www.johncstennismemorialhospital.com/jcsmh/

LAIRD HOSPITAL (O, 25 beds) 25117 Highway 15, Union, MS, Zip 39365–9099; tel. 601/774–8214; Thomas G. Bartlett III, Administrator

---

For explanation of codes following names, see page B2.
★ Indicates Type III membership in the American Hospital Association.

RUSH FOUNDATION HOSPITAL (O, 182 beds) 1314 19th Avenue, Meridian, MS, Zip 39301–4195; tel. 601/483–0011; Larkin Kennedy, Chief Executive Officer
Web address: www.rushhealthsystems.org/rfh/

SCOTT REGIONAL HOSPITAL (O, 25 beds) 317 Highway 13 South, Morton, MS, Zip 39117–3353, Mailing Address: P.O. Box 259, Zip 39117–0259, tel. 601/732–6301; Heather Davis, Administrator

SPECIALTY HOSPITAL OF MERIDIAN (O, 49 beds) 1314 19th Avenue, Meridian, MS, Zip 39301–4116; tel. 601/703–4211; Elizabeth C. Mitchell, Chief Executive Officer and Chief Operating Officer
Web address: www.specialtyhospitalofmeridian.com/shm/

Owned, leased, sponsored:	7 hospitals	356 beds
Contract-managed:	0 hospitals	0 beds
Totals:	7 hospitals	356 beds

★3855: **RUSH UNIVERSITY MEDICAL CENTER** (NP)
1653 West Congress Parkway, Chicago, IL, Zip 60612–3864; tel. 312/942–5000; Ranga Krishnan, M.D., Chief Executive Officer
(Moderately Centralized Health System)

ILLINOIS: RUSH OAK PARK HOSPITAL (O, 108 beds) 520 South Maple Avenue, Oak Park, IL, Zip 60304–1097; tel. 708/383–9300; Bruce M. Elegant, FACHE, President and Chief Executive Officer
Web address: www.roph.org

RUSH UNIVERSITY MEDICAL CENTER (O, 701 beds) 1653 West Congress Parkway, Chicago, IL, Zip 60612–3833; tel. 312/942–5000; Omar Lateef, D.O., Chief Executive Officer

RUSH-COPLEY MEDICAL CENTER (O, 210 beds) 2000 Ogden Avenue, Aurora, IL, Zip 60504–7222; tel. 630/978–6200; Barry C. Finn, President and Chief Executive Officer
Web address: www.rushcopley.com

Owned, leased, sponsored:	3 hospitals	1019 beds
Contract-managed:	0 hospitals	0 beds
Totals:	3 hospitals	1019 beds

★0994: **RWJBARNABAS HEALTH** (NP)
95 Old Short Hills Road, West Orange, NJ, Zip 07052–1008; tel. 973/322–4000; Barry Ostrowsky, President and Chief Executive Officer
(Decentralized Health System)

NEW JERSEY: CHILDREN'S SPECIALIZED HOSPITAL (O, 140 beds) 200 Somerset Street, New Brunswick, NJ, Zip 08901–1942; tel. 732/258–7000; Warren E. Moore, FACHE, President and Chief Executive Officer
Web address: www.childrens-specialized.org

CLARA MAASS MEDICAL CENTER (O, 352 beds) One Clara Maass Drive, Belleville, NJ, Zip 07109–3557; tel. 973/450–2000; Mary Ellen Clyne, Ph.D., President and Chief Executive Officer

COMMUNITY MEDICAL CENTER (O, 295 beds) 99 Route 37 West, Toms River, NJ, Zip 08755–6423; tel. 732/557–8000; Patrick Ahearn, Chief Executive Officer
Web address: www.barnabashealth.org/hospitals/community_medical/index.html

JERSEY CITY MEDICAL CENTER (O, 316 beds) 355 Grand Street, Jersey City, NJ, Zip 07302–4321; tel. 201/915–2000; Michael Prilutsky, President and Chief Executive Officer

MONMOUTH MEDICAL CENTER, LONG BRANCH CAMPUS (O, 296 beds) 300 Second Avenue, Long Branch, NJ, Zip 07740–6303; tel. 732/222–5200; Eric Carney, Chief Executive Officer
Web address: www.barnabashealth.org/hospitals/monmouth_medical/index.html

MONMOUTH MEDICAL CENTER, SOUTHERN CAMPUS (O, 124 beds) 600 River Avenue, Lakewood, NJ, Zip 08701–5237; tel. 732/363–1900; Frank J. Vozos, M.D., FACS, Chief Executive Officer, MMC Southern Campus

NEWARK BETH ISRAEL MEDICAL CENTER (O, 372 beds) 201 Lyons Avenue at Osborne Terrace, Newark, NJ, Zip 07112–2027; tel. 973/926–7000; Darrell K. Terry Sr, M.P.H., FACHE, President and Chief Executive Officer
Web address: www.barnabashealth.org/hospitals/newark_beth_israel/index.html

RWJBARNABAS HEALTH BEHAVIORAL HEALTH CENTER AND NETWORK (O, 40 beds) 1691 Highway 9, Toms River, NJ, Zip 8754; tel. 732/914–1688; Deanna Sperling, R.N., President and Chief Executive Officer

ROBERT WOOD JOHNSON UNIVERSITY HOSPITAL RAHWAY (O, 106 beds) 865 Stone Street, Rahway, NJ, Zip 07065–2797; tel. 732/381–4200; Kirk C. Tice, President and Chief Executive Officer
Web address: www.rwjuhr.com

ROBERT WOOD JOHNSON UNIVERSITY HOSPITAL SOMERSET (O, 228 beds) 110 Rehill Avenue, Somerville, NJ, Zip 08876–2598; tel. 908/685–2200; Anthony V. Cava, MS, FACHE, President
Web address: www.rwjuh.edu

ROBERT WOOD JOHNSON UNIVERSITY HOSPITAL AT HAMILTON (O, 164 beds) One Hamilton Health Place, Hamilton, NJ, Zip 08690–3599; tel. 609/586–7900; Richard Freeman, President and Chief Executive Officer
Web address: www.rwjhamilton.org

ROBERT WOOD JOHNSON UNIVERSITY HOSPITAL (O, 599 beds) 1 Robert Wood Johnson Place, New Brunswick, NJ, Zip 08901–1928; tel. 732/828–3000; John J. Gantner, President and Chief Executive Officer

SAINT BARNABAS MEDICAL CENTER (O, 561 beds) 94 Old Short Hills Rd, Livingston, NJ, Zip 07039–5672; tel. 973/322–5000; Stephen P. Zieniewicz, FACHE, President and Chief Executive Officer
Web address: www.barnabashealth.org/hospitals/saint_barnabas/index.html

Owned, leased, sponsored:	13 hospitals	3593 beds
Contract-managed:	0 hospitals	0 beds
Totals:	13 hospitals	3593 beds

0912: **SAFE HAVEN HEALTH CARE** (IO)
2520 South 5th Avenue, Pocatello, ID, Zip 83204–1923; tel. 800/261–2443; Scott Burpee, President

IDAHO: SAFE HAVEN HOSPITAL OF POCATELLO (O, 87 beds) 1200 Hospital Way, Pocatello, ID, Zip 83201–2708; tel. 208/232–2570; Karen Neilson, Administrator

SAFE HAVEN HOSPITAL OF TREASURE VALLEY (O, 22 beds) 8050 Northview Street, Boise, ID, Zip 83704–7126; tel. 208/327–0504; Scott Proctor, Chief Executive Officer
Web address: www.boisepsychhospital.com

Owned, leased, sponsored:	2 hospitals	109 beds
Contract-managed:	0 hospitals	0 beds
Totals:	2 hospitals	109 beds

★0254: **SAINT FRANCIS HEALTH SYSTEM** (CC)
6161 South Yale Avenue, Tulsa, OK, Zip 74136–1902; tel. 918/494–8454; Jake Henry Jr, President and Chief Executive Officer
(Centralized Health System)

OKLAHOMA: LAUREATE PSYCHIATRIC CLINIC AND HOSPITAL (O, 106 beds) 6655 South Yale Avenue, Tulsa, OK, Zip 74136–3329; tel. 918/481–4000; Brandon Keppner, Administrator
Web address: www.laureate.com

OKLAHOMA STATE UNIVERSITY MEDICAL CENTER (C, 191 beds) 744 West Ninth Street, Tulsa, OK, Zip 74127–9020; tel. 918/599–1000; Matthew Adams, Administrator
Web address: www.osumc.net

SAINT FRANCIS HOSPITAL MUSKOGEE (O, 160 beds) 300 Rockefeller Drive, Muskogee, OK, Zip 74401–5081; tel. 918/682–5501; Michele A. Keeling, Vice President and Administrator

SAINT FRANCIS HOSPITAL SOUTH (O, 90 beds) 10501 East 91st Street, Tulsa, OK, Zip 74133–5790; tel. 918/307–6010; David S. Weil, Senior Vice President and Administrator
Web address: www.saintfrancis.com/south/

For explanation of codes following names, see page B2.
★ Indicates Type III membership in the American Hospital Association.

SAINT FRANCIS HOSPITAL VINITA (O, 70 beds) 735 North Foreman Street, Vinita, OK, Zip 74301–1418, Mailing Address: P.O. Box 326, Zip 74301–0326, tel. 918/256–7551; Todd Schuster, Administrator
Web address: https://www.saintfrancis.com/vinita/Pages/default.aspx

SAINT FRANCIS HOSPITAL (O, 865 beds) 6161 South Yale Avenue, Tulsa, OK, Zip 74136–1902; tel. 918/494–2200; Douglas Williams, Senior Vice President, Administrator

Owned, leased, sponsored:	5 hospitals	1291 beds
Contract-managed:	1 hospitals	191 beds
Totals:	6 hospitals	1482 beds

★0120: SAINT LUKE'S HEALTH SYSTEM (NP)

901 East 104th Street, Mailstop 900N, Kansas City, MO, Zip 64131–4517, Mailing Address: 901 East 104th Street, Zip 64131–4517, tel. 816/932–2000; Melinda Estes, M.D., President and Chief Executive Officer
(Centralized Health System)

KANSAS: ANDERSON COUNTY HOSPITAL (L, 48 beds) 421 South Maple, Garnett, KS, Zip 66032–1334, Mailing Address: P.O. Box 309, Zip 66032–0309, tel. 785/448–3131; Rick McKain, Chief Executive Officer
Web address: www.saint-lukes.org

SAINT LUKE'S COMMUNITY HOSPITAL AT LEAWOOD (O, 8 beds) 13200 State Line Road, Leawood, KS, Zip 66209; tel. 913/222–8380; Teresa Collins, R.N., Chief Executive Officer and Chief Nursing Officer
Web address: www.saintlukescommunityhospital.org

SAINT LUKE'S CUSHING HOSPITAL (O, 25 beds) 711 Marshall Street, Leavenworth, KS, Zip 66048–3235; tel. 913/684–1100; Bobby Olm-Shipman, President and Chief Executive Officer

SAINT LUKE'S SOUTH HOSPITAL (O, 104 beds) 12300 Metcalf Avenue, Overland Park, KS, Zip 66213–1324; tel. 913/317–7000; Bobby Olm-Shipman, Chief Executive Officer
Web address: www.saintlukeshealthsystem.org/south

MISSOURI: HEDRICK MEDICAL CENTER (L, 25 beds) 2799 North Washington Street, Chillicothe, MO, Zip 64601–2902; tel. 660/646–1480; Steven M. Schieber, FACHE, Chief Executive Officer

SAINT LUKE'S EAST HOSPITAL (O, 203 beds) 100 NE Saint Luke's Boulevard, Lee's Summit, MO, Zip 64086–6000; tel. 816/347–5000; Ron Baker, FACHE, Chief Executive Officer
Web address: www.saintlukeskc.org

SAINT LUKE'S HOSPITAL OF KANSAS CITY (O, 485 beds) 4401 Wornall Road, Kansas City, MO, Zip 64111–3220; tel. 816/932–3800; Jani L. Johnson, R.N., MSN, Chief Executive Officer
Web address: www.saint-lukes.org

SAINT LUKE'S NORTH HOSPITAL – BARRY ROAD (O, 139 beds) 5830 NW Barry Road, Kansas City, MO, Zip 64154–2778; tel. 816/891–6000; Adele Ducharme, MSN, R.N., Chief Executive Officer

WRIGHT MEMORIAL HOSPITAL (L, 15 beds) 191 Iowa Boulevard, Trenton, MO, Zip 64683–8343; tel. 660/358–5700; Steven M. Schieber, FACHE, Interim Chief Executive Officer
Web address: www.saintlukeshealthsystem.org

Owned, leased, sponsored:	9 hospitals	1052 beds
Contract-managed:	0 hospitals	0 beds
Totals:	9 hospitals	1052 beds

0403: SALEM HEALTH (NP)

890 Oak Street Bldg B POB 14001, Salem, OR, Zip 97309–5014; tel. 503/561–5200; Norman F. Gruber, President and Chief Executive Officer
(Independent Hospital System)

OREGON: SALEM HEALTH WEST VALLEY (O, 6 beds) 525 SE Washington Street, Dallas, OR, Zip 97338–2834, Mailing Address: P.O. Box 378, Zip 97338–0378, tel. 503/623–8301; Bruce C. Rodgers, Chief Administrative Officer
Web address: www.salemhealth.org/wvh/

SALEM HOSPITAL (O, 441 beds) 890 Oak Street SE, Salem, OR, Zip 97301–3959, Mailing Address: P.O. Box 14001, Zip 97309–5014, tel. 503/561–5200; Cheryl R. Nester Wolfe, President and Chief Executive Officer
Web address: www.salemhealth.org

Owned, leased, sponsored:	2 hospitals	447 beds
Contract-managed:	0 hospitals	0 beds
Totals:	2 hospitals	447 beds

1002: SALINA REGIONAL HEALTH CENTER (NP)

400 South Santa Fe Avenue, Salina, KS, Zip 67401–4198, Mailing Address: PO Box 5080, Zip 67402–5080, tel. 785/452–7000; Micheal Terry, President and Chief Executive Officer
(Moderately Centralized Health System)

KANSAS: CLOUD COUNTY HEALTH CENTER (C, 25 beds) 1100 Highland Drive, Concordia, KS, Zip 66901–3923; tel. 785/243–1234; David Garnas, Administrator
Web address: www.cchc.com

LINDSBORG COMMUNITY HOSPITAL (C, 21 beds) 605 West Lincoln Street, Lindsborg, KS, Zip 67456–2328; tel. 785/227–3308; Larry VanDerWege, Administrator
Web address: www.lindsborghospital.org

SALINA REGIONAL HEALTH CENTER (O, 205 beds) 400 South Santa Fe Avenue, Salina, KS, Zip 67401–4198, Mailing Address: P.O. Box 5080, Zip 67402–5080, tel. 785/452–7000; Micheal Terry, President and Chief Executive Officer

Owned, leased, sponsored:	1 hospitals	205 beds
Contract-managed:	2 hospitals	46 beds
Totals:	3 hospitals	251 beds

★0186: SAMARITAN HEALTH SERVICES (NP)

3600 NW Samaritan Drive, Corvallis, OR, Zip 97330–3737, Mailing Address: P.O. Box 1068, Zip 97339–1068, tel. 541/768–5001; Doug Boysen, President and Chief Executive Officer
(Centralized Physician/Insurance Health System)

OREGON: GOOD SAMARITAN REGIONAL MEDICAL CENTER (O, 168 beds) 3600 NW Samaritan Drive, Corvallis, OR, Zip 97330–3737, Mailing Address: P.O. Box 1068, Zip 97339–1068, tel. 541/768–5111; Becky A. Pape, R.N., Chief Executive Officer

SAMARITAN ALBANY GENERAL HOSPITAL (O, 70 beds) 1046 Sixth Avenue, SW, Albany, OR, Zip 97321–1999; tel. 541/812–4000; David G. Triebes, Chief Executive Officer
Web address: www.samhealth.org

SAMARITAN LEBANON COMMUNITY HOSPITAL (O, 25 beds) 525 North Santiam Highway, Lebanon, OR, Zip 97355–4363, Mailing Address: P.O. Box 739, Zip 97355–0739, tel. 541/258–2101; Marty Cahill, Chief Executive Officer
Web address: www.samhealth.org

SAMARITAN NORTH LINCOLN HOSPITAL (C, 25 beds) 3043 NE 28th Street, Lincoln City, OR, Zip 97367–4518, Mailing Address: P.O. Box 767, Zip 97367–0767, tel. 541/994–3661; Lesley Ogden, M.D., Chief Executive Officer
Web address: www.samhealth.org

SAMARITAN PACIFIC COMMUNITIES HOSPITAL (C, 25 beds) 930 SW Abbey Street, Newport, OR, Zip 97365–4820, Mailing Address: P.O. Box 945, Zip 97365–0072, tel. 541/265–2244; Lesley Ogden, M.D., Chief Executive Officer
Web address: www.samhealth.org

Owned, leased, sponsored:	3 hospitals	263 beds
Contract-managed:	2 hospitals	50 beds
Totals:	5 hospitals	313 beds

★0914: SAN LUIS VALLEY HEALTH (NP)

106 Blanca Avenue, Alamosa, CO, Zip 81101–2340; tel. 719/589–2511; Konnie Martin, Chief Executive Officer
(Independent Hospital System)

For explanation of codes following names, see page B2.
★ Indicates Type III membership in the American Hospital Association.

Section B

COLORADO: SAN LUIS VALLEY HEALTH CONEJOS COUNTY HOSPITAL (O, 17 beds) 19021 U S Highway 285, La Jara, CO, Zip 81140–0639, Mailing Address: P.O. Box 639, Zip 81140–0639, tel. 719/274–5121; Kelly Gallegos, Administrator
Web address: www.sanluisvalleyhealth.org/locations/conejos-county-hospital

SAN LUIS VALLEY HEALTH (O, 44 beds) 106 Blanca Avenue, Alamosa, CO, Zip 81101–2393; tel. 719/589–2511; Konnie Martin, Chief Executive Officer

Owned, leased, sponsored:	2 hospitals	61 beds
Contract-managed:	0 hospitals	0 beds
Totals:	2 hospitals	61 beds

★**0530: SANFORD HEALTH** (NP)
2301 East 60th Street North, Sioux Falls, SD, Zip 57104–0569, Mailing Address: PO Box 5039, Zip 57117–5039, tel. 605/333–1000; Kelby K. Krabbenhoft, President and Chief Executive Officer **(Decentralized Health System)**

IOWA: ORANGE CITY AREA HEALTH SYSTEM (C, 114 beds) 1000 Lincoln Circle SE, Orange City, IA, Zip 51041–1862; tel. 712/737–4984; Martin W. Guthmiller, Chief Executive Officer
Web address: www.ochealthsystem.org

SANFORD SHELDON MEDICAL CENTER (O, 95 beds) 118 North Seventh Avenue, Sheldon, IA, Zip 51201–1235, Mailing Address: P.O. Box 250, Zip 51201–0250, tel. 712/324–5041; Richard E. Nordahl, Senior Director
Web address: www.sanfordsheldon.org

MINNESOTA: ARNOLD MEMORIAL HEALTH CARE CENTER (L, 50 beds) 601 Louisiana Avenue, Adrian, MN, Zip 56110–0279, Mailing Address: P.O. Box 279, Zip 56110–0279, tel. 507/483–2668; Michele Roban, Administrator

MAHNOMEN HEALTH CENTER (C, 50 beds) 414 West Jefferson Avenue, Mahnomen, MN, Zip 56557–4912, Mailing Address: P.O. Box 396, Zip 56557–0396, tel. 218/935–2511; Dale K. Kruger, Chief Executive Officer
Web address: www.mahnomenhealthcenter.com

MURRAY COUNTY MEDICAL CENTER (C, 20 beds) 2042 Juniper Avenue, Slayton, MN, Zip 56172–1017; tel. 507/836–6111; Michael Ladevich, FACHE, Interim Chief Executive Officer
Web address: www.murraycountymed.org

ORTONVILLE AREA HEALTH SERVICES (C, 102 beds) 450 Eastvold Avenue, Ortonville, MN, Zip 56278–1133; tel. 320/839–2502; David Rogers, Chief Executive Officer

PERHAM HEALTH (C, 121 beds) 1000 Coney Street West, Perham, MN, Zip 56573–1108; tel. 218/347–4500; Chuck Hofius, Chief Executive Officer
Web address: www.perhamhealth.org

SANFORD BAGLEY MEDICAL CENTER (O, 8 beds) 203 Fourth Street NW, Bagley, MN, Zip 56621–8307; tel. 218/694–6501; Robert Belanger, Administrator Director

SANFORD BEMIDJI MEDICAL CENTER (O, 196 beds) 1300 Anne Street NW, Bemidji, MN, Zip 56601–5103; tel. 218/751–5430; Bryan Nermoe, Executive Vice President
Web address: www.sanfordhealth.org/bemidji

SANFORD CANBY MEDICAL CENTER (L, 78 beds) 112 St Olaf Avenue South, Canby, MN, Zip 56220–1433; tel. 507/223–7277; Lori Sisk, R.N., Chief Executive Officer
Web address: www.sanfordcanby.org

SANFORD JACKSON MEDICAL CENTER (O, 16 beds) 1430 North Highway, Jackson, MN, Zip 56143–1093; tel. 507/847–2420; Dawn Schnell, Chief Nursing Officer and Interim Senior Director
Web address: www.sanfordjackson.org

SANFORD LUVERNE MEDICAL CENTER (O, 25 beds) 1600 North Kniss Avenue, Luverne, MN, Zip 56156–1067; tel. 507/283–2321; Tammy Loosbrock, Senior Director
Web address: www.sanfordluverne.org

SANFORD MEDICAL CENTER THIEF RIVER FALLS (O, 25 beds) 3001 Sanford Parkway, Thief River Falls, MN, Zip 56701–2700; tel. 218/681–4747; Brian J. Carlson, FACHE, Executive Officer
Web address: www.sanfordhealth.org

SANFORD THIEF RIVER FALLS BEHAVIORAL HEALTH CENTER (O, 16 beds) 120 LaBree Avenue South, Thief River Falls, MN, Zip 56701–2819, Mailing Address: 3001 Sanford Parkway, Zip 56701–2819, tel. 218/683–4349; Brian J. Carlson, FACHE, Chief Executive Officer

SANFORD TRACY MEDICAL CENTER (O, 25 beds) 251 Fifth Street East, Tracy, MN, Zip 56175–1536; tel. 507/629–8400; Stacy Barstad, Chief Executive Officer
Web address: www.sanfordtracy.org

SANFORD WESTBROOK MEDICAL CENTER (L, 8 beds) 920 Bell Avenue, Westbrook, MN, Zip 56183–9669, Mailing Address: P.O. Box 188, Zip 56183–0188, tel. 507/274–6121; Stacy Barstad, Chief Executive Officer
Web address: www.sanfordwestbrook.org

SANFORD WHEATON MEDICAL CENTER (O, 15 beds) 401 12th Street North, Wheaton, MN, Zip 56296–1099; tel. 320/563–8226; JoAnn M. Foltz, R.N., Chief Executive Officer
Web address: www.sanfordhealth.org

SANFORD WORTHINGTON MEDICAL CENTER (O, 48 beds) 1018 Sixth Avenue, Worthington, MN, Zip 56187–2202, Mailing Address: P.O. Box 997, Zip 56187–0997, tel. 507/372–2941; Jennifer . Weg, MS, R.N., Executive Director
Web address: www.sanfordhealth.org

WINDOM AREA HOSPITAL (C, 18 beds) 2150 Hospital Drive, Windom, MN, Zip 56101–0339, Mailing Address: P.O. Box 339, Zip 56101–0339, tel. 507/831–2400; Shelby Medina, Chief Executive Officer

NORTH DAKOTA: NORTHWOOD DEACONESS HEALTH CENTER (O, 57 beds) 4 North Park Street, Northwood, ND, Zip 58267–4102, Mailing Address: P.O. Box 190, Zip 58267–0190, tel. 701/587–6060; Pete Antonson, Chief Executive Officer
Web address: www.ndhc.net

SANFORD BISMARCK (O, 227 beds) 300 North Seventh Street, Bismarck, ND, Zip 58501–4439, Mailing Address: P.O. Box 5525, Zip 58506–5525, tel. 701/323–6000; Michael LeBeau, President

SANFORD HILLSBORO MEDICAL CENTER (C, 46 beds) 12 Third Street SE, Hillsboro, ND, Zip 58045–4840, Mailing Address: P.O. Box 609, Zip 58045–0609, tel. 701/636–3200; Jac McTaggart, Chief Executive Officer
Web address: www.hillsboromedicalcenter.com

SANFORD MAYVILLE MEDICAL CENTER (O, 10 beds) 42 Sixth Avenue SE, Mayville, ND, Zip 58257–1598; tel. 701/786–3800; Jac McTaggart, Chief Executive Officer
Web address: www.unionhospital.com

SANFORD MEDICAL CENTER FARGO (O, 540 beds) 801 Broadway North, Fargo, ND, Zip 58122–3641; tel. 701/234–2000; Nate White, Executive Vice President

SOUTH DAKOTA: COMMUNITY MEMORIAL HOSPITAL (C, 16 beds) 809 Jackson Street, Burke, SD, Zip 57523–2065, Mailing Address: P.O. Box 319, Zip 57523–0319, tel. 605/775–2621; Mistie Sachtjen, Chief Executive Officer
Web address: www.sanfordhealth.org

COTEAU DES PRAIRIES HOSPITAL (C, 25 beds) 205 Orchard Drive, Sisseton, SD, Zip 57262–2398; tel. 605/698–7647; Craig A. Kantos, Chief Executive Officer
Web address: www.cdphospital.com

PIONEER MEMORIAL HOSPITAL AND HEALTH SERVICES (C, 64 beds) 315 North Washington Street, Viborg, SD, Zip 57070–2002, Mailing Address: P.O. Box 368, Zip 57070–0368, tel. 605/326–5161; Thomas V. Richter, Chief Executive Officer
Web address: www.pioneermemorial.org

SANFORD ABERDEEN MEDICAL CENTER (O, 48 beds) 2905 3rd Avenue SE, Aberdeen, SD, Zip 57401–5420; tel. 605/626–4200; Ashley M. Erickson, Chief Executive Officer
Web address: www.sanfordaberdeen.org/

SANFORD CANTON-INWOOD MEDICAL CENTER (O, 11 beds) 440 North Hiawatha Drive, Canton, SD, Zip 57013–5800; tel. 605/764–1400; Scott C. Larson, Chief Executive Officer

SANFORD CHAMBERLAIN MEDICAL CENTER (O, 69 beds) 300 South Byron Boulevard, Chamberlain, SD, Zip 57325–9741; tel. 605/234–5511; Erica Peterson, Chief Executive Officer
Web address: www.sanfordchamberlain.org

SANFORD CLEAR LAKE MEDICAL CENTER (L, 10 beds) 701 Third Avenue South, Clear Lake, SD, Zip 57226–2016; tel. 605/874–2141; Lori Sisk, R.N., Chief Executive Officer
Web address: www.sanforddeuelcounty.org

SANFORD USD MEDICAL CENTER (O, 500 beds) 1305 West 18th Street, Sioux Falls, SD, Zip 57105–0496, Mailing Address: P.O. Box 5039, Zip 57117–5039, tel. 605/333–1000; Paul A. Hanson, FACHE, President

For explanation of codes following names, see page B2.
★ Indicates Type III membership in the American Hospital Association.

SANFORD VERMILLION MEDICAL CENTER (L, 120 beds) 20 South Plum Street, Vermillion, SD, Zip 57069–3346; tel. 605/677–3500; Timothy J. Tracy, Senior Director
Web address: www.sanfordvermillion.org

SANFORD WEBSTER MEDICAL CENTER (L, 20 beds) 1401 West 1st Street, Webster, SD, Zip 57274–1054, Mailing Address: P.O. Box 489, Zip 57274–0489, tel. 605/345–3336; Isaac Gerdes, Chief Executive Officer
Web address: www.sanfordhealth.org

WINNER REGIONAL HEALTHCARE CENTER (C, 104 beds) 745 East Eighth Street, Winner, SD, Zip 57580–2631; tel. 605/842–7100; Kevin Coffey, Chief Executive Officer

Owned, leased, sponsored:	24 hospitals	2217 beds
Contract-managed:	11 hospitals	680 beds
Totals:	35 hospitals	2897 beds

★**5095: SCL HEALTH** (CC)
500 Eldorado Boulevard, Suite 4300, Broomfield, CO, Zip 80021; tel. 303/813–5180; Lydia Jumonville, President and Chief Executive Officer
(Moderately Centralized Health System)

COLORADO: GOOD SAMARITAN MEDICAL CENTER (S, 176 beds) 200 Exempla Circle, Lafayette, CO, Zip 80026–3370; tel. 303/689–4000; Jennifer Alderfer, President
Web address: www.goodsamaritancolorado.org/

LUTHERAN MEDICAL CENTER (S, 368 beds) 8300 West 38th Avenue, Wheat Ridge, CO, Zip 80033–6005; tel. 303/425–4500; Grant Wicklund, President and Chief Executive Officer

PLATTE VALLEY MEDICAL CENTER (C, 70 beds) 1600 Prairie Center Parkway, Brighton, CO, Zip 80601–4006; tel. 303/498–1600; John R. Hicks, President and Chief Executive Officer
Web address: www.pvmc.org

SAINT JOSEPH HOSPITAL (O, 379 beds) 1375 East 19th Avenue, Denver, CO, Zip 80218–1126; tel. 303/837–7111; Jameson Smith, President
Web address: www.saintjosephdenver.org/

ST. MARY'S HOSPITAL AND MEDICAL CENTER (O, 309 beds) 2635 North 7th Street, Grand Junction, CO, Zip 81501–4209, Mailing Address: P.O. Box 1628, Zip 81502–1628, tel. 970/298–2273; Brian Davidson, M.D., President and Chief Medical Officer
Web address: www.stmarygj.com

MONTANA: HOLY ROSARY HEALTHCARE (O, 90 beds) 2600 Wilson Street, Miles City, MT, Zip 59301–5094; tel. 406/233–2600; Paul Lewis, Chief Executive Officer

ST. JAMES HEALTHCARE (O, 73 beds) 400 South Clark Street, Butte, MT, Zip 59701–2328; tel. 406/723–2500; Jay Doyle, President and Chief Executive Officer
Web address: www.stjameshealthcare.org

ST. VINCENT HEALTHCARE (O, 225 beds) 1233 North 30th Street, Billings, MT, Zip 59101–0165, Mailing Address: P.O. Box 35200, Zip 59107–5200, tel. 406/237–7000; Steve Loveless, President and Chief Executive Officer

Owned, leased, sponsored:	7 hospitals	1620 beds
Contract-managed:	1 hospitals	70 beds
Totals:	8 hospitals	1690 beds

★**1505: SCRIPPS HEALTH** (NP)
4275 Campus Point Court CP112, San Diego, CA, Zip 92121–1513, Mailing Address: 4275 Campus Point Court, Zip 92121–1513, tel. 858/678–7200; Chris D. Van Gorder, FACHE, President and Chief Executive Officer
(Centralized Health System)

CALIFORNIA: SCRIPPS GREEN HOSPITAL (O, 173 beds) 10666 North Torrey Pines Road, La Jolla, CA, Zip 92037–1093; tel. 858/455–9100; Carl J. Etter, Chief Executive Officer

SCRIPPS MEMORIAL HOSPITAL-ENCINITAS (O, 171 beds) 354 Santa Fe Drive, Encinitas, CA, Zip 92024–5182, Mailing Address: P.O. Box 230817, Zip 92023–0817, tel. 760/633–6501; Carl J. Etter, Chief Executive and Senior Vice President
Web address: www.scripps.org

SCRIPPS MEMORIAL HOSPITAL-LA JOLLA (O, 365 beds) 9888 Genesee Avenue, La Jolla, CA, Zip 92037–1200, Mailing Address: P.O. Box 28, Zip 92038–0028, tel. 858/626–4123; Carl J. Etter, Chief Executive Officer
Web address: www.scripps.org/locations/hospitals__scripps-memorial-hospital-la-jolla

SCRIPPS MERCY HOSPITAL (O, 392 beds) 4077 Fifth Avenue, San Diego, CA, Zip 92103–2105; tel. 619/294–8111; Thomas A. Gammiere, Chief Executive, Senior Vice President
Web address: www.scrippshealth.org

Owned, leased, sponsored:	4 hospitals	1101 beds
Contract-managed:	0 hospitals	0 beds
Totals:	4 hospitals	1101 beds

★**0181: SELECT MEDICAL CORPORATION** (IO)
4714 Gettysburg Road, Mechanicsburg, PA, Zip 17055–4325; tel. 717/972–1100; David S. Chernow, President and Chief Executive Officer
(Independent Hospital System)

ALABAMA: SELECT SPECIALTY HOSPITAL-BIRMINGHAM (O, 38 beds) 2010 Brookwood Medical Center Drive, 3rd Floor, Birmingham, AL, Zip 35209–6804; tel. 205/599–4600; Clifton Quinn, Chief Executive Officer
Web address: www.birmingham.selectspecialtyhospitals.com

ARIZONA: HONORHEALTH REHABILITATION HOSPITAL (O, 50 beds) 8850 East Pima Center Parkway, Scottsdale, AZ, Zip 85258–4619; tel. 480/800–3900; Scott R. Keen, Chief Executive Officer

SELECT SPECIALTY HOSPITAL-PHOENIX DOWNTOWN (O, 33 beds) 1012 East Wiletta Street, 4th Floor, Phoenix, AZ, Zip 85006; tel. 602/839–6550; David Selman, Chief Executive Officer
Web address: www.selectmedicalcorp.com

SELECT SPECIALTY HOSPITAL-PHOENIX (O, 48 beds) 350 West Thomas Road, 3rd Floor Main, Phoenix, AZ, Zip 85013–4409; tel. 602/406–6810; Karen Cawley, Chief Executive Officer

ARKANSAS: REGENCY HOSPITAL OF NORTHWEST ARKANSAS – SPRINGDALE (O, 25 beds) 609 West Maple Avenue, 6th Fl, Springdale, AR, Zip 72764; tel. 479/757–2600; Robert Poole, Chief Executive Officer
Web address: www.regencyhospital.com

SELECT SPECIALTY HOSPITAL-FORT SMITH (O, 34 beds) 1001 Towson Avenue, 6 Central, Fort Smith, AR, Zip 72901–4921; tel. 479/441–3960, Shannon Grams, Chief Executive Officer

CALIFORNIA: CALIFORNIA REHABILITATION INSTITUTE (O, 120 beds) 2070 Century Park East, Los Angeles, CA, Zip 90067–1907; tel. 424/363–1000; Scott T. Rotsted, Chief Executive Officer
Web address: www.californiarehabinstitute.com/

SELECT SPECIALTY HOSPITAL – SAN DIEGO (C, 80 beds) 555 Washington Street, San Diego, CA, Zip 92103–2294; tel. 619/260–8300; Yamcka Jones, Chief Executive Officer

DELAWARE: SELECT SPECIALTY HOSPITAL-WILMINGTON (O, 35 beds) 701 North Clayton Street, 5th Floor, Wilmington, DE, Zip 19805–3948; tel. 302/421–4545; Donna Gares, R.N., FACHE, MSN, Chief Executive Officer
Web address: www.wilmington.selectspecialtyhospitals.com

FLORIDA: PROMISE HOSPITAL OF FLORIDA AT THE VILLAGES (O, 40 beds) 5050 County Road 472, Oxford, FL, Zip 34484; tel. 352/689–6400; Hoyt Ross, Chief Executive Officer
Web address: www.promise-villages.com

PROMISE HOSPITAL OF FORT MYERS (O, 60 beds) 3050 Champion Ring Road, Fort Myers, FL, Zip 33905–5599; tel. 239/313–2900; Patrick G. Ryan, Chief Executive Officer
Web address: www.promisefortmyers.om

PROMISE HOSPITAL OF MIAMI (O, 60 beds) 14001 NW 82nd Avenue, Miami Lakes, FL, Zip 33016–1561; tel. 786/609–9200; Charles Doten, Chief Executive Officer

SELECT SPECIALTY HOSPITAL DAYTONA BEACH (O, 34 beds) 301 Memorial Medical Parkway, 11th Floor, Daytona Beach, FL, Zip 32117–5167; tel. 386/231–3436; Adrianne Lutes, Chief Executive Officer
Web address: www.daytonabeach.selectspecialtyhospitals.com

Section B

For explanation of codes following names, see page B2.
★ Indicates Type III membership in the American Hospital Association.

SELECT SPECIALTY HOSPITAL-GAINESVILLE (O, 44 beds) 1600 SW Archer Road, 5th Floor, Gainesville, FL, Zip 32610; tel. 352/337-3240; Ronnie Wagley, Market Chief Executive Officer

SELECT SPECIALTY HOSPITAL-MIAMI (O, 47 beds) 955 NW 3rd Street, Miami, FL, Zip 33128-1274; tel. 305/416-5700; Loretta Sheffield, Chief Executive Officer
Web address: www.selectspecialtyhospitals.com/company/locations/miami.aspx

SELECT SPECIALTY HOSPITAL-ORLANDO (O, 75 beds) 2250 Bedford Road, Orlando, FL, Zip 32803-1443; tel. 407/303-7869; Theodore Mena, Chief Executive Officer
Web address: www.selectspecialtyhospitals.com/company/locations/orlando.aspx

SELECT SPECIALTY HOSPITAL-PALM BEACH (O, 60 beds) 3060 Melaleuca Lane, Lake Worth, FL, Zip 33461-5174; tel. 561/357-7200; Larry Melby, Chief Executive Officer
Web address: www.selectspecialtyhospitals.com/company/locations/palmbeach.aspx

SELECT SPECIALTY HOSPITAL-PANAMA CITY (O, 30 beds) 615 North Bonita Avenue, 3rd Floor, Panama City, FL, Zip 32401-3623; tel. 850/767-3180; Randal S. Hamilton, Chief Executive Officer

SELECT SPECIALTY HOSPITAL-PENSACOLA (O, 75 beds) 7000 Cobble Creek Drive, Pensacola, FL, Zip 32504-8638; tel. 850/473-4800; Adam Principe, Chief Executive Officer
Web address: www.https://pensacola.selectspecialtyhospitals.com/

SELECT SPECIALTY HOSPITAL-TALLAHASSEE (O, 29 beds) 1554 Surgeons Drive, Tallahassee, FL, Zip 32308-4631; tel. 850/219-6950; Jay Faherty, Chief Executive Officer

UF HEALTH REHAB HOSPITAL (O, 121 beds) 2708 Southwest Archer Road, Gainesville, FL, Zip 32608-1316; tel. 352/265-5499; Marina T. Cecchini, Administrator
Web address: www.https://ufhealth.org/uf-health-shands-rehab-hospital

WEST GABLES REHABILITATION HOSPITAL (O, 60 beds) 2525 SW 75th Avenue, Miami, FL, Zip 33155-2800; tel. 305/262-6800; Walter Concepcion, Chief Executive Officer

GEORGIA: REGENCY HOSPITAL OF CENTRAL GEORGIA (O, 60 beds) 535 Coliseum Drive, Macon, GA, Zip 31217-0104; tel. 478/803-7300; Wayne B. Boutwell, Chief Executive Officer
Web address: www.regencyhospital.com

REGENCY HOSPITAL OF SOUTH ATLANTA (O, 40 beds) 1170 Cleveland Avenue, 4th Floor, East Point, GA, Zip 30344-3615; tel. 404/466-6250; Michelle Tenhengel-deVille, Chief Executive Officer

SELECT SPECIALTY HOSPITAL MIDTOWN ATLANTA (O, 72 beds) 705 Juniper Street NE, Atlanta, GA, Zip 30308-1307; tel. 404/873-2871; Adriene Kinnaird, Chief Executive Officer
Web address: www.selectspecialtyhospitals.com/

SELECT SPECIALTY HOSPITAL-AUGUSTA (O, 80 beds) 1537 Walton Way, Augusta, GA, Zip 30904-3764; tel. 706/731-1200; E Rick. Lowe, FACHE, Chief Executive Officer

SELECT SPECIALTY HOSPITAL-SAVANNAH (O, 40 beds) 5353 Reynolds Street, 4 South, Savannah, GA, Zip 31405-6015; tel. 912/819-7982; Greg Wuchter, R.N., MSN, Chief Executive Officer
Web address: www.savannah.selectspecialtyhospitals.com

INDIANA: REGENCY HOSPITAL OF NORTHWEST INDIANA (O, 61 beds) 4321 Fir Street, 4th Floor, East Chicago, IN, Zip 46312-3049; tel. 219/392-7799; Eleyce Winn, Chief Executive Officer
Web address: www.regencyhospital.com/company/locations/indiana-northwest-indiana.aspx

SELECT SPECIALTY HOSPITAL-EVANSVILLE (O, 51 beds) 400 SE 4th Street, Evansville, IN, Zip 47713-1206; tel. 812/421-2500; Scott A. Butler, Chief Executive Officer
Web address: www.selectspecialtyhospitals.com/company/locations/evansville.aspx

IOWA: SELECT SPECIALTY HOSPITAL-DES MOINES (O, 30 beds) 1111 6th Avenue, 4th Floor Main, Des Moines, IA, Zip 50314-2610; tel. 515/247-4400; Brent Hanson, Chief Executive Officer
Web address: www.selectspecialtyhospitals.com

SELECT SPECIALTY HOSPITAL-QUAD CITIES (O, 50 beds) 1111 West Kimberly Road, Davenport, IA, Zip 52806-5711; tel. 563/468-2000; Codie Dillie, Chief Executive Officer

KANSAS: SELECT SPECIALTY HOSPITAL-KANSAS CITY (O, 40 beds) 1731 North 90th Street, Kansas City, KS, Zip 66112-1515; tel. 913/732-5900; Bridgette Hunter, Chief Executive Officer
Web address: www.selectspecialtyhospitals.com

SELECT SPECIALTY HOSPITAL-WICHITA (O, 48 beds) 929 North St Francis Street, Wichita, KS, Zip 67214-3821; tel. 316/261-8303; Christopher Keith, Chief Executive Officer
Web address: www.selectspecialtyhospitals.com/company/locations/wichita.aspx

KENTUCKY: SELECT SPECIALTY HOSPITAL-LEXINGTON (O, 41 beds) 310 South Limestone Street, 3rd Floor, Lexington, KY, Zip 40508-3008; tel. 859/226-7096; Kim Pennington, Chief Executive Officer

SELECT SPECIALTY HOSPITAL-NORTHERN KENTUCKY (O, 33 beds) 85 North Grand Avenue, Fort Thomas, KY, Zip 41075-1793; tel. 859/572-3880; Mavis Bechtle, MSN, R.N., FACHE, Chief Executive Officer
Web address: www.selectspecialtyhospitals.com

LOUISIANA: OCHSNER REHABILITATON HOSPITAL WEST CAMPUS (O, 42 beds) 2614 Jefferson Highway, Jefferson, LA, Zip 70121-3828; tel. 504/291-5100; Sara Wriborg, Chief Executive Officer
Web address: https://www.ochsner.org/services/rehabilitation

MICHIGAN: SELECT SPECIALTY HOSPITAL – SPECTRUM HEALTH (O, 36 beds) 1840 Wealthy Street, Southeast, Grand Rapids, MI, Zip 49506-2921; tel. 616/774-3800; Jim Aldrich, Chief Executive Officer

SELECT SPECIALTY HOSPITAL-ANN ARBOR (O, 36 beds) 5301 East Huron River Drive, 7th Floor, Ypsilanti, MI, Zip 48197-1051; tel. 734/712-6751; Bryan Cutliff, Chief Executive Officer
Web address: www.annarbor.selectspecialtyhospitals.com/

SELECT SPECIALTY HOSPITAL-BATTLE CREEK (O, 25 beds) 300 North Avenue, Battle Creek, MI, Zip 49017-3307; tel. 269/245-4675; Robert Mach, Chief Executive Officer
Web address: www.battlecreek.selectspecialtyhospitals.com/

SELECT SPECIALTY HOSPITAL-DOWNRIVER (O, 71 beds) 2333 Biddle Avenue, 8th Floor, Wyandotte, MI, Zip 48192-4668; tel. 734/246-5500; John Ponczocha, Chief Executive Officer

SELECT SPECIALTY HOSPITAL-FLINT (O, 26 beds) 401 South Ballenger Highway, 5th Floor Central, Flint, MI, Zip 48532-3638; tel. 810/342-4545; Christina DeBlouw, Chief Executive Officer
Web address: www.selectspecialtyhospitals.com/company/locations/flint.aspx

SELECT SPECIALTY HOSPITAL-GROSSE POINTE (O, 30 beds) 468 Cadieux Road, 3 North East, Grosse Pointe, MI, Zip 48230-1507, Mailing Address: 22101 Moross Road, 6th Floor, Detroit, Zip 48236, tel. 313/473-6131; Zaahra Butt, Chief Executive Officer
Web address: www.grossepointe.selectspecialtyhospitals.com/

SELECT SPECIALTY HOSPITAL-MACOMB COUNTY (O, 36 beds) 215 North Avenue, Mount Clemens, MI, Zip 48043-1700; tel. 586/307-9000; Jon P. O'Malley, Chief Executive Officer

SELECT SPECIALTY HOSPITAL-MUSKEGON (O, 31 beds) 1700 Clinton Street, 3 South, Muskegon, MI, Zip 49442-5502; tel. 231/728-5811; Kerry McLane, Chief Executive Officer
Web address: www.greatlakesspecialtyhospital.com

SELECT SPECIALTY HOSPITAL-PONTIAC (O, 30 beds) 44405 Woodward Avenue, 8th Floor, Pontiac, MI, Zip 48341-5023; tel. 248/452-5252; Peggy Kingston, Chief Executive Officer

SELECT SPECIALTY HOSPITAL-SAGINAW (O, 32 beds) 1447 North Harrison Street, 8th Floor, Saginaw, MI, Zip 48602-4785; tel. 989/583-4235; Matthew J. Campbell Esq, Chief Executive Officer
Web address: www.selectspecialtyhospitals.com/company/locations/saginaw.aspx

MINNESOTA: REGENCY HOSPITAL OF MINNEAPOLIS (O, 92 beds) 1300 Hidden Lakes Parkway, Golden Valley, MN, Zip 55422-4286; tel. 763/588-2750; Sean Stricker, Chief Executive Officer
Web address: www.regencyhospital.com

MISSISSIPPI: REGENCY HOSPITAL OF MERIDIAN (O, 40 beds) 1102 Constitution Avenue, 2nd Floor, Meridian, MS, Zip 39301-4001; tel. 601/484-7900; William Heath, Chief Executive Officer

SELECT SPECIALTY HOSPITAL – BELHAVEN (O, 25 beds) 1225 North State Street, Jackson, MS, Zip 39202-2097, Mailing Address: P.O. Box 23695, Zip 39225-3695, tel. 601/968-1000; Robert Shannon. Canard, Chief Executive Officer
Web address: www.https://belhaven.selectspecialtyhospitals.com/

For explanation of codes following names, see page B2.
★ Indicates Type III membership in the American Hospital Association.

SELECT SPECIALTY HOSPITAL-GULFPORT (O, 61 beds) 1520 Broad Avenue, Suite 300, Gulfport, MS, Zip 39501–3601; tel. 228/575–7500; John O'Keefe, Chief Executive Officer
Web address: www.selectspecialtyhospitals.com/company/locations/gulfcoast.aspx

SELECT SPECIALTY HOSPITAL-JACKSON (O, 53 beds) 5903 Ridgewood Road, Suite 100, Jackson, MS, Zip 39211–3700; tel. 601/899–3800; Chandler Ewing, Chief Executive Officer

MISSOURI: SSM SELECT REHABILITATION HOSPITAL (O, 125 beds) 1027 Bellevue Avenue, 3rd Floor, Richmond Heights, MO, Zip 63117–1851, Mailing Address: 1027 Bellevue Avenue, Zip 63117–1851, tel. 314/768–5300; Patti Finnegan, Chief Operating Officer
Web address: www.ssm-select.com

SELECT SPECIALTY HOSPITAL-SPRINGFIELD (O, 44 beds) 1630 East Primrose Street, Springfield, MO, Zip 65804–7929; tel. 417/885–4700; Steve Patterson, Chief Executive Officer

SELECT SPECIALTY HOSPITAL-ST. LOUIS (O, 33 beds) 300 First Capitol Drive, Unit 1, Saint Charles, MO, Zip 63301–2844; tel. 636/947–5010; Phillip Readinger, Chief Executive Officer
Web address: www.selectspecialtyhospitals.com/company/locations/stlouis.aspx

NEBRASKA: SELECT SPECIALTY HOSPITAL – LINCOLN (O, 24 beds) 2300 South 16th Street, 7th Floor, Lincoln, NE, Zip 68502–3704; tel. 402/483–8444; Connie K. Siffring, Chief Executive Officer
Web address: www.selectmedical.com

SELECT SPECIALTY HOSPITAL-OMAHA (O, 52 beds) 1870 South 75th Street, Omaha, NE, Zip 68124–1700; tel. 402/361–5700; Kerry McLane, Interim Chief Executive Officer

NEW JERSEY: KESSLER INSTITUTE FOR REHABILITATION (O, 336 beds) 1199 Pleasant Valley Way, West Orange, NJ, Zip 07052–1424; tel. 973/731–3600; Bonnie A. Evans, Chief Executive Officer
Web address: www.kessler-rehab.com

KESSLER MARLTON REHABILITATION (O, 61 beds) 92 Brick Road, Marlton, NJ, Zip 08053–2177; tel. 856/988–8778; Phyllis J. Schlichtmann, R.N., Chief Executive Officer

SELECT SPECIALTY HOSPITAL-NORTHEAST NEW JERSEY (O, 62 beds) 96 Parkway, Rochelle Park, NJ, Zip 07662–4200; tel. 201/221–2352; Patrick T. Swift, Ph.D., FACHE, Chief Executive Officer
Web address: www.northeastnewjersey.selectspecialtyhospitals.com/about/

NORTH CAROLINA: SELECT SPECIALTY HOSPITAL-DURHAM (O, 30 beds) 3643 North Roxboro Road, 6th Floor, Durham, NC, Zip 27704–2702; tel. 919/470–9159; Jennifer Rawley, PharmD, Chief Executive Officer
Web address: www.selectspecialtyhospitals.com/company/locations/durham.aspx

SELECT SPECIALTY HOSPITAL-GREENSBORO (O, 30 beds) 1200 North Elm Street, 5th Floor, Greensboro, NC, Zip 27401–1004; tel. 336/832–8571; Deana Knight, Chief Executive Officer
Web address: www.selectspecialtyhospitals.com/company/locations/greensboro.aspx

OHIO: CLEVELAND CLINIC REHABILITATION HOSPITAL (O, 180 beds) 33355 Health Campus Boulevard, Avon, OH, Zip 44011; tel. 440/937–9099; Sam Bayoumy, Chief Executive Officer
Web address: www.my.clevelandclinic.org

OHIOHEALTH REHABILITATION HOSPITAL (O, 74 beds) 1087 Dennison Avenue, 4th Floor, Columbus, OH, Zip 43201–3201; tel. 614/484–9600; Eric Yap, Chief Executive Officer

REGENCY HOSPITAL CLEVELAND EAST (O, 87 beds) 4200 Interchange Corporate Center Road, Warrensville Heights, OH, Zip 44128–5631; tel. 216/910–3800; Lisa Deering, Chief Executive Officer
Web address: www.regencyhospital.com/

REGENCY HOSPITAL OF COLUMBUS (O, 66 beds) 1430 South High Street, Columbus, OH, Zip 43207–1045; tel. 614/456–0300; Kindra Marks, Chief Executive Officer
Web address: www.regencyhospital.com/

REGENCY HOSPITAL OF TOLEDO (O, 45 beds) 5220 Alexis Road, Sylvania, OH, Zip 43560–2504; tel. 419/318–5700; Gary Zaciewski, Chief Executive Officer

SELECT SPECIALTY HOSPITAL – BOARDMAN (O, 24 beds) 8401 Market Street, 7 South, Boardman, OH, Zip 44512–6725; tel. 330/729–1750; Jodi Costello, Chief Executive Officer
Web address: www.selectspecialtyhospitals.com/

SELECT SPECIALTY HOSPITAL – CINCINNATI NORTH (O, 41 beds) 10500 Montgomery Road, Cincinnati, OH, Zip 45242–4402; tel. 513/865–5300; David D. Muggli, FACHE, Interim Chief Executive Officer

SELECT SPECIALTY HOSPITAL – CLEVELAND GATEWAY (O, 143 beds) 2351 East 22nd Street, 7th Floor, Cleveland, OH, Zip 44115–3111; tel. 216/363–2671; Julie Idoine-Fries, Chief Executive Officer
Web address: www.selectspecialtyhospitals.com/

SELECT SPECIALTY HOSPITAL OF SOUTHEAST OHIO (O, 35 beds) 2000 Tamarack Road, Newark, OH, Zip 43055; tel. 740/588–7888; Linda Supplee, Chief Executive Officer
Web address: www.selectspecialtyhospitals.com/company/locations/zanesville.aspx

SELECT SPECIALTY HOSPITAL-AKRON (O, 60 beds) 200 East Market Street, Akron, OH, Zip 44308–2015; tel. 330/761–7500; Dawne Wheeler, Chief Executive Officer
Web address: www.selectspecialtyhospitals.com/company/locations/akron.aspx

SELECT SPECIALTY HOSPITAL-CANTON (O, 30 beds) 1320 Mercy Drive NW, 6th Floor, Canton, OH, Zip 44708–2614; tel. 330/489–8189; Sherri Becker, Chief Executive Officer
Web address: www.selectspecialtyhospitals.com/company/locations/canton.aspx

SELECT SPECIALTY HOSPITAL-CINCINNATI (O, 36 beds) 375 Dixmyth Avenue, 15th Floor, Cincinnati, OH, Zip 45220–2475; tel. 513/862–4444; David D. Muggli, FACHE, Chief Executive Officer

SELECT SPECIALTY HOSPITAL-COLUMBUS (O, 162 beds) 1087 Dennison Avenue, Columbus, OH, Zip 43201–3201; tel. 614/458–9000; Lisa J. Pettrey, MSN, R.N., Chief Executive Officer
Web address: www.selectspecialtyhospitals.com/company/locations/columbus.aspx

SELECT SPECIALTY HOSPITAL-YOUNGSTOWN (O, 56 beds) 1044 Belmont Avenue, Youngstown, OH, Zip 44504–1006; tel. 330/480–2349; Jodi Costello, Chief Executive Officer
Web address: www.selectspecialtyhospitals.com/company/locations/youngstown.aspx

TRIHEALTH REHABILITATION HOSPITAL (O, 60 beds) 2155 Dana Avenue, Cincinnati, OH, Zip 45207; tel. 513/601–0600; Daphne Glenn, Chief Executive Officer
Web address: www.trihealthrehab.com

OKLAHOMA: SELECT SPECIALTY HOSPITAL-OKLAHOMA CITY (O, 72 beds) 3524 NW 56th Street, Oklahoma City, OK, Zip 73112–4518; tel. 405/606–6700; Judy Webb-Hapgood, Chief Executive Officer
Web address: www.https://oklahomacity.selectspecialtyhospitals.com/

SELECT SPECIALTY HOSPITAL TULSA MIDTOWN (O, 56 beds) 1125 South Trenton Avenue, 3rd Floor, Tulsa, OK, Zip 74120–5418; tel. 918/579–7300; Charles D. Nasem, FACHE, Chief Executive Officer

PENNSYLVANIA: HELEN M. SIMPSON REHABILITATION HOSPITAL (C, 50 beds) 4300 Londonderry Road, Harrisburg, PA, Zip 17109–5317; tel. 717/920–4300; Mark Freeburn, Chief Executive Officer
Web address: www.simpson-rehab.com/

PENN STATE HERSHEY REHABILITATION HOSPITAL (O, 98 beds) 1135 Old West Chocolate Avenue, Hummelstown, PA, Zip 17036; tel. 717/832–2600; Michelle Von Arx, Chief Executive Officer

SELECT SPECIALTY HOSPITAL-CAMP HILL (O, 92 beds) 503 North 21st Street, 5th Floor, Camp Hill, PA, Zip 17011–2204; tel. 717/972–4575; John E. Simodejka, Chief Executive Officer
Web address: www.camphill.selectspecialtyhospitals.com/

SELECT SPECIALTY HOSPITAL-DANVILLE (O, 30 beds) 100 North Academy Avenue, 3rd Floor, Danville, PA, Zip 17822–3050; tel. 570/214–9653; Brian Mann, Chief Executive Officer

SELECT SPECIALTY HOSPITAL-ERIE (O, 50 beds) 252 West 11th Street, Erie, PA, Zip 16501–1702; tel. 814/874–5300; Karen Surkala, Chief Executive Officer
Web address: www.erie.selectspecialtyhospitals.com/

SELECT SPECIALTY HOSPITAL-JOHNSTOWN (O, 39 beds) 320 Main Street, 3rd Floor, Johnstown, PA, Zip 15901–1601; tel. 814/534–7300; Kelly Blake, Chief Executive Officer
Web address: www.selectspecialtyhospitals.com/company/locations/johnstown.aspx

For explanation of codes following names, see page B2.
★ Indicates Type III membership in the American Hospital Association.

Section B

SELECT SPECIALTY HOSPITAL-LAUREL HIGHLANDS (O, 40 beds) One Mellon Way, 3rd Floor, Latrobe, PA, Zip 15650–1197; tel. 724/539–3870; Eric Schwab, Chief Executive Officer

SELECT SPECIALTY HOSPITAL-MCKEESPORT (O, 30 beds) 1500 Fifth Avenue, 6th Floor, McKeesport, PA, Zip 15132–2422; tel. 412/664–2900; Patrick Tuer, Interim Chief Executive Officer
Web address: www.mckeesport.selectspecialtyhospitals.com/

SELECT SPECIALTY HOSPITAL-PITTSBURGH/UPMC (O, 32 beds) 200 Lothrop Street, E824, Pittsburgh, PA, Zip 15213–2536; tel. 412/586–9800; Darrell Jones, Chief Executive Officer

SOUTH CAROLINA: REGENCY HOSPITAL OF FLORENCE (O, 40 beds) 121 East Cedar Street, 4th Floor, Florence, SC, Zip 29506–2576; tel. 843/661–3471; Amy Metz, Chief Executive Officer
Web address: www.regencyhospital.com

REGENCY HOSPITAL OF GREENVILLE (O, 32 beds) One St Francis Drive, 4th Floor, Greenville, SC, Zip 29601–3955; tel. 864/255–1438; Tammy Ratliff, Chief Executive Officer
Web address: www.regencyhospital.com

SOUTH DAKOTA: SELECT SPECIALTY HOSPITAL-SIOUX FALLS (O, 24 beds) 1305 West 18th Street, Sioux Falls, SD, Zip 57105–0401; tel. 605/312–9500; Carol Ulmer, Chief Executive Officer
Web address: www.selectspecialtyhospitals.com/company/locations/siouxfalls.aspx

TENNESSEE: SELECT SPECIALTY HOSPITAL-MEMPHIS (O, 39 beds) 5959 Park Avenue, 12th Floor, Memphis, TN, Zip 38119–5200; tel. 901/765–1245; Marcia Taylor, Chief Executive Officer

SELECT SPECIALTY HOSPITAL-NASHVILLE (O, 70 beds) 2000 Hayes Street, Nashville, TN, Zip 37203–2318; tel. 615/284–4599; Jennifer Causey, Chief Executive Officer
Web address: www.selectspecialtyhospitals.com/company/locations/nashville.aspx

SELECT SPECIALTY HOSPITAL-NORTH KNOXVILLE (O, 33 beds) 7557B Dannaher Drive, Suite 145, Powell, TN, Zip 37849–3568; tel. 865/512–2450; Steve Plumlee, Chief Executive Officer
Web address: www.northknoxville.selectspecialtyhospitals.com/

SELECT SPECIALTY HOSPITAL-TRI CITIES (O, 33 beds) One Medical Park Boulevard, 5th Floor, Bristol, TN, Zip 37620–8964; tel. 423/844–5900; Jeffrey Radford, Chief Executive Officer
Web address: www.tricities.selectspecialtyhospitals.com/

TEXAS: BAYLOR SCOTT & WHITE INSTITUTE FOR REHABILITATION – LAKEWAY (O, 25 beds) 2000 Medical Drive, Lakeway, TX, Zip 78734–4200; tel. 512/263–4500; Deborah Hopps, R.N., FACHE, Chief Executive Officer
Web address: www.vrhlaketravis.com

BAYLOR SCOTT & WHITE INSTITUTE FOR REHABILITATION-FORT WORTH (C, 42 beds) 6601 Harris Parkway, Fort Worth, TX, Zip 76132–6108; tel. 817/433–9600; Ryan Seymour, Chief Executive Officer

BAYLOR SCOTT & WHITE INSTITUTE FOR REHABILITATION-FRISCO (O, 44 beds) 2990 Legacy Drive, Frisco, TX, Zip 75034–6066; tel. 469/888–5100; Ryan Seymour, Chief Executive Officer
Web address: www.baylorhealth.com/bir

SELECT REHABILITATION HOSPITAL OF DENTON (O, 44 beds) 2620 Scripture Street, Denton, TX, Zip 76201–4315; tel. 940/297–6500; Michelle Powell, Chief Executive Officer

SELECT REHABILITATION HOSPITAL OF SAN ANTONIO (O, 42 beds) 19126 Stonehue Road, San Antonio, TX, Zip 78258–3490; tel. 210/482–3400; John Deleon, Chief Executive Officer
Web address: www.sanantonio-rehab.com/

SELECT SPECIALTY HOSPITAL – DALLAS DOWNTOWN (O, 26 beds) 3500 Gaston Avenue, Floors 3&4 Jonsson, Dallas, TX, Zip 75246–2017; tel. 469/801–4500; Michael McAlister, Chief Executive Officer
Web address: www.dallasdowntown.selectspecialtyhospitals.com/

SELECT SPECIALTY HOSPITAL-DALLAS (O, 60 beds) 2329 West Parker Road, Carrollton, TX, Zip 75010–4713; tel. 469/892–1400; Jerome M. Brooks, Chief Executive Officer

SELECT SPECIALTY HOSPITAL-LONGVIEW (O, 32 beds) 700 East Marshall Avenue, 1st Floor, Longview, TX, Zip 75601–5580; tel. 903/315–1100; Andrew Meade, Chief Executive Officer
Web address: www.longview.selectspecialtyhospitals.com/

VIRGINIA: COASTAL VIRGINIA REHABILITATION (C, 50 beds) 245 Chesapeake Avenue, Newport News, VA, Zip 23607–6038; tel. 757/928–8000; Daniel Ballin, Administrator

SELECT SPECIALTY HOSPITAL HAMPTON ROADS (O, 25 beds) 245 Chesapeake Avenue, Newport News, VA, Zip 23607–6038; tel. 757/534–5000; Phillip L. Wright, FACHE, Chief Executive Officer
Web address: www.hamptonroadsspecialtyhospital.com

WEST VIRGINIA: SELECT SPECIALTY HOSPITAL-CHARLESTON (O, 32 beds) 333 Laidley Street, 3rd Floor East, Charleston, WV, Zip 25301–1614; tel. 304/720–7234; Frank Weber, Chief Executive Officer
Web address: www.selectspecialtyhospitals.com/company/locations/charleston.aspx

WISCONSIN: SELECT SPECIALTY HOSPITAL-MADISON (O, 58 beds) 801 Braxton Place, Madison, WI, Zip 53715–1415; tel. 608/260–2700; Catherine Heimbecher, Chief Executive Officer
Web address: www.madison.selectspecialtyhospitals.com

SELECT SPECIALTY HOSPITAL-MILWAUKEE (O, 34 beds) 8901 West Lincoln Avenue, 2nd Floor, Milwaukee, WI, Zip 53227–2409, West Allis, tel. 414/328–7700; Dennis Mattes, Chief Executive Officer

Owned, leased, sponsored:	103 hospitals	5558 beds
Contract-managed:	4 hospitals	222 beds
Totals:	107 hospitals	5780 beds

★2565: SENTARA HEALTHCARE (NP)
6015 Poplar Hall Drive, Norfolk, VA, Zip 23502–3819; tel. 757/455–7000; Howard P. Kern, Chief Executive Officer
(Centralized Physician/Insurance Health System)

NORTH CAROLINA: SENTARA ALBEMARLE MEDICAL CENTER (L, 109 beds) 1144 North Road Street, Elizabeth City, NC, Zip 27909–3473, Mailing Address: P.O. Box 1587, Zip 27906–1587, tel. 252/335–0531; Coleen F. Santa Ana, President
Web address: www.albemarlehealth.org

VIRGINIA: SENTARA CAREPLEX HOSPITAL (O, 169 beds) 3000 Coliseum Drive, Hampton, VA, Zip 23666–5963; tel. 757/736–1000; Kirkpatrick Conley, President

SENTARA HALIFAX REGIONAL HOSPITAL (O, 441 beds) 2204 Wilborn Avenue, South Boston, VA, Zip 24592–1638; tel. 434/517–3100; Jason A. Studley, FACHE, President
Web address: www.hrhs.org

SENTARA LEIGH HOSPITAL (O, 250 beds) 830 Kempsville Road, Norfolk, VA, Zip 23502–3920; tel. 757/261–6000; Joanne Inman, President

SENTARA MARTHA JEFFERSON HOSPITAL (O, 144 beds) 500 Martha Jefferson Drive, Charlottesville, VA, Zip 22911–4668; tel. 434/654–7000; Jonathan S. Davis, FACHE, President
Web address: www.marthajefferson.org

SENTARA NORFOLK GENERAL HOSPITAL (O, 483 beds) 600 Gresham Drive, Norfolk, VA, Zip 23507–1904; tel. 757/388–3000; Carolyn Carpenter, FACHE, President
Web address: www.sentara.com

SENTARA NORTHERN VIRGINIA MEDICAL CENTER (O, 183 beds) 2300 Opitz Boulevard, Woodbridge, VA, Zip 22191–3399; tel. 703/523–1000; Katherine Johnson, Ph.D., President
Web address: www.sentara.com/northernvirginia

SENTARA OBICI HOSPITAL (O, 175 beds) 2800 Godwin Boulevard, Suffolk, VA, Zip 23434–8038; tel. 757/934–4000; Steve Julian, M.D., President

SENTARA PRINCESS ANNE HOSPITAL (O, 160 beds) 2025 Glenn Mitchell Drive, Virginia Beach, VA, Zip 23456–0178; tel. 757/507–1000; Thomas B. Thames, M.D., President
Web address: www.sentara.com

SENTARA RMH MEDICAL CENTER (O, 244 beds) 2010 Health Campus Drive, Harrisonburg, VA, Zip 22801–3293; tel. 540/689–1000; Douglas J. Moyer, President

SENTARA VIRGINIA BEACH GENERAL HOSPITAL (O, 271 beds) 1060 First Colonial Road, Virginia Beach, VA, Zip 23454–3002; tel. 757/395–8000; Elwood Bernard. Boone III, FACHE, President
Web address: www.sentara.com

For explanation of codes following names, see page B2.
★ Indicates Type III membership in the American Hospital Association.

SENTARA WILLIAMSBURG REGIONAL MEDICAL CENTER (O, 145 beds) 100 Sentara Circle, Williamsburg, VA, Zip 23188–5713; tel. 757/984–6000; David J. Masterson, President
Web address: www.sentara.com

Owned, leased, sponsored:	12 hospitals	2774 beds
Contract-managed:	0 hospitals	0 beds
Totals:	12 hospitals	2774 beds

★2065: SHARP HEALTHCARE (NP)
8695 Spectrum Center Boulevard, San Diego, CA, Zip 92123–1489; tel. 858/499–4000; Christopher Howard, President and Chief Executive Officer
(Centralized Health System)

CALIFORNIA: SHARP CHULA VISTA MEDICAL CENTER (O, 338 beds) 751 Medical Center Court, Chula Vista, CA, Zip 91911–6699; tel. 619/502–5800; Pablo Velez, R.N., Ph.D., Chief Executive Officer

SHARP CORONADO HOSPITAL AND HEALTHCARE CENTER (L, 181 beds) 250 Prospect Place, Coronado, CA, Zip 92118–1999; tel. 619/522–3600; Susan Stone, R.N., Ph.D., Senior Vice President and Chief Executive Officer
Web address: www.sharp.com

SHARP GROSSMONT HOSPITAL (L, 524 beds) 5555 Grossmont Center Drive, La Mesa, CA, Zip 91942–3019, Mailing Address: PO Box 158, Zip 91944–0158, tel. 619/740–6000; Scott Evans, PharmD, FACHE, Senior Vice President and Chief Executive Officer
Web address: www.sharp.com

SHARP MEMORIAL HOSPITAL (O, 459 beds) 7901 Frost Street, San Diego, CA, Zip 92123–2701; tel. 858/939–3400; Tim Smith, Senior Vice President and Chief Executive Officer
Web address: www.sharp.com

SHARP MESA VISTA HOSPITAL (O, 162 beds) 7850 Vista Hill Avenue, San Diego, CA, Zip 92123–2717; tel. 858/278–4110; Trisha Khaleghi, Senior Vice President and Chief Executive Officer
Web address: www.sharp.com

Owned, leased, sponsored:	5 hospitals	1664 beds
Contract-managed:	0 hospitals	0 beds
Totals:	5 hospitals	1664 beds

4125: SHRINERS HOSPITALS FOR CHILDREN (NP)
2900 North Rocky Point Drive, Tampa, FL, Zip 33607–1435, Mailing Address: P.O. Box 31356, Zip 33631–3356, tel. 813/281–0300; John P. McCabe, Executive Vice President
(Independent Hospital System)

CALIFORNIA: SHRINERS HOSPITALS FOR CHILDREN-NORTHERN CALIFORNIA (O, 70 beds) 2425 Stockton Boulevard, Sacramento, CA, Zip 95817–2215; tel. 916/453–2000; Margaret Bryan, Administrator

FLORIDA: SHRINERS HOSPITALS FOR CHILDREN-TAMPA (O, 60 beds) 12502 USF Pine Drive, Tampa, FL, Zip 33612–9499; tel. 813/972–2250; Fleury Yelvington, Administrator
Web address: www.shrinershospitalsforchildren.org/Hospitals/Locations/Tampa.aspx

HAWAII: SHRINERS HOSPITALS FOR CHILDREN-HONOLULU (O, 16 beds) 1310 Punahou Street, Honolulu, HI, Zip 96826–1099; tel. 808/941–4466; Anton C. Smith, Administrator

ILLINOIS: SHRINERS HOSPITALS FOR CHILDREN-CHICAGO (O, 36 beds) 2211 North Oak Park Avenue, Chicago, IL, Zip 60707–3392; tel. 773/622–5400; Mark L. Niederpruem, FACHE, Administrator
Web address: www.shrinershospitalsforchildren.org/Hospitals/Locations/Chicago.aspx

LOUISIANA: SHRINERS HOSPITALS FOR CHILDREN-SHREVEPORT (O, 45 beds) 3100 Samford Avenue, Shreveport, LA, Zip 71103–4289; tel. 318/222–5704; Garry Kim. Green, FACHE, Administrator
Web address: www.shrinershospitalsforchildren.org/Hospitals/Locations/Shreveport.aspx

MASSACHUSETTS: SHRINERS HOSPITALS FOR CHILDREN-BOSTON (O, 12 beds) 51 Blossom Street, Boston, MA, Zip 02114–2601; tel. 617/722–3000; Eileen F. Skinner, FACHE, Administrator

SHRINERS HOSPITALS FOR CHILDREN-SPRINGFIELD (O, 20 beds) 516 Carew Street, Springfield, MA, Zip 01104–2396; tel. 413/787–2000; H Lee. Kirk Jr, FACHE, Administrator
Web address: www.shrinershospitalsforchildren.org/Hospitals/Locations/Springfield.aspx

MISSOURI: SHRINERS HOSPITALS FOR CHILDREN-ST. LOUIS (O, 12 beds) 4400 Clayton Avenue, Saint Louis, MO, Zip 63110–1624; tel. 314/432–3600; Phillip L. Grady, FACHE, Administrator
Web address: https://www.shrinershospitalsforchildren.org

OHIO: SHRINERS HOSPITALS FOR CHILDREN – CINCINNATI (O, 30 beds) 3229 Burnet Avenue, Cincinnati, OH, Zip 45229–3095; tel. 513/872–6000; Mark D. Shugarman, Administrator

OREGON: SHRINERS HOSPITALS FOR CHILDREN-PORTLAND (O, 12 beds) 3101 SW Sam Jackson Park Road, Portland, OR, Zip 97239–3009; tel. 503/241–5090; Dereesa Reid, Administrator
Web address: www.shrinershospitalsforchildren.org/portland

PENNSYLVANIA: SHRINERS HOSPITALS FOR CHILDREN-PHILADELPHIA (O, 39 beds) 3551 North Broad Street, Philadelphia, PA, Zip 19140–4160; tel. 215/430–4000; Ed Myers, Administrator
Web address: www.shrinershospitalsforchildren.org/Hospitals/Locations/Philadelphia.aspx

SOUTH CAROLINA: SHRINERS HOSPITALS FOR CHILDREN-GREENVILLE (O, 15 beds) 950 West Faris Road, Greenville, SC, Zip 29605–4277; tel. 864/271–3444; William Munley, Administrator
Web address: www.greenvilleshrinershospital.org

TEXAS: SHRINERS HOSPITALS FOR CHILDREN-GALVESTON (O, 20 beds) 815 Market Street, Galveston, TX, Zip 77550–2725; tel. 409/770–6600; Mary Jaco, Administrator

SHRINERS HOSPITALS FOR CHILDREN-HOUSTON (O, 40 beds) 6977 Main Street, Houston, TX, Zip 77030–3701; tel. 713/797–1616; Cathy Moniaci, Administrator
Web address: www.shrinershospitalsforchildren.org/Locations/houston

UTAH: SHRINERS HOSPITALS FOR CHILDREN-SALT LAKE CITY (O, 45 beds) 1275 East Fairfax Road, Salt Lake City, UT, Zip 84103–4399; tel. 801/536–3500; Kevin Martin, M.P.H., R.N., FACHE, Administrator
Web address: www.shrinershospitalsforchildren.org/Hospitals/Locations/SaltLakeCity.aspx

WASHINGTON: SHRINERS HOSPITALS FOR CHILDREN-SPOKANE (O, 30 beds) 911 West Fifth Avenue, Spokane, WA, Zip 99204–2901, Mailing Address: P.O. Box 2472, Zip 99210–2472, tel. 509/455–7844; Peter G. Brewer, Administrator
Web address: www.shrinershospitalsforchildren.org/Hospitals/Locations/Spokane.aspx

Owned, leased, sponsored:	16 hospitals	502 beds
Contract-managed:	0 hospitals	0 beds
Totals:	16 hospitals	502 beds

0360: SIGNATURE HEALTHCARE SERVICES (IO)
4238 Green River Road, Corona, CA, Zip 92880–1669; tel. 951/549–8032; Soon K. Kim, M.D., President and Chief Executive Officer
(Independent Hospital System)

ARIZONA: AURORA BEHAVIORAL HEALTH SYSTEM EAST (O, 70 beds) 6350 South Maple Street, Tempe, AZ, Zip 85283–2857; tel. 480/345–5400; Bruce Waldo, Chief Executive Officer
Web address: www.auroraarizona.com

AURORA BEHAVIORAL HEALTH SYSTEM WEST (O, 100 beds) 6015 West Peoria Avenue, Glendale, AZ, Zip 85302–1213; tel. 623/344–4400; Bruce Waldo, Chief Executive Officer

CALIFORNIA: AURORA BEHAVIORAL HEALTHCARE SAN DIEGO (O, 80 beds) 11878 Avenue of Industry, San Diego, CA, Zip 92128–3490; tel. 858/487–3200; Alain Azcona, Chief Executive Officer
Web address: www.sandiego.aurorabehavioral.com/

Section B

For explanation of codes following names, see page B2.
★ Indicates Type III membership in the American Hospital Association.

AURORA CHARTER OAK HOSPITAL (O, 146 beds) 1161 East Covina Boulevard, Covina, CA, Zip 91724-1599; tel. 626/966-1632; Todd A. Smith, Chief Executive Officer
Web address: www.charteroakhospital.com

AURORA SANTA ROSA HOSPITAL (O, 95 beds) 1287 Fulton Road, Santa Rosa, CA, Zip 95401-4923; tel. 707/800-7700; Kay E. Seim, Chief Executive Officer
Web address: www.aurorasantarosa.com

LAS ENCINAS HOSPITAL (O, 118 beds) 2900 East Del Mar Boulevard, Pasadena, CA, Zip 91107-4399; tel. 626/795-9901; Thomas J. Mahle, Chief Executive Officer
Web address: www.lasencinashospital.com

VISTA DEL MAR HOSPITAL (O, 87 beds) 801 Seneca Street, Ventura, CA, Zip 93001-1411; tel. 805/653-6434; Mayla Krebsbach, Chief Executive Officer
Web address: www.vistadelmarhospital.com

ILLINOIS: CHICAGO LAKESHORE HOSPITAL (O, 161 beds) 4840 North Marine Drive, Chicago, IL, Zip 60640-4296; tel. 773/878-9700; David Fletcher-Janzen, Chief Executive Officer
Web address: www.chicagolakeshorehospital.com

NEVADA: DESERT PARKWAY BEHAVIORAL HEALTHCARE HOSPITAL (O, 83 beds) 3247 South Maryland Parkway, Las Vegas, NV, Zip 89109-2412; tel. 702/776-3500; Allison Zednicek, Chief Executive Officer

RENO BEHAVIORAL HEALTHCARE HOSPITAL (O, 124 beds) 6940 Sierra Center Parkway, Reno, NV, Zip 89511; tel. 877/787-8518; Steve Shell, Chief Executive Officer
Web address: www.renobehavioral.com

TEXAS: DALLAS BEHAVIORAL HEALTHCARE HOSPITAL (O, 116 beds) 800 Kirnwood Drive, Desoto, TX, Zip 75115-2000; tel. 855/982-0897; Terrance O'Reilly, Chief Executive Officer
Web address: www.dallasbehavioral.com

GEORGETOWN BEHAVIORAL HEALTH INSTITUTE (O, 118 beds) 3101 South Austin Avenue, Georgetown, TX, Zip 78626-7541; tel. 512/819-1100; Monica Ochoa, Chief Executive Officer
Web address: www.georgetownbehavioral.com

HOUSTON BEHAVIORAL HEALTHCARE HOSPITAL (O, 25 beds) 2801 Gessner Road, Houston, TX, Zip 77080-2503; tel. 832/834-7710; Roy Hollis, Chief Executive Officer

SAN ANTONIO BEHAVIORAL HEALTHCARE HOSPITAL (O, 198 beds) 8550 Huebner Road, San Antonio, TX, Zip 78240-1803; tel. 877/514-0010; Aleen D. Arabit, Chief Executive Officer
Web address: www.sanantoniobehavioral.com

Owned, leased, sponsored:	14 hospitals	1521 beds
Contract-managed:	0 hospitals	0 beds
Totals:	14 hospitals	1521 beds

★0284: SINAI HEALTH SYSTEM (NP)
1500 South Fairfield Avenue, Chicago, IL, Zip 60608-1782; tel. 773/542-2000; Karen Teitelbaum, President and Chief Executive Officer
(Centralized Health System)

ILLINOIS: HOLY CROSS HOSPITAL (O, 209 beds) 2701 West 68th Street, Chicago, IL, Zip 60629-1882; tel. 773/884-9000; Lori Pacura, MSN, R.N., President

MOUNT SINAI HOSPITAL (O, 276 beds) 1500 South Fairfield Avenue, Chicago, IL, Zip 60608-1729; tel. 773/542-2000; Loren Chandler, President
Web address: www.sinai.org

SCHWAB REHABILITATION HOSPITAL (O, 73 beds) 1401 South California Avenue, Chicago, IL, Zip 60608-1858; tel. 773/522-2010; Karen Teitelbaum, Chief Executive Officer
Web address: www.schwabrehab.org

Owned, leased, sponsored:	3 hospitals	558 beds
Contract-managed:	0 hospitals	0 beds
Totals:	3 hospitals	558 beds

5125: SISTERS OF CHARITY HEALTH SYSTEM (CC)
2475 East 22nd Street, Cleveland, OH, Zip 44115-3221; tel. 216/363-2797; Thomas J. Strauss, Chief Executive Officer
(Moderately Centralized Health System)

OHIO: MERCY MEDICAL CENTER (O, 338 beds) 1320 Mercy Drive NW, Canton, OH, Zip 44708-2641; tel. 330/489-1000; Paul C. Hiltz, FACHE, President and Chief Executive Officer
Web address: www.cantonmercy.org

ST. VINCENT CHARITY MEDICAL CENTER (O, 208 beds) 2351 East 22nd Street, Cleveland, OH, Zip 44115-3111; tel. 216/861-6200; David F. Perse, M.D., President and Chief Executive Officer

Owned, leased, sponsored:	2 hospitals	546 beds
Contract-managed:	0 hospitals	0 beds
Totals:	2 hospitals	546 beds

5805: SISTERS OF MARY OF THE PRESENTATION HEALTH SYSTEM (CC)
1202 Page Drive SW, Fargo, ND, Zip 58103-2340, Mailing Address: P.O. Box 10007, Zip 58106-0007, tel. 701/237-9290; Aaron K. Alton, President and Chief Executive Officer
(Moderately Centralized Health System)

ILLINOIS: ST. MARGARET'S HOSPITAL (O, 44 beds) 600 East First Street, Spring Valley, IL, Zip 61362-1512; tel. 815/664-5311; Tim Muntz, President and Chief Executive Officer
Web address: www.aboutsmh.org

NORTH DAKOTA: PRESENTATION MEDICAL CENTER (O, 25 beds) 213 Second Avenue NE, Rolla, ND, Zip 58367-7153, Mailing Address: P.O. Box 759, Zip 58367-0759, tel. 701/477-3161; Chris Albertson, Chief Executive Officer
Web address: www.pmc-rolla.com

ST. ALOISIUS MEDICAL CENTER (O, 110 beds) 325 East Brewster Street, Harvey, ND, Zip 58341-1653; tel. 701/324-4651; Mike Zwicker, Chief Executive Officer

ST. ANDREW'S HEALTH CENTER (O, 25 beds) 316 Ohmer Street, Bottineau, ND, Zip 58318-1045; tel. 701/228-9300; Alfred Sams, President and Chief Executive Officer
Web address: www.standrewshealth.com

Owned, leased, sponsored:	4 hospitals	204 beds
Contract-managed:	0 hospitals	0 beds
Totals:	4 hospitals	204 beds

0997: SKAGIT REGIONAL HEALTH (NP)
1415 E Kincaid Street, Mount Vernon, WA, Zip 98274-4126; tel. 360/424-4111; Gregg Agustin. Davidson, FACHE, President and Chief Executive Officer
(Independent Hospital System)

WASHINGTON: CASCADE VALLEY HOSPITAL (L, 48 beds) 330 South Stillaguamish Avenue, Arlington, WA, Zip 98223-1642; tel. 360/435-2133; Brian K. Ivie, President and Chief Executive Officer

SKAGIT REGIONAL HEALTH (O, 202 beds) 1415 East Kincaid, Mount Vernon, WA, Zip 98274-4126, Mailing Address: P.O. Box 1376, Zip 98273-1376, tel. 360/424-4111; Brian K. Ivie, President and Chief Executive Officer
Web address: www.skagitregionalhealth.org

Owned, leased, sponsored:	2 hospitals	250 beds
Contract-managed:	0 hospitals	0 beds
Totals:	2 hospitals	250 beds

1042: SOLUTIONHEALTH (NP)
One Elliot Way, Manchester, NH, Zip 03103-3502; tel. 603/663-2990; Sherry Hausmann, President and Chief Executive Officer

For explanation of codes following names, see page B2.
★ Indicates Type III membership in the American Hospital Association.

Section B

NEW HAMPSHIRE: ELLIOT HOSPITAL (O, 268 beds) One Elliot Way, Manchester, NH, Zip 03103–3502; tel. 603/669–5300; Douglas F. Dean Jr, Chief Executive Officer

SOUTHERN NEW HAMPSHIRE MEDICAL CENTER (O, 162 beds) 8 Prospect Street, Nashua, NH, Zip 03060–3925, Mailing Address: P.O. Box 2014, Zip 03061–2014, tel. 603/577–2000; Michael S. Rose, President and Chief Executive Officer
Web address: www.snhhs.org

Owned, leased, sponsored:	2 hospitals	430 beds
Contract-managed:	0 hospitals	0 beds
Totals:	2 hospitals	430 beds

★1034: SOUTH GEORGIA MEDICAL CENTER (NP)

2501 North Patterson Street, Valdosta, GA, Zip 31602–1735, Mailing Address: P.O. Box 1727, Zip 31603–1727, tel. 229/333–1000; Bill Forbes, Interim Chief Executive Officer
(Independent Hospital System)

GEORGIA: SOUTH GEORGIA MEDICAL CENTER BERRIEN CAMPUS (O, 39 beds) 1221 East McPherson Avenue, Nashville, GA, Zip 31639–2326; tel. 229/433–8600; Richard Huth, Administrator
Web address: www.sgmc.org/

SOUTH GEORGIA MEDICAL CENTER LANIER CAMPUS (O, 87 beds) 116 West Thigpen Avenue, Lakeland, GA, Zip 31635–1011; tel. 229/482–3110; Richard Huth, Administrator

SOUTH GEORGIA MEDICAL CENTER (O, 203 beds) 2501 North Patterson Street, Valdosta, GA, Zip 31602–1735, Mailing Address: P.O. Box 1727, Zip 31603–1727, tel. 229/333–1000; Bill Forbes, Chief Executive Officer
Web address: www.sgmc.org

Owned, leased, sponsored:	3 hospitals	329 beds
Contract-managed:	0 hospitals	0 beds
Totals:	3 hospitals	329 beds

★0253: SOUTHEAST GEORGIA HEALTH SYSTEM (NP)

2415 Parkwood Drive, Brunswick, GA, Zip 31520–4722, Mailing Address: P.O. Box 1518, Zip 31521–1518, tel. 912/466–7000; Michael D. Scherneck, President and Chief Executive Officer

GEORGIA: SOUTHEAST GEORGIA HEALTH SYSTEM BRUNSWICK CAMPUS (O, 532 beds) 2415 Parkwood Drive, Brunswick, GA, Zip 31520–4722, Mailing Address: P.O. Box 1518, Zip 31521 1518, tel. 912/466–7000; Michael D. Scherneck, President and Chief Executive Officer
Web address: www.sghs.org

SOUTHEAST GEORGIA HEALTH SYSTEM CAMDEN CAMPUS (O, 40 beds) 2000 Dan Proctor Drive, Saint Marys, GA, Zip 31558–3810; tel. 912/576–6200; Howard W. Sepp Jr, Vice-President and Administrator
Web address: www.sghs.org

Owned, leased, sponsored:	2 hospitals	572 beds
Contract-managed:	0 hospitals	0 beds
Totals:	2 hospitals	572 beds

0628: SOUTHEASTHEALTH (NP)

1701 Lacey Street, Cape Girardeau, MO, Zip 63701–5230; tel. 573/334–4822; Kenneth Bateman, CPA, Chief Executive Officer
(Moderately Centralized Health System)

MISSOURI: SOUTHEAST HEALTH CENTER OF STODDARD COUNTY (L, 31 beds) 1200 North One Mile Road, Dexter, MO, Zip 63841–1000; tel. 573/624–5566; Sue Ann Williams, Chief Executive Officer
Web address: www.sehealth.org

SOUTHEAST HOSPITAL (O, 146 beds) 1701 Lacey Street, Cape Girardeau, MO, Zip 63701–5230; tel. 573/334–4822; Kenneth Bateman, CPA, President and Chief Executive Officer

Owned, leased, sponsored:	2 hospitals	177 beds
Contract-managed:	0 hospitals	0 beds
Totals:	2 hospitals	177 beds

4175: SOUTHERN ILLINOIS HEALTHCARE (NP)

1239 East Main Street, Carbondale, IL, Zip 62901–3114, Mailing Address: P.O. Box 3988, Zip 62902–3988, tel. 618/457–5200; Rex P. Budde, President and Chief Executive Officer
(Independent Hospital System)

ILLINOIS: HERRIN HOSPITAL (O, 114 beds) 201 South 14th Street, Herrin, IL, Zip 62948–3631; tel. 618/942–2171; Rodney Smith, Vice President and Administrator

MEMORIAL HOSPITAL OF CARBONDALE (O, 167 beds) 405 West Jackson Street, Carbondale, IL, Zip 62901–1467, Mailing Address: P.O. Box 10000, Zip 62902–9000, tel. 618/549–0721; Al Taylor, Vice President and Administrator
Web address: www.sih.net

ST. JOSEPH MEMORIAL HOSPITAL (O, 25 beds) 2 South Hospital Drive, Murphysboro, IL, Zip 62966–3333; tel. 618/684–3156; Susan Odle, Administrator
Web address: www.sih.net

Owned, leased, sponsored:	3 hospitals	306 beds
Contract-managed:	0 hospitals	0 beds
Totals:	3 hospitals	306 beds

0652: SOUTHWEST HEALTH SYSTEMS (NP)

215 Marion Avenue, Mccomb, MS, Zip 39648–2705, Mailing Address: P.O. Box 1307, Zip 39649–1307, tel. 601/249–5500; Norman M. Price, FACHE, Chief Executive Officer and Administrator
(Independent Hospital System)

MISSISSIPPI: LAWRENCE COUNTY HOSPITAL (O, 25 beds) Highway 84 East, Monticello, MS, Zip 39654–0788, Mailing Address: P.O. Box 788, Zip 39654–0788, tel. 601/587–4051; Phillip W. Langston, Administrator
Web address: www.smrmc.com

SOUTHWEST MISSISSIPPI REGIONAL MEDICAL CENTER (O, 143 beds) 215 Marion Avenue, McComb, MS, Zip 39648–2705, Mailing Address: P.O. Box 1307, Zip 39649–1307, tel. 601/249–5500; Norman M. Price, FACHE, Chief Executive Officer

Owned, leased, sponsored:	2 hospitals	168 beds
Contract-managed:	0 hospitals	0 beds
Totals:	2 hospitals	168 beds

0164: SOUTHWEST HEALTHCARE SYSTEM (IO)

7025 N Scottsdale Road Suite 9347, Scottsdale, AZ, Zip 85253–3675, Mailing Address: 7025 North Scottsdale Road, Suite 9347, Zip 85251–3331, tel. 480/518–5444; Paul R. Tuft, President
(Independent Hospital System)

CALIFORNIA: PACIFICA HOSPITAL OF THE VALLEY (O, 231 beds) 9449 San Fernando Road, Sun Valley, CA, Zip 91352–1489; tel. 818/767–3310; Ayman Mousa, R.N., Ph.D., Chief Executive Officer
Web address: www.pacificahospital.com

Owned, leased, sponsored:	1 hospitals	231 beds
Contract-managed:	0 hospitals	0 beds
Totals:	1 hospitals	231 beds

★1245: SPARROW HEALTH SYSTEM (NP)

1215 East Michigan Avenue, Lansing, MI, Zip 48912–1811; tel. 517/364–1000; James F. Dover, FACHE, President and Chief Executive Officer
(Centralized Health System)

MICHIGAN: SPARROW CARSON HOSPITAL (O, 48 beds) 406 East Elm Street, Carson City, MI, Zip 48811–9693, Mailing Address: P.O. Box 879, Zip 48811–0879, tel. 989/584–3131; William Roeser, Interim President and Chief Executive Officer
Web address: www.carsoncityhospital.com

For explanation of codes following names, see page B2.
★ Indicates Type III membership in the American Hospital Association.

Section B

SPARROW CLINTON HOSPITAL (O, 25 beds) 805 South Oakland Street, Saint Johns, MI, Zip 48879–2253; tel. 989/227–3400; Edward Bruun, President and Chief Executive Officer
Web address: www.sparrowclinton.org

SPARROW HOSPITAL (O, 632 beds) 1215 East Michigan Avenue, Lansing, MI, Zip 48912–1811; tel. 517/364–1000; Mark Brett, Chief Executive Officer

SPARROW IONIA HOSPITAL (O, 22 beds) 3565 South State Road, Ionia, MI, Zip 48846–1870; tel. 616/523–1400; William Roeser, President and Chief Executive Officer
Web address: www.sparrow.org/sparrowionia

SPARROW SPECIALTY HOSPITAL (O, 30 beds) 8 West Sparrow Hospital Tower, 1215 East Michigan Avenue, Lansing, MI, Zip 48912; tel. 517/364–4840; Lou Little, President and Chief Executive Officer

Owned, leased, sponsored:	5 hospitals	757 beds
Contract-managed:	0 hospitals	0 beds
Totals:	5 hospitals	757 beds

★4195: SPARTANBURG REGIONAL HEALTHCARE SYSTEM (NP)
101 East Wood Street, Spartanburg, SC, Zip 29303–3040; tel. 864/560–6000; Bruce Holstien, President and Chief Executive Officer
(Centralized Health System)

SOUTH CAROLINA: CHEROKEE MEDICAL CENTER (O, 45 beds) 1530 North Limestone Street, Gaffney, SC, Zip 29340–4738; tel. 864/487–4271; Cody Butts, President

PELHAM MEDICAL CENTER (O, 48 beds) 250 Westmoreland Road, Greer, SC, Zip 29651–9013; tel. 864/530–6000; Anthony Kouskolekas, FACHE, President
Web address: www.pelhammedicalcenter.com

SPARTANBURG HOSPITAL FOR RESTORATIVE CARE (O, 116 beds) 389 Serpentine Drive, Spartanburg, SC, Zip 29303–3026; tel. 864/560–3280; Anita M. Butler, Chief Executive Officer

SPARTANBURG MEDICAL CENTER – CHURCH STREET CAMPUS (O, 519 beds) 101 East Wood Street, Spartanburg, SC, Zip 29303–3040; tel. 864/560–6000; J Philip. Feisal, President and Chief Executive Officer
Web address: www.spartanburgregional.com

SPARTANBURG MEDICAL CENTER – MARY BLACK (O, 160 beds) 1700 Skylyn Drive, Spartanburg, SC, Zip 29307–1061, Mailing Address: P.O. Box 3217, Zip 29304–3217, tel. 864/573–3000; Parkes Coggins, Vice President Hospital Integration

UNION MEDICAL CENTER (O, 50 beds) 322 West South Street, Union, SC, Zip 29379–2857, Mailing Address: P.O. Box 789, Zip 29379–0789, tel. 864/301–2000; Paul R. Newhouse, President
Web address: https://www.spartanburgregional.com/locations/union-medical-center/

Owned, leased, sponsored:	6 hospitals	938 beds
Contract-managed:	0 hospitals	0 beds
Totals:	6 hospitals	938 beds

★0177: SPECTRUM HEALTH (NP)
221 Michigan Street NE, Suite 501, Grand Rapids, MI, Zip 49503–2543; tel. 616/391–1774; Christina Freese Decker, FACHE, President and Chief Executive Officer
(Centralized Physician/Insurance Health System)

MICHIGAN: LAKELAND HOSPITAL, WATERVLIET (O, 44 beds) 400 Medical Park Drive, Watervliet, MI, Zip 49098–9225; tel. 269/463–3111; Ray Cruse, Chief Executive Officer

SPECTRUM HEALTH – BUTTERWORTH HOSPITAL (O, 1412 beds) 100 Michigan Street NE, Grand Rapids, MI, Zip 49503–2560; tel. 616/391–1774; Gwen Sandefur, President, Spectrum Health Hospital Group
Web address: www.spectrumhealth.org

SPECTRUM HEALTH BIG RAPIDS HOSPITAL (O, 48 beds) 605 Oak Street, Big Rapids, MI, Zip 49307–2099; tel. 231/796–8691; Andrea M. Leslie, MSN, R.N., President
Web address: www.spectrumhealth.org

SPECTRUM HEALTH GERBER MEMORIAL (O, 25 beds) 212 South Sullivan Avenue, Fremont, MI, Zip 49412–1548; tel. 231/924–3300; Randall Kelley, FACHE, President
Web address: www.spectrumhealth.org

SPECTRUM HEALTH LAKELAND (O, 303 beds) 1234 Napier Avenue, Saint Joseph, MI, Zip 49085–2158; tel. 269/983–8300; Loren Hamel, M.D., President and Chief Executive Officer

SPECTRUM HEALTH LUDINGTON HOSPITAL (O, 30 beds) One Atkinson Drive, Ludington, MI, Zip 49431–1906, Mailing Address: PO Box 2408, Grand Rapids, Zip 49501–2408, tel. 231/843–2591; Randall Kelley, FACHE, President
Web address: www.mmcwm.com

SPECTRUM HEALTH PENNOCK (O, 39 beds) 1009 West Green Street, Hastings, MI, Zip 49058–1710; tel. 269/945–3451; Angela Ditmar, R.N., President

SPECTRUM HEALTH REED CITY HOSPITAL (O, 75 beds) 300 North Patterson Road, Reed City, MI, Zip 49677–8041, Mailing Address: P.O. Box 75, Zip 49677–0075, tel. 231/832–3271; Andrea M. Leslie, MSN, R.N., President
Web address: www.spectrumhealth.org/reedcity

SPECTRUM HEALTH UNITED HOSPITAL (O, 116 beds) 615 South Bower Street, Greenville, MI, Zip 48838–2614; tel. 616/754–4691; Andrea M. Leslie, MSN, R.N., President

SPECTRUM HEALTH ZEELAND COMMUNITY HOSPITAL (O, 50 beds) 8333 Felch Street, Zeeland, MI, Zip 49464–2608; tel. 616/772–4644; Ron Lewis, President
Web address: www.spectrumhealth.org/zeeland

Owned, leased, sponsored:	10 hospitals	2142 beds
Contract-managed:	0 hospitals	0 beds
Totals:	10 hospitals	2142 beds

1037: SPRINGSTONE (IO)
101 South Fifth Street, Suite 3850, Louisville, KY, Zip 40202–3127; tel. 855/595–2292; Robert Maha, M.D., President and Chief Executive Officer

COLORADO: DENVER SPRINGS (O, 96 beds) 8835 American Way, Englewood, CO, Zip 80112–7056; tel. 720/643–4300; Bill Snyder, Chief Executive Officer

INDIANA: BRENTWOOD SPRINGS (O, 48 beds) 4488 Roslin Road, Newburgh, IN, Zip 47630; tel. 812/858–7200; Mark Puckett, Chief Executive Officer
Web address: www.brentwoodmeadows.com

SYCAMORE SPRINGS HOSPITAL (O, 48 beds) 833 Park East Boulevard, Lafayette, IN, Zip 47905–0785; tel. 765/743–4400; Shelley Zimmerman, Chief Executive Officer

KANSAS: COTTONWOOD SPRINGS HOSPITAL (O, 72 beds) 13351 South Arapaho Drive, Olathe, KS, Zip 66062–1520; tel. 913/353–3000; Jason Toalson, Chief Executive Officer
Web address: www.cottonwoodsprings.com

NORTH CAROLINA: TRIANGLE SPRINGS HOSPITAL (O, 77 beds) 10901 World Trade Boulevard, Raleigh, NC, Zip 27617–4203; tel. 919/372–4408; Carla Hollis, Chief Executive Officer

OHIO: BECKETT SPRINGS (O, 96 beds) 8614 Shepherd Farm Drive, West Chester, OH, Zip 45069; tel. 513/942–9500; Jeff Pritchard, Chief Executive Officer
Web address: www.springstone.com/hospitals.stmhl

COLUMBUS DUBLIN SPRINGS (O, 144 beds) 7625 Hospital Drive, Dublin, OH, Zip 43016–9649; tel. 614/717–1800; Garry W. Hoyes, Chief Executive Officer

HIGHLAND SPRINGS HOSPITAL (O, 72 beds) 4199 Mill Pond Drive, Highland Hills, OH, Zip 44122–5731; tel. 602/314–7800; Matthew Winchester, Chief Executive Officer
Web address: https://www.highlandspringshealth.com

OKLAHOMA: OAKWOOD SPRINGS (O, 72 beds) 13101 Memorial Springs Court, Oklahoma City, OK, Zip 73114–2226; tel. 405/438–3000; Karen Walker, Chief Executive Officer
Web address: www.oakwoodsprings.com/

For explanation of codes following names, see page B2.
★ Indicates Type III membership in the American Hospital Association.

TEXAS: CARROLLTON SPRINGS (O, 78 beds) 2225 Parker Road, Carrollton, TX, Zip 75010–4711; tel. 972/242–4114; Samantha Castle, Chief Executive Officer
Web address: www.carrolltonsprings.com

MESA SPRINGS (O, 72 beds) 5560 Mesa Springs Drive, Fort Worth, TX, Zip 76123; tel. 817/292–4600; Barbara Schmidt, Chief Executive Officer
Web address: www.springstone.com/hospitals.stmhl

ROCK SPRINGS (O, 72 beds) 700 Southeast Inner Loop, Georgetown, TX, Zip 78626; tel. 512/819–9400; Jason McPherson, Chief Executive Officer
Web address: www.rockspringshealth.com/

WESTPARK SPRINGS (O, 72 beds) 6902 South Peek Road, Richmond, TX, Zip 77407; tel. 832/532–8107; Colleen McCammon, Chief Executive Officer

WOODLAND SPRINGS HOSPITAL (O, 96 beds) 15680 Old Conroe Road, Conroe, TX, Zip 77384; tel. 936/270–7520; Dustin Davis, Chief Executive Officer
Web address: https://www.woodlandspringshealth.com/

Owned, leased, sponsored:	14 hospitals	1115 beds
Contract-managed:	0 hospitals	0 beds
Totals:	14 hospitals	1115 beds

★**5455: SSM HEALTH** (CC)
10101 Woodfield Lane, Saint Louis, MO, Zip 63132–2937; tel. 314/994–7800; Laura Kaiser, President and Chief Executive Officer
(Decentralized Health System)

ILLINOIS: CLAY COUNTY HOSPITAL (C, 10 beds) 911 Stacy Burk Drive, Flora, IL, Zip 62839–3241, Mailing Address: P.O. Box 280, Zip 62839–0280, tel. 618/662–2131; Chris Hunt, President
Web address: www.claycountyhospital.org

GOOD SAMARITAN REGIONAL HEALTH CENTER (O, 134 beds) 1 Good Samaritan Way, Mount Vernon, IL, Zip 62864–2402; tel. 618/242–4600; Kerry Swanson, Regional President, President Good Samaritan
Web address: www.smgsi.com

SSM HEALTH ST. MARY'S HOSPITAL CENTRALIA (O, 124 beds) 400 North Pleasant Avenue, Centralia, IL, Zip 62801–3056; tel. 618/436–8000; Damon R. Harbison, President

MISSOURI: SSM CARDINAL GLENNON CHILDREN'S HOSPITAL (O, 176 beds) 1465 South Grand Boulevard, Saint Louis, MO, Zip 63104–1095; tel. 314/577–5600; Steven Durghart, President
Web address: www.cardinalglennon.com

SSM HEALTH DEPAUL HOSPITAL – ST. LOUIS (O, 529 beds) 12303 De Paul Drive, Bridgeton, MO, Zip 63044–2512; tel. 314/344–6000; Ellis Hawkins, President
Web address: www.ssmdepaul.com

SSM HEALTH SAINT LOUIS UNIVERSITY HOSPITAL (O, 356 beds) 3635 Vista at Grand Boulevard, Saint Louis, MO, Zip 63110–0250, Mailing Address: P.O. Box 15250, Zip 63110–0250, tel. 314/577–8000; Steven M. Scott, President
Web address: www.sluhospital.com

SSM HEALTH ST. CLARE HOSPITAL – FENTON (O, 184 beds) 1015 Bowles Avenue, Fenton, MO, Zip 63026–2394; tel. 636/496–2000; Tina Garrison, President

SSM HEALTH ST. JOSEPH – ST. CHARLES (O, 341 beds) 300 First Capitol Drive, Saint Charles, MO, Zip 63301–2844; tel. 636/947–5000; Lisle Wescott, President
Web address: www.ssmstjoseph.com

SSM HEALTH ST. JOSEPH HOSPITAL – LAKE SAINT LOUIS (O, 215 beds) 100 Medical Plaza, Lake Saint Louis, MO, Zip 63367–1366; tel. 636/625–5200; Lisle Wescott, President

SSM HEALTH ST. MARY'S HOSPITAL – AUDRAIN (O, 60 beds) 620 East Monroe Street, Mexico, MO, Zip 65265–2919; tel. 573/582–5000; Donna K. Jacobs, FACHE, President
Web address: www.ssmhealthmidmo.com

SSM HEALTH ST. MARY'S HOSPITAL – JEFFERSON CITY (O, 92 beds) 2505 Mission Drive, Jefferson City, MO, Zip 65109; tel. 573/681–3000; Michael A. Baumgartner, President

SSM HEALTH ST. MARY'S HOSPITAL – ST. LOUIS (O, 394 beds) 6420 Clayton Road, Saint Louis, MO, Zip 63117–1811; tel. 314/768–8000; Travis Capers, FACHE, President
Web address: www.stmarys-stlouis.com

OKLAHOMA: SSM HEALTH ST. ANTHONY HOSPITAL – OKLAHOMA CITY (O, 625 beds) 1000 North Lee Street, Oklahoma City, OK, Zip 73102–1080, Mailing Address: P.O. Box 205, Zip 73101–0205, tel. 405/272–7000; Tammy Powell, FACHE, M.P.H., President
Web address: www.saintsok.com

SSM HEALTH ST. ANTHONY HOSPITAL – SHAWNEE (O, 70 beds) 1102 West MacArthur Street, Shawnee, OK, Zip 74804–1744; tel. 405/273–2270; Charles E. Skillings, President and Chief Executive Officer

WISCONSIN: MONROE CLINIC (O, 58 beds) 515 22nd Avenue, Monroe, WI, Zip 53566–1598; tel. 608/324–2000; Michael B. Sanders, President and Chief Executive Officer
Web address: www.monroeclinic.org

RIPON MEDICAL CENTER (O, 16 beds) 845 Parkside Street, Ripon, WI, Zip 54971–8505, Mailing Address: P.O. Box 390, Zip 54971–0390, tel. 920/748–3101; DeAnn Thurmer, President and Chief Nursing Officer
Web address: www.agnesian.com

SSM HEALTH ST. CLARE HOSPITAL-BARABOO (O, 54 beds) 707 14th Street, Baraboo, WI, Zip 53913–1597; tel. 608/356–1400; Laura Walczak, President

SSM HEALTH ST. MARY'S HOSPITAL JANESVILLE (O, 50 beds) 515 22nd Ave, Monroe, WI, Zip 53566, Mailing Address: 3400 East Racine Steeet, Janesville, Zip 53546–2344, tel. 608/373–8000; Benjamin Layman, President
Web address: www.stmarysjanesville.com

SSM HEALTH ST. MARY'S HOSPITAL (O, 362 beds) 700 South Park Street, Madison, WI, Zip 53715–1830; tel. 608/251–6100; Jon Rozenfeld, President
Web address: www.stmarysmadison.com

ST. AGNES HOSPITAL (O, 139 beds) 430 East Division Street, Fond Du Lac, WI, Zip 54935–4560, Mailing Address: P.O. Box 385, Zip 54936–0385, tel. 920/929–2300; Katherine Vergos, FACHE, President

WAUPUN MEMORIAL HOSPITAL (O, 25 beds) 620 West Brown Street, Waupun, WI, Zip 53963–1799; tel. 920/324–5581; DeAnn Thurmer, President and Chief Nursing Officer
Web address: www.agnesian.com

Owned, leased, sponsored:	20 hospitals	4004 beds
Contract-managed:	1 hospitals	10 beds
Totals:	21 hospitals	4014 beds

★**0250: ST. CHARLES HEALTH SYSTEM, INC.** (NP)
2500 NE Neff Road, Bend, OR, Zip 97701–6015; tel. 541/382–4321; Joseph Sluka, President and Chief Executive Officer
(Centralized Physician/Insurance Health System)

OREGON: ST. CHARLES BEND (O, 259 beds) 2500 NE Neff Road, Bend, OR, Zip 97701–6015; tel. 541/382–4321; Aaron Adams, President

ST. CHARLES MADRAS (O, 25 beds) 470 NE 'A' Street, Madras, OR, Zip 97741–1844; tel. 541/475–3882; David Golda, Administrator and Vice President
Web address: www.stcharleshealthcare.org/Our-Locations/Madras

ST. CHARLES PRINEVILLE (O, 20 beds) 384 SE Combs Flat Road, Prineville, OR, Zip 97754–1206; tel. 541/447–6254; Todd Shields, Administrator
Web address: www.stcharleshealthcare.org

ST. CHARLES REDMOND (O, 48 beds) 1253 NW Canal Boulevard, Redmond, OR, Zip 97756–1395; tel. 541/548–8131; Aaron Adams, President
Web address: www.stcharleshealthcare.org

Owned, leased, sponsored:	4 hospitals	352 beds
Contract-managed:	0 hospitals	0 beds
Totals:	4 hospitals	352 beds

0618: ST. ELIZABETH HEALTHCARE (CC)
1 Medical Village Drive, Edgewood, KY, Zip 41017–3403; tel. 859/301–2000; Garren Colvin, Chief Executive Officer
(Centralized Physician/Insurance Health System)

For explanation of codes following names, see page B2.
★ Indicates Type III membership in the American Hospital Association.

Section B

KENTUCKY: ST. ELIZABETH EDGEWOOD (O, 510 beds) 1 Medical Village Drive, Edgewood, KY, Zip 41017–3403; tel. 859/301–2000; Garren Colvin, Chief Executive Officer
Web address: www.stelizabeth.com

ST. ELIZABETH FLORENCE (O, 147 beds) 4900 Houston Road, Florence, KY, Zip 41042–4824; tel. 859/212–5200; Garren Colvin, Chief Executive Officer
Web address: www.stelizabeth.com

ST. ELIZABETH FORT THOMAS (O, 147 beds) 85 North Grand Avenue, Fort Thomas, KY, Zip 41075–1796; tel. 859/572–3100; Garren Colvin, Chief Executive Officer
Web address: www.stelizabeth.com

ST. ELIZABETH GRANT (O, 24 beds) 238 Barnes Road, Williamstown, KY, Zip 41097–9482; tel. 859/824–8240; Garren Colvin, Chief Executive Officer
Web address: www.stelizabeth.com

Owned, leased, sponsored:	4 hospitals	828 beds
Contract-managed:	0 hospitals	0 beds
Totals:	4 hospitals	828 beds

0928: ST. LAWRENCE HEALTH SYSTEM (NP)
50 Leroy Street, Potsdam, NY, Zip 13676–1799; tel. 315/265–3300; David B. Acker, FACHE, President and CEO
(Independent Hospital System)

NEW YORK: CANTON-POTSDAM HOSPITAL (O, 87 beds) 50 Leroy Street, Potsdam, NY, Zip 13676–1799; tel. 315/265–3300; David B. Acker, FACHE, President and Chief Executive Officer
Web address: www.cphospital.org

GOUVERNEUR HOSPITAL (O, 25 beds) 77 West Barney Street, Gouverneur, NY, Zip 13642–1040; tel. 315/287–1000; David Bender, Chief Executive Officer
Web address: www.gvnrhospital.org

Owned, leased, sponsored:	2 hospitals	112 beds
Contract-managed:	0 hospitals	0 beds
Totals:	2 hospitals	112 beds

★0356: ST. LUKE'S HEALTH SYSTEM (NP)
190 East Bannock Street, Boise, ID, Zip 83712–6241; tel. 208/381–4200; David C. Pate, M.D., JD, President and Chief Executive Officer
(Moderately Centralized Health System)

IDAHO: ST. LUKE'S ELMORE (L, 63 beds) 895 North Sixth East Street, Mountain Home, ID, Zip 83647–2207, Mailing Address: P.O. Box 1270, Zip 83647–1270, tel. 208/587–8401; Lisa Melchiorre, R.N., MS, Chief Operating Officer and Chief Nursing Officer
Web address: www.stlukesonline.org/elmore/

ST. LUKE'S JEROME (O, 25 beds) 709 North Lincoln Street, Jerome, ID, Zip 83338–1851, Mailing Address: 709 North Lincoln Avenue, Zip 83338–1851, tel. 208/814–9500; Curtis Maier, Administrator

ST. LUKE'S MAGIC VALLEY MEDICAL CENTER (O, 224 beds) 801 Pole Line Road West, Twin Falls, ID, Zip 83301–5810, Mailing Address: P.O. Box 409, Zip 83303–0409, tel. 208/814–1000; Michael A. Fenello, Administrator and West Region Chief Executive Officer
Web address: www.stlukesonline.org

ST. LUKE'S MCCALL (L, 15 beds) 1000 State Street, McCall, ID, Zip 83638–3704; tel. 208/634–2221; Amber Green, R.N., Chief Operating Officer and Chief Nursing Officer

ST. LUKE'S NAMPA (O, 87 beds) 9850 West St.Luke's Drive, Nampa, ID, Zip 83687; tel. 208/505–2000; Ed Castledine, Chief Executive Officer

ST. LUKE'S REGIONAL MEDICAL CENTER (O, 604 beds) 190 East Bannock Street, Boise, ID, Zip 83712–6241; tel. 208/381–2222; David M. McFadyen, Administrator
Web address: www.stlukesonline.org/boise

ST. LUKE'S REHABILITATION HOSPITAL (O, 30 beds) 600 North Robbins Road, Boise, ID, Zip 83702–4565, Mailing Address: P.O. Box 1100, Zip 83701–1100, tel. 208/489–4444; Nolan Hoffer, Senior Director

ST. LUKE'S WOOD RIVER MEDICAL CENTER (O, 25 beds) 100 Hospital Drive, Ketchum, ID, Zip 83340, Mailing Address: P.O. Box 100, Zip 83340–0100, tel. 208/727–8800; Cody Langbehn, Administrator
Web address: www.slrmc.org

WEISER MEMORIAL HOSPITAL (C, 18 beds) 645 East Fifth Street, Weiser, ID, Zip 83672–2202; tel. 208/549–0370; Steven D. Hale, FACHE, Chief Executive Officer
Web address: www.weisermemorialhospital.org

Owned, leased, sponsored:	8 hospitals	1073 beds
Contract-managed:	1 hospitals	18 beds
Totals:	9 hospitals	1091 beds

0862: ST. LUKE'S UNIVERSITY HEALTH NETWORK (NP)
801 Ostrum Street, Bethlehem, PA, Zip 18015–1000; tel. 610/954–4000; Richard A. Anderson, President and Chief Executive Officer
(Moderately Centralized Health System)

NEW JERSEY: ST. LUKE'S HOSPITAL – WARREN CAMPUS (O, 92 beds) 185 Roseberry Street, Phillipsburg, NJ, Zip 08865–1690; tel. 908/859–6700; Scott R. Wolfe, CPA, President

PENNSYLVANIA: ST. LUKE'S – GNADEN HUETTEN CAMPUS (O, 250 beds) 211 North 12th Street, Lehighton, PA, Zip 18235–1138; tel. 610/377–1300; John L. Nespoli, President
Web address: www.blmtn.org

ST. LUKE'S HOSPITAL – ANDERSON CAMPUS (O, 108 beds) 1872 Riverside Circle, Easton, PA, Zip 18045–5669; tel. 484/503–3000; Edward Nawrocki, President

ST. LUKE'S HOSPITAL – MINERS CAMPUS (O, 97 beds) 360 West Ruddle Street, Coaldale, PA, Zip 18218–1027; tel. 570/645–2131; Wendy Lazo, President
Web address: www.slhn.org

ST. LUKE'S HOSPITAL – QUAKERTOWN CAMPUS (O, 62 beds) 1021 Park Avenue, Quakertown, PA, Zip 18951–1573; tel. 215/538–4500; Dennis Pfleiger, President and Chief Operating Officer
Web address: www.slhhn.org

ST. LUKE'S SACRED HEART CAMPUS (O, 155 beds) 421 West Chew Street, Allentown, PA, Zip 18102–3490; tel. 610/776–4500; Frank Ford, President

ST. LUKE'S UNIVERSITY HOSPITAL – BETHLEHEM CAMPUS (O, 572 beds) 801 Ostrum Street, Bethlehem, PA, Zip 18015–1065; tel. 484/526–4000; Carol Kuplen, R.N., MSN, President and Chief Executive Officer
Web address: www.slhn-lehighvalley.org

Owned, leased, sponsored:	7 hospitals	1336 beds
Contract-managed:	0 hospitals	0 beds
Totals:	7 hospitals	1336 beds

★0156: STANFORD HEALTH CARE (NP)
300 Pasteur Drive, Palo Alto, CA, Zip 94304–2299; tel. 650/723–4000; David Entwistle, President and Chief Executive Officer
(Centralized Physician/Insurance Health System)

CALIFORNIA: STANFORD HEALTH CARE – VALLEYCARE (O, 193 beds) 5555 West Las Positas Boulevard, Pleasanton, CA, Zip 94588–4000; tel. 925/847–3000; Tracey Lewis-Taylor, Chief Operating Officer
Web address: www.valleycare.com

STANFORD HEALTH CARE (O, 477 beds) 300 Pasteur Drive, Suite H3200, Palo Alto, CA, Zip 94304–2203; tel. 650/723–4000; David Entwistle, President and Chief Executive Officer
Web address: www.stanfordhealthcare.org

Owned, leased, sponsored:	2 hospitals	670 beds
Contract-managed:	0 hospitals	0 beds
Totals:	2 hospitals	670 beds

0141: STEWARD HEALTH CARE SYSTEM, LLC (IO)
1900 North Pearl Street, Suite 2400, Dallas, TX, Zip 75201; tel. 617/419–4700; Ralph de la Torre, M.D., Chairman and Chief Executive Officer
(Moderately Centralized Health System)

For explanation of codes following names, see page B2.
★ Indicates Type III membership in the American Hospital Association.

ARIZONA: MOUNTAIN VISTA MEDICAL CENTER (O, 172 beds) 1301 South Crismon Road, Mesa, AZ, Zip 85209–3767; tel. 480/358–6100; Jacob Golich, Chief Executive Officer

ST. LUKE'S BEHAVIORAL HEALTH CENTER (O, 85 beds) 1800 East Van Buren, Phoenix, AZ, Zip 85006–3742; tel. 602/251–8546; Gregory L. Jahn, R.N., Chief Executive Officer
Web address: www.iasishealthcare.com

ST. LUKE'S MEDICAL CENTER (O, 219 beds) 1800 East Van Buren Street, Phoenix, AZ, Zip 85006–3742; tel. 602/251–8100; James Flinn, JD, FACHE, Chief Executive Officer
Web address: www.stlukesmedcenter.com

ARKANSAS: WADLEY REGIONAL MEDICAL CENTER AT HOPE (O, 79 beds) 2001 South Main Street, Hope, AR, Zip 71801–8194; tel. 870/722–3800; Thomas D. Gilbert, FACHE, Chief Executive Officer
Web address: www.wadleyhealthathope.com

COLORADO: PIKES PEAK REGIONAL HOSPITAL (O, 15 beds) 16420 West Highway 24, Woodland Park, CO, Zip 80863; tel. 719/687–9999; Kimberly Monjesky, Chief Executive Officer

FLORIDA: MELBOURNE REGIONAL MEDICAL CENTER (O, 119 beds) 250 North Wickham Road, Melbourne, FL, Zip 32935–8625; tel. 321/752–1200; Ron Gicca, Chief Executive Officer
Web address: www.wuesthoff.com/locations/wuesthoff-medical-center-melbourne

ROCKLEDGE REGIONAL MEDICAL CENTER (O, 298 beds) 110 Longwood Avenue, Rockledge, FL, Zip 32955–2887, Mailing Address: P.O. Box 565002, Mail Stop 1, Zip 32956–5002, tel. 321/636–2211; Andrew Romine, Chief Executive Officer
Web address: www.wuesthoff.org

SEBASTIAN RIVER MEDICAL CENTER (O, 154 beds) 13695 North U S Hwy 1, Sebastian, FL, Zip 32958–3230, Mailing Address: Box 780838, Zip 32978–0838, tel. 772/589–3186; Kyle Sanders, President
Web address: https://www.sebastianrivermedical.org/

LOUISIANA: GLENWOOD REGIONAL MEDICAL CENTER (O, 278 beds) 503 McMillan Road, West Monroe, LA, Zip 71291–5327; tel. 318/329 4200; Jeremy M. Tinnerello, MSN, R.N., President
Web address: www.grmc.com

MASSACHUSETTS: CARNEY HOSPITAL (O, 81 beds) 2100 Dorchester Avenue, Boston, MA, Zip 02124–5615; tel. 617/296–4000; Tom Sands, Interim Chief Executive Officer

GOOD SAMARITAN MEDICAL CENTER (O, 190 beds) 235 North Pearl Street, Brockton, MA, Zip 02301–1794; tel. 508/427–3000; Harrison Bane, President
Web address: www.goodsamaritanmedical.org

HOLY FAMILY HOSPITAL (O, 329 beds) 70 East Street, Methuen, MA, Zip 01844–4597; tel. 978/687–0151; Craig A. Jesiolowski, FACHE, President
Web address: www.stewardhealth.org/Holy-Family-Hospital

MORTON HOSPITAL AND MEDICAL CENTER (O, 153 beds) 88 Washington Street, Taunton, MA, Zip 02780–2465; tel. 508/828–7000; Heidi Taylor, President
Web address: www.mortonhospital.org

NASHOBA VALLEY MEDICAL CENTER (O, 48 beds) 200 Groton Road, Ayer, MA, Zip 01432–3300; tel. 978/784–9000; Korry Dow, President

NEW ENGLAND SINAI HOSPITAL AND REHABILITATION CENTER (O, 212 beds) 150 York Street, Stoughton, MA, Zip 02072–1881; tel. 781/344–0600; Mary Beth Urquhart, Interim President, Vice President Patient Care Services and Chief Nursing Officer
Web address: www.newenglandsinai.org

NORWOOD HOSPITAL (O, 188 beds) 800 Washington Street, Norwood, MA, Zip 02062–3487; tel. 781/769–4000; Salvatore Perla, President

SAINT ANNE'S HOSPITAL (O, 160 beds) 795 Middle Street, Fall River, MA, Zip 02721–1798; tel. 508/674–5741; Michael Bushell, President
Web address: www.saintanneshospital.org

ST. ELIZABETH'S MEDICAL CENTER (O, 338 beds) 736 Cambridge Street, Brighton, MA, Zip 02135–2997; tel. 617/789–3000; Craig T. Williams, President

OHIO: HILLSIDE REHABILITATION HOSPITAL (O, 65 beds) 8747 Squires Lane NE, Warren, OH, Zip 44484–1649; tel. 330/841–3700; Krista McFadden, Interim Chief Executive Officer
Web address: www.https://valleycareofohio.steward.org

TRUMBULL MEMORIAL HOSPITAL (O, 292 beds) 1350 East Market Street, Warren, OH, Zip 44483–6628; tel. 330/841–9011; Ronald L. Bierman, Chief Executive Officer
Web address: www.https://trumbullmemorial.org/?_ga=2.209137234.1564767671.1497292183–315051339.1497292183

PENNSYLVANIA: EASTON HOSPITAL (O, 196 beds) 250 South 21st Street, Easton, PA, Zip 18042–3892; tel. 610/250–4000; Linda J. Grass, President

SHARON REGIONAL MEDICAL CENTER (O, 218 beds) 740 East State Street, Sharon, PA, Zip 16146–3395; tel. 724/983–3911; Joseph G. . Hugar, President
Web address: https://www.sharonregionalmedical.org

TEXAS: MEDICAL CENTER OF SOUTHEAST TEXAS (O, 17 beds) 6025 Metropolitan Drive, Beaumont, TX, Zip 77706–2407; tel. 409/617–7700; Becky Ames, Chief Executive Officer
Web address: www.medicalcentersetexas.com/

ODESSA REGIONAL MEDICAL CENTER (O, 213 beds) 520 East Sixth Street, Odessa, TX, Zip 79761–4565, Mailing Address: P.O. Box 4859, Zip 79760–4859, tel. 432/582–8000; Stacey L. Gerig, Chief Executive Officer

SCENIC MOUNTAIN MEDICAL CENTER (O, 82 beds) 1601 West 11th Place, Big Spring, TX, Zip 79720–4198; tel. 432/263–1211; Emma Krabill, Chief Executive Officer
Web address: www.smmccares.com

SOUTHWEST GENERAL HOSPITAL (O, 242 beds) 7400 Barlite Boulevard, San Antonio, TX, Zip 78224–1399; tel. 210/921–2000; P Craig. Desmond, Chief Executive Officer

ST. JOSEPH MEDICAL CENTER (O, 463 beds) 1401 St Joseph Parkway, Houston, TX, Zip 77002–8301; tel. 713/757–1000; Kimberly S. Bassett, R.N., President
Web address: www.sjmctx.com

THE MEDICAL CENTER OF SOUTHEAST TEXAS (O, 156 beds) 2555 Jimmy Johnson Boulevard, Port Arthur, TX, Zip 77640–2007; tel. 409/724–7389; Carl Bo"". Beaudry, President
Web address: www.medicalcentersetexas.com

WADLEY REGIONAL MEDICAL CENTER (O, 178 beds) 1000 Pine Street, Texarkana, TX, Zip 75501–5170; tel. 903/798–8000; Thomas D. Gilbert, FACHE, Chief Executive Officer

UTAH: DAVIS HOSPITAL AND MEDICAL CENTER (O, 221 beds) 1600 West Antelope Drive, Layton, UT, Zip 84041–1142; tel. 801/807–1000; Michael Jensen, Chief Executive Officer
Web address: www.davishospital.com

JORDAN VALLEY MEDICAL CENTER WEST VALLEY CAMPUS (O, 101 beds) 3460 South Pioneer Parkway, West Valley City, UT, Zip 84120 2049; tel. 801/561–8888; Jon R. Butterfield, Administrator and Chief Executive Officer

JORDAN VALLEY MEDICAL CENTER (O, 183 beds) 3580 West 9000 South, West Jordan, UT, Zip 84088–8812; tel. 801/561–8888; Jon Butterfield, Administrator and Chief Executive Officer
Web address: www.jordanvalleymc.com

SALT LAKE REGIONAL MEDICAL CENTER (O, 132 beds) 1050 East South Temple, Salt Lake City, UT, Zip 84102–1507; tel. 801/350–4111; Dale Johns, FACHE, Chief Executive Officer

Owned, leased, sponsored:	33 hospitals	5877 beds
Contract-managed:	0 hospitals	0 beds
Totals:	33 hospitals	5877 beds

0858: STRATEGIC BEHAVIORAL HEALTH, LLC (IO)
8295 Tournament Drive, Suite 201, Memphis, TN, Zip 38125–8913; tel. 901/969–3100; Jim Shaheen, President

COLORADO: PEAK VIEW BEHAVIORAL HEALTH (O, 112 beds) 7353 Sisters Grove, Colorado Springs, CO, Zip 80923–2615; tel. 719/444–8484; Dan Zarecky, Chief Executive Officer

NEVADA: MONTEVISTA HOSPITAL (O, 202 beds) 5900 West Rochelle Avenue, Las Vegas, NV, Zip 89103–3327; tel. 702/364–1111; Curtis Ohashi, Chief Executive Officer
Web address: www.montevistahospital.com

For explanation of codes following names, see page B2.
★ Indicates Type III membership in the American Hospital Association.

NEW MEXICO: PEAK BEHAVIORAL HEALTH SERVICES (O, 120 beds) 5065 McNutt Road, Santa Teresa, NM, Zip 88008–9442; tel. 575/589–3000; Peggy Cunningham, Chief Executive Officer

NORTH CAROLINA: STRATEGIC BEHAVIORAL HEALTH – CHARLOTTE (O, 60 beds) 1715 Sharon Road West, Charlotte, NC, Zip 28210–5663; tel. 704/944–0650; George G. Boykin, Chief Executive Officer
Web address: www.sbccharlotte.com/

STRATEGIC BEHAVIORAL HEALTH – RALEIGH (O, 50 beds) 3200 Waterfield Drive, Garner, NC, Zip 27529–7727; tel. 919/800–4400; Matt Doyle, Chief Executive Officer

STRATEGIC BEHAVIORAL HEALTH – WILMINGTON (O, 112 beds) 2050 Mercantile Drive, Leland, NC, Zip 28451–4053; tel. 910/371–2500; Daniel Kern, Chief Executive Officer
Web address: www.sbcwilmington.com/

TEXAS: ROCK PRAIRIE BEHAVIORAL HEALTH (O, 72 beds) 3550 Normand Drive, College Station, TX, Zip 77845–6399; tel. 979/703–8848; Orvin Fillman, Dr.PH, Chief Executive Officer
Web address: www.rockprairiebh.com/

WISCONSIN: WILLOW CREEK BEHAVIORAL HEALTH (O, 72 beds) 1351 Ontario Road, Green Bay, WI, Zip 54311–8302; tel. 920/328–1220; Teena Ahuja, Interim Chief Executive Officer and Regional Vice President of Operations

Owned, leased, sponsored:	8 hospitals	800 beds
Contract-managed:	0 hospitals	0 beds
Totals:	8 hospitals	800 beds

0517: SUCCESS HEALTHCARE (IO)
999 Yamato Road, 3rd Floor, Boca Raton, FL, Zip 33431–4477; tel. 561/869–6300; Peter R. Baronoff, President and Chief Executive Officer
(Independent Hospital System)

CALIFORNIA: SILVER LAKE MEDICAL CENTER (O, 175 beds) 1711 West Temple Street, Los Angeles, CA, Zip 90026–5421; tel. 213/989–6100; Brent A. Cope, Chief Executive Officer
Web address: www.silverlakemc.com

MISSOURI: ST. ALEXIUS HOSPITAL – BROADWAY CAMPUS (O, 190 beds) 3933 South Broadway, Saint Louis, MO, Zip 63118–4601; tel. 314/865–7000; Russell Kraeger, M.D., Interim Chief Executive Officer
Web address: www.stalexiushospital.com

Owned, leased, sponsored:	2 hospitals	365 beds
Contract-managed:	0 hospitals	0 beds
Totals:	2 hospitals	365 beds

0399: SUMMA HEALTH (NP)
1077 Gorge Boulevard, Akron, OH, Zip 44310; tel. 330/375–3000; T. Clifford Deveny, M.D., Interim Chief Executive Officer
(Centralized Physician/Insurance Health System)

OHIO: SUMMA HEALTH SYSTEM (O, 623 beds) 525 East Market Street, Akron, OH, Zip 44304–1619; tel. 330/375–3000; David Custodio, M.D., President Summa Health System Akron
Web address: www.summahealth.org

SUMMA REHAB HOSPITAL (O, 60 beds) 29 North Adams Street, Akron, OH, Zip 44304–1641; tel. 330/572–7300; Cheryl Henthorn, Chief Executive Officer
Web address: www.summarehabhospital.com/

Owned, leased, sponsored:	2 hospitals	683 beds
Contract-managed:	0 hospitals	0 beds
Totals:	2 hospitals	683 beds

★8795: SUTTER HEALTH (NP)
2200 River Plaza Drive, Sacramento, CA, Zip 95833–4134; tel. 916/733–8800; Sarah Krevans, President and Chief Executive Officer
(Centralized Health System)

CALIFORNIA: ALTA BATES SUMMIT MEDICAL CENTER – SUMMIT CAMPUS (O, 333 beds) 350 Hawthorne Avenue, Oakland, CA, Zip 94609–3100; tel. 510/655–4000; Charles Prosper, Chief Executive Officer
Web address: www.altabatessummit.com

ALTA BATES SUMMIT MEDICAL CENTER (O, 441 beds) 2450 Ashby Avenue, Berkeley, CA, Zip 94705–2067; tel. 510/204–4444; Julie A. Petrini, Chief Executive Officer
Web address: www.altabatessummit.org/

CALIFORNIA PACIFIC MEDICAL CENTER-DAVIES CAMPUS (O, 154 beds) Castro and Duboce Streets, San Francisco, CA, Zip 94114; tel. 415/600–6000; Mary Lanier, Vice President, Post Acute Services and Site Administrator
Web address: www.cpmc.org

CALIFORNIA PACIFIC MEDICAL CENTER-ST. LUKE'S CAMPUS (O, 175 beds) 3555 Cesar Chavez Street, San Francisco, CA, Zip 94110–4403; tel. 415/600–6000; Warren S. Browner, M.D., M.P.H., Chief Executive Officer
Web address: www.stlukes-sf.org

CALIFORNIA PACIFIC MEDICAL CENTER (O, 642 beds) 2333 Buchanan Street, San Francisco, CA, Zip 94115–1925, Mailing Address: P.O. Box 7999, Zip 94120–7999, tel. 415/600–6000; Warren S. Browner, M.D., M.P.H., Chief Executive Officer

EDEN MEDICAL CENTER (O, 130 beds) 20103 Lake Chabot Road, Castro Valley, CA, Zip 94546–5305; tel. 510/537–1234; Stephen Gray, Chief Executive Officer
Web address: www.edenmedcenter.org

MEMORIAL HOSPITAL LOS BANOS (O, 44 beds) 520 West 'I' Street, Los Banos, CA, Zip 93635–3498; tel. 209/826–0591; Doug Archer, Administrator
Web address: www.memoriallosbanos.org/

MEMORIAL MEDICAL CENTER (O, 222 beds) 1700 Coffee Road, Modesto, CA, Zip 95355–2869, Mailing Address: P.O. Box 942, Zip 95353–0942, tel. 209/526–4500; Eugene Patrizio, Chief Executive Officer
Web address: www.memorialmedicalcenter.org

MENLO PARK SURGICAL HOSPITAL (O, 16 beds) 570 Willow Road, Menlo Park, CA, Zip 94025–2617; tel. 650/324–8500; Jeanette Engle-Ramirez, Chief Executive Officer

MILLS-PENINSULA HEALTH SERVICES (O, 266 beds) 1501 Trousdale Drive, Burlingame, CA, Zip 94010–3282; tel. 650/696–5400; Janet Wagner, R.N., Chief Executive Officer
Web address: www.mills-peninsula.org

NOVATO COMMUNITY HOSPITAL (O, 40 beds) 180 Rowland Way, Novato, CA, Zip 94945–5009, Mailing Address: P.O. Box 1108, Zip 94948–1108, tel. 415/209–1300; Michael L. Purvis, Chief Executive Officer
Web address: www.novatocommunity.sutterhealth.org

STANISLAUS SURGICAL HOSPITAL (O, 23 beds) 1421 Oakdale Road, Modesto, CA, Zip 95355–3356; tel. 209/572–2700; Douglas V. Johnson, Chief Executive Officer

SUTTER AMADOR HOSPITAL (O, 52 beds) 200 Mission Boulevard, Jackson, CA, Zip 95642–2564; tel. 209/223–7500; Thomas C. Dickson, Chief Executive Officer
Web address: www.sutteramador.org

SUTTER AUBURN FAITH HOSPITAL (O, 72 beds) 11815 Education Street, Auburn, CA, Zip 95602–2410; tel. 530/888–4500; Mitchell J. Hanna, Chief Executive Officer

SUTTER CENTER FOR PSYCHIATRY (O, 71 beds) 7700 Folsom Boulevard, Sacramento, CA, Zip 95826–2608; tel. 916/386–3000; John W. Boyd, PsyD, Chief Executive Officer
Web address: www.sutterpsychiatry.org

SUTTER COAST HOSPITAL (O, 49 beds) 800 East Washington Boulevard, Crescent City, CA, Zip 95531–8359; tel. 707/464–8511; Mitchell J. Hanna, Chief Executive Officer

SUTTER DAVIS HOSPITAL (O, 48 beds) 2000 Sutter Place, Davis, CA, Zip 95616–6201, Mailing Address: P.O. Box 1617, Zip 95617–1617, tel. 530/756–6440; Rachael McKinney, FACHE, Chief Executive Officer
Web address: www.sutterhealth.org

SUTTER DELTA MEDICAL CENTER (O, 132 beds) 3901 Lone Tree Way, Antioch, CA, Zip 94509–6253; tel. 925/779–7200; Sherie C. Hickman, Chief Executive Officer

SUTTER LAKESIDE HOSPITAL (O, 25 beds) 5176 Hill Road East, Lakeport, CA, Zip 95453–6300; tel. 707/262–5000; Dan Peterson, Chief Administrative Officer
Web address: www.sutterlakeside.org

For explanation of codes following names, see page B2.
★ Indicates Type III membership in the American Hospital Association.

SUTTER MATERNITY AND SURGERY CENTER OF SANTA CRUZ (O, 30 beds) 2900 Chanticleer Avenue, Santa Cruz, CA, Zip 95065–1816; tel. 831/477–2200; Trina White, President and Chief Executive Officer

SUTTER MEDICAL CENTER, SACRAMENTO (O, 523 beds) 2801 'L' Street, Sacramento, CA, Zip 95816–5680; tel. 916/454–3333; David Cheney, Chief Executive Officer
Web address: www.sutterhealth.org

SUTTER OAKS NURSING CENTER (O, 100 beds) 2600 L Street, Sacramento, CA, Zip 95816–5612; tel. 916/552–2200; John W. Boyd, PsyD, Chief Administrative Officer

SUTTER ROSEVILLE MEDICAL CENTER (O, 328 beds) One Medical Plaza Drive, Roseville, CA, Zip 95661–3037; tel. 916/781–1000; Brian Alexander, Chief Executive Officer
Web address: www.sutterroseville.org

SUTTER SANTA ROSA REGIONAL HOSPITAL (O, 84 beds) 30 Mark West Springs Road, Santa Rosa, CA, Zip 95403; tel. 707/576–4000; Mike Purvis, Chief Administrative Officer
Web address: www.sutterhealth.org

SUTTER SOLANO MEDICAL CENTER (O, 108 beds) 300 Hospital Drive, CA, Zip 94589–2574, Mailing Address: P.O. Box 3189, Zip 94590–0669, tel. 707/554–4444; Abhishek Dosi, Chief Executive Officer
Web address: www.suttersolano.org

SUTTER SURGICAL HOSPITAL – NORTH VALLEY (O, 14 beds) 455 Plumas Boulevard, Yuba City, CA, Zip 95991–5074; tel. 530/749–5700; Shawndra Simpson, Interim Chief Executive Officer

SUTTER TRACY COMMUNITY HOSPITAL (O, 77 beds) 1420 North Tracy Boulevard, Tracy, CA, Zip 95376–3497; tel. 209/835–1500; David M. Thompson, Chief Executive Officer
Web address: www.suttertracy.org

HAWAII: SUTTER HEALTH KAHI MOHALA (O, 76 beds) 91–2301 Old Fort Weaver Road, Ewa Beach, HI, Zip 96706–3602; tel. 808/671–8511; Leonard Licina, Chief Executive Officer
Web address: www.kahimohala.org

Owned, leased, sponsored:	28 hospitals	4275 beds
Contract-managed:	0 hospitals	0 beds
Totals:	28 hospitals	4275 beds

★0871: SWEDISH HEALTH SERVICES (NP)
747 Broadway, Seattle, WA, Zip 98122–4379; tel. 206/386–6000; R. Guy Hudson, Chief Executive Officer
(Independent Hospital System)

WASHINGTON: SWEDISH MEDICAL CENTER-CHERRY HILL CAMPUS (O, 208 beds) 500 17th Avenue, Seattle, WA, Zip 98122–5711; tel. 206/320–2000; June Altaras, R.N., Chief Executive Officer
Web address: www.swedish.org

SWEDISH MEDICAL CENTER-FIRST HILL (O, 689 beds) 747 Broadway, Seattle, WA, Zip 98122–4307; tel. 206/386–6000; June Altaras, R.N., Chief Executive Officer

SWEDISH/EDMONDS (O, 185 beds) 21601 76th Avenue West, Edmonds, WA, Zip 98026–7506; tel. 425/640–4000; Sarah Zabel, Vice President, Operations
Web address: www.swedish.org

SWEDISH/ISSAQUAH (O, 153 beds) 751 NE Blakely Drive, Issaquah, WA, Zip 98029–6201; tel. 425/313–4000; Guy Hudson, Chief Executive Officer
Web address: www.swedish.org/issaquah

Owned, leased, sponsored:	4 hospitals	1235 beds
Contract-managed:	0 hospitals	0 beds
Totals:	4 hospitals	1235 beds

★0379: TAHOE FOREST HEALTH SYSTEM (NP)
10121 Pine Avenue, Truckee, CA, Zip 96161–4835; tel. 530/587–6011; Harry Weis, Chief Executive Officer

CALIFORNIA: TAHOE FOREST HOSPITAL DISTRICT (O, 62 beds) 10121 Pine Avenue, Truckee, CA, Zip 96161–4856, Mailing Address: P.O. Box 759, Zip 96160–0759, tel. 530/587–6011; Harry Weis, Chief Executive Officer
Web address: www.tfhd.com

NEVADA: INCLINE VILLAGE COMMUNITY HOSPITAL (O, 6 beds) 880 Alder Avenue, Incline Village, NV, Zip 89451–8335; tel. 775/833–4100; Judy Newland, R.N., Chief Nursing Officer

Owned, leased, sponsored:	2 hospitals	68 beds
Contract-managed:	0 hospitals	0 beds
Totals:	2 hospitals	68 beds

★0341: TANNER HEALTH SYSTEM (NP)
705 Dixie Street, Carrollton, GA, Zip 30117–3818; tel. 770/836–9580; Loy M. Howard, President and Chief Executive Officer

ALABAMA: TANNER MEDICAL CENTER/EAST ALABAMA (O, 15 beds) 1032 South Main Street, Wedowee, AL, Zip 36278–7428; tel. 256/357–2111; Jerry Morris, Administrator
Web address: www.tanner.org/eastalabama

GEORGIA: HIGGINS GENERAL HOSPITAL (O, 23 beds) 200 Allen Memorial Drive, Bremen, GA, Zip 30110–2012; tel. 770/824–2000; Jerry Morris, Administrator

TANNER MEDICAL CENTER-CARROLLTON (O, 146 beds) 705 Dixie Street, Carrollton, GA, Zip 30117–3818; tel. 770/836–9666; Loy M. Howard, Chief Operating Officer
Web address: www.tanner.org

TANNER MEDICAL CENTER-VILLA RICA (O, 132 beds) 601 Dallas Highway, Villa Rica, GA, Zip 30180–1202; tel. 770/456–3000; Eric Dalton, Administrator
Web address: www.tanner.org

Owned, leased, sponsored:	4 hospitals	316 beds
Contract-managed:	0 hospitals	0 beds
Totals:	4 hospitals	316 beds

★0169: TEMPLE UNIVERSITY HEALTH SYSTEM (NP)
3509 North Broad Street, 9th Floor, Philadelphia, PA, Zip 19140–4105; tel. 215/707–0900; Larry Kaiser, M.D., President and Chief Executive Officer
(Centralized Health System)

PENNSYLVANIA: FOX CHASE CANCER CENTER AMERICAN ONCOLOGIC HOSPITAL (O, 67 beds) 333 Cottman Avenue, Philadelphia, PA, Zip 19111–2434; tel. 215/728–6900; Richard Fisher, M.D., President and Chief Executive Officer
Web address: www.fccc.org

JEANES HOSPITAL (O, 146 beds) 7600 Central Avenue, Philadelphia, PA, Zip 19111–2499; tel. 215/728–2000; Marc P. Hurowitz, D.O., President and Chief Executive Officer
Web address: www.jeanes.com

TEMPLE UNIVERSITY HOSPITAL (O, 732 beds) 3401 North Broad Street, Philadelphia, PA, Zip 19140–5103; tel. 215/707–2000; Michael A. Young, FACHE, Chief Executive Officer
Web address: www.tuh.templehealth.org/content/default.htm

Owned, leased, sponsored:	3 hospitals	945 beds
Contract-managed:	0 hospitals	0 beds
Totals:	3 hospitals	945 beds

★0919: TENET HEALTHCARE CORPORATION (IO)
1445 Ross Avenue, Suite 1400, Dallas, TX, Zip 75202–2703, Mailing Address: P.O. Box 1390369, Zip 75313–9036, tel. 469/893–2200; Saumya Sutaria, M.D., Chief Operating Officer
(Decentralized Health System)

ALABAMA: BROOKWOOD BAPTIST MEDICAL CENTER (O, 607 beds) 2010 Brookwood Medical Center Drive, Birmingham, AL, Zip 35209–6875; tel. 205/877–1000; Timothy Puthoff, Chief Executive Officer

CITIZENS BAPTIST MEDICAL CENTER (O, 72 beds) 604 Stone Avenue, Talladega, AL, Zip 35160–2217, Mailing Address: P.O. Box 978, Zip 35161–0978, tel. 256/362–8111; Frank D. Thomas, Chief Executive Officer
Web address: www.brookwoodbaptisthealth.org

For explanation of codes following names, see page B2.
★ Indicates Type III membership in the American Hospital Association.

PRINCETON BAPTIST MEDICAL CENTER (O, 311 beds) 701 Princeton Avenue SW, Birmingham, AL, Zip 35211–1303; tel. 205/783–3000; Michael Neuendorf, Chief Executive Officer

SHELBY BAPTIST MEDICAL CENTER (O, 231 beds) 1000 First Street North, Alabaster, AL, Zip 35007–8703; tel. 205/620–8100; Daniel Listi, Chief Executive Officer
Web address: www.brookwoodbaptisthealth.com

WALKER BAPTIST MEDICAL CENTER (O, 178 beds) 3400 Highway 78 East, Jasper, AL, Zip 35501–8907, Mailing Address: P.O. Box 3547, Zip 35502–3547, tel. 205/387–4000; Robert A. Phillips, Chief Executive Officer
Web address: www.bhsala.com

ARIZONA: ABRAZO ARROWHEAD CAMPUS (O, 234 beds) 18701 North 67th Avenue, Glendale, AZ, Zip 85308–7100; tel. 623/561–1000; Jeff Patterson, Chief Executive Officer

ABRAZO CENTRAL CAMPUS (O, 172 beds) 2000 West Bethany Home Road, Phoenix, AZ, Zip 85015–2443; tel. 602/249–0212; Frank L. Molinaro, Chief Executive Officer
Web address: www.abrazohealth.com

ABRAZO SCOTTSDALE CAMPUS (O, 116 beds) 3929 East Bell Road, Phoenix, AZ, Zip 85032–2196; tel. 602/923–5000; Frank L. Molinaro, Chief Executive Officer
Web address: www.abrazoscottsdale.com

ABRAZO WEST CAMPUS (O, 188 beds) 13677 West McDowell Road, Goodyear, AZ, Zip 85395–2635; tel. 623/882–1500; Christina E. Oh, Chief Executive Officer

CARONDELET HOLY CROSS HOSPITAL (O, 25 beds) 1171 West Target Range Road, Nogales, AZ, Zip 85621–2415; tel. 520/285–3000; Debbie Knapheide, MSN, Site Administrator, Chief Nursing Officer and Chief Operating Officer
Web address: www.carondelet.org

CARONDELET ST. JOSEPH'S HOSPITAL (O, 486 beds) 350 North Wilmot Road, Tucson, AZ, Zip 85711–2678; tel. 520/873–3000; Mark A. Benz, President and Chief Executive Officer
Web address: www.carondelet.org

CARONDELET ST. MARY'S HOSPITAL (O, 300 beds) 1601 West St Mary's Road, Tucson, AZ, Zip 85745–2682; tel. 520/872–3000; Mark A. Benz, President and Chief Executive Officer
Web address: www.carondelet.org

CALIFORNIA: DESERT REGIONAL MEDICAL CENTER (L, 385 beds) 1150 North Indian Canyon Drive, Palm Springs, CA, Zip 92262–4872; tel. 760/323–6511; Michele Finney, Chief Executive Officer
Web address: www.desertregional.com

DOCTORS HOSPITAL OF MANTECA (O, 56 beds) 1205 East North Street, Manteca, CA, Zip 95336–4900; tel. 209/823–3111; Brandon May, Chief Executive Officer

DOCTORS MEDICAL CENTER OF MODESTO (O, 461 beds) 1441 Florida Avenue, Modesto, CA, Zip 95350–4418, Mailing Address: P.O. Box 4138, Zip 95352–4138, tel. 209/578–1211; Warren J. Kirk, Chief Executive Officer
Web address: www.dmc-modesto.com

EMANUEL MEDICAL CENTER (O, 209 beds) 825 Delbon Avenue, Turlock, CA, Zip 95382–2016, Mailing Address: P.O. Box 819005, Zip 95382, tel. 209/667–4200; Lani Dickinson, Chief Executive Officer
Web address: www.emanuelmedicalcenter.org

FOUNTAIN VALLEY REGIONAL HOSPITAL AND MEDICAL CENTER (O, 380 beds) 17100 Euclid Street, Fountain Valley, CA, Zip 92708–4043; tel. 714/966–7200; Kenneth D. McFarland, Chief Executive Officer

HI-DESERT MEDICAL CENTER (L, 179 beds) 6601 White Feather Road, Joshua Tree, CA, Zip 92284; tel. 760/366–3711; Karen Faulis, Chief Executive Officer
Web address: www.hdmc.org

JOHN F. KENNEDY MEMORIAL HOSPITAL (O, 145 beds) 47111 Monroe Street, Indio, CA, Zip 92201–6799; tel. 760/347–6191; Gary Honts, Chief Executive Officer

LAKEWOOD REGIONAL MEDICAL CENTER (O, 111 beds) 3700 East South Street, Lakewood, CA, Zip 90712–1498, Mailing Address: P.O. Box 6070, Zip 90712, tel. 562/531–2550; John A. Grah, FACHE, Chief Executive Officer
Web address: www.lakewoodregional.com

LOS ALAMITOS MEDICAL CENTER (O, 120 beds) 3751 Katella Avenue, Los Alamitos, CA, Zip 90720–3164; tel. 562/598–1311; Kent G. Clayton, Chief Executive Officer
Web address: www.losalamitosmedctr.com

PLACENTIA-LINDA HOSPITAL (O, 74 beds) 1301 North Rose Drive, Placentia, CA, Zip 92870–3899; tel. 714/993–2000; Kent G. Clayton, Interim Chief Executive Officer
Web address: www.placentialinda.com

SAN RAMON REGIONAL MEDICAL CENTER (O, 123 beds) 6001 Norris Canyon Road, San Ramon, CA, Zip 94583–5400; tel. 925/275–9200; Ann Lucena, Chief Executive Officer

SIERRA VISTA REGIONAL MEDICAL CENTER (O, 164 beds) 1010 Murray Avenue, San Luis Obispo, CA, Zip 93405–1806, Mailing Address: P.O. Box 1367, Zip 93405, tel. 805/546–7600; Mark P. Lisa, FACHE, Chief Executive Officer
Web address: www.sierravistaregional.com

TWIN CITIES COMMUNITY HOSPITAL (O, 89 beds) 1100 Las Tablas Road, Templeton, CA, Zip 93465–9796; tel. 805/434–3500; Mark P. Lisa, FACHE, Chief Executive Officer
Web address: www.twincitieshospital.com

FLORIDA: CORAL GABLES HOSPITAL (O, 256 beds) 3100 Douglas Road, Coral Gables, FL, Zip 33134–6914; tel. 305/445–8461; Cristina Jimenez, Chief Executive Officer
Web address: www.coralgableshospital.com

DELRAY MEDICAL CENTER (O, 536 beds) 5352 Linton Boulevard, Delray Beach, FL, Zip 33484–6580; tel. 561/498–4440; Margaret Gill, Chief Executive Officer

GOOD SAMARITAN MEDICAL CENTER (O, 226 beds) 1309 North Flagler Drive, West Palm Beach, FL, Zip 33401–3499; tel. 561/655–5511; Tara McCoy, Chief Executive Officer
Web address: www.goodsamaritanmc.com

HIALEAH HOSPITAL (O, 191 beds) 651 East 25th Street, Hialeah, FL, Zip 33013–3878; tel. 305/693–6100; Michael J. Bell, Chief Executive Officer

NORTH SHORE MEDICAL CENTER (O, 258 beds) 1100 NW 95th Street, Miami, FL, Zip 33150–2098; tel. 305/835–6000; Mark Racicot, Chief Executive Officer
Web address: www.northshoremedical.com

PALM BEACH GARDENS MEDICAL CENTER (L, 202 beds) 3360 Burns Road, Palm Beach Gardens, FL, Zip 33410–4323; tel. 561/622–1411; Teresa C. Urquhart, Chief Executive Officer
Web address: www.pbgmc.com

PALMETTO GENERAL HOSPITAL (O, 360 beds) 2001 West 68th Street, Hialeah, FL, Zip 33016–1898; tel. 305/823–5000; Ana J. Mederos, Chief Executive Officer
Web address: www.palmettogeneral.com

ST. MARY'S MEDICAL CENTER (O, 460 beds) 901 45th Street, West Palm Beach, FL, Zip 33407–2495; tel. 561/844–6300; Gabrielle Finley-Hazle, Chief Executive Officer

WEST BOCA MEDICAL CENTER (O, 195 beds) 21644 State Road 7, Boca Raton, FL, Zip 33428–1899; tel. 561/488–8000; Mitchell S. Feldman, Chief Executive Officer
Web address: www.westbocamedctr.com

MASSACHUSETTS: METROWEST MEDICAL CENTER (O, 160 beds) 115 Lincoln Street, Framingham, MA, Zip 01702–6342; tel. 508/383–1000; Andrew D. Harding, R.N., Chief Executive Officer

SAINT VINCENT HOSPITAL (O, 283 beds) 123 Summer Street, Worcester, MA, Zip 01608–1216; tel. 508/363–5000; Carolyn Jackson, Chief Executive Officer
Web address: www.stvincenthospital.com

MICHIGAN: DMC – CHILDREN'S HOSPITAL OF MICHIGAN (O, 227 beds) 3901 Beaubien Street, Detroit, MI, Zip 48201–2119; tel. 313/745–5852; Luanne T. Ewald, Chief Executive Officer
Web address: www.chmkids.org

DMC – DETROIT RECEIVING HOSPITAL (O, 187 beds) 4201 Saint Antoine Street, Detroit, MI, Zip 48201–2153; tel. 313/745–3000; Scott Steiner, FACHE, Chief Executive Officer
Web address: www.dmc.org

DMC – REHABILITATION INSTITUTE OF MICHIGAN (O, 69 beds) 261 Mack Avenue, Detroit, MI, Zip 48201–2495; tel. 313/745–1203; William Restum, Chief Executive Officer
Web address: www.rimrehab.org

DMC – SINAI-GRACE HOSPITAL (O, 285 beds) 6071 West Outer Drive, Detroit, MI, Zip 48235–2679; tel. 313/966–3300; Conrad L. Mallett Jr, Chief Executive Officer

For explanation of codes following names, see page B2.
★ Indicates Type III membership in the American Hospital Association.

DMC HARPER UNIVERSITY HOSPITAL (O, 348 beds) 3990 John 'R' Street, Detroit, MI, Zip 48201–2018; tel. 313/745–8040; Scott Steiner, FACHE, Chief Executive Officer
Web address: www.harperhospital.org

DMC HURON VALLEY-SINAI HOSPITAL (O, 156 beds) 1 William Carls Drive, Commerce Township, MI, Zip 48382–2201; tel. 248/937–3300; Karima Bentounsi, Chief Executive Officer
Web address: www.hvsh.org

SOUTH CAROLINA: COASTAL CAROLINA HOSPITAL (O, 35 beds) 1000 Medical Center Drive, Hardeeville, SC, Zip 29927–3446; tel. 843/784–8000; Joel Taylor, Chief Executive Officer

EAST COOPER MEDICAL CENTER (O, 140 beds) 2000 Hospital Drive, Mount Pleasant, SC, Zip 29464–3764; tel. 843/881–0100; Patrick Downes, Chief Executive Officer
Web address: www.eastcoopermedctr.com

HILTON HEAD HOSPITAL (O, 93 beds) 25 Hospital Center Boulevard, Hilton Head Island, SC, Zip 29926–2738; tel. 843/681–6122; Jeremy L. Clark, Market Chief Executive Officer

PIEDMONT MEDICAL CENTER (O, 279 beds) 222 Herlong Avenue, Rock Hill, SC, Zip 29732; tel. 803/329–1234; Mark Nosacka, Chief Executive Officer
Web address: www.piedmontmedicalcenter.com

TENNESSEE: SAINT FRANCIS HOSPITAL-BARTLETT (O, 156 beds) 2986 Kate Bond Road, Bartlett, TN, Zip 38133–4003; tel. 901/820–7000; Christopher Locke, Chief Executive Officer
Web address: www.saintfrancisbartlett.com

SAINT FRANCIS HOSPITAL (O, 415 beds) 5959 Park Avenue, Memphis, TN, Zip 38119–5198; tel. 901/765–1000; Audrey Gregory, R.N., MSN, Chief Executive Officer
Web address: www.saintfrancishosp.com

TEXAS: BAPTIST MEDICAL CENTER (O, 1531 beds) 111 Dallas Street, San Antonio, TX, Zip 78205–1230; tel. 210/297–7000; Matt Stone, President and Chief Executive Officer
Web address: www.baptisthealthsystem.com

BAYLOR SCOTT & WHITE MEDICAL CENTER – SUNNYVALE (O, 70 beds) 231 South Collins Road, Sunnyvale, TX, Zip 75182–4624; tel. 972/892–3000; Jon Duckert, FACHE, Chief Executive Officer
Web address: www.BaylorScottandWhite.com/Sunnyvale

NACOGDOCHES MEDICAL CENTER (O, 117 beds) 4920 NE Stallings Drive, Nacogdoches, TX, Zip 75965–1200; tel. 936/569–9481; Philip Koovakada, Chief Executive Officer

RESOLUTE HEALTH (O, 70 beds) 555 Creekside Crossing, New Braunfels, TX, Zip 78130–2594; tel. 830/500–6000; Mark L. Bernard, Chief Executive Officer
Web address: www.resolutehealth.com

THE HOSPITALS OF PROVIDENCE EAST CAMPUS (O, 182 beds) 3280 Joe Battle Boulevard, El Paso, TX, Zip 79938–2622; tel. 915/832–2000; Monica Vargas-Mahar, FACHE, Chief Executive Officer

THE HOSPITALS OF PROVIDENCE MEMORIAL CAMPUS (O, 332 beds) 2001 North Oregon Street, El Paso, TX, Zip 79902–3368; tel. 915/577–6625; Nicholas R. Tejeda, FACHE, Market Chief Executive Officer
Web address: www.thehospitalsofprovidence.com

THE HOSPITALS OF PROVIDENCE SIERRA CAMPUS (O, 180 beds) 1625 Medical Center Drive, El Paso, TX, Zip 79902–5005; tel. 915/747–4000; Rob Anderson, Chief Executive Officer

THE HOSPITALS OF PROVIDENCE TRANSMOUNTAIN CAMPUS (O, 106 beds) 2000 Transmountain Road, El Paso, TX, Zip 79911; tel. 915/877–8300; Tasha Hopper, Chief Executive Officer
Web address: https://www.thehospitalsofprovidence.com/our-locations/transmountain

VALLEY BAPTIST MEDICAL CENTER-BROWNSVILLE (O, 225 beds) P.O. Box 708, Rio Hondo, TX, Zip 78583, Mailing Address: P.O. Box 3590, Brownsville, Zip 78523–3590; tel. 956/698–5400; Leslie Bingham, Senior Vice President and Chief Executive Officer
Web address: www.valleybaptist.net/brownsville/index.htm

VALLEY BAPTIST MEDICAL CENTER-HARLINGEN (O, 432 beds) 2101 Pease Street, Harlingen, TX, Zip 78550–8307, Mailing Address: P O Drawer 2588, Zip 78551–2588, tel. 956/389–1100; Manuel Vela, President and Chief Executive Officer

Owned, leased, sponsored:	58 hospitals	14178 beds
Contract-managed:	0 hospitals	0 beds
Totals:	58 hospitals	14178 beds

0876: TENNESSEE HEALTH MANAGEMENT (IO)
52 West Eighth Street, Parsons, TN, Zip 38363–4656, Mailing Address: PO Box 10, Zip 38363–0010, tel. 731/847–6343; Dennis Berry, Chief Executive Officer

ALABAMA: UNITY PSYCHIATRIC CARE-HUNTSVILLE (O, 20 beds) 5315 Millennium Drive NW, Huntsville, AL, Zip 35806–2458; tel. 256/964–6700; Bradley Moss, Administrator
Web address: www.thmgt.com/locations/behavioral-healthcare-center-at-huntsville

TENNESSEE: UNITY PSYCHIATRIC CARE-CLARKSVILLE (O, 26 beds) 930 Professional Park Drive, Clarksville, TN, Zip 37040–5136; tel. 931/538–6420; Jennifer Robinson, Administrator

UNITY PSYCHIATRIC CARE-COLUMBIA (O, 16 beds) 1400 Rosewood Drive, Columbia, TN, Zip 38401–4878; tel. 931/388–6573; Paula Chennault, Administrator
Web address: www.unitypsych.com

UNITY PSYCHIATRIC CARE-MARTIN (O, 16 beds) 458 Hannings Lane, Martin, TN, Zip 38237–3308; tel. 731/588–2830; Carrie Brawley, Administrator
Web address: www.unitypsych.com

Owned, leased, sponsored:	4 hospitals	78 beds
Contract-managed:	0 hospitals	0 beds
Totals:	4 hospitals	78 beds

0020: TEXAS DEPARTMENT OF STATE HEALTH SERVICES (NP)
1100 West 49th Street, Austin, TX, Zip 78756–3199; tel. 512/458–7111; Stacey Thompson, Superintendent
(Independent Hospital System)

TEXAS: AUSTIN STATE HOSPITAL (O, 252 beds) 4110 Guadalupe Street, Austin, TX, Zip 78751–4296; tel. 512/452–0381; Stacey Thompson, Superintendent
Web address: www.dshs.state.tx.us/mhhospitals/austinsh/default.shtm

BIG SPRING STATE HOSPITAL (O, 180 beds) 1901 North Highway 87, Big Spring, TX, Zip 79720–0283; tel. 432/267–8216; Traci Phillips, Superintendent
Web address: www.dshs.state.tx.us/mhhospitals/BigSpringSH/default.shtm

EL PASO PSYCHIATRIC CENTER (O, 74 beds) 4615 Alameda Avenue, El Paso, TX, Zip 79905–2702; tel. 915/532–2202; Zulema Carrillo, Superintendent

KERRVILLE STATE HOSPITAL (O, 218 beds) 721 Thompson Drive, Kerrville, TX, Zip 78028–5154; tel. 830/896–2211; Leigh Ann Fitzpatrick, Superintendent
Web address: www.dshs.state.tx.us/mhhospitals/KerrvilleSH/default.shtm

NORTH TEXAS STATE HOSPITAL (O, 562 beds) Highway 70 Northwest, Vernon, TX, Zip 76384, Mailing Address: P.O. Box 2231, Zip 76385–2231, tel. 940/552–9901; James E. Smith, Superintendent

RIO GRANDE STATE CENTER/SOUTH TEXAS HEALTH CARE SYSTEM (O, 55 beds) 1401 South Rangerville Road, Harlingen, TX, Zip 78552–7638; tel. 956/364–8000; Sonia Hernandez-Keeble, Superintendent
Web address: www.dshs.state.tx.us/mhhospitals/RioGrandeSC/default.shtm

RUSK STATE HOSPITAL (O, 249 beds) 805 North Dickinson, Rusk, TX, Zip 75785–2333, Mailing Address: P.O. Box 318, Zip 75785–0318, tel. 903/683–3421; Brenda Slaton, Superintendent

SAN ANTONIO STATE HOSPITAL (O, 282 beds) 6711 South New Braunfels, Suite 100, San Antonio, TX, Zip 78223–3006; tel. 210/531–7711; Robert C. Arizpe, Superintendent
Web address: www.dshs.state.tx.us/mhhospitals/SanAntonioSH/default.shtm

TERRELL STATE HOSPITAL (O, 288 beds) 1200 East Brin Street, Terrell, TX, Zip 75160–2938, Mailing Address: P.O. Box 70, Zip 75160–9000, tel. 972/524–6452; Dorothy Floyd, Ph.D., Superintendent
Web address: www.dshs.state.tx.us/mhhospitals/terrellsh

TEXAS CENTER FOR INFECTIOUS DISEASE (O, 37 beds) 2303 SE Military Drive, San Antonio, TX, Zip 78223–3597; tel. 210/534–8857; James N. Elkins, FACHE, Director

Owned, leased, sponsored:	10 hospitals	2197 beds
Contract-managed:	0 hospitals	0 beds
Totals:	10 hospitals	2197 beds

For explanation of codes following names, see page B2.
★ Indicates Type III membership in the American Hospital Association.

Section B

★0129: TEXAS HEALTH RESOURCES (NP)
612 East Lamar Boulevard, Suite 900, Arlington, TX, Zip 76011–4130; tel. 682/236–7900; Barclay E. Berdan, FACHE, Chief Executive Officer
(Centralized Physician/Insurance Health System)

TEXAS: TEXAS HEALTH ARLINGTON MEMORIAL HOSPITAL (O, 252 beds) 800 West Randol Mill Road, Arlington, TX, Zip 76012–2503; tel. 817/548–6100; Blake Kretz, FACHE, President
Web address: www.arlingtonmemorial.org

TEXAS HEALTH HARRIS METHODIST HOSPITAL ALLIANCE (O, 101 beds) 10864 Texas Health Trail, Fort Worth, TX, Zip 76244–4897; tel. 682/212–2000; Clint Abernathy, President and Chief Operating Officer
Web address: https://www.texashealth.org/alliance/Pages/default.aspx

TEXAS HEALTH HARRIS METHODIST HOSPITAL AZLE (O, 31 beds) 108 Denver Trail, Azle, TX, Zip 76020–3614; tel. 817/444–8600; Tonya Sosebee, MSN, R.N., Chief Operating and Nursing Officer

TEXAS HEALTH HARRIS METHODIST HOSPITAL CLEBURNE (O, 92 beds) 201 Walls Drive, Cleburne, TX, Zip 76033–4007; tel. 817/641–2551; Ajith Pai, PharmD, FACHE, President
Web address: www.texashealth.org

TEXAS HEALTH HARRIS METHODIST HOSPITAL FORT WORTH (O, 650 beds) 1301 Pennsylvania Avenue, Fort Worth, TX, Zip 76104–2122; tel. 817/250–2000; Joseph DeLeon, President

TEXAS HEALTH HARRIS METHODIST HOSPITAL HURST-EULESS-BEDFORD (O, 285 beds) 1600 Hospital Parkway, Bedford, TX, Zip 76022–6913; tel. 817/685–4000; Fraser Hay, President
Web address: www.texashealth.org

TEXAS HEALTH HARRIS METHODIST HOSPITAL SOUTHWEST FORT WORTH (O, 235 beds) 6100 Harris Parkway, Fort Worth, TX, Zip 76132–4199; tel. 817/433–5000; Rebecca Tucker, President

TEXAS HEALTH HARRIS METHODIST HOSPITAL STEPHENVILLE (O, 50 beds) 411 North Belknap Street, Stephenville, TX, Zip 76401–3415; tel. 254/965–1500; Christopher Leu, President
Web address: www.texashealth.org/landing.cfm?id=108

TEXAS HEALTH PRESBYTERIAN HOSPITAL ALLEN (O, 52 beds) 1105 Central Expressway North, Suite 140, Allen, TX, Zip 75013–6103; tel. 972/747–1000; Jared Shelton, Chief Executive Officer
Web address: www.texashealth.org

TEXAS HEALTH PRESBYTERIAN HOSPITAL DALLAS (O, 553 beds) 8200 Walnut Hill Lane, Dallas, TX, Zip 75231–4426; tel. 214/345–6789; James Berg, FACHE, President

TEXAS HEALTH PRESBYTERIAN HOSPITAL DENTON (O, 197 beds) 3000 North I-35, Denton, TX, Zip 76201–5119; tel. 940/898–7000; Jeff Reecer, FACHE, Chief Executive Officer
Web address: www.dentonhospital.com

TEXAS HEALTH PRESBYTERIAN HOSPITAL KAUFMAN (O, 37 beds) 850 Ed Hall Drive, Kaufman, TX, Zip 75142–1861, Mailing Address: P.O. Box 1108, Zip 75142–5401, tel. 972/932–7200; Patsy Youngs, President
Web address: www.texashealth.org/Kaufman

TEXAS HEALTH PRESBYTERIAN HOSPITAL PLANO (O, 308 beds) 6200 West Parker Road, Plano, TX, Zip 75093–8185; tel. 972/981–8000; Joshua Floren, President
Web address: www.texashealth.org

TEXAS HEALTH SPECIALTY HOSPITAL (O, 10 beds) 1301 Pennsylvania Avenue, 4th Floor, Fort Worth, TX, Zip 76104–2190; tel. 817/250–5500; Pamela Duffey, DNP, RN, NEA-BC, MSN, R.N., Chief Executive Officer

Owned, leased, sponsored:	14 hospitals	2853 beds
Contract-managed:	0 hospitals	0 beds
Totals:	14 hospitals	2853 beds

1038: THE CARPENTER HEALTH NETWORK (IO)
10615 Jefferson Highway, Baton Rouge, LA, Zip 70809–7230; tel. 225/769–4180; Pat Mitchell, Chief Executive Officer

LOUISIANA: SAGE REHABILITATION HOSPITAL (O, 42 beds) 8000 Summa Avenue, Baton Rouge, LA, Zip 70809–3423, Mailing Address: P.O. Box 82681, Zip 70884–2681, tel. 225/819–0703; Scott McClelland, Administrator
Web address: www.sage-rehab.org

SAGE SPECIALTY HOSPITAL (LTAC) (O, 59 beds) 8375 Florida Boulevard, Denham Springs, LA, Zip 70726–7806; tel. 225/665–2664; Sharon Faulkner, Administrator
Web address: www.amgdenham.com/

Owned, leased, sponsored:	2 hospitals	101 beds
Contract-managed:	0 hospitals	0 beds
Totals:	2 hospitals	101 beds

★1040: THE UNIVERSITY OF KANSAS HEALTH SYSTEM (NP)
4000 Cambridge Street, Kansas City, KS, Zip 66160–0001; tel. 913/588–1227; Bob Page, President and Chief Executive Officer
(Moderately Centralized Health System)

KANSAS: HAYS MEDICAL CENTER (O, 127 beds) 2220 Canterbury Drive, Hays, KS, Zip 67601–2370, Mailing Address: P.O. Box 8100, Zip 67601–8100, tel. 785/623–5000; Edward Herrman, R.N., FACHE, President and Chief Executive Officer
Web address: www.haysmed.com

THE UNIVERSITY OF KANSAS HOSPITAL (O, 897 beds) 4000 Cambridge Street, MS 3011, Kansas City, KS, Zip 66160; tel. 913/588–5000; Bob Page, Chief Executive Officer
Web address: www.kumed.com

UNIVERSITY OF KANSAS HEALTH SYSTEM GREAT BEND CAMPUS (O, 33 beds) 514 Cleveland Street, Great Bend, KS, Zip 67530–3562; tel. 620/792–8833; Jesse Mock, Chief Executive Officer

UNIVERSITY OF KANSAS HEALTH SYSTEM PAWNEE VALLEY CAMPUS (O, 22 beds) 923 Carroll Avenue, Larned, KS, Zip 67550–2429; tel. 620/285–3161; Kendra Barker, Administrator
Web address: www.pawneevalleyhospital.com

Owned, leased, sponsored:	4 hospitals	1079 beds
Contract-managed:	0 hospitals	0 beds
Totals:	4 hospitals	1079 beds

2445: THEDACARE, INC. (NP)
122 East College Avenue, Appleton, WI, Zip 54911–5794, Mailing Address: P.O. Box 8025, Zip 54912–8025, tel. 920/830–5889; Imran A. Andrabi, M.D., President and Chief Executive Officer
(Moderately Centralized Health System)

WISCONSIN: THEDA CARE MEDICAL CENTER – WILD ROSE (O, 25 beds) 601 Grove Avenue, Wild Rose, WI, Zip 54984–6903, Mailing Address: P.O. Box 243, Zip 54984–0243, tel. 920/622–3257; Tammy Bending, Vice President
Web address: www.wildrosehospital.org

THEDACARE MEDICAL CENTER-BERLIN (O, 25 beds) 225 Memorial Drive, Berlin, WI, Zip 54923–1295; tel. 920/361–1313; Tammy Bending, Vice President, Critical Access Hospital

THEDACARE MEDICAL CENTER-NEW LONDON (O, 25 beds) 1405 Mill Street, New London, WI, Zip 54961–0307, Mailing Address: P.O. Box 307, Zip 54961–0307, tel. 920/531–2000; William Schmidt, President and Chief Executive Officer
Web address: www.thedacare.org

THEDACARE MEDICAL CENTER-SHAWANO (O, 22 beds) 100 County Road B, Shawano, WI, Zip 54166–2127; tel. 715/526–2111; William Schmidt, Chief Executive Officer
Web address: www.shawanomed.org

THEDACARE MEDICAL CENTER-WAUPACA (O, 25 beds) 800 Riverside Drive, Waupaca, WI, Zip 54981–1999; tel. 715/258–1000; David Corso, Vice President Critical Access Hospitals
Web address: www.riversidemedical.org

For explanation of codes following names, see page B2.
★ Indicates Type III membership in the American Hospital Association.

THEDACARE REGIONAL MEDICAL CENTER-APPLETON (O, 147 beds) 1818 North Meade Street, Appleton, WI, Zip 54911–3496; tel. 920/731–4101; Thomas J. Arquilla, Chief Strategy Officer

THEDACARE REGIONAL MEDICAL CENTER-NEENAH (O, 164 beds) 130 Second Street, Neenah, WI, Zip 54956–2883, Mailing Address: P.O. Box 2021, Zip 54957–2021, tel. 920/729–3100; Mark Thompson, System Chief Financial Officer
Web address: www.thedacare.org

Owned, leased, sponsored:	7 hospitals	433 beds
Contract-managed:	0 hospitals	0 beds
Totals:	7 hospitals	433 beds

★0643: THOMAS HEALTH SYSTEM, INC. (NP)
4605 MacCorkle Avenue SW, South Charleston, WV, Zip 25309–1311; tel. 304/766–3600; Daniel Lauffer, FACHE, President and Chief Executive Officer
(Independent Hospital System)

WEST VIRGINIA: SAINT FRANCIS HOSPITAL (O, 65 beds) 333 Laidley Street, Charleston, WV, Zip 25301–1628, Mailing Address: P.O. Box 471, Zip 25322–0471, tel. 304/347–6500; Daniel Lauffer, FACHE, President and Chief Executive Officer

THOMAS MEMORIAL HOSPITAL (O, 211 beds) 4605 MacCorkle Avenue SW, South Charleston, WV, Zip 25309–1398; tel. 304/766–3600; Daniel Lauffer, FACHE, President and Chief Executive Officer
Web address: www.thomashealth.org

Owned, leased, sponsored:	2 hospitals	276 beds
Contract-managed:	0 hospitals	0 beds
Totals:	2 hospitals	276 beds

★0812: TIDELANDS HEALTH (NP)
606 Black River Road, Georgetown, SC, Zip 29440–3304, Mailing Address: P.O. Box 421718, Zip 29442–4203, tel. 843/527–7000; Bruce P. Bailey, President and Chief Executive Officer

Owned, leased, sponsored:	0 hospitals	0 beds
Contract-managed:	0 hospitals	0 beds
Totals:	0 hospitals	0 beds

★0910: TIFT REGIONAL HEALTH SYSTEM (NP)
901 East 18th Street, Tifton, GA, Zip 31794–3648; tel. 229/353–6100; Christopher Dorman, President and Chief Executive Officer
(Independent Hospital System)

GEORGIA: COOK MEDICAL CENTER-A CAMPUS OF TIFT REGIONAL MEDICAL CENTER (O, 155 beds) 706 North Parrish Avenue, Adel, GA, Zip 31620–1511; tel. 229/896–8000; Michael L. Purvis, Chief Executive Officer

TIFT REGIONAL MEDICAL CENTER (O, 181 beds) 901 East 18th Street, Tifton, GA, Zip 31794–3648, Mailing Address: Drawer 747, Zip 31793–0747, tel. 229/382–7120; Christopher Dorman, President and Chief Executive Officer
Web address: www.tiftregional.com

Owned, leased, sponsored:	2 hospitals	336 beds
Contract-managed:	0 hospitals	0 beds
Totals:	2 hospitals	336 beds

★1029: TOWER HEALTH (NP)
Sixth Avenue and Spruce Street, West Reading, PA, Zip 19611; tel. 610/988–8000; Clinton Matthews, President and Chief Executive Officer
(Moderately Centralized Health System)

PENNSYLVANIA: BRANDYWINE HOSPITAL (O, 171 beds) 201 Reeceville Road, Coatesville, PA, Zip 19320–1536; tel. 610/383–8000; W. Jeffrey. Hunt, Chief Executive Officer

CHESTNUT HILL HOSPITAL (O, 212 beds) 8835 Germantown Avenue, Philadelphia, PA, Zip 19118–2718; tel. 215/248–8200; John D. . Cacciamani, M.D., Chief Executive Officer
Web address: www.chhealthsystem.com

JENNERSVILLE HOSPITAL (O, 63 beds) 1015 West Baltimore Pike, West Grove, PA, Zip 19390–9459; tel. 610/869–1000; Claire Bradley. Mooney, R.N., President and Chief Executive Officer
Web address: www.jennersville.com

PHOENIXVILLE HOSPITAL (O, 139 beds) 140 Nutt Road, Phoenixville, PA, Zip 19460–3900, Mailing Address: P.O. Box 3001, Zip 19460–0916, tel. 610/983–1000; Stephen M. Tullman, Chief Executive Officer

POTTSTOWN HOSPITAL (O, 232 beds) 1600 East High Street, Pottstown, PA, Zip 19464–5093; tel. 610/327–7000; Richard Newell, Chief Executive Officer
Web address: www.https://pottstown.towerhealth.org/

READING HOSPITAL (O, 713 beds) Sixth Avenue and Spruce Street, West Reading, PA, Zip 19611–1428, Mailing Address: P.O. Box 16052, Zip 19612–6052, tel. 610/988–8000; William Jennings, President and Chief Executive Officer
Web address: www.readinghospital.org

Owned, leased, sponsored:	6 hospitals	1530 beds
Contract-managed:	0 hospitals	0 beds
Totals:	6 hospitals	1530 beds

★0906: TRINITY HEALTH (CC)
20555 Victor Parkway, Livonia, MI, Zip 48152–7031; tel. 734/343–1000; Michael A. Slubowski, FACHE, President and Chief Executive Officer
(Decentralized Health System)

CALIFORNIA: SAINT AGNES MEDICAL CENTER (O, 436 beds) 1303 East Herndon Avenue, Fresno, CA, Zip 93720–3397; tel. 559/450–3000; Nancy Hollingsworth, R.N., MSN, President and Chief Executive Officer

CONNECTICUT: JOHNSON MEMORIAL MEDICAL CENTER (O, 78 beds) 201 Chestnut Hill Road, Stafford Springs, CT, Zip 06076–4005; tel. 860/684–4251; Stuart E. Rosenberg, President
Web address: www.jmmc.com

MOUNT SINAI REHABILITATION HOSPITAL (O, 38 beds) 490 Blue Hills Avenue, Hartford, CT, Zip 06112–1513; tel. 860/714–3500; Robert J. Krug, M.D., Chief Executive Officer

SAINT FRANCIS HOSPITAL AND MEDICAL CENTER (O, 416 beds) 114 Woodland Street, Hartford, CT, Zip 06105–1208; tel. 860/714–4000; John F. Rodis, M.D., President
Web address: www.saintfranciscare.com

SAINT MARY'S HOSPITAL (O, 187 beds) 56 Franklin Street, Waterbury, CT, Zip 06706–1281; tel. 203/709–6000; Steven E. Schneider, M.D., President
Web address: www.stmh.org

DELAWARE: ST. FRANCIS HOSPITAL (O, 154 beds) 701 North Clayton Street, Wilmington, DE, Zip 19805, Mailing Address: P.O. Box 2500, Zip 19805–0500, tel. 302/421–4100; Daniel J. Sinnott, President and Chief Executive Officer
Web address: www.stfrancishealthcare.org

FLORIDA: BARTOW REGIONAL MEDICAL CENTER (O, 72 beds) 2200 Osprey Boulevard, Bartow, FL, Zip 33830–3308; tel. 863/533–8111; Karen Kerr, R.N., President
Web address: www.bartowregional.com

BAYCARE ALLIANT HOSPITAL (S, 35 beds) 601 Main Street, MS#402, Dunedin, FL, Zip 34698–5848; tel. 727/736–9991; Jacqueline Arocho, Administrator
Web address: www.baycare.org

HOLY CROSS HOSPITAL (O, 367 beds) 4725 North Federal Highway, Fort Lauderdale, FL, Zip 33308–4668, Mailing Address: P.O. Box 23460, Zip 33307–3460, tel. 954/771–8000; Patrick Taylor, M.D., President and Chief Executive Officer
Web address: www.holy-cross.com

MEASE COUNTRYSIDE HOSPITAL (C, 311 beds) 3231 McMullen Booth Road, Safety Harbor, FL, Zip 34695–6607; tel. 727/725–6111; Matthew Novak, President

---

For explanation of codes following names, see page B2.
★ Indicates Type III membership in the American Hospital Association.

MEASE DUNEDIN HOSPITAL (C, 120 beds) 601 Main Street, Dunedin, FL, Zip 34698–5891; tel. 727/733–1111; Matthew Novak, President
Web address: www.mpmhealth.com

SOUTH FLORIDA BAPTIST HOSPITAL (S, 133 beds) 301 North Alexander Street, Plant City, FL, Zip 33563–4303; tel. 813/757–1200; Karen Kerr, R.N., President
Web address: www.https://baycare.org/sfbh

ST. ANTHONY'S HOSPITAL (S, 358 beds) 1200 Seventh Avenue North, Saint Petersburg, FL, Zip 33705–1388, Mailing Address: P.O. Box 12588, Zip 33733–2588, tel. 727/825–1100; M. Scott Smith, President
Web address: www.stanthonys.com/

ST. JOSEPH'S HOSPITAL (S, 1062 beds) 3001 West Martin Luther King Jr. Boulevard, Tampa, FL, Zip 33607–6387, Mailing Address: P.O. Box 4227, Zip 33677–4227, tel. 813/870–4000; Kimberly Guy, President

WINTER HAVEN HOSPITAL (S, 361 beds) 200 Avenue F NE, Winter Haven, FL, Zip 33881–4193; tel. 863/293–1121; Stephen A. Nierman, President
Web address: www.winterhavenhospital.org

GEORGIA: ST. MARY'S GOOD SAMARITAN HOSPITAL (O, 25 beds) 5401 Lake Oconee Parkway, Greensboro, GA, Zip 30642–4232; tel. 706/453–7331; Tanya M. Adcock, President

ST. MARY'S HEALTH CARE SYSTEM (O, 174 beds) 1230 Baxter Street, Athens, GA, Zip 30606–3791; tel. 706/389–3000; D. Montez. Carter, Chief Executive Officer
Web address: www.stmarysathens.com

ST. MARY'S SACRED HEART HOSPITAL (O, 41 beds) 367 Clear Creek Parkway, Lavonia, GA, Zip 30553–4173; tel. 706/356–7800; Jeff English, President
Web address: www.stmaryssacredheart.org/

IDAHO: SAINT ALPHONSUS MEDICAL CENTER – NAMPA (O, 106 beds) 4300 East Flamingo Avenue, Nampa, ID, Zip 83686–6008; tel. 208/205–1000; Travis Leach, President

SAINT ALPHONSUS REGIONAL MEDICAL CENTER (O, 392 beds) 1055 N Curtis Rd, Boise, ID, Zip 83706–1309, Mailing Address: 1055 North Curtis Road, Zip 83706–1309, tel. 208/367–2121; Andrew B. Cosentino, President
Web address: www.saintalphonsus.org

ILLINOIS: GOTTLIEB MEMORIAL HOSPITAL (O, 171 beds) 701 West North Avenue, Melrose Park, IL, Zip 60160–1612; tel. 708/681–3200; Lori Price, President
Web address: www.gottliebhospital.org

LOYOLA UNIVERSITY MEDICAL CENTER (O, 524 beds) 2160 South First Avenue, Maywood, IL, Zip 60153–3328; tel. 708/216–9000; Daniel J. Post, Interim President

MACNEAL HOSPITAL (O, 358 beds) 3249 South Oak Park Avenue, Berwyn, IL, Zip 60402–0715; tel. 708/783–9100; Mary Elizabeth. Cleary, President
Web address: www.macneal.com

MERCY HOSPITAL AND MEDICAL CENTER (O, 402 beds) 2525 South Michigan Avenue, Chicago, IL, Zip 60616–2333; tel. 312/567–2000; Carol L. Schneider, President and Chief Executive Officer
Web address: www.mercy-chicago.org

INDIANA: PLYMOUTH MEDICAL CENTER (O, 48 beds) 1915 Lake Avenue, Plymouth, IN, Zip 46563–9366, Mailing Address: P.O. Box 670, Zip 46563–0670, tel. 574/948–4000; Christopher J. Karam, President

SAINT JOSEPH HEALTH SYSTEM (O, 300 beds) 5215 Holy Cross Parkway, Mishawaka, IN, Zip 46545–1469; tel. 574/335–5000; Chad Towner, Chief Executive Officer
Web address: www.sjmed.com

IOWA: FRANKLIN GENERAL HOSPITAL (C, 77 beds) 1720 Central Avenue East, Suite A, Hampton, IA, Zip 50441–1867; tel. 641/456–5000; Kim Price, Chief Executive Officer
Web address: www.franklingeneral.com

HANCOCK COUNTY HEALTH SYSTEM (C, 25 beds) 532 First Street NW, Britt, IA, Zip 50423–1227; tel. 641/843–5000; Laura Zwiefel, Chief Executive Officer

HANSEN FAMILY HOSPITAL (C, 21 beds) 920 South Oak, Iowa Falls, IA, Zip 50126–9506; tel. 641/648–4631; Douglas E. Morse, Chief Executive Officer and Administrator
Web address: www.hansenfamilyhospital.com

HAWARDEN REGIONAL HEALTHCARE (C, 18 beds) 1111 11th Street, Hawarden, IA, Zip 51023–1999; tel. 712/551–3100; Jayson Pullman, Chief Executive Officer

KOSSUTH REGIONAL HEALTH CENTER (C, 23 beds) 1515 South Phillips Street, Algona, IA, Zip 50511–3649; tel. 515/295–2451; Darlene M. Elbert, R.N., MS, Chief Executive Officer and Chief Nursing Officer
Web address: www.krhc.com

MERCY MEDICAL CENTER-DUBUQUE (O, 231 beds) 250 Mercy Drive, Dubuque, IA, Zip 52001–7360; tel. 563/589–8000; Kay Takes, R.N., President
Web address: www.mercydubuque.com

MERCY MEDICAL CENTER-DYERSVILLE (O, 20 beds) 1111 Third Street SW, Dyersville, IA, Zip 52040–1725; tel. 563/875–7101; Kay Takes, R.N., President
Web address: www.mercydubuque.com/mercy-dyersville

MERCYONE CEDAR FALLS MEDICAL CENTER (C, 50 beds) 515 College Street, Cedar Falls, IA, Zip 50613–2500; tel. 319/268–3000; MaryJo Kavalier, Administrator

MERCYONE CLINTON MEDICAL CENTER (O, 193 beds) 1410 North Fourth Street, Clinton, IA, Zip 52732–2940; tel. 563/244–5555; Amy Berentes, R.N., MSN, Executive Vice President and Chief Operating Officer
Web address: www.mercyclinton.com

MERCYONE ELKADER MEDICAL CENTER (C, 15 beds) 901 Davidson Street NW, Elkader, IA, Zip 52043–9015; tel. 563/245–7000; Brooke Kensinger, Chief Executive Officer
Web address: www.centralcommunityhospital.com

MERCYONE NEW HAMPTON MEDICAL CENTER (O, 18 beds) 308 North Maple Avenue, New Hampton, IA, Zip 50659–1142; tel. 641/394–4121; Aaron Flugum, Chief Executive Officer
Web address: www.mercynewhampton.com

MERCYONE NORTH IOWA MEDICAL CENTER (O, 222 beds) 1000 Fourth Street SW, Mason City, IA, Zip 50401–2800; tel. 641/428–7000; Rod G. Schlader, President and Chief Executive Officer

MERCYONE OELWEIN MEDICAL CENTER (C, 64 beds) 201 Eighth Avenue SE, Oelwein, IA, Zip 50662–2447; tel. 319/283–6000; Terri Derflinger, Site Administrator
Web address: www.wheatoniowa.org

MERCYONE PRIMGHAR MEDICAL CENTER (O, 11 beds) 255 North Welch Avenue, Primghar, IA, Zip 51245–7765, Mailing Address: P.O. Box 528, Zip 51245–0528, tel. 712/957–2300; Misty Dulin, CAH, Director
Web address: www.baumharmon.org

MERCYONE SIOUXLAND MEDICAL CENTER (O, 197 beds) 801 Fifth Street, Sioux City, IA, Zip 51101–1326, Mailing Address: P.O. Box 3168, Zip 51102–3168, tel. 712/279–2010; Beth Hughes, President
Web address: www.mercysiouxcity.com

MERCYONE WATERLOO MEDICAL CENTER (C, 229 beds) 3421 West Ninth Street, Waterloo, IA, Zip 50702–5401; tel. 319/272–8000; Jack Dusenbery, President and Chief Executive Officer
Web address: www.wheatoniowa.org

MITCHELL COUNTY REGIONAL HEALTH CENTER (C, 25 beds) 616 North Eighth Street, Osage, IA, Zip 50461–1498; tel. 641/732–6000; Shelly Russell, Chief Executive Officer

PALO ALTO COUNTY HEALTH SYSTEM (C, 47 beds) 3201 First Street, Emmetsburg, IA, Zip 50536–2516; tel. 712/852–5500; Brett Antczak, Chief Executive Officer
Web address: www.pachs.com

REGIONAL HEALTH SERVICES OF HOWARD COUNTY (C, 19 beds) 235 Eighth Avenue West, Cresco, IA, Zip 52136–1098; tel. 563/547–2101; Robin M. Schluter, Chief Executive Officer

MARYLAND: HOLY CROSS GERMANTOWN HOSPITAL (O, 72 beds) 19801 Observation Drive, Germantown, MD, Zip 20876–4070; tel. 301/754–7000; Doug Ryder, President
Web address: www.holycrosshealth.org/germantown

HOLY CROSS HOSPITAL (O, 367 beds) 1500 Forest Glen Road, Silver Spring, MD, Zip 20910–1487; tel. 301/754–7000; Louis Damiano, M.D., President
Web address: www.holycrosshealth.org

MASSACHUSETTS: FARREN CARE CENTER (O, 72 beds) 340 Montague City Road, Turners Falls, MA, Zip 01376–9983; tel. 413/774–3111; James Clifford, Administrator

MERCY MEDICAL CENTER (O, 317 beds) 271 Carew Street, Springfield, MA, Zip 01104–2398, Mailing Address: P.O. Box 9012, Zip 01102–9012, tel. 413/748–9000; Mark M. Fulco, President
Web address: www.mercycares.com

For explanation of codes following names, see page B2.
★ Indicates Type III membership in the American Hospital Association.

MICHIGAN: MERCY HEALTH HACKLEY CAMPUS (O, 366 beds) 1700 Clinton Street, Muskegon, MI, Zip 49442–5502, Mailing Address: P.O. Box 3302, Zip 49443–3302, tel. 231/726–3511; Gary Allore, President
Web address: www.mercyhealthmuskegon.com

MERCY HEALTH SAINT MARY'S (O, 283 beds) 200 Jefferson Avenue Southeast, Grand Rapids, MI, Zip 49503–4598, Mailing Address: 200 Jefferson Avenue SE, Zip 49503–4598, tel. 616/685–5000; David Baumgartner, M.D., Interim President

MERCY HEALTH, LAKESHORE CAMPUS (O, 24 beds) 72 South State Street, Shelby, MI, Zip 49455–1299; tel. 231/861–2156; John T. Foss, Vice President, Operations
Web address: www.mercyhealthmuskegon.com

ST. JOSEPH MERCY ANN ARBOR (O, 483 beds) 5301 Mcauley Drive, Ypsilanti, MI, Zip 48197–1051, Mailing Address: P.O. Box 995, Ann Arbor, Zip 48106–0995, tel. 734/712–3456; Bill Manns, President

ST. JOSEPH MERCY CHELSEA (O, 96 beds) 775 South Main Street, Chelsea, MI, Zip 48118–1383; tel. 734/593–6000; Nancy Kay. Graebner, President and Chief Executive Officer
Web address: www.cch.org

ST. JOSEPH MERCY LIVINGSTON HOSPITAL (O, 38 beds) 620 Byron Road, Howell, MI, Zip 48843–1093; tel. 517/545–6000; John F. O'Malley, FACHE, President
Web address: www.stjoeslivingston.org/livingston

ST. JOSEPH MERCY OAKLAND (O, 396 beds) 44405 Woodward Avenue, Pontiac, MI, Zip 48341–5023; tel. 248/858–3000; Shannon Striebich, Chief Executive Officer
Web address: www.stjoesoakland.com

ST. MARY MERCY HOSPITAL (O, 304 beds) 36475 Five Mile Road, Livonia, MI, Zip 48154–1988; tel. 734/655–4800; David A. Spivey, President and Chief Executive Officer

NEBRASKA: MERCYONE OAKLAND MEDICAL CENTER (O, 18 beds) 601 East Second Street, Oakland, NE, Zip 68045–1499; tel. 402/685–5601; Rita Going, Director of Critical Access Hospitals
Web address: www.oaklandhospital.org

PENDER COMMUNITY HOSPITAL (C, 67 beds) 100 Hospital Drive, Pender, NE, Zip 68047–0100, Mailing Address: P.O. Box 100, Zip 68047–0100, tel. 402/385–3083; Melissa Kelly, Chief Executive Officer and Chief Financial Officer
Web address: www.pendercommunityhospital.com

NEW JERSEY: ST. FRANCIS MEDICAL CENTER (O, 142 beds) 601 Hamilton Avenue, Trenton, NJ, Zip 08629–1986; tel. 609/599–5000; Daniel P. Moen, President

NEW YORK: ALBANY MEMORIAL HOSPITAL (O, 74 beds) 600 Northern Boulevard, Albany, NY, Zip 12204–1083; tel. 518/471–3221; James K. Reed, M.D., Chief Executive Officer
Web address: www.nehealth.com

BURDETT BIRTH CENTER (O, 15 beds) 2215 Burdett Avenue, Suite 200, Troy, NY, Zip 12180–2466; tel. 518/271–3393
Web address: www.burdettbirthcenter.org/

SAMARITAN HOSPITAL – MAIN CAMPUS (O, 277 beds) 2215 Burdett Avenue, Troy, NY, Zip 12180–2475; tel. 518/271–3300; James K. Reed, M.D., Chief Executive Officer
Web address: www.nehealth.com

ST. JOSEPH'S HOSPITAL HEALTH CENTER (O, 451 beds) 301 Prospect Avenue, Syracuse, NY, Zip 13203–1807; tel. 315/448–5111; Leslie Paul. Luke, President and Chief Executive Officer

ST. PETER'S HOSPITAL (O, 442 beds) 315 South Manning Boulevard, Albany, NY, Zip 12208–1789; tel. 518/525–1550; James K. Reed, M.D., Chief Executive Officer
Web address: www.sphcs.org

SUNNYVIEW REHABILITATION HOSPITAL (O, 115 beds) 1270 Belmont Avenue, Schenectady, NY, Zip 12308–2104; tel. 518/382–4500; Edward Eisenman, Chief Executive Officer
Web address: www.sunnyview.org

NORTH CAROLINA: ST. JOSEPH OF THE PINES HOSPITAL (O, 204 beds) 590 Central Drive, Southern Pines, NC, Zip 28387; tel. 910/246–1000; Ken Cormier, President and Chief Executive Officer

OHIO: MOUNT CARMEL NEW ALBANY SURGICAL HOSPITAL (O, 60 beds) 7333 Smith's Mill Road, New Albany, OH, Zip 43054–9291; tel. 614/775–6600; Diane Doucette, R.N., President
Web address: www.mountcarmelhealth.com

MOUNT CARMEL ST. ANN'S (O, 294 beds) 500 South Cleveland Avenue, Westerville, OH, Zip 43081–8998; tel. 614/898–4000; Kim Unhee, President
Web address: www.mountcarmelhealth.com

MOUNT CARMEL (O, 612 beds) 793 West State Street, Columbus, OH, Zip 43222–1551; tel. 614/234–5000; Sean McKibben, President and Chief Operating Officer

OREGON: SAINT ALPHONSUS MEDICAL CENTER – BAKER CITY (S, 25 beds) 3325 Pocahontas Road, Baker City, OR, Zip 97814–1464; tel. 541/523–6461; Priscilla Lynn, President
Web address: https://www.saintalphonsus.org/bakercity

SAINT ALPHONSUS MEDICAL CENTER – ONTARIO (S, 37 beds) 351 SW Ninth Street, Ontario, OR, Zip 97914–2693; tel. 541/881–7000; Kenneth Hart, President
Web address: www.saintalphonsus.org/ontario

PENNSYLVANIA: MERCY FITZGERALD HOSPITAL (O, 340 beds) 1500 Lansdowne Avenue, Suite 100, Darby, PA, Zip 19023–1200; tel. 610/237–4000; Susan Cusack, Executive Director
Web address: www.mercyhealth.org

NAZARETH HOSPITAL (O, 147 beds) 2601 Holme Avenue, Philadelphia, PA, Zip 19152–2096; tel. 215/335–6000; Nancy Cherone, Executive Director and Administrator
Web address: www.nazarethhospital.org

ST. MARY MEDICAL CENTER (O, 353 beds) 1201 Langhorne-Newtown Road, Langhorne, PA, Zip 19047–1201; tel. 215/710–2000; Lawrence Brilliant, M.D., Vice President and Chief Medical Officer

Owned, leased, sponsored:	60 hospitals	13554 beds
Contract-managed:	15 hospitals	1111 beds
Totals:	75 hospitals	14665 beds

★9255: TRUMAN MEDICAL CENTERS (NP)
2301 Holmes Street, Kansas City, MO, Zip 64108–2677; tel. 816/404–1000; Charlie Shields, Chief Executive Officer
(Independent Hospital System)

MISSOURI: TRUMAN MEDICAL CENTER-HOSPITAL HILL (O, 249 beds) 2301 Holmes Street, Kansas City, MO, Zip 64108–2640; tel. 816/404–1000; Charlie Shields, President and Chief Executive Officer

TRUMAN MEDICAL CENTER-LAKEWOOD (O, 298 beds) 7900 Lee's Summit Road, Kansas City, MO, Zip 64139–1236; tel. 816/404–7000; Charlie Shields, Chief Executive Officer
Web address: www.trumed.org

Owned, leased, sponsored:	2 hospitals	547 beds
Contract-managed:	0 hospitals	0 beds
Totals:	2 hospitals	547 beds

★9105: UAB HEALTH SYSTEM (NP)
500 22nd Street South, Suite 408, Birmingham, AL, Zip 35233–3110; tel. 205/975–5362; William Ferniany, Ph.D., Chief Executive Officer
(Centralized Physician/Insurance Health System)

ALABAMA: BRYAN W. WHITFIELD MEMORIAL HOSPITAL (C, 47 beds) 105 U S Highway 80 East, Demopolis, AL, Zip 36732–3616, Mailing Address: P.O. Box 890, Zip 36732–0890, tel. 334/289–4000; Douglas L. Brewer, Chief Executive Officer
Web address: www.bwwmh.com

MEDICAL WEST (O, 231 beds) 995 Ninth Avenue SW, Bessemer, AL, Zip 35022–4527; tel. 205/481–7000; Brian Keith. Pennington, President and Chief Executive Officer

UNIVERSITY OF ALABAMA HOSPITAL (O, 1206 beds) 619 19th Street South, Birmingham, AL, Zip 35249–1900; tel. 205/934–4011; Reid F. Jones, Chief Executive Officer
Web address: www.uabmedicine.org

Owned, leased, sponsored:	2 hospitals	1437 beds
Contract-managed:	1 hospitals	47 beds
Totals:	3 hospitals	1484 beds

For explanation of codes following names, see page B2.
★ Indicates Type III membership in the American Hospital Association.

★**0082: UC HEALTH** (NP)
3200 Burnet Avenue, Cincinnati, OH, Zip 45229–3019;
tel. 513/585–6000; Richard P. Lofgren, M.D., M.P.H., President
and Chief Executive Officer
(Moderately Centralized Health System)

OHIO: DANIEL DRAKE CENTER FOR POST ACUTE CARE (O, 202 beds) 151
West Galbraith Road, Cincinnati, OH, Zip 45216–1015; tel. 513/418–
2500; Lafe Bauer, Vice President, Post Acute Care Services and Chief
Administrative Officer
Web address: www.uchealth.com/danieldrakecenter/

UNIVERSITY OF CINCINNATI MEDICAL CENTER (O, 579 beds) 234 Goodman
Street, Cincinnati, OH, Zip 45219–2316; tel. 513/584–1000; Ann Smith, Senior
Vice President, Inpatient Services and Interim Chief Administrative Officer

WEST CHESTER HOSPITAL (O, 174 beds) 7700 University Drive, West
Chester, OH, Zip 45069–2505; tel. 513/298–3000; Tom G. Daskalakis, Chief
Administrative Officer
Web address: www.uchealth.com/westchesterhospital

Owned, leased, sponsored:	3 hospitals	955 beds
Contract-managed:	0 hospitals	0 beds
Totals:	3 hospitals	955 beds

★**0381: UCHEALTH** (NP)
2315 East Harmony Road, Suite 200, Fort Collins, CO,
Zip 80528–8620; tel. 970/495–7000; Elizabeth B. Concordia,
President and Chief Executive Officer
(Moderately Centralized Health System)

COLORADO: UCHEALTH BROOMFIELD HOSPITAL (O, 18 beds) 11820
Destination Drive, Broomfield, CO, Zip 80021; tel. 303/460–6000; Lonnie
Cramer, President
Web address: www.uchealth.org/pages/OHAM/OrgUnitDetails.aspx?

UCHEALTH GRANDVIEW HOSPITAL (O, 22 beds) 5623 Pulpit Peak View,
Colorado Springs, CO, Zip 80918; tel. 719/272–3600; Derek Rushing, Chief
Executive Officer
Web address: https://www.uchealth.org/Pages/OHAM/OrgUnitDetails.
aspx?OrganizationalUnitId=514

UCHEALTH LONGS PEAK HOSPITAL (O, 47 beds) 1750 East Ken Pratt Boulevard,
Longmont, CO, Zip 80504–5311; tel. 970/237–7850; Lonnie Cramer, President
Web address: https://www.uchealth.org/locations/uchealth-longs-peak-hospital/

UCHEALTH MEDICAL CENTER OF THE ROCKIES (O, 174 beds) 2500 Rocky
Mountain Avenue, Loveland, CO, Zip 80538–9004; tel. 970/624–2500; Kevin
L. Unger, Ph.D., FACHE, President and Chief Executive Officer

UCHEALTH MEMORIAL HOSPITAL (L, 528 beds) 1400 East Boulder Street,
Colorado Springs, CO, Zip 80909–5599; tel. 719/365–5000; Joel P. Yuhas,
FACHE, President and Chief Executive Officer
Web address: www.uchealth.org/southerncolorado

UCHEALTH POUDRE VALLEY HOSPITAL (O, 255 beds) 1024 South Lemay
Avenue, Fort Collins, CO, Zip 80524–3998, Mailing Address: 2315 East
Harmony Road, Suite 200, Zip 80528, tel. 970/495–7000; Kevin L. Unger,
Ph.D., FACHE, President and Chief Executive Officer

UCHEALTH YAMPA VALLEY MEDICAL CENTER (O, 39 beds) 1024 Central
Park Drive, Steamboat Springs, CO, Zip 80487–8813; tel. 970/879–1322;
Thomas Downes, M.D., Interim Chief Executive Officer
Web address: https://www.uchealth.org/locations/uchealth-yampa-valley-
medical-center/

UNIVERSITY OF COLORADO HOSPITAL (O, 763 beds) 12401 East 17th
Avenue, MS F417, Aurora, CO, Zip 80045–2545; tel. 720/848–0000;
Christopher A. Gessner, President and Chief Executive Officer

Owned, leased, sponsored:	8 hospitals	1846 beds
Contract-managed:	0 hospitals	0 beds
Totals:	8 hospitals	1846 beds

★**0111: UF HEALTH SHANDS** (NP)
1600 SW Archer Road, Gainesville, FL, Zip 32610–0326;
tel. 352/733–1500; Edward Jimenez, Chief Executive Officer
(Moderately Centralized Health System)

FLORIDA: UF HEALTH JACKSONVILLE (O, 644 beds) 655 West Eighth Street,
Jacksonville, FL, Zip 32209–6595; tel. 904/244–0411; Leon L. Haley Jr,
M.D., Chief Executive Officer
Web address: www.ufhealthjax.org/

UF HEALTH SHANDS HOSPITAL (O, 1052 beds) 1600 SW Archer Road,
Gainesville, FL, Zip 32610–3003, Mailing Address: PO Box 100326,
Zip 32610–0326, tel. 352/265–0111; Edward Jimenez, Chief Executive
Officer
Web address: www.https://ufhealth.org/

Owned, leased, sponsored:	2 hospitals	1696 beds
Contract-managed:	0 hospitals	0 beds
Totals:	2 hospitals	1696 beds

★**0224: UMASS MEMORIAL HEALTH CARE, INC.** (NP)
1 Biotech Park, Worcester, MA, Zip 01605–2982; tel. 508/334–
0100; Eric Dickson, M.D., President and Chief Executive Officer
(Centralized Physician/Insurance Health System)

MASSACHUSETTS: UMASS MEMORIAL HEALTHALLIANCE-CLINTON HOSPITAL
(O, 163 beds) 60 Hospital Road, Leominster, MA, Zip 01453–2205;
tel. 978/466–2000; Steven P. Roach, FACHE, Interim Chief Executive
Officer

UMASS MEMORIAL MEDICAL CENTER (O, 661 beds) 119 Belmont Street,
Worcester, MA, Zip 01605–2982; tel. 508/334–1000; Michael Gustafson,
M.D., President
Web address: www.umassmemorial.org

UMASS MEMORIAL-MARLBOROUGH HOSPITAL (O, 67 beds) 157 Union ST,
Marlborough, MA, Zip 01752–1297; tel. 508/481–5000; Steven P. Roach,
FACHE, President and Chief Executive Officer
Web address: www.marlboroughhospital.org

Owned, leased, sponsored:	3 hospitals	891 beds
Contract-managed:	0 hospitals	0 beds
Totals:	3 hospitals	891 beds

★**0901: UNC HEALTH CARE** (NP)
101 Manning Drive, Chapel Hill, NC, Zip 27514–4220;
tel. 919/966–4131; Wesley Burks, M.D., Chief Executive Officer
(Moderately Centralized Health System)

NORTH CAROLINA: CALDWELL UNC HEALTH CARE (O, 82 beds) 321
Mulberry Street SW, Lenoir, NC, Zip 28645–5720, Mailing Address: P.O.
Box 1890, Zip 28645–1890, tel. 828/757–5100; Laura J. Easton,
President and Chief Executive Officer
Web address: www.caldwellmemorial.org

CHATHAM HOSPITAL (O, 25 beds) 475 Progress Boulevard, Siler City,
NC, Zip 27344–6787, Mailing Address: P.O. Box 649, Zip 27344–0649,
tel. 919/799–4000; Robert A. Enders Jr, President
Web address: www.chathamhospital.org

JOHNSTON HEALTH (C, 153 beds) 509 North Bright Leaf Blvd, Smithfield,
NC, Zip 27577–4407, Mailing Address: P.O. Box 1376, Zip 27577–1376,
tel. 919/934–8171; Charles W. Elliott Jr, Chief Executive Officer
Web address: www.johnstonhealth.org

MARGARET R. PARDEE MEMORIAL HOSPITAL (C, 158 beds) 800 North Justice
Street, Hendersonville, NC, Zip 28791–3410; tel. 828/696–1000; James M.
Kirby II, President and Chief Executive Officer

NASH UNC HEALTH CARE (C, 249 beds) 2460 Curtis Ellis Drive, Rocky Mount,
NC, Zip 27804–2237; tel. 252/962–8000; L Lee. Isley, FACHE, Ph.D.,
President and Chief Executive Officer
Web address: www.nhcs.org

UNC LENOIR HEALTHCARE (C, 176 beds) 100 Airport Road, Kinston, NC,
Zip 28501–1634, Mailing Address: P.O. Box 1678, Zip 28503–1678,
tel. 252/522–7000; Gary E. Black, President and Chief Executive Officer

UNC REX HEALTH CARE (O, 666 beds) 4420 Lake Boone Trail, Raleigh, NC,
Zip 27607–6599; tel. 919/784–3100; Stephen W. Burriss, President
Web address: www.rexhealth.com

UNC ROCKINGHAM HEALTH CARE (O, 188 beds) 117 East King's Highway,
Eden, NC, Zip 27288–5201; tel. 336/623–9711; Dana Weston, Chief
Executive Officer

For explanation of codes following names, see page B2.
★ Indicates Type III membership in the American Hospital Association.

© 2019 AHA Guide

UNIVERSITY OF NORTH CAROLINA HOSPITALS (O, 949 beds) 101 Manning Drive, Chapel Hill, NC, Zip 27514–4220; tel. 984/974–1000; Gary L. Park, President
Web address: www.unchealthcare.org

WAYNE UNC HEALTH CARE (C, 274 beds) 2700 Wayne Memorial Drive, Goldsboro, NC, Zip 27534–9494, Mailing Address: P.O. Box 8001, Zip 27533–8001, tel. 919/736–1110; Janie Jaberg, FACHE, President and Chief Executive Officer
Web address: www.waynehealth.org

Owned, leased, sponsored:	5 hospitals	1910 beds
Contract-managed:	5 hospitals	1010 beds
Totals:	10 hospitals	2920 beds

0922: UNION GENERAL HOSPITAL, INC. (NP)
35 Hospital Road, Blairsville, GA, Zip 30512–3139; tel. 706/745–2111; Mike Gowder, Chief Executive Officer

GEORGIA: CHATUGE REGIONAL HOSPITAL AND NURSING HOME (O, 150 beds) 110 Main Street, Hiawassee, GA, Zip 30546–3408, Mailing Address: P.O. Box 509, Zip 30546–0509, tel. 706/896–2222; Ryan Snow, Administrator
Web address: www.chatugeregionalhospital.org

UNION GENERAL HOSPITAL (O, 195 beds) 35 Hospital Road, Blairsville, GA, Zip 30512–3139; tel. 706/745–2111; Kevin Bierschenk, Chief Executive Officer
Web address: www.uniongeneralhospital.com

Owned, leased, sponsored:	2 hospitals	345 beds
Contract-managed:	0 hospitals	0 beds
Totals:	2 hospitals	345 beds

0288: UNITED HEALTH SERVICES (NP)
10–42 Mitchell Avenue, Binghamton, NY, Zip 13903–1617; tel. 607/762–2200; John M. Carrigg, President and Chief Executive Officer
(Independent Hospital System)

NEW YORK: UHS CHENANGO MEMORIAL HOSPITAL (O, 138 beds) 179 North Broad Street, Norwich, NY, Zip 13815–1097; tel. 607/337–4111; Drake M. Lamen, M.D., President, Chief Executive Officer and Chief Medical Officer

UHS DELAWARE VALLEY HOSPITAL (O, 25 beds) 1 Titus Place, Walton, NY, Zip 13856–1498; tel. 607/865–2100; Paul Summers, President and Chief Executive Officer
Web address: www.uhs.net/locations/

UNITED HEALTH SERVICES HOSPITALS-BINGHAMTON (O, 464 beds) 10–42 Mitchell Avenue, Binghamton, NY, Zip 13903–1678; tel. 607/763–6000; John M. Carrigg, President and Chief Executive Officer

Owned, leased, sponsored:	3 hospitals	627 beds
Contract-managed:	0 hospitals	0 beds
Totals:	3 hospitals	627 beds

9605: UNITED MEDICAL CORPORATION (IO)
603 Main Street, Windermere, FL, Zip 34786–3548, Mailing Address: P.O. Box 1100, Zip 34786–1100, tel. 407/876–2200; Donald R. Dizney, Chairman and Chief Executive Officer

PUERTO RICO: HOSPITAL PAVIA-HATO REY (O, 180 beds) 435 Ponce De Leon Avenue, San Juan, PR, Zip 00917–3428, Mailing Address: PO Box 190828, Zip 00917–3428, tel. 787/641–2323; Guillermo Pastrana, Executive Director
Web address: www.paviahealth.com

HOSPITAL PAVIA-SANTURCE (O, 197 beds) 1462 Asia Street, San Juan, PR, Zip 00909–2143, Mailing Address: Box 11137, Santurce Station, Zip 00910–1137, tel. 787/727–6060; Jose Luis. Rodriguez, Chief Executive Officer
Web address: www.paviahealth.com

HOSPITAL PEREA (O, 103 beds) 15 Basora Street, Mayaguez, PR, Zip 681, Mailing Address: P.O. Box 170, Zip 681, tel. 787/834–0101; Jorge I. Martinez, Executive Director

HOSPITAL SAN FRANCISCO (O, 133 beds) 371 Avenida De Diego, San Juan, PR, Zip 00923–1711, Mailing Address: P.O. Box 29025, Zip 00929–0025, tel. 787/767–5100; Marcos Aguila, Chief Executive Officer
Web address: www.metropavia.com/SanFrancisco.cfm

SAN JORGE CHILDREN'S HOSPITAL (O, 167 beds) 258 San Jorge Street, Santurce, Santurce, PR, Zip 00912–3310, Mailing Address: PO Box 6308, San Juan, Zip 00912–3310, tel. 787/727–1000; Domingo Cruz, Senior Vice President Operations
Web address: www.sanjorgechildrenshospital.com

TENNESSEE: TEN BROECK TENNESSEE TREATMENT FACILITY (O, 38 beds) 1 Medical Center Boulevard, 5 West, Cookeville, TN, Zip 38501; tel. 931/783–2570; Kelly Tripp, Chief Executive Officer
Web address: www.tenbroeck.com

Owned, leased, sponsored:	6 hospitals	818 beds
Contract-managed:	0 hospitals	0 beds
Totals:	6 hospitals	818 beds

0937: UNITED MEDICAL REHABILITATION HOSPITALS (IO)
3201 Wall Boulevard, Suite B, Gretna, LA, Zip 70056–7755; tel. 504/433–5551; John E.H. Mills, President and Chief Executive Officer

LOUISIANA: UNITED MEDICAL REHABILITATION HOSPITAL (O, 26 beds) 3201 Wall Boulevard, Suite B, Gretna, LA, Zip 70056–7755; tel. 504/433–5551; Elisha Johnson, Interim Administrator

UNITED MEDICAL REHABILITATION HOSPITAL (O, 20 beds) 15717 Belle Drive, Hammond, LA, Zip 70403–1439; tel. 985/340–5998; Jonathan Landreth, Administrator
Web address: www.umrhospital.com

Owned, leased, sponsored:	2 hospitals	46 beds
Contract-managed:	0 hospitals	0 beds
Totals:	2 hospitals	46 beds

0322: UNITED SURGICAL PARTNERS INTERNATIONAL (IO)
15305 Dallas Parkway, Suite 1600, Addison, TX, Zip 75001–6491; tel. 972/713–3500; Brett Brodnax, Chief Executive Officer
(Independent Hospital System)

ARIZONA: ARIZONA ORTHOPEDIC SURGICAL HOSPITAL (O, 24 beds) 2905 West Warner Road, Suite 1, Chandler, AZ, Zip 85224–1674; tel. 480/603–9000; Patricia K. Alice, Chief Executive Officer

OKLAHOMA: OKLAHOMA CENTER FOR ORTHOPEDIC AND MULTI-SPECIALTY SURGERY (O, 10 beds) 8100 South Walker, Suite C, Oklahoma City, OK, Zip 73139–9402, Mailing Address: P.O. Box 890609, Zip 73189–0609, tel. 405/602–6500; Daniel J. Coats, Chief Executive Officer
Web address: www.ocomhospital.com

TEXAS: BAYLOR SCOTT & WHITE MEDICAL CENTER-UPTOWN (O, 24 beds) 2727 East Lemmon Avenue, Dallas, TX, Zip 75204–2895; tel. 214/443–3000; Nick Taylor, Chief Executive Officer
Web address: www.bmcuptown.com

BAYLOR SCOTT & WHITE MEDICAL CENTER–FRISCO (O, 68 beds) 5601 Warren Parkway, Frisco, TX, Zip 75034–4069; tel. 214/407–5000; Trevor Castaneda, Chief Executive Officer

BAYLOR SURGICAL HOSPITAL AT LAS COLINAS (O, 12 beds) 400 West Interstate 635, Irving, TX, Zip 75063; tel. 972/868–4000; Deonna Unell, Chief Executive Officer
Web address: www.baylorhealth.com/About/Community/Assessments/West/ICSH/Pages/Default.aspx

TOPS SURGICAL SPECIALTY HOSPITAL (O, 15 beds) 17080 Red Oak Drive, Houston, TX, Zip 77090–2602; tel. 281/539–2900; Samuel H. Rossmann, Chief Executive Officer

Owned, leased, sponsored:	6 hospitals	153 beds
Contract-managed:	0 hospitals	0 beds
Totals:	6 hospitals	153 beds

For explanation of codes following names, see page B2.
★ Indicates Type III membership in the American Hospital Association.

Section B

★0061: UNITYPOINT HEALTH (NP)
1776 West Lakes Parkway, Suite 400, West Des Moines, IA, Zip 50266–8393; tel. 515/241–6161; Kevin Vermeer, President and Chief Executive Officer
(Decentralized Health System)

ILLINOIS: UNITYPOINT HEALTH – PEORIA (O, 269 beds) 221 NE Glen Oak Avenue, Peoria, IL, Zip 61636–4310; tel. 309/672–5522; Keith Knepp, M.D., President and Chief Executive Officer
Web address: www.unitypoint.org/peoria

UNITYPOINT HEALTH – PROCTOR (O, 131 beds) 5409 North Knoxville Avenue, Peoria, IL, Zip 61614–5069; tel. 309/691–1000; Keith Knepp, M.D., President and Chief Executive Officer
Web address: www.proctor.org

UNITYPOINT HEALTH – TRINITY ROCK ISLAND (O, 343 beds) 2701 17th Street, Rock Island, IL, Zip 61201–5393; tel. 309/779–5000; John C. Sheehan, FACHE, Interim President and Chief Executive Officer

UNITYPOINT HEALTH-PEKIN HOSPITAL (O, 98 beds) 600 South 13th Street, Pekin, IL, Zip 61554–4936; tel. 309/347–1151; Keith Knepp, M.D., President and Chief Executive Officer
Web address: www.pekinhospital.org

IOWA: BUCHANAN COUNTY HEALTH CENTER (O, 58 beds) 1600 First Street East, Independence, IA, Zip 50644–3155; tel. 319/332–0999; Steve Robert. Slessor, Chief Executive Officer
Web address: www.bchealth.info

BUENA VISTA REGIONAL MEDICAL CENTER (C, 35 beds) 1525 West Fifth Street, Storm Lake, IA, Zip 50588–3027, Mailing Address: P.O. Box 309, Zip 50588–0309, tel. 712/732–4030; Steven Colerick, Chief Executive Officer
Web address: www.bvrmc.org

CHEROKEE REGIONAL MEDICAL CENTER (O, 25 beds) 300 Sioux Valley Drive, Cherokee, IA, Zip 51012–1205; tel. 712/225–5101; Gary W. Jordan, FACHE, Chief Executive Officer

CLARKE COUNTY HOSPITAL (C, 25 beds) 800 South Fillmore Street, Osceola, IA, Zip 50213–1619; tel. 641/342–2184; Brian G. Evans, FACHE, Chief Executive Officer
Web address: www.clarkehosp.org

COMMUNITY MEMORIAL HOSPITAL (C, 16 beds) 909 West First Street, Sumner, IA, Zip 50674–1203, Mailing Address: P.O. Box 148, Zip 50674–0148, tel. 563/578–3275; Dawn Everding, President and Chief Financial Officer
Web address: www.cmhsumner.org

COMPASS MEMORIAL HEALTHCARE (O, 25 beds) 300 West May Street, Marengo, IA, Zip 52301–1261; tel. 319/642–5543; Barry Goettsch, FACHE, Chief Executive Officer

GREATER REGIONAL MEDICAL CENTER (C, 25 beds) 1700 West Townline Street Suite 3, Creston, IA, Zip 50801–1099; tel. 641/782–7091; Monte Neitzel, Chief Executive Officer
Web address: www.greaterregional.org

GREENE COUNTY MEDICAL CENTER (C, 85 beds) 1000 West Lincolnway, Jefferson, IA, Zip 50129–1645; tel. 515/386–2114; Carl P. Behne, Chief Executive Officer
Web address: www.gcmchealth.com

GRUNDY COUNTY MEMORIAL HOSPITAL (C, 25 beds) 201 East 'J' Avenue, Grundy Center, IA, Zip 50638–2096; tel. 319/824–5421; Adam Scherling, President

GUTHRIE COUNTY HOSPITAL (C, 17 beds) 710 North 12th Street, Guthrie Center, IA, Zip 50115–1544; tel. 641/332–2201; Patrick Peters, Chief Executive Officer
Web address: www.guthriecountyhospital.org

HUMBOLDT COUNTY MEMORIAL HOSPITAL (C, 49 beds) 1000 North 15th Street, Humboldt, IA, Zip 50548–1008; tel. 515/332–4200; Michelle Sleiter, Chief Executive Officer
Web address: www.humboldthospital.org

LORING HOSPITAL (C, 25 beds) 211 Highland Avenue, Sac City, IA, Zip 50583–2424; tel. 712/662–7105; Stacy Johnson, Chief Executive Officer
Web address: www.loringhospital.org

LUCAS COUNTY HEALTH CENTER (C, 25 beds) 1200 North Seventh Street, Chariton, IA, Zip 50049–1258; tel. 641/774–3000; Brian Sims, Chief Executive Officer

POCAHONTAS COMMUNITY HOSPITAL (C, 20 beds) 606 NW Seventh Street, Pocahontas, IA, Zip 50574–1099; tel. 712/335–3501; James D. Roetman, President and Chief Executive Officer
Web address: www.pocahontashospital.org

STEWART MEMORIAL COMMUNITY HOSPITAL (C, 25 beds) 1301 West Main, Lake City, IA, Zip 51449–1585; tel. 712/464–3171; Cynthia L. Carstens, R.N., Chief Executive Officer

STORY COUNTY MEDICAL CENTER (C, 82 beds) 640 South 19th Street, Nevada, IA, Zip 50201–2902; tel. 515/382–2111; Nate Thompson, Chief Executive Officer
Web address: www.storymedical.org

UNITYPOINT HEALTH – ALLEN HOSPITAL (O, 201 beds) 1825 Logan Avenue, Waterloo, IA, Zip 50703–1916; tel. 319/235–3941; Pamela K. Delagardelle, President and Chief Executive Officer
Web address: www.unitypoint.org/waterloo

UNITYPOINT HEALTH – FINLEY HOSPITAL (O, 109 beds) 350 North Grandview Avenue, Dubuque, IA, Zip 52001–6393; tel. 563/582–1881; Chad Wolbers, President and Chief Executive Officer

UNITYPOINT HEALTH – GRINNELL REGIONAL MEDICAL CENTER (O, 49 beds) 210 Fourth Avenue, Grinnell, IA, Zip 50112–1898; tel. 641/236–7511; Jennifer Havens, Chief Executive Officer
Web address: www.grmc.us

UNITYPOINT HEALTH – IOWA METHODIST MEDICAL CENTER (O, 459 beds) 1200 Pleasant Street, Des Moines, IA, Zip 50309–1406; tel. 515/241–6212; David A. Stark, FACHE, President and Chief Executive Officer

UNITYPOINT HEALTH – JONES REGIONAL MEDICAL CENTER (O, 22 beds) 1795 Highway 64 East, Anamosa, IA, Zip 52205–2112; tel. 319/462–6131; Eric Briesemeister, Chief Executive Officer
Web address: www.jonesregional.org

UNITYPOINT HEALTH – MARSHALLTOWN (O, 37 beds) 3 South Fourth Avenue, Marshalltown, IA, Zip 50158–2998; tel. 641/754–5151; Jennifer Friedly, President
Web address: www.https://marshalltown.unitypoint.org

UNITYPOINT HEALTH – ST. LUKE'S HOSPITAL (O, 345 beds) 1026 'A' Avenue NE, Cedar Rapids, IA, Zip 52402–3026, Mailing Address: P.O. Box 3026, Zip 52406–3026, tel. 319/369–7211; Michelle Niermann, President and Chief Executive Officer

UNITYPOINT HEALTH – ST. LUKES'S SIOUX CITY (O, 152 beds) 2720 Stone Park Boulevard, Sioux City, IA, Zip 51104–3734; tel. 712/279–3500; Lynn Wold, President and Chief Executive Officer
Web address: www.stlukes.org

UNITYPOINT HEALTH – TRINITY BETTENDORF (O, 86 beds) 4500 Utica Ridge Road, Bettendorf, IA, Zip 52722–1626; tel. 563/742–5000; John C. Sheehan, FACHE, Interim President and Chief Executive Officer

UNITYPOINT HEALTH – TRINITY MUSCATINE (O, 45 beds) 1518 Mulberry Avenue, Muscatine, IA, Zip 52761–3499; tel. 563/264–9100; Angela Johnson, Executive Director
Web address: www.unitypoint.org/quadcities/trinity-muscatine.aspx

UNITYPOINT HEALTH – TRINITY REGIONAL MEDICAL CENTER (O, 49 beds) 802 Kenyon Road, Fort Dodge, IA, Zip 50501–5795; tel. 515/573–3101; Leah Glasgo, Chief Executive Officer

UNITYPOINT HEALTH-IOWA LUTHERAN HOSPITAL (O, 207 beds) 700 East University Avenue, Des Moines, IA, Zip 50316–2392; tel. 515/263–5612; David A. Stark, FACHE, President and Chief Executive Officer
Web address: www.unitypoint.org

UNITYPOINT HEALTH-KEOKUK (O, 42 beds) 1600 Morgan Street, Keokuk, IA, Zip 52632–3456; tel. 319/524–7150; John Winenger, FACHE, Interim Chief Executive Officer
Web address: www.keokukhealthsystems.org

WISCONSIN: MEMORIAL HOSPITAL OF LAFAYETTE COUNTY (O, 25 beds) 800 Clay Street, Darlington, WI, Zip 53530–1228, Mailing Address: P.O. Box 70, Zip 53530–0070, tel. 608/776–4466; Kathleen Kuepers, Chief Executive Officer

UNITYPOINT HEALTH MERITER (O, 217 beds) 202 South Park Street, Madison, WI, Zip 53715–1507; tel. 608/417–6000; Sue Erickson, President and Chief Executive Officer
Web address: www.meriter.com

Owned, leased, sponsored:	22 hospitals	2994 beds
Contract-managed:	13 hospitals	454 beds
Totals:	35 hospitals	3448 beds

For explanation of codes following names, see page B2.
★ Indicates Type III membership in the American Hospital Association.

9555: UNIVERSAL HEALTH SERVICES, INC. (IO)
367 South Gulph Road, King of Prussia, PA, Zip 19406–3121, Mailing Address: P.O. Box 61558, Zip 19406–0958, tel. 610/768–3300; Alan B. Miller, Chairman and Chief Executive Officer
(Decentralized Health System)

ALABAMA: HILL CREST BEHAVIORAL HEALTH SERVICES (O, 80 beds) 6869 Fifth Avenue South, Birmingham, AL, Zip 35212–1866; tel. 205/833–9000; Steve McCabe, Chief Executive Officer
Web address: www.hillcrestbhs.com

LAUREL OAKS BEHAVIORAL HEALTH CENTER (O, 38 beds) 700 East Cottonwood Road, Dothan, AL, Zip 36301–3644; tel. 334/794–7373; Derek Johnson, Chief Executive Officer

ALASKA: NORTH STAR BEHAVIORAL HEALTH SYSTEM (O, 200 beds) 2530 DeBarr Circle, Anchorage, AK, Zip 99508–2948; tel. 907/258–7575; Andrew Mayo, Ph.D., Chief Executive Officer and Managing Director
Web address: www.northstarbehavioral.com

ARIZONA: PALO VERDE BEHAVIORAL HEALTH (O, 48 beds) 2695 North Craycroft Road, Tucson, AZ, Zip 85712–2244; tel. 520/322–2888; Melissa Eckstein, Chief Executive Officer

VALLEY HOSPITAL PHOENIX (O, 122 beds) 3550 East Pinchot Avenue, Phoenix, AZ, Zip 85018–7434; tel. 602/957–4000; Michelle David, Chief Executive Officer
Web address: www.valleyhospital-phoenix.com

ARKANSAS: PINNACLE POINTE HOSPITAL (O, 127 beds) 11501 Financial Center Parkway, Little Rock, AR, Zip 72211–3715; tel. 501/223–3322; Shane Frazier, Chief Executive Officer
Web address: www.pinnaclepointehospital.com

RIVENDELL BEHAVIORAL HEALTH SERVICES OF ARKANSAS (O, 80 beds) 100 Rivendell Drive, Benton, AR, Zip 72019–9100; tel. 501/316–1255; Ballard Sheppard, Chief Executive Officer
Web address: www.rivendellofarkansas.com

SPRINGWOODS BEHAVIORAL HEALTH HOSPITAL (O, 80 beds) 1955 West Truckers Drive, Fayetteville, AR, Zip 72704–5637; tel. 479/973–6000; Jordon Babcock, Chief Executive Officer
Web address: www.springwoodsbehavioral.com

THE BRIDGEWAY (I, 124 beds) 21 Bridgeway Road, North Little Rock, AR, Zip 72113–9516; tel. 501/771–1500; Sherrie James, R.N., Chief Executive Officer
Web address: www.thebridgeway.com

CALIFORNIA: BHC ALHAMBRA HOSPITAL (O, 97 beds) 4619 North Rosemead Boulevard, Rosemead, CA, Zip 91770–1478, Mailing Address: P.O. Box 369, Zip 91770–0369, tel. 626/286–1191; Peggy Minnick, R.N., Chief Executive Officer

CANYON RIDGE HOSPITAL (O, 106 beds) 5353 'G' Street, Chino, CA, Zip 91710–5250; tel. 909/590–3700; Burt Harris, Acting Chief Executive Officer
Web address: www.canyonridgehospital.com

CORONA REGIONAL MEDICAL CENTER (O, 147 beds) 800 South Main Street, Corona, CA, Zip 92882–3400; tel. 951/737–4343; Mark H. Uffer, Chief Executive Officer
Web address: www.coronaregional.com

DEL AMO HOSPITAL (O, 70 beds) 23700 Camino Del Sol, Torrance, CA, Zip 90505–5000; tel. 310/530–1151; Steven Hytry, PsyD, Chief Executive Officer
Web address: www.delamohospital.com

FREMONT HOSPITAL (O, 148 beds) 39001 Sundale Drive, Fremont, CA, Zip 94538–2005; tel. 510/796–1100; Tricia Williams, Chief Executive Officer

HERITAGE OAKS HOSPITAL (O, 120 beds) 4250 Auburn Boulevard, Sacramento, CA, Zip 95841–4164; tel. 916/489–3336; Shawn Silva, Chief Executive Officer
Web address: www.heritageoakshospital.com

PALMDALE REGIONAL MEDICAL CENTER (O, 184 beds) 38600 Medical Center Drive, Palmdale, CA, Zip 93551–4483; tel. 661/382–5000; Richard Allen, Chief Executive Officer

SIERRA VISTA HOSPITAL (O, 171 beds) 8001 Bruceville Road, Sacramento, CA, Zip 95823–2329; tel. 916/288–0300; Mike Zauner, Chief Executive Officer
Web address: www.sierravistahospital.com

SOUTHWEST HEALTHCARE SYSTEM (O, 231 beds) 25500 Medical Center Drive, Murrieta, CA, Zip 92562–5965; tel. 951/696–6000; Bradley D. Neet, FACHE, Chief Executive Officer

TEMECULA VALLEY HOSPITAL (O, 140 beds) 31700 Temecula Parkway, Temecula, CA, Zip 92592–5896; tel. 951/331–2216; Darlene Wetton, R.N., Chief Executive Officer
Web address: www.temeculavalleyhospital.com

COLORADO: CEDAR SPRINGS HOSPITAL (O, 110 beds) 2135 Southgate Road, Colorado Springs, CO, Zip 80906–2693; tel. 719/633–4114; Christopher D. Burke, Ph.D., Chief Executive Officer

CENTENNIAL PEAKS HOSPITAL (O, 72 beds) 2255 South 88th Street, Louisville, CO, Zip 80027–9716; tel. 303/673–9990; Elicia Bunch, Chief Executive Officer
Web address: www.centennialpeaks.com

HIGHLANDS BEHAVIORAL HEALTH SYSTEM (O, 86 beds) 8565 South Poplar Way, Littleton, CO, Zip 80130–3602; tel. 720/348–2800; Amy Alexander, Chief Executive Officer

DELAWARE: DOVER BEHAVIORAL HEALTH SYSTEM (O, 80 beds) 725 Horsepond Road, Dover, DE, Zip 19901–7232; tel. 302/741–0140; Jean-Charles Constant, Administrator
Web address: www.doverbehavioral.com

ROCKFORD CENTER (O, 138 beds) 100 Rockford Drive, Newark, DE, Zip 19713–2121; tel. 302/996–5480; John F. McKenna, Chief Executive Officer and Managing Director
Web address: www.rockfordcenter.com

DISTRICT OF COLUMBIA: GEORGE WASHINGTON UNIVERSITY HOSPITAL (O, 385 beds) 900 23rd Street NW, Washington, DC, Zip 20037–2342; tel. 202/715–4000; Kimberly Russo, Chief Executive Officer
Web address: www.gwhospital.com

FLORIDA: CENTRAL FLORIDA BEHAVIORAL HOSPITAL (O, 126 beds) 6601 Central Florida Parkway, Orlando, FL, Zip 32821–8064; tel. 407/370–0111; Vickie Lewis, Chief Executive Officer
Web address: www.centralfloridabehavioral.com

EMERALD COAST BEHAVIORAL HOSPITAL (O, 86 beds) 1940 Harrison Avenue, Panama City, FL, Zip 32405–4542; tel. 850/763–0017; Tim Bedford, Chief Executive Officer
Web address: www.emeraldcoastbehavioral.com

FORT LAUDERDALE HOSPITAL (L, 182 beds) 1601 East Las Olas Boulevard, Fort Lauderdale, FL, Zip 33301–2393, tel. 954/463–4321; Manuel R. Llano, Chief Executive Officer

LAKEWOOD RANCH MEDICAL CENTER (O, 120 beds) 8330 Lakewood Ranch Boulevard, Bradenton, FL, Zip 34202–5174; tel. 941/782–2100; Andrew Guz, Chief Executive Officer
Web address: www.lakewoodranchmedicalcenter.com

MANATEE MEMORIAL HOSPITAL (O, 319 beds) 206 Second Street East, Bradenton, FL, Zip 34208–1000; tel. 941/746–5111; Kevin DiLallo, Chief Executive Officer

RIVER POINT BEHAVIORAL HEALTH (O, 92 beds) 6300 Beach Boulevard, Jacksonville, FL, Zip 32216–2782; tel. 904/724–9202; Kevin McGee, Chief Executive Officer
Web address: www.riverpointbehavioral.com

SUNCOAST BEHAVIORAL HEALTH CENTER (O, 60 beds) 4480 51st Street West, Bradenton, FL, Zip 34210–2855; tel. 941/251–5000; Brandy Hamilton, Chief Executive Officer

THE VINES (O, 98 beds) 3130 SW 27th Avenue, Ocala, FL, Zip 34471–4306; tel. 352/671–3130; Stephen Quintyne, Chief Executive Officer
Web address: www.thevineshospital.com

WEKIVA SPRINGS (O, 60 beds) 3947 Salisbury Road, Jacksonville, FL, Zip 32216–6115; tel. 904/296–3533; Sheila Carr, Chief Executive Officer
Web address: www.wekivacenter.com

WELLINGTON REGIONAL MEDICAL CENTER (L, 233 beds) 10101 Forest Hill Boulevard, Wellington, FL, Zip 33414–6199; tel. 561/798–8500; Pamela S. Tahan, Chief Executive Officer
Web address: www.wellingtonregional.com

WINDMOOR HEALTHCARE OF CLEARWATER (O, 100 beds) 11300 U S 19 North, Clearwater, FL, Zip 33764; tel. 727/541–2646; Wendy Merson, Chief Executive Officer

GEORGIA: ANCHOR HOSPITAL (O, 122 beds) 5454 Yorktowne Drive, Atlanta, GA, Zip 30349–5317; tel. 770/991–6044; Lloyd Noble, Chief Executive Officer
Web address: www.anchorhospital.com

For explanation of codes following names, see page B2.
★ Indicates Type III membership in the American Hospital Association.

COASTAL HARBOR TREATMENT CENTER (O, 191 beds) 1150 Cornell Avenue, Savannah, GA, Zip 31406–2702; tel. 912/354–3911; Sally Perry, Chief Executive Officer
Web address: www.coastalharbor.com

PEACHFORD BEHAVIORAL HEALTH SYSTEM (O, 246 beds) 2151 Peachford Road, Atlanta, GA, Zip 30338–6599; tel. 770/455–3200; Matthew Crouch, Chief Executive Officer and Managing Director

SAINT SIMONS BY-THE-SEA HOSPITAL (O, 101 beds) 2927 Demere Road, Saint Simons Island, GA, Zip 31522–1620; tel. 912/638–1999; Chuck Flavio, Chief Executive Officer
Web address: www.ssbythesea.com

TURNING POINT HOSPITAL (O, 69 beds) 3015 Veterans Parkway South, Moultrie, GA, Zip 31788–6705, Mailing Address: P.O. Box 1177, Zip 31776–1177, tel. 229/985–4815; Judy H. Payne, Chief Executive Officer

IDAHO: INTERMOUNTAIN HOSPITAL (O, 135 beds) 303 North Allumbaugh Street, Boise, ID, Zip 83704–9208; tel. 208/377–8400; Jeffrey F. Morrell, Chief Executive Officer
Web address: www.intermountainhospital.com

ILLINOIS: GARFIELD PARK HOSPITAL (O, 88 beds) 520 North Ridgeway Avenue, Chicago, IL, Zip 60624–1232; tel. 773/265–3700; Steven Airhart, Chief Executive Officer
Web address: www.garfieldparkhospital.com

HARTGROVE HOSPITAL (O, 128 beds) 5730 West Roosevelt Road, Chicago, IL, Zip 60644–1580; tel. 773/413–1700; Steven Airhart, Chief Executive Officer
Web address: www.hartgrovehospital.com

LINCOLN PRAIRIE BEHAVIORAL HEALTH CENTER (O, 97 beds) 5230 South Sixth Street, Springfield, IL, Zip 62703–5128; tel. 217/585–1180; Mark Littrell, Chief Executive Officer

RIVEREDGE HOSPITAL (O, 224 beds) 8311 West Roosevelt Road, Forest Park, IL, Zip 60130–2500; tel. 708/771–7000; Carey Carlock, Chief Executive Officer
Web address: www.riveredgehospital.com

STREAMWOOD BEHAVIORAL HEALTH CENTER (O, 178 beds) 1400 East Irving Park Road, Streamwood, IL, Zip 60107–3203; tel. 630/837–9000; Ron Weglarz, Chief Executive Officer and Managing Director

THE PAVILION (O, 106 beds) 809 West Church Street, Champaign, IL, Zip 61820–3399; tel. 217/373–1700; Mark Littrell, Group Director
Web address: www.pavilionhospital.com

INDIANA: BLOOMINGTON MEADOWS HOSPITAL (O, 67 beds) 3600 North Prow Road, Bloomington, IN, Zip 47404–1616; tel. 812/331–8000; Christopher Dowers, Chief Executive Officer

MICHIANA BEHAVIORAL HEALTH CENTER (O, 75 beds) 1800 North Oak Drive, Plymouth, IN, Zip 46563–3492; tel. 574/936–3784; Michael Perry, Chief Executive Officer
Web address: www.michianabhc.com

VALLE VISTA HEALTH SYSTEM (O, 102 beds) 898 East Main Street, Greenwood, IN, Zip 46143–1400; tel. 317/887–1348; Sherri R. Jewett, Chief Executive Officer
Web address: www.vallevistahospital.com

WELLSTONE REGIONAL HOSPITAL (O, 100 beds) 2700 Vissing Park Road, Jeffersonville, IN, Zip 47130–5989; tel. 812/284–8000; Greg Stewart, Chief Executive Officer

KENTUCKY: CUMBERLAND HALL HOSPITAL (O, 97 beds) 270 Walton Way, Hopkinsville, KY, Zip 42240–6808; tel. 270/886–1919; Jason Staats, Chief Executive Officer
Web address: www.cumberlandhallhospital.com

LINCOLN TRAIL BEHAVIORAL HEALTH SYSTEM (O, 140 beds) 3909 South Wilson Road, Radcliff, KY, Zip 40160–8944, Mailing Address: P.O. Box 369, Zip 40159–0369, tel. 270/351–9444; Charles L. Webb Jr, Chief Executive Officer
Web address: www.lincolnbehavioral.com

RIDGE BEHAVIORAL HEALTH SYSTEM (O, 110 beds) 3050 Rio Dosa Drive, Lexington, KY, Zip 40509–1540; tel. 859/269–2325; Nina W. Eisner, Chief Executive Officer and Managing Director

RIVENDELL BEHAVIORAL HEALTH (O, 125 beds) 1035 Porter Pike, Bowling Green, KY, Zip 42103–9581; tel. 270/843–1199; Matt Ours, Chief Executive Officer and Managing Director
Web address: www.rivendellbehavioral.com

THE BROOK HOSPITAL – KMI (O, 98 beds) 8521 Old LaGrange Road, Louisville, KY, Zip 40242–3800; tel. 502/426–6380; Paul Andrews, Chief Executive Officer
Web address: www.thebrookhospitals.com

THE BROOK AT DUPONT (O, 88 beds) 1405 Browns Lane, Louisville, KY, Zip 40207–4608; tel. 502/896–0495; Paul Andrews, Chief Executive Officer

LOUISIANA: BRENTWOOD HOSPITAL (O, 176 beds) 1006 Highland Avenue, Shreveport, LA, Zip 71101–4103; tel. 318/678–7500; William Weaver, Chief Executive Officer
Web address: www.brentwoodbehavioral.com

RIVER OAKS HOSPITAL (O, 126 beds) 1525 River Oaks Road West, New Orleans, LA, Zip 70123–2162; tel. 504/734–1740; Deagan Watson, Chief Executive Officer
Web address: www.riveroakshospital.com

MASSACHUSETTS: ARBOUR H. R. I. HOSPITAL (O, 76 beds) 227 Babcock Street, Brookline, MA, Zip 02446–6799; tel. 617/731–3200; Jameson Pinette, Chief Executive Officer

ARBOUR HOSPITAL (O, 118 beds) 49 Robinwood Avenue, Boston, MA, Zip 02130–2156; tel. 617/522–4400; Eric Kennedy, Chief Executive Officer
Web address: www.arbourhealth.com

ARBOUR-FULLER HOSPITAL (O, 46 beds) 200 May Street, Attleboro, MA, Zip 02703–5520; tel. 508/761–8500; Rachel Legend, Chief Executive Officer
Web address: www.arbourhealth.com

PEMBROKE HOSPITAL (O, 115 beds) 199 Oak Street, Pembroke, MA, Zip 02359–1953; tel. 781/829–7000; Raymond Robinson, Chief Executive Officer

MICHIGAN: FOREST VIEW PSYCHIATRIC HOSPITAL (O, 108 beds) 1055 Medical Park Drive SE, Grand Rapids, MI, Zip 49546–3607; tel. 616/942–9610; Andrew Hotaling, Chief Executive Officer
Web address: www.forestviewhospital.com

HAVENWYCK HOSPITAL (O, 243 beds) 1525 University Drive, Auburn Hills, MI, Zip 48326–2673; tel. 248/373–9200; Julie Szyska, Chief Executive Officer and Managing Director

MISSISSIPPI: ALLIANCE HEALTH CENTER (O, 154 beds) 5000 Highway 39 North, Meridian, MS, Zip 39301–1021; tel. 601/483–6211; Jay Shehi, Chief Executive Officer
Web address: www.alliancehealthcenter.com

BRENTWOOD BEHAVIORAL HEALTHCARE OF MISSISSIPPI (O, 105 beds) 3531 East Lakeland Drive, Jackson, MS, Zip 39232–8839; tel. 601/936–2024; Michael J. Carney, Chief Executive Officer

GULFPORT BEHAVIORAL HEALTH SYSTEM (O, 48 beds) 11150 Highway 49 North, Gulfport, MS, Zip 39503–4110; tel. 228/831–1700; Michael A. Zieman, FACHE, Administrator
Web address: www.gulfportmemorial.com

PARKWOOD BEHAVIORAL HEALTH SYSTEM (O, 148 beds) 8135 Goodman Road, Olive Branch, MS, Zip 38654–2103; tel. 662/895–4900; Vince Brummett, Chief Executive Officer
Web address: www.parkwoodbhs.com

MISSOURI: HEARTLAND BEHAVIORAL HEALTH SERVICES (O, 69 beds) 1500 West Ashland Street, Nevada, MO, Zip 64772–1710; tel. 417/667–2666; Alyson Wysong-Harder, Chief Executive Officer
Web address: www.heartlandbehavioral.com

TWO RIVERS BEHAVIORAL HEALTH SYSTEM (O, 105 beds) 5121 Raytown Road, Kansas City, MO, Zip 64133–2141; tel. 816/382–6300; Greg Shannon, Chief Executive Officer

NEVADA: CENTENNIAL HILLS HOSPITAL MEDICAL CENTER (O, 165 beds) 6900 North Durango Drive, Las Vegas, NV, Zip 89149–4409; tel. 702/835–9700; Sajit Pullarkat, Chief Executive Officer and Managing Director
Web address: www.centennialhillshospital.com

DESERT SPRINGS HOSPITAL MEDICAL CENTER (O, 293 beds) 2075 East Flamingo Road, Las Vegas, NV, Zip 89119–5121; tel. 702/733–8800; Ryan Jensen, Chief Executive Officer
Web address: www.desertspringshospital.com

DESERT VIEW HOSPITAL (O, 25 beds) 360 South Lola Lane, Pahrump, NV, Zip 89048–0884; tel. 775/751–7500; Susan Davila, Chief Executive Officer

HENDERSON HOSPITAL (O, 145 beds) 1050 West Galleria Drive, Henderson, NV, Zip 89011; tel. 702/963–7000; Samuel Kaufman, Chief Executive Officer
Web address: www.hendersonhospital.com/

For explanation of codes following names, see page B2.
★ Indicates Type III membership in the American Hospital Association.

NORTHERN NEVADA MEDICAL CENTER (O, 108 beds) 2375 East Prater Way, Sparks, NV, Zip 89434–9641; tel. 775/331–7000; Alan C. Olive, Chief Executive Officer

SPRING MOUNTAIN SAHARA (O, 30 beds) 5460 West Sahara, Las Vegas, NV, Zip 89146–3307; tel. 702/216–8900; Darryl S. Dubroca, Chief Executive Officer and Managing Director
Web address: www.springmountainsahara.com

SPRING MOUNTAIN TREATMENT CENTER (L, 110 beds) 7000 West Spring Mountain Road, Las Vegas, NV, Zip 89117–3816; tel. 702/873–2400; C. Alan. Eaks, Chief Executive Officer and Managing Director

SPRING VALLEY HOSPITAL MEDICAL CENTER (O, 169 beds) 5400 South Rainbow Boulevard, Las Vegas, NV, Zip 89118–1859; tel. 702/853–3000; Leonard Freehof, Chief Executive Officer and Managing Director
Web address: www.springvalleyhospital.com

SUMMERLIN HOSPITAL MEDICAL CENTER (O, 148 beds) 657 Town Center Drive, Las Vegas, NV, Zip 89144–6367; tel. 702/233–7000; Robert S. Freymuller, Chief Executive Officer

VALLEY HOSPITAL MEDICAL CENTER (O, 365 beds) 620 Shadow Lane, Las Vegas, NV, Zip 89106–4119; tel. 702/388–4000; Claude Wise, Chief Executive Officer
Web address: www.valleyhospital.net

WEST HILLS HOSPITAL (O, 190 beds) 1240 East Ninth Street, Reno, NV, Zip 89512–2964; tel. 775/323–0478; Nadine Dexter, Chief Executive Officer
Web address: www.westhillshospital.net

NEW JERSEY: HAMPTON BEHAVIORAL HEALTH CENTER (O, 120 beds) 650 Rancocas Road, Westampton, NJ, Zip 08060–5613; tel. 609/267–7000; Craig Hilton, Chief Executive Officer and Managing Director
Web address: www.hamptonhospital.com

SUMMIT OAKS HOSPITAL (O, 90 beds) 19 Prospect Street, Summit, NJ, Zip 07901–2530; tel. 908/522–7000; Ross Friedman, Chief Executive Officer
Web address: www.summitoakshospital.com/

NEW MEXICO: MESILLA VALLEY HOSPITAL (O, 105 beds) 3751 Del Rey Boulevard, Las Cruces, NM, Zip 88012–8526; tel. 575/382–3500; Anna Laliotis, Chief Executive Officer

NORTH CAROLINA: BRYNN MARR HOSPITAL (O, 99 beds) 192 Village Drive, Jacksonville, NC, Zip 28546–7299; tel. 910/577–1400; Colin Weaver, Chief Executive Officer
Web address: www.brynnmarr.org

HOLLY HILL HOSPITAL (O, 228 beds) 3019 Falstaff Road, Raleigh, NC, Zip 27610–1812; tel. 919/250–7000; Amanda Johanson, Chief Executive Officer
Web address: www.hollyhillhospital.com

OLD VINEYARD BEHAVIORAL HEALTH SERVICES (O, 158 beds) 3637 Old Vineyard Road, Winston-Salem, NC, Zip 27104–4842; tel. 336/794–3550; Kevin Patton, Chief Executive Officer
Web address: www.oldvineyardbhs.com

NORTH DAKOTA: PRAIRIE ST. JOHN'S (O, 94 beds) 510 4th Street South, Fargo, ND, Zip 58103–1914; tel. 701/476–7200; Jeff Herman, Chief Executive Officer
Web address: www.prairie-stjohns.com

OHIO: ARROWHEAD BEHAVIORAL HEALTH HOSPITAL (O, 48 beds) 1725 Timber Line Road, Maumee, OH, Zip 43537–4015; tel. 419/891–9333; Theresa Contreras, Chief Executive Officer

BELMONT PINES HOSPITAL (O, 96 beds) 615 Churchill-Hubbard Road, Youngstown, OH, Zip 44505–1379; tel. 330/759–2700; Lisa Cocca, Chief Executive Officer
Web address: www.belmontpines.com

WINDSOR-LAURELWOOD CENTER FOR BEHAVIORAL MEDICINE (O, 159 beds) 35900 Euclid Avenue, Willoughby, OH, Zip 44094–4648; tel. 440/953–3000; Ric McAllister, Chief Executive Officer
Web address: www.windsorlaurelwood.com

OKLAHOMA: CEDAR RIDGE HOSPITAL (O, 172 beds) 6501 NE 50th Street, Oklahoma City, OK, Zip 73141–9118; tel. 405/605–6111; Heather Joseph, Chief Executive Officer
Web address: www.cedarridgebhs.com

ST. MARY'S REGIONAL MEDICAL CENTER (O, 124 beds) 305 South Fifth Street, Enid, OK, Zip 73701–5899, Mailing Address: P.O. Box 232, Zip 73702–0232, tel. 580/233–6100; Krista Roberts, Chief Executive Officer
Web address: www.stmarysregional.com

OREGON: CEDAR HILLS HOSPITAL (O, 78 beds) 10300 SW Eastridge Street, Portland, OR, Zip 97225–5004; tel. 503/944–5000; Elizabeth Hutter, Chief Executive Officer

PENNSYLVANIA: BROOKE GLEN BEHAVIORAL HOSPITAL (O, 146 beds) 7170 Lafayette Avenue, Fort Washington, PA, Zip 19034–2301; tel. 215/641–5300; Neil Callahan, Chief Executive Officer
Web address: www.brookeglenhospital.com

CLARION PSYCHIATRIC CENTER (O, 74 beds) 2 Hospital Drive, Clarion, PA, Zip 16214–8502; tel. 814/226–9545; Michael Post, Chief Executive Officer

FAIRMOUNT BEHAVIORAL HEALTH SYSTEM (O, 235 beds) 561 Fairthorne Avenue, Philadelphia, PA, Zip 19128–2499; tel. 215/487–4000; Mark L. Howard, Chief Executive Officer
Web address: www.fairmountbhs.com

FOUNDATIONS BEHAVIORAL HEALTH (O, 58 beds) 833 East Butler Avenue, Doylestown, PA, Zip 18901–2280; tel. 215/345–0444; Gina Fusco, Chief Executive Officer
Web address: www.fbh.com

FRIENDS HOSPITAL (O, 192 beds) 4641 Roosevelt Boulevard, Philadelphia, PA, Zip 19124–2343; tel. 215/831–4600; Michael S. McDonald Jr, Chief Executive Officer

HORSHAM CLINIC (O, 206 beds) 722 East Butler Pike, Ambler, PA, Zip 19002–2310; tel. 215/643–7800; Phyllis Weisfield, Chief Executive Officer and Managing Director
Web address: www.horshamclinic.com

MEADOWS PSYCHIATRIC CENTER (O, 119 beds) 132 The Meadows Drive, Centre Hall, PA, Zip 16828–9231; tel. 814/364–2161; David Grabowski, Chief Executive Officer
Web address: www.themeadows.net

ROXBURY TREATMENT CENTER (O, 94 beds) 601 Roxbury Road, Shippensburg, PA, Zip 17257–9302; tel. 800/648–4673; Shauna Mogerman, Chief Executive Officer

PUERTO RICO: FIRST HOSPITAL PANAMERICANO (O, 153 beds) State Road 787 KM 1 5, Cidra, PR, Zip 739, Mailing Address: P.O. Box 1400, Zip 739, tel. 787/739–5555; Astro Munoz, Executive Director
Web address: www.hospitalpanamericano.com

SOUTH CAROLINA: AIKEN REGIONAL MEDICAL CENTERS (O, 299 beds) 302 University Parkway, Aiken, SC, Zip 29801–6302; tel. 803/641–5000; James F. O'Loughlin, Chief Executive Officer
Web address: www.aikenregional.com

CAROLINA CENTER FOR BEHAVIORAL HEALTH (O, 138 beds) 2700 East Phillips Road, Greer, SC, Zip 29650–4816; tel. 864/235–2335; John Willingham, Chief Executive Officer and Managing Director
Web address: www.thecarolinacenter.com

LIGHTHOUSE BEHAVIORAL HEALTH HOSPITAL (O, 90 beds) 152 Waccamaw Medical Park Drive, Conway, SC, Zip 29526–8901; tel. 843/347–8871; Thomas L. Ryba, Chief Executive Officer

PALMETTO LOWCOUNTRY BEHAVIORAL HEALTH (O, 100 beds) 2777 Speissegger Drive, Charleston, SC, Zip 29405–8229; tel. 843/747–5830; Clint Hauger, Chief Executive Officer
Web address: www.palmettobehavioralhealth.com

THREE RIVERS BEHAVIORAL HEALTH (O, 122 beds) 2900 Sunset Boulevard, West Columbia, SC, Zip 29169–3422; tel. 803/796–9911; Shannon Marcus, Chief Executive Officer
Web address: www.threeriversbehavioral.org

TENNESSEE: LAKESIDE BEHAVIORAL HEALTH SYSTEM (O, 345 beds) 2911 Brunswick Road, Memphis, TN, Zip 38133–4199; tel. 901/377–4700; Joy Golden, Chief Executive Officer
Web address: www.lakesidebhs.com

ROLLING HILLS HOSPITAL (O, 120 beds) 2014 Quail Hollow Circle, Franklin, TN, Zip 37067–5967; tel. 615/628–5700; Laurel Roberts, R.N., MSN, Interim Chief Executive Officer

TEXAS: AUSTIN LAKES HOSPITAL (O, 58 beds) 1025 East 32nd Street, Austin, TX, Zip 78705–2714; tel. 512/544–5253; Robert J. Lerma, MS, Chief Executive Officer
Web address: www.austinlakeshospital.com

AUSTIN OAKS HOSPITAL (O, 80 beds) 1407 West Stassney Lane, Austin, TX, Zip 78745–2947; tel. 512/440–4800; Steve Kelly, Interim Chief Executive Officer
Web address: www.austinoakshospital.com

Section B

For explanation of codes following names, see page B2.
★ Indicates Type III membership in the American Hospital Association.

BEHAVIORAL HOSPITAL OF BELLAIRE (O, 122 beds) 5314 Dashwood Drive, Houston, TX, Zip 77081-4603; tel. 713/600-9500; Eric Amoh, Chief Executive Officer

CORNERSTONE REGIONAL HOSPITAL (L, 14 beds) 2302 Cornerstone Boulevard, Edinburg, TX, Zip 78539-8471; tel. 956/618-4444; Roxanna M. Godinez, Chief Executive Officer
Web address: www.cornerstoneregional.com

CYPRESS CREEK HOSPITAL (O, 128 beds) 17750 Cali Drive, Houston, TX, Zip 77090-2700; tel. 281/586-7600; Phuong Cardoza, Interim Chief Executive Officer

DOCTORS HOSPITAL OF LAREDO (O, 183 beds) 10700 McPherson Road, Laredo, TX, Zip 78045-6268; tel. 956/523-2000; James R. Resendez, Chief Executive Officer
Web address: www.doctorshosplaredo.com

EL PASO BEHAVIORAL HEALTH SYSTEM (O, 166 beds) 1900 Denver Avenue, El Paso, TX, Zip 79902-3008; tel. 915/544-4000; Phillip Sosa, Interim Chief Executive Officer
Web address: www.ubhelpaso.com/

FORT DUNCAN REGIONAL MEDICAL CENTER (O, 101 beds) 3333 North Foster Maldonado Boulevard, Eagle Pass, TX, Zip 78852-5893; tel. 830/773-5321; Eladio Montalvo, Chief Executive Officer

GARLAND BEHAVIORAL HOSPITAL (O, 72 beds) 2300 Marie Curie Boulevard, 5th Floor, Garland, TX, Zip 75402; tel. 972/487-5309; Kristin Harris, Chief Executive Officer
Web address: www.garlandbehavioralhospital.com/

GLEN OAKS HOSPITAL (O, 54 beds) 301 Division Street, Greenville, TX, Zip 75401-4101; tel. 903/454-6000; James Miller, Chief Executive Officer
Web address: www.glenoakshospital.com

HICKORY TRAIL HOSPITAL (O, 86 beds) 2000 Old Hickory Trail, Desoto, TX, Zip 75115-2242; tel. 972/298-7323; Kay McKennery, Interim Chief Executive Officer

KINGWOOD PINES HOSPITAL (O, 55 beds) 2001 Ladbrook Drive, Kingwood, TX, Zip 77339-3004; tel. 281/404-1001; Shanti Carter, Chief Executive Officer
Web address: www.kingwoodpines.com

LAUREL RIDGE TREATMENT CENTER (O, 208 beds) 17720 Corporate Woods Drive, San Antonio, TX, Zip 78259-3500; tel. 210/491-9400; Jacob Cuellar, M.D., Chief Executive Officer

MAYHILL HOSPITAL (O, 59 beds) 2809 South Mayhill Road, Denton, TX, Zip 76208-5910; tel. 940/239-3000; Loren Fouch, Chief Executive Officer
Web address: www.mayhillhospital.com

MILLWOOD HOSPITAL (O, 134 beds) 1011 North Cooper Street, Arlington, TX, Zip 76011-5517; tel. 817/261-3121; Brian Gill, Chief Executive Officer

NORTHWEST TEXAS HEALTHCARE SYSTEM (O, 430 beds) 1501 South Coulter Avenue, Amarillo, TX, Zip 79106-1770, Mailing Address: P.O. Box 1110, Zip 79105-1110, tel. 806/354-1000; Ryan Chandler, Chief Executive Officer
Web address: www.nwtexashealthcare.com

RIVER CREST HOSPITAL (O, 80 beds) 1636 Hunters Glen Road, San Angelo, TX, Zip 76901-5016; tel. 325/949-5722; Juana Giralt, Interim Chief Executive Officer

SOUTH TEXAS HEALTH SYSTEM (O, 810 beds) 1400 West Trenton Road, Edinburg, TX, Zip 78539-9105, Mailing Address: 1102 West Trenton Road, Zip 78539-9105, tel. 956/388-6000; Brenda Ivory, MSN, Chief Executive Officer
Web address: www.southtexashealthsystem.com

TEXAS NEUROREHAB CENTER (O, 47 beds) 1106 West Dittmar Road, Building 9, Austin, TX, Zip 78745-6328, Mailing Address: P.O. Box 150459, Zip 78715-0459, tel. 512/444-4835; Edgar E. Prettyman, PsyD, Chief Executive Officer

TEXOMA MEDICAL CENTER (O, 378 beds) 5016 South US Highway 75, Denison, TX, Zip 75020-4584, Mailing Address: P.O. Box 890, Zip 75021-0890, tel. 903/416-4000; Ronald T. Seal, Chief Executive Officer
Web address: www.texomamedicalcenter.net

UNIVERSITY BEHAVIORAL HEALTH OF DENTON (O, 104 beds) 2026 West University Drive, Denton, TX, Zip 76201-0644; tel. 940/320-8100; Ronald Rains, Chief Executive Officer
Web address: www.ubhdenton.com

WEST OAKS HOSPITAL (O, 144 beds) 6500 Hornwood Drive, Houston, TX, Zip 77074-5095; tel. 713/995-0909; Mandy Westerman, Chief Executive Officer

UTAH: PROVO CANYON BEHAVIORAL HOSPITAL (O, 80 beds) 1350 East 750 North, Orem, UT, Zip 84097-4345; tel. 801/852-2273; Jeremy Cottle, Ph.D., Chief Executive Officer
Web address: www.pcbh.com

SALT LAKE BEHAVIORAL HEALTH (O, 118 beds) 3802 South 700 East, Salt Lake City, UT, Zip 84106-1182; tel. 801/264-6000; Kreg Gillman, Chief Executive Officer
Web address: www.saltlakebehavioralhealth.com

VIRGINIA: CUMBERLAND HOSPITAL FOR CHILDREN AND ADOLESCENTS (O, 118 beds) 9407 Cumberland Road, New Kent, VA, Zip 23124-2029; tel. 804/966-2242; Patrice Gay. Brooks, Chief Executive Officer
Web address: www.cumberlandhospital.com

POPLAR SPRINGS HOSPITAL (O, 180 beds) 350 Poplar Drive, Petersburg, VA, Zip 23805-9367; tel. 804/733-6874; Nelson Smith, Chief Executive Officer
Web address: www.poplarsprings.com

VIRGINIA BEACH PSYCHIATRIC CENTER (O, 100 beds) 1100 First Colonial Road, Virginia Beach, VA, Zip 23454-2403; tel. 757/496-6000

WASHINGTON: FAIRFAX BEHAVIORAL HEALTH (O, 221 beds) 10200 NE 132nd Street, Kirkland, WA, Zip 98034-2899; tel. 425/821-2000; Beckie Shauinger, Chief Executive Officer
Web address: www.fairfaxhospital.com

WEST VIRGINIA: RIVER PARK HOSPITAL (O, 175 beds) 1230 Sixth Avenue, Huntington, WV, Zip 25701-2312, Mailing Address: P.O. Box 1875, Zip 25719-1875, tel. 304/526-9111; Terry A. Stephens, Chief Executive Officer
Web address: www.riverparkhospital.net

WYOMING: WYOMING BEHAVIORAL INSTITUTE (O, 129 beds) 2521 East 15th Street, Casper, WY, Zip 82609-4126; tel. 307/237-7444; Mike Phillips, Chief Executive Officer

Owned, leased, sponsored:	142 hospitals	19434 beds
Contract-managed:	0 hospitals	0 beds
Totals:	142 hospitals	19434 beds

★0896: **UNIVERSITY HEALTH CARE SYSTEM** (NP)
1350 Walton Way, Augusta, GA, Zip 30901-2629; tel. 706/722-9011; James R. Davis, President and Chief Executive Officer
(Independent Hospital System)

GEORGIA: UNIVERSITY HOSPITAL MCDUFFIE (O, 22 beds) 2460 Washington Road, NE, Thomson, GA, Zip 30824; tel. 706/595-1411; Bob Kepshire, R.N., MS, Administrator and Chief Nursing Officer

UNIVERSITY HOSPITAL SUMMERVILLE (O, 105 beds) 2260 Wrightsboro Road, Augusta, GA, Zip 30904-4726; tel. 706/481-7000; James R. Davis, Chief Executive Officer
Web address: www.universityhealth.org/summerville/

UNIVERSITY HOSPITAL (O, 566 beds) 1350 Walton Way, Augusta, GA, Zip 30901-2629; tel. 706/722-9011; James R. Davis, Chief Executive Officer
Web address: www.universityhealth.org

Owned, leased, sponsored:	3 hospitals	693 beds
Contract-managed:	0 hospitals	0 beds
Totals:	3 hospitals	693 beds

0961: **UNIVERSITY HEALTH SYSTEM** (NP)
1501 Kings Highway, Shreveport, LA, Zip 71103-4228; tel. 318/675-5000; Daniel J. Snyder, Chief Executive Officer
(Moderately Centralized Health System)

LOUISIANA: OCHSNER LSU HEALTH SHREVEPORT – MONROE MEDICAL CENTER (O, 108 beds) 4864 Jackson Street, Monroe, LA, Zip 71202-6497, Mailing Address: P.O. Box 1881, Zip 71210-8005, tel. 318/330-7000; Jonathan Phillips, Interim Administrator
Web address: www.uhsystem.com

OCHSNER LSU HEALTH SHREVPORT – ACADEMIC MEDICAL CENTER (O, 395 beds) 1501 Kings Highway, Shreveport, LA, Zip 71103-4228, Mailing Address: P.O. Box 33932, Zip 71130-3932, tel. 318/675-5000; Mark Randolph, President
Web address: www.lsuhscshreveport.edu

Owned, leased, sponsored:	2 hospitals	503 beds
Contract-managed:	0 hospitals	0 beds
Totals:	2 hospitals	503 beds

For explanation of codes following names, see page B2.
★ Indicates Type III membership in the American Hospital Association.

★0112: UNIVERSITY HOSPITALS (NP)
11100 Euclid Avenue, Cleveland, OH, Zip 44106–5000;
tel. 216/844–1000; Thomas F. Zenty III, President and Chief
Executive Officer
(Centralized Health System)

OHIO: ST. JOHN MEDICAL CENTER (O, 176 beds) 29000 Center Ridge Road,
Westlake, OH, Zip 44145–5293; tel. 440/835–8000; Robert G. David,
President
Web address: www.sjws.net

UH PORTAGE MEDICAL CENTER (O, 135 beds) 6847 North Chestnut Street,
Ravenna, OH, Zip 44266–3929, Mailing Address: P.O. Box 1204, Zip 44266–
1204, tel. 330/297–0811; M Steven. Jones, President

UH REGIONAL HOSPITALS (O, 101 beds) 27100 Chardon Road, Cleveland, OH,
Zip 44143–1116; tel. 440/585–6500; Brian Monter, MSN, R.N., President
Web address: www.uhhospitals.org

UNIVERSITY HOSPITALS AHUJA MEDICAL CENTER (O, 144 beds) 3999
Richmond Road, Beachwood, OH, Zip 44122–6046; tel. 216/593–5500;
Susan V. Juris, President

UNIVERSITY HOSPITALS CLEVELAND MEDICAL CENTER (O, 938 beds) 11100
Euclid Avenue, Cleveland, OH, Zip 44106–1716; tel. 216/844–1000; Daniel I.
Simon, M.D., President
Web address: www.UHhospitals.org

UNIVERSITY HOSPITALS CONNEAUT MEDICAL CENTER (O, 25 beds) 158 West
Main Road, Conneaut, OH, Zip 44030–2039; tel. 440/593–1131; M Steven.
Jones, President
Web address: www.uhhospitals.org

UNIVERSITY HOSPITALS ELYRIA MEDICAL CENTER (O, 202 beds) 630 East River
Street, Elyria, OH, Zip 44035–5902; tel. 440/329–7500; Kristi M. Sink, President
Web address: www.uhhospitals.org/elyria

UNIVERSITY HOSPITALS GEAUGA MEDICAL CENTER (O, 142 beds) 13207
Ravenna Road, Chardon, OH, Zip 44024–7032; tel. 440/269–6000; M
Steven. Jones, President

UNIVERSITY HOSPITALS GENEVA MEDICAL CENTER (O, 25 beds) 870 West
Main Street, Geneva, OH, Zip 44041–1295; tel. 440/466–1141; M Steven.
Jones, President
Web address: www.uhhs.com

UNIVERSITY HOSPITALS PARMA MEDICAL CENTER (O, 271 beds) 7007
Powers Boulevard, Parma, OH, Zip 44129–5495; tel. 440/743–3000; Peter
U. Bergmann, President

UNIVERSITY HOSPITALS SAMARITAN MEDICAL CENTER (O, 39 beds) 1025
Center Street, Ashland, OH, Zip 44805–4011; tel. 419/289–0491; Karen
McNeil, President
Web address: www.samaritanhospital.org

Owned, leased, sponsored:	11 hospitals	2198 beds
Contract-managed:	0 hospitals	0 beds
Totals:	11 hospitals	2198 beds

★0915: UNIVERSITY HOSPITALS AND HEALTH SYSTEM (NP)
2500 North State Street, Jackson, MS, Zip 39216–4500;
tel. 601/984–1000; Kevin S. Cook, Chief Executive Officer
(Decentralized Health System)

MISSISSIPPI: UNIVERSITY OF MISSISSIPPI MEDICAL CENTER GRENADA (C,
58 beds) 960 Avent Drive, Grenada, MS, Zip 38901–5230; tel. 662/227–
7000; Wes Sigler, Chief Executive Officer
Web address: www.glmc.net/

UNIVERSITY OF MISSISSIPPI MEDICAL CENTER HOLMES COUNTY (O, 25 beds)
239 Bowling Green Road, Lexington, MS, Zip 39095–5167; tel. 601/496–
5200; Wes Sigler, Chief Executive Officer
Web address: www.ummchealth.com/holmes/

UNIVERSITY OF MISSISSIPPI MEDICAL CENTER (O, 680 beds) 2500 North
State Street, Jackson, MS, Zip 39216–4505; tel. 601/984–1000; Kevin S.
Cook, Chief Executive Officer

Owned, leased, sponsored:	2 hospitals	705 beds
Contract-managed:	1 hospitals	58 beds
Totals:	3 hospitals	763 beds

**★6405: UNIVERSITY OF CALIFORNIA SYSTEMWIDE
ADMINISTRATION** (NP)
1111 Franklin Street, 11th Floor, Oakland, CA, Zip 94607–5200;
tel. 510/987–9071; John D. Stobo, M.D., Executive Vice President and Chief Executive Officer
(Decentralized Health System)

CALIFORNIA: RONALD REAGAN UCLA MEDICAL CENTER (O, 445 beds) 757
Westwood Plaza, Los Angeles, CA, Zip 90095–8358; tel. 310/825–9111;
Johnese Spisso, Chief Executive Officer
Web address: www.uclahealth.org

STEWART & LYNDA RESNICK NEUROPSYCHIATRIC HOSPITAL AT UCLA (O,
74 beds) 150 UCLA Medical Plaza, Los Angeles, CA, Zip 90095–8353;
tel. 310/825–9989; Peter Whybrow, M.D., Chief Executive Officer

UC IRVINE MEDICAL CENTER (O, 417 beds) 101 The City Drive South, Orange,
CA, Zip 92868–3298; tel. 714/456–6011; Richard Gannotta, Chief Executive
Officer
Web address: www.ucirvinehealth.org

UC SAN DIEGO HEALTH (O, 701 beds) 200 West Arbor Drive, San Diego,
CA, Zip 92103–9000; tel. 619/543–6222; Patty Maysent, Chief Executive
Officer
Web address: www.health.ucsd.edu

UCLA MEDICAL CENTER-SANTA MONICA (O, 265 beds) 1250 16th Street,
Santa Monica, CA, Zip 90404–1249; tel. 310/319–4000; Richard Azar, Chief
Operating Officer
Web address: www.healthcare.ucla.edu

UCSF MEDICAL CENTER (O, 859 beds) 500 Parnassus Avenue, San Francisco,
CA, Zip 94143–0296, Mailing Address: 500 Parnassus Avenue, Box 0296,
Zip 94143–0296, tel. 415/476–1000; Mark R. Laret, Chief Executive Officer

UNIVERSITY OF CALIFORNIA, DAVIS MEDICAL CENTER (O, 611 beds) 2315
Stockton Boulevard, Sacramento, CA, Zip 95817–2282; tel. 916/734–2011;
Brad Simmons, Interim Chief Executive Officer
Web address: www.ucdmc.ucdavis.edu

Owned, leased, sponsored:	7 hospitals	3372 beds
Contract-managed:	0 hospitals	0 beds
Totals:	7 hospitals	3372 beds

★0058: UNIVERSITY OF CHICAGO MEDICINE (NP)
5841 South Maryland Avenue, Chicago, IL, Zip 60637–1447;
tel. 773/702–6240; Sharon L. O'Keefe, President
(Centralized Health System)

ILLINOIS: INGALLS MEMORIAL HOSPITAL (O, 270 beds) One Ingalls Drive,
Harvey, IL, Zip 60426–3591; tel. 708/333–2300; Jonathan R. Goble,
FACHE, Interim President

UNIVERSITY OF CHICAGO MEDICAL CENTER (O, 668 beds) 5841 South
Maryland Avenue, Chicago, IL, Zip 60637–1443; tel. 773/702–1000; Sharon
L. O'Keefe, President
Web address: www.uchospitals.edu

Owned, leased, sponsored:	2 hospitals	938 beds
Contract-managed:	0 hospitals	0 beds
Totals:	2 hospitals	938 beds

★0216: UNIVERSITY OF MARYLAND MEDICAL SYSTEM (NP)
250 West Pratt Street, 24th Floor, Baltimore, MD, Zip 21201–
1595; tel. 410/328–8667; John W. Ashworth III, Interim President
and Chief Executive Officer
(Moderately Centralized Health System)

MARYLAND: MT. WASHINGTON PEDIATRIC HOSPITAL (O, 61 beds) 1708 West
Rogers Avenue, Baltimore, MD, Zip 21209–4545; tel. 410/578–8600;
Sheldon J. Stein, President and Chief Executive Officer

UNIVERSITY OF MARYLAND BALTIMORE WASHINGTON MEDICAL CENTER
(O, 272 beds) 301 Hospital Drive, Glen Burnie, MD, Zip 21061–5899;
tel. 410/787–4000; Karen E. Olscamp, President and Chief Executive Officer
Web address: www.mybwmc.org

For explanation of codes following names, see page B2.
★ Indicates Type III membership in the American Hospital Association.

UNIVERSITY OF MARYLAND CAPITAL REGION HEALTH PRINCE GEORGE'S HOSPITAL CENTER (O, 177 beds) 3001 Hospital Drive, Cheverly, MD, Zip 20785–1189; tel. 301/618–2000; Sherry B. Perkins, Ph.D., R.N., President and Chief Executive Officer
Web address: www.princegeorgeshospital.org

UNIVERSITY OF MARYLAND CHARLES REGIONAL MEDICAL CENTER (O, 109 beds) 5 Garrett Avenue, La Plata, MD, Zip 20646–5960, Mailing Address: P.O. Box 1070, Zip 20646–1070, tel. 301/609–4000; Noel A. Cervino, President and Chief Executive Officer
Web address: www.charlesregional.org

UNIVERSITY OF MARYLAND HARFORD MEMORIAL HOSPITAL (O, 85 beds) 501 South Union Avenue, Havre De Grace, MD, Zip 21078–3493; tel. 443/843–5000; Lyle Ernest. Sheldon, FACHE, President and Chief Executive Officer

UNIVERSITY OF MARYLAND MEDICAL CENTER MIDTOWN CAMPUS (O, 170 beds) 827 Linden Avenue, Baltimore, MD, Zip 21201–4606; tel. 410/225–8000; Mohan Suntha, M.D., President and Chief Executive Officer
Web address: www.ummidtown.org/

UNIVERSITY OF MARYLAND MEDICAL CENTER (O, 693 beds) 22 South Greene Street, Baltimore, MD, Zip 21201–1595; tel. 410/328–9199; Mohan Suntha, M.D., President and Chief Executive Officer
Web address: www.umm.edu

UNIVERSITY OF MARYLAND REHABILITATION & ORTHOPAEDIC INSTITUTE (O, 117 beds) 2200 Kernan Drive, Baltimore, MD, Zip 21207–6697; tel. 410/448–2500; Cynthia Kelleher, M.P.H., President and Chief Executive Officer

UNIVERSITY OF MARYLAND SHORE MEDICAL CENTER AT CHESTERTOWN (O, 124 beds) 100 Brown Street, Chestertown, MD, Zip 21620–1499; tel. 410/778–3300; Kenneth D. Kozel, FACHE, President and Chief Executive Officer
Web address: www.umms.org/hospitals/shore-health-system.htm

UNIVERSITY OF MARYLAND SHORE MEDICAL CENTER AT DORCHESTER (O, 47 beds) 300 Byrn Street, Cambridge, MD, Zip 21613–1908; tel. 410/228–5511; Kenneth D. Kozel, FACHE, President and Chief Executive Officer

UNIVERSITY OF MARYLAND SHORE MEDICAL CENTER AT EASTON (O, 132 beds) 219 South Washington Street, Easton, MD, Zip 21601–2996; tel. 410/822–1000; Kenneth D. Kozel, FACHE, President and Chief Executive Officer
Web address: www.shorehealth.org

UNIVERSITY OF MARYLAND ST. JOSEPH MEDICAL CENTER (O, 287 beds) 7601 Osler Drive, Towson, MD, Zip 21204–7582; tel. 410/337–1000; Thomas Smyth, President and Chief Executive Officer

UNIVERSITY OF MARYLAND UPPER CHESAPEAKE MEDICAL CENTER (O, 162 beds) 500 Upper Chesapeake Drive, Bel Air, MD, Zip 21014–4324; tel. 443/643–1000; Lyle Ernest. Sheldon, FACHE, President and Chief Executive Officer
Web address: www.uchs.org

Owned, leased, sponsored:	13 hospitals	2436 beds
Contract-managed:	0 hospitals	0 beds
Totals:	13 hospitals	2436 beds

★0227: UNIVERSITY OF MISSOURI HEALTH CARE (NP)
One Hospital Drive, DC 031, Columbia, MO, Zip 65212–0001; tel. 573/882–4141; Jonathan W. Curtright, Chief Executive Officer and Chief Operating Officer
(Moderately Centralized Health System)

MISSOURI: CAPITAL REGION MEDICAL CENTER (O, 114 beds) 1125 Madison Street, Jefferson City, MO, Zip 65101–5200, Mailing Address: P.O. Box 1128, Zip 65102–1128, tel. 573/632–5000; Gaspare Calvaruso, President
Web address: www.crmc.org

UNIVERSITY OF MISSOURI HEALTH CARE (O, 602 beds) One Hospital Drive, Columbia, MO, Zip 65212–0001; tel. 573/882–4141; Jonathan W. Curtright, Chief Executive Officer
Web address: www.muhealth.org

Owned, leased, sponsored:	2 hospitals	716 beds
Contract-managed:	0 hospitals	0 beds
Totals:	2 hospitals	716 beds

0021: UNIVERSITY OF NEW MEXICO HOSPITALS (NP)
915 Camino De Salud, Albuquerque, NM, Zip 87131–0001; tel. 505/272–5849; Michael Chicarelli, R.N., Interim Chief Executive Officer
(Moderately Centralized Health System)

NEW MEXICO: UNM SANDOVAL REGIONAL MEDICAL CENTER, INC. (O, 60 beds) 3001 Broadmoor Boulevard NE, Rio Rancho, NM, Zip 87131; tel. 505/994–7000; Jamie A. Silva-Steele, FACHE, R.N., President and Chief Executive Officer
Web address: www.hsc.unm.edu/health/locations/sandoval-regional-medical-center.html

UNIVERSITY OF NEW MEXICO HOSPITALS (O, 537 beds) 2211 Lomas Boulevard NE, Albuquerque, NM, Zip 87106–2745; tel. 505/272–2111; Kathleen R. Becker, M.P.H., JD, Chief Executive Officer

Owned, leased, sponsored:	2 hospitals	597 beds
Contract-managed:	0 hospitals	0 beds
Totals:	2 hospitals	597 beds

★0168: UNIVERSITY OF PENNSYLVANIA HEALTH SYSTEM (NP)
3400 Civic Center Bouelvard, Philadelphia, PA, Zip 19104–5127; tel. 215/662–2203; Kevin B. Mahoney, Chief Executive Officer
(Moderately Centralized Health System)

NEW JERSEY: PENN MEDICINE PRINCETON MEDICAL CENTER (O, 355 beds) One Plainsboro Road, Plainsboro, NJ, Zip 08536–1913; tel. 609/853–7100; Barry S. Rabner, President and Chief Executive Officer, Princeton Healthcare System
Web address: www.princetonhcs.org

PENNSYLVANIA: HOSPITAL OF THE UNIVERSITY OF PENNSYLVANIA (O, 805 beds) 3400 Spruce Street, Philadelphia, PA, Zip 19104–4206; tel. 215/662–4000; Regina Cunningham, Ph.D., R.N., Chief Executive Officer
Web address: www.pennmedicine.org

PENN MEDICINE CHESTER COUNTY HOSPITAL (O, 224 beds) 701 East Marshall Street, West Chester, PA, Zip 19380–4412; tel. 610/431–5000; Michael J. Duncan, President and Chief Executive Officer
Web address: www.chestercountyhospital.org

PENN MEDICINE LANCASTER GENERAL HOSPITAL (O, 616 beds) 555 North Duke Street, Lancaster, PA, Zip 17602–2250; tel. 717/544–5511; Jan L. Bergen, President and Chief Executive Officer

PENN PRESBYTERIAN MEDICAL CENTER (O, 375 beds) 51 North 39th Street, Philadelphia, PA, Zip 19104–2699; tel. 215/662–8000; Michele M. Volpe, Chief Executive Officer
Web address: www.pennmedicine.org/pmc/

PENNSYLVANIA HOSPITAL (O, 475 beds) 800 Spruce Street, Philadelphia, PA, Zip 19107–6192; tel. 215/829–3000; Theresa M. . Larivee, Chief Executive Officer

Owned, leased, sponsored:	6 hospitals	2850 beds
Contract-managed:	0 hospitals	0 beds
Totals:	6 hospitals	2850 beds

★0223: UNIVERSITY OF ROCHESTER MEDICAL CENTER (NP)
601 Elmwood Ave Box 623, Rochester, NY, Zip 14642–0002, Mailing Address: 601 Elmwood Avenue, Zip 14642–0002, tel. 585/275–2100; Mark B. Taubman, M.D., Chief Executive Officer
(Moderately Centralized Health System)

NEW YORK: F. F. THOMPSON HOSPITAL (O, 291 beds) 350 Parrish Street, Canandaigua, NY, Zip 14424–1731; tel. 585/396–6000; Michael Stapleton, President and Chief Executive Officer

HIGHLAND HOSPITAL (O, 261 beds) 1000 South Avenue, Rochester, NY, Zip 14620–2733; tel. 585/473–2200; Steven I. Goldstein, President and Chief Executive Officer
Web address: https://www.urmc.rochester.edu/highland

For explanation of codes following names, see page B2.
★ Indicates Type III membership in the American Hospital Association.

Section B

JONES MEMORIAL HOSPITAL (O, 33 beds) 191 North Main Street, Wellsville, NY, Zip 14895–1150, Mailing Address: P.O. Box 72, Zip 14895–0072, tel. 585/593–1100; Eva Benedict, R.N., President and Chief Executive Officer
Web address: www.jmhny.org

NICHOLAS H. NOYES MEMORIAL HOSPITAL (O, 48 beds) 111 Clara Barton Street, Dansville, NY, Zip 14437–9503; tel. 585/335–6001; Amy Pollard, R.N., President and Chief Executive Officer

ST. JAMES MERCY HOSPITAL (O, 127 beds) 411 Canisteo Street, Hornell, NY, Zip 14843–2197; tel. 607/324–8000; Leo P. Brideau, FACHE, Interim President and Chief Executive Officer
Web address: www.stjamesmercy.org

STRONG MEMORIAL HOSPITAL OF THE UNIVERSITY OF ROCHESTER (O, 869 beds) 601 Elmwood Avenue, Rochester, NY, Zip 14642–0002, Mailing Address: 601 Elmwood Avenue, Box 612, Zip 14642–0002, tel. 585/275–2100; Steven I. Goldstein, President and Chief Executive Officer
Web address: www.urmc.rochester.edu

Owned, leased, sponsored:	6 hospitals	1629 beds
Contract-managed:	0 hospitals	0 beds
Totals:	6 hospitals	1629 beds

★0033: UNIVERSITY OF TEXAS SYSTEM (NP)
601 Colorado Street, Suite 205, Austin, TX, Zip 78701–2904; tel. 512/499–4224; Raymond Greenberg, M.D., Executive Vice Chancellor
(Moderately Centralized Health System)

TEXAS: UT HEALTH NORTH CAMPUS TYLER (O, 114 beds) 11937 Highway 271, Tyler, TX, Zip 75708–3154; tel. 903/877–7777; Kirk A. Calhoun, M.D., President

UNIVERSITY OF TEXAS HARRIS COUNTY PSYCHIATRIC CENTER (C, 216 beds) 2800 South MacGregor Way, Houston, TX, Zip 77021–1000, Mailing Address: P.O. Box 20249, Zip 77225–0249, tel. 713/741–7870; Jair C. Soares, M.D., Executive Director
Web address: www.hcpc.uth.tmc.edu

UNIVERSITY OF TEXAS M.D. ANDERSON CANCER CENTER (O, 658 beds) 1515 Holcombe Boulevard, Unit 1491, Houston, TX, Zip 77030–4000; tel. 713/792–2121; Peter Pisters, M.D., President

UNIVERSITY OF TEXAS MEDICAL BRANCH (O, 480 beds) 301 University Boulevard, Galveston, TX, Zip 77555–0128; tel. 409/772–1011; Donna K. Sollenberger, Executive Vice President and Chief Executive Officer
Web address: www.utmb.edu

Owned, leased, sponsored:	3 hospitals	1252 beds
Contract-managed:	1 hospitals	216 beds
Totals:	4 hospitals	1468 beds

0137: UPMC (NP)
600 Grant Street, US Steel Tower, Suite 6262, Pittsburgh, PA, Zip 15219–2702; tel. 412/647–8762; Jeffrey A. Romoff, President and Chief Executive Officer
(Decentralized Health System)

NEW YORK: UPMC CHAUTAUQUA WCA (O, 111 beds) 207 Foote Avenue, Jamestown, NY, Zip 14701–7077, Mailing Address: P.O. Box 840, Zip 14702–0840, tel. 716/487–0141; Brian Durniok, Interim President and Chief Executive Officer

PENNSYLVANIA: UPMC ALTOONA (O, 346 beds) 620 Howard Avenue, Altoona, PA, Zip 16601–4804; tel. 814/889–2011; Jan E. Fisher, President
Web address: www.altoonaregional.org

UPMC BEDFORD MEMORIAL (O, 27 beds) 10455 Lincoln Highway, Everett, PA, Zip 15537–7046; tel. 814/623–6161; Jan E. Fisher, President
Web address: www.upmcbedfordmemorial.com

UPMC CARLISLE (O, 165 beds) 361 Alexander Spring Road, Carlisle, PA, Zip 17015–6940; tel. 717/249–1212; Christian H. . Caicedo, M.D., President

UPMC CHILDREN'S HOSPITAL OF PITTSBURGH (O, 305 beds) One Children's Hospital Drive, 4401 Penn Avenue, Pittsburgh, PA, Zip 15224–1334; tel. 412/692–5325; Mark Sevco, President
Web address: www.chp.edu

UPMC EAST (O, 155 beds) 2775 Mosside Boulevard, Monroeville, PA, Zip 15146–2760; tel. 412/357–3000; Mark O'Hern, President

UPMC HAMOT (O, 365 beds) 201 State Street, Erie, PA, Zip 16550–0002; tel. 814/877–6000; David Gibbons, President
Web address: www.upmc.com/locations/hospitals/hamot

UPMC HANOVER (O, 93 beds) 300 Highland Avenue, Hanover, PA, Zip 17331–2297; tel. 717/316–3711; Michael W. Gaskins, President
Web address: www.hanoverhospital.org

UPMC HORIZON (O, 77 beds) 2200 Memorial Drive, Farrell, PA, Zip 16121–1357; tel. 724/588–2100; Donald R. Owrey, President

UPMC JAMESON (O, 96 beds) 1211 Wilmington Avenue, New Castle, PA, Zip 16105–2516; tel. 724/658–9001; Donald R. Owrey, President
Web address: www.upmcjameson.com

UPMC KANE (O, 31 beds) 4372 Route 6, Kane, PA, Zip 16735–3060; tel. 814/837–8585; Mark Papalia, President

UPMC LITITZ (O, 148 beds) 1500 Highlands Drive, Lititz, PA, Zip 17543–7694; tel. 717/625–5000; Deborah J. Willwerth, R.N., MSN, Chief Executive Officer
Web address: www.heartoflancaster.com

UPMC MAGEE-WOMENS HOSPITAL (O, 321 beds) 300 Halket Street, Pittsburgh, PA, Zip 15213–3108; tel. 412/641–1000; Richard Beigi, M.D., President

UPMC MCKEESPORT (O, 190 beds) 1500 Fifth Avenue, McKeesport, PA, Zip 15132–2422; tel. 412/664–2000; Mark O'Hern, President
Web address: www.mckeesport.upmc.com

UPMC MEMORIAL (O, 100 beds) 325 South Belmont Street, York, PA, Zip 17403–2609, Mailing Address: P.O. Box 15118, Zip 17405–7118, tel. 717/843–8623; Curtis Herrin, Chief Financial Officer
Web address: www.mhyork.org

UPMC MERCY (O, 419 beds) 1400 Locust Street, Pittsburgh, PA, Zip 15219–5166; tel. 412/232–8111; Michael A. Grace, President

UPMC NORTHWEST (O, 128 beds) 100 Fairfield Drive, Seneca, PA, Zip 16346–2130; tel. 814/676–7600; Brian Durniok, President
Web address: www.upmc.com/locations/hospitals/northwest/Pages/default.aspx

UPMC PASSAVANT (O, 306 beds) 9100 Babcock Boulevard, Pittsburgh, PA, Zip 15237–5815; tel. 412/748–6700; Susan E. Hoolahan, R.N., MSN, President
Web address: www.upmc.edu/passavant

UPMC PINNACLE HARRISBURG (O, 655 beds) 111 South Front Street, Harrisburg, PA, Zip 17101–2010, Mailing Address: P.O. Box 8700, Zip 17105–8700, tel. 717/231–8900; Philip Guarneschelli, Interim Chief Executive Officer

UPMC PRESBYTERIAN (O, 1398 beds) 200 Lothrop Street, Pittsburgh, PA, Zip 15213–2536; tel. 412/647–2345; John Innocenti Sr, President and Chief Executive Officer
Web address: www.upmc.edu

UPMC SOMERSET HOSPITAL (O, 98 beds) 225 South Center Avenue, Somerset, PA, Zip 15501–2088; tel. 814/443–5000; Andrew G. Rush, Chief Executive Officer
Web address: www.somersethospital.com

UPMC ST. MARGARET (O, 208 beds) 815 Freeport Road, Pittsburgh, PA, Zip 15215–3301; tel. 412/784–4000; David J. Patton, President

Owned, leased, sponsored:	22 hospitals	5742 beds
Contract-managed:	0 hospitals	0 beds
Totals:	22 hospitals	5742 beds

★0066: UPMC SUSQUEHANNA (NP)
700 High Street, Williamsport, PA, Zip 17701–3100; tel. 570/321–1000; Steven P. Johnson, FACHE, President and Chief Executive Officer
(Moderately Centralized Health System)

PENNSYLVANIA: UPMC SUSQUEHANNA DIVINE PROVIDENCE CAMPUS (O, 31 beds) 1100 Grampian Boulevard, Williamsport, PA, Zip 17701–1995; tel. 570/326–8000; Robert E. Kane, Chief Administrative Officer
Web address: www.susquehannahealth.org

For explanation of codes following names, see page B2.
★ Indicates Type III membership in the American Hospital Association.

Section B

UPMC SUSQUEHANNA LOCK HAVEN (O, 102 beds) 24 Cree Drive, Lock Haven, PA, Zip 17745–2699; tel. 570/893–5000; Ronald J. Reynolds, President

UPMC SUSQUEHANNA MUNCY (O, 145 beds) 215 East Water Street, Muncy, PA, Zip 17756–8700; tel. 570/546–8282; Christine Ballard, President
Web address: www.susquehannahealth.org

UPMC SUSQUEHANNA SOLDIERS + SAILORS (O, 25 beds) 32–36 Central Avenue, Wellsboro, PA, Zip 16901–1899; tel. 570/724–1631; Janie Hilfiger, Chief Administrative Officer
Web address: www.susquehannahealth.org

UPMC SUSQUEHANNA SUNBURY (O, 16 beds) 350 North Eleventh Street, Sunbury, PA, Zip 17801–1611; tel. 570/286–3333; Robert E. Kane, Chief Executive Officer

UPMC SUSQUEHANNA WILLIAMSPORT (O, 224 beds) 700 High Street, Williamsport, PA, Zip 17701–3100; tel. 570/321–1000; Steven P. Johnson, FACHE, President
Web address: www.susquehannahealth.org

Owned, leased, sponsored:	6 hospitals	543 beds
Contract-managed:	0 hospitals	0 beds
Totals:	6 hospitals	543 beds

0816: UPPER ALLEGHENY HEALTH SYSTEM (NP)
130 South Union Street, Suite 300, Olean, NY, Zip 14760–3676; tel. 716/375–6190; Timothy J. Finan, FACHE, President and Chief Executive Officer
(Independent Hospital System)

NEW YORK: OLEAN GENERAL HOSPITAL (O, 186 beds) 515 Main Street, Olean, NY, Zip 14760–1513; tel. 716/373–2600; Timothy J. Finan, FACHE, President and Chief Executive Officer

PENNSYLVANIA: BRADFORD REGIONAL MEDICAL CENTER (O, 202 beds) 116 Interstate Parkway, Bradford, PA, Zip 16701–1036; tel. 814/368–4143; Timothy J. Finan, FACHE, President and Chief Executive Officer
Web address: www.brmc.com

Owned, leased, sponsored:	2 hospitals	388 beds
Contract-managed:	0 hospitals	0 beds
Totals:	2 hospitals	388 beds

9195: U. S. INDIAN HEALTH SERVICE (FG)
801 Thompson Avenue, Rockville, MD, Zip 20852–1627; tel. 301/443–1083; Yvette Roubideaux, M.D., M.P.H., Director
(Independent Hospital System)

ARIZONA: CHINLE COMPREHENSIVE HEALTH CARE FACILITY (O, 60 beds) Highway 191, Hospital Road, Chinle, AZ, Zip 86503, Mailing Address: Highway 191 Hospital Drive, Zip 86503–8000, tel. 928/674–7001; Darlene Chee, Acting Chief Executive Officer

HOPI HEALTH CARE CENTER (O, 15 beds) Highway 264 Mile Marker 388, Keams Canyon, AZ, Zip 86042, Mailing Address: P.O. Box 4000, Polacca, Zip 86042–4000, tel. 928/737–6000; Mose Herne, Chief Executive Officer
Web address: www.ihs.gov/index.asp

SAN CARLOS APACHE HEALTHCARE CORPORATION (O, 8 beds) 103 Medicine Way Road, Peridot, AZ, Zip 85542; tel. 928/475–1400; Victoria D. Began, R.N., MS, President and Chief Executive Officer
Web address: www.ihs.gov

U. S. PUBLIC HEALTH SERVICE INDIAN HOSPITAL-SELLS (O, 12 beds) Highway 86 & Topawa Road, Sells, AZ, Zip 85634, Mailing Address: P.O. Box 548, Zip 85634–0548, tel. 520/383–7251; Troy Klarkowski, Administrator and Chief Executive Officer

U. S. PUBLIC HEALTH SERVICE INDIAN HOSPITAL-WHITERIVER (O, 35 beds) 200 West Hospital Drive, Whiteriver, AZ, Zip 85941–0860, Mailing Address: State Route 73, Box 860, Zip 85941–0860, tel. 928/338–4911; Michelle Martinez, Chief Executive Officer
Web address: www.ihs.gov

U. S. PUBLIC HEALTH SERVICE INDIAN HOSPITAL (O, 20 beds) 12033 Agency Road, Parker, AZ, Zip 85344–7718; tel. 928/669–2137; Elizabeth Helsel, Chief Executive Officer

U. S. PUBLIC HEALTH SERVICE PHOENIX INDIAN MEDICAL CENTER (O, 127 beds) 4212 North 16th Street, Phoenix, AZ, Zip 85016–5389; tel. 602/263–1200; Deanna Dick, Chief Executive Officer
Web address: www.ihs.gov

MARYLAND: NATIONAL INSTITUTES OF HEALTH CLINICAL CENTER (O, 121 beds) 9000 Rockville Pike, Building 10, Room 6–2551, Bethesda, MD, Zip 20892–1504; tel. 301/496–4000; James K. Gilman, M.D., Chief Executive Officer
Web address: www.clinicalcenter.nih.gov

MINNESOTA: RED LAKE INDIAN HEALTH SERVICE HOSPITAL (O, 19 beds) 24760 Hospital Drive, Red Lake, MN, Zip 56671, Mailing Address: P.O. Box 497, Zip 56671–0497, tel. 218/679–3912; Norine Smith, Chief Executive Officer
Web address: www.rlnnredlakehospital.com/

U. S. PUBLIC HEALTH SERVICE INDIAN HOSPITAL (O, 9 beds) 425 7th Street North West, Cass Lake, MN, Zip 56633; tel. 218/335–3200; Louis P. Erdrich, Acting Chief Executive Officer

MONTANA: BLACKFEET COMMUNITY HOSPITAL (O, 25 beds) 760 New Hospital Circle, Saint Mary, MT, Zip 59417–0760, Mailing Address: P.O. Box 760, Browning, Zip 59417–0760, tel. 406/338–6100; Garland Stiffarm, Chief Executive Officer
Web address: www.ihs.gov

CROW/NORTHERN CHEYENNE HOSPITAL (O, 24 beds) 10110 South 7650 East, Crow Agency, MT, Zip 59022–0009, Mailing Address: P.O. Box 9, Zip 59022–0009, tel. 406/638–2626; Darren Crowe, Chief Executive Officer
Web address: https://www.ihs.gov/billings/healthcarefacilities/crow/

FORT BELKNAP SERVICE UNIT (O, 6 beds) 669 Agency Main Street, Harlem, MT, Zip 59526–9455; tel. 406/353–3100; Gregory Smith, M.D., Chief Executive Officer
Web address: www.ihs.gov

NEW MEXICO: ACOMA-CANONCITO-LAGUNA HOSPITAL (O, 6 beds) 80B Veterans Boulevard, Acoma, NM, Zip 87034, Mailing Address: P.O. Box 130, San Fidel, Zip 87049–0130, tel. 505/552–5300; Melody Price-Yonts, Chief Executive Officer
Web address: www.ihs.gov/albuquerque/index.cfm?module=dsp_abq_acoma_canoncito_laguna

GALLUP INDIAN MEDICAL CENTER (O, 58 beds) 516 East Nizhoni Boulevard, Gallup, NM, Zip 87301–5748, Mailing Address: P.O. Box 1337, Zip 87301, tel. 505/722–1000; John Meese, Acting Director

MESCALERO PUBLIC HEALTH SERVICE INDIAN HOSPITAL (O, 13 beds) 318 Abalone Loop, Mescalero, NM, Zip 88340, Mailing Address: Box 210, Zip 88340–0210, tel. 505/464–3801; Dorlynn Simmons, Chief Executive Officer
Web address: www.ihs.gov

NORTHERN NAVAJO MEDICAL CENTER (O, 68 beds) Highway 491 North, Shiprock, NM, Zip 87420–0160, Mailing Address: P.O. Box 160, Zip 87420–0160, tel. 505/368–6001; Fannessa Comer, Chief Executive Officer
Web address: www.ihs.gov/

PHS SANTA FE INDIAN HOSPITAL (O, 4 beds) 1700 Cerrillos Road, Santa Fe, NM, Zip 87505–3554; tel. 505/988–9821; Leslie Dye, Chief Executive Officer

U. S. PUBLIC HEALTH SERVICE INDIAN HOSPITAL (O, 12 beds) Route 9 and State Road 371, Crownpoint, NM, Zip 87313, Mailing Address: P.O. Box 358, Zip 87313–0358, tel. 505/786–5291; Anslem Roanhorse, Chief Executive Officer
Web address: www.ihs.gov

U. S. PUBLIC HEALTH SERVICE INDIAN HOSPITAL (O, 32 beds) Route 301 North B Street, Zuni, NM, Zip 87327, Mailing Address: P.O. Box 467, Zip 87327–0467, tel. 505/782–4431; Jean Othole, Chief Executive Officer
Web address: www.ihs.gov

NORTH DAKOTA: INDIAN HEALTH SERVICE – QUENTIN N. BURDICK MEMORIAL HEALTH CARE FACILITY (O, 27 beds) 1300 Hospital Loop, Belcourt, ND, Zip 58316, Mailing Address: P.O. Box 160, Zip 58316–0160, tel. 701/477–6111; Shelly Harris, Chief Executive Officer
Web address: www.ihs.gov

STANDING ROCK SERVICE UNIT, FORT YATES HOSPITAL, INDIAN HEALTH SERVICE, DHHS (O, 14 beds) 10 North River Road, Fort Yates, ND, Zip 58538, Mailing Address: P.O. Box 'J', Zip 58538, tel. 701/854–3831; Jana Gipp, Chief Executive Officer
Web address: www.ihs.gov

For explanation of codes following names, see page B2.
★ Indicates Type III membership in the American Hospital Association.

OKLAHOMA: CLAREMORE INDIAN HOSPITAL (O, 44 beds) 101 South Moore Avenue, Claremore, OK, Zip 74017–5091; tel. 918/342–6200; George Valliere, Chief Executive Officer
Web address: www.ihs.gov

LAWTON INDIAN HOSPITAL (O, 26 beds) 1515 Lawrie Tatum Road, Lawton, OK, Zip 73507–3099; tel. 580/353–0350; Travis Scott, Chief Executive Officer
Web address: www.ihs.gov

SOUTH DAKOTA: INDIAN HEALTH SERVICE HOSPITAL (O, 9 beds) 3200 Canyon Lake Drive, Rapid City, SD, Zip 57702–8197; tel. 605/355–2280; Kevin J. Stiffarm, Chief Executive Officer

U. S. PUBLIC HEALTH SERVICE INDIAN HOSPITAL (O, 8 beds) 317 Main Street, Eagle Butte, SD, Zip 57625–1012, Mailing Address: P.O. Box 1012, Zip 57625–1012, tel. 605/964–7724; Charles Fisher, Chief Executive Officer
Web address: www.ihs.gov

U. S. PUBLIC HEALTH SERVICE INDIAN HOSPITAL (O, 45 beds) East Highway 18, Pine Ridge, SD, Zip 57770, Mailing Address: P.O. Box 1201, Zip 57770–1201, tel. 605/867–5131; Travis Scott, Service Unit Director
Web address: www.ihs.gov

U. S. PUBLIC HEALTH SERVICE INDIAN HOSPITAL (O, 35 beds) Highway 18, Soldier Creek Road, Rosebud, SD, Zip 57570; tel. 605/747–2231; Kathey Wilson, Acting Chief Executive Officer
Web address: www.ihs.gov

Owned, leased, sponsored:	28 hospitals	882 beds
Contract-managed:	0 hospitals	0 beds
Totals:	28 hospitals	882 beds

★0057: USA HEALTH (NP)
2451 USA Medical Center Drive, Mobile, AL, Zip 36617–2300; tel. 251/471–7000; Owen Bailey, FACHE, Chief Executive Officer and Senior Associate Vice President for Medical Affairs
(Independent Hospital System)

ALABAMA: USA CHILDREN'S AND WOMEN'S HOSPITAL (O, 180 beds) 1700 Center Street, Mobile, AL, Zip 36604–3301; tel. 251/415–1000; Chris Jett, Administrator

USA HEALTH UNIVERSITY HOSPITAL (O, 150 beds) 2451 USA Medical Center Drive, Mobile, AL, Zip 36617–2293; tel. 251/471–7000; Sam Dean, Administrator
Web address: www.usahealthsystem.com/usamc

Owned, leased, sponsored:	2 hospitals	330 beds
Contract-managed:	0 hospitals	0 beds
Totals:	2 hospitals	330 beds

0868: USMD HEALTH SYSTEM (IO)
6333 North State Highway 161 Suite 200, Irving, TX, Zip 75038–2229; tel. 214/493–4000; Mike Bukosky, President, Hospital Division
(Independent Hospital System)

TEXAS: USMD HOSPITAL AT ARLINGTON (O, 34 beds) 801 West Interstate 20, Arlington, TX, Zip 76017–5851; tel. 817/472–3400; Marcia Crim, R.N., MSN, Chief Executive Officer
Web address: www.usmdarlington.com

USMD HOSPITAL AT FORT WORTH (O, 8 beds) 5900 Altamesa Boulevard, Fort Worth, TX, Zip 76132–5473; tel. 817/433–9100; Kathy Early, Chief Executive Officer and Chief Nursing Officer
Web address: www.usmdfortworth.com/

Owned, leased, sponsored:	2 hospitals	42 beds
Contract-managed:	0 hospitals	0 beds
Totals:	2 hospitals	42 beds

★0860: UVA HEALTH SYSTEM (NP)
1215 Lee Street, Charlottesville, VA, Zip 22908–0816; tel. 434/924–0211; Pamela Sutton-Wallace, Acting Executive Vice President for Health Affairs, UVA Health System and Chief Executive Officer, UVA Medical Center
(Centralized Health System)

VIRGINIA: UVA TRANSITIONAL CARE HOSPITAL (O, 30 beds) 2965 Ivy Rd (250 West), Charlottesville, VA, Zip 22903–9330; tel. 434/924–8245; Tracy Turman, Administrator
Web address: www.uvahealth.com/services/transitional-care-hospital

UNIVERSITY OF VIRGINIA MEDICAL CENTER (O, 612 beds) 1215 Lee Street, Charlottesville, VA, Zip 22908–0001, Mailing Address: P.O. Box 800809, Zip 22908–0809, tel. 434/924–0211; Pamela Sutton-Wallace, Chief Executive Officer

Owned, leased, sponsored:	2 hospitals	642 beds
Contract-managed:	0 hospitals	0 beds
Totals:	2 hospitals	642 beds

1009: UW HEALTH SYSTEM (IO)
600 Highland Avenue, Madison, WI, Zip 53792–0001; tel. 608/263–6400; Alan Kaplan, M.D., Chief Executive Officer
(Moderately Centralized Health System)

WISCONSIN: UW HEALTH REHABILITATION HOSPITAL (O, 40 beds) 5115 North Biltmore Lane, Madison, WI, Zip 53718–2161; tel. 608/592–8100; Mary Kay. Diderrich, R.N., Chief Executive Officer
Web address: www.uwhealth.org

UNIVERSITY HOSPITAL (O, 638 beds) 600 Highland Avenue, Madison, WI, Zip 53792–0002; tel. 608/263–6400; Alan Kaplan, M.D., Chief Executive Officer
Web address: www.uwhealth.org

Owned, leased, sponsored:	2 hospitals	678 beds
Contract-managed:	0 hospitals	0 beds
Totals:	2 hospitals	678 beds

★6415: UW MEDICINE (NP)
1959 NE Pacific Street, Seattle, WA, Zip 98195–0001, Mailing Address: P.O. Box 356350, Zip 98195–6350, tel. 206/543–7718; Paul G. Ramsey, M.D., Chief Executive Officer
(Independent Hospital System)

WASHINGTON: UW MEDICINE/HARBORVIEW MEDICAL CENTER (C, 413 beds) 325 Ninth Avenue, Seattle, WA, Zip 98104–2499, Mailing Address: P.O. Box 359717, Zip 98195–9717, tel. 206/744–3000; Paul Hayes, R.N., Executive Director

UW MEDICINE/NORTHWEST HOSPITAL & MEDICAL CENTER (O, 203 beds) 1550 North 115th Street, Seattle, WA, Zip 98133–8401; tel. 206/364–0500; Cynthia Hecker, R.N., Executive Director
Web address: www.uwmedicine.org/Patient-Care/Locations/nwh/Pages/default.aspx

UW MEDICINE/VALLEY MEDICAL CENTER (C, 311 beds) 400 South 43rd Street, Renton, WA, Zip 98055–5714, Mailing Address: P.O. Box 50010, Zip 98058–5010, tel. 425/228–3450; Richard D. Roodman, Chief Executive Officer

UNIVERSITY OF WASHINGTON MEDICAL CENTER (O, 492 beds) 1959 NE Pacific Street, Seattle, WA, Zip 98195–6151; tel. 206/598–3300; Geoff Austin, Executive Director
Web address: www.uwmedicine.org/uw-medical-center

Owned, leased, sponsored:	2 hospitals	695 beds
Contract-managed:	2 hospitals	724 beds
Totals:	4 hospitals	1419 beds

★0128: VALLEY HEALTH SYSTEM (NP)
220 Campus Boulevard, Suite 420, Winchester, VA, Zip 22601–2889, Mailing Address: P.O. Box 3340, Zip 22604–2540, tel. 540/536–8024; Mark H. Merrill, President and Chief Executive Officer
(Moderately Centralized Health System)

VIRGINIA: PAGE MEMORIAL HOSPITAL (O, 25 beds) 200 Memorial Drive, Luray, VA, Zip 22835–1005; tel. 540/743–4561; N Travis. Clark, President
Web address: www.valleyhealthlink.com/page

For explanation of codes following names, see page B2.
★ Indicates Type III membership in the American Hospital Association.

VALLEY HEALTH SHENANDOAH MEMORIAL HOSPITAL (O, 25 beds) 759 South Main Street, Woodstock, VA, Zip 22664–1127; tel. 540/459–1100; N Travis. Clark, President
Web address: www.valleyhealthlink.com/shenandoah

WARREN MEMORIAL HOSPITAL (O, 166 beds) 1000 North Shenandoah Avenue, Front Royal, VA, Zip 22630–3598; tel. 540/636–0300; Floyd Heater, President

WINCHESTER MEDICAL CENTER (O, 485 beds) 1840 Amherst Street, Winchester, VA, Zip 22601–2808, Mailing Address: P.O. Box 3340, Zip 22604–2540, tel. 540/536–8000; Grady W. Philips III, President
Web address: www.valleyhealthlink.com/WMC

WEST VIRGINIA: HAMPSHIRE MEMORIAL HOSPITAL (O, 44 beds) 363 Sunrise Boulevard, Romney, WV, Zip 26757–4607; tel. 304/822–4561; Thomas S. Kluge, President
Web address: www.valleyhealthlink.com/hampshire

WAR MEMORIAL HOSPITAL (O, 41 beds) One Healthy Way, Berkeley Springs, WV, Zip 25411–7463; tel. 304/258–1234; Thomas S. Kluge, President

Owned, leased, sponsored:	6 hospitals	786 beds
Contract-managed:	0 hospitals	0 beds
Totals:	6 hospitals	786 beds

★0387: VANDERBILT HEALTH (NP)

1211 22nd Avenue South, Nashville, TN, Zip 37232; tel. 615/322–5000; Charles Wright. Pinson, M.D., Deputy Chief Executive Officer
(Moderately Centralized Health System)

TENNESSEE: VANDERBILT UNIVERSITY MEDICAL CENTER (O, 1051 beds) 1211 Medical Center Drive, Nashville, TN, Zip 37232–2102; tel. 615/322–5000; Jeffrey R. Balsar, President and Chief Executive Officer Vanderbilt Medical Center and Dean, Vanderbilt University School of Medicine
Web address: www.mc.vanderbilt.edu

VANDERBILT WILSON COUNTY HOSPITAL (O, 245 beds) 1411 Baddour Parkway, Lebanon, TN, Zip 37087–2513; tel. 615/444–8262; Jay Hinesley, FACHE, Chief Executive Officer

Owned, leased, sponsored:	2 hospitals	1296 beds
Contract-managed:	0 hospitals	0 beds
Totals:	2 hospitals	1296 beds

★0939: VCU HEALTH SYSTEM (NP)

1200 East Marshall Street, Richmond, VA, Zip 23298, Mailing Address: P.O. Box 980510, Zip 23298–0510, tel. 804/828–9000; Marsha Rappley, M.D., Chief Executive Officer and Vice President for Health Sciences
(Moderately Centralized Health System)

VIRGINIA: CHILDREN'S HOSPITAL OF RICHMOND AT VCU-BROOK ROAD CAMPUS (O, 36 beds) 2924 Brook Road, Richmond, VA, Zip 23220–1298; tel. 804/321–7474; Elias Neujahr, Chief Executive Officer

VCU HEALTH COMMUNITY MEMORIAL HOSPITAL (O, 206 beds) 125 Buena Vista Circle, South Hill, VA, Zip 23970–1431, Mailing Address: P.O. Box 90, Zip 23970–0090, tel. 434/447–3151; W Scott. Burnette, Chief Executive Officer
Web address: www.cmh-sh.org

VCU MEDICAL CENTER (O, 812 beds) 1250 East Marshall Street, Richmond, VA, Zip 23298–5051, Mailing Address: P.O. Box 980510, Zip 23298–0510, tel. 804/828–9000; Deborah W. Davis, Chief Executive Officer and Vice President Clinical Services

Owned, leased, sponsored:	3 hospitals	1054 beds
Contract-managed:	0 hospitals	0 beds
Totals:	3 hospitals	1054 beds

1041: VERITAS COLLABORATIVE (IO)

4024 Stirrup Creek Drive, Durham, NC, Zip 27703–9464; tel. 855/875–5812; Stacie McEntyre, Chief Executive Officer

NORTH CAROLINA: VERITAS COLLABORATIVE (L, 40 beds) 4024 Stirrup Creek Drive, Durham, NC, Zip 27703–9464; tel. 919/908–9730; Sara Hofmeier, Executive Director

VERITAS COLLABORATIVE (L, 25 beds) 615 Douglas Street, Suite 500, Durham, NC, Zip 27705–6616; tel. 919/908–9730; Becca Eckstein, Executive Director
Web address: www.https://veritascollaborative.com

Owned, leased, sponsored:	2 hospitals	65 beds
Contract-managed:	0 hospitals	0 beds
Totals:	2 hospitals	65 beds

1075: VERITY HEALTH SYSTEM (NP)

2200 West Third Street, Suite 200, Los Angeles, CA, Zip 90057–1935, Mailing Address: 203 Redwood Shores Parkway, Suite 800, Redwood City, Zip 94065, tel. 650/551–6650; Richard Adcock, President and Chief Executive Officer
(Independent Hospital System)

CALIFORNIA: SETON MEDICAL CENTER COASTSIDE (O, 116 beds) 600 Marine Boulevard, Moss Beach, CA, Zip 94038–9641; tel. 650/563–7100; John Ferrelli, Chief Executive Officer

SETON MEDICAL CENTER (O, 397 beds) 1900 Sullivan Avenue, Daly City, CA, Zip 94015–2229; tel. 650/992–4000; Mark Fratzke, R.N., President and Chief Executive Officer
Web address: www.setonmedicalcenter.org

ST. FRANCIS MEDICAL CENTER (O, 323 beds) 3630 East Imperial Highway, Lynwood, CA, Zip 90262–2636; tel. 310/900–8900; Gerald T. Kozai, PharmD, President and Chief Executive Officer

ST. VINCENT MEDICAL CENTER (O, 271 beds) 2131 West Third Street, Los Angeles, CA, Zip 90057–1901, Mailing Address: P.O. Box 57992, Zip 90057–0992, tel. 213/484–7111; Frank J. Cracolici, President and Chief Executive Officer
Web address: www.stvincentmedicalcenter.com

Owned, leased, sponsored:	4 hospitals	1107 beds
Contract-managed:	0 hospitals	0 beds
Totals:	4 hospitals	1107 beds

★0299: VIBRA HEALTHCARE (IO)

4550 Lena Drive, Suite 225, Mechanicsburg, PA, Zip 17055–4920; tel. 717/591–5700; Brad Hollinger, Chairman and Chief Executive Officer
(Independent Hospital System)

CALIFORNIA: BALLARD REHABILITATION HOSPITAL (O, 60 beds) 1760 West 16th Street, San Bernardino, CA, Zip 92411–1160; tel. 909/473–1200; Mary Miles. Hunt, Chief Executive Officer

KENTFIELD REHABILITATION AND SPECIALTY HOSPITAL (O, 60 beds) 1125 Sir Francis Drake Boulevard, Kentfield, CA, Zip 94904–1455; tel. 415/456–9680; Varun Chauhan, Chief Executive Officer
Web address: www.kentfieldrehab.com

SAN JOAQUIN VALLEY REHABILITATION HOSPITAL (O, 62 beds) 7173 North Sharon Avenue, Fresno, CA, Zip 93720–3329; tel. 559/436–3600; Mary Jo Jacobson, Chief Executive Officer

VIBRA HOSPITAL OF NORTHERN CALIFORNIA (O, 88 beds) 2801 Eureka Way, Redding, CA, Zip 96001–0222; tel. 530/246–9000; Chris Jones, Chief Executive Officer
Web address: www.norcalrehab.com

VIBRA HOSPITAL OF SACRAMENTO (O, 58 beds) 330 Montrose Drive, Folsom, CA, Zip 95630–2720; tel. 916/351–9151; Kimberly C. Long, R.N., MSN, Chief Executive Officer

COLORADO: VIBRA HOSPITAL OF DENVER (O, 71 beds) 8451 Pearl Street, Thornton, CO, Zip 80229–4804; tel. 303/288–3000; Lamar McBride, Chief Executive Officer
Web address: www.vhdenver.com

IDAHO: VIBRA HOSPITAL OF BOISE (O, 60 beds) 6651 West Franklin Road, Boise, ID, Zip 83709–0914; tel. 877/801–2244; Cynthia Newsom, Chief Executive Officer

For explanation of codes following names, see page B2.
★ Indicates Type III membership in the American Hospital Association.

INDIANA: SOUTHERN INDIANA REHABILITATION HOSPITAL (O, 60 beds) 3104 Blackiston Boulevard, New Albany, IN, Zip 47150–9579; tel. 812/941–8300; William Boso, Executive Director, Administrator
Web address: www.sirh.org

VIBRA HOSPITAL OF NORTHWESTERN INDIANA (O, 40 beds) 9509 Georgia Street, Crown Point, IN, Zip 46307–6518; tel. 219/472–2200; Craig L. Johnson, FACHE, Chief Executive Officer
Web address: www.vhnwindiana.com/

KENTUCKY: GATEWAY REHABILITATION HOSPITAL (C, 40 beds) 5940 Merchant Street, Florence, KY, Zip 41042–1158; tel. 859/426–2400; Frank Schneider, FACHE, Chief Executive Officer
Web address: www.gatewayflorence.com/

SOUTHERN KENTUCKY REHABILITATION HOSPITAL (O, 60 beds) 1300 Campbell Lane, Bowling Green, KY, Zip 42104–4162; tel. 270/782–6900; Stuart Locke, Chief Executive Officer

MASSACHUSETTS: VIBRA HOSPITAL OF SOUTHEASTERN MASSACHUSETTS (O, 90 beds) 4499 Acushnet Avenue, New Bedford, MA, Zip 02745–4707; tel. 508/995–6900; Edward B. Leary, Chief Executive Officer
Web address: www.newbedfordrehab.com

VIBRA HOSPITAL OF WESTERN MASSACHUSETTS (O, 174 beds) 1400 State Street, Springfield, MA, Zip 01109–2550; tel. 413/726–6700; Edward B. Leary, Interim Chief Executive Officer
Web address: www.vhwmass.com

MICHIGAN: VIBRA HOSPITAL OF SOUTHEASTERN MICHIGAN, LLC (O, 220 beds) 26400 West Outer Drive, Lincoln Park, MI, Zip 48146–2088; tel. 313/386–2000; Reginald Lee, Chief Executive Officer
Web address: www.vhsemichigan.com/

NORTH DAKOTA: VIBRA HOSPITAL OF CENTRAL DAKOTAS (O, 41 beds) 1000 18th Street NW, Mandan, ND, Zip 58554–1612; tel. 701/667–2000; Glynda Troyo-Sauviac, Chief Executive Officer
Web address: www.vhcentraldakotas.com

VIBRA HOSPITAL OF FARGO (O, 31 beds) 1720 University Drive South, Fargo, ND, Zip 58103–4940; tel. 701/241–9099; Custer Huseby, Chief Executive Officer

OHIO: VIBRA HOSPITAL OF MAHONING VALLEY (O, 42 beds) 8049 South Avenue, Boardman, OH, Zip 44512–6154; tel. 330/726–5000; Nathan Mast, Chief Executive Officer
Web address: www.vhmvalley.com

OREGON: VIBRA SPECIALTY HOSPITAL OF PORTLAND (O, 68 beds) 10300 NE Hancock Street, Portland, OR, Zip 97220–3831; tel. 503/257–5500; Victor Jackson, Chief Executive Officer

SOUTH CAROLINA: VIBRA HOSPITAL OF CHARLESTON (O, 59 beds) 1200 Hospital Drive, Mt. Pleasant, SC, Zip 29464; tel. 843/375–4000; J. Scott Broome, Chief Executive Officer
Web address: www.vhcharleston.com

TEXAS: HIGHLANDS REHABILITATION HOSPITAL (O, 41 beds) 1395 George Dieter Drive, El Paso, TX, Zip 79936–7410; tel. 915/298–7222; Travis Rich, Chief Executive Officer
Web address: www.vrhhighlands.com/

VIBRA HOSPITAL OF AMARILLO (O, 72 beds) 7501 Wallace Boulevard, Amarillo, TX, Zip 79124–2150; tel. 806/467–7000; Eric Mueller, Chief Executive Officer and Market Chief Executive Officer

VIBRA REHABILITATION HOSPITAL OF AMARILLO (O, 44 beds) 7200 West 9th Avenue, Amarillo, TX, Zip 79106–1703; tel. 806/468–2900; Tammie Tabor, Chief Executive Officer
Web address: www.vrhamarillo.com

VIBRA SPECIALTY HOSPITAL AT DESOTO (O, 60 beds) 2700 Walker Way, Desoto, TX, Zip 75115–2088; tel. 972/298–1100; Thomas Alexander, Chief Executive Officer
Web address: www.vshdesoto.com

VIRGINIA: VIBRA HOSPITAL OF RICHMOND (O, 60 beds) 2220 Edward Holland Drive, Richmond, VA, Zip 23230–2519; tel. 804/678–7000; Linda Tiemens, Chief Executive Officer

Owned, leased, sponsored:	23 hospitals	1621 beds
Contract-managed:	1 hospitals	40 beds
Totals:	24 hospitals	1661 beds

★**0217: VIDANT HEALTH** (NP)
2100 Stantonsburg Road, Greenville, NC, Zip 27834–2818, Mailing Address: P.O. Box 6028, Zip 27835–6028, tel. 252/847–4100; Michael Waldrum, M.D., Chief Executive Officer
(Moderately Centralized Health System)

NORTH CAROLINA: THE OUTER BANKS HOSPITAL (O, 21 beds) 4800 South Croatan Highway, Nags Head, NC, Zip 27959–9704; tel. 252/449–4500; Ronald A. Sloan, FACHE, President
Web address: www.theouterbankshospital.com

VIDANT BEAUFORT HOSPITAL (L, 84 beds) 628 East 12th Street, Washington, NC, Zip 27889–3409; tel. 252/975–4100; Harvey Case, President
Web address: www.vidanthealth.com

VIDANT BERTIE HOSPITAL (L, 6 beds) 1403 South King Street, P.O. Box 40, Windsor, NC, Zip 27983–9666, Mailing Address: P.O. Box 40, Zip 27983–0040, tel. 252/794–6600; Jeffrey Sackrison, President
Web address: www.vidanthealth.com

VIDANT CHOWAN HOSPITAL (L, 19 beds) 211 Virginia Road, Edenton, NC, Zip 27932–9668, Mailing Address: P.O. Box 629, Zip 27932–0629, tel. 252/482–8451; Jeffrey Sackrison, President

VIDANT DUPLIN HOSPITAL (L, 47 beds) 401 North Main Street, Kenansville, NC, Zip 28349–8801, Mailing Address: P.O. Box 278, Zip 28349–0278, tel. 910/296–0941; Jay Briley, President
Web address: www.vidanthealth.com

VIDANT EDGECOMBE HOSPITAL (O, 65 beds) 111 Hospital Drive, Tarboro, NC, Zip 27886–2011; tel. 252/641–7700; Patrick Heins, President
Web address: https://www.vidanthealth.com/edgecombe/default.aspx

VIDANT MEDICAL CENTER (O, 974 beds) 2100 Stantonsburg Road, Greenville, NC, Zip 27834–2818, Mailing Address: P.O. Box 6028, Zip 27835–6028, tel. 252/847–4100; William Brian. Floyd, President

VIDANT ROANOKE-CHOWAN HOSPITAL (L, 71 beds) 500 South Academy Street, Ahoskie, NC, Zip 27910–3261, Mailing Address: P.O. Box 1385, Zip 27910–1385, tel. 252/209–3000; Judy Bruno, President
Web address: www.vidanthealth.com

Owned, leased, sponsored:	8 hospitals	1287 beds
Contract-managed:	0 hospitals	0 beds
Totals:	8 hospitals	1287 beds

0012: VIRGINIA DEPARTMENT OF MENTAL HEALTH (NP)
1220 Bank Street, Richmond, VA, Zip 23219–3645, Mailing Address: P.O. Box 1797, Zip 23218–1797, tel. 804/786–3921; James S. Reinhard, M.D., Commissioner
(Independent Hospital System)

VIRGINIA: CATAWBA HOSPITAL (O, 110 beds) 5525 Catawba Hospital Drive, Catawba, VA, Zip 24070–2115, Mailing Address: P.O. Box 200, Zip 24070–0200, tel. 540/375–4200; Walton F. Mitchell III, Director
Web address: www.catawba.dbhds.virginia.gov

CENTRAL STATE HOSPITAL (O, 277 beds) 26317 West Washington Street, Petersburg, VA, Zip 23803–2727, Mailing Address: P.O. Box 4030, Zip 23803–0030, tel. 804/524–7000; Rebecca Vauter, PsyD, Facility Director
Web address: www.csh.dbhds.virginia.gov

CENTRAL VIRGINIA TRAINING CENTER (O, 1112 beds) 210 East Colony Road, Madison Heights, VA, Zip 24572–2005, Mailing Address: P.O. Box 1098, Lynchburg, Zip 24505–1098, tel. 434/947–6326; David Cole, Assistant Director of Administration, Chief Financial Officer, Department of Behavioral Health and Developmental Service

COMMONWEALTH CENTER FOR CHILDREN AND ADOLESCENTS (O, 60 beds) 1355 Richmond Road, Staunton, VA, Zip 24401–9146, Mailing Address: Box 4000, Zip 24402–4000, tel. 540/332–2100; Mary Clare. Smith, Interim Facility Director
Web address: www.ccca.dbhds.virginia.gov

EASTERN STATE HOSPITAL (O, 300 beds) 4601 Ironbound Road, Williamsburg, VA, Zip 23188–2652; tel. 757/253–5161; John M. Favret, Director
Web address: www.esh.dmhmrsas.virginia.gov/

HIRAM W. DAVIS MEDICAL CENTER (O, 10 beds) 26317 West Washington Street, Petersburg, VA, Zip 23803–2727, Mailing Address: P.O. Box 4030, Zip 23803–0030, tel. 804/524–7420; Nichelle Williams, Director

Section B

For explanation of codes following names, see page B2.
★ Indicates Type III membership in the American Hospital Association.

NORTHERN VIRGINIA MENTAL HEALTH INSTITUTE (O, 134 beds) 3302 Gallows Road, Falls Church, VA, Zip 22042–3398; tel. 703/207–7100; Tammy Peacock, Ph.D., Facility Director
Web address: www.nvmhi.dbhds.virginia.gov

PIEDMONT GERIATRIC HOSPITAL (O, 135 beds) 5001 East Patrick Henry Hwy, Burkeville, VA, Zip 23922–3460, Mailing Address: P.O. Box 427, Zip 23922–0427, tel. 434/767–4401; Hilton McDaniel, President

SOUTHERN VIRGINIA MENTAL HEALTH INSTITUTE (O, 72 beds) 382 Taylor Drive, Danville, VA, Zip 24541–4023; tel. 434/799–6220; William Cook, Director
Web address: www.svmhi.dbhds.virginia.gov

SOUTHWESTERN VIRGINIA MENTAL HEALTH INSTITUTE (O, 166 beds) 340 Bagley Circle, Marion, VA, Zip 24354–3390; tel. 276/783–1200; Cynthia McClaskey, Ph.D., Director
Web address: www.swvmhi.dmhmrsas.virginia.gov/

WESTERN STATE HOSPITAL (O, 246 beds) 103 Valley Center Drive, Staunton, VA, Zip 24401–9146, Mailing Address: P.O. Box 2500, Zip 24402–2500, tel. 540/332–8000; Mary Clare. Smith, Director
Web address: www.dbhds.virginia.gov

Owned, leased, sponsored:	11 hospitals	2622 beds
Contract-managed:	0 hospitals	0 beds
Totals:	11 hospitals	2622 beds

0986: VIRGINIA MASON HEALTH SYSTEM (NP)

1100 Ninth Avenue, Seattle, WA, Zip 98101–2756, Mailing Address: P.O. Box 900, Zip 98111–0900, tel. 206/223–6600; Gary Kaplan, M.D., FACHE, Chief Executive Officer
(Moderately Centralized Health System)

WASHINGTON: VIRGINIA MASON MEDICAL CENTER (O, 245 beds) 1100 Ninth Avenue, Seattle, WA, Zip 98101–2756, Mailing Address: P.O. Box 900, Zip 98111–0900, tel. 206/223–6600; Gary Kaplan, M.D., FACHE, Chairman and Chief Executive Officer

VIRGINIA MASON MEMORIAL (O, 246 beds) 2811 Tieton Drive, Yakima, WA, Zip 98902–3761; tel. 509/575–8000; Russ Myers, Chief Executive Officer
Web address: www.yakimamemorial.org

Owned, leased, sponsored:	2 hospitals	491 beds
Contract-managed:	0 hospitals	0 beds
Totals:	2 hospitals	491 beds

★**6725: VIRTUA HEALTH** (NP)

303 Lippincott Drive, 4th Floor, Marlton, NJ, Zip 08053–4160; tel. 856/355–0010; Dennis W. Pullin, FACHE, President and Chief Executive Officer
(Centralized Health System)

NEW JERSEY: LOURDES MEDICAL CENTER OF BURLINGTON COUNTY (O, 169 beds) 218-A Sunset Road, Willingboro, NJ, Zip 08046–1162; tel. 609/835–2900; Mark Nessel, Executive Vice President and Chief Operating Officer
Web address: www.lourdesnet.org

OUR LADY OF LOURDES MEDICAL CENTER (O, 340 beds) 1600 Haddon Avenue, Camden, NJ, Zip 08103–3117; tel. 856/757–3500; Reginald Blaber, M.D., FACC, President

VIRTUA MARLTON (O, 185 beds) 90 Brick Road, Marlton, NJ, Zip 08053–2177; tel. 856/355–6000; Dennis W. Pullin, FACHE, President and Chief Executive Officer
Web address: www.virtua.org

VIRTUA MEMORIAL (O, 334 beds) 175 Madison Avenue, Mount Holly, NJ, Zip 08060–2099; tel. 609/267–0700; Dennis W. Pullin, FACHE, President and Chief Executive Officer
Web address: www.virtua.org

VIRTUA VOORHEES (O, 402 beds) 100 Bowman Drive, Voorhees, NJ, Zip 08043–9612; tel. 856/325–3000; Dennis W. Pullin, FACHE, President and Chief Executive Officer
Web address: www.virtua.org

Owned, leased, sponsored:	5 hospitals	1430 beds
Contract-managed:	0 hospitals	0 beds
Totals:	5 hospitals	1430 beds

★**0221: WAKE FOREST BAPTIST HEALTH** (NP)

Medical Center Boulevard, Winston-Salem, NC, Zip 27157; tel. 336/716–2011; Julie Ann . Freischlag, M.D., Chief Executive Officer
(Centralized Health System)

NORTH CAROLINA: HIGH POINT MEDICAL CENTER (O, 311 beds) 601 North Elm Street, High Point, NC, Zip 27262–4398, Mailing Address: P.O. Box HP-5, Zip 27261–1899, tel. 336/878–6000; James Hoekstra, M.D., President

WAKE FOREST BAPTIST HEALTH – WILKES MEDICAL CENTER (L, 92 beds) 1370 West 'D' Street, North Wilkesboro, NC, Zip 28659–3506, Mailing Address: P.O. Box 609, Zip 28659–0609, tel. 336/651–8100; J Gene. Faile, Chief Executive Officer and President
Web address: www.wilkesregional.com/

WAKE FOREST BAPTIST HEALTH-DAVIE MEDICAL CENTER (O, 25 beds) 329 NC Highway 801 North, Bermuda Run, NC, Zip 27006; tel. 336/998–1300; Chad J. Brown, M.P.H., President

WAKE FOREST BAPTIST HEALTH-LEXINGTON MEDICAL CENTER (O, 75 beds) 250 Hospital Drive, Lexington, NC, Zip 27292–6728, Mailing Address: P.O. Box 1817, Zip 27293–1817, tel. 336/248–5161; William B. James, FACHE, President
Web address: www.lexington.wakehealth.edu

WAKE FOREST BAPTIST MEDICAL CENTER (O, 800 beds) Medical Center Boulevard, Winston-Salem, NC, Zip 27157–0001; tel. 336/716–2011; Julie Ann . Freischlag, M.D., Chief Executive Officer
Web address: www.wakehealth.edu

Owned, leased, sponsored:	5 hospitals	1303 beds
Contract-managed:	0 hospitals	0 beds
Totals:	5 hospitals	1303 beds

★**6705: WAKEMED HEALTH & HOSPITALS** (NP)

3000 New Bern Avenue, Raleigh, NC, Zip 27610–1231; tel. 919/350–8000; Donald R. Gintzig, President and Chief Executive Officer
(Moderately Centralized Health System)

NORTH CAROLINA: WAKEMED CARY HOSPITAL (O, 178 beds) 1900 Kildaire Farm Road, Cary, NC, Zip 27518–6616; tel. 919/350–8000; Donald R. Gintzig, President and Chief Executive Officer
Web address: www.wakemed.org

WAKEMED RALEIGH CAMPUS (O, 695 beds) 3000 New Bern Avenue, Raleigh, NC, Zip 27610–1295; tel. 919/350–8000; Donald R. Gintzig, President and Chief Executive Officer

Owned, leased, sponsored:	2 hospitals	873 beds
Contract-managed:	0 hospitals	0 beds
Totals:	2 hospitals	873 beds

★**0979: WASHINGTON HEALTH SYSTEM** (NP)

155 Wilson Avenue, Washington, PA, Zip 15301–3336; tel. 724/225–7000; Brook Ward, President and Chief Executive Officer
(Independent Hospital System)

PENNSYLVANIA: WASHINGTON HEALTH SYSTEM GREENE (O, 49 beds) 350 Bonar Avenue, Waynesburg, PA, Zip 15370–1608; tel. 724/627–3101; Terry Wiltrout, President

WASHINGTON HOSPITAL (O, 206 beds) 155 Wilson Avenue, Washington, PA, Zip 15301–3398; tel. 724/225–7000; Gary B. Weinstein, President and Chief Executive Officer
Web address: www.washingtonhospital.org

Owned, leased, sponsored:	2 hospitals	255 beds
Contract-managed:	0 hospitals	0 beds
Totals:	2 hospitals	255 beds

For explanation of codes following names, see page B2.
★ Indicates Type III membership in the American Hospital Association.

© 2019 AHA Guide

Section B

★**0068: WELLSPAN HEALTH** (NP)
45 Monument Road, Suite 200, York, PA, Zip 17403–5071; tel. 717/851–2121; Roxanna L. Gapstur, Ph.D., R.N., President and Chief Executive Officer
(Centralized Physician/Insurance Health System)

PENNSYLVANIA: CHAMBERSBURG HOSPITAL (O, 273 beds) 112 North Seventh Street, Chambersburg, PA, Zip 17201–1720; tel. 717/267–3000; Patrick W. O'Donnell, CPA, President and Chief Executive Officer

WAYNESBORO HOSPITAL (O, 56 beds) 501 East Main Street, Waynesboro, PA, Zip 17268–2394; tel. 717/765–4000; Melissa Dubrow, Chief Operating Officer
Web address: www.summithealth.org

WELLSPAN EPHRATA COMMUNITY HOSPITAL (O, 130 beds) 169 Martin Avenue, Ephrata, PA, Zip 17522–1724, Mailing Address: P.O. Box 1002, Zip 17522–1002, tel. 717/733–0311

WELLSPAN GETTYSBURG HOSPITAL (O, 76 beds) 147 Gettys Street, Gettysburg, PA, Zip 17325–2534; tel. 717/334–2121; Jane E. Hyde, President
Web address: www.wellspan.org

WELLSPAN GOOD SAMARITAN HOSPITAL (O, 151 beds) Fourth and Walnut Streets, Lebanon, PA, Zip 17042–1281, Mailing Address: P.O. Box 1281, Zip 17042–1281, tel. 717/270–7500; Thomas R. Harlow, FACHE, President

WELLSPAN PHILHAVEN (O, 103 beds) 283 South Butler Road, Mount Gretna, PA, Zip 17064–6085, Mailing Address: P.O. Box 550, Zip 17064–0550, tel. 717/273–8871; Phil Hess, Chief Executive Officer
Web address: www.philhaven.org

WELLSPAN SURGERY AND REHABILLITATION HOSPITAL (O, 73 beds) 55 Monument Road, York, PA, Zip 17403–5023; tel. 717/812–6100; Barbara Yarrish, R.N., President

WELLSPAN YORK HOSPITAL (O, 573 beds) 1001 South George Street, York, PA, Zip 17403–3645; tel. 717/851–2345; Keith D. Noll, President
Web address: www.wellspan.org

Owned, leased, sponsored:	8 hospitals	1435 beds
Contract-managed:	0 hospitals	0 beds
Totals:	8 hospitals	1435 beds

★**0995: WELLSTAR HEALTH SYSTEM** (NP)
793 Sawyer Road, Marietta, GA, Zip 30062, tel. 770/792–5012; Candice Saunders, President and Chief Executive Officer
(Centralized Health System)

GEORGIA: WELLSTAR COBB HOSPITAL (O, 370 beds) 3950 Austell Road, Austell, GA, Zip 30106–1121; tel. 470/732–4000; Callie Andrews, President
Web address: www.wellstar.org

WELLSTAR DOUGLAS HOSPITAL (O, 108 beds) 8954 Hospital Drive, Douglasville, GA, Zip 30134–2282; tel. 770/949–1500; Craig A. Owens, President
Web address: www.wellstar.org

WELLSTAR KENNESTONE HOSPITAL (O, 657 beds) 677 Church Street, Marietta, GA, Zip 30060–1148; tel. 770/793–5000; Mary Chatman, Ph.D., Chief Executive Officer
Web address: www.wellstar.org

WELLSTAR PAULDING HOSPITAL (O, 294 beds) 2518 Jimmy Lee Smith Parkway, Hiram, GA, Zip 30141; tel. 470/644–7000; John Kueven, Senior Vice President and President

WELLSTAR WINDY HILL HOSPITAL (O, 55 beds) 2540 Windy Hill Road, Marietta, GA, Zip 30067–8632; tel. 770/644–1000; Mary Chatman, Ph.D., Chief Executive Officer
Web address: www.wellstar.org

WELLSTAR ATLANTA MEDICAL CENTER (O, 506 beds) 303 Parkway Drive NE, Atlanta, GA, Zip 30312–1212; tel. 404/265–4000; Kimberly Ryan, President

WELLSTAR NORTH FULTON HOSPITAL (O, 173 beds) 3000 Hospital Boulevard, Roswell, GA, Zip 30076–3899; tel. 770/751–2500; Jon-Paul Croom, President
Web address: www.nfultonhospital.com

WELLSTAR SPALDING REGIONAL HOSPITAL (O, 160 beds) 601 South Eighth Street, Griffin, GA, Zip 30224–4294, Mailing Address: P O Drawer 'V', Zip 30224–1168, tel. 770/228–2721; Tamara Ison, Senior Vice President and President

WELLSTAR SYLVAN GROVE HOSPITAL (O, 24 beds) 1050 McDonough Road, Jackson, GA, Zip 30233–1599; tel. 770/775–7861; Tamara Ison, Senior Vice President and President
Web address: www.sylvangrovehospital.com

WELLSTAR WEST GEORGIA MEDICAL CENTER (O, 390 beds) 1514 Vernon Road, Lagrange, GA, Zip 30240–4131; tel. 706/882–1411; Coleman Foss, Chief Executive Officer
Web address: www.wghealth.org/

Owned, leased, sponsored:	10 hospitals	2737 beds
Contract-managed:	0 hospitals	0 beds
Totals:	10 hospitals	2737 beds

★**0004: WEST TENNESSEE HEALTHCARE** (NP)
620 Skyline Drive, Jackson, TN, Zip 38301–3923; tel. 731/541–5000; James E. Ross, President and Chief Executive Officer
(Centralized Physician/Insurance Health System)

TENNESSEE: BOLIVAR GENERAL HOSPITAL (O, 25 beds) 650 Nuckolls Road, Bolivar, TN, Zip 38008–1532, Mailing Address: PO Box 509, Zip 38008–0509, tel. 731/658–3100; Ruby Kirby, Administrator
Web address: www.wth.net

CAMDEN GENERAL HOSPITAL (O, 25 beds) 175 Hospital Drive, Camden, TN, Zip 38320–1617; tel. 731/593–6300; Scott Barber, Vice President
Web address: www.wth.net

JACKSON-MADISON COUNTY GENERAL HOSPITAL (O, 672 beds) 620 Skyline Drive, Jackson, TN, Zip 38301–3923; tel. 731/541–5000; Deann Thelen, Chief Executive Officer
Web address: www.wth.org

MILAN GENERAL HOSPITAL (O, 28 beds) 4039 Highland Street, Milan, TN, Zip 38358–3483; tel. 731/686–1591; Sherry Scruggs, Administrator

PATHWAYS OF TENNESSEE (O, 25 beds) 238 Summar Drive, Jackson, TN, Zip 38301–3906; tel. 731/541–8200; Pam Henson, Executive Director
Web address: www.wth.net/pathways

WEST TENNESSEE HEALTHCARE DYERSBURG HOSPITAL (O, 124 beds) 400 East Tickle Street, Dyersburg, TN, Zip 38024–3120; tel. 731/285–2410; Reba Celsor, Chief Executive Officer

WEST TENNESSEE HEALTHCARE VOLUNTEER HOSPITAL (O, 41 beds) 161 Mount Pelia Road, Martin, TN, Zip 38237–3811; tel. 731/587–4261; Darrell Blaylock, Chief Executive Officer
Web address: www.wth.org/locations/west-tennessee-healthcare-volunteer-hospital

Owned, leased, sponsored:	7 hospitals	940 beds
Contract-managed:	0 hospitals	0 beds
Totals:	7 hospitals	940 beds

★**0119: WEST VIRGINIA UNIVERSITY HEALTH SYSTEM** (NP)
One Medical Center, Box 8136, Morgantown, WV, Zip 26506–8136; tel. 304/285–7150; Albert L. Wright Jr, PharmD, President and Chief Executive Officer
(Moderately Centralized Health System)

WEST VIRGINIA: BERKELEY MEDICAL CENTER (O, 195 beds) 2500 Hospital Drive, Martinsburg, WV, Zip 25401–3402; tel. 304/264–1000; Anthony Zelenka, President and Chief Operating Officer

CAMDEN CLARK MEDICAL CENTER (O, 239 beds) 800 Garfield Avenue, Parkersburg, WV, Zip 26101–5378, Mailing Address: P.O. Box 718, Zip 26102–0718, tel. 304/424–2111; Steve Altmiller, President and Chief Executive Officer
Web address: www.camdenclark.org

JEFFERSON MEDICAL CENTER (O, 25 beds) 300 South Preston Street, Ranson, WV, Zip 25438–1631; tel. 304/728–1600; Anthony Zelenka, President and Chief Executive Officer
Web address: www.wvuniversityhealthcare.com/locations/Jefferson-Medical-Center.aspx

For explanation of codes following names, see page B2.
★ *Indicates Type III membership in the American Hospital Association.*

POTOMAC VALLEY HOSPITAL (O, 25 beds) 100 Pin Oak Lane, Keyser, WV, Zip 26726–5908; tel. 304/597–3500; Mark G. Boucot, FACHE, President and Chief Executive Officer

REYNOLDS MEMORIAL HOSPITAL (O, 50 beds) 800 Wheeling Avenue, Glen Dale, WV, Zip 26038–1697; tel. 304/845–3211; David F. Hess, M.D., Chief Executive Officer
Web address: www.reynoldsmemorial.com

ST. JOSEPH'S HOSPITAL OF BUCKHANNON (O, 51 beds) 1 Amalia Drive, Buckhannon, WV, Zip 26201–2276; tel. 304/473–2000; Skip Gjolberg, FACHE, Administrator

UNITED HOSPITAL CENTER (O, 264 beds) 327 Medical Park Drive, Bridgeport, WV, Zip 26330–9006; tel. 681/342–1000; Michael C. Tillman, President and Chief Executive Officer
Web address: www.thenewuhc.com

WEST VIRGINIA UNIVERSITY HOSPITALS (O, 652 beds) 1 Medical Center Drive, Morgantown, WV, Zip 26506–4749; tel. 304/598–4000; Albert L. Wright Jr, PharmD, President and Chief Executive Officer

Owned, leased, sponsored:	8 hospitals	1501 beds
Contract-managed:	0 hospitals	0 beds
Totals:	8 hospitals	1501 beds

★**0811: WESTERN CONNECTICUT HEALTH NETWORK** (NP)
24 Hospital Avenue, Danbury, CT, Zip 06810–6099; tel. 203/739–7066; John M. Murphy, M.D., President and Chief Executive Officer
(Centralized Physician/Insurance Health System)

CONNECTICUT: DANBURY HOSPITAL (O, 284 beds) 24 Hospital Avenue, Danbury, CT, Zip 06810–6099; tel. 203/739–7000; John M. Murphy, M.D., President

NORWALK HOSPITAL (O, 151 beds) 34 Maple Street, Norwalk, CT, Zip 06850–3894; tel. 203/852–2000; Peter Cordeau, President
Web address: www.norwalkhospital.org

Owned, leased, sponsored:	2 hospitals	435 beds
Contract-managed:	0 hospitals	0 beds
Totals:	2 hospitals	435 beds

★**0468: WHITE RIVER HEALTH SYSTEM** (NP)
1710 Harrison Street, Batesville, AR, Zip 72501–7303; tel. 870/262–1200; Gary Paxson, Chief Executive Officer
(Independent Hospital System)

ARKANSAS: STONE COUNTY MEDICAL CENTER (O, 25 beds) 2106 East Main Street, Mountain View, AR, Zip 72560–6439, Mailing Address: P.O. Box 510, Zip 72560–0510, tel. 870/269–4361; Kevin Spears, Chief Executive Officer
Web address: www.whiteriverhealthsystem.com/doctors/facilities/stone-county-medical-center

WHITE RIVER MEDICAL CENTER (O, 210 beds) 1710 Harrison Street, Batesville, AR, Zip 72501–7303, Mailing Address: P.O. Box 2197, Zip 72503–2197, tel. 870/262–1200; Gary Paxson, Administrator

Owned, leased, sponsored:	2 hospitals	235 beds
Contract-managed:	0 hospitals	0 beds
Totals:	2 hospitals	235 beds

0646: WHITTIER HEALTH NETWORK (IO)
25 Railroad Square, Haverhill, MA, Zip 01832–5721; tel. 978/556–5858; Alfred L. Arcidi, M.D., President
(Independent Hospital System)

MASSACHUSETTS: WHITTIER PAVILION (O, 65 beds) 76 Summer Street, Haverhill, MA, Zip 01830–5814; tel. 978/373–8222; Alfred L. Arcidi, M.D., Chief Executive Officer

WHITTIER REHABILITATION HOSPITAL (O, 60 beds) 150 Flanders Road, Westborough, MA, Zip 01581–1017; tel. 508/871–2000; Alfred J. Arcidi, M.D., Senior Vice President
Web address: www.whittierhealth.com

WHITTIER REHABILITATION HOSPITAL (O, 60 beds) 145 Ward Hill Avenue, Bradford, MA, Zip 01835–6928; tel. 978/372–8000; Alfred J. Arcidi, M.D., Senior Vice President
Web address: www.whittierhealth.com

Owned, leased, sponsored:	3 hospitals	185 beds
Contract-managed:	0 hospitals	0 beds
Totals:	3 hospitals	185 beds

1945: WILLIS-KNIGHTON HEALTH SYSTEM (NP)
2600 Greenwood Road, Shreveport, LA, Zip 71103–3908; tel. 318/212–4000; James K. Elrod, LFACHE, President and Chief Executive Officer
(Moderately Centralized Health System)

LOUISIANA: DE SOTO REGIONAL HEALTH SYSTEM (C, 10 beds) 207 Jefferson Street, Mansfield, LA, Zip 71052–2603, Mailing Address: P.O. Box 1636, Zip 71052–1636, tel. 318/872–4610; Todd Eppler, FACHE, Chief Executive Officer
Web address: www.desotoregional.com

SPRINGHILL MEDICAL CENTER (C, 58 beds) 2001 Doctors Drive, Springhill, LA, Zip 71075–4526, Mailing Address: P.O. Box 920, Zip 71075–0920, tel. 318/539–1000; Michael Patronis, Chief Executive Officer
Web address: www.smccare.com

WILLIS-KNIGHTON MEDICAL CENTER (O, 758 beds) 2600 Greenwood Road, Shreveport, LA, Zip 71103–3908, Mailing Address: P.O. Box 32600, Zip 71130–2600, tel. 318/212–4600; James K. Elrod, LFACHE, Chief Executive Officer

Owned, leased, sponsored:	1 hospitals	758 beds
Contract-managed:	2 hospitals	68 beds
Totals:	3 hospitals	826 beds

1004: WMCHEALTH (NP)
100 Woods Road, Valhalla, NY, Zip 10595–1530; tel. 914/493–7000; Michael D. Israel, President and Chief Executive Officer
(Moderately Centralized Health System)

NEW YORK: BON SECOURS COMMUNITY HOSPITAL (O, 143 beds) 160 East Main Street, Port Jervis, NY, Zip 12771–2245, Mailing Address: P.O. Box 1014, Zip 12771–0268, tel. 845/858–7000; Mary Leahy, M.D., Chief Executive Officer

GOOD SAMARITAN REGIONAL MEDICAL CENTER (O, 308 beds) 255 Lafayette Avenue, Suffern, NY, Zip 10901–4869; tel. 845/368–5000; Mary Leahy, M.D., Chief Executive Officer
Web address: www.goodsamhosp.org

HEALTH ALLIANCE HOSPITAL – BROADWAY CAMPUS (O, 150 beds) 396 Broadway, Kingston, NY, Zip 12401–4692; tel. 845/331–3131; David Scarpino, President and Chief Executive Officer

HEALTH ALLIANCE HOSPITAL – MARY'S AVENUE CAMPUS (O, 120 beds) 105 Marys Avenue, Kingston, NY, Zip 12401–5894; tel. 845/338–2500; David Scarpino, President and Chief Executive Officer
Web address: www.hahv.org

MARGARETVILLE HOSPITAL (O, 15 beds) 42084 State Highway 28, Margaretville, NY, Zip 12455–2820; tel. 845/586–2631; Mark Pohar, Executive Director
Web address: www.margaretvillehospital.org

ST. ANTHONY COMMUNITY HOSPITAL (O, 60 beds) 15 Maple Avenue, Warwick, NY, Zip 10990–1028; tel. 845/986–2276; Mary Leahy, M.D., Chief Executive Officer
Web address: www.stanthonycommunityhosp.org

WESTCHESTER MEDICAL CENTER (O, 872 beds) 100 Woods Road, Valhalla, NY, Zip 10595–1530; tel. 914/493–7000; Michael D. Israel, President and Chief Executive Officer

Owned, leased, sponsored:	7 hospitals	1668 beds
Contract-managed:	0 hospitals	0 beds
Totals:	7 hospitals	1668 beds

For explanation of codes following names, see page B2.
★ Indicates Type III membership in the American Hospital Association.

★0157: YALE NEW HAVEN HEALTH (NP)
20 York St, PACU YSC EP3, New Haven, CT, Zip 06519–1304,
Mailing Address: 789 Howard Avenue, Zip 06519–1304,
tel. 203/688–4608; Marna P. Borgstrom, President and Chief
Executive Officer
(Centralized Physician/Insurance Health System)

CONNECTICUT: BRIDGEPORT HOSPITAL (O, 362 beds) 267 Grant Street,
Bridgeport, CT, Zip 06610–2805, Mailing Address: P.O. Box 5000,
Zip 06610–0120, tel. 203/384–3000; Michael Ivy, M.D., Interim Chief
Executive Officer

GREENWICH HOSPITAL (O, 184 beds) 5 Perryridge Road, Greenwich, CT,
Zip 06830–4697; tel. 203/863–3000; Norman G. Roth, President
Web address: www.greenhosp.org

LAWRENCE + MEMORIAL HOSPITAL (O, 251 beds) 365 Montauk Avenue, New
London, CT, Zip 06320–4769; tel. 860/442–0711; Patrick Green, FACHE,
President and Chief Executive Officer
Web address: www.lmhospital.org

YALE-NEW HAVEN HOSPITAL (O, 1424 beds) 20 York Street, New Haven, CT,
Zip 06510–3202; tel. 203/688–4242; Marna P. Borgstrom, Chief Executive
Officer

RHODE ISLAND: WESTERLY HOSPITAL (O, 75 beds) 25 Wells Street, Westerly,
RI, Zip 02891–2934; tel. 401/596–6000; Patrick Green, FACHE, President
and Chief Executive Officer
Web address: www.westerlyhospital.org

Owned, leased, sponsored:	5 hospitals	2296 beds
Contract-managed:	0 hospitals	0 beds
Totals:	5 hospitals	2296 beds

For explanation of codes following names, see page B2.
★ Indicates Type III membership in the American Hospital Association.

© 2019 AHA Guide Health Care Systems, Networks and Alliances **B149**

Geographically

United States

ALABAMA

Anniston: REGIONAL MEDICAL CENTER 400 East 10th Street, Zip 36207–4716; tel. 256/235–5121; Louis A. Bass, President and Chief Executive Officer, p. B108

Birmingham: BRADFORD HEALTH SERVICES 2101 Magnolia Avenue South, Suite 518, Zip 35205–2853; tel. 205/251–7753; Jerry W. Crowder, President and Chief Executive Officer, p. B25

★ ENCOMPASS HEALTH CORPORATION 3660 Grandview Parkway, Suite 200, Zip 35243–3332, Mailing Address: 9001 Liberty Parkway, Zip 35242–3332, tel. 205/967–7116; Mark J. Tarr, President and Chief Executive Officer, p. B49

NOLAND HEALTH SERVICES, INC. 600 Corporate Parkway, Suite 100, Zip 35242–5451; tel. 205/783–8484; Gary M. Glasscock, President and Chief Executive Officer, p. B49

★ UAB HEALTH SYSTEM 500 22nd Street South, Suite 408, Zip 35233–3110; tel. 205/975–5362; William Ferniany, Chief Executive Officer, p. B131

Guntersville: MARSHALL HEALTH SYSTEM 227 Britany Road, Zip 35976–5766; tel. 256/894–6615; Gary R. Gore, Chief Executive Officer, p. B79

Huntsville: HUNTSVILLE HOSPITAL HEALTH SYSTEM 101 Sivley Road SW, Zip 35801–4421; tel. 265/256–1000; David S. Spillers, Chief Executive Officer, p. B67

Mobile: ALTAPOINTE HEALTH SYSTEMS 5750-A Southland Drive, Zip 36693–3316; tel. 251/473–4423; J. Tuerk. Schlesinger, Chief Executive Officer, p. B10

INFIRMARY HEALTH SYSTEM 5 Mobile Infirmary Circle, Zip 36607–3513; tel. 251/435–5500; D Mark. Nix, President and Chief Executive Officer, p. B68

★ USA HEALTH 2451 USA Medical Center Drive, Zip 36617–2300; tel. 251/471–7000; Owen Bailey, Chief Executive Officer and Senior Associate Vice President for Medical Affairs, p. B143

Montgomery: BAPTIST HEALTH 301 Brown Springs Road, Zip 36117–7005; tel. 334/273–4400; W Russell. Tyner, President and Chief Executive Officer, p. B20

GILLIARD HEALTH SERVICES 3091 Carter Hill Road, Zip 36111–1801; tel. 334/265–5009; William G. McKenzie, President, Chief Executive Officer and Chairman, p. B57

Tuscaloosa: DCH HEALTH SYSTEM 809 University Boulevard East, Zip 35401–2029; tel. 205/759–7111; Bryan N. Kindred, President and Chief Executive Officer, p. B42

ARIZONA

Flagstaff: ★ NORTHERN ARIZONA HEALTHCARE 1200 North Beaver Street, Zip 86001–3118; tel. 928/779–3366; Florence (Flo). Spyrow, President and Chief Executive Officer, p. B91

Phoenix: ★ BANNER HEALTH 2901 North Central Avenue Suite 160, Zip 85012–2702, Mailing Address: P.O. Box 25489, Zip 85002–5489, tel. 602/747–4000; Peter S. Fine, President and Chief Executive Officer, p. B19

Scottsdale: ★ HONORHEALTH 8125 North Hayden Road, Zip 85258–2463; tel. 623/580–5800; Todd LaPorte, Chief Executive Officer, p. B66

SOUTHWEST HEALTHCARE SYSTEM 7025 N Scottsdale Road Suite 9347, Zip 85253–3675, Mailing Address: 7025 North Scottsdale Road, Suite 9347, Zip 85251–3331, tel. 480/518–5444; Paul R. Tuft, President, p. B119

ARKANSAS

Batesville: ★ WHITE RIVER HEALTH SYSTEM 1710 Harrison Street, Zip 72501–7303; tel. 870/262–1200; Gary Paxson, Chief Executive Officer, p. B148

Blytheville: ★ MISSISSIPPI COUNTY HOSPITAL SYSTEM 1520 North Division Street, Zip 72315–1448, Mailing Address: P.O. Box 108, Zip 72316–0108, tel. 870/838–7300; Chris Lee. Raymer, Chief Executive Officer, p. B86

Little Rock: ★ BAPTIST HEALTH 9601 Baptist Health Drive, Zip 72205–6321; tel. 501/202–2000; Troy R. Wells, Chief Executive Officer, p. B20

CALIFORNIA

Alhambra: AHMC & HEALTHCARE, INC. 55 South Raymond Avenue, Suite 105, Zip 91801–7101; tel. 626/457–9600; Jonathan Wu, President and Chairman, p. B8

Corona: SIGNATURE HEALTHCARE SERVICES 4238 Green River Road, Zip 92880–1669; tel. 951/549–8032; Soon K. Kim, President and Chief Executive Officer, p. B117

Covina: ★ CITRUS VALLEY HEALTH PARTNERS 210 West San Bernardino Road, Zip 91723–1515; tel. 626/331–7331; Robert H. Curry, President and Chief Executive Officer, p. B31

Cupertino: CRC HEALTH GROUP, INC. 20400 Stevens Creek Boulevard, Suite 600, Zip 95014–2217; tel. 866/540–5240; Jerome E. Rhodes, Chief Executive Officer, p. B41

El Segundo: AVANTI HOSPITALS 222 North Sepulveda Boulevard, Suite 950, Zip 90245–5614; tel. 310/356–0550; Michael A. Rembis, Corporate Chief Executive Officer, p. B17

Escondido: ★ PALOMAR HEALTH 456 East Grand Avenue, Zip 92025–3319; tel. 760/740–6393; Diane Hansen, Chief Executive Officer, p. B97

Fountain Valley: MEMORIALCARE 17360 Brookhurst Street, Zip 92708–3720, Mailing Address: P.O. Box 1428, Long Beach, Zip 90801–1428, tel. 714/377–2900; Barry S. Arbuckle, President and Chief Executive Officer, p. B83

Fresno: COMMUNITY MEDICAL CENTERS Fresno and Maddy Drive, Zip 93721, Mailing Address: P.O. Box 1232, Zip 93715–1232, tel. 559/459–6000; Tim A. Joslin, President and Chief Executive Officer, p. B39

Hemet: PHYSICIANS FOR HEALTHY HOSPITALS 1117 East Devonshire Avenue, Zip 92543–3083; tel. 951/652–2811; Joel M. Bergenfeld, Chief Executive Officer, p. B98

Irvine: ALECTO HEALTHCARE 16310 Bake Parkway, Suite 200, Zip 92618–4684; tel. 323/932–5963; Lex Reddy, Chief Executive Officer, p. B8

Loma Linda: LOMA LINDA UNIVERSITY ADVENTIST HEALTH SCIENCES CENTER 11175 Campus Street, Zip 92350–1700; tel. 909/558–7572; Richard H. Hart, President and Chief Executive Officer, p. B78

Los Angeles: KECK MEDICINE OF USC 1510 San Pablo Street, Suite 600, Zip 90033–5405; tel. 323/442–8500; Thomas E. Jackiewicz, Senior Vice President and Chief Executive Officer, p. B71

LOS ANGELES COUNTY-DEPARTMENT OF HEALTH SERVICES 313 North Figueroa Street, Room 912, Zip 90012–2691; tel. 213/240–8101; Mitchell H. Katz, Director, p. B78

PROSPECT MEDICAL HOLDINGS 10780 California Route 2 #400, Zip 90025; tel. 714/796–5900; Mitchell Lew, President, p. B103

VERITY HEALTH SYSTEM 2200 West Third Street, Suite 200, Zip 90057–1935, Mailing Address: 203 Redwood Shores Parkway, Suite 800, Redwood City, Zip 94065, tel. 650/551–6650; Richard Adcock, President and Chief Executive Officer, p. B144

Oakland: ★ KAISER FOUNDATION HOSPITALS One Kaiser Plaza, 27th Floor - Office #2743, Zip 94612–3600; tel. 510/271–5910; Bernard J. Tyson, Chairman and Chief Executive Officer, p. B70

★ UNIVERSITY OF CALIFORNIA SYSTEMWIDE ADMINISTRATION 1111 Franklin Street, 11th Floor, Zip 94607–5200; tel. 510/987–9071; John D. Stobo, Executive Vice President and Chief Executive Officer, p. B139

Ontario: ★ PRIME HEALTHCARE 3300 East Guasti Road, Zip 91761–8655; tel. 909/235–4400; Prem Reddy, Chairman, President and Chief Executive Officer, p. B100

Palo Alto: ★ STANFORD HEALTH CARE 300 Pasteur Drive, Zip 94304–2299; tel. 650/723–4000; David Entwistle, President and Chief Executive Officer, p. B122

Roseville: ★ ADVENTIST HEALTH One Adventist Health Way, Zip 95661–3266, Mailing Address: P.O. Box 619002, Zip 95661–9002, tel. 916/406–0000; Scott Reiner, Chief Executive Officer, p. B6

Sacramento: ★ SUTTER HEALTH 2200 River Plaza Drive, Zip 95833–4134; tel. 916/733–8800; Sarah Krevans, President and Chief Executive Officer, p. B124

San Diego: ★ SCRIPPS HEALTH 4275 Campus Point Court CP112, Zip 92121–1513, Mailing Address: 4275 Campus Point Court, Zip 92121–1513, tel. 858/678–7200; Chris D. Van Gorder, President and Chief Executive Officer, p. B113

★ SHARP HEALTHCARE 8695 Spectrum Center Boulevard, Zip 92123–1489; tel. 858/499–4000; Christopher Howard, President and Chief Executive Officer, p. B117

San Leandro: ALAMEDA HEALTH SYSTEM 15400 Foothill Boulevard, Zip 94578–1009; tel. 510/677–7920; Delvecchio Finley, Chief Executive Officer, p. B8

Santa Ana: KPC HEALTHCARE, INC. 1301 North Tustin Avenue, Zip 92705–8619; tel. 714/953–3652

Santa Barbara: ★ COTTAGE HEALTH 400 West Pueblo Street, Zip 93105–4353, Mailing Address: P.O. Box 689, Zip 93102–0689, tel. 805/569–7290; Ronald C. Werft, President and Chief Executive Officer, p. B40

Santa Fe Springs: COLLEGE HEALTH ENTERPRISES 11627 Telegraph Road, Suite 200, Zip 90670–6814; tel. 562/923–9449; Barry J. Weiss, Chairman of the Board, p. B31

Truckee: ★ TAHOE FOREST HEALTH SYSTEM 10121 Pine Avenue, Zip 96161–4835; tel. 530/587–6011; Harry Weis, Chief Executive Officer, p. B125

Ventura: COMMUNITY MEMORIAL HEALTH SYSTEM 147 North Brent Street, Zip 93003–2809; tel. 805/652–5011; Gary Wilde, President and Chief Executive Officer, p. B39

Walnut Creek: ★ JOHN MUIR HEALTH 1400 Treat Boulevard, Zip 94597–2142; tel. 925/941–2100; Calvin K, Knight, President and Chief Executive Officer, p. B70

West Hollywood: ★ CEDARS-SINAI HEALTH SYSTEM 8700 Beverly Boulevard, Zip 90048–1865, Mailing Address: Box 48750, Los Angeles, Zip 90048–0750, tel. 310/423–5000; Thomas M. Priselac, President and Chief Executive Officer, p. B29

Whittier: ★ PIH HEALTH 12401 Washington Boulevard, Zip 90602–1006; tel. 562/698–0811; James R. West, President and Chief Executive Officer, p. B98

COLORADO

Alamosa: ★ SAN LUIS VALLEY HEALTH 106 Blanca Avenue, Zip 81101–2340; tel. 719/589–2511; Konnie Martin, Chief Executive Officer, p. B111

Broomfield: ★ SCL HEALTH 500 Eldorado Boulevard, Suite 4300, Zip 80021; tel. 303/813–5180; Lydia Jumonville, President and Chief Executive Officer, p. B113

Fort Collins: ★ UCHEALTH 2315 East Harmony Road, Suite 200, Zip 80528–8620; tel. 970/495–7000; Elizabeth B. Concordia, President and Chief Executive Officer, p. B132

CONNECTICUT

Danbury: ★ WESTERN CONNECTICUT HEALTH NETWORK 24 Hospital Avenue, Zip 06810–6099; tel. 203/739–7066; John M. Murphy, President and Chief Executive Officer, p. B148

Hartford: CONNECTICUT DEPARTMENT OF MENTAL HEALTH AND ADDICTION SERVICES 410 Capitol Avenue, Zip 06106–1367, Mailing Address: P.O. Box 341431, Zip 06134–1431, tel. 860/418–7000; Miriam Delphin-Rittmon, Commissioner, p. B39

★ HARTFORD HEALTHCARE One State Street, 19th Floor, Zip 6103; tel. 860/263–4100; Elliot T. Joseph, Chief Executive Officer, p. B59

New Haven: ★ YALE NEW HAVEN HEALTH 20 York St, PACU YSC EP3, Zip 06519–1304, Mailing Address: 789 Howard Avenue, Zip 06519–1304, tel. 203/688–4608; Marna P. Borgstrom, President and Chief Executive Officer, p. B149

DELAWARE

Wilmington: ★ CHRISTIANA CARE HEALTH SYSTEM 501 West 14th Street, Zip 19801–1013, Mailing Address: P.O. Box 1668, Zip 19899–1668, tel. 302/733–1000; Janice E. Nevin, Chief Executive Officer, p. B30

DISTRICT OF COLUMBIA

Washington: ★ DEPARTMENT OF THE AIR FORCE 1420 Pentagon, Room 4E1084, Zip 20330–1420; tel. 202/767–4765, Lieutenant General, Thomas Travis, Surgeon General, p. B42

★ DEPARTMENT OF VETERANS AFFAIRS 810 Vermont Avenue NW, Zip 20420–0001; tel. 202/273–5781, Honorable, Robert Wilkie, Secretary, p. B43

FLORIDA

Altamonte Springs: ★ ADVENTHEALTH 900 Hope Way, Zip 32714–1502; tel. 407/357–1000; Terry Shaw, President and Chief Executive Officer, p. B5

Boca Raton: PROMISE HEALTHCARE 999 Yamato Road, 3rd Floor, Zip 33431–4477; tel. 561/869–3100; Peter R. Baronoff, Chief Executive Officer, p. B102

SUCCESS HEALTHCARE 999 Yamato Road, 3rd Floor, Zip 33431–4477; tel. 561/869–6300; Peter R. Baronoff, President and Chief Executive Officer, p. B124

Clearwater: MORTON PLANT MEASE HEALTH CARE 2985 Drew Street, Zip 33759, Mailing Address: P.O. Box 210, Zip 33757–0210, tel. 727/462–7000; Glenn D. Waters, President, p. B87

Coral Gables: ★ BAPTIST HEALTH SOUTH FLORIDA 6855 Red Road, Suite 600, Zip 33143–3632; tel. 786/662–7111; Brian E. Keeley, President and Chief Executive Officer, p. B21

Fort Lauderdale: ★ BROWARD HEALTH 1800 NW 49th Street, Zip 33309–3092; tel. 954/355–4400; Gino Santorio, President and Chief Executive Officer, p. B25

Fort Myers: ★ LEE HEALTH 2776 Cleveland Avenue, Zip 33901–5864, Mailing Address: P.O. Box 2218, Zip 33902–2218, tel. 239/343–2000; Lawrence Antonucci, President and Chief Executive Officer, p. B74

Gainesville: ★ UF HEALTH SHANDS 1600 SW Archer Road, Zip 32610–0326; tel. 352/733–1500; Edward Jimenez, Chief Executive Officer, p. B132

Hollywood: ★ MEMORIAL HEALTHCARE SYSTEM 3501 Johnson Street, Zip 33021–5421; tel. 954/987–2000; Aurelio Fernandez, Chief Executive Officer, p. B83

Jacksonville: ★ BAPTIST HEALTH 841 Prudential Drive, Suite 1601, Zip 32207–8202; tel. 904/202–2000; Brett McClung, President and Chief Executive Officer, p. B20

NEMOURS 10140 Centurion Parkway North, Zip 32256–0532; tel. 904/697–4100; R. Lawrence. Moss, President and Chief Executive Officer, p. B89

Lauderdale Lakes: CATHOLIC HEALTH SERVICES 4790 North State Road 7, Zip 33319–5860; tel. 954/484–1515; Joseph M. Catania, President and Chief Executive Officer, p. B28

Leesburg: CENTRAL FLORIDA HEALTH 600 East Dixie Avenue, Zip 34748–5925; tel. 352/323–5762; Donald G. Henderson, Chief Executive Officer, p. B29

Miami Lakes: PACER HEALTH CORPORATION 14100 Palmetto Frontage Road, Suite 110, Zip 33016; tel. 305/828–7660; Rainier Gonzalez, Chairman and Chief Executive Officer, p. B96

Orlando: ORLANDO HEALTH 1414 Kuhl Avenue, Zip 32806–2093; tel. 321/843–7000; David W. Strong, President and Chief Executive Officer, p. B96

Pensacola: ★ BAPTIST HEALTH CARE CORPORATION 1717 North 'E' Street, Suite 402, Zip 32501–6377, Mailing Address: P.O. Box 17500, Zip 32522–7500, tel. 850/434–4011; Mark T. Faulkner, President, p. B21

Rockledge: HEALTH FIRST, INC. 6450 US Highway 1, Zip 32955–5747; tel. 321/434–7000; Steven P. Johnson, President and Chief Executive Officer, p. B64

Tampa: SHRINERS HOSPITALS FOR CHILDREN 2900 North Rocky Point Drive, Zip 33607–1435, Mailing Address: P.O. Box 31356, Zip 33631–3356, tel. 813/281–0300; John P. McCabe, Executive Vice President, p. B117

Windermere: UNITED MEDICAL CORPORATION 603 Main Street, Zip 34786–3548, Mailing Address: P.O. Box 1100, Zip 34786–1100, tel. 407/876–2200; Donald R. Dizney, Chairman and Chief Executive Officer, p. B133

GEORGIA

Albany: ★ PHOEBE PUTNEY HEALTH SYSTEM 417 Third Avenue, Zip 31701–1943; tel. 229/312–1000; Scott Steiner, Chief Executive Officer, p. B98

Atlanta: ★ EMORY HEALTHCARE 1440 Clifton Road NE, Suite 400, Zip 30322–1102; tel. 404/778–5000; Jonathan S. Lewin, President, p. B49

★ NORTHSIDE HEALTHCARE SYSTEM 1000 Johnson Ferry Road NE, Zip 30342–1611; tel. 404/851–8000; Robert Quattrocchi, President and Chief Executive Officer, p. B92

Augusta: ★ UNIVERSITY HEALTH CARE SYSTEM 1350 Walton Way, Zip 30901–2629; tel. 706/722–9011; James R. Davis, President and Chief Executive Officer, p. B138

Blairsville: UNION GENERAL HOSPITAL, INC. 35 Hospital Road, Zip 30512–3139; tel. 706/745–2111; Mike Gowder, Chief Executive Officer, p. B133

Brunswick: ★ SOUTHEAST GEORGIA HEALTH SYSTEM 2415 Parkwood Drive, Zip 31520–4722, Mailing Address: P.O. Box 1518, Zip 31521–1518, tel. 912/466–7000; Michael D. Scherneck, President and Chief Executive Officer, p. B119

Carrollton: ★ TANNER HEALTH SYSTEM 705 Dixie Street, Zip 30117–3818; tel. 770/836–9580; Loy M. Howard, President and Chief Executive Officer, p. B125

Columbus: COLUMBUS REGIONAL HEALTHCARE SYSTEM 707 Center Street, Suite 400, Zip 31901–1575; tel. 706/660–6100; M. Scott. Hill, Chief Executive Officer, p. B31

Decatur: DEKALB REGIONAL HEALTH SYSTEM 2701 North Decatur Road, Zip 30033–5918; tel. 404/501–1000; Robert E. Wilson Esq, Chief Executive Officer, p. B42

Gainesville: NORTHEAST GEORGIA HEALTH SYSTEM 743 Spring Street NE, Zip 30501–3715; tel. 770/219–9000; Carol H. Burrell, President and Chief Executive Officer, p. B91

Lilburn: LIFEBRITE HOSPITAL GROUP, LLC 3970 Five Forks Trickum Road SW Suite A, Zip 30047–2339; tel. 678/505–9657; Christian Al. Fletcher, Chief Executive Officer, p. B75

Macon: NAVICENT HEALTH 777 Hemlock Street, MSC 105, Zip 31201–2155, Mailing Address: 777 Hemlock Street, Zip 31201–2155, tel. 478/633–1000; Ninfa M. Saunders, President and Chief Executive Officer, p. B88

Marietta: ★ WELLSTAR HEALTH SYSTEM 793 Sawyer Road, Zip 30062; tel. 770/792–5012; Candice Saunders, President and Chief Executive Officer, p. B147

Rome: FLOYD HEALTHCARE MANAGEMENT 304 Turner McCall Boulevard, Zip 30165–5621, Mailing Address: P.O. Box 233, Zip 30162–0233, tel. 706/509–5000; Kurt Stuenkel, President and Chief Executive Officer, p. B55

Roswell: PIEDMONT HEALTHCARE 1800 Howell Mill Road NW, Suite 850, Zip 30076, Atlanta, tel. 404/425–1314; Kevin Brown, President and Chief Executive Officer, p. B98

Thomasville: ★ ARCHBOLD MEDICAL CENTER 910 South Broad Street, Zip 31792–6113; tel. 229/228–2739; J. Perry Mustian, President and Chief Executive Officer, p. B11

Tifton: ★ TIFT REGIONAL HEALTH SYSTEM 901 East 18th Street, Zip 31794–3648; tel. 229/353–6100; Christopher Dorman, President and Chief Executive Officer, p. B129

Valdosta: ★ SOUTH GEORGIA MEDICAL CENTER 2501 North Patterson Street, Zip 31602–1735, Mailing Address: P.O. Box 1727, Zip 31603–1727, tel. 229/333–1000; Bill Forbes, Interim Chief Executive Officer, p. B119

Warner Robins: ★ HOUSTON HEALTHCARE SYSTEM 1601 Watson Boulevard, Zip 31093–3431, Mailing Address: P.O. Box 2886, Zip 31099–2886, tel. 478/922–4281; Cary Martin, Chief Executive Officer, p. B66

HAWAII

Honolulu: ★ HAWAII HEALTH SYSTEMS CORPORATION 3675 Kilauea Avenue, Zip 96816–2333; tel. 808/733–4151; Linda Rosen, Chief Executive Officer, p. B59

HAWAII PACIFIC HEALTH 55 Merchant Street, Zip 96813–4306; tel. 808/949–9355; Raymond P. Vara Jr, President and Chief Executive Officer, p. B60

★ QUEEN'S HEALTH SYSTEMS 1301 Punchbowl Street, Zip 96813–2402; tel. 808/535–5448; Arthur A. Ushijima, President and Chief Executive Officer, p. B107

IDAHO

Boise: ★ ST. LUKE'S HEALTH SYSTEM 190 East Bannock Street, Zip 83712–6241; tel. 208/381–4200; David C. Pate, President and Chief Executive Officer, p. B122

Pocatello: SAFE HAVEN HEALTH CARE 2520 South 5th Avenue, Zip 83204–1923; tel. 800/261–2443; Scott Burpee, President, p. B110

ILLINOIS

Carbondale: SOUTHERN ILLINOIS HEALTHCARE 1239 East Main Street, Zip 62901–3114, Mailing Address: P.O. Box 3988, Zip 62902–3988, tel. 618/457–5200; Rex P. Budde, President and Chief Executive Officer, p. B119

Chicago: ★ COMMONSPIRIT HEALTH 444 West Lake Street Suite 2500, Zip 60606–0097; tel. 312/741–7000; Lloyd H. Dean, Chief Executive Officer, p. B32

★ COOK COUNTY HEALTH AND HOSPITALS SYSTEM 1900 West Polk Street, Suite 220, Zip 60612–3723; tel. 312/864–6820; John Jay. Shannon, Chief Executive Officer, p. B40

NATIONAL SURGICAL HEALTHCARE 250 South Wacker Drive, Suite 500, Zip 60606–5897; tel. 312/627–8400; David Crane, Chief Executive Officer, p. B88

★ NORTHWESTERN MEMORIAL HEALTHCARE 251 East Huron Street, Zip 60611–2908; tel. 312/926–2000; Dean M. Harrison, President and Chief Executive Officer, p. B92

★ RUSH UNIVERSITY MEDICAL CENTER 1653 West Congress Parkway, Zip 60612–3864; tel. 312/942–5000; Ranga Krishnan, Chief Executive Officer, p. B110

★ SINAI HEALTH SYSTEM 1500 South Fairfield Avenue, Zip 60608–1782; tel. 773/542–2000; Karen Teitelbaum, President and Chief Executive Officer, p. B118

★ UNIVERSITY OF CHICAGO MEDICINE 5841 South Maryland Avenue, Zip 60637–1447; tel. 773/702–6240; Sharon L. O'Keefe, President, p. B139

Downers Grove: ★ ADVOCATE AURORA HEALTH 3075 Highland Parkway, Suite 600, Zip 60515–5563; tel. 630/929–8700; Jim Skogsbergh, President and Chief Executive Officer, p. B7

Evergreen Park: AMERICAN PROVINCE OF LITTLE COMPANY OF MARY SISTERS 9350 South California Avenue, Zip 60805–2595; tel. 708/229–5095, Sister, Carol Pacini, Region Leader, p. B10

Naperville: ★ EDWARD-ELMHURST HEALTHCARE 801 South Washington Street, Zip 60540–7430; tel. 630/527–3000; Mary Lou Mastro, System Chief Executive Officer, p. B48

Peoria: ★ OSF HEALTHCARE 800 NE Glen Oak Avenue, Zip 61603–3200; tel. 309/655–2850; Robert Sehring, Chief Executive Officer, p. B96

Schaumburg: CANCER TREATMENT CENTERS OF AMERICA 1336 Basswood Road, Zip 60173–4544; tel. 847/342–7400; Rajesh K. Garg, President and Chief Executive Officer, p. B26

Springfield: DIVISION OF MENTAL HEALTH, DEPARTMENT OF HUMAN SERVICES 319 East Madison Street, S-3B, Zip 62701–1035; tel. 217/785–6023; Lorrie Rickman. Jones, Director, p. B47

★ HSHS HOSPITAL SISTERS HEALTH SYSTEM 4936 LaVerna Road, Zip 62707–9797, Mailing Address: P.O. Box 19456, Zip 62794–9456, tel. 217/523–4747; Mary Starmann-Harrison, President and Chief Executive Officer, p. B67

★ MEMORIAL HEALTH SYSTEM 701 North First Street, Zip 62781–0001; tel. 217/788–3000; Edgar J. Curtis, President and Chief Executive Officer, p. B82

Urbana: ★ CARLE FOUNDATION 611 West Park Street, Zip 61801–2595; tel. 217/383–3311; James C. Leonard, President and Chief Executive Officer, p. B27

INDIANA

Evansville: ★ DEACONESS HEALTH SYSTEM 600 Mary Street, Zip 47710–1658; tel. 812/450–5000; Shawn W. McCoy, Chief Executive Officer, p. B42

Fort Wayne: ★ PARKVIEW HEALTH 10501 Corporate Drive, Zip 46845–1700; tel. 260/373–7001; Michael J. Packnett, President and Chief Executive Officer, p. B97

Hammond: COMMUNITY HEALTHCARE SYSTEM 901 MacArthur Boulevard, Zip 46321–2959; tel. 219/836–1600; Donald P. Fesko, President and Chief Executive Officer, p. B38

Indianapolis: ★ COMMUNITY HEALTH NETWORK 7330 Shadeland Station, Zip 46256–3957; tel. 317/355–1411; Bryan A. Mills, President and Chief Executive Officer, p. B35

★ INDIANA UNIVERSITY HEALTH 340 West 10th Street, Suite 6100, Zip 46202–3082, Mailing Address: P.O. Box 1367, Zip 46206–1367, tel. 317/962–2000; Dennis M. Murphy, President and Chief Executive Officer, p. B67

Mishawaka: FRANCISCAN HEALTH 1515 Dragoon Trail, Zip 46544–4710, Mailing Address: P.O. Box 1290, Zip 46546–1290, tel. 574/256–3935; Kevin D. Leahy, President and Chief Executive Officer, p. B56

NEUROPSYCHIATRIC HOSPITALS 1625 East Jefferson Boulevard, Zip 46545–7103; tel. 574/255–1400; Cameron R. Gilbert, President and Chief Executive Officer, p. B89

South Bend: ★ BEACON HEALTH SYSTEM 615 North Michigan Street, Zip 46601–1033; tel. 574/647–1000; Kreg Gruber, Chief Executive Officer, p. B23

IOWA

Clarion: ★ IOWA SPECIALTY HOSPITALS 1316 South Main Street, Zip 50525–2019; tel. 515/532–2811; Steven J. Simonin, Chief Executive Officer, p. B69

Clive: MERCYONE 1449 NW 128th Stret, Zip 50325–7400; tel. 515/358–9200; Robert P. Ritz, Chief Executive Officer, p. B85

Davenport: ★ GENESIS HEALTH SYSTEM 1227 East Rusholme Street, Zip 52803–2498; tel. 563/421–1000; Douglas P. Cropper, President and Chief Executive Officer, p. B57

West Des Moines: ★ UNITYPOINT HEALTH 1776 West Lakes Parkway, Suite 400, Zip 50266–8393; tel. 515/241–6161; Kevin Vermeer, President and Chief Executive Officer, p. B134

KANSAS

Kansas City: ★ THE UNIVERSITY OF KANSAS HEALTH SYSTEM 4000 Cambridge Street, Zip 66160–0001; tel. 913/588–1227; Bob Page, President and Chief Executive Officer, p. B128

Salina: SALINA REGIONAL HEALTH CENTER 400 South Santa Fe Avenue, Zip 67401–4198, Mailing Address: PO Box 5080, Zip 67402–5080, tel. 785/452–7000; Micheal Terry, President and Chief Executive Officer, p. B111

Wichita: ★ GREAT PLAINS HEALTH ALLIANCE, INC. 250 North Rock Road, Suite 160, Zip 67206–2241; tel. 316/685–1523; Dave Dellasega, President and Chief Executive Officer, p. B58

KENTUCKY

Bowling Green: MED CENTER HEALTH 800 Park Street, Zip 42101–2356; tel. 270/745–1500; Connie Smith, President and Chief Executive Officer, p. B82

Danville: EPHRAIM MCDOWELL HEALTH 217 South Third Street, Zip 40422–1823; tel. 859/239–1000; Daniel E. McKay, Chief Executive Officer, p. B53

Edgewood: ST. ELIZABETH HEALTHCARE 1 Medical Village Drive, Zip 41017–3403; tel. 859/301–2000; Garren Colvin, Chief Executive Officer, p. B121

Lexington: APPALACHIAN REGIONAL HEALTHCARE, INC. 2260 Executive Drive, Zip 40505–4810, Mailing Address: P.O. Box 8086, Zip 40533–8086, tel. 859/226–2440; Joseph Grossman, President and Chief Executive Officer, p. B11

Louisville: ALLIANT MANAGEMENT SERVICES 2650 Eastpoint Parkway, Suite 300, Zip 40223–5164; tel. 502/992–3525; Stephen E. Fischer, Regional Vice President, Finance, p. B9

★ BAPTIST HEALTH 2701 Eastpoint Parkway, Zip 40223; tel. 502/896–5000; Gerard Colman, Chief Executive Officer, p. B20

★ KINDRED HEALTHCARE 680 South Fourth Street, Zip 40202–2412; tel. 502/596–7300; Pete Kalmey, President, Hospital Division, p. B72

★ NORTON HEALTHCARE 4967 US Highway 42, Suite 100, Zip 40222–6363, Mailing Address: P.O. Box 35070, Zip 40232–5070, tel. 502/629–8000; Russell Cox, President and Chief Executive Officer, p. B93

SPRINGSTONE 101 South Fifth Street, Suite 3850, Zip 40202–3127; tel. 855/595–2292; Robert Maha, President and Chief Executive Officer, p. B120

Owensboro: OWENSBORO HEALTH 1201 Pleasant Valley Road, Zip 42303–9811; tel. 270/417–2000; Greg Strahan, Interim Chief Executive Officer, p. B96

LOUISIANA

Baton Rouge: ★ FRANCISCAN MISSIONARIES OF OUR LADY HEALTH SYSTEM, INC. 4200 Essen Lane, Zip 70809–2158; tel. 225/923–2701; Richard Vath, President and Chief Executive Officer, p. B56

LOUISIANA STATE HOSPITALS 628 North 4th Street, Zip 70802–5342, Mailing Address: P.O. Box 629, Zip 70821–0628, tel. 225/342–9500; Shelby Price, Chief Executive Officer, p. B78

THE CARPENTER HEALTH NETWORK 10615 Jefferson Highway, Zip 70809–7230; tel. 225/769–4180; Pat Mitchell, Chief Executive Officer, p. D129

Crowley: COMPASS HEALTH 713 North Avenue L, Zip 70526–3832; tel. 337/788–3330; Aimee Monaghan, Chief Executive Officer, p. B39

Gretna: UNITED MEDICAL REHABILITATION HOSPITALS 3201 Wall Boulevard, Suite B, Zip 70056–7755; tel. 504/433–5551; John E.H. Mills, President and Chief Executive Officer, p. B133

Hammond: NORTH OAKS HEALTH SYSTEM 15790 Paul Vega MD Drive, Zip 70403–1436, Mailing Address: P.O. Box 2668, Zip 70404–2668, tel. 985/345–2700; Michele Kidd. Sutton, President and Chief Executive Officer, p. B91

Lafayette: AMG INTEGRATED HEALTHCARE MANAGEMENT 101 La Rue France, Suite 500, Zip 70508–3144; tel. 337/269–9828; Timothy W. Howard, Chief Executive Officer, p. B10

LAFAYETTE GENERAL HEALTH 920 West Pinhook Road, Zip 70503–2455; tel. 337/289–7991; David L. Callecod, President and Chief Executive Officer, p. B74

LHC GROUP 420 West Pinhook Road, Zip 70503–2131; tel. 337/233–1307; Keith G. Myers, Chairman and Chief Executive Officer, p. B75

Lake Charles: OCEANS HEALTHCARE 2720 Rue de Jardin, Suite 100, Zip 70605–4050; tel. 337/721–1900; Jason Reed, President and Chief Executive Officer, p. B94

New Orleans: LCMC HEALTH 200 Henry Clay Avenue, Zip 70118–5720; tel. 504/899–9511; Greg Feirn, President and Chief Executive Officer, p. B74

★ OCHSNER HEALTH SYSTEM 1514 Jefferson Highway, Zip 70121–2429; tel. 800/874–8984; Warner L. Thomas, President and Chief Executive Officer, p. B94

Shreveport: ALLEGIANCE HEALTH MANAGEMENT 504 Texas Street, Suite 200, Zip 71101–3526; tel. 318/226–8202; Rock Bordelon, President and Chief Executive Officer, p. B9

UNIVERSITY HEALTH SYSTEM 1501 Kings Highway, Zip 71103–4228; tel. 318/675–5000; Daniel J. Snyder, Chief Executive Officer, p. B138

WILLIS-KNIGHTON HEALTH SYSTEM 2600 Greenwood Road, Zip 71103–3908; tel. 318/212–4000; James K. Elrod, President and Chief Executive Officer, p. B148

MAINE

Brewer: ★ NORTHERN LIGHT HEALTH 43 Whiting Hill Road, Zip 04412–1005; tel. 207/973–7045; M. Michelle. Hood, President and Chief Executive Officer, p. B92

Lewiston: CENTRAL MAINE HEALTHCARE 300 Main Street, Zip 04240–7027; tel. 207/795–0111; Jeffrey L. Brickman, Chief Executive Officer, p. B29

Portland: MAINEHEALTH 110 Free Street, Zip 04101–3537; tel. 207/661–7001; William L. Caron Jr, President, p. B79

MARYLAND

Baltimore: ★ JOHNS HOPKINS HEALTH SYSTEM 733 North Broadway, BRB 104, Zip 21205–1832; tel. 410/955–5000; Kevin W. Sowers, President, p. B70

LIFEBRIDGE HEALTH 2401 West Belvedere Avenue, Zip 21215–5216; tel. 410/601–5134; Neil M. Meltzer, President and Chief Executive Officer, p. B75

★ UNIVERSITY OF MARYLAND MEDICAL SYSTEM 250 West Pratt Street, 24th Floor, Zip 21201–1595; tel. 410/328–8667; John W. Ashworth III, Interim President and Chief Executive Officer, p. D130

Columbia: ★ MEDSTAR HEALTH 10980 Grantchester Way, Zip 21044–2665; tel. 410/772–6500; Kenneth A. Samet, President and Chief Executive Officer, p. B82

Gaithersburg: ADVENTIST HEALTHCARE 820 West Diamond Avenue, Suite 600, Zip 20878–1419; tel. 301/315–3185; Terry Forde, President and Chief Executive Officer, p. B7

Marriottsville: BON SECOURS MERCY HEALTH 1505 Marriottsville Road, Zip 21104–1399; tel. 410/442–5511; Richard Statuto, President and Chief Executive Officer, p. B24

Rockville: U. S. INDIAN HEALTH SERVICE 801 Thompson Avenue, Zip 20852–1627; tel. 301/443–1083; Yvette Roubideaux, Director, p. B142

Sparks Glencoe: FUNDAMENTAL LONG TERM CARE HOLDINGS, LLC 930 Ridgebrook Road, Zip 21152–9390; tel. 410/773–1000; W Bradley. Bennett, President and Chief Executive Officer, p. B57

MASSACHUSETTS

Boston: ★ BETH ISRAEL LAHEY HEALTH 109 Brookline Avenue, Zip 02215–3903; tel. 617/667–7000; Kevin Tabb, Chief Executive Officer, p. B24

MASSACHUSETTS DEPARTMENT OF MENTAL HEALTH 25 Staniford Street, Zip 02114–2575; tel. 617/626–8123; Joan Mikula, Interim Commissioner, p. B80

MASSACHUSETTS DEPARTMENT OF PUBLIC HEALTH 250 Washington Street, Zip 02108–4619; tel. 617/624–6000; Sandra Akers, Bureau Director, Public Health Hospitals, p. B80

★ PARTNERS HEALTHCARE SYSTEM, INC. 800 Boylston Street, Suite 1150, Zip 02199–8123; tel. 617/278–1004; Anne Klibanski, Chief Executive Officer, p. B97

Gardner: HEYWOOD HEALTHCARE 242 Green Street, Zip 01440–1336; tel. 978/632–3420; Winfield S. Brown, Chief Executive Officer, p. B66

Haverhill: WHITTIER HEALTH NETWORK 25 Railroad Square, Zip 01832–5721; tel. 978/556–5858; Alfred L. Arcidi, President, p. B148

Hyannis: ★ CAPE COD HEALTHCARE, INC. 27 Park Street, Zip 02601–5230; tel. 508/862–5121; Michael K. Lauf, President and Chief Executive Officer, p. B26

Pittsfield: ★ BERKSHIRE HEALTH SYSTEMS, INC. 725 North Street, Zip 01201–4124; tel. 413/447–2750; David E. Phelps, President and Chief Executive Officer, p. B23

Springfield: ★ BAYSTATE HEALTH, INC. 280 Chestnut Street, Zip 01199–0001; tel. 413/794–0000; Mark A. Keroack, President and Chief Executive Officer, p. B23

Tewksbury: ★ COVENANT HEALTH 100 Ames Pond Drive, Suite 102, Zip 01876–1240; tel. 978/654–6363; Stephen J. Grubbs, President and Chief Executive Officer, p. B40

Worcester: ★ UMASS MEMORIAL HEALTH CARE, INC. 1 Biotech Park, Zip 01605–2982; tel. 508/334–0100; Eric Dickson, President and Chief Executive Officer, p. B132

MICHIGAN

Detroit: ★ HENRY FORD HEALTH SYSTEM One Ford Place, Zip 48202–3450; tel. 313/876–8708; Wright L. Lassiter III, President and Chief Executive Officer, p. B65

Grand Blanc: MCLAREN HEALTH CARE CORPORATION 3373 Regency Park Drive, Zip 48439, Mailing Address: One McLaren Parkway, Zip 48439, tel. 810/342–1100; Philip A. Incarnati, President and Chief Executive Officer, p. B81

Grand Rapids: ★ SPECTRUM HEALTH 221 Michigan Street NE, Suite 501, Zip 49503–2543; tel. 616/391–1774; Christina Freese Decker, President and Chief Executive Officer, p. B120

Kalamazoo: ★ BRONSON HEALTHCARE GROUP 301 John Street, Zip 49007–5295; tel. 269/341–6000; Frank J. Sardone, President and Chief Executive Officer, p. B25

Lansing: ★ SPARROW HEALTH SYSTEM 1215 East Michigan Avenue, Zip 48912–1811; tel. 517/364–1000; James F. Dover, President and Chief Executive Officer, p. B119

Livonia: ★ TRINITY HEALTH 20555 Victor Parkway, Zip 48152–7031; tel. 734/343–1000; Michael A. Slubowski, President and Chief Executive Officer, p. B129

Midland: ★ MIDMICHIGAN HEALTH 4000 Wellness Drive, Zip 48670–0001; tel. 989/839–3000; Diane Postler-Slattery, President and Chief Executive Officer, p. B86

Southfield: ★ BEAUMONT HEALTH 2000 Town Center, Suite 1200, Zip 48075–1145, fraser, tel. 248/898–5000; John T. Fox, President and Chief Executive Officer, p. B23

Traverse City: ★ MUNSON HEALTHCARE 1105 Sixth Street, Zip 49684–2386; tel. 231/935–6703; Edwin Ness, President and Chief Executive Officer, p. B88

MINNESOTA

Bloomington: HEALTHPARTNERS 8170 33rd Avenue South, Zip 55425–4516; tel. 952/883–7600; Andrea Walsh, President and Chief Executive Officer, p. B65

Duluth: ★ ESSENTIA HEALTH 502 East Second Street, Zip 55805–1913; tel. 218/786–8376; David C. Herman, Chief Executive Officer, p. B54

Minneapolis: ★ ALLINA HEALTH 2925 Chicago Avenue, Zip 55407–1321, Mailing Address: P.O. Box 43, Zip 55440–0043, tel. 612/262–5000; Penny Ann. Wheeler, Chief Executive Officer, p. B9

★ FAIRVIEW HEALTH SERVICES 2450 Riverside Avenue, Zip 55454–1400; tel. 612/672–6141; James Hereford, President and Chief Executive Officer, p. B54

Robbinsdale: NORTH MEMORIAL HEALTH CARE 3300 Oakdale Avenue North, Zip 55422–2926; tel. 763/520–5200; J. Kevin. Croston, Chief Executive Officer, p. B91

Rochester: ★ MAYO CLINIC 200 First Street SW, Zip 55905–0002; tel. 507/284–2511; Gianrico Farrugia, President, p. B80

Saint Cloud: ★ CENTRACARE HEALTH 1406 Sixth Avenue North, Zip 56303–1900; tel. 320/251–2700; Kenneth D. Holmen, President and Chief Executive Officer, p. B29

Saint Paul: MINNESOTA DEPARTMENT OF HUMAN SERVICES 540 Cedar Street, Zip 55101–2208, Mailing Address: P.O. Box 64998, Zip 55164–0998, tel. 651/431–3212; Anne Barry, Deputy Commissioner, p. B86

Waconia: ★ RIDGEVIEW MEDICAL CENTER 500 South Maple Street, Zip 55387–1752; tel. 952/442–2191; Michael Phelps, President and Chief Executive Officer, p. B108

MISSISSIPPI

Jackson: MISSISSIPPI STATE DEPARTMENT OF MENTAL HEALTH 1101 Robert E Lee Building, 239 North Lamar Street, Zip 39201–1101; tel. 601/359–1288; Edwin C. LeGrand III, Executive Director, p. B86

★ UNIVERSITY HOSPITALS AND HEALTH SYSTEM 2500 North State Street, Zip 39216–4500; tel. 601/984–1000; Kevin S. Cook, Chief Executive Officer, p. B139

Mccomb: SOUTHWEST HEALTH SYSTEMS 215 Marion Avenue, Zip 39648–2705, Mailing Address: P.O. Box 1307, Zip 39649–1307, tel. 601/249–5500; Norman M. Price, Chief Executive Officer and Administrator, p. B119

Meridian: RUSH HEALTH SYSTEMS 1314 19th Avenue, Zip 39301–4116; tel. 601/483–0011; Larkin Kennedy, President and Chief Executive Officer, p. B109

Tupelo: ★ NORTH MISSISSIPPI HEALTH SERVICES, INC. 830 South Gloster Street, Zip 38801–4996; tel. 662/377–3136; M. Shane. Spees, President and Chief Executive Officer, p. B91

MISSOURI

Cape Girardeau: LANDMARK HOSPITALS 3255 Independence Street, Zip 63701–4914; tel. 573/335–1091; William K. Kapp III, President and Chief Executive Officer, p. B74

SOUTHEASTHEALTH 1701 Lacey Street, Zip 63701–5230; tel. 573/334–4822; Kenneth Bateman, Chief Executive Officer, p. B119

Chesterfield: ★ MERCY 14528 South Outer 40, Suite 100, Zip 63017–5743; tel. 314/579–6100; Lynn Britton, President and Chief Executive Officer, p. B83

Columbia: ★ UNIVERSITY OF MISSOURI HEALTH CARE One Hospital Drive, DC 031, Zip 65212–0001; tel. 573/882–4141; Jonathan W. Curtright, Chief Executive Officer and Chief Operating Officer, p. B140

Joplin: ★ FREEMAN HEALTH SYSTEM 1102 West 32nd Street, Zip 64804–3503; tel. 417/347–1111; Paula F. Baker, President and Chief Executive Officer, p. B56

Kansas City: RURAL COMMUNITY HOSPITALS OF AMERICA 1100 Main Street, Suite 2350, Zip 64105–5186; tel. 816/474–7800; Paul L. Nusbaum, President and Co-Owner, p. B109

★ SAINT LUKE'S HEALTH SYSTEM 901 East 104th Street, Mailstop 900N, Zip 64131–4517, Mailing Address: 901 East 104th Street, Zip 64131–4517, tel. 816/932–2000; Melinda Estes, President and Chief Executive Officer, p. B111

★ TRUMAN MEDICAL CENTERS 2301 Holmes Street, Zip 64108–2677; tel. 816/404–1000; Charlie Shields, Chief Executive Officer, p. B131

Saint Joseph: ★ MOSAIC LIFE CARE 5325 Faraon Street, Zip 64506–3488; tel. 816/271–6000; Samuel Mark. Laney, Chief Executive Officer, p. B87

Saint Louis: ★ ASCENSION HEALTHCARE 101 South Hanley Road, Suite 450, Zip 63105–3406; tel. 314/733–8000; Joseph R. Impicciche, President and Chief Executive Officer, p. B13

★ BJC HEALTHCARE 4901 Forest Park Avenue, Suite 1200, Zip 63108–1402; tel. 314/286–2000; Richard J. Liekweg, President and Chief Executive Officer, p. B24

★ SSM HEALTH 10101 Woodfield Lane, Zip 63132–2937; tel. 314/994–7800; Laura Kaiser, President and Chief Executive Officer, p. B121

Springfield: COXHEALTH 1423 North Jefferson Avenue, Zip 65802–1988; tel. 417/269–3108; Steven D. Edwards, President and Chief Executive Officer, p. B41

MONTANA

Great Falls: BENEFIS HEALTH SYSTEM 1101 26th Street South, Zip 59405–5161; tel. 406/455–5000; John H. Goodnow, Chief Executive Officer, p. B23

NEBRASKA

Lincoln: ★ BRYAN HEALTH 1600 South 48th Street, Zip 68506–1283, Mailing Address: 1600 S 48th ST, Zip 68506–1283, tel. 402/481–1111; Kimberly A. Russel, President and Chief Executive Officer, p. B25

Norfolk: FAITH REGIONAL HEALTH SERVICES 2700 West Norfolk Avenue, Zip 68701–4438, Mailing Address: P.O. Box 869, Zip 68702–0869, tel. 402/371–4880; Kelly Driscoll, President and Chief Executive Officer, p. B55

Omaha: ★ NEBRASKA METHODIST HEALTH SYSTEM, INC. 8511 West Dodge Road, Zip 68114–3403; tel. 402/354–5411; Stephen L. Goeser, President and Chief Executive Officer, p. B89

NEVADA

Reno: ★ RENOWN HEALTH 50 West Liberty Street, Suite 1100, Zip 89501–1951; tel. 775/982–5529; Anthony D. Slonim, President and Chief Executive Officer, p. B108

NEW HAMPSHIRE

Laconia: ★ LRGHEALTHCARE 80 Highland Street, Zip 03246–3298; tel. 603/524–3211; Kevin Donovan, President and Chief Executive Officer, p. B79

Littleton: NORTH COUNTRY HEALTHCARE 600 Saint Johnsbury Road, Zip 03561–3442; tel. 603/444–9000; Thomas Mee, Chief Executive Officer, p. B91

Manchester: SOLUTIONHEALTH One Elliot Way, Zip 03103–3502; tel. 603/663–2990; Sherry Hausmann, President and Chief Executive Officer, p. B118

Portsmouth: BRIDGEPOINT HEALTHCARE 155 Fleet Street, Zip 03801–4050; tel. 603/570–4888; Marc C. Ferrell, President and Chief Executive Officer, p. B25

NEW JERSEY

Edison: ★ HACKENSACK MERIDIAN HEALTH 343 Thornall Street, 8th Floor, Zip 08837–2206, Mailing Address: 343 Thornall Street, Zip 08837–2206, tel. 844/464–9355; Robert C. Garrett, Chief Executive Officer, p. B59

Jersey City: CAREPOINT HEALTH 10 Exchange Place, 15th Floor, Zip 07302–3918; tel. 877/791–7000; Natasha Deckmann, Chief Executive Officer, p. B27

Lakewood: CONCORD HEALTHCARE GROUP 111 Clifton AVenue, Zip 8701; tel. 214/396–3462; Joe Neuman, Chief Executive Officer, p. B39

Marlton: ★ VIRTUA HEALTH 303 Lippincott Drive, 4th Floor, Zip 08053–4160; tel. 856/355–0010; Dennis W. Pullin, President and Chief Executive Officer, p. B146

Morristown: ★ ATLANTIC HEALTH SYSTEM 475 South Street, Zip 07960–6459, Mailing Address: P.O. Box 1905, Zip 07962–1905, tel. 973/660–3270; Brian A. Gragnolati, President and Chief Executive Officer, p. B16

Mullica Hill: ★ INSPIRA HEALTH NETWORK 165 Bridgeton Pike, Zip 8062; tel. 856/641–8000; John A. DiAngelo, President and Chief Executive Officer, p. B68

Trenton: ★ CAPITAL HEALTH 750 Brunswick Avenue, Zip 08638–4143; tel. 609/394–6000; Al Maghazehe, President and Chief Executive Officer, p. B27

DIVISION OF MENTAL HEALTH AND ADDICTION SERVICES, DEPARTMENT OF HUMAN SERVICES, STATE OF NEW JERSEY 222 South Warren Street, Zip 08608–2306, Mailing Address: P.O. Box 700, Zip 08625–0700, tel. 609/777–0702; Lynn Kovich, Assistant Commissioner, p. B47

West Orange: ★ RWJBARNABAS HEALTH 95 Old Short Hills Road, Zip 07052–1008; tel. 973/322–4000; Barry Ostrowsky, President and Chief Executive Officer, p. B110

NEW MEXICO

Albuquerque: ERNEST HEALTH, INC. 7770 Jefferson Street NE, Suite 320, Zip 87109–4386; tel. 505/856–5300; Darby Brockette, Chief Executive Officer, p. B53

★ PRESBYTERIAN HEALTHCARE SERVICES 9521 San Mateo Blvd. NE, Zip 87113, Mailing Address: P.O. Box 26666, Zip 87125–6666, tel. 505/841–1234; Dale Maxwell, Chief Executive Officer, p. B100

UNIVERSITY OF NEW MEXICO HOSPITALS 915 Camino De Salud, Zip 87131–0001; tel. 505/272–5849; Michael Chicarelli, Interim Chief Executive Officer, p. B140

NEW YORK

Albany: NEW YORK STATE OFFICE OF MENTAL HEALTH 44 Holland Avenue, Zip 12208–3411; tel. 518/474–7056; Kristin M. Woodlock, Acting Commissioner, p. B89

Binghamton: UNITED HEALTH SERVICES 10–42 Mitchell Avenue, Zip 13903–1617; tel. 607/762–2200; John M. Carrigg, President and Chief Executive Officer, p. B133

Bronx: MONTEFIORE HEALTH SYSTEM 111 East 210th Street, Zip 10467–2490; tel. 718/920–4321; Steven M. Safyer, President and Chief Executive Officer, p. B87

Buffalo: ★ CATHOLIC HEALTH SYSTEM 144 Genesee Street, Zip 14203–1560; tel. 716/862–2410; Mark A. Sullivan, President and Chief Executive Officer, p. B28

Cooperstown: ★ BASSETT HEALTHCARE NETWORK 1 Atwell Road, Zip 13326–1301; tel. 607/547–3456; William F. Streck, President and Chief Executive Officer, p. B22

Elmira: ARNOT HEALTH 600 Roe Avenue, Zip 14905–1629; tel. 607/737–4100; Jonathan I. Lawrence, President and Chief Executive Officer, p. B12

Geneva: FINGER LAKES HEALTH 196 North Street, Zip 14456–1651; tel. 315/787–4000; Jose Acevedo, President and Chief Executive Officer, p. B55

Ithaca: ★ CAYUGA HEALTH SYSTEM 101 Dates Drive, Zip 14850–1342, tel. 607/274–4011; Martin Stallone, President and Chief Executive Officer, p. B28

Jamaica: ★ MEDISYS HEALTH NETWORK 8900 Van Wyck Expressway, Zip 11418–2832; tel. 718/206–6000; Bruce J. Flanz, President and Chief Executive Officer, p. B82

LaGrangeville: HEALTH QUEST SYSTEMS, INC. 1351 Route 55 Ste 200, Zip 12540–5108, Mailing Address: 1351 Route 55, Zip 12540–5108, tel. 845/475–9500; Robert Friedberg, President and Chief Executive Officer, p. B64

Middletown: ★ GREATER HUDSON VALLEY HEALTH SYSTEM 707 East Main Street, Zip 10940–2650; tel. 845/333–1000; Scott Batulis, President and Chief Executive Officer, p. B58

New Hyde Park: ★ NORTHWELL HEALTH 2000 Marcus Avenue, Zip 11042; tel. 516/465–8100; Michael J. Dowling, President and Chief Executive Officer, p. B92

New York: ★ MOUNT SINAI HEALTH SYSTEM One Gustave L. Levy Place, Zip 10029; tel. 212/659–8888; Kenneth L. Davis, President and Chief Executive Officer, p. B94

★ NEWYORK-PRESBYTERIAN 525 East 68th Street, Box 182, Zip 10065; tel. 212/746–3745; Steven J. Corwin, President and Chief Executive Officer, p. B90

★ NYC HEALTH + HOSPITALS 125 Worth Street, Room 514, Zip 10013–4006; tel. 212/788–3321; Mitchell H. Katz, Chief Executive Officer, p. B93

NYU LANGONE HEALTH 550 First Avenue, Zip 10016–6402; tel. 646/929–7870; Robert I. Grossman, Chief Executive Officer, p. B94

Olean: UPPER ALLEGHENY HEALTH SYSTEM 130 South Union Street, Suite 300, Zip 14760–3676; tel. 716/375–6190; Timothy J. Finan, President and Chief Executive Officer, p. B142

Potsdam: ST. LAWRENCE HEALTH SYSTEM 50 Leroy Street, Zip 13676–1799; tel. 315/265–3300; David B. Acker, President and CEO, p. B122

Rochester: ★ ROCHESTER REGIONAL HEALTH 1425 Portland Avenue, 5th Floor, Zip 14621–3001; tel. 585/922–4000; Eric Bieber, President and Chief Executive Officer, p. B109

★ UNIVERSITY OF ROCHESTER MEDICAL CENTER 601 Elmwood Ave Box 623, Zip 14642–0002, Mailing Address: 601 Elmwood Avenue, Zip 14642–0002, tel. 585/275–2100; Mark B. Taubman, Chief Executive Officer, p. B140

Rockville Centre: CATHOLIC HEALTH SERVICES OF LONG ISLAND 992 North Village Avenue, 1st Floor, Zip 11570–1002; tel. 516/705–3700; Alan D. Guerci, President and Chief Executive Officer, p. B28

Valhalla: WMCHEALTH 100 Woods Road, Zip 10595–1530; tel. 914/493–7000; Michael D. Israel, President and Chief Executive Officer, p. B148

NORTH CAROLINA

Boone: ★ APPALACHIAN REGIONAL HEALTHCARE SYSTEM 336 Deerfield Road, Zip 28607–5008, Mailing Address: P.O. Box 2600, Zip 28607–2600, tel. 828/262–4100; Charles Mantooth, President and Chief Executive Officer, p. B11

Chapel Hill: ★ UNC HEALTH CARE 101 Manning Drive, Zip 27514–4220; tel. 919/966–4131; Wesley Burks, Chief Executive Officer, p. B132

Charlotte: ★ ACUITYHEALTHCARE, LP 10200 Mallard Creek Road, Suite 300, Zip 28262–9705; tel. 704/887–7200; Edwin H. Cooper Jr, President and Chief Executive Officer, p. B5

★ ATRIUM HEALTH 1000 Blythe Boulevard, Zip 28203–5871, Mailing Address: PO Box 32861, Zip 28232–2861, tel. 704/355–2000; Eugene A. Woods, President and Chief Executive Officer, p. B16

Durham: ★ DUKE UNIVERSITY HEALTH SYSTEM 201 Trent Drive, Zip 27710–3037, Mailing Address: P.O. Box 3701, Zip 27710–3701, tel. 919/684–2255; A. Eugene. Washington, President and Chief Executive Officer, p. B48

VERITAS COLLABORATIVE 4024 Stirrup Creek Drive, Zip 27703–9464; tel. 855/875–5812; Stacie McEntyre, Chief Executive Officer, p. B144

Fayetteville: CAPE FEAR VALLEY HEALTH SYSTEM 1638 Owen Drive, Zip 28304–3424, Mailing Address: P.O. Box 2000, Zip 28302–2000, tel. 910/615–4000; Michael Nagowski, President and Chief Executive Officer, p. B27

Greensboro: CONE HEALTH 1200 North Elm Street, Zip 27401–1004; tel. 336/832–7000; Terry Akin, President and Chief Executive Officer, p. B39

Greenville: ★ VIDANT HEALTH 2100 Stantonsburg Road, Zip 27834–2818, Mailing Address: P.O. Box 6028, Zip 27835–6028, tel. 252/847–4100; Michael Waldrum, Chief Executive Officer, p. B145

Pinehurst: ★ FIRSTHEALTH OF THE CAROLINAS 155 Memorial Drive, Zip 28374–8710, Mailing Address: P.O. Box 3000, Zip 28374–3000, tel. 910/715–1000; Mickey Foster, Chief Executive Officer, p. B55

Raleigh: ★ WAKEMED HEALTH & HOSPITALS 3000 New Bern Avenue, Zip 27610–1231; tel. 919/350–8000; Donald R. Gintzig, President and Chief Executive Officer, p. B146

Wilmington: ★ NEW HANOVER REGIONAL MEDICAL CENTER 2131 South 17th Street, Zip 28401–7407; tel. 910/343–7040; John H. Gizdic, President and Chief Executive Officer, p. B89

Winston Salem: ★ NOVANT HEALTH 2085 Frontis Plaza Boulevard, Zip 27103–5614; tel. 336/718–5600; Carl S. Armato, President and Chief Executive Officer, p. B93

Winston-Salem: ★ WAKE FOREST BAPTIST HEALTH Medical Center Boulevard, Zip 27157; tel. 336/716–2011; Julie Ann . Freischlag, Chief Executive Officer, p. B146

NORTH DAKOTA

Fargo: SISTERS OF MARY OF THE PRESENTATION HEALTH SYSTEM 1202 Page Drive SW, Zip 58103–2340, Mailing Address: P.O. Box 10007, Zip 58106–0007, tel. 701/237–9290; Aaron K. Alton, President and Chief Executive Officer, p. B118

OHIO

Akron: SUMMA HEALTH 1077 Gorge Boulevard, Zip 44310; tel. 330/375–3000; T. Clifford Deveny, Interim Chief Executive Officer, p. B124

Canton: AULTMAN HEALTH FOUNDATION 2600 Sixth Street SW, Zip 44710–1702; tel. 330/363–6192; Edward J. Roth III, President and Chief Executive Officer, p. B17

Chillicothe: ADENA HEALTH SYSTEM 272 Hospital Road, Zip 45601–9031, Mailing Address: PO Box 802846, Kansas City, MO, Zip 64180–2846, tel. 740/779–7500; Jeff Graham, President and Chief Executive Officer, p. B5

Cincinnati: MERCY HEALTH 1701 Mercy Health Place, Zip 45237; tel. 513/639–2800; John M. Starcher, President and Chief Executive Officer, p. B84

★ UC HEALTH 3200 Burnet Avenue, Zip 45229–3019; tel. 513/585–6000; Richard P. Lofgren, President and Chief Executive Officer, p. B84

Cleveland: ★ CLEVELAND CLINIC HEALTH SYSTEM 9500 Euclid, Zip 44195–5108; tel. 216/444–2200; Tomislav Mihaljevic, Chief Executive Officer and President, p. B31

SISTERS OF CHARITY HEALTH SYSTEM 2475 East 22nd Street, Zip 44115–3221; tel. 216/363–2797; Thomas J. Strauss, Chief Executive Officer, p. B118

★ UNIVERSITY HOSPITALS 11100 Euclid Avenue, Zip 44106–5000; tel. 216/844–1000; Thomas F. Zenty III, President and Chief Executive Officer, p. B139

Columbus: OHIO DEPARTMENT OF MENTAL HEALTH 30 East Broad Street, 8th Floor, Zip 43215–3430; tel. 614/466–2297; Tracy Plouck, Director, p. B95

★ OHIO STATE UNIVERSITY HEALTH SYSTEM 370 West Ninth Avenue, Zip 43210–1238; tel. 614/685–9015; David P. McQuaid, Chief Executive Officer, p. B95

★ OHIOHEALTH 180 East Broad Street, Zip 43215–3707; tel. 614/544–4455; Stephen Markovich, President and Chief Executive Officer, p. B95

Dayton: ★ KETTERING HEALTH NETWORK 3965 Southern Boulevard, Zip 45429–1229; tel. 855/536–7543; Fred M. Manchur, Chief Executive Officer, p. B71

★ PREMIER HEALTH 110 North Main Street Suite 390, Zip 45402–3720; tel. 937/499–9401; Mary H. Boosalis, President and Chief Executive Officer, p. B100

Findlay: ★ BLANCHARD VALLEY HEALTH SYSTEM 1900 South Main Street, Zip 45840–1214; tel. 419/423–4500; Scott C. Malaney, President and Chief Executive Officer, p. B24

Galion: ★ AVITA HEALTH SYSTEM 269 Portland Way South, Zip 44833–2399; tel. 419/468–4841; Jerome Morasko, President and Chief Executive Officer, p. B18

Jackson: HOLZER HEALTH SYSTEM 500 Burlington Road, Zip 45640–9360; tel. 855/446–5937; Michael R. Canady, Chief Executive Officer, p. B66

Marietta: MEMORIAL HEALTH SYSTEM 401 Matthew Street, Zip 45750–1635; tel. 740/374–1400; J Scott. Cantley, President and Chief Executive Officer, p. B82

Toledo: ★ PROMEDICA HEALTH SYSTEM 100 Madison Avenue, Zip 43604–1516; tel. 567/585–9601; Randall D. Oostra, President and Chief Executive Officer, p. B102

OKLAHOMA

Duncan: DUNCAN REGIONAL HOSPITAL 1407 North Whisenant Drive, Zip 73533–1650; tel. 580/252–5300; Jay R. Johnson, President and Chief Executive Officer, p. B48

Oklahoma City: FIRST PHYSICIANS CAPITAL GROUP, INC. 4323 NW 63rd Street Suite 140, Zip 73116–1513; tel. 405/246–0218; Sean Kirrane, Chief Executive Officer, p. B55

FOUNDATION SURGICAL HOSPITAL AFFILIATES 14000 North Portland Avenue, Suite 204, Zip 73134–4002; tel. 405/608–1700; Thomas A. Michaud, Chief Executive Officer, p. B55

★ INTEGRIS HEALTH 3366 NW Expressway, Suite 800, Zip 73112–9756; tel. 405/949–6066; Timothy T. Pehrson, President and Chief Executive Officer, p. B69

OKLAHOMA DEPARTMENT OF MENTAL HEALTH AND SUBSTANCE ABUSE SERVICES 1200 NE 13th Street, Zip 73117–1022, Mailing Address: P.O. Box 53277, Zip 73152–3277, tel. 405/522–3908; Terri White, Commissioner, p. B95

Shawnee: PREFERRED MANAGEMENT CORPORATION 120 West MacArthur, Suite 121, Zip 74804–2005; tel. 405/878–0202; Donald Freeman, President and Chief Executive Officer, p. B99

Tulsa: ★ SAINT FRANCIS HEALTH SYSTEM 6161 South Yale Avenue, Zip 74136–1902; tel. 918/494–8454; Jake Henry Jr, President and Chief Executive Officer, p. B110

OREGON

Bend: ★ ST. CHARLES HEALTH SYSTEM, INC. 2500 NE Neff Road, Zip 97701–6015; tel. 541/382–4321; Joseph Sluka, President and Chief Executive Officer, p. B121

Corvallis: ★ SAMARITAN HEALTH SERVICES 3600 NW Samaritan Drive, Zip 97330–3737, Mailing Address: P.O. Box 1068, Zip 97339–1068, tel. 541/768–5001; Doug Boysen, President and Chief Executive Officer, p. B111

Medford: ★ ASANTE HEALTH SYSTEM 2650 Siskiyou Boulevard, Suite 200, Zip 97504–8170; tel. 541/789–4100; Scott A. Kelly, President and Chief Executive Officer, p. B12

Portland: ★ LEGACY HEALTH 1919 NW Lovejoy Street, Zip 97209–1503; tel. 503/415–5600; Kathryn G. Correia, President and Chief Executive Officer, p. B74

Salem: SALEM HEALTH 890 Oak Street Bldg B POB 14001, Zip 97309–5014; tel. 503/561–5200; Norman F. Gruber, President and Chief Executive Officer, p, B111

PENNSYLVANIA

Allentown: GOOD SHEPHERD REHABILITATION NETWORK 850 South Fifth Street, Zip 18103–3308; tel. 610/776–3100; John Kristel, President and Chief Executive Officer, p. B58

★ LEHIGH VALLEY HEALTH NETWORK 1200 South Cedar Crest Boulevard, Zip 18103–6202, Mailing Address: P.O. Box 689, Zip 18105–1556, tel. 610/402–8000; Brian A. Nester, President and Chief Executive Officer, p. B75

Beaver: HERITAGE VALLEY HEALTH SYSTEM 1000 Dutch Ridge Road, Zip 15009–9727; tel. 724/773–2024; Norman F. Mitry, President and Chief Executive Officer, p. B42

Bethlehem: ST. LUKE'S UNIVERSITY HEALTH NETWORK 801 Ostrum Street, Zip 18015–1000; tel. 610/954–4000; Richard A. Anderson, President and Chief Executive Officer, p. B122

Danville: ★ GEISINGER 100 North Academy Avenue, Zip 17822–9800; tel. 570/271–6211; Jaewon Ryu, President and Chief Executive Officer, p. B122

Enola: ★ POST ACUTE MEDICAL, LLC 1828 Good Hope Road, Suite 102, Zip 17025–1233; tel. 717/731–9660; Anthony F. Misitano, President and Chief Executive Officer, p. B99

Greensburg: EXCELA HEALTH 532 West Pittsburgh Street, Zip 15601, Mailing Address: 134 Industrial Park Road, Zip 15601–7328, tel. 724/832–5050; Robert Rogalski, Chief Executive Officer, p. B54

Hershey: PENN STATE HERSHEY HEALTH SYSTEM 500 University Drive, Zip 17033–2360; tel. 717/531–8521; Stephen M. Massini, Chief Executive Officer, p. B98

King of Prussia: UNIVERSAL HEALTH SERVICES, INC. 367 South Gulph Road, Zip 19406–3121, Mailing Address: P.O. Box 61558, Zip 19406–0958, tel. 610/768–3300; Alan B. Miller, Chairman and Chief Executive Officer, p. B135

Meadville: ★ MEADVILLE MEDICAL CENTER 751 Liberty Street, Zip 16335–2559; tel. 814/333–5000; Philip E. Pandolph, Chief Executive Officer, p. B81

Mechanicsburg: ★ SELECT MEDICAL CORPORATION 4714 Gettysburg Road, Zip 17055–4325; tel. 717/972–1100; David S. Chernow, President and Chief Executive Officer, p. B113

★ VIBRA HEALTHCARE 4550 Lena Drive, Suite 225, Zip 17055–4920; tel. 717/591–5700; Brad Hollinger, Chairman and Chief Executive Officer, p. B144

Philadelphia: AMERICAN ACADEMIC HEALTH SYSTEM 1500 Market Street, Centre Square Suite 24th Floor, Zip 19102–2100; tel. 215/255–3500; Joel Freedman, Chief Executive Officer, p. B10

EINSTEIN HEALTHCARE NETWORK 5501 Old York Road, Zip 19141–3098; tel. 215/456–7890; Barry R. Freedman, President and Chief Executive Officer, p. B49

★ JEFFERSON HEALTH 925 Chestnut Street, Suite 110, Zip 19107–4216; tel. 610/225–6200; Stephen K. Klasko, Chief Executive Officer, p. B70

★ TEMPLE UNIVERSITY HEALTH SYSTEM 3509 North Broad Street, 9th Floor, Zip 19140–4105; tel. 215/707–0900; Larry Kaiser, President and Chief Executive Officer, p. B125

★ UNIVERSITY OF PENNSYLVANIA HEALTH SYSTEM 3400 Civic Center Bouelvard, Zip 19104–5127; tel. 215/662–2203; Kevin B. Mahoney, Chief Executive Officer, p. B140

Pittsburgh: ★ ALLEGHENY HEALTH NETWORK 30 Isabella Street, Suite 300, Zip 15212–5862; tel. 412/359–3131; Cynthia Hundorfean, President and Chief Executive Officer, p. B8

UPMC 600 Grant Street, US Steel Tower, Suite 6262, Zip 15219–2702; tel. 412/647–8762; Jeffrey A. Romoff, President and Chief Executive Officer, p. B141

Sayre: ★ GUTHRIE CLINIC One Guthrie Square, Zip 18840–1625; tel. 570/888–5858; Joseph A. Scopelliti, President and Chief Executive Officer, p. B58

Villanova: DEVEREUX 444 Devereux Drive, Zip 19085–1932, Mailing Address: P.O. Box 638, Zip 19085–0638, tel. 610/520–3000; Robert Q. Kreider, President and Chief Executive Officer, p. B47

Washington: ★ WASHINGTON HEALTH SYSTEM 155 Wilson Avenue, Zip 15301–3336; tel. 724/225–7000; Brook Ward, President and Chief Executive Officer, p. B146

West Reading: ★ TOWER HEALTH Sixth Avenue and Spruce Street, Zip 19611; tel. 610/988–8000; Clinton Matthews, President and Chief Executive Officer, p. B129

Williamsport: ★ UPMC SUSQUEHANNA 700 High Street, Zip 17701–3100; tel. 570/321–1000; Steven P. Johnson, President and Chief Executive Officer, p. B141

York: ★ WELLSPAN HEALTH 45 Monument Road, Suite 200, Zip 17403–5071; tel. 717/851–2121; Roxanna L. Gapstur, President and Chief Executive Officer, p. B147

PUERTO RICO

San Juan: ★ PUERTO RICO DEPARTMENT OF HEALTH Building 'A' - Medical Center, Zip 936, Mailing Address: Call Box 70184, Zip 936, tel. 787/765–2929; Rafael Rodriguez. Mercado, Secretary of Health, p. B104

RHODE ISLAND

Providence: ★ CARE NEW ENGLAND HEALTH SYSTEM 45 Willard Avenue, Zip 02905–3218; tel. 401/453–7900; James E. Fanale, President, Chief Executive Officer and Chief Clinical Officer, p. B27

LIFESPAN CORPORATION 167 Point Street, Zip 02903–4771; tel. 401/444–3500; Timothy J. Babineau, President and Chief Executive Officer, p. B78

SOUTH CAROLINA

Anderson: ★ ANMED HEALTH 800 North Fant Street, Zip 29621–5793; tel. 864/512–1000; William T. Manson III, Chief Executive Officer, p. B11

Charleston: ROPER ST. FRANCIS HEALTHCARE 125 Doughty Street, Suite 760, Zip 29403–5785; tel. 843/402–2273; Lorraine Lutton, President and Chief Executive Officer, p. B109

Columbia: ★ PRISMA HEALTH - MIDLANDS 1301 Taylor Street, Suite 9-A, Zip 29201–2942, Mailing Address: P.O. Box 2266, Zip 29202–2266, tel. 803/296–2100; Mark O'Halla, President and Chief Executive Officer, Prisma Health, p. B101

Florence: MCLEOD HEALTH 555 East Cheves Street, Zip 29506–2617, Mailing Address: P.O. Box 100551, Zip 29502–0551, tel. 843/777–2000; Robert L. Colones, President and Chief Executive Officer, p. B81

Georgetown: ★ TIDELANDS HEALTH 606 Black River Road, Zip 29440–3304, Mailing Address: P.O. Box 421718, Zip 29442–4203, tel. 843/527–7000; Bruce P. Bailey, President and Chief Executive Officer, p. B129

Greenville: ★ PRISMA HEALTH - UPSTATE 701 Grove Road, Zip 29605–5611; tel. 864/455–7000; Spence Taylor, President of Prisma Health Upstate, p. B101

Spartanburg: ★ SPARTANBURG REGIONAL HEALTHCARE SYSTEM 101 East Wood Street, Zip 29303–3040; tel. 864/560–6000; Bruce Holstien, President and Chief Executive Officer, p. B120

SOUTH DAKOTA

Rapid City: ★ REGIONAL HEALTH 353 Fairmont Boulevard, Zip 57701–7375, Mailing Address: P.O. Box 6000, Zip 57709–6000, tel. 605/719–1000; Paulette Davidson, President and Chief Executive Officer, p. B108

Sioux Falls: ★ AVERA HEALTH 3900 West Avera Drive, Suite 300, Zip 57108–5721; tel. 605/322–4700; Bob Sutton, President and Chief Executive Officer, p. B17

★ SANFORD HEALTH 2301 East 60th Street North, Zip 57104–0569, Mailing Address: PO Box 5039, Zip 57117–5039, tel. 605/333–1000; Kelby K. Krabbenhoft, President and Chief Executive Officer, p. B112

TENNESSEE

Brentwood: ★ DUKE LIFEPOINT HEALTHCARE 330 Seven Springs Way, Zip 37027–5098; tel. 615/920–7000; Jeffrey G. Seraphine, President, p. B48

★ HEALTHTECH MANAGEMENT SERVICES 5110 Maryland Way Suite 200, Zip 37027–2307; tel. 615/309–6053; Derek Morkel, Chief Executive Officer, p. B65

★ LIFEPOINT HEALTH 330 Seven Springs Way, Zip 37027–4536; tel. 615/920–7000; David M. Dill, President and Chief Executive Officer, p. B76

★ QHR 1573 Mallory Lane, Suite 200, Zip 37027, Mailing Address: 1573 Mallory Lane, Suite 200, Zip 37027, tel. 800/233–1470; Bob Vento, President and Chief Executive Officer, p. B105

★ QUORUM HEALTH 1573 Mallory Lane, Suite 100, Zip 37027; tel. 615/221–1400; Robert D. Fish, Chief Executive Officer, p. B105

Chattanooga: ERLANGER HEALTH SYSTEM 975 East Third Street, Zip 37403–2147; tel. 423/778–7000; Kevin M. Spiegel, President and Chief Executive Officer, p. B53

Clinton: CURAE HEALTH 121 Leinart Street, Zip 37716–3632, Mailing Address: P.O. Box 358, Zip 37717–0358, tel. 865/269–4074; Steve Clapp, President and Chief Executive Officer, p. B41

Columbia: ★ MAURY REGIONAL HEALTH SYSTEM 1224 Trotwood Avenue, Zip 38401–4802; tel. 931/381–1111; H Alan. Watson, Chief Executive Officer, p. B80

Franklin: ACADIA HEALTHCARE COMPANY, INC. 830 Crescent Centre Drive, Suite 610, Zip 37067–7323; tel. 615/861–6000; Debra Osteen, Chief Executive Officer, p. B1

★ COMMUNITY HEALTH SYSTEMS, INC. 4000 Meridian Boulevard, Zip 37067–6325, Mailing Address: P.O. Box 689020, Zip 37068–9020, tel. 615/465–7000; Wayne T. Smith, Chairman, President and Chief Executive Officer, p. B35

Jackson: ★ WEST TENNESSEE HEALTHCARE 620 Skyline Drive, Zip 38301–3923; tel. 731/541–5000; James E. Ross, President and Chief Executive Officer, p. B147

Johnson City: BALLAD HEALTH 303 Med Tech Parkway, Zip 37604–2391; tel. 833/822–5523; Alan M. Levine, President and Chief Executive Officer, p. B18

Knoxville: COVENANT HEALTH 100 Fort Sanders West Boulevard, Zip 37922–3353; tel. 865/531–5555; James VanderSteeg, President and Chief Executive Officer, p. B41

Memphis: ★ BAPTIST MEMORIAL HEALTH CARE CORPORATION 350 North Humphreys Boulevard, Zip 38120–2177; tel. 901/227–5117; Jason Little, President and Chief Executive Officer, p. B21

★ METHODIST LE BONHEUR HEALTHCARE 1211 Union Avenue, Suite 700, Zip 38104–6600; tel. 901/516–0791; Michael Ugwueke, President and Chief Executive Officer, p. B86

STRATEGIC BEHAVIORAL HEALTH, LLC 8295 Tournament Drive, Suite 201, Zip 38125–8913; tel. 901/969–3100; Jim Shaheen, President, p. B123

Nashville: ★ ARDENT HEALTH SERVICES 1 Burton Hills Boulevard, Suite 250, Zip 37215–6195; tel. 615/296–3000; David T. Vandewater, President and Chief Executive Officer, p. B11

HAVEN BEHAVIORAL HEALTHCARE 652 West Iris Drive, Zip 37204–3191; tel. 615/250–9500; Kelly Gill, Chief Executive Officer, p. B59

★ HCA HEALTHCARE One Park Plaza, Zip 37203–1548; tel. 615/344–5248; Samuel Hazen, President and Chief Executive Officer, p. B60

★ VANDERBILT HEALTH 1211 22nd Avenue South, Zip 37232; tel. 615/322–5000; Charles Wright. Pinson, Deputy Chief Executive Officer, p. B144

Parsons: TENNESSEE HEALTH MANAGEMENT 52 West Eighth Street, Zip 38363–4656, Mailing Address: PO Box 10, Zip 38363–0010, tel. 731/847–6343; Dennis Berry, Chief Executive Officer, p. B127

TEXAS

Addison: UNITED SURGICAL PARTNERS INTERNATIONAL 15305 Dallas Parkway, Suite 1600, Zip 75001–6491; tel. 972/713–3500; Brett Brodnax, Chief Executive Officer, p. B133

Arlington: ★ TEXAS HEALTH RESOURCES 612 East Lamar Boulevard, Suite 900, Zip 76011–4130; tel. 682/236–7900; Barclay E. Berdan, Chief Executive Officer, p. B128

Austin: TEXAS DEPARTMENT OF STATE HEALTH SERVICES 1100 West 49th Street, Zip 78756–3199; tel. 512/458–7111; Stacey Thompson, Superintendent, p. B127

★ UNIVERSITY OF TEXAS SYSTEM 601 Colorado Street, Suite 205, Zip 78701–2904; tel. 512/499–4224; Raymond Greenberg, Executive Vice Chancellor, p. B141

Dallas: ★ BAYLOR SCOTT & WHITE HEALTH 4005 Crutcher Street, Suite 310, Zip 75246–1779; tel. 214/820–0111; James H. Hinton, Chief Executive Officer, p. B22

CHILDREN'S HEALTH 1935 Medical District Drive, Zip 75235–7701; tel. 214/456–7000; Christopher J. Durovich, President and Chief Executive Officer, p. B29

CORNERSTONE HEALTHCARE GROUP 2200 Ross Avenue, Suite 5400, Zip 75201–7984; tel. 469/621–6700; Steve Jakubcanin, President and Chief Executive Officer, p. B40

EVEREST REHABILITATION HOSPITALS, LLC 5100 Belt Line Road, Suite 310, Zip 75254–7559; tel. 469/713–1145; Jay Quintana, Chief Executive Officer and Co-Founder, p. B54

★ METHODIST HEALTH SYSTEM 1441 North Beckley Avenue, Zip 75203–1201, Mailing Address: P.O. Box 655999, Zip 75265–5999, tel. 214/947–8181; James C. Scoggin Jr, Chief Executive Officer, p. B85

STEWARD HEALTH CARE SYSTEM, LLC 1900 North Pearl Street, Suite 2400, Zip 75201; tel. 617/419–4700; Ralph de la Torre, Chairman and Chief Executive Officer, p. B122

★ TENET HEALTHCARE CORPORATION 1445 Ross Avenue, Suite 1400, Zip 75202–2703, Mailing Address: P.O. Box 1390369, Zip 75313–9036, tel. 469/893–2200; Saumya Sutaria, Chief Operating Officer, p. B125

Garland: CURAHEALTH HOSPITALS 650 Beebalm Lane, Suite 220, Zip 75040–2955; tel. 972/414–0070; Ken McGee, President and Chief Operating Officer, p. B41

Greenville: HUNT REGIONAL HEALTHCARE 4215 Joe Ramsey Boulevard, Zip 75401–7852, Mailing Address: P.O. Box 1059, Zip 75403–1059, tel. 903/408–5000; Richard Carter, Chief Executive Officer, p. B67

Houston: ★ HOUSTON METHODIST 6565 Fannin Street, D-200, Zip 77030–2707; tel. 713/441–2221; Marc L. Boom, Chief Executive Officer, p. B66

★ MEMORIAL HERMANN HEALTH SYSTEM 929 Gessner, Suite 2700, Zip 77024–2593; tel. 713/338–5555; David L. Callender, President and Chief Executive Officer, p. B83

NEXUS HEALTH SYSTEMS One Riverway, Suite 600, Zip 77056–1993; tel. 713/355–6111; John W. Cassidy, President, Chief Executive Officer and Chief Medical Officer, p. B90

NOBILIS HEALTH CORPORATION 11700 Katy Freeway Suite 300, Zip 77079–1218; tel. 713/355–8614; Harry Fleming, Chief Executive Officer, p. B90

Irving: ★ CHRISTUS HEALTH 919 Hidden Ridge Drive, Zip 75038; tel. 469/282–2000; Ernie W. Sadau, Chief Executive Officer, p. B30

USMD HEALTH SYSTEM 6333 North State Highway 161 Suite 200, Zip 75038–2229; tel. 214/493–4000; Mike Bukosky, President, Hospital Division, p. B143

Lubbock: ★ COVENANT HEALTH SYSTEM 3615 19th Street, Zip 79410–1203; tel. 806/725–0447; Richard H. Parks, President and Chief Executive Officer, p. B41

Plano: ★ COMMUNITY HOSPITAL CORPORATION 7800 North Dallas Parkway, Suite 200, Zip 75024–6116; tel. 972/943–6400; Jim R. Kendrick, President and Chief Executive Officer, p. B38

★ LIFECARE MANAGEMENT SERVICES 5340 Legacy Drive, Suite 150, Zip 75024–3131; tel. 469/241–2100; James E. Murray, Chief Executive Officer, p. B76

Sherman: CARRUS HOSPITALS 1810 West US Highway 82, Zip 75092–7069; tel. 903/870–2600; Ronald E. Dorris, Chief Executive Officer, p. B28

The Woodlands: EMERUS 10077 Grogan's Mill, Suite 100, Zip 77380–1022; tel. 281/292–2450; Craig Goguen, Chief Executive Officer, p. B49

UTAH

Nephi: ★ RURAL HEALTH GROUP 48 West 1500 North, Zip 84648–8900; tel. 435/623–4924; Mark R. Stoddard, President and Chairman, p. B109

Salt Lake City: ★ INTERMOUNTAIN HEALTHCARE, INC. 36 South State Street, 22nd Floor, Zip 84111–1453; tel. 801/442–2000; A. Marc. Harrison, President and Chief Executive Officer, p. B69

VIRGINIA

Charlottesville: ★ UVA HEALTH SYSTEM 1215 Lee Street, Zip 22908–0816; tel. 434/924–0211; Pamela Sutton-Wallace, Acting Executive Vice President for Health Affairs, UVA Health System and Chief Executive Officer, UVA Medical Center, p. B143

Falls Church: ★ BUREAU OF MEDICINE AND SURGERY, DEPARTMENT OF THE NAVY 7700 Arlington Boulevard, Suite 5126, Zip 22042; tel. 202/762–3701; Bryce H.P. Mendez, Healthcare Policy Analyst, p. B26

★ DEPARTMENT OF THE ARMY, OFFICE OF THE SURGEON GENERAL 5109 Leesburg Pike, Zip 22041–3215; tel. 703/681–3000, Lieutenant General, Nadja Y. West, Surgeon General, p. B43

★ INOVA HEALTH SYSTEM 8110 Gatehouse Road, Suite 200 East, Zip 22042–1252; tel. 703/289–2069; J Stephen. Jones, Chief Executive Officer, p. B68

Fredericksburg: ★ MARY WASHINGTON HEALTHCARE 1001 Sam Perry Boulevard, Zip 22401–4453; tel. 540/741–3100; Michael P. McDermott, President and Chief Executive Officer, p. B79

Lynchburg: ★ CENTRA HEALTH, INC. 1901 Tate Springs Road, Zip 24501–1109; tel. 434/200–3000; Andrew Mueller, President and Chief Executive Officer, p. B29

Newport News: RIVERSIDE HEALTH SYSTEM 701 Town Center Drive, Suite 1000, Zip 23606–4286; tel. 757/534–7000; William B. Downey, President and Chief Executive Officer, p. B29

Norfolk: ★ SENTARA HEALTHCARE 6015 Poplar Hall Drive, Zip 23502–3819; tel. 757/455–7000; Howard P. Kern, Chief Executive Officer, p. B116

Richmond: ★ VCU HEALTH SYSTEM 1200 East Marshall Street, Zip 23298, Mailing Address: P.O. Box 980510, Zip 23298–0510, tel. 804/828–9000; Marsha Rappley, Chief Executive Officer and Vice President for Health Sciences, p. B144

VIRGINIA DEPARTMENT OF MENTAL HEALTH 1220 Bank Street, Zip 23219–3645, Mailing Address: P.O. Box 1797, Zip 23218–1797, tel. 804/786–3921; James S. Reinhard, Commissioner, p. B145

Roanoke: ★ CARILION CLINIC 1906 Belleview Avenue SE, Zip 24014–1838, Mailing Address: P.O. Box 13727, Zip 24036–3727, tel. 540/981–7000; Nancy Howell. Agee, President and Chief Executive Officer, p. B27

Winchester: ★ VALLEY HEALTH SYSTEM 220 Campus Boulevard, Suite 420, Zip 22601–2889, Mailing Address: P.O. Box 3340, Zip 22604–2540, tel. 540/536–8024; Mark H. Merrill, President and Chief Executive Officer, p. B143

WASHINGTON

Mount Vernon: SKAGIT REGIONAL HEALTH 1415 E Kincaid Street, Zip 98274–4126; tel. 360/424–4111; Gregg Agustin. Davidson, President and Chief Executive Officer, p. B118

Renton: ★ PROVIDENCE ST. JOSEPH HEALTH 1801 Lind Avenue Southwest, 9016, Zip 98057–9016, Mailing Address: 181 Lind Avenue Southwest, 9016, Zip 98057–9016, tel. 425/525–3698; Rodney F. Hochman, President and Chief Executive Officer, p. B103

Seattle: ★ SWEDISH HEALTH SERVICES 747 Broadway, Zip 98122–4379; tel. 206/386–6000; R. Guy. Hudson, Chief Executive Officer, p. B125

★ UW MEDICINE 1959 NE Pacific Street, Zip 98195–0001, Mailing Address: P.O. Box 356350, Zip 98195–6350, tel. 206/543–7718; Paul G. Ramsey, Chief Executive Officer, p. 143

VIRGINIA MASON HEALTH SYSTEM 1100 Ninth Avenue, Zip 98101–2756, Mailing Address: P.O. Box 900, Zip 98111–0900, tel. 206/223–6600; Gary Kaplan, Chief Executive Officer, p. B146

Sunnyside: ASTRIA HEALTH 1806 Yakima Valley Highway, Zip 98944–2263; tel. 509/837–1330; John Gallagher, President and Chief Executive Officer, p. B16

Tacoma: MULTICARE HEALTH SYSTEM 315 Martin Luther King Jr Way, Zip 98405–4234, Mailing Address: P.O. Box 5299, Zip 98415–0299, tel. 253/403–1000; William G. Robertson, President and Chief Executive Officer, p. B87

Vancouver: ★ PEACEHEALTH 1115 SE 164th Avenue, Zip 98683; tel. 360/729–1000; Elizabeth Dunne, President and Chief Executive Officer, p. B97

WEST VIRGINIA

Elkins: ★ DAVIS HEALTH SYSTEM Reed Street and Gorman Avenue, Zip 26241, Mailing Address: P.O. Box 1697, Zip 26241–1697, tel. 304/636–3300; Vance Jackson, President and Chief Executive Officer, p. B42

Huntington: MOUNTAIN HEALTH NETWORK 517 9th Street, Zip 25701–2020; tel. 304/781–4466; Michael Mullins, President and Chief Executive Officer, p. B87

★ PALLOTTINE HEALTH SERVICES 2900 First Avenue, Zip 25702–1241; tel. 304/526–1234; Michael G. Sellards, Chief Executive Officer, p. B96

Morgantown: ★ MON HEALTH SYSTEM 1200 J. D. Anderson Drive, Zip 26505–3494; tel. 304/598–1200; David Goldberg, President and Chief Executive, p. B86

★ WEST VIRGINIA UNIVERSITY HEALTH SYSTEM One Medical Center, Box 8136, Zip 26506–8136; tel. 304/285–7150; Albert L. Wright Jr, President and Chief Executive Officer, p. B147

South Charleston: ★ THOMAS HEALTH SYSTEM, INC. 4605 MacCorkle Avenue SW, Zip 25309–1311; tel. 304/766–3600; Daniel Lauffer, President and Chief Executive Officer, p. B129

WISCONSIN

Appleton: THEDACARE, INC. 122 East College Avenue, Zip 54911–5794, Mailing Address: P.O. Box 8025, Zip 54912–8025, tel. 920/830–5889; Imran A. Andrabi, President and Chief Executive Officer, p. B128

Janesville: MERCY HEALTH SYSTEM 1000 Mineral Point Avenue, Zip 53548–2940, Mailing Address: P.O. Box 5003, Zip 53547–5003, tel. 608/756–6000; Javon R. Bea, President and Chief Executive Officer, p. B85

Madison: UW HEALTH SYSTEM 600 Highland Avenue, Zip 53792–0001; tel. 608/263–6400; Alan Kaplan, Chief Executive Officer, p. B143

Manitowoc: ★ FRANCISCAN SISTERS OF CHRISTIAN CHARITY SPONSORED MINISTRIES, INC. 1415 South Rapids Road, Zip 54220–9302; tel. 920/684–7071; Scott McConnaha, FACHE, President and Chief Executive Officer, p. B56

Marshfield: ★ MARSHFIELD CLINIC HEALTH SYSTEM 1000 North Oak Avenue, Zip 54449–5703; tel. 800/782–8581; Susan Turney, Chief Executive Officer, p. B79

Milwaukee: CHILDREN'S HOSPITAL AND HEALTH SYSTEM 9000 West Wisconsin Avenue, Zip 53226–4810, Mailing Address: P.O. Box 1997, Zip 53201–1997, tel. 414/226–2000; Peggy N. Troy, President and Chief Executive Officer, p. B30

FROEDTERT HEALTH 9200 West Wisconsin Avenue, Zip 53226–3596, Mailing Address: P.O. Box 26099, Zip 53226–0099, tel. 414/805–3000; Catherine A. Jacobson, President and Chief Executive Officer, p. B57

Waukesha: ★ PROHEALTH CARE, INC. N17 W24100 Riverwood Drive, Suite 130, Zip 53188; tel. 262/928–2242; Susan A. Edwards, President and Chief Executive Officer, p. B73

Wausau: ★ ASPIRUS, INC. 2200 Westwood Drive, Zip 54401–7806; tel. 715/847–2118; Matthew Heywood, Chief Executive Officer, p. B16

ARIZONA

HONORHEALTH
8125 North Hayden Road, Scottsdale, AZ, Zip 85258–2463; tel. 480/882–4000; Todd LaPorte, Chief Executive Officer

HONORHEALTH DEER VALLEY MEDICAL CENTER, 19829 North 27th Avenue, Phoenix, AZ, Zip 85027–4002; tel. 623/879–6100; David Price, Chief Executive Officer

HONORHEALTH JOHN C. LINCOLN MEDICAL CENTER, 250 East Dunlap Avenue, Phoenix, AZ, Zip 85020–2825; tel. 602/943–2381; Margaret Elizabeth. Griffin, Chief Executive Officer

HONORHEALTH REHABILITATION HOSPITAL, 8850 East Pima Center Parkway, Scottsdale, AZ, Zip 85258–4619; tel. 480/800–3900; Scott R. Keen, Chief Executive Officer

HONORHEALTH SCOTTSDALE OSBORN MEDICAL CENTER, 7400 East Osborn Road, Scottsdale, AZ, Zip 85251–6403; tel. 480/882–4000; Kimberly Post, Senior Vice President and Chief Executive Officer

HONORHEALTH SCOTTSDALE SHEA MEDICAL CENTER, 9003 East Shea Boulevard, Scottsdale, AZ, Zip 85260–6771; tel. 480/323–3000; Gary E. Baker, Senior Vice President and Chief Executive Officer

HONORHEALTH SCOTTSDALE THOMPSON PEAK MEDICAL CENTER, 7400 East Thompson Peak Parkway, Scottsdale, AZ, Zip 85255–4109; tel. 480/324–7000; David Price, Chief Executive Officer

NORTHERN ARIZONA HEALTHCARE
1200 North Beaver Street, Flagstaff, AZ Zip 86001–3118; tel. 928/779–3366; Robert P. Thames, President and Chief Executive Officer

FLAGSTAFF MEDICAL CENTER, 1200 North Beaver Street, Flagstaff, AZ, Zip 86001–3118; tel. 928/779–3366; Florence (Flo). Spyrow, Chief Administrative Officer

VERDE VALLEY MEDICAL CENTER, 269 South Candy Lane, Cottonwood, AZ, Zip 86326–4170; tel. 928/639–6000; Barbara Firminger, Chief Administrative Officer

CALIFORNIA

ADVENTIST HEALTH NORTHERN CALIFORNIA NETWORK
463 Aviation Boulevard, Santa Rosa, CA, Zip 95403–1079; tel. 707/371–2893; Jeff Eller, FACHE, President and Chief Executive Officer

ADVENTIST HEALTH CLEAR LAKE, 15630 18th Avenue, Clearlake, CA, Zip 95422–9336, Mailing Address: P.O. Box 6710, Zip 95422, tel. 707/994–6486; David Santos, President and Chief Executive Officer

ADVENTIST HEALTH HOWARD MEMORIAL, One Marcela Drive, Willits, CA, Zip 95490–4298; tel. 707/459–6801; Jason Wells, President and Chief Executive Officer

ADVENTIST HEALTH ST HELENA, 10 Woodland Road, Saint Helena, CA, Zip 94574–9554; tel. 707/963–3611; Steven Herber, M.D., FACS, President and Chief Executive Officer

ADVENTIST HEALTH ST. HELENA, 525 Oregon Street, Vallejo, CA, Zip 94590–3201; tel. 707/648–2200; Steven Herber, M.D., FACS, President and Chief Executive Officer

UKIAH VALLEY MEDICAL CENTER, 275 Hospital Drive, Ukiah, CA, Zip 95482–4531; tel. 707/462–3111; Gwen Matthews, R.N., MSN, Chief Executive Officer

PROVIDENCE HEALTH AND SERVICES – SOUTHERN CALIFORNIA
Regional Administration, 20555 Earl Street, Torrance, CA, Zip 90503–3006; tel. 310/793–8087; Erik G. Wexler, Chief Executive Officer

PROVIDENCE HOLY CROSS MEDICAL CENTER, 15031 Rinaldi Street, Mission Hills, CA, Zip 91345–1207; tel. 818/365–8051; Bernard Klein, M.D., Chief Executive

PROVIDENCE LITTLE COMPANY OF MARY MEDICAL CENTER – TORRANCE, 4101 Torrance Boulevard, Torrance, CA, Zip 90503–4664; tel. 310/540–7676; Garry M. Olney, Chief Executive Officer

PROVIDENCE LITTLE COMPANY OF MARY MEDICAL CENTER SAN PEDRO, 1300 West Seventh Street, San Pedro, CA, Zip 90732–3505; tel. 310/832–3311; Garry M. Olney, Chief Executive Officer

PROVIDENCE SAINT JOHN'S HEALTH CENTER, 2121 Santa Monica Boulevard, Santa Monica, CA, Zip 90404–2091; tel. 310/829–5511; Marcel C. Loh, FACHE, Chief Executive Officer

PROVIDENCE SAINT JOSEPH MEDICAL CENTER, 501 South Buena Vista Street, Burbank, CA, Zip 91505–4866; tel. 818/843–5111; Kelly Linden, Chief Executive Officer

PROVIDENCE TARZANA MEDICAL CENTER, 18321 Clark Street, Tarzana, CA, Zip 91356–3521; tel. 818/881–0800; Dale Surowitz, Chief Executive

ST. JOSEPH HOAG HEALTH
3345 Michelson Drive, Suite 100, Irvine, CA Zip 92612–0693; tel. 949/381–4019; Richard Afable, M.D., M.P.H., President and Chief Executive Officer

HOAG MEMORIAL HOSPITAL PRESBYTERIAN, One Hoag Drive, Newport Beach, CA, Zip 92663–4120, Mailing Address: P.O. Box 6100, Zip 92658–6100, tel. 949/764–4624; Robert Braithwaite, President and Chief Executive Officer

MISSION HOSPITAL, 27700 Medical Center Road, Mission Viejo, CA, Zip 92691–6474; tel. 949/364–1400; Seth R. Teigen, Chief Executive Officer

ST. JOSEPH HOSPITAL, 1100 West Stewart Drive, Orange, CA, Zip 92868–3849, Mailing Address: P.O. Box 5600, Zip 92863–5600, tel. 714/633–9111; Jeremy Zoch, Chief Executive

ST. MARY MEDICAL CENTER, 18300 Highway 18, Apple Valley, CA, Zip 92307–2206, Mailing Address: P.O. Box 7025, Zip 92307–0725, tel. 760/242–2311; Randall Castillo, Chief Executive Officer

COLORADO

CENTURA HEALTH
188 Inverness Drive West, Suite 500, Englewood, CO, Zip 80112–5204; tel. 303/290–6500; Peter D. Banko, FACHE, President and Chief Executive Officer

AVISTA ADVENTIST HOSPITAL, 100 Health Park Drive, Louisville, CO, Zip 80027–9583; tel. 303/673–1000; Jillyan McKinney, Chief Executive Officer

CASTLE ROCK ADVENTIST HOSPITAL, 2350 Meadows Boulevard, Castle Rock, CO, Zip 80109–8405; tel. 720/455–5000; Brandon M. Nudd, Chief Executive Officer

LITTLETON ADVENTIST HOSPITAL, 7700 South Broadway Street, Littleton, CO, Zip 80122–2628; tel. 303/730–8900; Geoff Lawton, Interim Chief Executive Officer

PARKER ADVENTIST HOSPITAL, 9395 Crown Crest Boulevard, Parker, CO, Zip 80138–8573; tel. 303/269–4000; Michael Goebel, Chief Executive Officer

PENROSE-ST. FRANCIS HEALTH SERVICES, 2222 North Nevada Avenue, Colorado Springs, CO, Zip 80907–6799; tel. 719/776–5000; Brian Erling, Interim Chief Executive Officer

PORTER ADVENTIST HOSPITAL, 2525 South Downing Street, Denver, CO, Zip 80210–5876; tel. 303/778–1955; Todd Folkenberg, Chief Executive Officer

RAWLINS COUNTY HEALTH CENTER, 707 Grant Street, Atwood, KS, Zip 67730–1526, Mailing Address: P.O. Box 47, Zip 67730–0047, tel. 785/626–3211; Ronald R. Robinson, M.D., M.P.H., FACHE, Chief Executive Officer and Chief Medical Officer

ST. ANTHONY HOSPITAL, 11600 West Second Place, Lakewood, CO, Zip 80228–1527; tel. 720/321–0000; Peter Powers, Chief Executive Officer

ST. ANTHONY NORTH HEALTH CAMPUS, 14300 Orchard Parkway, Westminster, CO, Zip 80023–9206; tel. 720/627–0000; Kevin Jenkins, President and Chief Executive Officer

ST. ANTHONY SUMMIT MEDICAL CENTER, 340 Peak One Drive, Frisco, CO, Zip 80443, Mailing Address: P.O. Box 738, Zip 80443–0738, tel. 970/668–3300; Lee Boyles, Chief Executive Officer

ST MARY-CORWIN MEDICAL CENTER, 1008 Minnequa Avenue, Pueblo, CO, Zip 81004–3798; tel. 719/557–4000; Michael Cafasso, Chief Executive Officer

ST. THOMAS MORE HOSPITAL, 1338 Phay Avenue, Canon City, CO, Zip 81212–2302; tel. 719/285–2000; Kristi Olson, Chief Executive Officer

ST. VINCENT GENERAL HOSPITAL DISTRICT, 822 West 4th Street, Leadville, CO, Zip 80461–3897; tel. 719/486–0230; Gary Campbell, Chief Executive Officer

COMMUNITY HEALTH PROVIDERS ORGANIZATION
2021 North 12th Street, Grand Junction, CO, Zip 81501–2980; tel. 970/256–6200; Chris Thomas, FACHE, President and Chief Executive Officer

COMMUNITY HOSPITAL, 2351 G Road, Grand Junction, CO, Zip 81505; tel. 970/242–0920; Chris Thomas, FACHE, President and Chief Executive Officer

HCA HEALTHONE, LLC
4900 South Monaco Street, Suite 380, Denver, CO, Zip 80237–3487; tel. 303/788–2500; Sylvia Young, President

MEDICAL CENTER OF AURORA, 1501 South Potomac Street, Aurora, CO, Zip 80012–5411; tel. 303/695–2600; Ryan Simpson, President and Chief Executive Officer

NORTH SUBURBAN MEDICAL CENTER, 9191 Grant Street, Thornton, CO, Zip 80229–4341; tel. 303/451–7800; Daphne G. David, President and Chief Executive Officer

PRESBYTERIAN-ST. LUKE'S MEDICAL CENTER, 1719 East 19th Avenue, Denver, CO, Zip 80218–1281; tel. 720/754–6000; Maureen Tarrant, President and Chief Executive Officer

ROSE MEDICAL CENTER, 4567 East Ninth Avenue, Denver, CO, Zip 80220–3941; tel. 303/320–2121; Ryan Tobin, President and Chief Executive Officer

SKY RIDGE MEDICAL CENTER, 10101 Ridge Gate Parkway, Lone Tree, CO, Zip 80124–5522; tel. 720/225–1000; Susan Hicks, Chief Executive Officer

SPALDING REHABILITATION HOSPITAL, 900 Potomac Steet, Aurora, CO, Zip 80011–6716; tel. 303/367–1166; Ryan Simpson, President and Chief Executive Officer

SWEDISH MEDICAL CENTER, 501 East Hampden Avenue, Englewood, CO, Zip 80113–2702; tel. 303/788–5000; Richard A. Hammett, President and Chief Executive Officer

CONNECTICUT

EASTERN CONNECTICUT HEALTH NETWORK
71 Haynes Street, Manchester, CT Zip 06040–4131; tel. 860/533–3400; Michael F. Collins, Interim President and Chief Executive Officer

MANCHESTER MEMORIAL HOSPITAL, 71 Haynes Street, Manchester, CT, Zip 06040–4188; tel. 860/646–1222; Michael F. Collins, Chief Executive Officer

ROCKVILLE GENERAL HOSPITAL, 31 Union Street, Vernon, CT, Zip 06066–3160; tel. 860/872–0501; Michael F. Collins, Chief Executive Officer

FLORIDA

BAYCARE HEALTH SYSTEM
2985 Drew Street, Clearwater, FL, Zip 33759–3012; tel. 877/692–2922; Tommy Inzina, President and Chief Executive Officer

BARTOW REGIONAL MEDICAL CENTER, 2200 Osprey Boulevard, Bartow, FL, Zip 33830–3308; tel. 863/533–8111; Karen Kerr, R.N., President

BAYCARE ALLIANT HOSPITAL, 601 Main Street, MS#402, Dunedin, FL, Zip 34698–5848; tel. 727/736–9991; Jacqueline Arocho, Administrator

MEASE COUNTRYSIDE HOSPITAL, 3231 McMullen Booth Road, Safety Harbor, FL, Zip 34695–6607; tel. 727/725–6111; Matthew Novak, President

MEASE DUNEDIN HOSPITAL, 601 Main Street, Dunedin, FL, Zip 34698–5891; tel. 727/733–1111; Matthew Novak, President

MORTON PLANT HOSPITAL, 300 Pinellas Street, Clearwater, FL, Zip 33756–3804, Mailing Address: P.O. Box 210, Zip 33757–0210, tel. 727/462–7000; Lou Galdieri, R.N., President

MORTON PLANT NORTH BAY HOSPITAL, 6600 Madison Street, New Port Richey, FL, Zip 34652–1900; tel. 727/842–8468; Sarah Naumowich, President

SOUTH FLORIDA BAPTIST HOSPITAL, 301 North Alexander Street, Plant City, FL, Zip 33563–4303; tel. 813/757–1200; Karen Kerr, R.N., President

ST. ANTHONY'S HOSPITAL, 1200 Seventh Avenue North, Saint Petersburg, FL, Zip 33705–1388, Mailing Address: P.O. Box 12588, Zip 33733–2588, tel. 727/825–1100; M. Scott Smith, President

ST. JOSEPH'S HOSPITAL, 3001 West Martin Luther King Jr. Boulevard, Tampa, FL, Zip 33607–6387, Mailing Address: P.O. Box 4227, Zip 33677–4227, tel. 813/870–4000; Kimberly Guy, President

WINTER HAVEN HOSPITAL, 200 Avenue F NE, Winter Haven, FL, Zip 33881–4193; tel. 863/293–1121; Stephen A. Nierman, President

GEORGIA

ST. JOSEPH'S/CANDLER HEALTH SYSTEM, INC.
5353 Reynolds Street, Savannah, GA, Zip 31405–6015; tel. 912/819–6000; Paul P. Hinchey, President and Chief Executive Officer

APPLING HEALTHCARE SYSTEM, 163 East Tollison Street, Baxley, GA, Zip 31513–0120; tel. 912/367–9841; Randy Crawford, Chief Executive Officer

CANDLER HOSPITAL, 5353 Reynolds Street, Savannah, GA, Zip 31405–6015; tel. 912/819–6000; Paul P. Hinchey, President and Chief Executive Officer

EFFINGHAM HOSPITAL, 459 Highway 119 South, Springfield, GA, Zip 31329–3021, Mailing Address: P.O. Box 386, Zip 31329–0386, tel. 912/754–6451; Francine Baker-Witt, R.N., Chief Executive Officer

EMORY UNIVERSITY HOSPITAL, 1364 Clifton Road NE, Atlanta, GA, Zip 30322; tel. 404/712–2000; Bryce D. Gartland, M.D., Chief Executive Officer

LIBERTY REGIONAL MEDICAL CENTER, 462 Elma G Miles Parkway, Hinesville, GA, Zip 31313–4000, Mailing Address: P.O. Box 919, Zip 31310–0919, tel. 912/369–9400; Tammy Mims, Interim Chief Executive Officer

MEADOWS REGIONAL MEDICAL CENTER, One Meadows Parkway, Vidalia, GA, Zip 30474–8759, Mailing Address: P.O. Box 1048, Zip 30475–1048, tel. 912/535–5555; Alan Kent, Chief Executive Officer

ST. JOSEPH'S HOSPITAL, 11705 Mercy Boulevard, Savannah, GA, Zip 31419–1791; tel. 912/819–4100; Paul P. Hinchey, President and Chief Executive Officer

IDAHO

THE HOSPITAL COOPERATIVE
500 South 11th Avenue Suite 503, Pocatello, ID, Zip 83201–4881; tel. 208/239–1951; Jon Smith, Executive Director

BEAR LAKE MEMORIAL HOSPITAL, 164 South Fifth Street, Montpelier, ID, Zip 83254–1597; tel. 208/847–1630; Leslie Crane, Interim Chief Executive Officer

BINGHAM MEMORIAL HOSPITAL, 98 Poplar Street, Blackfoot, ID, Zip 83221–1799; tel. 208/785–4100; Jake Erickson, Chief Executive Officer

CARIBOU MEMORIAL HOSPITAL AND LIVING CENTER, 300 South Third West, Soda Springs, ID, Zip 83276–1598; tel. 208/547–3341; Christina Thomas, R.N., FACHE, Chief Executive Officer

EASTERN IDAHO REGIONAL MEDICAL CENTER, 3100 Channing Way, Idaho Falls, ID, Zip 83404–7533, Mailing Address: P.O. Box 2077, Zip 83403–2077, tel. 208/529–6111; Jeff Sollis, Chief Executive Officer

FRANKLIN COUNTY MEDICAL CENTER, 44 North First East Street, Preston, ID, Zip 83263–1399; tel. 208/852–0137; Darin Dransfield, Chief Executive Officer

LOST RIVERS MEDICAL CENTER, 551 Highland Drive, Arco, ID, Zip 83213–9771, Mailing Address: P.O. Box 145, Zip 83213–0145, tel. 208/527–8206; Brad Huerta, Chief Executive Officer and Administrator

MADISON MEMORIAL HOSPITAL, 450 East Main Street, Rexburg, ID, Zip 83440–2048, Mailing Address: P.O. Box 310, Zip 83440–0310, tel. 208/359–6900; Rachel Ann. Gonzales, Chief Executive Officer

MINIDOKA MEMORIAL HOSPITAL, 1224 Eighth Street, Rupert, ID, Zip 83350–1599; tel. 208/436–0481; Tom Murphy, Chief Executive Officer

NELL J. REDFIELD MEMORIAL HOSPITAL, 150 North 200 West, Malad City, ID, Zip 83252–1239, Mailing Address: Box 126, Zip 83252–0126, tel. 208/766–2231; John Williams, Administrator and Chief Executive Officer

PORTNEUF MEDICAL CENTER, 777 Hospital Way, Pocatello, ID, Zip 83201–5175; tel. 208/239–1000; Daniel Ordyna, Chief Executive Officer

POWER COUNTY HOSPITAL DISTRICT, 510 Roosevelt Street, American Falls, ID, Zip 83211–1362, Mailing Address: P.O. Box 420, Zip 83211–0420, tel. 208/226–3200; Dallas Clinger, Administrator

STAR VALLEY MEDICAL CENTER, 901 Adams Street, Afton, WY, Zip 83110–9621, Mailing Address: P.O. Box 579, Zip 83110–0579, tel. 307/885–5800; Bren Lowe, Chief Executive Officer

STEELE MEMORIAL MEDICAL CENTER, 203 South Daisy Street, Salmon, ID, Zip 83467–4709; tel. 208/756–5600; Jeanine Gentry, Chief Executive Officer

TETON VALLEY HEALTH CARE, 120 East Howard Street, Driggs, ID, Zip 83422–5112; tel. 208/354–2383; Keith Gnagey, Chief Executive Officer

ILLINOIS

AMITA HEALTH
2601 Navistar Drive, Lisle, IL, Zip 60532–3661; tel. 224/273–4121; Mark A. Frey, President and Chief Executive Officer

ADVENTIST MEDICAL CENTER – HINSDALE, 120 North Oak Street, Hinsdale, IL, Zip 60521–3890; tel. 630/856–6001; Steven Province, President and Chief Executive Officer

ADVENTIST MEDICAL CENTER BOLINGBROOK, 500 Remington Boulevard, Bolingbrook, IL, Zip 60440–4906; tel. 630/312–5000; Bruce C. Christian, Chief Executive Officer

ADVENTIST MEDICAL CENTER GLENOAKS, 701 Winthrop Avenue, Glendale Heights, IL, Zip 60139–1403; tel. 630/545–8000; Bruce C. Christian, President and Chief Executive Officer

ADVENTIST MEDICAL CENTER LAGRANGE, 5101 South Willow Spring Road, La Grange, IL, Zip 60525–2600; tel. 708/245–9000; Michael Murrill, President and Chief Executive Officer

ALEXIAN BROTHERS BEHAVIORAL HEALTH HOSPITAL, 1650 Moon Lake Boulevard, Hoffman Estates, IL, Zip 60169–1010; tel. 847/882–1600; Clayton Ciha, President and Chief Executive Officer

MERCY HEALTH CORPORATION
2400 North Rockton Avenue, Rockford, IL, Zip 61103–3655; tel. 608/756–6000; Javon R. Bea, President and Chief Executive Officer

JAVON BEA HOSPITAL-ROCKTON, 2400 North Rockton Avenue, Rockford, IL, Zip 61103–3655; tel. 815/971–5000; Javon R. Bea, President and Chief Executive Officer

MERCYHEALTH HOSPITAL AND MEDICAL CENTER – HARVARD, 901 Grant Street, Harvard, IL, Zip 60033–1898, Mailing Address: P.O. Box 850, Zip 60033–0850, tel. 815/943–5431; Javon R. Bea, Chief Executive Officer

MERCYHEALTH HOSPITAL AND MEDICAL CENTER – WALWORTH, N2950 State Road 67, Lake Geneva, WI, Zip 53147–2655; tel. 262/245–0535; Javon R. Bea, President and Chief Executive Officer

MERCYHEALTH HOSPITAL AND TRAUMA CENTER – JANESVILLE, 1000 Mineral Point Avenue, Janesville, WI, Zip 53548–2982, Mailing Address: P.O. Box 5003, Zip 53547–5003, tel. 608/756–6000; Javon R. Bea, President and Chief Executive Officer

INDIANA

LUTHERAN HEALTH NETWORK
7950 West Jefferson Boulevard, Fort Wayne, IN, Zip 46804–4140; tel. 260/435–7001; Michael Poore, Regional Vice President

© 2018 AHA Guide

BLUFFTON REGIONAL MEDICAL CENTER, 303 South Main Street, Bluffton, IN, Zip 46714–2503; tel. 260/824–3210; Brent Parsons, Chief Executive Officer

DUKES MEMORIAL HOSPITAL, 275 West 12th Street, Peru, IN, Zip 46970–1638; tel. 765/472–8000; Debra Close, Chief Executive Officer

DUPONT HOSPITAL, 2520 East Dupont Road, Fort Wayne, IN, Zip 46825–1675; tel. 260/416–3000; Lorenzo Suter, Chief Executive Officer

KOSCIUSKO COMMUNITY HOSPITAL, 2101 East Dubois Drive, Warsaw, IN, Zip 46580–3288; tel. 574/267–3200; Jae Dale, Chief Executive Officer

LUTHERAN HOSPITAL OF INDIANA, 7950 West Jefferson Boulevard, Fort Wayne, IN, Zip 46804–4140; tel. 260/435–7001

ORTHOPAEDIC HOSPITAL OF LUTHERAN HEALTH NETWORK, 7952 West Jefferson Boulevard, Fort Wayne, IN, Zip 46804–4140; tel. 260/435–2999; Lorie Ailor, Chief Executive Officer

REHABILITATION HOSPITAL OF FORT WAYNE, 7970 West Jefferson Boulevard, Fort Wayne, IN, Zip 46804–4140; tel. 260/435–6100; Ryan Cassedy, Chief Administrative Officer

ST. JOSEPH HOSPITAL, 700 Broadway, Fort Wayne, IN, Zip 46802–1493; tel. 260/425–3000; Lisa Dolan, Interim Chief Executive Officer

ST. VINCENT HEALTH
10330 North Meridian Street, Indianapolis, IN, Zip 46290; tel. 317/338–2273; Jonathan Nalli, Senior Vice President, Ascension Health and Indiana Ministry Market Executive

ST. VINCENT ANDERSON, 2015 Jackson Street, Anderson, IN, Zip 46016–4339; tel. 765/649–2511; Mike K. Schroyer, FACHE, MSN, R.N., President

ST. VINCENT CARMEL HOSPITAL, 13500 North Meridian Street, Carmel, IN, Zip 46032–1456; tel. 317/582–7000; Julie Manas, Regional President

ST. VINCENT CLAY HOSPITAL, 1206 East National Avenue, Brazil, IN, Zip 47834–2797, Mailing Address: 1206 East National Ave, Zip 47834–0489, tel. 812/442–2500; Jerry Laue, Administrator

ST. VINCENT DUNN HOSPITAL, 1600 23rd Street, Bedford, IN, Zip 47421–4704; tel. 812/275–3331; Jerry Laue, Administrator

ST. VINCENT EVANSVILLE, 3700 Washington Avenue, Evansville, IN, Zip 47714–0541; tel. 812/485–4000; Daniel A. Parod, President

ST. VINCENT FISHERS HOSPITAL, 13861 Olio Road, Fishers, IN, Zip 46037–3487; tel. 317/415–9000; Julie Manas, Regional President

ST. VINCENT HEART CENTER, 10580 North Meridian Street, Indianapolis, IN, Zip 46290–1028; tel. 317/583–5000; Lori Shannon, President

ST. VINCENT INDIANAPOLIS HOSPITAL, 2001 West 86th Street, Indianapolis, IN, Zip 46260–1991, Mailing Address: P.O. Box 40970, Zip 46240–0970, tel. 317/338–2345; Joel Feldman, Regional President

ST. VINCENT JENNINGS HOSPITAL, 301 Henry Street, North Vernon, IN, Zip 47265–1097; tel. 812/352–4200; Dana M. Muntz, Chief Executive Officer

ST. VINCENT MERCY HOSPITAL, 1331 South 'A' Street, Elwood, IN, Zip 46036–1942; tel. 765/552–4600; Ann C. Yates, R.N., MSN, Administrator and Chief Nursing Officer

ST. VINCENT RANDOLPH HOSPITAL, 473 Greenville Avenue, Winchester, IN, Zip 47394–9436; tel. 765/584–0004; Carla Fouse, Administrator and Chief Nursing Officer

ST. VINCENT SALEM HOSPITAL, 911 North Shelby Street, Salem, IN, Zip 47167–1694; tel. 812/883–5881; Dana M. Muntz, Chief Executive Officer

ST. VINCENT SETON SPECIALTY HOSPITAL, 8050 Township Line Road, Indianapolis, IN, Zip 46260–2478; tel. 317/415–8500; Joel Feldman, Regional President

ST. VINCENT WARRICK, 1116 Millis Avenue, Boonville, IN, Zip 47601–2204; tel. 812/897–4800; Kathy J. Hall, Administrator

ST. VINCENT WILLIAMSPORT HOSPITAL, 412 North Monroe Street, Williamsport, IN, Zip 47993–1049; tel. 765/762–4000; Jane Craigin, Chief Executive Officer

SUBURBAN HEALTH ORGANIZATION
2780 Waterfront Parkway East Drive, Suite 300, Indianapolis, IN, Zip 46214; tel. 317/692–5222; Dave Lippincott, President

GOSHEN HEALTH, 200 High Park Avenue, Goshen, IN, Zip 46526–4899, Mailing Address: P.O. Box 139, Zip 46527–0139, tel. 574/533–2141; Randal Christophel, President and Chief Executive Officer

HANCOCK REGIONAL HOSPITAL, 801 North State Street, Greenfield, IN, Zip 46140–1270, Mailing Address: P.O. Box 827, Zip 46140–0827, tel. 317/462–5544; Steven V. Long, FACHE, President and Chief Executive Officer

HENDRICKS REGIONAL HEALTH, 1000 East Main Street, Danville, IN, Zip 46122–1948, Mailing Address: P.O. Box 409, Zip 46122–0409, tel. 317/745–4451; Kevin Speer, President and Chief Executive Officer

HENRY COMMUNITY HEALTH, 1000 North 16th Street, New Castle, IN, Zip 47362–4319, Mailing Address: P.O. Box 490, Zip 47362–0490, tel. 765/521–0890; Paul Janssen, President and Chief Executive Officer

JOHNSON MEMORIAL HOSPITAL, 1125 West Jefferson Street, Franklin, IN, Zip 46131–2140, Mailing Address: P.O. Box 549, Zip 46131–0549, tel. 317/736–3300, Larry Heydon, President and Chief Executive Officer

MAJOR HOSPITAL, 150 West Washington Street, Shelbyville, IN, Zip 46176–1236, Mailing Address: 2451 Intelliplex Drive, Zip 46176, tel. 317/392–3211; John M. Horner, President and Chief Executive Officer

MARGARET MARY HEALTH, 321 Mitchell Avenue, Batesville, IN, Zip 47006–8909, Mailing Address: P.O. Box 226, Zip 47006–0226, tel. 812/934–6624; Timothy L. Putnam, FACHE, President and Chief Executive Officer

RIVERVIEW HEALTH, 395 Westfield Road, Noblesville, IN, Zip 46060–1425, Mailing Address: P.O. Box 220, Zip 46061–0220, tel. 317/773–0760; Seth Warren, President and Chief Executive Officer

RUSH MEMORIAL HOSPITAL, 1300 North Main Street, Rushville, IN, Zip 46173–1198; tel. 765/932–4111; Bradley Smith, President and Chief Executive Officer

WITHAM HEALTH SERVICES, 2605 North Lebanon Street, Lebanon, IN, Zip 46052–1476, Mailing Address: P.O. Box 1200, Zip 46052–3005, tel. 765/485–8000; Raymond V. Ingham, Ph.D., President and Chief Executive Officer

IOWA

GENESIS HEALTH SYSTEM
1227 East Rusholme Street, Davenport, IA, Zip 52803–2459; tel. 563/421–1000; Douglas P. Cropper, President and Chief Executive Officer

GENESIS MEDICAL CENTER, DAVENPORT, 1227 East Rusholme Street, Davenport, IA, Zip 52803–2498; tel. 563/421–1000; Jordan Voigt, Administrator

GENESIS MEDICAL CENTER, DEWITT, 1118 11th Street, De Witt, IA, Zip 52742–1296; tel. 563/659–4200; Curt Coleman, FACHE, Chief Executive Officer

GENESIS MEDICAL CENTER, SILVIS, 801 Illini Drive, Silvis, IL, Zip 61282–1893; tel. 309/281–4000; Theresa Summers-Main, R.N., President

GENESIS MEDICAL CENTER-ALEDO, 409 NW Ninth Avenue, Aledo, IL, Zip 61231–1296; tel. 309/582–9100; Ted Rogalski, Administrator

MERCYONEX
1449 NW 128th Street, Building 5, Suite 200, Clive, IA, Zip 50325; tel. 515/358–9200; Robert P. Ritz, Chief Executive Officer

ADAIR COUNTY HEALTH SYSTEM, 609 SE Kent Street, Greenfield, IA, Zip 50849–9454; tel. 641/743–2123; Marcia Hendricks, FACHE, R.N., Chief Executive Officer

BOONE COUNTY HOSPITAL, 1015 Union Street, Boone, IA, Zip 50036–4821; tel. 515/432–3140; Joseph S. Smith, Chief Executive Officer

MERCYONE PRIMGHAR MEDICAL CENTER, 255 North Welch Avenue, Primghar, IA, Zip 51245–7765, Mailing Address: P.O. Box 528, Zip 51245–0528, tel. 712/957–2300; Misty Dulin, CAH, Director

KANSAS

HEALTH INNOVATIONS NETWORK OF KANSAS
1500 SW 10th Avenue, Topeka, KS, Zip 66604–1301; tel. 785/354–6137; Kristi Gosser, Network Operations Director

ASCENSION VIA CHRISTI HOSPITAL, MANHATTAN, 1823 College Avenue, Manhattan, KS, Zip 66502–3346, tel. 785/776–3322; Robert C. Copple, FACHE, Senior Administrator

ATCHISON HOSPITAL, 800 Raven Hill Drive, Atchison, KS, Zip 66002–9204; tel. 913/367–2131; Jeffery Perry, President and Chief Executive Officer

CLAY COUNTY MEDICAL CENTER, 617 Liberty Street, Clay Center, KS, Zip 67432–1564, Mailing Address: P.O. Box 512, Zip 67432–0512, tel. 785/632–2144; Austin M. Gillard, Chief Executive Officer

COFFEY COUNTY HOSPITAL, 801 North 4th Street, Burlington, KS, Zip 66839–2602; tel. 620/364–2121; Leonard Hernandez, Chief Executive Officer

COMMUNITY HEALTHCARE SYSTEM, 120 West Eighth Street, Onaga, KS, Zip 66521–9574; tel. 785/889–4272; Todd Willert, Chief Executive Officer

F. W. HUSTON MEDICAL CENTER, 408 Delaware Street, Winchester, KS, Zip 66097–4003; tel. 913/774–4340; LaMont Cook, Administrator

GEARY COMMUNITY HOSPITAL, 1102 St Mary's Road, Junction City, KS, Zip 66441–4196, Mailing Address: P.O. Box 490, Zip 66441–0490, tel. 785/238–4131; Joseph Stratton, FACHE, Chief Executive Officer

HERINGTON MUNICIPAL HOSPITAL, 100 East Helen Street, Herington, KS, Zip 67449–1606; tel. 785/258–2207; Isabel Schmedemann, Chief Executive Officer and Administrator

HIAWATHA COMMUNITY HOSPITAL, 300 Utah Street, Hiawatha, KS, Zip 66434–2314; tel. 785/742–2131; John Broberg, Chief Executive Officer

IRWIN ARMY COMMUNITY HOSPITAL, 600 Caisson Hill Road, Junction City, KS, Zip 66442–7037; tel. 785/239–7000, Colonel, Risa Ware, Commander

KANSAS REHABILITATION HOSPITAL, 1504 SW Eighth Avenue, Topeka, KS, Zip 66606–1632; tel. 785/235–6600; William J. Overbey, Chief Executive Officer

MORRIS COUNTY HOSPITAL, 600 North Washington Street, Council Grove, KS, Zip 66846–1422; tel. 620/767–6811; Kevin Leeper, Chief Executive Officer

NEMAHA VALLEY COMMUNITY HOSPITAL, 1600 Community Drive, Seneca, KS, Zip 66538–9739; tel. 785/336–6181; Kiley Floyd, Chief Executive Officer

NEWMAN REGIONAL HEALTH, 1201 West 12th Avenue, Emporia, KS, Zip 66801–2597; tel. 620/343–6800; Robert N. Wright, Chief Executive Officer

SABETHA COMMUNITY HOSPITAL, 14th and Oregon Streets, Sabetha, KS, Zip 66534–0229, Mailing Address: P.O. Box 229, Zip 66534–0229, tel. 785/284–2121; Lora Key, Chief Executive Officer

STORMONT VAIL HEALTH, 1500 SW Tenth Avenue, Topeka, KS, Zip 66604–1353; tel. 785/354–6000; Rob Kenagy, M.D., President and Chief Executive Officer

WAMEGO HEALTH CENTER, 711 Genn Drive, Wamego, KS, Zip 66547–1179; tel. 785/456–2295; Steve Land, Senior Administrator

WASHINGTON COUNTY HOSPITAL, 304 East Third Street, Washington, KS, Zip 66968–2033; tel. 785/325–2211; Roxanne Schottel, Chief Executive Officer

MED-OP, INC.
220 Canterbury Drive, Hays, KS, Zip 67601; tel. 785/623–2301; Shae Veach, Executive Director

CITIZENS MEDICAL CENTER, 100 East College Drive, Colby, KS, Zip 67701–3799; tel. 785/462–7511; Greg Unruh, Chief Executive Officer

CLARA BARTON HOSPITAL, 250 West Ninth Street, Hoisington, KS, Zip 67544–1706; tel. 620/653–2114; James Blackwell, President and Chief Executive Officer

GOODLAND REGIONAL MEDICAL CENTER, 220 West Second Street, Goodland, KS, Zip 67735–1602; tel. 785/890–3625; Ronald R. Robinson, M.D., M.P.H., FACHE, Chief Executive Officer and Chief Medical Officer

GOVE COUNTY MEDICAL CENTER, 520 West Fifth Street, Quinter, KS, Zip 67752–0129, Mailing Address: P.O. Box 129, Zip 67752–0129, tel. 785/754–3341; Coleen Tummons, Chief Executive Officer

GRAHAM COUNTY HOSPITAL, 304 West Prout Street, Hill City, KS, Zip 67642–1435; tel. 785/421–2121; Melissa Atkins, CPA, Chief Executive Officer

HAYS MEDICAL CENTER, 2220 Canterbury Drive, Hays, KS, Zip 67601–2370, Mailing Address: P.O. Box 8100, Zip 67601–8100, tel. 785/623–5000; Edward Herrman, R.N., FACHE, President and Chief Executive Officer

LOGAN COUNTY HOSPITAL, 211 Cherry Street, Oakley, KS, Zip 67748–1201; tel. 785/672–3211; Meldon L. Snow, Chief Executive Officer

NESS COUNTY HOSPITAL DISTRICT NO 2, 312 Custer Street, Ness City, KS, Zip 67560–1654; tel. 785/798–2291; Curt Thomas, Administrator

NORTON COUNTY HOSPITAL, 102 East Holme, Norton, KS, Zip 67654–1406, Mailing Address: P.O. Box 250, Zip 67654–0250, tel. 785/877–3351; Gina Frack, Chief Executive Officer

ROOKS COUNTY HEALTH CENTER, 1210 North Washington Street, Plainville, KS, Zip 67663–1632, Mailing Address: P.O. Box 389, Zip 67663–0389, tel. 785/434–4553; Anthony Thomas, Chief Executive Officer

RUSH COUNTY MEMORIAL HOSPITAL, 801 Locust Street, La Crosse, KS, Zip 67548–9673, Mailing Address: P.O. Box 520, Zip 67548–0520, tel. 785/222–2545; Brenda Legleiter, R.N., Chief Executive Officer

RUSSELL REGIONAL HOSPITAL, 200 South Main Street, Russell, KS, Zip 67665–2920; tel. 785/483–3131; Sharon Collins, Chief Executive Officer

SCOTT COUNTY HOSPITAL, 201 East Albert Avenue, Scott City, KS, Zip 67871–1203; tel. 620/872–5811; Mark Burnett, President and Chief Executive Officer

SHERIDAN COUNTY HEALTH COMPLEX, 826 18th Street, Hoxie, KS, Zip 67740–0167, Mailing Address: P.O. Box 167, Zip 67740–0167, tel. 785/675–3281; Niceta Farber, Chief Executive Officer

UNIVERSITY OF KANSAS HEALTH SYSTEM PAWNEE VALLEY CAMPUS, 923 Carroll Avenue, Larned, KS, Zip 67550–2429; tel. 620/285–3161; Kendra Barker, Administrator

PIONEER HEALTH NETWORK, INC.
310 East Walnut Street, Suite 210, Garden City, KS, Zip 67846–5565; tel. 620/276–6100; Mary Adam, Executive Director

BOB WILSON MEMORIAL GRANT COUNTY HOSPITAL, 415 North Main Street, Ulysses, KS, Zip 67880–2133; tel. 620/356–1266; Amanda Vaughan, Interim Administrator

CITIZENS MEDICAL CENTER, 100 East College Drive, Colby, KS, Zip 67701–3799; tel. 785/462–7511; Greg Unruh, Chief Executive Officer

EDWARDS COUNTY MEDICAL CENTER, 620 West Eighth Street, Kinsley, KS, Zip 67547–2329, Mailing Address: P.O. Box 99, Zip 67547–0099, tel. 620/659–3621; Jimmie W. Hansel, Ph.D., Chief Executive Officer

GREELEY COUNTY HEALTH SERVICES, 506 Third Street, Tribune, KS, Zip 67879–9684, Mailing Address: P.O. Box 338, Zip 67879–0338, tel. 620/376–4221; Burke Kline, Chief Executive Officer

HAMILTON COUNTY HOSPITAL, 700 North Huser Street, Syracuse, KS, Zip 67878–0948, Mailing Address: P.O. Box 948, Zip 67878–0948, tel. 620/384–7461; Malachi Lones, Interim Administrator

HODGEMAN COUNTY HEALTH CENTER, 809 Bramley Street, Jetmore, KS, Zip 67854–9320, Mailing Address: P.O. Box 310, Zip 67854–0310, tel. 620/357–8361; Phil Ginder, Chief Executive Officer

KEARNY COUNTY HOSPITAL, 500 Thorpe Street, Lakin, KS, Zip 67860–9625; tel. 620/355–7111; Benjamin Anderson, Chief Executive Officer and Administrator

LANE COUNTY HOSPITAL, 235 West Vine, Dighton, KS, Zip 67839–0969, Mailing Address: P.O. Box 969, Zip 67839–0969, tel. 620/397–5321; Mike Ruggiero, Interim Chief Executive Officer

LOGAN COUNTY HOSPITAL, 211 Cherry Street, Oakley, KS, Zip 67748–1201; tel. 785/672–3211; Meldon L. Snow, Chief Executive Officer

MEADE DISTRICT HOSPITAL, 510 East Carthage Street, Meade, KS, Zip 67864–6401, Mailing Address: P.O. Box 820, Zip 67864–0820, tel. 620/873–2141; Tara Ramlochan, Chief Executive Officer

MINNEOLA DISTRICT HOSPITAL, 212 Main Street, Minneola, KS, Zip 67865–8511, Mailing Address: P.O. Box 127, Zip 67865–0127, tel. 620/885–4264; Deborah Bruner, Chief Executive Officer and Administrator

MORTON COUNTY HEALTH SYSTEM, 445 Hilltop Street, Elkhart, KS, Zip 67950–0937, Mailing Address: P.O. Box 937, Zip 67950–0937, tel. 620/697–2141; Chad Thompson, Chief Executive Officer

SATANTA DISTRICT HOSPITAL AND LONG TERM CARE, 401 South Cheyenne Street, Satanta, KS, Zip 67870–0159, Mailing Address: P.O. Box 159, Zip 67870–0159, tel. 620/649–2761; Jeremy Clingenpeel, Administrator

SCOTT COUNTY HOSPITAL, 201 East Albert Avenue, Scott City, KS, Zip 67871–1203; tel. 620/872–5811; Mark Burnett, President and Chief Executive Officer

SOUTHWEST MEDICAL CENTER, 315 West 15th Street, Liberal, KS, Zip 67901–2455, Mailing Address: Box 1340, Zip 67905–1340, tel. 620/624–1651; William Ermann, President and Chief Executive Officer

ST. CATHERINE HOSPITAL, 401 East Spruce Street, Garden City, KS, Zip 67846–5679; tel. 620/272–2561; Scott J. Taylor, President and Chief Executive Officer

STANTON COUNTY HOSPITAL, 404 North Chestnut Street, Johnson, KS, Zip 67855–5001, Mailing Address: P.O. Box 779, Zip 67855–0779, tel. 620/492–6250; Jay Tusten, Chief Executive Officer

STEVENS COUNTY HOSPITAL, 1006 South Jackson Street, Hugoton, KS, Zip 67951–2858, Mailing Address: P.O. Box 10, Zip 67951–0010, tel. 620/544–8511; Linda Stalcup, Chief Executive Officer

WICHITA COUNTY HEALTH CENTER, 211 East Earl Street, Leoti, KS, Zip 67861–9620; tel. 620/375–2233; Teresa Clark, Chief Executive Officer and Administrator

SUNFLOWER HEALTH NETWORK
400 South Santa Fe Avenue, Salina, KS, Zip 67401–4144; tel. 785/452–6102; Heather Fuller, Executive Director

CLAY COUNTY MEDICAL CENTER, 617 Liberty Street, Clay Center, KS, Zip 67432–1564, Mailing Address: P.O. Box 512, Zip 67432–0512, tel. 785/632–2144; Austin M. Gillard, Chief Executive Officer

CLOUD COUNTY HEALTH CENTER, 1100 Highland Drive, Concordia, KS, Zip 66901–3923; tel. 785/243–1234; David Garnas, Administrator

ELLSWORTH COUNTY MEDICAL CENTER, 1604 Aylward Street, Ellsworth, KS, Zip 67439–0087, Mailing Address: P.O. Box 87, Zip 67439–0087, tel. 785/472–3111; Andrew P. Bair, Chief Executive Officer

HERINGTON MUNICIPAL HOSPITAL, 100 East Helen Street, Herington, KS, Zip 67449–1606; tel. 785/258–2207; Isabel Schmedemann, Chief Executive Officer and Administrator

HILLSBORO COMMUNITY HOSPITAL, 701 South Main Street, Hillsboro, KS, Zip 67063–1553; tel. 620/947–3114; Marion Regier, Chief Executive Officer

HOSPITAL DISTRICT NO 1 OF RICE COUNTY, 619 South Clark Street, Lyons, KS, Zip 67554–3003, Mailing Address: P.O. Box 828, Zip 67554–0828, tel. 620/257–5173; George M. Stover, Chief Executive Officer

JEWELL COUNTY HOSPITAL, 100 Crestvue Avenue, Mankato, KS, Zip 66956–2407, Mailing Address: P.O. Box 327, Zip 66956–0327, tel. 785/378–3137; Doyle L. McKimmy, FACHE, Chief Executive Officer

LINCOLN COUNTY HOSPITAL, 624 North Second Street, Lincoln, KS, Zip 67455–1738, Mailing Address: P.O. Box 406, Zip 67455–0406, tel. 785/524–4403; Steven L. Granzow, Chief Executive Officer

LINDSBORG COMMUNITY HOSPITAL, 605 West Lincoln Street, Lindsborg, KS, Zip 67456–2328; tel. 785/227–3308; Larry VanDerWege, Administrator

MEMORIAL HEALTH SYSTEM, 511 NE Tenth Street, Abilene, KS, Zip 67410–2153; tel. 785/263–2100; Harold Courtois, Chief Executive Officer

MITCHELL COUNTY HOSPITAL HEALTH SYSTEMS, 400 West Eighth, Beloit, KS, Zip 67420–1605, Mailing Address: P.O. Box 399, Zip 67420–0399, tel. 785/738–2266; Jeremy Armstrong, FACHE, Chief Executive Officer

OSBORNE COUNTY MEMORIAL HOSPITAL, 424 West New Hampshire Street, Osborne, KS, Zip 67473–2314, Mailing Address: P.O. Box 70, Zip 67473–0070, tel. 785/346–2121; Marianna Harris, Administrator

OTTAWA COUNTY HEALTH CENTER, 215 East Eighth, Minneapolis, KS, Zip 67467–1902, Mailing Address: P.O. Box 290, Zip 67467–0290, tel. 785/392–2122; Jody Parks, Administrator

REPUBLIC COUNTY HOSPITAL, 2420 'G' Street, Belleville, KS, Zip 66935–2400; tel. 785/527–2254; David-Paul Cavazos, Chief Executive Officer

SALINA REGIONAL HEALTH CENTER, 400 South Santa Fe Avenue, Salina, KS, Zip 67401–4198, Mailing Address: P.O. Box 5080, Zip 67402–5080, tel. 785/452–7000; Micheal Terry, President and Chief Executive Officer

SMITH COUNTY MEMORIAL HOSPITAL, 921 East Highway 36, Smith Center, KS, Zip 66967; tel. 785/282–6845; Allen Van Driel, FACHE, Administrator

KENTUCKY

COMMONWEALTH HEALTH CORPORATION
800 Park Street, Bowling Green, KY, Zip 42101–2356; tel. 270/745–1500; Connie Smith, FACHE, MSN, R.N., Chief Executive Officer

COMMONWEALTH REGIONAL SPECIALTY HOSPITAL, 250 Park Drive, 6th Floor, Bowling Green, KY, Zip 42101–1760, Mailing Address: P.O. Box 90010, Zip 42102–9010, tel. 270/796–6200; Christa Atkins, Administrator

MEDICAL CENTER AT BOWLING GREEN, 250 Park Street, Bowling Green, KY, Zip 42101-1795, Mailing Address: P.O. Box 90010, Zip 42102-9010, tel. 270/745-1000; Connie Smith, FACHE, MSN, R.N., Chief Executive Officer

MEDICAL CENTER AT FRANKLIN, 1100 Brookhaven Road, Franklin, KY, Zip 42134-2746; tel. 270/598-4800; Annette Runyon, Vice President and Administrator

MEDICAL CENTER AT SCOTTSVILLE, 456 Burnley Road, Scottsville, KY, Zip 42164-6355; tel. 270/622-2800; Eric Hagan, R.N., Executive Vice President and Administrator

COMMUNITY CARE NETWORK
110 A Second Street, Henderson, KY, Zip 42420; tel. 619/278-2273; Roberta Alexander, Director

BAPTIST HEALTH MADISONVILLE, 900 Hospital Drive, Madisonville, KY, Zip 42431-1694; tel. 270/825-5100; Robert L. Ramey, President

BAPTIST HEALTH PADUCAH, 2501 Kentucky Avenue, Paducah, KY, Zip 42003-3200; tel. 270/575-2100; Christopher Roty, President

CALDWELL MEDICAL CENTER, 100 Medical Center Drive, Princeton, KY, Zip 42445-2430, Mailing Address: P.O. Box 410, Zip 42445-0410, tel. 270/365-0300; Daniel Odegaard, FACHE, Chief Executive Officer

CRITTENDEN COUNTY HOSPITAL, 520 West Gum Street, Marion, KY, Zip 42064-1516, Mailing Address: P.O. Box 386, Zip 42064-0386, tel. 270/965-5281; Daniel Hiben, Chief Executive Officer

HEALTHSOUTH DEACONESS REHABILITATION HOSPITAL, 4100 Covert Avenue, Evansville, IN, Zip 47714-5567, Mailing Address: P.O. Box 5349, Zip 47716-5349, tel. 812/476-9983; Blake Bunner, Chief Executive Officer

JENNIE STUART MEDICAL CENTER, 320 West 18th Street, Hopkinsville, KY, Zip 42240-1965, Mailing Address: P.O. Box 2400, Zip 42241-2400, tel. 270/887-0100; Eric A. Lee, President and Chief Executive Officer

LINCOLN TRAIL BEHAVIORAL HEALTH SYSTEM, 3909 South Wilson Road, Radcliff, KY, Zip 40160-8944, Mailing Address: P.O. Box 369, Zip 40159-0369, tel. 270/351-9444; Charles L. Webb, Jr., Chief Executive Officer

LIVINGSTON HOSPITAL AND HEALTHCARE SERVICES, 131 Hospital Drive, Salem, KY, Zip 42078-8043; tel. 270/988-2299; Elizabeth Snodgrass, Chief Executive Officer

MEDICAL CENTER AT FRANKLIN, 1100 Brookhaven Road, Franklin, KY, Zip 42134-2746; tel. 270/598-4800; Annette Runyon, Vice President and Administrator

METHODIST HOSPITAL UNION COUNTY, 4604 Highway 60 West, Morganfield, KY, Zip 42437-9570; tel. 270/389-5000; Lynn R. Steinwachs, Vice President and Administrator

METHODIST HOSPITAL, 1305 North Elm Street, Henderson, KY, Zip 42420-2775, Mailing Address: P.O. Box 48, Zip 42419-0048, tel. 270/827-7700; Benny Nolen, President and Chief Executive Officer

MURRAY CALLOWAY COUNTY HOSPITAL, 803 Poplar Street, Murray, KY, Zip 42071-2432; tel. 270/762-1100, Colonel, Jerome Penner, Chief Executive Officer

NORTON CHILDREN'S HOSPITAL, 231 East Chestnut Street, Louisville, KY, Zip 40202-1821; tel. 502/629-6000; Emmett Ramser, Chief Administrative Officer

NORTON HOSPITAL, 200 East Chestnut Street, Louisville, KY, Zip 40202-1800, Mailing Address: P.O. Box 35070, Zip 40232-5070, tel. 502/629-8000; Matthew Ayers, Chief Administrative Officer

OHIO COUNTY HOSPITAL, 1211 Main Street, Hartford, KY, Zip 42347-1619; tel. 270/298-7411; Blaine Pieper, Chief Executive Officer

OWENSBORO HEALTH MUHLENBERG COMMUNITY HOSPITAL, 440 Hopkinsville Street, Greenville, KY, Zip 42345-1172, Mailing Address: P.O. Box 387, Zip 42345-0378, tel. 270/338-8000; Ed Heath, FACHE, Chief Executive Officer

RIVERVALLEY BEHAVIORAL HEALTH HOSPITAL, 1000 Industrial Drive, Owensboro, KY, Zip 42301-8715; tel. 270/689-6500; Wanda Figuerora Peralta, President and Chief Executive Officer

SAINT THOMAS WEST HOSPITAL, 4220 Harding Road, Nashville, TN, Zip 37205-2095, Mailing Address: P.O. Box 380, Zip 37202-0380, tel. 615/222-2111; Fahad Tahir, Chief Executive Officer

ST. VINCENT EVANSVILLE, 3700 Washington Avenue, Evansville, IN, Zip 47714-0541; tel. 812/485-4000; Daniel A. Parod, President

STS. MARY & ELIZABETH HOSPITAL, 1850 Bluegrass Avenue, Louisville, KY, Zip 40215-1199; tel. 502/361-6000; Charles Powell, President

TRIGG COUNTY HOSPITAL, 254 Main Street, Cadiz, KY, Zip 42211-9153, Mailing Address: P.O. Box 312, Zip 42211-0312, tel. 270/522-3215; John Sumner, Chief Executive Officer

KENTUCKYONE
200 Abraham Flexner Way, Louisville, KY, Zip 40202-2877; tel. 502/587-4011; Charles W. Neumann, Interim President and Chief Executive Officer

CHI FLAGET MEMORIAL HOSPITAL, 4305 New Shepherdsville Road, Bardstown, KY, Zip 40004-9019; tel. 502/350-5000; Jennifer Nolan, President and Chief Executive Officer

CHI OUR LADY OF PEACE, 2020 Newburg Road, Louisville, KY, Zip 40205-1879; tel. 502/479-4500; Jennifer Nolan, President and Chief Executive Officer

CHI SAINT JOSEPH BEREA, 305 Estill Street, Berea, KY, Zip 40403-1909; tel. 859/986-3151; Terrence G. Deis, CPA, FACHE, President

CHI SAINT JOSEPH EAST, 150 North Eagle Creek Drive, Lexington, KY, Zip 40509-1805; tel. 859/967-5000; Eric Gilliam, President

CHI SAINT JOSEPH HEALTH, One St Joseph Drive, Lexington, KY, Zip 40504-3754; tel. 859/278-3436; Bruce J. Tassin, President

CHI SAINT JOSEPH LONDON, 1001 Saint Joseph Lane, London, KY, Zip 40741-8345; tel. 606/330-6000; Terrence G. Deis, CPA, FACHE, President

CONTINUING CARE HOSPITAL, 1 Saint Joseph Drive, Lexington, KY, Zip 40504-3742; tel. 859/967-5744; Robert C. Desotelle, President and Chief Executive Officer

JEWISH HOSPITAL-SHELBYVILLE, 727 Hospital Drive, Shelbyville, KY, Zip 40065-1699; tel. 502/647-4000; Annessa Baker, Site Executive and Chief Nursing Officer

JEWISH HOSPITAL, 200 Abraham Flexner Way, Louisville, KY, Zip 40202-1886; tel. 502/587-4011; Deborah M. Lee-Eddie, Interim President and Chief Executive Officer

SAINT JOSEPH MOUNT STERLING, 225 Falcon Drive, Mount Sterling, KY, Zip 40353-1158, Mailing Address: P.O. Box 7, Zip 40353-0007, tel. 859/497-5000; Terrence G. Deis, CPA, FACHE, President

STS. MARY & ELIZABETH HOSPITAL, 1850 Bluegrass Avenue, Louisville, KY, Zip 40215-1199; tel. 502/361-6000; Charles Powell, President

ST. ELIZABETH HEALTHCARE
1 Medical Village Drive, Edgewood, KY, Zip 41017-3403; tel. 859/301-2000; Garren Colvin, Chief Executive Officer

ST. ELIZABETH EDGEWOOD, 1 Medical Village Drive, Edgewood, KY, Zip 41017-3403; tel. 859/301-2000; Garren Colvin, Chief Executive Officer

ST. ELIZABETH FLORENCE, 4900 Houston Road, Florence, KY, Zip 41042-4824; tel. 859/212-5200; Garren Colvin, Chief Executive Officer

ST. ELIZABETH FORT THOMAS, 85 North Grand Avenue, Fort Thomas, KY, Zip 41075-1796; tel. 859/572-3100; Garren Colvin, Chief Executive Officer

ST. ELIZABETH GRANT, 238 Barnes Road, Williamstown, KY, Zip 41097-9482; tel. 859/824-8240; Garren Colvin, Chief Executive Officer

MASSACHUSETTS

LAHEY HEALTH
41 Mall Road, Burlington, MA, Zip 01805-0001; tel. 781/744-7100; Howard R. Grant, M.D., President and Chief Executive Officer

BEVERLY HOSPITAL, 85 Herrick Street, Beverly, MA, Zip 01915-1777; tel. 978/922-3000; Philip M. Cormier, Chief Executive Officer

LAHEY HOSPITAL & MEDICAL CENTER, BURLINGTON, 41 Mall Road, Burlington, MA, Zip 01805-0001, Mailing Address: 31 Mall Road, Zip 01805-0001, tel. 781/744-5100; David L. Longworth, M.D., Chief Executive Officer

WINCHESTER HOSPITAL, 41 Highland Avenue, Winchester, MA, Zip 01890-1496; tel. 781/729-9000; Richard I. Welner, M.D., Chief Executive Officer and Chief Medical Officer

WELLFORCE
800 District Avenue, Suite 520, Burlington, MA, Zip 01803-5057; tel. 978/942-2220; Michael Wagner, M.D., Interim Chief Executive Officer

LOWELL GENERAL HOSPITAL, 295 Varnum Avenue, Lowell, MA, Zip 01854-2134; tel. 978/937-6000; Joseph White, FACHE, President and Chief Executive Officer

MELROSEWAKEFIELD HEALTHCARE, 585 Lebanon Street, Melrose, MA, Zip 02176-3225; tel. 781/979-3000; Susan Sandberg, R.N., Chief Executive Officer

TUFTS MEDICAL CENTER, 800 Washington Street, Boston, MA, Zip 02111-1552; tel. 617/636-5000; Michael Apkon, M.D., Ph.D., Chief Executive Officer

MICHIGAN

GENESYS HEALTH SYSTEM
1 Genesys Parkway, Grand Blanc, MI, Zip 48439-8065; tel. 810/606-5000; Elizabeth Aderholdt, Chief Executive Officer

ASCENSION MACOMB-OAKLAND HOSPITAL, 11800 East 12 Mile Road, Warren, MI, Zip 48093-3472; tel. 586/573-5000; Terry Hamilton, President

ASCENSION ST. JOSEPH HOSPITAL, 200 Hemlock Street, Tawas City, MI, Zip 48763-9237, Mailing Address: P.O. Box 659, Zip 48764-0659, tel. 989/362-3411; Jan Jacob, R.N., Interim Administrator

ASCENSION ST. MARY'S OF MICHIGAN, 800 South Washington Avenue, Saginaw, MI, Zip 48601-2594; tel. 989/907-8000; Chris Palazzolo, Health System President and Chief Executive Officer Mid-Michigan

LAKELAND REGIONAL HEALTH SYSTEM
1234 Napier Avenue, Saint Joseph, MI, Zip 49085-2112; tel. 269/983-8300; Loren Hamel, M.D., President and Chief Executive Officer

LAKELAND HOSPITAL, WATERVLIET, 400 Medical Park Drive, Watervliet, MI, Zip 49098-9225; tel. 269/463-3111; Ray Cruse, Chief Executive Officer

SPECTRUM HEALTH LAKELAND, 1234 Napier Avenue, Saint Joseph, MI, Zip 49085-2158; tel. 269/983-8300; Loren Hamel, M.D., President and Chief Executive Officer

ST. JOHN PROVIDENCE HEALTH SYSTEM
28000 Dequindre Drive, Warren, MI, Zip 48092; tel. 866/501–3627; Jean Meyer, President and Chief Executive Officer

ASCENSION BRIGHTON CENTER FOR RECOVERY, 12851 Grand River Road, Brighton, MI, Zip 48116–8506; tel. 810/227–1211; Raymond A. Waller, Director and Administrator

ASCENSION MACOMB-OAKLAND HOSPITAL, 11800 East 12 Mile Road, Warren, MI, Zip 48093–3472; tel. 586/573–5000; Terry Hamilton, President

ASCENSION RIVER DISTRICT HOSPITAL, 4100 River Road, East China, MI, Zip 48054–2909; tel. 810/329–7111; Robert E. Hoban, President

ASCENSION ST. JOHN HOSPITAL, 22101 Moross Road, Detroit, MI, Zip 48236–2148; tel. 313/343–4000; Robert E. Hoban, President

ASCENSION OF PROVIDENCE HOSPITAL, SOUTHFIELD CAMPUS, 16001 West Nine Mile Road, Southfield, MI, Zip 48075; tel. 248/849–3400; Joseph R. Hurshe, President

UPPER PENINSULA HEALTH CARE NETWORK (UPHCN)
228 West Washington Street, Marquette, MI, Zip 49855–4330; tel. 906/225–3146; Dennis Smith, Chief Executive Officer

ASPIRUS IRON RIVER HOSPITALS & CLINICS, INC., 1400 West Ice Lake Road, Iron River, MI, Zip 49935–9526; tel. 906/265–6121; Connie L. Koutouzos, R.N., MSN, Chief Executive Officer

ASPIRUS IRONWOOD HOSPITALS & CLINICS, INC., N10561 Grand View Lane, Ironwood, MI, Zip 49938–9622; tel. 906/932–2525; Paula L. Chermside, Chief Executive Officer

ASPIRUS KEWEENAW HOSPITAL, INC., 205 Osceola Street, Laurium, MI, Zip 49913–2134; tel. 906/337–6500; Rick L. Nevers, Interim President

ASPIRUS ONTONAGON HOSPITAL, INC., 601 South Seventh Street, Ontonagon, MI, Zip 49953–1459; tel. 906/884–8000; Dylan Taylor, Chief Administrative Officer

BARAGA COUNTY MEMORIAL HOSPITAL, 18341 U.S. Highway 41, L'Anse, MI, Zip 49946–8024; tel. 906/524–3300; Margie Hale, R.N., MSN, Chief Executive Officer

DICKINSON COUNTY HEALTHCARE SYSTEM, 1721 South Stephenson Avenue, Iron Mountain, MI, Zip 49801–3637; tel. 906/774–1313; Jeanne Goche, Interim Chief Executive Officer

HELEN NEWBERRY JOY HOSPITAL, Helen Newberry Joy Hospital Annex, 502 West Harrie Street, Newberry, MI, Zip 49868–1209; tel. 906/293–9200; Scott Pillion, Chief Executive Officer

MACKINAC STRAITS HEALTH SYSTEM, INC., 1140 North State Street, Saint Ignace, MI, Zip 49781–1048; tel. 906/643–8585; Karen Cheeseman, Chief Executive Officer

MUNISING MEMORIAL HOSPITAL, 1500 Sand Point Road, Munising, MI, Zip 49862–1406; tel. 906/387–4110; Melissa Hall, Chief Executive Officer

SCHOOLCRAFT MEMORIAL HOSPITAL, 7870W US Highway 2, Manistique, MI, Zip 49854–8992; tel. 906/341–3200; Robert Crumb, MS, Chief Executive Officer

UP HEALTH SYSTEM-BELL, 901 Lakeshore Drive, Ishpeming, MI, Zip 49849–1367; tel. 906/486–4431; Mitchell D. Leckelt, Chief Executive Officer

UP HEALTH SYSTEM-PORTAGE, 500 Campus Drive, Hancock, MI, Zip 49930–1569; tel. 906/483–1000; Randy Neiswonger, Chief Executive Officer

WAR MEMORIAL HOSPITAL, 500 Osborn Boulevard, Sault Sainte Marie, MI, Zip 49783–1884; tel. 906/635–4460; David B. Jahn, President and Chief Executive Officer

MINNESOTA

NORTHWEST METRO ALLIANCE
c/O Mercy Hospital, 4050 Coon Rapids Boulevard, Coon Rapids, MN, Zip 55433–2586; tel. 763/236–6000; Sara J. Criger, President

MERCY HOSPITAL, 4050 Coon Rapids Boulevard, Coon Rapids, MN, Zip 55433–2586; tel. 763/236–6000; Sara J. Criger, President

MISSOURI

HEALTH NETWORK OF MISSOURI
One Hospital Drive, Room C1213, DC 079.00, Columbia, MO, Zip 65212; tel. 573/815–8000; Marty McCormick, Chief Executive Officer

BOTHWELL REGIONAL HEALTH CENTER, 601 East 14th Street, Sedalia, MO, Zip 65301–5972, Mailing Address: P.O. Box 1706, Zip 65302–1706, tel. 660/826–8833; Lori Wightman, R.N., MSN, FACHE, Chief Executive Officer

CAPITAL REGION MEDICAL CENTER, 1125 Madison Street, Jefferson City, MO, Zip 65101–5200, Mailing Address: P.O. Box 1128, Zip 65102–1128, tel. 573/632–5000; Gaspare Calvaruso, President

HANNIBAL REGIONAL HOSPITAL, 6000 Hospital Drive, Hannibal, MO, Zip 63401–6887, Mailing Address: P.O. Box 551, Zip 63401–0551, tel. 573/248–1300; C Todd. Ahrens, President and Chief Executive Officer

LAKE REGIONAL HEALTH SYSTEM, 54 Hospital Drive, Osage Beach, MO, Zip 65065–3050; tel. 573/348–8000; Dane W. Henry, Chief Executive Officer

SAINT FRANCIS MEDICAL CENTER, 211 St Francis Drive, Cape Girardeau, MO, Zip 63703–5049; tel. 573/331–3000; Maryann Reese, R.N., FACHE, President and Chief Executive Officer

UNIVERSITY OF MISSOURI HEALTH CARE, One Hospital Drive, Columbia, MO, Zip 65212–0001; tel. 573/882–4141; Jonathan W. Curtright, Chief Executive Officer

MERCY HEALTH EAST
615 South New Ballas Road, Saint Louis, MO, Zip 63141–8221; tel. 314/364–3000; Donn Sorensen, Regional President, West Communities

MERCY HOSPITAL JEFFERSON, 1400 US Highway 61 South, Festus, MO, Zip 63028–4100, Mailing Address: P.O. Box 350, Crystal City, Zip 63019–0350, tel. 636/933–1000; Eric Ammons, President

MERCY HOSPITAL ST. LOUIS, 615 South New Ballas Road, Saint Louis, MO, Zip 63141–8277; tel. 314/251–6000; Stephen Mackin, President

MERCY HOSPITAL WASHINGTON, 901 East Fifth Street, Washington, MO, Zip 63090–3127; tel. 636/239–8000; Eric J. Eoloff, President

MOSAIC LIFE CARE X
5325 Faraon Street, Saint Joseph, MO, Zip 64506–3488; tel. 816/271–6000; Brady Dubois, President

LONG-TERM ACUTE CARE HOSPITAL, MOSAIC LIFE CARE AT ST. JOSEPH, 5325 Faraon Street, Saint Joseph, MO, Zip 64506–3488; tel. 816/271–6000; Dana Anderson, R.N., Administrator

MOSAIC LIFE CARE AT ST. JOSEPH – MEDICAL CENTER, 5325 Faraon Street, Saint Joseph, MO, Zip 64506–3488; tel. 816/271–6000; Samuel Mark. Laney, M.D., Chief Executive Officer

MOSAIC MEDICAL CENTER – ALBANY, 705 North College Street, Albany, MO, Zip 64402–1433; tel. 660/726–3941; Jon D. Doolittle, Regional President

MONTANA

MONTANA HEALTH NETWORK
519 Pleasant Street, Miles City, MT, Zip 59301–3030; tel. 406/234–1420; Janet Bastian, Chief Executive Officer

BILLINGS CLINIC, 2800 10th Avenue North, Billings, MT, Zip 59101–0703, Mailing Address: P.O. Box 37000, Zip 59107–7000, tel. 406/657–4000; Randall K. Gibb, M.D., Chief Executive Officer

CENTRAL MONTANA MEDICAL CENTER, 408 Wendell Avenue, Lewistown, MT, Zip 59457–2261; tel. 406/535–7711; Laura Bennett, Interim Chief Executive Officer

DAHL MEMORIAL HEALTHCARE ASSOCIATION, 215 Sandy Street, Ekalaka, MT, Zip 59324, Mailing Address: P.O. Box 46, Zip 59324–0046, tel. 406/775–8730; Ryan Tooke, Chief Executive Officer

DANIELS MEMORIAL HEALTHCARE CENTER, 105 Fifth Avenue East, Scobey, MT, Zip 59263, Mailing Address: P.O. Box 400, Zip 59263–0400, tel. 406/487–2296; Eric Connell, Chief Executive Officer

FALLON MEDICAL COMPLEX, 202 South 4th Street West, Baker, MT, Zip 59313–9156, Mailing Address: P.O. Box 820, Zip 59313–0820, tel. 406/778–3331; David Espeland, Chief Executive Officer

FRANCES MAHON DEACONESS HOSPITAL, 621 Third Street South, Glasgow, MT, Zip 59230–2699; tel. 406/228–3500; Randall G. Holom, Chief Executive Officer

GLENDIVE MEDICAL CENTER, 202 Prospect Drive, Glendive, MT, Zip 59330–1999; tel. 406/345–3306; Parker Powell, Chief Executive Officer

HOLY ROSARY HEALTHCARE, 2600 Wilson Street, Miles City, MT, Zip 59301–5094; tel. 406/233–2600; Paul Lewis, Chief Executive Officer

MCCONE COUNTY HEALTH CENTER, 605 Sullivan Avenue, Circle, MT, Zip 59215, Mailing Address: P.O. Box 48, Zip 59215–0048, tel. 406/485–3381; Nancy Rosaaen, Chief Executive Officer

PHILLIPS COUNTY HOSPITAL, 311 South 8th Avenue East, Malta, MT, Zip 59538–0640, Mailing Address: P.O. Box 640, Zip 59538–0640, tel. 406/654–1100; Ward C. VanWichen, Chief Executive Officer

ROOSEVELT MEDICAL CENTER, 818 Second Avenue East, Culbertson, MT, Zip 59218, Mailing Address: P.O. Box 419, Zip 59218–0419, tel. 406/787–6401; Audrey Stromberg, Administrator

SHERIDAN MEMORIAL HOSPITAL, 440 West Laurel Avenue, Plentywood, MT, Zip 59254–1596; tel. 406/765–3700; Gregory L. Maurer, Chief Executive Officer

SIDNEY HEALTH CENTER, 216 14th Avenue SW, Sidney, MT, Zip 59270–3586; tel. 406/488–2100; Jennifer Doty, Chief Executive Officer

STILLWATER BILLINGS CLINIC, 44 West Fourth Avenue North, Columbus, MT, Zip 59019–0959, Mailing Address: P.O. Box 959, Zip 59019–0959, tel. 406/322–5316; David Ryerse, Chief Executive Officer

WHEATLAND MEMORIAL HEALTHCARE, 530 Third Street North West, Harlowton, MT, Zip 59036, Mailing Address: P.O. Box 287, Zip 59036–0287, tel. 406/632–4351; Rick Poss, Interim Chief Executive Officer

NEBRASKA

CHI HEALTH
12809 West Dodge Road, Omaha, NE, Zip 68154–2155; tel. 402/343–4300; Cliff Robertson, M.D., President and Chief Executive Officer

Section B

CHI HEALTH CREIGHTON UNIVERSITY MEDICAL CENTER – BERGAN MERCY, 7500 Mercy Road, Omaha, NE, Zip 68124–2319; tel. 402/398–6060; Marie E. Knedler, R.N., FACHE, Interim President

CHI HEALTH GOOD SAMARITAN, 10 East 31st Street, Kearney, NE, Zip 68847–2926, Mailing Address: P.O. Box 1990, Zip 68848–1990, tel. 308/865–7100; Michael H. Schnieders, FACHE, President

CHI HEALTH IMMANUEL, 6901 North 72nd Street, Omaha, NE, Zip 68122–1799; tel. 402/572–2121; Ann Schumacher, R.N., MSN, FACHE, President

CHI HEALTH LAKESIDE, 6901 N 72nd St, Omaha, NE, Zip 68122, Mailing Address: 16901 Lakeside Hills Court, Zip 68130–2318, tel. 402/717–8000; Kevin Miller, President

CHI HEALTH MERCY CORNING, 603 Rosary Drive, Corning, IA, Zip 50841–1683; tel. 641/322–3121; Lisa Wolfe, President

CHI HEALTH MERCY COUNCIL BLUFFS, 800 Mercy Drive, Council Bluffs, IA, Zip 51503–3128; tel. 712/328–5000; Ann Schumacher, R.N., MSN, FACHE, President

CHI HEALTH MIDLANDS, 11111 South 84th Street, Papillion, NE, Zip 68046–4122; tel. 402/593–3000; Kevin Miller, President

CHI HEALTH MISSOURI VALLEY, 631 North Eighth Street, Missouri Valley, IA, Zip 51555–1102; tel. 712/642–2784; Jonathan Moe, President

CHI HEALTH NEBRASKA HEART, 7500 South 91st Street, Lincoln, NE, Zip 68526–9437; tel. 402/327–2700; Derek Vance, President

CHI HEALTH PLAINVIEW, 704 North Third Street, Plainview, NE, Zip 68769–2047, Mailing Address: P.O. Box 489, Zip 68769–0489, tel. 402/582–4245; Gregory Beckmann, Regional President

CHI HEALTH SAINT FRANCIS, 2620 West Faidley Avenue, Grand Island, NE, Zip 68803–4297, Mailing Address: P.O. Box 9804, Zip 68802–9804, tel. 308/384–4600; Edward J. Hannon, FACHE, President

CHI HEALTH SCHUYLER, 104 West 17th Street, Schuyler, NE, Zip 68661–1304; tel. 402/352–2441; Connie Peters, R.N., President

CHI HEALTH ST ELIZABETH, 555 South 70th Street, Lincoln, NE, Zip 68510–2494; tel. 402/219–8000; Derek Vance, President

CHI HEALTH ST. MARY'S, 1301 Grundman Boulevard, Nebraska City, NE, Zip 68410; tel. 402/873–3321; Daniel DeFreece, M.D., Interim President

NEBRASKA MEDICINE
987400 Nebraska Medical Center, Omaha, NE, Zip 68198–7400; tel. 877/763–0000; James Linder, M.D., Chief Executive Officer

NEBRASKA MEDICINE – BELLEVUE, 2500 Bellevue Medical Center Drive, Bellevue, NE, Zip 68123–1591; tel. 402/763–3000, Matt E. Pospisil, Vice President Perioperative Services

NEBRASKA MEDICINE – NEBRASKA MEDICAL CENTER, 987400 Nebraska Medical Center, Omaha, NE, Zip 68198–7400; tel. 402/552–2000; James Linder, M.D., Chief Executive Officer

NORTHEAST HEALTH SERVICES
704 North Third Street, c/o CHI Plainview, Plainview, NE, Zip 68769–2047; tel. 402/358–5700; Gregory Beckmann, Chief Executive Officer

AVERA CREIGHTON HOSPITAL, 1503 Main Street, Creighton, NE, Zip 68729–3007, Mailing Address: P.O. Box 186, Zip 68729–0186, tel. 402/358–5700; Todd Consbruck, Chief Executive Officer

CHI HEALTH PLAINVIEW, 704 North Third Street, Plainview, NE, Zip 68769–2047, Mailing Address: P.O. Box 489, Zip 68769–0489, tel. 402/582–4245; Gregory Beckmann, Regional President

OSMOND GENERAL HOSPITAL, 402 North Maple Street, Osmond, NE, Zip 68765–5726, Mailing Address: P.O. Box 429, Zip 68765–0429, tel. 402/748–3393; Lon Knievel, Chief Executive Officer

NEW HAMPSHIRE

CARING COMMUNITY NETWORK OF THE TWIN RIVERS
c/o First Health, 841 Central Street, Franklin, NH, Zip 03235–2026; tel. 603/934–0177; Rick Silverberg, Managing Director

FRANKLIN REGIONAL HOSPITAL, 15 Aiken Avenue, Franklin, NH, Zip 03235–1299; tel. 603/934–2060; Kevin Donovan, FACHE, President and Chief Executive Officer

NEW JERSEY

QUALCARE, INC.
242 Old New Brunswick Road, Piscataway, NJ, Zip 08854–3754; tel. 732/562–2800; Jerry Eisenberg, Network Contact

CAPITAL HEALTH MEDICAL CENTER-HOPEWELL, 1 Capital Way, Pennington, NJ, Zip 08534–2520; tel. 609/303–4000; Al Maghazehe, Ph.D., FACHE, President and Chief Executive Officer

CAREPOINT HEALTH CHRIST HOSPITAL, 176 Palisade Avenue, Jersey City, NJ, Zip 07306–1196, Mailing Address: 176 Palisades Avenue, Zip 07306–1196, tel. 201/795–8200; Marie Theresa Duffy, Chief Hospital Executive

CHILTON MEDICAL CENTER, 97 West Parkway, Pompton Plains, NJ, Zip 07444–1696; tel. 973/831–5000; Stephanie L. Schwartz, FACHE, Vice President AHS and President CMC

CLARA MAASS MEDICAL CENTER, One Clara Maass Drive, Belleville, NJ, Zip 07109–3557; tel. 973/450–2000; Mary Ellen Clyne, Ph.D., President and Chief Executive Officer

DEBORAH HEART AND LUNG CENTER, 200 Trenton Road, Browns Mills, NJ, Zip 08015–1705; tel. 609/893–6611; Joseph Chirichella, President and Chief Executive Officer

ENGLEWOOD HOSPITAL AND MEDICAL CENTER, 350 Engle Street, Englewood, NJ, Zip 07631–1898; tel. 201/894–3000; Warren Geller, President and Chief Executive Officer

HACKENSACK MERIDIAN HEALTH HACKENSACK UNIVERSITY MEDICAL CENTER, 30 Prospect Avenue, Hackensack, NJ, Zip 07601–1914; tel. 201/996–2000; Mark Sparta, President

HACKENSACK MERIDIAN HEALTH JFK MEDICAL CENTER, 65 James Street, Edison, NJ, Zip 8818; tel. 732/321–7000; Raymond F. Fredericks, Central Regional President

HACKENSACK MERIDIAN HEALTH OCEAN MEDICAL CENTER, 425 Jack Martin Boulevard, Brick Township, NJ, Zip 08724–7732; tel. 732/840–2200; Dean Q. Lin, FACHE, Regional President

HACKENSACK MERIDIAN HEALTH RARITAN BAY MEDICAL CENTER, 530 New Brunswick Avenue, Perth Amboy, NJ, Zip 08861–3654; tel. 732/442–3700; Thomas Shanahan, Chief Operating Officer

HACKENSACK MERIDIAN HEALTH RIVERVIEW MEDICAL CENTER, 1 Riverview Plaza, Red Bank, NJ, Zip 07701–1864; tel. 732/741–2700; Timothy J. Hogan, FACHE, President, RMC and BMC

HACKETTSTOWN MEDICAL CENTER, 651 Willow Grove Street, Hackettstown, NJ, Zip 07840–1799; tel. 908/852–5100; Joseph DiPaolo, FACHE, President

INSPIRA MEDICAL CENTER-VINELAND, 1505 West Sherman Avenue, Vineland, NJ, Zip 08360–6912; tel. 856/641–8000; John A. DiAngelo, President and Chief Executive Officer

PENN MEDICINE PRINCETON MEDICAL CENTER, One Plainsboro Road, Plainsboro, NJ, Zip 08536–1913; tel. 609/853–7100; Barry S. Rabner, President and Chief Executive Officer, Princeton Healthcare System

PIEDMONT MOUNTAINSIDE HOSPITAL, 1266 Highway 515 South, Jasper, GA, Zip 30143–4872; tel. 706/692–2441; Denise Ray, Chief Executive Officer

ROBERT WOOD JOHNSON UNIVERSITY HOSPITAL, 1 Robert Wood Johnson Place, New Brunswick, NJ, Zip 08901–1928; tel. 732/828–3000; John J. Gantner, President and Chief Executive Officer

SAINT MICHAEL'S MEDICAL CENTER, 111 Central Avenue, Newark, NJ, Zip 07102–1909; tel. 973/877–5350; Robert C. Iannaccone, JD, Chief Executive Officer

SALEM MEDICAL CENTER, 310 Woodstown Road, Salem, NJ, Zip 08079–2080; tel. 856/935–1000; Tammy Torres, R.N., MSN, Chief Executive Officer

ST. MARY'S GENERAL HOSPITAL, 350 Boulevard, Passaic, NJ, Zip 07055–2840; tel. 973/365–4300; Edward Condit, President and Chief Executive Officer

UNIVERSITY HOSPITAL, 150 Bergen Street, Newark, NJ, Zip 07103–2496; tel. 973/972–4300; Judith M. Persichilli, Acting President and Chief Executive Officer

VIRTUA MARLTON, 90 Brick Road, Marlton, NJ, Zip 08053–2177; tel. 856/355–6000; Dennis W. Pullin, FACHE, President and Chief Executive Officer

NEW MEXICO

NEW MEXICO RURAL HOSPITAL NETWORK
7471 Pan American Freeway NE, Albuquerque, NM, Zip 87109; tel. 505/346–0216; Stephen Stoddard, FACHE, Executive Director

ARTESIA GENERAL HOSPITAL, 702 North 13th Street, Artesia, NM, Zip 88210–1199; tel. 575/748–3333; Robert C. Tyk, Interim Chief Executive Officer

CIBOLA GENERAL HOSPITAL, 1016 East Roosevelt Avenue, Grants, NM, Zip 87020–2118; tel. 505/287–4446; Thomas Whelan, Chief Executive Officer

GUADALUPE COUNTY HOSPITAL, 117 Camino de Vida, Santa Rosa, NM, Zip 88435–2267; tel. 575/472–3417; Christina Campos, Administrator

HOLY CROSS HOSPITAL, 1397 Weimer Road, Taos, NM, Zip 87571–6253; tel. 575/758–8883; William D. Patten, Jr., Chief Executive Officer

MINERS' COLFAX MEDICAL CENTER, 200 Hospital Drive, Raton, NM, Zip 87740–2099; tel. 575/445–7700; Bo Beames, Interim Chief Executive Officer

NOR-LEA HOSPITAL DISTRICT, 1600 North Main Avenue, Lovington, NM, Zip 88260–2871; tel. 575/396–6611; David B. Shaw, Chief Executive Officer and Administrator

REHOBOTH MCKINLEY CHRISTIAN HEALTH CARE SERVICES, 1901 Red Rock Drive, Gallup, NM, Zip 87301–5683; tel. 505/863–7000; David Conejo, Chief Executive Officer

ROOSEVELT GENERAL HOSPITAL, 42121 U S Highway 70, Portales, NM, Zip 88130, Mailing Address: P.O. Box 868, Zip 88130–0868, tel. 575/359–1800; Kaye Green, FACHE, Chief Executive Officer

SIERRA VISTA HOSPITAL, 800 East Ninth Avenue, Truth or Consequences, NM, Zip 87901–1961; tel. 575/894–2111; David Faulkner, Interim Chief Executive Officer

UNION COUNTY GENERAL HOSPITAL, 300 Wilson Street, Clayton, NM, Zip 88415–3304, Mailing Address: P.O. Box 489, Zip 88415–0489, tel. 575/374–2585; Tammie Stump, R.N., Chief Executive Officer

NEW YORK

ARDENT SOLUTIONS, INC.
85 North Main Street, Suite 4, Wellsville, NY, Zip 14895–1254; tel. 585/593–5223; Carrie Whitwood, Executive Director

JONES MEMORIAL HOSPITAL, 191 North Main Street, Wellsville, NY, Zip 14895–1150, Mailing Address: P.O. Box 72, Zip 14895–0072, tel. 585/593–1100; Eva Benedict, R.N., President and Chief Executive Officer

ARNOT HEALTH
600 Roe Avenue, Elmira, NY, Zip 14905–1629; tel. 607/737–4100; Robert K. Lambert, M.D., FACHE, President and Chief Executive Officer

ARNOT OGDEN MEDICAL CENTER, 600 Roe Avenue, Elmira, NY, Zip 14905–1629; tel. 607/737–4100; Jonathan I. Lawrence, System Chief Operating Officer

IRA DAVENPORT MEMORIAL HOSPITAL, 7571 State Route 54, Bath, NY, Zip 14810–9590; tel. 607/776–8500; Elizabeth Weir, MSN, R.N., Site Administrator and Vice President of Nursing

ST. JOSEPH'S HOSPITAL, 555 St. Joseph's Boulevard, Elmira, NY, Zip 14901–3223; tel. 607/733–6541; Jonathan I. Lawrence, President and Chief Executive Officer

BASSETT HEALTHCARE NETWORK
1 Atwell Road, Cooperstown, NY, Zip 13326–1301; tel. 607/547–3456; William F. Streck, M.D., President and Chief Executive Officer

AURELIA OSBORN FOX MEMORIAL HOSPITAL, 1 Norton Avenue, Oneonta, NY, Zip 13820–2629; tel. 607/432–2000; Jeff Joyner, President

BASSETT MEDICAL CENTER, One Atwell Road, Cooperstown, NY, Zip 13326–1394; tel. 607/547–3456; William W. LeCates, M.D., President

COBLESKILL REGIONAL HOSPITAL, 178 Grandview Drive, Cobleskill, NY, Zip 12043–5144; tel. 518/254–3456; Eric H. Stein, FACHE, President

LITTLE FALLS HOSPITAL, 140 Burwell Street, Little Falls, NY, Zip 13365–1725; tel. 315/823–1000; Michael L. Ogden, President and Chief Executive Officer

O'CONNOR HOSPITAL, 460 Andes Road, State Route 28, Delhi, NY, Zip 13753–7407; tel. 607/746–0300; Scott Bonderoff, President

GREAT LAKES HEALTH SYSTEM OF WESTERN NEW YORK
726 Exchange Street, Suite 522, Buffalo, NY, Zip 14210–1485; tel. 716/859–8820; Jody Lomeo, Interim Chief Executive Officer

ERIE COUNTY MEDICAL CENTER, 462 Grider Street, Buffalo, NY, Zip 14215–3098; tel. 716/898–3000; Thomas J. Quatroche, Jr., President and Chief Executive Officer

KALEIDA HEALTH, 100 High Street, Buffalo, NY, Zip 14203–1154; tel. 716/859–5600; Jody Lomeo, Chief Executive Officer

LAKE ERIE REGIONAL HEALTH SYSTEM OF NEW YORK
529 Central Avenue, Dunkirk, NY Zip 14048–2514; tel. 716/366–1111; J. Gary Rhodes, FACHE, Interim Chief Executive Officer

BROOKS MEMORIAL HOSPITAL, 529 Central Avenue, Dunkirk, NY, Zip 14048–2599; tel. 716/366–1111; Mary E. LaRowe, FACHE, President and Chief Executive Officer

MOHAWK VALLEY HEALTH SYSTEM (MVHS)
1656 Champlin Avenue, Utica, NY, Zip 13502–4830; tel. 315/624–6002; Darlene Stromstad, FACHE, President and Chief Executive Officer

FAXTON ST. LUKE'S HEALTHCARE, 1656 Champlin Avenue, Utica, NY, Zip 13502–4830, Mailing Address: P.O. Box 479, Zip 13503–0479, tel. 315/624–6000; Scott H. Perra, FACHE, President and Chief Executive Officer

ST. ELIZABETH MEDICAL CENTER, 2209 Genesee Street, Utica, NY, Zip 13501–5999; tel. 315/798–8100; Scott H. Perra, FACHE, Chief Executive Officer

MOUNT SINAI NYU HEALTH NETWORK
One Gustave L. Levy Place, New York, NY, Zip 10029; tel. 212/659–8888; Arthur A. Klein, M.D., President

ENGLEWOOD HOSPITAL AND MEDICAL CENTER, 350 Engle Street, Englewood, NJ, Zip 07631–1898; tel. 201/894–3000; Warren Geller, President and Chief Executive Officer

HUDSON REGIONAL HOSPITAL, 55 Meadowlands Parkway, Secaucus, NJ, Zip 07094–2977; tel. 201/392–3100; Felicia Karsos, R.N., President and Chief Executive Officer

JAMES J. PETERS VETERANS AFFAIRS MEDICAL CENTER, 130 West Kingsbridge Road, Bronx, NY, Zip 10468–3904; tel. 718/584–9000; Erik Langhoff, M.D., Ph.D., Director

JERSEY CITY MEDICAL CENTER, 355 Grand Street, Jersey City, NJ, Zip 07302–4321; tel. 201/915–2000; Michael Prilutsky, President and Chief Executive Officer

MONTEFIORE ST. LUKE'S CORNWALL, 70 Dubois Street, Newburgh, NY, Zip 12550–4851; tel. 845/561–4400; Joan Cusack-McGuirk, President and Chief Executive Officer

MORRISTOWN MEDICAL CENTER, 100 Madison Avenue, Morristown, NJ, Zip 07960–6136; tel. 973/971–5000; Trish O'Keefe, Ph.D., R.N., President

MOUNT SINAI HOSPITAL, One Gustave L Levy Place, P.O. Box 1068, New York, NY, Zip 10029–0310; tel. 212/241–6500; David L. Reich, M.D., President and Chief Operating Officer

NYC HEALTH + HOSPITALS / ELMHURST, 79–01 Broadway, Elmhurst, NY, Zip 11373–1329; tel. 718/334–4000; Israel Rocha, Jr., Chief Executive Officer

NYC HEALTH + HOSPITALS / QUEENS, 82–68 164th Street, Jamaica, NY, Zip 11432–1104; tel. 718/883–3000; Christopher Roker, Chief Executive Officer

OVERLOOK MEDICAL CENTER, 99 Beauvoir Avenue, Summit, NJ, Zip 07901–3533; tel. 908/522–2000; Alan R. Lieber, President

PHELPS MEMORIAL HOSPITAL CENTER, 701 North Broadway, Sleepy Hollow, NY, Zip 10591–1020; tel. 914/366–3000; Daniel Blum, President

ST. JOHN'S RIVERSIDE HOSPITAL, 967 North Broadway, Yonkers, NY, Zip 10701–1399; tel. 914/964–4444; Ronald J. Corti, President and Chief Executive Officer

ST. JOSEPH'S UNIVERSITY MEDICAL CENTER, 703 Main Street, Paterson, NJ, Zip 07503–2691; tel. 973/754–2000; Kevin J. Slavin, FACHE, President and Chief Executive Officer

VASSAR BROTHERS MEDICAL CENTER, 45 Reade Place, Poughkeepsie, NY, Zip 12601–3947; tel. 845/454–8500; Ann McMackin, President

NEW YORK PRESBYTERIAN REGIONAL HOSPITAL NETWORK
525 East 68th Street, Box 182, New York, NY, Zip 10065–4870; tel. 212/746–3745; Steven J. Corwin, M.D., President and Chief Executive Officer

GRACIE SQUARE HOSPITAL, 420 East 76th Street, New York, NY, Zip 10021–3396; tel. 212/988–4400; David Wyman, President and Chief Executive Officer

NEW YORK COMMUNITY HOSPITAL, 2525 Kings Highway, Brooklyn, NY, Zip 11229–1705; tel. 718/692–5300; Barry Stern, President and Chief Executive Officer

NEWYORK-PRESBYTERIAN BROOKLYN METHODIST HOSPITAL, 506 Sixth Street, Brooklyn, NY, Zip 11215–3609; tel. 718/780–3000; Robert Guimento, President

RURAL HEALTH NETWORK OF OSWEGO COUNTY
10 George Street, Oswego, NY, Zip 13126; tel. 315/592–0827; Brian Coleman, Coordinator

OSWEGO HOSPITAL, 110 West Sixth Street, Oswego, NY, Zip 13126–2507; tel. 315/349–5511; Michael Harlovic, R.N., President and Chief Executive Officer

STELLARIS HEALTH
135 Bedford Rd, Armonk, NY, Zip 10504–1945; tel. 914/273–5454; Sharon A. Lucian, President and Chief Executive Officer

NORTHERN WESTCHESTER HOSPITAL, 400 East Main Street, Mount Kisco, NY, Zip 10549–3477, Mailing Address: 400 East Main Street, G-02, Zip 10549–3477, tel. 914/666–1200; Joel Seligman, President and Chief Executive Officer

PHELPS MEMORIAL HOSPITAL CENTER, 701 North Broadway, Sleepy Hollow, NY, Zip 10591–1020; tel. 914/366–3000; Daniel Blum, President

WHITE PLAINS HOSPITAL CENTER, 41 East Post Road, White Plains, NY, Zip 10601–4699; tel. 914/681–0600; Susan Fox, President and Chief Executive Officer

NORTH CAROLINA

COASTAL CAROLINAS HEALTH ALLIANCE
5305-M Wrightsville Avenue, Wilmington, NC, Zip 28403; tel. 910/332–8012; Yvonne Hughes, Chief Executive Officer

CAPE FEAR VALLEY – BLADEN COUNTY HOSPITAL, 501 South Poplar Street, Elizabethtown, NC, Zip 28337–9375, Mailing Address: P.O. Box 398, Zip 28337–0398, tel. 910/862–5100; Mark Cobb, Chief Executive Officer

COLUMBUS REGIONAL HEALTHCARE SYSTEM, 500 Jefferson Street, Whiteville, NC, Zip 28472–3634; tel. 910/642–8011; John E. Young, Interim Chief Executive Officer

J. ARTHUR DOSHER MEMORIAL HOSPITAL, 924 North Howe Street, Southport, NC, Zip 28461–3099; tel. 910/457–3800; Thomas R. Siemers, Chief Executive Officer

MCLEOD LORIS SEACOAST HOSPITAL, 3655 Mitchell Street, Loris, SC, Zip 29569–2827; tel. 843/716–7000; Edward D. Tinsley, III., Regional Administrator

MCLEOD REGIONAL MEDICAL CENTER, 555 East Cheves Street, Florence, SC, Zip 29506–2617, Mailing Address: P.O. Box 100551, Zip 29502–0551, tel. 843/777–2000; Robert L. Colones, President and Chief Executive Officer

NEW HANOVER REGIONAL MEDICAL CENTER, 2131 South 17th Street, Wilmington, NC, Zip 28401–7483, Mailing Address: P.O. Box 9000, Zip 28402–9000, tel. 910/343–7000; Andre Boyd, Sr., Executive Vice President, Hospital Division

PENDER MEMORIAL HOSPITAL, 507 East Freemont Street, Burgaw, NC, Zip 28425–5131; tel. 910/259–5451, Ruth Glaser, President

SAMPSON REGIONAL MEDICAL CENTER, 607 Beaman Street, Clinton, NC, Zip 28328–2697, Mailing Address: P.O. Box 260, Zip 28329–0260, tel. 910/592–8511; Shawn Howerton, M.D., Chief Executive Officer and President, Medical Staff

SCOTLAND HEALTH CARE SYSTEM, 500 Lauchwood Drive, Laurinburg, NC, Zip 28352–5599; tel. 910/291–7000; Gregory C. Wood, President and Chief Executive Officer

SOUTHEASTERN HEALTH, 300 West 27th Street, Lumberton, NC, Zip 28358–3075, Mailing Address: P.O. Box 1408, Zip 28359–1408, tel. 910/671–5000; Joann Anderson, President and Chief Executive Officer

VIDANT DUPLIN HOSPITAL, 401 North Main Street, Kenansville, NC, Zip 28349–8801, Mailing Address: P.O. Box 278, Zip 28349–0278, tel. 910/296–0941; Jay Briley, President

VIDANT MEDICAL CENTER, 2100 Stantonsburg Road, Greenville, NC, Zip 27834–2818, Mailing Address: P.O. Box 6028, Zip 27835–6028, tel. 252/847–4100; William Brian. Floyd, President

MISSION HEALTH SYSTEM
509 Biltmore Avenue, Asheville, NC, Zip 28801–4601; tel. 828/213–1111; Greg Lowe, President, North Carolina Division

ANGEL MEDICAL CENTER, 120 Riverview Street, Franklin, NC, Zip 28734–2612, Mailing Address: P.O. Box 1209, Zip 28744–0569, tel. 828/524–8411; Karen S. Gorby, R.N., MSN, FACHE, Chief Executive Officer and Chief Nursing Officer

ASHEVILLE SPECIALTY HOSPITAL, 428 Biltmore Avenue, 4th Floor, Asheville, NC, Zip 28801–4502; tel. 828/213–5400; Julie A. Dikos, President and Chief Executive Officer

BLUE RIDGE REGIONAL HOSPITAL, 125 Hospital Drive, Spruce Pine, NC, Zip 28777–3035; tel. 828/765–4201; Rebecca W. Carter, MSN, R.N., FACHE, President and Chief Nursing Officer

CAREPARTNERS HEALTH SERVICES, 68 Sweeten Creek Road, Asheville, NC, Zip 28803–2318, Mailing Address: P.O. Box 15025, Zip 28813–0025, tel. 828/277–4800; Tracy Buchanan, Chief Executive Officer and President

HIGHLANDS-CASHIERS HOSPITAL, 190 Hospital Drive, Highlands, NC, Zip 28741–7600, Mailing Address: P O Drawer 190, Zip 28741–0190, tel. 828/526–1200; Jacqueline Medland, MS, Ph.D., President and Chief Nursing Officer

MCDOWELL HOSPITAL, 430 Rankin Drive, Marion, NC, Zip 28752–6568, Mailing Address: P.O. Box 730, Zip 28752–0730, tel. 828/659–5000; Carol C. Wolfenbarger, FACHE, MSN, President

MISSION HOSPITAL, 509 Biltmore Avenue, Asheville, NC, Zip 28801–4690; tel. 828/213–1111; Jill Hoggard Green, Ph.D., R.N., President

TRANSYLVANIA REGIONAL HOSPITAL, 260 Hospital Drive, Brevard, NC, Zip 28712–3378; tel. 828/884–9111; Michele Pilon, President and Chief Nursing Officer

WNC HEALTH NETWORK, INC.
1200 Ridgefield Boulevard Suite 200, Asheville, NC, Zip 28806–2280; tel. 828/667–8220; Heather Gates, Executive Director

ADVENTHEALTH HENDERSONVILLE, 100 Hospital Drive, Hendersonville, NC, Zip 28792–5272; tel. 828/684–8501; Jimm Bunch, President and Chief Executive Officer

ANGEL MEDICAL CENTER, 120 Riverview Street, Franklin, NC, Zip 28734–2612, Mailing Address: P.O. Box 1209, Zip 28744–0569, tel. 828/524–8411; Karen S. Gorby, R.N., MSN, FACHE, Chief Executive Officer and Chief Nursing Officer

BLUE RIDGE REGIONAL HOSPITAL, 125 Hospital Drive, Spruce Pine, NC, Zip 28777–3035; tel. 828/765–4201; Rebecca W. Carter, MSN, R.N., FACHE, President and Chief Nursing Officer

CAREPARTNERS HEALTH SERVICES, 68 Sweeten Creek Road, Asheville, NC, Zip 28803–2318, Mailing Address: P.O. Box 15025, Zip 28813–0025, tel. 828/277–4800; Tracy Buchanan, Chief Executive Officer and President

CHARLES GEORGE VETERANS AFFAIRS MEDICAL CENTER, 1100 Tunnel Road, Asheville, NC, Zip 28805–2087; tel. 828/298–7911; Cynthia Breyfogle, FACHE, Director

CHEROKEE INDIAN HOSPITAL, 1 Hospital Road, Cherokee, NC, Zip 28719; tel. 828/497–9163; Casey Cooper, Chief Executive Officer

ERLANGER WESTERN CAROLINA HOSPITAL, 3990 U S Highway 64 East Alt, Murphy, NC, Zip 28906–7917; tel. 828/837–8161; Mark E. Kimball, Chief Executive Officer

HARRIS REGIONAL HOSPITAL, 68 Hospital Road, Sylva, NC, Zip 28779–2722; tel. 828/586–7000; Steve Heatherly, Chief Executive Officer

HAYWOOD REGIONAL MEDICAL CENTER, 262 Leroy George Drive, Clyde, NC, Zip 28721–7430; tel. 828/456–7311; Rod Harkleroad, R.N., Chief Executive Officer

HIGHLANDS-CASHIERS HOSPITAL, 190 Hospital Drive, Highlands, NC, Zip 28741–7600, Mailing Address: P O Drawer 190, Zip 28741–0190, tel. 828/526–1200; Jacqueline Medland, MS, Ph.D., President and Chief Nursing Officer

MARGARET R. PARDEE MEMORIAL HOSPITAL, 800 North Justice Street, Hendersonville, NC, Zip 28791–3410; tel. 828/696–1000; James M. Kirby, II., President and Chief Executive Officer

MCDOWELL HOSPITAL, 430 Rankin Drive, Marion, NC, Zip 28752–6568, Mailing Address: P.O. Box 730, Zip 28752–0730, tel. 828/659–5000; Carol C. Wolfenbarger, FACHE, MSN, President

MISSION HOSPITAL, 509 Biltmore Avenue, Asheville, NC, Zip 28801–4690; tel. 828/213–1111; Jill Hoggard Green, Ph.D., R.N., President

RUTHERFORD REGIONAL HEALTH SYSTEM, 288 South Ridgecrest Avenue, Rutherfordton, NC, Zip 28139–2838; tel. 828/286–5000; Rebecca Segal, Chief Executive Officer

ST. LUKE'S HOSPITAL, 101 Hospital Drive, Columbus, NC, Zip 28722–6418; tel. 828/894–3311; Michelle Fortune, R.N., Chief Executive Officer

SWAIN COMMUNITY HOSPITAL, 45 Plateau Street, Bryson City, NC, Zip 28713–4200; tel. 828/488–2155; Steve Heatherly, Chief Executive Officer

TRANSYLVANIA REGIONAL HOSPITAL, 260 Hospital Drive, Brevard, NC, Zip 28712–3378; tel. 828/884–9111; Michele Pilon, President and Chief Nursing Officer

NORTH DAKOTA

NORTHLAND HEALTHCARE ALLIANCE
2223 East Rosser Avenue, Bismarck, ND, Zip 58501–4949; tel. 701/250–0709; Timothy Cox, President

ASHLEY MEDICAL CENTER, 612 North Center Avenue, Ashley, ND, Zip 58413–7013, Mailing Address: P.O. Box 450, Zip 58413–0450, tel. 701/288–3433; Holly Wolff, Chief Executive Officer

CHI ST. ALEXIUS HEALTH – DICKINSON MEDICAL CENTER, 2500 Fairway Street, Dickinson, ND, Zip 58601–4399; tel. 701/456–4000; Reed Reyman, President

CHI ST. ALEXIUS HEALTH GARRISON, 407 Third Avenue SE, Garrison, ND, Zip 58540–7235; tel. 701/463–2275; Tod Graeber, Administrator

CHI ST. ALEXIUS HEALTH, 900 East Broadway, Bismarck, ND, Zip 58501–4586, Mailing Address: P.O. Box 5510, Zip 58506–5510, tel. 701/530–7000; Kurt Schley, Market Chief Executive Officer

COMMUNITY MEMORIAL HOSPITAL, 220 Fifth Avenue, Turtle Lake, ND, Zip 58575–4005, Mailing Address: P.O. Box 280, Zip 58575–0280, tel. 701/448–2331; Tod Graeber, Administrator

LINTON HOSPITAL, 518 North Broadway, Linton, ND, Zip 58552–7308, Mailing Address: P.O. Box 850, Zip 58552–0850, tel. 701/254–4511; Robert O. Black, Chief Executive Officer

MCKENZIE COUNTY HEALTHCARE SYSTEM, 516 North Main Street, Watford City, ND, Zip 58854–7310; tel. 701/842–3000; Daniel R. Kelly, Chief Executive Officer

MOBRIDGE REGIONAL HOSPITAL, 1401 Tenth Avenue West, Mobridge, SD, Zip 57601–1106, Mailing Address: P.O. Box 580, Zip 57601–0580, tel. 605/845–3692; John J. Ayoub, FACHE, Chief Executive Officer

PRESENTATION MEDICAL CENTER, 213 Second Avenue NE, Rolla, ND, Zip 58367–7153, Mailing Address: P.O. Box 759, Zip 58367–0759, tel. 701/477–3161; Chris Albertson, Chief Executive Officer

SAKAKAWEA MEDICAL CENTER, 510 Eighth Avenue NE, Hazen, ND, Zip 58545–4637; tel. 701/748–2225; Darrold Bertsch, Chief Executive Officer

SOUTHWEST HEALTHCARE SERVICES, 802 2nd Street Northwest, Bowman, ND, Zip 58623–4483, Mailing Address: P O Drawer 'C', Zip 58623, tel. 701/523–5265; Jerry Wiesner, Administrator and Chief Executive Officer

WEST RIVER REGIONAL MEDICAL CENTER, 1000 Highway 12, Hettinger, ND, Zip 50639–7530; tel. 701/567–4561; Matthew Shahan, Chief Executive Officer

WISHEK COMMUNITY HOSPITAL AND CLINICS, 1007 Fourth Avenue South, Wishek, ND, Zip 58495–7527, Mailing Address: P.O. Box 647, Zip 58495–0647, tel. 701/452–2326; Beverly Vilhauer, Chief Executive Officer

SANFORD HEALTH NETWORK – FARGO MARKET
736 Broadway North, Route 1000, Fargo, ND, Zip 58102–4421; tel. 701/234–6951; Bruce Vlessman, Vice President Operations

BOZEMAN HEALTH, 915 Highland Boulevard, Bozeman, MT, Zip 59715–6902; tel. 406/585–5000; John Hill, President and Chief Executive Officer

JAMESTOWN REGIONAL MEDICAL CENTER, 2422 20th Street SW, Jamestown, ND, Zip 58401–6201; tel. 701/252–1050; Michael Delfs, President and Chief Executive Officer

KITTSON MEMORIAL HEALTHCARE CENTER, 1010 South Birch Street, Hallock, MN, Zip 56728–4215, Mailing Address: P.O. Box 700, Zip 56728–0700, tel. 218/843–3612; Ashley Rivera, Chief Financial Officer and Chief Executive Officer

LIBERTY MEDICAL CENTER, 315 West Madison Avenue, Chester, MT, Zip 59522, Mailing Address: P.O. Box 705, Zip 59522–0705, tel. 406/759–5181; Matthew Waller, Chief Executive Officer

MAHNOMEN HEALTH CENTER, 414 West Jefferson Avenue, Mahnomen, MN, Zip 56557–4912, Mailing Address: P.O. Box 396, Zip 56557–0396, tel. 218/935–2511; Dale K. Kruger, Chief Executive Officer

MCKENZIE COUNTY HEALTHCARE SYSTEM, 516 North Main Street, Watford City, ND, Zip 58854–7310; tel. 701/842–3000; Daniel R. Kelly, Chief Executive Officer

NORTHWOOD DEACONESS HEALTH CENTER, 4 North Park Street, Northwood, ND, Zip 58267–4102, Mailing Address: P.O. Box 190, Zip 58267–0190, tel. 701/587–6060; Pete Antonson, Chief Executive Officer

PERHAM HEALTH, 1000 Coney Street West, Perham, MN, Zip 56573–1108; tel. 218/347–4500; Chuck Hofius, Chief Executive Officer

RIVERVIEW HEALTH, 323 South Minnesota Street, Crookston, MN, Zip 56716–1601; tel. 218/281–9200; Carrie Michalski, President and Chief Executive Officer

SANFORD BAGLEY MEDICAL CENTER, 203 Fourth Street NW, Bagley, MN, Zip 56621–8307; tel. 218/694–6501; Robert Belanger, Administrator Director

SANFORD BEMIDJI MEDICAL CENTER, 1300 Anne Street NW, Bemidji, MN, Zip 56601–5103; tel. 218/751–5430; Bryan Nermoe, Executive Vice President

SANFORD BISMARCK, 300 North Seventh Street, Bismarck, ND, Zip 58501–4439, Mailing Address: P.O. Box 5525, Zip 58506–5525, tel. 701/323–6000; Michael LeBeau, President

SANFORD MAYVILLE MEDICAL CENTER, 42 Sixth Avenue SE, Mayville, ND, Zip 58257–1598; tel. 701/786–3800; Jac McTaggart, Chief Executive Officer

SANFORD MEDICAL CENTER THIEF RIVER FALLS, 3001 Sanford Parkway, Thief River Falls, MN, Zip 56701–2700; tel. 218/681–4747; Brian J. Carlson, FACHE, Executive Director

SANFORD THIEF RIVER FALLS BEHAVIORAL HEALTH CENTER, 120 LaBree Avenue South, Thief River Falls, MN, Zip 56701–2819, Mailing Address: 3001 Sanford Parkway, Zip 56701–2819, tel. 218/683–4349; Brian J. Carlson, FACHE, Chief Executive Officer

SANFORD WHEATON MEDICAL CENTER, 401 12th Street North, Wheaton, MN, Zip 56296–1099; tel. 320/563–8226; JoAnn M. Foltz, R.N., Chief Executive Officer

SIDNEY HEALTH CENTER, 216 14th Avenue SW, Sidney, MT, Zip 59270–3586; tel. 406/488–2100; Jennifer Doty, Chief Executive Officer

OHIO

CLEVELAND HEALTH NETWORK
6000 West Creek Road, Suite 20, Independence, OH, Zip 44131–2139; tel. 216/986–1100; Fred M. DeGrandis, President

AKRON CHILDREN'S HOSPITAL, One Perkins Square, Akron, OH, Zip 44308–1063; tel. 330/543–1000; William H. Considine, President

ASHTABULA COUNTY MEDICAL CENTER, 2420 Lake Avenue, Ashtabula, OH, Zip 44004–4954; tel. 440/997–2262; Michael J. Habowski, President and Chief Executive Officer

CLEVELAND CLINIC CHILDREN'S HOSPITAL FOR REHABILITATION, 2801 Martin Luther King Jr Drive, Cleveland, OH, Zip 44104–3865; tel. 216/448–6400; Michelle Marks, D.O., Medical Director

CLEVELAND CLINIC FAIRVIEW HOSPITAL, 18101 Lorain Avenue, Cleveland, OH, Zip 44111–5656; tel. 216/476–7000; Neil Smith, D.O., President

CLEVELAND CLINIC, MEDINA HOSPITAL, 1000 East Washington Street, Medina, OH, Zip 44256–2170; tel. 330/725–1000; Richard K. Shewbridge, President

CLEVELAND CLINIC, 9500 Euclid Avenue, Cleveland, OH, Zip 44195–5108; tel. 216/444–2200; Tomislav Mihaljevic, M.D., President and Chief Executive Officer

EUCLID HOSPITAL, 18901 Lake Shore Boulevard, Euclid, OH, Zip 44119–1090; tel. 216/531–9000; Daniel Napierkowski, M.D., President

FIRELANDS REGIONAL HEALTH SYSTEM, 1111 Hayes Avenue, Sandusky, OH, Zip 44870–3323; tel. 419/557–7400; Daniel J. Moncher, Interim President and Chief Executive Officer

FISHER-TITUS MEDICAL CENTER, 272 Benedict Avenue, Norwalk, OH, Zip 44857–2374; tel. 419/668–8101; Brent Burkey, M.D., President and Chief Executive Officer

HILLCREST HOSPITAL, 6780 Mayfield Road, Cleveland, OH, Zip 44124–2203; tel. 440/312–4500; Richard Parker, M.D., President, Hillcrest Hospital

LUTHERAN HOSPITAL, 1730 West 25th Street, Cleveland, OH, Zip 44113–3170; tel. 216/696–4300; Donald A. Malone, Jr., President

MARYMOUNT HOSPITAL, 12300 McCracken Road, Garfield Heights, OH, Zip 44125–2975; tel. 216/581–0500; Daniel Napierkowski, M.D., President

METROHEALTH MEDICAL CENTER, 2500 MetroHealth Drive, Cleveland, OH, Zip 44109–1998; tel. 216/778–7800; Akram Boutros, M.D., FACHE, President and Chief Executive Officer

SOUTH POINTE HOSPITAL, 20000 Harvard Road, Warrensville Heights, OH, Zip 44122–6805; tel. 216/491–6000; Margaret McKenzie, M.D., President

SUMMA HEALTH SYSTEM, 525 East Market Street, Akron, OH, Zip 44304–1619; tel. 330/375–3000; David Custodio, M.D., President Summa Health System Akron

UNIVERSITY HOSPITALS ELYRIA MEDICAL CENTER, 630 East River Street, Elyria, OH, Zip 44035–5902; tel. 440/329–7500; Kristi M. Sink, President

UNIVERSITY HOSPITALS PARMA MEDICAL CENTER, 7007 Powers Boulevard, Parma, OH, Zip 44129–5495; tel. 440/743–3000; Peter U. Bergmann, President

WESTERN RESERVE HOSPITAL, 1900 23rd Street, Cuyahoga Falls, OH, Zip 44223–1499; tel. 330/971–7000; Robert Kent, D.O., President and Chief Executive Officer

MERCY HEALTH – SOUTHWEST OHIO
4600 McAuley Place, Cincinnati, OH, Zip 45242; tel. 513/981–6000; John M. Starcher, President and Chief Executive Officer

MERCY HEALTH – ANDERSON HOSPITAL, 7500 State Road, Cincinnati, OH, Zip 45255–2492; tel. 513/624–4500; Ken James, President and Chief Executive Officer of East Market

MERCY HEALTH – CLERMONT HOSPITAL, 3000 Hospital Drive, Batavia, OH, Zip 45103–1921; tel. 513/732–8200; Justin Krueger, FACHE, President

MERCY HEALTH – FAIRFIELD HOSPITAL, 3000 Mack Road, Fairfield, OH, Zip 45014–5335; tel. 513/870–7000; Thomas S. Urban, FACHE, President and Chief Executive Officer

MERCY HEALTH – WEST HOSPITAL, 3300 Mercy Health Boulevard, Cincinnati, OH, Zip 45211–1103; tel. 513/215–5000; Michael Kramer, Chief Executive Officer

THE JEWISH HOSPITAL – MERCY HEALTH, 4777 East Galbraith Road, Cincinnati, OH, Zip 45236–2725; tel. 513/686–3000; Patricia Davis-Hagens, R.N., Central Market Leader and President

PREMIER HEALTH
110 North Main Street, Suite 390, Dayton, OH, Zip 45402–3720; tel. 937/499–9401; Mary H. Boosalis, President and Chief Executive Officer

ATRIUM MEDICAL CENTER, One Medical Center Drive, Middletown, OH, Zip 45005–1066; tel. 513/424–2111; Michael Uhl, President

MIAMI VALLEY HOSPITAL, One Wyoming Street, Dayton, OH, Zip 45409–2793; tel. 937/208–8000; Michael J. Maiberger, President

UPPER VALLEY MEDICAL CENTER, 3130 North County Road 25A, Troy, OH, Zip 45373–1309; tel. 937/440–4000; Thomas Parker, President

THE OHIO STATE HEALTH NETWORK
660 Ackerman Road, Suite 601F, Columbus, OH, Zip 43202–4500; tel. 614/293–4425; Thomas Blincoe, Executive Director

AVITA ONTARIO HOSPITAL, 715 Richland Mall, Ontario, OH, Zip 44906–3802; tel. 567/307–7666; Jerome Morasko, President and Chief Executive Officer

BARNESVILLE HOSPITAL, 639 West Main Street, Barnesville, OH, Zip 43713–1039, Mailing Address: P.O. Box 309, Zip 43713–0309, tel. 740/425–3941; David D. Phillips, Chief Executive Officer and Administrator

BUCYRUS HOSPITAL, 629 North Sandusky Avenue, Bucyrus, OH, Zip 44820–1821; tel. 419/562–4677; Jerome Morasko, Chief Executive Officer

FAYETTE COUNTY MEMORIAL HOSPITAL, 1430 Columbus Avenue, Washington Court House, OH, Zip 43160–1791; tel. 740/335–1210; D Michael. Diener, Chief Executive Officer

GALION HOSPITAL, 269 Portland Way South, Galion, OH, Zip 44833–2399; tel. 419/468–4841; Jerome Morasko, President and Chief Executive Officer

HIGHLAND DISTRICT HOSPITAL, 1275 North High Street, Hillsboro, OH, Zip 45133–8273; tel. 937/393–6100; Randal P. Lennartz, CPA, President and Chief Executive Officer

HOCKING VALLEY COMMUNITY HOSPITAL, 601 State Route 664 North, Logan, OH, Zip 43138–8541, Mailing Address: P.O. Box 966, Zip 43138–0966, tel. 740/380–8000; Stacey Gabriel, R.N., President and Chief Executive Officer

MADISON HEALTH, 210 North Main Street, London, OH, Zip 43140–1115; tel. 740/845–7000; Dana E. Engle, Chief Executive Officer

MARY RUTAN HOSPITAL, 205 Palmer Avenue, Bellefontaine, OH, Zip 43311–2281; tel. 937/592–4015; Mandy C. Goble, President and Chief Executive Officer

MERCER HEALTH, 800 West Main Street, Coldwater, OH, Zip 45828–1698; tel. 419/678–2341; Lisa R. Klenke, R.N., Chief Executive Officer

OHIO STATE UNIVERSITY WEXNER MEDICAL CENTER, 410 West 10th Avenue, Columbus, OH, Zip 43210–1240; tel. 614/293–8000; David P. McQuaid, FACHE, Chief Operating Officer

WAYNE HEALTHCARE, 835 Sweitzer Street, Greenville, OH, Zip 45331–1077; tel. 937/548–1141; Wayne G. Deschambeau, President and Chief Executive Officer

WILSON MEMORIAL HOSPITAL, 915 West Michigan Street, Sidney, OH, Zip 45365–2491; tel. 937/498–2311; Duane Francis, Interim Chief Executive Officer

WYANDOT MEMORIAL HOSPITAL, 885 North Sandusky Avenue, Upper Sandusky, OH, Zip 43351–1098; tel. 419/294–4991; Ty Shaull, President and Chief Executive Officer

TRIHEALTH
619 Oak Street, Cincinnati, OH, Zip 45206; tel. 513/569–6507; Mark C. Clement, President and Chief Executive Officer

BETHESDA NORTH HOSPITAL, 10500 Montgomery Road, Cincinnati, OH, Zip 45242–4402; tel. 513/865–1111; Mark C. Clement, Chief Executive Officer

GOOD SAMARITAN HOSPITAL, 375 Dixmyth Avenue, Cincinnati, OH, Zip 45220–2489; tel. 513/862–1400; Jamie Easterling, Executive Director, Operations

MCCULLOUGH-HYDE MEMORIAL HOSPITAL/TRIHEALTH, 110 North Poplar Street, Oxford, OH, Zip 45056–1292; tel. 513/523–2111; Brett Kirkpatrick, Executive Director

TRIHEALTH EVENDALE HOSPITAL, 3155 Glendale Milford Road, Cincinnati, OH, Zip 45241–3134; tel. 513/454–2222; Kelvin Hanger, Chief Executive Officer

OKLAHOMA

ALLIANCEHEALTH OKLAHOMA
5300 North Grand Boulevard, Oklahoma City, OK, Zip 73112–5647; tel. 405/815–3900; Clay Franklin, Market Chief Executive Officer

ALLIANCEHEALTH CLINTON, 100 North 30th Street, Clinton, OK, Zip 73601–3117; tel. 580/323–2363; Landon E. Hise, Chief Executive Officer

ALLIANCEHEALTH DURANT, 1800 University Boulevard, Durant, OK, Zip 74701–3006, Mailing Address: P.O. Box 1207, Zip 74702–1207, tel. 580/924–3080; Charles Hall, Interim Chief Executive Officer

ALLIANCEHEALTH MADILL, 901 South Fifth Avenue, Madill, OK, Zip 73446–3640, Mailing Address: P.O. Box 827, Zip 73446–0827, tel. 580/795–3384; Charles Hall, Interim Chief Executive Officer

ALLIANCEHEALTH MIDWEST, 2825 Parklawn Drive, Midwest City, OK, Zip 73110–4258; tel. 405/610–4411; Clay Franklin, Chief Executive Officer

ALLIANCEHEALTH PONCA CITY, 1900 North 14th Street, Ponca City, OK, Zip 74601–2099; tel. 580/765–3321; Christopher Mendoza, Chief Executive Officer

ALLIANCEHEALTH SEMINOLE, 2401 Wrangler Boulevard, Seminole, OK, Zip 74868–1917; tel. 405/303–4000; Damon Brown, Interim Chief Executive Officer

ALLIANCEHEALTH WOODWARD, 900 17th Street, Woodward, OK, Zip 73801–2448; tel. 580/256–5511; Landon E. Hise, Interim Chief Executive Officer

INTEGRIS DEACONESS, 5501 North Portland Avenue, Oklahoma City, OK, Zip 73112–2099; tel. 405/604–6000; Rex Van Meter, President

MERCY HEALTH SYSTEM OF OKLAHOMA
4300 West Memorial Road, Oklahoma City, OK, Zip 73120–8304; tel. 405/752–3756; Diana Smalley, President and Chief Executive Officer

ARBUCKLE MEMORIAL HOSPITAL, 2011 West Broadway Street, Sulphur, OK, Zip 73086–4221, Mailing Address: P.O. Box 1109, Zip 73086–8109, tel. 580/622–2161; Jeremy A. Jones, Chief Executive Officer

MERCY HEALTH LOVE COUNTY, 300 Wanda Street, Marietta, OK, Zip 73448–1200; tel. 580/276–3347; Richard Barker, Administrator and Chief Executive Officer

MERCY HOSPITAL ADA, 430 North Monte Vista, Ada, OK, Zip 74820–4610; tel. 580/332–2323; Terence Farrell, President

MERCY HOSPITAL ARDMORE, 1011 14th Avenue NW, Ardmore, OK, Zip 73401–1828; tel. 580/223–5400; Daryle Voss, FACHE, President and Chief Executive Officer

MERCY HOSPITAL HEALDTON, 3462 Hospital Road, Healdton, OK, Zip 73438–6124, Mailing Address: P.O. Box 928, Zip 73438–0928, tel. 580/229–0701; Nichole Barrett, R.N., Interim Administrator

MERCY HOSPITAL KINGFISHER, 1000 Hospital Cirle, Kingfisher, OK, Zip 73750–5002, Mailing Address: P.O. Box 59, Zip 73750–0059, tel. 405/375–3141; Brian Denton, Administrator

MERCY HOSPITAL LOGAN COUNTY, 200 South Academy Road, Guthrie, OK, Zip 73044–8727, Mailing Address: P.O. Box 1017, Zip 73044–1017, tel. 405/202–6700, Bobby Stitt, R.N., Administrator

MERCY HOSPITAL OKLAHOMA CITY, 4300 West Memorial Road, Oklahoma City, OK, Zip 73120–8362; tel. 405/755–1515; Jim Gebhart, Jr., FACHE, President

MERCY HOSPITAL TISHOMINGO, 1000 South Byrd Street, Tishomingo, OK, Zip 73460–3299; tel. 580/371–2327; Lori McMillin, Administrator

MERCY HOSPITAL WATONGA, 500 North Clarence Nash Boulevard, Watonga, OK, Zip 73772–2945, Mailing Address: P.O. Box 370, Zip 73772–0370, tel. 580/623–7211; Bobby Stitt, R.N., Administrator

MERCY REHABILITATION HOSPITAL OKLAHOMA CITY, 5401 West Memorial Rd, Oklahoma City, OK, Zip 73142–2026; tel. 405/752–3935; Thomas Elliott, President

OKLAHOMA HEART HOSPITAL SOUTH CAMPUS, 5200 East I-240 Service Road, Oklahoma City, OK, Zip 73135; tel. 405/628–6000; John Harvey, M.D., Chief Executive Officer

OKLAHOMA HEART HOSPITAL, 4050 West Memorial Road, Oklahoma City, OK, Zip 73120–8382; tel. 405/608–3200; John Harvey, M.D., Chief Executive Officer

OKLAHOMA STATE UNIVERSITY MEDICAL CENTER, 744 West Ninth Street, Tulsa, OK, Zip 74127–9020; tel. 918/599–1000; Matthew Adams, Administrator

SEILING REGIONAL MEDICAL CENTER, Highway 60 NE, Seiling, OK, Zip 73663, Mailing Address: P.O. Box 720, Zip 73663–0720, tel. 580/377–1005; Rachel Farrow, Interim Chief Executive Officer

PENNSYLVANIA

ALLEGHENY HEALTH NETWORK
30 Isabella Street, Suite 300, Pittsburgh, PA, Zip 15212–5862; tel. 412/330–2400; Cynthia Hundorfean, President and Chief Executive Officer

ALLEGHENY GENERAL HOSPITAL, 320 East North Avenue, Pittsburgh, PA, Zip 15212–4756; tel. 412/359–3131; Jeffrey Cohen, M.D., President

ALLEGHENY VALLEY HOSPITAL, 1301 Carlisle Street, Natrona Heights, PA, Zip 15065–1152; tel. 724/224–5100; Jeffrey Carlson, Interim Chief Executive Officer

CANONSBURG HOSPITAL, 100 Medical Boulevard, Canonsburg, PA, Zip 15317–9762; tel. 724/745–6100; Louise Urban, R.N., President and Chief Executive Officer

FORBES HOSPITAL, 2570 Haymaker Road, Monroeville, PA, Zip 15146–3513; tel. 412/858–2000; Mark Rubino, M.D., President

JEFFERSON HOSPITAL, 565 Coal Valley Road, Jefferson Hills, PA, Zip 15025–3703, Mailing Address: Box 18119, Pittsburgh, Zip 15236–0119, tel. 412/469–5000; Louise Urban, R.N., President and Chief Executive Officer

SAINT VINCENT HOSPITAL, 232 West 25th Street, Erie, PA, Zip 16544–0002; tel. 814/452–5000; Christopher Clark, D.O., President and Chief Executive Officer

WEST PENN HOSPITAL, 4800 Friendship Avenue, Pittsburgh, PA, Zip 15224–1722; tel. 412/578–5000; Ronald J. Andro, R.N., MS, President and Chief Executive Officer

WESTFIELD MEMORIAL HOSPITAL, 189 East Main Street, Westfield, NY, Zip 14787–1195; tel. 716/326–4921; Henry J. Ward, Interim President

BRIDGES HEALTH PARTNERS
500 Commonwealth Drive, Warrendale, PA, Zip 15086–7516; tel. 724/300–8105

BUTLER HEALTH SYSTEM, 1 Hospital Way, Butler, PA, Zip 16001–4697; tel. 724/283–6666; Ken DeFurio, President and Chief Executive Officer

EXCELA FRICK HOSPITAL, 508 South Church Street, Mount Pleasant, PA, Zip 15666–1790; tel. 724/547–1500; Michael D. Busch, Executive Vice President and Chief Operating Officer

EXCELA HEALTH WESTMORELAND HOSPITAL, 532 West Pittsburgh Street, Greensburg, PA, Zip 15601–2282; tel. 724/832–4000; Robert Rogalski, Chief Executive Officer

EXCELA LATROBE AREA HOSPITAL, One Mellon Way, Latrobe, PA, Zip 15650–1096; tel. 724/537–1000; Michael D. Busch, Executive Vice President and Chief Operating Officer

ST. CLAIR HOSPITAL, 1000 Bower Hill Road, Pittsburgh, PA, Zip 15243–1873; tel. 412/942–4000; James M. Collins, President and Chief Executive Officer

WASHINGTON HEALTH SYSTEM GREENE, 350 Bonar Avenue, Waynesburg, PA, Zip 15370–1608; tel. 724/627–3101; Terry Wiltrout, President

WASHINGTON HOSPITAL, 155 Wilson Avenue, Washington, PA, Zip 15301–3398; tel. 724/225–7000; Gary B. Weinstein, President and Chief Executive Officer

COMMONWEALTH HEALTH
575 North River Street, Wilkes Barre, PA, Zip 18764–0999; tel. 570/829–8111; Cornelio R. Catena, Market President and Chief Executive Officer, Wilkes-Barre General Hospital

BERWICK HOSPITAL CENTER, 701 East 16th Street, Berwick, PA, Zip 18603–2397; tel. 570/759–5000; Thomas Neal, Chief Executive Officer

FIRST HOSPITAL WYOMING VALLEY, 562 Wyoming Avenue, Kingston, PA, Zip 18704–3721; tel. 570/552–3900; Greg Shannon, Chief Executive Officer

MOSES TAYLOR HOSPITAL, 700 Quincy Avenue, Scranton, PA, Zip 18510–1724; tel. 570/770–5000; Ronald Ziobro, Interim Chief Executive Officer

REGIONAL HOSPITAL OF SCRANTON, 746 Jefferson Avenue, Scranton, PA, Zip 18510–1624; tel. 570/348–7100; Ronald Ziobro, Interim Chief Executive Officer

TYLER MEMORIAL HOSPITAL, 5950 State Route 6, Tunkhannock, PA, Zip 18657–7905; tel. 570/836–2161; Ann Marie. Stevens, R.N., Chief Executive Officer

WILKES-BARRE GENERAL HOSPITAL, 575 North River Street, Wilkes-Barre, PA, Zip 18764–0001; tel. 570/829–8111; Cornelio R. Catena, President and Chief Executive Officer

PENN HIGHLANDS HEALTHCARE
204 Hospital Avenue, DuBois, PA, Zip 15801–0447; tel. 814/375–0400; Steven M. Fontaine, System Chief Executive Officer

PENN HIGHLANDS BROOKVILLE, 100 Hospital Road, Brookville, PA, Zip 15825–1367; tel. 814/849–2312; Julianne Peer, President

PENN HIGHLANDS CLEARFIELD, 809 Turnpike Avenue, Clearfield, PA, Zip 16830–1232, Mailing Address: P.O. Box 992, Zip 16830–0992, tel. 814/765–5341; Rhonda Halstead, President

PENN HIGHLANDS DUBOIS, 100 Hospital Avenue, DuBois, PA, Zip 15801–1440, Mailing Address: P.O. Box 447, Zip 15801–0447, tel. 814/371–2200; John Sutika, President

PENN HIGHLANDS ELK, 763 Johnsonburg Road, Saint Marys, PA, Zip 15857–3498; tel. 814/788–8000; Bradley Chapman, President

VANTAGE HEALTHCARE NETWORK, INC.
18282 Technology Drive, Suite 202, Meadville, PA, Zip 16335–8378; tel. 814/337–0000; David Petrarca, Director Retail Operations

BRADFORD REGIONAL MEDICAL CENTER, 116 Interstate Parkway, Bradford, PA, Zip 16701–1036; tel. 814/368–4143; Timothy J. Finan, FACHE, President and Chief Executive Officer

CLARION HOSPITAL, One Hospital Drive, Clarion, PA, Zip 16214–8501; tel. 814/226–9500; Steven T. Davis, Chief Executive Officer

MEADVILLE MEDICAL CENTER, 751 Liberty Street, Meadville, PA, Zip 16335–2559; tel. 814/333–5000; Philip E. Pandolph, FACHE, Chief Executive Officer

PENN HIGHLANDS BROOKVILLE, 100 Hospital Road, Brookville, PA, Zip 15825–1367; tel. 814/849–2312; Julianne Peer, President

PENN HIGHLANDS ELK, 763 Johnsonburg Road, Saint Marys, PA, Zip 15857–3498; tel. 814/788–8000; Bradley Chapman, President

PUNXSUTAWNEY AREA HOSPITAL, 81 Hillcrest Drive, Punxsutawney, PA, Zip 15767–2616; tel. 814/938–1800; Daniel D. Blough, Jr., Chief Executive Officer

TITUSVILLE AREA HOSPITAL, 406 West Oak Street, Titusville, PA, Zip 16354–1404; tel. 814/827–1851; Lee Clinton, FACHE, Chief Executive Officer

UPMC BEDFORD MEMORIAL, 10455 Lincoln Highway, Everett, PA, Zip 15537–7046; tel. 814/623–6161; Jan E. Fisher, President

UPMC HAMOT, 201 State Street, Erie, PA, Zip 16550–0002; tel. 814/877–6000; David Gibbons, President

UPMC JAMESON, 1211 Wilmington Avenue, New Castle, PA, Zip 16105–2516; tel. 724/658–9001; Donald R. Owrey, President

UPMC KANE, 4372 Route 6, Kane, PA, Zip 16735–3060; tel. 814/837–8585; Mark Papalia, President

UPMC MCKEESPORT, 1500 Fifth Avenue, McKeesport, PA, Zip 15132–2422; tel. 412/664–2000; Mark O'Hern, President

UPMC NORTHWEST, 100 Fairfield Drive, Seneca, PA, Zip 16346–2130; tel. 814/676–7600; Brian Durniok, President

UPMC PASSAVANT, 9100 Babcock Boulevard, Pittsburgh, PA, Zip 15237–5815; tel. 412/748–6700; Susan E. Hoolahan, R.N., MSN, President

UPMC ST. MARGARET, 815 Freeport Road, Pittsburgh, PA, Zip 15215–3301; tel. 412/784–4000; David J. Patton, President

WARREN GENERAL HOSPITAL, Two Crescent Park West, Warren, PA, Zip 16365–0068, Mailing Address: P.O. Box 68, Zip 16365–0068, tel. 814/723–4973; Richard Allen, Chief Executive Officer

SOUTH DAKOTA

REGIONAL HEALTH
353 Fairmont Boulevard, Rapid City, SD, Zip 57701–7375; tel. 605/719–1000; Brent R. Phillips, President and Chief Executive Officer

CUSTER REGIONAL HOSPITAL, 1039 Montgomery Street, Custer, SD, Zip 57730–1397; tel. 605/673–2229; Mark C. Schmidt, President

LEAD-DEADWOOD REGIONAL HOSPITAL, 61 Charles Street, Deadwood, SD, Zip 57732–1303; tel. 605/717–6000; Mark C. Schmidt, President

PHILIP HEALTH SERVICES, 503 West Pine Street, Philip, SD, Zip 57567–3300, Mailing Address: P.O. Box 790, Zip 57567–0790, tel. 605/859–2511; Jeremy Schultes, Administrator and Chief Executive Officer

RAPID CITY REGIONAL HOSPITAL, 353 Fairmont Boulevard, Rapid City, SD, Zip 57701–7393, Mailing Address: P.O. Box 6000, Zip 57709–6000, tel. 605/755–1000; John Pierce, Acting President

SPEARFISH REGIONAL HOSPITAL, 1440 North Main Street, Spearfish, SD, Zip 57783–1504; tel. 605/644–4000; Thomas Worsley, Chief Executive Officer

STURGIS REGIONAL HOSPITAL, 949 Harmon Street, Sturgis, SD, Zip 57785–2452; tel. 605/720–2400; Mark Schulte, FACHE, President

WESTON COUNTY HEALTH SERVICES, 1124 Washington Boulevard, Newcastle, WY, Zip 82701–2972; tel. 307/746–4491; Maureen K. Cadwell, Chief Executive Officer

SANFORD HEALTH NETWORK – SIOUX FALLS MARKET
1305 West 18th Street, Route 6145, Sioux Falls, SD, Zip 57105–0401; tel. 605/328–5513; Eric C. Hilmoe, Vice President Operations

COMMUNITY MEMORIAL HOSPITAL, 809 Jackson Street, Burke, SD, Zip 57523–2065, Mailing Address: P.O. Box 319, Zip 57523–0319, tel. 605/775–2621; Mistie Sachtjen, Chief Executive Officer

DOUGLAS COUNTY MEMORIAL HOSPITAL, 708 Eighth Street, Armour, SD, Zip 57313–2102; tel. 605/724–2159; Heath Brouwer, Administrator

MURRAY COUNTY MEDICAL CENTER, 2042 Juniper Avenue, Slayton, MN, Zip 56172–1017; tel. 507/836–6111; Michael Ladevich, FACHE, Interim Chief Executive Officer

ORANGE CITY AREA HEALTH SYSTEM, 1000 Lincoln Circle SE, Orange City, IA, Zip 51041–1862; tel. 712/737–4984; Martin W. Guthmiller, Chief Executive Officer

ORTONVILLE AREA HEALTH SERVICES, 450 Eastvold Avenue, Ortonville, MN, Zip 56278–1133; tel. 320/839–2502; David Rogers, Chief Executive Officer

PIONEER MEMORIAL HOSPITAL AND HEALTH SERVICES, 315 North Washington Street, Viborg, SD, Zip 57070–2002, Mailing Address: P.O. Box 368, Zip 57070–0368, tel. 605/326–5161; Thomas V. Richter, Chief Executive Officer

SANFORD ABERDEEN MEDICAL CENTER, 2905 3rd Avenue SE, Aberdeen, SD, Zip 57401–5420; tel. 605/626–4200; Ashley M. Erickson, Chief Executive Officer

SANFORD CANBY MEDICAL CENTER, 112 St Olaf Avenue South, Canby, MN, Zip 56220–1433; tel. 507/223–7277; Lori Sisk, R.N., Chief Executive Officer

SANFORD CANTON-INWOOD MEDICAL CENTER, 440 North Hiawatha Drive, Canton, SD, Zip 57013–5800; tel. 605/764–1400; Scott C. Larson, Chief Executive Officer

SANFORD CHAMBERLAIN MEDICAL CENTER, 300 South Byron Boulevard, Chamberlain, SD, Zip 57325–9741; tel. 605/234–5511; Erica Peterson, Chief Executive Officer

SANFORD CLEAR LAKE MEDICAL CENTER, 701 Third Avenue South, Clear Lake, SD, Zip 57226–2016; tel. 605/874–2141; Lori Sisk, R.N., Chief Executive Officer

SANFORD HILLSBORO MEDICAL CENTER, 12 Third Street SE, Hillsboro, ND, Zip 58045–4840, Mailing Address: P.O. Box 609, Zip 58045–0609, tel. 701/636–3200; Jac McTaggart, Chief Executive Officer

SANFORD JACKSON MEDICAL CENTER, 1430 North Highway, Jackson, MN, Zip 56143–1093; tel. 507/847–2420; Dawn Schnell, Chief Nursing Officer and Interim Senior Director

SANFORD LUVERNE MEDICAL CENTER, 1600 North Kniss Avenue, Luverne, MN, Zip 56156–1067; tel. 507/283–2321; Tammy Loosbrock, Senior Director

SANFORD SHELDON MEDICAL CENTER, 118 North Seventh Avenue, Sheldon, IA, Zip 51201–1235, Mailing Address: P.O. Box 250, Zip 51201–0250, tel. 712/324–5041; Richard E. Nordahl, Senior Director

SANFORD TRACY MEDICAL CENTER, 251 Fifth Street East, Tracy, MN, Zip 56175–1536; tel. 507/629–8400; Stacy Barstad, Chief Executive Officer

SANFORD USD MEDICAL CENTER, 1305 West 18th Street, Sioux Falls, SD, Zip 57105–0496, Mailing Address: P.O. Box 5039, Zip 57117–5039, tel. 605/333–1000; Paul A. Hanson, FACHE, President

SANFORD VERMILLION MEDICAL CENTER, 20 South Plum Street, Vermillion, SD, Zip 57069–3346; tel. 605/677–3500; Timothy J. Tracy, Senior Director

SANFORD WESTBROOK MEDICAL CENTER, 920 Bell Avenue, Westbrook, MN, Zip 56183–9669, Mailing Address: P.O. Box 188, Zip 56183–0188, tel. 507/274–6121; Stacy Barstad, Chief Executive Officer

SANFORD WORTHINGTON MEDICAL CENTER, 1018 Sixth Avenue, Worthington, MN, Zip 56187–2202, Mailing Address: P.O. Box 997, Zip 56187–0997, tel. 507/372–2941; Jennifer . Weg, MS, R.N., Executive Director

WEST HOLT MEDICAL SERVICES, 406 West Neely Street, Atkinson, NE, Zip 68713–4801; tel. 402/925–2811; Jeremy Bauer, Interim Chief Executive Officer

WINDOM AREA HOSPITAL, 2150 Hospital Drive, Windom, MN, Zip 56101–0339, Mailing Address: P.O. Box 339, Zip 56101–0339, tel. 507/831–2400; Shelby Medina, Chief Executive Officer

WINNER REGIONAL HEALTHCARE CENTER, 745 East Eighth Street, Winner, SD, Zip 57580–2631; tel. 605/842–7100; Kevin Coffey, Chief Executive Officer

TENNESSEE

TRISTAR HEALTH
110 Winners Circle, First Floor, Brentwood, TN, Zip 37027–5070; tel. 615/886–4900; Stephen Corbeil, President

CARTERSVILLE MEDICAL CENTER, 960 Joe Frank Harris Parkway, Cartersville, GA, Zip 30120–2129; tel. 770/382–1530; J. Christopher. Mosley, Chief Executive Officer

EASTSIDE MEDICAL CENTER, 1700 Medical Way, Snellville, GA, Zip 30078–2195; tel. 770/979–0200; Trent Lind, Chief Executive Officer

PARKRIDGE MEDICAL CENTER, 2333 McCallie Avenue, Chattanooga, TN, Zip 37404–3258; tel. 423/698–6061; Thomas H. Ozburn, Chief Executive Officer

REDMOND REGIONAL MEDICAL CENTER, 501 Redmond Road, Rome, GA, Zip 30165–1415, Mailing Address: P.O. Box 107001, Zip 30164–7001, tel. 706/291–0291; John Quinlivan, Chief Executive Officer

TRISTAR ASHLAND CITY MEDICAL CENTER, 313 North Main Street, Ashland City, TN, Zip 37015–1347; tel. 615/792–3030; Darrell White, R.N., Administrator and Chief Nursing Officer

TRISTAR CENTENNIAL MEDICAL CENTER, 2300 Patterson Street, Nashville, TN, Zip 37203–1528; tel. 615/342–1000; Scott A. Cihak, President and Chief Executive Officer

TRISTAR GREENVIEW REGIONAL HOSPITAL, 1801 Ashley Circle, Bowling Green, KY, Zip 42104–3362; tel. 270/793–1000; Michael Sherrod, Chief Executive Officer

TRISTAR HENDERSONVILLE MEDICAL CENTER, 355 New Shackle Island Road, Hendersonville, TN, Zip 37075–2479; tel. 615/338–1000; Regina Bartlett, Chief Executive Officer

TRISTAR HORIZON MEDICAL CENTER, 111 Highway 70 East, Dickson, TN, Zip 37055–2080; tel. 615/446–0446; Dustin Greene, Chief Executive Officer

TRISTAR SKYLINE MEDICAL CENTER, 3441 Dickerson Pike, Nashville, TN, Zip 37207–2539; tel. 615/769–2000; Steve Otto, Chief Executive Officer

TRISTAR SOUTHERN HILLS MEDICAL CENTER, 391 Wallace Road, Nashville, TN, Zip 37211–4859, Mailing Address: 3441 Dickerson Pike, Zip 37207, tel. 615/781–4000; Joanna J. Conley, FACHE, Chief Executive Officer

TRISTAR STONECREST MEDICAL CENTER, 200 StoneCrest Boulevard, Smyrna, TN, Zip 37167–6810; tel. 615/768–2000; Louis Caputo, Chief Executive Officer

TRISTAR SUMMIT MEDICAL CENTER, 5655 Frist Boulevard, Hermitage, TN, Zip 37076–2053; tel. 615/316–3000; Brian Marger, Chief Executive Officer

TEXAS

LITTLE RIVER HEALTHCARE
1700 Brazos Avenue, Rockdale, TX, Zip 76567–2517; tel. 512/446–4500; Jeffrey Madison, FACHE, Chief Executive Officer

CAMERON HOSPITAL, 806 North Crockett Avenue, Cameron, TX, Zip 76520–2553; tel. 254/605–1300; Troy Zinn, Chief Executive Officer

METHODIST HEALTHCARE SYSTEM
8109 Fredericksburg Road, San Antonio, TX, Zip 78229–3311; tel. 210/575–0355; Allen Harrison, Chief Executive Officer

METHODIST AMBULATORY SURGERY HOSPITAL – NORTHWEST, 9150 Huebner Road, Suite 100, San Antonio, TX, Zip 78240-1545; tel. 210/575-5000; Cathy Bump, R.N., Interim Chief Executive Officer

METHODIST HOSPITAL, 7700 Floyd Curl Drive, San Antonio, TX, Zip 78229-3993; tel. 210/575-4000; Daniel Miller, FACHE, Chief Executive Officer

METHODIST STONE OAK HOSPITAL, 1139 E Sonterra Boulevard, San Antonio, TX, Zip 78258-4347, Mailing Address: 1139 East Sonterra Boulevard, Zip 78258-4347, tel. 210/638-2100; Marc Strode, Chief Executive Officer

REGIONAL HEALTHCARE ALLIANCE
530 South Beckham Avenue, Tyler, TX, Zip 75702-8310; tel. 903/531-4449; John Webb, President

ALLEGIANCE SPECIALTY HOSPITAL OF KILGORE, 1612 South Henderson Boulevard, Kilgore, TX, Zip 75662-3594; tel. 903/984-3505; Karen Ross, Chief Executive Officer

BAYLOR UNIVERSITY MEDICAL CENTER, 3500 Gaston Avenue, Dallas, TX, Zip 75246-2088; tel. 214/820-0111; Steven R. Newton, FACHE, President

CHRISTUS MOTHER FRANCES HOSPITAL – JACKSONVILLE, 2026 South Jackson, Jacksonville, TX, Zip 75766-5822; tel. 903/541-4500; Anne Pileggi, Administrator and Associate Vice President

CHRISTUS MOTHER FRANCES HOSPITAL – SULPHUR SPRINGS, 115 Airport Road, Sulphur Springs, TX, Zip 75482-2105; tel. 903/885-7671; Paul Harvey, President and Chief Executive Officer

CHRISTUS MOTHER FRANCES HOSPITAL – TYLER, 800 East Dawson Street, Tyler, TX, Zip 75701-2036; tel. 903/593-8441; Jason J. Proctor, Chief Operating Officer

CHRISTUS TRINITY MOTHER FRANCES REHABILITATION HOSPITAL, A PARTNER OF ENCOMPASS HEALTH, 3131 Troup Highway, Tyler, TX, Zip 75701-8352; tel. 903/510-7000; Sharla Anderson, Chief Executive Officer

CHILDREN'S MEDICAL CENTER DALLAS, 1935 Medical District Drive, Pavilion, 3rd Floor, Dallas, TX, Zip 75235-7701; tel. 214/456-7000; Christopher J. Durovich, President and Chief Executive Officer

NACOGDOCHES MEDICAL CENTER, 4920 NE Stallings Drive, Nacogdoches, TX, Zip 75965-1200; tel. 936/569-9481; Philip Koovakada, Chief Executive Officer

PALESTINE REGIONAL MEDICAL CENTER-EAST, 2900 South Loop 256, Palestine, TX, Zip 75801-6958; tel. 903/731-1000; Roy Finch, Chief Executive Officer

PARIS REGIONAL MEDICAL CENTER, 865 Deshong Drive, Paris, TX, Zip 75460-9313, Mailing Address: P.O. Box 9070, Zip 75461-9070, tel. 903/785-4521; Steve Hyde, Chief Executive Officer

TITUS REGIONAL MEDICAL CENTER, 2001 North Jefferson Avenue, Mount Pleasant, TX, Zip 75455-2398; tel. 903/577-6000; Terry Scoggin, Chief Executive Officer

TYLER CONTINUECARE HOSPITAL, 800 East Dawson, 4th Floor, Tyler, TX, Zip 75701-2036; tel. 903/531-4080; Stephanie Hyde, R.N., MSN, Chief Executive Officer

UT HEALTH HENDERSON, 300 Wilson Street, Henderson, TX, Zip 75652-5956; tel. 903/657-7541; Mark Leitner, FACHE, Administrator

UT HEALTH NORTH CAMPUS TYLER, 11937 Highway 271, Tyler, TX, Zip 75708-3154; tel. 903/877-7777; Kirk A. Calhoun, M.D., President

ST. DAVID'S HEALTH NETWORK
98 San Jacinto Boulevard, Austin, TX, Zip 78701-4082; tel. 512/708-9700; David Huffstutler, President and Chief Executive Officer

ST. DAVID'S MEDICAL CENTER, 919 East 32nd Street, Austin, TX, Zip 78705-2709, Mailing Address: P.O. Box 4039, Zip 78765-4039, tel. 512/476-7111; Todd E. Steward, FACHE, Chief Executive Officer

ST. DAVID'S NORTH AUSTIN MEDICAL CENTER, 12221 North MoPac Expressway, Austin, TX, Zip 78758-2496; tel. 512/901-1000; Thomas W. Jackson, Chief Executive Officer

ST. DAVID'S ROUND ROCK MEDICAL CENTER, 2400 Round Rock Avenue, Round Rock, TX, Zip 78681-4097; tel. 512/341-1000; Jeremy Barclay, Chief Executive Officer

ST. DAVID'S SOUTH AUSTIN MEDICAL CENTER, 901 West Ben White Boulevard, Austin, TX, Zip 78704-6903; tel. 512/447-2211; Todd E. Steward, FACHE, Acting Chief Executive Officer

THE HOSPITALS OF PROVIDENCE
2001 North Oregon Street, El Paso, TX, Zip 79902-3320; tel. 915/577-6625; Nicholas R. Tejeda, FACHE, Market Chief Executive Officer

THE HOSPITALS OF PROVIDENCE EAST CAMPUS, 3280 Joe Battle Boulevard, El Paso, TX, Zip 79938-2622; tel. 915/832-2000; Monica Vargas-Mahar, FACHE, Chief Executive Officer

THE HOSPITALS OF PROVIDENCE MEMORIAL CAMPUS, 2001 North Oregon Street, El Paso, TX, Zip 79902-3368; tel. 915/577-6625; Nicholas R. Tejeda, FACHE, Market Chief Executive Officer

THE HOSPITALS OF PROVIDENCE SIERRA CAMPUS, 1625 Medical Center Drive, El Paso, TX, Zip 79902-5005; tel. 915/747-4000; Rob Anderson, Chief Executive Officer

THE HOSPITALS OF PROVIDENCE TRANSMOUNTAIN CAMPUS, 2000 Transmountain Road, El Paso, TX, Zip 79911; tel. 915/877-8300; Tasha Hopper, Chief Executive Officer

VERMONT

THE UNIVERSITY OF VERMONT HEALTH NETWORK
111 Colchester Avenue, Burlington, VT, Zip 05401-1473; tel. 802/847-3983; John R. Brumsted, M.D., President and Chief Executive Officer

THE UNIVERSITY OF VERMONT HEALTH NETWORK CENTRAL VERMONT MEDICAL CENTER, 130 Fisher Road, Berlin, VT, Zip 05602-9516, Mailing Address: P.O. Box 547, Barre, Zip 05641-0547, tel. 802/371-4100; Anna T. Noonan, President and Chief Operating Officer

THE UNIVERSITY OF VERMONT HEALTH NETWORK ELIZABETHTOWN COMMUNITY HOSPITAL, 75 Park Street, Elizabethtown, NY, Zip 12932, Mailing Address: P.O. Box 277, Zip 12932-0277, tel. 518/873-6377; John R. Remillard, President and Chief Executive Officer

THE UNIVERSITY OF VERMONT HEALTH NETWORK-CHAMPLAIN VALLEY PHYSICIANS HOSPITAL, 75 Beekman Street, Plattsburgh, NY, Zip 12901-1438; tel. 518/561-2000; Michelle Lebeau, President and Chief Operating Officer

UNIVERSITY OF VERMONT MEDICAL CENTER, 111 Colchester Avenue, Burlington, VT, Zip 05401-1473; tel. 802/847-0000; Eileen Whalen, R.N., President and Chief Operating Officer

VIRGINIA

VIRGINIA HEALTH NETWORK
7400 Beaufont Springs Drive, Suite 505, Richmond, VA, Zip 23225-5521; tel. 804/320-3837; James Brittain, President

AUGUSTA HEALTH, 78 Medical Center Drive, Fishersville, VA, Zip 22939-2332, Mailing Address: P.O. Box 1000, Zip 22939-1000, tel. 540/932-4000; Mary N. Mannix, FACHE, President and Chief Executive Officer

BATH COMMUNITY HOSPITAL, 106 Park Drive, Hot Springs, VA, Zip 24445-2921, Mailing Address: P.O. Box Z, Zip 24445-0750, tel. 540/839-7000; Kathy Landreth, Chief Executive Officer

BON SECOURS MARY IMMACULATE HOSPITAL, 2 Bernardine Drive, Newport News, VA, Zip 23602-4499; tel. 757/886-6000; Darlene Stephenson, Chief Executive Officer

BON SECOURS MARYVIEW MEDICAL CENTER, 3636 High Street, Portsmouth, VA, Zip 23707-3270; tel. 757/398-2200; Paul Gaden, Chief Executive Officer

BON SECOURS MEMORIAL REGIONAL MEDICAL CENTER, 8260 Atlee Road, Mechanicsville, VA, Zip 23116-1844; tel. 804/764-6000; Mark M. Gordon, Chief Executive Officer

BON SECOURS ST. FRANCIS MEDICAL CENTER, 13710 St Francis Boulevard, Midlothian, VA, Zip 23114-3267; tel. 804/594-7300; Chris Accashian, Chief Executive Officer

BON SECOURS ST. MARY'S HOSPITAL, 5801 Bremo Road, Richmond, VA, Zip 23226-1907; tel. 804/285-2011; Francine Barr, R.N., MS, Chief Executive Officer

BON SECOURS-DEPAUL MEDICAL CENTER, 150 Kingsley Lane, Norfolk, VA, Zip 23505-4650; tel. 757/889-5000; Paul Gaden, Chief Executive Officer

BON SECOURS-RICHMOND COMMUNITY HOSPITAL, 1500 North 28th Street, Richmond, VA, Zip 23223-5396, Mailing Address: P.O. Box 27184, Zip 23261-7184, tel. 804/225-1700; Mark M. Gordon, Chief Executive Officer

BUCHANAN GENERAL HOSPITAL, 1535 Slate Creek Road, Grundy, VA, Zip 24614-6974; tel. 276/935-1000; Robert D. Ruchti, Chief Executive Officer

CARILION FRANKLIN MEMORIAL HOSPITAL, 180 Floyd Avenue, Rocky Mount, VA, Zip 24151-1389; tel. 540/483-5277; Carl T. Cline, Chief Executive Officer

CARILION GILES COMMUNITY HOSPITAL, 159 Hartley Way, Pearisburg, VA, Zip 24134-2471; tel. 540/921-6000; William Flattery, Vice President and Administrator Western Division

CARILION NEW RIVER VALLEY MEDICAL CENTER, 2900 Lamb Circle, Christiansburg, VA, Zip 24073-6344, Mailing Address: P.O. Box 5, Radford, Zip 24143-0005, tel. 540/731-2000; William Flattery, Vice President and Administrator Western Division

CARILION ROANOKE MEMORIAL HOSPITAL, 1906 Belleview Avenue Southeast, Roanoke, VA, Zip 24014-1838, Mailing Address: P.O. Box 13367, Zip 24033-3367, tel. 540/981-7000; Steven C. Arner, President

CARILION STONEWALL JACKSON HOSPITAL, 1 Health Circle, Lexington, VA, Zip 24450-2492; tel. 540/458-3300; Greg T. Madsen, Chief Executive Officer

CARILION TAZEWELL COMMUNITY HOSPITAL, 141 Ben Bolt Avenue, Tazewell, VA, Zip 24651-9700, Mailing Address: 388 Ben Bolt Avenue, Zip 24651, tel. 276/988-8700; Kathren Dowdy, MSN, Regional Hospital Senior Director

CENTRA BEDFORD MEMORIAL HOSPITAL, 1613 Oakwood Street, Bedford, VA, Zip 24523-1213; tel. 540/586-2441; Patti Jurkus, Vice President and Chief Executive Officer

CENTRA SOUTHSIDE COMMUNITY HOSPITAL, 800 Oak Street, Farmville, VA, Zip 23901-1199; tel. 434/392-8811; Thomas Angelo, Chief Executive Officer

CHESAPEAKE REGIONAL MEDICAL CENTER, 736 Battlefield Boulevard North, Chesapeake, VA, Zip 23320-4941, Mailing Address: P.O. Box 2028, Zip 23327-2028, tel. 757/312-8121; Reese Jackson, President and Chief Executive Officer

CHILDREN'S HOSPITAL OF RICHMOND AT VCU-BROOK ROAD CAMPUS, 2924 Brook Road, Richmond, VA, Zip 23220–1298; tel. 804/321–7474; Elias Neujahr, Chief Executive Officer

CHILDREN'S HOSPITAL OF THE KING'S DAUGHTERS, 601 Children's Lane, Norfolk, VA, Zip 23507–1910; tel. 757/668–7000; James D. Dahling, President and Chief Executive Officer

CHIPPENHAM HOSPITAL, 7101 Jahnke Road, Richmond, VA, Zip 23225–4044; tel. 804/320–3911; Zachary McCluskey, Interim Chief Executive Officer

CLINCH VALLEY MEDICAL CENTER, 6801 Governor G C Peery Highway, Richlands, VA, Zip 24641–2194; tel. 276/596–6000; Peter Mulkey, Chief Executive Officer

COASTAL VIRGINIA REHABILITATION, 245 Chesapeake Avenue, Newport News, VA, Zip 23607–6038; tel. 757/928–8000; Daniel Ballin, Administrator

DOMINION HOSPITAL, 2960 Sleepy Hollow Road, Falls Church, VA, Zip 22044–2030; tel. 703/536–2000; Lee Higginbotham, Chief Executive Officer

ENCOMPASS HEALTH REHABILITATION HOSPITAL OF VIRGINIA, 5700 Fitzhugh Avenue, Richmond, VA, Zip 23226–1800; tel. 804/288–5700; Dan Gaskell, Chief Executive Officer

FAUQUIER HOSPITAL, 500 Hospital Drive, Warrenton, VA, Zip 20186–3099; tel. 540/316–5000; Chad Melton, Chief Executive Officer

HENRICO DOCTORS' HOSPITAL, 1602 Skipwith Road, Richmond, VA, Zip 23229–5205; tel. 804/289–4500; William Wagnon, Chief Executive Officer

INOVA ALEXANDRIA HOSPITAL, 4320 Seminary Road, Alexandria, VA, Zip 22304–1535; tel. 703/504–3167; Rina Bansal, Acting President and Chief Nursing Officer

INOVA FAIR OAKS HOSPITAL, 3600 Joseph Siewick Drive, Fairfax, VA, Zip 22033–1798; tel. 703/391–3600; Donald Brideau, M.D., Chief Executive Officer

INOVA FAIRFAX HOSPITAL, 3300 Gallows Road, Falls Church, VA, Zip 22042–3300; tel. 703/776–4001; Susan T. Carroll, FACHE, Acting President

INOVA LOUDOUN HOSPITAL, 44045 Riverside Parkway, Leesburg, VA, Zip 20176–5101, Mailing Address: P.O. Box 6000, Zip 20177–0600, tel. 703/858–6000; Deborah Addo, Chief Executive Officer

INOVA MOUNT VERNON HOSPITAL, 2501 Parker's Lane, Alexandria, VA, Zip 22306–3209; tel. 703/664–7000; Joseph Pina, M.D., Chief Executive Officer

JOHN RANDOLPH MEDICAL CENTER, 411 West Randolph Road, Hopewell, VA, Zip 23860–2938; tel. 804/541–1600; Joseph Mazzo, Chief Executive Officer

JOHNSTON MEMORIAL HOSPITAL, 16000 Johnston Memorial Drive, Abingdon, VA, Zip 24211–7659; tel. 276/258–1000; John Jeter, Chief Executive Officer

LEWISGALE HOSPITAL ALLEGHANY, One ARH Lane, Low Moor, VA, Zip 24457, Mailing Address: P.O. Box 7, Zip 24457–0007, tel. 540/862–6011; William Windham, Chief Executive Officer

LEWISGALE HOSPITAL PULASKI, 2400 Lee Highway, Pulaski, VA, Zip 24301–2326, Mailing Address: P.O. Box 759, Zip 24301–0759, tel. 540/994–8100; Sean Pressman, Chief Executive Officer

MARY WASHINGTON HOSPITAL, 1001 Sam Perry Boulevard, Fredericksburg, VA, Zip 22401–3354; tel. 540/741–1100; Michael P. McDermott, M.D., President and Chief Executive Officer

MOUNTAIN VIEW REGIONAL MEDICAL CENTER, 310 Third Street NE, Norton, VA, Zip 24273–1137; tel. 276/679–9100; Mark T. Leonard, Interim Chief Executive Officer

NORTHERN HOSPITAL OF SURRY COUNTY, 830 Rockford Street, Mount Airy, NC, Zip 27030–5365, Mailing Address: P.O. Box 1101, Zip 27030–1101, tel. 336/719–7000; Chris A. Lumsden, President and Chief Executive Officer

NOVANT HEALTH UVA HEALTH SYSTEM CULPEPER MEDICAL CENTER, 501 Sunset Lane, Culpeper, VA, Zip 22701–3917, Mailing Address: P.O. Box 592, Zip 22701–0500, tel. 540/829–4100; Jeff Hetmanski, President and Chief Operating Officer

NOVANT HEALTH UVA HEALTH SYSTEM PRINCE WILLIAM MEDICAL CENTER, 8700 Sudley Road, Manassas, VA, Zip 20110–4418, Mailing Address: P.O. Box 2610, Zip 20108–0867, tel. 703/369–8000; Stephen Smith, President and Chief Operating Officer

RAPPAHANNOCK GENERAL HOSPITAL, 101 Harris Drive, Kilmarnock, VA, Zip 22482–3880, Mailing Address: P.O. Box 1449, Zip 22482–1449, tel. 804/435–8000; Chris Accashian, Chief Executive Officer

RESTON HOSPITAL CENTER, 1850 Town Center Parkway, Reston, VA, Zip 20190–3219; tel. 703/689–9000; John A. Deardorff, President and Chief Executive, Northern Virginia Market

RIVERSIDE REGIONAL MEDICAL CENTER, 500 J Clyde Morris Boulevard, Newport News, VA, Zip 23601–1929; tel. 757/594–2000; Michael J. Doucette, Senior Vice President and Administrator

RIVERSIDE SHORE MEMORIAL HOSPITAL, 20480 Market Street, Onancock, VA, Zip 23417–4309, Mailing Address: P.O. Box 430, Zip 23417, tel. 757/302–2100; John Peterman, Vice President and Administrator

RIVERSIDE TAPPAHANNOCK HOSPITAL, 618 Hospital Road, Tappahannock, VA, Zip 22560–5000; tel. 804/443–3311; Esther Muscari. Desimini, Administrator

RIVERSIDE WALTER REED HOSPITAL, 7519 Hospital Drive, Gloucester, VA, Zip 23061–4178, Mailing Address: P.O. Box 1130, Zip 23061–1130, tel. 804/693–8800; Esther Muscari, Interim Administrator

RUSSELL COUNTY MEDICAL CENTER, 58 Carroll Street, Lebanon, VA, Zip 24266, Mailing Address: P.O. Box 3600, Zip 24266–0200, tel. 276/883–8000; Stephen K. Givens, Assistant Vice President and Administrator

SOVAH HEALTH-MARTINSVILLE, 320 Hospital Drive, Martinsville, VA, Zip 24112–1981, Mailing Address: P.O. Box 4788, Zip 24115–4788, tel. 276/666–7200; Alan Larson, Market President

SENTARA CAREPLEX HOSPITAL, 3000 Coliseum Drive, Hampton, VA, Zip 23666–5963; tel. 757/736–1000; Kirkpatrick Conley, President

SENTARA LEIGH HOSPITAL, 830 Kempsville Road, Norfolk, VA, Zip 23502–3920; tel. 757/261–6000; Joanne Inman, President

SENTARA MARTHA JEFFERSON HOSPITAL, 500 Martha Jefferson Drive, Charlottesville, VA, Zip 22911–4668; tel. 434/654–7000; Jonathan S. Davis, FACHE, President

SENTARA NORFOLK GENERAL HOSPITAL, 600 Gresham Drive, Norfolk, VA, Zip 23507–1904; tel. 757/388–3000; Carolyn Carpenter, FACHE, President

SENTARA NORTHERN VIRGINIA MEDICAL CENTER, 2300 Opitz Boulevard, Woodbridge, VA, Zip 22191–3399; tel. 703/523–1000; Katherine Johnson, Ph.D., President

SENTARA OBICI HOSPITAL, 2800 Godwin Boulevard, Suffolk, VA, Zip 23434–8038; tel. 757/934–4000; Steve Julian, M.D., President

SENTARA PRINCESS ANNE HOSPITAL, 2025 Glenn Mitchell Drive, Virginia Beach, VA, Zip 23456–0178; tel. 757/507–1000; Thomas B. Thames, M.D., President

SENTARA VIRGINIA BEACH GENERAL HOSPITAL, 1060 First Colonial Road, Virginia Beach, VA, Zip 23454–3002; tel. 757/395–8000; Elwood Bernard. Boone, III., FACHE, President

SENTARA WILLIAMSBURG REGIONAL MEDICAL CENTER, 100 Sentara Circle, Williamsburg, VA, Zip 23188–5713; tel. 757/984–6000; David J. Masterson, President

SHELTERING ARMS REHABILITATION HOSPITAL, 8254 Atlee Road, Mechanicsville, VA, Zip 23116–1844; tel. 804/764–1000; Mary A. Zweifel, MS, President and Chief Executive Officer

SMYTH COUNTY COMMUNITY HOSPITAL, 245 Medical Park Drive, Marion, VA, Zip 24354, Mailing Address: P.O. Box 880, Zip 24354–0880, tel. 276/378–1000; James E. Tyler, Chief Executive Officer

SOUTHAMPTON MEMORIAL HOSPITAL, 100 Fairview Drive, Franklin, VA, Zip 23851–1238, Mailing Address: P.O. Box 817, Zip 23851–0817, tel. 757/569–6100; Kimberly W. Marks, Chief Executive Officer

SOUTHERN VIRGINIA REGIONAL MEDICAL CENTER, 727 North Main Street, Emporia, VA, Zip 23847–1274; tel. 434/348–4400; Wilson A. Thomas, Chief Executive Officer

SOUTHSIDE REGIONAL MEDICAL CENTER, 200 Medical Park Boulevard, Petersburg, VA, Zip 23805–9274; tel. 804/765–5000; Trent Nobles, Chief Executive Officer

TWIN COUNTY REGIONAL HEALTHCARE, 200 Hospital Drive, Galax, VA, Zip 24333–2227; tel. 276/236–8181; Dale Alward, Chief Executive Officer

UVA-HEALTHSOUTH REHABILITATION HOSPITAL, 515 Ray C Hunt Drive, Charlottesville, VA, Zip 22903–2981; tel. 434/244–2000; Barbara Adcock Mohr, Chief Executive Officer

UNIVERSITY OF VIRGINIA MEDICAL CENTER, 1215 Lee Street, Charlottesville, VA, Zip 22908–0001, Mailing Address: P.O. Box 800809, Zip 22908–0809, tel. 434/924–0211; Pamela Sutton-Wallace, Chief Executive Officer

VCU HEALTH COMMUNITY MEMORIAL HOSPITAL, 125 Buena Vista Circle, South Hill, VA, Zip 23970–1431, Mailing Address: P.O. Box 90, Zip 23970–0090, tel. 434/447–3151; W Scott. Burnette, Chief Executive Officer

VCU MEDICAL CENTER, 1250 East Marshall Street, Richmond, VA, Zip 23298–5051, Mailing Address: P.O. Box 980510, Zip 23298–0510, tel. 804/828–9000; Deborah W. Davis, Chief Executive Officer and Vice President Clinical Services

VIRGINIA HOSPITAL CENTER, 1701 North George Mason Drive, Arlington, VA, Zip 22205–3698; tel. 703/558–5000; James B. Cole, President and Chief Executive Officer

WYTHE COUNTY COMMUNITY HOSPITAL, 600 West Ridge Road, Wytheville, VA, Zip 24382–1099; tel. 276/228–0200; Joseph Wilkins, Chief Executive Officer

WASHINGTON

GROUP HEALTH COOPERATIVE
320 Westlake Avenue North, Suite 100, Seattle, WA, Zip 98109–5233; tel. 206/448–5083; Scott Armstrong, Chief Executive Officer

ASTRIA REGIONAL MEDICAL CENTER, 110 South Ninth Avenue, Yakima, WA, Zip 98902–3315; tel. 509/575–5000; Jeff Egbert, Interim Chief Executive Officer

ASTRIA SUNNYSIDE HOSPITAL, 1016 Tacoma Avenue, Sunnyside, WA, Zip 98944–2263, Mailing Address: P.O. Box 719, Zip 98944–0719, tel. 509/837–1500; Brian P. Gibbons, Jr., Chief Executive Officer

ASTRIA TOPPENISH HOSPITAL, 502 West Fourth Avenue, Toppenish, WA, Zip 98948–1616, Mailing Address: P.O. Box 672, Zip 98948–0672, tel. 509/865–3105; Eric P. Jensen, Chief Executive Officer

CASCADE VALLEY HOSPITAL, 330 South Stillaguamish Avenue, Arlington, WA, Zip 98223–1642; tel. 360/435–2133; Brian K. Ivie, President and Chief Executive Officer

COLUMBIA COUNTY HEALTH SYSTEM, 1012 South Third Street, Dayton, WA, Zip 99328–1696; tel. 509/382–2531; Shane McGuire, Chief Executive Officer

HARRISON MEDICAL CENTER, 2520 Cherry Avenue, Bremerton, WA, Zip 98310–4229; tel. 360/744–3911; David W. Schultz, FACHE, President, Peninsula Region

ISLAND HOSPITAL, 1211 24th Street, Anacortes, WA, Zip 98221–2562; tel. 360/299–1300; Vincent Oliver, FACHE, Administrator

KADLEC REGIONAL MEDICAL CENTER, 888 Swift Boulevard, Richland, WA, Zip 99352–3514; tel. 509/946–4611; Reza Kaleel, Chief Executive Officer

KAISER PERMANENTE CAPITOL HILL CAMPUS, 201 16th Avenue East, Seattle, WA, Zip 98112–5226; tel. 206/326–3000; Carol M. Taylor, R.N., Regional Director Clinical Operations

KITTITAS VALLEY HEALTHCARE, 603 South Chestnut Street, Ellensburg, WA, Zip 98926–3875; tel. 509/962–7302; Julie Petersen, CPA, Chief Executive Officer

KOOTENAI HEALTH, 2003 Kootenai Health Way, Coeur D'Alene, ID, Zip 83814–2677; tel. 208/625–4000; Jon Ness, Chief Executive Officer

LOURDES MEDICAL CENTER, 520 North Fourth Avenue, Pasco, WA, Zip 99301–5257; tel. 509/547–7704; John Serle, FACHE, President and Chief Executive Officer

MULTICARE DEACONESS HOSPITAL, 800 West Fifth Avenue, Spokane, WA, Zip 99204–2803, Mailing Address: P.O. Box 248, Zip 99210–0248, tel. 509/458–5800; Laureen Driscoll, President

MULTICARE MARY BRIDGE CHILDREN'S HOSPITAL AND HEALTH CENTER, 317 Martin Luther King Jr Way, Tacoma, WA, Zip 98405–4234, Mailing Address: P.O. Box 5299, Zip 98415–0299, tel. 253/403–1400; Jeffrey S. Poltawsky, President and Market Leader

MULTICARE VALLEY HOSPITAL, 12606 East Mission Avenue, Spokane Valley, WA, Zip 99216–1090; tel. 509/924–6650; Gregory George. Repetti, III., FACHE, Chief Executive Officer

NORTHWEST SPECIALTY HOSPITAL, 1593 East Polston Avenue, Post Falls, ID, Zip 83854–5326; tel. 208/262–2300; Rick Rasmussen, Chief Executive Officer

OVERLAKE MEDICAL CENTER, 1035 116th Avenue NE, Bellevue, WA, Zip 98004–4604; tel. 425/688–5000; J. Michael Marsh, President and Chief Executive Officer

PEACEHEALTH ST. JOSEPH MEDICAL CENTER, 2901 Squalicum Parkway, Bellingham, WA, Zip 98225–1851; tel. 360/734–5400; Dale Zender, President Hospital Services NW

PEACEHEALTH UNITED GENERAL MEDICAL CENTER, 2000 Hospital Drive, Sedro-Woolley, WA, Zip 98284–4327; tel. 360/856–6021; Christopher Johnston, Chief Administrative Officer

PROSSER MEMORIAL HEALTH, 723 Memorial Street, Prosser, WA, Zip 99350–1524; tel. 509/786–2222; Craig J. Marks, FACHE, Chief Executive Officer

PROVIDENCE CENTRALIA HOSPITAL, 914 S Scheuber RD, Centralia, WA, Zip 98531–9027, Mailing Address: 914 South Scheuber Road, Zip 98531–9027, tel. 360/736–2803; Medrice Coluccio, R.N., Southwest Region Chief Executive

PROVIDENCE HOLY FAMILY HOSPITAL, 5633 North Lidgerwood Street, Spokane, WA, Zip 99208–1224; tel. 509/482–0111; Peggy M. Currie, R.N., Chief Operating Officer

PROVIDENCE REGIONAL MEDICAL CENTER EVERETT, 1321 Colby Avenue, Everett, WA, Zip 98201–1665, Mailing Address: P.O. Box 1147, Zip 98206–1147, tel. 425/261–2000; Kim Williams, R.N., MS, Chief Executive Officer

PROVIDENCE SACRED HEART MEDICAL CENTER & CHILDREN'S HOSPITAL, 101 West Eighth Avenue, Spokane, WA, Zip 99204–2364, Mailing Address: P.O. Box 2555, Zip 99220–2555, tel. 509/474–3131; Peggy M. Currie, R.N., Chief Operating Officer

PROVIDENCE ST. MARY MEDICAL CENTER, 401 W Poplar Street, Walla Walla, WA, Zip 99362–2846, Mailing Address: P.O. Box 1477, Zip 99362–0312, tel. 509/897–3320; Susan Blackburn, Chief Administrative Officer

PULLMAN REGIONAL HOSPITAL, 835 SE Bishop Boulevard, Pullman, WA, Zip 99163–5512; tel. 509/332–2541; Scott K. Adams, FACHE, Chief Executive Officer

SEATTLE CHILDREN'S HOSPITAL, 4800 Sand Point Way NE, Seattle, WA, Zip 98105–3901, Mailing Address: P.O. Box 5371, Zip 98145–5005, tel. 206/987–2000; Jeff Sperring, M.D., Chief Executive Officer

SKAGIT REGIONAL HEALTH, 1415 East Kincaid, Mount Vernon, WA, Zip 98274–4126, Mailing Address: P.O. Box 1376, Zip 98273–1376, tel. 360/424–4111; Brian K. Ivie, President and Chief Executive Officer

ST. FRANCIS HOSPITAL, 34515 Ninth Avenue South, Federal Way, WA, Zip 98003–6799; tel. 253/944–8100; Anthony McLean, Market President

ST. JOSEPH MEDICAL CENTER, 1717 South 'J' Street, Tacoma, WA, Zip 98405–3004, Mailing Address: P.O. Box 2197, Zip 98401–2197, tel. 253/426–4101; Syd Bersante, R.N., President

TRIOS HEALTH, 900 South Auburn Street, Kennewick, WA, Zip 99336–5621, Mailing Address: P.O. Box 6128, Zip 99336–0128, tel. 509/586–6111; John H. Solheim, Chief Executive Officer

VIRGINIA MASON MEDICAL CENTER, 1100 Ninth Avenue, Seattle, WA, Zip 98101–2756, Mailing Address: P.O. Box 900, Zip 98111–0900, tel. 206/223–6600; Gary Kaplan, M.D., FACHE, Chairman and Chief Executive Officer

VIRGINIA MASON MEMORIAL, 2811 Tieton Drive, Yakima, WA, Zip 98902–3761; tel. 509/575–8000; Russ Myers, Chief Executive Officer

WHIDBEYHEALTH, 101 North Main Street, Coupeville, WA, Zip 98239–3413; tel. 360/678–5151; Ron Telles, Interim Chief Executive Officer

WHITMAN HOSPITAL AND MEDICAL CENTER, 1200 West Fairview Street, Colfax, WA, Zip 99111–9579; tel. 509/397–3435; Hank Hanigan, FACHE, Chief Executive Officer

LINCOLN COUNTY HEALTH DEPARTMENT
90 Nichols Street, Davenport, WA, Zip 99122–9729; tel. 509/725–1001; Ed Dzedzy, Public Health Administration

LINCOLN HOSPITAL, 10 Nicholls Street, Davenport, WA, Zip 99122–9729; tel. 509/725–7101; Tyson Lacy, Chief Executive Officer and Superintendent

ODESSA MEMORIAL HEALTHCARE CENTER, 502 East Amende Drive, Odessa, WA, Zip 99159–7003, Mailing Address: P.O. Box 368, Zip 99159–0368, tel. 509/982–2611; Mo P. Sheldon, FACHE, Chief Executive Officer and Administrator

WEST VIRGINIA

HEALTH PARTNERS NETWORK, INC.
1000 Technology Drive, Suite 2320, Fairmont, WV, Zip 26554–8834; tel. 304/368–2740; William G. MacLean, Executive Director

BROADDUS HOSPITAL, 1 Healthcare Drive, Philippi, WV, Zip 26416–9405, Mailing Address: P.O. Box 930, Zip 26416–0930, tel. 304/457–1760; Dana L. Gould, Chief Executive Officer

CAMDEN CLARK MEDICAL CENTER, 800 Garfield Avenue, Parkersburg, WV, Zip 26101–5378, Mailing Address: P.O. Box 718, Zip 26102–0718, tel. 304/424–2111; Steve Altmiller, President and Chief Executive Officer

DAVIS MEDICAL CENTER, Gorman Avenue and Reed Street, Elkins, WV, Zip 26241, Mailing Address: P.O. Box 1484, Zip 26241–1484, tel. 304/636–3300; Vance Jackson, FACHE, Chief Executive Officer

ENCOMPASS HEALTH REHABILITATION HOSPITAL OF MORGANTOWN, 1160 Van Voorhis Road, Morgantown, WV, Zip 26505–3437; tel. 304/598–1100; Tracy Vinciguerra, Chief Executive Officer

GRAFTON CITY HOSPITAL, 1 Hospital Plaza, Grafton, WV, Zip 26354–1283; tel. 304/265–0400; Patrick D. Shaw, Chief Executive Officer

MINNIE HAMILTON HEALTHCARE CENTER, 186 Hospital Drive, Grantsville, WV, Zip 26147–7100; tel. 304/354–9244; Steve Whited, Chief Executive Officer

ST. JOSEPH'S HOSPITAL OF BUCKHANNON, 1 Amalia Drive, Buckhannon, WV, Zip 26201–2276; tel. 304/473–2000; Skip Gjolberg, FACHE, Administrator

STONEWALL JACKSON MEMORIAL HOSPITAL, 230 Hospital Plaza, Weston, WV, Zip 26452–8558; tel. 304/269–8000; Avah Stalnaker, Chief Executive Officer

UNITED HOSPITAL CENTER, 327 Medical Park Drive, Bridgeport, WV, Zip 26330–9006; tel. 681/342–1000; Michael C. Tillman, President and Chief Executive Officer

WEBSTER COUNTY MEMORIAL HOSPITAL, 324 Miller Mountain Drive, Webster Springs, WV, Zip 26288–1087, Mailing Address: P.O. Box 312, Zip 26288–0312, tel. 304/847–5682; Jim Parker, FACHE, Chief Executive Officer

WEST VIRGINIA UNIVERSITY HOSPITALS, 1 Medical Center Drive, Morgantown, WV, Zip 26506–4749; tel. 304/598–4000; Albert L. Wright, Jr., PharmD, President and Chief Executive Officer

PARTNERS IN HEALTH NETWORK, INC.
405 Capitol Street, Suite 505, Charleston, WV, Zip 25301–1783; tel. 304/388–7385; Robert D. Whitler, Executive Director

BOONE MEMORIAL HOSPITAL, 701 Madison Avenue, Madison, WV, Zip 25130–1699; tel. 304/369–1230; Virgil Underwood, Chief Executive Officer

BRAXTON COUNTY MEMORIAL HOSPITAL, 100 Hoylman DR, Gassaway, WV, Zip 26624–9318, Mailing Address: 100 Hoylman Drive, Zip 26624–9318, tel. 304/364–5156; Karen L. Bowling, MSN, R.N., Interim Chief Executive Officer

CHARLESTON AREA MEDICAL CENTER, 501 Morris Street, Charleston, WV, Zip 25301–1300, Mailing Address: P.O. Box 1547, Zip 25326–1547, tel. 304/388–5432; David L. Ramsey, President and Chief Executive Officer

CHARLESTON SURGICAL HOSPITAL, 1306 Kanawha Boulevard East, Charleston, WV, Zip 25301–3001, Mailing Address: P.O. Box 2271, Zip 25328–2271, tel. 304/343–4371; Christina Arvon, Administrator and Chief Executive Officer

HIGHLAND HOSPITAL, 300 56th Street SE, Charleston, WV, Zip 25304–2361, Mailing Address: P.O. Box 4107, Zip 25364–4107, tel. 304/926–1600; Cynthia A. Persily, Ph.D., R.N., Chief Executive Officer

JACKSON GENERAL HOSPITAL, 122 Pinnell Street, Ripley, WV, Zip 25271–9101, Mailing Address: P.O. Box 720, Zip 25271–0720, tel. 304/372–2731; Stephanie McCoy, President and Chief Executive Officer

MINNIE HAMILTON HEALTHCARE CENTER, 186 Hospital Drive, Grantsville, WV, Zip 26147–7100; tel. 304/354–9244; Steve Whited, Chief Executive Officer

MONTGOMERY GENERAL HOSPITAL, 401 Sixth Avenue, Montgomery, WV, Zip 25136–2116, Mailing Address: P.O. Box 270, Zip 25136–0270, tel. 304/442–5151; Vickie Gay, Chief Executive Officer

POCAHONTAS MEMORIAL HOSPITAL, 150 Duncan Road, Buckeye, WV, Zip 24924; tel. 304/799–7400; Mary Beth Barr, R.N., Chief Executive Officer

ROANE GENERAL HOSPITAL, 200 Hospital Drive, Spencer, WV, Zip 25276–1050; tel. 304/927–4444; Douglas E. Bentz, Chief Executive Officer

STONEWALL JACKSON MEMORIAL HOSPITAL, 230 Hospital Plaza, Weston, WV, Zip 26452–8558; tel. 304/269–8000; Avah Stalnaker, Chief Executive Officer

SUMMERSVILLE REGIONAL MEDICAL CENTER, 400 Fairview Heights Road, Summersville, WV, Zip 26651–9308; tel. 304/872–2891; Karen L. Bowling, MSN, R.N., Interim Chief Executive Officer

WEBSTER COUNTY MEMORIAL HOSPITAL, 324 Miller Mountain Drive, Webster Springs, WV, Zip 26288–1087, Mailing Address: P.O. Box 312, Zip 26288–0312, tel. 304/847–5682; Jim Parker, FACHE, Chief Executive Officer

WISCONSIN

ASCENSION WISCONSIN
1506 South Oneida Street, Appleton, WI, Zip 54915–1305; tel. 920/831–8912; Monica Hilt, President and Chief Executive Officer

ASCENSION CALUMET HOSPITAL, 614 Memorial Drive, Chilton, WI, Zip 53014–1597; tel. 920/849–2386; Jenny Derks, Chief Administrative Officer

ASCENSION NORTHEAST WISCONSIN MERCY HOSPITAL, 500 South Oakwood Road, Oshkosh, WI, Zip 54904–7944; tel. 920/223–2000; Denise Parrish, Interim Chief Administrative Officer

ASCENSION NORTHEAST WISCONSIN ST. ELIZABETH HOSPITAL, 1506 South Oneida Street, Appleton, WI, Zip 54915–1305; tel. 920/738–2000; Monica Hilt, President and Regional Vice President

ASPIRUS, INC.
2200 Westwood Drive, Wausau, WI, Zip 54401–7806; tel. 715/847–2118; Matthew Heywood, President and Chief Executive Officer

ASPIRUS IRON RIVER HOSPITALS & CLINICS, INC., 1400 West Ice Lake Road, Iron River, MI, Zip 49935–9526; tel. 906/265–6121; Connie L. Koutouzos, R.N., MSN, Chief Executive Officer

ASPIRUS IRONWOOD HOSPITALS & CLINICS, INC., N10561 Grand View Lane, Ironwood, MI, Zip 49938–9622; tel. 906/932–2525; Paula L. Chermside, Chief Executive Officer

ASPIRUS KEWEENAW HOSPITAL, INC., 205 Osceola Street, Laurium, MI, Zip 49913–2134; tel. 906/337–6500; Rick L. Nevers, Interim President

ASPIRUS LANGLADE HOSPITAL, 112 East Fifth Avenue, Antigo, WI, Zip 54409–2796; tel. 715/623–2331; Andrew J. Barth, Executive Director

ASPIRUS MEDFORD HOSPITAL & CLINICS, INC., 135 South Gibson Street, Medford, WI, Zip 54451; tel. 715/748–8100; Dale Hustedt, Chief Executive Officer

ASPIRUS ONTONAGON HOSPITAL, INC., 601 South Seventh Street, Ontonagon, MI, Zip 49953–1459; tel. 906/884–8000; Dylan Taylor, Chief Administrative Officer

ASPIRUS RIVERVIEW HOSPITAL AND CLINICS, INC., 410 Dewey Street, Wisconsin Rapids, WI, Zip 54494–4715, Mailing Address: P.O. Box 8080, Zip 54495–8080, tel. 715/423–6060; Todd Burch, Chief Executive Officer

ASPIRUS WAUSAU HOSPITAL, INC., 333 Pine Ridge Boulevard, Wausau, WI, Zip 54401–4187; tel. 715/847–2121; Darrell Lentz, President

COLUMBIA ST. MARY'S
2025 East Newport Avenue, Milwaukee, WI, Zip 53211–2906; tel. 414/961–3300; Travis Andersen, President and Chief Executive Officer

ASCENSION COLUMBIA ST. MARY'S HOSPITAL MILWAUKEE, 2301 North Lake Drive, Milwaukee, WI, Zip 53211–4508; tel. 414/291–1000; Travis Andersen, Chief Executive Officer

ASCENSION COLUMBIA ST. MARY'S HOSPITAL OZAUKEE, 13111 North Port Washington Road, Mequon, WI, Zip 53097–2416; tel. 262/243–7300; Kelly Elkins, President and Chief Executive Officer

ASCENSION COLUMBIA ST. MARY'S MILWAUKEE HOSPITAL, 2323 North Lake Drive, Milwaukee, WI, Zip 53211–4508, Mailing Address: 2301 North Lake Drive, Zip 53211–4508, tel. 414/585–1000; Kelly Elkins, President and Chief Executive Officer

COMMUNITY HEALTH NETWORK, INC.
225 Memorial Drive, Berlin, WI, Zip 54923–1243; tel. 920/361–5580

THEDA CARE MEDICAL CENTER – WILD ROSE, 601 Grove Avenue, Wild Rose, WI, Zip 54984–6903, Mailing Address: P.O. Box 54984–0243, tel. 920/622–3257; Tammy Bending, Vice President

THEDACARE MEDICAL CENTER-BERLIN, 225 Memorial Drive, Berlin, WI, Zip 54923–1295; tel. 920/361–1313; Tammy Bending, Vice President, Critical Access Hospital

GUNDERSEN HEALTH SYSTEM
1900 South Avenue, La Crosse, WI, Zip 54601–5467; tel. 608/782–7300; Scott W. Rathgaber, M.D., Chief Executive Officer

GUNDERSEN BOSCOBEL AREA HOSPITAL AND CLINICS, 205 Parker Street, Boscobel, WI, Zip 53805–1698; tel. 608/375–4112; David Hartberg, Chief Executive Officer

GUNDERSEN LUTHERAN MEDICAL CENTER, 1900 South Avenue, La Crosse, WI, Zip 54601–5467; tel. 608/782–7300; Scott W. Rathgaber, M.D., Chief Executive Officer

GUNDERSEN MOUNDVIEW HOSPITAL & CLINICS, 402 West Lake Street, Friendship, WI, Zip 53934–9699, Mailing Address: P.O. Box 40, Zip 53934–0040, tel. 608/339–3331; Francisco Perez-Guerra, Chief Executive Officer

GUNDERSEN PALMER LUTHERAN HOSPITAL AND CLINICS, 112 Jefferson Street, West Union, IA, Zip 52175–1022; tel. 563/422–3811; Patrice Kuennen, Chief Executive Officer

GUNDERSEN ST. JOSEPH'S HOSPITAL AND CLINICS, 400 Water Avenue, Hillsboro, WI, Zip 54634–9054, Mailing Address: P.O. Box 527, Zip 54634–0527, tel. 608/489–8000; Danielle Gearhart, Chief Executive Officer

GUNDERSEN TRI-COUNTY HOSPITAL AND CLINICS, 18601 Lincoln Street, Whitehall, WI, Zip 54773–8605; tel. 715/538–4361; Joni Olson, Chief Executive Officer

ALLIANCE OF INDEPENDENT ACADEMIC MEDICAL CENTERS
233 East Erie Street, Ste 306, Chicago, IL, Zip 60611; tel. 312/836–3712; Kimberly Pierce–Boggs, Executive Director

ARIZONA
Scottsdale
Alliance
HonorHealth

CALIFORNIA
Colton
Alliance
Arrowhead Regional Medical Center

Los Angeles
Alliance
Cedars–Sinai Medical Center

Oakland
Alliance
Kaiser Permanente Oakland Medical Center

COLORADO
Aurora
Alliance
Medical Center of Aurora

Denver
Alliance
Presbyterian–St. Luke's Medical Center

Rose Medical Center

Saint Joseph Hospital

Englewood
Alliance
Swedish Medical Center

Lone Tree
Alliance
Sky Ridge Medical Center

Thornton
Alliance
North Suburban Medical Center

CONNECTICUT
Hartford
Alliance
Saint Francis Hospital and Medical Center

DELAWARE
Newark
Alliance
Christiana Care Health System

FLORIDA
Hollywood
Alliance
Memorial Healthcare System

Orange Park
Alliance
Orange Park Medical Center

Orlando
Alliance
AdventHealth Orlando

Orlando Regional Medical Center

GEORGIA
Macon
Alliance
Coliseum Medical Centers

ILLINOIS
Chicago
Alliance
Advocate Illinois Masonic Medical Center

Oak Lawn
Alliance
Advocate Christ Medical Center

Park Ridge
Alliance
Advocate Lutheran General Hospital

Peoria
Alliance
OSF Saint Francis Medical Center

INDIANA
Indianapolis
Alliance
Community Health Network

IOWA
West Des Moines
Alliance
UnityPoint Health

LOUISIANA
Baton Rouge
Alliance
Our Lady of the Lake Regional Medical Center

New Orleans
Alliance
Ochsner Health System

MAINE
Portland
Alliance
Maine Medical Center

MARYLAND
Baltimore
Alliance
Sinai Hospital of Baltimore

MASSACHUSETTS
Burlington
Alliance
Lahey Hospital & Medical Center, Burlington

Springfield
Alliance
Baystate Medical Center

MICHIGAN
Grand Rapids
Alliance
Mercy Health Saint Mary's

Lansing
Alliance
Sparrow Hospital

Rochester
Alliance
Ascension Crittenton Hospital Medical Center

MINNESOTA
Bloomington
Alliance
HealthPartners

MONTANA
Billings
Alliance
Billings Clinic

NEW JERSEY
Brick Township
Alliance
Hackensack Meridian Health Ocean Medical Center

Holmdel
Alliance
Hackensack Meridian Health Bayshore Community Hospital

Livingston
Alliance
Saint Barnabas Medical Center

Long Branch
Alliance
Monmouth Medical Center, Long Branch Campus

Manahawkin
Alliance
Hackensack Meridian Health Southern Ocean Medical Center

Neptune
Alliance
Hackensack Meridian Health Jersey Shore University Medical Center

Newark
Alliance
Newark Beth Israel Medical Center

Perth Amboy
Alliance
Hackensack Meridian Health Raritan Bay Medical Center

Phillipsburg
Alliance
St. Luke's Hospital – Warren Campus

Red Bank
Alliance
Hackensack Meridian Health Riverview Medical Center

NEW YORK
Brooklyn
Alliance
Maimonides Medical Center

Cooperstown
Alliance
Bassett Medical Center

Mineola
Alliance
NYU Winthrop Hospital

NORTH CAROLINA
Charlotte
Alliance
Atrium Health's Carolinas Medical Center

OHIO
Akron
Alliance
Cleveland Clinic Akron General

Cincinnati
Alliance
Christ Hospital

TriHealth Evendale Hospital

Cleveland
Alliance
Cleveland Clinic

Columbus
Alliance
OhioHealth Grant Medical Center

OhioHealth Riverside Methodist Hospital

OREGON
Hood River
Alliance
Providence Hood River Memorial Hospital

Milwaukie
Alliance
Providence Milwaukie Hospital

Portland
Alliance
Providence Portland Medical Center

Providence St. Vincent Medical Center

PENNSYLVANIA
Bethlehem
Alliance
St. Luke's University Hospital – Bethlehem Campus

Philadelphia
Alliance
Einstein Medical Center Philadelphia

Sayre
Alliance
Guthrie Robert Packer Hospital

Wynnewood
Alliance
Lankenau Medical Center

York
Alliance
WellSpan York Hospital

SOUTH CAROLINA
Charleston
Alliance
Trident Medical Center

Myrtle Beach
Alliance
Grand Strand Regional Medical Center

TEXAS
Dallas
Alliance
Baylor Scott & White Health

Fort Worth
Alliance
JPS Health Network

Lubbock
Alliance
Covenant Children's Hospital

Covenant Medical Center

WASHINGTON
Seattle
Alliance
Kaiser Permanente Capitol Hill Campus

Swedish Medical Center–Cherry Hill Campus

Swedish Medical Center–First Hill

Virginia Mason Medical Center

WEST VIRGINIA
Charleston
Alliance
Charleston Area Medical Center

WISCONSIN
Marshfield
Alliance
Marshfield Medical Center

CAPSTONE HEALTH ALLIANCE

1200 Ridgefield Boulevard, Suite 200, Asheville, NC, Zip 28806; tel. 828/418–5050; Tim Bugg, President and Chief Executive Officer

ALABAMA
Butler
Alliance
Choctaw General Hospital

Dothan
Alliance
Southeast Alabama Medical Center

Eufaula
Alliance
Medical Center Barbour

Opelika
Alliance
East Alabama Medical Center

Wedowee
Alliance
Tanner Medical Center/East Alabama

ARKANSAS
Batesville
Alliance
White River Medical Center

Calico Rock
Alliance
Izard County Medical Center

Fordyce
Alliance
Dallas County Medical Center

Harrison
Alliance
North Arkansas Regional Medical Center

Mountain View
Alliance
Stone County Medical Center

Pine Bluff
Alliance
Jefferson Regional Medical Center

DELAWARE
Lewes
Alliance
Beebe Healthcare

GEORGIA
Bremen
Alliance
Higgins General Hospital

Carrollton
Alliance
Tanner Medical Center–Carrollton

Jesup
Alliance
Wayne Memorial Hospital

Lagrange
Alliance
Wellstar West Georgia Medical Center

Savannah
Alliance
Candler Hospital

St. Joseph's Hospital

Villa Rica
Alliance
Tanner Medical Center–Villa Rica

ILLINOIS
Centreville
Alliance
Touchette Regional Hospital

Chicago
Alliance
Loretto Hospital

Norwegian American Hospital

Thorek Memorial Hospital

Dixon
Alliance
Katherine Shaw Bethea Hospital

Elmhurst
Alliance
Elmhurst Hospital

Hoopeston
Alliance
Carle Hoopeston Regional Health Center

Kankakee
Alliance
Riverside Medical Center

Naperville
Alliance
Edward Hospital

Linden Oaks Hospital

Urbana
Alliance
Carle Foundation Hospital

INDIANA
Greenfield
Alliance
Hancock Regional Hospital

Rushville
Alliance
Rush Memorial Hospital

KANSAS
Manhattan
Alliance
Manhattan Surgical

KENTUCKY
Albany
Alliance
The Medical Center Albany

Bowling Green
Alliance
Commonwealth Regional Specialty Hospital

Medical Center at Bowling Green

Danville
Alliance
Ephraim McDowell Regional Medical Center

Edgewood
Alliance
St. Elizabeth Edgewood

Florence
Alliance
St. Elizabeth Florence

Fort Thomas
Alliance
St. Elizabeth Fort Thomas

Franklin
Alliance
Medical Center at Franklin

Glasgow
Alliance
T. J. Samson Community Hospital

Henderson
Alliance
Methodist Hospital

Horse Cave
Alliance
The Medical Center at Caverna

Morganfield
Alliance
Methodist Hospital Union County

Murray
Alliance
Murray–Calloway County Hospital

Scottsville
Alliance
Medical Center at Scottsville

Stanford
Alliance
Ephraim McDowell Fort Logan Hospital

Williamstown
Alliance
St. Elizabeth Grant

LOUISIANA
Abbeville
Alliance
Abbeville General Hospital

Baton Rouge
Alliance
Baton Rouge General Medical Center

Baton Rouge Rehabilitation Hospital

Spine Hospital of Louisiana (formally the NeuroMedical Center Surgical Hospital)

The NeuroMedical Center Rehabilitation Hospital

Woman's Hospital

Breaux Bridge
Alliance
St. Martin Hospital

Bunkie
Alliance
Bunkie General Hospital

Church Point
Alliance
Acadia–St. Landry Hospital

Columbia
Alliance
Citizens Medical Center

Crowley
Alliance
Acadia General Hospital

Delhi
Alliance
Richland Parish Hospital

Hammond
Alliance
North Oaks Medical Center

North Oaks Rehabilitation Hospital

Houma
Alliance
Terrebonne General Medical Center

Jennings
Alliance
Jennings American Legion Hospital

Kaplan
Alliance
Abrom Kaplan Memorial Hospital

Kinder
Alliance
Allen Parish Community Healthcare

Lafayette
Alliance
Lafayette General Medical Center

Lafayette General Surgical Hospital

Louisiana Extended Care Hospital of Lafayette

University Hospital and Clinics

Marrero
Alliance
Bridgepoint Continuing Care Hospital

Monroe
Alliance
Specialty Hospital

Natchitoches
Alliance
Louisiana Extended Care
Hospital of Natchitoches

New Iberia
Alliance
Iberia Medical Center

New Orleans
Alliance
Extended Care Hospital

Opelousas
Alliance
St. Landry Extended Care Hospital

Rayville
Alliance
Richardson Medical Center

West Monroe
Alliance
Louisiana Extended Care
Hospital West Monroe

Winnsboro
Alliance
Franklin Medical Center

MARYLAND
Annapolis
Alliance
Anne Arundel Medical Center

Baltimore
Alliance
Greater Baltimore Medical Center

Levindale Hebrew Hospital and Nursing

Mercy Medical Center

Sinai Hospital of Baltimore

Berlin
Alliance
Atlantic General Hospital

Cumberland
Alliance
Western Maryland Regional Medical Center

Elkton
Alliance
Union Hospital

Frederick
Alliance
Frederick Regional Health System

Lanham
Alliance
Doctors Community Hospital

Randallstown
Alliance
Northwest Hospital

Salisbury
Alliance
Peninsula Regional Medical Center

Westminster
Alliance
Carroll Hospital Center

MICHIGAN
Ypsilanti
Alliance
Forest Health Medical Center

MINNESOTA
Blue Earth
Alliance
United Hospital District

MISSISSIPPI
Bay Springs
Alliance
Jasper General Hospital

Carthage
Alliance
Baptist Medical Center Leake

Charleston
Alliance
Tallahatchie General Hospital

De Kalb
Alliance
John C. Stennis Memorial Hospital

Jackson
Alliance
Mississippi Baptist Medical Center

Kosciusko
Alliance
Baptist Medical Center Attala

Laurel
Alliance
South Central Regional Medical Center

Louisville
Alliance
Winston Medical Center

Magee
Alliance
Magee General Hospital

Mendenhall
Alliance
Simpson General Hospital

Meridian
Alliance
Rush Foundation Hospital

Morton
Alliance
Scott Regional Hospital

Quitman
Alliance
H. C. Watkins Memorial Hospital

Ruleville
Alliance
North Sunflower Medical Center

Union
Alliance
Laird Hospital

Water Valley
Alliance
Yalobusha General Hospital

Yazoo City
Alliance
Baptist Medical Center Yazoo

NEBRASKA
Kearney
Alliance
Kearney Regional Medical Center

NORTH CAROLINA
Asheville
Alliance
Asheville Specialty Hospital

CarePartners Health Services

Mission Hospital

Boone
Alliance
Watauga Medical Center

Brevard
Alliance
Transylvania Regional Hospital

Bryson City
Alliance
Swain Community Hospital

Cherokee
Alliance
Cherokee Indian Hospital

Clyde
Alliance
Haywood Regional Medical Center

Columbus
Alliance
St. Luke's Hospital

Dunn
Alliance
Harnett Health System

Elizabeth City
Alliance
Sentara Albemarle Medical Center

Elizabethtown
Alliance
Cape Fear Valley – Bladen County Hospital

Fayetteville
Alliance
Cape Fear Valley Medical Center

Highsmith–Rainey Specialty Hospital

Franklin
Alliance
Angel Medical Center

Gastonia
Alliance
CaroMont Regional Medical Center

Goldsboro
Alliance
Wayne UNC Health Care

Hendersonville
Alliance
AdventHealth Hendersonville

Margaret R. Pardee Memorial Hospital

Hickory
Alliance
Catawba Valley Medical Center

Highlands
Alliance
Highlands–Cashiers Hospital

Marion
Alliance
McDowell Hospital

Morehead City
Alliance
Carteret Health Care

Newland
Alliance
Charles A. Cannon Memorial Hospital

Oxford
Alliance
Granville Health System

Pinehurst
Alliance
FirstHealth Moore Regional Hospital

Raeford
Alliance
Hoke Hospital

Roanoke Rapids
Alliance
Halifax Regional Medical Center

Spruce Pine
Alliance
Blue Ridge Regional Hospital

Statesville
Alliance
Iredell Health System

Troy
Alliance
FirstHealth Montgomery Memorial Hospital

NORTH DAKOTA
Cavalier
Alliance
Pembina County Memorial Hospital and Wedgewood Manor

OHIO
Amherst
Alliance
Specialty Hospital of Lorain

Bowling Green
Alliance
Wood County Hospital

Cleveland
Alliance
Grace Hospital

Cuyahoga Falls
Alliance
Western Reserve Hospital

Salem
Alliance
Salem Regional Medical Center

Steubenville
Alliance
Life Line Hospital

PENNSYLVANIA

Corry
Alliance
LECOM Corry Memorial Hospital

Erie
Alliance
LECOM Health Millcreek Community Hospital

Kittanning
Alliance
ACMH Hospital

Langhorne
Alliance
Barix Clinics of Pennsylvania

Meadville
Alliance
Meadville Medical Center

State College
Alliance
Mount Nittany Medical Center

Titusville
Alliance
Titusville Area Hospital

Tyrone
Alliance
Tyrone Hospital

Windber
Alliance
Chan Soon–Shiong
Medical Center

SOUTH CAROLINA

Conway
Alliance
Conway Medical Center

West Columbia
Alliance
Lexington Medical Center

TENNESSEE

Crossville
Alliance
Cumberland Medical Center

Elizabethton
Alliance
Sycamore Shoals Hospital

Erwin
Alliance
Unicoi County Memorial Hospital

Greeneville
Alliance
Greeneville Community Hospital East

Johnson City
Alliance
Franklin Woods Community Hospital

Johnson City Medical Center

Quillen Rehabilitation Hospital

Kingsport
Alliance
Indian Path Medical Center

Knoxville
Alliance
University of Tennessee
Medical Center

Maryville
Alliance
Blount Memorial Hospital

Mountain City
Alliance
Johnson County Community Hospital

TEXAS

The Woodlands
Alliance
Woodlands Specialty Hospital

VIRGINIA

Abingdon
Alliance
Johnston Memorial Hospital

Chesapeake
Alliance
Chesapeake Regional Medical Center

Christiansburg
Alliance
Carilion New River Valley Medical Center

Clintwood
Alliance
Dickenson Community Hospital

Front Royal
Alliance
Warren Memorial Hospital

Gloucester
Alliance
Riverside Walter Reed Hospital

Grundy
Alliance
Buchanan General Hospital

Lebanon
Alliance
Russell County Medical Center

Lexington
Alliance
Carilion Stonewall Jackson Hospital

Luray
Alliance
Page Memorial Hospital

Marion
Alliance
Smyth County Community Hospital

Newport News
Alliance
Riverside Regional Medical Center

Norton
Alliance
Norton Community Hospital

Onancock
Alliance
Riverside Shore Memorial Hospital

Pearisburg
Alliance
Carilion Giles Community Hospital

Roanoke
Alliance
Carilion Roanoke Memorial Hospital

Rocky Mount
Alliance
Carilion Franklin Memorial Hospital

South Hill
Alliance
VCU Health Community
Memorial Hospital

Tappahannock
Alliance
Riverside Tappahannock Hospital

Tazewell
Alliance
Carilion Tazewell Community Hospital

Williamsburg
Alliance
Riverside Doctors' Hospital Williamsburg

Winchester
Alliance
Winchester Medical Center

Woodstock
Alliance
Valley Health Shenandoah
Memorial Hospital

WEST VIRGINIA

Berkeley Springs
Alliance
War Memorial Hospital

Charleston
Alliance
Saint Francis Hospital

Elkins
Alliance
Davis Medical Center

Huntington
Alliance
Cabell Huntington Hospital

St. Mary's Medical Center

Kingwood
Alliance
Preston Memorial Hospital

Morgantown
Alliance
Mon Health Medical Center

Point Pleasant
Alliance
Pleasant Valley Hospital

Romney
Alliance
Hampshire Memorial Hospital

South Charleston
Alliance
Thomas Memorial Hospital

CATHOLIC CEO HEALTHCARE CONNECTION
50 South Main Street, Suite 200,
Naperville, IL, Zip 60540–5484;
tel. 630/352–2220; Roger N. Butler,
Executive Director

COLORADO

Broomfield
Alliance
SCL Health

ILLINOIS

Peoria
Alliance
OSF Healthcare

Springfield
Alliance
HSHS Hospital Sisters Health System

LOUISIANA

Baton Rouge
Alliance
Franciscan Missionaries of Our Lady Health System, Inc.

MARYLAND

Marriottsville
Alliance
Bon Secours Mercy Health

MISSOURI

Chesterfield
Alliance
Mercy

Saint Louis
Alliance
Ascension Healthcare

SSM Health

OHIO

Cincinnati
Alliance
Mercy Health

SOUTH DAKOTA

Sioux Falls
Alliance
Avera Health

TEXAS

Irving
Alliance
  CHRISTUS Health

WASHINGTON

Renton
Alliance
  Providence St. Joseph Health

Vancouver
Alliance
  PeaceHealth

WISCONSIN

Manitowoc
Alliance
  Franciscan Sisters of Christian Charity Sponsored
  Ministries, Inc.

HEALTH ENTERPRISES COOPERATIVE
5825 Dry Creek Lane NE, Cedar Rapids,
IA, Zip 52402–1225; tel. 319/368–
3619; Judy L. Sadler, President and
Chief Executive Officer

IOWA

Ames
Alliance
  Mary Greeley Medical Center

Chariton
Alliance
  Lucas County Health Center

Charles City
Alliance
  Floyd County Medical Center

Cherokee
Alliance
  Cherokee Regional Medical Center

Davenport
Alliance
  Genesis Health System

Denison
Alliance
  Crawford County Memorial Hospital

Des Moines
Alliance
  Broadlawns Medical Center

Fairfield
Alliance
  Jefferson County Health Center

Grinnell
Alliance
  UnityPoint Health – Grinnell Regional
  Medical Center

Guthrie Center
Alliance
  Guthrie County Hospital

Humboldt
Alliance
  Humboldt County Memorial Hospital

Ida Grove
Alliance
  Horn Memorial Hospital

Independence
Alliance
  Buchanan County Health Center

Iowa City
Alliance
  MercyOne Iowa City Medical Center

Manchester
Alliance
  Regional Medical Center

Maquoketa
Alliance
  Jackson County Regional Health Center

Marshalltown
Alliance
  UnityPoint Health – Marshalltown

Mount Pleasant
Alliance
  Henry County Health Center

Newton
Alliance
  MercyOne Newton Medical Center

Oskaloosa
Alliance
  Mahaska Health Partnership

Pella
Alliance
  Pella Regional Health Center

Pocahontas
Alliance
  Pocahontas Community Hospital

Sac City
Alliance
  Loring Hospital

Waukon
Alliance
  Veterans Memorial Hospital

Waverly
Alliance
  Waverly Health Center

West Burlington
Alliance
  Great River Health System

MISSOURI

Bethany
Alliance
  Harrison County Community Hospital

Fairfax
Alliance
  Community Hospital–Fairfax

HOSPITAL NETWORK VENTURES, LLC
6212 American Avenue, Portage,
MI, Zip 49002; tel. 269/329–3200;
Gregory L. Hedegore, President and
Chief Executive Officer

MICHIGAN

Allegan
Alliance
  Allegan General Hospital

Kalamazoo
Alliance
  Bronson Healthcare Group

  Bronson Methodist Hospital

Marshall
Alliance
  Oaklawn Hospital

Sturgis
Alliance
  Sturgis Hospital

HOSPITAL SHARED SERVICES ASSOCIATION
P O Box 19741, Seattle, WA,
Zip 98109–6741; tel. 206/399–0865;
Joe McNamee, Executive Director

OREGON

Salem
Alliance
  Oregon State Hospital

WASHINGTON

Bellevue
Alliance
  Overlake Medical Center

Chelan
Alliance
  Lake Chelan Community Hospital and Clinics

Clarkston
Alliance
  Tri–State Memorial Hospital

Davenport
Alliance
  Lincoln Hospital

Edmonds
Alliance
  Swedish/Edmonds

Ephrata
Alliance
  Columbia Basin Hospital

Grand Coulee
Alliance
  Coulee Medical Center

Kirkland
Alliance
  EvergreenHealth

Medical Lake
Alliance
  Eastern State Hospital

Moses Lake
Alliance
  Samaritan Healthcare

Mount Vernon
Alliance
  Skagit Regional Health

Newport
Alliance
  Newport Hospital and Health Services

Odessa
Alliance
  Odessa Memorial Healthcare Center

Othello
Alliance
  Othello Community Hospital

Prosser
Alliance
  Prosser Memorial Health

Pullman
Alliance
  Pullman Regional Hospital

Quincy
Alliance
  Quincy Valley Medical Center

Republic
Alliance
  Ferry County Memorial Hospital

Ritzville
Alliance
  East Adams Rural Healthcare

Tacoma
Alliance
  Western State Hospital

Tonasket
Alliance
  North Valley Hospital

KENTUCKY HEALTH COLLABORATIVE
651 Perimeter Drive, Suite 650,
Lexington, KY, Zip 40517–4134;
tel. 859/286–3107; David Zimba,
Managing Director

KENTUCKY

Bowling Green
Alliance
  Medical Center at Bowling Green

Danville
Alliance
  Ephraim McDowell Health

Edgewood
Alliance
  St. Elizabeth Healthcare

Lexington
Alliance
  Appalachian Regional Healthcare, Inc.

  University of Kentucky Albert B. Chandler Hospital

Louisville
Alliance
  Baptist Health

  Norton Healthcare

Morehead
Alliance
  St. Claire HealthCare

Owensboro
Alliance
  Owensboro Health

TENNESSEE

Brentwood
Alliance
LifePoint Health

MEDI–SOTA, INC.
1280 Locust Street Suite 16, Dawson, MN Zip 56232–2375; tel. 320/769–2269; Deb Ranallo, Executive Director

MINNESOTA

Appleton
Alliance
Appleton Area Health Services

Arlington
Alliance
Ridgeview Sibley Medical Center

Benson
Alliance
Swift County – Benson Health Services

Blue Earth
Alliance
United Hospital District

Canby
Alliance
Sanford Canby Medical Center

Dawson
Alliance
Johnson Memorial Health Services

Elbow Lake
Alliance
Prairie Ridge Hospital and Health Services

Glencoe
Alliance
Glencoe Regional Health

Glenwood
Alliance
Glacial Ridge Health System

Graceville
Alliance
Essentia Health–Graceville

Granite Falls
Alliance
Granite Falls Health

Hendricks
Alliance
Hendricks Community Hospital Association

Litchfield
Alliance
Meeker Memorial Hospital

Madelia
Alliance
Madelia Community Hospital

Madison
Alliance
Madison Healthcare Services

Mahnomen
Alliance
Mahnomen Health Center

Marshall
Alliance
Avera Marshall Regional Medical Center

Montevideo
Alliance
CCM Health

Olivia
Alliance
RC Hospital and Clinics

Ortonville
Alliance
Ortonville Area Health Services

Paynesville
Alliance
CentraCare Health–Paynesville

Perham
Alliance
Perham Health

Pipestone
Alliance
Pipestone County Medical Center Avera

Redwood Falls
Alliance
Carris Health – Redwood

Saint Peter
Alliance
River's Edge Hospital and Clinic

Slayton
Alliance
Murray County Medical Center

Sleepy Eye
Alliance
Sleepy Eye Medical Center

Staples
Alliance
Lakewood Health System

Tracy
Alliance
Sanford Tracy Medical Center

Tyler
Alliance
Avera Tyler Hospital

Wadena
Alliance
Tri–County Hospital

Willmar
Alliance
Rice Memorial Hospital

Windom
Alliance
Windom Area Hospital

NORTHWEST KANSAS HEALTH ALLIANCE
2220 Canterbury Drive, Hays, KS, Zip 67601–2370; tel. 785/623–2300; Edward Herrman, R.N., FACHE, President and Chief Executive Officer

KANSAS

Ashland
Alliance
Ashland Health Center

Atwood
Alliance
Rawlins County Health Center

Beloit
Alliance
Mitchell County Hospital Health Systems

Colby
Alliance
Citizens Medical Center

Dighton
Alliance
Lane County Hospital

Dodge City
Alliance
Western Plains Medical Complex

Ellsworth
Alliance
Ellsworth County Medical Center

Garden City
Alliance
St. Catherine Hospital

Goodland
Alliance
Goodland Regional Medical Center

Great Bend
Alliance
University of Kansas Health System Great Bend Campus

Greensburg
Alliance
Kiowa County Memorial Hospital

Hill City
Alliance
Graham County Hospital

Hoisington
Alliance
Clara Barton Hospital

Hoxie
Alliance
Sheridan County Health Complex

Hutchinson
Alliance
Hutchinson Regional Medical Center

Jetmore
Alliance
Hodgeman County Health Center

Kinsley
Alliance
Edwards County Medical Center

La Crosse
Alliance
Rush County Memorial Hospital

Larned
Alliance
University of Kansas Health System Pawnee Valley Campus

Lawrence
Alliance
LMH Health

Leoti
Alliance
Wichita County Health Center

Lincoln
Alliance
Lincoln County Hospital

Lyons
Alliance
Hospital District No 1 of Rice County

Minneola
Alliance
Minneola District Hospital

Ness City
Alliance
Ness County Hospital District No 2

Norton
Alliance
Norton County Hospital

Oakley
Alliance
Logan County Hospital

Oberlin
Alliance
Decatur Health Systems

Osborne
Alliance
Osborne County Memorial Hospital

Ottawa
Alliance
Ransom Memorial Hospital

Phillipsburg
Alliance
Phillips County Health Systems

Plainville
Alliance
Rooks County Health Center

Quinter
Alliance
Gove County Medical Center

Ransom
Alliance
Grisell Memorial Hospital District One

Russell
Alliance
Russell Regional Hospital

Saint Francis
Alliance
Cheyenne County Hospital

Salina
Alliance
Salina Regional Health Center

Satanta
Alliance
Satanta District Hospital and Long Term Care

Scott City
Alliance
Scott County Hospital

Smith Center
Alliance
Smith County Memorial Hospital

Stafford
Alliance
Stafford County Hospital

Tribune
Alliance
Greeley County Health Services

Wakeeney
Alliance
Trego County–Lemke Memorial Hospital

OHSU PARTNERS
3303 SW Bond Avenue, Suite 6100, Mail Code: CH6P, Portland, OR, Zip 97239–4501; tel. 503/494–4036; Peter F. Rapp, Chief Executive Officer

OREGON
Hillsboro
Alliance
Tuality Healthcare

Salem
Alliance
Salem Health

PANDION SOURCING & CONSULTING REGIONAL CORPORATION
3445 Winton Place, Suite 222, Rochester, NY, Zip 14623–2950; tel. 888/732–4282; Travis Heider, President and Chief Executive Officer

GEORGIA
Fort Oglethorpe
Alliance
CHI Memorial Hospital – Georgia

NEW JERSEY
Berkeley Heights
Alliance
Runnells Center for Rehabilitation and Healthcare

Newark
Alliance
Columbus Hospital LTACH

NEW YORK
Batavia
Alliance
United Memorial Medical Center

Bath
Alliance
Bath Veterans Affairs Medical Center

Ira Davenport Memorial Hospital

Buffalo
Alliance
Erie County Medical Center

Roswell Park Comprehensive Cancer Center

Sisters of Charity Hospital of Buffalo

Canandaigua
Alliance
F. F. Thompson Hospital

Clifton Springs
Alliance
Clifton Springs Hospital and Clinic

Corning
Alliance
Guthrie Corning Hospital

Dansville
Alliance
Nicholas H. Noyes Memorial Hospital

Dunkirk
Alliance
Brooks Memorial Hospital

Elmira
Alliance
Arnot Ogden Medical Center

St. Joseph's Hospital

Geneva
Alliance
Finger Lakes Hospital

Hornell
Alliance
St. James Mercy Hospital

Ithaca
Alliance
Cayuga Medical Center at Ithaca

Jamestown
Alliance
UPMC Chautauqua WCA

Kenmore
Alliance
Kenmore Mercy Hospital

Lewiston
Alliance
Mount St. Mary's Hospital and Health Center

Montour Falls
Alliance
Schuyler Hospital

Newark
Alliance
Newark–Wayne Community Hospital

Niagara Falls
Alliance
Niagara Falls Memorial Medical Center

Olean
Alliance
Olean General Hospital

Penn Yan
Alliance
Soldiers and Sailors Memorial Hospital of Yates County

Rochester
Alliance
Highland Hospital

Rochester General Hospital

Strong Memorial Hospital of the University of Rochester

Unity Hospital

Springville
Alliance
Bertrand Chaffee Hospital

Wellsville
Alliance
Jones Memorial Hospital

PENNSYLVANIA
Bradford
Alliance
Bradford Regional Medical Center

PANDION SOURCING NATIONAL LLC
3445 Winton Place, Suite 222, Rochester, NY, Zip 14623–2950; tel. 888/732–4282; Travis Heider, President and Chief Executive Officer

GEORGIA
Fort Oglethorpe
Alliance
CHI Memorial Hospital – Georgia

NEW JERSEY
Berkeley Heights
Alliance
Runnells Center for Rehabilitation and Healthcare

Newark
Alliance
Columbus Hospital LTACH

NEW YORK
Dansville
Alliance
Nicholas H. Noyes Memorial Hospital

Geneva
Alliance
Finger Lakes Hospital

Lockport
Alliance
Eastern Niagara Hospital

Penn Yan
Alliance
Soldiers and Sailors Memorial Hospital of Yates County

Springville
Alliance
Bertrand Chaffee Hospital

Wellsville
Alliance
Jones Memorial Hospital

PENNANT HEALTH ALLIANCE
2122 Health Drive SW Suite 100, Wyoming, MI, Zip 49519–9698; tel. 616/252–6800; Michael D. Faas, Chief Executive Officer

MICHIGAN
Ann Arbor
Alliance
Michigan Medicine

Cadillac
Alliance
Munson Healthcare Cadillac Hospital

Grand Rapids
Alliance
Mary Free Bed Rehabilitation Hospital

Mercy Health Saint Mary's

Grayling
Alliance
Munson Healthcare Grayling Hospital

Wyoming
Alliance
Metro Health – University of Michigan Health

PREMIER, INC.
13034 Ballantyne Corporate Place, Charlotte, NC, Zip 28277–1498; tel. 704/816 5353; Susan DeVore, President and Chief Executive Officer

ALABAMA
Dothan
Alliance
Southeast Alabama Medical Center

Opelika
Alliance
East Alabama Medical Center

ARIZONA
Phoenix
Alliance
Banner Health

Scottsdale
Alliance
HonorHealth

ARKANSAS
Batesville
Alliance
White River Medical Center

Pine Bluff
Alliance
Jefferson Regional Medical Center

CALIFORNIA
Fresno
Alliance
Community Medical Centers

Loma Linda
Alliance
Loma Linda University Medical Center

Los Angeles
Alliance
Verity Health System

Mountain View
Alliance
El Camino Hospital

Rancho Mirage
Alliance
Eisenhower Medical Center

Roseville
Alliance
  Adventist Health

CONNECTICUT
Hartford
Alliance
  Saint Francis Hospital and Medical Center

Waterbury
Alliance
  Saint Mary's Hospital

DELAWARE
Dover
Alliance
  Bayhealth Medical Center

Lewes
Alliance
  Beebe Healthcare

FLORIDA
Altamonte Springs
Alliance
  AdventHealth

Clearwater
Alliance
  BayCare Health System

Coral Gables
Alliance
  Baptist Health South Florida

Dunedin
Alliance
  BayCare Alliant Hospital

Jacksonville
Alliance
  Baptist Health
  Nemours

Miami Beach
Alliance
  Mount Sinai Medical Center

Tampa
Alliance
  H. Lee Moffitt Cancer Center and Research Institute

Vero Beach
Alliance
  Cleveland Clinic Indian River Hospital

Winter Haven
Alliance
  Winter Haven Hospital

GEORGIA
Carrollton
Alliance
  Tanner Medical Center–Carrollton

Lagrange
Alliance
  Wellstar West Georgia Medical Center

Savannah
Alliance
  Memorial Health
  St. Joseph's Hospital

HAWAII
Honolulu
Alliance
  Kuakini Medical Center

ILLINOIS
Chicago
Alliance
  Mount Sinai Hospital

Harvey
Alliance
  Ingalls Memorial Hospital

Naperville
Alliance
  Edward Hospital

Peoria
Alliance
  UnityPoint Health – Peoria

Urbana
Alliance
  Carle Foundation Hospital

INDIANA
Gary
Alliance
  Methodist Hospitals

KENTUCKY
Ashland
Alliance
  King's Daughters Medical Center

Bowling Green
Alliance
  Commonwealth Regional Specialty Hospital

Danville
Alliance
  Ephraim McDowell Regional Medical Center

Edgewood
Alliance
  St. Elizabeth Edgewood

Glasgow
Alliance
  T. J. Samson Community Hospital

Henderson
Alliance
  Methodist Hospital

Louisville
Alliance
  Alliant Management Services
  Baptist Health
  Norton Healthcare

Murray
Alliance
  Murray–Calloway County Hospital

LOUISIANA
Baton Rouge
Alliance
  Woman's Hospital

Hammond
Alliance
  North Oaks Health System

Houma
Alliance
  Terrebonne General Medical Center

Lafayette
Alliance
  Lafayette General Medical Center

Marrero
Alliance
  West Jefferson Medical Center

MAINE
Lewiston
Alliance
  Central Maine Medical Center

MARYLAND
Annapolis
Alliance
  Anne Arundel Medical Center

Baltimore
Alliance
  Greater Baltimore Medical Center
  Johns Hopkins Health System
  Mercy Medical Center
  Sinai Hospital of Baltimore

Cumberland
Alliance
  Western Maryland Regional Medical Center

Elkton
Alliance
  Union Hospital

Frederick
Alliance
  Frederick Regional Health System

Gaithersburg
Alliance
  Adventist HealthCare

Hagerstown
Alliance
  Meritus Medical Center

Lanham
Alliance
  Doctors Community Hospital

Marriottsville
Alliance
  Bon Secours Mercy Health

Randallstown
Alliance
  Northwest Hospital

Salisbury
Alliance
  Peninsula Regional Medical Center

Westminster
Alliance
  Carroll Hospital Center

MASSACHUSETTS
Boston
Alliance
  Tufts Medical Center

Fall River
Alliance
  Southcoast Hospitals Group

Springfield
Alliance
  Baystate Health, Inc.

MICHIGAN
Detroit
Alliance
  Henry Ford Health System

Grand Blanc
Alliance
  McLaren Health Care Corporation

Jackson
Alliance
  Henry Ford Allegiance Health

MINNESOTA
Minneapolis
Alliance
  Fairview Health Services

MISSISSIPPI
Laurel
Alliance
  South Central Regional Medical Center

Meridian
Alliance
  Rush Health Systems

MISSOURI
Saint Joseph
Alliance
  Mosaic Life Care at St. Joseph – Medical Center

Saint Louis
Alliance
  SSM Health

MONTANA
Billings
Alliance
  Billings Clinic

NEW MEXICO
Albuquerque
Alliance
  Presbyterian Healthcare Services

NEW YORK
Rochester
Alliance
  Pandion Sourcing National LLC
  Rochester Regional Health

NORTH CAROLINA
Asheboro
Alliance
  Randolph Hospital

Boone
Alliance
  Watauga Medical Center

Charlotte
Alliance
  Atrium Health

Fayetteville
Alliance
Cape Fear Valley Health System

Gastonia
Alliance
CaroMont Regional Medical Center

Goldsboro
Alliance
Wayne UNC Health Care

Greensboro
Alliance
Moses H. Cone Memorial Hospital

Hendersonville
Alliance
Margaret R. Pardee Memorial Hospital

Hickory
Alliance
Catawba Valley Medical Center

Kinston
Alliance
UNC Lenoir Healthcare

Lumberton
Alliance
Southeastern Health

Morehead City
Alliance
Carteret Health Care

Pinehurst
Alliance
FirstHealth of the Carolinas

Roanoke Rapids
Alliance
Halifax Regional Medical Center

Statesville
Alliance
Iredell Health System

OHIO
Akron
Alliance
Summa Health System

Cincinnati
Alliance
Mercy Health

Cleveland
Alliance
University Hospitals

Elyria
Alliance
University Hospitals Elyria
Medical Center

Kettering
Alliance
Kettering Medical Center

Middleburg Heights
Alliance
Southwest General Health Center

Parma
Alliance
University Hospitals Parma
Medical Center

Sandusky
Alliance
Firelands Regional Health System

OKLAHOMA
Tulsa
Alliance
Saint Francis Hospital

OREGON
Salem
Alliance
Salem Hospital

PENNSYLVANIA
Beaver
Alliance
Heritage Valley Health System

Bethlehem
Alliance
St. Luke's University Health Network

Danville
Alliance
Geisinger

King of Prussia
Alliance
Universal Health Services, Inc.

Philadelphia
Alliance
Einstein Healthcare Network

Washington
Alliance
Washington Hospital

SOUTH CAROLINA
Anderson
Alliance
AnMed Health Medical Center

Conway
Alliance
Conway Medical Center

Greenwood
Alliance
Self Regional Healthcare

West Columbia
Alliance
Lexington Medical Center

SOUTH DAKOTA
Rapid City
Alliance
Rapid City Regional Hospital

Sioux Falls
Alliance
Avera Health

TENNESSEE
Crossville
Alliance
Cumberland Medical Center

Greeneville
Alliance
Greeneville Community Hospital East

Knoxville
Alliance
University of Tennessee Medical Center

Maryville
Alliance
Blount Memorial Hospital

TEXAS
Arlington
Alliance
Texas Health Resources

Dallas
Alliance
Methodist Health System

University of Texas Southwestern Medical Center

Galveston
Alliance
University of Texas Medical Branch

Houston
Alliance
Harris Health System

University of Texas M.D. Anderson Cancer Center

Lubbock
Alliance
University Medical Center

VIRGINIA
Abingdon
Alliance
Johnston Memorial Hospital

Chesapeake
Alliance
Chesapeake Regional Medical Center

Falls Church
Alliance
Inova Health System

Marion
Alliance
Smyth County Community Hospital

Newport News
Alliance
Riverside Health System

Roanoke
Alliance
Carilion Clinic

South Hill
Alliance
VCU Health Community
Memorial Hospital

Winchester
Alliance
Valley Health System

WASHINGTON
Seattle
Alliance
Kaiser Permanente Capitol Hill Campus

Vancouver
Alliance
PeaceHealth

WEST VIRGINIA
Elkins
Alliance
Davis Medical Center

Huntington
Alliance
Cabell Huntington Hospital

Pallottine Health Services

Morgantown
Alliance
Mon Health Medical Center

Parkersburg
Alliance
Camden Clark Medical Center

Point Pleasant
Alliance
Pleasant Valley Hospital

South Charleston
Alliance
Thomas Memorial Hospital

Weirton
Alliance
Weirton Medical Center

THE NEW JERSEY COUNCIL OF TEACHING HOSPITALS
154 West State Street, Trenton, NJ, Zip 8608; tel. 609/656-9600; Deborah S. Briggs, President

NEW JERSEY
Camden
Alliance
Cooper University Health Care

Hackensack
Alliance
Hackensack Meridian Health
Hackensack University Medical Center

Marlton
Alliance
Weisman Children's Rehabilitation Hospital

Montclair
Alliance
Hackensack Meridian Health Mountainside Medical Center

Morristown
Alliance
Atlantic Health System

Morristown Medical Center

New Brunswick
Alliance
Children's Specialized Hospital

North Bergen
Alliance
Hackensack Meridian Health Palisades Medical Center

Paterson
Alliance
St. Joseph's University Medical Center

Summit
Alliance
   Overlook Medical Center

UNITED IROQUOIS SHARED SERVICES, INC.
   15 Executive Park Drive, Clifton Park, NY, Zip 12065–5631; tel. 518/383–5060; Gary J. Fitzgerald, President

NEW YORK
Albany
Alliance
   Albany Memorial Hospital

   St. Peter's Hospital

Alexandria Bay
Alliance
   River Hospital

Amsterdam
Alliance
   St. Mary's Healthcare

Auburn
Alliance
   Auburn Community Hospital

Binghamton
Alliance
   Our Lady of Lourdes Memorial Hospital, Inc.

   United Health Services Hospitals–Binghamton

Buffalo
Alliance
   Roswell Park Comprehensive Cancer Center

Carthage
Alliance
   Carthage Area Hospital

Cobleskill
Alliance
   Cobleskill Regional Hospital

Cooperstown
Alliance
   Bassett Medical Center

Cortland
Alliance
   Cortland Regional Medical Center

Cuba
Alliance
   Cuba Memorial Hospital

Delhi
Alliance
   O'Connor Hospital

Elizabethtown
Alliance
   The University of Vermont Health Network Elizabethtown Community Hospital

Glens Falls
Alliance
   Glens Falls Hospital

Glenville
Alliance
   Conifer Park

Gloversville
Alliance
   Nathan Littauer Hospital and Nursing Home

Hamilton
Alliance
   Community Memorial Hospital

Hudson
Alliance
   Columbia Memorial Hospital

Ithaca
Alliance
   Cayuga Medical Center at Ithaca

Little Falls
Alliance
   Little Falls Hospital

Lowville
Alliance
   Lewis County General Hospital

Malone
Alliance
   The University of Vermont Health Network – Alice Hyde Medical Center

Margaretville
Alliance
   Margaretville Hospital

Massena
Alliance
   Massena Memorial Hospital

Norwich
Alliance
   UHS Chenango Memorial Hospital

Ogdensburg
Alliance
   Claxton–Hepburn Medical Center

Olean
Alliance
   Olean General Hospital

Oneida
Alliance
   Oneida Healthcare

Oneonta
Alliance
   Aurelia Osborn Fox Memorial Hospital

Oswego
Alliance
   Oswego Hospital

Plattsburgh
Alliance
   The University of Vermont Health Network–Champlain Valley Physicians Hospital

Potsdam
Alliance
   Canton–Potsdam Hospital

Rome
Alliance
   Rome Memorial Hospital

Saranac Lake
Alliance
   Adirondack Health

Saratoga Springs
Alliance
   Saratoga Hospital

Schenectady
Alliance
   Ellis Hospital

   Sunnyview Rehabilitation Hospital

Springville
Alliance
   Bertrand Chaffee Hospital

Star Lake
Alliance
   Clifton–Fine Hospital

Syracuse
Alliance
   Crouse Health

   Upstate University Hospital

Troy
Alliance
   Samaritan Hospital – Main Campus

Utica
Alliance
   Faxton St. Luke's Healthcare

   St. Elizabeth Medical Center

Walton
Alliance
   UHS Delaware Valley Hospital

Watertown
Alliance
   Samaritan Medical Center

UNIVERSITY OF IOWA HEALTH ALLIANCE
   1755 59th Place, West Des Moines, IA, Zip 50266–7737; tel. 515/643–4000; Jennifer Vermeer, President and Chief Executive Officer

ILLINOIS
Aledo
Alliance
   Genesis Medical Center–Aledo

Silvis
Alliance
   Genesis Medical Center, Silvis

IOWA
Albia
Alliance
   Monroe County Hospital and Clinics

Algona
Alliance
   Kossuth Regional Health Center

Audubon
Alliance
   Audubon County Memorial Hospital and Clinics

Belmond
Alliance
   Iowa Specialty Hospital–Belmond

Bloomfield
Alliance
   Davis County Hospital

Britt
Alliance
   Hancock County Health System

Cedar Falls
Alliance
   MercyOne Cedar Falls Medical Center

Cedar Rapids
Alliance
   Mercy Medical Center – Cedar Rapids

Centerville
Alliance
   MercyOne Centerville Medical Center

Clarinda
Alliance
   Clarinda Regional Health Center

Clarion
Alliance
   Iowa Specialty Hospital–Clarion

Clinton
Alliance
   MercyOne Clinton Medical Center

Corydon
Alliance
   Wayne County Hospital

Cresco
Alliance
   Regional Health Services of Howard County

Davenport
Alliance
   Genesis Medical Center, Davenport

De Witt
Alliance
   Genesis Medical Center, DeWitt

Des Moines
Alliance
   Mercy Medical Center–Des Moines

Dubuque
Alliance
   Mercy Medical Center–Dubuque

Dyersville
Alliance
   Mercy Medical Center–Dyersville

Elkader
Alliance
   MercyOne Elkader Medical Center

Emmetsburg
Alliance
   Palo Alto County Health System

Fairfield
Alliance
   Jefferson County Health Center

Greenfield
Alliance
   Adair County Health System

Grinnell
Alliance
UnityPoint Health – Grinnell Regional Medical Center

Hampton
Alliance
Franklin General Hospital

Hawarden
Alliance
Hawarden Regional Healthcare

Iowa City
Alliance
University of Iowa Hospitals and Clinics

Iowa Falls
Alliance
Hansen Family Hospital

Keosauqua
Alliance
Van Buren County Hospital

Knoxville
Alliance
Knoxville Hospital & Clinics

Leon
Alliance
Decatur County Hospital

Manning
Alliance
Manning Regional Healthcare Center

Maquoketa
Alliance
Jackson County Regional Health Center

Mason City
Alliance
MercyOne North Iowa Medical Center

Mount Ayr
Alliance
Ringgold County Hospital

Mount Pleasant
Alliance
Henry County Health Center

New Hampton
Alliance
MercyOne New Hampton Medical Center

Oelwein
Alliance
MercyOne Oelwein Medical Center

Osage
Alliance
Mitchell County Regional Health Center

Pella
Alliance
Pella Regional Health Center

Perry
Alliance
Dallas County Hospital

Primghar
Alliance
MercyOne Primghar Medical Center

Sigourney
Alliance
Keokuk County Health Center

Sioux City
Alliance
MercyOne Siouxland Medical Center

Vinton
Alliance
Virginia Gay Hospital

Washington
Alliance
Washington County Hospital and Clinics

Waterloo
Alliance
MercyOne Waterloo Medical Center

Waverly
Alliance
Waverly Health Center

Webster City
Alliance
Van Diest Medical Center

Winterset
Alliance
Madison County Health Care System

NEBRASKA
Oakland
Alliance
MercyOne Oakland Medical Center

Pender
Alliance
Pender Community Hospital

VANTAGE HEALTHCARE NETWORK, INC.
18282 Technology Drive, Suite 202, Meadville, PA, Zip 16335; tel. 814/337–0000; David Petrarca, Director Retail Operations

PENNSYLVANIA
Corry
Alliance
LECOM Corry Memorial Hospital

DuBois
Alliance
Penn Highlands DuBois

Ellwood City
Alliance
Ellwood City Medical Center, LLC

Erie
Alliance
LECOM Health Millcreek Community Hospital

Saint Vincent Hospital

Farrell
Alliance
UPMC Horizon

Kane
Alliance
UPMC Kane

Kittanning
Alliance
ACMH Hospital

Meadville
Alliance
Meadville Medical Center

Saint Marys
Alliance
Penn Highlands Elk

Seneca
Alliance
UPMC Northwest

Titusville
Alliance
Titusville Area Hospital

Warren
Alliance
Warren General Hospital

VIZIENT, INC.
290 East John Carpenter Freeway, Irving, TX Zip 75062–2730; tel. 972/830–0000; Curtis W. Nonomaque, President and Chief Executive Officer

ALABAMA
Alexander City
Alliance
Russell Medical

Anniston
Alliance
RMC Anniston

Athens
Alliance
Athens–Limestone Hospital

Atmore
Alliance
Atmore Community Hospital

Bay Minette
Alliance
North Baldwin Infirmary

Bessemer
Alliance
Medical West

Birmingham
Alliance
University of Alabama Hospital

Boaz
Alliance
Marshall Medical Center South

Brewton
Alliance
D. W. McMillan Memorial Hospital

Carrollton
Alliance
Pickens County Medical Center

Decatur
Alliance
Decatur Morgan Hospital

Fairhope
Alliance
Thomas Hospital

Fayette
Alliance
Fayette Medical Center

Guntersville
Alliance
Marshall Health System

Marshall Medical Center North

Huntsville
Alliance
Huntsville Hospital

Mobile
Alliance
Mobile Infirmary Medical Center

USA Children's and Women's Hospital

USA Health University Hospital

Montgomery
Alliance
Baptist Medical Center East

Baptist Medical Center South

Opp
Alliance
Mizell Memorial Hospital

Ozark
Alliance
Dale Medical Center

Prattville
Alliance
Prattville Baptist Hospital

Red Bay
Alliance
Red Bay Hospital

Scottsboro
Alliance
Highlands Medical Center

Sheffield
Alliance
Helen Keller Hospital

Tuscaloosa
Alliance
DCH Health System

DCH Regional Medical Center

Union Springs
Alliance
Bullock County Hospital

ALASKA
Anchorage
Alliance
Providence Alaska Medical Center

St. Elias Specialty Hospital

Cordova
Alliance
Cordova Community Medical Center

Kodiak
Alliance
Providence Kodiak Island Medical Center

Alliances

Seward
Alliance
Providence Seward Medical Center

Valdez
Alliance
Providence Valdez Medical Center

Wrangell
Alliance
Wrangell Medical Center

AMERICAN SAMOA

Pago Pago
Alliance
Lyndon B. Johnson Tropical Medical Center

ARIZONA

Benson
Alliance
Benson Hospital

Bisbee
Alliance
Copper Queen Community Hospital

Flagstaff
Alliance
Flagstaff Medical Center

Green Valley
Alliance
Santa Cruz Valley Regional Hospital

Kingman
Alliance
Kingman Regional Medical Center

Phoenix
Alliance
Maricopa Integrated Health System
Mayo Clinic Hospital

Safford
Alliance
Mt. Graham Regional Medical Center

Tucson
Alliance
Banner – University Medical Center South
Banner – University Medical Center Tucson
TMC HealthCare

Willcox
Alliance
Northern Cochise Community Hospital

ARKANSAS

Arkadelphia
Alliance
Baptist Health Medical Center–Arkadelphia

Booneville
Alliance
Mercy Hospital Booneville

Clinton
Alliance
Ozark Health Medical Center

Conway
Alliance
Conway Regional Medical Center

Fayetteville
Alliance
Washington Regional Medical Center

Heber Springs
Alliance
Baptist Health Medical Center–Heber Springs

Hot Springs
Alliance
CHI St. Vincent Hot Springs

Jonesboro
Alliance
NEA Baptist Memorial Hospital
St. Bernards Medical Center

Little Rock
Alliance
Baptist Health Extended Care Hospital
Baptist Health Medical Center–Little Rock
Baptist Health
CHI St. Vincent Infirmary Medical Center

Malvern
Alliance
Baptist Health Medical Center–Hot Spring County

Morrilton
Alliance
CHI St. Vincent Morrilton

North Little Rock
Alliance
Baptist Health Medical Center – North Little Rock

Paragould
Alliance
Arkansas Methodist Medical Center

Piggott
Alliance
Piggott Community Hospital

Stuttgart
Alliance
Baptist Health Medical Center–Stuttgart

Walnut Ridge
Alliance
Lawrence Memorial Hospital

Wynne
Alliance
CrossRidge Community Hospital

CALIFORNIA

Alameda
Alliance
Alameda Hospital

Antioch
Alliance
Kaiser Permanente Antioch Medical Center

Arcadia
Alliance
Methodist Hospital of
Southern California

Auburn
Alliance
Sutter Auburn Faith Hospital

Bakersfield
Alliance
Kern Medical Center

Berkeley
Alliance
Alta Bates Medical Center–Herrick Campus
Alta Bates Summit Medical Center

Burbank
Alliance
Providence Saint Joseph Medical Center

Burlingame
Alliance
Mills–Peninsula Health Services

Castro Valley
Alliance
Eden Medical Center

Colton
Alliance
Arrowhead Regional Medical Center

Concord
Alliance
John Muir Medical Center, Concord

Covina
Alliance
Citrus Valley Health Partners
Citrus Valley Medical Center–Inter
Community Campus

Crescent City
Alliance
Sutter Coast Hospital

Davis
Alliance
Sutter Davis Hospital

Downey
Alliance
PIH Health Hospital – Downey
Rancho Los Amigos National Rehabilitation Center

El Centro
Alliance
El Centro Regional Medical Center

Escondido
Alliance
Palomar Health
Palomar Medical Center

Fairfield
Alliance
NorthBay Medical Center

Fremont
Alliance
Kaiser Permanente Fremont Medical Center
Washington Hospital Healthcare System

French Camp
Alliance
San Joaquin General Hospital

Fresno
Alliance
Community Medical Centers
Saint Agnes Medical Center

Glendora
Alliance
Foothill Presbyterian Hospital

Jackson
Alliance
Sutter Amador Hospital

King City
Alliance
Mee Memorial Hospital

Lakeport
Alliance
Sutter Lakeside Hospital

Lancaster
Alliance
Antelope Valley Hospital

Los Angeles
Alliance
Cedars–Sinai Medical Center
LAC+USC Medical Center
Martin Luther King, Jr. Community Hospital
Ronald Reagan UCLA Medical Center
Stewart & Lynda Resnick
Neuropsychiatric Hospital at UCLA
USC Norris Comprehensive Cancer Center

Los Banos
Alliance
Memorial Hospital Los Banos

Manteca
Alliance
Kaiser Permanente Manteca Medical Center

Marina Del Rey
Alliance
Marina Del Rey Hospital

Mariposa
Alliance
John C. Fremont Healthcare District

Martinez
Alliance
Contra Costa Regional Medical Center

Menlo Park
Alliance
Menlo Park Surgical Hospital

Mission Hills
Alliance
Providence Holy Cross Medical Center

Modesto
Alliance
Memorial Medical Center

Monterey
Alliance
Community Hospital of the Monterey Peninsula

Moreno Valley
Alliance
Riverside University Health System–Medical Center

Mountain View
Alliance
El Camino Hospital

Novato
Alliance
Novato Community Hospital

Oakland
Alliance
Alta Bates Summit Medical Center – Summit Campus
Highland Hospital
Kaiser Permanente Oakland Medical Center

Oceanside
Alliance
Tri–City Medical Center

Ojai
Alliance
Ojai Valley Community Hospital

Orange
Alliance
UC Irvine Medical Center

Palo Alto
Alliance
Lucile Salter Packard Children's Hospital Stanford
Stanford Health Care

Pleasanton
Alliance
Stanford Health Care – ValleyCare

Pomona
Alliance
Pomona Valley Hospital Medical Center

Porterville
Alliance
Sierra View Medical Center

Portola
Alliance
Eastern Plumas Health Care

Poway
Alliance
Palomar Medical Center Poway

Redlands
Alliance
Redlands Community Hospital

Redwood City
Alliance
Kaiser Permanente Redwood City Medical Center

Roseville
Alliance
Kaiser Permanente Roseville Medical Center
Sutter Roseville Medical Center

Sacramento
Alliance
Kaiser Permanente Sacramento Medical Center
Kaiser Permanente South Sacramento Medical Center
Shriners Hospitals for Children–Northern California
Sutter Center for Psychiatry
Sutter Health
Sutter Medical Center, Sacramento
University of California, Davis Medical Center

Salinas
Alliance
Natividad Medical Center

San Diego
Alliance
Scripps Health
UC San Diego Health

San Francisco
Alliance
California Pacific Medical Center–Davies Campus
California Pacific Medical Center–St. Luke's Campus
California Pacific Medical Center
Chinese Hospital
Kaiser Permanente San Francisco Medical Center
UCSF Medical Center
Zuckerberg San Francisco General Hospital and Trauma Center

San Jose
Alliance
Kaiser Permanente San Jose Medical Center
Santa Clara Valley Medical Center

San Leandro
Alliance
San Leandro Hospital

San Mateo
Alliance
San Mateo Medical Center

San Pedro
Alliance
Providence Little Company of Mary Medical Center
San Pedro

San Rafael
Alliance
Kaiser Permanente San Rafael Medical Center

Santa Barbara
Alliance
Cottage Health
Goleta Valley Cottage Hospital
Santa Barbara Cottage Hospital

Santa Clara
Alliance
Kaiser Permanente Santa Clara Medical Center

Santa Cruz
Alliance
Sutter Maternity and Surgery Center of Santa Cruz

Santa Monica
Alliance
Providence Saint John's Health Center
UCLA Medical Center–Santa Monica

Santa Rosa
Alliance
Kaiser Permanente Santa Rosa Medical Center
Sutter Santa Rosa Regional Hospital

Solvang
Alliance
Santa Ynez Valley Cottage Hospital

South San Francisco
Alliance
Kaiser Permanente South San Francisco

Stockton
Alliance
Dameron Hospital

Sylmar
Alliance
LAC–Olive View–UCLA Medical Center

Tarzana
Alliance
Providence Tarzana Medical Center

Torrance
Alliance
Harbor–UCLA Medical Center
Providence Little Company of Mary Medical Center – Torrance
Torrance Memorial Medical Center

Tracy
Alliance
Sutter Tracy Community Hospital

Vacaville
Alliance
Kaiser Permanente Vacaville Medical Center

Vallejo
Alliance
Kaiser Permanente Vallejo Medical Center
Sutter Solano Medical Center

Ventura
Alliance
Community Memorial Hospital

Walnut Creek
Alliance
John Muir Health
John Muir Medical Center, Walnut Creek
Kaiser Permanente Walnut Creek Medical Center

Whittier
Alliance
PIH Health Hospital – Whittier

Yuba City
Alliance
Sutter Surgical Hospital – North Valley

COLORADO
Alamosa
Alliance
San Luis Valley Health

Aurora
Alliance
University of Colorado Hospital

Boulder
Alliance
Boulder Community Health

Canon City
Alliance
St. Thomas More Hospital

Colorado Springs
Alliance
Penrose–St. Francis Health Services
UCHealth Memorial Hospital

Denver
Alliance
Denver Health
National Jewish Health

Durango
Alliance
Mercy Regional Medical Center

Englewood
Alliance
Craig Hospital

Estes Park
Alliance
Estes Park Medical Center

Fort Collins
Alliance
UCHealth Poudre Valley Hospital

Grand Junction
Alliance
St. Mary's Hospital and Medical Center

Gunnison
Alliance
Gunnison Valley Hospital

La Jara
Alliance
San Luis Valley Health Conejos
County Hospital

Lakewood
Alliance
St. Anthony Hospital

Loveland
Alliance
UCHealth Medical Center of the Rockies

Pueblo
Alliance
St. Mary–Corwin Medical Center

Steamboat Springs
Alliance
UCHealth Yampa Valley Medical Center

Westminster
Alliance
St. Anthony North Health Campus

Yuma
Alliance
Yuma District Hospital

CONNECTICUT
Bridgeport
Alliance
Bridgeport Hospital

Bristol
Alliance
Bristol Hospital

Danbury
Alliance
Danbury Hospital

Farmington
Alliance
UConn, John Dempsey Hospital

Greenwich
Alliance
Greenwich Hospital

Hartford
Alliance
Hartford Hospital
Saint Francis Hospital and Medical Center

Manchester
Alliance
Manchester Memorial Hospital

Middletown
Alliance
Connecticut Valley Hospital
Middlesex Hospital

Milford
Alliance
Milford Hospital

New Haven
Alliance
Connecticut Mental Health Center
Yale New Haven Health
Yale–New Haven Hospital

New London
Alliance
Lawrence + Memorial Hospital

Norwalk
Alliance
Norwalk Hospital

Putnam
Alliance
Day Kimball Hospital

Stamford
Alliance
Stamford Hospital

Torrington
Alliance
Charlotte Hungerford Hospital

Vernon
Alliance
Rockville General Hospital

DELAWARE
Wilmington
Alliance
St. Francis Hospital

DISTRICT OF COLUMBIA
Washington
Alliance
Howard University Hospital
MedStar Georgetown University Hospital
MedStar Washington Hospital Center
Sibley Memorial Hospital

FLORIDA
Apalachicola
Alliance
George E. Weems Memorial Hospital

Boca Raton
Alliance
Boca Raton Regional Hospital

Boynton Beach
Alliance
Bethesda Hospital East

Clermont
Alliance
South Lake Hospital

Cocoa Beach
Alliance
Health First Cape Canaveral Hospital

Coral Gables
Alliance
Baptist Health South Florida, Doctors Hospital

Daytona Beach
Alliance
Halifax Health Medical Center of Daytona Beach

Gainesville
Alliance
UF Health Shands Hospital

Gulf Breeze
Alliance
Gulf Breeze Hospital

Homestead
Alliance
Baptist Health South Florida, Homestead Hospital

Jacksonville
Alliance
Mayo Clinic Hospital in Florida

Jay
Alliance
Jay Hospital

Lakeland
Alliance
Lakeland Regional Health Medical Center

Leesburg
Alliance
Leesburg Regional Medical Center

Melbourne
Alliance
Health First Holmes Regional Medical Center

Miami
Alliance
Baptist Health South Florida, Baptist Hospital of Miami
Baptist Health South Florida, West Kendall Baptist Hospital
Jackson Health System

Milton
Alliance
West Florida Community Care Center

Naples
Alliance
NCH Baker Hospital

Ocoee
Alliance
Health Central Hospital

Orlando
Alliance
Orlando Health
Orlando Regional Medical Center

Palm Bay
Alliance
Health First Palm Bay Hospital

Panama City
Alliance
Bay Medical Sacred Heart

Pensacola
Alliance
Baptist Health Care Corporation
Baptist Hospital

Perry
Alliance
Doctor's Memorial Hospital

Rockledge
Alliance
Health First, Inc.

Starke
Alliance
Shands Starke Regional Medical Center

Stuart
Alliance
Cleveland Clinic Martin North Hospital

Tallahassee
Alliance
Tallahassee Memorial HealthCare

Tampa
Alliance
H. Lee Moffitt Cancer Center and Research Institute
Shriners Hospitals for Children–Tampa
Tampa General Hospital

Tavernier
Alliance
Baptist Health South Florida, Mariners Hospital

The Villages
Alliance
The Villages Regional Hospital

Titusville
Alliance
Parrish Medical Center

Vero Beach
Alliance
Cleveland Clinic Indian River Hospital

Weston
Alliance
Cleveland Clinic Florida

GEORGIA
Adel
Alliance
Cook Medical Center–A Campus of Tift Regional Medical Center

Albany
Alliance
Phoebe Putney Health System
Phoebe Putney Memorial Hospital

Americus
Alliance
Phoebe Sumter Medical Center

Athens
Alliance
Piedmont Athens Regional Medical Center
St. Mary's Health Care System

Atlanta
Alliance
Emory Saint Joseph's Hospital of Atlanta
Emory University Hospital Midtown
Emory University Hospital
Grady Memorial Hospital
Northside Hospital
Wellstar Atlanta Medical Center

Augusta
Alliance
Augusta University Medical Center
Charlie Norwood Veterans Affairs Medical Center
University Hospital

Austell
Alliance
WellStar Cobb Hospital

Braselton
Alliance
Northeast Georgia Medical Center Braselton

Brunswick
Alliance
Southeast Georgia Health System Brunswick Campus
Southeast Georgia Health System

Bryon
Alliance
Medical Center of Peach County, Navicent Health

Cairo
Alliance
Grady General Hospital

Camilla
Alliance
Mitchell County Hospital

Canton
Alliance
Northside Hospital–Cherokee

Cedartown
Alliance
Polk Medical Center

Claxton
Alliance
Evans Memorial Hospital

Columbus
Alliance
Columbus Regional Healthcare System
Columbus Specialty Hospital
Piedmont Columbus Regional Midtown
Piedmont Columbus Regional Northside

Cordele
Alliance
Crisp Regional Hospital

Cumming
Alliance
Northside Hospital–Forsyth

Cuthbert
Alliance
Southwest Georgia Regional Medical Center

Dalton
Alliance
Hamilton Medical Center

Decatur
Alliance
Emory Long–Term Acute Care

Douglas
Alliance
Coffee Regional Medical Center

Douglasville
Alliance
WellStar Douglas Hospital

Eatonton
Alliance
Putnam General Hospital

Fitzgerald
Alliance
Dorminy Medical Center

Gainesville
Alliance
Northeast Georgia Medical Center

Hiram
Alliance
WellStar Paulding Hospital

Homerville
Alliance
Clinch Memorial Hospital

Jackson
Alliance
Wellstar Sylvan Grove Hospital

Johns Creek
Alliance
Emory Johns Creek Hospital

Lakeland
Alliance
South Georgia Medical Center Lanier Campus

Lawrenceville
Alliance
Gwinnett Hospital System

Lithonia
Alliance
Emory Hillandale Hospital

Macon
Alliance
Medical Center, Navicent Health
Rehabilitation Hospital, Navicent Health

Marietta
Alliance
WellStar Health System
WellStar Kennestone Hospital
WellStar Windy Hill Hospital

Moultrie
Alliance
Colquitt Regional Medical Center

Nashville
Alliance
South Georgia Medical Center Berrien Campus

Newnan
Alliance
Southeastern Regional Medical Center

Perry
Alliance
Perry Hospital

Quitman
Alliance
Brooks County Hospital

Riverdale
Alliance
Southern Regional Medical Center

Rome
Alliance
Floyd Medical Center

Roswell
Alliance
Wellstar North Fulton Hospital

Saint Marys
Alliance
Southeast Georgia Health System C
amden Campus

Sandersville
Alliance
Washington County Regional Medical Center

Savannah
Alliance
Memorial Health

Swainsboro
Alliance
Emanuel Medical Center

Sylvester
Alliance
Phoebe Worth Medical Center

Thomasville
Alliance
Archbold Medical Center
John D. Archbold Memorial Hospital

Thomson
Alliance
University Hospital McDuffie

Tifton
Alliance
Tift Regional Medical Center

Valdosta
Alliance
South Georgia Medical Center

Warm Springs
Alliance
Roosevelt Warm Springs Rehabilitation
Hospital – Rehab
Roosevelt Warm Springs Rehabilitation and Specialty
Hospitals – LTAC

Warner Robins
Alliance
Houston Medical Center

Waycross
Alliance
Memorial Satilla Health

GUAM
Dededo
Alliance
Guam Regional Medical City

HAWAII
Aiea
Alliance
Pali Momi Medical Center

Ewa Beach
Alliance
Sutter Health Kahi Mohala

Honolulu
Alliance
Kaiser Permanente Medical Center
Queen's Health Systems
Shriners Hospitals for Children–Honolulu
Straub Medical Center
The Queen's Medical Center

Kamuela
Alliance
North Hawaii Community Hospital

Kaunakakai
Alliance
Molokai General Hospital

Wahiawa
Alliance
Wahiawa General Hospital

IDAHO
American Falls
Alliance
Power County Hospital District

Blackfoot
Alliance
Bingham Memorial Hospital

Boise
Alliance
Saint Alphonsus Regional Medical Center
St. Luke's Health System

Bonners Ferry
Alliance
Boundary Community Hospital

Cascade
Alliance
Cascade Medical Center

Coeur D'Alene
Alliance
Kootenai Health

Cottonwood
Alliance
St. Mary's Hospital

Emmett
Alliance
Valor Health

Orofino
Alliance
Clearwater Valley Hospital and Clinics

Preston
Alliance
Franklin County Medical Center

Rupert
Alliance
Minidoka Memorial Hospital

Sandpoint
Alliance
Bonner General Hospital

Weiser
Alliance
Weiser Memorial Hospital

ILLINOIS
Alton
Alliance
Alton Memorial Hospital

Arlington Heights
Alliance
Northwest Community Hospital

Aurora
Alliance
Rush–Copley Medical Center

Barrington
Alliance
Advocate Good Shepherd Hospital

Belleville
Alliance
Memorial Hospital

Bloomington
Alliance
OSF St. Joseph Medical Center

Canton
Alliance
Graham Hospital Association

Carbondale
Alliance
Memorial Hospital of Carbondale
Southern Illinois Healthcare

Chester
Alliance
Memorial Hospital

Chicago
Alliance
AMITA Health Resurrection Medical Center
Advocate Illinois Masonic Medical Center
Advocate Trinity Hospital
Ann & Robert H. Lurie Children's Hospital of Chicago
John H. Stroger Jr. Hospital of Cook County
La Rabida Children's Hospital
Louis A. Weiss Memorial Hospital
Mercy Hospital and Medical Center

Methodist Hospital of Chicago

Northwestern Memorial Hospital

Norwegian American Hospital

Provident Hospital of Cook County

Rush University Medical Center

Shriners Hospitals for Children–Chicago

Swedish Covenant Hospital

University of Chicago Medical Center

University of Illinois Hospital & Health Sciences System

Decatur
Alliance
Decatur Memorial Hospital

Downers Grove
Alliance
Advocate Good Samaritan Hospital

Eldorado
Alliance
Ferrell Hospital

Elgin
Alliance
Advocate Sherman Hospital

Elmhurst
Alliance
Elmhurst Hospital

Evanston
Alliance
NorthShore University Health System

Evergreen Park
Alliance
Little Company of Mary Hospital and Health Care Centers

Freeport
Alliance
FHN Memorial Hospital

Galesburg
Alliance
OSF St. Mary Medical Center

Geneva
Alliance
Northwestern Medicine Delnor Hospital

Greenville
Alliance
HSHS Holy Family Hospital in Greenville

Harvey
Alliance
Ingalls Memorial Hospital

Hazel Crest
Alliance
Advocate South Suburban Hospital

Herrin
Alliance
Herrin Hospital

Hinsdale
Alliance
Adventist Medical Center – Hinsdale

RML Specialty Hospital

Hoffman Estates
Alliance
Alexian Brothers Behavioral Health Hospital

Jacksonville
Alliance
Passavant Area Hospital

Jerseyville
Alliance
Jersey Community Hospital

Joliet
Alliance
AMITA Health Saint Joseph Medical Center

Kewanee
Alliance
OSF Saint Luke Medical Center

Lake Forest
Alliance
Northwestern Medicine Lake Forest Hospital

Libertyville
Alliance
Advocate Condell Medical Center

Lincoln
Alliance
Abraham Lincoln Memorial Hospital

Macomb
Alliance
McDonough District Hospital

Maryville
Alliance
Anderson Hospital

Mattoon
Alliance
Sarah Bush Lincoln Health Center

Maywood
Alliance
Loyola University Medical Center

McHenry
Alliance
Northwestern Medicine McHenry

Monticello
Alliance
Kirby Medical Center

Murphysboro
Alliance
St. Joseph Memorial Hospital

New Lenox
Alliance
Silver Cross Hospital

Oak Lawn
Alliance
Advocate Christ Medical Center

Oak Park
Alliance
Rush Oak Park Hospital

Palos Heights
Alliance
Palos Health

Park Ridge
Alliance
Advocate Lutheran General Hospital

Peoria
Alliance
OSF Saint Francis Medical Center

UnityPoint Health – Peoria

Pittsfield
Alliance
Illini Community Hospital

Pontiac
Alliance
OSF Saint James – John W. Albrecht Medical Center

Quincy
Alliance
Blessing Hospital

Rock Island
Alliance
UnityPoint Health – Trinity Rock Island

Rockford
Alliance
OSF Saint Anthony Medical Center

SwedishAmerican – A Division of UW Health

Rushville
Alliance
Sarah D. Culbertson Memorial Hospital

Salem
Alliance
Salem Township Hospital

Shelbyville
Alliance
HSHS Good Shepherd Hospital

Shiloh
Alliance
Memorial Hospital East

Springfield
Alliance
Memorial Health System

Memorial Medical Center

Taylorville
Alliance
Taylorville Memorial Hospital

Urbana
Alliance
Carle Foundation Hospital

Winfield
Alliance
Northwestern Medicine Central DuPage Hospital

INDIANA
Anderson
Alliance
Community Hospital of Anderson & Madison County

Angola
Alliance
Cameron Memorial Community Hospital

Auburn
Alliance
DeKalb Health

Avon
Alliance
Indiana University Health West Hospital

Batesville
Alliance
Margaret Mary Health

Bedford
Alliance
Indiana University Health Bedford Hospital

Bloomington
Alliance
Indiana University Health Bloomington Hospital

Carmel
Alliance
Indiana University Health North Hospital

Clinton
Alliance
Union Hospital Clinton

Columbia City
Alliance
Parkview Whitley Hospital

Columbus
Alliance
Columbus Regional Hospital

Danville
Alliance
Hendricks Regional Health

Elkhart
Alliance
Elkhart General Hospital

Evansville
Alliance
Deaconess Health System

Deaconess Midtown Hospital

Fort Wayne
Alliance
Parkview Ortho Hospital

Parkview Health

Parkview Regional Medical Center

Frankfort
Alliance
Indiana University Health Methodist Hospital

Franklin
Alliance
Johnson Memorial Hospital

Goshen
Alliance
Goshen Health

Hartford City
Alliance
Indiana University Health Blackford Hospital

Huntington
Alliance
Parkview Huntington Hospital

Indianapolis
Alliance
Community Health Network

Community Hospital East

Community Hospital North

Community Hospital South

Eskenazi Health

Indiana University Health University Hospital

Jasper
Alliance
Memorial Hospital and Health Care Center

Kendallville
Alliance
Parkview Noble Hospital

Knox
Alliance
Starke Hospital

Kokomo
Alliance
Community Howard Regional Health

La Porte
Alliance
La Porte Hospital

LaGrange
Alliance
Parkview LaGrange Hospital

Lafayette
Alliance
Indiana University Health Arnett Hospital

Logansport
Alliance
Logansport Memorial Hospital

Madison
Alliance
King's Daughters' Health

Marion
Alliance
Marion General Hospital

Monticello
Alliance
Indiana University Health White Memorial Hospital

Muncie
Alliance
Indiana University Health Ball Memorial Hospital

New Albany
Alliance
Baptist Health Floyd
Southern Indiana Rehabilitation Hospital

New Castle
Alliance
Henry Community Health

Newburgh
Alliance
Deaconess Gateway Hospital
The Women's Hospital

Noblesville
Alliance
Riverview Health

Paoli
Alliance
Indiana University Health Paoli Hospital

Portland
Alliance
Indiana University Health Jay Hospital

Richmond
Alliance
Reid Health

Rochester
Alliance
Woodlawn Hospital

Seymour
Alliance
Schneck Medical Center

Shelbyville
Alliance
Major Hospital

South Bend
Alliance
Healthwin Hospital
Memorial Hospital of South Bend

Terre Haute
Alliance
Union Hospital

Tipton
Alliance
Indiana University Health Tipton Hospital

Vincennes
Alliance
Good Samaritan Hospital

Wabash
Alliance
Parkview Wabash Hospital

IOWA

Anamosa
Alliance
UnityPoint Health – Jones Regional Medical Center

Atlantic
Alliance
Cass County Memorial Hospital

Bettendorf
Alliance
UnityPoint Health – Trinity Bettendorf

Cedar Rapids
Alliance
UnityPoint Health – St. Luke's Hospital

Centerville
Alliance
MercyOne Centerville Medical Center

Clarinda
Alliance
Clarinda Regional Health Center

Clinton
Alliance
MercyOne Clinton Medical Center

Corning
Alliance
CHI Health Mercy Corning

Council Bluffs
Alliance
Methodist Jennie Edmundson Hospital

Decorah
Alliance
Winneshiek Medical Center

Des Moines
Alliance
Mercy Medical Center–Des Moines
UnityPoint Health–Iowa Lutheran Hospital

Dubuque
Alliance
Mercy Medical Center–Dubuque
UnityPoint Health – Finley Hospital

Fort Dodge
Alliance
UnityPoint Health – Trinity Regional Medical Center

Grundy Center
Alliance
Grundy County Memorial Hospital

Guttenberg
Alliance
Guttenberg Municipal Hospital

Hamburg
Alliance
George C Grape Community Hospital

Hampton
Alliance
Franklin General Hospital

Harlan
Alliance
Myrtue Medical Center

Iowa City
Alliance
University of Iowa Hospitals and Clinics

Iowa Falls
Alliance
Hansen Family Hospital

Jefferson
Alliance
Greene County Medical Center

Keokuk
Alliance
UnityPoint Health–Keokuk

Keosauqua
Alliance
Van Buren County Hospital

Lake City
Alliance
Stewart Memorial Community Hospital

Le Mars
Alliance
Floyd Valley Healthcare

Marengo
Alliance
Compass Memorial Healthcare

Mason City
Alliance
MercyOne North Iowa Medical Center

Missouri Valley
Alliance
CHI Health Missouri Valley

Muscatine
Alliance
UnityPoint Health – Trinity Muscatine

Nevada
Alliance
Story County Medical Center

New Hampton
Alliance
MercyOne New Hampton Medical Center

Orange City
Alliance
Orange City Area Health System

Osceola
Alliance
Clarke County Hospital

Pella
Alliance
Pella Regional Health Center

Red Oak
Alliance
Montgomery County Memorial Hospital

Sheldon
Alliance
Sanford Sheldon Medical Center

Shenandoah
Alliance
Shenandoah Medical Center

Sigourney
Alliance
Keokuk County Health Center

Sioux City
Alliance
MercyOne Siouxland Medical Center
UnityPoint Health – St. Lukes's Sioux City

Sumner
Alliance
Community Memorial Hospital

Waverly
Alliance
Waverly Health Center

West Des Moines
Alliance
UnityPoint Health – Methodist
West Hospital

West Union
Alliance
Gundersen Palmer Lutheran Hospital and Clinics

KANSAS

Abilene
Alliance
Memorial Health System

Ashland
Alliance
Ashland Health Center

Atchison
Alliance
Atchison Hospital

Alliances

Atwood
Alliance
Rawlins County Health Center

Belleville
Alliance
Republic County Hospital

Beloit
Alliance
Mitchell County Hospital Health Systems

Clay Center
Alliance
Clay County Medical Center

Colby
Alliance
Citizens Medical Center

Coldwater
Alliance
Comanche County Hospital

Concordia
Alliance
Cloud County Health Center

Dighton
Alliance
Lane County Hospital

El Dorado
Alliance
Susan B. Allen Memorial Hospital

Ellinwood
Alliance
Ellinwood District Hospital

Ellsworth
Alliance
Ellsworth County Medical Center

Emporia
Alliance
Newman Regional Health

Fredonia
Alliance
Fredonia Regional Hospital

Garden City
Alliance
St. Catherine Hospital

Garnett
Alliance
Anderson County Hospital

Girard
Alliance
Girard Medical Center

Goodland
Alliance
Goodland Regional Medical Center

Great Bend
Alliance
University of Kansas Health System Great Bend Campus

Greensburg
Alliance
Kiowa County Memorial Hospital

Hays
Alliance
Hays Medical Center

Herington
Alliance
Herington Municipal Hospital

Hiawatha
Alliance
Hiawatha Community Hospital

Hill City
Alliance
Graham County Hospital

Hoisington
Alliance
Clara Barton Hospital

Hoxie
Alliance
Sheridan County Health Complex

Junction City
Alliance
Geary Community Hospital

Kansas City
Alliance
The University of Kansas Hospital

La Crosse
Alliance
Rush County Memorial Hospital

Larned
Alliance
University of Kansas Health System Pawnee Valley Campus

Lawrence
Alliance
LMH Health

Leavenworth
Alliance
Saint Luke's Cushing Hospital

Lincoln
Alliance
Lincoln County Hospital

Lindsborg
Alliance
Lindsborg Community Hospital

Mankato
Alliance
Jewell County Hospital

Medicine Lodge
Alliance
Medicine Lodge Memorial Hospital

Minneapolis
Alliance
Ottawa County Health Center

Minneola
Alliance
Minneola District Hospital

Ness City
Alliance
Ness County Hospital District No 2

Norton
Alliance
Norton County Hospital

Oakley
Alliance
Logan County Hospital

Overland Park
Alliance
Menorah Medical Center
Overland Park Regional Medical Center
Saint Luke's South Hospital

Parsons
Alliance
Labette Health

Phillipsburg
Alliance
Phillips County Health Systems

Plainville
Alliance
Rooks County Health Center

Pratt
Alliance
Pratt Regional Medical Center

Quinter
Alliance
Gove County Medical Center

Ransom
Alliance
Grisell Memorial Hospital District One

Russell
Alliance
Russell Regional Hospital

Sabetha
Alliance
Sabetha Community Hospital

Saint Francis
Alliance
Cheyenne County Hospital

Salina
Alliance
Salina Regional Health Center
Salina Surgical Hospital

Satanta
Alliance
Satanta District Hospital and Long Term Care

Scott City
Alliance
Scott County Hospital

Smith Center
Alliance
Smith County Memorial Hospital

Stafford
Alliance
Stafford County Hospital

Topeka
Alliance
Stormont Vail Health

Wakeeney
Alliance
Trego County–Lemke Memorial Hospital

Wichita
Alliance
Great Plains Health Alliance, Inc.
Kansas Spine and Specialty Hospital

KENTUCKY

Bardstown
Alliance
CHI Flaget Memorial Hospital

Berea
Alliance
CHI Saint Joseph Berea

Cynthiana
Alliance
Harrison Memorial Hospital

Florence
Alliance
St. Elizabeth Florence

Lexington
Alliance
CHI Saint Joseph East
CHI Saint Joseph Health
Eastern State Hospital
University of Kentucky Albert B. Chandler Hospital

London
Alliance
CHI Saint Joseph London

Louisville
Alliance
CHI Our Lady of Peace
Jewish Hospital
University of Louisville Hospital

Martin
Alliance
ARH Our Lady of the Way

Morehead
Alliance
St. Claire HealthCare

Mount Sterling
Alliance
Saint Joseph Mount Sterling

Mount Vernon
Alliance
Rockcastle Regional Hospital and Respiratory Care Center

Owensboro
Alliance
Owensboro Health Regional Hospital

Pikeville
Alliance
Pikeville Medical Center

Shelbyville
Alliance
Jewish Hospital–Shelbyville

LOUISIANA

Baton Rouge
Alliance
Franciscan Missionaries of Our Lady Health System, Inc.
Ochsner Medical Center – Baton Rouge
Our Lady of the Lake Regional Medical Center

Bogalusa
Alliance
Our Lady of the Angels Hospital

Church Point
Alliance
Acadia–St. Landry Hospital

Covington
Alliance
St. Tammany Parish Hospital

De Ridder
Alliance
Beauregard Health System

Ferriday
Alliance
Riverland Medical Center

Jennings
Alliance
Jennings American Legion Hospital

Kenner
Alliance
Ochsner Medical Center – Kenner

Lafayette
Alliance
Lafayette General Medical Center

Our Lady of Lourdes Regional Medical Center

Lake Charles
Alliance
Lake Charles Memorial Hospital

Memorial Specialty Hospital

Mansfield
Alliance
De Soto Regional Health System

Monroe
Alliance
Ochsner LSU Health Shreveport – Monroe Medical Center

St. Francis Medical Center

Napoleonville
Alliance
Assumption Community Hospital

Natchitoches
Alliance
Natchitoches Regional Medical Center

New Iberia
Alliance
Iberia Medical Center

New Orleans
Alliance
Touro Infirmary

Raceland
Alliance
Ochsner St. Anne General Hospital

Shreveport
Alliance
Ochsner LSU Health Shrevport – Academic Medical Center

Shriners Hospitals for Children–Shreveport

Willis–Knighton Health System

Willis–Knighton Medical Center

Slidell
Alliance
Ochsner Medical Center – North Shore

Springhill
Alliance
Springhill Medical Center

Sulphur
Alliance
West Calcasieu Cameron Hospital

Vivian
Alliance
North Caddo Medical Center

MAINE

Augusta
Alliance
MaineGeneral Medical Center–Augusta Campus

MaineGeneral Medical Center

Bangor
Alliance
Northern Light Eastern Maine Medical Center

The Acadia Hospital

Bar Harbor
Alliance
Mount Desert Island Hospital

Belfast
Alliance
Waldo County General Hospital Maine Health

Biddeford
Alliance
Southern Maine Health Care – Biddeford Medical Center

Blue Hill
Alliance
Northern Light Blue Hill Hospital

Brewer
Alliance
Northern Light Health

Brunswick
Alliance
Mid Coast Hospital

Damariscotta
Alliance
LincolnHealth

Dover–Foxcroft
Alliance
Mayo Regional Hospital

Ellsworth
Alliance
Northern Light Maine Coast Hospital

Farmington
Alliance
Franklin Memorial Hospital

Fort Kent
Alliance
Northern Maine Medical Center

Greenville
Alliance
Northern Light CA Dean Hospital

Houlton
Alliance
Houlton Regional Hospital

Machias
Alliance
Down East Community Hospital

Millinocket
Alliance
Millinocket Regional Hospital

Norway
Alliance
Stephens Memorial Hospital

Pittsfield
Alliance
Northlight Sebasticook Valley Hospital

Portland
Alliance
Maine Medical Center

Northern Light Mercy Hospital

Presque Isle
Alliance
The Aroostook Medical Center

Rockport
Alliance
Pen Bay Medical Center

Skowhegan
Alliance
Redington–Fairview General Hospital

Waterville
Alliance
Northern Light Inland Hospital

Westbrook
Alliance
Spring Harbor Hospital

MARYLAND

Baltimore
Alliance
Greater Baltimore Medical Center

Johns Hopkins Bayview Medical Center

Johns Hopkins Hospital

MedStar Franklin Square Medical Center

MedStar Good Samaritan Hospital

MedStar Harbor Hospital

MedStar Union Memorial Hospital

Mercy Medical Center

Mt. Washington Pediatric Hospital

University of Maryland Medical Center Midtown Campus

University of Maryland Medical Center

University of Maryland Rehabilitation & Orthopaedic Institute

Bel Air
Alliance
University of Maryland Upper Chesapeake Medical Center

Bethesda
Alliance
Suburban Hospital

Cambridge
Alliance
University of Maryland Shore Medical Center at Dorchester

Chestertown
Alliance
University of Maryland Shore Medical Center at Chestertown

Cheverly
Alliance
University of Maryland Capital Region Health Prince George's Hospital Center

Clinton
Alliance
MedStar Southern Maryland Hospital Center

Columbia
Alliance
Howard County General Hospital

MedStar Health

Easton
Alliance
University of Maryland Shore Medical Center at Easton

Elkton
Alliance
Union Hospital

Glen Burnie
Alliance
University of Maryland Baltimore Washington Medical Center

Hagerstown
Alliance
Meritus Medical Center

Havre De Grace
Alliance
University of Maryland Harford Memorial Hospital

La Plata
Alliance
University of Maryland Charles Regional Medical Center

Leonardtown
Alliance
MedStar St. Mary's Hospital

Olney
Alliance
MedStar Montgomery Medical Center

Prince Frederick
Alliance
CalvertHealth Medical Center

Randallstown
Alliance
Northwest Hospital

Rockville
Alliance
  Adventist Healthcare Shady Grove Medical Center

Silver Spring
Alliance
  Holy Cross Hospital

Takoma Park
Alliance
  Adventist Healthcare Washington Adventist Hospital

MASSACHUSETTS
Athol
Alliance
  Athol Hospital

Ayer
Alliance
  Nashoba Valley Medical Center

Belmont
Alliance
  McLean Hospital

Beverly
Alliance
  Beverly Hospital

Boston
Alliance
  Beth Israel Deaconess Medical Center
  Boston Medical Center
  Brigham and Women's Faulkner Hospital
  Brigham and Women's Hospital
  Carney Hospital
  Dana–Farber Cancer Institute
  Massachusetts Eye and Ear
  Massachusetts General Hospital
  Partners HealthCare System, Inc.
  Shriners Hospitals for Children–Boston
  Tufts Medical Center

Brighton
Alliance
  St. Elizabeth's Medical Center

Brockton
Alliance
  Good Samaritan Medical Center
  Signature Healthcare Brockton Hospital

Burlington
Alliance
  Lahey Hospital & Medical Center, Burlington

Cambridge
Alliance
  Cambridge Health Alliance
  Mount Auburn Hospital
  Spaulding Hospital for Continuing Medical Care Cambridge

Charlestown
Alliance
  Spaulding Rehabilitation Hospital

Concord
Alliance
  Emerson Hospital

East Sandwich
Alliance
  Spaulding Rehabilitation Hospital Cape Cod

Fall River
Alliance
  Saint Anne's Hospital

Gardner
Alliance
  Heywood Hospital

Greenfield
Alliance
  Baystate Franklin Medical Center

Holyoke
Alliance
  Holyoke Medical Center

Hyannis
Alliance
  Cape Cod Healthcare, Inc.

Leominster
Alliance
  UMass Memorial HealthAlliance–Clinton Hospital

Lowell
Alliance
  Lowell General Hospital

Marlborough
Alliance
  UMass Memorial–Marlborough Hospital

Melrose
Alliance
  Melrose–Wakefield Hospital

Methuen
Alliance
  Holy Family Hospital

Milton
Alliance
  Beth Israel Deaconess Hospital–Milton

Nantucket
Alliance
  Nantucket Cottage Hospital

Newton Lower Falls
Alliance
  Newton–Wellesley Hospital

Northampton
Alliance
  Cooley Dickinson Hospital

Norwood
Alliance
  Norwood Hospital

Oak Bluffs
Alliance
  Martha's Vineyard Hospital

Palmer
Alliance
  Baystate Wing Hospital

Plymouth
Alliance
  Beth Israel Deaconess Hospital Plymouth

Salem
Alliance
  North Shore Medical Center

South Weymouth
Alliance
  South Shore Hospital

Southbridge
Alliance
  Harrington Hospital

Springfield
Alliance
  Baystate Medical Center
  Shriners Hospitals for Children–Springfield

Taunton
Alliance
  Morton Hospital and Medical Center

Winchester
Alliance
  Winchester Hospital

Worcester
Alliance
  UMass Memorial Medical Center

MICHIGAN
Alma
Alliance
  MidMichigan Medical Center–Gratiot

Alpena
Alliance
  MidMichigan Medical Center – Alpena

Ann Arbor
Alliance
  Michigan Medicine

Battle Creek
Alliance
  Bronson Battle Creek Hospital

Bay City
Alliance
  McLaren Bay Region
  McLaren Bay Special Care

Big Rapids
Alliance
  Spectrum Health Big Rapids Hospital

Cadillac
Alliance
  Munson Healthcare Cadillac Hospital

Carson City
Alliance
  Sparrow Carson Hospital

Cass City
Alliance
  Hills & Dales General Hospital

Chelsea
Alliance
  St. Joseph Mercy Chelsea

Coldwater
Alliance
  ProMedica Coldwater Regional Hospital

Dearborn
Alliance
  Beaumont Hospital – Dearborn

Detroit
Alliance
  Henry Ford Hospital

Farmington Hills
Alliance
  Beaumont Hospital – Farmington Hills

Flint
Alliance
  McLaren Flint

Fremont
Alliance
  Spectrum Health Gerber Memorial

Grand Haven
Alliance
  North Ottawa Community Hospital

Grand Rapids
Alliance
  Mary Free Bed Rehabilitation Hospital
  Pine Rest Christian Mental Health Services
  Spectrum Health – Butterworth Hospital
  Spectrum Health

Grayling
Alliance
  Munson Healthcare Grayling Hospital

Greenville
Alliance
  Spectrum Health United Hospital

Grosse Pointe
Alliance
  Beaumont Hospital – Grosse Pointe

Hastings
Alliance
  Spectrum Health Pennock

Holland
Alliance
  Holland Hospital

Ionia
Alliance
  Sparrow Ionia Hospital

Iron River
Alliance
  Aspirus Iron River Hospitals & Clinics, Inc.

Ironwood
Alliance
  Aspirus Ironwood Hospitals & Clinics, Inc.

Kalamazoo
Alliance
  Bronson Healthcare Group
  Bronson Methodist Hospital

Lansing
Alliance
  Sparrow Hospital
  Sparrow Specialty Hospital

Laurium
Alliance
  Aspirus Keweenaw Hospital, Inc.

Section B

Ludington
Alliance
   Spectrum Health Ludington Hospital

Marlette
Alliance
   Marlette Regional Hospital

Marshall
Alliance
   Oaklawn Hospital

Midland
Alliance
   MidMichigan Medical Center–Midland

Monroe
Alliance
   ProMedica Monroe Regional Hospital

Mount Clemens
Alliance
   McLaren Macomb

Mount Pleasant
Alliance
   McLaren Central Michigan

Muskegon
Alliance
   Mercy Health Hackley Campus

Ontonagon
Alliance
   Aspirus Ontonagon Hospital, Inc.

Paw Paw
Alliance
   Bronson LakeView Hospital

Petoskey
Alliance
   McLaren Northern Michigan

Pontiac
Alliance
   McLaren Oakland
   St. Joseph Mercy Oakland

Port Huron
Alliance
   McLaren Port Huron

Reed City
Alliance
   Spectrum Health Reed City Hospital

Royal Oak
Alliance
   Beaumont Hospital – Royal Oak

Saginaw
Alliance
   Covenant Healthcare

Saint Johns
Alliance
   Sparrow Clinton Hospital

Saint Joseph
Alliance
   Spectrum Health Lakeland

Sheridan
Alliance
   Sheridan Community Hospital

South Haven
Alliance
   Bronson South Haven Hospital

Taylor
Alliance
   Beaumont Hospital – Taylor

Tecumseh
Alliance
   ProMedica Herrick Hospital

Trenton
Alliance
   Beaumont Hospital – Trenton

Troy
Alliance
   Beaumont Hospital – Troy

Vicksburg
Alliance
   Bronson Vicksburg Hospital

Watervliet
Alliance
   Lakeland Hospital, Watervliet

Wayne
Alliance
   Beaumont Hospital, Wayne

West Branch
Alliance
   MidMichigan Medical Center –
   West Branch

Wyoming
Alliance
   Metro Health – University of Michigan Health

Zeeland
Alliance
   Spectrum Health Zeeland Community Hospital

MINNESOTA
Ada
Alliance
   Essentia Health Ada

Albert Lea
Alliance
   Mayo Clinic Health System – Albert Lea and Austin

Arlington
Alliance
   Ridgeview Sibley Medical Center

Aurora
Alliance
   Essentia Health Northern Pines Medical Center

Bagley
Alliance
   Sanford Bagley Medical Center

Baudette
Alliance
   CHI LakeWood Health

Bemidji
Alliance
   Sanford Bemidji Medical Center

Benson
Alliance
   Swift County – Benson Health Services

Blue Earth
Alliance
   United Hospital District

Brainerd
Alliance
   Essentia Health St. Joseph's Medical Center

Buffalo
Alliance
   Buffalo Hospital

Burnsville
Alliance
   Fairview Ridges Hospital

Cambridge
Alliance
   Cambridge Medical Center

Canby
Alliance
   Sanford Canby Medical Center

Cannon Falls
Alliance
   Mayo Clinic Health System in Cannon Falls

Coon Rapids
Alliance
   Mercy Hospital

Crookston
Alliance
   RiverView Health

Deer River
Alliance
   Essentia Health–Deer River

Detroit Lakes
Alliance
   Essentia Health St. Mary's – Detroit Lakes

Duluth
Alliance
   Essentia Health Duluth

   Essentia Health St. Mary's
   Medical Center

   Essentia Health

   St. Luke's Hospital

Fairmont
Alliance
   Mayo Clinic Health System in Fairmont

Faribault
Alliance
   District One Hospital

Fergus Falls
Alliance
   Lake Region Healthcare

Fosston
Alliance
   Essentia Health Fosston

Glencoe
Alliance
   Glencoe Regional Health

Graceville
Alliance
   Essentia Health–Graceville

Grand Rapids
Alliance
   Grand Itasca Clinic and Hospital

Granite Falls
Alliance
   Granite Falls Health

Hallock
Alliance
   Kittson Memorial Healthcare Center

Hastings
Alliance
   Regina Hospital

Hutchinson
Alliance
   Hutchinson Health

Jackson
Alliance
   Sanford Jackson Medical Center

Lake City
Alliance
   Mayo Clinic Health System in Lake City

Little Falls
Alliance
   CHI St. Gabriel's Health

Long Prairie
Alliance
   CentraCare Health–Long Prairie

Luverne
Alliance
   Sanford Luverne Medical Center

Madelia
Alliance
   Madelia Community Hospital

Mahnomen
Alliance
   Mahnomen Health Center

Mankato
Alliance
   Mayo Clinic Health System in Mankato

Maple Grove
Alliance
   Maple Grove Hospital

Melrose
Alliance
   CentraCare Health–Melrose

Minneapolis
Alliance
   Abbott Northwestern Hospital

   Allina Health

   Hennepin Healthcare

   Phillips Eye Institute

Monticello
Alliance
   CentraCare Health–Monticello

New Prague
Alliance
   Mayo Clinic Health System in New Prague

New Ulm
Alliance
   New Ulm Medical Center

Section B

Ortonville
Alliance
Ortonville Area Health Services

Owatonna
Alliance
Owatonna Hospital

Park Rapids
Alliance
CHI St. Joseph's Health

Paynesville
Alliance
CentraCare Health–Paynesville

Perham
Alliance
Perham Health

Princeton
Alliance
Fairview Northland Medical Center

Red Wing
Alliance
Mayo Clinic Health System in Red Wing

Redwood Falls
Alliance
Carris Health – Redwood

Robbinsdale
Alliance
North Memorial Health Hospital

Rochester
Alliance
Mayo Clinic Hospital – Rochester

Mayo Clinic

Roseau
Alliance
LifeCare Medical Center

Saint Cloud
Alliance
CentraCare Health

St. Cloud Hospital

Saint James
Alliance
Mayo Clinic Health System in Saint James

Saint Paul
Alliance
Regions Hospital

United Hospital

Sandstone
Alliance
Essentia Health Sandstone

Sauk Centre
Alliance
CentraCare Health–Sauk Centre

Shakopee
Alliance
St. Francis Regional Medical Center

Slayton
Alliance
Murray County Medical Center

Springfield
Alliance
Mayo Clinic Health System in Springfield

Stillwater
Alliance
Lakeview Hospital

Thief River Falls
Alliance
Sanford Medical Center Thief River Falls

Sanford Thief River Falls Behavioral
Health Center

Tracy
Alliance
Sanford Tracy Medical Center

Two Harbors
Alliance
Lake View Hospital

Virginia
Alliance
Essentia Health–Virginia

Waconia
Alliance
Ridgeview Medical Center

Warren
Alliance
North Valley Health Center

Waseca
Alliance
Mayo Clinic Health System in Waseca

Westbrook
Alliance
Sanford Westbrook Medical Center

Wheaton
Alliance
Sanford Wheaton Medical Center

Willmar
Alliance
Rice Memorial Hospital

Windom
Alliance
Windom Area Hospital

Worthington
Alliance
Sanford Worthington Medical Center

Wyoming
Alliance
Fairview Lakes Health Services

MISSISSIPPI
Booneville
Alliance
Baptist Memorial Hospital–Booneville

Columbia
Alliance
Marion General Hospital

Columbus
Alliance
Baptist Memorial Hospital–Golden Triangle

Corinth
Alliance
Magnolia Regional Health Center

Greenville
Alliance
Delta Regional Medical Center

Greenwood
Alliance
Greenwood Leflore Hospital

Grenada
Alliance
University of Mississippi Medical Center Grenada

Gulfport
Alliance
Memorial Hospital at Gulfport

Hattiesburg
Alliance
Forrest General Hospital

Indianola
Alliance
South Sunflower County Hospital

Jackson
Alliance
St. Dominic–Jackson Memorial Hospital

University of Mississippi Medical Center

Leakesville
Alliance
Greene County Hospital

Lexington
Alliance
University of Mississippi Medical Center Holmes County

Lucedale
Alliance
George Regional Hospital

Magnolia
Alliance
Beacham Memorial Hospital

McComb
Alliance
Southwest Mississippi Regional Medical Center

Meridian
Alliance
Anderson Regional Health System South

Anderson Regional Health System

Monticello
Alliance
Lawrence County Hospital

New Albany
Alliance
Baptist Memorial Hospital–Union County

Olive Branch
Alliance
Methodist Healthcare Olive Branch Hospital

Oxford
Alliance
Baptist Memorial Hospital–North Mississippi

Pascagoula
Alliance
Singing River Health System

Philadelphia
Alliance
Neshoba County General Hospital

Picayune
Alliance
Highland Community Hospital

Prentiss
Alliance
Jefferson Davis Community Hospital

Southaven
Alliance
Baptist Memorial Hospital–Desoto

Starkville
Alliance
OCH Regional Medical Center

Tupelo
Alliance
North Mississippi Health Services, Inc.

Tylertown
Alliance
Walthall County General Hospital

MISSOURI
Appleton City
Alliance
Ellett Memorial Hospital

Belton
Alliance
Belton Regional Medical Center

Bolivar
Alliance
Citizens Memorial Hospital

Bonne Terre
Alliance
Parkland Health Center–Bonne Terre

Branson
Alliance
Cox Medical Center Branson

Brookfield
Alliance
Pershing Memorial Hospital

Cameron
Alliance
Cameron Regional Medical Center

Cape Girardeau
Alliance
Saint Francis Medical Center

Chillicothe
Alliance
Hedrick Medical Center

Clinton
Alliance
Golden Valley Memorial Healthcare

Columbia
Alliance
Boone Hospital Center

University of Missouri Health Care

Farmington
Alliance
Parkland Health Center – Farmington Community

Independence
Alliance
  Centerpoint Medical Center

Jefferson City
Alliance
  Capital Region Medical Center

Joplin
Alliance
  Freeman Health System
  Freeman Hospital East

Kansas City
Alliance
  Children's Mercy Hospital Kansas City
  Research Medical Center
  Saint Luke's Health System
  Saint Luke's Hospital of Kansas City
  Saint Luke's North Hospital – Barry Road
  Truman Medical Center–Hospital Hill
  Truman Medical Center–Lakewood

Lamar
Alliance
  Cox Barton County Memorial Hospital

Lee's Summit
Alliance
  Lee's Summit Medical Center
  Saint Luke's East Hospital

Lexington
Alliance
  Lafayette Regional Health Center

Liberty
Alliance
  Liberty Hospital

Macon
Alliance
  Samaritan Hospital

Marshall
Alliance
  Fitzgibbon Hospital

Milan
Alliance
  Sullivan County Memorial Hospital

Monett
Alliance
  Cox Monett Hospital

Neosho
Alliance
  Freeman Neosho Hospital

O'Fallon
Alliance
  Progress West Hospital

Osage Beach
Alliance
  Lake Regional Health System

Potosi
Alliance
  Washington County Memorial Hospital

Saint Louis
Alliance
  BJC HealthCare
  Barnes–Jewish Hospital
  Barnes–Jewish West County Hospital
  Christian Hospital
  Missouri Baptist Medical Center
  Shriners Hospitals for Children–St. Louis
  St. Louis Children's Hospital

Saint Peters
Alliance
  Barnes–Jewish St. Peters Hospital

Salem
Alliance
  Salem Memorial District Hospital

Sikeston
Alliance
  Missouri Delta Medical Center

Springfield
Alliance
  Cox Medical Center North
  Cox Medical Centers
  CoxHealth

Ste Genevieve
Alliance
  Ste. Genevieve County Memorial Hospital

Sullivan
Alliance
  Missouri Baptist Sullivan Hospital

Trenton
Alliance
  Wright Memorial Hospital

Warrensburg
Alliance
  Western Missouri Medical Center

MONTANA

Anaconda
Alliance
  Community Hospital of Anaconda

Bozeman
Alliance
  Bozeman Health

Columbus
Alliance
  Stillwater Billings Clinic

Conrad
Alliance
  Pondera Medical Center

Deer Lodge
Alliance
  Deer Lodge Medical Center

Ennis
Alliance
  Madison Valley Medical Center

Hamilton
Alliance
  Marcus Daly Memorial Hospital

Helena
Alliance
  St. Peter's Hospital

Kalispell
Alliance
  Kalispell Regional Healthcare
  The HealthCenter

Libby
Alliance
  Cabinet Peaks Medical Center

Missoula
Alliance
  Providence St. Patrick Hospital

Philipsburg
Alliance
  Granite County Medical Center

Plains
Alliance
  Clark Fork Valley Hospital

Polson
Alliance
  Providence St. Joseph Medical Center

Ronan
Alliance
  St. Luke Community Healthcare

Sidney
Alliance
  Sidney Health Center

Townsend
Alliance
  Broadwater Health Center

White Sulphur Springs
Alliance
  Mountainview Medical Center

NEBRASKA

Alliance
Alliance
  Box Butte General Hospital

Alma
Alliance
  Harlan County Health System

Atkinson
Alliance
  West Holt Medical Services

Beatrice
Alliance
  Beatrice Community Hospital and Health Center

Bellevue
Alliance
  Nebraska Medicine – Bellevue

Blair
Alliance
  Memorial Community Hospital and
  Health System

Bridgeport
Alliance
  Morrill County Community Hospital

Broken Bow
Alliance
  Jennie M. Melham Memorial Medical Center

Columbus
Alliance
  Columbus Community Hospital

Crete
Alliance
  Crete Area Medical Center

Falls City
Alliance
  Community Medical Center, Inc.

Franklin
Alliance
  Franklin County Memorial Hospital

Gordon
Alliance
  Gordon Memorial Health Services

Grand Island
Alliance
  CHI Health Saint Francis

Hastings
Alliance
  Mary Lanning Healthcare

Kearney
Alliance
  CHI Health Good Samaritan

Lexington
Alliance
  Lexington Regional Health Center

Lincoln
Alliance
  Bryan Health
  Bryan Medical Center
  CHI Health Nebraska Heart
  CHI Health St Elizabeth
  Madonna Rehabilitation Hospital

Lynch
Alliance
  Niobrara Valley Hospital

Minden
Alliance
  Kearney County Health Services

Nebraska City
Alliance
  CHI Health St. Mary's

Neligh
Alliance
  Antelope Memorial Hospital

Norfolk
Alliance
  Faith Regional Health Services

O'Neill
Alliance
  Avera St. Anthony's Hospital

Omaha
Alliance
CHI Health Creighton University Medical Center –
Bergan Mercy
CHI Health Immanuel
CHI Health Lakeside
Nebraska Medicine – Nebraska Medical Center
Nebraska Methodist Health System, Inc.
Nebraska Methodist Hospital
OrthoNebraska Hospital

Ord
Alliance
Valley County Health System

Oshkosh
Alliance
Regional West Garden County

Osmond
Alliance
Osmond General Hospital

Papillion
Alliance
CHI Health Midlands

Plainview
Alliance
CHI Health Plainview

Schuyler
Alliance
CHI Health Schuyler

Scottsbluff
Alliance
Regional West Medical Center

York
Alliance
York General

NEVADA
Las Vegas
Alliance
Sunrise Hospital and Medical Center
University Medical Center

NEW HAMPSHIRE
Claremont
Alliance
Valley Regional Hospital

Colebrook
Alliance
Upper Connecticut Valley Hospital

Dover
Alliance
Wentworth–Douglass Hospital

Keene
Alliance
Cheshire Medical Center

Lancaster
Alliance
Weeks Medical Center

Lebanon
Alliance
Alice Peck Day Memorial Hospital
Dartmouth–Hitchcock Medical Center

Nashua
Alliance
Southern New Hampshire Medical Center

New London
Alliance
New London Hospital

North Conway
Alliance
Memorial Hospital

Peterborough
Alliance
Monadnock Community Hospital

Plymouth
Alliance
Speare Memorial Hospital

Woodsville
Alliance
Cottage Hospital

NEW JERSEY
Atlantic City
Alliance
AtlantiCare Regional Medical Center

Camden
Alliance
Cooper University Health Care

Cape May Court House
Alliance
Cape Regional Health System

Denville
Alliance
Saint Clare's Denville Hospital

Edison
Alliance
Hackensack Meridian Health JFK Medical Center

Elmer
Alliance
Inspira Medical Center–Elmer

Flemington
Alliance
Hunterdon Healthcare

Hamilton
Alliance
Robert Wood Johnson University
Hospital at Hamilton

Marlton
Alliance
Virtua Marlton

Morristown
Alliance
Morristown Medical Center

Mount Holly
Alliance
Virtua Memorial

Mullica Hill
Alliance
Inspira Health Network

New Brunswick
Alliance
Robert Wood Johnson University Hospital

Newark
Alliance
University Hospital

Newton
Alliance
Newton Medical Center

Pomona
Alliance
Bacharach Institute for Rehabilitation

Pompton Plains
Alliance
Chilton Medical Center

Rahway
Alliance
Robert Wood Johnson University
Hospital Rahway

Ridgewood
Alliance
Valley Hospital

Somers Point
Alliance
Shore Medical Center

Summit
Alliance
Overlook Medical Center

Trenton
Alliance
Capital Health

Vineland
Alliance
Inspira Medical Center–Vineland

Voorhees
Alliance
Virtua Voorhees

Woodbury
Alliance
Inspira Medical Center–Woodbury

NEW MEXICO
Albuquerque
Alliance
University of New Mexico Hospitals

Farmington
Alliance
San Juan Regional Medical Center

Gallup
Alliance
Rehoboth McKinley Christian Health Care Services

Rio Rancho
Alliance
UNM Sandoval Regional Medical Center, Inc.

Santa Fe
Alliance
CHRISTUS St. Vincent Regional Medical Center

NEW YORK
Albany
Alliance
Albany Medical Center
St. Peter's Hospital

Alexandria Bay
Alliance
River Hospital

Binghamton
Alliance
United Health Services Hospitals–Binghamton

Bronx
Alliance
Montefiore Medical Center
NYC Health + Hospitals / Jacobi
NYC Health + Hospitals / North Central Bronx

Brooklyn
Alliance
Brooklyn Hospital Center
NYC Health + Hospitals / Coney Island
NYC Health + Hospitals / Woodhull
New York Community Hospital
NewYork–Presbyterian Brooklyn
Methodist Hospital
SUNY Downstate Medical Center University Hospital

Buffalo
Alliance
Erie County Medical Center
Roswell Park Comprehensive Cancer Center

Canandaigua
Alliance
F. F. Thompson Hospital

Cooperstown
Alliance
Bassett Medical Center

Corning
Alliance
Guthrie Corning Hospital

Cortlandt Manor
Alliance
New York–Presbyterian/Hudson Valley Hospital

Elizabethtown
Alliance
The University of Vermont Health Network
Elizabethtown Community Hospital

Elmhurst
Alliance
NYC Health + Hospitals / Elmhurst

Flushing
Alliance
New York–Presbyterian Queens

Geneva
Alliance
Finger Lakes Health

Greenport
Alliance
Eastern Long Island Hospital

Hamilton
Alliance
Community Memorial Hospital

Ithaca
Alliance
Cayuga Medical Center at Ithaca

Jamaica
Alliance
NYC Health + Hospitals / Queens

Jamestown
Alliance
UPMC Chautauqua WCA

Malone
Alliance
The University of Vermont Health Network – Alice Hyde Medical Center

Mineola
Alliance
NYU Winthrop Hospital

Montour Falls
Alliance
Schuyler Hospital

Mount Vernon
Alliance
Montefiore Mount Vernon

New Rochelle
Alliance
Montefiore New Rochelle

New York
Alliance
Gracie Square Hospital

Lenox Hill Hospital

Mount Sinai Hospital

NYC Health + Hospitals / Bellevue

NYC Health + Hospitals / Harlem

NYC Health + Hospitals / Henry J Carter Specialty Hospital and Medical Center

NYU Langone Hospitals

New York–Presbyterian Hospital

New York–Presbyterian/Columbia University Medical Center

Rockefeller University Hospital

Norwich
Alliance
UHS Chenango Memorial Hospital

Nyack
Alliance
Nyack Hospital

Ogdensburg
Alliance
Claxton–Hepburn Medical Center

Plattsburgh
Alliance
The University of Vermont Health Network–Champlain Valley Physicians Hospital

Riverhead
Alliance
Peconic Bay Medical Center

Rochester
Alliance
Highland Hospital

Strong Memorial Hospital of the University of Rochester

University of Rochester Medical Center

Sleepy Hollow
Alliance
Phelps Memorial Hospital Center

Staten Island
Alliance
Staten Island University Hospital

Stony Brook
Alliance
Stony Brook University Hospital

Syracuse
Alliance
Crouse Health

Upstate University Hospital

Valhalla
Alliance
Westchester Medical Center

Walton
Alliance
UHS Delaware Valley Hospital

NORTH CAROLINA

Ahoskie
Alliance
Vidant Roanoke–Chowan Hospital

Bermuda Run
Alliance
Wake Forest Baptist Health–Davie Medical Center

Bolivia
Alliance
Novant Health Brunswick Medical Center

Cary
Alliance
WakeMed Cary Hospital

Chapel Hill
Alliance
University of North Carolina Hospitals

Charlotte
Alliance
Atrium Health

Novant Health Charlotte Orthopaedic Hospital

Novant Health Presbyterian Medical Center

Clinton
Alliance
Sampson Regional Medical Center

Dunn
Alliance
Harnett Health System

Durham
Alliance
Duke Regional Hospital

Duke University Hospital

Eden
Alliance
UNC Rockingham Health Care

Edenton
Alliance
Vidant Chowan Hospital

Elizabeth City
Alliance
Sentara Albemarle Medical Center

Elkin
Alliance
Hugh Chatham Memorial Hospital

Greenville
Alliance
Vidant Medical Center

Huntersville
Alliance
Novant Health Huntersville Medical Center

Jefferson
Alliance
Ashe Memorial Hospital

Kenansville
Alliance
Vidant Duplin Hospital

Lexington
Alliance
Wake Forest Baptist Health–Lexington Medical Center

Matthews
Alliance
Novant Health Matthews Medical Center

Morehead City
Alliance
Carteret Health Care

Nags Head
Alliance
The Outer Banks Hospital

New Bern
Alliance
CarolinaEast Health System

Raleigh
Alliance
Duke Raleigh Hospital

UNC REX Health Care

WakeMed Health & Hospitals

WakeMed Raleigh Campus

Roanoke Rapids
Alliance
Halifax Regional Medical Center

Rocky Mount
Alliance
Nash UNC Health Care

Salisbury
Alliance
Novant Health Rowan Medical Center

Siler City
Alliance
Chatham Hospital

Sparta
Alliance
Alleghany Memorial Hospital

Tarboro
Alliance
Vidant Edgecombe Hospital

Thomasville
Alliance
Novant Health Thomasville Medical Center

Washington
Alliance
Vidant Beaufort Hospital

Wilson
Alliance
Wilson Medical Center

Windsor
Alliance
Vidant Bertie Hospital

Winston Salem
Alliance
Novant Health

Winston–Salem
Alliance
Novant Health Forsyth Medical Center

Novant Health Medical Park Hospital

Wake Forest Baptist Medical Center

NORTH DAKOTA

Bismarck
Alliance
Sanford Bismarck

Devils Lake
Alliance
CHI St. Alexius Health Devils Lake Hospital

Dickinson
Alliance
CHI St. Alexius Health – Dickinson Medical Center

Fargo
Alliance
Sanford Medical Center Fargo

Grand Forks
Alliance
Altru Health System

Hillsboro
Alliance
Sanford Hillsboro Medical Center

Jamestown
Alliance
Jamestown Regional Medical Center

Kenmare
Alliance
Kenmare Community Hospital

Lisbon
Alliance
CHI Lisbon Health

Mayville
Alliance
Sanford Mayville Medical Center

Mcville
Alliance
  Nelson County Health System

Minot
Alliance
  Trinity Health

Northwood
Alliance
  Northwood Deaconess Health Center

Oakes
Alliance
  CHI Oakes Hospital

Valley City
Alliance
  CHI Mercy Health

OHIO
Akron
Alliance
  Akron Children's Hospital

  Cleveland Clinic Akron General

Alliance
Alliance
  Alliance Community Hospital

Ashland
Alliance
  University Hospitals Samaritan Medical Center

Ashtabula
Alliance
  Ashtabula County Medical Center

Athens
Alliance
  O'Bleness Memorial Hospital

Barnesville
Alliance
  Barnesville Hospital

Bellefontaine
Alliance
  Mary Rutan Hospital

Bluffton
Alliance
  Bluffton Hospital

Bucyrus
Alliance
  Bucyrus Hospital

Cadiz
Alliance
  Harrison Community Hospital

Cambridge
Alliance
  Southeastern Ohio Regional Medical Center

Canton
Alliance
  Aultman Hospital

Chardon
Alliance
  University Hospitals Geauga Medical Center

Cincinnati
Alliance
  Christ Hospital

  Cincinnati Children's Hospital Medical Center

  Good Samaritan Hospital

  Shriners Hospitals for Children – Cincinnati

  The Jewish Hospital – Mercy Health

  UC Health

  University of Cincinnati Medical Center

Circleville
Alliance
  Berger Health System

Cleveland
Alliance
  Cleveland Clinic Fairview Hospital

  Cleveland Clinic

  Lutheran Hospital

  MetroHealth Medical Center

  University Hospitals Cleveland
  Medical Center

Coldwater
Alliance
  Mercer Health

Columbus
Alliance
  Ohio State University Wexner Medical Center

  OhioHealth Doctors Hospital

  OhioHealth Grant Medical Center

  OhioHealth Riverside Methodist Hospital

  OhioHealth

Conneaut
Alliance
  University Hospitals Conneaut
  Medical Center

Coshocton
Alliance
  Coshocton Regional Medical Center

Cuyahoga Falls
Alliance
  Edwin Shaw Rehab

Dayton
Alliance
  Miami Valley Hospital

Defiance
Alliance
  ProMedica Defiance Regional Hospital

Delaware
Alliance
  OhioHealth Grady Memorial Hospital

Dover
Alliance
  Cleveland Clinic Union Hospital

Dublin
Alliance
  OhioHealth Dublin Methodist Hospital

Euclid
Alliance
  Euclid Hospital

Findlay
Alliance
  Blanchard Valley Hospital

Fostoria
Alliance
  ProMedica Fostoria Community Hospital

Fremont
Alliance
  ProMedica Memorial Hospital

Galion
Alliance
  Galion Hospital

Garfield Heights
Alliance
  Marymount Hospital

Geneva
Alliance
  University Hospitals Geneva Medical Center

Greenville
Alliance
  Wayne HealthCare

Hamilton
Alliance
  Fort Hamilton Hospital

Kenton
Alliance
  OhioHealth Hardin Memorial Hospital

Lima
Alliance
  Lima Memorial Health System

Lodi
Alliance
  Cleveland Clinic Akron General Lodi Hospital

Logan
Alliance
  Hocking Valley Community Hospital

London
Alliance
  Madison Health

Mansfield
Alliance
  OhioHealth MedCentral Mansfield Hospital

Marion
Alliance
  OhioHealth Marion General Hospital

Martins Ferry
Alliance
  East Ohio Regional Hospital

Marysville
Alliance
  Memorial Health

Mason
Alliance
  Lindner Center of HOPE

Maumee
Alliance
  St. Luke's Hospital

Medina
Alliance
  Cleveland Clinic, Medina Hospital

Middleburg Heights
Alliance
  Southwest General Health Center

Millersburg
Alliance
  Pomerene Hospital

Mount Gilead
Alliance
  Morrow County Hospital

New Albany
Alliance
  Mount Carmel New Albany
  Surgical Hospital

Newark
Alliance
  Licking Memorial Hospital

Norwalk
Alliance
  Fisher–Titus Medical Center

Orrville
Alliance
  Aultman Orrville Hospital

Paulding
Alliance
  Paulding County Hospital

Portsmouth
Alliance
  Southern Ohio Medical Center

Rock Creek
Alliance
  Glenbeigh Hospital and Outpatient Centers

Shelby
Alliance
  OhioHealth MedCentral Shelby Hospital

Sidney
Alliance
  Wilson Memorial Hospital

Sylvania
Alliance
  ProMedica Flower Hospital

Toledo
Alliance
  ProMedica Health System

  ProMedica Toledo Hospital

  The University of Toledo Medical Center

Troy
Alliance
  Upper Valley Medical Center

Upper Sandusky
Alliance
  Wyandot Memorial Hospital

Van Wert
Alliance
  Van Wert County Hospital

Warrensville Heights
Alliance
  South Pointe Hospital

Washington Court House
Alliance
Fayette County Memorial Hospital

Westerville
Alliance
Mount Carmel St. Ann's

Westlake
Alliance
St. John Medical Center

Zanesville
Alliance
Genesis HealthCare System

OKLAHOMA

Altus
Alliance
Jackson County Memorial Hospital

Antlers
Alliance
Pushmataha Hospital

Atoka
Alliance
Atoka County Medical Center

Bethany
Alliance
The Children's Center Rehabilitation Hospital

Carnegie
Alliance
Carnegie Tri–County Municipal Hospital

Chickasha
Alliance
Grady Memorial Hospital

Duncan
Alliance
Duncan Regional Hospital

Edmond
Alliance
INTEGRIS Health Edmond

Elk City
Alliance
Great Plains Regional Medical Center

Enid
Alliance
Integris Bass Baptist Health Center
Integris Bass Pavilion

Grove
Alliance
INTEGRIS Grove Hospital

Hobart
Alliance
Elkview General Hospital

Hugo
Alliance
Choctaw Memorial Hospital

Lawton
Alliance
Comanche County Memorial Hospital

McAlester
Alliance
McAlester Regional Health Center

Miami
Alliance
INTEGRIS Miami Hospital

Norman
Alliance
Norman Regional Health System

Oklahoma City
Alliance
INTEGRIS Baptist Medical Center
INTEGRIS Health
INTEGRIS Southwest Medical Center
Lakeside Women's Hospital

Stillwater
Alliance
Stillwater Medical Center

Tahlequah
Alliance
Northeastern Health System

Waurika
Alliance
Jefferson County Hospital

Yukon
Alliance
INTEGRIS Canadian Valley Hospital

OREGON

Forest Grove
Alliance
Tuality Forest Grove Hospital

Grants Pass
Alliance
Asante Three Rivers Medical Center

Hillsboro
Alliance
Tuality Healthcare

Hood River
Alliance
Providence Hood River Memorial Hospital

Medford
Alliance
Asante Rogue Regional Medical Center
Providence Medford Medical Center

Milwaukie
Alliance
Providence Milwaukie Hospital

Newberg
Alliance
Providence Newberg Medical Center

Ontario
Alliance
Saint Alphonsus Medical Center – Ontario

Oregon City
Alliance
Providence Willamette Falls Medical Center

Pendleton
Alliance
CHI St. Anthony Hospital

Portland
Alliance
OHSU Hospital
Providence Portland Medical Center
Providence St. Vincent Medical Center
Shriners Hospitals for Children–Portland

Roseburg
Alliance
Mercy Medical Center

Salem
Alliance
Salem Hospital

Seaside
Alliance
Providence Seaside Hospital

Silverton
Alliance
Legacy Silverton Medical Center

The Dalles
Alliance
Mid–Columbia Medical Center

PENNSYLVANIA

Abington
Alliance
Abington Hospital

Allentown
Alliance
Lehigh Valley Hospital

Brookville
Alliance
Penn Highlands Brookville

Bryn Mawr
Alliance
Bryn Mawr Hospital

Butler
Alliance
Butler Health System

Chambersburg
Alliance
Chambersburg Hospital

Clearfield
Alliance
Penn Highlands Clearfield

Darby
Alliance
Mercy Fitzgerald Hospital

Drexel Hill
Alliance
Delaware County Memorial Hospital

DuBois
Alliance
Penn Highlands DuBois

East Norriton
Alliance
Einstein Medical Center Montgomery

East Stroudsburg
Alliance
Lehigh Valley Hospital – Pocono

Ephrata
Alliance
WellSpan Ephrata Community Hospital

Gettysburg
Alliance
WellSpan Gettysburg Hospital

Greensburg
Alliance
Excela Health Westmoreland Hospital

Hanover
Alliance
UPMC Hanover

Harrisburg
Alliance
PinnacleHealth at Community General Osteopathic
Hospital
UPMC Pinnacle Harrisburg

Hazleton
Alliance
Lehigh Valley Hospital – Hazleton

Hershey
Alliance
Penn State Milton S. Hershey Medical Center

Huntingdon
Alliance
J. C. Blair Memorial Hospital

Indiana
Alliance
Indiana Regional Medical Center

Jefferson Hills
Alliance
Jefferson Hospital

Lancaster
Alliance
Penn Medicine Lancaster General Hospital

Langhorne
Alliance
St. Mary Medical Center

Lansdale
Alliance
Abington–Lansdale Hospital
Jefferson Health

Latrobe
Alliance
Excela Latrobe Area Hospital

Lebanon
Alliance
WellSpan Good Samaritan Hospital

Lehighton
Alliance
St. Luke's – Gnaden Huetten Campus

Malvern
Alliance
Bryn Mawr Rehabilitation Hospital

Meadowbrook
Alliance
Holy Redeemer Hospital

Media
Alliance
  Riddle Hospital

Monongahela
Alliance
  Monongahela Valley Hospital

Mount Pleasant
Alliance
  Excela Frick Hospital

Muncy
Alliance
  UPMC Susquehanna Muncy

New Castle
Alliance
  UPMC Jameson

Paoli
Alliance
  Paoli Hospital

Philadelphia
Alliance
  Children's Hospital of Philadelphia
  Einstein Medical Center Philadelphia
  Fox Chase Cancer Center–American
  Oncologic Hospital
  Hospital of the University of Pennsylvania
  Jeanes Hospital
  Jefferson Health Northeast
  Magee Rehabilitation Hospital
  Penn Presbyterian Medical Center
  Pennsylvania Hospital
  Temple University Hospital
  University of Pennsylvania Health System

Pittsburgh
Alliance
  St. Clair Hospital
  UPMC Presbyterian

Pottsville
Alliance
  Lehigh Valley Hospital – Schuylkill

Reading
Alliance
  Penn State Health St. Joseph

Saint Marys
Alliance
  Penn Highlands Elk

Sayre
Alliance
  Guthrie Clinic
  Guthrie Robert Packer Hospital

Sellersville
Alliance
  Grand View Health

Towanda
Alliance
  Guthrie Towanda
  Memorial Hospital

Troy
Alliance
  Guthrie Troy Community Hospital

Uniontown
Alliance
  Uniontown Hospital

Upland
Alliance
  Crozer–Chester Medical Center

Waynesboro
Alliance
  Waynesboro Hospital

Wellsboro
Alliance
  UPMC Susquehanna Soldiers + Sailors

West Chester
Alliance
  Penn Medicine Chester County Hospital

West Reading
Alliance
  Reading Hospital

Williamsport
Alliance
  UPMC Susquehanna
  UPMC Susquehanna Divine
  Providence Campus
  UPMC Susquehanna Williamsport

Wynnewood
Alliance
  Lankenau Medical Center

York
Alliance
  WellSpan Health
  WellSpan York Hospital

RHODE ISLAND
Newport
Alliance
  Newport Hospital

Providence
Alliance
  Butler Hospital
  Care New England Health System
  Lifespan Corporation
  Miriam Hospital
  Rhode Island Hospital
  Women & Infants Hospital of Rhode Island

Warwick
Alliance
  Kent County Memorial Hospital

Westerly
Alliance
  Westerly Hospital

SOUTH CAROLINA
Charleston
Alliance
  MUSC Health of Medical University of South Carolina

Cheraw
Alliance
  McLeod Health Cheraw

Clinton
Alliance
  Prisma Health Laurens County Hospital

Columbia
Alliance
  ContinueCARE Hospital at
  Palmetto Health Baptist
  Prisma Health Baptist Hospital
  Prisma Health Baptist Parkridge Hospital
  Prisma Health Richland Hospital
  Providence Hospital

Darlington
Alliance
  McLeod Medical Center Darlington

Dillon
Alliance
  McLeod Medical Center Dillon

Easley
Alliance
  Prisma Health Baptist Easley Hospital

Florence
Alliance
  McLeod Regional Medical Center

Georgetown
Alliance
  Tidelands Georgetown Memorial Hospital

Greenville
Alliance
  Prisma Health Greenville Memorial Hospital
  Prisma Health Patewood Hospital
  Shriners Hospitals for Children–Greenville

Greenwood
Alliance
  Self Regional Healthcare

Greer
Alliance
  Prisma Health Greer Memorial Hospital

Loris
Alliance
  McLeod Loris Seacoast Hospital

Murrells Inlet
Alliance
  Tidelands Waccamaw Community Hospital

Seneca
Alliance
  Prisma Health Oconee Memorial Hospital

Simpsonville
Alliance
  Prisma Health Hillcrest Hospital

Sumter
Alliance
  Prisma Health Tuomey Hospital

Travelers Rest
Alliance
  Prisma Health North Greenville LTACH

SOUTH DAKOTA
Aberdeen
Alliance
  Sanford Aberdeen Medical Center

Armour
Alliance
  Douglas County Memorial Hospital

Burke
Alliance
  Community Memorial Hospital

Canton
Alliance
  Sanford Canton–Inwood Medical Center

Chamberlain
Alliance
  Sanford Chamberlain Medical Center

Clear Lake
Alliance
  Sanford Clear Lake Medical Center

Sioux Falls
Alliance
  Sanford Health
  Sanford USD Medical Center

Vermillion
Alliance
  Sanford Vermillion Medical Center

Viborg
Alliance
  Pioneer Memorial Hospital and
  Health Services

Watertown
Alliance
  Prairie Lakes Healthcare System

Webster
Alliance
  Sanford Webster Medical Center

Winner
Alliance
  Winner Regional Healthcare Center

TENNESSEE
Chattanooga
Alliance
  Erlanger Health System
  Erlanger North Hospital

Collierville
Alliance
  Baptist Memorial Hospital–Collierville

Columbia
Alliance
  Maury Regional Hospital

Covington
Alliance
  Baptist Memorial Hospital–Tipton

Franklin
Alliance
  Williamson Medical Center

Harriman
Alliance
  Roane Medical Center

Huntingdon
Alliance
  Baptist Memorial Hospital–Carroll County

Knoxville
Alliance
  Covenant Health

  Fort Sanders Regional Medical Center

  Parkwest Medical Center

  University of Tennessee Medical Center

Lenoir City
Alliance
  Fort Loudoun Medical Center

Lewisburg
Alliance
  Marshall Medical Center

Memphis
Alliance
  Baptist Memorial Health Care Corporation

  Baptist Memorial Hospital – Memphis

  Baptist Memorial Hospital for Women

  Methodist Healthcare Memphis Hospitals

  Regional One Health

  St. Jude Children's Research Hospital

Morristown
Alliance
  Morristown–Hamblen Healthcare System

Nashville
Alliance
  Vanderbilt University Medical Center

Oak Ridge
Alliance
  Methodist Medical Center of Oak Ridge

Sevierville
Alliance
  LeConte Medical Center

Tazewell
Alliance
  Claiborne Medical Center

Union City
Alliance
  Baptist Memorial Hospital–Union City

Waynesboro
Alliance
  Wayne Medical Center

TEXAS
Andrews
Alliance
  Permian Regional Medical Center

Baytown
Alliance
  Houston Methodist Baytown Hospital

Bellville
Alliance
  CHI St. Joseph Health Bellville Hospital

Dallas
Alliance
  Baylor Scott & White Health

  Children's Medical Center Dallas

  Methodist Health System

  Parkland Health & Hospital System

  William P. Clements, Jr. University Hospital

El Paso
Alliance
  University Medical Center of El Paso

Fort Worth
Alliance
  JPS Health Network

Galveston
Alliance
  Shriners Hospitals for Children–Galveston

  University of Texas Medical Branch

Houston
Alliance
  Baylor St. Luke's Medical Center

  CHI St. Luke's Hospital – The Vintage Hospital

  Harris Health System

  Houston Methodist Hospital

  Houston Methodist West Hospital

  Houston Methodist Willowbrook Hospital

  Memorial Hermann – Texas Medical Center

  Memorial Hermann Greater Heights Hospital

  Memorial Hermann Health System

  Memorial Hermann Memorial City Medical Center

  Shriners Hospitals for Children–Houston

  TIRR Memorial Hermann

Humble
Alliance
  Memorial Hermann Northeast

Katy
Alliance
  Houston Methodist Continuing Care Hospital

  Memorial Hermann Katy Hospital

Livingston
Alliance
  CHI St. Luke's Health Memorial Livingston

Lubbock
Alliance
  Covenant Health System

  Covenant Medical Center–Lakeside

Lufkin
Alliance
  CHI St. Luke's Health Memorial Lufkin

Midland
Alliance
  Midland Memorial Hospital

Pasadena
Alliance
  CHI St. Luke's Health – Patients Medical Center

Pearsall
Alliance
  Frio Regional Hospital

Plano
Alliance
  Community Hospital Corporation

San Antonio
Alliance
  University Health System

San Augustine
Alliance
  CHI St. Luke's Health Memorial San Augustine

Sugar Land
Alliance
  Houston Methodist Sugar Land Hospital

  Memorial Hermann Sugar Land Hospital

Sweeny
Alliance
  Sweeny Community Hospital

The Woodlands
Alliance
  CHI St. Luke's Health–Lakeside Hospital

  CHI St. Luke's Health–The Woodlands Hospital

Tyler
Alliance
  CHRISTUS Mother Frances Hospital – Tyler

  UT Health North Campus Tyler

UTAH
Gunnison
Alliance
  Gunnison Valley Hospital

Provo
Alliance
  Utah State Hospital

Salt Lake City
Alliance
  Shriners Hospitals for Children–Salt Lake City

  University of Utah Health

  University of Utah Neuropsychiatric Institute

VERMONT
Bennington
Alliance
  Southwestern Vermont Medical Center

Berlin
Alliance
  The University of Vermont Health Network Central
  Vermont Medical Center

Brattleboro
Alliance
  Brattleboro Memorial Hospital

  Brattleboro Retreat

Burlington
Alliance
  University of Vermont Medical Center

Morrisville
Alliance
  Copley Hospital

Newport
Alliance
  North Country Hospital and Health Center

Rutland
Alliance
  Rutland Regional Medical Center

Saint Johnsbury
Alliance
  Northeastern Vermont Regional Hospital

Springfield
Alliance
  Springfield Hospital

Townshend
Alliance
  Grace Cottage Hospital

Windsor
Alliance
  Mt. Ascutney Hospital and Health Center

VIRGIN ISLANDS
Saint Thomas
Alliance
  Schneider Regional Medical Center

VIRGINIA
Bedford
Alliance
  Centra Bedford Memorial Hospital

Charlottesville
Alliance
  Sentara Martha Jefferson Hospital

  UVA-HEALTHSOUTH Rehabilitation
  Hospital

  University of Virginia Medical Center

Culpeper
Alliance
  Novant Health UVA Health System
  Culpeper Medical Center

Farmville
Alliance
  Centra Southside Community Hospital

Fishersville
Alliance
  Augusta Health

Fredericksburg
Alliance
  Mary Washington Hospital

Hampton
Alliance
  Sentara CarePlex Hospital

Harrisonburg
Alliance
  Sentara RMH Medical Center

Lynchburg
Alliance
  Centra Lynchburg General Hospital

Manassas
Alliance
  Novant Health UVA Health System Prince William
  Medical Center

Section B

Norfolk
Alliance
Hospital for Extended Recovery

Sentara Healthcare

Sentara Leigh Hospital

Sentara Norfolk General Hospital

Richmond
Alliance
Children's Hospital of Richmond at VCU–Brook Road Campus

VCU Medical Center

South Boston
Alliance
Sentara Halifax Regional Hospital

Stafford
Alliance
Stafford Hospital

Suffolk
Alliance
Sentara Obici Hospital

Virginia Beach
Alliance
Sentara Princess Anne Hospital

Sentara Virginia Beach General Hospital

Williamsburg
Alliance
Sentara Williamsburg Regional
Medical Center

Woodbridge
Alliance
Sentara Northern Virginia Medical Center

WASHINGTON
Aberdeen
Alliance
Grays Harbor Community Hospital

Auburn
Alliance
MultiCare Auburn Medical Center

Bellingham
Alliance
PeaceHealth St. Joseph Medical Center

Bremerton
Alliance
Harrison Medical Center

Burien
Alliance
Highline Medical Center

Centralia
Alliance
Providence Centralia Hospital

Chewelah
Alliance
Providence St. Joseph's Hospital

Colfax
Alliance
Whitman Hospital and Medical Center

Colville
Alliance
Providence Mount Carmel Hospital

Dayton
Alliance
Columbia County Health System

Edmonds
Alliance
Swedish/Edmonds

Enumclaw
Alliance
St. Elizabeth Hospital

Everett
Alliance
Providence Regional Medical
Center Everett

Gig Harbor
Alliance
St. Anthony Hospital

Ilwaco
Alliance
Ocean Beach Hospital

Issaquah
Alliance
Swedish/Issaquah

Lakewood
Alliance
St. Clare Hospital

Morton
Alliance
Arbor Health, Morton Hospital

Olympia
Alliance
Providence St. Peter Hospital

Pomeroy
Alliance
Garfield County Public Hospital District

Port Angeles
Alliance
Olympic Medical Center

Prosser
Alliance
Prosser Memorial Health

Puyallup
Alliance
MultiCare Good Samaritan Hospital

Renton
Alliance
UW Medicine/Valley Medical Center

Richland
Alliance
Kadlec Regional Medical Center

Seattle
Alliance
Swedish Medical Center–Cherry Hill Campus

Swedish Medical Center–First Hill

UW Medicine/Harborview Medical Center

UW Medicine/Northwest Hospital & Medical Center

University of Washington Medical Center

Spokane
Alliance
Providence Holy Family Hospital

Providence Sacred Heart Medical Center & Children's
Hospital

Shriners Hospitals for Children–Spokane

St. Luke's Rehabilitation Institute

Tacoma
Alliance
MultiCare Health System

MultiCare Tacoma General Hospital

St. Joseph Medical Center

Walla Walla
Alliance
Providence St. Mary Medical Center

WEST VIRGINIA
Charleston
Alliance
CAMC Women and Children's Hospital

Charleston Area Medical Center

Gassaway
Alliance
Braxton County Memorial Hospital

Madison
Alliance
Boone Memorial Hospital

Martinsburg
Alliance
Berkeley Medical Center

Montgomery
Alliance
Montgomery General Hospital

Morgantown
Alliance
West Virginia University Hospitals

Princeton
Alliance
Princeton Community Hospital

Ranson
Alliance
Jefferson Medical Center

Ripley
Alliance
Jackson General Hospital

Spencer
Alliance
Roane General Hospital

Wheeling
Alliance
Ohio Valley Medical Center

WISCONSIN
Antigo
Alliance
Aspirus Langlade Hospital

Appleton
Alliance
ThedaCare, Inc.

Barron
Alliance
Mayo Clinic Health System – Northland in Barron

Beaver Dam
Alliance
Beaver Dam Community Hospitals

Beloit
Alliance
Beloit Health System

Bloomer
Alliance
Mayo Clinic Health System – Chippewa Valley in
Bloomer

Boscobel
Alliance
Gundersen Boscobel Area Hospital and Clinics

Eau Claire
Alliance
Mayo Clinic Health System in Eau Claire

Friendship
Alliance
Gundersen Moundview Hospital & Clinics

Green Bay
Alliance
Bellin Hospital

Bellin Psychiatric Center

Hillsboro
Alliance
Gundersen St. Joseph's Hospital and Clinics

Hudson
Alliance
Hudson Hospital and Clinic

La Crosse
Alliance
Gundersen Lutheran Medical Center

Mayo Clinic Health System – Franciscan Healthcare in
La Crosse

Madison
Alliance
UnityPoint Health Meriter

University Hospital

Marinette
Alliance
Aurora Medical Center – Bay Area

Medford
Alliance
Aspirus Medford Hospital & Clinics, Inc.

Menomonee Falls
Alliance
Community Memorial Hospital

Menomonie
Alliance
Mayo Clinic Health System – Red Cedar
in Menomonie

Milwaukee
Alliance
Froedtert and the Medical College of Wisconsin
Froedtert Hospital

Section B

Neenah
Alliance
ThedaCare Regional Medical Center–Neenah

Neillsville
Alliance
Marshfield Medical Center – Neilsville

New Richmond
Alliance
Westfields Hospital and Clinic

Oconomowoc
Alliance
Oconomowoc Memorial Hospital

Oconto
Alliance
Bellin Health Oconto Hospital

Osseo
Alliance
Mayo Clinic Health System – Oakridge in Osseo

Portage
Alliance
Divine Savior Healthcare

River Falls
Alliance
River Falls Area Hospital

Sparta
Alliance
Mayo Clinic Health System – Franciscan Healthcare in Sparta

Superior
Alliance
Essentia Health St. Mary's Hospital of Superior

Waukesha
Alliance
ProHealth Care, Inc.
Waukesha Memorial Hospital

Waupaca
Alliance
ThedaCare Medical Center–Waupaca

Wausau
Alliance
Aspirus Wausau Hospital, Inc.
North Central Health Care

West Bend
Alliance
St. Joseph's Hospital

Whitehall
Alliance
Gundersen Tri–County Hospital and Clinics

Wild Rose
Alliance
Theda Care Medical Center – Wild Rose

Wisconsin Rapids
Alliance
Aspirus Riverview Hospital and Clinics, Inc.

WYOMING

Buffalo
Alliance
Johnson County Healthcare Center

Casper
Alliance
Wyoming Medical Center

Cheyenne
Alliance
Cheyenne Regional Medical Center

Douglas
Alliance
Memorial Hospital of Converse County

Laramie
Alliance
Ivinson Memorial Hospital

Lusk
Alliance
Niobrara Health and Life Center

Sheridan
Alliance
Sheridan Memorial Hospital

YANKEE ALLIANCE
138 River Road, Andover, MA,
Zip 01810–1083; tel. 978/470–2000;
James W. Oliver, President and Chief
Executive Officer

CALIFORNIA

Long Beach
Alliance
College Medical Center

Oceanside
Alliance
Tri–City Medical Center

CONNECTICUT

Derby
Alliance
Griffin Hospital

Hartford
Alliance
Saint Francis Hospital and Medical Center

New London
Alliance
Lawrence + Memorial Hospital

Stafford Springs
Alliance
Johnson Memorial Medical Center

FLORIDA

Boca Raton
Alliance
Promise Healthcare

Coral Gables
Alliance
Baptist Health South Florida, Doctors Hospital

Homestead
Alliance
Baptist Health South Florida, Homestead Hospital

Miami Beach
Alliance
Mount Sinai Medical Center

Miami
Alliance
Baptist Health South Florida, Baptist Hospital of Miami
Baptist Health South Florida, South Miami Hospital
Baptist Health South Florida, West Kendall Baptist Hospital

Miramar
Alliance
Memorial Hospital Miramar

Pembroke Pines
Alliance
Memorial Hospital Pembroke
Memorial Hospital West

South Miami
Alliance
Larkin Community Hospital–South Miami Campus

Tavernier
Alliance
Baptist Health South Florida, Mariners Hospital

ILLINOIS

Geneva
Alliance
Northwestern Medicine Delnor Hospital

Winfield
Alliance
Northwestern Medicine Central DuPage Hospital

INDIANA

Gary
Alliance
Methodist Hospitals

Mishawaka
Alliance
Unity Medical & Surgical Hospital

KENTUCKY

Ashland
Alliance
King's Daughters Medical Center

Benton
Alliance
Marshall County Hospital

Corbin
Alliance
Baptist Health Corbin

Elizabethtown
Alliance
Hardin Memorial Health

La Grange
Alliance
Baptist Health La Grange

Lexington
Alliance
Baptist Health Lexington

Louisville
Alliance
Baptist Health Louisville

Madisonville
Alliance
Baptist Health Madisonville

Paducah
Alliance
Baptist Health Paducah

Prestonsburg
Alliance
Highlands ARH Regional Medical Center

Richmond
Alliance
Baptist Health Richmond

MAINE

Bangor
Alliance
St. Joseph Hospital

Lewiston
Alliance
St. Mary's Regional Medical Center

MASSACHUSETTS

Attleboro
Alliance
Sturdy Memorial Hospital

Boston
Alliance
Boston Medical Center
New England Baptist Hospital
Tufts Medical Center

Brockton
Alliance
Signature Healthcare Brockton Hospital

Burlington
Alliance
Lahey Hospital & Medical Center, Burlington

Fall River
Alliance
Southcoast Hospitals Group

Great Barrington
Alliance
Fairview Hospital

Lowell
Alliance
Lowell General Hospital

Milford
Alliance
Milford Regional Medical Center

Newburyport
Alliance
Anna Jaques Hospital

Oak Bluffs
Alliance
Martha's Vineyard Hospital

Pittsfield
Alliance
Berkshire Medical Center

Westfield
Alliance
Baystate Noble Hospital

Winchester
Alliance
  Winchester Hospital

NEW HAMPSHIRE

Concord
Alliance
  Concord Hospital

Exeter
Alliance
  Exeter Hospital

Franklin
Alliance
  Franklin Regional Hospital

Laconia
Alliance
  Lakes Region General Hospital

Manchester
Alliance
  Catholic Medical Center
  Elliot Hospital

Nashua
Alliance
  St. Joseph Hospital

North Conway
Alliance
  Memorial Hospital

Rochester
Alliance
  Frisbie Memorial Hospital

Salem
Alliance
  Northeast Rehabilitation Hospital

NEW YORK

Batavia
Alliance
  United Memorial Medical Center

Bath
Alliance
  Ira Davenport Memorial Hospital

Elizabethtown
Alliance
  The University of Vermont Health Network
  Elizabethtown Community Hospital

Elmira
Alliance
  Arnot Ogden Medical Center
  St. Joseph's Hospital

Glens Falls
Alliance
  Glens Falls Hospital

Gloversville
Alliance
  Nathan Littauer Hospital and Nursing Home

Plattsburgh
Alliance
  The University of Vermont Health Network–Champlain
  Valley Physicians Hospital

Warsaw
Alliance
  Wyoming County Community Hospital

OHIO

Logan
Alliance
  Hocking Valley Community Hospital

Montpelier
Alliance
  Community Hospitals and Wellness Centers–Montpelier

Salem
Alliance
  Salem Regional Medical Center

Seaman
Alliance
  Adams County Regional Medical Center

Sidney
Alliance
  Wilson Memorial Hospital

Steubenville
Alliance
  Life Line Hospital

PENNSYLVANIA

Honesdale
Alliance
  Wayne Memorial Hospital

Langhorne
Alliance
  Barix Clinics of Pennsylvania

Washington
Alliance
  Advanced Surgical Hospital

RHODE ISLAND

Providence
Alliance
  Roger Williams Medical Center

Wakefield
Alliance
  South County Hospital

Westerly
Alliance
  Westerly Hospital

SOUTH CAROLINA

Columbia
Alliance
  Providence Hospital

Fairfax
Alliance
  Allendale County Hospital

TEXAS

Austin
Alliance
  Arise Austin Medical Center

Houston
Alliance
  Healthbridge Children's Hospital of
  Houston

New Braunfels
Alliance
  Post Acute/Warm Springs Specialty
  Hospital of New Braunfels

Plainview
Alliance
  Covenant Hospital Plainview

WEST VIRGINIA

New Martinsville
Alliance
  Wetzel County Hospital

Abbreviations Used in the AHA Guide

AB, Army Base
ACSW, Academy of Certified Social Workers
AEC, Atomic Energy Commission
AFB, Air Force Base
AHA, American Hospital Association
AK, Alaska
AL, Alabama
AODA, Alcohol and Other Drug Abuse
APO, Army Post Office
AR, Arkansas
A.R.T., Accredited Record Technician
A.S.C., Ambulatory Surgical Center
A.T.C., Alcoholism Treatment Center
Ave., Avenue
AZ, Arizona

B.A., Bachelor of Arts
B.B.A., Bachelor of Business Administration
B.C., British Columbia
Blvd., Boulevard
B.S., Bachelor of Science
B.S.Ed., Bachelor of Science in Education
B.S.H.S., Bachelor of Science in Health Studies
B.S.N., Bachelor of Science in Nursing
B.S.W., Bachelor of Science and Social Worker

CA, California; Controller of Accounts
C.A.A.D.A.C., Certified Alcohol and Drug Abuse Counselor
CAC, Certified Alcoholism Counselor
CAE, Certified Association Executive
CAP, College of American Pathologists
CAPA, Certified Ambulatory Post Anesthesia
C.A.S., Certificate of Advanced Study
CCDC, Certified Chemical Dependency Counselor
C.D., Commander of the Order of Distinction
CDR, Commander
CDS, Chemical Dependency Specialist
CFACHE, Certified Fellow American College of Healthcare Executives
CFRE, Certified Fund Raising Executive
C.G., Certified Gastroenterology
CHC, Certified Health Consultant
CHE, Certified Healthcare Executive
C.L.D., Clinical Laboratory Director
CLU, Certified Life Underwriter, Chartered Life Underwriter
CMA, Certified Medical Assistant
C.M.H.A., Certified Mental Health Administrator
CNHA, Certified Nursing Home Administrator
CNM, Certified Nurse Midwife
CNOR, Certified Operating Room Nurse
C.N.S., Clinical Nurse Specialist
CO, Colorado; Commanding Officer
COA, Certified Ophthalmic Assistant
COMT, Commandant
C.O.M.T., Certified Ophthalmic Medical Technician
Conv., Conventions
Corp., Corporation; Corporate
C.O.T., Certified Ophthalmic Technician
CPA, Certified Public Accountant
C.P.H.Q., Certified Professional in Health Care Quality
CPM, Certified Public Manager
CRNA, Certified Registered Nurse Anesthetist
CRNH, Certified Registered Nurse Hospice
C.S.J.B., Catholic Saint John the Baptist
CSW, Certified Social Worker
CT, Connecticut
CWO, Chief Warrant Officer

D.B.A., Doctor of Business Administration
DC, District of Columbia
D.D., Doctor of Divinity
D.D.S., Doctor of Dental Surgery
DE, Delaware
Diet, Dietitian; Dietary; Dietetics
D.M.D., Doctor of Dental Medicine
D.MIN., Doctor of Ministry
D.O., Doctor of Osteopathic Medicine and Surgery, Doctor of Osteopathy
DPA, Doctorate Public Administration
D.P.M., Doctor of Podiatric Medicine
Dr., Drive
Dr.P.h., Doctor of Public Health
D.Sc., Doctor of Science
D.S.W., Doctor of Social Welfare
D.V.M., Doctor of Veterinary Medicine

E., East
Ed.D., Doctor of Education
Ed.S., Specialist in Education
ENS, Ensign
Esq., Esquire
Expwy., Expressway
ext., extension

FAAN, Fellow of the American Academy of Nursing
FACATA, Fellow of the American College of Addiction Treatment Administrators
FACHE, Fellow of the American College of Healthcare Executives
FACMGA, Fellow of the American College of Medical Group Administrators
FACP, Fellow of the American College of Physicians
FACS, Fellow of the American College of Surgeons
FAX, Facsimile
FL, Florida
FPO, Fleet Post Office
FRCPSC, Fellow of the Royal College of Physicians and Surgeons of Canada
FT, Full-time

GA, Georgia
Govt., Government; Governmental

HHS, Department of Health and Human Services
HI, Hawaii
HM, Helmsman
HMO, Health Maintenance Organization
Hon., Honorable; Honorary
H.S.A., Health System Administrator
Hts., Heights
Hwy., Highway

IA, Iowa
ID, Idaho
IL, Illinois
IN, Indiana
Inc., Incorporated

J.D., Doctor of Law
J.P., Justice of the Peace
Jr., Junior

KS, Kansas
KY, Kentucky

LA, Louisiana
LCDR, Lieutenant Commander
LCSW, Licensed Certified Social Worker
L.H.D., Doctor of Humanities

L.I.S.W., Licensed Independent Social Worker
LL.D., Doctor of Laws
L.L.P., Limited Licensed Practitioner
L.M.H.C., Licensed Master of Health Care
L.M.S.W., Licensed Master of Social Work
L.N.H.A., Licensed Nursing Home Administrator
L.P.C., Licensed Professional Counselor
LPN, Licensed Practical Nurse
L.P.N., Licensed Practical Nurse
L.S.W., Licensed Social Worker
Lt., Lieutenant
LTC, Lieutenant Colonel
Ltd., Limited
LT.GEN., Lieutenant General
LTJG, Lieutenant (junior grade)

MA, Massachusetts
M.A., Master of Arts
Maj., Major
M.B., Bachelor of Medicine
M.B.A., Masters of Business Administration
MC, Medical Corps; Marine Corps
M.C., Member of Congress
MD, Maryland
M.D., Doctor of Medicine
ME, Maine
M.Ed., Master of Education
MFCC, Marriage/Family/Child Counselor
MHA, Mental Health Association
M.H.S., Masters in Health Science; Masters in Human Service
MI, Michigan
MM, Masters of Management
MN, Minnesota
M.N., Master of Nursing
MO, Missouri
M.P.A., Master of Public Administration; Master Public Affairs
M.P.H., Master of Public Health
M.P.S., Master of Professional Studies; Master of Public Science
MS, Mississippi
M.S., Master of Science
MSC, Medical Service Corps
M.S.D., Doctor of Medical Science
MSHSA, Master of Science Health Service Administration
M.S.N., Master of Science in Nursing
M.S.P.H., Master of Science in Public Health
M.S.S.W., Master of Science in Social Work
M.S.W., Master of Social Work
MT, Montana
Mt., Mount

N., North
NC, North Carolina
N.C.A.D.C., National Certification of Alcohol and Drug Counselors
ND, North Dakota
NE, Nebraska
NH, New Hampshire
NHA, National Hearing Association; Nursing Home Administrator
NJ, New Jersey
NM, New Mexico
NPA, National Perinatal Association
NV, Nevada
NY, New York

OCN, Oncology Certified Nurse
O.D., Doctor of Optometry
O.F.M., Order Franciscan Monks, Order of Friars Minor
OH, Ohio
OK, Oklahoma
OR, Oregon

O.R., Operating Room
O.R.S., Operating Room Supervisor
OSF, Order of St. Francis

PA, Pennsylvania
P.A., Professional Association
P.C., Professional Corporation
Pharm.D., Doctor of Pharmacy
Ph.B., Bachelor of Philosophy
Ph.D., Doctor of Philosophy
PHS, Public Health Service
Pkwy., Parkway
Pl., Place
PR, Puerto Rico
PS, Professional Services
PSRO, Professional Standards Review Organization

RADM, Rear Admiral
RD, Rural Delivery
Rd., Road
R.F.D., Rural Free Delivery
RI, Rhode Island
R.M., Risk Manager
R.N., Registered Nurse
RNC, Republican National Committee; Registered Nurse or Board Certified
R.Ph., Registered Pharmacist
RRA, Registered Record Administrator
R.S.M., Religious Sisters of Mercy
Rte., Route

S., South
SC, South Carolina
S.C., Surgery Center
SCAC, Senior Certified Addiction Counselor
Sc.D., Doctor of Science
Sci., Science, Scientific
SD, South Dakota
SHCC, Statewide Health Coordinating Council

Sgt., Sergeant
SNA, Surgical Nursing Assistant
SNF, Skilled Nursing Facility
Sq., Square
Sr., Senior, Sister
St., Saint, Street
Sta., Station
Ste., Saint; Suite

Tel., Telephone
Terr., Terrace
TN, Tennessee
Tpke., Turnpike
Twp., Township
TX, Texas

USA, United States Army
USAF, United States Air Force
USMC, United States Marine Corps
USN, United States Navy
USPHS, United States Public Health Service
UT, Utah

VA, Virginia
VADM, Vice Admiral
VI, Virgin Islands
Vlg., Village
VT, Vermont
W., West

WA, Washington
WI, Wisconsin
WV, West Virginia
WY, Wyoming

Index

Abbreviations Used in the AHA Guide, C1
Acknowledgements, v
AHA Offices, Officers, and Historical Data, ix
AHA Guide Hospital Listing Requirements, A2
Alliances, B174
    defined, B2
Ambulatory Centers and Home Care
    Agencies, A1023
Annual Survey, A5
Approval Codes, A3
Associate Members, A1023
    defined, A1023
Associated University Programs in Health
    Administration, A1019
Blue Cross Plans, A1023
Control and Service Classifications, A12
Explanation of Hospital Listings, A3
Facility Codes
    defined, A4
    numerically, A3
Health Care Professionals alphabetically, A771
Health Care Systems
    and their hospitals, B4
    defined, B2
    geographically, B149
    introduced, B2
    Statistics for Multihospital Health Care Systems
        and their Hospitals, B3
Hospital Listing Requirements, A2
Hospital Schools of Nursing, A1020

Hospitals in Areas Associated with the United States,
    by Area, A711
Hospitals in the United States, by state, A13
Index of Health Care Professionals, A771
Index of Hospitals, A719
Introduction, vi
    accredited Hospitals, A2
Membership Categories, A1017
Networks and their Hospitals, B158
    defined, B2
Nonhospital Preacute and Postacute Care Facilities,
    A1021
Nonreporting defined, A3
Other Associate Members, A1024
Other Institutional Members, A1018
    defined, A1018
Provisional Hospitals, A944
Types of Hospitals, A2
    general, A2
    psychiatric, A2
    rehabilitation and chronic disease, A2
    special, A2
U.S. Government Hospitals Outside the United
    States, by Area, A718
Utilization Data, A3
    defined, A3
    expense, A3
    facilities, A4
    personnel, A3